S0-AEI-081

PATTERSON'S

AMERICAN EDUCATION

2017 Edition
VOLUME CXIII

Editorial Staff

Editor	Wayne Moody
Assistant Editor	Rita Ostdick
Assistant Editor	James Thiessen

EDUCATIONAL DIRECTORIES INC.

Educational Directories Inc.
PO Box 68097
Schaumburg IL 60168-0097
(847) 891-1250 or (800) 357-6183
www.ediusa.com

First edition published 1904. One Hundred Thirteenth edition 2017

ISBN 978-0-9883500-8-3
ISSN 0079-0230
Library of Congress Catalog Card Number: 04-012953
Printed in the United States of America

CONTENTS

How To Use This Directory iv
Guide To Editorial Style vi

Secondary Schools Alphabetically By State 1
Charter Schools 681
Bureau of Indian Affairs Schools 736
Department of Defense Dependent Schools 738
Catholic School Superintendents 739
Lutheran School Superintendents 740
Seventh-Day Adventists School Superintendents 741

HOW TO USE THIS DIRECTORY

Patterson's AMERICAN EDUCATION (published annually since 1904) is THE standard directory to secondary schools and is the first in a series of school directories published by Educational Directories Inc. Patterson's ELEMENTARY EDUCATION (published annually since 1989) is identical in format to Patterson's AMERICAN EDUCATION but is a directory to elementary schools. The two volumes combined fulfill the need for a single, systematized, comprehensive directory to our nation's schools from kindergarten through post-graduate studies.

Patterson's AMERICAN EDUCATION contains 10,884 public school districts, 30,979 public secondary schools, 6,477 private and Catholic secondary schools and more than 7,000 post-secondary schools in an easy-to-use and consistent format. It is an invaluable resource for anyone involved in education or educational research. School registrars, guidance counselors, principals, superintendents, directors of admissions, financial aid officers, schools of education, public libraries, government agencies, armed forces, and business people find it a welcome replacement for the multitude of other directories required for national coverage of our nation's school systems with their variation in size, content, format and publishing date.

One of the primary objectives of this directory is to make available the latest, most comprehensive information about secondary and post-secondary schools in a condensed and easily accessible format. Its general organization is geographical. Entries are arranged alphabetically, by state, then by community (post office) and then by District and School name. Each state begins with a listing of the officials in its Department of Education followed by the head of the State Board of Education. If a state has intermediate superintendents (a level of superintendent between the state superintendent of schools and the superintendents who actually supervise the schools) they appear in a table preceding the community listings. Community listings follow and include the community name, county name, community population, district name, total district student enrollment, the superintendent's name, address, telephone, fax number and website where available followed by a listing of the district schools, showing their enrollment, grade range and the principal's name, address, telephone number and fax number. A district may be responsible for schools in more than one community. To achieve consistency, the district office is listed in the community in which it is located. A cross-reference is provided to and from the schools of the district located in other communities.

A short line may appear at the end of the listing of public secondary schools. This line separates the public secondary schools from the private and Catholic secondary schools and the post-secondary schools located in the community. Private and Catholic school listings include their enrollment, grade range and the principal's name, address, telephone number and fax number. Post-secondary school listings include their name, address and telephone number. Please refer to page vi, "Guide to Editorial Style," for an example of how these elements work together to provide an easy-to-use format.

Schools Listed

Patterson's AMERICAN EDUCATION lists the following types of schools

- **Middle Schools** usually teach any combination of grades five through eight.
- **Junior High Schools** usually teach grades seven through nine.
- **Junior-Senior High Schools** usually teach any combination of grades five through eight and include nine through twelve.
- **High Schools** usually teach grades nine through twelve or ten through twelve.
- **K-12 Schools**
- **Vocational-Technical Schools**

The following are included:

- All graded state approved public secondary schools.
- All graded secondary schools belonging to the National Catholic Education Association.
- All graded, regionally accredited, private secondary schools.
- Private secondary schools belonging to the member associations of the Council of American Private Education.

Non graded, special education schools and other non-traditional secondary schools are not listed.

Patterson's ELEMENTARY EDUCATION lists Kindergarten Schools, Primary Schools, Elementary Schools, Middle Schools and K-12 Schools.

ABBREVIATIONS

ALT . . . Alternative School
AVC. . . Area Vocational Center
AVTS . . Area Vocational Technical School
CCSD. . Community Consolidated School District
CDC . . Child Development Center
CESD. . Consolidated Elementary School District
CISD . . City Independent School District
CSD. . . City School District
CUSD. . Community Unit School District
ECC. . . Early Childhood Center
ECCSD . Elementary Community Consolidated School District
EHSD . . Elementary-High School District
ES . . . Elementary School
ESD. . . Elementary School District
EVD. . . Exempted Village District
HS . . . High School
HSD. . . High School District
IS. . . . Intermediate School
ISD . . . Independent School District
JESD . . Joint Elementary School District
JHS . . . Junior High School
JSD . . . Joint School District
JSHS . . Junior-Senior High School
JUESD . Joint Unified Elementary School District
JUHSD . Joint Unified High School District
JUNESD Joint Union Elementary School District
JUNHSD Joint Union High School District
JUSD . . Joint Unified School District
JVSD . . Joint Vocational School District
K . . . . Kindergarten
MS . . . Middle School
MSHS. . Middle School High School
PS . . . Primary School
RHSD. . Rural High School District
RISD . . Rural Independent School District
ROC . . Regional Occupational Center
ROP . . Regional Occupational Program
RSD. . . Reorganized School District
S . . . . School
SAD. . . School Administrative District
SC . . . School Corporation
SD . . . School District
SHS. . . Senior High School
SSD. . . Separate School District
UESD . . Unified Elementary School District
UFD. . . Union Free District
UHSD. . Unified High School District
UNESD . Union Elementary School District
UNHSD . Union High School District
UNSD. . Union School District
USD. . . Unified School District
Vo/Tech. Vocational/Technical

GUIDE TO EDITORIAL STYLE

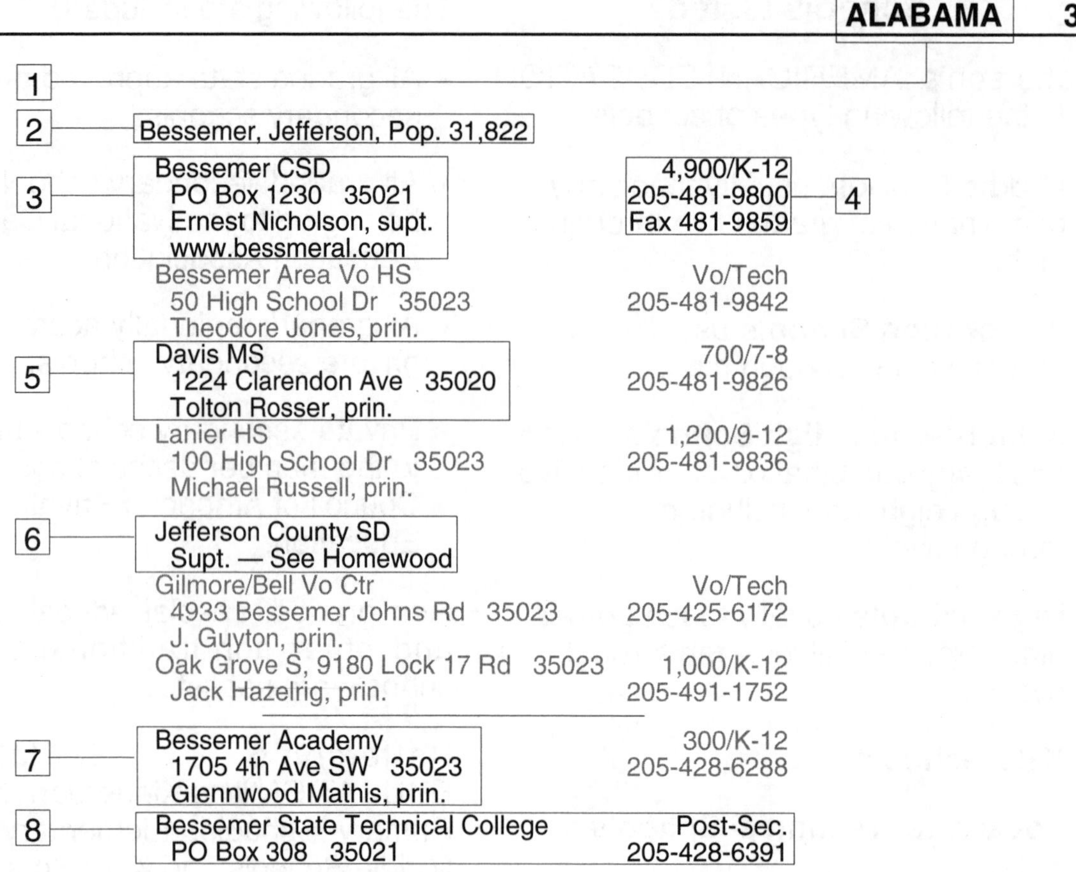

1. State.

2. City, county and city population.

3. Community school districts - school district name (refer to page v for abbreviations), address, superintendent's name and website (please enter as shown to access districts website).

4. Enrollment, grade range and phone number (fax number is included where available).

5. Community schools - school name, address and principal's name.

6. If the school district office is not located in this city, a cross-reference will show office location.

7. Private and Catholic secondary schools appear below a short line in the cities where they are located.

8. Post-secondary schools also appear below the line in the cities where they are located.

SECONDARY SCHOOL COUNTS BY STATE

	Public								
State	Districts	5-9	7-12	9-12	10-12	K-12	Private	Catholic	Total
Alabama	132	229	90	188	10	79	104	10	842
Alaska	54	35	16	36	0	180	16	2	339
Arizona	111	213	7	191	6	4	38	13	583
Arkansas	246	166	132	94	49	3	35	8	733
California	415	1,242	47	946	11	7	616	125	3,409
Colorado	178	263	71	216	4	7	84	10	833
Connecticut	123	168	9	149	1	1	50	26	527
Delaware	16	32	2	23	1	0	34	8	116
District Of Columbia	1	19	0	14	0	0	12	7	53
Florida	67	530	41	360	7	12	438	36	1,491
Georgia	175	448	19	334	9	6	199	12	1,202
Hawaii	1	36	6	33	0	6	36	7	125
Idaho	109	97	34	72	14	14	24	1	365
Illinois	485	704	50	612	22	1	144	80	2,098
Indiana	292	316	102	243	5	4	88	25	1,075
Iowa	337	264	110	233	9	0	28	31	1,012
Kansas	288	228	95	226	8	1	31	18	895
Kentucky	169	222	28	198	3	6	51	29	706
Louisiana	70	213	65	168	4	63	88	52	723
Maine	117	98	13	97	1	9	37	5	377
Maryland	24	233	6	185	0	2	113	38	601
Massachusetts	227	289	40	230	0	2	96	55	939
Michigan	520	553	81	472	21	30	194	54	1,925
Minnesota	328	216	184	161	20	13	63	31	1,016
Mississippi	148	151	61	136	7	41	81	9	634
Missouri	447	335	196	290	13	3	66	47	1,397
Montana	160	213	0	168	0	0	12	7	560
Nebraska	254	105	171	98	2	2	12	30	674
Nevada	16	90	13	65	6	6	31	2	229
New Hampshire	77	82	2	76	0	2	37	7	283
New Jersey	267	392	34	287	10	0	118	71	1,179
New Mexico	89	133	21	92	8	0	40	3	386
New York	646	782	247	713	20	76	355	139	2,978
North Carolina	115	452	11	422	5	5	231	4	1,245
North Dakota	152	38	113	38	5	2	7	5	360
Ohio	611	604	130	582	7	8	121	85	2,148
Oklahoma	428	278	24	377	52	2	41	5	1,207
Oregon	175	199	36	182	3	22	68	11	696
Pennsylvania	497	493	166	386	39	1	251	88	1,921
Rhode Island	32	48	1	43	0	1	20	10	155
South Carolina	85	237	18	167	8	2	97	4	618
South Dakota	156	159	2	156	0	1	12	7	493
Tennessee	119	297	39	246	5	19	150	12	887
Texas	973	1,372	158	984	51	111	267	58	3,974
Utah	40	125	22	31	57	2	47	4	328
Vermont	52	27	21	27	1	10	26	2	166
Virginia	132	332	42	284	16	2	138	16	962
Washington	247	344	47	250	29	23	112	16	1,068
West Virginia	55	121	19	94	3	2	33	8	335
Wisconsin	380	342	64	345	7	11	93	54	1,296
Wyoming	46	57	10	47	5	6	4	1	176
Total	10,884	14,622	2,916	12,067	564	810	5,089	1,388	48,340

SECONDARY SCHOOLS

ALABAMA

ALABAMA DEPARTMENT OF EDUCATION
PO Box 302101, Montgomery 36130
Telephone 334-242-9700
Fax 334-242-9708
Website http://www.alsde.edu

State Superintendent of Education Michael Sentance

ALABAMA BOARD OF EDUCATION
PO Box 302101, Montgomery 36130-2101

President Governor Robert Bentley

PUBLIC, PRIVATE AND CATHOLIC SECONDARY SCHOOLS

Abbeville, Henry, Pop. 2,658
Henry County SD 2,600/PK-12
300 N Trawick St 36310 334-585-2206
Lesa Knowles, supt. Fax 585-2551
www.henrycountyboe.org
Abbeville JSHS 400/7-12
411 Graball Cutoff 36310 334-585-2065
Darryl Brooks, prin. Fax 585-6562
Other Schools – See Headland

Abbeville Christian Academy 200/K-12
PO Box 9 36310 334-585-5100

Adamsville, Jefferson, Pop. 4,485
Jefferson County SD
Supt. — See Birmingham
Minor HS 1,000/9-12
2285 Minor Pkwy 35005 205-379-4750
Kalvin Eaton, prin. Fax 379-4795
Minor MS 800/6-8
400 Hillcrest Rd 35005 205-379-2550
Taki Sarhaan, prin. Fax 379-2553

Addison, Winston, Pop. 756
Winston County SD
Supt. — See Double Springs
Addison HS 300/7-12
PO Box 240 35540 256-747-2286
Micah Smothers, prin. Fax 747-6410

Alabaster, Shelby, Pop. 29,944
Alabaster CSD 6,100/K-12
1953 Municipal Way Ste 200 35007 205-663-8400
Dr. Wayne Vickers, supt. Fax 663-8408
www.alabasterschools.org
Thompson HS 1,800/9-12
100 Warrior Dr 35007 205-682-5700
Dr. Wesley Hester, prin. Fax 682-5705
Thompson MS 900/7-8
1509 Kent Dairy Rd 35007 205-685-8100
Neely Woodley, prin. Fax 685-0446

Evangel Classical Christian S 400/K-12
423 Thompson Rd 35007 205-216-0149
Kingwood Christian S 400/PK-12
1351 Royalty Dr 35007 205-663-3973

Albertville, Marshall, Pop. 20,874
Albertville CSD 4,700/PK-12
107 W Main St 35950 256-891-1183
Dr. Frederic Ayer, supt. Fax 891-6303
www.albertk12.org
Albertville HS 1,100/9-12
402 E Mccord Ave 35950 256-878-6580
Diedra Robinson, prin. Fax 891-6305
Albertville MS 600/7-8
600 E Alabama Ave 35950 256-878-2341
Lance Kitchens, prin. Fax 891-6334

Marshall County SD
Supt. — See Guntersville
Asbury MSHS 500/6-12
1990 Asbury Rd 35951 256-878-4068
Amy Childress, prin. Fax 878-5233

Marshall Christian Academy 200/PK-12
1631 Brashers Chapel Rd 35951 256-279-0192
Roy Bryant, admin. Fax 891-4160

Alexander City, Tallapoosa, Pop. 14,759
Alexander City SD 3,100/K-12
375 Lee St 35010 256-234-5074
Dr. J. Darrell Cooper, supt. Fax 329-6547
www.alexcityschools.net
Alexander City MS 500/7-8
359 State St 35010 256-234-8660
Reginald Clifton, prin. Fax 234-8659
Russell HS 1,000/9-12
225 Heard Blvd 35010 256-234-8611
Anthony Wilkinson, prin. Fax 234-8680

Central Alabama Community College Post-Sec.
1675 Cherokee Rd 35010 256-234-6346

Alexandria, Calhoun, Pop. 3,872
Calhoun County SD
Supt. — See Anniston
Alexandria HS 1,100/6-12
PO Box 180 36250 256-741-4400
Mack Holley, prin. Fax 820-7161

Aliceville, Pickens, Pop. 2,445
Pickens County SD
Supt. — See Carrollton
Aliceville HS 300/9-12
417 3rd St SE 35442 205-373-6378
Terry Sterling, prin. Fax 373-6730
Aliceville MS 300/5-8
1000 Columbus Rd NW 35442 205-373-6900
Fred Young, prin. Fax 373-8296

Alpine, Talladega
Talladega County SD
Supt. — See Talladega
Genesis Alternative Education Center Alt
22501 AL Highway 21 35014 256-315-5580
Joann Swain, prin. Fax 315-5585
Winterboro HS 300/5-12
22601 AL Highway 21 35014 256-315-5370
Emily Harris, prin. Fax 315-5380

Andalusia, Covington, Pop. 8,865
Andalusia CSD 1,600/K-12
1201 C C Baker Ave, 334-222-3186
Ted Watson, supt. Fax 222-8631
andalusia.schoolinsites.com
Andalusia HS 500/9-12
701 3rd St 36420 334-222-7569
Dr. Daniel Shakespeare, prin. Fax 222-5834
Andalusia JHS 300/7-8
408 4th Ave 36420 334-222-7569
Dr. Daniel Shakespeare, prin. Fax 222-5834

Covington County SD 3,100/PK-12
807 C C Baker Ave, 334-222-7571
Shannon Driver, supt. Fax 222-7573
www.cov.k12.al.us
Pleasant Home S 500/PK-12
12548 Falco Rd 36420 334-222-1315
Craig Nichols, prin. Fax 222-4415
Straughn HS 400/9-12
29448 Straughn School Rd, 334-222-2511
Donny Powell, prin. Fax 222-4010
Straughn MS 300/6-8
29324 Straughn School Rd, 334-222-4090
Cassandra Scott, prin. Fax 222-4132
Other Schools – See Florala, Red Level

Lurleen B. Wallace Community College Post-Sec.
PO Box 1418 36420 334-222-6591

Anniston, Calhoun, Pop. 22,755
Anniston CSD 1,800/PK-12
PO Box 1500 36202 256-231-5000
Darren Douthitt, supt. Fax 231-5073
www.annistonschools.com/
Anniston HS 500/9-12
1301 Woodstock Ave 36207 256-231-5010
Dr. Sherron Jinadu, prin. Fax 231-5069
Anniston MS 400/6-8
4800 Mcclellan Blvd 36206 256-231-5020
Kimberly Garrick, prin. Fax 231-5024

Calhoun County SD 9,300/K-12
PO Box 2084 36202 256-741-7400
Joe Dyar, supt. Fax 237-5332
www.ccboe.us
Saks HS 500/8-12
4401 Saks Rd 36206 256-741-7000
Jody Whaley, prin. Fax 236-5121
Wellborn HS 600/7-12
135 Pinson Rd 36201 256-741-7600
Chris Hayes, prin. Fax 237-7071
White Plains HS 400/9-12
250 White Plains Rd 36207 256-741-7800
Andy Ward, prin. Fax 237-3301
White Plains MS 500/5-8
5800 AL Highway 9 36207 256-741-4700
Courtney Wilburn, prin. Fax 238-1715

Other Schools – See Alexandria, Jacksonville, Ohatchee, Weaver

Donoho S 400/PK-12
2501 Henry Rd 36207 256-237-5477
James Hutchins, head sch Fax 237-6474
Faith Christian S 300/PK-12
4100 Ronnaki Rd 36207 256-236-4499
Robert Phillips, hdmstr. Fax 236-4673
IQRA Math and Science Academy 50/K-12
1821 McCall Dr 36207 256-403-6161
Sacred Heart S 200/PK-12
16 Morton Rd 36205 256-237-4231
Charlie Maniscalco, prin. Fax 237-2353
Sharp-Dean S of Continuing Studies 200/K-12
1910 Noble St 36201 256-238-0466

Arab, Marshall, Pop. 7,960
Arab CSD 2,600/PK-12
750 Arabian Dr NE 35016 256-586-6011
John Mullins, supt. Fax 586-6013
www.arabcityschools.org
Arab HS 900/9-12
511 Arabian Dr NE 35016 256-586-6026
Brad Cooper, prin. Fax 586-1948
Arab JHS 600/6-8
911 Old Cullman Rd SW 35016 256-586-6074
John Ingram, prin. Fax 586-1348

Ardmore, Limestone, Pop. 1,178
Limestone County SD
Supt. — See Athens
Ardmore JSHS 1,000/6-12
30285 Ardmore Ave 35739 256-423-2685
Glenn Bryant, prin. Fax 423-4991

Ariton, Dale, Pop. 752
Dale County SD
Supt. — See Ozark
Ariton S 700/K-12
PO Box 750 36311 334-445-5560
Joshua Herring, prin. Fax 445-5561

Arley, Winston, Pop. 344
Winston County SD
Supt. — See Double Springs
Meek HS 300/7-12
6615 County Road 41 35541 205-384-5825
Marla Murrah, prin. Fax 384-6825

Ashford, Houston, Pop. 2,133
Houston County SD
Supt. — See Dothan
Ashford JSHS 700/7-12
607 Church St 36312 334-899-5411
James Odom, prin. Fax 899-7450
Houston County AVC Vo/Tech
PO Box 3005 36312 334-899-3308
Glenn Maloy, prin. Fax 899-8854

Ashland, Clay, Pop. 2,015
Clay County SD 1,500/K-12
PO Box 278 36251 256-396-1475
William Walker, supt. Fax 354-5415
www.claycoboe.org
Other Schools – See Lineville

Ashville, Saint Clair, Pop. 2,172
Saint Clair County SD 8,800/PK-12
410 Roy Dr 35953 205-594-7131
Jenny Seals, supt. Fax 594-4441
www.sccboe.org
Ashville HS 400/9-12
33215 US Highway 231 35953 205-594-7943
Patti Johnson, prin. Fax 594-4349
Ashville MS 400/5-8
33221 US Highway 231 35953 205-594-7044
Rusty St. John, prin. Fax 594-2241
Eden Career-Technical Center Vo/Tech
45 County Road 33 35953 205-594-7055
Fax 594-4124
Yancy Alternative S Alt
466 10th St 35953 205-594-7492
David Gray, prin. Fax 594-3258
Other Schools – See Moody, Odenville, Ragland, Springville

Athens, Limestone, Pop. 21,523
Athens CSD 3,800/K-12
455 US Highway 31 N 35611 256-233-6600
Dr. Trey Holladay, supt. Fax 233-6640
www.acs-k12.org
Athens HS 900/9-12
PO Box 109 35612 256-233-6613
Dr. Travis Schrimsher, prin. Fax 233-6617
Athens MS 500/7-8
601 S Clinton St 35611 256-233-6620
Melanie Barkley, prin. Fax 233-6623
Athens Renaissance School 500/K-12
405 South St E 35611 256-614-3708
Dr. Joanna May, prin. Fax 233-6640

Limestone County SD 9,000/K-12
300 S Jefferson St 35611 256-232-5353
Dr. Tom Sisk, supt. Fax 233-6461
www.lcsk12.org
Clements MSHS 600/6-12
7730 US Highway 72 35611 256-729-6564
Keith Hairrell, prin. Fax 729-1029
East Limestone JSHS 1,200/6-12
15641 E Limestone Rd 35613 256-233-6660
Louis Berry, prin. Fax 230-9366
Limestone County Career Technical Center Vo/Tech
505 E Sanderfer Rd 35611 256-233-6463
Vince Green, prin. Fax 233-6667
Other Schools – See Ardmore, Elkmont, Lester, Tanner

Athens Bible S 300/K-12
507 Hoffman St 35611 256-232-3525
Athens State University Post-Sec.
300 N Beaty St 35611 256-233-8100
Lindsay Lane Christian Academy 300/PK-12
1300 Lindsay Ln S 35613 256-262-5323
Stephen Murr M.Ed., hdmstr. Fax 232-0425

Atmore, Escambia, Pop. 10,046
Escambia County SD
Supt. — See Brewton
Escambia County HS 500/9-12
1215 S Presley St 36502 251-368-9181
Dennis Fuqua, prin. Fax 368-0674
Escambia County MS 500/5-8
PO Box 1236 36504 251-368-9105
Deborah L. Bolden, prin. Fax 368-0969

Escambia Academy 300/PK-12
268 Cowpen Creek Rd 36502 251-368-2080
Jefferson Davis Community College Post-Sec.
PO Box 1119 36504 251-368-8118

Attalla, Etowah, Pop. 5,935
Attalla CSD 1,500/PK-12
101 Case Ave SE 35954 256-538-8051
David Bowman, supt. Fax 538-8388
www.attalla.k12.al.us
Etowah HS 800/9-12
201 Case Ave SE 35954 256-538-8381
Ryan Barkley, prin. Fax 538-2136
Etowah MS 400/6-8
429 4th St SW 35954 256-538-9221
Jeff Johnson, prin. Fax 538-3232

Etowah County SD
Supt. — See Gadsden
Career Technical Center Vo/Tech
105 Burke Ave SE 35954 256-538-3312
Mark Stancil, dir. Fax 538-1090
Etowah County Alternative S 200/Alt
106 Burke Ave SE 35954 256-538-8431
Larry Shoemaker, prin. Fax 538-8431

Auburn, Lee, Pop. 52,538
Auburn CSD 7,300/K-12
PO Box 3270 36831 334-887-2100
Dr. Karen T. DeLano, supt. Fax 887-2107
auburnschools.org
Auburn HS 1,600/10-12
405 Dean Rd 36830 334-887-4970
Dr. Shannon Pignato, prin. Fax 887-4177
Auburn JHS 1,200/8-9
332 E Samford Ave 36830 334-887-1960
Ross Reed, prin. Fax 887-4160

Auburn University 36849 Post-Sec.
334-844-4000
Lee-Scott Academy 600/PK-12
1601 Academy Dr 36830 334-821-2430
Dr. Stan Cox, hdmstr. Fax 821-0876

Autaugaville, Autauga, Pop. 858
Autauga County SD
Supt. — See Prattville
Autaugaville S 300/K-12
PO Box 99 36003 334-365-8329
Susan Butts, prin. Fax 365-8043

Bay Minette, Baldwin, Pop. 7,923
Baldwin County SD 29,900/PK-12
2600 Hand Ave 36507 251-937-0306
Eddie Tyler, supt. Fax 580-1856
www.bcbe.org
Baldwin County HS 1,200/9-12
1 Tiger Dr 36507 251-937-2341
Craig Smith, prin. Fax 937-2933
Bay Minette MS 500/7-8
1311 W 13th St 36507 251-580-2960
Kyle Nobles, prin. Fax 580-5120
North Baldwin Center for Tech Vo/Tech
505 W Hurricane Rd 36507 251-937-6751
Holly Resmondo, prin. Fax 937-4688
Other Schools – See Daphne, Elberta, Fairhope, Foley, Gulf Shores, Robertsdale, Spanish Fort

---

James H. Faulkner State Comm. College Post-Sec.
1900 S US Highway 31 36507 251-580-2100

Bayou La Batre, Mobile, Pop. 2,494
Mobile County SD
Supt. — See Mobile
Alba MS 600/6-8
14180 S Wintzell Ave 36509 251-824-4134
Rhonda Mayfield, prin. Fax 824-1324

Bear Creek, Marion, Pop. 1,062
Marion County SD
Supt. — See Hamilton
Phillips HS 200/7-12
142 School Ave 35543 205-486-3737
Keith Smith, prin. Fax 486-1716

Beatrice, Monroe, Pop. 301
Monroe County SD
Supt. — See Monroeville
Shields S 300/PK-12
17688 Highway 21 N 36425 251-789-2168
Ramona Dailey, prin. Fax 789-2715

Berry, Fayette, Pop. 1,134
Fayette County SD
Supt. — See Fayette
Berry HS 300/7-12
18242 Highway 18 E 35546 205-689-4467
Trevor Kribbs, prin. Fax 689-8819

Bessemer, Jefferson, Pop. 27,229
Bessemer CSD 3,000/PK-12
PO Box 1230 35021 205-432-3000
Dr. Keith Stewart, supt. Fax 432-3085
www.bessk12.org
Bessemer Center for Technology Vo/Tech
4940 Premiere Pkwy 35022 205-432-3805
Iverson Dudley, dir. Fax 432-0041
Bessemer City HS 9-12
4950 Premiere Pkwy 35022 205-432-3700
Reginald Ware, prin. Fax 434-2816
Bessemer City MS 1,000/6-8
100 High School Dr 35022 205-432-3600
Albert Soles, prin. Fax 432-3607
New Horizon S Alt
1701 6th Ave N 35020 205-432-3036
Edith Hunter, prin. Fax 432-3062

Jefferson County SD
Supt. — See Birmingham
Oak Grove HS 900/6-12
9494 Oak Grove Pkwy 35023 205-379-5000
Pamela Dennis, prin. Fax 379-5045

Bessemer Academy 300/K-12
1705 4th Ave SW 35022 205-428-6288

Billingsley, Autauga, Pop. 144
Autauga County SD
Supt. — See Prattville
Billingsley S 700/K-12
PO Box 118 36006 334-365-5516
Micheal Blair, prin. Fax 755-1633

Birmingham, Jefferson, Pop. 210,274
Alabama School of Fine Arts SD 400/7-12
1800 Rev Abraham Woods Blvd 35203
205-252-9241
Dr. Michael Meeks, supt. Fax 251-9541
www.asfa.k12.al.us
Alabama S of Fine Arts JSHS 400/7-12
1800 Rev Abraham Woods Blvd 35203
205-252-9241
Dr. Michael Meeks, supt. Fax 251-9541

Birmingham CSD 23,900/PK-12
PO Box 10007 35202 205-231-4600
Dr. Kelley Castlin-Gacutan, supt.
www.bhamcityschools.org
Arrington MS 500/6-8
2101 Jefferson Ave SW 35211 205-231-1130
Anthony Moss, prin. Fax 231-1133
Carver HS 900/9-12
3900 24th St N 35207 205-231-3900
Dr. Charles Willis, prin. Fax 231-3973
Dupuy Alternative S 100/Alt
4500 14th Ave N 35212 205-231-3250
Dr. Shirley Graham-Burrell, prin. Fax 231-3267
Green Acres MS 300/6-8
1220 67th St W 35228 205-231-1370
Dr. Willie Goldsmith, prin. Fax 231-1414
Huffman HS 1,300/9-12
950 Springville Rd 35215 205-231-5000
John Lyons, prin. Fax 231-5056
Huffman MS 300/6-8
517 Huffman Rd 35215 205-231-5370
WaShunda Gill, prin. Fax 231-5426
Jackson-Olin HS 1,100/9-12
510 12th Street Ensley 35218 205-231-6431
Dr. Janice Drake, prin. Fax 231-6527
Jones Valley MS 500/6-8
2000 31st St SW 35221 205-231-1040
Carolyn Denson, prin. Fax 231-1088
Mitchell MS 300/6-8
501 81st St S 35206 205-231-9400
Rameka Davis, prin. Fax 231-9464
Parker HS 900/9-12
400 Abraham Woods Jr Blvd 35204 205-231-2370
Darrell Hudson, prin. Fax 231-2916
Putnam MS 300/6-8
1757 Montclair Rd 35210 205-231-8680
Dr. Sakema Porterfield, prin. Fax 231-8685
Ramsay HS 800/Alt
1800 13th Ave S 35205 205-231-7000
Cassandra Fells, prin. Fax 231-7076
Smith MS 600/6-8
1124 Five Mile Rd 35215 205-231-5675
Dr. Demarcus Gates, prin. Fax 231-5899
Wenonah HS 800/9-12
2800 Wilson Rd SW 35221 205-231-1675
Regina Hope, prin. Fax 231-1655

Wilkerson MS 300/6-8
116 11th Ct W 35204 205-231-2740
Davida Hill-Johnson, prin. Fax 231-2790
Woodlawn HS 900/9-12
5620 1st Ave N 35212 205-231-8000
Dr. Fanchon Muhammad, prin. Fax 231-8084

Hoover CSD
Supt. — See Hoover
Berry MS 1,200/6-8
4500 Jaguar Dr 35242 205-439-2000
Christopher Robbins, prin. Fax 439-2001

Jefferson County SD 35,600/K-12
2100 18th St S 35209 205-379-2000
Dr. Craig Pouncey, supt. Fax 379-2311
www.jefcoed.com
Center Point HS 800/9-12
1000 Eagle Dr 35215 205-379-3400
Van Phillips, prin. Fax 379-3425
Erwin MS 700/6-8
532 23rd Ave NW 35215 205-379-3430
Serra Peterson, prin. Fax 856-6663
Fultondale JSHS 600/6-12
1450 Carson Rd N 35217 205-379-3500
Dr. Stephanie Robinson, prin. Fax 379-3545
Irondale MS 600/6-8
6200 Old Leeds Rd 35210 205-379-3800
Carita Venable, prin. Fax 379-3845
Jefferson Co. Counseling/Lrng Ctr-East Alt
50 Long St 35217 205-379-4250
Jason Wilson, prin. Fax 379-4295
Shades Valley Technical Academy Vo/Tech
5191 Pine Whispers Dr 35210 205-379-3300
Mary Beth Blankenship, prin. Fax 379-5397
Other Schools – See Adamsville, Bessemer, Dora, Gardendale, Hueytown, Irondale, Kimberly, Mc Calla, Pinson, Pleasant Grove, Trussville, Warrior

Pelham CSD
Supt. — See Pelham
Riverchase MS 700/6-8
853 Willow Oak Dr 35244 205-682-5510
Susan Hyatt, prin. Fax 682-5515

Shelby County SD
Supt. — See Columbiana
Oak Mountain HS 1,600/9-12
5476 Caldwell Mill Rd 35242 205-682-5200
Dr. Kristi Sayers, prin. Fax 682-5205
Oak Mountain MS 1,200/6-8
5650 Cahaba Valley Rd 35242 205-682-5210
Larry Haynes, prin. Fax 682-5215

Altamont S 300/5-12
4801 Altamont Rd S 35222 205-879-2006
Sarah Whiteside, head sch Fax 871-5666
Banks Academy 50/9-10
PO Box 590049 35259 205-834-5433
Dr. Kathy King, prin.
Birmingham-Southern College Post-Sec.
900 Arkadelphia Rd 35254 800-523-5793
Briarwood Christian S 1,900/PK-12
2204 Briarwood Way 35243 205-776-5800
Dr. Barrett Mosbacker, admin. Fax 776-5815
Carroll HS 600/9-12
300 Lakeshore Pkwy 35209 205-940-2400
Charlie McGrath, prin. Fax 945-7429
Central Park Christian S 200/K-12
1900 43rd St W 35208 205-786-4811
Cornerstone S of Alabama 300/PK-12
PO Box 320309 35232 205-591-7600
Dr. Nita Carr, pres. Fax 769-0063
Fortis Institute Post-Sec.
100 London Pkwy Ste 150 35211 205-940-7800
Herzing University Post-Sec.
280 W Valley Ave 35209 205-916-2800
Holy Family Catholic Academy 100/6-8
1916 19th Street Ensley 35218 205-780-5858
Sidney Moore, prin. Fax 785-2666
Holy Family Cristo Rey HS 200/9-12
2001 19th Street Ensley 35218 205-787-9937
Rev. Jon Chalmers, pres. Fax 787-8530
Hoover Christian S 100/PK-12
2113 Old Rocky Ridge Rd 35216 205-987-3376
Lori Abbott, prin. Fax 987-4428
Jefferson State Community College Post-Sec.
2601 Carson Rd 35215 205-853-1200
Lawson State Community College Post-Sec.
3060 Wilson Rd SW 35221 205-925-2515
Samford University Post-Sec.
800 Lakeshore Dr 35229 205-726-2011
Southeastern Bible College Post-Sec.
2545 Valleydale Rd 35244 205-970-9200
Southeastern School of Cosmetology Post-Sec.
849 Dennison Ave SW Ste 101 35211 205-925-0011
Strayer University Post-Sec.
3570 Grandview Pkwy Ste 200 35243 205-453-6300
University of Alabama at Birmingham Post-Sec.
1720 2nd Ave S 35294 205-934-4011
University of Alabama Hospital Post-Sec.
619 19th St S 35249 205-934-5490
Virginia College Post-Sec.
488 Palisades Blvd 35209 205-802-1200
Westminster S at Oak Mountain 500/K-12
5080 Cahaba Valley Trce 35242 205-995-9694

Blountsville, Blount, Pop. 1,659
Blount County SD
Supt. — See Oneonta
Moore HS 600/7-12
4040 Susan Moore Rd 35031 205-466-7663
Mike Stansberry, prin. Fax 466-7858
Pennington HS 600/7-12
81 College St 35031 205-429-4101
Brian Kirk, prin. Fax 429-4104

Boaz, Marshall, Pop. 9,410
Boaz CSD 2,200/PK-12
126 Newt Parker Dr 35957 256-593-8180
Dr. Timothy Morgan, supt. Fax 593-8181
www.boazk12.org
Boaz HS 600/9-12
907 Brown St 35957 256-593-2401
Gary Minnick, prin. Fax 593-2403
Boaz MS 500/6-8
140 Newt Parker Dr 35957 256-593-0799
Dr. Richard Rutledge, prin. Fax 593-0729

Etowah County SD
Supt. — See Gadsden
Sardis MS 400/6-8
1415 Sardis Dr 35956 256-622-1120
Chris Royal, prin. Fax 622-1119

Snead State Community College Post-Sec.
PO Box 734 35957 256-593-5120

Brantley, Crenshaw, Pop. 786
Crenshaw County SD
Supt. — See Luverne
Brantley S 600/PK-12
PO Box 86 36009 334-527-8879
Kris Odom, prin. Fax 527-3405

Bremen, Cullman
Cullman County SD
Supt. — See Cullman
Cold Springs HS 300/9-12
PO Box 130 35033 256-287-1787
Tim Burleson, prin. Fax 287-2841

Brewton, Escambia, Pop. 5,355
Brewton CSD 1,100/K-12
811 Belleville Ave 36426 251-867-8400
Dr. Kenneth Varner, supt. Fax 867-8403
www.brewtoncityschools.org/
Brewton MS 300/5-8
1384 Old Castleberry Rd 36426 251-867-8420
Madelyn Cave, prin. Fax 867-8422
Miller HS 300/9-12
1835 Douglas Ave 36426 251-867-8430
Ronald Snell, prin. Fax 867-8407

Escambia County SD 4,300/K-12
PO Box 307 36427 251-867-6251
John J. Knott, supt. Fax 867-6252
www.escambiak12.net
Escambia Career Readiness Center Vo/Tech
2824 Pea Ridge Rd 36426 251-867-7829
David Lanier, dir. Fax 867-7064
Other Schools – See Atmore, East Brewton, Flomaton

Jefferson Davis Community College Post-Sec.
PO Box 958 36427 251-867-4832

Bridgeport, Jackson, Pop. 2,317
Jackson County SD
Supt. — See Scottsboro
Bridgeport MS 200/5-8
629 Dr Lee Ave 35740 256-495-2967
A.J. Buckner, prin. Fax 495-2850

Brilliant, Marion, Pop. 893
Marion County SD
Supt. — See Hamilton
Brilliant HS 200/7-12
PO Box 90 35548 205-465-2322
Jack Hayes, prin. Fax 465-2382

Brookwood, Tuscaloosa, Pop. 1,803
Tuscaloosa County SD
Supt. — See Tuscaloosa
Brookwood HS 1,000/9-12
12250 George Richmond Pkwy 35444 205-342-2777
Mark Franks, prin. Fax 247-4162

Brundidge, Pike, Pop. 2,052
Pike County SD
Supt. — See Troy
Pike County JSHS 500/7-12
552 S Main St 36010 334-735-2389
Willie Wright, prin. Fax 735-3176

Bryant, Jackson

Mountain View Christian Academy 100/PK-12
3665 AL Highway 73 35958 256-597-3467
Jonathan Aultman, prin. Fax 597-3467

Buhl, Tuscaloosa
Tuscaloosa County SD
Supt. — See Tuscaloosa
Sipsey Valley HS 500/9-12
15815 Romulus Rd 35446 205-342-2850
Dennis Alvarez, prin. Fax 342-2851
Sipsey Valley MS 400/6-8
15817 Romulus Rd 35446 205-342-2870
Frank Kelly, prin. Fax 342-2871

Butler, Choctaw, Pop. 1,876
Choctaw County SD 1,700/PK-12
107 Tom Orr Dr 36904 205-459-3031
Dorothy Banks, supt. Fax 459-3037
www.choctawal.org
Choctaw County HS 400/7-12
277 Tom Orr Dr 36904 205-459-2139
Celester Bolden, prin. Fax 459-2277
Other Schools – See Gilbertown

Patrician Academy 300/PK-12
901 S Mulberry Ave 36904 205-459-3605

Calera, Shelby, Pop. 11,417
Shelby County SD
Supt. — See Columbiana
Calera HS 700/9-12
100 Calera Eagle Dr 35040 205-682-6100
Joel Dixon, prin. Fax 682-6105

Camden, Wilcox, Pop. 2,011
Wilcox County SD 1,900/PK-12
PO Box 160 36726 334-682-4716
Andre Saulsberry, supt. Fax 682-4179
www.wilcox.k12.al.us
Camden S of Arts & Technology 300/7-8
PO Box 698 36726 334-682-4514
Andre Davis, prin. Fax 682-5934
Wilcox Central HS 500/9-12
PO Box 1089 36726 334-682-9239
Duane Hale, prin. Fax 682-5411
Wilcox County Alternative S Alt
PO Box 160 36726 334-682-5074
Robert Stallworth, admin. Fax 682-4769

Wilcox Academy 300/PK-12
PO Box 1149 36726 334-682-9619

Camp Hill, Tallapoosa, Pop. 1,004
Tallapoosa County SD
Supt. — See Dadeville
Bell Career Tech Center Vo/Tech
251 M L King St 36850 256-896-0160
Chad McKelvey, prin. Fax 896-0170

Lyman Ward Military Academy 100/6-12
PO Box 550 36850 256-798-9151
Dr. Roy Berwick, pres. Fax 896-4661

Carbon Hill, Walker, Pop. 1,992
Walker County SD
Supt. — See Jasper
Carbon Hill HS 400/9-12
217 Bulldog Blvd 35549 205-924-8821
Jody Claborn, prin. Fax 924-8877

Carrollton, Pickens, Pop. 1,006
Pickens County SD 2,700/K-12
377 Ladow Center Cir 35447 205-367-2082
Jamie Chapman, supt. Fax 367-8404
www.pickenscountyschools.net
Pickens County Career Center Vo/Tech
377 Ladow Center Cir 35447 205-367-2080
William Chan Mullenix, admin. Fax 367-8404
Other Schools – See Aliceville, Gordo, Reform

Pickens Academy 300/PK-12
225 Ray Bass Rd 35447 205-367-8144

Cecil, Montgomery

Macon East Academy 400/PK-12
15396 Vaughn Rd 36013 334-277-6566

Cedar Bluff, Cherokee, Pop. 1,779
Cherokee County SD
Supt. — See Centre
Cedar Bluff S 600/K-12
3655 Old Highway 9 35959 256-779-6211
Aubrey Thrasher, prin. Fax 779-8328

Centre, Cherokee, Pop. 3,423
Cherokee County SD 4,000/PK-12
130 E Main St 35960 256-927-3362
Mitchell Guice, supt. Fax 927-3399
www.cherokeek12.org
Centre MS 500/5-8
1920 E Main St 35960 256-927-5656
Jennifer Mackey, prin. Fax 927-4656
Cherokee Co. Career & Technology Center Vo/Tech
600 Bay Springs Rd 35960 256-927-5351
Brett Keasler, prin. Fax 927-3501
Cherokee County HS 500/9-12
910 Warrior Dr 35960 256-927-3625
Wisdom Neyman, prin. Fax 927-6445
Other Schools – See Cedar Bluff, Gaylesville, Sand Rock, Spring Garden

Centreville, Bibb, Pop. 2,751
Bibb County SD 3,300/PK-12
721 Walnut St 35042 205-926-9881
Duane McGee, supt. Fax 926-5075
www.bibbed.org/
Bibb County HS 500/9-12
220 Birmingham Rd 35042 205-926-9071
James Alston, prin. Fax 926-6848
Centreville MS 500/5-8
1621 Montgomery Hwy 35042 205-926-9861
Dr. Ernie Cutts, prin. Fax 926-3917
Other Schools – See West Blocton

Cahawba Christian Academy 100/PK-12
2415 Montevallo Rd 35042 205-926-4676
Gail Sammons, prin. Fax 926-4633

Chatom, Washington, Pop. 1,283
Washington County SD 3,100/K-12
PO Box 1359 36518 251-847-2401
Tim Savage, supt. Fax 847-3611
www.wcbek12.org
Washington County AVC Vo/Tech
PO Box 1298 36518 251-847-2040
David Wofford, prin. Fax 847-3489
Washington County JSHS 500/5-12
PO Box 1329 36518 251-847-2851
Rodney Smith, prin. Fax 847-2825
Other Schools – See Fruitdale, Leroy, Mc Intosh, Millry

Chelsea, Shelby, Pop. 10,063
Shelby County SD
Supt. — See Columbiana
Chelsea HS 1,100/9-12
PO Box 639 35043 205-682-7200
Kenneth Trucks, prin. Fax 682-7205
Chelsea MS 1,000/6-8
2321 Highway 39 35043 205-682-7210
Andrew Gunn, prin. Fax 682-7215

Cherokee, Colbert, Pop. 1,027
Colbert County SD
Supt. — See Tuscumbia
Cherokee HS 300/7-12
850 High School Dr 35616 256-359-4434
Pam Worsham, prin. Fax 359-4060

Chickasaw, Mobile, Pop. 6,039
Chickasaw CSD 900/PK-12
201 N Craft Hwy 36611 251-452-2256
Kathy Odom, supt. Fax 380-8380
www.chickasawschools.com
Chickasaw HS 400/6-12
50 Chieftan Way 36611 251-380-8120
Chris Pennington, prin. Fax 380-8115

Childersburg, Talladega, Pop. 5,086
Talladega County SD
Supt. — See Talladega
Childersburg HS 500/9-12
122 Faye S Perry Dr 35044 256-315-5475
Jesse Hooks, prin. Fax 315-5495
Childersburg MS 500/5-8
800 4th St SE 35044 256-315-5505
Jena Jones, prin. Fax 315-5520

Citronelle, Mobile, Pop. 3,830
Mobile County SD
Supt. — See Mobile
Citronelle HS 800/9-12
8200 E Lebaron Ave 36522 251-221-3444
Thomas Campbell, prin. Fax 221-3448
Lott MS 500/6-8
17740 Celeste Rd 36522 251-221-2240
Jason Golden, prin. Fax 221-2247

Clanton, Chilton, Pop. 8,519
Chilton County SD 7,700/PK-12
1705 Lay Dam Rd 35045 205-280-3000
Tommy Glasscock, supt. Fax 755-6549
www.chilton.k12.al.us
Chilton County HS 800/9-12
1214 7th St S 35045 205-280-2710
Dr. Cynthia Stewart, prin. Fax 755-0618
Clanton MS 700/6-8
835 Temple Rd 35045 205-280-2750
Carla White, prin. Fax 755-2446
LeCroy Career Technical Center Vo/Tech
2829 4th Ave N 35045 205-280-2920
Dara Norman, prin. Fax 755-2035
Other Schools – See Jemison, Maplesville, Thorsby, Verbena

Clayton, Barbour, Pop. 3,001
Barbour County SD 800/PK-12
PO Box 429 36016 334-775-3453
David Hobdy, supt. Fax 775-7301
barbourschools.org
Barbour County JSHS 200/7-12
PO Box 339 36016 334-775-3545
Undrea Johnson, prin. Fax 775-8861

Cleveland, Blount, Pop. 1,288
Blount County SD
Supt. — See Oneonta
Blount County Career Technology Vo/Tech
PO Box 125 35049 205-625-3424
Johnny Pullen, dir. Fax 625-3427
Cleveland HS 400/7-12
71 High School St 35049 205-274-9915
Chris Lakey, prin. Fax 274-0201

Collinsville, DeKalb, Pop. 1,945
De Kalb County SD
Supt. — See Rainsville
Collinsville S 900/K-12
802 S Valley Ave 35961 256-524-2111
Donny Jones, prin. Fax 524-7526

Columbia, Houston, Pop. 730
Houston County SD
Supt. — See Dothan
Houston County JSHS 400/7-12
200 W Church St 36319 334-696-2221
Derrick Morris, prin. Fax 696-4677

Columbiana, Shelby, Pop. 4,133
Shelby County SD 18,600/K-12
PO Box 1910 35051 205-682-7000
Randy Fuller, supt. Fax 682-7005
www.shelbyed.org
Columbiana MS 500/6-8
222 Joiner Town Rd 35051 205-682-6610
Dr. Kerry Rush, prin. Fax 682-6615
New Direction Alt
701 Highway 70 35051 205-682-5910
Michael Jones, prin. Fax 682-5915
Shelby County College & Career Center Vo/Tech
701 Highway 70 35051 205-682-6650
Zac McWhorter, prin. Fax 682-6655
Shelby County HS 600/9-12
101 Washington St 35051 205-682-6600
Barbara Snyder, prin. Fax 682-6605
Other Schools – See Birmingham, Calera, Chelsea, Helena, Montevallo, Vincent

---

Cornerstone Christian S 200/PK-12
24975 Highway 25 35051 205-669-7777
Tim Smith, dir. Fax 395-8304

Cordova, Walker, Pop. 2,077
Walker County SD
Supt. — See Jasper
Bankhead MS 300/5-8
110 School Rd 35550 205-483-7245
Amber Freeman, prin. Fax 483-7244

Cordova HS 500/9-12
183 School Rd 35550 205-483-7404
Kathy Vintson, prin. Fax 483-1934

Cottondale, Tuscaloosa
Tuscaloosa CSD
Supt. — See Tuscaloosa
Bryant HS 900/9-12
6315 Mary Harmon Bryant Dr 35453 205-759-3538
Linda Harper, prin. Fax 759-8315
Eastwood MS 600/6-8
6314 Mary Harmon Bryant Dr 35453 205-759-3613
Portia Martin, prin. Fax 759-3798

Tuscaloosa County SD
Supt. — See Tuscaloosa
Davis - Emerson MS 400/6-8
1500 Bulldog Blvd 35453 205-342-2750
Marlon Murray, prin. Fax 247-4169

Tuscaloosa Christian S 300/PK-12
1601 Prude Mill Rd 35453 205-553-4303
Dan Lancaster, prin. Fax 553-4259

Cottonwood, Houston, Pop. 1,266
Houston County SD
Supt. — See Dothan
Cottonwood S 700/K-12
663 Houston St 36320 334-691-2587
Judy Fowler, prin. Fax 691-4200

Courtland, Lawrence, Pop. 595
Lawrence County SD
Supt. — See Moulton
Hubbard HS 200/7-12
12905 Jessie Jackson Pkwy 35618 256-637-3010
Jewell Satchel, prin. Fax 637-3006

Crossville, DeKalb, Pop. 1,821
De Kalb County SD
Supt. — See Rainsville
Crossville HS 500/7-12
5405 County Road 28 35962 256-528-7858
David Uptain, prin. Fax 528-7840

Cullman, Cullman, Pop. 14,641
Cullman CSD 3,100/PK-12
301 1st St NE 35055 256-734-2233
Dr. Susan Patterson, supt. Fax 737-9621
www.cullmancats.net
Cullman City Career Tech S Vo/Tech
301 1st St NE 35055 256-734-2233
Joshua Swindall, prin. Fax 737-9621
Cullman HS 900/9-12
510 13th St NE 35055 256-734-3923
Kim Hall, prin. Fax 734-9570
Cullman MS 500/7-8
800 2nd Ave NE 35055 256-734-7959
Patrick Hill, prin. Fax 734-7711

Cullman County SD 9,500/PK-12
PO Box 1590 35056 256-734-2933
Shane Barnette, supt. Fax 736-2486
www.ccboe.org
CARE Alternative S Alt
192 County Road 940 35057 256-747-6371
Mike Grantham, coord. Fax 747-7376
Cullman Area Technology Academy Vo/Tech
17640 US Highway 31 35058 256-734-7740
Billy Troutman, prin. Fax 734-7464
Fairview HS 500/9-12
841 Welcome Rd 35058 256-796-5106
Dr. Chris Gambrill, prin. Fax 796-9025
Fairview MS 300/6-8
841 Welcome Rd 35058 256-796-0883
Trina Walker, prin. Fax 796-0885
Good Hope HS 400/9-12
210 Good Hope School Rd 35057 256-734-3807
John Hood, prin. Fax 734-3427
Good Hope MS 400/6-8
216 Good Hope School Rd 35057 256-734-9600
Alan Dunkling, prin. Fax 734-9704
West Point HS 600/9-12
4314 County Road 1141 35057 256-734-5375
Heith Yearwood, prin. Fax 775-6047
Other Schools – See Bremen, Hanceville, Holly Pond, Vinemont

St. Bernard Prep HS 100/9-12
101 Saint Bernard Ave SE 35055 256-739-6682
Dan Baillargeon, hdmstr. Fax 734-2925

Dadeville, Tallapoosa, Pop. 3,198
Tallapoosa County SD 3,100/PK-12
679 E Columbus St 36853 256-825-0746
Joseph Windle, supt. Fax 825-8224
www.tallapoosak12.org
Dadeville HS 500/7-12
227 Weldon St 36853 256-825-7848
Chris Hand, prin. Fax 825-0697
Tallapoosa County Alternative S 50/Alt
227 Weldon St 36853 256-825-7848
Raymond Porter, prin. Fax 825-0697
Other Schools – See Camp Hill, New Site, Notasulga

Daleville, Dale, Pop. 5,083
Daleville CSD 1,100/PK-12
626 N Daleville Ave 36322 334-598-2456
Dr. Diane Flournoy, supt. Fax 598-9006
www.daleville.k12.al.us
Daleville JSHS 600/7-12
626 N Daleville Ave 36322 334-598-4461
Joshua Robertson, prin. Fax 598-3850

Danville, Morgan
Morgan County SD
Supt. — See Decatur
Danville HS 400/9-12
9235 Danville Rd 35619 256-773-9909
Marty Chambers, prin. Fax 773-5622
Danville MS 400/5-8
5933 Highway 36 W 35619 256-773-7723
Gary Walker, prin. Fax 773-7708

Daphne, Baldwin, Pop. 21,279
Baldwin County SD
Supt. — See Bay Minette
Daphne HS 1,200/9-12
9300 Champions Way 36526 251-626-8787
Dr. Meredith Foster, prin. Fax 626-3024
Daphne MS 600/7-8
1 Jody Davis Cir 36526 251-626-2845
Tiffany Irby, prin. Fax 626-0025

Bayside Academy 800/PK-12
303 Dryer Ave 36526 251-338-6300
Michael Papa, head sch Fax 338-6310
United States Sports Academy Post-Sec.
1 Academy Dr 36526 251-626-3303

Deatsville, Elmore, Pop. 1,131
Autauga County SD
Supt. — See Prattville
Marbury HS 600/9-12
2360 US Highway 31 N 36022 334-387-1910
Donna Finch, prin. Fax 387-1920

Elmore County SD
Supt. — See Wetumpka
Holtville HS 500/9-12
10425 Holtville Rd 36022 334-569-3034
Kyle Futral, prin. Fax 569-1013
Holtville MS 500/5-8
655 Bulldog Ln 36022 334-569-1596
Lee Jackson, prin. Fax 569-3258

J. F. Ingram State Technical College Post-Sec.
PO Box 220350 36022 334-285-5177

Decatur, Morgan, Pop. 54,679
Decatur CSD 8,500/PK-12
302 4th Ave NE 35601 256-552-3000
Dr. Dan Brigman, supt. Fax 552-3981
www.dcs.edu
Austin HS 1,400/9-12
1625 Danville Rd SW 35601 256-552-3060
Dr. Melissa Scott, prin. Fax 350-7802
Brookhaven MS 400/6-8
1302 5th Ave SW 35601 256-552-3045
Anita Clarke, prin. Fax 552-3047
Cedar Ridge MS 900/6-8
2715 Danville Rd SW 35603 256-552-4622
Johnnie Renick, prin. Fax 552-4623
Decatur HS 1,000/9-12
1011 Prospect Dr SE 35601 256-552-3011
Dr. Johnny Berry, prin. Fax 308-2535
Oak Park MS 700/6-8
1218 16th Ave SE 35601 256-552-3035
Wes Black, prin. Fax 552-3082

Morgan County SD 7,800/PK-12
235 Highway 67 S 35603 256-353-6442
Bill Hopkins, supt. Fax 309-2187
www.morgank12.org
Priceville HS 400/9-12
317 Highway 67 S 35603 256-353-1950
Mark Mason, prin. Fax 353-2802
Priceville JHS 400/6-8
317 Highway 67 S 35603 256-355-5104
Mary Speegle, prin. Fax 355-5932
Other Schools – See Danville, Falkville, Hartselle, Somerville, Trinity

---

Calhoun Community College Post-Sec.
PO Box 2216 35609 256-306-2500
Decatur Heritage Christian Academy 400/K-12
PO Box 5659 35601 256-351-4275
Scott Mayo, hdmstr. Fax 355-4738

Demopolis, Marengo, Pop. 7,436
Demopolis CSD 2,200/PK-12
PO Box 759 36732 334-289-1670
Kyle Kallhoff, supt. Fax 289-1689
www.dcsedu.com
Demopolis HS 700/9-12
701 US Highway 80 W 36732 334-289-0294
Chris Tangle, prin. Fax 289-8777
Demopolis MS 600/6-8
300 E Pettus St 36732 334-289-4242
Blaine Hathcock, prin. Fax 289-2670

Dixons Mills, Marengo
Marengo County SD
Supt. — See Linden
Marengo S 200/PK-12
212 Panther Dr 36736 334-992-2395
David Miller, prin. Fax 992-2197

Dora, Walker, Pop. 1,996
Jefferson County SD
Supt. — See Birmingham
Corner HS 500/9-12
4301 Warrior Jasper Rd 35062 205-379-3200
Ronald Cooper, prin. Fax 379-3245

Walker County SD
Supt. — See Jasper
Dora HS 500/9-12
330 Glenn C Gant Cir 35062 205-648-6863
Paige Skalnik, prin. Fax 648-4709

Dothan, Houston, Pop. 64,426
Dothan CSD 9,400/PK-12
500 Dusy St 36301 334-793-1397
Dr. Charles Ledbetter, supt. Fax 794-1499
www.dothan.k12.al.us
Beverlye Magnet MS 500/6-8
1025 S Beverlye Rd 36301 334-794-1432
Maria Johnson, prin. Fax 792-0886
Carver Magnet MS 600/6-8
1001 Webb Rd 36303 334-794-1440
Dr. Donnie Chambers, prin. Fax 794-1587
Dothan HS 1,200/9-12
1236 S Oates St 36301 334-794-1400
Stan Eldridge, prin. Fax 677-0099
Dothan Technology Center Vo/Tech
3165 Reeves St 36303 334-794-1436
Joey Meigs, prin. Fax 794-1439
Girard MS 500/6-8
600 Girard Ave 36303 334-794-1426
Darius McKay, prin. Fax 794-6373
Honeysuckle MS 600/6-8
1665 Honeysuckle Rd 36305 334-794-1420
Jeffrey Torrence, prin. Fax 678-6546
Northview HS 1,300/9-12
3209 Reeves St 36303 334-794-1410
Charles Corbitt, prin. Fax 702-4802
PASS Academy Alt
201 E Wilson St 36303 334-671-1474
Edward Fleming, prin. Fax 677-7480

Houston County SD 6,300/PK-12
404 W Washington St 36301 334-792-8331
David Sewell, supt. Fax 792-1016
hcboe.us
Houston County Alternative S Alt
315 N Foster St 36303 334-671-9295
Scott Stephens, prin. Fax 794-1016
Rehobeth HS 700/9-12
373 Malvern Rd 36301 334-677-7002
Bobby Boyd, prin. Fax 677-2699
Rehobeth MS 500/6-8
5631 County Road 203 36301 334-677-5153
John Dixon, prin. Fax 677-5947
Other Schools – See Ashford, Columbia, Cottonwood, Newton

Alabama College of Osteopathic Medicine Post-Sec.
445 Health Sciences Blvd 36303 334-699-2266
Emmanuel Christian S 500/PK-12
178 Earline Rd 36305 334-792-0935
Mark Redmond, admin. Fax 702-7410
Flowers Hospital Post-Sec.
PO Box 6907 36302 334-793-5000
Fortis College Post-Sec.
200 Vulcan Way 36303 334-677-2832
Houston Academy 600/PK-12
901 Buena Vista Dr 36303 334-794-4106
Dr. Scott Phillipps, hdmstr. Fax 793-4053
Northside Methodist Academy 400/PK-12
2600 Redmond Rd 36303 334-794-7273
Bill Reif, head sch Fax 702-8941
Providence Christian S 700/1-12
4847 Murphy Mill Rd 36303 334-702-8933
Emory Latta, head sch Fax 702-0700
Southeast Alabama Medical Center Post-Sec.
PO Box 6987 36302 334-793-8100
Wallace Community College Post-Sec.
1141 Wallace Dr 36303 334-983-3521

Double Springs, Winston, Pop. 1,073
Winston County SD 2,600/PK-12
PO Box 9 35553 205-489-5018
Gregory Pendley, supt. Fax 717-3391
www.winstonk12.org
Double Springs MS 300/5-8
PO Box 669 35553 205-489-3813
Ben Aderholt, prin. Fax 717-3392
Winston County HS 300/9-12
PO Box 549 35553 205-489-5593
Jeff Cole, prin. Fax 489-8204
Winston County Technical Center Vo/Tech
PO Box 1000 35553 205-489-2190
Barton Shannon, prin. Fax 717-3396
Other Schools – See Addison, Arley, Lynn

Douglas, Marshall, Pop. 724
Marshall County SD
Supt. — See Guntersville
Douglas HS 500/9-12
PO Box 300 35964 256-593-2810
Craig Ross, prin. Fax 840-5489
Douglas MS 500/6-8
PO Box 269 35964 256-593-1240
Rita Walker, prin. Fax 593-1259

Duncanville, Tuscaloosa
Tuscaloosa County SD
Supt. — See Tuscaloosa
Duncanville MS 500/6-8
11205 Eagle Pkwy 35456 205-342-2830
Darrell Williams, prin. Fax 759-1998

East Brewton, Escambia, Pop. 2,446
Escambia County SD
Supt. — See Brewton
Neal HS 400/9-12
801 Andrew Jackson St 36426 251-867-4645
Patricia Frazier, prin. Fax 867-4642
Neal MS 400/5-8
703 Williamson St 36426 251-867-5035
Dr. Laura Leigh Rambach, prin. Fax 867-5051

Eclectic, Elmore, Pop. 979
Elmore County SD
Supt. — See Wetumpka
Eclectic MS 500/5-8
170 S Ann St 36024 334-541-2131
Blair Andress, prin. Fax 541-3556
Elmore County HS 500/9-12
155 N College Ave 36024 334-541-3662
Wes Rogers, prin. Fax 541-4441

Eight Mile, See Prichard
Mobile County SD
Supt. — See Mobile
Blount HS 1,000/9-12
5450 Lott Rd 36613 251-221-3070
Jerome Woods, prin. Fax 221-3075

Elba, Coffee, Pop. 3,889
Coffee County SD 2,000/PK-12
400 Reddoch Hill Rd 36323 334-897-5016
Terry Weeks, supt. Fax 897-6207
www.coffeecountyschools.org
Other Schools – See Jack, Kinston, New Brockton

Elba CSD 700/K-12
131 Tiger Dr 36323 334-897-2801
Chresal Threadgill, supt. Fax 897-5601
www.elbaed.com
Elba Area Vocational HS Vo/Tech
371 Tiger Dr 36323 334-897-2266
Fax 897-5106
Elba HS 300/7-12
371 Tiger Dr 36323 334-897-2266
Chris Moseley, prin. Fax 897-5106

Elberta, Baldwin, Pop. 1,467
Baldwin County SD
Supt. — See Bay Minette
Elberta MS 500/4-8
13355 Main St 36530 251-986-8127
Claude Eilert, prin. Fax 986-7472

Elkmont, Limestone, Pop. 433
Limestone County SD
Supt. — See Athens
Elkmont S 1,100/K-12
25630 Evans Ave 35620 256-732-4291
William Tribble, prin. Fax 732-3418

Elmore, Elmore

Edgewood Academy 300/PK-12
PO Box 160 36025 334-567-5102
Clint Welch, head sch Fax 567-8316

Enterprise, Coffee, Pop. 25,851
Enterprise CSD 5,600/PK-12
PO Box 311790 36331 334-347-9531
Dr. Camille Wright, supt. Fax 347-5102
www.enterpriseschools.net/
Coppinville JHS 500/7-8
301 N Ouida St 36330 334-347-2215
David West, prin. Fax 347-7895
Dauphin JHS 300/7-8
1271 Dauphin Street Ext 36330 334-347-1141
Judy Thomas, prin. Fax 347-0845
Enterprise HS 1,600/9-12
1801 Boll Weevil Cir 36330 334-347-2640
Matt Rodgers, prin. Fax 347-3144

Enterprise State Community College Post-Sec.
PO Box 1300 36331 334-347-2623

Eufaula, Barbour, Pop. 13,021
Eufaula CSD 2,900/PK-12
333 State Docks Rd 36027 334-687-1100
Dr. Elisabeth Davis, supt. Fax 687-1150
www.ecs.k12.al.us
Eufaula HS 800/9-12
530 Lake Dr 36027 334-687-1110
Steve Hawkins, prin. Fax 687-1121
Moorer MS 600/6-8
101 Saint Francis Rd 36027 334-687-1130
Tania McKey, prin. Fax 687-1138

Lakeside S 300/PK-12
1020 Lake Dr 36027 334-687-5748

Eutaw, Greene, Pop. 2,918
Greene County SD 900/PK-12
220 Main St 35462 205-372-3161
Dr. James Carter, supt. Fax 372-3247
www.greene.k12.al.us
Brown MS 100/7-8
720 Greensboro St 35462 205-372-4816
Barbara Martin, prin. Fax 372-4828
Greene County Career Center Vo/Tech
627 Mesopotamia St 35462 205-372-4636
Dr. Rhinnie Scott, prin. Fax 372-2358
Greene County HS 300/9-12
PO Box 658 35462 205-372-3789
Garry Rice, prin. Fax 372-3404

Evergreen, Conecuh, Pop. 3,925
Conecuh County SD 1,600/PK-12
100 Jackson St 36401 251-578-1752
Zickeyous Byrd Ed.D., supt. Fax 578-7061
www.conecuh.k12.al.us
Genesis S Alt
111 Perryman St 36401 251-578-5291
Susan Brewton-Coleman, prin. Fax 578-2377
Hillcrest HS 400/9-12
1989 Jaguar Dr 36401 251-578-1126
Katrina Roper-Smith, prin. Fax 578-7071
Marshall MS 200/6-8
428 Reynolds Ave 36401 251-578-2866
LaTonya Gill, prin. Fax 578-7067

Reid State Technical College Post-Sec.
PO Box 588 36401 251-578-1313
Sparta Academy 200/PK-12
300 Pierce St 36401 251-578-2852
Wayne Hammonds, prin. Fax 578-2878

Excel, Monroe, Pop. 708
Monroe County SD
Supt. — See Monroeville
Excel S 1,100/PK-12
PO Box 429 36439 251-765-2351
Marty Hanks, prin. Fax 765-9153

Fairfield, Jefferson, Pop. 11,062
Fairfield CSD 1,900/K-12
6405 Avenue D 35064 205-783-6850
Walter Gonsoulin Ph.D., supt. Fax 783-6805
fairfield.cyberschool.com
Fairfield Alternative S Alt
6405 Avenue D 35064 205-264-9501
Dr. Gordon Fears, prin. Fax 783-6810
Fairfield Area Vocational HS Vo/Tech
610 Valley Rd 35064 205-785-5176
Valerie Holmes, prin. Fax 783-6748
Fairfield Preparatory HS 600/9-12
610 Valley Rd 35064 205-785-5176
Michelle Hayes, prin. Fax 783-6748
Forest Hills Community Development Ctr 300/7-8
610 Valley Rd 35064 205-264-9655
Shun Williams, prin.

Miles College Post-Sec.
5500 Myron Massey Blvd 35064 205-929-1000
Restoration Academy 300/K-12
PO Box 30 35064 205-785-8805
Brian Goessling, prin. Fax 785-8809

Fairhope, Baldwin, Pop. 15,206
Baldwin County SD
Supt. — See Bay Minette
Fairhope HS 1,500/9-12
1 Pirate Dr 36532 251-928-8309
Jan Cardwell, prin. Fax 990-2053
Fairhope MS 800/7-8
2 Pirate Dr 36532 251-928-2573
Angie Hall, prin. Fax 990-0403

Bayshore Christian S 200/K-12
23050 US Highway 98 36532 251-929-0011
Dr. Pamela McKee, head sch
St. Michael Catholic HS 100/9-10
11732 Higbee Rd 36532 251-459-0210
Faustin Weber, prin.

Falkville, Morgan, Pop. 1,257
Morgan County SD
Supt. — See Decatur
Falkville JSHS 400/6-12
43 Clark Dr 35622 256-784-5248
Dennis Morris, prin. Fax 784-9438

Fayette, Fayette, Pop. 4,573
Fayette County SD 2,400/PK-12
PO Box 686 35555 205-932-4611
Jim Burkhalter, supt. Fax 932-7246
www.fayette.k12.al.us
Fayette County HS 500/9-12
202 Tiger Dr 35555 205-932-6313
Dr. Jeremy Madden, prin. Fax 932-8361
Fayette MS 500/5-8
418 3rd Ave NE 35555 205-932-7660
Rodney Hannah, prin. Fax 932-7661
Hubbertville S 400/PK-12
7360 County Road 49 35555 205-487-2845
Tim Dunavant, prin. Fax 487-3375
Other Schools – See Berry

Flomaton, Escambia, Pop. 1,423
Escambia County SD
Supt. — See Brewton
Escambia County Alternative S Alt
21280 Highway 31 36441 251-296-4113
Dr. Anthony Morris, prin. Fax 296-4075
Flomaton HS 300/9-12
21200 Highway 31 36441 251-296-2627
Scott Hammond, prin. Fax 296-2625

Florala, Covington, Pop. 1,935
Covington County SD
Supt. — See Andalusia
Florala HS 200/7-12
22114 Begonia St 36442 334-858-3765
Max Whittaker, prin. Fax 858-6925

Florence, Lauderdale, Pop. 38,649
Florence CSD 4,400/PK-12
PO Box 10 35631 256-768-3000
Dr. Janet Womack, supt. Fax 768-3009
www.florencek12.org/
Florence Career Technical Education Vo/Tech
PO Box 10 35631 256-768-3021
Darrin Lett, admin. Fax 768-3010
Florence Freshman Center 400/9-9
1203 Bradshaw Dr 35630 256-768-2400
Rod Sheppard, prin. Fax 768-2405
Florence HS 900/10-12
1201 Bradshaw Dr 35630 256-768-2200
Lynne Hice, prin. Fax 768-2205
Florence MS 700/7-8
1603 Appleby Blvd 35630 256-768-3100
Aimee Rainey, prin. Fax 768-3105

Lauderdale County SD 8,600/PK-12
PO Box 278 35631 256-760-1300
Dr. Jennifer Gray, supt. Fax 766-5815
www.lcschools.org
Central S 1,400/PK-12
3000 County Road 200 35633 256-764-2903
Duane Keener, prin. Fax 764-5409
Rogers S 1,200/PK-12
300 Rogers Ln 35634 256-757-3106
David Matthews, prin. Fax 757-9625
Wilson S 1,300/PK-12
7601 Highway 17 35634 256-764-8470
Gary Horton, prin. Fax 764-1304
Other Schools – See Killen, Lexington, Rogersville, Waterloo

Heritage Christian University Post-Sec.
PO Box HCU 35630 256-766-6610
Mars Hill Bible S 600/PK-12
698 Cox Creek Pkwy 35630 256-767-1203
Dexter Rutherford, pres. Fax 767-6304
Shoals Christian S 200/PK-12
301 Heathrow Dr 35633 256-767-7070
Jim Koan M.A., hdmstr. Fax 766-5677
University of North Alabama Post-Sec.
1 Harrison Plz 35632 256-765-4100

Foley, Baldwin, Pop. 14,389
Baldwin County SD
Supt. — See Bay Minette
Foley HS 1,700/9-12
1 Pride Pl 36535 251-943-2221
Russ Moore, prin. Fax 943-3538
Foley MS 700/7-8
201 N Pine St 36535 251-943-1255
Danny McDuffie, prin. Fax 943-8221

Alabama Gulf Coast Christian Academy 100/PK-12
18930 County Road 28 36535 251-989-2333
Fortis College Post-Sec.
200 E Laurel Ave 36535 251-970-1460

Fort Deposit, Lowndes, Pop. 1,336
Lowndes County SD
Supt. — See Hayneville
Lowndes County MS 200/6-8
PO Box 393 36032 334-227-4206
Archie Curtis, prin. Fax 227-4125

Fort Payne, DeKalb, Pop. 13,756
Fort Payne CSD 3,100/PK-12
PO Box 681029 35968 256-845-0915
James Cunningham, supt. Fax 845-4962
www.ftpayk12.org
Fort Payne HS 800/9-12
201 45th St NE 35967 256-845-0535
Brian Jett, prin. Fax 845-7868
Fort Payne MS 900/5-8
4910 Martin Ave NE 35967 256-845-7501
Shane Byrd, prin. Fax 845-8292

Fruitdale, Washington, Pop. 184
Washington County SD
Supt. — See Chatom
Fruitdale S 400/K-12
PO Box 448 36539 251-827-6655
Curtis Stagner, prin. Fax 827-6573

Fyffe, DeKalb, Pop. 992
De Kalb County SD
Supt. — See Rainsville
Fyffe S 1,000/K-12
PO Box 7 35971 256-623-2116
Ricky Bryant, prin. Fax 623-4388

Gadsden, Etowah, Pop. 36,211
Etowah County SD 9,100/PK-12
3200 W Meighan Blvd 35904 256-549-7560
Dr. Alan Cosby, supt. Fax 549-7589
www.ecboe.org
Gaston S 600/K-12
4550 US Highway 411 35901 256-547-0047
Tammy George, prin. Fax 543-7124
Hokes Bluff HS 400/9-12
1865 Appalachian Hwy 35903 256-492-1360
Scott Calhoun, prin. Fax 492-7502
Hokes Bluff MS 300/6-8
3121 Appalachian Hwy 35903 256-492-1963
Greg Watkins, prin. Fax 492-1950
Other Schools – See Attalla, Boaz, Glencoe, Rainbow City, Sardis City, Southside, Walnut Grove

Gadsden CSD 5,900/K-12
PO Box 184 35902 256-543-3512
Dr. Ed Miller, supt. Fax 549-2950
www.gcs.k12.al.us
Gadsden City HS 1,600/9-12
1917 Black Creek Pkwy 35904 256-543-3614
Jeffrey Colegrove, prin. Fax 543-4251
Gadsden MS 500/6-8
612 Tracy St 35901 256-547-6341
Joel Gulledge, prin. Fax 547-6323
Litchfield MS 200/6-8
1109 Hoke St 35903 256-492-6793
Dr. Charlie Parker, prin. Fax 492-4010
Sansom MS 500/6-8
2210 W Meighan Blvd 35904 256-546-4992
Russell Waits, prin. Fax 543-1060
Secondary Alternative S 600/Alt
607 S 12th St 35901 256-547-5446
Donna Smoots, prin. Fax 547-5448

Coosa Christian S 300/PK-12
2736 Wills Creek Rd 35904 256-547-1841
Amanda Justus, admin. Fax 547-0045
Gadsden State Community College Post-Sec.
PO Box 227 35902 256-549-8200
Holy Comforter Episcopal Day S 100/PK-12
156 S 9th St 35901 256-546-9071
Laura McCartney, hdmstr. Fax 546-7912

Gardendale, Jefferson, Pop. 13,766
Jefferson County SD
Supt. — See Birmingham
Bragg MS 900/6-8
840 Ash Ave 35071 205-379-2600
Larry Robertson, prin. Fax 379-2645
Gardendale HS 1,100/9-12
800 Main St 35071 205-379-3600
Jeff Caufield, prin. Fax 379-3645

Alabama State College of Barber Styling Post-Sec.
753 Main St 35071 205-631-8898

Gaylesville, Cherokee, Pop. 143
Cherokee County SD
Supt. — See Centre
Gaylesville S 400/PK-12
760 Trojan Way 35973 256-422-3401
Scott Hays, prin. Fax 422-3165

Geneva, Geneva, Pop. 4,382
Geneva CSD 1,300/K-12
511 Panther Dr 36340 334-684-1090
Rhonda Stringham, supt. Fax 684-3128
www.genevacity.schoolinsites.com
Geneva HS 300/9-12
505 Panther Dr 36340 334-684-9379
Mickey Bennett, prin. Fax 684-0303
Geneva MS 300/6-8
501 Panther Dr 36340 334-684-6431
Danny Bedsole, prin. Fax 684-0476

Geneva County SD 2,700/K-12
PO Box 250 36340 334-684-5690
Becky Birdsong, supt. Fax 684-5601
genevacounty.schoolinsites.com/
Other Schools – See Hartford, Samson, Slocomb

Georgiana, Butler, Pop. 1,722
Butler County SD
Supt. — See Greenville
Georgiana S 500/K-12
PO Box 680 36033 334-376-9130
Bryant Marlow, prin. Fax 376-2956

Geraldine, DeKalb, Pop. 882
De Kalb County SD
Supt. — See Rainsville
Geraldine S 1,200/K-12
13011 AL Highway 227 35974 256-659-2142
Steven Street, prin. Fax 659-4296

Gilbertown, Choctaw, Pop. 214
Choctaw County SD
Supt. — See Butler
Southern Choctaw HS 400/7-12
10941 Highway 17 36908 251-843-5645
Dr. Leo Leddon, prin. Fax 843-5649

Glencoe, Etowah, Pop. 5,099
Etowah County SD
Supt. — See Gadsden
Glencoe HS 300/9-12
803 Lonesome Bend Rd 35905 256-492-2250
Charlton Giles, prin. Fax 492-2265
Glencoe MS 300/5-8
809 Lonesome Bend Rd 35905 256-492-5627
Tisha Howell, prin. Fax 492-7076

Gordo, Pickens, Pop. 1,715
Pickens County SD
Supt. — See Carrollton
Gordo JSHS 500/7-12
630 4th St NW 35466 205-364-7353
Mark Capps, prin. Fax 364-6160

Goshen, Pike, Pop. 265
Pike County SD
Supt. — See Troy
Goshen JSHS 500/7-12
286 Eagle Cir 36035 334-484-3245
Major Lane, prin. Fax 484-3247

Grady, Montgomery

South Montgomery County Academy 100/PK-12
PO Box 10 36036 334-562-3235
Dannelly Martin, head sch Fax 562-9059

Grand Bay, Mobile, Pop. 3,617
Mobile County SD
Supt. — See Mobile
Grand Bay MS 800/6-8
12800 Cunningham Rd 36541 251-865-6511
Wendell Ellis, prin. Fax 221-2405

Grant, Marshall, Pop. 887
Marshall County SD
Supt. — See Guntersville
Smith DAR HS 500/9-12
6077 Main St 35747 256-728-4238
Stacy Anderton, prin. Fax 728-8900
Smith DAR MS 400/5-8
6077 Main St 35747 256-728-5950
Tim Isbill, prin. Fax 728-8447

Greensboro, Hale, Pop. 2,483
Hale County SD 2,300/PK-12
1115 Powers St 36744 334-624-8836
Osie A. Pickens, supt. Fax 624-3415
www.halek12.org
College and Career Academy Vo/Tech
PO Box 517 36744 334-624-3691
James Essex, prin. Fax 624-1090
Greensboro HS 400/9-12
620 Carver St 36744 334-624-9156
Dr. Jessica Constant, prin. Fax 624-9157
Greensboro MS 300/6-8
620 Carver St 36744 334-624-4005
Anthony Sanders, prin. Fax 624-0308
Other Schools – See Moundville

Southern Academy 200/PK-12
407 College St 36744 334-624-8111
Marc Mickleboro, hdmstr. Fax 624-3778

Greenville, Butler, Pop. 8,092
Butler County SD 3,200/K-12
211 School Highlands Rd 36037 334-382-2665
Amy Bryan, supt. Fax 382-8607
www.butlerco.k12.al.us
Butler County Area Vocational HS Vo/Tech
100 Tiger Dr 36037 334-382-0266
Jennifer Burt, prin. Fax 382-8607
Greenville HS 700/9-12
100 Tiger Dr 36037 334-382-2608
Joseph Dean, prin. Fax 382-7202
Greenville MS 700/5-8
300 Overlook Rd 36037 334-382-3450
Catherine Tanner, prin. Fax 382-0686
Other Schools – See Georgiana, Mc Kenzie

Fort Dale Academy 400/K-12
1100 Gamble St 36037 334-382-2606

Grove Hill, Clarke, Pop. 1,558
Clarke County SD 3,100/PK-12
PO Box 936 36451 251-275-3255
Larry Bagley, supt. Fax 275-8061
www.clarkecountyschools.org/
Clarke County HS 400/9-12
PO Box 937 36451 251-275-3368
Debra Dennis, prin. Fax 275-4132
Wilson Hall MS 400/5-8
401 Carter Dr 36451 251-275-8993
Carolyn Taite, prin. Fax 275-4688
Other Schools – See Jackson

Clarke Preparatory S 300/PK-12
20100 Highway 43 36451 251-275-8576
Doug Bradford, hdmstr. Fax 275-8579

Guin, Marion, Pop. 2,339
Marion County SD
Supt. — See Hamilton
Marion County HS 300/7-12
PO Box 549 35563 205-468-3377
Jason Bourland, prin. Fax 468-8047

Gulf Shores, Baldwin, Pop. 9,533
Baldwin County SD
Supt. — See Bay Minette
Gulf Shores HS 800/9-12
600 E 15th Ave 36542 251-968-4747
Dr. Ernie Rosado, prin. Fax 968-4770
Gulf Shores MS 500/7-8
450 E 15th Ave 36542 251-968-8719
Kyle McCartney, prin. Fax 967-1577

South Baldwin Christian Academy PK-12
6900 Highway 59 36542 251-968-1230
Dawn Cranston, head sch Fax 265-3349

Guntersville, Marshall, Pop. 8,040
Guntersville CSD 2,000/PK-12
PO Box 129 35976 256-582-3159
Brett Stanton, supt. Fax 582-6158
www.guntersvilleboe.com
Guntersville HS 600/9-12
14227 US Highway 431 35976 256-582-2046
Roseanne Mabrey, prin. Fax 582-4742
Guntersville MS 500/6-8
901 Sunset Dr 35976 256-582-5182
Jeff Jones, prin. Fax 582-4477

Marshall County SD 5,600/PK-12
12380 US Highway 431 35976 256-582-3171
Dr. Cindy Wigley, supt. Fax 582-3178
www.marshallk12.org
Brindlee Mountain HS 400/9-12
994 Scant City Rd 35976 256-753-2800
David McCollum, prin. Fax 753-2802
Brindlee Mountain MS 300/6-8
1050 Scant City Rd 35976 256-753-2820
Mike Little, prin. Fax 753-2822
Marshall Technical HS Vo/Tech
12312 US Highway 431 35976 256-582-5629
Sherman Leeth, prin. Fax 582-2580
Other Schools – See Albertville, Douglas, Grant

Gurley, Madison, Pop. 783
Madison County SD
Supt. — See Huntsville
Madison County HS 500/9-12
174 Brock Rd 35748 256-851-3270
Jeremy Lowry, prin. Fax 851-3272

Hackleburg, Marion, Pop. 1,499
Marion County SD
Supt. — See Hamilton
Hackleburg HS 200/7-12
PO Box 310 35564 205-935-3223
John Hardin, prin. Fax 935-8092

Haleyville, Winston, Pop. 4,111
Haleyville CSD 1,700/PK-12
2011 20th St 35565 205-486-9231
Alan Miller, supt. Fax 486-8833
haley-k12.us
Haleyville Center of Technology Vo/Tech
2007 20th St 35565 205-486-9481
William Bishop, prin. Fax 486-8735
Haleyville HS 500/9-12
2001 20th St 35565 205-486-3122
Holly Sutherland, prin. Fax 486-1660
Haleyville MS 400/6-8
2014 20th Ave 35565 205-486-9240
Richard Wilcoxson, prin. Fax 486-9244

Hamilton, Marion, Pop. 6,817
Marion County SD 3,500/PK-12
188 Winchester Dr 35570 205-921-3191
Ryan Hollingsworth, supt. Fax 921-7336
www.mcbe.net
Hamilton HS 500/9-12
211 Aggie Ave 35570 205-921-3281
Ronnie Miller, prin. Fax 921-2333
Hamilton MS 600/5-8
400 Military St S 35570 205-921-7030
Steven Deavours, prin. Fax 921-3821
Marion County Alternative S 50/Alt
188 Winchester Dr 35570 205-952-9083
Patrick Sutton, lead tchr. Fax 952-9083
Other Schools – See Bear Creek, Brilliant, Guin, Hackleburg

Hampton Cove, Madison
Huntsville CSD
Supt. — See Huntsville

Hampton Cove MS 600/6-8
261 Old Highway 431 Ste B 35763 256-428-8380
Dr. Debi Edwards, prin. Fax 428-8383

Hanceville, Cullman, Pop. 2,928
Cullman County SD
Supt. — See Cullman
Hanceville HS 400/9-12
801 Commercial St SE 35077 256-352-6111
Jimmy Collins, prin. Fax 352-6491
Hanceville MS 300/6-8
805 Commercial St SE 35077 256-352-6175
Cynthia Roden, prin. Fax 352-9741

Wallace State Community College Post-Sec.
PO Box 2000 35077 256-352-8000

Harpersville, Shelby, Pop. 1,615

Coosa Valley Academy 300/K-12
PO Box 250 35078 205-672-7326

Hartford, Geneva, Pop. 2,582
Geneva County SD
Supt. — See Geneva
Geneva County HS 200/9-12
301 Lily St 36344 334-588-2943
Kevin LeSueur, prin. Fax 588-3650
Geneva County MS 200/6-8
301 Lily St 36344 334-588-2943
Leslie Habbard, prin. Fax 588-3650

Hartselle, Morgan, Pop. 14,036
Hartselle CSD 2,600/PK-12
305 College St NE 35640 256-773-5419
Dr. Vic Wilson, supt. Fax 773-5433
www.hartselletigers.org
Hartselle HS 1,000/9-12
1000 Bethel Rd NE 35640 256-751-5615
Dr. Jeff Hyche, prin. Fax 751-5638
Hartselle JHS 500/7-8
904 Sparkman St SW 35640 256-773-5426
Dr. Robbie Smith, prin. Fax 751-5658

Morgan County SD
Supt. — See Decatur
Morgan County Learning Center Alt
72 Plainview St 35640 256-773-6458
Layne Dillard, prin. Fax 309-2158

Harvest, Madison, Pop. 5,123
Madison County SD
Supt. — See Huntsville
Sparkman HS 1,800/10-12
2616 Jeff Rd 35749 256-837-0331
Chris Shaw, prin. Fax 837-7673
Sparkman Ninth Grade S 700/9-9
2680 Jeff Rd 35749 256-851-4560
Martin Hester, prin. Fax 851-4561

Hayden, Blount, Pop. 432
Blount County SD
Supt. — See Oneonta
Hayden HS 900/8-12
125 Atwood Rd 35079 205-647-0397
Allen Hargett, prin. Fax 647-8633

Hayneville, Lowndes, Pop. 928
Lowndes County SD 1,700/K-12
PO Box 755 36040 334-548-2131
Dr. Daniel Boyd, supt. Fax 548-2161
www.lowndesboe.org/
Central HS 200/9-12
145 Main St 36040 334-563-7311
Toriano Baker, prin. Fax 563-7299
Hayneville MS 200/6-8
PO Box 307 36040 334-548-2184
Keith Scissum, prin. Fax 548-5237
Project Success Learning Center Alt
147 Main St 36040 334-563-9869
Fax 563-9869
Other Schools – See Fort Deposit, Letohatchee

Hazel Green, Madison, Pop. 3,538
Madison County SD
Supt. — See Huntsville
Hazel Green HS 1,400/9-12
14380 Highway 231 431 N 35750 256-851-3220
Darrell Long, prin. Fax 851-3221
Meridianville MS 700/7-8
12975 Highway 231 431 N 35750 256-851-4550
David Manning, prin. Fax 851-4551

Headland, Henry, Pop. 4,460
Henry County SD
Supt. — See Abbeville
Headland HS 400/10-12
8 Sporman St 36345 334-585-7086
Jason Bradford, prin. Fax 585-7088
Headland MS 500/6-9
1 Martin Luther King Dr 36345 334-585-7083
Kevin Sanders, prin. Fax 585-7085

Heflin, Cleburne, Pop. 3,431
Cleburne County SD 2,700/PK-12
141 Davenport Dr 36264 256-463-5624
Claire Dryden, supt. Fax 463-5709
www.cleburneschools.net
Cleburne County Career Technical S Vo/Tech
11200 Highway 46 36264 256-748-2961
Eric Lovvorn, prin. Fax 748-3904
Cleburne County HS 700/8-12
520 Evans Bridge Rd 36264 256-463-2012
Valrie Bain, prin. Fax 463-5504
Other Schools – See Ranburne

Helena, Shelby, Pop. 16,576
Shelby County SD
Supt. — See Columbiana

Helena HS 9-12
1310 Hillsboro Pkwy 35080 205-682-3650
April Brand, prin. Fax 682-3655
Helena MS 900/6-8
1299 Hillsboro Pkwy 35080 205-682-5300
Scott Knight, prin. Fax 682-5305

Higdon, Jackson
Jackson County SD
Supt. — See Scottsboro
North Sand Mountain S 700/K-12
PO Box 129 35979 256-597-2111
Dustin Roden, prin. Fax 597-2505

Highland Home, Crenshaw
Crenshaw County SD
Supt. — See Luverne
Highland Home S 800/PK-12
18434 Montgomery Hwy 36041 334-537-4379
Cliff Maddox, prin. Fax 537-9805

Holly Pond, Cullman, Pop. 794
Cullman County SD
Supt. — See Cullman
Holly Pond HS 300/9-12
160 New Hope Rd 35083 256-796-5169
Kim Butler, prin. Fax 796-5199
Holly Pond MS 300/6-8
91 Buckner Rd 35083 256-796-5898
Dr. Chuck Gambrill, prin. Fax 796-0680

Hollywood, Jackson, Pop. 967
Jackson County SD
Supt. — See Scottsboro
Pruett Center of Technology Vo/Tech
29490 US Highway 72 35752 256-574-6079
Kerry Wright, prin. Fax 259-1644

Homewood, Jefferson, Pop. 24,859
Homewood CSD 3,800/K-12
450 Dale Ave 35209 205-870-4203
Dr. Bill Cleveland, supt. Fax 877-4544
www.homewood.k12.al.us
Homewood HS 1,000/9-12
1901 Lakeshore Dr S 35209 205-871-9663
Dr. Zack Barnes, prin. Fax 879-0879
Homewood MS 900/6-8
395 Mecca Ave 35209 205-870-0878
Jimmie Pearson, prin. Fax 877-4573

Islamic Academy of Alabama 200/PK-12
1810 25th Ct S 35209 205-870-0422

Hoover, Jefferson, Pop. 80,440
Hoover CSD 13,900/K-12
2810 Metropolitan Way 35243 205-439-1000
Dr. Kathy Murphy, supt. Fax 439-1003
www.hoover.k12.al.us
Bumpus MS 900/7-8
6055 Fleming Pkwy 35244 205-439-2200
Dr. Tamala Maddox, prin. Fax 439-2201
Crossroads S Alt
1000 Buccaneer Dr 35244 205-439-1800
Anna Whitney, prin. Fax 439-1899
Hoover HS 2,800/9-12
1000 Buccaneer Dr 35244 205-439-1200
Don Hulin, prin. Fax 439-1201
Simmons MS 800/6-8
1575 Patton Chapel Rd 35226 205-439-2100
Brian Cain, prin. Fax 439-2101
Other Schools – See Birmingham, Vestavia Hills

Shades Mountain Christian S 400/PK-12
2290 Old Tyler Rd 35226 205-978-6001
Brian Willett, prin. Fax 978-9120

Hope Hull, Montgomery

Hooper Academy 400/PK-12
380 Fischer Rd 36043 334-288-5980

Hueytown, Jefferson, Pop. 15,960
Jefferson County SD
Supt. — See Birmingham
Hueytown HS 1,100/9-12
4881 15th Street Rd 35023 205-379-4150
Joseph Garner, prin. Fax 379-4195
Hueytown MS 800/6-8
701 Sunrise Blvd 35023 205-379-5150
Chris Anders, prin. Fax 379-5195
Jefferson Co. Counseling/Lrng Ctr-West Alt
131 Dabbs Ave 35023 205-379-4130
Jason Wilson, prin. Fax 379-4135

Valley Creek Academy 50/K-12
3253 Virginia Dr 35023 205-491-3330
Kim Dobbs, dir.

Huntsville, Madison, Pop. 175,870
Huntsville CSD, PO Box 1256 35807 20,500/PK-12
Dr. E. Casey Wardynski, supt. 256-428-6800
www.huntsvillecityschools.org
Challenger MS 500/6-8
13555 Chaney Thompson Rd SE 35803
256-428-7620
Dianne Hasty, prin. Fax 428-7621
Columbia HS 700/9-12
300 Explorer Blvd NW 35806 256-428-7576
Clifford Porter, prin. Fax 428-7579
Grissom HS 1,800/9-12
7901 Bailey Cove Rd SE 35802 256-428-8000
Becky Balentine, prin. Fax 428-8001
Huntsville Center for Technology Vo/Tech
2800 Drake Ave SW 35805 256-428-7810
Shelton Cobb, prin. Fax 428-7811
Huntsville HS 1,700/9-12
2304 Billie Watkins St SW 35801 256-428-8050
Aaron King, prin. Fax 428-8051
Huntsville JHS 400/7-8
817 Adams St SE 35801 256-428-7700
Stephanie Wieseman, prin. Fax 428-7701
Jemison HS, 5000 Pulaski Pike 35810 9-12
Michael Morris, prin. 256-428-8100
Lee HS 800/9-12
2500 Meridian St N 35811 256-428-8150
Anne Jobe, prin. Fax 428-8151
McNair JHS 400/7-8
5000 Pulaski Pike 35810 256-428-7660
Chrystapher Walker, prin. Fax 428-7661
New Century Technology HS 400/9-12
2500 Meridian St N 35811 256-428-7800
Sheila Roby, prin. Fax 428-7801
Westlawn MS 600/6-8
4217 9th Ave SW 35805 256-428-7760
Amber Hall, prin. Fax 428-7761
Other Schools – See Hampton Cove

Madison County SD 18,800/PK-12
PO Box 226 35804 256-852-2557
Matthew Massey, supt. Fax 852-2538
www.mcssk12.org
Madison County Career Technical Center Vo/Tech
1275 Jordan Rd 35811 256-852-2170
Michael Romine, prin. Fax 851-9790
Monrovia MS 1,100/6-8
1216 Jeff Rd NW 35806 256-851-4580
Anthony Thompson, prin. Fax 851-4581
PACE Academy Alt
1275 Jordan Rd 35811 256-859-1148
Tandy Shumate, prin. Fax 859-1033
Other Schools – See Gurley, Harvest, Hazel Green, New Hope, New Market, Toney

---

Alabama A & M University Post-Sec.
4900 Meridian St N 35810 256-372-5000
Grace Lutheran S 100/PK-11
3405 Memorial Pkwy SW 35801 256-881-0553
Joshua Swartz, prin. Fax 881-0563
Huntsville Bible College Post-Sec.
904 Oakwood Ave NW 35811 256-539-0834
Huntsville Hospital Post-Sec.
101 Sivley Rd SW 35801 256-533-8123
J. F. Drake State Technical College Post-Sec.
3421 Meridian St N 35811 256-539-8161
Oakwood Adventist Academy 300/K-12
7000 Adventist Blvd NW 35896 256-726-7010
Oakwood University Post-Sec.
7000 Adventist Blvd NW 35896 256-726-7000
Providence Classical S 200/K-12
605 Clinton Ave E 35801 256-852-8884
Pattie Steward, admin. Fax 852-8884
Randolph S 1,000/K-12
1005 Drake Ave SE 35802 256-799-6100
Jay Rainey, hdmstr. Fax 881-1784
St. John Paul II Catholic HS 400/9-12
7301 Old Madison Pike NW 35806 256-430-1760
Vince Aquila, prin. Fax 430-1766
University of Alabama in Huntsville Post-Sec.
301 Sparkman Dr NW 35805 256-824-1000
Valley Fellowship Christian Academy 200/PK-12
3616 Holmes Ave NW 35816 256-533-5248
Patti Simon M.A., head sch Fax 533-5253
Virginia College Post-Sec.
2021 Drake Ave SW 35801 256-533-7387
Westminster Christian Academy 500/6-12
237 Johns Rd NW 35806 256-705-8000
Stephen Hooks, head sch Fax 705-8001
Whitesburg Christian Academy 400/PK-12
7290 Whitesburg Dr SW 35802 256-704-7373
Jerry Reeder, hdmstr. Fax 650-6115

Ider, DeKalb, Pop. 708
De Kalb County SD
Supt. — See Rainsville
Ider S 800/K-12
1064 Crabapple Ln 35981 256-632-2302
Jeff Watkins, prin. Fax 632-3481

Indian Springs, Shelby, Pop. 2,352

Indian Springs S 300/8-12
190 Woodward Dr 35124 205-988-3350
Dr. Sharon Howell, head sch Fax 988-3797

Irondale, Jefferson, Pop. 12,191
Jefferson County SD
Supt. — See Birmingham
Shades Valley HS 1,300/9-12
6100 Old Leeds Rd 35210 205-379-5350
Mary Beth Blankenship, prin. Fax 379-5395

Jefferson Christian Academy 200/PK-12
1500 Heritage Place Dr 35210 205-956-9111

Irvington, Mobile
Mobile County SD
Supt. — See Mobile
Bryant Career Technical S Vo/Tech
8950 Padgett Switch Rd 36544 251-957-2845
Thomas Reed, prin. Fax 221-5420
Bryant HS 1,700/9-12
14001 Hurricane Blvd 36544 251-824-3213
Doug Estle, prin. Fax 221-3605

Jack, Coffee
Coffee County SD
Supt. — See Elba
Zion Chapel S 800/PK-12
29256 Highway 87 36346 334-897-6275
Vohn Enloe, prin. Fax 897-5136

Jackson, Clarke, Pop. 5,191
Clarke County SD
Supt. — See Grove Hill
Jackson HS 700/9-12
321 Stanley Dr 36545 251-246-2571
Stuart Etheredge, prin. Fax 246-3190
Jackson MS 400/6-8
235 College Ave 36545 251-246-3597
Adam Andrews, prin. Fax 246-6017

Jackson Academy 200/K-12
PO Box 838 36545 251-246-5552

Jacksonville, Calhoun, Pop. 12,298
Calhoun County SD
Supt. — See Anniston
Calhoun County Alternative S Alt
1200 Church Ave SE 36265 256-741-7900
Robin Kines, dir. Fax 435-0745
Calhoun County Career Technical Center Vo/Tech
1200 Church Ave SE 36265 256-741-4600
Kevin Lockridge, prin. Fax 435-4221
Pleasant Valley HS 500/7-12
4141 Pleasant Valley Rd 36265 256-741-6700
Mark Proper, prin. Fax 435-0171

Jacksonville CSD 1,500/PK-12
123 College St SW 36265 256-782-5682
Mark Petersen, supt. Fax 782-5685
www.jcsboe.org
Jacksonville HS 700/7-12
1000 George Douthit Dr SW 36265 256-782-8800
Bill Singleton, prin. Fax 782-8801

Jacksonville Christian Academy 200/K-12
831 Alexandria Rd SW 36265 256-435-3333
Dr. Tommy Miller, prin. Fax 435-2059
Jacksonville State University Post-Sec.
700 Pelham Rd N 36265 256-782-5781

Jasper, Walker, Pop. 14,147
Jasper CSD 2,800/PK-12
PO Box 500 35502 205-384-6880
Dr. Ann Jackson, supt. Fax 387-5213
www.jasper.k12.al.us
Maddox MS 600/6-8
201 Panther Trl 35501 205-384-3235
Dr. Steven Hall, prin. Fax 387-5208
Walker HS 800/9-12
1501 Viking Dr 35501 205-221-9277
Kenneth Abbott, prin. Fax 387-5228

Walker County SD 6,800/PK-12
PO Box 311 35502 205-387-0555
Dr. Jason Adkins, supt. Fax 221-5636
www.walkercountyschools.com
Curry HS 500/9-12
155 Yellow Jacket Dr 35503 205-384-3887
Rod Aaron, prin. Fax 221-7381
Curry MS 300/6-8
115 Yellow Jacket Dr 35503 205-384-3441
Barry Wilson, prin. Fax 384-1110
Walker County Alternative S Alt
1100 Viking Dr 35501 205-387-9984
Rickey Pate, prin. Fax 387-7239
Walker County Center for Tech Vo/Tech
1100 Viking Dr 35501 205-387-0561
Christopher McCullar, prin. Fax 384-5170
Other Schools – See Carbon Hill, Cordova, Dora, Oakman, Sumiton

---

Bevill State Community College Post-Sec.
1411 Indiana Ave 35501 205-387-0511

Jemison, Chilton, Pop. 2,561
Chilton County SD
Supt. — See Clanton
Jemison HS 800/8-12
25125 US Highway 31 35085 205-280-4860
Diane Calloway, prin. Fax 688-4761

Killen, Lauderdale, Pop. 1,097
Lauderdale County SD
Supt. — See Florence
Brooks JSHS 800/7-12
4300 Highway 72 35645 256-757-2115
Stephen Howard, prin. Fax 757-1136
Thornton Career Technical Center Vo/Tech
7275 Highway 72 35645 256-757-2101
Kelley Joiner, dir. Fax 757-8692

Kimberly, Jefferson, Pop. 2,694
Jefferson County SD
Supt. — See Birmingham
Jordan HS 800/9-12
1920 Blue Devil Dr 35091 205-379-4850
Clifton Kanaday, prin. Fax 379-4895
North Jefferson MS 600/6-8
8350 Warrior Kimberly Rd 35091 205-379-4000
Terry Henderson, prin. Fax 379-4045

Kinston, Coffee, Pop. 531
Coffee County SD
Supt. — See Elba
Kinston S 500/PK-12
201 College St 36453 334-565-3016
Jennifer Lee, prin. Fax 565-3494

Lafayette, Chambers, Pop. 2,991
Chambers County SD 3,800/PK-12
PO Box 408 36862 334-864-9343
Kelli Hodge, supt. Fax 864-0119
www.chambersk12.org
Chambers County Career Tech Center Vo/Tech
PO Box 318 36862 334-864-8863
Ken Sealy, prin. Fax 864-9394
Lafayette HS 200/9-12
214 1st Ave SE 36862 334-864-9881
Don Turner, prin. Fax 864-0650
Powell MS 200/6-8
700 Martin Luther King Dr 36862 334-864-8876
Daron Brooks, prin. Fax 864-8169
Other Schools – See Valley

Chambers Academy 100/K-12
15048 US Highway 431 36862 334-864-9852

Lanett, Chambers, Pop. 6,366
Lanett CSD 900/K-12
105 N Lanier Ave 36863 334-644-5900
Phillip Johnson, supt. Fax 644-5910
www.lanettcityschools.org
Lanett HS 200/9-12
1301 S 8th Ave 36863 334-644-5965
Jennifer Boyd, prin. Fax 644-5979
Lanett JHS 100/7-8
1301 S 8th Ave 36863 334-644-5950
Donna Bell, prin. Fax 644-5964

Springwood S 300/PK-12
PO Box 1030 36863 334-644-2191

Leeds, Jefferson, Pop. 11,579
Leeds CSD 1,200/PK-PK, 1-
PO Box 1029 35094 205-699-5437
John Moore, supt. Fax 699-6629
www.leedsk12.org/
Leeds HS 500/9-12
1500 Greenwave Dr 35094 205-699-4510
Brent Shaw, prin. Fax 699-4515
Leeds MS 400/6-8
1771 Whitmire St 35094 205-699-4505
Dr. Bobby Byrd, prin. Fax 699-4509

Leighton, Colbert, Pop. 711
Colbert County SD
Supt. — See Tuscumbia
Colbert County HS 500/7-12
2200 High School St 35646 256-446-8214
Melcha Satchel, prin. Fax 446-8951

Leroy, Washington, Pop. 902
Washington County SD
Supt. — See Chatom
Leroy S 700/K-12
PO Box 40 36548 251-246-2000
Danny Patterson, prin. Fax 246-2199

Lester, Limestone, Pop. 111
Limestone County SD
Supt. — See Athens
West Limestone S 1,100/K-12
10945 W School House Rd 35647 256-233-6687
Charlotte Craig, prin. Fax 233-8034

Letohatchee, Lowndes
Lowndes County SD
Supt. — See Hayneville
Calhoun HS 300/9-12
8213 County Road 33 36047 334-227-4515
Nicholas Townsend, prin. Fax 227-8335

Lexington, Lauderdale, Pop. 728
Lauderdale County SD
Supt. — See Florence
Lexington S 900/K-12
101 School St 35648 256-229-6622
Willie Joiner, prin. Fax 229-6636

Lincoln, Talladega, Pop. 6,180
Talladega County SD
Supt. — See Talladega
Drew MS 300/7-8
78975 AL Highway 21 35096 256-315-5280
Dr. Rhonda Lee, prin. Fax 315-5290
Lincoln HS 500/9-12
78989 AL Highway 77 35096 256-315-5295
Evan Blair, prin. Fax 315-5315

Linden, Marengo, Pop. 2,103
Linden CSD 500/PK-12
PO Box 480609 36748 334-295-8802
Dr. Timothy Thurman, supt. Fax 295-8801
www.lindencity.org
Austin JHS 100/6-8
PO Box 480699 36748 334-295-5378
Terry Gosa, prin. Fax 295-5376
Linden HS 200/9-12
PO Box 480729 36748 334-295-4287
Dr. Timothy Thurman, prin. Fax 295-0988

Marengo County SD 1,100/PK-12
PO Box 480339 36748 334-295-4123
Luke Hallmark, supt. Fax 295-2259
www.marengocounty.schoolinsites.com/
Other Schools – See Dixons Mills, Sweet Water, Thomaston

Marengo Academy 200/K-12
2103 S Main St 36748 334-295-4151

Lineville, Clay, Pop. 2,331
Clay County SD
Supt. — See Ashland
Central HS of Clay County 500/9-12
1 Bob Riley Dr 36266 256-396-1400
Steve Giddens, prin. Fax 396-2452
Central JHS of Clay County 7-8
1 Bob Riley Dr 36266 256-396-1401
Russell Hathcock, prin. Fax 396-2452

Livingston, Sumter, Pop. 3,462
Sumter County SD 1,800/PK-12
PO Box 10 35470 205-652-9605
Dr. Tyrone Yarbrough, supt. Fax 652-9641
www.sumter.k12.al.us
Bell-Brown Career Technical Center Vo/Tech
PO Box 1380 35470 205-652-9469
Fax 652-9487
Other Schools – See York

University of West Alabama Post-Sec.
UWA Station 04 35470 205-652-3400

Loachapoka, Lee, Pop. 179
Lee County SD
Supt. — See Opelika
Loachapoka HS 300/7-12
PO Box 187 36865 334-887-8038
Zelda Kitt, prin. Fax 887-5228

Locust Fork, Blount, Pop. 1,182
Blount County SD
Supt. — See Oneonta
Locust Fork HS 600/7-12
77 School Rd 35097 205-681-7846
Thomas Smitherman, prin. Fax 681-6175

Lowndesboro, Lowndes, Pop. 112

Lowndes Academy 200/K-12
PO Box 99 36752 334-278-3366

Luverne, Crenshaw, Pop. 2,775
Crenshaw County SD 2,200/PK-12
183 Votec Dr 36049 334-335-6519
Dr. Boyd English, supt. Fax 335-6510
crenshawcounty.schoolinsites.com
Crenshaw County AVTS Vo/Tech
183 Votec Dr 36049 334-335-6519
Ashley Catrett, prin. Fax 335-6510
Luverne S 800/PK-12
194 First Ave 36049 334-335-3331
Jamie Howard, prin. Fax 335-2246
Other Schools – See Brantley, Highland Home

Crenshaw Christian Academy 200/K-12
608 Country Club Dr 36049 334-335-5749

Lynn, Winston, Pop. 651
Winston County SD
Supt. — See Double Springs
Lynn HS 200/8-12
531 E Main St 35575 205-893-5471
Timothy Tittle, prin. Fax 893-2484

Mc Calla, Jefferson
Jefferson County SD
Supt. — See Birmingham
McAdory HS 1,000/9-12
4800 McAdory School Rd 35111 205-379-4700
Michael Humphries, prin. Fax 481-8037
McAdory MS 800/6-8
5450 Yellow Jacket Blvd 35111 205-379-4730
James McLeod, prin. Fax 379-4745

Mc Intosh, Washington, Pop. 237
Washington County SD
Supt. — See Chatom
McIntosh HS 200/6-12
PO Box 359 36553 251-944-2449
Jamelle Sauls, prin. Fax 944-8779

Mc Kenzie, Butler, Pop. 519
Butler County SD
Supt. — See Greenville
Mc Kenzie S 400/K-12
PO Box 158 36456 334-374-2711
Miles Brown, prin. Fax 374-8108

Madison, Madison, Pop. 41,860
Madison CSD 9,600/PK-12
211 Celtic Dr 35758 256-464-8370
Dr. Dee Fowler, supt. Fax 464-8291
www.madisoncity.k12.al.us
Academy Alt
11306 County Line Rd 35756 256-216-5313
Dr. Treva Stewart, prin. Fax 216-5314
Clemens HS 1,400/9-12
11306 County Line Rd 35756 256-216-5313
Dr. Brian Clayton, prin. Fax 216-5314
Discovery MS 800/7-8
1304 Hughes Rd 35758 256-837-3735
Eric Terrell, prin. Fax 837-1573
Jones HS 1,900/9-12
650 Hughes Rd 35758 256-772-2547
Sylvia Lambert, prin. Fax 772-6698
Liberty MS 700/7-8
281 Dock Murphy Dr 35758 256-430-0001
Nelson Brown, prin. Fax 430-0282

Madison Academy 900/PK-12
325 Slaughter Rd 35758 256-469-6400

Maplesville, Chilton, Pop. 698
Chilton County SD
Supt. — See Clanton
Isabella S 700/K-12
11338 County Road 15 36750 205-280-2770
Ricky Porter, prin. Fax 755-8549
Maplesville S 500/K-12
1256 AL Highway 139 36750 205-280-4900
Steven Hunter, prin. Fax 366-2531

Marbury, Autauga, Pop. 1,390
Autauga County SD
Supt. — See Prattville
Marbury MS 500/6-8
PO Box A 36051 334-365-3522
Jerome Barrington, prin. Fax 755-3168

Marion, Perry, Pop. 3,671
Perry County SD 800/PK-12
PO Box 900 36756 334-683-6528
John Heard, supt. Fax 683-8427
www.perrycountyal.org
Marion S 400/PK-12
PO Box 150 36756 334-683-6741
Dr. Cathy Trimble, prin. Fax 683-8838
Other Schools – See Uniontown

Judson College Post-Sec.
302 Bibb St 36756 800-447-9472

Marion Academy 100/PK-12
1820 Prier Dr 36756 334-683-8204
Ben Miller, prin. Fax 683-4938
Marion Military Institute Post-Sec.
1101 Washington St 36756 800-664-1842

Midfield, Jefferson, Pop. 5,311
Midfield CSD 1,200/K-12
417 Parkwood St 35228 205-923-2262
Demica Sanders, supt. Fax 929-0585
www.midfield.k12.al.us/
Midfield Area Vocational HS Vo/Tech
1600 High School Dr 35228 205-923-2833
Marcus Harris, coord. Fax 929-0593
Midfield HS 400/9-12
1600 High School Dr 35228 205-923-2833
Shun Williams, prin. Fax 929-0593
Rutledge MS 400/5-8
1221 8th St 35228 205-780-8647
Marcus Harris, prin. Fax 780-3664

Midland City, Dale, Pop. 2,267
Dale County SD
Supt. — See Ozark
Dale County HS 400/9-12
11470 S County Road 59 36350 334-983-3541
Matthew Humphrey, prin. Fax 983-1549

Millbrook, Elmore, Pop. 14,375
Elmore County SD
Supt. — See Wetumpka
Millbrook MS 1,300/5-8
4228 Chapman Rd 36054 334-285-2100
Ayena Jackson, prin. Fax 285-2102
Stanhope Elmore HS 1,100/9-12
4300 Main St 36054 334-285-4263
Jamey McGowin, prin. Fax 285-4575

Millport, Lamar, Pop. 1,035
Lamar County SD
Supt. — See Vernon
South Lamar S 500/K-12
300 Sls Rd 35576 205-662-4411
Jason Williams, prin. Fax 662-4544

Millry, Washington, Pop. 541
Washington County SD
Supt. — See Chatom
Millry S 500/K-12
PO Box 65 36558 251-846-2987
John Carter, prin. Fax 846-2986

Mobile, Mobile, Pop. 192,396
Mobile County SD 57,500/PK-12
PO Box 180069 36618 251-221-4000
Martha Peek, supt. Fax 221-4399
www.mcpss.com
Baker HS 2,500/9-12
8901 Airport Blvd 36608 251-221-3000
Clem Richardson, prin. Fax 221-3004
Burns MS 1,000/6-8
6175 Girby Rd 36693 251-221-2025
Jason Laffitte, prin. Fax 221-2021
Calloway-Smith MS 700/6-8
350 N Lawrence St 36603 251-221-2042
D.H. Walton, prin. Fax 221-2041
Causey MS 1,500/6-8
2205 McFarland Rd 36695 251-221-2060
John Poiroux, prin. Fax 221-2062
Chastang MS 400/6-8
2800 Berkley Ave 36617 251-221-2081
Bernard Everett, prin. Fax 221-2080
Clark-Shaw Magnet S 900/5-8
5960 Arlberg St 36608 251-221-2106
Mary Divincenzo, prin. Fax 221-2108
Davidson HS 1,500/9-12
3900 Pleasant Valley Rd 36609 251-221-3084
Lewis Copeland, prin. Fax 221-3083
Denton Magnet S of Technology 700/6-8
3800 Pleasant Valley Rd 36609 251-221-2148
James Gill, prin. Fax 221-2152
Dunbar Magnet S 600/4-8
500 Saint Anthony St 36603 251-221-2160
Timesha Dumas, prin. Fax 221-2162
Evening Educational Options 100/9-12
2051 Military Rd 36605 251-221-6292
Kim Walker, prin.
LeFlore Magnet HS 1,000/9-12
700 Donald St 36617 251-221-3125
Alvin Dailey, prin. Fax 221-3667
Murphy HS 2,200/9-12
100 S Carlen St 36606 251-221-3184
William Smith, prin. Fax 221-3188
Pathway S Alt
800 1/2 Whitley St 36610 251-221-5010
Francine Craig, prin. Fax 221-6801
Phillips Preparatory S 900/6-8
3255 Old Shell Rd 36607 251-221-2286
Brenda Hartzog, prin. Fax 221-2285
Pillans MS 500/6-8
2051 Military Rd 36605 251-221-2300
Ed Sanderson, prin. Fax 221-2314
Rain HS 800/9-12
3125 Dauphin Island Pkwy 36605 251-221-3233
Marlon Firle, prin. Fax 221-3229
Scarborough MS 400/6-8
1800 Phillips Ln 36618 251-221-2323
Andrea Dennis, prin. Fax 221-2321
Washington MS 300/6-8
1961 Andrews St 36617 251-221-2361
Angie Brown, prin. Fax 221-2367
Williamson HS 700/6-12
1567 E Dublin St 36605 251-221-3411
Kirven Lang, prin. Fax 221-3414
Continuous Learning Center Adult
1870 Pleasant Ave 36617 251-221-2122
Aithan Brewer, prin. Fax 221-2124
Other Schools – See Bayou La Batre, Citronelle, Eight Mile, Grand Bay, Irvington, Prichard, Semmes, Theodore

Bishop State Community College Post-Sec.
351 N Broad St 36603 251-405-7000
Blue Cliff Career College Post-Sec.
2970 Cottage Hill Rd # 175 36606 251-473-2220
Cottage Hill Christian Academy 200/9-12
7355 Creekwood Dr 36695 251-634-2513
Jimmy Messer, head sch Fax 634-2566
Faith Academy 1,900/PK-12
8650 Tanner Williams Rd 36608 251-633-7267
Tim Skelton, hdmstr. Fax 633-9133
Fortis College Post-Sec.
3590 Pleasant Valley Rd 36609 251-344-1203
Fortis College Post-Sec.
300 Azalea Rd Ste F 36609 251-342-3230
McGill-Toolen HS 1,100/9-12
1501 Old Shell Rd 36604 251-445-2900
Michelle Haas, prin. Fax 433-8356
Mobile Christian S 600/PK-12
5900 Cottage Hill Rd 36609 251-661-1613
David Pahman, hdmstr. Fax 661-1396
Remington College Post-Sec.
828 Downtowner Loop W 36609 251-343-8200
St. Luke's Episcopal MSHS 700/6-12
1400 S University Blvd 36609 251-666-2991
Mike Notaro M.S., hdmstr. Fax 410-6183
St. Paul's Episcopal S 1,300/PK-12
161 Dogwood Ln 36608 251-342-6700
F. Martin Lester, hdmstr. Fax 342-1844
Spring Hill College Post-Sec.
4000 Dauphin St 36608 251-380-4000
UMS Wright Preparatory S 1,300/PK-12
65 Mobile St 36607 251-479-6551
Dr. Tony Havard, hdmstr. Fax 470-9010
University of Mobile Post-Sec.
5735 College Pkwy 36613 800-946-7267
University of South Alabama Post-Sec.
307 University Blvd N 36688 251-460-6101
Virginia College Post-Sec.
3725 Airport Blvd Ste 165 36608 251-343-7227

Monroeville, Monroe, Pop. 6,440
Monroe County SD 3,700/PK-12
109 Pickens St 36460 251-575-2168
Gregory L. Shehan, supt. Fax 575-9353
www.monroe.k12.al.us/
Carmichael Alternative S Alt
1323 Veterans Dr 36460 251-575-4189
Larry Woolfolk, prin. Fax 575-9648
Monroe County Career Technical Center Vo/Tech
230 Tiger Dr 36460 251-575-4381
Edna Richardson, prin. Fax 575-2017
Monroe County HS 500/9-12
212 Tiger Dr 36460 251-575-3258
Maurice Woody, prin. Fax 575-2019
Monroeville MS 500/5-8
201 York St 36460 251-575-4121
Valerie Stevens, prin. Fax 575-2934
Other Schools – See Beatrice, Excel, Uriah

Alabama Southern Community College Post-Sec.
PO Box 2000 36461 251-575-3156
Monroe Academy 500/PK-12
4096 S Alabama Ave 36460 251-743-3932

Montevallo, Shelby, Pop. 6,221
Shelby County SD
Supt. — See Columbiana
Calera MS 600/6-8
9178 Highway 22 35115 205-682-6140
Branden Vincent, prin. Fax 682-6145
Montevallo HS 400/9-12
980 Oak St 35115 205-682-6400
Brandon Turner, prin. Fax 682-6405
Montevallo MS 300/6-8
235 Samford St 35115 205-682-6410
Sheila Lewis, prin. Fax 682-6415

University of Montevallo 35115 Post-Sec.
205-665-6000

Montgomery, Montgomery, Pop. 203,255
Montgomery County SD 31,300/K-12
PO Box 1991 36102 334-223-6700
Margaret Allen, supt. Fax 269-3076
www.mps.k12.al.us
Baldwin Arts & Academics Magnet S 600/6-8
410 S McDonough St 36104 334-269-3870
Jannette Wright, prin. Fax 269-3918
Bellingrath MS 700/6-8
3350 S Court St 36105 334-269-3623
Sonya Floyd, prin. Fax 269-6173
Brewbaker MS 1,000/6-8
4425 Brewbaker Dr 36116 334-284-8008
Cameron Whitlow, prin. Fax 284-8052
Brewbaker Technology Magnet HS 600/9-12
4405 Brewbaker Dr 36116 334-284-7100
April Wise-Lee, prin. Fax 284-7110
Capitol Heights MS 700/6-8
116 Federal Dr 36107 334-260-1000
Cheryl Smith-Fountain, prin. Fax 260-1049
Carr MS 800/6-8
1610 Ray Thorington Rd 36117 334-244-4005
Brittany Aarestad, prin. Fax 244-4009
Carver HS 1,400/9-12
2001 W Fairview Ave 36108 334-269-3636
Gary Hall, prin. Fax 269-3680
Davis HS 2,100/9-12
3420 Carter Hill Rd 36111 334-269-3712
Bobby Abrams, prin. Fax 269-3715
Fews Secondary Acceleration Academy 100/Alt
321 Early St 36104 334-269-3665
Sabrina Johnson, prin. Fax 269-3743
Floyd MS for Math Science & Technology 500/6-8
3444 Le Bron Rd 36111 334-284-7130
Vince Johnson, prin. Fax 284-7125
Goodwyn MS 600/6-8
209 Perry Hill Rd 36109 334-260-1021
Curtis Black, prin. Fax 260-1079
Lanier HS 900/9-12
1756 S Court St 36104 334-269-3726
Antonio Williams, prin. Fax 269-6180
Lee HS 1,700/9-12
225 Ann St 36107 334-269-3742
Lorenza Pharrams, prin. Fax 269-3888
Loveless Academic Magnet HS 500/9-12
215 Hall St 36104 334-269-3839
Matthew Monson, prin. Fax 269-3961
McKee MS 900/6-8
4017 McInnis Dr 36116 334-284-7528
Patrick Nelson, prin. Fax 241-5308
Montgomery Prep Acad Career Technologies Alt
2901 East South Blvd 36116 334-241-5307
Marsha Baugh, prin. Fax 613-7562
Park Crossing HS 500/9-12
8000 Park Xing 36117 334-260-8121
Tracy Hubbert, prin. Fax 215-0706
Progressive Academy of Creative Ed 100/Alt
3315 Hayneville Rd 36108 334-269-3760
Sabrina Johnson, prin. Fax 269-3989
Southlawn MS 700/6-8
5333 Mobile Hwy 36108 334-284-8086
Jarmar Muhammad, prin. Fax 284-8094
Washington Magnet HS 400/9-12
632 S Union St 36104 334-269-3617
Dr. Quesha Starks, prin. Fax 269-6140
Other Schools – See Pike Road

Alabama Christian Academy 1,000/PK-12
4700 Wares Ferry Rd 36109 334-277-1985
Dr. Misty Overman, head sch Fax 279-0604
Alabama State University Post-Sec.
915 S Jackson St 36104 334-229-4100
Amridge University Post-Sec.
1200 Taylor Rd 36117 888-790-8080
Auburn University at Montgomery Post-Sec.
PO Box 244023 36124 334-244-3000
Baptist Medical Center Post-Sec.
301 Brown Springs Rd 36117 334-273-4400
Canterbury HS 100/6-12
3701 Atlanta Hwy 36109 334-834-2273
Community College of the Air Force Post-Sec.
100 S Turner Blvd 36114 334-649-5000
Cornerstone Classical Christian Academy 100/K-12
125 Calhoun Rd 36109 334-356-7788
Eastwood Christian S 400/K-12
1701 E Trinity Blvd 36106 334-272-8195
Evangel Christian Academy 300/PK-12
3975 Vaughn Rd 36106 334-272-3882
Rev. Scott Matthes, admin. Fax 272-5662
Faulkner University Post-Sec.
5345 Atlanta Hwy 36109 334-272-5820
Fortis College Post-Sec.
3736 Atlanta Hwy 36109 334-272-3857
Huntingdon College Post-Sec.
1500 E Fairview Ave 36106 334-833-4222
Montgomery Academy 500/5-12
3240 Vaughn Rd 36106 334-272-8210
Jay Spencer, hdmstr. Fax 277-3240
Montgomery Catholic Prep HS 300/9-12
5350 Vaughn Rd 36116 334-272-7220
Justin Castanza, prin. Fax 272-2440
Montgomery Catholic Prep MS 200/7-8
5350 Vaughn Rd 36116 334-272-2465
Justin Castanza, prin. Fax 272-2330
St. James S 1,000/PK-12
6010 Vaughn Rd 36116 334-277-8033
Dr. Larry McLemore, head sch Fax 277-2542
South University Post-Sec.
5355 Vaughn Rd 36116 334-395-8800
Success Unlimited Academy 200/PK-12
2328 Fairlane Dr 36116 334-213-0803
The Hair Academy Post-Sec.
3150 McGeehee Rd 36111 334-281-0411
The Robert B. Adams/LabCorp CLS Program Post-Sec.
543 S Hull St 36104 334-263-5745
Trenholm State Technical College Post-Sec.
PO Box 10048 36108 334-420-4200
Trinity Presbyterian S 900/PK-12
1700 E Trinity Blvd 36106 334-213-2100
Kerry Palmer, head sch Fax 213-2171
Valiant Cross Academy 100/6-8
301 Dexter Ave 36104 334-301-0478
Virginia College Post-Sec.
6200 Atlanta Hwy 36117 334-277-3390

Moody, Saint Clair, Pop. 11,564
Saint Clair County SD
Supt. — See Ashville
Moody HS 700/9-12
714 High School Dr 35004 205-640-5127
Cheryl Kuyk, prin. Fax 640-2300
Moody JHS 400/7-8
600 High School Dr 35004 205-640-2040
Cassandra Taylor, prin. Fax 640-3036

Moulton, Lawrence, Pop. 3,330
Lawrence County SD 4,600/PK-12
14131 Market St 35650 256-905-2400
Johnny Yates, supt. Fax 905-2406
www.lawrenceal.org
Jester Learning Center Alt
371 School St 35650 256-974-3252
Craig Owens, prin. Fax 974-3296
Lawrence County Center of Technology Vo/Tech
179 College St 35650 256-974-3751
Robert Vinzant, prin. Fax 905-2482
Lawrence County JSHS 600/9-12
102 College St 35650 256-905-2440
Thomas Jones, prin. Fax 905-2444
Moulton MS 600/5-8
660 College St 35650 256-905-2460
Stacie Givens, prin. Fax 905-2481
Other Schools – See Courtland, Town Creek, Trinity

Moundville, Hale, Pop. 2,391
Hale County SD
Supt. — See Greensboro
Hale County HS 300/9-12
PO Box 188 35474 205-371-2514
Cathy Seale, prin. Fax 371-6800
Hale County MS 300/6-8
120 Wildcat Way 35474 205-371-7000
Eric Perry, prin. Fax 371-7099

Mountain Brook, Jefferson, Pop. 20,299
Mountain Brook CSD 4,500/K-12
32 Vine St, Birmingham AL 35213 205-871-4608
Dr. Richard Barlow, supt. Fax 802-1629
www.mtnbrook.k12.al.us
Mountain Brook HS 1,000/10-12
3650 Bethune Dr 35223 205-414-3800
Amanda Hood, prin. Fax 969-8113
Mountain Brook JHS 1,100/7-9
205 Overbrook Rd, Birmingham AL 35213
205-871-3516
Donald Clayton, prin. Fax 969-8113

Munford, Talladega, Pop. 1,274
Talladega County SD
Supt. — See Talladega
Mumford MS, 360 Cedars Rd 36268 400/6-8
Angel Carter, prin. 256-315-5235
Munford HS 500/9-12
300 Cedars Rd 36268 256-315-5220
Tim Young, prin. Fax 315-5240

Muscle Shoals, Colbert, Pop. 12,952
Muscle Shoals CSD 2,900/PK-12
PO Box 2610 35662 256-389-2600
Dr. Brian Lindsey, supt. Fax 389-2605
www.mscs.k12.al.us
Muscle Shoals Career Academy Vo/Tech
321 Jim Holland Dr 35661 256-389-2660
Caryn Hairell, prin. Fax 389-2662
Muscle Shoals HS 900/9-12
1900 Avalon Ave 35661 256-389-2682
Chad Holden, prin. Fax 389-2689
Muscle Shoals MS 700/6-8
100 Trojan Dr 35661 256-389-2640
Kevin Davis, prin. Fax 389-2647

Northwest-Shoals Community College Post-Sec.
PO Box 2545 35662 256-331-5200

New Brockton, Coffee, Pop. 1,118
Coffee County SD
Supt. — See Elba
New Brockton HS 300/7-12
PO Box 399 36351 334-894-2350
Gray Harrison, prin. Fax 894-5204

New Hope, Madison, Pop. 2,743
Madison County SD
Supt. — See Huntsville
New Hope HS 400/9-12
5216 Main Dr 35760 256-851-3280
Lavell Everett, prin. Fax 851-3281

New Market, Madison, Pop. 1,576
Madison County SD
Supt. — See Huntsville
Buckhorn HS 1,400/9-12
4123 Winchester Rd 35761 256-851-3300
Todd Markham, prin. Fax 851-3301
Buckhorn MS 700/7-8
4185 Winchester Rd 35761 256-851-3230
April McCutcheon, prin. Fax 851-3231

New Site, Tallapoosa, Pop. 769
Tallapoosa County SD
Supt. — See Dadeville
Horseshoe Bend S 800/K-12
10684 Highway 22 E 36256 256-329-9110
James Aulner, prin. Fax 329-9119

Newton, Dale, Pop. 1,478
Houston County SD
Supt. — See Dothan
Wicksburg S 1,000/K-12
1172 S State Highway 123 36352 334-692-5549
Cheryl Smith, prin. Fax 692-3184

Northport, Tuscaloosa, Pop. 23,073
Tuscaloosa County SD
Supt. — See Tuscaloosa
Collins-Riverside MS 500/6-8
1400 3rd St 35476 205-342-2680
Craig Henson, prin. Fax 752-8024
Echols MS 700/6-8
2701 Echols Ave 35476 205-342-2884
Jason Stapp, prin. Fax 339-1064
Northside HS 500/9-12
19230 Northside Pkwy 35475 205-342-2755
Cynthia Long, prin. Fax 339-3437
Northside MS 400/6-8
19130 Northside Pkwy 35475 205-342-2740
Bobby Beasley, prin. Fax 247-4188
Tuscaloosa County HS 1,500/9-12
12500 Wildcat Dr 35475 205-342-2670
Cynthia Simpson, prin. Fax 333-3197

Notasulga, Macon, Pop. 958
Macon County SD
Supt. — See Tuskegee
Notasulga S 300/PK-12
500 E Main St 36866 334-724-1240
Brelinda Sullen, prin. Fax 257-4228

Tallapoosa County SD
Supt. — See Dadeville
Reeltown S 800/PK-12
4090 AL Highway 120 36866 334-257-1670
Thomas Cochran, prin. Fax 257-3978

Oakman, Walker, Pop. 785
Walker County SD
Supt. — See Jasper
Oakman HS 300/9-12
PO Box 286 35579 205-622-3381
Patrick Gann, prin. Fax 622-3542

Odenville, Saint Clair, Pop. 3,535
Saint Clair County SD
Supt. — See Ashville
Odenville MS 500/6-8
100 1st Ave 35120 205-629-2280
Walker Cook, prin. Fax 620-2282
St. Clair County HS 600/9-12
16700 US Highway 411 35120 205-629-6222
Stanley Howard, prin. Fax 629-2228

Ohatchee, Calhoun, Pop. 1,146
Calhoun County SD
Supt. — See Anniston
Ohatchee HS 500/7-12
100 Cherokee Trl 36271 256-741-4900
Bobby Tittle, prin. Fax 892-9181

Oneonta, Blount, Pop. 6,492
Blount County SD 8,300/K-12
PO Box 578 35121 205-625-4102
Rodney Green, supt. Fax 625-4100
www.blountboe.net
Allgood Alternative S Alt
45 Community Rd 35121 205-274-9865
Jeff Dean, prin. Fax 274-9865
Appalachian S 600/K-12
350 County Highway 12 35121 205-274-9712
Jonathan Cleveland, prin. Fax 274-9706
Other Schools – See Blountsville, Cleveland, Hayden, Locust Fork, Remlap

Oneonta CSD 1,100/K-12
27605 State Highway 75 35121 205-625-4106
Dr. Michael Douglas, supt. Fax 274-2910
www.oneontacityschools.com
Oneonta HS 400/9-12
27605 State Highway 75 35121 205-625-3801
Lauren Wilson, prin. Fax 625-5015
Oneonta MS 6-8
27605 State Highway 75 35121 205-625-3018
Brad Newton, prin. Fax 625-3059

Opelika, Lee, Pop. 26,170
Lee County SD 8,800/K-12
2410 Society Hill Rd 36804 334-705-6000
James McCoy, supt. Fax 745-9822
www.lee.k12.al.us
Beauregard HS 700/9-12
7343 AL Highway 51 36804 334-745-5916
Richard Brown, prin. Fax 749-6421
Sanford MS 600/5-8
1500 Lee Road 11 36804 334-745-5023
Lura Reed, prin. Fax 745-5685
Other Schools – See Loachapoka, Smiths Station, Valley

Opelika CSD 4,400/PK-12
300 Simmons St 36801 334-745-9700
Dr. Mark Neighbors, supt. Fax 745-9706
www.opelikaschools.org
Opelika HS 1,300/9-12
1700 Lafayette Pkwy 36801 334-745-9715
Dr. Farrell Seymore, prin. Fax 745-9721
Opelika Learning Center 100/Alt
214 Jeter Ave 36801 334-741-5603
Steven Carson, prin. Fax 741-5604
Opelika MS 1,000/6-8
1206 Denson Dr 36801 334-745-9726
Keith York, prin. Fax 745-9730

Southern Union State Community College Post-Sec.
1701 Lafayette Pkwy 36801 334-745-6437
Trinity Christian S 200/K-12
PO Box 311 36803 334-745-2464

Opp, Covington, Pop. 6,581
Opp CSD 1,300/K-12
PO Box 840 36467 334-493-3173
Michael Smithart, supt. Fax 493-3060
www.oppcityschools.com
Opp HS 400/9-12
502 N Maloy St 36467 334-493-4561
Aaron Hightower, prin. Fax 493-2146
Opp MS 400/5-8
303 E Stewart Ave 36467 334-493-6332
Sharon Spurlin, prin. Fax 493-1120

Orange Beach, Baldwin, Pop. 5,326

Columbia Southern University Post-Sec.
21982 University Ln 36561 251-981-3771

Orrville, Dallas, Pop. 204
Dallas County SD
Supt. — See Selma
Keith MSHS 300/6-12
1166 County Road 115 36767 334-996-8464
Frederick Hardy, prin. Fax 996-0918

Oxford, Calhoun, Pop. 21,062
Oxford CSD 4,200/K-12
PO Box 7670 36203 256-241-3140
Dr. Jeff Goodwin, supt. Fax 241-3938
www.oxfordcityschools.com
Oxford Area Vo HS Vo/Tech
1 Yellow Jacket Dr 36203 256-241-3166
Fax 241-3943
Oxford HS 1,200/9-12
1 Yellow Jacket Dr 36203 256-241-3166
Heath Harmon, prin. Fax 241-3943
Oxford MS 700/7-8
1750 US Highway 78 W 36203 256-241-3816
Michael Maniscalco, prin. Fax 241-3831

Ozark, Dale, Pop. 14,570
Dale County SD 3,000/K-12
202 S Highway 123 Ste E 36360 334-774-2355
Ben Baker, supt. Fax 774-3503
www.dalecountyboe.org
Other Schools – See Ariton, Midland City, Pinckard, Skipperville

Ozark CSD 1,700/PK-12
1044 Andrews Ave 36360 334-774-5197
Dr. Richard McInturf, supt. Fax 774-2685
www.ozarkcityschools.net
Carroll HS 700/9-12
141 Eagle Way 36360 334-774-4915
Sean Clark, prin. Fax 774-1865
Carroll HS Career Center Vo/Tech
227 Faust Ave 36360 334-774-4949
Dana Griggs, prin. Fax 774-8314
Smith MS 500/6-8
994 Andrews Ave 36360 334-774-4913
Danelle Peterman, prin. Fax 774-0568

Pelham, Shelby, Pop. 21,087
Pelham CSD 4,000/K-12
3113 Cummings St 35124 205-624-3700
Dr. Scott Coefield, supt. Fax 624-3980
www.pelhamcityschools.org
Pelham HS 1,800/9-12
2500 Panther Cir 35124 205-682-5500
Jason Yohn, prin. Fax 682-5505
Other Schools – See Birmingham

Pell City, Saint Clair, Pop. 12,505
Pell City CSD 4,100/PK-12
3105 15th Ave N 35125 205-884-4440
Dr. Michael Barber, supt. Fax 814-1010
www.pellcityschools.net
Duran JHS 300/8-8
309 Williamson Dr 35125 205-338-2825
Richard Garris, prin. Fax 884-6502
Pell City HS 1,200/9-12
1300 Cogswell Ave 35125 205-338-2250
Tony Dowdy, prin. Fax 338-2838

Victory Christian S 400/PK-12
PO Box 710 35125 205-338-2901

Phenix City, Russell, Pop. 32,176
Phenix City SD 6,700/PK-12
PO Box 460 36868 334-298-0534
Randy Wilkes, supt. Fax 298-2674
www.pcboe.net
Central HS 1,300/10-12
2400 Dobbs Dr 36870 334-298-3626
Tommy Vickers, prin. Fax 298-7690
Central HS Freshman Academy 400/9-9
2800 Dobbs Dr 36870 334-448-8880
Rachael Fowler, prin. Fax 448-8690
South Girard S 500/8-8
521 Fontaine Rd 36869 334-298-2527
Kerry McDonald, prin. Fax 297-8274
Success Academy Alt
1700 17th Ave 36867 334-298-9876

Russell County SD 3,600/K-12
PO Box 400 36868 706-321-2224
Brenda Coley Ed.D., supt. Fax 448-8314
rcsd-al.schoolloop.com/
Other Schools – See Seale

Chattahoochee Valley Community College Post-Sec.
2602 College Dr 36869 334-291-4900

Phil Campbell, Franklin, Pop. 1,134
Franklin County SD
Supt. — See Russellville
Phil Campbell HS 400/7-12
PO Box 849 35581 256-331-2150
Gary Odom, prin. Fax 331-2151

Piedmont, Calhoun, Pop. 4,787
Piedmont CSD 1,200/K-12
502 W Hood St 36272 256-447-8831
Dr. Matthew Akin, supt. Fax 447-6486
www.piedmont.k12.al.us/
Piedmont HS 300/9-12
750 Tom Bible Memorial Hwy 36272 256-447-2829
Adam Clemons, prin. Fax 447-8722
Piedmont MS 300/6-8
401 N Main St 36272 256-447-6165
Jerry Snow, prin. Fax 447-8070

Pike Road, Montgomery, Pop. 5,366
Montgomery County SD
Supt. — See Montgomery
Washington MS 700/6-8
696 Georgia Washington Rd 36064 334-215-8290
Orlando Ledyard, prin. Fax 215-1304

Pinckard, Dale, Pop. 638
Dale County SD
Supt. — See Ozark
South Dale MS 400/5-8
PO Box D 36371 334-983-3077
Bucky Sconyers, prin. Fax 983-5882

Pinson, Jefferson, Pop. 7,099
Jefferson County SD
Supt. — See Birmingham
Clay-Chalkville HS 1,300/9-12
6623 Roe Chandler Rd 35126 205-379-3050
Michael Lee, prin. Fax 680-8128
Pinson Valley HS 1,000/9-12
6895 Highway 75 35126 205-379-5100
Michael Turner, prin. Fax 379-5145
Rudd MS 800/6-8
4526 Rudd School Rd 35126 205-379-5300
Susan Slaney, prin. Fax 680-8124

Pisgah, Jackson, Pop. 710
Jackson County SD
Supt. — See Scottsboro
Pisgah S 700/K-12
60 Metcalf St 35765 256-451-3241
Billy Duncan, prin. Fax 451-3457

Plantersville, Dallas
Dallas County SD
Supt. — See Selma
Dallas County HS 600/9-12
PO Box 145 36758 334-366-2232
Todd Reece, prin. Fax 366-4015

Pleasant Grove, Jefferson, Pop. 10,034
Jefferson County SD
Supt. — See Birmingham
JCIB Pleasant Grove 400/6-8
805 7th Ave 35127 205-379-5280
Sandy Jolivette, prin. Fax 379-5295
Pleasant Grove HS 500/7-12
100 Spartan Dr 35127 205-379-5250
Jarvis Watkins, prin. Fax 379-5265

Prattville, Autauga, Pop. 33,381
Autauga County SD 9,500/K-12
153 W 4th St 36067 334-365-5706
Spence Agee, supt. Fax 361-3828
www.acboe.net
Autauga County Tech Center Vo/Tech
1301 Upper Kingston Rd 36067 334-361-0258
Brock Dunn, admin. Fax 361-3839
Prattville HS 2,000/9-12
PO Box 680810 36068 334-365-8804
Richard Dennis, prin. Fax 358-0011
Prattville JHS 1,100/7-8
1089 Martin Luther King Dr 36067 334-365-6697
Janice Stockman, prin. Fax 361-3870
Second Chance Alternative S Alt
816 Cardinal Ln 36067 334-361-3834
Darryl Pickett, prin. Fax 361-3834
Other Schools – See Autaugaville, Billingsley, Deatsville, Marbury

---

Autauga Academy 300/PK-12
497 Golson Rd 36067 334-365-4343
East Memorial Christian Academy 300/K-12
1320 Old Ridge Rd E 36066 334-358-4085
Bryan Easley, admin. Fax 358-9226
Prattville Christian Academy 700/PK-12
322 Old Farm Ln N 36066 334-285-0077
Dr. Ron Mitchell, pres. Fax 285-1777

Prichard, Mobile, Pop. 22,453
Mobile County SD
Supt. — See Mobile
Faulkner Career Tech Center Vo/Tech
33 W Elm St 36610 251-221-5431
William White, prin. Fax 221-5433
Mobile County Training MS 200/6-8
800 Whitley St 36610 251-221-2267
Rashad Stallworth, prin. Fax 221-2269
Vigor HS 800/9-12
913 N Wilson Ave 36610 251-221-3045
Gerald Cunningham, prin. Fax 221-3378

Princeton, Jackson
Jackson County SD
Supt. — See Scottsboro
Paint Rock Valley S 100/K-12
PO Box 150 35766 256-776-2628
Clay Webber, prin. Fax 776-0042

Ragland, Saint Clair, Pop. 1,613
Saint Clair County SD
Supt. — See Ashville
Ragland S 500/K-12
1060 Main St 35131 205-472-2123
Jennifer Ball, prin. Fax 472-0086

Rainbow City, Etowah, Pop. 9,471
Etowah County SD
Supt. — See Gadsden
Rainbow MS 700/6-8
454 Lumbley Rd 35906 256-442-1095
Matt Brooks, prin. Fax 442-1028

Westbrook Christian S 600/PK-12
100 Westminster Dr 35906 256-442-7457

Rainsville, DeKalb, Pop. 4,882
De Kalb County SD 8,700/K-12
PO Box 1668 35986 256-638-6921
Hugh Taylor, supt. Fax 638-6972
www.dekalbk12.org
De Kalb Vocational S Vo/Tech
PO Box 529 35986 256-638-4421
Jonathan Phillips, prin. Fax 638-4420
Plainview S 1,100/K-12
PO Box 469 35986 256-638-3510
Tony Richards, prin. Fax 638-6811
Other Schools – See Collinsville, Crossville, Fyffe, Geraldine, Ider, Sylvania, Valley Head

---

Northeast Alabama Community College Post-Sec.
PO Box 159 35986 256-638-4418

Ranburne, Cleburne, Pop. 406
Cleburne County SD
Supt. — See Heflin
Ranburne MSHS 500/5-12
21045 Main St 36273 256-568-3402
Tim Ward, prin. Fax 568-2605

Red Bay, Franklin, Pop. 3,100
Franklin County SD
Supt. — See Russellville
Red Bay S 800/PK-12
PO Box 1518 35582 256-331-2270
Kenny Sparks, prin. Fax 331-2281

Red Level, Covington, Pop. 487
Covington County SD
Supt. — See Andalusia
Red Level HS 300/7-12
PO Box D 36474 334-469-5315
Randy McGlaun, prin. Fax 469-6192

Reform, Pickens, Pop. 1,691
Pickens County SD
Supt. — See Carrollton
Pickens County JSHS 300/7-12
205 4th Ave SE 35481 205-375-2344
SheMia Wilson, prin. Fax 375-8151

Remlap, Blount
Blount County SD
Supt. — See Oneonta
Southeastern S 600/K-12
18770 State Highway 75 35133 205-681-3964
Billy Puckett, prin. Fax 681-3975

Roanoke, Randolph, Pop. 6,021
Roanoke CSD 1,500/PK-12
PO Box 1367 36274 334-863-2628
Chuck Marcum, supt. Fax 863-2849
www.roanokecityschools.org/
Handley HS 500/9-12
PO Box 1393 36274 334-863-6815
Greg Foster, prin. Fax 863-6284
Handley MS 600/4-8
PO Box 725 36274 334-863-4174
Lynn Robinson, prin. Fax 863-6129

Robertsdale, Baldwin, Pop. 5,180
Baldwin County SD
Supt. — See Bay Minette
Central Baldwin MS 700/7-8
PO Box 930 36567 251-947-2327
Phillip Fountain, prin. Fax 947-1949
Robertsdale HS 1,300/9-12
PO Box 69 36567 251-947-4154
Joseph Roh, prin. Fax 947-2666
South Baldwin Center for Tech Vo/Tech
19200 Carolina St 36567 251-947-5041
Kendall Mowdy, prin. Fax 947-4837
Taylor Alternative S 50/Alt
19150 Wilters St 36567 251-970-4415
Don Johnson, prin. Fax 970-4416

Central Christian S 300/PK-12
17395 State Highway 104 36567 251-947-5043
Tim Shelton, admin. Fax 947-2572

Rockford, Coosa, Pop. 477
Coosa County SD 1,100/K-12
PO Box 37 35136 256-377-4913
Dennis Sanford, supt. Fax 377-2385
www.coosaschools.k12.al.us
Central HS Coosa County 300/9-12
243 Coosa County Road 75 35136 256-377-4384
Delynn Bouldin, prin. Fax 377-4658
Central MS Coosa County 400/5-8
97 Coosa County Road 75 35136 256-377-1490
Christian Ivey, prin. Fax 377-1493
Coosa County Technology Center Vo/Tech
17768 US Highway 231 35136 256-377-4678
Jocelyn Marbury, dir. Fax 377-4589

Rogersville, Lauderdale, Pop. 1,248
Lauderdale County SD
Supt. — See Florence
Lauderdale County S 1,200/PK-12
201 Cedar St 35652 256-247-3414
Eric Cornelius, prin. Fax 247-3444

Russellville, Franklin, Pop. 9,705
Franklin County SD 3,200/PK-12
PO Box 610 35653 256-332-1360
Gary Williams, supt. Fax 331-0069
www.franklin.k12.al.us/
Belgreen S 500/PK-12
14220 Highway 187 35653 256-332-1376
Myra Frederick, prin. Fax 332-7209
Franklin County Career Technical Center Vo/Tech
85 Jail Springs Rd 35653 256-332-2127
Scott Wiginton, dir. Fax 332-2219
Tharptown HS 300/7-12
255 Highway 80 35654 256-332-6485
Barry Laster, prin. Fax 332-2840
Other Schools – See Phil Campbell, Red Bay, Vina

Russellville CSD 2,500/K-12
1945 Waterloo Rd 35653 256-331-2000
Heath Grimes, supt. Fax 332-7323
www.rcs.k12.al.us
Russellville HS 700/9-12
1865 Waterloo Rd 35653 256-332-2110
Jason Goodwin, prin. Fax 332-8447
Russellville MS 600/6-8
765 Summit St 35653 256-331-2120
Dr. Karen Thorn, prin. Fax 332-8453

Samson, Geneva, Pop. 1,902
Geneva County SD
Supt. — See Geneva
Samson HS 200/9-12
209 N Broad St 36477 334-898-2371
R. DeWayne Hamilton, prin. Fax 898-7576
Samson MS 200/7-8
209 N Broad St 36477 334-898-2371
Ashley Sanders, prin. Fax 898-7576

Sand Rock, Cherokee, Pop. 556
Cherokee County SD
Supt. — See Centre
Sand Rock S 900/K-12
1950 Sand Rock Ave 35983 256-523-3564
John East, prin. Fax 523-3507

Saraland, Mobile, Pop. 13,216
Saraland CSD 2,700/PK-12
943 Highway 43 S 36571 251-375-5420
Dr. Aaron Milner, supt. Fax 375-5430
www.saralandboe.org
Saraland HS 900/9-12
1115 Industrial Pkwy 36571 251-602-8970
Beverly Spondike, prin. Fax 602-8994
Saraland MS - Nelson Adams Campus 800/5-8
401 Baldwin Rd 36571 251-679-9405
Alex Crane, prin. Fax 679-9456

Sardis City, Etowah, Pop. 1,693
Etowah County SD
Supt. — See Gadsden
Sardis HS 500/9-12
1420 Church St 35956 256-593-5221
Wendy Gibbs, prin. Fax 593-5223

Satsuma, Mobile, Pop. 6,101
Satsuma City SD 1,100/PK-12
PO Box 939 36572 251-380-8200
Joe Walters, supt. Fax 380-8201
satsumacity.schoolinsites.com/
Satsuma HS 700/7-12
1 Gator Cir 36572 251-380-8190
Joshua Verkouille, prin. Fax 380-8191

Scottsboro, Jackson, Pop. 14,491
Jackson County SD 5,700/PK-12
PO Box 490 35768 256-259-9500
Dr. Bart Reeves, supt. Fax 259-0076
www.jackson.k12.al.us
Jackson County Alternative S Alt
PO Box 490 35768 256-574-6446
Kerry Wright, prin. Fax 259-1392
Skyline S 500/K-12
897 County Road 25 35768 256-587-6561
Kevin Dukes, prin. Fax 587-6562
Other Schools – See Bridgeport, Higdon, Hollywood, Pisgah, Princeton, Section, Stevenson, Woodville

Scottsboro CSD 2,600/K-12
305 S Scott St 35768 256-218-2100
Dr. Sandra Spivey, supt. Fax 218-2190
www.scottsboroschools.net
Scottsboro HS 800/9-12
25053 John T Reid Pkwy 35768 256-218-2000
Brad Dudley, prin. Fax 218-2090
Scottsboro JHS 400/7-8
1601 Jefferson St 35768 256-218-2300
Jason Hass, prin. Fax 218-2390

Seale, Russell
Russell County SD
Supt. — See Phenix City
Russell County HS 1,000/9-12
4699 Old Seale Hwy 36875 706-321-2246
Sheila Baker, prin. Fax 855-4042
Russell County MS 600/7-8
4716 Old Seale Hwy 36875 706-321-2261
Rebecca Johnston, prin. Fax 855-4487

Section, Jackson, Pop. 755
Jackson County SD
Supt. — See Scottsboro
Section S 600/K-12
PO Box 10 35771 256-228-6718
Gene Roberts, prin. Fax 228-6252

Selma, Dallas, Pop. 20,594
Dallas County SD 3,400/PK-12
PO Box 1056 36702 334-875-3440
Hattie Shelton, supt. Fax 876-4497
www.dallask12.org
Dallas County Alternative S Alt
Craig Industrial Bldg 37 36701 334-872-6761
Curtis Williams, prin. Fax 872-6761
Dallas County Career Technical Center Vo/Tech
1306 Roosevelt St 36701 334-872-8031
Jerolene Williams, dir. Fax 872-5697
Southside HS 400/9-12
7975 US Highway 80 E 36701 334-872-0518
Michael Walker, prin. Fax 872-0295
Tipton MS 200/7-8
2500 Tipton St 36701 334-872-8080
Jackie Averhart, prin. Fax 872-8008
Other Schools – See Orrville, Plantersville, Valley Grande

Selma CSD 3,600/PK-12
PO Box 350 36702 334-874-1600
Dr. Angela Mangum, supt. Fax 874-1604
www.selmacityschools.org
Hudson MS 500/7-8
1701 Summerfield Rd 36701 334-874-1675
LaShonda Moorer, prin. Fax 874-1679
Phoenix S 100/Alt
501 Plant St 36703 334-874-1718
Latonzia Bullard-Dillard, prin. Fax 874-1649
Selma HS 1,000/9-12
2180 Broad St 36701 334-874-1680
Emma Alexander, prin. Fax 874-9450

Concordia College Alabama Post-Sec.
1712 Broad St 36701 334-874-5700
Ellwood Christian Academy 200/PK-12
1 Bell Rd 36701 334-877-1586
George C. Wallace State Comm College Post-Sec.
PO Box 2530 36702 334-876-9227
Meadowview Christian S 200/PK-12
1512 Old Orrville Rd 36701 334-872-8448
Morgan Academy 500/K-12
2901 W Dallas Ave 36701 334-875-4464
Mark Knight, hdmstr. Fax 875-4465
Selma University Post-Sec.
1501 Lapsley St 36701 334-872-2533

Semmes, Mobile
Mobile County SD
Supt. — See Mobile
Montgomery HS 2,100/9-12
4275 Snow Rd N 36575 251-221-3153
Joe Toomey, prin. Fax 221-3150
Semmes MS 1,600/6-8
4566 Ed George Rd 36575 251-221-2344
Brenda Shenesey, prin. Fax 221-2347

Sheffield, Colbert, Pop. 8,895
Sheffield CSD 1,100/PK-12
300 W 6th St 35660 256-383-0400
Daniel Lankford, supt. Fax 386-5704
www.scs.k12.al.us
Sheffield HS 300/9-12
2800 E 19th Ave 35660 256-383-6052
Joseph Burch, prin. Fax 386-5707
Sheffield JHS 200/7-8
1803 E 30th St 35660 256-386-5735
Eric Kirkman, prin. Fax 386-5706

Skipperville, Dale
Dale County SD
Supt. — See Ozark
Long HS 400/7-12
2565 County Road 60 36374 334-774-2380
Jason Steed, prin. Fax 774-3937

Slocomb, Geneva, Pop. 1,949
Geneva County SD
Supt. — See Geneva
Slocomb HS 400/9-12
591 S County Road 9 36375 334-886-2008
Harold Birge, prin. Fax 886-9889
Slocomb MS 300/6-8
591 S County Road 9 36375 334-886-2008
Zeb Brown, prin. Fax 886-9889

Smiths, Lee, Pop. 3,456

Glenwood S 400/PK-12
5801 Summerville Rd 36877 334-297-3614

Smiths Station, Lee, Pop. 4,838
Lee County SD
Supt. — See Opelika
Smiths Station Freshman Center 500/9-9
1150 Lee Road 298 36877 334-664-4063
Dr. Brad Cook, prin.
Smiths Station HS 1,400/10-12
4228 Lee Road 430 36877 334-298-0969
Joaquin Richards, prin. Fax 298-1304
Smiths Station JHS 7-8
1100 Lee Road 298 36877 334-664-4070
Rick Harris, prin.

Somerville, Morgan, Pop. 713
Morgan County SD
Supt. — See Decatur
Brewer HS 900/9-12
59 Eva Rd 35670 256-778-8634
Jeremy Childers, prin. Fax 778-8012
Brewer Vocational HS Vo/Tech
59 Eva Rd 35670 256-309-2119
Christal Blevins, prin. Fax 309-2180

Southside, Etowah, Pop. 8,359
Etowah County SD
Supt. — See Gadsden
Southside HS 900/9-12
2361 School Dr 35907 256-442-2172
Chris Winningham, prin. Fax 442-2183

Spanish Fort, Baldwin, Pop. 6,701
Baldwin County SD
Supt. — See Bay Minette
Spanish Fort HS 1,100/9-12
1 Plaza De Toros Dr 36527 251-625-3259
Brian Williamson, prin. Fax 615-5648
Spanish Fort MS 900/6-8
33899 Jimmy Faulkner Dr 36527 251-625-3271
Oliver Sinclair, prin. Fax 626-7201

Spring Garden, Cherokee, Pop. 234
Cherokee County SD
Supt. — See Centre
Spring Garden S 500/K-12
PO Box 31 36275 256-447-7045
Michael Welsh, prin. Fax 447-6947

Springville, Saint Clair, Pop. 4,042
Saint Clair County SD
Supt. — See Ashville
Springville HS 700/9-12
8295 US Highway 11 35146 205-467-7833
Virgil Winslett, prin. Fax 467-2734
Springville MS 500/6-8
6691 US Highway 11 35146 205-467-2740
Kimberly Brown, prin. Fax 467-2742

Stevenson, Jackson, Pop. 1,968
Jackson County SD
Supt. — See Scottsboro
North Jackson HS 500/9-12
45549 AL Highway 277 35772 256-437-2136
Sam Houston, prin. Fax 437-2400
Stevenson MS 300/5-8
701 Kentucky Ave 35772 256-437-2945
Dr. Rob Paradise, prin. Fax 437-2747

Sulligent, Lamar, Pop. 1,890
Lamar County SD
Supt. — See Vernon
Sulligent S 800/K-12
PO Box 909 35586 205-698-9254
Dr. Lisa Stamps, prin. Fax 698-8497

Sumiton, Walker, Pop. 2,483
Walker County SD
Supt. — See Jasper
Sumiton MS 400/5-8
275 1st St N 35148 205-648-2390
Chris Stephenson, prin. Fax 648-0183

Sumiton Christian S 400/PK-12
155 Hosanna Dr 35148 205-648-6643
Cheryl Capps, prin. Fax 648-9893

Sweet Water, Marengo, Pop. 258
Marengo County SD
Supt. — See Linden
Sweet Water S 700/PK-12
PO Box 127 36782 334-994-4263
Phyllis Mabowitz, prin. Fax 994-4686

Sylacauga, Talladega, Pop. 12,625
Sylacauga CSD 2,400/PK-12
43 N Broadway Ave 35150 256-245-5256
Michael Freeman, supt. Fax 245-6665
www.sylacauga.k12.al.us
Nichols-Lawson MS 600/6-8
1550 Talladega Hwy 35150 256-245-4376
Gary Rivers, prin. Fax 245-4071
Sylacauga HS 700/9-12
701 N Broadway Ave 35150 256-249-0911
Charles Murphy, prin. Fax 245-1026

Talladega County SD
Supt. — See Talladega
Comer Memorial HS 500/7-12
801 Seminole Ave 35150 256-315-5400
Judson Warlick, prin. Fax 315-5420
Fayetteville S 700/K-12
170 WW Averitte Dr 35151 256-315-5550
Amy Smith, prin. Fax 315-5575

Knollwood Christian S 50/PK-11
PO Box 340 35150 256-249-4750
Joyce Lilly, admin.

Sylvania, DeKalb, Pop. 1,781
De Kalb County SD
Supt. — See Rainsville
Sylvania S 900/K-12
133 Second St N 35988 256-638-2030
Westley King, prin. Fax 638-7839

Talladega, Talladega, Pop. 15,505
Talladega CSD 2,200/PK-12
PO Box 946 35161 256-315-5600
Terry Roller, supt. Fax 315-5606
www.talladega-cs.net
Ellis JHS 300/7-8
414 Elm St 35160 256-315-5700
Shari Dye, prin. Fax 315-5704
Talladega High Career Tech Vo/Tech
110 Picadilly Cir 35160 256-315-5688
Trisha Howell-Turner, dir. Fax 315-5690
Talladega HS 600/9-12
1177 McMillan St E 35160 256-315-5656
Darius Williams, admin. Fax 315-5670

Talladega County SD 7,600/K-12
PO Box 887 35161 256-315-5100
Dr. Suzanne Lacey, supt. Fax 315-5126
www.tcboe.org
Talladega County Central HS 200/7-12
5104 Howell Cove Rd 35160 256-315-5340
Quentin Lee, prin. Fax 315-5350
Other Schools – See Alpine, Childersburg, Lincoln, Munford, Sylacauga

---

Alabama Institute for the Deaf and Blind Post-Sec.
PO Box 698 35161 256-761-3207
Talladega College Post-Sec.
627 Battle St W 35160 256-362-0206

Tallassee, Elmore, Pop. 4,755
Tallassee CSD 1,900/K-12
308 King St 36078 334-283-6864
Wade Shipman, supt. Fax 283-4338
www.tcschools.com
Southside MS 600/5-8
901 EB Payne Sr Dr 36078 334-283-2151
Bruce Dean, prin. Fax 283-3577
Tallassee HS 500/9-12
502 Barnett Blvd 36078 334-283-2187
Matt Coker, prin. Fax 283-6210

Tanner, Limestone
Limestone County SD
Supt. — See Athens
Tanner S 800/K-12
12060 Sommers Rd 35671 256-233-6682
Billy Owens, prin. Fax 233-6449

Tarrant, Jefferson, Pop. 6,300
Tarrant CSD 1,100/PK-12
1318 Alabama St 35217 205-849-3700
Dr. Shelly Mize, supt. Fax 849-3728
www.tarrant.k12.al.us/
Tarrant HS 500/7-12
91 Black Creek Rd 35217 205-849-0172
Amy Banaszek, prin. Fax 849-3724

Theodore, Mobile, Pop. 6,002
Mobile County SD
Supt. — See Mobile
Hankins MS 800/6-8
5750 Katherine Hankins Dr 36582 251-221-2200
David Diaz, prin. Fax 221-2204
Theodore HS 1,600/9-12
6201 Swedetown Rd N 36582 251-221-3351
Charles Menton, prin. Fax 221-3355

Thomaston, Marengo, Pop. 414
Marengo County SD
Supt. — See Linden
Johnson S 200/K-12
PO Box 67 36783 334-627-3364
Lepolean Peterson, prin. Fax 627-3396

Thomasville, Clarke, Pop. 4,190
Thomasville CSD 1,500/PK-12
PO Box 458 36784 334-636-9955
Dr. Vic Adkison, supt. Fax 636-4096
www.thomasvilleschools.org/
Thomasville HS 500/9-12
777 Gates Dr 36784 334-636-4451
Chuck Alford, prin. Fax 636-0022
Thomasville MS 400/5-8
781 Gates Dr 36784 334-636-4928
Gerald McAnally, prin. Fax 636-4924

Thorsby, Chilton, Pop. 1,968
Chilton County SD
Supt. — See Clanton
Thorsby S 800/K-12
54 Opportunity Dr 35171 205-280-4880
Russ Bryan, prin. Fax 646-2197

Toney, Madison
Madison County SD
Supt. — See Huntsville
Sparkman MS 800/6-8
2697 Carters Gin Rd 35773 256-851-4610
Ronnie Blair, prin. Fax 851-4611

Town Creek, Lawrence, Pop. 1,049
Lawrence County SD
Supt. — See Moulton
Hatton HS 400/7-12
6909 AL Highway 101 35672 256-685-4010
Brent Gillespie, prin. Fax 685-4007

Toxey, Choctaw, Pop. 137

South Choctaw Academy 300/PK-12
PO Box 160 36921 251-843-2426
Monteil Robinson, prin. Fax 843-2088

Trinity, Morgan, Pop. 2,059
Lawrence County SD
Supt. — See Moulton
East Lawrence HS 400/9-12
55 County Road 370 35673 256-905-2430
Jacki Hall, prin. Fax 905-2424
East Lawrence MS 400/5-8
99 County Road 370 35673 256-905-2420
Baine Garner, prin. Fax 905-2477

Morgan County SD
Supt. — See Decatur
West Morgan HS 400/9-12
261 S Greenway Dr 35673 256-353-5214
Keith Harris, prin. Fax 351-0161
West Morgan MS 400/5-8
261 S Greenway Dr 35673 256-353-5214
Jill Jones, prin. Fax 355-8713

Troy, Pike, Pop. 17,799
Pike County SD 2,200/PK-12
101 W Love St 36081 334-566-1850
Dr. Mark Bazzell M.Ed., supt. Fax 566-2580
www.pikecountyschools.com
Troy-Pike Regional Center for Technology Vo/Tech
285 Gibbs St 36081 334-566-5395
Julie Simmons, prin. Fax 566-1690
Other Schools – See Brundidge, Goshen

Troy CSD 1,900/K-12
PO Box 529 36081 334-566-3741
Lee Hicks, supt. Fax 566-1425
www.troyschools.net
Henderson HS 600/9-12
PO Box 1006 36081 334-566-3510
Brock Kelley, prin. Fax 566-4940
Henderson MS 300/6-8
PO Box 925 36081 334-566-5770
Aaron Brown, prin. Fax 566-3071

Pike Liberal Arts S 400/PK-12
PO Box 329 36081 334-566-2023
Troy University 36082 Post-Sec.
334-670-3100

Trussville, Jefferson, Pop. 19,764
Jefferson County SD
Supt. — See Birmingham
Clay-Chalkville MS 1,000/6-8
6700 Trussville Clay Rd 35173 205-379-3100
Ron Tillman, prin. Fax 379-3145

Trussville City SD 3,400/K-12
113 N Chalkville Rd 35173 205-228-3018
Dr. Patricia Neill, supt. Fax 228-3001
trussvillecityschools.com/
Hewitt-Trussville HS 1,400/9-12
6450 Husky Pkwy 35173 205-228-4000
Timothy Salem, prin. Fax 228-4001
Hewitt-Trussville MS 1,000/6-8
5275 Trussville Clay Rd 35173 205-228-3700
Lisa Berry, prin. Fax 228-3701

Tuscaloosa, Tuscaloosa, Pop. 89,545
Tuscaloosa CSD 9,700/PK-12
PO Box 38991 35403 205-759-3700
Mike Daria, supt. Fax 759-3542
www.tusc.k12.al.us
Central HS 700/9-12
905 15th St 35401 205-759-3720
Clarence Sutton, prin. Fax 759-3756
Northridge HS 1,200/9-12
2901 Northridge Rd 35406 205-759-3590
Kyle Ferguson, prin. Fax 759-3605
Rock Quarry MS 600/6-8
2100 Rock Quarry Dr 35406 205-759-3578
Lynda Ingram, prin. Fax 759-3582
Tuscaloosa Career and Technology Academy Vo/Tech
2800 ML King Jr Blvd 35401 205-759-3649
Danielle Morton, prin. Fax 759-3767
Tuscaloosa Magnet MS 100/6-8
315 McFarland Blvd E 35404 205-759-3653
Kristi Thomson, prin. Fax 759-3784
University Place MS 100/6-8
2010 1st Ave 35401 205-759-3631
Tom Danner, prin. Fax 759-3635
Westlawn MS 400/6-8
1715 ML King Jr Blvd 35401 205-759-3673
Tiffany Davis, prin. Fax 759-3770
Other Schools – See Cottondale

Tuscaloosa County SD 17,800/PK-12
PO Box 2568 35403 205-758-0411
Dr. Walter Davie, supt. Fax 758-2990
www.tcss.net
Hillcrest HS 1,300/9-12
300 Patriot Pkwy 35405 205-342-2800
Jeff Hinton, prin. Fax 247-4178
Hillcrest MS 600/6-8
401 Hillcrest School Rd 35405 205-342-2820
C'Kimba Hobbs, prin. Fax 247-4177
Holt HS 400/9-12
3801 Alabama Ave NE 35404 205-342-2768
Jacqueline McNealey, prin. Fax 247-4179
Other Schools – See Brookwood, Buhl, Cottondale, Duncanville, Northport, Vance

---

American Christian Academy 900/PK-12
2300 Veterans Memorial Pkwy 35404 205-553-5963
Dr. Dan Carden, hdmstr. Fax 553-5942
Capitol S 100/PK-12
2828 6th St 35401 205-758-2828
Dr. Barbara Rountree, dir. Fax 750-0280
DCH Regional Medical Center Post-Sec.
809 University Blvd E 35401 205-759-7111
Holy Spirit HS 200/7-12
601 James I Harrison Jr E 35405 205-553-5606
Scott Perry, prin. Fax 566-7103
North River Christian Academy 300/PK-12
1785 McFarland Blvd N 35406 205-349-4881
Dan Habrial, admin. Fax 349-3246
Riverwood Classical School 50/K-11
501 Rice Valley Rd N 35406 205-758-5502
Shelton State Community College Post-Sec.
9500 Old Greensboro Rd 35405 205-391-2211
Stillman College Post-Sec.
PO Box 1430 35403 205-349-4240
Tuscaloosa Academy 400/PK-12
420 Rice Valley Rd N 35406 205-758-4462
Dr. Isaac Espy, hdmstr. Fax 758-4418
University of Alabama 35487 Post-Sec.
205-348-6010

Tuscumbia, Colbert, Pop. 8,279
Colbert County SD 2,700/PK-12
PO Box 538 35674 256-386-8565
Dr. Gale Satchel, supt. Fax 381-9375
colbert.k12.al.us/
Colbert Heights HS 500/7-12
6825 Woodmont Dr 35674 256-383-7875
Thomas Casteel, prin. Fax 389-8319
Other Schools – See Cherokee, Leighton

Tuscumbia CSD 1,500/K-12
303 N Commons St E 35674 256-389-2900
Darryl Aikerson, supt. Fax 389-2903
www.tuscumbia.k12.al.us
Deshler Career Technical Center Vo/Tech
200 N Commons St E 35674 256-389-2900
Vickey Moon, coord. Fax 389-2903
Deshler HS 500/9-12
200 N Commons St E 35674 256-389-2910
Russell Tate, prin. Fax 389-2915
Deshler MS 400/6-8
598 N High St 35674 256-389-2920
Bryan Murner, prin. Fax 389-2921
Tuscumbia City Alternative S Alt
303 N Commons St E 35674 256-389-2900
Paul Pickett, prin. Fax 389-2903

Covenant Christian S 200/PK-12
1900 Covenant Dr 35674 256-383-4436
Donny Davis, admin. Fax 381-4437

Tuskegee, Macon, Pop. 9,751
Macon County SD 2,200/PK-12
PO Box 830090 36083 334-727-1600
Dr. Jacqueline Brooks, supt. Fax 724-9990
www.maconk12.org
Washington HS 600/9-12
3803 W Martin Luther King 36083 334-727-0073
Brelinda Sullen, prin. Fax 724-0222
Other Schools – See Notasulga, Tuskegee Institute

Tuskegee University Post-Sec.
1200 W Montgomery Rd 36088 334-727-8011

Tuskegee Institute, See Tuskegee
Macon County SD
Supt. — See Tuskegee
Macon County Area Vocational Center Vo/Tech
1902 Taylor St 36088 334-724-1236
Tuskegee Institute MS 300/7-8
1809 Franklin Rd 36088 334-727-2580
Rosemary Wright, prin. Fax 727-5089

Union Springs, Bullock, Pop. 3,959
Bullock County SD 1,500/K-12
PO Box 231 36089 334-738-2860
Elliott Harris, supt. Fax 738-2802
bullockcounty.schoolinsites.com
Bullock County Career Technical Ctr Vo/Tech
304 Blackmon Ave E 36089 334-738-4370
James Foulks, dir. Fax 738-4369
Bullock County HS 500/9-12
PO Box 5108 36089 334-738-2198
Derrick Harris, prin. Fax 738-2606

South Highlands MS 400/5-8
PO Box 111 36089 334-738-2896
Sean Dees, prin. Fax 738-5746

Uniontown, Perry, Pop. 1,770
Perry County SD
Supt. — See Marion
Hatch S 400/PK-12
PO Box 709 36786 334-628-4061
Leslie Turner, prin. Fax 683-4935

Uriah, Monroe, Pop. 280
Monroe County SD
Supt. — See Monroeville
Blacksher S 700/PK-12
15933 Highway 21 S 36480 251-862-2130
Donald Baggett, prin. Fax 862-2808

Valley, Chambers, Pop. 9,430
Chambers County SD
Supt. — See Lafayette
Burns MS 700/6-8
292 Johnson St 36854 334-756-3567
Dr. Frankie Bell, prin. Fax 756-7511
Valley HS 900/9-12
501 US Highway 29 36854 334-756-4105
Sherry Ashe, prin. Fax 756-9602

Lee County SD
Supt. — See Opelika
Beulah HS 600/7-12
4848 Lee Road 270 36854 334-745-5010
Cincrystal Poythress, prin. Fax 749-1914

Valley Grande, Dallas, Pop. 3,989
Dallas County SD
Supt. — See Selma
Martin MS 300/7-8
2863 County Road 81, 334-872-6417
Paul Thomas, prin. Fax 875-4013

Valley Head, DeKalb, Pop. 541
De Kalb County SD
Supt. — See Rainsville
Valley Head S 500/K-12
PO Box 149 35989 256-635-6228
William Monroe, prin. Fax 635-6229

Vance, Tuscaloosa, Pop. 1,508
Tuscaloosa County SD
Supt. — See Tuscaloosa
Brookwood MS 800/6-8
17021 Brookwood Pkwy 35490 205-342-2748
Daniel Bray, prin. Fax 553-9910

Verbena, Chilton
Chilton County SD
Supt. — See Clanton
Verbena S 600/K-12
202 County Road 510 36091 205-280-2820
Todd Davis, prin. Fax 755-0393

Vernon, Lamar, Pop. 1,977
Lamar County SD 2,400/K-12
PO Box 1379 35592 205-695-7615
Garth Moss, supt. Fax 695-7678
www.lamarcountyschools.net
Lamar County S 700/4-12
8990 Highway 18 35592 205-695-7717
Vance Herron, prin. Fax 695-8218
Lamar County School of Technology Vo/Tech
43880 Highway 17 35592 205-695-7129
Ken Dawkins, prin. Fax 695-6153
Other Schools – See Millport, Sulligent

Vestavia Hills, Jefferson, Pop. 33,714
Hoover CSD
Supt. — See Hoover

Spain Park HS 1,600/9-12
4700 Jaguar Dr 35242 205-439-1400
Larry Giangrosso, prin. Fax 439-1401

Vestavia Hills CSD 6,700/K-12
PO Box 660826 35266 205-402-5100
Sheila Phillips, supt. Fax 402-5134
www.vestavia.k12.al.us
Liberty Park MS 500/6-8
17035 Liberty Pkwy 35242 205-402-5450
Kacy Pierce, prin. Fax 402-5450
Pizitz MS 1,100/6-8
2020 Pizitz Dr 35216 205-402-5350
Meredith Hanson, prin. Fax 402-5354
Vestavia Hills HS 1,900/9-12
2235 Lime Rock Rd 35216 205-402-5250
Dr. Tyler Burgess, prin. Fax 402-5262

Vina, Franklin, Pop. 354
Franklin County SD
Supt. — See Russellville
Vina S 300/PK-12
8250 Highway 23 35593 256-331-2260
James Pharr, prin. Fax 331-2292

Vincent, Shelby, Pop. 1,969
Shelby County SD
Supt. — See Columbiana
Vincent MSHS 500/6-12
42505 Highway 25 35178 205-682-7300
Dr. Michele Edwards, prin. Fax 682-7305

Vinemont, Cullman
Cullman County SD
Supt. — See Cullman
Vinemont HS 300/9-12
PO Box 189 35179 256-734-0571
Ferrell Runge, prin. Fax 739-8605
Vinemont MS 200/6-8
170 High School Rd 35179 256-739-1943
Dr. Vicky Spear, prin. Fax 737-1664
West Point MS 400/6-8
4545 County Road 1141 35179 256-734-5904
Clark Farley, prin. Fax 736-2354

Wadley, Randolph, Pop. 735
Randolph County SD
Supt. — See Wedowee
Wadley S 400/K-12
105 Bailey 36276 256-395-2286
Lori Carlisle, prin. Fax 395-4488

Southern Union State Community College Post-Sec.
PO Box 1000 36276 256-395-2211

Walnut Grove, Etowah, Pop. 690
Etowah County SD
Supt. — See Gadsden
West End HS 400/7-12
4515 Elm St 35990 256-622-1112
Butch Dixon, prin. Fax 622-1081

Warrior, Jefferson, Pop. 3,120
Jefferson County SD
Supt. — See Birmingham
Corner MS 300/5-8
10005 Corner School Rd 35180 205-379-3230
Michael Manning, prin. Fax 379-3246

Waterloo, Lauderdale, Pop. 203
Lauderdale County SD
Supt. — See Florence
Waterloo S 300/PK-12
PO Box 68 35677 256-766-3100
Dr. Gary Dan Williams, prin. Fax 766-3194

Weaver, Calhoun, Pop. 2,963
Calhoun County SD
Supt. — See Anniston

Weaver HS 600/7-12
917 Clairmont Dr 36277 256-741-7200
Michael Allison, prin. Fax 820-0811

Wedowee, Randolph, Pop. 821
Randolph County SD 2,200/K-12
182 Circle Dr 36278 256-357-4611
Rance Kirby, supt. Fax 357-4844
www.randolphboe.org
Randolph County HS 400/7-12
465 Woodland Ave W 36278 256-357-4751
Darren Anglin, prin. Fax 357-2310
Randolph-Roanoke Career Tech Vo/Tech
960 Main St S 36278 256-357-2839
Christy Fordham, prin. Fax 357-4580
Other Schools – See Wadley, Woodland

West Blocton, Bibb, Pop. 1,231
Bibb County SD
Supt. — See Centreville
Bibb County Career Academy Vo/Tech
17191 Highway 5 35184 205-938-7434
Dr. Terry Holder, prin. Fax 938-2037
West Blocton HS 500/9-12
4734 Truman Aldrich Pkwy 35184 205-938-9002
Terry Lawley, prin. Fax 938-9546
West Blocton MS 500/5-8
4721 Truman Aldrich Pkwy 35184 205-938-2451
Dr. Greg Blake, prin. Fax 938-3261

Wetumpka, Elmore, Pop. 6,406
Elmore County SD 11,100/PK-12
100 H H Robinson Dr 36092 334-567-1200
Andre Harrison, supt. Fax 567-1405
www.elmoreco.com
Elmore County Technical Center Vo/Tech
800 Kelly Fitzpatrick Dr 36092 334-567-1218
Jimmy Hull, dir. Fax 567-1417
Wetumpka HS 1,100/9-12
1251 Coosa River Pkwy 36092 334-567-5158
Robert Slater, prin. Fax 567-1178
Wetumpka MS 1,000/5-8
1000 Micanopy St 36092 334-567-1413
Tremeca Jackson, prin. Fax 567-1408
Other Schools – See Deatsville, Eclectic, Millbrook

Winfield, Marion, Pop. 4,666
Winfield CSD 1,300/K-12
PO Box 70 35594 205-487-4255
Dr. Keith Davis, supt. Fax 487-4603
www.winfield.k12.al.us
Winfield HS 400/9-12
232 Pirate Cv 35594 205-487-6900
Benny Parrish, prin. Fax 487-4257
Winfield MS 400/5-8
481 Apple Ave 35594 205-487-6901
Wendell Goodwin, prin. Fax 487-6258

Woodland, Randolph, Pop. 182
Randolph County SD
Supt. — See Wedowee
Woodland S 800/K-12
24574 Highway 48 36280 256-449-2315
Jeffery Thompson, prin. Fax 449-2316

Woodville, Jackson, Pop. 730
Jackson County SD
Supt. — See Scottsboro
Woodville S 600/PK-12
290 County Road 63 35776 256-776-2874
Bruce Maples, prin. Fax 776-4718

York, Sumter, Pop. 2,533
Sumter County SD
Supt. — See Livingston
Sumter Central HS 600/9-12
13878 U S Highway 11 36925 205-652-1501
Stoney Pritchett, prin. Fax 652-1513

Sumter Academy 200/K-12
181 Sumter Academy Rd 36925 205-392-5238

ALASKA

ALASKA DEPARTMENT OF EDUCATION
PO Box 110500, Juneau 99811-0500
Telephone 907-465-2800
Fax 907-465-4165
Website http://www.eed.state.ak.us/

Commissioner of Education Dr. Michael Johnson

ALASKA BOARD OF EDUCATION
PO Box 110500, Juneau 99811-0500

Chairperson James Fields

PUBLIC, PRIVATE AND CATHOLIC SECONDARY SCHOOLS

Adak, Aleutians West, Pop. 290
Aleutian Region SD
Supt. — See Anchorage
Adak S 50/PK-12
PO Box 2083 99546 907-592-3820
Julie Plummer, lead tchr. Fax 592-2249

Akhiok, Kodiak Island, Pop. 51
Kodiak Island Borough SD
Supt. — See Kodiak
Akhiok S 50/PK-12
PO Box 5049 99615 907-836-2223
Kendra Bartz, prin. Fax 836-2206

Akiachak, Bethel, Pop. 621
Yupiit SD 400/PK-12
PO Box 51190 99551 907-825-3600
Rayna Hartz, supt. Fax 825-2404
www.yupiit.org
Akiachak S, PO Box 51189 99551 200/K-12
William Richards, prin. 907-825-3616
Other Schools – See Akiak, Tuluksak

Akiak, Bethel, Pop. 339
Yupiit SD
Supt. — See Akiachak
Akiak S, PO Box 49 99552 100/PK-12
Charles Burns, prin. 907-765-4600

Akutan, Aleutians East, Pop. 979
Aleutian East Borough SD
Supt. — See Sand Point
Akutan S 50/PK-12
PO Box 25 99553 907-698-2205
Shiloh McManus, prin. Fax 698-2216

Alakanuk, Wade Hampton, Pop. 660
Lower Yukon SD
Supt. — See Mountain Village
Alakanuk S 200/PK-12
PO Box 9 99554 907-238-3312
Herbert Hooper, prin. Fax 238-3417

Allakaket, Yukon-Koyukuk, Pop. 101
Yukon-Koyukuk SD
Supt. — See Fairbanks
Allakaket S 50/PK-12
PO Box 69 99720 907-968-2205
Larry Parker, prin. Fax 968-2250

Ambler, Northwest Arctic, Pop. 248
Northwest Arctic Borough SD
Supt. — See Kotzebue
Ambler S 100/PK-12
PO Box 109 99786 907-445-2154
Scott Lefebvre, prin. Fax 445-2159

Anaktuvuk Pass, North Slope, Pop. 294
North Slope Borough SD
Supt. — See Barrow
Nunamiut S 100/PK-12
PO Box 21029 99721 907-661-3226
Patrick Manning, prin. Fax 661-3402

Anchorage, Anchorage, Pop. 265,438
Aleutian Region SD 50/PK-12
PO Box 92230 99509 907-277-2648
Joe Beckford, supt. Fax 277-2649
www.aleutregion.org
Other Schools – See Adak, Atka

Anchorage SD 47,800/PK-12
5530 E Northern Lights Blvd 99504 907-742-4000
Dr. Deena Paramo, supt. Fax 742-4318
www.asdk12.org
ACE / ACT Program Alt
3745 Community Park Loop 99508 907-742-3950
Robyn Harris, prin. Fax 742-3988
AVAIL Program 100/Alt
425 C St 99501 907-742-4930
Nichelle Mauk, prin. Fax 742-4933
Bartlett HS 1,600/9-12
1101 Golden Bear Dr 99504 907-742-1800
Sean Prince, prin. Fax 742-1825
Begich MS 1,000/6-8
7440 Creekside Center Dr 99504 907-742-0500
Brian Singleton, prin. Fax 742-0510
Benson Secondary S 300/Alt
4515 Campbell Airstrip Rd 99507 907-742-2050
Frank Reuter, prin. Fax 742-2060
Central MS of Science 500/7-8
1405 E St 99501 907-742-5100
Joel Roylance, prin. Fax 742-5125
Clark MS 1,100/6-8
150 Bragaw St 99508 907-742-4700
Cessilye Williams, prin. Fax 742-4756
Dimond HS 1,600/9-12
2909 W 88th Ave 99502 907-742-7000
Tina Johnson-Harris, prin. Fax 742-7007
East Anchorage HS 2,100/9-12
4025 E Northern Lights Blvd 99508 907-742-2100
Sam Spinella, prin. Fax 742-2134
Goldenview MS 700/7-8
15800 Golden View Dr 99516 907-348-8626
Wendy Pondolfino, prin. Fax 742-8273
Hanshew MS 800/7-8
10121 Lake Otis Pkwy 99507 907-349-1561
Nancy Brain, prin. Fax 349-2835
King Career Center Vo/Tech
2650 E Northern Lights Blvd 99508 907-742-8900
Lou Pondolfino, prin. Fax 742-8907
Mears MS 800/7-8
2700 W 100th Ave 99515 907-742-6400
Michael Perkins, prin. Fax 742-6444
New Path HS 50/Alt
1400 E 4th Ave 99501 907-742-4939
Nichelle Mauk, prin. Fax 742-4933
Polaris S 500/Alt
6200 Ashwood St 99507 907-742-8700
Carol Bartholomew, prin. Fax 742-8777
Romig MS 800/7-8
2500 Minnesota Dr 99503 907-742-5200
Sven Gustafson, prin. Fax 742-5252
SAVE HS 200/Alt
410 E 56th Ave 99518 907-742-1250
Karin Parker, prin. Fax 742-1266
Service HS 1,700/9-12
5577 Abbott Rd 99507 907-742-8100
Frank Hauser, prin. Fax 742-6615
South Anchorage HS 1,400/9-12
13400 Elmore Rd 99516 907-742-6200
K. Johnson-Struempler, prin. Fax 742-6207
Steller Secondary S 300/Alt
2508 Blueberry Rd 99503 907-742-4950
Reed Whitmore, prin. Fax 742-4966
Wendler MS 500/7-8
2905 Lake Otis Pkwy 99508 907-742-7300
Brendan Wilson, prin. Fax 742-7350
West Anchorage HS 1,800/9-12
1700 Hillcrest Dr 99517 907-742-2500
Rick Stone, prin. Fax 742-2525
Other Schools – See Chugiak, Eagle River

Chugach SD 100/PK-12
9312 Vanguard Dr Ste 100 99507 907-522-7400
Bob Crumley, supt. Fax 522-3399
www.chugachschools.com
Other Schools – See Chenega Bay, Tatitlek, Whittier

Alaska Career College Post-Sec.
1415 E Tudor Rd 99507 907-563-7575
Alaska Pacific University Post-Sec.
4101 University Dr 99508 800-252-7528
Anchorage Christian S 700/PK-12
6575 E Northern Lights Blvd 99504 907-337-9575
Thomas Cobaugh, admin. Fax 338-3903
Charter College Post-Sec.
2221 E Northern Lights #120 99508 907-277-1000
Grace Christian S 600/K-12
12407 Pintail St 99516 907-868-1203
Christopher Gionet, prin. Fax 644-2261
Holy Rosary Academy 100/K-12
1010 W Fireweed Ln 99503 907-276-5822
Catherine Neumayr, prin. Fax 258-1055
Lumen Christi JSHS 100/7-12
8110 Jewel Lake Rd Bldg D 99502 907-245-9231
John Harmon, prin. Fax 245-9232
University of Alaska Anchorage Post-Sec.
3211 Providence Dr 99508 907-786-1800

Anderson, Denali, Pop. 234
Denali Borough SD
Supt. — See Healy
Anderson S 50/K-12
PO Box 3120 99744 907-582-2700
Jeni Mason, prin. Fax 582-2000

Angoon, Skagway-Hoonah-Angoon, Pop. 409
Chatham SD 200/K-12
PO Box 109 99820 907-788-3302
Bernie Grieve, supt. Fax 788-3252
chathamsd.schoolwires.net
Angoon S 100/K-12
PO Box 209 99820 907-788-3811
Jim Parkin, prin. Fax 788-3812
Other Schools – See Gustavus, Haines, Tenakee Springs

Aniak, Bethel, Pop. 452
Kuspuk SD 400/PK-12
PO Box 49 99557 907-675-4250
Susan L. Johnson, supt. Fax 675-4305
www.kuspuk.org
Aniak JSHS, PO Box 29 99557 100/7-12
Dr. David Hamilton, prin. 907-675-4330
Other Schools – See Chuathbaluk, Crooked Creek, Kalskag, Sleetmute, Stony River

Anvik, Yukon-Koyukuk, Pop. 82
Iditarod Area SD
Supt. — See Mc Grath
Blackwell S 50/PK-12
PO Box 90 99558 907-663-6348
Doug Goben, prin. Fax 663-6349

Arctic Village, Yukon-Koyukuk, Pop. 142
Yukon Flats SD
Supt. — See Fort Yukon
Arctic Village S 50/PK-12
PO Box 22049 99722 907-587-5211
Terry Reed, lead tchr. Fax 587-5210

Atka, Aleutians West, Pop. 61
Aleutian Region SD
Supt. — See Anchorage
Netsvetov S 50/K-12
PO Box 47050 99547 907-839-2210
Sally Swetzof, lead tchr. Fax 839-2212

Atmautluak, Bethel, Pop. 277
Lower Kuskokwim SD
Supt. — See Bethel
Alexie Memorial S 100/PK-12
PO Box ATT 99559 907-553-5112
Tania Erickson-Grant, prin. Fax 553-5129

Atqasuk, North Slope, Pop. 231
North Slope Borough SD
Supt. — See Barrow
Meade River S 100/PK-12
PO Box 91030 99791 907-633-6315
Debbe Lancaster, prin. Fax 633-6215

Barrow, North Slope, Pop. 3,772
North Slope Borough SD 2,000/PK-12
PO Box 169 99723 907-852-5311
Peggy Cowan, supt. Fax 852-9503
www.nsbsd.org/
Barrow HS 200/9-12
PO Box 960 99723 907-852-8950
Sherry McKenzie, prin. Fax 852-8969
Hopson MS 200/6-8
PO Box 509 99723 907-852-3880
Roger Wells, prin. Fax 852-7794
Kiita Learning Community 50/Alt
PO Box 169 99723 907-852-9677
Robert Johnson, prin. Fax 852-4334
Other Schools – See Anaktuvuk Pass, Atqasuk, Kaktovik, Nuiqsut, Point Hope, Point Lay, Wainwright

---

Ilisagvik College Post-Sec.
PO Box 749 99723 907-852-3333

Beaver, Yukon-Koyukuk, Pop. 83
Yukon Flats SD
Supt. — See Fort Yukon

Cruikshank S 50/PK-12
PO Box 24050 99724 907-628-6313
Clayton Ellsworth, lead tchr. Fax 628-6615

Bethel, Bethel, Pop. 5,648
Lower Kuskokwim SD 4,300/PK-12
PO Box 305 99559 907-543-4800
Jacob Jensen, supt. Fax 543-4904
www.lksd.org
Bethel Regional HS 500/7-12
PO Box 700 99559 907-543-3957
Elizabeth Balcerek, prin. Fax 543-2327
Kuskokwim Learning Academy 100/Alt
PO Box 1949 99559 907-543-5610
Doug Boyer, prin. Fax 543-5603
Other Schools – See Atmautluak, Chefornak, Eek, Goodnews Bay, Kasigluk, Kipnuk, Kongiganak, Kwethluk, Kwigillingok, Mekoryuk, Napakiak, Napaskiak, Newtok, Nightmute, Nunapitchuk, Platinum, Quinhagak, Toksook Bay, Tuntutuliak, Tununak

Big Lake, Matanuska-Susitna, Pop. 3,191
Matanuska-Susitna Borough SD
Supt. — See Palmer
Houston HS 400/9-12
12501 W Hawk Ln, 907-892-9400
William Johnson, prin. Fax 892-9460
Houston MS 400/6-8
PO Box 520920 99652 907-892-9500
Benjamin Howard, prin. Fax 892-9560

Brevig Mission, Nome, Pop. 377
Bering Strait SD
Supt. — See Unalakleet
Brevig Mission S 100/PK-12
General Delivery 99785 907-642-4021
Diane Crockett, prin. Fax 642-4031

Buckland, Northwest Arctic, Pop. 408
Northwest Arctic Borough SD
Supt. — See Kotzebue
Buckland S 200/PK-12
PO Box 91 99727 907-494-2127
Matthew Berlin, prin. Fax 494-2106

Cantwell, Denali, Pop. 205
Denali Borough SD
Supt. — See Healy
Cantwell S 50/K-12
PO Box 29 99729 907-768-2372
Jeni Mason, prin. Fax 768-2500

Chalkyitsik, Yukon-Koyukuk, Pop. 69
Yukon Flats SD
Supt. — See Fort Yukon
Tsuk Taih S 50/PK-12
1 Marten Hill 99788 907-848-8113
Fax 848-8312

Chefornak, Bethel, Pop. 415
Lower Kuskokwim SD
Supt. — See Bethel
Chaputnquak S 200/PK-12
PO Box 50 99561 907-867-8700
Andrea Engbretsen, prin. Fax 867-8727

Chenega Bay, Valdez-Cordova, Pop. 94
Chugach SD
Supt. — See Anchorage
Chenega Bay S 50/PK-12
PO Box 8030 99574 907-573-5123
Charley Rininger, lead tchr. Fax 573-5137

Chevak, Wade Hampton, Pop. 915
Kashunamiut SD 300/PK-12
PO Box 345 99563 907-858-7712
Larry Parker, supt. Fax 858-6150
www.chevakschool.org/
Chevak S 300/PK-12
PO Box 345 99563 907-858-7712
Molli Sipe, prin. Fax 858-6150

Chignik, Lake and Peninsula, Pop. 87
Lake & Peninsula SD
Supt. — See King Salmon
Chignik Bay S 50/K-12
PO Box 9 99564 907-749-2213
Kitza Durlop, prin. Fax 749-2261

Chignik Lagoon, Lake and Peninsula, Pop. 69
Lake & Peninsula SD
Supt. — See King Salmon
Chignik Lagoon S 50/PK-12
PO Box 50 99565 907-840-2210
Joe Ward, prin. Fax 840-2265

Chignik Lake, Lake and Peninsula, Pop. 71
Lake & Peninsula SD
Supt. — See King Salmon
Chignik Lake S 50/K-12
General Delivery 99548 907-845-2210
Joe Ward, lead tchr. Fax 845-2254

Chiniak, Kodiak Island, Pop. 45
Kodiak Island Borough SD
Supt. — See Kodiak
Chiniak S 50/K-10
PO Box 5529 99615 907-486-8323
Kendra Bartz, prin. Fax 486-3185

Chuathbaluk, Bethel, Pop. 112
Kuspuk SD
Supt. — See Aniak
Crow Village Sam S 50/PK-12
PO Box CHU 99557 907-467-4229
Steven B. Porter, prin. Fax 467-4122

Chugiak, See Anchorage
Anchorage SD
Supt. — See Anchorage
Chugiak HS 1,100/9-12
16525 S Birchwood Loop Rd 99567 907-742-3050
David Legg, prin. Fax 742-3148
Mirror Lake MS 700/6-8
22901 Lake Hill Dr 99567 907-742-3500
Alexandra Hagler, prin. Fax 742-3545

Birchwood Christian S 100/PK-12
22208 Birchwood Loop Rd 99567 907-688-2228
Todd Clark, prin. Fax 688-2159

Circle, Yukon-Koyukuk, Pop. 98
Yukon Flats SD
Supt. — See Fort Yukon
Circle S 50/PK-12
PO Box 49 99733 907-773-1250
Mathew Potter, lead tchr. Fax 773-1259

Coffman Cove, Prince of Wales-Outer Ketchikan, Pop. 173
Southeast Island SD
Supt. — See Thorne Bay
Valentine S 50/K-12
PO Box 18002 99918 907-329-2244
James Hughes, lead tchr. Fax 329-2210

Cooper Landing, Kenai Peninsula, Pop. 282
Kenai Peninsula Borough SD
Supt. — See Soldotna
Cooper Landing S 50/K-12
19030 Bean Creek Rd 99572 907-595-1244
Douglas Hayman, prin. Fax 595-1461

Copper Center, Valdez-Cordova, Pop. 312
Copper River SD
Supt. — See Glennallen
Kenny Lake S 100/1-12
HC 60 Box 224 99573 907-822-3870
Shaun Streyle, lead tchr. Fax 822-3794

Cordova, Valdez-Cordova, Pop. 2,067
Cordova CSD 300/PK-12
PO Box 1330 99574 907-424-3265
Rich Carlson, supt. Fax 424-3271
cordovasd.org
Cordova JSHS 100/7-12
PO Box 1330 99574 907-424-3266
Rob O'Neal, prin. Fax 424-5215

Craig, Prince of Wales-Outer Ketchikan, Pop. 1,047
Craig CSD 300/PK-12
PO Box 800 99921 907-826-3274
Jack Walsh, supt. Fax 826-3322
www.craigschools.com
Craig HS 100/9-12
PO Box 800 99921 907-826-2274
Michael Silverman, prin. Fax 826-3016
Craig MS 100/6-8
PO Box 800 99921 907-826-3274
Jackie Hanson, prin. Fax 826-3309

Southeast Island SD
Supt. — See Thorne Bay
Hollis S 50/PK-12
PO Box 803 99921 907-530-7108
Julie Vasquez, lead tchr. Fax 530-7111

Crooked Creek, Bethel, Pop. 96
Kuspuk SD
Supt. — See Aniak
John Sr. S 50/PK-12
PO Box 20 99575 907-432-2205
Steven Porter, prin. Fax 432-2206

Deering, Northwest Arctic, Pop. 117
Northwest Arctic Borough SD
Supt. — See Kotzebue
Deering S 50/PK-12
PO Box 36009 99736 907-363-2121
Perrian Windhausen, prin. Fax 363-2128

Delta Junction, Southeast Fairbanks, Pop. 919
Delta-Greely SD 600/PK-12
PO Box 527 99737 907-895-4657
Laural Jackson, supt. Fax 895-4781
www.dgsd.us
Delta Junction HS 200/9-12
PO Box 647 99737 907-895-4460
Bob Burkhart, prin. Fax 895-4049
Gerstle River S 50/PK-12
PO Box 369 99737 907-895-1043
Jeff Lansing, prin. Fax 895-5198
New Horizons HS 50/Alt
PO Box 369 99737 907-895-4655
Laural Jackson, prin. Fax 895-4246
Other Schools – See Fort Greely

Dillingham, Dillingham, Pop. 2,086
Dillingham CSD 500/PK-12
PO Box 170 99576 907-842-5223
Danny Frazier, supt. Fax 530-8877
www.dlgsd.org
Dillingham MSHS 300/6-12
PO Box 170 99576 907-842-5221
Monte Thacker, prin. Fax 842-4395

Southwest Region SD 600/K-12
PO Box 90 99576 907-842-5287
David Piazza, supt. Fax 842-5428
www.swrsd.org/
Other Schools – See Koliganek, Manokotak, New Stuyahok, Togiak

Diomede, Nome, Pop. 111
Bering Strait SD
Supt. — See Unalakleet
Diomede S 50/PK-12
PO Box 7099 99762 907-686-3021
Frank Stanek, prin. Fax 686-3022

Dot Lake, Southeast Fairbanks, Pop. 12
Alaska Gateway SD
Supt. — See Tok
Dot Lake S 50/K-12
PO Box 2280 99737 907-882-2663
Julie Selves, prin. Fax 882-2112

Eagle, Southeast Fairbanks, Pop. 85
Alaska Gateway SD
Supt. — See Tok
Eagle Community S 50/K-12
PO Box 168 99738 907-547-2210
Kristy Robbins, prin. Fax 547-2302

Eagle River, See Anchorage
Anchorage SD
Supt. — See Anchorage
Eagle River HS 800/9-12
8701 Yosemite Dr 99577 907-742-2700
Martin Lang, prin. Fax 742-2710
Gruening MS 600/7-8
9601 Lee St 99577 907-742-3600
Bobby Jefts, prin. Fax 742-3666

Matanuska-Susitna Borough SD
Supt. — See Palmer
Alaska Middle College S 100/11-12
10928 Eagle River Rd # 115 99577 907-746-8494
Kathy Moffitt, admin. Fax 746-8485

Eagle River Christian S 100/K-12
10336 E Eagle River Loop Rd 99577 907-694-4602
Michelle Caldwell, admin. Fax 694-4141

Eek, Bethel, Pop. 296
Lower Kuskokwim SD
Supt. — See Bethel
Eek S 100/PK-12
PO Box 50 99578 907-536-5227
Brett Stirling, prin. Fax 536-5628

Egegik, Lake and Peninsula, Pop. 97
Lake & Peninsula SD
Supt. — See King Salmon
Egegik S 50/K-12
PO Box 10 99579 907-233-2210
April LeFevere, lead tchr. Fax 233-2254

Eielson AFB, Fairbanks North Star, Pop. 2,496
Fairbanks North Star Borough SD
Supt. — See Fairbanks
Eielson JSHS 400/7-12
675 Ravens Way 99702 907-372-3110
Mario Gatto, prin. Fax 372-3202

Elim, Nome, Pop. 322
Bering Strait SD
Supt. — See Unalakleet
Aniguiin S 100/PK-12
PO Box 29 99739 907-890-3021
Jack Kingsford, prin. Fax 890-3031

Emmonak, Wade Hampton, Pop. 759
Lower Yukon SD
Supt. — See Mountain Village
Emmonak S 200/PK-12
General Delivery 99581 907-949-1248
Thomas Gobeske, prin. Fax 949-1148

Fairbanks, Fairbanks North Star, Pop. 29,138
Fairbanks North Star Borough SD 13,900/PK-12
520 5th Ave 99701 907-452-2000
Dr. Karen Gaborik Ed.D., supt. Fax 451-6160
www.k12northstar.org
Fairbanks B.E.S.T. 300/Alt
520 5th Ave 99701 907-452-2000
Kathy Hughes, dir. Fax 451-1009
Hutchison HS Vo/Tech
3750 Geist Rd 99709 907-479-2261
Tyrone Oates, prin. Fax 479-8286
Lathrop HS 1,100/9-12
901 Airport Way 99701 907-456-7794
Bob Meade, prin. Fax 452-6735
Ryan MS 400/7-8
951 Airport Way 99701 907-452-4751
Heather Stewart, prin. Fax 451-8834
Smith MS 300/7-8
1401 Bainbridge Blvd 99701 907-458-7600
Dave Dershin, prin. Fax 458-7676
Tanana MS 500/7-8
600 Trainor Gate Rd 99701 907-452-8145
Greg Platt, prin. Fax 456-2780
West Valley HS 1,000/9-12
3800 Geist Rd 99709 907-479-4221
Dave Foshee, prin. Fax 474-8901
Other Schools – See Eielson AFB, North Pole

Yukon-Koyukuk SD 300/PK-12
4762 Old Airport Rd 99709 907-374-9400
Kerry Boyd, supt. Fax 374-9440
www.yksd.com
Other Schools – See Allakaket, Hughes, Huslia, Kaltag, Koyukuk, Manley Hot Springs, Minto, Nulato, Ruby

---

Aurora Tutoring S 50/PK-12
201 Old Steese Hwy Ste 6 99701 907-374-8852
Baubi Jo Reid, prin. Fax 374-8853
Monroe Catholic JSHS 200/7-12
615 Monroe St 99701 907-456-4574
Patrick Riggs, prin. Fax 452-5978
University of Alaska Fairbanks Post-Sec.
PO Box 757500 99775 907-474-7500

False Pass, Aleutians East, Pop. 35
Aleutian East Borough SD
Supt. — See Sand Point
False Pass S 50/PK-12
PO Box 30 99583 907-548-2224
Annette Barnett, prin. Fax 548-2304

Fort Greely, Southeast Fairbanks, Pop. 513
Delta-Greely SD
Supt. — See Delta Junction
Delta Junction MS 200/6-8
Building 725, 907-869-1043
Jeff Lansing, prin.

Fort Yukon, Yukon-Koyukuk, Pop. 569
Yukon Flats SD 200/PK-12
PO Box 350 99740 907-662-2515
Dr. Lance Bowie, supt. Fax 662-2519
www.yukonflats.net
Fort Yukon S 100/PK-12
PO Box 129 99740 907-662-2352
Debra Van Dyke, prin. Fax 662-2958
Other Schools – See Arctic Village, Beaver, Chalkyitsik, Circle, Venetie

Fritz Creek, Kenai Peninsula, Pop. 1,832
Kenai Peninsula Borough SD
Supt. — See Soldotna
Kachemak-Selo S 100/PK-12
PO Box 15007 99603 907-235-5552
Tim Whip, prin. Fax 235-5644
Voznesenka S 100/PK-12
PO Box 15336 99603 907-235-8549
Michael Wojciak, prin. Fax 235-6086

Galena, Yukon-Koyukuk, Pop. 441
Galena CSD 300/PK-12
PO Box 299 99741 907-656-1205
Chris Reitan, supt. Fax 656-1368
www.galenaalaska.org
Galena Interior Learning Academy 200/9-12
PO Box 359 99741 907-656-2053
John Riddle, prin. Fax 656-2107
Huntington JSHS 50/7-12
PO Box 299 99741 907-656-1205
Beth Buchanan, prin. Fax 656-1368

Gambell, Nome, Pop. 678
Bering Strait SD
Supt. — See Unalakleet
Gambell S 200/PK-12
PO Box 169 99742 907-985-5515
Robert Cooper, prin. Fax 985-5435

Glennallen, Valdez-Cordova, Pop. 422
Copper River SD 400/K-12
PO Box 108 99588 907-822-3234
Dr. Michael Johnson, supt. Fax 822-3949
www.crsd.us
Glennallen JSHS 100/7-12
PO Box 108 99588 907-822-5286
Jack Von Thaer, prin. Fax 822-8501
Other Schools – See Copper Center, Slana

Alaska Bible College Post-Sec.
PO Box 289 99588 907-822-3201

Golovin, Nome, Pop. 153
Bering Strait SD
Supt. — See Unalakleet
Olson S 100/PK-12
PO Box 62040 99762 907-779-3021
Gay Jacobson, prin. Fax 779-3031

Goodnews Bay, Bethel, Pop. 241
Lower Kuskokwim SD
Supt. — See Bethel
Rocky Mountain S 100/PK-12
PO Box 153 99589 907-967-8213
Shannon Hutson, prin. Fax 967-8228

Grayling, Yukon-Koyukuk, Pop. 182
Iditarod Area SD
Supt. — See Mc Grath
David-Louis Memorial S 50/PK-12
PO Box 90 99590 907-453-5135
Michael Willyerd, prin. Fax 453-5165

Gustavus, Skagway-Hoonah-Angoon, Pop. 422
Chatham SD
Supt. — See Angoon
Gustavus S 100/K-12
PO Box 120 99826 907-697-2248
Ann Hilburn, prin. Fax 697-2378

Haines, Haines, Pop. 1,608
Chatham SD
Supt. — See Angoon
Klukwan S 50/K-12
HC 60 Box 2222 99827 907-767-5551
Katherine Carl, lead tchr. Fax 767-5573

Haines Borough SD 200/K-12
PO Box 1289 99827 907-766-6700
Anthony Habra, supt. Fax 766-6794
www.hbsd.net
Haines HS 100/7-12
PO Box 1289 99827 907-766-6700
Rene Martin, prin. Fax 766-6791

Healy, Denali, Pop. 980
Denali Borough SD 800/PK-12
PO Box 280 99743 907-683-2278
Dan Polta, supt. Fax 683-2514
www.dbsd.org
Denali PEAK 600/Alt
PO Box 280 99743 907-683-7325
Jeni Mason, prin. Fax 683-0329
Tri-Valley S 200/K-12
PO Box 400 99743 907-683-2267
Nathan Pitt, prin. Fax 683-2632
Other Schools – See Anderson, Cantwell

Holy Cross, Yukon-Koyukuk, Pop. 171
Iditarod Area SD
Supt. — See Mc Grath
Holy Cross S 50/PK-12
PO Box 210 99602 907-476-7131
Jeff Bader, prin. Fax 476-7161

Homer, Kenai Peninsula, Pop. 4,783
Kenai Peninsula Borough SD
Supt. — See Soldotna
Homer Flex S 50/Alt
4122 Ben Walters Ln 99603 907-235-5558
Christopher Brown, prin. Fax 235-5633
Homer HS 400/9-12
600 E Fairview Ave 99603 907-235-4600
Doug Waclawski, prin. Fax 235-8933
Homer MS 200/7-8
500 Sterling Hwy 99603 907-235-5700
Kari Dendurent, prin. Fax 235-2513
Razdolna S 100/PK-12
PO Box 15098 99603 907-235-6870
Timothy Whip, prin. Fax 235-6485

Hoonah, Skagway-Hoonah-Angoon, Pop. 657
Hoonah CSD 100/PK-12
PO Box 157 99829 907-945-3611
Dr. P.J. Ford Slack Ph.D., supt. Fax 945-3492
www.hoonahschools.org
Hoonah JSHS 50/7-12
PO Box 157 99829 907-945-3613
Ralph Watkins, prin. Fax 945-3607

Hooper Bay, Wade Hampton, Pop. 1,055
Lower Yukon SD
Supt. — See Mountain Village
Hooper Bay S 400/PK-12
PO Box 249 99604 907-758-1200
Hammond Gracy, prin. Fax 758-1280

Hope, Kenai Peninsula, Pop. 178
Kenai Peninsula Borough SD
Supt. — See Soldotna
Hope S 50/K-12
PO Box 47 99605 907-782-3202
Michael Hanson, admin. Fax 782-3140

Hughes, Yukon-Koyukuk, Pop. 77
Yukon-Koyukuk SD
Supt. — See Fairbanks
Oldman S 50/K-12
PO Box 30 99745 907-889-2204
Patty White, admin. Fax 889-2220

Huslia, Yukon-Koyukuk, Pop. 272
Yukon-Koyukuk SD
Supt. — See Fairbanks
Huntington S 100/PK-12
PO Box 110 99746 907-829-2220
Casey Weter, prin. Fax 829-2270

Hydaburg, Prince of Wales-Outer Ketchikan, Pop. 342
Hydaburg CSD 100/K-12
PO Box 109 99922 907-285-3491
Lauren Burch, supt. Fax 285-3391
www.hydaburg.k12.ak.us
Hydaburg S 100/K-12
PO Box 109 99922 907-285-3591
Fax 285-3391

Hyder, Prince of Wales-Outer Ketchikan, Pop. 82
Southeast Island SD
Supt. — See Thorne Bay
Hyder S 50/K-12
PO Box 130 99923 250-636-2800
Chadwick Dillman, lead tchr. Fax 636-2880

Igiugig, Lake and Peninsula, Pop. 34
Lake & Peninsula SD
Supt. — See King Salmon
Igiugig S 50/K-12
PO Box 4010 99613 907-533-3220
Tate Gooden, lead tchr. Fax 533-3221

Iliamna, Lake and Peninsula, Pop. 96
Lake & Peninsula SD
Supt. — See King Salmon
Newhalen S 100/PK-12
PO Box 89 99606 907-571-1211
Ed Lester, prin. Fax 571-1466

Juneau, Juneau, Pop. 28,325
Juneau Borough SD 4,700/PK-12
10014 Crazy Horse Dr 99801 907-523-1700
Mark Miller, supt. Fax 523-1708
www.juneauschools.org
Dryden MS 500/6-8
10014 Crazy Horse Dr 99801 907-463-1850
Jim Thompson, prin. Fax 463-1828
Heeni MS 500/6-8
10014 Crazy Horse Dr 99801 907-463-1899
Molly Yerkes, prin. Fax 463-1877
Juneau-Douglas HS 700/9-12
10014 Crazy Horse Dr 99801 907-523-1500
Paula Casperson, prin. Fax 523-1616
Thunder Mountain HS 700/9-12
10014 Crazy Horse Dr 99801 907-780-1900
Dan Larson, prin. Fax 780-1909
YaaKoosge Daakahidi Alternative HS 100/Alt
10014 Crazy Horse Dr 99801 907-523-1800
Kristin Garot, prin. Fax 523-1819

University of Alaska Southeast Post-Sec.
11120 Glacier Hwy 99801 907-796-6000

Kake, Wrangell-Petersburg, Pop. 485
Kake CSD 100/PK-12
PO Box 450 99830 907-785-3741
Kevin Shipley, supt. Fax 785-6439
www.kakeschools.com
Kake S 100/PK-12
PO Box 450 99830 907-785-3741
Kevin Shipley, supt. Fax 785-6439

Kaktovik, North Slope, Pop. 236
North Slope Borough SD
Supt. — See Barrow
Kaveolook S 100/PK-12
PO Box 20 99747 907-640-6626
Todd Washburn, prin. Fax 640-6718

Kalskag, Bethel, Pop. 186
Kuspuk SD
Supt. — See Aniak
Morgan HS 100/7-12
PO Box 30 99607 907-471-2288
Severin Gardner, prin. Fax 471-2242

Kaltag, Yukon-Koyukuk, Pop. 185
Yukon-Koyukuk SD
Supt. — See Fairbanks
Kaltag S 50/PK-12
PO Box 30 99748 907-534-2204
Patty White, prin. Fax 534-2227

Karluk, Kodiak Island, Pop. 37
Kodiak Island Borough SD
Supt. — See Kodiak
Karluk S 50/K-12
General Delivery 99608 907-241-2217
Kendra Bartz, prin. Fax 241-2207

Kasaan, Prince of Wales-Outer Ketchikan, Pop. 44
Southeast Island SD
Supt. — See Thorne Bay
Kasaan S 50/K-12
117 Kasaan Rd 99901 907-542-2217
Shane Scamahorn, lead tchr. Fax 542-2219

Kasigluk, Bethel, Pop. 558
Lower Kuskokwim SD
Supt. — See Bethel
Akiuk Memorial S 100/PK-12
General Delivery 99609 907-477-6829
Christina Powers, prin. Fax 477-6314
Akula Elitnaurvik S 100/PK-12
PO Box 79 99609 907-477-6615
Ross Bolding, prin. Fax 477-6715

Kenai, Kenai Peninsula, Pop. 6,541
Kenai Peninsula Borough SD
Supt. — See Soldotna
Kenai Alternative HS 100/Alt
705 Frontage Rd Ste C 99611 907-335-2870
Loren Reese, prin. Fax 283-6463
Kenai Central HS 500/9-12
9583 Kenai Spur Hwy 99611 907-283-2100
Alan Fields, prin. Fax 283-3230
Kenai MS 400/6-8
201 N Tinker Ln 99611 907-283-1700
Vaughn Dosko, prin. Fax 283-3180
Marathon S 50/Alt
405 Marathon Rd 99611 907-335-3343
Melissa Linton, prin. Fax 335-3342

Ketchikan, Ketchikan Gateway, Pop. 7,299
Ketchikan Gateway Borough SD 2,300/PK-12
333 Schoenbar Rd 99901 907-225-2118
Robert Boyle, supt. Fax 247-3820
www.kgbsd.org
Ketchikan HS 600/9-12
2610 Fourth Ave 99901 907-225-9815
Sam Nelson, prin. Fax 247-5761
Revilla JSHS 100/7-12
3131 Baranof Ave 99901 907-225-6681
Kurt Lindemann, prin. Fax 247-6681
Schoenbar MS 300/7-8
217 Schoenbar Rd 99901 907-228-7200
Casey Robinson, prin.

Southeast Island SD
Supt. — See Thorne Bay
Naukati S 50/PK-12
PO Box NKI 99950 907-629-4121
Ryan Nelson, lead tchr. Fax 629-4122
Port Protection S 50/PK-12
PO Box PPV 99950 907-489-2228
Jeff Theurer, lead tchr. Fax 489-2235
Whale Pass S 50/PK-12
126 Bayview Rd 99950 907-846-5320
Christine Cook, lead tchr. Fax 846-5319

Kiana, Northwest Arctic, Pop. 351
Northwest Arctic Borough SD
Supt. — See Kotzebue
Kiana S 100/PK-12
PO Box 190 99749 907-475-2115
Rex Kilburn, prin. Fax 475-2120

King Cove, Aleutians East, Pop. 905
Aleutian East Borough SD
Supt. — See Sand Point
King Cove S 100/PK-12
PO Box 69 99612 907-497-2354
Jason Martinez, prin. Fax 497-2408

King Salmon, Bristol Bay, Pop. 341
Lake & Peninsula SD 300/PK-12
PO Box 498 99613 907-246-4280
Ty Mase, supt. Fax 246-4473
www.lpsd.com
Other Schools – See Chignik, Chignik Lagoon, Chignik Lake, Egegik, Igiugig, Iliamna, Kokhanok, Levelock, Nondalton, Perryville, Pilot Point, Port Alsworth, Port Heiden

Kipnuk, Bethel, Pop. 637
Lower Kuskokwim SD
Supt. — See Bethel
Chief Paul Memorial S 200/PK-12
PO Box 19 99614 907-896-5011
LaDorothy Lightfoot, prin. Fax 896-5428

Kivalina, Northwest Arctic, Pop. 368
Northwest Arctic Borough SD
Supt. — See Kotzebue
McQueen S 100/PK-12
General Delivery 99750 907-645-2125
Dr. Zoe Theoharis, prin. Fax 645-2124

Klawock, Prince of Wales-Outer Ketchikan, Pop. 670
Klawock CSD 100/PK-12
PO Box 9 99925 907-755-2220
Jim Holien, supt. Fax 755-2320
www.klawockschool.com/
Klawock City S 100/PK-12
PO Box 9 99925 907-755-2220
Kelli Larson, prin. Fax 755-2913

Kobuk, Northwest Arctic, Pop. 151
Northwest Arctic Borough SD
Supt. — See Kotzebue
Kobuk S 100/PK-12
PO Box 40 99751 907-948-2231
Jay Denton, lead tchr. Fax 948-2225

Kodiak, Kodiak Island, Pop. 5,742
Kodiak Island Borough SD 2,400/PK-12
722 Mill Bay Rd 99615 907-481-6200
Stewart McDonald, supt. Fax 481-6255
www.kibsd.org/
Kodiak HS 800/9-12
722 Mill Bay Rd 99615 907-481-2501
Phillip Johnson, prin. Fax 481-2505
Kodiak MS 500/6-8
722 Mill Bay Rd 99615 907-481-2200
Ron Bryant, prin. Fax 481-2201
Other Schools – See Akhiok, Chiniak, Karluk, Larsen Bay, Old Harbor, Ouzinkie, Port Lions

Kokhanok, Lake and Peninsula, Pop. 153
Lake & Peninsula SD
Supt. — See King Salmon
Kokhanok S 50/K-12
PO Box 1109 99606 907-282-2210
Nicole Metzgar, prin. Fax 282-2247

Koliganek, Dillingham, Pop. 207
Southwest Region SD
Supt. — See Dillingham
Koliganek S 100/K-12
PO Box 5052 99576 907-596-3444
Cody McCanna, prin. Fax 596-3484

Kongiganak, Bethel, Pop. 430
Lower Kuskokwim SD
Supt. — See Bethel
Ayagina'ar Elitnaurvik S 200/PK-12
PO Box 5109, 907-557-5551
Lewis Beaver, prin. Fax 557-5639

Kotlik, Wade Hampton, Pop. 574
Lower Yukon SD
Supt. — See Mountain Village
Kotlik S 200/PK-12
PO Box 20129 99620 907-899-4415
John Harris, prin. Fax 899-4515

Kotzebue, Northwest Arctic, Pop. 2,953
Northwest Arctic Borough SD 2,100/PK-12
PO Box 51 99752 907-442-1800
Dr. Annmarie O'Brien, supt. Fax 442-2246
www.nwarctic.org
Alaska Technical Center Vo/Tech
PO Box 51 99752 907-442-1500
Cheryl Edenshaw, dir. Fax 442-2764
Kotzebue MSHS 300/6-12
PO Box 264 99752 907-442-1876
Mike Lane, prin. Fax 442-2141
Star of the Northwest Magnet S Vo/Tech
PO Box 51 99752 907-442-1800
Paul Bartos, prin. Fax 442-2392
Other Schools – See Ambler, Buckland, Deering, Kiana, Kivalina, Kobuk, Noatak, Noorvik, Selawik, Shungnak

Koyuk, Nome, Pop. 308
Bering Strait SD
Supt. — See Unalakleet
Koyuk-Malemute S 100/PK-12
PO Box 53009 99753 907-963-3021
Mary Huntington, prin. Fax 963-2428

Koyukuk, Yukon-Koyukuk, Pop. 94
Yukon-Koyukuk SD
Supt. — See Fairbanks
Vernetti S 50/PK-10
PO Box 70 99754 907-927-2212
Patty White, admin. Fax 927-2251

Kwethluk, Bethel, Pop. 696
Lower Kuskokwim SD
Supt. — See Bethel
Ket'acik and Aap'alluk Memorial S 300/PK-12
PO Box 150 99621 907-757-6014
Darrell Richard, prin. Fax 757-6013

Kwigillingok, Bethel, Pop. 316
Lower Kuskokwim SD
Supt. — See Bethel
Kwigillingok S 100/PK-12
PO Box 109 99622 907-588-8629
Megan Rosendall, prin. Fax 588-8613

Larsen Bay, Kodiak Island, Pop. 83
Kodiak Island Borough SD
Supt. — See Kodiak
Larsen Bay S 50/PK-12
PO Box 70 99624 907-847-2252
Kendra Bartz, prin. Fax 847-2260

Levelock, Lake and Peninsula, Pop. 65
Lake & Peninsula SD
Supt. — See King Salmon
Levelock S 50/K-12
PO Box 89 99625 907-287-3060
Cathy Pusch, lead tchr. Fax 287-3021

Mc Grath, Yukon-Koyukuk, Pop. 277
Iditarod Area SD 300/PK-12
PO Box 90 99627 907-524-1200
Dr. Rodman Weston, supt. Fax 524-3217
www.iditarodsd.org
Mc Grath S 100/PK-12
PO Box 290 99627 907-524-3388
Fax 524-3751
Other Schools – See Anvik, Grayling, Holy Cross, Nikolai, Shageluk, Takotna

Manley Hot Springs, Yukon-Koyukuk, Pop. 75
Yukon-Koyukuk SD
Supt. — See Fairbanks
Dart S 50/PK-12
PO Box 29 99756 907-672-3202
Patty White, admin. Fax 672-3201

Manokotak, Dillingham, Pop. 440
Southwest Region SD
Supt. — See Dillingham
Manokotak S 100/K-12
PO Box 30 99628 907-289-1013
Debra Forkner, prin. Fax 289-2050

Marshall, Wade Hampton, Pop. 404
Lower Yukon SD
Supt. — See Mountain Village
Marshall S 100/PK-12
PO Box 89 99585 907-679-6112
Joseph Gaylord, prin. Fax 679-6637

Mekoryuk, Bethel, Pop. 184
Lower Kuskokwim SD
Supt. — See Bethel
Nuniwarmiut S 50/PK-12
PO Box 49 99630 907-827-8415
Walt Betz, prin. Fax 827-8613

Mentasta Lake, Southeast Fairbanks, Pop. 111
Alaska Gateway SD
Supt. — See Tok
Mentasta Lake S 50/K-12
PO Box 6039 99780 907-291-2317
Craig Roach, prin. Fax 291-2327

Metlakatla, Prince of Wales-Outer Ketchikan, Pop. 1,313
Annette Islands SD 300/PK-12
PO Box 7 99926 907-886-6332
Eugene Avey M.A., supt. Fax 886-5130
aisdk12.org
Leask MS 100/6-8
PO Box 7 99926 907-886-6000
Jason Pipkin, admin. Fax 886-5119
Metlakatla HS 100/9-12
PO Box 7 99926 907-886-6000
Taw Lindsey M.A., prin. Fax 886-5120

Minto, Yukon-Koyukuk, Pop. 200
Yukon-Koyukuk SD
Supt. — See Fairbanks
Minto S 50/PK-12
PO Box 81 99758 907-798-7212
Vicky Charlie, prin. Fax 798-7282

Mountain Village, Wade Hampton, Pop. 788
Lower Yukon SD 2,000/PK-12
PO Box 32089 99632 907-591-2411
Jon Wehde, supt. Fax 591-2449
www.loweryukon.org
Beans S 200/PK-12
PO Box 32105 99632 907-591-2204
Diane Reed, prin. Fax 591-2819
Other Schools – See Alakanuk, Emmonak, Hooper Bay, Kotlik, Marshall, Pilot Station, Russian Mission, Scammon Bay, Sheldon Point

Naknek, Bristol Bay, Pop. 421
Bristol Bay Borough SD 200/PK-12
PO Box 169 99633 907-246-4225
Bill Hill, supt. Fax 246-4447
www.bbbsd.net
Bristol Bay MSHS 100/7-12
PO Box 169 99633 907-246-4265
Rick Luthi, prin. Fax 246-4447

Nanwalek, Kenai Peninsula, Pop. 231
Kenai Peninsula Borough SD
Supt. — See Soldotna
Nanwalek S 100/K-12
PO Box 8007 99603 907-281-2210
Nancy Kleine, prin. Fax 281-2211

Napakiak, Bethel, Pop. 354
Lower Kuskokwim SD
Supt. — See Bethel
Miller Memorial S 100/PK-12
PO Box 34050 99634 907-589-2420
Linda Jennings, prin. Fax 589-2515

Napaskiak, Bethel, Pop. 403
Lower Kuskokwim SD
Supt. — See Bethel
Qugcuun Memorial S 50/PK-12
PO Box 6199 99559 907-737-7214
Nick Straw, prin. Fax 737-7211
Williams Memorial S 200/K-12
PO Box 6089 99559 907-737-7212
Talbert Bentley, prin. Fax 737-7967

Nenana, Yukon-Koyukuk, Pop. 357
Nenana CSD 1,000/K-12
PO Box 10 99760 907-832-5464
Eric Gebhart, supt. Fax 832-5625
nenanalynx.org
Nenana City S 200/K-12
PO Box 10 99760 907-832-5464
Sherelyn Carattini, prin. Fax 832-5625

New Stuyahok, Dillingham, Pop. 495
Southwest Region SD
Supt. — See Dillingham
Chief Blunka S 100/K-12
PO Box 29 99636 907-693-3144
Robin Jones, prin. Fax 693-3163

Newtok, Bethel, Pop. 352
Lower Kuskokwim SD
Supt. — See Bethel
Ayaprun S 200/PK-12
PO Box WWT 99559 907-237-2504
Grant Kashatok, prin. Fax 237-2506

Nightmute, Bethel, Pop. 279
Lower Kuskokwim SD
Supt. — See Bethel
Negtemiut Elitnaurviat S 100/PK-12
General Delivery 99690 907-647-6313
Jerry White, prin. Fax 647-6227

Nikiski, Kenai Peninsula, Pop. 4,284
Kenai Peninsula Borough SD
Supt. — See Soldotna
Nikiski MSHS 400/6-12
PO Box 7112 99635 907-776-9400
Dan Carstens, prin. Fax 776-3486

Nikolaevsk, Kenai Peninsula, Pop. 307
Kenai Peninsula Borough SD
Supt. — See Soldotna
Nikolaevsk S 100/PK-12
PO Box 5129 99556 907-235-8972
Mike Sellers, prin. Fax 235-3617

Nikolai, Yukon-Koyukuk, Pop. 83
Iditarod Area SD
Supt. — See Mc Grath
Top of the Kuskokwim S 50/PK-12
PO Box 9190 99691 907-293-2427
Fax 293-2214

Ninilchik, Kenai Peninsula, Pop. 836
Kenai Peninsula Borough SD
Supt. — See Soldotna
Ninilchik S 100/K-12
15735 Sterling Hwy 99639 907-567-3301
Jeffrey Ambrosier, prin. Fax 567-3504

Noatak, Northwest Arctic, Pop. 502
Northwest Arctic Borough SD
Supt. — See Kotzebue
Napaaqtugmiut S 200/PK-12
PO Box 49 99761 907-485-2153
Stan VanAmburg, lead tchr. Fax 485-2150

Nome, Nome, Pop. 3,196
Nome SD 700/PK-12
PO Box 131 99762 907-443-2231
Shawn Arnold, supt. Fax 443-5144
www.nomeschools.com
Nome-Beltz JSHS 300/7-12
PO Box 131 99762 907-443-6151
Scott Handley, prin. Fax 443-3626

Nondalton, Lake and Peninsula, Pop. 130
Lake & Peninsula SD
Supt. — See King Salmon
Nondalton S 50/K-12
1000 School Rd 99640 907-294-2210
Ed Cox, prin. Fax 294-2265

Noorvik, Northwest Arctic, Pop. 618
Northwest Arctic Borough SD
Supt. — See Kotzebue
Aqqaluk / Noorvik S 200/PK-12
PO Box 165 99763 907-636-2178
Faith Jurs, prin. Fax 636-2160

North Pole, Fairbanks North Star, Pop. 1,997
Fairbanks North Star Borough SD
Supt. — See Fairbanks
North Pole HS 800/9-12
601 NPHS Blvd 99705 907-488-3761
Annie Keep-Barnes, prin. Fax 488-1488
North Pole MS 700/6-8
300 E 8th Ave 99705 907-488-2271
Rich Smith, prin. Fax 488-9213

North Pole Christian S 100/PK-12
2936 Badger Rd 99705 907-488-0133
David Pearson, prin. Fax 488-8248

Northway, Southeast Fairbanks, Pop. 65
Alaska Gateway SD
Supt. — See Tok
Northway S 50/PK-12
PO Box 519 99764 907-778-2287
Cathy Pusch, prin. Fax 778-2221

Nuiqsut, North Slope, Pop. 391
North Slope Borough SD
Supt. — See Barrow
Nuiqsut Trapper S 100/PK-12
PO Box 89167 99789 907-480-6712
John Lamont, prin. Fax 480-6621

Nulato, Yukon-Koyukuk, Pop. 263
Yukon-Koyukuk SD
Supt. — See Fairbanks
Demoski S 50/PK-12
PO Box 65029 99765 907-898-2204
Jason Johnson, prin. Fax 898-2340

Nunapitchuk, Bethel, Pop. 487
Lower Kuskokwim SD
Supt. — See Bethel
Tobeluk Memorial S 200/K-12
PO Box 150 99641 907-527-5701
Edward Pekar, prin. Fax 527-5610

Old Harbor, Kodiak Island, Pop. 215
Kodiak Island Borough SD
Supt. — See Kodiak
Old Harbor S 50/K-12
PO Box 49 99643 907-286-2213
Kendra Bartz, prin. Fax 286-2222

Ouzinkie, Kodiak Island, Pop. 146
Kodiak Island Borough SD
Supt. — See Kodiak
Ouzinkie S 50/K-12
PO Box 49 99644 907-680-2204
Steve Doerksen, prin. Fax 680-2288

Palmer, Matanuska-Susitna, Pop. 5,499
Matanuska-Susitna Borough SD 17,800/PK-12
501 N Gulkana St 99645 907-746-9200
Gene Stone, supt. Fax 746-4076
www.matsuk12.us
Beryozova S 50/K-12
501 N Gulkana St 99645 907-495-2500
Carl Chamblee, prin. Fax 495-2502
Colony HS 1,100/9-12
9550 E Colony Schools Dr 99645 907-861-5500
Cydney Duffin, prin. Fax 861-5509
Colony MS 700/6-8
9250 E Colony Schools Dr 99645 907-761-1500
Mary McMahon, prin. Fax 761-1592
Palmer HS 800/9-12
1170 W Arctic Ave 99645 907-746-8400
Reese Everett, prin. Fax 746-8481
Palmer MS 600/6-8
1159 S Chugach St 99645 907-761-4300
Thomas Lytle, prin. Fax 761-4372
Valley Pathways HS 200/7-12
PO Box 4897 99645 907-761-4650
James Wanser, prin. Fax 761-4680
Other Schools – See Big Lake, Eagle River, Sutton, Talkeetna, Wasilla

---

Amazing Grace Academy PK-12
2238 Inner Springer Loop 99645 907-745-2691

Pelican, Skagway-Hoonah-Angoon, Pop. 82
Pelican CSD 50/PK-12
PO Box 90 99832 907-735-2236
Larry Wilson, supt. Fax 735-2263
Pelican S 50/PK-12
PO Box 90 99832 907-735-2236
Larry Wilson, admin. Fax 735-2263

Perryville, Lake and Peninsula, Pop. 111
Lake & Peninsula SD
Supt. — See King Salmon
Perryville S 50/K-12
PO Box 103 99648 907-853-2210
Lindsey Moore, lead tchr. Fax 853-2267

Petersburg, Wrangell-Petersburg, Pop. 2,720
Petersburg SD 400/K-12
PO Box 289 99833 907-772-4271
Erica Kludt-Painter, supt. Fax 772-4719
www.pcsd.us
Mitkof MS 100/6-8
PO Box 289 99833 907-772-3860
Rick Dormer, prin. Fax 772-3617
Petersburg HS 100/9-12
PO Box 289 99833 907-772-3861
Rick Dormer, prin. Fax 772-4168

Pilot Point, Lake and Peninsula, Pop. 56
Lake & Peninsula SD
Supt. — See King Salmon
Pilot Point S 50/PK-12
PO Box 467 99649 907-797-2210
Kitza Durlop, prin. Fax 797-2267

Pilot Station, Wade Hampton, Pop. 567
Lower Yukon SD
Supt. — See Mountain Village
Pilot Station S 200/PK-12
PO Box 5090 99650 907-549-3212
Cory Stringer, prin. Fax 549-3335

Platinum, Bethel, Pop. 58
Lower Kuskokwim SD
Supt. — See Bethel
Arviq S 50/PK-12
PO Box 28 99651 907-979-8111
Georgia Berry, prin. Fax 979-8308

Point Hope, North Slope, Pop. 647
North Slope Borough SD
Supt. — See Barrow
Tikigaq S 200/PK-12
PO Box 148 99766 907-368-2662
Gene Burke, prin. Fax 368-2770

Point Lay, North Slope, Pop. 187
North Slope Borough SD
Supt. — See Barrow
Kali S 100/PK-12
PO Box 59077 99759 907-833-2311
Glenn Cole, prin. Fax 833-2315

Port Alexander, Wrangell-Petersburg, Pop. 51
Southeast Island SD
Supt. — See Thorne Bay
Port Alexander S 50/PK-12
PO Box 8170 99836 907-568-2205
Kale Peacock, lead tchr. Fax 568-2261

Port Alsworth, Lake and Peninsula, Pop. 150
Lake & Peninsula SD
Supt. — See King Salmon
Tanalian S 100/PK-12
1400 School Rd 99653 907-781-2210
Nathan Davis, prin. Fax 781-2254

Port Graham, Kenai Peninsula, Pop. 143
Kenai Peninsula Borough SD
Supt. — See Soldotna
Port Graham S 50/PK-12
PO Box 5550 99603 907-284-2210
Nancy Klein, prin. Fax 284-2213

Port Heiden, Lake and Peninsula, Pop. 100
Lake & Peninsula SD
Supt. — See King Salmon
Meshik S 50/K-12
General Delivery 99549 907-837-2210
Derek Luke, prin. Fax 837-2265

Port Lions, Kodiak Island, Pop. 189
Kodiak Island Borough SD
Supt. — See Kodiak
Port Lions S 50/K-12
PO Box 109 99550 907-454-2237
Steve Doerksen, prin. Fax 454-2377

Quinhagak, Bethel, Pop. 642
Lower Kuskokwim SD
Supt. — See Bethel
Kuinerrarmiut Elitnaurviat S 200/PK-12
General Delivery 99655 907-556-8628
Peggie Price, prin. Fax 556-8228

Ruby, Yukon-Koyukuk, Pop. 156
Yukon-Koyukuk SD
Supt. — See Fairbanks
Kangas S 50/PK-12
PO Box 68110 99768 907-468-4465
Anne Titus, prin. Fax 468-4444

Russian Mission, Wade Hampton, Pop. 309
Lower Yukon SD
Supt. — See Mountain Village
Russian Mission S 100/PK-12
PO Box 90 99657 907-584-5126
Jason Moen, prin. Fax 584-5412

Saint Marys, Wade Hampton, Pop. 483
Saint Mary's SD 200/PK-12
PO Box 9 99658 907-438-2411
David Herbert, supt. Fax 438-2735
www.smcsd.us
Saint Mary's S 200/PK-12
PO Box 9 99658 907-438-2411
Dewayne Bahnsen, prin. Fax 438-2735

Saint Michael, Nome, Pop. 392
Bering Strait SD
Supt. — See Unalakleet
Andrews S 200/PK-12
100 Baker St 99659 907-923-3041
Craig Sherwood, prin. Fax 923-3031

Saint Paul Island, Aleutians West, Pop. 459
Pribilof SD 100/PK-12
PO Box 905 99660 907-546-3331
Connie Newman M.Ed., supt. Fax 546-2327
psd-k12.org
St. Paul S 100/PK-12
PO Box 905 99660 907-546-3331
Connie Newman M.Ed., prin. Fax 546-2356

Sand Point, Aleutians East, Pop. 929
Aleutian East Borough SD 200/PK-12
PO Box 429 99661 907-383-5222
Michael Seifert, supt. Fax 383-3496
www.aebsd.org
Sand Point S 100/PK-12
PO Box 269 99661 907-383-2393
Chris Bennett, prin. Fax 383-3833
Other Schools – See Akutan, False Pass, King Cove

Savoonga, Nome, Pop. 668
Bering Strait SD
Supt. — See Unalakleet
Kingeekuk Memorial S 200/PK-12
PO Box 200 99769 907-984-6811
Ralph Lindquist, prin. Fax 984-6413

Scammon Bay, Wade Hampton, Pop. 473
Lower Yukon SD
Supt. — See Mountain Village
Scammon Bay S 200/PK-12
103 Askinuk St 99662 907-558-5312
Melissa Rivers, prin. Fax 558-5320

Selawik, Northwest Arctic, Pop. 742
Northwest Arctic Borough SD
Supt. — See Kotzebue
Davis-Ramoth S 300/PK-12
PO Box 29 99770 907-484-2142
Lois Ballard, prin. Fax 484-2127

Seldovia, Kenai Peninsula, Pop. 230
Kenai Peninsula Borough SD
Supt. — See Soldotna
English S 50/K-12
PO Box 171 99663 907-234-7616
Alan Haskins, prin. Fax 234-7884

Seward, Kenai Peninsula, Pop. 2,478
AVTEC SD
PO Box 889 99664 907-224-6151
Daniel Repasky, dir. Fax 224-4401
www.avtec.edu
AVTEC-Alaska's Institute of Technology Vo/Tech
PO Box 889 99664 907-224-6151
Daniel Repasky, dir. Fax 224-4401

Kenai Peninsula Borough SD
Supt. — See Soldotna
Seward HS 200/9-12
PO Box 1049 99664 907-224-3351
Trevan Walker, prin. Fax 224-3306
Seward MS 100/6-8
PO Box 1149 99664 907-224-9000
Andy Rothenberger, prin. Fax 224-9001

Alaska Vocational Technical School Post-Sec.
PO Box 889 99664 907-224-3322

Shageluk, Yukon-Koyukuk, Pop. 78
Iditarod Area SD
Supt. — See Mc Grath
Innoko River S 50/PK-12
PO Box 53 99665 907-473-8233
Joy Hamilton, prin. Fax 473-8268

Shaktoolik, Nome, Pop. 250
Bering Strait SD
Supt. — See Unalakleet
Shaktoolik S 100/PK-12
PO Box 40 99771 907-955-3021
Steven Sammons, prin. Fax 955-3031

Sheldon Point, Wade Hampton, Pop. 121
Lower Yukon SD
Supt. — See Mountain Village
Sheldon Point S 100/PK-12
PO Box 32, Nunam Iqua AK 99666 907-498-4112
James Vansandt, prin. Fax 498-4111

Shishmaref, Nome, Pop. 556
Bering Strait SD
Supt. — See Unalakleet
Shishmaref S 200/PK-12
1 Seaview Ln 99772 907-649-3021
Matt Palmer, prin. Fax 649-3031

Shungnak, Northwest Arctic, Pop. 262
Northwest Arctic Borough SD
Supt. — See Kotzebue
Shungnak S 100/PK-12
PO Box 79 99773 907-437-2151
Roger Franklin, prin. Fax 437-2177

Sitka, Sitka, Pop. 8,072
Mt. Edgecumbe HSD 400/9-12
1330 Seward Ave 99835 907-966-3200
Bill Hutton, supt. Fax 966-2442
www.mehs.us
Mt. Edgecumbe HS 400/9-12
1330 Seward Ave 99835 907-966-3200
Bernie Gurule, prin. Fax 966-2442

Sitka SD 1,400/PK-12
300 Kostrometinoff St 99835 907-747-8622
Dr. Mary Wegner, supt. Fax 966-1260
www.sitkaschools.org
Blatchley MS 300/6-8
601 Halibut Point Rd 99835 907-747-8672
Ben White, prin. Fax 966-1460
Pacific HS 50/Alt
509 Lincoln St 99835 907-747-0525
Mandy Summer, prin. Fax 747-7310
Sitka HS 300/9-12
1000 Lake St 99835 907-747-3263
Lyle Sparrowgrove, prin. Fax 747-3229

Skagway, Skagway-Hoonah-Angoon, Pop. 884
Skagway SD 100/PK-12
PO Box 497 99840 907-983-2960
Dr. Joshua Coughran, supt. Fax 983-2964
www.skagwayschool.org
Skagway S 100/PK-12
PO Box 497 99840 907-983-2960
Dr. Joshua Coughran, supt. Fax 983-2964

Slana, Valdez-Cordova, Pop. 142
Copper River SD
Supt. — See Glennallen
Slana S 50/1-12
HC 63 Box 1002 99586 907-822-5868
Linda Bates, lead tchr. Fax 822-3850

Sleetmute, Bethel, Pop. 86
Kuspuk SD
Supt. — See Aniak
Egnaty Sr. S 50/K-12
PO Box 69 99668 907-449-4216
Steven B. Porter, prin. Fax 449-4217

Soldotna, Kenai Peninsula, Pop. 3,894
Kenai Peninsula Borough SD 8,500/PK-12
148 N Binkley St 99669 907-714-8888
Sean Dusek, supt. Fax 262-9645
www.kpbsd.k12.ak.us
Connections S 700/Alt
143 E Park Ave 99669 907-714-8880
Richard Bartolowits, prin. Fax 262-2859
River City Academy 100/7-12
426 W Redoubt Ave 99669 907-714-8945
Dawn Edwards-Smith, prin. Fax 714-8946
Skyview MS 400/7-8
46188 Sterling Hwy 99669 907-260-2500
Sarge Truesdell, prin. Fax 262-7036
Soldotna HS 400/10-12
425 W Marydale Ave 99669 907-260-7000
Tony Graham, prin. Fax 262-4288
Soldotna Prep S 9-9
426 W Redoubt Ave 99669 907-260-2300
Curtis Schmidt, prin. Fax 262-6555
Other Schools – See Cooper Landing, Fritz Creek, Homer, Hope, Kenai, Nanwalek, Nikiski, Nikolaevsk, Ninilchik, Port Graham, Seldovia, Seward, Tyonek

---

Alaska Christian College Post-Sec.
35109 Royal Pl 99669 907-260-7422
Cook Inlet Academy 100/PK-12
45872 Kalifornsky Beach Rd 99669 907-262-5101
Mary Rowley, prin. Fax 262-1541

Stebbins, Nome, Pop. 556
Bering Strait SD
Supt. — See Unalakleet
Tukurngailnguq S 200/K-12
General Delivery 99671 907-934-3021
John Juvinall, prin. Fax 934-3031

Stony River, Bethel, Pop. 49
Kuspuk SD
Supt. — See Aniak
Michael S, General Delivery 99557 50/K-12
Steven B. Porter, prin. 907-537-3225

Sutton, Matanuska-Susitna, Pop. 308
Matanuska-Susitna Borough SD
Supt. — See Palmer

Glacier View S 50/K-12
65975 S Wolverine Cir 99674 907-861-5650
Wendy Taylor, prin. Fax 861-5680

Takotna, Yukon-Koyukuk, Pop. 38
Iditarod Area SD
Supt. — See Mc Grath
Takotna S 50/PK-12
PO Box 90 99675 907-298-2115
Fax 298-2316

Talkeetna, Matanuska-Susitna, Pop. 845
Matanuska-Susitna Borough SD
Supt. — See Palmer
Susitna Valley JSHS 200/7-12
HC 89 Box 8580 99676 907-733-9300
Jason Mabry, prin. Fax 733-9380

Tanana, Yukon-Koyukuk, Pop. 238
Tanana CSD 50/K-12
PO Box 89 99777 907-366-7203
M. Therese Ashton, supt. Fax 366-7201
aktcsd.schoolwires.net
Sommer S 50/K-12
PO Box 89 99777 907-366-7203
M. Therese Ashton, supt. Fax 366-7201

Tatitlek, Valdez-Cordova, Pop. 84
Chugach SD
Supt. — See Anchorage
Tatitlek Community S 50/K-12
PO Box 167 99677 907-325-2252
Jed Palmer, lead tchr. Fax 325-2299

Teller, Nome, Pop. 229
Bering Strait SD
Supt. — See Unalakleet
Isabell S 100/PK-12
100 Airport Ave 99778 907-642-3041
Susette Carroll, prin. Fax 642-3031

Tenakee Springs, Skagway-Hoonah-Angoon, Pop. 127
Chatham SD
Supt. — See Angoon
Tenakee Springs S 50/K-12
PO Box 62 99841 907-736-2204
Anne Connelly, lead tchr. Fax 736-2204

Tetlin, Southeast Fairbanks, Pop. 122
Alaska Gateway SD
Supt. — See Tok
Tetlin S 50/PK-12
100 Main St 99779 907-324-2104
Robert Litwack, prin. Fax 324-2120

Thorne Bay, Prince of Wales-Outer Ketchikan, Pop. 450
Southeast Island SD 200/PK-12
PO Box 19569 99919 907-828-8254
Lauren Burch, supt. Fax 828-8257
www.sisd.org/
Thorne Bay S 100/K-12
PO Box 19005 99919 907-828-3921
Rob O'Neal, prin. Fax 828-3901
Other Schools – See Coffman Cove, Craig, Hyder, Kasaan, Ketchikan, Port Alexander

Togiak, Dillingham, Pop. 691
Southwest Region SD
Supt. — See Dillingham
Togiak S 200/K-12
PO Box 50 99678 907-493-5829
Sam Gosuk, prin. Fax 493-5933

Tok, Southeast Fairbanks, Pop. 1,157
Alaska Gateway SD 400/PK-12
PO Box 226 99780 907-883-5151
Scott MacManu, supt. Fax 883-5154
www.agsd.us/
Tok S 200/PK-12
PO Box 249 99780 907-883-5161
Jason Roslansky, prin. Fax 883-5165
Other Schools – See Dot Lake, Eagle, Mentasta Lake, Northway, Tetlin

Toksook Bay, Bethel, Pop. 578
Lower Kuskokwim SD
Supt. — See Bethel
Nelson Island Area S 200/PK-12
General Delivery 99637 907-427-7815
Daryl Daugaard, prin. Fax 427-7612

Tuluksak, Bethel, Pop. 370
Yupiit SD
Supt. — See Akiachak
Tuluksak S, PO Box 115 99679 100/PK-12
David Macri, prin. 907-695-5600

Tuntutuliak, Bethel, Pop. 403
Lower Kuskokwim SD
Supt. — See Bethel
Angapak Memorial S 100/PK-12
General Delivery 99680 907-256-2415
Zachary Bastoky, prin. Fax 256-2527

Tununak, Bethel, Pop. 322
Lower Kuskokwim SD
Supt. — See Bethel
Albert Memorial S 100/PK-12
PO Box 49 99681 907-652-6827
Randy Heinrichs, prin. Fax 652-6028

Tyonek, Kenai Peninsula, Pop. 165
Kenai Peninsula Borough SD
Supt. — See Soldotna
Tebughna S 50/K-12
PO Box 82010 99682 907-583-2291
Pamela Potter, prin. Fax 583-2692

Unalakleet, Nome, Pop. 644
Bering Strait SD 1,900/PK-12
PO Box 225 99684 907-624-4261
Dr. Bobby Bolen, supt. Fax 624-3099
www.bssd.org
Unalakleet S 200/PK-12
PO Box 130 99684 907-624-3444
Perry Corsetti, prin. Fax 624-3388
Other Schools – See Brevig Mission, Diomede, Elim, Gambell, Golovin, Koyuk, Saint Michael, Savoonga, Shaktoolik, Shishmaref, Stebbins, Teller, Wales, White Mountain

Unalaska, Aleutians West, Pop. 4,083
Unalaska CSD 400/PK-12
PO Box 570 99685 907-581-3151
John Conwell, supt. Fax 581-3152
www.ucsd.net
Unalaska City HS 200/7-12
PO Box 570 99685 907-581-1222
Jim Wilson, prin. Fax 581-2428

Valdez, Valdez-Cordova, Pop. 3,714
Valdez CSD 600/PK-12
PO Box 398 99686 907-835-4357
Jim Nygaard, supt. Fax 835-4964
www.valdezcityschools.org/
Gilson MS 100/6-8
PO Box 398 99686 907-835-2244
Rodney Morrison, prin. Fax 835-2540
Valdez HS 200/9-12
PO Box 398 99686 907-835-4767
Rodny Schug, prin. Fax 835-2596

Prince William Sound Community College Post-Sec.
PO Box 97 99686 907-834-1600

Venetie, Yukon-Koyukuk, Pop. 159
Yukon Flats SD
Supt. — See Fort Yukon
Fredson S 100/PK-12
PO Box 81089 99781 907-849-8415
Jake Kramer, lead tchr. Fax 849-8630

Wainwright, North Slope, Pop. 547
North Slope Borough SD
Supt. — See Barrow
Alak S 200/PK-12
PO Box 10 99782 907-763-2541
Bob Grimes, prin. Fax 763-2565

Wales, Nome, Pop. 132
Bering Strait SD
Supt. — See Unalakleet
Wales S 50/PK-12
PO Box 490 99783 907-664-3021
Roxanne Meneguin, prin. Fax 664-3031

Wasilla, Matanuska-Susitna, Pop. 7,351
Matanuska-Susitna Borough SD
Supt. — See Palmer
Burchell HS 300/Alt
1775 W Parks Hwy 99654 907-864-2600
Adam Mokelke, prin. Fax 864-2680
Mat-Su Career and Technical HS Vo/Tech
2472 N Seward Meridian Pkwy 99654 907-352-0400
Mark Okeson, prin. Fax 352-0480
Mat-Su Day S 100/Alt
2360 N Tait Dr 99654 907-864-6000
Wolfgang Winter, prin. Fax 864-6080
Teeland MS 700/6-8
2788 N Seward Meridian Pkwy 99654 907-352-7500
Katherine Ellsworth, prin. Fax 352-7585
Wasilla HS 1,200/9-12
701 E Bogard Rd 99654 907-352-8200
Amy Spargo, prin. Fax 352-8280
Wasilla MS 800/6-8
650 E Bogard Rd 99654 907-352-5300
Casey Hull, prin. Fax 352-5380

Charter College Post-Sec.
721 W Parks Hwy Ste 5 99654 907-952-1000
Wasilla Lake Christian S 200/PK-12
2001 Palmer Wasilla Hwy 99654 907-373-6439
Alison Elder, prin. Fax 373-6438

White Mountain, Nome, Pop. 178
Bering Strait SD
Supt. — See Unalakleet
White Mountain S 100/PK-12
PO Box 55 99784 907-638-3041
David Fair, prin. Fax 638-3031

Whittier, Valdez-Cordova, Pop. 187
Chugach SD
Supt. — See Anchorage
Whittier Community S 50/PK-12
PO Box 638 99693 907-472-2575
Melody Clifford, lead tchr. Fax 472-2409

Wrangell, Wrangell-Petersburg, Pop. 2,153
Wrangell SD 300/K-12
PO Box 2319 99929 907-874-2347
Patrick Mayer, supt. Fax 874-3137
www.wpsd.us
Stikine MS 100/6-8
PO Box 1935 99929 907-874-3393
William Schwan, prin. Fax 874-3149
Wrangell HS 100/9-12
PO Box 651 99929 907-874-3395
William Schwan, prin. Fax 874-3143

Yakutat, Yakutat, Pop. 549
Yakutat SD 100/PK-12
PO Box 429 99689 907-784-3317
Robin Gray, supt. Fax 784-3446
www.yakutatschools.org
Yakutat S 100/PK-12
PO Box 429 99689 907-784-3317
Robin Gray, supt. Fax 784-3446

ARIZONA

ARIZONA DEPARTMENT OF EDUCATION
1535 W Jefferson St, Phoenix 85007-3280
Telephone 602-542-5393
Fax 602-542-5440
Website http://www.azed.gov

Superintendent of Public Instruction Diane Douglas

ARIZONA BOARD OF EDUCATION
1535 W Jefferson St, Phoenix 85007-3280

President Greg Miller

COUNTY SUPERINTENDENTS OF SCHOOLS

Apache County Office of Education
R. Barry Williams, supt. 928-337-7539
PO Box 548, Saint Johns 85936 Fax 337-2033
schools.apachecounty.net

Cochise County Office of Education
Trudy Berry, supt. 520-432-8950
PO Box 208, Bisbee 85603 Fax 432-7136
www.cochise.az.gov/schools/home

Coconino County Office of Education
Risha VanderWey, supt. 928-679-8070
2384 N Steves Blvd Fax 679-8077
Flagstaff 86004
ccesa.az.gov

Gila County Office of Education
Dr. Linda O'Dell, supt. 928-402-8784
1400 E Ash St, Globe 85501 Fax 402-0038
www.gilacountyaz.gov

Graham County Office of Education
Donna McGaughey, supt. 928-428-2880
921 W Thatcher Blvd Fax 428-8824
Safford 85546
www.graham.az.gov/school-superintendent

Greenlee County Office of Education
Tom Powers, supt. 928-865-2822
PO Box 1595, Clifton 85533 Fax 865-4417
www.co.greenlee.az.us/schools/

Lapaz County Office of Education
Jacquline Price, supt. 928-669-6183
1112 S Joshua Ave Ste 205 Fax 669-4406
Parker 85344
www.lapazschools.org

Maricopa County Education Service Agency
Dr. Don Covey, supt. 602-506-3866
4041 N Central Ave Ste 1200 Fax 506-3753
Phoenix 85012
education.maricopa.gov/

Mohave County Office of Education
Michael File, supt. 928-753-0747
PO Box 7000, Kingman 86402 Fax 718-4958
www.mohavecounty.us/ContentPage.aspx?id=130

Navajo County Office of Education
Jalyn Gerlich, supt. 928-524-4204
PO Box 668, Holbrook 86025 Fax 524-4209
www.navajocountyaz.gov/departments/superintendent-of-schools

Pima County Office of Education
Dr. Linda Arzoumanian, supt. 520-724-8451
200 N Stone Ave, Tucson 85701 Fax 770-4210
www.schools.pima.gov

Pinal County Office of Education
Jill Broussard, supt. 520-866-6565
PO Box 769, Florence Fax 866-6973
www.ecrsc.org/pinalesa/

Santa Cruz County Office of Education
Alfredo Velasquez, supt. 520-375-7940
2150 N Congress Dr Fax 375-7958
Nogales 85621
www.co.santa-cruz.az.us/294/Superintendent-of-Schools

Yavapai County Office of Education
Tim Carter, supt. 928-771-3326
2970 Centerpointe East Dr Fax 771-3329
Prescott 86301
www.ycesa.com

Yuma County Office of Education
Thomas Tyree, supt. 928-373-1006
210 S 1st Ave, Yuma 85364 Fax 329-2008
www.yumasupt.org

PUBLIC, PRIVATE AND CATHOLIC SECONDARY SCHOOLS

Ajo, Pima, Pop. 3,253
Ajo USD 15 400/PK-12
111 N Well Rd 85321 520-387-5618
Dr. Robert Dooley, supt. Fax 387-6545
www.ajoschools.org/
Ajo HS 100/9-12
111 N Well Rd 85321 520-387-7602
Dr. Lauren Carriere, prin. Fax 387-7603

Anthem, Maricopa, Pop. 21,203
Deer Valley USD 97
Supt. — See Phoenix
Boulder Creek HS 2,600/9-12
40404 N Gavilan Peak Pkwy 85086 623-445-8600
Lauren Sheahan, prin. Fax 445-8680

Apache Junction, Pinal, Pop. 35,261
Apache Junction USD 43 3,900/K-12
1575 W Southern Ave, 480-982-1110
Dr. Chad Wilson, supt. Fax 982-6474
www.ajusd.org
Apache Junction HS 1,400/9-12
2525 S Ironwood Dr, 480-982-1110
Larry LaPrise, prin. Fax 982-3787
Cactus Canyon JHS 800/7-8
801 W Southern Ave, 480-982-1110
Courtney Castelhano, prin. Fax 983-4913

Central Arizona College Post-Sec.
805 S Idaho Rd, 480-677-7700

Ash Fork, Yavapai, Pop. 392
Ash Fork JUSD 31 200/K-12
PO Box 247 86320 928-637-2561
Seth Staples, admin. Fax 637-2623
www.afjusd.org/
Ash Fork HS 100/9-12
PO Box 247 86320 928-637-2561
Seth Staples, prin. Fax 637-2623
Ash Fork MS 100/6-8
PO Box 247 86320 928-637-2561
Seth Staples, prin. Fax 637-2623

Avondale, Maricopa, Pop. 74,219
Agua Fria UNHSD 216 7,200/9-12
1481 N Eliseo Felix Jr Way 85323 623-932-7000
Dr. Dennis Runyan, supt. Fax 932-2796
www.aguafria.org
Agua Fria HS 1,700/9-12
530 E Riley Dr 85323 623-932-7300
Ernest Molina, prin. Fax 932-0650
Other Schools – See Buckeye, Goodyear

Avondale ESD 44 5,600/PK-8
295 W Western Ave 85323 623-772-5000
Dr. Betsy Hargrove, supt. Fax 772-5001
www.avondale.k12.az.us
Avondale MS 400/5-8
1406 N Central Ave 85323 623-772-4500
Lillian Linn, prin. Fax 772-4520

Tolleson UNHSD 214
Supt. — See Tolleson
La Joya Community HS 1,900/9-12
11650 W Whyman Ave 85323 623-478-4400
Brandi Haskins, prin. Fax 478-7225
Westview HS 2,500/9-12
10850 W Garden Lakes Pkwy, 623-478-4600
Dr. Michele Wilson, prin. Fax 478-4669

Estrella Mountain Community College Post-Sec.
3000 N Dysart Rd, 623-935-8000
Maricopa Beauty College Post-Sec.
515 W Western Ave 85323 623-932-4414
Universal Technical Institute Post-Sec.
10695 W Pierce St 85323 623-245-4600

Bagdad, Yavapai, Pop. 1,847
Bagdad USD 20 500/PK-12
PO Box 427 86321 928-633-4101
Bryan Bullington, supt. Fax 633-4345
bagdadschools.org
Bagdad HS 100/9-12
PO Box 427 86321 928-633-2201
Tom Finnerty, prin. Fax 633-4345
Bagdad MS 100/6-8
PO Box 427 86321 928-633-2201
Tom Finnerty, prin. Fax 633-4345

Beaver Dam, Mohave, Pop. 1,928
Littlefield USD 9 400/PK-12
3490 E Rio Virgin Rd 86432 928-347-5486
Lael Calton, supt. Fax 347-5967
www.lusd9.com/
Beaver Dam JSHS 200/7-12
3475 E Rio Virgin Rd 86432 928-347-5252
Lael Calton, prin. Fax 347-5151

Benson, Cochise, Pop. 5,014
Benson USD 9 1,100/PK-12
360 S Patagonia St 85602 520-720-6700
Micah Mortensen, supt. Fax 720-6701
www.bensonsd.k12.az.us
Benson HS 400/9-12
360 S Patagonia St 85602 520-720-6840
Ben Rodriguez, prin. Fax 720-6710
Benson MS 300/5-8
360 S Patagonia St 85602 520-720-6801
Tammara Ragsdale, prin. Fax 720-6709

Bisbee, Cochise, Pop. 5,464
Bisbee USD 2 900/PK-12
100 Old Douglas Rd 85603 520-432-5381
James Phillips, supt. Fax 432-7622
www.busd.k12.az.us
Bisbee HS 400/9-12
100 Old Douglas Rd 85603 520-432-5714
Laura Miller, prin. Fax 432-6105
Lowell JHS 200/5-8
100 Old Douglas Rd 85603 520-432-5391
Tari Hardy, prin. Fax 432-6106

Blue, Greenlee
Blue ESD 22 50/PK-12
PO Box 80 85922 928-339-4346
Sally Hulsey, hdmstr. Fax 339-4116
Blue S 50/PK-12
PO Box 80 85922 928-339-4346
Sally Hulsey, prin. Fax 339-4116

Bowie, Cochise, Pop. 442
Bowie USD 14 50/K-12
PO Box 157 85605 520-847-2545
Jeff St. Clair, supt. Fax 847-2546
www.bowieschools.org
Bowie MSHS 50/6-12
PO Box 157 85605 520-847-2545
Jeff St. Clair, supt. Fax 847-2546

Buckeye, Maricopa, Pop. 49,727
Agua Fria UNHSD 216
Supt. — See Avondale
Verrado HS 1,700/9-12
20050 W Indian School Rd, 623-932-7400
Dr. Terry Maurer, prin. Fax 853-0369

Buckeye UNHSD 201 3,800/9-12
1000 E Narramore Ave 85326 623-386-9700
Eric Godfrey, supt. Fax 386-9923
www.buhsd.org
Buckeye Union HS 1,300/9-12
1000 E Narramore Ave 85326 623-386-9700
Tawn Argeris, prin. Fax 386-9711
Youngker HS 1,600/9-12
3000 S Apache Rd 85326 623-474-0100
Randy Stillman, prin. Fax 474-0200
Other Schools – See Goodyear

Litchfield ESD 79
Supt. — See Litchfield Park
Verrado MS 1,000/6-8
20880 W Main St, 623-547-1300
Karen Williams, prin. Fax 853-2358

Bullhead City, Mohave, Pop. 38,810
Bullhead City ESD 15 3,000/PK-8
1004 Hancock Rd 86442 928-758-3961
Riley Frei, supt. Fax 758-4996
www.bullheadschools.com
Bullhead City JHS 500/6-8
1062 Hancock Rd 86442 928-758-3921
Pat Young, prin. Fax 758-7428
Fox Creek JHS 500/6-8
3101 Desert Sky Blvd 86442 928-704-2500
Jon Jones, prin. Fax 704-2504

Colorado River UNHSD 2 2,000/9-12
PO Box 21479 86439 928-758-3961
Riley Frei, supt. Fax 219-3050
coloradoriverschools.org/
Mohave HS 1,300/9-12
2251 Highway 95 86442 928-758-3916
Steve Lawrence, prin. Fax 758-7145
Other Schools – See Mohave Valley

Camp Verde, Yavapai, Pop. 10,552
Camp Verde USD 28 1,500/PK-12
410 Camp Lincoln Rd 86322 928-567-8000
Dr. Dennis Goodwin, admin. Fax 567-8004
www.campverdeschools.org
Camp Verde HS 400/9-12
1326 N Montezuma Castle Hwy 86322 928-567-8035
Robert Weir, prin. Fax 567-8045
Camp Verde MS 300/6-8
370 Camp Lincoln Rd 86322 928-567-8014
Danny Howe, prin. Fax 567-8022

United Christian S 100/K-12
PO Box 3126 86322 928-567-0415
Kathy Becker, admin. Fax 567-9774

Casa Grande, Pinal, Pop. 47,575
Casa Grande ESD 4 7,000/PK-8
220 W Kortsen Rd, 520-836-2111
Dr. Frank Davidson, supt. Fax 426-3712
www.cgesd.org
Cactus MS 900/6-8
1220 E Kortsen Rd, 520-421-3330
Kendra Tate, prin. Fax 421-7425
Casa Grande MS 600/6-8
300 W McMurray Blvd, 520-836-7310
Jennifer Murrieta, prin. Fax 836-2399
Villago MS 800/6-8
574 E Lakeside Pkwy, 520-423-0176
Jeffrey Lavender, prin. Fax 423-0177

Casa Grande UNHSD 82 3,300/9-12
1362 N Casa Grande Ave, 520-316-3360
Dr. Shannon Goodsell, supt. Fax 316-3352
www.cguhsd.org
Casa Grande Union HS 1,500/9-12
2730 N Trekell Rd, 520-836-8500
Thomas Trigalet, prin. Fax 316-3353
Vista Grande HS 1,800/9-12
1556 N Arizola Rd, 520-876-9400
Glenda Sulley, prin. Fax 876-5348

Logos Christian Academy 50/K-12
PO Box 11493, 520-421-1220
Dan Bradfield M.Ed., prin.

Chandler, Maricopa, Pop. 229,946
Chandler USD 80 40,800/PK-12
1525 W Frye Rd 85224 480-812-7000
Dr. Camille Casteel, supt. Fax 224-9128
www.cusd80.com
Andersen JHS 900/6-8
1255 N Dobson Rd 85224 480-883-5300
Dr. Joyce Meyer, prin. Fax 883-5320
Arizona College Prep - Erie 400/7-12
1150 W Erie St 85224 480-424-8000
Robert Bickes, prin. Fax 224-9268
Arizona College Prep - Oakland 500/6-8
191 W Oakland St 85225 480-224-3930
Jayson Phillips, prin. Fax 224-3940
Basha Accelerated MS 6-8
5990 S Val Vista Dr 85249 480-224-2100
David Loutzenheiser, prin. Fax 224-2120
Basha HS 2,500/9-12
5990 S Val Vista Dr 85249 480-224-2100
David Loutzenheiser, prin. Fax 224-2120
Bogle JHS 1,200/7-8
1600 W Queen Creek Rd 85248 480-883-5500
Susie Avey, prin. Fax 224-9140
Chandler Early College 9-12
2626 E Pecos Rd 85225 480-224-3060
Shawn Mitchell, head sch Fax 224-9345
Chandler HS 3,100/9-12
350 N Arizona Ave 85225 480-812-7700
Larry Rother, prin. Fax 812-7720
Elite Performance Academy 3-8
1825 S Alma School Rd, 480-812-2060
Thuy Padilla, admin.
Hamilton HS 3,700/9-12
3700 S Arizona Ave 85248 480-883-5000
Ken James, prin. Fax 883-5020
Hill Learning Academy 200/Alt
290 S Cooper Rd 85225 480-812-7150
Dave Constance, prin. Fax 224-9066
Santan JHS 1,300/7-8
1550 E Chandler Heights Rd 85249 480-883-4600
Barbara Kowalinski, prin. Fax 883-4648
Willis JHS 900/7-8
401 S McQueen Rd 85225 480-883-5700
Jeff Delp, prin. Fax 883-5720
Other Schools – See Gilbert, Queen Creek

Kyrene ESD 28
Supt. — See Tempe
Kyrene Aprende MS 1,000/6-8
777 N Desert Breeze Blvd E 85226 480-541-6200
Renee Kory, prin. Fax 541-6210
Kyrene Del Pueblo MS 900/6-8
360 S Twelve Oaks Blvd 85226 480-541-6800
Kelly Alexander, prin. Fax 541-6810

Chandler-Gilbert Community College Post-Sec.
2626 E Pecos Rd 85225 480-732-7000
Empire Beauty School Post-Sec.
2978 N Alma School Rd Ste 3 85224 480-855-7901
Golf Academy of America Post-Sec.
2031 N Arizona Ave Ste 2 85225 800-342-7342
International Baptist College Post-Sec.
2211 W Germann Rd, 480-245-7903
Quantum Helicopters Post-Sec.
2401 S Heliport Way, 480-814-8118
Seton Catholic Preparatory HS 600/9-12
1150 N Dobson Rd 85224 480-963-1900
Patricia Collins, prin. Fax 963-1974
Tri-City Christian Academy 300/K-12
2211 W Germann Rd, 480-245-7902
Dr. Mike Sproul, admin. Fax 245-7908
Valley Christian HS 400/9-12
6900 W Galveston St 85226 480-705-8888
Dan Kuiper, prin. Fax 705-8889

Chinle, Apache, Pop. 4,452
Chinle USD 24 3,500/K-12
PO Box 587 86503 928-674-9600
Quincy Natay, supt. Fax 674-9608
www.chinleusd.k12.az.us/
Chinle HS 1,000/9-12
PO Box 587 86503 928-674-9500
Douglas Clauschee, prin. Fax 674-9599
Chinle JHS 400/7-8
PO Box 587 86503 928-674-9400
Tammy Smith, prin. Fax 674-9499

Chino Valley, Yavapai, Pop. 10,639
Chino Valley USD 51 1,900/PK-12
650 E Center St 86323 928-636-2458
John Scholl, supt. Fax 636-1434
www.cvsd.k12.az.us
Chino Valley HS 700/9-12
760 E Center St 86323 928-636-2298
Wes Brownfield, prin. Fax 636-6219
Heritage MS 500/6-8
1076 N Road 1 W 86323 928-636-4464
Julie Bryce, prin. Fax 636-6214

Colorado City, Mohave, Pop. 4,817
Colorado City USD 14 200/PK-12
PO Box 309 86021 928-875-9000
Carol Timpson, supt. Fax 875-8066
www.elcap.us
El Capitan HS 200/6-12
PO Box 309 86021 928-875-9000
Shauna Hammon, prin. Fax 875-8068

Coolidge, Pinal, Pop. 11,531
Coolidge USD 21 3,700/PK-12
450 N Arizona Blvd, 520-723-2040
Charie Wallace, admin. Fax 723-2442
www.coolidgeschools.org/
Coolidge HS 700/9-12
684 W Northern Ave, 520-723-2305
Dawn Dee Hodge, prin. Fax 723-8249
Hohokam MS 500/6-8
684 W Northern Ave, 520-723-2304
Dawn Dee Hodge, prin. Fax 723-8249

Central Arizona College Post-Sec.
8470 N Overfield Rd, 520-494-5444

Corona, Pima, Pop. 5,546
Vail USD 20
Supt. — See Vail
Corona Foothills MS 500/6-8
16705 S Houghton Rd 85641 520-879-3500
Margaret Steuer, prin. Fax 879-3501

Cottonwood, Yavapai, Pop. 11,102
Cottonwood-Oak Creek ESD 6 2,100/PK-8
1 N Willard St 86326 928-634-2288
Barbara U'Ren, supt. Fax 634-2309
www.cocsd.us
Cottonwood MS 500/6-8
1 N Willard St 86326 928-634-2231
Mathew Schumacher, prin. Fax 634-2874

Mingus UNHSD 4 1,200/9-12
1801 E Fir St 86326 928-634-8901
Eric Harmon, supt. Fax 649-4399
www.mingusunion.com
Mingus Union HS 1,200/9-12
1801 E Fir St 86326 928-634-7531
Jennifer Chilton, prin. Fax 639-4236

Dewey, Yavapai, Pop. 3,640
Humboldt USD 22
Supt. — See Prescott Valley
Bradshaw Mountain MS 300/7-8
12255 E Turquoise Cir 86327 928-759-4900
Jessica Bennett, prin. Fax 759-4920

Dolan Springs, Mohave, Pop. 1,994
Kingman USD 20
Supt. — See Kingman
Mt. Tipton S 100/K-12
PO Box 248 86441 928-767-3350
Deb Warren, prin. Fax 767-4330

Douglas, Cochise, Pop. 17,315
Douglas USD 27 3,700/PK-12
PO Box 1237 85608 520-364-2447
Ronald V. Aguallo, supt. Fax 224-2470
www.dusd.k12.az.us
Borane MS 400/6-8
PO Box 1237 85608 520-364-2461
Katie Walker, prin. Fax 364-5537
Douglas HS 1,300/9-12
PO Box 1237 85608 520-364-3462
Dr. Andrea Overman, prin. Fax 805-4171
Huber MS 400/6-8
PO Box 1237 85608 520-364-2840
Jeremy Long, prin. Fax 364-2421

Cochise College Post-Sec.
4190 W Highway 80 85607 800-966-7943

Duncan, Greenlee, Pop. 683
Duncan USD 2 300/K-12
PO Box 710 85534 928-359-2472
Eldon Merrell, supt. Fax 359-2807
dusdwildkats.org
Duncan ES 200/3-8
PO Box 710 85534 928-359-2471
Kent Baldwin, prin. Fax 359-1105
Duncan HS 100/9-12
PO Box 710 85534 928-359-2474
Steve Korzan, prin. Fax 359-1141

Eagar, Apache, Pop. 4,784
Round Valley USD 10
Supt. — See Springerville
Round Valley HS 400/9-12
550 N Butler St 85925 928-333-6800
Slade Morgan, prin. Fax 333-6819
Round Valley MS 400/5-8
126 W 2nd St 85925 928-333-6700
John Allen, prin. Fax 333-5252
White Mountain Academy Alt
550 N Butler St 85925 928-333-6890
Chris Matthews, lead tchr.

Elfrida, Cochise, Pop. 454
Valley UNHSD 22 100/9-12
PO Box 158 85610 520-642-3492
Kyle Hart, admin. Fax 642-3523
www.vuhs.net
Valley Union HS 100/9-12
PO Box 158 85610 520-642-3492
Kyle Hart, admin. Fax 642-3523

El Mirage, Maricopa, Pop. 30,983
Dysart USD 89
Supt. — See Surprise
Dysart HS 1,600/9-12
11425 N Dysart Rd 85335 623-876-7500
Amy Hartjen, prin. Fax 876-7572

Eloy, Pinal, Pop. 15,495
Eloy ESD 11 800/PK-8
1011 N Sunshine Blvd, 520-466-2100
Ruby James, supt. Fax 466-2101
www.eloyesd.org
Eloy JHS 200/6-8
1011 N Sunshine Blvd, 520-466-2140
Kevin Oursler, prin. Fax 466-2150

Pinal County Office of Education
Supt. — See Florence
Villa Oasis Interscholastic Center 100/Alt
3740 N Toltec Rd, 520-450-4450
Ector Rodriguez, prin. Fax 450-4301

Santa Cruz Valley UNHSD 840 400/9-12
900 N Main St, 520-466-2220
Orlenda Roberts M.Ed., supt. Fax 466-2222
www.scvuhs.org/
Santa Cruz Valley Union HS 400/9-12
900 N Main St, 520-466-2200
Orante Jenkins, prin. Fax 466-2222

Flagstaff, Coconino, Pop. 64,141
Flagstaff USD 1 9,700/PK-12
3285 E Sparrow Ave 86004 928-527-6000
Barbara Hickman, supt. Fax 527-6015
www.fusd1.org
Coconino HS 1,400/9-12
2801 N Izabel St 86004 928-773-8200
Stacie Zanzucchi, prin. Fax 773-8247
Flagstaff HS 1,500/9-12
400 W Elm Ave 86001 928-773-8100
Tony Cullen, prin. Fax 773-8146
Mount Elden MS 800/6-8
3223 N 4th St 86004 928-773-8250
Yvette Harpe, prin. Fax 773-8269
Sinagua MS 1,000/6-8
3950 E Butler Ave 86004 928-527-5500
Tari Popham, prin. Fax 527-5561
Summit HS TAPP Alternative S 100/Alt
4000 N Cummings St 86004 928-773-8198
Chris Koenker, prin. Fax 773-8427

Coconino Community College Post-Sec.
2800 S Lone Tree Rd, 928-527-1222
CollegeAmerica Post-Sec.
3012 E Route 66 86004 928-213-6060
Empire Beauty School Post-Sec.
1790 E Route 66 86004 928-774-7146
Northern Arizona University Post-Sec.
S San Francisco St 86011 928-523-9011

Florence, Pinal, Pop. 25,223
Florence USD 1 7,800/PK-12
PO Box 2850, 520-866-3500
Dr. Amy Fuller, supt. Fax 868-2302
www.fusdaz.com
Florence HS 700/9-12
PO Box 2850, 520-866-3560
Thad Gates, prin. Fax 868-2329
Other Schools – See San Tan Valley

Pinal County Office of Education 200/
PO Box 769 85132 520-866-6565
Jill Broussard, supt. Fax 866-6973
www.ecrsc.org/pinalesa/
Other Schools – See Eloy

Fort Defiance, Apache, Pop. 3,530
Window Rock USD 8 1,700/K-12
PO Box 559 86504 928-729-6705
Lynnette Michalski, supt. Fax 729-5780
www.wrschool.net
Tsehootsooi MS 300/7-8
PO Box 559 86504 928-729-6803
David Moore, prin. Fax 729-6814
Window Rock HS 600/9-12
PO Box 559 86504 928-729-7004
Eric Harmon, prin. Fax 729-7661

Fort Huachuca, See Sierra Vista
Fort Huachuca Accommodation SD 00 1,100/PK-8
PO Box 12954 85670 520-458-5082
Bonnie Austin, supt. Fax 515-5972
www.fthuachuca.k12.az.us
Smith MS 300/6-8
PO Box 12954 85670 520-459-8892
Sandy Larson, prin. Fax 335-6803

Fort Thomas, Graham, Pop. 360
Fort Thomas USD 7 600/K-12
PO Box 300 85536 928-485-9423
Shane Hawkins, supt. Fax 485-3019
www.ftusd.org/
Fort Thomas JSHS 200/7-12
PO Box 28 85536 928-485-2427
McKay DeSpain, prin. Fax 485-2834

Fountain Hills, Maricopa, Pop. 22,214
Fountain Hills USD 98 1,800/PK-12
16000 E Palisades Blvd 85268 480-664-5000
Dr. Patrick Sweeney, supt. Fax 664-5099
www.fhusd.org
Fountain Hills HS 600/9-12
16100 E Palisades Blvd 85268 480-664-5500
Cain Jagodzinski, prin. Fax 664-5599
Fountain Hills MS 400/6-8
15414 N McDowell Mountain R 85268 480-664-5400
Anita Gomez, prin. Fax 664-5499

American Institute of Interior Design Post-Sec.
13014 N Saguaro Blvd # 206 85268 480-946-9601

Fredonia, Coconino, Pop. 1,295
Fredonia-Moccasin USD 6 200/PK-12
PO Box 247 86022 928-643-7333
Joseph Wright, supt. Fax 643-7044
www.fredonia.org/
Fredonia-Moccasin HS 100/7-12
PO Box 247 86022 928-643-7333
Brett Waite, prin. Fax 643-7044

Ganado, Apache, Pop. 1,188
Ganado USD 20 1,100/K-12
PO Box 1757 86505 928-755-1011
James Phillips, supt. Fax 755-1012
www.ganado.k12.az.us
Ganado HS 500/9-12
PO Box 1757 86505 928-755-1500
Elissa James, prin. Fax 755-1502
Ganado MS 300/6-8
PO Box 1757 86505 928-755-1400
Steve Wyble, prin. Fax 755-1402

Gila Bend, Maricopa, Pop. 1,896
Gila Bend USD 24 300/PK-12
PO Box V 85337 928-683-2225
Dr. Anthony J. Perkins, supt. Fax 683-2671
www.gbusd.org
Gila Bend HS 100/6-12
PO Box V 85337 928-683-2225
Lilian Bester, prin. Fax 683-2671

Gilbert, Maricopa, Pop. 202,881
Chandler USD 80
Supt. — See Chandler
Perry HS 2,800/9-12
1919 E Queen Creek Rd 85297 480-224-2800
Dan Serrano, prin. Fax 224-2820

Gilbert Unified SD 37,700/PK-12
140 S Gilbert Rd 85296 480-497-3300
Dr. Christina Kishimoto, supt. Fax 507-1320
www.gilbertschools.net
Campo Verde HS 2,100/9-12
3870 S Quartz St 85297 480-545-3100
Michael DeLaTorre, prin. Fax 545-3111
Gilbert Classical Academy 200/7-12
55 N Greenfield Rd 85234 480-497-4034
Dan Hood, prin. Fax 507-1645
Gilbert HS 2,600/9-12
1101 E Elliot Rd 85234 480-497-0177
Christopher Stroud, prin. Fax 497-5673
Gilbert JHS 600/7-8
1016 N Burk St 85234 480-892-6908
Sam Valles, prin. Fax 813-8240
Greenfield JHS 1,000/7-8
101 S Greenfield Rd 85296 480-813-1770
Brian Yee, prin. Fax 813-7279
Highland HS 3,000/9-12
4301 E Guadalupe Rd 85234 480-813-0051
Melinda Murphy, prin. Fax 813-0258
Mesquite HS 2,000/9-12
500 S McQueen Rd 85233 480-632-4750
Ken Fetter, prin. Fax 632-4777
Mesquite JHS 800/7-8
130 W Mesquite St 85233 480-926-1433
Dan Johnson, prin. Fax 813-9002
South Valley JHS 1,300/7-8
2034 S Lindsay Rd, 480-855-0015
Tim Cannon, prin. Fax 855-3542
Other Schools – See Mesa

Higley USD 60 11,100/PK-12
2935 S Recker Rd, 480-279-7000
Dr. Mike Thomason, supt. Fax 279-7500
www.husd.org
Higley HS 1,700/9-12
4068 E Pecos Rd, 480-279-7300
Nancy Diab-Scott, prin. Fax 279-7305
Williams Field HS 1,600/9-12
2076 S Higley Rd, 480-279-8000
Dr. Terri Wattawa, prin. Fax 279-8005
Other Schools – See Queen Creek

Conservatory of Recording Arts/Sciences Post-Sec.
1205 N Fiesta Blvd 85233 480-858-9400
Gilbert Christian S 600/PK-12
3632 E Jasper Dr 85296 480-699-1215
Jim Desmarchais, supt. Fax 809-6677

Glendale, Maricopa, Pop. 221,458
Alhambra ESD 68
Supt. — See Phoenix
Barcelona MS 700/4-8
6530 N 44th Ave 85301 623-842-8616
Paige Brill, prin. Fax 842-1384

Deer Valley USD 97
Supt. — See Phoenix
Deer Valley HS 1,900/9-12
18424 N 51st Ave 85308 602-467-6700
Kim Crooks, prin. Fax 467-6780
Desert Sky MS 600/7-8
5130 W Grovers Ave 85308 602-467-6500
Patricia Resetar, prin. Fax 467-6580
Hillcrest MS 1,000/7-8
22833 N 71st Ave 85310 623-376-3300
Matt Hreha, prin. Fax 376-3380
Mountain Ridge HS 2,300/9-12
22800 N 67th Ave 85310 623-376-3000
Shona Miranda, prin. Fax 376-3080

Glendale ESD 40 13,600/PK-8
7301 N 58th Ave 85301 623-237-7100
Dr. Joe Quintana, supt. Fax 237-7291
www.gesd40.org/
Bicentennial North S 800/4-8
7237 W Missouri Ave 85303 623-237-4009
Diane Pesch, prin. Fax 237-4915
Challenger MS 700/4-8
6905 W Maryland Ave 85303 623-237-4011
Tiffany Molina, prin. Fax 237-5115
Mensendick IS 1,000/4-8
5535 N 67th Ave 85301 623-237-4006
Michelle Brady, prin. Fax 237-4615

Glendale UNHSD 205 15,100/9-12
7650 N 43rd Ave 85301 623-435-6000
Brian Capistran, supt. Fax 435-6078
www.guhsdaz.org
Apollo HS 2,000/9-12
8045 N 47th Ave 85302 623-435-6300
Brooke Parsons, prin. Fax 435-6369
Glendale HS 1,600/9-12
6216 W Glendale Ave 85301 623-435-6200
Kevin Cashatt, prin. Fax 435-6270
Independence HS 2,000/9-12
6602 N 75th Ave 85303 623-435-6100
Rob Ambrose, prin. Fax 435-6157
Other Schools – See Phoenix

Peoria USD 11 36,300/PK-12
6330 W Thunderbird Rd 85306 623-486-6000
Dr. Darwin Stiffler, supt. Fax 486-6009
www.peoriaud.k12.az.us
Cactus HS 1,400/9-12
6330 W Greenway Rd 85306 623-412-5000
Kristi Hammer, prin. Fax 412-5020
Ironwood HS 2,000/9-12
6051 W Sweetwater Ave 85304 623-486-6400
Vance Setka, prin. Fax 486-6424
Kellis HS 1,800/9-12
8990 W Orangewood Ave 85305 623-412-5425
Jeffrey Wooten, prin. Fax 412-5447
Other Schools – See Peoria

Tolleson UNHSD 214
Supt. — See Tolleson
Copper Canyon HS 2,000/9-12
9126 W Camelback Rd 85305 623-478-4800
Mindy Marsit, prin. Fax 478-4802

Washington ESD 6 23,000/PK-8
4650 W Sweetwater Ave 85304 602-347-2600
Dr. Paul Stanton, supt. Fax 347-2720
www.wesdschools.org
Other Schools – See Phoenix

Arizona Automotive Institute Post-Sec.
6829 N 46th Ave 85301 888-419-9440
Arizona College Post-Sec.
4425 W Olive Ave Ste 300 85302 602-222-9300
Arrowhead Christian Academy 100/K-12
4030 W Yorkshire Dr 85308 623-582-6871
Mark French, head sch Fax 581-9311
Glendale Community College Post-Sec.
6000 W Olive Ave 85302 623-845-3000
Herberger Young Scholars Academy 200/7-12
4701 W Thunderbird Rd 85306 602-543-8274
Robert Walker, prin. Fax 543-6164
Joy Christian S 600/PK-12
21000 N 75th Ave 85308 623-561-2000
Danielle Root, supt. Fax 362-3202
Midwestern University Post-Sec.
19555 N 59th Ave 85308 623-572-3200
Thunderbird School of Global Management Post-Sec.
1 Global Pl 85306 602-978-7100

Globe, Gila, Pop. 7,446
Globe USD 1 1,800/PK-12
460 N Willow St 85501 928-402-6000
Jerry Jennex, supt. Fax 425-8912
www.globeschools.org
Globe HS 600/9-12
460 N Willow St 85501 928-402-6000
Bobby Armenta, prin. Fax 425-8909
High Desert MS 500/5-8
460 N Willow St 85501 928-402-5900
Lori Rodriquez, prin. Fax 425-8710

Goodyear, Maricopa, Pop. 63,699
Agua Fria UNHSD 216
Supt. — See Avondale
Desert Edge HS 1,600/9-12
15778 W Yuma Rd 85338 623-932-7500
Julie Jones, prin. Fax 932-7502
Millennium HS 2,200/9-12
14802 W Wigwam Blvd, 623-932-7200
Tamee Gressett, prin. Fax 932-7204

Buckeye UNHSD 201
Supt. — See Buckeye
Estrella Foothills HS 1,000/9-12
13033 S Estrella Pkwy 85338 623-327-2400
Dr. Leslie Standerfer, prin. Fax 327-2499

Litchfield ESD 79
Supt. — See Litchfield Park
Western Sky MS 900/6-8
4905 N 144th Ave, 623-535-6300
Tami Garrett, prin. Fax 935-9536

Grand Canyon, Coconino
Grand Canyon USD 4 200/K-12
PO Box 519 86023 928-638-2461
Dr. Shonny Bria Ph.D., supt. Fax 638-2045
www.grandcanyonschool.org
Grand Canyon S 200/K-12
PO Box 519 86023 928-638-2461
Tom Rowlin, prin. Fax 638-2045

Heber, Navajo, Pop. 1,581
Heber-Overgaard USD 6 400/PK-12
PO Box 547 85928 928-535-4622
Ron Tenney, supt. Fax 535-5146
www.heberovergaardschools.org
Mogollon JSHS 100/7-12
PO Box 279 85928 928-535-4238
Reed Porter, prin. Fax 535-3933

Holbrook, Navajo, Pop. 4,904
Holbrook USD 3 2,100/PK-12
PO Box 640 86025 928-524-6144
Dr. Robbie Koerperich, supt. Fax 524-3073
www.holbrook.k12.az.us
Holbrook HS 700/9-12
PO Box 640 86025 928-524-2815
Lance Phaturos, prin. Fax 524-3537
Holbrook JHS 400/6-8
PO Box 640 86025 928-524-3959
Dr. Jeri McKinnon, prin. Fax 524-3766
Phenix S Alt
PO Box 640 86025 928-524-9091
Lance Phaturos, prin. Fax 524-2311

Northland Pioneer College Post-Sec.
PO Box 610 86025 928-524-7311

Joseph City, Navajo, Pop. 1,364
Joseph City USD 2 300/PK-12
PO Box 8 86032 928-288-3307
Bryan Fields, supt. Fax 288-3309
www.josephcityschools.org
Joseph City JSHS 100/7-12
PO Box 8 86032 928-288-3361
Bryan Fields, prin. Fax 288-3825

Kayenta, Navajo, Pop. 5,074
Kayenta USD 27 1,800/K-12
PO Box 337 86033 928-697-3251
Dr. Bryce Anderson, supt. Fax 697-2160
www.kayenta.k12.az.us
Kayenta MS 500/5-8
PO Box 337 86033 928-697-2303
David Hawley, prin. Fax 697-2308
Monument Valley HS 700/9-12
PO Box 337 86033 928-697-2175
Jack Gilmore, prin. Fax 697-2195

Kearny, Pinal, Pop. 1,932
Ray USD 3 500/PK-12
PO Box 427, 520-363-5515
Curt Cook, supt. Fax 363-5642
www.rayusd.org
Ray Jr-Sr HS 300/7-12
PO Box 427, 520-363-5515
Curt Cook, prin. Fax 363-5642

Kingman, Mohave, Pop. 27,434
Kingman USD 20 6,300/PK-12
3033 McDonald Ave 86401 928-753-5678
Roger Jacks, supt. Fax 753-6910
www.kusd.org
Kingman HS 1,300/10-12
4182 N Bank St, 928-692-6480
Rusty Moomey, prin. Fax 692-6418
Kingman MS 600/6-8
1969 Detroit Ave 86401 928-753-3588
Don Burton, prin. Fax 753-1336
White Cliffs MS 700/6-8
3550 Prospector St 86401 928-753-6216
Tonia Cobanovich, prin. Fax 753-4042
Williams HS 300/9-9
400 Grandview Ave 86401 928-718-6000
Gretchen Dorner, prin. Fax 718-1058
Other Schools – See Dolan Springs

Mohave Community College Post-Sec.
1971 E Jagerson Ave, 928-757-4331

Lake Havasu City, Mohave, Pop. 51,709
Lake Havasu USD 1 5,400/PK-12
2200 Havasupai Blvd 86403 928-505-6900
Diana M. Asseier, supt. Fax 505-6999
www.havasu.k12.az.us/
Lake Havasu HS 1,900/9-12
2675 Palo Verde Blvd S 86403 928-854-5001
Scott Becker, prin. Fax 854-5499
Thunderbolt MS 900/7-8
695 Thunderbolt Ave 86406 928-854-7224
Marijo Mulligan, prin. Fax 854-7482

Charles of Italy Beauty College Post-Sec.
1987 McCulloch Blvd #205 86403 928-453-6666

Lakeside, Navajo, Pop. 4,210
Blue Ridge USD 32 2,200/PK-12
1200 W White Mountain Blvd 85929 928-368-6126
Michael Wright, supt. Fax 368-5570
www.brusd.org
Blue Ridge HS 700/9-12
1200 W White Mountain Blvd 85929 928-368-6126
Jay Cox M.Ed., prin. Fax 368-9572
Blue Ridge JHS 400/7-8
1200 W White Mountain Blvd 85929 928-368-2350
Loren Webb M.Ed., prin. Fax 368-2399

Laveen, Maricopa
Phoenix UNHSD 210
Supt. — See Phoenix
Chavez HS 2,600/9-12
3921 W Baseline Rd 85339 602-764-4000
Matthew Georgia, prin. Fax 764-4054
Fairfax HS, 8225 S 59th Ave 85339 1,900/9-12
Phillip Wooley, prin. 602-764-9000

Litchfield Park, Maricopa, Pop. 5,366
Litchfield ESD 79 11,300/PK-8
272 E Sagebrush St 85340 623-535-6000
Dr. Julianne Lein, supt. Fax 935-1448
www.lesd.k12.az.us
Heck MS 700/6-8
272 E Sagebrush St 85340 623-547-1700
Dr. Ron Sterr, prin. Fax 536-5955
Wigwam Creek MS 900/6-8
272 E Sagebrush St 85340 623-547-1100
John Scudder, prin. Fax 547-0873
Other Schools – See Buckeye, Goodyear

Marana, Pima, Pop. 34,148
Marana USD 6 12,300/PK-12
11279 W Grier Rd Ste 106 85653 520-682-4774
Dr. Doug Wilson, supt. Fax 682-2421
www.maranausd.org
Marana Career and Technical HS 100/Alt
13650 N McDuff Rd 85653 520-682-4773
Denise Coronado, dir. Fax 682-4106
Marana MS 1,000/7-8
11279 W Grier Rd 85653 520-682-4730
Heather Pletnick, prin. Fax 682-4790
Other Schools – See Tucson

Maricopa, Pinal, Pop. 42,031
Maricopa USD 20 5,800/PK-12
44150 W Maricopa Casa Grand,
520-568-5100
Steve Chestnut Ed.D., supt. Fax 568-5110
maricopausd.org/
Desert Wind MS 400/7-8
44150 W Maricopa Casa Grand,
520-568-7110
June Celaya, prin. Fax 568-7119

Maricopa HS 1,700/9-12
44150 W Maricopa Casa Grand, 520-568-8100
Renita Myers, prin. Fax 568-8119

Mayer, Yavapai, Pop. 1,462
Mayer USD 43 600/PK-12
PO Box 1059 86333 928-642-1000
Dean Slaga, supt. Fax 632-4005
www.mayerschools.org
Mayer HS 200/9-12
PO Box 1059 86333 928-642-1201
Jeff Duncan, prin. Fax 632-5714

Orme S 100/8-12
HC 63 Box 3040 86333 928-632-7601
Bruce Sanborn, head sch Fax 632-7605

Mesa, Maricopa, Pop. 428,892
East Valley Institute of Tech. SD 401
1601 W Main St 85201 480-461-4000
Dr. Sally Downey Ed.D., supt. Fax 461-4089
evit.com
East Valley Institute of Technology Vo/Tech
1601 W Main St 85201 480-461-4000
Dr. Sally Downey Ed.D., supt. Fax 461-4169
East Valley Institute of Technology East Vo/Tech
6625 S Power Rd 85212 480-308-4600
Craig Pearson, admin. Fax 308-4608

Gilbert Unified SD
Supt. — See Gilbert
Canyon Valley S 200/Alt
7007 E Guadalupe Rd 85212 480-507-0519
Chad Fitzgerald, prin. Fax 507-3978
Desert Ridge HS 2,800/9-12
10045 E Madero Ave, 480-984-8947
Mike Deignan, prin. Fax 354-5090
Desert Ridge JHS 1,400/7-8
10211 E Madero Ave, 480-635-2025
Jean Woods, prin. Fax 635-2044
Highland JHS 1,300/7-8
6915 E Guadalupe Rd 85212 480-632-4739
Lance Smith, prin. Fax 632-4729

Mesa USD 4 63,700/PK-12
63 E Main St 85201 480-472-0000
Dr. Michael Cowan, supt. Fax 472-0204
www.mpsaz.org
Carson JHS 1,000/7-8
525 N Westwood 85201 480-472-2900
Tony Elmer, prin. Fax 472-2899
Crossroads S 100/Alt
855 W 8th Ave 85210 480-472-9350
Patricia Goolsby, prin. Fax 472-9393
Dobson HS 2,700/9-12
1501 W Guadalupe Rd 85202 480-472-3000
Tamara Addis, prin. Fax 472-3075
East Valley Academy 300/Alt
855 W 8th Ave 85210 480-472-9350
Pat Goolsby, prin. Fax 472-9393
Franklin JHS 200/7-8
4949 E Southern Ave 85206 480-472-2600
Jeffrey Abrams, prin. Fax 472-2698
Fremont JHS 1,000/7-8
1001 N Power Rd 85205 480-472-8300
Todd Roberts, prin. Fax 472-8333
Kino JHS 1,000/7-8
848 N Horne 85203 480-472-2400
Keiko Dilbeck, prin. Fax 472-2549
Mesa Academy for Advanced Studies 400/4-8
6919 E Brown Rd 85207 480-308-7400
Bob Crispin, prin. Fax 308-7428
Mesa HS 3,300/9-12
1630 E Southern Ave 85204 480-472-5900
Kirk Thomas, prin. Fax 472-5995
Mountain View HS 3,200/9-12
2700 E Brown Rd 85213 480-472-6900
Greg Milbrandt, prin. Fax 472-6983
Poston JHS 1,000/7-8
2433 E Adobe St 85213 480-472-2100
Allen Flax, prin. Fax 472-2105
Red Mountain HS 3,300/9-12
7301 E Brown Rd 85207 480-472-8000
Jared Ryan, prin. Fax 472-8008
Rhodes JHS 1,000/7-8
1860 S Longmore 85202 480-472-2300
Patricia Christie, prin. Fax 472-2299
Riverview HS 100/Alt
1731 N Country Club Dr 85201 480-472-5350
Greg Mendez, prin. Fax 472-5355
Shepherd JHS 700/7-8
1407 N Alta Mesa Dr 85205 480-472-1800
Renea Kennedy, prin. Fax 472-1888
Skyline HS 2,600/9-12
845 S Crismon Rd 85208 480-472-9400
Tom Brennan, prin. Fax 472-9406
Smith JHS 1,000/7-8
10100 E Adobe Rd 85207 480-472-9900
Casey Eagleburger, prin. Fax 472-9999
Stapley JHS 900/7-8
3250 E Hermosa Vista Dr 85213 480-472-2700
Ken Erickson, prin. Fax 472-2828
Superstition HS 50/Alt
10222 E Southern Ave, 480-472-9650
Lilia Gomez-Napier, prin. Fax 472-9660
Taylor JHS 1,100/7-8
705 S 32nd St 85204 480-472-1500
Gina Piraino, prin. Fax 472-1616
Westwood HS 3,100/9-12
945 W Rio Salado Pkwy 85201 480-472-4400
Shawn Lynch, prin. Fax 472-4509

Arizona Sch of Dentistry & Oral Health Post-Sec.
5850 E Still Cir 85206 866-626-2878
Arizona School of Health Sciences Post-Sec.
5850 E Still Cir 85206 866-626-2878
Avalon School of Cosmetology Post-Sec.
2111 S Alma School Rd #21 85210 480-897-1688
Carrington College Post-Sec.
1001 W Southern Ave Ste 130 85210 480-212-1600
DeVry University - Mesa Center Post-Sec.
1201 S Alma School Rd #5450 85210 480-827-1511
Everest College Post-Sec.
5416 E Baseline Rd Ste 200 85206 480-830-5151
Faith Christian S 100/PK-12
PO Box 9086 85214 480-833-1983
Dick Buckingham, admin. Fax 325-1096
International Academy of Hair Design Post-Sec.
1445 W Southern Ave # 2006 85202 480-820-9422
Mesa Community College Post-Sec.
1833 W Southern Ave 85202 480-461-7000
Pima Medical Institute Post-Sec.
957 S Dobson Rd 85202 480-644-0267
Redeemer Christian S 100/K-12
719 N Stapley Dr 85203 480-962-5003
Dr. Denise Monroe Ed.D., prin. Fax 833-7502
Sch of Osteopathic Medicine - AT Still U Post-Sec.
5850 E Still Cir 85206 866-626-2878

Miami, Gila, Pop. 1,817
Miami USD 40 1,100/K-12
PO Box 2070 85539 928-425-3271
Dr. Sherry Dorathy, supt. Fax 425-7419
www.miamiusd40.org
Miami JSHS 500/7-12
PO Box 2070 85539 928-425-3271
Glen Lineberry, prin. Fax 425-7027

Mohave Valley, Mohave, Pop. 2,530
Colorado River UNHSD 2
Supt. — See Bullhead City
River Valley HS 700/9-12
2250 E Laguna Rd 86440 928-768-2300
Dorn Wilcox, prin. Fax 768-6156

Mohave Valley ESD 16 600/PK-8
8450 S Olive Ave 86440 928-768-2507
Whitney Crow, supt. Fax 768-2510
www.mvesd16.org
Mohave Valley JHS 300/6-8
6565 S Girard Ave 86440 928-768-9196
Christina Stahl, prin. Fax 768-1129

Morenci, Greenlee, Pop. 1,476
Morenci USD 18 1,500/PK-12
PO Box 1060 85540 928-865-2081
Dr. David Woodall, supt. Fax 865-3130
www.morenci.k12.az.us/
Fairbanks MS 400/5-8
PO Box 1060 85540 928-865-3501
Anna VanZile, prin. Fax 865-5980
Morenci HS 400/9-12
PO Box 1060 85540 928-865-3631
Bryan Boling, prin. Fax 865-3614

Nogales, Santa Cruz, Pop. 20,797
Nogales USD 1 5,900/K-12
PO Box 5000 85628 520-287-0800
Fernando Parra, supt. Fax 287-3586
www.nusd.k12.az.us
Carpenter Middle Academy 700/6-8
595 W Kino St 85621 520-287-0820
Dr. Roman Soltero, prin. Fax 287-0817
Desert Shadows MS 800/6-8
340 Boulevard Del Rey David 85621 520-377-2646
Joan Molera, prin. Fax 377-2674
Nogales HS 1,700/9-12
1905 N Apache Blvd 85621 520-377-2021
Cesar Miranda, prin. Fax 281-4448
Pierson Vocational HS Vo/Tech
451 N Arroyo Blvd 85621 520-287-0915
Joel Kramer, lead tchr. Fax 287-0918

Lourdes HS 100/9-12
555 E Patagonia Hwy 85621 520-287-5659
Sandra Contreras, prin. Fax 287-2910

Oro Valley, Pima, Pop. 40,283
Amphitheater USD 10
Supt. — See Tucson
Canyon Del Oro HS 1,600/9-12
25 W Calle Concordia 85704 520-696-5560
Paul DeWeerdt, prin. Fax 696-5746
Ironwood Ridge HS 1,900/9-12
2475 W Naranja Dr, 520-696-3900
Natalie Burnett, prin. Fax 696-3999

Page, Coconino, Pop. 6,933
Page USD 8 2,700/K-12
PO Box 1927 86040 928-608-4100
Robert Varner, supt. Fax 645-2805
pageusd.org
Page HS 900/9-12
PO Box 1927 86040 928-608-4138
Paul Gagnon, prin. Fax 645-9243
Page MS 600/6-8
PO Box 1927 86040 928-608-4300
Ray Webb, prin. Fax 645-9285

Paradise Valley, Maricopa, Pop. 12,621

Gateway Academy 50/K-12
3939 E Shea Blvd, 480-998-1071
Robin Sweet, dir. Fax 872-7089
Phoenix Country Day S 700/PK-12
3901 E Stanford Dr 85253 602-955-8200
Andrew Rodin, head sch Fax 955-1286

Parker, LaPaz, Pop. 2,994
Parker USD 27 1,900/PK-12
PO Box 1090 85344 928-669-9244
James Lotts, supt. Fax 669-2515
www.parkerusd.org
Parker HS 500/9-12
PO Box 1090 85344 928-669-2202
Paul Olson, prin. Fax 669-2315
Wallace JHS 300/6-8
PO Box 1090 85344 928-669-2141
Amanda Maxwell, prin. Fax 669-2515

Patagonia, Santa Cruz, Pop. 909
Patagonia SD 200/PK-12
PO Box 254 85624 520-394-3000
Denise Blake, supt. Fax 394-3001
www.patagonia.k12.az.us
Patagonia Union HS 100/9-12
PO Box 254 85624 520-394-3050
Denise Blake, prin. Fax 394-3051

Payson, Gila, Pop. 15,087
Payson USD 10 2,400/K-12
PO Box 919 85547 928-474-2070
Greg Wyman, supt. Fax 472-2013
www.pusd.k12.az.us/
Payson Center for Success 100/Alt
PO Box 919 85547 928-472-2011
Linda Gibson, lead tchr. Fax 472-2039
Payson HS 700/9-12
PO Box 919 85547 928-474-2233
Brian Mabb, prin. Fax 472-2010
Rim Country MS 500/6-8
PO Box 919 85547 928-474-4511
Jennifer White, prin. Fax 472-2044

Payson Christian S 100/PK-12
1000 E Frontier St 85541 928-474-8050
David Callahan M.Ed., admin. Fax 474-3252

Peoria, Maricopa, Pop. 150,709
Peoria USD 11
Supt. — See Glendale
Centennial HS 2,100/9-12
14388 N 79th Ave 85381 623-412-4400
Christine Lopezlira, prin. Fax 412-4420
Liberty HS 2,100/9-12
9621 W Speckled Gecko Dr 85383 623-773-6525
John Croteau, prin. Fax 773-6540
Peoria Flex Academy 100/Alt
11200 N 83rd Ave 85345 623-412-5475
Cybil Jacob, dir. Fax 486-6022
Peoria HS 1,600/9-12
11200 N 83rd Ave 85345 623-486-6300
Paul Bower, prin. Fax 486-6330
Sunrise Mountain HS 1,600/9-12
21200 N 83rd Ave 85382 623-487-5125
David Svorinic, prin. Fax 487-5140

Phoenix, Maricopa, Pop. 1,416,459
Alhambra ESD 68 13,600/PK-8
4510 N 37th Ave 85019 602-336-2920
Mark Yslas, supt. Fax 336-2270
www.alhambraesd.org/
Andalucia MS 1,100/4-8
4730 W Campbell Ave 85031 623-848-8646
Raul Ruiz, prin. Fax 846-6044
Granada East MS 1,100/4-8
3022 W Campbell Ave 85017 602-589-0110
Dr. Randy Martinez, prin. Fax 589-0140
Sevilla West S 1,200/4-8
3851 W Missouri Ave 85019 602-347-0232
Garry Glay, prin. Fax 347-9906
Simpson MS 800/4-8
5330 N 23rd Ave 85015 602-246-0699
Alana Ragland, prin. Fax 246-4305
Other Schools – See Glendale

Cartwright ESD 83 19,100/PK-8
5220 W Indian School Rd 85031 623-691-4000
Dr. Jacob A. Chavez, supt. Fax 691-5926
www.csd83.org
Atkinson MS 1,400/6-8
4315 N Maryvale Pkwy 85031 623-691-1700
Dr. Diana Romito, prin. Fax 691-1720
Castro MS 900/6-8
2730 N 79th Ave 85035 623-691-5300
Sarah Hernandez, prin. Fax 691-5320
Desert Sands MS 1,100/6-8
6308 W Campbell Ave 85033 623-691-4900
Michael Dellisanti, prin. Fax 691-4920
Estrella MS 1,300/6-8
3733 N 75th Ave 85033 623-691-5400
Ryan Anderson, prin. Fax 691-5420

Cave Creek USD 93
Supt. — See Scottsdale
Sonoran Trails MS 800/7-8
5555 E Pinnacle Vista Dr 85085 480-272-8600
Bill Dolezal, prin. Fax 272-8699

Deer Valley USD 97 32,700/PK-12
20402 N 15th Ave 85027 623-445-5000
Dr. James Veitenheimer, supt. Fax 445-5086
www.dvusd.org
Deer Valley MS 700/7-8
21100 N 27th Ave 85027 623-445-3300
Tamela Harris, prin. Fax 445-3380
Goldwater HS 1,900/9-12
2820 W Rose Garden Ln 85027 623-445-3000
Dr. Mike Andersen, prin. Fax 445-3080
O'Connor HS 2,600/9-12
25250 N 35th Ave, 623-445-7100
Dr. Lynn Miller, prin. Fax 445-7180
Vista Peak S Alt
19825 N 15th Ave 85027 623-445-3900
Brian Fineberg, prin. Fax 445-3980
Other Schools – See Anthem, Glendale

Fowler ESD 45 4,600/PK-8
1617 S 67th Ave 85043 623-707-4500
Dr. Marvene Lobato, supt. Fax 707-4560
www.fesd.org
Santa Maria MS 700/6-8
7250 W Lower Buckeye Rd 85043 623-707-1100
Dr. Desiree Castillo, prin. Fax 707-1110
Western Valley MS 800/6-8
6250 W Durango St 85043 623-707-2200
Trent Lyon, prin. Fax 707-2204

Glendale UNHSD 205
Supt. — See Glendale
Cortez HS 1,200/9-12
8828 N 31st Ave 85051 623-915-8200
Walter Sampson, prin. Fax 915-8244
Greenway HS 1,500/9-12
3930 W Greenway Rd 85053 623-915-8500
Jon Vreeken, prin. Fax 915-8560
Moon Valley HS 1,500/9-12
3625 W Cactus Rd 85029 623-915-8000
Anat Salyer, prin. Fax 915-8070
Sunnyslope HS 2,000/9-12
35 W Dunlap Ave 85021 623-915-8760
Steven Ducey, prin. Fax 915-8762
Thunderbird HS 1,500/9-12
1750 W Thunderbird Rd 85023 623-915-8900
Jeannie Paparella, prin. Fax 915-8971
Washington HS 1,800/9-12
2217 W Glendale Ave 85021 623-915-8400
Tami Strege, prin. Fax 915-8437

Isaac ESD 5 7,200/PK-8
3348 W McDowell Rd 85009 602-455-6700
Dr. Mario Ventura, supt. Fax 278-1693
www.isaacschools.org
Isaac MS 800/6-8
3402 W McDowell Rd 85009 602-455-6800
Bree Honeycutt, prin. Fax 455-6899
Udall MS 700/6-8
3715 W Roosevelt St 85009 602-442-2700
Foster Leaf, admin. Fax 442-2799

Kyrene ESD 28
Supt. — See Tempe
Kyrene Akimel A-al MS 1,100/6-8
2720 E Liberty Ln 85048 480-541-5800
Stephanie Phillips, prin. Fax 541-5810
Kyrene Altadena MS 1,100/6-8
14620 S Desert Foothills 85048 480-541-6000
James Martin, prin. Fax 541-6010
Kyrene Centennial MS 1,000/6-8
13808 S 36th St 85044 480-541-6400
Michelle Anderson, prin. Fax 541-6410

Madison ESD 38 5,900/PK-11
5601 N 16th St 85016 602-664-7900
Quinn Kellis Ed.D., supt. Fax 664-7999
www.madisonaz.org
Madison # 1 MS 900/5-8
5525 N 16th St 85016 602-664-7100
Pam Warren, prin. Fax 664-7199
Madison Meadows MS 800/5-8
225 W Ocotillo Rd 85013 602-664-7600
Pat Carney, prin. Fax 664-7699
Madison Park MS 400/5-8
1431 E Campbell Ave 85014 602-664-7500
Todd Stevens, prin. Fax 664-7599

Osborn ESD 8 3,000/PK-8
1226 W Osborn Rd 85013 602-707-2000
Patricia Tate, supt. Fax 707-2040
www.osbornnet.org
Osborn MS 600/7-8
1102 W Highland Ave 85013 602-707-2400
Marty Makar, prin. Fax 707-2440

Paradise Valley USD 32,000/PK-12
15002 N 32nd St 85032 602-449-2000
James Lee Ed.D., supt. Fax 449-2005
www.pvschools.net
Explorer MS 800/7-8
22401 N 40th St 85050 602-449-4200
Kyle Shappee, prin. Fax 449-4205
Greenway MS 500/7-8
3002 E Nisbet Rd 85032 602-449-2400
Dr. Ibi Haghighat, prin. Fax 449-2405
Mountain Trail MS 800/7-8
2323 E Mountain Gate Pass 85024 602-449-4600
Craig Lahlum, prin. Fax 449-4605
North Canyon HS 2,000/9-12
1700 E Union Hls Dr 85024 602-449-5000
Elaine Jacobs, prin. Fax 449-5005
Paradise Valley HS 1,800/9-12
3950 E Bell Rd 85032 602-449-7000
Ian Deonise, prin. Fax 449-7005
Pinnacle HS 2,400/9-12
3535 E Mayo Blvd 85050 602-449-4000
Dr. Chad Lanese, prin. Fax 449-4205
Shadow Mountain HS 1,500/9-12
2902 E Shea Blvd 85028 602-449-3000
David Appleman, prin. Fax 449-3005
Shea MS 600/7-8
2728 E Shea Blvd 85028 602-449-3500
Dan Knak, prin. Fax 449-3505
Star Tech Professional Center Vo/Tech
3950 E Bell Rd 85032 602-449-7036
Tony Maldonado, dir. Fax 449-2333
Sweetwater Community S Alt
4215 E Andora Dr 85032 602-449-2300
Diane Silvestri, prin. Fax 449-2305
Vista Verde MS 700/7-8
2826 E Grovers Ave 85032 602-449-5300
Andrea Hoffler, prin. Fax 449-5305
Other Schools – See Scottsdale

Phoenix UNHSD 210 26,600/9-12
4502 N Central Ave 85012 602-764-1100
Chad Gestson Ed.D., supt. Fax 271-3593
www.phoenixunion.org
Abril Education Academy 200/Alt
3000 N 19th Ave 85015 602-764-0050
Rick Beck, prin. Fax 744-1221
Alhambra HS 2,700/9-12
3839 W Camelback Rd 85019 602-764-6022
Karen Cardenas, prin. Fax 271-3497
Bostrom Alternative Center 200/Alt
3535 N 27th Ave 85017 602-764-1700
Alvin Watson, prin. Fax 271-2923
Browne HS 3,000/9-12
7402 W Catalina Dr 85033 602-764-8500
Tony Camp, prin. Fax 440-6803
Camelback HS 2,000/9-12
4612 N 28th St 85016 602-764-7000
Dana Cook, prin. Fax 271-2295
Central HS 2,300/9-12
4525 N Central Ave 85012 602-764-7500
John Biera, prin. Fax 271-2385
Franklin Police and Fire HS 300/9-12
1645 W McDowell Rd 85007 602-764-0200
Lorenzo Cabrera, prin. Fax 258-2868
Hayden Community HS 2,100/9-12
3333 W Roosevelt St 85009 602-764-3000
Ricardo Cordova, prin. Fax 229-8387
Maryvale HS 2,800/9-12
3415 N 59th Ave 85033 602-764-2000
Manuel Silvas, prin. Fax 271-2597
Metro Tech HS 1,700/9-12
1900 W Thomas Rd 85015 602-764-8000
Bryan Reynoso, prin. Fax 452-5302
North HS 2,600/9-12
1101 E Thomas Rd 85014 602-764-6500
Juan A. Nunez, prin. Fax 271-2765
Phoenix Coding Academy 100/9-9
4445 N Central Ave 85012 602-764-5700
Seth Beute, prin.
Phoenix Union Bioscience HS 300/9-12
512 E Pierce St 85004 602-764-5600
Holly Batsell, prin. Fax 253-9013

South Mountain HS 1,700/9-12
5401 S 7th St 85040 602-764-5000
Brian Guliford, prin. Fax 271-2880
Other Schools – See Laveen

Riverside ESD 2 900/PK-8
1414 S 51st Ave 85043 602-477-8900
Jaime Rivera Ed.D., supt. Fax 272-8378
resdonline.org/
Kings Ridge Preparatory Academy 400/5-8
3650 S 64th Ln 85043 602-477-8960
Talmadge Tanks, prin. Fax 936-5531

Roosevelt ESD 66 9,700/PK-8
6000 S 7th St 85042 602-243-4800
Dr. Jeanne Koba, supt. Fax 243-2637
www.rsd.k12.az.us
Greenfield MS 600/4-8
7009 S 10th St 85042 602-232-4240
Stuart Starky, prin. Fax 243-4973

Scottsdale USD 48
Supt. — See Scottsdale
Arcadia HS 1,700/9-12
4703 E Indian School Rd 85018 480-484-6300
Nathan Slater, prin. Fax 484-6301
Ingleside MS 700/6-8
5402 E Osborn Rd 85018 480-484-4900
Christopher Thuman, prin. Fax 484-4901

Tempe UNHSD 213
Supt. — See Tempe
Desert Vista HS 3,100/9-12
16440 S 32nd St 85048 480-706-7900
Dr. Christine Barela, prin. Fax 706-7976
Mountain Pointe HS 2,600/9-12
4201 E Knox Rd 85044 480-759-8449
Bruce Kipper, prin. Fax 759-8458

Tolleson UNHSD 214
Supt. — See Tolleson
Sierra Linda HS 1,800/9-12
3434 S 67th Ave 85043 623-474-7700
Tim Madrid, prin. Fax 474-7790

Washington ESD 6
Supt. — See Glendale
Cholla MS 700/7-8
3120 W Cholla St 85029 602-896-5400
Phil Garitson, prin. Fax 896-5420
Desert Foothills JHS 700/7-8
3333 W Banff Ln 85053 602-896-5500
Susan Smith, prin. Fax 896-5520
Mountain Sky JHS 700/7-8
16225 N 7th Ave 85023 602-896-6100
Perry Mason, prin. Fax 896-6120
Palo Verde MS 900/7-8
7502 N 39th Ave 85051 602-347-2500
Jill Sarraino, prin. Fax 347-2520

Wilson ESD 7 1,300/PK-8
3025 E Fillmore St 85008 602-681-2200
Antonio Sanchez, supt. Fax 275-7517
www.wsd.k12.az.us
Wilson MS 600/4-8
2929 E Fillmore St 85008 602-683-2400
Cindy Campton, prin. Fax 275-8677

American Indian Coll of Assemblies/God Post-Sec.
10020 N 15th Ave 85021 602-944-3335
American Institute of Technology Post-Sec.
440 S 54th Ave 85043 602-457-3294
Anthem College Post-Sec.
1515 E Indian School Rd 85014 602-279-9700
Argosy University/Phoenix Post-Sec.
2233 W Dunlap Ave 85021 602-216-2600
Arizona Christian University Post-Sec.
2625 E Cactus Rd 85032 800-247-2697
Arizona Cultural Academy & College Prep 300/PK-12
7810 S 42nd Pl 85042 602-454-1222
Samah Bkhaitan, prin. Fax 453-3222
Arizona Lutheran Academy 200/9-12
6036 S 27th Ave 85041 602-268-8686
Kurt Rosenbaum M.Ed., prin. Fax 243-1353
Arizona Summit Law School Post-Sec.
1 N Central Ave Ste 1400 85004 602-682-6800
Bourgade Catholic HS 400/9-12
4602 N 31st Ave 85017 602-973-4000
Kathy Rother, prin. Fax 973-5854
Brookline College Post-Sec.
2445 W Dunlap Ave Ste 100 85021 602-242-6265
Brophy College Prep Catholic HS 1,300/9-12
4701 N Central Ave 85012 602-264-5291
Bob Ryan, prin. Fax 266-3642
Bryman School Post-Sec.
2250 W Peoria Ave Ste A100 85029 602-274-4300
Carrington College Post-Sec.
8503 N 27th Ave 85051 877-206-2106
Carrington College - Westside Post-Sec.
2701 W Bethany Home Rd 85017 602-433-1333
Chamberlain College of Nursing Post-Sec.
2149 W Dunlap Ave 85021 602-331-2720
CollegeAmerica Post-Sec.
9801 N Metro Pkwy E 85051 602-257-7522
Collins College Post-Sec.
4750 S 44th Pl 85040 480-966-3000
DeVry University - Phoenix Campus Post-Sec.
2149 W Dunlap Ave 85021 602-870-9222
Dunlap-Stone University Post-Sec.
19820 N 7th St Ste 100 85024 800-474-8013
Empire Beauty School Post-Sec.
2727 W Glendale Ave Ste 200 85051 623-939-8364
Everest College Post-Sec.
10400 N 25th Ave Ste 190 85021 602-942-4141
Fortis College Post-Sec.
555 N 18th St Ste 110 85006 602-254-3099
Gateway Community College Post-Sec.
108 N 40th St 85034 602-286-8000
Grand Canyon University Post-Sec.
3300 W Camelback Rd 85017 602-639-7500
Motorcycle Mechanics Institute Post-Sec.
2844 W Deer Valley Rd 85027 623-869-9644
National Paralegal College Post-Sec.
717 E Maryland Ave 85014 800-371-6105
91st Psalm Christian S 100/PK-12
2020 E Baseline Rd 85042 602-243-1900
Rob Arthurs, prin. Fax 243-5919

North Valley Christian Academy 100/PK-12
42101 N 41st Dr 85086 623-551-3454
Nate Kretzmann M.Ed., dir. Fax 551-4067
Northwest Christian S 1,300/PK-12
16401 N 43rd Ave 85053 602-978-5134
Geoffrey Brown, supt. Fax 978-5804
Ottawa University Arizona Post-Sec.
10020 N 25th Ave 85021 602-371-1188
Paradise Valley Christian College Prep S 300/PK-12
11875 N 24th St 85028 602-992-8140
Sheryl Temple M.A., hdmstr. Fax 992-8152
Paradise Valley Community College Post-Sec.
18401 N 32nd St 85032 602-787-6500
Phoenix Christian Preparatory S 300/PK-12
1751 W Indian School Rd 85015 602-265-4707
Joe Bradley, pres. Fax 277-7170
Phoenix College Post-Sec.
1202 W Thomas Rd 85013 602-285-7800
Phoenix Institute of Herbal Medicine Post-Sec.
301 E Bethany Home Rd #A100 85012
602-274-1885
Phoenix Seminary Post-Sec.
4222 E Thomas Rd Ste 400 85018 602-850-8000
Refrigeration School Post-Sec.
4210 E Washington St 85034 602-275-7133
Roberto-Venn School of Luthiery Post-Sec.
1012 Grand Ave 85007 602-243-1179
St. Marys Catholic HS 500/9-12
2525 N 3rd St 85004 602-251-2500
Suzanne Fessler, prin. Fax 251-2595
Scottsdale Christian Academy 800/PK-12
14400 N Tatum Blvd 85032 602-992-5100
Brent Hodges, supt. Fax 992-0575
Shearim Torah HS for Girls 50/9-12
715 E Sierra Vista Dr Ste 1 85014 602-324-3406
South Mountain Community College Post-Sec.
7050 S 24th St 85042 602-243-8000
The Art Institute of Phoenix Post-Sec.
2233 W Dunlap Ave 85021 602-331-7500
Valley Lutheran HS 200/9-12
5199 N 7th Ave 85013 602-230-1600
Robert Koehne M.A., prin. Fax 230-1602
West Coast Ultrasound Institute Post-Sec.
4250 E Camelback Rd 85018 602-954-3834
Xavier College Prep Catholic HS 1,200/9-12
4710 N 5th St 85012 602-277-3772
Sr. Joan Nuckols, prin. Fax 279-1346
Yeshiva HS of Arizona 50/9-12
727 E Glendale Ave 85020 623-266-1213

Pima, Graham, Pop. 2,335
Pima USD 6 800/K-12
PO Box 429 85543 928-387-8000
Sean Rickert, supt. Fax 387-8020
www.pimaschools.org
Gila Valley Learning Center 50/Alt
PO Box 429 85543 928-387-8015
Craig Lunt, dir. Fax 387-8020
Pima HS 200/9-12
PO Box 429 85543 928-387-8151
Cody Barlow, prin. Fax 387-8023
Pima JHS 100/7-8
PO Box 429 85543 928-387-8100
Mark Squires, prin. Fax 387-8021

Pinon, Navajo, Pop. 897
Pinon USD 4 1,300/PK-12
PO Box 839 86510 928-725-3450
Dr. Jasvir Sethi, supt. Fax 725-2123
www.pusdatsa.org
Pinon HS 400/9-12
PO Box 839 86510 928-725-2401
Lori Chee, prin. Fax 725-2470
Pinon MS 300/6-8
PO Box 839 86510 928-725-2300
Lariza Turner, prin. Fax 725-2370

Prescott, Yavapai, Pop. 39,213
Prescott USD 1 3,400/PK-12
146 S Granite St 86303 928-445-5400
Joe Howard, supt. Fax 776-0243
www.prescottschools.com
Prescott HS 1,600/9-12
1050 Ruth St 86301 928-445-2322
Stephanie Hillig, prin. Fax 778-6106
Prescott Mile High MS 400/7-8
300 S Granite St 86303 928-717-3241
Mark Goligoski, prin. Fax 717-3298

Yavapai Accommodation SD 100/9-12
2972 Centerpointe East Dr 86301 928-759-8126
Kellie Burns, dir. Fax 759-8136
yasd99.com
Aspire HS 100/Alt
2972 Centerpointe East Dr 86301 928-759-8126
Kellie Burns, dir. Fax 759-8136
Other Schools – See Prescott Valley

Embry-Riddle Aeronautical University Post-Sec.
3700 Willow Creek Rd 86301 800-888-3728
Empire Beauty School Post-Sec.
410 W Goodwin St 86303 928-778-5064
Prescott College Post-Sec.
220 Grove Ave 86301 877-350-2100
Trinity Christian S 200/K-12
1077 Mogollon Rd 86301 928-445-6306
Kyle Maestri, hdmstr. Fax 445-7210
Yavapai College Post-Sec.
1100 E Sheldon St 86301 928-445-7300

Prescott Valley, Yavapai, Pop. 38,121
Humboldt USD 22 5,800/PK-12
6411 N Robert Rd 86314 928-759-4000
Dan Streeter, supt. Fax 759-4020
www.humboldtunified.com
Bradshaw Mountain HS 1,600/9-12
6000 E Long Look Dr 86314 928-759-4100
Kort Miner, prin. Fax 759-4120
Glassford Hill MS 400/7-8
6901 Panther Path 86314 928-759-4600
Melissa Tannehill, prin. Fax 759-4620
Other Schools – See Dewey

Yavapai Accommodation SD
Supt. — See Prescott
Yavapai County HS 50/Alt
6325 Baja Circle 86314 928-759-8126
Kellie Burns, dir. Fax 759-8136

Northcentral University — Post-Sec.
10000 E University Dr 86314 — 928-541-7777

Queen Creek, Maricopa, Pop. 25,755
Chandler USD 80
Supt. — See Chandler
Casteel HS — 7-12
24901 S Power Rd, — 480-424-8100
Sandy Lundberg, prin. — Fax 224-9406
Payne JHS — 1,400/7-8
7655 S Higley Rd, — 480-224-2400
Paul Bollard, prin. — Fax 224-2420

Higley USD 60
Supt. — See Gilbert
Sossaman MS — 900/7-8
18655 E Jacaranda Blvd, — 480-279-8500
John Dolan, prin. — Fax 279-8505

Queen Creek USD 95 — 4,700/PK-12
20217 E Chandler Heights Rd, — 480-987-5935
Dr. Perry Berry, supt. — Fax 987-9714
www.qcusd.org/
Barney JHS — 800/6-8
24937 S Sossaman Rd, — 480-474-6700
Denise Johnson, prin. — Fax 882-3181
Queen Creek HS — 1,800/9-12
22149 E Ocotillo Rd, — 480-987-5973
Paul Gagnon, prin. — Fax 882-1276
Queen Creek MS — 300/6-8
20435 S Old Ellsworth Rd, — 480-987-5940
Joseph McKnight, prin. — Fax 987-5947

Ambassador Christian Academy — 50/K-12
19248 E San Tan Blvd, — 480-387-0902
Amy Crislip, admin. — Fax 452-0316
Freedom Christian Academy — 100/PK-12
39731 N Kennedy Dr, — 480-987-5488
Ben Koshtaka, admin. — Fax 987-9344

Red Valley, Apache, Pop. 30
Red Mesa USD 27
Supt. — See Teec Nos Pos
Red Valley/Cove HS — 50/9-12
Navaho Route 13 86544 — 928-653-4200
Glen White Eagle, prin. — Fax 653-4204

Rio Rico, Santa Cruz, Pop. 18,904
Santa Cruz Valley USD 35 — 3,000/PK-12
1374 W Frontage Rd 85648 — 520-375-8282
David Verdugo, supt. — Fax 281-7093
www.santacruz.k12.az.us
Coatimundi MS — 400/6-8
1374 W Frontage Rd 85648 — 520-375-8800
Lerona Dickson, prin. — Fax 761-4669
Rio Rico HS — 1,100/9-12
1374 W Frontage Rd 85648 — 520-375-8700
Shelly Vroegh, prin. — Fax 377-9556

Sacaton, Pinal, Pop. 2,641
Sacaton ESD 18 — 400/PK-8
PO Box 98, — 520-562-8600
Dr. Douglas Price, supt. — Fax 763-4410
sacatonschools.org
Sacaton MS — 200/5-8
PO Box 98, — 520-562-8600
Philip Bonds, prin. — Fax 763-4420

Safford, Graham, Pop. 9,405
Safford USD 1 — 3,300/PK-12
734 W 11th St 85546 — 928-348-7000
Ken VanWinkle, supt. — Fax 348-7001
www.saffordusd.com
Mt. Graham HS — 100/Alt
300 W Discovery Park Blvd 85546 — 928-348-7060
Lori VanScyoc, prin. — Fax 348-7061
Safford HS — 900/9-12
1400 W 11th St 85546 — 928-348-7050
Rich DeRidder, prin. — Fax 348-7057
Safford MS — 500/7-8
612 W 11th St 85546 — 928-348-7040
Clay Emery, prin. — Fax 348-7041

Safford College of Beauty Culture — Post-Sec.
1550 W Thatcher Blvd 85546 — 928-428-0331

Sahuarita, Pima, Pop. 24,638
Sahuarita USD 30 — 5,700/PK-12
350 W Sahuarita Rd 85629 — 520-625-3502
Dr. Manuel Valenzuela, supt. — Fax 625-4609
www.susd30.us
Sahuarita HS — 900/9-12
350 W Sahuarita Rd 85629 — 520-625-3502
John Kneup, prin. — Fax 399-1223
Sahuarita MS — 600/6-8
350 W Sahuarita Rd 85629 — 520-625-3502
Stephanie Silman, prin. — Fax 393-7043
Walden Grove HS — 900/9-12
350 W Sahuarita Rd 85629 — 520-625-3502
Teresa Hill, prin. — Fax 393-7048

Saint David, Cochise, Pop. 1,668
Saint David USD 21 — 400/PK-12
PO Box 70 85630 — 520-720-4781
Mark Goodman, supt. — Fax 720-4783
www.stdavidschools.org/
Saint David HS — 100/9-12
PO Box 70 85630 — 520-720-4781
Andrew Brogan, prin. — Fax 720-4783

Saint Johns, Apache, Pop. 3,399
Saint Johns USD 1 — 800/K-12
PO Box 3030 85936 — 928-337-2255
Ed Burgoyne, supt. — Fax 337-2263
www.sjusd.net
Saint Johns HS — 300/9-12
PO Box 429 85936 — 928-337-2221
Roger Heap, prin. — Fax 337-2867
Saint Johns Learning Center — 50/Alt
PO Box 3030 85936 — 928-337-2221
Kim Fejes, dir. — Fax 337-2263
Saint Johns MS — 300/4-8
PO Box 3060 85936 — 928-337-2132
Tim Raban, prin. — Fax 337-3147

Saint Michaels, Apache, Pop. 1,404

St. Michael Indian S — 300/PK-12
PO Box 650 86511 — 928-871-4636
Tom Sorci, prin. — Fax 871-2467

Salome, LaPaz, Pop. 1,511
Bicentennial UNHSD 76 — 100/9-12
PO Box 519 85348 — 928-859-3453
Byron Maynes, supt. — Fax 859-3875
www.salomehs.org
Salome HS — 100/9-12
PO Box 519 85348 — 928-859-3453
Byron Maynes, supt. — Fax 859-3875

San Carlos, Gila, Pop. 4,011
San Carlos USD 20 — 1,400/PK-12
PO Box 207 85550 — 928-475-2315
Debroah Dennison Ph.D., supt. — Fax 475-2301
www.sancarlosbraves.org
San Carlos Alternative S — Alt
PO Box 207 85550 — 928-475-5538
Carol Slim, prin. — Fax 475-2301
San Carlos JSHS — 500/7-12
PO Box 207 85550 — 928-475-2378
Tyron Draper, prin. — Fax 475-2697

Sanders, Apache, Pop. 600
Sanders USD 18 — 800/K-12
PO Box 250 86512 — 928-688-4750
Dan Hute, supt. — Fax 688-4723
www.sandersusd.net
Sanders MS — 200/6-8
PO Box 250 86512 — 928-688-4770
Sheryl Soderstrom, prin. — Fax 688-4776
Valley HS — 300/9-12
PO Box 250 86512 — 928-688-4200
Verlynn Goldtooth, prin. — Fax 688-4202

San Luis, Yuma, Pop. 25,496
Gadsden ESD 32 — 5,300/PK-8
PO Box 6870 85349 — 928-627-6540
Raymond Aguilera, supt. — Fax 627-3635
www.gesd32.org/
San Luis MS — 700/7-8
PO Box 6870 85349 — 928-627-6920
Rafael Sanchez, prin. — Fax 627-9339
Southwest JHS — 700/7-8
PO Box 6870 85349 — 928-627-6580
Jose Urena, prin. — Fax 627-9266

Yuma UNHSD 70
Supt. — See Yuma
San Luis HS — 2,600/9-12
PO Box 7380 85349 — 928-502-6100
Tamara Ray, prin. — Fax 502-6222

San Manuel, Pinal, Pop. 3,491
Mammoth-San Manuel USD 8 — 700/PK-12
PO Box 406 85631 — 520-385-2337
John Ryan, supt. — Fax 385-2621
www.msmusd.org
San Manuel JSHS — 300/7-12
PO Box 406 85631 — 520-385-2336
Julie Dale-Scott, prin. — Fax 385-3035

San Simon, Cochise, Pop. 160
San Simon USD 18 — 100/K-12
PO Box 38 85632 — 520-845-2275
Jonathan Truschke, supt. — Fax 845-2480
www.sansimon.k12.az.us
San Simon S — 100/K-12
PO Box 38 85632 — 520-845-2275
Jonathan Truschke, admin. — Fax 845-2480

San Tan Valley, Pinal, Pop. 79,014
Florence USD 1
Supt. — See Florence
Mountain Vista Academy — Alt
33622 N Mountain Vista Blvd, — 480-474-6175
Robert Edwards, prin.
Poston Butte HS — 1,600/9-12
32375 N Gantzel Rd, — 480-474-6100
Steve Tannenbaum, prin. — Fax 888-0679
San Tan Foothills HS — 600/9-12
1255 W Silverdale Rd, — 480-474-6240
Dr. Tim Richard, prin. — Fax 888-2611

J.O. Combs USD 44 — 4,500/PK-12
301 E Combs Rd, — 480-987-5300
Dr. Gayle A. Blanchard, supt. — Fax 987-3487
www.jocombs.org
Combs HS — 1,200/9-12
301 E Combs Rd, — 480-882-3540
Brooke Davis, prin. — Fax 987-0837
Combs MS — 700/7-8
301 E Combs Rd, — 480-882-3510
Mark Mauro, prin. — Fax 888-8049

Scottsdale, Maricopa, Pop. 213,310
Cave Creek USD 93 — 5,400/PK-12
33616 N 60th St 85266 — 480-575-2000
Dr. Debbi Burdick, supt. — Fax 488-7055
www.ccusd93.org
Cactus Shadows HS — 1,700/9-12
5802 E Dove Valley Rd 85266 — 480-575-2400
Dr. Steve Bebee, prin. — Fax 488-6701
Other Schools – See Phoenix

Paradise Valley USD
Supt. — See Phoenix
Desert Shadows MS — 800/7-8
5858 E Sweetwater Ave 85254 — 602-449-6800
Derek Hummert, prin. — Fax 449-6805
Horizon HS — 2,300/9-12
5601 E Greenway Rd 85254 — 602-449-6000
Linda Ihnat, prin. — Fax 449-6005
Sunrise MS — 600/7-8
4960 E Acoma Dr 85254 — 602-449-6100
Gregory Martin, prin. — Fax 449-6105

Scottsdale USD 48 — 24,800/PK-12
7575 E Main St 85251 — 480-484-6100
Dr. A. Denise Birdwell, supt. — Fax 484-6287
www.susd.org
Chaparral HS — 2,100/9-12
6935 E Gold Dust Ave 85253 — 480-484-6500
Gayle Holland, prin. — Fax 484-6501
Cocopah MS — 900/6-8
6615 E Cholla St 85254 — 480-484-4400
Lance Huffman, prin. — Fax 484-4401
Coronado HS — 1,100/9-12
7501 E Virginia Ave 85257 — 480-484-6800
Alyssa Tarkington, prin. — Fax 484-6801
Desert Canyon MS — 600/6-8
10203 E McDowell Mtn Ranch 85255 — 480-484-4600
Dale Link, prin. — Fax 484-4601
Desert Mountain HS — 2,300/9-12
12575 E Via Linda 85259 — 480-484-7000
Nicole Wilfert, prin. — Fax 484-7001
Mohave MS — 800/6-8
8490 E Jackrabbit Rd 85250 — 480-484-5200
Chris Asmussen, prin. — Fax 484-5201
Mountainside MS — 800/6-8
11256 N 128th St 85259 — 480-484-5500
Terri Kellen, prin. — Fax 484-5501
Saguaro HS — 1,300/9-12
6250 N 82nd St 85250 — 480-484-7100
Ann Achtziger, prin. — Fax 484-7101
Other Schools – See Phoenix

Arizona Culinary Institute — Post-Sec.
10585 N 114th St Ste 401 85259 — 480-603-1066
Automotive Dealership Institute — Post-Sec.
6613 N Scottsdale Rd 85250 — 480-998-7200
Bella Vista College Preparatory S — 50/4-12
PO Box 28096 85255 — 480-575-6001
Brighton College — Post-Sec.
7332 E Butherus Dr Ste 102 85260 — 800-354-1254
Cortiva Institute - Scottsdale — Post-Sec.
8010 E McDowell Rd Ste 214 85257 — 480-684-1275
Devereux-Arizona Treatment Network — Post-Sec.
11000 N Scottsville Rd #260 85254 — 480-998-2920
Empire Beauty School — Post-Sec.
7730 E McDowell Rd 85257 — 480-949-7557
Frank Lloyd Wright Sch of Architecture — Post-Sec.
PO Box 4430 85261 — 480-860-2700
Le Cordon Bleu College of Culinary Arts — Post-Sec.
8100 E Camelback Rd # 1001 85251 — 480-990-3773
Notre Dame Preparatory Catholic HS — 900/9-12
9701 E Bell Rd 85260 — 480-634-8200
Jerome Zander, prin. — Fax 634-8299
Penn Foster College — Post-Sec.
14300 N Northsight Ste 120 85260 — 480-947-6644
Penrose Academy — Post-Sec.
13402 N Scottsdale Rd #B160 85254 — 480-222-9540
Phoenix HS of Jewish Studies — 50/9-12
12701 N Scottsdale Rd 85254 — 480-634-8050
Rancho Solano Preparatory S — 600/PK-12
9180 E Via de Ventura 85258 — 480-646-8200
Scott Cole Academy — Post-Sec.
7201 E Camelback Rd Ste 100 85251 — 480-994-4222
Scottsdale Community College — Post-Sec.
9000 E Chaparral Rd 85256 — 480-423-6000
Sonoran Desert Institute — Post-Sec.
10245 E Via Linda Ste 110 85258 — 480-314-2102
The Paralegal Institute — Post-Sec.
7332 E Butherus Dr Ste 102 85260 — 800-354-1254
Thunderbird Adventist Academy — 100/9-12
7410 E Sutton Dr 85260 — 480-948-3300

Sedona, Coconino, Pop. 9,896
Sedona-Oak Creek JUSD 9 — 1,200/K-12
221 Brewer Rd Ste 100 86336 — 928-204-6800
David Lykins, supt. — Fax 282-0232
www.sedona.k12.az.us
Sedona Red Rock HS — 500/7-12
995 Upper Red Rock Loop Rd 86336 — 928-204-6700
Darrin Karuzas, prin. — Fax 282-5992

Verde Valley S — 100/9-12
3511 Verde Valley School Rd 86351 — 928-284-2272

Seligman, Yavapai, Pop. 428
Seligman USD 40 — 100/K-12
PO Box 650 86337 — 928-422-3233
Diane Pritchett, supt. — Fax 422-3642
www.seligmanschools.org/
Seligman HS — 100/9-12
PO Box 650 86337 — 928-216-4123
Marvin Baker, prin. — Fax 422-3642

Sells, Pima, Pop. 2,459
Baboquivari USD 40 — 900/K-12
PO Box 248 85634 — 520-383-6746
Dr. Edna Morris, supt. — Fax 383-5441
busd40.org
Indian Oasis JSHS — 100/Alt
PO Box 248 85634 — 520-383-6746
Andy Vurrola, prin. — Fax 383-5441
Other Schools – See Topawa

Tohono O'odham Community College — Post-Sec.
PO Box 3129 85634 — 520-383-8401

Show Low, Navajo, Pop. 10,473
Show Low USD 10 — 2,100/PK-12
500 W Old Linden Rd 85901 — 928-537-6000
Shad Housley, supt. — Fax 537-6009
www.show-low.k12.az.us
Show Low HS — 800/9-12
500 W Old Linden Rd 85901 — 928-537-6200
Farrell Adams, prin. — Fax 537-6299
Show Low JHS — 600/6-8
500 W Old Linden Rd 85901 — 928-537-6100
Meghan Dorsett, prin. — Fax 537-6149
White Mountain Institute — 50/Alt
500 W Old Linden Rd 85901 — 928-537-6201
Farrell Adams, prin. — Fax 537-6299

American Indian Christian S — 50/3-8
924 Mission Ln Lot 1 85901 — 928-537-5912
Leslie Solliday, dir. — Fax 537-5620

Sierra Vista, Cochise, Pop. 41,754
Sierra Vista USD 68 — 5,700/PK-12
3555 E Fry Blvd 85635 — 520-515-2701
Kriss Hagerl, supt. — Fax 515-2744
www.svusd68.org
Buena HS — 2,200/9-12
3555 E Fry Blvd 85635 — 520-515-2800
Joe Farmer, prin. — Fax 515-2877
Clark MS — 800/7-8
3555 E Fry Blvd 85635 — 520-515-2930
Roger Hill, prin. — Fax 515-2941

DeVoe College of Beauty Post-Sec.
PO Box 1571 85636 520-458-8660
Veritas Christian Community S 100/K-12
215 Taylor Dr 85635 520-417-1113
Jason Tinney, head sch Fax 417-0180

Snowflake, Navajo, Pop. 5,508
Snowflake USD 5 2,500/K-12
682 W School Bus Ln 85937 928-536-4156
Hollis Merrell, supt. Fax 536-2634
home.susd5.org
Snowflake HS 700/9-12
682 W School Bus Ln 85937 928-536-4156
Larry Titus, prin. Fax 536-4240
Snowflake JHS 400/7-8
682 W School Bus Ln 85937 928-536-4156
Brian Hoopes, prin. Fax 536-3007

Somerton, Yuma, Pop. 14,249
Somerton ESD 11 2,800/PK-8
PO Box 3200 85350 928-341-6000
Dr. Laura Noel, supt. Fax 341-6090
www.somerton.k12.az.us
Somerton MS 900/6-8
PO Box 3200 85350 928-341-6100
Elizabeth Garza, prin. Fax 341-6190

Springerville, Apache, Pop. 1,931
Round Valley USD 10 1,300/K-12
PO Box 610 85938 928-333-6580
Travis Udall, supt. Fax 333-2823
www.elks.net
Other Schools – See Eagar

Sun City, Maricopa, Pop. 37,274

Walter Boswell Memorial Hospital Post-Sec.
10401 W Thunderbird Blvd 85351 623-977-7211

Sun Valley, Navajo, Pop. 299

Native American Christian Academy 50/3-8
PO Box 4013 86029 928-524-6211
Kristopher Miller, admin. Fax 524-3230

Superior, Pinal, Pop. 2,804
Superior USD 15 400/PK-12
1500 W Panther Dr, 520-689-3000
Stephen Estatico, supt. Fax 689-3170
www.superiorusd.org
Superior HS 100/9-12
100 W Panther Dr, 520-689-3002
William Duarte, prin. Fax 689-3197
Superior JHS 100/7-8
100 W Panther Dr, 520-689-3002
William Duarte, prin. Fax 689-3197

Surprise, Maricopa, Pop. 114,476
Dysart USD 89 25,700/K-12
15802 N Parkview Pl 85374 623-876-7000
Dr. Gail Pletnick, supt. Fax 876-7042
www.dysart.org
Shadow Ridge HS 1,500/9-12
10909 N Perryville Rd, 623-523-5100
Michael Hawkins, prin. Fax 523-5111
Sundown Mountain Alternative Program Alt
23251 N 166th Dr 85387 623-876-7250
Anthony Capuano, prin. Fax 876-7261
Valley Vista HS 2,400/9-12
15550 N Parkview Pl 85374 623-523-8800
Roberta Lockhart, prin. Fax 523-8811
Willow Canyon HS 2,100/9-12
17901 W Lundberg St, 623-523-8000
Jayne Wieferich, prin. Fax 523-8097
Other Schools – See El Mirage

Teec Nos Pos, Apache, Pop. 721
Red Mesa USD 27 600/K-12
HC 61 Box 40 86514 928-656-4108
Kim Pearce, supt. Fax 656-4302
www.rmusd.net
Red Mesa HS 200/9-12
HC 61 Box 40 86514 928-656-4177
Glen White Eagle, prin. Fax 656-4178
Other Schools – See Red Valley

Immanuel Mission S 100/K-12
PO Box 1080 86514 830-200-0351
John Bloom, prin. Fax 435-7041

Tempe, Maricopa, Pop. 156,729
Kyrene ESD 28 17,300/PK-8
8700 S Kyrene Rd 85284 480-541-1000
Dr. Jan Vesely, supt. Fax 541-1860
www.kyrene.org
Kyrene MS 1,100/6-8
1050 E Carver Rd 85284 480-541-6600
Sheryl Houston, prin. Fax 541-6610
Other Schools – See Chandler, Phoenix

Tempe ESD 3 11,800/PK-8
3205 S Rural Rd 85282 480-730-7100
Christine Busch, supt. Fax 730-7177
www.tempeschools.org
Connolly MS 1,000/6-8
2002 E Concorda Dr 85282 480-967-8933
Katherine Mullery, prin. Fax 929-9695
Fees College Preparatory Academy 1,000/6-8
1600 E Watson Dr 85283 480-897-6063
Kacy Baxter, prin. Fax 838-0853
Gililland MS 1,000/6-8
1025 S Beck Ave 85281 480-966-7114
JoLyn Gibbons, prin. Fax 829-6178
Tempe Academy of International Studies 100/6-8
2250 S College Ave 85282 480-459-5048
David Owen, prin. Fax 621-6577

Tempe UNHSD 213 14,000/9-12
500 W Guadalupe Rd 85283 480-839-0292
Dr. Kenneth Baca, supt. Fax 413-0685
www.tuhsd.k12.az.us
Compadre Academy 600/Alt
500 W Guadalupe Rd 85283 480-752-3560
Ed Flores, prin. Fax 285-3252
Corona Del Sol HS 2,700/9-12
1001 E Knox Rd 85284 480-752-8888
Nathan Kleve, prin. Fax 820-3632

Marcos De Niza HS 1,600/9-12
6000 S Lakeshore Dr 85283 480-838-3200
Sean McDonald, prin. Fax 730-7665
McClintock HS 1,800/9-12
1830 E Del Rio Dr 85282 480-839-4222
Derek Hoffland, prin. Fax 752-8661
Tempe HS 1,500/9-12
1730 S Mill Ave 85281 480-967-1661
Dr. Stacia Wilson, prin. Fax 736-4096
Other Schools – See Phoenix

Acacia University Post-Sec.
7665 S Research Dr 85284 480-428-6034
Arizona State University Post-Sec.
PO Box 870112 85287 480-965-2100
Brookline College Post-Sec.
1140 S Priest Dr 85281 480-545-8755
Bryan University Post-Sec.
350 W Washington St Ste 100 85281 602-384-2555
Carsten Aveda Institute Post-Sec.
3345 S Rural Rd 85282 480-491-0449
Conservatory of Recording Arts/Sciences Post-Sec.
2300 E Broadway Rd 85282 480-858-9400
Harrison Middleton University Post-Sec.
1105 E Broadway Rd 85282 877-248-6724
International Academy of Hair Post-Sec.
4812 S Mill Ave 85282 480-964-8675
Rio Salado College Post-Sec.
2323 W 14th St 85281 480-517-8000
Sessions College of Professional Design Post-Sec.
398 S Mill Ave Ste 300 85281 480-212-1704
Southwest Coll of Naturopathic Medicine Post-Sec.
2140 E Broadway Rd 85282 480-858-9100
Southwest Institute of Healing Arts Post-Sec.
1100 E Apache Blvd 85281 480-994-9244
University of Advancing Technology Post-Sec.
2625 W Baseline Rd 85283 800-658-5744
University of Phoenix Post-Sec.
1625 W Fountainhead Pkwy 85282 602-557-2000
Western International University Post-Sec.
1601 W Fountainhead Pkwy 85282 602-943-2311

Thatcher, Graham, Pop. 4,760
Thatcher USD 4 1,500/K-12
PO Box 610 85552 928-348-7200
Paul Nelson, supt. Fax 348-7220
www.thatcherud.org
Thatcher HS 400/9-12
601 N 3rd Ave 85552 928-348-7270
Carol McAtee, prin. Fax 348-7273
Thatcher MS 200/7-8
1130 N 4th Ave 85552 928-348-7260
Hal Mullenaux, prin. Fax 348-7263

Eastern Arizona College Post-Sec.
615 N Stadium Ave 85552 800-678-3808

Tolleson, Maricopa, Pop. 6,455
Tolleson UNHSD 214 10,600/9-12
9801 W Van Buren St 85353 623-478-4000
Nora Gutierrez, supt. Fax 936-5048
www.tuhsd.org
Tolleson Union HS 1,900/9-12
9419 W Van Buren St 85353 623-478-4200
Richard Stinnett, prin. Fax 478-4226
University HS 500/9-12
9419 W Van Buren St 85353 623-478-4212
Susan Thompson, dean Fax 478-4226
Other Schools – See Avondale, Glendale, Phoenix

Union ESD 62 1,400/K-8
3834 S 91st Ave 85353 623-478-5005
Lorah Neville M.Ed., supt. Fax 478-5006
unionesd.org
Hurley Ranch S 500/3-8
8950 W Illini Rd 85353 623-478-5100
Dudley Butts, prin. Fax 742-9625

Tombstone, Cochise, Pop. 1,359
Tombstone USD 1 1,000/PK-12
PO Box 1000 85638 520-457-2217
Robert Devere, supt. Fax 457-3270
www.tombstoneschools.org
Tombstone HS 400/9-12
PO Box 1000 85638 520-457-2215
David Thursby, prin. Fax 457-3643

Tonalea, Coconino, Pop. 542
San Juan SD
Supt. — See Blanding, UT
Navajo Mountain HS 50/9-12
PO Box 10040 86044 435-678-1287
Gary Rock, admin. Fax 678-1289

Tonopah, Maricopa, Pop. 60
Saddle Mountain USD 90 1,400/K-12
38201 W Indian School Rd 85354 623-474-5115
Dr. Paul Tighe, supt. Fax 474-5190
www.smusd90.org
Tonopah Valley HS 400/9-12
38201 W Indian School Rd 85354 623-474-5201
Edgar Garcia, prin. Fax 474-5214

Topawa, Pima, Pop. 298
Baboquivari USD 40
Supt. — See Sells
Baboquivari JSHS 200/6-12
Indian Route 19 85639 520-383-6800
Yolanda Nunez, prin. Fax 383-4852

Tsaile, Apache, Pop. 1,179

Din College Post-Sec.
1 Circle Dr 86556 928-724-6600

Tuba City, Coconino, Pop. 8,486
Tuba City USD 15 1,600/PK-12
PO Box 67 86045 928-283-1000
Dr. Harold Begay, supt. Fax 283-1200
www.tcusd.org
Nizhoni Accelerated Academy 50/Alt
PO Box 67 86045 928-283-1070
Charles Henderson, dir. Fax 283-1226
Tuba City HS 700/9-12
PO Box 67 86045 928-283-1050
Fax 283-1204

Tuba City JHS 200/7-8
PO Box 67 86045 928-283-1040
Harriett Sloan-Carter, prin. Fax 283-1218

Tucson, Pima, Pop. 507,980
Altar Valley ESD 51 600/PK-8
10105 S Sasabe Rd 85736 520-822-1484
Dr. David Dumon, supt. Fax 822-1798
altarvalleyschools.org
Altar Valley MS 300/5-8
10105 S Sasabe Rd 85736 520-822-9343
Joshua Peebles, prin. Fax 822-5801

Amphitheater USD 10 14,300/PK-12
701 W Wetmore Rd 85705 520-696-5000
Patrick Nelson, supt. Fax 696-5015
www.amphi.com
Amphitheater HS 1,200/9-12
125 W Yavapai Rd 85705 520-696-5340
Jon Lansa, prin. Fax 696-5555
Amphitheater MS 600/6-8
315 E Prince Rd 85705 520-696-6230
Tassi Call, prin. Fax 696-6236
Cross MS 700/6-8
1000 W Chapala Dr 85704 520-696-5920
Andy Heinemann, prin. Fax 696-5996
La Cima MS 500/6-8
5600 N La Canada Dr 85704 520-696-6730
Christine Sullivan, prin. Fax 696-6793
Other Schools – See Oro Valley

Catalina Foothills USD 16 5,000/PK-12
2101 E River Rd 85718 520-209-7500
Dr. Mary Kamerzell, supt. Fax 209-7570
www.cfsd16.org/
Catalina Foothills HS 1,700/9-12
4300 E Sunrise Dr 85718 520-209-8300
Dr. Angela Chomokos, prin. Fax 209-8520
Esperero Canyon MS 600/6-8
5801 N Sabino Canyon Rd 85750 520-209-8100
Mary Setliff, prin. Fax 209-8170
Orange Grove MS 600/6-8
1911 E Orange Grove Rd 85718 520-209-8200
Susan Rosenthal, prin. Fax 209-8275

Flowing Wells USD 8 5,700/PK-12
1556 W Prince Rd 85705 520-696-8800
Dr. David Baker, supt. Fax 690-2400
www.flowingwellsschools.org
Flowing Wells HS 1,700/9-12
3725 N Flowing Wells Rd 85705 520-696-8002
Jim Brunenkant, prin. Fax 690-2379
Flowing Wells JHS 900/7-8
4545 N La Cholla Blvd 85705 520-696-8550
Dr. Kimberley Parkinson, prin. Fax 690-2420
Sentinel Peak HS 100/Alt
4125 W Aerie Dr 85741 520-696-8900
Alan Schmidt, prin. Fax 579-3773

Marana USD 6
Supt. — See Marana
Marana HS 2,000/9-12
12000 W Emigh Rd 85743 520-616-6400
David Mandel, prin. Fax 616-6426
Mountain View HS 1,800/9-12
3901 W Linda Vista Blvd 85742 520-579-4400
Todd Garelick, prin. Fax 579-7384
Tortolita MS 900/7-8
4101 W Hardy Rd 85742 520-579-4600
Rex Scott, prin. Fax 579-4646

Sunnyside USD 12 15,600/PK-12
2238 E Ginter Rd 85706 520-545-2000
Steve Holmes, supt. Fax 545-2120
www.susd12.org
Apollo MS 500/6-8
265 W Nebraska St 85706 520-545-4500
Roy Massani, prin. Fax 545-4516
Challenger MS 700/6-8
100 E Elvira Rd, 520-545-4600
John Benavidez, prin. Fax 545-4616
Desert View HS 2,100/9-12
4101 E Valencia Rd 85706 520-545-5100
Jose Gastelum, prin. Fax 545-5116
Gallego IS 4-8
3700 E Alvord Rd 85706 520-545-4700
Anna Warmbrand, prin. Fax 545-4716
Lauffer MS 900/6-8
5385 E Littletown Rd, 520-545-4900
Thom Luedemann, prin. Fax 545-4916
S.T.A.R. Academic Center 300/Alt
5093 S Liberty Ave 85706 520-545-2300
Marsha Flores, prin. Fax 545-2316
Sunnyside HS 2,300/9-12
1725 E Bilby Rd 85706 520-545-5300
Dr. Michael Marcos, prin. Fax 545-5316

Tanque Verde USD 13 2,000/PK-12
2300 N Tanque Verde Loop Rd 85749 520-749-5751
Kimberly C. Sharp M.Ed., supt. Fax 749-5400
www.tanqueverdeschools.org
Gray JHS 400/7-8
11150 E Tanque Verde Rd 85749 520-749-3838
Greg Miller, prin. Fax 749-9668
Tanque Verde HS 500/9-12
4201 N Melpomene Way 85749 520-760-0801
A.J. Malis, prin. Fax 749-9668

Tucson USD 1 48,500/PK-12
1010 E 10th St 85719 520-225-6000
H.T. Sanchez Ed.D., supt. Fax 225-6174
www.tusd.k12.az.us
Catalina Magnet HS 1,000/9-12
3645 E Pima St 85716 520-232-8400
Kathryn Shaw, prin. Fax 232-8401
Cholla Magnet HS 1,700/9-12
2001 W Starr Pass Blvd 85713 520-225-4000
Frank Armenta, prin. Fax 225-4001
Dodge Magnet MS 400/6-8
5831 E Pima St 85712 520-731-4100
Daniel Schulter, prin. Fax 731-4101
Doolen MS 800/6-8
2400 N Country Club Rd 85716 520-232-6900
Venessa Morales, prin. Fax 232-6901
Gridley MS 700/6-8
350 S Harrison Rd 85748 520-731-4600
Kamren Taravati, prin. Fax 731-4601

Lawrence IS 400/3-8
4850 W Jeffrey Rd, 520-908-3900
Ann Kobritz, prin. Fax 908-3901
Life Skills/Core Plus 50/Alt
1010 E 10th St 85719 520-225-2600
Israel Macias-Reyes, coord. Fax 225-2601
Magee MS 600/6-8
8300 E Speedway Blvd 85710 520-731-5000
Jason Lindsay, prin. Fax 731-5001
Mansfeld MS 800/6-8
1300 E 6th St 85719 520-225-1800
Richard Sanchez, prin. Fax 225-1801
Palo Verde Magnet HS 900/9-12
1302 S Avenida Vega 85710 520-584-7400
Eric Brock, prin. Fax 584-7441
Pistor MS 1,000/6-8
5455 S Cardinal Ave 85746 520-908-5400
Angela Wichers, prin. Fax 908-5411
Project M.O.R.E. HS 100/Alt
440 S Park Ave 85719 520-225-2600
Israel Macias-Reyes, prin. Fax 225-2601
Pueblo Magnet HS 1,500/9-12
3500 S 12th Ave 85713 520-225-4300
Augustine Romero Ph.D., prin. Fax 225-4301
Rincon HS 1,100/9-12
421 N Arcadia Ave 85711 520-232-5600
Alissa Welch, prin. Fax 232-5601
Sabino HS 1,100/9-12
5000 N Bowes Rd 85749 520-584-7700
Russell Doty, prin. Fax 584-7701
Sahuaro HS 1,800/9-12
545 N Camino Seco 85710 520-731-7100
Roberto Estrella, prin. Fax 731-7101
Santa Rita HS 900/9-12
3951 S Pantano Rd 85730 520-731-7500
James Palacios, prin. Fax 731-7501
Secrist MS 600/6-8
3400 S Houghton Rd 85730 520-731-5300
Deborah Garcia, prin. Fax 731-5301
Tucson Magnet HS 3,200/9-12
400 N 2nd Ave 85705 520-225-5000
Shawna Rodriguez, prin. Fax 225-5221
University HS 1,000/9-12
421 N Arcadia Ave 85711 520-232-5900
Amy Cislak, prin. Fax 232-5911
Utterback Magnet MS 700/6-8
3233 S Pinal Vis 85713 520-225-3500
Robin Dunbar, prin. Fax 225-3501
Vail MS 700/6-8
5350 E 16th St 85711 520-584-5400
Larissa Filler, prin. Fax 584-5401
Valencia MS 1,000/6-8
4400 W Irvington Rd 85746 520-908-4500
Michael Beck, prin. Fax 908-4501

Vail USD 20
Supt. — See Vail
Andrada Polytechnic HS 600/9-12
12960 S Houghton Rd 85747 520-879-3300
Julia Kaiser, prin. Fax 879-3301
Desert Sky MS 700/6-8
9850 E Rankin Loop 85747 520-879-2700
Katie Dabney, prin. Fax 879-2701
Empire HS 800/9-12
10701 E Mary Ann Cleveland 85747 520-879-3000
Matt Donaldson, prin. Fax 879-3001
Pantano HS 100/Alt
13010 S Houghton Rd 85747 520-879-1200
Monica Wright, prin. Fax 879-1201

Arizona Academy of Beauty Post-Sec.
5631 E Speedway Blvd 85712 520-885-4120
AZ School of Acupuncture & Oriental Med Post-Sec.
4646 E Ft Lowell Rd Ste 103 85712 520-795-0787
AZ State School for the Deaf & Blind Post-Sec.
PO Box 85000 85754 520-770-3719
Brookline College Post-Sec.
5441 E 22nd St Ste 125 85711 520-748-9799
Calvary Chapel Christian S 100/K-11
8725 E Speedway Blvd 85710 520-731-2100
Catherine Swearingen, admin.
Carondelet Saint Marys Hospital Post-Sec.
1601 W Saint Marys Rd 85745 520-622-5833
Carrington College Post-Sec.
3550 N Oracle Rd 85705 520-888-5885
Cortiva Institute - Tucson Post-Sec.
6390 E Broadway Blvd 85710 520-407-5160
Desert Christian HS 200/9-12
7525 E Speedway Blvd 85710 520-298-5817
John O'Hair, hdmstr. Fax 298-9312
Empire Beauty School Post-Sec.
3030 E Speedway Blvd 85716 520-327-6544
Fenster S 50/6-12
8505 E Ocotillo Dr 85750 520-749-3340
Tony Tsang M.S., head sch Fax 749-3349
Green Fields S 200/K-12
6000 N Camino De La Tierra 85741 520-297-2288
Rebecca Cordier M.Ed., head sch Fax 618-2599
Gregory S 300/5-12
3231 N Craycroft Rd 85712 520-327-6395
Dr. Julie Sherrill, head sch Fax 327-8276

Han University of Traditional Medicine Post-Sec.
2856 E Fort Lowell Rd 85716 520-322-6330
HDS Truck Driving Institute Post-Sec.
PO Box 17600 85731 520-721-5825
Imago Dei MS, PO Box 3056 85702 100/5-8
Rev. Anne Sawyer, head sch 520-882-4008
Immaculate Heart HS 100/9-12
625 E Magee Rd 85704 520-297-2851
Dan Ethridge, prin. Fax 797-7374
Pima Community College Post-Sec.
4905 E Broadway Blvd 85709 520-206-4500
Pima Medical Institute Post-Sec.
3350 E Grant Rd 85716 520-326-1600
Pusch Ridge Christian Academy 500/6-12
9500 N Oracle Rd 85704 520-797-0107
Allen Cooney, hdmstr. Fax 797-0598
St. Augustine Catholic HS 100/9-12
8800 E 22nd St 85710 520-751-8300
Lynn Cuffari, prin. Fax 751-8304
Salpointe Catholic HS 1,100/9-12
1545 E Copper St 85719 520-327-6581
Sr. Helen Timothy, prin. Fax 327-8477
San Miguel HS 300/9-12
6601 S San Fernando Rd, 520-294-6403
Armando Valenzuela, prin. Fax 294-6417
San Pedro Valley Academy 50/9-12
6107 E Grant Rd 85712 877-304-3329
Southwest University of Visual Arts Post-Sec.
2525 N Country Club Rd 85716 520-325-0123
The Art Institute of Tucson Post-Sec.
5099 E Grant Rd Ste 100 85712 520-318-2700
Tucson College Post-Sec.
5151 E Broadway Blvd # 155 85711 800-915-2096
University of Arizona 85721 Post-Sec.
520-621-2211
Veritas Academy of Tucson 100/K-11
PO Box 35263 85740 520-576-0427
Rev. Christopher Barnes, head sch

Vail, Pima, Pop. 9,882
Vail USD 20 11,400/K-12
PO Box 800 85641 520-879-2000
Calvin Baker, supt. Fax 879-2001
www.vail.k12.az.us
Cienega HS 1,900/9-12
12775 Mary Ann Cleveland 85641 520-879-2800
Nemer Hassey, prin. Fax 879-2801
Other Schools – See Corona, Tucson

Wellton, Yuma, Pop. 2,851
Antelope UNHSD 50 300/9-12
9168 S Avenue 36 E 85356 928-785-3344
Dr. Andrew Smith, supt. Fax 785-9566
www.antelopeunion.org
Antelope Union HS 300/9-12
9168 S Avenue 36 E 85356 928-785-3344
Barton Rud, prin. Fax 785-9566

Whiteriver, Navajo, Pop. 4,055
Whiteriver USD 20 2,300/PK-12
PO Box 190 85941 928-358-5800
Dr. Rea Goklish, supt. Fax 358-5801
www.wusd.us
Alchesay HS 500/9-12
PO Box 190 85941 928-358-5690
Leeann Lacapa, prin. Fax 358-5691
Canyon Day JHS 400/6-8
PO Box 190 85941 928-358-5680
Vajra Miller, prin. Fax 358-5681

East Fork Lutheran S 100/K-10
PO Box 489 85941 928-338-4455
Darrell Dobberpuhl, prin. Fax 338-1575

Wickenburg, Maricopa, Pop. 6,301
Wickenburg USD 9 1,500/PK-12
40 W Yavapai St 85390 928-668-5350
Dr. Howard Carlson, supt. Fax 668-5390
www.wickenburgschools.org/
Vulture Peak MS 200/6-8
920 S Vulture Mine Rd 85390 928-684-6700
Jennifer Lougee, prin. Fax 684-6746
Wickenburg HS 700/9-12
1090 S Vulture Mine Rd 85390 928-684-6600
Derek Streeter, prin. Fax 684-6628

Gospel Outreach Christian S 50/PK-12
515 W Wickenburg Way 85390 928-684-5227
Victor Bedoian, supt. Fax 684-2878
Wickenburg Christian Academy 100/PK-12
260 W Yavapai St 85390 928-684-5916

Willcox, Cochise, Pop. 3,704
Willcox USD 13 1,200/PK-12
480 N Bisbee Ave 85643 520-384-8600
Kevin Davis, supt. Fax 384-4401
www.wusd13.org
Willcox HS 400/9-12
240 N Bisbee Ave 85643 520-384-8601
Jeff Thompson, prin. Fax 384-4006

Willcox MS 400/5-8
360 N Bisbee Ave 85643 520-384-8602
Mike Patterson, prin. Fax 384-6322

Williams, Coconino, Pop. 2,960
Williams USD 2 600/PK-12
PO Box 427 86046 928-635-4473
Rick Honsinger, supt. Fax 635-4767
www.wusd2.org
Williams HS 200/9-12
PO Box 427 86046 928-635-4474
Dr. Carissa Morrison, prin. Fax 635-2796

Winkelman, Gila, Pop. 352
Hayden-Winkelman USD 41 200/K-12
PO Box 409, 520-356-7876
Jeff Gregorich, supt. Fax 356-7303
www.hwusd.org
Hayden HS 100/9-12
PO Box 409, 520-356-7876
Jeff Gregorich, prin. Fax 356-7303

Winslow, Navajo, Pop. 9,382
Winslow USD 1 1,900/PK-12
PO Box 580 86047 928-288-8101
Lance Heister, supt. Fax 288-8292
www.wusd1.org
Winslow HS 700/9-12
PO Box 580 86047 928-288-8100
Chris Gilmore, prin. Fax 288-8290
Winslow JHS 300/7-8
PO Box 580 86047 928-288-8300
Darlene McCauley, prin. Fax 288-8393

Young, Gila, Pop. 657
Young ESD 5 50/PK-12
PO Box 390 85554 928-462-3244
Linda Cheney, supt. Fax 462-3283
www.youngschool.org
Young S 50/PK-12
PO Box 390 85554 928-462-3244
Linda Cheney, prin. Fax 462-3283

Yuma, Yuma, Pop. 91,424
Crane ESD 13 6,100/PK-8
4250 W 16th St 85364 928-373-3400
Robert Klee, supt. Fax 782-6831
www.craneschools.org
Centennial MS 700/7-8
2650 W 20th St 85364 928-373-3300
Helen Coffeen, prin. Fax 376-7742
Crane MS 800/7-8
4450 W 32nd St 85364 928-373-3200
Kari Neumann, prin. Fax 344-6821

Yuma ESD 1 8,900/PK-8
450 W 6th St 85364 928-502-4300
Darwin Stiffler, supt. Fax 502-4442
www.yuma.org
Castle Dome MS 800/6-8
2353 S Otondo Dr 85365 928-502-7300
Lori Sheffield, prin. Fax 341-1700
Fourth Avenue JHS 400/6-8
450 S 4th Ave 85364 928-502-7000
Jose Cazares, prin. Fax 783-2195
Gila Vista JHS 500/6-8
2245 S Arizona Ave 85364 928-502-7100
Thad Dugan, prin. Fax 782-1483
Watson MS 400/6-8
9851 E 28th St 85365 928-502-7400
Donna Franklin, prin. Fax 502-7403
Woodard JHS 700/6-8
2250 S 8th Ave 85364 928-502-7200
Daniel Acosta, prin. Fax 782-4596

Yuma UNHSD 70 10,700/9-12
3150 S Avenue A 85364 928-502-4600
Toni Badone, supt. Fax 344-9157
www.yumaunion.org/
Cibola HS 2,600/9-12
4100 W 20th St 85364 928-502-5700
Tim Brienza, prin. Fax 502-6046
Gila Ridge HS 1,800/9-12
7150 E 24th St 85365 928-502-6400
Shawn Wehrer, prin. Fax 502-6749
Kofa HS 2,200/9-12
3100 S Avenue A 85364 928-502-5400
Mike Sharp, prin. Fax 502-5693
Vista Alternative S 200/Alt
2350 S Virginia Dr 85364 928-343-2521
Laura Campbell, prin. Fax 343-2582
Yuma HS 1,300/9-12
400 S 6th Ave 85364 928-502-5000
Faith Klostreich, prin. Fax 502-5338
Other Schools – See San Luis

Arizona Western College Post-Sec.
PO Box 929 85366 928-317-6000
Yuma Catholic HS 300/9-12
2100 W 28th St 85364 928-317-7900
Rhett Stallworth, prin. Fax 317-8558

ARKANSAS

ARKANSAS DEPARTMENT OF EDUCATION
4 State Capitol Rm 304A, Little Rock 72201
Telephone 501-682-4475
Fax 501-682-1079
Website http://www.arkansased.org/

Commissioner of Education Johnny Key

ARKANSAS BOARD OF EDUCATION
4 State Capitol, Little Rock 72201

Chairperson Toyce Newton

EDUCATION SERVICE COOPERATIVES (ESC)

Arch Ford ESC
Phillip Young, dir. 501-354-2269
101 Bulldog Dr, Plumerville 72127 Fax 354-0167
www.afsc.k12.ar.us/

Arkansas River ESC
Barbara Warren, dir. 870-730-2900
912 W 6th Ave, Pine Bluff 71601 Fax 534-2847
www.aresc.k12.ar.us

Crowley's Ridge ESC
John Manning, dir. 870-578-5426
1606 Pine Grove Ln Fax 578-5896
Harrisburg 72432
crowleys.crsc.k12.ar.us/

Dawson ESC
Ron Wright, dir. 870-246-3077
711 Clinton St Ste 201 Fax 246-5892
Arkadelphia 71923
dawsonesc.com

De Queen/Mena ESC
John Ponder, dir. 870-386-2251
PO Box 110, Gillham 71841 Fax 386-7731
dmesc.org

Great Rivers ESC
Suzann McCommon, dir. 870-338-6461
PO Box 2837, West Helena 72390 Fax 338-7905
www.grsc.k12.ar.us/

Northcentral Arkansas ESC
Gerald Cooper, dir. 870-581-3600
PO Box 739, Melbourne 72556 Fax 368-4920
naesc.k12.ar.us

Northeast Arkansas ESC
Donna Harris, dir., 211 W Hickory St 870-886-7717
Walnut Ridge 72476 Fax 886-7719
nea.k12.ar.us

Northwest Arkansas ESC
Dr. Charles Cudney, dir. 479-267-7450
4 N Double Springs Rd Fax 267-7456
Farmington 72730
www.starfishnw.org

Ozarks Unlimited Resource Cooperative
Rick Nance, dir. 870-429-9100
5823 Resource Dr, Harrison 72601 Fax 429-9099
www.oursc.k12.ar.us

South Central ESC
Marsha Daniels, dir. 870-836-1600
2235 California Ave SW Fax 836-1629
Camden 71701
www.scsc.k12.ar.us

Southeast Arkansas ESC
Karen Eoff, dir. 870-367-6848
1022 Scogin Dr, Monticello 71655 Fax 367-9877
se.sesc.k12.ar.us/

Southwest Arkansas ESC
Phoebe Bailey, dir. 870-777-3076
2502 S Main St, Hope 71801 Fax 777-5793
www.swaec.org

Western Arkansas ESC
Roy Hester, dir. 479-965-2191
3010 Highway 22 E Ste A Fax 965-2723
Branch 72928
sites.google.com/a/wscstarfish.com/waesc/home

Wilbur D. Mills ESC
Jeff Williams, dir. 501-882-5467
PO Box 850, Beebe 72012 Fax 882-2155
www.wilbur.k12.ar.us

PUBLIC, PRIVATE AND CATHOLIC SECONDARY SCHOOLS

Alexander, Saline, Pop. 2,843
Bryant SD
Supt. — See Bryant
Bethel MS 900/6-8
5415 Northlake Rd 72002 501-316-0937
Todd Sellers, prin. Fax 653-5830

Avilla Christian Academy 100/PK-12
302 Avilla E 72002 501-408-4631
Rich Meyers, prin.

Alma, Crawford, Pop. 5,279
Alma SD 3,300/K-12
PO Box 2359 72921 479-632-4791
David Woolly, supt. Fax 632-4793
www.almasd.net
Alma HS 1,100/9-12
PO Box 2139 72921 479-632-2162
Jerry Valentine, prin. Fax 632-5070
Alma MS 800/6-8
PO Box 2229 72921 479-632-2168
Bob Wolfe, prin. Fax 632-2160

Alpena, Boone, Pop. 380
Alpena SD 500/K-12
PO Box 270 72611 870-437-2220
Andrea Martin, supt. Fax 437-2133
alpenaschools.k12.ar.us/
Alpena JSHS 200/7-12
PO Box 270 72611 870-437-2228
Steven Watkins, prin. Fax 437-5638

Amity, Clark, Pop. 719
Centerpoint SD 1,000/PK-12
755 Highway 8 E 71921 870-356-2912
Dan Breshears, supt. Fax 356-4637
www.goknights.us
Centerpoint HS 500/6-12
755 Highway 8 E 71921 870-356-3612
Nic Mounts, prin. Fax 356-4519

Arkadelphia, Clark, Pop. 10,545
Arkadelphia SD 2,000/K-12
235 N 11th St 71923 870-246-5564
Donnie Whitten, supt. Fax 246-1144
www.arkadelphiaschools.org
Arkadelphia HS 600/9-12
401 High School Rd 71923 870-246-7373
David Maxwell, prin. Fax 246-1154
Goza MS 400/6-8
1305 Caddo St 71923 870-246-4291
Angela Garner, prin. Fax 246-1153

Arkadelphia Beauty College Post-Sec.
203 S 26th St 71923 870-246-6726
Henderson State University Post-Sec.
1100 Henderson St 71999 870-230-5000
Ouachita Baptist University Post-Sec.
410 Ouachita St 71998 870-245-5000

Armorel, Mississippi
Armorel SD 400/PK-12
PO Box 99 72310 870-763-6639
Sally Bennett, supt. Fax 763-0028
armorel.k12.ar.us/
Armorel JSHS 200/7-12
PO Box 99 72310 870-763-7121
Teresa Lawrence, prin. Fax 763-7020

Ashdown, Little River, Pop. 4,622
Ashdown SD 1,200/K-12
751 Rankin St 71822 870-898-3208
Jason Sanders, supt. Fax 898-3709
www.ashdownschools.org
Ashdown HS 500/9-12
171 S Locust St 71822 870-898-3562
Kay York, prin. Fax 898-4452
Ashdown JHS 300/6-8
600 S Ellen Dr 71822 870-898-5138
James Jones, prin. Fax 898-4472

Atkins, Pope, Pop. 2,978
Atkins SD 1,000/K-12
307 N Church St 72823 479-641-7871
Joe Fisher, supt. Fax 641-7569
www.atkinsschools.org
Atkins HS 300/9-12
403 Avenue 3 NW 72823 479-641-7872
Mary Beth Cox, prin. Fax 641-1306
Atkins MS 300/5-8
611 NW 4th St 72823 479-641-1008
Darrell Webb, prin. Fax 641-5504

Augusta, Woodruff, Pop. 2,163
Augusta SD 500/PK-12
10 Red Devil Dr 72006 870-347-2241
Cathy Tanner, supt. Fax 347-5423
www.augustasd.org
Augusta HS 200/7-12
10 Red Devil Dr 72006 870-347-2515
Lisa Martin, prin. Fax 347-8113

Bald Knob, White, Pop. 2,847
Bald Knob SD 1,200/K-12
103 W Park Ave 72010 501-724-3273
Bradley Roberts, supt. Fax 724-6621
www.baldknobschools.org
Bald Knob HS 400/9-12
901 N Hickory St 72010 501-724-3843
Thomas Garner, prin. Fax 724-8323
Bald Knob MS 300/5-8
103 W Park Ave 72010 501-724-5652
Lori Finley, prin. Fax 724-2062

Batesville, Independence, Pop. 10,067
Batesville SD 3,000/K-12
955 Water St 72501 870-793-6831
Gary Anderson, supt. Fax 793-6760
www.batesvilleschools.com
Batesville HS 600/10-12
1 Pioneer Dr 72501 870-793-6846
David Campbell, prin. Fax 793-0607
Batesville JHS 700/7-9
2 Pioneer Dr 72501 870-793-7533
Matt Douglas, prin. Fax 793-0626
Other Schools – See Cushman

Southside SD 1,700/PK-12
70 Scott Dr 72501 870-251-2341
Roger Rich, supt. Fax 251-3316
southsideschools.org
Southside HS 500/9-12
70 Scott Dr 72501 870-251-2662
Roger Reid, prin. Fax 251-3316
Southside JHS 200/7-8
70 Scott Dr 72501 870-251-4003
George Sitkowski, prin. Fax 251-4011

Bee-Jay's Hairstyling Academy Post-Sec.
130 W Main St 72501 870-793-3898
Lyon College Post-Sec.
PO Box 2317 72503 870-307-7000
University of Arkansas Community College Post-Sec.
PO Box 3350 72503 870-612-2000

Bauxite, Saline, Pop. 486
Bauxite SD 1,500/PK-12
800 School St 72011 501-557-5453
Matt Donaghy, supt. Fax 557-2235
www.edline.net/pages/Bauxite_SD
Bauxite HS 500/9-12
800 School St 72011 501-557-5303
Ann Webb, prin. Fax 557-2274
Bauxite MS 400/6-8
6725 Benton Rd 72011 501-557-5491
Kim Arnold, prin. Fax 557-5509

Eaton Barber College Post-Sec.
8333 Sagebrush Cir 72011 501-375-0211

Bay, Craighead, Pop. 1,780
Bay SD 600/K-12
PO Box 39 72411 870-781-3296
Oliver Layne, supt. Fax 781-3712
www.edline.net/pages/bay
Bay JSHS 300/7-12
PO Box 39 72411 870-781-3297
Jodi Cobb, prin. Fax 781-3687

Bearden, Ouachita, Pop. 942
Bearden SD 600/K-12
100 Oak Ave 71720 870-687-2236
Denny Rozenberg, supt. Fax 687-3683
www.beardenschools.org
Bearden JSHS 300/7-12
635 N Plum St 71720 870-687-2913
Felecia Doster, prin. Fax 687-2514

Beebe, White, Pop. 7,140
Beebe SD 3,000/PK-12
1201 W Center St 72012 501-882-5463
Dr. Belinda Shook, supt. Fax 882-5465
beebebadgers.org
Beebe HS 900/9-12
1201 W Center St 72012 501-882-5463
Scott Jennings, prin. Fax 882-8404
Beebe JHS 500/7-8
1201 W Center St 72012 501-882-5463
Chris Ellis, prin. Fax 882-8416

Arkansas State University - Beebe Post-Sec.
PO Box 1000 72012 501-882-3600

Bee Branch, Van Buren
South Side SD 500/PK-12
334 Southside Rd 72013 501-654-2633
Billy Jackson, supt. Fax 654-2336
www.ssbb.k12.ar.us
South Side JSHS 200/7-12
334 Southside Rd 72013 501-654-2242
Tim Smith, prin. Fax 654-2331

Benton, Saline, Pop. 30,248
Benton SD 4,900/K-12
PO Box 939 72018 501-778-4861
Dr. Mike Skelton, supt. Fax 776-5777
ww2.bentonschools.org
Benton HS 1,100/10-12
211 N Border St 72015 501-778-3288
Curt Barger, prin. Fax 776-5783
Benton JHS 800/8-9
411 N Border St 72015 501-778-7698
Lori Kellogg, prin. Fax 776-5744

Harmony Grove SD 800/K-12
2621 N Highway 229 72015 501-778-6271
Daniel Henley, supt. Fax 778-6271
www.harmonygrovesd.org
Harmony Grove HS 300/10-12
2621 N Highway 229 72015 501-776-2337
Chad Withers, prin. Fax 776-2337
Harmony Grove JHS 7-9
2621 N Highway 229 72015 501-778-6907
Sarah Gober, prin. Fax 778-6907

Bentonville, Benton, Pop. 34,453
Bentonville SD 15,100/PK-12
500 Tiger Blvd 72712 479-254-5000
Michael Poore, supt. Fax 271-1159
bentonvillek12.org
Bentonville HS 4,100/9-12
1801 SE J St 72712 479-254-5100
Jack Loyd, prin. Fax 271-1184
Fulbright JHS 700/7-8
5303 SW Bright Rd 72712 479-802-7000
Bradley Webber, prin.
Lincoln JHS 800/7-8
1206 Leopard Ln 72712 479-254-5250
Don Hoover, prin. Fax 271-1128
Washington JHS 800/7-8
1501 NE Wildcat Way 72712 479-254-5345
Tim Sparacino, prin. Fax 271-1191

Ambassadors For Christ Academy 100/PK-12
PO Box 924 72712 479-273-5635
David Welshenbaugh, admin. Fax 273-0684
Northwest Arkansas Community College Post-Sec.
1 College Dr 72712 479-636-9222

Bergman, Boone, Pop. 427
Bergman SD 1,100/K-12
PO Box 1 72615 870-741-5213
Joe Couch, supt. Fax 741-6701
bergman.k12.ar.us
Bergman HS 300/9-12
PO Box 1 72615 870-741-1414
Tami Richey, prin. Fax 741-6701
Bergman MS 300/5-8
PO Box 1 72615 870-741-8557
Sarah Alexander, prin. Fax 741-3490

Berryville, Carroll, Pop. 5,283
Berryville SD 2,000/K-12
902 W Trimble Ave 72616 870-423-7065
Owen Powell, supt. Fax 423-6824
bobcat.k12.ar.us
Berryville HS 600/9-12
902 W Trimble Ave 72616 870-480-4632
David Gilmore, prin. Fax 480-4635
Berryville MS 500/6-8
902 W Trimble Ave 72616 870-480-4633
John McClellan, prin. Fax 480-4634

Bigelow, Perry, Pop. 315
East End SD 600/K-12
114 W Panther Dr 72016 501-759-2808
Dr. Doug Harris, supt. Fax 759-2667
eastendpanthers.com
Bigelow JSHS 300/7-12
114 W Panther Dr 72016 501-759-2602
Dr. Brad Gist, prin. Fax 759-3081

Bismarck, Hot Spring
Bismarck SD 1,000/K-12
11636 Highway 84 71929 501-865-4888
Susan Stewart, supt. Fax 865-3626
www.bismarcklions.net/
Bismarck HS 300/9-12
11636 Highway 84 71929 501-865-4541
Larry Newsom, prin. Fax 865-4542
Bismarck MS 300/5-8
11636 Highway 84 71929 501-865-4543
Michael Spraggins, prin. Fax 865-4505

Blevins, Hempstead, Pop. 310
Blevins SD 500/K-12
PO Box 98 71825 870-874-2801
Billy Lee, supt. Fax 874-2889
blevinshornets.weebly.com/
Blevins JSHS 200/7-12
PO Box 98 71825 870-874-2281
Jeffrey Steed, prin. Fax 874-2450

Blytheville, Mississippi, Pop. 15,417
Blytheville SD 2,500/PK-12
PO Box 1169 72316 870-762-2053
Richard Atwill, supt. Fax 762-0168
www.blythevilleschools.com
Blytheville HS - A New Tech S 800/9-12
600 N 10th St 72315 870-762-2772
Bobby Ashley, prin. Fax 762-0175
Blytheville MS 500/6-8
700 Chickasawba St 72315 870-762-2983
Mike Wallace, prin. Fax 762-0174

Arkansas Northeastern College Post-Sec.
2501 S Division St 72315 870-762-1020

Bonnerdale, Hot Spring, Pop. 50

Ewing Jr Academy 50/K-10
709 Adventist Church Rd 71933 870-356-2780

Booneville, Logan, Pop. 3,888
Booneville SD 1,300/K-12
381 W 7th St 72927 479-675-3504
John Parrish, supt. Fax 675-3186
www.booneville.k12.ar.us/
Booneville HS 300/10-12
945 N Plum St 72927 479-675-3277
Trent Goff, prin. Fax 675-3214
Booneville JHS 300/7-9
835 E 8th St 72927 479-675-5247
Josh Walker, prin. Fax 675-0793

Bradford, White, Pop. 744
Bradford SD 500/K-12
PO Box 60 72020 501-344-2707
Arthur Dunn, supt. Fax 344-2706
bradford.k12.ar.us
Bradford JSHS 200/7-12
PO Box 60 72020 501-344-2607
Rick Wood, prin. Fax 344-2706

Bradley, Lafayette, Pop. 627
Emerson-Taylor-Bradley SD
Supt. — See Taylor
Bradley HS 200/7-12
521 School Dr 71826 870-894-3316
Mike Lyons, prin. Fax 894-3344

Branch, Franklin, Pop. 358
County Line SD 500/PK-12
12092 W State Highway 22 72928 479-635-2222
Taylor Gattis, supt. Fax 635-2087
indians.wsc.k12.ar.us
County Line JSHS 200/7-12
12092 W State Highway 22 72928 479-635-2441
Eric Parsons, prin. Fax 635-2452

Brinkley, Monroe, Pop. 3,151
Brinkley SD 500/K-12
200 Tigers Dr 72021 870-734-5000
Dr. Arthur Tucker, supt. Fax 734-5187
www.brinkleyschools.com
Brinkley JSHS 300/7-12
100 Tigers Dr 72021 870-734-5005
Samuel White, prin. Fax 734-1354

Brockwell, Izard
Izard County Consolidated SD 500/K-12
PO Box 115 72517 870-258-7700
Fred Walker, supt. Fax 258-3140
icc.k12.ar.us/
Izard County Consolidated HS 100/9-12
PO Box 115 72517 870-258-7788
David Harmon, prin. Fax 258-3140
Izard County Consolidated MS 100/5-8
PO Box 115 72517 870-258-7788
William McBride, prin. Fax 258-3140

Brookland, Craighead, Pop. 1,612
Brookland SD 1,700/PK-12
200 W School St 72417 870-932-2080
Keith McDaniel, supt. Fax 932-2088
www.brooklandbearcats.org
Brookland HS 400/10-12
100 W School St 72417 870-932-2080
Steven Hovis, prin. Fax 932-1251
Brookland JHS 400/7-9
100 W School St 72417 870-932-8610
Bart Hyde, prin. Fax 974-9762

Bryant, Saline, Pop. 16,446
Bryant SD 8,900/PK-12
200 NW 4th St 72022 501-847-5600
Dr. Tom W. Kimbrell, supt. Fax 847-5695
www.bryantschools.org
Bryant HS 2,700/9-12
200 NW 4th St 72022 501-847-5605
Dr. Jay Pickering, prin. Fax 847-5612
Bryant MS 1,100/6-8
200 NW 4th St 72022 501-847-5651
Todd Sellers, prin. Fax 847-5654
Other Schools – See Alexander

Arkansas Christian Academy 200/PK-12
21815 Highway 30 West 72022 501-847-0112
Tina Goddard, admin. Fax 847-0177

Burdette, Mississippi, Pop. 191

Cotton Boll Technical Institute Post-Sec.
PO Box 36 72321 870-763-1486

Cabot, Lonoke, Pop. 23,349
Cabot SD 9,600/PK-12
602 N Lincoln St 72023 501-843-3363
Dr. Tony Thurman, supt. Fax 843-0576
www.cabotschools.org
Cabot Freshman Academy 9-9
18 Spirit Dr 72023 501-743-3576
Tanya Spillane, prin. Fax 941-1505
Cabot HS 2,100/10-12
401 N Lincoln St 72023 501-843-3562
Henry Hawkins, prin. Fax 843-4231
Cabot JHS North 800/7-8
38 Spirit Dr 72023 501-743-3572
Charlotte Sandage, prin. Fax 605-8472
Cabot JHS South 800/7-8
39 Panther Trl 72023 501-743-3573
John West, prin. Fax 941-7746

Calico Rock, Izard, Pop. 1,531
Calico Rock SD 400/K-12
PO Box 220 72519 870-297-8339
Jerry Skidmore, supt. Fax 297-4233
pirates.k12.ar.us/
Calico Rock JSHS 200/7-12
PO Box 220 72519 870-297-3745
Anita Cook, prin. Fax 297-3168

Camden, Ouachita, Pop. 11,970
Camden Fairview SD 2,400/K-12
625 Clifton St 71701 870-836-4193
Mark Keith, supt. Fax 836-6039
cfsd.k12.ar.us
Camden Fairview HS 700/9-12
1750 Cash Rd SW 71701 870-837-1300
Gary Steelman, prin. Fax 837-2330
Camden Fairview MS 500/6-8
647 J A Dooley Womack Dr 71701 870-836-9361
Edgar Cooper, prin. Fax 836-3717

Harmony Grove SD 1,000/K-12
401 Ouachita 88 71701 870-574-0971
Walton Pigott, supt. Fax 574-2765
www.hgsd1.com
Harmony Grove JSHS 400/7-12
401 Ouachita 88 71701 870-574-0867
Jeff Mock, prin. Fax 574-2765
Other Schools – See Sparkman

Southern Arkansas University Tech Post-Sec.
100 Carr Rd 71701 870-574-4500
Victory Christian S K-12
1244 Maul Rd 71701 870-836-6300

Carlisle, Lonoke, Pop. 2,193
Carlisle SD 800/PK-12
520 Center St 72024 870-552-3931
Jason Clark, supt. Fax 552-7967
bison.wmsc.k12.ar.us
Carlisle JSHS 400/7-12
520 Center St 72024 870-552-3931
Brad Horn, prin. Fax 552-3032

Cave City, Sharp, Pop. 1,876
Cave City SD 1,000/K-12
PO Box 600 72521 870-283-5391
Steven Green, supt. Fax 283-6887
www.cavecity.k12.ar.us
Cave City HS 400/9-12
PO Box 600 72521 870-283-3333
Marc Walling, prin. Fax 283-3322
Cave City MS 200/6-8
PO Box 600 72521 870-283-5392
Mark Smith, prin. Fax 266-3258

Cedarville, Crawford, Pop. 1,339
Cedarville SD 900/K-12
PO Box 97 72932 479-474-7220
Kerry Schneider, supt. Fax 410-1804
www.cedarvilleschools.org
Cedarville HS 300/9-12
PO Box 97 72932 479-474-7021
Darren Busch, prin. Fax 410-1804
Cedarville MS 300/5-8
PO Box 97 72932 479-474-5847
Chris Ross, prin. Fax 471-7036

Center Ridge, Conway, Pop. 385
Nemo Vista SD 500/PK-12
5690 Highway 9 72027 501-893-2925
Cody Beene, supt. Fax 893-2367
socs.nemo.k12.ar.us
Nemo Vista HS 100/9-12
5690 Highway 9 72027 501-893-2811
Shade Gilbert, prin. Fax 893-6472
Nemo Vista MS 100/6-8
5690 Highway 9 72027 501-893-6494
Tresa Virden, prin. Fax 893-6494

Centerton, Benton, Pop. 9,305

Life Way Christian S 500/PK-12
PO Box 220 72719 479-795-9322
Dr. Luke Bowers, admin. Fax 795-9399

Charleston, Franklin, Pop. 2,451
Charleston SD 800/PK-12
PO Box 188 72933 479-965-7160
Jeff Stubblefield, supt. Fax 965-9989
tigers.wsc.k12.ar.us/

Charleston HS 300/9-12
PO Box 188 72933 479-965-7150
Shane Storey, prin. Fax 965-9989
Charleston MS 100/5-8
PO Box 188 72933 479-965-7170
Melissa Moore, prin. Fax 965-7949

Clarendon, Monroe, Pop. 1,643
Clarendon SD 600/K-12
PO Box 248 72029 870-747-3351
Lee Vent, supt. Fax 747-5963
lions.grsc.k12.ar.us
Clarendon HS 300/7-12
PO Box 248 72029 870-747-3326
Cathy Tanne, prin. Fax 747-5444

Clarksville, Johnson, Pop. 9,041
Clarksville SD 2,600/K-12
1701 W Clark Rd 72830 479-705-3200
Dr. David Hopkins, supt. Fax 754-3748
www.csdar.org/
Clarksville JHS 600/7-9
1801 W Clark Rd 72830 479-705-3224
Paul Dean, prin. Fax 754-7431
Clarksville SHS 500/10-12
1703 W Clark Rd 72830 479-705-3212
John Burke, prin. Fax 754-2492

University of the Ozarks Post-Sec.
415 N College Ave 72830 479-979-1000

Clinton, Van Buren, Pop. 2,548
Clinton SD 1,300/K-12
765 Yellowjacket Ln 72031 501-508-2030
Andrew Vining, supt. Fax 745-2475
www.clintonsd.org
Clinton HS 300/10-12
489 Yellowjacket Ln 72031 501-508-2035
Frank McMurry, prin. Fax 745-2450
Clinton JHS 300/7-9
443 Yellowjacket Ln 72031 501-508-2020
Michael Wells, prin. Fax 745-6065

Conway, Faulkner, Pop. 57,689
Conway SD 10,000/PK-12
2220 Prince St 72034 501-450-4800
Dr. Greg Murry, supt. Fax 450-4898
www.conwayschools.org
Conway Area Career Center Vo/Tech
2300 Prince St 72034 501-450-4888
Donna Lyon, admin. Fax 450-6658
Conway HS 2,100/10-12
2300 Prince St 72034 501-450-4880
Jason Lawrence, prin. Fax 450-4884
Conway JHS 1,400/8-9
1815 Prince St 72034 501-450-4860
Ben Darley, prin. Fax 450-6651

Arkansas Beauty School - Conway Post-Sec.
1061 Markham St 72032 501-329-8303
Central Baptist College Post-Sec.
1501 College Ave 72034 501-329-6872
Conway Christian S 500/PK-12
500 E German Ln 72032 501-336-9067
Jason Carson, pres. Fax 336-9251
Hendrix College Post-Sec.
1600 Washington Ave 72032 501-329-6811
St. Joseph S 500/K-12
502 Front St 72032 501-327-1204
Diane Wolfe, prin. Fax 513-6805
University of Central Arkansas Post-Sec.
201 Donaghey Ave 72035 501-450-5000

Corning, Clay, Pop. 3,348
Corning SD 1,000/K-12
PO Box 479 72422 870-857-6818
Kellee Smith, supt. Fax 857-5086
www.corningschools.k12.ar.us/
Corning JSHS 500/7-12
PO Box 479 72422 870-857-3041
Andrew Eubanks, prin. Fax 857-6797

Cotter, Baxter, Pop. 947
Cotter SD 700/K-12
PO Box 70 72626 870-435-6171
Donald Sharp, supt. Fax 435-1300
www.cotterschools.net
Cotter JSHS 300/7-12
PO Box 70 72626 870-435-6323
Amanda Britt, prin. Fax 435-1300

Cove, Polk, Pop. 372
Cossatot River SD
Supt. — See Wickes
Cossatot River HS 400/7-12
6330 Highway 71 S 71937 870-387-4200
Ladonna White, prin. Fax 387-4250

Crossett, Ashley, Pop. 5,460
Crossett SD 1,900/PK-12
219 Main St 71635 870-364-3112
Gary Williams, supt. Fax 304-2525
www.crossettschools.org
Crossett HS 500/9-12
301 W 9th Ave 71635 870-364-2625
Alicia Brown, prin. Fax 364-4792
Crossett MS 500/5-8
100 Petersburg Rd 71635 870-364-4712
Lou Gregorio, prin. Fax 364-3771

University of Arkansas - Monticello Post-Sec.
1326 Highway 52 W 71635 870-364-6414

Cushman, Independence, Pop. 440
Batesville SD
Supt. — See Batesville
White River Academy Alt
PO Box 370 72526 870-698-1145
Roger Head, dir. Fax 698-1455

Danville, Yell, Pop. 2,373
Danville SD 800/K-12
PO Box 939 72833 479-495-4800
Gregg Grant, supt. Fax 495-4803
www.dps-littlejohns.net
Danville HS 200/9-12
PO Box 939 72833 479-495-4810
Kim Foster, prin. Fax 495-4832
Danville MS 200/5-8
PO Box 939 72833 479-495-4827
Teddy Qualls, prin. Fax 495-4831

Dardanelle, Yell, Pop. 4,680
Dardanelle SD 1,900/K-12
102 S Front St 72834 479-229-4111
John Thompson, supt. Fax 229-1387
www.dardanellepublicschools.org
Dardanelle HS 600/9-12
1079 N State Highway 28 72834 479-229-4655
Marcia Lawrence, prin. Fax 229-4687
Dardanelle MS 300/6-8
2306 State Highway 7 N 72834 479-229-4550
John Keeling, prin. Fax 229-1697

Decatur, Benton, Pop. 1,637
Decatur SD 600/PK-12
1498 Stadium Ave 72722 479-752-3986
Jeff Gravette, supt. Fax 752-2490
www.decatursd.com
Decatur JSHS 200/7-12
1498 Stadium Ave 72722 479-752-3983
Toby Conrad, prin. Fax 752-2491

Deer, Newton
Deer / Mt. Judea SD 400/K-12
PO Box 56 72628 870-428-5433
Andrew Curry, supt. Fax 428-5901
deermtjudea.k12.ar.us
Deer JSHS 100/7-12
PO Box 56 72628 870-428-5288
Elvis Middleton, prin. Fax 428-5901
Other Schools – See Mount Judea

De Queen, Sevier, Pop. 6,482
De Queen SD 2,300/K-12
101 N 9th St 71832 870-584-4312
Bruce Hill, supt. Fax 642-8881
www.dequeenleopards.org
De Queen HS 500/10-12
1803 W Coulter Ave 71832 870-642-2426
Bryan Blackwood, prin. Fax 642-4931
De Queen JHS 300/8-9
1803 W Coulter Ave 71832 870-642-3077
William Huddleston, prin. Fax 642-3355

Cossatot Community College Univ. of AR Post-Sec.
PO Box 960 71832 870-584-4471

Dermott, Chicot, Pop. 2,294
Dermott SD 400/K-12
PO Box 380 71638 870-538-1000
Kristi Ridgell, supt. Fax 538-1005
www.dermott.k12.ar.us
Dermott JSHS 200/7-12
PO Box 380 71638 870-538-1030
Heather Hardin, prin. Fax 538-1067

Des Arc, Prairie, Pop. 1,696
Des Arc SD 600/K-12
600 Main St 72040 870-256-4164
Nicholas Hill, supt. Fax 256-3701
www.desarc.wmsc.k12.ar.us
Des Arc JSHS 300/7-12
600 Main St 72040 870-256-4166
Joshua Kessler, prin. Fax 256-3701

De Witt, Arkansas, Pop. 3,250
De Witt SD 1,300/PK-12
PO Box 700 72042 870-946-3576
Lynne Dardenne, supt. Fax 946-1491
www.dewittschooldistrict.net
De Witt HS 400/9-12
1614 S Grandview Dr 72042 870-946-4661
Marty Weaver, prin. Fax 946-2746
De Witt MS 300/6-8
1209 W 16th St 72042 870-946-3708
Julie Blevins, prin. Fax 946-1301

Dierks, Howard, Pop. 1,118
Dierks SD 600/K-12
PO Box 124 71833 870-286-2191
Holly Cothren, supt. Fax 286-2450
www.dierksschools.org
Dierks JSHS 300/7-12
PO Box 124 71833 870-286-3234
Jody Cowart, prin. Fax 286-2450

Donaldson, Hot Spring, Pop. 298
Ouachita SD 500/K-12
166 Schoolhouse Rd 71941 501-384-2318
Ronnie Kissire, supt. Fax 384-5615
www.ouachitasd.org
Ouachita JSHS 200/7-12
258 Schoolhouse Rd 71941 501-384-2323
Dr. David Thigpen, prin. Fax 384-5614

Dover, Pope, Pop. 1,350
Dover SD 1,300/K-12
PO Box 325 72837 479-331-2916
Jerry Owens, supt. Fax 331-2205
www.doverschools.net
Dover HS 400/9-12
PO Box 325 72837 479-331-2120
Jo Lynn Taverner, prin. Fax 331-3286
Dover MS 300/5-8
PO Box 325 72837 479-331-4814
Donald Forehand, prin. Fax 331-4965

Dumas, Desha, Pop. 4,687
Dumas SD 1,500/PK-12
213 Adams St 71639 870-382-4571
Kelvin Gragg, supt. Fax 382-4874
dpsd.k12.ar.us
Dumas HS 300/10-12
709 Dan Gill Dr 71639 870-382-4151
Lorrie Holt, prin. Fax 382-8904
Dumas JHS 400/7-9
315 S College St 71639 870-382-4476
Ronnieus Thompson, prin. Fax 382-2162

Earle, Crittenden, Pop. 2,397
Earle SD 600/K-12
PO Box 637 72331 870-792-8486
Rickey Nicks, supt. Fax 792-8897
www.earle.crsc.k12.ar.us/
Earle JSHS 300/7-12
PO Box 637 72331 870-792-8716
Juanita Bohannon, prin. Fax 792-1004

Edmondson, Crittenden, Pop. 415
West Memphis SD
Supt. — See West Memphis
West Memphis Learning Center 100/Alt
200 B J Taylor St 72332 870-735-5113
Larry Rooks, dir. Fax 732-8653

El Dorado, Union, Pop. 18,658
El Dorado SD 4,700/K-12
200 W Oak St 71730 870-864-5001
Jim Tucker, supt. Fax 864-5015
www.eldoradopublicschools.com
Barton JHS 700/7-8
400 W Faulkner St 71730 870-864-5051
Sherry Hill, prin. Fax 864-5064
El Dorado HS 1,300/9-12
2000 Wild Cat Dr 71730 870-864-5100
Alva Reibe, prin. Fax 863-3309
Murmil Heights Educational Center 200/Alt
2000 Ripley St 71730 870-864-5021
Jerry Langston, prin.

Parkers Chapel SD 800/PK-12
401 Parkers Chapel Rd 71730 870-862-4641
Michael White, supt. Fax 881-5092
www.parkerschapelschool.com
Parkers Chapel JSHS 300/7-12
401 Parkers Chapel Rd 71730 870-862-2360
Seth Williams, prin. Fax 881-5095

South Arkansas Community College Post-Sec.
PO Box 7010 71731 870-862-8131
West Side Christian S 100/PK-12
2400 W Hillsboro St 71730 870-863-5636
Robin Colley, admin. Fax 863-3529

Elkins, Washington, Pop. 2,568
Elkins SD 1,100/K-12
349 N Center St 72727 479-643-2172
Dan Jordan, supt. Fax 643-3605
www.elkinsdistrict.org
Elkins HS 400/9-12
349 N Center St 72727 479-643-3381
Steve Watkins, prin. Fax 643-2726
Elkins MS 300/6-8
349 N Center St 72727 479-643-2552
Steve Denzer, prin. Fax 643-4272

Emerson, Columbia, Pop. 368
Emerson-Taylor-Bradley SD
Supt. — See Taylor
Emerson HS 100/7-12
212 Grayson St 71740 870-547-2862
Jim Deloach, prin. Fax 547-2011

England, Lonoke, Pop. 2,789
England SD 800/PK-12
501 Pine Bluff Hwy 72046 501-842-2996
Barry Scott, supt. Fax 842-3698
england.k12.ar.us
England JSHS 400/7-12
501 Pine Bluff Hwy 72046 501-842-2031
Eddie Nally, prin. Fax 842-3263

Eureka Springs, Carroll, Pop. 2,008
Eureka Springs SD 600/K-12
147 Greenwood Hollow Rd 72632 479-253-5999
Bryan Pruitt, supt. Fax 253-5955
eurekaspringsschools.k12.ar.us
Eureka Springs HS 200/9-12
2 Lake Lucern Rd 72632 479-253-8875
Fax 253-8390
Eureka Springs MS 200/5-8
142 Greenwood Hollow Rd 72632 479-253-7716
Cindy Holt, prin. Fax 253-7809

Clear Spring S 100/PK-12
PO Box 511 72632 479-253-7888
Phyllis Poe, head sch Fax 253-0768

Everton, Marion, Pop. 128
Ozark Mountain SD
Supt. — See Saint Joe
Bruno-Pyatt JSHS 100/7-12
4754 Highway 125 S 72633 870-427-5227
Nichole Cunningham, prin. Fax 427-5255

Farmington, Washington, Pop. 5,772
Farmington SD 2,100/K-12
42 S Double Springs Rd 72730 479-266-1800
Bryan Law, supt. Fax 267-6030
www.farmcards.org/
Farmington Freshman Academy 9-9
278 W Main St 72730 479-266-1861
Bob Echols, prin. Fax 267-6040
Farmington HS 500/10-12
278 W Main St 72730 479-266-1860
Jon Purifoy, prin. Fax 267-6065

Lynch MS 500/6-8
359 Rheas Mill Rd 72730 479-266-1840
Terry Lakey, prin. Fax 267-6051

Fayetteville, Washington, Pop. 71,413
Fayetteville SD 9,400/K-12
1000 W Bulldog Blvd 72701 479-444-3000
Dr. Matthew Wendt, supt. Fax 973-8670
district.fayar.net/pages/Fayetteville_SD
Fayetteville SHS 1,900/10-12
994 W Martin Luther King Bl 72701 479-444-3050
Dr. Chad Scott, prin. Fax 444-3056
Ramay JHS 600/8-9
401 S Sang Ave 72701 479-444-3064
Lori Linam, prin. Fax 444-3013
Woodland JHS 800/8-9
1 E Poplar St 72703 479-444-3067
David McClure, prin. Fax 444-3039

Blue Cliff College Post-Sec.
3448 N College Ave 72703 479-521-2914
Fayetteville Christian S 200/PK-12
2006 E Mission Blvd 72703 479-442-2565
Paul Mitchell The School Post-Sec.
2167 W 6th St 72701 479-442-5181
Prism Education Center 200/K-11
2190 S Razorback Rd 72701 479-249-6113
University of Arkansas at Fayetteville Post-Sec.
1 University of Arkansas 72701 479-575-2000

Flippin, Marion, Pop. 1,337
Flippin SD 800/K-12
210 Alford St 72634 870-453-2270
Kelvin Hudson, supt. Fax 453-5059
www.flippinschools.com
Flippin HS 200/9-12
103 Alford St 72634 870-453-2233
Cassie Gilley, prin. Fax 453-7380
Flippin MS 200/6-8
308 N 1st St 72634 870-453-6464
Gregg Yarbrough, prin. Fax 453-6465

Fordyce, Dallas, Pop. 4,245
Fordyce SD 900/PK-12
PO Box 706 71742 870-352-3005
Albert Snow, supt. Fax 352-7187
www.fordyceschools.org/
Fordyce HS 400/7-12
PO Box 706 71742 870-352-2126
Judy Hubbell, prin. Fax 352-3953

Foreman, Little River, Pop. 984
Foreman SD 500/K-12
PO Box 480 71836 870-542-7211
George Kennedy, supt. Fax 542-7225
www.foremanschools.org
Foreman JSHS 300/7-12
PO Box 480 71836 870-542-7212
Kim Cody, prin. Fax 542-7227

Forrest City, Saint Francis, Pop. 15,183
Forrest City SD 3,100/PK-12
625 Irving St 72335 870-633-1485
Tiffany Hardrick Ph.D., supt. Fax 633-1415
mustang.grsc.k12.ar.us/
Forrest City HS 900/9-12
467 Victoria St 72335 870-633-1464
Osceola Hicks, prin. Fax 261-1844
Forrest City JHS 400/7-8
1133 N Division St 72335 870-633-3230
Carlos Fuller, prin. Fax 633-6066
Other Schools – See Madison

Calvary Christian S 100/PK-12
1611 N Washington St 72335 870-633-5333
Crowley's Ridge Technical Institute Post-Sec.
1620 New Castle Rd 72335 870-633-5411
East Arkansas Community College Post-Sec.
1700 New Castle Rd 72335 870-633-4480

Fort Smith, Sebastian, Pop. 83,397
Fort Smith SD 14,500/PK-12
PO Box 1948 72902 479-785-2501
Ben Gooden Ed.D., supt. Fax 785-1722
www.fortsmithschools.org
Belle Point Alternative Center 50/Alt
1501 Dodson Ave 72901 479-783-7034
Maria Arnold, dir. Fax 784-8161
Chaffin JHS 900/7-9
3025 Massard Rd 72903 479-452-2226
Todd Marshell, prin. Fax 478-3103
Darby JHS 600/7-9
616 N 14th St 72901 479-783-4159
Darren McKinney Ed.D., prin. Fax 784-8165
Kimmons JHS 900/7-9
2201 N 50th St 72904 479-785-2451
David Watkins, prin. Fax 784-8177
Northside SHS 1,600/10-12
2301 N B St 72901 479-783-1171
Ginni McDonald, prin. Fax 784-8144
Ramsey JHS 900/7-9
3201 Jenny Lind Rd 72901 479-783-5115
Dennis Siebenmorgen, prin. Fax 784-8178
Southside SHS 1,600/10-12
4100 Gary St 72903 479-646-7371
Wayne Haver, prin. Fax 648-8204
Adult Education Adult
501 S 20th St 72901 479-785-1232
Dr. Gary Udouj, dir. Fax 782-3401

Academy of Salon and Spa Post-Sec.
311 S 16th St 72901 479-782-5059
Trinity JHS 200/7-9
1205 S Albert Pike Ave 72903 479-782-2451
Dr. Karen Hollenbeck, prin. Fax 782-7263
Union Christian Academy 200/PK-12
4201 Windsor Dr 72904 479-783-7327
Paul Bridges, supt. Fax 783-9342

University of Arkansas at Fort Smith Post-Sec.
PO Box 3649 72913 479-788-7000

Fouke, Miller, Pop. 849
Fouke SD 1,100/PK-12
PO Box 20 71837 870-653-4311
Forrest Mulkey, supt. Fax 653-2856
fouke.schoolfusion.us
Fouke HS 300/9-12
PO Box 20 71837 870-653-4551
Carman Cross, prin. Fax 653-3313
Smith MS 200/6-8
PO Box 20 71837 870-653-2304
Amanda Whitehead, prin. Fax 653-7840

Fox, Stone
Mountain View SD
Supt. — See Mountain View
Rural Special HS 100/7-12
13237 Highway 263 72051 870-363-4365
Junior Barham, prin. Fax 363-4222

Gentry, Benton, Pop. 3,064
Gentry SD 1,400/K-12
201 S Giles Ave 72734 479-736-2253
Dr. Randy C. Barrett, supt. Fax 736-2245
www.gentrypioneers.com/
Gentry HS 400/9-12
201 S Giles Ave 72734 479-736-2666
Brae Harper, prin. Fax 736-5202
Gentry MS 400/6-8
201 S Giles Ave 72734 479-736-2251
Larry Cozens, prin. Fax 736-3414

Ozark Adventist Academy 100/9-12
20997 Dawn Hill East Rd 72734 479-736-2221

Gosnell, Mississippi, Pop. 3,483
Gosnell SD 1,300/K-12
600 N State Highway 181 72315 870-532-4000
Bonard Mace, supt. Fax 532-4002
www.gosnellschool.net
Gosnell JSHS 600/7-12
600 N State Highway 181 72315 870-532-4010
Len Whitehead, prin. Fax 532-4031

Gravette, Benton, Pop. 2,243
Gravette SD 1,900/PK-12
609 Birmingham St SE 72736 479-787-4100
Dr. Richard Page Ed.D., supt. Fax 787-4108
gravetteschools.net
Gravette HS 600/9-12
325 Lion Dr S 72736 479-787-4180
Jay Chalk, prin. Fax 787-4188
Gravette MS 500/6-8
607 Dallas St SE 72736 479-787-4160
Duane Thomas, prin. Fax 787-4178

Greenbrier, Faulkner, Pop. 4,616
Greenbrier SD 3,400/PK-12
4 School Dr 72058 501-679-4808
Scott Spainhour, supt. Fax 679-1024
www.greenbrierschools.org
Greenbrier HS 700/10-12
72 Green Valley Dr 72058 501-679-4236
Steve Landers, prin. Fax 679-5765
Greenbrier JHS 500/8-9
10 School Dr 72058 501-679-3433
Jason Miller, prin. Fax 679-3658

Green Forest, Carroll, Pop. 2,720
Green Forest SD 1,200/K-12
PO Box 1950 72638 870-438-5201
Matt Summers, supt. Fax 438-6214
www.gf.k12.ar.us
Green Forest HS 400/9-12
PO Box 1950 72638 870-438-5203
Terry Darnell, prin. Fax 438-4588
Green Forest MS 300/6-8
PO Box 1950 72638 870-438-5242
Tim Booth, prin. Fax 438-6343

Greenland, Washington, Pop. 1,236
Greenland SD 800/PK-12
PO Box 57 72737 479-521-2366
Dr. Larry Ben, supt. Fax 521-1480
www.greenlandsd.com
Greenland HS 300/9-12
PO Box 57 72737 479-521-2366
Gary Orr, prin. Fax 521-1350
Greenland MS 300/5-8
PO Box 57 72737 479-521-2366
Phil Costner, prin. Fax 251-1203

Greenwood, Sebastian, Pop. 8,785
Greenwood SD 3,600/K-12
420 N Main St 72936 479-996-4142
John Ciesla, supt. Fax 996-4143
www.greenwoodk12.com/
Greenwood HS 800/10-12
440 E Gary St 72936 479-996-4141
Jerry Efurd, prin. Fax 996-6548
Greenwood JHS 600/8-9
300 E Gary St 72936 479-996-7440
Cody Chatman, prin. Fax 996-7469

Greers Ferry, Cleburne, Pop. 887
West Side SD 400/K-12
7295 Greers Ferry Rd 72067 501-825-6258
Andy Chisum, supt. Fax 825-6258
www.westsideeagles.org
West Side JSHS 200/7-12
7295 Greers Ferry Rd 72067 501-825-7241
Matthew Irwin, prin. Fax 825-7241

Gurdon, Clark, Pop. 2,184
Gurdon SD 800/K-12
1 Go Devil Dr 71743 870-353-4454
Allen Blackwell, supt. Fax 353-4455
www.go-devils.net

Cabe MS 200/5-8
7780 Highway 67 S 71743 870-353-4454
Amanda Jones, prin. Fax 353-5149
Gurdon HS 200/9-12
7777 Highway 67 S 71743 870-353-5123
Harvey Sellers, prin. Fax 353-5131

Guy, Faulkner, Pop. 699
Guy-Perkins SD 400/K-12
492 Highway 25 N 72061 501-679-7224
Robert Stewart, supt. Fax 679-3508
www.gptbirds.org
Guy-Perkins HS 200/7-12
492 Highway 25 N 72061 501-679-3507
Karen Hoskins M.A., prin. Fax 679-3508

Hackett, Sebastian, Pop. 782
Hackett SD 1,000/PK-12
102 N Oak St 72937 479-638-8822
Edward Ray, supt. Fax 638-7106
www.hackettschools.org
Hackett JSHS 300/7-12
102 N Oak St 72937 479-638-7003
Michael Freeman, prin. Fax 638-8210
Other Schools – See Hartford

Hamburg, Ashley, Pop. 2,843
Hamburg SD 2,000/PK-12
202 E Parker St 71646 870-853-9851
Max Dyson, supt. Fax 853-2842
www.hsdlions.org
Hamburg HS 600/9-12
1119 S Main St 71646 870-853-9856
Nick Adams, prin. Fax 853-2850
Hamburg MS 500/6-8
1109 Cub Dr 71646 870-853-2811
John Spradlin, prin. Fax 853-2835

Hampton, Calhoun, Pop. 1,315
Hampton SD 500/K-12
PO Box 1176 71744 870-798-2742
Jimmy Cunningham, supt. Fax 798-2239
www.edline.net/pages/Hampton_Public_Schools
Hampton JSHS 200/7-12
PO Box 1176 71744 870-798-2742
Bryan Sanders, prin. Fax 798-2090

Harrisburg, Poinsett, Pop. 2,253
Harrisburg SD 1,300/K-12
207 W Estes St 72432 870-578-2416
Danny Sample, supt. Fax 578-9366
www.hbgsd.org/
Harrisburg HS 400/9-12
401 W South St 72432 870-578-2417
Brandon Craig, prin. Fax 578-2338
Harrisburg MS 400/5-8
401 W South St 72432 870-578-2410
Cindy Armstrong, prin. Fax 578-6201

Harrison, Boone, Pop. 12,739
Harrison SD 2,800/PK-12
110 S Cherry St 72601 870-741-7600
Dr. Melinda Moss, supt. Fax 741-4520
harrison.k12.ar.us/
Harrison JHS 600/7-9
515 S Pine St 72601 870-741-3496
Mike Stokes, prin. Fax 741-0101
Harrison SHS 600/10-12
925 Goblin Dr 72601 870-741-8223
Bill Keaster, prin. Fax 741-2606

North Arkansas College Post-Sec.
1515 Pioneer Dr 72601 870-743-3000

Hartford, Sebastian, Pop. 634
Hackett SD
Supt. — See Hackett
Hartford HS 200/7-12
512 Ludlow St 72938 479-639-2239
David Lee, prin. Fax 639-2158

Hartman, Johnson, Pop. 516
Westside SD 600/K-12
1535 Rabbit Hill Rd 72840 479-497-1991
Shane Gordon, supt. Fax 497-9037
www.westsiderebels.net
Westside JSHS 300/7-12
400 Highway 164 72840 479-497-1171
Chase Carter, prin. Fax 497-1537

Hattieville, Conway
Wonderview SD 400/K-12
2436 Highway 95 72063 501-354-0211
J. Carroll Purtle, supt. Fax 354-6071
www.wonderviewschools.org
Wonderview JSHS 200/7-12
2436 Highway 95 72063 501-354-8668
Jason Reynolds, prin. Fax 354-8602

Havana, Yell, Pop. 375
Western Yell County SD 400/K-12
PO Box 214 72842 479-476-4116
Joe Staton, supt. Fax 476-4115
wolverines.k12.ar.us
Western Yell County JSHS 200/7-12
PO Box 214 72842 479-476-4100
Scott Smith, prin. Fax 476-4111

Hazen, Prairie, Pop. 1,454
Hazen SD 700/PK-12
305 N Hazen Ave 72064 870-255-4549
Nanette Belford, supt. Fax 255-4508
www.hazen.k12.ar.us
Hazen HS 200/9-12
305 N Hazen Ave 72064 870-255-4546
Roxanne Bradow, prin. Fax 255-4559

Heber Springs, Cleburne, Pop. 7,068
Heber Springs SD 1,800/K-12
1100 W Pine St 72543 501-362-6712
Dr. Alan Stauffacher, supt. Fax 362-0613
hssd.k12.ar.us
Heber Springs HS 500/9-12
1100 W Pine St 72543 501-362-3141
Marc Griffin, prin. Fax 362-9931
Heber Springs MS 400/6-8
1100 W Pine St 72543 501-362-2488
Rita Watkins, prin. Fax 362-2193

Hector, Pope, Pop. 441
Hector SD 600/K-12
11520 SR 27 72843 479-284-2021
Mark Taylor, supt. Fax 284-2350
wildcats.afsc.k12.ar.us/
Hector JSHS 300/7-12
11601 SR 27 72843 479-284-3536
Harry Alvis, prin. Fax 284-5023

Helena, Phillips, Pop. 5,687
Helena/West Helena SD 1,700/PK-12
305 Valley Dr 72342 870-338-4425
John Hoy, supt. Fax 338-4411
hwh.grsc.k12.ar.us/
Other Schools – See West Helena

Phillips Comm. Coll. of the Univ. of AR Post-Sec.
PO Box 785 72342 870-338-6474

Hermitage, Bradley, Pop. 823
Hermitage SD 500/PK-12
PO Box 38 71647 870-463-2246
Dr. Tracy Tucker, supt. Fax 463-8520
hermitageschools.org
Hermitage HS 200/7-12
PO Box 190 71647 870-463-2235
Mistie McGhee, prin. Fax 463-2122

Highland, Sharp, Pop. 1,030
Highland SD 1,600/K-12
1627 Highway 62 412, 870-856-3275
Tracy Webb, supt. Fax 856-2765
highlandrebels.k12.ar.us/
Highland JSHS 600/8-12
1627 Highway 62 412, 870-856-3273
Annette Scribner, prin. Fax 856-2768

Hope, Hempstead, Pop. 9,935
Hope SD 2,800/K-12
117 E 2nd St 71801 870-722-2700
Bobby Hart, supt. Fax 777-4087
hpsdistrict.org
Hope HS 700/9-12
1701 S Main St 71801 870-777-3451
Bill Hoglund, prin. Fax 722-2736
Yerger MS 400/7-8
400 E 9th St 71801 870-722-2770
Josclyn Wiley, prin. Fax 722-2707

Spring Hill SD 600/K-12
633 Highway 355 W 71801 870-777-8236
Angela Raney, supt. Fax 777-9200
sites.google.com/a/springhill.k12.ar.us/web/home
Spring Hill JSHS 300/7-12
633 Highway 355 W 71801 870-722-7430
Steve Britton, prin. Fax 722-7425

Garrett Memorial Christian S 200/PK-12
PO Box 223 71802 870-777-3256
University of Arkansas Community College Post-Sec.
PO Box 140 71802 870-777-5722

Horatio, Sevier, Pop. 1,021
Horatio SD 900/PK-12
204 Lawson Ln 71842 870-832-1940
Lee Smith, supt. Fax 832-4465
www.horatioschools.org
Horatio JSHS 400/7-12
PO Box 435 71842 870-832-1900
Stephanie Rowe, prin. Fax 832-2174

Hot Springs National Park, Garland, Pop. 34,276
Cutter-Morning Star SD 600/K-12
2801 Spring St 71901 501-262-2414
Nancy Anderson, supt. Fax 262-0670
eaglesnest.dsc.k12.ar.us/
Cutter-Morning Star JSHS 300/7-12
2801 Spring St 71901 501-262-1883
Pike Palmer, prin. Fax 262-3757

Fountain Lake SD 1,300/K-12
4207 Park Ave 71901 501-701-1700
Darin Beckwith, supt. Fax 623-6447
www.flcobras.net
Fountain Lake HS 400/9-12
4207 Park Ave 71901 501-701-1706
Donald Westerman, prin. Fax 624-4053
Fountain Lake MS Cobra Digital Prep Acad 400/5-8
4207 Park Ave 71901 501-701-1730
Frank Janaskie, prin. Fax 318-6922

Hot Springs SD 3,700/PK-12
400 Linwood Ave 71913 501-624-3372
Dr. Mike Hernandez Ed.D., supt. Fax 620-7829
www.hssd.net
Hot Springs MS 500/7-8
700 Main St 71913 501-624-5228
Natasha Lenox, prin. Fax 620-7828
Hot Springs World Class HS 800/9-12
701 Emory St 71913 501-624-5286
Lloyd Jackson, prin. Fax 620-7820

Lakeside SD 3,300/PK-12
2837 Malvern Ave 71901 501-262-1880
Shawn Cook, supt. Fax 262-2732
lakesidesd.com
Lakeside HS 1,200/8-12
2871 Malvern Ave 71901 501-262-1530
Darin Landry, prin. Fax 262-6205

Christian Ministries Academy 100/K-12
PO Box 8500 71910 501-624-1952
David Pate, prin. Fax 318-2624
Hot Springs Beauty College Post-Sec.
100 Cones Rd 71901 501-624-0203
National Park Community College Post-Sec.
101 College Dr 71913 501-760-4222

Hoxie, Lawrence, Pop. 2,716
Hoxie SD 900/PK-12
PO Box 240 72433 870-886-2401
Radius Baker, supt. Fax 886-4252
hoxieschools.com
Hoxie HS 400/7-12
PO Box 240 72433 870-886-4254
Kelly Gillham, prin. Fax 886-4255

Huntsville, Madison, Pop. 2,295
Huntsville SD 2,300/K-12
PO Box F 72740 479-738-2011
Clint Jones, supt. Fax 738-2563
www.huntsvilleschooldistrict.org
Huntsville HS 600/9-12
PO Box 1377 72740 479-738-2500
Roxanne Enix, prin. Fax 738-2849
Huntsville MS 500/6-8
PO Box G 72740 479-738-6520
Chip Greenwell, prin. Fax 738-6259
Other Schools – See Saint Paul

Imboden, Lawrence, Pop. 668
Sloan-Hendrix SD 600/K-12
PO Box 1080 72434 870-869-2384
Clifford Rorex, supt. Fax 869-2380
shsd.k12.ar.us
Sloan-Hendrix HS 300/8-12
PO Box 1080 72434 870-869-2361
Marty Moore, prin. Fax 869-2362

Jacksonville, Pulaski, Pop. 27,377
Jacksonville North Pulaski SD 3,800/PK-12
1414 W Main 72076 501-241-2080
Tony Wood, supt. Fax 241-2092
jnpsd.org
Jacksonville HS 800/9-12
2400 Linda Ln 72076 501-982-2128
Jacob Smith, prin. Fax 982-1692
Jacksonville MS, 718 Harris Rd 72076 600/6-8
Mike Hudgeons, prin. 501-982-9436

Arthur's Beauty College Post-Sec.
2600 John Harden Dr 72076 501-982-8987

Jasper, Newton, Pop. 462
Jasper SD 900/K-12
PO Box 446 72641 870-446-2223
Jeff Cantrell, supt. Fax 446-2305
jasper.k12.ar.us
Jasper JSHS 200/7-12
PO Box 446 72641 870-446-2223
Jeff Lewis, prin. Fax 446-5549
Other Schools – See Kingston, Oark

Jessieville, Garland
Jessieville SD 900/K-12
PO Box 4 71949 501-984-5381
Ralph Carter, supt. Fax 984-4200
www.jsdlions.net
Jessieville HS 300/9-12
PO Box 4 71949 501-984-5011
Toby Packard, prin. Fax 984-4200
Jessieville MS 200/6-8
PO Box 4 71949 501-984-5610
Toby Packard, prin. Fax 984-4200

Jonesboro, Craighead, Pop. 66,085
Jonesboro SD 5,900/PK-12
2506 Southwest Sq 72401 870-933-5800
Dr. Kim Wilbanks, supt. Fax 933-5838
www.jonesboroschools.net
Area Technical Center Vo/Tech
1727 S Main St 72401 870-933-5891
Eddie Crain, dir. Fax 933-5890
Camp JHS 600/7-9
1814 W Nettleton Ave 72401 870-933-5820
William Cheatham, prin. Fax 933-5837
Jonesboro SHS 1,100/10-12
301 Hurricane Dr 72401 870-933-5881
Leigh Ann Rainey, prin. Fax 933-5812
MacArthur JHS 600/7-9
1615 Wilkins Ave 72401 870-933-5840
Dr. Brad Faught, prin. Fax 933-5848
SUCCESS Alt
613 N Fisher St 72401 870-931-9647
Todd Rhoades, dir. Fax 934-3555

Nettleton SD 3,200/K-12
3300 One Pl 72404 870-910-7800
James Dunivan, supt. Fax 910-7854
nettletonschools.net
Nettleton HS 900/9-12
4207 Race St 72401 870-910-7805
Brian Carter, prin. Fax 910-7804
Nettleton JHS 500/7-8
4208 Chieftain Ln 72401 870-910-7819
David Shipman, prin. Fax 910-6984

Valley View SD 1,900/PK-12
2131 Valley View Dr 72404 870-935-6200
Bryan Russell, supt. Fax 972-0373
www.valleyviewschools.net
Valley View HS 500/10-12
2116 Yarbrough Dr 72404 870-935-4602
David Goodin, prin. Fax 935-6202
Valley View JHS 600/7-9
2118 Valley View Dr 72404 870-935-4602
Barry Jones, prin. Fax 932-2291

Westside Consolidated SD 1,800/PK-12
1630 Highway 91 W 72404 870-935-7501
Scott Gaunt, supt. Fax 935-2123
www.westsideschools.org
Westside HS 700/8-12
1630 Highway 91 W 72404 870-935-7501
Michael Graham, prin. Fax 268-9119

Concordia Christian Academy 100/PK-12
1812 Rains St 72401 870-935-2273
Kory O'Brien, prin. Fax 935-4717
Ridgefield Christian S 300/PK-12
3824 Casey Springs Rd 72404 870-932-7540
Marica Elder, admin. Fax 931-9711

Judsonia, White, Pop. 1,987
White County Central SD 700/K-12
3259 Highway 157 72081 501-729-3947
Sheila Whitlow, supt. Fax 729-3992
wccbears.org
White County Central JSHS 300/7-12
3259 Highway 157 72081 501-729-3947
Jackwlyn Underwood, prin. Fax 729-3947

Junction City, Union, Pop. 576
Junction City SD 500/K-12
PO Box 790 71749 870-924-4575
William Lowe, supt. Fax 924-4565
junctioncity.k12.ar.us/
Junction City JSHS 300/7-12
PO Box 790 71749 870-924-4576
Melanie Mason, prin. Fax 924-4565

Kingston, Madison
Jasper SD
Supt. — See Jasper
Kingston JSHS 100/7-12
PO Box 149 72742 479-665-2835
Marsha Shaver, prin. Fax 665-2577

Kirby, Pike, Pop. 768
Kirby SD 300/K-12
PO Box 9 71950 870-398-4212
Jeff Alexander, supt. Fax 398-4442
www.kirbytrojans.net/
Kirby HS 200/7-12
PO Box 9 71950 870-398-4211
Bobby Applegate, prin. Fax 398-5413

Lake City, Craighead, Pop. 2,050
Riverside SD 800/K-12
PO Box 178 72437 870-237-4329
Tommy Knight, supt. Fax 237-4867
riverside.k12.ar.us
Riverside HS 400/7-12
PO Box 178 72437 870-237-4328
Jeffery Priest, prin. Fax 237-9929

Lake Village, Chicot, Pop. 2,553
Lakeside SD 1,200/PK-12
1110 S Lakeshore Dr 71653 870-265-7300
Dr. Billy Adams, supt. Fax 265-5466
www.lsschool.org
Lakeside HS 300/9-12
1110 S Lakeshore Dr 71653 870-265-2232
Linda Armour, prin. Fax 265-7302
Lakeside MS 200/6-8
1110 S Lakeshore Dr 71653 870-265-2970
Arthur Gray, prin. Fax 265-7309

Lamar, Johnson, Pop. 1,567
Lamar SD 1,100/K-12
301 Elberta St 72846 479-885-3907
Jay Holland, supt. Fax 885-2380
lamarwarriors.org
Lamar HS 400/8-12
301 Elberta St 72846 479-885-3344
Charles Harris, prin. Fax 885-3842

Lavaca, Sebastian, Pop. 2,248
Lavaca SD 900/PK-12
PO Box 8 72941 479-674-5611
Steve Rose, supt. Fax 674-2271
www.lavacaschools.com
Lavaca HS 200/9-12
PO Box 8 72941 479-674-5612
Felicia Owen, prin. Fax 674-0087
Lavaca MS 300/5-8
PO Box 8 72941 479-674-5618
Kenny Holland, prin. Fax 674-2271

Leachville, Mississippi, Pop. 1,967
Buffalo Island Central SD
Supt. — See Monette
Buffalo Island Central JHS 200/7-9
PO Box 110 72438 870-539-6883
Mark Hurst, prin. Fax 539-6696

Lead Hill, Boone, Pop. 266
Lead Hill SD 300/K-12
PO Box 20 72644 870-436-5250
Wanda Van Dyke, supt. Fax 436-5946
leadhillschools.net
Lead Hill JSHS 200/5-12
PO Box 20 72644 870-436-5677
Bryce Harrison, prin. Fax 436-6827

Lepanto, Poinsett, Pop. 1,866
East Poinsett County SD 700/PK-12
502 McClellan St 72354 870-475-2472
Michael Pierce, supt. Fax 475-3531
epc.k12.ar.us
East Poinsett County JSHS 300/7-12
502 McClellan St 72354 870-475-2331
John Kelly, prin. Fax 475-2206

Leslie, Searcy, Pop. 431
Searcy County SD
Supt. — See Marshall
North Central Career Center Vo/Tech
402 Oak St 72645 870-447-6111
Tommy Welch, dir. Fax 447-2872

Lewisville, Lafayette, Pop. 1,260
Lafayette County SD 700/K-12
PO Box 950 71845 870-921-5500
Robert Edwards, supt. Fax 921-4277
www.lcscougars.org
Other Schools – See Stamps

South Arkansas Christian S 50/K-12
PO Box 990 71845 870-921-5050
Br. Andy Hawkins, hdmstr. Fax 921-5050

Lexa, Phillips, Pop. 285
Barton-Lexa SD 800/PK-12
9546 Highway 85 72355 870-572-7294
David Tollett, supt. Fax 572-4713
www.bartonsd.org
Barton JSHS 400/7-12
9546 Highway 85 72355 870-572-6867
Christopher Goodin, prin. Fax 572-4713

Lincoln, Washington, Pop. 2,196
Lincoln Consolidated SD 48 1,100/PK-12
107 E School St 72744 479-824-7310
Mary Ann Spears, supt. Fax 824-3045
www.lincolncsd.com
Lincoln HS 300/8-12
1392 E Pridemore Dr 72744 479-824-7451
Courtney Jones, prin. Fax 824-3042

Little Rock, Pulaski, Pop. 190,562
Little Rock SD 25,800/PK-12
810 W Markham St 72201 501-447-1000
Baker Kurrus, supt. Fax 447-1159
www.lrsd.org
Accelerated Learning Center 200/Alt
7701 Scott Hamilton Dr 72209 501-447-1350
Brenda Allen, prin. Fax 447-1351
Central HS 2,500/9-12
1500 S Park St 72202 501-447-1400
Nancy Rousseau, prin. Fax 447-1401
Dunbar Magnet MS 700/6-8
1100 Wright Ave 72206 501-447-2600
Eunice Thrasher, prin. Fax 447-2601
Fair Magnet HS 800/9-12
13420 David O Dodd Rd 72210 501-447-1700
LaGail Biggs, prin. Fax 447-1701
Hall HS 1,100/9-12
6700 H St 72205 501-447-1900
Larry Schleicher, prin. Fax 447-1901
Hamilton Learning Academy 200/Alt
3301 S Bryant St 72204 501-447-3400
Willie Vinson, prin. Fax 447-3401
Henderson Magnet MS 700/6-8
401 John Barrow Rd 72205 501-447-2800
Frank Williams, prin. Fax 447-2801
Mann Magnet MS 800/6-8
1000 E Roosevelt Rd 72206 501-447-3100
Keith McGee, prin. Fax 447-3101
McClellan Magnet HS 900/9-12
9417 Geyer Springs Rd 72209 501-447-2100
Henry Anderson, prin. Fax 447-2101
Metropolitan Career-Tech Center Vo/Tech
7701 Scott Hamilton Dr 72209 501-447-1200
Shameka Montgomery, prin. Fax 447-1201
Parkview Magnet HS 1,000/9-12
2501 John Barrow Rd 72204 501-447-2300
Dr. Dexter Booth, prin. Fax 447-2301
Pulaski Heights MS 800/6-8
401 N Pine St 72205 501-447-3200
Darryl Powell, prin. Fax 447-3201
Adult Education Center Adult
4800 W 26th St 72204 501-447-1850
Linda Kindy, coord. Fax 447-1897
Other Schools – See Mabelvale

Pulaski County Special SD 12,700/PK-12
925 E Dixon Rd 72206 501-234-2000
Dr. Jerry Guess, supt. Fax 490-0483
www.pcssd.org
Fuller MS 500/6-8
808 E Dixon Rd 72206 501-490-5730
Leslie Ireland, prin. Fax 490-5736
Mills HS 700/9-12
1205 E Dixon Rd 72206 501-490-5700
Duane Clayton, prin. Fax 490-5709
Robinson HS 500/9-12
21501 Highway 10 72223 501-868-2400
Mary Bailey, prin. Fax 868-2405
Robinson MS 400/6-8
21001 Highway 10 72223 501-868-2410
Lance LeVar, prin. Fax 868-2441
Other Schools – See Maumelle, Sherwood

Arkansas Baptist College Post-Sec.
1621 Dr Martin Luther King 72202 501-370-4000
Arkansas Baptist S 800/PK-12
62 Pleasant Valley Dr 72212 501-227-7077
Arkansas Beauty School Post-Sec.
5108 Baseline Rd 72209 501-562-5673
Arkansas College of Barbering Post-Sec.
8521 Geyer Springs Rd #30 72209 501-376-9696
AR College of Barbering & Hair Design Post-Sec.
2500 S State St 72206 501-376-9696
Arkansas School for the Blind Post-Sec.
PO Box 668 72203 501-296-1810
Arkansas School for the Deaf Post-Sec.
2400 W Markham St 72205 501-324-9506
Baptist Preparatory Upper S 300/7-12
8400 Ranch Blvd 72223 501-868-5121
Randy Goldsmith, prin. Fax 868-5403
Baptist Schools of Allied Health Post-Sec.
11900 Colonel Glenn Rd 72210 501-202-6200
Catholic HS for Boys 700/9-12
6300 Father Tribou St 72205 501-664-3939
Steve Straessle, prin. Fax 664-6549
Central Arkansas Radiation Therapy Inst. Post-Sec.
PO Box 55050 72215 501-664-8573
Eastern College of Health Vocations Post-Sec.
200 S University Ave 72205 501-568-0211
Episcopal Collegiate S 700/PK-12
1701 Cantrell Rd 72201 501-372-1194
Christopher Tompkins, head sch Fax 372-2160
Little Rock Adventist Academy 50/K-10
8708 N Rodney Parham Rd 72205 501-225-6183
Little Rock Christian Academy 1,300/K-12
19010 Cantrell Rd 72223 501-868-9822
Dr. Gary Arnold, head sch Fax 868-8766
Mt. St. Mary Academy 500/9-12
3224 Kavanaugh Blvd 72205 501-664-8006
Angie Collins, prin. Fax 666-4382
Philander Smith College Post-Sec.
900 W Daisy L Gatson Bates 72202 501-375-9845
Pinnacle Classical Academy 50/PK-11
PO Box 241822 72223 501-240-9080
Chad Muller, hdmstr.
Pulaski Academy 1,400/PK-12
12701 Hinson Rd 72212 501-604-1910
Matthew Walsh, head sch Fax 225-1974
Remington College Post-Sec.
10600 Colonel Glenn Rd #100 72204 501-312-0007
St. Vincent Infirmary Medical Center Post-Sec.
2 Saint Vincent Cir 72205 501-660-3910
Southwest Christian Academy 500/PK-12
11301 Geyer Springs Rd 72209 501-565-3276
University of Arkansas at Little Rock Post-Sec.
2801 S University Ave 72204 501-569-3000
University of Arkansas/Medical Sciences Post-Sec.
4301 W Markham St 72205 501-686-5000
Velvatex College of Beauty Culture Post-Sec.
1520 Dr Martin Luther King 72202 501-372-9678
Washington Barber College Post-Sec.
5300 W 65th St 72209 501-568-8800

Lonoke, Lonoke, Pop. 4,204
Lonoke SD 1,800/K-12
401 W Holly St 72086 501-676-2042
Dr. Suzanne Bailey, supt. Fax 676-7074
lonokeschools.org/
Lonoke HS 600/9-12
405 W Academy St 72086 501-676-2476
Sandi King, prin. Fax 676-3716
Lonoke MS 400/6-8
1100 W Palm St 72086 501-676-6670
Jeannie Holt, prin. Fax 676-7013

Mabelvale, Pulaski
Little Rock SD
Supt. — See Little Rock
Mabelvale Magnet MS 600/6-8
10811 Mabelvale West Rd 72103 501-447-3000
Rhonda Hall, prin. Fax 447-3001

Mc Crory, Woodruff, Pop. 1,707
Mc Crory SD 600/PK-12
PO Box 930 72101 870-731-2535
Bob Casteel, supt. Fax 731-2536
mccrory.k12.ar.us/
Mc Crory JSHS 300/7-12
PO Box 930 72101 870-731-2851
Aaron Wiggins, prin. Fax 731-2574

Mc Gehee, Desha, Pop. 4,181
McGehee SD 1,200/K-12
PO Box 767 71654 870-222-3670
Thomas Gathen, supt. Fax 222-6957
www.mcgeheeschools.org
McGehee JSHS 500/7-12
PO Box 767 71654 870-222-5026
Derrell Thompson, prin. Fax 222-5838

Baptist School of Nursing-SE Post-Sec.
Highway 1 NE 71654

Madison, Saint Francis, Pop. 758
Forrest City SD
Supt. — See Forrest City
Madison Academy ALE 50/Alt
105 N 5th St 72359 870-633-1081
Patti Long, admin.

Magazine, Logan, Pop. 835
Magazine SD 600/PK-12
485 E Priddy St 72943 479-969-2566
Brett Bunch, supt. Fax 969-8740
magazinerattlers.k12.ar.us
Leftwich HS 300/7-12
292 E Priddy St 72943 479-969-2640
Randy Bryan, prin. Fax 969-2610

Magnolia, Columbia, Pop. 11,431
Magnolia SD 2,900/PK-12
PO Box 649 71754 870-234-4933
John D. Ward, supt. Fax 901-2508
www.magnoliaschools.net
Magnolia JHS 600/7-9
PO Box 649 71754 870-234-2206
Gwen Carter, prin. Fax 234-1293
Magnolia SHS 700/10-12
PO Box 649 71754 870-234-2610
Roger Loper, prin. Fax 901-2509

Columbia Christian S 300/PK-12
250 Warnock Springs Rd 71753 870-234-2831
Ted Waller, supt. Fax 234-1497
Southern Arkansas University Post-Sec.
100 E University 71753 870-235-4000

Malvern, Hot Spring, Pop. 10,082
Glen Rose SD 1,000/PK-12
14334 Highway 67 72104 501-332-3694
Tim Holicer, supt. Fax 332-3031
www.grbeavers.org
Glen Rose HS 300/9-12
14334 Highway 67 72104 501-332-3694
Susan Blockburger, prin. Fax 332-3902
Glen Rose MS 300/5-8
14334 Highway 67 72104 501-332-3694
Shawn Pilgrim, prin. Fax 332-3799

Magnet Cove SD 600/K-12
472 Magnet School Rd 72104 501-332-5468
Danny Thomas, supt. Fax 337-4119
magnetcove.k12.ar.us
Magnet Cove HS 300/7-12
472 Magnet School Rd 72104 501-332-5466
Jeff Eskola, prin. Fax 337-8711

Malvern SD 2,200/K-12
1620 S Main St 72104 501-332-7500
Brian Golden, supt. Fax 332-7501
malvernleopards.org
Malvern MS 300/7-8
339 E Donnelly St 72104 501-332-7530
Velda Keeney, prin. Fax 332-7532
Malvern SHS 600/9-12
525 E Highland Ave 72104 501-332-6905
Jennifer Shnaekel, prin. Fax 332-7523

College of the Ouachitas Post-Sec.
1 College Cir 72104 501-337-5000

Mammoth Spring, Fulton, Pop. 962
Mammoth Spring SD 500/K-12
410 Goldsmith Ave 72554 870-625-3612
David Turnbough, supt. Fax 625-3609
www.mammothspringschools.com
Mammoth Spring HS 200/7-12
410 Goldsmith Ave 72554 870-625-7212
Brian Davis, prin. Fax 625-3609

Manila, Mississippi, Pop. 3,321
Manila SD 1,100/PK-12
PO Box 670 72442 870-561-4419
Pamela Castor, supt. Fax 561-4410
mps.crsc.k12.ar.us
Manila HS 300/9-12
PO Box 670 72442 870-561-4417
Mark Manchester, prin. Fax 561-4243
Manila MS 300/5-8
PO Box 670 72442 870-561-4815
LeAnn Helms, prin. Fax 561-4828

Mansfield, Scott, Pop. 1,119
Mansfield SD 900/K-12
402 Grove St 72944 479-928-4006
Robert Ross, supt. Fax 928-4482
mansfieldtigers.org
Mansfield HS 300/9-12
2500 Highway 71 S 72944 479-928-1105
James Best, prin. Fax 928-1108
Mansfield MS 300/5-8
400 Grove St 72944 479-928-4451
Floyd Fisher, prin. Fax 928-4323

Marianna, Lee, Pop. 4,065
Lee County SD 1,000/PK-12
175 Walnut St 72360 870-295-7100
Willie Murdock, supt. Fax 295-7125
lcsd1.grsc.k12.ar.us
Lee HS 400/7-12
523 Forest Ave 72360 870-295-7130
Phylistia Stanley, prin. Fax 295-7313

Lee Academy 200/PK-12
973 Highway 243 72360 870-295-3444

Marion, Crittenden, Pop. 12,214
Marion SD 4,200/K-12
200 Manor St 72364 870-739-5100
Don Johnston, supt. Fax 739-5156
www.msd3.org/
Marion JHS 700/8-9
801 Carter Dr 72364 870-739-5140
Elmer West, prin. Fax 739-5142
Marion SHS 900/10-12
1 Patriot Dr 72364 870-739-5130
Lincoln Daniels, prin. Fax 739-5135

Marked Tree, Poinsett, Pop. 2,530
Marked Tree SD 500/PK-12
406 Saint Francis St 72365 870-358-2913
Annesa Thompson, supt. Fax 358-3953
mtree.k12.ar.us
Marked Tree JSHS 200/7-12
406 Saint Francis St 72365 870-358-2891
Matt Wright, prin. Fax 358-3953

Delta Technical Institute Post-Sec.
PO Box 280 72365 870-358-2117

Marmaduke, Greene, Pop. 1,093
Marmaduke SD 700/K-12
1010 Greyhound Dr 72443 870-597-2723
Tim Gardner, supt. Fax 597-4693
www.mhs.nesc.k12.ar.us
Marmaduke JSHS 300/7-12
1010 Greyhound Dr 72443 870-597-2723
Bill Muse, prin. Fax 597-4693

Marshall, Searcy, Pop. 1,315
Searcy County SD 900/K-12
952 Highway 65 N 72650 870-448-3011
Alan Yarbrough, supt. Fax 448-3012
scsd.info
Marshall MSHS 400/7-12
950 Highway 65 N 72650 870-448-3331
Robin Morris, prin. Fax 448-5306
Other Schools – See Leslie

Marvell, Phillips, Pop. 1,170
Marvell-Elaine SD 400/PK-12
PO Box 1870 72366 870-829-2101
Dr. Joyce Cottoms Ph.D., supt. Fax 829-2044
marvell.grsc.k12.ar.us/
Marvell-Elaine HS 200/7-12
PO Box 1870 72366 870-829-1351
Sylvia Moore M.S., prin. Fax 829-3150

Marvell Academy 200/PK-12
PO Box 277 72366 870-829-2931
Dr. Susan Lgion, hdmstr. Fax 829-3601

Maumelle, Pulaski, Pop. 16,888
Pulaski County Special SD
Supt. — See Little Rock
Maumelle HS 1,100/9-12
100 Victory Ln 72113 501-851-5350
Jeff Senn, prin. Fax 851-5356
Maumelle MS 900/6-8
1000 Carnahan Dr 72113 501-851-8990
Ryan Burgess, prin. Fax 851-8988

Mayflower, Faulkner, Pop. 2,195
Mayflower SD 1,200/PK-12
7 Ashmore Dr 72106 501-470-0506
John Gray, supt. Fax 470-1343
www.mayflowerschools.org
Mayflower HS 400/9-12
10 Leslie King N 72106 501-470-0388
T.J. Slough, prin. Fax 470-2106
Mayflower MS 400/5-8
18 Eagle Circle 72106 501-470-2111
John Pipkins, prin. Fax 470-2116

Maynard, Randolph, Pop. 421
Maynard SD 500/K-12
74 Campus Dr 72444 870-647-3500
Patricia Rawlings, supt. Fax 647-2301
maynard.nesc.k12.ar.us/
Maynard JSHS 200/7-12
74 Campus Dr 72444 870-647-3500
Cindy Dauck, prin. Fax 647-2301

Melbourne, Izard, Pop. 1,832
Melbourne SD 800/K-12
PO Box 250 72556 870-368-7070
Dennis Sublett, supt. Fax 368-7071
bearkatz.k12.ar.us/
Melbourne JSHS 400/7-12
PO Box 250 72556 870-368-4345
Jim Carroll, prin. Fax 368-4349

Ozarka College Post-Sec.
PO Box 10 72556 870-368-7371

Mena, Polk, Pop. 5,622
Mena SD 1,800/K-12
501 Hickory Ave 71953 479-394-1710
Benny Weston, supt. Fax 394-1713
www.menaschools.org
Mena HS 600/9-12
PO Box 1810 71953 479-394-1144
Shane Torix, prin. Fax 394-1145
Mena MS 400/6-8
700 Morrow St S 71953 479-394-2572
Michael Hobson, prin. Fax 394-0258

Ouachita River SD 700/K-12
143 Polk Road 96 71953 479-394-2348
Jerrall Strasner, supt. Fax 394-6687
www.ouachitariversd.org
Acorn JSHS 200/7-12
143 Polk Road 96 71953 479-394-5544
Shannon Lyle, prin. Fax 394-1041
Other Schools – See Oden

Rich Mountain Community College Post-Sec.
1100 College Dr 71953 479-394-7622

Mineral Springs, Howard, Pop. 1,190
Mineral Springs SD 400/K-12
PO Box 189 71851 870-287-4748
Curtis Turner, supt. Fax 287-5301
mssd2.k12.ar.us/
Mineral Springs HS 200/7-12
PO Box 189 71851 870-287-4747
Josh Kessler, prin. Fax 287-5300

Monette, Craighead, Pop. 1,489
Buffalo Island Central SD 800/PK-12
PO Box 730 72447 870-486-5411
Gaylon Taylor, supt. Fax 486-2657
www.bicschools.net
Buffalo Island Central SHS 200/10-12
PO Box 730 72447 870-486-5512
Randy Rose, prin. Fax 486-2657
Other Schools – See Leachville

Monticello, Drew, Pop. 9,357
Drew Central SD 900/K-12
250 University Dr 71655 870-367-5369
Billy Williams, supt. Fax 367-1932
www.drewcentral.org/
Drew Central HS 300/9-12
250 University Dr 71655 870-367-6076
Melissia Vincent, prin. Fax 460-5501
Drew Central MS 300/5-8
250 University Dr 71655 870-367-5235
Patti Smith, prin. Fax 460-5502

Monticello SD 2,100/K-12
935 Scogin Dr 71655 870-367-4000
Sandra Lanehart, supt. Fax 367-1531
www.billies.org
Monticello HS 600/9-12
390 Clyde Ross Dr 71655 870-367-4050
Judy Holaway, prin. Fax 367-3699
Monticello MS 500/6-8
180 Clyde Ross Dr 71655 870-367-4040
Kevin Hancock, prin. Fax 367-5437
Occupational Education Center Vo/Tech
741 Scogin Dr 71655 870-367-4060
Randy Lay, dir. Fax 367-1385

University of Arkansas at Monticello Post-Sec.
346 University Dr 71656 870-460-1026

Morrilton, Conway, Pop. 6,618
South Conway County SD 2,200/K-12
100 Baramore St 72110 501-354-9400
Shawn Halbrook, supt. Fax 354-9464
www.sccsd.org
Morrilton HS 700/9-12
701 E Harding St 72110 501-354-9430
Danny Ketcherside, prin. Fax 354-9468
Morrilton JHS 400/7-8
1400 Poor Farm Rd 72110 501-354-9437
Robert Hogan, prin. Fax 354-9429

Sacred Heart S 200/PK-12
106 N Saint Joseph St 72110 501-354-8113
Buddy Greeson, prin. Fax 354-2001
University of Arkansas Community College Post-Sec.
1537 University Blvd 72110 501-354-2465

Mountainburg, Crawford, Pop. 624
Mountainburg SD 700/K-12
129 Highway 71 SW 72946 479-369-2121
Dennis Copeland, supt. Fax 369-2138
www.mountainburg.org
Mountainburg HS 200/9-12
129 Highway 71 SW 72946 479-369-2146
Jason Rutherford, prin. Fax 369-2845
Mountainburg MS 200/5-8
129 Highway 71 SW 72946 479-369-4506
Paul Roper, prin. Fax 369-4355

Mountain Home, Baxter, Pop. 12,291
Mountain Home SD 3,900/K-12
2465 Rodeo Dr 72653 870-425-1201
Dr. Jake Long, supt. Fax 425-1316
bombers.k12.ar.us
Mountain Home HS Career Academies 1,200/9-12
500 Bomber Blvd 72653 870-425-1215
Dana Brown, prin. Fax 508-6097
Mountain Home JHS 300/8-8
2301 Rodeo Dr 72653 870-425-1231
Ron Czanstkowski, prin. Fax 424-4797

Arkansas State University Mountain Home Post-Sec.
1600 S College St 72653 870-508-6100
Marsha Kay Beauty College Post-Sec.
408 Highway 201 N 72653 870-425-7575
Mountain Home Christian Academy 100/PK-12
1989 Glenbriar Dr 72653 870-424-6622
Lori Mathis, prin. Fax 424-6622

Mountain Pine, Garland, Pop. 749
Mountain Pine SD 600/PK-12
PO Box 1 71956 501-767-1540
Bobby Applegate, supt. Fax 767-1589
www.mpsdrd.com
Mountain Pine JSHS 300/7-12
PO Box 1 71956 501-767-6917
Denise Taylor, prin. Fax 767-0170

Mountain View, Stone, Pop. 2,714
Mountain View SD 1,600/PK-12
210 High School Rd 72560 870-269-3443
Rowdy Ross, supt. Fax 269-3446
mountainviewschooldistrict.k12.ar.us/
Mountain View HS 400/9-12
210 High School Rd 72560 870-269-3943
Kim Cruce, prin. Fax 269-2372
Mountain View MS 400/5-8
210 High School Rd 72560 870-269-4335
Robert Ross, prin. Fax 269-4447
Other Schools – See Fox, Timbo

Mount Ida, Montgomery, Pop. 1,049
Mount Ida SD 500/K-12
PO Box 1230 71957 870-867-2771
Hal Landrith, supt. Fax 867-3734
www.mountidaschools.com
Mount Ida JSHS 300/7-12
PO Box 1230 71957 870-867-2771
Ron McGuire, prin. Fax 867-3734

Mount Judea, Newton
Deer / Mt. Judea SD
Supt. — See Deer
Mount Judea JSHS 100/7-12
PO Box 40 72655 870-434-5362
Roxanna Holt, prin. Fax 434-5359

Mount Vernon, Faulkner, Pop. 139
Mount Vernon-Enola SD 500/K-12
38 Garland Springs Rd 72111 501-849-2220
Larry Walters, supt. Fax 849-3076
www.mve.k12.ar.us
Mount Vernon-Enola JSHS 200/7-12
38 Garland Springs Rd 72111 501-849-2221
Rudy Beavers, prin. Fax 849-3302

Mulberry, Crawford, Pop. 1,638
Mulberry/Pleasant View Bi-County SD 300/K-12
424 Alma Ave 72947 479-997-1715
Lonnie Myers Ed.D., supt. Fax 997-1897
www.mpvschools.com
Mulberry HS 100/9-12
424 Alma Ave 72947 479-997-1363
Melvin Williams, prin. Fax 997-1491
Other Schools – See Ozark

Murfreesboro, Pike, Pop. 1,612
South Pike County SD 700/K-12
PO Box 339 71958 870-285-2189
Roger Featherston, supt. Fax 285-2276
www.rattlers.org
Murfreesboro JSHS 300/7-12
PO Box 339 71958 870-285-2184
Kathaleen Cole, prin. Fax 285-2276

Nashville, Howard, Pop. 4,566
Nashville SD 1,900/K-12
600 N 4th St 71852 870-845-3425
Douglas Graham, supt. Fax 845-7344
www.nashvillesd.com
Nashville JHS 400/7-9
1000 N 8th St 71852 870-845-3418
Deb Tackett, prin. Fax 845-7334
Nashville SHS 400/10-12
1301 Mount Pleasant Dr 71852 870-845-3261
Tate Gordon, prin. Fax 845-7345

Newark, Independence, Pop. 1,165
Cedar Ridge SD 800/PK-12
1502 N Hill St 72562 870-799-8691
Andy Ashley, supt. Fax 799-8647
www.cedarwolves.org
Cedar Ridge JSHS 400/6-12
1500 N Hill St 72562 870-799-8691
Greg Thetford, prin. Fax 799-3225

Newport, Jackson, Pop. 7,757
Newport SD 1,200/PK-12
406 Wilkerson Dr 72112 870-523-1312
Dr. Larry Bennett, supt. Fax 523-1388
www.newportschools.org
Newport HS 400/7-12
406 Wilkerson Dr 72112 870-523-1321
Terri Kane, prin. Fax 523-1383

Arkansas State University - Newport Post-Sec.
7648 Victory Blvd 72112 870-512-7800

Norfork, Baxter, Pop. 502
Norfork SD 400/K-12
44 Fireball Ln 72658 870-499-5228
Mike Seay, supt. Fax 499-5109
norfork.k12.ar.us
Norfork JSHS 200/7-12
136 Mildred Simpson Dr 72658 870-499-7191
Bob Hulse, prin. Fax 499-5659

Norman, Montgomery, Pop. 367
Caddo Hills SD 600/PK-12
2268 Highway 8 E 71960 870-356-5700
Deric Owens, supt. Fax 356-3426
www.caddohills.org
Caddo Hills JSHS 300/7-12
2268 Highway 8 E 71960 870-356-3857
Todd Baxley, prin. Fax 356-3444

Norphlet, Union, Pop. 829
Smackover-Norphlet SD
Supt. — See Smackover
Norphlet MS 100/6-8
PO Box 50 71759 870-546-2781
Keith Coleman, prin. Fax 546-9554

North Little Rock, Pulaski, Pop. 61,111
North Little Rock SD 7,200/PK-12
PO Box 687 72115 501-771-8000
Kelly Rodgers, supt. Fax 771-8069
www.nlrsd.org
North Little Rock Academy 100/9-12
5500 Lynch Dr 72117 501-955-3600
Charles Jones, prin. Fax 955-3603
North Little Rock HS 2,500/9-12
101 W 22nd St 72114 501-771-8100
Randy Rutherford, prin. Fax 771-8283
North Little Rock MS 1,100/6-8
2400 Lakeview Rd 72116 501-771-8200
Lee Tackett, prin. Fax 771-8206

AR College of Barbering & Hair Design Post-Sec.
200 E Washington Ave 72114 501-376-9696
Central Arkansas Christian S 500/PK-12
1 Windsong Dr 72113 501-758-3160
Lee's School of Cosmetology Post-Sec.
2700 W Pershing Blvd 72114 501-758-2800
New Tyler Barber College Post-Sec.
1221 Bishop Lindsey Ave 72114 501-375-0377
Pulaski Technical College Post-Sec.
3000 W Scenic Dr 72118 501-812-2200
Shorter College Post-Sec.
604 N Locust St 72114 501-374-6305

Oark, Johnson
Jasper SD
Supt. — See Jasper
Oark JSHS 100/7-12
370 Highway 215 72852 479-292-3353
David Westenhover, prin. Fax 292-3435

Oden, Montgomery, Pop. 227
Ouachita River SD
Supt. — See Mena
Oden JSHS 100/7-12
135 School Dr 71961 870-326-4311
William Edwards, prin. Fax 326-5552

Ola, Yell, Pop. 1,269
Two Rivers SD 800/K-12
17727 E State Highway 28 72853 479-272-3113
Jimmy Loyd, supt. Fax 272-3125
www.trgators.org/

Two Rivers JSHS 500/5-12
17727 E State Highway 28 72853 479-272-3150
Barry Fisher, prin. Fax 272-3149

Omaha, Boone, Pop. 159
Omaha SD 400/K-12
522 College Rd 72662 870-426-3366
Jerry Parrett, supt. Fax 426-3355
omahaschool.weebly.com
Omaha JSHS 200/7-12
522 College Rd 72662 870-426-3373
Nathan White, prin. Fax 426-3360

Osceola, Mississippi, Pop. 7,648
Osceola SD 1,400/PK-12
2750 W Semmes Ave 72370 870-563-2561
Michael Cox, supt. Fax 563-2181
www.osd1.org/
Osceola HS 400/9-12
2800 W Semmes Ave 72370 870-563-2192
Tiffany Morgan, prin. Fax 622-1003

Ozark, Franklin, Pop. 3,615
Mulberry/Pleasant View Bi-County SD
Supt. — See Mulberry
Pleasant View Campus 50/7-8
5750 Hornet Ln 72949 479-997-8469
Dennis Fisher, prin. Fax 997-1667

Ozark SD 1,400/PK-12
PO Box 135 72949 479-667-4118
James Ford, supt. Fax 667-4092
www.ozarkhillbillies.org/
Ozark JHS 300/8-9
1301 Walden Dr 72949 479-667-4747
Michael Burns, prin. Fax 667-0898
Ozark SHS 400/10-12
1631 Hillbilly Dr 72949 479-667-4118
Jody Jenkins, prin. Fax 667-5921

Arkansas Technical University Ozark Cmps Post-Sec.
1700 Helberg Ln 72949 866-225-2884

Palestine, Saint Francis, Pop. 671
Palestine-Wheatley SD 600/PK-12
PO Box 790 72372 870-581-2646
Jon Estes, supt. Fax 581-4420
www.edline.net/pages/Palestine-Wheatley_School_Dist/
Palestine-Wheatley HS 200/9-12
PO Box 790 72372 870-581-2425
Randy Cannon, prin. Fax 581-4421
Palestine-Wheatley JHS 200/5-8
PO Box 790 72372 870-581-2246
Zenna Smith, prin.

Pangburn, White, Pop. 587
Pangburn SD 800/K-12
1100 Short St 72121 501-728-4511
Dr. Kathy Berryhill, supt. Fax 728-4514
www.pangburnschools.org
Pangburn MSHS 400/7-12
1100 Short St 72121 501-728-3513
David Rolland, prin. Fax 728-2212

Paragould, Greene, Pop. 25,788
Greene County Technical SD 3,700/PK-12
5413 W Kingshighway 72450 870-236-2762
Gene Weeks, supt. Fax 236-7333
www.gctsd.k12.ar.us/
Greene County Technical HS 700/10-12
4601 Linwood Dr 72450 870-215-4460
Chad Jordan, prin. Fax 239-6976
Greene County Technical JHS 600/8-9
5201 W Kingshighway 72450 870-215-4450
Michael Todd, prin. Fax 239-2148

Paragould SD 3,100/PK-12
1501 W Court St 72450 870-239-2105
Debbie Smith, supt. Fax 239-4697
paragould.k12.ar.us
Paragould HS 800/9-12
1701 W Court St 72450 870-240-2271
Luke Lovins, prin. Fax 240-2276
Paragould JHS 500/7-8
1713 W Court St 72450 870-240-2261
Laurel Taylor, prin. Fax 240-2263

Crowleys Ridge Academy 300/PK-12
606 Academy Dr 72450 870-236-6909
Crowley's Ridge College Post-Sec.
100 College Dr 72450 870-236-6901

Paris, Logan, Pop. 3,477
Paris SD 1,200/PK-12
602 N 10th St 72855 844-963-3243
Wayne Fawcett, supt. Fax 208-7554
www.parisschools.org
Paris HS 300/9-12
2000 E Wood St 72855 844-963-3243
Bryan Hutson, prin. Fax 208-7564
Paris MS 300/5-8
602 N 10th St 72855 844-963-3243
Mike Nichols, prin. Fax 208-7482

Pearcy, Garland
Lake Hamilton SD 4,500/K-12
205 Wolf St 71964 501-767-2306
Steve Anderson, supt. Fax 767-5573
www.lhwolves.net
Lake Hamilton JHS 700/8-9
281 Wolf St 71964 501-767-2731
J.J. Humphries, prin. Fax 767-1711
Lake Hamilton SHS 1,000/10-12
280 Wolf St 71964 501-767-9311
Kirk Nance, prin. Fax 767-9318
New Horizon's Alternative S 100/Alt
382 Adam Brown Rd 71964 501-760-1720
Jodi Chalmers, dir. Fax 760-4857

Pea Ridge, Benton, Pop. 4,709
Pea Ridge SD 1,800/K-12
781 W Pickens Rd 72751 800-451-0032
Rick Neal, supt. Fax 431-6095
www.prs.k12.ar.us/
Pea Ridge HS 500/9-12
781 W Pickens Rd 72751 800-451-1343
Jon Laffoon, prin. Fax 431-6090
Pea Ridge MS 400/6-8
1391 Weston St 72751 800-451-0692
Matthew Wood, prin. Fax 431-6169

Perryville, Perry, Pop. 1,437
Perryville SD 1,000/K-12
614 S Fourche Ave 72126 501-889-2327
Dr. Ron Wilson, supt. Fax 889-5191
www.perryvilleschool.org
Perryville JSHS 500/7-12
325 Houston Ave 72126 501-889-2326
Kevin Campbell, prin. Fax 889-5006

Piggott, Clay, Pop. 3,820
Piggott SD 900/K-12
PO Box 387 72454 870-598-2572
Charnelsa Powell, supt. Fax 598-5283
www.piggottschools.net
Piggott HS 400/7-12
PO Box 387 72454 870-598-3815
Barry DeHart, prin. Fax 598-1560

Pine Bluff, Jefferson, Pop. 48,534
Dollarway SD 1,400/PK-12
4900 Dollarway Rd 71602 870-534-7003
Barbara Warren, supt. Fax 534-7859
www.dollarwayschools.org
Dollarway HS 400/9-12
4900 Dollarway Rd 71602 870-534-3878
Jeff Spaletta, prin. Fax 534-1455
Morehead MS 300/6-8
2602 W Fluker Ave 71601 870-534-5243
Yolanda Prim, prin. Fax 535-1215

Pine Bluff SD 3,100/PK-12
PO Box 7678 71611 870-543-4200
Dr. T.C. Wallace, supt. Fax 543-4208
www.pinebluffschools.org
Pine Bluff HS 900/9-12
711 W 11th Ave 71601 870-543-4300
Dr. Michael Nellums, prin. Fax 543-4302
Robey JHS 300/7-8
4101 S Olive St 71603 870-543-4290
Donald Booth, prin. Fax 850-2027

Watson Chapel SD 2,900/K-12
4100 Camden Rd 71603 870-879-0220
Dr. Connie Hathorn, supt. Fax 879-0588
wc-web.k12.ar.us
Watson Chapel JHS 700/7-9
3900 Camden Rd 71603 870-879-4420
Henry Webb, prin. Fax 879-4426
Watson Chapel SHS 700/10-12
4000 Camden Rd 71603 870-879-3230
Leydel Willis, prin. Fax 879-1842

Jefferson Regional Medical Center Post-Sec.
1600 W 40th Ave 71603 870-541-7858
Ridgway Christian S 300/K-12
3201 Ridgway Rd 71603 870-879-6264
Southeast Arkansas College Post-Sec.
1900 S Hazel St 71603 870-543-5900
University of Arkansas at Pine Bluff Post-Sec.
1200 University Dr 71601 870-575-8000

Pleasant Plains, Independence, Pop. 344
Midland SD 500/K-12
PO Box 630 72568 501-345-8844
Dewayne Wammack, supt. Fax 345-2086
www.midlandschools.org
Midland JSHS 200/7-12
PO Box 630 72568 501-345-2610
Edwin Butterworth, prin. Fax 345-3355

Pocahontas, Randolph, Pop. 6,538
Pocahontas SD 1,800/K-12
2300 N Park St 72455 870-892-4573
Shannon Fish, supt. Fax 892-8857
www.pocahontaspsd.com
Pocahontas HS 400/10-12
2312 Stadium Dr 72455 870-892-4573
Lesa Grooms, prin. Fax 892-8857
Pocahontas JHS 400/7-9
2405 N Park St 72455 870-892-4573
Brent Miller, prin. Fax 892-8857

Black River Technical College Post-Sec.
PO Box 468 72455 870-248-4000

Pottsville, Pope, Pop. 2,791
Pottsville SD 1,600/K-12
7000 SR 247 72858 479-968-8101
Larry Dugger, supt. Fax 968-6339
www.pottsvilleschools.org
Pottsville HS 300/10-12
500 Apache Dr 72858 479-968-6334
Jonathan Bradley, prin. Fax 968-3442
Pottsville JHS 400/7-9
250 Apache Dr 72858 479-968-6574
Kenneth Bell, prin. Fax 498-2345

Poyen, Grant, Pop. 289
Poyen SD 600/PK-12
PO Box 209 72128 501-332-8884
Jerry Newton, supt. Fax 332-8886
www.poyenschool.com
Poyen JSHS 300/7-12
PO Box 209 72128 501-332-2939
Dennis Emerson, prin. Fax 332-7809

Prairie Grove, Washington, Pop. 4,291
Prairie Grove SD 1,400/PK-12
110 School St 72753 479-846-4242
Dr. Allen Williams, supt. Fax 846-2015
pgtigers.org
Prairie Grove HS 600/9-12
500 Cole Dr 72753 479-846-4212
Ron Bond, prin. Fax 846-4207
Prairie Grove MS 600/5-8
806 N Mock St 72753 479-846-4221
Reba Holmes, prin. Fax 846-4275

Prescott, Nevada, Pop. 3,248
Prescott SD 900/K-12
762 Martin St 71857 870-887-3016
Robert Poole, supt. Fax 887-5021
www.curleywolves.org
Prescott HS 500/7-12
736 Martin St 71857 870-887-3123
Missy Walley, prin. Fax 887-3682

Quitman, Cleburne, Pop. 754
Quitman SD 700/PK-12
PO Box 178 72131 501-589-3156
Dennis Truxler, supt. Fax 589-3523
www.quitman.k12.ar.us
Quitman JSHS 300/7-12
PO Box 178 72131 501-589-2554
Michael Stacks, prin. Fax 589-3524

Rector, Clay, Pop. 1,960
Rector SD 600/K-12
PO Box 367 72461 870-595-3151
Johnny Fowler, supt. Fax 595-9067
www.rector.k12.ar.us
Rector HS 200/7-12
PO Box 367 72461 870-595-3553
Wade Williams, prin. Fax 595-3554

Rison, Cleveland, Pop. 1,329
Cleveland County SD 800/K-12
PO Box 600 71665 870-325-6344
Johnnie Johnson, supt. Fax 325-7094
www.rison.k12.ar.us
Rison JSHS 400/7-12
PO Box 600 71665 870-325-6241
Davy King, prin. Fax 325-6799

Woodlawn SD 600/K-12
6760 Highway 63 71665 870-357-8108
Dudley Hume, supt. Fax 357-8718
bears.k12.ar.us
Woodlawn JSHS 300/7-12
6760 Highway 63 71665 870-357-8171
Jeffery Wylie, prin. Fax 357-8022

Rogers, Benton, Pop. 54,921
Rogers SD 14,800/K-12
500 W Walnut St 72756 479-636-3910
Dr. Janie Darr, supt. Fax 631-3504
www.rogersschools.net/
Annex Alternative Center Alt
2922 S 1st St 72758 479-631-3690
Cindy Ford, prin. Fax 631-3612
Elmwood MS 800/6-8
1610 S 13th St 72758 479-631-3600
Bob White, prin. Fax 631-3603
Kirksey MS 1,000/6-8
2930 S 1st St 72758 479-631-3625
Mel Ahart, prin. Fax 631-3624
Lingle MS 900/6-8
901 N 13th St 72756 479-631-3590
Mary Elmore, prin. Fax 631-3594
Oakdale MS 700/6-8
511 N Dixieland Rd 72756 479-631-3615
Donna Charlton, prin. Fax 631-3617
Rogers Heritage HS 2,000/9-12
1114 S 5th St 72756 479-631-3579
Karen Steen, prin. Fax 631-3580
Rogers HS 2,100/9-12
2300 S Dixieland Rd 72758 479-636-2202
Charles Lee, prin. Fax 631-3554
Rogers New Technology HS 300/9-12
2922 S 1st St 72758 479-631-3621
Lance Arbuckle, prin. Fax 631-3637

Bryan University Post-Sec.
3704 W Walnut St 72756 479-899-6644
Providence Classical Christian Academy 200/K-12
4911 W Pleasant Grove Rd 72758 479-263-8861
Jason Ross M.Ed., hdmstr. Fax 439-8130

Rose Bud, White, Pop. 462
Rose Bud SD 900/PK-12
124 School Rd 72137 501-556-5815
Curtis Spann, supt. Fax 556-6000
rosebudschools.com
Rose Bud JSHS 400/7-12
124 School Rd 72137 501-556-5404
Danny Starkey, prin. Fax 556-6005

Rosston, Nevada, Pop. 259
Nevada SD 400/K-12
PO Box 50 71858 870-871-2418
Rick McAfee, supt. Fax 871-2419
www.nevadaschooldistrict.net/
Nevada JSHS 200/7-12
PO Box 50 71858 870-871-2478
Michael Odom, prin. Fax 871-2419

Russellville, Pope, Pop. 27,404
Russellville SD 5,200/PK-12
PO Box 928 72811 479-968-1306
Randall Williams, supt. Fax 968-6381
www.russellvilleschools.net/
Russellville HS 1,100/10-12
2203 S Knoxville Ave 72802 479-968-3151
Sheila Jacobs, prin. Fax 968-4264

Russellville JHS 700/8-9
2000 W Parkway Dr 72802 479-968-1599
Al Harpenau, prin. Fax 890-6419

Arkansas Beauty College Post-Sec.
109 N Commerce Ave 72801 479-968-3075
Arkansas Tech University Post-Sec.
1509 N Boulder Ave 72801 479-968-0389
Community Christian S 50/K-12
PO Box 1786 72811 479-968-1429
Rebecca Partain, admin. Fax 968-1436
River Valley School of Massage Post-Sec.
2003 E Parkway Dr 72802 479-890-7876

Saint Joe, Searcy, Pop. 132
Ozark Mountain SD 600/K-12
250 S Highway 65 72675 870-439-2218
James Jones, supt. Fax 439-2604
www.omsd.k12.ar.us
Saint Joe JSHS 100/7-12
250 S Highway 65 72675 870-439-2213
Jess Knapp, prin. Fax 439-2604
Other Schools – See Everton, Western Grove

Saint Paul, Madison, Pop. 113
Huntsville SD
Supt. — See Huntsville
Saint Paul JSHS 100/7-12
PO Box 125 72760 479-677-2411
Audra Kimball, prin. Fax 677-2210

Salem, Fulton, Pop. 1,613
Salem SD 800/K-12
313 Highway 62 E Ste 1 72576 870-895-2516
Wayne Guiltner, supt. Fax 895-4062
www.salemschools.net/
Salem JSHS 400/7-12
313 Highway 62 E Ste 2 72576 870-895-3293
Cody Curtis, prin. Fax 895-5937

Scranton, Logan, Pop. 220
Scranton SD 400/K-12
103 N 10th St 72863 479-938-7121
Dr. James Bridges, supt. Fax 938-7564
www.scrantonrockets.net
Scranton JSHS 200/7-12
103 N 10th St 72863 479-938-7121
Mark Siebenmorgen, prin. Fax 938-7564

Searcy, White, Pop. 22,441
Riverview SD 1,400/K-12
800 Raider Dr 72143 501-279-0540
David Rutledge, supt. Fax 279-0737
riverview.k12.ar.us
Riverview HS 400/9-12
810 Raider Dr 72143 501-279-7700
George Lucas, prin. Fax 279-2848
Riverview JHS 200/7-8
820 Raider Dr 72143 501-279-7111
Stuart Hill, prin. Fax 279-7166

Searcy SD 4,200/K-12
801 N Elm St 72143 501-268-3517
Diane Barrett, supt. Fax 278-2220
www.searcyschools.org/
Ahlf JHS 700/7-8
308 W Vine Ave 72143 501-268-3158
Gene Hodges, prin. Fax 278-2212
Searcy HS 1,200/9-12
301 N Ella St 72143 501-268-8315
Claude Smith, prin. Fax 267-2249

Arkansas State University Searcy Campus Post-Sec.
PO Box 909 72145 501-207-4014
Harding Academy 700/PK-12
PO Box 10775 72149 501-279-7200
Harding University Post-Sec.
915 E Market Ave 72149 501-279-4000
Searcy Beauty College Post-Sec.
1004 S Main St 72143 501-268-6300

Sheridan, Grant, Pop. 4,558
Sheridan SD 3,700/PK-12
400 N Rock St 72150 870-942-3135
Jerrod Williams, supt. Fax 942-2931
www.sheridanschools.org
Sheridan HS 900/10-12
700 W Vine St 72150 870-942-3137
Rodney Williams, prin. Fax 942-7546
Sheridan JHS 700/7-9
500 N Rock St 72150 870-942-3813
Jason Burks, prin. Fax 942-3034

Sherwood, Pulaski, Pop. 28,899
Pulaski County Special SD
Supt. — See Little Rock
Sylvan Hills HS 900/9-12
484 Bear Paw Rd 72120 501-833-1100
Tracy Allen, prin. Fax 833-1104
Sylvan Hills MS 900/6-8
10001 Johnson Dr 72120 501-833-1120
Jo Wilcox, prin. Fax 833-1137

Abundant Life S 300/K-12
9200 Highway 107 72120 501-835-3120
Justin Moseley, supt. Fax 835-4428

Shirley, Van Buren, Pop. 283
Shirley SD 400/K-12
199 School Dr 72153 501-723-8191
Betty McGruder, supt. Fax 723-4020
www.shirley.k12.ar.us/
Shirley JSHS 200/7-12
201 Blue Devil Dr 72153 501-723-8192
Randy Moore, prin. Fax 723-8114

Siloam Springs, Benton, Pop. 14,431
Siloam Springs SD 4,200/PK-12
PO Box 798 72761 479-524-3191
Kendall Ramey, supt. Fax 524-8002
www.siloamschools.com
Siloam Springs HS 1,300/9-12
700 N Progress Ave 72761 479-524-5134
Jason Jones, prin. Fax 524-8211
Siloam Springs MS 600/7-8
600 S Dogwood St 72761 479-524-6184
Teresa Morgan, prin. Fax 524-3228

John Brown University Post-Sec.
2000 W University St 72761 479-524-9500

Smackover, Union, Pop. 1,823
Smackover-Norphlet SD 900/K-12
112 E 8th St 71762 870-725-3132
Dave Wilcox, supt. Fax 725-1250
www.smackover.net
Smackover HS 300/9-12
1 Buckaroo Ln 71762 870-725-3101
Jan Henderson, prin. Fax 725-2540
Other Schools – See Norphlet

Sparkman, Dallas, Pop. 421
Harmony Grove SD
Supt. — See Camden
Sparkman HS 100/7-12
PO Box 37 71763 870-678-9312
Todd Lewis, prin. Fax 678-2917

Springdale, Washington, Pop. 64,520
Springdale SD 20,500/PK-12
PO Box 8 72765 479-750-8800
Dr. Jim Rollins, supt. Fax 750-8812
www.sdale.org
Archer Learning Center 300/Alt
500 E Meadow Ave 72764 479-750-8773
Mr. Shawna Lyons, prin. Fax 750-8778
Central JHS 900/8-9
2811 W Huntsville Ave 72762 479-750-8854
Paul Griep, prin. Fax 750-8700
George JHS 700/8-9
3200 Powell St 72764 479-750-8750
La Dena Eads, prin. Fax 750-8756
Har-Ber HS 1,800/10-12
300 Jones Rd 72762 479-750-8777
Dr. Daniel Brackett, prin. Fax 306-4250
Lakeside JHS 700/8-9
3050 Hylton Rd 72764 479-750-8885
Dr. Michael Shepherd, prin. Fax 750-8701
Sonora MS 800/6-8
17051 E Highway 412 72764 479-750-8821
Martha Dodson, prin. Fax 750-8823
Southwest JHS 700/8-9
1807 Princeton Ave 72762 479-750-8849
Shannon Tisher, prin. Fax 750-8704
Springdale HS 2,200/10-12
101 S Pleasant St 72764 479-750-8832
Peter Joenks, prin. Fax 750-8811

Baptist School of Nursing-NW Post-Sec.
610 E Emma Ave 72764 479-750-6200
Ecclesia College Post-Sec.
9653 Nations Dr 72762 479-248-7236
Northwest Technical Institute Post-Sec.
PO Box 2000 72765 479-751-8824
Shiloh Christian S 900/PK-12
1707 Johnson Rd 72762 479-756-1140
Greg Jones, pres. Fax 756-7229

Stamps, Columbia, Pop. 1,678
Lafayette County SD
Supt. — See Lewisville
Lafayette County HS 300/7-12
1209 Alexander Ln 71860 870-533-4464
Opal Anderson, prin. Fax 533-2367

Star City, Lincoln, Pop. 2,243
Star City SD 1,600/K-12
400 E Arkansas St 71667 870-628-4237
Jon Laffoon, supt. Fax 628-4228
www.starcityschools.com
Star City HS 500/9-12
400 E Arkansas St 71667 870-628-4111
Mike Walker, prin. Fax 628-4165
Star City MS 400/6-8
400 E Arkansas St 71667 870-628-5125
Gina Richard, prin. Fax 628-1393

State University, Craighead

Arkansas State University Post-Sec.
PO Box 600 72467 870-972-2100

Strawberry, Lawrence, Pop. 295
Hillcrest SD 400/K-12
PO Box 50 72469 870-528-3856
Greg Crabtree, supt. Fax 528-3383
hillcrest.k12.ar.us
Hillcrest JSHS 200/7-12
PO Box 50 72469 870-528-3856
Mike Smith, prin. Fax 528-3383

Strong, Union, Pop. 548
Strong-Huttig SD 400/K-12
PO Box 735 71765 870-797-3040
Jeff Alphin, supt. Fax 797-3012
strong.k12.ar.us
Strong HS 200/7-12
PO Box 735 71765 870-797-7322
Jeff Alphin, admin. Fax 797-2257

Stuttgart, Arkansas, Pop. 9,196
Stuttgart SD 1,700/K-12
2501 S Main St 72160 870-673-8701
Nathan Gills, supt. Fax 673-7337
www.stuttgartschools.org
Stuttgart HS 500/9-12
2501 S Main St 72160 870-673-3561
Donnie Boothe, prin. Fax 673-7337
Stuttgart JHS 200/7-8
2501 S Main St 72160 870-673-3562
Cedric Hawkins, prin. Fax 673-7337

Subiaco, Logan, Pop. 567

Subiaco Academy 200/7-12
405 N Subiaco Ave 72865 479-934-1005
Matt Stengel, hdmstr. Fax 934-1033

Taylor, Columbia, Pop. 562
Emerson-Taylor-Bradley SD 1,000/PK-12
506 E Pine St 71861 870-694-2251
Gary Hines, supt. Fax 694-1261
www.etbsd.org
Taylor HS 100/7-12
506 E Pine St 71861 870-694-2251
David Downs, prin. Fax 694-2901
Other Schools – See Bradley, Emerson

Texarkana, Miller, Pop. 29,379
Genoa Central SD 1,100/PK-12
12472 Highway 196 71854 870-653-4343
Angie Bryant, supt. Fax 653-2624
www.dragons1.k12.ar.us
Cobb MS 300/5-8
11986 Highway 196 71854 870-653-2132
Deloris Coe, prin. Fax 653-6944
Genoa Central HS 300/9-12
12472 Highway 196 71854 870-653-2272
Debbie Huff, prin. Fax 653-6967

Texarkana Arkansas SD 4,300/K-12
3435 Jefferson Ave 71854 870-772-3371
Dr. Becky Kesler, supt. Fax 773-2602
www.tasd7.net
Arkansas Magnet HS 1,100/9-12
3512 Grand Ave 71854 870-774-7641
Eva Nadeau, prin. Fax 773-8408
North Heights Magnet JHS 600/7-8
3512 Grand Ave 71854 870-773-1091
Theresa Cowling, prin. Fax 772-2722
Texarkana Career & Technology Center Vo/Tech
3512 Grand Ave 71854 870-774-7641
Natasha Hampton, prin.

Trinity Christian S 300/PK-12
3107 Trinity Blvd 71854 870-779-1009
Veritas Academy 50/K-12
2101 E 50th St 71854 870-772-0646
Ben House, hdmstr.

Timbo, Stone
Mountain View SD
Supt. — See Mountain View
Timbo S 100/K-12
23747 Highway 263 72680 870-746-4303
Jimmy Lowery, prin. Fax 746-4844

Trumann, Poinsett, Pop. 7,174
Trumann SD 1,400/K-12
221 N Pine Ave 72472 870-483-6444
Myra Graham, supt. Fax 483-2602
www.trumannwildcat.com
Trumann HS 400/9-12
1620 W Main St 72472 870-483-5301
Joshua Shepherd, prin. Fax 483-0227
Trumann IS 200/5-8
221 N Pine Ave 72472 870-483-5356
Josh Byard, prin. Fax 483-2602

Tuckerman, Jackson, Pop. 1,848
Jackson County SD 900/PK-12
PO Box 1070 72473 870-349-2232
Chester Shannon, supt. Fax 349-2355
bulldogs.k12.ar.us/
Tuckerman HS 300/8-12
PO Box 1070 72473 870-349-2657
Michael Holland, prin. Fax 349-2294

Umpire, Howard
Cossatot River SD
Supt. — See Wickes
Umpire HS 100/7-12
PO Box 60 71971 870-583-2141
Carla Golden, prin. Fax 583-6364

Valley Springs, Boone, Pop. 182
Valley Springs SD 900/K-12
PO Box 640 72682 870-429-9200
Judith Green, supt. Fax 429-5551
valley.k12.ar.us
Valley Springs HS 300/9-12
PO Box 640 72682 870-429-9200
Ronnie Ruff, prin. Fax 429-8160
Valley Springs MS 300/5-8
PO Box 640 72682 870-429-9200
Tony Mincer, prin. Fax 429-8121

Van Buren, Crawford, Pop. 22,172
Van Buren SD 5,500/K-12
2221 E Pointer Trl 72956 479-474-7942
Dr. Harold Jeffcoat, supt. Fax 471-3146
www.vbsd.us
Butterfield Trail MS 700/6-8
310 N 11th St 72956 479-474-6838
Dr. Karen Endel, prin. Fax 471-3101
Northridge MS 700/6-8
120 Northridge Dr 72956 479-471-3126
Lonnie Mitchell, prin. Fax 471-3129
Van Buren Freshman Academy 200/9-9
821 E Pointer Trl 72956 479-471-3160
Lisa Miller, prin. Fax 471-0249
Van Buren HS 1,300/10-12
2001 E Pointer Trl 72956 479-474-6821
Eddie Tipton, prin. Fax 471-3199

Vilonia, Faulkner, Pop. 3,760
Vilonia SD 2,100/K-12
PO Box 160 72173 501-796-2113
David Stephens, supt. Fax 796-3134
www.viloniaschools.org
Vilonia Freshman Academy 200/9-9
1164 Main St Ste A 72173 501-796-2037
Ronnie Simmons, prin. Fax 796-4326
Vilonia MS 300/7-8
49 Eagle St 72173 501-796-2940
Lori Lombardi, prin. Fax 796-4697
Vilonia SHS 700/10-12
1164 Main St 72173 501-796-2111
Matt Sewell, prin. Fax 796-8895

Viola, Fulton, Pop. 326
Viola SD 400/K-12
PO Box 380 72583 870-458-2323
John May, supt. Fax 458-2214
violaschool.k12.ar.us
Viola JSHS 200/7-12
PO Box 380 72583 870-458-2213
Vicki Hurst, prin. Fax 458-4049

Waldron, Scott, Pop. 3,541
Waldron SD 1,500/PK-12
1560 W 6th St 72958 479-637-3179
Roy Wayman, supt. Fax 637-3177
waldron.k12.ar.us
Waldron HS 500/9-12
736 W Highway 80 72958 479-637-3405
Daniel Fielding, prin. Fax 637-5624
Waldron MS 500/5-8
2075 Rice St 72958 479-637-4549
Kimberly Solomon, prin. Fax 637-3165

Walnut Ridge, Lawrence, Pop. 4,854
Lawrence County SD 800/K-12
508 E Free St 72476 870-886-6634
Terry Belcher, supt. Fax 886-6635
www.bobcats.k12.ar.us
Walnut Ridge JSHS 400/7-12
508 E Free St 72476 870-886-6623
Jacob Kersey, prin. Fax 819-0403

Williams Baptist College Post-Sec.
60 W Fulbright St 72476 870-886-6741

Western Grove, Newton, Pop. 373
Ozark Mountain SD
Supt. — See Saint Joe
Western Grove JSHS 100/7-12
300 School St 72685 870-429-5215
William Carter, prin. Fax 429-5276

West Fork, Washington, Pop. 2,246
West Fork SD 1,200/K-12
359 School Ave 72774 479-839-2231
John Karnes, supt. Fax 839-8412
www.westforkschools.org
West Fork HS 400/9-12
359 School Ave 72774 479-839-3131
John Crowder, prin. Fax 839-8412
West Fork MS 400/5-8
333 School Ave 72774 479-839-3342
Becky Ramsey, prin. Fax 839-8412

West Helena, Phillips, Pop. 7,876
Helena/West Helena SD
Supt. — See Helena
Central HS 800/7-12
103 School Rd 72390 870-572-6744
Earnest Simpson, prin. Fax 572-4502

De Soto S 300/PK-12
PO Box 2807 72390 870-572-6717

West Memphis, Crittenden, Pop. 26,012
West Memphis SD 5,600/K-12
301 S Avalon St 72301 870-735-1915
Jon Collins, supt. Fax 732-8643
www.wmsd.net
Academies Of West Memphis Charter S 1,100/10-12
501 W Broadway St 72301 870-735-3660
Gary Jackson, prin. Fax 732-8510
East JHS 300/7-9
1151 Goodwin Ave 72301 870-735-2081
Arther Quarrels, prin. Fax 732-8583
West JHS 500/7-9
331 W Barton Ave 72301 870-735-3161
Charlie Tyler, prin. Fax 732-8566
Wonder JHS 400/7-9
1401 Madison Ave 72301 870-735-8522
Dr. Palmer Quarrels, prin. Fax 732-8584
Other Schools – See Edmondson

Mid-South Community College Post-Sec.
2000 W Broadway St 72301 870-733-6722
West Memphis Christian S 200/PK-12
PO Box 996 72303 870-400-4000
Mary Anne Pike, hdmstr. Fax 400-4001

White Hall, Jefferson, Pop. 5,470
White Hall SD 3,000/K-12
1020 W Holland Ave 71602 870-247-2002
Dr. Larry Smith, supt. Fax 247-3707
www.whitehallsd.org/
White Hall HS 900/9-12
700 Bulldog Dr 71602 870-247-3255
Don Stringer, prin. Fax 247-2756
White Hall MS 700/6-8
8106 Dollarway Rd 71602 870-247-2711
Douglas Dorris, prin. Fax 247-4879

Wickes, Polk, Pop. 743
Cossatot River SD 1,100/PK-12
130 School Dr 71973 870-385-7101
Donnie Davis, supt. Fax 385-2238
www.cossatot.us
Other Schools – See Cove, Umpire

Wilson, Mississippi, Pop. 888
Rivercrest SD 1,000/PK-12
22 N Jefferson St 72395 870-655-8633
Mike Smith, supt. Fax 655-8841
www.smccolts.com
Rivercrest HS 400/9-12
1700 W State Highway 14 72395 870-655-8111
Dr. Tom Bennett, prin. Fax 655-8507
Rivercrest JHS 200/7-8
1702 W State Highway 14 72395 870-655-8421
William Fortson, prin. Fax 655-9980

Wynne, Cross, Pop. 8,285
Wynne SD 2,700/K-12
PO Box 69 72396 870-238-5020
Carl Easley, supt. Fax 238-5011
wynne.k12.ar.us
Wynne HS 800/9-12
PO Box 69 72396 870-238-5070
Keith Watson, prin. Fax 238-5009
Wynne JHS 600/6-8
PO Box 69 72396 870-238-5040
David Stepp, prin. Fax 238-5043

Yellville, Marion, Pop. 1,190
Yellville-Summit SD 500/K-12
1124 N Panther Ave 72687 870-449-4061
Wes Henderson, supt. Fax 449-5003
yellvillesummitschools.com
Yellville-Summit HS 300/7-12
1124 N Panther Ave 72687 870-449-4066
David Wyatt, prin. Fax 449-4773

CALIFORNIA

CALIFORNIA DEPARTMENT OF EDUCATION
1430 N St, Sacramento 95814-5901
Telephone 916-319-0800
Fax 916-319-0100
Website http://www.cde.ca.gov

Superintendent of Public Instruction Tom Torlakson

CALIFORNIA BOARD OF EDUCATION
1430 N St, Sacramento 95814-5901

President Dr. Michael Kirst

COUNTY SUPERINTENDENTS OF SCHOOLS

Alameda County Office of Education
Karen Monroe, supt. 510-887-0152
313 W Winton Ave, Hayward 94544 Fax 670-4146
www.acoe.org

Alpine County Office of Education
Patrick Traynor, supt. 530-694-2230
43 Hawkside Dr Fax 694-2379
Markleeville 96120
www.alpinecoe.k12.ca.us

Amador County Office of Education
Dick Glock, supt. 209-257-5353
217 Rex Ave, Jackson 95642 Fax 257-5360
www.amadorcoe.org/

Butte County Office of Education
Tim Taylor, supt. 530-532-5650
1859 Bird St, Oroville 95965 Fax 532-5762
www.bcoe.org

Calaveras County Office of Education
Kathy Northington, supt. 209-736-4662
PO Box 760, Angels Camp 95221 Fax 736-2138
www.ccoe.k12.ca.us

Colusa County Office of Education
Michael West, supt. 530-458-0350
345 5th St Ste A, Colusa 95932 Fax 458-8054
www.ccoe.net

Contra Costa County Office of Education
Dr. Karen Sakata, supt. 925-942-3388
77 Santa Barbara Rd Fax 472-0875
Pleasant Hill 94523
www.cccoe.k12.ca.us

Del Norte County Office of Education
Jeff Harris, supt. 707-464-0200
301 W Washington Blvd Fax 464-0238
Crescent City 95531
www.delnortecoe.org

El Dorado County Office of Education
Ed Manansala, supt. 530-622-7130
6767 Green Valley Rd Fax 621-2543
Placerville 95667
www.edcoe.org

Fresno County Office of Education
Jim Yovino, supt. 559-265-3000
1111 Van Ness Ave, Fresno 93721 Fax 265-4005
www.fcoe.org

Glenn County Office of Education
Tracey Quarne, supt. 530-934-6575
311 S Villa Ave, Willows 95988 Fax 934-6576
www.glenncoe.org

Humboldt County Office of Education
Garry Eagles Ph.D., supt. 707-445-7000
901 Myrtle Ave, Eureka 95501 Fax 445-7143
www.humboldt.k12.ca.us

Imperial County Office of Education
Jonathan Finnell, supt. 760-312-6464
1398 Sperber Rd, El Centro Fax 312-6568
www.icoe.org

Inyo County Office of Education
Dr. Lisa Fontana, supt. 760-878-2426
PO Box G, Independence 93526 Fax 878-2279
www.inyo.k12.ca.us

Kern County Office of Education
Christine Frazier, supt. 661-636-4000
1300 17th St, Bakersfield 93301 Fax 636-4130
www.kern.org/

Kings County Office of Education
Tim Bowers, supt. 559-584-1441
1144 W Lacey Blvd, Hanford 93230 Fax 589-7000
www.kings.k12.ca.us

Lake County Office of Education
Brock Falkenberg, supt. 707-262-4100
1152 S Main St, Lakeport 95453 Fax 263-0197
www.lakecoe.org

Lassen County Office of Education
Patricia Gunderson, supt. 530-257-2196
472-013 Johnstonville Rd Fax 257-2518
Susanville 96130
www.lcoe.org

Los Angeles County Office of Education
Dr. Debra Duardo, supt. 562-922-6111
9300 Imperial Hwy, Downey 90242 Fax 922-6768
www.lacoe.edu

Madera County Office of Education
Cecilia Massetti Ed.D., supt. 559-673-6051
1105 S Madera Ave, Madera 93637 Fax 673-5569
www.maderacoe.k12.ca.us

Marin County Office of Education
Mike Grant, supt. 415-472-4110
PO Box 4925, San Rafael 94913 Fax 491-6625
www.marinschools.org/

Mariposa County Office of Education
Robin Hopper, supt. 209-742-0250
PO Box 8, Mariposa 95338 Fax 966-4549
www.mariposa.k12.ca.us

Mendocino County Office of Education
Warren Galletti, supt. 707-467-5000
2240 Old River Rd, Ukiah 95482 Fax 462-0379
www.mcoe.us

Merced County Office of Education
Steven Gomes Ed.D., supt. 209-381-6600
632 W 13th St, Merced 95341 Fax 381-6767
www.mcoe.org

Modoc County Office of Education
Mike Martin, supt. 530-233-7100
139 Henderson St, Alturas 96101 Fax 233-5531
www.modoccoe.k12.ca.us

Mono County Office of Education
Stacey Adler, supt. 760-932-7311
PO Box 477, Bridgeport 93517 Fax 932-7278
www.monocoe.org

Monterey County Office of Education
Dr. Nancy Kotowski, supt. 831-755-0300
PO Box 80851, Salinas 93912 Fax 753-6473
www.montereycoe.org

Napa County Office of Education
Barbara Nemko, supt. 707-253-6800
2121 Imola Ave, Napa 94559 Fax 253-6841
www.napacoe.org

Nevada County Office of Education
Holly Hermansen, supt. 530-478-6400
112 Nevada City Hwy Fax 478-6410
Nevada City 95959
www.nevco.org/

Orange County Office of Education
Al Mijares, supt. 714-966-4000
PO Box 9050, Costa Mesa 92628 Fax 662-3570
www.ocde.us

Placer County Office of Education
Gayle Garbolino-Mojica, supt. 530-889-8020
360 Nevada St, Auburn 95603 Fax 888-1367
www.placercoe.k12.ca.us

Plumas County Office of Education
Terry Oestreich, admin. 530-283-6500
1446 E Main St, Quincy 95971 Fax 283-6530
www.pcoe.k12.ca.us

Riverside County Office of Education
Kenneth Young, supt. 951-826-6530
PO Box 868, Riverside 92502 Fax 826-6199
www.rcoe.us

Sacramento County Office of Education
David Gordon, supt. 916-228-2500
10474 Mather Blvd, Mather 95655 Fax 228-2403
www.scoe.net

San Benito County Office of Education
Lorna Gilbert, supt. 831-637-5393
460 5th St, Hollister 95023 Fax 637-0140
www.sbcoe.org

San Bernardino Co. Office of Education
Ted Alejandre, supt. 909-386-2704
601 N E St, San Bernardino 92415 Fax 386-2478
www.sbcss.k12.ca.us

San Diego County Office of Education
Randolph Ward, supt. 858-292-3500
6401 Linda Vista Rd Fax 292-3653
San Diego 92111
www.sdcoe.net

San Francisco County Office of Education
Myong Leigh, supt., 555 Franklin St 415-241-6000
San Francisco 94102 Fax 241-6012
www.sfusd.edu

San Joaquin County Office of Education
Dr. James Mousalimas, supt. 209-468-4800
PO Box 213030, Stockton 95213 Fax 468-4819
www.sjcoe.org

San Luis Obispo Co. Office of Education
James Brescia, supt. 805-543-7732
3350 Education Dr Fax 541-1105
San Luis Obispo 93405
www.slocoe.org

San Mateo County Office of Education
Anne Campbell, supt. 650-802-5300
101 Twin Dolphin Dr Fax 802-5564
Redwood City 94065
www.smcoe.org

Santa Barbara County Office of Education
William Cirone, supt. 805-964-4711
PO Box 6307, Santa Barbara 93160 Fax 964-4712
sbceo.org

Santa Clara County Office of Education
Dr. Jon Gundry, supt. 408-453-6500
1290 Ridder Park Dr Fax 453-6601
San Jose 95131
www.sccoe.org

Santa Cruz County Office of Education
Michael Watkins, supt. 831-466-5600
400 Encinal St, Santa Cruz 95060 Fax 466-5607
www.santacruz.k12.ca.us

Shasta County Office of Education
Tom Armelino, supt. 530-225-0200
1644 Magnolia Ave Fax 225-0329
Redding 96001
www.shastacoe.org

Sierra County Office of Education
Merrill Grant, supt. 530-993-1660
PO Box 955, Loyalton 96118 Fax 993-0828
www.sierracountyofficeofeducation.org/

Siskiyou County Office of Education
Kermith Walters, dir. 530-842-8400
609 S Gold St, Yreka 96097 Fax 842-8436
www.siskiyoucoe.net/

Solano County Office of Education
Jay Speck, supt. 707-399-4400
5100 Business Center Dr Fax 863-4174
Fairfield
www.solanocoe.net/

Sonoma County Office of Education
Steven D. Herrington Ph.D., supt. 707-524-2600
5340 Skylane Blvd Fax 578-0220
Santa Rosa 95403
www.scoe.org/

Stanislaus County Office of Education
Tom Changnon, supt. 209-238-1700
1100 H St, Modesto 95354 Fax 238-4201
www.stancoe.org/

Sutter County Office of Education
Bill Cornelius, supt. 530-822-2900
970 Klamath Ln, Yuba City 95993 Fax 671-3422
www.sutter.k12.ca.us

Tehama County Department of Education
Richard DuVarney, supt. 530-527-5811
1135 Lincoln St, Red Bluff 96080 Fax 529-4120
www.tehamaschools.org/

Trinity County Office of Education
Bettina Blackwell, supt. 530-623-2861
PO Box 1256, Weaverville 96093 Fax 623-4489
www.tcoek12.org/

Tulare County Office of Education
Jim Vidak, supt. 559-733-6300
PO Box 5091, Visalia 93278 Fax 737-4378
www.tcoe.org/

Tuolumne County Office of Education
Marguerite Bulkin, supt. 209-536-2000
175 Fairview Ln, Sonora 95370 Fax 536-2003
www.tcsos.us

Ventura County Office of Education
Stan Mantooth, supt. 805-383-1900
5189 Verdugo Way Fax 383-1908
Camarillo 93012
www.vcoe.org

Yolo County Office of Education
Jesse Ortiz, supt. 530-668-6700
1280 Santa Anita Ct Ste 100 Fax 668-3848
Woodland 95776
www.ycoe.org

Yuba County Office of Education
Francisco Reveles, supt. 530-749-4900
935 14th St, Marysville 95901 Fax 741-6500
www.yuba.net/

PUBLIC, PRIVATE AND CATHOLIC SECONDARY SCHOOLS

Acton, Los Angeles, Pop. 7,398
Acton-Agua Dulce USD 1,300/K-12
32248 Crown Valley Rd 93510 661-269-5999
Dr. Brent Woodard, supt. Fax 269-0849
aadusd.k12.ca.us/
High Desert MS 300/6-8
3620 Antelope Woods Rd 93510 661-269-0310
Lynn David, prin. Fax 269-9336
Vasquez HS 400/9-12
33630 Red Rover Mine Rd 93510 661-269-0410
Tyrone Devoe, prin. Fax 269-5325

Adelanto, San Bernardino, Pop. 30,727
Adelanto ESD 8,300/K-8
PO Box 70 92301 760-246-8691
Dr. Edwin Gomez, supt. Fax 246-8259
www.aesd.net
Columbia MS 400/7-8
PO Box 70 92301 760-530-1950
Richard Upshaw, prin. Fax 530-1953
Other Schools – See Victorville

Agoura Hills, Los Angeles, Pop. 19,692
Las Virgenes USD
Supt. — See Calabasas
Agoura HS 2,200/9-12
28545 Driver Ave 91301 818-889-1262
Brian Mercer, prin. Fax 597-0816
Indian Hills Continuation HS - West 50/Alt
28545 Driver Ave 91301 818-889-1262
Brian Mercer, prin. Fax 597-0816
Lindero Canyon MS 1,000/6-8
5844 Larboard Ln 91301 818-889-2134
Dr. Abbe Irshay, prin. Fax 889-9432

Alameda, Alameda, Pop. 69,145
Alameda City USD 10,600/PK-12
2060 Challenger Dr 94501 510-337-7000
Sean McPhetridge Ed.D., supt. Fax 522-6926
www.alameda.k12.ca.us
Alameda HS 1,800/9-12
2201 Encinal Ave 94501 510-337-7022
Robert Ithurburn, prin. Fax 521-4740
Alameda Science & Technical Institute 200/9-12
2060 Challenger Dr 94501 510-337-7059
Tracy Corbally, dean Fax 337-7163
Encinal JSHS 1,000/6-12
210 Central Ave 94501 510-748-4023
Kirsten Zazo, prin. Fax 521-4956
Island Continuation HS 200/Alt
500 Pacific Ave 94501 510-748-4024
Ben Washofsky, prin. Fax 769-7417
Lincoln MS 1,000/6-8
1250 Fernside Blvd 94501 510-748-4018
Michael Hans, prin. Fax 523-6217
Wood MS 400/6-8
420 Grand St 94501 510-748-4015
Cammie Harris, prin. Fax 523-8829
Alameda Adult S Adult
500 Pacific Ave 94501 510-522-3858
Joy Chua, prin. Fax 522-0846

Regional Occupational Center & Program
Supt. — None
East Bay ROP Vo/Tech
1900 3rd St Rm 23 94501 510-879-3037
Brigitte Marshall, dir.

Alameda Beauty College Post-Sec.
2318 Central Ave 94501 510-523-1050
Argosy University San Francisco Campus Post-Sec.
1005 Atlantic Ave 94501 510-217-4700
College of Alameda Post-Sec.
555 Ralph Appezzato Mem Pky 94501
510-522-7221
St. Joseph Notre Dame HS 400/9-12
1011 Chestnut St 94501 510-523-1526
Milt Werner, prin. Fax 523-2181

Alamo, Contra Costa, Pop. 14,161
San Ramon Valley USD
Supt. — See Danville
Stone Valley MS 600/6-8
3001 Miranda Ave 94507 925-855-5800
Jon Campopiano, prin. Fax 838-5680

Albany, Alameda, Pop. 17,446
Albany City USD 3,800/PK-12
1051 Monroe St 94706 510-558-3750
Valerie Williams, supt. Fax 559-6560
www.ausdk12.org
Albany HS 1,200/9-12
603 Key Route Blvd 94706 510-558-2500
Jeff Anderson, prin. Fax 559-6584
Albany MS 900/6-8
1259 Brighton Ave 94706 510-558-3600
Deborah Brill, prin. Fax 559-6547
MacGregor Continuation HS 50/Alt
603 Key Route Blvd 94706 510-559-6570
Daren McNally, prin. Fax 559-6572

Tilden Preparatory S 100/6-12
1231 Solano Ave 94706 510-525-5506

Alhambra, Los Angeles, Pop. 81,736
Alhambra USD 17,700/K-12
1515 W Mission Rd 91803 626-943-3000
Laura Tellez-Gagliano Ed.D., supt. Fax 943-8050
www.ausd.us
Alhambra HS 2,700/9-12
101 S 2nd St 91801 626-943-6910
Duane Russell, prin. Fax 308-2344
Century HS 200/Alt
20 S Marengo Ave 91801 626-943-6680
Phuong Nguyen, prin. Fax 308-2299
Independence HS 100/Alt
20 S Marengo Ave 91801 626-943-6681
Phuong Nguyen, prin. Fax 308-2299
Keppel HS 2,400/9-12
501 E Hellman Ave 91801 626-943-6710
John Scanlan, prin. Fax 572-2217
Other Schools – See San Gabriel

Alhambra Beauty College Post-Sec.
200 W Main St 91801 626-282-6433
Alhambra Medical University Post-Sec.
25 S Raymond Ave Ste 201 91801 626-289-7719
Alliant International University Post-Sec.
1000 S Fremont Ave Unit 5 91803 626-270-3300
Everest College Post-Sec.
2215 W Mission Rd 91803 626-979-4940
Foothill Preparatory S 50/9-12
101 S Atlantic Blvd 91801 626-282-9936
Lily Liu, dir. Fax 282-9937
Platt College Alhambra Post-Sec.
1000 S Fremont Ave Ste A9W 91803 626-300-5444
Ramona Convent Secondary S 300/9-12
1701 W Ramona Rd 91803 626-282-4151
Mary Mansell, prin. Fax 281-0797

Aliso Viejo, Orange, Pop. 45,578
Capistrano USD
Supt. — See San Juan Capistrano
Aliso Niguel HS 3,000/9-12
28000 Wolverine Way 92656 949-831-5590
Deni Christensen, prin. Fax 448-9854
Aliso Viejo MS 1,100/6-8
111 Park Ave 92656 949-831-2622
Cynthia Steinert, prin. Fax 643-2784
Avila MS 1,200/6-8
26278 Wood Canyon Dr 92656 949-362-0348
Josh Wellikson, prin. Fax 362-9076

Soka University of America Post-Sec.
1 University Dr 92656 949-480-4000

Alpaugh, Tulare, Pop. 1,021
Alpaugh USD 600/PK-12
PO Box 9 93201 559-949-8413
Dr. Robert Hudson, supt. Fax 949-8173
www.tcoe.org/districts/alpaugh.shtm
Alpaugh JSHS 100/7-12
PO Box 9 93201 559-949-8413
Nancy Ruble, prin. Fax 949-8173
Tule Continuation HS 50/Alt
PO Box 9 93201 559-949-8644
Dr. Robert Hudson, dir. Fax 949-8173

Alpine, San Diego, Pop. 13,892
Alpine UNESD 1,800/PK-8
1323 Administration Way 91901 619-445-3236
Dr. Richard Newman, supt. Fax 445-7045
www.alpineschools.net
MacQueen MS 600/6-8
2001 Tavern Rd 91901 619-445-3245
Theresa Meyerott, prin. Fax 445-6503

Altadena, Los Angeles, Pop. 40,865
Pasadena USD
Supt. — See Pasadena
Eliot MS 600/6-8
2184 Lake Ave 91001 626-396-5680
Lori Touloumian, prin. Fax 794-7238

Pasadena Waldorf S 200/PK-12
209 E Mariposa St 91001 626-794-9564
Renaissance Academy 100/K-12
119 W Palm St 91001 626-765-9358
Sandra Staffer, dir. Fax 765-9360

Alta Loma, San Bernardino
Alta Loma ESD 6,000/K-8
9390 Baseline Rd 91701 909-484-5151
James Moore, supt. Fax 484-5155
www.alsd.k12.ca.us/pages/Alta_Loma_School_District
Alta Loma JHS 700/7-8
9000 Lemon Ave 91701 909-484-5100
Susanne Melton, prin. Fax 484-5105
Vineyard JHS 800/7-8
6440 Mayberry Ave 91737 909-484-5120
Sandy Rose, prin. Fax 484-5125

Chaffey JUNHSD
Supt. — See Ontario
Alta Loma HS 2,600/9-12
8880 Baseline Rd 91701 909-989-5511
Jason Kaylor, prin. Fax 391-5336

Altaville, Calaveras
Bret Harte UNHSD
Supt. — See Angels Camp
Vallecito Continuation HS 50/Alt
364 Murphys Grade Rd 95221 209-736-8327
Tracie Baughn, prin. Fax 736-0598

Alturas, Modoc, Pop. 2,746
Modoc JUSD 800/K-12
906 W 4th St 96101 530-233-7201
Tom O'Malley, supt. Fax 233-4362
www.modoc.k12.ca.us
High Desert Community Day S 50/Alt
802 N East St 96101 530-233-7201
Tom O'Malley, prin. Fax 233-5158
Modoc HS 200/9-12
900 N Main St 96101 530-233-7201
Brian Norby, prin. Fax 233-7306
Modoc MS 200/6-8
906 W 4th St 96101 530-233-7201
Noelle Knight, prin. Fax 233-7503
Warner Continuation HS 50/Alt
802 N East St 96101 530-233-7201
Tom O'Malley, prin. Fax 233-5158

Regional Occupational Center & Program
Supt. — None
Modoc County ROP Vo/Tech
139 Henderson St 96101 530-233-7102
Marian Hall, dir.

American Canyon, Napa, Pop. 18,364
Napa Valley USD
Supt. — See Napa
American Canyon HS 1,500/9-12
3000 Newell Dr 94503 707-267-2710
Damon Wright, prin. Fax 644-1139
American Canyon MS 1,000/6-8
300 Benton Way 94503 707-259-8592
Dan Scudero, prin. Fax 259-8800
Legacy HS, 3000 Newell Dr 94503 50/Alt
Damon Wright, prin. 707-265-2710

Anaheim, Orange, Pop. 327,991
Anaheim UNHSD 31,600/7-12
501 N Crescent Way 92801 714-999-3511
Michael B. Matsuda, supt. Fax 535-1706
www.auhsd.us
Anaheim HS 3,200/9-12
811 W Lincoln Ave 92805 714-999-3717
Dr. Anna Corral, prin. Fax 772-6537
Ball JHS 1,100/7-8
1500 W Ball Rd 92802 714-999-3663
Dr. Karen Dabney-Lieras, prin. Fax 563-9214
Brookhurst JHS 1,200/7-8
601 N Brookhurst St 92801 714-999-3613
Sam Joo, prin. Fax 999-1764
Dale JHS 1,200/7-8
900 S Dale Ave 92804 714-220-4210
Lorena Moreno, prin. Fax 220-4076
Gilbert HS 800/Alt
1800 W Ball Rd 92804 714-999-3738
Jei Garlitos, coord. Fax 999-5651
Katella HS 2,600/9-12
2200 E Wagner Ave 92806 714-999-3621
Dr. Ben Carpenter, prin. Fax 535-3991
Loara HS 2,500/9-12
1765 W Cerritos Ave 92804 714-999-3677
Katrina Callaway, prin. Fax 999-3703
Magnolia HS 1,900/9-12
2450 W Ball Rd 92804 714-220-4221
Daphne Hammer, prin. Fax 220-4233
Orangeview JHS 900/7-8
3715 W Orange Ave 92804 714-220-4205
Robert Saldivar, prin. Fax 220-3023
Polaris HS 200/Alt
1800 W Ball Rd 92804 714-999-3738
Jei Garlitos, coord. Fax 999-5651
Savanna HS 2,100/9-12
301 N Gilbert St 92801 714-220-4262
Carlos Hernandez, prin. Fax 995-2544
South JHS 1,600/7-8
2320 E South St 92806 714-999-3667
Fax 999-3721
Sycamore JHS 1,500/7-8
1801 E Sycamore St 92805 714-999-3616
Gary Brown, prin. Fax 776-3879
Western HS 2,200/9-12
501 S Western Ave 92804 714-220-4040
Joe Carmona, prin. Fax 220-4027
Other Schools – See Cypress, La Palma

Orange USD
Supt. — See Orange
Canyon HS 2,400/9-12
220 S Imperial Hwy 92807 714-532-8000
James Abercrombie, prin. Fax 921-0278

Placentia-Yorba Linda USD
Supt. — See Placentia
Esperanza HS 1,800/9-12
1830 N Kellogg Dr 92807 714-985-7540
Ken Fox, prin. Fax 693-7527

Regional Occupational Center & Program
Supt. — None
North Orange County ROP Vo/Tech
385 N Muller St 92801 714-502-5800
Dr. Michael Worley, supt. Fax 766-3880

Acaciawood S 100/1-12
2530 W La Palma Ave 92801 714-995-1800
American Career College - Orange County Post-Sec.
1200 N Magnolia Ave 92801 714-763-9066
Anaheim University Post-Sec.
1240 S State College # 110 92806 714-772-3330
Bethesda University of California Post-Sec.
730 N Euclid St 92801 714-517-1945
Bristol University Post-Sec.
2390 E Orangewood Ave # 485 92806714-542-8086
Brownson Technical School Post-Sec.
1110 S Technology Cir Ste D 92805 714-774-9443
California Career School Post-Sec.
1100 S Technology Cir 92805 714-635-6585
CA University of Management and Sciences Post-Sec.
721 N Euclid St 92801 714-533-3946
Connelly HS 200/9-12
2323 W Broadway 92804 714-776-1717
Sr. Francine Gunther, head sch Fax 776-2534
Evangelia University Post-Sec.
2660 W Woodland Dr Ste 200 92801 714-527-0691
Everest College Post-Sec.
511 N Brookhurst St Ste 300 92801 714-953-6500
Fairmont Preparatory Academy 700/9-12
2200 W Sequoia Ave 92801 714-999-5055
Robert Mendoza, hdmstr. Fax 999-0150
Integrity Christian S 100/1-12
4905 E La Palma Ave 92807 714-693-2022
Shelly Kitada, prin.
Orange County Christian S 300/PK-12
641 S Western Ave 92804 714-821-6227
David Lewis, admin. Fax 952-8823

Servite HS 1,000/9-12
1952 W La Palma Ave 92801 714-774-7575
Michael Brennan, prin. Fax 774-1404
South Baylo University Post-Sec.
1126 N Brookhurst St 92801 714-533-1495
Southern California Institute of Tech Post-Sec.
525 N Muller St 92801 714-300-0300
West Coast University Post-Sec.
1477 S Manchester Ave 92802 714-782-1700
Westwood College - Anaheim Post-Sec.
1551 S Douglass Rd 92806 714-704-2720

Anderson, Shasta, Pop. 9,521
Anderson UNHSD 2,000/9-12
1469 Ferry St 96007 530-378-0568
Tim Azevedo, supt. Fax 378-0834
www.auhsd.net
Anderson HS 700/9-12
1471 Ferry St 96007 530-365-2741
Brian Parker, prin. Fax 365-5446
North Valley HS 100/Alt
20083 Olinda Rd 96007 530-365-6054
Brandt Shriner, prin. Fax 378-1264
Oakview HS 100/Alt
20083 Olinda Rd 96007 530-378-6895
Brandt Shriner, prin. Fax 365-0801
Anderson Adult Education Adult
5250 W Anderson Dr 96007 530-365-3334
Brandt Shriner, prin. Fax 365-8440
Other Schools – See Cottonwood

Cascade UNESD 1,200/K-8
1645 Mill St 96007 530-378-7000
Jason Provence, supt. Fax 378-7001
www.cuesd.com
Anderson MS 500/5-8
1646 Ferry St 96007 530-378-7060
Christopher Cerbone, prin. Fax 378-7061

Happy Valley UNESD 500/K-8
17480 Palm Ave 96007 530-357-2134
Janet Tufts, supt. Fax 357-4143
www.hvesd.org
Happy Valley MS 200/5-8
17480 Palm Ave 96007 530-357-2111
Janet Tufts, prin. Fax 357-4193

Angels Camp, Calaveras, Pop. 2,997
Bret Harte UNHSD 700/9-12
PO Box 7000 95221 209-736-8340
Michael Chimente, supt. Fax 736-8367
www.bhuhsd.k12.ca.us
Bret Harte Union HS 700/9-12
364 Murphys Grade Rd 95222 209-736-2507
Tracie Baughn, prin. Fax 736-8383
Vierra HS 50/Alt
364 Murphys Grade Rd 95222 209-736-8327
Tracie Baughn, prin. Fax 736-0598
Other Schools – See Altaville

Calaveras County Office of Education 500/
PO Box 760 95221 209-736-4662
Kathy Northington, supt. Fax 736-2138
www.ccoe.k12.ca.us
Calaveras County Adult Education Adult
PO Box 760 95221 209-754-1996
Colby Barker, prin. Fax 754-4261
Other Schools – See San Andreas

Angwin, Napa, Pop. 2,912

Pacific Union College Post-Sec.
1 Angwin Ave 94508 707-965-6311
Pacific Union College Prep S 100/9-12
1 Angwin Ave 94508 707-200-2648

Antelope, Sacramento, Pop. 42,966
Center JUSD 4,600/K-12
8408 Watt Ave 95843 916-338-6330
Scott Loehr, supt. Fax 338-6411
www.centerusd.k12.ca.us
Center HS 1,300/9-12
3111 Center Court Ln 95843 916-338-6420
Mike Jordan, prin. Fax 338-6370
McClellan Continuation HS 100/Alt
8725 Watt Ave 95843 916-338-6440
David French, prin. Fax 338-6535
Center Adult S Adult
3401 Scotland Dr 95843 916-338-6387
Fax 338-6386
Other Schools – See Roseville

Dry Creek JESD
Supt. — See Roseville
Antelope Crossing MS 1,000/6-8
9200 Palmerson Dr 95843 916-745-2100
Jon Smith, prin. Fax 745-2135

Roseville JUNHSD
Supt. — See Roseville
Antelope HS 1,800/9-12
7801 Titan Dr 95843 916-726-1400
John Becker, prin. Fax 726-0700

Antioch, Contra Costa, Pop. 96,748
Antioch USD 17,900/K-12
510 G St 94509 925-779-7500
Stephanie Anello Ed.D., supt. Fax 779-7509
www.antioch.k12.ca.us
Antioch HS 1,800/9-12
700 W 18th St 94509 925-779-7550
Louie Rocha, prin. Fax 779-7567
Antioch MS 800/6-8
1500 D St 94509 925-779-7400
Lindsay Wisely, prin. Fax 779-7414
Bidwell HS 200/Alt
800 Gary Ave 94509 925-779-7520
Carol Lowart, prin. Fax 779-7521

Black Diamond MS 700/6-8
4730 Sterling Hill Dr 94531 925-776-5500
Phyllis James, prin. Fax 779-2600
Dallas Ranch MS 1,300/6-8
1401 Mount Hamilton Dr 94531 925-779-7485
Ed Dacus, prin. Fax 706-1933
Deer Valley HS 2,600/9-12
4700 Lone Tree Way 94531 925-776-5555
Kenneth Gardner, prin. Fax 754-8094
Dozier-Libbey Medical HS 600/9-12
4900 Sand Creek Rd 94531 925-779-7540
Scott Bergerhouse, prin. Fax 779-7542
Live Oak Continuation HS 200/Alt
1708 F St 94509 925-779-7440
Tim Cooper, prin. Fax 779-7441
Park MS 1,000/6-8
1 Spartan Way 94509 925-779-7420
John Jimno, prin. Fax 779-7421
Prospects HS 400/Alt
820 W 2nd St 94509 925-779-7490
Mike Santos, prin. Fax 779-7491
Antioch Adult S Adult
820 W 2nd St 94509 925-779-7490
Carol Lowart, prin. Fax 775-7491

Cornerstone Christian S 500/PK-12
1745 E 18th St 94509 925-779-2010
Heritage Baptist Academy 100/K-12
5200 Heidorn Ranch Rd 94531 925-778-2234
Rev. Jim Oesterwind M.A., admin. Fax 757-2848

Anza, Riverside, Pop. 2,927
Hemet USD
Supt. — See Hemet
Hamilton HS 300/9-12
57430 Mitchell Rd 92539 951-763-1865
Dave Farkas, prin. Fax 763-5420

Apple Valley, San Bernardino, Pop. 66,794
Apple Valley USD 14,400/PK-12
12555 Navajo Rd 92308 760-247-8001
Thomas Hoegerman, supt. Fax 247-4103
www.avusd.org
Apple Valley HS 2,200/9-12
11837 Navajo Rd 92308 760-247-7206
Dustin Conrad, prin. Fax 247-2092
Granite Hills HS 1,600/9-12
22900 Esaws Rd 92307 760-961-2290
Charles McCall, prin. Fax 961-8755
Apple Valley Adult S Adult
21950 Nisqually Rd 92308 760-240-4252
Kim Brock, prin. Fax 240-1261

Apple Valley Christian S 200/PK-12
22230 Ottawa Rd 92308 760-995-3516
Rev. John Richart, admin. Fax 995-3524

Aptos, Santa Cruz, Pop. 6,003
Pajaro Valley USD
Supt. — See Watsonville
Aptos HS 1,400/9-12
100 Mariner Way 95003 831-688-6565
Peggy Pughe, prin. Fax 688-6430
Aptos JHS 700/7-8
1001 Huntington Dr 95003 831-688-3234
Rich Moran, prin. Fax 728-8139

Cabrillo College Post-Sec.
6500 Soquel Dr 95003 831-479-6100
St. Abraham's Classical Christian Acad 100/K-11
1940 Bonita Dr 95003 831-239-4657

Arbuckle, Colusa, Pop. 2,990
Pierce JUSD 1,400/K-12
PO Box 239 95912 530-476-2892
Carol Geyer, supt. Fax 476-2289
www.pierce.k12.ca.us
Arbuckle Alternative HS 50/Alt
960 Wildwood Rd 95912 530-476-2173
Nicole Newman, prin. Fax 476-2674
Johnson JHS 300/6-8
938 Wildwood Rd 95912 530-476-3261
Ron Fisher, prin. Fax 476-2017
Pierce HS 400/9-12
960 Wildwood Rd 95912 530-476-2277
Nicole Newman, prin. Fax 476-3285

Arcadia, Los Angeles, Pop. 55,191
Arcadia USD 9,700/PK-12
150 S 3rd Ave 91006 626-821-8300
Dr. David Vannasdall, supt. Fax 821-8647
site.ausd.net
Arcadia HS 3,500/9-12
180 Campus Dr 91007 626-821-8370
Dr. Brent Forsee, prin. Fax 821-1712
Dana MS 800/6-8
1401 S 1st Ave 91006 626-821-8361
Dr. Daniel Hacking, prin. Fax 447-1965
First Avenue MS 800/6-8
301 S 1st Ave 91006 626-821-8362
Semeen Issa Ed.D., prin. Fax 446-1660
Foothills MS 800/6-8
171 E Sycamore Ave 91006 626-821-8363
Ben Acker, prin. Fax 303-7983
Rancho Learning Center 100/Alt
150 S 3rd Ave 91006 626-821-8371
Laurie McQuaid, prin. Fax 574-3806

Arroyo Pacific Academy 100/9-12
41 W Santa Clara St 91007 626-294-0661
Joseph Blackman, prin. Fax 294-0677
Rio Hondo Preparatory S 200/6-12
PO Box 662080 91066 626-444-9531

Arcata, Humboldt, Pop. 16,233
Arcata ESD 1,000/K-8
1435 Buttermilk Ln 95521 707-822-0351
Barbara Short Ed.D., supt. Fax 822-6589
arcataschooldistrict.org
Sunny Brae MS 200/6-8
1430 Buttermilk Ln 95521 707-822-5988
Lynda Yeoman, prin. Fax 822-7002

Northern Humboldt UNHSD
Supt. — See Mc Kinleyville
Arcata HS 800/9-12
1720 M St 95521 707-825-2400
Dave Navarre, prin. Fax 825-2407
Pacific Coast HS 50/Alt
1720 M St 95521 707-825-2443
Jon Larson, prin. Fax 825-2130

Humboldt State University Post-Sec.
1 Harpst St 95521 707-826-3011

Arleta, See Los Angeles
Los Angeles USD
Supt. — See Los Angeles
Arleta HS 1,600/9-12
14200 Van Nuys Blvd 91331 818-686-4100
Michael Browne, prin. Fax 890-1040

Armona, Kings, Pop. 4,080
Armona UNESD 1,100/PK-12
PO Box 368 93202 559-583-5000
Dr. Xavier Pena Ed.D., supt. Fax 583-5004
www.auesd.com
Parkview MS 400/5-8
PO Box 368 93202 559-583-5020
Dr. Xavier Pina Ed.D., prin. Fax 583-5030

Armona Union Academy 100/K-12
PO Box 397 93202 559-582-4468

Arroyo Grande, San Luis Obispo, Pop. 16,717
Lucia Mar USD 10,600/PK-12
602 Orchard Ave 93420 805-474-3000
Dr. Raynee Daley, supt. Fax 481-1398
www.lmusd.org
Arroyo Grande HS 2,200/9-12
495 Valley Rd 93420 805-474-3200
Conan Bowers, prin. Fax 473-4222
Lopez HS 100/Alt
1055 Mesa View Dr 93420 805-474-3750
Charlissa Skinner, prin. Fax 473-5518
Mesa MS 500/7-8
2555 S Halcyon Rd 93420 805-474-3400
Brett Gimlin, prin. Fax 473-4396
Paulding MS 700/7-8
600 Crown Hill St 93420 805-474-3500
Edward Arrigoni, prin. Fax 473-5525
Other Schools – See Nipomo, Pismo Beach

Regional Occupational Center & Program
Supt. — None
Santa Lucia ROP Vo/Tech
602 Orchard St 93420 805-474-3000
James Souza, dir. Fax 473-5593

Valley View Adventist Academy 100/K-10
230 Vernon St 93420 805-489-2687

Artesia, Los Angeles, Pop. 16,099
ABC USD
Supt. — See Cerritos
Ross MS 600/7-8
17707 Elaine Ave 90701 562-229-7785
Ricardo Brown, prin. Fax 402-6145

Angeles Institute Post-Sec.
11688 South St Ste 205 90701 562-531-4100

Arvin, Kern, Pop. 19,155
Arvin UNSD 3,100/PK-8
737 Bear Mountain Blvd 93203 661-854-6500
Michelle McLean Ed.D., supt. Fax 854-2362
www.arvinschools.com
Haven Drive MS 700/7-8
737 Bear Mountain Blvd 93203 661-854-6540
Aurora Moran Ed.D., prin. Fax 854-1440

Kern UNHSD
Supt. — See Bakersfield
Arvin HS 2,500/9-12
900 Varsity Rd 93203 661-854-5561
Ed Watts, prin. Fax 854-5943

Atascadero, San Luis Obispo, Pop. 27,543
Atascadero USD 4,700/K-12
5601 West Mall 93422 805-462-4200
Thomas Butler, supt. Fax 462-4421
www.atasusd.org/
Atascadero Fine Arts Academy 200/4-8
6100 Olmeda Ave 93422 805-460-2500
Kibbe Rubin, prin. Fax 460-2522
Atascadero HS 1,300/9-12
1 High School Hill Rd 93422 805-462-4300
Bill Neely, prin. Fax 462-4387
Atascadero JHS 700/6-8
6501 Lewis Ave 93422 805-462-4360
Jessica Lloyd, prin. Fax 462-4373
Del Rio Continuation HS 100/Alt
5601 West Mall 93422 805-462-4350
Chris Balogh, prin. Fax 462-0837
West Mall Alternative HS 50/Alt
5601 West Mall 93422 805-462-4238
Chris Balogh, prin. Fax 462-0837

Laurus College Post-Sec.
8693 El Camino Real 93422 805-267-1690
North County Christian S 200/PK-12
PO Box 6017 93423 805-466-4457
Dr. Robert McLaughlin, admin. Fax 466-4457

Atherton, San Mateo, Pop. 6,660
Menlo Park City ESD 2,900/K-8
181 Encinal Ave 94027 650-321-7140
Maurice Ghysels Ed.D., supt. Fax 321-7184
www.mpcsd.org
Other Schools – See Menlo Park

Sequoia UNHSD
Supt. — See Redwood City
Menlo-Atherton HS 2,100/9-12
555 Middlefield Rd 94027 650-322-5311
Simone Kennel, prin. Fax 323-1411

Menlo College Post-Sec.
1000 El Camino Real 94027 650-543-3753
Menlo S 800/6-12
50 Valparaiso Ave 94027 650-330-2000
Than Healy, head sch Fax 330-2002
Sacred Heart Prep S 600/9-12
150 Valparaiso Ave 94027 650-322-1866
Jennie Whitcomb, prin. Fax 322-7151

Atwater, Merced, Pop. 27,459
Atwater ESD 4,600/K-8
1401 Broadway Ave 95301 209-357-6100
Dr. Sandra Schiber, supt. Fax 357-6163
www.aesd.edu
Atwater Senior Academy 50/Alt
1800 Juniper Ave 95301 209-357-6515
Aaron Delworth, prin.
Mitchell Senior ES 800/7-8
1753 5th St 95301 209-357-6124
Aaron Delworth, prin. Fax 357-6506

Merced County Office of Education
Supt. — See Merced
Valley Atwater Community Day S 100/Alt
1800 Matthews Ave 95301 209-381-4550
Carrie Harkreader, prin. Fax 385-5380

Merced UNHSD 10,000/9-12
3430 A St 95301 209-325-2000
Alan Peterson, supt. Fax 385-6442
www.muhsd.org
Atwater HS 1,800/9-12
PO Box 835 95301 209-357-6000
Torrin Johnson, prin. Fax 357-6067
Buhach Colony HS 1,800/9-12
PO Box 753 95301 209-357-6600
Lance Morrow, prin. Fax 357-6602
Other Schools – See Livingston, Merced

Sierra Academy of Aeronautics Post-Sec.
3515 Hardstand Ave Ste B 95301 209-722-7522

Auburn, Placer, Pop. 12,869
Placer UNHSD 4,200/9-12
13000 New Airport Rd 95603 530-886-4400
George Sziraki, supt. Fax 886-4439
sites.google.com/a/puhsd.k12.ca.us/puhsd-us/
Chana Continuation HS 200/Alt
3775 Richardson Dr 95602 530-885-8401
Stan Parker, prin. Fax 885-1657
Maidu HS 100/Alt
3775 Richardson Dr 95602 530-885-8401
Stanton Parker, prin. Fax 885-1657
Placer HS 1,400/9-12
275 Orange St 95603 530-885-4581
Peter Efstathiu, prin. Fax 823-5770
Placer S for Adults Adult
390 Finley St 95603 530-885-8585
Bill Bettencourt, prin. Fax 823-1406
Other Schools – See Colfax, Foresthill, Loomis

Regional Occupational Center & Program
Supt. — None
Forty-Niner ROP Vo/Tech
360 Nevada St 95603 530-889-5940
Ward Andrus, dir. Fax 887-1704

Forest Lake Christian S 400/K-12
12515 Combie Rd 95602 530-269-1535
Carol Holt, supt. Fax 269-1541
Pine Hills Adventist Academy 100/K-12
13500 Richards Ln 95603 530-885-9447

Avalon, Los Angeles, Pop. 3,671
Long Beach USD
Supt. — See Long Beach
Avalon S 600/K-12
PO Box 557 90704 310-510-0790
Christopher Lounsbery, prin. Fax 510-2986

Avenal, Kings, Pop. 15,241
Reef-Sunset USD 2,600/PK-12
205 N Park Ave 93204 559-386-9083
Dr. David East, supt. Fax 386-5303
www.rsusd.org
Avenal HS 600/9-12
601 E Mariposa St 93204 559-386-5253
Juan Ruiz, prin. Fax 386-9413
Reef-Sunset MS 400/7-8
608 N 1st Ave 93204 559-386-4128
Fred Guerrero, prin. Fax 386-4918
Reef Sunset Sec Community Day S 50/Alt
205 N Park Ave 93204 559-386-0460
Estela Jimenez, prin. Fax 386-5303
Sunrise Continuation HS 50/Alt
209 N Park Ave 93204 559-386-4162
Estela Jimenez, prin. Fax 386-4937
Avenal Adult S Adult
205 N Park Ave 93204 559-386-9083
Estela Jimenez, prin. Fax 386-1752
Other Schools – See Kettleman City

Avery, Calaveras, Pop. 622
Vallecito UNSD 600/PK-8
PO Box 329 95224 209-795-8500
Don Ogden, supt. Fax 795-8505
vallecito-ca.schoolloop.com
Avery MS 200/6-8
PO Box 329 95224 209-795-8520
Jared Hungerford, prin. Fax 795-8539

Azusa, Los Angeles, Pop. 45,586
Azusa USD 9,400/PK-12
PO Box 500 91702 626-967-6211
Linda Kaminski, supt. Fax 858-6137
www.azusa.org
Azusa HS 1,300/9-12
PO Box 500 91702 626-815-3400
Ramiro Rubalcaba, prin. Fax 815-3430
Center MS 600/6-8
PO Box 500 91702 626-815-5184
Zepure Hacopian, prin. Fax 815-2601
Foothill MS 600/6-8
PO Box 500 91702 626-815-6600
Sam Perdomo, prin. Fax 815-1027
Slauson MS 800/6-8
PO Box 500 91702 626-815-5144
Dayna Mitchell, prin. Fax 815-5147
Other Schools – See Covina, Glendora

Azusa Pacific University Post-Sec.
PO Box 7000 91702 626-969-3434
Christbridge Academy 100/K-12
405 S Azusa Ave 91702 626-969-7400
Dr. Daniel Simonson, admin. Fax 969-6888

Baker, San Bernardino, Pop. 711
Baker Valley USD 200/K-12
PO Box 460 92309 760-733-4567
Ronda Tremblay, supt. Fax 733-4605
www.baker.k12.ca.us
Baker HS 100/9-12
PO Box 460 92309 760-733-4567
Ronda Tremblay, supt. Fax 733-4605
Baker JHS 50/6-8
PO Box 460 92309 760-733-4567
Ronda Tremblay, supt. Fax 733-4605
Baker Valley Adult S Adult
PO Box 460 92309 760-733-4567
Ronda Tremblay, supt. Fax 733-4605

Bakersfield, Kern, Pop. 338,954
Bakersfield CSD 29,700/PK-8
1300 Baker St 93305 661-631-4600
Doc Ervin Ed.D., supt. Fax 631-4623
www.bcsd.com
Cato MS, 4115 Vineland Rd 93306 6-8
Brooke Smothers-Strizic, prin. 661-631-5245
Chipman JHS 900/7-8
2905 Eissler St 93306 661-631-5210
Russell Taylor, prin. Fax 631-3229
Compton JHS 700/7-8
3211 Pico Ave 93306 661-631-5230
Jennifer Payne, prin. Fax 631-3166
Curran MS 900/6-8
1116 Lymric Way 93309 661-631-5240
Jason Brannen, prin. Fax 631-4538
Emerson MS 900/6-8
801 4th St 93304 661-631-5260
Kempton Coman, prin. Fax 327-8505
Sequoia MS 1,000/6-8
900 Belle Terrace 93304 661-631-5940
Gary McCloskey, prin. Fax 631-3236
Sierra MS 800/6-8
3017 Center St 93306 661-631-5470
Tomas Prieto, prin. Fax 631-4541
Stiern MS 1,400/6-8
2551 Morning Dr 93306 661-631-5480
Julie Short, prin. Fax 631-3241
Washington MS 700/6-8
1101 Noble Ave 93305 661-631-5810
Abraham Rivera, prin. Fax 631-3172

Beardsley ESD 1,800/K-8
1001 Roberts Ln 93308 661-393-8550
Paul Miller, supt. Fax 393-5965
www.beardsleyschool.org/
Beardsley JHS 300/7-8
1001 Roberts Ln 93308 661-392-9254
David Hilton, prin. Fax 399-3925

Edison ESD 1,100/K-8
11518 School St 93307 661-363-5394
Erica Andrews, supt. Fax 363-4631
www.edline.net/pages/Edison_Elementary
Edison MS 500/5-8
721 S Edison Rd 93307 661-366-8216
Duane Grumling, prin. Fax 366-0922

Fairfax ESD 2,100/K-8
1500 S Fairfax Rd 93307 661-366-7221
Michael Coleman, supt. Fax 366-1901
www.fairfax.k12.ca.us
Fairfax JHS 500/7-8
1500 S Fairfax Rd 93307 661-366-4461
Wendy Burkhead, prin. Fax 366-5831

Fruitvale SD 3,300/K-8
7311 Rosedale Hwy 93308 661-589-3830
Dr. Mary Westendorf, supt. Fax 589-3674
www.fruitvale.k12.ca.us
Fruitvale JHS 700/7-8
2114 Calloway Dr 93312 661-589-3933
Leslie Roberts, prin. Fax 588-3259

Greenfield UNESD 9,200/K-8
1624 Fairview Rd 93307 661-837-6000
Chris Crawford, supt. Fax 832-2873
www.gfusd.net
Greenfield Community S 50/Alt
725 Capitola Dr 93307 661-837-3717
Matt Earls, dir. Fax 837-3719
Greenfield MS 900/6-8
1109 Pacheco Rd 93307 661-837-6110
Sandra Welch, prin. Fax 832-7431
McKee MS 900/6-8
205 McKee Rd 93307 661-837-6060
Brandon Duncan, prin. Fax 834-7566
Ollivier MS 1,000/6-8
7310 Monitor St 93307 661-837-6120
Sheila Johnson, prin. Fax 396-0963

Kern County Office of Education 4,100/
1300 17th St 93301 661-636-4000
Christine Frazier, supt. Fax 636-4130
www.kern.org/
Kern County Community S 1,200/Alt
1300 17th St 93301 661-636-4346
Warcester Williams, dir. Fax 636-4127

Kern UNHSD 37,100/9-12
5801 Sundale Ave 93309 661-827-3100
Dr. Bryon Schaefer, supt. Fax 827-3302
www.kernhigh.org
Bakersfield HS 2,800/9-12
1241 G St 93301 661-324-9841
David Reese, prin. Fax 324-3401
Centennial HS 1,900/9-12
8601 Hageman Rd 93312 661-588-8601
Dean Juola, prin. Fax 588-8608
East Bakersfield HS 2,100/9-12
2200 Quincy Dr 93306 661-871-7221
Leo Holland, prin. Fax 872-6980
Foothill HS 2,000/9-12
501 Park Dr 93306 661-366-4491
Gail Bentley, prin. Fax 363-6223
Frontier HS 2,300/9-12
6401 Allen Rd, 661-829-1107
Vicky Thompson, prin. Fax 829-1185
Golden Valley HS 2,400/9-12
801 Hosking Ave 93307 661-827-0800
Paul Helman, prin. Fax 827-0480
Highland HS 1,900/9-12
2900 Royal Scots Way 93306 661-872-2777
Debra Vigstrom, prin. Fax 871-6052
Independence HS 2,000/9-12
8001 Old River Rd 93311 661-834-8001
Debbie Thompson, prin. Fax 398-0899
Liberty HS 1,900/9-12
925 Jewetta Ave 93312 661-587-0925
Libby Wyatt, prin. Fax 587-1299
Mira Monte HS 2,100/9-12
1800 S Fairfax Rd 93307 661-366-1800
William Sandoval, prin. Fax 363-6475
North HS 1,600/9-12
300 Galaxy Ave 93308 661-399-3351
Mark Balch, prin. Fax 393-5918
Ridgeview HS 2,200/9-12
8501 Stine Rd 93313 661-398-3100
Steve Holmes, prin. Fax 398-9758
Ruggenberg Career Center Vo/Tech
610 Ansol Ln 93306 661-366-4401
John Eldridge, coord. Fax 363-0828
Schuetz Career Center Vo/Tech
8600 Shannon Dr 93307 661-827-4800
Misty Krugman, admin. Fax 827-4804
South HS 1,900/9-12
1101 Planz Rd 93304 661-831-3680
Connie Grumling, prin. Fax 837-2756
Stockdale HS 2,100/9-12
2800 Buena Vista Rd 93311 661-665-2800
Ramon Hendrix, prin. Fax 665-0914
Tierra Del Sol Continuation HS 400/Alt
3700 E Belle Ter 93307 661-832-3700
Chris Dutton, admin. Fax 832-9807
Vista Continuation HS 200/Alt
200 P St 93304 661-327-8561
Tracey Lozano, admin. Fax 631-0558
Vista West Continuation HS 300/Alt
7115 Rosedale Hwy 93308 661-589-4242
Mike Mullings, admin. Fax 588-1627
West HS 2,100/9-12
1200 New Stine Rd 93309 661-832-2822
Terrie Bernardin, prin. Fax 831-5606
Bakersfield Adult HS Adult
501 S Mount Vernon Ave 93307 661-835-1855
Mark Wyatt, prin. Fax 835-9612
Other Schools – See Arvin, Lake Isabella, Lamont, Shafter

Lamont ESD
Supt. — See Lamont
Mountain View MS 600/7-8
8001 Weedpatch Hwy 93307 661-845-2291
Jonathan Martinez, prin. Fax 845-1839

Norris SD 3,900/K-8
6940 Calloway Dr 93312 661-387-7000
Kelly Miller, supt. Fax 399-9750
www.norris.k12.ca.us/
Norris MS 900/6-8
6940 Calloway Dr 93312 661-387-7060
Ryan Carr, prin. Fax 399-9356

Panama-Buena Vista UNSD 17,500/K-8
4200 Ashe Rd 93313 661-831-8331
Dr. Kevin Silberberg, supt. Fax 398-2141
www.pbvusd.k12.ca.us
Actis JHS 600/7-8
2400 Westholme Blvd 93309 661-833-1250
Patrick Spears, prin. Fax 833-9656
Stonecreek JHS 900/7-8
8000 Akers Rd 93313 661-834-4521
Matthew Kennedy, prin. Fax 834-6908
Tevis JHS 700/7-8
3901 Pin Oak Park Blvd 93311 661-664-7211
Paul Coon, prin. Fax 664-9659
Thompson JHS 800/7-8
4200 Planz Rd 93309 661-832-8011
Darryl Pope, prin. Fax 832-5165

Warren JHS 900/7-8
4615 Mountain Vista Dr 93311 661-665-9210
George Thornburgh, prin. Fax 665-9507

Regional Occupational Center & Program
Supt. — None
Kern HSD ROC Vo/Tech
501 S Mount Vernon Ave 93307 661-831-3327
Brian Miller, admin. Fax 398-8239

Rio Bravo-Greeley UNESD 1,000/K-8
6521 Enos Ln, 661-589-2696
Joost DeMoes, supt. Fax 589-2218
www.rbgusd.k12.ca.us
Rio Bravo-Greeley MS 400/5-8
6601 Enos Ln, 661-589-2505
Becky Macquarrie, prin. Fax 588-7204

Rosedale UNESD 5,400/K-8
2553 Old Farm Rd 93312 661-588-6000
John Mendiburu Ed.D., supt. Fax 588-6009
www.ruesd.net
Freedom MS 600/7-8
11445 Noriega Rd 93312 661-588-6044
Russell Sentes, prin. Fax 588-6048
Rosedale MS 700/7-8
12463 Rosedale Hwy 93312 661-588-6030
Becky Devahl, prin. Fax 588-6039

Standard ESD 2,900/K-8
1200 N Chester Ave 93308 661-392-2110
Paul Meyers Ed.D., supt. Fax 392-0681
district.standard.k12.ca.us
Standard MS 900/6-8
1222 N Chester Ave 93308 661-392-2130
Jason Hodgson, prin. Fax 392-2134

Vineland ESD 800/K-8
14713 Weedpatch Hwy 93307 661-845-3713
Matthew Ross, supt. Fax 845-8449
vineland.k12.ca.us
Sunset S 300/5-8
8301 Sunset Blvd 93307 661-845-1320
Charles Monaco, prin. Fax 845-3952

Bakersfield Adventist Academy 100/K-12
3333 Bernard St 93306 661-871-1591
Bakersfield Christian HS 500/9-12
12775 Stockdale Hwy, 661-410-7000
John Buetow, pres. Fax 410-7007
Bakersfield College Post-Sec.
1801 Panorama Dr 93305 661-395-4011
Bethel Christian S 100/K-12
2236 E California Ave 93307 661-325-2661
Brightwood College Post-Sec.
1914 Wible Rd 93304 661-836-6300
California State University-Bakersfield Post-Sec.
9001 Stockdale Hwy 93311 661-654-2782
DeVry University Post-Sec.
3000 Ming Ave 93304 661-833-7120
Garces Memorial HS 600/9-12
2800 Loma Linda Dr 93305 661-327-2578
Myka Peck, prin. Fax 327-5427
Lyle's College of Beauty Post-Sec.
2935 F St 93301 661-327-9784
Milan Institute Post-Sec.
2822 F St 93301 661-325-8900
San Joaquin Valley College Post-Sec.
201 New Stine Rd 93309 661-834-0126
Santa Barbara Business College Post-Sec.
5300 California Ave 93309 866-749-7222

Baldwin Park, Los Angeles, Pop. 74,883
Baldwin Park USD 14,500/PK-12
3699 Holly Ave 91706 626-962-3311
Froilan N. Mendoza, supt. Fax 856-4901
www.bpusd.net
Baldwin Park HS 2,100/9-12
3900 Puente Ave 91706 626-960-5431
Anthony Ippolito, prin. Fax 856-4059
Holland MS 500/6-8
4733 Landis Ave 91706 626-962-8412
James Michael Rust, prin. Fax 813-6148
Jones JHS 500/7-8
14250 Merced Ave 91706 626-962-8312
Elizabeth Cox, prin. Fax 856-4291
North Park Continuation HS 400/Alt
4600 Bogart Ave 91706 626-337-4407
Harris Vincent Pratt, prin. Fax 856-4402
Olive MS 500/6-8
13701 Olive St 91706 626-962-8416
Blanca Risco, prin. Fax 856-4568
Santa Fe S 400/3-8
4650 Baldwin Park Blvd 91706 626-856-1525
Margie Clark, prin. Fax 813-0614
Sierra Vista HS 2,000/9-12
3600 Frazier St 91706 626-960-7741
Christine Simmons, prin. Fax 856-4050
Sierra Vista JHS 800/7-8
13400 Foster Ave 91706 626-962-1300
Lorena Chavira, prin. Fax 856-4577
Baldwin Park Adult & Community Education Adult
4640 Maine Ave 91706 626-939-4456
John Kerr Ed.D., admin. Fax 856-4384

Ballico, Merced, Pop. 398
Ballico-Cressey ESD 400/PK-8
11818 Gregg Ave 95303 209-394-9600
Bryan Ballenger, supt. Fax 632-8929
www.ballicocressey.com
Ballico MS 200/3-8
11818 Gregg Ave 95303 209-394-9400
Bryan Ballenger, supt. Fax 632-8929

Banning, Riverside, Pop. 28,937
Banning USD 4,500/K-12
161 W Williams St 92220 951-922-0200
Robert Guillen, supt. Fax 922-0227
www.banning.k12.ca.us
Banning HS 1,100/9-12
100 W Westward Ave 92220 951-922-0285
Matthew Valdivia, prin. Fax 922-2137
Banning Independent Study 100/Alt
1151 W Wilson St 92220 951-922-0268
David Sanchez, prin. Fax 922-2723
New Horizons Continuation HS 100/Alt
1151 W Wilson St 92220 951-922-0250
David Sanchez, prin. Fax 922-2750
Nicolet MS 1,000/6-8
101 E Nicolet St 92220 951-922-0280
Albert Evinger, prin. Fax 922-2748

Calvary Christian S 100/PK-12
1325 Mountain Ave 92220 951-849-1877

Barstow, San Bernardino, Pop. 21,497
Barstow USD 5,800/K-12
551 S Avenue H 92311 760-255-6000
Jeff Malan, supt. Fax 255-8965
www.barstow.k12.ca.us
Barstow HS 1,300/9-12
551 S Avenue H 92311 760-255-6105
Derrick Delton, prin. Fax 256-4076
Barstow JHS 800/7-8
551 S Avenue H 92311 760-255-6200
Jose Rubio, prin. Fax 255-6205
Barstow STEM Academy 6-8
551 S Avenue H 92311 760-255-6150
Vinney Williams, prin. Fax 255-6104
BUSD School of Opportunity 50/Alt
551 S Avenue H 92311 760-255-6063
Carolyn Norman, prin. Fax 255-6063
Central Continuation HS 300/Alt
551 S Avenue H 92311 760-255-6063
Carolyn Norman, prin. Fax 256-2125
Barstow Adult S Adult
551 S Avenue H 92311 760-255-6131
Sonya Smith, prin. Fax 255-6130

Barstow Community College Post-Sec.
2700 Barstow Rd 92311 760-252-2411

Bay Point, Contra Costa, Pop. 20,582
Mount Diablo USD
Supt. — See Concord
Gateway HS 50/Alt
235 Pacifica Ave 94565 925-458-1316
Rachelle Buckner, admin. Fax 458-1487
Riverview MS 700/6-8
205 Pacifica Ave 94565 925-458-3216
Eric Wood, prin. Fax 458-0875

Beaumont, Riverside, Pop. 35,877
Beaumont USD 9,000/K-12
PO Box 187 92223 951-845-1631
Terrence Davis, supt. Fax 845-2039
www.beaumont-ca.schoolloop.com
Beaumont HS 2,600/9-12
PO Box 187 92223 951-845-3171
Christina Pierce, prin. Fax 769-9289
Glen View HS 100/Alt
PO Box 187 92223 951-845-6012
Bobbi Burnett Ed.D., prin. Fax 769-8760
Mountain View MS 1,000/6-8
PO Box 187 92223 951-845-1627
Michael Breyere, prin. Fax 845-8679
San Gorgônio MS 1,000/6-8
PO Box 187 92223 951-769-4391
Drew Scherrer, prin. Fax 769-8750
21st Century Learning Institute 100/Alt
PO Box 187 92223 951-845-1133
Bobbi Burnett Ed.D., prin. Fax 845-1134
Beaumont Adult S Adult
PO Box 187 92223 951-845-6012
Matt Russo Ed.D., prin. Fax 769-8760

Bell, Los Angeles, Pop. 35,263
Los Angeles USD
Supt. — See Los Angeles
Bell HS 3,400/9-12
4328 Bell Ave 90201 323-832-4700
Rafael Balderas, prin. Fax 560-7874
Orchard Academy #2B 500/6-8
6411 Orchard Ave 90201 323-826-3951
David Manzo, prin. Fax 826-3951
Orchard Academy #2C 500/6-8
6411 Orchard Ave 90201 323-826-3975
Rosa Guerrero, prin. Fax 826-3976

Bellflower, Los Angeles, Pop. 74,379
Bellflower USD 13,300/K-12
16703 Clark Ave 90706 562-866-9011
Brian Jacobs Ed.D., supt. Fax 866-7713
www.busd.k12.ca.us/
Bellflower MSHS 2,800/7-12
15301 Mcnab Ave 90706 562-920-1801
Michael Lundgren, prin. Fax 804-2387
Somerset Continuation HS 300/Alt
9242 Laurel St 90706 562-804-6548
Mark Kailiponi, prin. Fax 804-6587
Other Schools – See Lakewood

St. John Bosco HS 800/9-12
13640 Bellflower Blvd 90706 562-920-1734
Casey Yeazel, prin. Fax 867-5322

Bell Gardens, Los Angeles, Pop. 41,928
Montebello USD
Supt. — See Montebello
Bell Gardens HS 3,100/9-12
6119 Agra St 90201 323-826-5151
Juan Herrera, prin. Fax 887-7959
Bell Gardens IS 1,200/6-8
5841 Live Oak St 90201 562-927-1319
Ricardo Mendez, prin. Fax 806-5131
Suva IS 900/6-8
6660 Suva St 90201 562-927-2679
Dr. Teresa Alonzo Ed.D., prin. Fax 806-5132
Bell Gardens Adult Education Adult
6119 Agra St 90201 323-887-7955
Kathy Brendzal, prin. Fax 887-7958
Ford Park Adult S Adult
7800 Scout Ave 90201 562-927-7750
Kathy Brendzal, prin. Fax 806-5133

InterAmerican Adult S 300/9-12
PO Box 541 90201 888-356-8110
Gladys Rendon, admin.

Belmont, San Mateo, Pop. 24,354
Belmont-Redwood Shores ESD 3,700/K-8
2960 Hallmark Dr 94002 650-637-4800
Michael Milliken Ph.D., supt. Fax 637-4811
www.brssd.org
Ralston IS 1,100/6-8
2675 Ralston Ave 94002 650-637-4880
Michael Dougherty, prin. Fax 637-4888

Sequoia UNHSD
Supt. — See Redwood City
Carlmont HS 2,200/9-12
1400 Alameda De Las Pulgas 94002 650-595-0210
Ralph Crame, prin. Fax 591-6067

Notre Dame de Namur University Post-Sec.
1500 Ralston Ave 94002 650-508-3500
Notre Dame HS 400/9-12
1540 Ralston Ave 94002 650-595-1913
Maryann Osmond, prin. Fax 595-2116

Benicia, Solano, Pop. 25,504
Benicia USD 4,900/K-12
350 E K St 94510 707-747-8300
Charles Young, supt. Fax 748-0146
www.beniciaunified.org
Benicia HS 1,600/9-12
1101 Military W 94510 707-747-8325
Brianna Kleinschmidt, prin. Fax 745-6769
Benicia MS 1,200/6-8
1100 Southampton Rd 94510 707-747-8340
Damian Scott, prin. Fax 747-8349
Community Day S, 426 E K St 94510 Alt
Shelly Nissen, prin. 707-746-0569
Liberty Continuation HS 100/Alt
351 E J St 94510 707-747-8323
JoAnn Severson, prin. Fax 748-2684

Ben Lomond, Santa Cruz, Pop. 6,022
San Lorenzo Valley USD 4,500/K-12
325 Marion Ave 95005 831-336-5194
Dr. Laurie Bruton, supt. Fax 336-9531
www.slvusd.org
Other Schools – See Felton

Berkeley, Alameda, Pop. 106,371
Berkeley USD 10,100/PK-12
2020 Bonar St 94702 510-644-4500
Donald Evans, supt. Fax 540-5358
www.berkeleyschools.net
Berkeley HS 3,100/9-12
1980 Allston Way 94704 510-644-6120
Kristin Glenchur, prin. Fax 548-4221
Berkeley Technology Academy 100/Alt
2701 M L King Jr Way 94703 510-644-6159
Sheila Quintana, prin. Fax 644-4597
King MS 900/6-8
1781 Rose St 94703 510-644-6280
Janet Levenson, prin. Fax 644-8783
Longfellow Arts & Technology MS 500/6-8
1500 Derby St 94703 510-644-6360
Marcos Garcia, prin. Fax 644-8707
Willard MS 500/6-8
2425 Stuart St 94705 510-644-6330
Debbie Dean, prin. Fax 548-4219
Berkeley Adult S Adult
1701 San Pablo Ave 94702 510-644-6130
Burr Guthrie, prin. Fax 644-6784

Acupuncture & Integrative Medicine Coll. Post-Sec.
2550 Shattuck Ave 94704 510-666-8248
American Baptist Seminary of the West Post-Sec.
2606 Dwight Way 94704 510-841-1905
Bayhill HS 100/9-12
1940 Virginia St 94709 510-984-0599
Berkeley City College Post-Sec.
2050 Center St 94704 510-981-2800
Church Divinity School of the Pacific Post-Sec.
2451 Ridge Rd 94709 510-204-0700
Dominican School of Philosophy/Theology Post-Sec.
2301 Vine St 94708 510-849-2030
Franciscan School of Theology Post-Sec.
1712 Euclid Ave 94709 510-848-5232
Graduate Theological Union Post-Sec.
2400 Ridge Rd 94709 510-649-2400
Maybeck HS 100/9-12
2727 College Ave 94705 510-841-8489
William Webb, dir. Fax 704-0473
Pacific Lutheran Theological Seminary Post-Sec.
2770 Marin Ave 94708 510-524-5264
Pacific School of Religion Post-Sec.
1798 Scenic Ave 94709 510-849-8200
St. Marys College HS 600/9-12
1294 Albina Ave 94706 510-526-9242
Peter Imperial, prin. Fax 559-6277
Starr King School for the Ministry Post-Sec.
2441 Le Conte Ave 94709 510-845-6232
University of California Post-Sec.
110 Sproul Hall 94720 510-642-6000
Wright Institute Post-Sec.
2728 Durant Ave 94704 510-841-9230

Bermuda Dunes, Riverside, Pop. 7,164

Desert Christian Academy 500/PK-12
40700 Yucca Ln, 760-345-2848
Debbee Scott, head sch Fax 345-8173

Beverly Hills, Los Angeles, Pop. 32,498
Beverly Hills USD 4,300/PK-12
255 S Lasky Dr 90212 310-551-5100
Steve Kessler, supt. Fax 286-2138
www.bhusd.org/
Beverly Hills HS 1,700/9-12
241 S Moreno Dr 90212 310-229-3685
Dave Jackson, prin. Fax 286-7446
Moreno Continuation HS 50/Alt
241 S Moreno Dr 90212 310-551-5100
Jennifer Tedford, head sch

Academy of Couture Art Post-Sec.
8484 Wilshire Blvd Ste 730 90211 310-360-8888
West Coast Ultrasound Institute Post-Sec.
291 S La Cienega Blvd # 500 90211 310-289-5123

Bieber, Lassen, Pop. 307
Big Valley JUSD 200/K-12
PO Box 157 96009 530-294-5266
Paula Silva, supt. Fax 294-5396
www.bigvalleyschool.org
Big Valley JSHS 100/7-12
PO Box 157 96009 530-294-5231
Paula Silva, prin. Fax 294-5100

Big Bear Lake, San Bernardino, Pop. 4,883
Bear Valley USD 2,600/PK-12
PO Box 1529 92315 909-866-4631
Mary Suzuki Ed.D., supt. Fax 866-2040
www.bearvalleyusd.org
Big Bear MS 400/7-8
PO Box 1607 92315 909-866-4634
Dena Arbaugh, prin. Fax 866-5679
Other Schools – See Sugarloaf

Biggs, Butte, Pop. 1,654
Biggs USD 500/PK-12
300 B St 95917 530-868-1281
Doug Kaelin, supt. Fax 868-1615
www.biggs.org/
Biggs HS, 3046 2nd St 95917 100/9-12
Mandy Leahy, prin. 530-868-5825
Biggs Secondary Community Day S 50/Alt
300 B St 95917 – Doug Kaelin, prin. 530-868-1281

Big Pine, Inyo, Pop. 1,716
Big Pine USD 200/K-12
PO Box 908 93513 760-938-2005
Pamela Jones, supt. Fax 938-2310
www.bp.k12.ca.us
Big Pine HS 50/9-12
PO Box 908 93513 760-938-2222
Ed Dardenne-Ankringa, prin. Fax 938-2310

Bishop USD
Supt. — See Bishop
Palisade Glacier Continuation HS 50/Alt
PO Box 938 93513 760-938-2001
Katie Kolker, prin. Fax 938-2310

Big Sur, Monterey
Big Sur USD 100/PK-12
69325 Highway 1 93920 805-927-4507
Gordon Piffero, supt. Fax 927-8123
www.bigsurunified.org
Pacific Valley S 50/PK-12
69325 Highway 1 93920 805-927-4507
Gordon Piffero, supt. Fax 927-8123

Bishop, Inyo, Pop. 3,811
Bishop USD 1,500/K-12
301 N Fowler St 93514 760-872-3680
Barry Simpson, supt. Fax 872-6016
bishop-ca.schoolloop.com
Bishop Union HS 700/9-12
301 N Fowler St 93514 760-873-4275
Allen Van Velzen, prin. Fax 873-3065
Home Street MS 400/6-8
201 Home St 93514 760-872-1381
Patrick Twomey, prin. Fax 872-1877
Other Schools – See Big Pine

Inyo County Office of Education
Supt. — See Independence
Boothe S 50/Alt
166 Grandview Dr 93514 760-873-3262
Dr. Lisa Fontana, prin. Fax 873-3324

Bloomington, San Bernardino, Pop. 23,603
Colton JUSD
Supt. — See Colton
Baca MS 900/7-8
1640 S Lilac Ave 92316 909-580-5014
Mike Williford, prin. Fax 876-4195
Bloomington HS 2,100/9-12
10750 Laurel Ave 92316 909-580-5004
Sandy Torres, prin. Fax 876-6326
Harris MS 800/7-8
11150 Alder Ave 92316 909-580-5020
Cynthia Aguilar-Munoz Ed.D., prin. Fax 820-2238
Slover Mountain Continuation HS 300/Alt
18829 Orange St 92316 909-580-5013
Kristi Richardson, prin. Fax 876-6363

Bloomington Christian S 900/PK-12
955 Bloomington Ave 92316 909-877-1239

Blue Jay, San Bernardino
Rim of the World USD 3,300/K-12
27315 N Bay Rd 92317 909-336-2031
Dr. Giovanni Annous, supt. Fax 337-4527
www.rimsd.k12.ca.us
Other Schools – See Lake Arrowhead

Blue Lake, Humboldt, Pop. 1,210

Dell'Arte International School Post-Sec.
PO Box 816 95525 707-668-5663

Blythe, Riverside, Pop. 20,420
Palo Verde USD 2,800/PK-12
295 N 1st St 92225 760-922-4164
Fax 922-5942
www.pvusd.us
Palo Verde HS 900/9-12
667 N Lovekin Blvd 92225 760-922-7148
Brandy Cox, prin. Fax 922-8916
Twin Palms Continuation S 100/Alt
811 W Chanslor Way 92225 760-922-4884
Rachel Angel, prin. Fax 922-1177

Palo Verde College Post-Sec.
1 College Dr 92225 760-921-5500

Bonsall, San Diego, Pop. 3,866
Bonsall USD 2,300/K-12
31505 Old River Rd 92003 760-631-5200
Justin Cunningham Ed.D., supt. Fax 941-4409
www.bonsallusd.com
Bonsall HS, 7350 W Lilac Rd 92003 9-12
Lee Fleming, prin. 760-631-5209
Sullivan MS 500/6-8
7350 W Lilac Rd 92003 760-631-5210
Joseph Clevenger, prin. Fax 631-5230

Boonville, Mendocino, Pop. 1,016
Anderson Valley USD 500/PK-12
PO Box 457 95415 707-895-3774
Michelle Hutchins, supt. Fax 895-2665
www.avusd.k12.ca.us
Anderson Valley JSHS 300/7-12
PO Box 130 95415 707-895-3496
Keri St. Jeor, prin. Fax 895-3153
Rancheria Continuation S 50/Alt
PO Box 457 95415 707-895-3151
Keri St. Jeor, lead tchr. Fax 895-2665
Anderson Valley Adult S Adult
PO Box 457 95415 707-895-2953
Katherine Reddick, prin. Fax 895-2665

Boron, Kern, Pop. 2,180
Muroc JUSD
Supt. — See North Edwards
Boron JSHS 300/7-12
26831 Prospect St 93516 760-762-5121
David Wiggs, prin. Fax 762-5040

Borrego Springs, San Diego, Pop. 3,399
Borrego Springs USD 500/PK-12
1315 Palm Canyon Dr 92004 760-767-5357
Mark Stevens, supt. Fax 767-0494
www.bsusd.com
Borrego Springs HS 100/9-12
1315 Palm Canyon Dr 92004 760-767-5335
Steve Dunn, prin. Fax 767-5999
Borrego Springs MS 100/6-8
1315 Palm Canyon Dr 92004 760-767-5335
Steve Dunn, prin. Fax 767-5999

Brawley, Imperial, Pop. 24,758
Brawley ESD 3,300/K-8
261 D St 92227 760-344-2330
Ronald Garcia, supt. Fax 344-8928
www.besd.org
Worth JHS 500/7-8
385 W D St 92227 760-344-2153
Terri Mason, prin. Fax 351-5043

Brawley UNHSD 1,900/9-12
480 N Imperial Ave 92227 760-312-6063
Simon Canalez, supt. Fax 344-9520
www.brawleyhigh.org
Brawley HS 1,700/9-12
480 N Imperial Ave 92227 760-312-6073
Jesse Sanchez, prin. Fax 312-6064
BUHS Renaissance Community Day S 50/Alt
480 N Imperial Ave 92227 760-312-5109
Antonio Munguia, admin. Fax 344-7425
Desert Valley Continuation HS 200/Alt
480 N Imperial Ave 92227 760-312-5110
Antonio Munguia, prin. Fax 344-7425

Brawley Christian Academy 100/K-12
430 N 2nd St 92227 760-344-3911
Tony Flores, prin. Fax 344-5864

Brea, Orange, Pop. 38,164
Brea-Olinda USD 6,000/K-12
PO Box 300 92822 714-990-7800
Dr. Brad Mason, supt. Fax 529-2137
www.bousd.us
Brea Canyon HS 100/Alt
689 Wildcat Way 92821 714-990-7882
Eric Barrientos, prin. Fax 990-7587
Brea JHS 900/7-8
400 N Brea Blvd 92821 714-990-7500
Kelly Kennedy, prin. Fax 990-7585
Brea-Olinda HS 1,900/9-12
789 N Wildcat Way 92821 714-990-7850
Jerry Halpin, prin. Fax 990-7547

Brea School of Exceptional Children Post-Sec.
875 N Brea Blvd 92821

Brentwood, Contra Costa, Pop. 49,001
Brentwood UNESD 8,500/PK-8
255 Guthrie Ln 94513 925-513-6300
Dr. Dana Eaton, supt. Fax 634-8583
www.brentwood.k12.ca.us
Adams MS 1,000/6-8
401 American Ave 94513 925-513-6450
Mike Wood, prin. Fax 513-3470
Bristow MS 1,100/6-8
855 Minnesota Ave 94513 925-513-6460
Jon Ovick, prin. Fax 516-8725
Hill MS 900/6-8
140 Birch St 94513 925-513-6440
Kirsten Jobb, prin. Fax 513-0696

Liberty UNHSD 7,900/9-12
20 Oak St 94513 925-634-2166
Eric Volta, supt. Fax 634-1687
libertyunion.schoolwires.net
Heritage HS 2,400/9-12
101 American Ave 94513 925-634-0037
Larry Oshodi, prin. Fax 240-0662
Independence HS 400/Alt
929 2nd St 94513 925-634-2589
Guy Rognlien, dir. Fax 634-5317
La Paloma Continuation HS 200/Alt
400 Ghiggeri Dr 94513 925-634-2888
Chris Holland, prin. Fax 634-6578
Liberty HS 2,400/9-12
850 2nd St 94513 925-634-3521
Patrick Walsh, prin. Fax 513-2739
Liberty Adult Education Adult
929 2nd St 94513 925-634-2565
Guy Rognlien, dir. Fax 634-5317
Other Schools – See Oakley

Bridgeport, Mono, Pop. 560
Eastern Sierra USD 400/K-12
PO Box 575 93517 760-932-7443
Don Clark, supt. Fax 932-7140
www.esusd.org
Other Schools – See Coleville, Lee Vining

Mono County Office of Education 200/
PO Box 477 93517 760-932-7311
Stacey Adler, supt. Fax 932-7278
www.monocoe.org
Other Schools – See Coleville, Lee Vining, Mammoth Lakes

Regional Occupational Center & Program
Supt. — None
Mono County ROP Vo/Tech
PO Box 477 93517 760-932-7311
Rhea Kerby, dir. Fax 932-7278

Brisbane, San Mateo, Pop. 4,026
Brisbane ESD 500/K-8
1 Solano St 94005 415-467-0550
Ronan Collver, supt. Fax 467-2914
www.brisbanesd.org
Lipman MS 200/6-8
1 Solano St 94005 415-467-9541
Jolene Heckerman, prin. Fax 467-5073

Buellton, Santa Barbara, Pop. 4,686
Buellton UNESD 600/PK-8
595 2nd St 93427 805-686-2767
Randal Haggard, supt. Fax 686-2719
www.buelltonusd.org
Jonata MS 200/6-8
301 2nd St 93427 805-688-4222
Hans Rheinschild, prin. Fax 688-6611

Buena Park, Orange, Pop. 78,169
Buena Park ESD 5,200/K-8
6885 Orangethorpe Ave 90620 714-522-8412
Greg Magnuson, supt. Fax 994-1506
www.bpsd.k12.ca.us/
Buena Park JHS 1,100/7-8
6931 Orangethorpe Ave 90620 714-522-8491
Erik Bagger, prin. Fax 523-1602

Fullerton JUNHSD
Supt. — See Fullerton
Buena Park HS 1,900/9-12
8833 Academy Dr 90621 714-992-8601
Jim Coombs, prin. Fax 992-8619

Bethel Baptist Academy 200/1-12
8251 La Palma Ave 90620 714-521-5586

Burbank, Los Angeles, Pop. 99,967
Burbank USD 15,200/PK-12
1900 W Olive Ave 91506 818-729-4400
Matt Hill, supt. Fax 729-4483
www.burbankusd.org
Burbank Community Day S 50/Alt
223 E Santa Anita Ave 91502 818-558-4693
Christine Krohn, prin. Fax 846-3404
Burbank HS 2,600/9-12
902 N 3rd St 91502 818-558-4700
Michael Bertram, prin. Fax 845-6122
Burbank MS 1,100/6-8
3700 W Jeffries Ave 91505 818-558-4646
Dr. Oscar Macias, prin. Fax 842-3727
Burroughs HS 2,600/9-12
1920 W Clark Ave 91506 818-558-4777
Deborah Madrigal, prin. Fax 846-9268
Independent Learning Academy Alt
3715 W Allan Ave 91505 818-558-5353
Emilio Urioste, prin.
Jordan MS 1,100/6-8
420 S Mariposa St 91506 818-558-4622
Stacy Cashman, prin. Fax 843-3509
Monterey Continuation HS 200/Alt
1915 W Monterey Ave 91506 818-558-5455
Ann Brooks, prin. Fax 841-2446
Muir MS 1,300/6-8
1111 N Kenneth Rd 91504 818-558-5320
Dr. Greg Miller, prin. Fax 841-4637
Burbank Adult S Adult
3811 W Allan Ave 91505 818-558-4611
Emilio Urioste, dir. Fax 558-4620

Bellarmine-Jefferson HS 200/9-12
465 E Olive Ave 91501 818-972-1400
Michael Stumpf, prin. Fax 559-6387

Brighton Hall S 100/3-12
755 N Whitnall Hwy 91505 818-985-9485
Niranjala Peiris, dir. Fax 861-7326
Elegante Beauty College Post-Sec.
200 N San Fernando Blvd 91502 818-954-8894
Intercoast Colleges Post-Sec.
175 E Olive Ave Fl 3 91502 818-500-8400
Intl S of Los Angeles - Burbank Campus 300/6-12
1105 W Riverside Dr 91506 818-900-1895
Anneli Harvey, dir. Fax 859-7355
Make-up Designory Post-Sec.
129 S San Fernando Blvd 91502 818-729-9420
New York Film Academy Post-Sec.
4444 W Lakeside Dr 91505 818-295-2020
Providence HS 400/9-12
511 S Buena Vista St 91505 818-846-8141
Joe Sciuto, head sch Fax 843-8421
Woodbury University Post-Sec.
7500 N Glenoaks Blvd 91504 818-767-0888

Burlingame, San Mateo, Pop. 27,534
Burlingame ESD 3,200/K-8
1825 Trousdale Dr 94010 650-259-3800
Maggie MacIsaac Ed.D., supt. Fax 259-3820
www.burlingameschools.org
Burlingame IS 1,000/6-8
1715 Quesada Way 94010 650-259-3830
Pamela Scott, prin. Fax 259-3843

San Mateo UNHSD
Supt. — See San Mateo
Burlingame HS 1,300/9-12
1 Mangini Way 94010 650-558-2899
Pyongduk Yim, prin. Fax 558-2852

Mercy HS 500/9-12
2750 Adeline Dr 94010 650-343-3631
Karen Hanrahan, head sch Fax 343-3358
Mills Peninsula Health Services Post-Sec.
1783 El Camino Real 94010 650-696-5678

Burney, Shasta, Pop. 3,044
Fall River JUSD 1,200/K-12
20375 Tamarack Ave 96013 530-335-4538
Greg Hawkins, supt. Fax 335-3115
www.frjusd.org
Burney Community Day S 50/Alt
20375 Tamarack Ave 96013 530-335-5189
Greg Hawkins, prin. Fax 335-3115
Burney JSHS 200/7-12
37571 Mountain View Rd 96013 530-335-4576
Ray Guerrero, prin. Fax 335-3554
Mountain View Continuation HS 50/Alt
20375 Tamarack Ave 96013 530-335-5189
Greg Hawkins, prin. Fax 335-3115
Other Schools – See Mc Arthur

Byron, Contra Costa, Pop. 1,236
Byron UNESD 1,600/PK-8
14301 Byron Hwy 94514 925-809-7500
Debbie Gold Ed.D., supt. Fax 634-9421
www.byronunionschooldistrict.us
Excelsior MS 600/6-8
14301 Byron Hwy 94514 925-809-7530
Paul Gengler, prin. Fax 634-5120

Calabasas, Los Angeles, Pop. 22,176
Las Virgenes USD 11,200/PK-12
4111 Las Virgenes Rd 91302 818-880-4000
Dan Stepenosky Ed.D., supt. Fax 880-4200
www.lvusd.org
Calabasas HS 1,700/9-12
22855 Mulholland Hwy 91302 818-222-7177
C.J. Foss, prin. Fax 223-8477
Indian Hills Continuation HS - East 50/Alt
22855 Mulholland Hwy 91302 818-222-7177
C.J. Foss, prin. Fax 223-8477
Stelle MS 800/6-8
22450 Mulholland Hwy 91302 818-224-4107
Ryan Emery, prin. Fax 224-4989
Wright MS 800/6-8
4029 Las Virgenes Rd 91302 818-880-4614
Elias Miles, prin. Fax 878-0453
Other Schools – See Agoura Hills

Mesivta of Greater Los Angeles S 100/9-12
25115 Mureau Rd 91302 818-876-0550
MUSE MSHS 100/6-12
4345 Las Virgenes Rd 91302 818-880-5437
Jeff King, head sch Fax 880-5430
Viewpoint S 1,200/K-12
23620 Mulholland Hwy 91302 818-591-6500
Mark McKee, head sch Fax 591-0834

Calexico, Imperial, Pop. 38,495
Calexico USD 9,100/K-12
901 Andrade Ave 92231 760-768-3888
Maria Ambriz, supt. Fax 768-3856
www2.cusdk12.org/nsite/
Aurora HS 200/Alt
641 Rockwood Ave 92231 760-768-3940
John Moreno, prin. Fax 768-1459
Calexico HS 2,900/9-12
1030 Encinas Ave 92231 760-768-3980
Gabrielle Williams, prin. Fax 357-9640
Camarena JHS 700/7-8
800 E Rivera Ave 92231 760-768-3808
Diego Romero, prin. Fax 768-3807
Moreno JHS 800/7-8
1202 Kloke Ave 92231 760-768-3960
Mariano Velez, prin. Fax 768-1905
Morales Adult Education Center Adult
1201 Kloke Ave 92231 760-768-3914
John Moreno, admin. Fax 768-3916

Calexico Mission S 300/K-12
601 E 1st St 92231 760-357-3711

Vincent Memorial HS 300/9-12
525 Sheridan St 92231 760-357-3461
Sr. Guadalupe Hernandez, prin. Fax 357-0902

California City, Kern, Pop. 13,467
Mojave USD
Supt. — See Mojave
California City HS 500/9-12
8567 Raven Way 93505 760-373-5263
Michael Vogenthaler, prin. Fax 373-9028
California City MS 300/7-8
9736 Redwood Blvd 93505 760-373-3241
Ron Riley, prin. Fax 373-1355

Calimesa, Riverside, Pop. 7,727
Yucaipa-Calimesa JUSD
Supt. — See Yucaipa
Mesa View MS 800/6-8
800 Mustang Way 92320 909-790-8008
John Moore, prin. Fax 795-6810

Mesa Grande Academy 300/PK-12
975 Fremont St 92320 909-795-1112
Alfred Riddle, prin. Fax 795-1653

Calipatria, Imperial, Pop. 7,613
Calipatria USD 1,200/K-12
501 W Main St 92233 760-348-2892
Douglas Kline, supt. Fax 344-8926
www.calipatriahornets.org
Calipatria HS 300/9-12
601 W Main St 92233 760-348-2254
Joe Derma, prin. Fax 348-2431
Young MS 400/5-8
220 S International Blvd 92233 760-348-2842
Virginia Calsada-Medina, prin. Fax 348-2848

Calistoga, Napa, Pop. 5,085
Calistoga JUSD 800/K-12
1520 Lake St 94515 707-942-4703
Dr. Esmeralda Mondragon, supt. Fax 942-6589
www.calistogaschools.org
Calistoga JSHS 300/7-12
1608 Lake St 94515 707-942-6278
David Kumamoto, prin. Fax 942-6592
Palisades HS 50/Alt
1507 Grant St 94515 707-942-5255
David Kumamoto, prin. Fax 942-5255

Camarillo, Ventura, Pop. 63,018
Oxnard UNHSD
Supt. — See Oxnard
Camarillo HS 2,600/9-12
4660 Mission Oaks Blvd 93012 805-389-6407
Kimberly Stephenson, prin. Fax 484-8087
Frontier HS 400/Alt
545 Airport Way 93010 805-389-6450
Wayne Lamas, prin. Fax 389-6466
Rancho Campana HS 9-12
4235 Mar Vista Dr 93010 805-385-2500
Roger Adams, prin.

Pleasant Valley SD 7,000/PK-8
600 Temple Ave 93010 805-482-2763
Angelica Ramsey, supt. Fax 987-5511
www.pvsd.k12.ca.us
Las Colinas MS 900/6-8
5750 Fieldcrest Dr 93012 805-484-0461
Erik Goldman, prin. Fax 482-2443
Monte Vista MS 900/6-8
888 Lantana St 93010 805-482-8891
Joseph Herzog, prin. Fax 987-8951

Regional Occupational Center & Program
Supt. — None
Ventura County ROP Vo/Tech
465 Horizon Way 93010 805-388-4423
Peggy Velarde, dir. Fax 388-4428

Ventura County Office of Education 2,800/
5189 Verdugo Way 93012 805-383-1900
Stan Mantooth, supt. Fax 383-1908
www.vcoe.org
Gateway Community S 100/Alt
200 Horizon Way 93010 805-437-1460
James Koenig, prin. Fax 437-1493

Beacon Hill Classical Academy 100/K-10
2304 Antonio Ave 93010 805-389-6581
California State University-Channel Isle Post-Sec.
1 University Dr 93012 805-437-8400
Saint John's Seminary Post-Sec.
5012 Seminary Rd 93012 805-482-2755

Cambria, San Luis Obispo, Pop. 5,934
Coast USD 700/K-12
1350 Main St 93428 805-927-3880
Victoria Schumacher, supt. Fax 927-0312
www.coastusd.org
Coast Union HS 200/9-12
2950 Santa Rosa Creek Rd 93428 805-927-3889
Scott Ferguson, prin. Fax 924-2933
Leffingwell Continuation HS 50/Alt
2820 Santa Rosa Creek Rd 93428 805-927-7148
Bob Watt, prin. Fax 927-6741
Santa Lucia MS 200/6-8
2850 Schoolhouse Ln 93428 805-927-3693
John Calandro, prin. Fax 927-4615

Cameron Park, El Dorado, Pop. 17,664
Buckeye UNSD
Supt. — See El Dorado Hills
Camerado Springs MS 600/6-8
2480 Merrychase Dr 95682 530-677-1658
Doug Shupe, prin. Fax 677-9537

Campbell, Santa Clara, Pop. 37,545
Campbell UNESD 7,600/K-8
155 N 3rd St 95008 408-364-4200
Dr. Eric Andrew, supt. Fax 341-7280
www.campbellusd.org

Campbell MS 700/5-8
295 Cherry Ln 95008 408-364-4222
Norma Jeanne Ready, prin. Fax 341-7150
Other Schools – See Los Gatos, San Jose

Campbell UNHSD
Supt. — See San Jose
Westmont HS 1,600/9-12
4805 Westmont Ave 95008 408-626-3406
Abra Evanoff, prin. Fax 379-1720

The International Culinary Center Post-Sec.
700 W Hamilton Ave 95008 408-370-5555
Valley International Academy 9-12
1 W Campbell Ave Ste B20 95008 408-866-9988

Canoga Park, See Los Angeles
Los Angeles USD
Supt. — See Los Angeles
Canoga Park HS 1,700/9-12
6850 Topanga Canyon Blvd 91303 818-673-1300
Robert Garcia, prin. Fax 702-8942
Columbus MS 800/6-8
22250 Elkwood St 91304 818-702-1200
Debra McIntyre-Sciarrino, prin. Fax 348-2894
Owensmouth Continuation HS 100/Alt
6921 Jordan Ave 91303 818-340-7663
Jason Camp, prin. Fax 340-2947
Sutter MS 1,100/6-8
7330 Winnetka Ave 91306 818-773-5800
Kelly Welsh, prin. Fax 341-3039

AGBU Manoogian-Demirdjian S 800/PK-12
6844 Oakdale Ave 91306 818-883-2428
Arpi Avanesian-Idolor, prin. Fax 883-8353
Faith Baptist S 1,200/PK-12
7644 Farralone Ave 91304 818-340-6131
Valley College of Medical Careers Post-Sec.
8399 Topanga Canyon Ste 200 91304 888-271-1444

Canyon Country, See Santa Clarita
William S. Hart UNHSD
Supt. — See Santa Clarita
Canyon HS 2,500/9-12
19300 Nadal St 91351 661-252-6110
Jason d'Autremont, prin. Fax 251-1419
Sierra Vista JHS 1,200/7-8
19425 Stillmore St 91351 661-252-3113
Carolyn Hoffman, prin. Fax 252-2790

Charter College Canyon Country Post-Sec.
27125 Sierra Hwy Ste 329 91351 661-252-1864
Santa Clarita Christian S 500/K-12
27249 Luther Dr 91351 661-252-7371
Kirk Huckabone, admin. Fax 252-4354

Capistrano Beach, See Dana Point

San Clemente Christian S 100/PK-10
25975 Domingo Ave 92624 949-496-3513
Dr. Nicky Magnuson, prin. Fax 496-2138

Capitola, Santa Cruz, Pop. 9,578
Soquel UNESD 2,000/PK-8
620 Monterey Ave 95010 831-464-5633
Scott Turnbull, supt. Fax 479-7182
www.soqueldo.santacruz.k12.ca.us/
New Brighton MS 700/6-8
250 Washburn Ave 95010 831-464-5660
Craig Broadhurst, prin. Fax 475-8236

Carlsbad, San Diego, Pop. 101,706
Carlsbad USD 11,000/K-12
6225 El Camino Real 92009 760-331-5000
Benjamin Churchill Ed.D., supt. Fax 431-6707
www.carlsbadusd.k12.ca.us
Aviara Oaks MS 1,100/6-8
6225 El Camino Real 92009 760-331-6100
Bryan Brockett, prin. Fax 729-3040
Calavera Hills MS 500/6-8
6225 El Camino Real 92009 760-331-6400
Michael Ecker, prin. Fax 729-3040
Carlsbad HS 3,000/9-12
6225 El Camino Real 92009 760-331-5100
Joshua Porter, prin. Fax 729-6830
Carlsbad Seaside Academy 100/Alt
6225 El Camino Real 92009 760-331-5299
Jorge Espinoza, prin. Fax 729-1791
Carlsbad Village Academy 100/Alt
6225 El Camino Real 92009 760-331-5100
Jorge Espinoza, prin. Fax 729-1791
Sage Creek HS 300/9-12
6225 El Camino Real 92009 760-331-6600
Cesar Morales, prin. Fax 730-9698
Valley MS 1,000/6-8
6225 El Camino Real 92009 760-331-5300
Nicole Johnston, prin. Fax 720-2326

San Dieguito UNHSD
Supt. — See Encinitas
La Costa Canyon HS 2,000/9-12
1 Maverick Way 92009 760-436-6136
Bryan Marcus, prin. Fax 943-3539

APT College Post-Sec.
PO Box 131717 92013 800-431-8488
Army and Navy Academy 300/7-12
PO Box 3000 92018 760-729-2385
Arthur M. Bartell, pres. Fax 434-5948
Gemological Institute of America Post-Sec.
5345 Armada Dr 92008 760-603-4000
Golf Academy of America Post-Sec.
1950 Camino Vida Roble #125 92008 760-734-1208
Pacific Ridge S 400/7-12
6269 El Fuerte St 92009 760-448-9820
Dr. Bob Ogle, head sch Fax 683-6003

Carmel, Monterey, Pop. 3,645
Carmel USD 2,500/PK-12
PO Box 222700 93922 831-624-1546
Karen Hendricks, supt. Fax 626-4052
www.carmelunified.org
Carmel HS 800/9-12
PO Box 222780 93922 831-624-1821
Rick Lopez, prin. Fax 626-4313
Carmel MS 600/6-8
PO Box 222740 93922 831-624-2785
Dan Morgan, prin. Fax 624-0839
Carmel Valley HS 50/Alt
PO Box 222700 93922 831-624-4462
Tom Stewart, prin. Fax 624-4487
Carmel Adult Education Adult
PO Box 222700 93922 831-624-1714
Karen Hendricks, prin. Fax 624-8747

Carmichael, Sacramento, Pop. 58,920
San Juan USD 45,400/PK-12
PO Box 477 95609 916-971-7700
Kent Kern, supt. Fax 971-7758
www.sanjuan.edu
Barrett MS 700/6-8
4243 Barrett Rd 95608 916-971-7842
Brent Givens, prin. Fax 971-7839
Churchill MS 1,000/6-8
4900 Whitney Ave 95608 916-971-7324
Michael Dolan, prin. Fax 971-7856
Other Schools – See Citrus Heights, Fair Oaks, Orangevale, Sacramento

---

Jesuit HS 1,100/9-12
1200 Jacob Ln 95608 916-482-6060
Michael Wood, prin. Fax 482-2310
Sacramento Adventist Academy 200/PK-12
5601 Winding Way 95608 916-481-2300
Victory Christian S 200/K-12
3045 Garfield Ave 95608 916-488-5601
John Huffman, supt. Fax 488-2589

Carpinteria, Santa Barbara, Pop. 12,835
Carpinteria USD 2,300/K-12
1400 Linden Ave 93013 805-684-4511
Micheline G. Miglis, supt. Fax 684-0218
www.cusd.net
Carpinteria HS 700/9-12
4810 Foothill Rd 93013 805-684-4107
Gerardo Cornejo, prin. Fax 566-5952
Carpinteria MS 500/6-8
5351 Carpinteria Ave 93013 805-684-4544
John Merritt, prin. Fax 566-3839
Foothill Alternative HS 50/Alt
4698 Foothill Rd 93013 805-684-3277
Barnaby Gloger, prin. Fax 566-9707
Rincon Continuation S 50/Alt
4698 Foothill Rd 93013 805-684-3277
Barnaby Gloger, prin. Fax 566-9707

Cate S 300/9-12
1960 Cate Mesa Rd 93013 805-684-4127
Benjamin Williams, hdmstr. Fax 684-8940
International Sports Sciences Post-Sec.
1015 Mark Ave 93013 805-745-8111
Pacifica Graduate Institute Post-Sec.
249 Lambert Rd 93013 805-969-3626

Carson, Los Angeles, Pop. 87,081
Long Beach USD
Supt. — See Long Beach
California Academy of Math & Science 700/9-12
1000 E Victoria St 90747 310-243-2025
Wendy Poffenberger, prin. Fax 516-4041

Los Angeles USD
Supt. — See Los Angeles
Academy of Education and Empowerment 600/9-12
22328 Main St 90745 310-847-6000
Michelle Bryant, prin.
Academy of Medical Arts at Carson HS 500/9-12
22328 Main St 90745 310-847-6000
Melinda Martes, prin.
Carnegie MS 900/6-8
21820 Bonita St 90745 310-952-5700
Cheryl Nakata, prin. Fax 830-9015
Carson HS 1,500/9-12
22328 Main St 90745 310-847-6000
Windy Warren, prin. Fax 518-5817
Curtiss MS 700/6-8
1254 E Helmick St 90746 310-661-4500
Gina Russell-Williams, prin. Fax 537-2115
Eagle Tree Continuation S 100/Alt
22628 Main St 90745 310-549-0970
Jaiyawanda Gant, prin. Fax 518-5746
White MS 1,700/6-8
22102 Figueroa St 90745 310-783-4900
Adaina Brown, prin. Fax 782-8954

California State Univ.-Dominguez Hills Post-Sec.
1000 E Victoria St 90747 310-243-3300
Carson Christian S 100/K-12
17705 Central Ave 90746 310-609-2300

Caruthers, Fresno, Pop. 2,460
Caruthers USD 1,400/K-12
PO Box 127 93609 559-864-6500
Orin Hirschkorn, supt. Fax 864-8857
www.caruthers.k12.ca.us
Caruthers HS 600/9-12
PO Box 545 93609 559-864-6500
Mark Fowler, prin. Fax 864-8303
MARC HS, PO Box 545 93609 50/Alt
Tod Tompkins, dir. 559-495-6443

Castaic, Los Angeles, Pop. 18,337
Castaic UNSD
Supt. — See Valencia
Castaic MS 900/6-8
28900 Hillcrest Pkwy 91384 661-257-4550
Bob Brauneisen, prin. Fax 294-9714

Castro Valley, Alameda, Pop. 58,286
Castro Valley USD 9,300/PK-12
PO Box 2146 94546 510-537-3000
Parvin Ahmadi, supt. Fax 886-8962
www.cv.k12.ca.us
Canyon MS 1,400/6-8
19600 Cull Canyon Rd 94552 510-538-8833
Matthew Steinecke, prin. Fax 247-9439
Castro Valley HS 3,000/9-12
19400 Santa Maria Ave 94546 510-537-5910
Blaine Torpey, prin. Fax 582-3924
Creekside MS 800/6-8
19722 Center St 94546 510-247-0665
Jaliza Eagles, prin. Fax 581-6617
Redwood HS 100/Alt
18400 Clifton Way 94546 510-537-3193
Erica Ehmann, prin. Fax 247-3397
Castro Valley Adult & Career Education Adult
4430 Alma Ave 94546 510-886-1000
Susie Passeggi, dir. Fax 537-8537

Castroville, Monterey, Pop. 6,411
North Monterey County USD
Supt. — See Moss Landing
North Monterey County HS 1,100/9-12
13990 Castroville Blvd 95012 831-633-5221
Antonio Vela, prin. Fax 633-2520
North Monterey County MS 600/7-8
10301 Seymour St 95012 831-633-3391
Marisa Martinez, prin. Fax 633-3680

Cathedral City, Riverside, Pop. 50,401
Palm Springs USD
Supt. — See Palm Springs
Cathedral City HS 2,000/9-12
69250 Dinah Shore Dr 92234 760-770-0100
Guillermo Chavez, prin. Fax 770-0149
Coffman MS 1,100/6-8
34603 Plumley Rd 92234 760-770-8617
Carlos Flores, prin. Fax 770-8623
Mt. San Jacinto Continuation HS 400/Alt
30800 Landau Blvd 92234 760-770-8563
Milt Jones, prin. Fax 770-8568
Workman MS 1,400/6-8
69300 30th Ave 92234 760-770-8540
Brad Sauer, prin. Fax 770-8545

Mayfield College Post-Sec.
35325 Date Palm Dr Ste 101 92234 760-328-5554

Cedarville, Modoc, Pop. 502
Surprise Valley JUSD 100/K-12
PO Box 100 96104 530-279-6141
Janelle Anderson, supt. Fax 279-2210
www.svjusd.org
Surprise Valley HS 50/9-12
PO Box 100 96104 530-279-6141
Rikki-Lee Carey, prin. Fax 279-2210

Ceres, Stanislaus, Pop. 43,964
Ceres USD 12,300/PK-12
PO Box 307 95307 209-556-1500
Scott Siegel, supt. Fax 556-1090
www.ceres.k12.ca.us
Argus and Endeavor HS 300/Alt
PO Box 307 95307 209-556-1800
Jan Gordon, prin. Fax 538-1027
Blaker-Kinser JHS 600/7-8
PO Box 307 95307 209-556-1810
Paul Rutishauser, prin. Fax 541-0174
Central Valley HS 1,700/9-12
PO Box 307 95307 209-556-1900
Dan Pangrazio, prin. Fax 531-2748
Ceres HS 1,600/9-12
PO Box 307 95307 209-556-1920
Linda Stubbs, prin. Fax 538-8978
Chavez JHS 600/7-8
PO Box 307 95307 209-556-1830
Rosemarie Kloepfer, prin. Fax 538-3970
Hensley JHS 600/7-8
PO Box 307 95307 209-556-1820
Carol Lubinsky, prin. Fax 538-9428
Ceres Adult S Adult
2491 Lawrence St 95307 556-556-1557
Dustin Pack, prin.

Stanislaus County Office of Education
Supt. — See Modesto
Stanislaus County Institute of Learning Alt
3113 Mitchell Road 95307 209-238-8750
Marcelo Briones, prin. Fax 238-8774

Central Valley Christian Academy 200/PK-12
2020 Academy Pl 95307 209-537-4521

Cerritos, Los Angeles, Pop. 47,521
ABC USD 20,700/K-12
16700 Norwalk Blvd 90703 562-926-5566
Mary Sieu, supt. Fax 404-1092
www.abcusd.k12.ca.us
Carmenita MS 700/7-8
13435 166th St 90703 562-229-7775
Robert Castillo, prin. Fax 404-7807
Cerritos HS 2,200/9-12
12500 183rd St 90703 562-228-7815
Patrick Walker, prin. Fax 924-3187
Gahr HS 2,000/9-12
11111 Artesia Blvd 90703 562-229-7730
Crechena Wise, prin. Fax 924-8136
Haskell MS 500/7-8
11525 Del Amo Blvd 90703 562-229-7815
Camille Lewis, prin. Fax 809-7250
Tetzlaff MS 600/7-8
12351 Del Amo Blvd 90703 562-229-7795
Kester Song, prin. Fax 402-6412
Tracy Continuation HS 400/Alt
12222 Cuesta Dr 90703 562-229-7760
Jeff Green, prin. Fax 926-8740
Whitney JSHS 1,000/7-12
16800 Shoemaker Ave 90703 562-229-7745
John Briquelet Ed.D., prin. Fax 926-2751
ABC Adult HS Adult
12254 Cuesta Dr 90703 562-229-7960
Pao-Ling Guo, prin. Fax 921-9958
Other Schools – See Artesia, Hawaiian Gardens, Lakewood

Fremont College Post-Sec.
18000 Studebaker Rd # 900A 90703 800-373-6668
PCI College Post-Sec.
17215 Studebaker Rd Ste 310 90703 562-916-5055
Valley Christian HS 600/9-12
17700 Dumont Ave 90703 562-865-0281
Troy Stahl, prin. Fax 865-0082
Valley Christian MS 300/7-8
18100 Dumont Ave 90703 562-865-6519
John Tiersma, prin. Fax 403-3159

Chatsworth, See Los Angeles
Los Angeles USD
Supt. — See Los Angeles
Aggeler Community Day S 100/Alt
21050 Plummer St 91311 818-341-1232
Alex Placencio, prin. Fax 349-1404
Lawrence MS 1,500/6-8
10100 Variel Ave 91311 818-678-7900
Maria Pigliapoco, prin. Fax 349-4539
Stoney Point Continuation HS 100/Alt
10010 De Soto Ave 91311 818-678-3491
George Padgett, prin. Fax 773-1796

Chaminade College Prep MS 700/6-8
19800 Devonshire St 91311 818-363-8127
Michael Valentine, prin. Fax 363-1219
Phillips Graduate Institute Post-Sec.
19900 Plummer St 91311 818-386-5660
Sierra Canyon S 500/7-12
20801 Rinaldi St 91311 818-882-8121
James Skrumbis, hdmstr. Fax 534-2398
Univ of West Los Angeles School of Law Post-Sec.
9201 Oakdale Ave Ste 201 91311 818-775-4500

Chester, Plumas, Pop. 2,075
Plumas USD
Supt. — See Quincy
Chester JSHS 200/7-12
PO Box 797 96020 530-258-2126
Terry Hernandez, prin. Fax 258-2306

Chico, Butte, Pop. 82,892
Butte County Office of Education
Supt. — See Oroville
LEAD Alt
2345 Fair St 95928 530-532-5642
Cheri Gamette, prin. Fax 532-5699

Chico USD 12,400/PK-12
1163 E 7th St 95928 530-891-3000
Kelly Staley, supt. Fax 891-3220
www.chicousd.org
Academy for Change 50/Alt
290 East Ave 95926 530-895-4047
Andrew Moll, prin. Fax 895-4048
Bidwell JHS 600/6-8
2376 North Ave 95926 530-891-3080
Leonard Lopez, prin. Fax 891-3082
Chico HS 1,800/9-12
901 Esplanade 95926 530-891-3026
Mark Beebe, prin. Fax 891-3284
Chico JHS 600/6-8
280 Memorial Way 95926 530-891-3066
Pedro Caldera, prin. Fax 891-3264
Fair View HS 200/Alt
290 East Ave 95926 530-891-3092
Andrew Moll, prin. Fax 891-3232
Marsh JHS 600/6-8
2253 Humboldt Rd 95928 530-895-4110
Jay Marchant, prin. Fax 895-4111
Pleasant Valley HS 1,900/9-12
1475 East Ave 95926 530-879-5100
John Shepherd, prin. Fax 879-5263

Regional Occupational Center & Program
Supt. — None
Butte County ROP Vo/Tech
2491 Carmichael Dr Ste 100 95928 530-879-7462
Susan Steward, dir. Fax 879-7458

California State University-Chico Post-Sec.
400 W 1st St 95929 530-898-6116

Chino, San Bernardino, Pop. 76,369
Chino Valley USD 29,100/K-12
5130 Riverside Dr 91710 909-628-1201
Wayne Joseph, supt. Fax 548-6096
www.chino.k12.ca.us
Buena Vista Continuation HS 200/Alt
13509 Ramona Ave 91710 909-628-9903
Rigoberto Vasquez, prin. Fax 548-6027
Chino HS 2,400/9-12
5472 Park Pl 91710 909-627-7351
Felix Melendez, prin. Fax 548-6004
Lugo HS 1,900/9-12
13400 Pipeline Ave 91710 909-591-3902
Kimberly Cabrera, prin. Fax 548-6020
Magnolia JHS 800/7-8
13150 Mountain Ave 91710 909-627-9263
John Miller, prin. Fax 627-2165
Ramona JHS 600/7-8
4575 Walnut Ave 91710 909-627-9144
Andrea Boden, prin. Fax 548-6055

Chino Community Adult — Adult
12970 3rd St 91710 — 909-628-1201
Carl Hampton, prin. — Fax 548-6016
Other Schools – See Chino Hills, Ontario

Chino Hills, San Bernardino, Pop. 72,538
Chino Valley USD
Supt. — See Chino
Ayala HS — 2,500/9-12
14255 Peyton Dr 91709 — 909-627-3584
Diana Yarboi, prin. — Fax 464-9239
Boy's Republic HS — 100/Alt
1907 Boys Republic Dr 91709 — 909-628-1217
Carl Hampton, prin. — Fax 628-9847
Canyon Hills JHS — 1,100/7-8
2500 Madrugada Dr 91709 — 909-464-9938
Ryan Cummins, prin. — Fax 548-6058
Chino Hills HS — 3,100/9-12
16150 Pomona Rincon Rd 91709 — 909-606-7540
Isabel Brenes, prin. — Fax 548-6041
Townsend JHS — 1,100/7-8
15359 Ilex Dr 91709 — 909-591-2161
Robert Nelson, prin. — Fax 548-6057

Orion International Academy — 9-12
15659 Pipeline Ave 91709 — 323-898-5188
Marco Menendez, prin.

Chowchilla, Madera, Pop. 17,893
Alview-Dairyland UNESD — 400/K-8
12861 Avenue 18 1/2 93610 — 559-665-2394
Loren York M.A., supt. — Fax 665-7347
www.adusd.k12.ca.us
Dairyland MS — 200/4-8
12861 Avenue 18 1/2 93610 — 559-665-2394
Loren York M.A., prin. — Fax 665-7347

Chowchilla ESD — 2,200/PK-8
PO Box 910 93610 — 559-665-8000
Dr. Charles Martin, supt. — Fax 665-5134
www.chowchillaelem.k12.ca.us
Wilson MS — 500/7-8
PO Box 910 93610 — 559-665-8070
Zach White, prin. — Fax 665-8004

Chowchilla UNHSD — 1,000/9-12
805 Humboldt Ave 93610 — 559-665-1331
Ronald Seals, supt. — Fax 665-1881
www.chowchillahigh.k12.ca.us
Chowchilla HS — 1,000/9-12
805 Humboldt Ave 93610 — 559-665-1331
Dr. Justin Miller, prin. — Fax 665-1881
Gateway Continuation HS — 50/Alt
805 Humboldt Ave 93610 — 559-665-1331
Michelle Irwin, prin. — Fax 665-2220

Chula Vista, San Diego, Pop. 235,860
Sweetwater UNHSD — 40,100/K-12
1130 5th Ave 91911 — 619-691-5500
Dr. Karen Janney, supt. — Fax 498-1997
www.sweetwaterschools.org
Bonita Vista HS — 2,400/9-12
751 Otay Lakes Rd 91913 — 619-397-2000
Bettina Batista, prin. — Fax 656-1203
Bonita Vista MS — 1,100/7-8
650 Otay Lakes Rd 91910 — 619-397-2200
Eduardo Reyes, prin. — Fax 482-9356
Castle Park HS — 1,600/9-12
1395 Hilltop Dr 91911 — 619-585-2000
Viky Mitrovich, prin. — Fax 427-5967
Castle Park MS — 800/7-8
160 Quintard St 91911 — 619-498-6000
Gina Galvez-Mallari, prin. — Fax 427-8045
Chula Vista HS — 2,700/9-12
820 4th Ave 91911 — 619-476-3300
Mary Rose Peralta, prin. — Fax 427-5824
Chula Vista MS — 1,000/7-8
415 5th Ave 91910 — 619-498-6800
Julissa Gracias, prin. — Fax 427-5723
Eastlake HS — 3,000/9-12
1120 Eastlake Pkwy 91915 — 619-397-3800
Maria Esther Lizarraga, prin. — Fax 656-9736
Eastlake MS — 1,700/7-8
900 Duncan Ranch Rd 91914 — 619-591-4000
Juan Ulloa, prin. — Fax 482-0553
Hilltop HS — 2,200/9-12
555 Claire Ave 91910 — 619-476-4200
Thomas Gray, prin. — Fax 425-3284
Hilltop MS — 1,200/7-8
44 E J St 91910 — 619-498-2700
Griselda Delgado, prin. — Fax 585-3576
Olympian HS — 2,200/9-12
1925 Magdalena Ave 91913 — 619-656-2400
Ernesto Zamudio, prin. — Fax 216-0650
Options Secondary S — 200/Alt
467 Moss St 91911 — 619-585-7896
Mercedes Lopez, prin. — Fax 420-5663
Otay Ranch HS — 2,700/9-12
1250 Olympic Pkwy 91913 — 619-591-5000
Jose Brosz, prin. — Fax 591-5010
Palomar Continuation HS — 400/Alt
480 Palomar St 91911 — 619-407-4800
Sarita Fuentes, prin. — Fax 585-6232
Rancho del Rey MS — 1,700/7-8
1174 E J St 91910 — 619-397-2500
Anna Pedroza, prin. — Fax 656-3810
Chula Vista Adult S — Adult
1034 4th Ave 91911 — 619-796-7000
Wes Braddock, prin. — Fax 425-5447
Other Schools – See Imperial Beach, National City, San Diego, San Ysidro

---

Brightwood College — Post-Sec.
555 Broadway Ste 144 91910 — 619-498-4100
Calvary Christian Academy — 400/PK-12
1771 E Palomar St 91913 — 619-591-2260
Dr. Richard Andujo, hdmstr. — Fax 591-2261

Covenant Christian S — 100/K-12
505 E Naples St 91911 — 619-421-8822
Thomas McManus, prin. — Fax 216-9846
Lutheran HS of San Diego — 100/9-12
810 Buena Vista Way 91910 — 619-262-4444
Scott Dufresne M.A., dir. — Fax 691-0424
Mater Dei Catholic HS — 700/9-12
PO Box 210760 91921 — 619-423-2121
George Milke, prin. — Fax 423-6910
Pima Medical Institute — Post-Sec.
780 Bay Blvd Ste 101 91910 — 619-425-3200
Southwestern College — Post-Sec.
900 Otay Lakes Rd 91910 — 619-421-6700
United States University — Post-Sec.
830 Bay Blvd 91911 — 619-477-6310

Citrus Heights, Sacramento, Pop. 79,798
San Juan USD
Supt. — See Carmichael
Mesa Verde HS — 900/9-12
7501 Carriage Dr 95621 — 916-971-5288
Colin Bross, prin. — Fax 971-5215
New San Juan HS — 700/9-12
7551 Greenback Ln 95610 — 916-971-5112
Vanessa Adolphson, prin. — Fax 971-5111
Sylvan MS — 500/7-8
7085 Auburn Blvd 95621 — 916-971-7873
Kristen Schnepp, prin. — Fax 971-7896
Sunrise Tech Center — Adult
7322 Sunrise Blvd 95610 — 916-971-7654
Bill Bettencourt, prin. — Fax 971-7695

Carrington College California — Post-Sec.
7301 Greenback Ln Bldg A 95621 — 916-722-8200

City of Industry, Los Angeles, Pop. 217
Bassett USD
Supt. — See La Puente
Torch MS — 800/6-8
751 Vineland Ave 91746 — 626-931-2700
Monica Murray, prin. — Fax 931-2702

Hacienda La Puente USD — 19,900/K-12
PO Box 60002 91716 — 626-933-1000
Cynthia Parulan-Colfer, supt. — Fax 855-3505
www.hlpschools.org
Workman HS — 1,200/9-12
16303 Temple Ave 91744 — 626-933-8801
Ben Webster, prin. — Fax 855-3148
Other Schools – See Hacienda Heights, La Puente

Elegante Beauty College — Post-Sec.
1600 S Azusa Ave Unit 244 91748 — 626-965-2532
Everest College — Post-Sec.
12801 Crossroads Pkwy S 91746 — 562-908-2500

Claremont, Los Angeles, Pop. 33,627
Claremont USD — 7,000/PK-12
170 W San Jose Ave 91711 — 909-398-0609
James Elsasser Ed.D., supt. — Fax 398-0690
www.cusd.claremont.edu
Claremont HS — 2,400/9-12
1601 N Indian Hill Blvd 91711 — 909-624-9053
Dr. Brett O'Connor, prin. — Fax 624-2128
Community Day S — 50/Alt
125 W San Jose Ave 91711 — 909-398-0316
Sean Delgado, prin. — Fax 398-0384
El Roble IS — 1,100/7-8
665 N Mountain Ave 91711 — 909-398-0343
Scott Martinez, prin. — Fax 398-0399
San Antonio HS — 100/Alt
125 W San Jose Ave 91711 — 909-398-0316
Sean Delgado, prin. — Fax 398-0384
Claremont Adult S — Adult
170 W San Jose Ave Ste 100 91711 — 909-398-0609
Felipe Delvasto, coord. — Fax 626-5109

Claremont Graduate University — Post-Sec.
150 E 10th St 91711 — 909-621-8000
Claremont McKenna College — Post-Sec.
500 E 9th St 91711 — 909-621-8000
Claremont School of Theology — Post-Sec.
1325 N College Ave 91711 — 909-447-2500
Harvey Mudd College — Post-Sec.
301 Platt Blvd 91711 — 909-621-8000
Keck Graduate Institute — Post-Sec.
535 Watson Dr 91711 — 909-607-7855
Pitzer College — Post-Sec.
1050 N Mills Ave 91711 — 909-621-8219
Pomona College — Post-Sec.
333 N College Way 91711 — 909-621-8000
Scripps College — Post-Sec.
1030 Columbia Ave 91711 — 909-621-8000
Webb S — 400/9-12
1175 W Baseline Rd 91711 — 909-626-3587
Taylor Stockdale, head sch — Fax 621-4582

Clarksburg, Yolo, Pop. 410
River Delta USD
Supt. — See Rio Vista
Clarksburg MS — 200/7-9
52870 Netherlands Ave 95612 — 916-744-1717
Laura Uslan, prin. — Fax 744-5704
Delta HS — 200/10-12
52810 Netherlands Ave 95612 — 916-744-1714
Laura Uslan, prin. — Fax 744-1673

Clayton, Contra Costa, Pop. 10,503
Mount Diablo USD
Supt. — See Concord
Diablo View MS — 600/6-8
300 Diablo View Ln 94517 — 925-672-0898
Patti Bannister, prin. — Fax 672-4327

Clearlake, Lake, Pop. 14,540
Konocti USD
Supt. — See Lower Lake

Konocti Education Center — Alt
15850A Dam Road Ext 95422 — 707-994-6447
Melissa Lambert, prin. — Fax 994-4121

Cloverdale, Sonoma, Pop. 8,447
Cloverdale USD — 1,400/PK-12
97 School St 95425 — 707-894-1920
Jeremy Decker, supt. — Fax 894-1922
www.cusd.org/
Cloverdale HS — 400/9-12
509 N Cloverdale Blvd 95425 — 707-894-1900
Kirsten Sanft, prin. — Fax 894-4804
Eagle Creek Community S — 50/Alt
322 N Washington St 95425 — 707-894-1900
Kirsten Sanft, prin. — Fax 894-1922
Echols-Hansen Continuation HS — 50/Alt
322 N Washington St 95425 — 707-894-1925
Kirsten Sanft, prin. — Fax 894-1922
Washington MS — 400/5-8
129 S Washington St 95425 — 707-894-1940
Mark Lucchetti, prin. — Fax 894-1946

Clovis, Fresno, Pop. 92,614
Clovis USD — 38,200/K-12
1450 Herndon Ave 93611 — 559-327-9000
Janet Young Ed.D., supt. — Fax 327-9109
www.cusd.com
Alta Sierra IS — 1,400/7-8
380 W Teague Ave, — 559-327-3500
Steve Pagani, prin. — Fax 327-3590
Buchanan HS — 2,600/9-12
1560 N Minnewawa Ave, — 559-327-3000
Ricci Ulrich, prin. — Fax 327-3090
Clark IS — 1,500/7-8
902 5th St 93612 — 559-327-1500
Teresa Barber, prin. — Fax 327-1556
Clovis Community Day Secondary S — 50/Alt
1715 David E Cook Way 93611 — 559-327-1980
Tom Judd, prin. — Fax 327-1989
Clovis HS — 2,900/9-12
1055 Fowler Ave 93611 — 559-327-1000
Denver Stairs, prin. — Fax 327-1010
Gateway HS / Enterprise — 200/Alt
1550 Herndon Ave 93611 — 559-327-1800
Rees Warne, prin. — Fax 327-1890
Reagan Educational Center — 2,100/7-12
2940 Leonard Ave, — 559-327-4000
Kevin Kerney, prin. — Fax 327-4190
Clovis Adult S — Adult
1452 David E Cook Way 93611 — 559-327-2800
Kevin Cookingham, prin. — Fax 327-2889
Other Schools – See Fresno

Brightwood College — Post-Sec.
44 Shaw Ave 93612 — 559-325-5101
Institute of Technology — Post-Sec.
564 W Herndon Ave 93612 — 559-297-4500
Milan Institute — Post-Sec.
731 W Shaw Ave 93612 — 559-323-2800
San Joaquin College of Law — Post-Sec.
901 5th St 93612 — 559-323-2100
Tower Christian S — 100/K-12
8753 Chickadee Ln, — 559-298-2772

Coachella, Riverside, Pop. 40,549
Coachella Valley USD
Supt. — See Thermal
Cahuilla Desert Academy — 900/7-8
82489 Avenue 52 92236 — 760-398-0097
Michael Reule, prin. — Fax 398-0088
Duke MS — 700/7-8
85358 Bagdad Ave 92236 — 760-398-0139
Encarnacion Becerra, prin. — Fax 398-5399
Coachella Valley Adult Education — Adult
1099 Orchard Ave 92236 — 760-398-6302
Jereme Weischedel, prin. — Fax 398-0436

Coalinga, Fresno, Pop. 13,188
Coalinga-Huron USD — 4,400/K-12
657 Sunset St 93210 — 559-935-7500
Dr. Helen Foster, supt. — Fax 935-5329
www.chusd.org
Cambridge HS — 100/Alt
516 Baker St 93210 — 559-935-7578
Jeff Hardig, prin. — Fax 935-1692
Coalinga HS — 1,200/9-12
750 Van Ness St 93210 — 559-935-7520
Margo Perkins, prin. — Fax 935-3571
Coalinga MS — 600/6-8
265 Cambridge Ave 93210 — 559-935-7550
Gary Miller, prin. — Fax 934-1311
Culwell Community Day S — 50/Alt
275 Cambridge Ave 93210 — 559-935-7660
Jeff Hardig, prin. — Fax 935-5601
Other Schools – See Huron

Faith Christian Academy — 100/PK-12
450 W Elm Ave 93210 — 559-935-9209
Tara Davis, prin. — Fax 935-0745
West Hills College Coalinga — Post-Sec.
300 W Cherry Ln 93210 — 559-935-2000

Coarsegold, Madera, Pop. 1,773
Yosemite USD
Supt. — See Oakhurst
Meadowbrook Community Day S — 50/Alt
45426 Road 415 93614 — 559-683-3533
Dr. Stacy Nicol, prin. — Fax 683-3533
Yosemite Falls Education Center — 50/Alt
35572 Highway 41 93614 — 559-658-8801
Stacy Nicol, prin. — Fax 658-2359

Coleville, Mono, Pop. 479
Eastern Sierra USD
Supt. — See Bridgeport
Coleville HS — 100/9-12
111591 US Highway 395 96107 — 530-495-2231
Steve Childs, prin. — Fax 495-2730

Mono County Office of Education
Supt. — See Bridgeport
Sawtooth Ridge Community S 50/7-12
111591 Highway 395 96107 760-934-0031
Janet Hunt, prin.

Colfax, Placer, Pop. 1,892
Placer UNHSD
Supt. — See Auburn
Colfax HS 700/9-12
24995 Ben Taylor Rd 95713 530-346-2284
Paul Lundberg, prin. Fax 346-6476

Colma, San Mateo, Pop. 1,713
Jefferson ESD
Supt. — See Daly City
Franklin IS 500/7-8
700 Stewart Ave, Daly City CA 94015 650-991-1200
James Parrish, prin. Fax 756-5475

Colton, San Bernardino, Pop. 51,046
Colton JUSD 23,300/PK-12
1212 Valencia Dr 92324 909-580-5000
Jerry Almendarez, supt. Fax 433-9471
www.cjusd.net
Colton HS 1,900/9-12
777 W Valley Blvd 92324 909-580-5005
Joda Murphy, prin. Fax 876-4093
Colton MS 1,000/7-8
670 W Laurel St 92324 909-580-5009
John Abbott, prin. Fax 876-4095
Washington Alternative HS 100/Alt
900 E C St 92324 909-580-5011
Pete Tasaka, prin. Fax 876-6352
Other Schools – See Bloomington, Grand Terrace

Rialto USD
Supt. — See Rialto
Jehue MS 1,500/6-8
1500 N Eucalyptus Ave 92324 909-421-7377
Armando Urteaga, prin. Fax 421-7376

Coast Career Institute Post-Sec.
1250 E Cooley Dr 92324 877-277-7170
DeVry University Post-Sec.
1090 E Washington St Ste H 92324 909-514-1808
Four-D College Post-Sec.
1020 E Washington St 92324 909-783-9331

Colusa, Colusa, Pop. 5,849
Colusa County Office of Education 100/
345 5th St Ste A 95932 530-458-0350
Michael West, supt. Fax 458-8054
www.ccoe.net
Other Schools – See Williams

Colusa USD 1,400/K-12
745 10th St 95932 530-458-7791
Dwayne Newman, supt. Fax 458-4030
www.colusa.k12.ca.us
Colusa Alternative HS 50/Alt
901 Colus Ave 95932 530-458-2156
Rebecca Changus, prin. Fax 458-5783
Colusa HS 300/9-12
901 Colus Ave 95932 530-458-2156
Darren Brown, prin. Fax 458-5783
Egling MS 500/4-8
813 Webster St 95932 530-458-7631
Jody Johnston, prin. Fax 458-8107

Commerce, Los Angeles, Pop. 12,764

National Polytechnic College Post-Sec.
6630 Telegraph Rd 90040 323-728-9636

Compton, Los Angeles, Pop. 94,840
Compton USD 22,400/PK-12
501 S Santa Fe Ave 90221 310-639-4321
Dr. Carmella Franco, supt. Fax 632-3014
www.compton.k12.ca.us
Bunche MS 600/6-8
12338 S Mona Blvd 90222 310-898-6010
Gipson Lyles, prin. Fax 638-4935
Centennial HS 900/9-12
2600 N Central Ave 90222 310-635-2715
Shauna Harris, prin. Fax 631-9164
Chavez Continuation HS 400/Alt
12501 S Wilmington Ave 90222 310-898-6340
Laura Henry, prin. Fax 763-4186
Community Day MS Alt
2300 W Caldwell St Bldg A 90220 310-639-7329
Fredricka Brown, prin. Fax 632-7304
Community Day S 50/Alt
417 W Alondra Blvd 90220 310-898-6154
Fredricka Brown, prin. Fax 632-7304
Compton Early College HS 9-12
601 S Acacia Ave 90220 310-639-4321
Lawrence Smith, prin.
Compton HS 2,200/9-12
601 S Acacia Ave 90220 310-635-3881
Rigoberto Roman, prin. Fax 898-6402
Davis MS 900/6-8
621 W Poplar St 90220 310-898-6020
Lakeyshua Washington, prin. Fax 631-5725
Dominguez HS 2,100/9-12
15301 S San Jose Ave 90221 562-630-0142
Stephen Franklin, prin. Fax 408-2367
Enterprise MS 500/6-8
2600 W Compton Blvd 90220 310-898-6030
David Herrera, prin. Fax 632-4183
Marshall Alternative S 50/Alt
12501 S Wilmington Ave 90222 310-604-2780
Laura Henry, prin. Fax 223-0970
Roosevelt MS 1,000/6-8
1200 E Alondra Blvd 90221 310-898-6040
Dr. Kevin Curry, prin. Fax 631-3298
Walton MS 500/6-8
900 W Greenleaf Dr 90220 310-898-6060
Dr. Bobbi Walker, prin. Fax 631-3409

Whaley MS 800/6-8
14401 S Gibson Ave 90221 310-898-6070
Dr. Candice Waters, prin. Fax 638-7079
Willowbrook MS 400/6-8
2601 N Wilmington Ave 90222 310-898-6080
David Brutus, prin. Fax 537-2932
Compton Adult S Adult
1104 E 148th St 90220 310-898-6490
Synee Pearson, admin. Fax 898-6477
Other Schools – See Los Angeles

Regional Occupational Center & Program
Supt. — None
Compton Unified ROP Vo/Tech
700 N Bullis Rd 90221 310-898-6000
Ryan Whetstone, dir. Fax 763-3871

El Camino College Compton Center Post-Sec.
1111 E Artesia Blvd 90221 310-900-1600
St. Albert the Great MS 100/6-8
823 E Compton Blvd 90220 310-515-3891
Tina Johnson, prin. Fax 515-1413
Universal College of Beauty Post-Sec.
718 W Compton Blvd 90220 310-635-6969

Concord, Contra Costa, Pop. 116,303
Mount Diablo USD 31,700/PK-12
1936 Carlotta Dr 94519 925-682-8000
Dr. Nellie Meyer, supt. Fax 689-1649
www.mdusd.org
Concord HS 1,500/9-12
4200 Concord Blvd 94521 925-687-2030
Rianne Pfalsgraff, prin. Fax 682-4613
Crossroads HS 50/Alt
2701 Willow Pass Rd 94519 925-689-6852
Samantha Allen, admin. Fax 603-1771
Diablo Community Day S 50/Alt
1026 Mohr Ln 94518 925-676-6862
Thom Kwiatkowski, admin. Fax 682-9352
El Dorado MS 1,100/6-8
1750 West St 94521 925-682-5700
Christopher Clausen, prin. Fax 685-1460
Mount Diablo HS 1,300/9-12
2450 Grant St 94520 925-682-4030
Liane Cismowski, prin. Fax 687-9658
Oak Grove MS 700/6-8
2050 Minert Rd 94518 925-682-1843
Christina Filios, prin. Fax 682-2083
Olympic Continuation HS 300/Alt
2730 Salvio St 94519 925-687-0363
Lynsie Castellano, prin. Fax 798-6317
Pine Hollow MS 700/6-8
5522 Pine Hollow Rd 94521 925-672-5444
Shelley Bain, prin. Fax 672-9751
Summit Continuation HS 50/Alt
4200 Concord Blvd 94521 925-689-0991
Brook Penca, prin. Fax 603-1770
Summit HS 50/Alt
4200 Concord Blvd 94521 925-687-0991
Edward Penca, prin. Fax 603-1770
Ygnacio Valley HS 1,200/9-12
755 Oak Grove Rd 94518 925-685-8414
Efa Huckaby, prin. Fax 685-1435
Mount Diablo Adult Center Adult
1266 San Carlos Ave 94518 925-685-7340
Vittoria Abbate, dir. Fax 687-8217
Other Schools – See Bay Point, Clayton, Pleasant Hill, Walnut Creek

---

Carondelet HS 800/9-12
1133 Winton Dr 94518 925-686-5353
Kevin Cushing, prin. Fax 671-9429
De La Salle HS 1,000/9-12
1130 Winton Dr 94518 925-288-8100
Br. Robert Wickman, prin. Fax 686-3474
Heald College Post-Sec.
5130 Commercial Cir 94520 925-288-5800
Paris Beauty College Post-Sec.
1655 Willow Pass Rd 94520 925-685-7600

Corcoran, Kings, Pop. 24,292
Corcoran JUSD 3,300/PK-12
1520 Patterson Ave 93212 559-992-8888
Rich Merlo, supt. Fax 992-3957
www.corcoranunified.com/
Corcoran HS 900/9-12
1520 Patterson Ave 93212 559-992-8884
Antonia Stone, prin. Fax 992-5066
Kings Lake Education Center 50/Alt
1520 Patterson Ave 93212 559-992-8885
John Arriola, admin. Fax 992-4858
Muir MS 700/6-8
1520 Patterson Ave 93212 559-992-8886
David Whitmore, prin. Fax 992-4423

Corning, Tehama, Pop. 7,468
Corning UNESD 2,000/K-8
1590 South St 96021 530-824-7700
Richard Fitzpatrick, supt. Fax 824-2493
www.corningelementary.org
Maywood MS 300/7-8
1666 Marguerite Ave 96021 530-824-7730
Dave Cory, prin. Fax 824-7742

Corning UNHSD 1,000/9-12
643 Blackburn Ave 96021 530-824-8000
John Burch, supt. Fax 824-8005
www.corninghs.org/
Centennial Continuation HS 50/Alt
250 E Fig Ln 96021 530-824-7400
Jason Armstrong, prin. Fax 824-7405
Corning HS 900/9-12
643 Blackburn Ave 96021 530-824-8000
Charlie Troughton, prin. Fax 824-8005
Corning Adult S, 250 E Fig Ln 96021 Adult
Jason Armstrong, prin. 530-824-7400

Corona, Riverside, Pop. 147,939
Alvord USD 19,400/K-12
9 KPC Pkwy 92879 951-509-5070
Dr. Sid Salazar, supt. Fax 509-6070
alvordschools.org
Other Schools – See Riverside

Corona-Norco USD
Supt. — See Norco
Auburndale IS 600/7-8
1255 River Rd 92880 951-736-3231
Ben Sanchez, prin. Fax 736-3360
Centennial HS 3,300/9-12
1820 Rimpau Ave 92881 951-739-5670
Dr. Ben Roberts, prin. Fax 739-5693
Citrus Hills IS 1,100/7-8
3211 S Main St 92882 951-736-4600
Andrew Roberts, prin. Fax 736-4623
Corona Fundamental IS 1,200/7-8
1230 S Main St 92882 951-736-3321
Kelli Jakubik, prin. Fax 736-3417
Corona HS 3,000/9-12
1150 W 10th St 92882 951-736-3211
Dr. Danny Kim, prin. Fax 736-3408
El Cerrito MS 1,300/6-8
7610 El Cerrito Rd 92881 951-736-3216
Dr. Shelly Yarbrough, prin. Fax 736-3286
Orange Grove HS 200/Alt
300 S Buena Vista Ave 92882 951-736-3339
Henry Torres, prin. Fax 736-3435
Pollard HS 800/Alt
185 Magnolia Ave 92879 951-736-3367
Mike Ridgway, prin. Fax 736-7104
Raney IS 800/6-8
1010 W Citron St 92882 951-736-3221
Michele Sanchez, prin. Fax 736-3439
Santiago HS 3,600/9-12
1395 Foothill Pkwy 92881 951-739-5600
Dr. Seth Bond, prin. Fax 739-5639
Corona-Norco Adult Education Adult
300 S Buena Vista Ave 92882 951-736-3325
JoDee Slyter, prin. Fax 736-7159

Christian Heritage S 300/K-12
PO Box 1780 92878 951-736-3033
Crossroads Christian S 1,000/PK-12
2380 Fullerton Ave 92881 951-278-3199
Doug Husen, supt. Fax 493-2169
Grace Christian Academy 100/PK-12
2781 S Lincoln Ave 92882 951-736-7466
Charlene Owens, prin.
JEM College Post-Sec.
271 Ott St Ste 23 92882 951-549-0693

Coronado, San Diego, Pop. 18,310
Coronado USD 3,100/PK-12
201 6th St 92118 619-522-8900
Karl Mueller, supt. Fax 437-6570
coronadousd.net
Coronado HS 1,200/9-12
650 D Ave 92118 619-522-8907
Karl Mueller, prin. Fax 437-0236
Coronado MS 700/6-8
550 F Ave 92118 619-522-8921
Karin Mellina, prin. Fax 522-6948

Costa Mesa, Orange, Pop. 106,497
Newport - Mesa USD 22,000/K-12
2985 Bear St 92626 714-424-5000
Frederick Navarro Ed.D., supt. Fax 424-5018
www.nmusd.us
Back Bay HS 100/Alt
390 Monte Vista Ave 92627 949-515-6900
Debbie Lucker-Davis, prin. Fax 515-3380
Costa Mesa JSHS 1,800/7-12
2650 Fairview Rd 92626 714-424-8700
Jacob Haley, prin. Fax 424-8770
Early College HS 200/9-12
2990 Mesa Verde Dr E 92626 714-241-6108
David Martinez, prin. Fax 241-6185
Estancia HS 1,200/9-12
2323 Placentia Ave 92627 949-515-6500
Michael Halt, prin. Fax 515-6571
Monte Vista HS 100/Alt
390 Monte Vista Ave 92627 949-515-6900
Debbie Lucker-Davis, prin. Fax 515-3380
TeWinkle MS 700/7-8
3224 California St 92626 714-424-7965
Kira Hurst, prin. Fax 424-5680
Newport Mesa Adult Education Adult
2045 Meyer Pl 92627 949-515-6996
Becky Goegel, prin.
Other Schools – See Newport Beach

Regional Occupational Center & Program
Supt. — None
Coastline ROP Vo/Tech
1001 Presidio Sq 92626 714-979-1955
Carol Hume, supt. Fax 557-6812

James Albert School of Cosmetology Post-Sec.
1835 Newport Blvd 92627 949-642-0606
Orange Coast College Post-Sec.
PO Box 5005 92628 714-432-5072
Pacific College Post-Sec.
3160 Red Hill Ave 92626 714-662-4402
Paul Mitchell The School Post-Sec.
3309 Hyland Ave Ste J 92626 714-546-8786
Vanguard University of Southern CA Post-Sec.
55 Fair Dr 92626 714-556-3610
Waldorf S of Orange County 300/PK-12
2350 Canyon Dr 92627 949-574-7775

Cottonwood, Shasta, Pop. 3,202
Anderson UNHSD
Supt. — See Anderson

West Valley HS 900/9-12
3805 Happy Valley Rd 96022 530-347-7171
Emmett Koerperich, prin. Fax 347-0481

Cottonwood UNESD 1,100/K-8
20512 1st St 96022 530-347-3165
David Alexander Ed.D., supt. Fax 347-0247
cwusd.com
West Cottonwood JHS 400/5-8
20512 1st St 96022 530-347-3123
Douglas Geren, prin. Fax 347-0247

Evergreen UNSD 1,000/PK-12
19500 Learning Way 96022 530-347-3411
Brad Mendenhall, supt. Fax 347-7954
www.evergreenusd.org
Evergreen MS 400/5-8
19500 Learning Way 96022 530-347-3411
Felicia Ross, prin. Fax 347-7953

Coulterville, Mariposa, Pop. 195
Mariposa County USD
Supt. — See Mariposa
Coulterville HS 50/9-12
10326 Fiske Rd 95311 209-878-3028
Tracie Baughn, prin. Fax 878-3067

Courtland, Sacramento, Pop. 350
River Delta USD
Supt. — See Rio Vista
Mokelumne HS 50/Alt
PO Box 574 95615 916-775-9160
Maria Elena Becerra, prin. Fax 775-1797
River Delta Community Day S 50/Alt
160 Courtland High School 95615 916-775-9160
Maria Elena Becerra, prin. Fax 775-1797

Covelo, Mendocino, Pop. 1,175
Round Valley USD 400/K-12
PO Box 276 95428 707-983-6171
Mike Gorman, supt. Fax 983-6655
www.roundvalleyschools.org/
Round Valley Continuation HS 50/Alt
PO Box 276 95428 707-983-6171
Mark Smith, prin. Fax 983-6179
Round Valley HS 100/9-12
PO Box 276 95428 707-983-6171
Mark Smith, prin. Fax 983-6179

Covina, Los Angeles, Pop. 46,744
Azusa USD
Supt. — See Azusa
Gladstone HS 1,200/9-12
1340 N Enid Ave 91722 626-815-3600
Scott Magnusson, prin. Fax 815-3655

Charter Oak USD 5,300/K-12
20240 E Cienega Ave 91724 626-966-8331
Dr. Michael Hendricks Ed.D., supt. Fax 967-9580
www.cousd.net
Charter Oak HS 1,800/9-12
1430 E Covina Blvd 91724 626-915-5841
Dr. Ivan Ayro, prin. Fax 915-3398
Royal Oak MS 800/7-8
303 S Glendora Ave 91724 626-967-6354
Maria Thompson, prin. Fax 331-2074
Other Schools – See Glendora

Covina-Valley USD 12,600/K-12
519 E Badillo St 91723 626-974-7000
Dr. Richard Sheehan, supt. Fax 974-7032
www.c-vusd.org
Covina HS 1,400/9-12
463 S Hollenbeck Ave 91723 626-974-6020
Christiana Kraus, prin. Fax 974-6045
Fairvalley HS 200/Alt
758 W Grondahl St 91722 626-974-4800
Dana Craig, prin. Fax 974-4815
Las Palmas MS 900/6-8
641 N Lark Ellen Ave 91722 626-974-7200
Nicole Higuera, prin. Fax 974-7215
Northview HS 1,400/9-12
1016 W Cypress St 91722 626-974-6120
Dr. Julie Harrison, prin. Fax 974-6145
Sierra Vista MS 1,000/6-8
777 E Puente St 91723 626-974-7300
Danielle Travieso, prin. Fax 974-7315
Business Center Adult
342 S 4th Ave 91723 626-974-6800
Claudia Karnoski, prin. Fax 974-6814
Tri Community Adult Ed.-Griswold Center Adult
342 S 4th Ave 91723 626-472-7680
Dan Gribbon, prin. Fax 472-7681
Other Schools – See West Covina

American Graduate University Post-Sec.
733 N Dodsworth Ave 91724 626-966-4576
Firm Foundation Christian Academy 100/PK-12
541 S Aldenville Ave 91723 626-938-1199
Mary Carnighan, head sch

Crescent City, Del Norte, Pop. 7,317
Del Norte County Office of Education 400/
301 W Washington Blvd 95531 707-464-0200
Jeff Harris, supt. Fax 464-0238
www.delnortecoe.org
Del Norte Community Day S 50/Alt
400 W Harding Ave 95531 707-464-0750
Rob Parker, prin. Fax 464-5116
McCarthy Center 50/Alt
301 W Washington Blvd 95531 707-464-0399
Robert Parker, prin. Fax 465-5116

Del Norte County USD 3,900/K-12
301 W Washington Blvd 95531 707-464-6141
Jeff Harris, supt. Fax 464-0238
www.delnorte.k12.ca.us
Crescent Elk MS 500/6-8
994 G St 95531 707-464-0320
Paige Swan, prin. Fax 464-7920

Del Norte Community S Alt
400 W Harding Ave 95531 707-464-0750
Robert Parker, prin. Fax 465-5116
Del Norte County HS 900/9-12
1301 El Dorado St 95531 707-464-0260
Randy Fugate, prin. Fax 464-0785
Sunset Continuation HS 100/Alt
2500 Elk Valley Cross Rd 95531 707-464-0380
Tony Fabricius, prin. Fax 465-5346

Regional Occupational Center & Program
Supt. — None
Del Norte County ROP Vo/Tech
1301 El Dorado St 95531 707-464-0274
Colleen Parker, dir. Fax 465-6923

Crockett, Contra Costa, Pop. 2,949
John Swett USD
Supt. — See Rodeo
Carquinez MS 400/6-8
1099 Pomona St 94525 510-787-1081
Annie Flores-Aikey, prin. Fax 787-2359
Swett HS 500/9-12
1098 Pomona St 94525 510-787-1088
Jeff Brauning, prin. Fax 787-1930
Willow Continuation HS 100/Alt
1650 Crockett Blvd 94525 510-787-1286
Ken Nelson, prin. Fax 787-4770

Crowley Lake, Mono, Pop. 853

Eastern Sierra Christian Academy 50/K-10
384 S Landing Rd 93546 760-935-4272
Rena Davis, dir. Fax 935-4273

Crows Landing, Stanislaus, Pop. 352
Chatom UNESD
Supt. — See Turlock
Mountain View MS 200/6-8
10001 Crows Landing Rd 95313 209-664-8515
Monica Schut, prin. Fax 669-1733

Cudahy, Los Angeles, Pop. 23,704
Los Angeles USD
Supt. — See Los Angeles
Elizabeth Learning Center 1,800/K-12
4811 Elizabeth St 90201 323-271-3600
Damian Lenon, prin. Fax 560-8412

Culver City, Los Angeles, Pop. 36,982
Culver City USD 6,700/K-12
4034 Irving Pl 90232 310-842-4220
Dr. Joshua Arnold, supt. Fax 842-4205
www.ccusd.org
Culver City HS 2,100/9-12
4401 Elenda St 90230 310-842-4200
Dr. Lisa Cooper, prin. Fax 842-4303
Culver City MS 1,500/6-8
4601 Elenda St 90230 310-842-4200
Dr. Linsey Gotanda, prin. Fax 842-4304
Culver City USD Academy Alt
4601 Elenda St 90230 310-842-4200
Veronica Montes, prin.
Culver Park Continuation HS 100/Alt
4601 Elenda St 90230 310-390-8886
Veronica Montes, prin. Fax 390-3796
Culver City Adult S Adult
4909 Overland Ave 90230 310-842-4300
Veronica Montes, prin. Fax 842-4343

Antioch University Los Angeles Post-Sec.
400 Corporate Pointe 90230 310-578-1080
West Los Angeles College Post-Sec.
9000 Overland Ave 90230 310-287-4200

Cupertino, Santa Clara, Pop. 56,415
Cupertino UNSD
Supt. — See Sunnyvale
Hyde MS 1,000/6-8
19325 Bollinger Rd 95014 408-252-6290
Lisa Taormina, prin. Fax 255-3288
Kennedy MS 1,500/6-8
821 Bubb Rd 95014 408-253-1525
Steven Hamm, prin. Fax 257-5777
Lawson MS 1,100/6-8
10401 Vista Dr 95014 408-255-7500
Kit Bragg, prin. Fax 446-4987

Fremont UNHSD
Supt. — See Sunnyvale
Cupertino HS 2,100/9-12
10100 Finch Ave 95014 408-366-7300
Kami Tomberlain, prin. Fax 255-8466
Homestead HS 2,400/9-12
21370 Homestead Rd 95014 408-522-2500
Greg Giglio, prin. Fax 738-8631
Monta Vista HS 2,300/9-12
21840 McClellan Rd 95014 408-366-7600
April Scott, prin. Fax 252-1519

DeAnza College Post-Sec.
21250 Stevens Creek Blvd 95014 408-864-5678
Legend College Preparatory S 200/6-12
21050 McClellan Rd 95014 408-865-0366

Cutler, Tulare, Pop. 4,971
Cutler-Orosi JUSD
Supt. — See Orosi
Lovell HS 100/Alt
12724 Avenue 392 93615 559-528-4703
Martha Calderon, prin. Fax 528-0102

Cypress, Orange, Pop. 46,012
Anaheim UNHSD
Supt. — See Anaheim
Cypress HS 2,700/9-12
9801 Valley View St 90630 714-220-4144
Jodie Wales Ed.D., prin. Fax 220-4174

Lexington JHS 1,300/7-8
4351 Orange Ave 90630 714-220-4201
Amber Houston, prin. Fax 761-4989
Oxford Academy 1,200/7-12
5172 Orange Ave 90630 714-220-3055
Ron Hoshi, prin. Fax 527-7128

Cypress College Post-Sec.
9200 Valley View St 90630 714-484-7000
Trident University International Post-Sec.
5757 Plaza Dr Ste 100 90630 800-579-3197
Wisdom Mission Christian S K-12
5851 Newman St 90630 714-995-1900
Rev. Sae Chung, prin. Fax 995-1910

Daggett, San Bernardino
Silver Valley USD
Supt. — See Yermo
Calico Continuation HS 50/Alt
33525 Ponnay St 92327 760-254-2715
Michael Cox, prin. Fax 254-2194
Silver Valley Academy 50/Alt
33525 Ponnay St 92327 760-254-2715
Michael Cox, prin. Fax 254-2194
Silver Valley Community Day S 50/Alt
33525 Ponnay 92327 760-254-2715
Michael Cox, prin. Fax 254-2194
Silver Valley Adult S Adult
33525 Ponnay 92327 760-254-2715
Michael Cox, prin. Fax 254-2194

Daly City, San Mateo, Pop. 97,070
Bayshore ESD 400/K-8
1 Martin St 94014 415-467-5443
Dr. Audra Pittman, supt. Fax 467-1542
www.bayshore.k12.ca.us
Robertson IS 200/5-8
1 Martin St 94014 415-467-5443
Dr. Sergio Nesterov, prin. Fax 467-1542

Jefferson ESD 6,200/K-8
101 Lincoln Ave 94015 650-991-1000
Bernardo Vidales, supt. Fax 992-2265
www.jsd.k12.ca.us/
Pollicita MS 700/6-8
550 E Market St 94014 650-991-1216
Benjamin Turner, prin. Fax 755-2170
Rivera IS 400/7-8
1255 Southgate Ave 94015 650-991-1225
Dina Conti, prin. Fax 755-6273
Other Schools – See Colma

Jefferson UNHSD 4,700/9-12
699 Serramonte Blvd Ste 100 94015 650-550-7900
Dan Burns, supt. Fax 550-7888
www.juhsd.net
Jefferson HS 1,100/9-12
6996 Mission St 94014 650-550-7700
Mark Beshirs, prin. Fax 550-7790
Thornton HS 200/Alt
115 1st Ave 94014 650-550-7840
Monica Casey, prin. Fax 758-2092
Westmoor HS 1,700/9-12
131 Westmoor Ave 94015 650-550-7400
Thomas Orput, prin. Fax 550-7490
Adult Education Divison Adult
699 Serramonte Blvd Ste 111 94015 650-550-7890
Francisca Wentworth, prin. Fax 550-7889
Other Schools – See Pacifica

DeVry University Post-Sec.
2001 Junipero Serra Ste 161 94014 650-991-3520
Hilltop Beauty School Post-Sec.
6317 Mission St 94014 650-756-2720

Dana Point, Orange, Pop. 32,532
Capistrano USD
Supt. — See San Juan Capistrano
Dana Hills HS 2,700/9-12
33333 Golden Lantern St 92629 949-496-6666
Jason Allemann, prin. Fax 489-8317

Danville, Contra Costa, Pop. 40,475
San Ramon Valley USD 31,300/PK-12
699 Old Orchard Dr 94526 925-552-5500
Rick Schmitt, supt. Fax 838-3147
www.srvusd.net/
Del Amigo Continuation HS 50/Alt
189 Del Amigo Rd 94526 925-855-2600
Amy Gillespie-Oss, prin. Fax 838-5372
Diablo Vista MS 900/6-8
4100 Camino Tassajara 94506 925-855-7600
Becky Ingram, prin. Fax 648-7167
Los Cerros MS 700/6-8
968 Blemer Rd 94526 925-855-6800
Evan Powell, prin. Fax 837-3512
Monte Vista HS 2,200/9-12
3131 Stone Valley Rd 94526 925-552-2800
Kevin Ahern, prin. Fax 743-1744
San Ramon Valley HS 2,200/9-12
501 Danville Blvd 94526 925-552-3000
Ruth Steele, prin. Fax 552-3060
Wood MS 1,100/6-8
600 El Capitan Dr 94526 925-855-4400
Christopher George, prin. Fax 820-1857
Other Schools – See Alamo, San Ramon

Athenian S 500/6-12
2100 Mount Diablo Scenic 94506 925-837-5375
Eric Niles, head sch Fax 362-7292

Davis, Yolo, Pop. 62,607
Davis JUSD 8,500/K-12
526 B St 95616 530-757-5300
Dr. John Bowes, supt. Fax 757-5323
www.djusd.net
Davis S for Independent Study 100/Alt
526 B St 95616 530-757-5333
Michelle Flowers, prin. Fax 757-5382

Davis SHS 1,700/10-12
315 W 14th St 95616 530-757-5400
William Brown, prin. Fax 757-5492
Emerson JHS 400/7-9
2121 Calaveras Ave 95616 530-757-5430
Stacy Desideri, prin. Fax 757-5434
Harper JHS 600/7-9
4000 E Covell Blvd 95618 530-757-5330
Kerin Kelleher, prin. Fax 757-5350
Holmes JHS 700/7-9
1220 Drexel Dr 95616 530-757-5445
Derek Brothers, prin. Fax 757-5435
King Continuation HS 50/Alt
635 B St 95616 530-757-5425
Michelle Flowers, prin. Fax 757-5440
Davis Adult S Adult
315 W 14th St 95616 530-757-5380
Grace Sauser, prin. Fax 757-5381

D-Q University Post-Sec.
PO Box 409 95617 530-758-0470
University of California Post-Sec.
1 Shields Ave 95616 530-752-1011

Delano, Kern, Pop. 52,490
Delano JUNHSD 4,300/9-12
1720 Norwalk St 93215 661-725-4000
Dr. Terr Nuckols, supt. Fax 721-9390
www.djuhsd.org/
Chavez HS 1,400/9-12
1720 Norwalk St 93215 661-720-4502
Ben DeLeon, prin. Fax 725-8875
Delano HS 1,700/9-12
1720 Norwalk St 93215 661-720-4121
Rene Ayon, prin. Fax 720-4119
Kennedy HS 1,000/9-12
1720 Norwalk St 93215 661-720-5102
Raudel Rojas, prin. Fax 721-0833
Valley HS 100/Alt
1720 Norwalk St 93215 661-720-4374
Chris Juarez, prin. Fax 725-7611
Delano Adult S Adult
1720 Norwalk St 93215 661-720-4173
Julio Segura, dir. Fax 725-5852

Delano UNESD 7,700/PK-8
1405 12th Ave 93215 661-721-5000
Rosalina Rivera, supt. Fax 725-2201
www.duesd.org
Almond Tree MS 700/6-8
200 W 15th Ave 93215 661-721-3641
Rodney Del Rio, prin. Fax 721-3649
La Vina MS 700/6-8
1331 Browning Rd 93215 661-721-3601
Jennifer Townson, prin. Fax 721-3662

Delhi, Merced, Pop. 10,554
Delhi USD 2,400/K-12
9716 Hinton Ave 95315 209-656-2000
Adolfo Melara, supt. Fax 656-2000
www.delhi.k12.ca.us
Delhi HS 700/9-12
9716 Hinton Ave 95315 209-656-2050
Vincent Gonzalez, prin. Fax 669-3168
Delhi MS 200/7-8
9716 Hinton Ave 95315 209-656-2050
Vincent Gonzalez, prin. Fax 669-3168
Shattuck Educational Park HS 50/Alt
9716 Hinton Ave 95315 209-656-2012
Francisca Briones, prin. Fax 669-6165
Delhi Adult S Adult
9716 Hinton Ave 95315 209-656-2012
Francisca Briones, prin. Fax 669-6165

Del Mar, San Diego, Pop. 4,073

Winston S of San Diego 100/4-12
215 9th St 92014 858-259-8155

Denair, Stanislaus, Pop. 4,321
Denair USD 1,400/PK-12
3460 Lester Rd 95316 209-632-7514
Dr. Aaron Rosander, supt. Fax 632-9194
dusd.k12.ca.us
Denair HS 300/9-12
3460 Lester Rd 95316 209-632-9911
Kara Backman, prin. Fax 632-8153
Denair MS 300/6-8
3460 Lester Rd 95316 209-632-2510
Kelly Beard, prin. Fax 632-0269

Desert Hot Springs, Riverside, Pop. 25,289
Palm Springs USD
Supt. — See Palm Springs
Desert Hot Springs Alternative Center Alt
11695 Palm Dr 92240 760-329-3330
Milt Jones, prin. Fax 329-6677
Desert Hot Springs HS 1,800/9-12
65850 Pierson Blvd 92240 760-288-7000
George Bullis, prin. Fax 288-7010
Desert Springs MS 900/6-8
66755 Two Bunch Palms Trl 92240 760-251-7200
Kiela Snider, prin. Fax 251-7206
Painted Hills MS 800/6-8
9250 Sonora Dr 92240 760-251-1551
Michael Grainger, prin. Fax 251-5330

Diamond Bar, Los Angeles, Pop. 54,094
Pomona USD
Supt. — See Pomona
Lorbeer MS 700/7-8
501 S Diamond Bar Blvd 91765 909-397-4527
Angelique Butler, prin. Fax 396-9022

Walnut Valley USD
Supt. — See Walnut
Chaparral MS 1,300/6-8
1405 Spruce Tree Dr 91765 909-861-6227
Ronald Thibodeaux, prin. Fax 396-0749

Diamond Bar HS 3,000/9-12
21400 Pathfinder Rd 91765 909-594-1405
Reuben Jones, prin. Fax 595-8301

California Intercontinental University Post-Sec.
1470 Valley Vista Dr # 150 91765 909-396-6090
Institute of Knowledge 200/K-10
1009 Via Sorella, 909-595-2401

Diamond Springs, El Dorado, Pop. 10,676
El Dorado UNHSD
Supt. — See Placerville
Independence HS 100/Alt
385 Pleasant Valley Rd 95619 530-622-7090
Alison Gennai, prin. Fax 642-2291

Dinuba, Tulare, Pop. 21,288
Dinuba USD 6,500/K-12
1327 E El Monte Way 93618 559-595-7200
Joe Hernandez Ed.D., supt. Fax 591-3334
www.dinuba.k12.ca.us
Dinuba HS 1,900/9-12
1327 E El Monte Way 93618 559-595-7220
Michael Roberts, prin. Fax 591-3655
Reagan Academy 200/Alt
1327 E El Monte Way 93618 559-595-7295
Suzanne Rodriguez, prin. Fax 595-7248
Sierra Vista HS 100/Alt
1327 E El Monte Way 93618 559-595-7240
Suzanne Rodriguez, prin. Fax 595-8198
Washington IS 900/7-8
1327 E El Monte Way 93618 559-595-7252
Jonathan Torres, prin. Fax 595-8158
Dinuba Adult S Adult
1327 E El Monte Way 93618 559-595-7242
Suzanne Rodriguez, prin. Fax 595-7248

Dixon, Solano, Pop. 17,699
Dixon USD 3,400/K-12
180 S 1st St 95620 707-693-6300
Brian Dolan, supt. Fax 678-0726
www.dixonusd.org
Dixon Community Day S 50/Alt
180 S 1st St 95620 707-678-4061
Yvette Ramos, prin.
Dixon HS 1,100/9-12
555 College Way 95620 707-693-6330
Nick Girimonte, prin. Fax 678-9318
Jacobs IS 600/7-8
200 N Lincoln St 95620 707-678-9222
Dan Bledsoe, prin. Fax 678-1245
Maine Prairie HS 100/Alt
305 E C St 95620 707-678-4560
Yvette Ramos, prin. Fax 678-4892

Dorris, Siskiyou, Pop. 895
Butte Valley USD 300/K-12
PO Box 709 96023 530-397-4000
Heidi Gerig, supt. Fax 397-3999
www.bvalusd.org/
Butte Valley HS 100/9-12
PO Box 709 96023 530-397-3990
Jason Allen, lead tchr. Fax 397-3989
Butte Valley MS 50/7-8
PO Box 709 96023 530-397-3900
Heidi Gerig, prin. Fax 397-3899
Cascade Continuation HS 50/Alt
PO Box 709 96023 530-397-3363
Nikki Lane, lead tchr. Fax 397-3360
Butte Valley Adult S Adult
PO Box 709 96023 530-397-3363
Linda Tracy, lead tchr. Fax 397-3360

Dos Palos, Merced, Pop. 4,873
Dos Palos Oro Loma JUSD 2,400/K-12
2041 Almond St 93620 209-392-0200
William Spalding, supt. Fax 392-3347
www.dpol.net
Bryant MS 500/6-8
16695 Bryant Ave 93620 209-392-0240
Laura Andrews, prin. Fax 392-2636
Dos Palos HS 700/9-12
1701 E Blossom St 93620 209-392-0300
Heather Ruiz, prin. Fax 392-2705
Other Schools – See South Dos Palos

Downey, Los Angeles, Pop. 110,312
Downey USD 22,800/K-12
PO Box 7017 90241 562-469-6500
Dr. John Garcia Ph.D., supt. Fax 469-6515
www.dusd.net
Columbus Continuation HS 300/Alt
12330 Woodruff Ave 90241 562-904-3552
Anthony Zegarra, prin. Fax 469-7320
Doty MS 1,400/6-8
10301 Woodruff Ave 90241 562-904-3586
Brent Shubin, prin. Fax 469-7240
Downey HS 4,400/9-12
11040 Brookshire Ave 90241 562-869-7301
Tom Houts, prin. Fax 469-7340
Griffiths MS 1,400/6-8
9633 Tweedy Ln 90240 562-904-3580
Dr. Rani Bertsch Ed.D., prin. Fax 469-7260
Stauffer MS 1,500/6-8
11985 Old River School Rd 90242 562-904-3565
Alyda Mir, prin. Fax 469-7300
Sussman MS 1,200/6-8
12500 Birchdale Ave 90242 562-904-3572
Dr. Robert Jagielski Ed.D., prin. Fax 469-7280
Warren HS 3,800/9-12
8141 De Palma St 90241 562-869-7306
Laura Rivas, prin. Fax 469-7360
Downey Adult S Adult
12340 Woodruff Ave 90241 562-940-6200
Blanca Rochin, prin. Fax 940-6221

Los Angeles County Office of Education 6,100/
9300 Imperial Hwy 90242 562-922-6111
Dr. Debra Duardo, supt. Fax 922-6768
www.lacoe.edu
Alternative Opportunity Programs 200/Alt
9300 Imperial Hwy 90242 562-803-8203
Mary Laihee, dir. Fax 401-5742
Other Schools – See Hawthorne, Los Angeles, Monterey Park, Pomona

Regional Occupational Center & Program
Supt. — None
Los Angeles County ROP Vo/Tech
9300 Imperial Hwy 90242 562-922-6850
Jimmy Benavides, dir. Fax 940-1672

Calvary Chapel Christian S 1,000/PK-12
12808 Woodruff Ave 90242 562-803-4076
Roger Stahlhut B.A., admin. Fax 803-1292
Los Amigos Research & Education Inst. Post-Sec.
PO Box 3500 90242 562-401-8111
St. Pius X / St. Matthias Academy 200/9-12
7851 Gardendale St 90242 562-861-2271
Erick Rubalcava, prin. Fax 869-8652

Downieville, Sierra, Pop. 276
Sierra-Plumas JUSD
Supt. — See Loyalton
Downieville JSHS 50/7-12
PO Box B 95936 530-289-3473
Merrill Grant Ed.D., supt. Fax 289-3693

Duarte, Los Angeles, Pop. 20,755
Duarte USD 3,700/K-12
1620 Huntington Dr 91010 626-599-5000
Dr. Allan Mucerino, supt. Fax 599-5069
www.duarte.k12.ca.us
Duarte HS 1,100/9-12
1565 Central Ave 91010 626-599-5700
Mark Sims, prin. Fax 599-5784
Mt. Olive Innovation and Technology S 50/Alt
1400 Mount Olive Dr 91010 626-599-5900
Kevin Morris, prin. Fax 599-5984
Northview IS 500/7-8
1401 Highland Ave 91010 626-599-5600
Mark Newell, prin. Fax 599-5684

Irell & Manella Grad Sch of Biological Post-Sec.
1500 Duarte Rd 91010 626-256-4673

Dublin, Alameda, Pop. 43,591
Dublin USD 8,300/K-12
7471 Larkdale Ave 94568 925-828-2551
Dr. Leslie Boozer, supt. Fax 829-6532
www.dublin.k12.ca.us
Dublin HS 1,900/9-12
8151 Village Pkwy 94568 925-833-3300
Maureen Byrne, prin. Fax 833-3322
Fallon MS 1,000/6-9
3601 Kohnen Way 94568 925-875-9376
Sheryl Sweeney, prin. Fax 829-6532
Valley Continuation HS 100/Alt
6901 York Dr 94568 925-829-4322
Megan Pettis, prin. Fax 833-7609
Wells MS 800/6-8
6800 Penn Dr 94568 925-828-6227
Ean Ainsworth, prin. Fax 829-8851
Dublin Adult Education Adult
6901 York Dr 94568 925-829-4322
Bill Branca, prin. Fax 833-7609

Golden State College of Court Reporting Post-Sec.
6543 Regional St 94568 925-829-0115
Quarry Lane S 800/PK-12
6363 Tassajara Rd, 925-829-8000
Valley Christian S 800/PK-12
7500 Inspiration Dr 94568 925-560-6200
Dr. Michael Chen, supt. Fax 828-5623

Dunsmuir, Siskiyou, Pop. 1,565
Dunsmuir JUNHSD 100/9-12
5805 High School Way 96025 530-235-4835
Ray Kellar, supt. Fax 235-2224
www.dunsmuirhigh.k12.ca.us/
Dunsmuir Community Day S 50/Alt
5805 High School Way 96025 530-235-2225
Ray Kellar, supt. Fax 235-2224
Dunsmuir HS 100/9-12
5805 High School Way 96025 530-235-4835
Ray Kellar, supt. Fax 235-2224

Durham, Butte, Pop. 5,377
Durham USD 1,000/K-12
PO Box 300 95938 530-895-4675
Len Foreman, supt. Fax 895-4692
www.durhamunified.org/
Durham HS 300/9-12
PO Box 600 95938 530-895-4685
Terry Bennett, prin. Fax 895-4688
Durham IS 200/6-8
PO Box 310 95938 530-895-4690
Jeff Kuhn, prin. Fax 895-4305

Earlimart, Tulare, Pop. 8,499
Earlimart ESD 2,000/K-8
PO Box 11970 93219 661-849-3386
Philip Nystrom, supt. Fax 849-2352
www.earlimart.org
Earlimart Community Day S 50/Alt
PO Box 11970 93219 661-849-4841
Raylene Welch, lead tchr. Fax 849-2352
Earlimart MS 600/6-8
PO Box 11970 93219 661-849-2611
Scott Staton, prin. Fax 849-4214

East Palo Alto, San Mateo, Pop. 25,414
Ravenswood City ESD 3,700/PK-12
2120 Euclid Ave 94303 650-329-2800
Dr. Gloria Hernandez-Goff, supt. Fax 323-1072
www.ravenswoodschools.org
Chavez Academy 200/6-8
2450 Ralmar Ave 94303 650-329-6700
Amika Guillaume, prin. Fax 326-8902
McNair Academy 200/6-8
2033 Pulgas Ave 94303 650-329-2888
Jennifer Gravem, prin. Fax 473-9247

Eastside College Preparatory S 300/6-12
1041 Myrtle St 94303 650-688-0850

Eastvale, Riverside, Pop. 51,943
Corona-Norco USD
Supt. — See Norco
Ramirez IS 1,100/7-8
6905 Harrison Ave, 951-736-8241
Kim Seheult, prin. Fax 273-3145
River Heights IS 1,100/7-8
7227 Scholar Way, 951-738-2155
Teri Dudley, prin. Fax 738-2175
Roosevelt HS 3,700/9-12
7447 Scholar Way, 951-738-2100
Jeremy Goins, prin. Fax 738-2104

Edwards, Kern
Muroc JUSD
Supt. — See North Edwards
Desert JSHS 600/7-12
1575 Payne Ave 93523 661-258-4411
Dr. David Ellms Ed.D., prin. Fax 258-5029

El Cajon, San Diego, Pop. 94,267
Cajon Valley UNESD 16,200/K-8
PO Box 1007 92022 619-588-3000
David Miyashiro Ed.D., supt. Fax 588-7653
www.cajonvalley.net
Cajon Valley Community Day S 50/Alt
165 Roanoke Rd 92020 619-588-3265
Karen Minshew, prin. Fax 588-3168
Cajon Valley MS 900/6-8
550 E Park Ave 92020 619-588-3092
Justin Goodrich, prin. Fax 579-4817
Emerald MS 600/6-8
1221 Emerald Ave 92020 619-588-3097
Steven Bailey, prin. Fax 588-3225
Greenfield MS 600/6-8
1495 Greenfield Dr 92021 619-588-3103
Greg Calvert, prin. Fax 588-3648
Hillsdale MS 1,500/6-8
1301 Brabham St 92019 619-441-6156
Jacob Launder, prin. Fax 441-6185
Los Coches Creek MS 700/6-8
9669 Dunbar Ln 92021 619-441-5741
Dana Stevenson, prin. Fax 938-1850
Montgomery MS 800/6-8
1570 Melody Ln 92019 619-588-3107
Jacqueline Luzak, prin. Fax 441-6122

Grossmont UNHSD
Supt. — See La Mesa
Chaparral HS 300/Alt
1600 N Cuyamaca St 92020 619-956-4600
David Napoleon, prin. Fax 596-7815
El Cajon Valley HS 1,800/9-12
1035 E Madison Ave 92021 619-401-4700
Kim Patterson, prin. Fax 447-3943
Elite Academy 100/Alt
230 Jamacha Blvd 92019 619-588-3545
Barbara Schmidt, admin.
Granite Hills HS 2,600/9-12
1719 E Madison Ave 92019 619-593-5500
Mike Fowler, prin. Fax 588-9389
Grossmont HS 2,300/9-12
1100 Murray Dr 92020 619-668-6000
Daniel Barnes, prin. Fax 463-7108
Grossmont Middle College HS 100/11-12
8800 Grossmont College Dr 92020 619-644-7524
David Napoleon, prin. Fax 644-7011
IDEA Center 600/9-12
1600 N Cuyamaca St 92020 619-956-4332
David Napoleon, prin. Fax 596-7815
Phoenix Independent Study 100/Alt
1600 N Cuyamaca St 92020 619-956-4625
Kathy Burton, admin. Fax 258-3750
Valhalla HS 2,100/9-12
1725 Hillsdale Rd 92019 619-593-5300
Mary Beth Kastan, prin. Fax 588-9713
East Region Adult S Adult
1550 Melody Ln 92019 619-588-3500
Robyn Wiggins, dir. Fax 579-9291

Advanced Training Associates Post-Sec.
1810 Gillespie Way Ste 104 92020 619-596-2766
Bellus Academy Post-Sec.
1073 E Main St 92021 619-442-3407
Christian JSHS 500/7-12
2100 Greenfield Dr 92019 619-201-8800
Pat McCarty, supt. Fax 201-8898
Cuyamaca College Post-Sec.
900 Rancho San Diego Pkwy 92019 619-660-4000
Foothills Christian HS 300/9-12
2321 Dryden Rd 92020 619-303-8035
Foothills Christian MS 100/6-8
350 Cypress Ln 92020 619-303-1641
Lanell Lenzkes, prin. Fax 312-1923
Grossmont College Post-Sec.
8800 Grossmont College Dr 92020 619-644-7000
San Diego Christian College Post-Sec.
2100 Greenfield Dr 92019 619-201-8700
Southern California Seminary Post-Sec.
2075 E Madison Ave 92019 888-389-7244

El Centro, Imperial, Pop. 42,253
Central UNHSD 5,100/9-12
351 W Ross Ave, 760-336-4500
Renato Montano, supt. Fax 353-3606
www.cuhsd.net
Central Union HS 1,900/9-12
1001 W Brighton Ave, 760-336-4300
Craig Lyon, prin. Fax 353-3570
Desert Oasis HS 200/Alt
1302 S 3rd St, 760-336-4555
Fernando O'Campo, prin. Fax 337-3952
Southwest HS 2,000/9-12
2001 Ocotillo Dr, 760-336-4100
Bernardo Valenzuela, prin. Fax 353-0467
Central Union Adult Education Adult
1302 S 3rd St, 760-336-4544
Tish Thompson, dir. Fax 336-4547

El Centro ESD 6,000/K-8
1256 Broadway Ave, 760-352-5712
Jon LeDoux, supt. Fax 312-9522
www.ecesd.com
Kennedy MS 400/7-8
900 N 6th St, 760-352-0444
Michael Castillo, prin. Fax 353-0325
Wilson JHS 700/7-8
600 S Wilson St, 760-352-5341
Rauna Fox, prin. Fax 337-3800

Regional Occupational Center & Program
Supt. — None
Imperial Valley ROP Vo/Tech
687 W State St, 760-482-2600
Edwin Obergfell, supt. Fax 482-2751

El Cerrito, Contra Costa, Pop. 22,213
West Contra Costa USD
Supt. — See Richmond
El Cerrito HS 1,300/9-12
540 Ashbury Ave 94530 510-231-1437
Edith Jordan-McCormick, prin. Fax 525-1810
Korematsu MS 500/6-8
1021 Navellier St 94530 510-524-0405
Matthew Burnham, prin. Fax 559-8784

Prospect Sierra MS 300/5-8
960 Avis Dr 94530 510-809-9000
Katherine Dinh, head sch Fax 527-3728

El Dorado, El Dorado
El Dorado UNHSD
Supt. — See Placerville
Union Mine HS 1,100/9-12
6530 Koki Ln 95623 530-621-4003
Paul Neville, prin. Fax 622-6034

El Dorado Hills, El Dorado, Pop. 40,513
Buckeye UNSD 4,700/PK-8
PO Box 4768 95762 916-985-2183
Dr. David Roth, supt. Fax 934-0920
www.buckeyeusd.org/
Rolling Hills MS 1,000/6-8
7141 Silva Valley Pkwy 95762 916-933-9290
Debra Bowers, prin. Fax 939-7454
Other Schools – See Cameron Park

El Dorado UNHSD
Supt. — See Placerville
Oak Ridge HS 2,300/9-12
1120 Harvard Way 95762 916-933-6980
Aaron Palm, prin. Fax 933-6987

Rescue UNESD
Supt. — See Rescue
Marina Village MS 800/6-8
1901 Francisco Dr 95762 916-933-3993
George Tapanes, prin. Fax 933-3995

Guiding Hands S 100/PK-12
4900 Windplay Dr 95762 916-939-0553

Elk Creek, Glenn, Pop. 158
Stony Creek JUSD 100/K-12
3430 County Road 309 95939 530-968-5361
Laurel Hill-Ward, supt. Fax 968-5102
www.scjusd.org
Bidwell Point HS 50/Alt
3430 County Road 309 95939 530-968-5361
Laurel Hill-Ward, prin. Fax 968-5535
Elk Creek JSHS 50/7-12
3430 County Road 309 95939 530-968-5361
Laurel Hill-Ward, prin. Fax 968-5102

Elk Grove, Sacramento, Pop. 142,334
Elk Grove USD 61,500/PK-12
9510 Elk Grove Florin Rd 95624 916-686-5085
Christopher Hoffman, supt. Fax 686-7787
www.egusd.net
Albiani MS 1,400/7-8
9140 Bradshaw Rd 95624 916-686-5210
Danielle Storey, prin. Fax 686-5538
Cosumnes Oaks HS 2,000/9-12
8350 Lotz Pkwy, 916-683-7670
Maria Osborne, prin. Fax 683-4522
Eddy MS 1,000/7-8
9329 Soaring Oaks Dr 95758 916-683-1302
Mark Benson, prin. Fax 684-6142
Elk Grove HS 1,800/9-12
9800 Elk Grove Florin Rd 95624 916-686-7741
Catherine Guy, prin. Fax 685-5515
Franklin HS 2,700/9-12
6400 Whitelock Pkwy, 916-714-8150
Chantelle Albiani, prin. Fax 714-8155
Harris MS 1,200/7-8
8691 Power Inn Rd 95624 916-688-0080
Charles Amey, prin. Fax 688-0084
Johnson MS 1,300/7-8
10099 Franklin High Rd, 916-714-8181
Patrick McDougall, prin. Fax 714-8177

Kerr MS 900/7-8
8865 Elk Grove Blvd 95624 916-686-7728
Dawnelle Maffei, prin. Fax 685-2952
Laguna Creek HS 1,600/9-12
9050 Vicino Dr 95758 916-683-1339
Douglas Craig, prin. Fax 683-3128
Monterey Trail HS 2,200/9-12
8661 Power Inn Rd 95624 916-688-0050
Jana Durham, prin. Fax 688-0058
Pinkerton MS 1,000/7-8
8365 Whitelock Pkwy, 916-683-7680
Chandra Victor, prin. Fax 685-5703
Pleasant Grove HS 2,500/9-12
9531 Bond Rd 95624 916-686-0230
Hank Meyer, prin. Fax 686-0239
Other Schools – See Sacramento

DeVry University Post-Sec.
2216 Kausen Dr 95758 916-478-2847
Lutheran HS 100/9-12
9270 Bruceville Rd 95758 916-691-2277
James Maddock, prin. Fax 691-2292

El Monte, Los Angeles, Pop. 112,772
El Monte UNHSD 9,300/9-12
3537 Johnson Ave 91731 626-444-9005
Edward Zuniga, supt. Fax 350-1095
emuhsd.org
Arroyo HS 2,300/9-12
4921 Cedar Ave 91732 626-444-9201
Angelita Gonzales-Hernan, prin. Fax 443-1175
El Monte HS 1,900/9-12
3048 Tyler Ave 91731 626-444-7701
Robin Torres, prin. Fax 442-6594
Ledesma HS 400/Alt
12347 Ramona Blvd 91732 626-442-0481
Freddy Arteaga, prin. Fax 442-7260
Mountain View HS 1,600/9-12
2900 Parkway Dr 91732 626-443-6181
Larry Cecil, prin. Fax 442-7284
El Monte-Rosemead Adult Education Adult
10807 Ramona Blvd 91731 626-258-5800
Dr. Deborah Kerr, prin. Fax 258-5809
Other Schools – See Rosemead, South El Monte

Mountain View ESD 7,500/K-8
3320 Gilman Rd 91732 626-652-4000
Lillian Maldonado French, supt. Fax 652-4052
www.mtviewschools.com/
Kranz IS 800/7-8
12460 Fineview St 91732 626-652-4200
Sean Grycel, prin. Fax 652-4215
Madrid MS 900/6-8
3300 Gilman Rd 91732 626-652-4300
Cesar Flores, prin. Fax 652-4315
Magnolia Learning Center Alt
11919 Magnolia St 91732 626-652-4938
Terri Thomas, admin. Fax 652-4939

International Theological Seminary Post-Sec.
3225 Tyler Ave 91731 626-448-0023
Logos Evangelical Seminary Post-Sec.
9358 Telstar Ave 91731 626-571-5110
Palladium Technical Academy Post-Sec.
10503 Valley Blvd 91731 626-444-0880
Professional Institute of Beauty Post-Sec.
10801 Valley Mall 91731 626-443-9401

El Segundo, Los Angeles, Pop. 15,912
El Segundo USD 3,400/K-12
641 Sheldon St 90245 310-615-2650
Dr. Melissa Moore, supt.
www.elsegundousd.net
Arena HS 50/Alt
641 Sheldon St 90245 310-615-2650
Marisa Janicek, prin. Fax 322-7939
El Segundo HS 1,300/9-12
640 Main St 90245 310-615-2662
Jaime Mancilla, prin. Fax 640-8079
El Segundo MS 800/6-8
332 Center St 90245 310-615-2690
Dr. Jack Plotkin, prin. Fax 640-9634

Vistamar S 200/9-12
737 Hawaii St 90245 310-643-7377
Dr. Karen Eshoo, head sch Fax 643-7371

El Sobrante, Contra Costa, Pop. 11,868
West Contra Costa USD
Supt. — See Richmond
Crespi MS 600/7-8
1121 Allview Ave 94803 510-231-1447
Guthrie Fleischman, prin. Fax 243-2090

El Sobrante Christian JSHS 100/7-12
5070 Appian Way 94803 510-223-1966
Danyiel Wright, prin. Fax 223-5344

Elverta, Sacramento, Pop. 5,268
Elverta JESD 300/K-12
7900 Eloise Ave 95626 916-991-2244
Michael Borgaard, supt. Fax 991-0271
www.ejesd.net
Alpha Technology MS 100/6-8
7900 Eloise Ave 95626 916-991-4726
Michael Borgaard, prin.

Emeryville, Alameda, Pop. 9,492
Emery USD 700/K-12
1275 61st St 94608 510-601-4000
Dr. John Rubio, supt. Fax 601-4913
www.emeryusd.org/
Emery HS 200/9-12
915 54th St 94608 510-601-4000
Douglas Ferber, prin. Fax 601-4988

Expression College for Digital Arts Post-Sec.
6601 Shellmound St 94608 510-654-2934

Encinitas, San Diego, Pop. 57,785
San Dieguito UNHSD 12,400/7-12
710 Encinitas Blvd 92024 760-753-6491
Eric Dill, supt. Fax 943-3501
www.sduhsd.net
Diegueno MS 900/7-8
710 Encinitas Blvd 92024 760-944-1892
Jeffrey Copeland, prin. Fax 944-3717
Oak Crest MS 900/7-8
710 Encinitas Blvd 92024 760-753-6241
Ben Taylor, prin. Fax 942-0520
San Dieguito HS Academy 1,600/9-12
710 Encinitas Blvd 92024 760-753-1121
Bjorn Paige, prin. Fax 753-8142
Sunset HS 100/Alt
710 Encinitas Blvd 92024 760-753-3860
Rick Ayala, prin. Fax 753-8469
Other Schools – See Carlsbad, San Diego, Solana Beach

Encinitas Country Day 300/K-12
3616 Manchester Ave 92024 760-942-1111
Grauer S 100/7-12
1500 S El Camino Real 92024 760-944-6777
Dr. Stuart Grauer, head sch Fax 944-6784
Pacific Academy 50/7-12
679 Encinitas Blvd Ste 205 92024 760-634-1188
Mario Gonzales, prin. Fax 436-5718

Encino, See Los Angeles

Crespi Carmelite HS 600/9-12
5031 Alonzo Ave 91316 818-345-1672
Dr. Jonathan Schild, prin. Fax 705-0209
Ferrahian HS 300/6-12
5300 White Oak Ave 91316 818-784-6228
Westmark S 200/1-12
5461 Louise Ave 91316 818-986-5045
Claudia Koochek, head sch Fax 986-2605

Escalon, San Joaquin, Pop. 7,002
Escalon USD 2,800/K-12
1520 Yosemite Ave 95320 209-838-3591
Ron Costa, supt. Fax 838-6703
www.escalonusd.org/
El Portal MS 600/6-8
805 1st St 95320 209-838-7095
Mark Vos, prin. Fax 838-3017
Escalon HS 900/9-12
1528 Yosemite Ave 95320 209-838-7073
Stephanie Parker, prin. Fax 838-6127
Vista HS 50/Alt
1520 Yosemite Ave 95320 209-838-1450
George McGenney, admin. Fax 838-1922

Escondido, San Diego, Pop. 140,582
Escondido UNHSD 9,200/9-12
302 N Midway Dr 92027 760-291-3200
Steve Boyle, supt. Fax 480-3163
www.euhsd.org
Del Lago Academy Applied Science Campus 300/9-12
1740 Scenic Trails Way 92029 760-291-2500
Keith Nuthall, prin.
Escondido HS 2,500/9-12
1535 N Broadway 92026 760-291-4000
Richard Watkins, prin. Fax 739-7313
Orange Glen HS 2,100/9-12
2200 Glenridge Rd 92027 760-291-5000
Stacey Adams, prin. Fax 739-7314
San Pasqual HS 2,300/9-12
3300 Bear Valley Pkwy S 92025 760-291-6000
Martin Casas, prin. Fax 739-7315
Valley HS 400/Alt
410 Hidden Trails Rd 92027 760-291-2240
Dan Barajas, prin. Fax 741-7605
Escondido Adult S Adult
220 W Crest St 92025 760-739-7300
Dom Gagliardi, prin. Fax 739-7310

Escondido Union SD 19,900/PK-8
2310 Aldergrove Ave 92029 760-432-2400
Luis Rankins-Ibarra Ed.D., supt. Fax 735-2874
www.eusd.org
Bear Valley MS 1,100/6-8
3003 Bear Valley Pkwy S 92025 760-432-4060
Susan Freeman, prin. Fax 504-0158
Del Dios Academy of Arts and Sciences 800/6-8
1400 W 9th Ave 92029 760-432-2439
Albert Ngo, prin. Fax 432-0728
Hidden Valley MS 1,200/6-8
2700 Reed Rd 92027 760-432-2457
Trent Smith, prin. Fax 480-0845
Mission MS 1,000/6-8
939 E Mission Ave 92025 760-432-2452
Dr. Carlos Ulloa, prin. Fax 737-9085
Rincon MS 1,300/6-8
925 Lehner Ave 92026 760-432-2491
Beth Crooks, prin. Fax 743-6713

Balboa City S 100/1-12
130 Woodward Ave 92025 760-294-4490
Zachary Jones, dir. Fax 294-4209
Calvin Christian JSHS 300/6-12
2000 N Broadway 92026 760-489-6430
Frank Steidl, prin. Fax 489-7055
Escondido Adventist Academy 200/K-12
1301 Deodar Rd 92026 760-746-1800
Escondido Christian S 400/PK-12
923 Idaho Ave 92025 760-745-2071
Matt Conway, prin. Fax 745-1905
Westminster Seminary California Post-Sec.
1725 Bear Valley Pkwy 92027 760-480-8474

Esparto, Yolo, Pop. 3,053
Esparto USD 1,200/PK-12
26675 Plainfield St 95627 530-787-3446
Hortencia Phifer, supt. Fax 787-3033
www.espartok12.org
Esparto HS 300/9-12
26675 Plainfield St 95627 530-787-3405
Jennifer Wiese, prin. Fax 787-4850
Esparto MS 200/6-8
26675 Plainfield St 95627 530-787-4151
Hortencia Phifer M.Ed., prin. Fax 787-3890
Other Schools – See Madison

Etiwanda, See Rancho Cucamonga
Chaffey JUNHSD
Supt. — See Ontario
Etiwanda HS 3,300/9-12
13500 Victoria St 91739 909-899-2531
Don Jaramillo, prin. Fax 899-3661

Etiwanda SD 13,600/K-8
6061 East Ave 91739 909-899-2451
Shawn Judson Ed.D., supt. Fax 899-1235
www.etiwanda.k12.ca.us
Day Creek IS 1,200/6-8
12345 Coyote Dr 91739 909-803-3300
Alicia Lyon, prin. Fax 803-3309
Etiwanda Community Day S 50/Alt
5959 East Ave 91739 909-899-2451
Jeff Sipos, dir. Fax 803-3024
Etiwanda IS 1,300/6-8
6925 Etiwanda Ave 91739 909-899-1701
Justin Kooyman, prin. Fax 899-5676
Summit IS 1,100/6-8
5959 East Ave 91739 909-899-1704
Ben Nakamura, prin. Fax 899-7596
Other Schools – See Fontana

Etna, Siskiyou, Pop. 666
Scott Valley USD
Supt. — See Fort Jones
Etna HS 200/9-12
PO Box 721 96027 530-467-3244
Regina Hanna, prin. Fax 467-5763
Scott River HS 50/Alt
PO Box 59 96027 530-467-5279
Regina Hanna, prin. Fax 467-3459
Scott Valley Adult S Adult
PO Box 59 96027 530-467-3244
Regina Hanna, admin. Fax 467-5763

Eureka, Humboldt, Pop. 25,748
Eureka City SD 3,700/K-12
2100 J St 95501 707-441-2400
Fred Van Vleck Ed.D., supt. Fax 441-3326
www.eurekacityschools.org
Barnum Continuation HS 100/Alt
216 W Harris St 95503 707-441-2467
Omar Khattab, prin. Fax 441-0299
Eureka HS 1,200/9-12
1915 J St 95501 707-441-2508
Jennifer Johnson, prin. Fax 445-1956
Winship MS, 2500 Cypress Ave 95503 300/6-8
Shellye Horowitz, prin. 707-441-2488
Zane MS 600/6-8
2155 S St 95501 707-441-2470
Randall Simms, prin. Fax 441-0286
Eureka Adult Education Adult
2100 J St 95501 707-441-2448
Omar Khattab, prin. Fax 442-1403

Fortuna UNHSD
Supt. — See Fortuna
Academy of the Redwoods 200/Alt
7351 Tompkins Hill Rd 95501 707-476-4203
Luke Biesecker, prin. Fax 476-4439

Humboldt County Office of Education 300/
901 Myrtle Ave 95501 707-445-7000
Garry Eagles Ph.D., supt. Fax 445-7143
www.humboldt.k12.ca.us
Eureka Community S 100/Alt
1820 6th St 95501 707-445-7108
Jennifer Fairbanks, prin. Fax 445-7071
Other Schools – See Fortuna, Garberville

Regional Occupational Center & Program
Supt. — None
Humboldt County ROP Vo/Tech
901 Myrtle Ave 95501 707-445-7018
Lori Breyer, dir. Fax 445-7143

College of the Redwoods Post-Sec.
7351 Tompkins Hill Rd 95501 707-476-4100
Frederick and Charles Beauty College Post-Sec.
831 F St 95501 707-443-2733
Gospel Outreach S 50/K-12
2845 Saint James Pl 95503 707-445-2214
David Sczepanski, prin. Fax 445-2212
St. Bernard Academy 300/7-12
222 Dollison St 95501 707-443-2735
Paul Shanahan, prin. Fax 443-4723

Exeter, Tulare, Pop. 10,133
Exeter USD 2,900/PK-12
215 N Crespi Ave 93221 559-592-9421
Tim Hire, supt. Fax 592-9445
www.exeter.k12.ca.us/
Exeter Union HS 1,000/9-12
505 Rocky Hill Dr 93221 559-592-2127
Robert Mayo, prin. Fax 592-3539
Kaweah Continuation HS 100/Alt
1107 Rocky Hill Dr 93221 559-592-4420
Darin Pace, prin. Fax 592-5246
Wilson MS 700/6-8
710 W Maple St 93221 559-592-2144
Sonia Wilson, prin. Fax 592-5536

Sierra View Junior Academy 100/K-10
19933 Avenue 256 93221 559-592-3689

Fairfax, Marin, Pop. 7,179
Ross Valley ESD
Supt. — See San Anselmo
White Hill MS 700/6-8
101 Glen Dr 94930 415-454-8390
David Finnane, prin. Fax 454-3980

Fairfield, Solano, Pop. 97,586
Fairfield-Suisun USD 21,300/PK-12
2490 Hilborn Rd, 707-399-5000
Kris Corey, supt. Fax 399-5160
www.fsusd.org
Armijo HS 2,400/9-12
824 Washington St 94533 707-422-7500
Eric Tretten, prin. Fax 438-3390
Fairfield HS 1,400/9-12
205 E Atlantic Ave 94533 707-438-3000
Will Cushman, prin. Fax 422-0178
Garcia Career and College Academy 100/6-12
1100 Civic Center Dr 94533 707-424-9400
Jacqueline Kearns, prin.
Grange MS 1,200/6-8
1975 Blossom Ave 94533 707-421-4175
Christine Harrison, prin. Fax 422-4004
Green Valley MS 800/6-8
1350 Gold Hill Rd, 707-646-7000
Kristen Cherry, prin. Fax 864-1503
Public Safety Academy Vo/Tech
230 Atlantic Ave 94533 707-421-4100
Laurie Halcomb, prin.
Rodriguez HS 1,900/9-12
5000 Red Top Rd, 707-863-7950
Clarence Isadore, prin. Fax 863-7974
Sam Yeto Satellite Alt
824 Washington St 94533 707-438-3478
Sherry McCormick, prin.
Sem Yeto Continuation HS 500/Alt
205 Alaska Ave 94533 707-438-3170
Sherry McCormick, prin.
Fairfield-Suisun Adult Education Adult
900 Travis Blvd 94533 707-421-4155
James Woods, prin. Fax 421-4158
Other Schools – See Suisun City

Solano County Office of Education 300/
5100 Business Center Dr, 707-399-4400
Jay Speck, supt. Fax 863-4174
www.solanocoe.net/
Solano County Community S 100/Alt
2460 Clay Bank Rd 94533 707-399-4840
Rick Vaccaro, prin.

Travis USD 5,500/K-12
2751 De Ronde Dr 94533 707-437-4604
Kate Wren Gavlak, supt. Fax 437-8122
travisusd.org
Golden West MS 900/7-8
2651 De Ronde Dr 94533 707-437-8240
Jackie Tretten, prin. Fax 437-3416
Travis Community Day S 50/Alt
2785 De Ronde Dr 94533 707-437-8265
Allyson Rude Azevedo, prin.
Travis Education Center HS 100/Alt
2775 De Ronde Dr 94533 707-437-8265
Allyson Rude Azevedo, prin. Fax 437-0141
Vanden HS 1,600/9-12
2951 Markeley Ln 94533 707-437-7333
William Sarty, prin. Fax 437-7220

Fairfield Christian S 100/PK-12
PO Box 2172 94533 707-427-2665
Shawn Fortney, prin. Fax 237-2307
Milan Institute of Cosmetology Post-Sec.
934 Missouri St 94533 707-425-2288
Solano Christian Academy 100/PK-12
2200 Fairfield Ave 94533 707-425-7715
John Reed, head sch Fax 429-2999
Solano Community College Post-Sec.
4000 Suisun Valley Rd, 707-864-7000

Fair Oaks, Sacramento, Pop. 29,764
San Juan USD
Supt. — See Carmichael
Bella Vista HS 2,100/9-12
8301 Madison Ave 95628 916-971-5052
Peggy Haskins, prin. Fax 971-5011
Del Campo HS 1,800/9-12
4925 Dewey Dr 95628 916-971-5664
Brett Wolfe, prin. Fax 971-5640
El Sereno Independent Study S 200/Alt
10700 Fair Oaks Blvd 95628 916-971-5060
Mia Funk, prin. Fax 971-5070
Rogers MS 700/6-8
4924 Dewey Dr 95628 916-971-7889
Gabriel Cooper, prin. Fax 971-7903

Freedom Christian S 100/K-12
7736 Sunset Ave 95628 916-962-3247
Annette Coller, admin. Fax 962-0783
Rudolf Steiner College Post-Sec.
9200 Fair Oaks Blvd 95628 916-961-8727
Sacramento Waldorf S 400/K-12
3750 Bannister Rd 95628 916-961-3900

Fallbrook, San Diego, Pop. 29,874
Fallbrook UNESD 5,400/PK-8
321 Iowa St 92028 760-731-5420
Stephanie Weaver, supt. Fax 723-3895
www.fuesd.k12.ca.us
Potter IS 800/7-8
1743 Reche Rd 92028 760-731-4150
Brian Frost, prin. Fax 723-5740

Fallbrook UNHSD 2,600/9-12
2234 S Stage Coach Ln 92028 760-723-6332
Dr. Hugo A. Pedroza Ph.D., supt. Fax 723-1795
www.fuhsd.net
Fallbrook HS 2,300/9-12
2400 S Stage Coach Ln 92028 760-723-6300
Larry Boone, prin. Fax 723-6343

Ivy HS 100/Alt
1056 Winter Haven Rd 92028 760-723-6395
John Hayek, prin. Fax 723-6392
Oasis Alternative HS 100/Alt
2208 S Stage Coach Ln 92028 760-723-1886
John Hayek, prin. Fax 723-6411

Farmersville, Tulare, Pop. 10,466
Farmersville USD 2,600/K-12
571 E Citrus Dr 93223 559-592-2010
Randy DeGraw, supt. Fax 592-2203
www.farmersville.k12.ca.us
Deep Creek Academy 100/Alt
281 S Farmersville Blvd 93223 559-747-6205
Fax 747-0591
Farmersville HS 700/9-12
631 E Walnut Ave 93223 559-594-4567
Lisa Whitworth, prin. Fax 594-5287
Farmersville JHS 400/7-8
650 N Virginia Ave 93223 559-747-0764
Dago Garcia, prin. Fax 747-2704

Felton, Santa Cruz, Pop. 3,909
San Lorenzo Valley USD
Supt. — See Ben Lomond
San Lorenzo Valley HS 700/9-12
7105 Highway 9 95018 831-335-4425
Jeff Calden, prin. Fax 335-1531
San Lorenzo Valley MS 500/6-8
7179 Hacienda Way 95018 831-335-4452
Shannon Calden, prin. Fax 335-3812

Ferndale, Humboldt, Pop. 1,343
Ferndale USD 500/PK-12
1231 Main St 95536 707-786-5900
Jack Lakin, supt. Fax 786-4865
www.ferndalek12.org/
Ferndale HS 200/9-12
1231 Main St 95536 707-786-5900
Jack Lakin, prin. Fax 786-4865

Fillmore, Ventura, Pop. 14,823
Fillmore USD 3,800/PK-12
PO Box 697 93016 805-524-6000
Adrian Palazuelos, supt. Fax 524-6060
www.fillmore.k12.ca.us
Fillmore HS 1,000/9-12
PO Box 697 93016 805-524-6100
Thomas Ito, prin. Fax 524-6121
Fillmore MS 900/6-8
PO Box 697 93016 805-524-6055
Scott Carroll, prin. Fax 524-6063
Sierra HS 100/Alt
PO Box 697 93016 805-524-8202
Cynthia Frutos, prin. Fax 524-6080
Fillmore Adult S Adult
PO Box 697 93016 805-524-8232
Stefan Cvijanovich, prin. Fax 524-6060

Firebaugh, Fresno, Pop. 7,529
Firebaugh-Las Deltas JUSD 2,200/PK-12
1976 Morris Kyle Dr 93622 559-659-1476
Russell Freitas, supt. Fax 659-2355
www.fldusd.org/
El Puente Continuation HS 50/Alt
1976 Morris Kyle Dr 93622 559-659-3899
Terr Anderson, admin. Fax 659-1511
Firebaugh HS 700/9-12
1976 Morris Kyle Dr 93622 559-659-1415
Anthony Catalat, prin. Fax 659-2636
Firebaugh MS 500/6-8
1976 Morris Kyle Dr 93622 559-659-1481
Marc Sosa, prin. Fax 659-7106
Firebaugh-Las Deltas Adult S Adult
1976 Morris Kyle Dr 93622 559-659-3899
Terry Anderson, admin. Fax 659-1511

Folsom, Sacramento, Pop. 69,359
Folsom-Cordova USD
Supt. — See Rancho Cordova
Folsom HS 2,100/9-12
1655 Iron Point Rd 95630 916-294-2400
Howard Cadenhead, prin. Fax 355-1110
Folsom Lake HS 100/Alt
955 Riley St 95630 916-294-9055
Leane Linson, prin. Fax 294-9728
Folsom MS 1,300/6-8
500 Blue Ravine Rd 95630 916-294-9040
John Bliss, prin. Fax 983-3462
Sutter MS 1,400/6-8
715 Riley St 95630 916-985-3644
Keri Phillips, prin. Fax 985-7044
Vista Del Lago HS 1,400/9-12
1970 Broadstone Pkwy 95630 916-294-2410
Lori Emmington, prin. Fax 294-2411

Folsom Lake College Post-Sec.
10 College Pkwy 95630 916-608-6500

Fontana, San Bernardino, Pop. 192,303
Etiwanda SD
Supt. — See Etiwanda
Heritage IS 1,300/6-8
13766 S Heritage Cir 92336 909-357-1345
Laura Rowland, prin. Fax 357-8945

Fontana USD 40,000/PK-12
9680 Citrus Ave 92335 909-357-7600
Randal Bassett Ph.D., supt. Fax 357-5012
www.fusd.net
Alder MS 1,200/6-8
7555 Alder Ave 92336 909-357-5330
Rosario Gomez, prin. Fax 357-5348
Almeria MS 900/6-8
7723 Almeria Ave 92336 909-357-5350
Letitia Bradley, prin. Fax 357-5360
Birch HS 300/Alt
7930 Locust Ave 92336 909-357-5310
Ed Campbell, prin. Fax 357-5319

Citrus Continuation HS 600/Alt
9820 Citrus Ave 92335 909-357-5300
Ed Campbell, prin. Fax 357-5302
Fontana HS 2,500/9-12
9453 Citrus Ave 92335 909-357-5500
Ofelia Hinojosa, prin. Fax 357-5629
Fontana MS 1,100/6-8
8425 Mango Ave 92335 909-357-5370
Sergio Chavez, prin. Fax 357-5391
Jurupa Hills HS 2,100/9-12
10700 Oleander Ave 92337 909-357-6300
Lorraine Trollinger, prin. Fax 357-7540
Kaiser HS 2,400/9-12
11155 Almond Ave 92337 909-357-5900
Terry Abernathy, prin. Fax 357-5997
Miller HS 2,500/9-12
6821 Oleander Ave 92336 909-357-5800
Moises Merlos, prin. Fax 357-7680
Ruble MS 1,200/6-8
6762 Juniper Ave 92336 909-357-5530
Caroline Labonte, prin. Fax 357-5539
Sequoia MS 1,100/7-8
9452 Hemlock Ave 92335 909-357-5400
Gorge Santiago, prin. Fax 357-5419
Southridge MS 1,100/6-8
14500 Live Oak Ave 92337 909-357-5420
Gerald Mullins, prin. Fax 822-4609
Summit HS 2,500/9-12
15551 Summit Ave 92336 909-357-5950
Fax 357-5959
Truman MS 1,200/6-8
16224 Mallory Dr 92335 909-357-5190
Kim Hall, prin. Fax 357-5199
Fontana Adult S Adult
10755 Oleander Ave 92337 909-357-5490
Cindy Gleason, prin. Fax 357-5556

Foresthill, Placer, Pop. 1,441
Placer UNHSD
Supt. — See Auburn
Foresthill HS 200/9-12
23319 Foresthill Rd 95631 530-367-5244
Randy Ittner, prin. Fax 367-4623

Forestville, Sonoma, Pop. 3,212
West Sonoma County UNHSD
Supt. — See Sebastopol
El Molino HS 600/9-12
7050 Covey Rd 95436 707-824-6570
Matt Dunkle, prin. Fax 887-0448

Fort Bragg, Mendocino, Pop. 7,053
Fort Bragg USD 1,900/PK-12
312 S Lincoln St 95437 707-961-2850
Rebecca Walker, supt. Fax 964-5002
www.fbusd.us
Fort Bragg HS 500/9-12
300 Dana St 95437 707-961-2880
Bruce Triplett, prin. Fax 961-2884
Fort Bragg MS 400/6-8
500 N Harold St 95437 707-961-2870
Lura Vieira, prin. Fax 964-9416
Lighthouse Community Day S 50/Alt
250 S Sanderson Way 95437 707-964-1017
Coni Belli, prin.
Noyo HS 50/Alt
250 S Sanderson Way 95437 707-961-2889
Coni Belli, prin. Fax 964-1017
Shelter Cove S 50/Alt
310 S Lincoln St 95437 707-961-2889
Coni Belli, prin. Fax 964-1017
Coastal Adult S Adult
250 S Sanderson Way 95437 707-961-2889
Coni Belli, prin. Fax 964-1017

Fort Irwin, San Bernardino, Pop. 8,282
Silver Valley USD
Supt. — See Yermo
Fort Irwin MS 400/6-8
1700 Pork Chop Hill St 92310 760-386-1133
Heidi Chavez, prin. Fax 386-2448

Fort Jones, Siskiyou, Pop. 789
Scott Valley USD 600/K-12
PO Box 687 96032 530-468-2727
Dr. Allan Carver, supt. Fax 468-2729
www.svusd.us/
Scott Valley Community Day S 50/Alt
11033 Quartz Valley Rd 96032 530-467-5279
Allan Carver, admin. Fax 467-3459
Scott Valley JHS 100/6-9
237 Butte St 96032 530-468-5565
Tana Piersall, prin. Fax 468-5658
Other Schools – See Etna

Fortuna, Humboldt, Pop. 11,506
Fortuna ESD 1,300/PK-8
500 9th St 95540 707-725-2293
Jeff Northern M.A., supt. Fax 725-2228
fesd-ca.schoolloop.com
Fortuna MS 300/5-8
843 L St 95540 707-725-3415
Vince Zinselmeir B.A., prin. Fax 725-6240
Thomas MS 300/5-8
2800 Thomas St 95540 707-725-5197
Julie Johansen M.A., prin. Fax 725-8637

Fortuna UNHSD 1,100/9-12
379 12th St 95540 707-725-4461
Glen Senestraro, supt. Fax 725-6085
www.fuhsdistrict.org
East HS 100/Alt
379 12th St 95540 707-725-4461
Brian Schoenfield, prin. Fax 725-1628
Fortuna Union HS 800/9-12
379 12th St 95540 707-725-4461
Clint Duey, prin. Fax 725-5511
Other Schools – See Eureka

Humboldt County Office of Education
Supt. — See Eureka
Eel River Community S 100/Alt
2292 Newburg Rd 95540 707-725-0209
Jennifer Fairbanks, prin. Fax 725-0326

New Life Christian S 100/PK-12
PO Box 404 95540 707-725-9136
Karen Johnson, prin. Fax 725-1638

Foster City, San Mateo, Pop. 29,077
San Mateo-Foster City ESD 11,700/K-8
1170 Chess Dr 94404 650-312-7700
Dr. Joan Rosas Ph.D., supt. Fax 312-7348
www.smfcsd.net
Bowditch MS 1,000/6-8
1450 Tarpon St 94404 650-312-7680
Heather Gomez, prin. Fax 312-7639
Other Schools – See San Mateo

Fountain Valley, Orange, Pop. 53,408
Fountain Valley ESD 6,300/K-8
10055 Slater Ave 92708 714-843-3200
Mark Johnson Ed.D., supt. Fax 841-0356
www.fvsd.k12.ca.us
Fulton MS 800/6-8
8778 El Lago Cir 92708 714-375-2816
Kevin Johnson, prin. Fax 375-2825
Masuda MS 800/6-8
17415 Los Jardines W 92708 714-378-4250
Jay Adams, prin. Fax 378-4259
Other Schools – See Huntington Beach

Garden Grove USD
Supt. — See Garden Grove
Los Amigos HS 1,800/9-12
16566 Newhope St 92708 714-663-6288
Vicki Braddock, prin. Fax 663-6518

Huntington Beach UNHSD
Supt. — See Huntington Beach
Fountain Valley HS 3,700/9-12
17816 Bushard St 92708 714-962-3301
Morgan Smith, prin. Fax 964-0491
Valley Vista HS 300/Alt
9600 Dolphin St 92708 714-964-7766
Kerry Clitheroe, prin. Fax 964-3045

Ocean View SD
Supt. — See Huntington Beach
Vista View MS 700/6-8
16250 Hickory St 92708 714-842-0626
Scott Mooney, prin. Fax 843-9156

Coastline Community College Post-Sec.
11460 Warner Ave 92708 714-546-7600
Modern Technology School Post-Sec.
16560 Harbor Blvd Ste K 92708 714-418-9100

Fowler, Fresno, Pop. 5,491
Fowler USD 2,400/K-12
658 E Adams Ave 93625 559-834-6080
Eric Cederquist, supt. Fax 834-3390
www.fowlerusd.org
Fowler HS 700/9-12
701 E Main St 93625 559-834-6160
Rick Romero, prin. Fax 834-3284
Fowler Unified Alternative Education 50/Alt
658 E Adams Ave 93625 559-834-6098
Jonathan Farley, prin. Fax 834-6721
Sutter MS 600/6-8
701 E Walter Ave 93625 559-834-6180
Gary Geringer, prin. Fax 834-4739

Fremont, Alameda, Pop. 203,344
Fremont USD 33,700/K-12
PO Box 5008 94537 510-657-2350
James Morris Ed.D., supt. Fax 659-2597
www.fremont.k12.ca.us
American HS 2,000/9-12
36300 Fremont Blvd 94536 510-796-1776
Steven Musto, prin. Fax 791-5331
Centerville JHS 900/7-8
37720 Fremont Blvd 94536 510-797-2072
Weste Petersen, prin. Fax 794-7588
Hopkins JHS 1,000/7-8
600 Driscoll Rd 94539 510-656-3500
Corey Brown, prin. Fax 656-3731
Horner JHS 1,100/7-8
41365 Chapel Way 94538 510-656-4000
Jana Holmes, prin. Fax 656-2793
Irvington HS 2,200/9-12
41800 Blacow Rd 94538 510-656-5711
Sarah Smoot, prin. Fax 623-9805
Kennedy HS 1,400/9-12
39999 Blacow Rd 94538 510-657-4070
Eddie Velez, prin. Fax 438-9287
Mission San Jose HS 2,200/9-12
41717 Palm Ave 94539 510-657-3600
Zachary Larsen, prin. Fax 657-2302
Robertson Continuation HS 200/Alt
4455 Seneca Park Ave 94538 510-657-9155
Sal Herrera, prin. Fax 657-5535
Thornton JHS 1,100/7-8
4357 Thornton Ave 94536 510-793-9090
Stan Hicks, prin. Fax 793-9756
Vista Alternative S 100/Alt
4455 Seneca Park Ave 94538 510-657-7028
Salvador Herrera, prin. Fax 657-0733
Walters JHS 800/7-8
39600 Logan Dr 94538 510-656-7211
Brian Weems, prin. Fax 656-4056
Washington HS 1,800/9-12
38442 Fremont Blvd 94536 510-505-7300
Rob Moran, prin. Fax 794-8437
Fremont Adult S Adult
4700 Calaveras Ave 94538 510-793-6465
Gladys Nazario, prin. Fax 793-2271

Regional Occupational Center & Program
Supt. — None
Mission Valley ROP — Vo/Tech
5019 Stevenson Blvd 94538 — 510-657-1865
Thomas Hanson, supt. — Fax 438-0378

Alsion Montessori MSHS — 100/7-12
PO Box 3296 94539 — 510-445-1127
Averroes HS — 9-12
43174 Osgood Rd 94539 — 510-580-4566
California School for the Blind — Post-Sec.
500 Walnut Ave 94536
California School for the Deaf — Post-Sec.
39350 Gallaudet Dr 94538 — 510-794-3684
DeVry University — Post-Sec.
6600 Dumbarton Cir 94555 — 510-574-1200
Fremont Christian S — 800/PK-12
4760 Thornton Ave 94536 — 510-744-2241
Dr. Tricia Meyer, head sch — Fax 744-2255
Northwestern Polytechnic University — Post-Sec.
47671 Westinghouse Dr 94539 — 510-592-9688
Ohlone College — Post-Sec.
43600 Mission Blvd 94539 — 510-659-6000
Queen of the Holy Rosary College — Post-Sec.
43326 Mission Blvd 94539 — 510-657-2468
Unitek College — Post-Sec.
4670 Auto Mall Pkwy 94538 — 888-735-4355
Wyotech — Post-Sec.
420 Whitney Pl 94539 — 510-490-6900

Fresno, Fresno, Pop. 482,604
Central USD — 15,500/K-12
4605 N Polk Ave 93722 — 559-274-4700
Mark G. Sutton, supt. — Fax 271-8200
www.centralunified.org
Central HS East Campus — 4,100/9-12
3535 N Cornelia Ave 93722 — 559-276-0280
Robert Perez, prin. — Fax 276-5653
Central HS West Campus — 9-12
2045 N Dickenson Ave, — 559-276-5276
Robert Perez, prin. — Fax 276-6380
Central Unified Alternative S — 300/Alt
2698 N Brawley Ave 93722 — 559-276-5230
Jose Reyes, prin. — Fax 276-8204
El Capitan MS — 600/7-8
4443 W Weldon Ave 93722 — 559-276-5270
Jeff Wimp, prin. — Fax 276-3121
Glacier Point MS — 900/7-8
4055 N Bryan Ave, — 559-276-3105
Heather Kuyper, prin. — Fax 276-3152
Pathway Community Day School — 50/Alt
11 S Teilman Ave 93706 — 559-487-1201
Nick Hustedde, prin. — Fax 487-1204
Pershing Continuation HS — 100/Alt
855 W Nielsen Ave 93706 — 559-268-2272
Nick Hustedde, prin. — Fax 268-2279
Rio Vista MS — 800/7-8
6240 W Palo Alto Ave 93722 — 559-276-3185
Joe Bracamonte, prin. — Fax 276-3199
Central Unified Adult Education — Adult
2698 N Brawley Ave 93722 — 559-276-5230
Jose Reyes, prin. — Fax 276-8204

Clovis USD
Supt. — See Clovis
Clovis North Educational Center — 2,200/7-12
2770 E International Ave, — 559-327-5000
Scott Dille, prin. — Fax 327-5290
Clovis West HS — 2,200/9-12
1070 E Teague Ave 93720 — 559-327-2000
Marc Hammack, prin. — Fax 327-2490
Kastner IS — 1,100/7-8
7676 N 1st St 93720 — 559-327-2500
Ryan Eisele, prin. — Fax 327-2790

Fresno County Office of Education — 1,900/
1111 Van Ness Ave 93721 — 559-265-3000
Jim Yovino, supt. — Fax 265-4005
www.fcoe.org
Heintz Education Academy — 100/Alt
4939 E Yale Ave 93727 — 559-443-4863
Bill Johnson, prin. — Fax 443-4856
Koontz Education Complex — 100/Alt
1320 N Mariposa St 93703 — 559-443-4863
Bill Johnson, prin. — Fax 264-6398

Fresno USD — 72,600/PK-12
2309 Tulare St 93721 — 559-457-3000
Michael Hanson, supt. — Fax 457-3786
www.fresnounified.org
Ahwahnee MS — 700/7-8
1127 E Escalon Ave 93710 — 559-451-4300
Jose Guzman, prin. — Fax 439-1808
Baird MS — 600/5-8
5500 N Maroa Ave 93704 — 559-451-4310
Janetta McGensy, prin. — Fax 432-4075
Bullard HS — 2,600/9-12
5445 N Palm Ave 93704 — 559-451-4320
Carlos Castillo, prin. — Fax 451-4339
Cambridge Continuation HS — 400/Alt
1001 S Chestnut Ave 93702 — 559-253-6560
Pete Pulos, prin. — Fax 266-9776
Computech MS — 800/7-8
555 E Belgravia Ave 93706 — 559-457-2640
Andrew Scherrer, prin. — Fax 457-2643
Cooper MS — 500/7-8
2277 W Bellaire Way 93705 — 559-248-7050
Kristine Belcher, prin. — Fax 224-7255
Design Science HS — 300/9-12
2004 E Cambridge Ave 93703 — 559-248-7353
Roy Exum, prin.
Dewolf Continuation HS — 200/Alt
2445 W Dakota Ave 93705 — 559-457-2990
Frank Duran, prin. — Fax 224-2840
Duncan Polytechnical HS — Vo/Tech
4330 E Garland Ave 93726 — 559-248-7080
Carol Hansen, prin. — Fax 222-6186

Edison HS — 2,300/9-12
540 E California Ave 93706 — 559-457-2650
Lindsay Sanders, prin. — Fax 457-2742
Ft. Miller MS — 900/7-8
1302 E Dakota Ave 93704 — 559-248-7100
Mike Jones, prin. — Fax 221-7548
Fresno HS — 2,300/9-12
1839 N Echo Ave 93704 — 559-457-2780
John Forbes, prin. — Fax 457-2801
Gaston MS, 1100 E Church Ave 93706 — 6-8
Felicia Treadwell, prin. — 559-457-3400
Hoover HS, 5550 N 1st St 93710 — 1,900/9-12
Rebecca Wheeler, prin. — 559-451-4000
Kings Canyon MS — 800/7-8
5117 E Tulare Ave 93727 — 559-253-6470
Clark Mello, prin. — Fax 253-1005
McLane HS — 1,900/9-12
2727 N Cedar Ave 93703 — 559-248-5100
Scott Lamm, prin. — Fax 255-5253
Patino S of Entrepreneurship — 10-12
2000 E Cambridge Ave 93703 — 559-248-7360
Dr. Brett Taylor, prin.
Phoenix Secondary Academy — 50/Alt
5090 E Church Ave 93725 — 559-253-6520
Mark McAleenan, prin.
Roosevelt HS — 2,100/9-12
4250 E Tulare St 93702 — 559-253-5200
Michael Allen, prin. — Fax 253-5319
Scandinavian MS — 800/7-8
3216 N Sierra Vista Ave 93726 — 559-253-6510
Julie Goorabian-Ellis, prin. — Fax 252-7608
Sequoia MS — 800/7-8
4050 E Hamilton Ave 93702 — 559-457-3210
Matt Ward, prin. — Fax 497-1745
Sunnyside HS — 3,100/9-12
1019 S Peach Ave 93727 — 559-253-6700
Tim Liles, prin. — Fax 253-6799
Tehipite MS — 400/7-8
630 N Augusta St 93701 — 559-457-3420
Yvonne Zysling, prin. — Fax 457-3423
Tenaya MS — 900/7-8
1239 W Mesa Ave 93711 — 559-451-4570
Heather Garcia, prin. — Fax 431-0771
Terronez MS — 700/7-8
2300 S Willow Ave 93725 — 559-253-6570
Virginia Mendez-Buelna, prin. — Fax 253-6572
Tioga MS — 800/7-8
3232 E Fairmont Ave 93726 — 559-248-7280
Kevin Evangilinos, prin. — Fax 226-1296
Wawona MS — 600/7-8
4524 N Thorne Ave 93704 — 559-248-7310
Kimberly Wong Villescaz, prin. — Fax 227-5206
Yosemite MS — 600/7-8
1292 N 9th St 93703 — 559-457-3450
Nichole Horn, prin. — Fax 264-0933
Young Academic Center — 1,100/Alt
822 N Abby St 93701 — 559-457-3190
Janice Trimble, prin. — Fax 457-3193
Chavez Adult S — Adult
2500 Stanislaus St 93721 — 559-457-6000
Sally Fowler, prin. — Fax 457-6001

Regional Occupational Center & Program
Supt. — None
Fresno ROP — Vo/Tech
1318 E Shaw Ave Ste 420 93710 — 559-497-3850
Valerie Vuicich, admin. — Fax 497-3806

Washington USD — 2,900/PK-12
7950 S Elm Ave 93706 — 559-495-5600
Joey Campbell, supt.
www.washingtonunified.org
Easton Community S — 50/Alt
6041 S Elm Ave 93706 — 559-485-8805
Glen Freeman, dir. — Fax 237-0270
Easton Continuation HS — 50/Alt
5865 S Clara Ave 93706 — 559-485-8805
Glen Freeman, dir. — Fax 237-0270
Elm HS, 5865 S Clara Ave 93706 — Alt
Glen Freeman, dir. — 559-485-8805
Washington Union HS — 1,000/9-12
6041 S Elm Ave 93706 — 559-485-8805
Derek Cruz, prin. — Fax 485-4435
West Fresno MS — 300/6-8
2888 S Ivy Ave 93706 — 559-495-5607
Lucio Cortez, prin. — Fax 485-3006

Advanced Career Institute — Post-Sec.
2953 S East Ave 93725 — 559-441-4345
Alliant International University — Post-Sec.
5130 E Clinton Way 93727 — 559-253-2200
California Christian College — Post-Sec.
4881 E University Ave 93703 — 559-251-4215
California State University-Fresno — Post-Sec.
5241 N Maple Ave 93740 — 559-278-4240
Clovis Community College — Post-Sec.
10309 N Willow Ave, — 559-325-5200
DeVry University — Post-Sec.
7575 N Fresno St 93720 — 559-439-8595
Fresno Adventist Academy — 200/K-12
5397 E Olive Ave 93727 — 559-251-5548
Fresno Christian S — 300/K-12
7280 N Cedar Ave 93720 — 559-299-1695
Jeremy Brown, supt. — Fax 299-1051
Fresno City College — Post-Sec.
1101 E University Ave 93741 — 559-442-4600
Fresno Pacific University — Post-Sec.
1717 S Chestnut Ave 93702 — 559-453-2000
Heald College — Post-Sec.
255 W Bullard Ave 93704 — 559-438-4222
Lyle's College of Beauty — Post-Sec.
6735 N 1st St Ste 112 93710 — 559-431-6060
Manchester Beauty College — Post-Sec.
3756 N Blackstone Ave 93726 — 559-224-4242
San Joaquin Memorial HS — 600/9-12
1406 N Fresno St 93703 — 559-268-9251
Jimmy Monreal, head sch — Fax 268-1351

San Joaquin Valley College — Post-Sec.
295 E Sierra Ave 93710 — 559-448-8282
San Joaquin Valley College — Post-Sec.
4985 E Andersen Ave 93727 — 559-453-0123
Sierra Valley College of Court Reporting — Post-Sec.
4747 N 1st St # D 93726 — 559-222-0947
United Education Institute — Post-Sec.
2002 N Gateway Blvd 93727 — 559-456-0623

Fullerton, Orange, Pop. 131,685
Fullerton JUNHSD — 14,400/9-12
1051 W Bastanchury Rd 92833 — 714-870-2800
Scott Scambray, supt. — Fax 870-2807
www.fjuhsd.org
Fullerton Union HS — 2,200/9-12
201 E Chapman Ave 92832 — 714-626-3801
Rani Goyal, prin. — Fax 626-3839
La Sierra HS — 600/Alt
951 N State College Blvd 92831 — 714-447-7820
Sandi Layana, prin.
La Vista HS — 500/Alt
909 N State College Blvd 92831 — 714-447-5500
Sandi Layana, prin.
Sunny Hills HS — 2,300/9-12
1801 Warburton Way 92833 — 714-626-4201
Allen Whitten, prin. — Fax 738-3728
Troy HS — 2,700/9-12
2200 Dorothy Ln 92831 — 714-626-4401
Will Mynster, prin. — Fax 626-4492
Other Schools – See Buena Park, La Habra

Fullerton SD — 13,800/K-8
1401 W Valencia Dr 92833 — 714-447-7400
Dr. Bob Pletka Ed.D., supt. — Fax 447-7414
www.fullertonsd.org
Ladera Vista JHS — 900/7-8
1700 E Wilshire Ave 92831 — 714-447-7765
Randa Schmalfeld, prin. — Fax 447-7554
Nicolas JHS — 800/7-8
1100 W Olive Ave 92833 — 714-447-7775
Robyn Clemente, prin. — Fax 447-7586
Parks JHS — 1,000/7-8
1710 Rosecrans Ave 92833 — 714-447-7785
Sherry Dustin, prin. — Fax 447-7753

California State University-Fullerton — Post-Sec.
PO Box 34080 92834 — 657-278-2011
Eastside Christian S — 200/K-12
1701 W Valencia Dr 92833 — 714-525-7200
Kim Van Geloof, head sch — Fax 525-7200
Fullerton College — Post-Sec.
321 E Chapman Ave 92832 — 714-992-7000
Grace Christian Academy — 100/K-12
1619 W Louise Pl 92833 — 714-315-1619
Grace Mission University — Post-Sec.
1645 W Valencia Dr 92833 — 714-525-0088
Hope International University — Post-Sec.
2500 Nutwood Ave 92831 — 714-879-3901
Marshall B. Ketchum University — Post-Sec.
2575 Yorba Linda Blvd 92831 — 714-449-7444
Rosary Academy — 600/9-12
1340 N Acacia Ave 92831 — 714-879-6302
Jen Almand, admin. — Fax 879-0853
Veritas Classical Academy — 100/K-12
1601 W Malvern Ave 92833 — 949-557-1311
Dr. David Kim, hdmstr.
Western State University College of Law — Post-Sec.
1111 N State College Blvd 92831 — 714-738-1000

Galt, Sacramento, Pop. 22,880
Galt JUNESD — 3,800/K-8
1018 C St Ste 210 95632 — 209-744-4545
Karen Schauer, supt. — Fax 744-4553
www.galt.k12.ca.us
McCaffrey MS — 900/7-8
997 Park Terrace Dr 95632 — 209-745-5462
Julie Grandinetti, prin. — Fax 745-5465

Galt JUNHSD — 2,300/9-12
12945 Marengo Rd 95632 — 209-745-0249
Elizabeth Kaufman Ed.D., supt. — Fax 745-0881
www.ghsd.k12.ca.us
Estrellita Continuation HS — 200/Alt
12935 Marengo Rd 95632 — 209-745-2167
Lisa Pettis, prin. — Fax 745-7026
Galt HS — 1,000/9-12
145 N Lincoln Way 95632 — 209-745-3081
Bob Rappleye, prin. — Fax 745-4786
Liberty Ranch HS — 1,200/9-12
12945 Marengo Rd 95632 — 209-744-4250
Anahi Perez, prin. — Fax 745-2601
Adult Education — Adult
150 Camellia Way 95632 — 209-745-5852
Tony Lara, dir. — Fax 745-7026

Garberville, Humboldt, Pop. 894
Humboldt County Office of Education
Supt. — See Eureka
Southern Humboldt Community S — 50/Alt
286 Sprowl Creek Rd 95542 — 707-923-2550
Jennifer Fairbanks, prin.

Gardena, Los Angeles, Pop. 56,918
Los Angeles USD
Supt. — See Los Angeles
Gardena HS — 1,700/9-12
1301 W 182nd St 90248 — 310-354-5000
Rosemarie Martinez, prin. — Fax 366-6943
Moneta Continuation HS — 100/Alt
1230 W 177th St 90248 — 310-354-4951
Antonio Morreale, prin. — Fax 352-4027
Peary MS — 1,400/6-8
1415 W Gardena Blvd 90247 — 310-225-4200
Marva Patton, prin. — Fax 329-3957

Everest College — Post-Sec.
1045 W Rdnd Bch Blvd #275 90247 — 310-527-7105

Junipero Serra HS 600/9-12
14830 Van Ness Ave 90249 310-324-6675
Jeff Guzman, prin. Fax 352-4953
Pacific Lutheran HS 100/9-12
1473 W 182nd St 90248 310-538-6863
Lucas Fitzgerald, prin.
United Education Institute Post-Sec.
661 W Redondo Beach Blvd 90247 424-246-3000

Garden Grove, Orange, Pop. 166,793
Garden Grove USD 46,700/PK-12
10331 Stanford Ave 92840 714-663-6000
Gabriela Mafi, supt. Fax 663-6100
www.ggusd.us/
Alamitos IS 800/7-8
12381 Dale St 92841 714-663-6101
Christina Pflughoft, prin. Fax 663-6277
Bell IS 700/7-8
11852 Knott St 92841 714-663-6466
Matt Lambert, prin. Fax 663-6238
Bolsa Grande HS 2,000/9-12
9401 Westminster Ave 92844 714-663-6424
Louise Milner, prin. Fax 663-6029
Doig IS 900/7-8
12752 Trask Ave 92843 714-663-6241
Louie Gomez, prin. Fax 663-6845
Garden Grove HS 2,500/9-12
11271 Stanford Ave 92840 714-663-6115
Steve Osborne, prin. Fax 663-6030
Hare HS 400/Alt
12012 Magnolia St 92841 714-663-6508
Todd Nirk, prin. Fax 663-6510
Irvine IS 900/7-8
10552 Hazard Ave 92843 714-663-6551
Bill Gates, prin. Fax 663-6013
Jordan IS 800/7-8
9821 Woodbury Ave 92844 714-663-6124
Tracy Conway, prin. Fax 663-6123
Lake IS 600/7-8
10801 Orangewood Ave 92840 714-663-6506
Tahnee Phan, prin. Fax 663-6065
Pacifica HS 1,800/9-12
6851 Lampson Ave 92845 714-663-6515
Robin Patterson, prin. Fax 663-6037
Ralston IS 700/7-8
10851 Lampson Ave 92840 714-663-6366
Ruth Dietze, prin. Fax 638-7155
Rancho Alamitos HS 1,800/9-12
11351 Dale St 92841 714-663-6415
Mary Hibbard, prin. Fax 663-6439
Santiago HS 2,300/9-12
12342 Trask Ave 92843 714-663-6215
Michael Kennedy, prin. Fax 530-0764
Walton IS 600/7-8
12181 Buaro St 92840 714-663-6040
Janis Cody, prin. Fax 534-4814
Lincoln Education Center Adult
11262 Garden Grove Blvd 92843 714-663-6291
Connie Van Luit Ed.D., dir.
Other Schools – See Fountain Valley, Santa Ana, Westminster

Career Academy of Beauty Post-Sec.
12471 Valley View St 92845 714-897-3010
Concorde Career Institute Post-Sec.
12951 Euclid St Ste 101 92840 714-703-1900
Lola Beauty College Post-Sec.
11883 Valley View St 92845 714-894-3366
Orangewood Academy 200/PK-12
13732 Clinton St 92843 714-534-4694
Stanton University Post-Sec.
12666 Brookhurst St 92840 714-539-6561
Thanh Le College School of Cosmetology Post-Sec.
12875 Chapman Ave 92840 714-971-5844
Trinity Christian S K-12
12761 Euclid St 92840 714-971-4159

Garden Valley, El Dorado
Black Oak Mine USD
Supt. — See Georgetown
Golden Sierra JSHS 600/7-12
5101 Garden Valley Rd 95633 530-333-8330
Jeremy Meyers, prin. Fax 333-8333

Georgetown, El Dorado, Pop. 2,308
Black Oak Mine USD 1,400/K-12
6540 Wentworth Springs Rd 95634 530-333-8300
Elizabeth Haines Ed.D., supt. Fax 333-8303
www.bomusd.org/
Other Schools – See Garden Valley, Greenwood

Geyserville, Sonoma, Pop. 841
Geyserville USD 300/K-12
1300 Moody Ln 95441 707-857-3592
Deborah Bertolucci, supt. Fax 857-3071
www.gusd.com
Buena Vista HS 50/Alt
1300 Moody Ln 95441 707-433-3207
Deborah Bertolucci, prin.
Geyersville New Tech Academy 100/6-12
1300 Moody Ln 95441 707-857-3592
Deborah Bertolucci, prin. Fax 857-3071

Gilroy, Santa Clara, Pop. 47,703
Gilroy USD 11,500/PK-12
7810 Arroyo Cir 95020 408-847-2700
Dr. Deborah A. Flores, supt. Fax 847-4717
www.gilroyunified.org
Brownell MS 1,000/6-8
7800 Carmel St 95020 408-847-3377
David Laboranti, prin. Fax 846-7521
Christopher HS 1,800/9-12
850 Day Rd 95020 408-848-7171
Paul Winslow, prin. Fax 847-7256
Gilroy HS 1,400/9-12
750 W 10th St 95020 408-847-2424
Dr. Marco Sanchez, prin. Fax 842-3311

Mt. Madonna HS 300/Alt
8750 Hirasaki Ct 95020 408-842-4313
Dianne Padilla, prin. Fax 842-2918
Owens Gilroy Early College Academy 200/9-12
5055 Santa Teresa Blvd 95020 408-846-4909
Sonia Flores, prin. Fax 848-4730
Solorsano MS 900/6-8
7121 Grenache Way 95020 408-848-4121
Maria Walker, prin. Fax 848-7121
South Valley MS 800/6-8
385 I O O F Ave 95020 408-847-2828
Patricia Mondragon, prin. Fax 847-5708

Regional Occupational Center & Program
Supt. — None
Santa Clara County ROP South Vo/Tech
700 W 6th St Ste L 95020 408-842-0361
Dr. David Matuszak, dir. Fax 842-0653

Gavilan College Post-Sec.
5055 Santa Teresa Blvd 95020 408-848-4800
Pacific Point JSHS 6-12
2220 Pacheco Pass Hwy 95020 408-847-0111
Sergio Montenegro, supt. Fax 847-0147

Glendale, Los Angeles, Pop. 184,933
Glendale USD 25,900/PK-12
223 N Jackson St 91206 818-241-3111
Winfred Roberson, supt. Fax 548-9041
www.gusd.net
Daily Continuation HS 200/Alt
220 N Kenwood St 91206 818-247-4805
Dr. Rene Valdes Ed.D., prin. Fax 547-3081
Glendale HS 2,700/9-12
1440 E Broadway 91205 818-242-3161
Benjamin Wolf, prin. Fax 244-6309
Hoover HS 1,800/9-12
651 Glenwood Rd 91202 818-242-6801
Dr. Jennifer Earl Ed.D., prin. Fax 247-8825
Jewel City Community Day S 50/Alt
223 N Jackson St 91206 818-549-4812
Dr. Rene Valdes Ed.D., dir. Fax 547-5715
Roosevelt MS 800/6-8
1017 S Glendale Ave 91205 818-242-6845
Dr. Mary Mason Ed.D., prin. Fax 552-5188
Toll MS 1,100/6-8
700 Glenwood Rd 91202 818-244-8414
Dr. Thomas Crowther Ed.D., prin. Fax 500-1487
Wilson MS 1,300/6-8
1221 Monterey Rd 91206 818-244-8145
Dr. Chris Coulter Ed.D., prin. Fax 244-2050
Other Schools – See La Crescenta

Brand College Post-Sec.
529 Hahn Ave Ste 101 91203 818-550-0770
Glendale Adventist Academy 600/K-12
700 Kimlin Dr 91206 818-244-8671
Glendale Community College Post-Sec.
1500 N Verdugo Rd 91208 818-240-1000
Holy Family HS 200/9-12
400 E Lomita Ave 91205 818-241-3178
Dr. Nancy O'Sullivan, prin. Fax 241-7753
Integrated Digital Technologies Post-Sec.
130 N Brand Blvd Ste 300 91203 818-396-3500
Moro Beauty College Post-Sec.
124 N Brand Blvd 91203 818-246-7376
North-West College Post-Sec.
221 N Brand Blvd 91203 818-242-0205
Uni Health America/Glendale Mem Hospital Post-Sec.
1420 S Central Ave 91204 818-502-2334

Glendora, Los Angeles, Pop. 48,747
Azusa USD
Supt. — See Azusa
Sierra HS 200/Alt
1134 S Barranca Ave 91740 626-852-8300
Mari Bordona, prin. Fax 914-3797
Azusa Adult Educ Center Adult
1134 S Barranca Ave 91740 626-852-8400
Mary Ketza, prin. Fax 852-8407

Charter Oak USD
Supt. — See Covina
Arrow Continuation HS 100/Alt
1505 Sunflower Ave 91740 626-914-3961
Lisa Raigosa, prin. Fax 335-3941
Bridges Community Day S 50/Alt
1507 Sunflower Ave 91740 626-914-3961
Lisa Raigosa, prin. Fax 335-3941

Glendora USD 7,600/PK-12
500 N Loraine Ave 91741 626-963-1611
Dr. Ann Keyes, supt. Fax 335-2196
www.glendora.k12.ca.us
Glendora HS 2,400/9-12
1600 E Foothill Blvd 91741 626-963-5731
Paul Lopez, prin. Fax 963-2880
Goddard MS 900/6-8
859 E Sierra Madre Ave 91741 626-852-4500
Jennifer Prince, prin. Fax 852-4520
Sandburg MS 900/6-8
819 W Bennett Ave 91741 626-852-4530
Eric Osborne, prin. Fax 852-4521
Whitcomb Continuation HS 100/Alt
350 W Mauna Loa Ave 91740 626-852-4550
Ron Letourneau, prin. Fax 852-4519
Glendora Adult S Adult
350 W Mauna Loa Ave 91740 626-852-4550
Ron Letourneau, prin. Fax 852-4519

Citrus College Post-Sec.
1000 W Foothill Blvd 91741 626-963-0323
Grace Communion Seminary Post-Sec.
PO Box 5005 91740 626-650-2306
St. Lucy's Priory HS 700/9-12
655 W Sierra Madre Ave 91741 626-335-3322
Gina Giuliucci, prin. Fax 335-4373

Gold River, Sacramento, Pop. 7,625

Bryan University Post-Sec.
2317 Gold Meadow Way 95670 866-649-2400

Goleta, Santa Barbara, Pop. 29,028
Santa Barbara USD
Supt. — See Santa Barbara
Dos Pueblos HS 2,100/9-12
7266 Alameda Ave 93117 805-968-2541
Shawn Carey, prin. Fax 968-2891
Goleta Valley JHS 900/7-8
6100 Stow Canyon Rd 93117 805-967-3486
Mauricio Ortega, prin. Fax 967-8176

Gonzales, Monterey, Pop. 8,098
Gonzales USD 2,500/K-12
PO Box G 93926 831-675-0100
Candice McFarland, supt. Fax 675-2763
www.gonzalesusd.net
Fairview MS 700/5-8
PO Box G 93926 831-675-3704
Avetik Atoian, prin. Fax 675-3274
Gonzales HS 700/9-12
PO Box G 93926 831-675-2495
Cheryl Alves De Souza, prin. Fax 675-8054
Somavia HS 50/Alt
PO Box G 93926 831-675-1081
John McKenzie, admin. Fax 675-1084

Granada Hills, See Los Angeles
Los Angeles USD
Supt. — See Los Angeles
Addams Continuation HS 200/Alt
16341 Donmetz St 91344 818-271-2946
Paul Purkhiser, prin. Fax 271-2569
Frost MS 1,500/6-8
12314 Bradford Pl 91344 818-332-6900
Jose Ayala, prin. Fax 360-9584
Henry MS 1,000/6-8
17340 San Jose St 91344 818-832-3870
Sandra Cruz, prin. Fax 368-7333
Kennedy HS 2,100/9-12
11254 Gothic Ave 91344 818-271-2900
Richard Chavez, prin. Fax 368-9527
Porter MS 1,700/6-8
15960 Kingsbury St 91344 818-920-2050
Suzanne Blake, prin. Fax 891-7826
Valley Academy of Arts & Sciences 1,200/9-12
10445 Balboa Blvd 91344 818-832-7750
Kelly Hanock, prin. Fax 368-5140

Newberry School of Beauty Post-Sec.
16852 Devonshire St 91344 818-366-3211

Grand Terrace, San Bernardino, Pop. 11,712
Colton JUSD
Supt. — See Colton
Grand Terrace HS 2,200/9-12
21810 Main St 92313 909-580-5006
James Western, prin. Fax 876-4001
Terrace Hills MS 1,000/7-8
22579 De Berry St 92313 909-580-5022
Scott Boggs, prin. Fax 783-3836

Granite Bay, Placer, Pop. 19,714
Eureka UNSD 3,400/PK-8
5455 Eureka Rd 95746 916-791-4939
Tom Janis, supt. Fax 791-5527
www.eureka-usd.k12.ca.us
Cavitt JHS 400/7-8
7200 Fuller Dr 95746 916-791-4152
Jennifer Platt, prin. Fax 791-7414
Other Schools – See Roseville

Roseville JUNHSD
Supt. — See Roseville
Granite Bay HS 2,100/9-12
1 Grizzly Way 95746 916-786-8676
Jennifer Leighton, prin. Fax 786-0766

Grass Valley, Nevada, Pop. 12,474
Grass Valley ESD 1,700/PK-8
10840 Gilmore Way 95945 530-273-4483
Eric Fredrickson, supt. Fax 273-0248
www.gvsd.us
Gilmore MS 500/5-8
10837 Rough and Ready Hwy 95945 530-273-8479
Christopher Roberts, prin. Fax 273-1675

Nevada County Office of Education
Supt. — See Nevada City
Jamieson HS 50/Alt
12338 McCourtney Rd 95949 530-272-5464
Lisa Sanford, admin. Fax 272-5870

Nevada JUNHSD 3,300/9-12
11645 Ridge Rd 95945 530-273-3351
Louise Johnson, supt. Fax 273-3372
www.njuhsd.com
Bear River HS 800/9-12
11130 Magnolia Rd 95949 530-268-3700
Amy Besler, prin. Fax 268-8372
Ghidotti HS 200/9-12
250 Sierra College Dr 95945 530-274-5270
Noah Levinson, prin. Fax 274-5272
Nevada Union HS 1,900/9-12
11761 Ridge Rd 95945 530-273-4431
Dan Frisella, prin. Fax 477-9317
North Point Academy 100/Alt
11761 Ridge Rd 95945 530-477-1225
Michael Hughes, prin. Fax 272-8564
NU Tech1 HS Vo/Tech
11761 Ridge Rd 95945 530-273-4431
Michael Hughes, admin. Fax 477-9317
Silver Springs HS 200/Alt
140 Park Ave 95945 530-272-2635
Marty Mathiesen, prin. Fax 272-2687

Nevada Adult Education — Adult
12338 McCourtney Rd 95949 — 530-272-2643
Melissa Madigan, admin. — Fax 272-3422

Pleasant Ridge UNESD — 1,300/K-8
22580 Kingston Ln 95949 — 530-268-2800
Rusty Clark, supt. — Fax 268-2804
www.prsd.us
Magnolia IS — 500/6-8
22431 Kingston Ln 95949 — 530-268-2815
Gene Morgan, prin. — Fax 268-2819

Union Hill ESD — 600/K-8
10879 Bartlett Dr 95945 — 530-273-0647
David Curry, supt. — Fax 273-5626
www.uhsd.k12.ca.us
Union Hill MS — 100/7-8
11638 Colfax Hwy 95945 — 530-273-8456
Joe Limov, prin. — Fax 273-0152

Graton, Sonoma, Pop. 1,648

Pacific Christian Academy — 50/K-12
PO Box 369 95444 — 707-823-2880

Greenfield, Monterey, Pop. 16,188
Greenfield UNSD — 2,800/K-8
493 El Camino Real 93927 — 831-674-2840
Kimberly Berman, supt. — Fax 674-3712
www.greenfield.k12.ca.us
Vista Verde MS — 800/6-8
1199 Elm Ave 93927 — 831-674-1420
Julie Croy, prin. — Fax 674-1425

South Monterey JUNHSD
Supt. — See King City
Greenfield HS — 900/9-12
225 S El Camino Real 93927 — 831-674-2751
Frank Lynch, prin. — Fax 674-2646

Greenville, Plumas, Pop. 1,068
Plumas USD
Supt. — See Quincy
Greenville JSHS — 100/7-12
117 Grand St 95947 — 530-284-7197
Dr. Jerry Merica-Jones, prin. — Fax 284-6710

Greenwood, El Dorado
Black Oak Mine USD
Supt. — See Georgetown
Divide HS — 50/Alt
4405 State Highway 193 95635 — 530-333-8315
Cerrene Cervantes, admin. — Fax 333-8317

Gridley, Butte, Pop. 6,408
Gridley USD — 2,100/K-12
429 Magnolia St 95948 — 530-846-4721
Jordan Reeves, supt. — Fax 846-4595
www.gusd.org
Esperanza Continuation HS — 50/Alt
581 Jackson St 95948 — 530-846-4383
Cindy Kershaw, prin. — Fax 846-2435
Gridley HS — 700/9-12
300 E Spruce St 95948 — 530-846-4791
Joey Adame, prin. — Fax 846-3412
Sycamore MS — 400/6-8
1125 Sycamore St 95948 — 530-846-3636
Clint Johnson, prin. — Fax 846-6796

Groveland, Tuolumne, Pop. 585
Big Oak Flat-Groveland USD — 400/K-12
PO Box 1397 95321 — 209-962-5765
Dave Urquhart, supt. — Fax 962-6108
www.bofg.k12.ca.us
Moccasin Community Day S — 50/Alt
PO Box 1397 95321 — 209-962-7160
Wynette Hilton, prin. — Fax 962-7160
Tioga HS — 100/9-12
19304 Ferretti Rd 95321 — 209-962-4763
Ryan Dutton, prin. — Fax 962-4507
Other Schools – See La Grange

Guadalupe, Santa Barbara, Pop. 6,975
Guadalupe UNESD — 1,200/K-8
PO Box 788 93434 — 805-343-2114
Ed Cora, supt. — Fax 343-6155
www.guadusd.org
McKenzie JHS — 400/6-8
PO Box 788 93434 — 805-343-1951
Gabriel Solorio, prin. — Fax 343-6931

Gustine, Merced, Pop. 5,420
Gustine USD — 1,800/K-12
1500 Meredith Ave 95322 — 209-854-3784
Bill Morones, supt. — Fax 854-9164
www.gustine.k12.ca.us
Gustine HS — 500/9-12
501 North Ave 95322 — 209-854-6414
John Petrone, prin. — Fax 854-1955
Gustine MS — 400/6-8
28075 Sullivan Rd 95322 — 209-854-5030
Michael Bunch, prin. — Fax 854-9592
Pioneer HS — 50/Alt
501 North Ave 95322 — 209-854-6414
Adam Cano, prin. — Fax 854-9581

Hacienda Heights, Los Angeles, Pop. 53,234
Hacienda La Puente USD
Supt. — See City of Industry
Los Altos HS — 2,000/9-12
15325 Los Robles Ave 91745 — 626-934-5418
Cheli McReynolds, prin. — Fax 855-3145
Newton MS — 600/6-8
15616 Newton St 91745 — 626-933-2401
Dan Ma, prin. — Fax 855-3832
Orange Grove MS — 600/6-8
14505 Orange Grove Ave 91745 — 626-933-7001
Maria Elena Navarro, prin. — Fax 855-3837
Puente Hills HS — 100/Alt
15430 Shadybend Dr 91745 — 626-933-3400
Joaquin Martinez, prin. — Fax 855-3719
Valley Alternative S — 100/Alt
15430 Shadybend Dr 91745 — 626-933-3400
Joaquin Martinez, prin. — Fax 855-3719
Wilson HS — 1,600/9-12
16455 Wedgeworth Dr 91745 — 626-934-4410
Dr. Danielle Kenfield, prin. — Fax 855-3792
Dibble Adult S — Adult
1600 Pontenova Ave 91745 — 626-933-8301
Elbia Sarabia, dir. — Fax 855-3528

Half Moon Bay, San Mateo, Pop. 11,097
Cabrillo USD — 3,300/K-12
498 Kelly Ave 94019 — 650-712-7100
Jane Yuster, supt. — Fax 726-0279
www.cabrillo.k12.ca.us/
Cunha IS — 700/6-8
600 Church St 94019 — 650-712-7190
Jarrett Dooley, prin. — Fax 712-7195
Half Moon Bay HS — 1,000/9-12
498 Kelly Ave 94019 — 650-712-7200
John Nazar, prin. — Fax 712-7232
Pilarcitos Continuation HS — 50/Alt
498 Kelly Ave 94019 — 650-712-7224
Rajan Bechar, prin. — Fax 712-7225
Cabrillo Adult S — Adult
498 Kelly Ave 94019 — 650-712-7224
Rajan Bechar, prin. — Fax 712-7225

Hamilton City, Glenn, Pop. 1,746
Hamilton USD — 700/K-12
PO Box 488 95951 — 530-826-3261
Charles Tracy, supt. — Fax 826-0440
www.husdschools.org
Barkley HS — 50/Alt
Hwy 32 & Los Robles St 95951 — 530-826-3331
Charles Tracy, prin. — Fax 826-3929
Hamilton Community Day S — 50/Alt
535 Sacramento Ave 95951 — 530-826-3261
Charles Tracy, prin. — Fax 826-3929
Hamilton HS — 300/9-12
620 Canal St 95951 — 530-826-3261
Cris Oseguera, prin. — Fax 826-0440
Hamilton Adult S — Adult
300 6th St 95951 — 530-826-3331
Sylvia Robles, dir. — Fax 826-3929

Hanford, Kings, Pop. 52,527
Hanford ESD — 5,800/K-8
PO Box 1067 93232 — 559-585-3601
Paul Terry, supt. — Fax 584-7833
www.hesd.k12.ca.us/
Kennedy JHS — 500/7-8
PO Box 1067 93232 — 559-585-3850
Jason Strickland, prin. — Fax 585-2374
Wilson JHS — 600/7-8
PO Box 1067 93232 — 559-585-3870
Kenneth Eggert, prin. — Fax 585-2336

Hanford JUNHSD — 4,400/9-12
823 W Lacey Blvd 93230 — 559-583-5901
William Fishbough, supt. — Fax 589-9769
www.hjuhsd.k12.ca.us
Hanford Community Day S — 50/Alt
120 E Grangeville Blvd 93230 — 559-583-5902
Scott Pickle, prin. — Fax 582-5229
Hanford HS — 1,500/9-12
120 E Grangeville Blvd 93230 — 559-583-5902
Scott Pickle, prin. — Fax 582-5229
Hanford Night Continuation HS — 50/Alt
1201 N Douty St 93230 — 559-583-5904
Heather Keran, prin. — Fax 583-6580
Hanford West HS — 1,300/9-12
1150 W Lacey Blvd 93230 — 559-583-5903
Darin Parson, prin. — Fax 583-6708
Johnson HS — 100/Alt
1201 N Douty St 93230 — 559-583-5904
Heather Keran, prin. — Fax 583-6580
Sierra Pacific HS — 800/9-12
1259 13th Ave 93230 — 559-583-5912
Tim Smith, prin. — Fax 583-5914
Hanford Adult S — Adult
905 Campus Dr 93230 — 559-583-5905
Heather Keran, prin. — Fax 589-9564

Kings County Office of Education — 400/
1144 W Lacey Blvd 93230 — 559-584-1441
Tim Bowers, supt. — Fax 589-7000
www.kings.k12.ca.us
Kings County Community S — 100/Alt
146 W Highland St 93230 — 559-589-2608
Rebecca Villa, prin. — Fax 582-0731

Regional Occupational Center & Program
Supt. — None
Kings County ROP — Vo/Tech
1144 W Lacey Blvd 93230 — 559-589-7026
Margie Newton, dir. — Fax 589-7007

Happy Camp, Siskiyou, Pop. 1,130
Siskiyou UNHSD
Supt. — See Mount Shasta
Happy Camp HS — 100/9-12
PO Box 437 96039 — 530-493-2697
Steve Van Ert, prin. — Fax 493-2605

Harbor City, See Los Angeles
Los Angeles USD
Supt. — See Los Angeles
Humanities & Arts Academy of LA — 9-12
24300 Western Ave 90710 — 310-257-7100
Gregory Fisher, prin. — Fax 326-1805
Narbonne HS — 2,800/9-12
24300 Western Ave 90710 — 310-257-7100
Gerald Kobata, prin. — Fax 326-1805
Patton Continuation HS — 100/Alt
24514 Western Ave 90710 — 310-257-4740
Reginald Obiamalu, prin. — Fax 257-4742

Hawaiian Gardens, Los Angeles, Pop. 14,073
ABC USD
Supt. — See Cerritos
Fedde MS — 400/7-8
21409 Elaine Ave 90716 — 562-229-7805
Ricardo Lois, prin. — Fax 809-6895

Hawthorne, Los Angeles, Pop. 81,457
Centinela Valley UNHSD
Supt. — See Lawndale
Hawthorne HS — 2,100/9-12
4859 W El Segundo Blvd 90250 — 310-263-4400
Dr. Vanessa Landesfeind, prin. — Fax 675-7017
Centinela Valley Adult S — Adult
4859 W El Segundo Blvd 90250 — 310-263-4469
Paul Guzman, prin. — Fax 644-6142

Hawthorne SD — 8,900/PK-12
14120 S Hawthorne Blvd 90250 — 310-676-2276
Dr. Helen Morgan Ed.D., supt. — Fax 675-9464
www.hawthorne.k12.ca.us
Carson MS — 800/6-8
13838 S Yukon Ave 90250 — 310-676-1908
Mark Silva, prin. — Fax 676-0634
Hawthorne MS — 900/6-8
4366 W 129th St 90250 — 310-676-0167
Rudy Salas, prin. — Fax 675-0924
Prairie Vista MS — 1,000/6-8
13600 Prairie Ave 90250 — 310-679-1003
Dr. Patricia Ray, prin. — Fax 679-1142

Los Angeles County Office of Education
Supt. — See Downey
Renaissance Community Day S — 200/Alt
14600 Cerise Ave 90250 — 310-970-9914
Zan Mason, prin. — Fax 679-8106

Wiseburn USD — 3,900/K-12
13530 Aviation Blvd 90250 — 310-643-3025
Dr. Tom Johnstone, supt. — Fax 643-7659
www.wiseburn.k12.ca.us
Dana MS — 1,000/6-8
5504 W 135th St 90250 — 310-725-4700
Aileen Harbeck, prin. — Fax 536-9091

Hayfork, Trinity, Pop. 2,231
Mountain Valley USD — 300/PK-12
PO Box 339 96041 — 530-628-5265
Debbie Miller, supt. — Fax 628-5267
www.mvusd.us
Hayfork HS — 100/9-12
PO Box 10 96041 — 530-628-5261
Debbie Miller, prin. — Fax 628-3091
Valley Continuation HS — 50/Alt
PO Box 339 96041 — 530-628-5294
Wendy Platt, prin. — Fax 628-5344
Mountain Valley Adult S — Adult
231 Oak Ave 96041 — 530-628-5265
Debbie Miller, prin.

Hayward, Alameda, Pop. 133,787
Alameda County Office of Education — 2,200/
313 W Winton Ave 94544 — 510-887-0152
Karen Monroe, supt. — Fax 670-4146
www.acoe.org
Alameda County Community S — 300/K-12
313 W Winton Ave 94544 — 510-670-6619
Carolyn Hobbs, prin. — Fax 293-9201

Hayward USD — 21,500/K-12
PO Box 5000 94540 — 510-784-2600
Stan Dobbs, supt. — Fax 784-2641
www.husd.us
Brenkwitz Alternative HS — 200/Alt
PO Box 5000 94540 — 510-723-3160
Kwasi Reed, prin. — Fax 582-6376
Chavez MS — 500/7-8
PO Box 5000 94540 — 510-723-3110
Sean Moffatt, prin. — Fax 538-8478
Harte MS — 700/7-8
PO Box 5000 94540 — 510-723-3100
Seana Condit-Gordon, prin. — Fax 886-5926
Hayward HS — 1,600/9-12
PO Box 5000 94540 — 510-723-3170
David Seymour, prin. — Fax 581-3145
King MS — 800/7-8
PO Box 5000 94540 — 510-723-3120
Estella Santos, prin. — Fax 781-6129
Mt. Eden HS — 1,900/9-12
PO Box 5000 94540 — 510-723-3180
Greg Fobbs, prin. — Fax 786-2269
Ochoa MS — 600/7-8
PO Box 5000 94540 — 510-723-3130
Ariel Dolowich, prin. — Fax 786-0559
Tennyson HS — 1,300/9-12
PO Box 5000 94540 — 510-723-3190
George Mitsopoulos, prin. — Fax 582-0964
Winton MS — 500/7-8
PO Box 5000 94540 — 510-723-3140
Lisa Tess, prin. — Fax 733-9043
Hayward Adult Education Center — Adult
PO Box 5000 94540 — 510-293-8595
Guy Zakrevsky, prin. — Fax 727-1139

New Haven USD
Supt. — See Union City
Conley-Caraballo HS — 50/Alt
541 Blanche St 94544 — 510-471-5126
Ramon Camacho, prin. — Fax 475-3949

Regional Occupational Center & Program
Supt. — None
Eden Area ROP — Vo/Tech
26316 Hesperian Blvd 94545 — 510-293-2900
Linda Granger, dir. — Fax 783-2955

San Lorenzo USD
Supt. — See San Lorenzo
East Bay Arts HS — 300/9-12
20450 Royal Ave 94541 — 510-317-4471
Abigail Kotzin, prin. — Fax 317-4495
Royal Sunset HS — 200/Alt
20450 Royal Ave 94541 — 510-317-4400
Abigail Kotzin, prin. — Fax 317-4495

California Crosspoint MSHS 200/6-12
25500 Industrial Blvd 94545 510-995-5333
Robin Hom, supt. Fax 995-5335
California State University-East Bay Post-Sec.
25800 Carlos Bee Blvd 94542 510-885-3000
Chabot College Post-Sec.
25555 Hesperian Blvd 94545 510-723-6600
Heald College Post-Sec.
25500 Industrial Blvd 94545 510-783-2100
Life Chiropractic College West Post-Sec.
25001 Industrial Blvd 94545 800-788-4476
Moreau HS 900/9-12
27170 Mission Blvd 94544 510-881-4300
Lisa Tortorich, prin. Fax 581-5669
NCP College of Nursing Post-Sec.
21615 Hesperian Blvd Ste A 94541 510-785-0454

Healdsburg, Sonoma, Pop. 11,079
Healdsburg USD 2,300/K-12
1028 Prince Ave 95448 707-431-3488
Chris Vanden Heuvel, supt. Fax 433-8403
www.husd.com
Healdsburg HS 600/9-12
1024 Prince Ave 95448 707-431-3420
Dr. Lori Rhodes, prin. Fax 431-3467
Healdsburg JHS 400/6-8
315 Grant St 95448 707-431-3410
Bill Halliday, prin. Fax 431-3593
Marce Becerra Academy 50/Alt
1024 Prince Ave 95448 707-431-3420
Dr. Lori Rhodes, prin. Fax 431-3467

Rio Lindo Adventist Academy 200/9-12
3200 Rio Lindo Ave 95448 707-431-5100
Doug Schmidt, admin. Fax 431-5115

Heber, Imperial, Pop. 4,270
Heber ESD 1,300/K-8
1052 Heber Ave 92249 760-337-6530
Jaime Silva, supt. Fax 353-3421
hesdk8.org
Heber ES 700/4-8
1052 Heber Ave 92249 760-337-6530
Patty Marcial, prin. Fax 353-3421

Helendale, San Bernardino
Helendale ESD 1,500/K-12
PO Box 249 92342 760-952-1180
Ross Swearingen, supt. Fax 952-1178
www.helendalesd.org
Riverview MS 100/7-8
PO Box 249 92342 760-952-1266
William Brown, prin. Fax 952-1178

Helm, Fresno
Golden Plains USD
Supt. — See San Joaquin
Rio Del Rey Continuation HS 50/Alt
PO Box 158 93627 559-866-5757
Joel Ramirez, prin. Fax 866-5209

Hemet, Riverside, Pop. 76,330
Hemet USD 21,300/K-12
1791 W Acacia Ave 92545 951-765-5100
Christi Barrett, supt. Fax 765-5115
www.hemetusd.org
Acacia MS 700/6-8
1200 E Acacia Ave 92543 951-765-1620
Jeff Franks, prin. Fax 765-5149
Accelerated Core Education Alt
831 E Devonshire Ave 92543 951-925-2324
Frank Green, prin. Fax 765-5729
Alessandro HS 500/Alt
831 E Devonshire Ave 92543 951-765-5182
Tara O'Malley, prin. Fax 925-7548
ASPIRE Community Day S Alt
26866 San Jacinto St 92543 951-929-3071
Cristian Miley, prin.
Dartmouth MS 900/6-8
41535 Mayberry Ave 92544 951-765-2550
Jennifer Martin, prin. Fax 765-2559
Diamond Valley MS 1,100/6-8
291 W Chambers Ave 92543 951-925-2899
Robert Dominguez, prin. Fax 925-6297
Hemet HS 2,400/9-12
41701 Stetson Ave 92544 951-765-5150
Dr. Emily Shaw, prin. Fax 765-5177
Jackson College Prep HS 200/Alt
26400 Dartmouth St 92544 951-765-5193
Frank Green, prin. Fax 765-5195
Rancho Viejo MS 1,200/6-8
985 N Cawston Ave 92545 951-765-6287
Jon Workman, prin. Fax 925-5244
Tahquitz HS 1,600/9-12
4425 Titan Trl 92545 951-765-6300
Eric Dahlstrom, prin. Fax 765-6344
West Valley HS 1,800/9-12
3401 Mustang Way 92545 951-765-1600
Janice Jones, prin. Fax 765-1607
Hemet Adult Education Adult
831 E Devonshire Ave 92543 951-765-5190
Tara O'Malley, prin. Fax 925-7478
Other Schools – See Anza

Hercules, Contra Costa, Pop. 22,834
West Contra Costa USD
Supt. — See Richmond
Hercules HS 1,000/9-12
1900 Refugio Valley Rd 94547 510-231-1429
Paul Mansingh, prin. Fax 245-1089
Hercules MS 700/6-8
1900 Refugio Valley Rd 94547 510-231-1429
Renee Lama, prin. Fax 245-1089

Herlong, Lassen, Pop. 264
Fort Sage USD 200/K-12
PO Box 35 96113 530-827-2129
Patrick Condon, supt. Fax 827-2019
www.fortsage.org
Fort Sage MS 50/7-8
PO Box 35 96113 530-827-2101
Patrick Condon, prin. Fax 827-3362
Herlong HS 100/9-12
PO Box 97 96113 530-827-2101
Patrick Condon, prin. Fax 827-3362

Hermosa Beach, Los Angeles, Pop. 18,753
Hermosa Beach City ESD 1,400/K-8
1645 Valley Dr 90254 310-937-5877
Patricia Escalante, supt. Fax 376-4974
www.hbcsd.org
Hermosa Valley ES 900/3-8
1645 Valley Dr 90254 310-937-5888
Kimberly Taylor, prin. Fax 798-4365

Fusion Academy 6-12
1601 Pacific Coast Ste 26 90254 310-376-5139

Hesperia, San Bernardino, Pop. 88,087
Hesperia USD 23,400/K-12
15576 Main St 92345 760-244-4411
David McLaughlin, supt. Fax 244-2806
www.hesperiausd.org
Canyon Ridge HS 200/Alt
12850 Muscatel St, 760-244-6530
Scott Ahlgren, prin. Fax 244-7210
Cedar MS 1,100/7-8
13565 Cedar St, 760-244-6093
Kelly Maxwell, prin. Fax 244-5439
Hesperia Community Day S 50/Alt
16527 1/2 Lemon St 92345 760-244-1771
Nate Lambdin, prin. Fax 948-0508
Hesperia HS 2,000/9-12
9898 Maple Ave 92345 760-244-9898
Michelle Estrada, prin. Fax 244-0939
Hesperia JHS 900/7-8
10275 Cypress Ave 92345 760-244-9386
Lisa Kelly, prin. Fax 244-0595
Mojave HS 300/Alt
16633 Lemon St 92345 760-948-3999
Nate Lambdin, prin. Fax 948-0508
Ranchero MS 1,000/7-8
17607 Ranchero Rd 92345 760-948-0175
Isaac Newman-Gomez, prin. Fax 948-0381
Shadow Ridge Alternative S 200/Alt
12850 Muscatel St, 760-949-8267
Chris Cusino, admin. Fax 948-7976
Sultana HS 2,100/9-12
17311 Sultana St 92345 760-947-6777
Lawrence Bird, prin. Fax 947-6788
Adult Education Center Adult
16527 Lemon St 92345 760-244-1771
Kim Walker, prin. Fax 948-3508
Other Schools – See Oak Hills

Hesperia Christian S 300/PK-12
16775 Olive St 92345 760-244-6164
Sharon Romero, admin. Fax 244-9756
San Joaquin Valley College Post-Sec.
9331 Mariposa Rd, 760-948-1947

Highland, San Bernardino, Pop. 51,532
Redlands USD
Supt. — See Redlands
Beattie MS 1,200/6-8
7800 Orange St 92346 909-307-2400
Angela Neuhaus, prin. Fax 307-2416

San Bernardino City USD
Supt. — See San Bernardino
San Andreas SHS 600/Alt
3232 Pacific St 92346 909-388-6521
Edward Hensley, prin. Fax 425-0523
San Bernadino Alternative Learning Ctr. 50/Alt
3236 Pacific St 92346 909-388-6221
Robyn Eberhardt, coord. Fax 388-6223
Serrano MS 800/7-8
3131 Piedmont Dr 92346 909-388-6530
Michelle Cleveland, prin. Fax 864-6232

Hillsborough, San Mateo, Pop. 10,401
Hillsborough CSD 1,500/K-8
300 El Cerrito Ave 94010 650-342-5193
Anthony Ranii, supt. Fax 342-6964
www.hcsd.k12.ca.us
Crocker MS 500/6-8
2600 Ralston Ave 94010 650-342-6331
Jamie Adams, prin. Fax 579-5943

Crystal Springs Uplands S 400/6-12
400 Uplands Dr 94010 650-342-4175
Amy Richards, head sch Fax 342-7623

Hilmar, Merced, Pop. 3,392
Hilmar USD 2,200/K-12
7807 Lander Ave 95324 209-667-5701
Isabel Cabral-Johnson, supt. Fax 667-1721
www.hilmar.k12.ca.us
Colony HS 50/Alt
7807 Lander Ave 95324 209-667-0276
Darlene Carvalho, prin. Fax 667-1532
Hilmar HS 700/9-12
7807 Lander Ave 95324 209-667-5903
Melissa Brewer, prin. Fax 667-7628
Hilmar MS 500/6-8
7807 Lander Ave 95324 209-632-8847
Amy Fitzgerald, prin. Fax 667-7018
Irwin HS 50/Alt
7807 Lander Ave 95324 209-667-0276
Darlene Carvalho, prin. Fax 667-1532

Hollister, San Benito, Pop. 34,317
Hollister SD 5,000/PK-8
2690 Cienega Rd 95023 831-630-6300
Dr. Lisa Andrew, supt. Fax 634-2080
www.hesd.org
Accelerated Achievement Academy 100/4-8
1151 Buena Vista Rd 95023 831-636-4460
Diana Herbst, admin. Fax 634-4970
Maze MS 600/6-8
900 Meridian St 95023 831-636-4480
Bill Sachau, prin. Fax 636-4488
Rancho San Justo MS 600/6-8
1201 Rancho Dr 95023 831-636-4450
Lisa Jelinek, prin. Fax 634-4952

San Benito County Office of Education 100/
460 5th St 95023 831-637-5393
Lorna Gilbert, supt. Fax 637-0140
www.sbcoe.org
Pinnacles Community S Alt
3230 Southside Rd 95023 831-636-2870
Colleen Grimes, prin. Fax 636-7885
San Benito County Opportunity S 100/Alt
460 5th St 95023 831-637-9269
Colleen Grimes, dir. Fax 636-7769

San Benito HSD 3,000/9-12
1220 Monterey St 95023 831-637-5831
John Perales, supt. Fax 637-6524
www.sbhsd.k12.ca.us
San Andreas Continuation HS 100/Alt
191 Alvarado St 95023 831-637-9269
David Burke, prin. Fax 636-0376
San Benito HS 2,900/9-12
1220 Monterey St 95023 831-637-5831
Adrian Ramirez, prin. Fax 637-6524

Hollywood, See Los Angeles
Los Angeles USD
Supt. — See Los Angeles
Bernstein HS 600/9-12
1309 N Wilton Pl 90028 323-817-6400
Andre Spicer, prin. Fax 860-9711
Le Conte MS 900/6-8
1316 N Bronson Ave 90028 323-308-1700
Rosemary Hindinger, prin. Fax 856-3053

American Academy of Dramatic Arts Post-Sec.
1336 N La Brea Ave 90028 800-463-8990
Elegance International Post-Sec.
1622 N Highland Ave 90028 323-871-8318
Los Angeles Film School Post-Sec.
6363 W Sunset Blvd 90028 323-860-0789
Musicians Institute Post-Sec.
6752 Hollywood Blvd 90028 323-462-1384

Holtville, Imperial, Pop. 5,905
Holtville USD 1,600/PK-12
621 E 6th St 92250 760-356-2974
Celso Ruiz, supt. Fax 356-4936
www.husd.net
Freedom Academy of the Imperial Valley Vo/Tech
524 W 8th St 92250 760-356-5718
Dennis Bourland, admin.
Holtville HS 500/9-12
755 Olive Ave 92250 760-356-2926
Jeff Magin, prin. Fax 356-1206
Holtville JHS 300/6-8
800 Beale Ave 92250 760-356-2811
Mario Garcia, prin. Fax 356-5741
Webb Continuation HS 50/Alt
522 W 8th St 92250 760-356-1304
Celso Ruiz, prin. Fax 356-5621

Homeland, Riverside, Pop. 5,870
Romoland ESD 3,000/K-8
25900 Leon Rd 92548 951-926-9244
Dr. Julie A. Vitale, supt. Fax 926-2170
www.romoland.net
Other Schools – See Menifee

Hoopa, Humboldt
Klamath-Trinity JUSD 1,000/PK-12
PO Box 1308 95546 530-625-5600
John Ray, supt. Fax 625-5611
www.ktjusd.k12.ca.us/
Hoopa Valley HS 200/9-12
PO Box 1308 95546 530-625-5600
Dustin Rossman, prin. Fax 625-5619
John Continuation HS 50/Alt
PO Box 1308 95546 530-625-5600
Jennifer Lane, prin. Fax 625-4840
Two Rivers Community Day S 50/Alt
PO Box 1308 95546 530-625-5600
Craig Kimball, prin. Fax 625-4840

Hughson, Stanislaus, Pop. 6,490
Hughson USD 2,100/K-12
PO Box 189 95326 209-883-4428
Brian Beck, supt. Fax 883-4639
www.hughson.k12.ca.us
Dickens HS 50/Alt
6937 Fox Rd 95326 209-883-4182
Debra Davis, admin. Fax 883-4726
Hughson HS 700/9-12
PO Box 99 95326 209-883-0469
Debra Davis, prin. Fax 883-0870
Ross MS 500/6-8
7448 Fox Rd 95326 209-883-4425
Ryan Smith, prin. Fax 883-2017
Valley Community Day S 50/Alt
PO Box 99 95326 209-883-0469
Andrew Reese, admin. Fax 883-0870

Keyes UNESD
Supt. — See Keyes
Spratling MS 200/6-8
5277 Washington Rd 95326 209-664-3833
John Stuart, prin. Fax 656-2384

Huntington Beach, Orange, Pop. 183,010
Fountain Valley ESD
Supt. — See Fountain Valley

Talbert MS 700/6-8
9101 Brabham Dr, 714-378-4220
Jennifer Morgan, prin. Fax 378-4229

Huntington Beach City ESD 7,000/PK-8
17011 Beach Blvd Ste 560, 714-964-8888
Gregg Haulk, supt. Fax 963-9565
www.hbcsd.us
Dwyer MS 1,300/6-8
1502 Palm Ave, 714-536-7507
Darrenn Platt, prin. Fax 960-0955
Sowers MS 1,200/6-8
9300 Indianapolis Ave, 714-962-7738
Dr. Cynthia Guerrero, prin. Fax 968-5580

Huntington Beach UNHSD 16,400/9-12
5832 Bolsa Ave 92649 714-903-7000
Alan Rasmussen, supt. Fax 892-5750
www.hbuhsd.edu
Coast HS, 17231 Gothard St, 100/Alt
Angela Harding, prin. 714-842-4227
Edison HS 2,600/9-12
21400 Magnolia St, 714-962-1356
Jennifer Graves, prin. Fax 963-4280
Huntington Beach HS 2,900/9-12
1905 Main St, 714-536-2514
Daniel Morris, prin. Fax 960-7042
Marina HS 2,600/9-12
15871 Springdale St, 714-893-6571
Jessie Marion, prin. Fax 892-7855
Ocean View HS 1,500/9-12
17071 Gothard St, 714-848-0656
Courtney Robinson, prin. Fax 843-0541
Huntington Beach Adult Education Adult
17231 Gothard St, 714-901-8106
Steve Curiel, prin. Fax 373-5245
Other Schools – See Fountain Valley, Westminster

Ocean View SD 9,200/PK-8
17200 Pinehurst Ln 92647 714-847-2551
Dr. Carol Hansen, supt. Fax 847-1430
www.ovsd.org
Marine View MS 800/6-8
5682 Tilburg Dr, 714-846-0624
Bill Lynch, prin. Fax 846-2074
Mesa View MS 800/6-8
17601 Avilla Ln, 714-842-6608
Randy Lempert, prin. Fax 842-8798
Spring View MS 800/6-8
16662 Trudy Ln, 714-846-2891
Jason Blade, prin. Fax 377-9821
Other Schools – See Fountain Valley

Westminster SD
Supt. — See Westminster
Stacey MS 900/6-8
6311 Larchwood Dr, 714-894-7212
Heidi DeBritton, prin. Fax 373-0478

Apollos University Post-Sec.
17011 Beach Blvd Ste 900, 714-375-6697
Brethren Christian JSHS 300/6-12
21141 Strathmoor Ln, 714-962-6617
Rick Niswonger, prin. Fax 962-3171
Fusion Academy 6-12
7711 Center Ave Ste 120, 657-200-2300
Maryam Pourmohsen J.D., head sch
Golden West College Post-Sec.
15744 Goldenwest St, 714-892-7711
Hebrew Academy 300/PK-12
14401 Willow Ln, 714-898-0051
Rabbi Yitzchok Newman, head sch Fax 898-0051
Liberty Christian S 200/PK-12
7661 Warner Ave, 714-842-5992
David Whitmire, prin. Fax 848-7484

Huntington Park, Los Angeles, Pop. 57,940
Los Angeles USD
Supt. — See Los Angeles
Gage MS 1,900/6-8
2880 E Gage Ave 90255 323-826-1500
Cesar Quezada, prin. Fax 589-6925
Huntington Park HS 2,000/9-12
6020 Miles Ave 90255 323-826-2300
Lupe Hernandez, prin. Fax 583-0463
Marquez HPIAM HS 9-12
6361 Cottage St 90255 323-584-3800
Jonathan Chaikittirattan, prin. Fax 583-1305
Marquez LIBRA Academy 9-12
6361 Cottage St 90255 323-584-3800
Lisa Davis, prin. Fax 583-1305
Marquez School of Social Justice HS 9-12
6361 Cottage St 90255 323-584-3800
Kyle Boswell, prin. Fax 583-1305
Nimitz MS 2,000/6-8
6021 Carmelita Ave 90255 323-887-5400
Lorenzo Garcia, prin. Fax 773-5201
San Antonio Continuation HS 100/Alt
2911 Belgrave Ave 90255 323-826-2420
Robert Reimann, prin. Fax 826-2427
Huntington Park-Bell Community Adult S Adult
2945 Belgrave Ave 90255 323-826-2400
Clifton DeCordoba, prin. Fax 826-2413

ICDC College Post-Sec.
6812 Pacific Blvd 90255 323-277-0240
United Education Institute Post-Sec.
6055 Pacific Blvd 90255 323-319-9500

Huron, Fresno, Pop. 6,708
Coalinga-Huron USD
Supt. — See Coalinga
Huron MS 400/6-8
PO Box 99 93234 559-945-2926
Javier Gonzalez, prin. Fax 945-8482

Idyllwild, Riverside, Pop. 2,853

Idyllwild Arts Academy 300/9-12
PO Box 38 92549 951-659-2171
Pamela Jordan, head sch Fax 659-2323

Imperial, Imperial, Pop. 14,611
Imperial USD 3,800/K-12
219 N E St 92251 760-355-3200
Bryan Thomason, supt. Fax 355-4511
www.imperialusd.org
Imperial Avenue Holbrook S 100/Alt
322 N Imperial Ave 92251 760-355-3207
Victor Torres, prin. Fax 355-3258
Imperial HS 1,100/9-12
517 W Barioni Blvd 92251 760-355-3220
Joe Apodaca, prin. Fax 355-0869
Wright MS 900/6-8
885 N Imperial Ave 92251 760-355-3240
Diego Lopez, prin. Fax 355-3256

Imperial Valley College Post-Sec.
380 E Aten Rd 92251 760-352-8320

Imperial Beach, San Diego, Pop. 25,203
Sweetwater UNHSD
Supt. — See Chula Vista
Mar Vista HS 1,700/9-12
505 Elm Ave 91932 619-628-5700
Juan Gonzalez, prin. Fax 424-6232
Sweetwater Community Day MS 50/Alt
505 1/2 Elm Ave 91932 619-628-3056
Fax 628-3060

Independence, Inyo, Pop. 646
Inyo County Office of Education 100/
PO Box G 93526 760-878-2426
Dr. Lisa Fontana, supt. Fax 878-2279
www.inyo.k12.ca.us
Other Schools – See Bishop

Owens Valley USD 100/K-12
PO Box E 93526 760-878-2405
Dan Moore M.Ed., supt. Fax 878-2405
www.ovusd.org
Owens Valley HS 50/9-12
PO Box E 93526 760-878-2405
Dan Moore M.Ed., prin. Fax 878-2626

Indio, Riverside, Pop. 75,249
Desert Sands USD
Supt. — See La Quinta
Amistad Continuation HS 300/Alt
83501 Dillon Ave 92201 760-775-3570
David Gustafson, prin. Fax 775-3575
Desert Ridge Academy 1,100/6-8
79767 Avenue 39 92203 760-393-5500
Bradley Fisher, prin. Fax 393-5502
Glenn MS of International Studies 1,400/6-8
79655 Miles Ave 92201 760-200-3700
Dr. Majid Salehi, prin. Fax 200-3709
Indio HS 2,000/9-12
81750 Avenue 46 92201 760-775-3550
Derrick Lawson, prin. Fax 775-3565
Indio MS 800/6-8
81195 Miles Ave 92201 760-775-3800
Jesus Jimenez, prin. Fax 775-3807
Jefferson MS 600/6-8
83089 US Highway 111 92201 760-863-3660
Margo McCormick, prin. Fax 775-3597
Shadow Hills HS 1,700/9-12
39225 Jefferson St 92203 760-393-5400
Marcus Wood, prin. Fax 200-1967

Milan Institute Post-Sec.
45691 Monroe St Ste 2 92201 760-347-5000

Inglewood, Los Angeles, Pop. 107,237
Inglewood USD 12,200/K-12
401 S Inglewood Ave 90301 310-419-2700
Dr. Vincent Matthews, admin. Fax 680-5144
myiusd.net/
Crozier MS 700/7-8
1210 W Regent St 90301 310-680-5280
La Royce Murphy, prin. Fax 680-5299
Inglewood Continuation HS 50/Alt
106 E Manchester Blvd 90301 310-680-5300
Debbie Tate, prin.
Inglewood HS 1,400/9-12
231 S Grevillea Ave 90301 310-680-5200
Kyle Douglas, prin. Fax 680-5201
Monroe MS 500/6-8
10711 S 10th Ave 90303 310-680-5310
Franklin Tilley, prin. Fax 680-5317
Morningside HS 1,100/9-12
10500 Yukon Ave 90303 310-680-5230
Isaac Burgess, prin. Fax 680-5257
ICASS Adult
106 E Manchester Ave 90301 310-330-4424
Debbie Tate, prin. Fax 330-5218

Crimson Technical College Post-Sec.
8911 Aviation Blvd 90301 866-451-0818
Daniel Freeman Mem. Hospital Post-Sec.
333 N Prairie Ave 90301 310-674-7050
Marinello School of Beauty Post-Sec.
240 S Market St 90301 310-674-8100
St. Marys Academy 300/9-12
701 Grace Ave 90301 310-674-8470
Nancy Portillo, prin. Fax 674-6255
Univ of West Los Angeles School of Law Post-Sec.
9800 S La Cienega Blvd 90301 310-342-5200

Ione, Amador, Pop. 7,650
Amador County USD
Supt. — See Jackson
Ione JHS 300/6-8
450 S Mill St 95640 209-257-5500
Dr. Jessica Dorris, prin. Fax 274-0671

Irvine, Orange, Pop. 201,858
Irvine USD 30,100/PK-12
5050 Barranca Pkwy 92604 949-936-5000
Terry L. Walker, supt. Fax 936-5259
www.iusd.org
Creekside HS 100/9-12
3387 Barranca Pkwy 92606 949-936-7400
Rebecca Roberts, prin. Fax 936-7409
Irvine HS 1,900/9-12
4321 Walnut Ave 92604 949-936-7000
Monica Colunga, prin. Fax 936-7009
Jeffrey Trail MS 700/7-8
155 Visions 92620 949-936-8700
Michael Georgino, prin. Fax 936-8709
Lakeside MS 700/7-8
3 Lemongrass 92604 949-559-1601
Gina Cuneo, prin. Fax 936-6109
Northwood HS 2,000/9-12
4515 Portola Pkwy 92620 949-936-7200
Leslie Roach, prin. Fax 936-7209
Portola HS, 1001 Cadence 92618 9-12
John Pehrson, prin. 949-936-8202
Rancho San Joaquin MS 900/7-8
4861 Michelson Dr 92612 949-936-6500
Mike Modeer, prin. Fax 936-6509
San Joaquin Alternative Education 100/Alt
3387 Barranca Pkwy 92606 949-936-7440
Rebecca Roberts, dir. Fax 936-7409
Sierra Vista MS 800/7-8
2 Liberty 92620 949-936-6600
Lynn Matassarin, prin. Fax 936-6609
South Lake MS 700/7-8
655 W Yale Loop 92614 949-936-6700
Belinda Averill, prin. Fax 936-6709
University HS 2,400/9-12
4771 Campus Dr 92612 949-936-7600
Kevin Astor, prin. Fax 936-7609
Venado MS 600/7-8
4 Deerfield Ave 92604 949-936-6800
Luis Torrez, prin. Fax 936-6809
Woodbridge HS 2,400/9-12
2 Meadowbrook 92604 949-786-1104
Christopher Krebs, prin.
Irvine Adult S Adult
3387 Barranca Pkwy 92606 949-936-7400
Rebecca Roberts, prin. Fax 936-7459

Tustin USD
Supt. — See Tustin
Beckman HS 2,600/9-12
3588 Bryan 92602 714-734-2900
Dr. Donnie Rafter Ed.D., prin. Fax 505-9676
Orchard Hills S 1,100/4-8
11555 Culver Dr 92602 714-430-2078
Cindy Agopian, prin. Fax 430-2278

Alliant International University Post-Sec.
2855 Michelle Ste 300 92606 949-833-2651
Brandman University Post-Sec.
16355 Laguna Canyon Rd 92618 949-753-4774
California Southern University Post-Sec.
930 Roosevelt 92620 714-882-7800
Chicago Sch of Professional Psychology Post-Sec.
4199 Campus Dr 92612 949-737-5460
Concordia University Post-Sec.
1530 Concordia 92612 949-854-8002
Crean Lutheran South HS 500/9-12
12500 Sand Canyon Ave 92618 949-387-1199
Jeffrey Beavers, prin. Fax 387-1200
FIDM Fashion Institute of Design Post-Sec.
17590 Gillette Ave 92614 949-851-6200
Irvine Valley College Post-Sec.
5500 Irvine Center Dr 92618 949-451-5100
Pacific Academy 100/7-12
4947 Alton Pkwy 92604 949-398-5288
Keith Corpus, prin. Fax 398-5289
Stanbridge College Post-Sec.
2041 Business Center Dr 107 92612 949-794-9090
Tarbut V'Torah Day MSHS 300/6-12
5 Federation Way 92603 949-509-9500
Dr. Jeffrey Davis, head sch Fax 509-7866
University of California 92697 Post-Sec.
949-824-5011

Irwindale, Los Angeles, Pop. 1,410

Premiere Career College Post-Sec.
12901 Ramona Blvd Ste D 91706 626-814-2080
Public Health Foundation Enterprises Post-Sec.
12781 Schabarum Ave 91706 626-856-6376

Jackson, Amador, Pop. 4,513
Amador County Office of Education 500/
217 Rex Ave 95642 209-257-5353
Dick Glock, supt. Fax 257-5360
www.amadorcoe.org/
Other Schools – See Sutter Creek

Amador County USD 3,700/K-12
217 Rex Ave 95642 209-223-1750
Amy Slavensky Ph.D., supt. Fax 296-3133
www.amadorcoe.org
Argonaut HS 500/9-12
501 Argonaut Ln 95642 209-257-7700
Kelly Hunkins, prin. Fax 223-3149
Jackson JHS 200/6-8
747 Sutter St 95642 209-257-5700
Janet DeLeo, prin. Fax 257-5757
Other Schools – See Ione, Sutter Creek

Regional Occupational Center & Program
Supt. — None
Amador County ROP Vo/Tech
217 Rex Ave 95642 209-259-5339
Elizabeth Chapin-Pinotti, dir.

Jacumba, San Diego, Pop. 550
Mountain Empire USD
Supt. — See Pine Valley
Jacumba MS 100/6-8
44343 Old Highway 80 91934 619-766-4464
Gary Brannon, prin. Fax 766-4532

Jamul, San Diego, Pop. 5,990
Jamul-Dulzura UNSD 1,000/K-12
14581 Lyons Valley Rd 91935 619-669-7700
Nadine Bennett, supt. Fax 669-0254
www.jdusd.net
Oak Grove MS 200/6-8
14344 Olive Vista Dr 91935 619-669-2700
Liz Bystedt, prin. Fax 669-7632

Joshua Tree, San Bernardino, Pop. 7,144

Copper Mountain College Post-Sec.
PO Box 1398 92252 760-366-3791

Julian, San Diego, Pop. 1,474
Julian UNESD 3,500/PK-12
PO Box 337 92036 760-765-0661
Brian Duffy, supt. Fax 765-0220
www.juesd.net
Julian JHS 100/6-8
PO Box 337 92036 760-765-0575
Brian Duffy, prin. Fax 765-3340

Julian UNHSD 100/9-12
PO Box 417 92036 760-765-0606
Dr. Patrick Hefflin, supt. Fax 765-2926
www.juhsd.org
Julian Union HS 100/9-12
PO Box 417 92036 760-765-0606
Dr. Partick Hefflin, supt. Fax 765-2926

Jurupa Valley, Riverside
Jurupa USD 19,400/PK-12
4850 Pedley Rd, 951-360-4100
Elliott Duchon, supt. Fax 360-4194
www.jusd.k12.ca.us
Jurupa MS 1,200/7-8
8700 Galena St, 951-360-2846
Terri Stevens, prin. Fax 360-8928
Jurupa Valley HS 1,700/9-12
10551 Bellegrave Ave, 951-360-2600
Kimberly Corbin, prin. Fax 360-2612
Mira Loma MS 900/7-8
5051 Steve Ave, 951-360-2883
Mary Boules, prin. Fax 685-7405
Mission MS 800/7-8
5961 Mustang Ln, 951-222-7842
Dr. RoseMarie Hickman, prin. Fax 369-1407
Nueva Vista Continuation HS 400/Alt
6836 34th St, 951-360-2802
Dr. Michael Rogers, prin. Fax 360-0928
Patriot HS 2,200/9-12
4355 Camino Real, 951-361-6500
Monty Owens, prin. Fax 361-6526
Rubidoux HS 1,700/9-12
4250 Opal St, 951-222-7700
Dr. Jose Araux, prin. Fax 275-0079
Steps Community Day S 50/Alt
4041 Pacific Ave, 951-222-7739
Michael Gray, prin. Fax 788-8689
Adult Education Adult
4041 Pacific Ave, 951-222-7739
Michael Gray, prin. Fax 788-8689

Kelseyville, Lake, Pop. 3,286
Kelseyville USD 1,700/K-12
4410 Konocti Rd 95451 707-279-1511
Dave McQueen, supt. Fax 279-9221
www.kvusd.org
Donaldson Continuation HS 50/Alt
4410 Konocti Rd 95451 707-279-8414
Diana Davidson, admin. Fax 279-4404
Kelseyville Community Day S 50/Alt
3980 Gard St 95451 707-279-2415
Diana Davidson, admin. Fax 279-4404
Kelseyville HS 500/9-12
5480 Main St 95451 707-279-4923
Matt Cockerton, prin. Fax 279-9173
Mountain Vista MS 400/6-8
5081 Konocti Rd 95451 707-279-4060
Tavis Perkins, prin. Fax 279-8835

Kentfield, Marin, Pop. 6,290
Kentfield ESD 1,200/K-8
750 College Ave 94904 415-458-5130
Elizabeth Schott, supt. Fax 458-5137
www.kentfieldschools.org/
Kent MS 500/5-8
800 College Ave 94904 415-458-5970
Skip Kniesche, prin. Fax 458-5973

College of Marin Post-Sec.
835 College Ave 94904 415-457-8811
Marin Catholic HS 700/9-12
675 Sir Francis Drake Blvd 94904 415-464-3898
Chris Valdez, prin. Fax 461-6943

Kerman, Fresno, Pop. 13,348
Kerman USD 4,900/K-12
151 S 1st St 93630 559-843-9000
Robert Frausto, supt. Fax 840-4283
www.kermanusd.com
Enterprise HS 100/Alt
15405 W Sunset Ave 93630 559-843-9580
Rebecca Sanchez, prin. Fax 717-4233
Kerman HS 1,300/9-12
205 S 1st St 93630 559-843-9700
Pam Sellick, prin. Fax 840-4287
Kerman MS 800/7-8
601 S 1st St 93630 559-843-9600
Amanda Guizar, prin. Fax 840-4291

Kettleman City, Kings, Pop. 1,426
Reef-Sunset USD
Supt. — See Avenal
Adelante Continuation HS 50/Alt
PO Box 149 93239 559-386-9081
Estela Jimenez, prin. Fax 386-0207

Keyes, Stanislaus, Pop. 5,468
Keyes UNESD 1,100/PK-12
PO Box 310 95328 209-669-2921
Cynthia Schaefer, supt. Fax 669-2923
www.keyes.k12.ca.us/
Other Schools – See Hughson

King City, Monterey, Pop. 12,778
King City UNSD 2,600/K-8
435 Pearl St 93930 831-385-2940
Rory Livingston, supt. Fax 386-0372
www.kcusd.org
Chalone Peaks MS 800/6-8
667 Meyer St 93930 831-385-4400
Matt Daniels, prin. Fax 385-4422
Phoenix Academy Community Day S 5-8
667 Meyer St 93930 831-385-2940
Mike Barbree, prin. Fax 386-0372

South Monterey JUNHSD 2,000/9-12
800 Broadway St 93930 831-385-0606
Daniel Moirao, supt. Fax 385-0695
www.smcjuhsd.org
King City HS 900/9-12
720 Broadway St 93930 831-385-5461
Janet Sanchez Matos, prin. Fax 385-0901
Portola-Butler Continuation HS 100/Alt
760 Broadway St 93930 831-385-4661
Dr. Steven James, dir. Fax 385-0643
Other Schools – See Greenfield

Kings Beach, Placer, Pop. 3,765

Tahoe Expedition Academy 100/K-12
8651 Speckled Ave 96143 530-546-5253
Mark Kushner, head sch Fax 579-3206

Kingsburg, Fresno, Pop. 11,129
Kingsburg JUNHSD 1,200/9-12
1900 18th Ave 93631 559-897-7721
Randy Morris, supt. Fax 897-7759
kjuhsd.com
Kingsburg HS 1,100/9-12
1900 18th Ave 93631 559-897-5156
Fred Cogan, prin. Fax 897-7759
Oasis Continuation HS 50/Alt
1900 18th Ave 93631 559-897-3880
Ryan Phelan, prin. Fax 897-0458

La Canada Flintridge, Los Angeles, Pop. 19,647
La Canada USD 4,000/K-12
4490 Cornishon Ave 91011 818-952-8300
Wendy Sinnette, supt. Fax 952-8309
www.lcusd.net
La Canada JSHS 2,100/7-12
4463 Oak Grove Dr 91011 818-952-4200
Ian McFeat, prin. Fax 952-4214

Flintridge Preparatory S 500/7-12
4543 Crown Ave 91011 818-790-1178
Peter Bachmann, hdmstr. Fax 952-6247
Flintridge Sacred Heart Academy 400/9-12
440 Saint Katherine Dr 91011 626-685-8500
Sr. Celeste Botello, prin. Fax 685-8555
St. Francis HS 700/9-12
200 Foothill Blvd 91011 818-790-0325
Thomas Moran, prin. Fax 790-5542

La Crescenta, Los Angeles, Pop. 19,112
Glendale USD
Supt. — See Glendale
Clark Magnet HS 1,100/9-12
4747 New York Ave 91214 818-248-8324
Lena Kortoshian, prin. Fax 957-2954
Crescenta Valley HS 2,800/9-12
2900 Community Ave 91214 818-249-5871
Dr. Linda Junge Ed.D., prin. Fax 541-9531
Rosemont MS 1,200/7-8
4725 Rosemont Ave 91214 818-248-4224
Dr. Cynthia Livingston Ed.D., prin. Fax 248-3790

Ladera Ranch, Orange, Pop. 21,970
Capistrano USD
Supt. — See San Juan Capistrano
Ladera Ranch MS 1,400/6-8
29551 Sienna Pkwy 92694 949-234-5922
George Duarte, prin. Fax 364-1149

Lafayette, Contra Costa, Pop. 22,962
Acalanes UNHSD 5,300/9-12
1212 Pleasant Hill Rd 94549 925-280-3900
Dr. John Nickerson Ed.D., supt. Fax 280-3903
www.acalanes.k12.ca.us
Acalanes HS 1,300/9-12
1200 Pleasant Hill Rd 94549 925-280-3970
Travis Bell, prin. Fax 280-3971
Other Schools – See Moraga, Orinda, Walnut Creek

Lafayette SD 3,500/PK-8
3477 School St 94549 925-927-3500
Rachel Zinn, supt. Fax 284-1525
www.lafsd.k12.ca.us
Stanley MS 1,200/6-8
3455 School St 94549 925-927-3530
David Schrag, prin. Fax 283-1797

Bentley Upper S - Lafayette Campus 300/9-12
1000 Upper Happy Valley Rd 94549 925-283-2101
Arlene Hogan, head sch Fax 299-0469

La Grange, Stanislaus
Big Oak Flat-Groveland USD
Supt. — See Groveland

Pedro HS 50/9-12
3090 Merced Falls Rd 95329 209-852-2864
Rob Egger, prin. Fax 852-2125

Laguna Beach, Orange, Pop. 22,111
Laguna Beach USD 2,800/PK-12
550 Blumont St 92651 949-497-7700
Jason Viloria Ed.D., supt. Fax 497-6021
www.lbusd.org
Laguna Beach HS 800/9-12
625 Park Ave 92651 949-497-7750
Christopher Herzfeld, prin. Fax 497-7766
Thurston MS 800/6-8
2100 Park Ave 92651 949-497-7785
Jennifer Salberg, prin. Fax 497-7798

Laguna College of Art and Design Post-Sec.
2222 Laguna Canyon Rd 92651 949-376-6000

Laguna Hills, Orange, Pop. 29,183
Saddleback Valley USD
Supt. — See Mission Viejo
Laguna Hills HS 1,700/9-12
25401 Paseo De Valencia 92653 949-770-5447
Bill Hinds, prin. Fax 830-0295

Allied American University Post-Sec.
22952 Alcalde Dr 92653 888-384-0849
Lake Forest Beauty College Post-Sec.
23565 Moulton Pkwy Ste A 92653 949-951-8883

Laguna Niguel, Orange, Pop. 60,641
Capistrano USD
Supt. — See San Juan Capistrano
Niguel Hills MS 1,300/6-8
29070 Paseo De La Escuela 92677 949-234-5360
Tim Reece, prin. Fax 249-2069

Laguna Niguel Jr. Academy 100/K-10
29702 Kensington Dr 92677 949-495-3428

La Habra, Orange, Pop. 59,112
Fullerton JUNHSD
Supt. — See Fullerton
La Habra HS 2,200/9-12
801 Highlander Ave 90631 562-266-5200
Karl Zener, prin. Fax 691-8280
Sonora HS 1,900/9-12
401 S Palm St 90631 562-266-2001
Adam Bailey Ph.D., prin. Fax 266-2040

La Habra City ESD 5,100/K-8
PO Box 307 90633 562-690-2305
Marc Winger Ed.D., supt. Fax 690-4154
www.lahabraschools.org
Imperial MS 900/6-8
PO Box 307 90633 562-690-2344
Cathy Seighman, prin. Fax 526-3678
Washington MS 900/6-8
PO Box 307 90633 562-690-2374
Mario Carlos, prin. Fax 690-7834

Whittier Christian HS 700/9-12
501 N Beach Blvd 90631 562-694-3803
Carl Martinez M.A., head sch Fax 697-1673

La Jolla, See San Diego
San Diego USD
Supt. — See San Diego
La Jolla HS 1,600/9-12
750 Nautilus St 92037 858-454-3081
Chuck Podhorsky, prin. Fax 459-2188
Muirlands MS 1,000/6-8
1056 Nautilus St 92037 858-459-4211
Harlan Klein, prin. Fax 459-8075

Bishop's S 800/6-12
7607 La Jolla Blvd 92037 858-459-4021
Aimeclaire Roche, head sch Fax 459-3914
La Jolla Country Day S 1,200/PK-12
9490 Genesee Ave 92037 858-453-3440
Dr. Gary Krahn, head sch Fax 453-8210
National University Post-Sec.
11255 N Torrey Pines Rd 92037 858-642-8000
Sanford-Burnham Graduate School Post-Sec.
10901 N Torrey Pines Rd 92037 858-646-3100
Scripps Memorial Hospital Post-Sec.
9888 Genesee Ave 92037 858-457-6100
Scripps Research Institute Post-Sec.
10550 N Torrey Pines Rd 92037 858-784-8469
University of California Post-Sec.
9500 Gilman Dr 92093 858-534-2230

Lake Arrowhead, San Bernardino, Pop. 12,063
Rim of the World USD
Supt. — See Blue Jay
Henck IS 900/6-8
PO Box 430 92352 909-336-0360
Kenneth Decroo, prin. Fax 336-3449
Rim of the World HS 1,200/9-12
PO Box 430 92352 909-336-2038
Derek Swem, prin. Fax 336-0254

Lake Elsinore, Riverside, Pop. 50,250
Lake Elsinore USD 21,900/PK-12
545 Chaney St 92530 951-253-7000
Doug Kimberly Ed.D., supt. Fax 253-7084
www.leusd.k12.ca.us
Canyon Lake MS 1,300/6-8
33005 Canyon Hills Rd 92532 951-244-2123
Preston Perez Ed.D., prin. Fax 244-2103
Elsinore MS 700/6-8
1203 W Graham Ave 92530 951-674-2118
James Judziewicz, prin. Fax 674-6302
Lakeside HS 1,900/9-12
32593 Riverside Dr 92530 951-253-7300
Peter Hopping Ed.D., prin. Fax 253-7335

McCarthy Academy 200/Alt
1405 Education Way 92530 951-253-7777
Ryan Mulvanny, prin. Fax 245-1988
Ortega Continuation HS 200/Alt
520 Chaney St 92530 951-253-7065
Greg Cleave, prin. Fax 245-1988
Temescal Canyon HS 2,100/9-12
28755 El Toro Rd 92532 951-253-7250
Whitney D'Amico Ed.D., prin. Fax 253-7266
Terra Cotta MS 1,200/6-8
29291 Lake St 92530 951-253-7380
Kathy Nash, prin. Fax 674-5191
Valley Adult S Adult
520 Chaney St 92530 951-253-7093
Greg Cleave, prin. Fax 253-7039
Other Schools – See Wildomar

Lake Forest, Orange, Pop. 74,539
Saddleback Valley USD
Supt. — See Mission Viejo
El Toro HS 2,600/9-12
25255 Toledo Way 92630 949-586-6333
Terri Gusiff, prin. Fax 380-9874
Serrano IS 1,200/7-8
24642 Jeronimo Rd 92630 949-586-3221
Robert Sherlock, prin. Fax 586-3773

Elegante Beauty College Post-Sec.
23635 El Toro Rd Ste K 92630 949-586-4900

Lake Isabella, Kern, Pop. 3,311
Kern UNHSD
Supt. — See Bakersfield
Kern Valley HS 500/9-12
3340 Erskine Creek Rd 93240 760-379-2611
John Meyers, prin. Fax 379-8314

Kernville UNESD 800/K-8
3240 Erskine Creek Rd 93240 760-379-3651
Robin Shive, supt. Fax 379-3812
www.kernvilleusd.org
Rio Vista Community Day S 50/Alt
3240 Erskine Creek Rd 93240 760-379-4863
Brian Polston, prin. Fax 379-1324
Wallace MS 300/5-8
3240 Erskine Creek Rd 93240 760-379-4646
Jill Shaw, prin. Fax 379-1322

Lakeport, Lake, Pop. 4,650
Lake County Office of Education 50/
1152 S Main St 95453 707-262-4100
Brock Falkenberg, supt. Fax 263-0197
www.lakecoe.org
Hance Community S 50/Alt
1510 Argonaut Rd 95453 707-263-5819
Lori LaBrie, lead tchr. Fax 263-6262

Lakeport USD 1,500/K-12
2508 Howard Ave 95453 707-262-3000
Erin Smith-Hagberg, supt. Fax 263-7332
www.lakeport.k12.ca.us
Clear Lake HS 400/9-12
2508 Howard Ave 95453 707-262-3010
David Chamberlain, prin. Fax 262-3026
Lakeport Alternative S 50/Alt
2508 Howard Ave 95453 707-262-3013
Erin Smith-Hagberg, admin. Fax 263-6304
Lakeport Community Day S 50/Alt
2508 Howard Ave 95453 707-262-3013
Erin Smith-Hagberg, admin. Fax 263-6304
Natural Continuation HS 50/Alt
2508 Howard Ave 95453 707-262-3013
Erin Smith-Hagberg, admin. Fax 263-6304
Terrace MS 500/4-8
2508 Howard Ave 95453 707-262-3007
Rachel Paarsch, prin. Fax 262-5532

Regional Occupational Center & Program
Supt. — None
Lake County ROP Vo/Tech
1152 S Main St 95453 707-262-4162
Brock Falkenberg, dir. Fax 262-0197

Lakeside, San Diego, Pop. 20,041
Grossmont UNHSD
Supt. — See La Mesa
El Capitan HS 1,600/9-12
10410 Ashwood St 92040 619-938-9100
Laura Whitaker, prin. Fax 390-8503

Lakeside UNSD 5,100/PK-12
12335 Woodside Ave 92040 619-390-2600
David Lorden, supt. Fax 561-7929
www.lsusd.net
Lakeside MS 900/6-8
11833 Woodside Ave 92040 619-390-2636
Stephen Mull, prin. Fax 390-2643
Tierra Del Sol MS 500/6-8
9611 Petite Ln 92040 619-390-2670
Scott Goergens, prin. Fax 390-2518

Lakewood, Los Angeles, Pop. 76,583
ABC USD
Supt. — See Cerritos
Artesia HS 1,500/9-12
12108 Del Amo Blvd 90715 562-229-7700
Sergio Garcia, prin. Fax 809-5604

Bellflower USD
Supt. — See Bellflower
Mayfair MSHS 3,200/7-12
6000 Woodruff Ave 90713 562-925-9981
Julie Stanley, prin. Fax 804-1656

Long Beach USD
Supt. — See Long Beach
Hoover MS 900/6-8
3501 Country Club Dr 90712 562-421-1213
Stephanie Cooper, prin. Fax 421-8063
Lakewood HS 3,700/9-12
4400 Briercrest Ave 90713 562-425-1281
Shawn Abbate, prin. Fax 421-9616

Paramount USD
Supt. — See Paramount
Buena Vista HS Alt
3717 Michelson St 90712 562-602-8090
Dr. Andrea Aguilare-Nuno, prin. Fax 602-8091

St. Joseph HS 700/9-12
5825 Woodruff Ave 90713 562-925-5073
Dr. Teresa Mendoza, prin. Fax 925-3315

La Mesa, San Diego, Pop. 54,494
Grossmont UNHSD 23,100/7-12
PO Box 1043 91944 619-644-8000
Tim Glover Ed.D., supt. Fax 465-1349
www.guhsd.net
Other Schools – See El Cajon, Lakeside, Santee, Spring Valley

La Mesa-Spring Valley SD 12,000/K-8
4750 Date Ave 91942 619-668-5700
Brian Marshall, supt. Fax 668-5809
www.lmsvsd.org
La Mesa Arts Academy 600/4-8
4200 Parks Ave 91941 619-668-5730
Beth Thomas, prin. Fax 668-8303
Parkway MS 800/7-8
9009 Park Plaza Dr 91942 619-668-5810
Mary Beason, prin. Fax 668-5779
Other Schools – See Spring Valley

California Hair Design Academy Post-Sec.
8011 University Ave Ste A2 91942 619-461-8600

La Mirada, Los Angeles, Pop. 47,368
Norwalk-La Mirada USD
Supt. — See Norwalk
Benton MS 600/6-8
15709 Olive Branch Dr 90638 562-943-1553
Michael Gotto, prin. Fax 947-3861
Hutchinson MS 500/6-8
13900 Estero Rd 90638 562-944-3268
Robin Padget, prin. Fax 944-3269
La Mirada HS 2,200/9-12
13520 Adelfa Dr 90638 562-868-0431
L. Reed, prin. Fax 943-7872
Los Coyotes MS 600/6-8
14640 Mercado Ave 90638 714-523-2051
Jacob Muniz, prin. Fax 739-2368
La Mirada Adult S Adult
15920 Barbata Rd 90638 562-670-9279
Sharon Todd, dir. Fax 670-1654

Biola University Post-Sec.
13800 Biola Ave 90639 562-903-6000
Heights Christian JHS 300/5-8
12900 Bluefield Ave 90638 562-947-3309
Rebecca Neal, prin. Fax 947-1001

Lamont, Kern, Pop. 15,088
Kern UNHSD
Supt. — See Bakersfield
Nueva Continuation HS 100/Alt
8600 Palm Ave 93241 661-845-1532
Mark Weir, admin. Fax 845-9523

Lamont ESD 2,900/K-8
7915 Burgundy Ave 93241 661-845-0751
Ricardo Robles, supt. Fax 845-0689
www.lamontschooldistrict.org
Other Schools – See Bakersfield

Lancaster, Los Angeles, Pop. 151,168
Antelope Valley UNHSD 23,600/7-12
44811 Sierra Hwy 93534 661-948-7655
David Vierra, supt. Fax 942-8744
www.avdistrict.org
Antelope Valley HS 1,700/9-12
44900 Division St 93535 661-948-8552
Jodie Radford, prin. Fax 945-8867
Desert Winds Continuation HS 800/Alt
45030 3rd St E 93535 661-948-7555
Will Laird, prin. Fax 948-5947
Eastside HS 2,400/9-12
3200 E Avenue J8 93535 661-946-3800
Kristen Tepper, prin. Fax 946-3850
Lancaster HS 2,300/9-12
44701 Eagle Way 93536 661-726-7649
Jose Barajas, prin. Fax 726-7694
Phoenix HS Community Day 100/Alt
225 E Avenue H8 93535 661-729-3936
Will Laird, prin.
SOAR HS 400/9-12
3041 W Avenue K 93536 661-722-6509
Chris Grado, prin. Fax 722-6583
Antelope Valley Adult HS Adult
45110 3rd St E 93535 661-942-3042
Steve Radford, prin. Fax 948-0846
Other Schools – See Littlerock, Palmdale, Quartz Hill

Eastside UNSD 3,300/K-8
45006 30th St E 93535 661-952-1200
Mark Marshall Ed.D., supt. Fax 952-1220
www.eastside.k12.ca.us
Cole MS 800/6-8
3126 E Avenue I 93535 661-946-1041
Francisco Pinto, prin. Fax 946-0166

Lancaster ESD 15,000/PK-8
44711 Cedar Ave 93534 661-948-4661
Dr. Michele Bowers Ed.D., supt. Fax 942-9452
www.lancsd.org
Amargosa Creek MS 1,000/6-8
44333 27th St W 93536 661-729-6064
Richelle Pulos, prin. Fax 729-6858
Endeavour MS 800/6-8
43755 45th St W 93536 661-723-0351
Cheri Newlander, prin. Fax 723-1362
Fulton & Alsbury Acad Arts & Engineering 6-8
831 E Avenue K2 93535 661-206-0120
Dr. Andrew Glatfelter, prin.
Lancaster Virtual Alternative Academy 100/Alt
44310 Hardwood Ave 93534 661-726-4354
Kimberly Porter, coord. Fax 726-5457
New Vista MS 1,000/6-8
753 E Avenue K2 93535 661-726-4271
Kymberlee Cochran, prin. Fax 726-4278
Piute MS 800/6-8
425 E Avenue H11 93535 661-942-9508
Michael Davis, prin. Fax 940-6676

Westside UNESD
Supt. — See Quartz Hill
Westside Academy 50/Alt
5606 W Avenue L8 93536 661-206-3711
Debbie Rutkowski-Hines, prin. Fax 722-1046

Wilsona SD
Supt. — See Palmdale
Challenger MS 600/5-8
41725 170th St E 93535 661-264-1790
Janice Stowers, prin. Fax 264-1793
Wilsona Achievement Academy 50/Alt
41725 170th St E 93535 661-264-1790
Janice Stowers, prin. Fax 264-1793

Antelope Valley Christian S 300/PK-12
44514 20th St W 93534 661-943-0044
Antelope Valley College Post-Sec.
3041 W Avenue K 93536 661-722-6300
Bethel Christian S 400/PK-12
3100 W Avenue K 93536 661-943-2224
Mathias Konnerth, prin. Fax 943-6574
Charter College Lancaster Post-Sec.
43141 Business Ctr Pkwy 102 93535 661-341-3500
Desert Christian HS 400/9-12
2340 W Avenue J8 93536 661-723-7441
Brian Roseborough, prin. Fax 723-7437
Desert Christian MS 200/6-8
44662 15th St W 93534 661-723-0665
Lisa Costello, dir. Fax 723-6774
Lancaster Baptist S 400/K-12
4020 E Lancaster Blvd 93535 661-946-4668
Jim Lee, admin. Fax 946-7374
Lancaster Beauty School Post-Sec.
44646 10th St W 93534 661-948-1672
Paraclete HS 700/9-12
42145 30th St W 93536 661-943-3255
John Anson, prin. Fax 722-9455
University of Antelope Valley Post-Sec.
44055 Sierra Hwy 93534 661-726-1911

La Palma, Orange, Pop. 15,047
Anaheim UNHSD
Supt. — See Anaheim
Kennedy HS 2,300/9-12
8281 Walker St 90623 714-220-4101
Russell Earnest, prin. Fax 995-1833
Walker JHS 1,100/7-8
8132 Walker St 90623 714-220-4051
Kirsten Levitin Ed.D., prin. Fax 220-2237

La Puente, Los Angeles, Pop. 39,527
Bassett USD, 904 Willow Ave 91746 4,100/K-12
Alex Rojas, supt. 626-931-3000
www.bassettusd.org
Bassett HS 1,100/9-12
904 Willow Ave 91746 626-931-2800
Gabriel Griego, prin. Fax 931-2850
Nueva Vista Continuation HS 100/Alt
904 Willow Ave 91746 626-931-3177
Gabriel Fernandez, prin. Fax 931-3145
Bassett Adult S, 904 Willow Ave 91746 Adult
Albert Michel, prin. 626-931-3102
Other Schools – See City of Industry

Hacienda La Puente USD
Supt. — See City of Industry
La Puente HS 1,500/9-12
15615 Nelson Ave 91744 626-934-6797
Fernando Sanchez, prin. Fax 855-3798
Sierra Vista MS 300/7-8
15801 Sierra Vista Ct 91744 626-933-4001
Lisa Carrera, prin. Fax 855-3817
Sparks MS 500/7-8
15100 Giordano St 91744 626-933-5001
Collin Miller, prin. Fax 855-3848
Hacienda La Puente Adult Education Adult
14101 Nelson Ave 91746 626-934-2987
Elena Paul, dir. Fax 934-2986
Willow Adult S Adult
14101 Nelson Ave 91746 626-934-2801
Elena Paul, dir.

Regional Occupational Center & Program
Supt. — None
La Puente Valley ROP Vo/Tech
341 La Seda Rd 91744 626-810-3300
Esperanza Fernandez, supt. Fax 581-9108

Rowland USD
Supt. — See Rowland Heights
Nogales HS 2,100/9-12
401 Nogales St 91744 626-965-3437
Yousef Nasouf, prin. Fax 965-4587
Santana Alternative Education Center 200/Alt
341 La Seda Rd 91744 626-965-5971
Stephen Edmunds, prin. Fax 854-2225

Bishop Amat HS 1,400/9-12
14301 Fairgrove Ave 91746 626-962-2495
Dr. Richard Beck, prin. Fax 960-0994
Hacienda LaPuente Valley Adult Education Post-Sec.
14101 Nelson Ave 91746 626-934-2800

La Quinta, Riverside, Pop. 36,785
Desert Sands USD 28,700/K-12
47950 Dune Palms Rd 92253 760-777-4200
Dr. Gary Rutherford, supt. Fax 771-8505
www.dsusd.us
Horizon S 300/Alt
43330 Palm Royale Dr 92253 760-238-9720
Rudy Wilson, prin. Fax 360-2182
La Quinta HS 2,900/9-12
79255 Blackhawk Way 92253 760-772-4150
Rebecca Cook, prin. Fax 772-4166
La Quinta MS 500/6-8
78900 Avenue 50 92253 760-777-4220
Dan Borgen, prin. Fax 777-4216
Paige MS 900/6-8
43495 Palm Royale Dr 92253 760-238-9710
Janet Seto, prin. Fax 345-1202
Summit HS 300/Alt
43330 Palm Royale Dr 92253 760-238-9760
Rudy Wilson, prin. Fax 238-9751
Other Schools – See Indio, Palm Desert

Larkspur, Marin, Pop. 11,461
Larkspur-Corte Madera SD 1,800/K-8
230 Doherty Dr 94939 415-927-6960
Valerie Pitts, supt. Fax 927-6964
www.lcmschools.org
Hall MS 600/5-8
200 Doherty Dr 94939 415-927-6978
Tom Utic, prin. Fax 927-6985

Tamalpais UNHSD 4,000/9-12
PO Box 605 94977 415-945-3600
David Yoshihara, supt. Fax 945-3719
www.tamdistrict.org
Redwood HS 1,600/9-12
395 Doherty Dr 94939 415-924-6200
David Sondheim, prin. Fax 945-3675
San Andreas HS 100/Alt
599 William Ave 94939 415-945-3770
David Luongo, prin. Fax 945-3754
Tamiscal HS 100/Alt
PO Box 605 94977 415-945-3750
Corbett Elsen, prin. Fax 945-3752
Other Schools – See Mill Valley, San Anselmo

La Selva Beach, Santa Cruz, Pop. 2,748
Pajaro Valley USD
Supt. — See Watsonville
Renaissance HS 200/Alt
11 Spring Valley Rd 95076 831-728-6344
Andrew Singleton, prin. Fax 728-6419

Monterey Bay Academy 200/9-12
783 San Andreas Rd 95076 831-728-1481

Lathrop, San Joaquin, Pop. 17,283
Manteca USD
Supt. — See Manteca
Lathrop HS 1,200/9-12
647 Spartan Way 95330 209-938-6350
Michael Horwood, prin. Fax 938-6390

Laton, Fresno, Pop. 1,814
Laton USD 700/K-12
PO Box 248 93242 559-922-4015
Larry Audet, supt. Fax 923-4791
latonunified.org
Conejo MS 200/6-8
PO Box 7 93242 559-922-4030
Lori Montejano, prin. Fax 923-9651
Laton HS 200/9-12
PO Box 278 93242 559-922-4080
Jason Krikava, prin. Fax 923-4072

La Verne, Los Angeles, Pop. 30,232
Bonita USD
Supt. — See San Dimas
Bonita HS 2,000/9-12
3102 D St 91750 909-971-8220
Derek Bub, prin. Fax 971-8229
Ramona MS 1,300/6-8
3490 Ramona Ave 91750 909-971-8260
Anne Neal, prin. Fax 971-8269

Calvary Baptist S 100/PK-12
2990 Damien Ave 91750 909-593-4672
Taylor Dial, prin. Fax 392-9533
Damien HS 1,000/9-12
2280 Damien Ave 91750 909-596-1946
Dr. Merritt Hemenway, prin. Fax 596-1946
Lutheran HS 100/9-12
3960 Fruit St 91750 909-593-4494
Dr. Lance Ebel, prin. Fax 596-3744
University of La Verne Post-Sec.
1950 3rd St 91750 909-593-3511

Lawndale, Los Angeles, Pop. 31,604
Centinela Valley UNHSD 6,600/9-12
14901 Inglewood Ave 90260 310-263-3200
Gregory O'Brien Ph.D., supt. Fax 675-8286
www.centinela.k12.ca.us/
Centinela Valley Independent Study HS 200/Alt
4409 Redondo Beach Blvd 90260 424-255-4066
Michael Martinez, prin. Fax 978-3995
Lawndale HS 2,400/9-12
14901 Inglewood Ave 90260 310-263-3100
Paula Hart Rodas, prin. Fax 675-8174
Leuzinger HS 1,700/9-12
4118 Rosecrans Ave 90260 310-263-2200
Dr. Pamela Brown, prin. Fax 675-7023
Lloyde Continuation HS 200/Alt
4951 Marine Ave 90260 310-263-3264
James Tarouilly, prin. Fax 978-3995
South Bay Academy Community Day S Alt
4409 Redondo Beach Blvd 90260 424-255-4066
Michael Martinez, prin. Fax 285-5377
Other Schools – See Hawthorne

Lawndale ESD 5,900/K-12
4161 W 147th St 90260 310-973-1300
Dr. Ellen Dougherty Ed.D., supt. Fax 675-6462
lesd-ca.schoolloop.com
Addams MS 900/6-8
4161 W 147th St 90260 310-676-4806
Dennis Perry, prin. Fax 676-8621
Rogers MS 900/6-8
4161 W 147th St 90260 310-676-1197
Dr. Maurita De La Torre Ed.D., prin. Fax 675-0489

Laytonville, Mendocino, Pop. 1,182
Laytonville USD 400/K-12
PO Box 868 95454 707-984-6414
Joan Potter, supt. Fax 984-8223
layt.k12.ca.us
Laytonville Continuation HS 50/Alt
PO Box 868 95454 707-984-6811
Tim Henry, prin. Fax 984-8066
Laytonville HS 100/9-12
PO Box 868 95454 707-984-6108
Tim Henry, prin. Fax 984-8066

Lebec, Kern, Pop. 1,432
El Tejon USD 800/K-12
PO Box 876 93243 661-248-6247
Rodney Wallace, supt. Fax 248-6714
www.el-tejon.k12.ca.us
El Tejon MS 200/5-8
PO Box 876 93243 661-248-6680
Rosalie Jimenez, prin. Fax 248-5203
Frazier Mountain HS 300/9-12
PO Box 876 93243 661-248-0310
Sara Haflich, prin. Fax 248-0403

Lee Vining, Mono, Pop. 220
Eastern Sierra USD
Supt. — See Bridgeport
Lee Vining HS 100/9-12
PO Box 268 93541 760-647-6366
Roger Yost, prin. Fax 647-6695

Mono County Office of Education
Supt. — See Bridgeport
TIOGA Community S 50/Alt
132 Lee Vining Ave 93541 760-206-6014
Janet Hunt, prin. Fax 934-1443

Leggett, Mendocino, Pop. 105
Leggett Valley USD 100/PK-12
PO Box 186 95585 707-925-6230
Anthony Loumena, supt. Fax 925-6396
www.leggett.k12.ca.us
Leggett Valley HS 50/9-12
PO Box 186 95585 707-925-6285
Anthony Loumena, prin. Fax 925-6396
Other Schools – See Whitethorn

Le Grand, Merced, Pop. 1,644
Le Grand UNHSD 500/9-12
12961 Le Grand Rd 95333 209-389-9403
Donna Alley M.A., supt. Fax 389-9414
www.lghs.k12.ca.us/
Granada HS 50/Alt
12961 E Le Grand Rd 95333 209-382-0202
Donna Alley, prin. Fax 382-1443
Le Grand Union HS 500/9-12
12961 Le Grand Rd 95333 209-389-9400
Javier Martinez, prin. Fax 389-4065

Lemon Grove, San Diego, Pop. 24,153
Lemon Grove SD 3,900/PK-8
8025 Lincoln St 91945 619-825-5600
Ernest Anastos, supt. Fax 462-7959
www.lgsd.k12.ca.us
Lemon Grove Academy MS 700/7-8
7866 Lincoln St 91945 619-825-5628
Rick Oser, prin. Fax 825-5781

Lemoore, Kings, Pop. 23,462
Lemoore ESD 3,200/K-8
100 Vine St 93245 559-924-6800
Cheryl Hunt, supt. Fax 924-6809
www.luesd.k12.ca.us
Bridges Academy 50/Alt
1200 W Cinnamon Dr 93245 559-925-7040
Brooke Warkentin, dir. Fax 924-6809
Liberty MS 600/7-8
100 Vine St 93245 559-924-6860
Ben Luis, prin. Fax 924-6869

Lemoore UNHSD 2,300/9-12
5 Powell Ave 93245 559-924-6610
Debbie Muro, supt. Fax 924-9212
www.luhsd.k12.ca.us/
Jamison Alternative Education HS 100/Alt
351 E Bush St 93245 559-924-6620
Sandi Lowe, prin. Fax 924-6637
Lemoore HS 2,000/9-12
101 E Bush St 93245 559-924-6600
Rodney Brumit, prin. Fax 924-5086
Lemoore Adult S Adult
351 E Bush St 93245 559-924-6620
Sandi Lowe, prin. Fax 924-6637

Kings Christian S 300/PK-12
900 E D St 93245 559-924-8301
Kevin Dalafu, admin. Fax 924-0607
West Hills College Lemoore Post-Sec.
555 College Dr 93245 559-925-3000

Lennox, Los Angeles, Pop. 22,462
Lennox ESD 7,000/K-12
10319 Firmona Ave 90304 310-695-4000
Kent Taylor, supt. Fax 677-3817
www.lennox.k12.ca.us
Lennox MS 1,600/6-8
11033 Buford Ave 90304 310-419-1800
Raul Roman Ed.D., prin. Fax 677-4635

Lincoln, Placer, Pop. 41,451
Western Placer USD 8,000/PK-12
600 6th St Ste 400 95648 916-645-6350
Scott Leaman, supt. Fax 645-6356
www.wpusd.k12.ca.us
Edwards MS 700/6-8
204 L St 95648 916-645-6370
Stacey Brown, prin. Fax 645-6379
Lincoln HS 1,600/9-12
790 J St 95648 916-645-6360
Jay Berns, prin. Fax 645-6349
Phoenix Continuation HS 100/Alt
870 J St 95648 916-645-6395
Charles Whitecotton, prin. Fax 645-6347
Twelve Bridges MS 800/6-8
770 Westview Dr 95648 916-434-5270
Randy Woods, prin. Fax 434-5240

Linden, San Joaquin, Pop. 1,741
Linden USD 2,300/K-12
18527 E Highway 26 95236 209-887-3894
Rick Hall, supt. Fax 887-2250
www.lindenusd.com
Linden HS 700/9-12
18527 E Front St 95236 209-887-3073
Richard Schmidig, prin. Fax 887-3815
Other Schools – See Stockton

Lindsay, Tulare, Pop. 11,716
Lindsay USD 4,200/PK-12
371 E Hermosa St 93247 559-562-5111
Thomas L. Rooney, supt. Fax 562-4637
www.lindsay.k12.ca.us
Cairns Continuation HS 100/Alt
467 E Honolulu St 93247 559-562-5913
Dennis Doane, prin. Fax 562-1753
Lindsay Community Day S 50/Alt
270 N Harvard 93247 559-562-5913
Dennis Doane, prin.
Lindsay HS 1,000/9-12
1849 E Tulare Rd 93247 559-562-5911
Heather Rocha, prin. Fax 562-4291

Littlerock, Los Angeles, Pop. 1,327
Antelope Valley UNHSD
Supt. — See Lancaster
Littlerock HS 1,500/9-12
10833 E Avenue R 93543 661-944-5209
Karen Parker, prin. Fax 944-5191

Keppel UNESD
Supt. — See Pearblossom
Desert View Community Day S 50/Alt
9330 E Avenue U 93543 661-944-2152
Gary Schatz, prin. Fax 944-0694
Keppel Academy 400/5-8
9330 E Avenue U 93543 661-944-2152
Gary Schatz, prin. Fax 944-0694

Live Oak, Sutter, Pop. 8,180
Live Oak USD 1,700/K-12
2201 Pennington Rd 95953 530-695-5400
Mathew Gulbrandsen, supt. Fax 695-5460
www.lousd.k12.ca.us
Live Oak Alternative S 50/Alt
2207 Pennington Rd 95953 530-695-5430
James VonBargen, prin. Fax 695-5432
Live Oak HS 500/9-12
2351 Pennington Rd 95953 530-695-5415
Tony Walton, prin. Fax 695-5422
Live Oak MS 500/5-8
2082 Pennington Rd 95953 530-695-5435
Parm Virk, prin. Fax 695-5443

Livermore, Alameda, Pop. 77,773
Livermore Valley JUSD 14,000/K-12
685 E Jack London Blvd 94551 925-606-3200
Kelly Bowers, supt. Fax 606-3329
www.livermoreschools.com
Christensen MS 700/6-8
5757 Haggin Oaks Ave 94551 925-606-4702
Pat Avilla, prin. Fax 606-4705
Del Valle Continuation HS 100/Alt
2253 5th St 94550 925-606-4709
Darrel Avilla, prin. Fax 606-3371
East Avenue MS 600/6-8
3951 East Ave 94550 925-606-4711
Helen Gladden, prin. Fax 606-4763
Granada HS 2,000/9-12
400 Wall St 94550 925-606-4800
P.J. Daley, prin. Fax 606-4808
Livermore HS 1,800/9-12
600 Maple St 94550 925-606-4812
Vicki Scudder, prin. Fax 606-4851
Mendenhall MS 1,000/6-8
1701 El Padro Dr 94550 925-606-4731
Susan Sambuceti, prin. Fax 606-4737
Vineyard Alternative S 100/Alt
1401 Almond Ave 94550 925-606-4722
Alex Eckert, prin. Fax 606-4799
Livermore Adult Community Education Adult
1401 Almond Ave 94550 925-606-4722
Alex Eckert, prin. Fax 606-3389

Regional Occupational Center & Program
Supt. — None
Tri-Valley ROP Vo/Tech
1040 Florence Rd 94550 925-455-4800
Julie Duncan, supt. Fax 449-9126

Las Positas College Post-Sec.
3000 Campus Hill Dr 94551 925-424-1000
TriValley Classical Christian S 100/K-12
945 Concannon Blvd 94550 925-961-4664

Livingston, Merced, Pop. 12,876
Livingston UNSD 2,600/K-8
922 B St 95334 209-394-5400
Andres Zamora, supt. Fax 394-5401
www.livingstonusd.org

Livingston MS 900/6-8
101 F St 95334 209-394-5450
Victoria Bradshaw, prin. Fax 394-5451

Merced County Office of Education
Supt. — See Merced
Schelby S 100/Alt
6738 Sultana Dr 95334 209-394-1800
Lissa Mitchell, coord. Fax 394-7818

Merced UNHSD
Supt. — See Atwater
Livingston HS 1,100/9-12
1617 Main St 95334 209-394-7961
Mandy Ballenger, prin. Fax 358-1093

Lodi, San Joaquin, Pop. 60,610
Lodi USD 28,600/PK-12
1305 E Vine St 95240 209-331-7000
Dr. Cathy Nichols-Washer Ed.D., supt. Fax 331-7256
www.lodiusd.net
Henderson S 100/Alt
13451 N Extension Rd 95242 209-331-7331
Dominee Muller-Kimball, prin. Fax 331-8274
Independence S 200/Alt
13451 N Extension Rd 95242 209-331-8946
Dominee Muller-Kimball, prin. Fax 331-8274
Katnich Community Day S 50/Alt
13451 N Extension Rd 95242 209-331-7331
Marie Caffese, prin.
Liberty Continuation HS 100/Alt
660 W Walnut St 95240 209-331-7633
Tamara Dillon, prin. Fax 331-7624
Lincoln Technical Academy Vo/Tech
542 E Pine St 95240 209-331-7616
Deborah Chiene, prin. Fax 331-7526
Lodi HS 2,100/9-12
3 S Pacific Ave 95242 209-331-7819
Bob Lofsted, prin. Fax 331-7779
Lodi MS 800/7-8
945 S Ham Ln 95242 209-331-7540
Scott McGregor, prin. Fax 331-7550
Millswood MS 900/7-8
233 N Mills Ave 95242 209-331-8332
Erin Lenzi, prin. Fax 331-8347
Tokay HS 2,100/9-12
1111 W Century Blvd 95240 209-331-7990
Erik Sandstrom, prin. Fax 331-7168
Lodi Adult S Adult
542 E Pine St 95240 209-331-7605
Deborah Chiene, prin. Fax 331-7167
Other Schools – See Stockton

Elliot Christian HS 200/9-12
2695 W Vine St 95242 209-368-2800
Dr. Mark Stewart, admin. Fax 333-5208
Lodi Academy 100/9-12
1230 S Central Ave 95240 209-368-2781
Vineyard Christian MS 100/6-8
2301 W Lodi Ave 95242 209-333-8300
Randal Oliver, prin. Fax 339-4327

Loma Linda, San Bernardino, Pop. 22,264

Loma Linda Academy 1,300/K-12
10656 Anderson St 92354 909-796-0161
Loma Linda University 92350 Post-Sec.
909-558-1000

Lomita, Los Angeles, Pop. 19,339
Los Angeles USD
Supt. — See Los Angeles
Fleming MS 1,600/6-8
25425 Walnut St 90717 310-257-4500
Peter Hastings, prin. Fax 326-9071

Lompoc, Santa Barbara, Pop. 41,015
Lompoc USD 9,900/K-12
PO Box 8000 93438 805-742-3300
Trevor McDonald, supt. Fax 735-8452
www.lusd.org
Cabrillo HS 1,400/9-12
PO Box 8000 93438 805-742-2900
Jeff Wagonseller, prin. Fax 733-4156
Forinash Community Day S Alt
PO Box 8000 93438 805-742-3135
Katherine Wallace, prin.
Lompoc HS 1,400/9-12
PO Box 8000 93438 805-742-3000
Paul Bommersbach, prin. Fax 742-3004
Lompoc Valley MS 600/7-8
PO Box 8000 93438 805-742-2600
Schel Brown, prin. Fax 737-9480
Maple HS 200/Alt
PO Box 8000 93438 805-742-3150
Katherine Wallace, prin. Fax 742-3163
Lompoc Adult Education Adult
PO Box 8000 93438 805-742-3100
Mary Coggins, coord. Fax 742-3085
Other Schools – See Vandenberg AFB

Lone Pine, Inyo, Pop. 1,990
Lone Pine USD 400/K-12
PO Box 159 93545 760-876-5579
Heidi Torix, supt. Fax 876-5438
lpusd-ca.schoolloop.com
Lone Pine HS 100/9-12
PO Box 159 93545 760-876-5577
Heidi Torix, prin. Fax 876-1037
Sierra Alternative Learning Academy 50/Alt
PO Box 159 93545 760-876-5577
Heidi Torix, prin.
Lone Pine Adult S Adult
PO Box 159 93545 760-876-5579
Heidi Torix, prin. Fax 876-5438

Long Barn, Tuolumne, Pop. 153
Summerville UNHSD
Supt. — See Tuolumne
Cold Springs HS 50/Alt
25910 Long Barn Rd 95335 209-586-3011
Diana Harford, prin. Fax 928-1422
Long Barn HS 50/Alt
25910 Long Barn Dr 95335 209-586-3011
Diana Harford, prin. Fax 928-1422

Long Beach, Los Angeles, Pop. 443,652
Long Beach USD 79,700/PK-12
1515 Hughes Way 90810 562-997-8000
Christopher Steinhauser, supt. Fax 997-8280
www.lbschools.net
Bancroft MS 1,000/6-8
5301 E Centralia St 90808 562-425-7461
Pilar Perossio, prin. Fax 425-9741
Beach HS, 3701 E Willow St 90815 300/Alt
Troy Bennett, prin. 562-595-8893
Cabrillo HS 3,000/9-12
2001 Santa Fe Ave 90810 562-951-7700
Cheryl Cornejo, prin. Fax 951-7797
Educational Partnership HS 1,000/Alt
1794 Cedar Ave 90813 562-218-0493
Gregory Mendoza, prin. Fax 218-1573
Franklin Classical MS 1,100/6-8
540 Cerritos Ave 90802 562-435-4952
Wendy Sowinski, prin. Fax 432-6308
Hamilton MS 900/6-8
1060 E 70th St 90805 562-602-0302
Kathleen Cruz, prin. Fax 602-1354
Hughes MS 1,600/6-8
3846 California Ave 90807 562-595-0831
Edward Samuels, prin. Fax 595-9221
Jefferson Leadership Academies 1,000/6-8
750 Euclid Ave 90804 562-438-9904
Kevin Maddox, prin. Fax 439-3718
Jordan HS 3,500/9-12
6500 Atlantic Ave 90805 562-423-1471
Veronica Coleman, prin. Fax 422-9091
Keller Dual Immersion MS 6-8
7020 Brittain St 90808 562-421-8851
Thomas Espinoza, prin.
Lindbergh STEM Academy 600/6-8
1022 E Market St 90805 562-422-2845
Connie Magee, prin. Fax 423-8176
Lindsey Academy 900/6-8
5075 Daisy Ave 90805 562-423-6451
Renny Chu, prin. Fax 422-3800
Marshall Academy of the Arts 900/6-8
5870 E Wardlow Rd 90808 562-429-7013
Marie Hatwan, prin. Fax 429-6973
McBride HS 200/9-12
7025 E Parkcrest St 90808 562-425-3539
Steve Rockenbach, prin. Fax 420-9590
Millikan HS 4,000/9-12
2800 Snowden Ave 90815 562-425-7441
Michael Navia, prin. Fax 425-1151
Polytechnic HS Vo/Tech
1600 Atlantic Ave 90813 562-591-0581
Diane Prince, prin. Fax 591-0631
Reid Continuation HS 300/Alt
2153 W Hill St 90810 562-989-2098
Jeff Cornejo, prin. Fax 989-2097
Renaissance HS for the Arts 500/9-12
235 E 8th St 90813 562-901-0168
Kimberly Holland, prin. Fax 435-7147
Rogers MS 900/6-8
365 Monrovia Ave 90803 562-434-7411
Douglas Jordan, prin. Fax 434-0581
Sato Academy of Mathematics and Science 9-12
1100 Iroquois Ave 90815 562-598-7611
Mona Merlo, prin.
Stanford MS 1,300/6-8
5871 E Los Arcos St 90815 562-594-9793
David Costa, prin. Fax 594-8591
Stephens MS 800/6-8
1830 W Columbia St 90810 562-595-0841
Salvador Madrigal, prin. Fax 426-5631
Washington MS 1,100/6-8
1450 Cedar Ave 90813 562-591-2434
Megan Traver, prin. Fax 591-6888
Wilson HS 4,100/9-12
4400 E 10th St 90804 562-433-0481
Sandy Blazer, prin. Fax 433-2731
Long Beach School for Adults Adult
3701 E Willow St 90815 562-595-8893
Peter Davis, prin. Fax 988-1486
Other Schools – See Avalon, Carson, Lakewood, Signal Hill

Los Angeles USD
Supt. — See Los Angeles
Rancho Dominguez Preparatory S 1,200/6-12
4110 Santa Fe Ave 90810 310-847-6400
Keri Lew, prin. Fax 518-1022

Regional Occupational Center & Program
Supt. — None
Long Beach USD ROP Vo/Tech
3701 E Willow St Ste B 90815 562-595-8893
Matt Saldana, dir. Fax 424-8976

California State University-Long Beach Post-Sec.
1250 N Bellflower Blvd 90840 562-985-4111
Charter College Long Beach Post-Sec.
100 W Broadway Ste 3000 90802 562-216-7500
DeVry University Post-Sec.
3880 Kilroy Airport Way 90806 562-427-0861
John Wesley Intl. Barber/Beauty Coll Post-Sec.
717 Pine Ave 90813 562-435-7060
Long Beach City College Post-Sec.
4901 E Carson St 90808 562-938-4111
North-West College Post-Sec.
3799 E Burnett St 90815 562-546-5171
Pacific Baptist S 200/K-12
3332 Magnolia Ave 90806 562-426-5214
Br. Charlie Chim, admin. Fax 424-3324
St. Anthony HS 400/9-12
620 Olive Ave 90802 562-435-4496
Mike Schabert, prin. Fax 437-3055
WyoTech Post-Sec.
2161 Technology Pl 90810 562-624-9530

Loomis, Placer, Pop. 6,199
Placer UNHSD
Supt. — See Auburn
Del Oro HS 1,700/9-12
3301 Taylor Rd 95650 916-652-7243
Dan Gayaldo, prin. Fax 652-3706

Los Alamitos, Orange, Pop. 10,908
Los Alamitos USD 9,900/PK-12
10293 Bloomfield St 90720 562-799-4700
Dr. Sherry Kropp Ed.D., supt. Fax 799-4730
www.losal.org
Los Alamitos HS 3,200/9-12
3591 Cerritos Ave 90720 562-799-4780
Dr. Brandon Martinez Ed.D., prin. Fax 799-4798
McAuliffe MS 1,300/6-8
4112 Cerritos Ave 90720 714-816-3320
Ann Allen, prin. Fax 816-3362
Oak MS 1,100/6-8
10821 Oak St 90720 562-799-4740
Erin Kominsky, prin. Fax 799-4773

Los Altos, Santa Clara, Pop. 27,727
Los Altos ESD 4,500/K-8
201 Covington Rd 94024 650-947-1150
Jeffrey Baier, supt. Fax 947-0118
www.lasdschools.org/
Blach IS 500/7-8
1120 Covington Rd 94024 650-934-3800
Bhavna Narula, prin. Fax 968-3918
Egan IS 600/7-8
100 W Portola Ave 94022 650-917-2200
Keith Rocha, prin. Fax 949-3748

Mountain View-Los Altos UNHSD
Supt. — See Mountain View
Los Altos HS 1,800/9-12
201 Almond Ave 94022 650-960-8811
Wynne Satterwhite, prin. Fax 948-8672

Los Altos Hills, Santa Clara, Pop. 7,599

Foothill College Post-Sec.
12345 S El Monte Rd 94022 650-949-7777
Pinewood S - Upper Campus 300/7-12
26800 W Fremont Rd 94022 650-209-3010
Scott Riches, pres. Fax 209-3011

Los Angeles, Los Angeles, Pop. 3,699,911
Compton USD
Supt. — See Compton
Vanguard Learning Center 300/6-8
13305 S San Pedro St 90061 310-898-6050
Doi Johnson, prin. Fax 327-7180

Los Angeles County Office of Education
Supt. — See Downey
Los Angeles County HS for the Arts 600/Alt
5151 State University Dr 90032 323-343-2787
Mitzi Lizarraga, prin. Fax 343-2549

Los Angeles USD 617,100/PK-12
333 S Beaudry Ave 90017 213-241-1000
Michelle King, supt. Fax 241-8442
www.lausd.net
Academic Leadership Community S 400/9-12
322 Lucas Ave 90017 213-240-3815
Tadeo Climaco, prin. Fax 482-0232
Academy for Multilingual Arts & Science 600/9-12
8800 S San Pedro St 90003 323-565-4600
Simone Charles, prin. Fax 750-1084
Adams MS 1,000/6-8
151 W 30th St 90007 213-745-3700
Henry Torres, prin. Fax 749-8542
Alonzo Community Day S 200/7-12
5755 Fountain Ave 90028 323-817-6500
Joseph Zanki, prin. Fax 817-6599
Ambassador School of Global Leadership 700/6-12
701 S Catalina St 90005 213-480-4540
Gregory Jackson, prin. Fax 480-4599
Apex Academy 300/7-12
1309 N Wilton Pl 90028 323-817-6550
Cesar Lopez, prin. Fax 817-6555
Audubon MS 700/6-8
4120 11th Ave 90008 323-290-6300
Charmain Young, prin. Fax 296-2433
Bancroft MS 900/6-8
929 N Las Palmas Ave 90038 323-993-3400
Maria Rico, prin. Fax 461-8246
Belmont HS 1,000/9-12
1575 W 2nd St 90026 213-241-4300
Kristen McGregor, prin. Fax 250-9706
Belvedere MS 1,400/6-8
312 N Record Ave 90063 323-266-5400
Helen Carrillo, prin. Fax 269-6769
Berendo MS 1,000/6-8
1157 S Berendo St 90006 213-739-5600
Rosa Trujillo, prin. Fax 382-8599
Bethune MS 1,400/6-8
155 W 69th St 90003 323-541-1800
L.G. Garrett, prin. Fax 759-1271
Boyle Heights Continuation S 100/Alt
544 S Mathews St 90033 323-264-8070
Leigh Orr, prin. Fax 266-7177
Bravo Medical Magnet HS 1,900/9-12
1200 Cornwell St 90033 323-227-4400
Maria Flores, prin. Fax 342-9139
Burbank MS 900/6-8
6460 N Figueroa St 90042 323-340-4400
Christine Moore, prin. Fax 257-7420
Burroughs MS 1,900/6-8
600 S McCadden Pl 90005 323-549-5000
Steve Martinez, prin. Fax 934-9051

Business and Technology S 6-8
1420 E Adams Blvd 90011 323-846-2235
Maria Ozaeta, prin.
Carver MS 1,100/6-8
4410 McKinley Ave 90011 323-846-2900
Latasha Buck, prin. Fax 232-5344
Castro MS 500/6-8
1575 W 2nd St 90026 213-241-4415
Erick Mitchell, prin. Fax 241-4418
Central HS Tri-C 600/Alt
716 E 14th St 90021 213-745-1901
Helene Cameron, prin. Fax 748-3458
Cheviot Hills Continuation S 100/Alt
9200 Cattaraugus Ave 90034 310-838-8462
Mary Reid, prin. Fax 839-4051
City of Angels Independent Study 1,900/Alt
221 S Eastman Ave 90063 323-415-8350
Vince Carbino, prin. Fax 261-0618
Clinton MS 900/6-8
3500 S Hill St 90007 323-235-7200
Andres Favela, prin. Fax 846-0054
Cochran MS 1,000/6-8
4066 W Johnnie Cochran Vst 90019 323-730-4300
Gilberto Samuel, prin. Fax 733-9106
Communication and Technology S 500/9-12
6100 S Central Ave 90001 323-846-2118
Cynthia Gonzalez, prin.
Cortines S of Visual & Performing Arts 1,700/9-12
450 N Grand Ave 90012 213-217-8600
Kenneth Martinez, prin. Fax 928-0933
Crenshaw STEM Magnet HS 1,100/9-12
5010 11th Ave 90043 323-290-7800
Lenalda Corley, prin. Fax 292-6712
Dorsey HS 1,200/9-12
3537 Farmdale Ave 90016 323-298-8400
Sean Gaston, prin. Fax 298-8501
Downtown Business HS 1,000/9-12
1081 W Temple St 90012 213-481-0371
Jared DuPree, prin. Fax 482-0792
Drew MS 1,000/6-8
8511 Compton Ave 90001 323-826-1700
Nnamdi Uzor, prin. Fax 583-6030
Eagle Rock JSHS 2,600/7-12
1750 Yosemite Dr 90041 323-340-3500
Mylene Keipp, prin. Fax 255-3398
Early College Academy 200/10-12
400 W Washington Blvd 90015 323-521-1200
Michael Dean, prin.
Edison MS 1,200/6-8
6500 Hooper Ave 90001 323-826-2500
Salvador Velasco, prin. Fax 581-8389
Ellington Continuation HS 100/Alt
1541 W 110th St 90047 323-418-4130
Cecil McLinn, prin. Fax 754-1281
El Sereno MS 1,300/6-8
2839 N Eastern Ave 90032 323-224-4700
Joyce Dara, prin. Fax 223-9024
Environmental & Social Policy Magnet 300/9-12
3501 N Broadway 90031 323-441-4577
David Ayala, prin. Fax 224-5992
Fairfax HS 2,100/9-12
7850 Melrose Ave 90046 323-370-1200
Carmina Nacorda, prin. Fax 651-5803
Fine and Performing Arts Academy 700/9-12
300 E 53rd St 90011 323-846-4700
Hugo Carlos, prin. Fax 846-4714
Foshay Learning Center 2,000/Alt
3751 S Harvard Blvd 90018 323-373-2700
Tracy Triplett-Murray, prin. Fax 733-2120
Franklin HS 1,500/9-12
820 N Avenue 54 90042 323-550-2000
Regina Marquez Martinez, prin. Fax 258-5940
Fremont HS 2,300/9-12
7676 S San Pedro St 90003 323-565-1200
Pedro Avalos, prin. Fax 971-5890
Garfield HS 2,400/9-12
5101 E 6th St 90022 323-981-5500
Mario Cantu, prin. Fax 268-4957
Girls Academic Leadership Academy 6-12
1067 West Blvd 90019 323-900-4533
Elizabeth Hicks, prin.
Gompers MS 800/6-8
234 E 112th St 90061 323-241-4000
Elizabeth Pratt, prin. Fax 418-0778
Green Design S 400/9-12
6100 S Central Ave 90001 323-846-2108
William Lupejkis, prin.
Griffith MS 1,400/6-8
4765 E 4th St 90022 323-266-7400
Rose Anne Ruiz, prin. Fax 268-6375
Hamilton HS 3,000/9-12
2955 S Robertson Blvd 90034 310-280-1400
Brenda Pensamiento, prin. Fax 842-8663
Harte Prep MS 900/6-8
9301 S Hoover St 90044 323-242-5400
Luz Cortes, prin. Fax 757-0408
Hawkins Community Health Advocates S 9-12
825 W 60th St 90044 323-789-1282
Claudia Rojas, prin.
Hawkins Critical Design and Gaming S 9-12
825 W 60th St 90044 323-789-1282
Patricia Hanson, prin.
Hawkins RISE S, 825 W 60th St 90044 9-12
Anthony Terry, prin. 323-789-1282
Highland Park Continuation S 100/Alt
928 N Avenue 53 90042 323-254-3421
Irene Narvaez, prin. Fax 340-8132
Hollenbeck MS 1,300/6-8
2510 E 6th St 90023 323-780-3000
Randy Romero, prin. Fax 269-8137
Hollywood HS 1,500/9-12
1521 N Highland Ave 90028 323-993-1700
Alejandra Sanchez, prin. Fax 957-0238
Hope Continuation S 100/Alt
7840 Towne Ave 90003 323-565-1292
Tipawan McGee, prin. Fax 565-1319

Irving Magnet MS 600/6-8
3010 Estara Ave 90065 323-259-3700
Kirk Roskam, prin. Fax 254-6447
Jefferson HS 1,100/9-12
1319 E 41st St 90011 323-521-1200
Agustin Gonzalez, prin. Fax 231-4755
Kahlo Continuation HS 200/Alt
1924 S Los Angeles St 90011 213-763-1090
Sandra Washington, prin. Fax 763-1092
Kim Academy 800/6-8
615 Shatto Pl 90005 213-739-6500
Edward Colacion, prin. Fax 384-3083
King-Drew Medical Magnet HS 1,600/9-12
1601 E 120th St 90059 323-566-0420
Reginald Brookens, prin. Fax 567-1429
King MS 1,700/6-8
4201 Fountain Ave 90029 323-644-6700
Mark Naulls, prin. Fax 913-3594
LACES Magnet S 1,600/6-12
5931 W 18th St 90035 323-549-5900
Harold Boger, prin. Fax 938-8737
Liechty MS 1,200/6-8
650 S Union Ave 90017 213-989-1200
Adalberto Vega, prin. Fax 484-2700
Lincoln HS 1,300/9-12
3501 N Broadway 90031 323-441-4600
Jose Torres, prin. Fax 223-1291
Los Angeles Academy 1,600/6-8
644 E 56th St 90011 323-238-1800
Raul Correa, prin. Fax 231-0136
Los Angeles HS 1,500/9-12
4650 W Olympic Blvd 90019 323-900-2700
Helena Yoon-Fontamillas, prin. Fax 936-8455
Los Angeles HS For The Arts 400/9-12
701 S Catalina St 90005 213-480-4600
Susan Canjura, prin. Fax 480-4650
Los Angeles River S 300/9-12
2050 N San Fernando Rd 90065 323-276-5535
Kristine Puich, prin. Fax 276-5544
Los Angeles S of Global Studies 400/9-12
322 Lucas Ave 90017 213-240-3850
Christian Quintero, prin. Fax 240-3875
Los Angeles Technology Center Vo/Tech
3721 W Washington Blvd 90018 323-732-0153
Juan Jimenez, prin. Fax 731-1568
Mann JHS 500/6-8
7001 S St Andrews Pl 90047 323-541-1900
Orlando Johnson, prin. Fax 758-8203
Manual Arts HS 1,500/9-12
4131 S Vermont Ave 90037 323-846-7300
Erica Thomas, prin. Fax 232-0837
Marina Del Rey MS 700/6-8
12500 Braddock Dr 90066 310-578-2700
Lorraine Machado, prin. Fax 821-3248
Markham MS 1,200/6-8
1650 E 104th St 90002 323-568-5500
Luis Montoya, prin. Fax 569-6066
Marlton S 300/Alt
4000 Santo Tomas Dr 90008 323-296-7680
Annick Draghi, prin. Fax 290-1794
Marshall HS 2,500/9-12
3939 Tracy St 90027 323-671-1400
Patricia Heideman, prin. Fax 665-8682
McAlister JSHS 200/Alt
611 S Carondelet St 90057 213-381-2823
Tara Thurston, prin. Fax 384-8947
Mendez HS 700/9-12
1200 Plaza Del Sol St 90033 323-981-5400
Mauro Bautista, prin. Fax 307-0788
Metropolitan Continuation S 200/Alt
727 Wilson St 90021 213-623-4272
Nancy Luna, prin. Fax 629-1069
Middle College HS 400/9-12
1600 W Imperial Hwy Bldg 16 90047 323-418-4700
Betty Washington, prin. Fax 242-2449
Monterey Continuation HS 100/Alt
466 Fraser Ave 90022 323-269-0786
Janine Antoine, prin. Fax 526-0795
Muir MS 1,100/6-8
5929 S Vermont Ave 90044 323-565-2200
Aminika Readeux, prin. Fax 778-9824
Newmark Continuation HS 200/Alt
1575 W 2nd St 90026 213-250-9675
Justin Lauer, prin. Fax 482-3697
New Open World Academy 1,100/K-12
3201 W 8th St 90005 213-480-3700
Charles Smith, prin. Fax 389-1559
Nightingale MS 800/6-8
3311 N Figueroa St 90065 323-224-4800
Rafael Gaeta, prin. Fax 222-4506
Obama Global Preparation Academy 900/6-8
1700 W 46th St 90062 323-421-1700
David Devereaux, prin. Fax 293-2003
Palms MS 1,500/6-8
10860 Woodbine St 90034 310-253-7600
Derek Moriuchi, prin. Fax 559-0397
Partnership Academy for the Arts 9-12
2265 E 103rd St 90002 323-568-4100
Carlos Montes, prin. Fax 249-4709
Performing Arts Community S 400/9-12
6100 S Central Ave 90001 323-846-2136
Sally Lopez, prin.
Phoenix Continuation HS 100/Alt
12971 Zanja St 90066 310-306-8775
Nancy Huerta, prin. Fax 827-3876
Pio Pico MS 600/6-8
1512 Arlington Ave 90019 323-733-8801
Miranda Conston-Ra, prin. Fax 735-2665
Public Service Community S 400/9-12
6100 S Central Ave 90001 323-846-2128
Dennis Fulgoni, prin. Fax 846-2122
Pueblo de los Angeles Continuation HS 100/Alt
2506 Alta St 90031 323-223-3258
Michael Olivo, prin. Fax 223-4537
Ramona Opportunity HS 100/Alt
231 S Alma Ave 90063 323-266-7600
Anna Carrasco, prin. Fax 415-8077

Riley HS - Cyesis 200/Alt
1524 E 103rd St 90002 323-563-6692
Linda Roussel, prin. Fax 566-6379
Roosevelt Communication/Media/Tech HS 2,100/9-12
456 S Mathews St 90033 323-780-6500
Benjamin Gertner, prin. Fax 269-5473
Roybal Learning Center 1,200/9-12
1200 Colton St 90026 213-580-6430
Sarah Usmani, prin. Fax 580-6499
Santee Education Complex 1,800/9-12
1921 Maple Ave 90011 213-763-1000
Martin Gomez, prin. Fax 742-9883
School for Visual Arts & Humanities 9-12
701 S Catalina St 90005 213-480-4700
Eftihia Danellis, prin. Fax 480-4750
School of Arts and Culture 6-8
1420 E Adams Blvd 90011 323-846-2245
Anita Maxon, prin.
School of Business and Tourism 500/9-12
322 Lucas Ave 90017 213-240-3800
Nova. Meza, prin. Fax 482-0232
School of History & Dramatic Arts 300/9-12
2050 N San Fernando Rd 90065 323-276-5500
Elsa Mendoza, prin. Fax 276-5514
School of Sci/Tech/ Engineering/Math 9-12
456 S Mathews St 90033 323-780-6537
Jose Espinoza, prin. Fax 269-5473
School of Social Justice 9-12
322 Lucas Ave 90017 213-240-3800
Nova Meza, prin. Fax 482-0232
Solis Learning Academy 200/9-12
319 N Humphreys Ave 90022 323-729-1700
Daniel Gettinger, prin. Fax 264-2002
STEM @ Bernstein S 9-12
1309 N Wilton Pl 90028 323-817-6461
Paul Hirsch, prin. Fax 817-6465
STEM Academy of Boyle Heights 9-12
456 S Mathews Blvd 90033 323-268-1031
Adriana Trejo, prin. Fax 780-3069
Stevenson MS 1,800/6-8
725 S Indiana St 90023 323-780-6400
Leo Gonzalez, prin. Fax 265-3952
Studio S 6-8
2050 San Fernando Rd 90065 323-225-4542
Leah Raphael, prin. Fax 276-5444
32nd Street / USC MaST S 1,100/K-12
822 W 32nd St 90007 213-748-0126
Ezequiel Gonzalez, prin. Fax 744-1608
Torres Engineering and Technology Acad 100/9-12
4211 Dozier St 90063 323-265-6795
Luis Rodriguez, prin. Fax 265-6796
Torres Humanitas Visual Arts & Tech 100/9-12
4211 Dozier St 90063 323-265-6830
Deborah Lowe, prin. Fax 265-6831
Torres Performing Arts Academy 200/9-11
4211 Dozier St 90063 323-265-6725
Carolyn McKnight, prin. Fax 265-6726
Torres Renaissance Academy 100/9-12
4211 Dozier St 90063 323-265-6760
Raul Fernandez, prin. Fax 265-6761
Torres Social Justice Leadership Academy 100/9-12
4211 Dozier St 90063 323-265-6665
Roseann Cazares, prin. Fax 265-6866
Twain MS 700/6-8
2224 Walgrove Ave 90066 310-305-3100
Althea Ford, prin. Fax 398-1627
UCLA Community S 1,000/K-12
700 S Mariposa Ave 90005 213-480-3750
Leyda Garcia, prin. Fax 480-3759
University HS 1,800/9-12
11800 Texas Ave 90025 310-914-3500
Eric Davidson, prin. Fax 478-6535
USC Hybrid HS 200/9-12
350 S Figueroa St Ste 100 90071 213-929-1046
Mide Macaulay, prin. Fax 929-1047
Venice HS 2,100/9-12
13000 Venice Blvd 90066 310-577-4200
Oryla Wiedoeft, prin. Fax 306-3249
View Park Continuation HS 100/Alt
4701 Rodeo Rd 90016 323-292-0331
Donald Moorer, prin. Fax 292-7920
Virgil MS 1,000/6-8
152 N Vermont Ave 90004 213-368-2800
William Gurr, prin. Fax 383-8774
Washington Preparatory HS 1,300/9-12
10860 S Denker Ave 90047 323-418-4000
Dechele Byrd, prin. Fax 754-3517
Webster MS 500/6-8
11330 Graham Pl 90064 310-235-4600
Peter Benefiel, prin. Fax 477-0146
WESM Health/Sports Medicine HS 1,300/9-12
7400 W Manchester Ave 90045 310-338-2400
Debra Bryant, prin. Fax 410-1067
West Adams Preparatory HS 1,700/9-12
1500 W Washington Blvd 90007 323-373-2500
Erica Nava, prin. Fax 373-2518
West Hollywood Community Day School 100/Alt
1049 N Fairfax Ave 90046 323-654-4155
Karen Cheval, prin. Fax 654-5635
Whitman Continuation HS 100/Alt
7795 Rosewood Ave 90036 323-651-0645
Mark Leos, prin. Fax 653-9214
Widney HS 200/Alt
2302 S Gramercy Pl 90018 323-731-8633
Carrie Delisle, prin. Fax 734-8048
Wilson HS 1,700/9-12
4500 Multnomah St 90032 323-276-1600
Luis Lopez, prin. Fax 223-7936
Wright Magnet MS 600/6-8
6550 W 80th St 90045 310-258-6600
Christina Wantz, prin. Fax 568-8942
Young Continuation HS 50/Alt
3051 W 52nd St 90043 323-296-3258
Wanda Robinson, prin. Fax 292-6595
East Los Angeles Occupational Center Adult
2100 Marengo St 90033 323-276-7000
Andrea Rodriguez, prin. Fax 223-6365

East Los Angeles Skills Center Adult
3921 Selig Pl 90031 323-224-5970
Donna Brashear, prin. Fax 222-2351
Evans Community Adult Education Adult
717 N Figueroa St 90012 213-626-7151
Clifton DeCordoba, prin. Fax 626-4487
Friedman Occupational Center Adult
1646 S Olive St 90015 213-765-2400
Bernadine Gonzalez, prin. Fax 748-7406
Waters Employment Preparation Center Adult
10925 S Central Ave 90059 323-564-1431
Elsa Madrid, prin. Fax 566-0147
Other Schools – See Arleta, Bell, Canoga Park, Carson, Chatsworth, Cudahy, Gardena, Granada Hills, Harbor City, Hollywood, Huntington Park, Lomita, Long Beach, Maywood, Mission Hills, North Hills, North Hollywood, Northridge, Pacoima, Panorama City, Rancho Palos Verdes, Reseda, San Fernando, San Pedro, Sherman Oaks, South Gate, Sunland, Sun Valley, Sylmar, Tarzana, Tujunga, Van Nuys, Venice, Walnut Park, Wilmington, Woodland Hills

Regional Occupational Center & Program
Supt. — None
Los Angeles USD ROC/P Vo/Tech
333 S Beaudry Ave 90017 213-241-3162
Joseph Stark, dir.

ABCO Technology Post-Sec.
6733 S Sepulveda Blvd #106 90045 310-216-3067
Abraham Lincoln University Post-Sec.
3530 Wilshire Blvd Ste 1430 90010 213-252-5100
Academy for Jewish Religion Post-Sec.
574 Hilgard Ave 90024 310-824-1586
Advanced Computing Institute Post-Sec.
3470 Wilshire Blvd Ste 1100 90010 213-383-8999
AMDA College and Conservatory Post-Sec.
6305 Yucca St 90028 323-469-3300
American Career College - Los Angeles Post-Sec.
4021 Rosewood Ave 90004 323-668-7555
American Evangelical University Post-Sec.
1818 S Western Ave Ste 409 90006 323-643-0301
American Film Institute Conservatory Post-Sec.
2021 N Western Ave 90027 323-856-7600
American Jewish University Post-Sec.
15600 Mulholland Dr 90077 310-476-9777
American University Prep S 50/9-12
345 S Figueroa St Ste 100 90071 213-400-4585
Dr. Gary Woods, head sch
Angeles College Post-Sec.
3440 Wilshire Blvd Ste 310 90010 213-487-2211
Archer S for Girls 400/6-12
11725 W Sunset Blvd 90049 310-873-7000
Elizabeth English, head sch Fax 873-7070
Arete Preparatory Academy 50/9-12
11500 W Olympic Blvd # 318 90064 310-478-9900
Argosy University Los Angeles Post-Sec.
5230 Pacific Concourse #200 90045 310-531-9700
Associated Technical College Post-Sec.
1670 Wilshire Blvd 90017 213-353-1845
Bais Yaakov S 300/9-12
7353 Beverly Blvd 90036 323-938-3231
Bishop Conaty-Our Lady Loretto HS 400/9-12
2900 W Pico Blvd 90006 323-737-0012
Richard Spicer, prin. Fax 737-1749
Bishop Mora Salesian HS 500/9-12
960 S Soto St 90023 323-261-7124
Sam Robles, prin. Fax 261-7600
Bnos Devorah HS 50/9-12
461 N La Brea Ave 90036 323-930-0047
Shulamith May, head sch Fax 930-1901
Bnos Esther HS 9-12
116 N La Brea Ave 90036 310-933-4171
Brentwood JSHS 700/7-12
100 S Barrington Pl 90049 310-476-9633
Dr. Michael Riera, head sch Fax 476-4087
Bryan University Post-Sec.
3580 Wilshire Blvd Ste 400 90010 213-484-8850
California Healing Arts College Post-Sec.
12217 Santa Monica Blvd 90025 310-826-7622
California State University-Los Angeles Post-Sec.
5151 State University Dr 90032 323-343-3000
Cathedral HS 700/9-12
1253 Bishops Rd 90012 323-225-2438
Br. John Montgomery, prin. Fax 222-7223
CBD College Post-Sec.
3699 Wilshire Blvd Ste 400 90010 213-427-2200
Charles R. Drew Univ. of Med. & Science Post-Sec.
1731 E 120th St 90059 323-563-4800
Chicago Sch. of Professional Psychology Post-Sec.
617 W 7th St 90017 800-721-8072
Chicago Sch of Professional Psychology Post-Sec.
1145 Gayley Ave 90024 310-208-4240
Children's Hospital of Los Angeles Post-Sec.
4650 W Sunset Blvd 90027 323-669-2301
Coast Career Institute Post-Sec.
1354 S Hill St 90015 213-235-0606
Colburn School Post-Sec.
200 S Grand Ave 90012 213-621-2200
Concord Law School of Kaplan University Post-Sec.
10866 Wilshire Blvd # 1200 90024 310-689-3200
Dongguk University Post-Sec.
440 Shatto Pl 90020 213-487-0110
East Los Angeles Occupational Center Post-Sec.
2100 Marengo St 90033 323-223-1283
Episcopal S of Los Angeles 50/6-12
6325 Santa Monica Blvd 90038 323-462-3752
Rev. Maryetta Anschutz, head sch
Everest College Post-Sec.
3460 Wilshire Blvd Ste 500 90010 213-388-9950
Everest College Post-Sec.
3000 S Robertson Blvd # 300 90034 310-840-5777
FIDM Fashion Institute of Design Post-Sec.
919 S Grand Ave 90015 213-624-1200
Fremont College Post-Sec.
3440 Wilshire Blvd Fl 10 90010 800-373-6668
Fusion Academy 6-12
1640 S Sepulveda Blvd # 100 90025 310-445-2516
Fusion Academy 6-12
825 Colorado Blvd Ste 118 90041 323-258-2012
Gnomon School of Visual Effects Post-Sec.
1015 N Cahuenga Blvd 90038 323-466-6663
Harvard-Westlake MS 700/7-9
700 N Faring Rd 90077 310-274-7281
Jeanne Huybrechts, head sch Fax 288-3331
Hebrew Union College Post-Sec.
3077 University Ave 90007 213-749-3424
Holy Trinity S 100/5-8
3716 Boyce Ave 90039 323-663-2064
Karen Lloyd, prin. Fax 664-2581
ICDC College Post-Sec.
5422 W Sunset Blvd 90027 323-468-0404
ICL Academy 9-12
1201 W 5th St Ste F-160 90017 424-285-5519
Immaculate Heart MSHS 700/6-12
5515 Franklin Ave 90028 323-461-3651
Virginia Hurst, pres. Fax 462-0610
International Christian Education Coll. Post-Sec.
3807 Wilshire Blvd Ste 730 90010 213-368-0316
International Reformed University/Sem Post-Sec.
125 S Vermont Ave 90004 213-381-0081
John Tracy Clinic Post-Sec.
806 W Adams Blvd 90007 213-748-5481
Kabbaz HS 200/9-12
3261 Overland Ave 90034 310-836-3464
Learnet Academy Post-Sec.
3251 W 6th St 90020 213-387-4242
Los Angeles Adventist Academy 200/PK-12
846 E El Segundo Blvd 90059 323-743-8818
Dr. Lilly Nelson, prin. Fax 324-3207
Los Angeles City College Post-Sec.
855 N Vermont Ave 90029 323-953-4000
Los Angeles Co. Coll. Nursing/Alld Hlth Post-Sec.
1237 N Mission Rd 90033 323-226-4911
Los Angeles ORT College Post-Sec.
6435 Wilshire Blvd 90048 323-966-5444
Los Angeles Pacific College Post-Sec.
3550 Wilshire Blvd Ste 460 90010 213-384-2318
Los Angeles Southwest College Post-Sec.
1600 W Imperial Hwy 90047 323-241-5225
Los Angeles Trade-Technical College Post-Sec.
400 W Washington Blvd 90015 213-763-7000
Loyola HS 1,200/9-12
1901 Venice Blvd 90006 213-381-5121
Frank Kozakowski, prin. Fax 368-3819
Loyola Marymount University Post-Sec.
1 LMU Dr 90045 310-338-2700
Marinello School of Beauty Post-Sec.
1241 S Soto St Ste 101 90023 323-980-9253
Marinello School of Beauty Post-Sec.
6111 Wilshire Blvd 90048 323-938-2005
Marlborough S 500/7-12
250 S Rossmore Ave 90004 323-935-1147
Priscilla Sands, head sch Fax 933-0542
Marymount HS 400/9-12
10643 W Sunset Blvd 90077 310-472-1205
Jacqueline Landry, head sch Fax 476-0910
Mesivta Birkas Yitzchok 100/9-12
6022 W Pico Blvd 90035 323-937-4748
Methodist Theological Seminary Post-Sec.
2525 James M Wood Blvd 90006 213-386-0080
Milken Community S 700/7-12
15800 Zeldins Way 90049 310-440-3500
Gary Weisserman, head sch Fax 471-5139
Mt. St. Mary's College Post-Sec.
12001 Chalon Rd 90049 310-954-4000
Mt. St. Mary's College - Doheny Campus Post-Sec.
10 Chester Pl 90007 213-477-2500
New Covenant Academy 100/K-12
3119 W 6th St 90020 213-487-5437
Dr. Jason Song, prin. Fax 487-5430
Notre Dame Academy for Girls 400/9-12
2851 Overland Ave 90064 310-839-5289
Lilliam Paetzold, prin. Fax 839-7957
Occidental College Post-Sec.
1600 Campus Rd 90041 323-259-2500
Otis College of Art and Design Post-Sec.
9045 Lincoln Blvd 90045 310-665-6800
Pacific States University Post-Sec.
3450 Wilshire Blvd Fl 5 90010 323-731-2383
Pacific Union College Post-Sec.
1720 E Cesar E Chavez Ave 90033 323-268-5000
Pilgrim S 300/PK-12
540 S Commonwealth Ave 90020 213-385-7351
Paul Barsky, head sch Fax 386-7264
Pilibos Armenian S 700/K-12
1615 N Alexandria Ave 90027 323-668-2661
Price III Christian S 200/PK-12
7901 S Vermont Ave 90044 323-565-4199
Madeline Butler, prin. Fax 753-6770
Ribet Academy 400/PK-12
2911 N San Fernando Rd 90065 323-344-4330
Sacred Heart HS 200/9-12
2111 Griffin Ave 90031 323-225-2209
Raymond Saborio, prin. Fax 225-5046
SAE Institute of Technology Post-Sec.
6565 W Sunset Blvd Ste 100 90028 323-466-6323
St. Mary Magdalen S 100/5-8
1223 S Corning St 90035 310-652-4723
Nuria Gordillo, prin. Fax 933-7453
Shalhevet HS 200/9-12
910 S Fairfax Ave 90036 323-930-9333
Rabbi Ari Segal, head sch Fax 930-9444
Shepherd University School of Theology Post-Sec.
3200 N San Fernando Rd 90065 323-550-8888
Southern California Inst. Architecture Post-Sec.
960 E 3rd St 90013 213-613-2200
Southern CA Univ School of Oriental Med. Post-Sec.
1541 Wilshire Blvd Fl 3 90017 213-413-9500
Southwestern Law School Post-Sec.
3050 Wilshire Blvd 90010 213-738-6700
STAR Prep Academy 100/6-12
1518 S Robertson Blvd 90035 323-842-8808
Zahir Robb, head sch
SUTECH School of Voc/Tech Training Post-Sec.
3455 E Olympic Blvd 90023 323-262-3210
Theatre of Arts Post-Sec.
6755 Hollywood Blvd Fl 2 90028 323-463-2500
Union Institute & University Post-Sec.
6701 Center Dr W Ste 1200 90045 310-417-3500
United Healthcare Careers College Post-Sec.
1625 W Olympic Blvd Ste 708 90015 213-384-0900
Universal College of Beauty Post-Sec.
8619 S Vermont Ave 90044 323-750-5750
Universal College of Beauty Post-Sec.
3419 W 43rd Pl 90008 323-298-0045
University of California Post-Sec.
1147 Murphy Hall # 951436 90095 310-825-4321
University of Philosophical Research Post-Sec.
3910 Los Feliz Blvd 90027 323-663-2167
University of Southern California Post-Sec.
University Park 90089 213-740-2311
Verbum Dei HS 300/9-12
11100 S Central Ave 90059 323-564-6651
Dr. Michael Mandala, prin. Fax 564-9009
Virginia School Center Post-Sec.
1033 S Broadway 90015 213-747-8292
West Los Angeles VA Medical Center Post-Sec.
Wilshire & Sawtelle Blvds 90073 310-824-3132
Westwood College - Los Angeles Post-Sec.
3250 Wilshire Blvd Fl 400 90010 213-739-9999
Wildwood S 300/K-12
11811 W Olympic Blvd 90064 310-478-7189
Landis Green, head sch Fax 478-6875
Windward S 500/7-12
11350 Palms Blvd 90066 310-391-7127
Thomas Gilder, head sch Fax 397-5655
World Mission University Post-Sec.
500 Shatto Pl Ste 600 90020 213-385-2322
Yeshiva Gedolah of Los Angeles HS 100/9-12
5444 W Olympic Blvd 90036 323-938-2071
Rabbi Yossi Gross, dir. Fax 938-4650
Yeshiva Ohr Elchonon Chabad Post-Sec.
7215 Waring Ave 90046 323-937-3763
Yeshiva Ohr Elchonon Chabad West Coast 100/9-12
7215 Waring Ave 90046 323-937-3763
Yeshivat Ohr Chanoch 9-12
8906 W Pico Blvd 90035 323-274-9800
Yeshiva University Girls HS 200/9-12
1619 S Robertson Blvd 90035 310-203-0755
Rabbi Abraham Lieberman, head sch Fax 551-0312
Yeshiva University Los Angeles Boys HS 200/9-12
9760 W Pico Blvd 90035 310-203-3180
Yo San Univ. of Traditional Chinese Med. Post-Sec.
13315 W Washington Blvd 90066 310-577-3000

Los Banos, Merced, Pop. 35,167

Los Banos USD 10,000/K-12
1717 S 11th St 93635 209-826-3801
Dean Bubar, supt. Fax 826-6810
www.losbanosusd.k12.ca.us
Creekside JHS 7-8
1401 Prairie Springs Dr 93635 209-826-1005
Carolina Moreno, prin. Fax 826-1051
Crossroads Alternative Education Center 100/Alt
265 Mercey Springs Rd Ste C 93635 209-826-4013
Barbara Severns Ed.D., prin. Fax 826-4104
Los Banos HS 1,200/9-12
1966 S 11th St 93635 209-826-6033
Veli Gurgen, prin. Fax 827-4156
Los Banos JHS 1,600/7-8
1750 San Luis St 93635 209-826-0867
Deolinda Brasil, prin. Fax 826-8532
Pacheco HS 1,500/9-12
200 Ward Rd 93635 209-827-4506
Daniel Sutton, prin. Fax 827-4715
San Luis HS 200/Alt
125 7th St 93635 209-826-8410
Chan Meas, prin. Fax 826-2252

Merced County Office of Education
Supt. — See Merced
Valley Los Banos Community S 100/Alt
715 W H St 93635 209-827-5600
Lori Gattuso, prin. Fax 827-1486

Merced College-Los Banos Campus Post-Sec.
22240 Highway 152 93635 209-826-3495

Los Gatos, Santa Clara, Pop. 28,259

Campbell UNESD
Supt. — See Campbell
Rolling Hills MS 1,000/5-8
1585 More Ave 95032 408-364-4235
Cynthia Dodd, prin. Fax 341-7070

Loma Prieta JUNESD 500/PK-8
23800 Summit Rd 95033 408-353-1101
Corey Kidwell, supt. Fax 353-8051
www.loma.k12.ca.us
English MS 200/6-8
23800 Summit Rd 95033 408-353-1123
Denee Signorelli, prin. Fax 353-5024

Los Gatos UNESD 3,300/K-8
17010 Roberts Rd 95032 408-335-2000
Diana Abbati, supt. Fax 395-6481
www.lgusd.org
Fisher MS 1,200/6-8
19195 Fisher Ave 95032 408-335-2300
Lisa Fraser, prin. Fax 356-7616

Los Gatos-Saratoga JUNHSD 3,200/9-12
17421 Farley Rd W 95030 408-354-2520
Bob Mistele, supt. Fax 354-4198
www.lgsuhsd.org
Los Gatos HS 1,800/9-12
20 High School Ct 95030 408-354-2730
Kristina Grasty, prin. Fax 354-3742
Other Schools – See Saratoga

Fusion Academy 6-12
50 University Ave Ste A300 95030 408-354-0743
Melissa Mayes, head sch

Los Molinos, Tehama, Pop. 1,963
Los Molinos USD 600/K-12
7851 State Highway 99E 96055 530-384-7826
Charles Ward, supt. Fax 384-7832
www.lmusd.net
Los Molinos Community Day S 50/Alt
7851 State Highway 99E 96055 530-384-7900
Cliff Curry, coord.
Los Molinos HS 200/9-12
PO Box 609 96055 530-384-7900
Cliff Curry, prin. Fax 384-1534

Los Nietos, Los Angeles, Pop. 24,164
Los Nietos ESD 1,800/PK-8
8324 Westman Ave 90606 562-692-0271
Jonathan Vasquez, supt. Fax 699-0082
www.losnietos.k12.ca.us
Los Nietos MS 400/7-8
11425 Rivera Rd 90606 562-695-0637
Shanonn Brann Zelaya, prin. Fax 695-3805

Los Olivos, Santa Barbara, Pop. 1,116

Dunn S 200/6-12
PO Box 98 93441 805-688-6471
Mike Beck, head sch Fax 686-2078
Midland S 100/9-12
PO Box 8 93441 805-688-5114
Christopher Barnes, head sch Fax 686-2470

Los Osos, San Luis Obispo, Pop. 13,912
San Luis Coastal USD
Supt. — See San Luis Obispo
Los Osos MS 600/6-8
1555 El Morro Ave 93402 805-534-2835
Andre Illig, prin. Fax 528-5133

Lost Hills, Kern, Pop. 2,409
Lost Hills Union ESD 600/K-8
21109 Highway 46 93249 661-797-2626
Harrison Favereaux, supt. Fax 797-2580
www.losthills.k12.ca.us
Thomas MS 200/6-8
20979 Lobos Ct 93249 661-797-2626
Veronica Sanchez-Gregory, prin. Fax 797-3015

Lower Lake, Lake, Pop. 1,225
Konocti USD 2,800/K-12
PO Box 759 95457 707-994-6475
Donna Becnel, supt. Fax 994-0210
www.konoctiusd.org
Blue Heron S 100/Alt
9345 Winchester St 95457 707-994-1033
Heather Koehler, prin. Fax 994-4121
Carle Continuation HS 100/Alt
PO Box 309 95457 707-994-1033
Matthew Strahl, prin. Fax 994-4121
Lewis Alternative S 100/Alt
PO Box 5000 95457 707-994-2045
Melissa Lambert, prin. Fax 994-6807
Lower Lake HS 700/8-12
PO Box 799 95457 707-994-6471
Melissa Lambert, prin. Fax 994-4050
Other Schools – See Clearlake

Loyalton, Sierra, Pop. 752
Sierra-Plumas JUSD 400/K-12
PO Box 955 96118 530-993-1660
Merrill Grant Ed.D., supt. Fax 993-0828
www.sierracountyofficeofeducation.org
Loyalton HS 100/7-12
PO Box 37 96118 530-993-4454
Tom Jones, prin. Fax 993-4667
Sierra Pass HS, PO Box 37 96118 50/Alt
Tom Jones, prin. 530-993-1660
Other Schools – See Downieville

Lucerne Valley, San Bernardino, Pop. 5,647
Lucerne Valley USD 2,700/PK-12
8560 Aliento Rd 92356 760-248-6108
Peter Livingston, supt. Fax 248-6677
lucernevalleyusd.org
Community Day S 50/Alt
8560 Aliento Rd 92356 760-248-2408
Peter Livingston, admin. Fax 248-6677
Lucerne Valley JSHS 200/7-12
8560 Aliento Rd 92356 760-248-2124
Douglas Ferber, prin. Fax 248-2162
Mountain View HS 50/Alt
8560 Aliento Rd 92356 760-248-2408
Peter Livingston, admin. Fax 248-6677

Lynwood, Los Angeles, Pop. 69,209
Lynwood USD 14,200/K-12
11321 Bullis Rd 90262 310-886-1600
Paul Gothold, supt. Fax 763-0959
www.lynwood.k12.ca.us
Chavez MS 700/6-8
3898 Abbott Rd 90262 310-886-7300
Dr. Maria Pimienta, prin. Fax 603-2048
Firebaugh HS 1,400/10-12
5246 Martin Luther King Blv 90262 310-886-5200
Hector Preciado, prin. Fax 637-8041
Hosler MS 700/7-8
11300 Spruce St 90262 310-603-1447
Hector Marquez, prin. Fax 764-4124
Lynwood HS 2,300/9-12
4050 E Imperial Hwy 90262 310-603-1582
Carlos Zaragoza, prin. Fax 638-9253
Lynwood MS 1,000/7-9
12124 Bullis Rd 90262 310-603-1466
John Terry, prin. Fax 638-2156
Vista Continuation HS 200/Alt
11300 Wright Rd 90262 310-603-1516
Nina Denson, prin. Fax 537-7295

Lynwood Adult S Adult
4050 E Imperial Hwy 90262 310-604-3096
Bambi Smith, prin. Fax 635-9107

American Career College Post-Sec.
3680 E Imperial Hwy Ste 500 90262 310-900-8050

Mc Arthur, Shasta, Pop. 335
Fall River JUSD
Supt. — See Burney
Fall River Community Day HS 50/Alt
44144 A St 96056 530-336-7154
Greg Hawkins, prin. Fax 336-7071
Fall River JSHS 200/7-12
PO Box 340 96056 530-336-5515
Jeanne Utterback, prin. Fax 336-6256
Soldier Mountain Continuation HS 50/Alt
44144 A St 96056 530-336-7159
Greg Hawkins, prin. Fax 336-7071

Mc Clellan, Sacramento
Twin Rivers USD 26,300/PK-12
5115 Dudley Blvd Bay A 95652 916-566-1600
Dr. Steven Martinez, supt. Fax 566-1784
www.twinriversusd.org
Adult S McClellan Center Adult
5703 Skvarla Ave 95652 916-566-2785
Jackie White, dir. Fax 566-3524
Other Schools – See North Highlands, Rio Linda, Sacramento

Mc Cloud, Siskiyou, Pop. 1,075
Siskiyou UNHSD
Supt. — See Mount Shasta
McCloud HS 50/9-12
PO Box 1530 96057 530-964-2181
Jessica Bowman, prin. Fax 964-2011

Mc Farland, Kern, Pop. 12,620
McFarland USD 3,400/K-12
601 2nd St 93250 661-792-3081
Victor Hopper, supt. Fax 792-2447
www.mcfarlandusd.com
Mc Farland HS 800/9-12
259 W Sherwood Ave 93250 661-792-3126
Brian Bell, prin. Fax 792-2315
McFarland Independent S 50/Alt
599 5th St 93250 661-792-6312
Lori Schultz, admin. Fax 792-6758
Mc Farland MS 700/6-8
405 Mast Ave 93250 661-792-3340
Manuel Cantu, prin. Fax 792-5681
San Joaquin HS 50/Alt
599 5th St 93250 661-792-6312
Lori Schultz, prin. Fax 792-6758

Mc Kinleyville, Humboldt, Pop. 14,503
McKinleyville UNESD 1,200/K-8
2275 Central Ave 95519 707-839-1549
Jan Schmidt, supt. Fax 839-1540
www.edline.net/pages/McKinleyville_Union_Elementary
McKinleyville MS 400/6-8
2285 Central Ave 95519 707-839-1508
Julie Giannini-Previde, prin. Fax 839-2548

Northern Humboldt UNHSD 1,700/K-12
2755 McKinleyville Ave 95519 707-839-6470
Chris Hartley, supt. Fax 839-6457
www.nohum.k12.ca.us
Mc Kinleyville HS 600/9-12
1300 Murray Rd 95519 707-839-6400
Roger Macdonald, prin. Fax 839-6407
Tsurai HS 50/Alt
1300 Murray Rd 95519 707-839-6480
Jack Sheppard, prin. Fax 839-6494
Other Schools – See Arcata

Madera, Madera, Pop. 60,700
Golden Valley USD 2,000/PK-12
37479 Avenue 12, 559-645-7500
Andrew Alvarado, supt. Fax 645-7144
www.gvusd.k12.ca.us
Centennial Independent Study 50/Alt
12150 Road 36, 559-645-3580
Kuljeet Mann, admin.
Independence Continuation HS 50/Alt
12150 Road 36, 559-645-3580
Kuljeet Mann, prin. Fax 645-3581
Liberty HS 600/9-12
12220 Road 36, 559-645-3500
Kirk Delmas, prin. Fax 645-4769
Lincoln Community Day S 50/Alt
12150 Road 36, 559-645-3580
Kuljeet Mann, admin.
Ranchos MS 300/7-8
12455 Road 35 1/2, 559-645-3550
Felipe Piedra, prin. Fax 645-3565
Valley Teen Ranch 50/Alt
12150 Road 36, 559-645-3580
Kuljeet Mann, admin.

Madera County Office of Education 900/
1105 S Madera Ave 93637 559-673-6051
Cecilia Massetti Ed.D., supt. Fax 673-5569
www.maderacoe.k12.ca.us
Enterprise Secondary S 100/Alt
1105 S Madera Ave 93637 559-661-3570
Alyson Crafton, prin. Fax 673-5569

Madera USD 20,200/K-12
1902 Howard Rd 93637 559-675-4500
Edward Gonzalez, supt. Fax 661-7764
www.maderausd.org
Desmond MS 800/7-8
26490 Martin St 93638 559-664-1775
Prince Marshall, prin. Fax 664-1308
Furman HS 200/Alt
955 W Pecan Ave 93637 559-675-4482
David Raygoza, prin. Fax 675-3811

Jefferson MS 1,100/7-8
1407 Sunset Ave 93637 559-673-9286
Jesse Carrasco, prin. Fax 673-6930
King MS 700/7-8
601 Lilly St 93638 559-674-4681
Sabrina Rodriquez, prin. Fax 674-4261
Madera HS 2,200/9-12
200 S L St 93637 559-675-4444
Alan Hollman, prin. Fax 675-4531
Madera South HS 2,700/9-12
705 W Pecan Ave 93637 559-675-4450
Oracio Rodriguez, prin. Fax 675-9985
Mountain Vista HS 50/Alt
1901 Clinton St 93637 559-675-4580
Aimee Anderson, prin. Fax 675-4568
Ripperdan Community Day S Alt
26133 Avenue 7 93637 559-674-0059
Fermin Guzman, prin. Fax 674-7422
Madera Adult S Adult
955 W Pecan Ave 93637 559-675-4425
David Raygoza, prin. Fax 675-4562

Madera Beauty College Post-Sec.
325 N Gateway Dr 93637 559-673-9201

Madison, Yolo, Pop. 493
Esparto USD
Supt. — See Esparto
Madison Community HS 50/Alt
17923 Stephens St 95653 530-787-3165
Veronica Michael, prin. Fax 662-1521

Mad River, Trinity, Pop. 402
Southern Trinity JUSD 100/K-12
680 Van Duzen Rd, 707-574-6237
Peggy Canale, supt. Fax 574-6538
stjusd.org
Mt. Lassic HS 50/Alt
600 Van Duzen Rd, 707-574-6239
Peggy Canale, prin. Fax 574-6538
Southern Trinity HS 50/9-12
600 Van Duzen Rd, 707-574-6239
Peggy Canale, prin. Fax 574-1067

Magalia, Butte, Pop. 10,902
Paradise USD
Supt. — See Paradise
Ridgeview HS 100/Alt
13665 Skyway 95954 530-872-6478
Michael Lerch, prin. Fax 872-6481

Malibu, Los Angeles, Pop. 12,292
Santa Monica-Malibu USD
Supt. — See Santa Monica
Malibu MSHS 1,200/6-12
30215 Morning View Dr 90265 310-457-6801
Brandon Gallagher, prin. Fax 457-4984

Pepperdine University Post-Sec.
24255 Pacific Coast Hwy 90263 310-506-4000

Mammoth Lakes, Mono, Pop. 8,104
Mammoth USD 1,200/K-12
PO Box 3509 93546 760-934-6802
Lois Klein, supt. Fax 934-6803
www.mammothusd.org
Mammoth HS 300/9-12
PO Box 3149 93546 760-934-8541
Chris Powell, prin. Fax 934-3008
Mammoth MS 300/6-8
PO Box 2429 93546 760-934-7072
Annie Rinaldi, prin. Fax 934-7073
Sierra Continuation HS 50/Alt
PO Box 3509 93546 760-934-3702
Lois Klein, supt. Fax 924-0062

Mono County Office of Education
Supt. — See Bridgeport
Work Community S 200/Alt
451 Sierra Park Rd 93546 760-934-0031
Janet Hunt, prin. Fax 934-1443
Mono County Adult S Adult
451 Sierra Park Rd 93546 760-934-0031
Janet Hunt, prin. Fax 934-1443

Manhattan Beach, Los Angeles, Pop. 33,631
Manhattan Beach USD 6,900/PK-12
325 S Peck Ave 90266 310-318-7345
Dr. Michael Matthews, supt. Fax 303-3822
www.mbusd.org
Manhattan Beach MS 1,500/6-8
325 S Peck Ave 90266 310-545-4878
Kim Linz, prin. Fax 303-3829
Mira Costa HS 2,500/9-12
325 S Peck Ave 90266 310-318-7337
Dr. Ben Dale, prin. Fax 303-3814

Manteca, San Joaquin, Pop. 64,370
Manteca USD 22,800/K-12
PO Box 32 95336 209-825-3200
Jason Messer, supt. Fax 858-7570
www.mantecausd.net
Calla Continuation HS 200/Alt
130 S Austin Rd 95336 209-858-7230
Kathy Crouse, prin. Fax 858-7505
East Union HS 1,500/9-12
1700 N Union Rd 95336 209-858-7270
Raul Mora, prin. Fax 825-3148
Manteca Community Day S 50/Alt
737 W Yosemite Ave 95337 209-858-7380
Gerald Braxton, prin. Fax 858-7526
Manteca HS 1,500/9-12
450 E Yosemite Ave 95336 209-858-7340
Frank Gonzales, prin. Fax 825-3158
Manteca Unified Vocational Academy Vo/Tech
2271 W Louise Ave 95337 209-858-7460
Diane Medeiros, prin. Fax 858-7524

McParland S | 700/3-8
1601 Northgate Dr 95336 | 209-858-7290
Dale Borgeson, prin. | Fax 858-7510
Sierra HS | 1,400/9-12
1700 Thomas St 95337 | 209-858-7410
Steve Clark, prin. | Fax 825-3198
Manteca Adult S | Adult
2271 W Louise Ave 95337 | 209-858-7330
Diane Medeiros, prin. | Fax 858-7524
Other Schools – See Lathrop, Stockton

Maricopa, Kern, Pop. 1,126
Maricopa USD | 1,000/K-12
955 Stanislaus St 93252 | 661-769-8231
Scott Meier, supt. | Fax 769-8168
maricopaschools.org
Maricopa HS | 100/9-12
955 Stanislaus St 93252 | 661-769-8231
Scott Meier, prin. | Fax 769-8168
Maricopa MS | 100/6-8
955 Stanislaus St 93252 | 661-769-8231
Fax 769-8168

Marina, Monterey, Pop. 17,783
Monterey Peninsula USD
Supt. — See Monterey
Los Arboles MS | 600/6-8
294 Hillcrest Ave 93933 | 831-384-3550
Stephanie Herrera, prin. | Fax 384-6353
Marina HS | 600/9-12
298 Patton Pkwy 93933 | 831-583-2060
Rebecca Tyson, prin. | Fax 384-2288

Mariposa, Mariposa, Pop. 2,123
Mariposa County Office of Education | 100/
PO Box 8 95338 | 209-742-0250
Robin Hopper, supt. | Fax 966-4549
www.mariposa.k12.ca.us
Community S, 5171 Silva Rd 95338 | 50/Alt
David Naranjo, admin. | 209-742-0290

Mariposa County USD | 1,800/K-12
PO Box 8 95338 | 209-742-0250
Robin Hopper, supt. | Fax 966-4549
www.mariposa.k12.ca.us/
Mariposa County HS | 500/9-12
PO Box 127 95338 | 209-742-0260
Celeste Azevedo, prin. | Fax 742-0264
Other Schools – See Coulterville, Yosemite National Park

Markleeville, Alpine, Pop. 204
Alpine County Office of Education | 50/
43 Hawkside Dr 96120 | 530-694-2230
Patrick Traynor, supt. | Fax 694-2379
www.alpinecoe.k12.ca.us
Alpine County Opportunity S | 50/Alt
43 Hawkside Dr 96120 | 530-694-2230
Patrick Traynor, prin. | Fax 694-2379

Alpine County USD | 100/K-12
43 Hawkside Dr 96120 | 530-694-2230
Patrick Traynor, admin. | Fax 694-2379
www.alpinecoe.k12.ca.us
Alpine County Community Day S | 50/Alt
43 Hawkside Dr 96120 | 530-694-9423
Dr. Patrick Traynor, supt.

Martinez, Contra Costa, Pop. 34,098
Contra Costa County Office of Education
Supt. — See Pleasant Hill
Golden Gate Community S | 100/Alt
222 Glacier Dr 94553 | 925-313-2950
Edward Brown, prin. | Fax 313-2955

Martinez USD | 4,100/K-12
921 Susana St 94553 | 925-335-5800
C.J. Cammack, supt. | Fax 335-5961
www.martinezusd.net
Alhambra HS | 1,200/9-12
150 E St 94553 | 925-335-5810
Tom Doppe, prin. | Fax 335-5870
Briones S | 50/Alt
614 F St 94553 | 925-228-9232
Lori O'Connor, prin. | Fax 335-5889
Martinez Continuation HS | 100/Alt
614 F St 94553 | 925-228-9232
Lori O'Connor, prin. | Fax 335-5889
Martinez JHS | 900/6-8
1600 Court St 94553 | 925-335-5820
Michael DeFrancesco, prin. | Fax 335-5829
Martinez Adult Center | Adult
600 F St 94553 | 925-228-3276
Kathy Farwell, dir. | Fax 228-6989

Martinez Adult Education | Post-Sec.
600 F St 94553 | 925-228-3276

Marysville, Yuba, Pop. 11,483
Marysville JUSD | 9,200/K-12
1919 B St 95901 | 530-741-6000
Gay Todd Ed.D., supt. | Fax 741-7894
www.mjusd.com
Foothill IS | 100/7-8
5351 Fruitland Rd 95901 | 530-741-6130
Kathleen Hansen, prin. | Fax 741-6017
Marysville Community Day S | Alt
1919 B St 95901 – David Gray, prin. | 530-749-6919
Marysville HS | 900/9-12
12 E 18th St 95901 | 530-741-6180
Gary Cena, prin. | Fax 741-7828
McKenney IS | 500/6-8
1904 Huston St 95901 | 530-741-6187
Shevaun Mathews, prin. | Fax 741-6004
Other Schools – See Olivehurst

Yuba County Office of Education | 600/
935 14th St 95901 | 530-749-4900
Francisco Reveles, supt. | Fax 741-6500
www.yuba.net/
Mathews Community S | 50/Alt
1010 I St 95901 | 530-741-6349
Christopher Meyer, prin.

Yuba College | Post-Sec.
2088 N Beale Rd 95901 | 530-741-6700

Mather, Sacramento, Pop. 4,082
Regional Occupational Center & Program
Supt. — None
Sacramento County ROP | Vo/Tech
10474 Mather Blvd 95655 | 916-228-2500
Tim Taylor, admin. | Fax 228-2459

Sacramento County Office of Education | 1,100/
10474 Mather Blvd 95655 | 916-228-2500
David Gordon, supt. | Fax 228-2403
www.scoe.net
Other Schools – See Sacramento

Maxwell, Colusa, Pop. 1,095
Maxwell USD | 300/K-12
PO Box 788 95955 | 530-438-2291
Zach Thurman, supt. | Fax 438-2693
www.maxwell.k12.ca.us
Maxwell HS | 100/7-12
PO Box 788 95955 | 530-438-2291
Zach Thurman, prin. | Fax 438-2693

Maywood, Los Angeles, Pop. 27,328
Los Angeles USD
Supt. — See Los Angeles
Maywood Academy | 1,300/9-12
6125 Pine Ave 90270 | 323-838-6000
Jose Gonzalez, prin. | Fax 560-9206

Meadow Vista, Placer, Pop. 3,116
Placer Hills UNESD | 500/K-8
16801 Placer Hills Rd 95722 | 530-878-2606
Cindy Uptain, supt. | Fax 878-9475
www.phusd.org
Other Schools – See Weimar

Mendocino, Mendocino, Pop. 866
Mendocino USD | 500/K-12
PO Box 1154 95460 | 707-937-5868
Jason Morse, supt. | Fax 937-0714
www.mendocinousd.org/
Mendocino Alternative S | 50/Alt
PO Box 1154 95460 | 707-937-3703
Gail Dickenson, prin. | Fax 937-6806
Mendocino HS | 200/9-12
PO Box 226 95460 | 707-937-5871
Gail Dickenson, prin. | Fax 937-1552
Mendocino Sunrise HS | 50/Alt
PO Box 226 95460 | 707-937-9232
Gail Dickenson, prin. | Fax 937-5629

Mendota, Fresno, Pop. 10,983
Mendota USD | 3,000/K-12
115 McCabe Ave 93640 | 559-655-4942
Paul Lopez, supt. | Fax 655-4944
www.musdaztecs.com
Mendota Continuation HS | 50/Alt
211 Smoot Ave 93640 | 559-655-4471
Rebecca Gamez, prin. | Fax 655-2440
Mendota HS | 800/9-12
1200 Belmont Ave 93640 | 559-655-1993
Travis Kirby, prin. | Fax 655-0223
Mendota JHS | 400/7-8
1258 Belmont Ave 93640 | 559-655-4301
Randy Jarrett, prin. | Fax 655-1229

Menifee, Riverside, Pop. 75,080
Menifee UNESD | 10,600/PK-12
29775 Haun Rd, | 951-672-1851
Steve Kennedy Ed.D., supt. | Fax 672-1385
www.menifeeusd.org
Bell Mountain MS | 1,200/6-8
28525 La Piedra Rd 92584 | 951-301-8496
Ernie Lizarraga, prin. | Fax 301-5286
Christensen MS | 800/6-8
27625 Sherman Rd, | 951-679-8356
Michelle Randall, prin. | Fax 679-4090
Menifee Valley MS | 1,000/6-8
26255 Garbani Rd 92584 | 951-672-6400
Ed Resnick, prin. | Fax 672-6415

Perris UNHSD
Supt. — See Perris
Heritage HS | 2,600/9-12
26001 Briggs Rd, | 951-940-5447
Frank Arce, prin. | Fax 325-5449
Paloma Valley HS | 2,700/9-12
31375 Bradley Rd 92584 | 951-672-6030
Don Williamson, prin. | Fax 672-6037

Romoland ESD
Supt. — See Homeland
Chase MS | 700/6-8
28100 Calm Horizon Dr, | 951-566-4400
Chris Hernandez, prin. | Fax 639-5943

Menlo Park, San Mateo, Pop. 30,400
Las Lomitas ESD | 1,400/K-8
1011 Altschul Ave 94025 | 650-854-2880
Lisa Cesario, supt. | Fax 854-0882
www.llesd.k12.ca.us
La Entrada MS | 800/4-8
2200 Sharon Rd 94025 | 650-854-3962
Mark Jones, prin. | Fax 854-5947

Menlo Park City ESD
Supt. — See Atherton
Hillview MS | 900/6-8
1100 Elder Ave 94025 | 650-326-4341
Willy Haug, prin. | Fax 325-3861

Sequoia UNHSD
Supt. — See Redwood City
Sequoia District Adult S | Adult
3247 Middlefield Rd 94025 | 650-306-8866
Lionel de Maine, admin. | Fax 365-2420

Mid-Peninsula HS | 100/9-12
1340 Willow Rd 94025 | 650-321-1991
Dr. Douglas Thompson, head sch | Fax 321-9921
St. Patrick's Seminary & University | Post-Sec.
320 Middlefield Rd 94025 | 650-325-5621

Merced, Merced, Pop. 76,840
Merced City ESD | 10,100/K-8
444 W 23rd St 95340 | 209-385-6600
Rosemary Parga Duran Ed.D., supt. | Fax 385-6316
www.mcsd.k12.ca.us
Cruickshank MS | 500/7-8
601 Mercy Ave 95340 | 209-385-6330
Jill Settera, prin. | Fax 385-6338
Hoover MS | 500/7-8
800 E 26th St 95340 | 209-385-6631
Julie Rivard, prin. | Fax 385-6799
Rivera MS | 600/7-8
945 Buena Vista Dr 95348 | 209-385-6680
Sergio Mendez, prin. | Fax 385-6702
Tenaya MS | 600/7-8
760 W 8th St 95341 | 209-385-6687
Anthony Arista, prin. | Fax 385-6365

Merced County Office of Education | 1,200/
632 W 13th St 95341 | 209-381-6600
Steven Gomes Ed.D., supt. | Fax 381-6767
www.mcoe.org
Valley Community S | 300/Alt
632 W 13th St 95341 | 209-381-4500
Derrek Dean, prin. | Fax 385-8308
Other Schools – See Atwater, Livingston, Los Banos

Merced UNHSD
Supt. — See Atwater
El Capitan HS | 800/9-12
100 Farmland Ave 95340 | 209-384-5500
Lee Shaw, prin.
Golden Valley HS | 1,900/9-12
PO Box 2188 95344 | 209-385-8000
Kevin Swartwood, prin. | Fax 385-8002
Independence HS | 50/Alt
1900 G St 95340 | 209-385-6515
Chas Jolly, prin. | Fax 385-6435
Merced HS | 2,100/9-12
PO Box 2167 95344 | 209-385-6465
Jon Schaefer, prin. | Fax 385-6556
Sequoia HS | 100/Alt
123 E 18th St 95340 | 209-385-8950
Paul Bristow, prin. | Fax 385-6535
Yosemite Continuation HS | 400/Alt
1900 G St 95340 | 209-385-6425
Chas Jolly, prin. | Fax 385-6435
Merced Adult S | Adult
50 E 20th St 95340 | 209-385-6524
Steve Hobbs, prin. | Fax 385-6430

Regional Occupational Center & Program
Supt. — None
Merced County ROP | Vo/Tech
632 W 13th St 95341 | 209-381-6677
Holly Newlon, supt. | Fax 381-6766

Weaver UNSD | 2,900/PK-8
3076 E Childs Ave 95341 | 209-723-7606
John Curry M.A., supt. | Fax 725-7128
www.weaverusd.k12.ca.us
Weaver MS | 900/6-8
3076 E Childs Ave 95341 | 209-723-2174
Elias Villa M.A., prin. | Fax 725-7116

Merced College | Post-Sec.
3600 M St 95348 | 209-384-6000
Sierra College of Beauty | Post-Sec.
1340 W 18th St 95340 | 209-723-2989
Stone Ridge Christian HS | 100/9-12
500 Buena Vista Dr 95348 | 209-386-0322
Randy Postmus, prin. | Fax 386-0334
University of California | Post-Sec.
5200 N Lake Rd 95343 | 209-228-4400
WestMed College-Merced | Post-Sec.
330 E Yosemite Ave 95340 | 209-386-6300

Middletown, Lake, Pop. 1,281
Middletown USD | 1,600/K-12
20932 Big Canyon Rd 95461 | 707-987-4100
Catherine Stone, supt. | Fax 987-4105
www.middletownusd.org
Loconoma Vally HS | 50/Alt
20932 Big Canyon Rd 95461 | 707-987-4170
Catherine Stone, prin. | Fax 987-4171
Middletown HS | 500/9-12
20932 Big Canyon Rd 95461 | 707-987-4140
Bill Roderick, prin. | Fax 987-4146
Middletown MS | 200/7-8
20932 Big Canyon Rd 95461 | 707-987-4160
Mitch Tucker, prin. | Fax 987-4162

Middletown Christian S | 100/PK-12
PO Box 989 95461 | 707-987-2556
Anna Mayfield, admin. | Fax 987-2126

Midway City, Orange, Pop. 8,289

Huntington College of Dental Technology | Post-Sec.
14848 Monroe St 92655

Millbrae, San Mateo, Pop. 20,615
Millbrae ESD | 2,400/K-8
555 Richmond Dr 94030 | 650-697-5693
Vahn Phayprasert, supt. | Fax 697-6865
www.millbraeschooldistrict.org

Taylor MS 900/6-8
850 Taylor Blvd 94030 650-697-4096
Phillip Hophan, prin. Fax 697-8435

San Mateo UNHSD
Supt. — See San Mateo
Mills HS 1,200/9-12
400 Murchison Dr 94030 650-558-2599
Paul Belzer, prin. Fax 558-2552

Mill Valley, Marin, Pop. 13,420
Mill Valley ESD 3,300/K-8
411 Sycamore Ave 94941 415-389-7700
Paul Johnson, supt. Fax 389-7773
www.mvschools.org
Mill Valley MS 1,000/6-8
425 Sycamore Ave 94941 415-389-7711
Anna Lazzarini, prin. Fax 389-7780

Tamalpais UNHSD
Supt. — See Larkspur
Tamalpais HS 1,300/9-12
700 Miller Ave 94941 415-388-3292
J.C. Farr, prin. Fax 380-3526

Milpitas, Santa Clara, Pop. 64,272
Milpitas USD 10,200/PK-12
1331 E Calaveras Blvd 95035 408-635-2600
Cheryl Jordan, supt. Fax 635-2616
www.musd.org
Calaveras Hills HS 100/Alt
1331 E Calaveras Blvd 95035 408-635-2690
Carl Stice, prin. Fax 635-2615
Milpitas HS 3,000/9-12
1285 Escuela Pkwy 95035 408-635-2800
Philip Morales, prin. Fax 635-2851
Rancho Milpitas MS 700/7-8
1915 Yellowstone Ave 95035 408-635-2656
Casey McMurray, prin. Fax 635-2661
Russell MS 800/7-8
1500 Escuela Pkwy 95035 408-635-2864
Damon James, prin. Fax 635-2869
Milpitas Adult S Adult
1331 E Calaveras Blvd 95035 408-635-2692
Usha Narayanan, prin. Fax 635-2611

Heald College Post-Sec.
341 Great Mall Pkwy 95035 408-934-4900

Miranda, Humboldt, Pop. 496
Southern Humbolt JUSD 800/PK-12
PO Box 650 95553 707-943-1789
Catherine Scott, supt. Fax 943-1921
apps.humboldt.k12.ca.us/sohumwp
Miranda JHS 100/7-8
PO Box 188 95553 707-943-3144
Jeff Landry, prin. Fax 943-3129
Osprey Learning Center 50/Alt
PO Box 188 95553 707-943-3144
Jeff Landry, prin. Fax 943-3627
South Fork HS 200/9-12
PO Box 188 95553 707-943-3144
Jeff Landry, prin. Fax 943-3129

Mission Hills, Los Angeles, Pop. 3,460
Los Angeles USD
Supt. — See Los Angeles
North Valley Occupational Center Vo/Tech
11450 Sharp Ave 91345 818-365-9645
Carlynn Huddleston, prin. Fax 365-2695

Bishop Alemany HS 1,700/9-12
11111 Alemany Dr 91345 818-363-3925
David Chambers, prin. Fax 365-2064

Mission Viejo, Orange, Pop. 89,770
Capistrano USD
Supt. — See San Juan Capistrano
Capistrano Valley HS 2,400/9-12
26301 Via Escolar 92692 949-364-6100
Josh Hill, prin. Fax 347-0514
Newhart MS 1,300/6-8
25001 Veterans Way 92692 949-855-0162
Jeff Jones, prin. Fax 770-1262

Saddleback Valley USD 29,800/PK-12
25631 Peter A Hartman Way 92691 949-586-1234
Peggy Lynch Ed.D., supt. Fax 951-0994
svwp.svusd.org
La Paz IS 1,000/7-8
25151 Pradera Dr 92691 949-830-1720
Jean Carroll, prin. Fax 830-3320
Los Alisos IS 900/7-8
25171 Moor Ave 92691 949-830-9700
Rich Freda, prin. Fax 472-3968
Mira Monte Alternative HS 100/Alt
25632 Peter A Hartman Way 92691 949-830-8857
Darrell De Leon, prin. Fax 462-0352
Mission Viejo HS 2,500/9-12
25025 Chrisanta Dr 92691 949-837-7722
Ray Gatfield, prin. Fax 830-0782
Silverado Continuation HS 200/Alt
25632 Peter A Hartman Way 92691 949-586-8800
David Gordon, prin. Fax 583-9865
Trabuco Hills HS 3,100/9-12
27501 Mustang Run 92691 949-768-1934
Craig Collins, prin. Fax 588-0763
Adult Education Center Adult
25598 Peter A Hartman Way 92691 949-837-8830
David Gordon, dean Fax 837-1921
Other Schools – See Laguna Hills, Lake Forest, Rancho Santa Margarita

Fusion Academy 6-12
23456 Madero Ste 140 92691 949-716-7384
Heritage Christian S 200/PK-10
22081 Hidalgo 92691 949-598-9166
George Gay M.A., prin. Fax 598-1892

Master's Academy 50/K-12
23052 Alicia Pkwy Ste H107 92692 949-500-3059
Rebekah Milligan, admin. Fax 888-7420
Saddleback College Post-Sec.
28000 Marguerite Pkwy 92692 949-582-4500

Modesto, Stanislaus, Pop. 192,307
Empire UNESD 3,000/PK-8
116 N McClure Rd 95357 209-521-2800
David Garcia, supt. Fax 526-6421
www.empire.k12.ca.us
Glick MS 600/7-8
400 Frazine Rd 95357 209-577-3945
Isaias Rumayor, prin. Fax 577-3975

Modesto CSD 29,900/K-12
426 Locust St 95351 209-576-4011
Pamela Able, supt. Fax 576-4184
www.monet.k12.ca.us
Beyer HS 1,900/9-12
1717 Sylvan Ave 95355 209-576-4311
Dan park, prin. Fax 576-4352
Davis HS 1,400/9-12
1200 W Rumble Rd 95350 209-576-4500
Mike Rich, prin. Fax 576-4028
Downey HS 2,000/9-12
1000 Coffee Rd 95355 209-576-4211
Richard Baum, prin. Fax 576-4258
Elliott Alternative & Continuing Educ 600/Alt
1440 Sunrise Ave 95350 209-576-4005
Eric Andersen, prin. Fax 576-4863
Enochs HS 2,400/9-12
3201 Sylvan Ave 95355 209-550-3400
Deborah Rowe, prin. Fax 550-3413
Gregori HS 2,100/9-12
3701 Pirrone Rd 95356 209-550-3420
Jeff Albritton, prin. Fax 550-3433
Hanshaw MS 800/7-8
1725 Las Vegas St 95358 209-576-4847
Derek Pendley, prin. Fax 576-4723
Johansen HS 1,700/9-12
641 Norseman Dr 95357 209-576-4702
Nathan Schar, prin. Fax 576-4752
La Loma JHS 700/7-8
1800 Encina Ave 95354 209-576-4627
Marie McDonald, prin. Fax 576-4631
Modesto HS 2,400/9-12
18 H St 95351 209-576-4401
Jason Manning, prin. Fax 576-4434
Roosevelt JHS 800/7-8
1330 College Ave 95350 209-576-4871
David Sanchez, prin. Fax 569-2713
Twain JHS 800/7-8
707 S Emerald Ave 95351 209-576-4814
Richard Caldwell, prin. Fax 576-4843

Regional Occupational Center & Program
Supt. — None
Yosemite ROP, 1100 H St 95354 Vo/Tech
Cindy Young, admin. 209-238-1500

Stanislaus County Office of Education 2,100/
1100 H St 95354 209-238-1700
Tom Changnon, supt. Fax 238-4201
www.stancoe.org/
Petersen Alternative Center 300/Alt
715 13th St 95354 209-238-6717
John Luis, prin. Fax 238-6796
Other Schools – See Ceres, Turlock

Stanislaus UNESD 3,200/K-8
2410 Janna Ave 95350 209-529-9546
Britta Skavdahl, supt. Fax 529-0243
www.stanunion.k12.ca.us
Prescott JHS 700/7-8
2243 W Rumble Rd 95350 209-529-9892
Harjinder Mattu, prin. Fax 529-4406

Sylvan Union ESD 8,200/K-8
605 Sylvan Ave 95350 209-574-5000
Debra M. Hendricks, supt. Fax 524-2672
www.sylvan.k12.ca.us
Savage MS 1,000/6-8
1900 Maid Mariane Ln 95355 209-552-3300
Michael Stagnaro, prin. Fax 552-3305
Somerset MS 900/6-8
1037 Floyd Ave 95350 209-574-5300
Mary Smyth, prin. Fax 529-1110
Ustach MS 1,000/6-8
2701 Kodiak Dr 95355 209-552-3000
Gary Miller, prin. Fax 552-3010

Adrian's Beauty College Post-Sec.
124 Floyd Ave 95350 209-526-2040
Big Valley Christian S 700/PK-12
4040 Tully Rd Ste D 95356 209-527-3481
Bobby Kirchner, supt. Fax 571-4810
Brethren Heritage S 100/K-12
3549 Dakota Ave 95358 209-543-7860
John Fall, prin. Fax 543-7862
California Beauty College Post-Sec.
1115 15th St 95354 209-524-5184
Central Catholic HS 400/9-12
200 S Carpenter Rd 95351 209-524-9611
Bruce Sawyer, prin. Fax 524-4913
Community Business College Post-Sec.
3800 McHenry Ave 95356 209-529-3648
Computer Tutor Business & Technical Inst Post-Sec.
4306 Sisk Rd 95356 209-545-5200
Institute of Technology - Modesto Campus Post-Sec.
5601 Stoddard Rd 95356 209-545-3100
Modesto Christian S 300/PK-12
5755 Sisk Rd 95356 209-343-2330
Dr. Jonathan Burton, supt. Fax 545-0584
Modesto Junior College Post-Sec.
435 College Ave 95350 209-575-6550
Western Pacific Truck School Post-Sec.
2316 Nickerson Dr 95358 209-531-9226

Mojave, Kern, Pop. 4,110
Mojave USD 2,700/K-12
3500 Douglas Ave 93501 661-824-4001
Dr. Aaron Haughton, supt. Fax 824-2686
www.mojave.k12.ca.us/
Mojave JSHS 300/7-12
15732 O St 93501 661-824-4088
Scott Small, prin. Fax 824-3406
Other Schools – See California City

Regional Occupational Center & Program
Supt. — None
Kern County ROP Vo/Tech
15926 K St 93501 661-824-9313
Tom Anspach, admin. Fax 824-9316

National Test Pilot School Post-Sec.
PO Box 658 93502 661-824-2977

Monrovia, Los Angeles, Pop. 35,498
Monrovia USD 6,000/PK-12
325 E Huntington Dr 91016 626-471-2000
Dr. Katherine Thorossian, supt. Fax 471-2077
www.monroviaschools.net
Canyon Oaks HS 100/Alt
930 Royal Oaks Dr 91016 626-471-3000
Flint Fertig, prin. Fax 471-3033
Clifton MS 700/6-8
226 S Ivy Ave 91016 626-471-2600
Jennifer Gates, prin. Fax 471-2610
Monrovia HS 1,700/9-12
845 W Colorado Blvd 91016 626-471-2800
Kirk McGinnis, prin. Fax 471-2810
Mountain Park HS 100/Alt
950 S Mountain Ave 91016 626-471-3029
Flint Fertig, prin. Fax 471-3077
Santa Fe MS 700/6-8
148 W Duarte Rd 91016 626-471-2700
Dr. Caroline Sweeney, prin. Fax 471-2710
Monrovia Community Adult Education Adult
920 S Mountain Ave 91016 626-471-3035
Flint Fertig, prin. Fax 471-3036

Mt. Sierra College Post-Sec.
101 E Huntington Dr 91016 626-873-2144

Montclair, San Bernardino, Pop. 36,107
Chaffey JUNHSD
Supt. — See Ontario
Montclair HS 3,100/9-12
4725 Benito St 91763 909-621-6781
Martin Alvarado, prin. Fax 391-5323

Ontario-Montclair SD
Supt. — See Ontario
Serrano MS 800/7-8
4725 San Jose St 91763 909-624-0029
Mauricio Gormaz, prin. Fax 445-1687
Vernon MS 800/7-8
9775 Vernon Ave 91763 909-624-5036
Kim Tovar, prin. Fax 445-1720

Montebello, Los Angeles, Pop. 62,028
Montebello USD 29,900/K-12
123 S Montebello Blvd 90640 323-887-7900
Susanna Contreras Smith, supt. Fax 887-5890
www.montebello.k12.ca.us
Applied Technology Center Vo/Tech
1200 W Mines Ave 90640 323-248-2500
Sterling Schubert, prin. Fax 727-0739
Eastmont IS 1,000/6-8
400 Bradshawe St 90640 323-721-5133
Cecilia Ramirez, prin. Fax 887-3058
La Merced IS 1,300/6-8
215 E Avenida De La Merced 90640 323-722-7262
Alice Jacquez, prin. Fax 887-5816
Montebello Community Day S 100/Alt
123 S Montebello Blvd 90640 323-887-7900
Benedetta Kennedy, dir. Fax 887-5895
Montebello HS 3,000/9-12
2100 W Cleveland Ave 90640 323-728-0121
Helen Meltzer, prin. Fax 887-7848
Montebello IS 1,200/6-8
1600 W Whittier Blvd 90640 323-721-5111
Leticia Alvidrez, prin. Fax 887-3192
Schurr HS 3,000/9-12
820 N Wilcox Ave 90640 323-887-3090
Francisco Arregui, prin. Fax 887-3097
Vail Continuation HS 300/Alt
1230 S Vail Ave 90640 323-728-1940
Horacio Perez, prin. Fax 887-3004
Montebello Adult Education Adult
149 N 21st St 90640 323-887-7844
Kathy Brendzal, prin. Fax 724-8175
Schurr Adult Education Adult
820 N Wilcox Ave 90640 323-887-3088
Luz Hernandez, prin. Fax 887-3098
Other Schools – See Bell Gardens, Monterey Park

Cantwell-Sacred Heart of Mary HS 500/9-12
329 N Garfield Ave 90640 323-887-2066
Robert Fraley, prin. Fax 724-4332
Montebello Beauty College Post-Sec.
2201 W Whittier Blvd 90640 323-727-7851

Monterey, Monterey, Pop. 26,593
Monterey Peninsula USD 10,800/PK-12
PO Box 1031 93942 831-645-1200
Dr. Daniel Diffenbaugh, supt. Fax 649-4175
www.mpusd.k12.ca.us
Colton MS 700/6-8
100 Toda Vis 93940 831-649-1951
Janet Mikkelsen, prin. Fax 649-4692
Monterey HS 1,200/9-12
101 Herrmann Dr 93940 831-392-3801
Marcie Plummer, prin. Fax 649-1154
Other Schools – See Marina, Seaside

Monterey Institute of Intl. Studies — Post-Sec.
460 Pierce St 93940 — 831-647-4100
Monterey Peninsula College — Post-Sec.
980 Fremont St 93940 — 831-646-4000
Santa Catalina S — 500/PK-12
1500 Mark Thomas Dr 93940 — 831-655-9300
Margaret Bradley, head sch — Fax 649-3056
Trinity Christian HS — 100/9-12
680 Belden St 93940 — 831-656-9434
Rick Fitzgerald, prin. — Fax 656-9670
York S — 200/8-12
9501 York Rd 93940 — 831-372-7338
Chuck Harmon, head sch — Fax 372-8055

Monterey Park, Los Angeles, Pop. 59,435
Los Angeles County Office of Education
Supt. — See Downey
East Los Angeles Community Day S — 200/Alt
1260 Monterey Pass Rd 91754 — 323-262-2263
Ray Donahue, prin.

Montebello USD
Supt. — See Montebello
Macy IS — 900/6-8
2101 Lupine Ave 91755 — 323-722-0260
Jacinto Zavala, prin. — Fax 887-3068

East Los Angeles College — Post-Sec.
1301 Avenida Cesar Chavez 91754 — 323-265-8650

Montrose, See La Crescenta

St. Monica Academy — 200/1-12
2361 Del Mar Rd 91020 — 818-369-7310
Marguerite Grimm, hdmstr. — Fax 369-7305

Moorpark, Ventura, Pop. 33,338
Moorpark USD — 6,800/K-12
5297 Maureen Ln 93021 — 805-378-6300
Dr. Kelli Hays, supt. — Fax 529-8592
www.mrpk.org
Chaparral MS — 600/6-8
280 Poindexter Ave 93021 — 805-378-6302
Joshua Stephenson, prin. — Fax 378-6324
Community Continuation HS — 100/Alt
4500 Tierra Rejada Rd 93021 — 805-378-6304
Carrie Pentis, prin. — Fax 531-6448
Mesa Verde MS — 700/6-8
14000 Peach Hill Rd 93021 — 805-378-6309
Adam Rauch, prin. — Fax 531-6622
Moorpark HS — 2,100/9-12
4500 Tierra Rejada Rd 93021 — 805-378-6305
Carrie Pentis, prin. — Fax 531-6498
HS at Moorpark College — 100/Alt
7075 Campus Rd 93021 — 805-378-1444
Ruby Delery, prin. — Fax 378-1440

Moorpark College — Post-Sec.
7075 Campus Rd 93021 — 805-378-1400

Moraga, Contra Costa, Pop. 15,277
Acalanes UNHSD
Supt. — See Lafayette
Campolindo HS — 1,300/9-12
300 Moraga Rd 94556 — 925-280-3950
John Walker, prin. — Fax 280-3951

Moraga ESD — 1,800/PK-8
1540 School St 94556 — 925-376-5943
Bruce K. Burns, supt. — Fax 376-8132
www.moraga.k12.ca.us
Moraga IS — 600/6-8
1010 Camino Pablo 94556 — 925-376-7206
Joan Danilson, prin. — Fax 376-6836

St. Mary's College of California — Post-Sec.
1928 Saint Marys Rd 94556 — 925-631-4000

Moreno Valley, Riverside, Pop. 186,933
Moreno Valley USD — 34,200/K-12
25634 Alessandro Blvd 92553 — 951-571-7500
Dr. Judy D. White, supt. — Fax 571-7550
www.mvusd.net
Alessandro S — 100/Alt
23311 Dracaea Ave 92553 — 951-571-4510
Karen Tomei, admin. — Fax 571-4515
Badger Springs MS — 1,200/6-8
24750 Delphinium Ave 92553 — 951-571-4200
Jason Barney, prin. — Fax 571-4205
Canyon Springs HS — 2,400/9-12
23100 Cougar Canyon Dr 92557 — 951-571-4760
Tamara Kerr, prin. — Fax 571-4765
Landmark MS — 1,300/6-8
15261 Legendary Dr 92555 — 951-571-4220
Scott Walker, prin. — Fax 571-4225
March Mountain HS — 300/Alt
24551 Dracaea Ave 92553 — 951-571-4800
Sean McMurray, prin. — Fax 571-4805
March Valley HS — 100/Alt
24551 Dracaea Ave 92553 — 951-571-4800
Sean McMurray, prin. — Fax 571-4805
Moreno Valley HS — 2,400/9-12
23300 Cottonwood Ave 92553 — 951-571-4820
LaToysha Brown, prin. — Fax 571-4825
Mountain View MS — 1,200/6-8
13130 Morrison St 92555 — 951-571-4240
Jon Black, prin. — Fax 571-4245
Palm MS — 1,300/6-8
11900 Slawson Ave 92557 — 951-571-4260
Mallanie Avinger, prin. — Fax 571-4265
Sunnymead MS — 1,500/6-8
23996 Eucalyptus Ave 92553 — 951-571-4280
Jennifer Castillo, prin. — Fax 571-4285
Valley View HS — 2,600/9-12
13135 Nason St 92555 — 951-571-4850
Karen Johnson, prin. — Fax 571-4855
Vista Del Lago HS — 2,200/9-12
15150 Lasselle St 92551 — 951-571-4880
Dr. Erik Swanson, prin. — Fax 571-4885
Vista Heights MS — 1,400/6-8
23049 Old Lake Dr 92557 — 951-571-4300
Mark Hasson, prin. — Fax 571-4305
Moreno Valley Community Adult S — Adult
13350 Indian St 92553 — 951-571-4790
Dr. Tammy Guzzetta, prin. — Fax 571-4795

Val Verde USD
Supt. — See Perris
March MS — 800/6-8
15800 Indian St 92551 — 951-490-0430
Jim Owen, prin. — Fax 490-0435
Rancho Verde HS — 3,200/9-12
17750 Lasselle St 92551 — 951-485-6200
Dr. Charil Macaraeg, prin. — Fax 485-6218
Val Verde Academy — 50/Alt
25100 Red Maple Ln 92551 — 951-443-2450
Vanessa Karwan, prin.
Vista Verde MS — 1,000/6-8
25777 Krameria St 92551 — 951-485-6270
Esperanza Arce, prin. — Fax 485-6278

Calvary Chapel Christian S — 300/K-12
28010 Ironwood Ave 92555 — 951-485-6088
Tim Hamilton, prin. — Fax 485-6718
Elegante Beauty College — Post-Sec.
24741 Alessandro Blvd 92553 — 951-247-2047
Moreno Valley College — Post-Sec.
16130 Lasselle St 92551 — 951-571-6100
Sage College — Post-Sec.
12125 Day St Ste L 92557 — 951-781-2727
Westech College — Post-Sec.
22515 Alessandro Blvd 92553 — 951-653-8300

Morgan Hill, Santa Clara, Pop. 36,440
Morgan Hill USD — 8,600/PK-12
15600 Concord Cir 95037 — 408-201-6000
Steve Betando, supt. — Fax 201-6007
www.mhusd.org
Britton MS — 600/6-8
80 W Central Ave 95037 — 408-201-6160
Chris Moore, prin. — Fax 201-6175
Central HS — 100/Alt
85 Tilton Ave 95037 — 408-201-6300
Vera Gomes, prin. — Fax 201-6310
Live Oak HS — 1,100/9-12
1505 E Main Ave 95037 — 408-201-6100
Lloyd Webb, prin. — Fax 201-6143
Sobrato HS — 1,400/9-12
401 Burnett Ave 95037 — 408-201-6200
Courtney Macko, prin. — Fax 201-6241
Community Adult Education — Adult
17940 Monterey St 95037 — 408-201-6520
Dennis Browne, prin. — Fax 201-6525
Other Schools – See San Jose

Oakwood S — 400/PK-12
105 John Wilson Way 95037 — 408-782-7177

Morro Bay, San Luis Obispo, Pop. 10,002
San Luis Coastal USD
Supt. — See San Luis Obispo
Morro Bay HS — 800/9-12
235 Atascadero Rd 93442 — 805-771-1845
Dr. Kyle Pruitt, prin. — Fax 772-5944

Moss Landing, Monterey, Pop. 194
North Monterey County USD — 4,400/K-12
8142 Moss Landing Rd 95039 — 831-633-3343
Kari Yeater, supt. — Fax 633-2937
www.nmcusd.org
Other Schools – See Castroville, Salinas

Mountain House, San Joaquin, Pop. 9,039
Lammersville USD — 3,800/PK-10
111 S De Anza Blvd 95391 — 209-836-7400
Dr. Kirk Nicholas, supt. — Fax 836-7402
www.lammersvilleschooldistrict.net
Mountain House HS — 500/9-10
1090 S Central Pkwy 95391 — 209-836-7460
Ben Fobert, admin. — Fax 836-7462

Mountain View, Santa Clara, Pop. 70,771
Mountain View Whisman SD — 5,000/K-8
750A San Pierre Way 94043 — 650-526-3500
Ayinde Rudolph, supt. — Fax 964-8907
www.mvwsd.org
Crittenden MS — 600/6-8
1701 Rock St 94043 — 650-903-6945
Angie Dillman, prin. — Fax 967-1707
Graham MS — 800/6-8
1175 Castro St 94040 — 650-526-3570
Kim Thompson, prin. — Fax 965-9278

Mountain View-Los Altos UNHSD — 3,700/9-12
1299 Bryant Ave 94040 — 650-940-4650
Dr. Jeff Harding, supt. — Fax 961-1346
www.mvla.net/
Alta Vista HS — 100/Alt
1325 Bryant Ave 94040 — 650-691-2433
Bill Pierce, prin. — Fax 691-2469
Mountain View HS — 1,800/9-12
3535 Truman Ave 94040 — 650-940-4600
David Grissom, prin. — Fax 961-6349
Mountain View/Los Altos Adult Education — Adult
333 Moffett Blvd 94043 — 650-940-1333
Keith Moody, dir. — Fax 967-4699
Other Schools – See Los Altos

German International S of Silicon Valley — 400/PK-12
310 Easy St 94043 — 650-254-0748
Michael Koops, head sch — Fax 254-0749
Mountain View Academy — 100/9-12
360 S Shoreline Blvd 94041 — 650-967-2324
Gerald Corson, prin. — Fax 967-6886
Palo Alto Prep S — 100/8-12
2462 Wyandotte St Ste A 94043 — 650-493-7071
St. Francis HS — 1,700/9-12
1885 Miramonte Ave 94040 — 650-968-1213
Patricia Tennant, prin. — Fax 968-1706
Waldorf S of the Peninsula — 100/6-12
180 N Rengstorff Ave 94043 — 650-417-7600
Sue Levine, admin. — Fax 417-7676

Mount Madonna, Santa Cruz

Mount Madonna S — 200/PK-12
491 Summit Rd, — 408-847-2717
Mary McDonald, head sch — Fax 847-5633

Mount Shasta, Siskiyou, Pop. 3,264
Mount Shasta UNSD — 500/K-8
595 E Alma St 96067 — 530-926-6007
Barry Barnhart, supt. — Fax 926-6103
www.mtshastaandweedschooldistricts.com/
Sisson S — 300/4-8
601 E Alma St 96067 — 530-926-3846
Kale Riccomini, prin. — Fax 926-2152

Siskiyou UNHSD — 600/9-12
624 Everitt Memorial Hwy 96067 — 530-926-3006
Michael Matheson, supt. — Fax 926-3113
www.sisuhsd.net/
Jefferson Continuation HS — 50/Alt
720 Rockfellow Dr 96067 — 530-926-0425
Jessica Bowman, prin. — Fax 926-0586
Mount Shasta HS — 300/9-12
710 Everitt Memorial Hwy 96067 — 530-926-2614
Dr. Jennifer McKinnon, prin. — Fax 926-5162
South County Community Day S — 50/Alt
720 Rockfellow Dr 96067 — 530-926-0425
Jessica Bowman, prin. — Fax 926-0586
Siskiyou Adult S — Adult
720 Rockfellow Dr 96067 — 530-926-0425
Jessica Bowman, prin. — Fax 926-0586
Other Schools – See Happy Camp, Mc Cloud, Weed

Murrieta, Riverside, Pop. 99,237
Murrieta Valley USD — 22,900/K-12
41870 McAlby Ct 92562 — 951-696-1600
Patrick Kelley, supt. — Fax 304-1523
www.murrieta.k12.ca.us
Creekside HS — 200/Alt
24150 Hayes Ave 92562 — 951-696-1409
Martina Beach-Hedges, prin. — Fax 304-1665
McElhinney MS — 1,300/6-8
35125 Briggs Rd 92563 — 951-304-1885
Thomas Patane, prin. — Fax 304-1889
Murrieta Canyon Academy — 100/Alt
24150 Hayes Ave 92562 — 951-304-1661
Martina Beach-Hedges, dir. — Fax 304-1665
Murrieta Mesa HS — 2,100/9-12
24801 Monroe Ave 92562 — 951-677-0568
Steve Ellis, prin. — Fax 304-1895
Murrieta Valley HS — 2,400/9-12
42200 Nighthawk Way 92562 — 951-696-1408
Eric Mooney, prin. — Fax 304-1803
Shivela MS — 1,500/6-8
24515 Lincoln Ave 92562 — 951-696-1406
Mark Pettengill, prin. — Fax 304-1643
Thompson MS — 1,700/6-8
24040 Hayes Ave 92562 — 951-696-1410
John Fox, prin. — Fax 304-1691
Vista Murrieta HS — 3,400/9-12
28251 Clinton Keith Rd 92563 — 951-894-5750
Mick Wager, prin. — Fax 304-1832
Warm Springs MS — 900/6-8
39245 Calle de Fortuna 92563 — 951-696-3503
Terry Picchiottino, prin. — Fax 304-1611
Murrieta Valley Adult S — Adult
24150 Hayes Ave 92562 — 951-696-3805
Tom Petrich, coord. — Fax 304-1664

Temecula Valley USD
Supt. — See Temecula
Bella Vista MS — 1,200/6-8
31650 Browning St 92563 — 951-294-6600
Shery Stewart, prin. — Fax 294-6624

Calvary Murrieta Christian S — 700/PK-12
24225 Monroe Ave 92562 — 951-834-9190
Desmond Starr, supt. — Fax 698-4896
Veritas Evangelical Seminary — Post-Sec.
39407 Murrieta Hot Springs 92563 — 951-698-6389

Napa, Napa, Pop. 75,253
Napa County Office of Education — 100/
2121 Imola Ave 94559 — 707-253-6800
Barbara Nemko, supt. — Fax 253-6841
www.napacoe.org
Napa County Community S — 100/Alt
2121 Imola Ave 94559 — 707-253-6817
Caroline Wilson, dir. — Fax 253-6983

Napa Valley USD — 18,400/K-12
2425 Jefferson St 94558 — 707-253-3511
Patrick J. Sweeney Ed.D., supt. — Fax 253-3855
www.nvusd.k12.ca.us
Harvest Magnet MS — 700/6-8
2449 Old Sonoma Rd 94558 — 707-259-8866
Monica Ready, prin. — Fax 253-4013
Napa HS — 1,900/9-12
2475 Jefferson St 94558 — 707-253-3711
Annie Petrie, prin. — Fax 253-3906
Napa Valley Independent Studies — 200/Alt
3310 Linda Vista Ave 94558 — 707-259-8577
Susan Hartman, prin. — Fax 259-8494
New Technology HS — Vo/Tech
920 Yount St 94559 — 707-259-8557
Riley Johnson, prin. — Fax 253-8558
Redwood MS — 1,000/6-8
3600 Oxford St 94558 — 707-253-3415
Maryanne Christoffersen, prin. — Fax 259-0718

Silverado MS 800/6-8
1133 Coombsville Rd 94558 707-253-3688
Jen Kohl, prin. Fax 253-3830
Valley Oak HS 200/Alt
1600 Myrtle Ave 94558 707-253-3791
Maria Cisneros, prin. Fax 253-3437
Vintage HS 1,800/9-12
1375 Trower Ave 94558 707-253-3601
Mike Pearson, prin. Fax 253-3604
Napa Valley Adult Education Adult
1600 Lincoln Ave 94558 707-253-3594
Lori-Leanne Parris, prin. Fax 253-3828
Other Schools – See American Canyon

Regional Occupational Center & Program
Supt. — None
Napa County ROP Vo/Tech
2121 Imola Ave 94559 707-253-6830
Tammie Holloway, dir. Fax 253-6917

Justin-Siena HS 600/9-12
4026 Maher St 94558 707-255-0950
John Bordelon, prin. Fax 255-1334
Kolbe Academy Trinity Prep 100/PK-12
2055 Redwood Rd 94558 707-258-9030
John Bertolini, hdmstr. Fax 258-9031
Napa Christian S 100/K-12
2201 Pine St 94559 707-255-5233
Napa State Hospital Post-Sec.
2100 Napa Vallejo Hwy 94558 707-253-5428
Napa Valley College Post-Sec.
2277 Napa Vallejo Hwy 94558 707-253-3000

National City, San Diego, Pop. 57,012
Sweetwater UNHSD
Supt. — See Chula Vista
Granger JHS 1,000/7-9
2101 Granger Ave 91950 619-472-6000
Richard Carreon, prin. Fax 267-4107
National City MS 800/7-8
1701 D Ave 91950 619-336-2600
Arturo Montano, prin. Fax 474-1756
Sweetwater HS 2,800/9-12
2900 Highland Ave 91950 619-474-9700
Maribel Gavin, prin. Fax 474-7635
National City Adult S Adult
517 Mile of Cars Way 91950 619-336-9400
Bernard Balanay, prin. Fax 336-0641

Bellus Academy Post-Sec.
1520 E Plaza Blvd 91950 619-474-6607
San Diego Academy 300/K-12
2800 E 4th St 91950 619-267-9550
Nicholas Lindquist, prin. Fax 267-8662

Needles, San Bernardino, Pop. 4,672
Needles USD 900/K-12
1900 Erin Dr 92363 760-326-3891
Mary McNeil, supt. Fax 326-4218
www.needlesusd.org
Educational Training Center 50/Alt
1900 Erin Dr 92363 760-326-2092
Amy Avila, prin. Fax 326-2191
Needles Community Day S Alt
1900 Erin Dr 92363 760-326-3891
Marie Armijo, prin.
Needles HS 200/9-12
1900 Erin Dr 92363 760-326-2191
Amy Avila, prin. Fax 326-1212
Needles MS 200/6-8
1900 Erin Dr 92363 760-326-3894
Amy Avila, prin. Fax 326-4052

Nevada City, Nevada, Pop. 2,983
Nevada City ESD 900/K-8
800 Hoover Ln 95959 530-265-1820
Trisha Dellis, supt. Fax 265-1822
www.ncsd.k12.ca.us
Seven Hills IS 400/5-8
700 Hoover Ln 95959 530-265-1840
Sam Schug, prin. Fax 265-1846

Nevada County Office of Education 3,400/
112 Nevada City Hwy 95959 530-478-6400
Holly Hermansen, supt. Fax 478-6410
www.nevco.org/
Other Schools – See Grass Valley

Ananda Living Wisdom S 100/PK-12
14618 Tyler Foote Rd 95959 530-478-7640
Diane Atwell, dir. Fax 478-7646

Newark, Alameda, Pop. 40,127
Newark USD 6,300/K-12
5715 Musick Ave 94560 510-818-4112
Dr. Partick Sanchez, supt. Fax 794-2199
www.newarkunified.org
Bridgepoint Continuation HS 100/Alt
35753 Cedar Blvd 94560 510-818-3200
Marc Lopes, prin. Fax 818-3255
Crossroads HS 50/Alt
35753 Cedar Blvd 94560 510-818-3720
Marc Lopes, prin. Fax 818-3255
Newark JHS 900/7-8
6201 Lafayette Ave 94560 510-818-3050
Mark Neal, prin. Fax 794-2079
Newark Memorial HS 1,800/9-12
39375 Cedar Blvd 94560 510-818-4350
Phillip Morales, prin. Fax 794-2120
Newark Adult S Adult
35753 Cedar Blvd 94560 510-818-3700
Marc Lopes, prin. Fax 818-3738

Newbury Park, See Thousand Oaks
Conejo Valley USD
Supt. — See Thousand Oaks
Conejo Valley HS Alt/Continuation 100/Alt
1872 Newbury Rd 91320 805-498-6646
Martin Manzer, prin. Fax 498-1423

Newbury Park HS 2,500/9-12
456 N Reino Rd 91320 805-498-3676
Josh Eby, prin. Fax 499-3549
Sequoia MS 1,100/6-8
2855 Borchard Rd 91320 805-498-3617
Steve Lepire, prin. Fax 375-5605

Newbury Park Adventist Academy 200/9-12
180 Academy Dr 91320 805-498-2191

New Cuyama, Santa Barbara, Pop. 510
Cuyama JUSD 200/PK-12
2300 Highway 166 93254 661-766-2482
Dr. F. Paul Chounet, supt. Fax 766-2255
www.cuyamaunified.org
Cuyama Valley HS 100/9-12
2300 Highway 166 93254 661-766-2293
Dr. F. Paul Chounet, admin. Fax 766-2593
Sierra Madre Continuation HS 50/Alt
2300 Highway 166 93254 661-766-2293
Dr. F. Paul Chounet, admin. Fax 766-2593

Newhall, See Santa Clarita
William S. Hart UNHSD
Supt. — See Santa Clarita
Hart HS 2,200/9-12
24825 Newhall Ave 91321 661-259-7575
Dr. Collyn Nielsen, prin. Fax 254-6436
Placerita JHS 1,100/7-8
25015 Newhall Ave 91321 661-259-1551
Jan Hayes-Rennels, prin. Fax 287-9748

Master's College and Seminary Post-Sec.
21726 Placerita Canyon Rd 91321 661-259-3540

Newman, Stanislaus, Pop. 10,029
Newman-Crows Landing USD 2,900/PK-12
1162 Main St 95360 209-862-2933
Randy Fillpot, supt. Fax 862-0113
www.nclusd.k12.ca.us/
Foothill Community Day S 50/Alt
890 Main St 95360 209-862-2309
Rick Gonzalez, prin. Fax 862-2316
Newman Independent Study 50/Alt
890 Main St 95360 209-862-2309
Rick Gonzalez, prin. Fax 862-2316
Orestimba HS 800/9-12
707 Hardin Rd 95360 209-862-2916
Justin Pruett, prin. Fax 862-0259
Westside Valley Continuation HS 50/Alt
890 Main St 95360 209-862-2309
Rick Gonzalez, prin. Fax 862-2316
Yolo MS 600/6-8
901 Hoyer Rd 95360 209-862-2984
Eva Luna, prin. Fax 862-3734

Newport Beach, Orange, Pop. 82,964
Newport - Mesa USD
Supt. — See Costa Mesa
Corona Del Mar JSHS 2,500/7-12
2101 Eastbluff Dr 92660 949-515-6000
Kathy Scott, prin. Fax 515-6070
Ensign IS 1,100/7-8
2000 Cliff Dr 92663 949-515-6910
Michael Sciacca, prin. Fax 515-3370
Newport Harbor HS 2,500/9-12
600 Irvine Ave 92663 949-515-6300
Sean Boulton, prin. Fax 515-6370

Interior Designers Institute Post-Sec.
1061 Camelback St 92660 949-675-4451
Pacifica Christian HS 9-12
883 W 15th St 92663 949-887-2070
David O'Neil, head sch Fax 887-2620
Southern States University Post-Sec.
1601 Dove St Ste 105 92660 949-833-8868

Newport Coast, Orange

Sage Hill S 400/9-12
20402 Newport Coast Dr 92657 949-219-0100
Patricia Merz, head sch Fax 219-1399

Nicolaus, Sutter, Pop. 204
East Nicolaus JUNHSD 300/9-12
2454 Nicolaus Ave 95659 530-656-2255
Mary Lynch, supt. Fax 656-1065
www.eastnicolaus.k12.ca.us
East Nicolaus HS 300/9-12
2454 Nicolaus Ave 95659 530-656-2255
Mary Lynch, prin. Fax 656-1065

Nipomo, San Luis Obispo, Pop. 16,314
Lucia Mar USD
Supt. — See Arroyo Grande
Central Coast New Tech HS 200/9-12
525 N Thompson Ave 93444
Christian Holst, prin.
Nipomo HS 1,000/9-12
525 N Thompson Ave 93444 805-474-3300
John Denno, prin. Fax 929-2551

Norco, Riverside, Pop. 26,516
Corona-Norco USD 53,500/K-12
2820 Clark Ave 92860 951-736-5000
Michael H. Lin Ed.D., supt. Fax 736-5015
www.cnusd.k12.ca.us
Kennedy HS 500/10-12
1951 3rd St 92860 951-738-2200
Sarah Ragusa, prin. Fax 738-2212
Norco HS 2,300/9-12
2065 Temescal Ave 92860 951-736-3241
Rob Ibbetson, prin. Fax 736-3282
Norco IS 800/7-8
2711 Temescal Ave 92860 951-736-3206
Amy Shainman, prin. Fax 736-3208
Other Schools – See Corona, Eastvale

Norco College Post-Sec.
2001 3rd St 92860 951-372-7000

Norden, Nevada

Sugar Bowl Academy 50/6-12
PO Box 68 95724 530-426-1844
Tracy Keller, head sch Fax 426-1860

North Edwards, Kern, Pop. 1,016
Muroc JUSD 2,000/PK-12
17100 Foothill Ave 93523 760-769-4821
Dr. Michael McCoy Ph.D., supt. Fax 769-4241
www.muroc.k12.ca.us
Other Schools – See Boron, Edwards

North Fork, Madera
Chawanakee USD 1,100/K-12
PO Box 400 93643 559-877-6209
Darren Sylvia, supt. Fax 877-2065
www.chawanakee.k12.ca.us
Manzanita Community Day S 50/Alt
PO Box 339 93643 559-877-6209
Gary Talley, prin. Fax 877-4430
Mountain Oaks HS 50/9-12
PO Box 339 93643 559-877-4440
Gary Talley, prin. Fax 877-4430
Other Schools – See O Neals

North Highlands, Sacramento, Pop. 40,275
Twin Rivers USD
Supt. — See Mc Clellan
Highlands HS 800/9-12
6601 Guthrie St 95660 916-566-3465
Darryl Hawthrone, prin. Fax 566-7810
Pacific Career & Technology HS Vo/Tech
6560 Melrose Dr 95660 916-566-2715
Shane Yang, prin. Fax 566-3558

North Hills, Los Angeles
Los Angeles USD
Supt. — See Los Angeles
Einstein Continuation HS 100/Alt
15938 Tupper St 91343 818-892-4367
Flor Ayala, prin. Fax 893-3423
Monroe HS 2,500/9-12
9229 Haskell Ave 91343 818-830-4200
Christopher Rosas, prin. Fax 892-5622
Sepulveda MS 1,600/6-8
15330 Plummer St 91343 818-920-2130
Gabriel Ortega, prin. Fax 891-5754

Centers of Learning 100/PK-12
PO Box 2037 91393 818-894-3213
Heritage Christian S South Campus 700/6-12
9825 Woodley Ave 91343 818-894-5742
Lance Haliday, prin. Fax 892-5018

North Hollywood, See Los Angeles
Los Angeles USD
Supt. — See Los Angeles
Earhart Continuation S 100/Alt
5355 Colfax Ave 91601 818-769-4877
John Berns, prin. Fax 980-1794
East Valley HS 800/9-12
5525 Vineland Ave 91601 818-753-4400
Timothy Lino, prin. Fax 487-6922
Madison MS 1,700/6-8
13000 Hart St 91605 818-255-5200
Estelle Baptiste, prin. Fax 765-4692
North Hollywood HS 2,800/9-12
5231 Colfax Ave 91601 818-753-6200
Ricardo Rosales, prin. Fax 508-7124
Reed MS 1,700/6-8
4525 Irvine Ave 91602 818-487-7600
Jeanne Gamba, prin. Fax 766-9069
Romer MS 1,200/6-8
6501 Laurel Canyon Blvd 91606 818-505-2200
Manuel Diaz, prin. Fax 761-9343

Anderson Medical Career College Post-Sec.
10752 Burbank Blvd 91601 818-762-7095
Art Institute of California - Hollywood Post-Sec.
5250 Lankershim Blvd 91601 818-299-5100
Brightwood College Post-Sec.
6180 Laurel Canyon Ste 101 91606 818-763-2563
Campbell Hall S 1,100/K-12
4533 Laurel Canyon Blvd 91607 818-980-7280
Rev. Julian Bull, hdmstr. Fax 505-5362
Concorde Career College Post-Sec.
12412 Victory Blvd 91606 818-766-8151
Marinello School of Beauty Post-Sec.
6219 Laurel Canyon Blvd 91606 818-980-1300
Oakwood S 500/7-12
11600 Magnolia Blvd 91601 818-732-3000
Dr. James Astman, hdmstr.
Southern California Health Institute Post-Sec.
5200 Lankershim Blvd 91601 818-980-8990
Valley Torah Girls HS 200/9-12
12003 Riverside Dr 91607 818-755-1697
West Coast University Post-Sec.
12215 Victory Blvd 91606 818-299-5500

Northridge, See Los Angeles
Los Angeles USD
Supt. — See Los Angeles
Holmes MS 1,600/6-8
9351 Paso Robles Ave 91325 818-678-4100
Hanh Aloisio, prin. Fax 886-3358
Northridge Academy HS 1,100/9-12
9601 Zelzah Ave 91325 818-700-2222
Nidia Castro, prin. Fax 718-2239
Northridge MS 800/6-8
17960 Chase St 91325 818-678-5100
Adrienne Shaha, prin. Fax 885-1461

CA National University Advanced Studies Post-Sec.
8550 Balboa Blvd Ste 210 91325 800-782-2422

California State University-Northridge Post-Sec.
18111 Nordhoff St 91330 818-677-1200
Highland Hall Waldorf S 300/PK-12
17100 Superior St 91325 818-349-1394
Lynn Kern, admin. Fax 349-2390
San Fernando Valley Academy 100/PK-12
17601 Lassen St 91325 818-349-1373

Norwalk, Los Angeles, Pop. 103,851
Little Lake City SD
Supt. — See Santa Fe Springs
Lakeside MS 700/6-8
11000 Kenney St 90650 562-868-9422
Ana Gutierrez, prin. Fax 863-9252

Norwalk-La Mirada USD 19,300/PK-12
12820 Pioneer Blvd 90650 562-868-0431
Dr. Hasmik Danielian Ed.D., supt. Fax 864-9857
www.nlmusd.k12.ca.us
Corvallis MS 800/6-8
11032 Leffingwell Rd 90650 562-868-2678
Bob Easton, prin. Fax 863-4755
Glenn HS 1,600/9-12
13520 Shoemaker Ave 90650 562-868-0431
Greg Puccia, prin. Fax 802-1596
Los Alisos MS 1,200/6-8
14800 Jersey Ave 90650 562-868-0865
Mike Garcia, prin. Fax 864-2967
Norwalk HS 2,000/9-12
11356 Leffingwell Rd 90650 562-868-0431
Christina Stanley Ed.D., prin. Fax 864-0796
Waite MS 700/6-8
14320 Norwalk Blvd 90650 562-921-7981
Dr. Susan Newcomb, prin. Fax 921-8114
Norwalk Adult S Adult
15711 Pioneer Blvd 90650 562-868-9858
Sharon Todd, dir. Fax 863-2159
Other Schools – See La Mirada, Whittier

Regional Occupational Center & Program
Supt. — None
Southeast ROP Vo/Tech
12940 Foster Rd 90650 562-860-1927
Gilbert Montano, prin. Fax 929-2474

ATI College Post-Sec.
12440 Firestone Blvd # 2001 90650 562-864-0506
Cerritos College Post-Sec.
11110 Alondra Blvd 90650 562-860-2451
New Harvest Christian S 100/PK-12-
PO Box 529 90651 562-929-6034
NTMA Training Center of Southern CA Post-Sec.
14926 Bloomfield Ave 90650 562-921-3722

Novato, Marin, Pop. 49,983
Novato USD 8,000/K-12
1015 7th St 94945 415-897-4201
Jim Hogeboom, supt. Fax 898-5790
www.nusd.org
Marin Oaks HS 100/Alt
720 Diablo Ave 94947 415-892-8733
Kessa Early, prin. Fax 897-4229
Nexus Academy 50/Alt
720 Diablo Ave 94947 415-506-3066
Kessa Early, prin.
Nova Education Center/Adult Education 100/Alt
720 Diablo Ave 94947 415-897-7653
Kessa Early, prin. Fax 897-5603
Novato HS 1,400/9-12
625 Arthur St 94947 415-898-2125
Matt Baldwin, prin. Fax 897-4242
San Jose MS 700/6-8
1000 Sunset Pkwy 94949 415-883-7831
Justin Mori, prin. Fax 883-0624
San Marin HS 900/9-12
15 San Marin Dr 94945 415-898-2121
Adam Littlefield, prin. Fax 892-8284
Sinaloa MS 900/6-8
2045 Vineyard Rd 94947 415-897-2111
Jim Larson, prin. Fax 892-1201

College of Marin Post-Sec.
1800 Ignacio Blvd 94949 415-457-8811
Marin Christian Academy 200/PK-12
1370 S Novato Blvd 94947 415-892-5713
Christopher Mychajluk, supt. Fax 892-4719
North Bay Christian Academy 100/9-12
6965 Redwood Blvd 94945 415-892-8921
Brian Niehausen, prin. Fax 899-1300

Nuevo, Riverside, Pop. 6,326
Nuview UNESD 2,700/K-12
29780 Lakeview Ave 92567 951-928-0066
David Pyle, supt. Fax 928-0324
www.nuview.k12.ca.us
Mountain Shadows MS 400/7-8
30401 Reservoir Ave 92567 951-928-3836
Debra Orona, prin. Fax 928-3015

Oakdale, Stanislaus, Pop. 20,174
Oakdale JUSD 5,300/PK-12
168 S 3rd Ave 95361 209-848-4884
Marc Malone, supt. Fax 847-0155
www.ojusd.org
East Stanislaus HS 100/Alt
250 Hinkley Ave 95361 209-847-1735
Dennis Hitch, prin. Fax 847-9627
Oakdale HS 1,600/9-12
739 W G St 95361 209-847-3007
Michael Moore, prin. Fax 848-0314
Oakdale JHS 800/7-8
400 S Maag Ave 95361 209-847-2294
Jon Webb, prin. Fax 847-8521
Valley Oak JSHS 50/Alt
200 Hinkley Ave 95361 209-847-3097
Dennis Hitch, prin. Fax 848-4359

Oak Hills, San Bernardino, Pop. 8,716
Hesperia USD
Supt. — See Hesperia
Oak Hills HS 2,400/9-12
7625 Cataba Rd, 760-244-2283
Michael Capps, prin. Fax 244-0351

Oakhurst, Madera, Pop. 2,743
Bass Lake JUNESD 900/K-8
40096 Indian Springs Rd 93644 559-642-1555
Glenn Reid, supt. Fax 642-1556
www.basslakeschooldistrict.com/
Oak Creek IS 200/6-8
40094 Indian Springs Rd 93644 559-642-1570
Brad Barcus, prin. Fax 683-7279

Yosemite USD 2,000/K-12
50200 Road 427 93644 559-683-8801
Jim Sargent, supt. Fax 683-4160
www.yosemiteusd.com/
Ahwahnee Continuation HS 50/Alt
50200 Road 427 93644 559-683-8801
Dr. Stacy Nicol, prin. Fax 658-2034
Campbell High Community Day S 50/Alt
50200 Road 427 93644 559-683-8801
Dr. Stacy Nicol, prin. Fax 658-2359
Evergreen HS 50/Alt
50200 Road 427 93644 559-683-5544
Dr. Stacy Nicol, prin. Fax 658-2359
Yosemite HS 700/9-12
50200 Road 427 93644 559-683-4667
Randy Seals, prin. Fax 683-8392
Yosemite Adult HS Adult
50200 Road 427 93644 559-683-8801
Dr. Stacy Nicol, prin. Fax 642-4334
Other Schools – See Coarsegold, Raymond

Oakland, Alameda, Pop. 373,354
Oakland USD 42,400/PK-12
2111 International Blvd 94606 510-434-7790
Antwan Wilson, supt.
www.ousd.org
Alliance Academy 400/6-8
1800 98th Ave 94603 510-639-2893
Stacey Wyatt, prin. Fax 639-3387
Brewer MS 800/6-8
3748 13th Ave 94610 510-531-6600
Aubrey Lane, prin. Fax 531-6626
Bunche Continuation S 100/Alt
1240 18th St 94607 510-874-3300
Betsye Steele, prin. Fax 874-3305
Castlemont HS 600/9-12
8601 MacArthur Blvd 94605 510-639-1466
William Chavarin, prin. Fax 639-4271
Claremont MS 400/6-8
5750 College Ave 94618 510-654-7337
Jonathan Mayer, prin. Fax 654-7341
Coliseum College Prep Academy 500/6-12
1390 66th Ave 94621 510-639-3201
Amy Carozza, prin. Fax 639-3214
Community Day MSHS 50/Alt
4917 Mountain Blvd 94619 510-531-6800
Mekael Johnson, prin. Fax 482-7144
Dewey Academy 200/Alt
1111 2nd Ave 94606 510-874-3660
Robin Glover, prin. Fax 874-3661
Elmhurst Community Prep S 400/6-8
1800 98th Ave 94603 510-639-2888
Kilian Betlach, prin. Fax 639-2891
Fremont HS 700/9-12
4610 Foothill Blvd 94601 510-434-5257
Tom Skjerheim, prin. Fax 434-2018
Frick MS 300/6-8
2845 64th Ave 94605 510-729-7736
Jeffrey Taylor, prin. Fax 729-7739
Gateway to College S 100/Alt
900 Fallon St 94607 510-986-6941
Rogeair Purnell, prin. Fax 464-3231
Harte MS 500/6-8
3700 Coolidge Ave 94602 510-531-6400
Bianca D'Allesandro, prin. Fax 482-7272
LIFE Academy 400/6-12
2101 35th Ave 94601 510-534-0282
Aryn Bowman, prin. Fax 534-0283
Madison Park Academy 500/6-12
400 Capistrano Dr 94603 510-636-2701
Lucinda Taylor, prin. Fax 636-2704
McClymonds HS 300/9-12
2608 Myrtle St 94607 510-238-8607
Plashan McCune, prin. Fax 874-3796
MetWest HS 100/Alt
314 East Tenth St 94606 510-451-5902
Charlie Plant, prin. Fax 451-5903
Montera MS 900/6-8
5555 Ascot Dr 94611 510-531-6070
Darren Avent, prin. Fax 531-6354
Oakland HS 1,600/9-12
1023 MacArthur Blvd 94610 510-874-3676
Matin Abdel-Qawi, prin. Fax 874-3675
Oakland International HS 400/Alt
4521 Webster St 94609 510-597-4287
Carmelita Welsh-Reyes, prin. Fax 597-4292
Oakland Technical HS Vo/Tech
4351 Broadway 94611 510-450-5400
Staci Ross-Morrison, prin. Fax 450-5428
Roosevelt MS 600/6-8
1926 E 19th St 94606 510-535-2877
Clifford Hong, prin. Fax 535-2883
ROOTS International Academy 300/6-8
1390 66th Ave 94621 510-639-3226
Geoff Vu, prin. Fax 639-3214
Rudsdale Continuation S 100/Alt
8251 Fontaine St 94605 510-729-4303
Willie Thompson, prin. Fax 569-7402
Skyline HS 1,800/9-12
12250 Skyline Blvd 94619 510-482-7109
Vinnie Blye, prin. Fax 482-7296

Sojourner Truth S 200/Alt
8251 Fontaine St 94605 510-729-4308
Willie Thompson, prin. Fax 636-4701
Street Academy 100/Alt
417 29th St 94609 510-874-3630
Gina Hill, prin. Fax 874-3633
United for Success Academy 400/6-8
2101 35th Ave 94601 510-535-3880
Nicole Pierce, prin. Fax 535-7139
Urban Promise Academy 300/6-8
3031 E 18th St 94601 510-436-3636
Claire Fisher, prin. Fax 436-3638
Westlake MS 600/6-8
2629 Harrison St 94612 510-879-2130
Misha Karigica, prin. Fax 835-7170
West Oakland MS 200/6-8
991 14th St 94607 510-874-6788
Neha Ummat, prin. Fax 874-6790
Neighborhood Centers Adult S Adult
750 International Blvd 94606 510-451-7300
Chris Nelson, prin. Fax 451-7320

Academy of Chinese Culture & Health Sci. Post-Sec.
1601 Clay St 94612 510-763-7787
American University of Armenia Post-Sec.
300 Lakeside Dr Fl 12 94612 510-987-9452
Aviation Institute of Maintenance Post-Sec.
9636 Earhart Rd 94621 510-553-9600
Bishop O'Dowd HS 1,100/9-12
9500 Stearns Ave 94605 510-577-9100
James Childs, prin. Fax 638-3259
College Preparatory S 400/9-12
6100 Broadway 94618 510-652-0111
Monique DeVane, head sch Fax 652-7467
DeVry University Post-Sec.
505 14th St Ste 100 94612 510-267-1340
Head-Royce S 800/K-12
4315 Lincoln Ave 94602 510-531-1300
Crystal Land, head sch Fax 531-2649
Holy Names HS 200/9-12
4660 Harbord Dr 94618 510-450-1110
Dr. Connie Hubbard, prin. Fax 547-3111
Holy Names University Post-Sec.
3500 Mountain Blvd 94619 510-436-1000
Laney College Post-Sec.
900 Fallon St 94607 510-834-5740
Lincoln University Post-Sec.
401 15th St 94612 510-628-8010
Mentoring Academy 8-12
5951 College Ave 94618 510-400-7696
Merritt College Post-Sec.
12500 Campus Dr 94619 510-531-4911
Mills College Post-Sec.
5000 MacArthur Blvd 94613 510-430-2255
Moler Barber College Post-Sec.
3815 Telegraph Ave 94609 510-652-4177
Morgan S for Girls 200/6-8
PO Box 9966 94613 510-632-6000
Sandra Luna, head sch Fax 632-6301
Patten Academy of Christian Education 100/K-12
2430 Coolidge Ave 94601 510-533-3121
Dr. Sharon Anderson, prin. Fax 535-9381
Patten University Post-Sec.
2433 Coolidge Ave 94601 510-261-8500
St. Elizabeth HS 200/9-12
1530 34th Ave 94601 510-532-8947
Martin Procaccio, prin. Fax 532-9754
St. Martin de Porres S 100/6-8
1630 10th St 94607 510-832-1757
Dr. Hollis Pierce-Jenkins, pres. Fax 832-6481
Samuel Merritt University Post-Sec.
3100 Telegraph Ave Ste 1000 94609 510-869-6511
SUM Bible College & Theological Seminary Post-Sec.
735 105th Ave 94603 510-567-6174

Oakley, Contra Costa, Pop. 33,914
Liberty UNHSD
Supt. — See Brentwood
Freedom HS 2,600/9-12
1050 Neroly Rd 94561 925-625-5900
Kelly Manke, prin. Fax 625-0396

Oakley UNESD 4,900/K-8
91 Mercedes Ln 94561 925-625-0700
Greg Hetrick Ed.D., supt. Fax 625-1863
www.ouesd.k12.ca.us
Delta Vista MS 800/6-8
4901 Frank Hengel Way 94561 925-625-6840
Harvey Yurkovich, prin. Fax 625-6850
O'Hara Park MS 900/6-8
1100 OHara Ave 94561 925-625-5060
Colleen Creswell, prin. Fax 625-5096

Oak Park, Ventura, Pop. 13,435
Oak Park USD 4,700/PK-12
5801 Conifer St 91377 818-735-3200
Dr. Anthony Knight, supt. Fax 879-0372
www.opusd.org
Medea Creek MS 1,100/6-8
1002 Doubletree Rd 91377 818-707-7922
Brad Benioff, prin. Fax 865-8641
Oak Park HS 1,500/9-12
899 Kanan Rd 91377 818-735-3300
Kevin Buchanan, prin. Fax 707-7970
Oak Park Independent S 200/Alt
5801 Conifer St 91377 818-735-3260
Stewart McGugan, prin. Fax 735-3290
Oak View HS 50/Alt
5701 Conifer St 91377 818-735-3217
Stewart McGugan, prin. Fax 735-3290

Oceanside, San Diego, Pop. 159,148
Oceanside USD 21,200/K-12
2111 Mission Ave 92058 760-966-4000
Dr. Duane Coleman, supt. Fax 433-8620
ousd.ca.schoolloop.com

Chavez MS 700/6-8
202 Oleander Dr 92057 760-966-4900
Jenny Morgan, prin. Fax 945-4665
El Camino HS 3,100/9-12
400 Rancho Del Oro Dr 92057 760-901-8000
Alexander Bennet, prin. Fax 757-5321
Jefferson MS 700/6-8
823 Acacia Ave 92058 760-966-4700
Christy Dayhoff, prin. Fax 757-5791
King MS 1,500/6-8
1290 Ivey Ranch Rd 92057 760-901-8800
Dr. Greg Smedley, prin. Fax 967-4154
Lincoln MS 900/6-8
2000 California St 92054 760-901-8900
Steve Bessant, prin. Fax 433-2035
Ocean Shores HS 200/Alt
3131 Oceanside Blvd 92056 760-901-8600
Tina Cornish, prin. Fax 439-5588
Oceanside HS 2,200/9-12
1 Pirates Cove Way 92054 760-722-8201
Teresa Hill-Collis, prin. Fax 757-2419

Vista USD
Supt. — See Vista
Madison MS 1,200/6-8
4930 Lake Blvd 92056 760-940-0176
Susan Ford, prin. Fax 940-2081
Mission Vista HS 1,400/9-12
1306 Melrose Dr 92057 760-758-6800
Craig Wiblemo, prin. Fax 758-6832
Roosevelt MS 1,100/6-8
850 Sagewood Dr 92057 760-726-8003
Fax 726-8596

MediaTech Institute Post-Sec.
302 Oceanside Blvd 92054 760-231-5368
MiraCosta College Post-Sec.
1 Barnard Dr 92056 760-757-2121
Oceanside College of Beauty Post-Sec.
1575 S Coast Hwy 92054 760-757-6161

Ojai, Ventura, Pop. 7,310
Ojai USD 2,800/PK-12
PO Box 878 93024 805-640-4300
Dr. Hank Bangser, supt. Fax 640-4419
www.ojai.k12.ca.us
Chaparral Continuation HS 100/Alt
PO Box 878 93024 805-640-4330
Becky Beckett, lead tchr. Fax 640-4341
Matilija JHS 400/7-8
703 El Paseo Rd 93023 805-640-4355
Bill Rosen, prin. Fax 640-4398
Nordhoff HS 800/9-12
1401 Maricopa Hwy 93023 805-640-4343
Greg Bayless, prin. Fax 640-4336
Ojai Adult, 414 E Ojai Ave 93024 Adult
Becky Beckett, prin. 805-640-4330

Besant Hill S 100/9-12
PO Box 850 93024 805-646-4343
Randy Bertin, head sch Fax 646-4371
Laurel Springs S 1,600/K-12
302 El Paseo Rd 93023 805-646-2473
Oak Grove S 200/PK-12
220 W Lomita Ave 93023 805-646-8236
Willem Zwart, head sch Fax 646-6509
Ojai Valley S 300/PK-12
723 El Paseo Rd 93023 805-646-1423
Michael Hall-Mounsey, pres. Fax 646-0362
Thacher S 300/9-12
5025 Thacher Rd 93023 805-646-4377
Michael Mulligan, head sch Fax 646-9490
Villanova Preparatory HS 300/9-12
12096 N Ventura Ave 93023 805-646-1464
Nancy O'Sullivan, hdmstr. Fax 646-4430

Olivehurst, Yuba, Pop. 13,017
Marysville JUSD
Supt. — See Marysville
Lindhurst HS 1,100/9-12
4446 Olive Ave 95961 530-741-6150
Bob Eckardt, prin. Fax 741-6171
South Lindhurst Continuation HS 100/Alt
4446 Olive Ave 95961 530-741-6918
David Jones, prin. Fax 741-7875
Yuba Gardens IS 700/7-8
1964 11th Ave 95961 530-741-6194
Kari Ylst, prin. Fax 741-7847

New Life Christian S 100/PK-12
5736 Arboga Rd 95961 530-742-3033
John Lewallen, admin. Fax 741-8221

Olympic Valley, Placer

Squaw Valley Academy 100/9-12
PO Box 2667 96146 530-583-9393
Bill Grant, hdmstr. Fax 581-1111

O Neals, Madera
Chawanakee USD
Supt. — See North Fork
Minarets HS 300/9-12
PO Box 186 93645 559-868-8689
Daniel Ching, prin. Fax 868-3407
Chawanakee Adult Education Adult
PO Box 186 93645 559-868-4200
Gary Talley, prin. Fax 868-4222

Ontario, San Bernardino, Pop. 161,020
Chaffey JUNHSD 24,700/9-12
211 W 5th St 91762 909-988-8511
Mathew Holton, supt. Fax 467-5177
cjuhsd-ca.schoolloop.com
Chaffey Community Day S 50/Alt
1802 E 7th St 91764 909-460-5663
Bart Goldstein, prin.
Chaffey HS 3,600/9-12
1245 N Euclid Ave 91762 909-988-5560
Dr. George Matamala, prin. Fax 988-0146
Colony HS 2,200/9-12
3850 E Riverside Dr 91761 909-930-2929
Dr. Kern Oduro, prin. Fax 460-5856
Ontario HS 2,600/9-12
901 W Francis St 91762 909-988-7411
Eduardo Zaldivar, prin. Fax 391-5220
Valley View Continuation HS 500/Alt
1801 E 6th St 91764 909-985-0966
Bart Goldstein, prin. Fax 981-2159
Chaffey Adult S Adult
1802 E 7th St 91764 909-391-5365
Todd Haag, prin. Fax 391-5234
Other Schools – See Alta Loma, Etiwanda, Montclair, Rancho Cucamonga

Chino Valley USD
Supt. — See Chino
Woodcrest JHS 400/7-8
2725 S Campus Ave 91761 909-923-3455
Sue Pederson, prin. Fax 548-6059

Mountain View ESD 2,700/K-8
2585 S Archibald Ave 91761 909-947-2205
Dr. Rick Carr, supt. Fax 947-2291
www.mtnview.k12.ca.us
Yokley MS, 2947 S Turner Ave 91761 900/6-8
Jeremy Currier, prin. 909-947-6774

Ontario-Montclair SD 22,700/PK-8
950 W D St 91762 909-459-2500
Dr. James Hammond, supt. Fax 459-2542
www.omsd.net
Danks MS 900/7-8
1020 N Vine Ave 91762 909-983-2691
Anthony Ortiz, prin. Fax 459-2959
De Anza MS 600/7-8
1450 S Sultana Ave 91761 909-986-8577
Adriana Gonzalez, prin. Fax 459-2673
Oaks MS 900/7-8
1221 S Oaks Ave 91762 909-988-2050
Dave Foley, prin. Fax 988-2081
Wiltsey MS 1,000/6-8
1450 E G St 91764 909-986-5838
Henry Romero, prin. Fax 459-2834
Other Schools – See Montclair

Regional Occupational Center & Program
Supt. — None
Baldy View ROP Vo/Tech
2890 Inland Empire Blvd 91764 909-980-6490
Forest DeRenzo, supt.

American Career College Post-Sec.
3130 Sedona Ct 91764 909-218-3253
Argosy University Inland Empire Post-Sec.
3401 Centre Lake Dr Ste 200 91761 909-472-0800
Everest College Post-Sec.
1460 S Milliken Ave 91761 909-984-5027
Everest College Post-Sec.
1819 Excise Ave 91761 909-484-4311
Franklin Career College Post-Sec.
1274 Slater Cir 91761 909-937-9007
Golden Gate Baptist Theological Seminary Post-Sec.
3210 E Guasti Rd 91761 415-380-1300
Marinello School of Beauty Post-Sec.
940 N Mountain Ave 91762 909-984-5884
NTMA Training Center of Southern CA Post-Sec.
1717 S Grove Ave 91761 909-947-9363
Ontario Christian HS 500/9-12
931 W Philadelphia St 91762 909-984-1756
Tim Hoekstra, prin. Fax 460-0176
Platt College Post-Sec.
3700 Inland Empire Ste 400 91764 909-941-9410
Richard's Beauty College Post-Sec.
200 N Euclid Ave 91762 909-988-7584
San Antonio Christian S 100/K-10
1722 E 8th St 91764 909-982-2301
West Coast Ultrasound Institute Post-Sec.
3700 Inland Empire Blvd 235 91764 909-483-3808
West Coast University Post-Sec.
2855 E Guasti Rd 91761 909-467-6100
Westech College Post-Sec.
3491 Concours 91764 909-980-4474

Orange, Orange, Pop. 133,187
Orange USD 29,500/PK-12
PO Box 11022 92856 714-628-4001
Michael Christenson M.A., supt. Fax 628-4041
www.orangeusd.org/
Career Education Center Vo/Tech
250 S Yorba St 92869 714-997-6066
Justin Stanfield, coord. Fax 997-6035
El Modena HS 2,100/9-12
3920 E Spring St 92869 714-997-6331
Dustin Saxton, prin. Fax 997-0705
Orange HS 1,900/9-12
525 N Shaffer St 92867 714-997-6211
Dennis McCuistion, prin. Fax 633-6460
OUSD Community Day S 50/Alt
250 S Yorba St 92869 714-628-5479
Justin Stanfield, prin. Fax 538-8941
Portola MS 800/6-8
270 N Palm Dr 92868 714-997-6361
Jill Katevas, prin. Fax 978-0274
Richland Continuation HS 300/Alt
615 N Lemon St 92867 714-997-6167
Elsie Simonovski, prin. Fax 771-5967
Yorba MS 500/7-8
935 N Cambridge St 92867 714-997-6161
Tracy Knibb, prin. Fax 532-4759
Other Schools – See Anaheim, Villa Park

Argosy University Orange County Post-Sec.
601 S Lewis St 92868 714-620-3700
Camelot Academy of Arts Science & Tech PK-12
815 S Esplanade St 92869 714-602-7797
Chapman University Post-Sec.
1 University Dr 92866 714-997-6815
CNI College Post-Sec.
702 W Town and Country Rd 92868 714-437-9697
COBA Academy Post-Sec.
102 N Glassell St 92866 714-633-5950
Eldorado Emerson Private S 100/PK-12
4100 E Walnut Ave 92869 714-633-4774
Sean Kelley, hdmstr. Fax 744-3304
Lutheran HS of Orange County 1,300/9-12
2222 N Santiago Blvd 92867 714-998-5151
Todd Eklund M.A., prin. Fax 998-1371
St. Joseph Hospital Post-Sec.
1100 W Stewart Dr 92868 714-771-8111
Santiago Canyon College Post-Sec.
8045 E Chapman Ave 92869 714-628-4900
South Coast College Post-Sec.
2011 W Chapman Ave 92868 866-266-8779

Orange Cove, Fresno, Pop. 9,005
Kings Canyon JUSD
Supt. — See Reedley
Citrus MS 600/6-8
1400 Anchor Ave 93646 559-305-7370
Patricia Ledesma, prin. Fax 626-7255
Orange Cove HS 600/9-12
1700 Anchor Ave 93646 559-626-5900
Angel Durazo, prin. Fax 626-7217

Orangevale, Sacramento, Pop. 32,766
San Juan USD
Supt. — See Carmichael
Carnegie MS 1,000/6-8
5820 Illinois Ave 95662 916-971-7853
Mark Siewert, prin. Fax 971-7849
Casa Roble Fundamental HS 1,400/9-12
9151 Oak Ave 95662 916-971-5452
Michele Lorenzo, prin. Fax 971-5495
Pasteur MS 700/6-8
8935 Elm Ave 95662 916-971-7891
Janet Deal, prin. Fax 971-7893

Orcutt, Santa Barbara, Pop. 28,086
Orcutt UNESD 5,100/K-12
500 Dyer St 93455 805-938-8900
Deborah Blow, supt. Fax 938-8919
www.orcutt-schools.net
Orcutt JHS 500/7-8
608 Pinal Ave 93455 805-938-8700
Kelly Osborne, prin. Fax 938-8749
Other Schools – See Santa Maria

Orinda, Contra Costa, Pop. 16,885
Acalanes UNHSD
Supt. — See Lafayette
Miramonte HS 1,100/9-12
750 Moraga Way 94563 925-280-3930
Julie Parks, prin. Fax 280-3931

Orinda UNESD 2,500/K-8
8 Altarinda Rd 94563 925-254-4901
Carolyn Seaton Ed.D., supt. Fax 254-5261
www.orindaschools.org/
Orinda IS 900/6-8
80 Ivy Dr 94563 925-258-3090
Michael Randall, prin. Fax 631-7985

Orinda Academy 100/8-12
19 Altarinda Rd 94563 925-254-7553
Ronald Graydon, hdmstr. Fax 254-4768

Orland, Glenn, Pop. 7,173
Orland JUSD 2,200/K-12
903 South St 95963 530-865-1200
Dr. Ken Geisick, supt. Fax 865-1202
www.orlandusd.net
North Valley HS 50/Alt
903 South St 95963 530-865-1285
Fax 865-1285
Orland Community Day S 50/Alt
903 South St 95963 530-865-1264
Orland HS 700/9-12
903 South St 95963 530-865-1210
Victor Perry, prin. Fax 865-1215
Price IS 500/6-8
903 South St 95963 530-865-1225
Kelly Haight, prin. Fax 865-1227

Providence Christian S 100/K-12
1148 E Walker St 95963 530-865-4924
Gordon Wiens, supt. Fax 865-4926

Orosi, Tulare, Pop. 8,702
Cutler-Orosi JUSD 4,100/K-12
12623 Avenue 416 93647 559-528-4763
Yolanda Valdez, supt. Fax 528-3132
www.cojusd.org
Cutler-Orosi Community Day S 50/Alt
12623 Avenue 416 93647 559-528-4703
Martha Calderon, prin. Fax 528-0102
El Monte MS 900/6-8
12623 Avenue 416 93647 559-528-3017
Michelle Kettle, prin. Fax 528-2822
Esperanza HS 100/Alt
12623 Avenue 416 93647 559-528-4703
Martha Calderon, prin. Fax 528-0102
Orosi HS 1,000/9-12
12623 Avenue 416 93647 559-528-4731
Roberto Vaca, prin. Fax 528-4930
Cutler-Orosi Adult S Adult
12623 Avenue 416 93647 559-528-4763
Melissa Calvero, dir.
Other Schools – See Cutler

Oroville, Butte, Pop. 14,775
Butte County Office of Education 1,400/
1859 Bird St 95965 530-532-5650
Tim Taylor, supt. Fax 532-5762
www.bcoe.org
Other Schools – See Chico, Paradise

Oroville City ESD 2,600/PK-8
2795 Yard St 95966 530-532-3000
Penny Chennell-Carter, supt. Fax 532-3050
www.ocesd.org
Central MS 400/7-8
2565 Mesa Ave 95966 530-532-3002
Mikeial Williamson, prin. Fax 532-3042
Ishi Hills MS 300/6-8
1 Ishi Hills Way 95966 530-532-3078
Chris Renzullo, prin. Fax 532-3040

Oroville UNHSD 2,400/9-12
2211 Washington Ave 95966 530-538-2300
Dr. Corey Willenberg, supt. Fax 538-2308
www.ouhsd.org
Las Plumas HS 1,100/9-12
2380 Las Plumas Ave 95966 530-538-2310
Dana Ramos, prin. Fax 534-5974
Oroville Community Day S 50/Alt
2120 2nd St 95965 530-538-2330
Dennis Spasbo, prin. Fax 533-2338
Oroville HS 1,100/9-12
1535 Bridge St 95966 530-538-2320
Doug Williams, prin. Fax 534-6203
Prospect Continuation HS 100/Alt
2060 2nd St 95965 530-538-2330
Dennis Spasbo, prin. Fax 533-2338
Oroville Adult Education Adult
2750 Mitchell Ave 95966 530-538-5350
Jeff Ochs, dir. Fax 538-5396

Thermalito UNESD 1,400/K-8
400 Grand Ave 95965 530-538-2900
Gregory Blake, supt. Fax 538-2908
www.thermalito.org
Heritage Community Day S 50/Alt
2080 6th St 95965 530-532-4376
S. Bowman, prin. Fax 538-2949
Nelson Avenue MS 400/6-8
2255 6th St 95965 530-538-2940
Rochelle Simmons, prin. Fax 538-2949

Butte College Post-Sec.
3536 Butte Campus Dr 95965 530-895-2511
Northwest Lineman College Post-Sec.
2009 Challenger Ave 95965 530-534-7260

Oxnard, Ventura, Pop. 194,223
Hueneme ESD
Supt. — See Port Hueneme
Blackstock JHS 1,200/6-8
701 E Bard Rd 93033 805-488-3644
Tom Beneke, prin. Fax 488-1250
Green JHS 1,000/6-8
3739 S C St 93033 805-986-8750
Heidi Haines, prin. Fax 986-8756

Ocean View ESD 2,600/PK-8
4200 Olds Rd 93033 805-488-4441
Dr. Craig Helmstedter Ed.D., supt. Fax 986-6797
www.oceanviewsd.org
Ocean View JHS 800/6-8
4300 Olds Rd 93033 805-488-6421
Heather Hendrix, prin. Fax 488-4132

Oxnard SD 15,700/K-8
1051 S A St 93030 805-385-1501
Dr. Cesar Morales, supt. Fax 483-7426
www.oxnardsd.org
Frank MS 1,300/6-8
701 N Juanita Ave 93030 805-385-1536
Dr. Liam Joyce, prin. Fax 981-1754
Fremont MS 1,100/6-8
1130 N M St 93030 805-385-1539
Greg Brisbine, prin. Fax 485-2486
Haydock MS 800/6-8
647 Hill St 93033 805-385-1545
Dr. Edd Bond, prin. Fax 487-7159

Oxnard UNHSD 16,500/K-12
309 S K St 93030 805-385-2500
Dr. Penelope DeLeon, supt. Fax 483-3069
www.ouhsd.k12.ca.us
Channel Islands HS 2,600/9-12
1400 Raiders Way 93033 805-385-2787
Ray Senesac, prin. Fax 385-2748
Condor HS Alt
4000 S Rose Ave 93033 805-385-5884
Kathy Greaves, prin. Fax 385-5208
Hueneme HS 1,900/9-12
500 W Bard Rd 93033 805-385-2667
Gary Mayeda Ed.D., prin. Fax 385-2817
Oxnard HS 2,900/9-12
3400 W Gonzales Rd, 805-278-2907
Eric Riegert, prin. Fax 278-2912
Pacifica HS 3,200/9-12
600 E Gonzales Rd, 805-278-5000
Ted Lawrence, prin. Fax 278-7187
Rio Mesa HS 2,100/9-12
545 Central Ave, 805-278-5500
Mark Contreras, prin. Fax 278-5525
Oxnard Adult S Adult
1101 W 2nd St 93030 805-385-2578
Diana Batista, prin. Fax 385-2581
Other Schools – See Camarillo

Rio SD 4,800/PK-8
2500 E Vineyard Ave, 805-485-3111
Dr. John Puglisi Ph.D., supt. Fax 981-7736
rioschools.org
Rio Del Valle MS 700/6-8
3100 N Rose Ave, 805-485-3119
Dr. Adrienne Peralta Ed.D., prin. Fax 981-7737
Rio Vista MS 700/6-8
3050 Thames River Dr, 805-981-1507
Matt Klinefelter, prin. Fax 981-6791

Calvary Christian HS 9-12
936 W 5th St 93030 805-487-7200
Charter College - Oxnard Post-Sec.
2000 Outlet Center Dr # 150, 805-973-1240
Laurus College Post-Sec.
2351 Lockwood St, 805-267-1690
Modern Beauty Academy Post-Sec.
699 S C St 93030 805-483-4994
Oxnard College Post-Sec.
4000 S Rose Ave 93033 805-986-5800
Pacific Coast Trade School Post-Sec.
1690 Universe Cir 93033 805-487-9260
St. John's Regional Medical Center Post-Sec.
1600 N Rose Ave 93030 805-988-2500
Santa Clara HS 300/9-12
2121 Saviers Rd 93033 805-483-9502
Dr. Edward Robillard, prin. Fax 483-1588

Pacifica, San Mateo, Pop. 35,016
Jefferson UNHSD
Supt. — See Daly City
Oceana HS 600/9-12
401 Paloma Ave 94044 650-550-7300
Jonas Barbour, prin. Fax 550-7310
Terra Nova HS 1,100/9-12
1450 Terra Nova Blvd 94044 650-550-7600
Megan Carey, prin. Fax 550-7690

Pacifica SD 3,200/PK-8
375 Reina Del Mar Ave 94044 650-738-6600
Dr. Wendy Tukloff, supt. Fax 557-9672
www.pacificasd.org/
Lacy MS 600/6-8
1427 Palmetto Ave 94044 650-738-6665
Daniel Lyttle, prin. Fax 738-6669

Alma Heights Christian S 300/K-12
1295 Seville Dr 94044 650-359-0555
Dr. David Gross, dir. Fax 359-5020

Pacific Grove, Monterey, Pop. 14,485
Pacific Grove USD 2,100/K-12
435 Hillcrest Ave 93950 831-646-6520
Ralph Porras, supt. Fax 646-6500
pgusd.org
Community HS 50/Alt
435 Hillcrest Ave 93950 831-646-6535
Matt Bell, prin. Fax 648-8417
Pacific Grove HS 600/9-12
615 Sunset Dr 93950 831-646-6590
Matt Bell, prin. Fax 646-6660
Pacific Grove MS 500/6-8
835 Forest Ave 93950 831-646-6568
Sean Roach, prin. Fax 646-6652
Pacific Grove Adult Education Adult
1025 Lighthouse Ave 93950 831-646-6580
Craig Beller, prin. Fax 646-6578

Stanford University Hopkins Marine Post-Sec.
120 Ocean View Blvd 93950 831-655-6200

Pacoima, See Los Angeles
Los Angeles USD
Supt. — See Los Angeles
MacLay MS 900/6-8
12540 Pierce St 91331 818-686-3800
Carlos Tobar, prin. Fax 834-1012
Pacoima MS 1,500/6-8
9919 Laurel Canyon Blvd 91331 818-686-4200
Simerjit Garcha, prin. Fax 834-2021

Palermo, Butte, Pop. 5,130
Palermo UNESD 1,300/K-8
7390 Bulldog Way 95968 530-533-4842
Dr. Bryan Caples, supt. Fax 532-1047
www.palermoschools.org
Palermo MS 400/6-8
7350 Bulldog Way 95968 530-533-4708
Kathleen Andoe, prin. Fax 532-7801

Palmdale, Los Angeles, Pop. 148,782
Antelope Valley UNHSD
Supt. — See Lancaster
Highland HS 3,000/9-12
39055 25th St W 93551 661-538-0304
Steve Ford, prin. Fax 538-0405
Knight HS 3,200/9-12
37423 70th St E 93552 661-533-9000
Richie Romero, prin. Fax 533-0111
Palmdale HS 2,700/9-12
2137 E Avenue R 93550 661-273-3181
Kristina Ramos, prin. Fax 273-1093
Parris Continuation HS 800/Alt
38801 Clock Tower Plaza Dr 93550 661-274-1230
Will Laird, prin. Fax 274-1168

Palmdale ESD 21,500/K-12
39139 10th St E 93550 661-947-7191
Raul Maldonado, supt. Fax 273-5137
www.palmdalesd.org
Cactus IS 900/7-8
3243 E Avenue R8 93550 661-273-0847
Danny Kanga, prin. Fax 273-5514
Desert Willow IS 500/7-8
36555 Sunny Ln 93550 661-285-5866
Gerilyn Cherland, prin. Fax 456-1145
Millen IS 500/7-8
39221 22nd St W 93551 661-947-3075
Ryan Beardsley, prin. Fax 538-9035
Shadow Hills IS 900/7-8
37315 60th St E 93552 661-533-7400
Dr. Donna Campbell, prin. Fax 533-7445

Regional Occupational Center & Program
Supt. — None
Antelope Valley ROP Vo/Tech
1156 E Avenue S 93550 661-575-1026
Betsy McKinstry, dir. Fax 575-1037

Westside UNESD
Supt. — See Quartz Hill
Hillview MS 1,000/6-8
40525 Peonza Ln 93551 661-722-9993
Rodney Lots, prin. Fax 722-9483

Wilsona SD 1,300/K-8
18050 E Avenue O 93591 661-264-1111
Teresa Grey, supt. Fax 261-3259
www.wilsonasd.net
Other Schools – See Lancaster

DeVry University Post-Sec.
39115 Trade Center Dr # 100 93551 866-986-9388

Palm Desert, Riverside, Pop. 47,665
Desert Sands USD
Supt. — See La Quinta
Palm Desert HS 2,000/9-12
74910 Aztec Rd 92260 760-862-4300
Bob Hicks, prin. Fax 862-4390

College of the Desert Post-Sec.
43500 Monterey Ave 92260 760-346-8041
Xavier College Preparatory HS 500/9-12
34200 Cook St 92211 760-601-3900
Jimmy Tricco, prin. Fax 601-3901

Palm Springs, Riverside, Pop. 43,639
Palm Springs USD 23,300/K-12
980 E Tahquitz Canyon Way 92262 760-416-6000
Sandra Lyon, supt. Fax 416-6015
www.psusd.us
Cree MS 1,000/6-8
1011 E Vista Chino 92262 760-416-8283
Bernie Marez, prin. Fax 416-8287
Desert Learning Academy 100/Alt
2248 E Ramon Rd 92264 760-778-0487
Dr. Todd Reed, prin. Fax 778-0497
Palm Springs HS 1,900/9-12
2401 E Baristo Rd 92262 760-778-0400
Ryan Woll, prin. Fax 778-0481
Other Schools – See Cathedral City, Desert Hot Springs, Rancho Mirage

---

Brightwood College Post-Sec.
2475 E Tahquitz Canyon Way 92262 760-778-3540
California Nurses Educational Institute Post-Sec.
5200 E Ramon Rd Ste I1 92264 760-416-5955
Desert Chapel Christian S 200/K-12
630 S Sunrise Way 92264 760-327-2772
Frank Marshall, admin. Fax 325-7048

Palo Alto, Santa Clara, Pop. 61,626
Palo Alto USD 12,300/PK-12
25 Churchill Ave 94306 650-329-3700
Glenn McGee Ph.D., supt. Fax 329-3803
www.pausd.org
Gunn HS 1,900/9-12
780 Arastradero Rd 94306 650-354-8200
Denise Herrmann, prin. Fax 493-7801
Jordan MS 1,000/6-8
750 N California Ave 94303 650-494-8120
Katie Kinnamon, prin. Fax 858-1310
Palo Alto HS 1,900/9-12
50 Embarcadero Rd 94301 650-329-3701
Kim Diorio, prin. Fax 329-3753
Stanford MS 1,000/6-8
480 E Meadow Dr 94306 650-856-5188
Lisa Hickey, prin. Fax 856-3248
Terman MS 700/6-8
655 Arastradero Rd 94306 650-856-9810
Pier Angeli La Place, prin. Fax 856-9878
Palo Alto Adult S Adult
50 Embarcadero Rd 94301 650-329-3752
Katya Villalobos, prin. Fax 329-8515

Bay Area College of Nursing Post-Sec.
824 San Antonio Rd 94303 650-858-6810
Castilleja S 400/6-12
1310 Bryant St 94301 650-328-3160
Nanci Kauffman, head sch Fax 326-8036
Girls' MS 200/6-8
3400 W Bayshore Rd 94303 650-968-8338
Jennifer Ayer, head sch Fax 968-4775
Hope Technology S 100/K-10
2525 E Bayshore Rd 94303 650-565-8391
Sharon Siu, admin.
Kehillah Jewish HS 200/9-12
3900 Fabian Way 94303 650-213-9600
Rabbi Darren Kleinberg Ph.D., head sch Fax 213-9601
Meira Academy 9-12
3921 Fabian Way 94303 650-485-3589
Devorah Lewis, prin.
Palo Alto University Post-Sec.
1791 Arastradero Rd 94304 800-818-6136
Sofia University Post-Sec.
1069 E Meadow Cir 94303 650-493-4430

Palo Cedro, Shasta, Pop. 1,232
Shasta UNHSD
Supt. — See Redding
Foothill HS 1,300/9-12
9733 Deschutes Rd 96073 530-547-1700
Steve Abbott, prin. Fax 245-2700
Foothill Plus HS 50/Alt
9733 Deschutes Rd 96073 530-245-2715
Steve Abbott, prin. Fax 245-2700

Redding Christian S 500/PK-12
21945 Old 44 Dr 96073 530-547-5600
Erika Piper, prin. Fax 547-5655

Palos Verdes Estates, Los Angeles, Pop. 12,975
Palos Verdes Peninsula USD 11,700/PK-12
375 Via Almar 90274 310-378-9966
Donald Austin Ed.D., supt. Fax 378-0732
www.pvpusd.net
Palos Verdes HS 1,700/9-12
600 Cloyden Rd 90274 310-378-8471
Charles Park Ed.D., prin. Fax 378-0311
Palos Verdes IS 1,000/6-8
2161 Via Olivera 90274 310-544-4816
Frank Califano, prin. Fax 265-5944
Other Schools – See Rancho Palos Verdes, Rolling Hills

Palos Verdes Peninsula, See Rolling Hills Estates

Chadwick S 800/K-12
26800 Academy Dr 90274 310-377-1543
Dr. John Creeden, head sch Fax 377-0380

Panorama City, See Los Angeles
Los Angeles USD
Supt. — See Los Angeles
Burke HS 200/Alt
14630 Lanark St 91402 818-781-7665
Phillip Koch, prin. Fax 781-3226
Panorama HS 1,500/9-12
8015 Van Nuys Blvd 91402 818-909-4500
Elias De La Torre, prin. Fax 786-6991

St. Genevieve HS 600/9-12
13967 Roscoe Blvd 91402 818-894-6417
Dan Horn, prin. Fax 892-9853
Western Beauty Institute Post-Sec.
8700 Van Nuys Blvd 91402 818-894-9550

Paradise, Butte, Pop. 25,494
Butte County Office of Education
Supt. — See Oroville
Paradise IS - RISE 50/Alt
5657 Recreation Dr 95969 530-532-5642
Cheri Gamette, prin. Fax 532-5794

Paradise USD 4,300/PK-12
6696 Clark Rd 95969 530-872-6400
Donna Colosky, supt. Fax 872-6409
www.pusdk12.org
Honey Run Academy 50/Alt
622 Pearson Rd 95969 530-872-6461
Dena Kapsalis, prin. Fax 872-9708
Paradise HS 1,100/9-12
5911 Maxwell Dr 95969 530-872-6425
John Christie, prin. Fax 872-6427
Paradise IS 400/6-8
5657 Recreation Dr 95969 530-872-6465
Reiner Light, prin. Fax 876-1852
Paradise Adult S Adult
622 Pearson Rd 95969 530-872-6424
Mary Ficcardi, dir. Fax 872-9708
Other Schools – See Magalia

Paradise Adventist Academy 200/K-12
PO Box 2169 95967 530-877-6540

Paramount, Los Angeles, Pop. 53,159
Paramount USD 15,900/K-12
15110 California Ave 90723 562-602-6000
Ruth Perez, supt. Fax 602-8123
www.paramount.k12.ca.us
Alondra MS 900/6-8
16200 Downey Ave 90723 562-602-8004
Lynn Butler, prin. Fax 602-8005
Jackson MS 800/4-8
7220 Jackson St 90723 562-602-8020
Kelly Anderson, prin. Fax 602-8021
Paramount Community Day S 50/Alt
14507 Paramount Blvd 90723 562-602-8084
Jerry King, prin. Fax 602-8085
Paramount HS 3,700/10-12
14429 Downey Ave 90723 562-602-6064
Greg Buckner Ed.D., prin. Fax 602-6099
Paramount HS - West Campus 1,300/9-9
14708 Paramount Blvd 90723 562-602-8073
Elizabeth Salcido, prin. Fax 602-8075
Paramount Park MS 800/6-8
14608 Paramount Blvd 90723 562-602-8052
Kevin Longworth, prin. Fax 602-8053
Zamboni MS 1,000/6-8
15733 Orange Ave 90723 562-602-8048
Sue Saikaly, prin. Fax 602-8049
Paramount Adult Education Adult
14507 Paramount Blvd 90723 562-602-8080
Jerry King, prin. Fax 602-8081
Other Schools – See Lakewood

Infotech Career College Post-Sec.
8527 Alondra Blvd Ste 174 90723 562-804-1239
Marinello School of Beauty Post-Sec.
8527 Alondra Blvd Ste 129 90723 714-998-7461

Parlier, Fresno, Pop. 14,454
Parlier USD 3,400/K-12
900 S Newmark Ave 93648 559-646-2731
Edward M. Lucero, supt. Fax 888-0210
www.parlierunified.org
Parlier HS 800/9-12
603 3rd St 93648 559-646-3573
Fax 646-2856
Parlier JHS 500/7-8
1200 E Parlier Ave 93648 559-646-1660
Julissa Alvarado, prin. Fax 646-1633
San Joaquin Valley HS 100/Alt
900 S Newmark Ave 93648 559-646-2723
Israel Almendarez, prin. Fax 646-0959

Pasadena, Los Angeles, Pop. 132,725
Pasadena USD 18,400/K-12
351 S Hudson Ave 91101 626-396-3600
Dr. Brian McDonald, supt. Fax 795-5309
www.pusd.us/
Blair HS 900/7-12
1135 5th St Ste A 91106 626-396-5820
David Ibarra, prin. Fax 799-2189
Center for Independent Study 200/Alt
2925 E Sierra Madre Blvd 91107 626-396-5883
Jack Loos, dir. Fax 398-8793
Marshall Fundamental JSHS 1,900/6-12
990 N Allen Ave 91104 626-396-5810
Dr. Mark Anderson, prin. Fax 798-0643
Muir HS 1,000/9-12
1905 Lincoln Ave 91103 626-396-5600
Timothy Sippel, prin. Fax 791-3499
Pasadena HS 1,900/9-12
2925 E Sierra Madre Blvd 91107 626-798-8901
Dr. Gilbert Barraza, prin. Fax 798-1875
Rose City HS 200/Alt
351 S Hudson Ave 91101 626-396-5620
Jack Loos, prin. Fax 683-9309
Washington MS 500/6-8
1505 N Marengo Ave 91103 626-396-5830
Dr. Shannon Malone, prin. Fax 798-2844
Wilson MS 600/6-8
300 Madre St 91107 626-396-5800
Sarah Rudchenko, prin. Fax 584-9895
Twilight Adult Ed Adult
351 S Hudson St 91101 626-396-5883
Jack Loos, prin. Fax 398-8793
Other Schools – See Altadena, Sierra Madre

AGBU Vatche & Tamar Manoukian HS 200/9-12
2495 E Mountain St 91104 626-794-0363
Dr. Armine Movsisyan, prin. Fax 240-0818
Art Center College of Design Post-Sec.
1700 Lida St 91103 626-396-2200
California Institute of Technology Post-Sec.
1200 E California Blvd 91125 626-395-6811
Excelsior S 100/9-12
1539 E Howard St 91104 626-398-2388
Fuller Theological Seminary Post-Sec.
135 N Oakland Ave 91182 626-584-5200
Huntington Memorial Hospital Post-Sec.
100 W California Blvd 91105 626-397-5000
Judson International S 100/K-12
1610 E Elizabeth St 91104 626-398-2476
Diana Bjoraker, prin. Fax 398-2222
La Salle HS 700/9-12
3880 E Sierra Madre Blvd 91107 626-351-8951
Christopher Brady, prin. Fax 351-0275
Le Cordon Bleu College of Culinary Arts Post-Sec.
530 E Colorado Blvd 91101 626-229-1300
Los Angeles College of Music Post-Sec.
370 S Fair Oaks Ave 91105 626-568-8850
Maranatha HS 600/9-12
169 S Saint John Ave 91105 626-817-4000
Dr. Steven Sherman, head sch Fax 817-4040
Mayfield Senior S 300/9-12
500 Bellefontaine St 91105 626-799-9121
Kate Morin, head sch Fax 799-8576
North-West College Post-Sec.
530 E Union St 91101 626-796-5815
Pacific Oaks College Post-Sec.
55 Eureka St 91103 626-529-8061
Pasadena City College Post-Sec.
1570 E Colorado Blvd 91106 626-585-7123
Polytechnic S 900/K-12
1030 E California Blvd 91106 626-396-6300
John Bracker, head sch Fax 796-2249
Providence Christian College Post-Sec.
1539 E Howard St 91104 866-323-0233
Sequoyah HS 9-12
301 N Orange Grove Blvd 91103 626-441-2076
Marc Alongi, dir.
Waverly S 100/PK-12
67 W Bellevue Dr 91105 626-792-5940
Westridge S 500/4-12
324 Madeline Dr 91105 626-799-1153
Elizabeth McGregor, head sch Fax 799-9236

Paso Robles, San Luis Obispo, Pop. 20,187
Paso Robles JUSD 6,500/K-12
PO Box 7010 93447 805-769-1000
Chris Williams, supt. Fax 237-3339
www.pasoschools.org
Culinary Arts Academy Vo/Tech
PO Box 7010 93447 805-769-1133
Gregg Wangard, dir. Fax 237-3449
Flamson MS 700/6-8
PO Box 7010 93447 805-769-1400
Dr. Gene Miller, prin. Fax 237-3427
Independence HS 100/Alt
PO Box 7010 93447 805-769-1620
Nate Maas, dir. Fax 237-3374
Lewis MS 800/6-8
PO Box 7010 93447 805-769-1450
Erin Haley, prin. Fax 237-3458
Liberty HS 100/Alt
PO Box 7010 93447 805-769-1600
Nate Maas, prin. Fax 237-3466
Paso Robles HS 2,000/9-12
PO Box 7010 93447 805-769-1500
Eric Martinez, prin. Fax 237-3424

ACTS Advanced Christian Training S 50/K-12
3025 Adelaida Rd 93446 805-239-0707
Dr. William Thompson, supt. Fax 238-1133

Patterson, Stanislaus, Pop. 19,584
Patterson JUSD 6,000/PK-12
510 Keystone Blvd 95363 209-895-7700
Philip Alfano Ed.D., supt. Fax 892-5803
www.patterson.k12.ca.us
Creekside MS 1,200/6-8
535 Peregrine Dr 95363 209-892-4710
Catherine Aumoeualogo, prin. Fax 892-7101
Del Puerto HS 100/Alt
640 M St 95363 209-892-4720
Jose Sanchez, prin. Fax 892-3533
Patterson HS 1,700/9-12
200 N 7th St 95363 209-892-4750
Tonya Bibbins, prin. Fax 892-7093

Patton, San Bernardino, Pop. 1,000

Patton State Hospital Post-Sec.
3102 E Highland Ave 92369 909-425-7297

Pearblossom, Los Angeles
Keppel UNESD 2,700/K-8
PO Box 186 93553 661-944-2155
Dr. Ruben Zepeda, supt. Fax 944-2933
www.keppel.k12.ca.us
Other Schools – See Littlerock

Pebble Beach, Monterey, Pop. 3,600

Stevenson S 500/9-12
3152 Forest Lake Rd 93953 831-625-8300
Dr. Kevin Hicks, pres. Fax 625-5208

Penn Valley, Nevada, Pop. 1,545
Penn Valley Union ESD 700/K-12
14806 Pleasant Valley Rd 95946 530-432-7311
Torie England Ed.D., supt. Fax 432-7314
www.pennvalleyschools.k12.ca.us/pages/Penn_Valley_Union_Elem_SD
Pleasant Valley S 200/4-8
14685 Pleasant Valley Rd 95946 530-432-7333
Teena Corker, prin. Fax 432-7338

Perris, Riverside, Pop. 66,780
Perris UNHSD 10,400/5-12
155 E 4th St 92570 951-943-6369
Grant Bennett, supt. Fax 940-5378
www.puhsd.org
Academy Community Day S 100/Alt
515 E 7th St 92570 951-657-2174
Pauline Garcia Ed.D., prin. Fax 657-8102
Perris HS 2,400/9-12
175 E Nuevo Rd 92571 951-657-2171
Nick Hilton, prin. Fax 940-5717
Perris Lake HS 300/Alt
418 W Ellis Ave 92570 951-657-7357
Dean Hauser, prin. Fax 940-5305
Pinacate MS 1,100/7-8
1990 S A St 92570 951-943-6441
Rebecca Brown, prin. Fax 940-5344
Other Schools – See Menifee

Val Verde USD 19,000/PK-12
975 Morgan St 92571 951-940-6100
Michael McCormick, supt. Fax 940-6121
www.valverde.edu
Citrus Hill HS 2,300/9-12
18150 Wood Rd 92570 951-490-0400
Nereyda Gonzalez, prin. Fax 490-0405
Lakeside MS 1,200/7-8
27720 Walnut St 92571 951-443-2440
John Parker, prin. Fax 443-2445
Orange Vista HS 9-10
1400 Orange Ave 92571 951-490-4660
Joshua Workman, admin. Fax 490-4665
Rivera MS 1,000/6-8
21675 Martin St 92570 951-940-8570
Esteban Lizarraga, prin. Fax 940-6133
Val Verde Continuation HS 400/Alt
972 Morgan St 92571 951-940-6155
Steve Coelho, prin. Fax 940-6158
Other Schools – See Moreno Valley

Pescadero, San Mateo, Pop. 633
La Honda-Pescadero USD 300/PK-12
PO Box 189 94060 650-879-0286
Amy Wooliever, supt. Fax 879-0816
www.lhpusd.com
Pescadero MSHS 100/6-12
350 Butano Cut Off 94060 650-879-0274
Patricia Talbot, prin. Fax 879-0589

Petaluma, Sonoma, Pop. 56,146
Petaluma SD 7,800/PK-12
200 Douglas St 94952 707-778-4604
Gary Callahan, supt. Fax 778-4736
www.petalumacityschools.org
Carpe Diem HS 50/Alt
199 Fair St 94952 707-778-4796
Greg Stevenson, prin. Fax 762-7099
Casa Grande HS 1,700/9-12
333 Casa Grande Rd 94954 707-778-4677
Eric Backman, prin. Fax 778-4687
Crossroads S 50/Alt
700 Bantam Way 94952 707-778-4793
Jonathan Tallent, prin.
Kenilworth JHS 900/7-8
800 Riesling Rd 94954 707-778-4710
Bennett Holley, prin. Fax 766-8231
Petaluma HS 1,300/9-12
201 Fair St 94952 707-778-4651
David Stirrat, prin. Fax 778-4767
Petaluma JHS 700/7-8
700 Bantam Way 94952 707-778-4724
Renee Semik, prin. Fax 778-4600
San Antonio HS 100/Alt
500 Vallejo St 94952 707-778-4758
Rebecca Lofton, prin. Fax 778-4899
Sonoma Mountain HS 50/Alt
299 Casa Grande Rd 94954 707-778-4738
Greg Stevenson, prin. Fax 778-1350
Valley Oaks Alternative S 100/Alt
540 Vallejo St 94952 707-778-4794
Rebecca Lofton, prin. Fax 778-4898

Petaluma Adult S — Adult
200 Douglas St 94952 — 707-778-4633
Carol Waxman, prin. — Fax 778-4785

St. Vincent de Paul HS — 300/9-12
849 Keokuk St 94952 — 707-763-1032
Dr. John Walker, prin. — Fax 763-9448
Santa Rosa Junior College — Post-Sec.
680 Sonoma Mountain Pkwy 94954 — 707-778-2415

Petrolia, Humboldt
Mattole USD — 700/PK-12
PO Box 211 95558 — 707-629-3311
Richard Graey, supt. — Fax 629-3575
www.humboldt.k12.ca.us/mattole_usd
Mattole Triple Junction HS — 50/9-12
PO Box 211 95558 — 707-629-3250
Karen Ashmore, prin. — Fax 629-3551

Phelan, San Bernardino, Pop. 13,933
Snowline JUSD — 7,800/K-12
PO Box 296000 92329 — 760-868-5817
Dr. Ryan Holman, supt. — Fax 868-5309
www.snowlineschools.com/
Chaparral HS — 200/Alt
PO Box 296000 92329 — 760-868-5400
Dave Smith, prin. — Fax 868-4725
Eagle Summit Community S — 50/Alt
PO Box 296000 92329 — 760-868-3442
Dave Smith, coord. — Fax 868-6402
Pinon Mesa MS — 700/6-8
PO Box 296000 92329 — 760-868-3126
Burt Umstead, prin. — Fax 868-3033
Quail Valley MS — 1,000/6-8
PO Box 296000 92329 — 760-949-4888
Dennis Zimmerman, prin. — Fax 949-3663
Serrano HS — 2,300/9-12
PO Box 296000 92329 — 760-868-3222
Dan Andrus, prin. — Fax 868-3803
Snowline Virtual S — 100/Alt
PO Box 296000 92329 — 760-868-6277
Dave Smith, prin. — Fax 868-4024
Snowline Adult S — Adult
PO Box 296000 92329 — 760-701-9755
Matt Wells, coord. — Fax 868-3803

Pico Rivera, Los Angeles, Pop. 62,624
El Rancho USD — 9,300/PK-12
9333 Loch Lomond Dr 90660 — 562-942-1500
Martin Galindo, supt. — Fax 949-2821
erusd.org
El Rancho HS — 2,800/9-12
6501 Passons Blvd 90660 — 562-801-5295
Sam Genis, prin. — Fax 801-5293
North Park Academy of the Arts — 800/6-8
4450 Durfee Ave 90660 — 562-801-5137
Priscilla Rodriguez, prin. — Fax 801-5143
Ochoa Prep Academy — 9-12
8110 Paramount Blvd 90660 — 562-928-2180
Elias Vargas, prin. — Fax 928-2926
Rivera MS — 800/6-8
7200 Citronell Ave 90660 — 562-801-5088
Yvette Ventura-Rincon, prin. — Fax 801-9158
Salazar Continuation HS — 200/Alt
9115 Balfour St 90660 — 562-801-5021
Reynaldo Reyes, prin. — Fax 942-9458
STEAM Academy @ Burke — 500/6-8
8101 Orange Ave 90660 — 562-801-5059
Elias Vargas, prin. — Fax 801-5067
El Rancho Adult Education Center — Adult
9515 Haney St 90660 — 562-801-5009
Charles Collings, prin. — Fax 948-2041

Armenian Mesrobian S — 200/PK-12
8420 Beverly Rd 90660 — 562-699-2057

Piedmont, Alameda, Pop. 10,117
Piedmont City USD — 2,600/K-12
760 Magnolia Ave 94611 — 510-594-2600
Randall Booker, supt. — Fax 654-7374
www.piedmont.k12.ca.us
Millennium HS — 100/Alt
760 Magnolia Ave 94611 — 510-594-2703
Satyendra Shah, prin. — Fax 594-2791
Piedmont HS — 800/9-12
800 Magnolia Ave 94611 — 510-594-2626
Brent Daniels, prin. — Fax 450-0425
Piedmont MS — 600/6-8
740 Magnolia Ave 94611 — 510-594-2660
Ryan Fletcher, prin. — Fax 595-3523
Piedmont Adult S — Adult
740 Magnolia Ave 94611 — 510-594-2655
Michael Brady, dir. — Fax 595-8173

Pinecrest, Tuolumne
Summerville UNHSD
Supt. — See Tuolumne
Mountain HS — 50/Alt
2 Pinecrest School Rd 95364 — 209-965-4046
Diana Harford, prin. — Fax 928-1422

Pine Valley, San Diego, Pop. 1,469
Mountain Empire USD — 2,200/PK-12
3291 Buckman Springs Rd 91962 — 619-473-9022
Dr. Kathy Granger, supt. — Fax 473-9728
meusd.schoolwires.net
Mountain Empire HS — 400/9-12
3305 Buckman Springs Rd 91962 — 619-473-8601
Patrick Keeley, prin. — Fax 473-8038
Pine Valley MS — 100/6-8
PO Box 571 91962 — 619-473-8693
Gary Brannon, prin. — Fax 473-8026
Other Schools – See Jacumba

Pinole, Contra Costa, Pop. 17,432
West Contra Costa USD
Supt. — See Richmond
Pinole MS — 600/7-8
1575 Mann Dr 94564 — 510-231-1436
Denise Van Hook, prin. — Fax 724-9583
Pinole Valley HS — 1,300/9-12
2900 Pinole Valley Rd 94564 — 510-231-1442
Sue Kahn, prin. — Fax 758-6054

Pismo Beach, San Luis Obispo, Pop. 7,494
Lucia Mar USD
Supt. — See Arroyo Grande
Judkins MS — 500/7-8
680 Wadsworth Ave 93449 — 805-474-3600
Ian Penton, prin. — Fax 473-4376

Coastal Christian S — 200/K-12
1005 Oak Park Blvd 93449 — 805-489-1213
Dave Rehnberg M.A., prin. — Fax 489-5394

Pittsburg, Contra Costa, Pop. 60,137
Pittsburg USD — 10,700/PK-12
2000 Railroad Ave 94565 — 925-473-2300
Janet Schulze Ed.D., supt. — Fax 473-4274
www.pittsburg.k12.ca.us
Black Diamond HS — 300/Alt
1131 Stoneman Ave 94565 — 925-473-2510
Brian Wilson, prin.
Hillview JHS — 900/6-8
333 Yosemite Dr 94565 — 925-473-2380
Maria Gonzalez, prin. — Fax 473-4406
King JHS, 2012 Carion Ct 94565 — 700/6-8
Angela Stevenson, prin. — 925-473-2500
Pittsburg HS — 2,900/9-12
1750 Harbor St 94565 — 925-473-2390
Todd Whitmire, prin. — Fax 473-4183
Rancho Medanos JHS — 900/6-8
2301 Range Rd 94565 — 925-473-2490
Eric Peyko, prin. — Fax 473-1060
Pittsburg Adult Education Center — Adult
1151 Stoneman Ave 94565 — 925-473-4460
Lynne Nicodemus, prin. — Fax 473-4470

Los Medanos College — Post-Sec.
2700 E Leland Rd 94565 — 925-439-2181

Pixley, Tulare, Pop. 3,289
Pixley UNESD — 1,100/PK-8
300 N School St 93256 — 559-757-5207
Heather Elick, supt. — Fax 757-0705
www.pixley.k12.ca.us/
Pixley MS — 300/6-8
1520 E Court Ave 93256 — 559-757-3018
Jose Perez, prin. — Fax 757-3507

Placentia, Orange, Pop. 49,404
Placentia-Yorba Linda USD — 25,600/K-12
1301 E Orangethorpe Ave 92870 — 714-986-7000
Gregory S.Plutko Ed.D., supt. — Fax 524-3034
www.pylusd.org/
El Camino Real Continuation HS — 200/Alt
1351 E Orangethorpe Ave 92870 — 714-986-7060
Gordon Chamberlin, prin. — Fax 996-0294
El Dorado HS — 1,900/9-12
1651 Valencia Ave 92870 — 714-986-7580
Joey Davis, prin. — Fax 524-2458
Kraemer MS — 1,000/6-8
645 N Angelina Dr 92870 — 714-996-1551
Keith Carmona, prin. — Fax 996-8407
Parkview S — 100/Alt
2189 N Kraemer Blvd 92870 — 714-986-7050
Tuffree MS — 700/7-8
2151 N Kraemer Blvd 92870 — 714-986-7480
Cindy Freeman, prin. — Fax 993-6359
Valadez MS Academy — 700/6-8
161 E La Jolla St 92870 — 714-986-7440
James Hardin, prin. — Fax 238-9159
Valencia HS — 2,700/9-12
500 N Bradford Ave 92870 — 714-996-4970
Hector Vasquez, prin. — Fax 996-3159
Other Schools – See Anaheim, Yorba Linda

Placerville, El Dorado, Pop. 10,089
El Dorado County Office of Education — 800/
6767 Green Valley Rd 95667 — 530-622-7130
Ed Manansala, supt. — Fax 621-2543
www.edcoe.org
El Dorado COE Adult Education — Adult
6767 Green Valley Rd 95667 — 530-295-0007
David Publicover, dir. — Fax 621-1395

El Dorado UNHSD — 6,800/9-12
4675 Missouri Flat Rd 95667 — 530-622-5081
Stephen Wehr, supt. — Fax 642-0806
www.eduhsd.k12.ca.us
El Dorado HS — 1,300/9-12
561 Canal St 95667 — 530-622-3634
Chas Prior, prin. — Fax 622-1802
Vista HS — 100/Alt
561 Canal St 95667 — 530-622-3634
Ann Clark, prin. — Fax 622-1802
Other Schools – See Diamond Springs, El Dorado, El Dorado Hills, Shingle Springs

Gold Oak UNESD — 500/PK-8
3171 Pleasant Valley Rd 95667 — 530-626-3150
Meg Enns, supt. — Fax 626-3145
www.gousd.org
Pleasant Valley MS — 200/6-8
4120 Pleasant Valley Rd 95667 — 530-644-9620
Meg Enns, prin. — Fax 644-9622

Gold Trail UNESD — 600/K-8
1575 Old Ranch Rd 95667 — 530-626-3194
Joe Murchison, supt. — Fax 626-3199
www.gtusd.org
Gold Trail MS — 300/4-8
889 Cold Springs Rd 95667 — 530-626-2595
Scott Lyons, head sch — Fax 626-3289

Mother Lode UNESD — 1,100/K-8
3783 Forni Rd 95667 — 530-622-6464
Marcy Guthrie, supt. — Fax 622-6163
www.mlusd.net
Green MS — 500/5-8
3781 Forni Rd 95667 — 530-622-4668
Leslie Redkey, prin. — Fax 622-4680

Placerville UNSD — 1,300/K-8
1032 Thompson Way 95667 — 530-622-7216
Eric Bonniksen, supt. — Fax 622-0336
www.pusdk8.us/
Markham MS — 400/6-8
2800 Moulton Dr 95667 — 530-622-0403
Terry Edinger, prin. — Fax 622-5584

Regional Occupational Center & Program
Supt. — None
Central Sierra ROP — Vo/Tech
4675 Missouri Flat Rd 95667 — 530-621-0123
Carolyn Zachary, dir.

El Dorado Adventist S — 200/K-12
1900 Broadway 95667 — 530-622-3560

Planada, Merced, Pop. 4,571
Planada ESD — 800/PK-8
PO Box 236 95365 — 209-382-0756
Jose L. Gonzalez, supt. — Fax 382-1750
www.planada.org
Chavez MS — 200/6-8
PO Box 236 95365 — 209-382-0768
Christopher Busch, prin. — Fax 382-0775

Playa Del Rey, See Los Angeles

St. Bernard HS — 400/9-12
9100 Falmouth Ave 90293 — 310-823-4651
Dr. Cynthia Hoepner, prin. — Fax 827-3365

Pleasant Hill, Contra Costa, Pop. 31,678
Contra Costa County Office of Education — 3,100/
77 Santa Barbara Rd 94523 — 925-942-3388
Dr. Karen Sakata, supt. — Fax 472-0875
www.cccoe.k12.ca.us
Other Schools – See Martinez, Richmond

Mount Diablo USD
Supt. — See Concord
College Park HS — 1,900/9-12
201 Viking Dr 94523 — 925-682-7670
Joseph Alvarez, prin. — Fax 676-7892
Horizons — 200/Alt
1 Santa Barbara Rd 94523 — 925-938-2564
Sharon Brockman, admin. — Fax 937-6271
Pleasant Hill MS — 1,000/6-8
1 Santa Barbara Rd 94523 — 925-256-0791
Terry McCormick, prin. — Fax 937-6271
Prospect HS — 50/Alt
1 Santa Barbara Rd 94523 — 925-945-7902
Sharon Brockman, admin. — Fax 937-6271
Sequoia MS — 900/6-8
265 Boyd Rd 94523 — 925-934-8174
Kevin Honey, prin. — Fax 946-9063
Valley View MS — 900/6-8
181 Viking Dr 94523 — 925-686-6136
Ean Ainsworth, prin. — Fax 687-5381
Pleasant Hill Adult Center — Adult
1 Santa Barbara Rd 94523 — 925-937-1530
Fax 937-6271

Regional Occupational Center & Program
Supt. — None
Contra Costa County ROP — Vo/Tech
77 Santa Barbara Rd 94523 — 925-942-3368
Janet Haun, dir. — Fax 934-1057

Carrington College California — Post-Sec.
380 Civic Dr Ste 300 94523 — 925-298-6299
Diablo Valley College — Post-Sec.
321 Golf Club Rd 94523 — 925-685-1230
John F. Kennedy University — Post-Sec.
100 Ellinwood Way 94523 — 925-969-3300
Pleasant Hill Adventist Academy — 200/K-12
796 Grayson Rd 94523 — 925-934-9261
Susan Walters, prin. — Fax 934-5871

Pleasanton, Alameda, Pop. 67,470
Pleasanton USD — 14,700/K-12
4665 Bernal Ave 94566 — 925-462-5500
Richard Rubino, supt. — Fax 484-3591
pleasantonusd.net
Amador Valley HS — 2,600/9-12
1155 Santa Rita Rd 94566 — 925-461-6100
Michael Williams, prin. — Fax 461-6133
Foothill HS — 2,200/9-12
4375 Foothill Rd 94588 — 925-461-6650
Jason Krolikowski, prin. — Fax 461-6633
Hart MS — 1,100/6-8
4433 Willow Rd 94588 — 925-426-3102
Leslie Heller, prin. — Fax 460-0799
Harvest Park MS — 1,200/6-8
4900 Valley Ave 94566 — 925-426-4444
Ethan Cheever, prin. — Fax 426-9613
Pleasanton MS — 1,200/6-8
5001 Case Ave 94566 — 925-426-4390
Jill Butler, prin. — Fax 426-1382
Village Continuation HS — 100/Alt
4645 Bernal Ave 94566 — 925-426-4260
Dana Chavez, prin. — Fax 426-8394

Plumas Lake, Yuba, Pop. 5,494
Plumas Lake ESD — 1,100/PK-8
2743 Plumas School Rd, — 530-743-4428
Jeff Roberts, supt. — Fax 743-1408
www.plusd.org
Riverside Meadows IS — 300/6-8
1751 Cimarron Dr, — 530-743-1271
Julie Rojo, prin. — Fax 743-8970

Point Arena, Mendocino, Pop. 438
Point Arena SD 500/K-12
PO Box 87 95468 707-882-2803
Brent Cushenbery Ed.D., supt. Fax 882-2848
www.pointarenaschools.org
Point Arena HS 200/9-12
PO Box 7 95468 707-882-2134
Rebekah Barakos-Cartwrig, prin. Fax 882-3453
South Coast Continuation HS 50/Alt
PO Box 87 95468 707-882-2307
Leah Martini, prin. Fax 882-2309

Pollock Pines, El Dorado, Pop. 6,676
Pollock Pines ESD 700/K-8
2701 Amber Trl 95726 530-644-5416
Pat Atkins, supt. Fax 644-5483
www.ppesd.org
Sierra Ridge MS 300/5-8
2700 Amber Trl 95726 530-644-2031
Kim Little, prin. Fax 644-0198

Pomona, Los Angeles, Pop. 146,537
Los Angeles County Office of Education
Supt. — See Downey
International Polytechnic HS 600/Alt
3801 W Temple Ave 91768 909-869-4567
Bruce Petersen, prin. Fax 869-2202

Pomona USD 26,000/PK-12
PO Box 2900 91769 909-397-4800
Richard Martinez, supt. Fax 397-4881
www.pusd.org
Diamond Ranch HS 1,800/9-12
100 Diamond Ranch Rd 91766 909-397-4715
S. Steinsefer-Ripley, prin. Fax 591-9374
Emerson MS 700/6-8
635 Lincoln Ave 91767 909-397-4516
Jesus Altamirano, prin. Fax 397-5280
Fremont Academy of Engineeing & Design Vo/Tech
725 W Franklin Ave 91766 909-397-4521
Elizabeth Harper, prin. Fax 620-6229
Ganesha HS 1,200/9-12
1151 Fairplex Dr 91768 909-397-4400
Jennifer Francev, prin. Fax 629-4069
Garey HS 1,800/9-12
321 W Lexington Ave 91766 909-397-4451
Stacey Wilkins, prin. Fax 620-1575
Marshall MS 500/6-8
1921 Arroyo Ave 91768 909-397-4532
Juan Ortiz, prin. Fax 629-8275
Palomares Academy of Health Sciences Vo/Tech
2211 N Orange Grove Ave 91767 909-397-4539
Camille Ramos-Beal, prin. Fax 625-0337
Park West HS 300/Alt
1460 E Holt Ave Ste 100 91767 909-397-4900
Luis Rodriguez, prin. Fax 865-2423
Pomona Alternative S 50/Alt
1460 E Holt Ave Ste 100 91767 909-397-4900
Luis Rodriguez, prin. Fax 865-2423
Pomona Community Day S 50/Alt
605 N Park Ave 91768 909-397-4491
Tom Sweeney, dir.
Pomona HS 1,400/9-12
475 Bangor St 91767 909-397-4498
Roger Fasting, prin. Fax 629-1410
Simons MS 800/6-8
900 E Franklin Ave 91766 909-397-4544
Cristine Goens, prin. Fax 623-4691
Village Academy HS Vo/Tech
1444 E Holt Ave 91767 909-397-4900
Marco Sanchez, prin. Fax 865-9250
Pomona Adult & Career Education Adult
1515 W Mission Blvd 91766 909-469-2333
Dr. Enrique Medina, dir. Fax 623-3841
Other Schools – See Diamond Bar

Regional Occupational Center & Program
Supt. — None
San Antonio ROP Vo/Tech
1425 E Holt Ave Ste 101 91767 909-469-2304
Enrique Medina, dir.

California State Polytechnic University Post-Sec.
3801 W Temple Ave 91768 909-869-7659
Carrington College California Post-Sec.
901 Corporate Center Dr 300 91768 909-366-4122
City of Knowledge S 200/PK-12
3285 N Garey Ave 91767 909-392-0251
DeVry University Post-Sec.
901 Corporate Center Dr 91768 909-622-8866
North-West College Post-Sec.
134 W Holt Ave 91768 909-623-1552
Pomona Catholic HS 300/6-12
533 W Holt Ave 91768 909-623-5297
Samuel Torres, prin. Fax 620-6057
Western University of Health Sciences Post-Sec.
309 E 2nd St 91766 909-623-6116

Porterville, Tulare, Pop. 53,236
Burton ESD 4,600/K-12
264 N Westwood St 93257 559-781-8020
Sharon Kamberg Ed.D., supt. Fax 781-1403
www.burtonschools.org
Burton MS 500/7-8
1155 N Elderwood St 93257 559-781-2671
Chastity Lollis Ed.D., prin. Fax 788-6424

Pleasant View ESD 600/PK-8
14004 Road 184 93257 559-784-6769
Mark Odsather, supt. Fax 784-6819
www.pleasant-view.org
Pleasant View West S 200/5-8
14004 Road 184 93257 559-784-6769
Mark Odsather, supt. Fax 784-6819

Porterville USD 13,800/K-12
600 W Grand Ave 93257 559-793-2400
Ken Gibbs Ed.D., supt. Fax 793-1088
www.portervilleschools.org
Bartlett MS 500/7-8
600 W Grand Ave 93257 559-782-7100
Mike Tsuboi, prin. Fax 784-3432
Citrus Continuation HS 200/Alt
600 W Grand Ave 93257 559-782-7130
Scott Braden, prin. Fax 782-3643
Granite Hills HS 1,100/9-12
600 W Grand Ave 93257 559-782-7075
Apolinar Marroquin, prin. Fax 789-9357
Monache HS 1,800/9-12
600 W Grand Ave 93257 559-782-7150
Eric Barba Ed.D., prin. Fax 781-3377
Pioneer MS 600/6-8
600 W Grand Ave 93257 559-782-7200
Angel Valdez, prin. Fax 784-3507
Porterville HS 1,900/9-12
600 W Grand Ave 93257 559-782-7210
Jose Valdez, prin. Fax 782-7215
Prospect Education Center 100/Alt
600 W Grand Ave 93257 559-782-7095
Dawn Crater, dir. Fax 781-6846
Sequoia MS 600/7-8
600 W Grand Ave 93257 559-788-0925
Joe Santos Ed.D., prin. Fax 788-0927
Vine Street Community Day S 50/Alt
600 W Grand Ave 93257 559-782-6650
Monty Newkirk, prin. Fax 782-6652
Porterville Adult S Adult
600 W Grand Ave 93257 559-782-7030
Fernando Carrera, dir. Fax 781-4943
Other Schools – See Strathmore

Regional Occupational Center & Program
Supt. — None
Tulare Co. Organization/Vocational Educ Vo/Tech
600 W Grand Ave 93257 559-793-2406
Melinda Brown, dir.

Porterville College Post-Sec.
100 E College Ave 93257 559-791-2200

Port Hueneme, Ventura, Pop. 20,969
Hueneme ESD 8,400/K-8
205 N Ventura Rd 93041 805-488-3588
Dr. Christine Walker, supt. Fax 986-8755
www.huensd.k12.ca.us
Other Schools – See Oxnard

Portola, Plumas, Pop. 2,059
Plumas USD
Supt. — See Quincy
Beckwourth HS 50/Alt
155 6th Ave 96122 530-832-4284
Kristy Warren, dir. Fax 832-5582
Portola JSHS 200/7-12
155 6th Ave 96122 530-832-4284
Sara Sheridan, prin. Fax 832-5582

Portola Valley, San Mateo, Pop. 4,271
Portola Valley ESD 700/K-8
4575 Alpine Rd 94028 650-851-1777
Dr. Lisa Gonzales, supt. Fax 851-3700
www.pvsd.net
Corte Madera MS 400/4-8
4575 Alpine Rd 94028 650-851-1777
Cyndi Maijala, prin. Fax 529-8553

Woodside Priory HS 300/9-12
302 Portola Rd 94028 650-851-8221
Tim Molak, head sch Fax 851-2839
Woodside Priory MS 100/6-8
302 Portola Rd 94028 650-851-8221
Caitha Ambler, prin. Fax 851-2839

Potter Valley, Mendocino, Pop. 628
Potter Valley Community USD 200/PK-12
PO Box 219 95469 707-743-2101
Damon Dickinson, supt. Fax 743-1930
www.pottervalleyschools.us
Centerville HS 50/Alt
PO Box 219 95469 707-743-1762
Mindi Juszczak, prin. Fax 743-2879
Potter Valley JSHS 100/7-12
PO Box 219 95469 707-743-1142
Mindi Juszczak, prin. Fax 743-2879

Poway, San Diego, Pop. 46,170
Poway USD
Supt. — See San Diego
Abraxas Continuation HS 200/Alt
12450 Glenoak Rd 92064 858-748-5900
David MacLeod, prin. Fax 679-1739
Meadowbrook MS 1,300/6-8
12320 Meadowbrook Ln 92064 858-748-0802
Miguel Carrillo, prin. Fax 679-0149
Poway HS 2,400/9-12
15500 Espola Rd 92064 858-748-0245
Ron Garrett, prin. Fax 679-6879
Twin Peaks MS 1,200/6-8
14640 Tierra Bonita Rd 92064 858-748-5131
Kelly Burke, prin. Fax 679-6823
Poway Adult S Adult
13626 Twin Peaks Rd 92064 858-668-4024
Kathleen Porter, dir. Fax 748-7423

Poway Academy of Hair Design Post-Sec.
13266 Poway Rd 92064 858-748-1490

Prather, Fresno, Pop. 30
Sierra USD 1,300/K-12
29143 Auberry Rd 93651 559-855-3662
Melissa Ireland Ed.D., supt. Fax 855-3585
www.sierrausd.org
Other Schools – See Tollhouse

Princeton, Colusa, Pop. 299
Princeton JUSD 200/K-12
PO Box 8 95970 530-439-2261
Cody Walker, supt. Fax 439-2113
www.pjusd.org
Princeton JSHS 100/7-12
PO Box 8 95970 530-439-2261
Cody Walker, prin. Fax 439-2113

Prunedale, Monterey, Pop. 16,965

Prunedale Christian Academy 100/PK-12
8145 Prunedale North Rd 93907 831-663-2211
Rev. Betty Moon, prin. Fax 663-1663

Quartz Hill, Los Angeles, Pop. 10,599
Antelope Valley UNHSD
Supt. — See Lancaster
Quartz Hill HS 3,100/9-12
6040 W Avenue L 93536 661-718-3100
Matt Anderson, prin. Fax 943-8203

Westside UNESD 8,900/K-8
41914 50th St W 93536 661-722-0716
Regina Rossall, supt. Fax 206-3645
www.westside.k12.ca.us
Walker MS 900/6-8
5632 W Avenue L8 93536 661-943-3258
Steve Wood, prin. Fax 943-2969
Other Schools – See Lancaster, Palmdale

Quincy, Plumas, Pop. 1,652
Plumas County Office of Education 50/
1446 E Main St 95971 530-283-6500
Terry Oestreich, admin. Fax 283-6530
www.pcoe.k12.ca.us
Plumas County Community S 50/Alt
1446 E Main St 95971 530-283-6500
Kristy Warren, prin. Fax 283-6509
Plumas County Opportunity S 50/Alt
1446 E Main St 95971 530-283-6500
Kristy Warren, prin. Fax 283-6530

Plumas USD 2,100/K-12
1446 E Main St 95971 530-283-6500
Terry Oestreich, supt. Fax 283-6530
www.pcoe.k12.ca.us
Quincy JSHS 300/7-12
6 Quincy Junction Rd 95971 530-283-6510
Fax 283-6519
Other Schools – See Chester, Greenville, Portola

Regional Occupational Center & Program
Supt. — None
Plumas County ROP Vo/Tech
50 Church St Ste B 95971 530-283-6500
Terry Oestreich, dir. Fax 283-6509

Feather River College Post-Sec.
570 Golden Eagle Ave 95971 530-283-0202

Ramona, San Diego, Pop. 19,844
Ramona USD 5,700/K-12
720 9th St 92065 760-787-2000
Dr. Anne Staffieri, supt. Fax 789-9168
www.ramonausd.net
Future Bound Independent Study 100/Alt
720 9th St 92065 760-787-2068
Fax 788-3754
Montecito HS 100/Alt
720 9th St 92065 760-787-4300
Dave Lohman, prin. Fax 789-0928
Peirce MS 800/7-8
1521 Hanson Ln 92065 760-787-2400
Pauline Leavitt, prin. Fax 788-5014
Ramona Community S 500/Alt
1010 Ramona St 92065 760-788-5130
Kathryn Gunderson, prin. Fax 788-5918
Ramona HS 1,700/9-12
1401 Hanson Ln 92065 760-787-4000
Rowena Mak Ed.D., prin. Fax 789-4596

Rancho Cordova, Sacramento, Pop. 60,932
Folsom-Cordova USD 19,300/PK-12
1965 Birkmont Dr 95742 916-294-9000
Debbie Bettencourt, supt. Fax 294-9020
www.fcusd.org
Cordova HS 1,700/9-12
2239 Chase Dr 95670 916-294-2450
Dan Anklam, prin. Fax 294-9080
Kinney Continuation HS 200/Alt
2710 Kilgore Rd 95670 916-635-1292
Dana Carrigan, prin. Fax 635-0719
Mills MS 800/6-8
10439 Coloma Rd 95670 916-363-6544
Peter Maroon, prin. Fax 361-3744
Mitchell MS 700/6-8
2100 Zinfandel Dr 95670 916-635-8460
Jim Huber, prin. Fax 635-8979
Prospect Community Day S 100/Alt
2710 Kilgore Rd 95670 916-294-9060
Dana Carrigan, coord. Fax 364-1637
Walnutwood Independent Study HS 100/Alt
10850 Gadsten Way 95670 916-638-2598
Charlie Linebarger, prin. Fax 635-6147
Folsom-Cordova Adult Education Adult
10850 Gadsten Way 95670 916-635-6810
Charlie Linebarger, prin. Fax 635-0905
Other Schools – See Folsom

California Northstate Coll of Pharmacy Post-Sec.
10811 International Dr 95670 916-631-8108
Heald College Post-Sec.
2910 Prospect Park Dr 95670 916-638-1616
National Career Education Post-Sec.
11080 White Rock Rd Ste 100 95670 916-969-4900
San Joaquin Valley College Post-Sec.
11050 Olson Dr Ste 210 95670 916-638-7582

Rancho Cucamonga, San Bernardino, Pop. 159,896
Central ESD 4,700/K-8
10601 Church St Ste 112 91730 909-989-8541
Donna Libutti, supt. Fax 941-1732
www.csd-ca.schoolloop.com
Cucamonga MS 800/6-8
7611 Hellman Ave 91730 909-987-1788
Allan Morales, prin. Fax 483-3201
Musser MS 1,000/5-8
10789 Terra Vista Pkwy 91730 909-980-1230
Mary Kate Perez, prin. Fax 980-3042

Chaffey JUNHSD
Supt. — See Ontario
Los Osos HS 3,200/9-12
6001 Milliken Ave 91737 909-477-6900
Joshua Kirk, prin. Fax 460-5872
Rancho Cucamonga HS 3,400/9-12
11801 Lark Dr 91701 909-989-1600
Cary Willborn, prin. Fax 945-5355

Cucamonga ESD 2,500/K-8
8776 Archibald Ave 91730 909-987-8942
Janet Temkin, supt. Fax 980-3628
www.cucamonga-ca.schoolloop.com
Rancho Cucamonga MS 800/6-8
8776 Archibald Ave 91730 909-980-0969
Bruce LaVallee, prin. Fax 481-5381

American Christian Military Acad ExcIlnc 8-12
9229 Utica Ave Ste 130 91730 877-226-2399
Dr. Pauline Stone Ed.D., prin. Fax 226-2388
Chaffey College Post-Sec.
5885 Haven Ave 91737 909-652-6000
San Joaquin Valley College Post-Sec.
10641 Church St 91730 909-948-7582
Universal Technical Institute Post-Sec.
9494 Haven Ave 91730 909-484-1929
Upland Christian Academy 400/K-12
10900 Civic Center Dr 91730 909-758-8747
Tim Hoy, supt. Fax 204-4555

Rancho Mirage, Riverside, Pop. 16,964
Palm Springs USD
Supt. — See Palm Springs
Rancho Mirage HS 900/9-12
31001 Rattler Rd 92270 760-202-6455
Ken Wagner Ed.D., prin.

Eisenhower Memorial Hospital Post-Sec.
39000 Bob Hope Dr 92270 760-340-3911
Palm Valley S 400/PK-12
35525 Da Vall Dr 92270 760-328-0861
Susan Rice, head sch Fax 770-4541
Santa Barbara Business College Post-Sec.
34275 Monterey Ave 92270 866-749-7222

Rancho Palos Verdes, Los Angeles, Pop. 39,919
Los Angeles USD
Supt. — See Los Angeles
Dodson MS 1,900/6-8
28014 S Montereina Dr 90275 310-241-1900
John Vladovic, prin. Fax 832-4709

Palos Verdes Peninsula USD
Supt. — See Palos Verdes Estates
Miraleste IS 900/6-8
29323 Palos Verdes Dr E 90275 310-732-0900
Brent Kuykendall, prin. Fax 521-8915
Ridgecrest IS 900/6-8
28915 Northbay Rd 90275 310-544-2747
Kelli Keller, prin. Fax 265-1716

Marymount California University Post-Sec.
30800 Palos Verdes Dr E 90275 310-377-5501
Salvation Army College Officer Training Post-Sec.
30840 Hawthorne Blvd 90275 310-377-0481

Rancho Santa Fe, San Diego, Pop. 3,061
Rancho Sante Fe ESD 700/K-8
PO Box 809 92067 858-756-1141
David Jaffe, supt. Fax 756-0912
www.rsfschool.net/
Rowe MS 300/6-8
PO Box 809 92067 858-756-1141
Garrett Corduan, prin. Fax 759-0712

Horizon Prep 500/PK-12
PO Box 9070 92067 858-756-5599
Dr. Ken Kush, head sch Fax 759-5827

Rancho Santa Margarita, Orange, Pop. 46,094
Capistrano USD
Supt. — See San Juan Capistrano
Las Flores MS 1,100/6-8
25862 Antonio Pkwy 92688 949-589-6543
Sean McNamara, prin. Fax 589-9286
Tesoro HS 2,300/9-12
1 Tesoro Creek Rd 92688 949-234-5310
William Mocnik, prin. Fax 766-3370

Saddleback Valley USD
Supt. — See Mission Viejo
Rancho Santa Margarita IS 1,400/7-8
21931 Alma Aldea 92688 949-459-8253
Rick Jameson, prin. Fax 459-8258

Santa Margarita Catholic HS 1,600/9-12
22062 Antonio Pkwy 92688 949-766-6000
Ray Dunne, prin. Fax 766-6005

Raymond, Madera
Yosemite USD
Supt. — See Oakhurst
Raymond Granite HS 50/Alt
PO Box 228 93653 559-689-3490
J.D. Burnett, prin.

Red Bluff, Tehama, Pop. 13,607
Antelope ESD 700/K-8
22630 Antelope Blvd 96080 530-527-1272
Richard Hassay, supt. Fax 527-0656
www.antelopeschools.org/
Berrendos MS 200/6-8
401 Chestnut Ave 96080 530-527-6700
Jim Weber, prin. Fax 527-2506

Red Bluff JUNHSD 1,500/9-12
PO Box 1507 96080 530-529-8700
Todd Brose, supt. Fax 529-8709
www.rbhsd.org
Red Bluff HS 1,400/9-12
1260 Union St 96080 530-529-8710
Mike Tambini, prin. Fax 529-8739
Salisbury HS 100/Alt
1050 Kimball Rd 96080 530-529-8766
Barbara Thomas, prin. Fax 529-8840

Red Bluff UNESD 2,100/K-8
1755 Airport Blvd 96080 530-527-7200
Claudia Salvestrin, supt. Fax 527-9308
www.rbuesd.org
Vista Preparatory Academy 600/6-8
1770 S Jackson St 96080 530-527-7840
Shane Humphreys, prin. Fax 527-9374

Regional Occupational Center & Program
Supt. — None
Tehama County ROP Vo/Tech
PO Box 689 96080 530-528-7341
Larry Champion, admin. Fax 529-4120

Mercy HS 100/9-12
233 Riverside Way 96080 530-527-8314
Paul Weber, prin. Fax 527-3058

Redding, Shasta, Pop. 86,489
Columbia ESD 800/PK-8
10140 Old Oregon Trl 96003 530-223-1915
Clay Ross, supt. Fax 223-4168
www.columbiasd.com
Mountain View MS 400/5-8
675 Shasta View Dr 96003 530-221-5224
Shannon Angstadt, prin. Fax 221-5620

Enterprise ESD 3,800/PK-8
1155 Mistletoe Ln 96002 530-224-4100
Brian Winstead Ed.D., supt. Fax 224-4101
www.eesd.net/
Parsons JHS 600/6-8
750 Hartnell Ave 96002 530-224-4190
Tony Moebes, prin. Fax 224-4191

Gateway USD 3,600/PK-12
4411 Mountain Lakes Blvd 96003 530-245-7900
James Harrell, supt. Fax 245-7920
www.gateway-schools.org
Gateway Educational Options 100/Alt
3500 Tamarack Dr 96003 530-245-7960
Kyle Turner, prin. Fax 245-7963
Other Schools – See Shasta Lake

Pacheco UNESD 600/K-8
7424 Pacheco School Rd 96002 530-224-4599
John Greene Ed.D., supt. Fax 224-4591
www.pacheco.k12.ca.us
Pacheco S 300/4-8
7430 Pacheco School Rd 96002 530-224-4585
Katy Pearce, prin. Fax 224-4588

Redding ESD 3,400/K-12
5885 E Bonnyview Rd 96001 530-225-0011
Rick Fauss, supt. Fax 225-0015
www.reddingschools.net/
Sequoia MS 800/4-8
5885 E Bonnyview Rd 96001 530-225-0020
Cindy Bishop, prin. Fax 225-0029

Regional Occupational Center & Program
Supt. — None
Shasta-Trinity ROP Vo/Tech
4659 Eastside Rd 96001 530-246-3302
Charlie Hoffman, supt. Fax 246-3306

Shasta County Office of Education 200/
1644 Magnolia Ave 96001 530-225-0200
Tom Armelino, supt. Fax 225-0329
www.shastacoe.org
Career Pathways to Success Alt
3711 Oasis Rd 96003 530-225-0360
Jodie VanOrnum, prin. Fax 225-0366

Shasta UNHSD 5,700/6-12
2200 Eureka Way Ste B 96001 530-241-3261
Jim Cloney, supt. Fax 225-8499
www.suhsd.net
Enterprise HS 1,200/9-12
3411 Churn Creek Rd 96002 530-222-6601
Ryan Johnson, prin. Fax 222-5138
Enterprise Plus HS 50/Alt
3411 Churn Creek Rd 96002 530-245-2714
Ryan Johnson, prin. Fax 222-5138
Freedom HS 50/Alt
2650 8th St 96001 530-243-1880
Elsbeth Prigmore, prin. Fax 243-0753
North State Independence HS 100/Alt
2200 Eureka Way Ste B 96001 530-245-2760
Elsbeth Prigmore, prin. Fax 245-2761
Pioneer Continuation HS 200/Alt
2650 8th St 96001 530-243-1880
Elsbeth Prigmore, prin. Fax 243-0753
Shasta HS 1,500/9-12
2500 Eureka Way 96001 530-241-4161
Leo Perez, prin. Fax 241-9571
Shasta Plus HS 50/Alt
2500 Eureka Way 96001 530-245-2716
Leo Perez, prin. Fax 241-9571
Shasta Adult S Adult
2200 Eureka Way 96001 530-245-2626
Milan Wollard, admin. Fax 245-2682
Other Schools – See Palo Cedro

Institute of Technology - Redding Campus Post-Sec.
1755 Hilltop Dr 96002 530-224-1000
Liberty Christian S 200/PK-12
3782 Churn Creek Rd 96002 530-222-2232
Tom Adams, head sch Fax 222-1784
Shasta Bible College & Graduate School Post-Sec.
2951 Goodwater Ave 96002 530-221-4275
Shasta College Post-Sec.
PO Box 496006 96049 530-242-7500
Simpson University Post-Sec.
2211 College View Dr 96003 530-224-5600

Redlands, San Bernardino, Pop. 66,575
Redlands USD 21,000/K-12
PO Box 3008 92373 909-307-5300
Lori Rhodes, supt. Fax 748-6711
www.redlands.k12.ca.us
Citrus Valley HS 2,300/9-12
PO Box 3008 92373 909-799-2300
Rhonda Bruce, prin. Fax 799-2349
Clement MS 1,000/6-8
501 E Pennsylvania Ave 92374 909-307-5400
Robert Clarey, prin. Fax 307-5414
Cope MS 1,400/6-8
1000 W Cypress Ave 92373 909-307-5420
Lisa Bruich, prin. Fax 307-5436
Moore MS 1,100/6-8
1550 E Highland Ave 92374 909-307-5440
Jamie Cortz, prin. Fax 307-5453
Orangewood HS 300/Alt
515 Texas St 92374 909-307-5380
Carol Ruhm, prin. Fax 307-5384
Redlands East Valley HS 2,200/9-12
31000 Colton Ave 92374 909-389-2500
John Maloney, prin. Fax 389-2517
Redlands HS 2,300/9-12
840 E Citrus Ave 92374 909-307-5500
Katherine Pearne, prin. Fax 307-5524
Redlands Adult S Adult
820 W Stuart Ave 92374 909-748-6930
David Finley, prin. Fax 307-5393
Other Schools – See Highland

Regional Occupational Center & Program
Supt. — None
Colton-Redlands-Yucaipa ROP Vo/Tech
PO Box 8640 92375 909-793-3115
Stephanie Houston, supt. Fax 793-6901

Ashdown College of Health Sciences Post-Sec.
101 E Redlands Blvd Ste 285 92373 909-793-4263
Community Christian College Post-Sec.
1849 N Wabash Ave 92374 909-335-8863
Packinghouse Christian Academy 200/K-12
27165 San Bernardino Ave 92374 909-793-4984
Jeff Lindeman, prin. Fax 307-1852
Redlands Adventist Academy 500/K-12
130 Tennessee St 92373 909-793-1000
Linda Woolley, prin. Fax 793-9862
Redlands Christian S 400/6-12
105 Tennessee St 92373 909-793-0601
Daniel Cole, head sch Fax 792-5691
University of Redlands Post-Sec.
PO Box 3080 92373 909-793-2121

Redondo Beach, Los Angeles, Pop. 63,466
Redondo Beach Unified SD 9,100/K-12
1401 Inglewood Ave 90278 310-379-5449
Steven Keller Ed.D., supt. Fax 798-8610
www.rbusd.org
Adams MS 900/6-8
2600 Ripley Ave 90278 310-798-8636
Anthony Taranto, prin. Fax 318-3064
Parras MS 1,100/6-8
200 N Lucia Ave 90277 310-798-8616
Dr. Lars Nygren, prin. Fax 798-8620
Redondo Shores HS 100/Alt
1000 Del Amo St 90277 310-798-8690
Sue Hall, prin. Fax 798-5287
Redondo Union HS 2,600/9-12
1 Sea Hawk Way 90277 310-798-8665
Dr. Jens Brandt, prin. Fax 798-4685
South Bay Adult S Adult
3401 Inglewood Ave 90278 310-937-3340
Anthony Taranto, dir. Fax 937-3345

Redwood City, San Mateo, Pop. 73,481
Redwood City ESD 9,100/PK-8
750 Bradford St 94063 650-423-2200
Dr. John R. Baker, supt. Fax 423-2204
www.rcsdk8.net
Kennedy MS 800/6-8
2521 Goodwin Ave 94061 650-482-2409
Stephen Brady, prin. Fax 367-4362
McKinley Institute of Technology 400/6-8
400 Duane St 94062 650-366-3827
Nick Fanourgiakis, prin. Fax 367-4363
North Star Academy 500/3-8
400 Duane St 94062 650-482-2411
Sara Shackel, prin. Fax 482-5980

Regional Occupational Center & Program
Supt. — None
San Mateo County ROP Vo/Tech
101 Twin Dolphin Dr 94065 650-598-2000
Ken San Filippo, dir. Fax 802-5414

San Mateo County Office of Education 300/
101 Twin Dolphin Dr 94065 650-802-5300
Anne Campbell, supt. Fax 802-5564
www.smcoe.org
Other Schools – See San Mateo

Sequoia UNHSD 9,200/9-12
480 James Ave 94062 650-369-1411
James Lianides, supt. Fax 306-8870
www.seq.org
Redwood HS 300/Alt
1968 Old County Rd 94063 650-369-1411
Frank Wells, prin. Fax 261-0213
Sequoia HS 2,000/9-12
1201 Brewster Ave 94062 650-367-9780
Sean Priest, prin. Fax 368-5180
Other Schools – See Atherton, Belmont, Menlo Park, Woodside

Canada College Post-Sec.
4200 Farm Hill Blvd 94061 650-306-3100

Redwood Valley, Mendocino, Pop. 1,695
Ukiah USD
Supt. — See Ukiah
Eagle Peak MS 400/5-8
8601 West Rd 95470 707-472-5250
Dan Stearns, prin. Fax 485-9542

Reedley, Fresno, Pop. 23,944
Kings Canyon JUSD 9,900/PK-12
675 W Manning Ave 93654 559-305-7010
Juan Garza, supt. Fax 637-1292
www.kcusd.com
Grant MS 500/6-8
360 N East Ave 93654 559-305-7330
Sharon Matsuzaki, prin. Fax 638-6772
Mountain View S 300/Alt
877 E North Ave 93654 559-305-7080
Ron Pack, dir. Fax 637-7778
Navelencia MS 300/6-8
22620 Wahtoke Ave 93654 559-305-7350
Josh Darnell, prin. Fax 637-1316
Reedley HS 1,900/9-12
740 W North Ave 93654 559-305-7100
Roberto Gutierrez, prin. Fax 637-0458
Reedly Middle College HS 100/9-12
995 N Reed Ave 93654 559-305-7010
Alejandro Juarez, prin. Fax 637-1292
Kings Canyon Adult S Adult
675 W Manning Ave 93654 559-305-7085
Ron Pack, dir. Fax 637-9486
Other Schools – See Orange Cove

Immanuel S 400/K-12
1128 S Reed Ave 93654 559-638-2529
Ryan Wood, supt. Fax 638-7030
Reedley College Post-Sec.
995 N Reed Ave 93654 559-638-3641

Rescue, El Dorado
Rescue UNESD 3,800/K-8
2390 Bass Lake Rd 95672 530-677-4461
David Swart, supt. Fax 677-0719
www.rescueusd.org
Pleasant Grove MS 600/6-8
2540 Green Valley Rd 95672 530-672-4400
Hope Migliaccio, prin. Fax 677-5829
Other Schools – See El Dorado Hills

Reseda, See Los Angeles
Los Angeles USD
Supt. — See Los Angeles
Grey Continuation S 200/Alt
18230 Kittridge St 91335 818-758-3769
Harry Haskell, prin. Fax 758-3714
Reseda HS 1,800/9-12
18230 Kittridge St 91335 818-758-3600
Melanie Welsh, prin. Fax 776-0452
Sherman Oaks Ctr for Enriched Studies 2,100/4-12
18605 Erwin St 91335 818-758-5600
Martin Price, prin. Fax 344-5909
Wooden HS 200/Alt
18741 Elkwood St 91335 818-345-0203
Laura Novak, prin. Fax 996-9008

Everest College Post-Sec.
18040 Sherman Way Ste 400 91335 818-774-0550
Marinello School of Beauty Post-Sec.
18442 Sherman Way 91335 818-881-2521

Rialto, San Bernardino, Pop. 97,244
Rialto USD 26,400/K-12
182 E Walnut Ave 92376 909-820-7700
Dr. Cuauhtemoc Avila, supt. Fax 873-0448
www.rialto.k12.ca.us
Carter HS 2,400/9-12
2630 N Linden Ave 92377 909-854-4100
Chavez Patricia, prin. Fax 574-7313
Eisenhower HS 2,400/9-12
1321 N Lilac Ave 92376 909-820-7777
Scott Sparks, prin. Fax 421-7640
Frisbie MS 1,300/6-8
1442 N Eucalyptus Ave 92376 909-820-7887
Akinlana Osonduagwuike, prin. Fax 820-7885
Kolb MS 1,000/6-8
2351 N Spruce Ave 92377 909-820-7849
Carolyn Eide, prin. Fax 875-0374
Kucera MS 1,200/6-8
2140 W Buena Vista Dr 92377 909-421-7662
Monique Conway, prin. Fax 421-7681
Milor Continuation HS 300/Alt
266 W Randall Ave 92376 909-820-7785
Andres Luna, prin. Fax 421-7617
Rialto HS 3,000/9-12
595 S Eucalyptus Ave 92376 909-421-7500
Arnie Ayala, prin. Fax 421-7584
Rialto MS 1,200/6-8
1262 W Rialto Ave 92376 909-879-7308
Rhea McIver-Gibbs, prin. Fax 877-4893
Zupanic HS 100/Alt
266 W Randall Ave 92376 909-820-7955
Andres Luna, admin. Fax 421-7617
Rialto Adult S Adult
595 S Eucalyptus Ave 92376 909-879-6010
Veronica Smith-Iszard, dir. Fax 879-6011
Other Schools – See Colton

Richmond, Contra Costa, Pop. 99,595
Contra Costa County Office of Education
Supt. — See Pleasant Hill
Contra Costa Adult S Adult
5555 Giant Hwy 94806 510-262-4340
Angela Hatter, prin. Fax 262-4343

West Contra Costa USD 30,400/PK-12
1108 Bissell Ave 94801 510-231-1100
Matthew Duffy, supt. Fax 236-6784
www.wccusd.net
De Anza HS 1,100/9-12
5000 Valley View Rd 94803 510-231-1440
Summer Sigler, prin. Fax 223-7984
DeJean MS 600/7-8
3400 MacDonald Ave 94805 510-231-1430
William McGee, prin. Fax 236-6680
Kennedy HS 800/9-12
4300 Cutting Blvd 94804 510-231-1433
Roxanne Brown-Garcia, prin. Fax 235-1915
Richmond HS 1,500/9-12
1250 23rd St 94804 510-231-1450
Jose DeLeon, prin. Fax 235-0316
West CC Adult Ed - Serra Adult
6028 Ralston Ave 94805 510-215-4666
Valerie Garrett, prin. Fax 215-0430
Other Schools – See El Cerrito, El Sobrante, Hercules, Pinole, San Pablo

---

Kaiser Permanente Medical Center Post-Sec.
938 Marina Way S 94804 510-231-5000
Salesian HS 600/9-12
2851 Salesian Ave 94804 510-234-4433
Tim Chambers, prin. Fax 236-4636

Ridgecrest, Kern, Pop. 26,434
Sierra Sands USD 4,900/K-12
113 W Felspar Ave 93555 760-499-1600
Ernest Bell, supt. Fax 375-3338
www.ssusdschools.org
Burroughs HS 1,400/9-12
500 E French Ave 93555 760-499-1800
Bryan Auld, prin. Fax 375-1735
Mesquite Continuation HS 100/Alt
140 Drummond Ave 93555 760-499-1810
JoAnne McClelland, prin. Fax 446-3328
Monroe MS 500/6-8
340 W Church Ave 93555 760-499-1830
Bonny Porter, prin. Fax 375-8781
Murray MS 600/6-8
921 E Inyokern Rd 93555 760-446-5525
Kirsti Smith, prin. Fax 446-3838
Sierra Sands Adult S Adult
1327 N Norma St Ste 143 93555 760-499-1725
JoAnne McClelland, prin. Fax 446-1391

Cerro Coso Community College Post-Sec.
3000 College Heights Blvd 93555 760-384-6100
Immanuel Christian S 200/K-12
201 W Graaf Ave 93555 760-446-6114
Lisa Waddill, prin. Fax 284-8320

Rio Dell, Humboldt, Pop. 3,219
Rio Dell ESD 300/K-8
95 Center St 95562 707-764-5694
Leslie Yale, supt. Fax 764-2656
riodell.schoolwires.com
Monument MS 100/6-8
95 Center St 95562 707-764-3783
Leslie Yale, supt. Fax 764-2656

Rio Linda, Sacramento, Pop. 14,536
Twin Rivers USD
Supt. — See Mc Clellan
Rio Linda HS 1,800/9-12
6309 Dry Creek Rd 95673 916-566-2725
Paul Orlando, prin. Fax 566-1718
Rio Linda Preparatory Academy 400/5-8
1101 G St 95673 916-566-2720
Cindy Harrison, prin. Fax 566-3578

Rio Vista, Solano, Pop. 7,140
River Delta USD 2,300/K-12
445 Montezuma St 94571 707-374-1700
Don Beno, supt. Fax 374-2995
www.rdusd.org
Rio Vista HS 400/9-12
410 S 4th St 94571 707-374-6336
Vicky Turk, prin. Fax 374-6810
River Delta S 50/Alt
400 Elm Way 94571 707-374-1719
Nicholas Casey, prin. Fax 374-5623
Riverview MS 200/6-8
525 S 2nd St 94571 707-374-2345
Sonia Rambo, prin. Fax 374-5623
Wind River Adult S Adult
525 S 2nd St 94571 707-374-1731
Nicholas Casey, prin. Fax 374-1723
Other Schools – See Clarksburg, Courtland

Ripon, San Joaquin, Pop. 13,864
Ripon USD 3,000/PK-12
304 N Acacia Ave 95366 209-599-2131
Dr. Ziggy Robeson Ed.D., supt. Fax 599-6271
www.riponusd.net
Harvest HS, 729 W Main St 95366 50/Alt
Sergei Samborski, prin. 209-599-5009
Ripon HS 900/9-12
301 N Acacia Ave 95366 209-599-4287
Keith Rangel, prin. Fax 599-6410

Ripon Christian HS 200/9-12
435 Maple Ave 95366 209-599-2155
Eric Segaar, prin. Fax 599-2170

Riverbank, Stanislaus, Pop. 22,058
Riverbank USD 2,800/K-12
6715 7th St 95367 209-869-2538
Dr. Daryl Camp, supt. Fax 869-1487
www.riverbank.k12.ca.us
Adelante Continuation HS 100/Alt
6801 7th St 95367 209-869-2383
Rebecca Evans, prin. Fax 869-7433
Cardozo MS 500/6-8
3525 Santa Fe St 95367 209-869-2591
Kevin Bizzini, prin. Fax 869-2714
Riverbank HS 700/9-12
6200 Claus Rd 95367 209-869-1891
Dr. Sean Richey, prin. Fax 869-2116

Riverdale, Fresno, Pop. 3,092
Riverdale JUSD 1,600/K-12
PO Box 1058 93656 559-867-8200
Jeff Percell, supt. Fax 867-6722
www.rjusd.org
Horizon HS 50/Alt
PO Box 726 93656 559-867-3614
Melissa Locke, prin. Fax 867-4575
Riverdale ES 600/4-8
PO Box 338 93656 559-867-3589
Chris Stilson, prin. Fax 867-3393
Riverdale HS 500/9-12
PO Box 726 93656 559-867-3562
Melissa Locke, prin. Fax 867-4750

Riverside, Riverside, Pop. 295,499
Alvord USD
Supt. — See Corona
Alvord Alternative Continuation HS 100/Alt
10365 Campbell Ave 92505 951-509-6120
Jason Marquez, admin. Fax 509-6119
Alvord Continuation HS 200/Alt
3606 Pierce St 92503 951-358-1715
Sandy Fielding, prin. Fax 358-1716
Arizona MS 1,100/6-8
11045 Arizona Ave 92503 951-358-1675
Jason Jones, prin. Fax 358-1676
Hillcrest HS 900/9-12
1180 Indiana Ave 92503 951-358-1755
Sherri Kemp, prin. Fax 358-1756
La Sierra HS 2,500/9-12
4145 La Sierra Ave 92505 951-358-1725
Josh Moss, prin. Fax 358-1726
Loma Vista MS 1,100/6-8
11050 Arlington Ave 92505 951-358-1685
Diane Kammeyer, prin. Fax 358-1686
Norte Vista HS 2,200/9-12
6585 Crest Ave 92503 951-358-1740
Susan Boyd, prin. Fax 358-1741
Villegas MS 1,300/6-8
3754 Harvill Ln 92503 951-358-1695
David Ferguson, prin. Fax 358-1696
Wells MS 1,000/6-8
10000 Wells Ave 92503 951-358-1705
Karin Ribaudo, prin. Fax 358-1706

Regional Occupational Center & Program
Supt. — None
Riverside County ROP Vo/Tech
PO Box 868 92502 951-826-6797
Nancy Pavelsky, dir. Fax 826-6440

Riverside USD 42,100/PK-12
PO Box 2800 92516 951-788-7135
David Hansen Ed.D., supt. Fax 778-5668
www.rusdlink.org
Arlington HS 2,100/9-12
2951 Jackson St 92503 951-352-8316
Steven Ybarra, prin. Fax 328-7311
Central MS 700/7-8
4795 Magnolia Ave 92506 951-788-7282
Lynn McCown, prin. Fax 328-2580
Chemawa MS 1,000/7-8
8830 Magnolia Ave 92503 951-352-8244
Raul Ayala, prin. Fax 328-2980
Earhart MS 1,000/7-8
20202 Aptos St 92508 951-697-5700
Sean Curtin, prin. Fax 328-7580
Gage MS 1,000/7-8
6400 Lincoln Ave 92506 951-788-7350
Dr. Gary Reller, prin. Fax 328-5680
King HS 3,300/9-12
9301 Wood Rd 92508 951-789-5690
Michael West, prin. Fax 778-5680
Lincoln HS 200/Alt
4341 Victoria Ave 92507 951-788-7371
Anthony Rice, prin. Fax 328-2931
Miller MS 1,000/7-8
17925 Krameria Ave 92504 951-789-8181
Chuck Hiroto, prin. Fax 328-2912
North HS 2,300/9-12
1550 3rd St 92507 951-788-7311
Dr. Pamela Mshana, prin. Fax 328-2581
Polytechnic HS 2,800/9-12
5450 Victoria Ave 92506 951-788-7203
Dr. Michael Roe, prin. Fax 328-2901
Raincross HS 200/Alt
6401 Lincoln Ave 92506 951-276-7670
Dennis Deets, dir. Fax 778-5623
Ramona HS 2,200/9-12
7675 Magnolia Ave 92504 951-352-8429
Dr. Jamie Angulo, prin. Fax 328-2532
Riverside STEM Academy 500/5-9
4466 Mt Vernon Ave 92507 951-788-7308
Dale Moore, prin. Fax 328-2513
Sierra MS 900/7-8
4950 Central Ave 92504 951-788-7501
Ratmony Yee, prin. Fax 328-2552
Summit View S 300/Alt
6401 Lincoln Ave 92506 951-276-7670
Dennis Deets, dir. Fax 276-7685
University Heights MS 800/7-8
1155 Massachusetts Ave 92507 951-788-7388
Coleman Kells, prin. Fax 328-2566

Riverside Adult S — Adult
6735 Magnolia Ave 92506 — 951-788-7185
Rachel Bramlett, prin. — Fax 328-2523

Bethel Christian S — 200/PK-12
2425 Van Buren Blvd 92503 — 951-359-1123
Dr. Michael Crites, supt. — Fax 359-1719
Brightwood College — Post-Sec.
4040 Vine St 92507 — 951-276-1704
California Baptist University — Post-Sec.
8432 Magnolia Ave 92504 — 951-689-5771
Carnegie S - Riverside — 600/PK-12
8775 Magnolia Ave 92503 — 951-687-0077
Dr. Tiffany Edwards, supt. — Fax 687-3340
La Sierra Academy — 700/K-12
4900 Golden Ave 92505 — 951-351-1445
La Sierra University — Post-Sec.
4500 Riverwalk Pkwy 92505 — 951-785-2000
North-West College — Post-Sec.
4550 La Sierra Ave 92505 — 951-351-7750
Notre Dame HS — 500/9-12
7085 Brockton Ave 92506 — 951-275-5896
Matt Luttringer, prin. — Fax 781-9020
Platt College — Post-Sec.
6465 Sycamore Canyon # 100 92507 — 626-300-5444
Riverside City College — Post-Sec.
4800 Magnolia Ave 92506 — 951-222-8000
The Fab School — Post-Sec.
2001 3rd St Ste E 92507 — 951-782-0567
United Education Institute — Post-Sec.
1860 University Ave 92507 — 851-300-5500
University of California — Post-Sec.
900 University Ave 92521 — 951-827-1012
Woodcrest Christian S — 500/7-12
18401 Van Buren Blvd 92508 — 951-780-2010
James Sullivan, supt. — Fax 780-2079

Rocklin, Placer, Pop. 54,666
Rocklin USD — 12,800/PK-12
2615 Sierra Meadows Dr 95677 — 916-624-2428
Roger Stock, supt. — Fax 630-2229
www.rocklinusd.org
Granite Oaks MS — 900/7-8
2600 Wyckford Blvd 95765 — 916-315-9009
Jay Holmes, prin. — Fax 315-9885
Rocklin HS — 1,900/9-12
5301 Victory Ln 95765 — 916-632-1600
Davis Stewart, prin. — Fax 632-0305
Spring View MS — 800/7-8
5040 5th St 95677 — 916-624-3381
Elizabeth Davidson, prin. — Fax 624-5737
Victory HS — 100/Alt
3250 Victory Dr 95765 — 916-632-3195
Wayne Hauptman, prin. — Fax 632-8630
Whitney HS — 1,900/9-12
701 Wildcat Blvd 95765 — 916-632-6500
Justin Cutts, prin. — Fax 435-2542

Sierra College — Post-Sec.
5000 Rocklin Rd 95677 — 916-624-3333
William Jessup University — Post-Sec.
333 Sunset Blvd 95765 — 916-577-2200

Rodeo, Contra Costa, Pop. 8,152
John Swett USD — 1,700/K-12
400 Parker Ave 94572 — 510-245-4300
Rob Stockberger, supt. — Fax 245-4312
www.jsusd.org
Other Schools – See Crockett

Rohnert Park, Sonoma, Pop. 39,217
Cotati-Rohnert Park USD — 5,800/K-12
7165 Burton Ave 94928 — 707-792-4722
Robert Haley, supt. — Fax 792-4537
www.crpusd.org
El Camino HS, 5450 Snyder Ln 94928 — 50/Alt
Amie Carter, prin. — 707-792-4750
Jones MS — 900/6-8
5154 Snyder Ln 94928 — 707-588-5600
Scott Johnson, prin. — Fax 588-5607
Rancho Cotate HS — 1,500/9-12
5450 Snyder Ln 94928 — 707-792-4750
Amie Carter, prin. — Fax 792-4758
Technology HS — Vo/Tech
1801 E Cotati Ave 94928 — 707-792-4825
Dawn Mawhinney, prin. — Fax 792-4727
Technology MS — 300/6-8
7165 Burton Ave 94928 — 707-792-4800
Sara McKenna-McKee, prin. — Fax 792-4516

Bergin University of Canine Studies — Post-Sec.
5860 Labath Ave 94928 — 707-545-3647
Sonoma State University — Post-Sec.
1801 E Cotati Ave 94928 — 707-664-2880

Rolling Hills, Los Angeles, Pop. 1,810
Palos Verdes Peninsula USD
Supt. — See Palos Verdes Estates
Palos Verdes Peninsula HS — 2,600/9-12
27118 Silver Spur Rd 90274 — 310-377-4888
Mitzi Cress, prin. — Fax 544-4378
Rancho Del Mar HS — 100/Alt
38 Crest Rd W 90274 — 310-377-6691
Rosemary Humphrey, prin. — Fax 544-5526
PVPUSD Adult Education — Adult
38 Crest Rd W 90274 — 310-541-7626
Rosemary Humphrey, prin. — Fax 265-5967

Rosamond, Kern, Pop. 17,416
Southern Kern USD — 3,000/K-12
PO Box CC 93560 — 661-256-5000
Jeffrey Weinstein, supt. — Fax 256-1247
www.skusd.k12.ca.us
Lincoln Alternative Education — 100/Alt
PO Box CC 93560 — 661-256-5090
Patrick Holmes, prin. — Fax 256-6868
Rare Earth Continuation HS — 100/Alt
PO Box CC 93560 — 661-256-5090
Patrick Holmes, prin. — Fax 256-6868
Rosamond HS — 800/9-12
PO Box CC 93560 — 661-256-5020
Harold Roney, prin. — Fax 256-6880
Tropico MS — 600/6-8
PO Box CC 93560 — 661-256-5040
Nat Adams, prin. — Fax 256-0630

Rosemead, Los Angeles, Pop. 53,367
El Monte UNHSD
Supt. — See El Monte
Rosemead HS — 1,700/9-12
9063 Mission Dr 91770 — 626-286-3141
Dr. Brian Bristol, prin. — Fax 286-6396

Garvey ESD — 5,200/K-8
2730 Del Mar Ave 91770 — 626-307-3400
Anita Chu, supt. — Fax 307-1964
www.garvey.k12.ca.us
Garvey IS — 800/7-8
2720 Jackson Ave 91770 — 626-307-3385
Gema Macias, prin. — Fax 307-3443
Temple IS — 500/7-8
8470 Fern Ave 91770 — 626-307-3360
Robert Boyd, prin. — Fax 307-8162

Rosemead ESD — 2,700/PK-8
3907 Rosemead Blvd 91770 — 626-312-2900
Dr. Amy Enomoto-Perez Ed.D., supt. — Fax 312-2906
www.rosemead.k12.ca.us
Muscatel MS — 600/7-8
4201 Ivar Ave 91770 — 626-287-1139
Jessica Ancona, prin. — Fax 307-6185

Don Bosco Technical Institute — Post-Sec.
1151 San Gabriel Blvd 91770 — 626-307-6500
Don Bosco Technical Institute — 500/9-12
1151 San Gabriel Blvd 91770 — 626-940-2000
Xavier Jimenez, prin. — Fax 940-2001
Rosemead Beauty School — Post-Sec.
8531 Valley Blvd 91770 — 626-286-2147
University of the West — Post-Sec.
1409 Walnut Grove Ave 91770 — 626-571-8811

Roseville, Placer, Pop. 114,218
Center JUSD
Supt. — See Antelope
Riles MS — 700/7-8
4747 PFE Rd 95747 — 916-787-8100
Joyce Frisch, prin. — Fax 773-4131

Dry Creek JESD — 6,400/K-8
9707 Cook Riolo Rd 95747 — 916-770-8800
Brad Tooker, supt. — Fax 771-0650
www.drycreek.k12.ca.us
Silverado MS — 1,100/6-8
2525 Country Club Dr 95747 — 916-780-2620
Priscilla Rasanen, prin. — Fax 780-2635
Other Schools – See Antelope

Eureka UNSD
Supt. — See Granite Bay
Olympus JHS — 600/7-8
2625 La Croix Dr 95661 — 916-782-1667
Sean Healy, prin. — Fax 782-1339

Roseville City ESD — 10,100/K-8
1050 Main St 95678 — 916-771-1600
Derk Garcia, supt. — Fax 771-1620
www.rcsdk8.org
Buljan MS — 1,100/6-8
100 Hallissy Dr 95678 — 916-771-1720
Ryan Hartsoch, prin. — Fax 773-2696
Chilton MS — 300/6-8
4501 Bob Doyle Dr 95747 — 916-771-1870
Jeff Ancker, prin. — Fax 771-1871
Cooley MS — 1,000/6-8
9300 Prairie Woods Way 95747 — 916-771-1740
Karen Calkins, prin. — Fax 786-3003
Eich MS — 700/6-8
1509 Sierra Gardens Dr 95661 — 916-771-1770
Marc Buljan, prin. — Fax 783-7292

Roseville JUNHSD — 10,200/9-12
1750 Cirby Way 95661 — 916-786-2051
Ron Severson, supt. — Fax 786-2681
www.rjuhsd.us
Adelante HS — 100/Alt
350 Atlantic St 95678 — 916-782-3155
Amy Lloyd, prin. — Fax 782-4064
Independence HS — 200/Alt
125 Berry St 95678 — 916-786-0793
Debbie Latteri, prin. — Fax 786-3389
Oakmont HS — 1,800/9-12
1710 Cirby Way 95661 — 916-782-3781
Rob Hasty, prin. — Fax 782-4943
Roseville HS — 2,000/9-12
1 Tiger Way 95678 — 916-782-3753
David Byrd, prin. — Fax 786-3846
Woodcreek HS — 2,200/9-12
2551 Woodcreek Oaks Blvd 95747 — 916-771-6565
Rebecca Rood, prin. — Fax 771-6596
Roseville Adult S — Adult
200 Branstetter St 95678 — 916-782-3952
Joyce Lude, dir. — Fax 782-4361
Other Schools – See Antelope, Granite Bay

Christian Life Academy — 50/K-12
1301 Coloma Way 95661 — 916-956-4662
Gary Gubitz, prin. — Fax 786-7916
Heald College — Post-Sec.
7 Sierra Gate Plz 95678 — 916-789-8600
Valley Christian Academy — 300/PK-12
301 W Whyte Ave 95678 — 916-728-5500

Ross, Marin, Pop. 2,341

Branson S — 300/9-12
PO Box 887 94957 — 415-454-3612
Christina Mazzola, head sch — Fax 454-2327

Rowland Heights, Los Angeles, Pop. 48,135
Rowland USD — 15,100/K-12
1830 Nogales St 91748 — 626-965-2541
Julie Mitchell Ed.D., supt. — Fax 854-8302
www.rowlandschools.org
Alvarado IS — 800/7-8
1901 Desire Ave 91748 — 626-964-2358
Scott Cavanias, prin. — Fax 810-5579
Community Day S — 50/Alt
1928 Nogales St 91748 — 626-935-8210
Dr. Mari Bordona, prin. — Fax 964-6450
Rowland HS — 2,400/9-12
2000 Otterbein Ave 91748 — 626-965-3448
Mitch Brunyer, prin. — Fax 810-4859
Rowland Adult & Continuing Education — Adult
2100 Lerona Ave 91748 — 626-965-5975
Rocky Bettar, dir. — Fax 854-1191
Other Schools – See La Puente, West Covina

Oxford S — 100/7-12
18760 Colima Rd 91748 — 626-964-9588
Southlands Christian S — 400/PK-12
18550 Farjardo St 91748 — 909-598-9733
Glenn Duncan, pres. — Fax 468-9943

Sacramento, Sacramento, Pop. 437,732
Elk Grove USD
Supt. — See Elk Grove
Calvine HS — 200/Alt
8333 Vintage Park Dr 95828 — 916-689-7502
Gregory Alburn, prin. — Fax 689-7546
Daylor HS — 100/Alt
6131 Orange Ave 95823 — 916-427-5428
Katherine Whiteside, prin. — Fax 391-2017
Florin HS — 1,500/9-12
7956 Cottonwood Ln 95828 — 916-689-8600
Denise Escobar, prin. — Fax 689-7430
Jackman MS — 900/7-8
7925 Kentwall Dr 95823 — 916-393-2352
Michael Anderson, prin. — Fax 393-4053
Las Flores Independent Study — 200/Alt
5900 Bamford Dr 95823 — 916-422-5604
Alan Williams, admin. — Fax 428-8307
Rio Cazadero HS — 200/Alt
7825 Grandstaff Dr 95823 — 916-422-3058
Douglas Wendle, prin. — Fax 422-0604
Rutter MS — 900/7-8
7350 Palmer House Dr 95828 — 916-422-7590
Kenneth Smith, prin. — Fax 422-8354
Sheldon HS — 2,300/9-12
8333 Kingsbridge Dr 95829 — 916-681-7500
Paula Duncan, prin. — Fax 681-7505
Smedberg MS — 1,100/7-8
8239 Kingsbridge Dr 95829 — 916-681-7525
Richard Wall, prin. — Fax 681-7530
Valley HS — 1,500/9-12
6300 Ehrhardt Ave 95823 — 916-689-6500
Richard Gutierrez, prin. — Fax 682-1528
Adult/Community Education — Adult
8401 Gerber Rd 95828 — 916-686-7717
Kathy Hamilton, dir. — Fax 689-5752

Natomas USD — 12,800/PK-12
1901 Arena Blvd 95834 — 916-567-5400
Chris Evans, supt. — Fax 567-5405
www.natomas.k12.ca.us
Discovery HS — 200/Alt
3401 Fong Ranch Rd 95834 — 916-928-5200
Keven MacDonald, prin. — Fax 928-5222
Inderkum HS — 1,600/9-12
2500 New Market Dr 95835 — 916-567-5640
Dan Motherspaw, prin. — Fax 567-5649
Natomas Gateways MS — 7-8
3301 Fong Ranch Rd 95834 — 916-567-5430
Lore Carrillo, prin.
Natomas HS — 1,100/9-12
3301 Fong Ranch Rd 95834 — 916-641-4960
Yuri Penermon, prin. — Fax 641-5455
Natomas MS — 700/7-8
3200 N Park Dr 95835 — 916-567-5540
Shea Borges Ed.D., prin. — Fax 567-5549

Sacramento City USD — 45,500/PK-12
PO Box 246870 95824 — 916-643-9000
Jose Banda, supt. — Fax 643-9480
www.scusd.edu
American Legion HS — 300/Alt
3801 Broadway 95817 — 916-277-6600
Richard Baranowski, prin. — Fax 277-6800
Bacon MS — 700/7-8
4140 Cuny Ave 95823 — 916-433-5000
Mary Coronado, prin. — Fax 433-5166
Benjamin Health Professions HS — 300/9-12
451 McClatchy Way 95818 — 916-264-3262
Marla Johnson, prin. — Fax 264-3245
Brannan MS — 700/7-8
5301 Elmer Way 95822 — 916-264-4350
Enrique Flores, prin. — Fax 264-4481
Burbank HS — 1,600/9-12
3500 Florin Rd 95823 — 916-433-5100
Jim Peterson, prin. — Fax 433-5199
California MS — 700/7-8
1600 Vallejo Way 95818 — 916-264-4550
Andrea Egan, prin. — Fax 264-4477
Capital City Independent Study — 600/Alt
7222 24th St 95822 — 916-433-5187
Michael Salman, prin. — Fax 433-5195
Carson MS — 300/7-10
5301 N St 95819 — 916-277-6750
Santiago Chapa, prin. — Fax 277-6550

Einstein MS 700/7-8
9325 Mirandy Dr 95826 916-228-5800
Garrett Kirkland, prin. Fax 228-5813
Johnson HS 1,500/9-12
6879 14th Ave 95820 916-277-6300
Kal Phan, prin. Fax 277-6740
Kennedy HS 2,100/9-12
6715 Gloria Dr 95831 916-433-5200
David Van Natten, prin. Fax 433-5511
McClatchy HS 2,300/9-12
3066 Freeport Blvd 95818 916-264-4400
Peter Lambert, prin. Fax 264-4499
Rosemont HS 1,300/9-12
9594 Kiefer Blvd 95827 916-228-5844
Elizabeth Vigil, prin. Fax 228-5733
School of Engineering and Sciences 500/7-12
7345 Gloria Dr 95831 916-433-2960
Jim Hays, prin. Fax 433-2959
Success Academy 50/Alt
5601 47th Ave 95824 916-643-2338
Cyndi Swindle, prin. Fax 433-5301
Sutter MS 1,100/7-8
3150 I St 95816 916-264-4150
Cristin Tahara-Martin, prin. Fax 264-3436
West Campus HS 900/9-12
5022 58th St 95820 916-277-6400
David Rodriguez, prin. Fax 277-6593
Wood MS 700/7-8
6201 Lemon Hill Ave 95824 916-382-5900
Tuan Duong, prin. Fax 382-5914
Jones Skills Center Adult
5451 Lemon Hill Ave 95824 916-433-2600
Susan Gilmore, dir. Fax 433-2640
McClaskey Adult Education Center Adult
5241 J St 95819 916-277-6625
Susan Gilmore, prin. Fax 277-6810

Sacramento County Office of Education
Supt. — See Mather
Gerber JSHS 100/Alt
PO Box 269003 95826 916-228-2329
Sharon Barnes, contact Fax 689-3730
Hickey JSHS 100/Alt
PO Box 269003 95826 916-566-2074
Lisa Alcala, prin. Fax 566-2018
North Area Community S 100/Alt
PO Box 269003 95826 916-566-1302
Lisa Alcala, prin. Fax 566-1304

San Juan USD
Supt. — See Carmichael
Arcade Fundamental MS 500/6-8
3500 Edison Ave 95821 916-971-7300
LeeAnn Hopton, prin. Fax 971-7821
Arden MS 900/6-8
1640 Watt Ave 95864 916-971-7306
Jeff Banks, prin. Fax 971-7830
El Camino Fundamental HS 1,600/9-12
4300 El Camino Ave 95821 916-971-7430
Shelley Friery, prin. Fax 971-7429
Encina Preparatory HS 1,000/6-12
1400 Bell St 95825 916-971-7538
Richard Judge, prin. Fax 971-7555
La Entrada Continuation HS 100/Alt
5320 Hemlock St 95841 916-979-8050
Glen Odabashian, prin. Fax 971-7302
Mira Loma HS 1,700/9-12
4000 Edison Ave 95821 916-971-7465
Rich Nichols, prin. Fax 971-7483
Rio Americano HS 1,600/9-12
4540 American River Dr 95864 916-971-7494
Brian Ginter, prin. Fax 971-7513

Twin Rivers USD
Supt. — See Mc Clellan
Foothill HS 1,100/9-12
5000 McCloud Dr 95842 916-566-3445
Brian Welborn, prin. Fax 566-3526
Foothill Ranch MS 600/5-8
5001 Diablo Dr 95842 916-566-3440
Howard Holcomb, prin. Fax 566-3574
Grant Union HS 2,000/9-12
1400 Grand Ave 95838 916-566-3450
Darris Hinson, prin. Fax 566-3501
Keema HS 600/Alt
1281 North Ave 95838 916-566-3410
Robert Pope, prin. Fax 566-3572
King Technology Academy 400/7-8
3051 Fairfield St 95815 916-566-3490
Shana Henry, prin. Fax 566-7815
Norwood JHS 800/6-8
4601 Norwood Ave 95838 916-566-2710
Diedre Barlow, prin. Fax 566-3529
NOVA Opportunity S 50/Alt
2035 North Ave 95838 916-566-2750
Bob Wilkerson, prin. Fax 566-3541
Rio Tierra JHS 600/6-8
3201 Northstead Dr 95833 916-566-2730
Micah Simmons, prin. Fax 566-3533
Vista Nueva Career & Tech HS Vo/Tech
2035 North Ave 95838 916-566-2750
Bob Wilkerson, prin. Fax 566-3542

Al-Arqam Islamic S 300/PK-12
6990 65th St 95823 916-391-3333
Noor Duso, prin. Fax 391-3334
Alliant International University Post-Sec.
2030 W El Camino Ave # 200 95833 916-565-2955
American River College Post-Sec.
4700 College Oak Dr 95841 916-484-8011
Anthem College Post-Sec.
9738 Lincoln Village # 100 95827 916-929-9700
Art Institute of California - Sacramento Post-Sec.
2850 Gateway Oaks Dr # 100 95833 800-477-1957
Bradshaw Christian S 1,200/PK-12
8324 Bradshaw Rd 95829 916-688-0521
Michelle Reynolds, supt. Fax 688-0502
Brightwood College Post-Sec.
4330 Watt Ave Ste 400 95821 916-649-8168
California State University-Sacramento Post-Sec.
6000 J St 95819 916-278-6011
Capital Christian S 1,100/PK-12
9470 Micron Ave 95827 916-856-5600
Todd W. Jacobs, supt. Fax 856-5951
Carrington College California Post-Sec.
8909 Folsom Blvd 95826 916-361-1660
Christian Brothers HS 1,000/9-12
4315 Mrtn Lthr King Jr Blvd 95820 916-733-3600
Mary Hesser, prin. Fax 733-3657
Cornerstone Christian S 200/K-12
5073 Andrea Blvd 95842 916-334-6236
Richard Batista, hdmstr. Fax 334-6200
Cosumnes River College Post-Sec.
8401 Center Pkwy 95823 916-691-7344
Cristo Rey HS 300/9-12
8475 Jackson Rd 95826 916-733-2660
Andreas Agos, prin. Fax 739-1310
Emergency Medical Sciences Training Inst Post-Sec.
3105 Fite Cir Ste 108 95827 800-500-0711
Epic Bible College Post-Sec.
4330 Auburn Blvd 95841 916-348-4689
Federico College of Hairstyling Post-Sec.
1515 Sports Dr 95834 916-929-4242
Le Cordon Bleu Academy of Culinary Arts Post-Sec.
2450 Del Paso Rd 95834 888-807-8222
MTI College Post-Sec.
5221 Madison Ave 95841 916-339-1500
My-Le's Beauty College Post-Sec.
5972 Stockton Blvd 95824 916-422-0223
Sacramento City College Post-Sec.
3835 Freeport Blvd 95822 916-558-2111
Sacramento Country Day S 500/PK-12
2636 Latham Dr 95864 916-481-8811
Lee Thomsen, head sch Fax 481-6016
St. Francis HS 1,100/9-12
5900 Elvas Ave 95819 916-452-3461
Theresa Rodgers, prin. Fax 452-1591
Truck Driving Academy Post-Sec.
3100 Fite Cir Ste 105 95827 916-381-2285
Union Institute & University Post-Sec.
160 Promenade Cir Ste 115 95834 916-564-3100
Unitek College Post-Sec.
1111 Howe Ave Ste 300 95825 818-518-6601
Universal Technical Institute Post-Sec.
4100 Duckhorn Dr 95834 916-263-9100
Western Pacific Truck School Post-Sec.
8720 Fruitridge Rd 95826 800-333-1233

Saint Helena, Napa, Pop. 5,723
St. Helena USD 1,300/PK-12
465 Main St 94574 707-967-2708
Dr. Marylou Wilson Ed.D., supt. Fax 963-1335
www.sthelena.k12.ca.us
St. Helena HS 500/9-12
1401 Grayson Ave 94574 707-967-2740
Ben Scinto, prin. Fax 967-2735
Stevenson MS 300/6-8
1316 Hillview Pl 94574 707-967-2725
Karin Cox, prin. Fax 967-2734

Culinary Institute of America Greystone Post-Sec.
2555 Main St 94574 707-967-1100

Salida, Stanislaus, Pop. 13,232
Salida UNESD 3,000/K-8
4801 Sisk Rd 95368 209-545-0339
Twila Tosh, supt. Fax 545-2682
www.salida.k12.ca.us/
Salida MS - Vella Campus 900/6-8
5041 Toomes Rd 95368 209-545-1633
Dean Way, prin. Fax 545-0831

Brightwood College Post-Sec.
5172 Kiernan Ct 95368 209-543-7000
Heald College Modesto Post-Sec.
5260 Pirrone Ct 95368 209-416-3700
San Joaquin Valley College Post-Sec.
5380 Pirrone Rd 95368 209-543-8800

Salinas, Monterey, Pop. 147,570
Monterey County Office of Education 1,700/
PO Box 80851 93912 831-755-0300
Dr. Nancy Kotowski, supt. Fax 753-6473
www.montereycoe.org
Salinas Community S 300/Alt
1420 Natividad Rd 93906 831-755-3790
Chandalee Wood, prin. Fax 753-1042

North Monterey County USD
Supt. — See Moss Landing
Central Bay Continuation HS 100/Alt
17500 Pesante Rd 93907 831-663-2997
Aida Ramirez, prin. Fax 663-1151
N Monterey Co. Ctr for Independent Study 100/K-12
17500 Pesante Rd 93907 831-663-7050
Aida Ramirez, prin. Fax 663-6184

Regional Occupational Center & Program
Supt. — None
Mission Trails ROP Vo/Tech
867 E Laurel Dr 93905 831-753-4209
Randy Bangs, dir. Fax 422-5115

Salinas UNHSD 13,800/7-12
431 W Alisal St 93901 831-796-7000
Tim Vanoli, supt. Fax 796-7005
www.salinas.k12.ca.us
Alisal HS 2,400/9-12
777 Williams Rd 93905 831-796-7600
Ernesto Garcia, prin. Fax 796-7605
Carr Lake Community Day S 50/Alt
10 Sherwood Pl 93906 831-796-7770
Richard Moreno, prin.
El Puente S, 20 Sherwood Dr 93901 400/Alt
August Caresani, prin. 831-796-7770
El Sausal MS 900/7-8
1155 E Alisal St 93905 831-796-7200
Francisco Huerta, prin. Fax 796-7205
Everret Alvarez HS 2,400/9-12
1900 Independence Blvd 93906 831-796-7800
Jacqui Axtell, prin. Fax 796-7805
Harden MS 1,200/7-8
1561 McKinnon St 93906 831-796-7300
Alberto Verduzco, prin. Fax 796-7305
La Paz MS 900/7-8
1300 N Sanborn Rd 93905 831-796-7900
Irelia Dominguez, prin. Fax 796-7905
Mount Toro HS 200/Alt
10 Sherwood Pl 93906 831-796-7700
Richarad Moreno, prin. Fax 424-7325
North Salinas HS 1,900/9-12
55 Kip Dr 93906 831-796-7500
Barabara Emanuel, prin. Fax 796-7505
Salinas HS 2,500/9-12
726 S Main St 93901 831-796-7400
Judith Peterson, prin. Fax 796-7405
Washington MS 1,100/7-8
560 Iverson St 93901 831-796-7100
Anthony Hinton, prin. Fax 796-7105
Salinas Adult S Adult
20 Sherwood Pl 93906 831-796-6900
Todd Farr, prin. Fax 796-6905

Santa Rita UNSD 3,200/K-8
57 Russell Rd 93906 831-443-7200
Dr. Shelly Morr, supt. Fax 442-1729
www.santaritaschools.org
Bolsa Knolls MS 500/6-8
1031 Rogge Rd 93906 831-443-3300
John Gutierrez, prin. Fax 443-4766
Gavilan View MS 500/6-8
18250 Van Buren Ave 93906 831-443-7212
Abel Valdez, prin. Fax 443-0908

Spreckels UNESD
Supt. — See Spreckels
Buena Vista MS 400/6-8
18250 Tara Dr 93908 831-455-8936
Eric Tarallo, prin. Fax 455-8832

Washington UNESD 900/K-8
43 San Benancio Rd 93908 831-484-2166
Dr. Kevin Vaughn, supt. Fax 484-2828
www.washingtonusd.org
San Benancio MS 300/6-8
43 San Benancio Rd 93908 831-484-1172
Gina Uccelli, prin. Fax 484-6509

Hartnell College Post-Sec.
411 Central Ave 93901 831-755-6700
Heald College Post-Sec.
1450 N Main St 93906 831-443-1700
Notre Dame HS 300/9-12
455 Palma Dr 93901 831-751-1850
Colleen Eagleson, prin. Fax 757-5749
Palma HS 500/7-12
919 Iverson St 93901 831-422-6391
David Sullivan, prin. Fax 422-5065

Salton City, Imperial, Pop. 3,695
Coachella Valley USD
Supt. — See Thermal
West Shores HS 400/7-12
2381 Shore Hawk Ave, 760-848-1360
Richard Pimentel, prin. Fax 394-0971

San Andreas, Calaveras, Pop. 2,665
Calaveras County Office of Education
Supt. — See Angels Camp
Calaveras River Academy 50/Alt
PO Box 249 95249 209-754-1996
Mike Nagano, prin. Fax 754-4261
Oakendell S 50/Alt
PO Box 249 95249 209-754-1961
Mike Nagano, prin. Fax 754-1659

Calaveras USD 3,100/K-12
PO Box 788 95249 209-754-2300
Mark Campbell, supt. Fax 754-2215
www.calaveras.k12.ca.us
Calaveras HS 1,000/9-12
PO Box 607 95249 209-754-1811
Michael Merrill, prin. Fax 754-0276
Gold Strike Continuation HS 100/Alt
PO Box 788 95249 209-754-2123
Rene Malamed, prin. Fax 754-1268
Other Schools – See Valley Springs

San Anselmo, Marin, Pop. 11,931
Ross Valley ESD 2,200/PK-8
110 Shaw Dr 94960 415-454-2162
Dr. Rick E. Bagley Ed.D., supt. Fax 454-6840
rossvalleyschools.org
Other Schools – See Fairfax

Tamalpais UNHSD
Supt. — See Larkspur
Sir Francis Drake HS 1,000/9-12
1327 Sir Francis Drake Blvd 94960 415-453-8770
Liz Seabury, prin. Fax 458-3429

San Domenico HS 100/9-12
1500 Butterfield Rd 94960 415-258-1990
John Berry, prin. Fax 258-1901
San Domenico MS 200/6-8
1500 Butterfield Rd 94960 415-258-1900
Carrie Robley, prin. Fax 258-1901
San Francisco Theological Seminary Post-Sec.
105 Seminary Rd 94960 415-451-2800

San Bernardino, San Bernardino, Pop. 204,762
Regional Occupational Center & Program
Supt. — None

San Bernadino County ROP Vo/Tech
601 N E St 92415 909-386-2449
Kit Alvarez, admin. Fax 386-2479

San Bernardino City USD 51,500/PK-12
777 N F St 92410 909-381-1100
Dr. Dale Marsden, supt. Fax 885-6392
www.sbcusd.k12.ca.us/
Arrowview MS 700/7-8
2299 N G St 92405 909-881-8109
Berenice Rios, prin. Fax 881-8119
Arroyo Valley HS 2,600/9-12
1881 W Base Line St 92411 909-381-4295
Lissette Magana, prin. Fax 386-2577
Cajon HS 2,800/9-12
1200 W Hill Dr 92407 909-881-8120
Teenya Bishop, prin. Fax 881-8141
Chavez MS 1,300/6-8
6650 Magnolia Ave 92407 909-386-2050
Ernestine Hopwood, prin. Fax 473-8443
Curtis MS 900/6-8
1050 Del Rosa Ave 92410 909-388-6332
Marlene Bicondova, prin. Fax 388-6339
Del Vallejo MS 600/6-8
1885 E Lynwood Dr 92404 909-881-8280
William Prudhomme, prin. Fax 881-8285
Golden Valley MS 800/6-8
3800 N Waterman Ave 92404 909-881-8168
Kristen Vicondova, prin. Fax 881-5196
Indian Springs HS 1,500/9-12
650 Del Rosa Dr 92410 909-383-1360
Dr. Alan Kay, prin. Fax 383-1750
King MS 700/6-8
1250 Medical Center Dr 92411 909-388-6350
Maria Jauregui, prin. Fax 388-6361
Middle College HS 300/9-12
1260 Esperanza St 92410 909-888-4041
James Espinoza, prin.
Pacific HS 1,600/9-12
1020 Pacific St 92404 909-388-6419
Hector Vasquez, prin. Fax 388-6427
Richardson Prep MS 600/6-8
455 S K St 92410 909-388-6438
Natalie Raymundo, prin. Fax 383-0368
Rodriguez Prep MS 500/6-8
1985 Guthrie St 92404 909-884-6030
Sudha Venkatesan, prin. Fax 863-7869
San Bernardino HS 1,800/9-12
1850 N E St 92405 909-881-8217
Antoinette Fulcher Gutie, prin. Fax 881-8245
San Gorgonio HS 2,100/9-12
2299 Pacific St 92404 909-388-6524
Dion Clark, prin. Fax 388-6498
Shandin Hills MS 800/6-8
4301 Little Mountain Dr 92407 909-880-6666
Victoria Flores, prin. Fax 880-6672
Sierra HS 400/Alt
570 E 9th St 92410 909-388-6478
Rose Lalama, prin. Fax 889-4188
Inland Career Education Adult
1200 N E St 92405 909-388-6000
Karen Bautista, prin. Fax 381-2887
Other Schools – See Highland

San Bernardino Co. Office of Education 2,500/
601 N E St 92415 909-386-2704
Ted Alejandre, supt. Fax 386-2478
www.sbcss.k12.ca.us
Other Schools – See Victorville

Aquinas HS 400/9-12
2772 Sterling Ave 92404 909-886-4659
Christopher Barrows, prin. Fax 886-7717
California State Univ.-San Bernardino Post-Sec.
5500 University Pkwy 92407 909-537-5000
Concorde Career College Post-Sec.
201 E Airport Dr # A 92408 909-884-8891
Dikaios Christian Academy 200/K-12
PO Box 9067 92427 909-881-8310
Jerry Sommerville, dir. Fax 881-8315
Everest College Post-Sec.
217 E Club Center Dr Ste A 92408 909-777-3300
Hair Masters University of Beauty Post-Sec.
208 W Highland Ave 92405 909-882-2987
Marinello School of Beauty Post-Sec.
721 W 2nd St Ste E 92410 909-884-8747
Rock Christian S 100/PK-12
2345 S Waterman Ave 92408 909-825-8887
Jackie Flores, prin.
San Bernardino Valley College Post-Sec.
701 S Mount Vernon Ave 92410 909-384-4400
The Art Institute of CA - Inland Empire Post-Sec.
674 E Brier Dr 92408 909-915-2100

San Bruno, San Mateo, Pop. 37,955
San Bruno Park ESD 2,800/K-8
500 Acacia Ave 94066 650-624-3100
Cheryl Olson, supt. Fax 266-9626
sbpsd.k12.ca.us
Parkside MS 900/6-8
1801 Niles Ave 94066 650-624-3180
Kerry Dees, prin. Fax 877-8195

San Mateo UNHSD
Supt. — See San Mateo
Capuchino HS 1,100/9-12
1501 Magnolia Ave 94066 650-558-2799
Shamar Shanks, prin. Fax 558-2752
Peninsula Alternative HS 200/Alt
300 Piedmont Ave 94066 650-558-2499
Ron Campana, prin. Fax 866-4120

Skyline College Post-Sec.
3300 College Dr 94066 650-738-4100

San Carlos, San Mateo, Pop. 27,121
San Carlos ESD 3,000/PK-8
1200 Industrial Rd Ste 9 94070 650-508-7333
Dr. Craig Baker, supt. Fax 508-7340
www.scsdk8.org
Central MS 500/6-8
757 Cedar St 94070 650-508-7321
Tom Domer, prin. Fax 508-7342

San Clemente, Orange, Pop. 61,767
Capistrano USD
Supt. — See San Juan Capistrano
Ayer MS 900/6-8
1271 Calle Sarmentoso 92673 949-366-9607
Nick Stever, prin. Fax 366-1519
San Clemente HS 3,100/9-12
700 Avenida Pico 92673 949-492-4165
Chris Carter, prin. Fax 361-5175
Shorecliffs MS 1,000/6-8
240 Via Socorro 92672 949-498-1660
Brad Baker, prin. Fax 498-0826
Vista del Mar MS 600/6-8
1130 Avenida Talega 92673 949-234-5955
Michelle Benham, prin. Fax 940-0262

San Diego, San Diego, Pop. 1,256,111
Poway USD 35,200/K-12
15250 Avenue of Science 92128 858-521-2800
Mel Robertson, supt.
www.powayusd.com
Bernardo Heights MS 1,400/6-8
12990 Paseo Lucido 92128 858-485-4850
Tim Biland, prin. Fax 485-4865
Black Mountain MS 1,300/6-8
9353 Oviedo St 92129 858-484-1300
Charan Kirpalani, prin. Fax 538-9440
Del Norte HS 1,800/9-12
16601 Night Hawk Ln 92127 858-487-0877
Greg Mizel, prin. Fax 487-2443
Mesa Verde MS 1,300/6-8
8375 Entreken Way 92129 858-538-5478
Cliff Mitchell, prin. Fax 538-8636
Mt. Carmel HS 2,000/9-12
9550 Carmel Mountain Rd 92129 858-484-1180
Greg Magno, prin. Fax 538-9426
Oak Valley MS 1,400/6-8
16055 Winecreek Rd 92127 858-487-2939
Casey Currigan, prin. Fax 457-0991
Rancho Bernardo HS 2,200/9-12
13010 Paseo Lucido 92128 858-485-4800
David LeMaster, prin. Fax 485-4822
Westview HS 2,300/9-12
13500 Camino Del Sur 92129 858-780-2000
Todd Cassen, prin. Fax 780-2054
Other Schools – See Poway

Regional Occupational Center & Program
Supt. — None
San Diego County ROP Vo/Tech
6401 Linda Vista Rd Ste 408 92111 858-292-3500
Steve Pinning, dir. Fax 268-9726

San Diego County Office of Education 2,000/
6401 Linda Vista Rd 92111 858-292-3500
Randolph Ward, supt. Fax 292-3653
www.sdcoe.net
Monarch S 300/K-12
1625 Newton Ave 92113 858-652-4100
Fax 652-4107
Other Schools – See San Marcos

San Diego USD 127,200/PK-12
4100 Normal St 92103 619-725-8000
Cindy Marten, supt. Fax 291-7182
www.sandi.net
A. L. B. A. S 50/Alt
4041 Oregon St 92104 619-344-3900
Andy Trakas, prin. Fax 344-3940
Bell MS 900/6-8
620 Briarwood Rd 92139 619-430-1000
Precious Hubbard-Jackson, prin. Fax 470-6054
Challenger MS 1,000/6-8
10810 Parkdale Ave 92126 858-586-7001
Diane Ryan, prin. Fax 271-5203
Clairemont HS 1,100/9-12
4150 Ute Dr 92117 858-273-0201
Jennifer Roberson, prin. Fax 272-4219
Clark MS 1,100/6-8
4388 Thorn St 92105 619-344-4200
Thomas Liberto, prin. Fax 344-4274
Correia MS 800/7-8
4302 Valeta St 92107 619-222-0476
Jonathan McDade, prin. Fax 221-0147
Crawford HS 1,100/9-12
4191 Colts Way 92115 619-362-3700
Richard Lawrence, dir. Fax 593-9207
Creative Performing & Media Arts S 900/6-8
5050 Conrad Ave 92117 858-800-5550
Scott Thomason, prin.
De Portola MS 1,000/6-8
11010 Clairemont Mesa Blvd 92124 858-496-8080
Ryan Brock, prin. Fax 576-4419
East Village HS, 1405 Park Blvd 92101 100/Alt
Elizabeth Larkin, prin. 619-525-2000
Farb MS 500/6-8
4880 La Cuenta Dr 92124 858-697-6750
Courtney Rizzo, prin. Fax 697-6790
Foster Construction Tech Academy 300/9-12
7651 Wellington Way 92111 858-496-8370
Ana Diaz-Booz, dir. Fax 496-4907
Garfield HS 200/Alt
1255 16th St 92101 619-362-4500
Jolie Pickett, prin. Fax 362-4549
Henry HS 2,500/9-12
6702 Wandermere Dr 92120 619-286-7700
Elizabeth Gillingh, prin. Fax 229-0370
Hoover HS 2,000/9-12
4474 El Cajon Blvd 92115 619-344-4500
Joe Austin, prin. Fax 344-4649

Innovation MS 500/7-8
5095 Arvinels Ave 92117 858-278-5948
Nicola Labas, prin.
Kearny Digital Media and Design HS 400/9-12
1954 Komet Way 92111 858-496-8370
Ana Diaz-Booz, prin. Fax 278-6349
Kearny HS College Connections 400/9-12
1954 Komet Way 92111 858-496-8370
Ana Diaz-Booz, prin. Fax 496-8379
Kearny Science Connections & Tech HS 300/9-12
1954 Komet Way 92111 858-496-8370
Ana Diaz-Booz, dir. Fax 715-9504
Lewis MS 1,000/6-8
5170 Greenbrier Ave 92120 619-583-3233
Brad Callahan, prin. Fax 229-1338
Lincoln HS, 4777 Imperial Ave 92113 1,500/9-12
John Ross, prin. 619-266-6500
Madison HS 1,200/9-12
4833 Doliva Dr 92117 858-496-8410
Richard Nash, prin. Fax 496-8421
Mann MS 800/6-8
4345 54th St 92115 619-582-8990
Allen Teng, prin. Fax 583-2637
Marshall MS 1,500/6-8
9700 Avenue of Nations 92131 858-549-5400
Michelle Irwin, prin. Fax 549-5490
Marston MS 800/6-8
3799 Clairemont Dr 92117 858-273-2030
Dr. John Gollias, prin. Fax 272-3460
Memorial Prep for Scholars & Athletes 500/6-8
2850 Logan Ave 92113 619-344-4350
Mirna Estrada, prin. Fax 344-4424
Millennial Tech MS 600/6-8
1110 Carolina Ln 92102 619-527-6933
William Neil, prin.
Mira Mesa HS 2,600/9-12
10510 Reagan Rd 92126 858-566-2262
Scott Giusti, prin. Fax 549-9541
Mission Bay HS 1,200/9-12
2475 Grand Ave 92109 858-273-1313
Ernest Remillard, prin. Fax 270-8294
Montgomery MS 500/6-8
2470 Ulric St 92111 858-397-6600
Stephanie Brown, prin. Fax 397-6642
Morse HS 1,900/9-12
6905 Skyline Dr 92114 619-262-0763
Harry Shelton, prin. Fax 262-6835
Mt. Everest Academy 300/Alt
4350 Mount Everest Blvd 92117 858-496-8778
Courtney Browne, prin. Fax 496-8797
Muir S 300/Alt
4431 Mount Herbert Ave 92117 858-268-1954
Laura Bellofato, prin. Fax 627-9289
New Dawn 100/Alt
5650 Mount Ackerly Dr 92111 858-496-1655
Georgina Barajas-Aguirre, prin.
Pacific Beach MS 600/6-8
4676 Ingraham St 92109 858-273-9070
Kimberly Meng, prin. Fax 270-8063
Pershing MS 800/6-8
8204 San Carlos Dr 92119 619-465-3234
Susan Levy, prin. Fax 461-5447
Point Loma HS 1,900/9-12
2335 Chatsworth Blvd 92106 619-223-3121
Barbara Samilson, prin. Fax 225-1298
Roosevelt International MS 900/6-8
3366 Park Blvd 92103 619-293-4450
Dr. Christina Casillas, prin. Fax 497-0918
San Diego HS of Business 700/9-12
1405 Park Blvd 92101 619-525-7461
Carmen Garcia, prin. Fax 525-7337
San Diego International Studies HS 800/9-12
1405 Park Blvd 92101 619-525-7464
Carmen Garcia, prin. Fax 744-7651
San Diego Metro Career & Tech HS Vo/Tech
7250 Mesa College Dr 92111 619-388-2299
Sara Leonard, prin.
San Diego Science & Technology HS 600/9-12
1405 Park Blvd 92101 619-525-7459
Dianne Cordero, prin. Fax 744-7677
School of Creative & Performing Arts 1,300/6-12
2425 Dusk Dr 92139 619-470-0555
Tim Farson, prin. Fax 470-9430
Scripps Ranch HS 2,200/9-12
10410 Treena St 92131 858-621-9020
Ann Menna, prin. Fax 621-0646
Serra HS 1,900/9-12
5156 Santo Rd 92124 858-496-8342
Vincent Mays, prin. Fax 571-3457
Standley MS 1,000/6-8
6298 Radcliffe Dr 92122 858-455-0550
William Pearson, prin. Fax 546-7627
Taft MS 500/6-8
9191 Gramercy Dr 92123 858-935-2650
Michael George, prin. Fax 496-8138
TRACE S 600/Alt
2555 Camino del Rio S 92108 619-574-1073
Amy Perez, prin.
Twain HS 200/Alt
6402 Linda Vista Rd 92111 858-800-5300
Emma Martinez, prin. Fax 800-5340
University City HS 1,700/9-12
6949 Genesee Ave 92122 858-457-3040
Jeff Olivero, prin. Fax 458-9432
Wangenheim MS 1,000/6-8
9230 Gold Coast Dr 92126 858-578-1400
Matthew Fallon, prin. Fax 578-9481
Whittier S, 3401 Clairemont Dr 92117 50/Alt
Cathie Whitley, prin. 858-490-2770
Wilson MS 600/6-8
3838 Orange Ave 92105 619-362-3400
David Downey, prin. Fax 362-3474
Other Schools – See La Jolla

San Dieguito UNHSD
Supt. — See Encinitas
Canyon Crest Academy 1,900/9-12
5951 E Village Center Loop 92130 858-350-0253
Brett Killeen, prin. Fax 350-0280
Carmel Valley MS 1,500/7-8
3800 Mykonos Ln 92130 858-481-8221
Cara Dolnik, prin. Fax 481-8256
Pacific Trails MS 7-8
5975 Village Center Loop Rd 92130 760-509-1000
Mary Anne Nuskin, prin. Fax 509-1005
Torrey Pines HS 2,700/9-12
3710 Del Mar Heights Rd 92130 858-755-0125
Rob Coppo, prin. Fax 481-0098

Sweetwater UNHSD
Supt. — See Chula Vista
Mar Vista Academy 900/Alt
1267 Thermal Ave 92154 619-628-5100
Thomas Winters, prin. Fax 423-8431
Montgomery HS 1,700/9-12
3250 Palm Ave 92154 619-628-3800
Tom Rodrigo, prin. Fax 424-6473
Montgomery MS 800/7-8
1051 Picador Blvd 92154 619-662-8200
Louie Zumstein, prin. Fax 428-6517
San Ysidro HS 2,400/9-12
5353 Airway Rd 92154 619-710-2300
Hector Espinoza, prin. Fax 710-2318
Southwest HS 1,700/9-12
1685 Hollister St 92154 619-628-3600
Lee Romero, prin. Fax 423-8253
Southwest MS 700/7-8
2710 Iris Ave 92154 619-628-4000
Oscar Medina, prin. Fax 423-1151
Montgomery Adult S Adult
3240 Palm Ave 92154 619-600-3800
Kevin McClelland, prin. Fax 423-7876

Academy of Our Lady of Peace 800/9-12
4860 Oregon St 92116 619-297-2266
Lauren Lek, prin. Fax 297-2473
Alliant International University Post-Sec.
10455 Pomerado Rd 92131 866-825-5426
Arch Academy K-12
9445 Farnham St Ste 101 92123 619-201-3834
Cheryl Allcock, head sch Fax 384-6608
Argosy University San Diego Post-Sec.
1615 Murray Canyon Ste 100 92108 619-321-3000
Art Institute of California - San Diego Post-Sec.
7650 Mission Valley Rd 92108 858-598-1200
Associated Technical College Post-Sec.
707 Broadway Ste 300 92101 619-234-2181
Avance Beauty College Post-Sec.
750 Beyer Way Ste B 92154 619-575-1511
Bethel Seminary Post-Sec.
6116 Arosa St 92115 619-325-5200
Brightwood College Post-Sec.
9055 Balboa Ave 92123 800-935-1857
Cal Coast Academy 50/6-12
11555 Clews Ranch Rd 92130 858-481-0882
Jan Dunning, head sch Fax 481-8583
California College San Diego Post-Sec.
2820 Camino Del Rio S # 300 92108 619-293-0190
CA International Business University Post-Sec.
520 W Ash St 92101 619-702-9400
California Miramar University Post-Sec.
9750 Miramar Rd Ste 180 92126 858-653-3000
California Univ of Management & Sciences Post-Sec.
8525 Gibbs Dr Ste 105 92123 858-277-6700
California Western School of Law Post-Sec.
225 Cedar St 92101 619-239-0391
Cambridge S 100/PK-10
PO Box 720508 92172 858-484-3488
Jean Kim, head sch Fax 484-3458
Career College of San Diego Post-Sec.
3350 Market St 92102 619-338-0813
Cathedral Catholic HS 1,700/9-12
5555 Del Mar Heights Rd 92130 858-523-4000
Kevin Calkins, prin. Fax 523-4097
Childrens Creative/Performing Arts Acad 200/PK-12
3051 El Cajon Blvd 92104 619-584-2454
Janet Cherif, dir. Fax 584-2422
Coleman University Post-Sec.
8888 Balboa Ave 92123 858-499-0202
Concorde Career Institute Post-Sec.
4393 Imperial Ave Ste 100 92113 619-688-0800
Design Institute of San Diego Post-Sec.
8555 Commerce Ave 92121 858-566-1200
DeVry University Post-Sec.
2655 Camino Del Rio N #350 92108 619-683-2446
FIDM Fashion Institute of Design Post-Sec.
350 10th Ave Fl 3 92101 619-235-2049
High Tech High Graduate School of Educ Post-Sec.
2855 Farragut Rd 92106 619-398-4902
Horizon Christian Academy 500/PK-12
5331 Mount Alifan Dr 92111 858-244-0333
Chris Johnson, prin. Fax 654-3054
Horizon University Post-Sec.
5331 Mount Alifan Dr 92111 858-695-8587
International Prof School of Body Work Post-Sec.
9025 Balboa Ave Ste 130 92123 858-505-1000
John Paul the Great Catholic University Post-Sec.
10174 Old Grove Rd Ste 200 92131 858-653-6740
Kuyper Preparatory S 50/K-12
7997 Paradise Valley Rd 92139 877-458-9737
Gabriela Lozoya, admin. Fax 458-9737
Maranatha Christian S 500/PK-12
9050 Maranatha Dr 92127 858-759-9737
Jess Hetherington, supt. Fax 759-4001
Marinello School of Beauty Post-Sec.
7550 Miramar Rd Ste 440 92126 858-547-9260
Maritime Institute Post-Sec.
1310 Rosecrans St Ste G 92106 619-225-1783
Mueller College Post-Sec.
123 Camino De La Reina 92108 619-291-9811
Nativity Prep Academy 6-8
2755 55th St 92105 619-544-9455
Newschool of Architecture & Design Post-Sec.
1249 F St 92101 619-684-8800
Ocean View Christian Academy 300/PK-12
2460 Palm Ave 92154 619-424-7875
Stephen Johnson, prin. Fax 621-5274
Pacific College of Oriental Medicine Post-Sec.
7445 Mission Valley Rd #105 92108 619-574-6909
Parker S 800/PK-12
6501 Linda Vista Rd 92111 858-569-7900
Kevin Yaley, head sch Fax 569-0621
Platt College Post-Sec.
6250 El Cajon Blvd 92115 619-265-0107
Point Loma Nazarene University Post-Sec.
3900 Lomaland Dr 92106 619-849-2200
Rock Academy 400/K-12
2277 Rosecrans St 92106 619-764-5200
Scott Marshall, head sch Fax 764-5202
Sage College Post-Sec.
2820 Camino Del Rio S # 100 92108 619-683-2727
St. Augustine HS 700/9-12
3266 Nutmeg St 92104 619-282-2184
Jim Horne, prin. Fax 282-1203
San Diego City College Post-Sec.
1313 Park Blvd 92101 619-388-3400
San Diego Jewish Academy 600/PK-12
11860 Carmel Creek Rd 92130 858-704-3700
Chaim Heller, head sch Fax 704-3850
San Diego Mesa College Post-Sec.
7250 Mesa College Dr 92111 619-388-2600
San Diego Miramar College Post-Sec.
10440 Black Mountain Rd 92126 619-388-7800
San Diego State University Post-Sec.
5500 Campanile Dr 92182 619-594-5200
Southern California Yeshiva HS 9-12
3410 Mount Acadia Blvd 92111 858-560-1818
Southern States University Post-Sec.
123 Camino De La Reina #100 92108 619-298-1829
Thomas Jefferson School of Law Post-Sec.
1155 Island Ave 92101 619-297-9700
Torah HS of San Diego 50/9-12
9001 Towne Centre Dr 92122 858-558-6880
Rabbi Michoel Peikes, head sch Fax 558-6835
Travel University International Post-Sec.
3625 Ruffin Rd Ste 308 92123 858-292-9755
University of San Diego Post-Sec.
5998 Alcala Park 92110 619-260-4600
Veterans Affairs Medical Center Post-Sec.
3350 La Jolla Village Dr 92161 858-552-8585
Waldorf S of San Diego 300/PK-12
3547 Altadena Ave 92105 619-280-8016
Rachel Davis, admin. Fax 280-8071
Warren-Walker MS 100/6-8
2231 Camino Del Rio S 92108 619-260-3663
Suzanne Pettigrew, dean Fax 260-3573

San Dimas, Los Angeles, Pop. 32,412
Bonita USD 9,900/K-12
115 W Allen Ave 91773 909-971-8200
Christina Goennier, supt. Fax 971-8329
www.bonita.k12.ca.us
Chaparral HS 100/Alt
115 W Allen Ave 91773 909-971-8240
Christine Black, prin. Fax 971-8249
Lone Hill MS 900/6-8
115 W Allen Ave 91773 909-971-8270
Jason Coss, prin. Fax 971-8279
San Dimas HS 1,300/9-12
115 W Allen Ave 91773 909-971-8230
Michael Kelly, prin. Fax 971-8239
Vista Alternative S 50/Alt
115 W Allen Ave 91773 909-971-8242
Christine Black, prin. Fax 971-8249
Other Schools – See La Verne

Life Pacific College Post-Sec.
1100 W Covina Blvd 91773 800-356-0001

San Fernando, Los Angeles, Pop. 23,530
Los Angeles USD
Supt. — See Los Angeles
Academy of Scientific Exploration 9-12
1001 Arroyo St 91340 818-838-3926
Dana Neill, prin. Fax 838-3945
Arts, 1001 Arroyo St 91340 9-12
John Lawler, prin. 818-837-6428
Mission Continuation HS 100/Alt
11015 Omelveny Ave 91340 818-361-1777
Nicolas Mize, prin. Fax 365-2592
San Fernando HS 2,400/9-12
11133 Omelveny Ave 91340 818-898-7600
Florentina Mendoza-Werne, prin. Fax 365-7255
San Fernando Institute of Applied Media 400/6-8
130 N Brand Blvd 91340 818-837-5455
Pearl Arredondo, prin. Fax 365-8911
San Fernando MS 800/6-8
130 N Brand Blvd 91340 818-837-5400
Freddy Ortiz, prin. Fax 365-8911
Social Justice Humanities Academy 9-12
1001 Arroyo St 91340 818-838-3915
Jose Navarro, prin. Fax 838-6759
Teacher Preparation Academy 9-12
1001 Arroyo St 91340 818-838-3946
Elizabeth Beltran, prin.

San Francisco, San Francisco, Pop. 773,534
Regional Occupational Center & Program
Supt. — None
San Francisco County ROP Vo/Tech
750 25th Ave 94121 415-355-7711
Sharon Zimmern, coord. Fax 355-7744

San Francisco County Office of Education 100/
555 Franklin St 94102 415-241-6000
Myong Leigh, supt. Fax 241-6012
www.sfusd.edu
Civic Center Secondary S 100/Alt
727 Golden Gate Ave 94102 415-241-3000
Elisa Villafuerte, prin. Fax 241-6192

San Francisco USD 55,500/PK-12
555 Franklin St 94102 415-241-6000
Myong Leigh, supt. Fax 241-6012
www.sfusd.edu
Academy of Arts & Sciences 400/9-12
555 Portola Dr 94131 415-695-5700
Gregory Markwith, prin. Fax 695-5326
Aptos MS 1,100/6-8
105 Aptos Ave 94127 415-469-4520
Doug Dent, prin. Fax 333-9038
Asawa San Francisco S of the Arts 600/9-12
555 Portola Dr 94131 415-695-5700
Barnaby Payne, prin. Fax 695-5326
Balboa HS 1,300/9-12
1000 Cayuga Ave 94112 415-469-4090
Susan Ritter, prin. Fax 469-0859
Brown MS 6-8
2055 Silver Ave 94124 415-642-8901
Bill Kappenhagen, prin. Fax 641-1120
Burton Academic HS 1,000/9-12
400 Mansell St 94134 415-469-4550
Sam Bass, prin. Fax 239-6806
Civic Center Secondary S 50/Alt
727 Golden Gate Ave 94102 415-241-3000
Elisa Villafuerte, prin. Fax 241-6192
Denman MS 600/6-8
241 Oneida Ave 94112 415-469-4535
Teresa Kohler, prin. Fax 585-8402
Downtown HS 200/9-12
693 Vermont St 94107 415-695-5860
Ellen Wong, prin. Fax 695-5863
Everett MS 400/6-8
450 Church St 94114 415-241-6344
Richard Curci, prin. Fax 241-6361
Francisco MS 600/6-8
2190 Powell St 94133 415-291-7900
Patricia Theel, prin. Fax 291-7910
Galileo Academy of Science & Technology 1,900/9-12
1150 Francisco St 94109 415-749-3430
Michael Reimer, prin. Fax 771-2322
Gateway to College Alt
50 Phelan Ave Science Hall 94112 415-452-5773
Thomas Graven, prin.
Giannini MS 1,200/6-8
3151 Ortega St 94122 415-759-2770
Tai-Sun Schoeman, prin. Fax 664-8541
Hoover MS 1,000/6-8
2290 14th Ave 94116 415-759-2783
Thomas Graven, prin. Fax 759-2881
Independence HS 200/Alt
1350 7th Ave 94122 415-242-2528
Anastasia Klafter, prin. Fax 242-2533
Jordan S for Equity 200/Alt
325 La Grande Ave 94112 415-452-4922
Jessica Huang, admin. Fax 452-4927
King Academic MS 500/6-8
350 Girard St 94134 415-330-1500
Michael Essien, prin. Fax 468-7295
Lick MS 600/6-8
1220 Noe St 94114 415-695-5675
Bita Nazarian, prin. Fax 695-5360
Lilienthal S Winifred Scott Campus 400/Alt
3630 Divisadero St 94123 415-749-3516
Tyler Graff, prin. Fax 749-3431
Lincoln HS 2,000/9-12
2162 24th Ave 94116 415-759-2700
Sharimar Manalang, prin. Fax 566-2224
Lowell HS 2,700/9-12
1101 Eucalyptus Dr 94132 415-759-2730
Andrew Ishibashi, prin. Fax 759-2742
Marina MS 800/6-8
3500 Fillmore St 94123 415-749-3495
Joanna Fong, prin. Fax 921-7539
Marshall HS 500/9-12
45 Conkling St 94124 415-695-5612
Martha Torres, prin. Fax 695-5438
Mission HS 900/9-12
3750 18th St 94114 415-241-6240
Eric Guthertz, prin. Fax 626-1641
O'Connell HS 500/9-12
2355 Folsom St 94110 415-695-5370
Mark Alvarado, prin. Fax 695-5379
Presidio MS 1,100/6-8
450 30th Ave 94121 415-750-8435
Thomas Ekno, prin. Fax 750-8445
Rooftop Alternative S - Mayeda Campus 300/Alt
500 Corbett Ave 94114 415-522-6757
Michael Reichle, prin. Fax 522-6763
Roosevelt MS 700/6-8
460 Arguello Blvd 94118 415-750-8446
Michael Stachon, prin. Fax 750-8455
San Francisco International HS 400/9-12
1050 York St 94110 415-695-5781
Julia Kessler, prin. Fax 695-5402
Visitacion Valley MS 500/6-8
450 Raymond Ave 94134 415-469-4590
Joe Truss, prin. Fax 469-4703
Wallenberg HS 700/9-12
40 Vega St 94115 415-749-3469
Cheryl Foster, prin. Fax 346-7303
Washington HS 2,000/9-12
600 32nd Ave 94121 415-750-8400
Susan Saunders, prin. Fax 750-8417
Wells HS 200/Alt
1099 Hayes St 94117 415-241-6315
Catherine Pringle, prin. Fax 241-6317

Academy of Art University Post-Sec.
79 New Montgomery St Fl 4 94105 415-274-2200

Alliant International University Post-Sec.
1 Beach St Ste 100 94133 415-955-2100
Alliant International University Post-Sec.
20 Haight St 94102 415-626-5550
American Coll of Traditional Chinese Med Post-Sec.
455 Arkansas St 94107 415-282-7600
American Conservatory Theater Post-Sec.
30 Grant Ave Fl 6 94108 415-439-2350
Archbishop Riordan HS 600/9-12
175 Phelan Ave 94112 415-586-8200
Vittorio Anastasio, prin. Fax 587-1310
Art Institute of California - San Fran Post-Sec.
1170 Market St 94102 888-493-3261
Bay Area Medical Academy Post-Sec.
1 Hallidie Plz Ste 406 94102 415-217-0077
Bay S of San Francisco 300/9-12
35 Keyes Ave 94129 415-561-5800
Luke Felker, hdmstr. Fax 561-5808
California College of the Arts Post-Sec.
1111 8th St 94107 415-703-9500
California Institute of Integral Studies Post-Sec.
1453 Mission St 94103 415-575-6100
City College of San Francisco Post-Sec.
50 Phelan Ave 94112 415-239-3000
Convent of the Sacred Heart HS 200/9-12
2222 Broadway St 94115 415-563-2900
Rachel Simpson, prin. Fax 931-0244
Cornerstone Academy Cambridge Campus 300/6-12
501 Cambridge St 94134 415-585-5183
De Marillac Academy 100/4-8
175 Golden Gate Ave 94102 415-552-5220
Christopher Giangregorio, prin. Fax 520-6969
Drew S 300/9-12
2901 California St 94115 415-409-3739
David Frankenberg, head sch Fax 346-0720
Fei Tian Academy of the Arts California 6-12
1950 Page St 94117 415-431-3161
FIDM Fashion Institute of Design Post-Sec.
55 Stockton St 94108 415-675-5200
French-American International S 1,000/PK-12
150 Oak St 94102 415-558-2000
Dr. Melinda Bihn, head sch Fax 558-2024
Fusion Academy 6-12
1160 Battery St Ste 40 94111 415-765-9078
Golden Gate University Post-Sec.
536 Mission St 94105 415-442-7000
Heald College Post-Sec.
875 Howard St Ste 100 94103 415-808-3000
Immaculate Conception Academy 200/9-12
3625 24th St 94110 415-824-2052
Lisa Graham, prin. Fax 821-4677
Jewish Community HS of the Bay 200/9-12
1835 Ellis St 94115 415-345-9777
Rabbi Howard Jacoby Ruben, head sch Fax 345-1888
Kampner Hebrew Academy 100/1-12
645 14th Ave 94118 415-752-7333
Le Cordon Bleu College of Culinary Arts Post-Sec.
350 Rhode Island St 94103 415-771-3500
Lick-Wilmerding HS 400/9-12
755 Ocean Ave 94112 415-333-4021
Eric Temple, head sch Fax 586-0737
Lycee Francais de San Francisco 900/6-12
1201 Ortega St 94122 415-661-5232
Philippe Legendre, hdmstr. Fax 564-6677
Mercy HS 400/9-12
3250 19th Ave 94132 415-334-0525
Scott McLarty, head sch Fax 334-9726
New Charter University Post-Sec.
543 Howard St Fl 5 94105 415-813-5970
Olivet University Post-Sec.
250 4th St 94103 415-371-0002
Presidio Graduate School Post-Sec.
36 Lincoln Blvd 94129 415-561-6555
Proof S, 555 Post St 94102 50/6-11
Dr. Sam Vandervelde, head sch 415-624-3910
Sacred Heart Cathedral Prep S 1,300/9-12
1055 Ellis St 94109 415-775-6626
Gary Cannon, prin. Fax 931-6941
SAE Institute - San Francisco Post-Sec.
450 Bryant St 94107 415-344-0886
St. Ignatius College Prep S 1,400/9-12
2001 37th Ave 94116 415-731-7500
Patrick Ruff, prin. Fax 731-2227
St. John of San Fran Orthodox Academy 100/PK-12
6210 Geary Blvd 94121 415-221-3484
Mary Najjarian, prin.
San Francisco Art Institute Post-Sec.
800 Chestnut St 94133 415-771-7020
San Francisco Christian S 200/K-12
25 Whittier St 94112 415-586-1117
Mike Allen, admin. Fax 841-0833
San Francisco Conservatory of Music Post-Sec.
50 Oak St 94102 800-899-7326
San Francisco State University Post-Sec.
1600 Holloway Ave 94132 415-338-1111
San Francisco University HS 400/9-12
3065 Jackson St 94115 415-447-3100
Julia Eells, head sch Fax 447-5801
San Francisco Waldorf HS 100/9-12
470 West Portal Ave 94127 415-431-2736
Gerhard Engels, dir. Fax 431-1712
Saybrook University Post-Sec.
747 Front St Fl 3 94111 800-825-4480
Stuart Hall HS 100/9-12
1715 Octavia St 94109 415-345-5811
Anthony Farrell, prin. Fax 563-3005
University of California Post-Sec.
513 Parnassus Ave # S-126 94143 415-476-9000
University of CA Hastings College of Law Post-Sec.
200 McAllister St 94102 415-565-4600
University of San Francisco Post-Sec.
2130 Fulton St 94117 415-422-5555
Urban S of San Francisco 400/9-12
1563 Page St 94117 415-626-2919
Mark Salkind, head sch Fax 626-1125
Woodside International S 100/9-12
1555 Irving St 94122 415-564-1063

San Gabriel, Los Angeles, Pop. 39,114
Alhambra USD
Supt. — See Alhambra
San Gabriel HS 2,400/9-12
801 S Ramona St 91776 626-943-6810
Debbie Stone, prin. Fax 308-2332

San Gabriel USD 5,300/K-12
408 Junipero Serra Dr 91776 626-451-5400
John Pappalardo Ed.D., supt. Fax 451-5494
www.sgusd.k12.ca.us
Del Mar HS 100/Alt
312 S Del Mar Ave 91776 626-291-5723
Lon Sellers, prin. Fax 291-2540
Gabrielino HS 1,800/9-12
1327 S San Gabriel Blvd 91776 626-573-2453
Sharron Heinrich, prin. Fax 573-5089
Jefferson MS 1,200/6-8
1372 E Las Tunas Dr 91776 626-287-5260
Dr. Matthew Arnold, prin. Fax 285-5387

San Gabriel Academy 500/PK-12
8827 E Broadway 91776 626-292-1156
San Gabriel Mission HS 200/9-12
254 S Santa Anita St 91776 626-282-3181
Marielle Sallo, prin. Fax 282-4209

Sanger, Fresno, Pop. 24,008
Regional Occupational Center & Program
Supt. — None
Valley ROP Vo/Tech
1305 Q St 93657 559-876-2122
Deborah Marvin-Deeter, dir. Fax 876-2102

Sanger USD 11,100/K-12
1905 7th St 93657 559-524-6521
Matt Navo, supt. Fax 875-0311
www.sanger.k12.ca.us/
Community Day S 50/Alt
818 L St 93657 559-524-6630
Johnny Gonzalez, prin. Fax 875-6379
Kings River Continuation HS 100/Alt
1801 7th St 93657 559-524-6490
Rick Church, prin. Fax 875-0676
Sanger HS 2,700/9-12
1045 Bethel Ave 93657 559-524-7121
Dan Chacon, prin. Fax 875-5721
Taft Independent Study 100/Alt
1801 7th St 93657 559-524-6490
Rick Church, prin. Fax 875-0676
Washington Academic MS 1,700/6-8
1705 10th St 93657 559-524-7015
Jamie Nino, prin. Fax 875-6365
Sanger Adult S Adult
1045 Bethel Ave 93657 559-524-7203
Nancy Penny, prin. Fax 875-1820

San Jacinto, Riverside, Pop. 42,978
San Jacinto USD 10,100/PK-12
2045 S San Jacinto Ave 92583 951-929-7700
Diane Perez, supt. Fax 658-3574
www.sanjacinto.k12.ca.us/
Monte Vista MS 900/6-8
181 N Ramona Blvd 92583 951-654-9361
Janet Covacevich, prin. Fax 654-0173
Mountain View HS Mountain Heights Acad 300/Alt
1000 N Ramona Blvd 92582 951-487-7710
Ken Swanson, prin. Fax 487-7718
North Mountain MS 1,000/6-8
1202 E 7th St 92583 951-487-7797
Dr. Karen Kirschinger, prin. Fax 487-7799
San Jacinto HS 2,400/9-12
500 Idyllwild Dr 92583 951-654-7374
Dr. Frank Jimenez, prin. Fax 654-7702
San Jacinto Leadership Academy 200/6-8
1599 Malaga Dr 92583 951-929-1954
Col. Francis Sick, prin.

Mt. San Jacinto College Post-Sec.
1499 N State St 92583 951-487-6752

San Joaquin, Fresno, Pop. 3,985
Golden Plains USD 1,900/K-12
PO Box 937 93660 559-693-1115
Martin Macias, supt. Fax 693-2526
www.gpusd.org
Other Schools – See Helm, Tranquillity

San Jose, Santa Clara, Pop. 914,803
Alum Rock UNESD 12,300/PK-8
2930 Gay Ave 95127 408-928-6800
Dr. Hilaria Bauer Ph.D., supt. Fax 928-6400
www.arusd.org
Fischer MS of Business and Communication 500/6-8
1720 Hopkins Dr 95122 408-928-7500
Dr. Imee Almazan Ed.D., prin. Fax 928-7501
George MS 600/6-8
277 Mahoney Dr 95127 408-928-7600
Barbara Campbell, prin. Fax 928-7601
Mathson Institute of Technology 500/6-8
2050 Kammerer Ave 95116 408-928-7950
Vince Iwasaki, prin. Fax 928-7951
Ocala STEAM Academy 600/6-8
2800 Ocala Ave 95148 408-928-8350
Tracy Leathers, prin. Fax 928-8351
Renaissance Academy at Fischer 300/6-8
1720 Hopkins Dr 95122 408-928-1950
Doug Kleinhenz, prin. Fax 928-1951
Renaissance Academy at Mathson 200/6-8
2050 Kammerer Ave 95116 408-928-8500
Doug Kleinhenz, prin. Fax 928-8501
Sheppard MS 700/6-8
480 Rough and Ready Rd 95133 408-928-8800
Jackie Montejano, prin. Fax 928-8801

Berryessa UNESD 7,900/K-8
1376 Piedmont Rd 95132 408-923-1800
Will Ector, supt. Fax 923-0623
www.berryessa.k12.ca.us
Morrill MS 800/6-8
1970 Morrill Ave 95132 408-923-1930
Joann Vaars, prin. Fax 946-0776
Piedmont MS 800/6-8
955 Piedmont Rd 95132 408-923-1945
Stefani Garino, prin. Fax 251-2392
Sierramont MS 1,100/6-8
3155 Kimlee Dr 95132 408-923-1955
Chris Mosley, prin. Fax 729-5840

Campbell UNESD
Supt. — See Campbell
Monroe MS 900/5-8
1055 S Monroe St 95128 408-556-0360
Dawnel Sonntag, prin. Fax 341-7020

Campbell UNHSD 7,300/9-12
3235 Union Ave 95124 408-371-0960
Robert Bravo Ed.D., supt. Fax 558-3006
www.cuhsd.org/
Boynton Alternative HS 300/Alt
901 Boynton Ave 95117 408-626-3404
Sarah Thomas, prin. Fax 984-8917
Branham HS 1,400/9-12
1570 Branham Ln 95118 408-626-3407
Cheryl Lawton, prin. Fax 267-2676
Del Mar HS 1,100/9-12
1224 Del Mar Ave Ste A 95128 408-626-3403
Jennifer Baldwin, prin. Fax 295-9476
Leigh HS 1,600/9-12
5210 Leigh Ave 95124 408-626-3405
Kara Butler, prin. Fax 265-7525
Campbell Adult & Community Education Adult
1224 Del Mar Ave 95128 408-371-0960
Dr. Bob Harper Ed.D., dir. Fax 947-2342
Other Schools – See Campbell, Saratoga

Cupertino UNSD
Supt. — See Sunnyvale
Miller MS 1,300/6-8
6151 Rainbow Dr 95129 408-252-3755
Steven Burrell, prin. Fax 255-5269

East Side UNHSD 26,300/K-12
830 N Capitol Ave 95133 408-347-5000
Chris Funk, supt. Fax 347-5045
www.esuhsd.org
Apollo Continuation HS 200/Alt
1835 Cunningham Ave 95122 408-928-5400
Vito Chiala, dir.
Calero HS 100/9-12
420 Calero Ave 95123 408-347-7600
Robert Ibarra, prin. Fax 347-5015
Evergreen Valley HS 2,700/9-12
3300 Quimby Rd 95148 408-347-7000
Lauren Kelly, prin. Fax 347-7175
Foothill HS 300/Alt
230 Pala Ave 95127 408-928-9100
George Sanchez, prin. Fax 928-9115
Hill HS 2,100/9-12
3200 Senter Rd 95111 408-347-4100
Jose Hernandez, prin. Fax 347-4115
Independence HS 3,100/9-12
1776 Educational Park Dr 95133 408-928-9500
Bjorn Berg, prin. Fax 928-9515
Lick HS 1,200/9-12
57 N White Rd 95127 408-347-4400
Kelly Daugherty, prin. Fax 347-4415
Mt. Pleasant HS 1,500/9-12
1750 S White Rd 95127 408-937-2800
Martha Guerrero, prin. Fax 937-2815
Oak Grove HS 1,900/9-12
285 Blossom Hill Rd 95123 408-347-6500
Martha Brazil, prin. Fax 347-6515
Overfelt HS 1,400/9-12
1835 Cunningham Ave 95122 408-347-5900
Vito Chiala, prin. Fax 347-5915
Pegasus HS 100/Alt
1776 Educational Park Dr 95133 408-928-9597
Bjorn Berg, coord. Fax 928-9535
Phoenix HS 100/Alt
6150 Snell Ave 95123 408-347-6291
Greg Louie, prin. Fax 347-6295
Piedmont Hills HS 2,200/9-12
1377 Piedmont Rd 95132 408-347-3800
Traci Williams, prin. Fax 347-3805
Santa Teresa HS 2,300/9-12
6150 Snell Ave 95123 408-347-6200
Greg Louie, prin. Fax 347-6215
Silver Creek HS 2,400/9-12
3434 Silver Creek Rd 95121 408-347-5600
Adolfo Laguna, prin. Fax 347-5615
Yerba Buena HS 1,700/9-12
1855 Lucretia Ave 95122 408-347-4700
Tom Huynh, prin. Fax 347-4715
East Side Adult Center Adult
625 Educational Park Dr 95133 408-928-9300
Richard Uribe, dir. Fax 928-9309

Evergreen ESD 13,200/K-8
3188 Quimby Rd 95148 408-270-6800
Kathy Gomez, supt. Fax 274-3894
www.eesd.org/
Chaboya MS 1,200/7-8
3276 Fowler Rd 95135 408-270-6900
Derrick Watkins, prin. Fax 270-6916
LeyVa IS 1,000/7-8
1865 Monrovia Dr 95122 408-270-4993
James Sherman, prin. Fax 270-5462
Quimby Oak MS 1,000/7-8
3190 Quimby Rd 95148 408-270-6735
Phil Bond, prin. Fax 223-4533

Franklin-McKinley ESD 11,100/PK-8
645 Wool Creek Dr 95112 408-283-6006
Juan Cruz, supt. Fax 283-6022
www.fmsd.org
College Connection Academy 100/Alt
1855 Lucretia Ave 95122 408-347-4827
Amber Andrade, prin.
Lairon College Preparatory Academy 500/4-8
3975 Mira Loma Way 95111 408-363-5775
Maria Dehghanfard, prin. Fax 363-5642
Sylvandale MS 800/7-8
653 Sylvandale Ave 95111 408-363-5700
Dan Fowler, prin. Fax 363-5649

Fremont UNHSD
Supt. — See Sunnyvale
Lynbrook HS 1,900/9-12
1280 Johnson Ave 95129 408-366-7700
Maria Jackson, prin. Fax 257-0551

Moreland SD 5,200/K-8
4711 Campbell Ave 95130 408-874-2900
Mary Kay Going, supt. Fax 374-8863
www.moreland.org
Moreland MS 1,000/6-8
4600 Student Ln 95130 408-875-3300
Ann Doumanian, prin. Fax 379-3622

Morgan Hill USD
Supt. — See Morgan Hill
Murphy MS 500/6-8
141 Avenida Espana 95139 408-201-6260
Heather Nursement, prin. Fax 201-6270

Mount Pleasant ESD 2,500/PK-8
3434 Marten Ave 95148 408-223-3700
Mariann Engle, supt. Fax 223-3715
www.mountpleasant.k12.ca.us
Boeger MS 600/6-8
1944 Flint Ave 95148 408-223-3770
Mia Cruz, prin. Fax 223-6959

Oak Grove ESD 11,100/K-8
6578 Santa Teresa Blvd 95119 408-227-8300
Jose Manzo, supt. Fax 629-7183
www.ogsd.net
Academy 50/Alt
6578 Santa Teresa Blvd 95119 408-226-2350
Oscar Ortiz, prin. Fax 227-2719
Bernal IS 800/7-8
6610 San Ignacio Ave 95119 408-578-5731
Jamal Splane, prin. Fax 578-7367
Davis IS 700/7-8
5035 Edenview Dr 95111 408-227-0616
Kim Kianidehkian, prin. Fax 224-8957
Herman IS 900/5-8
5955 Blossom Ave 95123 408-226-1886
Laura Meusel, prin. Fax 226-1897

Regional Occupational Center & Program
Supt. — None
Silicon Valley Career Technical Ed Vo/Tech
760 Hillsdale Ave 95136 408-723-6464
Susan Glass, supt. Fax 723-7266

San Jose USD 32,900/K-12
855 Lenzen Ave 95126 408-535-6000
Dr. Vincent Matthews, supt. Fax 535-2362
www.sjusd.org
Broadway HS 300/Alt
4825 Speak Ln 95118 408-535-6285
Giovanni Bui, prin. Fax 264-6392
Burnett Academy 900/6-8
850 N 2nd St 95112 408-535-6267
Fax 298-1675
Castillero MS 1,200/6-8
6384 Leyland Park Dr 95120 408-535-6385
Darbi O'Connell, prin. Fax 268-4489
Gunderson HS 1,200/9-12
622 Gaundabert Ln 95136 408-535-6340
Fax 224-2209
Gunderson Plus Continuation HS 50/Alt
622 Gaundabert Ln 95136 408-972-8629
Cecilia Molina, prin.
Harte MS 1,200/6-8
7050 Bret Harte Dr 95120 408-535-6270
Tina VanLaarhoven, prin. Fax 927-0698
Hoover MS 1,100/6-8
1635 Park Ave 95126 408-535-6274
Don McCloskey, prin. Fax 286-4864
Leland HS 1,800/9-12
6677 Camden Ave 95120 408-535-6290
Brad Craycroft, prin. Fax 927-6448
Leland Plus Continuation HS 50/Alt
6677 Camden Ave 95120 408-535-6100
Cecilia Molina, prin.
Liberty MSHS 300/Alt
5845 Allen Ave 95123 408-229-0722
Cecilia Molina, prin. Fax 225-5348
Lincoln HS 1,800/9-12
555 Dana Ave 95126 408-535-6300
Matt Hewitson, prin. Fax 535-2352
Lincoln Plus S, 1999 Olive Ave 95128 50/Alt
Cecilia Molina, prin. 408-292-3794
Middle College HS 50/Alt
2100 Moorpark Ave 95128 408-288-3100
Cecilia Molina, prin.
Muir MS 1,200/6-8
1260 Branham Ln 95118 408-535-6281
Jeannette Harding, prin. Fax 535-2319
O'Connor Career Academy Vo/Tech
2105 Forest Ave 95128 408-947-2852
Cecilia Molina, prin.
Pioneer HS 1,600/9-12
1290 Blossom Hill Rd 95118 408-535-6310
Herb Espiritu, prin. Fax 535-2357
Pioneer Plus Continuation HS 50/Alt
1290 Blossom Hill Rd 95118 408-264-4428
Cecilia Molina, prin.

San Jose High Academy Plus 50/Alt
275 N 24th St 95116 408-287-1631
Cecilia Molina, prin.
San Jose HS Academy 1,100/9-12
275 N 24th St 95116 408-535-6320
Gloria Marchant, prin. Fax 535-2355
Willow Glen HS 1,700/9-12
2001 Cottle Ave 95125 408-535-6330
Randy Shmidt, prin. Fax 535-2353
Willow Glen MS 1,200/6-8
2105 Cottle Ave 95125 408-535-6277
Paul Slayton, prin. Fax 535-2353
Willow Glen Plus HS 50/Alt
2001 Cottle Ave 95125 408-264-4422
Cecilia Molina, prin.
Silicon Valley Adult Education Adult
760 Hillsdale Ave 95136 408-723-6464
Susan Glass, prin. Fax 264-7266

Union ESD 5,300/K-8
5175 Union Ave 95124 408-377-8010
Denise Clay Ed.D., supt. Fax 377-7182
www.unionsd.org
Dartmouth MS 800/6-8
5575 Dartmouth Dr 95118 408-264-1122
Randy Martino, prin. Fax 264-9332
Union MS 900/6-8
2130 Los Gatos Almaden Rd 95124 408-371-0366
Todd Feinberg, prin. Fax 371-1217

Apostles Lutheran S 200/PK-12
5828 Santa Teresa Blvd 95123 408-578-4800
Joel Walker M.Ed., prin. Fax 225-0720
Archbishop Mitty HS 1,700/9-12
5000 Mitty Way 95129 408-252-6610
Timothy Brosnan, prin. Fax 252-6967
BASIS Independent Silicon Valley 600/5-12
1290 Parkmoor Ave 95126 408-291-0907
Bellarmine College Prep S 1,600/9-12
960 W Hedding St 95126 408-294-9224
Kristina Luscher, prin. Fax 297-5585
Cambrian Academy 6-12
1774 Foxworthy Ave 95124 408-833-7050
Carrington College California Post-Sec.
6201 San Ignacio Ave 95119 408-360-0840
Center of Employment Training Post-Sec.
701 Vine St 95110 408-287-7924
Cristo Rey HS 100/9-12
1390 Five Wounds Ln 95116 408-293-0425
Joe Albers, prin.
DeVry University Post-Sec.
2160 Lundy Ave Ste 250 95131 408-571-3760
East Valley Christian S 200/K-12
2715 S White Rd 95148 408-270-2500
Evergreen Valley College Post-Sec.
3095 Yerba Buena Rd 95135 408-274-7900
Ex'pression College Post-Sec.
1751 Fox Dr 95131 408-620-3300
Five Branches University Post-Sec.
3031 Tisch Way Ste 507 95128 408-260-0208
Harker MS 400/6-8
3800 Blackford Ave 95117 408-248-2510
Christopher Nikoloff, head sch Fax 248-2502
Harker Upper S 700/9-12
500 Saratoga Ave 95129 408-249-2510
Christopher Nikoloff, hdmstr. Fax 984-2325
International Technological University Post-Sec.
355 W San Fernando St 95110 888-488-4968
Liberty Baptist S 200/PK-12
2790 S King Rd 95122 408-274-5613
National Hispanic University Post-Sec.
14271 Story Rd 95127 408-254-6900
Notre Dame HS 600/9-12
596 S 2nd St 95112 408-294-1113
Mary Beth Riley, prin. Fax 293-9779
Palmer College of Chiropractic West Cmps Post-Sec.
90 E Tasman Dr 95134 866-303-7939
Presentation HS 800/9-12
2281 Plummer Ave 95125 408-264-1664
Mary Miller, prin. Fax 266-3028
Sacred Heart Nativity Schools 100/6-8
310 Edwards Ave 95110 408-993-1293
Lorraine Shepherd, prin. Fax 993-0675
San Jose City College Post-Sec.
2100 Moorpark Ave 95128 408-298-2181
San Jose State University Post-Sec.
1 Washington Sq 95192 408-924-1000
Silicon Valley University Post-Sec.
2160 Lundy Ave Ste 110 95131 408-435-8989
Stratford MS, 1718 Andover Ln 95124 200/6-8
Maggie Schwartz, prin. 408-626-0001
Valley Christian HS 1,300/9-12
100 Skyway Dr Ste 110 95111 408-513-2400
Mark Lodewyk, prin. Fax 513-2527
Valley Christian JHS 500/6-8
100 Skyway Dr Ste 140 95111 408-513-2460
Lisa Arnett, prin. Fax 513-2472
WestMed College-San Jose Post-Sec.
3031 Tisch Way 95128 408-236-1170

San Juan Bautista, San Benito, Pop. 1,810
Aromas/San Juan USD 1,100/PK-12
2300 San Juan Hwy 95045 831-623-4500
Michele Huntoon, supt. Fax 623-4907
www.asjusd.k12.ca.us
Anzar HS 400/9-12
2000 San Juan Hwy 95045 831-623-7660
Charlene McKowen, prin. Fax 623-7676

San Juan Capistrano, Orange, Pop. 33,954
Capistrano USD 52,500/K-12
33122 Valle Rd 92675 949-234-9200
Kirsten Vital, supt. Fax 493-8729
capousd.ca.schoolloop.com
Forster MS 1,400/6-8
25601 Camino Del Avion 92675 949-234-5907
Carrie Bertini, prin. Fax 488-3567

Junipero Serra HS 200/Alt
31422 Camino Capistrano 92675 949-489-7216
Meg Ervais, prin. Fax 496-2007
San Juan Hills HS 2,200/9-12
29211 Stallion Ridge 92675 949-234-5900
Jennifer Smalley, prin. Fax 488-9727
Capistrano Unified Adult Education Adult
31431 El Camino Real 92675 949-493-0658
Jolene Dougherty, prin. Fax 489-1421
Other Schools – See Aliso Viejo, Dana Point, Ladera Ranch, Laguna Niguel, Mission Viejo, Rancho Santa Margarita, San Clemente

Regional Occupational Center & Program
Supt. — None
College and Career Advantage Vo/Tech
33122 Valle Rd Ste 1000 92675 949-234-9464
Patricia Romo, dir.

Capistrano Valley Christian S 400/PK-12
32032 Del Obispo St 92675 949-493-5683
Christopher Rutz, head sch Fax 493-6057
JSerra HS 1,000/9-12
26351 Junipero Serra Rd 92675 949-493-9307
Eric Stroupe, admin. Fax 493-9308
Saddleback Valley Christian S 900/PK-12
26333 Oso Rd 92675 949-443-4050
Erick Streelman, head sch Fax 443-3941
St. Margaret Episcopal S 1,100/PK-12
31641 La Novia Ave 92675 949-661-0108
William Moseley, head sch Fax 661-8637

San Leandro, Alameda, Pop. 81,465
San Leandro USD 8,600/K-12
14735 Juniper St 94579 510-667-3500
Dr. Mike McLaughlin, supt. Fax 667-3569
www.sanleandro.k12.ca.us
Bancroft MS 900/6-8
1150 Bancroft Ave 94577 510-618-4380
Valentin Del Rio, prin. Fax 895-4113
Lincoln HS 100/Alt
2600 Teagarden St 94577 510-618-4600
Benjamin Redmond, prin. Fax 614-2018
Muir MS 1,000/6-8
1444 Williams St 94577 510-618-4400
Vernon Walton, prin. Fax 667-3545
San Leandro HS 2,600/9-12
2200 Bancroft Ave 94577 510-618-4600
Reginald Richardson, prin. Fax 347-1064
San Leandro Adult S Adult
1448 Williams St 94577 510-667-6287
Bradley Frazier, prin. Fax 357-8794

San Lorenzo USD
Supt. — See San Lorenzo
Washington Manor MS 800/6-8
1170 Fargo Ave 94579 510-317-5500
Theresa Armada, prin. Fax 317-5597

Carrington College California Post-Sec.
15555 E 14th St Ste 500 94578 510-276-3888
Insight Christian S 100/7-12
562 Lewelling Blvd 94579 510-351-3684

San Lorenzo, Alameda, Pop. 22,527
San Lorenzo USD 12,200/PK-12
15510 Usher St 94580 510-317-4600
Dr. Fred Brill, supt. Fax 278-4344
www.slzusd.org
Arroyo HS 1,700/9-12
15701 Lorenzo Ave 94580 510-317-4000
James Gray, prin. Fax 278-9067
Bohannon MS 900/6-8
800 Bockman Rd 94580 510-317-3800
Gwendolyn Rehling, prin. Fax 278-7794
Edendale MS 700/6-8
16160 Ashland Ave 94580 510-317-5100
Evelyn Baffico, prin. Fax 317-5190
San Lorenzo HS 1,500/9-12
50 E Lewelling Blvd 94580 510-317-3000
Allison Silvestri, prin. Fax 278-0547
San Lorenzo Adult S Adult
820 Bockman Rd 94580 510-317-4200
Sara Walke, prin. Fax 317-4291
Other Schools – See Hayward, San Leandro

Redwood Christian MSHS 400/6-12
1000 Paseo Grande 94580 510-317-8990
Al Hearne, supt. Fax 278-5064

San Luis Obispo, San Luis Obispo, Pop. 43,697
San Luis Coastal USD 7,500/PK-12
1500 Lizzie St 93401 805-549-1200
Dr. Eric Prater, supt. Fax 549-9074
www.slcusd.org
Laguna MS 700/7-8
11050 Los Osos Valley Rd 93405 805-596-4055
John Calandro, prin. Fax 544-2449
Pacific Beach HS 100/Alt
11950 Los Osos Valley Rd 93405 805-596-4023
Andrew Marinello, prin.
San Luis Obispo HS 1,400/9-12
1499 San Luis Dr 93401 805-596-4040
Leslie O'Connor, prin. Fax 542-9075
Adult S Adult
1500 Lizzie St Bldg G 93401 805-549-1222
Sally Ames, coord. Fax 544-0638
Other Schools – See Los Osos, Morro Bay

California Polytechnic State University Post-Sec.
1 Grand Ave 93407 805-756-1111
Central CA School of Continuing Educ. Post-Sec.
3195 McMillan Ave Ste F 93401 805-543-9123
Cuesta College Post-Sec.
PO Box 8106 93403 805-546-3100
Laurus College Post-Sec.
81 Higuera St Ste 110 93401 805-267-1690

Mission College Preparatory Catholic HS 300/9-12
682 Palm St 93401 805-543-2131
James Childs, prin. Fax 543-4359
San Luis Obispo Classical Academy 300/PK-12
165 Grand Ave 93405 805-548-8700
Susan Theule Ph.D., dir.

San Marcos, San Diego, Pop. 80,807
San Diego County Office of Education
Supt. — See San Diego
North Coastal Consortium S 100/PK-12
255 Pico Ave 92069 760-761-5110
Theresa Kurtz, prin.

San Marcos USD 20,100/K-12
255 Pico Ave Ste 250 92069 760-752-1299
Kevin Holt Ed.D., supt.
www.smusd.org/
Foothills HS 100/Alt
158 Cassou Rd 92069 760-290-2544
Mary Bunker, prin. Fax 736-2221
Mission Hills HS 2,600/9-12
1 E Mission Hills Ct 92069 760-290-2700
Courtney Goode, prin. Fax 290-2680
San Elijo MS 1,700/6-8
1600 Schoolhouse Way 92078 760-290-2800
Gary DeBora, prin. Fax 290-2828
San Marcos HS 2,500/9-12
1615 W San Marcos Blvd 92078 760-290-2200
Tiffany Campbell, prin. Fax 736-8275
San Marcos MS 1,300/6-8
650 W Mission Rd 92069 760-290-2500
Spencer Wavra, prin. Fax 744-0893
Twin Oaks HS 200/Alt
158 Cassou Rd 92069 760-290-2555
Mary Bunker, prin. Fax 736-2221
Woodland Park MS 1,300/6-8
1270 Rock Springs Rd 92069 760-290-2455
Josh Way, prin. Fax 741-6178

California College San Diego Post-Sec.
277 Rancheros Dr Ste 200 92069 760-621-4333
California State University-San Marcos Post-Sec.
333 S Twin Oaks Valley Rd 92096 760-750-4000
Palomar College Post-Sec.
1140 W Mission Rd 92069 760-744-1150
Palomar Institute of Cosmetology Post-Sec.
355 Via Vera Cruz Ste 3 92078 760-744-7900
St. Joseph Academy K-12
500 Las Flores Dr 92078 760-305-8505
Anthony Biese, prin. Fax 305-8466
Univ of St. Augustine for Health Science Post-Sec.
700 Windy Point Dr 92069 800-241-1027

San Marino, Los Angeles, Pop. 12,791
San Marino USD 3,100/K-12
1665 West Dr 91108 626-299-7000
Alex Cherniss, supt. Fax 299-7010
www.smusd.us
Huntington MS 800/6-8
1700 Huntington Dr 91108 626-299-7060
Jason Kurtenbach, prin. Fax 299-7064
San Marino HS 1,200/9-12
2701 Huntington Dr 91108 626-299-7020
Mary Johnson, prin. Fax 299-7037

Southwestern Academy 200/6-12
2800 Monterey Rd 91108 626-799-5010

San Mateo, San Mateo, Pop. 91,447
San Mateo County Office of Education
Supt. — See Redwood City
Gateway Center 100/Alt
35 Tower Rd 94402 650-598-2150
Nancy Magee, prin. Fax 598-2191

San Mateo UNHSD 8,100/9-12
650 N Delaware St 94401 650-558-2299
Dr. Kevin Skelly, supt. Fax 762-0249
www.smuhsd.org
Aragon HS 1,400/9-12
900 Alameda De Las Pulgas 94402 650-558-2999
Patricia Kurtz, prin. Fax 558-2952
Hillsdale HS 1,300/9-12
3115 Del Monte St 94403 650-558-2699
Jeff Gilbert, prin. Fax 574-4173
San Mateo HS 1,500/9-12
506 N Delaware St 94401 650-558-2399
Yvonne Shiu, prin. Fax 558-2352
San Mateo Adult S Adult
789 E Poplar Ave 94401 650-558-2100
Lawrence Teshara, dir. Fax 762-0232
Other Schools – See Burlingame, Millbrae, San Bruno

San Mateo-Foster City ESD
Supt. — See Foster City
Abbott MS 800/6-8
600 36th Ave 94403 650-312-7600
Joe Hadley, prin. Fax 312-7605
Bayside S.T.E.M. Academy 600/6-8
2025 Kehoe Ave 94403 650-312-7660
John Cosmos, prin. Fax 312-7634
Borel MS 900/6-8
425 Barneson Ave 94402 650-312-7670
Kenyetta Cook, prin. Fax 312-7644

College of San Mateo Post-Sec.
1700 W Hillsdale Blvd 94402 650-574-6161
Dawn Christian Academy 100/K-12
525 42nd Ave 94403 650-212-4222
Chris Chu, prin.
Fusion Academy 6-12
2000 Alameda de las Pulgas 94403 650-312-8305
Gurnick Academy of Medical Arts Post-Sec.
2121 S El Camino Real 94403 650-685-6616
Junipero Serra HS 900/9-12
451 W 20th Ave 94403 650-345-8207
Dr. Barry Thornton, prin. Fax 573-6638

Pacific Rim International S 100/PK-12
454 Peninsula Ave 94401 650-685-1881

San Pablo, Contra Costa, Pop. 28,206
West Contra Costa USD
Supt. — See Richmond
Helms MS 1,000/7-8
2500 Road 20 94806 510-233-3988
Jessica Petrilli, prin. Fax 234-5977
Middle College HS 300/9-12
2600 Mission Bell Dr 94806 510-215-3881
Finy Prak, prin. Fax 215-7927
Vista S 300/Alt
2625 Barnard St 94806 510-231-1431
Sylvia Greenwood, prin. Fax 222-8357

Contra Costa College Post-Sec.
2600 Mission Bell Dr 94806 510-235-7800

San Pedro, See Los Angeles
Los Angeles USD
Supt. — See Los Angeles
Angels Gate Continuation S 100/Alt
3607 S Gaffey St 90731 310-221-4600
Joan D'Amore, prin. Fax 221-4629
Dana MS 1,500/6-8
1501 S Cabrillo Ave 90731 310-241-1100
Steven Gebhart, prin. Fax 514-9925
Johnston Community Day S 200/7-12
2210 N Taper Ave 90731 310-832-0376
Barbara Politz, prin. Fax 832-7914
San Pedro HS 2,700/9-12
1001 W 15th St 90731 310-241-5800
Jeanette Stevens, prin. Fax 547-3183
Harbor Occupational Center Adult
740 N Pacific Ave 90731 310-547-5551
Gertrude Hawkins, prin. Fax 547-4979

Mary Star of the Sea HS 500/9-12
2500 N Taper Ave 90731 310-547-1138
Rita Dever, prin. Fax 547-1827
Rolling Hills Preparatory S 200/6-12
1 Rolling Hills Prep Way 90732 310-791-1101
Peter McCormack, head sch Fax 373-4931

San Rafael, Marin, Pop. 55,927
Dixie ESD 1,900/PK-8
380 Nova Albion Way 94903 415-492-3700
Dr. Thomas Lohwasser, supt. Fax 492-3707
dixieschooldistrict.org
Miller Creek MS 600/6-8
2255 Las Gallinas Ave 94903 415-492-3760
Kristy Treewater, prin. Fax 492-3765

Marin County Office of Education 200/
PO Box 4925 94913 415-472-4110
Mike Grant, supt. Fax 491-6625
www.marinschools.org/
Marin County Community S 100/Alt
PO Box 4925 94913 415-491-0581
Raquel Rose, dir. Fax 491-0981

Regional Occupational Center & Program
Supt. — None
Marin County ROP Vo/Tech
PO Box 4925 94913 415-499-5892
Gene Abbott, coord. Fax 491-6622

San Rafael CSD 6,700/PK-12
310 Nova Albion Way 94903 415-492-3233
Dr. Michael Watenpaugh, supt. Fax 492-3245
www.srcs.org
Davidson MS 1,000/6-8
280 Woodland Ave 94901 415-485-2400
Robert Marcucci, prin. Fax 485-2476
Madrone Continuation HS 100/Alt
185 Mission Ave 94901 415-485-2435
Jane Songer, prin. Fax 485-2438
San Rafael HS 1,100/9-12
185 Mission Ave 94901 415-485-2330
Glenn Dennis, prin. Fax 485-2345
Terra Linda HS 1,000/9-12
320 Nova Albion Way 94903 415-492-3100
Katy Dunlap, prin. Fax 492-3105

Dominican University of California Post-Sec.
50 Acacia Ave 94901 415-457-4440
Fusion Academy 6-12
1600 Los Gamos Dr Ste 380 94903 415-472-1421
Marin Academy 400/9-12
1600 Mission Ave 94901 415-453-4550
Travis Brownley, head sch Fax 453-8538
Marin S 100/9-12
150 N San Pedro Rd 94903 415-339-9336
Barbara J. Brown Ed.D., head sch Fax 339-9337

San Ramon, Contra Costa, Pop. 68,811
San Ramon Valley USD
Supt. — See Danville
California HS 2,600/9-12
9870 Broadmoor Dr 94583 925-803-3200
Sarah Cranford, prin. Fax 803-9341
Dougherty Valley HS 2,400/9-12
10550 Albion Rd, 925-479-6400
Daniel Hillman, prin. Fax 479-6597
Gale Ranch MS 1,000/6-8
6400 Main Branch Rd, 925-479-1500
Susan Goldman, prin. Fax 479-1595
Iron Horse MS 1,000/6-8
12601 Alcosta Blvd 94583 925-790-2500
Joe Nguyen, prin. Fax 824-2830
Pine Valley MS 1,000/6-8
3000 Pine Valley Rd 94583 925-479-7700
Jason Law, prin. Fax 828-1972
Venture Independent Study S 200/Alt
10540 Albion Rd, 925-479-1200
Matt Chamberlain, prin. Fax 479-1297

Windemere Ranch MS 1,200/6-8
11611 E Branch Pkwy, 925-479-7400
David Bolin, prin. Fax 479-7469

Santa Ana, Orange, Pop. 321,180
Garden Grove USD
Supt. — See Garden Grove
Fitz IS 700/7-8
4600 W McFadden Ave 92704 714-663-6351
Mischelle Repsher, prin. Fax 663-6527

Regional Occupational Center & Program
Supt. — None
Central Orange County CTE Partnership Vo/Tech
2323 N Broadway Ste 301 92706 714-996-3528
Al Mijares, dir.

Santa Ana USD 57,500/PK-12
1601 E Chestnut Ave 92701 714-558-5501
Stefanie Phillips Ed.D., supt. Fax 558-5610
www.sausd.us
Carr IS 1,600/6-8
2120 W Edinger Ave 92704 714-480-4100
Jose Luis Pedroza, prin. Fax 957-8766
Century HS 1,900/9-12
1401 S Grand Ave 92705 714-568-7000
Michael Parra, prin. Fax 568-7038
Chavez HS 300/Alt
2128 Cypress Ave 92707 714-430-5700
Matthew Cruz, prin. Fax 430-5799
Godinez Fundamental HS 2,600/9-12
3002 W Centennial Rd 92704 714-433-6600
Cindy Landsiedel, prin. Fax 433-6731
Lathrop IS 1,100/6-8
1111 S Broadway 92707 714-567-3300
Julie Infante, prin. Fax 567-3399
MacArthur Fundamental IS 1,300/6-8
600 W Alton Ave 92707 714-568-7700
David Casper, prin. Fax 568-7799
McFadden IS 1,500/6-8
2701 S Raitt St 92704 714-479-4000
Ignacio Muniz, prin. Fax 479-4099
Mendez Fundamental IS 1,400/6-8
2000 N Bristol St 92706 714-972-7800
Kathy Ochoa, prin. Fax 972-7899
Middle College HS 300/9-12
1530 W 17th St 92706 714-953-3900
Kathy Apps Ed.D., prin. Fax 953-3999
REACH Academy 100/Alt
804 N Fairview St 92703 714-796-9000
Trucker Clark, prin. Fax 796-9099
Saddleback HS 1,800/9-12
2802 S Flower St 92707 714-569-6300
Edward Bustamante Ed.D., prin. Fax 569-6399
Santa Ana HS 2,800/9-12
520 W Walnut St 92701 714-567-4900
Jeff Bishop, prin. Fax 567-4952
Segerstrom HS 2,500/9-12
2301 W MacArthur Blvd 92704 714-241-5000
Duncan McCulloch, prin. Fax 241-5099
Sierra Preparatory Academy 1,000/6-8
2021 N Grand Ave 92705 714-567-3500
Jesse Church, prin. Fax 567-3591
Spurgeon IS 900/6-8
2701 W 5th St 92703 714-480-2200
Stuart Caldwell, prin. Fax 480-2215
Valley HS 2,200/9-12
1801 S Greenville St 92704 714-241-6410
David Richey, prin. Fax 241-6599
Villa Fundamental IS 1,400/6-8
1441 E Chestnut Ave 92701 714-558-5100
Jonathan Swanson, prin. Fax 558-5199
Willard IS 900/6-8
1342 N Ross St 92706 714-480-4800
Amy Scruton, prin. Fax 480-4899

Tustin USD
Supt. — See Tustin
Foothill HS 2,600/9-12
19251 Dodge Ave 92705 714-730-7464
Dr. Mike Williams Ed.D., prin. Fax 573-9376
Hewes MS 900/6-8
13232 Hewes Ave 92705 714-730-7348
Eric Kilian, prin. Fax 730-7315

Art Institute of California - Orange Co. Post-Sec.
3601 W Sunflower Ave 92704 714-830-0200
Bethel Baptist S 200/PK-12
901 S Euclid St 92704 714-839-3600
California Coast University Post-Sec.
925 N Spurgeon St 92701 888-228-8648
Calvary Chapel S 1,500/K-12
3800 S Fairview St 92704 714-662-7485
Colleen O'Hara's Beauty Academy Post-Sec.
109 W 4th St Fl 2 92701 714-568-5399
Everest College Post-Sec.
500 W Santa Ana Blvd 92701 714-656-1000
Mater Dei HS 2,000/9-12
1202 W Edinger Ave 92707 714-754-7711
Frances Clare, prin. Fax 754-1880
Newbridge College Post-Sec.
1840 E 17th St Ste 140 92705 714-550-8000
North-West College Post-Sec.
1840 E 17th St 92705 714-795-2800
Santa Ana College Post-Sec.
1530 W 17th St 92706 714-564-6000
Taft Law School Post-Sec.
3700 S Susan St Ste 200 92704 714-850-4800

Santa Barbara, Santa Barbara, Pop. 86,425
Santa Barbara County Office of Education 300/
PO Box 6307 93160 805-964-4711
William Cirone, supt. Fax 964-4712
sbceo.org
Other Schools – See Santa Maria

Santa Barbara USD 15,500/PK-12
720 Santa Barbara St 93101 805-963-4338
Cary Matsuoka, supt. Fax 962-3146
www.sbunified.org
Alta Vista Alternative HS 200/Alt
215 E Ortega St 93101 805-965-1916
Elise Simmons, prin.
La Colina JHS 800/7-8
4025 Foothill Rd 93110 805-967-4506
David Ortiz, prin. Fax 967-3056
La Cuesta Continuation HS 100/Alt
710 Santa Barbara St 93101 805-966-0883
Elise Simmons, prin. Fax 963-8006
La Cumbre JHS 500/7-8
2255 Modoc Rd 93101 805-687-0761
Jo Ann Caines, prin. Fax 563-4636
San Marcos HS 1,900/9-12
4750 Hollister Ave 93110 805-967-4581
Ed Behrens, prin. Fax 967-8358
Santa Barbara HS 2,200/9-12
700 E Anapamu St 93103 805-966-9101
John Becchio, prin. Fax 965-6872
Santa Barbara JHS 900/7-8
721 E Cota St 93103 805-963-7751
Lito Garcia, prin. Fax 962-7196
Other Schools – See Goleta

Anacapa S 50/7-12
814 Santa Barbara St 93101 805-965-0228
Antioch University Santa Barbara Post-Sec.
602 Anacapa St 93101 805-962-8179
Avalon Beauty College Post-Sec.
504 N Milpas St 93103 805-966-1931
Bishop Garcia Diego HS 300/9-12
4000 La Colina Rd 93110 805-967-1266
Dr. Paul Harrington, head sch Fax 964-3178
Fielding Graduate University Post-Sec.
2020 De La Vina St 93105 805-687-1099
Garden Street Academy 100/K-12
2300 Garden St 93105 805-687-3717
Angela Jevons, admin. Fax 456-1897
Laguna Blanca S 300/PK-12
4125 Paloma Dr 93110 805-687-2461
Robert Hereford, head sch Fax 682-2553
Providence A Santa Barbara Christian S 100/7-12
630 E Canon Perdido St 93103 805-962-4400
Dr. Scott Lisea, head sch Fax 962-0132
Santa Barbara Business College Post-Sec.
506 Chapala St 93101 866-749-7222
Santa Barbara City College Post-Sec.
721 Cliff Dr 93109 805-965-0581
Santa Barbara Cottage & Gen. Hosp. Post-Sec.
PO Box 689 93102 805-569-7290
Santa Barbara MS 100/6-9
1321 Alameda Padre Serra 93103 805-682-2989
Brian McWilliams, hdmstr. Fax 682-0893
University of California 93106 Post-Sec.
805-893-8000
Westmont College Post-Sec.
955 La Paz Rd 93108 805-565-6000

Santa Clara, Santa Clara, Pop. 111,315

Santa Clara USD 15,400/K-12
PO Box 397 95052 408-423-2000
Dr. Stanley Rose, supt. Fax 423-2285
www.santaclarausd.org
Buchser MS 1,000/6-8
1111 Bellomy St 95050 408-423-3000
Monica Stoffal, prin. Fax 423-3080
Cabrillo MS 800/6-8
2550 Cabrillo Ave 95051 408-423-3700
Stan Garber, prin. Fax 423-3780
New Valley Continuation HS 200/Alt
1875 Lawrence Rd 95051 408-423-2300
Antonio Vela, prin. Fax 423-2380
Santa Clara Community Day S 50/Alt
3450 Brookdale Dr 95051 408-423-2090
Deborah Bauer, prin.
Santa Clara HS 1,800/9-12
3000 Benton St 95051 408-423-2600
Greg Shelby, prin. Fax 423-2681
Wilcox HS 1,900/9-12
3250 Monroe St 95051 408-423-2400
Kristin Gonzalez, prin. Fax 423-2480
Wilson Alternative S 300/Alt
1840 Benton St 95050 408-423-3600
Pamela Galano, prin. Fax 423-3580
Santa Clara Adult Education Adult
1840 Benton St 95050 408-423-3500
Kathy Martarano, dir. Fax 423-3580
Other Schools – See Sunnyvale

California Cosmetology College Post-Sec.
955 Monroe St 95050 408-247-2200
Granada Islamic S 400/PK-10
3003 Scott Blvd 95054 408-980-1161
Henley-Putnam University Post-Sec.
2804 Mission Coll Blvd #240 95054 408-453-9900
Institute for Business and Technology Post-Sec.
2400 Walsh Ave 95051 800-915-3562
Mission College Post-Sec.
3000 Mission College Blvd 95054 408-988-2200
North Valley Baptist S 200/K-12
941 Clyde Ave 95054 408-988-8883
Chris Fanara, prin.
Santa Clara University Post-Sec.
500 El Camino Real 95053 408-554-4000
Sierra S 100/K-12
220 Blake Ave 95051 408-247-4740

Santa Clarita, Los Angeles, Pop. 171,060

Regional Occupational Center & Program
Supt. — None
Hart District ROP Vo/Tech
21515 Centre Pointe Pkwy 91350 661-259-0033
Dave LeBarron, coord. Fax 260-1909

William S. Hart UNHSD 23,700/7-12
21380 Centre Pointe Pkwy 91350 661-259-0033
Vicki Engbrecht, supt. Fax 254-8653
www.hartdistrict.org
Academy of the Canyons 400/Alt
26455 Rockwell Canyon Rd 91355 661-362-3056
Pete Getz, prin. Fax 255-2954
Bowman Continuation HS 500/Alt
21508 Centre Pointe Pkwy 91350 661-253-4400
Robin Geissler, prin. Fax 253-4125
Golden Valley HS 2,200/9-12
27051 Robert C Lee Pkwy 91350 661-298-8140
Sal Frias, prin. Fax 250-8362
La Mesa JHS 1,100/7-8
26623 May Way 91351 661-250-0022
Michele Krantz, prin. Fax 252-3326
Learning Post HS 100/Alt
26455 Rockwell Canyon Rd 91355 661-255-8338
Pete Getz, prin. Fax 255-3801
Rio Norte JHS 1,200/7-8
28771 Rio Norte Dr 91354 661-295-3700
Vince Ferry, prin. Fax 257-1413
Other Schools – See Canyon Country, Newhall, Saugus, Stevenson Ranch, Valencia

---

Advantage Preparatory S 100/K-12
PO Box 802274 91380 661-296-5466
College of the Canyons Post-Sec.
26455 Rockwell Canyon Rd 91355 661-259-7800

Santa Cruz, Santa Cruz, Pop. 57,302

Live Oak SD 2,100/PK-12
984 Bostwick Ln Ste 1 95062 831-475-6333
Tamra Taylor, supt. Fax 475-2638
www.losd.ca
Shoreline MS 500/6-8
855 17th Ave 95062 831-475-6565
Colleen Martin, prin. Fax 462-1653

Regional Occupational Center & Program
Supt. — None
Santa Cruz County ROP Vo/Tech
399 Encinal St 95060 831-466-5760
Mark Hodges, dir. Fax 466-5769

Santa Cruz CSD
Supt. — See Soquel
Alternative Family Education 200/Alt
840 N Branciforte Ave 95062 831-429-3898
Lysa Tabachnick, prin. Fax 429-3912
ARK Independent S 100/Alt
840 N Branciforte Ave 95062 831-429-3432
Lysa Tabachnick, prin. Fax 429-3912
Branciforte MS 400/6-8
315 Poplar Ave 95062 831-429-3883
Kristin Pfotenhauer, prin. Fax 429-3962
Costanoa Continuation HS 100/Alt
840 N Branciforte Ave 95062 831-429-3898
Lysa Tabachnick, prin. Fax 429-3912
Harbor HS 1,000/9-12
300 La Fonda Ave 95062 831-429-3810
Richard Davis, prin. Fax 429-3982
Mission Hill MS 700/6-8
425 King St 95060 831-429-3860
Julia Hodges, prin. Fax 427-4846
Santa Cruz HS 1,000/9-12
415 Walnut Ave 95060 831-429-3960
Karen Edmonds, prin. Fax 429-3944
Santa Cruz Adult Education Adult
319 La Fonda Ave 95062 831-429-3966
Lysa Tabachnick, prin. Fax 429-3061

Santa Cruz County Office of Education 1,200/
400 Encinal St 95060 831-466-5600
Michael Watkins, supt. Fax 466-5607
www.santacruz.k12.ca.us
Santa Cruz County Community S 600/Alt
400 Encinal St 95060 831-466-5728
Johnny Rice, dir. Fax 466-5730

Five Branches University Post-Sec.
200 7th Ave 95062 831-476-9424
Kirby Preparatory S 200/6-12
425 Encinal St 95060 831-423-0658
Laura Lucas, dir. Fax 423-0679
University of California Post-Sec.
1156 High St 95064 831-459-0111

Santa Fe Springs, Los Angeles, Pop. 16,058

Little Lake City SD 4,600/K-8
10515 Pioneer Blvd 90670 562-868-8241
William Crean Ed.D., supt. Fax 868-1192
www.llcsd.net
Lake Center MS 900/6-8
10503 Pioneer Blvd 90670 562-868-4977
Jack Sokoloff, prin. Fax 929-4527
Other Schools – See Norwalk

Whittier UNHSD
Supt. — See Whittier
Santa Fe HS 2,600/9-12
10400 Orr and Day Rd 90670 562-698-8121
Craig Campbell, prin. Fax 868-8277

Presbyterian Theological Seminary Post-Sec.
15605 Carmenita Rd 90670 562-926-1023
St. Paul HS 700/9-12
9635 Greenleaf Ave 90670 562-698-6246
Kate Aceves, prin. Fax 696-8396

Santa Maria, Santa Barbara, Pop. 97,930

Orcutt UNESD
Supt. — See Orcutt
Lakeview JHS 500/7-8
3700 Orcutt Rd 93455 805-938-8600
Ted Lyon, prin. Fax 938-8649

Regional Occupational Center & Program
Supt. — None
Santa Barbara County ROP Vo/Tech
4893 Bethany Ln 93455 805-937-8427
Tony Bauer, dir. Fax 569-2507

Santa Barbara County Office of Education
Supt. — See Santa Barbara
Fitzgerald Community S 100/Alt
402 Farnel Rd 93458 805-928-0698
Fax 928-5414

Santa Maria JUNHSD 7,700/9-12
2560 Skyway Dr 93455 805-922-4573
Mark Richardson Ed.D., supt. Fax 928-9916
www.smjuhsd.k12.ca.us
Delta HS 600/Alt
4893 Bethany Ln 93455 805-937-6356
Esther Prieto-Chavez, prin. Fax 934-4743
Pioneer Valley HS 2,700/9-12
675 Panther Dr 93454 805-922-1305
Shanda Herrera, prin. Fax 928-9916
Righetti HS 2,100/9-12
941 E Foster Rd 93455 805-937-2051
Karen Rotondi, prin. Fax 934-0819
Santa Maria HS 2,300/9-12
901 S Broadway 93454 805-925-2567
Joseph Domingues, prin. Fax 922-0215

Santa Maria-Bonita ESD 15,500/K-8
708 S Miller St 93454 805-928-1783
Luke Ontiveros, supt. Fax 928-7874
www.smbsd.org
Arellanes JHS 600/7-8
1890 Sandalwood Dr 93455 805-361-6820
Stacie Rivera, prin. Fax 346-8535
El Camino JHS 700/7-8
219 W El Camino St 93458 805-361-7800
Betty Romero, prin. Fax 346-1851
Fesler JHS 900/7-8
1100 E Fesler St 93454 805-361-7880
Anjanette Winckler, prin. Fax 346-1849
Kunst JHS 800/7-8
930 Hidden Pines Way 93458 805-361-5800
Sharon Shell, prin. Fax 925-8239

Allan Hancock College Post-Sec.
800 S College Dr 93454 805-922-6966
Laurus College Post-Sec.
325 E Betteravia Rd Ste B8 93454 805-267-1690
St. Joseph HS 500/9-12
4120 S Bradley Rd 93455 805-937-2038
Joanne Poloni, prin. Fax 937-4248
Santa Barbara Business College Post-Sec.
303 Plaza Dr 93454 866-749-7222
Valley Christian Academy 300/PK-12
2970 Santa Maria Way 93455 805-937-6317

Santa Monica, Los Angeles, Pop. 86,130

Santa Monica-Malibu USD 11,300/PK-12
1651 16th St 90404 310-450-8338
Dr. Chris King, supt. Fax 450-1667
www.smmusd.org
Adams MS 1,000/6-8
2425 16th St 90405 310-452-2326
Steven Richardson, prin. Fax 452-5352
Lincoln MS 1,000/6-8
1501 California Ave 90403 310-393-9227
Dr. Florence Culpepper, prin. Fax 393-4297
Olympic Continuation HS 100/Alt
721 Ocean Park Blvd 90405 310-392-2494
Dr. Anthony Fuller, prin. Fax 392-9741
Santa Monica HS 3,000/9-12
601 Pico Blvd 90405 310-395-3204
Eva Mayoral, prin. Fax 395-5842
Santa Monica-Malibu Adult Education Adult
2510 Lincoln Blvd 90405 310-664-6222
Dr. Anthony Fuller, prin. Fax 664-6220
Other Schools – See Malibu

Art Institute of California-Los Angeles Post-Sec.
2900 31st St 90405 310-752-4700
Crossroads S for Arts & Sciences 1,100/K-12
1714 21st St 90404 310-829-7391
Bob Riddle, head sch Fax 828-5636
Emperor's Coll. of Trad. Oriental Med. Post-Sec.
1807 Wilshire Blvd Ste 200 90403 310-453-8300
Lighthouse Christian Academy 100/9-12
1424 Yale St 90404 310-829-2522
Jack Mefford, prin. Fax 829-5544
New Roads MSHS 400/6-12
3131 Olympic Blvd 90404 310-828-5582
Luthern Williams, head sch Fax 828-2582
Pacifica Christian HS 200/9-12
1730 Wilshire Blvd 90403 310-828-7015
Jim Knight, head sch Fax 829-2063
Pardee RAND Grad Sch of Policy Studies Post-Sec.
1776 Main St 90401 310-393-0411
St. Monica HS 500/9-12
1030 Lincoln Blvd 90403 310-394-3701
Alex Chacon, prin. Fax 458-1353
Santa Monica College Post-Sec.
1900 Pico Blvd 90405 310-434-4000

Santa Paula, Ventura, Pop. 29,121

Briggs ESD 600/PK-8
12465 Foothill Rd 93060 805-525-7540
Deborah Cuevas, supt. Fax 933-1111
www.briggsesd.org
Briggs MS 300/5-8
14438 W Telegraph Rd 93060 805-525-7151
Samuel Pacheco, prin. Fax 933-3565

Santa Paula USD 5,400/K-12
201 S Steckel Dr 93060 805-933-8800
Alfonso Gamino, supt. Fax 933-8026
www.santapaulaunified.org
Isbell MS 1,100/6-8
221 S 4th St 93060 805-933-8880
Dr. Ricardo Araiza, prin. Fax 933-5582
Renaissance Continuation HS 100/Alt
333 N Palm Ave 93060 805-525-4407
Robin Gillette, prin. Fax 525-2294
Santa Paula HS 1,500/9-12
404 N 6th St 93060 805-525-4400
Elizabeth Garcia, prin. Fax 525-1690

Thomas Aquinas College Post-Sec.
10000 Ojai Rd 93060 800-634-9797

Santa Rosa, Sonoma, Pop. 161,788
Regional Occupational Center & Program
Supt. — None
Sonoma County ROP Vo/Tech
5340 Skylane Blvd 95403 707-524-2720
Stephen Jackson, dir. Fax 524-2789

Santa Rosa CSD 16,100/K-12
211 Ridgway Ave 95401 707-528-5388
Diann Kitamura, supt. Fax 528-5440
www.srcs.k12.ca.us
Allen HS 1,000/9-12
599 Bellevue Ave 95407 707-528-5020
Mary Gail Stablein, prin. Fax 528-5023
Carillo HS 1,600/9-12
6975 Montecito Blvd 95409 707-528-5790
Vicki Zands, prin. Fax 528-5789
Comstock MS 400/7-8
2750 W Steele Ln 95403 707-528-5266
Laura Hendrickson, prin. Fax 528-5480
Cook MS 400/7-8
2480 Sebastopol Rd 95407 707-528-5156
Matthew Pollack, prin. Fax 528-5163
Grace Necessary Small HS 100/Alt
1702 Fulton Rd 95403 707-528-5756
Tony Negri, prin. Fax 528-5246
Lewis Opportunity S 50/Alt
2230 Lomitas Ave 95404 707-284-8225
Tracy Anderson, prin. Fax 284-8232
Mesa Necessary Small HS 50/Alt
1237 Mendocino Ave 95401 707-528-5227
Brad Coscarelli, prin. Fax 528-5724
Midrose Necessary Small HS 100/Alt
597 Bellevue Ave 95407 707-528-5041
Tony Negri, prin. Fax 528-5027
Montgomery HS 1,800/9-12
1250 Hahman Dr 95405 707-528-5191
Randy Burbank, prin. Fax 528-5056
Piner HS 900/9-12
1700 Fulton Rd 95403 707-528-5245
Tim Zalunardo, prin. Fax 528-5246
Ridgway Continuation HS 300/Alt
325 Ridgway Ave 95401 707-528-5325
Gabriel Albavera, prin. Fax 528-5717
Rincon Valley MS 800/7-8
4650 Badger Rd 95409 707-528-5255
Ed Navarro, prin. Fax 528-5644
Santa Rosa HS 2,000/9-12
1235 Mendocino Ave 95401 707-528-5291
Brad Coscarelli, prin. Fax 528-5724
Santa Rosa MS 700/7-8
500 E St 95404 707-528-5281
Tom Fierro, prin. Fax 528-5283
Slater MS 700/7-8
3500 Sonoma Ave 95405 707-528-5241
Rachele Cunningham, prin. Fax 528-5733

Cardinal Newman HS 700/9-12
50 Ursuline Rd 95403 707-546-6470
Graham Rutherford, prin. Fax 544-8502
Empire College Post-Sec.
3035 Cleveland Ave 95403 707-546-4000
Lytle's Redwood Empire Beauty College Post-Sec.
186 Wikiup Dr 95403 707-545-8490
Redwood Adventist Academy 100/K-12
385 Mark West Springs Rd 95404 707-545-1697
Rincon Valley Christian S 400/PK-12
4585 Badger Rd 95409 707-539-1486
Paul Eggenberger, admin. Fax 539-1493
Santa Rosa Junior College Post-Sec.
1501 Mendocino Ave 95401 707-527-4011
Sonoma Academy 200/9-12
2500 Farmers Ln 95404 707-545-1770
Janet Durgin, head sch Fax 636-2474
Summerfield Waldorf S 400/PK-12
655 Willowside Rd 95401 707-575-7194

Santa Ynez, Santa Barbara, Pop. 4,319
Santa Ynez Valley UNHSD 1,000/9-12
PO Box 398 93460 805-688-6487
Scott Cory, supt. Fax 686-4454
www.syvuhsd.org
Refugio HS 50/Alt
PO Box 398 93460 805-688-6487
Scott Cory, prin. Fax 686-5627
Santa Ynez Valley Union HS 1,000/9-12
PO Box 398 93460 805-688-6487
Mark Swanitz, prin. Fax 688-1913

Santee, San Diego, Pop. 51,246
Grossmont UNHSD
Supt. — See La Mesa
Santana HS 1,500/9-12
9915 N Magnolia Ave 92071 619-956-0200
Tim Schwuchow, prin. Fax 449-3119
West Hills HS 2,000/9-12
8756 Mast Blvd 92071 619-956-0400
Robin Ballarin, prin. Fax 258-3750

San Ysidro, See San Diego
San Ysidro ESD 5,100/PK-8
4350 Otay Mesa Rd 92173 619-428-4476
Julio Fonseca Ed.D., supt. Fax 428-1505
www.sysd.k12.ca.us
San Ysidro MS 600/7-8
4345 Otay Mesa Rd 92173 619-428-5551
Roberto Carrillo, prin. Fax 690-2837

Sweetwater UNHSD
Supt. — See Chula Vista
San Ysidro Adult S Adult
4220 Otay Mesa Rd 92173 619-428-7200
Sheryl Sanchez, prin. Fax 428-0295

Saratoga, Santa Clara, Pop. 28,911
Campbell UNHSD
Supt. — See San Jose
Prospect HS 1,300/9-12
18900 Prospect Rd 95070 408-626-3408
Joell Hanson, prin. Fax 973-1759

Los Gatos-Saratoga JUNHSD
Supt. — See Los Gatos
Saratoga HS 1,400/9-12
20300 Herriman Ave 95070 408-867-3411
Paul Robinson, prin. Fax 867-3577

Saratoga UNESD 2,100/K-8
20460 Forrest Hills Dr 95070 408-867-3424
Nancy Johnson, supt. Fax 867-2312
www.saratogausd.org
Redwood MS 900/6-8
13925 Fruitvale Ave 95070 408-867-3042
Barbara Neal, prin. Fax 867-3195

West Valley College Post-Sec.
14000 Fruitvale Ave 95070 408-867-2200

Saugus, See Santa Clarita
William S. Hart UNHSD
Supt. — See Santa Clarita
Saugus HS 2,400/9-12
21900 Centurion Way 91350 661-297-3900
Bill Bolde, prin. Fax 297-7491

Scotts Valley, Santa Cruz, Pop. 11,122
Scotts Valley USD 2,500/K-12
4444 Scotts Valley Dr # 5B 95066 831-438-1820
Tanya Krause, supt. Fax 438-2314
www.scottsvalleyusd.org
Scotts Valley HS 800/9-12
555 Glenwood Dr 95066 831-439-9555
Valerie Bariteau, prin. Fax 439-9501
Scotts Valley MS 600/6-8
8 Bean Creek Rd 95066 831-438-0610
Mary Lonhart, prin. Fax 439-8935

Seaside, Monterey, Pop. 30,879
Monterey Peninsula USD
Supt. — See Monterey
Central Coast HS 100/Alt
200 Coe Ave 93955 831-392-3560
Alan Crawford, prin. Fax 392-3561
Monterey Peninsula Community Day S 50/Alt
200 Coe Ave 93955 831-392-3822
Alan Crawford, admin. Fax 649-6621
Seaside HS 1,100/9-12
2200 Noche Buena St 93955 831-392-3530
Carlos Moran, prin. Fax 899-0212
Seaside MS 800/6-8
999 Coe Ave 93955 831-899-7080
Manuel Nunez, prin. Fax 899-0663
Adult Education Adult
1713 Broadway Ave 93955 831-392-3565
Alan Crawford, admin.

California State University-Monterey Bay Post-Sec.
100 Campus Ctr 93955 831-582-3000
Chartwell S 100/2-12
2511 Numa Watson Rd 93955 831-394-3468
Steve Henderson M.Ed., head sch Fax 394-6809

Sebastopol, Sonoma, Pop. 7,156
Gravenstein UNESD 700/K-8
3840 Twig Ave 95472 707-823-7008
Jennifer Schwinn, supt. Fax 823-2108
www.grav.k12.ca.us/
Hillcrest MS 300/6-8
725 Bloomfield Rd 95472 707-823-7653
Brad Carn, prin. Fax 823-4630

Sebastopol UNESD 800/PK-8
7611 Huntley St 95472 707-829-4570
Linda Irving, supt. Fax 829-7427
www.sebastopolschools.org
Brook Haven MS 200/5-8
7905 Valentine Ave 95472 707-829-4590
Deborah Hanks, prin. Fax 829-6285

West Sonoma County UNHSD 2,100/9-12
462 Johnson St 95472 707-824-6403
Dr. Steven Kellner, supt. Fax 824-6499
wscuhsd.k12.ca.us
Analy HS 1,400/9-12
6950 Analy Ave 95472 707-824-2300
Raul Guerrero, prin. Fax 827-7936
Laguna Continuation HS 100/Alt
445 Taft St 95472 707-824-6485
Kent Cromwell, prin. Fax 829-7910
Other Schools – See Forestville

Selma, Fresno, Pop. 22,943
Selma USD 6,300/PK-12
3036 Thompson Ave 93662 559-898-6500
Dr. Tanya A. Fisher Ed.D., supt. Fax 896-7147
www.selmausd.org
Heartland Alternative HS 100/Alt
2269 Sylvia St 93662 559-898-6670
Drew Sylvia, prin. Fax 896-4635

Lincoln MS 1,000/7-8
1239 Nelson Blvd 93662 559-898-6600
Charles Coleman, prin. Fax 896-0733
Selma HS 1,700/9-12
3125 Wright St 93662 559-898-6550
Mark Babiarz, prin. Fax 896-1110
Selma Adult S Adult
3125 Wright St 93662 559-898-6590
Drew Sylvia, dir. Fax 896-4333

Shafter, Kern, Pop. 16,846
Kern UNHSD
Supt. — See Bakersfield
Central Valley Continuation HS 100/Alt
526 Mannel Ave 93263 661-746-4281
John Brown, admin. Fax 746-0521
Shafter HS 1,400/9-12
526 Mannel Ave 93263 661-746-4961
Russell Shipley, prin. Fax 746-6743

Richland UNESD 3,500/PK-8
331 N Shafter Ave 93263 661-746-8600
Richard Stotler, supt. Fax 746-8614
www.rsdshafter.org
Richland JHS 700/7-8
331 N Shafter Ave 93263 661-746-8630
Kenneth Wright, prin. Fax 746-8614

Shandon, San Luis Obispo, Pop. 1,278
Shandon JUSD 300/K-12
PO Box 79 93461 805-238-0286
Teresa Taylor, supt. Fax 238-0777
www.shandonschools.org
Shandon HS 100/9-12
PO Box 79 93461 805-238-0286
Teresa Taylor, supt. Fax 238-0777

Shasta Lake, Shasta, Pop. 9,765
Gateway USD
Supt. — See Redding
Central Valley HS 800/9-12
4066 La Mesa Ave 96019 530-275-7075
Kyle Turner, prin. Fax 275-7065
Mountain Lakes HS 50/Alt
17752 Shasta Dam Blvd 96019 530-275-7000
Mark Telles, prin. Fax 275-7006

Sherman Oaks, See Los Angeles
Los Angeles USD
Supt. — See Los Angeles
Millikan MS 2,200/6-8
5041 Sunnyslope Ave 91423 818-528-1600
John Plevack, prin. Fax 990-7651
Millikan STEM Magnet S 6-12
5041 Sunnyslope Ave 91423 818-528-1662
Carlos Lauchu, prin. Fax 528-1665

Buckley S 800/K-12
3900 Stansbury Ave 91423 818-783-1610
Dr. James Busby, head sch Fax 461-6714
DeVry University Post-Sec.
15301 Ventura Blvd Ste 100 91403 818-713-8111
Notre Dame HS 1,200/9-12
13645 Riverside Dr 91423 818-933-3600
Stephanie Connelly, prin. Fax 501-0507

Shingle Springs, El Dorado, Pop. 4,277
El Dorado UNHSD
Supt. — See Placerville
Ponderosa HS 1,800/9-12
3661 Ponderosa Rd 95682 530-677-2281
Lisa Garrett, prin. Fax 676-1401

Latrobe SD 100/K-8
7900 S Shingle Rd 95682 530-677-0260
Natalie Miller, supt. Fax 672-0463
www.latrobeschool.com
Miller's Hill S 100/4-8
7900 S Shingle Rd 95682 530-677-0260
Natalie Miller, admin. Fax 672-0463

Shingletown, Shasta, Pop. 2,210
Black Butte UNESD 200/PK-8
7752 Ponderosa Way 96088 530-474-3125
Don Aust, supt. Fax 474-3118
www.blackbutteschool.org
Black Butte JHS 100/6-8
7946 Ponderosa Way 96088 530-474-3441
Don Aust, admin. Fax 474-1361

Shoshone, Inyo, Pop. 30
Death Valley USD 50/K-12
PO Box 217 92384 760-852-4303
James Copeland, supt. Fax 852-4395
www.inyo.k12.ca.us
Death Valley Academy 50/7-12
PO Box 217 92384 760-852-4303
Craig Hill, prin. Fax 852-4395
Shoshone Continuation HS 50/Alt
PO Box 217 92384 760-852-4303
Craig Hill, prin. Fax 852-4395

Sierra Madre, Los Angeles, Pop. 10,555
Pasadena USD
Supt. — See Pasadena
Sierra Madre MS 400/6-8
160 N Canon Ave 91024 626-836-2947
Garret Newson, prin. Fax 836-2964

Alverno Heights Academy 200/9-12
200 N Michillinda Ave 91024 626-355-3463
Julia Fanara, head sch Fax 355-3153

Sierraville, Sierra, Pop. 200
Regional Occupational Center & Program
Supt. — None
Rouse ROP Vo/Tech
PO Box 157 96126 530-994-1044
Stan Hardeman, supt. Fax 994-1045

Signal Hill, Los Angeles, Pop. 10,477
Long Beach USD
Supt. — See Long Beach
Nelson Academy 800/6-8
1951 Cherry Ave, 562-591-6041
Sparkle Peterson, prin. Fax 591-8690

American University of Health Science Post-Sec.
1600 E Hill St Bldg 1, 562-988-2278

Silverado, Orange

St. Michaels Preparatory S 100/9-12
19292 El Toro Rd 92676 949-858-0222
Fr. Victor Szczurek, hdmstr. Fax 858-7365

Simi Valley, Ventura, Pop. 120,233
Simi Valley USD 17,600/K-12
875 Cochran St 93065 805-520-6500
Dr. Jason Peplinski, supt. Fax 520-6504
www.simivalleyusd.org
Apollo HS 200/Alt
3150 School St 93065 805-520-6150
Shanna Sarris, prin. Fax 520-6655
Hillside MS 700/6-8
2222 Fitzgerald Rd 93065 805-520-6810
Timothy Bednar, prin. Fax 520-6156
Monte Vista S 200/Alt
1220 4th St 93065 805-579-6326
Stephen Pietrolungo Ed.D., prin. Fax 579-6329
Royal HS 2,100/9-12
1402 Royal Ave 93065 805-306-4875
Keith Derrick, prin. Fax 520-6644
Santa Susana HS 1,300/9-12
3570 Cochran St 93063 805-520-6800
Jerry Block, prin. Fax 579-6385
Simi Valley HS 2,300/9-12
5400 Cochran St 93063 805-577-1400
Dean May, prin. Fax 520-6633
Sinaloa MS 1,000/6-8
601 Royal Ave 93065 805-520-6830
Diana Janke, prin. Fax 520-6835
Valley View MS 1,400/6-8
3347 Tapo St 93063 805-520-6820
Michael Hall, prin. Fax 520-6157
Simi Institute of Career Education Adult
1880 Blackstock Ave 93065 805-579-6200
Michele Arso, dir. Fax 522-8902

Eternity Bible College Post-Sec.
2136 Winifred St 93063 805-581-1233
Grace Brethren JSHS 400/7-12
1350 Cherry Ave 93065 805-522-4667
John Hynes, prin. Fax 522-5617
Heritage Christian Academy 100/K-12
1559 Rosita Dr 93065 805-428-2511
Simi Valley Adult Education Post-Sec.
1880 Blackstock Ave 93065 805-579-6200

Solana Beach, San Diego, Pop. 12,580
San Dieguito UNHSD
Supt. — See Encinitas
Warren MS 700/7-8
155 Stevens Ave 92075 858-755-1558
Adam Camacho, prin. Fax 755-0891

Fusion Academy 6-12
512 Via De La Valle Ste 201 92075 858-792-2300
Santa Fe Christian S 1,000/PK-12
838 Academy Dr 92075 858-755-8900
Dr. Tom Bennett, head sch Fax 755-2480

Soledad, Monterey, Pop. 25,398
Soledad USD 4,800/PK-12
1261 Metz Rd 93960 831-678-3987
Fax 678-2866
www.soledadusd.org
Main Street MS 700/7-8
441 Main St 93960 831-678-6460
Jessie Swift, prin. Fax 678-0797
Pinnacles HS 100/Alt
690 Main St 93960 831-678-6300
Jeffrey Lopez, prin. Fax 678-0162
Soledad HS 1,300/9-12
425 Gabilan Dr 93960 831-678-6400
Jeffrey James, prin. Fax 678-0449

Somerset, El Dorado
Pioneer UNESD 300/K-8
6862 Mount Aukum Rd 95684 530-620-3556
Annette Lane, supt. Fax 620-4932
www.pioneerusd.org
Mountain Creek MS 100/5-8
6862 Mount Aukum Rd 95684 530-620-4393
John Sanguinetti, prin. Fax 620-6509

Sonoma, Sonoma, Pop. 10,444
Sonoma Valley USD 4,600/K-12
17850 Railroad Ave 95476 707-935-6000
Louann Carlomagno Ph.D., supt. Fax 939-2235
svusdca.org/
Altimira MS 500/6-8
17805 Arnold Dr 95476 707-935-6020
William Deeths, prin. Fax 935-6027
Creekside HS 50/Alt
20000 Broadway 95476 707-933-4046
Sydney Smith, prin. Fax 933-4095
Harrison MS 400/6-8
1150 Broadway 95476 707-935-6080
Mary Ann Spitzer, prin. Fax 935-6083
Sonoma Valley HS 1,300/9-12
20000 Broadway 95476 707-933-4010
Kathleen Hawing, prin. Fax 935-4205

Sonora, Tuolumne, Pop. 4,736
Sonora UNHSD 1,100/9-12
100 School St 95370 209-533-8510
Patrick Chabot, supt. Fax 532-4513
www.sonorahs.k12.ca.us/
Bird HS 100/Alt
251 Barretta St 95370 209-533-2923
Roy Morlan, prin. Fax 533-0980
Cassina Continuation HS 50/Alt
251 Barretta St 95370 209-532-1587
Roy Morlan, prin. Fax 533-0980
Sonora HS 1,000/9-12
430 N Washington St 95370 209-532-5511
Ben Howell, prin. Fax 533-1158

Columbia College Post-Sec.
11600 Columbia College Dr 95370 209-588-5100
Mother Lode Adventist Junior Academy 100/K-10
80 N Forest Rd 95370 209-532-2855
Patrice Osborne, prin. Fax 532-7757

Soquel, Santa Cruz, Pop. 9,255
Santa Cruz CSD 7,000/K-12
405 Old San Jose Rd 95073 831-429-3410
Kris Munro, supt. Fax 429-3439
sccs.net
Soquel HS 1,100/9-12
401 Old San Jose Rd 95073 831-429-3909
Gail Atlansky, prin. Fax 429-3311
Other Schools – See Santa Cruz

South Dos Palos, Merced, Pop. 1,600
Dos Palos Oro Loma JUSD
Supt. — See Dos Palos
Westside HS 100/Alt
22369 6th St 93665 209-392-0280
Frank Lemos, prin. Fax 392-1043

South El Monte, Los Angeles, Pop. 19,998
El Monte UNHSD
Supt. — See El Monte
South El Monte HS 1,500/9-12
1001 Durfee Ave 91733 626-442-0218
Dr. Amy Avina, prin. Fax 442-4794

Valle Lindo ESD 1,200/K-8
1431 Central Ave 91733 626-580-0610
Dr. Mary Labrucherie, supt. Fax 575-1534
www.vallelindo.k12.ca.us
Shively MS 600/5-8
1431 Central Ave 91733 626-580-0610
Lynn Bulgin, prin. Fax 575-1534

South Gate, Los Angeles, Pop. 94,017
Los Angeles USD
Supt. — See Los Angeles
International Studies Learning Center 800/6-12
5225 Tweedy Blvd 90280 323-357-7521
Guillermina Jauregui, prin. Fax 569-7139
Odyssey Continuation HS 100/Alt
8693 Dearborn Ave 90280 323-567-5536
Julieta Badgley, prin. Fax 563-3468
Rodia Continuation HS 100/Alt
2701 Sequoia Dr 90280 323-569-7140
Victorio Gutierrez, prin. Fax 569-7139
Science Tech Engineering Arts & Math HS 9-12
5225 Tweedy Blvd 90280 323-357-7545
Carla Barrera-Ortiz, prin. Fax 357-7590
South East HS 2,300/9-12
2720 Tweedy Blvd 90280 323-568-3400
Jesus Nunez, prin. Fax 566-7918
Southeast MS 1,200/6-8
2560 Tweedy Blvd 90280 323-568-3100
Wanda Sequeira, prin. Fax 564-9398
South Gate HS 3,000/9-12
3351 Firestone Blvd 90280 323-568-5600
Gerardo Llamas, prin. Fax 249-0237
South Gate MS 2,300/6-8
4100 Firestone Blvd 90280 323-568-4000
Janet Mack, prin. Fax 564-7434
Visual and Performing Arts HS 300/9-12
5225 Tweedy Blvd 90280 323-357-7500
Edward Trims, prin. Fax 564-8371

Advanced College Post-Sec.
13180 Paramount Blvd 90280 562-408-6969
Career College of America Post-Sec.
5612 Imperial Hwy 90280 562-861-8702
GDS Institute Post-Sec.
7916 Long Beach Blvd 90280 323-585-5577

South Lake Tahoe, El Dorado, Pop. 20,898
Lake Tahoe USD 3,900/PK-12
1021 Al Tahoe Blvd 96150 530-541-2850
Dr. James Tarwater, supt. Fax 541-5930
www.ltusd.org/
Mt. Tallac Continuation HS 100/Alt
1735 Lake Tahoe Blvd 96150 530-543-2245
Chad Houck, prin. Fax 542-1036
South Tahoe HS 1,000/9-12
1735 Lake Tahoe Blvd 96150 530-541-4111
Chad Houck, prin. Fax 541-4157
South Tahoe MS 800/6-8
2940 Lake Tahoe Blvd 96150 530-541-6404
John Simons, prin. Fax 541-4624
Transition Learning Center 50/Alt
1735 Lake Tahoe Blvd 96150 530-543-2264
Chad Houck, prin. Fax 542-1036

Lake Tahoe Community College Post-Sec.
1 College Dr 96150 530-541-4660

South Pasadena, Los Angeles, Pop. 24,612
South Pasadena USD 4,700/PK-12
1020 El Centro St 91030 626-441-5810
Dr. Geoff Yantz, supt. Fax 441-5815
www.spusd.net
South Pasadena HS 1,500/9-12
1401 Fremont Ave 91030 626-441-5820
Janet Anderson, prin. Fax 441-5825
South Pasadena MS 1,100/6-8
1500 Fair Oaks Ave 91030 626-441-5830
Dave Kubela, prin. Fax 441-5835

South San Francisco, San Mateo, Pop. 60,202
South San Francisco USD 9,200/K-12
398 B St 94080 650-877-8700
Shawnterra Moore, supt. Fax 583-4717
www.ssfusd.org
Alta Loma MS 800/6-8
116 Romney Ave 94080 650-877-8797
Lou Delorio, prin. Fax 877-8824
Baden HS 100/Alt
825 Southwood Dr 94080 650-877-8769
Michael Coyne, prin. Fax 737-9072
El Camino HS 1,500/9-12
1320 Mission Rd 94080 650-877-8806
David Lunt, prin. Fax 589-2343
Parkway Heights MS 600/6-8
650 Sunset Ave 94080 650-877-8788
Marco Lopez, prin. Fax 225-9427
South San Francisco HS 1,500/9-12
400 B St 94080 650-877-8754
Anthony Limoges, prin. Fax 871-7943
Westborough MS 700/6-8
2570 Westborough Blvd 94080 650-877-8848
April Holland, prin. Fax 871-5356
South San Francisco Adult Adult
825 Southwood Dr 94080 650-877-8844
Michael Coyne, prin. Fax 877-8786

NCP College of Nursing Post-Sec.
257 Longford Dr Ste 5 94080 650-871-0701

Spreckels, Monterey, Pop. 663
Spreckels UNESD 1,000/K-8
PO Box 7362 93962 831-455-2550
Eric Tarallo Ed.D., supt. Fax 455-1871
Other Schools – See Salinas

Spring Valley, San Diego, Pop. 26,795
Grossmont UNHSD
Supt. — See La Mesa
Monte Vista HS 1,700/9-12
3230 Sweetwater Springs Blv 91977 619-660-3000
Fax 670-9749
Mt. Miguel HS 1,500/9-12
8585 Blossom Ln 91977 619-667-6400
Kimberlee Hedrick Ed.D., prin. Fax 697-0794

La Mesa-Spring Valley SD
Supt. — See La Mesa
Quest Academy 6-8
8805 Tyler St 91977 619-668-5890
Kimberly Libenguth, prin. Fax 668-8335
Spring Valley Academy 500/4-8
3900 Conrad Dr 91977 619-668-5750
Margaret Jacobsen, prin. Fax 668-8302
STEAM Academy @ La Presa 500/4-8
1001 Leland St 91977 619-668-5720
Mike Allmann, prin. Fax 668-8305

Stanford, Santa Clara, Pop. 12,819

Stanford University Post-Sec.
450 Serra Mall 94305 650-723-2300

Stevenson Ranch, Los Angeles, Pop. 16,902
William S. Hart UNHSD
Supt. — See Santa Clarita
Rancho Pico JHS 1,000/7-8
26250 Valencia Blvd 91381 661-284-3260
Erum Jones, prin. Fax 255-7523
West Ranch HS 2,500/9-12
26255 Valencia Blvd 91381 661-222-1220
Mark Crawford, prin. Fax 290-2676

Stockton, San Joaquin, Pop. 279,493
Lincoln USD 9,200/PK-12
2010 W Swain Rd 95207 209-953-8700
Thomas Uslan, supt. Fax 474-7817
www.lusd.net
Lincoln HS 2,800/9-12
6844 Alexandria Pl 95207 209-953-8920
Terry Asplund, prin. Fax 952-4646
McCandless STEM Charter S Alt
2020 W Swain Rd 95207 209-953-8740
Phyllis Kahl, prin.
Sierra MS 600/7-8
6768 Alexandria Pl 95207 209-953-8749
Scott Tatum, prin. Fax 953-8747
Village Oaks HS 200/Alt
1900 W Swain Rd 95207 209-953-8687
Josef Schallberger, prin. Fax 953-8741

Linden USD
Supt. — See Linden
Pride Continuation HS 50/Alt
100 N Jack Tone Rd 95215 209-887-3894
Jane Steinkamp, prin.
Waterloo MS 400/5-8
7007 Pezzi Rd 95215 209-931-0818
Shannon Roberson, prin. Fax 931-2915

Lodi USD
Supt. — See Lodi
Bear Creek HS 1,900/9-12
10555 Thornton Rd 95209 209-953-8234
Hillary Harrell, prin. Fax 953-8247
Delta Sierra MS 400/7-8
2255 Wagner Heights Rd 95209 209-953-8510
Brad Watson, prin. Fax 953-8139
Elkhorn MS 300/4-8
10505 Davis Rd 95209 209-953-8312
Pat White, prin. Fax 953-8319

McAuliffe MS 1,000/7-8
3880 Iron Canyon Cir 95209 209-953-9431
Pierre Kirby, prin. Fax 953-9430
McNair HS 1,800/9-12
9550 Ronald E McNair Way 95210 209-953-9245
Jim Davis, prin. Fax 953-9261
Middle College HS 200/9-12
5151 Pacific Ave 95207 209-954-5790
Sherry Balian, prin. Fax 954-5875
Morada MS 700/7-8
5001 Eastview Dr 95212 209-953-8490
Janet Godina Perez, prin. Fax 953-8502
Plaza Robles Continuation HS 200/Alt
9434 Thornton Rd 95209 209-953-8068
Mark Dawson, prin. Fax 953-8064

Manteca USD
Supt. — See Manteca
Great Valley Annex S 500/7-8
4550 Star Way 95206 209-938-6310
Patricia Boutte, prin. Fax 938-6383
New Vision HS 200/Alt
4726 McCuen Ave 95206 209-938-6225
Sonya Arellano, prin. Fax 938-6394
Weston Ranch HS 1,200/9-12
4606 McCuen Ave 95206 209-938-6245
Francine Baird, prin. Fax 938-6397

Regional Occupational Center & Program
Supt. — None
San Joaquin County ROC/P Vo/Tech
PO Box 213030 95213 209-468-5930
Christopher Kleinert, dir.

Stockton USD 36,300/PK-12
701 N Madison St 95202 209-933-7000
Eliseo Davalos Ph.D., supt. Fax 933-7071
www.stocktonusd.net
Chavez HS 2,100/9-12
2929 Windflower Ln 95212 209-933-7480
William Nelson, prin. Fax 475-9097
Edison HS 2,000/9-12
1425 S Center St 95206 209-933-7425
Brain Biedermann, prin. Fax 942-2106
Franklin HS 1,900/9-12
300 N Gertrude Ave 95215 209-933-7435
Juan Salas, prin. Fax 464-4708
Frederick Continuation S 300/Alt
1141 E Weber Ave 95205 209-933-7340
Chris Anderson, prin. Fax 933-7341
Merlo Institute of Environmental Tech 200/9-12
1670 E 6th St 95206 209-933-7190
Bukky Oyebade, prin. Fax 469-3740
Stagg HS 1,500/9-12
1621 Brookside Rd 95207 209-933-7445
Andre Phillips, prin. Fax 954-9037
Weber Institute Vo/Tech
302 W Weber Ave 95203 209-933-7330
Katrina Johnson Leon, dir. Fax 464-4917
School for Adults Adult
1525 Pacific Ave 95204 209-933-7455
Carol Hirota, prin. Fax 464-4917

Brookside Christian S 200/K-12
915 Rosemarie Ln 95207 209-954-7650
Jessica Carter, prin. Fax 954-7670
Carrington College California Post-Sec.
1313 W Robinhood Dr Ste B 95207 209-956-1240
Heald College Post-Sec.
1605 E March Ln 95210 209-473-5200
Humphreys College Post-Sec.
6650 Inglewood Ave 95207 209-478-0800
MTI Business College of Stockton Post-Sec.
6006 N El Dorado St 95207 209-957-3030
St. Mary HS 1,000/9-12
PO Box 7247 95267 209-957-3340
Kathy Smith, prin. Fax 957-0861
San Joaquin Delta College Post-Sec.
5151 Pacific Ave 95207 209-954-5151
San Joaquin General Hospital Post-Sec.
PO Box 1020 95201 209-468-6600
Stockton Christian S 200/K-12
9021 West Ln 95210 209-957-3043
Tim Miller, prin. Fax 957-4120
Teachers College of San Joaquin Post-Sec.
2857 Transworld Dr 95206 209-468-9155
University of the Pacific Post-Sec.
3601 Pacific Ave 95211 209-946-2285
Western Pacific Truck School Post-Sec.
1002 N Broadway Ave 95205 209-465-1191

Strathmore, Tulare, Pop. 2,793
Porterville USD
Supt. — See Porterville
Strathmore HS 300/9-12
22568 Avenue 196 93267 559-568-1731
John Buckley, prin. Fax 568-0091

Strathmore UNESD 900/K-8
PO Box 247 93267 559-568-1283
Shelly Long Ed.D., supt. Fax 568-1262
www.suesd.k12.ca.us
Strathmore MS 300/5-8
PO Box 247 93267 559-568-9293
Joanie Stone, prin. Fax 568-2944

Studio City, See Los Angeles

Bridges Academy 100/4-12
3921 Laurel Canyon Blvd 91604 818-506-1091
Carl Sabatino M.A., head sch Fax 506-8094
Emerson Academy 5-12
12749 Ventura Blvd 91604 818-761-4898
Harvard-Westlake HS 900/10-12
3700 Coldwater Canyon Ave 91604 818-980-6692
Jeanne Huybrechts, head sch Fax 487-6631

Sugarloaf, San Bernardino
Bear Valley USD
Supt. — See Big Bear Lake
Big Bear HS 800/9-12
351 Maple Ln 92386 909-585-6892
Tina Fulmer, prin. Fax 585-6809
Chautauqua HS 50/Alt
525 Maple Ln 92386 909-585-2521
Tina Fulmer, prin. Fax 585-3311

Suisun City, Solano, Pop. 25,805
Fairfield-Suisun USD
Supt. — See Fairfield
Crystal MS 900/6-8
400 Whispering Bay Ln 94585 707-435-5800
Monifa Williams, prin. Fax 435-5806

Sunland, See Los Angeles
Los Angeles USD
Supt. — See Los Angeles
Mt. Gleason MS 1,000/6-8
10965 Mount Gleason Ave 91040 818-951-2580
Deborah Acosta, prin. Fax 352-6209

Sunnyvale, Santa Clara, Pop. 134,677
Cupertino UNSD 19,200/PK-8
1309 S Mary Ave 94087 408-252-3000
Dr. Wendy Gudalewicz, supt. Fax 343-2801
www.edline.net/pages/Cupertino_Union_SD
Cupertino MS 1,400/6-8
1650 S Bernardo Ave 94087 408-245-0303
Mara Milazzo, prin. Fax 732-4152
Other Schools – See Cupertino, San Jose

Fremont UNHSD 10,600/9-12
589 W Fremont Ave 94087 408-522-2200
Polly Bove, supt. Fax 245-5325
www.fuhsd.org
Fremont HS 2,000/9-12
1279 Sunnyvale Saratoga Rd 94087 408-522-2400
Bryan Emmert, prin. Fax 522-2401
Adult & Community Education Adult
591 W Fremont Ave 94087 408-522-2700
Peggy Raun-Linde, prin. Fax 522-2799
Other Schools – See Cupertino, San Jose

Santa Clara USD
Supt. — See Santa Clara
Peterson MS 900/6-8
1380 Rosalia Ave 94087 408-423-2800
Susan Harris, prin. Fax 423-2880

Sunnyvale ESD 6,800/K-8
PO Box 3217 94088 408-522-8200
Benjamin Picard Ed.D., supt. Fax 522-8221
www.sesd.org
Columbia MS 700/6-8
739 Morse Ave 94085 408-522-8247
Mary Beth Allmann, prin. Fax 522-8254
Sunnyvale MS 1,200/6-8
1080 Mango Ave 94087 408-522-8288
Nabil Shahin, prin. Fax 522-8296

Art Institute of California - Sunnyvale Post-Sec.
1120 Kifer Rd 94086 408-962-6400
Cogswell Polytechnical College Post-Sec.
1175 Bordeaux Dr 94089 408-541-0100
King's Academy 900/6-12
562 N Britton Ave 94085 408-481-9900
Scott Meadows, prin. Fax 481-9932
Stratford S - Raynor MS 6-8
1500 Partridge Ave 94087 408-247-4400
Becky Turner, prin.
University of East West Medicine Post-Sec.
595 Lawrence Expy 94085 408-733-1878

Sun Valley, See Los Angeles
Los Angeles USD
Supt. — See Los Angeles
Byrd MS 1,700/6-8
8501 Arleta Ave 91352 818-394-4300
Deborah Wiltz, prin. Fax 768-1837
Francis Polytechnic HS 2,900/9-12
12431 Roscoe Blvd 91352 818-394-3600
Ari Bennett, prin. Fax 771-0452
Lewis Continuation S 100/Alt
12508 Wicks St 91352 818-394-3980
Robert Eiseman, prin. Fax 394-3981
Sun Valley HS 600/9-12
9171 Telfair Ave 91352 818-394-4600
Michael Gitomer, prin. Fax 767-8125
Sun Valley MS 1,000/6-8
7330 Bakman Ave 91352 818-255-5100
Roberto Lee, prin. Fax 503-9846

Village Christian HS 400/9-12
8930 Village Ave 91352 818-767-8382
Bruce Osgood, prin.
Village Christian MS 200/6-8
8930 Village Ave 91352 818-767-8382
Bruce Osgood, prin.

Susanville, Lassen, Pop. 17,110
Lassen UNHSD 900/7-12
1000 Main St 96130 530-257-5134
Willard McCabe, supt. Fax 251-0475
www.lassenhigh.org
Lassen Community Day S 50/Alt
1110 Main St 96130 530-257-2141
Robbin Pedrett, prin. Fax 257-5852
Lassen HS 900/9-12
1110 Main St 96130 530-257-2141
Robbin Pedrett, prin. Fax 251-1173
Diploma Gold Adult S Adult
1000 Main St 96130 530-257-2703
Robbin Pedrett, prin.

Regional Occupational Center & Program
Supt. — None
Lassen County ROP Vo/Tech
472-013 Johnstonville Rd 96130 530-252-1673
Rich Duvarney, dir.

Susanville ESD 1,000/K-8
109 S Gilman St 96130 530-257-8200
Jason Waddell, supt. Fax 257-8246
www.susanvillesd.org
Diamond View MS 300/6-8
850 Richmond Rd 96130 530-257-5144
Jamie Huber, prin. Fax 257-7232

Lassen Community College Post-Sec.
PO Box 3000 96130 530-257-6181

Sutter, Sutter, Pop. 2,803
Sutter UNHSD 700/9-12
PO Box 498 95982 530-822-5161
Ryan Robison, supt. Fax 822-5168
www.sutterhigh.k12.ca.us/
Butte View HS 50/Alt
PO Box 498 95982 530-822-5161
Jedsen Nunes, prin. Fax 822-5168
Sutter HS 700/9-12
PO Box 498 95982 530-822-5161
Ryan Robison, prin. Fax 822-5168

Sutter Creek, Amador, Pop. 2,442
Amador County Office of Education
Supt. — See Jackson
County Community S 300/Alt
525 Independence Dr 95685 209-257-5100
Frank Wagner, prin. Fax 245-3864

Amador County USD
Supt. — See Jackson
Amador HS 600/9-12
330 Spanish St 95685 209-257-7300
Jared Critchfield, prin. Fax 267-5942
Independence HS 100/Alt
525 Independence Dr 95685 209-257-5100
Butch Wagner, prin. Fax 267-5497
North Star S 100/Alt
525 Independence Dr 95685 209-257-5150
Dr. Thomas Littlefair, prin. Fax 267-5847

Sylmar, See Los Angeles
Los Angeles USD
Supt. — See Los Angeles
Evergreen Continuation S 100/Alt
13101 Dronfield Ave 91342 818-367-5989
Robinson Acosta, prin. Fax 367-2796
Olive Vista MS 1,200/6-8
14600 Tyler St 91342 818-833-3900
Rodney Wright, prin. Fax 367-8273
Sylmar Biotech Health Academy 9-12
13050 Borden Ave 91342 818-833-3723
Maria Herrera, prin. Fax 833-5121

Delphi Academy of Los Angeles 200/PK-12
11341 Brainard Ave 91342 818-583-1070
Karen Dale, head sch Fax 583-1082
Los Angeles Mission College Post-Sec.
13356 Eldridge Ave 91342 818-364-7600
Olive View/UCLA Medical Centers Post-Sec.
14445 Olive View Dr 91342 818-364-4224

Taft, Kern, Pop. 9,099
Taft CSD 2,000/K-8
820 6th St 93268 661-763-1521
Julie Graves, supt. Fax 763-1495
www.taftcityschools.org
Lincoln JHS 600/6-8
810 6th St 93268 661-765-2127
Brandi Swearengin, prin. Fax 763-3970

Taft UNHSD 1,000/9-12
701 Wildcat Way 93268 661-763-2300
Blanca Cavazos, supt. Fax 763-1445
www.taft.k12.ca.us/
Buena Vista Continuation HS 100/Alt
701 Wildcat Way 93268 661-763-2383
Chelle Koerner, prin. Fax 763-2393
Career Technical Education Center Vo/Tech
515 9th St 93268 661-763-2390
Sandra Mittelsteadt, dir. Fax 763-2375
Taft Union HS 1,000/9-12
701 Wildcat Way 93268 661-763-2300
Mary Alice Finn, prin. Fax 763-4736

Taft College Post-Sec.
29 Emmons Park Dr 93268 661-763-7700

Tahoe City, Placer, Pop. 1,643
Tahoe Truckee USD
Supt. — See Truckee
Cold Stream Alternative S 50/Alt
740 Timberland Ln 96145 530-582-2640
Greg Wohlman, prin. Fax 581-3457
North Tahoe HS 300/9-12
PO Box 5099 96145 530-581-7000
Joanna Mitchell, prin. Fax 581-3252
North Tahoe S 400/5-8
PO Box 794 96145 530-581-7050
Chad Lindeen, prin. Fax 581-1237

Tarzana, See Los Angeles
Los Angeles USD
Supt. — See Los Angeles
Portola MS 1,800/6-8
18720 Linnet St 91356 818-654-3300
Stephanie McClay, prin. Fax 996-0292

Columbia College Hollywood Post-Sec.
18618 Oxnard St 91356 800-785-0585
Hypnosis Motivation Institute Post-Sec.
18607 Ventura Blvd Ste 310 91356 800-479-9464

Tehachapi, Kern, Pop. 14,166
Tehachapi USD 4,200/K-12
300 S Robinson St 93561 661-822-2100
Susan Andreas-Bervel, supt. Fax 822-2159
www.teh.k12.ca.us
Jacobsen MS 900/6-8
711 Anita Dr 93561 661-822-2150
Paul Kaminski, prin. Fax 822-2156
Monroe HS 100/Alt
126 S Snyder Ave 93561 661-822-2124
Steve Bsharah, prin. Fax 822-2188
Tehachapi HS 1,200/9-12
801 S Dennison Rd 93561 661-822-2130
Scott Heitman, prin. Fax 822-1854
Tehachapi Adult S Adult
126 S Snyder Ave 93561 661-822-2112
Steve Bsharah, prin. Fax 822-2188

Heritage Oak S 100/K-12
20915 Schout Rd 93561 661-823-0885
Amy Walker, head sch Fax 823-0863

Temecula, Riverside, Pop. 95,946
Temecula Valley USD 29,900/K-12
31350 Rancho Vista Rd 92592 951-676-2661
Timothy Ritter, supt. Fax 695-7121
www.tvusd.k12.ca.us
Chaparral HS 3,000/9-12
27215 Nicolas Rd 92591 951-695-4200
Nicole Dayus, prin. Fax 695-4219
Day MS 1,000/6-8
40775 Camino Campos Verde 92591 951-699-8138
Tina Miller, prin. Fax 699-4198
Gardner MS 1,100/6-8
45125 Via Del Coronado 92592 951-699-0080
Michael McTasney, prin. Fax 699-0081
Great Oak HS 3,700/9-12
32555 Deer Hollow Way 92592 951-294-6450
Marc Horton, prin. Fax 294-6477
Margarita MS 900/6-8
30600 Margarita Rd 92591 951-695-7370
Duane Legg, prin. Fax 695-7378
Nelson S 200/Alt
32225 Pio Pico Rd 92592 951-695-7360
Fax 294-6303
Rancho Vista HS 200/Alt
32225 Pio Pico Rd 92592 951-695-7320
Fax 294-6304
Temecula MS 1,000/6-8
42075 Meadows Pkwy 92592 951-302-5151
Rob Sousa, prin. Fax 302-5160
Temecula Valley HS 2,700/9-12
31555 Rancho Vista Rd 92592 951-695-7300
Allen Williams, prin. Fax 695-7311
Vail Ranch MS 1,300/6-8
33340 Camino Piedra Rojo 92592 951-302-5188
Kevin Groepper, prin. Fax 302-5195
Temecula Valley Adult S Adult
43000 Margarita Rd 92592 951-294-6512
Fax 294-6521
Other Schools – See Murrieta

Health Staff Training Institute Post-Sec.
28671 Calle Cortez Ste F 92590 951-694-4784
Linfield Christian S 700/PK-12
31950 Pauba Rd 92592 951-676-8111
Drake Charles, head sch Fax 695-1291
Professional Golfers Career College Post-Sec.
26109 Ynez Rd 92591 800-877-4380
Rancho Christian S 500/PK-12
31300 Rancho Community Way 92592
951-303-1408
Jim Kunau, dir. Fax 302-1580
Royale College of Beauty Post-Sec.
27485 Commerce Center Dr 92590 951-676-0833

Temple City, Los Angeles, Pop. 34,921
Temple City USD 5,900/K-12
9700 Las Tunas Dr 91780 626-548-5000
Kathryn Perini, supt. Fax 548-5022
www.tcusd.net
Oak Avenue IS 1,000/7-8
6623 Oak Ave 91780 626-548-5060
Lawton Gray, prin. Fax 548-5170
Sears Learning Center 50/Alt
9229 Pentland St 91780 626-548-5113
Chris Sewell, prin. Fax 548-5118
Temple City HS 2,100/9-12
9501 Lemon Ave 91780 626-548-5040
Mary Jo Fosselman-King, prin. Fax 548-5045
Temple City Adult Education Adult
9229 Pentland St 91780 626-548-5050
Chris Sewell, prin. Fax 548-5118

United Beauty College Post-Sec.
10229 Lower Azusa Rd 91780 626-443-0900

Templeton, San Luis Obispo, Pop. 7,486
Templeton USD 2,400/PK-12
960 Old County Rd 93465 805-434-5800
Joe Koski, supt. Fax 434-5879
tusd.ca.schoolloop.com/
Eagle Canyon HS 50/9-12
950 Old County Rd 93465 805-434-5833
Kari Fisher Gibson, prin. Fax 434-3879
Templeton HS 700/9-12
1200 S Main St 93465 805-434-5888
Erik Lewis, prin. Fax 434-0743
Templeton Independent Study HS 100/Alt
960 Old County Rd 93465 805-434-5846
Kari Fisher Gibson, prin. Fax 434-5848
Templeton MS 500/6-8
925 Old County Rd 93465 805-434-5813
Kristina Benson, prin. Fax 434-5812

Terra Bella, Tulare, Pop. 3,287
Terra Bella UNESD 900/PK-8
9121 Road 240 93270 559-535-4451
Guadalupe Roman, supt. Fax 535-0314
www.tbuesd.org
Smith MS 300/6-8
23825 Avenue 92 93270 559-535-4451
Guadalupe Roman, prin. Fax 535-0829

Thermal, Riverside, Pop. 2,856
Coachella Valley USD 18,700/K-12
PO Box 847 92274 760-399-5137
Darryl Adams, supt. Fax 399-1052
www.cvusd.us
Coachella Valley HS 2,700/9-12
83800 Airport Blvd 92274 760-399-5183
Victor Uribe, prin. Fax 399-0089
Desert Mirage HS 2,000/9-12
86150 Avenue 66 92274 760-397-2255
Maria McLeod, prin. Fax 397-8760
La Familia Continuation HS 100/Alt
56-615 Olive St 92274 760-399-5929
Arthur Kimball, prin. Fax 399-5169
Toro Canyon MS 1,100/7-8
86150 Avenue 66 92274 760-397-2244
Charles Housewright, prin. Fax 397-8760
Other Schools – See Coachella, Salton City

Thousand Oaks, Ventura, Pop. 122,978
Conejo Valley USD 20,200/PK-12
1400 E Janss Rd 91362 805-497-9511
Ann Bonitatibus Ed.D., supt. Fax 371-9170
www.conejousd.org
Century Academy 100/Alt
1025 Old Farm Rd 91360 805-496-0286
Martin Manzer, prin. Fax 496-5169
Colina MS 1,100/6-8
1500 E Hillcrest Dr 91362 805-495-7429
Shane Frank, prin. Fax 374-1163
Los Cerritos MS 900/6-8
2100 E Ave De Las Flores 91362 805-492-3538
Jason Klinger, prin. Fax 493-8854
Redwood MS 1,000/6-8
233 W Gainsborough Rd 91360 805-497-7264
Shauna Ashmore, prin. Fax 497-3734
Thousand Oaks HS 2,300/9-12
2323 N Moorpark Rd 91360 805-495-7491
Lou Lichtl, prin. Fax 374-1165
Conejo Valley Adult Education Adult
1025 Old Farm Rd 91360 805-497-2761
Michael Sanders, prin. Fax 374-1167
Other Schools – See Newbury Park, Westlake Village

California Lutheran University Post-Sec.
60 W Olsen Rd 91360 805-492-2411
Hillcrest Christian S 300/PK-12
384 Erbes Rd 91362 805-497-7501
Kathy Horan J.D., prin. Fax 494-9355
La Reina HS 600/6-12
106 W Janss Rd 91360 805-495-6494
Dr. Michael Bates, head sch Fax 494-4966
Trinity Pacific Christian S 400/K-12
3389 Camino Calandria 91360 805-492-0863

Tiburon, Marin, Pop. 8,606
Reed UNESD 1,600/K-8
277 Karen Way Ste A 94920 415-381-1112
Nancy Lynch Ed.D., supt. Fax 384-0890
www.reedschools.org
Del Mar MS 500/6-8
105 Avenida Miraflores 94920 415-435-1468
Dr. Alan Vann Gardner, prin. Fax 435-6190

Tollhouse, Fresno
Sierra USD
Supt. — See Prather
Oak Meadow Community Day S 50/Alt
33411 Lodge Rd 93667 559-855-4347
Ara Keledjian, prin. Fax 855-4348
Sandy Bluffs Alternative Education Ctr. 50/Alt
33280 Lodge Rd 93667 559-855-3020
Ara Keledjian, prin. Fax 855-3081
Sierra HS 500/9-12
33326 Lodge Rd 93667 559-855-8311
Sean Osterberg, prin. Fax 855-2162
Sierra JHS 200/7-8
33326 Lodge Rd 93667 559-855-8311
Sean Osterberg, prin. Fax 855-2162

Tomales, Marin, Pop. 200
Shoreline USD 600/K-12
PO Box 198 94971 707-878-2266
Bob Raines, supt. Fax 878-2554
www.shorelineunified.org
Tomales HS 200/9-12
PO Box 25 94971 707-878-2286
Adam Jennings, prin. Fax 878-2787

Torrance, Los Angeles, Pop. 138,782
Regional Occupational Center & Program
Supt. — None
Southern California ROC Vo/Tech
2300 Crenshaw Blvd 90501 310-224-4220
Laurie St. Gean, supt. Fax 320-1029

Torrance USD 24,100/PK-12
2335 Plaza Del Amo 90501 310-972-6500
Dr. George Mannon Ed.D., supt. Fax 972-6012
www.tusd.org
Calle Mayor MS 800/6-8
4800 Calle Mayor 90505 310-533-4548
David Mosley, prin. Fax 972-6389
Casimir MS 700/6-8
17220 Casimir Ave 90504 310-533-4498
Susan Holmes, prin. Fax 972-6391
Drevno Community Day S 50/Alt
2291 Washington Ave 90501 310-972-6962
Jamie Jimenez, prin. Fax 972-6964
Hull MS 700/6-8
2080 W 231st St 90501 310-533-4516
Patty Girgis, prin. Fax 972-6397
Jefferson MS 600/6-8
21717 Talisman St 90503 310-533-4794
Kara Heinrich-Daugherty, prin. Fax 972-6398
Lynn MS 700/6-8
5038 Halison St 90503 310-533-4495
Leroy Jackson, prin. Fax 972-6401
Madrona MS 700/6-8
21364 Madrona Ave 90503 310-533-4562
Chris Lipsey, prin. Fax 972-6402
Magruder MS 600/6-8
4100 W 185th St 90504 310-533-4527
Chris Sheck, prin. Fax 972-6403
North HS 2,000/9-12
3620 W 182nd St 90504 310-533-4412
Dr. Ronald Richardson, prin. Fax 972-6404
Richardson MS 700/6-8
23751 Nancylee Ln 90505 310-533-4790
Ian Drummond, prin. Fax 972-6405
Shery Continuation HS 100/Alt
2600 Vine Ave 90501 310-533-4440
Jamie Jimenez, prin. Fax 972-6408
South HS 2,100/9-12
4801 Pacific Coast Hwy 90505 310-533-4352
Dr. Scott McDowell, prin. Fax 972-6454
Torrance HS 2,100/9-12
2200 W Carson St 90501 310-533-4396
Karim Girgis, prin. Fax 972-6455
West HS 2,200/9-12
20401 Victor St 90503 310-533-4299
Pamela Metz, prin. Fax 972-6483
Griffith Adult Education Center Adult
2291 Washington Ave 90501 310-533-4454
James Jones, prin. Fax 972-6394
Hamilton Adult Education Center Adult
2606 W 182nd St 90504 310-533-4459
Dr. Wayne Diulio, dir. Fax 972-6395
Levy Adult Education Center Adult
3420 W 229th Pl 90505 310-533-4689
James Jones, prin. Fax 972-6399

Ambassador HS 100/9-12
540 Maple Ave 90503 310-356-0950
Dr. Michael Barker Ed.D., head sch Fax 618-8985
Bishop Montgomery HS 1,000/9-12
5430 Torrance Blvd 90503 310-540-2021
Rosemary Libbon, prin. Fax 792-1273
El Camino College Post-Sec.
16007 Crenshaw Blvd 90506 310-532-3670
Everest College Post-Sec.
1231 Cabrillo Ave Ste 201 90501 310-320-3200
Los Angeles Co. Harbor UCLA Medical Ctr. Post-Sec.
1000 W Carson St 90502 310-533-2101
South Bay Junior Academy 200/PK-10
4400 Del Amo Blvd 90503 310-370-6215
Westwood College - South Bay Campus Post-Sec.
19700 S Vermont Ave Ste 100 90502 310-965-0888

Tracy, San Joaquin, Pop. 78,298
Jefferson ESD 2,400/K-8
1219 Whispering Wind Dr 95377 209-836-3388
James W. Bridges Ed.D., supt. Fax 836-2930
www.jeffersonschooldistrict.com
Jefferson S 400/5-8
7500 W Linne Rd 95304 209-835-3053
Alyssa Wooten, prin. Fax 835-4419

Tracy JUSD 17,300/K-12
1875 W Lowell Ave 95376 209-830-3200
Brian Stephens, supt. Fax 830-3204
www.tracy.k12.ca.us
Duncan-Russell Continuation S 50/Alt
164 W Grant Line Rd 95376 209-830-3357
Dave Pickering, prin. Fax 830-3358
Kimball HS 2,200/9-12
3200 Jaguar Run 95377 209-832-6600
Rob Pecot, prin. Fax 832-6601
Monte Vista MS 900/6-8
751 W Lowell Ave 95376 209-830-3340
Barbara Silver, prin. Fax 830-3341
Stein Continuation HS 100/Alt
650 W 10th St 95376 209-830-3395
Cynthia Johannes, prin. Fax 830-3396
Tracy HS 2,000/9-12
315 E 11th St 95376 209-830-3360
Jason Noll, prin. Fax 830-3361
West HS 2,000/9-12
1775 W Lowell Ave 95376 209-830-3370
Troy Brown, prin. Fax 830-3371
Williams MS 1,100/6-8
1600 Tennis Ln 95376 209-830-3345
Barbara Montgomery, prin. Fax 830-3346
Willow Community Day S 50/Alt
164 W Grant Line Rd 95376 209-830-3357
Dave Pickering, admin. Fax 830-3358
Tracy Adult S Adult
1895 W Lowell Ave 95376 209-830-3384
Dave Pickering, prin. Fax 830-3385

Notre Dame de Namur University Tracy Post-Sec.
50 E 6th St 95376 209-833-5020

Tranquillity, Fresno, Pop. 794
Golden Plains USD
Supt. — See San Joaquin
Tranquillity HS 500/9-12
PO Box 457 93668 559-698-7205
James Reed, prin. Fax 698-7632

Trona, San Bernardino, Pop. 18
Trona JUSD 200/K-12
83600 Trona Rd 93562 760-372-2861
Keith Tomes, supt. Fax 372-4534
www.trona.k12.ca.us

Trona HS 100/7-12
83600 Trona Rd 93562 760-372-2824
Joseph Wolfe, prin. Fax 372-4504

Truckee, Nevada, Pop. 15,914
Tahoe Truckee USD 3,900/K-12
11603 Donner Pass Rd 96161 530-582-2500
Robert Leri Ed.D., supt. Fax 582-7606
www.ttusd.org
Alder Creek MS 500/6-8
10931 Alder Dr 96161 530-582-2750
Hein Larson, prin. Fax 582-7640
Sierra HS 50/Alt
11661 Donner Pass Rd 96161 530-582-2640
Greg Wohlman, prin. Fax 582-7687
Tahoe Truckee HS 600/9-12
11725 Donner Pass Rd 96161 530-582-2600
John Carlson, prin. Fax 582-7636
Other Schools – See Tahoe City

Tujunga, See Los Angeles
Los Angeles USD
Supt. — See Los Angeles
Mt. Lukens Continuation HS 100/Alt
7705 Summitrose St 91042 818-352-4039
Douglas Franklin, prin. Fax 352-2499
Verdugo Hills HS 1,600/9-12
10625 Plainview Ave 91042 818-951-5400
Arturo Barcenas, prin. Fax 352-3577

Tulare, Tulare, Pop. 58,086
Tulare CSD 9,500/K-8
600 N Cherry St 93274 559-685-7200
Clare Gist Ed.D., supt. Fax 685-7287
www.tcsdk8.org/
Cherry Avenue MS 700/6-8
540 N Cherry St 93274 559-685-7320
Greg Anderson, prin. Fax 685-5621
Live Oak MS 600/7-8
980 N Laspina St 93274 559-685-7310
Michelle McPhetridge, prin. Fax 685-7313
Los Tules MS 600/6-8
801 W Gail Ave 93274 559-687-3156
Ira Porchia, prin. Fax 685-7374
Mulcahy MS 700/5-8
1001 W Sonora Ave 93274 559-685-7250
Tracey Jenkins, prin. Fax 687-6412
Tulare City Community Day S Alt
909 E Cedar Ave 93274 559-685-7227
Philip Pierschbacher, admin.

Tulare JUNHSD 5,300/9-12
426 N Blackstone St 93274 559-688-2021
Dr. Sarah Koligian, supt. Fax 687-7317
www.tjuhsd.org
Countryside HS Community Day School 50/Alt
1084 S Pratt St 93274 559-687-7400
Steve Ramirez, prin. Fax 687-7414
Mission Oak HS 1,500/9-12
3442 E Bardsley Ave 93274 559-687-7308
Michele Borges, prin. Fax 687-7383
Tulare Technical Preparatory S Vo/Tech
737 W Bardsley Ave 93274 559-687-7400
Steve Ramirez, prin. Fax 687-7414
Tulare Union HS 1,800/9-12
755 E Tulare Ave 93274 559-686-4761
Dr. Michelle Nunley, prin. Fax 687-7367
Tulare Western HS 1,700/9-12
824 W Maple Ave 93274 559-686-8751
Kevin Covert, prin. Fax 687-7341
Tulare Adult S Adult
575 W Maple Ave 93274 559-686-0225
Larriann Torrez, dir. Fax 687-7447

Tulare Beauty College Post-Sec.
1400 W Inyo Ave 93274 559-688-2901

Tulelake, Siskiyou, Pop. 985
Tulelake Basin JUSD 500/K-12
PO Box 640 96134 530-667-2295
Vanessa Jones, supt. Fax 667-4298
www.tulelake.k12.ca.us
Tulelake Continuation HS 50/Alt
PO Box 640 96134 530-667-2280
Dean Teig, prin. Fax 667-4298
Tulelake HS 200/7-12
PO Box 640 96134 530-667-2292
Dean Teig, prin. Fax 667-4298

Tuolumne, Tuolumne
Summerville UNHSD 1,100/K-12
17555 Tuolumne Rd 95379 209-928-3498
Robert Griffith, supt. Fax 928-1321
www.summbears.k12.ca.us
Summerville HS 400/9-12
17555 Tuolumne Rd 95379 209-928-4228
Diana Harford, prin. Fax 928-1422
Other Schools – See Long Barn, Pinecrest, Twain Harte

Turlock, Stanislaus, Pop. 66,239
Chatom UNESD 600/PK-8
7201 Clayton Rd 95380 209-664-8505
Cherise Olvera, supt. Fax 664-8508
www.chatom.k12.ca.us
Other Schools – See Crows Landing

Stanislaus County Office of Education
Supt. — See Modesto
Allard Community S 500/Alt
350 North Kilroy Rd 95380 209-238-6600
Daniel Vannest, prin. Fax 238-6699

Turlock USD 13,900/K-12
PO Box 819013 95381 209-667-0632
Dana Trevethan Ed.D., supt. Fax 667-6520
www.turlock.k12.ca.us
Dutcher MS 700/7-8
1441 Colorado Ave 95380 209-667-8817
Scott Lucas, prin. Fax 667-1332
Pitman HS 2,200/9-12
2525 W Christoffersen Pkwy 95382 209-656-1592
Amy Curd, prin. Fax 656-1639
Roselawn HS 200/Alt
312 S Roselawn Ave 95380 209-634-9311
Felipe Meraz, prin. Fax 634-8730
Turlock HS 2,200/9-12
1600 E Canal Dr 95380 209-667-2055
Marie Russell, prin. Fax 634-2698
Turlock JHS 1,300/7-8
3951 N Walnut Rd 95382 209-667-0881
Robert Ruiz, prin. Fax 668-3985
Turlock Adult Education Adult
1574 E Canal Dr 95380 209-667-0643
David Lattig, prin. Fax 667-0695

Adrian's Beauty College of Turlock Post-Sec.
1340 W Main St 95380 209-632-2233
California State University-Stanislaus Post-Sec.
1 University Cir 95382 209-667-3122
Turlock Christian JSHS 200/7-12
PO Box 1540 95381 209-632-2337
David Schnurstein, prin. Fax 632-5859

Tustin, Orange, Pop. 73,165
Tustin USD 23,400/K-12
300 S C St 92780 714-730-7305
Dr. Gregory Franklin Ed.D., supt. Fax 730-7436
www.tustin.k12.ca.us
Columbus Tustin MS 900/6-8
17952 Beneta Way 92780 714-730-7352
Maggie Burdette, prin. Fax 730-7512
Currie MS 700/6-8
1402 Sycamore Ave 92780 714-730-7360
Erick Fineberg, prin. Fax 730-7593
Hillview HS 200/Alt
15400 Lansdowne Rd 92782 714-730-7356
Tim O'Donoghue, prin. Fax 730-7584
Pioneer MS 1,300/6-8
2700 Pioneer Rd 92782 714-730-7534
Tracey Vander Hayden, prin. Fax 730-5405
Tustin Adult/Sycamore HS 50/Alt
15400 Landsdowne Rd 92782 714-730-7395
Tim O'Donoghue, prin. Fax 730-4895
Tustin HS 2,200/9-12
1171 El Camino Real 92780 714-730-7414
Christine Matos, prin. Fax 730-7568
Utt MS 1,000/6-8
13601 Browning Ave 92780 714-730-7573
Dr. C.K. Green Ed.D., prin. Fax 750-7576
Other Schools – See Irvine, Santa Ana

Spirit Christian Academy 200/K-12
1372 Irvine Blvd 92780 714-731-2630
Pamela Costes, admin. Fax 731-2630

Twain Harte, Tuolumne, Pop. 2,173
Summerville UNHSD
Supt. — See Tuolumne
South Fork HS 50/Alt
25611 Lyons Dam Rd 95383 209-586-5672
Diana Harford, prin. Fax 928-1422

Twentynine Palms, San Bernardino, Pop. 23,540
Morongo USD 8,500/K-12
PO Box 1209 92277 760-367-9191
Tom Baumgarten, supt. Fax 367-7189
www.morongousd.com
Twentynine Palms HS 800/9-12
72750 Wild Cat Way 92277 760-367-9591
Justin Monical, prin. Fax 367-2106
Twentynine Palms JHS 500/7-8
5798 Utah Trl 92277 760-367-9507
Stacy Smalling, prin. Fax 367-0742
Other Schools – See Yucca Valley

Twin Peaks, San Bernardino

Lake Arrowhead Christian S 100/K-12
PO Box 870 92391 909-337-3739
Linda Huffman M.Ed., prin. Fax 337-4550

Ukiah, Mendocino, Pop. 15,561
Mendocino County Office of Education 100/
2240 Old River Rd 95482 707-467-5000
Warren Galletti, supt. Fax 462-0379
www.mcoe.us
Mendocino County Community S 100/Alt
2240 Old River Rd 95482 707-467-5155
Antonio Lopez, dir. Fax 467-5164
Orr Creek S 50/Alt
2240 Old River Rd 95482 707-467-2517
Barbara Bloom, dir. Fax 467-2531

Regional Occupational Center & Program
Supt. — None
Mendocino County ROP Vo/Tech
2240 Old River Rd 95482 707-467-5123
Dennis Aseltyne, dir. Fax 468-8212

Ukiah USD 6,400/PK-12
511 S Orchard Ave 95482 707-472-5000
Debra Kubin, supt. Fax 463-2120
www.uusd.net
Pomolita MS 800/6-8
740 N Spring St 95482 707-472-5350
Bryan Barrett, prin. Fax 463-5203
South Valley Continuation HS 200/Alt
429 S Dora St 95482 707-472-5150
Kris Swett, prin. Fax 462-9654
Ukiah HS 1,500/9-12
1000 Low Gap Rd 95482 707-472-5750
Gordon Oslund, prin. Fax 463-4859
Ukiah Independent Study Academy 100/Alt
1000 Low Gap Rd 95482 707-472-5062
Holly Rodgers, prin. Fax 463-2120
Ukiah Adult Education Adult
1056 N Bush St 95482 707-463-5217
Holly Rodgers, dir. Fax 463-0718
Other Schools – See Redwood Valley

Instilling Goodness Developing Virtue S 100/K-12
4951 Bodhi Way 95482 707-468-3896
Jin Jr Shi, prin.
Mendocino College Post-Sec.
1000 Hensley Creek Rd 95482 707-468-3000
Ukiah Junior Academy 100/K-10
180 Stipp Ln 95482 707-462-6350

Union City, Alameda, Pop. 65,266
New Haven USD 12,400/PK-12
34200 Alvarado Niles Rd 94587 510-471-1100
Dr. Arlando Smith, supt. Fax 471-7108
www.mynhusd.org
Chavez MS 1,300/6-8
2801 Hop Ranch Rd 94587 510-487-1700
Mireya Casarez, prin. Fax 475-3938
Decoto School for Independent Study 100/Alt
600 G St 94587 510-476-2696
Grace Kim, coord.
Itliong-Vera Cruz MS 1,400/6-8
31604 Alvarado Blvd 94587 510-489-0700
Heather Thorner, prin. Fax 475-3936
Logan HS 3,900/9-12
1800 H St 94587 510-471-2520
Abhi Brar, prin. Fax 471-0514
New Haven Adult S Adult
600 G St 94587 510-489-2185
Jessica Wilder, prin. Fax 471-0554
Other Schools – See Hayward

Purple Lotus S 1-12
33615 9th St 94587 510-429-8808

Upland, San Bernardino, Pop. 71,871
Upland USD 11,700/PK-12
390 N Euclid Ave 91786 909-985-1864
Nancy Kelly Ed.D., supt. Fax 949-7872
www.upland.k12.ca.us
Hillside HS 200/Alt
1558 W 9th St 91786 909-949-8400
Jerry Adams, prin. Fax 949-7840
Pioneer JHS 900/7-8
245 W 18th St 91784 909-949-7770
Aaron Dover, prin. Fax 949-7778
Upland HS 3,500/9-12
565 W 11th St 91786 909-949-7880
Pamela Salgado, prin. Fax 949-7895
Upland JHS 900/7-8
444 E 11th St 91786 909-949-7810
Richie Vega, prin. Fax 949-7817
Upland Adult S Adult
565 W 11th St 91786 909-949-7880

Western Christian HS 400/9-12
100 W 9th St 91786 909-920-5858
John Attwood, prin. Fax 985-3449
Westwood College - Inland Empire Post-Sec.
20 W 7th St 91786 909-931-7550

Upper Lake, Lake, Pop. 1,026
Upper Lake USD 800/K-12
675 Clover Valley Rd 95485 707-275-2338
Patrick Iaccino, supt. Fax 275-9750
www.ulusd.org
Clover Valley HS 50/Alt
682 Clover Valley Rd 95485 707-275-0840
Don Boyd, lead tchr. Fax 275-0208
Upper Lake Community Day HS 50/Alt
675 Clover Valley Rd 95485 707-275-0840
Don Boyd, lead tchr. Fax 275-0208
Upper Lake HS 300/9-12
675 Clover Valley Rd 95485 707-275-2338
Patrick Iaccino, prin. Fax 275-0239
Upper Lake Union MS 200/6-8
PO Box 36 95485 707-275-0223
Tony Loumena, prin. Fax 275-2911
Upper Lake Adult Education Adult
675 Clover Valley Rd 95485 707-275-0840
Patrick Iaccino, admin. Fax 275-0208

Vacaville, Solano, Pop. 87,007
Vacaville USD 12,900/K-12
401 Nut Tree Rd 95687 707-453-6100
Jane Shamieh, supt. Fax 453-7114
www.vacavilleusd.org
Country HS 200/Alt
100 McClellan St Ste B 95688 707-453-6215
Mike Sullivan, prin. Fax 451-3875
Jepson MS 900/7-8
580 Elder St 95688 707-453-6280
Kelley Birch, prin. Fax 447-7128
Vaca Pena MS 900/7-8
200 Keith Way 95687 707-453-6270
Ramon Cusi, prin. Fax 451-9501
Vacaville HS 2,000/9-12
100 W Monte Vista Ave 95688 707-453-6011
Ed Santopadre, prin. Fax 447-5604
Wood HS 1,600/9-12
998 Marshall Rd 95687 707-453-6900
Adam Rich, prin. Fax 451-3656
Adult Education Adult
100 McClellan St Ste A 95688 707-453-6018
Mark Frazier, prin. Fax 453-6959

Blake Austin College Post-Sec.
611 Orange Dr Ste K 95687 707-455-0557
Vacaville Christian S 1,000/PK-12
1117 Davis St 95687 707-446-1776
Paul Harrell, head sch Fax 446-1538

Valencia, See Santa Clarita
Castaic UNSD 2,700/K-8
28131 Livingston Ave 91355 661-257-4500
Steven Doyle, supt. Fax 257-3596
castaicusd.com
Other Schools – See Castaic

William S. Hart UNHSD
Supt. — See Santa Clarita
Arroyo Seco JHS 1,300/7-8
27171 Vista Delgado Dr 91354 661-296-0991
Rhondi Durand, prin. Fax 296-3436
Valencia HS 3,100/9-12
27801 Dickason Dr 91355 661-294-1188
John Costanzo, prin. Fax 294-3828
Golden Oak Adult S Adult
23201 Dalbey Dr 91355 661-253-0583
Cherise Moore, admin. Fax 260-1371

California Institute of the Arts Post-Sec.
24700 McBean Pkwy 91355 661-255-1050
Trinity Classical Academy 200/PK-12
28310 Kelly Johnson Pkwy 91355 661-296-2601

Vallejo, Solano, Pop. 108,826
Vallejo City USD 14,600/K-12
665 Walnut Ave 94592 707-556-8921
Ramona Bishop, supt. Fax 649-3907
www.vallejo.k12.ca.us
Bethel HS 1,800/9-12
1800 Ascot Pkwy 94591 707-556-5700
Lloyd Cartwright, prin. Fax 556-5703
Franklin MS 700/6-8
501 Starr Ave 94590 707-556-8470
Michelle Jordan-Faucett, prin. Fax 556-8475
Hogan MS 1,100/6-8
850 Rosewood Ave 94591 707-556-8510
Rosalind Hines, prin. Fax 556-8529
Peoples Continuation HS 200/Alt
233 Hobbs Ave 94589 707-556-8670
Ernani Santos, prin. Fax 556-8674
Solano MS 700/6-8
1025 Corcoran Ave 94589 707-556-8600
Shayla Bowman, prin. Fax 556-8615
Vallejo Education Academy 50/Alt
301 Farragut Ave 94590 707-649-3909
Linda Combs, prin.
Vallejo HS 1,800/9-12
840 Nebraska St 94590 707-556-1700
Sheila Quintana, prin. Fax 556-8729
Vallejo Adult Education Adult
436 Del Sur St 94591 707-556-8620
Paul Jacobs, prin. Fax 556-8624

California Maritime Academy Post-Sec.
200 Maritime Academy Dr 94590 707-654-1000
North Hills Christian S 300/PK-12
200 Admiral Callaghan Ln 94591 707-644-5284
Florence Wright, supt. Fax 644-5295
St. Patrick-St. Vincent HS 500/9-12
1500 Benicia Rd 94591 707-644-4425
Coleen Martin, prin. Fax 644-3107
Touro University - California Post-Sec.
1310 Club Dr 94592 707-638-5200

Valley Center, San Diego, Pop. 9,007
Valley Center-Pauma USD 4,200/K-12
28751 Cole Grade Rd 92082 760-749-0464
Mary Gorsuch, supt. Fax 749-1208
www.vcpusd.net
Oak Glen HS 100/Alt
28751 Cole Grade Rd 92082 760-751-0455
Dennis Zabinsky, prin. Fax 749-0767
Valley Center HS 1,200/9-12
28751 Cole Grade Rd 92082 760-751-5500
Ron McCowan, prin. Fax 751-5509
Valley Center MS 800/6-8
28751 Cole Grade Rd 92082 760-751-4295
Jon Peterson, prin. Fax 751-4259
Valley Center Prep S 100/Alt
28751 Cole Grade Rd 92082 760-751-5590
Dennis Zabinsky, prin.

Valley Glen, Los Angeles

Los Angeles Valley College Post-Sec.
5800 Fulton Ave, 818-947-2600

Valley Springs, Calaveras, Pop. 3,427
Calaveras USD
Supt. — See San Andreas
Toyon MS 500/7-8
PO Box 1510 95252 209-754-2137
Amy Hasselwander, prin. Fax 754-5327

Valley Village, See Los Angeles

Valley Torah Boys HS 100/9-12
12517 Chandler Blvd 91607 818-505-7999
Yeshivas Ner Aryeh 9-12
12422 Chandler Blvd 91607 818-509-5909
Rabbi Yochanan Weiner, prin. Fax 980-1971

Vandenberg AFB, Santa Barbara, Pop. 3,111
Lompoc USD
Supt. — See Lompoc
Vandenberg MS 800/7-8
Mountain View Blvd 93437 805-742-2700
Joel Jory, prin. Fax 742-2759

Van Nuys, See Los Angeles
Los Angeles USD
Supt. — See Los Angeles
Fulton College Prep S 1,900/6-12
7477 Kester Ave 91405 818-947-2100
Raquel George, prin. Fax 994-2284
Grant HS 2,200/9-12
13000 Oxnard St 91401 818-756-2700
Pamela Damonte, prin. Fax 908-0774
Independence Continuation HS 100/Alt
6501 Balboa Blvd 91406 818-881-7737
Marsha Coates, prin. Fax 609-0764
London HS 100/Alt
12924 Oxnard St 91401 818-756-2794
Norbert Sznajder, prin. Fax 902-9671
Mulholland MS 1,300/6-8
17120 Vanowen St 91406 818-609-2500
Gregory Vallone, prin. Fax 345-1933
Pearl Journalism & Communications HS 400/9-12
6649 Balboa Blvd 91406 818-654-3775
Deborah Smith, prin. Fax 654-3701
Rogers Continuation HS 200/Alt
14711 Gilmore St 91411 818-778-6895
Sunshine Sepulveda-Klus, prin. Fax 904-0675
Valley Alternative S 600/Alt
6701 Balboa Blvd 91406 818-342-6133
Karen O'Riley, prin. Fax 342-8645
Van Nuys HS 2,700/9-12
6535 Cedros Ave 91411 818-778-6800
Yolanda Gardea, prin. Fax 781-5181
Van Nuys MS 1,300/6-8
5435 Vesper Ave 91411 818-267-5900
Cristina Serrano, prin. Fax 909-7274
Vista MS 1,400/6-8
15040 Roscoe Blvd 91402 818-901-2727
Guiseppe Nardulli, prin. Fax 901-2740

American Pacific College Post-Sec.
14435 Sherman Way Ste 210 91405 818-781-0001
California Institute of Locksmithing Post-Sec.
14719 1/2 Oxnard St 91411 818-994-7425
Casa Loma College Post-Sec.
6725 Kester Ave 91405 818-785-2726
ICDC College Post-Sec.
14434 Sherman Way 91405 818-787-0008
National Career College Post-Sec.
6850 Van Nuys Blvd Fl 3 91405 888-988-2301
Nick Harris Detective Academy Post-Sec.
14721 Oxnard St 91411 818-343-6611
The Kings University Post-Sec.
14800 Sherman Way 91405 818-779-8040

Venice, See Los Angeles
Los Angeles USD
Supt. — See Los Angeles
Venice Adult Skills Center Adult
611 5th Ave 90291 310-664-5820
Carl Badeau, prin. Fax 392-3461

Ventura, Ventura, Pop. 103,287
Ventura USD 17,400/K-12
255 W Stanley Ave Ste 100 93001 805-641-5000
Michael Babb, supt. Fax 653-7855
www.venturausd.org
Anacapa MS 800/6-8
100 S Mills Rd 93003 805-289-7900
Barbara Boggio, prin. Fax 289-7909
Balboa MS 1,200/6-8
247 S Hill Rd 93003 805-289-1800
Wes Wade, prin. Fax 289-1806
Buena HS 2,000/9-12
5670 Telegraph Rd 93003 805-289-1826
Bobbi Powers, prin. Fax 289-1854
Cabrillo MS 1,000/6-8
1426 E Santa Clara St 93001 805-641-5155
Lorelle Dawes, prin. Fax 641-5377
De Anza Academy 900/6-8
2060 Cameron St 93001 805-641-5165
Hector Guerrero, prin. Fax 641-5282
El Camino HS 300/9-12
61 Day Rd 93003 805-289-7955
Cheryl Burns, prin. Fax 658-6315
Foothill Technology HS Vo/Tech
100 Day Rd 93003 805-289-0023
Joe Bova, prin. Fax 289-0029
Pacific HS 200/Alt
501 College Dr 93003 805-289-7950
Cynthia Frutos, prin. Fax 289-7962
Ventura HS 2,100/9-12
2 N Catalina St 93001 805-641-5116
Carlos Cohen, prin. Fax 641-5310
Ventura Adult and Continuing Education Adult
5200 Valentine Rd 93003 805-289-7925
Carolyn Van Walker, prin. Fax 289-7931

Brooks Institute Post-Sec.
5301 N Ventura Ave 93001 805-585-8000
St. Augustine Academy 100/K-12
PO Box 4506 93007 805-672-0411
Michael Van Hecke, hdmstr. Fax 672-0177
St. Bonaventure HS 600/9-12
3167 Telegraph Rd 93003 805-648-6836
Marc Groff, prin. Fax 648-4903
Santa Barbara Business College Post-Sec.
4839 Market St 93003 866-749-7222
Santa Barbara Business College - Online Post-Sec.
1834 Palma Dr 93003 866-749-7222
Ventura College Post-Sec.
4667 Telegraph Rd 93003 805-654-6400
Ventura County Christian S 50/K-12
96 MacMillan Ave 93001 805-641-0187
Tanja Geue, admin. Fax 641-0252

Victorville, San Bernardino, Pop. 111,837
Adelanto ESD
Supt. — See Adelanto
Davis Academy of Excellence 6-8
15831 Diamond Rd 92394 760-530-7650
Kathy Youskievicz, prin.
Mesa Linda MS 800/7-8
13001 Mesa Linda Ave 92392 760-246-6363
Eric Groeber, prin. Fax 956-7456

San Bernardino Co. Office of Education
Supt. — See San Bernardino
Desert Mountain Community S 100/Alt
15733 1st St, 760-843-5490
Bernadine Hollingsworth, dir.
Victor Valley UNHSD 11,400/7-12
16350 Mojave Dr, 760-955-3200
Ron Williams, supt. Fax 245-3128
www.vvuhsd.org
Adelanto HS 1,200/9-12
13853 Seneca Rd 92392 760-246-3909
Ebony Purcell, prin. Fax 261-7023
Cobalt Institute of Math & Science 600/7-12
14045 Topaz Rd 92392 760-955-2530
Dr. Melda Gaskins, prin. Fax 955-2437
Goodwill Education Center 200/Alt
16350 Mojave Dr, 760-955-3440
Kevan Loyd, prin. Fax 843-7384
Hook JHS 900/7-8
15000 Hook Blvd 92394 760-955-3360
Carlos Cerna, prin. Fax 245-5839
Lakeview Leadership Academy 800/7-8
12484 Tamarisk Rd, 760-955-3400
Kent Crosby, prin. Fax 955-1992
Silverado HS 2,700/9-12
14048 Cobalt Rd 92392 760-955-3353
Heather Conkle, prin. Fax 955-3439
University Preparatory S 1,100/Alt
13853 Seneca Rd 92392 760-243-5940
Valerie Hatcher, prin. Fax 951-2803
Victor Valley HS 2,100/9-12
16500 Mojave Dr, 760-955-3300
Nancy Noyer, prin. Fax 955-3319
Victor Valley Adult Education Adult
13853 Seneca Rd 92392 760-955-3440
Kevan Loyd, coord. Fax 241-0115

Four-D College Post-Sec.
16534 Victor St, 760-962-1325
Victor Valley Beauty College Post-Sec.
16515 Mojave Dr, 760-245-2522
Victor Valley Christian S 300/PK-12
15260 Nisqualli Rd, 760-241-8827
Deb Clarkson, admin. Fax 243-0654
Victor Valley College Post-Sec.
18422 Bear Valley Rd, 760-245-4271
Westech College Post-Sec.
14554 7th St, 760-951-5050

Villa Park, Orange, Pop. 5,691
Orange USD
Supt. — See Orange
Cerro Villa MS 1,100/7-8
17852 Serrano Ave 92861 714-997-6251
Lisa Ogan Ed.D., prin. Fax 921-9331
Villa Park HS 2,500/9-12
18042 Taft Ave 92861 714-532-8020
Kenneth Miller Ed.D., prin. Fax 628-4302

Visalia, Tulare, Pop. 121,741
Visalia USD 28,100/K-12
5000 W Cypress Ave 93277 559-730-7300
Todd Oto Ed.D., supt. Fax 730-7508
www.vusd.org
Divisadero MS 900/7-8
1200 S Divisadero St 93277 559-730-7661
Irene Del Cid, prin. Fax 730-7908
El Diamante HS 1,900/9-12
5100 W Whitendale Ave 93277 559-735-3501
Angela Sanchez, prin. Fax 735-3579
Golden West HS 1,600/9-12
1717 N McAuliff St 93292 559-730-7801
Jose Fregoso, prin. Fax 730-7408
Green Acres MS 1,300/7-8
1147 N Mooney Blvd 93291 559-730-7671
Andy Di Meo, prin. Fax 730-7918
La Joya MS 1,000/7-8
4711 W La Vida Ave 93277 559-730-7921
Travis Hambleton, prin. Fax 730-7505
Mt. Whitney HS 1,600/9-12
900 S Conyer St 93277 559-730-7602
Rick Hamilton, prin. Fax 730-7679
Redwood HS 2,100/9-12
1001 W Main St 93291 559-730-7367
Matt Shin, prin. Fax 730-7741
Sequoia HS 300/Alt
901 N Mooney Blvd 93291 559-730-7649
Adolfo Reyes, prin. Fax 730-7487
Valley Oak MS 900/7-8
2000 N Lovers Ln 93292 559-730-7681
Michael Hernandez, prin. Fax 730-7822
Visalia Technical Early College HS Vo/Tech
2049 S Linwood St 93277 559-622-3212
Victoria Porter, prin. Fax 322-6214
Visalia Adult Education Adult
3110 E Houston Ave 93292 559-730-7655
Melissa Calvero, prin. Fax 635-0372

Advanced Career Institute Post-Sec.
1728 N Kelsey St 93291 559-651-1978
Central Valley Christian S 900/PK-12
5600 W Tulare Ave 93277 559-734-9481
Larry Baker, supt. Fax 734-7963
College of the Sequoias Post-Sec.
915 S Mooney Blvd 93277 559-730-3700
Estes Inst. Cosmetology Arts & Sciences Post-Sec.
324 E Main St 93291 559-733-3617
Milan Institute of Cosmetology Post-Sec.
6500 S Mooney Blvd Unit A 93277 559-735-3829
San Joaquin Valley College Post-Sec.
8400 W Mineral King Ave 93291 559-651-2500

Vista, San Diego, Pop. 90,562
Vista USD 25,500/K-12
1234 Arcadia Ave 92084 760-726-2170
Dr. Devin Vodicka, supt. Fax 758-7838
www.vistausd.org
Alta Vista HS 200/Alt
1575 Bonair Rd 92084 760-724-3775
Michael Sterner, prin. Fax 724-0410
Murray Continuation S 200/Alt
215 N Melrose Dr 92083 760-631-2502
Chuck Hoover, prin. Fax 643-2685

Rancho Buena Vista HS 2,600/9-12
1601 Longhorn Dr, 760-727-7284
Chuck Schindler, prin. Fax 598-7062
Rancho Minerva MS 900/6-8
2245 Foothill Dr 92084 760-631-4500
Benjamin Gaines, prin. Fax 643-2490
Vista HS 2,500/9-12
1 Panther Way 92084 760-726-5611
Anthony Barela, prin. Fax 630-9738
Vista Innovation & Design Academy 700/6-8
740 Olive Ave 92083 760-724-7115
Dr. Eric Chagala, prin. Fax 941-6912
Vista Magnet MS 800/6-8
151 Civic Center Dr 92084 760-726-5766
Anne Green, prin. Fax 945-4273
Vista Visions Academy 100/Alt
305 E Bobier Dr 92084 760-724-4785
Fax 630-4206
Vista Adult S Adult
510 Sunset Dr, 760-758-7122
Elizabeth O'Shea-West, prin. Fax 726-3277
Other Schools – See Oceanside

Brightwood College Post-Sec.
2022 University Dr 92083 760-630-1555
Tri City Christian S 600/PK-12
302 N Emerald Dr 92083 760-630-8227
Clark Gilbert, supt. Fax 724-6643

Walnut, Los Angeles, Pop. 28,480
Walnut Valley USD 14,600/K-12
880 S Lemon Ave 91789 909-595-1261
Dr. Robert Taylor, supt. Fax 444-3435
www.wvusd.k12.ca.us
Hockwalt Academies 50/Alt
476 S Lemon Ave 91789 909-595-1261
Donna Hunter, prin. Fax 594-1272
South Pointe MS 1,100/6-8
20671 Larkstone Dr 91789 909-595-8171
Susan Arzola, prin. Fax 468-5201
Suzanne MS 1,400/6-8
525 Suzanne Rd 91789 909-594-1657
Lester Ojeda, prin. Fax 598-6741
Walnut HS 2,800/9-12
400 Pierre Rd 91789 909-594-1333
Brandon Dade, prin. Fax 598-7282
Other Schools – See Diamond Bar

Mt. San Antonio College Post-Sec.
1100 N Grand Ave 91789 909-594-5611

Walnut Creek, Contra Costa, Pop. 61,759
Acalanes UNHSD
Supt. — See Lafayette
Acalanes Center for Independent Study 50/Alt
1963 Tice Valley Blvd 94595 925-280-3945
Steven France, dir. Fax 280-3947
Las Lomas HS 1,500/9-12
1460 S Main St 94596 925-280-3920
Matt Campbell, prin. Fax 280-3921
Acalanes Adult S & Center Adult
1963 Tice Valley Blvd 94595 925-280-3980
Steven France, dir. Fax 395-3981

Mount Diablo USD
Supt. — See Concord
Foothill MS 1,100/6-8
2775 Cedro Ln 94598 925-939-8600
April Bush, prin. Fax 256-4281
Northgate HS 1,600/9-12
425 Castle Rock Rd 94598 925-938-0900
Michael McAlister, prin. Fax 945-6429

Walnut Creek ESD 3,600/K-8
960 Ygnacio Valley Rd 94596 925-944-6850
Marie Morgan Ed.D., supt. Fax 944-1768
www.walnutcreeksd.org
Walnut Creek IS 1,200/6-8
2425 Walnut Blvd 94597 925-944-6840
Brandy Byers, prin. Fax 933-1922

Berean Christian HS 500/9-12
245 El Divisadero Ave 94598 925-945-6464
Dr. Nelson Noriega, prin. Fax 945-7473
Contra Costa Christian S 300/PK-12
2721 Larkey Ln 94597 925-934-4964
Chris Winters, head sch Fax 934-4966
Fusion Academy 6-12
3003 Oak Rd Ste 150 94597 925-296-0053

Walnut Park, Los Angeles, Pop. 15,927
Los Angeles USD
Supt. — See Los Angeles
Science Tech Engineering & Math Academy 6-8
7500 Marbrisa Ave 90255 323-277-2600
Linda Park, prin. Fax 589-1529
S of Social Justice and Service Learning 6-8
7500 Marbrisa Ave 90255 323-277-2600
Aida Coronado-Delon, prin. Fax 589-1529

Warner Springs, San Diego
Warner USD 300/PK-12
PO Box 8 92086 760-782-3517
Melissa Brown M.Ed., supt. Fax 782-9117
www.warnerusd.net
Warner JSHS 100/7-12
PO Box 8 92086 760-782-3517
Melissa Brown M.Ed., supt. Fax 782-0605

Wasco, Kern, Pop. 25,343
Regional Occupational Center & Program
Supt. — None
North Kern Vocational Training Center Vo/Tech
2150 7th St 93280 661-758-3045
Amy Bean, dir. Fax 758-5956

Wasco UNESD 3,500/PK-8
1102 5th St 93280 661-758-7100
Kelly Richers, supt. Fax 758-7110
www.wuesd.org
Jefferson MS 800/7-8
305 Griffith Ave 93280 661-758-7140
Steve Davis, prin. Fax 758-9366

Wasco UNHSD 1,700/9-12
2100 7th St 93280 661-758-8447
Lori Albrecht, supt. Fax 758-4946
www.wascouhsd.org
Independence HS 100/Alt
1445 Poso Dr 93280 661-758-7450
Martin Lonza, prin. Fax 758-7451
Wasco HS 1,600/9-12
1900 7th St 93280 661-758-7400
Kevin Tallon, prin. Fax 758-9201

Waterford, Stanislaus, Pop. 8,248
Waterford USD 4,000/K-12
219 N Reinway Ave 95386 209-874-1809
Donald J. Davis Ed.D., supt. Fax 874-3109
www.waterford.k12.ca.us
Sentinel HS 50/Alt
121 S Reinway Ave 95386 209-874-9017
Peggy Herndon, prin. Fax 874-9065
Waterford HS 600/9-12
121 S Reinway Ave 95386 209-874-9060
Dr. Ignacio Ramirez, prin. Fax 874-9065
Waterford JHS 200/7-8
12916 Bentley St 95386 209-874-2382
Paul Patterson, prin. Fax 874-3652
Waterford Adult Education Adult
12916 Bentley St 95386 209-596-1511
Jose Aldaco, prin. Fax 874-3109

Watsonville, Santa Cruz, Pop. 50,582
Pajaro Valley USD 20,200/K-12
294 Green Valley Rd 95076 831-786-2100
Dorma Baker, supt. Fax 728-4288
www.pvusd.net
Chavez MS 600/6-8
440 Arthur Rd 95076 831-761-7699
Benjamin Benavidez, prin. Fax 728-6477
Hall MS 600/6-8
201 Brewington Ave 95076 831-728-6270
Adelina Cervero, prin. Fax 761-6150
Lakeview MS 700/6-8
2350 E Lake Ave 95076 831-728-6454
Dr. Rosa Hernandez, prin. Fax 728-6480
New S 50/Alt
165 Harkins Slough Rd 95076 831-761-6140
Artemisa Cortez, prin. Fax 761-6188
Pajaro MS 400/6-8
250 Salinas Rd 95076 831-728-6238
Dr. Victoria Sorensen, prin. Fax 728-6219
Rolling Hills MS 600/6-8
130 Herman Ave 95076 831-728-6341
Rick Ito, prin. Fax 724-7323
Watsonville HS 1,900/9-12
250 E Beach St 95076 831-728-6390
Elaine Legorreta, prin. Fax 761-6013
Adult Education Green Valley Center Adult
294 Green Valley Rd 95076 831-786-2160
Dr. Nancy Bilicich, dir. Fax 786-2193
Other Schools – See Aptos, La Selva Beach

Green Valley Christian S 200/K-12
376 S Green Valley Rd 95076 831-724-6505
Troy Martin, prin. Fax 288-0214
Monte Vista Christian S 800/6-12
2 School Way 95076 831-722-8178
Stephen Sharp, head sch Fax 722-6003
St. Francis Central Coast Catholic HS 200/9-12
PO Box 2649 95077 831-724-5933
Patrick Lee, prin. Fax 724-5995

Weaverville, Trinity, Pop. 3,455
Trinity Alps USD 700/PK-12
PO Box 1227 96093 530-623-6104
Tom Barnett, supt. Fax 623-3418
www.tausd.org
Alps View HS 50/Alt
PO Box 1227 96093 530-623-6104
Tom Barnett, supt. Fax 623-3418
Trinity HS 300/9-12
PO Box 1060 96093 530-623-6127
Bob Anderson, prin. Fax 623-6661
Trinity River Community Day S 50/Alt
PO Box 2789 96093 530-623-6104
Tom Barnett, prin. Fax 623-3418
Trinity Adult S Adult
PO Box 1227 96093 530-623-6104
Tom Barnett, supt. Fax 623-3418

Weed, Siskiyou, Pop. 2,802
Siskiyou UNHSD
Supt. — See Mount Shasta
Weed HS 200/9-12
909 Hillside Dr 96094 530-938-4774
Mike Matheson, prin. Fax 938-1319

College of the Siskiyous Post-Sec.
800 College Ave 96094 530-938-5555

Weimar, Placer, Pop. 1,300
Placer Hills UNESD
Supt. — See Meadow Vista
Weimar Hills MS 200/4-8
PO Box 255 95736 530-637-4121
Rebecca Evers, prin. Fax 637-4054

West Covina, Los Angeles, Pop. 103,993
Covina-Valley USD
Supt. — See Covina
South Hills HS 1,800/9-12
645 S Barranca St 91791 626-974-6220
Matt Dalton, prin. Fax 974-6245
Traweek MS 900/6-8
1941 E Rowland Ave 91791 626-974-7400
Mathew Kodama, prin. Fax 974-7415
Tri Community Adult Ed.-Pioneer Center Adult
1651 E Rowland Ave 91791 626-974-6821
Dan Gribbon, prin. Fax 974-6830

Regional Occupational Center & Program
Supt. — None
East San Gabriel Valley ROP Vo/Tech
1501 Del Norte St 91790 626-962-5080
Dr. Laurel Adler, supt. Fax 472-5145

Rowland USD
Supt. — See Rowland Heights
Giano IS 700/7-8
3223 S Giano Ave 91792 626-965-2461
Carlos Ochoa, prin. Fax 854-2212

West Covina USD 10,500/K-12
1717 W Merced Ave 91790 626-939-4600
Dr. Charles Hinman Ed.D., supt. Fax 939-4701
www.wcusd.org
Coronado Alternative HS 200/Alt
1500 E Francisquito Ave 91791 626-931-1810
Veronica Pendleton, prin. Fax 931-1819
Edgewood HS 800/9-12
1301 Trojan Way 91790 626-939-4900
Veronica Maddox, prin. Fax 939-0800
Edgewood MS 600/6-8
1625 W Durness St 91790 626-939-4900
Veronica Maddox, prin. Fax 939-4999
Hollencrest MS 800/6-8
2101 E Merced Ave 91791 626-931-1760
Devon Rose, prin. Fax 931-1762
Walnut Grove IS 500/7-8
614 W Vine Ave 91790 626-919-7018
Rich Nambu, prin. Fax 919-7207
West Covina HS 2,400/9-12
1609 E Cameron Ave 91791 626-859-2900
Stephen Glass, prin. Fax 859-3950

American Beauty College Post-Sec.
646 S Sunset Ave 91790
Marinello School of Beauty Post-Sec.
118 Plaza Dr 91790 626-962-1021
North-West College Post-Sec.
2121 W Garvey Ave N 91790 626-960-5046
South Hills Academy 300/PK-12
1600 E Francisquito Ave 91791 626-919-2000
Dr. Gabriel Ramirez, head sch Fax 918-7730

West Hills, Los Angeles

Chaminade College Prep HS 1,300/9-12
7500 Chaminade Ave 91304 818-347-8300
Br. Stephen Lepire, prin. Fax 348-8374
de Toledo HS 400/9-12
22622 Vanowen St 91307 818-348-0048
Dr. Bruce Powell, head sch Fax 348-0092
West Valley Christian S 200/PK-12
22450 Sherman Way 91307 818-884-4710
Derek Swales, admin. Fax 884-4749

West Hollywood, Los Angeles, Pop. 33,330

Cedars-Sinai Graduate Program Post-Sec.
8700 Beverly Blvd Atrium 90048 310-423-8294
Pacific Hills S 200/6-12
8628 Holloway Dr 90069 310-276-3068
Touro College Los Angeles Post-Sec.
1317 N Crescent Hts Blvd 90046 323-822-9700
West Hollywood College Preparatory S 100/PK-12
1317 N Crescent Heights Blv 90046 323-822-7900

Westlake Village, Los Angeles, Pop. 8,064
Conejo Valley USD
Supt. — See Thousand Oaks
Westlake HS 2,400/9-12
100 N Lakeview Canyon Rd 91362 805-497-6711
Jason Branham, prin. Fax 497-2606

Oaks Christian S 1,400/5-12
31749 La Tienda Rd 91362 818-575-9201
Robert Black, head sch Fax 575-9951

Westminster, Orange, Pop. 87,394
Garden Grove USD
Supt. — See Garden Grove
La Quinta HS 2,200/9-12
10372 McFadden Ave 92683 714-663-6315
Denise Halstead, prin. Fax 775-7307
McGarvin IS 800/7-8
9802 Bishop Pl 92683 714-663-6218
Margaret Feliciani, prin. Fax 663-6163

Huntington Beach UNHSD
Supt. — See Huntington Beach
Westminster HS 2,600/9-12
14325 Goldenwest St 92683 714-893-1381
Joseph Fraser, prin. Fax 898-4721

Westminster SD 9,700/PK-8
14121 Cedarwood St 92683 714-894-7311
Dr. Marian Phelps, supt. Fax 899-2781
www.wsdk8.us
Johnson MS 800/6-8
13603 Edwards St 92683 714-894-7244
Daniel Owens, prin. Fax 379-0784
Warner MS 1,100/6-8
14171 Newland St 92683 714-894-7281
Amy Kwon, prin. Fax 895-2378
Other Schools – See Huntington Beach

Asian American Intl Beauty College Post-Sec.
7871 Westminster Blvd 92683 714-891-0508

West Sacramento, Yolo, Pop. 45,910
Washington USD 7,800/PK-12
930 Westacre Rd 95691 916-375-7600
Linda Luna Ed.D., supt. Fax 375-7619
www.wusd.k12.ca.us
River City HS 2,000/9-12
1 Raider Ln 95691 916-375-7800
Stan Mojsich, prin. Fax 375-7809
West Sacramento S for Independent Study 50/Alt
1200 Anna St 95605 916-375-7650
Alejandro Ramos, dir. Fax 375-7771
Yolo HS 100/Alt
919 Westacre Rd 95691 916-375-7740
Alejandro Ramos, prin. Fax 375-0928
Washington Adult S Adult
919 Westacre Rd 95691 916-375-7740
Alejandro Ramos, prin. Fax 375-7744

Western Truck School Post-Sec.
4519 W Capitol Ave 95691 800-929-1320
WyoTech Post-Sec.
980 Riverside Pkwy 95605 916-376-8888

Westwood, Lassen, Pop. 1,610
Westwood USD 300/K-12
PO Box 1225 96137 530-256-2311
Randy Bobby, supt. Fax 256-3539
www.westwoodusd.org/
Westwood HS 100/6-12
PO Box 1510 96137 530-256-3235
Marci Johnson, prin. Fax 256-3693

Wheatland, Yuba, Pop. 3,292
Wheatland SD 1,300/PK-8
111 Main St 95692 530-633-3130
Craig Guensler, supt. Fax 633-4807
www.wheatlandsd.com
Bear River S 500/4-8
100 Wheatland Park Dr 95692 530-633-3135
Angela Gouker, prin. Fax 633-3142

Wheatland UNHSD 700/7-12
1010 Wheatland Rd 95692 530-633-3100
Vic Ramos Ed.D., supt. Fax 633-3109
www.wheatlandhigh.org
Wheatland Community Day S Alt
1010 Wheatland Rd 95692 530-633-3100
Lynne Tafoya, prin.
Wheatland Union HS 700/9-12
1010 Wheatland Rd 95692 530-633-3100
Vic Ramos Ed.D., prin. Fax 633-3109

Whitethorn, Humboldt
Leggett Valley USD
Supt. — See Leggett
Whale Gulch HS 50/9-12
76811 Usal Rd 95589 707-925-6285
Anthony Loumena, prin.

Whittier, Los Angeles, Pop. 84,209
East Whittier City ESD 9,200/PK-8
14535 Whittier Blvd 90605 562-907-5959
Mary Branca, supt. Fax 696-9256
www.ewcsd.org/
East Whittier MS 1,300/6-8
14421 Whittier Blvd 90605 562-789-7220
Gabriela Aldana, prin. Fax 945-3542
Granada MS 1,100/6-8
15337 Lemon Dr 90604 562-464-2330
Justin Mayernik, prin. Fax 943-5413
Hillview MS 700/6-8
10931 Stamy Rd 90604 562-789-2000
Wendy Davio, prin. Fax 946-3066

Lowell JSD 3,200/PK-8
11019 Valley Home Ave 90603 562-943-0211
Dr. Bonnie Bell, supt. Fax 947-7874
www.ljsd.org
Rancho-Starbuck IS 800/7-8
16430 Woodbrier Dr 90604 562-902-4261
Linda Takacs, prin. Fax 947-9911

Norwalk-La Mirada USD
Supt. — See Norwalk
El Camino HS 300/Alt
14625 Keese Dr 90604 562-868-0431
R. Cummins, prin. Fax 944-1843

Regional Occupational Center & Program
Supt. — None
Tri-Cities ROP Vo/Tech
10800 Ben Avon St 90606 562-698-9571
Maura Murabito, supt. Fax 696-5352

South Whittier ESD 3,200/K-8
11200 Telechron Ave 90605 562-944-6231
Gail Baxter, supt. Fax 946-4301
www.swhittier.k12.ca.us
Graves MS 800/7-8
13243 Los Nietos Rd 90605 562-944-0135
Dr. Matthew Fraijo, prin. Fax 944-9433

Whittier City ESD 6,200/K-8
7211 Whittier Ave 90602 562-789-3075
Dr. Ron Carruth, supt. Fax 698-6534
www.whittiercity.net
Dexter MS 1,100/6-8
11532 Floral Dr 90601 562-789-3090
Robert Allard Ed.D., prin. Fax 789-3095
Edwards MS 800/6-8
6812 Norwalk Blvd 90606 562-789-3120
Andrew Alvidrez, prin. Fax 789-3133

Whittier UNHSD 13,100/9-12
9401 Painter Ave 90605 562-698-8121
Martin Plourde, supt. Fax 693-0221
www.wuhsd.org
California HS 3,000/9-12
9800 Mills Ave 90604 562-698-8121
Bill Schloss, prin. Fax 946-6094
Frontier HS 500/Alt
9401 Painter Ave 90605 562-698-8121
Margie Moriarty, prin. Fax 945-7451
La Serna HS 2,800/9-12
15301 Youngwood Dr 90605 562-698-8121
Ann Fitzgerald, prin. Fax 698-6918
Pioneer HS 1,400/9-12
10800 Ben Avon St 90606 562-698-8121
Lilia Bozigian, prin. Fax 692-9194
Sierra Vista Alternative HS 400/Alt
9401 Painter Ave 90605 562-698-8121
Nicki Buchholz, dir. Fax 698-0004
Whittier HS 2,300/9-12
12417 Philadelphia St 90601 562-698-8121
Timothy Liggett, prin. Fax 698-8925
Adult Education Center Adult
9401 Painter Ave 90605 562-698-8121
Debbie Roberts, dir. Fax 693-5354
Other Schools – See Santa Fe Springs

Marinello School of Beauty Post-Sec.
6538 Greenleaf Ave 90601 562-698-0068
Rio Hondo College Post-Sec.
3600 Workman Mill Rd 90601 562-692-0921
Southern CA University of Health Science Post-Sec.
16200 Amber Valley Dr 90604 562-947-8755
Whittier Christian S 200/K-12
6548 Newlin Ave 90601 562-698-0527
Karen Holmes-Mura, prin. Fax 698-2859
Whittier College Post-Sec.
PO Box 634 90608 562-907-4200

Wildomar, Riverside, Pop. 31,160
Lake Elsinore USD
Supt. — See Lake Elsinore
Brown MS 1,000/6-8
21861 Grand Ave 92595 951-253-7430
Karen Gaither, prin. Fax 253-7437
Elsinore HS 2,200/9-12
21800 Canyon Dr 92595 951-253-7200
Robbin Hamilton Ed.D., prin. Fax 253-7209

California Lutheran HS 100/9-12
PO Box 1570 92595 951-678-7000
Andrew Aguilar, supt. Fax 678-0172
Cornerstone Christian S 200/PK-12
34570 Monte Vista Dr 92595 951-674-9381
Sharon Privett, head sch Fax 674-8462
Faith Baptist Academy 200/K-12
PO Box 1030 92595 951-245-8748

Williams, Colusa, Pop. 5,073
Colusa County Office of Education
Supt. — See Colusa
Abel Community S Alt
499 Marguerite St 95987 530-473-1350
Maria Arvizu De Espinoza, prin.

Williams USD 1,300/PK-12
PO Box 7 95987 530-473-2550
Edgar Lampkin, supt. Fax 473-5894
www.williamsusd.net
Mid Valley HS 50/Alt
PO Box 7 95987 530-473-5369
Nicholas Richter, prin. Fax 473-5540
Williams JSHS 600/7-12
PO Box 7 95987 530-473-5369
Dr. Nicholas Richter, prin. Fax 473-5540

Willits, Mendocino, Pop. 4,738
Willits USD 1,600/K-12
1277 Blosser Ln 95490 707-459-5314
Mark Westerburg, supt. Fax 459-7862
www.willitsunified.com
Baechtel Grove MS 300/6-8
1150 Magnolia St 95490 707-459-2417
Maria Mungia, prin. Fax 459-7881
New Horizons S 50/Alt
1277 Blosser Ln 95490 707-459-4801
Robert Chavez, prin. Fax 459-6580
Sanhedrin Continuation HS 50/Alt
120 N Main St 95490 707-459-4801
Robert Chavez, prin. Fax 459-6580
Willits HS 500/9-12
299 N Main St 95490 707-459-7700
Robert Chavez, prin. Fax 459-7741

Willows, Glenn, Pop. 6,043
Glenn County Office of Education 300/
311 S Villa Ave 95988 530-934-6575
Tracey Quarne, supt. Fax 934-6576
www.glenncoe.org
Glenn Adult Program Adult
451 S Villa Ave 95988 530-934-6320
Jhan Dunn, dir. Fax 934-6325

Regional Occupational Center & Program
Supt. — None
Glenn County ROP Vo/Tech
311 S Villa Ave 95988 530-934-6575
John Dunn, dir. Fax 934-6576

Willows USD 1,400/K-12
823 W Laurel St 95988 530-934-6600
Dr. Mort Geivett, supt. Fax 934-6609
www.willowsunified.org
Willows Community HS 50/Alt
823 W Laurel St 95988 530-934-6605
Dr. Mort Geivett, prin. Fax 934-6609
Willows HS 400/9-12
203 N Murdock Ave 95988 530-934-6611
David Johnstone, prin. Fax 934-6619
Willows IS 300/6-8
1145 W Cedar St 95988 530-934-6633
Steve Sailsbery, prin. Fax 934-6697

Wilmington, See Los Angeles
Los Angeles USD
Supt. — See Los Angeles
Avalon Continuation HS 100/Alt
1425 N Avalon Blvd 90744 310-549-2112
David Bonneau, prin. Fax 549-3287
Banning Academies Creative Science 9-12
1527 Lakme Ave 90744 310-847-3789
Paul Valanis, prin. Fax 830-5515
Banning HS 2,600/9-12
1527 Lakme Ave 90744 310-847-3700
Rudy Mendoza, prin. Fax 830-5515
Harbor Teacher Preparation Academy 400/Alt
1111 Figueroa Pl 90744 310-834-3932
Jan Murata, admin. Fax 834-4194
Wilmington STEAM MS 1,500/6-8
1700 Gulf Ave 90744 310-847-1500
Karen Mercado, prin. Fax 549-5307

Los Angeles Harbor College Post-Sec.
1111 Figueroa Pl 90744 310-233-4000
Pacific Harbor Christian S 200/PK-12
1530 N Wilmington Blvd 90744 310-835-5665
Kathy Gutierrez, head sch Fax 835-6316

Wilton, Sacramento, Pop. 5,148

Wilton Christian S 100/PK-12
9697 Dillard Rd 95693 916-687-7693
Rev. John Schmidt, admin. Fax 687-6587

Windsor, Sonoma, Pop. 26,016
Windsor USD 5,400/PK-12
9291 Old Redwood Hwy 95492 707-837-7700
Steve Jorgensen, supt. Fax 838-4031
www.wusd.org
Windsor HS 1,700/9-12
8695 Windsor Rd 95492 707-837-7767
Marc Elin, prin. Fax 837-7773
Windsor MS 900/6-8
9500 Brooks Rd S 95492 707-837-7737
Brian Williams, prin. Fax 837-7743
Windsor Oaks Academy 100/Alt
8681 Windsor Rd 95492 707-837-7771
Susan Nystrom, prin. Fax 837-7770

Winterhaven, Imperial, Pop. 381
San Pasqual Valley USD 800/K-12
676 Base Line Rd 92283 760-572-0222
Dr. Rauna Fox, supt. Fax 572-0711
www.spvusd.org/
Manes HS 50/Alt
676 Base Line Rd 92283 760-572-0095
Darrell Pechtl, prin. Fax 572-0829
San Pasqual Valley HS 200/9-12
676 Base Line Rd 92283 760-572-0222
Darrell Pechtl, prin. Fax 572-0881
San Pasqual Valley MS 200/6-8
676 Base Line Rd 92283 760-572-0222
Mary Kay Monson, prin. Fax 572-0829

Winters, Yolo, Pop. 6,490
Winters JUSD 1,500/K-12
909 Grant Ave 95694 530-795-6100
Dr. Todd Cutler, supt. Fax 795-6114
www.wintersjusd.org
Winters HS 500/9-12
101 Grant Ave 95694 530-795-6140
Dr. Nicole Reyherme, prin. Fax 795-6147
Winters MS 400/6-8
425 Anderson Ave 95694 530-795-6130
John Barsotti, prin. Fax 795-6137
Wolfskill Continuation HS 50/Alt
200 Baker St 95694 530-795-6154
Matt Moran, lead tchr. Fax 795-6162

Winton, Merced, Pop. 10,450
Merced River UNESD 100/PK-8
4402 Oakdale Rd 95388 209-358-5679
Richard Lopez, supt. Fax 358-2855
www.mrusd.us
Washington MS 100/4-8
4402 Oakdale Rd 95388 209-358-5679
Richard Lopez, supt. Fax 358-2855

Winton SD 1,900/PK-8
PO Box 8 95388 209-357-6175
Randall Heller, supt. Fax 357-1994
www.winton.k12.ca.us
Winton MS 600/6-8
PO Box 1299 95388 209-357-6189
Craig Perry, prin. Fax 358-5889

Woodlake, Tulare, Pop. 7,217
Woodlake USD 2,300/K-12
300 W Whitney Ave 93286 559-564-8081
Drew Sorensen, supt. Fax 564-3831
www.w-usd.org
Bravo Lake HS 50/Alt
450 W Sequoia Ave 93286 559-564-8716
Tony Casares, prin. Fax 564-2695
Woodlake Community Day S 50/Alt
36220 Millwood Dr 93286 559-564-8716
Tony Casares, dir. Fax 564-2695
Woodlake Union HS 700/9-12
400 W Whitney Ave 93286 559-564-3307
Ricardo Rodriguez, admin. Fax 564-3320
Woodlake Valley MS 500/6-8
497 N Palm St 93286 559-564-8061
Antonio Rivera, prin. Fax 564-0702

Woodland, Yolo, Pop. 54,082
Regional Occupational Center & Program
Supt. — None
Yolo County ROP Vo/Tech
1280 Santa Anita Ct Ste 100 95776 530-668-3770
Ronda Adams, coord. Fax 668-3850

Woodland JUSD 9,900/K-12
435 6th St 95695 530-662-0201
Dr. Maria Armstrong, supt. Fax 662-6956
www.wjusd.org
Douglass MS 800/7-8
525 Granada Dr 95695 530-666-2191
Derek Cooper, prin. Fax 668-9217
Lee MS 700/7-8
520 West St 95695 530-662-0251
Armando Olvera, prin. Fax 662-9423
Pioneer HS 1,500/9-12
1400 Pioneer Ave 95776 530-406-1148
Sandra Reese, prin. Fax 662-3661
Woodland HS 1,300/9-12
21 N West St 95695 530-662-4678
Karrie Sequeira, prin. Fax 662-7464
Woodland Adult Education Adult
575 Hays St 95695 530-662-0798
Susan Moylan, prin. Fax 662-8039
Other Schools – See Yolo

Yolo County Office of Education 100/
1280 Santa Anita Ct Ste 100 95776 530-668-6700
Jesse Ortiz, supt. Fax 668-3848
www.ycoe.org
Chavez Community S 50/Alt
255 W Beamer St 95695 530-668-3090
Angelina Arias, dir. Fax 662-6873

Cambridge Junior College Post-Sec.
501 Main St 95695 855-564-2293
Woodland Christian S 300/PK-12
1787 Matmor Rd 95776 530-406-8800
Justin Smith, admin. Fax 406-0900
Woodland Community College Post-Sec.
2300 E Gibson Rd 95776 530-661-5700

Woodland Hills, See Los Angeles
Los Angeles USD
Supt. — See Los Angeles
Thoreau Continuation HS 100/Alt
5429 Quakertown Ave 91364 818-340-4395
Eric Diaz, prin. Fax 347-4235
Woodland Hills Academy 1,100/6-8
20800 Burbank Blvd 91367 818-226-2900
Ted Yamane, prin. Fax 716-0649
West Valley Occupational Center Adult
6200 Winnetka Ave 91367 818-346-3540
Candace Lee, prin. Fax 346-3858

Fusion Academy 6-12
21650 Oxnard St Ste 100 91367 818-712-9521
Hojjat Sandi M.Ed., head sch
Los Angeles Pierce College Post-Sec.
6201 Winnetka Ave 91371 818-347-0551
Louisville HS 400/9-12
22300 Mulholland Dr 91364 818-346-8812
Myra McPartland, pres. Fax 346-9483

Woodside, San Mateo, Pop. 5,153
Sequoia UNHSD
Supt. — See Redwood City
Woodside HS 1,800/9-12
199 Churchill Ave 94062 650-367-9750
Diane Burbank, prin. Fax 367-7263

Yermo, San Bernardino
Silver Valley USD 2,400/PK-12
PO Box 847 92398 760-254-2916
Jill Kemock, supt. Fax 254-2091
www.svusdk12.net
Silver Valley HS 400/9-12
PO Box 847 92398 760-254-2963
Marc Lacey, prin. Fax 254-3043
Other Schools – See Daggett, Fort Irwin

Yolo, Yolo, Pop. 447
Woodland JUSD
Supt. — See Woodland
Cache Creek HS 100/Alt
PO Box 298 95697 530-662-4331
William Jarrel, prin. Fax 666-9082

Yorba Linda, Orange, Pop. 62,269
Placentia-Yorba Linda USD
Supt. — See Placentia
La Entrada HS 100/Alt
4175 Fairmont Blvd 92886 714-779-4170
Carrie Bisgard, prin. Fax 779-6825
Yorba Linda HS 1,800/9-12
19900 Bastanchury Rd 92886 714-986-7500
Dave Flynn, prin. Fax 986-7501
Yorba Linda MS 900/6-8
4777 Casa Loma Ave 92886 714-986-7080
Cameron Malotte, prin. Fax 996-2752
Yorba MS 700/7-8
5350 Fairmont Blvd 92886 714-986-7400
Ken Valburg, prin. Fax 970-1647

Friends Christian MS 400/5-8
4231 Rose Dr 92886 714-524-5240
Joy Swift, prin. Fax 524-5784

Yosemite National Park, Mariposa
Mariposa County USD
Supt. — See Mariposa
Yosemite Park HS 50/9-12
9670 Rancheria Flat Rd 95389 209-372-2382
Sean Jacobs, lead tchr. Fax 379-9138

Yreka, Siskiyou, Pop. 7,387
Regional Occupational Center & Program
Supt. — None
Siskiyou County ROP Vo/Tech
431 Knapp St 96097 530-842-6155
Kim Greene, dir. Fax 842-1759

Yreka UNHSD 700/9-12
400 Preece Way 96097 530-842-2521
Mark Greenfield, supt. Fax 842-1759
www.yuhsd.net
Discovery HS 50/9-12
400 Preece Way 96097 530-842-1659
Randy Baker, prin. Fax 841-1057
Yreka HS 700/9-12
400 Preece Way 96097 530-842-6151
Marie Caldwell, prin. Fax 841-0740
Yreka Union Community Day S Alt
400 Preece Way 96097 530-842-1659
Randy Baker, prin.
Yreka Union HS Adult Education Adult
400 Preece Way 96097 530-842-7829
Randy Baker, dir. Fax 842-1759

Yreka UNSD 1,000/K-8
309 Jackson St 96097 530-842-1168
Dave Parsons, supt. Fax 842-4576
www.yrekausd.net
Jackson Street ES 500/4-8
405 Jackson St 96097 530-842-3561
Chris Harris, prin. Fax 842-1716

Yuba City, Sutter, Pop. 62,225
Regional Occupational Center & Program
Supt. — None
Tri-County ROP Vo/Tech
970 Klamath Ln 95993 530-822-2952
Randy Page, dir. Fax 822-3003

Sutter County Office of Education 400/
970 Klamath Ln 95993 530-822-2900
Bill Cornelius, supt. Fax 671-3422
www.sutter.k12.ca.us
Feather River Academy 100/Alt
1895 Lassen Blvd 95993 530-822-2400
Bill Embleton, prin. Fax 822-3267

Yuba City USD 13,400/PK-12
750 N Palora Ave 95991 530-822-5200
Nancy Aaberg, supt. Fax 671-2454
www.ycusd.org
Gray Avenue MS 700/6-8
808 Gray Ave 95991 530-822-5240
Brian Gault, prin. Fax 822-5057
Powell Continuation HS 200/Alt
1875 Clark Ave 95991 530-822-5210
Jen Cates, prin. Fax 822-5053
River Valley HS 1,700/9-12
801 El Margarita Rd 95993 530-822-2500
Tom Reusser, prin. Fax 822-2589
Yuba City HS 1,700/9-12
850 B St 95991 530-674-4900
Bruce Morton, prin. Fax 671-7814
Yuba City Unified Alternative S 100/Alt
984 B St 95991 530-822-5244
Bruce Morton, prin. Fax 822-5096

Cambridge Junior College Post-Sec.
990 Klamath Ln Ste A 95993 530-674-9199
Faith Christian JSHS 200/7-12
PO Box 1690 95992 530-674-5474
Steve Finlay, prin. Fax 674-0194

Yucaipa, San Bernardino, Pop. 50,145
Yucaipa-Calimesa JUSD 9,700/K-12
12797 3rd St 92399 909-797-0174
Cali Binks, supt. Fax 797-5751
www.yucaipaschools.com
Green Valley Continuation HS 100/Alt
35948 Susan St 92399 909-790-8580
Cara Prentiss, prin. Fax 790-8584
Green Valley Independent Study 50/Alt
35948 Susan St 92399 909-790-8580
Cara Prentiss, prin.
Oak View HS & Education Center 100/Alt
12358 6th St 92399 909-797-7931
Sam Spencer, prin. Fax 797-7962
Park View MS 600/7-8
34875 Tahoe Dr 92399 909-790-3285
Frank Tucci, prin. Fax 790-3295
Yucaipa HS 2,700/9-12
33000 Yucaipa Blvd 92399 909-797-0106
Shad Kirkland, prin. Fax 790-3200
Yucaipa Adult S Adult
35948 Susan St 92399 909-797-0121
Cara Prentiss, prin. Fax 790-6115
Other Schools – See Calimesa

Crafton Hills College Post-Sec.
11711 Sand Canyon Rd 92399 909-794-2161

Yucca Valley, San Bernardino, Pop. 20,139
Morongo USD
Supt. — See Twentynine Palms
Black Rock HS 100/Alt
59273 Sunnyslope Dr 92284 760-369-6310
Vonda Viland, prin. Fax 365-3366
La Contenta MS 800/7-8
7050 La Contenta Rd 92284 760-228-1802
Garrett Gruwell, prin. Fax 369-6324
Yucca Valley HS 1,400/9-12
7600 Sage Ave 92284 760-365-3391
Carl Phillips, prin. Fax 365-1845

Joshua Springs Christian S 200/PK-12
57373 Joshua Ln 92284 760-365-3599
Fem Ontiveros, admin. Fax 369-0315

COLORADO

COLORADO DEPARTMENT OF EDUCATION
201 E Colfax Ave, Denver 80203-1799
Telephone 303-866-6646
Fax 303-830-0793
Website http://www.cde.state.co.us

Commissioner of Education Dr. Katy Anthes

COLORADO BOARD OF EDUCATION
201 E Colfax Ave, Denver 80203-1704

Chairperson Steve Durham

BOARDS OF COOPERATIVE EDUCATIONAL SERVICES (BOCES)

Adams County BOCES
Eric Wiant, dir. 303-286-7294
1400 W 122nd Ave Ste 110 Fax 286-9078
Denver 80234
www.aboces.org

Centennial BOCES
Dr. Randy Zila, dir. 970-352-7404
2020 Clubhouse Dr, Greeley 80634 Fax 352-7350
www.cboces.org

Colorado Digital BOCES
Kim McClelland, dir., 4035 Tutt Blvd 719-418-5276
Colorado Springs 80922
www.cdboces.org

East Central BOCES
Don Anderson, dir. 719-775-2342
PO Box 910, Limon 80828 Fax 775-9714
www.ecboces.org

Expeditionary BOCES
Chad Burns, dir. 303-759-2076
1700 S Holly St, Denver 80222 Fax 757-7442
www.rmsel.org

Front Range BOCES
Hi Howard, dir. 720-561-5096
6500 Arapahoe Rd, Boulder 80303
www.frboces.org

Grand Valley BOCES
Bridgitte Sunderman, dir. 970-255-2700
2508 Blichman Ave Fax 255-2626
Grand Junction 81505

Mountain BOCES
Troy Lange, dir. 719-486-2603
1713 Mount Lincoln Dr W Fax 486-2109
Leadville 80461
www.mtnboces.org/

Mount Evans BOCES
Terri Jones, dir. 303-567-3878
PO Box 3399, Idaho Springs 80452 Fax 567-3880
mtevansboces.com

Northeast Colorado BOCES
Bret Miles, dir. 970-774-6152
PO Box 98, Haxtun 80731 Fax 774-6157
www.neboces.org

Northwest Colorado BOCES
Paul McCarty, dir., PO Box 773390 970-879-0391
Steamboat Springs 80477 Fax 879-0442
www.nwboces.org

Pikes Peak BOCES
Deborah Montgomery, dir. 719-570-7474
2883 S Circle Dr Fax 380-9685
Colorado Springs 80906
www.ppboces.org

Rio Blanco BOCES
Teresa Schott, dir. 970-675-2064
402 W Main St Ste 219 Fax 675-5738
Rangely 81648
www.rioblancoboces.org

San Juan BOCES
Mary Rubadeau, dir. 970-247-3261
201 E 12th St, Durango 81301 Fax 247-8333
www.sjboces.org

San Luis Valley BOCES
Nita McAuliffe, dir. 719-589-5851
2261 Enterprise Dr, Alamosa 81101 Fax 589-5007
www.slvbocs.org

Santa Fe Trail BOCES
Sandy Malouff, dir. 719-383-2623
PO Box 980, La Junta 81050 Fax 383-2627
www.sftboces.org

South Central BOCES
Dr. Henry Roman, dir. 719-647-0023
323 S Purcell Blvd, Pueblo 81007 Fax 647-0136
www.sc-boces.org

Southeastern BOCES
Loraine Saffer, dir. 719-336-9046
PO Box 1137, Lamar 81052 Fax 336-9679
www.seboces.org

Uncompahgre BOCS
Tammy Johnson, dir. 970-626-2977
PO Box 728, Ridgway 81432 Fax 626-2978

Ute Pass BOCES
Marcy Palmer, dir., 405 El Monte Pl 719-685-2640
Manitou Springs 80829 Fax 685-4536
www.upboces.org

PUBLIC, PRIVATE AND CATHOLIC SECONDARY SCHOOLS

Aguilar, Las Animas, Pop. 527
Aguilar RSD 6 100/PK-12
PO Box 567 81020 719-941-4188
Dr. Stacy Houser, supt. Fax 941-4279
www.aguilarschools.org
Aguilar JSHS 50/7-12
PO Box 567 81020 719-941-4188
Dr. Stacy Houser, supt. Fax 941-4279

Akron, Washington, Pop. 1,685
Akron SD R-1 300/PK-12
PO Box 429 80720 970-345-2053
Brian Christensen, supt. Fax 345-6508
akronrams.schoolwires.net
Akron JSHS 100/7-12
600 Elm Ave 80720 970-345-2268
Ed Lundquist, prin. Fax 345-6508

Alamosa, Alamosa, Pop. 8,620
Alamosa SD RE-11J 2,000/K-12
209 Victoria Ave 81101 719-587-1600
Rob Alejo, supt. Fax 587-1712
www.alamosa.k12.co.us/
Alamosa HS 500/9-12
805 Craft Dr 81101 719-587-6000
Andy Lavier, prin. Fax 587-6069
Ortega MS 500/6-8
401 Victoria Ave 81101 719-587-1650
Denise Cordova, prin. Fax 587-1721

Adams State University Post-Sec.
208 Edgemont Blvd 81101 719-587-7011

Anton, Washington, Pop. 40
Arickaree SD R-2 100/PK-12
12155 County Road NN 80801 970-383-2202
S. Shane Walkinshaw, supt. Fax 383-2205
www.arickaree.org
Arickaree JSHS 100/6-12
12155 County Road NN 80801 970-383-2202
S. Shane Walkinshaw, supt. Fax 383-2205

Antonito, Conejos, Pop. 772
South Conejos SD RE-10 200/K-12
PO Box 398 81120 719-376-5512
Carla Archuleta, supt. Fax 376-5425
southconejos.com
Antonito HS 100/9-12
PO Box 398 81120 719-376-7000
Angela Montoya, prin. Fax 376-5425
Antonito MS 50/7-8
PO Box 398 81120 719-376-7000
Angela Montoya, prin. Fax 376-5425

Arvada, Jefferson, Pop. 104,595
Jefferson County SD R-1
Supt. — See Golden
Arvada HS 900/9-12
7951 W 65th Ave 80004 303-982-0162
Georgina Yacovetta-Rivas, prin. Fax 982-0163
Arvada West HS 1,700/9-12
11595 Allendale Dr 80004 303-982-1303
Robert Bishop, prin. Fax 982-1304
Drake MS 700/7-8
12550 W 52nd Ave 80002 303-982-1510
Rod Pugnetti, prin. Fax 982-1511
Moore MS 500/7-8
8455 W 88th Ave 80005 303-982-0400
Brenda Fletcher, prin. Fax 982-0462
North Arvada MS 400/7-8
7285 Pierce St 80003 303-982-0528
Sohne Van Selus, prin. Fax 982-0529
Oberon MS 600/7-8
7300 Quail St 80005 303-982-2020
Tara Pena, prin. Fax 982-2021
Pomona HS 1,400/9-12
8101 W Pomona Dr 80005 303-982-0710
Andy Geise, prin. Fax 982-0709
Ralston Valley HS 1,700/9-12
13355 W 80th Ave 80005 303-982-5600
Gordon Goodrich, prin. Fax 982-5601
Warren Tech North Vo/Tech
11325 Allendale Dr 80004 303-982-9360
Joseph Shaw, prin. Fax 982-9361

Faith Christian Academy HS 400/9-12
4890 Carr St 80002 303-424-7310
Andrew Hasz, prin. Fax 403-2730
Faith Christian Academy MS 300/6-8
6250 Wright St 80004 303-424-7310
Michael Cook, prin. Fax 403-2720

Aspen, Pitkin, Pop. 6,573
Aspen SD 1 1,700/PK-12
235 High School Rd 81611 970-925-3760
Dr. John Maloy, supt. Fax 925-5721
www.aspenk12.net/
Aspen HS 600/9-12
235 High School Rd 81611 970-925-3760
Tharyn Mulberry, prin. Fax 925-1205
Aspen MS 500/5-8
235 High School Rd 81611 970-925-3760
Craig Rogers, prin. Fax 925-8374

Ault, Weld, Pop. 1,488
Weld County SD RE-9 800/K-12
PO Box 1390 80610 970-834-1345
Robert Ring, supt. Fax 834-1347
www.weldre9.k12.co.us
Highland HS 200/9-12
PO Box 1390 80610 970-834-2816
Randy Yaussi, prin. Fax 834-2858
Highland MS 200/6-8
PO Box 1390 80610 970-834-2829
Clay Naughton, prin. Fax 834-2663

Aurora, Arapahoe, Pop. 313,203
Aurora SD 40,300/PK-12
15701 E 1st Ave 80011 303-365-7800
Rico Munn, supt. Fax 326-1280
aurorak12.org
Aurora Central HS 2,100/9-12
11700 E 11th Ave 80010 303-340-1600
Geraldo De La Garza, prin. Fax 326-1270
Aurora Hills MS 900/6-8
1009 S Uvalda St 80012 303-341-7450
Nichole Brooks, prin. Fax 326-1250
Aurora West College Preparatory S 1,200/6-12
10100 E 13th Ave 80010 303-366-2671
Brian Duwe, prin. Fax 326-1260
Columbia MS 700/6-8
17600 E Columbia Ave 80013 303-690-6570
Steve Hamilton, prin. Fax 326-1251
East MS 1,000/6-8
1275 Fraser St 80011 303-340-0660
Biaze Houston, prin. Fax 326-1252
Futures Academy 100/Alt
14707 E 2nd Ave Ste 260 80011 720-949-0253
Joy Smith, prin.
Gateway HS 1,700/9-12
1300 S Sable Blvd 80012 303-755-7160
Dackri Davis, prin. Fax 326-1272
Hinkley HS 2,100/9-12
1250 Chambers Rd 80011 303-340-1500
Matthew Willis, prin. Fax 326-1274
Mrachek MS 900/6-8
1955 S Telluride St 80013 303-750-2836
Michelle Davis, prin. Fax 326-1254
North MS 900/6-8
12095 Montview Blvd 80010 303-364-7411
Brett Stringer, prin. Fax 326-1256
Rangeview HS 2,400/9-12
17599 E Iliff Ave 80013 303-695-6848
Ron Fay, prin. Fax 326-1276
Smith HS 300/9-12
400 Airport Blvd 80011 303-364-8715
David Roll, prin. Fax 326-1278

South MS 700/6-8
12310 E Parkview Dr 80011 303-364-7623
Courtney Goertz, prin. Fax 326-1258
Vista PEAK Preparatory HS 900/9-12
24500 E 6th Ave 80018 303-340-0121
Garrett Rosa, prin. Fax 326-1262

Cherry Creek SD 5
Supt. — See Greenwood Village
Cherokee Trail HS 2,600/9-12
25901 E Arapahoe Rd 80016 720-886-1900
Kim Rauh, prin. Fax 886-1989
Falcon Creek MS 1,000/6-8
6100 S Genoa St 80016 720-886-7700
Lisa Ruiz, prin. Fax 886-7788
Fox Ridge MS 1,100/6-8
26301 E Arapahoe Rd 80016 720-886-4400
Marquetta Thomas, prin. Fax 886-4488
Grandview HS 2,600/9-12
20500 E Arapahoe Rd 80016 720-886-6500
Lisa Sprague, prin. Fax 886-6698
Horizon Community MS 1,000/6-8
3981 S Reservoir Rd 80013 720-886-6100
Nickie Bell, prin. Fax 886-6253
I Team - Estate Alt
4360 S Pitkin St 80015 720-886-5850
Allison Witkin, prin. Fax 886-5865
I Team - Manor Alt
1820 S Joliet St 80012 720-747-2955
Allison Witkin, prin. Fax 747-2951
I Team - Ranch Alt
7250 S Gartrell Rd 80016 720-886-6880
Allison Witkin, prin. Fax 886-6888
Laredo MS 1,100/6-8
5000 S Laredo St 80015 720-886-5000
Edie Alvarez, prin. Fax 886-5298
Liberty MS 1,100/6-8
21500 E Dry Creek Rd 80016 720-886-2400
Kevin Doherty, prin. Fax 886-2688
Overland HS 2,300/9-12
12400 E Jewell Ave 80012 720-747-3700
Leon Lundie, prin. Fax 747-3895
Prairie MS 1,700/6-8
12600 E Jewell Ave 80012 720-747-3000
David Gonzales, prin. Fax 747-3097
Sky Vista MS 900/6-8
4500 S Himalaya St 80015 720-886-4700
Michelle McCourt, prin. Fax 886-4788
Smoky Hill HS 2,100/9-12
16100 E Smoky Hill Rd 80015 720-886-5300
Chuck Puga, prin. Fax 886-5408

American Sentinel University Post-Sec.
2260 S Xanadu Way Ste 310 80014 303-991-1575
Anthem College Post-Sec.
350 Blackhawk St 80011 720-859-7900
CedarWood Christian Academy 100/K-12
PO Box 111389 80042 303-361-6456
Gene Oborny, admin. Fax 340-0971
Colorado Technical University Post-Sec.
3151 S Vaughn Way 80014 303-632-2300
Community College of Aurora Post-Sec.
16000 E Centretech Pkwy 80011 303-360-4700
Concorde Career College Post-Sec.
111 Havana St 80010 303-861-1151
Ecotech Institute Post-Sec.
1400 S Abilene St 80012 877-326-5576
Everest College Post-Sec.
14280 E Jewell Ave Ste 100 80012 303-745-6244
Pickens Technical Center Post-Sec.
500 Airport Blvd 80011 303-344-4910
Pima Medical Institute Post-Sec.
13750 E Mississippi Ave 80012 303-368-7462
Platt College Post-Sec.
3100 S Parker Rd 80014 303-369-5151
Regis Jesuit HS for Boys 1,600/9-12
6400 S Lewiston Way 80016 303-269-8000
Regis Jesuit HS for Girls 700/9-12
6300 S Lewiston Way 80016 303-269-8100
Xenon International Post-Sec.
2231 S Peoria St 80014 303-752-1560

Bailey, Park, Pop. 150
Platte Canyon SD 1 1,000/PK-12
PO Box 1069 80421 303-838-7666
Dr. Brenda Krage Ed.D., supt. Fax 679-7504
www.plattecanyonschools.org
Fitzsimmons MS 200/6-8
PO Box 1069 80421 303-838-7666
Ginger Slocum, prin. Fax 679-7506
Platte Canyon HS 300/9-12
PO Box 1069 80421 303-838-7666
Michael Schmidt, prin. Fax 679-7497

Basalt, Pitkin, Pop. 3,792
Roaring Fork SD RE-1
Supt. — See Glenwood Springs
Basalt HS 400/9-12
600 Southside Dr 81621 970-384-5959
Peter Mueller, prin. Fax 384-5955
Basalt MS 500/5-8
51 School St 81621 970-384-5900
Jennifer Ellsperman, prin. Fax 384-5905

Cornerstone Classical S 50/PK-12
20449 Highway 82 81621 970-927-9106

Bayfield, LaPlata, Pop. 2,294
Bayfield SD 10 JT-R 1,300/PK-12
24 S Clover Dr 81122 970-884-2496
Troy Zabel, supt. Fax 884-4284
www.bayfield.k12.co.us
Bayfield HS 400/9-12
24 S Clover Dr 81122 970-884-9521
Leon Hanhardt, prin. Fax 884-4226
Bayfield MS 300/6-8
24 S Clover Dr 81122 970-884-9592
Tod Lokey, prin. Fax 884-4110

Bennett, Adams, Pop. 2,268
Bennett SD 29J 1,000/PK-12
610 7th St 80102 303-644-3234
Robin Purdy, supt. Fax 644-4121
www.bennett29j.k12.co.us
Bennett HS 300/9-12
610 7th St 80102 303-644-3234
Rich Campbell, prin. Fax 644-3894
Bennett MS 300/6-8
455 8th St 80102 303-644-3234
Zachary Stall, prin. Fax 644-4398

Berthoud, Larimer, Pop. 5,034
Thompson SD R-2J
Supt. — See Loveland
Berthoud HS 700/9-12
850 Spartan Ave 80513 970-613-7700
Chris Garcia, prin. Fax 613-7728
Turner MS 500/6-8
950 Massachusetts Ave 80513 970-613-7400
Derrick Martin, prin. Fax 613-7420

Bethune, Kit Carson, Pop. 236
Bethune SD R-5 100/PK-12
PO Box 127 80805 719-346-7513
Shila Adolf, supt. Fax 346-5048
bethuneschool.com
Bethune JSHS 100/7-12
PO Box 127 80805 719-343-7513
Shila Adolf, prin. Fax 346-5048

Black Hawk, Gilpin, Pop. 118
Gilpin County SD RE-1 400/PK-12
10595 Highway 119 80422 303-582-3444
Dr. David MacKenzie, supt. Fax 582-3346
www.gilpin.k12.co.us
Gilpin County JSHS 200/6-12
10595 Highway 119 80422 303-582-3444
Alexis Donaldson, prin. Fax 582-3346

Blanca, Costilla, Pop. 380
Sierra Grande SD R-30 300/K-12
17523 E Highway 160 81123 719-379-3259
Darren Edgar, supt. Fax 379-2572
www.sierragrandeschool.net
Sierra Grande HS 100/9-12
17523 E Highway 160 81123 719-379-3257
Brandon Mizokami, prin. Fax 379-2572
Sierra Grande MS 100/6-8
17523 E Highway 160 81123 719-379-3257
Manuel Montano, prin. Fax 379-2572

Boulder, Boulder, Pop. 95,063
Boulder Valley SD RE-2 30,100/PK-12
PO Box 9011 80301 303-447-1010
Bruce Messinger Ph.D., supt. Fax 561-5134
www.bvsd.org
Arapahoe Campus 100/9-12
6600 Arapahoe Rd 80303 720-561-5220
Dr. Joan Bludorn, prin. Fax 561-5258
Boulder HS 1,900/9-12
1604 Arapahoe Ave 80302 720-561-2200
James Hill, prin. Fax 561-5317
Casey MS 600/6-8
1301 High St 80304 720-561-2700
Justin McMillan, prin. Fax 561-2701
Centennial MS 600/6-8
2205 Norwood Ave 80304 720-561-5441
Dana Ellis, prin. Fax 561-2090
Fairview HS 2,100/9-12
1515 Greenbriar Blvd 80305 720-561-3100
Don Stensrud, prin. Fax 561-5353
Manhattan S of Arts and Academics 500/6-8
290 Manhattan Dr 80303 720-561-6300
John Riggs, prin. Fax 561-6301
New Vista HS 300/9-12
700 20th St 80302 720-561-8700
Kirk Quitter, prin. Fax 561-8701
Platt MS 500/6-8
6096 Baseline Rd 80303 720-561-5536
Theo Robison, prin. Fax 561-6898
Southern Hills MS 600/6-8
1500 Knox Dr 80305 720-561-3400
Chavonne Gloster, prin. Fax 561-3401
Other Schools – See Broomfield, Lafayette, Louisville, Nederland

---

Naropa University Post-Sec.
2130 Arapahoe Ave 80302 303-444-0202
Rolf Institute of Structural Integration Post-Sec.
5055 Chaparral Ct Ste 103 80301 303-449-5903
September HS 50/9-12
1902 Walnut St 80302 303-443-9933
Shining Mountain Waldorf S 300/PK-12
999 Violet Ave 80304 303-444-7697
Jane M. Zeender, dir. Fax 444-7701
Southwest Acupuncture College Post-Sec.
6620 Gunpark Dr 80301 303-581-9955
Tara Performing Arts HS 50/9-12
4180 19th St 80304 303-440-4510
Greg Fisher, admin. Fax 448-0090
Temple Grandin S 50/6-12
6446 Jay Rd 80301 303-554-7363
Jen Wilger, dir. Fax 494-7558
University of Colorado Boulder 80309 Post-Sec.
303-492-1411
Watershed S 100/6-12
1661 Alpine Ave 80304 303-440-7520
Greg Bamford, head sch Fax 440-7521

Branson, Las Animas, Pop. 73
Branson RSD 82 400/K-12
PO Box 128 81027 719-946-5531
Brad Caldwell, supt. Fax 946-5619
www.bransonschoolonline.com
Branson S Online 400/Alt
PO Box 128 81027 719-946-5531
Brad Caldwell, prin. Fax 946-5619

Briggsdale, Weld, Pop. 225
Briggsdale SD RE-10 200/PK-12
PO Box 129 80611 970-656-3417
Rick Mondt, supt. Fax 656-3479
www.briggsdaleschool.org/
Briggsdale JSHS 100/6-12
PO Box 129 80611 970-656-3417
Fax 656-3479

Brighton, Adams, Pop. 32,801
SD 27J 16,500/PK-12
18551 E 160th Ave 80601 303-655-2900
Chris Fiedler Ed.D., supt. Fax 655-2870
www.sd27j.org/
Brighton HS 1,800/9-12
270 S 8th Ave 80601 303-655-4200
John Biner, prin. Fax 655-2885
Heritage Academy 100/Alt
830 E Bridge St 80601 303-655-2850
Kenlyn Newman, prin. Fax 655-2886
Overland Trail MS 700/6-8
455 N 19th Ave 80601 303-655-4000
Eric Lambright, prin. Fax 655-2880
Vikan MS 600/6-8
879 Jessup St 80601 303-655-4050
Trina Norris-Buck, prin. Fax 655-2881
Other Schools – See Commerce City, Henderson

Brighton Adventist Academy 100/K-10
820 S 5th Ave 80601 303-659-1223
Laura Groessel, lead tchr. Fax 558-8774
Elmwood Baptist Academy 100/PK-12
13100 E 144th Ave 80601 303-659-3818

Broomfield, Boulder, Pop. 54,716
Adams 12 Five Star SD
Supt. — See Thornton
Legacy HS 2,200/9-12
2701 W 136th Ave, 720-972-6700
Sara Marx, prin. Fax 972-6897
Westlake MS 1,100/6-8
2800 W 135th Ave 80020 720-972-5200
Rachel Heide, prin. Fax 972-5239

Boulder Valley SD RE-2
Supt. — See Boulder
Broomfield Heights MS 600/6-8
1555 Daphne St 80020 720-561-8400
Chris Meyer, prin. Fax 561-8401
Broomfield HS 1,400/9-12
1 Eagle Way 80020 720-561-8100
Ginger Ramsey, prin. Fax 561-5390

Holy Family HS 600/9-12
5195 W 144th Ave, 303-410-1411
Matthew Hauptly, prin. Fax 466-1935
Redstone College Post-Sec.
10851 W 120th Ave 80021 303-466-1714
Westwood College - Online Post-Sec.
10249 Church Ranch Way 80021 720-887-8888

Brush, Morgan, Pop. 5,401
Brush SD RE-2(J) 1,400/PK-12
PO Box 585 80723 970-842-5176
Dr. Bill Wilson, supt. Fax 842-4481
www.brushschools.org
Brush HS 500/9-12
PO Box 585 80723 970-842-5171
Rocky Schneider, prin. Fax 842-2804
Brush MS 200/7-8
PO Box 585 80723 970-842-5035
Connie Dreitz, prin. Fax 842-3009

Buena Vista, Chaffee, Pop. 2,579
Buena Vista SD R-31 1,000/PK-12
PO Box 2027 81211 719-395-7000
Lisa Yates, supt. Fax 395-7007
www.bvschools.org
Buena Vista HS 300/9-12
PO Box 2027 81211 719-395-7100
Brian Yates, prin. Fax 395-7106
Chaffee County HS 50/Alt
PO Box 2027 81211 719-395-4064
Mike Post, prin. Fax 395-8267
McGinnis MS 200/6-8
PO Box 2027 81211 719-395-7060
John Emilsson, prin. Fax 395-7090

Link S 50/9-12
18885 County Road 367 81211 719-395-6797
Patterson Christian Academy 100/PK-12
PO Box 1243 81211 719-395-6046
Amy Taylor, admin. Fax 395-2055

Burlington, Kit Carson, Pop. 4,206
Burlington SD RE-6J 800/PK-12
PO Box 369 80807 719-346-8737
Tom Satterly, supt. Fax 346-8541
www.burlingtonk12.org/
Burlington HS 200/9-12
380 Mike Lounge Dr 80807 719-346-8455
Michael Clark, prin. Fax 346-5599
Burlington MS 200/5-8
2600 Rose Ave 80807 719-346-5440
Pam Pekarek, prin. Fax 346-7900

Byers, Arapahoe, Pop. 1,139
Byers SD 32J 600/PK-12
444 E Front St 80103 303-822-5292
Tom Turrell, supt. Fax 822-9592
www.byers32j.k12.co.us
Byers HS 200/7-12
444 E Front St 80103 303-822-5292
Kelly Boren, prin. Fax 822-8616

Calhan, El Paso, Pop. 759
Calhan SD RJ-1 500/PK-12
780 8th St 80808 719-347-2541
Linda Miller, supt. Fax 347-2144
calhanschool.org
Calhan HS 100/9-12
780 8th St 80808 719-347-2766
David Slothower, prin. Fax 347-2108
Calhan MS 100/6-8
780 8th St 80808 719-347-2766
David Slothower, prin. Fax 347-2108

Campo, Baca, Pop. 109
Campo SD RE-6 50/PK-12
PO Box 70 81029 719-787-2226
Nikki Johnson, supt. Fax 787-0140
www.campok12.org

Campo JSHS 50/6-12
PO Box 70 81029 719-787-2226
Kim Jenkins, prin. Fax 787-0140

Canon City, Fremont, Pop. 16,140
Canon City SD RE-1 3,700/K-12
101 N 14th St 81212 719-276-5700
Dr. Robin Gooldy, supt. Fax 276-5739
www.canoncityschools.org/
Canon City HS 1,100/9-12
1313 College Ave 81212 719-276-5870
Brett Meuli, prin. Fax 276-5950
Canon City MS 400/6-8
1215 Main St 81212 719-276-5740
Tim Renn, prin. Fax 276-5795

Carbondale, Garfield, Pop. 6,354
Roaring Fork SD RE-1
Supt. — See Glenwood Springs
Bridges HS 100/Alt
455 S 3rd St 81623 970-384-6160
Lyn Bair, prin. Fax 384-6165
Carbondale MS 400/5-8
180 Snowmass Dr 81623 970-384-5700
Jennifer Lamont, prin. Fax 384-5705
Roaring Fork HS 300/9-12
2270 Highway 133 81623 970-384-5757
Drew Adams, prin. Fax 384-5755

Colorado Rocky Mountain S 200/9-12
1493 County Road 106 81623 970-963-2562
Jeff Leahy, head sch Fax 963-9865

Castle Rock, Douglas, Pop. 47,126
Douglas County SD RE-1 61,200/PK-12
620 Wilcox St 80104 303-387-0100
Erin Kane, supt. Fax 387-0107
www.dcsdk12.org
Castle Rock MS 900/7-8
2575 Meadows Pkwy, 303-387-1300
LeeAnn Hayen, prin. Fax 387-1301
Castle View HS 1,800/9-12
5254 Meadows Dr, 303-387-9000
Rex Corr, prin. Fax 387-9001
Douglas County HS 1,800/9-12
2842 Front St 80104 303-387-1000
Tony Kappas, prin. Fax 387-1001
Mesa MS 1,000/7-8
365 N Mitchell St 80104 303-387-4750
Anthony Jackowski, prin. Fax 387-4751
Oakes HS 200/Alt
961 Plum Creek Blvd 80104 303-387-0650
Derek Fleshman, prin. Fax 387-0651
Other Schools – See Highlands Ranch, Littleton, Parker

Cedaredge, Delta, Pop. 2,222
Delta County SD 50(J)
Supt. — See Delta
Cedaredge HS 200/9-12
575 SE Deer Creek Dr 81413 970-856-6882
Randy Brown, prin. Fax 856-6616
Cedaredge MS 200/6-8
845 SE Deer Creek Dr 81413 970-856-3118
Delaine Hudson, prin. Fax 856-3235

Centennial, Arapahoe, Pop. 97,891
Cherry Creek SD 5
Supt. — See Greenwood Village
Eaglecrest HS 2,500/9-12
5100 S Picadilly St 80015 720-886-1000
Gwen Hansen-Vigil, prin. Fax 886-1029
Endeavor Academy Alt
14076 E Briarwood Ave 80112 720-886-7200
Mark Morgan, prin. Fax 886-7288
Thunder Ridge MS 1,300/6-8
5250 S Picadilly St 80015 720-886-1500
Angie Zehner, prin. Fax 886-1582

Littleton SD
Supt. — See Littleton
Arapahoe HS 2,300/9-12
2201 E Dry Creek Rd 80122 303-347-6000
Natalie Pramenko, prin. Fax 347-6004
Newton MS 600/6-8
4001 E Arapahoe Rd 80122 303-347-7900
James O'Tremba, prin. Fax 347-3945

College for Financial Planning Post-Sec.
9000 E Nichols Ave Ste 200 80112 303-220-1200
Jones International University Post-Sec.
9697 E Mineral Ave 80112 303-784-8904

Center, Saguache, Pop. 2,207
Center Consolidated SD 26JT 700/PK-12
550 Sylvester Ave 81125 719-754-3442
Chris Vance, supt. Fax 754-3952
www.center.k12.co.us
Academic Recovery Center 50/Alt
550 Sylvester Ave 81125 719-251-3334
Joy Werner, dir. Fax 754-3952
Center HS 200/9-12
550 Sylvester Ave 81125 719-754-2232
Kevin Jones, prin. Fax 754-2856
Skoglund MS 100/6-8
550 Sylvester Ave 81125 719-754-2232
Luis Murillo, prin. Fax 754-2856

Cheraw, Otero, Pop. 245
Cheraw SD 31 200/PK-12
PO Box 160 81030 719-853-6655
Tonya Rodwell, supt. Fax 853-6322
cheraw.k12.co.us
Cheraw HS 100/9-12
PO Box 160 81030 719-853-6655
Todd Werner, prin. Fax 853-6322
Cheraw MS 100/6-8
PO Box 160 81030 719-853-6655
Todd Werner, prin. Fax 853-6322

Cheyenne Wells, Cheyenne, Pop. 839
Cheyenne County SD RE-5 200/PK-12
PO Box 577 80810 719-767-5866
Glen Bradshaw, supt. Fax 767-8773
www.cheyennesd.net/

Cheyenne Wells HS 50/9-12
PO Box 577 80810 719-767-5612
Mike Miller, prin. Fax 767-5749
Cheyenne Wells MS 50/7-8
PO Box 577 80810 719-767-5656
Mike Miller, prin. Fax 767-5136

Clifton, Mesa, Pop. 19,453
Mesa County Valley SD 51
Supt. — See Grand Junction
Mt. Garfield MS 600/6-8
3475 Front St 81520 970-254-4720
Hal Templeton, prin. Fax 464-0536

Collbran, Mesa, Pop. 699
Plateau Valley SD 50 500/PK-12
56600 Highway 330 81624 970-487-3547
Gregory Randall, supt. Fax 487-3876
www.pvsd50.org
Grand Mesa HS 100/Alt
56600 Highway 330 81624 970-487-2017
Kristi Mease, prin.
Plateau Valley HS 100/9-12
56600 Highway 330 81624 970-487-3547
Leroy Gutierrez, prin. Fax 487-3876
Plateau Valley MS 100/6-8
56600 Highway 330 81624 970-487-3547
Leroy Gutierrez, prin. Fax 487-3876

Colorado City, Pueblo, Pop. 2,165
Pueblo County SD 70
Supt. — See Pueblo
Craver MS 200/6-8
PO Box 19369 81019 719-676-3030
Gene Padilla, prin. Fax 676-3511

Colorado Springs, El Paso, Pop. 400,464
Academy SD 20 26,400/PK-12
1110 Chapel Hills Dr 80920 719-234-1200
Dr. Mark Hatchell, supt. Fax 234-1299
www.asd20.org/
Aspen Valley Campus 100/7-12
1450 Chapel Hills Dr 80920 719-234-6000
George Stone, prin. Fax 234-6099
Challenger MS 800/6-8
10215 Lexington Dr 80920 719-234-3000
Tony Scott, prin. Fax 234-3199
Discovery Canyon Campus 2,500/PK-12
1810 N Gate Blvd 80921 719-234-1800
Jim Bailey, prin. Fax 234-1899
Eagleview MS 1,000/6-8
1325 Vindicator Dr 80919 719-234-3400
John Jamison, prin. Fax 234-3599
Liberty HS 1,600/9-12
8720 Scarborough Dr 80920 719-234-2200
Alan Thimmig, prin. Fax 234-2399
Mountain Ridge MS 1,100/6-8
9150 Lexington Dr 80920 719-234-3200
Jeff Sterk, prin. Fax 234-3399
Pine Creek HS 1,500/9-12
10750 Thunder Mountain Ave 80908 719-234-2600
Kolette Back, prin. Fax 234-2799
Rampart HS 1,500/9-12
8250 Lexington Dr 80920 719-234-2000
Pete Alvarez, prin. Fax 234-2199
Timberview MS 1,100/6-8
8680 Scarborough Dr 80920 719-234-3600
Brett Smith, prin. Fax 234-3799
Other Schools – See USAF Academy

Cheyenne Mountain SD 12 4,700/PK-12
1775 LaClede St 80905 719-475-6100
Dr. Walter Cooper, supt. Fax 475-6106
www.cmsd.k12.co.us
Cheyenne Mountain HS 1,300/9-12
1200 Cresta Rd 80906 719-475-6110
Don Fortenberry, prin. Fax 475-6116
Cheyenne Mountain JHS 600/7-8
1200 W Cheyenne Rd 80906 719-475-6120
Greg Watkins, prin. Fax 475-6123

Colorado Springs SD 11 27,700/PK-12
1115 N El Paso St 80903 719-520-2000
Dr. Nicholas Gledich, supt. Fax 577-4546
www.d11.org
Bijou S 100/Alt
2115 Afton Way 80909 719-328-2065
Kathryn Presnal, dir. Fax 328-2101
Coronado HS 1,600/9-12
1590 W Fillmore St 80904 719-328-3600
Darin Smith, prin. Fax 328-3601
Digital HS Alt
2115 Afton Way 80909 719-328-3012
John Bailey, prin. Fax 328-3071
Doherty HS 2,200/9-12
4515 Barnes Rd 80917 719-328-6400
Kevin Gardner, prin. Fax 328-6401
Early College HS 100/9-12
2115 Afton Way 80909 719-328-2030
Aurora Umana-Arko, prin. Fax 328-2029
Galileo S of Math & Science 500/6-8
1600 N Union Blvd 80909 719-328-2200
Richard Law, prin. Fax 448-0498
Holmes MS 700/6-8
2455 Mesa Rd 80904 719-328-3800
Robert Utter, prin. Fax 448-0358
Jenkins MS 1,000/6-8
6410 Austin Bluffs Pkwy, 719-328-5300
Darren Joiner, prin. Fax 266-5276
Mann MS 500/6-8
1001 E Van Buren St 80907 719-328-2300
Shawn Limberg, prin. Fax 488-0354
Mitchell HS 1,300/9-12
1205 Potter Dr 80909 719-328-6600
Carlos Perez, prin. Fax 328-6601
North MS 700/6-8
612 E Yampa St 80903 719-328-2400
Christopher Kilroy, prin. Fax 448-0268
Palmer HS 2,100/9-12
301 N Nevada Ave 80903 719-328-5000
Lara Disney, prin. Fax 328-5001
Russell MS 700/6-8
3825 Montebello Dr W 80918 719-328-5200
Julie Johnson, prin. Fax 531-5520

Sabin MS 900/6-8
3605 N Carefree Cir 80917 719-328-7000
Jared Welch, prin. Fax 573-4960
Springs Community Night S Alt
2115 Afton Way 80909 719-328-2160
Tanya Nash, prin. Fax 328-2161
Swigert Aerospace Academy 500/6-8
4220 E Pikes Peak Ave 80909 719-328-6900
James Nason, prin. Fax 573-5295
Tesla Educational Opportunity Center 200/Alt
2115 Afton Way 80909 719-328-2100
Greg Wiley, prin. Fax 328-2101
West MS 300/6-8
1920 W Pikes Peak Ave 80904 719-328-3900
Shalah Sims, prin. Fax 448-0141
Adult Education Center Adult
2115 Afton Way 80909 719-328-3001
M. Burkhardt-Shields, dir. Fax 630-2286

Falcon SD 49
Supt. — See Falcon
Horizon MS 600/6-8
1750 Piros Dr 80915 719-495-5210
Dustin Horras, prin. Fax 495-5209
Sand Creek HS 1,200/9-12
7005 N Carefree Cir 80922 719-495-1160
Fax 495-1196
Skyview MS 1,000/6-8
6350 Windom Peak Blvd, 719-495-5566
Catherine Tinucci, prin. Fax 495-5569
Vista Ridge HS 1,200/9-12
6888 Black Forest Rd, 719-494-8800
Bruce Grose, prin. Fax 494-8838

Hanover SD 28 200/PK-12
17050 S Peyton Hwy 80928 719-683-2247
Dr. Grant Schmidt, supt. Fax 683-2299
www.hanoverhornets.org
Hanover JSHS 100/5-12
17050 S Peyton Hwy 80928 719-683-2247
Danielle Van Esselstine, prin. Fax 683-3805

Harrison SD 2 11,100/PK-12
1060 Harrison Rd 80905 719-579-2000
Andre Spencer Ed.D., supt. Fax 579-2019
www.hsd2.org
Carmel MS 400/6-8
1740 Pepperwood Dr 80910 719-579-3210
Lorna Breske, prin. Fax 579-2695
Fox Meadow MS 500/6-8
1450 Cheyenne Meadows Rd 80906 719-527-7100
John Rogerson, prin. Fax 576-0918
Harrison HS 900/9-12
2755 Janitell Rd 80906 719-579-2080
Cheri Martinez, prin. Fax 538-4832
High School Preparatory Academy Alt
2250 Jet Wing Dr 80916 719-579-2580
Damon DiFabio, prin. Fax 579-2582
Panorama MS 500/6-8
2145 S Chelton Rd 80916 719-579-3220
Elizabeth Domangue, prin. Fax 579-2756
Sierra HS 900/9-12
2250 Jet Wing Dr 80916 719-579-2090
Aaron Griffen, prin. Fax 579-2536

Widefield SD 3 9,400/PK-12
1820 Main St 80911 719-391-3000
Scott Campbell, supt. Fax 390-4372
www.wsd3.org
Discovery HS 100/Alt
701 Widefield Dr 80911 719-391-3121
Steven Hutchcraft, prin. Fax 391-3091
Mesa Ridge HS 1,300/9-12
6070 Mesa Ridge Pkwy 80911 719-391-3600
Scott Sage, prin. Fax 390-9697
Sproul JHS 600/6-8
235 Sumac Dr 80911 719-391-3215
Maureen di Stasio, prin. Fax 391-3215
Watson JHS 700/6-8
136 Fontaine Blvd 80911 719-391-3255
Justin Lee, prin. Fax 392-3419
Widefield HS 1,300/9-12
615 Widefield Dr 80911 719-391-3200
Aaron Hoffman, prin. Fax 391-8072
Other Schools – See Fountain

CollegeAmerica - Colorado Springs Post-Sec.
2020 N Academy Blvd 80909 719-227-0170
Colorado Acad of Veterinary Technology Post-Sec.
2766 Janitell Rd 80906 719-219-9636
Colorado College Post-Sec.
14 E Cache La Poudre St 80903 719-389-6000
Colorado School for the Deaf and Blind Post-Sec.
33 N Institute St 80903 719-578-2100
Colorado Springs Christian S 800/K-12
4855 Mallow Rd 80907 719-599-3553
Dr. Roland DeRenzo, supt. Fax 268-2184
Colorado Springs S 300/PK-12
21 Broadmoor Ave 80906 719-475-9747
Aaron Schubach, head sch Fax 475-9864
Colorado Technical University Post-Sec.
4435 N Chestnut St 80907 719-598-0200
DeVry University Post-Sec.
1175 Kelly Johnson Blvd 80920 719-632-3000
Evangelical Christian Academy 200/7-12
4052 S Nonchalant Cir 80917 719-597-3675
Dr. Jim Johnson, supt. Fax 597-6983
Everest College Post-Sec.
1815 Jet Wing Dr 80916 719-638-6580
Fountain Valley S of Colorado 200/9-12
6155 Fountain Valley School 80911 719-390-7035
William Webb, head sch Fax 391-9039
IntelliTec College Post-Sec.
2315 E Pikes Peak Ave 80909 719-632-7626
IntelliTec Medical Institute Post-Sec.
6805 Corporate Dr Ste 100 80919 719-596-7400
International Salon and Spa Academy Post-Sec.
5705 N Academy Blvd 80918 719-597-1413
National American University Post-Sec.
1915 Jamboree Dr Ste 185 80920 719-590-8300
Nazarene Bible College Post-Sec.
1111 Academy Park Loop 80910 719-884-5000
Pikes Peak Christian S 400/PK-12
5905 Flintridge Dr 80918 719-598-8610

Pikes Peak Community College Post-Sec.
5675 S Academy Blvd 80906 719-502-2000
St. Mary HS 300/9-12
2501 E Yampa St 80909 719-635-7540
Jim Felice, prin. Fax 471-7623
Toni & Guy Hairdressing Academy Post-Sec.
332 Main St 80911 719-390-9898
UCH Memorial Hospital School of Rad Tech Post-Sec.
1400 E Boulder St 80909 719-365-8291
University of Colorado Colorado Springs Post-Sec.
1420 Austin Bluffs Pkwy 80918 719-255-8227
University of the Rockies Post-Sec.
555 E Pikes Peak Ave # 108 80903 719-442-0505
University S 100/PK-12
2713 W Cucharras St 80904 719-302-3751
Jeff Cooper, admin. Fax 377-3903

Commerce City, Adams, Pop. 45,019
Adams County SD 14 7,600/PK-12
5291 E 60th Ave 80022 303-853-3333
Dr. Javier Abrego, supt. Fax 286-9753
www.adams14.org
Adams City HS 1,700/9-12
7200 Quebec Pkwy 80022 303-289-3111
Gionni Thompson, prin. Fax 288-6113
Adams City MS 800/6-8
4451 E 72nd Ave 80022 303-289-5881
Matt Schwartz, prin. Fax 288-8574
Arnold HS 200/9-12
6500 E 72nd Ave 80022 303-289-2983
Paul Sandos, prin. Fax 289-7167
Kearney MS 800/6-8
6160 Kearney St 80022 303-287-0261
Veronica Jeffers, prin. Fax 287-0432

SD 27J
Supt. — See Brighton
Stuart MS 600/6-8
15955 E 101st Way 80022 720-685-5500
Dr. Richard Patterson, prin. Fax 685-5506

Rocky Mountain Lutheran HS 100/9-12
10391 Luther Ct 80022 303-346-1947
Rick Lohmiller, prin. Fax 451-0817

Conifer, Jefferson, Pop. 600
Jefferson County SD R-1
Supt. — See Golden
Conifer HS 800/9-12
10441 Highway 73 80433 303-982-5255
Wesley Paxton, prin. Fax 982-5256
West Jefferson MS 600/6-8
9449 Barnes Ave 80433 303-982-3056
Rebecca Brown, prin. Fax 982-3057

Cortez, Montezuma, Pop. 8,328
Montezuma-Cortez SD RE-1 2,800/PK-12
PO Box R 81321 970-565-7522
Alex Carter, supt. Fax 565-2161
www.cortez.k12.co.us
Cortez MS 600/6-8
450 W 2nd St 81321 970-565-7824
Glenn Smith, prin. Fax 565-5120
Montezuma-Cortez HS 700/9-12
418 S Sligo St 81321 970-565-3722
Dr. Jason Wayman, prin. Fax 565-5118

Cotopaxi, Fremont, Pop. 45
Cotopaxi SD RE-3 100/PK-12
PO Box 385 81223 719-942-4131
Randy Bohlander, supt. Fax 942-4134
www.cotopaxire3.org/
Cotopaxi S 100/PK-12
PO Box 385 81223 719-942-4131
Jackie Crabtree, prin. Fax 942-4134

Craig, Moffat, Pop. 9,327
Moffat County SD RE-1 2,200/PK-12
775 Yampa Ave 81625 970-824-3268
Brent Curtice, supt. Fax 824-6655
moffatsd.org
Craig MS 500/6-8
915 Yampa Ave 81625 970-824-3289
Dave Grabowski, prin. Fax 824-3858
Moffat County HS 500/9-12
900 Finley Ln 81625 970-824-7036
Kelly McCormick, prin. Fax 824-3130

Creede, Mineral, Pop. 412
Creede SD 100/PK-12
PO Box 429 81130 719-658-2220
Buck Stroh, supt. Fax 658-2942
www.creedek12.net
Creede MSHS 50/6-12
PO Box 429 81130 719-658-2220
John Goss, prin. Fax 658-2942

Crested Butte, Gunnison, Pop. 1,477
Gunnison Watershed SD RE 1J
Supt. — See Gunnison
Crested Butte Community S 600/K-12
PO Box 339 81224 970-641-7720
Stephanie Niemi, prin. Fax 641-7729

Cripple Creek, Teller, Pop. 1,167
Cripple Creek-Victor SD RE-1 400/PK-12
PO Box 897 80813 719-689-2685
Leslie Lindauer, supt. Fax 689-2256
www.ccvschools.org
Cripple Creek-Victor JSHS 200/7-12
PO Box 897 80813 719-689-2661
Dr. Tory Richey, prin. Fax 389-2256

De Beque, Mesa, Pop. 499
De Beque SD 49JT 100/PK-12
PO Box 70 81630 970-283-5418
Alan Dillon, supt. Fax 283-5598
www.dbschools.org
De Beque JSHS 100/7-12
PO Box 70 81630 970-283-5596
Alan Dillon, prin. Fax 283-5598

Deer Trail, Arapahoe, Pop. 538
Deer Trail SD 26J 200/PK-12
PO Box 129 80105 303-769-4421
Kevin Schott, supt. Fax 769-4600
www.dt26j.org
Deer Trail JSHS 100/6-12
PO Box 129 80105 303-769-4421
Dave Casey, prin. Fax 769-4600

Del Norte, Rio Grande, Pop. 1,670
Del Norte SD C-7 400/K-12
770 11th St 81132 719-657-4040
Chris Burr, supt. Fax 657-2546
delnorte.schoolfusion.us
Del Norte HS 100/9-12
770 11th St 81132 719-657-4020
Russelll Randolph, prin. Fax 657-4024
Del Norte MS 100/5-8
770 11th St 81132 719-657-4030
Amy Duda, prin. Fax 657-9087

Delta, Delta, Pop. 8,798
Delta County SD 50(J) 4,600/PK-12
7655 2075 Rd 81416 970-874-4438
Caryn Gibson, supt. Fax 874-5744
www.deltaschools.com
Delta Academy of Applied Learning 50/Alt
PO Box 224 81416 970-874-0835
Kim Egging, dir. Fax 874-8684
Delta County Opportunity S 100/Alt
1765 US Highway 50 81416 970-874-7671
John Jones, prin. Fax 874-8796
Delta HS 600/9-12
1400 Pioneer Rd 81416 970-874-8031
Derek Carlson, prin. Fax 874-8034
Delta MS 500/6-8
910 Grand Ave 81416 970-874-8046
Jennifer Erwin, prin. Fax 874-8049
Other Schools – See Cedaredge, Hotchkiss, Paonia

Denver, Denver, Pop. 585,815
Denver County SD 1 83,600/PK-12
1860 N Lincoln St 80203 720-423-3200
Tom Boasberg, supt. Fax 423-3413
www.dpsk12.org/
Bear Valley International S 6-8
3005 S Golden Way 80227 720-423-9600
Lindsay Meier, prin.
CEC Middle College of Denver 400/9-12
2650 Eliot St 80211 720-423-6600
Jamie Lofaro, prin. Fax 423-6604
Collegiate Prep Academy at Noel 400/9-12
5290 Kittredge St 80239 720-424-0850
Martha Gustafson, prin. Fax 424-0945
Compassion Road Academy 100/9-12
1000 Cherokee St 80204 720-424-2200
Kimberly Ortiz, prin.
Contemporary Learning Academy 200/Alt
200 E 9th Ave 80203 720-423-6900
Shawne Anderson, prin. Fax 423-6999
Crittenton HS 100/Alt
55 S Zuni St 80223 303-423-7900
Michelle Wright, admin. Fax 423-7905
DCIS at Montbello 700/6-12
5000 Crown Blvd 80239 720-423-5900
Julie Murgal, prin. Fax 423-5390
Denver Center for 21st Century Learning 200/Alt
1690 N Williams St 80218 720-424-2980
Renard Simmons, prin. Fax 424-3031
Denver Center for International Studies 800/6-12
574 W 6th Ave 80204 720-423-9000
Therese McCorquodale, prin. Fax 423-9075
Denver Discovery S 6-8
3480 Syracuse St 80238 720-424-4790
Kristen Atwood, prin. Fax 424-4791
Denver Montessori JSHS 7-12
4250 Shoshone St 80211 720-424-2600
Katy Myers, prin.
S of Innovation & Sustainable Design 9-12
150 S Pearl St 80209 720-424-2000
Danny Medved, prin.
Denver S of the Arts 1,100/6-12
7111 Montview Blvd 80220 720-424-1700
William Kohut, prin. Fax 424-1845
East HS 2,400/9-12
1600 City Park Esplanade 80206 720-423-8300
Andy Mendelsberg, prin. Fax 423-8306
Escuela Tlatelolco 100/Alt
2949 Federal Blvd 80211 303-964-8993
Nita Gonzales, prin. Fax 964-9795
Excel Academy 100/9-12
1825 S Federal Blvd 80219 720-424-2250
Cynthia Navarro, prin.
Gilliam S 50/Alt
2844 N Downing St 80205 303-291-8929
Wes Montoya, dir. Fax 292-9348
Grant Beacon MS 400/6-8
1751 S Washington St 80210 720-423-9360
Michelle Saab, prin. Fax 423-9385
Griffith HS, 1860 Lincoln St 80203 400/Alt
David Daves, prin. 720-423-4900
Hamilton MS 900/6-8
8600 E Dartmouth Ave 80231 720-423-9500
Christian Sawyer, prin. Fax 423-9445
Henry World MS 800/6-8
3005 S Golden Way 80227 720-423-9560
Don Roy, prin. Fax 423-9585
High Tech Early College 400/9-12
11200 E 45th Ave 80239 720-424-2450
Stacy Parish, prin. Fax 424-2460
Hill MS Campus of Arts & Sciences 800/6-8
451 Clermont St 80220 720-423-9680
Sean Kavanaugh, prin. Fax 423-9709
Jefferson HS 1,100/9-12
3950 S Holly St 80237 720-423-7000
Mike Christoff, prin. Fax 423-7047
Kennedy HS 1,300/9-12
2855 S Lamar St 80227 720-423-4300
Christian De La Oliva, prin. Fax 423-4309
Kepner Beacon MS 6-8
911 S Hazel Ct 80219 720-424-0027
Alex Magana, prin.
Kepner MS 800/6-8
911 S Hazel Ct 80219 720-424-0000
Elza Guajardo, prin. Fax 424-0023
King Early College HS 1,200/6-12
19535 E 46th Ave 80249 720-424-0420
Kimberly Grayson, prin. Fax 424-0557
Kunsmiller Creative Arts Academy 900/K-12
2250 S Quitman Way 80219 720-424-0200
Peter Castillo, prin. Fax 424-0145
Lake International MS 400/6-8
1820 Lowell Blvd 80204 720-424-0260
Rebecca Marques-Guerrero, prin. Fax 424-0380
Legacy Options HS Alt
6850 Argonne St 80249 720-424-3100
Anthony McWright, prin. Fax 424-3103
Lincoln HS 1,500/9-12
2285 S Federal Blvd 80219 720-423-5000
Larry Irvin, prin. Fax 423-5098
Manual HS 400/9-12
1700 E 28th Ave 80205 720-423-6300
Nickolas Dawkins, prin. Fax 423-6302
McAuliffe International MS 400/6-8
2540 Holly St 80207 720-424-1540
Kurt Dennis, prin. Fax 424-1565
McAuliffe Manual MS 6-8
2540 Holly St 80207 720-423-6550
Jessica Long, prin.
Merrill MS 500/6-8
1551 S Monroe St 80210 720-424-0600
Christina Sylvester, prin. Fax 424-0625
Morey MS 600/6-8
840 E 14th Ave 80218 720-424-0700
Noah Tonk, prin. Fax 424-0727
Noel Community Arts HS 600/6-12
5000 Crown Blvd 80239 720-423-5840
Deborah Blair-Minter, prin. Fax 423-5863
Northfield HS 9-12
5500 Central Park Blvd 80238 720-423-8000
Amy Bringedahl, prin.
North HS 800/9-12
2960 N Speer Blvd 80211 720-423-2700
Scott Wolf, prin. Fax 423-2708
North HS Engagement Center 100/Alt
2960 N Speer Blvd 80211 720-423-2700
Teresa Steele, prin. Fax 423-2708
P.R.E.P. Academy 200/Alt
2727 Columbine St 80205 720-424-8451
Eric Rowe, prin. Fax 424-8477
P.U.S.H. Academy 200/Alt
4501 Airport Way 80239 720-423-7200
Karen Powell, prin. Fax 423-7259
Randolph MSHS 900/6-12
3955 N Steele St 80205 720-424-1080
Cesar Cedillo, prin. Fax 424-1241
Respect Academy at Lincoln 100/Alt
2285 S Federal Blvd 80219 720-423-5203
Wauneta Vann, prin.
Skinner MS 500/6-8
3435 W 40th Ave 80211 720-424-1420
Michelle Koyama, prin. Fax 424-1446
South HS 1,400/9-12
1700 E Louisiana Ave 80210 720-423-6000
Jen Hanson, prin. Fax 423-6280
Summit Academy 200/Alt
5590 W Evans Ave 80227 720-424-2400
Bobby Thomas, prin.
Vista Academy 200/6-12
4800 Telluride St 80249 720-423-7650
Anthony Smith, prin. Fax 423-7667
Washington HS 1,400/9-12
655 S Monaco Pkwy 80224 720-423-8600
Scott Lessard, prin. Fax 423-8614
West Career Academy 100/Alt
951 Elati St 80204 720-423-5390
Jessica Newman, prin.
West Early College HS 6-12
951 Elati St 80204 720-423-5300
Ana Mendoza, prin.
West Leadership Academy 400/6-12
951 Elati St 80204 720-423-5300
Teresa Klava, prin.

Jefferson County SD R-1
Supt. — See Golden
D'Evelyn JSHS 1,000/7-12
10359 W Nassau Ave 80235 303-982-2600
Anthony Edwards, prin. Fax 982-2601

Mapleton SD 1 8,500/PK-12
591 E 80th Ave 80229 303-853-1000
Charlotte Ciancio, supt. Fax 853-1087
www.mapleton.us
Global Intermediate Academy 4-8
7480 N Broadway 80221 303-853-1930
Tiffany Dragoo, dir. Fax 853-1956
Global Leadership Academy 400/9-12
7480 N Broadway 80221 303-853-1930
Jeremy Jimenez, dir. Fax 853-1956
Other Schools – See Thornton

Sheridan SD 2
Supt. — See Sheridan
Ft. Logan Northgate S 300/3-8
4000 S Lowell Blvd 80236 720-833-6853
Nelson Van Vranken, prin. Fax 833-6746
S.O.A.R. Academy 100/Alt
3201 W Oxford Ave 80236 720-833-6796
Christian Ramaker, dir.
Sheridan HS 400/9-12
3201 W Oxford Ave 80236 720-833-6987
Michele Kelley, prin. Fax 833-6833

Westminster SD
Supt. — See Westminster
Carpenter MS 600/6-8
7001 Lipan St 80221 303-428-8583
Chad Anderson, prin. Fax 657-3962
Ranum MS 800/6-8
2401 W 80th Ave 80221 303-428-9577
Shannon Willy, prin. Fax 657-3952

Accelerated Schools 50/K-12
2160 S Cook St 80210 303-758-2003
Jane Queen, dir. Fax 757-4336

American Pathways University — Post-Sec.
2227 Franklin St 80205 — 303-839-2551
American University of Paris — Post-Sec.
700 Colorado Blvd # 502 80206 — 303-993-4326
Argosy University / Denver — Post-Sec.
7600 E Eastman Ave 80231 — 303-923-4110
Arrupe Jesuit HS — 300/9-12
4343 Utica St 80212 — 303-455-7449
Art Institute of Colorado — Post-Sec.
1200 Lincoln St 80203 — 303-837-0825
Aspen University — Post-Sec.
720 S Colorado Blvd #1150N 80246 — 800-441-4746
Bel-Rea Institute of Animal Technology — Post-Sec.
1681 S Dayton St, — 303-751-8700
Beth Jacob HS of Denver — 100/9-12
5100 W 14th Ave 80204 — 303-893-1333
Bishop Machebeuf Catholic HS — 400/9-12
458 Uinta Way 80230 — 303-344-0082
Marc Nestorick, prin. — Fax 344-1582
Centura-St. Anthony Hospital — Post-Sec.
4231 W 16th Ave 80204 — 303-629-4350
CollegeAmerica - Denver — Post-Sec.
1385 S Colorado Blvd Fl 5 80222 — 303-534-0226
Colorado Academy — 900/PK-12
3800 S Pierce St 80235 — 303-986-1501
Michael Davis Ph.D., hdmstr. — Fax 914-2583
Colorado Ctr for Medical Laboratory Sci. — Post-Sec.
1719 E 19th Ave 80218 — 303-839-6485
Colorado Heights University — Post-Sec.
3001 S Federal Blvd 80236 — 303-937-4225
CO Sch of Traditional Chinese Medicine — Post-Sec.
1441 York St Ste 202 80206 — 303-329-6355
Community College of Denver — Post-Sec.
PO Box 173363 80217 — 303-556-2600
Denver Academy — 400/1-12
4400 E Iliff Ave 80222 — 303-777-5870
Mark Twarogowski, hdmstr. — Fax 777-5893
Denver Academy of Torah — 100/PK-12
6825 E Alameda Ave 80224 — 720-859-6806
Denver Health Medical Center — Post-Sec.
660 Bannock St 80204 — 303-436-6611
Denver Jewish Day School — 400/K-12
2450 S Wabash St 80231 — 303-369-0663
Avi Halzel, head sch — Fax 369-0664
Denver Waldorf S — 300/PK-12
2100 S Pennsylvania St 80210 — 303-777-0531
Kelly Church, admin. — Fax 744-1216
Emily Griffith Opportunity School — Post-Sec.
1250 Welton St 80204 — 720-423-4700
Iliff School of Theology — Post-Sec.
2201 S University Blvd 80210 — 303-744-1287
Johnson & Wales University-Denver Campus — Post-Sec.
7150 Montview Blvd 80220 — 303-256-9300
Lincoln College of Technology — Post-Sec.
11194 E 45th Ave 80239 — 303-722-5724
Metropolitan State University — Post-Sec.
PO Box 173362 80217 — 303-556-2400
Mullen HS — 800/9-12
3601 S Lowell Blvd 80236 — 303-761-1764
Janell Kloostermann, prin. — Fax 761-0502
National American University — Post-Sec.
1325 S Colorado Blvd #100 80222 — 303-876-7100
Phlebotomy Learning Center — Post-Sec.
1780 S Bellaire St Ste 780 80222 — 303-584-0575
Pima Medical Institute — Post-Sec.
7475 Dakin St 80221 — 303-426-1800
Redstone College — Post-Sec.
7350 Broadway 80221 — 303-466-1714
Regis University — Post-Sec.
3333 Regis Blvd 80221 — 303-458-4100
Rocky Mountain College of Art & Design — Post-Sec.
1600 Pierce St 80214 — 800-888-2787
St. John Vianney Theological Seminary — Post-Sec.
1300 S Steele St 80210 — 303-282-3427
University of Colorado Denver — Post-Sec.
1250 14th St 80202 — 303-556-2400
University of Denver — Post-Sec.
2199 S University Blvd 80210 — 303-871-2000
Westwood College - Denver North — Post-Sec.
7350 Broadway 80221 — 303-650-5050
Westwood College - Denver South — Post-Sec.
3150 S Sheridan Blvd 80227 — 303-934-1122
William Howard Taft University — Post-Sec.
600 S Cherry St Ste 525 80246 — 303-867-1155
Yeshiva Toras Chaim HS — 100/9-12
PO Box 40067 80204 — 303-629-8200
Yeshiva Toras Chaim Talmudical Seminary — Post-Sec.
1555 Stuart St 80204 — 303-629-8200

Dolores, Montezuma, Pop. 903
Dolores SD RE-4A — 700/PK-12
PO Box 727 81323 — 970-882-7255
Dr. Scott Cooper, supt. — Fax 882-7685
www.doloresschools.org
Dolores HS — 200/9-12
PO Box 727 81323 — 970-882-7288
Jenifer Hufman, prin. — Fax 882-7685
Dolores MS — 100/7-8
PO Box 727 81323 — 970-882-7288
Jenifer Hufman, admin. — Fax 882-7289

Dove Creek, Dolores, Pop. 714
Dolores County SD RE-2J — 300/PK-12
PO Box 459 81324 — 970-677-2522
Bruce Hankins, supt. — Fax 677-2712
www.dc2j.org
Dove Creek HS — 100/6-12
PO Box 459 81324 — 970-677-2237
Ty Gray, prin. — Fax 677-2927

Durango, LaPlata, Pop. 16,541
Durango SD 9-R — 4,900/PK-12
201 E 12th St 81301 — 970-247-5411
Dan Snowberger, supt. — Fax 247-9581
www.durangoschools.org
Durango Big Picture HS — 100/9-12
215 E 12th St 81301 — 970-259-0203
Alain Henry, prin. — Fax 382-0588
Durango HS — 1,100/9-12
2390 Main Ave 81301 — 970-259-1630
LeAnne Garcia, prin. — Fax 385-1493
Escalante MS — 500/6-8
141 Baker Ln 81303 — 970-247-9490
Jeremy Voss, prin. — Fax 385-1194
Miller MS — 400/6-8
2608 Junction St 81301 — 970-247-1418
Cito Nuhn, prin. — Fax 385-1191

Fort Lewis College — Post-Sec.
1000 Rim Dr 81301 — 970-247-7010

Eads, Kiowa, Pop. 605
Kiowa County SD RE-1 — 200/PK-12
210 W 10th St 81036 — 719-438-2218
Glenn Smith, supt. — Fax 438-2272
www.eadseagles.org
Eads HS — 100/9-12
210 W 10th St 81036 — 719-438-2214
Betsy Barnett, prin. — Fax 438-2272
Eads MS — 50/6-8
900 Maine St 81036 — 719-438-2216
Betsy Barnett, prin. — Fax 438-2272

Eagle, Eagle, Pop. 6,436
Eagle County SD RE-50 — 6,500/PK-12
PO Box 740 81631 — 970-328-6321
Jason Glass, supt. — Fax 328-1024
www.eagleschools.net
Eagle Valley MS — 300/6-8
PO Box 1019 81631 — 970-328-6224
Katie Jarnot, prin. — Fax 328-8915
Other Schools – See Edwards, Gypsum

Eaton, Weld, Pop. 4,298
Eaton SD RE-2 — 1,800/K-12
211 1st St 80615 — 970-454-3402
Randy Miller Ed.D., supt. — Fax 454-5193
www.eaton.k12.co.us
Eaton HS — 500/9-12
114 Park Ave 80615 — 970-454-3374
Mark Naill, prin. — Fax 454-5190
Eaton MS — 400/6-8
225 Juniper Ave 80615 — 970-454-3358
Jim Orth, prin. — Fax 454-1337

Edgewater, Jefferson, Pop. 5,086
Jefferson County SD R-1
Supt. — See Golden
Jefferson HS — 600/7-12
2305 Pierce St 80214 — 303-982-6056
Michael James, prin. — Fax 982-6057

Edwards, Eagle, Pop. 10,187
Eagle County SD RE-50
Supt. — See Eagle
Battle Mountain HS — 800/9-12
151 Miller Ranch Rd 81632 — 970-328-2930
Dr. Lourra Barthuly, prin. — Fax 328-2935
Berry Creek MS — 400/6-8
1000 Miller Ranch Rd 81632 — 970-328-2960
Amy Vanwel, prin. — Fax 926-4137
Red Canyon HS — 200/Alt
1002 Miller Ranch Rd 81632 — 970-328-2852
Wade Hill, prin. — Fax 328-2855

Vail Christian HS — 100/9-12
31621 Highway 6 81632 — 970-926-3015
Fax 766-3016

Elbert, Elbert, Pop. 225
Elbert SD 200 — 200/PK-12
PO Box 38 80106 — 303-648-3030
Kelli Thompson, supt. — Fax 648-3652
www.elbertschool.org
Elbert JSHS — 100/6-12
PO Box 38 80106 — 303-648-3030
Shawn Graves, prin. — Fax 648-3652

Elizabeth, Elbert, Pop. 1,335
Elizabeth SD C-1 — 2,500/PK-12
PO Box 610 80107 — 303-646-1836
Douglas Bissonette, supt. — Fax 646-0337
elizabeth.k12.co.us/
Elizabeth HS — 800/9-12
34500 County Road 13 80107 — 303-646-4616
Bret McClendon, prin. — Fax 646-6030
Elizabeth MS — 500/6-8
34427 County Road 13 80107 — 303-646-4520
Pamela Eschief, prin. — Fax 646-0980
Frontier HS — 100/Alt
589 S Banner St 80107 — 303-646-1798
Robert McMullen, dir. — Fax 646-1329

Ellicott, El Paso, Pop. 1,094
Ellicott SD 22 — 1,000/PK-12
322 S Ellicott Hwy 80808 — 719-683-2700
Patrick Cullen Ed.D., supt. — Fax 941-7500
www.ellicottschools.org
Ellicott HS — 200/9-12
375 S Ellicott Hwy 80808 — 719-683-2700
Mark McPherson, prin. — Fax 683-2705
Ellicott MS — 200/6-8
350 S Ellicott Hwy 80808 — 719-683-2700
Chris Smith, prin. — Fax 683-5430

Englewood, Arapahoe, Pop. 29,512
Cherry Creek SD 5
Supt. — See Greenwood Village
Campus MS — 1,400/6-8
4785 S Dayton St 80111 — 720-554-2677
Greg Connellan, prin. — Fax 554-2795

Englewood SD 1 — 2,800/PK-12
4101 S Bannock St 80110 — 303-761-7050
Wendy Rubin Ed.D., supt. — Fax 806-2064
www.englewoodschools.net
Colorado's Finest Alternative HS — 300/Alt
300 W Chenango Ave 80110 — 303-934-5786
Bobbie Skaggs, prin. — Fax 934-9183
Englewood HS — 600/9-12
3800 S Logan St, — 303-806-2266
Jon Fore, prin. — Fax 806-2296
Englewood Leadership Academy — 100/6-8
3800 S Logan St, — 303-806-2266
Jon Fore, prin. — Fax 806-2296
Englewood MS — 300/7-8
3800 S Logan St, — 303-781-7817
Mandy Braun, prin. — Fax 806-2399

Columbia HealthOne — Post-Sec.
501 E Hampden Ave, — 303-788-6484
Elliot Christian S — 100/6-12
8505 S Valley Hwy 80112 — 303-922-0011
Wayne Embry, admin. — Fax 922-0159
Kent Denver S — 700/6-12
4000 E Quincy Ave, — 303-770-7660
Dr. Randal Harrington, head sch — Fax 770-7137
St. Mary's Academy — 700/PK-12
4545 S University Blvd, — 303-762-8300
Vicki Schwartz, pres. — Fax 783-6201

Erie, Weld, Pop. 17,723
St. Vrain Valley SD RE-1J
Supt. — See Longmont
Erie HS — 800/9-12
3180 County Road 5 80516 — 303-828-4213
Matt Buchler, prin. — Fax 494-3869
Erie MS — 700/6-8
650 Main St 80516 — 303-828-3391
Kim Watry, prin. — Fax 652-8293

Estes Park, Larimer, Pop. 5,792
Estes Park SD R-3 — 1,100/PK-12
1605 Brodie Ave 80517 — 970-586-2361
Sheldon Rosenkrance, supt. — Fax 586-1108
www.psdr3.k12.co.us
Estes Park HS — 300/9-12
1600 Manford Ave 80517 — 970-586-5321
Charles Scott, prin. — Fax 586-1102
Estes Park MS — 200/6-8
1500 Manford Ave 80517 — 970-586-4439
Janet Bielmaier, prin. — Fax 586-1100

Eagle Rock S — 100/9-12
2750 Notaiah Rd 80517 — 970-586-0600
Jeff Liddle, head sch — Fax 586-4805

Evans, Weld, Pop. 18,255
Weld County SD 6
Supt. — See Greeley
Prairie Heights MS — 6-8
3737 65th Ave, — 970-348-3600
Dr. Dawn Hillman Ed.D., admin. — Fax 348-3632

Evergreen, Jefferson, Pop. 8,923
Clear Creek SD RE-1
Supt. — See Idaho Springs
Clear Creek HS — 200/9-12
185 Beaver Brook Canyon Rd 80439 — 303-679-4600
Elizabeth Gardner, prin. — Fax 679-4603
Clear Creek MS — 100/7-8
185 Beaver Brook Canyon Rd 80439 — 303-670-4600
Jeff Miller, prin. — Fax 670-4690

Jefferson County SD R-1
Supt. — See Golden
Evergreen HS — 1,000/9-12
29300 Buffalo Park Rd 80439 — 303-982-5140
Brandon Brekke, prin. — Fax 982-5141
Evergreen MS — 700/6-8
2059 Hiwan Dr 80439 — 303-982-5020
Timothy Vialpando, prin. — Fax 982-5021

Fairplay, Park, Pop. 659
Park County SD RE-2 — 600/PK-12
PO Box 189 80440 — 719-836-3111
Becky Minnis, supt. — Fax 836-2275
www.parkcountyre2.org/
South Park HS — 100/9-12
PO Box 189 80440 — 719-836-2006
Jane Newman, prin. — Fax 836-4429
South Park MS — 100/6-8
PO Box 189 80440 — 719-836-4406
Jane Newman, prin. — Fax 836-4429

Falcon, El Paso, Pop. 200
Falcon SD 49 — 17,600/PK-12
10850 E Woodmen Rd 80831 — 719-495-1100
Peter Hilts, admin. — Fax 494-8900
www.d49.org
Other Schools – See Colorado Springs, Peyton

Firestone, Weld, Pop. 9,981
St. Vrain Valley SD RE-1J
Supt. — See Longmont
Coal Ridge MS — 800/6-8
6201 Booth Dr 80504 — 303-833-4176
Liza Nybo, prin. — Fax 494-3813

Flagler, Kit Carson, Pop. 558
Arriba-Flagler SD C-20 — 100/PK-12
PO Box 218 80815 — 719-765-4684
Valorie McCleary, supt. — Fax 765-4418
flaglerschools.co.afs.schoolinsites.com
Flagler S — 100/PK-12
PO Box 218 80815 — 719-765-4684
Valorie McCleary, admin. — Fax 765-4418

Fleming, Logan, Pop. 408
Frenchman SD RE-3 — 200/PK-12
506 N Fremont Ave 80728 — 970-265-2111
Steve McCracken, supt. — Fax 265-2815
www.flemingschools.org
Fleming HS — 100/7-12
506 N Fremont Ave 80728 — 970-265-2111
Stacy McDaniel, prin. — Fax 265-2815

Florence, Fremont, Pop. 3,816
Fremont SD RE-2 — 1,500/K-12
403 W 5th St 81226 — 719-784-6312
Rhonda Roberts, supt. — Fax 784-4140
www.re-2.org/
Florence HS — 500/9-12
2006 Highway 67 81226 — 719-784-6414
Brian Schipper, prin. — Fax 784-2727
Fremont MS — 300/6-8
215 Maple St 81226 — 719-784-4856
Andy Fieth, prin. — Fax 784-3821

Fort Carson, El Paso, Pop. 13,113
Fountain-Fort Carson SD 8
Supt. — See Fountain
Carson MS — 700/6-8
6200 Prussman Blvd, — 719-382-1610
Josh Hobgood, prin. — Fax 382-8526

Fort Collins, Larimer, Pop. 140,582
Poudre SD R-1 27,800/PK-12
2407 Laporte Ave 80521 970-482-7420
Dr. Sandra Smysor, supt. Fax 490-3514
www.psdschools.org
Blevins MS 500/6-8
2101 S Taft Hill Rd 80526 970-488-4000
David Linehan, prin. Fax 488-4011
Boltz MS 600/6-8
720 Boltz Dr 80525 970-472-3700
Brett Larsen, prin. Fax 472-3730
Centennial HS 100/Alt
330 E Laurel St 80524 970-488-4940
Mike Roberts, prin. Fax 488-4942
Fort Collins HS 1,500/9-12
3400 Lambkin Way 80525 970-488-8021
Mark Eversole, prin. Fax 488-8008
Fossil Ridge HS 2,100/9-12
5400 Ziegler Rd 80528 970-488-6260
Will Allen, prin. Fax 488-6263
Kinard Core Knowledge MS 800/6-8
3002 E Trilby Rd 80528 970-488-5400
Jesse Morrill, prin. Fax 488-5402
Lesher MS 700/6-8
1400 Stover St 80524 970-472-3800
Thomas Dodd, prin. Fax 472-3880
Lincoln MS 500/6-8
1600 Lancer Dr 80521 970-488-5700
Penny Stires, prin. Fax 488-5752
Polaris Expeditionary Learning S 300/K-12
1905 Orchard Pl 80521 970-488-8260
Joe Gawronski, prin. Fax 488-8262
Poudre Community Academy 100/Alt
2540 LaPorte Ave 80521 970-490-3295
Troy Krotz, prin. Fax 490-3402
Poudre HS 1,800/9-12
201 S Impala Dr 80521 970-488-6000
Kathy Mackay, prin. Fax 488-6060
Preston MS 1,100/6-8
4901 Corbett Dr 80528 970-488-7300
Scott Nielsen, prin. Fax 488-7307
Rocky Mountain HS 2,000/9-12
1300 W Swallow Rd 80526 970-488-7023
Craig Woodall, prin. Fax 488-7001
Webber MS 800/6-8
4201 Seneca St 80526 970-488-7800
Christopher Keiffer, prin. Fax 488-7811
Other Schools – See Laporte, Wellington

At-Home Professions Post-Sec.
2001 Lowe St 80525 970-225-6300
CollegeAmerica - Fort Collins Post-Sec.
4601 S Mason St 80525 970-221-2769
Colorado State University Post-Sec.
1062 Campus Delivery 80523 970-491-6909
Front Range Baptist Academy 100/PK-12
625 E Harmony Rd 80525 970-223-2173
Front Range Community College Post-Sec.
4616 S Shields St 80526 970-226-2500
Hair Dynamics Education Center Post-Sec.
PO Box 272389 80527 970-223-9943
Heritage Christian Academy 200/PK-12
2506 Zurich Dr 80524 970-494-1022
Mike Cuckler, admin. Fax 494-1025
Institute of Business & Medical Careers Post-Sec.
3842 S Mason St 80525 970-223-2669
McKinley College Post-Sec.
2001 Lowe St 80525 970-207-4550
US Career Institute Post-Sec.
2001 Lowe St 80525 800-347-7899

Fort Lupton, Weld, Pop. 7,284
Weld County SD RE-8 2,600/PK-12
301 Reynolds St 80621 303-857-3200
Alan Kaylor, supt. Fax 857-3219
www.weld8.org
Fort Lupton HS 600/9-12
530 Reynolds St 80621 303-857-7100
Marci Hester, prin. Fax 857-7179
Fort Lupton MS 500/6-8
201 S McKinley Ave 80621 303-857-7200
Candace Kensinger, prin. Fax 857-7287

Fort Morgan, Morgan, Pop. 11,188
Ft. Morgan SD RE-3 3,000/PK-12
715 W Platte Ave 80701 970-867-5633
Ron Echols, supt. Fax 867-0262
www.morgan.k12.co.us
Fort Morgan HS 900/9-12
709 E Riverview Ave 80701 970-867-5648
Ben Bauman, prin. Fax 867-3347
Fort Morgan MS 500/6-8
605 Education Ave 80701 970-867-8253
Jason Frasco, prin. Fax 867-4876
Lincoln HS 50/Alt
230 Walnut St 80701 970-867-2924
Vicki Davis, prin. Fax 867-4958

Morgan Community College Post-Sec.
920 Barlow Rd 80701 970-542-3100

Fountain, El Paso, Pop. 24,314
Fountain-Fort Carson SD 8 8,100/PK-12
10665 Jimmy Camp Rd 80817 719-382-1300
Dr. Keith Owen, supt. Fax 382-7338
www.ffc8.org
Fountain-Fort Carson HS 1,700/9-12
900 Jimmy Camp Rd 80817 719-382-1640
Burnie Hibbard, prin. Fax 382-3228
Fountain MS 900/6-8
515 N Santa Fe Ave 80817 719-382-1580
Kathy Van't Hul, prin. Fax 382-9065
Welte Education Center 100/Alt
330 Lyckman Pl 80817 719-382-1550
Sally Conboy, prin. Fax 382-5782
Other Schools – See Fort Carson

Widefield SD 3
Supt. — See Colorado Springs
Janitell JHS 800/6-8
7635 Fountain Mesa Rd 80817 719-391-3295
David Gish, prin. Fax 390-7869

Fowler, Otero, Pop. 1,170
Fowler SD R-4J 400/K-12
PO Box 218 81039 719-263-4224
Steven Grasmick, supt. Fax 263-4625
www.fowler.k12.co.us
Fowler HS 100/9-12
PO Box 218 81039 719-263-4279
Russell Bates, prin. Fax 263-4625
Fowler JHS 100/7-8
PO Box 218 81039 719-263-4224
Russell Bates, prin. Fax 263-4625

Frederick, Weld, Pop. 8,509
St. Vrain Valley SD RE-1J
Supt. — See Longmont
Frederick HS 1,000/9-12
5690 Tipple Pkwy 80504 303-833-3533
Brian Young, prin. Fax 494-3887

Frisco, Summit, Pop. 2,654
Summit SD RE-1 3,300/PK-12
PO Box 7 80443 970-368-1000
Dr. Heidi Pace, supt. Fax 368-1049
www.summit.k12.co.us
Snowy Peaks HS 50/Alt
PO Box 7 80443 970-368-1145
James Smith, prin. Fax 368-1299
Summit HS 800/9-12
PO Box 7 80443 970-368-1100
Drew Adkins, prin. Fax 368-1199
Summit MS 700/6-8
PO Box 7 80443 970-368-1200
Joel Rivera, prin. Fax 368-1299

Peak S, PO Box 550 80443 50/6-12
Steven Coleman, head sch 970-368-5601

Fruita, Mesa, Pop. 12,442
Mesa County Valley SD 51
Supt. — See Grand Junction
Fruita 8th & 9th Grade S 700/8-9
1835 J Rd 81521 970-254-6720
Jason Plantiko, prin. Fax 858-7751
Fruita Monument HS 1,300/10-12
1102 Wildcat Ave 81521 970-254-6600
Todd McClaskey, prin. Fax 858-9661

Gateway, Mesa, Pop. 7,510
Mesa County Valley SD 51
Supt. — See Grand Junction
Gateway S 50/K-12
PO Box 240 81522 970-254-7080
Mark Allen, prin. Fax 931-2883

Gilcrest, Weld, Pop. 1,023
Weld County SD RE-1 1,900/PK-12
PO Box 157 80623 970-737-2403
Don Rangel, supt. Fax 737-2516
www.weld-re1.k12.co.us
Valley HS 500/9-12
PO Box 156 80623 970-737-2494
Rich Dalgliesh, prin. Fax 737-2203
Other Schools – See La Salle, Platteville

Glenwood Springs, Garfield, Pop. 9,485
Roaring Fork SD RE-1 5,600/PK-12
1405 Grand Ave 81601 970-384-6000
Dr. Rob Stein, supt. Fax 384-6005
www.rfschools.com
Glenwood Springs HS 800/9-12
1521 Grand Ave 81601 970-384-5555
Paul Freeman, prin. Fax 384-5556
Glenwood Springs MS 600/6-8
120 Soccerfield Rd 81601 970-384-5500
Joel Hathaway, prin. Fax 384-5505
Other Schools – See Basalt, Carbondale

Colorado Mountain College Post-Sec.
802 Grand Ave 81601 970-945-8691
Glenwood Beauty Academy Post-Sec.
51241 Highway 6 Ste 1 81601 970-945-0485

Golden, Jefferson, Pop. 18,494
Jefferson County SD R-1 82,600/PK-12
PO Box 4001 80402 303-982-6500
Dan McMinimee, supt. Fax 982-6814
www.jeffcopublicschools.org/
Bell MS 600/6-8
1001 Ulysses St 80401 303-982-4280
Bridget Jones, prin. Fax 982-4281
Golden HS 1,300/9-12
701 24th St 80401 303-982-4200
Brian Conroy, prin. Fax 982-4201
Manning Options S 500/Alt
13200 W 32nd Ave 80401 303-982-6340
Barb Bares, prin. Fax 982-6341
Other Schools – See Arvada, Conifer, Denver, Edgewater, Evergreen, Lakewood, Littleton, Westminster, Wheat Ridge

---

Colorado School of Mines Post-Sec.
1500 Illinois St 80401 303-273-3000
Holmes Institute of Consciousness Stds Post-Sec.
573 Park Point Dr 80401 720-496-1370

Granada, Prowers, Pop. 515
Granada SD RE-1 200/PK-12
PO Box 259 81041 719-734-5492
Ty Kemp, supt. Fax 734-5495
www.granadaschools.org
Granada JSHS 100/7-12
PO Box 259 81041 719-734-5492
Ty Kemp, prin. Fax 734-5495

Granby, Grand, Pop. 1,839
East Grand SD 2 1,300/PK-12
PO Box 125 80446 970-887-2581
Dr. Jody Mimmack, supt. Fax 887-2635
www.egsd.org
East Grand MS 300/6-8
PO Box 2210 80446 970-887-3382
Jenny Rothboeck, prin. Fax 887-9234
Middle Park HS 300/9-12
PO Box 130 80446 970-887-2104
Thom Schnellinger, prin. Fax 887-9454

Grand Junction, Mesa, Pop. 57,510
Mesa County Valley SD 51 21,300/PK-12
2115 Grand Ave 81501 970-254-5100
Steven Schultz, supt. Fax 245-2714
www.d51schools.org
Bookcliff MS 600/6-8
540 29 1/4 Rd 81504 970-254-6220
Jim Butterfield, prin. Fax 245-7812
Career Center Vo/Tech
2935 North Ave 81504 970-254-6000
Lee Searcy, prin. Fax 255-8465
Central HS 1,500/9-12
550 Warrior Way 81504 970-254-6200
Lanc Sellden, prin. Fax 254-6169
East MS 500/6-8
830 Gunnison Ave 81501 970-254-5020
Leah Gonyeau, prin. Fax 242-0513
Grand Junction HS 1,700/9-12
1400 N 5th St 81501 970-254-6900
Ari Goldberg, prin. Fax 241-5154
Grand Mesa MS 600/6-8
585 31 1/2 Rd 81504 970-254-6270
Jennifer Marsh, prin. Fax 523-5938
Orchard Mesa MS 500/6-8
2736 C Rd 81503 970-254-6320
Cheryl Vana, prin. Fax 245-7343
R-5 HS 200/Alt
2150 Grand Ave 81501 970-254-6880
Donald Trujillo, prin. Fax 242-4465
Redlands MS 600/6-8
2200 Broadway, 970-254-7000
Jory Sorensen, prin. Fax 245-1985
Valley S West Alt
2508 Blichmann Ave 81505 970-255-2708
Sara Krick, prin. Fax 255-2711
West MS 400/6-8
123 W Orchard Ave 81505 970-254-5090
Vernon Walker, prin. Fax 243-0574
Other Schools – See Clifton, Fruita, Gateway, Palisade

Colorado Mesa University Post-Sec.
1100 North Ave 81501 970-248-1020
IntelliTec College Post-Sec.
772 Horizon Dr 81506 970-245-8101

Greeley, Weld, Pop. 91,409
Weld County SD 6 19,000/PK-12
1025 9th Ave 80631 970-348-6000
Dr. Deirdre Pilch Ed.D., supt. Fax 348-6231
www.greeleyschools.org
Brentwood MS 600/6-8
2600 24th Avenue Ct 80634 970-348-3000
Nicole Petersen, prin. Fax 348-3030
Early College Academy 9-12
5590 W 11th St 80634 970-348-5800
Gordon Boschman, admin. Fax 348-5830
Franklin MS 800/6-8
818 35th Ave 80634 970-348-3200
Chris Joseph, prin. Fax 348-3230
Greeley Central HS 1,400/9-12
1515 14th Ave 80631 970-348-5000
Kent Henson, prin. Fax 348-5030
Greeley-Evans Alternative Program Alt
1113 10th Ave 80631 970-348-4900
Dave Shaffer, admin. Fax 348-4930
Greeley West HS 1,500/9-12
2401 35th Ave 80634 970-348-5400
Jeff Cranson, prin. Fax 348-5430
Heath MS 700/6-8
2223 16th St 80631 970-348-3400
Dr. Blakley Wallace, prin. Fax 348-3430
Jefferson HS 400/9-12
1315 4th Ave 80631 970-348-1600
Larry Green, prin. Fax 348-1630
Northridge HS 1,100/9-12
100 N 71st Ave 80634 970-348-5200
Insoon Olson, prin. Fax 348-5230
Other Schools – See Evans

Academy of Natural Therapy Post-Sec.
625 8th Ave 80631 970-352-1181
Aims Community College Post-Sec.
5401 W 20th St 80634 970-330-8008
Dayspring Christian Academy 300/PK-12
3734 W 20th St 80634 970-330-1151
Weston Kurz, dir. Fax 330-0565
Institute of Business & Medical Careers Post-Sec.
2863 35th Ave 80634 970-356-4733
University of Northern Colorado Post-Sec.
501 20th St 80639 970-351-1890

Greenwood Village, Arapahoe, Pop. 13,663
Cherry Creek SD 5 52,700/PK-12
4700 S Yosemite St 80111 303-773-1184
Dr. Harry Bull, supt. Fax 773-9370
www.cherrycreekschools.org
Cherry Creek HS 3,500/9-12
9300 E Union Ave 80111 720-554-2285
Ryan Silva, prin. Fax 554-2239
West MS 1,200/6-8
5151 S Holly St 80121 720-554-5180
Kate Bergles, prin. Fax 554-5181
Other Schools – See Aurora, Centennial, Englewood

Colorado State University Global Campus Post-Sec.
8000 E Maplewood Bdg 5 #250 80111
720-279-0159
DeVry University Post-Sec.
6312 S Fiddlers Green #150E 80111 303-329-3000
Tri-County Health Nutrition Services Post-Sec.
6162 S Willow Dr Ste 100 80111 303-220-9200

Grover, Weld, Pop. 137
Pawnee SD RE-12 50/PK-12
PO Box 220 80729 970-895-2222
Bret Robinson, supt. Fax 895-2221
www.pawneeschool.org
Pawnee S 50/PK-12
PO Box 220 80729 970-895-2222
Bret Robinson, prin. Fax 895-2221

Gunnison, Gunnison, Pop. 5,730
Gunnison Watershed SD RE 1J 1,900/PK-12
800 N Boulevard St 81230 970-641-7770
Doug Tredway, supt. Fax 641-7777
www.gunnisonschools.net/
Gunnison HS 300/9-12
800 W Ohio Ave 81230 970-641-7700
Andy Hanks, prin. Fax 641-7709
Gunnison MS 300/6-8
1099 N 11th St 81230 970-641-7710
Todd Witzel, prin. Fax 641-7739
Other Schools – See Crested Butte

Western State Colorado University Post-Sec.
600 N Adams St 81231 970-943-0120

Gypsum, Eagle, Pop. 6,422
Eagle County SD RE-50
Supt. — See Eagle
Eagle Valley HS 700/9-12
PO Box 188 81637 970-328-8960
Greg Doan, prin. Fax 328-8965
Gypsum Creek MS 400/6-8
PO Box 5129 81637 970-328-8980
David Russell, prin. Fax 328-8985

Haxtun, Phillips, Pop. 937
Haxtun SD RE-2J 300/PK-12
201 W Powell St 80731 970-774-6111
Darcy Garretson, supt. Fax 774-7568
www.haxtunschools.com
Haxtun HS 100/9-12
201 W Powell St 80731 970-774-6111
Alan Nall, prin. Fax 774-7568

Hayden, Routt, Pop. 1,785
Hayden SD RE-1 400/PK-12
PO Box 70 81639 970-276-3864
Phil Kasper, supt. Fax 276-4217
haydenschools.org
Hayden HS 100/9-12
PO Box 70 81639 970-276-3761
Regina Zabel, prin. Fax 276-4374
Hayden MS 100/6-8
PO Box 70 81639 970-276-3762
Regina Zabel, prin. Fax 276-7235

Henderson, Adams, Pop. 500
SD 27J
Supt. — See Brighton
Prairie View HS 1,800/9-12
12909 E 120th Ave 80640 303-655-8800
Jaime White, prin. Fax 655-8920
Prairie View MS 800/6-8
12915 E 120th Ave 80640 720-685-5400
Cristina Costas-Bissell, prin. Fax 685-5404

American Institute of Technology Post-Sec.
9239 Brighton Rd Unit 201 80640 303-558-3152

Highlands Ranch, Douglas, Pop. 94,597
Douglas County SD RE-1
Supt. — See Castle Rock
Cresthill MS 900/7-8
9195 Cresthill Ln 80130 303-387-2800
Sid Rundle, prin. Fax 387-2801
Highlands Ranch HS 1,600/9-12
9375 Cresthill Ln 80130 303-387-2500
Chris Page, prin. Fax 387-2501
Mountain Ridge MS 1,100/7-8
10590 Mountain Vista Rdg 80126 303-387-1800
Shannon Clarke, prin. Fax 387-1801
Mountain Vista HS 2,100/9-12
10585 Mountain Vista Rdg 80126 303-387-1500
Michael Weaver, prin. Fax 387-1501
Ranch View MS 1,000/7-8
1731 W Wildcat Reserve Pkwy 80129 303-387-2300
Tanner Fitch, prin. Fax 387-2301
Rock Canyon HS 1,900/9-12
5810 McArthur Ranch Rd 80124 303-387-3000
Andrew Abner, prin. Fax 387-3021
ThunderRidge HS 2,000/9-12
1991 W Wildcat Reserve Pkwy 80129 303-387-2000
Chris Tabeling, prin. Fax 387-2001
Eagle Academy Adult
9375 Cresthill Ln 80130 303-387-2700
Chris Eberhardt, prin. Fax 470-7376

Mile High Academy 100/PK-12
1733 Dad Clark Dr 80126 303-744-1069
Valor Christian HS 800/9-12
3775 Grace Blvd 80126 303-471-3000
Kurt Unruh, head sch Fax 471-3001

Hoehne, Las Animas, Pop. 111
Hoehne RSD 3 200/K-12
PO Box 91 81046 719-846-4457
Christine Barela, supt. Fax 846-2208
www.hoehnesd.org/
Hoehne S 200/K-12
PO Box 91 81046 719-846-4457
Joseph DeAngelis, prin. Fax 846-2208

Holly, Prowers, Pop. 799
Holly SD RE-3 200/PK-12
PO Box 608 81047 719-537-6616
Randy Holmen, supt. Fax 537-0315
www.hollyschool.org
Holly JSHS 100/7-12
PO Box 608 81047 719-537-6512
Randy Holmen, prin. Fax 537-6519

Holyoke, Phillips, Pop. 2,299
Holyoke SD RE-1J 600/K-12
435 S Morlan Ave 80734 970-854-3634
John McCleary, supt. Fax 854-4049
holyoke.schoolfusion.us
Holyoke Alternative HS Alt
545 E Hale St 80734 970-854-2284
Cindi Beavers, dir. Fax 854-4578
Holyoke JSHS 300/7-12
545 E Hale St 80734 970-854-2284
Susan Ortner, prin. Fax 854-4578

Hotchkiss, Delta, Pop. 933
Delta County SD 50(J)
Supt. — See Delta
Hotchkiss HS 200/9-12
438 Bulldog St 81419 970-872-3882
Paul Rodriguez, prin. Fax 872-2390

Hugo, Lincoln, Pop. 718
Genoa-Hugo SD C113 200/PK-12
PO Box 247 80821 719-743-2428
Frank Reeves, supt. Fax 743-2194
www.genoahugo.org
Genoa-Hugo HS 50/9-12
PO Box 247 80821 719-743-2428
Shari Humphrey, prin. Fax 743-2194
Genoa-Hugo MS 50/6-8
PO Box 247 80821 719-743-2428
Shari Humphrey, prin. Fax 743-2194

Idaho Springs, Clear Creek, Pop. 1,695
Clear Creek SD RE-1 900/PK-12
PO Box 3399 80452 303-567-3850
Roslin Marshall, supt. Fax 567-3861
www.ccsdre1.org/
Other Schools – See Evergreen

Idalia, Yuma, Pop. 88
Idalia SD RJ-3 200/PK-12
PO Box 40 80735 970-354-7298
Tim Krause, supt. Fax 354-7416
www.idaliaco.us
Idalia JSHS 100/6-12
PO Box 40 80735 970-354-7298
Tim Krause, admin. Fax 354-7416

Ignacio, LaPlata, Pop. 652
Ignacio SD 11 JT 600/K-12
PO Box 460 81137 970-563-0500
Rocco Fuschetto Ed.D., supt. Fax 563-4524
www.ignacioschools.org
Ignacio HS 200/9-12
PO Box 460 81137 970-563-0515
Melanie Taylor, prin. Fax 563-9463
Ignacio MS 200/6-8
PO Box 460 81137 970-563-0600
Chris deKay, prin. Fax 563-0234

Iliff, Logan, Pop. 261
Valley SD RE-1
Supt. — See Sterling
Caliche JSHS 100/7-12
26308 County Road 65 80736 970-522-8200
Doug Stutzman, prin. Fax 522-9400

Joes, Yuma, Pop. 78
Liberty SD J-4 50/PK-12
PO Box 112 80822 970-358-4288
Richard Walter, supt. Fax 358-4282
www.libertyschoolj4.com
Liberty S 50/PK-12
PO Box 112 80822 970-358-4288
Richard Walter, admin. Fax 358-4282

Johnstown, Weld, Pop. 9,738
Weld County SD RE-5J
Supt. — See Milliken
Roosevelt HS 800/9-12
616 N 2nd St 80534 970-587-6000
Trevor Long, prin. Fax 587-2608

Julesburg, Sedgwick, Pop. 1,216
Julesburg SD RE-1 300/PK-12
102 W 6th St 80737 970-474-3365
Shawn Ehnes, supt. Fax 474-3742
www.julesburg.org
Julesburg JSHS 100/7-12
102 W 6th St 80737 970-474-3364
Shawn Ehnes, prin. Fax 474-3742

Karval, Lincoln, Pop. 50
Karval SD RE-23 100/PK-12
PO Box 5 80823 719-446-5311
Floyd Beard, supt. Fax 446-5332
www.karvalschool.org
Karval JSHS 50/6-12
PO Box 5 80823 719-446-5311
Kenneth Bridges, supt. Fax 446-5332

Keenesburg, Weld, Pop. 1,112
Weld County SD RE-3J 2,300/PK-12
PO Box 269 80643 303-536-2000
Dr. Greg Rabenhorst, supt. Fax 536-2010
www.re3j.com
Weld Central HS 600/9-12
4715 County Road 59 80643 303-536-2100
Dan Kennedy, prin. Fax 536-2110
Weld Central MS 500/6-8
4977 County Road 59 80643 303-536-2700
Jamie Jeffery, prin. Fax 536-2710

Kersey, Weld, Pop. 1,432
Weld County SD RE-7 1,100/PK-12
PO Box 485 80644 970-336-8500
Dr. E. Glenn McClain Ed.D., supt. Fax 336-8511
www.plattevalley.k12.co.us
Platte Valley HS 300/9-12
PO Box 487 80644 970-336-8700
Brad Joens, prin. Fax 336-8794
Platte Valley MS 300/6-8
PO Box 515 80644 970-336-8610
Jason Taylor, prin. Fax 336-8635

Kim, Las Animas, Pop. 73
Kim RSD 88 50/PK-12
PO Box 100 81049 719-643-5295
Blake Byall, supt. Fax 643-5299
www.kimk12.org
Kim JSHS 50/6-12
PO Box 100 81049 719-643-5295
Blake Byall, prin. Fax 643-5299

Kiowa, Elbert, Pop. 708
Kiowa SD C-2 300/PK-12
PO Box 128 80117 303-621-2220
Jason Westfall, supt. Fax 621-2239
www.kiowaschool.org
Kiowa HS 100/9-12
PO Box 128 80117 303-621-2115
Amy Smith, prin. Fax 621-2566
Kiowa MS 100/6-8
PO Box 128 80117 303-621-2785
Amy Smith, prin. Fax 621-2239

Kit Carson, Cheyenne, Pop. 230
Kit Carson SD R-1 100/PK-12
PO Box 185 80825 719-962-3219
Robert Framel, supt. Fax 962-3317
www.kcsdr1.org
Carson JSHS 100/6-12
PO Box 185 80825 719-962-3219
Jim Trahern, prin. Fax 962-3317

Kremmling, Grand, Pop. 1,417
West Grand SD 1-JT 200/K-12
PO Box 515 80459 970-724-3217
Mike Page, supt. Fax 724-9373
www.wgsd.us
West Grand HS 100/9-12
PO Box 515 80459 970-724-3425
Mike Page, prin. Fax 724-3450

Lafayette, Boulder, Pop. 23,902
Boulder Valley SD RE-2
Supt. — See Boulder
Angevine MS 600/6-8
1150 W South Boulder Rd 80026 720-561-7100
Mike Medina, prin. Fax 561-7101
Centaurus HS 1,000/9-12
10300 E South Boulder Rd 80026 720-561-7500
Terry Gillach, prin. Fax 561-5368

Dawson S 500/K-12
10455 Dawson Dr 80026 303-665-6679
George Moore, head sch Fax 665-0757

La Jara, Conejos, Pop. 805
North Conejos SD RE-1J 1,000/PK-12
PO Box 72 81140 719-274-5174
Curt Wilson, supt. Fax 274-5621
www.northconejos.com
Centauri HS 300/9-12
17889 US Highway 285 81140 719-274-5178
Brian Loch, prin. Fax 274-5637
Centauri MS 200/6-8
17891 US Highway 285 81140 719-274-4301
Tyler Huffaker, prin. Fax 274-4306
North Conejos Alternative Program 100/Alt
PO Box 72 81140 719-274-4220
Susan Hamilton, admin. Fax 274-3809

La Junta, Otero, Pop. 6,961
East Otero SD R-1 1,300/K-12
301 Raton Ave 81050 719-384-6900
Rick Lovato, supt. Fax 384-6910
www.lajuntaschools.org
La Junta JSHS 500/7-12
1817 Smithland Ave 81050 719-384-4467
John Haberman, prin. Fax 384-2581

Otero Junior College Post-Sec.
1802 Colorado Ave 81050 719-384-6831

Lake City, Hinsdale, Pop. 393
Hinsdale County SD RE 1 100/PK-12
PO Box 39 81235 970-944-2314
Dr. Leslie Nichols, supt. Fax 944-2662
www.lakecityschool.org
Lake City Community S 100/PK-12
PO Box 39 81235 970-944-2314
Dr. Leslie Nichols, prin. Fax 944-2662

Lakewood, Jefferson, Pop. 140,229
Jefferson County SD R-1
Supt. — See Golden
Alameda International JSHS 900/7-12
1255 S Wadsworth Blvd 80232 303-982-8160
Susie VanScoyk, prin. Fax 982-8161
Bear Creek HS 1,700/9-12
9800 W Dartmouth Pl 80227 303-982-8855
Donald Torr, prin. Fax 982-8856
Brady Exploration S 200/Alt
5220 W Ohio Ave 80226 303-982-6722
Troy Braley, prin. Fax 982-6723
Carmody MS 600/7-8
2050 S Kipling St 80227 303-982-8930
Wendy Doran, prin. Fax 982-8931
Creighton MS 700/7-8
50 S Kipling St 80226 303-982-6282
Nick Kemmer, prin. Fax 982-6283
Dunstan MS 600/7-8
1855 S Wright St 80228 303-982-9270
Jennifer Kirksey, prin. Fax 982-9269
Green Mountain HS 1,100/9-12
13175 W Green Mountain Dr 80228 303-982-9500
Colleen Owens, prin. Fax 982-9501
Jefferson County Open S 300/PK-12
7655 W 10th Ave 80214 303-982-7045
Scott Bain, prin. Fax 982-7046
Lakewood HS 2,100/9-12
9700 W 8th Ave 80215 303-982-7096
Lisa Ritchey, prin. Fax 982-7097
Long View HS 100/Alt
13301 W 2nd Pl 80228 303-982-8523
Chris Eberhardt, prin. Fax 982-8568
McClain Community HS 100/Alt
13600 W 2nd Pl 80228 303-982-7460
Chris Eberhardt, prin. Fax 982-7494
Warren Tech S Vo/Tech
13300 W 2nd Pl 80228 303-982-8600
Joe Shaw, prin. Fax 982-8622

Augustine Classical Academy 100/PK-12
480 S Kipling St 80226 720-446-6286
Colorado Christian University Post-Sec.
8787 W Alameda Ave 80226 303-963-3000
Colorado School of Healing Arts Post-Sec.
7655 W Mississippi #100 80226 303-986-2320
Colorado School of Trades Post-Sec.
1575 Hoyt St 80215 303-233-4697

Denver Christian S 200/PK-12
3898 S Teller St 80235 303-733-2421
Todd Lanting, dir. Fax 733-7734
Ohio Center for Broadcasting - Colorado Post-Sec.
404 S Upham St 80226 303-937-7070
Red Rocks Community College Post-Sec.
13300 W 6th Ave 80228 303-914-6600

Lamar, Prowers, Pop. 7,721
Lamar SD RE-2 1,700/PK-12
210 W Pearl St 81052 719-336-3251
Dave Tecklenburg, supt. Fax 336-2817
www.lamarschools.org
Lamar HS 400/9-12
1900 S 11th St 81052 719-336-3488
Allan Medina, prin. Fax 336-3026
Lamar MS 400/6-8
104 W Park St 81052 719-336-7436
Matt Snyder, prin. Fax 336-5457

Lamar Community College Post-Sec.
2401 S Main St 81052 719-336-2248

Laporte, Larimer, Pop. 2,391
Poudre SD R-1
Supt. — See Fort Collins
Cache La Poudre MS 300/6-8
3515 W County Road 54G 80535 970-488-7400
Alicia Bono, prin. Fax 488-7433

La Salle, Weld, Pop. 1,932
Weld County SD RE-1
Supt. — See Gilcrest
North Valley MS 300/6-8
300 2nd Ave 80645 970-284-5508
Martin Pearson, prin. Fax 284-6595

Las Animas, Bent, Pop. 2,388
Las Animas SD RE-1 500/PK-12
1021 2nd St 81054 719-456-0161
Elsie Goines, supt. Fax 456-1117
la-schools.com
Las Animas HS 100/9-12
300 Grove Ave 81054 719-456-0211
Tom Meardon, prin. Fax 456-0932
Las Animas JHS 100/7-8
1021 2nd St 81054 719-456-0228
Tom Meardon, prin. Fax 456-0241

La Veta, Huerfano, Pop. 774
La Veta SD RE-2 200/PK-12
PO Box 85 81055 719-742-3562
Bree Lessar, supt. Fax 742-3959
www.laveta.k12.co.us
La Veta JSHS 100/6-12
PO Box 85 81055 719-742-3662
Bree Lessar, prin. Fax 742-5799

Leadville, Lake, Pop. 2,564
Lake County SD R-1 700/PK-12
107 Spruce St 80461 719-486-6800
Wendy Wyman, supt. Fax 486-2048
www.lakecountyschools.net/
Lake County HS 300/7-12
1000 W 4th St 80461 719-486-6950
Ben Cairnes, prin. Fax 486-8157

Limon, Lincoln, Pop. 1,854
Limon SD RE-4J 500/K-12
PO Box 249 80828 719-775-2350
Dave Marx, supt. Fax 775-9052
www.limonbadgers.com/
Limon JSHS 200/6-12
PO Box 249 80828 719-775-2350
Traci Weisensee, prin. Fax 775-9052

Littleton, Arapahoe, Pop. 40,946
Douglas County SD RE-1
Supt. — See Castle Rock
Rocky Heights MS 1,400/6-8
11033 Monarch Blvd 80124 303-387-3300
Celine Wicks, prin. Fax 387-3301

Jefferson County SD R-1
Supt. — See Golden
Chatfield HS 1,800/9-12
7227 S Simms St 80127 303-982-3670
Chad Broer, prin. Fax 982-3671
Columbine HS 1,700/9-12
6201 S Pierce St 80123 303-982-4400
Kenneth Somers, prin. Fax 982-4401
Dakota Ridge HS 1,500/9-12
13399 W Coal Mine Ave 80127 303-982-1970
Dr. James Jelinek, prin. Fax 982-1971
Deer Creek MS 500/6-8
9201 W Columbine Dr 80128 303-982-3820
Rob Hoover, prin. Fax 982-3821
Falcon Bluffs MS 600/6-8
8449 S Garrison St 80128 303-982-9900
Thomas Burns, prin. Fax 982-9901
Ken Caryl MS 700/7-8
6509 W Ken Caryl Ave 80128 303-982-4710
Christie Hurt, prin. Fax 982-4711
Summit Ridge MS 800/7-8
11809 W Coal Mine Ave 80127 303-982-9013
Daniel Brennan, prin. Fax 982-8998

Littleton SD 15,900/PK-12
5776 S Crocker St 80120 303-347-3300
Brian Ewert, supt. Fax 347-4350
www.littletonpublicschools.net
Euclid MS 700/6-8
777 W Euclid Ave 80120 303-347-7800
Gary Hein, prin. Fax 347-7830
Goddard MS 700/6-8
3800 W Berry Ave 80123 303-347-7850
Bryan Breuer, prin. Fax 347-7880
Heritage HS 1,700/9-12
1401 W Geddes Ave 80120 303-347-7600
Stacey Riendeau, prin. Fax 347-7604
Littleton HS 1,400/9-12
199 E Littleton Blvd 80121 303-347-7700
Dr. Amy Oaks Ed.D., prin. Fax 347-3772
Options Secondary HS Program 100/Alt
6558 S Acoma St 80120 303-347-3580
Greg Sumlin, prin. Fax 347-3590
Options Secondary MS Program Alt
6557 S Acoma St 80120 303-347-4725
Ashley Broer, prin. Fax 347-4747
Powell MS 900/6-8
8000 S Corona Way 80122 303-347-7950
Steve Wolf, prin. Fax 347-3975
Other Schools – See Centennial

Arapahoe Community College Post-Sec.
PO Box 9002 80160 303-797-4222
Denver Seminary Post-Sec.
6399 S Santa Fe Dr 80120 303-761-2482
Front Range Christian S 400/PK-12
6657 W Ottawa Ave Ste A17 80128 720-922-3269
David Cooper, head sch Fax 922-3296
Hope Christian Academy 100/PK-12
7462 S Everett St 80128 303-979-6839
Nancy Thurston, prin. Fax 979-6907
Truth Christian Academy 50/PK-12
PO Box 621961 80162 303-670-3360
Stanley Silverman, admin. Fax 978-0770

Lonetree, See Littleton

University of Phoenix Post-Sec.
10004 Park Meadows Dr 80124 303-755-9090

Longmont, Boulder, Pop. 84,733
St. Vrain Valley SD RE-1J 29,700/PK-12
395 S Pratt Pkwy 80501 303-776-6200
Don Haddad Ed.D., supt. Fax 682-7396
www.svvsd.org
Altona MS 800/6-8
4600 Clover Basin Dr 80503 720-494-3980
Jeremy LaCrosse, prin. Fax 494-3989
Longmont HS 1,200/9-12
1040 Sunset St 80501 303-776-6014
Rick Olsen, prin. Fax 494-3916
Longs Peak MS 400/5-8
1500 14th Ave 80501 303-776-5611
Ann Reed, prin. Fax 494-3663
Mead HS 800/9-12
12750 County Road 7 80504 720-494-3940
Rachael Ayers, prin. Fax 494-3959
Olde Columbine HS 100/Alt
1200 S Sunset St 80501 720-494-3961
Deniece Cook, prin. Fax 494-3977
Silver Creek HS 1,100/9-12
4901 Nelson Rd 80503 720-494-3721
Erick Finnestead, prin. Fax 494-3730
Skyline HS 1,400/9-12
600 E Mountain View Ave 80504 720-494-3741
Heidi Ringer, prin. Fax 682-7382
Sunset MS 600/6-8
1300 S Sunset St 80501 303-776-3963
Dr. Dawn Macy, prin. Fax 494-3703
Trail Ridge MS 700/6-8
1000 Button Rock Dr 80504 720-494-3820
Eddie Cloke, prin. Fax 494-3829
Westview MS 700/6-8
1651 Airport Rd 80503 303-772-3134
Mark Spencer, prin. Fax 494-3786
Other Schools – See Erie, Firestone, Frederick, Lyons, Mead, Niwot

---

Institute of Business & Medical Careers Post-Sec.
2315 Main St 80501 303-651-6819
Longmont Christian S 300/PK-12
1440 Collyer St 80501 303-776-3254
Donnie Bennett, prin. Fax 485-6937

Louisville, Boulder, Pop. 17,982
Boulder Valley SD RE-2
Supt. — See Boulder
Louisville MS 600/6-8
1341 Main St 80027 720-561-7400
Ginny Vidulich, prin. Fax 561-7401
Monarch HS 1,600/9-12
329 Campus Dr 80027 720-561-4200
Jerry Anderson, prin. Fax 561-5650

Institute of Taoist Educ & Acupuncture Post-Sec.
325 W South Boulder Rd # 2 80027 720-890-8922

Loveland, Larimer, Pop. 65,828
Thompson SD R-2J 16,100/PK-12
800 S Taft Ave 80537 970-613-5000
Dr. Stan Scheer, supt. Fax 613-5095
www.thompsonschools.org
Ball MS 700/6-8
2660 Monroe Ave 80538 970-613-7300
Tiffany Miller, prin. Fax 613-7341
Clark MS 500/6-8
2605 Carlisle Dr 80537 970-613-5400
Christine Smith, prin. Fax 613-5420
Erwin MS 900/6-8
4700 Lucerne Ave 80538 970-613-7600
Tim Ridder, prin. Fax 613-7619
Ferguson HS 100/Alt
1101 Hilltop Dr 80537 970-613-5300
Fax 613-5395
Loveland HS 1,500/9-12
920 W 29th St 80538 970-613-5200
Todd Ball, prin. Fax 613-7191
Mountain View HS 1,200/9-12
3500 Mountain Lion Dr 80537 970-613-7800
Kim Young, prin. Fax 613-7820
Reed MS 700/6-8
370 W 4th St 80537 970-613-7200
Arnold Jahnke, prin. Fax 613-7287
Thompson Valley HS 1,200/9-12
1669 Eagle Dr 80537 970-613-7900
Lanny Hass, prin. Fax 613-7909
Other Schools – See Berthoud

Campion Academy 200/9-12
300 42nd St SW 80537 970-667-5592
Don Reeder B.S., prin. Fax 667-5104
Resurrection Christian S 800/PK-12
6508 E Crossroads Blvd 80538 970-612-0674
Rev. Allen Howlett M.A., supt. Fax 612-0975

Lyons, Boulder, Pop. 2,004
St. Vrain Valley SD RE-1J
Supt. — See Longmont
Lyons MSHS 400/6-12
100 McConnell Dr 80540 303-823-6631
Greg Winger, prin. Fax 494-3855

Mc Clave, Bent, Pop. 150
McClave SD RE-2 300/PK-12
PO Box 1 81057 719-829-4517
Terry Weber, supt. Fax 829-4430
www.mcclaveschool.org
Mc Clave JSHS 100/7-12
PO Box 1 81057 719-829-4517
Rachel Dunning, prin. Fax 829-4430

Mancos, Montezuma, Pop. 1,302
Mancos SD RE-6 400/PK-12
395 W Grand Ave 81328 970-533-7748
Brian Hanson, supt. Fax 533-7954
www.mancosre6.edu
Mancos HS 100/9-12
355 W Grand Ave 81328 970-533-7746
Adam Priestley, prin. Fax 533-7537
Mancos MS 100/6-8
100 S Beech St 81328 970-533-9143
Adam Priestley, prin. Fax 533-1463

San Juan Basin Technical College Post-Sec.
33057 Highway 160 81328 970-565-8457

Manitou Springs, El Paso, Pop. 4,882
Manitou Springs SD 14 1,500/PK-12
405 El Monte Pl 80829 719-685-2024
Ed Longfield, supt. Fax 685-4536
www.mssd14.org
Manitou Springs HS 500/9-12
401 El Monte Pl 80829 719-685-2074
Glenn Hard, prin. Fax 685-4755
Manitou Springs MS 400/6-8
415 El Monte Pl 80829 719-685-2127
Cameron Jones, prin. Fax 685-4552

Manzanola, Otero, Pop. 429
Manzanola SD 3J 100/K-12
PO Box 148 81058 719-462-5527
Tom Wilke, supt. Fax 462-5708
www.manzanola.k12.co.us/
Manzanola JSHS 100/6-12
PO Box 148 81058 719-462-5528
Tom Wilke, admin. Fax 462-5115

Mead, Weld, Pop. 3,346
St. Vrain Valley SD RE-1J
Supt. — See Longmont
Mead MS 400/6-8
620 Welker Ave 80542 970-535-4446
Joshua Barnett, prin. Fax 494-3686

Meeker, Rio Blanco, Pop. 2,417
Meeker SD RE-1 700/PK-12
PO Box 1089 81641 970-878-9040
Chris Selle, supt. Fax 878-3682
www.meeker.k12.co.us
Barone MS 200/6-8
PO Box 690 81641 970-878-9060
Jim Hanks, prin. Fax 878-4291
Meeker HS 200/9-12
PO Box 159 81641 970-878-9070
Amy Chinn, prin. Fax 878-3633

Merino, Logan, Pop. 281
Buffalo SD RE-4J 300/K-12
PO Box 198 80741 970-522-7424
Robert Sanders, supt. Fax 522-1541
merino.k12.co.us
Merino JSHS 200/7-12
PO Box 198 80741 970-522-7424
Lonnie Brungardt, prin. Fax 522-1541

Milliken, Weld, Pop. 5,520
Weld County SD RE-5J 3,500/PK-12
110 Centennial Dr Ste A 80543 970-587-6050
Dr. Martin Foster, supt. Fax 587-2607
www.weldre5j.k12.co.us
Milliken MS 700/6-8
PO Box 339 80543 970-587-6300
Ron Hruby, prin. Fax 587-5749
Other Schools – See Johnstown

Moffat, Saguache, Pop. 116
Moffat SD 2, PO Box 428 81143 200/PK-12
Kirk Banghart, supt. 719-745-7821
www.moffatschools.org
Moffat S, PO Box 127 81143 100/PK-12
Michelle Hashbarger, prin. 719-745-7821

Monte Vista, Rio Grande, Pop. 4,392
Monte Vista SD C-8 1,000/PK-12
349 E Prospect Ave 81144 719-852-5996
Robert Webb, supt. Fax 852-6184
www.monte.k12.co.us
Monte Vista HS 300/9-12
295 E Prospect Ave 81144 719-852-3586
Scott Wiedeman, prin. Fax 852-6121
Monte Vista MS 200/6-8
3720 Sherman Ave 81144 719-852-5984
Tom Tichy, prin. Fax 852-6199

Sargent SD RE-33J 400/K-12
7090 N County Road 2 E 81144 719-852-4023
Steven Marantino, supt. Fax 852-9890
www.sargent.k12.co.us
Sargent JSHS 100/7-12
7090 N County Road 2 E 81144 719-852-4025
Ronna Cochran, prin. Fax 852-9672

Montrose, Montrose, Pop. 18,812
Montrose County SD RE-1J 6,200/PK-12
PO Box 10000 81402 970-249-7726
Steve Schiell, supt. Fax 249-7173
www.mcsd.org
Centennial MS 600/6-8
PO Box 10000 81402 970-249-2576
Joe Simo, prin. Fax 240-6461

Columbine MS 500/6-8
PO Box 10000 81402 970-249-2581
Ben Stephenson, prin. Fax 240-6404
Montrose HS 1,400/9-12
PO Box 10000 81402 970-249-6636
James Barnhill, prin. Fax 240-6414
Other Schools – See Olathe

Colorado West Christian S 100/PK-12
2705 Sunnyside Rd 81401 970-249-1094

Monument, El Paso, Pop. 5,337
Lewis-Palmer SD 38 6,300/PK-12
PO Box 40 80132 719-488-4700
Karen Brofft, supt. Fax 488-4704
www.lewispalmer.org
Lewis-Palmer HS 1,000/9-12
1300 Higby Rd 80132 719-488-4720
Sandi Brandl, prin. Fax 488-4723
Lewis-Palmer MS 800/7-8
1776 Woodmoor Dr 80132 719-488-4776
Seann O'Connor, prin. Fax 488-4780
Palmer Ridge HS 1,100/9-12
19255 Monument Hill Rd 80132 719-867-8600
Gary Gabel, prin. Fax 867-8605

Mosca, Alamosa, Pop. 180
Sangre De Cristo SD RE-22J 300/PK-12
8751 Lane 7 N 81146 719-378-2321
Brady Stagner, supt. Fax 378-2327
sdc.schooldesk.net
Sangre De Cristo JSHS 100/7-12
8751 Lane 7 N 81146 719-378-2321
John Stephens, prin. Fax 378-2327

Nederland, Boulder, Pop. 1,417
Boulder Valley SD RE-2
Supt. — See Boulder
Nederland MSHS 300/6-12
597 County Road 130 80466 720-561-4900
Carrie Yantzer, prin. Fax 561-4901

New Castle, Garfield, Pop. 4,478
Garfield SD RE-2
Supt. — See Rifle
Coal Ridge HS 500/9-12
35947 Highway 6 81647 970-665-6700
Rick Elertson, prin. Fax 665-6701
Riverside MS 700/5-8
215 Alder Ave 81647 970-665-7800
Eugenia Williams, prin. Fax 665-7846

New Raymer, Weld, Pop. 95
Prairie SD RE-11 200/PK-12
PO Box 68 80742 970-437-5351
Joe Kimmel, supt. Fax 437-5732
www.prairieschool.org
Prairie JSHS 100/6-12
PO Box 68 80742 970-437-5351
Tabitha Piel, prin. Fax 437-5732

Niwot, Boulder, Pop. 3,929
St. Vrain Valley SD RE-1J
Supt. — See Longmont
Niwot HS 1,300/9-12
8989 Niwot Rd 80503 303-652-2550
Eric Rauschkolb, prin. Fax 494-3928

Northglenn, Adams, Pop. 35,024
Adams 12 Five Star SD
Supt. — See Thornton
Crossroads Alternative MS 100/Alt
10900 Huron St 80234 720-972-5900
Alan Hollenbeck, prin. Fax 972-5919
Northglenn HS 1,800/9-12
601 W 100th Pl 80260 720-972-4600
Sharee Blunt, prin. Fax 972-4739
Northglenn MS 800/6-8
1123 Muriel Dr 80233 720-972-5080
Jami Miller, prin. Fax 972-5119
Vantage Point HS 300/Alt
10900 Huron St 80234 720-972-5800
Alan Hollenbeck, prin. Fax 972-5814

Thorncreek Christian S 200/PK-12
11980 Irma Dr 80233 303-452-7514
Joseph Davis, admin. Fax 452-4904

Norwood, San Miguel, Pop. 505
Norwood SD R-2J 300/PK-12
PO Box 448 81423 970-327-4336
David Crews, supt. Fax 327-4116
norwoodk12.org
Norwood HS 100/6-12
PO Box 448 81423 970-327-4336
Perri Gipner, prin. Fax 327-4116

Nucla, Montrose, Pop. 704
West End SD RE-2 300/PK-12
PO Box 570 81424 970-864-7350
Michael Epright, supt. Fax 864-7269
www.westendschools.org
Nucla HS 100/9-12
PO Box 570 81424 970-864-7350
Michael Epright, supt. Fax 864-7269

Oak Creek, Routt, Pop. 865
South Routt SD RE-3 400/PK-12
PO Box 158 80467 970-736-2313
Darci Mohr, supt. Fax 736-2458
www.southroutt.k12.co.us
Soroco HS 100/9-12
PO Box 158 80467 970-736-2531
Lynda McCarty, prin. Fax 736-0211
Soroco MS 100/6-8
PO Box 158 80467 970-736-8531
Lynda McCarty, prin. Fax 736-0182

Olathe, Montrose, Pop. 1,821
Montrose County SD RE-1J
Supt. — See Montrose
Olathe HS 400/9-12
410 Highway 50 81425 970-252-7950
Scot Brown, prin. Fax 323-5947
Olathe MS 300/6-8
410 Highway 50 81425 970-252-7950
Scot Brown, prin. Fax 323-5947

Ordway, Crowley, Pop. 1,058
Crowley County SD RE-1-J 200/PK-12
1001 Main St 81063 719-267-3117
Scott Cuckow, supt. Fax 267-3130
www.cck12.net/
Crowley County MSHS 100/6-12
602 Main St 81063 719-267-3582
Lisa Bauer, prin. Fax 267-3585

Otis, Washington, Pop. 462
Lone Star SD 101 100/K-12
44940 County Road 54 80743 970-848-2778
Susan Sonnenberg, supt. Fax 848-0340
www.lonestarschool.net
Lone Star JSHS 50/6-12
44940 County Road 54 80743 970-848-2778
Michael Bowers, prin. Fax 848-0340

Otis SD R-3 200/PK-12
518 Dungan St 80743 970-246-3486
Kendra Anderson, supt. Fax 246-0518
www.osdco.com
Otis JSHS 100/7-12
301 Work St 80743 970-246-3486
Michelle Patterson, supt. Fax 246-3487

Ouray, Ouray, Pop. 990
Ouray SD R-1 200/PK-12
PO Box N 81427 970-325-4505
Scott Pankow, supt. Fax 325-7343
www.ouray.k12.co.us
Ouray HS 100/9-12
PO Box N 81427 970-325-4505
Scott Pankow, prin. Fax 325-7343
Ouray MS 50/7-8
PO Box N 81427 970-325-4505
Scott Pankow, prin. Fax 325-7343

Ovid, Sedgwick, Pop. 314
Revere SD 100/PK-12
500 Main St 80744 970-463-5477
Sharon Green, supt. Fax 503-2318
www.plattvalley.schoolfusion.us
Revere JSHS 100/7-12
500 Main St 80744 970-463-5477
Brandon Marquez, prin. Fax 503-2318

Pagosa Springs, Archuleta, Pop. 1,685
Archuleta SD 50 JT 1,300/K-12
PO Box 1498 81147 970-264-2228
Linda Reed, supt. Fax 264-4631
www.mypagosaschools.com
Pagosa Springs HS 400/9-12
PO Box 1498 81147 970-264-2231
Sean O'Donnell, prin. Fax 264-2239
Pagosa Springs MS 400/5-8
PO Box 1498 81147 970-264-2794
Chris Hinger, prin. Fax 264-6112

Palisade, Mesa, Pop. 2,644
Mesa County Valley SD 51
Supt. — See Grand Junction
Palisade HS 1,100/9-12
3679 G Rd 81526 970-254-4800
Dan Bollinger, prin. Fax 464-5102

Paonia, Delta, Pop. 1,427
Delta County SD 50(J)
Supt. — See Delta
Paonia JSHS 200/7-12
846 Grand Ave 81428 970-527-4882
Randal Palmer, prin. Fax 527-4080

Parachute, Garfield, Pop. 1,062
Garfield County SD 16 1,100/PK-12
PO Box 68 81635 970-285-5701
Dr. Ken Haptonstall, supt. Fax 285-5711
www.garfield16.org
Grand Valley HS 300/9-12
PO Box 68 81635 970-285-5705
Ryan Frink, prin. Fax 285-5715
Grand Valley MS 200/6-8
PO Box 68 81635 970-285-5707
Kelly McCormick, prin. Fax 285-5717

Parker, Douglas, Pop. 44,230
Douglas County SD RE-1
Supt. — See Castle Rock
Chaparral HS 2,100/9-12
15655 Brookstone Dr 80134 303-387-3500
Greg Gotchey, prin. Fax 387-3501
Cimarron MS 1,000/7-8
12130 Canterberry Pkwy 80138 303-433-0120
Christopher Zimmerman, prin. Fax 433-0121
Legend HS 2,000/9-12
22219 Hilltop Rd 80138 303-387-4500
Jason Jacob, prin. Fax 387-4501
Ponderosa HS 1,200/9-12
7007 Bayou Gulch Rd 80134 303-387-4000
David Haggerty, prin. Fax 387-4101
Sagewood MS 1,000/6-8
4725 Fox Sparrow Rd 80134 303-387-4300
Daniel Winsor, prin. Fax 387-4301
Sierra MS 1,100/7-8
6651 E Pine Ln 80138 303-387-3800
Kathyrn Teel, prin. Fax 387-3801

Lutheran HS 200/9-12
11249 Newlin Gulch Blvd 80134 303-841-5551
David Ness, prin. Fax 842-1015
Rocky Vista University Post-Sec.
8401 S Chambers Rd 80134 303-373-2008

Peetz, Logan, Pop. 237
Peetz Plateau SD RE-5 200/PK-12
311 Coleman Ave 80747 970-334-2361
Mark Collard, supt. Fax 334-2360
www.peetzschool.org
Peetz JSHS 100/7-12
311 Coleman Ave 80747 970-334-2361
Mark Collard, prin. Fax 334-2360

Peyton, El Paso, Pop. 247
Falcon SD 49
Supt. — See Falcon
Falcon HS 1,200/9-12
10255 Lambert Rd 80831 719-495-5522
Jodi Fletcher, prin. Fax 495-5521
Falcon MS 900/6-8
9755 Towner Ave 80831 719-495-5232
Brian Smith, prin. Fax 495-5237
Patriot HS 200/Alt
11990 Swingline Rd 80831 719-495-5505
Daniel Mulay, prin. Fax 495-5506
Pikes Peak Early College 9-12
11990 Swingline Rd 80831 719-345-7732
Dave Knoche, prin. Fax 323-6465

Peyton SD 23 JT 500/PK-12
18320 Main St 80831 719-749-2330
Tim Kistler, supt. Fax 749-2368
www.peyton.k12.co.us
CTEF Vo/Tech
18320 Main St 80831 719-749-2330
Mary Krisko, admin. Fax 749-2368
Peyton JSHS 200/7-12
13885 Bradshaw Rd 80831 719-749-0417
Brian Rea, prin. Fax 749-0150

Platteville, Weld, Pop. 2,448
Weld County SD RE-1
Supt. — See Gilcrest
South Valley MS 200/6-8
1004 Main St 80651 970-785-2205
Jeff Angus, prin. Fax 785-2182

Pritchett, Baca, Pop. 140
Pritchett SD RE-3 100/PK-12
PO Box 7 81064 719-523-4045
Dr. Terry Bishop, supt. Fax 523-6991
www.pritchettre3.org
Pritchett HS 50/9-12
PO Box 7 81064 719-523-4045
Dr. Terry Bishop, prin. Fax 523-6991
Pritchett JHS 50/6-8
PO Box 7 81064 719-523-4045
Dr. Terry Bishop, prin. Fax 523-6991

Pueblo, Pueblo, Pop. 104,988
Pueblo CSD 60 17,700/PK-12
315 W 11th St 81003 719-549-7100
Dr. Constance Jones, supt. Fax 549-7112
www.pueblocityschools.us
Centennial HS 1,300/9-12
2525 Mountview Dr 81008 719-549-7335
Javin Baker, prin. Fax 549-7634
Central HS 800/9-12
216 E Orman Ave 81004 719-549-7300
Dr. Lynn Seifert, prin. Fax 549-7306
Corwin International Magnet MS 600/4-8
1500 Lakeview Ave 81004 719-549-7400
Sulema James, prin. Fax 253-5264
East HS 1,000/9-12
9 MacNeil Rd 81001 719-549-7222
Dr. Patrick Krumholz, prin. Fax 253-5248
Health Academy 9-12
2525 Mountview Dr 81008 719-549-7632
William McAuliffe, coord.
Heaton MS 700/6-8
6 Adair Rd 81001 719-549-7420
Jayme Cardinal, prin. Fax 549-7838
Paragon Learning Center Alt
3000 Lake Ave 81005 719-423-3573
Yolanda Ortega, prin. Fax 253-6268
Pueblo Academy of Arts 400/6-8
29 Lehigh Ave 81005 719-549-7430
Karen Ortiz, prin. Fax 549-7878
Risley International Academy 400/6-8
625 N Monument Ave 81001 719-549-7440
Charlotte Macaluso, prin. Fax 549-7926
Roncalli STEM Academy 500/6-8
4202 W State Highway 78 81005 719-549-7450
Marci Imes, prin. Fax 549-7469
South HS 1,400/9-12
1801 Hollywood Dr 81005 719-549-7255
Aaron Bravo, prin. Fax 549-7759

Pueblo County SD 70 9,100/PK-12
24951 E US Highway 50 81006 719-542-0220
C. Edward Smith, supt. Fax 542-0225
www.district70.org
Pleasant View MS 400/6-8
23600 Everett Rd 81006 719-542-7813
Ronda Rein, prin. Fax 545-6291
Pueblo County HS 800/9-12
1050 35th Ln 81006 719-948-3351
Brian Dilka, prin. Fax 948-0196
Vineland MS 300/6-8
1132 36th Ln 81006 719-948-3336
Sandy Gibbs, prin. Fax 948-2323
Other Schools – See Colorado City, Pueblo West, Rye

Colorado State University - Pueblo Post-Sec.
2200 Bonforte Blvd 81001 719-549-2100
IntelliTec College Post-Sec.
3673 Parker Blvd Ste 250 81008 719-542-3181
Parkview Medical Center Post-Sec.
400 W 16th St 81003 719-584-4573
Pueblo Community College Post-Sec.
900 W Orman Ave 81004 719-549-3200
St. Therese Catholic S 200/PK-12
320 Goodnight Ave 81004 719-561-1121
Nadine Montoya, prin. Fax 561-2252

Pueblo West, Pueblo, Pop. 29,092
Pueblo County SD 70
Supt. — See Pueblo
Liberty Point International S 500/6-8
484 S Maher Dr 81007 719-547-3752
Cody Kuhlman, prin. Fax 547-0499
Pueblo West HS 1,400/9-12
661 W Capistrano Ave 81007 719-547-8050
Martha Nogare, prin. Fax 547-8041
Skyview MS 600/6-8
1047 S Camino De Bravo 81007 719-547-1175
Robert DiPietro, prin. Fax 647-9667

Rangely, Rio Blanco, Pop. 2,325
Rangely SD RE-4 600/PK-12
402 W Main St 81648 970-675-2207
Matt Scoggins, supt. Fax 675-5023
www.rangelyk12.org/
Rangely JSHS 200/6-12
234 S Jones Ave 81648 970-675-2253
Dr. Kevin Bryant, prin. Fax 675-5403

Colorado Northwestern Community College Post-Sec.
500 Kennedy Dr 81648 800-562-1105

Ridgway, Ouray, Pop. 910
Ridgway SD R-2 300/PK-12
1115 Clinton St 81432 970-626-4320
Steve Smith, supt. Fax 626-4337
www.ridgway.k12.co.us
Ridgway HS 100/9-12
1200 Green St 81432 970-626-5788
Jeremy Voytko, prin. Fax 626-3249
Ridgway MS 100/6-8
1200 Green St 81432 970-626-5788
Jeremy Voytko, prin. Fax 626-3249

Rifle, Garfield, Pop. 9,029
Garfield SD RE-2 4,800/PK-12
839 Whiteriver Ave 81650 970-665-7600
Dave Lindenberg, supt. Fax 665-7623
www.garfieldre2.org/
Rifle HS 700/9-12
1350 Prefontaine Ave 81650 970-665-7725
Todd Ellis, prin. Fax 665-7785
Rifle MS 800/5-8
753 Railroad Ave 81650 970-665-7900
Kevin Marlatt, prin. Fax 665-7930
Other Schools – See New Castle

Rocky Ford, Otero, Pop. 3,914
Rocky Ford SD R-2 800/PK-12
601 S 8th St 81067 719-254-7423
Kermit Snyder, supt. Fax 254-7425
www.rockyfordk12.org
Rocky Ford JSHS 300/7-12
601 S 8th St 81067 719-254-7431
Cindy Cowan, prin. Fax 254-7436

Rush, El Paso, Pop. 100
Miami-Yoder SD 60 JT 200/PK-12
420 S Rush Rd 80833 719-478-2206
Dwight Barnes, supt. Fax 478-5380
www.miamiyoder.com
Miami-Yoder JSHS 100/6-12
420 S Rush Rd 80833 719-478-2186
Dwight Barnes, prin. Fax 478-5380

Rye, Pueblo, Pop. 153
Pueblo County SD 70
Supt. — See Pueblo
Rye HS 200/9-12
PO Box 10 81069 719-489-2271
Michelle Mann, prin. Fax 489-2278

Saguache, Saguache, Pop. 479
Mountain Valley SD RE-1 100/PK-12
PO Box 127 81149 719-655-2578
Travis Garoutte, supt. Fax 655-2875
www.mountainvalleyschool.org
Mountain Valley HS 50/9-12
PO Box 127 81149 719-655-2578
Travis Garoutte, prin. Fax 655-2875
Mountain Valley MS 50/6-8
PO Box 127 81149 719-655-2578
Kathy Hill, prin. Fax 655-2875

Salida, Chaffee, Pop. 5,163
Salida SD R-32 1,200/PK-12
349 E 9th St 81201 719-530-5200
Darryl Webb, supt. Fax 539-6220
salidaschools.com
Horizons Exploratory Academy 50/Alt
349 E 9th St 81201 719-530-5204
Albert Lionelle, prin. Fax 539-6220
Salida HS 300/9-12
26 Jones Ave 81201 719-530-5400
Tami Thompson, prin. Fax 539-2407
Salida MS 300/5-8
520 Milford St 81201 719-530-5300
Will Wooddell, prin. Fax 530-5364

Sanford, Conejos, Pop. 874
Sanford SD 6J 400/PK-12
PO Box 39 81151 719-274-5167
Kevin Edgar M.Ed., supt. Fax 274-5830
www.sanfordschools.org
Sanford JSHS 200/7-12
PO Box 39 81151 719-274-5167
David Judd, prin. Fax 274-5830

San Luis, Costilla, Pop. 618
Centennial SD R-1 200/PK-12
PO Box 350 81152 719-672-3322
Brian Crowther, supt. Fax 672-3345
www.centennialschool.net
Centennial HS 50/9-12
PO Box 350 81152 719-672-3322
Arlen Arguello, prin. Fax 672-3345
Centennial JHS 100/6-8
PO Box 350 81152 719-672-3322
Arlen Arguello, prin. Fax 672-3345

Seibert, Kit Carson, Pop. 178
Hi-Plains SD R-23 100/PK-12
PO Box 238 80834 970-664-2636
Michael Warren, supt. Fax 664-2283
www.hp-patriots.com/
Hi-Plains JSHS 100/7-12
PO Box 238 80834 970-664-2616
Michael Warren, admin. Fax 664-2622

Sheridan, Arapahoe, Pop. 5,532
Sheridan SD 2 1,300/PK-12
4150 S Hazel Ct 80110 720-833-6616
Michael Clough, supt. Fax 833-6650
www.ssd2.org
Other Schools – See Denver

Sheridan Lake, Kiowa, Pop. 88
Kiowa County SD RE-2 100/PK-12
13997 County Road 71 81071 719-729-3331
Melissa Parks, supt. Fax 729-3451
www.plainviewhawks.org
Plainview JHSH 50/6-12
13997 County Road 71 81071 719-729-3331
Melissa Parks, admin. Fax 729-3451

Silverton, San Juan, Pop. 625
Silverton SD 1 100/K-12
PO Box 128 81433 970-387-5543
Kim White, supt. Fax 387-5791
www.silvertonschool.org
Silverton HS 50/9-12
PO Box 128 81433 970-387-5543
Kim White, admin. Fax 387-5791
Silverton MS 50/6-8
PO Box 128 81433 970-387-5543
Kim White, prin. Fax 387-5791

Simla, Elbert, Pop. 614
Big Sandy SD 100J 200/PK-12
PO Box 68 80835 719-541-2292
Steve Wilson, supt. Fax 541-2186
bigsandy100j.com
Simla JSHS 100/6-12
PO Box 68 80835 719-541-2291
Sammi Swennes, prin. Fax 541-2443

Springfield, Baca, Pop. 1,423
Springfield SD RE-4 300/PK-12
389 Tipton St 81073 719-523-6654
Richard Hargrove, supt. Fax 523-4192
www.spre4.org
Springfield HS 100/9-12
389 Tipton St 81073 719-523-6522
Dr. Kirk Salmela, prin. Fax 523-4361
Springfield JHS 50/7-8
389 Tipton St 81073 719-523-6522
Dr. Kirk Salmela, prin. Fax 523-4361

Steamboat Springs, Routt, Pop. 11,946
Northwest Colorado BOCES 50/
PO Box 773390 80477 970-879-0391
Paul McCarty, dir. Fax 879-0442
www.nwboces.org
Yampa Valley HS 50/Alt
PO Box 773390 80477 970-879-0391
Jane Toothaker, dir.

Steamboat Springs SD RE-2 2,400/PK-12
325 7th St 80487 970-871-3199
Dr. Brad Meeks, supt. Fax 879-3943
www.sssd.k12.co.us
Steamboat Springs HS 700/9-12
45 Maple St 80487 970-879-1562
Kevin Taulman, prin. Fax 879-8039
Steamboat Springs MS 500/6-8
39610 Amethyst St 80487 970-879-1058
Jerry Buelter, prin. Fax 870-0368
Yampa Valley HS 50/Alt
325 7th St 80487 970-871-3299
Chuck Rosemond, lead tchr. Fax 871-3943

Steamboat Mountain S 100/9-12
42605 County Road 36 80487 970-879-1350
Meg Morse, head sch Fax 879-0506

Sterling, Logan, Pop. 14,616
Valley SD RE-1 2,300/PK-12
301 Hagen St 80751 970-522-0792
Dr. Jan DeLay Ph.D., supt. Fax 522-0525
www.re1valleyschools.org
Sterling HS 600/9-12
407 W Broadway St 80751 970-522-2944
Dianna Chrisman, prin. Fax 522-1540
Sterling MS 400/6-8
1177 Pawnee Ave 80751 970-522-1041
Robert Hall, prin. Fax 522-0209
Other Schools – See Iliff

Northeastern Junior College Post-Sec.
100 College Ave 80751 970-521-6600

Strasburg, Adams, Pop. 2,413
Strasburg SD 31J 1,100/PK-12
56729 Colorado Ave 80136 303-622-9211
Monica Johnson, supt. Fax 622-9224
www.strasburg31j.com
Hemphill MS 200/6-8
2100 Wagner St 80136 303-622-9213
Sara Turrell, prin. Fax 622-2613
Strasburg HS 400/9-12
56729 Colorado Ave 80136 303-622-9211
Jeffrey Rasp, prin. Fax 622-6921

Stratton, Kit Carson, Pop. 658
Stratton SD R-4 200/PK-12
219 Illinois Ave 80836 719-348-5369
Jeff Durbin, supt. Fax 348-5555
www.strattonschools.org
Stratton HS 50/9-12
219 Illinois Ave 80836 719-348-5369
Dave Gottmann, prin. Fax 348-5555
Stratton MS 50/6-8
219 Illinois Ave 80836 719-348-5369
Dave Gottmann, prin. Fax 348-5555

Swink, Otero, Pop. 607
Swink SD 33 300/K-12
PO Box 487 81077 719-384-8103
Libby Hiza, supt. Fax 384-5471
www.swinkk12.net/
Swink JSHS 200/7-12
PO Box 487 81077 719-384-8103
Nancy Westfall, prin. Fax 384-5471

Tabernash, Grand, Pop. 408

Winter Park Christian S 100/K-12
PO Box 518 80478 970-887-9784

Telluride, San Miguel, Pop. 2,291
Telluride SD R-1 600/PK-12
725 W Colorado Ave 81435 970-728-6617
Michael Gass, supt. Fax 728-9490
www.tellurideschool.org
Telluride MSHS 200/7-12
725 W Colorado Ave 81435 970-728-4377
Sara Kimble, prin. Fax 728-0257

Telluride Mountain S 100/PK-12
200 San Miguel River Dr 81435 970-728-1969
Karen Walker, head sch Fax 369-4412

Thornton, Adams, Pop. 116,276
Adams 12 Five Star SD 36,800/PK-12
1500 E 128th Ave 80241 720-972-4000
Chris Gdowski, supt. Fax 972-4008
www.adams12.org
Bollman Technical Education Center Vo/Tech
9451 Washington St 80229 720-972-5820
Janet Renden, prin. Fax 972-5869
Century MS 1,100/6-8
13000 Lafayette St 80241 720-972-5240
Howard Holbrook, prin. Fax 972-5279
Horizon HS 2,000/9-12
5321 E 136th Ave 80602 720-972-4400
David Shadwell, prin. Fax 972-4598
International S 800/6-8
9451 Hoffman Way 80229 720-972-5160
Jessica Fiedler, prin. Fax 972-5199
Pathways Future Center S 400/Alt
550 E 124th Ave 80241 720-972-4723
Matthew Schmidt, prin. Fax 972-8279
Rocky Top MS 1,200/6-8
14150 York St 80602 720-972-2200
Chelsea Behana, prin. Fax 972-2303
Shadow Ridge MS 1,000/6-8
12551 Holly St 80241 720-972-5040
Susie Wickham, prin. Fax 972-5079
Thornton HS 1,800/9-12
9351 Washington St 80229 720-972-4800
Jennifer Skrobela, prin. Fax 972-4999
Other Schools – See Broomfield, Northglenn, Westminster

Mapleton SD 1
Supt. — See Denver
Academy HS 400/9-12
8970 York St 80229 303-853-1730
Sheri Kangas, dir. Fax 853-1779
Big Picture College and Career Academy 9-10
8990 York St 80229 303-853-1690
Matt Coates, dir. Fax 853-1689
Mapleton Early College HS 200/9-12
8980 York St 80229 303-853-1960
James Long, dir. Fax 853-1996
Mapleton Expeditionary S of the Arts 600/7-12
8980 York St 80229 303-853-1270
Chris Byrd, dir. Fax 853-1296
York International S 700/K-12
9200 York St 80229 303-853-1600
Laura Nelson, dir. Fax 853-1656
North Valley S for Young Adults Adult
8990 York St 80229 303-853-1790
Allison Lusero-Hoffman, dir. Fax 853-1798

Empire Beauty School Post-Sec.
3811 E 120th Ave 80233 303-451-5808
Everest College Post-Sec.
9065 Grant St 80229 303-457-2757
HealthONE North Suburban Medical Center Post-Sec.
9191 Grant St 80229 303-451-7800

Trinidad, Las Animas, Pop. 8,973
Trinidad SD 1 1,100/PK-12
612 Park St 81082 719-846-3324
Scott Mader, supt. Fax 846-2957
www.tsd1.org
Trinidad HS 200/9-12
816 West St 81082 719-846-2971
George Dasko, prin. Fax 846-7488
Trinidad MS 300/6-8
607 Miner Dr 81082 719-846-4411
Deana Pachelli, prin. Fax 846-4740

Grace Christian Center 50/K-12
1001 Obregon St 81082 719-846-6133
Fax 846-6133
Heritage Christian S 50/K-12
PO Box 801 81082 719-859-3508
Jean Griffis, admin.
Trinidad State Junior College Post-Sec.
600 Prospect St 81082 719-846-5011

USAF Academy, El Paso, Pop. 9,062
Academy SD 20
Supt. — See Colorado Springs
Air Academy HS 1,400/9-12
6910 Carlton Dr, 719-234-2400
Dan Olson, prin. Fax 234-2599

United States Air Force Academy Post-Sec.
2304 Cadet Dr Ste 2300, 800-443-9266

Vail, Eagle, Pop. 5,245

Vail Mountain S 300/K-12
3000 Booth Falls Rd 81657 970-476-3850
Mike Imperi, head sch Fax 476-3860

Vilas, Baca, Pop. 112
Vilas SD RE-5 100/PK-12
PO Box 727 81087 719-523-6738
Samantha Yocum, supt. Fax 523-4818
www.vilasre5.us
Vilas Undivided HS 50/7-12
PO Box 727 81087 719-523-6738
Samantha Yocum, dean Fax 523-4818

Walden, Jackson, Pop. 599
North Park SD R-1 200/PK-12
PO Box 798 80480 970-723-3300
Robert Fulton, supt. Fax 723-8486
npk12.org
North Park JSHS 100/6-12
PO Box 798 80480 970-723-3300
Jack Daly, prin. Fax 723-4702

Walsenburg, Huerfano, Pop. 3,036
Huerfano SD RE-1 500/PK-12
201 E 5th St 81089 719-738-1520
Mike Moore, supt. Fax 738-3148
huerfano.k12.co.us
Mall HS 100/9-12
335 W Pine St 81089 719-738-1610
Gunnison Pagnotta, prin. Fax 738-2541

Walsh, Baca, Pop. 543
Walsh SD RE-1 200/PK-12
PO Box 68 81090 719-324-5632
Kyle Hebberd, supt. Fax 324-5426
www.walsheagles.com
Walsh JSHS 100/7-12
PO Box 68 81090 719-324-5221
Ryan Renquist, prin. Fax 324-5734

Weldona, Morgan, Pop. 139
Weldon Valley SD RE-20(J) 200/PK-12
911 North Ave 80653 970-645-2411
Doug Pfau M.S., supt. Fax 645-2377
www.weldonvalley.org/
Weldon Valley HS 100/9-12
911 North Ave 80653 970-645-2411
Jeff Sparrow, prin. Fax 645-2377
Weldon Valley JHS 50/7-8
911 North Ave 80653 970-645-2411
Jeff Sparrow, prin. Fax 645-2377

Wellington, Larimer, Pop. 6,177
Poudre SD R-1
Supt. — See Fort Collins
Wellington MS 400/6-8
4001 Wilson Ave 80549 970-488-6600
Alicia Durand, prin. Fax 488-6602

Westcliffe, Custer, Pop. 555
Custer County SD C-1 400/PK-12
PO Box 730 81252 719-783-2357
Mark Payler, supt. Fax 783-2334
www.custercountyschools.org
Custer County HS 100/9-12
PO Box 730 81252 719-783-2291
John Christensen, prin. Fax 783-4944
Custer County JHS 100/6-8
PO Box 730 81252 719-783-2291
Holly Anderson, prin. Fax 783-4944

Westminster, Adams, Pop. 103,933
Adams 12 Five Star SD
Supt. — See Thornton
Mountain Range HS 2,000/9-12
12500 Huron St 80234 720-972-6300
Julie Enger, prin. Fax 972-6529
Silver Hills MS 1,100/6-8
12400 Huron St 80234 720-972-5000
Julie Evans, prin. Fax 972-5039

Jefferson County SD R-1
Supt. — See Golden
Carle MS 400/7-8
10200 W 100th Ave 80021 303-982-9070
John White, prin. Fax 982-9071
Mandalay MS 400/7-8
9651 Pierce St 80021 303-982-9802
John Schalk, prin. Fax 982-9813
Standley Lake HS 1,300/9-12
9300 W 104th Ave 80021 303-982-3311
Jeff Pierson, prin. Fax 982-3312

Westminster SD 10,100/PK-12
6933 Raleigh St 80030 303-428-3511
Dr. Pamela Swanson, supt. Fax 428-2810
www.westminsterpublicschools.org
Hidden Lake HS 300/Alt
7300 Lowell Blvd 80030 303-428-2600
James Steward, prin. Fax 428-2142
Shaw Heights MS 600/6-8
8780 Circle Dr 80031 303-428-9533
Mike Carlson, prin. Fax 657-3973
Westminster HS 2,400/9-12
6933 Raleigh St 80030 303-657-3980
Kiffany Kiewiet, prin. Fax 657-3989
Other Schools – See Denver

Belleview Christian S 300/PK-12
3455 W 83rd Ave 80031 303-427-5459
Dr. Peggy Polson, prin. Fax 426-6768
Cornerstone Christian Academy 200/PK-12
12000 Zuni St 80234 303-451-1421
Larry Zimbelman, prin.
DeVry University Post-Sec.
1870 W 122nd Ave 80234 303-280-7400
Front Range Community College Post-Sec.
3645 W 112th Ave 80031 303-404-5000
Hyland Christian S 100/K-12
5255 W 98th Ave 80020 303-466-1673
LIFE Christian Academy 200/PK-12
11500 Sheridan Blvd 80020 303-438-1260
Cheri Strong, admin. Fax 438-1866

Weston, Las Animas, Pop. 54
Primero RSD RE-2 200/PK-12
20200 State Highway 12 81091 719-868-2715
Bill Naccarato, supt. Fax 868-2241
www.primeroschool.org
Primero JSHS 100/6-12
20200 State Highway 12 81091 719-868-2715
Heidi Dasko, prin. Fax 868-2241

Wheat Ridge, Jefferson, Pop. 29,601
Jefferson County SD R-1
Supt. — See Golden
Everitt MS 400/7-8
3900 Kipling St 80033 303-982-1580
Jeff Gomez, prin. Fax 982-1581
Wheat Ridge HS 1,300/9-12
9505 W 32nd Ave 80033 303-982-7695
Griff Wirth, prin. Fax 982-7696

Beth Eden Baptist S 200/K-12
2600 Wadsworth Blvd 80033 303-232-2313

Wiggins, Morgan, Pop. 888
Wiggins SD RE-50(J) 500/PK-12
320 Chapman St 80654 970-483-7762
Gary Bruntz, supt. Fax 483-6205
www.wiggins50.k12.co.us
Wiggins MSHS 200/6-12
320 Chapman St 80654 970-483-7763
Trent Kerr, prin. Fax 483-7796

Wiley, Prowers, Pop. 402
Wiley SD RE-13 JT 100/PK-12
PO Box 247 81092 719-829-4806
Dave Eastin, supt. Fax 829-4808
www.wileyschool.org
Wiley S 100/PK-12
PO Box 247 81092 719-829-4806
Michelle Wallace, prin. Fax 829-4805

Windsor, Weld, Pop. 18,391
Weld County SD RE-4 4,800/PK-12
PO Box 609 80550 970-686-8000
Dan Seegmiller, supt. Fax 686-8001
www.weldre4.org
Severance MS 400/6-8
1801 Avery Plaza St 80550 970-674-5200
Jay Tapia, prin. Fax 674-5201
Windsor HS 1,200/9-12
1100 Main St 80550 970-686-8100
Michelle Scallon, prin. Fax 686-0935
Windsor MS 600/6-8
900 Main St 80550 970-686-8200
Eric Johnson, prin. Fax 686-7122

Woodland Park, Teller, Pop. 7,047
Woodland Park SD RE-2 2,600/PK-12
PO Box 99 80866 719-686-2000
Jed Bowman Ph.D., supt. Fax 687-8408
www.wpsdk12.org/
Woodland Park HS 900/9-12
PO Box 6820 80866 719-686-2067
Del Garrick, prin. Fax 687-3880
Woodland Park MS 600/6-8
PO Box 6790 80866 719-686-2200
Jeff Wallingford, prin. Fax 687-8458

Woodrow, Washington, Pop. 20
Woodlin SD R-104 100/PK-12
15400 County Road L 80757 970-386-2223
Rose Cronk, supt. Fax 386-2241
www.woodlinschool.com
Woodlin Undivided HS 50/6-12
15400 County Road L 80757 970-386-2223
Rose Cronk, supt. Fax 386-2241

Wray, Yuma, Pop. 2,328
Wray SD RD-2 700/PK-12
30222 County Road 35 80758 970-332-5764
Levi Kramer, admin. Fax 332-5773
www.wrayschools.org
Buchanan MS 200/5-8
620 W 7th St 80758 970-332-3600
Laurie Unger, prin. Fax 332-3356
Wray HS 200/9-12
30074 County Road 35 80758 970-332-3767
Rick Ward, prin. Fax 332-4476

Yoder, El Paso, Pop. 40
Edison SD 54 JT 200/PK-12
14550 Edison Rd 80864 719-478-2125
Patrick Bershinsky, supt. Fax 478-3000
www.edison54jt.schoolfusion.us
Edison JSHS 100/6-12
14550 Edison Rd 80864 719-478-2125
Fax 478-3000

Yuma, Yuma, Pop. 3,498
Yuma SD-1 800/PK-12
PO Box 327 80759 970-848-5831
Dianna Chrisman, supt. Fax 848-2256
www.yumaschools.org
Yuma HS 200/9-12
1000 S Albany St 80759 970-848-5488
Jodene Boerner, prin. Fax 848-0314
Yuma MS 200/5-8
500 S Elm St 80759 970-848-2000
Brenda Kloberdanz, prin. Fax 848-4261

CONNECTICUT

CONNECTICUT DEPARTMENT OF EDUCATION
165 Capitol Ave, Hartford 06106-1659
Telephone 860-713-6500
Fax 860-713-7001
Website http://www.sde.ct.gov

Commissioner of Education Dianna Wentzell

CONNECTICUT BOARD OF EDUCATION
165 Capitol Ave, Hartford 06106-1659

Chairperson Allan Taylor

REGIONAL EDUCATIONAL SERVICE CENTERS

Area Coop. Educational Services RESC
Thomas Danehy Ed.D., dir. 203-498-6800
350 State St, North Haven 06473 Fax 498-6890
www.aces.org

Capitol Region Education Council RESC
Dina Crowl, supt. 860-247-2732
111 Charter Oak Ave
Hartford 06106
www.crec.org

Cooperative Educational Services RESC
Dr. Evan Pitkoff, supt. 203-365-8803
40 Lindeman Dr, Trumbull 06611 Fax 365-8804
www.ces.k12.ct.us

Eastconn RESC
Paula Colen, dir. 860-455-0707
376 Hartford Tpke, Hampton 06247 Fax 455-8026
www.eastconn.org

Education Connection RESC
Dr. Danuta Thibodeau Ph.D., dir. 860-567-0863
PO Box 909, Litchfield 06759 Fax 567-3381
www.educationconnection.org

Learn RESC
Dr. Eileen Howley, dir. 860-434-4800
44 Hatchetts Hill Rd Fax 434-4837
Old Lyme 06371
www.learn.k12.ct.us

PUBLIC, PRIVATE AND CATHOLIC SECONDARY SCHOOLS

Ansonia, New Haven, Pop. 18,821
Ansonia SD 2,200/K-12
42 Grove St 06401 203-736-5095
Carol Merlone Ed.D., supt. Fax 736-5098
www.ansonia.org
Ansonia HS 600/9-12
20 Pulaski Hwy 06401 203-736-5060
Terri Goldson, prin. Fax 736-5068
Ansonia MS 400/7-8
115 Howard Ave 06401 203-736-5070
Joseph Dobbins, prin. Fax 736-1044

Connecticut Technical HS System
Supt. — See Middletown
O'Brien Technical HS Vo/Tech
141 Prindle Ave 06401 203-732-1800
Laurie Lebouthillier, prin. Fax 735-6236

Avon, Hartford
Avon SD 3,300/PK-12
34 Simsbury Rd 06001 860-404-4700
Gary Mala, supt. Fax 404-4702
www.avon.k12.ct.us
Avon HS 1,100/9-12
510 W Avon Rd 06001 860-404-4740
Chris Tranberg, prin. Fax 404-4743
Avon MS 600/7-8
375 W Avon Rd 06001 860-404-4770
Marco Famiglietti, prin. Fax 404-4773

Avon Old Farms S 400/9-12
500 Old Farms Rd 06001 860-404-4100
Kenneth LaRocque, hdmstr. Fax 404-4135

Baltic, New London, Pop. 1,192

Academy of the Holy Family 100/9-12
PO Box 691 06330 860-822-9272
Mary Riquier, prin. Fax 822-1318

Beacon Falls, New Haven
Regional SD 16
Supt. — See Prospect
Woodland Regional HS 700/9-12
135 Back Rimmon Rd 06403 203-881-5551
Kurt Ogren, prin. Fax 881-2015

Berlin, Hartford
Berlin SD 3,000/PK-12
238 Kensington Rd 06037 860-828-6581
David B. Erwin, supt. Fax 829-0832
www.berlinschools.org
Berlin HS 900/9-12
139 Patterson Way 06037 860-828-6577
Francis Kennedy, prin. Fax 829-2169
McGee MS 700/6-8
899 Norton Rd 06037 860-828-0323
Salvatore Urso, prin. Fax 828-0676

Bethany, New Haven
Regional SD 5
Supt. — See Woodbridge
Amity Regional MS 400/7-8
190 Luke Hill Rd 06524 203-393-3102
Richard Dellinger, prin. Fax 393-0583

Bethel, Fairfield, Pop. 9,266
Bethel SD 3,000/PK-12
PO Box 253 06801 203-794-8601
Dr. Christine Carver, supt. Fax 794-8723
www.bethel.k12.ct.us
Bethel HS 900/9-12
300 Whittlesey Dr 06801 203-794-8600
Christopher Troetti, prin. Fax 778-7448
Bethel MS 700/6-8
600 Whittlesey Dr 06801 203-794-8670
Nicholas DaPonte, prin. Fax 830-7318

Bethlehem, Litchfield

Woodhall S 50/9-12
PO Box 550 06751 203-266-7788
Matthew C. Woodhall, head sch Fax 266-5896

Bloomfield, Hartford, Pop. 7,200
Bloomfield SD 2,100/PK-12
1133 Blue Hills Ave 06002 860-769-4200
Dr. James Thompson, supt. Fax 769-4215
www.bloomfieldschools.org
Arace MS 200/7-8
390 Park Ave 06002 860-286-2622
Trevor Ellis, prin. Fax 242-0347
Bloomfield HS 600/9-12
5 Huckleberry Ln 06002 860-286-2630
Daniel Moleti, prin. Fax 242-9491
Global Experience Magnet S 200/6-12
44 Griffin Rd S 06002 860-769-6600
Sabin Loveland, prin. Fax 769-6605
Harris Agriscience & Tech Center Vo/Tech
5 Huckleberry Ln 06002 860-286-2630
Jaunice Edwards, dir.

Capitol Region Education Council RESC
Supt. — See Hartford
Metropolitan Learning Center 700/6-12
1551 Blue Hills Ave 06002 860-242-7834
Sasha Douglas, prin. Fax 242-0732

Bolton, Tolland
Bolton SD 900/PK-12
72 Brandy St 06043 860-643-1569
Kristin B. Heckt, supt. Fax 647-8452
www.boltonpublicschools.com/
Bolton HS 300/9-12
72 Brandy St 06043 860-643-2768
Joseph Maselli, prin. Fax 645-8374

Branford, New Haven, Pop. 27,603
Branford SD, 1111 Main St 06405 3,200/PK-12
Hamlet Hernandez, supt. 203-488-7276
www.branfordschools.org/
Branford HS 1,100/9-12
185 E Main St 06405 203-488-7291
Lee Panagoulias, prin. Fax 315-6740
Walsh IS 900/5-8
185 Damascus Rd 06405 203-488-8317
Robin Goeler, prin. Fax 481-2785

Branford Hall Career Institute Post-Sec.
1 Summit Pl 06405 203-488-2525
Porter and Chester Institute Post-Sec.
221 W Main St 06405 203-315-1060

Bridgeport, Fairfield, Pop. 139,433
Bridgeport SD 20,000/PK-12
45 Lyon Ter Rm 203 06604 203-275-1000
Frances Rabinowitz, supt. Fax 576-8488
www.bridgeportedu.com
Bassick HS 1,100/9-12
1181 Fairfield Ave 06605 203-275-3083
Tomas Ramirez, prin. Fax 337-0143
Bridgeport Learning Center 100/Alt
280 Tesiny Ave 06606 203-275-1136
Marilyn Earle, admin. Fax 337-0189
Bridgeport Military Academy 100/9-12
641 Mill Hill Ave 06610 203-275-3961
Diana Soares, prin.
Bridgeport Regional-Aquaculture S Vo/Tech
60 Saint Stephens Rd 06605 203-275-2926
Lea Catherman, dir. Fax 337-0168
Central HS 1,800/9-12
1 Lincoln Blvd 06606 203-275-1502
Eric Graf, prin. Fax 337-0173
FWC Information Technology HS 9-12
840 Old Town Rd 06606 203-275-3372
Victor Black, prin.
FWC Physical Science HS 9-12
840 Old Town Rd 06606 203-275-3343
Joseph Lipp, prin.
FWC Zoological Science HS 9-12
840 Old Town Rd 06606 203-275-3413
Michael Watson, prin.
Harding HS 1,100/9-12
1734 Central Ave 06610 203-275-2751
Dane Brown, prin. Fax 337-0177

Connecticut Technical HS System
Supt. — See Middletown
Bullard-Havens Technical HS Vo/Tech
500 Palisade Ave 06610 203-579-6333
Richard Cavallaro, prin. Fax 579-6904

Bridgeport Hospital Post-Sec.
267 Grant St 06610 203-384-3464
Bridgeport Hospital School of Nursing Post-Sec.
200 Mill Hill Ave 06610 203-384-3022
Bridgeport International Academy 100/9-12
285 Lafayette St 06604 203-334-3434
Dr. Frank LaGrotteria, pres. Fax 334-8651
Housatonic Community College Post-Sec.
900 Lafayette Blvd 06604 203-332-5000
Kolbe Cathedral HS 300/9-12
33 Calhoun Pl 06604 203-335-2554
Henry Rondon, prin. Fax 335-2556
Leon Institute of Hair Design Post-Sec.
111 Wall St 06604 203-333-1465
New England Tractor Trailer Training Sch Post-Sec.
510 Barnum Ave Ste 4 06608 203-368-9069
St. Augustine Academy 100/4-8
63 Pequonnock St 06604 203-366-6500
Dr. Deborah Boccanfuso, prin. Fax 362-2934
St. Vincent's College Post-Sec.
2800 Main St 06606 203-576-5235
University of Bridgeport Post-Sec.
126 Park Ave 06604 800-392-3582

Bristol, Hartford, Pop. 59,288
Bristol SD 8,200/PK-12
PO Box 450 06011 860-584-7000
Ellen W. Solek Ed.D., supt. Fax 584-7611
www.bristol.k12.ct.us
Bristol Central HS 1,200/9-12
PO Box 700 06011 860-584-7735
Peter Wininger, prin. Fax 584-7713
Bristol Eastern HS 1,300/9-12
PO Box 580 06011 860-584-7876
Carly Fortin, prin. Fax 584-4886
Bristol Prep Academy Alt
632 King St 06010 860-584-7709
Ed Mongeon, coord. Fax 584-7763
Chippins Hill MS 700/6-8
551 Peacedale St 06010 860-584-3881
Matthew Harnett, prin. Fax 584-4833
Northeast MS 500/6-8
530 Stevens St 06010 860-584-7839
Daniel Sonstrom, prin. Fax 584-7837

Connecticut Technical HS System
Supt. — See Middletown
Bristol Technical Education Center Vo/Tech
431 Minor St 06010 860-584-8433
Luz Manson, admin. Fax 584-0795

St. Paul Catholic HS 300/9-12
1001 Stafford Ave 06010 860-584-0911
Cary Dupont, pres. Fax 585-8815

Broad Brook, Hartford, Pop. 3,997
East Windsor SD
Supt. — See East Windsor
East Windsor MS 300/5-8
38 Main St 06016 860-623-4488
Kimberly Hellerich, prin. Fax 654-1915

Brookfield, Fairfield
Brookfield SD 2,800/PK-12
PO Box 5194 06804 203-775-7620
John Barile, supt. Fax 740-3195
www.brookfieldps.org
Brookfield HS 900/9-12
45 Long Meadow Hill Rd 06804 203-775-7725
Marc Balanda, prin. Fax 775-7773
Whisconier MS 900/5-8
17 W Whisconier Rd 06804 203-775-7710
Deane Renda, prin. Fax 775-7615

Brooklyn, Windham, Pop. 976
Brooklyn SD 900/PK-8
119 Gorman Rd 06234 860-774-9153
Dr. Mary Conway, supt. Fax 774-6938
www.brooklynschools.org
Brooklyn MS 400/5-8
119 Gorman Rd 06234 860-774-9153
Alan Yanku, prin. Fax 774-6938

Burlington, Hartford
Regional SD 10 2,600/PK-12
24 Lyon Rd 06013 860-673-2538
Alan Beitman, supt. Fax 673-4976
www.region10ct.org
Har-Bur MS 800/5-8
24 Lyon Rd 06013 860-673-6163
Kenneth Smith, prin. Fax 673-3481
Mills HS 800/9-12
24 Lyon Rd 06013 860-673-0423
Christopher Rau, prin. Fax 673-9128

Canterbury, Windham
Canterbury SD 500/PK-8
45 Westminster Rd 06331 860-546-6950
Dr. Lois DaSilva-Knapton, supt. Fax 546-6423
www.canterburypublicschools.org/
Baldwin MS 200/5-8
45 Westminster Rd 06331 860-546-9421
Ryan Earley, prin. Fax 546-6289

Canton, Hartford
Canton SD 1,700/PK-12
4 Market St Ste 100 06019 860-693-7704
Kevin Case, supt. Fax 693-7706
www.cantonschools.org
Canton HS 500/9-12
76 Simonds Ave 06019 860-693-7707
Andrew DiPippo, prin. Fax 693-7812
Canton MS 300/7-8
76 Simonds Ave 06019 860-693-7712
Pamela Hamad, prin. Fax 693-7812

Central Village, Windham
Plainfield SD
Supt. — See Plainfield
Plainfield HS 700/9-12
PO Box 218 06332 860-564-6422
James Worth, prin. Fax 564-2116

Chaplin, Windham
Regional SD 11 300/7-12
304 Parish Hill Rd 06235 860-455-9306
Kenneth Henrici, supt. Fax 455-1263
www.parishhill.org/
Parish Hill JSHS 300/7-12
304 Parish Hill Rd 06235 860-455-9584
Brian Tedeschi, prin. Fax 455-9081

Cheshire, New Haven, Pop. 25,684
Cheshire SD 4,600/PK-12
29 Main St 06410 203-250-2400
Jeffrey Solan, supt. Fax 250-2453
www.cheshire.k12.ct.us
Cheshire HS 1,500/9-12
525 S Main St 06410 203-250-2511
Mary Joscelyn-Gadd Ed.D., prin. Fax 250-2563
Dodd MS 700/7-8
100 Park Pl 06410 203-272-3249
Michael Woods, prin. Fax 250-7614
Humiston S 50/Alt
30 Spring St 06410 203-250-2442
Christopher Brown, dir. Fax 250-2453

Cheshire Academy 300/9-12
10 Main St 06410 203-272-5396
John Nozell, head sch Fax 250-7209

Clinton, Middlesex, Pop. 3,326
Clinton SD 2,000/PK-12
137B Glenwood Rd 06413 860-664-6500
Maryann O'Donnell, supt. Fax 664-6580
www.clintonpublic.net
Eliot MS 500/6-8
69 Fairy Dell Rd 06413 860-664-6503
Linda Tucker, prin. Fax 664-6583
Morgan S 600/9-12
71 Killingworth Tpke 06413 860-664-6504
Keri Hagness, prin. Fax 664-6549

Colchester, New London, Pop. 4,696
Colchester SD 2,700/PK-12
127 Norwich Ave Ste 202 06415 860-537-7260
Jeffry Mathieu, supt. Fax 537-1252
www.colchesterct.org/
Bacon Academy 900/9-12
611 Norwich Ave 06415 860-537-2378
Matthew Peel, prin. Fax 537-5410
Johnston MS 700/6-8
360 Norwich Ave 06415 860-537-2313
Christopher Bennett, prin. Fax 537-6258

Coventry, Tolland, Pop. 10,063
Coventry SD 1,700/PK-12
1700 Main St 06238 860-742-7317
David Petrone, supt. Fax 742-4567
www.coventrypublicschools.org/
Coventry HS 500/9-12
78 Ripley Hill Rd 06238 860-742-7346
Joseph Blake, prin. Fax 742-4591
Hale MS 400/6-8
1776 Main St 06238 860-742-7334
Dena DeJulius, prin. Fax 742-4565

Cromwell, Middlesex
Cromwell SD 1,900/PK-12
9 Mann Memorial Dr 06416 860-632-4830
Dr. Paula Talty, supt. Fax 632-4865
www.cromwell.k12.ct.us/
Cromwell HS 500/9-12
1 Donald Harris Dr 06416 860-632-4841
Frances DiFiore, prin. Fax 613-3363
Cromwell MS 500/6-8
9 Mann Memorial Dr 06416 860-632-4853
Ann Cocchiola, prin. Fax 632-4855

Holy Apostles College and Seminary Post-Sec.
33 Prospect Hill Rd 06416 860-632-3010
Lincoln Technical Institute Post-Sec.
106 Sebethe Dr 06416 860-613-3350

Danbury, Fairfield, Pop. 77,029
Connecticut Technical HS System
Supt. — See Middletown
Abbott Technical HS Vo/Tech
21 Hayestown Ave 06811 203-797-4460
Stacy Butkus, prin. Fax 797-4382

Danbury SD 10,500/PK-12
63 Beaver Brook Rd 06810 203-797-4701
Sal Pascarella Ed.D., supt. Fax 830-6560
www.danbury.k12.ct.us
Alternative Center for Excellence 100/Alt
26 Locust Ave 06810 203-797-4786
Sandra Atanasoff, prin. Fax 830-6544
Broadview MS 1,100/6-8
72 Hospital Ave 06810 203-797-4861
Edie Thomas, prin. Fax 790-2856
Danbury HS 2,900/9-12
43 Clapboard Ridge Rd 06811 203-797-4800
Dan Donovan, prin. Fax 797-4730
Rogers Park MS 1,200/6-8
21 Memorial Dr 06810 203-797-4880
Patricia Joaquim, prin. Fax 790-2829
Westside MS Academy 6-8
1 School Ridge Rd 06811 203-329-6700
Dr. Frank LaBanca, prin.

Danbury Hospital Post-Sec.
24 Hospital Ave 06810 203-797-7210
Immaculate HS 400/9-12
73 Southern Blvd 06810 203-744-1510
Joe Carmen, prin. Fax 744-1275
Paul Mitchell the School Post-Sec.
109 South St 06810 203-744-0900
Ridley-Lowell Business & Technical Inst Post-Sec.
44 Shelter Rock Rd 06810 203-797-0551
Western Connecticut State University Post-Sec.
181 White St 06810 203-837-8200
Wooster S 300/PK-12
91 Miry Brook Rd 06810 203-830-3900
Matt Byrnes, head sch Fax 790-7147

Danielson, Windham, Pop. 3,941
Connecticut Technical HS System
Supt. — See Middletown
Ellis Technical HS Vo/Tech
613 Upper Maple St 06239 860-412-7500
Dr. Brian Mignault, prin. Fax 779-2565

Quinebaug Valley Community College Post-Sec.
742 Upper Maple St 06239 860-412-7200

Darien, Fairfield, Pop. 20,500
Darien SD 4,900/PK-12
PO Box 1167 06820 203-656-7400
Dr. Dan Brenner, supt. Fax 656-3052
www.darienps.org
Darien HS 1,400/9-12
80 High School Ln 06820 203-655-3981
Ellen Dunn, prin. Fax 655-3864
Middlesex MS 1,100/6-8
204 Hollow Tree Ridge Rd 06820 203-655-2518
Deborah Boccanfuso, prin. Fax 655-1627

Dayville, Windham
Killingly SD
Supt. — See Killingly
Killingly HS 900/9-12
226 Putnam Pike 06241 860-779-6620
Michael Vose Ph.D., prin. Fax 774-0846
Killingly IS 800/5-8
1599 Upper Maple St 06241 860-779-6700
Heather Taylor, prin. Fax 779-9639

Deep River, Middlesex, Pop. 2,444
Regional SD 4 1,000/7-12
PO Box 187 06417 860-526-2417
Dr. Ruth Levy, supt. Fax 526-5469
www.reg4.k12.ct.us
Valley Regional HS 600/9-12
256 Kelsey Hill Rd 06417 860-526-5328
Michael Barile, prin. Fax 526-8123
Winthrop MS 400/7-8
1 Winthrop Rd 06417 860-526-9546
William Duffy, prin. Fax 526-3721

Derby, New Haven, Pop. 12,664
Derby SD 1,500/PK-12
PO Box 373 06418 203-736-5027
Matthew Conway, supt. Fax 736-5031
www.derbyps.org/
Derby HS 400/9-12
8 Nutmeg Ave 06418 203-736-5032
Martin Pascale, prin. Fax 736-5056
Derby MS 400/6-8
10 Nutmeg Ave 06418 203-736-1426
William Vitelli, prin. Fax 736-3234

Durham, Middlesex, Pop. 2,900
Regional SD 13 1,700/PK-12
135A Pickett Ln 06422 860-349-7200
Kathryn Veronesi Ed.D., supt. Fax 349-7203
www.rsd13ct.org/
Coginchaug Regional HS 600/9-12
135 Pickett Ln 06422 860-349-7215
Brian Falcone, prin. Fax 349-7136
Strong MS 300/7-8
191 Main St 06422 860-349-7222
Scott Sadinsky, prin. Fax 349-7225

Lake Grove School at Durham Post-Sec.
459R Wallingford Rd 06422 860-349-3467

East Granby, Hartford
East Granby SD 900/PK-12
PO Box 674 06026 860-653-6486
Dr. Christine Mahoney, supt. Fax 413-9075
www.eastgranby.k12.ct.us/
East Granby HS 300/9-12
95 S Main St 06026 860-653-2541
David Peling, prin. Fax 413-9092
East Granby MS 200/6-8
95 S Main St 06026 860-653-7113
Melissa Bavaro-Grande, prin. Fax 413-9126

East Hampton, Middlesex, Pop. 2,637
East Hampton SD 1,900/PK-12
94 Main St 06424 860-365-4000
Paul Smith, supt. Fax 365-4004
www.easthamptonps.org
East Hampton HS 500/9-12
15 N Maple St 06424 860-365-4030
John Fidler, prin. Fax 365-4034
East Hampton MS 400/6-8
19 Childs Rd 06424 860-365-4060
Jason Lehmann, prin. Fax 365-4064

East Hartford, Hartford, Pop. 50,077
Capitol Region Education Council RESC
Supt. — See Hartford
Two Rivers Magnet MS 700/6-8
337 E River Dr 06108 860-290-5320
Jill Wnuk, prin. Fax 509-3609

East Hartford SD 6,600/PK-12
1110 Main St 06108 860-622-5107
Nathan Quesnel M.A., supt. Fax 622-5119
www.easthartford.org
CT International Baccalaureate Academy 200/9-12
857 Forbes St 06118 860-622-5560
Caryn Stedman, prin. Fax 622-5555
East Hartford HS 1,700/9-12
869 Forbes St 06118 860-622-5200
Matt Ryan, prin. Fax 622-5223
East Hartford MS 1,100/6-8
777 Burnside Ave 06108 860-622-5600
Anthony Menard, prin. Fax 622-5619
Stevens Alternative HS 100/Alt
40 Butternut Dr 06118 860-622-5999
Dr. Craig Outhouse, prin. Fax 622-5990
Sunset Ridge MS 100/6-8
450 Forbes St 06118 860-622-5800
Dan Catlin, prin. Fax 622-5819

Hartford SD
Supt. — See Hartford
Pathways Academy of Technology & Design 300/9-12
2 Pent Rd 06118 860-695-9450
David Goldblum, prin. Fax 569-5569

Learn RESC
Supt. — See Old Lyme
Connecticut River Academy 400/9-12
9 Riverside Dr 06118 860-913-2200
Tara Amatrudo, prin. Fax 216-9640

Goodwin College Post-Sec.
1 Riverside Dr 06118 860-528-4111
New Testament Baptist Church S 100/PK-12
111 Ash St 06108 860-290-6696
Dr. Michael Stoddard, prin. Fax 290-6698
Stone Academy Post-Sec.
745 Burnside Ave 06108 860-569-0618

East Haven, New Haven, Pop. 28,923
East Haven SD 2,800/PK-12
35 Wheelbarrow Ln 06513 203-468-3261
Dr. Portia S. Bonner, supt. Fax 468-3918
www.east-haven.k12.ct.us
East Haven HS 900/9-12
35 Wheelbarrow Ln 06513 203-468-3267
Vincent DeNuzzo, prin. Fax 468-3818
Melillo MS 600/6-8
67 Hudson St 06512 203-468-3227
Laura Lynn, prin. Fax 468-3866

East Lyme, New London
East Lyme SD 2,800/PK-12
PO Box 220 06333 860-739-3966
Jeffrey Newton, supt. Fax 739-1215
www.eastlymeschools.org
East Lyme HS 1,100/9-12
30 Chesterfield Rd 06333 860-739-6946
Michael Susi, prin. Fax 739-1241
Other Schools – See Niantic

Easton, Fairfield
Easton SD 1,000/PK-8
PO Box 500 06612 203-261-2513
Thomas McMorran Ed.D., supt. Fax 261-7936
www.er9.org
Keller MS 400/6-8
360 Sport Hill Rd 06612 203-268-8651
Susan Kaplan, prin. Fax 268-6105

Redding SD 1,000/K-8
PO Box 500 06612 203-261-2513
Thomas McMorran, supt. Fax 261-7936
www.er9.org
Other Schools – See Redding

Regional SD 9 1,100/9-12
PO Box 500 06612 203-261-2513
Thomas McMorran Ed.D., supt. Fax 261-4549
www.er9.org
Other Schools – See Redding

Easton Country Day S 200/PK-12
660 Morehouse Rd 06612 203-268-5530

East Windsor, Hartford
East Windsor SD 1,200/PK-12
70 S Main St 06088 860-623-3346
Dr. Theresa Kane, supt. Fax 292-6817
www.eastwindsork12.org
East Windsor HS 300/9-12
76 S Main St 06088 860-623-3361
Edward Keleher, prin. Fax 623-7197
Other Schools – See Broad Brook

Lincoln Technical Institute Post-Sec.
97 Newberry Rd 06088 800-243-4242

Ellington, Tolland
Ellington SD 2,200/PK-12
PO Box 179 06029 860-896-2300
Dr. Scott Nicol, supt. Fax 896-2312
www.ellingtonpublicschools.org
Ellington HS 800/9-12
PO Box 149 06029 860-896-2352
Neil Rinaldi, prin. Fax 896-2366
Ellington MS 400/7-8
46 Middle Butcher Rd 06029 860-896-2339
David Pearson, prin. Fax 896-2351

Enfield, Hartford, Pop. 45,500
Capitol Region Education Council RESC
Supt. — See Hartford
Public Safety Academy 400/6-12
1617 King St 06082 860-253-0274
Jeff Larson, prin. Fax 253-0406

Enfield SD 4,100/PK-12
27 Shaker Rd 06082 860-253-6500
Dr. Jeffrey A. Schumann, supt. Fax 253-6510
www.enfieldschools.org
Enfield HS 700/9-12
1264 Enfield St 06082 860-253-5540
Andrew Longey, prin. Fax 253-5555
Kennedy MS 1,100/6-8
155 Raffia Rd 06082 860-763-8855
Steve Sargalski, prin. Fax 763-8888

Asnuntuck Community College Post-Sec.
170 Elm St 06082 860-253-3000
Porter and Chester Institute Post-Sec.
132 Weymouth Rd 06082 860-741-2561

Fairfield, Fairfield, Pop. 54,400
Fairfield SD 10,300/PK-12
PO Box 320189, 203-255-8371
Dr. Stephen Tracy Ed.D., supt. Fax 255-8245
fairfieldschools.org
Fairfield Ludlowe HS 1,500/9-12
785 Unquowa Rd, 203-255-7201
Greg Hatzis, hdmstr. Fax 255-7213
Fairfield Warde HS 1,500/9-12
755 Melville Ave, 203-255-8449
David Ebling, hdmstr. Fax 255-8284
Fairfield Woods MS 900/6-8
1115 Fairfield Woods Rd, 203-255-8334
Dr. Gary Rosato, prin. Fax 255-8210
Ludlowe MS 900/6-8
689 Unquowa Rd, 203-255-8345
Meg Tiley, prin. Fax 255-8214
Tomlinson MS 700/6-8
200 Unquowa Rd, 203-255-8336
Anthony Formato, prin. Fax 255-8211

Fairfield College Prep S 900/9-12
1073 N Benson Rd, 203-254-4200
Dr. Robert Perrotta, prin. Fax 254-4108
Fairfield University Post-Sec.
1073 N Benson Rd, 203-254-4000
Notre Dame HS 400/9-12
220 Jefferson St, 203-372-6521
Christopher Cipriano, prin. Fax 374-4167
Sacred Heart University Post-Sec.
5151 Park Ave, 203-371-7999

Falls Village, Litchfield, Pop. 534
Regional SD 1 400/9-12
246 Warren Tpke 06031 860-824-0855
Patricia Chamberlain, supt. Fax 824-1271
www.region1schools.org
Housatonic Valley Regional HS 400/9-12
246 Warren Tpke 06031 860-824-5123
Dr. Jose Martinez, prin. Fax 824-5419

Farmington, Hartford, Pop. 2,500
Farmington SD 3,900/PK-12
1 Monteith Dr 06032 860-673-8268
Kathleen Greider, supt. Fax 673-8224
www.fpsct.org
Farmington HS 1,300/9-12
10 Monteith Dr 06032 860-673-2514
Dr. Bill Silva, prin. Fax 673-7284
Robbins MS 600/7-8
20 Wolf Pit Rd 06032 860-677-2683
Ted Donahue, prin. Fax 676-0697

Miss Porter's S 300/9-12
60 Main St 06032 860-409-3500
Dr. Katherine Windsor, head sch Fax 409-3525
Tunxis Community College Post-Sec.
271 Scott Swamp Rd 06032 860-255-3500
University of Connecticut Health Center Post-Sec.
263 Farmington Ave 06030 860-679-2000

Gales Ferry, New London, Pop. 1,137
Ledyard SD
Supt. — See Ledyard
Ledyard MS 300/7-8
1860 Route 12 06335 860-464-3188
Christopher Pomroy, prin. Fax 464-2155

Glastonbury, Hartford, Pop. 27,901
Glastonbury SD 6,400/PK-12
PO Box 191 06033 860-652-7951
Dr. Alan Bookman, supt. Fax 652-7982
www.glastonburyus.org
Glastonbury HS 2,100/9-12
330 Hubbard St 06033 860-652-7200
Dr. Nancy Bean, prin. Fax 652-7267
Smith MS 1,000/7-8
216 Addison Rd 06033 860-652-7040
Donna Schilke, prin. Fax 652-4450

Granby, Hartford
Granby SD 1,600/PK-12
15B N Granby Rd 06035 860-844-5250
Dr. Alan Addley, supt. Fax 844-6081
www.granby.k12.ct.us
Granby Memorial HS 700/9-12
315 Salmon Brook St 06035 860-844-3014
Michael Dunn, prin. Fax 844-3026
Granby Memorial MS 300/6-8
321 Salmon Brook St 06035 860-844-3029
Sue Henneberry, prin. Fax 844-3039

Greens Farms, Fairfield

Greens Farms Academy 700/PK-12
PO Box 998, 203-256-0717
Janet Hartwell, head sch Fax 256-7501

Greenwich, Fairfield, Pop. 12,646
Greenwich SD 8,800/K-12
290 Greenwich Ave 06830 203-625-7400
Dr. William McKersie, supt. Fax 618-9379
www.greenwich.k12.ct.us
Central MS 600/6-8
9 Indian Rock Ln 06830 203-661-8500
Shelley Somers, prin. Fax 661-2576
Greenwich HS 2,600/9-12
10 Hillside Rd 06830 203-625-8000
Chris Winters, hdmstr. Fax 863-8888
Western MS 500/6-8
1 Western Junior Hwy 06830 203-531-5700
Gordon Beinstein, prin. Fax 531-5220
Other Schools – See Riverside

Brunswick S 900/PK-12
100 Maher Ave 06830 203-625-5800
Daniel Griffin, dir. Fax 625-5889
Convent of Sacred Heart S 700/PK-12
1177 King St 06831 203-531-6500
Pamela Hayes, head sch Fax 531-5206
Greenwich Academy 900/PK-12
200 N Maple Ave 06830 203-625-8900
Molly King, head sch Fax 869-4921
Stanwich S 400/PK-12
257 Stanwich Rd 06830 203-542-0000
Charlie Sachs, head sch Fax 542-0025

Griswold, See Jewett City
Griswold SD 2,000/PK-12
211 Slater Ave 06351 860-376-7600
Sean McKenna, supt. Fax 376-7607
www.griswold.k12.ct.us
Griswold Alternative S Alt
1553 Glasgo Rd 06351 860-376-9129
Christopher Champlin, prin. Fax 376-9122
Griswold HS 600/9-12
267 Slater Ave 06351 860-376-7640
Erin Palonen M.S., prin. Fax 376-7684
Griswold MS 600/5-8
211 Slater Ave 06351 860-376-7630
Michele Raynor, prin. Fax 376-7631

Groton, New London, Pop. 9,886
Connecticut Technical HS System
Supt. — See Middletown
Grasso Technical HS Vo/Tech
189 Fort Hill Rd 06340 860-448-0220
Patricia Feeney, prin. Fax 446-9895

Groton SD
Supt. — See Mystic
Fitch HS 1,100/9-12
101 Groton Long Point Rd 06340 860-449-7200
Joseph Arcarese, prin. Fax 449-7255
West Side MS 500/6-8
250 Brandegee Ave 06340 860-449-5630
John Jones, prin. Fax 449-5628

Learn RESC
Supt. — See Old Lyme
Marine Science Magnet HS 300/9-12
130 Shennecossett Rd 06340 860-446-9380
Dr. Nicholas Spera, prin. Fax 446-9381

Connecticut Center for Massage Therapy Post-Sec.
1154 Poquonnock Rd 06340 877-295-2268
University of Connecticut Post-Sec.
1084 Shennecossett Rd 06340 860-405-9000

Guilford, New Haven, Pop. 19,848
Guilford SD 3,500/PK-12
PO Box 367 06437 203-453-8200
Dr. Paul Freeman Ed.D., supt. Fax 453-8211
www.guilfordschools.org
Adams MS 600/7-8
233 Church St 06437 203-453-2755
Catherine Walker, prin. Fax 453-8446
Guilford HS 1,100/9-12
605 New England Rd 06437 203-453-2741
Rick Misenti, prin. Fax 453-6768

Hamden, New Haven, Pop. 52,600
Connecticut Technical HS System
Supt. — See Middletown
Whitney Technical HS Vo/Tech
100 Fairview Ave 06514 203-397-4031
Dr. Mary Moran, prin. Fax 397-4129

Hamden SD 5,800/PK-12
60 Putnam Ave 06517 203-407-2000
Jody Goeler, supt. Fax 407-2001
www.hamden.org
Hamden Collaborative Learning Center 50/Alt
306 Circular Ave 06514 203-407-2133
Jonathan Pearce, coord.
Hamden HS 1,800/9-12
2040 Dixwell Ave 06514 203-407-2040
Nadine Gannon, prin. Fax 407-2041
Hamden MS 900/7-8
2623 Dixwell Ave 06518 203-407-3140
Dan Levy, prin. Fax 407-3141

Eli Whitney Tech. High School Post-Sec.
71 Jones Rd 06514 203-397-4031
Hamden Hall Country Day S 600/PK-12
1108 Whitney Ave 06517 203-752-2600
Robert Izzo, head sch Fax 752-2651
Paier College of Art Post-Sec.
20 Gorham Ave 06514 203-287-3031
Quinnipiac University Post-Sec.
275 Mount Carmel Ave 06518 203-582-8200
Sacred Heart Academy 500/9-12
265 Benham St 06514 203-288-2309
Sr. Maureen Flynn, prin. Fax 230-9680
West Woods Christian Academy 100/K-12
2105 State St 06517 203-562-9922
William Kane, prin. Fax 786-4730

Hartford, Hartford, Pop. 121,829
Capitol Region Education Council RESC 5,300/
111 Charter Oak Ave 06106 860-247-2732
Dina Crowl, supt.
www.crec.org
Greater Hartford Academy of the Arts 400/9-12
15 Vernon St 06106 860-757-6300
Jeffrey Ostroff, prin. Fax 757-6399
Greater Hartford Academy of the Arts MS 6-8
75 Van Dyke Ave 06106 860-724-0685
Bo Ryan, prin.
Two Rivers Magnet HS 200/9-12
15 Van Dyke Ave 06106 860-422-7095
Robert McCain, prin. Fax 244-9064
Other Schools – See Bloomfield, East Hartford, Enfield, New Britain, Windsor

Connecticut Technical HS System
Supt. — See Middletown
Prince Technical HS Vo/Tech
401 Flatbush Ave 06106 860-951-7112
Sheila Williams, prin. Fax 951-1529
Connecticut Aero Tech HS Adult
500 Lindbergh Dr 06114 860-566-1234
Robert Sartoris, prin. Fax 566-1350

Hartford SD 21,500/PK-12
960 Main St 06103 860-695-8000
Fax 722-6161
www.hartfordschools.org
Betances STEM Magnet S 4-8
585 Wethersfield Ave 06114 860-695-2970
Ventine Richardson, prin.
Bulkeley HS 400/9-12
300 Wethersfield Ave 06114 860-695-1000
Gayle Allen-Greene, prin. Fax 247-3491
Capital Preparatory Magnet S 700/PK-12
1304 Main St 06103 860-695-9800
Kitsia Ferguson, prin. Fax 722-8520
Classical Magnet S 400/9-12
85 Woodland St 06105 860-695-9100
Zandralyn Gordon, prin. Fax 722-6449
Culinary Arts Academy 300/9-12
85 Sigourney St 06105 860-695-1733
Sheldon Neal, prin.
Global Communications Academy 500/K-12
85 Edwards St 06120 860-695-6020
Kimberly Stone, prin.
Hartford Magnet Trinity College Academy 900/6-12
53 Vernon St 06106 860-695-7201
Sally Biggs, prin. Fax 722-6954
High School Inc. 300/9-12
275 Asylum St 06103 860-695-7100
Audrey Boutaugh, prin. Fax 768-1487
HPHS Academy of Nursing & Health Science 500/9-12
55 Forest St 06105 860-695-1325
Melony Brady-Shanley, prin. Fax 722-8764
HPHS Engineering & Green Technology Acad 400/9-12
55 Forest St 06105 860-695-1315
Michael Maziarz, prin. Fax 722-8765
HPHS Law and Government Academy 500/9-12
55 Forest St 06105 860-695-1320
Jose Colon, prin. Fax 722-8768
Journalism and Media Academy 200/9-12
150 Tower Ave 06120 860-695-7564
Leonard Epps, prin.
Kinsella Sch of Performing Arts 800/PK-12
65 Van Block Ave 06106 860-695-4140
Kenneth O'Brien, prin. Fax 522-0004
McDonough Expeditionary Learning S 300/6-8
111 Hillside Ave 06106 860-695-4260
Bethany Sullivan, prin. Fax 722-8825
OPPortunity HS Alt
110 Washington St 06106 860-722-8529
Rodney Powell, prin.
Renzulli Gifted & Talented Academy 100/4-8
110 Washington St 06106 860-695-2140
Tina Jeter, prin. Fax 722-8529
Sport & Medical Sciences Academy 700/6-12
280 Huyshope Ave 06106 860-695-6900
John Laverty, prin. Fax 722-8017
University HS of Science & Engineering 400/9-12
351 Mark Twain Dr 06112 860-695-9020
Martin Folam, prin. Fax 722-6408
Other Schools – See East Hartford, Manchester

Capital Community College Post-Sec.
950 Main St 06103 860-906-5000

Connecticut Childrens Medical Center — Post-Sec.
282 Washington St 06106 — 860-545-8514
Connecticut Institute for the Blind — Post-Sec.
120 Holcomb St 06112 — 860-242-2274
Covenant Preparatory S — 5-8
135 Broad St 06105 — 860-547-0289
Glenn Winfree, head sch — Fax 547-0361
Hartford Area SDA S — 100/PK-10
474 Woodland St 06112 — 860-724-5777
Hartford Hospital — Post-Sec.
PO Box 5037 06102 — 860-545-2100
Hartford Seminary — Post-Sec.
77 Sherman St 06105 — 860-509-9500
Institute of Living Schools — Post-Sec.
400 Washington St 06106
Lincoln Technical Institute — Post-Sec.
85 Sigourney St 06105 — 800-762-4337
Prince Regional Vocational Tech School — Post-Sec.
500 Brookfield St 06106 — 860-246-8594
Rensselaer at Hartford — Post-Sec.
275 Windsor St 06120 — 860-548-2400
Trinity College — Post-Sec.
300 Summit St 06106 — 860-297-2000
Watkinson S — 200/6-12
180 Bloomfield Ave 06105 — 860-236-5618
Teri Schrader, head sch — Fax 233-8295

Hebron, Tolland
Regional SD 8 — 1,700/7-12
PO Box 1438 06248 — 860-228-2115
Dr. Robert Siminski Ed.D., supt. — Fax 228-4346
www.reg8.k12.ct.us/
RHAM HS — 1,100/9-12
85 Wall St 06248 — 860-228-9474
Scott Leslie, prin. — Fax 228-5312
RHAM MS — 600/7-8
25 RHAM Rd 06248 — 860-228-9423
Dr. Michael Seroussi, prin. — Fax 228-5316

Higganum, Middlesex, Pop. 1,666
Regional SD 17 — 2,300/PK-12
57 Little City Rd 06441 — 860-345-4534
Howard Thiery, supt. — Fax 345-2817
rsd17.org
Haddam-Killingworth HS — 600/9-12
95 Little City Rd 06441 — 860-345-8541
Donna Hayward, prin. — Fax 345-8252
Other Schools – See Killingworth

Kent, Litchfield

Kent S — 600/9-12
PO Box 2006 06757 — 860-927-6111
Rev. Richardson Schell, hdmstr. — Fax 927-6109
Marvelwood S — 200/9-12
PO Box 3001 06757 — 860-927-0047
Arthur Goodearl, head sch — Fax 927-5325

Killingly, Windham
Killingly SD — 2,100/PK-12
PO Box 210 06239 — 860-779-6600
Kevin Farr, supt. — Fax 779-3798
www.killinglyschools.org
Other Schools – See Dayville

Killingworth, Middlesex
Regional SD 17
Supt. — See Higganum
Haddam-Killingworth MS — 800/5-8
451 Route 81 06419 — 860-663-1241
Dr. Jennifer Olsen, prin. — Fax 663-2071

Lakeville, Litchfield, Pop. 909

Hotchkiss S — 600/9-12
11 Interlaken Rd 06039 — 860-435-2591
Craig Bradley, head sch — Fax 435-8056

Lebanon, New London
Lebanon SD — 1,100/PK-12
891 Exeter Rd 06249 — 860-642-7795
Robert Angeli, supt. — Fax 642-4589
www.lebanonct.org
Lebanon MS — 400/5-8
891 Exeter Rd 06249 — 860-642-4702
Robert Laskarzewski, prin. — Fax 642-3534
Lyman Memorial HS — 400/9-12
917 Exeter Rd 06249 — 860-642-7567
James Apicelli, prin. — Fax 642-3521

Ledyard, New London
Ledyard SD — 2,600/PK-12
4 Blonder Blvd 06339 — 860-464-9255
Jay Hartling, supt. — Fax 464-8589
ledyard.net
Ledyard HS — 900/9-12
24 Gallup Hill Rd 06339 — 860-464-9600
Amanda Fagan, prin. — Fax 464-1990
Other Schools – See Gales Ferry

Litchfield, Litchfield, Pop. 1,239
Litchfield SD — 1,000/PK-12
PO Box 110 06759 — 860-567-7500
Sherri Turner, supt. — Fax 567-7508
www.litchfieldschools.org
Litchfield HS — 300/9-12
PO Box 110 06759 — 860-567-7530
Kristen Della Volpe, prin. — Fax 567-7538
Litchfield MS — 200/7-8
PO Box 110 06759 — 860-567-7530
Stephanie Kubisek, admin. — Fax 567-7538

Regional SD 6 — 900/PK-12
98 Wamogo Rd 06759 — 860-567-7400
Edward Drapp, supt. — Fax 567-6652
www.rsd6.org
Wamogo Regional JSHS — 600/7-12
98 Wamogo Rd 06759 — 860-567-7410
Fax 567-6651

Connecticut Junior Republic — Post-Sec.
PO Box 161 06759

Madison, New Haven, Pop. 15,485
Madison SD — 3,300/K-12
PO Box 71 06443 — 203-245-6300
Thomas Scarice, supt. — Fax 245-6336
www.madison.k12.ct.us
Hand HS — 1,300/9-12
286 Green Hill Rd 06443 — 203-245-6350
Anthony Salutari, prin. — Fax 245-6356
Polson MS — 600/7-8
302 Green Hill Rd 06443 — 203-245-6480
Frank Henderson, prin. — Fax 245-6494

Manchester, Hartford, Pop. 29,743
Connecticut Technical HS System
Supt. — See Middletown
Cheney Technical HS — Vo/Tech
791 Middle Tpke W 06040 — 860-649-5396
Robert Sartoris, prin. — Fax 649-5263

Hartford SD
Supt. — See Hartford
Great Path Academy — 200/9-12
PO Box 1046 06045 — 860-512-3700
Tory Niles-Outler, prin. — Fax 512-3701

Manchester SD — 6,200/PK-12
45 N School St, — 860-647-3441
Matt Geary, supt. — Fax 647-5042
publicschools.manchesterct.gov
Bentley Alternative Education S — Alt
134 Middle Tpke E 06040 — 860-647-3342
James Fromme, prin. — Fax 647-5038
Illing MS — 800/7-8
227 Middle Tpke E 06040 — 860-647-3400
Beth Hayes, prin. — Fax 647-5008
Manchester HS — 1,600/9-12
134 Middle Tpke E 06040 — 860-647-3530
Jill Krieger, prin. — Fax 646-3727

Cornerstone Christian S — 200/PK-12
236 Main St, — 860-643-0792
Tonya Snyder, prin. — Fax 647-9291
East Catholic HS — 700/9-12
115 New State Rd, — 860-649-5336
Thomas Maynard, prin. — Fax 649-7191
Manchester Community College — Post-Sec.
PO Box 1046 06045 — 860-512-3000

Meriden, New Haven, Pop. 59,747
Area Coop. Educational Services RESC
Supt. — See North Haven
Edison MS — 700/6-8
1355 N Broad St 06450 — 203-639-8403
Karen Habegger, prin. — Fax 639-8323

Connecticut Technical HS System
Supt. — See Middletown
Wilcox Technical HS — Vo/Tech
298 Oregon Rd 06451 — 203-238-6260
Joyce Mowrey, prin. — Fax 238-6602

Meriden SD — 8,100/PK-12
22 Liberty St 06450 — 203-630-4171
Mark Benigni Ed.D., supt. — Fax 630-0110
www.meridenk12.org
Lincoln MS — 800/6-8
164 Centennial Ave 06451 — 203-238-2381
Dianne Vumback, prin. — Fax 238-7258
Maloney HS — 1,200/9-12
121 Gravel St 06450 — 203-238-2334
Jennifer Straub, prin. — Fax 630-7011
Platt HS — 1,200/9-12
220 Coe Ave 06451 — 203-235-7962
Robert Montemurro, prin. — Fax 630-4011
Washington MS — 800/6-8
1225 N Broad St 06450 — 203-235-6606
Raymond Southland, prin. — Fax 235-6040

Marinello School of Beauty — Post-Sec.
1231 E Main St 06450 — 203-237-6683

Middlebury, New Haven, Pop. 4,100
Regional SD 15 — 4,000/PK-12
PO Box 395 06762 — 203-758-8259
Regina Botsford, supt. — Fax 758-1908
www.region15.org
Memorial MS — 500/6-8
PO Box 903 06762 — 203-758-2496
Dr. John Sieller, prin. — Fax 758-9594
Other Schools – See Southbury

Westover S — 200/9-12
1237 Whittemore Rd 06762 — 203-758-2423
Julie Faulstich, head sch

Middletown, Middlesex, Pop. 46,173
Connecticut Technical HS System
25 Industrial Park Rd 06457 — 860-807-2200
Dr. Nivea Torres, supt. — Fax 807-2196
www.cttech.org
Vinal Technical HS — Vo/Tech
60 Daniels St 06457 — 860-344-7100
Richard Shellman, prin. — Fax 344-2622
Other Schools – See Ansonia, Bridgeport, Bristol, Danbury, Danielson, Groton, Hamden, Hartford, Manchester, Meriden, Milford, New Britain, Norwich, Stamford, Stratford, Torrington, Waterbury, Willimantic

Middletown SD — 4,800/PK-12
311 Hunting Hill Ave 06457 — 860-638-1401
Patricia Charles Ed.D., supt. — Fax 638-1495
www.middletownschools.org
Middletown HS — 1,300/9-12
200 La Rosa Ln 06457 — 860-704-4500
Colleen Weiner, prin. — Fax 347-2044
Wilson MS — 700/7-8
370 Hunting Hill Ave 06457 — 860-347-8594
Cheryl Gonzales, prin. — Fax 347-2158

Mercy HS — 700/9-12
1740 Randolph Rd 06457 — 860-346-6659
Sr. Mary McCarthy, pres. — Fax 344-9887
Middlesex Community College — Post-Sec.
100 Training Hill Rd 06457 — 860-343-5800

Wesleyan University 06459 — Post-Sec.
860-685-2000
Xavier HS — 900/9-12
181 Randolph Rd 06457 — 860-346-7735
Br. Brian Davis, hdmstr. — Fax 346-6859

Milford, New Haven, Pop. 50,507
Connecticut Technical HS System
Supt. — See Middletown
Platt Technical HS — Vo/Tech
600 Orange Ave, — 203-783-5300
Scott Zito, prin. — Fax 783-3970

Milford SD — 6,500/PK-12
70 W River St 06460 — 203-783-3400
Dr. Elizabeth E. Feser, supt. — Fax 783-3475
www.milforded.org
Academy — 100/Alt
140 Gulf St 06460 — 203-783-3652
Sarah Scionti, admin. — Fax 783-3469
East Shore MS — 500/6-8
240 Chapel St 06460 — 203-783-3559
Catherine Williams, prin. — Fax 301-5060
Foran HS — 1,000/9-12
80 Foran Rd 06460 — 203-783-3502
Max Berkowitz, prin. — Fax 783-3635
Harborside MS — 600/6-8
175 High St 06460 — 203-783-3523
Steve Gottlieb, prin. — Fax 783-3687
Law HS — 1,000/9-12
20 Lansdale Ave 06460 — 203-783-3574
Francis Thompson, prin. — Fax 783-3586
West Shore MS — 500/6-8
70 Kay Ave 06460 — 203-783-3553
Paul Cavanna, prin. — Fax 783-4827

Academy of Our Lady of Mercy — 500/9-12
200 High St 06460 — 203-877-2786
Cynthia Gallant, prin. — Fax 876-9760

Monroe, Fairfield
Monroe SD — 3,400/PK-12
375 Monroe Tpke 06468 — 203-452-2860
James Agostine, supt. — Fax 452-5818
www.monroeps.org
Jockey Hollow S — 800/6-8
365 Fan Hill Rd 06468 — 203-452-2905
John Ceccolini, prin. — Fax 452-2444
Masuk HS — 1,200/9-12
1014 Monroe Tpke 06468 — 203-452-5823
Joe Kobza, prin. — Fax 452-5835

Montville, New London
Montville SD
Supt. — See Oakdale
Palmer Building — 50/Alt
PO Box 27 06353 — 860-848-7816
Heather Sangermano, prin. — Fax 848-9159

Moodus, Middlesex, Pop. 1,397
East Haddam SD — 1,200/PK-12
26 Plains Rd 06469 — 860-873-5090
Brian Reas, supt. — Fax 873-5092
www.easthaddamschools.org
Hale-Ray HS — 400/9-12
PO Box 404 06469 — 860-873-5065
Eric Spencer, prin. — Fax 873-5074
Hale-Ray MS — 500/4-8
PO Box 363 06469 — 860-873-5081
Jason Peacock, prin. — Fax 873-5086

Mystic, New London, Pop. 4,136
Groton SD — 4,700/PK-12
1300 Flanders Rd 06355 — 860-572-2100
Dr. Michael Graner Ph.D., supt. — Fax 572-2107
www.groton.k12.ct.us
Cutler MS — 400/6-8
160 Fishtown Rd 06355 — 860-572-5830
Peter Bass, prin. — Fax 572-5834
Other Schools – See Groton

Stonington SD
Supt. — See Old Mystic
Mystic MS — 400/5-8
204 Mistuxet Ave 06355 — 860-536-9613
Gregory Keith, prin. — Fax 536-4508

Naugatuck, New Haven, Pop. 31,134
Naugatuck SD — 4,200/PK-12
497 Rubber Ave 06770 — 203-720-5265
Sharon Locke, supt. — Fax 720-5434
www.naugy.net
City Hill MS — 700/7-8
441 City Hill St 06770 — 203-720-5250
Eileen Mezzo, prin. — Fax 720-5256
Naugatuck HS — 1,300/9-12
543 Rubber Ave 06770 — 203-720-5400
Janice Saam, prin. — Fax 720-5444
Adult & Continuing Education — Adult
543 Rubber Ave 06770 — 203-720-5282
Heather Pelletier, prin. — Fax 720-5281

New Britain, Hartford, Pop. 71,606
Capitol Region Education Council RESC
Supt. — See Hartford
Medical Professions & Teacher Prep Acad — 400/PK-PK, 6-
600 Slater Rd 06053 — 860-223-0726
Andrew Skarzynski, prin. — Fax 223-0742

Connecticut Technical HS System
Supt. — See Middletown
Goodwin Regional Technical HS — Vo/Tech
735 Slater Rd 06053 — 860-827-7736
Daniel Mello, prin. — Fax 827-7862

New Britain SD — 9,500/PK-12
PO Box 1960 06050 — 860-827-2200
Nancy Sarra, supt. — Fax 612-1533
www.csdnb.org
Alternative Center S — 50/Alt
505 S Main St 06051 — 860-224-6450
Dr. Ann Marie Niedzwiecki, prin.
HALS Academy — 200/6-8
40 Goodwin St 06051 — 860-826-1866
Elizabeth Crooks, prin. — Fax 826-1867

New Britain HS 2,500/9-12
110 Mill St 06051 860-225-6300
Joseph Pinchera, prin. Fax 225-6350
Pulaski MS 600/6-8
755 Farmington Ave 06053 860-225-7665
Mark Fernandes, prin. Fax 223-3840
Satellite Careers Academy Alt
40 Goodwin St 06051 860-826-1065
Michael Foran, prin.
Slade MS 600/6-8
183 Steele St 06052 860-225-6395
Todd Verdi, prin. Fax 826-7894

Central Connecticut State University Post-Sec.
1615 Stanley St 06053 860-832-3200
Charter Oak State College Post-Sec.
55 Paul Manafort Dr 06053 860-515-3800
Lincoln Technical Institute Post-Sec.
200 John Downey Dr 06051 860-225-8641

New Canaan, Fairfield, Pop. 17,864
New Canaan SD 4,200/PK-12
39 Locust Ave 06840 203-594-4000
Dr. Bryan D. Luizzi, supt. Fax 594-4035
www.newcanaan.k12.ct.us
New Canaan HS 1,300/9-12
11 Farm Rd 06840 203-594-4600
Dr. William Egan, prin. Fax 972-4700
Saxe MS 1,300/5-8
468 South Ave 06840 203-594-4500
Greg Macedo, prin. Fax 594-4565

St. Luke's S 500/5-12
377 N Wilton Rd 06840 203-966-5612
Mark Davis, head sch Fax 972-3409

New Fairfield, Fairfield, Pop. 12,911
New Fairfield SD 2,700/PK-12
3 Brush Hill Rd 06812 203-312-5770
Dr. Alicia Roy, supt. Fax 312-5609
www.newfairfieldschools.org
New Fairfield HS 1,000/9-12
54 Gillotti Rd 06812 203-312-5800
Dr. Richard Sanzo, prin. Fax 312-5803
New Fairfield MS 600/6-8
56 Gillotti Rd 06812 203-312-5885
Christine Baldelli, prin. Fax 312-5887

New Haven, New Haven, Pop. 126,396
Area Coop. Educational Services RESC
Supt. — See North Haven
Educational Center for the Arts 300/9-12
55 Audubon St 06510 203-777-5451
Jason Hiruo, prin. Fax 782-3596

New Haven SD 20,300/PK-12
54 Meadow St 06519 475-220-1000
Reginald Mayo, supt. Fax 946-7300
www.nhps.net
Brennan/Rogers S of Arts and Sciences 200/3-8
200 Wilmot Rd 06515 203-946-8640
Dr. Gail DeBlasio, prin. Fax 946-7516
Cooperative Arts & Humanities HS 600/9-12
177 College St 06510 475-220-2400
Val-Jean Belton, prin. Fax 691-2404
Cross HS 1,400/9-12
181 Mitchell Dr 06511 475-220-7400
Edith Johnson, prin. Fax 946-6932
Dixwell New Light HS 50/Alt
21 Wooster Pl 06511 203-946-5617
Larry Conaway, prin. Fax 946-5821
DOMUS Academy 50/Alt
560 Ella T Grasso Blvd 06519 475-220-6762
Marc Donald, prin. Fax 946-2343
Engineering & Science S 500/6-12
130B Leeder Hill Dr 06517 203-946-6610
Medria Blue-Ellis, prin. Fax 946-6376
High School in the Community 300/9-12
175 Water St 06511 203-946-7022
Matthew Brown, admin. Fax 946-7132
Hillhouse HS 1,000/9-12
480 Sherman Pkwy 06511 475-220-7500
Glen Worthy, prin. Fax 946-8487
Hill Regional Career HS 700/9-12
140 Legion Ave 06519 475-220-5845
Dr. Zakia Parrish, prin. Fax 946-5949
Hooker MS 300/3-8
691 Whitney Ave 06511 475-220-7200
Evelyn Robles-Rivas, prin. Fax 497-7205
McCabe Center 50/Alt
400 Canner St 06511 475-220-3484
Belinda Carberry, prin. Fax 946-5374
Metropolitan Business HS 400/9-12
115 Water St 06511 475-220-7700
Judy Puglisi, prin. Fax 497-7705
New Haven Academy 300/9-12
804 State St 06511 203-946-8995
Greg Baldwin, prin. Fax 946-8428
New Horizons HS Alt
103 Hallock Ave 06519 203-946-2411
Maureen Bransfield, prin. Fax 946-2412
Riverside Educational Academy 100/9-12
560 Ella T Grasso Blvd 06519 475-220-6700
Larry Conaway, prin. Fax 946-2380
Ross Arts MS 500/5-8
150 Kimberly Ave 06519 203-946-8974
Shawn True, prin. Fax 946-5824
Sound HS 300/9-12
60 S Water St 06519 203-946-6937
Rebecca Gratz, prin. Fax 946-6874
Adult & Continuing Education Center Adult
580 Ella T Grasso Blvd 06519 203-492-0213
Fallon Daniels, prin. Fax 946-6384
Other Schools – See North Haven

Albertus Magnus College Post-Sec.
700 Prospect St 06511 203-773-8550
Berkeley Divinity School Post-Sec.
409 Prospect St 06511 203-432-9285
Gateway Community College Post-Sec.
20 Church St 06510 203-285-2000
Hopkins S 700/7-12
986 Forest Rd 06515 203-397-1001
Kai Bynum, head sch Fax 389-3506
St. Martin de Porres Academy 100/5-8
208 Columbus Ave 06519 203-772-2424
Allison Rivera, prin. Fax 772-2425
Southern Connecticut State University Post-Sec.
501 Crescent St 06515 203-392-5200
Yale-New Haven Hospital Post-Sec.
20 York St 06510 203-785-5074
Yale University Post-Sec.
38 Hillhouse Ave 06511 203-432-4771
Yeshiva of New Haven HS 50/9-12
765 Elm St 06511 203-777-7199

Newington, Hartford, Pop. 30,076
Newington SD 4,200/PK-12
131 Cedar St 06111 860-665-8610
Dr. William C. Collins, supt. Fax 665-8616
www.npsct.org
Kellogg MS 600/5-8
155 Harding Ave 06111 860-666-5418
Jason Lambert, prin. Fax 666-5925
Newington HS 1,400/9-12
605 Willard Ave 06111 860-666-5611
James Wenker, prin. Fax 666-8224
Wallace MS 700/5-8
71 Halleran Dr 06111 860-667-5888
David Milardo, prin. Fax 667-5893

Connecticut Center for Massage Therapy Post-Sec.
75 Kitts Ln 06111 860-667-1886
Hanger Orthopedic Group Post-Sec.
181 Patricia M Genova Dr 06111 860-667-5304

New London, New London, Pop. 26,373
New London SD 3,200/PK-12
134 Williams St 06320 860-447-6000
Dr. Manuel J. Rivera, supt. Fax 447-6016
www.newlondon.org
Jackson MS 600/6-8
36 Waller St 06320 860-437-6480
Dr. Alison Burdick, prin. Fax 437-6494
New London HS 900/9-12
490 Jefferson Ave 06320 860-437-6400
Tommy Thompson, prin. Fax 271-4321
Science & Technology Magnet HS of SE CT 9-12
490 Jefferson Ave 06320 860-437-6496
Laurelle Texidor, dir. Fax 439-7774
New London Adult Education Adult
3 Shaws Cv 06320 860-437-2385
Maria Pukas, dir. Fax 437-6460

Connecticut College Post-Sec.
270 Mohegan Ave 06320 860-447-1911
Mitchell College Post-Sec.
437 Pequot Ave 06320 860-701-5000
Ridley-Lowell Business & Technical Inst. Post-Sec.
470 Bank St 06320 860-443-7441
United States Coast Guard Academy Post-Sec.
31 Mohegan Ave 06320 800-883-8724
Williams S 300/6-12
182 Mohegan Ave 06320 860-443-5333
Mark Fader, head sch Fax 439-2796

New Milford, Litchfield, Pop. 6,408
New Milford SD 3,500/PK-12
50 East St 06776 860-355-8406
Joshua Smith, supt. Fax 210-4132
www.newmilfordps.org
New Milford HS 1,400/9-12
388 Danbury Rd 06776 860-350-6647
Greg Shugrue, prin. Fax 210-2256
Schaghticoke MS 700/6-8
23 Hipp Rd 06776 860-354-2204
Dr. Christopher Longo, prin. Fax 210-2216

Canterbury HS 300/9-12
101 Aspetuck Ave 06776 860-210-3800
Rachel Stone, hdmstr. Fax 350-4425
Faith Preparatory S 100/K-12
600 Danbury Rd Ste 2 06776 860-210-3677
Jaclyn Mattison, prin. Fax 210-3685

Newtown, Fairfield, Pop. 1,929
Newtown SD 4,500/PK-12
3 Primrose St 06470 203-426-7600
Dr. Joseph Erardi Ed.D., supt. Fax 270-6199
www.newtown.k12.ct.us
Newtown MS 900/7-8
11 Queen St 06470 203-426-7642
Thomas Einhorn, prin. Fax 270-6102
Other Schools – See Sandy Hook

Niantic, New London, Pop. 3,074
East Lyme SD
Supt. — See East Lyme
East Lyme MS 900/5-8
31 Society Rd 06357 860-739-4491
Dr. Judy DeLeeuw, prin. Fax 691-5400

North Branford, New Haven, Pop. 12,996
North Branford SD
Supt. — See Northford
North Branford HS 600/9-12
49 Caputo Rd 06471 203-484-1465
Todd Stoeffler, prin. Fax 484-1233
North Branford IS 500/6-8
654 Foxon Rd 06471 203-484-1500
Alan Davis, prin. Fax 484-1505

Northford, New Haven, Pop. 3,200
North Branford SD 2,000/K-12
PO Box 129 06472 203-484-1440
Scott Schoonmaker, supt. Fax 484-1445
www.northbranfordschools.org
Other Schools – See North Branford

North Grosvenordale, Windham, Pop. 1,481
Thompson SD 1,100/PK-12
785 Riverside Dr 06255 860-923-9581
Michael Jolin Ph.D., supt. Fax 923-9638
www.thompsonk12.org
Thompson MS 300/5-8
785 Riverside Dr 06255 860-923-9380
Tina Chahanovich, prin. Fax 923-9638
Tourtellotte Memorial HS 300/9-12
785 Riverside Dr 06255 860-923-9303
Megan Baker, prin. Fax 923-3752

North Haven, New Haven, Pop. 23,822
Area Coop. Educational Services RESC 2,100/
350 State St 06473 203-498-6800
Thomas Danehy Ed.D., dir. Fax 498-6890
www.aces.org
Other Schools – See Meriden, New Haven

New Haven SD
Supt. — See New Haven
Creed Health & Sports HS 9-12
88 Bassett Rd 06473 475-220-7060
Laura Roblee, prin. Fax 946-6161

North Haven SD 3,400/PK-12
5 Linsley St 06473 203-239-2581
Robert Cronin Ph.D., supt. Fax 234-9811
www.north-haven.k12.ct.us/
North Haven HS 1,100/9-12
221 Elm St 06473 203-239-1641
Russell Dallai Ph.D., prin. Fax 234-7436
North Haven MS 800/6-8
55 Bailey Rd 06473 203-239-1683
Philip Piazza, prin. Fax 234-2846

Gal Mar Academy of Hairdressing Post-Sec.
97 Washington Ave Ste 8 06473 203-281-4477

North Stonington, New London
North Stonington SD 800/PK-12
297 Norwich Westerly Rd 06359 860-535-2800
Peter Nero, supt. Fax 535-1470
www.northstonington.k12.ct.us
Wheeler HS 200/9-12
298 Norwich Westerly Rd 06359 860-535-0377
Kristen St. Germain, prin. Fax 535-2536
Wheeler MS 200/6-8
298 Norwich Westerly Rd 06359 860-535-0377
Kristen St. Germain, prin. Fax 535-2536

North Stonington Christian Academy 100/PK-12
12 Stillman Rd 06359 860-599-5071
Pamela Wilkinson, dir. Fax 599-2815

Norwalk, Fairfield, Pop. 84,099
Norwalk SD 10,900/PK-12
PO Box 6001 06852 203-854-4000
Dr. Steven Adamowski, supt. Fax 838-3299
www.norwalkps.org
Hale MS 600/6-8
176 Strawberry Hill Ave 06851 203-899-2910
Dr. Albert Sackey, prin. Fax 899-2914
McMahon HS 1,700/9-12
300 Highland Ave 06854 203-852-9488
Suzanne Koroshetz, prin. Fax 899-2813
Norwalk HS 1,500/9-12
23 Calvin Murphy Dr 06851 203-838-4481
Reginald Roberts, prin. Fax 899-2815
Norwalk Pathways Academy 100/Alt
350 Main Ave 06851 203-899-2820
Dr. Marie Allan, prin. Fax 899-2824
Ponus Ridge MS 600/6-8
21 Hunters Ln 06850 203-847-3557
Dr. Damon Lewis, prin. Fax 899-2924
Roton MS 400/6-8
201 Highland Ave 06853 203-899-2930
Joseph Vellucci, prin. Fax 899-2934
West Rocks MS 700/6-8
81 W Rocks Rd 06851 203-899-2970
Dr. Lynne Moore, prin. Fax 899-2974

Norwalk Community College Post-Sec.
188 Richards Ave 06854 203-857-7000
Norwalk Hospital Post-Sec.
24 Stevens St 06850 203-852-2211

Norwich, New London, Pop. 38,601
Connecticut Technical HS System
Supt. — See Middletown
Norwich Technical HS Vo/Tech
7 Mahan Dr 06360 860-889-8453
Dr. Nikitoula Menounos, prin. Fax 886-4632

Endowed & Incorporated Academies 2,300/9-12
305 Broadway 06360 860-425-5500
David Klein, head sch Fax 887-2004
www.norwichfreeacademy.com
Norwich Free Academy 2,300/9-12
305 Broadway 06360 860-887-2505
David Klein, head sch Fax 887-2004

Learn RESC
Supt. — See Old Lyme
Three Rivers Middle College HS 100/11-12
574 New London Tpke 06360 860-215-9055
Brad Columbus, prin. Fax 215-9913

Norwich SD 3,200/PK-8
90 Town St 06360 860-823-4245
Abby I. Dolliver, supt. Fax 823-1880
www.norwichpublicschools.org
Kelly MS 400/7-8
25 Mahan Dr 06360 860-823-4211
William Peckrul, prin. Fax 892-4302

Three Rivers Community College Post-Sec.
574 New London Tpke 06360 860-886-0177

Oakdale, New London
Montville SD 2,400/PK-12
800 Old Colchester Rd 06370 860-848-1228
Brian Levesque, supt. Fax 848-0589
www.montvilleschools.org
Montville HS 700/9-12
800 Old Colchester Rd 06370 860-848-9208
Jeffrey Theodoss, prin. Fax 848-3872

Tyl MS 600/6-8
166 Chesterfield Rd 06370 860-848-2822
Mary Jane Dix, prin. Fax 848-8854
Other Schools – See Montville

St. Thomas More S 100/8-12
45 Cottage Rd 06370 860-859-1900
James Hanrahan M.Ed., hdmstr. Fax 859-2989

Oakville, Litchfield, Pop. 8,924
Watertown SD
Supt. — See Watertown
Swift MS 700/6-8
250 Colonial St 06779 860-945-4830
Marylu Lerz, prin. Fax 945-6449

Old Lyme, New London
Learn RESC 2,100/
44 Hatchetts Hill Rd 06371 860-434-4800
Dr. Eileen Howley, dir. Fax 434-4837
www.learn.k12.ct.us
Other Schools – See East Hartford, Groton, Norwich, Waterford

Regional SD 18 1,200/K-12
49 Lyme St 06371 860-434-7238
Ian Neviaser, supt. Fax 434-9959
www.region18.org
Lyme-Old Lyme HS 400/9-12
69 Lyme St 06371 860-434-1651
James Wygonik, prin. Fax 434-8234
Lyme-Old Lyme MS 400/6-8
53 Lyme St 06371 860-434-2568
Michelle Dean, prin. Fax 434-0717

Lyme Academy College of Fine Arts Post-Sec.
84 Lyme St 06371 860-434-5232

Old Mystic, New London, Pop. 3,422
Stonington SD 2,300/K-12
PO Box 479 06372 860-572-0506
Dr. Van Riley, supt. Fax 572-8155
www.stoningtonschools.org
Other Schools – See Mystic, Pawcatuck

Old Saybrook, Middlesex, Pop. 9,552
Old Saybrook SD 1,400/PK-12
50 Sheffield St 06475 860-395-3157
Jan Perruccio, supt. Fax 395-3162
www.oldsaybrookschools.org
Old Saybrook HS 500/9-12
1111 Boston Post Rd 06475 860-395-3175
Sheila Riffle, prin. Fax 395-3179
Old Saybrook MS 600/4-8
60 Sheffield St 06475 860-395-3168
Mandy Ryan, prin. Fax 395-3350

Orange, New Haven, Pop. 13,774
Regional SD 5
Supt. — See Woodbridge
Amity Regional MS 400/7-8
100 Ohman Ave 06477 203-392-3200
Kathleen Fuller-Cutler, prin. Fax 387-7603

Oxford, New Haven
Oxford SD 2,000/PK-12
1 Great Hill Rd 06478 203-888-7754
Anna Ortiz, supt. Fax 888-5955
www.oxfordpublicschools.org
Great Oak MS 500/6-8
50 Great Oak Rd 06478 203-888-5418
Anthony Hibbert, prin. Fax 888-7798
Oxford HS 600/9-12
61 Quaker Farms Rd 06478 203-888-2468
Dorothy Potter, prin. Fax 881-5250

Pawcatuck, New London, Pop. 5,474
Stonington SD
Supt. — See Old Mystic
Pawcatuck MS 300/5-8
40 Field St 06379 860-599-5696
Tim Smith, prin. Fax 599-8948
Stonington HS 800/9-12
176 S Broad St 06379 860-599-5781
Mark Friese, prin. Fax 599-5784

Plainfield, Windham, Pop. 14,363
Plainfield SD 2,400/PK-12
651 Norwich Rd 06374 860-564-6403
Kenneth DiPietro, supt. Fax 564-6412
www.plainfieldschools.org
Plainfield Central S 600/6-8
75 Canterbury Rd 06374 860-564-6437
Scott Gagnon, prin. Fax 564-1147
Other Schools – See Central Village

Plainville, Hartford, Pop. 17,932
Plainville SD 2,300/PK-12
1 Central Sq 06062 860-793-3210
Dr. Maureen Brummett, supt. Fax 747-6790
www.plainvilleschools.org
Plainville HS 700/9-12
47 Robert Holcomb Way 06062 860-793-3220
Roberto Medic, prin. Fax 793-3224
MS of Plainville 500/6-8
150 Northwest Dr 06062 860-793-3250
Matthew Guarino, prin. Fax 793-3265

Plantsville, Hartford, Pop. 7,000
Southington SD
Supt. — See Southington
Kennedy MS 800/6-8
1071 S Main St 06479 860-628-3275
Richard Terino, prin. Fax 628-3404

Pomfret, Windham

Pomfret S 400/9-12
PO Box 128 06258 860-963-6100
Timothy Richards, head sch Fax 963-2086

Portland, Middlesex, Pop. 5,757
Portland SD 1,300/PK-12
33 E Main St 06480 860-342-6790
Dr. Philip O'Reilly, supt. Fax 342-6791
www.portlandctschools.org
Portland HS 400/9-12
95 High St 06480 860-342-1720
Kathryn Lawson, prin. Fax 342-2906
Portland MS 300/7-8
93 High St 06480 860-342-1880
Scott Giegerich, prin. Fax 342-3934

Preston, New London
Preston SD 400/PK-8
325 Shetucket Tpke 06365 860-889-6098
Dr. John Welch, supt. Fax 889-8685
www.prestonschools.org/
Preston Plains MS 200/6-8
1 Route 164 06365 860-889-3831
Ivy Davis-Tomczuk, prin. Fax 204-0126

Prospect, New Haven, Pop. 7,775
Regional SD 16 1,700/PK-12
PO Box 7038 06712 203-758-6671
Michael Yamin, supt. Fax 758-5797
www.region16ct.org
Long River MS 600/6-8
38 Columbia Ave 06712 203-758-4421
Derek Muharem, prin. Fax 758-6948
Other Schools – See Beacon Falls

Putnam, Windham, Pop. 7,034
Putnam SD 1,200/PK-12
126 Church St 06260 860-963-6900
William Hull, supt. Fax 963-6903
www.putnam.k12.ct.us/
Putnam HS 300/9-12
152 Woodstock Ave 06260 860-963-6905
Jacqueline Vetrovec, prin. Fax 963-6911
Putnam MS 300/6-8
35 Wicker St 06260 860-963-6920
Teri Bruce, prin. Fax 963-6921

Putnam Science Academy 50/9-12
18 Maple St 06260 860-928-5010
Donald Cushing, hdmstr. Fax 928-1666

Redding, Fairfield
Redding SD
Supt. — See Easton
Read MS 500/5-8
486 Redding Rd 06896 203-938-2533
Diane Martin, prin. Fax 938-8667

Regional SD 9
Supt. — See Easton
Barlow HS 1,100/9-12
100 Black Rock Tpke 06896 203-938-2508
Gina Pin, prin. Fax 938-0327

Ridgefield, Fairfield, Pop. 7,542
Ridgefield SD 5,300/PK-12
70 Prospect St 06877 203-894-5550
Dr. Karen Baldwin, supt. Fax 431-2811
www.ridgefield.org
East Ridge MS 800/6-8
10 E Ridge Rd 06877 203-894-5500
Patricia Raneri, prin. Fax 431-2843
Ridgefield HS 1,800/9-12
700 N Salem Rd 06877 203-894-5725
Dr. Stacey Gross Ed.D., prin. Fax 431-2891
Scotts Ridge MS 500/6-8
750 N Salem Rd 06877 203-894-5725
Tim Salem, prin. Fax 894-3411

Riverside, Fairfield, Pop. 8,283
Greenwich SD
Supt. — See Greenwich
Eastern MS 800/6-8
51 Hendrie Ave 06878 203-637-1744
Ralph Mayo, prin. Fax 637-3567

Rocky Hill, Hartford, Pop. 16,554
Rocky Hill SD 2,400/PK-12
PO Box 627 06067 860-258-7701
Dr. Mark Zito, supt. Fax 258-7710
www.rockyhillps.com
Griswold MS 600/5-8
144 Bailey Rd 06067 860-258-7741
Richard Watson, prin. Fax 258-7746
Rocky Hill HS 700/9-12
50 Chapin Ave 06067 860-258-7721
Mario Almeida, prin. Fax 258-7735

Porter and Chester Institute Post-Sec.
30 Waterchase Dr 06067 860-529-2519

Salisbury, Litchfield

Salisbury S 300/9-12
251 Canaan Rd 06068 860-435-5700
Chisholm Chandler, hdmstr. Fax 435-5750

Sandy Hook, Fairfield
Newtown SD
Supt. — See Newtown
Newtown HS 1,700/9-12
12 Berkshire Rd 06482 203-426-7646
Lorrie Rodrigue, prin. Fax 426-6573

Seymour, New Haven, Pop. 14,288
Seymour SD 2,000/PK-12
98 Bank St 06483 203-888-4564
Christine Syriac, supt. Fax 888-1704
www.seymourschools.org
Seymour HS 600/9-12
2 Botsford Rd 06483 203-888-2561
James Freund, prin. Fax 888-7476
Seymour MS 600/6-8
211 Mountain Rd 06483 203-888-4513
Bernadette Hamad, prin. Fax 881-7535

Shelton, Fairfield, Pop. 39,118
Shelton SD 4,900/PK-12
382 Long Hill Ave 06484 203-924-1023
Dr. Christopher Clouet, supt. Fax 924-5894
www.sheltonpublicschools.org
Shelton HS 1,600/9-12
120 Meadow St 06484 203-922-3004
Dr. Beth Smith, hdmstr. Fax 924-8236
Shelton IS 800/7-8
675 Constitution Blvd N 06484 203-926-2000
Kenneth Saranich, hdmstr. Fax 926-2017

Lincoln Technical Institute Post-Sec.
8 Progress Dr 06484 203-929-0592

Simsbury, Hartford, Pop. 22,023
Simsbury SD 4,300/PK-12
933 Hopmeadow St 06070 860-651-3361
Matthew Curtis, supt. Fax 651-4343
www.simsbury.k12.ct.us
James Memorial MS 700/7-8
155 Firetown Rd 06070 860-651-3341
Brian White, prin. Fax 658-3629
Simsbury HS 1,500/9-12
34 Farms Village Rd 06070 860-658-0451
Andrew O'Brien, prin. Fax 658-2439

Walker S 200/6-12
230 Bushy Hill Rd 06070 860-408-4200
Dr. Meera Viswanathan, head sch Fax 408-4201
Westminster S 400/9-12
995 Hopmeadow St 06070 860-408-3000
William Philip, hdmstr. Fax 408-3001

Somers, Tolland, Pop. 1,774
Somers SD 1,500/PK-12
1 Vision Blvd 06071 860-749-2270
Dr. Maynard Suffredini, supt. Fax 763-0748
www.somers.k12.ct.us
Avery MS 400/6-8
1 Vision Blvd 06071 860-749-2270
Clay Krevolin, prin. Fax 763-2073
Somers HS 500/9-12
5 Vision Blvd 06071 860-749-2270
Gary Cotzin, prin. Fax 749-9264

New England Tractor Trailer Training Post-Sec.
32 Field Rd 06071 860-749-0711

Southbury, New Haven, Pop. 15,818
Regional SD 15
Supt. — See Middlebury
Pomperaug Regional HS 1,300/9-12
234 Judd Rd 06488 203-262-3200
Glenn Lungarini, prin. Fax 262-6806
Rochambeau MS 500/6-8
100 Peter Rd 06488 203-264-2711
Michael Bernardi, prin. Fax 264-6638

Southington, Hartford, Pop. 39,200
Southington SD 6,700/PK-12
200 N Main St 06489 860-628-3200
Timothy J. Connellan, supt. Fax 821-8056
www.southingtonschools.org
ALTA at Pyne Center Alt
242 N Main St 06489 860-628-3379
Jess Levin, dir. Fax 628-3458
DePaolo MS 800/6-8
385 Pleasant St 06489 860-628-3260
Frank Pepe, prin. Fax 628-3403
Southington HS 2,000/9-12
720 Pleasant St 06489 860-628-3229
Brian Stranieri, prin. Fax 628-3397
Other Schools – See Plantsville

Branford Hall Career Institute Post-Sec.
35 N Main St 06489 860-276-0600
Lincoln College of New England Post-Sec.
2279 Mount Vernon Rd 06489 860-628-4751

South Kent, Litchfield

South Kent S 200/9-12
40 Bulls Bridge Rd 06785 860-927-3539
Andrew J. Vadnais, head sch Fax 803-0040

South Windsor, Hartford, Pop. 22,090
South Windsor SD 4,200/PK-12
1737 Main St 06074 860-291-1200
Kate Carter Ed.D., supt. Fax 291-1291
www.southwindsorschools.org
Edwards MS 1,000/6-8
100 Arnold Way 06074 860-648-5030
Nancy Larson, prin. Fax 648-5029
South Windsor HS 1,400/9-12
161 Nevers Rd 06074 860-648-5000
Daniel Sullivan, prin. Fax 648-5013

Stafford Springs, Tolland, Pop. 4,869
Stafford SD 1,600/PK-12
16 Levinthal Run 06076 860-684-2208
Dr. Patricia Collin, supt. Fax 684-5172
www.stafford.k12.ct.us
Stafford HS 500/9-12
145 Orcuttville Rd 06076 860-684-4233
Marco Pelliccia, prin. Fax 684-0424
Stafford MS 300/6-8
21 Levinthal Run 06076 860-684-2785
Jennifer Hoffman, prin. Fax 684-4671

Stamford, Fairfield, Pop. 120,428
Connecticut Technical HS System
Supt. — See Middletown
Wright Technical HS Vo/Tech
120 Bridge St 06905 203-324-7363
Eric Hilversum, prin. Fax 674-5801

Stamford SD 15,700/PK-12
888 Washington Blvd Fl 5 06901 203-977-4105
Earl Kim, supt. Fax 977-5964
www.stamfordpublicschools.org/
Academy of Info Technology & Engineering 700/9-12
411 High Ridge Rd 06905 203-977-4336
Tina Rivera, prin. Fax 977-6638
Cloonan MS 600/6-8
11 W North St 06902 203-977-4544
David Tate, prin. Fax 977-4867
Dolan MS 600/6-8
51 Toms Rd 06906 203-977-4441
Charmaine Tourse, prin. Fax 977-4880

Rippowam MS 700/5-8
381 High Ridge Rd 06905 203-977-5255
Jason Martin, prin. Fax 977-5154
Scofield Magnet MS 600/5-8
641 Scofieldtown Rd 06903 203-977-2750
Scott Clayton, prin. Fax 977-2766
Stamford HS 1,900/9-12
55 Strawberry Hill Ave 06902 203-977-4227
Raymond Manka, prin. Fax 356-1720
Turn of River MS 500/6-8
117 Vine Rd 06905 203-977-4284
Brendan Fox, prin. Fax 977-5037
Westhill HS 2,100/9-12
125 Roxbury Rd 06902 203-977-4477
Camille Figluizzi, prin. Fax 977-4996

Beacon S 50/3-12
111 W North St 06902 203-200-7244
Marge Ullrich, admin. Fax 829-6075
Beth Benjamin Academy of Connecticut Post-Sec.
132 Prospect St 06901 203-325-4351
Jewish HS of Connecticut 50/9-12
1937 W Main St 06902 203-357-0850
Rabbi Elisha Paul, head sch Fax 363-9826
King S 700/PK-12
1450 Newfield Ave 06905 203-322-3496
Thomas Main, hdmstr. Fax 461-9988
St. Basil College Seminary Post-Sec.
195 Glenbrook Rd 06902 203-324-4578
Stamford Hospital Post-Sec.
PO Box 9317 06904 203-276-7877
Trinity Catholic HS 400/9-12
926 Newfield Ave 06905 203-322-3401
David Williams, prin. Fax 322-5330
Trinity Catholic MS 200/6-8
948 Newfield Ave 06905 203-322-7383
Abbey Camillery, prin. Fax 324-4435

Storrs, Tolland, Pop. 14,985
Mansfield SD 1,200/PK-8
4 S Eagleville Rd 06268 860-429-3350
Kelly Lyman, supt. Fax 429-3379
www.mansfieldct.gov/content/11150/default.aspx
Mansfield MS 500/5-8
205 Spring Hill Rd 06268 860-429-9341
Candace Morell, prin. Fax 429-1020

Regional SD 19 1,200/9-12
1235 Storrs Rd 06268 860-487-1862
Bruce Silva, supt. Fax 429-0085
www.eosmith.org
Smith HS 1,200/9-12
1235 Storrs Rd 06268 860-487-0877
Dr. Louis DeLoreto, prin. Fax 429-7892

University of Connecticut 06269 Post-Sec.
860-486-2000

Stratford, Fairfield, Pop. 50,391
Connecticut Technical HS System
Supt. — See Middletown
Stratford S for Aviation Maintenance Adult
200 Great Meadow Rd 06615 203-381-9250
Scott Zito, prin. Fax 381-0764

Stratford SD 6,900/PK-12
1000 E Broadway 06615 203-385-4210
Dr. Janet Robinson, supt. Fax 381-2012
stratfordk12.org
Bunnell HS 1,200/9-12
1 Bulldog Blvd 06614 203-385-4250
Dr. Nancy Dowling, prin. Fax 381-2014
Flood MS 600/7-8
490 Chapel St 06614 203-385-4280
Lea Ann Bradford, prin. Fax 381-2033
Stratford HS 1,000/9-12
45 N Parade St 06615 203-385-4230
John Dellapiano, prin. Fax 381-2021
Wooster MS 500/7-8
150 Lincoln St 06614 203-385-4275
Bryan Darcy, prin. Fax 381-6918

Porter and Chester Institute Post-Sec.
670 Lordship Blvd 06615 203-375-4463

Suffield, Hartford
Suffield SD 2,400/PK-12
350 Mountain Rd 06078 860-668-3800
Karen Berasi, supt. Fax 668-3805
www.suffield.org
Suffield MS 600/6-8
350 Mountain Rd 06078 860-668-3820
Damon Pearce, prin. Fax 668-3088
Other Schools – See West Suffield

Suffield Academy 400/9-12
185 N Main St 06078 860-386-4400
Charles Cahn, hdmstr. Fax 386-4411

Terryville, Litchfield, Pop. 5,299
Plymouth SD 1,500/PK-12
77 Main St 06786 860-314-8005
Dr. Martin Semmel, supt. Fax 314-2766
www.plymouth.k12.ct.us
Terry MS 400/6-8
21 N Main St 06786 860-314-2790
Angela Suffridge, prin. Fax 314-2768
Terryville HS 500/9-12
33 N Harwinton Ave 06786 860-314-2777
Michael Hults, prin. Fax 314-2785

Thomaston, Litchfield, Pop. 1,888
Thomaston SD 900/PK-12
PO Box 166 06787 860-283-4796
Francine Coss, supt. Fax 283-6708
www.thomastonschools.net/
Thomaston HS 400/7-12
185 Branch Rd 06787 860-283-3030
John Perrucci, prin. Fax 283-3040

Thompson, Windham

Marianapolis Prep S 300/9-12
PO Box 304 06277 860-923-9565
Joseph Hanrahan, hdmstr. Fax 923-3730

Tolland, Tolland
Tolland SD 2,700/PK-12
51 Tolland Grn 06084 860-870-6850
Walter Willett Ph.D., supt. Fax 870-7737
www.tolland.k12.ct.us
Tolland HS 800/9-12
1 Eagle Hill Dr 06084 860-870-6818
Domonique Fox, prin. Fax 870-8168
Tolland MS 700/6-8
1 Falcon Way 06084 860-870-6860
Daniel Uriano, prin. Fax 870-5737

Torrington, Litchfield, Pop. 35,694
Connecticut Technical HS System
Supt. — See Middletown
Wolcott Technical HS Vo/Tech
75 Oliver St 06790 860-496-5300
Robert Axon, prin. Fax 496-9022

Torrington SD 4,300/PK-12
355 Migeon Ave 06790 860-489-2327
Lynda T. Reitman, supt. Fax 489-0726
www.torrington.org
Torrington HS 1,100/9-12
50 Major Besse Dr 06790 860-489-2294
Eric Baim, prin. Fax 489-2853
Torrington MS 1,000/6-8
200 Middle School Dr 06790 860-496-4050
Eric Baim, prin. Fax 496-1089

Trumbull, Fairfield, Pop. 35,588
Trumbull SD 6,800/PK-12
6254 Main St 06611 203-452-4300
Gary Cialfi, supt. Fax 452-4305
www.trumbullps.org
Hillcrest MS 800/6-8
530 Daniels Farm Rd 06611 203-452-4466
Stafford Thomas, prin. Fax 452-4479
Madison MS 800/6-8
4630 Madison Ave 06611 203-452-4499
Valerie Forshaw, prin. Fax 452-4490
Trumbull HS 2,100/9-12
72 Strobel Rd 06611 203-452-4555
Marc Guarino, prin. Fax 452-4593

Christian Heritage S 500/K-12
575 White Plains Rd 06611 203-261-6230
Dr. Brian Modarelli, head sch Fax 452-1531
St. Joseph HS 800/9-12
2320 Huntington Tpke 06611 203-378-9378
Dr. James Keane, prin. Fax 378-7306

Uncasville, New London, Pop. 2,975

St. Bernard S 400/6-12
1593 Norwich New London Tpk 06382
860-848-3007
Donald Macrino, hdmstr. Fax 848-0261

Vernon Rockville, Tolland, Pop. 28,900
Vernon SD 3,300/PK-12
PO Box 600 06066 860-870-6000
Joseph Macary, supt. Fax 870-6005
vernonpublicschools.org
Rockville HS 900/9-12
70 Loveland Hill Rd 06066 860-870-6050
Andrew Rockett, prin. Fax 870-6314
Vernon Center MS 700/6-8
777 Hartford Tpke 06066 860-870-6070
James Harrison, prin. Fax 870-6318

Wallingford, New Haven, Pop. 41,700
Wallingford SD 6,000/PK-12
100 S Turnpike Rd 06492 203-949-6500
Dr. Salvatore Menzo, supt. Fax 949-6550
www.wallingford.k12.ct.us
Hall HS 1,100/9-12
70 Pond Hill Rd 06492 203-294-5350
Joseph Corso, prin. Fax 294-5353
Hammarskjold MS 700/6-8
106 Pond Hill Rd 06492 203-294-3700
Sashi Govin, prin. Fax 294-3749
Moran MS 700/6-8
141 Hope Hill Rd 06492 203-741-2900
Joseph Piacentini, prin. Fax 741-2939
Sheehan HS 900/9-12
142 Hope Hill Rd 06492 203-294-5900
Rosemary Duthie, prin. Fax 294-5980

Choate Rosemary Hall 800/9-12
333 Christian St 06492 203-697-2000
Dr. Alex Curtis, hdmstr. Fax 697-2720

Washington, Litchfield
Regional SD 12
Supt. — See Washington Depot
Shepaug Valley JSHS 300/6-12
159 South St 06793 860-868-7326
Kimberly Gallo, prin. Fax 868-6260

Devereux Center in Connecticut Post-Sec.
81 Sabbaday Ln 06793 860-868-7377
Gunnery 300/9-12
99 Green Hill Rd 06793 860-868-7334
Peter Becker, head sch Fax 868-1614

Washington Depot, Litchfield
Regional SD 12 600/PK-12
PO Box 386 06794 860-868-6100
Patricia Cosentino Ed.D., supt. Fax 868-6103
www.region-12.org
Other Schools – See Washington

Waterbury, New Haven, Pop. 106,427
Connecticut Technical HS System
Supt. — See Middletown
Kaynor Technical HS Vo/Tech
43 Tompkins St 06708 203-596-4302
David Telesca, prin. Fax 596-4308

Waterbury SD 18,300/PK-12
236 Grand St 06702 203-574-8000
Dr. Kathleen Ouellette, supt. Fax 574-8010
www.waterbury.k12.ct.us
Crosby HS 1,400/9-12
300 Pierpont Rd 06705 203-574-8061
Jade Gopie, prin. Fax 574-8072
Enlightenment S 200/Alt
30 Church St 06702 203-574-8050
Richard Arroyo, prin. Fax 573-6634
Kennedy HS 1,300/9-12
422 Highland Ave 06708 203-574-8150
Robert Johnston, prin. Fax 574-8154
North End MS 1,100/6-8
534 Bucks Hill Rd 06704 203-574-8097
Jacquelyn Gilmore, prin. Fax 574-8203
Wallace MS 1,200/6-8
3465 E Main St 06705 203-574-8140
Michael LoRusso, prin. Fax 574-8141
Waterbury Arts Magnet S 500/6-12
16 S Elm St 06706 203-573-6300
Lauren Elias, prin. Fax 573-6325
Waterbury Career Academy HS Vo/Tech
175 Birch St 06704 203-574-6000
Dr. Louis Padua, prin. Fax 578-3929
West Side MS 1,000/6-8
483 Chase Pkwy 06708 203-574-8120
Maria Burns, prin. Fax 574-8130
Wilby HS 1,300/9-12
568 Bucks Hill Rd 06704 203-574-8100
Michele Buerkle, prin. Fax 574-6896

Bais Yaakov of Waterbury HS 9-12
66 Buckingham St 06710 917-805-8401
Ita Selengut, prin.
Chase Collegiate S 500/PK-12
565 Chase Pkwy 06708 203-236-9500
Dr. Polly Peterson Ph.D., head sch Fax 236-9539
Holy Cross HS 700/9-12
587 Oronoke Rd 06708 203-757-9248
Margaret Leger, prin. Fax 757-3423
Industrial Management and Training Post-Sec.
233 Mill St 06706 203-753-7910
Mesivta Ateres Shmuel of Waterbury 9-12
359 Cooke St 06710 203-756-1800
Naugatuck Valley Community College Post-Sec.
750 Chase Pkwy 06708 203-575-8040
Post University Post-Sec.
PO Box 2540 06723 203-596-4500
Sacred Heart HS 300/9-12
142 S Elm St 06706 203-753-1605
Anthony Azzara, prin. Fax 597-1686
St. Mary's Hospital Post-Sec.
56 Franklin St 06706 203-574-6300
Stone Academy Post-Sec.
101 Pierpont Rd 06705 203-756-5500
University of Connecticut Post-Sec.
99 E Main St 06702 203-236-9800

Waterford, New London, Pop. 2,818
Learn RESC
Supt. — See Old Lyme
Dual Language & Arts Magnet MS 100/6-8
51 Daniels Ave 06385 860-443-0461
Christina Chamberlain, dir. Fax 443-0468

Waterford SD 2,500/K-12
15 Rope Ferry Rd 06385 860-444-5801
Thomas Giard, supt. Fax 444-5870
www.waterfordschools.org
Clark Lane MS 700/6-8
105 Clark Ln 06385 860-443-2837
James Sachs, prin. Fax 437-6985
Waterford HS 800/9-12
20 Rope Ferry Rd 06385 860-437-6956
Andre Hauser, prin. Fax 447-7928

Watertown, Litchfield, Pop. 6,000
Watertown SD 2,900/PK-12
10 Deforest St 06795 860-945-4801
Dr. B. Heston Carnemolla, supt. Fax 945-2775
www.watertownps.org/
Watertown HS 900/9-12
324 French St 06795 860-945-4810
Paul Jones Ed.D., prin. Fax 945-3348
Other Schools – See Oakville

Porter and Chester Institute Post-Sec.
320 Sylvan Lake Rd 06779 860-274-9294
Taft S 600/9-12
110 Woodbury Rd 06795 860-945-7777
William MacMullen, hdmstr. Fax 945-7720

Westbrook, Middlesex, Pop. 2,342
Westbrook SD 800/PK-12
158 McVeagh Rd 06498 860-399-6432
Patricia Ciccone, supt. Fax 399-8817
www.westbrookctschools.org/
Westbrook HS 300/9-12
156 McVeagh Rd 06498 860-399-6214
Tara Winch, prin. Fax 399-2007
Westbrook MS 300/5-8
154 McVeagh Rd 06498 860-399-2010
Cori DiMaggio, prin. Fax 399-2006

Oxford Academy 50/9-12
1393 Boston Post Rd 06498 860-399-6247
Philip Cocchiola, head sch Fax 399-5555

West Hartford, Hartford, Pop. 61,804
West Hartford SD 9,800/PK-12
50 S Main St, 860-561-6600
Thomas Moore, supt. Fax 561-6910
www.whps.org
Bristow MS 400/6-8
34 Highland St, 860-231-2100
Steven Cook, prin. Fax 231-2107
Conard HS 1,500/9-12
110 Beechwood Rd, 860-231-5000
Julio Duarte, prin. Fax 521-6699

Hall HS 1,500/9-12
975 N Main St, 860-232-4561
Dan Zittoun, prin. Fax 236-0366
King Philip MS 900/6-8
100 King Philip Dr, 860-233-8236
Joy Wright, prin. Fax 233-0812
Sedgwick MS 800/6-8
128 Sedgwick Rd, 860-521-0610
Andrew Clapsaddle, prin. Fax 521-7502

American Institute Post-Sec.
99 South St, 860-947-2299
American School for the Deaf Post-Sec.
139 N Main St, 860-570-2309
Hebrew HS of New England 100/9-12
300 Bloomfield Ave, 860-231-0317
Kingswood Oxford S 500/6-12
170 Kingswood Rd, 860-233-9631
Dennis Bisgaard, head sch Fax 236-3651
Northwest Catholic HS 600/9-12
29 Wampanoag Dr, 860-236-4221
David Eustis, pres. Fax 586-0911
St. Timothy MS 100/6-8
225 King Philip Dr, 860-236-0614
Tara Bellefleur M.Ed., prin. Fax 920-0293
University of Hartford Post-Sec.
200 Bloomfield Ave, 860-768-4100
University of Saint Joseph Post-Sec.
1678 Asylum Ave, 860-232-4571

West Haven, New Haven, Pop. 54,140
West Haven SD 5,900/PK-12
PO Box 26010 06516 203-937-4300
Neil Cavallaro, supt. Fax 937-4315
www.whschools.org
Bailey MS 900/7-8
106 Morgan Ln 06516 203-937-4380
Anthony Cordone Ed.D., prin. Fax 937-4385
West Haven HS 1,600/9-12
1 McDonough Plz 06516 203-937-4360
Pamela Gardner, prin. Fax 934-4370

Notre Dame HS 600/9-12
24 Ricardo St 06516 203-933-1673
Robert Curis, pres. Fax 933-2474
Stone Academy Post-Sec.
560 Saw Mill Rd 06516 203-288-7474
University of New Haven Post-Sec.
300 Boston Post Rd 06516 203-932-7000

Weston, Fairfield
Weston SD 2,400/PK-12
24 School Rd 06883 203-291-1400
Dr. Colleen Palmer Ph.D., supt. Fax 291-1415
www.westonps.org
Weston HS 800/9-12
115 School Rd 06883 203-291-1600
Lisa Deorio, prin. Fax 291-1603
Weston MS 600/6-8
135 School Rd 06883 203-291-1500
Dan Doak, prin. Fax 291-1516

Westport, Fairfield, Pop. 25,982
Westport SD 5,800/PK-12
110 Myrtle Ave 06880 203-341-1010
Colleen Palmer, supt. Fax 341-1029
www.westport.k12.ct.us/
Bedford MS 900/6-8
88 North Ave 06880 203-341-1510
Adam Rosen, prin. Fax 341-1508
Coleytown MS 500/6-8
255 North Ave 06880 203-341-1600
Kris Szabo, prin. Fax 341-1614
Staples HS 1,800/9-12
70 North Ave 06880 203-341-1200
Mark Karagus, prin. Fax 341-1202

Connecticut Center for Massage Therapy Post-Sec.
25 Sylvan Rd S 06880 203-221-7325
Pierrepont S, 1 Sylvan Rd N 06880 100/K-12
Nancy Webber, head sch 203-226-1891

West Simsbury, Hartford, Pop. 2,411

Master's S 300/PK-12
36 Westledge Rd 06092 860-651-9361
Ray Lagan, admin. Fax 651-9363

West Suffield, Hartford
Suffield SD
Supt. — See Suffield
Suffield HS 800/9-12
1060 Sheldon St 06093 860-668-3810
Steve Moccio, prin. Fax 668-3037

Wethersfield, Hartford, Pop. 26,301
Wethersfield SD 3,600/PK-12
127 Hartford Ave 06109 860-571-8100
Michael Emmett, supt. Fax 571-8130
www.wethersfield.k12.ct.us/
Deane MS 600/7-8
551 Silas Deane Hwy 06109 860-571-8300
Susan Czapla, prin. Fax 563-0563
Wethersfield HS 1,200/9-12
411 Wolcott Hill Rd 06109 860-571-8200
Thomas Moore, prin. Fax 571-8240

Connecticut Childrens Medical Center Post-Sec.
170 Ridge Rd 06109 860-545-8551

Willimantic, Windham, Pop. 17,404
Connecticut Technical HS System
Supt. — See Middletown
Windham Technical HS Vo/Tech
210 Birch St 06226 860-456-3879
Mark Ambruso, prin. Fax 450-0630

Windham SD 3,200/PK-12
322 Prospect St 06226 860-465-2300
Patricia Garcia Ph.D., supt. Fax 456-2311
www.windham.k12.ct.us/
Windham HS 600/9-12
355 High St 06226 860-465-2460
Yvette Santiesteban, prin. Fax 465-2463
Windham MS 700/6-8
123 Quarry St 06226 860-465-2350
Brett DuBow, prin. Fax 465-2353

Eastern Connecticut State University Post-Sec.
83 Windham St 06226 860-456-5000
Windham Community Memorial Hospital Post-Sec.
112 Mansfield Ave 06226 860-456-6800

Willington, Tolland
Willington SD 500/PK-8
40 Old Farms Rd Ste A 06279
David Harding, supt.
www.willingtonpublicschools.org
Hall Memorial MS 300/4-8
111 River Rd 06279 860-429-9391
Kenneth Craig, prin. Fax 429-5682

Wilton, Fairfield, Pop. 7,200
Wilton SD 4,300/PK-12
PO Box 277 06897 203-762-3381
Dr. Kevin Smith, supt. Fax 762-2177
www.wilton.k12.ct.us
Middlebrook MS 1,100/6-8
131 School Rd 06897 203-762-8388
Lauren Feltz, prin. Fax 762-1716
Wilton HS 1,300/9-12
395 Danbury Rd 06897 203-762-0381
Robert O'Donnell, prin. Fax 834-0164

Windsor, Hartford, Pop. 27,817
Capitol Region Education Council RESC
Supt. — See Hartford
Academy of Aerospace & Engineering 6-12
1101 Kennedy Rd 06095 860-243-0857
Paul Brenton, prin. Fax 286-2842
Greater Hartford Academy of Math/Science 200/9-12
1101 Kennedy Rd 06095 860-243-0857
Paul Brenton, prin. Fax 286-2842

Windsor SD 3,200/PK-12
601 Matianuck Ave 06095 860-687-2000
Dr. Craig Cooke, supt. Fax 687-2009
www.windsorct.org
Sage Park MS 700/6-8
25 Sage Park Rd 06095 860-687-2030
Paul Cavaliere, prin. Fax 687-2039
Windsor HS 1,100/9-12
50 Sage Park Rd 06095 860-687-2020
Russell Sills, prin. Fax 687-2029

Branford Hall Career Institute Post-Sec.
995 Day Hill Rd 06095 860-683-4900
Loomis Chaffee S 700/9-12
4 Batchelder Rd 06095 860-687-6000
Sheila Culbert, head sch Fax 687-6552
Madina Academy 200/PK-12
519 Palisado Ave 06095 860-219-0569
Masuda Vohra, prin.
Praise Power & Prayer Christian S 100/K-12
PO Box 474 06095 860-285-8898
Rev. Raymond McMahon, prin.

Windsor Locks, Hartford, Pop. 12,219
Windsor Locks SD 1,700/PK-12
58 S Elm St 06096 860-292-5000
Susan Bell, supt. Fax 292-5003
www.wlps.org
Pine Meadow Academy Alt
7 Center St 06096 860-292-6984
Joshua Robinson, prin.
Windsor Locks HS 500/9-12
58 S Elm St 06096 860-292-5032
Steven Swensen, prin. Fax 292-5039
Windsor Locks MS 400/6-8
7 Center St 06096 860-292-5012
David Prinstein, prin. Fax 292-5017

Winsted, Litchfield, Pop. 7,586
Endowed & Incorporated Academies 500/7-12
200 Williams Ave 06098 860-379-8521
Dr. Anthony Serio Ed.D., supt. Fax 379-6163
gilbertschool.org
Gilbert S 500/7-12
200 Williams Ave 06098 860-379-8521
Alan J. Strauss, prin. Fax 379-6163

Regional SD 7 1,100/7-12
PO Box 656 06098 860-379-1084
Dr. Judith Palmer, supt. Fax 379-0618
www.nwr7.com
Northwestern Regional HS 700/9-12
100 Battistoni Rd 06098 860-379-8525
Kenneth Chichester, prin. Fax 738-6059
Northwestern Regional MS 400/7-8
100 Battistoni Rd 06098 860-379-7243
Candy Perez, prin. Fax 738-6205

Northwestern CT Comm. Technical College Post-Sec.
2 Park Pl 06098 860-738-6300

Wolcott, New Haven, Pop. 13,700
Wolcott SD 2,500/PK-12
154 Center St 06716 203-879-8183
Dr. Tony Gasper, supt. Fax 879-8182
www.wolcottps.org
Tyrrell MS 700/6-8
500 Todd Rd 06716 203-879-8151
Arline Tansley, prin. Fax 879-8419
Wolcott HS 800/9-12
457 Bound Line Rd 06716 203-879-8164
Joseph Monroe, prin. Fax 879-8167

Connecticut Institute of Hair Design Post-Sec.
1681 Meriden Rd 06716 203-879-4247

Woodbridge, New Haven, Pop. 7,924
Regional SD 5 2,400/7-12
25 Newton Rd 06525 203-392-2106
Charles Dumais, supt. Fax 397-4864
www.amityregion5.org
Amity Regional HS 1,600/9-12
25 Newton Rd 06525 203-397-4830
Charles Britton, prin. Fax 397-4866
Other Schools – See Bethany, Orange

Woodbury, Litchfield, Pop. 8,131
Regional SD 14 1,900/PK-12
PO Box 469 06798 203-263-4330
Dr. Anna Leonard, supt. Fax 263-0372
www.ctreg14.org
Nonnewaug HS 800/9-12
5 Minortown Rd 06798 203-263-2186
Alice Jones, prin. Fax 263-3570
Woodbury MS 400/6-8
67 Washington Ave 06798 203-263-4306
Eric Bergeron, prin. Fax 263-0825

Woodstock, Windham
Endowed & Incorporated Academies 1,000/9-12
57 Academy Rd 06281 860-928-6575
Christopher Sandford, hdmstr. Fax 963-7222
www.woodstockacademy.org
Woodstock Academy 1,000/9-12
57 Academy Rd 06281 860-928-6575
Christopher Sandford, hdmstr. Fax 963-7222

Woodstock SD 900/PK-8
147A Route 169 06281 860-928-7453
Viktor Toth, supt. Fax 928-0206
www.woodstockschools.net
Woodstock MS 400/5-8
147B Route 169 06281 860-963-6575
Paul Gamache, prin. Fax 963-6577

Hyde S - Woodstock 200/9-12
PO Box 237 06281 860-963-9096
Robert Felt, dir. Fax 963-0164

DELAWARE

DELAWARE DEPARTMENT OF EDUCATION
401 Federal St Ste 2, Dover 19901-3639
Telephone 302-735-4000
Fax 302-739-4654
Website http://www.doe.k12.de.us

Secretary of Education Susan Bunting

DELAWARE BOARD OF EDUCATION
1006 Tulip Tree Ln, Newark 19713-1128

President Teri Quinn Gray

PUBLIC, PRIVATE AND CATHOLIC SECONDARY SCHOOLS

Bear, New Castle, Pop. 18,842

Academy of Massage & Bodywork Post-Sec.
1218 Pulaski Hwy Ste 324 19701 302-392-6768
Aquinas Academy 100/PK-12
2370 Red Lion Rd 19701 302-838-9601
John Moore, prin. Fax 838-9602
Caravel Academy 1,200/PK-12
2801 Del Laws Rd 19701 302-834-8938
Fairwinds Christian S 200/PK-12
801 Seymour Rd 19701 302-328-7404
Red Lion Christian Academy 700/PK-12
1390 Red Lion Rd 19701 302-834-2526
Sam Osbourn, prin. Fax 836-6346
Tall Oaks Classical S 200/K-12
1390 Red Lion Rd 19701 302-738-3337
Jonathan Jones, prin. Fax 836-6346

Bridgeville, Sussex, Pop. 1,988
Woodbridge SD 1,700/PK-12
16359 Sussex Hwy 19933 302-337-7990
Heath Chasanov, supt. Fax 337-7998
www.woodbridgeraiders.net
Woodbridge MS 600/6-8
307 S Laws St 19933 302-337-8289
Delores Tunstall, prin. Fax 337-0631
Other Schools – See Greenwood

Camden, Kent, Pop. 3,311
Caesar Rodney SD
Supt. — See Wyoming
Fifer MS 800/6-8
109 E Camden Wyoming Ave 19934 302-698-8400
Brian Smith, prin. Fax 698-8409
Postlethwait MS 800/6-8
2841 S State St 19934 302-698-8410
Derek Prillaman, prin. Fax 698-8419
Rodney HS 2,000/9-12
239 Old North Rd 19934 302-697-2161
Sherry Kijowski Ed.D., prin. Fax 697-6888

Claymont, New Castle, Pop. 8,108
Brandywine SD
Supt. — See Wilmington
Brandywine Community S Alt
500 Darley Rd 19703 302-792-3920
Dr. Kim Allen, dir. Fax 792-3814

Archmere Academy 500/9-12
3600 Philadelphia Pike 19703 302-798-6632
John Jordan, prin. Fax 798-7290

Dagsboro, Sussex, Pop. 782
Indian River SD
Supt. — See Selbyville
Indian River HS 900/9-12
29772 Armory Rd 19939 302-732-1500
Bennett Murray, prin. Fax 732-1514

Delmar, Sussex, Pop. 1,524
Delmar SD 1,300/5-12
200 N 8th St 19940 302-846-9544
Charity Phillips, supt. Fax 846-2793
www.delmar.k12.de.us
Delmar HS 600/9-12
200 N 8th St 19940 302-846-9544
William Rickard, prin. Fax 846-5056
Delmar MS 700/5-8
200 N 8th St 19940 302-846-9544
Andy O'Neal, prin. Fax 846-5056

Dover, Kent, Pop. 34,742
Caesar Rodney SD
Supt. — See Wyoming
Dover AFB MS 200/6-8
3100 Hawthorne Dr 19901 302-674-3284
David Santore Ed.D., prin. Fax 730-4283

Capital SD 6,400/PK-12
198 Commerce Way 19904 302-672-1500
Dr. Dan Shelton, supt. Fax 672-1714
www.capital.k12.de.us
Central MS 900/7-8
211 Delaware Ave 19901 302-672-1772
Shan Green, prin. Fax 672-1733
Dover HS, 1 Dover High Dr 19904 1,700/9-12
Dr. Courtney Voshell, prin. 302-241-2400
Kent County Alternative S 100/Alt
631 Ridgely St 19904 302-736-5355
William Buczynski, prin. Fax 736-5263

Bayhealth Medical Center Post-Sec.
640 S State St 19901 302-674-7001
Calvary Christian Academy 300/PK-12
1143 E Lebanon Rd 19901 302-697-7860
Aaron Coon, admin. Fax 697-0284
Delaware State University Post-Sec.
1200 N Dupont Hwy 19901 302-857-6060
Delaware Technical & Community College Post-Sec.
100 Campus Dr 19904 302-857-1000
Harris School of Business Post-Sec.
97 Commerce Way Ste 105 19904 302-674-8060
Wesley College Post-Sec.
120 N State St 19901 302-736-2300

Ellendale, Sussex, Pop. 363

Cross Christian Academy 50/K-12
PO Box 1 19941 302-270-9182
Donald Porter, dir. Fax 422-5425

Felton, Kent, Pop. 1,251
Lake Forest SD 3,700/PK-12
5423 Killens Pond Rd 19943 302-284-3020
Dr. Brenda Wynder, supt. Fax 284-4491
www.lf.k12.de.us
Lake Forest HS 900/9-12
5407 Killens Pond Rd 19943 302-284-9291
Theodora White, prin. Fax 284-5833
Other Schools – See Harrington

Frankford, Sussex, Pop. 835
Indian River SD
Supt. — See Selbyville
Carver Educational Center 50/Alt
30207 Frankford School Rd 19945 302-732-3800
Charlynne Hopkins Ed.D., dir. Fax 732-3790

Georgetown, Sussex, Pop. 6,322
Indian River SD
Supt. — See Selbyville
Georgetown MS 600/6-8
301 W Market St 19947 302-856-1900
Mike Williams, prin. Fax 856-1915
Sussex Central HS 1,200/9-12
26026 Patriots Way 19947 302-934-3166
Bradley Layfield Ed.D., prin. Fax 934-3234

Sussex Technical SD
PO Box 351 19947 302-856-2541
Dr. A.J. Lathbury Ed.D., supt. Fax 856-7078
www.sussexvt.k12.de.us
Sussex Technical HS Vo/Tech
PO Box 351 19947 302-856-0961
Dr. John Demby Ed.D., prin. Fax 856-1760
Sussex Extended Learning Division Adult
PO Box 351 19947 302-856-9035
Dr. Michael Owens, admin. Fax 856-7875

Delaware Technical & Community College Post-Sec.
PO Box 610 19947 302-856-5400
Delmarva Christian HS 200/9-12
21777 Sussex Pines Rd 19947 302-856-4040
Mike Vonhof, head sch Fax 856-6878

Greenwood, Sussex, Pop. 943
Woodbridge SD
Supt. — See Bridgeville
Woodbridge HS 600/9-12
14712 Woodbridge Rd 19950 302-232-3333
Robert Adams, prin. Fax 349-0237

Greenwood Mennonite S 200/PK-12
12802 Mennonite School Rd 19950 302-349-4131
Duane Miller, admin. Fax 349-5076

Harrington, Kent, Pop. 3,428
Lake Forest SD
Supt. — See Felton
Chipman MS 1,000/6-8
101 W Center St 19952 302-398-8197
Don DeHart, prin. Fax 398-8375

Hockessin, New Castle, Pop. 13,327
Red Clay Consolidated SD
Supt. — See Wilmington
DuPont MS 800/6-8
735 Meeting House Rd 19707 302-239-3420
Jason Bastianelli, prin. Fax 239-3450

Sanford S 600/PK-12
6900 Lancaster Pike 19707 302-235-6500
Mark Anderson, head sch Fax 239-5389
Wilmington Christian S 500/PK-12
825 Loveville Rd 19707 302-239-2121
William Stevens, head sch Fax 239-2778

Laurel, Sussex, Pop. 3,540
Laurel SD 1,800/PK-12
1160 S Central Ave 19956 302-875-6100
Shawn Larrimore, supt. Fax 875-6106
www.laurel.k12.de.us
Laurel HS 500/9-12
1133 S Central Ave 19956 302-875-6120
Matthew Marine, prin. Fax 875-6123
Laurel MS 300/5-8
1131 S Central Ave 19956 302-875-6110
Dr. Richard Evans, prin. Fax 875-6109

Lewes, Sussex, Pop. 2,714
Cape Henlopen SD 5,000/K-12
1270 Kings Hwy 19958 302-645-6686
Robert S. Fulton M.Ed., supt. Fax 645-6684
www.capehenlopenschools.com/
Beacon MS 600/6-8
19483 John J Williams Hwy 19958 302-645-6288
David Frederick, prin. Fax 644-6118
Cape Henlopen HS 1,300/9-12
1250 Kings Hwy 19958 302-645-7711
Brian Donahue, prin. Fax 645-1356
Other Schools – See Milton

American College Delaware Post-Sec.
404 E Savannah Rd 19958 302-793-1101
Beebe Medical Center School of Nursing Post-Sec.
424 Savannah Rd 19958 302-645-3251

Lincoln, Sussex

Geneva Academy 50/K-12
11146 Ponder Rd 19960 302-500-2087
Kandi Playford, prin. Fax 500-2087

Magnolia, Kent, Pop. 218

St. Thomas More Academy 200/9-12
133 Thomas More Dr 19962 302-697-8100
Rachael Casey, prin. Fax 697-8122

Middletown, New Castle, Pop. 18,350
Appoquinimink SD
Supt. — See Odessa
Appoquinimink HS 1,500/9-12
1080 Bunker Hill Rd 19709 302-449-3840
Keisha Brinkley, prin. Fax 378-5130
Meredith MS 700/6-8
504 S Broad St 19709 302-378-5001
Nick Hoover, prin. Fax 378-5008
Middletown HS 1,300/9-12
120 Silver Lake Rd 19709 302-376-4141
Dr. Matt Donovan Ed.D., prin. Fax 378-5268
Redding MS 800/6-8
201 New St 19709 302-378-5030
Dr. Edward Small, prin. Fax 378-5080
Waters MS 900/6-8
1235 Cedar Lane Rd 19709 302-449-3490
Thomas Poehlmann, prin. Fax 449-3496

New Castle County Voc-Tech SD
Supt. — See Wilmington
St. Georges Technical HS Vo/Tech
555 Hyetts Corner Rd 19709 302-449-3360
Shanta Reynolds, prin. Fax 376-6796

St. Andrew's S 300/9-12
350 Noxontown Rd 19709 302-378-9511
Daniel T. Roach, hdmstr. Fax 378-7120

Milford, Sussex, Pop. 9,349
Milford SD 4,000/PK-12
906 Lakeview Ave 19963 302-422-1600
Dr. Kevin Dickerson, supt. Fax 422-1608
www.milfordschooldistrict.org/
Milford Central Academy 1,000/6-8
1021 N Walnut St 19963 302-424-7900
Dr. Nancy Carnevale, prin. Fax 424-4163
Milford HS 1,000/9-12
1019 N Walnut St 19963 302-422-1610
Shawn Snyder, prin. Fax 424-5463

Millsboro, Sussex, Pop. 3,755
Indian River SD
Supt. — See Selbyville
Millsboro MS 700/6-8
302 E State St 19966 302-934-3200
Renee Jerns Ed.D., prin. Fax 934-3215

Milton, Sussex, Pop. 2,504
Cape Henlopen SD
Supt. — See Lewes
Mariner MS 500/6-8
16391 Harbeson Rd 19968 302-684-8516
Fred Best, prin. Fax 684-5606

Newark, New Castle, Pop. 30,774
Christina SD
Supt. — See Wilmington
Christiana HS 800/9-12
190 Salem Church Rd 19713 302-631-2400
Noreen LaSorsa, prin. Fax 454-3490
Gauger-Cobbs MS 1,100/6-8
50 Gender Rd 19713 302-454-2358
Sean Mulrine, prin. Fax 454-3482
Glasgow HS 1,000/9-12
1901 S College Ave 19702 302-631-5600
Dr. Dean Ivory, prin. Fax 454-5453
Kirk MS 800/6-8
140 Brennen Dr 19713 302-451-7021
Brian Curtis, prin. Fax 454-3491
Networks S for Entrepreneurial Sciences Vo/Tech
30 Blue Hen Dr 19713 302-454-2233
Norma Brister, prin. Fax 454-5446
Newark HS 1,500/9-12
750 E Delaware Ave 19711 302-631-4700
Timothy Slade, prin. Fax 454-2155
Shue-Medill MS 1,000/6-8
1500 Capitol Trl 19711 302-454-2171
Michele Savage, prin. Fax 454-3492

New Castle County Voc-Tech SD
Supt. — See Wilmington
Hodgson Vocational-Technical HS Vo/Tech
2575 Glasgow Ave 19702 302-834-0990
Jerry Lamey Ed.D., prin. Fax 834-0598

Delaware Technical & Community College Post-Sec.
400 Stanton Christiana Rd 19713 302-454-3900
Schilling-Douglas School of Hair Design Post-Sec.
70 Amstel Ave 19711 302-737-5100
University of Delaware Post-Sec.
210 S College Ave 19716 302-831-2792

New Castle, New Castle, Pop. 5,184
Colonial SD 9,700/K-12
318 E Basin Rd 19720 302-323-2700
Dolon Blakey Ed.D., supt. Fax 323-2748
www.colonialschooldistrict.org
Bedford MS 1,000/6-8
801 Cox Neck Rd 19720 302-832-6280
Andrew Moffett, prin. Fax 834-6729
McCullough MS 800/6-8
20 Chase Ave 19720 302-429-4000
Ige Purnell, prin. Fax 429-4005
Penn HS 2,200/9-12
713 E Basin Rd 19720 302-323-2800
Brian Erskine, prin. Fax 323-2955
Read MS 700/6-8
314 E Basin Rd 19720 302-323-2760
Holly Sage, prin. Fax 323-2763
Wallin S Alt
701 E Basin Rd 19720 302-323-2952
Kevin White, prin. Fax 323-2787

Serviam Girls Academy 50/5-8
14 Halcyon Dr 19720 302-651-9700
Kate Lucyk, prin. Fax 651-9703
Wilmington University Post-Sec.
320 N Dupont Hwy 19720 302-356-4636

Odessa, New Castle, Pop. 353
Appoquinimink SD 10,200/PK-12
PO Box 4010 19730 302-376-4128
Matthew Burrows, supt. Fax 378-5007
www.apposchooldistrict.com
Other Schools – See Middletown

Seaford, Sussex, Pop. 6,739
Seaford SD 2,400/K-12
390 N Market Street Ext 19973 302-629-4587
David Perrington, supt. Fax 629-2619
www.seafordbluejays.org
Seaford HS 700/9-12
399 N Market Street Ext 19973 302-629-4587
Teresa Carson, prin. Fax 628-4417
Seaford MS 800/6-8
500 E Stein Hwy 19973 302-629-4587
Dr. Stephanie Smith, prin. Fax 628-4485

Selbyville, Sussex, Pop. 2,147
Indian River SD 9,100/PK-12
31 Hosier St 19975 302-436-1000
Susan Bunting Ed.D., supt. Fax 436-1034
www.irsd.net/
Selbyville MS 700/6-8
80 Bethany Rd 19975 302-436-1020
Jason Macrides, prin. Fax 436-1035
Other Schools – See Dagsboro, Frankford, Georgetown, Millsboro

Smyrna, Kent, Pop. 9,689
Smyrna SD 5,200/PK-12
82 Monrovia Ave 19977 302-653-8585
Deborah Wicks, supt. Fax 653-3149
www.smyrna.k12.de.us
Smyrna HS 1,500/9-12
500 Duck Creek Pkwy 19977 302-653-8581
Stacy Cook, prin. Fax 653-3139
Smyrna MS 800/7-8
700 Duck Creek Pkwy 19977 302-653-8584
Steven Gott, prin. Fax 653-3424

Wilmington, New Castle, Pop. 69,534
Brandywine SD 10,800/K-12
1311 Brandywine Blvd 19809 302-793-5000
Dr. Mark Holodick, supt. Fax 792-3823
www.brandywineschools.org
Brandywine HS 900/9-12
1400 Foulk Rd 19803 302-479-1600
Keith Rolph, prin. Fax 479-1604
Concord HS 1,100/9-12
2501 Ebright Rd 19810 302-475-3951
Yolanda McKinney, prin. Fax 529-3094
duPont MS 1,000/6-8
701 W 34th St 19802 302-762-7146
Lewis Cheatwood, prin. Fax 762-7196
Mt. Pleasant HS 1,000/9-12
5201 Washington Blvd 19809 302-762-7125
Heather Austin, prin. Fax 762-7042
Springer MS 900/6-8
2220 Shipley Rd 19803 302-479-1621
Dr. Tracy Woodson, prin. Fax 479-1628
Talley MS 700/6-8
1110 Cypress Rd 19810 302-475-3976
Mark Mayer, prin. Fax 475-3998
Other Schools – See Claymont

Christina SD 15,900/PK-12
600 N Lombard St 19801 302-552-2630
Dr. Robert Andrzejewski, supt. Fax 429-3944
www.christina.k12.de.us/
Bayard MS 500/6-8
200 S Dupont St 19805 302-429-4118
Victoir Cahoon, prin. Fax 429-4153
Douglas S 50/Alt
1800 Prospect Rd 19805 302-429-4146
John Martin, prin. Fax 429-4920
Pyle Academy 100/Alt
501 N Lombard St 19801 302-429-4158
Kristina MacBury, prin. Fax 429-3959
Other Schools – See Newark

New Castle County Voc-Tech SD
1417 Newport Rd 19804 302-995-8050
Victoria Gehrt Ed.D., supt. Fax 995-1579
www.nccvotech.com
Delcastle Technical HS Vo/Tech
1417 Newport Rd 19804 302-995-8100
Dr. Clifton Hayes, prin. Fax 995-8197
Howard HS of Technology Vo/Tech
401 E 12th St 19801 302-571-5400
Stanley Spoor Ed.D., prin. Fax 571-5843
Delaware Skills Center Adult
13th & Clifford Brown Walk 19801 302-654-5392
Eric Wells, head sch Fax 654-9418
Other Schools – See Middletown, Newark

Red Clay Consolidated SD 18,400/PK-12
1502 Spruce Ave 19805 302-552-3700
Dr. Mervin Daugherty, supt. Fax 992-7820
redclay.schoolwires.net
Calloway S of Arts 900/6-12
100 N Dupont Rd 19807 302-651-2700
Julie Rumschlag, dean Fax 425-4594
Conrad S of Science 1,200/6-12
201 Jackson Ave 19804 302-992-5545
Mark Pruitt, prin. Fax 992-5585
Dickinson HS 800/9-12
1801 Milltown Rd 19808 302-992-5500
Byron Murphy, prin. Fax 992-5506
DuPont HS 1,100/9-12
50 Hillside Rd 19807 302-651-2626
Kevin Palladinetti, prin. Fax 651-2757
DuPont MS 500/6-8
3130 Kennett Pike 19807 302-651-2690
Susan Huffman, prin. Fax 425-4585
McKean HS 900/9-12
301 Mckennans Church Rd 19808 302-992-5520
Brian Mattix, prin. Fax 992-5525
Skyline MS 800/6-8
2900 Skyline Dr 19808 302-454-3410
Frank Rumford, prin. Fax 454-3541
Stanton MS 700/6-8
1800 Limestone Rd 19804 302-992-5540
Tawanda Bond, prin. Fax 992-5586
Groves Adult Education Adult
1621 Telegraph Rd 19804 302-651-2709
Kellie Tetrick, prin. Fax 658-7137
Other Schools – See Hockessin

Christiana Care Health Services Post-Sec.
PO Box 1668 19899 302-428-2571
Concord Christian Academy 200/PK-12
2510 Marsh Rd 19810 302-475-3247
Dawn Career Institute Post-Sec.
3700 Lancaster Pike 19805 302-633-9075
Delaware College of Art and Design Post-Sec.
600 N Market St 19801 302-622-8000
Delaware Technical & Community College Post-Sec.
333 N Shipley St 19801 302-571-5300
Goldey-Beacom College Post-Sec.
4701 Limestone Rd 19808 302-998-8814
Harris School of Business Post-Sec.
1413 Foulk Rd 19803 302-478-8890
National Massage Therapy Institute Post-Sec.
1601 Concord Pike 19803 800-509-5058
Nativity Preparatory S 50/5-8
1515 Linden St 19805 302-777-1015
Paul Webster, prin. Fax 777-1225
Padua Academy 600/9-12
905 N Broom St 19806 302-421-3739
Cindy Hayes-Mann, head sch Fax 421-3748
St. Elizabeth HS 400/9-12
1500 Cedar St 19805 302-656-3369
Dr. Nicholas Huck, prin. Fax 656-7513
St. Marks HS 1,100/9-12
2501 Pike Creek Rd 19808 302-738-3300
Richard Bayhan, prin. Fax 738-5132
Salesianum S 1,000/9-12
1801 N Broom St 19802 302-654-2495
Rev. Christian Beretta, prin. Fax 654-7767
Tatnall S 700/PK-12
1501 Barley Mill Rd 19807 302-998-2292
Timothy Burns Ph.D., head sch Fax 892-4389
Tower Hill S 800/PK-12
2813 W 17th St 19806 302-575-0550
Elizabeth C. Speers, head sch Fax 657-8366
Ursuline Academy 500/PK-12
1106 Pennsylvania Ave 19806 302-658-7158
Cathie Field-Lloyd, pres. Fax 658-4297
Widener University School of Law Post-Sec.
PO Box 7474 19803 302-477-2162
Wilmington Friends S 800/PK-12
101 School Rd 19803 302-576-2900
Ken Aldridge, head sch Fax 576-2939

Woodside, Kent, Pop. 178
POLYTECH SD
PO Box 22 19980 302-697-2170
Dr. Deborah Zych, supt. Fax 697-6749
polytechschooldistrict.com
POLYTECH HS, PO Box 97 19980 Vo/Tech
Dr. Ryan Fuller, prin. 302-697-3255

Wyoming, Kent, Pop. 1,263
Caesar Rodney SD 7,600/K-12
7 Front St 19934 302-698-4800
Kevin Fitzgerald Ed.D., supt. Fax 697-3406
www.cr.k12.de.us
Other Schools – See Camden, Dover

DISTRICT OF COLUMBIA

DISTRICT OF COLUMBIA PUBLIC SCHOOLS
1200 1st St NE, Washington 20002
Telephone 202-442-5885
Fax 202-442-5026
Website dcps.dc.gov/

Chancellor Antwan Wilson

DISTRICT OF COLUMBIA BOARD OF EDUCATION
441 4th St NW Ste 723N, Washington 20001-2714

Director John-Paul Hayworth

PUBLIC, PRIVATE AND CATHOLIC SECONDARY SCHOOLS

Washington, District of Columbia, Pop. 587,406

District of Columbia SD 45,700/PK-12
1200 1st St NE 20002 202-442-5885
John Davis, chncllr. Fax 442-5026
dcps.dc.gov

Anacostia HS 800/9-12
1601 16th St SE 20020 202-698-2155
Eric Fraser, prin. Fax 698-2188

Ballou HS 700/9-12
3401 4th St SE 20032 202-645-3400
Yetunde Reeves, prin. Fax 645-3397

Banneker HS 400/9-12
800 Euclid St NW 20001 202-671-6320
Anita Berger, prin. Fax 673-2231

Brookland MS 6-8
1150 Michigan Ave NE 20017 202-759-1999
Norah Lycknell, prin. Fax 671-6251

Brown College Prep HS 9-12
4800 Meade St NE 20019 202-729-4343
Benjamin Williams, prin. Fax 729-2156

Cardozo HS 700/6-12
1200 Clifton St NW 20009 202-673-7385
Tanya Roane, prin. Fax 673-2232

CHOICE Academy 50/Alt
300 Bryant St NW 20001 202-939-4350
Michael Alexander, dir. Fax 673-8123

Columbia Heights Education Campus 1,300/6-12
3101 16th St NW 20010 202-939-7700
Maria Tukeva, prin. Fax 576-9147

Coolidge HS 400/9-12
6315 5th St NW 20011 202-671-6080
Richard Jackson, prin. Fax 576-3147

Deal MS 1,200/6-8
3815 Fort Dr NW 20016 202-939-2010
James Albright, prin. Fax 282-1116

Dunbar HS 600/9-12
101 N St NW 20001 202-698-3762
Abdullah Zaki, prin. Fax 673-2233

Eastern HS 800/9-12
1700 E Capitol St NE 20003 202-698-4500
Sah Brown, prin. Fax 698-4800

Eliot-Hine MS 300/6-8
1830 Constitution Ave NE 20002 202-939-5380
Isamar Vargas, prin. Fax 673-8063

Ellington HS of the Arts 500/9-12
2501 11th St NW 20001 202-282-0123
Desepe de Vargas, prin. Fax 337-7847

Ellington HS of the Arts 9-12
2001 10th St NW 20001 202-282-0123
Desepe de Vargas, prin. Fax 337-7847

Hardy MS 400/6-8
1819 35th St NW 20007 202-729-4350
Patricia Pride, prin. Fax 576-9443

Hart MS 600/6-8
601 Mississippi Ave SE 20032 202-671-6426
Charlette Butler, prin. Fax 645-3426

Jefferson MS Academy 300/6-8
801 7th St SW 20024 202-729-3270
Greg Dohmann, prin. Fax 724-2459

Johnson MS 300/6-8
1400 Bruce Pl SE 20020 202-939-3140
Courtney Aldridge, prin. Fax 645-5882

Kramer MS 400/6-8
1700 Q St SE 20020 202-939-3150
Roman Smith, prin. Fax 698-1169

McKinley MS 200/6-8
151 T St NE 20002 202-281-3950
Mary Louise Jones, prin. Fax 832-1293

McKinley Technology HS Vo/Tech
151 T St NE 20002 202-281-3950
Mary Louise Jones, prin. Fax 576-6279

Miller MS 500/6-8
301 49th St NE 20019 202-388-6870
Kortni Stafford, prin. Fax 727-8330

Moore HS 400/Alt
1001 Monroe St NE 20017 202-281-3600
Jada Langston, prin. Fax 526-5022

Oyster-Adams Bilingual MS 300/4-8
2020 19th St NW 20009 202-673-7311
Mayra Canizales, prin. Fax 673-6500

Phelps Architecture Construction & Eng S 300/9-12
704 26th St NE 20002 202-729-4360
Willie Jackson, prin. Fax 442-8438

Roosevelt HS 400/9-12
4301 13th St NW 20011 202-576-6130
Aqueelha James, prin. Fax 541-6449

School Without Walls HS 600/9-12
2130 G St NW 20037 202-645-9690
Richard Trogisch, prin. Fax 724-8536

Sousa MS 300/6-8
3650 Ely Pl SE 20019 202-729-3260
Courtney Wilkerson, prin. Fax 645-0456

Stuart-Hobson MS 400/6-8
410 E St NE 20002 202-671-6010
Dawn Clemens, prin. Fax 698-4720

Washington Metropolitan HS 300/Alt
300 Bryant St NW 20001 202-939-3610
Michael Alexander, prin. Fax 671-2101

Wilson HS 1,700/9-12
3950 Chesapeake St NW 20016 202-282-0120
Kimberly Martin, prin. Fax 282-0077

Woodson HS 800/9-12
540 55th St NE 20019 202-939-2030
Darrin Slade, prin. Fax 645-4193

Youth Services Center 100/Alt
1000 Mount Olivet Rd NE 20002 202-576-8388
Soncyree Lee, prin. Fax 576-9073

Ballou STAY HS Adult
3401 4th St SE 20032 202-645-3390
Cara Fuller, prin. Fax 645-3935

Roosevelt STAY HS Adult
4301 13th St NW 20011 202-576-8399
Eugenia Young, prin. Fax 576-8478

Academia de la Recta Porta Christian S 100/K-12
7614 Georgia Ave NW 20012 202-726-8737
Annette Miles M.A., admin. Fax 726-8759

American University Post-Sec.
4400 Massachusetts Ave NW 20016 202-885-1000

Archbishop Carroll HS 500/9-12
4300 Harewood Rd NE 20017 202-529-0900
Katy Dunn, prin. Fax 526-8879

Bennett Career Institute Post-Sec.
700 Monroe St NE 20017 202-526-1400

Blyth-Templeton Academy 100/9-12
921 Pennsylvania Ave SE 20003 202-847-0779
Lee Palmer, head sch Fax 838-1101

British S of Washington 400/PK-12
2001 Wisconsin Ave NW 20007 202-829-3700
Ian Piper, prin. Fax 829-6522

Burke S 300/6-12
4101 Connecticut Ave NW 20008 202-362-8882
Damian Jones, head sch Fax 362-1914

Catholic University of America Post-Sec.
620 Michigan Ave NE 20064 202-319-5000

Chicago Sch of Professional Psychology Post-Sec.
901 15th St NW 20005 202-706-5052

Corcoran College of Art & Design Post-Sec.
500 17th St NW 20006 202-639-1800

Cornerstone S of Washington DC 100/PK-12
3742 Ely Pl SE 20019 202-575-0027
Derrick Max, head sch Fax 575-0669

Dudley Beauty College Post-Sec.
2031 Rhode Island Ave NE 20018 202-269-3666

Field S 300/6-12
2301 Foxhall Rd NW 20007 202-295-5800
Dale Johnson, head sch Fax 295-5858

Gallaudet University Post-Sec.
800 Florida Ave NE 20002 202-651-5000

Georgetown Day HS 500/9-12
4200 Davenport St NW 20016 202-274-3200
Russell Shaw, head sch Fax 338-0480

Georgetown University Post-Sec.
37th and O St NW 20057 202-687-0100

Georgetown Visitation Prep HS 500/9-12
1524 35th St NW 20007 202-337-3350
MaryKate Blaine, prin. Fax 342-5733

George Washington University Post-Sec.
2121 I St NW 20052 202-994-1000

Gonzaga College HS 1,000/9-12
19 I St NW 20001 202-336-7100
Thomas Every, hdmstr. Fax 336-7164

Graduate School USA Post-Sec.
600 Maryland Ave SW 20024 202-314-3300

Howard University Post-Sec.
2400 6th St NW 20059 202-806-6100

Howard University School of Divinity Post-Sec.
1400 Shepherd St NE 20017 202-806-0500

Johns Hopkins University Post-Sec.
1740 Massachusetts Ave NW 20036 202-663-5600

Lab S of Washington 200/1-12
4759 Reservoir Rd NW 20007 202-965-6600
Katherine Schantz, head sch Fax 965-5015

Levine School of Music Post-Sec.
2801 Upton St NW 20008 202-686-8000

Maret S 600/K-12
3000 Cathedral Ave NW 20008 202-939-8800
Marjo Talbott, hdmstr. Fax 939-8845

Medtech College Post-Sec.
529 14th St NW 20045 202-872-4700

Model Secondary School for the Deaf Post-Sec.
800 Florida Ave NE 20002 202-651-5031

National Cathedral S 600/4-12
3612 Woodley Rd NW 20016 202-537-6300
Kathleen Jamieson, head sch Fax 537-5743

National Conservatory of Dramatic Arts Post-Sec.
1556 Wisconsin Ave NW 20007 202-333-2202

Pontifical Faculty Immaculate Conception Post-Sec.
487 Michigan Ave NE 20017 202-495-3820

Pontifical John Paul II Institute Post-Sec.
620 Michigan Ave NE 20064 202-526-3799

Preparatory S of the DC 100/PK-12
805 Rock Creek Church Rd NW 20010
202-722-5080
Betty North, dir. Fax 722-5060

Radians College Post-Sec.
1025 Vermont Ave NW Ste 200 20005 202-291-9020

St. Albans S 600/4-12
Mount Saint Alban 20016 202-537-6435
Vance Wilson, hdmstr. Fax 537-6434

St. Anselms Abbey S 200/6-12
4501 South Dakota Ave NE 20017 202-269-2350
Bill Crittenberger, hdmstr. Fax 269-2373

St. Johns College HS 1,000/9-12
2607 Military Rd NW 20015 202-363-2316
Christopher Themistos, prin. Fax 363-2916

San Miguel MS 100/6-8
7705 Georgia Ave NW 20012 202-232-8345
Dave Palank, prin. Fax 232-3987

Sidwell Friends S 1,100/PK-12
3825 Wisconsin Ave NW 20016 202-537-8100
Bryan Garman, head sch Fax 537-8138

Strayer University Post-Sec.
1133 15th St NW Ste 200 20005 202-408-2400

Technical Learning Center Post-Sec.
1720 I St NW Ste 200 20006 202-223-3500

The Institute of World Politics Post-Sec.
1521 16th St NW 20036 202-462-2101

Trinity University Post-Sec.
125 Michigan Ave NE 20017 202-884-9000

University of the District of Columbia Post-Sec.
4200 Connecticut Ave NW 20008 202-274-5000

University of the Potomac Post-Sec.
1401 H St NW Ste 100 20005 202-686-0876

Walter Reed Medical Center Post-Sec.
6825 16th St NW 20306 202-782-6104

Washington International S 500/6-12
3100 Macomb St NW 20008 202-243-1800
Clayton Lewis, head sch Fax 243-1802

Washington Jesuit Academy 100/5-8
900 Varnum St NE 20017 202-832-7679
Marcus Washington, hdmstr. Fax 832-8098

Washington MS for Girls 100/3-8
1901 Mississippi Ave SE 20020 202-678-1113
Sr. Mary Bourdon, head sch Fax 678-1114

Washington Theological Union Post-Sec.
1600 Webster St NE 20017 202-526-1221

Wesley Theological Seminary Post-Sec.
4500 Massachusetts Ave NW 20016 202-885-8600

FLORIDA

FLORIDA DEPARTMENT OF EDUCATION
325 W Gaines St, Tallahassee 32399-0400
Telephone 850-245-0505
Fax 850-245-9667
Website http://www.fldoe.org/

Commissioner of Education Pam Stewart

FLORIDA BOARD OF EDUCATION
325 W Gaines St, Tallahassee 32399-0400

Chairperson Marva Johnson

PUBLIC, PRIVATE AND CATHOLIC SECONDARY SCHOOLS

Alachua, Alachua, Pop. 8,873
Alachua County SD
Supt. — See Gainesville
Mebane MS 400/6-8
16401 NW 140th St 32615 386-462-1648
Manda Bessner, prin. Fax 273-4632
Santa Fe HS 1,100/9-12
16213 NW US Highway 441 32615 386-462-1125
Dr. Beth LeClear, prin. Fax 448-1691

Forest Grove Christian Academy 100/PK-12
22575 NW 94th Ave 32615 386-462-3921

Altamonte Springs, Seminole, Pop. 40,483
Seminole County SD
Supt. — See Sanford
Lake Brantley HS 2,700/9-12
991 Sand Lake Rd 32714 407-746-3450
Dr. Trent Daniel, prin. Fax 746-3600
Teague MS 1,400/6-8
1350 Mcneil Rd 32714 407-320-1550
Debra Abbott, prin. Fax 320-1545

Altamonte Christian S 300/K-12
601 Palm Springs Dr 32701 407-831-0950
City College Post-Sec.
177 Montgomery Rd 32714 407-831-9816
Everglades University Post-Sec.
887 E Altamonte Dr 32701 407-277-0311

Altha, Calhoun, Pop. 529
Calhoun County SD
Supt. — See Blountstown
Altha S 600/PK-12
25793 N Main St 32421 850-762-3121
Sue Price, prin. Fax 762-9502

Apopka, Orange, Pop. 40,626
Orange County SD
Supt. — See Orlando
Amikids Orlando 50/Alt
1461 S Lake Pleasant Rd 32703 407-886-5405
William Tovine, prin.
Apopka HS 3,000/9-12
555 Martin St 32712 407-905-5500
Matthew Arnold, prin. Fax 814-6130
Apopka MS 1,100/6-8
425 N Park Ave 32712 407-884-2208
Kelly Pelletier, prin. Fax 884-2217
Piedmont Lakes MS 1,200/6-8
2601 Lakeville Rd 32703 407-884-2265
Edward Thompson, prin. Fax 884-2287
Wekiva HS 2,300/9-12
2501 N Hiawassee Rd 32703 407-297-4900
Michele Erickson, prin. Fax 297-4970
Wolf Lake MS 1,200/6-8
1725 W Ponkan Rd 32712 407-464-3317
Caroll Grimando, prin. Fax 464-3336

Champion Preparatory Academy 300/PK-12
1935 S Orange Blossom Trl 32703 407-788-0018
Community Christian Learning Center 100/K-12
PO Box 2347 32704 407-410-0049
Forest Lake Academy 400/9-12
500 Education Loop 32703 407-862-8411
Frank Jones, prin. Fax 862-7050
Golf Academy of America Post-Sec.
510 S Hunt Club Blvd 32703 800-342-7342

Arcadia, DeSoto, Pop. 7,533
De Soto County SD 4,600/PK-12
PO Box 2000 34265 863-494-4222
Dr. Karyn Gary, supt. Fax 494-0389
www.desotoschools.com
DeSoto HS 1,100/9-12
1710 E Gibson St 34266 863-494-3434
Tod Baldwin, prin. Fax 494-7867
DeSoto MS 1,100/6-8
420 E Gibson St 34266 863-494-4133
Dr. Christina Britton, prin. Fax 494-6263
DeSoto County Adult Education Center Adult
310 W Whidden St 34266 863-993-1333
Kathy Severson, prin. Fax 993-9181

Atlantic Beach, Duval, Pop. 12,332
Duval County SD
Supt. — See Jacksonville
Marine Science Education Center Vo/Tech
1347 Palmer St 32233 904-247-5973
Donald Nelson, prin. Fax 247-5976
Mayport MS 900/6-8
2600 Mayport Rd 32233 904-247-5977
Katrina McCray, prin. Fax 247-5987

Auburndale, Polk, Pop. 13,305
Polk County SD
Supt. — See Bartow
Auburndale HS 1,700/9-12
1 Bloodhound Trl 33823 863-965-6200
John Hill, prin. Fax 965-6245
Stambaugh MS 800/6-8
226 N Main St 33823 863-965-5494
Trish Butler, prin. Fax 965-5496
East Area Adult S Adult
300 E Bridgers Ave 33823 863-965-5475
Marc Hutek, prin. Fax 965-5477

Southern Technical College Post-Sec.
298 Havendale Blvd 33823 407-438-6000

Ave Maria, Collier

Ave Maria University Post-Sec.
5050 Ave Maria Blvd 34142 877-283-8648

Avon Park, Highlands, Pop. 8,676
Highlands County SD
Supt. — See Sebring
Avon Park HS 900/9-12
700 E Main St 33825 863-452-4311
Danielle Erwin, prin. Fax 452-4324
Avon Park MS 700/6-8
401 S Lake Ave 33825 863-452-4333
Seth Lambert, prin. Fax 452-4341
Highlands Career Institute Vo/Tech
600 W College Dr 33825 863-784-7209
Julia Burnett, lead tchr. Fax 784-7211

Community Christian Academy 50/PK-12
1400 County Road 17A N 33825 863-452-0644
Hannah Okwengu, admin.
South Florida State College Post-Sec.
600 W College Dr 33825 863-453-6661
Walker Memorial Academy 200/K-12
1525 W Avon Blvd 33825 863-453-3131
Jacqueline Colon-Diaz, prin. Fax 453-4925

Babson Park, Polk, Pop. 1,321

Webber International University Post-Sec.
PO Box 96 33827 863-638-1431

Baker, Okaloosa
Okaloosa County SD
Supt. — See Fort Walton Beach
Baker S 1,400/K-12
1369 14th St 32531 850-689-7279
Michael Martello, prin. Fax 689-7416

Baldwin, Duval, Pop. 1,376
Duval County SD
Supt. — See Jacksonville
Baldwin MSHS 1,100/6-12
291 Mill St W 32234 904-266-1200
Denise Hall, prin. Fax 266-1220

Bartow, Polk, Pop. 17,008
Polk County SD 97,500/PK-12
PO Box 391 33831 863-534-0500
Jacqueline Byrd, supt. Fax 519-8231
www.polk-fl.net
Bartow HS 2,000/9-12
1270 S Broadway Ave 33830 863-534-7400
Emilean Clemons, prin. Fax 534-0077
Bartow MS 800/6-8
550 E Clower St 33830 863-534-7415
Christopher Roberts, prin. Fax 534-7418
Gause Academy of Leadership 200/6-12
1395 Polk St 33830 863-534-7425
Daraford Jones, prin. Fax 519-3716
International Baccalaureate HS at Bartow 200/9-12
1270 S Broadway Ave 33830 863-534-0194
Brenda Hardman, prin. Fax 534-0077
Summerlin Academy 9-12
1500 S Jackson Ave 33830 863-519-7504
Steve Cochran, prin. Fax 519-8774
Union Academy 400/6-8
1795 E Wabash St 33830 863-534-7435
Joel McGuire, prin. Fax 534-7487
Other Schools – See Auburndale, Davenport, Dundee, Eagle Lake, Fort Meade, Frostproof, Haines City, Lake Alfred, Lakeland, Lake Wales, Mulberry, Poinciana, Winter Haven

Bell, Gilchrist, Pop. 455
Gilchrist County SD
Supt. — See Trenton
Bell HS 700/6-12
930 S Main St 32619 352-463-3232
Sherry Lindsey, prin. Fax 463-3294

Belle Glade, Palm Beach, Pop. 17,323
Palm Beach County SD
Supt. — See West Palm Beach
Crossroads Academy 200/Alt
225 SW 12th St 33430 561-993-8400
Diane Howard, prin. Fax 993-8450
Glades Central Community HS 1,000/9-12
1001 SW Avenue M 33430 561-993-4400
Angela Avery-Moore, prin. Fax 993-9462
Lake Shore MS 700/6-8
425 W Canal St N 33430 561-829-1100
Anthony Lockhart, prin. Fax 829-1130

Glades Day S 300/PK-12
400 Gator Blvd 33430 561-996-6769
Amie Pitts, admin. Fax 992-9274

Belleview, Marion, Pop. 4,408
Marion County SD
Supt. — See Ocala
Belleview HS 1,500/9-12
10400 SE 36th Ave 34420 352-671-6210
Mike Kelly, prin. Fax 671-6212
Belleview MS 1,000/6-8
10500 SE 36th Ave 34420 352-671-6235
David Ellers, prin. Fax 671-6239

Souls Harbor Christian Academy 200/PK-12
12650 SE County Highway 484 34420 352-245-6252
Taylor College Post-Sec.
5190 SE 125th St 34420 352-245-4119

Blountstown, Calhoun, Pop. 2,466
Calhoun County SD 2,200/PK-12
20859 Central Ave E Ste G20 32424 850-674-5927
Ralph Yoder, supt. Fax 674-5814
www.calhounflschools.org
Blountstown HS 400/9-12
18597 NE State Road 69 32424 850-674-5724
Debbie Williams, prin. Fax 674-8865
Blountstown MS 300/6-8
17586 Main St N 32424 850-674-8234
Neva Miller, prin. Fax 674-6480
Calhoun County Adult Education Center Adult
17283 NW Charlie Johns St 32424 850-674-6490
Barbara Hathaway, lead tchr.
Other Schools – See Altha

Boca Raton, Palm Beach, Pop. 83,145
Palm Beach County SD
Supt. — See West Palm Beach
Boca Raton Community HS 3,100/9-12
1501 NW 15th Ct 33486 561-338-1400
Dr. Susie King, prin. Fax 338-1440
Boca Raton Community MS 1,400/6-8
1251 NW 8th St 33486 561-416-8700
Peter Slack, prin. Fax 416-8777
Eagles Landing MS 1,300/6-8
19500 Coral Ridge Dr 33498 561-470-7000
Cynthia Chiapetta, prin. Fax 470-7030
Estridge High Tech MS 1,200/6-8
1798 NW Spanish River Blvd 33431 561-989-7800
Laura Riopelle, prin. Fax 989-7810
Loggers Run Community MS 1,000/6-8
11584 W Palmetto Park Rd 33428 561-883-8000
Edmund Capitano, prin. Fax 883-8027
Olympic Heights Community HS 2,000/9-12
20101 Lyons Rd 33434 561-852-6900
Dave Clark, prin. Fax 852-6974

Omni MS 1,400/6-8
5775 Jog Rd 33496 561-989-2800
Gerald Riopelle, prin. Fax 981-9651
Spanish River Community HS 2,400/9-12
5100 Jog Rd 33496 561-241-2200
William Latson, prin. Fax 241-2236
West Boca Raton Community HS 2,100/9-12
12811 Glades Rd 33498 561-672-2001
Craig Sommer, prin. Fax 672-2014

Boca Raton Christian S 500/PK-12
315 NW 4th St 33432 561-391-2727
Robert Tennies Ed.D., hdmstr. Fax 226-0617
Boca Raton Prep International S 200/PK-12
10333 Diego Dr S 33428 561-852-1410
Digital Media Arts College Post-Sec.
5400 Broken Sound Blvd NW 33487 561-391-1148
Everglades University Post-Sec.
5002 T Rex Ave Ste 100 33431 561-912-1211
Florida Atlantic University Post-Sec.
PO Box 3091 33431 561-297-3000
Garden of the Sahaba Academy 300/PK-11
3100 NW 5th Ave 33431 561-395-3011
Dr. Radwan Baytiyeh, prin. Fax 395-3029
Grandview Preparatory S 200/PK-12
336 NW Spanish River Blvd 33431 561-416-9737
Klein Jewish Academy 700/K-12
9701 Donna Klein Blvd 33428 561-852-3300
Lynn University Post-Sec.
3601 N Military Trl 33431 561-237-7000
PC Professor Post-Sec.
7056 Beracasa Way 33433 561-750-7879
St. Andrew's S 1,300/PK-12
3900 Jog Rd 33434 561-210-2000
Dr. Jim Byer, head sch Fax 210-2007
St. John Paul II Academy 500/9-12
4001 N Military Trl 33431 561-314-2100
Edward Bernot, prin. Fax 989-8582
Weinbaum Yeshiva HS 300/9-12
7902 Montoya Cir N 33433 561-417-7422
West Boca Medical Center Post-Sec.
21644 State Road 7 33428 561-488-8000

Bonifay, Holmes, Pop. 2,723
Holmes County SD 3,300/PK-12
701 E Pennsylvania Ave 32425 850-547-9341
Eddie Dixon, supt. Fax 547-0381
www.hdsb.org
Bethlehem S 500/PK-12
2767 Highway 160 32425 850-547-3621
Brent Jones, prin. Fax 547-4856
Bonifay MS 500/5-8
401 Mclaughlin Ave 32425 850-547-2754
Donald Etheridge, prin. Fax 547-3685
Graduate Alternative S 50/Alt
401 McLaughlin Ave 32425 850-547-0470
Ron Dixon, prin. Fax 547-0474
Holmes County HS 400/9-12
825 W Highway 90 32425 850-547-9000
Mickey Hudson, prin. Fax 547-6694
Other Schools – See Graceville, Ponce de Leon

Bonita Springs, Lee, Pop. 43,637
Lee County SD
Supt. — See Fort Myers
Bonita Springs MS for the Arts 800/6-8
10141 W Terry St 34135 239-992-4422
Melissa Layner, prin. Fax 992-9157

Southern Technical College Post-Sec.
24311 Walden Center Dr #101 34134 877-347-5492

Boynton Beach, Palm Beach, Pop. 66,992
Palm Beach County SD
Supt. — See West Palm Beach
Boynton Beach Community HS 1,700/9-12
4975 Park Ridge Blvd 33426 561-752-1200
Fred Barch, prin. Fax 752-1205
Congress MS 1,000/6-8
101 S Congress Ave 33426 561-374-5600
Denise O'Conner, prin. Fax 374-5642
McAuliffe MS 1,100/6-8
6500 Le Chalet Blvd, 561-374-6600
Jeff Silverman, prin. Fax 374-6636
Odyssey MS 900/6-8
6161 W Woolbright Rd 33437 561-752-1300
Bonnie Fox, prin. Fax 752-1305

Bethesda Memorial Hospital Post-Sec.
2815 S Seacrest Blvd 33435 561-737-7733
Florida Career College Post-Sec.
1743 N Congress Ave 33426 561-634-7400
Lake Worth Christian S 500/PK-12
7592 High Ridge Rd 33426 561-493-3100
Jim Harwood, supt. Fax 493-3848
St. Vincent DePaul Regional Seminary Post-Sec.
10701 S Military Trl 33436 561-732-4424

Bradenton, Manatee, Pop. 48,642
Manatee County SD 44,600/PK-12
PO Box 9069 34206 941-708-8770
Dr. Diana Greene, supt. Fax 708-8686
www.manateeschools.net
Bayshore HS 1,400/9-12
5401 34th St W 34210 941-751-7004
David Underhill, prin. Fax 753-0953
Braden River HS 1,900/9-12
6545 State Road 70 E 34203 941-751-8230
Jennifer Gilray, prin. Fax 751-8250
Braden River MS 1,000/6-8
6215 River Club Blvd 34202 941-751-7080
Randy Petrilla, prin. Fax 751-7085
Haile MS 1,100/6-8
9501 E State Road 64 34212 941-714-7240
Sharon Scarbrough, prin. Fax 714-7245
Harllee MS 500/6-8
6423 9th St E 34203 941-751-7027
Verdya Bradley, prin. Fax 751-7030
Horizons Academy 600/Alt
1910 27th St E 34208 941-714-7470
James Hird, dir. Fax 708-6417
Johnson MS 500/6-8
2121 26th Ave E 34208 941-741-3344
Angela Lindsey, prin. Fax 741-3345
King MS 1,100/6-8
600 75th St NW 34209 941-798-6820
Michele Romeo, prin. Fax 798-6835
Lakewood Ranch HS 2,100/9-12
5500 Lakewood Ranch Blvd 34211 941-727-6100
Craig Little, prin. Fax 727-6099
Lee MS 1,000/6-8
4000 53rd Ave W 34210 941-727-6500
Scott Cooper, prin. Fax 727-6513
Manatee HS 2,500/9-12
902 33rd Street Ct W 34205 941-714-7300
Don Sauer, prin. Fax 741-3443
Manatee Technical College - East Vo/Tech
5520 Lakewood Ranch Blvd 34211 941-752-8100
Doug Wagner, dir. Fax 727-6257
Manatee Technical College - Main Vo/Tech
6305 State Road 70 E 34203 941-751-7900
Doug Wagner, dir. Fax 405-1367
Manatee Technical College - West Vo/Tech
5505 34th St W 34210 941-209-6800
Doug Wagner, dir. Fax 751-7927
Nolan MS 1,100/6-8
6615 Greenbrook Blvd 34202 941-751-8200
Scot Boice, prin. Fax 751-8210
Southeast HS 1,300/9-12
1200 37th Ave E 34208 941-741-3366
Rosa Daughtry, prin. Fax 741-3372
Sugg MS 800/6-8
3801 59th St W 34209 941-741-3157
Ann McDonald, prin. Fax 741-3514
Other Schools – See Palmetto

Bradenton Christian S 500/PK-12
3304 43rd St W 34209 941-792-5454
Dan Vande Pol, supt. Fax 795-7190
Community Christian S 200/PK-12
5500 18th St E 34203 941-756-8748
Edison Academics 100/6-12
7700 Cortez Rd W 34210 941-792-7500
Paula Cavitt-Jackson, admin. Fax 792-7559
Florida College of Natural Health Post-Sec.
616 67th Street Cir E 34208 941-744-1244
Gulfcoast Christian Academy 50/K-12
1700 51st Ave E 34203 941-755-0332
Carol Pope, admin. Fax 981-1564
GUTI - Bradenton Post-Sec.
4212 Cortez Rd W 34210 941-761-4400
IMG Academy 600/PK-12
5650 Bollettieri Blvd 34210 800-872-6425
Fax 752-2630
Inspiration Academy 50/6-12
7900 40th Ave W 34209 941-795-5466
Lake Erie College\Osteopathic Medicine Post-Sec.
5000 Lakewood Ranch Blvd 34211 941-756-0690
Manatee Learning Academy 200/PK-10
6210 17th Ave W 34209 941-794-0088
Manatee Technical Institute Post-Sec.
5603 34th St W 34210 941-751-7900
St. Stephen's Episcopal S 600/PK-12
315 41st St W 34209 941-746-2121
Dr. Janet Pullen, head sch Fax 746-5699
State College of FL Manatee-Sarasota Post-Sec.
PO Box 1849 34206 941-752-5000

Brandon, Hillsborough, Pop. 100,869
Hillsborough County SD
Supt. — See Tampa
Brandon HS 1,900/9-12
1101 Victoria St 33510 813-744-8120
Jennifer Sparano, prin. Fax 744-8129
Burns MS 1,300/6-8
615 Brooker Rd 33511 813-744-8383
Matthew DiPrima, prin. Fax 740-3623
Mann MS 1,100/6-8
409 E Jersey Ave 33510 813-744-8400
Barbara Fillhart, prin. Fax 744-6707
McLane MS 900/6-8
306 N Knights Ave 33510 813-744-8100
Dina Langston, prin. Fax 744-8135
Brandon Adult Education Adult
1101 Victoria St 33510 813-744-8131
Susan Balke, admin. Fax 664-8393

Central Baptist Christian S 300/PK-12
402 E Windhorst Rd 33510 813-689-6133
Faith Baptist Christian S 100/K-12
1118 N Parsons Ave 33510 813-654-4936
Southern Technical College Post-Sec.
608 E Bloomingdale Ave 33511 813-654-8800

Branford, Suwannee, Pop. 686
Suwannee County SD
Supt. — See Live Oak
Branford HS 700/6-12
405 Reynolds St NE 32008 386-935-5600
Jimmy Wilkerson, prin. Fax 935-3867

Bristol, Liberty, Pop. 982
Liberty County SD 1,400/PK-12
PO Box 429 32321 850-643-2275
David Summers, supt. Fax 643-2533
www.lcsb.org
Liberty County HS 300/9-12
PO Box 519 32321 850-643-2241
Aaron Day, prin. Fax 643-4153
Liberty County Adult S Adult
PO Box 429 32321 850-643-1016
Terrell Sykes, prin.

Bronson, Levy, Pop. 1,084
Levy County SD 4,900/PK-12
480 Marshburn Dr 32621 352-486-5231
Robert Hastings, supt. Fax 486-5237
www.levy.k12.fl.us
Bronson MSHS 600/6-12
351 Ishie Ave 32621 352-486-5261
Gary Masters, prin. Fax 486-5263
Levy Learning Academy Alt
320 Mongo St 32621 352-486-5388
Dennis Webber, prin.
Other Schools – See Cedar Key, Chiefland, Williston

Brooksville, Hernando, Pop. 7,591
Hernando County SD 21,600/PK-12
919 N Broad St 34601 352-797-7000
Dr. Lori Romano Ph.D., supt. Fax 797-7101
www.hernandoschools.org
Central HS 1,200/9-12
14075 Ken Austin Pkwy 34613 352-797-7020
John Stratton, prin. Fax 797-7120
Discovery Academy Alt
14063 Ken Austin Pkwy 34613 352-797-7013
Steve Crognale, prin. Fax 797-7113
Endeavor Academy 100/Alt
14063 Ken Austin Pkwy 34613 352-797-7013
Steve Crognale, prin. Fax 797-7113
Hernando HS 1,300/9-12
700 Bell Ave 34601 352-797-7015
Leechele Booker, prin. Fax 797-7115
Nature Coast Technical HS Vo/Tech
4057 California St 34604 352-797-7088
Toni-Ann Noyes, prin. Fax 797-7188
Parrott MS 800/6-8
19220 Youth Dr 34601 352-797-7075
Brent Gaustad, prin. Fax 797-7175
Powell MS 800/6-8
4100 Barclay Ave 34609 352-797-7095
Thomas Dye, prin. Fax 797-7195
West Hernando MS 700/6-8
14325 Ken Austin Pkwy 34613 352-797-7035
Lori Lessley, prin. Fax 797-7135
Other Schools – See Spring Hill, Weeki Wachee

Hernando Christian Academy 200/PK-12
7200 Emerson Rd 34601 352-796-0616
Ken Alvarez, supt. Fax 799-3400
Pasco-Hernando Community College Post-Sec.
11415 Ponce De Leon Blvd 34601 352-796-6726

Bunnell, Flagler, Pop. 2,615
Flagler County SD 12,700/PK-12
PO Box 755 32110 386-437-7526
Jacob Oliva, supt. Fax 586-2351
www.flaglerschools.com
Other Schools – See Palm Coast

Bushnell, Sumter, Pop. 2,367
Sumter County SD 7,500/PK-12
2680 W C 476 33513 352-793-2315
Richard Shirley, supt. Fax 793-4180
www.sumter.k12.fl.us
South Sumter HS 1,000/9-12
706 N Main St 33513 352-793-3131
Dr. Preston Morgan, prin. Fax 793-2992
Other Schools – See Sumterville, Webster, Wildwood

Callahan, Nassau, Pop. 1,111
Nassau County SD
Supt. — See Fernandina Beach
Callahan MS 800/6-8
450121 Old Dixie Hwy 32011 904-491-7935
Kimberly Harrison, prin. Fax 879-2860
West Nassau County HS 1,000/9-12
1 Warrior Dr 32011 904-491-7942
Curtis Gaus, prin. Fax 879-5843

Sonshine Christian Academy 300/PK-12
PO Box 5026 32011 904-879-1260

Cantonment, Escambia, Pop. 4,500
Escambia County SD
Supt. — See Pensacola
Ransom MS 1,400/6-8
1000 W Kingsfield Rd 32533 850-937-2220
Brent Brummet, prin. Fax 937-2232
Tate HS 2,000/9-12
1771 Tate Rd 32533 850-937-2300
Rick Shackle, prin. Fax 937-2328

Cape Coral, Lee, Pop. 151,800
Lee County SD
Supt. — See Fort Myers
Baker HS 1,700/9-12
3500 Agualinda Blvd 33914 239-458-6690
Jami Covert, prin. Fax 458-6691
Caloosa MS 900/6-8
610 Del Prado Blvd S 33990 239-574-3232
Dr. Ann Cole, prin. Fax 574-2660
Cape Coral HS 1,700/9-12
2300 Santa Barbara Blvd 33991 239-574-6766
Dr. Jeff Spiro, prin. Fax 574-7799
Cape Coral Technical College Vo/Tech
360 Santa Barbara Blvd N 33993 239-574-4440
Judy Johnson, dir. Fax 458-3721
Challenger MS 1,100/6-8
624 SW Trafalgar Pkwy 33991 239-242-4341
Teri Cannady, prin. Fax 242-7217
Diplomat MS 800/6-8
1039 NE 16th Ter 33909 239-574-5257
Maura Bennington, prin. Fax 574-4008
Gulf MS 800/6-8
1809 SW 36th Ter 33914 239-549-0606
Dr. Michelle Cort-Mora, prin. Fax 549-2806
Island Coast HS 1,500/9-12
2125 De Navarra Pkwy 33909 239-458-0362
Kristin Bueno, prin. Fax 772-8405
Mariner HS 1,500/9-12
701 Chiquita Blvd N 33993 239-772-3324
Dr. Robert Butz, prin. Fax 772-4880
Mariner MS 900/6-8
425 Chiquita Blvd N 33993 239-772-1848
Rachel Gould, prin. Fax 242-1256
Trafalgar MS 900/6-8
2120 SW Trafalgar Pkwy 33991 239-283-2001
Dr. Michael Galbreath, prin. Fax 283-5620

Cape Coral Christian S 100/PK-12
811 Santa Barbara Blvd 33991 239-574-3707
Lee County High Tech Center North Post-Sec.
360 Santa Barbara Blvd N 33993 239-574-4440

Casselberry, Seminole, Pop. 25,625
Seminole County SD
Supt. — See Sanford

South Seminole MS 1,300/6-8
101 S Winter Park Dr 32707 407-746-1350
Dr. Mia Coleman-Baker, prin. Fax 746-1420

Aviation Institute of Maintenance Post-Sec.
2725 S US Highway 17/92 32707 888-349-5387
Florida Institute of Animal Arts Post-Sec.
493 Semoran Blvd 32707 407-869-7387
Socrates Preparatory S 100/1-12
3955 Red Bug Lake Rd 32707 407-422-0825

Cedar Key, Levy, Pop. 698
Levy County SD
Supt. — See Bronson
Cedar Key S 300/PK-12
951 Whiddon Ave 32625 352-543-5223
Josh Slemp, prin. Fax 543-5988

Celebration, Osceola, Pop. 7,281
Osceola County SD
Supt. — See Kissimmee
Celebration HS 2,100/9-12
1809 Celebration Blvd 34747 321-939-6600
Jonathan Rasmussen, prin. Fax 939-6652

Century, Escambia, Pop. 1,651
Escambia County SD
Supt. — See Pensacola
Northview HS 500/9-12
4100 W Highway 4 32535 850-327-6681
Gayle Weaver, prin. Fax 327-6106

Chiefland, Levy, Pop. 2,173
Levy County SD
Supt. — See Bronson
Chiefland MSHS 800/6-12
808 N Main St 32626 352-493-6000
Matt McLelland, prin. Fax 493-6018
Adult HS Adult
114 Rodgers Blvd 32626 352-493-9533
Fax 493-9994

Chipley, Washington, Pop. 3,525
Washington County SD 3,100/PK-12
652 3rd St 32428 850-638-6222
Joseph Taylor, supt. Fax 638-6226
www.wcsdschools.com
Chipley HS 600/9-12
1545 Brickyard Rd 32428 850-638-6100
Kyle Newsom, prin. Fax 638-6017
Florida Panhandle Technical College HS Vo/Tech
757 Hoyt St 32428 850-638-1180
Martha Compton, dir. Fax 638-6177
Roulhac MS 400/6-8
1535 Brickyard Rd 32428 850-638-6170
Nancy Holley, prin. Fax 638-6319
Washington Inst for Specialized Educ 100/Alt
680 2nd St 32428 850-638-6020
Sam Cox, lead tchr. Fax 415-5024
Other Schools – See Vernon

Washington County Christian S 100/PK-12
1405 Brickyard Rd 32428 850-638-9227
Jason Haddock, admin. Fax 638-9234

Citra, Marion
Marion County SD
Supt. — See Ocala
North Marion HS 1,300/9-12
151 W Highway 329 32113 352-671-6010
Ben Whitehouse, prin. Fax 671-6011
North Marion MS 800/6-8
2085 W Highway 329 32113 352-671-6035
Philip Leppert, prin. Fax 671-6044

Citrus Springs, Citrus, Pop. 8,462
Citrus County SD
Supt. — See Inverness
Citrus Springs MS 800/6-8
150 W Citrus Springs Blvd 34434 352-344-2244
John Weed, prin. Fax 249-2111

Clearwater, Pinellas, Pop. 105,537
Pinellas County SD
Supt. — See Largo
Bayside HS 400/Alt
14405 49th St N 33762 727-507-4730
Patricia Fuller, prin. Fax 507-4735
Clearwater Fundamental MS 800/6-8
1660 Palmetto St 33755 727-298-1609
Linda Burris, prin. Fax 298-1614
Clearwater HS 1,800/9-12
540 S Hercules Ave 33764 727-298-1620
Keith Mastorides, prin. Fax 469-5981
Clearwater IS 300/Alt
1220 Palmetto St 33755 727-298-1616
Philip Wirth, prin. Fax 469-4189
Countryside HS 2,200/9-12
3000 State Road 580 33761 727-725-7956
Gerald Schlereth, prin. Fax 725-7990
Oak Grove MS 1,100/6-8
1370 S Belcher Rd 33764 727-524-4430
Dr. Dawn Coffin, prin. Fax 524-4416
Pinellas Technical College Clearwater Vo/Tech
6100 154th Ave N 33760 727-538-7167
Jakub Prokop, dir. Fax 507-4423
Rodriguez Academy Alt
3030 McMullen Booth Rd 33761 727-793-3522
Jayme Pecci, dir. Fax 726-8553
Clearwater Adult Education Center Adult
540 S Hercules Ave 33764 727-469-4190
James Joyner, admin. Fax 469-4193

Allendale Academy 800/K-12
2655 Ulmerton Rd Ste 402 33762 727-531-2481
Calvary Christian HS 500/9-12
110 N McMullen Booth Rd 33759 727-449-2247
David Kilgore, head sch Fax 461-5421
Church of Scientology Cadet S 100/6-12
1875 Drew St 33765 727-639-1080
Clearwater Academy International 200/PK-12
801 Drew St 33755 727-446-1722
Jim Zwers, dir. Fax 443-5252
Clearwater Central Catholic HS 500/9-12
2750 Haines Bayshore Rd 33760 727-531-1449
James Deputy, prin. Fax 535-7034
Clearwater Christian College Post-Sec.
3400 Gulf To Bay Blvd 33759 727-726-1153
Florida Career College Post-Sec.
410 Park Place Blvd 33759 727-724-1037
Iva Christian S 100/K-12
1430 Bellair Rd 33756 727-442-2424
Lakeside Christian S 300/K-12
1897 Sunset Point Rd 33765 727-461-3311
Jim Jensen, head sch Fax 445-1835
National Aviation Academy Post-Sec.
6225 Ulmerton Rd 33760 727-531-2080
Pinellas Technical Education Center Post-Sec.
6100 154th Ave N 33760 727-538-7167
St. Petersburg Theological Seminary Post-Sec.
3190 Gulf to Bay Blvd 33759 727-399-0276
Sunstate Academy Post-Sec.
2525 Drew St 33765 727-538-3827
Ultimate Medical Academy Post-Sec.
1255 Cleveland St 33755 727-298-8685
Washburn Academy 100/PK-12
222 S Lincoln Ave 33756 727-647-1668

Clermont, Lake, Pop. 27,603
Lake County SD
Supt. — See Tavares
Clermont MS 700/6-8
301 East Ave 34711 352-243-2460
Robert McCue, prin. Fax 243-1407
East Ridge HS 2,100/9-12
13322 Excalibur Rd 34711 352-242-2080
Julie Robinson-Leuallen, prin. Fax 242-2090
East Ridge MS 1,100/6-8
13201 Excalibur Rd 34711 352-536-8020
Stephanie Mayuski, prin. Fax 536-8039
Windy Hill MS 1,300/6-8
3575 Hancock Rd 34711 352-394-2123
William Roberts, prin. Fax 394-7901

Family Christian S of Clermont 200/K-12
2500 S Hwy 27 34711 352-241-0323
Dr. Mercy Nyman, prin. Fax 243-8501
Real Life Christian Academy 300/PK-12
1501 Steves Rd 34711 352-394-5575
Michael Fernandes, admin. Fax 394-7860

Clewiston, Hendry, Pop. 7,087
Hendry County SD
Supt. — See LaBelle
Clewiston HS 900/9-12
1501 S Francisco St 33440 863-983-1520
Roberto Sanchez, prin. Fax 983-2168
Clewiston MS 700/6-8
601 W Pasadena Ave 33440 863-983-1530
Lori Duckstein, prin. Fax 983-1541

Cocoa, Brevard, Pop. 16,719
Brevard County SD
Supt. — See Melbourne
Cocoa HS 1,400/7-12
2000 Tiger Trl 32926 321-632-5300
Dr. Stephanie Soliven, prin. Fax 636-1218
Space Coast JSHS 1,500/7-12
6150 Banyan St 32927 321-638-0750
Sylvia Mijuskovic, prin. Fax 638-0766
Clearlake Education Center Adult
1225 Clearlake Rd 32922 321-633-3660
Jeff Arnott, prin. Fax 633-3488

Eastern Florida State College Post-Sec.
1519 Clearlake Rd 32922 321-632-1111
Space Coast Christian Academy 100/PK-12
1950 Michigan Ave 32922 321-636-0883

Cocoa Beach, Brevard, Pop. 11,096
Brevard County SD
Supt. — See Melbourne
Cocoa Beach JSHS 1,200/7-12
1500 Minutemen Cswy 32931 321-783-1776
Karyle Green, prin. Fax 868-6602

Coconut Creek, Broward, Pop. 51,291
Broward County SD
Supt. — See Fort Lauderdale
Atlantic Technical Center HS Vo/Tech
4700 Coconut Creek Pkwy 33063 754-321-5100
Robert Crawford, prin. Fax 321-5380
Coconut Creek HS 1,400/9-12
1400 NW 44th Ave 33066 754-322-0350
Scott Fiske, prin. Fax 322-0481
Lyons Creek MS 1,800/6-8
4333 Sol Press Blvd 33073 754-322-3700
Horace Hamm, prin. Fax 322-3785
Monarch HS 2,300/9-12
5050 Wiles Rd 33073 754-322-1400
James Neer, prin. Fax 322-1530
Thomas Education Center West Alt
4690 Coconut Creek Pkwy 33063 754-321-6800
Tracy Lockhart-Talley, prin. Fax 321-6840

Atlantic Technical Center Post-Sec.
4700 Coconut Creek Pkwy 33063 754-321-5100
Broward College Post-Sec.
1000 Coconut Creek Blvd 33066 954-201-2240
North Broward Preparatory S 1,400/PK-12
7600 Lyons Rd 33073 954-247-0179

Coconut Grove, See Miami

Carrollton S of the Sacred Heart 800/PK-12
3747 Main Hwy 33133 305-446-5673
Olen Kalkus, hdmstr. Fax 592-6533
Ransom Everglades S 1,100/6-12
3575 Main Hwy 33133 305-460-8800
Penny Townsend, head sch Fax 854-1846

Cooper City, Broward, Pop. 28,003
Broward County SD
Supt. — See Fort Lauderdale
Cooper City HS 2,100/9-12
9401 Stirling Rd 33328 754-323-0200
Wendy Doll, prin. Fax 323-0330
Pioneer MS 1,300/6-8
5350 SW 90th Ave 33328 754-323-4100
Michael Consaul, prin. Fax 323-4185

Cooper City Christian Academy 100/K-12
5201 S Flamingo Rd 33330 954-779-6221
Nur Ul-Islam Academy 300/PK-12
10600 SW 59th St 33328 954-434-3288
Westlake Preparatory S & Academy 100/K-12
8950 Stirling Rd 33024 954-236-2300

Coral Gables, Miami-Dade, Pop. 46,270
Miami-Dade County SD
Supt. — See Miami
Carver MS 1,000/6-8
4901 Lincoln Dr 33133 305-444-7388
Shelley Stroleny, prin. Fax 529-5148
Coral Gables HS 3,300/9-12
450 Bird Rd 33146 305-443-4871
Adolfo Costa, prin. Fax 441-8094
De Leon MS 1,100/6-8
5801 Augusto St 33146 305-661-1611
Martha Chang, prin. Fax 666-3140
International Studies Preparatory Acad 300/9-12
1570 Madruga Ave 33146 305-663-7200
Alejandro Perez, prin. Fax 661-0196
Coral Gables Adult Education Center Adult
450 Bird Rd 33146 305-443-4871
Alan Bashaw, prin. Fax 446-2507

New Professions Technical Institute Post-Sec.
4000 W Flagler St 33134 305-461-2223
Riviera Day S and Riviera Preparatory S 600/PK-12
6800 Nervia St 33146 305-666-1856
SABER Post-Sec.
3990 W Flagler St Ste 103 33134 305-443-9170
University of Miami Post-Sec.
PO Box 248006 33124 305-284-2211

Coral Springs, Broward, Pop. 117,909
Broward County SD
Supt. — See Fort Lauderdale
Coral Glades HS 2,400/9-12
2700 Sportsplex Dr 33065 754-322-1250
Steven Carruth, prin. Fax 322-1380
Coral Springs HS 2,500/9-12
7201 W Sample Rd 33065 754-322-0500
Susan Leon, prin. Fax 322-0630
Coral Springs MS 1,300/6-8
10300 Wiles Rd 33076 754-322-3000
Ian Murray, prin. Fax 322-3085
Forest Glen MS 1,400/6-8
6501 Turtle Run Blvd 33067 754-322-3400
Ronald Foresman, prin. Fax 322-3485
Ramblewood MS 1,200/6-8
8505 W Atlantic Blvd 33071 754-322-4300
Cory Smith, prin. Fax 322-4385
Sawgrass Springs MS 1,200/6-8
12500 W Sample Rd 33065 754-322-4500
James Cecil, prin. Fax 322-4585
Taravella HS 3,100/9-12
10600 Riverside Dr 33071 754-322-2300
Jason Nault, prin. Fax 322-2430

Coral Springs Christian Academy 900/PK-12
2251 Riverside Dr 33065 954-752-2870
Joseph E. Sanelli, head sch Fax 346-1112
Florida Medical Training Institute Post-Sec.
7451 Wiles Rd Ste 105 33067 954-752-1414
Mesivta of Coral Springs 9-12
1730 N University Dr 33071 954-464-0416
Phyl's Academy Preparatory S 50/7-12
11411 NW 56th Dr 33076 954-731-7524

Cottondale, Jackson, Pop. 899
Jackson County SD
Supt. — See Marianna
Cottondale JSHS 500/6-12
2680 Levy St 32431 850-482-9821
Ken Granger, prin. Fax 482-9827

Crawfordville, Wakulla, Pop. 3,618
Wakulla County SD 4,800/PK-12
PO Box 100 32326 850-926-0065
Robert Pearce, supt. Fax 926-0123
wakulla.schooldesk.net
Riversprings MS 600/6-8
800 Spring Creek Hwy 32327 850-926-2300
Michele Yeomans, prin. Fax 926-2111
Wakulla County HS 1,200/9-12
3237 Coastal Hwy 32327 850-926-7125
Michael Barwick, prin. Fax 926-8571
Wakulla MS 600/6-8
22 Jean Dr 32327 850-926-7143
Tolar Griffin, prin. Fax 926-3752

Crescent City, Putnam, Pop. 1,539
Putnam County SD
Supt. — See Palatka
Crescent City JSHS 800/7-12
2201 S US Highway 17 32112 386-698-1629
Mechele Higginbotham, prin. Fax 698-3073

Crestview, Okaloosa, Pop. 20,112
Okaloosa County SD
Supt. — See Fort Walton Beach
Crestview HS 2,000/9-12
1250 N Ferdon Blvd 32536 850-689-7177
Dexter Day, prin. Fax 689-7332
Davidson MS 900/6-8
6261 Old Bethel Rd 32536 850-683-7500
Jay Sanders, prin. Fax 683-7523
Shoal River MS 900/6-8
3200 E Redstone Ave 32539 850-689-7229
Gary Massey, prin. Fax 689-7245

Cross City, Dixie, Pop. 1,699
Dixie County SD 2,000/PK-12
16077 NE Highway 19 32628 352-498-6131
Mike Thomas, supt. Fax 498-1308
www.dixie.k12.fl.us/
Dixie County HS 500/9-12
16077 SE Highway 19 32628 352-498-6410
Diana Locke, prin. Fax 498-1287

Rains MS 400/6-8
981 SE Highway 351 32628 352-498-1346
Chris Lord, prin. Fax 498-1283
Other Schools – See Old Town

Crystal River, Citrus, Pop. 3,056
Citrus County SD
Supt. — See Inverness
Crystal River HS 1,300/9-12
3195 Crystal River High Dr 34428 352-795-4641
Dr. Linda Connors, prin. Fax 249-2106
Crystal River MS 800/6-8
344 NE Crystal St 34428 352-795-2116
Inge Frederick, prin. Fax 249-2108

Cutler Bay, Miami-Dade, Pop. 39,453
Miami-Dade County SD
Supt. — See Miami
Cutler Bay HS 200/9-12
8601 SW 212th St, 305-235-1581
Lucas DelaTorre, prin. Fax 234-8071
Cutler Bay MS 1,100/6-8
19400 Gulfstream Rd, 305-235-4761
Paul Pfeiffer, prin. Fax 254-3746

College of Business & Technology Post-Sec.
19151 S Dixie Hwy, 305-764-3165
Fortis College Post-Sec.
19600 S Dixie Hwy Ste B, 786-345-5300

Dade City, Pasco, Pop. 6,339
Pasco County SD
Supt. — See Land O Lakes
Centennial MS 600/6-8
38505 Centennial Rd 33525 352-524-9700
Rick Saylor, prin. Fax 524-9791
Irvin Education Center 100/Alt
35830 State Road 52 33525 352-524-5700
Cloty Davis, prin. Fax 524-5791
Pasco HS 1,500/9-12
36850 State Road 52 33525 352-524-5500
Kari Kadluv, prin. Fax 524-5591
Pasco MS 900/6-8
13925 14th St 33525 352-524-8400
Jeffrey Wolff, prin. Fax 524-8491
Moore-Mickens Education Center Adult
38301 Martin Luther King Bl 33525 352-524-9000
Cloty Davis, prin. Fax 524-9091

East Pasco Adventist Academy 100/PK-10
38434 Centennial Rd 33525 352-567-3646
Pasco-Hernando Community College Post-Sec.
36727 Blanton Rd 33523 352-567-6701

Dania Beach, Broward, Pop. 29,112
Broward County SD
Supt. — See Fort Lauderdale
Olsen MS 900/6-8
330 SE 11th Ter 33004 754-323-3800
Valerie Harris, prin. Fax 323-3885

Key College Post-Sec.
225 E Dania Beach Blvd 33004 800-581-8292

Davenport, Polk, Pop. 2,854
Polk County SD
Supt. — See Bartow
Davenport Community Campus 200/Alt
8 W Palmetto St 33837 863-419-3486
Fax 419-3491
Ridge Community HS 2,400/9-12
500 Orchid Dr 33837 863-419-3315
Russell Donnelly, prin. Fax 419-3321

Ridge Christian Academy 200/PK-12
41219 Highway 27 33837 863-420-2885

Davie, Broward, Pop. 90,050
Broward County SD
Supt. — See Fort Lauderdale
College Academy 300/11-12
3501 Davie Rd 33314 754-321-6900
Deborah Davey, prin. Fax 321-6940
Indian Ridge MS 1,800/6-8
1355 S Nob Hill Rd 33324 754-323-3300
Frank Zagari, prin. Fax 323-3385
McFatter Technical HS Vo/Tech
6500 Nova Dr 33317 754-321-5700
Jeanette Johnson, prin. Fax 321-5980
Nova HS 2,100/9-12
3600 College Ave 33314 754-323-1650
John LaCasse, prin. Fax 323-1780
Nova MS 1,200/6-8
3602 College Ave 33314 754-323-3700
Jermaine Fleming, prin. Fax 323-3785
Western HS 3,100/9-12
1200 SW 136th Ave 33325 754-323-2400
Jimmy Arrojo, prin. Fax 323-2530

American Preparatory Academy 100/K-12
4850 S Pine Island Rd 33328 954-434-8936
ASM Beauty World Academy Post-Sec.
6423 Stirling Rd 33314 954-321-8411
Broward College Post-Sec.
3501 Davie Rd 33314 954-201-6800
Nova Southeastern University Post-Sec.
3301 College Ave 33314 954-262-7300
Posnack Jewish Day S 500/K-12
5810 S Pine Island Rd 33328 954-583-6100
Dr. Richard Cuenca, hdmstr. Fax 791-5463
Trinity International University Post-Sec.
8190 W State Road 84 33324 954-382-6400

Daytona Beach, Volusia, Pop. 59,727
Volusia County SD
Supt. — See De Land
Campbell MS, 625 S Keech St 32114 900/6-8
Kelly Lewis, prin. 386-258-4661
Hinson MS 900/6-8
1860 N Clyde Morris Blvd 32117 386-258-4682
Robert Ouellette, prin. Fax 506-5064
Mainland HS 1,900/9-12
1255 W Intl Speedway Blvd 32114 386-258-4665
Dr. Cheryl Salerno, prin. Fax 506-5069
Riverview Learning Center 50/Alt
801 N Wild Olive Ave 32118 386-258-4673
Dr. Jerry Picott, prin. Fax 239-6218
Seabreeze HS 1,700/9-12
2700 N Oleander Ave 32118 386-258-4674
Joseph Rawlings, prin. Fax 506-5071

Bethune-Cookman University Post-Sec.
640 Dr Mary Mcleod Bthn Blvd 32114 386-481-2000
Daytona State College Post-Sec.
PO Box 2811 32120 386-506-3000
Embry-Riddle Aeronautical University Post-Sec.
600 S Clyde Morris Blvd 32114 800-222-3728
Embry-Riddle Aeronautical Univ-Worldwide Post-Sec.
600 S Clyde Morris Blvd 32114 800-522-6787
Father Lopez HS 300/9-12
3918 LPGA Blvd 32124 386-253-5213
Pat LaMorte, prin. Fax 252-6101
Halifax Academy 100/4-12
275 N Williamson Blvd 32114 386-252-9557
Joseph Dougherty M.A., prin. Fax 252-9414
Halifax Medical Center Post-Sec.
PO Box 2830 32120 386-254-4065
Keiser University Post-Sec.
1800 Business Park Blvd 32114 386-274-5060
Phoenix East Aviation Post-Sec.
561 Pearl Harbor Dr 32114 386-258-0703

De Bary, Volusia, Pop. 19,046
Volusia County SD
Supt. — See De Land
Highbanks Learning Center 50/Alt
336 E Highbanks Rd 32713 386-968-0039
Dr. Jerry Picott, prin.

Deerfield Beach, Broward, Pop. 72,542
Broward County SD
Supt. — See Fort Lauderdale
Deerfield Beach HS 2,400/9-12
910 SW 15th St 33441 754-322-0650
Jon Marlow, prin. Fax 322-0780
Deerfield Beach MS 1,200/6-8
701 SE 6th Ave 33441 754-322-3300
Francine Baugh, prin. Fax 322-3385

South Florida Bible College Post-Sec.
1100 S Federal Hwy 33441 954-545-4500
Zion Lutheran Christian S 500/PK-12
959 SE 6th Ave 33441 954-421-3146
Joann Halem, prin. Fax 421-4250

De Funiak Springs, Walton, Pop. 5,054
Walton County SD 8,000/PK-12
145 S Park St Ste 2 32435 850-892-1100
Russell Hughes, supt. Fax 892-1191
www.walton.k12.fl.us
Emerald Coast Technical College Vo/Tech
761 N 20th St 32433 850-892-1240
Charlie Morse, dir. Fax 892-1249
Walton HS 700/9-12
449 Walton Rd 32433 850-892-1270
Janet Currid, prin. Fax 892-1279
Walton Learning Center 50/Alt
286 Gene Hurley Rd 32435 850-892-1100
Ray Sansom, dir. Fax 892-8584
Walton MS 700/6-8
605 Bruce Ave 32435 850-892-1281
Jason Campbell, prin. Fax 892-1289
Other Schools – See Freeport, Paxton, Santa Rosa Beach

De Land, Volusia, Pop. 26,549
Volusia County SD 60,500/PK-12
PO Box 2118 32721 386-734-7190
James Russell, supt. Fax 822-6790
myvolusiaschools.org
DeLand HS 2,300/9-12
800 N Hill Ave 32724 386-822-6909
Mitch Moyer, prin. Fax 626-0556
DeLand MS 1,100/6-8
1400 Aquarius Ave 32724 386-822-5678
William Dunnigan, prin. Fax 822-6583
Southwestern MS 700/6-8
605 W New Hampshire Ave 32720 386-822-6815
Jacquese Slocum, prin. Fax 822-6708
Other Schools – See Daytona Beach, De Bary, Deltona, New Smyrna Beach, Orange City, Ormond Beach, Pierson, Port Orange

---

Florida Technical College Post-Sec.
1199 S Woodland Blvd 32720 386-734-3303
Lighthouse Christian Prep Academy 200/K-12
126 S Ridgewood Ave 32720 386-734-5380
Paul Bryan, admin. Fax 734-5627
Stetson University Post-Sec.
421 N Woodland Blvd 32723 386-822-7000

Delray Beach, Palm Beach, Pop. 59,547
Palm Beach County SD
Supt. — See West Palm Beach
Atlantic Community HS 2,100/9-12
2455 W Atlantic Ave 33445 561-243-1500
Tara Dellegrotti, prin. Fax 243-1532
Carver Community MS 900/6-8
101 Barwick Rd 33445 561-638-2100
Kiwana Prophete, prin. Fax 638-2181
Village Academy 800/K-12
400 SW 12th Ave 33444 561-243-6100
Latoya Dixon, prin. Fax 243-6150

American Heritage S Boca Delray 1,200/PK-12
6200 Linton Blvd 33484 561-495-7272
Cambridge Institute Allied Health/Tech Post-Sec.
5150 Linton Blvd Ste 340 33484 561-381-4990

Deltona, Volusia, Pop. 83,518
Volusia County SD
Supt. — See De Land
Deltona HS 1,700/9-12
100 Wolf Pack Run 32725 386-575-4153
Carolyn Carbonell, prin. Fax 968-0014
Deltona MS 1,100/6-8
250 Enterprise Rd 32725 386-575-4150
Dr. Rick Inge, prin. Fax 968-0015
Galaxy MS 1,100/6-8
2400 Eustace Ave 32725 386-575-4144
Patricia Corr, prin. Fax 968-0016
Heritage MS 1,200/6-8
1001 Parnell Ct 32738 386-575-4113
Thomas Vaughan, prin. Fax 708-0020
Pine Ridge HS 1,600/9-12
926 Howland Blvd 32738 386-575-4195
John Atkinson, prin. Fax 688-9502

Deltona Christian S 200/PK-12
1200 Providence Blvd 32725 386-574-1971
Trinity Christian Academy 600/PK-12
875 Elkcam Blvd 32725 386-789-4515
Dr. Dennis Robinson, hdmstr. Fax 789-0210

Destin, Okaloosa, Pop. 11,900
Okaloosa County SD
Supt. — See Fort Walton Beach
Destin MS 700/5-8
4608 Legendary Marina Dr 32541 850-833-7655
Grant Meyer, prin. Fax 833-7677

Doral, Miami-Dade, Pop. 45,331
Miami-Dade County SD
Supt. — See Miami
Reagan/Doral HS 2,100/9-12
8600 NW 107th Ave, 305-805-1900
Juan Boue, prin. Fax 805-1901
School for Advanced Studies West 11-12
3800 NW 115th Ave, 305-237-0510
Dr. Omar Monteagudo, prin. Fax 237-0511

Divine Savior Lutheran Academy 400/PK-12
10311 NW 58th St, 305-597-4545
Timothy Biesterfeld, head sch Fax 597-4077
Miami-Dade College Post-Sec.
3800 NW 115th Ave, 305-237-8000
Millenia Atlantic University Post-Sec.
3801 NW 97th Ave, 786-331-1000
Polytechnic University of Puerto Rico Post-Sec.
8180 NW 36th St Ste 401, 305-418-4220
San Ignacio College Post-Sec.
10395 NW 41st St Ste 125, 305-629-2929

Dover, Hillsborough, Pop. 3,664
Hillsborough County SD
Supt. — See Tampa
Strawberry Crest HS 2,200/9-12
4691 Gallagher Rd 33527 813-707-7522
David Brown, prin. Fax 707-7526

Dundee, Polk, Pop. 3,628
Polk County SD
Supt. — See Bartow
Dundee Ridge Middle Academy 1,000/6-8
5555 Lake Trask Rd 33838 863-419-3088
Stacy Gideons, prin. Fax 419-3157
Woods Opportunity Center 100/Alt
213 Lake Ave 33838 863-421-3325
Rodney Bellamy, prin. Fax 421-3390

Dunedin, Pinellas, Pop. 34,705
Pinellas County SD
Supt. — See Largo
Dunedin Highland MS 1,100/6-8
70 Patricia Ave 34698 727-469-4112
Chris Bates, prin. Fax 469-4115
Dunedin HS 1,500/9-12
1651 Pinehurst Rd 34698 727-469-4100
Kyle Johnson, prin. Fax 469-4143

Dunnellon, Marion, Pop. 1,711
Marion County SD
Supt. — See Ocala
Dunnellon HS 1,100/9-12
10055 SW 180th Avenue Rd 34432 352-465-6745
Stephen Ayres, prin. Fax 465-6746
Dunnellon MS 600/6-8
21005 Chestnut St 34431 352-465-6720
Delbert Smallridge, prin. Fax 465-6721

Dunnellon Christian Academy 200/PK-12
20831 Powell Rd 34431 352-489-7716
Kristy Nelson, admin. Fax 489-5760

Eagle Lake, Polk, Pop. 2,207
Polk County SD
Supt. — See Bartow
Lake Region HS 1,900/9-12
1995 Thunder Rd 33839 863-297-3099
Deborah Kindel, prin. Fax 297-3097

Eastpoint, Franklin, Pop. 2,298
Franklin County SD 1,200/K-12
85 School Rd Ste 1 32328 850-670-2810
Nina Marks, supt. Fax 670-8579
www.franklincountyschools.org
Franklin County S 900/K-12
1250 US Highway 98 32328 850-670-2800
Chip Clatto, prin. Fax 670-2801
Franklin County Adult S Adult
85 School Rd Ste 1 32328 850-670-2810
Nick O'Grady, dir. Fax 670-8579

El Portal, Miami-Dade, Pop. 2,243
Miami-Dade County SD
Supt. — See Miami
Academy for Community Education 100/Alt
8950 NW 2nd Ave 33150 305-460-2946
Dr. Deborah Carter, prin. Fax 460-2944

Englewood, Sarasota, Pop. 14,723
Charlotte County SD
Supt. — See Port Charlotte
Lemon Bay HS 1,300/9-12
2201 Placida Rd 34224 941-474-7702
Bob Bedford, prin. Fax 475-5260

Estero, Lee, Pop. 22,447
Lee County SD
Supt. — See Fort Myers
Estero HS 1,700/9-12
21900 River Ranch Rd 33928 239-947-9400
Clayton Simmons, prin. Fax 947-5017

Eustis, Lake, Pop. 18,227
Lake County SD
Supt. — See Tavares
Eustis HS - Curtright Campus 400/9-9
1801 Bates Ave 32726 352-589-1510
Nancy Velez, prin. Fax 589-1605
Eustis MS 1,000/6-8
18725 Bates Ave 32736 352-357-3366
Johnathan Owens, prin. Fax 357-5963
Eustis SHS 900/10-12
1300 E Washington Ave 32726 352-357-4147
Nancy Velez, prin. Fax 357-7449

Lake Technical Center Post-Sec.
2001 Kurt St 32726 352-589-2250

Everglades City, Collier
Collier County SD
Supt. — See Naples
Everglades City S 200/PK-12
PO Box 170 34139 239-377-9800
James Ragusa, prin. Fax 377-9801

Fernandina Beach, Nassau, Pop. 11,315
Nassau County SD 11,200/PK-12
1201 Atlantic Ave 32034 904-491-9900
Kathy Burns, supt. Fax 277-9042
www.nassau.k12.fl.us
Fernandina Beach HS 900/9-12
435 Citrona Dr 32034 904-491-7937
Dr. Spencer Lodree, prin. Fax 277-3754
Fernandina Beach MS 600/6-8
315 Citrona Dr 32034 904-491-7938
Dr. John Mazzella, prin. Fax 261-8919
Nassau County Adult S Adult
1201 Atlantic Ave 32034 904-548-1750
Brent Lemond, prin. Fax 548-4499
Other Schools – See Callahan, Hilliard, Yulee

Fern Park, Seminole, Pop. 7,563

Lincoln Tech Fern Park Campus Post-Sec.
7275 Estapona Cir 32730 407-673-7406

Florahome, Putnam
Putnam County SD
Supt. — See Palatka
Roberts JSHS 200/7-12
901 State Road 100 32140 386-659-1737
Dr. Melissa Coleman, prin. Fax 659-1986

Fort Lauderdale, Broward, Pop. 162,648
Broward County SD 251,700/PK-12
600 SE 3rd Ave 33301 754-321-0000
Robert Runcie, supt. Fax 321-2701
www.browardschools.com
Dandy MS 1,100/6-8
2400 NW 26th St 33311 754-322-3200
Shernette Grant, prin. Fax 322-3285
Dillard MSHS 1,900/6-12
2501 NW 11th St 33311 754-322-0800
Cassandra Robinson, prin. Fax 322-0930
Fort Lauderdale HS 2,100/9-12
1600 NE 4th Ave 33305 754-322-1100
Priscilla Ribeiro, prin. Fax 322-1230
New River MS 1,400/6-8
3100 Riverland Rd 33312 754-323-3600
Melinda Wessinger, prin. Fax 323-3685
Pine Ridge Education Center 100/Alt
1251 SW 42nd Ave 33317 754-321-7250
Belinda Hope, prin. Fax 321-7290
Sheridan Technical Center Vo/Tech
3775 SW 16th St 33312 754-321-7450
Daniel Boegli, prin. Fax 321-7490
Stranahan HS 1,600/9-12
1800 SW 5th Pl 33312 754-323-2100
Michelle Padura, prin. Fax 323-2230
Sunrise MS 1,300/6-8
1750 NE 14th St 33304 754-322-4700
Michael Walker, prin. Fax 322-4785
Whiddon-Rodgers Education Center 1,100/Alt
700 SW 26th St 33315 754-321-7550
Wylie Howard, prin. Fax 321-7590
Other Schools – See Coconut Creek, Cooper City, Coral Springs, Dania Beach, Davie, Deerfield Beach, Hallandale Beach, Hollywood, Lauderdale Lakes, Lauderhill, Margate, Miramar, North Lauderdale, Oakland Park, Parkland, Pembroke Pines, Plantation, Pompano Beach, Sunrise, Tamarac, Weston

---

Alternative Education Foundation Prep S 200/PK-12
4650 SW 61st Ave 33314 954-581-8222
Art Institute of Fort Lauderdale Post-Sec.
1799 SE 17th St 33316 954-463-3000
Atlantic Institute of Oriental Medicine Post-Sec.
100 E Broward Blvd Ste 100 33301 954-763-9840
Calvary Christian Academy 1,700/PK-12
2401 W Cypress Creek Rd 33309 954-905-5100
Jason Rachels, head sch Fax 653-2991
Cardinal Gibbons HS 1,100/9-12
2900 NE 47th St 33308 954-491-2900
Paul Ott, prin. Fax 772-1025
City College Post-Sec.
2000 W Commercial Blvd #200 33309 954-492-5353
Coral Ridge Training School Post-Sec.
2121 W Oakland Park Blvd 33311 954-714-0061
Cosmix School of Makeup Artistry Post-Sec.
2635 E Oakland Park Blvd 33306 954-564-4181
DeVry University Post-Sec.
600 Corporate Dr Ste 200 33334 954-938-3083
Faith Lutheran S 100/PK-12
1161 SW 30th Ave 33312 954-581-2918
Karen Johnson, prin. Fax 581-0029
Fortis College Post-Sec.
4850 W Oakland Park Ste 200 33313 954-587-7100
Fort Lauderdale Preparatory S 200/PK-12
3275 W Oakland Park Blvd 33311 954-485-7500
Keiser University Post-Sec.
1500 NW 49th St 33309 954-776-4456
Knox Theological Seminary Post-Sec.
5554 N Federal Hwy 33308 954-771-0376
Merryfield School of Pet Grooming Post-Sec.
5040 NE 13th Ave 33334 954-771-4030
NSU University S 1,900/PK-12
3375 SW 75th Ave 33314 954-262-4506
Dr. William Kopas, head sch
St. Thomas Aquinas HS 2,200/9-12
2801 SW 12th St 33312 954-581-0700
Dr. Denise Aloma, prin. Fax 581-8263
Sanford-Brown College Post-Sec.
1201 W Cypress Creek Rd 33309 954-308-7400
Strayer University Post-Sec.
2307 W Broward Blvd Ste 100 33312 954-745-6960
Westminster Academy 900/PK-12
5601 N Federal Hwy 33308 954-771-4600
Joel Satterly, hdmstr.

Fort Meade, Polk, Pop. 5,552
Polk County SD
Supt. — See Bartow
Fort Meade MSHS 700/6-12
700 Edgewood Dr N 33841 863-285-1180
Amy Hardee, prin. Fax 285-1186

Fort Myers, Lee, Pop. 60,807
Lee County SD 84,300/PK-12
2855 Colonial Blvd 33966 239-334-1102
Gregory Adkins Ed.D., supt. Fax 337-8301
www.leeschools.net
Cypress Lake HS 1,500/9-12
6750 Panther Ln 33919 239-481-2233
Angela Roles, prin. Fax 481-9838
Cypress Lake MS 800/6-8
8901 Cypress Lake Dr 33919 239-481-1533
Kelly Maniscalco, prin. Fax 481-3121
Dunbar HS 1,200/9-12
3800 Edison Ave 33916 239-461-5322
Carl Burnside, prin. Fax 461-5110
Dunbar MS 1,000/6-8
4750 Winkler Ave, 239-334-1357
Dr. Nathan Shaker, prin. Fax 334-7633
Fort Myers HS 1,900/9-12
2635 Cortez Blvd 33901 239-334-2167
David LaRosa, prin. Fax 334-3095
Fort Myers Middle Academy 400/6-8
3050 Central Ave 33901 239-936-1759
Ron Schuyler, prin. Fax 936-4350
Fort Myers Technical College Vo/Tech
3800 Michigan Ave 33916 239-334-4544
Brian Mangan, prin. Fax 332-4839
Lexington MS 1,000/6-8
16351 Summerlin Rd 33908 239-454-6130
Linda Berry, prin. Fax 489-3419
Oak Hammock MS 1,100/6-8
5321 Tice St 33905 239-693-0469
Jennifer Sneddon, prin. Fax 694-4089
Riverdale HS 1,900/6-12
2600 Buckingham Rd 33905 239-694-4141
Scott Cook, prin. Fax 694-3527
South Fort Myers HS 1,800/9-12
14020 Plantation Rd 33912 239-561-0060
Edward Mathews, prin. Fax 561-3612
Success Academy 200/Alt
3650 Michigan Ave 33916 239-334-3416
Dr. Marti Iovine, prin. Fax 332-7772
Three Oaks MS 1,000/6-8
18500 3 Oaks Pkwy, 239-267-5757
Mike Carson, prin. Fax 267-4007
Adult & Career Education Adult
2855 Colonial Blvd, 239-939-6310
Rita Effing, dir. Fax 334-4568
Dunbar Community S Adult
1857 High St 33916 239-334-2941
Ken Burns, admin. Fax 334-3519
Other Schools – See Bonita Springs, Cape Coral, Estero, Lehigh Acres, North Fort Myers

---

Bishop Verot Catholic HS 600/9-12
5598 Sunrise Dr 33919 239-274-6700
Dr. Denny Denison, prin. Fax 274-6798
Canterbury S 600/PK-12
8141 College Pkwy 33919 239-481-4323
Rick Kirschner, head sch Fax 481-8339
Edison State College Post-Sec.
8099 College Pkwy 33919 239-489-9300
Evangelical Christian S 800/PK-12
8237 Beacon Blvd 33907 239-936-3319
Florida Gulf Coast University Post-Sec.
10501 FGCU Blvd 33965 239-590-1000
Fort Myers Institute of Technology Post-Sec.
3800 Michigan Ave 33916 239-334-4544
Keiser University Post-Sec.
9100 Forum Corporate Pkwy 33905 239-277-1336
Rasmussen College Post-Sec.
9160 Forum Corporate # 100 33905 239-477-2100
Sonshine Christian Academy 200/PK-12
12925 Palm Beach Blvd 33905 239-694-8882
Loretta Dezarn, dir. Fax 694-8885
Southwest Florida Christian Academy 500/K-12
3750 Colonial Blvd, 239-936-8865
Lisa Kleinmann, hdmstr. Fax 936-7095
Southwest Florida College Post-Sec.
1685 Medical Ln 33907 239-939-4766
Sunstate Academy Post-Sec.
2040 Colonial Blvd 33907 239-278-1311

Fort Pierce, Saint Lucie, Pop. 40,874
St. Lucie County SD 40,600/PK-12
4204 Okeechobee Rd 34947 772-429-3600
E. Wayne Gent, supt. Fax 429-3916
www.stlucieschools.org
Forest Grove MS 900/6-8
3201 S 25th St 34981 772-468-5885
Terrance Davis, prin. Fax 595-1187
Fort Pierce Central HS 2,500/9-12
4101 S 25th St 34981 772-468-5888
Todd Smith, prin. Fax 468-5761
Fort Pierce Westwood HS 1,400/9-12
1801 Panther Ln 34947 772-468-5400
John Lynch, prin. Fax 468-5465
Lincoln Park Academy 1,800/6-12
1806 Avenue I 34950 772-468-5474
Henry Sanabria, prin. Fax 468-5485
McCarty MS 600/6-8
1201 Mississippi Ave 34950 772-468-5700
Lisa Sullivan, prin. Fax 468-5737
Performance Based Preparatory Academy Alt
2909 Delaware Ave 34947 772-468-5880
Keith Davis, admin. Fax 468-5795
Other Schools – See Port Saint Lucie

Aviator College of Aeronautical Sci/Tech Post-Sec.
3800 Saint Lucie Blvd 34946 800-635-9032
Fort Pierce Beauty Academy Post-Sec.
3028 S US 1 34982 772-464-4885
Indian River State College Post-Sec.
3209 Virginia Ave 34981 772-462-4772
John Carroll HS 400/9-12
3402 Delaware Ave 34947 772-464-5200
Ben Hopper, prin. Fax 464-5233
Liberty Baptist Academy 500/PK-12
3660 W Midway Rd 34981 772-461-2731
St. Andrew's Episcopal Academy 200/PK-12
210 S Indian River Dr 34950 772-461-7689
Suzanne Barry, head sch Fax 461-4683

Fort Walton Beach, Okaloosa, Pop. 18,836
Okaloosa County SD 29,800/PK-12
120 Lowery Pl SE 32548 850-833-3100
Mary Beth Jackson, supt. Fax 833-3436
www.okaloosaschools.com
Bruner MS 800/6-8
322 Holmes Blvd NW 32548 850-833-3266
Dr. Cynthia Hudson, prin. Fax 833-3434
Choctawhatachee HS 1,600/9-12
110 Racetrack Rd NW 32547 850-833-3614
Dr. Lee Hale, prin. Fax 833-3410
CHOICE HS & Technical Center Vo/Tech
1976 Lewis Turner Blvd 32547 850-833-3500
Jerry Sansom, prin. Fax 833-3466
Fort Walton Beach HS 1,700/9-12
400 Hollywood Blvd SW 32548 850-833-3300
John Spolski, prin. Fax 833-3332
Pryor MS 600/6-8
201 Racetrack Rd NW 32547 850-833-3613
Brooke Barron, prin. Fax 833-4276
Other Schools – See Baker, Crestview, Destin, Laurel Hill, Niceville, Shalimar, Valparaiso

---

Calvary Christian Academy 200/PK-12
535 Clifford St 32547 850-862-1414

Fort White, Columbia, Pop. 554
Columbia County SD
Supt. — See Lake City
Fort White HS 1,200/6-12
17828 SW State Road 47 32038 386-497-5952
Keith Couey, prin. Fax 497-5951

Freeport, Walton, Pop. 1,743
Walton County SD
Supt. — See De Funiak Springs
Freeport HS 300/9-12
12615 331 Business 32439 850-892-1200
Tripp Hope, prin. Fax 892-1209
Freeport MS 400/5-8
360 Kylea Laird Dr 32439 850-892-1221
Josh Harrison, prin. Fax 892-1229

Frostproof, Polk, Pop. 2,965
Polk County SD
Supt. — See Bartow
Frostproof MSHS 1,000/6-12
1000 N Palm Ave 33843 863-635-7809
Kyle Windham, prin. Fax 635-7812

Fruitland Park, Lake, Pop. 3,984

Holy Trinity Episcopal S 50/6-12
2201 Spring Lake Rd 34731 352-787-8855
Dr. Nancy Bryson Ed.D., head sch Fax 787-8063

Gainesville, Alachua, Pop. 121,031
Alachua County SD 26,800/PK-12
620 E University Ave 32601 352-955-7300
Dr. Owen Roberts, supt. Fax 955-6700
www.sbac.edu
Bishop MS 700/6-8
1901 NE 9th St 32609 352-955-6701
Mike Gamble, prin. Fax 316-7370
Buchholz HS 2,200/9-12
5510 NW 27th Ave 32606 352-955-6702
Mike DeLucas, prin. Fax 955-7285
Eastside HS 1,300/9-12
1201 SE 43rd St 32641 352-955-6704
Shane Andrew, prin. Fax 955-7291
Ft. Clarke MS 800/6-8
9301 NW 23rd Ave 32606 352-333-2800
Kelly Brill Jones, prin. Fax 333-2806
Gainesville HS 1,800/9-12
1900 NW 13th St 32609 352-955-6707
David Shelnutt, prin. Fax 955-7283
Kanapaha MS 1,000/6-8
5005 SW 75th St 32608 352-955-6960
Sherry Estes, prin. Fax 955-6858
Lincoln MS 700/6-8
1001 SE 12th St 32641 352-955-6711
Latroy Strappy, prin. Fax 955-7133
Professional Academies Magnet at Loften Vo/Tech
3000 E University Ave 32641 352-955-6839
Bill McElroy, prin. Fax 955-6999
Westwood MS 1,000/6-8
3215 NW 15th Ave 32605 352-955-6718
James TenBieg, prin. Fax 955-6897
Other Schools – See Alachua, Hawthorne, Newberry

Academy for Five Element Acupuncture Post-Sec.
305 SE 2nd Ave 32601 352-335-2332
Christian Life Academy 100/PK-12
12000 SW Archer Rd 32608 352-495-3040
City College Post-Sec.
7001 NW 4th Blvd 32607 352-335-4000

Cornerstone Academy 200/PK-12
PO Box 357430 32635 352-378-9337
Doug Lawson, hdmstr. Fax 378-7708
Countryside Christian S 100/PK-12
10926 NW 39th Ave 32606 352-332-1493
Dragon Rises College Oriental Medicine Post-Sec.
1000 NE 16th Ave Bldg F 32601 352-371-2833
Florida School of Massage Post-Sec.
6421 SW 13th St 32608 352-378-7891
Oak Hall Upper S 400/6-12
8009 SW 14th Ave 32607 352-332-3609
Richard Gehman, hdmstr. Fax 332-4975
Rock S 300/PK-12
9818 SW 24th Ave 32607 352-331-7625
St. Francis HS 200/9-12
4100 NW 115th Ter 32606 352-376-6545
Ernest Herrington, prin. Fax 248-0418
Santa Fe College Post-Sec.
3000 NW 83rd St 32606 352-395-5000
University of Florida Post-Sec.
PO Box 114000 32611 352-392-3261

Gibsonton, Hillsborough, Pop. 13,940
Hillsborough County SD
Supt. — See Tampa
East Bay HS 2,300/9-12
7710 Old Big Bend Rd 33534 813-671-5134
Maria Gsell, prin. Fax 671-5139
Eisenhower MS 1,200/6-8
7620 Old Big Bend Rd 33534 813-671-5121
Fax 671-5039

Glen Saint Mary, Baker, Pop. 430
Baker County SD
Supt. — See Macclenny
Baker County HS 1,200/9-12
1 Wildcat Dr 32040 904-259-6286
Allen Murphy, prin. Fax 259-5617

Gotha, Orange, Pop. 1,873

Central Florida Preparatory S 200/PK-12
1450 Citrus Oaks Ave 34734 407-290-8073
Rowena Flanders-Ramos, dir. Fax 298-6443
Crenshaw S 50/PK-12
2342 Hempel Ave 34734 407-757-2241
Brenda Crenshaw, head sch Fax 613-5845

Graceville, Jackson, Pop. 2,229
Holmes County SD
Supt. — See Bonifay
Poplar Springs S 400/PK-12
3726 Atomic Dr 32440 850-263-6260
Gordon Wells, prin. Fax 263-1252

Jackson County SD
Supt. — See Marianna
Graceville JSHS 300/6-12
5539 Brown St 32440 850-263-4451
Julie Burdeshaw, prin. Fax 263-3605

The Baptist College of Florida Post-Sec.
5400 College Dr 32440 800-328-2660

Greenacres, Palm Beach, Pop. 36,906
Palm Beach County SD
Supt. — See West Palm Beach
Leonard HS 3,000/9-12
4701 10th Ave N 33463 561-641-1200
Edward Tierney, prin. Fax 491-8350
Swain MS 1,200/6-8
5332 Lake Worth Rd 33463 561-649-6900
James Thomas, prin. Fax 649-6906
Tradewinds MS 1,200/6-8
5090 S Haverhill Rd 33463 561-493-6400
Rebecca Subin, prin. Fax 493-6410

Greenacres Christian Academy 100/PK-12
4982 Cambridge St 33463 561-965-0363
Southeastern College Post-Sec.
6812 Forest Hill Blvd # D1 33413 561-433-2330

Green Cove Springs, Clay, Pop. 6,779
Clay County SD 34,800/PK-12
900 Walnut St 32043 904-284-6500
Addison Davis, supt. Fax 284-6525
www.oneclay.net
Bannerman Learning Center 200/Alt
608 Mill St 32043 904-529-2100
Mike Elia, prin. Fax 529-1025
Clay HS 1,400/9-12
2025 State Road 16 W 32043 904-529-3000
Cary Dicks, prin. Fax 529-3214
Green Cove Springs JHS 800/7-8
1220 Bonaventure Ave 32043 904-336-5175
Jen Halter, prin. Fax 336-6563
Lake Asbury JHS 1,100/7-8
2851 Sandridge Rd 32043 904-291-5582
Becky Murphy, prin. Fax 291-5593
Other Schools – See Keystone Heights, Middleburg, Orange Park, Starke

Groveland, Lake, Pop. 8,373
Lake County SD
Supt. — See Tavares
Gray MS 1,000/6-8
205 E Magnolia St 34736 352-429-3322
Pam Chateauneuf, prin. Fax 429-0133
South Lake HS 1,600/9-12
15600 Silver Eagle Rd 34736 352-394-2100
Steven Benson, prin. Fax 394-1972

Gulf Breeze, Santa Rosa, Pop. 5,682
Santa Rosa County SD
Supt. — See Milton
Gulf Breeze HS 1,500/9-12
675 Gulf Breeze Pkwy 32561 850-916-4100
Dan Brothers, prin. Fax 916-4109
Gulf Breeze MS 900/6-8
649 Gulf Breeze Pkwy 32561 850-934-4080
Michael Brandon, prin. Fax 934-4085
Woodlawn Beach MS 1,000/6-8
1500 Woodlawn Way 32563 850-934-4010
Victor Lowrimore, prin. Fax 934-4015

Gulfport, Pinellas, Pop. 11,800
Pinellas County SD
Supt. — See Largo
Boca Ciega HS 1,600/9-12
924 58th St S 33707 727-893-2780
Michael Vigue, prin. Fax 893-1382

Haines City, Polk, Pop. 20,261
Polk County SD
Supt. — See Bartow
Boone MS 800/6-8
225 S 22nd St 33844 863-421-3302
Sharon Chipman, prin. Fax 421-3305
Haines City HS 2,400/9-12
2800 Hornet Dr 33844 863-421-3281
Adam Lane, prin. Fax 421-3283
Haines City HS - IB 200/9-12
2800 Hornet Dr 33844 863-419-3371
Adam Lane, prin. Fax 419-3373
Jenkins Academy of Technology 500/6-8
701 Ledwith Ave 33844 863-421-3267
Brad Tarver, prin. Fax 421-3269

Landmark Christian S 200/PK-12
2020 E Hinson Ave 33844 863-422-2037

Hallandale Beach, Broward, Pop. 36,609
Broward County SD
Supt. — See Fort Lauderdale
Hallandale HS 1,300/9-12
720 NW 9th Ave, 754-323-0900
Mark Howard, prin. Fax 323-1030
Lanier-James Education Center 100/Alt
1050 NW 7th Ct, 754-321-7350
Kelvin Lee, prin. Fax 321-7390
Perry Education Center Adult
1000 SW 3rd St, 754-321-7050
Bardetta Haygood, prin. Fax 321-7135

Havana, Gadsden, Pop. 1,746
Gadsden County SD
Supt. — See Quincy
East Gadsden HS 800/9-12
27001 Blue Star Hwy 32333 850-662-2300
Sonya Jackson, prin. Fax 539-2863

Tallavana Christian S 200/PK-12
5840 Havana Hwy 32333 850-539-5300

Hawthorne, Alachua, Pop. 1,398
Alachua County SD
Supt. — See Gainesville
Hawthorne MSHS 300/6-12
21403 SE 69th Ave 32640 352-481-1900
Libby Hartwell, prin. Fax 481-4859

Hialeah, Miami-Dade, Pop. 224,295
Miami-Dade County SD
Supt. — See Miami
American HS 2,200/9-12
18350 NW 67th Ave 33015 305-557-3770
Francisco Garnica, prin. Fax 828-7380
Filer MS 1,100/6-8
531 W 29th St 33012 305-822-6601
Emirce Ladaga, prin. Fax 822-2063
Hialeah HS 2,900/9-12
251 E 47th St 33013 305-822-1500
Herberto Sanchez, prin. Fax 828-5513
Hialeah-Miami Lakes HS 1,700/9-12
7977 W 12th Ave 33014 305-823-1330
Lisa Garcia, prin. Fax 362-4188
Hialeah MS 900/6-8
6027 E 7th Ave 33013 305-681-3527
Nelson Gonzalez, prin. Fax 681-6225
Marti MAST 6-12 Academy 500/6-12
5701 W 24th Ave 33016 305-557-5931
Jose Enriquez, prin. Fax 556-6917
Palm Springs MS 1,200/6-9
1025 W 56th St 33012 305-821-2460
Leonard Torres, prin. Fax 828-3987
Westland Hialeah HS 2,200/9-12
4000 W 18th Ave 33012 305-818-3000
Giovanna Blanco, prin. Fax 818-3002
American Adult Education Adult
18350 NW 67th Ave 33015 305-557-3770
Alexis Cazanas, prin. Fax 827-7935
Hialeah HS Adult Education Center Adult
251 E 47th St 33013 305-822-1500
Manuel Gonzalez, prin. Fax 821-6018
Hialeah-Miami Lakes Adult Ed Center Adult
7977 W 12th Ave 33014 305-823-1330
Alexis Cazanas, prin. Fax 828-8929

Advance Science Institute Post-Sec.
3750 W 12th Ave 33012 305-827-5452
American Christian S 100/PK-12
5888 W 20th Ave 33016 305-827-6544
Beauty Academy of South Florida Post-Sec.
1305 W 49th St 33012 305-817-3577
Beauty Schools of America Post-Sec.
1060 W 49th St 33012 305-362-9003
Champagnat Catholic S 300/6-12
1851 Palm Ave 33010 305-888-3760
Nuria Allonza-Sanchez, prin. Fax 883-1174
College of Business & Technology Post-Sec.
935 W 49th St 33012 305-764-3165
Compu-Med Vocational Careers Post-Sec.
2900 W 12th Ave 3rd Flr 33012 305-888-9200
Edison Private S 400/PK-12
3720 E 4th Ave 33013 305-824-0303
Florida Career College Post-Sec.
3750 W 18th Ave 33012 305-825-3231
Florida National University Post-Sec.
4425 W 20th Ave 33012 305-821-3333
Florida National University Post-Sec.
4206 W 12th Ave 33012 305-231-3326
Florida National University Online Post-Sec.
4425 W 20th Ave 33012 305-821-3333
Futura Career Institute Post-Sec.
4512 W 12th Ave 33012 305-825-7660
Horeb Christian S 200/PK-12
795 W 68th St 33014 305-557-6811
La Belle Beauty School Post-Sec.
1495 W 49th St 33012 305-558-0562

Lincoln-Marti S 300/1-12
1750 E 4th Ave 33010 305-884-1570
Miami-Dade College Post-Sec.
1780 W 49th St 33012 305-237-8700
Nouvelle Institute Post-Sec.
500 W 49th St Fl 2 33012 305-557-3017
Total International Career Institute Post-Sec.
3060 W 12th Ave 33012 305-681-6622
Trinity Christian Academy 100/PK-12
1498 W 84th St 33014 305-819-8999
Joseph N. Jimenez, dir. Fax 819-2554

Hialeah Gardens, Miami-Dade, Pop. 21,719
Miami-Dade County SD
Supt. — See Miami
Hialeah Gardens HS 3,100/9-12
11700 Hialeah Gardens Blvd 33018 305-698-5000
Dr. Louis Algaze, prin. Fax 698-5001
Hialeah Gardens MS 1,800/6-8
11690 NW 92nd Ave 33018 305-817-0017
Maritza Jimenez, prin. Fax 817-0018

Hilliard, Nassau, Pop. 3,050
Nassau County SD
Supt. — See Fernandina Beach
Hilliard MSHS 800/6-12
1 Flashes Ave 32046 904-491-7940
Tammy Johnson, prin. Fax 845-7662

Hobe Sound, Martin, Pop. 11,387

Hobe Sound Bible College Post-Sec.
11298 SE Gomez Ave 33455 772-546-5534
Hobe Sound Christian Academy 200/PK-12
PO Box 1065 33475 772-545-1455
Pine S 200/K-12
12350 SE Federal Hwy 33455 772-675-7005
Phyllis Parker, hdmstr. Fax 675-7006

Holiday, Pasco, Pop. 21,981
Pasco County SD
Supt. — See Land O Lakes
Anclote HS 1,300/9-12
1540 Sweetbriar Dr 34691 727-246-3000
Elaine Williams, prin. Fax 246-3091
Smith MS 1,100/6-8
1410 Sweetbriar Dr 34691 727-246-3200
Joel DiVincent, prin. Fax 246-3291

Hollywood, Broward, Pop. 137,985
Broward County SD
Supt. — See Fort Lauderdale
Apollo MS 1,200/6-8
6800 Arthur St 33024 754-323-2900
Shawn Aycock, prin. Fax 323-2985
Attucks MS 700/6-8
3500 N 22nd Ave 33020 754-323-3000
Errol Evans, prin. Fax 323-3085
Driftwood MS 1,500/6-8
2751 NW 70th Ter 33024 754-323-3100
Steven Williams, prin. Fax 323-3185
Hollywood Hills HS 2,100/9-12
5400 Stirling Rd 33021 754-323-1050
Lourdes Gonzalez, prin. Fax 323-1180
McArthur HS 2,200/9-12
6501 Hollywood Blvd 33024 754-323-1200
Todd LaPace, prin. Fax 323-1330
McNicol MS 900/6-8
1602 S 27th Ave 33020 754-323-3400
Melissa Gurreonero, prin. Fax 323-3485
South Broward HS 2,000/9-12
1901 N Federal Hwy 33020 754-323-1800
Olayemi Awofadeju, prin. Fax 323-1930

Chaminade-Madonna College Prep HS 600/9-12
500 E Chaminade Dr 33021 954-989-5150
Raiza Echemendia, prin. Fax 983-4663
City College Post-Sec.
6565 Taft St Ste 200 33024 954-744-1777
Hollywood Christian S 300/PK-12
1708 N State Road 7 33021 954-322-4375
Dr. Mike Hill, head sch Fax 322-4383
Lamb Athletic and Art Academy 100/K-12
1704 Buchanan St 33020 954-935-5023
Sha'arei Bina Torah Academy for Girls 50/6-12
2907 Taylor St 33020 954-927-5544
Rabbi Elchonon Abramchik, head sch Fax 927-3444
Sheridan Hills Christian S 500/PK-12
3751 Sheridan St 33021 954-966-7995
Eric Spee, head sch Fax 961-1359
Sheridan Technical Center Post-Sec.
5400 Sheridan St 33021 754-321-5400

Homestead, Miami-Dade, Pop. 59,655
Miami-Dade County SD
Supt. — See Miami
Center for International Education 9-12
900 NE 23rd Ave 33033 305-248-7911
Lisa Pizzimenti-Bradshaw, prin. Fax 248-3518
Homestead HS 1,700/9-12
2351 SE 12th Ave 33034 305-245-7000
Guillermo Munoz, prin. Fax 247-5757
Homestead MS 500/6-8
650 NW 2nd Ave 33030 305-247-4221
Keith Anderson, prin. Fax 247-1098
Medical Academy for Science & Technology 500/9-12
1220 NW 1st Ave 33030 305-257-4500
Lisa Noffo, prin. Fax 257-4501
Redland MS 500/6-8
16001 SW 248th St 33031 305-247-6112
Gregory Beckford, prin. Fax 248-0628
School for Advanced Studies - Homestead 100/11-12
500 College Ter 33030 305-237-5062
Dr. Omar Monteagudo, prin. Fax 237-5232
South Dade HS 3,300/9-12
28401 SW 167th Ave 33030 305-247-4244
Juan De Armas, prin. Fax 248-3867
South Dade MS 1,200/4-8
29100 SW 194th Ave 33030 305-224-5200
John Galardi, prin. Fax 224-5201
South Dade Skill Center Vo/Tech
28300 SW 152nd Ave 33033 305-247-7839
Dr. Susana Mauri, prin. Fax 247-2375

South Dade Technical S — Adult
109 NE 8th St 33030 — 305-248-5723
Dr. Susana Mauri, prin. — Fax 248-9164

Colonial Christian S — 200/PK-12
17105 SW 296th St 33030 — 305-246-8608
Faith Fellowship S — 50/PK-12
28945 SW 187th Ave 33030 — 305-246-5534
Monica Upegui B.A., prin. — Fax 246-5586
Miami-Dade College — Post-Sec.
500 College Ter 33030 — 305-237-5000
Redland Christian Academy — 300/PK-12
17700 SW 280th St 33031 — 305-247-7399
Daniel Carrillo M.A., admin. — Fax 247-1147

Hudson, Pasco, Pop. 12,006
Pasco County SD
Supt. — See Land O Lakes
Fivay HS — 1,400/9-12
12115 Chicago Ave 34669 — 727-246-4000
Marsha VanHook, prin. — Fax 246-4091
Hudson HS — 1,200/9-12
14410 Cobra Way 34669 — 727-774-4200
David LaRoche, prin. — Fax 774-4291
Hudson MS — 800/6-8
14540 Cobra Way 34669 — 727-774-8200
Joseph Musselman, prin. — Fax 774-8291

Grace Christian S — 100/K-12
9403 Scot St 34669 — 727-863-1825
Glenwood Pratt, prin. — Fax 862-4484

Immokalee, Collier, Pop. 23,830
Collier County SD
Supt. — See Naples
Immokalee HS — 1,400/9-12
701 Immokalee Dr 34142 — 239-377-1800
Ken Fairbanks, prin. — Fax 377-1801
Immokalee MS — 800/6-8
401 N 9th St 34142 — 239-377-4200
Abel Jaimes, prin. — Fax 377-4201
Immokalee Technical Center — Vo/Tech
508 N 9th St 34142 — 239-377-9900
Dorin Oxender, prin. — Fax 377-7101

Indialantic, Brevard, Pop. 2,676
Brevard County SD
Supt. — See Melbourne
Hoover MS — 600/7-8
2000 Hawk Haven Dr 32903 — 321-727-1611
Lena Wiebelt, prin. — Fax 725-0076

Indiantown, Martin, Pop. 6,057
Martin County SD
Supt. — See Stuart
Indiantown MS — 500/5-8
16303 SW Farm Rd 34956 — 772-597-2146
Jeff Raimann, prin. — Fax 597-5854

Interlachen, Putnam, Pop. 1,381
Putnam County SD
Supt. — See Palatka
Interlachen HS — 700/9-12
126 N County Road 315 32148 — 386-684-2116
Bryan Helms, prin. — Fax 684-3915
Price MS — 600/6-8
140 N County Road 315 32148 — 386-684-2113
Leah Lundy, prin. — Fax 684-3908

Inverness, Citrus, Pop. 7,057
Citrus County SD — 15,000/PK-12
1007 W Main St 34450 — 352-726-1931
Sandra Himmel, supt. — Fax 726-4418
www.citrus.k12.fl.us
Citrus HS — 1,500/9-12
600 W Highland Blvd 34452 — 352-726-2241
Rich Hilgert, prin. — Fax 249-2102
Inverness MS — 1,000/6-8
1950 Highway 41 N 34450 — 352-726-1471
Ernest Hopper, prin. — Fax 249-2133
Withlachoochee Technical College — Vo/Tech
1201 W Main St 34450 — 352-726-2430
Gloria Bishop, dir. — Fax 249-2157
Other Schools – See Citrus Springs, Crystal River, Lecanto

Inverness Christian Academy — 200/PK-12
4222 S Florida Ave 34450 — 352-726-3759

Islamorada, Monroe, Pop. 1,220

Island Christian S — 200/PK-12
83400 Overseas Hwy 33036 — 305-664-4933
Jodi Martin, prin. — Fax 664-8170

Jacksonville, Duval, Pop. 800,944
Duval County SD — 121,600/PK-12
1701 Prudential Dr 32207 — 904-390-2000
Dr. Nikolai Vitti Ed.D., supt. — Fax 390-2586
www.duvalschools.org
Anderson HS of the Arts — 1,200/9-12
2445 San Diego Rd 32207 — 904-346-5620
Jackie Cornelius, prin. — Fax 346-5636
Arlington MS — 700/6-8
8141 Lone Star Rd 32211 — 904-720-1680
Maysha Shelton, prin. — Fax 720-1702
Atlantic Coast HS — Vo/Tech
9735 R G Skinner Pkwy 32256 — 904-538-5120
Debra Lynch, prin. — Fax 538-5159
Bridge to Success Acad at W Jacksonville — Alt
2115 W Commonwealth Ave 32209 — 904-630-6592
Aleya Prier, prin.
Butler MS — 600/6-8
900 Acorn St 32209 — 904-630-6900
Truitte Moreland, prin. — Fax 630-6913
Darnell-Cookman MSHS — 1,200/6-12
1701 N Davis St 32209 — 904-630-6805
Carol Daniels, prin. — Fax 630-6811
Davis MS — 1,100/6-8
7050 Melvin Rd 32210 — 904-573-1060
Nidia Ashby, prin. — Fax 573-1066
DuPont MS — 800/6-8
2710 Dupont Ave 32217 — 904-739-5200
Marilyn Barnwell, prin. — Fax 739-5321
Englewood HS — 1,800/9-12
4412 Barnes Rd 32207 — 904-739-5212
Sara Bravo, prin. — Fax 739-5324
First Coast HS — 2,300/9-12
590 Duval Station Rd 32218 — 904-757-0080
Timothy Simmons, prin. — Fax 696-8721
Ft. Caroline MS — 700/6-8
3787 University Club Blvd 32277 — 904-745-4927
Meghan Green, prin. — Fax 745-4937
Gilbert MS — 500/6-8
1424 Franklin St 32206 — 904-630-6700
Jamelle Goodwin, prin. — Fax 630-6713
Grand Park Education Center — 200/Alt
2335 W 18th St 32209 — 904-630-6894
Tyrone Blue, prin. — Fax 630-6898
Highlands MS — 900/6-8
10913 Pine Estates Rd E 32218 — 904-696-8771
Jackie Simmons, prin. — Fax 696-8782
Jackson HS — 700/9-12
3816 N Main St 32206 — 904-630-6950
Evan Daniels, prin. — Fax 630-6955
Johnson College Prep MS — 1,100/6-8
3276 Norman E Thagard Blvd 32254 — 904-693-7600
Sharwonda Peek, prin. — Fax 693-7661
Kernan MS — 1,200/6-8
2271 Kernan Blvd S 32246 — 904-220-1350
Julie Hemphill, prin. — Fax 220-1355
Kirby-Smith MS — 1,000/6-8
2034 Hubbard St 32206 — 904-630-6600
Kenya Griffin, prin. — Fax 630-6605
Lake Shore MS — 1,200/6-8
2519 Bayview Rd 32210 — 904-381-7440
Christopher Begley, prin. — Fax 381-7437
Landmark MS — 1,200/6-8
101 Kernan Blvd N 32225 — 904-221-7125
David Gilmore, prin. — Fax 221-8847
Landon MS — 700/6-8
1819 Thacker Ave 32207 — 904-346-5650
Timothy Feagins, prin. — Fax 346-5657
LaVilla S of the Arts — 1,100/6-8
501 N Davis St 32202 — 904-633-6069
Lianna Knight, prin. — Fax 633-8089
Lee HS — 1,800/9-12
1200 McDuff Ave S 32205 — 904-381-3930
Scott Schneider, prin. — Fax 381-3945
Mandarin HS — 2,600/9-12
4831 Greenland Rd 32258 — 904-260-3911
Donna Richardson, prin. — Fax 260-5439
Mandarin MS — 1,300/6-8
5100 Hood Rd 32257 — 904-292-0555
Tonya Marx, prin. — Fax 260-5415
Northwestern MS — 400/6-8
2100 W 45th St 32209 — 904-924-3100
Shawn Platts, prin. — Fax 924-3284
Oceanway MS — 1,200/6-8
143 Oceanway Ave 32218 — 904-714-4680
Emily Kristansen, prin. — Fax 714-4685
Parker HS — 1,500/9-12
7301 Parker School Rd 32211 — 904-720-1650
Megan Pardue, prin. — Fax 720-1700
Paxon HS for Advanced Studies — 1,500/9-12
3239 Norman E Thagard Blvd 32254 — 904-693-7583
Royce Turner, prin. — Fax 693-7597
Peterson Academy of Technology — Vo/Tech
7450 Wilson Blvd 32210 — 904-573-1150
Jessica Parrish, prin. — Fax 573-3206
Raines HS — 1,000/9-12
3663 Raines Ave 32209 — 904-924-3049
Vincent Hall, prin. — Fax 924-3058
Randolph Academies of Technology — Vo/Tech
1157 Golfair Blvd 32209 — 904-924-3011
Cathy Barnes, prin. — Fax 924-3125
Ribault HS — 1,200/9-12
3701 Winton Dr 32208 — 904-924-3092
Christopher Jackson, prin. — Fax 924-3154
Ribault MS — 600/6-8
3610 Ribault Scenic Dr 32208 — 904-924-3062
Angela Maxey, prin. — Fax 924-3167
Rutherford Alternative Education Center — 100/Alt
1514 Hubbard St 32206 — 904-630-6782
Maurice Nesmith, prin. — Fax 630-6789
Sandalwood HS — 3,000/9-12
2750 John Prom Blvd 32246 — 904-646-5100
Vickie Schultz, prin. — Fax 646-5126
Schools for the Future Academy — 800/Alt
1824 N Pearl St 32206 — 904-354-7799
Vincent Foster, prin. — Fax 359-2637
Southside MS — 700/6-8
2948 Knights Ln E 32216 — 904-739-5238
Zeina Spaulding, prin. — Fax 739-5244
Stanton College Preparatory HS — 1,500/9-12
1149 W 13th St 32209 — 904-630-6760
Nongongoma Majova-Seane, prin. — Fax 630-6758
Stilwell MS — 900/6-8
7840 Burma Rd 32221 — 904-693-7523
Jennifer Campese, prin. — Fax 693-7539
Stuart MS — 900/6-8
4815 Wesconnett Blvd 32210 — 904-573-1000
Sadie Milliner-Smith, prin. — Fax 573-3213
Twin Lakes Academy MS — 1,300/6-8
8050 Point Meadows Dr 32256 — 904-538-0825
Tamara Tuschhoff, prin. — Fax 538-0840
Westside HS — 1,300/9-12
5530 Firestone Rd 32244 — 904-573-1170
Gregory Bostic, prin. — Fax 573-1177
White HS — 1,600/9-12
1700 Old Middleburg Rd N 32210 — 904-693-7620
Jason Bloom, prin. — Fax 693-7639
Wolfson HS — 1,300/9-12
7000 Powers Ave 32217 — 904-739-5265
Terry Connor, prin. — Fax 739-5272
Other Schools – See Atlantic Beach, Baldwin, Jacksonville Beach, Neptune Beach

---

Arlington Country Day S — 400/PK-12
5725 Fort Caroline Rd 32277 — 904-762-0123
Art Institute of Jacksonville — Post-Sec.
8775 Baypine Rd 32256 — 904-486-3000
ATP Flight School — Post-Sec.
855 St Johns Bluff Rd N 603 32225 — 800-255-2877
Baptist Medical Centers — Post-Sec.
800 Prudential Dr 32207 — 904-393-2001
Baptist/St. Vincent's Health System — Post-Sec.
1 Shircliff Way 32204 — 904-387-7300
Bishop John J. Snyder HS — 500/9-12
5001 Samaritan Way 32210 — 904-771-1029
David Yazdiya, prin. — Fax 908-8988
Bishop Kenny HS — 1,200/9-12
1055 Kingman Ave 32207 — 904-398-7545
Todd Orlando, prin. — Fax 398-5728
Bolles S - Bartrum Campus — 400/6-8
2264 Bartram Rd 32207 — 904-724-8850
David Farace, pres. — Fax 724-8862
Bolles S - San Jose Campus — 1,600/9-12
7400 San Jose Blvd 32217 — 904-733-9292
David Farace, pres. — Fax 739-9363
Cedar Creek Christian S — 300/PK-12
1372 Lane Ave S 32205 — 904-781-9151
Chamberlain College of Nursing — Post-Sec.
5200 Belfort Rd 32256 — 904-251-8100
Chatman's Early Learning Christian Acdmy — 200/PK-12
1614 Leonid Rd 32218 — 904-751-9803
Christ's Church Academy — 400/K-12
10850 Old Saint Augustine 32257 — 904-268-8667
Dr. Madison Nichols, head sch — Fax 880-3251
Concorde Career Institute — Post-Sec.
7259 Salisbury Rd 32256 — 904-725-0525
Cornerstone Christian S — 300/PK-12
9039 Beach Blvd 32216 — 904-730-5500
Donna Stables, prin. — Fax 730-5502
DeVry University — Post-Sec.
5200 Belfort Rd Ste 175 32256 — 904-367-4942
Eagle's View Academy — 400/K-12
7788 Ramona Blvd W 32221 — 904-786-1411
Scott Kinlaw, admin. — Fax 786-1445
Edward Waters College — Post-Sec.
1658 Kings Rd 32209 — 904-470-8000
Episcopal S of Jacksonville — 900/6-12
4455 Atlantic Blvd 32207 — 904-396-5751
Rev. Adam Greene, head sch — Fax 396-7209
Esprit De Corps Center for Learning — 200/K-12
9840 Wagner Rd 32219 — 904-924-2000
Dr. Jeannette Holmes-Vann, admin. — Fax 766-8870
Everest University - Jacksonville Campus — Post-Sec.
8226 Philips Hwy 32256 — 904-731-4949
First Coast Christian S — 600/PK-12
7587 Blanding Blvd 32244 — 904-777-3040
Richard Spain, admin. — Fax 777-3045
Florida Career College — Post-Sec.
6600 Youngerman Cir 32244 — 904-573-1900
Florida Coastal School of Law — Post-Sec.
8787 Baypine Rd 32256 — 904-680-7700
Florida State College — Post-Sec.
3939 Roosevelt Blvd 32205 — 904-381-3400
Florida State College — Post-Sec.
4501 Capper Rd 32218 — 904-766-6500
Florida State College — Post-Sec.
11901 Beach Blvd 32246 — 904-646-2111
Florida State College - Jacksonville — Post-Sec.
101 State St W 32202 — 904-646-2300
Fortis Institute — Post-Sec.
5995 University Blvd W #2 32216 — 904-443-6300
Foundation Academy — 200/PK-12
3675 San Pablo Rd S 32224 — 904-493-7300
Harvest Community S — 200/PK-12
2360 Saint Johns Bluff Rd S 32246 — 904-997-1882
Patty Wilcox, admin. — Fax 997-1862
Heart to Heart Christian Academy — 100/PK-12
8247 W Ramona Blvd 32221 — 904-783-8638
Dr. Juanita White, admin. — Fax 224-1183
Jacksonville University — Post-Sec.
2800 University Blvd N 32211 — 904-256-8000
Jones College — Post-Sec.
5353 Arlington Expy 32211 — 904-743-1122
Jones College — Post-Sec.
1195 Edgewood Ave S 32205 — 904-743-1122
J Tech Institute — Post-Sec.
8813 Western Way 32256 — 877-447-0442
Kaplan College — Post-Sec.
7450 Beach Blvd 32216 — 904-855-2400
Keiser University — Post-Sec.
6430 Southpoint Pkwy 32216 — 904-296-3440
Normandy Beauty School of Jacksonville — Post-Sec.
5373 Lenox Ave 32205 — 904-786-6250
North Florida Educational Institute — 300/PK-12
580 Lawton Ave 32208 — 904-764-0084
Old Plank Christian Academy — 200/PK-12
8964 Old Plank Rd 32220 — 904-783-4888
Parsons Christian Academy — 200/PK-12
5705 Fort Caroline Rd 32277 — 904-745-4588
Providence S — 1,400/PK-12
2701 Hodges Blvd 32224 — 904-223-5270
Don Barfield, head sch — Fax 223-3028
St. Luke's Hospital/Mayo Clinic — Post-Sec.
4201 Belfort Rd 32216 — 904-296-3733
Sanford-Brown Institute — Post-Sec.
10255 Fortune Pkwy Ste 501 32256 — 904-363-6221
Seacoast Christian Academy — 200/6-12
8057 Arlington Expy 32211 — 904-722-1738
Dr. Elton Brooke, prin. — Fax 725-5085
Shands Jacksonville Medical Center — Post-Sec.
655 W 8th St 32209 — 904-244-0411
Southeastern College — Post-Sec.
6700 Southpoint Pkwy # 400 32216 — 904-448-9499
Temple Christian Academy — 200/K-12
4200 Georgetown Rd 32210 — 904-778-8655
Trinity Baptist College — Post-Sec.
800 Hammond Blvd 32221 — 800-786-2206
Trinity Christian Academy — 1,500/PK-12
800 Hammond Blvd 32221 — 904-596-2400
Dr. Clay Lindstam, admin. — Fax 596-2531
Tulsa Welding School — Post-Sec.
3500 Southside Blvd 32216 — 904-646-9353
University Christian S — 500/PK-12
5520 University Blvd W 32216 — 904-737-6330
Heath Nivens, head sch — Fax 483-3572
University of North Florida — Post-Sec.
1 U N F Dr 32224 — 904-620-1000
Victory Christian Academy — 200/PK-12
10613 Lem Turner Rd 32218 — 904-764-7781
Virginia College — Post-Sec.
5940 Beach Blvd 32207 — 904-520-7400

Jacksonville Beach, Duval, Pop. 20,925
Duval County SD
Supt. — See Jacksonville

Fletcher MS 1,100/6-8
2000 3rd St N 32250 904-247-5929
Teresa Mowbray, prin. Fax 247-5940

Jasper, Hamilton, Pop. 4,513
Hamilton County SD 1,700/PK-12
5683 US Highway 129 S # 1 32052 386-792-1228
Thomas Moffses, supt. Fax 792-3681
www.hamiltonfl.com
Hamilton County HS 700/7-12
5683 US Highway 129 S 32052 386-792-6540
Kip McLeod, prin. Fax 792-6594

Corinth Christian Academy 100/K-12
7042 SW 41st Ave 32052 386-938-2270

Jay, Santa Rosa, Pop. 529
Santa Rosa County SD
Supt. — See Milton
Jay JSHS 400/7-12
3741 School St 32565 850-675-4507
Stephen Knowlton, prin. Fax 675-8573

Jensen Beach, Martin, Pop. 11,571
Martin County SD
Supt. — See Stuart
Jensen Beach HS 1,700/9-12
2875 NW Goldenrod Rd 34957 772-232-3500
Lori Vogel, prin. Fax 232-3699

Jupiter, Palm Beach, Pop. 54,490
Palm Beach County SD
Supt. — See West Palm Beach
Independence MS 1,300/6-8
4001 Greenway Dr 33458 561-799-7500
Kathy Koerner, prin. Fax 799-7505
Jupiter Community HS 2,700/9-12
500 Military Trl 33458 561-744-7900
Dr. Colleen Iannitti, prin. Fax 744-7978
Jupiter MS 1,200/6-8
15245 Military Trl 33458 561-745-7200
Lisa Hastey, prin. Fax 745-7242

Jupiter Christian S 600/PK-12
700 S Delaware Blvd 33458 561-746-7800
Daniel Steinfield, pres. Fax 746-1955

Key Biscayne, Miami-Dade, Pop. 12,269
Miami-Dade County SD
Supt. — See Miami
Maritime & Science Technology Academy 700/9-12
3979 Rickenbacker Cswy 33149 305-365-6278
Josephine Otero, prin. Fax 361-0996

Keystone Heights, Clay, Pop. 1,326
Clay County SD
Supt. — See Green Cove Springs
Keystone Heights JSHS 1,200/7-12
900 Orchid Ave, 352-473-2761
Angela Gentry, prin. Fax 473-5920

Key West, Monroe, Pop. 24,199
Monroe County SD 8,200/PK-12
241 Trumbo Rd 33040 305-293-1400
Mark Porter, supt. Fax 293-1407
keysschools.schoolfusion.us/
Key West HS 1,200/9-12
2100 Flagler Ave 33040 305-293-1549
Amber Bosco, prin. Fax 293-1547
Other Schools – See Marathon, Tavernier

Florida Keys Community College Post-Sec.
5901 College Rd 33040 305-296-9081

Kissimmee, Osceola, Pop. 58,578
Osceola County SD 56,300/PK-12
817 Bill Beck Blvd 34744 407-870-4600
Debra Pace, supt. Fax 870-4010
www.osceolaschools.net
Denn John MS 1,100/6-8
2001 Denn John Ln 34744 407-935-3560
Hank Hoyle, prin. Fax 935-3572
Discovery IS 1,200/6-8
5350 San Miguel Rd 34758 407-343-7300
Alan Ramos, prin. Fax 343-7310
Gateway HS 2,500/9-12
93 Panther Paws Trl 34744 407-935-3600
Larry Meadows, prin. Fax 935-3609
Horizon MS 1,200/6-8
2020 Ham Brown Rd 34746 407-943-7240
Michelle Henninger, prin. Fax 943-7250
Kissimmee MS 1,300/6-8
2410 Dyer Blvd 34741 407-870-0857
Gary Weeden, prin. Fax 870-5669
Liberty HS 1,900/9-12
4250 Pleasant Hill Rd 34746 407-933-3910
Evelith Olmeda-Garcia, prin. Fax 933-9990
Neptune MS 1,400/6-8
2727 Neptune Rd 34744 407-935-3500
Joumana Moukaddam, prin. Fax 935-3519
New Beginnings Educational Center 200/Alt
2599 W Vine St 34741 407-348-4466
Nina Wehmeyer, prin. Fax 348-4069
Osceola County S for the Arts 900/6-12
3151 N Orange Blossom Trl 34744 407-931-4803
Chundra Evens, prin. Fax 931-3019
Osceola HS 2,600/9-12
420 S Thacker Ave 34741 407-518-5400
Edward Jones, prin. Fax 943-7909
Parkway MS 1,000/6-8
857 Florida Pkwy 34743 407-344-7000
Megan Gould, prin. Fax 348-2797
PATHS @ TECO Vo/Tech
501 Simpson Rd 34744 407-518-5407
Paula Evans, prin. Fax 344-2467
Poinciana HS 1,500/9-12
2300 S Poinciana Blvd 34758 407-870-4860
Michael Meechin, prin. Fax 870-0382
Technical Education Center Vo/Tech
1030 Cypress Pkwy 34759 407-343-7341
Thomas Ott, prin. Fax 870-1417
Technical Education Center Vo/Tech
501 Simpson Rd 34744 407-344-5080
Thomas Ott, dir. Fax 344-5089

Zenith Learning Academy 100/Alt
2218 E Irlo Bronson Mem Hwy 34744 407-846-3976
Robert Studly, prin. Fax 933-9920
Adult Learning Center Adult
2320 New Beginnings Rd 34744 407-518-8140
Beth Rattie, dir. Fax 518-8141
Adult Learning Center Adult
1030 Cypress Pkwy 34759 407-343-7341
Beth Rattie, prin. Fax 870-1417
Other Schools – See Celebration, Saint Cloud

American Inst Coll of Health Professions Post-Sec.
1420 Celebration Blvd 34747 407-738-4488
City of Life Christian Academy 400/PK-12
2874 E Irlo Bronson Mem Hwy 34744 407-847-5184
Dr. Kathy Harkema, prin. Fax 870-2679
Florida Technical College Post-Sec.
3831 W Vine St 34741 407-483-5700
Freedomland Christian Academy PK-12
1210 N Main St 34744 407-935-9088
Heritage Christian S 500/K-12
1500 E Vine St 34744 407-847-4087
Johnson University Florida Post-Sec.
1011 Bill Beck Blvd 34744 407-847-8966
Life Christian Academy 300/PK-12
2269 Partin Settlement Rd 34744 407-847-8222
Jessica Wilkinson, prin. Fax 932-4431
North Kissimmee Christian S 100/PK-12
425 W Donegan Ave 34741 407-847-2877
PHA Preparatory S 200/PK-12
1820 Armstrong Blvd 34741 407-343-1905
Southland Christian S 400/PK-12
2440 Fortune Rd 34744 407-201-7999

LaBelle, Hendry, Pop. 4,611
Hendry County SD 6,800/PK-12
PO Box 1980 33975 863-674-4642
Paul K. Puletti, supt. Fax 674-4090
www.hendry-schools.org
La Belle HS 1,000/9-12
4050 E Cowboy Way 33935 863-674-4120
David Kelley, prin. Fax 674-4571
La Belle MS 700/6-8
8000 E Cowboy Way 33935 863-674-4646
Kenneth Pickles, prin. Fax 674-4645
Other Schools – See Clewiston

Lake Alfred, Polk, Pop. 4,919
Polk County SD
Supt. — See Bartow
Lake Alfred-Addair MS 800/6-8
925 N Buena Vista Dr 33850 863-295-5988
Julie Grice, prin. Fax 295-5989

Lake Butler, Union, Pop. 1,869
Union County SD 2,300/PK-12
55 SW 6th St 32054 386-496-2045
Carlton Faulk, supt. Fax 496-2580
www.union.k12.fl.us
Lake Butler MS 700/5-8
150 SW 6th St 32054 386-496-3046
Carolyn Parrish, prin. Fax 496-4352
Union County HS 600/9-12
1000 S Lake Ave 32054 386-496-3040
Mike Ripplinger, prin. Fax 496-4187
Union County Adult HS Adult
208 SE 6th St 32054 386-496-1300
Barry Sams, dir. Fax 496-4919

Lake City, Columbia, Pop. 11,774
Columbia County SD 9,900/PK-12
372 W Duval St 32055 386-755-8000
Terry Huddleston, supt. Fax 755-8008
www.columbia.k12.fl.us
Challenge Learning Center 100/Alt
1301 NW LaBonte Ln 32055 386-755-8296
Lex Carswell, prin. Fax 755-8291
Columbia HS 1,800/9-12
469 SE Fighting Tiger Dr 32025 386-755-8080
Donnie Harrison, prin. Fax 755-8082
Lake City MS 1,000/6-8
843 SW Arlington Blvd 32025 386-758-4800
Sonya Judkins, prin. Fax 758-4839
Richardson MS 600/6-8
646 SE Pennsylvania St 32025 386-755-8130
Angela Coppock, prin. Fax 755-8154
Career and Adult Education Adult
409 SW Saint Johns St 32025 386-758-4872
Kay Dekle, dir. Fax 758-4967
Other Schools – See Fort White

Florida Gateway College Post-Sec.
149 SE College Pl 32025 386-752-1822
Lake City Christian Academy 100/PK-12
3035 SW Pinemount Rd 32024 386-758-0055
Tana Norris, dir. Fax 758-3018
New Generation Christian S 200/K-12
608 SW Marvin Burnett Rd 32025 386-758-4710

Lakeland, Polk, Pop. 95,497
Polk County SD
Supt. — See Bartow
Chiles Middle Academy 700/6-8
400 N Florida Ave 33801 863-499-2742
Brian Andrews, prin. Fax 499-2774
Crystal Acad of Science and Engineering 6-8
2410 N Crystal Lake Dr 33801 863-668-3055
Ronda Cotter, prin.
Crystal Lake MS 1,100/6-8
2410 N Crystal Lake Dr 33801 863-499-2970
Ronda Cotter, prin. Fax 603-6267
Duncan Opportunity Center 200/Alt
3333 Winter Lake Rd 33803 863-499-2860
Dr. Leigh Anne Cooley, prin. Fax 499-2863
Harrison S for the Arts 400/9-12
750 Hollingsworth Rd 33801 863-499-2855
Daryl Ward, prin. Fax 499-2938
Jenkins HS 2,200/9-12
6000 Lakeland Highlands Rd 33813 863-648-3566
Buddy Thomas, prin. Fax 648-3573
Kathleen HS 2,100/9-12
1100 Red Devil Way 33815 863-499-2655
Donna Drisdom, prin. Fax 499-2726

Kathleen MS 800/6-8
3627 Kathleen Pnes 33810 863-853-6040
Sheila Gregory, prin. Fax 853-6037
Lake Gibson HS 1,800/9-12
7007 N Socrum Loop Rd 33809 863-853-6100
Ryan Vann, prin. Fax 853-6108
Lake Gibson MS 1,100/6-8
6901 N Socrum Loop Rd 33809 863-853-6151
Alain Douge, prin. Fax 853-6171
Lakeland Highlands MS 1,300/6-8
740 Lake Miriam Dr 33813 863-648-3500
Telay Kendrick, prin. Fax 648-3580
Lakeland HS 2,000/9-12
726 Hollingsworth Rd 33801 863-499-2900
Arthur Martinez, prin. Fax 499-2917
REAL Academy Alt
951 Mount Airy Ave 33801 863-413-2837
John Wilson, prin. Fax 413-2531
Sleepy Hill MS 800/6-8
2215 Sleepy Hill Rd 33810 863-815-6577
Kathryn Blackburn, prin. Fax 815-6586
Southwest MS 900/6-8
2815 Eden Pkwy 33803 863-499-2840
Tye Bruno, prin. Fax 499-2762
Tenoroc HS 1,100/9-12
4905 Saddle Creek Rd 33801 863-614-9183
Jason Looney, prin. Fax 614-9192
Traviss Career Center Vo/Tech
3225 Winter Lake Rd 33803 863-499-2700
Wayne Dickens, prin. Fax 499-2706
West Area Adult & Community S Adult
604 S Central Ave 33815 863-499-2835
Marc Hutek, prin. Fax 499-2727

Everest University - Lakeland Campus Post-Sec.
995 E Memorial Blvd Ste 110 33801 863-686-1444
Excel Christian Academy 200/PK-12
6505 Odom Rd 33809 863-853-9235
Florida Southern College Post-Sec.
111 Lake Hollingsworth Dr 33801 863-680-4111
Florida Technical College Post-Sec.
4715 S Florida Ave Ste 4 33813 863-619-6200
Geneva Classical Academy 100/PK-12
4204 Lakeland Highlands Rd 33813 863-644-1408
Rich Cali, admin. Fax 619-5841
Keiser University Post-Sec.
2400 Interstate Dr 33805 863-682-6020
Lakeland Christian S 1,000/PK-12
1111 Forest Park St 33803 863-688-2771
Dr. Michael Sligh, hdmstr. Fax 682-5637
Lakeland Regional Medical Center Post-Sec.
1324 Lakeland Hills Blvd 33805 863-687-1100
Santa Fe Catholic HS 300/9-12
3110 US Highway 92 E 33801 863-665-4188
Matthew Franzino, prin. Fax 665-4151
Southeastern University Post-Sec.
1000 Longfellow Blvd 33801 863-667-5000
Traviss Career Center Post-Sec.
3225 Winter Lake Rd 33803 863-499-2700
Victory Christian Academy 300/PK-12
1401 Griffin Rd 33810 863-858-5614
Whitestone Academy 100/PK-12
3151 Hardin Combee Rd 33801 863-665-4187

Lake Mary, Seminole, Pop. 13,545
Seminole County SD
Supt. — See Sanford
Greenwood Lakes MS 1,000/6-8
601 Lake Park Dr 32746 407-320-7650
Breezi Erickson, prin. Fax 320-7699
Lake Mary HS 2,700/9-12
655 Longwood Lake Mary Rd 32746 407-320-9550
Michael Kotkin, prin. Fax 320-9512
Markham Woods MS 1,100/6-8
6003 Markham Woods Rd 32746 407-871-1750
Byron Durias, prin. Fax 871-1799

Lake Mary Preparatory S 700/PK-12
650 Rantoul Ln 32746 407-805-0095
Remington College of Nursing Post-Sec.
660 Century Pt Ste 1050 32746 800-294-4434
Remington College - Online Post-Sec.
500 International Pkwy #200 32746 800-560-6192

Lake Park, Palm Beach, Pop. 7,949

Palm Beach Academy of Health & Beauty Post-Sec.
1220 10th St Ste A 33403 561-845-1400

Lake Placid, Highlands, Pop. 2,195
Highlands County SD
Supt. — See Sebring
Lake Placid HS 800/9-12
202 Green Dragon Dr 33852 863-699-5010
Toni Stivender, prin. Fax 699-5094
Lake Placid MS 600/6-8
201 S Tangerine Ave 33852 863-699-5030
Jennifer Sanchez, prin. Fax 699-5029

Lake Wales, Polk, Pop. 13,989
Polk County SD
Supt. — See Bartow
McLaughlin MS and Fine Arts Academy 700/6-8
800 4th St S 33853 863-678-4233
Eileen Killebrew, prin. Fax 678-4033
Roosevelt Academy 300/6-12
115 E St 33853 863-678-4252
Debra Edwards, prin. Fax 678-4250

Candlelight Christian Academy 200/K-12
209 E Sessoms Ave 33853 863-676-0049
Endtime Christian S of Excellence 50/PK-12
200 S 3rd St 33853 863-676-8299
Betty Hill, prin. Fax 678-1193
Warner University Post-Sec.
13895 Hwy 27 33859 863-638-1426

Lake Worth, Palm Beach, Pop. 34,358
Palm Beach County SD
Supt. — See West Palm Beach
Intensive Transition South S 100/Alt
1509 Barton Rd 33460 561-202-0600
Reginald Jeudy, prin. Fax 202-0650

Lake Worth Community HS 2,300/9-12
1701 Lake Worth Rd 33460 561-533-6300
George Lockhart, prin. Fax 493-0888
Lake Worth MS 1,000/6-8
1300 Barnett Dr 33461 561-540-5500
Mike Williams, prin. Fax 540-5559
Park Vista Community HS 2,900/9-12
7900 S Jog Rd 33467 561-491-8400
Reginald Myers, prin. Fax 493-6854
Woodlands MS 1,200/6-8
5200 Lyons Rd 33467 561-357-0300
Jeffrey Eassa, prin. Fax 357-0307

Palm Beach State College Post-Sec.
4200 S Congress Ave 33461 561-967-7222
Trinity Christian Academy 600/PK-12
7259 S Military Trl 33463 561-967-1900
Tobi Manke, prin. Fax 965-4347

Land O Lakes, Pasco, Pop. 31,370
Pasco County SD 68,500/PK-12
7227 Land O Lakes Blvd 34638 813-794-2000
Kurt Browning, supt. Fax 794-2716
www.pasco.k12.fl.us
Land O'Lakes HS 1,700/9-12
20325 Gator Ln, 813-794-9400
Ric Mellin, prin. Fax 794-9491
Pine View MS 900/6-8
5334 Parkway Blvd 34639 813-794-4800
Jennifer Warren, prin. Fax 794-4891
Rushe MS 1,300/6-8
18654 Mentmore Blvd, 813-346-1200
David Salerno, prin. Fax 346-1291
Sunlake HS 1,700/9-12
3023 Sunlake Blvd, 813-346-1000
Michael Cloyd, prin. Fax 346-1091
Other Schools – See Dade City, Holiday, Hudson, New Port Richey, Port Richey, Spring Hill, Wesley Chapel, Zephyrhills

Academy at the Lakes - McCormick 200/5-12
2331 Collier Pkwy 34639 813-948-7600
Mark Heller, head sch Fax 949-0563
Land O' Lakes Christian S 200/PK-12
5105 School Rd, 813-995-9040
Rev. David Nichols, admin. Fax 996-6106

Lantana, Palm Beach, Pop. 10,206
Palm Beach County SD
Supt. — See West Palm Beach
Lantana Community MS 800/6-8
1225 W Drew St 33462 561-540-3400
Edward Burke, prin. Fax 540-3435
Santaluces Community HS 2,400/9-12
6880 Lawrence Rd 33462 561-642-6200
Tameka Robinson, prin. Fax 642-6255

Kentwood Preparatory S 200/1-12
6210 S Congress Ave 33462 561-649-6141
Paolo Preparatory Academy 50/PK-12
125 Hypoluxo Rd 33462 561-299-4792

Largo, Pinellas, Pop. 76,001
Pinellas County SD 101,500/PK-12
301 4th St SW 33770 727-588-6000
Dr. Michael Grego, supt. Fax 588-6200
www.pcsb.org
Fitzgerald MS 1,200/6-8
6410 118th Ave 33773 727-547-4526
Michael Hernandez, prin. Fax 549-6631
Largo HS 1,700/9-12
410 Missouri Ave N 33770 727-588-3758
Bradley Finkbiner, prin. Fax 588-4037
Largo MS 800/6-8
155 8th Ave SE 33771 727-588-4600
Stephanie Joyner, prin. Fax 588-3720
Pinellas Gulf Coast Academy 300/Alt
1197 East Bay Dr 33770 727-474-8836
Bonnie Solinsky, prin. Fax 581-9557
Pinellas Park HS 2,200/9-12
6305 118th Ave 33773 727-538-7410
Brett Patterson, prin. Fax 507-4563
Other Schools – See Clearwater, Dunedin, Gulfport, Palm Harbor, Pinellas Park, Safety Harbor, Saint Petersburg, Seminole, Tarpon Springs

ATA Career Education Post-Sec.
12360 66th St 33773 727-576-9597
Everest University - Largo Campus Post-Sec.
1199 E Bay Dr 33770 727-725-2688
Fortis College Post-Sec.
6565 Ulmerton Rd 33771 727-531-5900
Indian Rocks Christian S 800/PK-12
12685 Ulmerton Rd 33774 727-596-4342
Walter Weller, supt. Fax 593-8778
Schiller International University Post-Sec.
8560 Ulmerton Rd 33771 800-261-9751

Lauderdale Lakes, Broward, Pop. 31,785
Broward County SD
Supt. — See Fort Lauderdale
Anderson HS 1,800/9-12
3050 NW 41st St 33309 754-322-0200
Angel Almanzar, prin. Fax 322-0330
Lauderdale Lakes MS 1,000/6-8
3911 NW 30th Ave 33309 754-322-3500
James Griffin, prin. Fax 322-3585

Florida Career College Post-Sec.
3383 N State Road 7 33319 954-535-8700

Lauderhill, Broward, Pop. 65,234
Broward County SD
Supt. — See Fort Lauderdale
Lauderhill MSHS 700/6-12
1901 NW 49th Ave 33313 754-322-3600
Dr. Ryan Reardon, prin. Fax 322-3685
Parkway MS 1,600/6-8
3600 NW 5th Ct 33311 754-322-4000
Bradford Mattair, prin. Fax 322-4085

Intl School of Health Beauty and Tech Post-Sec.
5950 W Oakland Park Blvd 33313 954-741-0088

University of Fort Lauderdale Post-Sec.
4093 NW 16th St 33313 954-486-7728

Laurel Hill, Okaloosa, Pop. 532
Okaloosa County SD
Supt. — See Fort Walton Beach
Laurel Hill S 400/PK-12
8078 4th St 32567 850-652-4111
Lee Martello, prin. Fax 652-4659

Lecanto, Citrus, Pop. 5,799
Citrus County SD
Supt. — See Inverness
Lecanto HS 1,600/9-12
3810 W Educational Path 34461 352-746-2334
Jason Koon, prin. Fax 249-2136
Lecanto MS 700/6-8
3800 W Educational Path 34461 352-746-2050
Brian Lancaster, prin. Fax 249-2138
Renaissance Center 100/Alt
3630 W Educational Path 34461 352-527-4567
Heather Nieb, prin. Fax 249-2144

Seven Rivers Christian S 300/PK-12
4221 W Gulf to Lake Hwy 34461 352-746-5696

Leesburg, Lake, Pop. 19,677
Lake County SD
Supt. — See Tavares
Carver MS 800/6-8
1200 Beecher St 34748 352-787-7868
Mollie Cunningham, prin. Fax 787-1339
Leesburg HS 1,600/9-12
1401 Yellow Jacket Way 34748 352-787-5047
Dennis Neal, prin. Fax 787-5091
Oak Park MS 600/6-8
2101 South St 34748 352-787-3232
Barbara Longo, prin. Fax 326-2177

Beacon College Post-Sec.
105 E Main St 34748 352-787-7660
First Academy-Leesburg 300/PK-12
219 N 13th St 34748 352-787-7762
Gregory Frescoln, admin. Fax 323-1773
Lake-Sumter State College Post-Sec.
9501 US Highway 441 34788 352-787-3747

Lehigh Acres, Lee, Pop. 85,066
Lee County SD
Supt. — See Fort Myers
East Lee County HS 1,700/9-12
715 Thomas Sherwin Ave S, 239-369-2932
Susan Zellers, prin. Fax 369-3213
Harns Marsh MS 1,100/6-8
1820 Unice Ave N 33971 239-690-2025
Linda Maere, prin. Fax 690-2028
Lehigh Acres MS 1,100/6-8
104 Arthur Ave 33936 239-369-6108
Neketa Watson, prin. Fax 369-8808
Lehigh HS 1,800/9-12
901 Gunnery Rd N 33971 239-693-5353
Jackie Corey, prin. Fax 693-6702
Varsity Lakes MS 1,000/6-8
801 Gunnery Rd N 33971 239-694-3464
Daman Essert, prin. Fax 694-7093

Lithia, Hillsborough
Hillsborough County SD
Supt. — See Tampa
Barrington MS 1,200/6-8
5925 Village Center Dr 33547 813-657-7266
Amy Rappleyea, prin. Fax 657-7369
Newsome HS 2,400/9-12
16550 Fishhawk Blvd 33547 813-740-4600
Carla Bruning, prin. Fax 740-4604
Randall MS 1,300/6-8
16510 Fishhawk Blvd 33547 813-740-3900
Claire Mawhinney, prin. Fax 740-3910

Live Oak, Suwannee, Pop. 6,744
Suwannee County SD 5,900/PK-12
702 2nd St NW 32064 386-647-4600
Jerry Scarborough, supt. Fax 364-2635
www.suwannee.k12.fl.us
RIVEROAK Technical College Vo/Tech
415 Pinewood Dr SW 32064 386-647-4200
Walter Boatright, prin. Fax 364-4698
Suwannee HS 1,300/9-12
1314 Pine Ave SW 32064 386-647-4000
Malcolm Hines, prin. Fax 364-2794
Suwannee MS 1,000/6-8
1730 Walker Ave SW 32064 386-647-4500
Jay Jolicoeur, prin. Fax 208-1474
Other Schools – See Branford

Melody Christian Academy 200/PK-12
PO Box 100 32064 386-364-4800
Westwood Christian S 100/PK-12
920 11th St SW 32064 386-362-3735

Longwood, Seminole, Pop. 13,382
Seminole County SD
Supt. — See Sanford
Lyman HS 2,500/9-12
865 S Ronald Reagan Blvd 32750 407-746-2050
Mike Rice, prin. Fax 746-2024
Milwee MS 1,200/6-8
1341 S Ronald Reagan Blvd 32750 407-746-3850
James Kubis, prin. Fax 746-3899
Rock Lake MS 900/6-8
250 Slade Dr 32750 407-746-9350
Jordan Rodriguez, prin. Fax 746-9399

One S of the Arts 100/PK-12
1675 Dixon Rd 32779 407-774-0168

Loxahatchee, Palm Beach
Palm Beach County SD
Supt. — See West Palm Beach
Osceola Creek MS 600/6-8
6775 180th Ave N 33470 561-422-2500
Nicole Daly, prin. Fax 422-2510

Seminole Ridge Community HS 2,400/9-12
4601 Seminole Pratt Whitney 33470 561-422-2600
James Campbell, prin. Fax 422-2623

Lutz, Hillsborough, Pop. 19,035
Hillsborough County SD
Supt. — See Tampa
Martinez MS 1,100/6-8
5601 W Lutz Lake Fern Rd 33558 813-558-1190
Scott Weaver, prin. Fax 558-1226
Steinbrenner HS 2,200/9-12
5575 W Lutz Lake Fern Rd 33558 813-792-5131
Kelly King, prin. Fax 792-5135

Tampa Christian Community S 100/PK-12
960 W Lutz Lake Fern Rd 33548 813-949-2144
Melissa Walker, prin. Fax 877-3111

Lynn Haven, Bay, Pop. 18,004
Bay County SD
Supt. — See Panama City
Mosley HS 1,700/9-12
501 Mosley Dr 32444 850-767-4400
Sandy Harrison, prin. Fax 872-4453
Mowat MS 1,000/6-8
1903 W Highway 390 32444 850-767-4040
Ed Sheffield, prin. Fax 265-2179

Macclenny, Baker, Pop. 6,242
Baker County SD 5,000/PK-12
392 South Blvd E 32063 904-259-6251
Sherrie Raulerson, supt. Fax 259-1387
www.baker.k12.fl.us
Baker County MS 1,100/6-8
211 E Jonathan St 32063 904-259-2226
Debbie Fraser, prin. Fax 259-7955
Baker County Adult Center Adult
270 South Blvd E 32063 904-259-6251
Ann Watts, prin. Fax 259-0378
Other Schools – See Glen Saint Mary

Madison, Madison, Pop. 2,801
Madison County SD 2,400/PK-12
210 NE Duval Ave 32340 850-973-5022
Doug Brown, supt. Fax 973-5027
www.madison.k12.fl.us
Madison Co. Excel Alternative Ed. Center 50/Alt
2523 W US 90 32340 850-973-5054
Jada Williams, prin. Fax 973-5047
Madison County HS 600/9-12
2649 W US 90 32340 850-973-5061
Ben Killingsworth, prin. Fax 973-5066

North Florida Community College Post-Sec.
325 NW Turner Davis Dr 32340 850-973-2288

Maitland, Orange, Pop. 15,449
Orange County SD
Supt. — See Orlando
Maitland MS 900/6-8
701 N Thistle Ln 32751 407-623-1462
Andrew Leftakis, prin. Fax 623-1474

Florida College of Natural Health Post-Sec.
2600 Lake Lucien Dr Ste 140 32751 407-261-0319
Orangewood Christian S 700/PK-12
1300 W Maitland Blvd 32751 407-339-0223
Fax 339-4148

Malone, Jackson, Pop. 2,054
Jackson County SD
Supt. — See Marianna
Malone S 500/PK-12
5361 9th St 32445 850-482-9950
Doug Powell, prin. Fax 482-9981

Marathon, Monroe, Pop. 8,204
Monroe County SD
Supt. — See Key West
Marathon MSHS 600/6-12
350 Sombrero Beach Rd 33050 305-289-2480
Wendy McPherson, prin. Fax 289-2486

Margate, Broward, Pop. 51,792
Broward County SD
Supt. — See Fort Lauderdale
Margate MS 1,400/6-8
500 NW 65th Ave 33063 754-322-3800
Ernest Toliver, prin. Fax 322-3885

American Institute Post-Sec.
5000 Coconut Creek Pkwy # C 33063 888-283-1671
Florida Career College Post-Sec.
3271 N State Road 7 33063 954-862-7260
Margate School of Beauty Post-Sec.
5281 Coconut Creek Pkwy 33063 954-972-9630

Marianna, Jackson, Pop. 5,957
Jackson County SD 6,600/PK-12
PO Box 5958 32447 850-482-1200
Steve Benton, supt. Fax 482-1299
www.jcsb.org
Jackson Alternative S 100/Alt
2701 Technology Cir 32448 850-482-9666
Rex Suggs, prin. Fax 482-9800
Marianna HS 700/9-12
3546 Caverns Rd 32446 850-482-9605
Hunter Nolen, prin. Fax 482-1247
Marianna MS 700/6-8
4144 South St 32448 850-482-9609
Eddie Ellis, prin. Fax 482-9795
Adult Education Adult
2971 Guyton St 32446 850-482-9617
John Ellerbee, prin. Fax 482-1201
Other Schools – See Cottondale, Graceville, Malone, Sneads

Chipola College Post-Sec.
3094 Indian Cir 32446 850-526-2761
Dayspring Christian Academy 200/PK-12
4685 Meadowview Rd 32446 850-526-4919

Mayo, Lafayette, Pop. 1,208
LaFayette County SD 1,200/PK-12
363 NE Crawford St 32066 386-294-1351
Robert Edwards, supt. Fax 294-3072
lafayette.schooldesk.net
LaFayette JSHS 600/6-12
160 NE Hornet Ln 32066 386-294-1701
Ray Stewart Hancock, prin. Fax 294-4197
Adult Education Adult
363 NE Crawford St 32066 386-294-1649
Kris Bracewell, admin. Fax 294-4197

Lighthouse Christian Academy 100/PK-12
772 N State Road 51 32066 386-294-2994
Bobby Ur, admin. Fax 294-3449

Melbourne, Brevard, Pop. 74,011
Brevard County SD 68,900/PK-12
2700 Judge Fran Jamieson 32940 321-633-1000
Dr. Desmond Blackburn, supt. Fax 633-3432
www.edline.net/pages/Brevard_County_Schools
Eau Gallie HS 1,700/9-12
1400 Commodore Blvd 32935 321-242-6400
Jeremy Salmon, prin. Fax 242-6427
Johnson MS 800/7-8
2155 Croton Rd 32935 321-242-6430
Robert Fish, prin. Fax 242-6436
Melbourne HS 2,000/9-12
74 Bulldog Blvd 32901 321-952-5880
James Kirk, prin. Fax 952-5898
Palm Bay HS 1,500/9-12
101 Pirate Ln 32901 321-952-5900
Karl Kaminski, prin. Fax 676-2891
Stone MS 800/7-8
1101 E University Blvd 32901 321-723-0741
Mary Bland, prin. Fax 951-1497
West Shore JSHS 1,000/7-12
250 Wildcat Aly 32935 321-242-4730
Eric Fleming, prin. Fax 242-4740
Palm Bay Adult Center Adult
101 Pirate Ln 32901 321-952-5914
Fax 676-2891
South Area Adult Center Adult
1362 S Babcock St 32901 321-952-5977
Jeff Arnott, prin. Fax 952-5831
Other Schools – See Cocoa, Cocoa Beach, Indialantic, Merritt Island, Palm Bay, Rockledge, Satellite Beach, Titusville, Viera, West Melbourne

---

Community Christian S 100/K-12
1616 Ferndale Ave 32935 321-259-1590
Laurel Earls, prin. Fax 259-5301
Everest University - Melbourne Campus Post-Sec.
2401 N Harbor City Blvd 32935 321-253-2929
Florida Institute of Technology Post-Sec.
150 W University Blvd 32901 321-674-8000
Florida Preparatory Academy 300/5-12
1950 Academy Dr 32901 321-723-3211
James Dwight, pres. Fax 676-9548
Harris-Casel Institute Post-Sec.
5000 Stack Blvd Ste A4 32901 321-676-4066
Holy Trinity Episcopal Academy 500/7-12
5625 Holy Trinity Dr 32940 321-723-8323
Nancy Giangrisostomi, head sch Fax 241-6422
Keiser University Post-Sec.
900 S Babcock St 32901 321-409-4800
Melbourne Central Catholic HS 400/9-12
100 E Florida Ave 32901 321-727-0793
Ernest Herrington, prin. Fax 727-1134
New Covenant S 100/K-12
1990 W New Haven Ave # 306 32904 321-724-9603
Sandra Hancock, prin. Fax 724-6932
Shiloh Christian Academy 100/PK-12
155 E University Blvd 32901 321-956-1404
West Melbourne Christian Academy 100/K-12
3150 Milwaukee Ave 32904 321-725-3743

Merritt Island, Brevard, Pop. 33,904
Brevard County SD
Supt. — See Melbourne
Edgewood JSHS 900/7-12
180 E Merritt Ave 32953 321-454-1030
Jackie Ingratta, prin. Fax 452-1176
Jefferson MS 600/7-8
1275 S Courtenay Pkwy 32952 321-453-5154
Dr. Lori Spinner, prin. Fax 459-2854
Merritt Island HS 1,500/9-12
100 Mustang Way 32953 321-454-1000
Mollie Vega, prin. Fax 454-1013

Avalon School of Cosmetology Post-Sec.
2088 N Courtenay Pkwy 32953 321-452-8490
Brevard Private Academy 100/7-12
508 S Plumosa St 32952 321-459-3466
Merritt Island Christian S 500/PK-12
140 Magnolia Ave 32952 321-453-2710
Dr. Nanci Dettra, supt. Fax 452-6580

Miami, Miami-Dade, Pop. 396,081
Miami-Dade County SD 338,900/PK-12
1450 NE 2nd Ave 33132 305-995-1000
Alberto Carvalho, supt. Fax 995-1488
www.dadeschools.net/
Ammons MS 1,200/6-8
17990 SW 142nd Ave 33177 305-971-0158
Maria Costa, prin. Fax 971-0179
Arvida MS 1,300/6-8
10900 SW 127th Ave 33186 305-385-7144
Nancy Aragon, prin. Fax 383-9472
Baker Aviation S Vo/Tech
3275 NW 42nd Ave 33142 305-871-3143
Ciro Hidalgo, prin. Fax 871-5840
Bell MS 500/6-8
11800 NW 2nd St 33182 305-220-2075
Ingrid Soto, prin. Fax 229-0798
BioTECH @ Richmond Heights HS 9-12
15015 SW 103rd Ave 33176 786-573-5353
Daniel Mateo, prin. Fax 573-5350
Braddock HS 3,400/9-12
3601 SW 147th Ave 33185 305-225-9729
Manuel Garcia, prin. Fax 221-3312
Brownsville MS 500/7-9
4899 NW 24th Ave 33142 305-633-1481
Ebony Dunn, prin. Fax 635-8702
Canosa MS 2,000/6-8
15735 SW 144th St 33196 305-252-5900
Elio Falcon, prin. Fax 252-5901
Chiles MS 600/6-8
8190 NW 197th St 33015 305-816-9101
Nelson Izquierdo, prin. Fax 816-9248
Citrus Grove MS 900/6-8
2153 NW 3rd St 33125 305-642-5055
Dr. Cory Rodriguez, prin. Fax 642-9349
Coral Reef HS 3,200/9-12
10101 SW 152nd St 33157 305-232-2044
Thomas Ennis, prin. Fax 252-3454
Country Club MS 1,200/6-8
18305 NW 75th Pl 33015 305-820-8800
Cynthia Prado, prin. Fax 820-8801
Curry MS 1,100/6-8
15750 SW 47th St 33185 305-222-2775
Jean Baril, prin. Fax 229-1521
Dario MS 600/6-8
350 NW 97th Ave 33172 305-226-0179
Dr. Verona McCarthy, prin. Fax 559-0919
De Diego MS 600/6-8
3100 NW 5th Ave 33127 305-573-7229
Dr. April Williams, prin. Fax 573-6415
Design & Architectural Magnet HS 500/9-12
4001 NE 2nd Ave 33137 305-573-7135
Ana Alvarez-Arimon, prin. Fax 573-8253
Ferguson HS 4,200/9-12
15900 SW 56th St 33185 305-408-2700
Rafael Villalobos, prin. Fax 408-6487
Glades MS 1,100/6-8
9451 SW 64th Ter 33173 305-271-3342
Cynthia Valdes-Garcia, prin. Fax 271-0402
Hammocks MS 1,100/6-8
9889 Hammocks Blvd 33196 305-385-0896
Deborah Leal, prin. Fax 382-0861
Highland Oaks MS 1,200/6-8
2375 NE 203rd St 33180 305-932-3810
Cheryl Kushi, prin. Fax 932-0676
Hopkins Technical Center Vo/Tech
750 NW 20th St 33127 305-324-6070
Nyce Daniel, prin. Fax 545-6397
iPreparatory Academy 200/9-12
1500 Biscayne Blvd 33132 305-995-1929
Alberto Carvalho, prin. Fax 523-8405
iTech @ Thomas A. Edison Educational Ctr 9-12
6101 NW 2nd Ave 33127 305-762-5000
Layda Nasr, prin. Fax 757-2219
Jefferson MS 300/7-9
525 NW 147th St 33168 305-681-7481
Robin Atkins, prin. Fax 688-5912
Jones-Ayers MS 500/6-8
1331 NW 46th St 33142 305-634-9787
Bernard Edwards, prin. Fax 638-8254
Kinloch Park MS 1,200/6-8
4340 NW 3rd St 33126 305-445-5467
Scott Weiner, prin. Fax 445-3110
Krop HS 2,700/9-12
1410 NE 215th St 33179 305-652-6808
Dr. Allison Harley, prin. Fax 651-8043
Law Enforcement Officers Memorial HS 400/9-12
300 NW 2nd Ave 33128 305-371-0400
David Ladd, prin. Fax 371-0401
Madison MS 500/6-8
3400 NW 87th St 33147 305-836-2610
Dr. Philippe Napoleon, prin. Fax 696-5249
Mann MS 800/6-8
8950 NW 2nd Ave 33150 305-757-9537
Leon Maycock, prin. Fax 754-0724
MAST @ FIU Biscayne Bay 100/9-12
3000 NE 151st St 33181 305-919-4450
Dr. Matthew Welker, prin. Fax 919-4456
Mays Conservatory of the Arts 400/6-12
11700 SW 216th St 33170 305-233-2300
Martin Reid, prin. Fax 251-5462
McMillan MS 900/6-8
13100 SW 59th St 33183 305-385-6877
Hilca Thomas, prin. Fax 387-9641
Miami Arts Studio 6-12 6-12
15015 SW 24th St 33185 305-485-2323
Dr. Miguel Balsera, prin. Fax 485-2324
Miami Central HS 2,000/9-12
1781 NW 95th St 33147 305-696-4161
Gregory Bethune, prin. Fax 836-2872
Miami Coral Park HS 2,900/9-12
8865 SW 16th St 33165 305-226-6565
Alicia Hidalgo, prin. Fax 553-4658
Miami Edison HS 900/9-12
6161 NW 5th Ct 33127 305-751-7337
Trynegwa Diggs, prin. Fax 759-4561
Miami HS 2,900/9-12
2450 SW 1st St 33135 305-649-9800
Benny Valdes, prin. Fax 649-9475
Miami Jackson HS 1,500/9-12
1751 NW 36th St 33142 305-634-2621
Carlos Rios, prin. Fax 634-7477
Miami Killian HS 2,500/9-12
10655 SW 97th Ave 33176 305-271-3311
Magda Pereira, prin. Fax 275-5494
Miami Northwestern HS 1,600/9-12
1100 NW 71st St 33150 305-836-0991
Wallace Aristide, prin. Fax 691-4955
Miami Southridge HS 2,100/9-12
19355 SW 114th Ave 33157 305-238-6110
Humberto Miret, prin. Fax 253-4456
Miami Sunset HS 1,900/9-12
13125 SW 72nd St 33183 305-385-4255
John Lux, prin. Fax 385-6458
Morgan Educational Center HS Vo/Tech
18180 SW 122nd Ave 33177 305-253-9920
Reginald Fox, prin. Fax 259-1495
New World S of the Arts 500/9-12
25 NE 2nd St 33132 305-237-3135
Evonne Alvarez, prin. Fax 237-3794
Richmond Heights MS 600/6-8
15015 SW 103rd Ave 33176 305-238-2316
Larhonda Donaldson, prin. Fax 251-3712
Riviera MS 800/6-8
10301 SW 48th St 33165 305-226-4286
Jorge Rivas, prin. Fax 226-1025
Rockway MS 1,000/6-8
9393 SW 29th Ter 33165 305-221-8212
Melanie Megias, prin. Fax 221-5940
School for Advanced Studies - North 100/11-12
11380 NW 27th Ave Ste 1111 33167 305-237-1089
Dr. Omar Monteagudo, prin. Fax 237-1610
School for Advanced Studies-South 200/11-12
11011 SW 104th St Ste 706 33176 305-237-0510
Dr. Omar Monteagudo, prin. Fax 237-0511
School for Advanced Studies-Wolfson 100/11-12
25 NE 2nd St 33132 305-237-7270
Dr. Omar Monteagudo, prin. Fax 237-7271
Shenandoah MS 1,100/6-8
1950 SW 19th St 33145 305-856-8282
Bianca Calzadilla, prin. Fax 856-7049
South Miami HS 2,300/9-12
6856 SW 53rd St 33155 305-666-5871
Gilberto Bonce, prin. Fax 666-6359
Southwest Miami HS 3,200/9-12
8855 SW 50th Ter 33165 305-274-0181
Carlos Diaz, prin. Fax 596-7370
TERRA Environmental Research Institute 1,800/9-12
11005 SW 84th St 33173 305-412-5800
Jose Sirven, prin. Fax 412-5801
Thomas MS 1,100/6-8
13001 SW 26th St 33175 305-995-3800
Allen Breeding, prin. Fax 995-3537
Turner Technical Arts HS Vo/Tech
10151 NW 19th Ave 33147 305-691-8324
Lavette Hunter, prin. Fax 693-9463
Varela HS 3,200/9-12
15255 SW 96th St 33196 305-752-7900
Nery Fins, prin. Fax 386-8987
Wallace C.O.P.E. Center 100/Alt
10225 SW 147th Ter 33176 305-233-1044
Annette Burks, prin. Fax 256-8694
Washington HS 900/9-12
1200 NW 6th Ave 33136 305-324-8900
William Aristide, prin. Fax 324-4676
West Miami MS 900/6-8
7525 SW 24th St 33155 305-261-8383
Katyna Lopez-Martin, prin. Fax 267-8204
Westview MS 400/6-8
1901 NW 127th St 33167 305-681-6647
Ron Steiger, prin. Fax 685-3192
Young Mens Preparatory Academy 200/6-12
3001 NW 2nd Ave 33127 305-571-1111
Pierre Edouard, prin. Fax 571-1112
Young Women's Preparatory Academy 400/6-12
1150 SW 1st St 33130 305-575-1200
Concepcion Martinez, prin. Fax 325-8071
Dorsey Education Center Adult
7100 NW 17th Ave 33147 305-693-2490
Dr. Angela Thomas-Dupree, prin. Fax 691-7492
English Center Adult
3501 SW 28th St 33133 305-445-7731
Yamila Carballo, prin. Fax 441-2150
Miami Coral Park Adult Education Ctr Adult
8865 SW 16th St 33165 305-226-6565
Robert Novak, prin. Fax 559-7415
Miami Jackson Adult Education Center Adult
1751 NW 36th St 33142 305-634-2621
Joey Bautista, prin. Fax 633-8191
Miami Palmetto Adult Education Center Adult
7460 SW 118th St 33156 305-235-1360
Octavia Williams, prin. Fax 253-3898
Miami Senior Adult Education Center Adult
2450 SW 1st St 33135 305-649-9800
Alan Bashaw, prin. Fax 643-2395
Miami Sunset Adult Education Center Adult
13125 SW 72nd St 33183 305-385-4255
Julian Cazanas, prin. Fax 386-9218
Southwest Adult Education Ctr. Adult
8855 SW 50th Ter 33165 305-274-0181
Robert Novak, prin. Fax 274-3351
Turner Tech Adult Ed Center Adult
10151 NW 19th Ave 33147 305-691-8324
Uwezo Frazier, prin. Fax 693-9463
Other Schools – See Coral Gables, Cutler Bay, Doral, El Portal, Hialeah, Hialeah Gardens, Homestead, Key Biscayne, Miami Beach, Miami Gardens, Miami Lakes, Miami Springs, Naranja, North Miami, North Miami Beach, Opa Locka, Palmetto Bay, Pinecrest, South Miami

---

Acupuncture & Massage College Post-Sec.
10506 N Kendall Dr 33176 305-595-9500
American HS Academy 600/6-12
10300 SW 72nd St Ste 427 33173 305-270-1440
Sr. R. Valentino, dir. Fax 598-8003
American Medical Acadmey Post-Sec.
12215 SW 112th St 33186 305-271-6555
Archbishop Coleman Carroll HS 500/9-12
10300 SW 167th Ave 33196 305-388-6700
Sr. Margaret Ann Laechelin, prin. Fax 388-4371
Archbishop Curley-Notre Dame HS 300/6-12
4949 NE 2nd Ave 33137 305-751-8367
Douglas Romanik, prin. Fax 751-3517
Atlantis University Post-Sec.
1442 Biscayne Blvd 33132 305-377-8817
Beis Chana S for Girls 500/9-12
17330 NW 7th Ave 33169 305-653-8770
Belen Jesuit Preparatory HS 1,500/6-12
500 SW 127th Ave 33184 305-223-8600
Jose Roca, prin. Fax 227-2565
Brito Miami Private S 300/PK-12
2732 SW 32nd Ave 33133 305-448-1463
Calusa Preparatory S 200/PK-12
12515 SW 72nd St 33183 305-596-3787
Carlos Albizu University Post-Sec.
2173 NW 99th Ave 33172 305-593-1223
Center of Cinematography Art & TV Post-Sec.
1637 NW 27th Ave 33125 305-634-0550
City College Post-Sec.
9300 S Dadeland Blvd # 200 33156 305-666-9242
College of Business & Technology Post-Sec.
8230 W Flagler St 33144 305-764-3165
College of Business & Technology Post-Sec.
8765 SW 165th Ave Ste 114 33193 305-764-3165
Columbus HS 1,400/9-12
3000 SW 87th Ave 33165 305-223-5650
David Pugh, prin. Fax 559-4306

Compu-Med Vocational Careers — Post-Sec.
9738 SW 24th St 33165 — 305-553-2898
Dade Christian S — 900/PK-12
6601 NW 167th St 33015 — 305-822-7690
Douglas Flores, prin. — Fax 826-4072
DeVry University — Post-Sec.
8700 W Flagler St Ste 100 33174 — 305-229-4833
Educating Hands School of Massage — Post-Sec.
3883 Biscayne Blvd 33137 — 305-285-6991
Eureka Institute of Health and Beauty — Post-Sec.
11373 W Flagler St Ste 209 33174 — 305-480-1005
Everest Institute — Post-Sec.
9020 SW 137th Ave 33186 — 305-386-9900
Everest Institute — Post-Sec.
111 NW 183rd St Ste 200 33169 — 305-949-9500
Florida Career College — Post-Sec.
1321 SW 107th Ave Ste 201B 33174 — 305-553-6065
Florida Career College — Post-Sec.
11731 Mills Dr Bldg 2 33183 — 888-852-7272
Florida Christian S — 1,400/PK-12
4200 SW 89th Ave 33165 — 305-226-8152
Florida College of Natural Health — Post-Sec.
7925 NW 12th St Ste 201 33126 — 305-597-9599
Florida International University — Post-Sec.
11200 SW 8th St 33199 — 305-348-2000
Florida National University — Post-Sec.
11865 SW 26th St Ste H3 33175 — 305-266-9999
Fortis College — Post-Sec.
7757 W Flagler St 33144 — 305-717-7000
Future Tech Institute — Post-Sec.
3446 SW 8th St Ste 213 33135 — 305-774-0227
George T. Baker Aviation School — Post-Sec.
3275 NW 42nd Ave 33142 — 305-871-3143
Grace Christian Preparatory S — 100/K-12
11000 SW 216th St 33170 — 305-259-1929
Greater Miami Adventist Academy — 300/PK-12
500 NW 122nd Ave 33182 — 305-220-5955
Luis Cortes Ph.D., prin. — Fax 220-5970
Hope Center — Post-Sec.
1411 NW 14th Ave 33125 — 305-545-7572
Immaculata - La Salle HS — 800/9-12
3601 S Miami Ave 33133 — 305-854-2334
Sr. Kim Keraitis, prin. — Fax 858-5971
Interamerican Technical Institute — Post-Sec.
9600 SW 8th St Ste 42 33174 — 305-554-9281
International Training Careers — Post-Sec.
7360 Coral Way 33155 — 800-649-8139
Jackson Memorial Medical Center — Post-Sec.
1611 NW 12th Ave 33136 — 305-585-6754
Keiser University — Post-Sec.
2101 NW 117th Ave 33172 — 305-596-2226
Keystone National HS — 800/9-12
12840 NW 1st Ct 33168 — 866-257-6011
Dr. Clarence Watson Ph.D., prin. — Fax 454-2394
Killian Oaks Academy — 100/PK-12
10545 SW 97th Ave 33176 — 305-274-2221
La Belle Beauty Academy — Post-Sec.
2960 SW 8th St 33135 — 305-649-2800
La Progressiva Presbyterian S — 400/PK-12
2480 NW 7th St 33125 — 305-642-8600
Lincoln-Marti S — 1,100/PK-12
931 SW 1st St 33130 — 305-324-4060
Lindsey Hopkins Technical Education Ctr — Post-Sec.
750 NW 20th St 33127 — 305-324-6070
Management Resources Institute — Post-Sec.
10 NW 42nd Ave Ste 400 33126 — 305-442-9223
Marti S — 100/4-8
1685 SW 32nd Ave 33145 — 305-441-0565
Edith Ysada, prin. — Fax 443-9359
Miami Christian S — 300/PK-12
200 NW 109th Ave 33172 — 305-221-7754
Dr. Lorena Morrison Ed.D., head sch — Fax 221-7783
Miami Country Day S — 1,000/PK-12
601 NE 107th St 33161 — 305-779-7200
Dr. John Davies, head sch — Fax 397-0370
Miami Dade College — Post-Sec.
300 NE 2nd Ave 33132 — 305-237-8888
Miami-Dade College — Post-Sec.
950 NW 20th St 33127 — 305-237-4160
Miami-Dade College — Post-Sec.
11380 NW 27th Ave 33167 — 305-237-1000
Miami-Dade College — Post-Sec.
11011 SW 104th St 33176 — 305-237-2000
Miami-Dade College — Post-Sec.
627 SW 27th Ave 33135 — 305-237-6000
Miami International Univ of Art & Design — Post-Sec.
1501 Biscayne Blvd Ste 100 33132 — 305-428-5700
Miami Media School — Post-Sec.
901 S Miami Ave Ste 303 33130 — 305-728-1120
New Concept Massage & Beauty School — Post-Sec.
2022 SW 1st St 33135 — 305-642-3020
New World School of the Arts — Post-Sec.
300 NE 2nd Ave 33132 — 305-237-7007
Northwest Christian Academy — 300/PK-12
951 NW 136th St 33168 — 305-685-8734
Jerry Nelson, admin. — Fax 685-5341
Nouvelle Institute — Post-Sec.
3271 NW 7th St Ste 106 33125 — 305-643-3360
Our Lady of Lourdes Academy — 800/9-12
5525 SW 84th St 33143 — 305-667-1623
Sr. Kathryn Donze, prin. — Fax 663-3121
Professional Training Center — Post-Sec.
13926 SW 47th St 33175 — 305-220-4120
Revelation S of Florida — 500/PK-12
10658 SW 186th St 33157 — 305-969-9448
Riviera Preparatory S — 200/6-12
9775 SW 87 Ave 33176 — 786-300-0300
St. Brendan HS — 1,200/9-12
2950 SW 87th Ave 33165 — 305-223-5181
Dr. Jose Rodelgo-Bueno, prin. — Fax 220-7434
St. John Vianney College Seminary — Post-Sec.
2900 SW 87th Ave 33165 — 305-223-4561
Schoolhouse Preparatory S — 100/9-12
3800 SW 108th Ave 33165 — 305-552-1200
South Florida Institute of Technology — Post-Sec.
720 NW 27th Ave Fl 2 33125 — 305-649-2050
The Praxis Institute — Post-Sec.
1850 SW 8th St 33135 — 305-642-4104
Universal Beauty School — Post-Sec.
10720 W Flagler St Ste 21 33174 — 305-485-7700
Westwood Christian S — 500/PK-12
5801 SW 120th Ave 33183 — 305-274-3380

Worshipers House of Prayer Academy — 100/K-12
8350 NW 7th Ave 33150 — 305-200-3245
Marie Zizi, prin. — Fax 460-8045

Miami Beach, Miami-Dade, Pop. 86,463
Miami-Dade County SD
Supt. — See Miami
Miami Beach HS — 2,500/9-12
2231 Prairie Ave 33139 — 305-532-4515
John Donohue, prin. — Fax 531-9209
Nautilus MS — 700/7-8
4301 N Michigan Ave 33140 — 305-532-3481
Rene Bellmas, prin. — Fax 532-8906
Miami Beach Adult Center — Adult
1424 Drexel Ave 33139 — 305-531-0451
Judith DelGado, prin. — Fax 531-2352

Hebrew Academy (RASG) — 500/PK-12
2400 Pine Tree Dr 33140 — 305-532-6421
Rabbi Zvi Kahn, head sch — Fax 674-6895
Klurman Mesivta HS — 100/7-12
1140 Alton Rd 33139 — 305-653-8770
Mechina HS of South Florida — 100/7-12
4000 Alton Rd 33140 — 305-534-7050
Miami Ad School — Post-Sec.
955 Alton Rd 33139 — 305-538-3193
Mt. Sinai Medical Center — Post-Sec.
4300 Alton Rd 33140 — 305-674-2222
Talmudic University — Post-Sec.
4000 Alton Rd 33140 — 305-534-7050
Yeshiva Gedolah Rabbinical College — Post-Sec.
1140 Alton Rd 33139 — 305-653-8770

Miami Gardens, Miami-Dade, Pop. 105,806
Miami-Dade County SD
Supt. — See Miami
Andover MS — 900/6-8
121 NE 207th St, — 305-654-2727
Rennina Turner, prin. — Fax 654-2728
Carol City MS — 500/6-8
3737 NW 188th St, — 305-624-2652
Maria Medina, prin. — Fax 623-2955
Lake Stevens MS — 700/6-8
18484 NW 48th Pl, — 305-620-1294
Jorge Bulnes, prin. — Fax 620-1345
Miami Carol City HS — 1,700/9-12
3301 Miami Gardens Dr, — 305-621-5681
Jamarv Dunn, prin. — Fax 620-8862
Miami Norland HS — 1,600/9-12
1193 NW 193rd St, — 305-653-1416
Reginald Lee, prin. — Fax 651-6175
Norland MS — 900/6-8
1235 NW 192nd Ter, — 305-653-1210
Ronald Redmon, prin. — Fax 654-1237
North Dade MS — 800/6-8
1840 NW 157th St, — 305-624-8415
Kharim Armand, prin. — Fax 628-2954

Azure College — Post-Sec.
1525 NW 167th St, — 305-751-0001
College of Business and Technology — Post-Sec.
5190 NW 167th St 33014 — 305-764-3165
Florida Memorial University — Post-Sec.
15800 NW 42nd Ave, — 305-626-3600
Monsignor Edward Pace HS — 900/9-12
15600 NW 32nd Ave, — 305-624-8534
Ana Garcia, prin. — Fax 521-0185
St. Thomas University — Post-Sec.
16401 NW 37th Ave, — 305-628-6546

Miami Lakes, Miami-Dade, Pop. 29,182
Miami-Dade County SD
Supt. — See Miami
Goleman HS — 1,700/9-12
14100 NW 89th Ave 33018 — 305-362-0676
Joaquin Hernandez, prin. — Fax 827-0249
Miami Lakes Educational Center — Vo/Tech
5780 NW 158th St 33014 — 305-557-1100
Lourdes Diaz, prin. — Fax 827-9317
Miami Lakes MS — 1,000/6-8
6425 Miami Lakeway N 33014 — 305-557-3900
Dr. Manuel Sanchez, prin. — Fax 828-6753

Southeastern College — Post-Sec.
17395 NW 59th Ave 33015 — 305-820-5003

Miami Shores, Miami-Dade, Pop. 10,271

Barry University — Post-Sec.
11300 NE 2nd Ave 33161 — 305-899-3000

Miami Springs, Miami-Dade, Pop. 13,739
Miami-Dade County SD
Supt. — See Miami
Miami Springs HS — 1,800/9-12
751 Dove Ave 33166 — 305-885-3585
Edward Smith, prin. — Fax 884-2632
Miami Springs MS — 1,500/6-8
150 S Royal Poinciana Blvd 33166 — 305-888-6457
Kimberly Emmanuel, prin. — Fax 887-5281
Miami Springs Adult Education Center — Adult
751 Dove Ave 33166 — 305-885-3585
Miguel Veloso, prin. — Fax 884-2632

Middleburg, Clay, Pop. 12,797
Clay County SD
Supt. — See Green Cove Springs
Middleburg HS — 1,700/9-12
3750 County Road 220 32068 — 904-213-2100
Robert Feltner, prin. — Fax 291-5462
Wilkinson JHS — 800/7-8
5025 County Road 218 32068 — 904-291-5500
Christina Cornwell, prin. — Fax 291-5510

Milton, Santa Rosa, Pop. 8,470
Santa Rosa County SD — 25,600/PK-12
5086 Canal St 32570 — 850-983-5000
Tim Wyrosdick, supt. — Fax 983-5013
www.santarosa.k12.fl.us/
Avalon MS — 800/6-8
5445 King Arthurs Way 32583 — 850-983-5540
David Sigurnjak, prin. — Fax 983-5545
Central S — 500/K-12
6180 Central School Rd 32570 — 850-983-5640
Sean Twitty, prin. — Fax 983-5645
Hobbs MS — 700/6-8
5317 Glover Ln 32570 — 850-983-5630
Wesley Underwood, prin. — Fax 983-5635
King MS — 600/6-8
5928 Stewart St 32570 — 850-983-5660
Darren Brock, prin. — Fax 983-5665
Learning Academy — 100/Alt
5880 Stewart St 32570 — 850-983-3495
Kara Whitney, admin. — Fax 983-8098
Locklin Technical Center — Vo/Tech
5330 Berryhill Rd 32570 — 850-983-5700
Maria LaDouceur, prin. — Fax 983-5715
Milton HS — 1,800/9-12
5445 Stewart St 32570 — 850-983-5600
Tim Short, prin. — Fax 983-5610
Santa Rosa HS — Adult
5332 Berryhill Rd 32570 — 850-983-5710
Donna Christopher, prin. — Fax 983-5345
Other Schools – See Gulf Breeze, Jay, Navarre, Pace

Radford M. Locklin Technical Center — Post-Sec.
5330 Berryhill Rd 32570 — 850-983-5700
Santa Rosa Christian S — 300/PK-12
6331 Chestnut St 32570 — 850-623-4671
West Florida Baptist Academy — 200/K-12
5621 Highway 90 32583 — 850-623-9307

Minneola, Lake, Pop. 9,082
Lake County SD
Supt. — See Tavares
Lake Minneola HS — 1,900/9-12
101 N Hancock Rd, — 352-394-9600
Linda Shepherd-Miller, prin. — Fax 394-9601

Miramar, Broward, Pop. 118,644
Broward County SD
Supt. — See Fort Lauderdale
Everglades HS — 2,400/9-12
17100 SW 48th Ct 33027 — 754-323-0500
Haleh Darbar, prin. — Fax 323-0640
Glades MS — 1,500/6-8
16700 SW 48th Ct 33027 — 754-323-4600
Ricardo Reyes, prin. — Fax 323-4685
Miramar HS — 2,600/9-12
3601 SW 89th Ave 33025 — 754-323-1350
Maria Formoso, prin. — Fax 323-1480
New Renaissance MS — 1,100/6-8
10701 Miramar Blvd 33025 — 754-323-3500
Janet Morales, prin. — Fax 323-3585

Chamberlain College of Nursing — Post-Sec.
2300 SW 145th Ave 33027 — 954-885-3510
Concorde Career Institute — Post-Sec.
10933 Marks Way 33025 — 954-731-8880
DeVry University — Post-Sec.
2300 SW 145th Ave 33027 — 954-499-9700
Le Cordon Bleu College of Culinary Arts — Post-Sec.
3221 Enterprise Way 33025 — 954-438-8882
Unilatina International College — Post-Sec.
3130 Commerce Pkwy 33025 — 954-607-4344

Monticello, Jefferson, Pop. 2,477
Jefferson County SD — 900/PK-12
1490 W Washington St 32344 — 850-342-0100
Al Cooksey, supt. — Fax 342-0108
www.jeffersonschooldistrict.org
Jefferson County MSHS — 300/6-12
50 David Rd 32344 — 850-997-3555
Dr. Baron McCombs, prin. — Fax 997-4773
Turning Point Alternative S — Alt
575 S Water St 32344 — 850-342-0100
Nancy Whitty, prin.
Jefferson County Adult Center — Adult
575 S Water St 32344 — 850-342-0100
Sherman Stroman, prin. — Fax 342-0108

Aucilla Christian Academy — 300/PK-12
7803 Aucilla Rd 32344 — 850-997-3597

Montverde, Lake, Pop. 1,436

Montverde Academy — 900/PK-12
17235 7th St 34756 — 407-469-2561
Dr. Kasey Kesselring, hdmstr. — Fax 469-3711

Moore Haven, Glades, Pop. 1,667
Glades County SD — 1,400/PK-12
PO Box 459 33471 — 863-946-0202
Scott Bass, supt. — Fax 946-1529
www.gladesedu.org
Moore Haven MSHS — 300/6-12
PO Box 99 33471 — 863-946-0811
Tim Wilder, prin. — Fax 946-1532

Mount Dora, Lake, Pop. 12,205
Lake County SD
Supt. — See Tavares
Mount Dora HS — 1,100/9-12
700 N Highland St 32757 — 352-383-2177
Dr. Rhonda Boone, prin. — Fax 383-6466
Mount Dora MS — 800/6-8
1405 Lincoln Ave 32757 — 352-383-6101
Jacob Stein, prin. — Fax 383-4949

Mount Dora Christian Academy — 600/PK-12
301 W 13th Ave 32757 — 352-383-2155
Dr. Brad Moser, head sch — Fax 383-3112
Solid Rock Christian S — 100/PK-12
21951 US Highway 441 32757 — 352-735-5777
Southern Technical College — Post-Sec.
2799 W Old US Highway 441 32757 — 352-383-4242

Mulberry, Polk, Pop. 3,765
Polk County SD
Supt. — See Bartow
Mulberry HS — 1,000/9-12
1 NE 4th Cir 33860 — 863-701-1104
Michael Young, prin. — Fax 701-1109

Mulberry MS 1,000/6-8
500 Dr MLK Jr Ave 33860 863-701-1066
Cynthia Cangelose, prin. Fax 701-1068
New Horizons S 50/Alt
6980 State Road 37 S 33860 863-428-1520
Brett Butler, prin. Fax 428-2204

Fortis Institute Post-Sec.
5925 Imperial Pkwy Ste 200 33860 863-646-1400

Naples, Collier, Pop. 19,366
Collier County SD 43,800/PK-12
5775 Osceola Trl 34109 239-377-0001
Dr. Kamela Patton, supt. Fax 377-0206
www.collierschools.com
Beacon HS 300/Alt
3710 Estey Ave 34104 239-377-1060
Dr. Cynthia Janssen, prin. Fax 377-1051
Collier HS 1,700/9-12
5600 Cougar Dr 34109 239-377-1200
Jose Hernandez, prin. Fax 377-1201
Corkscrew MS 700/6-8
1165 County Road 858 34120 239-377-3400
Dennis Snider, prin. Fax 377-3401
Cypress Palm MS 800/6-8
4255 18th Ave NE 34120 239-377-5200
John Kasten, prin. Fax 377-5201
East Naples MS 1,100/6-8
4100 Estey Ave 34104 239-377-3600
Dr. Darren Burkett, prin. Fax 377-3601
Golden Gate HS 1,600/9-12
2925 Titan Way 34116 239-377-1600
Dr. Tobin Walcott, prin. Fax 377-1601
Golden Gate MS 1,000/6-8
2701 48th Ter SW 34116 239-377-3800
Dr. Mason Clark, prin. Fax 377-3801
Gulf Coast HS 2,000/9-12
7878 Shark Way 34119 239-377-1400
Joseph Mikulski, prin. Fax 377-1401
Gulfview MS 700/6-8
255 6th St S 34102 239-377-4000
Kevin Huelsman, prin. Fax 377-4001
Lely HS 1,500/9-12
1 Lely High School Blvd 34113 239-377-2000
Ryan Nemeth, prin. Fax 377-2001
Manatee MS 900/6-8
1920 Manatee Rd 34114 239-377-4400
Pamela Vickaryous, prin. Fax 377-4401
Naples HS 1,600/9-12
1100 Golden Eagle Cir 34102 239-377-2200
Kevin Saba, prin. Fax 377-2201
New Beginnings S - Naples 50/Alt
3710 Estey Ave 34104 239-377-1050
Eric Peltz, lead tchr. Fax 377-1051
North Naples MS 900/6-8
16165 Learning Ln 34110 239-377-4600
Margaret Jackson, prin. Fax 377-4601
Oakridge MS 1,000/6-8
14975 Collier Blvd 34119 239-377-4800
Kimberly Lonergan, prin. Fax 377-4801
Palmetto Ridge HS 1,800/9-12
1655 Victory Ln 34120 239-377-2400
Jon Bremseth, prin. Fax 377-2401
Pine Ridge MS 1,000/6-8
1515 Pine Ridge Rd 34109 239-377-5000
Dr. Sean Kinsley, prin. Fax 377-5001
Walker Technical HS Vo/Tech
3702 Estey Ave 34104 239-377-3300
Fax 377-3301
Other Schools – See Everglades City, Immokalee

Ave Maria School of Law Post-Sec.
1025 Commons Cir 34119 239-687-5300
Community S of Naples 700/PK-12
13275 Livingston Rd 34109 239-597-7575
Dr. David Watson, head sch Fax 598-2973
First Baptist Academy 500/PK-12
3000 Orange Blossom Dr 34109 239-597-2233
Thomas Rider, admin. Fax 597-4187
Hodges University Post-Sec.
2655 Northbrooke Dr 34119 239-513-1122
Lorenzo Walker Institute of Technology Post-Sec.
3702 Estey Ave 34104 239-377-0900
Nicaea Academy 200/PK-12
14785 Collier Blvd 34119 239-353-9099
St. John Neumann Catholic HS 200/9-12
3000 53rd St SW 34116 239-455-3044
Sr. Patricia Roche, prin. Fax 455-2966
Seacrest Country Day S 500/PK-12
7100 Davis Blvd 34104 239-793-1986
D. John Watson Ph.D., head sch Fax 793-1460
Wolford College Post-Sec.
1336 Creekside Blvd Ste 2 34108 239-513-1135

Naranja, Miami-Dade, Pop. 8,180
Miami-Dade County SD
Supt. — See Miami
Miami MacArthur South HS 100/Alt
13990 SW 264th St 33032 305-258-7200
Marcus Miller, prin. Fax 258-7201

Navarre, Santa Rosa, Pop. 30,113
Santa Rosa County SD
Supt. — See Milton
Holley-Navarre MS 800/6-8
1976 Williams Creek Dr 32566 850-936-6040
Joie DeStefano, prin. Fax 936-6049
Navarre HS 1,900/9-12
8600 High School Blvd 32566 850-936-6080
Brian Noack, prin. Fax 936-6088

Neptune Beach, Duval, Pop. 6,907
Duval County SD
Supt. — See Jacksonville
Fletcher HS 2,200/9-12
700 Seagate Ave 32266 904-247-5905
Dean Ledford, prin. Fax 247-5920

Beaches Chapel Christian S 300/PK-12
610 Florida Blvd 32266 904-241-4211
Vivian Pinner, prin. Fax 249-2046

Newberry, Alachua, Pop. 4,851
Alachua County SD
Supt. — See Gainesville
Newberry HS 600/9-12
400 SW 258th St 32669 352-472-1101
Kevin Purvis, prin. Fax 472-1116
Oak View MS 600/6-8
1203 SW 250th St 32669 352-472-1102
Katherine Munn, prin. Fax 472-1131

New Port Richey, Pasco, Pop. 14,612
Pasco County SD
Supt. — See Land O Lakes
Bayonet Point MS 700/6-8
11125 Little Rd 34654 727-774-7400
Shelley Carrino, prin. Fax 774-7491
Gulf HS 1,300/9-12
5355 School Rd 34652 727-774-3300
Kim Davis, prin. Fax 774-3391
Gulf MS 800/6-8
6419 Louisiana Ave 34653 727-774-8000
Jason Joens, prin. Fax 774-8091
Marchman Technical Education Center Vo/Tech
7825 Campus Dr 34653 727-774-1700
Robert Aguis, prin. Fax 774-1791
Mitchell HS 1,800/9-12
2323 Little Rd 34655 727-774-9200
Jessica Schultz, prin. Fax 774-9291
Ridgewood HS 1,100/9-12
7650 Orchid Lake Rd 34653 727-774-3900
Angie Murphy, prin. Fax 774-3991
River Ridge HS 1,500/9-12
11646 Town Center Rd 34654 727-774-7200
Toni Zetzsche, prin. Fax 774-7291
River Ridge MS 1,100/6-8
11646 Town Center Rd 34654 727-774-7000
Marcy Nettles, prin. Fax 774-7291
Seven Springs MS 1,400/6-8
2441 Little Rd 34655 727-774-6700
Christopher Dunning, prin. Fax 774-6791
Schwettman Education Center Adult
5520 Grand Blvd 34652 727-774-0000
Randy Koenigsfeld, prin. Fax 774-0091

Benes International School of Beauty Post-Sec.
7027 US Highway 19 34652 727-848-8415
Elfers Christian S 200/PK-12
5630 Olympia St 34652 727-845-0235
Genesis Preparatory S 100/6-12
7710 Osteen Rd 34653 727-846-8407
Millennium Academy 100/K-12
1005 Ridge Rd 34654 727-845-8150
New Port Richey SDA S 100/PK-12
4416 Thys Rd 34653 727-842-8919
Keith Nelson, prin. Fax 842-1517
Pasco-Hernando Community College Post-Sec.
10230 Ridge Rd 34654 727-847-2727
Rasmussen College Post-Sec.
8661 Citizens Dr 34654 727-942-0069
Southeastern College Post-Sec.
6014 US Highway 19 Ste 250 34652 727-487-6855

New Smyrna Beach, Volusia, Pop. 22,191
Volusia County SD
Supt. — See De Land
New Smyrna Beach HS 1,900/9-12
1015 10th St 32168 386-424-2555
Karen Chenoweth, prin. Fax 424-2505
New Smyrna Beach MS 1,200/6-8
1200 S Myrtle Ave 32168 386-424-2550
Elizabeth Johnson, prin. Fax 424-2504

Niceville, Okaloosa, Pop. 12,288
Okaloosa County SD
Supt. — See Fort Walton Beach
Niceville HS 2,000/9-12
800 John Sims Pkwy E 32578 850-833-4114
Charlie Marello, prin. Fax 833-4267
Ruckel MS 1,000/6-8
201 Partin Dr N 32578 850-833-4142
Paul Whiddon, prin. Fax 833-3291

Northwest Florida State College Post-Sec.
100 College Blvd E 32578 850-678-5111
Rocky Bayou Christian S 600/PK-12
2101 Partin Dr N 32578 850-729-7227
Dr. Michael Mosley, supt. Fax 729-2513
Wellspring Performing Arts Christian S 50/PK-12
201 Redwood Ave 32578 850-678-9355
Lucille Hearn, head sch

North Fort Myers, Lee, Pop. 39,050
Lee County SD
Supt. — See Fort Myers
North Fort Myers HS 1,600/9-12
5000 Orange Grove Blvd 33903 239-995-2117
Debbie Diggs, prin. Fax 995-1243

Temple Christian S 100/PK-12
18841 State Road 31 33917 239-543-3222

North Lauderdale, Broward, Pop. 39,771
Broward County SD
Supt. — See Fort Lauderdale
Silver Lakes MS 800/6-8
7600 Tam Oshanter Blvd 33068 754-322-4600
Alison Trautmann, prin. Fax 322-4685

North Miami, Miami-Dade, Pop. 57,562
Miami-Dade County SD
Supt. — See Miami
North Miami HS 2,500/9-12
13110 NE 8th Ave 33161 305-891-6590
Daryl Branton, prin. Fax 895-1788
North Miami MS 700/7-9
700 NE 137th St 33161 305-891-5611
Patrick Lacouty, prin. Fax 891-4057
North Miami Adult Education Center Adult
13110 NE 8th Ave 33161 305-981-6774
Franklyn Glasford, prin. Fax 895-6248

Johnson & Wales University Post-Sec.
1701 NE 127th St 33181 305-892-7000
Miami Union Academy 300/PK-12
12600 NW 4th Ave 33168 305-953-9907

North Miami Beach, Miami-Dade, Pop. 40,525
Miami-Dade County SD
Supt. — See Miami
Kennedy MS 1,200/6-8
1075 NE 167th St 33162 305-947-1451
Mary Parton, prin. Fax 949-9046
Mourning HS 1,800/9-12
2601 NE 151st St 33160 305-919-2000
Christopher Shinn, prin. Fax 919-2001
North Miami Beach HS 2,000/9-12
1247 NE 167th St 33162 305-949-8381
Randy Milliken, prin. Fax 949-0491

Allison Academy 100/6-12
1881 NE 164th St 33162 305-940-3922
Bais Yaakov S for Girls 300/6-12
1110 NE 163rd St 33162 305-957-1670
Chames HS 100/9-12
1025 NE Miami Gardens Dr 33179 305-944-5344
Rohr MS 6-8
1051 N Miami Beach Blvd 33162 305-947-7779
SAE Institute of Technology Post-Sec.
16051 W Dixie Hwy Ste 200 33160 305-944-7494
Scheck Hillel Community S 900/PK-12
19000 NE 25th Ave, Miami FL 33180 305-931-2831
Dr. Ezra Levy, hdmstr. Fax 932-7463
Union Institute & University Post-Sec.
16853 NE 2nd Ave Ste 102 33162 305-653-7141

North Palm Beach, Palm Beach, Pop. 11,885

Baldwin Prep S 100/K-12
200 Castlewood Dr 33408 561-844-7700
Benjamin S 1,300/PK-12
11000 Ellison Wilson Rd 33408 561-626-3747
Robert Goldberg, head sch Fax 626-8752

North Port, Sarasota, Pop. 56,337
Sarasota County SD
Supt. — See Sarasota
Heron Creek MS 900/6-8
6501 W Price Blvd, 941-480-3371
Matthew Gruhl, prin. Fax 480-3398
North Port HS 2,300/9-12
6400 W Price Blvd, 941-423-8558
Brandon Johnson, prin. Fax 480-3199
Woodland MS 800/6-8
2700 Panacea Blvd 34289 941-240-8590
Dr. Cindy Hall, prin. Fax 240-8589

Oakland Park, Broward, Pop. 40,410
Broward County SD
Supt. — See Fort Lauderdale
Northeast HS 1,900/9-12
700 NE 56th St 33334 754-322-1550
Anthony Valachovic, prin. Fax 322-1680
Rickards MS 1,000/6-8
6000 NE 9th Ave 33334 754-322-4400
Washington Collado, prin. Fax 322-4485

Ocala, Marion, Pop. 55,278
Marion County SD 41,200/PK-12
PO Box 670 34478 352-671-7700
Heidi Maier Ph.D., supt. Fax 671-7581
www.marionschools.net
Forest HS 2,100/9-12
5000 SE Maricamp Rd 34480 352-671-4700
Brent Carson, prin. Fax 671-4702
Fort King MS 1,100/6-8
545 NE 17th Ave 34470 352-671-4725
Gary Smallridge, prin. Fax 671-4726
Horizon Academy at Marion Oak 800/5-8
365 Marion Oaks Dr 34473 352-671-6290
Troy Sanford, prin. Fax 671-6291
Howard MS 1,200/6-8
1655 NW 10th St 34475 352-671-7225
Robert Hensel, prin. Fax 671-7226
Lake Weir HS 1,700/9-12
10351 SE Maricamp Rd 34472 352-671-4820
Jennifer Beasley, prin. Fax 671-4829
Liberty MS 1,100/6-8
4773 SW 95th St 34476 352-291-7930
Renee Jones, prin. Fax 291-7931
Marion Technical Institute 50/9-12
1614 E Fort King St 34471 352-671-4765
Jim Wohrley, prin. Fax 671-4766
Osceola MS 900/6-8
526 SE Tuscawilla Ave 34471 352-671-7100
Suzette Parker, prin. Fax 671-7101
Vanguard HS 1,800/9-12
7 NW 28th St 34475 352-671-4900
John Kerley, prin. Fax 671-4903
West Port HS 2,500/9-12
3733 SW 80th Ave 34481 352-291-4000
Ken McAteer, prin. Fax 291-4001
Other Schools – See Belleview, Citra, Dunnellon, Summerfield

College of Central Florida Post-Sec.
3001 SW College Rd 34474 352-873-5800
First Assembly Christian S 300/PK-12
1827 NE 14th St 34470 352-351-1913
Earlene Carte, prin. Fax 351-5170
Marion Co. School Radiologic Technology Post-Sec.
1014 SW 7th Rd 34471 352-671-7200
Meadowbrook Academy 300/K-12
4741 SW 20th St Bldg 1 34474 352-861-0700
Tina Stelogeannis, prin. Fax 861-0533
Ocala Christian Academy 400/PK-12
1714 SE 36th Ave 34471 352-694-4178
Tim Rowe, admin. Fax 694-7192
Rasmussen College Post-Sec.
4755 SW 46th Ct 34474 352-629-1941
Redeemer Christian S 200/PK-10
155 SW 87th Pl 34476 352-854-2999
St. John Lutheran S 400/PK-12
1915 SE Lake Weir Ave 34471 352-622-7275
Tim Schmidt, prin. Fax 433-2540
Trinity Catholic HS 500/9-12
2600 SW 42nd St 34471 352-622-9025
Louis Pereira, pres. Fax 861-8164

Ocoee, Orange, Pop. 34,484
Orange County SD
Supt. — See Orlando
Ocoee HS 2,400/9-12
1925 Ocoee Crown Point Pkwy 34761 407-905-3000
Laura Beusse, prin. Fax 905-3099
Ocoee MS 1,400/6-8
300 S Bluford Ave 34761 407-877-5035
Samuel Davis, prin. Fax 877-5045

Victory Christian Academy 200/K-12
1601 A D Mims Rd 34761 407-656-1295
Dr. Bradley Phillips, admin. Fax 656-6895

Odessa, Hillsborough, Pop. 7,133
Hillsborough County SD
Supt. — See Tampa
Walker MS 900/6-8
8282 North Mobley Rd 33556 813-631-4726
Anthony Jones, prin. Fax 631-4738

Odessa Christian S 200/K-12
19521 Michigan Ave 33556 813-792-1825
Erin Ciulla, head sch Fax 749-6690

Okeechobee, Okeechobee, Pop. 5,542
Okeechobee County SD 6,000/PK-12
700 SW 2nd Ave 34974 863-462-5000
Ken Kenworthy, supt. Fax 462-5151
www.okee.k12.fl.us
Okeechobee Achievement Academy 100/Alt
1000 NW 34th St 34972 863-462-5125
Randal Weigum, prin. Fax 462-5295
Okeechobee HS 1,200/10-12
2800 US Highway 441 N 34972 863-462-5025
Dylan Tedders, prin. Fax 462-5037
Okeechobee HS Freshman Campus 500/9-9
610 SW 2nd Ave 34974 863-462-5288
Carol Revels, head sch Fax 462-5258
Osceola MS 700/6-8
825 SW 28th St 34974 863-462-5070
Sean Downing, prin. Fax 462-5076
Yearling MS 700/6-8
925 NW 23rd Ln 34972 863-462-5056
Jody Hays, prin. Fax 462-5062

Okeechobee Christian Academy 100/PK-12
701 S Parrott Ave 34974 863-763-3072
Sabina Guthrie, prin. Fax 213-1339

Oldsmar, Pinellas, Pop. 13,296

Oldsmar Christian S 200/PK-12
650 Burbank Rd 34677 813-855-5746

Old Town, Dixie
Dixie County SD
Supt. — See Cross City
Dixie County Adult Center Adult
328 SE 349 Ave 32680 352-498-6141
Buddy Schofield, dir. Fax 498-1279

Dixie County Learning Academy 100/K-12
1357 NE 82nd Ave 32680 352-542-3306
Dr. Sylvia Lamenta, prin. Fax 542-7291

Opa Locka, Miami-Dade, Pop. 15,115
Miami-Dade County SD
Supt. — See Miami
Mann Opportunity S 100/Alt
16101 NW 44th Ct 33054 305-625-0855
Samuel Johnson, prin. Fax 625-1605

Betesda Christian S 100/K-12
PO Box 540392 33054 305-685-8255

Orange City, Volusia, Pop. 10,438
Volusia County SD
Supt. — See De Land
River Springs MS 1,400/6-8
900 W Ohio Ave 32763 386-968-0011
Stacy Gotlib, prin. Fax 456-5355
University HS 2,800/9-12
1000 W Rhode Island Ave 32763 386-968-0013
Dr. Julian Jones, prin. Fax 968-0019

Sunshine State S of Leadership 100/PK-12
2700 Enterprise Rd 32763 386-218-3906

Orange Park, Clay, Pop. 8,196
Clay County SD
Supt. — See Green Cove Springs
Fleming Island HS 2,100/9-12
2233 Village Square Pkwy 32003 904-336-7500
Tom Pittman, prin. Fax 336-7478
Lakeside JHS 800/7-8
2750 Moody Ave 32073 904-213-1800
Dr. David McDonald, prin. Fax 213-2987
Oakleaf HS 2,000/9-12
4035 Plantation Oaks Blvd 32065 904-218-1900
Treasure Pickett, prin. Fax 336-8382
Oakleaf JHS 900/6-8
4085 Plantation Oaks Blvd 32065 904-213-5500
Anthony Williams, prin. Fax 529-2170
Orange Park HS 1,600/9-12
2300 Kingsley Ave 32073 904-272-8110
Clayton Anderson, prin. Fax 272-8181
Orange Park JHS 700/7-8
1500 Gano Ave 32073 904-278-2000
Al DeJesus, prin. Fax 278-2009
Ridgeview HS 1,500/9-12
466 Madison Ave 32065 904-213-5203
Debbie Segreto, prin. Fax 213-3033

Everest University Post-Sec.
805 Wells Rd 32073 904-264-9122
Fortis College Post-Sec.
560 Wells Rd 32073 904-269-7086
HighPoint Christian Academy 50/7-12
84 Knight Boxx Rd 32065 904-272-7949
National Heavy Equipment Operator School Post-Sec.
PO Box 65789 32065 904-272-4000
R. Webber Institute for Worship Studies Post-Sec.
151 Kingsley Ave 32073 904-264-2172
St. Johns Country Day S 600/PK-12
3100 Doctors Lake Dr 32073 904-264-9572
Todd Zehner, hdmstr. Fax 264-0375

Orlando, Orange, Pop. 231,839
Orange County SD 183,800/PK-12
445 W Amelia St 32801 407-317-3200
Dr. Barbara Jenkins, supt. Fax 317-3401
www.ocps.net
Acceleration Academy 300/Alt
2274 S Semoran Blvd 32822 407-992-0917
Douglas Loftus, prin. Fax 207-4961
Acceleration Academy West 100/Alt
2751 Lake Stanley Rd 32818 407-521-2358
George Morse, prin. Fax 521-2369
Avalon MS 1,600/6-8
13914 Mailer Blvd 32828 407-207-7839
Karen Furno, prin. Fax 207-7872
Boone HS 2,900/9-12
1000 E Kaley St 32806 407-893-7200
Dusty Johns, prin. Fax 897-2466
Carver MS 700/6-8
4500 Columbia St 32811 407-296-5110
Hector Maestre, prin. Fax 296-6407
Chain of Lakes MS 1,300/6-8
8700 Conroy Windermere Rd 32835 407-909-5400
Cheron Anderson, prin. Fax 909-5410
Colonial 9th Grade Center 900/9-9
7775 Valencia College Ln 32807 407-249-6369
Jose Martinez, prin. Fax 249-6297
Colonial HS 2,400/10-12
6100 Oleander Dr 32807 407-482-6300
Jose Martinez, prin. Fax 737-1450
Conway MS 1,000/6-8
4600 Anderson Rd 32812 407-249-6420
Darrell Canamas, prin. Fax 249-6429
Corner Lake MS 1,300/6-8
1700 Chuluota Rd 32820 407-568-0510
Luis Tousent, prin. Fax 568-0920
Cypress Creek HS 3,100/9-12
1101 Bear Crossing Dr 32824 407-852-3400
Dr. Walton McHale, prin. Fax 850-5160
Discovery MS 1,000/6-8
601 Woodbury Rd 32828 407-384-1555
Gloria Fernandez, prin. Fax 384-1580
East Orlando Education Center 50/Alt
2510 Gulfstream Rd 32805 407-245-1555
William Tovine, prin. Fax 245-1561
East River HS 1,800/9-12
654 Columbia School Rd 32833 407-956-8550
Heather Hilton, prin. Fax 956-8565
Edgewater HS 1,700/9-12
3100 Edgewater Dr 32804 407-835-4900
Dr. Mark Shanoff, prin. Fax 245-2758
Evans HS 2,600/9-12
4949 Silver Star Rd 32808 407-522-3400
Jenny Gibson-Linkh, prin. Fax 522-3458
Freedom HS 3,200/9-12
2500 W Taft Vineland Rd 32837 407-816-5600
Rolando Bailey, prin. Fax 816-5616
Freedom MS 1,000/6-8
2850 W Taft Vineland Rd 32837 407-858-6130
Cheri Godek, prin. Fax 858-6132
Glenridge MS 1,400/6-8
2900 Upper Park Rd 32814 407-623-1415
Trevor Honahan, prin. Fax 623-1427
Howard MS 1,000/6-8
800 E Robinson St 32801 407-245-1780
Michael Martucci, prin. Fax 245-1785
Hunters Creek MS 1,100/6-8
13400 Town Loop Blvd 32837 407-858-4620
Amy McHale, prin. Fax 858-4621
Jackson MS 1,400/6-8
6000 Stonewall Jackson Rd 32807 407-249-6430
Dr. Jhunu Mohapatra, prin. Fax 249-6438
Jones HS 800/9-12
801 S Rio Grande Ave 32805 407-835-2300
Roderick Walton, prin. Fax 245-2765
Lake Nona HS 2,000/9-12
12500 Narcoossee Rd 32832 407-956-8300
Margaret Nampon, prin. Fax 956-8315
Lake Nona MS 1,400/6-8
13700 Narcoossee Rd 32832 407-858-5522
Stephanie Jackson, prin. Fax 858-5530
Lee MS 1,000/6-8
1201 Maury Rd 32804 407-245-1800
Cynthia Haupt, prin. Fax 245-1809
Legacy MS 900/6-8
11398 Lake Underhill Rd 32825 407-658-5330
Shannon Battoe, prin. Fax 658-5334
Liberty MS 1,000/6-8
3405 S Chickasaw Trl 32829 407-249-6440
James Russo, prin. Fax 249-6449
Lockhart MS 800/6-8
3411 Dr Love Rd 32810 407-296-5120
Alison Kirby, prin. Fax 296-6549
Meadowbrook MS 1,100/6-8
6000 North Ln 32808 407-296-5130
Robin Brown, prin. Fax 296-5139
Meadow Woods MS 1,100/6-8
1800 Rhode Island Woods Cir 32824 407-850-5180
Marisol Mendez, prin. Fax 850-5190
Memorial MS 800/6-8
2220 29th St 32805 407-245-1810
Gracemarie Howland, prin. Fax 245-1820
Mid Florida Tech Vo/Tech
2900 W Oak Ridge Rd 32809 407-855-5880
Alex Heidelberg, prin. Fax 251-6197
Oak Ridge HS 2,400/9-12
700 W Oak Ridge Rd 32809 407-852-3200
Jennifer Bellinger, prin. Fax 850-5152
Odyssey MS 900/6-8
9290 Lee Vista Blvd 32829 407-207-3850
Ann Hembrook, prin. Fax 207-3871
Olympia HS 3,000/9-12
4301 S Apopka Vineland Rd 32835 407-905-6400
Guy Swenson, prin. Fax 905-6465
Orlando Tech Ctr Vo/Tech
301 W Amelia St 32801 407-246-7060
Andrew Jenkins, dir. Fax 317-3372
Pace Center for Girls 50/Alt
728 Gear Lake Ave 32803 407-992-0456
William Tovine, admin. Fax 992-0455
Phillips HS 3,500/9-12
6500 Turkey Lake Rd 32819 407-355-3200
Suzanne Knight, prin. Fax 370-7232
Positive Pathways Transition Center Alt
6125 N Orange Blossom Trl 32810 407-992-0599
Francis Pons, prin. Fax 992-0914
Robinswood MS 1,300/6-8
6305 Balboa Dr 32818 407-296-5140
Nicole Jefferson, prin. Fax 296-5148
Simon Youth Academy Alt
5253 International Dr 32819 407-858-6114
William Tovine, prin. Fax 858-6119
South Creek MS 1,000/6-8
3801 Wetherbee Rd 32824 407-251-2413
Sean Brown, prin. Fax 251-2464
Southwest MS 1,200/6-8
6450 Dr Phillips Blvd 32819 407-370-7200
Raymond Yockel, prin. Fax 370-7210
Timber Creek HS 3,000/9-12
1001 Avalon Park South Blvd 32828 321-235-7800
Kelly Paduano, prin. Fax 253-7821
Union Park MS 900/6-8
1844 Westfall Dr 32817 407-249-6309
Melanie May, prin. Fax 249-4404
Universal Education Center 50/Alt
1000 Universal Studios Plz 32819 407-224-6634
William Tovine, prin. Fax 224-6636
University HS 3,000/9-12
2450 Cougar Way 32817 407-482-8700
Dr. Anne Carcara, prin. Fax 737-1455
Walker MS 1,000/6-8
150 Amidon Ln 32809 407-858-3210
Julio Valle, prin. Fax 858-3218
Westridge MS 1,200/6-8
3800 W Oak Ridge Rd 32809 407-354-2640
Christopher Camacho, prin. Fax 354-2637
Avalon Center for Tech Excellence Adult
2201 Crown Hill Blvd 32828 407-281-5100
Capildeo Jadonath, prin. Fax 281-5127
Other Schools – See Apopka, Maitland, Ocoee, Windermere, Winter Garden, Winter Park

Adventist University of Health Sciences Post-Sec.
671 Winyah Dr 32803 407-303-9798
Agape Christian Academy 400/PK-12
2425 N Hiawassee Rd 32818 407-298-1111
American College for Medical Careers Post-Sec.
5959 Lake Ellenor Dr 32809 407-738-4488
Asbury Theological Seminary Post-Sec.
8401 Valencia College Ln 32825 407-482-7500
Avalon S 100/K-12
5002 Andrus Ave 32804 407-297-4353
Bishop Moore HS 1,100/9-12
3901 Edgewater Dr 32804 407-293-7561
Scott Brogan, prin. Fax 296-8135
Central Florida Blood Bank Post-Sec.
8669 Commodity Cir 32819 407-849-6100
Central Florida Christian Academy 200/PK-12
700 Good Homes Rd 32818 407-850-2322
Dr. Robert Gilliland, hdmstr. Fax 293-6914
Centura Institute Post-Sec.
6359 Edgewater Dr 32810 407-275-9696
Concorde Career Institute Post-Sec.
3444 McCrory Pl 32803 407-812-3060
Conrad Academy 200/K-12
2008 N Goldenrod Rd 32807 407-243-2211
DAVE School Post-Sec.
2500 Universal Studios # 25 32819 855-328-3839
Devereux-Florida Treatment Network Post-Sec.
5850 T G Lee Blvd Ste 400 32822 407-812-4555
DeVry University Post-Sec.
4000 Millenia Blvd 32839 407-345-2800
DeVry University Post-Sec.
1800 Pembrook Dr Ste 160 32810 407-659-0900
Downey Christian S 300/K-12
10201 E Colonial Dr 32817 407-275-0340
Dr. C.C. Dees, admin. Fax 275-1481
Eastland Christian S 300/PK-12
9000 Lake Underhill Rd 32825 407-277-5858
Everest University - North Orlando Cmps Post-Sec.
5421 Diplomat Cir 32810 407-628-5870
Everest University-South Orlando Campus Post-Sec.
9200 Southpark Center Loop 32819 407-851-2525
Faith Christian Academy 400/PK-12
9307 Curry Ford Rd 32825 407-275-8031
Dr. Andrew Rumbaugh, admin. Fax 281-3710
Family Christian Academy 100/K-10
9580 Curry Ford Rd 32825 407-568-9837
FCC Anthem College Post-Sec.
989 N Semoran Blvd 32807 407-628-5870
First Academy 1,000/PK-12
2667 Bruton Blvd 32805 407-206-8600
Steve Whitaker Ph.D., head sch
Florida College of Integrative Medicine Post-Sec.
7100 Lake Ellenor Dr 32809 407-888-8689
Florida Technical College Post-Sec.
12900 Challenger Pkwy 32826 407-447-7300
Heritage Prep S 200/PK-12
6000 W Colonial Dr 32808 407-293-6000
IEC Christian Academy 100/PK-10
2500 W Oak Ridge Rd 32809 407-581-6120
Keiser University Post-Sec.
5600 Lake Underhill Rd 32807 407-273-5800
Lake Highland Preparatory S 2,000/PK-12
901 Highland Ave 32803 407-206-1900
Dr. David Rowe, pres.
Leaders Preparatory S 200/PK-12
1021 N Goldenrod Rd 32807 407-382-9900
Le Cordon Bleu College of Culinary Arts Post-Sec.
8511 Commodity Cir # 100 32819 407-888-4000
Medtech Institute Post-Sec.
2000 N Alafaya Trl Ste 300 32826 407-691-3391
Mt. Sinai Jr Academy 100/K-10
2610 Orange Center Blvd 32805 407-298-7871
Dr. Betty Nugent, prin. Fax 286-2914
Orlando Christian Prep S 400/PK-12
500 S Semoran Blvd 32807 407-823-9744
Pamela Piorkowski M.Ed., admin. Fax 380-1186
Orlando Medical Institute Post-Sec.
6220 S Orange Blossom #410 32809 407-251-0007

Pine Castle Christian Academy 200/PK-12
7101 Lake Ellenor Dr 32809 407-313-7222
Shane Lightfoot, admin. Fax 313-7226
Saints Academy 100/K-12
PO Box 680487 32868 407-683-5537
Vivian Williams, prin.
Sanford-Brown College Post-Sec.
6039 S Rio Grande Ave 32809 407-857-2300
Southern Technical College Post-Sec.
1485 Florida Mall Ave 32809 407-438-6000
South Orlando Christian Academy 200/PK-12
5815 Makoma Dr 32839 407-859-9511
Strayer University Post-Sec.
2200 N Alafaya Trl Ste 500 32826 407-926-2000
Treasure of Knowledge Christian Academy 200/PK-12
13001 Landstar Blvd 32824 407-859-8755
Universal Technical Institute Post-Sec.
2202 W Taft Vineland Rd 32837 321-281-9810
University of Central Florida Post-Sec.
PO Box 160000 32816 407-823-2000
Valencia College Post-Sec.
PO Box 3028 32802 407-299-5000
Victory Christian Academy 100/K-12
240 N Ivey Ln 32811 407-295-3332
West Oaks Academy 200/PK-12
8624 A D Mims Rd 32818 407-292-8481

Ormond Beach, Volusia, Pop. 37,607
Volusia County SD
Supt. — See De Land
Ormond Beach MS 1,100/6-8
151 Domicilio Ave 32174 386-258-4667
Matt Krajewski, prin. Fax 676-1258

Calvary Christian Academy 400/PK-12
1687 W Granada Blvd 32174 386-672-2081
Dr. Aaron Gonzalez, hdmstr. Fax 615-3736
Daytona College Post-Sec.
425 S Nova Rd 32174 386-267-0565
Harry Wendelstedt Umpire School Post-Sec.
88 S Saint Andrews Dr 32174 800-818-1690
Riverbend Academy 300/PK-12
2080 W Granada Blvd 32174 386-615-0986
Jason Karr, hdmstr. Fax 672-7945
WyoTech Post-Sec.
470 Destination Daytona Ln 32174 386-255-0295

Oviedo, Seminole, Pop. 32,607
Seminole County SD
Supt. — See Sanford
Chiles MS 1,300/6-8
1240 Sanctuary Dr 32766 407-871-7050
Linda Mumey, prin. Fax 871-7099
Hagerty HS 2,200/9-12
3225 Lockwood Blvd 32765 407-871-0750
Dr. Mary Williams, prin. Fax 871-0749
Jackson Heights MS 1,200/6-8
41 Academy Ave 32765 407-320-4550
Sarah Mansur, prin. Fax 320-4599
Oviedo HS 2,400/9-12
601 King St 32765 407-320-4050
Joe Trybus, prin. Fax 320-4000
Tuskawilla MS 1,100/6-8
1801 Tuskawilla Rd 32765 407-746-8550
Kate Eglof, prin. Fax 746-8599

Master's Academy of Central Florida 900/PK-12
1500 Lukas Ln 32765 407-971-2221
Rev. Mike Armstrong, admin. Fax 706-0254
Reformed Theological Seminary Post-Sec.
1231 Reformation Dr 32765 407-366-9493

Pace, Santa Rosa, Pop. 19,523
Santa Rosa County SD
Supt. — See Milton
Pace HS 1,800/9-12
4065 Norris Rd 32571 850-995-3600
Stephen Shell, prin. Fax 995-3620
Sims MS 900/6-8
5500 Education Dr 32571 850-995-3676
Emily Donalson, prin. Fax 995-3696

Pahokee, Palm Beach, Pop. 5,609
Palm Beach County SD
Supt. — See West Palm Beach
Pahokee HS 500/9-12
900 Larrimore Rd 33476 561-924-6400
Michael Aronson, prin. Fax 924-6457
Pahokee MS 400/6-8
850 Larrimore Rd 33476 561-924-6500
Dwayne Dennard, prin. Fax 924-6550

Palatka, Putnam, Pop. 10,395
Putnam County SD 11,100/PK-12
200 Reid St 32177 386-329-0538
Rick Surrency, supt. Fax 312-4918
www.putnamschools.org
Jenkins MS 700/7-8
1100 N 19th St 32177 386-329-0588
Randall Hedstrom, prin. Fax 329-0636
Palatka HS 1,300/9-12
302 Mellon Rd 32177 386-329-0577
J.T. Stout, prin. Fax 329-0624
Other Schools – See Crescent City, Florahome, Interlachen

Hillcrest Academy 50/K-12
2009 President St 32177 386-328-6514
Peniel Baptist Academy 300/PK-12
110 Peniel Church Rd 32177 386-328-1707
St. John's River State College Post-Sec.
5001 Saint Johns Ave 32177 386-312-4200

Palm Bay, Brevard, Pop. 100,267
Brevard County SD
Supt. — See Melbourne
Bayside HS 1,600/9-12
1901 Degroodt Rd SW 32908 321-956-5000
Christine Moore, prin. Fax 956-5021
Heritage HS 1,800/9-12
2351 Malabar Rd NW 32907 321-722-4178
Dr. John Harris, prin. Fax 722-4198
Southwest MS 1,000/7-8
451 Eldron Blvd SE 32909 321-952-5800
Todd Scheuerer, prin. Fax 952-5819

Covenant Christian S 300/PK-12
720 Emerson Dr NE 32907 321-727-2661
Ron Fischer, head sch Fax 728-9574
Darlyne McGee's Academy of Cosmetology Post-Sec.
1975 Palm Bay Rd NE Ste 106 32905 321-951-0595

Palm Beach, Palm Beach, Pop. 8,309

Palm Beach Day Academy 200/4-9
241 Seaview Ave 33480 561-655-1188
Dr. Edwin Gordon, hdmstr. Fax 655-5794

Palm Beach Gardens, Palm Beach, Pop. 47,764
Palm Beach County SD
Supt. — See West Palm Beach
Duncan MS 1,300/6-8
5150 117th Ct N 33418 561-776-3500
Phillip D'Amico, prin. Fax 776-3550
Dwyer HS 2,100/9-12
13601 N Military Trl 33410 561-625-7800
Joe DePasquale, prin. Fax 625-7870
Palm Beach Gardens Community HS 2,500/9-12
4245 Holly Dr 33410 561-694-7300
Larry Clawson, prin. Fax 691-0515
Watkins MS 800/6-8
9480 MacArthur Blvd 33403 561-776-3600
Don Hoffman, prin. Fax 776-3603

Strayer University Post-Sec.
11025 RCA Center Dr Ste 200 33410 561-904-3000

Palm City, Martin, Pop. 22,880
Martin County SD
Supt. — See Stuart
Hidden Oaks MS 1,100/6-8
2801 SW Martin Hwy 34990 772-219-1655
Jeri Eckler, prin. Fax 219-1663

Palm Coast, Flagler, Pop. 73,538
Flagler County SD
Supt. — See Bunnell
Flagler Palm Coast HS 2,400/9-12
5500 E Highway 100 32164 386-437-7540
Dustin Sims, prin. Fax 437-7546
Flagler Technical Institute Vo/Tech
5400 E Highway 100 32164 386-446-7612
Kevin McCarthy, dir. Fax 446-7620
Indian Trails MS 800/7-8
5505 Belle Terre Pkwy 32137 386-446-6732
Paul Peacock, prin. Fax 446-7662
Matanzas HS 1,600/9-12
3535 Old Kings Rd N 32137 386-447-1575
Earl Johnson, prin. Fax 447-1597
Taylor MS 1,000/7-8
4500 Belle Terre Pkwy 32164 386-446-6700
Nathan Lovelette M.Ed., prin. Fax 446-6711

Palmetto, Manatee, Pop. 12,420
Manatee County SD
Supt. — See Bradenton
Buffalo Creek MS 1,000/6-8
7320 69th St E 34221 941-721-2260
Dustin Dahlquist, prin. Fax 721-2275
Lincoln MS 600/6-8
305 17th St E 34221 941-721-6840
Ed Hundley, prin. Fax 721-6853
Manatee Technical College - North Vo/Tech
801 9th St W 34221 941-845-2092
Doug Wagner, dir. Fax 845-2102
Palmetto HS 1,900/9-12
1200 17th St W 34221 941-723-4848
Carl Auckerman, prin. Fax 723-4952

Palmetto Bay, Miami-Dade
Miami-Dade County SD
Supt. — See Miami
Southwood MS 1,400/6-8
16301 SW 80th Ave, 305-251-5361
Raul Garcia, prin. Fax 251-7464

Palmer Trinity S 700/6-12
7900 SW 176th St, 305-251-2230
Patrick Roberts, head sch Fax 251-2917
Westminster Christian S 1,000/PK-12
6855 SW 152nd St, 305-233-2030
Peter Cabrera, supt. Fax 238-2259

Palm Harbor, Pinellas, Pop. 56,551
Pinellas County SD
Supt. — See Largo
Carwise MS 1,200/6-8
3301 Bentley Dr 34684 727-724-1442
Robert Vicari, prin. Fax 724-1446
Palm Harbor MS 1,400/6-8
1800 Tampa Rd 34683 727-669-1146
Victoria Hawkins, prin. Fax 669-1244
Palm Harbor University HS 2,500/9-12
1900 Omaha St 34683 727-669-1131
Christen Gonzalez, prin. Fax 725-7936
Palm Harbor Community S Adult
1900 Omaha St 34683 727-669-1140
Anne Januario, prin. Fax 725-7936

Panama City, Bay, Pop. 35,536
Bay County SD 26,100/PK-12
1311 Balboa Ave 32401 850-767-4100
William Husfelt, supt.
www.bay.k12.fl.us
Arnold HS 1,400/9-12
550 N Alf Coleman Rd 32407 850-767-3700
Keith Bland, prin. Fax 236-3068
Bay HS 1,300/9-12
1200 Harrison Ave 32401 850-767-4600
Billy May, prin. Fax 767-4651
Bozeman S 1,100/K-12
13410 Highway 77 32409 850-767-1300
Josh Balkom, prin. Fax 265-5377
Brown MS 800/6-8
5044 Merritt Brown Way 32404 850-767-3976
Charlotte Marshall, prin. Fax 872-7625
Everitt MS 800/6-8
608 School Ave 32401 850-767-3776
Phillip Mullins, prin. Fax 872-7721
Haney Technical Center Vo/Tech
3016 Highway 77 32405 850-767-5500
Ann Leonard, dir. Fax 747-5555
Jinks MS 600/6-8
600 W 11th St 32401 850-767-4695
Britt Smith, prin. Fax 872-7612
Rosenwald HS 300/9-12
924 Bay Ave 32401 850-767-4580
Chandra Tyson, prin. Fax 872-7615
Rutherford HS 1,200/9-12
1000 School Ave 32401 850-767-4500
L. Coy Pilson, prin. Fax 872-4827
Surfside MS 700/6-8
300 Nautilus St 32413 850-767-5180
Dr. Sue Harrell, prin. Fax 233-5193
Washington Academy 100/Alt
924 Bay Ave 32401 850-767-5576
Todd Harless, prin. Fax 914-6429
Other Schools – See Lynn Haven

Covenant Christian S 300/PK-12
2350 Frankford Ave 32405 850-769-7448
Gooding Institute of Nurse Anesthesia Post-Sec.
615 N Bonita Ave 32401 850-747-6918
Gulf Coast State College Post-Sec.
5230 W Highway 98 32401 850-769-1551
Panama City Advanced S 100/PK-12
3332 Token Rd 32405 850-784-2520

Parkland, Broward, Pop. 23,535
Broward County SD
Supt. — See Fort Lauderdale
Stoneman Douglas HS 3,000/9-12
5901 Pine Island Rd 33076 754-322-2150
Ty Thompson, prin. Fax 322-2280
Westglades MS 1,400/6-8
11000 Holmberg Rd 33076 754-322-4800
Jack Vesey, prin. Fax 322-4835

Paxton, Walton, Pop. 626
Walton County SD
Supt. — See De Funiak Springs
Paxton S 700/PK-12
21893 US Highway 331 N 32538 850-892-1230
Cindy Neale, prin. Fax 892-1239

Pembroke Pines, Broward, Pop. 151,189
Broward County SD
Supt. — See Fort Lauderdale
Flanagan HS 2,900/9-12
12800 Taft St 33028 754-323-0650
Michelle Kefford, prin. Fax 323-0780
Pines MS 1,400/6-8
200 NW Douglas Rd 33024 754-323-4000
Carlton Campbell, prin. Fax 323-4085
Silver Trail MS 1,500/6-8
18300 Sheridan St 33331 754-323-4300
Stephen Frazier, prin. Fax 323-4385
West Broward HS 2,700/9-12
500 NW 209th Ave 33029 754-323-2600
Teresa Hall, prin. Fax 323-2730
Young MS 1,200/6-8
901 NW 129th Ave 33028 754-323-4500
Harold Osborn, prin. Fax 323-4585

Broward College Post-Sec.
7200 Pines Blvd 33024 954-201-8100
Florida Career College Post-Sec.
7891 Pines Blvd 33024 954-965-7272
Florida Technical College Post-Sec.
12520 Pines Blvd 33027 954-556-1900
Jose Maria Vargas University Post-Sec.
8300 S Palm Dr 33025 954-322-4460
Keiser University Post-Sec.
1640 SW 145th Ave 33027 954-431-4300
Pelican Flight Training Center Post-Sec.
1601 SW 75th Ave 33023 954-966-9750

Pensacola, Escambia, Pop. 50,807
Escambia County SD 39,500/PK-12
75 N Pace Blvd 32505 850-432-6121
Malcolm Thomas, supt. Fax 469-6379
escambiaschools.net
Bailey MS 1,500/6-8
4110 Bauer Rd 32506 850-492-6136
Janet Penrose, prin. Fax 492-9860
Bellview MS 1,000/6-8
6201 Mobile Hwy 32526 850-941-6080
Melia Adams, prin. Fax 941-6073
Brown-Barge MS 500/6-8
201 Hancock Ln 32503 850-494-5640
Joe Snyder, prin. Fax 494-5699
Escambia HS 1,700/9-12
1310 N 65th Ave 32506 850-453-3221
Frank Murphy, prin. Fax 453-7502
Ferry Pass MS 1,000/6-8
8355 Yancey Ave 32514 850-494-5650
Sherri Mims, prin. Fax 494-5653
Pensacola HS 1,500/9-12
500 W Maxwell St 32501 850-595-1500
David Williams, prin. Fax 595-1519
Pine Forest HS 1,700/9-12
2500 Longleaf Dr 32526 850-941-6150
Laura Touchstone, prin. Fax 941-6163
Stone Career Center Vo/Tech
2400 Longleaf Dr 32526 850-941-6200
Thomas Rollins, prin. Fax 941-6215
Warrington MS 600/6-8
450 S Old Corry Field Rd 32507 850-453-7440
Dr. Reggie Lipnick, prin. Fax 453-7572
Washington HS 1,700/9-12
6000 College Pkwy 32504 850-475-5257
Dr. Michael Roberts, prin. Fax 494-7297
West Florida HS of Advanced Technology 1,300/9-12
2400 Longleaf Dr 32526 850-941-6221
Sheena Payne, prin. Fax 941-6210
Woodham MS 700/6-8
150 E Burgess Rd 32503 850-494-7140
Wilson Taylor, prin. Fax 494-7484

Workman MS 1,000/6-8
6299 Lanier Dr 32504 850-494-5665
Traci Ursery, prin. Fax 494-5697
Andrews Center Adult
129 N Merritt St 32507 850-453-7462
LaDon Boyd, prin.
Other Schools – See Cantonment, Century, Walnut Hill

Aletheia Christian Academy 200/PK-12
PO Box 10568 32524 850-969-0088
Jeff Caulfield-James, admin. Fax 969-0906
East Hill Christian S 200/PK-12
1301 E Gonzalez St 32501 850-438-7746
Glenn Dickson, hdmstr. Fax 434-7384
Florida Institute of Ultrasound Post-Sec.
8800 University Pkwy Ste A4 32514 850-478-7300
Fortis Institute Post-Sec.
4081 E Olive Rd Ste B 32514 850-476-7607
George Stone Vocational Technical Ctr. Post-Sec.
2400 Longleaf Dr 32526 850-941-6200
Jones Christian Academy 200/PK-12
100 Boeing St 32507 850-456-2249
Pensacola Catholic HS 600/9-12
3043 W Scott St 32505 850-436-6400
Sr. Kierstin Martin, prin. Fax 436-6405
Pensacola Christian Academy 2,300/PK-12
10 Brent Ln 32503 850-478-8483
Pensacola Christian College Post-Sec.
PO Box 18000 32523 850-478-8496
Pensacola School of Massage Therapy Post-Sec.
2409 Creighton Rd 32504 850-474-1330
Pensacola State College Post-Sec.
1000 College Blvd 32504 850-484-1000
Trinitas Christian S 200/K-12
3301 E Johnson Ave 32514 850-484-3515
University of West Florida Post-Sec.
11000 University Pkwy 32514 850-474-2000
Virginia College Post-Sec.
19 W Garden St 32502 850-436-8444

Perry, Taylor, Pop. 6,889
Taylor County SD 3,000/PK-12
318 N Clark St 32347 850-838-2500
Paul Dyal, supt. Fax 838-2501
www.taylor.k12.fl.us
Taylor County HS 600/9-12
900 N Johnson Stripling Rd 32347 850-838-2525
Audie Ash, prin. Fax 838-2521
Taylor County MS 600/6-8
610 E Lafayette St 32347 850-838-2516
Kiki Puhl, prin. Fax 838-2559
Taylor Technical Institute Vo/Tech
3233 S Byron Butler Pkwy 32348 850-838-2535
Jodi Tillman, dir. Fax 838-2546

Taylor Technical Institute Post-Sec.
3233 S Byron Butler Pkwy 32348 850-838-2545

Pierson, Volusia, Pop. 1,725
Volusia County SD
Supt. — See De Land
Taylor MSHS 1,100/6-12
100 E Washington Ave 32180 386-749-9800
Jeff Miller, prin. Fax 626-0051

Pinecrest, Miami-Dade
Miami-Dade County SD
Supt. — See Miami
Miami Palmetto HS 2,700/9-12
7460 SW 118th St 33156 305-235-1360
Victoria Dobbs, prin. Fax 378-9724
Palmetto MS 700/7-9
7351 SW 128th St 33156 305-238-3911
Jesus Gonzalez, prin. Fax 233-4849

Gulliver Academy - Montgomery Dr Campus 100/5-8
7500 SW 120th St 33156 305-238-3424
Frank Steel, head sch Fax 675-7744
Gulliver Preparatory S 800/9-12
6575 N Kendall Dr 33156 305-666-7937
Frank Steel, head sch Fax 665-3791

Pinellas Park, Pinellas, Pop. 47,904
Pinellas County SD
Supt. — See Largo
Pinellas Park MS 1,100/6-8
6940 70th Ave N 33781 727-545-6400
David Rosenberger, prin. Fax 547-7894
Pinellas Secondary S 100/Alt
8570 66th St N 33781 727-549-6550
Darren Hammond, prin. Fax 549-6555

Classical Christian S for the Arts 100/K-12
PO Box 1455 33780 727-547-6820
Rev. Daniel Baker, dir. Fax 545-3579
Cortiva Institute-Florida Post-Sec.
4045 Park Blvd N 33781 727-865-4940
National University of Health Sciences Post-Sec.
9200 113th St 33781 800-826-6285

Plantation, Broward, Pop. 82,808
Broward County SD
Supt. — See Fort Lauderdale
Plantation HS 2,200/9-12
6901 NW 16th St 33313 754-322-1850
Alona Dipaolo, prin. Fax 322-1980
Plantation MS 1,000/6-8
6600 W Sunrise Blvd 33313 754-322-4100
Sherri Wilson, prin. Fax 322-4185
Seminole MS 1,100/6-8
6200 SW 16th St 33317 754-323-4200
Kathryn Marlow, prin. Fax 323-4285
South Plantation HS 2,400/9-12
1300 Paladin Way 33317 754-323-1950
Christine Henschel, prin. Fax 323-2080

Allied Health Institute Post-Sec.
51 N State Road 7 33317 877-959-3570
American Heritage S 2,300/PK-12
12200 W Broward Blvd 33325 954-472-0022
William Laurie, pres.

Plant City, Hillsborough, Pop. 34,205
Hillsborough County SD
Supt. — See Tampa
Durant HS 2,200/9-12
4748 Cougar Path 33567 813-757-9075
Pamela Bowden, prin. Fax 707-7079
Marshall MS 800/6-8
18 S Maryland Ave, 813-757-9360
Daphne Blanton, prin. Fax 707-7385
Plant City HS 2,200/9-12
1 Raider Pl, 813-757-9370
Susan Sullivan, prin. Fax 757-9135
Simmons Career Center Vo/Tech
1202 W Grant St, 813-707-7430
Cleto Chazares, prin. Fax 707-7435
Tomlin MS 1,600/6-8
501 N Woodrow Wilson St, 813-757-9400
Traci Durrance, prin. Fax 707-7024
Turkey Creek MS 1,000/6-8
5005 Turkey Creek Rd 33567 813-757-9442
Fredda Johnson, prin. Fax 757-9451
Plant City Adult Education Adult
1 Raider Pl, 813-707-7147
James Rich, prin. Fax 707-7149

Hillsborough Community College Post-Sec.
1206 N Park Rd, 813-757-2100

Poinciana, Osceola, Pop. 51,604
Polk County SD
Supt. — See Bartow
Lake Marion Creek MS 800/5-8
3055 Lake Marion Creek Dr 34759 863-427-1471
Maryjo Costine, prin. Fax 427-1502

Pompano Beach, Broward, Pop. 97,655
Broward County SD
Supt. — See Fort Lauderdale
Blanche Ely HS 2,000/9-12
1201 NW 6th Ave 33060 754-322-0950
Karlton Johnson, prin. Fax 322-1080
Crystal Lake MS 1,400/6-8
3551 NE 3rd Ave 33064 754-322-3100
Sabine Phillips, prin. Fax 322-3185
Cypress Run Education Center 100/Alt
2800 NW 30th Ave 33069 754-321-6500
Gastride Harrigan, prin. Fax 321-6540
Pompano Beach HS 1,200/9-12
600 NE 13th Ave 33060 754-322-2000
Hudson Thomas, prin. Fax 322-2130
Pompano Beach MS 1,100/6-8
310 NE 6th St 33060 754-322-4200
Sonja Braziel, prin. Fax 322-4285
Thomas Education Center East Adult
180 SW 2nd St 33060 754-321-6750
Wade Edmond, prin. Fax 321-6790

Everest University-Pompano Beach Campus Post-Sec.
225 N Federal Hwy 33062 954-783-7339
Florida Barber Academy Post-Sec.
3269 N Federal Hwy 33064 954-781-6066
Florida College of Natural Health Post-Sec.
2001 W Sample Rd Ste 100 33064 954-975-6400
Highlands Christian Academy 500/PK-12
501 NE 48th St 33064 954-421-1747
New Life Preparatory Academy 100/9-12
2111 NW 2nd St 33069 954-440-8333
Progressive Training Center Post-Sec.
98 E McNab Rd Ste 98 33060 954-946-2022

Ponce de Leon, Holmes, Pop. 585
Holmes County SD
Supt. — See Bonifay
Ponce De Leon JSHS 300/6-12
1477 Ammons Rd 32455 850-836-4242
Brian Morgan, prin. Fax 836-5388

Ponte Vedra Beach, Saint Johns
St. Johns County SD
Supt. — See Saint Augustine
Landrum MS 1,300/6-8
230 Landrum Ln 32082 904-547-8410
Ryan Player, prin. Fax 547-8415
Nease HS 1,800/9-12
10550 Ray Rd, 904-547-8300
Kyle Dresback, prin. Fax 547-8305
Ponte Vedra HS 1,500/9-12
460 Davis Park Rd, 904-547-7350
Steve McCormick, prin. Fax 547-7355

Port Charlotte, Charlotte, Pop. 53,337
Charlotte County SD 15,800/PK-12
1445 Education Way 33948 941-255-0808
Steve Dionisio, supt. Fax 255-7571
yourcharlotteschools.net
Academy Alt
18300 Cochran Blvd 33948 941-255-7545
Jack Ham, prin. Fax 255-7548
Charlotte Technical College HS Vo/Tech
18150 Murdock Cir 33948 941-255-7500
DeeLynn Bennett, dir. Fax 255-7509
Murdock MS 800/6-8
17325 Mariner Way 33948 941-255-7525
Demetrius Revelas, prin. Fax 255-7533
Port Charlotte HS 1,700/9-12
18200 Cochran Blvd 33948 941-255-7485
Lou Long, prin. Fax 255-7493
Port Charlotte MS 800/6-8
23000 Midway Blvd 33952 941-255-7460
John LeClair, prin. Fax 255-7469
Adult & Community Education Adult
1441 Tamiami Trl Unit 365 33948 941-255-7430
Jack Ham, dir. Fax 255-7433
Other Schools – See Englewood, Punta Gorda, Rotonda West

Community Christian S 300/PK-12
20035 Quesada Ave 33952 941-625-8977
Dr. Sarah Mielke, head sch Fax 625-1735
Port Charlotte Adventist S 100/K-12
2100 Loveland Blvd 33980 941-625-5237
Southwest Florida College Post-Sec.
950 Tamiami Trl Unit 109 33953 877-270-9786

Port Orange, Volusia, Pop. 55,114
Volusia County SD
Supt. — See De Land
Atlantic HS 1,000/9-12
1250 Reed Canal Rd 32129 386-322-6100
JamesTager, prin. Fax 506-0001
Creekside MS 1,100/6-8
6801 Airport Rd 32128 386-322-6155
John Cash, prin. Fax 506-0002
Silver Sands MS 1,100/6-8
1300 Herbert St 32129 386-322-6175
Rose Roland, prin. Fax 322-7574
Spruce Creek HS 2,700/9-12
801 Taylor Rd 32127 386-322-6272
Todd Sparger, prin. Fax 506-5045

Palmer College of Chiropractic FL Campus Post-Sec.
4777 City Center Pkwy 32129 866-585-9677

Port Richey, Pasco, Pop. 2,626
Pasco County SD
Supt. — See Land O Lakes
Chasco MS 700/6-8
7702 Ridge Rd 34668 727-774-1300
David Huyck, prin. Fax 774-1391

Port Saint Joe, Gulf, Pop. 3,399
Gulf County SD 1,900/PK-12
150 Middle School Dr 32456 850-229-8256
Jim Norton, supt. Fax 229-6089
www.gulf.k12.fl.us
Port Saint Joe JSHS 500/7-12
100 Shark Dr 32456 850-229-8251
Sandra Cook Ph.D., prin. Fax 227-1803
Gulf County Adult S Adult
150 Middle School Dr 32456 850-229-8256
Billy Hoover, coord. Fax 229-6089
Other Schools – See Wewahitchka

Port Saint Lucie, Saint Lucie, Pop. 160,756
St. Lucie County SD
Supt. — See Fort Pierce
College Preparatory Academy 200/9-12
501 NW California Blvd 34986 772-323-3747
Erika Rains, admin.
Port Saint Lucie HS 1,600/9-12
1201 SE Jaguar Ln 34952 772-337-6770
Adrian Ocampo, prin. Fax 337-6780
St. Lucie West Centennial HS 2,500/9-12
1485 SW Cashmere Blvd 34986 772-344-4400
Andrea Popwell, prin. Fax 785-6679
Southern Oaks MS 1,000/6-8
5500 NE Saint James Dr 34983 772-785-5640
Bridgette Hargadine, prin. Fax 785-5660
Southport MS 800/6-8
2420 SE Morningside Blvd 34952 772-337-5900
Nicole Telese, prin. Fax 337-5903
Treasure Coast HS 2,500/9-12
1000 SW Darwin Blvd 34953 772-807-4300
Susan Seal, prin. Fax 807-4320

Barnabas Christian Academy 100/K-12
1860 SW Fountainview Blvd 34986 772-344-1643
Bill Reed, admin. Fax 344-1443
Keiser University Post-Sec.
10330 S US Highway 1 34952 772-398-9990
Morningside Academy 200/6-12
1631 SE Greendon Ave 34952 772-335-2096
Helen Klassen, admin. Fax 335-2095
Port St. Lucie Beauty Academy Post-Sec.
7644 S US 1 34983 772-340-3540

Princeton, Miami-Dade, Pop. 21,761

Princeton Christian S 300/PK-12
PO Box 924916 33092 305-257-3644

Punta Gorda, Charlotte, Pop. 16,453
Charlotte County SD
Supt. — See Port Charlotte
Charlotte HS 1,900/9-12
1250 Cooper St 33950 941-575-5450
Cathy Corsaletti, prin. Fax 575-5464
Punta Gorda MS 1,100/6-8
1001 Education Ave 33950 941-575-5485
Justina Dionisio, prin. Fax 575-5491

Quincy, Gadsden, Pop. 7,889
Gadsden County SD 5,200/PK-12
35 Martin Luther King Jr Bl 32351 850-627-9651
Reginald James, supt. Fax 627-2760
www.gcps.k12.fl.us
Carter-Paramore Academy 200/Alt
631 S Stewart St 32351 850-627-6030
Keith Dowdell, prin. Fax 875-3197
Gadsden Central Academy 50/Alt
655 S Stewart St 32351 850-875-7249
Laronda Frazier-Lee, admin. Fax 627-1802
Gadsden Technical Institute Vo/Tech
201 Martin Luther King Jr 32351 850-875-8324
Dr. Sylvia Jackson, dir. Fax 875-7297
Shanks MS 600/6-8
1400 W King St 32351 850-875-8737
Juanita Ellis, prin. Fax 875-8775
West Gadsden HS 400/7-12
200 Providence Rd 32351 850-442-9500
James Mills, prin. Fax 442-6126
Other Schools – See Havana

Munroe Day S 200/PK-12
91 Old Mt Pleasant Rd 32352 850-856-5500

Riverview, Hillsborough, Pop. 68,857
Hillsborough County SD
Supt. — See Tampa
Giunta MS 1,000/6-8
4202 S Falkenburg Rd, 813-740-4888
Michael Bobo, prin. Fax 740-4892
Riverview HS 2,300/9-12
11311 Boyette Rd 33569 813-671-5011
Danielle Shotwell, prin. Fax 671-5012
Rodgers MS 700/6-8
11910 Tucker Rd 33569 813-671-5288
Michael Miranda, prin. Fax 671-5245

Spoto HS 1,400/9-12
8538 Eagle Palm Dr, 813-672-5405
David New, prin. Fax 672-5423

Florida Career College Post-Sec.
2662 S Falkenburg Rd, 813-621-5775
Providence Christian S 200/PK-12
5416 Providence Rd, 813-661-0588
David Hubbart, admin. Fax 681-3852

Riviera Beach, Palm Beach, Pop. 31,825
Palm Beach County SD
Supt. — See West Palm Beach
Kennedy MS 800/6-8
1901 Avenue S 33404 561-845-4500
Corey Brooks, prin. Fax 845-4537
Riviera Beach Prep & Achievement Academy 100/Alt
7071 Garden Rd 33404 561-881-4740
Elaine Hubbard-Williams, prin. Fax 881-4731
Suncoast HS 1,500/9-12
1717 Avenue S 33404 561-882-3400
Karen Whetsell, prin. Fax 882-3443

North Technical Education Center Post-Sec.
7071 Garden Rd 33404 561-881-4600

Rockledge, Brevard, Pop. 24,317
Brevard County SD
Supt. — See Melbourne
Kennedy MS 600/7-8
2100 S Fiske Blvd 32955 321-633-3500
Richard Myers, prin. Fax 633-3509
McNair Magnet MS 500/7-8
1 Challenger Dr 32955 321-633-3630
Rosette Brown, prin. Fax 633-3639
Rockledge HS 1,400/9-12
220 Raider Rd 32955 321-636-3711
Victoria Hickey, prin. Fax 632-6064

Rosemary Beach, Walton

Ohana Institute, 82 S Barret Sq 32461 100/3-12
Robert Walsh, prin. 850-231-1140

Rotonda West, Charlotte
Charlotte County SD
Supt. — See Port Charlotte
Ainger MS 900/6-8
245 Cougar Way 33947 941-697-5800
Jeff Harvey, prin. Fax 697-5470

Royal Palm Beach, Palm Beach, Pop. 33,307
Palm Beach County SD
Supt. — See West Palm Beach
Crestwood MS 1,000/6-8
64 Sparrow Dr 33411 561-753-5000
Stephanie Nance, prin. Fax 753-5035
Royal Palm Beach Community HS 2,200/9-12
10600 Okeechobee Blvd 33411 561-753-4000
Jesus Armas, prin. Fax 753-4015

South University Post-Sec.
9801 Belvedere Rd 33411 561-273-6500

Ruskin, Hillsborough, Pop. 16,985
Hillsborough County SD
Supt. — See Tampa
Lennard HS 1,900/9-12
2342 E Shell Point Rd 33570 813-641-5611
Mary Freitas, prin. Fax 641-5610
Shields MS 1,500/6-8
15732 Beth Shields Way 33573 813-672-5338
Tia Brown, prin. Fax 672-5342
South County Career Center Vo/Tech
2810 John Sherman Way 33570 813-233-3335
Tibor Kovacs, prin. Fax 233-3339
Lennard Adult Education Adult
2342 E Shell Point Rd 33570 813-658-2075
Sandra Tune, prin. Fax 658-2078

Hillsborough Community College Post-Sec.
551 24th St NE 33570 813-253-7000
Ruskin Christian S 200/PK-12
820 W College Ave 33570 813-645-6441
Tim Vanderveer, admin. Fax 641-2073

Safety Harbor, Pinellas, Pop. 16,579
Pinellas County SD
Supt. — See Largo
Safety Harbor MS 1,400/6-8
901 1st Ave N 34695 727-724-1400
Alison Kennedy, prin. Fax 724-1407

Saint Augustine, Saint Johns, Pop. 12,760
St. Johns County SD 33,100/PK-12
40 Orange St 32084 904-547-7500
Joseph Joyner Ed.D., supt. Fax 547-7515
www.stjohns.k12.fl.us
First Coast Technical College Vo/Tech
2980 Collins Ave 32084 904-547-3282
Cathy Mittelstadt, admin. Fax 547-3388
Gaines and Transition S 100/Alt
1 Christopher St 32084 904-547-8560
Tish McMahon, prin. Fax 547-8555
Menendez HS 1,300/9-12
600 State Road 206 W 32086 904-547-8660
Dr. Clay Carmichael, prin. Fax 547-8675
Murray MS 800/6-8
150 N Holmes Blvd 32084 904-547-8483
Tom Schwarm, prin. Fax 547-8475
Pacetti Bay MS 1,000/6-8
245 Meadowlark Ln 32092 904-547-8760
Jay Willets, prin. Fax 547-8765
Rogers MS 800/6-8
6250 US Highway 1 S 32086 904-547-8700
Greg Bergamasco, prin. Fax 547-8705
Saint Augustine HS 1,700/9-12
3205 Varella Ave 32084 904-547-8530
Dr. DeArmas Graham, prin. Fax 547-8535
St. Johns Technical HS Vo/Tech
2980 Collins Ave 32084 904-547-8500
Cynthia Williams, prin. Fax 547-8505

Sebastian MS 600/6-8
2955 Lewis Speedway 32084 904-547-3840
Wayne King, prin. Fax 547-3845
Other Schools – See Ponte Vedra Beach, Saint Johns

Beacon of Hope Christian S 100/K-12
1230 Kings Estate Rd 32086 904-797-6996
First Coast Technical College Post-Sec.
2980 Collins Ave 32084 904-547-3282
Flagler College Post-Sec.
74 King St 32084 904-829-6481
Florida School for the Deaf and Blind Post-Sec.
207 San Marco Ave 32084 904-827-2200
St. Joseph Academy 300/9-12
155 State Road 207 32084 904-824-0431
Todd DeClemente, prin. Fax 826-4477
Univ. of St. Augustine for Health Sci. Post-Sec.
1 University Blvd 32086 904-826-0084
Victory Prep S K-12
110 Masters Dr 32084 904-810-0534

Saint Cloud, Osceola, Pop. 34,423
Osceola County SD
Supt. — See Kissimmee
Harmony HS 1,900/9-12
3601 Arthur Gallagher Blvd 34771 407-933-9900
Grover Butler, prin. Fax 933-9901
Narcoossee MS 1,100/6-8
2700 N Narcoossee Rd 34771 407-891-6600
Frank Telemko, prin. Fax 891-6610
Saint Cloud HS 2,200/9-12
2000 Bulldog Ln 34769 407-891-3100
Nathaniel Fancher, prin. Fax 891-3114
Saint Cloud MS 1,100/6-8
1975 Michigan Ave 34769 407-891-3200
Cynthia Chiavini, prin. Fax 891-3206
Technical Education Center Vo/Tech
2901 17th St 34769 407-343-7342
Thomas Ott, prin. Fax 870-1409
Adult Learning Center Adult
2901 17th St 34769 407-343-7342
Beth Rattie, prin. Fax 518-8141

Saint Johns, Saint Johns
St. Johns County SD
Supt. — See Saint Augustine
Bartram Trail HS 1,800/9-12
7399 Longleaf Pine Pkwy, 904-547-8340
Chris Phelps, prin. Fax 547-8359
Creekside HS 1,900/9-12
100 Knights Ln, 904-547-7300
Randy Johnson, prin. Fax 547-7305
Fruit Cove MS 1,300/6-8
3180 Race Track Rd, 904-547-7880
Lynn O'Connor, prin. Fax 547-7885
Switzerland Point MS 1,300/6-8
777 Greenbriar Rd, 904-547-8650
Lisa Kunze, prin. Fax 547-8645

Saint Leo, Pasco, Pop. 1,297

St. Leo University Post-Sec.
33701 State Road 52 33574 352-588-8200

Saint Petersburg, Pinellas, Pop. 239,351
Pinellas County SD
Supt. — See Largo
Azalea MS 1,000/6-8
7855 22nd Ave N 33710 727-893-2606
Dr. Solomon Lowery, prin. Fax 893-2624
Bay Point MS 900/6-8
2151 62nd Ave S 33712 727-893-1153
Jason Shedrick, prin. Fax 893-1181
Gibbs HS 1,300/9-12
850 34th St S 33711 727-893-5452
Reuben Hepburn, prin. Fax 893-5461
Hollins HS 1,800/9-12
4940 62nd St N 33709 727-547-7876
Robert Florio, prin. Fax 547-7727
Hopkins MS 900/6-8
701 16th St S 33705 727-893-2400
Barry Brown, prin. Fax 893-1600
Lakewood HS 1,200/9-12
1400 54th Ave S 33705 727-893-2916
Erin Savage, prin. Fax 893-1387
Lealman Innovation Academy 300/6-12
4900 28th St N 33714 727-528-5802
Connisheia Matthews, prin. Fax 528-5807
Marshall Fundamental MS 900/6-8
3901 22nd Ave S 33711 727-552-1737
Nicole Wilson, prin. Fax 552-1741
Meadowlawn MS 1,200/6-8
6050 16th St N 33703 727-570-3097
Claudius Effiom, prin. Fax 570-3396
Northeast HS 1,800/9-12
5500 16th St N 33703 727-570-3138
Kevin Hendrick, prin. Fax 217-7318
Pinellas Technical Coll St. Petersburg Vo/Tech
901 34th St S 33711 727-893-2500
Sylvester Norwood, dir. Fax 893-2776
St. Petersburg HS 2,300/9-12
2501 5th Ave N 33713 727-893-1842
Albert Bennett, prin. Fax 893-1399
Tyrone MS 900/6-8
6421 22nd Ave N 33710 727-893-1819
Robin Mobley, prin. Fax 893-1946
Hollins Evening Adult Education Ctr Adult
4940 62nd St N 33709 727-547-7872
Brenda Vlach, admin. Fax 547-7873
Lakewood Community S Adult
1400 54th Ave S 33705 727-893-2955
Harriet Davis, admin. Fax 893-1375
Northeast Community S Adult
1717 54th Ave N 33714 727-570-3193
Dr. Kathy Gregg, admin. Fax 217-7449
Tomlinson Adult Learning Center Adult
296 Mirror Lake Dr N 33701 727-893-2723
Godfrey Watson, dir. Fax 893-2782

Admiral Farragut Academy 400/PK-12
501 Park St N 33710 727-384-5500
Robert Fine, hdmstr. Fax 347-5160

Bayfront Medical Center Post-Sec.
701 6th St S 33701 727-893-6604
Canterbury S of Florida -Knowlton Campus 300/5-12
990 62nd Ave NE 33702 727-525-1419
Mac Hall, head sch Fax 525-2545
Eckerd College Post-Sec.
4200 54th Ave S 33711 727-867-1166
Keswick Christian S 500/PK-12
10101 54th Ave N 33708 727-393-9100
Nick Stratis, supt. Fax 397-5378
Loraine's Academy Post-Sec.
1012 58th St N 33710 727-347-4247
Northside Christian S 600/PK-12
7777 62nd Ave N 33709 727-541-7593
Dr. Don James, hdmstr. Fax 546-5836
Pinellas Technical Education Center Post-Sec.
901 34th St S 33711 727-893-2500
Poynter Institute for Media Studies Post-Sec.
801 3rd St S 33701 888-769-6837
St. Petersburg Catholic HS 500/9-12
6333 9th Ave N 33710 727-344-4065
Rev. Richard Rosin, prin. Fax 343-9311
St. Petersburg College Post-Sec.
PO Box 13489 33733 727-341-4772
Shorecrest Preparatory S 1,000/PK-12
5101 1st St NE 33703 727-522-2111
Michael Murphy, hdmstr. Fax 527-4191
Southeastern College Post-Sec.
11208 Blue Heron Blvd Ste A 33716 727-576-6500
University of South Florida Post-Sec.
140 7th Ave S 33701 727-873-4873

Sanford, Seminole, Pop. 52,277
Seminole County SD 64,400/PK-12
400 E Lake Mary Blvd 32773 407-320-0000
Dr. Walt Griffin, supt. Fax 320-0281
www.scps.k12.fl.us
Crooms Academy of Information Technology 600/9-12
2200 W 13th St 32771 407-320-5750
Demetria Faison, prin. Fax 320-5798
Journeys Academy 200/Alt
1722 W Airport Blvd 32771 407-320-7850
Kenneth Bevan, prin. Fax 320-7849
Millennium MS 1,600/6-8
21 Lakeview Ave 32773 407-320-6550
Dr. Maggie Gunderson, prin. Fax 320-6599
Polk Alternative S Alt
211 Bush Blvd 32773 407-665-1405
Sanford MS 1,500/6-8
1700 S French Ave 32771 407-320-6150
Randy Shuler, prin. Fax 320-6265
Seminole HS 3,000/9-12
2701 Ridgewood Ave 32773 407-320-5050
Dr. Connie Collins, prin. Fax 320-5024
Other Schools – See Altamonte Springs, Casselberry, Lake Mary, Longwood, Oviedo, Winter Park, Winter Springs

---

Aerosim Flight Academy Post-Sec.
2700 Flightline Ave 32773 407-330-7020
Holy Cross Academy 5-10
100 Aero Ln 32771 407-936-3636
Rob Sinninger, prin. Fax 936-0041
Liberty Christian S 100/PK-12
2626 S Palmetto Ave 32773 407-323-1583
William Simpson, prin. Fax 323-1588
Seminole State College of Florida Post-Sec.
100 Weldon Blvd 32773 407-708-4722
Southern Technical College Post-Sec.
2910 S Orlando Dr 32773 407-323-4141

Santa Rosa Beach, Walton
Walton County SD
Supt. — See De Funiak Springs
Emerald Coast MS 700/5-8
4019 Highway 98 E 32459 850-622-5025
Jeff Infinger, prin. Fax 622-5027
South Walton HS 500/9-12
645 Greenway Trl 32459 850-622-5020
Dr. Alexis Tibbetts, prin. Fax 622-5039

Sarasota, Sarasota, Pop. 51,038
Sarasota County SD 40,400/PK-12
1960 Landings Blvd 34231 941-927-9000
Lori White, supt.
sarasotacountyschools.net
Booker HS 1,100/9-12
3201 N Orange Ave 34234 941-355-2967
Dr. Rachel Shelley, prin. Fax 359-5757
Booker MS 800/6-8
2250 Myrtle St 34234 941-359-5824
LaShawn Houston-Frost, prin. Fax 359-5898
Brookside MS 800/6-8
3636 S Shade Ave 34239 941-361-6472
Kristine Lawrence, prin. Fax 361-6508
McIntosh MS 800/6-8
701 Mcintosh Rd 34232 941-361-6520
Dr. Harriet Moore, prin. Fax 361-6340
Riverview HS 2,500/9-12
1 Ram Way 34231 941-923-1484
Paul Burns, prin. Fax 361-6175
Sarasota HS 2,000/9-12
1000 S School Ave 34237 941-955-0181
David Jones, prin. Fax 361-6380
Sarasota MS 1,200/6-8
4826 Ashton Rd 34233 941-361-6464
Janel Dorn, prin. Fax 361-6798
Suncoast Polytechnical HS Vo/Tech
4650 Beneva Rd 34233 941-921-3981
Trent Terry, dir. Fax 921-9900
Suncoast Technical College Vo/Tech
4748 Beneva Rd 34233 941-924-1365
Dr. Todd Bowden, dir. Fax 921-7902
YMCA Triad North/South 100/Alt
4430 Beneva Rd 34233 941-925-6693
Margaret King, dir. Fax 925-6696
Other Schools – See North Port, Venice

Argosy University/Sarasota Post-Sec.
5250 17th St 34235 941-379-0404
Cardinal Mooney Catholic HS 500/9-12
4171 Fruitville Rd 34232 941-371-4917
Tim Gallic, prin. Fax 371-6924

East West College of Natural Medicine — Post-Sec.
3808 N Tamiami Trl 34234 — 941-355-9080
Everglades University — Post-Sec.
6001 Lake Osprey Dr Ste 110 34240 — 941-907-2262
Fashion Focus Hair Academy — Post-Sec.
2184 Gulf Gate Dr 34231 — 941-921-4877
Keiser University — Post-Sec.
6151 Lake Osprey Dr 34240 — 941-907-3900
Meridian College — Post-Sec.
7020 Professional Pkwy E 34240 — 941-377-4880
New College of Florida — Post-Sec.
5800 Bay Shore Rd 34243 — 941-487-5000
NewGate S — 100/PK-12
5237 Ashton Rd 34233 — 941-922-4949
Out of Door Academy — 400/6-12
5950 Deer Dr 34240 — 941-349-3223
David Mahler, head sch — Fax 907-1251
Potter's Wheel Academy — 100/K-12
PO Box 50203 34232 — 941-284-4076
Glenna Palmer, dir.
Providence Community S — 200/PK-12
5600 Deer Dr 34240 — 941-727-6860
Ringling College of Art & Design — Post-Sec.
2700 N Tamiami Trl 34234 — 941-351-5100
Sarasota Christian S — 400/PK-12
5415 Bahia Vista St 34232 — 941-371-6481
Ryan Lehman, head sch — Fax 371-0898
Sarasota County Technical Institute — Post-Sec.
4748 Beneva Rd 34233 — 941-924-1365
Sarasota Memorial Hospital — Post-Sec.
1700 S Tamiami Trl 34239 — 941-917-1080
Sarasota School of Massage Therapy — Post-Sec.
5899 Whitfield Ave Ste 301 34243 — 941-957-0577
University of S Florida Sarasota-Manatee — Post-Sec.
8350 N Tamiami Trl 34243 — 941-359-4200

Satellite Beach, Brevard, Pop. 9,911
Brevard County SD
Supt. — See Melbourne
DeLaura MS — 700/7-8
300 Jackson Ave 32937 — 321-773-7581
Robert Pruett, prin. — Fax 773-0702
Satellite HS — 1,300/9-12
300 Scorpion Ct 32937 — 321-779-2000
Mark Elliott, prin. — Fax 773-0703

Sebastian, Indian River, Pop. 21,634
Indian River County SD
Supt. — See Vero Beach
Sebastian River HS — 1,900/9-12
9001 90th Ave 32958 — 772-564-4170
Todd Racine, prin. — Fax 564-4182
Sebastian River MS — 900/6-8
9400 County Road 512 32958 — 772-564-5111
Jody Idlette, prin. — Fax 564-5225

Sebring, Highlands, Pop. 10,311
Highlands County SD — 12,100/PK-12
426 School St 33870 — 863-471-5555
Wally Cox, supt. — Fax 471-5600
www.highlands.k12.fl.us
Hill-Gustat MS — 700/6-8
4700 Schumacher Rd 33872 — 863-471-5437
Chris Doty, prin. — Fax 314-5245
Sebring HS — 1,600/9-12
3514 Kenilworth Blvd 33870 — 863-471-5500
Anne Lindsay, prin. — Fax 471-5507
Sebring MS — 700/6-8
500 E Center Ave 33870 — 863-471-5700
Kevin Tunning, prin. — Fax 471-5710
Other Schools – See Avon Park, Lake Placid

Seffner, Hillsborough, Pop. 7,410
Hillsborough County SD
Supt. — See Tampa
Armwood HS — 1,700/9-12
12000 E US Highway 92 33584 — 813-744-8040
Joseph Castelli, prin. — Fax 744-8048
Brandon Alternative S — 100/Alt
1019 N Parsons Ave 33584 — 813-651-2165
Essie Johnson Wilson, admin. — Fax 651-2173
Burnett MS — 900/6-8
1010 N Kingsway Rd 33584 — 813-744-6745
Dante Jones, prin. — Fax 744-8973
Jennings MS — 800/6-8
9325 Governors Run Dr 33584 — 813-740-4575
Richard Scionti, prin. — Fax 740-4579

Seffner Christian Academy — 700/PK-12
11605 E US Highway 92 33584 — 813-626-0001
Roger Duncan, admin. — Fax 627-0330

Seminole, Pinellas, Pop. 17,030
Pinellas County SD
Supt. — See Largo
Career Academies of Seminole — Vo/Tech
12611 86th Ave 33776 — 727-545-6405
Barbara Clare, prin. — Fax 545-6408
Osceola Fundamental HS — 1,800/9-12
9751 98th St 33777 — 727-547-7717
Michael Bohnet, prin. — Fax 545-6412
Osceola MS — 1,200/6-8
9301 98th St 33777 — 727-547-7689
Susan Arsenault, prin. — Fax 547-7667
Seminole HS — 2,100/9-12
8401 131st St 33776 — 727-547-7536
Thomas Brittain, prin. — Fax 547-7503
Seminole MS — 1,200/6-8
8701 131st St 33776 — 727-547-4520
Wendy Bryan, prin. — Fax 547-7741

Shalimar, Okaloosa, Pop. 699
Okaloosa County SD
Supt. — See Fort Walton Beach
Meigs MS — 500/6-8
150 Richbourg Ave 32579 — 850-833-4301
Shiva McCraw, prin. — Fax 833-9392

Sneads, Jackson, Pop. 1,817
Jackson County SD
Supt. — See Marianna
Sneads HS — 400/9-12
8066 Old Spanish Trl 32460 — 850-482-9007
John Shouse, prin. — Fax 482-9058

South Daytona, Volusia, Pop. 12,013

International Academy — Post-Sec.
2550 S Ridgewood Ave 32119 — 386-767-4600
Warner Christian Academy — 700/PK-12
1730 S Ridgewood Ave 32119 — 386-767-5451
Mark Tress, supt. — Fax 760-6834

South Miami, Miami-Dade, Pop. 11,508
Miami-Dade County SD
Supt. — See Miami
South Miami MS — 1,000/6-8
6750 SW 60th St 33143 — 305-661-3481
Fabiola Izaguirre, prin. — Fax 665-6728

Southwest Ranches, Broward, Pop. 7,178

Archbishop Edward McCarthy HS — 1,500/9-12
5451 S Flamingo Rd, — 954-434-8820
Richard Jean, prin. — Fax 680-4835

Spring Hill, Hernando, Pop. 96,871
Hernando County SD
Supt. — See Brooksville
Fox Chapel MS — 600/6-8
9412 Fox Chapel Ln 34606 — 352-797-7025
Ray Pinder, prin. — Fax 797-7125
Springstead HS — 1,600/9-12
3300 Mariner Blvd 34609 — 352-797-7010
Carmine Ruffa, prin. — Fax 797-7110

Pasco County SD
Supt. — See Land O Lakes
Achieve Center of Pasco — Alt
18950 Michigan Ln 34610 — 727-346-2000
Kelly Long, prin.
Crews Lake MS — 700/6-8
15144 Shady Hills Rd 34610 — 727-246-1600
Adam Kennedy, prin. — Fax 246-1691

ATA Career Education — Post-Sec.
7355 Spring Hill Dr 34606 — 352-684-3007
Bene's International School of Beauty — Post-Sec.
1486 Pinehurst Dr 34606 — 352-263-2744
Bishop McLaughlin HS — 200/9-12
13651 Hays Rd 34610 — 727-857-2600
Camille Jowanna, prin. — Fax 857-2610
Pasco-Hernando Community College — Post-Sec.
450 Beverly Ct 34606 — 352-688-8798
Spring Hill Christian Academy — 300/PK-12
3140 Mariner Blvd 34609 — 352-683-8485
Michael Willis, prin. — Fax 683-5087
West Hernando Christian S — 300/PK-12
2250 Osowaw Blvd 34607 — 352-688-9918
Wider Horizons S — 100/PK-12
4060 Castle Ave 34609 — 352-686-1934

Starke, Bradford, Pop. 5,317
Bradford County SD — 3,100/PK-12
501 W Washington St 32091 — 904-966-6018
Chad Farnsworth, supt. — Fax 966-6030
www.bradfordschools.org
Bradford HS — 800/9-12
581 N Temple Ave 32091 — 904-966-6075
Bryan Boyer, prin. — Fax 966-6020
Bradford MS — 700/6-8
527 N Orange St 32091 — 904-966-6705
Mallory McConnell, prin. — Fax 966-6714
Bradford Union Career Technical Center — Vo/Tech
609 N Orange St 32091 — 904-966-6766
David Harris, coord. — Fax 966-6786

Clay County SD
Supt. — See Green Cove Springs
Florida Youth Challenge Academy — 50/Alt
Route 1 Box 550 32091 — 904-682-4036
Saryn Hatcher, dir. — Fax 682-3990

Bradford-Union Area Vo-Tech Center — Post-Sec.
609 N Orange St 32091 — 904-966-6764
Hope Christian Academy — 200/PK-12
3900 SE State Road 100 32091 — 352-473-4040
Tori Schenck, prin. — Fax 473-2024
Northside Christian Academy — 200/PK-12
7415 NW County Road 225 32091 — 904-964-7124
Alicia Etheridge, prin. — Fax 966-2350

Stuart, Martin, Pop. 15,329
Martin County SD — 18,100/PK-12
500 SE Ocean Blvd 34994 — 772-219-1200
Laurie J. Gaylord, supt. — Fax 219-1231
www.martinschools.org
Anderson MS — 900/6-8
7000 SE Atlantic Ridge Dr 34997 — 772-221-7100
Timothy Aitken, prin. — Fax 221-7149
Martin County HS — 2,100/9-12
2801 S Kanner Hwy 34994 — 772-219-1800
Al Fabrizio, prin. — Fax 219-1821
Murray MS — 800/6-8
4400 SE Murray St 34997 — 772-219-1670
Amy Laws, prin. — Fax 219-1677
South Fork HS — 1,900/9-12
10000 SW Bulldog Way 34997 — 772-219-1840
Dave Hall, prin. — Fax 219-1860
Spectrum JSHS — 100/Alt
800 SE Bahama Ave 34994 — 772-219-1870
Janice Mills, prin. — Fax 219-1873
Stuart MS — 1,000/6-8
575 SE Georgia Ave 34994 — 772-219-1685
David Krakoff, prin. — Fax 219-1690
Stuart Community Adult HS — Adult
1150 SE Saint Josephs Ave 34996 — 772-219-1296
Melissa Eversdyke, coord. — Fax 219-1299
Other Schools – See Indiantown, Jensen Beach, Palm City

Chapman School of Seamanship — Post-Sec.
4343 SE Saint Lucie Blvd 34997 — 772-283-8130
Community Christian Academy — 300/PK-12
777 SE Salerno Rd 34997 — 772-288-7227
First Baptist Christian S — 200/PK-12
201 SW Ocean Blvd 34994 — 772-287-5161
Stuart Shumway, hdmstr. — Fax 287-7735

Star Academy for Pet Stylists — Post-Sec.
2201 SE Indian St Unit C6 34997 — 772-221-9330

Summerfield, Marion
Marion County SD
Supt. — See Ocala
Lake Weir MS — 1,300/6-8
10220 SE Sunset Harbor Rd 34491 — 352-671-6120
Stephanie Calloway, prin. — Fax 671-6121

Sumterville, Sumter
Sumter County SD
Supt. — See Bushnell
Sumter Alternative S — 50/Alt
709 N West St 33585 — 352-568-1113
James Presley, prin. — Fax 793-6508
Sumter County Adult Center — Adult
1425 CR 526A 33585 — 352-793-5719
Chris Burke, prin. — Fax 793-6508

Sunrise, Broward, Pop. 82,120
Broward County SD
Supt. — See Fort Lauderdale
Bair MS — 900/6-8
9100 NW 21st Mnr 33322 — 754-322-2900
Fax 322-2985
Piper HS — 2,500/9-12
8000 NW 44th St 33351 — 754-322-1700
Angel Gomez, prin. — Fax 322-1830
Westpine MS — 1,200/6-8
9393 NW 50th St 33351 — 754-322-4900
Paula Meadows, prin. — Fax 322-4985

Tallahassee, Leon, Pop. 177,584
Leon County SD — 32,600/PK-12
2757 W Pensacola St 32304 — 850-487-7100
Jackie Pons, supt. — Fax 487-7141
www.leonschools.net
Chiles HS — 1,900/9-12
7200 Lawton Chiles Ln 32312 — 850-488-1756
Joe Burgess, prin. — Fax 488-1218
Cobb MS — 900/6-8
915 Hillcrest Ave 32308 — 850-488-3364
Tonja Fitzgerald, prin. — Fax 922-2452
Deerlake MS — 900/6-8
9902 Deer Lk W 32312 — 850-922-6545
Laura Brooks, prin. — Fax 488-3275
Fairview MS — 800/6-8
3415 Zillah St 32305 — 850-488-6880
Scott Hansen, prin. — Fax 922-6326
Godby HS — 1,200/9-12
1717 W Tharpe St 32303 — 850-617-4700
Shelly Bell, prin. — Fax 922-4162
Griffin MS — 500/6-8
800 Alabama St 32304 — 850-617-5353
Gwendolyn Lynn-Thomas, prin. — Fax 617-5354
Leon HS — 2,000/9-12
550 E Tennessee St 32308 — 850-617-5700
Billy Epting, prin. — Fax 922-5311
Lincoln HS — 2,100/9-12
3838 Trojan Trl 32311 — 850-487-2110
Allen Burch, prin. — Fax 922-4173
Lively-Technical Center — Vo/Tech
500 Appleyard Dr 32304 — 850-487-7555
Vernea Randolph, prin. — Fax 922-3880
Montford MS — 1,100/6-8
5789 Pimlico Dr 32309 — 850-922-6011
Lewis Blessing, prin. — Fax 922-7974
Nims MS — 500/6-8
723 W Orange Ave 32310 — 850-488-5960
Desmond Cole, prin. — Fax 922-0203
Raa MS — 900/6-8
401 W Tharpe St 32303 — 850-488-6287
Giselle Marsh, prin. — Fax 922-5835
Rickards HS — 1,200/9-12
3013 Jim Lee Rd 32301 — 850-414-5500
Doug Cook, prin. — Fax 922-7104
SAIL HS — 400/9-12
2006 Jackson Bluff Rd 32304 — 850-488-2468
Tiffany Thomas, prin. — Fax 922-8483
Second Chance S — Alt
860 Blountstown St 32304 — 850-488-2087
Richard Richardson, prin. — Fax 410-1531
Success Academy at Ghazvini Learning Ctr — 100/Alt
854 Blountstown St 32304 — 850-488-2087
Richard Richardson, prin. — Fax 410-3353
Swift Creek MS — 800/6-8
2100 Pedrick Rd 32317 — 850-414-2670
Sue Rishell, prin. — Fax 414-2650
Adult & Community Education — Adult
283 Trojan Trl 32311 — 850-922-5343
Regina Browning, prin. — Fax 922-5352

Betton Hills S — 100/2-12
2205 Thomasville Rd 32308 — 850-656-9211
Caroline Accorsini, dir. — Fax 656-9602
Community Christian S — 300/PK-12
4859 Kerry Forest Pkwy 32309 — 850-893-6628
David Pinson, hdmstr. — Fax 668-3966
Core Institute — Post-Sec.
223 W Carolina St 32301 — 866-830-0108
Florida A&M University — Post-Sec.
1601 Martin Luther King Jr 32307 — 850-599-3000
Florida State University — Post-Sec.
600 W College Ave 32306 — 850-644-2525
John Paul II Catholic HS — 100/9-12
5100 Terrebonne Dr 32311 — 850-201-5744
Sr. Maureen Martin, prin. — Fax 205-3299
Keiser University — Post-Sec.
1700 Halstead Blvd Ste 2 32309 — 850-906-9494
Lively Area Vocational Technical School — Post-Sec.
500 Appleyard Dr 32304 — 850-487-7555
Maclay S — 900/PK-12
3737 N Meridian Rd 32312 — 850-893-2138
James Milford, head sch — Fax 893-7434
North Florida Christian S — 800/PK-12
3000 N Meridian Rd 32312 — 850-386-6327
Dr. Tom Phillips, admin. — Fax 386-8409
North Florida Cosmetology Institute — Post-Sec.
2424 Allen Rd 32312 — 850-878-5269
Tallahassee Community College — Post-Sec.
444 Appleyard Dr 32304 — 850-201-6200
Tallahassee Memorial Hospital — Post-Sec.
1300 Miccosukee Rd 32308 — 850-681-5385

Tamarac, Broward, Pop. 59,173
Broward County SD
Supt. — See Fort Lauderdale
Millennium MS 1,300/6-8
5803 NW 94th Ave 33321 754-322-3900
Dr. Cheryl Cendan, prin. Fax 322-3985

Tampa, Hillsborough, Pop. 328,173
Hillsborough County SD 198,600/PK-12
PO Box 3408 33601 813-272-4000
Jeff Eakins, supt. Fax 272-4510
www.sdhc.k12.fl.us
Adams MS 1,100/6-8
10201 N Boulevard 33612 813-975-7665
Heath Beauregard, prin. Fax 632-6889
Alonso HS 2,500/9-12
8302 Montague St 33635 813-356-1525
Kenneth Hart, prin. Fax 356-1529
Benito MS 1,100/6-8
10101 Cross Creek Blvd 33647 813-631-4694
John Sanders, prin. Fax 631-4706
Blake HS 1,700/9-12
1701 N Boulevard 33607 813-272-3422
Jesse Salters, prin. Fax 272-3715
Bowers/Whitley Career Center Vo/Tech
13609 N 22nd St 33613 813-558-1750
Derrick Gaines, prin. Fax 558-1761
Buchanan MS 700/6-8
1001 W Bearss Ave 33613 813-975-7600
Scott Hilgenberg, prin. Fax 975-7610
Chamberlain HS 1,800/9-12
9401 N Boulevard 33612 813-975-7677
Celeste Liccio, prin. Fax 975-7687
Coleman MS 900/6-8
1724 S Manhattan Ave 33629 813-872-5335
Michael Hoskinson, prin. Fax 872-5338
Davidsen MS 1,000/6-8
10501 Montague St 33626 813-558-5300
Brent McBrien, prin. Fax 558-5299
Dowdell MS 600/6-8
1208 Wishing Well Way 33619 813-744-8322
Roger Stanley, prin. Fax 740-3616
Farnell MS 1,400/6-8
13912 Nine Eagles Dr 33626 813-356-1640
John Cobb, prin. Fax 356-1644
Ferrell Girls Prep Academy 400/6-8
4302 N 24th St 33610 813-276-5608
Karen French, prin. Fax 276-5615
Franklin Boys Prep Academy 400/6-8
3915 E 21st Ave 33605 813-744-8108
John Haley, prin. Fax 744-8579
Freedom HS 2,100/9-12
17410 Commerce Park Blvd 33647 813-558-1185
Kevin Stephenson, prin. Fax 558-1189
Gaither HS 2,100/9-12
16200 N Dale Mabry Hwy 33618 813-975-7340
Thomas Morrill, prin. Fax 975-7349
Hill MS 900/6-8
5200 Ehrlich Rd 33624 813-975-7325
Ronald Mason, prin. Fax 975-4819
Hillsborough HS 1,900/9-12
5000 N Central Ave 33603 813-276-5620
Gary Brady, prin. Fax 276-5629
Jefferson HS 1,500/9-12
4401 W Cypress St 33607 813-872-5241
Robert Quinn, prin. Fax 872-5250
King HS 1,800/9-12
6815 N 56th St 33610 813-744-8333
Michael Rowan, prin. Fax 744-8343
Leto HS 1,800/9-12
4409 W Sligh Ave 33614 813-872-5300
Hilda Genco, prin. Fax 872-5314
Liberty MS 1,100/6-8
17400 Commerce Park Blvd 33647 813-558-1180
James Ammirati, prin. Fax 558-1184
Madison MS 800/6-8
4444 W Bay Vista Ave 33611 813-272-3050
Joseph Brown, prin. Fax 233-2796
Memorial MS 700/6-8
4702 N Central Ave 33603 813-872-5230
Henry Lefler, prin. Fax 872-5238
Middleton HS 1,300/9-12
4801 N 22nd St 33610 813-233-3360
Kim Moore, prin. Fax 233-3364
Monroe MS 500/6-8
4716 W Montgomery Ave 33616 813-272-3020
Peter Megara, prin. Fax 272-3027
North Tampa Alternative S 200/Alt
8602 N Armenia Ave 33604 813-631-4426
Cornelius Bobo, prin. Fax 631-4429
Orange Grove Magnet MS 600/6-8
3415 N 16th St 33605 813-276-5717
Shannon Butler, prin. Fax 276-5857
Pierce MS 1,100/6-8
5511 N Hesperides St 33614 813-872-5344
Pablo Gallego, prin. Fax 871-7978
Plant HS 2,300/9-12
2415 S Himes Ave 33629 813-272-3033
Robert Nelson, prin. Fax 272-0624
Progress Village Magnet MS 900/6-8
8113 Zinnia Dr 33619 813-671-5110
Andrew Olson, prin. Fax 671-5240
Robinson HS 1,600/9-12
6311 S Lois Ave 33616 813-272-3006
Robert Bhoolai, prin. Fax 272-3014
Sickles HS 2,100/9-12
7950 Gunn Hwy 33626 813-631-4742
Jake Russell, prin. Fax 631-4754
Sligh MS 600/6-8
2011 E Sligh Ave 33610 813-276-5596
Shellie Blackwood-Green, prin. Fax 276-5606
Smith MS 900/6-8
14303 Citrus Pointe Dr 33625 813-792-5125
JoAnn Johnson, prin. Fax 792-5129
Stewart MS 900/6-8
1125 W Spruce St 33607 813-276-5691
Baretta Wilson, prin. Fax 276-5698
Tampa Bay Technical HS 2,000/9-12
6410 Orient Rd 33610 813-744-8360
Michael Ippolito, prin. Fax 744-8368
Van Buren MS 600/6-8
8715 N 22nd St 33604 813-975-7652
Ovette Wilson, prin. Fax 631-4312
Waters Career Center Vo/Tech
2704 N Highland Ave 33602 813-233-2655
Holly Frazier, admin. Fax 233-2659
Webb MS 800/6-8
6035 Hanley Rd 33634 813-872-5351
Frank Diaz, prin. Fax 872-5359
Wharton HS 2,300/9-12
20150 Bruce B Downs Blvd 33647 813-631-4710
Bradley Woods, prin. Fax 631-4722
Williams MS 800/6-8
5020 N 47th St 33610 813-744-8600
Arlene Castelli, prin. Fax 744-8665
Wilson MS 600/6-8
1005 W Swann Ave 33606 813-276-5682
Colleen Faucett, prin. Fax 233-2540
Young Magnet MS 600/6-8
1807 E Dr Martin L King Jr 33610 813-276-5739
Nadine Johnson, prin. Fax 276-5893
Aparicio-Levy Tech Center Adult
10119 E Ellicott St 33610 813-740-4884
AnnMarie Courtney, prin. Fax 740-4885
Bowers/Whitley Adult Education Adult
13609 N 22nd St 33613 813-463-9528
Dr. Sheila Washington, prin. Fax 558-1761
Brewster Tech Center Adult
2222 N Tampa St 33602 813-276-5448
Paul Gansemer, prin. Fax 276-5756
Chamberlain Adult Education Adult
9401 N Boulevard 33612 813-631-4500
Marcia Monk, prin. Fax 631-4513
Erwin Tech Center Adult
2010 E Hillsborough Ave 33610 813-769-5180
Steve Briant, prin. Fax 769-5185
Gary Adult S Adult
5101 N 40th St 33610 813-740-7660
Edward Cristiano, prin. Fax 740-7674
Jefferson Adult Education Adult
4401 W Cypress St 33607 813-356-1288
Pam Elles, prin. Fax 356-1291
Learey Technical Center Adult
7010 N Manhattan Ave 33614 813-769-2123
Dr. James Goode, prin. Fax 769-4615
Leto Adult Education Adult
4409 W Sligh Ave 33614 813-872-5300
Dr. Olaniyi Popoola, prin. Fax 356-1010
Other Schools – See Brandon, Dover, Gibsonton, Lithia, Lutz, Odessa, Plant City, Riverview, Ruskin, Seffner, Temple Terrace, Valrico

---

Academy of the Holy Names HS 400/9-12
3319 Bayshore Blvd 33629 813-839-5371
Stephanie Nitchals, prin. Fax 839-3924
Academy Prep Center of Tampa 100/5-8
1407 E Columbus Dr 33605 813-248-5600
American Youth Academy 400/PK-12
5905 E 130th Ave 33617 813-987-9282
Br. Feras Abuzayda, prin. Fax 987-9262
Argosy University/Tampa Post-Sec.
1403 N Howard Ave 33607 813-393-5290
Art Institute of Tampa Post-Sec.
4401 N Himes Ave Ste 150 33614 813-873-2112
Bayshore Christian S 200/PK-12
3909 S MacDill Ave 33611 813-839-4297
Melanie Humenansky, head sch Fax 835-1404
Berkeley Preparatory S 1,300/PK-12
4811 Kelly Rd 33615 813-885-1673
Joseph Seivold, hdmstr. Fax 886-6933
Cambridge Christian S 600/PK-12
6101 N Habana Ave 33614 813-872-6744
Shawn Minks M.Ed., head sch Fax 872-6013
Carrollwood Day S 800/PK-12
1515 W Bearss Ave 33613 813-920-2288
Ryan Kelly, head sch Fax 960-9269
Citrus Park Christian S 400/PK-12
7705 Gunn Hwy 33625 813-920-3960
Barry Yellets, head sch Fax 926-1240
Concorde Career Institute Post-Sec.
4202 W Spruce St 33607 813-874-0094
Cristo Rey Tampa HS 9-12
6400 E Chelsea St 33610 813-621-8300
Jim Madden, prin. Fax 620-1500
DeVry University Post-Sec.
5540 W Executive Dr Ste 100 33609 813-287-6700
DeVry University Post-Sec.
6700 Lakeview Center # 150 33619 813-664-4260
Everest University - Brandon Campus Post-Sec.
3924 Coconut Palm Dr 33619 813-621-0041
Everest University - Tampa Campus Post-Sec.
3319 W Hillsborough Ave 33614 813-879-6000
Faith Outreach Academy 200/PK-12
7607 Sheldon Rd 33615 813-887-5546
Gateway Christian Academy 100/PK-12
14205 N Florida Ave 33613 813-964-9800
Henry W. Brewster Technical Center Post-Sec.
2222 N Tampa St 33602 813-276-5448
Hillsborough Community College Post-Sec.
10414 E Columbus Dr 33619 813-253-7802
Hillsborough Community College Post-Sec.
PO Box 30030 33630 813-253-7000
Hillsborough Community College Ybor Camp Post-Sec.
2112 N 15th St 33605 813-253-7601
Hillsdale Christian Academy 100/PK-12
6201 Ehrlich Rd 33625 813-884-8250
Tanya B. Henry M.A., prin. Fax 886-5251
James Haley Veteran's Hospital Post-Sec.
13000 Bruce B Downs Blvd 33612 813-972-2000
Jesuit HS 700/9-12
4701 N Himes Ave 33614 813-877-5344
Barry Neuburger, prin. Fax 872-1853
Keiser University Post-Sec.
5002 W Waters Ave 33634 813-885-4900
LaSalle Computer Learning Center Post-Sec.
1111 N West Shore Blvd #110 33607 888-482-6877
Manhattan Beauty School Post-Sec.
2317 E Fletcher Ave 33612 813-264-3535
Manhattan Hairstyling Academy Post-Sec.
1906 W Platt St 33606 813-837-2525
Paideia S of Tampa Bay 100/K-12
7834 N 56th St 33617 813-988-7700
Dr. Tim Bridges, hdmstr. Fax 988-7740
Rasmussen College Post-Sec.
4042 Park Oaks Blvd Ste 100 33610 813-246-7600
Remington College Post-Sec.
6302 E ML King Blvd Ste 400 33619 813-935-5700
Sanford-Brown College Post-Sec.
7702 Woodland Center # 100 33614 847-781-3600
Sanford-Brown Institute Post-Sec.
3725 W Grace St 33607 813-881-0007
Southeastern College Post-Sec.
5225 Memorial Hwy 33634 813-961-2837
Southwest Florida College Post-Sec.
3910 Riga Blvd 33619 813-630-4401
Strayer University Post-Sec.
6302 E M L King Blvd # 450 33619 813-663-0100
Strayer University Post-Sec.
4902 Eisenhower Blvd # 100 33634 813-882-0100
Tampa Adventist Academy 100/PK-10
3205 N Boulevard 33603 813-228-7950
Tampa Bay Christian Academy 300/PK-12
6815 N Rome Ave 33604 813-343-0600
Natasha Sherwood, head sch Fax 343-0601
Tampa Catholic HS 700/9-12
4630 N Rome Ave 33603 813-870-0860
Robert Lees, prin. Fax 877-9136
Tampa General Hospital Post-Sec.
PO Box 1289 33601 813-844-7985
Tampa Preparatory S 600/6-12
727 W Cass St 33606 813-251-8481
Kevin Plummer, hdmstr. Fax 254-2106
The Salon Professional Academy Post-Sec.
4802 Gunn Hwy Ste 144 33624 813-908-8020
Ultimate Medical Academy Post-Sec.
9309 N Florida Ave Ste 100 33612 813-386-6350
Universal Academy of Florida 400/PK-12
6801 Orient Rd 33610 813-664-0695
University of South Florida Post-Sec.
4202 E Fowler Ave 33620 813-974-2011
University of Tampa Post-Sec.
401 W Kennedy Blvd 33606 813-253-3333
West Gate Christian S 100/PK-12
5121 Kelly Rd 33615 813-884-5147

Tarpon Springs, Pinellas, Pop. 23,056
Pinellas County SD
Supt. — See Largo
East Lake HS 2,200/9-12
1300 Silver Eagle Dr 34688 727-942-5419
Carmela Haley, prin. Fax 942-5441
East Lake MS Academy of Engineering 6-8
1200 Silver Eagle Dr 34688 727-940-7624
Karen Huzar, prin. Fax 754-8653
Tarpon Springs HS 1,400/9-12
1411 Gulf Rd 34689 727-943-4900
Leza Fatolitis, prin. Fax 943-4907
Tarpon Springs MS 1,000/6-8
501 N Florida Ave 34689 727-943-5511
Raquel Giles, prin. Fax 943-5519

St. Petersburg College Post-Sec.
600 E Klosterman Rd 34689 727-791-2400

Tavares, Lake, Pop. 13,762
Lake County SD 39,400/PK-12
201 W Burleigh Blvd 32778 352-253-6500
Susan Moxley Ed.D., supt. Fax 253-6503
www.lake.k12.fl.us/
Tavares HS 1,200/9-12
603 N New Hampshire Ave 32778 352-343-3007
Dr. Janice Boyd, prin. Fax 343-0892
Tavares MS 1,000/6-8
1335 Lane Park Cutoff 32778 352-343-4545
Trella Mott, prin. Fax 343-7212
Other Schools – See Clermont, Eustis, Groveland, Leesburg, Minneola, Mount Dora, Umatilla

---

Adventure Christian Academy 100/K-12
3800 State Road 19 32778 352-742-4543
Gary Johnson, admin. Fax 343-3820
Liberty Christian Prep 200/PK-12
2451 Dora Ave 32778 352-343-0061

Tavernier, Monroe, Pop. 2,111
Monroe County SD
Supt. — See Key West
Coral Shores HS 700/9-12
89901 Overseas Hwy 33070 305-853-3222
Blake Fry, prin. Fax 853-3228

Temple Terrace, Hillsborough, Pop. 23,889
Hillsborough County SD
Supt. — See Tampa
Greco MS 900/6-8
6925 E Fowler Ave 33617 813-987-6926
Valerie Newton, prin. Fax 987-6863

Florida College Post-Sec.
119 N Glen Arven Ave 33617 813-988-5131

Titusville, Brevard, Pop. 42,761
Brevard County SD
Supt. — See Melbourne
Astronaut HS 1,100/9-12
800 War Eagle Blvd 32796 321-264-3000
Krista Miller, prin. Fax 264-3013
Jackson MS 500/7-8
1515 Knox Mcrae Dr 32780 321-269-1812
Annetha Jones, prin. Fax 269-7811
Madison MS 500/7-8
3375 Dairy Rd 32796 321-264-3120
Sherry Tomlinson, prin. Fax 264-3124
Titusville HS 1,300/9-12
150 Terrier Trl S 32780 321-264-3100
Gary Preisser, prin. Fax 264-3103
South Lake Education Center Adult
3755 Garden St 32796 321-264-3088
Jeff Arnott, prin. Fax 264-3042

Bristow Academy Post-Sec.
365 Golden Knights Blvd 32780 321-567-0382
Melbourne Beauty School Post-Sec.
106 Julia St 32796 - -
Temple Christian S 100/PK-12
1400 N Washington Ave 32780 321-269-2837

Trenton, Gilchrist, Pop. 1,949
Gilchrist County SD 2,600/PK-12
310 NW 11th Ave 32693 352-463-3200
Robert G. Rankin, supt. Fax 463-3276
gilchristschools.schoolfusion.us
Trenton HS 600/6-12
1013 N Main St 32693 352-463-3210
Cheri Langford, prin. Fax 463-3264
Other Schools – See Bell

Trinity, Pasco, Pop. 10,776

Trinity College of Florida Post-Sec.
2430 Welbilt Blvd 34655 727-376-6911

Umatilla, Lake, Pop. 3,433
Lake County SD
Supt. — See Tavares
Umatilla HS 800/9-12
320 N Trowell Ave 32784 352-669-3131
Randy Campbell, prin. Fax 669-6606
Umatilla MS 600/6-8
305 E Lake St 32784 352-669-3171
Thomas Sanders, prin. Fax 669-5424

Valparaiso, Okaloosa, Pop. 4,829
Okaloosa County SD
Supt. — See Fort Walton Beach
Okaloosa STEMM Academy 100/6-8
379 Edge Ave 32580 850-833-4120
Wanda Avery, admin. Fax 833-4177

Valrico, Hillsborough, Pop. 34,795
Hillsborough County SD
Supt. — See Tampa
Bloomingdale HS 2,200/9-12
1700 Bloomingdale Ave, 813-744-8018
Susan Burkett, prin. Fax 744-8026
Mulrennan MS 1,100/6-8
4215 Durant Rd, 813-651-2100
Tim Ducker, prin. Fax 651-2104

Foundation Christian Academy 200/PK-12
3955 Lithia Pinecrest Rd, 813-654-2969
Jonathan Smith, pres. Fax 655-4780
Grace Christian S 200/PK-12
1425 N Valrico Rd 33594 813-689-8815
Manhattan Hairstyling Academy Post-Sec.
3244 Lithia Pinecrest #103 33594 813-655-4545

Venice, Sarasota, Pop. 20,602
Sarasota County SD
Supt. — See Sarasota
Venice HS 1,900/9-12
1 Indian Ave 34285 941-488-6726
Eric Jackson, prin. Fax 486-2034
Venice MS 500/6-8
1900 Center Rd 34292 941-486-2100
Dr. Karin Schmidt, prin. Fax 486-2108

Venice Christian S 200/PK-12
1200 Center Rd 34292 941-496-4411
Jerry Frimmel, admin. Fax 408-8362

Vernon, Washington, Pop. 673
Washington County SD
Supt. — See Chipley
Vernon HS 400/9-12
3232 Moss Hill Rd 32462 850-535-2046
Brian Riviere, prin. Fax 535-6244
Vernon MS 300/6-8
3206 Moss Hill Rd 32462 850-535-2807
Kimberly Register, prin. Fax 535-1683

Vero Beach, Indian River, Pop. 15,009
Indian River County SD 17,000/PK-12
6500 57th St 32968 772-564-3000
Dr. Mark Rendell, supt. Fax 564-3054
www.indianriverschools.org
Alternative Center for Education 100/Alt
4680 28th Ct 32967 772-564-6240
Denny Hart, prin. Fax 564-6265
Gifford MS 900/6-8
4530 28th Ct 32967 772-564-3550
Roxanne Decker, prin. Fax 564-3561
Oslo MS 900/6-8
480 20th Ave SW 32962 772-564-3980
Beth Hofer, prin. Fax 564-4029
Storm Grove MS 900/6-8
6400 57th St 32967 772-564-6400
Tosha Jones, prin. Fax 564-6321
Vero Beach Freshman Learning Center 9-9
1507 19th St 32960 772-564-5800
Shawn O'Keefe, prin. Fax 564-4928
Vero Beach HS 2,000/10-12
1707 16th St 32960 772-564-5400
Shawn O'Keefe, prin. Fax 564-5553
Technical Center for Career & Adult Ed Adult
1426 19th St 32960 772-564-4970
Christi Shields, prin. Fax 564-4977
Other Schools – See Sebastian

FlightSafety Academy Post-Sec.
2805 Airport Dr 32960 772-564-7600
Glendale Christian S 100/PK-12
790 27th Ave 32968 772-569-1095
Master's Academy 200/PK-12
1105 58th Ave 32966 772-794-4655
Dr. Wayne Smith, hdmstr. Fax 794-4655
St. Edward's S 500/PK-12
1895 Saint Edwards Dr 32963 772-231-4136
Michael Mersky, head sch Fax 231-2427

Viera, Brevard
Brevard County SD
Supt. — See Melbourne
Viera HS 2,000/9-12
6103 Stadium Pkwy 32940 321-632-1770
Miguel Alba, prin. Fax 433-4338

Walnut Hill, Escambia
Escambia County SD
Supt. — See Pensacola
Ward MS 500/6-8
7650 Highway 97 32568 850-327-4283
Nancy Perry, prin. Fax 327-4991

Wauchula, Hardee, Pop. 4,954
Hardee County SD 5,100/PK-12
PO Box 1678 33873 863-773-9058
David Durastanti, supt. Fax 773-0069
www.hardee.k12.fl.us
Hardee HS 1,300/9-12
830 Altman Rd 33873 863-773-3181
Dr. Michele Polk Ed.D., prin. Fax 773-4390
Hardee JHS 1,200/6-8
2401 US Highway 17 N 33873 863-773-3147
Todd Durden, prin. Fax 773-3167
Other Schools – See Zolfo Springs

Webster, Sumter, Pop. 770
Sumter County SD
Supt. — See Bushnell
South Sumter MS 800/6-8
773 NW 10th Ave 33597 352-793-2232
Allen Shirley, prin. Fax 793-3976

Weeki Wachee, Hernando, Pop. 12
Hernando County SD
Supt. — See Brooksville
Weeki Wachee HS 1,400/9-12
12150 Vespa Way 34614 352-797-7029
Troy LaBarbara, prin. Fax 797-7129

Wellington, Palm Beach, Pop. 55,375
Palm Beach County SD
Supt. — See West Palm Beach
Emerald Cove MS 1,200/6-8
9950 Stribling Way 33414 561-803-8000
Eugina Feaman, prin. Fax 803-8050
Palm Beach Central HS 2,900/9-12
8499 Forest Hill Blvd, 561-304-1000
Darren Edgecomb, prin. Fax 304-1017
Polo Park MS 800/6-8
11901 Lake Worth Rd, 561-333-5500
Ann Clark, prin. Fax 333-5505
Wellington Community HS 2,400/9-12
2101 Greenview Shores Blvd 33414 561-795-4900
Mario Crocetti, prin. Fax 795-4948
Wellington Landings MS 1,100/6-8
1100 Aero Club Dr 33414 561-792-8100
Blake Bennett, prin. Fax 792-8106

Wesley Chapel, Pasco, Pop. 42,858
Pasco County SD
Supt. — See Land O Lakes
Long MS 1,600/6-8
2025 Mansfield Blvd 33543 813-346-6200
Christine Wolff, prin. Fax 346-6291
Weightman MS 1,200/6-8
30649 Wells Rd, 813-794-0200
Brandon Bracciale, prin. Fax 794-0291
Wesley Chapel HS 1,500/9-12
30651 Wells Rd, 813-794-8700
Carin Nettles, prin. Fax 794-8791
Wiregrass Ranch HS 2,200/9-12
2909 Mansfield Blvd 33543 813-346-6000
Robyn White, prin. Fax 346-6091

Saddlebrook Preparatory S 100/3-12
5700 Saddlebrook Way 33543 813-907-4500

West Melbourne, Brevard, Pop. 17,945
Brevard County SD
Supt. — See Melbourne
Central MS 1,300/7-8
2600 Wingate Blvd 32904 321-722-4150
Gregory Potter, prin. Fax 722-4165

Bethany Christian S 300/PK-12
1100 Dorchester Ave 32904 321-727-2038

West Miami, Miami-Dade, Pop. 5,942

Florida Education Institute Post-Sec.
5818 SW 8th St 33144 305-263-9990

Weston, Broward, Pop. 64,228
Broward County SD
Supt. — See Fort Lauderdale
Cypress Bay HS 4,400/9-12
18600 Vista Park Blvd 33332 754-323-0350
Charles Neely, prin. Fax 323-0363
Falcon Cove MS 2,200/6-8
4251 Bonaventure Blvd 33332 754-323-3200
Dr. Mark Kaplan, prin. Fax 323-3285
Tequesta Trace MS 1,400/6-8
1800 Indian Trce 33326 754-323-4400
Paul Micensky, prin. Fax 323-4485

American InterContinental University Post-Sec.
2250 N Commerce Pkwy 33326 954-446-6100
Sagemont S - Upper School Campus 500/6-12
2585 Glades Cir 33327 954-389-2454
Gayle Iacono, prin. Fax 389-8106

West Palm Beach, Palm Beach, Pop. 98,081
Palm Beach County SD 176,500/PK-12
3300 Forest Hill Blvd 33406 561-434-8000
Robert Avossa Ed.D., supt. Fax 434-8571
www.palmbeachschools.org/
Bak MS of the Arts 1,300/6-8
1725 Echo Lake Dr 33407 561-882-3870
Sally Rozanski, prin. Fax 882-3879
Bear Lakes MS 800/6-8
3505 Shenandoah Rd 33409 561-615-7700
Kirk Howell, prin. Fax 615-7756
Conniston Community MS 1,100/6-8
3630 Parker Ave 33405 561-802-5400
Oscar Otero, prin. Fax 802-5409
Dreyfoos S of the Arts 1,300/9-12
501 S Sapodilla Ave 33401 561-802-6000
Susan Atherley, prin. Fax 802-6059
Forest Hill Community HS 2,000/9-12
6901 Parker Ave 33405 561-540-2400
Mary Stratos, prin. Fax 540-2440
Gold Coast Community S 100/Alt
4260 Westgate Ave 33409 561-687-6300
Timothy Abrams, prin. Fax 687-6350
Jeaga MS 1,200/6-8
3777 N Jog Rd 33411 561-242-8000
Kevin Gatlin, prin. Fax 242-8005
Okeeheelee MS 1,500/6-8
2200 Pinehurst Dr 33413 561-434-3200
David Samore, prin. Fax 434-3244
PACE Center for Girls 50/Alt
1225 S Military Trl Ste D 33415 561-472-1990
Fax 472-1991
Palm Beach Lakes Community HS 1,900/9-12
3505 Shiloh Dr 33407 561-640-5000
David Alfonso, prin. Fax 688-5340
Palm Springs Community MS 1,600/6-8
1560 Kirk Rd 33406 561-434-3300
Sandra Jinks, prin. Fax 434-3303
Roosevelt Community MS 1,100/6-8
1900 N Australian Ave 33407 561-822-0200
Moneek McTier, prin. Fax 882-0222
Turning Points Academy 100/Alt
1950 Benoist Farms Rd 33411 561-681-3700
Anthony Allen Ph.D., prin. Fax 681-3750
Western Pines MS 1,100/6-8
5949 140th Ave N 33411 561-792-2500
Robert Hatcher, prin. Fax 792-2530
Adult Education Center of Palm Beach Adult
2161 N Military Trl 33409 561-616-7800
Fax 616-7850
Other Schools – See Belle Glade, Boca Raton, Boynton Beach, Delray Beach, Greenacres, Jupiter, Lake Worth, Lantana, Loxahatchee, Pahokee, Palm Beach Gardens, Riviera Beach, Royal Palm Beach, Wellington

---

Academy for Nursing & Health Occupations Post-Sec.
5154 Okechobee Blvd #201 33417 561-683-1400
Atlantic Christian Academy 300/PK-12
4900 Summit Blvd 33415 561-686-8081
Jim Rozendal, hdmstr. Fax 640-7613
Berean Christian S 600/PK-12
8350 Okeechobee Blvd 33411 561-798-9300
William Dupere, hdmstr. Fax 792-3073
Cardinal Newman HS 700/9-12
512 Spencer Dr 33409 561-683-6266
Dr. Christine Higgins, prin. Fax 683-7307
Florida Career College Post-Sec.
6058 Okeechobee Blvd 33417 561-689-0550
Health Career Institute Post-Sec.
1764 N Congress Ave 33409 561-586-0121
Keiser University Post-Sec.
2085 Vista Pkwy 33411 561-471-6000
King's Academy 1,000/PK-12
8401 Belvedere Rd 33411 561-686-4244
Douglas Raines, hdmstr. Fax 686-8017
Lincoln College of Technology Post-Sec.
2410 Metrocentre Blvd 33407 561-842-8324
MCI Institute of Technology Post-Sec.
3650 Shawnee Ave Ste 12 33409 888-318-9310
Northwood University Post-Sec.
2600 N Military Trl 33409 800-458-8325
Oxbridge Academy 300/9-12
3151 N Military Trl 33409 561-972-9600
John Klemme, head sch
Palm Beach Atlantic University Post-Sec.
901 S Flagler Dr 33401 888-468-6722
PC Professor Post-Sec.
6080 Okeechobee Blvd #200 33417 561-684-3333

Wewahitchka, Gulf, Pop. 1,928
Gulf County SD
Supt. — See Port Saint Joe
Wewahitchka JSHS 400/7-12
1 Gator Cir 32465 850-639-2228
Jay Bidwell, prin. Fax 639-5394

Wildwood, Sumter, Pop. 6,607
Sumter County SD
Supt. — See Bushnell
Wildwood MSHS 700/6-12
700 Huey St 34785 352-748-1314
Richard Hampton, prin. Fax 748-7668

Williston, Levy, Pop. 2,726
Levy County SD
Supt. — See Bronson
Williston MSHS 500/6-12
350 SW 12th Ave 32696 352-528-3542
Lindsay Legler, admin. Fax 528-2723

Williston Central Christian Academy 100/K-11
PO Box 680 32696 352-529-0900
Julie Alexander, admin. Fax 529-0901

Windermere, Orange, Pop. 2,437
Orange County SD
Supt. — See Orlando
Gotha MS 1,300/6-8
9155 Gotha Rd 34786 407-521-2360
Patrice Knowles, prin. Fax 521-2361

Windermere Preparatory S 1,100/PK-12
6189 Winter Garden Vineland 34786 407-905-7737
Dr. Thomas Marcy, hdmstr. Fax 905-7710

Winter Garden, Orange, Pop. 33,427
Orange County SD
Supt. — See Orlando
Bridgewater MS 1,100/6-8
5600 Tiny Rd 34787 407-905-3710
Lisa James, prin. Fax 905-3858
Lakeview MS 1,000/6-8
1200 W Bay St 34787 407-877-5010
Athena Adams, prin. Fax 877-5019
Sunridge MS 1,200/6-8
14955 Sunridge Blvd 34787 407-656-0794
Patricia Bowen-Painter, prin. Fax 656-0806
West Orange HS 3,700/9-12
1625 Beulah Rd 34787 407-905-2400
William Floyd, prin. Fax 656-4970
Westside Tech Ctr Vo/Tech
955 E Story Rd 34787 407-905-2000
Crystal Davidson, dir. Fax 656-3970

Foundation Academy - South Campus 400/6-12
15304 Tilden Rd 34787 407-877-2744
David Buckles, pres. Fax 877-1985
Professional Golfers Career College Post-Sec.
16349 Phil Ritson Way 34787 407-905-2200

Winter Haven, Polk, Pop. 33,292
Polk County SD
Supt. — See Bartow
Denison MS 800/6-8
400 Avenue A SE 33880 863-291-5353
Terri Christian, prin. Fax 291-5347
Jewett Middle Academy 600/6-8
601 Avenue T NE 33881 863-291-5320
Jacquelyn Moore, prin. Fax 297-3049
Ridge Career Center Vo/Tech
7700 State Road 544 33881 863-419-3060
Kenneth Reddick, dir. Fax 419-3062
Westwood MS 800/6-8
3520 Avenue J NW 33881 863-965-5484
Todd Bennett, prin. Fax 965-5585
Winter Haven HS 1,900/9-12
600 6th St SE 33880 863-291-5330
Gina Williams, prin. Fax 297-3024

All Saints' Academy 600/PK-12
5001 State Road 540 W 33880 863-293-5980
Carolyn Baldwin, hdmstr. Fax 294-2819
Christian Academy of Winter Haven 200/K-12
PO Box 392 33882 863-294-8934
Sr. Ida Kilpatrick, prin. Fax 299-2489
Heritage Christian Academy 100/PK-11
244 Avenue D SW 33880 863-293-0012
Dr. John Scott, hdmstr. Fax 299-4146
Oasis Christian Academy 200/PK-12
151 King Rd 33880 863-293-0930
Matt Wiggins, admin. Fax 293-0429
Polk Community College Post-Sec.
999 Avenue H NE 33881 863-297-1000
Ridge Career Center Post-Sec.
7700 State Road 544 33881 863-419-3060
Winter Haven Christian S 200/PK-12
1700 Buckeye Loop Rd 33881 863-294-4135

Winter Park, Orange, Pop. 27,399
Orange County SD
Supt. — See Orlando
Winter Park 9th Grade Center 900/9-9
528 Huntington Ave 32789 407-623-1476
Paul Maldonado, prin. Fax 623-1485
Winter Park Education Center Alt
1045 Azalea Ln 32789 407-245-1555
William Tovine, prin. Fax 245-1561
Winter Park HS 2,300/10-12
2100 Summerfield Rd 32792 407-622-3200
Timothy Smith, prin. Fax 975-2434
Winter Park Tech Center Vo/Tech
901 W Webster Ave 32789 407-622-2900
Capildeo Jadonath, prin. Fax 975-2435

Seminole County SD
Supt. — See Sanford
Lake Howell HS 2,200/9-12
4200 Dike Rd 32792 407-746-9050
Frank Casillo, prin. Fax 746-9025

Fortis College Post-Sec.
1573 W Fairbanks Ave #100 32789 407-843-3984
Full Sail University Post-Sec.
3300 University Blvd 32792 407-679-0100
Geneva S 500/PK-12
2025 State Road 436 32792 407-332-6363
Herzing University Post-Sec.
1865 State Road 436 32792 407-478-0500
International Community S 400/PK-12
4800 Howell Branch Rd 32792 407-645-2343
Robyn Terwilleger, prin.
Rollins College Post-Sec.
1000 Holt Ave 32789 407-646-2000
Trinity Preparatory S 800/6-12
5700 Trinity Prep Ln 32792 407-671-4140
Byron Lawson, head sch Fax 671-6935
Walden Community S 50/PK-12
4595 Howell Branch Rd 32792 407-677-8225

Winter Springs, Seminole, Pop. 32,650
Seminole County SD
Supt. — See Sanford
Indian Trails MS 1,000/6-8
415 Tuskawilla Rd 32708 407-320-4350
Dr. Lesley Sileo Robinson, prin. Fax 320-4399
Winter Springs HS 2,300/9-12
130 Tuskawilla Rd 32708 407-320-8750
Dr. Mickey Reynolds, prin. Fax 320-8700

Yulee, Nassau, Pop. 11,311
Nassau County SD
Supt. — See Fernandina Beach
Yulee HS 1,100/9-12
85375 Miner Rd 32097 904-491-7949
Natasha Drake, prin. Fax 225-8658
Yulee MS 900/6-8
85439 Miner Rd 32097 904-491-7944
Amanda Cooper, prin. Fax 225-0104

Zellwood, Orange, Pop. 2,799

Hampden DuBose Academy 100/K-12
PO Box 639 32798 407-880-4321

Zephyrhills, Pasco, Pop. 13,107
Pasco County SD
Supt. — See Land O Lakes
Stewart MS 1,000/6-8
38505 10th Ave, 813-794-6500
Shae Davis, prin. Fax 794-6591
Zephyrhills HS 1,500/9-12
6335 12th St, 813-794-6100
Angela Stone, prin. Fax 794-6191

Zephyrhills Christian Academy 100/K-12
34927 Eiland Blvd 33541 813-779-1648

Zolfo Springs, Hardee, Pop. 1,811
Hardee County SD
Supt. — See Wauchula
Pioneer Career Academy 50/Alt
2630 Academy Dr 33890 863-735-2300
Gilbert Vasquez, dir. Fax 735-2155

GEORGIA

GEORGIA DEPARTMENT OF EDUCATION

2066 Twin Towers E, Atlanta 30334-9050
Telephone 404-656-2800
Fax 404-651-8737
Website http://www.doe.k12.ga.us

State Superintendent of Schools Richard Woods

GEORGIA BOARD OF EDUCATION

2053 Twin Towers East, Atlanta 30334

Chairperson Mike Royal

REGIONAL EDUCATIONAL SERVICE AGENCIES (RESA)

Central Savannah River Area RESA
Gene Sullivan, dir. 706-556-6225
4683 Augusta Hwy, Dearing 30808 Fax 556-8891
www.csraresa.net

Chattahoochee-Flint RESA
Norman Carter, dir. 229-937-5341
PO Box 1150, Ellaville 31806 Fax 937-5754
www.cfresa.org

Coastal Plains RESA
Harold Chambers, dir. 229-546-4094
245 N Robinson St, Lenox 31637 Fax 546-4167
www.cpresa.org

First District RESA
Dr. Whit Myers, dir. 912-842-5000
PO Box 780, Brooklet 30415 Fax 842-5161
www.fdresa.org/

Griffin RESA
Dr. Stephanie Gordy, dir. 770-229-3247
440 Tilney Ave, Griffin 30224 Fax 228-7316
www.griffinresa.net/

Heart of Georgia RESA
Dr. Steven Miletto, dir. 478-374-2240
1141 Cochran Hwy Fax 374-1524
Eastman 31023
www.hgresa.org/

Metro RESA
Leigh Ann Putman, dir. 770-432-2404
1870 Teasley Dr SE, Smyrna 30080 Fax 432-6105
www.ciclt.net/mresa

Middle Georgia RESA
Carolyn Williams, dir. 478-988-7170
80 Cohen Walker Dr Fax 988-7176
Warner Robins 31088
www.mgresa.org/

Northeast Georgia RESA
Dr. Keith Everson, dir. 706-742-8292
375 Winter St, Winterville 30683 Fax 742-8928
www.negaresa.org

North Georgia RESA
Alexander Rainey, dir. 706-276-1111
4731 Old Highway 5 S Fax 276-1114
Ellijay 30540
www.ngresa.org

Northwest Georgia RESA
Dexter Mills, dir. 706-295-6189
3167 Cedartown Hwy SE Fax 295-6098
Rome 30161
www.nwgaresa.com/

Oconee RESA
Dr. Hayward Cordy, dir. 478-552-5178
206 S Main St, Tennille 31089 Fax 552-6499
www.oconeeresa.org

Okefenokee RESA
Dr. Peggy Stovall, dir. 912-285-6151
1450 N Augusta Ave Fax 287-6650
Waycross 31503
www.okresa.org

Pioneer RESA
Justin Old, dir. 706-865-2141
PO Box 1789, Cleveland 30528 Fax 865-6748
www.pioneerresa.org/

Southwest Georgia RESA
Tim Helms, dir. 229-207-0600
570 Martin Luther King Jr Fax 336-2888
Camilla 31730
www.swresa.org

West Georgia RESA
Rachel Spates, dir. 770-583-2528
99 Brown School Dr Fax 583-3223
Grantville 30220
www.garesa.org

PUBLIC, PRIVATE AND CATHOLIC SECONDARY SCHOOLS

Abbeville, Wilcox, Pop. 2,863
Wilcox County SD 1,200/PK-12
395 College St W 31001 229-467-2141
Julie Childers, supt. Fax 467-2302
www.wilcox.k12.ga.us
Other Schools – See Rochelle

Acworth, Cobb, Pop. 19,875
Cobb County SD
Supt. — See Marietta
Allatoona HS 1,800/9-12
3300 Dallas Acworth Hwy NW 30101 770-975-6503
John Kelly, prin. Fax 529-7744
Barber MS 1,000/6-8
4222 Cantrell Rd NW 30101 770-975-6764
Tia Amlett, prin. Fax 529-0325
Durham MS 1,000/6-8
2891 Mars Hill Rd NW 30101 770-975-6641
Dr. Patricia Alford, prin. Fax 975-6643

Chattahoochee Technical College Post-Sec.
5198 Ross Rd SE 30102 770-975-4000
Cornerstone Preparatory Academy 400/K-12
3588 Hickory Grove Rd NW 30101 770-529-7077
Jeanne Borders, head sch Fax 529-7477

Adairsville, Bartow, Pop. 4,584
Bartow County SD
Supt. — See Cartersville
Adairsville HS 900/9-12
519 Old Highway 41 NW 30103 770-606-5841
Bruce Mulkey, prin. Fax 773-2722
Adairsville MS 700/6-8
485 Old Highway 41 NW 30103 770-606-5842
Dr. Brian Knuchel, prin. Fax 606-5179

Adel, Cook, Pop. 5,286
Cook County SD 3,300/PK-12
1109 N Parrish Ave 31620 229-896-2294
Dr. Jeff Shealey Ed.D., supt. Fax 896-3443
www.cook.k12.ga.us
Cook HS 900/9-12
9900 Highway 37 31620 229-896-2213
Keith Croft, prin. Fax 896-3423
Other Schools – See Sparks

Ailey, Montgomery, Pop. 429
Montgomery County SD
Supt. — See Mount Vernon
Montgomery County MS 200/6-8
800 Martin Luther King Dr 30410 912-583-2351
Dr. Scott Barrow, prin. Fax 583-4469

Alamo, Wheeler, Pop. 2,788
Wheeler County SD 1,000/PK-12
18 McRae St 30411 912-568-7198
Dr. Mark Davidson, supt. Fax 568-1985
www.wheelercountyschools.org
Wheeler County MSHS 500/6-12
50 Snowhill Rd 30411 912-568-7166
Hal Ford, prin. Fax 568-7141

Albany, Dougherty, Pop. 76,579
Dougherty County SD 15,000/PK-12
200 Pine Ave 31701 229-431-1285
Dr. David Mosely, supt. Fax 431-1276
www.docoschools.org
Albany HS 900/9-12
801 W Residence Ave 31701 229-431-3300
Rodney Bullard, prin. Fax 431-3481
Albany MS 700/6-8
1700 Cordell Ave 31705 229-431-3325
Eddie Johnson, prin. Fax 431-3474
College and Career Learning Center 9-12
900 Lippett Dr 31705 229-431-6321
Gloria Baker, prin.
Cross MS 500/6-8
324 Lockett Station Rd, 229-431-3362
Thelma Chunn, prin. Fax 431-3476
Dougherty HS 1,000/9-12
1800 Pearce Ave 31705 229-431-3310
Dr. Jeffrey Ross, prin. Fax 431-1302
Merry Acres MS 900/6-8
1601 Florence Dr 31707 229-431-3338
Dr. Gail Griffin, prin. Fax 431-1204
Monroe HS 1,100/9-12
900 Lippitt Dr 31701 229-431-3316
Vinson Davis, prin. Fax 431-3380
Radium Springs MS 700/6-8
2600 Radium Springs Rd 31705 229-431-3346
Dr. Valerie Williams, prin. Fax 431-3552
South GA Regional Achievement Center Alt
1001 W Highland Ave 31701 229-431-1218
Marcel Loving, prin. Fax 431-3478
Southside MS 600/6-8
1615 Newton Rd 31701 229-431-3351
Dr. Frederick Polite, prin. Fax 431-1209
Westover HS 1,200/9-12
2600 Partridge Dr 31707 229-431-3320
William Chunn, prin. Fax 431-3349

Albany State University Post-Sec.
504 College Dr 31705 229-430-4600
Albany Technical College Post-Sec.
1704 S Slappey Blvd 31701 229-430-3500
Byne Christian S 100/PK-12
2832 Ledo Rd 31707 229-436-0173
James Wagenschutz, hdmstr. Fax 434-0039
Darton State College Post-Sec.
2400 Gillionville Rd 31707 229-317-6000
Deerfield-Windsor S 800/PK-12
PO Box 71149 31708 229-435-1301
David Davies, hdmstr. Fax 888-6085
Sherwood Christian Academy 400/PK-12
1418 Old Pretoria Rd, 229-883-5677
Dr. Brian Dougherty, hdmstr. Fax 883-5794

Alma, Bacon, Pop. 3,400
Bacon County SD 2,100/PK-12
102 W 4th St 31510 912-632-7363
Dr. Laine Reichert, supt. Fax 632-2454
www.bcraiders.com/
Bacon County HS 500/9-12
1190 US Highway 1 S 31510 912-632-4414
Ross New, prin. Fax 632-6603
Bacon County MS 500/6-8
1188 US Highway 1 S 31510 912-632-4662
Charlie Powell, prin. Fax 632-6603

Alpharetta, Fulton, Pop. 56,130
Forsyth County SD
Supt. — See Cumming
DeSana MS 700/6-8
625 James Rd 30004 770-667-2591
Terri North, prin. Fax 667-2592

Fulton County SD
Supt. — See Atlanta
Alpharetta HS 2,100/9-12
3595 Webb Bridge Rd 30005 770-521-7640
Shannon Kersey, prin. Fax 521-7653
Haynes Bridge MS 700/6-8
10665 Haynes Bridge Rd 30022 470-254-7030
Lauren Malekebu, prin. Fax 254-2842
Holcomb Bridge MS 800/6-8
2700 Holcomb Bridge Rd 30022 470-254-5280
Christopher Shearer, prin. Fax 254-3333
Independence HS 300/Alt
86 School Dr 30009 470-254-7611
Tabatha Taylor, prin. Fax 254-7621
Webb Bridge MS 1,400/6-8
4455 Webb Bridge Rd 30005 470-254-2940
Susan Opferman, prin. Fax 254-2948

DeVry University Post-Sec.
2555 Northwinds Pkwy 30009 770-619-3600
King's Ridge Christian S 700/PK-12
2765 Bethany Bnd 30004 770-754-5738
David Rhodes, hdmstr. Fax 754-9785
Mill Springs Academy 300/1-12
13660 New Providence Rd 30004 770-360-1336
Robert Moore, hdmstr. Fax 360-1341
Rivers Academy 200/4-12
38 N Main St 30009 770-475-0081

Americus, Sumter, Pop. 16,892
Sumter County SD 3,000/PK-12
100 Learning Ln, 229-931-8500
Donnie Smith, supt. Fax 931-8555
www.sumterschools.org

Americus Sumpter HS 900/10-12
805 Harrold Ave 31709 229-924-3653
Kimothy Hadley, prin. Fax 924-1556
Americus Sumter Ninth Grade Academy 300/9-9
915 N Lee St, 229-924-5914
Coleman Price, prin. Fax 928-8618
Ombudsman Learning Center Alt
1540 E Forsyth St 31709 229-931-9771
Arthur Young, prin. Fax 931-9772
Sumter County MS 300/7-8
200 Industrial Blvd, 229-924-1010
Stacy Favors, prin. Fax 928-5571

Georgia Southwestern State University Post-Sec.
800 GSW State University Dr 31709 229-928-1273
South Georgia Technical College Post-Sec.
900 S Georgia Tech Pkwy 31709 229-931-2394
Southland Academy 600/PK-12
PO Box 1127 31709 229-924-4406

Armuchee, Floyd
Floyd County SD
Supt. — See Rome
Armuchee MS 500/6-8
471 Floyd Springs Rd NE 30105 706-378-7924
Jeanie Hubbard, prin. Fax 378-7983

Ashburn, Turner, Pop. 4,108
Turner County SD 1,500/PK-12
423 N Cleveland St 31714 229-567-3338
Dr. Jeff McDaniel, supt. Fax 567-3285
www.turner.k12.ga.us
Turner County HS 400/9-12
316 Lamar St 31714 229-567-4377
Bernice Martin, prin. Fax 567-9243
Turner County MS 300/6-8
316 Lamar St 31714 229-567-4343
Bernice Martin, prin. Fax 567-9243

Athens, Clarke, Pop. 113,262
Clarke County SD 12,800/PK-12
PO Box 1708 30603 706-546-7721
Dr. Jack Parish, supt. Fax 208-9124
www.clarke.k12.ga.us
Burney-Harris-Lyons MS 600/6-8
1600 Tallassee Rd 30606 706-548-7208
Melanie Sigler, prin. Fax 357-5263
Cedar Shoals HS 1,400/9-12
1300 Cedar Shoals Dr 30605 706-546-5375
DeAnne Varitek, prin. Fax 357-5291
Clarke Central HS 1,500/9-12
350 S Milledge Ave 30605 706-357-5200
Marie Yuran, prin. Fax 357-5358
Clarke MS 600/6-8
1235 Baxter St 30606 706-543-6547
Theodore MacMillan, prin. Fax 548-0257
Classic City Performance Learning Center 100/Alt
440 Dearing Ext Bldg 3 30606 706-353-2323
Dr. David Cole, dir. Fax 353-3877
Coile MS 600/6-8
110 Old Elberton Rd 30601 706-357-5318
Dwight Manzy, prin. Fax 357-5321
Hilsman MS 700/6-8
870 Gaines School Rd 30605 706-548-7281
Utevia Tolbert, prin. Fax 357-5295

Athens Academy 1,000/PK-12
PO Box 6548 30604 706-549-9225
John Thorsen, head sch Fax 354-3775
Athens Christian S 800/PK-12
1270 Highway 29 N 30601 706-549-7586
Steve Cummings, head sch Fax 549-2899
Athens Technical College Post-Sec.
800 Highway 29 N 30601 706-355-5000
Georgia Institute of Cosmetology Post-Sec.
3529 Atlanta Hwy 30606 706-549-6400
Msgr. Walter J. Donovan HS 100/9-12
590 Lavender Rd 30606 706-433-0223
Patrick Yuran, prin. Fax 433-0229
University of Georgia Post-Sec.
0 UGA 30602 706-542-3000

Atlanta, Fulton, Pop. 412,360
Atlanta CSD 44,700/PK-12
130 Trinity Ave SW 30303 404-802-3500
Meria Carstarphen Ed.D., supt. Fax 802-1803
www.atlantapublicschools.us
B.E.S.T. Academy 300/6-12
1890 D L Hollowell Pkwy NW 30318 404-802-4950
Dr. Timothy Jones, prin.
Brown MS 700/6-8
225 James P Brawley Dr SW 30314 404-802-6800
Tiauna Crooms, prin.
Bunche MS 700/6-8
1925 Niskey Lake Rd SW 30331 404-802-6700
Mario Watkins, prin.
Carver Early College HS 300/9-12
55 McDonough Blvd SE 30315 404-802-4405
Marcene Thornton, prin.
Carver HS 400/9-12
55 McDonough Blvd SE 30315 404-802-5890
Yusuf Muhammad, prin. Fax 521-3201
Crim Open Campus HS 300/Alt
256 Clifton St SE 30317 404-802-5800
Dawn Parker, prin. Fax 371-4889
Douglass HS 800/9-12
225 Hamilton E Holmes Dr NW 30318 404-802-3100
Ellis Duncan, prin. Fax 799-8022
Forrest Hill Academy 200/Alt
2930 Forrest Hills Dr SW 30315 404-802-6950
Zawadaski Robinson, prin. Fax 802-6996
Grady HS 1,300/9-12
929 Charles Allen Dr NE 30309 404-802-3001
Betsy Bockman, prin. Fax 802-3090
Harper-Archer MS 600/6-8
3399 Collier Dr NW 30331 404-802-6500
Marques Stewart, prin. Fax 699-4569
Inman MS 1,000/6-8
774 Virginia Ave NE 30306 404-802-3200
Betsy Bockman, prin. Fax 802-3299
Jackson HS 1,000/9-12
801 Glenwood Ave SE 30316 404-802-5200
Stephanie Johnson, prin. Fax 802-5299
King MS 500/6-8
545 Hill St SE 30312 404-802-5400
Paul Brown, prin. Fax 802-5499
King Young Womens Leadership Academy 300/9-12
1190 Northwest Dr NW 30318 404-802-4900
Eulonda Washington, prin.
Long MS 700/6-8
3200 Latona Dr SW 30354 404-802-4800
Lisa Hill, prin. Fax 802-4899
Mays HS 1,600/9-12
3450 Benjamin E Mays Dr SW 30331
Richard Fowler, prin. 404-802-5100
North Atlanta HS 1,600/9-12
4111 Northside Pkwy NW 30327 404-802-4700
Dr. Curtis Douglass, prin.
Price MS 300/6-8
1670 B W Bickers Dr SE 30315 404-802-6300
Luqman Abdur-Rahman, prin. Fax 624-5137
South Atlanta HS 300/9-12
800 Hutchens Rd SE 30354 404-802-5000
Dr. Patricia Ford, prin.
Sutton MS 1,500/6-8
2875 Northside Dr NW 30305 404-802-5600
Gail Johnson, prin.
Sylvan Hills MS 600/6-8
1461 Sylvan Rd SW 30310 404-802-6200
Artesa Portee, prin. Fax 802-6299
Therrell HS 400/9-12
3099 Panther Trl SW 30311 404-802-5300
Shelly Powell, prin.
Washington HS 300/9-12
45 Whitehouse Dr SW 30314 404-802-4600
Dr. Tasharah Wilson, prin. Fax 752-6063
West End Academy Alt
1445 Maynard Rd NW 30331 404-802-2900
Dr. Evelyn Mobley, prin. Fax 802-2949
Young MS 1,000/6-8
3116 Benjamin E Mays Dr SW 30311 404-802-5900
Fax 802-5999

DeKalb County SD
Supt. — See Stone Mountain
Cross Keys HS 1,200/9-12
1626 N Druid Hills Rd NE 30319 678-874-6102
Jason Heard, prin. Fax 874-6110
Druid Hills HS 1,500/9-12
1798 Haygood Dr NE 30307 678-874-6302
Brittany Cunningham, prin. Fax 874-6310
Henderson MS 1,500/6-8
2830 Henderson Mill Rd 30341 678-874-2902
Rochelle Patillo, prin. Fax 874-2910
Lakeside HS 2,000/9-12
3801 Briarcliff Rd NE 30345 678-874-6702
Damian Bounds, prin. Fax 874-6710
McNair HS 900/9-12
1804 Bouldercrest Rd SE 30316 678-874-4902
Loukisha Walker, prin. Fax 874-4910

Fulton County SD 94,500/PK-12
6201 Powers Ferry Rd 30339 470-254-3600
Dr. Jeff Rose, supt. Fax 254-1246
www.fultonschools.org
Sandtown MS 1,200/6-8
5400 Campbellton Rd SW 30331 404-346-6500
Estella Cook, prin. Fax 346-6510
Westlake HS 1,900/9-12
2400 Union Rd SW 30331 470-254-6400
Alexandra Bates, prin. Fax 254-6410
Other Schools – See Alpharetta, College Park, East Point, Fairburn, Johns Creek, Milton, Roswell, Sandy Springs

---

American InterContinental University Post-Sec.
6600 Peachtree Dunwoody Rd 30328 404-965-6500
Argosy University/Atlanta Post-Sec.
980 Hammond Dr Ste 100 30328 770-671-1200
Art Institute of Atlanta Post-Sec.
6600 Peachtree Dunwoody Rd 30328 770-394-8300
Atlanta Country Day S 50/7-12
8725 Dunwoody Pl 30350 770-998-0311
Atlanta Girls' S 200/6-12
3254 Northside Pkwy NW 30327 404-845-0900
Ayanna Hill-Gill, head sch Fax 869-9718
Atlanta International S 1,000/PK-12
2890 N Fulton Dr NE 30305 404-841-3840
Kevin Glass, hdmstr. Fax 841-3896
Atlanta Jewish Academy Upper S 100/9-12
5200 Northland Dr 30342 770-451-5299
Rabbi Ari Leubitz, head sch Fax 451-5571
Atlanta Medical Center Post-Sec.
303 Parkway Dr NE 30312 404-265-4203
Atlanta Metro State College Post-Sec.
1630 Metropolitan Pkwy SW 30310 404-756-4000
Atlanta School of Massage Post-Sec.
2 Dunwoody Park 30338 877-291-4485
Atlanta's John Marshall Law School Post-Sec.
1422 W Peachtree St NW 30309 404-872-3593
Atlanta Technical College Post-Sec.
1560 Metropolitan Pkwy SW 30310 404-225-4400
Bauder College Post-Sec.
384 Northyards Blvd NW #190 30313 404-237-7573
Beulah Heights University Post-Sec.
PO Box 18145 30316 404-627-2681
Brandon Hall S 100/6-12
1701 Brandon Hall Dr 30350 770-394-8177
Dean Fusto, head sch Fax 868-1444
Bright Futures Academy 100/6-12
1300 Joseph E Boone Blvd NW 30314
Eddie Echols, prin. 404-564-7751
Brown College of Court Reporting Post-Sec.
1900 Emery St NW Ste 200 30318 404-876-1227
Carver College Post-Sec.
3870 Cascade Rd SW 30331 404-527-4520
Chamberlain College of Nursing Post-Sec.
5775 Peachtree Dunwdy A100 30342 404-250-8500
Clark Academy 100/5-8
228 Margaret St SE 30315 678-651-2100
Clark Atlanta University Post-Sec.
223 James P Brawley Dr 30314 404-880-8000
Cristo Rey Atlanta Jesuit HS 9-10
680 W Peachtree St NW 30308 404-637-2800
Diane K. Bush, prin. Fax 637-2888
Dar Un Noor Academy 200/PK-10
434 14th St NW 30318 404-876-5051
Br. Halit Erdogdu, prin. Fax 874-6740
DeVry University Post-Sec.
5775 Peachtree Dunwoody NE 30342 404-236-1310
DeVry University Post-Sec.
100 Galleria Pkwy SE #100 30339 770-916-3704
Emory University Post-Sec.
201 Dowman Dr 30322 404-727-6123
Everest College Post-Sec.
2841 Greenbriar Pkwy SW 30331 678-500-3400
Franklin Academy 100/9-12
1585 Clifton Rd NE 30329 404-633-7404
Galloway S 700/PK-12
215 W Wieuca Rd NW 30342 404-252-8389
Suzanna Jemsby, head sch Fax 252-7770
Georgia Christian University Post-Sec.
6789 Peachtree Industrial 30360 770-279-0507
Georgia Institute of Technology Post-Sec.
225 North Ave NW 30332 404-894-2000
Georgia Perimeter College Post-Sec.
2101 Womack Rd 30338 770-274-5000
Georgia State University Post-Sec.
PO Box 3965 30302 404-413-2000
Grady Health System Post-Sec.
PO Box 26189 30303 404-616-4252
Greater Atlanta Adventist Academy 200/9-12
401 Hamilton E Holmes Dr NW 30318 404-799-0337
Johnny Holliday, prin. Fax 225-7250
Herzing University Post-Sec.
3393 Peachtree Rd NE # 1003 30326 404-816-4533
Holy Innocents' Episcopal S 1,300/PK-12
805 Mount Vernon Hwy 30327 404-255-4026
Paul Barton, head sch Fax 250-0815
Holy Spirit College Post-Sec.
4465 Northside Dr NW 30327 678-904-4959
Holy Spirit Preparatory S 600/PK-12
4449 Northside Dr NW 30327 678-904-2811
Kyle Pietrantonio, head sch Fax 904-4983
Interdenominational Theological Center Post-Sec.
700 Mrtn Lthr King Jr Dr SW 30314 404-527-7700
International School Skin Nail Massage Post-Sec.
5600 Roswell Rd 30342 404-843-1005
Keller Graduate School of Management Post-Sec.
3575 Piedmont Rd NE Lvl 100 30305 404-760-1400
Lovett S 1,600/K-12
4075 Paces Ferry Rd NW 30327 404-262-3032
William Peebles, hdmstr. Fax 261-1967
Marist S 1,100/7-12
3790 Ashford Dunwoody Rd NE 30319
770-457-7201
Fr. Joel Konzen, prin. Fax 457-8402
Medtech Institute Post-Sec.
4501 Circle 75 Pkwy SE 30339 770-859-9779
Medtech Institute Post-Sec.
2800 Century Pkwy NE # 100 30345 770-938-4711
Mercer University - Day Grad/Prof Campus Post-Sec.
3001 Mercer University Dr 30341 678-547-6000
Mohammed Schools of Atlanta 200/PK-12
735 Fayetteville Rd SE 30316 404-378-4219
Morehouse College Post-Sec.
830 Westview Dr SW 30314 404-681-2800
Morehouse School of Medicine Post-Sec.
720 Westview Dr SW 30310 404-752-1500
Mt. Vernon Presbyterian S 700/PK-12
471 Mount Vernon Hwy NE 30328 404-252-3448
Dr. Brett Jacobsen, head sch Fax 252-6777
Oglethorpe University Post-Sec.
4484 Peachtree Rd NE 30319 404-261-1441
Omnitech Institute Post-Sec.
1800 Phoenix Blvd 30349 404-888-1800
Pace Academy 1,000/K-12
966 W Paces Ferry Rd NW 30327 404-262-1345
Frederick Assaf, head sch Fax 264-9376
Paideia S 1,000/PK-12
1509 Ponce De Leon Ave NE 30307 404-377-3491
Paul Bianchi, hdmstr. Fax 377-0032
Portfolio Center Post-Sec.
125 Bennett St NW 30309 404-351-5055
Richmont Graduate University Post-Sec.
2055 Mount Paran Rd NW 30327 404-233-3949
SAE Institute Post-Sec.
215 Peachtree St NE Ste 300 30303 404-526-9366
St. Joseph's Hospital Post-Sec.
5665 Pchtree Dunwoody Rd 30342 404-851-7120
St. Pius X HS 1,100/9-12
2674 Johnson Rd NE 30345 404-636-3023
Steven Spellman, prin. Fax 633-8387
Sanford-Brown College Post-Sec.
1140 Hammond Dr Ste A1150 30328 770-576-4498
Savannah College of Art & Design Post-Sec.
PO Box 77300 30357 404-253-2700
Sophia Academy 100/PK-12
2880 Dresden Dr 30341 404-303-8722
Jenni Ellis, head sch Fax 303-8883
Southwest Atlanta Christian Academy 200/PK-12
PO Box 310750 31131 404-346-2080
Spelman College Post-Sec.
350 Spelman Ln SW 30314 404-681-3643
Strayer University Post-Sec.
3355 Northeast Expy NE #100 30341 770-454-9270
Strayer University Post-Sec.
3101 TowerCreek Pkwy SE 700 30339 770-612-2170
Temima HS 100/9-12
1839 LaVista Rd 30329 404-315-0507
University of Atlanta Post-Sec.
6685 Peachtree Industrial 30360 770-744-0370
Weber Jewish Community HS 200/9-12
6751 Roswell Rd 30328 404-917-2500
Rabbi Ed Harwitz, head sch Fax 917-2501
Westminster S 1,900/K-12
1424 W Paces Ferry Rd NW 30327 404-355-8673
Keith Evans, pres. Fax 355-6606
Westwood College Post-Sec.
1100 Spring St NW Ste 102 30309 404-745-9862
Westwood College Post-Sec.
2309 Parklake Dr NE 30345 770-743-3000
Yeshiva Ohr Yisrael of Atlanta 50/9-12
1458 Holly Ln NE 30329 404-320-1444

Augusta, Richmond, Pop. 193,101
Richmond County SD 30,800/PK-12
864 Broad St 30901 706-826-1000
Dr. Angela Pringle, supt. Fax 826-4612
www.rcboe.org
Academy of Richmond County 1,300/9-12
910 Russell St 30904 706-737-7152
Scott McClintock, prin. Fax 737-7155
Alternative Education Center at Lamar Alt
970 Baker Ave 30904 706-796-4965
Charles Givens, prin. Fax 796-4643
Butler HS 800/9-12
2011 Lumpkin Rd 30906 706-796-4959
Dr. Stacey Mabray, prin. Fax 796-4780
Cross Creek HS 1,300/9-12
3855 Old Waynesboro Rd 30906 706-772-8140
Dr. Glenda Collingsworth, prin. Fax 772-8153
Davidson Fine Arts Magnet JSHS 800/6-12
615 12th St 30901 706-823-6924
Dr. Renee Kelly, prin. Fax 823-4373
Glenn Hills HS 800/9-12
2840 Glenn Hills Dr 30906 706-796-4924
Dr. Bobby Williams, prin. Fax 796-4932
Glenn Hills MS 700/6-8
2941 Glenn Hills Dr 30906 706-796-4705
Dr. Bernard Chatman, prin. Fax 796-4716
Johnson Health Science HS 600/6-12
1324 Laney Walker Blvd 30901 706-823-6933
Charlie Tudor, prin. Fax 823-6931
Josey HS 700/9-12
1701 15th St 30901 706-737-7360
Chauncey Scott, prin. Fax 737-7363
Laney HS 700/9-12
1339 Laney Walker Blvd 30901 706-823-6900
Virgil Smith, prin. Fax 823-6918
Langford MS 900/6-8
3019 Walton Way Ext 30909 706-737-7301
Victoria Reese, prin. Fax 737-7302
Richmond Co. Technical Career Magnet S Vo/Tech
32000B Augusta Tech Dr 30906 706-823-5580
Melisa Clark, prin. Fax 796-4889
Sego MS 600/6-8
3420 Julia Ave 30906 706-796-4944
Pauline Andrews, prin. Fax 796-4670
Tutt MS 500/6-8
495 Boy Scout Rd 30909 706-737-7288
Angela Sheahan, prin. Fax 481-1620
Westside HS 900/9-12
1002 Patriots Way 30907 706-868-4030
Elizabeth Schad, prin. Fax 868-4005
Performance Learning Center Adult
1740 Walton Way 30904 706-796-4965
Gregory Thompson, admin. Fax 796-4643
Other Schools – See Hephzibah

Alleluia Community S 200/K-12
2819 Peach Orchard Rd 30906 706-793-9663
Aquinas HS 300/9-12
1920 Highland Ave 30904 706-736-5516
Maureen Lewis, prin. Fax 736-2678
Augusta Technical College Post-Sec.
3200 Augusta Tech Dr 30906 706-771-4000
Curtis Baptist S 400/PK-12
1326 Broad St 30901 706-828-6624
Mark Sterling, head sch Fax 828-6627
Georgia Regents University Post-Sec.
1120 15th St 30912 706-721-0211
Miller-Motte Technical College Post-Sec.
621 NW Frontage Rd 30907 706-396-8000
Paine College Post-Sec.
1235 15th St 30901 706-821-8200
University Hospital Health System Post-Sec.
1350 Walton Way 30901 706-722-9011
Virginia College Post-Sec.
2807 Wylds Road Ext 30909 706-288-2500
Westminster S of Augusta 500/PK-12
3067 Wheeler Rd 30909 706-731-5260
Brian Case, head sch Fax 731-5274

Austell, Cobb, Pop. 6,416
Cobb County SD
Supt. — See Marietta
Cooper MS 900/6-8
4605 Ewing Rd 30106 770-819-2438
Dr. Vanessa Watkins, prin. Fax 819-2440
Garrett MS 800/6-8
5235 Austell Pwdr Sprgs Rd 30106 770-819-2466
Kimberly Jackson, prin. Fax 819-2468
South Cobb HS 2,000/9-12
1920 Clay Rd 30106 770-819-2611
Clint Terza, prin. Fax 819-2613

Avondale Estates, DeKalb, Pop. 2,893
DeKalb County SD
Supt. — See Stone Mountain
DeKalb S of the Arts 400/8-12
1192 Clarendon Ave 30002 678-676-2502
Susan McCauley, prin. Fax 676-2510

Bainbridge, Decatur, Pop. 12,559
Decatur County SD 5,500/PK-12
100 S West St, 229-248-2200
Tim Cochran, supt. Fax 248-2252
www.dcboe.com
Bainbridge HS 1,500/9-12
1 Bearcat Blvd, 229-248-2230
Tommie Howell, prin. Fax 248-2260
Bainbridge MS 800/7-8
1301 E College St, 229-248-2206
John Wooden, prin. Fax 248-2817

Bainbridge College Post-Sec.
PO Box 990, 229-248-2500
Grace Christian Academy 300/PK-12
1302 Lake Douglas Rd, 229-243-8851
Rob Starner, head sch Fax 243-0515

Barnesville, Lamar, Pop. 6,625
Lamar County SD 2,600/PK-12
100 Victory Ln 30204 770-358-5891
Dr. Jute Wilson, supt. Fax 358-5858
www.lamar.k12.ga.us
Lamar County HS 700/9-12
1 Trojan Way 30204 770-358-8641
Dr. David Boland, prin. Fax 358-8649
Lamar County MS 600/6-8
100 Burnette Rd 30204 770-358-8652
Dr. Julie Steele, prin. Fax 358-8657

Gordon State College Post-Sec.
419 College Dr 30204 678-359-5555

Baxley, Appling, Pop. 4,360
Appling County SD 3,600/PK-12
249 Blackshear Hwy 31513 912-367-8600
Dr. Scarlett Copeland, supt. Fax 367-1011
www.appling.k12.ga.us
Appling County HS 1,000/9-12
482 Blackshear Hwy 31513 912-367-8610
Dr. Gene Starr, prin. Fax 367-9877
Appling County MS 800/6-8
2997 Blackshear Hwy 31513 912-367-8630
Cathy Campbell, prin. Fax 367-8803

Bellville, Evans, Pop. 123

Pinewood Christian Academy 600/PK-12
PO Box 7 30414 912-739-1272
Clay Hill, hdmstr. Fax 739-2321

Bethlehem, Barrow, Pop. 594
Barrow County SD
Supt. — See Winder
Barrow Co. Alternative Education Program Alt
54 W Star 30620 770-867-2900
Chuck Torbett, prin. Fax 867-1264

Bethlehem Christian Academy 400/PK-12
PO Box 187 30620 770-307-1574
Rhonda Whiting, head sch Fax 425-6553

Black Creek, Bryan
Bryan County SD 8,300/PK-12
8810 US Highway 280 E 31308 912-851-4000
Dr. Paul Brooksher, supt. Fax 851-4093
www.bryan.k12.ga.us/
Other Schools – See Pembroke, Richmond Hill

Blackshear, Pierce, Pop. 3,390
Pierce County SD 3,700/PK-12
PO Box 349 31516 912-449-2044
Terri DeLoach, supt. Fax 449-2046
www.pierce.k12.ga.us/
Pierce County HS 1,100/9-12
4850 County Farm Rd 31516 912-449-2055
Dara Bennett, prin. Fax 449-2061
Pierce County MS 900/6-8
5216 County Farm Rd 31516 912-449-2077
Perry Tison, prin. Fax 449-2075

Blairsville, Union, Pop. 642
Union County SD 2,700/PK-12
124 Hughes St 30512 706-745-2322
Gary Steppe, supt. Fax 745-5025
www.ucschools.org
Union County HS 800/9-12
153 Panther Cir 30512 706-745-2216
John Hill, prin. Fax 745-4122
Union County MS 600/6-8
367 Wellborn St 30512 706-745-2483
Gwen Stafford, prin. Fax 781-6200
Other Schools – See Suches

North Georgia Technical College Post-Sec.
121 Meeks Ave 30512 706-439-6300

Blakely, Early, Pop. 5,032
Early County SD 2,200/PK-12
11927 Columbia St, 229-723-4337
Bronwyn Ragan-Martin Ed.D., supt. Fax 723-8183
www.early.k12.ga.us
Early County HS 700/9-12
12020 Columbia St, 229-723-3006
David Ferry, prin. Fax 723-8690
Early County MS 500/6-8
12053 Columbia St, 229-723-3746
Anthony Yarbrough, prin. Fax 723-3942
Learning and Opportunity Academy Alt
544 Howell St, 229-723-3943
James McCoy, prin. Fax 723-6385

Bloomingdale, Chatham, Pop. 2,668
Savannah-Chatham County SD
Supt. — See Savannah
New Hampstead HS 1,300/9-12
2451 Little Neck Rd 31302 912-395-6789
Tawn Foltz, prin. Fax 201-7699

Blue Ridge, Fannin, Pop. 1,269
Fannin County SD 3,000/PK-12
2290 E First St 30513 706-632-3771
Mark Henson, supt. Fax 632-7583
www.fannin.k12.ga.us
Fannin County HS 900/9-12
360 Rebels Cir 30513 706-632-2081
Erik Cioffi, prin. Fax 632-6908
Fannin County MS 800/6-8
4560 Old Highway 76 30513 706-632-6100
Keith Nuckolls, prin. Fax 632-0461

Bogart, Clarke, Pop. 1,021
Oconee County SD
Supt. — See Watkinsville
Malcom Bridge MS 800/6-8
2500 Malcom Bridge Rd 30622 706-310-1992
Dr. Merideth Blackburn, prin. Fax 310-1993
North Oconee HS 1,100/9-12
1081 Rocky Branch Rd 30622 706-769-7760
Dr. Philip Brown, prin. Fax 769-4766

Prince Avenue Christian S 700/PK-12
2201 Ruth Jackson Rd 30622 678-726-2300
Seth Hathaway, head sch Fax 726-2301

Bonaire, Houston
Houston County SD
Supt. — See Perry
Bonaire MS 1,000/6-8
125 GA Highway 96 E 31005 478-929-6235
Cindy Randall, prin. Fax 929-6245

Bowdon, Carroll, Pop. 1,987
Carroll County SD
Supt. — See Carrollton
Bowdon HS 400/9-12
504 W College St 30108 770-258-5408
Zoe Evans, prin. Fax 258-7278
Bowdon MS 300/6-8
129 N Jonesville Rd 30108 770-258-1778
Scott Estes, prin. Fax 258-4374

Braselton, Jackson, Pop. 7,379

Braselton Christian Academy 50/K-12
401 Zion Church Rd 30517 706-824-9943

Bremen, Haralson, Pop. 6,130
Bremen CSD 2,100/PK-12
501 Pacific Ave 30110 770-537-5508
Dr. David Hicks, supt. Fax 537-0610
www.bremencs.com
Bremen HS 600/9-12
504 Georgia Ave S 30110 770-537-2592
Tim Huff, prin. Fax 537-0714
Bremen MS 500/6-8
2440 Crosstown Pkwy 30110 770-537-4874
Silas Brown, prin. Fax 537-5043

Brooklet, Bulloch, Pop. 1,369
Bulloch County SD
Supt. — See Statesboro
Southeast Bulloch HS 900/9-12
9184 Brooklet Denmark Rd 30415 912-842-8440
Donna Clifton, prin. Fax 842-9411
Southeast Bulloch MS 700/6-8
9124 Brooklet Denmark Rd 30415 912-842-8400
Torian White, prin. Fax 842-9559

Brunswick, Glynn, Pop. 15,115
Glynn County SD, PO Box 1677 31521 12,800/PK-12
Howard Mann, supt. 912-267-4100
www.glynn.k12.ga.us
Brunswick HS 1,700/9-12
3885 Altama Ave 31520 912-267-4200
Toriano Gilbert, prin. Fax 261-4433
Coastal Education HS 50/Alt
3700 Altama Ave 31520 912-267-4100
Jill Smith, coord.
Glynn Academy 1,700/9-12
1001 Mansfield St 31520 912-267-4210
Dr. Scott Spence, prin. Fax 267-4246
Glynn MS 800/6-8
635 Lanier Blvd 31520 912-267-4150
Matthew Blackstone, prin. Fax 267-4158
Jackson Learning Center Alt
1405 H St 31520 912-280-4030
Robert Pope, lead tchr. Fax 280-6754
Macon MS 700/6-8
201 McKenzie Dr 31523 912-265-3337
Michele Seals, prin. Fax 267-4118
Needwood MS 700/6-8
669 Harry Driggers Blvd 31525 912-261-4488
Marlowe Hinson, prin. Fax 261-4491
Risley MS 600/6-8
707 S Port Pkwy 31523 912-280-4020
Lori Joiner, prin. Fax 261-3252

Brunswick Christian Academy 200/PK-12
4231 US Highway 17 N 31525 912-264-4546
College of Coastal Georgia Post-Sec.
1 College Dr 31520 912-279-5700
Heritage Christian Academy 200/PK-12
4265 Norwich Street Ext 31520 912-264-5491
Cindy Zangla, admin. Fax 264-0799

Buena Vista, Marion, Pop. 2,149
Marion County SD 1,400/PK-12
PO Box 391 31803 229-649-2234
Richard McCorkle, supt. Fax 649-7423
www.marion.k12.ga.us/
Marion County MSHS 700/6-12
1 Eagle Dr 31803 229-649-7520
Glenn Tidwell, prin. Fax 649-5945

Buford, Gwinnett, Pop. 12,025
Buford CSD 4,000/K-12
2625 Sawnee Ave 30518 770-945-5035
Dr. Geye Hamby, supt. Fax 945-4629
www.bufordcityschools.org
Buford HS 1,100/9-12
2750 Sawnee Ave 30518 770-945-6768
Dr. Banks Bitterman, prin. Fax 932-7570
Buford MS 1,000/6-8
2700 Robert Bell Pkwy 30518 770-904-3690
Melanie Reed, prin. Fax 904-3689

Gwinnett County SD
Supt. — See Suwanee
Jones MS 1,300/6-8
3575 Ridge Rd 30519 770-904-5450
Dr. Richard Holland, prin. Fax 904-5452
Twin Rivers MS 1,500/6-8
2300 Braselton Hwy 30519 678-407-7550
Linda Boyd, prin. Fax 407-7560

Butler, Taylor, Pop. 1,959
Taylor County SD 1,500/PK-12
PO Box 1930 31006 478-862-5224
Dr. Gary Gibson, supt. Fax 862-5818
taylor.schooldesk.net
Taylor County HS 400/9-12
PO Box 1930 31006 478-862-3314
Ken Camp, prin. Fax 862-3099
Taylor County MS 200/7-8
PO Box 580 31006 478-862-5285
Shonda Green, prin. Fax 862-5368

Byron, Peach, Pop. 4,436
Peach County SD
Supt. — See Fort Valley
Byron MS 400/6-8
201 Linda Dr 31008 478-825-9660
Dr. Jeff Bell, prin. Fax 956-3916

Cairo, Grady, Pop. 9,480
Grady County SD 4,700/PK-12
122 N Broad St, 229-377-3701
Dr. Kermit Gilliard Ed.D., supt. Fax 377-3437
www.grady.k12.ga.us
Washington MS 600/6-8
1277 Martin Luther King Jr, 229-377-2106
Tilda Brimm, prin. Fax 377-7779

Calhoun, Gordon, Pop. 15,378
Calhoun CSD 3,700/PK-12
380 Barrett Rd 30701 706-629-2900
Dr. Michele Taylor, supt. Fax 629-3235
www.calhounschools.org
Calhoun HS 1,000/9-12
355 S River St 30701 706-602-6770
Greg Green, prin. Fax 602-6652
Calhoun MS 800/6-8
399 S River St 30701 706-629-3340
Michelle Knight, prin. Fax 629-0236

Gordon County SD 6,500/PK-12
PO Box 12001 30703 706-629-7366
Dr. Susan Remillard, supt. Fax 625-5671
www.gcbe.org
Ashworth MS 700/6-8
PO Box 12001 30703 706-625-9545
Scott McClanahan, prin. Fax 879-5073
College and Career Academy Vo/Tech
PO Box 12001 30703 706-879-5370
Steffan Larson, admin. Fax 879-5371
Gordon Central HS 800/9-12
PO Box 12001 30703 706-629-7391
Doug Clark, prin. Fax 879-5399
Sonoraville HS 1,000/8-12
PO Box 12001 30703 706-602-0320
Bruce Potts, prin. Fax 879-5165

Georgia-Cumberland Academy 200/9-12
397 Academy Dr SW 30701 706-629-4591
Dr. Greg Gerard, prin. Fax 629-1272
Georgia Northwestern Technical College Post-Sec.
1151 Highway 53 Spur SW 30701 706-624-1100

Camilla, Mitchell, Pop. 5,311
Mitchell County SD 1,700/PK-12
108 S Harney St 31730 229-336-2100
Victor Hill, supt. Fax 336-3870
www.mitchell.k12.ga.us
Mitchell County HS 400/9-12
1000 Newton Rd 31730 229-336-0970
Robert Adams, prin. Fax 336-2171
Mitchell County MS 400/6-8
55 Griffin Rd 31730 229-336-0980
Patricia English, prin. Fax 336-2139

Westwood S 400/PK-12
255 Fuller St 31730 229-336-7992

Canton, Cherokee, Pop. 22,432
Cherokee County SD 39,500/PK-12
111 Academy St 30114 770-479-1871
Dr. Brian Hightower, supt. Fax 479-7758
cherokeek12.net
ACE Academy Alt
8871 Knox Bridge Hwy 30114 770-721-6680
Richard Landolt, prin.
Cherokee HS 2,200/9-12
930 Marietta Hwy 30114 770-721-5300
Todd Miller, prin. Fax 479-8421
Creekland MS 1,400/6-8
1555 Owens Store Rd 30115 770-704-4460
Dr. Deborah Wiseman, prin.
Creekview HS 1,800/9-12
1550 Owens Store Rd 30115 770-704-4400
Dr. Mark Merges, prin.
Freedom MS 1,200/6-8
10550 Bells Ferry Rd 30114 770-704-1100
Sheila Grimes, prin.
Rusk MS, 2761 E Cherokee Dr 30115 900/7-8
Cindy Cooper, prin. 770-704-1135
Sequoyah HS 1,600/9-12
4485 Hickory Rd 30115 770-721-3200
Elliott Berman, prin. Fax 345-5498
Teasley MS 900/6-8
151 Hickory Log Dr 30114 770-721-5420
Dr. Susan Zinkil, prin. Fax 479-3275
Other Schools – See Woodstock

Carnesville, Franklin, Pop. 574
Franklin County SD 3,600/PK-12
280 Busha Rd 30521 706-384-4554
Wayne Randall, supt. Fax 384-7472
www.franklin.k12.ga.us
Franklin County HS 1,100/9-12
6570 Highway 145 30521 706-384-4525
Brad Roberts, prin. Fax 384-3534
Franklin County MS 900/6-8
485 Turkey Creek Rd 30521 706-384-4581
Lucy Floyd, prin. Fax 384-2285

Carrollton, Carroll, Pop. 23,838
Carroll County SD 14,600/PK-12
164 Independence Dr 30116 770-832-3568
Scott Cowart, supt. Fax 834-6399
www.carrollcountyschools.com/
Central HS 1,100/9-12
113 Central High Rd 30116 770-834-3386
Jared Griffis, prin. Fax 832-0103
Central MS 900/6-8
155 Whooping Creek Rd 30116 770-832-8114
Jimmy LeBlanc, prin. Fax 836-2782
GOAL Program Alt
1095 Newnan Rd 30116 770-830-5012
Deaidra Wilson, prin. Fax 830-8634
Mount Zion HS 400/9-12
280 Eureka Church Rd 30117 770-834-6654
Tracey Barrow, prin. Fax 832-9497
Other Schools – See Bowdon, Mount Zion, Temple, Villa Rica

Carrollton CSD 4,800/PK-12
106 Trojan Dr 30117 770-832-9633
Dr. Kent Edwards, supt. Fax 836-9950
www.carrolltoncityschools.net/
Carrollton HS 1,300/9-12
202 Trojan Dr 30117 770-834-7726
Dr. Mark Albertus, prin. Fax 834-8714
Carrollton JHS 700/7-8
510 Ben Scott Blvd 30117 770-832-6535
Dr. Todd Simpson, prin. Fax 832-7003
Performance Learning Center Alt
510 Ben Scott Blvd 30117 770-836-2842
Aprill Jones-Byrd, prin.

Oak Mountain Academy 200/PK-12
222 Cross Plains Rd 30116 770-834-6651
Paula Gillispie, head sch Fax 834-6785
University of West Georgia Post-Sec.
1601 Maple St 30118 678-839-5000
West Georgia Technical College Post-Sec.
997 Newnan Rd 30116 770-836-6800

Cartersville, Bartow, Pop. 19,341
Bartow County SD 14,200/PK-12
PO Box 200007 30120 770-606-5800
John Harper Ed.D., supt. Fax 606-5855
www.bartow.k12.ga.us
Cass MS 1,000/6-8
195 Fire Tower Rd NW 30120 770-606-5846
Dr. Kristy Arnold, prin. Fax 606-3835
Woodland HS 1,700/9-12
800 Old Alabama Rd SE 30120 770-606-5870
Dr. Wes Dickey, prin. Fax 606-2080
Other Schools – See Adairsville, Emerson, Euharlee, White

Cartersville CSD 4,000/PK-12
PO Box 3310 30120 770-382-5880
Dr. J. Howard Hinesley Ed.D., supt. Fax 387-7476
www.cartersville.k12.ga.us
Cartersville HS 1,100/9-12
320 E Church St 30120 770-382-3200
Marc Feuerbach, prin. Fax 382-0701
Cartersville MS 1,000/6-8
825 Douthit Ferry Rd 30120 770-382-3666
Ken MacKenzie, prin. Fax 387-7495

Excel Christian Academy 300/K-12
325 Old Mill Rd 30120 770-382-9488
Tammy Griffith, prin. Fax 606-9884
Trinity S 100/PK-11
814 West Ave 30120 770-386-7479
Stephanie K. Dietz, head sch Fax 606-9942

Cave Spring, Floyd, Pop. 1,186

Georgia School for the Deaf Post-Sec.
232 Perry Farm Rd SW 30124 706-777-2200

Cedartown, Polk, Pop. 9,595
Polk County SD 7,700/PK-12
612 S College St 30125 770-748-3821
Dr. William A. Hunter, supt. Fax 748-5131
www.polk.k12.ga.us/
Cedartown HS 1,100/9-12
167 Frank Lott Dr 30125 770-748-0490
Dr. Darrell Wetherington, prin. Fax 749-1872
Cedartown MS 1,000/6-8
1664 Syble W Brannon Pkwy 30125 770-749-8850
Tamra Walker, prin. Fax 749-2795
Other Schools – See Rockmart

Centerville, Houston, Pop. 6,978
Houston County SD
Supt. — See Perry
Thomson MS 800/6-8
301 Thomson St 31028 478-953-0489
Dr. Walter Stephens, prin. Fax 953-0484

Chamblee, DeKalb, Pop. 9,782
DeKalb County SD
Supt. — See Stone Mountain
Chamblee MS 900/6-8
3601 Sexton Woods Dr 30341 678-874-8202
John Martin, prin. Fax 874-8210

Interactive College of Technology Post-Sec.
5303 New Peachtree Rd 30341 770-216-2960
Iverson Institute Post-Sec.
5522 New Peachtree Rd # 114 30341 770-446-1333

Chatsworth, Murray, Pop. 4,251
Murray County SD 7,600/PK-12
PO Box 40 30705 706-695-4531
Eric McFee Ed.D., supt. Fax 695-8425
www.murray.k12.ga.us
Bagley MS 500/7-8
4600 Highway 225 N 30705 706-695-1115
Shalina Stone, prin. Fax 695-7289
Gladden MS 600/7-8
700 Old Dalton Ellijay Rd 30705 706-695-7448
Dr. Phillip Greeson, prin. Fax 517-2479
Murray County HS 900/9-12
1001 Green Rd 30705 706-695-1414
Gina Linder, prin. Fax 517-2625
North Murray HS 1,000/9-12
2568 Mount Carmel Church Rd 30705 706-695-7760
Dr. Maria Bradley, prin. Fax 517-5526
Other Schools – See Eton

Chickamauga, Walker, Pop. 3,044
Chickamauga CSD 1,400/K-12
402 Cove Rd 30707 706-382-3100
Melody Day, supt. Fax 375-5364
chickamaugacityschools.org
Lee HS 500/9-12
105 Lee Cir 30707 706-382-3100
Cyril Simmons, prin. Fax 375-5881
Lee MS 300/6-8
300 Crescent Ave 30707 706-382-3100
Benny Ashley, prin. Fax 375-1020

Chula, Tift

Tiftarea Academy 500/PK-12
PO Box 10 31733 229-382-0436
Stacey Bell, hdmstr. Fax 382-7742

Clarkesville, Habersham, Pop. 1,712
Habersham County SD 7,000/PK-12
PO Box 70 30523 706-754-2118
Matthew Cooper, supt. Fax 754-1549
www.habershamschools.com/
North Habersham MS 500/6-8
1500 Wall Bridge Rd 30523 706-754-2915
Elizabeth Tuck, prin. Fax 754-8218
Other Schools – See Cornelia, Demorest, Mount Airy

North Georgia Technical College Post-Sec.
PO Box 65 30523 706-754-7700

Clarkston, DeKalb, Pop. 7,202
DeKalb County SD
Supt. — See Stone Mountain
Clarkston HS 1,500/9-12
618 N Indian Creek Dr 30021 678-676-5302
Dr. Michelle Jones, prin. Fax 676-5310
DeKalb HS of Technology South Vo/Tech
618 N Indian Creek Dr 30021 678-676-5302
Dr. Vikki Williams, prin. Fax 676-5310

Atlanta Area School for the Deaf Post-Sec.
890 N Indian Creek Dr 30021 404-296-7101
Georgia Perimeter College Post-Sec.
555 N Indian Creek Dr 30021 678-891-3200
Georgia Piedmont Technical College Post-Sec.
495 N Indian Creek Dr 30021 404-297-9522

Claxton, Evans, Pop. 2,710
Evans County SD 1,900/PK-12
613 W Main St 30417 912-739-3544
Marty Waters, supt. Fax 739-2492
www.evans.k12.ga.us
Claxton HS 400/9-12
102 N Clark St 30417 912-739-3993
Todd Veland, prin. Fax 739-2029
Claxton MS 400/6-8
600 Hendrix St 30417 912-739-3646
Dr. Diane Holland, prin. Fax 739-7217

Cleveland, White, Pop. 3,334
White County SD 3,900/PK-12
136 Warriors Path 30528 706-865-2315
Jeffrey Wilson Ed.D., supt. Fax 865-7784
www.white.k12.ga.us
White County HS 800/10-12
2600 Highway 129 N 30528 706-865-2312
John Osborne, prin. Fax 865-5981
White County MS 900/6-8
283 Old Blairsville Rd 30528 706-865-4060
Kristi Gerrells, prin. Fax 865-1947
White County Ninth Grade Academy 300/9-9
328 Old Blairsville Rd 30528 706-865-0727
John Osborne, prin. Fax 865-0737

Truett McConnell College Post-Sec.
100 Alumni Dr 30528 706-865-2134

Cochran, Bleckley, Pop. 5,096
Bleckley County SD 2,300/PK-12
PO Box 516 31014 478-934-2821
Steve Smith, supt. Fax 934-9595
www.bleckley.k12.ga.us
Bleckley County HS 700/9-12
1 Royal Dr 31014 478-934-6258
Dr. Trey Belflower, prin. Fax 934-9707
Bleckley County MS 500/6-8
590 GA Highway 26 E 31014 478-934-7270
Michele Dyal, prin. Fax 934-6502
Bleckley County Success Academy Alt
140 Country Club Rd 31014 478-934-1685
Denise Warren, prin. Fax 271-5910

College Park, Fulton, Pop. 13,682
Clayton County SD
Supt. — See Jonesboro
North Clayton HS 800/9-12
1525 Norman Dr, 770-994-4035
Lonnie Farmer, prin. Fax 994-4038
North Clayton MS 900/6-8
5517 W Fayetteville Rd, 770-994-4025
Shakira Rice, prin. Fax 994-4028

Fulton County SD
Supt. — See Atlanta
Banneker HS 1,500/9-12
6015 Feldwood Rd, 770-969-3410
Duke Bradley, prin. Fax 969-3418
Camp Creek MS 700/6-8
4345 Welcome All Rd SW, 470-254-8030
Keynun Campbell, prin. Fax 254-8228
McClarin Alternative HS 300/Alt
3605 Main St 30337 470-254-8080
Dr. Leteshia Woodley, prin. Fax 254-8089
McNair MS 800/6-8
2800 Burdett Rd, 470-254-4160
John Madden, prin. Fax 254-4165

Woodward Academy 2,800/PK-12
1662 Rugby Ave 30337 404-765-4000
F. Stuart Gulley Ph.D., pres. Fax 765-4009

Colquitt, Miller, Pop. 1,979
Miller County SD 1,100/PK-12
96 Perry St, 229-758-5592
Dr. Allen Kicklighter, supt. Fax 758-6040
www.millercountyschools.schoolinsites.com
Miller County HS 300/9-12
996 Phillipsburg Rd, 229-758-4130
David Kirkland, prin. Fax 758-3244
Miller County MS 200/6-8
996 Phillipsburg Rd, 229-758-4130
Robert Melton, prin. Fax 758-3244

Columbus, Muscogee, Pop. 184,779
Muscogee County SD 31,100/PK-12
PO Box 2427 31902 706-748-2000
Dr. David Lewis, supt. Fax 748-2001
www.muscogee.k12.ga.us
Arnold Magnet Academy 700/6-8
2011 51st St 31904 706-748-2436
Stacy Day, prin. Fax 748-2435
Baker MS 600/6-8
1215 Benning Dr 31903 706-683-8721
Ramona Horn, prin. Fax 683-8731
Blackmon Road MS 600/6-8
7251 Blackmon Rd 31909 706-565-2998
Penny Bowen, prin. Fax 565-3006
Carver STEM HS 1,200/9-12
3100 8th St 31906 706-748-2499
Chris Lindsey, prin. Fax 748-2512
Columbus HS 1,300/9-12
1700 Cherokee Ave 31906 706-748-2534
Dr. Marvin Crumbs, prin. Fax 748-2546
Double Churches MS 500/6-8
7611 Whitesville Rd 31904 706-748-2678
Craig Fitts, prin. Fax 748-2682
Early College Academy 200/9-12
2701 11th Ave 31904 706-748-2948
Susan Willard, dean Fax 748-2951
East Columbus Magnet Academy 700/6-8
6100 Georgetown Dr 31907 706-565-3026
Tamura Magwood, prin. Fax 565-3031
Eddy MS 500/6-8
2100 S Lumpkin Rd 31903 706-683-8782
Shermaine Derrick, prin. Fax 683-8789
Fort MS 600/6-8
2900 Woodruff Farm Rd 31907 706-569-3740
Sonja Coaxum, prin. Fax 569-3616
Hardaway HS 1,500/9-12
2901 College Dr 31906 706-748-2766
Matt Bell, prin. Fax 748-2776
Jordan Vocational HS 700/9-12
3200 Howard Ave 31904 706-748-2819
Amy Wohler, prin. Fax 748-2829
Kendrick HS 800/9-12
6015 Georgetown Dr 31907 706-565-2960
Dr. Alonzo James, prin. Fax 565-2971
Northside HS 1,300/9-12
2002 American Way 31909 706-748-2920
Martin Richburg, prin. Fax 748-2931
Richards MS 800/6-8
2892 Edgewood Rd 31906 706-569-3697
Lance Henderson, prin. Fax 569-3704
Rothschild Leadership Academy 600/6-8
1136 Hunt Ave 31907 706-569-3709
Dr. Michael Forte, prin. Fax 569-3717
St. Elmo Center for Gifted Education K-12
2101 18th Ave 31901 706-748-3115
Christine Hull, dir. Fax 748-3118
Shaw HS 1,200/9-12
7579 Raider Way 31909 706-569-3638
Adam Herring, prin. Fax 569-3648
Spencer HS 800/9-12
4340 Victory Dr 31903 706-683-8701
Dr. Johnny Freeman, prin. Fax 683-8716
Veterans Memorial MS 600/6-8
2008 Old Guard Rd 31909 706-748-3203
Melanie Knight, prin. Fax 748-3211
Other Schools – See Midland

Brookstone S 800/PK-12
440 Bradley Park Dr 31904 706-324-1392
Marty Lester, head sch Fax 571-0178
Calvary Christian S 600/PK-12
7556 Old Moon Rd 31909 706-323-0467
Dr. Ricky Smith, hdmstr. Fax 323-1491
Columbus State University Post-Sec.
4225 University Ave 31907 706-507-8800
Columbus Technical College Post-Sec.
928 Manchester Expy 31904 706-649-1800
Grace Christian S 100/PK-12
2915 14th Ave 31904 706-323-9161
Medical Center Post-Sec.
PO Box 951 31902 706-571-1200
Miller-Motte Technical College Post-Sec.
1800 Box Rd 31907 706-225-5002
Rivertown School of Beauty Post-Sec.
4747 Hamilton Rd Ste B 31904 706-653-8032
St. Anne Pacelli Catholic S 500/PK-12
2020 Kay Cir 31907 706-561-8232
Jocelyn Smith, prin. Fax 563-0211
Southeastern Beauty School Post-Sec.
PO Box 12483 31917 706-687-1054
Virginia College Post-Sec.
5601 Veterans Pkwy 31904 762-207-1600

Comer, Madison, Pop. 1,110
Madison County SD
Supt. — See Danielsville
Madison County MS 1,100/6-8
3215 Highway 172 30629 706-783-2400
Chuck Colquitt, prin. Fax 783-4390

Commerce, Jackson, Pop. 6,437
Banks County SD 2,800/K-12
1989 Historic Homer Hwy 30529 706-677-2224
Stan Davis, supt. Fax 677-2223
www.banks.k12.ga.us
Other Schools – See Homer

Commerce CSD 1,500/PK-12
PO Box 29 30529 706-335-5500
Dr. Joy Tolbert, supt. Fax 335-5214
www.commercecityschools.org
Commerce HS 400/9-12
272 Lakeview Dr 30529 706-335-5942
Donnie Drew, prin. Fax 336-6955
Commerce MS 500/5-8
7690 Jefferson Rd 30529 706-335-5594
Derrick Maxwell, prin. Fax 335-6222

Jackson County SD
Supt. — See Jefferson
East Jackson Comprehensive HS 1,000/9-12
1435 Hoods Mill Rd 30529 706-336-8900
Jamie Dixon, prin. Fax 335-2928
East Jackson MS 800/6-8
1880 Hoods Mill Rd 30529 706-335-2083
Tiffany Barnett, prin. Fax 335-0935

Conyers, Rockdale, Pop. 14,890
Rockdale County SD 16,000/PK-12
PO Box 1199 30012 770-860-4211
Richard Autry, supt. Fax 860-4285
www.rockdale.k12.ga.us
Alpha Alternative S Alt
1045 North St NW 30012 770-922-8636
Alex Guilford, prin. Fax 918-0248
Conyers MS 900/6-8
400 Sigman Rd NW 30012 770-483-3371
Allison Barbour, prin. Fax 483-9448
Edwards MS 1,000/6-8
2633 Stanton Rd SE 30094 770-483-3255
Fred Middleton, prin. Fax 483-3676
Heritage HS 1,700/9-12
2400 Granade Rd SW 30094 770-483-5428
Greg Fowler, prin. Fax 483-9435
Magnet S for Science/Technology 9-12
1174 Bulldog Cir NE 30012 770-483-8737
Dr. Debra Arnold, dir. Fax 483-7379
Memorial MS 900/6-8
3205 Underwood Rd SE 30013 770-922-0139
Michell Glover, prin. Fax 922-6192
Open Campus S Alt
1115 West Ave SW 30012 770-388-5727
Andrea Nelson, prin. Fax 388-5728
Rockdale County HS 1,900/9-12
1174 Bulldog Cir NE 30012 770-483-8754
Frank Daniels, prin. Fax 483-8708
Salem HS 1,400/9-12
3551 Underwood Rd SE 30013 770-929-0176
Tonya Bloodworth, prin. Fax 922-1292
Other Schools – See Stockbridge

GDA Inc Post-Sec.
1448 V F W Dr SW 30012 770-918-8501
Georgia Career Institute Post-Sec.
1820 Highway 20 SE Ste 208 30013 770-922-7653
Young Americans Christian S 600/PK-12
1701 Honey Creek Rd SE 30013 770-760-7902
Dr. David Taylor Ed.D., admin. Fax 760-7981

Cordele, Crisp, Pop. 11,020
Crisp County SD 2,400/PK-12
PO Box 729 31010 229-276-3400
Dr. David Mims, supt. Fax 276-3406
www.crispschools.org
Crisp County HS 1,100/9-12
2402 Cougar Aly 31015 229-276-3430
Dr. Rusty Sowell, prin. Fax 276-3436
Crisp County MS 900/6-8
1116 E 24th Ave 31015 229-276-3460
Brandon Williams, prin. Fax 276-3466

Crisp Academy 200/PK-12
150 Crisp Academy Dr 31015 229-273-6330
South Georgia Technical College Post-Sec.
402 N Midway Rd 31015 229-271-4040

Cornelia, Habersham, Pop. 4,030
Habersham County SD
Supt. — See Clarkesville
South Habersham MS 500/6-8
237 Old Athens Hwy 30531 706-778-7121
Daphne Penick, prin. Fax 778-2110

Covington, Newton, Pop. 12,895
Newton County SD 19,200/PK-12
PO Box 1469 30015 770-787-1330
Samantha Fuhrey, supt. Fax 784-2950
www.newtoncountyschools.org
Alcovy HS 1,900/9-12
14567 Highway 36 30014 770-784-4995
Dr. Sandra Owens, prin. Fax 625-6117
Clements MS 700/6-8
66 Jack Neely Rd 30016 770-784-2934
Joy Scavella, prin. Fax 784-2992
Cousins MS 900/6-8
8187 Carlton Trl NW 30014 770-786-7311
Dr. Makeba Clark, prin. Fax 784-2991
Eastside HS 1,300/9-12
10245 Eagle Dr 30014 770-784-2920
Jeff Cher, prin. Fax 784-2918
Indian Creek MS 1,100/6-8
11051 Covington by Pass Rd 30014 770-385-6453
Dr. Renee Mallard, prin. Fax 385-6456
Liberty MS 900/6-8
5225 Salem Rd 30016 678-625-6617
Keisa Taylor, prin. Fax 625-6200
Newton HS 2,100/9-12
1 Ram Way 30014 770-787-2250
John Ellenberg, prin. Fax 784-2957
Veterans Memorial MS 700/6-8
13357 Brown Bridge Rd 30016 770-385-6893
Dr. Takila Curry, prin. Fax 385-6899

Georgia Perimter College Post-Sec.
239 Cedar Ln 30014 770-278-1200
Peachtree Academy 200/PK-12
14101 Highway 278 E 30014 678-729-9111

Crawford, Oglethorpe, Pop. 804
Oglethorpe County SD
Supt. — See Lexington
Oglethorpe County MS 500/6-8
270 Buddy Faust Rd 30630 706-743-8146
Beverley Levine, prin. Fax 743-0849

Cumming, Forsyth, Pop. 5,371
Forsyth County SD 42,200/PK-12
1120 Dahlonega Hwy 30040 770-887-2461
Dr. Jeff Bearden, supt. Fax 781-6632
www.forsyth.k12.ga.us
Forsyth Central HS 1,800/9-12
131 Elm St 30040 770-887-8151
Mitch Young, prin. Fax 781-2289
Gateway Academy Alt
136 Elm St 30040 770-781-2299
Betty Pope, dir. Fax 888-1193
Lakeside MS 1,100/6-8
2565 Echols Rd 30041 678-965-5080
Kim Head, prin. Fax 965-5081
Liberty MS 900/6-8
7465 Wallace Tatum Rd 30028 770-781-4889
Cheryl Riddle, prin. Fax 513-3877
Little Mill MS 900/6-8
6800 Little Mill Rd 30041 678-965-5000
Connie McCrary, prin. Fax 965-5001
North Forsyth HS 2,400/9-12
3635 Coal Mountain Dr 30028 770-781-6637
Jeff Cheney, prin. Fax 781-2273
North Forsyth MS 1,000/6-8
3645 Coal Mountain Dr 30028 770-889-0743
Todd McClelland, prin. Fax 888-1210
Otwell MS 1,100/6-8
605 Tribble Gap Rd 30040 770-887-5248
Steve Miller, prin. Fax 888-1214
Piney Grove MS 1,200/6-8
8135 Majors Rd 30041 678-965-5010
Pam Pajerski, prin. Fax 965-5011
South Forsyth HS 2,500/9-12
585 Peachtree Pkwy 30041 770-781-2264
Laura Wilson, prin. Fax 888-1224
South Forsyth MS 1,000/6-8
4670 Windermere Pkwy 30041 770-888-3170
Sandy Tinsley, prin. Fax 888-3175
Vickery Creek MS 1,200/6-8
6240 Post Rd 30040 770-667-2580
Drew Hayes, prin. Fax 667-2589
West Forsyth HS 2,300/9-12
4155 Drew Rd 30040 770-888-3470
Heather Gordy, prin. Fax 888-3471
Other Schools – See Alpharetta, Suwanee

Covenant Christian Academy 200/PK-12
6905 Post Rd 30040 770-674-2990
Johnathan Arnold, hdmstr. Fax 674-2989
Fideles Christian S 100/PK-12
1390 Weber Industrial Dr 30041 770-888-6705
Carla Rutherford, dir. Fax 888-9720
Horizon Christian Academy 300/K-12
PO Box 2715 30028 678-947-0711
Gary Bennett, head sch Fax 947-0721
Pinecrest Academy 800/PK-12
955 Peachtree Pkwy 30041 770-888-4477
Dr. Edward Lindekugel, head sch Fax 888-0404

Cusseta, Chattahoochee, Pop. 1,258
Chattahoochee County SD 900/PK-12
326 Broad St 31805 706-989-3774
David McCurry, supt. Fax 989-3776
www.chattco.org
ACE Academy Alternative S Alt
326 Broad St 31805 706-989-3243
Bo Oates, dir. Fax 989-3776
Chattahoochee County HS 500/9-12
360 GA Highway 26 31805 706-989-3678
Sandi Veliz, prin. Fax 989-0649
Chattahoochee County MS 200/6-8
360 GA Highway 26 31805 706-989-3678
Sandi Veliz, prin. Fax 989-0649

Cuthbert, Randolph, Pop. 3,851
Randolph County SD 1,100/PK-12
98 School Dr, 229-732-3601
Dr. Marvin Howard, supt. Fax 732-3840
www.sowegak12.org/
Randolph-Clay HS 300/9-12
3451 GA Highway 266, 229-732-2101
Willie Williams, prin. Fax 732-5633
Randolph-Clay MS 200/6-8
3451 GA Highway 266, 229-732-2790
Ronald Gadson, prin. Fax 732-5633

Andrew College Post-Sec.
501 College St, 229-732-2171

Dacula, Gwinnett, Pop. 4,365
Gwinnett County SD
Supt. — See Suwanee
Dacula HS 1,900/9-12
123 Broad St 30019 770-963-6664
Dr. Bryan Long, prin. Fax 338-4665
Dacula MS 1,600/6-8
137 Dacula Rd 30019 770-963-1110
Dr. Kellye Riggins, prin. Fax 338-4632

Dacula Classical Academy 100/PK-12
PO Box 986 30019 678-377-0080
Hebron Christian Academy 600/6-12
775 Dacula Rd 30019 770-963-9250
Tracey Pritchard, head sch Fax 277-3581
Oak Hill Classical S 100/PK-12
2955 Old Fountain Rd 30019 770-338-7945
James Cain, hdmstr. Fax 261-1721

Dahlonega, Lumpkin, Pop. 5,151
Lumpkin County SD 3,800/PK-12
56 Indian Dr 30533 706-864-3611
Dr. Robert W. Brown, supt. Fax 864-3755
www.lumpkinschools.com
Lumpkin County HS 1,100/9-12
2001 Indian Dr 30533 706-864-6186
Rick Conner, prin. Fax 864-4929
Lumpkin County MS 900/6-8
44 School Dr 30533 706-864-6189
Chris Froggatt, prin. Fax 864-0199

North Georgia College & State University Post-Sec.
82 College Cir 30597 706-864-1400

Dallas, Paulding, Pop. 11,233
Paulding County SD 28,300/K-12
3236 Atlanta Hwy 30132 770-443-8000
Cliff Cole, supt. Fax 443-8089
www.paulding.k12.ga.us
East Paulding HS 1,700/9-12
3320 E Paulding Dr 30157 770-445-5100
Jason Freeman, prin. Fax 443-6357
East Paulding MS 800/6-8
2945 Hiram Acworth Hwy 30157 770-443-7000
Tom Alverson, prin. Fax 443-0116

Jones MS 700/6-8
100 Stadium Dr 30132 770-443-8024
Glen Bigham, prin. Fax 443-8026
McClure MS 1,100/6-8
315 Bob Grogan Dr 30132 770-505-3700
Jaynath Hayes, prin. Fax 505-7253
Moses MS 500/6-8
1066 Old County Farm Rd 30132 770-443-8727
Scott Viness, prin. Fax 443-8078
New Hope Education Center Alt
4555 Dallas Acworth Hwy 30132 770-445-2656
Vladimir Labossiere, prin. Fax 443-7006
North Paulding HS 2,000/9-12
300 N Paulding Dr 30132 770-443-9400
Dr. Mark Crowe, prin. Fax 363-8544
Paulding County HS 1,700/9-12
1297 Villa Rica Hwy 30157 770-443-8008
Craig Wilcox, prin. Fax 443-7030
Ritch MS 600/6-8
60 Old Country Trl 30157 770-443-1449
Christine Carson, prin. Fax 443-4339
Scoggins MS 700/6-8
1663 Mulberry Rock Rd 30157 770-456-4188
Tammy Allen, prin. Fax 456-4189
South Paulding MS 500/6-8
592 Nebo Rd 30157 770-445-8500
Sandra Webb, prin. Fax 445-9989
Other Schools – See Douglasville, Hiram, Powder Springs

Dalton, Whitfield, Pop. 32,710
Dalton CSD 7,700/PK-12
PO Box 1408 30722 706-876-4000
Dr. Jim Hawkins Ph.D., supt. Fax 226-4583
www.daltonpublicschools.com/
Dalton HS 1,600/9-12
1500 Manly St 30720 706-876-4800
Steve Bartoo, prin. Fax 226-2430
Dalton MS 1,700/6-8
1250 Cross Plains Trl 30721 706-278-3903
Dr. Phil Jones, prin. Fax 428-7852
Morris Innovative HS 400/Alt
104 Fort Hill Ter 30721 706-876-4150
Pat Hunt, prin. Fax 278-4998

Whitfield County SD 13,400/PK-12
PO Box 2167 30722 706-217-6780
Dr. Judy Gilreath, supt. Fax 217-6755
www.whitfield.k12.ga.us
Coahulla Creek HS 1,000/9-12
3361 Crow Rd NE 30721 706-694-4900
Tracy Mardis, prin. Fax 694-5033
Crossroads Academy Alt
2818 Airport Rd 30721 706-271-2495
Donna Harris, prin. Fax 271-2496
Eastbrook MS 700/6-8
1382 Eastbrook Rd SE 30721 706-278-6135
Dr. Gregory Bailey, prin. Fax 226-9859
New Hope MS 600/6-8
1111 New Hope Rd NW 30720 706-673-2295
Stephen Vess, prin. Fax 673-2086
North Whitfield MS 900/6-8
3264 Cleveland Hwy 30721 706-259-3381
Andrea Bradley, prin. Fax 259-8168
Southeast Whitfield County HS 1,300/9-12
1954 Riverbend Rd 30721 706-876-7000
Denise Pendley, prin. Fax 278-3433
Valley Point MS 500/6-8
3796 S Dixie Rd 30721 706-277-9662
Joe Barnett, prin. Fax 277-7035
Phoenix HS Adult
2300 Maddox Chapel Rd NE 30721 706-260-2206
Fred Toney, prin. Fax 260-2200
Other Schools – See Rocky Face, Tunnel Hill

Christian Heritage S 400/K-12
PO Box 2066 30722 706-277-1198
Dalton State College Post-Sec.
650 College Dr 30720 706-272-4436
Georgia Beauty Academy Post-Sec.
PO Box 3516 30719 866-418-4522
Georgia Northwestern Technical College Post-Sec.
2310 Maddox Chapel Rd NE 30721 706-272-2966

Damascus, Early, Pop. 251

Southwest Georgia Academy 400/PK-12
14105 GA Highway 200, 229-725-4792

Danielsville, Madison, Pop. 548
Madison County SD 4,800/PK-12
PO Box 37 30633 706-795-2191
Dr. Allen McCannon, supt. Fax 795-5029
www.madison.k12.ga.us
Madison County HS 1,400/9-12
600 Madison St 30633 706-795-2197
George Bullock, prin. Fax 795-3116
Other Schools – See Comer

Darien, McIntosh, Pop. 1,951
McIntosh County SD 1,700/PK-12
200 Pine St SE 31305 912-437-6645
Dr. John Barge, supt. Fax 437-2140
www.mcintosh.k12.ga.us/
McIntosh County Academy 500/9-12
8945 US Highway 17 31305 912-437-6691
Dr. Scott Barrow, prin. Fax 437-3077
McIntosh County MS 400/6-8
500 Greene St 31305 912-437-6685
Carolyn Smith, prin. Fax 437-5676

Dawson, Terrell, Pop. 4,502
Terrell County SD 1,500/PK-12
PO Box 151, 229-995-4425
Robert Aaron, supt. Fax 995-4632
www.terrell.k12.ga.us
Terrell County HS 400/9-12
201 Greenwave Blvd, 229-995-2544
Douglas Bell, prin. Fax 995-4523
Terrell County MS 300/6-8
201 Greenwave Blvd, 229-995-2828
Valencia Gardner, prin. Fax 995-5418

Terrell Academy 300/K-12
602 Academy Dr SE, 229-995-4242

Dawsonville, Dawson, Pop. 2,501
Dawson County SD 3,100/PK-12
28 Main St 30534 706-265-3246
Dr. Damon Gibbs, supt. Fax 265-1226
www.dawsoncountyschools.org
Dawson County HS 1,100/9-12
PO Box 129 30534 706-265-6555
Richard Crumley, prin. Fax 265-3936
Dawson County JHS 100/8-8
332 Highway 9 N 30534 706-216-5801
Jeffrey Clapper, prin. Fax 265-7252
Hightower Academy Alt
175 Tiger Cir 30534 706-265-1244
Richard Crumley, prin. Fax 265-2867

Decatur, DeKalb, Pop. 18,866
City Schools of Decatur 4,600/PK-12
125 Electric Ave 30030 404-371-3601
Dr. David Dude, supt. Fax 371-3601
www.csdecatur.net
Decatur HS 1,000/9-12
310 N McDonough St 30030 404-370-4420
Arlethea Williams, prin. Fax 370-4434
Renfroe MS 900/6-8
220 W College Ave 30030 404-370-4440
Johnathan Clark, prin. Fax 370-4449

DeKalb County SD
Supt. — See Stone Mountain
Bethune MS 900/6-8
5200 Covington Hwy 30035 678-875-0302
Myron Broome, prin. Fax 875-0310
Cedar Grove MS 900/6-8
2300 Wildcat Rd 30034 678-874-4202
Dr. Candace Alexander, prin. Fax 874-4210
Chapel Hill MS 900/6-8
3535 Dogwood Farm Rd 30034 678-676-8502
Lisa McGhee, prin. Fax 676-8510
Columbia HS 1,200/9-12
2106 Columbia Dr 30032 678-874-0802
Dr. Derrica Boochee-Davis, prin. Fax 874-0810
Columbia MS 1,000/6-8
3001 Columbia Dr 30034 678-875-0502
Dr. Keith Jones, prin. Fax 875-0510
Druid Hills MS 1,000/6-8
3100 Mount Olive Dr 30033 678-874-7602
Jacqueline Taylor, prin. Fax 874-7610
International Student Center 300/Alt
3318 Midway Rd 30032 678-676-0902
Dr. Terry Segovis, prin. Fax 676-6608
McNair MS 700/6-8
2190 Wallingford Dr 30032 678-874-5102
Ronald Mitchell, prin. Fax 874-5110
Miller Grove MS 1,000/6-8
2215 Miller Rd 30035 678-676-8902
Thaddeus Dixon, prin. Fax 676-8910
Southwest DeKalb HS 1,300/9-12
2863 Kelley Chapel Rd 30034 678-874-1902
Dr. Thomas Glanton, prin. Fax 874-1910
Towers HS 1,000/9-12
3919 Brookcrest Cir 30032 678-874-2202
Vincent Denson, prin. Fax 874-2210

Academe of the Oaks 100/9-12
146 New St 30030 404-405-2173
Eva Handschin, dir. Fax 377-7178
Agnes Scott College Post-Sec.
141 E College Ave 30030 404-471-6000
American Professional Institute Post-Sec.
141 Sams St 30030 404-371-3338
Columbia Theological Seminary Post-Sec.
PO Box 520 30031 404-378-8821
DeKalb Medical Center Post-Sec.
2701 N Decatur Rd 30033 404-501-5206
DeVry University Post-Sec.
1 W Court Sq Ste 100 30030 404-270-2706
Georgia Perimeter College Post-Sec.
3251 Panthersville Rd 30034 678-891-2300
Greenforest-McCalep Christian Academy 500/PK-12
3250 Rainbow Dr 30034 404-486-6737
Millicent Black Ph.D., prin. Fax 486-1127
Gupton-Jones College of Funeral Service Post-Sec.
5141 Snapfinger Woods Dr 30035 770-593-2257
Laurus Technical Institute Post-Sec.
523 Church St 30030 404-303-2929

Demorest, Habersham, Pop. 1,780
Habersham County SD
Supt. — See Clarkesville
Wilbanks MS 500/6-8
3115 Demorest Mt Airy Hwy 30535 706-894-1341
Marybeth Thomas, prin. Fax 894-1342

Piedmont College Post-Sec.
PO Box 10 30535 706-778-3000

Dexter, Laurens, Pop. 568
Laurens County SD
Supt. — See Dublin
West Laurens HS 1,200/9-12
3692 GA Highway 257 31019 478-875-1000
Clifford Garnto, prin. Fax 875-2860

Donalsonville, Seminole, Pop. 2,610
Seminole County SD 1,700/PK-12
800 S Woolfork Ave, 229-524-2433
Brinson Register, supt. Fax 524-2212
www.seminole.k12.ga.us
Seminole County MSHS 900/6-12
5582 GA Highway 39, 229-524-5135
Kent Richardson, prin. Fax 524-5178

Doraville, DeKalb, Pop. 8,200
DeKalb County SD
Supt. — See Stone Mountain
Sequoyah MS 1,200/6-8
3456 Aztec Rd 30340 678-676-7902
Sedrick Anthony, prin. Fax 676-7910

Douglas, Coffee, Pop. 11,434
Coffee County SD 7,800/PK-12
1311 Peterson Ave S 31533 912-384-2086
Dr. Morris Leis, supt. Fax 383-5333
www.coffee.k12.ga.us
Carver HS Freshman Campus 500/9-9
1020 Gaskin Ave S 31533 912-384-1342
Abe Morris, prin. Fax 383-4160
Coffee Alternative Education Center Alt
1303 Peterson Ave S 31533 912-383-4100
Tonya LeSure, dir. Fax 383-4124
Coffee HS 1,300/10-12
159 Trojan Way 31533 912-384-2094
Dr. Rowland Cummings, prin. Fax 383-4142
Coffee MS 1,700/6-8
901 Connector 206 N 31533 912-720-1011
Sherri Berry, prin. Fax 720-1032
Wiregrass Regional Coll & Career Academy Vo/Tech
706 W Baker Hwy Ste A 31533 912-389-6851
Scott Gillis, prin. Fax 720-9849

Citizens Christian Academy 200/PK-12
PO Box 1064 31534 912-384-8862
South Georgia State College Post-Sec.
100 College Park Dr W 31533 912-260-4200

Douglasville, Douglas, Pop. 30,224
Douglas County SD 25,400/K-12
PO Box 1077 30133 770-651-2000
Dr. Gordon Pritz, supt. Fax 920-4159
www.douglas.k12.ga.us
Alexander HS 1,600/9-12
6500 Alexander Pkwy 30135 770-651-6000
Nathan Hand, prin. Fax 920-4514
Chapel Hill HS 1,200/9-12
4899 Chapel Hill Rd 30135 770-651-6200
Dr. Sean Kelly, prin. Fax 947-7512
Chapel Hill MS 1,100/6-8
3989 Chapel Hill Rd 30135 770-651-5000
Dr. Jolene Morris, prin. Fax 920-4242
Chestnut Log MS 700/6-8
2544 Pope Rd 30135 770-651-5100
Dr. Nicole Hayes, prin. Fax 651-5103
Douglas County HS 1,900/9-12
8705 Campbellton St 30134 770-651-6500
Andre Weaver, prin. Fax 920-4456
Factory Shoals MS 800/6-8
3301 Shoals School Rd 30135 770-651-5800
Angela Carter, prin. Fax 920-4356
Fairplay MS 500/6-8
8311 Highway 166 30135 770-651-5300
Yvonne Kidney, prin. Fax 651-5303
New Manchester HS 1,700/9-12
4925 Highway 92/166 30135 770-651-2700
Marco Holland, prin.
Stewart MS 600/6-8
8138 Malone St 30134 770-651-5400
Robyn Scott, prin. Fax 920-4229
Yeager MS 600/6-8
4000 Kings Hwy 30135 770-651-5600
Dr. Fred Ervin, prin. Fax 947-7374
Other Schools – See Lithia Springs, Winston

Paulding County SD
Supt. — See Dallas
Austin MS 900/6-8
3490 Ridge Rd 30134 770-942-0316
Greg Musgrove, prin. Fax 942-0548
South Paulding HS 1,700/9-12
1364 Winn Rd 30134 770-949-9221
Dr. Keith Rowland, prin. Fax 949-9239

Harvester Christian Academy 300/PK-12
4241 Central Church Rd 30135 770-942-1583
Joel Slater, hdmstr. Fax 942-9332
Heirway Christian Academy 200/PK-12
6758 Spring St 30134 770-489-4392
Timothy Thomas, hdmstr. Fax 489-4318
Kings Way Christian S 300/PK-12
6456 The Kings Way 30135, 770-949-0812
Dr. Ray Conway, admin. Fax 949-1045
Strayer University Post-Sec.
4655 Timber Ridge Dr 30135 678-715-2200
West Georgia Technical College Post-Sec.
4600 Timber Ridge Dr 30135 770-947-7200

Dublin, Laurens, Pop. 16,025
Dublin CSD 2,200/PK-12
207 Shamrock Dr 31021 478-353-8000
Dr. Fred Williams, supt. Fax 353-8001
www.dublincityschools.us
Dublin HS 600/9-12
1127 Hillcrest Pkwy 31021 478-353-8040
Dr. Tyrone Kellogg, prin. Fax 353-8041
Dublin MS 600/5-8
1501 N Jefferson St 31021 478-353-8130
Raymond Braziel, prin. Fax 353-8131
Moore Street S 100/Alt
1405 W Moore St 31021 478-353-8400
Emory Bostic, prin. Fax 353-8401

Laurens County SD 6,400/PK-12
467 Firetower Rd 31021 478-272-4767
Juli Alligood, supt. Fax 277-2619
www.lcboe.net
East Laurens HS 600/9-12
920 US Highway 80 E 31027 478-272-3144
Eddie Morris, prin. Fax 609-2175
East Laurens MS 500/6-8
920 US Highway 80 E 31027 478-272-1201
Dr. Otha Hall, prin. Fax 609-2176
West Laurens MS 1,000/6-8
332 W Laurens School Rd 31021 478-272-8452
Tim Franks, prin. Fax 609-2202
Other Schools – See Dexter

Oconee Fall Line Technical College Post-Sec.
560 Pinehill Rd 31021 478-275-6589
Trinity Christian S 400/PK-12
200 Trinity Rd 31021 478-272-7699
Stan Couey, hdmstr. Fax 272-7685

Duluth, Gwinnett, Pop. 25,917
Gwinnett County SD
Supt. — See Suwanee
Coleman MS 6-8
3057 Main St 30096 678-407-7400
J.W. Mozley, prin. Fax 407-7436
Duluth HS 2,700/9-12
3737 Brock Rd 30096 770-476-5206
Anthony Smith, prin. Fax 232-3332
Duluth MS 2,000/6-8
3200 Pleasant Hill Rd 30096 770-476-3372
Deborah Fusi, prin. Fax 232-3295
Hull MS 2,300/6-8
1950 Old Peachtree Rd 30097 770-232-3200
Denise Showell, prin. Fax 232-3203
Radloff MS 1,800/6-8
3939 Shackleford Rd 30096 678-245-3400
Dr. Sarah Skinner, prin. Fax 245-3403

Atlanta Adventist Academy 200/9-12
PO Box 4088 30096 404-699-1400
Matt Jones, prin. Fax 512-9999
Atlanta Institute of Music Post-Sec.
2875 Breckinridge Blvd #700 30096 770-242-7717
Aviation Institute of Maintenance Post-Sec.
2025 Satellite Pointe 30096 678-377-5600
Childcare Education Institute Post-Sec.
3059 Peachtree Indstrl #100 30097 800-499-9907
DeVry University Post-Sec.
3505 Koger Blvd Ste 170 30096 770-381-4400

Dunwoody, DeKalb, Pop. 45,357
DeKalb County SD
Supt. — See Stone Mountain
Dunwoody HS 1,600/9-12
5035 Vermack Rd 30338 678-874-8502
Tom McFerrin, prin. Fax 874-8510

Empire Beauty School Post-Sec.
4719 Ashford-Dunwoody #205 30338 770-672-2448

Eastman, Dodge, Pop. 4,921
Dodge County SD 3,100/K-12
720 College St 31023 478-374-3783
T. Michael Hilliard, supt. Fax 374-6697
www.dodge.k12.ga.us
Dodge County HS 900/9-12
350 Pearl Bates Ave 31023 478-374-7711
Dr. Susan Long, prin. Fax 374-6987
Dodge County MS 700/6-8
5911 Oak St 31023 478-374-6492
Dr. Elvis Davis, prin. Fax 374-6484

East Point, Fulton, Pop. 33,152
Fulton County SD
Supt. — See Atlanta
Tri-Cities HS 1,700/9-12
2575 Harris St 30344 470-254-8200
Termerion McCrary-Lakes, prin. Fax 254-8158
West MS 800/6-8
2376 Headland Dr 30344 470-254-8130
Pammy Darden, prin. Fax 254-8121
Woodland MS 1,100/6-8
2745 Stone Rd 30344 404-305-2182
Jason Stamper, prin. Fax 305-2190

Eatonton, Putnam, Pop. 6,410

Gatewood S 400/PK-12
139 Phillips Dr 31024 706-485-8231

Edison, Calhoun, Pop. 1,517
Calhoun County SD
Supt. — See Morgan
Calhoun County HS 200/9-12
700 Manry St, 229-213-0148
Henry Acres, prin. Fax 213-5000
Calhoun County MS 200/6-8
PO Box 364, 229-213-0146
Craveous Butler, prin. Fax 213-0146

Elberton, Elbert, Pop. 4,600
Elbert County SD 2,000/PK-12
50 Laurel Dr 30635 706-213-4000
Charles Bell, supt. Fax 283-6674
www.elbert.k12.ga.us
Elbert County Comprehensive HS 800/9-12
600 Abernathy Cir 30635 706-213-4100
Jason Kouns, prin. Fax 283-1183
Elbert County MS 900/5-8
1108 Athens Tech Rd 30635 706-213-4200
Jon Jarvis, prin. Fax 283-1117

Ellaville, Schley, Pop. 1,796
Schley County SD 1,400/PK-12
PO Box 66 31806 229-937-2405
Adam Hathaway, supt. Fax 937-5180
www.schleyk12.org/
Schley County MSHS 700/6-12
2131 US Highway 19 S 31806 229-937-0560
Todd West, prin. Fax 937-0565

Ellenwood, Clayton
DeKalb County SD
Supt. — See Stone Mountain
Cedar Grove HS 1,000/9-12
2360 River Rd 30294 678-874-4002
Pamela Benford, prin. Fax 874-4010

Anointed Word Christian S International 50/PK-12
3800 Linecrest Rd 30294 404-241-8200
Markell Davis-Haynes, admin. Fax 328-9801

Ellijay, Gilmer, Pop. 1,600

North Georgia Christian Academy 100/PK-12
191 Harold Pritchett Rd 30540 706-635-6422
Mary Pierce, admin. Fax 635-6425

Emerson, Bartow, Pop. 1,449
Bartow County SD
Supt. — See Cartersville
South Central MS 600/6-8
224 Old Alabama Rd SE 30137 770-606-5865
Tia Hawkins, prin. Fax 606-5168

Eton, Murray, Pop. 907
Murray County SD
Supt. — See Chatsworth
Pleasant Valley Innovative S 200/Alt
273 Harris St 30724 706-517-5355
Marcus Richardson, prin. Fax 517-5339

Euharlee, Bartow, Pop. 4,058
Bartow County SD
Supt. — See Cartersville
Woodland MS 800/6-8
1061 Euharlee Rd, 770-606-5871
Matt Gibson, prin. Fax 606-2092

Evans, Columbia, Pop. 28,398
Columbia County SD 24,900/PK-12
4781 Hereford Farm Rd 30809 706-541-0650
Dr. Sandra Carraway, supt. Fax 541-2723
www.ccboe.net
CCBOE Alternative S Alt
628 Gibbs Rd 30809 706-868-5715
Dr. Ja'net Bishop, prin. Fax 854-5819
Evans HS 1,800/9-12
4550 Cox Rd 30809 706-863-1198
Michael Johnson, prin. Fax 854-5807
Evans MS 900/6-8
4785 Hereford Farm Rd 30809 706-863-2275
Sandra Thompson, prin. Fax 854-5810
Greenbrier HS 1,700/9-12
5114 Riverwood Pkwy 30809 706-650-6040
Chris Segraves, prin. Fax 855-3886
Greenbrier MS 600/6-8
5120 Riverwood Pkwy 30809 706-650-6080
Chip Fulmer, prin. Fax 854-5800
Lakeside HS 1,600/9-12
533 Blue Ridge Dr 30809 706-863-0027
Steven Cummings, prin. Fax 854-5802
Lakeside MS 700/6-8
527 Blue Ridge Dr 30809 706-855-6900
Felicia Turner, prin. Fax 854-5805
Riverside MS 700/6-8
1095 Furys Ferry Rd 30809 706-868-3712
Yvette Foster, prin. Fax 854-5824
Other Schools – See Grovetown, Harlem, Martinez

Augusta School of Massage Post-Sec.
608 Ponder Place Dr 30809 706-863-4799

Fairburn, Fulton, Pop. 12,742
Fulton County SD
Supt. — See Atlanta
Bear Creek MS 1,000/6-8
7415 Herndon Rd 30213 470-254-6080
Anthony Newbold, prin. Fax 254-3584
Creekside HS 1,400/9-12
7405 Herndon Rd 30213 470-254-4300
Ronald Maxwell, prin. Fax 254-4313
Hughes HS 1,800/9-12
7510 Hall Rd 30213 770-774-3620
Brandy Reeves, prin. Fax 774-3633
Renaissance MS 1,300/6-8
7155 Hall Rd 30213 770-306-4330
Creseda Hawk, prin. Fax 306-4338

Arlington Christian S 300/K-12
4500 Ridge Rd 30213 770-964-9872
Landmark Christian S 800/PK-12
50 SE Broad St 30213 770-306-0647
Mike Titus, hdmstr. Fax 969-6551

Fayetteville, Fayette, Pop. 15,530
Fayette County SD 20,100/PK-12
PO Box 879 30214 770-460-3535
Dr. Joseph Barrow, supt. Fax 460-8191
www.fcboe.org
Bennetts Mill MS 1,000/6-8
210 Lester Rd 30215 770-716-3982
Dr. Marcus Broadhead, prin. Fax 716-3983
Fayette County Alternative S Alt
450 Grady Ave 30214 770-460-3551
Tim Carder, prin. Fax 460-3905
Fayette County HS 1,300/9-12
1 Tiger Trl 30214 770-460-3540
Dr. Dan Lane, prin. Fax 460-3410
Rising Starr MS 1,000/6-8
183 Panther Path 30215 770-486-2721
Nancy Blair, prin. Fax 486-2727
Starr's Mill HS 1,500/9-12
193 Panther Path 30215 770-486-2710
Allen Leonard, prin. Fax 486-2716
Whitewater HS 1,400/9-12
100 Wildcat Way 30215 770-460-3935
Roy Rabold, prin. Fax 716-3973
Whitewater MS 900/6-8
1533 Highway 85 S 30215 770-460-3450
Connie Baldwin, prin. Fax 460-0362
Other Schools – See Peachtree City, Tyrone

Fayette Beauty Academy Post-Sec.
386 Glynn St N 30214 770-461-4669
GRACE Christian Academy 200/PK-12
355 McDonough Rd 30215 770-461-0137
Charlotte Sanders, prin. Fax 461-1190
Our Lady of Mercy Catholic HS 400/9-12
861 Highway 279 30214 770-461-2202
Brian Newhall, prin. Fax 461-9353
Solid Rock Academy 200/PK-12
106 Commerce St 30214 770-997-9744

Fitzgerald, Ben Hill, Pop. 8,940
Ben Hill County SD 3,100/PK-12
509 W Palm St 31750 229-409-5500
Dr. J. Shawn Haralson, supt. Fax 409-5513
benhillcounty.schoolinsites.com
Ben Hill County MS 700/6-8
134 JC Hunter Rd 31750 229-409-5578
Dr. Lisa Stone, prin. Fax 409-5580
Fitzgerald HS 800/9-12
601 W Cypress St 31750 229-409-5530
Dawn Clements, prin. Fax 409-5534

Flintstone, Walker
Walker County SD
Supt. — See La Fayette
Chattanooga Valley MS 500/6-8
847 Allgood Rd 30725 706-820-0735
Wade Breeden, prin. Fax 820-0736

Flowery Branch, Hall, Pop. 5,590
Hall County SD
Supt. — See Gainesville
Davis MS 1,200/6-8
4450 Hog Mountain Rd 30542 770-965-3020
Eddie Millwood, prin. Fax 965-3025
South Hall MS 1,200/6-8
4335 Falcon Pkwy 30542 770-532-4416
Paula Stubbs, prin. Fax 967-5852

Lanier Christian Academy 200/PK-12
5285 Strickland Rd 30542 678-828-8350
Dwayne Daniels, prin. Fax 828-8357

Folkston, Charlton, Pop. 2,443
Charlton County SD 1,700/PK-12
1259 Third St 31537 912-496-2596
Dr. John Lairsey, supt. Fax 496-2595
www.charlton.k12.ga.us
Bethune MS 600/4-8
285 Little Phoebe Church Rd 31537 912-496-2360
Danny McCoy, prin. Fax 496-3766
Charlton County HS 400/9-12
994 Indian Trl 31537 912-496-2501
Dr. Joshua Howard, prin. Fax 496-3732

Forest Park, Clayton, Pop. 18,177
Clayton County SD
Supt. — See Jonesboro
Babb MS 800/6-8
5500 Reynolds Rd 30297 404-473-3248
Brenda Ross, prin. Fax 473-3252
Forest Park HS 1,700/9-12
5452 Phillips Dr 30297 770-473-2775
Dr. Derrick Manning, prin. Fax 473-3228
Forest Park MS 700/6-8
930 Finley Dr 30297 770-472-2817
Monique Drewry, prin. Fax 472-2833

Arnold/Padrick's Univ of Cosmetology Post-Sec.
4971 Courtney Dr 30297 404-361-5641
Beauty College of America Post-Sec.
1171 Main St 30297 404-361-4098

Forsyth, Monroe, Pop. 3,748
Monroe County SD 3,900/PK-12
PO Box 1308 31029 478-994-2031
Dr. Mike Hickman, supt. Fax 994-3364
www.monroe.k12.ga.us
Monroe County Achievement Ctr Alt
25 Brooklyn Ave 31029 478-994-7072
Grady Caldwell, coord. Fax 994-7074
Monroe County MS - Banks Stephens Campus 600/7-8
66 Thornton Rd 31029 478-994-6186
Dr. Efrem Yarber, prin. Fax 994-7061
Persons HS 1,200/9-12
300 Montpelier Ave 31029 478-994-2812
Jim Finch, prin. Fax 994-7065

Fort Gaines, Clay, Pop. 1,094
Clay County SD 300/PK-11
111 Commerce St E, 229-768-2232
Johnnie Grimsley, supt. Fax 768-3654
www.clay.k12.ga.us
Clay County MSHS 100/6-11
200 Hobbs Ln, 229-768-0160
Michelle Oliver, prin. Fax 768-2363

Fort Oglethorpe, Catoosa, Pop. 9,051
Catoosa County SD
Supt. — See Ringgold
Lakeview-Fort Oglethorpe HS 1,000/9-12
1850 Battlefield Pkwy 30742 706-866-0342
Terri Vandiver, prin. Fax 861-6645
Performance Learning Center Alt
2 Barnhardt Cir 30742 706-861-2772
Sharon Vaughn, prin. Fax 861-6643

Fort Valley, Peach, Pop. 9,695
Peach County SD 3,800/K-12
523 Vineville St 31030 478-825-5933
Daryl Fineran, supt. Fax 825-9970
www.peachschools.org
Fort Valley MS 500/6-8
712 Peggy Dr 31030 478-825-2413
Damika Glover, prin. Fax 825-1332
Peach County HS 1,000/9-12
900 Campus Dr 31030 478-825-8258
Albert Pollard, prin. Fax 825-2290
Other Schools – See Byron

Fort Valley State University Post-Sec.
1005 State University Dr 31030 478-825-6211

Franklin, Heard, Pop. 969
Heard County SD 2,000/PK-12
PO Box 1330 30217 706-675-3320
Jerry Prince, supt. Fax 675-3357
www.heard.k12.ga.us
Heard County HS 600/9-12
545 Main St 30217 706-675-3656
Brent Tisdale, prin. Fax 675-8729
Heard County MS 500/6-8
269 Old Field Rd 30217 706-675-9247
Brian Hadley, prin. Fax 675-9255

Franklin Springs, Franklin, Pop. 938

Emmanuel College Post-Sec.
PO Box 129 30639 800-860-8800

Gainesville, Hall, Pop. 33,306
Gainesville CSD 7,600/PK-12
508 Oak St 30501 770-536-5275
Dr. Wanda Creel, supt. Fax 287-2019
www.gcssk12.net/

Gainesville HS 1,700/9-12
830 Century Pl 30501 770-536-4441
Tom Smith, prin. Fax 287-2031
Gainesville MS 1,600/6-8
1581 Community Way 30501 770-534-4237
Dr. Rose Prejean-Harris, prin. Fax 287-2022

Hall County SD 26,500/PK-12
711 Green St NW 30501 770-534-1080
Will Schofield, supt. Fax 535-7404
www.hallco.org
Chestatee HS 1,200/9-12
3005 Sardis Rd 30506 770-532-1162
Suzanne Jarrard, prin. Fax 532-2202
Da Vinci Academy 6-8
3215 Poplar Springs Rd 30507 770-533-4004
Paula Stubbs, prin. Fax 533-4018
East Hall HS 1,100/9-12
3534 E Hall Rd 30507 770-536-9921
Jeff Cooper, prin. Fax 535-1184
East Hall MS 900/6-8
4120 E Hall Rd 30507 770-531-9457
Kristin Finley, prin. Fax 531-2327
Johnson HS 1,300/9-12
3305 Poplar Springs Rd 30507 770-536-2394
Stan Lewis, prin. Fax 531-3046
Lanier Career Academy Alt
2723 Tumbling Creek Rd 30504 770-531-2330
Dr. Cindy Blakley, prin. Fax 450-5978
North Hall HS 1,100/9-12
4885 Mount Vernon Rd 30506 770-983-7331
Jamey Moore, prin. Fax 983-7941
North Hall MS 900/6-8
4856 Rilla Rd 30506 770-983-9749
Tamara Etterling, prin. Fax 983-9993
Other Schools – See Flowery Branch, Oakwood

Brenau University Post-Sec.
500 Washington St SE 30501 800-252-5119
Interactive College of Technology Post-Sec.
2323 Browns Bridge Rd 30504 678-450-0550
Lakeview Academy 500/PK-12
796 Lakeview Dr 30501 770-532-4383
Dr. John P. Kennedy, head sch Fax 536-6142
Riverside Military Academy 400/7-12
2001 Riverside Dr 30501 800-462-2338
William Gallagher, pres. Fax 291-3364

Georgetown, Quitman, Pop. 912
Quitman County SD 300/PK-12
215 Kaigler Rd, 229-334-4189
Allen Fort, supt. Fax 334-2109
www.quitman.k12.ga.us/
Quitman HS 100/9-12
173 Kaigler Rd, 229-334-4298
Jon-Erik Jones, prin. Fax 334-4700

Glennville, Tattnall, Pop. 3,528
Tattnall County SD
Supt. — See Reidsville
Glennville MS 300/6-8
721 E Barnard St 30427 912-654-1467
Cindy Boyett, prin. Fax 654-1300

Gray, Jones, Pop. 3,239
Jones County SD 5,500/PK-12
125 Stewart Ave 31032 478-986-3032
Charles Gibson, supt. Fax 986-4412
jones.schooldesk.net/
Gray Station MS 700/6-8
324 GA Highway 18 E 31032 478-986-2090
Wes Cavender, prin. Fax 986-2099
Jones County HS 1,600/9-12
339 Railroad St 31032 478-986-5444
Mary Stewart, prin. Fax 986-1589
Other Schools – See Macon

Grayson, Gwinnett, Pop. 2,619
Gwinnett County SD
Supt. — See Suwanee
Bay Creek MS 1,000/6-8
821 Cooper Rd 30017 678-344-7570
Dr. Maggie Fehrman, prin. Fax 736-6908
Couch MS 1,000/6-8
1777 Grayson Hwy 30017 678-407-7272
Devon Williams, prin. Fax 407-7326

Greensboro, Greene, Pop. 3,310
Greene County SD 2,100/PK-12
101 E Third St 30642 706-453-7688
Dr. Chris Houston, supt. Fax 453-9019
www.greene.k12.ga.us
Carson MS 300/6-8
1010 S Main St 30642 706-453-3308
Brock Miller, prin. Fax 453-4674
Greene County HS 500/9-12
1002 S Main St 30642 706-453-2271
Corey Stephens, prin. Fax 453-3311

Greenville, Meriwether, Pop. 862
Meriwether County SD 3,100/PK-12
PO Box 70 30222 706-672-4297
Dr. Tim Dixon, supt. Fax 672-1618
www.mcssga.org
Greenville HS 300/9-12
17656 Roosevelt Hwy 30222 706-672-4930
Thaddeus Jackson, prin. Fax 672-1424
Greenville MS 300/6-8
17656 Roosevelt Hwy 30222 706-672-4930
Michael Perry, prin. Fax 672-1424
Other Schools – See Manchester

Griffin, Spalding, Pop. 23,259
Griffin Spalding County School System 10,600/PK-12
PO Box N 30224 770-229-3700
Jim Smith, supt. Fax 229-3708
www.spalding.k12.ga.us
Carver Road MS 500/6-8
2185 Carver Rd 30224 770-229-3739
Tiffany Taylor, prin. Fax 229-3712
Cowan Road MS 600/6-8
1185 Cowan Rd 30223 770-229-3722
Laura Jordan, prin. Fax 227-8583
Griffin HS 1,400/9-12
1617 W Poplar St 30224 770-229-3752
Darrell Evans, prin. Fax 467-4644
Kennedy Road MS 500/6-8
280 Kennedy Rd 30223 770-229-3760
Dexter Sands, prin. Fax 467-4626
Rehoboth Road MS 700/6-8
1500 Rehoboth Rd 30224 770-229-3727
Larry Jones, prin. Fax 229-3770
Spalding HS 1,200/9-12
433 Wilson Rd 30224 770-229-3775
Lindy Pruitt, prin. Fax 227-6899

Southern Crescent Technical College Post-Sec.
501 Varsity Rd 30223 770-228-7348

Grovetown, Columbia, Pop. 10,773
Columbia County SD
Supt. — See Evans
Columbia MS 900/6-8
2013 Raider Way 30813 706-541-1252
Eli Putnam, prin. Fax 854-5820
Grovetown HS 1,600/9-12
2010 Warrior Way 30813 706-541-2723
Craig Baker, prin. Fax 447-2109
Grovetown MS 900/6-8
5463 Harlem Grovetown Rd 30813 706-855-2514
Tom Smallwood, prin. Fax 854-5822

Guyton, Effingham, Pop. 1,661
Effingham County SD
Supt. — See Springfield
Effingham County MS 800/6-8
1659 GA Highway 119 S 31312 912-772-7001
April Hodges, prin. Fax 772-7005
South Effingham HS 1,500/9-12
1220 Noel C Conaway Rd 31312 912-728-7511
Dr. Mark Winters, prin. Fax 728-7529
South Effingham MS 1,000/6-8
1200 Noel C Conaway Rd 31312 912-728-7500
Brigid Nesmith, prin. Fax 728-7508

Hahira, Lowndes, Pop. 2,695
Lowndes County SD
Supt. — See Valdosta
Hahira MS 800/6-8
101 S Nelson St 31632 229-316-8601
Stacy Dickey, prin. Fax 316-8606

Valwood S 400/PK-12
4380 Old US 41 N 31632 229-242-8491
Dr. Darren Pascavage, hdmstr. Fax 245-7894

Hamilton, Harris, Pop. 1,001
Harris County SD 5,200/PK-12
132 Barnes Mill Rd 31811 706-628-4206
Dr. James Martin, supt. Fax 628-5609
harriscounty.ga.schoolwebpages.com
Harris County - Carver MS 800/7-8
11696 US Highway 27 E 31811 706-628-4951
Stacey Carlisle, prin. Fax 628-5737
Harris County HS 1,600/9-12
8281 GA Highway 116 31811 706-628-4278
Roger Couch, prin. Fax 628-4335
Performance Learning Center Alt
8281 GA Highway 116 31811 706-628-7452
Sanders Denham, prin. Fax 628-7480

Hampton, Henry, Pop. 6,827
Clayton County SD
Supt. — See Jonesboro
Lovejoy HS 2,000/9-12
1587 Mcdonough Rd 30228 770-473-2920
Arthur Carter, prin. Fax 473-2928

Henry County SD
Supt. — See Mc Donough
Dutchtown HS 1,500/9-12
149 Mitchell Rd 30228 770-515-7510
Nicole Shaw, prin. Fax 515-7518
Dutchtown MS 1,000/6-8
155 Mitchell Rd 30228 770-515-7500
April Madden, prin. Fax 515-7505
Hampton HS 9-12
795 Hampton Locust Grove Rd 30228 770-946-7461
Martin Gore, prin. Fax 946-7468
Hampton MS 800/6-8
799 Hampton Locust Grove Rd 30228 770-707-2130
Jason Shadden, prin. Fax 946-3545

Bible Baptist Christian S 200/PK-12
2780 Mount Carmel Rd 30228 770-946-4700

Harlem, Columbia, Pop. 2,608
Columbia County SD
Supt. — See Evans
Harlem HS 700/9-12
1070 Appling Harlem Rd 30814 706-556-5980
Dietmar Perez, prin. Fax 854-5813
Harlem MS 500/6-8
375 W Forrest St 30814 706-556-5990
Carl Jackson, prin. Fax 854-5816

Hartwell, Hart, Pop. 4,400
Hart County SD 3,400/K-12
PO Box 696 30643 706-376-5141
Jaybez Floyd, supt. Fax 376-7046
www.hart.k12.ga.us
Hart College and Career Academy Vo/Tech
59 Fifth St 30643 706-376-5461
Dr. Mark Crenshaw, admin.
Hart County HS 1,000/9-12
59 Fifth St 30643 706-376-5461
Kevin Gaines, prin. Fax 856-7237
Hart County MS 800/6-8
176 Powell Rd 30643 706-376-5431
Bryan Edwards, prin. Fax 376-2207

Hawkinsville, Pulaski, Pop. 4,540
Pulaski County SD 1,300/PK-12
72 Warren St 31036 478-783-7200
Jane Williams, supt. Fax 783-7204
www.pulaski.k12.ga.us
Alternative Learning Center Alt
Warren St 31036 478-783-7265
Marvin Hill, dir. Fax 783-7204
Hawkinsville HS 400/9-12
24 Red Devil Dr 31036 478-783-7210
Russell Lawley, prin. Fax 783-7251
Pulaski County MS 300/6-8
8 Red Devil Dr 31036 478-892-7215
Natasha Kilgore, prin. Fax 783-7297

Hazlehurst, Jeff Davis, Pop. 4,181
Jeff Davis County SD 3,100/PK-12
PO Box 1780 31539 912-375-6700
Dr. Rob Brown, supt. Fax 375-6703
www.jeff-davis.k12.ga.us
Davis HS 800/9-12
156 Collins St 31539 912-375-6760
Cecelia McLoon, prin. Fax 375-0945
Davis MS 700/6-8
93 Collins St 31539 912-375-6750
Barry Waller, prin. Fax 375-6756

Hephzibah, Richmond, Pop. 3,910
Richmond County SD
Supt. — See Augusta
Hephzibah HS 1,000/9-12
4558 Brothersville Rd 30815 706-592-2089
Dr. Larina Thomas, prin. Fax 592-3975
Hephzibah MS 500/6-8
2427 Mims Rd 30815 706-592-4534
Cameron Henry, prin. Fax 592-3979
Morgan Road MS 500/6-8
3635 Hiers Blvd 30815 706-796-4992
Dr. Shontier Barnes, prin. Fax 560-3947
Pine Hill MS 600/6-8
2147 McElmurray Rd 30815 706-592-3730
Brian Hadden, prin. Fax 592-3741
Spirit Creek MS 500/6-8
115 Dolphin Way 30815 706-592-3987
Kierstin Johnson, prin. Fax 592-3999

Hiawassee, Towns, Pop. 877
Towns County SD 1,100/PK-12
67 Lakeview Cir Ste C 30546 706-896-2279
Dr. Darren Berrong, supt. Fax 896-2632
www.towns.k12.ga.us
Towns County HS 400/9-12
1400 Highway 76 E 30546 706-896-4131
Dr. Connie Hobbs, prin. Fax 896-6628
Towns County MS 300/6-8
1400 Highway 76 E 30546 706-896-4131
Erica Chastain, prin. Fax 896-6628

Hinesville, Liberty, Pop. 31,826
Liberty County SD 9,800/PK-12
200 Bradwell St 31313 912-876-2161
Dr. Valya Lee, supt. Fax 368-6201
www.liberty.k12.ga.us/
Bradwell Institute HS 1,700/9-12
100 Pafford St 31313 912-876-6121
Scott Carrier, prin. Fax 876-6914
Frasier MS 800/6-8
910 Long Frasier Dr 31313 912-877-5367
Jermaine Williams, prin. Fax 877-3291
Liberty County HS 1,100/9-12
3216 E Oglethorpe Hwy 31313 912-876-4316
Stephanie Woods, prin. Fax 876-4303
Snelson-Golden MS 700/6-8
465 Coates Rd 31313 912-877-3112
Roland VanHorn, prin. Fax 368-5342
Other Schools – See Midway

First Presbyterian Christian Academy 300/PK-12
308 E Court St 31313 912-876-0441
Shannon Hickey, head sch Fax 369-6686

Hiram, Paulding, Pop. 3,455
Paulding County SD
Supt. — See Dallas
Hiram HS 1,600/9-12
702 Virgie Ballentine Dr 30141 770-443-1182
Misty Cooksey, prin. Fax 439-5053

Grace Christian Academy 300/PK-12
5790 Powder Springs/Dallas 30141 770-222-8955
Eddie Fincher, hdmstr. Fax 222-3321
Vogue Beauty School Post-Sec.
3655 Macland Rd 30141 770-943-6811

Hogansville, Troup, Pop. 3,003
Troup County SD
Supt. — See LaGrange
Callaway HS 800/9-12
221 Whitfield Rd 30230 706-845-2070
Jonathan Laney, prin. Fax 845-2071

Homer, Banks, Pop. 1,123
Banks County SD
Supt. — See Commerce
Banks County HS 900/9-12
1486 Historic Homer Hwy # A 30547 706-677-2221
Dr. Joseph Goodroe, prin. Fax 677-2688
Banks County MS 700/6-8
712 Thompson St 30547 706-677-2277
Hank Ramey, prin. Fax 677-5227

Homerville, Clinch, Pop. 2,408
Clinch County SD 1,400/PK-12
46 S College St 31634 912-487-5321
Dr. Donna Ryan, supt. Fax 487-5068
www.clinchcounty.com/
Clinch County HS 500/8-12
863 Carswell St 31634 912-487-5366
Denise Brown, prin. Fax 487-3272

Hoschton, Jackson, Pop. 1,352
Gwinnett County SD
Supt. — See Suwanee
Mill Creek HS 3,700/9-12
4400 Braselton Hwy 30548 678-714-5850
Jason Lane, prin. Fax 714-5863
Osborne MS 1,600/6-8
4404 Braselton Hwy 30548 770-904-5400
Kenney Wells, prin. Fax 765-5981

Irwinton, Wilkinson, Pop. 587
Wilkinson County SD 1,600/PK-12
PO Box 206 31042 478-946-5521
Dr. Aaron Geter, supt. Fax 946-5565
www.wilkinson.k12.ga.us/
Wilkinson County HS 400/9-12
PO Box 547 31042 478-946-2441
Jerome Miles, prin. Fax 946-7134
Wilkinson County MS 300/6-8
PO Box 527 31042 478-946-2541
Dr. Angela Smith, prin. Fax 946-8981

Jackson, Butts, Pop. 4,955
Butts County SD 3,400/PK-12
181 N Mulberry St 30233 770-504-2300
Robert Costley, supt. Fax 504-2305
www.butts.k12.ga.us
Henderson MS 700/6-8
494 George Tate Dr 30233 770-504-2310
Tracey Allen, prin. Fax 504-2315
Jackson HS 1,000/9-12
717 S Harkness St 30233 770-504-2340
Dr. Todd Simpson, prin. Fax 504-2341

Jasper, Pickens, Pop. 3,647
Pickens County SD 4,300/PK-12
100 D B Carrol 30143 706-253-1700
Dr. Charles Webb, supt. Fax 253-1710
www.pickenscountyschools.org
Jasper MS 500/6-8
339 W Church St 30143 706-253-1760
Anita Walker, prin. Fax 253-1765
Pickens County HS 1,300/9-12
500 Dragon Dr 30143 706-253-1800
Dr. Chad Flatt, prin. Fax 253-1815
Pickens County MS 500/6-8
1802 Refuge Rd 30143 706-253-1830
Pennie Fowler, prin. Fax 253-1835

Chattahoochee Technical College Post-Sec.
100 Campus Dr 30143 706-253-4500

Jefferson, Jackson, Pop. 9,285
Jackson County SD 6,900/PK-12
1660 Winder Hwy 30549 706-367-5151
April Howard Ed.D., supt. Fax 367-9457
www.jackson.k12.ga.us
Jackson County Comprehensive HS 1,000/9-12
1668 Winder Hwy 30549 706-367-5003
Pete Jones, prin. Fax 367-5007
West Jackson MS 900/6-8
400 Gum Springs Church Rd 30549 706-654-2775
Joe Cobb, prin. Fax 824-1969
Other Schools – See Commerce

Jefferson CSD 3,000/PK-12
345 Storey Ln 30549 706-367-2880
Dr. John Jackson, supt. Fax 367-2291
www.jeffcityschools.org/
Jefferson HS 900/9-12
575 Washington St 30549 706-367-2881
Dr. Kevin Smith, prin. Fax 367-1884
Jefferson MS 700/6-8
100 Dragon Dr 30549 706-367-2882
Kenneth Martin, prin. Fax 367-5207

Jeffersonville, Twiggs, Pop. 1,016
Twiggs County SD 800/PK-12
952 Main St 31044 478-945-3127
Elgin Dixon, supt. Fax 945-3078
www.twiggs.k12.ga.us
Twiggs County HS 200/9-12
375 Watson Dr 31044 478-945-3112
T. Makaya, prin. Fax 945-3140
Twiggs County MS 200/6-8
375 Watson Dr 31044 478-945-3113
J. Thomas, prin. Fax 945-3140

Twiggs Academy 100/PK-12
961 Hamlin Floyd Rd 31044 478-945-3175

Jesup, Wayne, Pop. 10,029
Wayne County SD 5,500/PK-12
555 Sunset Blvd 31545 912-427-1000
Dr. Jay Brinson, supt. Fax 427-1004
www.wayne.k12.ga.us
Puckett MS 600/6-8
475 Durrence Rd 31545 912-427-1061
Dr. Pam Shuman, prin. Fax 427-1069
Wayne County HS 1,400/9-12
1 Jacket Dr 31545 912-427-1088
Hubert Adams, prin. Fax 427-1081
Williams MS 600/6-8
1175 S US Highway 301 31546 912-427-1025
Dr. Reggie Burgess, prin. Fax 427-1032

Altamaha Technical College Post-Sec.
1777 W Cherry St 31545 912-427-5800

Johns Creek, Fulton, Pop. 74,864
Fulton County SD
Supt. — See Atlanta
Autrey Mill MS 1,400/6-8
4110 Old Alabama Rd, 770-521-7622
Trey Martin, prin. Fax 521-7630
Chattahoochee HS 1,900/9-12
5230 Taylor Rd, 770-521-7600
Tim Corrigan, prin. Fax 521-7659
Johns Creek HS 2,000/9-12
5575 State Bridge Rd, 770-623-2138
Fax 623-2139
Northview HS 1,900/9-12
10625 Parsons Rd, 770-497-3828
Brian Downey, prin. Fax 497-3844
River Trail MS 1,400/6-8
10795 Rogers Cir, 470-254-3860
Dawn Melin, prin. Fax 254-3866
Taylor Road MS 1,000/6-8
5150 Taylor Rd, 470-254-7090
Ed Williamson, prin. Fax 254-5609

Mt. Pisgah Christian S 800/PK-12
9820 Nesbit Ferry Rd, 678-336-3443
Ruston Pierce, head sch Fax 336-3399

Jonesboro, Clayton, Pop. 4,639
Clayton County SD 52,200/PK-12
1058 5th Ave 30236 770-473-2700
Luvenia Jackson, supt. Fax 473-2706
www.clayton.k12.ga.us
Jonesboro HS 1,300/9-12
7728 Mount Zion Blvd 30236 770-473-2855
Felicia Brown, prin. Fax 603-5177
Jonesboro MS 900/6-8
1308 Arnold St 30236 678-610-4331
Fax 610-4347
Kendrick MS 800/6-8
7971 Kendrick Rd 30238 770-472-8400
Dr. Kimberly Dugger, prin. Fax 472-8413
Mt. Zion HS 1,600/9-12
2535 Mount Zion Pkwy 30236 770-473-2940
Melvin Blocker, prin. Fax 473-2784
Mundy's Mill HS 1,700/9-12
9652 Fayetteville Rd 30238 678-817-3000
Dr. William Greene, prin. Fax 817-3007
Mundy's Mill MS 800/6-8
1251 Mundys Mill Rd 30238 770-473-2880
Sharra Cunningham, prin. Fax 603-5779
Perry Learning Center Alt
137 Spring St 30236 770-515-7601
Dr. Terry Young, dir. Fax 515-7689
Pointe South MS 800/6-8
8495 Thomas Rd 30238 770-473-2890
Sandra Nicholson, prin. Fax 477-4603
Roberts MS 800/6-8
1905 Walt Stephens Rd 30236 678-479-0100
Charmine Johnson, prin. Fax 479-0114
Stillwell Fine Arts Magnet HS 9-12
2580 Mount Zion Pkwy 30236 770-472-2838
Dr. Michael Robinson, prin. Fax 472-2839
Other Schools – See College Park, Forest Park, Hampton, Lovejoy, Morrow, Rex, Riverdale

---

Everest Institute Post-Sec.
6431 Tara Blvd 30236 770-603-0000
Laurus Technical Institute Post-Sec.
9540 Tara Blvd 30236 770-477-2799

Kathleen, Houston
Houston County SD
Supt. — See Perry
Mossy Creek MS 700/6-8
200 Danny Carpenter Dr 31047 478-988-6171
Dr. Andy Gentry, prin. Fax 218-7538
Veterans HS 1,300/9-12
340 Piney Grove Rd 31047 478-218-7537
Christopher Brown, prin. Fax 217-7570

Kennesaw, Cobb, Pop. 28,907
Cobb County SD
Supt. — See Marietta
Awtrey MS 800/6-8
3601 Nowlin Rd NW 30144 770-975-6615
Jeffrey Crawford, prin. Fax 975-6617
Harrison HS 2,000/9-12
4500 Due West Rd NW 30152 678-594-8104
Ashlynn Campbell, prin. Fax 594-8106
Kennesaw Mountain HS 2,100/9-12
1898 Kennesaw Due West NW 30152 678-594-8190
Dr. Mark Trachtenbroit, prin. Fax 594-8192
Lost Mountain MS 900/6-8
700 Old Mountain Rd NW 30152 678-594-8224
Candace Wilkes, prin. Fax 594-8226
McClure MS 1,100/6-8
3660 Old Stilesboro Rd NW 30152 678-331-8131
Kelly Metcalfe, prin. Fax 331-8132
North Cobb HS 2,800/9-12
3400 Highway 293 N 30144 770-975-6685
Joseph Horton, prin. Fax 975-6687
Palmer MS 1,000/6-8
690 N Booth Rd NW 30144 770-591-5020
Lisa Jackson, prin. Fax 591-5032
Pine Mountain MS 700/6-8
2720 Pine Mountain Cir NW 30152 678-594-8252
Dr. Jasmine Kullar, prin. Fax 594-8254

Cobb Beauty College Post-Sec.
3096 Cherokee St NW 30144 770-424-6915
Devereux-Georgia Treatment Network Post-Sec.
PO Box 1688 30156 800-342-3357
Empire Beauty School Post-Sec.
425 Ernest Barrett Pkwy #H2 30144 770-419-2303
Kennesaw State University Post-Sec.
1000 Chastain Rd NW 30144 770-423-6000
Mount Paran Christian S 1,200/PK-12
1275 Stanley Rd NW 30152 770-578-0182
Dr. David Tilley, hdmstr. Fax 977-9284
North Cobb Christian S 800/PK-12
4500 Eagle Dr 30144 770-975-0252
Todd Clingman, head sch Fax 975-9051
Shiloh Hills Christian S 300/PK-12
260 Hawkins Store Rd NE 30144 770-926-7729
Terry Farrant, admin. Fax 926-3762
TLE Christian Academy 50/1-12
2765 S Main St NW 30144 770-218-1790

Kingsland, Camden, Pop. 15,425
Camden County SD 9,200/PK-12
311 S East St 31548 912-729-5687
Dr. William Hardin, supt. Fax 729-1489
www.camden.k12.ga.us
Camden County HS 2,600/9-12
6300 Laurel Island Pkwy 31548 912-729-7318
Dr. John Tucker, prin. Fax 729-7627
Camden MS 1,100/6-8
1300 Middle School Rd 31548 912-729-3113
Thomas McClendon, prin. Fax 729-7489
Other Schools – See Saint Marys

La Fayette, Walker, Pop. 6,986
Walker County SD 9,200/PK-12
201 S Duke St 30728 706-638-1240
Damon Raines, supt. Fax 638-7827
www.walkerschools.org
La Fayette HS 1,200/9-12
100 Rambler Dr 30728 706-638-2342
Mike Culberson, prin. Fax 638-4767
La Fayette MS 700/6-8
419 Roadrunner Blvd 30728 706-638-6440
Kelly Long, prin. Fax 638-7616
Other Schools – See Flintstone, Rossville

LaGrange, Troup, Pop. 29,111
Troup County SD 12,300/PK-12
PO Box 1228 30241 706-812-7900
Dr. Cole Pugh, supt. Fax 812-7904
www.troup.org/
Callaway MS 700/6-8
2244 Hammett Rd 30241 706-845-2080
Melissa Trimeloni, prin. Fax 845-2081
Gardner Newman MS 1,100/6-8
101 Shannon Dr 30241 706-883-1535
Derek Pitts, prin. Fax 883-1562
HOPE Academy Alt
200 Mooty Bridge Rd 30240 706-812-7988
Karla Fagg, prin. Fax 812-7927
La Grange HS 1,300/9-12
516 N Greenwood St 30240 706-883-1590
Alton White, prin. Fax 812-7976
Long Cane MS 1,000/6-8
326 Long Cane Rd 30240 706-845-2085
Chip Giles, prin. Fax 845-2086
Troup County Comprehensive HS 1,300/9-12
1920 Hamilton Rd 30241 706-812-7957
Chip Medders, prin. Fax 812-7960
Other Schools – See Hogansville

Lafayette Christian S 300/PK-12
1904 Hamilton Rd 30241 706-884-6684
John Cipolla, hdmstr. Fax 882-2515
LaGrange Academy 200/PK-12
1501 Vernon Rd 30240 706-882-8097
Carl Parke, head sch Fax 882-8640
LaGrange College Post-Sec.
601 Broad St 30240 706-880-8000
West Georgia Technical College Post-Sec.
1 College Cir 30240 706-845-4323

Lakeland, Lanier, Pop. 3,308
Lanier County SD 1,800/PK-12
247 S Highway 221 31635 229-482-3966
Dr. Keith Humphrey, supt. Fax 482-3020
www.lanier.k12.ga.us/
Lanier County HS 400/9-12
52 W Patten Ave 31635 229-482-3868
Howard Akers, prin. Fax 482-3368
Lanier County MS 400/6-8
52 W Patten Ave 31635 229-482-8247
Reada Hamm, prin. Fax 482-3643

Lawrenceville, Gwinnett, Pop. 27,847
Gwinnett County SD
Supt. — See Suwanee
Archer HS 2,300/9-12
2255 New Hope Rd 30045 678-407-7700
Ken Johnson, prin. Fax 407-7725
Central Gwinnett HS 2,600/9-12
564 W Crogan St 30046 770-963-8041
Maryanne Grimes, prin. Fax 442-5152
Creekland MS 2,200/6-8
170 Russell Rd 30043 770-338-4700
Dr. Eddie Maresh, prin. Fax 338-4703
Crews MS 1,300/6-8
1000 Old Snellville Hwy 30044 770-982-6940
Dr. Stacey Schepens, prin. Fax 982-6942
Discovery HS 9-12
1335 Old Norcross Rd 30046 678-226-4250
Dr. Gene Taylor, prin. Fax 377-3983
Five Forks MS 1,100/6-8
3250 River Dr 30044 770-972-1506
Christine Douthart, prin. Fax 736-4547
Gwinnett InterVention Education Ctr East 200/Alt
723 Hi Hope Rd 30043 770-338-4855
Durrant Williams, prin. Fax 338-4899
Jordan MS 6-8
8 Village Way 30046 770-822-6500
Melissa Walker, prin. Fax 407-8889
Maxwell HS of Technology Vo/Tech
990 McElvaney Ln 30044 770-963-6838
Dr. Jeff Hall, prin. Fax 338-4612
Moore MS 1,000/6-8
1221 Lawrenceville Hwy 30046 678-226-7100
Lamont Mays, prin. Fax 226-7103
Mountain View HS 2,000/9-12
2351 Sunny Hill Rd 30043 678-407-7600
Keith Chaney, prin. Fax 407-7605
Phoenix HS 500/9-12
501 W Pike St 30046 770-513-6862
Donna Scott, prin. Fax 513-6864
Richards MS 1,500/6-8
3555 Sugarloaf Pkwy 30044 770-995-7133
Mark McCain, prin. Fax 338-4791
Sweetwater MS 1,900/6-8
3500 Cruse Rd 30044 770-923-4131
Jay Nebel, prin. Fax 806-8930

Empire Beauty School Post-Sec.
1455 Pleasant Hill Rd #105 30044 770-564-0725
Georgia Gwinnett College Post-Sec.
1000 University Center Ln 30043 678-407-5000
Gerard Preparatory S 200/PK-12
263 Jackson St 30046 770-277-4722
Dr. J.G. Sinclair, admin. Fax 277-4365
Gwinnett Technical College Post-Sec.
5150 Sugarloaf Pkwy 30043 770-962-7580
Strong Wall Academy 100/PK-12
PO Box 1647 30046 678-679-3070
Anthony Knight, hdmstr. Fax 679-3075

Leesburg, Lee, Pop. 2,853
Lee County SD 6,100/PK-12
PO Box 399 31763 229-903-2100
Dr. Jason Miller, supt. Fax 903-2130
www.lee.k12.ga.us
Lee County 9th Grade Campus 500/9-9
370 Leslie Hwy 31763 229-903-3590
Tim Mears, prin. Fax 903-3595
Lee County HS 1,300/10-12
1 Trojan Way 31763 229-903-2260
Kevin Dowling, prin. Fax 903-2291

Lee County MS East 700/6-8
185 Firetower Rd 31763 229-903-3500
Kelli Duke, prin. Fax 903-3521
Lee County MS West 800/6-8
190 Smithville Rd N 31763 229-903-2140
John Savelle, prin. Fax 903-2160
Transitional Learning Center Alt
190 Smithville Rd N 31763 229-903-3920
Aaron Edmondson, dir. Fax 903-3925

Lexington, Oglethorpe, Pop. 225
Oglethorpe County SD 2,300/PK-12
735 Athens Rd 30648 706-743-8128
Beverly Levine, supt. Fax 743-3211
www.oglethorpe.k12.ga.us
Oglethorpe County HS 700/9-12
749 Athens Rd 30648 706-743-8124
Susie Johnson, prin. Fax 743-3536
Other Schools – See Crawford

Lilburn, Gwinnett, Pop. 11,365
Gwinnett County SD
Supt. — See Suwanee
Berkmar HS 3,400/9-12
405 Pleasant Hill Rd NW 30047 770-806-3700
Alfred Taylor, prin. Fax 806-3715
Berkmar MS 1,100/6-8
4355 Lawrenceville Hwy NW 30047 770-638-2300
Nicole Tubbs, prin. Fax 638-2309
Lilburn MS 1,700/6-8
4994 Lawrenceville Hwy NW 30047 770-921-1776
Dr. Yvette Arthur, prin. Fax 806-3866
Parkview HS 2,800/9-12
998 Cole Dr SW 30047 770-921-2874
David Smith, prin. Fax 806-3797
Trickum MS 2,000/6-8
130 Killian Hill Rd SW 30047 770-921-2705
Ryan Queen, prin. Fax 806-3742

Al-Falah Academy 200/PK-10
4805 Lawrenceville Hwy #220 30047 678-502-7211
Gwinnett College Post-Sec.
4230 Lawrencevll Hwy NW #11 30047 770-381-7200
Killian Hill Christian S 400/K-12
151 Arcado Rd SW 30047 770-921-3224
Doug Abels, admin. Fax 921-9395
Providence Christian Academy 600/K-12
4575 Lawrenceville Hwy NW 30047 770-279-7200
Dr. Sean Chapman, head sch Fax 279-8258

Lincolnton, Lincoln, Pop. 1,557
Lincoln County SD 1,200/PK-12
423 Metasville Rd 30817 706-359-3742
Dr. Samuel Light, supt. Fax 359-7938
www.lincolncountyschools.org
Lincoln County HS 300/9-12
200 Charles Ward Elam Dr 30817 706-359-3121
Howie Gunby, prin. Fax 359-3552
Lincoln County MS 300/6-8
200B Charles Ward Elam Dr 30817 706-359-3069
Patty Arthur, prin. Fax 359-2200

Lindale, Floyd, Pop. 4,135
Floyd County SD
Supt. — See Rome
Pepperell HS 900/9-12
3 Dragon Dr SE 30147 706-236-1844
Jamey Alcorn, prin. Fax 236-1846
Pepperell MS 700/6-8
200 Hughes Dairy Rd SE 30147 706-236-1849
Becky McCoy, prin. Fax 802-6776

Lithia Springs, Douglas, Pop. 15,167
Douglas County SD
Supt. — See Douglasville
Lithia Springs HS 1,400/9-12
2520 E County Line Rd 30122 770-651-6700
Dr. Garrick Askew, prin. Fax 732-2644
Turner MS 800/6-8
7101 Turner Dr 30122 770-651-5500
Darron Franklin, prin. Fax 651-5503

Colonial Hills Christian S 300/PK-12
7131 Mount Vernon Rd 30122 770-941-6342
David Hicks, admin. Fax 941-2090

Lithonia, DeKalb, Pop. 1,901
DeKalb County SD
Supt. — See Stone Mountain
Arabia Mountain HS 1,400/9-12
6610 Browns Mill Rd 30038 678-875-3602
Dr. Rodney Swanson, prin. Fax 875-3610
King HS 1,600/9-12
3991 Snapfinger Rd 30038 678-874-5402
Ennis Harvey, prin. Fax 874-5410
Lithonia HS 1,300/9-12
2440 Phillips Rd 30058 678-676-2902
Yolanda Peek, prin. Fax 676-2910
Lithonia MS 1,200/6-8
2451 Randall Ave 30058 678-875-0702
Debra Phillips, prin. Fax 875-0710
Miller Grove HS 1,500/9-12
2645 DeKalb Medical Pkwy 30058 678-875-1102
Matthew Priester, prin. Fax 875-1110
Redan MS 800/6-8
1775 Young Rd 30058 678-874-7902
Dr. Donald Mason, prin. Fax 874-7910
Salem MS 1,100/6-8
5333 Salem Rd 30038 678-676-9402
Terrence Harvey, prin. Fax 676-9410

Luther Rice College and Seminary Post-Sec.
3038 Evans Mill Rd 30038 770-484-1204

Locust Grove, Henry, Pop. 5,279
Henry County SD
Supt. — See Mc Donough
Locust Grove HS 1,300/9-12
3275 S Ola Rd 30248 770-898-1452
Lisa Gugino, prin. Fax 898-7076
Locust Grove MS 1,000/6-8
3315 S Ola Rd 30248 770-957-6055
Tony Townsend, prin. Fax 957-7160

Luella HS 2,100/9-12
603 Walker Dr 30248 770-898-9822
Jerry Smith, prin. Fax 898-9625
Luella MS 800/6-8
2075 Hmpton Locust Grove Rd 30248 678-583-8919
Mary Carol Stanley, prin. Fax 583-8920

Strong Rock Christian S 700/PK-12
4200 Strong Rock Pkwy 30248 678-833-1200
Patrick Stuart M.A., head sch Fax 833-1395

Loganville, Walton, Pop. 10,219
Gwinnett County SD
Supt. — See Suwanee
Grayson HS 2,600/9-12
50 Hope Hollow Rd 30052 770-554-1071
Dana Pugh, prin. Fax 554-1074
McConnell MS 1,600/6-8
550 Ozora Rd 30052 770-554-1000
Clent Chatham, prin. Fax 554-1003
Snell MS 1,100/6-8
3800 Brushy Fork Rd 30052 770-554-7750
Allen Craine, prin. Fax 554-7749

Walton County SD
Supt. — See Monroe
Loganville HS 1,500/9-12
100 Trident Trl 30052 678-684-2880
Mike Robison, prin. Fax 684-2955
Loganville MS 1,100/6-8
4869 Bay Creek Church Rd 30052 678-684-2960
Christy Bowman, prin. Fax 684-2983
Walnut Grove HS 1,300/9-12
4863 Guthrie Cemetery Rd 30052 678-507-3900
Dr. Sean Callahan, prin. Fax 507-3901
Walton County Alternative Education Alt
4869 Bay Creek Church Rd 30052 678-684-2980
Meredith Cannon, dir. Fax 684-2983
Youth MS 1,100/6-8
1804 Highway 81 30052 770-466-6849
David Todd, prin. Fax 466-8596

Covenant Christian Academy 300/PK-12
3425 Loganville Hwy 30052 770-466-7890
Emmaline McKinnon, admin. Fax 466-2833
Loganville Christian Academy 600/PK-12
2575 Highway 81 30052 770-554-9888
Christy Monda, admin. Fax 554-9881
True Partnership Christian Academy 50/K-12
434 Conyers Rd 30052 770-299-9760
Carolyn Odom, admin. Fax 609-1390

Lookout Mountain, Walker, Pop. 1,588

Covenant College Post-Sec.
14049 Scenic Hwy 30750 706-820-1560

Louisville, Jefferson, Pop. 2,485
Jefferson County SD 2,800/PK-12
1001 Peachtree St 30434 478-625-7626
Dr. Molly Howard, supt. Fax 625-7459
www.jefferson.k12.ga.us
Hi Tech S Alt
1200 School St 30434 478-625-7764
Ken Hildebrant, prin. Fax 625-3120
Jefferson County HS 800/9-12
1157 Warrior Trl 30434 478-625-9991
Dr. Alan Long, prin. Fax 625-8988
Louisville MS 400/6-8
1200 School St 30434 478-625-7764
Ken Hildebrant, prin. Fax 625-3120
Other Schools – See Wrens

Jefferson Academy 200/K-12
2264 US Highway 1 N 30434 478-625-8861

Lovejoy, Clayton, Pop. 6,281
Clayton County SD
Supt. — See Jonesboro
Lovejoy MS 700/6-8
1588 Lovejoy Rd 30250 770-473-2933
Dr. Debra Bostick-Smith, prin. Fax 603-5777

Ludowici, Long, Pop. 1,650
Long County SD 3,000/K-12
PO Box 428 31316 912-545-2367
Dr. Robert Waters, supt. Fax 545-2380
www.longcountyps.com
Long County HS 800/9-12
1844 GA Highway 57 31316 912-545-2135
David Edwards, prin. Fax 545-2136
Long County MS 700/6-8
PO Box 729 31316 912-545-2069
Heath Crane, prin. Fax 545-2775

Lumpkin, Stewart, Pop. 2,722
Stewart County SD 500/PK-12
PO Box 547 31815 229-838-4329
Valerie Roberts, supt. Fax 838-6984
www.stewart.k12.ga.us/
Stewart County HS 100/9-12
PO Box 547 31815 229-838-4301
Dr. Joseph Gardner, admin. Fax 838-4352
Stewart County MS 100/6-8
PO Box 547 31815 229-838-4374
Caroly Hamilton, prin. Fax 838-4352

Lyons, Toombs, Pop. 4,285
Toombs County SD 3,100/PK-12
117 E Wesley Ave 30436 912-526-3141
Richard Smith, supt. Fax 526-3291
www.toombscountyschools.org
Toombs County HS 800/9-12
500 Bulldog Rd 30436 912-526-4286
Melanie McLemore, prin. Fax 526-4287
Toombs County MS 700/6-8
701 Bulldog Rd 30436 912-526-8363
Renee Garbutt, prin. Fax 526-0240

Toombs Christian Academy 300/PK-12
PO Box 227 30436 912-526-8938

Mableton, Cobb, Pop. 36,289
Cobb County SD
Supt. — See Marietta
Floyd MS 1,000/6-8
4803 Floyd Rd SW 30126 770-819-2453
Dr. Teresa Hargrett, prin. Fax 819-2455
Lindley MS 1,300/7-8
50 Veterans Memorial Hwy SE 30126 770-819-2496
Lisa Williams, prin. Fax 819-2498
Pebblebrook HS 2,100/9-12
991 Old Alabama Rd SW 30126 770-819-2521
Travis Joshua, prin. Fax 819-2523

Cumberland Christian Academy 100/6-8
4900 Floyd Rd SW 30126 678-426-1600
Dr. Lee Campbell, hdmstr. Fax 819-9091
Whitefield Academy 700/PK-12
1 Whitefield Dr SE 30126 678-305-3000
Dr. Kevin Bracher Ph.D., hdmstr. Fax 305-3010

Mc Donough, Henry, Pop. 21,578
Henry County SD 39,700/K-12
33 N Zack Hinton Pkwy 30253 770-957-6601
Rodney Bowler, supt. Fax 914-6178
www.henry.k12.ga.us
Eagle's Landing HS 1,200/9-12
301 Tunis Rd 30253 770-954-9515
Gabriel Crerie, prin. Fax 914-9789
Eagle's Landing MS 900/6-8
295 Tunis Rd 30253 770-914-8189
Derrick Thomas, prin. Fax 914-2989
EXCEL Academy 6-12
330 Tomlinson St 30253 770-957-4101
Dr. Kimberly Anderson, prin. Fax 957-0372
Henry County HS 1,000/9-12
401 Tomlinson St 30253 770-957-3943
Scott John, prin. Fax 957-5052
Henry County MS 800/6-8
166 Holly Smith Dr 30253 770-957-3945
James Mercer, prin. Fax 898-4986
Mainstay Academy Alt
354 N Ola Rd 30252 678-432-2310
Monica Brantley, coord. Fax 507-6259
Ola HS 1,600/9-12
357 N Ola Rd 30252 770-288-3222
David Shedd, prin. Fax 288-3230
Ola MS 1,200/6-8
353 N Ola Rd 30252 770-288-2108
Kathleen Truitt, prin. Fax 288-2114
Union Grove HS 1,600/9-12
120 E Lake Rd 30252 678-583-8502
Ryan Meeks, prin. Fax 583-8850
Union Grove MS 1,100/6-8
210 E Lake Rd 30252 678-583-8978
Dr. Matt Isenberg, prin. Fax 583-8580
Other Schools – See Hampton, Locust Grove, Stockbridge

Creekside Christian Academy 500/PK-12
175 Foster Dr 30253 770-961-9300
Rodney Knox, hdmstr. Fax 960-1875
Eagle's Landing Christian Academy 1,100/PK-12
2400 Highway 42 N 30253 770-957-2927
Chuck Gilliam, head sch Fax 957-2290

Macon, Bibb, Pop. 90,157
Bibb County SD 21,700/PK-12
484 Mulberry St 31201 478-765-8711
Dr. Curtis L. Jones, supt. Fax 765-8549
www.bcsdk12.net
Appling MS 600/6-8
1210 Shurling Dr 31211 478-779-2200
Dr. Christopher Ridley, prin. Fax 779-2202
Ballard-Hudson MS 400/6-8
1070 Anthony Rd 31204 478-779-3400
Eclan David, prin. Fax 779-3396
Central HS 1,100/9-12
2155 Napier Ave 31204 478-779-2300
Emanuel Frazier, prin. Fax 779-2307
Howard HS 1,100/9-12
6400 Forsyth Rd 31210 478-779-4850
Dr. Shannon Norfleet, prin. Fax 779-4860
Howard MS 1,000/6-8
6600 Forsyth Rd 31210 478-779-3500
Lindsey Allen, prin. Fax 779-3458
Miller Magnet MS 900/6-8
751 Hendley St 31204 478-779-4050
Jim Montgomery, prin. Fax 779-4032
Northeast HS 700/9-12
1646 Upper River Rd 31211 478-779-4100
Steven Jones, prin. Fax 779-4136
Rutland HS 1,000/9-12
6250 Skipper Rd 31216 478-779-3100
Kent Sparks, prin. Fax 779-3045
Rutland MS 900/6-8
6260 Skipper Rd 31216 478-779-4400
Richard Key, prin. Fax 779-4373
Soar Academy Alt
2011 Riverside Dr 31204 478-779-4814
Dr. Shawn Martin, dir.
Southwest HS 900/9-12
1775 Williamson Rd 31206 478-779-4500
Dexter Martin, prin. Fax 779-4484
Weaver MS 900/6-8
2570 Heath Rd 31206 478-779-4650
Dr. Sherri Flagg, prin. Fax 779-4627
Westside HS 1,000/9-12
2851 Heath Rd 31206 478-779-3800
Dr. Julia Daniely, prin. Fax 779-3832

Jones County SD
Supt. — See Gray
Clifton Ridge MS 600/6-8
169 Dusty Ln 31211 478-743-5182
Charles Lundy, prin. Fax 743-8282

American Professional Institute Post-Sec.
1667 Eisenhower Pkwy 31206 478-314-4444
Central Fellowship Christian Academy 300/PK-12
8460 Hawkinsville Rd 31216 478-788-6909
Central Georgia Technical College Post-Sec.
3300 Macon Tech Dr 31206 478-757-3400

Covenant Academy 400/PK-12
4652 Ayers Rd 31210 478-471-0285
First Presbyterian Day S 1,000/PK-12
5671 Calvin Dr 31210 478-477-6505
Gregg Thompson, hdmstr. Fax 477-2804
Georgia Academy for the Blind Post-Sec.
2895 Vineville Ave 31204 478-751-6083
Medical Center of Central Georgia Post-Sec.
777 Hemlock St 31201 478-633-1234
Mercer University in Macon Post-Sec.
1400 Coleman Ave 31207 478-301-2700
Middle Georgia State College Post-Sec.
100 College Station Dr 31206 478-471-2700
Miller-Motte Technical College Post-Sec.
175 Tom Hill Sr Blvd 31210 478-803-4800
Montessori of Macon 100/PK-12
855 Tolliver Pl 31210 478-757-8927
Mount de Sales Academy 700/6-12
851 Orange St 31201 478-751-3240
David Held, pres. Fax 751-3241
Stratford Academy 900/PK-12
6010 Peake Rd 31220 478-477-8073
Dr. Robert Veto, head sch Fax 477-0299
Tattnall Square Academy 600/PK-12
111 Trojan Trl 31210 478-477-6760
Virginia College Post-Sec.
1901 Paul Walsh Dr 31206 478-803-4600
Wesleyan College Post-Sec.
4760 Forsyth Rd 31210 800-447-6610
Windsor Academy 200/PK-12
4150 Jones Rd 31216 478-781-1621

Mc Rae, Telfair, Pop. 5,685
Telfair County SD 1,700/PK-12
PO Box 240 31055 229-868-5661
Lenard Harrelson, supt. Fax 868-5549
www.telfairschools.org
Telfair County HS 400/9-12
PO Box 240 31055 229-868-6096
Daymond Ray, prin. Fax 868-7221
Telfair County MS 400/6-8
PO Box 240 31055 229-868-7465
Christopher Ellis, prin. Fax 868-2616

Manchester, Meriwether, Pop. 4,197
Meriwether County SD
Supt. — See Greenville
Manchester HS 500/9-12
405 N 5th Ave 31816 706-846-8445
Henry Acree, prin. Fax 846-2082
Manchester MS 400/6-8
231 W Perry St 31816 706-846-2846
Lashanda Acres, prin. Fax 846-8242

Marietta, Cobb, Pop. 54,999
Cobb County SD 109,300/PK-12
514 Glover St SE 30060 770-426-3300
Chris Ragsdale, supt. Fax 426-3329
www.cobb.k12.ga.us
Daniell MS 1,000/6-8
2900 Scott Rd 30066 678-594-8048
David Nelson, prin. Fax 594-8050
Dickerson MS 1,200/6-8
855 Woodlawn Dr NE 30068 770-578-2710
Dr. Carole Brink, prin. Fax 578-2712
Dodgen MS 1,200/6-8
1725 Bill Murdock Rd 30062 770-578-2726
Dr. Loralee Hill, prin. Fax 578-2728
East Cobb MS 1,300/6-8
380 Holt Rd NE 30068 770-578-2740
Leetonia Young, prin. Fax 578-2742
Hightower Trail MS 1,000/6-8
3905 Post Oak Tritt Rd 30062 770-578-7225
Laura Montgomery, prin. Fax 578-7227
Kell HS 1,500/9-12
4770 Lee Waters Rd 30066 678-494-7844
Andy Bristow, prin. Fax 494-7846
Lassiter HS 2,000/9-12
2601 Shallowford Rd 30066 678-494-7863
Dr. Chris Richie, prin. Fax 494-7865
Mabry MS 900/6-8
2700 Jims Rd NE 30066 770-928-5546
Merrilee Heflin, prin. Fax 928-5548
McCleskey MS 700/6-8
4080 Maybreeze Rd 30066 770-928-5560
Claire Lyons, prin. Fax 928-5562
Oakwood Digital Academy 100/Alt
1560 Joyner Ave SE 30060 678-594-8240
David Pearce, prin. Fax 594-8241
Osborne HS 2,000/9-12
2451 Favor Rd SW 30060 770-437-5900
Josh Morreale, prin. Fax 437-5902
Performance Learning Center Alt
1560 Joyner Ave SE 30060 678-331-1098
Lugenia Purnell, prin. Fax 331-1058
Pope HS 1,800/9-12
3001 Hembree Rd NE 30062 770-578-7900
Dr. Robert Downs, prin. Fax 578-7902
Simpson MS 900/6-8
3340 Trickum Rd NE 30066 770-971-4711
Ansley Daniel, prin. Fax 971-4507
Smitha MS 1,000/6-8
2025 Powder Springs Rd SW 30064 678-594-8267
Chris Salter, prin. Fax 594-8269
Sprayberry HS 1,800/9-12
2525 Sandy Plains Rd 30066 770-578-3200
Joseph Sharp, prin. Fax 578-3202
Wheeler HS 2,100/9-12
375 Holt Rd NE 30068 770-578-3266
Dr. Peter Giles, prin. Fax 578-3268
Adult Education Center Adult
240 Barber Rd SE 30060 678-594-8011
Francia Browne, admin. Fax 594-8015
Other Schools – See Acworth, Austell, Kennesaw, Mableton, Powder Springs, Smyrna

Marietta CSD 8,800/K-12
250 Howard St NE 30060 770-422-3500
Dr. Emily Lembeck, supt. Fax 425-4095
www.marietta-city.org
Marietta HS 2,100/9-12
1171 Whitlock Ave SW 30064 770-428-2631
Forrestella Taylor, prin. Fax 429-3151
Marietta MS 1,300/7-8
121 Winn St NW 30064 770-422-0311
Gabe Carmona, prin. Fax 429-3162
Marietta Performance Learning Center Alt
353 Lemon St NE Ste B 30060 770-429-3188
Tammie Roach, admin. Fax 429-3189

Chattahoochee Technical College Post-Sec.
980 S Cobb Dr SE 30060 770-528-4545
Covenant Christian Ministries Academy 100/PK-12
PO Box 4065 30061 770-919-0022
Vanessa Anderson, supt. Fax 919-2098
Cumberland Christian Academy 100/9-12
2115 Pair Rd SW 30008 678-426-1600
Dr. Lee Campbell, hdmstr. Fax 423-0366
Dominion Christian JSHS 200/6-12
4607 Burnt Hickory Rd NW 30064 770-420-2153
David Raines, hdmstr. Fax 420-2510
Everest Institute Post-Sec.
1600 Terrell Rd Ste G 30067 770-303-7997
Johnson Ferry Christian Academy 300/K-12
955 Johnson Ferry Rd 30068 678-784-5231
Kimberly Maiocco, head sch Fax 795-3240
Life University Post-Sec.
1269 Barclay Cir SE 30060 770-426-2600
Lincoln College of Technology Post-Sec.
2359 Windy Hill Rd Ste 100 30067 770-226-0056
Mt. Bethel Christian Academy 500/PK-12
4385 Lower Roswell Rd 30068 770-971-0245
Jim R. Callis, head sch Fax 971-3770
Southern Polytech State University Post-Sec.
1100 S Marietta Pkwy SE 30060 678-915-7778
Toni & Guy Hairdressing Academy Post-Sec.
1355 Roswell Rd Ste 150 30062 770-565-3285
Walker S 1,100/PK-12
700 Cobb Pkwy N 30062 770-427-2689
Jack Hall, head sch Fax 514-8122

Martinez, Columbia, Pop. 34,798
Columbia County SD
Supt. — See Evans
Stallings Island MS 600/6-8
3830 Blackstone Camp Rd 30907 706-447-2106
Don Putnam, prin. Fax 447-2103

Augusta Christian S 500/PK-12
313 Baston Rd 30907 706-863-2905
Les Walden, head sch Fax 860-6618
Augusta Preparatory Day S 500/PK-12
285 Flowing Wells Rd 30907 706-863-1906
Peter Huestis, head sch Fax 863-6198
Community Christian Academy 100/PK-10
4594 Columbia Rd 30907 706-868-7249
Wayne Gaines, admin. Fax 650-3107

Metter, Candler, Pop. 4,108
Candler County SD 2,000/PK-12
210 S College St 30439 912-685-5713
Dr. Bubba Longgrear, supt. Fax 685-3068
www.metter.org
Metter HS 600/9-12
34905 GA Highway 129 S 30439 912-685-2134
John Jordan, prin. Fax 685-2897
Metter MS 400/6-8
33661 GA Highway 129 S 30439 912-685-5580
Ralph Carlyle, prin. Fax 685-4970

Midland, Muscogee
Muscogee County SD
Supt. — See Columbus
Cohn MS 500/6-8
7352 Garrett Rd 31820 706-569-3801
Richard Green, prin. Fax 569-3825
Midland MS 400/6-8
6990 Warm Springs Rd 31820 706-569-3673
Barrie Clarke, prin. Fax 569-3678

Midway, Liberty, Pop. 2,059
Liberty County SD
Supt. — See Hinesville
Midway MS 800/6-8
425 Edgewater Dr 31320 912-884-6677
Debra Frazier, prin. Fax 884-5944

Milledgeville, Baldwin, Pop. 17,451
Baldwin County SD 5,900/PK-12
PO Box 1188 31059 478-453-4176
Dr. Noris Price, supt. Fax 457-3327
www.baldwin-county-schools.com
Baldwin HS 1,300/9-12
155 GA Highway 49 W 31061 478-453-6429
Dr. Cloise Williams, prin. Fax 451-3032
Oak Hill MS 1,200/6-8
356 Blandy Rd NW 31061 478-457-3370
Daymond Ray, prin. Fax 457-2422

American Professional Institute Post-Sec.
2485 N Columbia St Ste 114 31061 478-452-3900
Central Georgia Technical College Post-Sec.
54 GA Highway 22 W 31061
Georgia College & State University Post-Sec.
231 W Hancock St 31061 478-445-5004
Georgia Military College Post-Sec.
201 E Greene St 31061 478-387-4900
Georgia Military College Prep S 500/6-12
201 E Greene St 31061 478-387-4878
Pam Grant, prin.
Milledge Academy 500/PK-12
197 Log Cabin Rd NE 31061 478-452-5570
Mark Hopkins M.Ed., head sch Fax 452-5000

Millen, Jenkins, Pop. 3,092
Jenkins County SD 1,400/PK-12
1152 E Winthrope Ave 30442 478-982-6000
Tara Cooper, supt. Fax 982-6002
www.jchs.com/
Jenkins County Alternative S Alt
Barney Ave 30442 478-982-6023
Rob Gray, prin. Fax 982-6002
Jenkins County HS 400/9-12
433 Barney Ave 30442 478-982-4791
Rob Gray, prin. Fax 982-6015
Jenkins County MS 300/6-8
409 Barney Ave 30442 478-982-1063
Rob Gray, prin. Fax 982-6015

Milner, Lamar, Pop. 597

Rock Springs Christian Academy 200/PK-12
219 Rock Springs Rd 30257 678-692-0192
Derrell Jeffcoat, head sch Fax 692-0601
St. George's Episcopal S 100/PK-10
103 Birch St 30257 770-358-9432
Dr. Larry Collins, hdmstr. Fax 358-9495

Milton, Fulton, Pop. 31,916
Fulton County SD
Supt. — See Atlanta
Cambridge HS 1,500/9-12
2845 Bethany Bnd, 770-667-2883
Dr. Edward Spurka, prin. Fax 667-2927
Hopewell MS 1,300/6-8
13060 Cogburn Rd, 678-297-3240
Michael LeMoyne, prin. Fax 297-3250
Milton HS 2,000/9-12
13025 Birmingham Hwy, 770-740-7000
Brian Jones, prin. Fax 667-2844
Northwestern MS 1,300/6-8
12805 Birmingham Hwy, 470-254-2870
Charles Chester, prin. Fax 254-2878

Monroe, Walton, Pop. 12,993
Walton County SD 13,700/PK-12
200 Double Spring Church SW 30656 770-266-4417
Dr. Nathan Franklin, supt. Fax 266-4420
www.walton.k12.ga.us
Carver MS 1,000/6-8
1095 Good Hope Rd 30655 770-207-3333
Alan Satterfield, prin. Fax 207-3332
Monroe Area HS 1,100/9-12
300 Double Springs Church 30656 770-266-4599
Bryan Hicks, prin. Fax 266-4598
Other Schools – See Loganville

Walton Academy 900/PK-12
1 Bulldog Dr 30655 770-267-7578

Montezuma, Macon, Pop. 3,439
Macon County SD
Supt. — See Oglethorpe
Macon County HS 500/9-12
615 Vienna Rd 31063 478-472-8579
Nakia Parks, prin. Fax 472-6206

Monticello, Jasper, Pop. 2,623
Jasper County SD 2,300/PK-12
1411 College St 31064 706-468-6350
Dr. Mike Newton, supt. Fax 468-0045
www.jasper.k12.ga.us
Jasper County HS 600/9-12
14477 GA Highway 11 N 31064 706-468-5016
Camille Murner, prin. Fax 468-5021
Jasper County MS 500/6-8
1289 College St 31064 706-468-2227
Cheryl Marrett, prin. Fax 468-1847

Piedmont Academy 300/PK-12
PO Box 231 31064 706-468-8818

Morgan, Calhoun, Pop. 236
Calhoun County SD 700/PK-12
PO Box 39 39866 229-213-0189
Dr. Yolanda Turner, supt. Fax 213-3837
www.calhoun.k12.ga.us
Other Schools – See Edison

Morganton, Union, Pop. 300

Mountain Area Christian Academy 200/PK-12
14090 Old Highway 76 30560 706-374-6222

Morrow, Clayton, Pop. 6,303
Clayton County SD
Supt. — See Jonesboro
Elite Scholars Academy 500/6-12
5968 Maddox Rd 30260 770-472-2823
Dr. Shonda Shaw, prin. Fax 472-2837
Morrow HS 1,700/9-12
2299 Old Rex Morrow Rd 30260 770-473-3241
Dr. Pamela Pitts, prin. Fax 473-3244
Morrow MS 700/6-8
5934 Trammell Rd 30260 770-210-4001
Matthew Smith, prin. Fax 210-4002

Clayton State University Post-Sec.
2000 Clayton State Blvd 30260 678-466-4000
Interactive College of Technology Post-Sec.
1580 Southlake Pkwy Ste C 30260 770-960-1298
Pacific Institute of Technology Post-Sec.
1388 Southlake Plaza Dr 30260 678-610-5900

Moultrie, Colquitt, Pop. 14,082
Colquitt County SD 9,700/PK-12
PO Box 2708 31776 229-890-6200
Dr. Samuel A. DePaul, supt. Fax 890-6246
www.colquitt.k12.ga.us/
Achievement Center 100/Alt
1800 Park Ave SE 31768 229-890-6197
Darius Dawson, prin. Fax 890-6181
Gray JHS 1,300/8-9
812 11th Ave NW 31768 229-890-6189
Frederick Smith, prin. Fax 890-6123
Other Schools – See Norman Park

Colquitt Christian Academy 50/PK-12
2929 S Main St 31768 229-668-2000
Moultrie Technical College Post-Sec.
800 Veterans Pkwy N, 229-891-7000

Mount Airy, Habersham, Pop. 1,271
Habersham County SD
Supt. — See Clarkesville
Habersham Central SHS 1,300/10-12
2059 Highway 197 30563 706-778-7161
Wesley McGee, prin. Fax 778-1258

Habersham Ninth Grade Academy 500/9-9
171 Raider Cir 30563 706-778-0830
Connie Franklin, prin. Fax 778-0848
Habersham Success Academy 100/6-12
171 Raider Cir 30563 706-894-3056
Rodney Long, prin. Fax 778-0848

Trinity Classical S 50/PK-12
243 Hazel Creek Church Rd 30563 706-894-2404

Mount Berry, Floyd

Berry College Post-Sec.
2277 Martha Berry Hwy NW 30149 706-232-5374

Mount Vernon, Montgomery, Pop. 2,411
Montgomery County SD 1,100/PK-12
703 Dobbins St 30445 912-583-2301
Hugh Kight, supt. Fax 583-4822
www.montgomery.k12.ga.us
Montgomery County HS 400/9-12
701 Dobbins St 30445 912-583-2296
Dr. Scott Barrow, prin. Fax 583-2302
Other Schools – See Ailey

Brewton-Parker College Post-Sec.
PO Box 197 30445 912-583-2241

Mount Zion, Carroll, Pop. 1,655
Carroll County SD
Supt. — See Carrollton
Mount Zion MS 300/6-8
132 Eagle Dr 30150 770-834-3389
Connie Robison, prin. Fax 214-7794

Nahunta, Brantley, Pop. 1,033
Brantley County SD 3,500/PK-12
272 School Cir 31553 912-462-6176
Dr. Greg Jacobs, supt. Fax 462-6731
www.brantley.k12.ga.us
Brantley County HS 1,000/9-12
10804 Highway 82 31553 912-462-5121
Nehemiah Cummings, prin. Fax 462-5123
Brantley County MS 500/7-8
10990 Highway 82 31553 912-462-7092
Dr. Angela Haney, prin. Fax 462-6785

Nashville, Berrien, Pop. 4,886
Berrien County SD 3,200/PK-12
810 S Dogwood Dr 31639 229-686-2081
Dr. Lili Wylam Drawdy, supt. Fax 686-9002
www.berrien.k12.ga.us
Berrien HS 800/9-12
500 E Smith Ave 31639 229-686-7428
Angie Lovein, prin. Fax 686-6251
Berrien MS 700/6-8
800 Tifton Hwy 31639 229-686-2021
Margo Mathis, prin. Fax 686-6546

Newborn, Newton, Pop. 690

Shiloh Christian Academy 50/K-12
9595 Highway 142 30056 706-468-2606

Newnan, Coweta, Pop. 32,285
Coweta County SD 22,500/PK-12
PO Box 280 30264 770-254-2800
Dr. Steve Barker, supt. Fax 254-2807
www.cowetaschools.net
Arnall MS 900/6-8
700 Lora Smith Rd 30265 770-254-2765
Dr. Jan Franks, prin. Fax 254-2770
Brown MS Alt
32 Clark St 30263 770-304-5930
Skip Seagraves, prin. Fax 254-2806
Dowdell Academy Alt
1 Dowdell St 30263 770-254-2870
Kevin Jones, prin. Fax 304-5919
Evans MS 800/6-8
41 Evans Dr 30263 770-254-2780
Vera Perry-Harris, prin. Fax 254-2783
Madras MS 1,100/6-8
240 Edgeworth Rd 30263 770-254-2744
Lorraine Johnson, prin. Fax 304-5928
Newnan HS 2,300/9-12
190 Lagrange St 30263 770-254-2880
Chase Puckett, prin. Fax 254-2797
Northgate HS 1,800/9-12
3220 Fischer Rd 30265 770-463-5585
Bill Harrison, prin. Fax 463-4982
Smokey Road MS 700/6-8
965 Smokey Rd 30263 770-254-2840
Keafer Triplett, prin. Fax 304-5933
Other Schools – See Senoia, Sharpsburg

Heritage S 400/PK-12
2093 Highway 29 N 30263 770-253-9898
Kristin Skelly, head sch Fax 253-4850
West Georgia Technical College Post-Sec.
160 Martin Luther King Dr 30263 770-755-7440

Newton, Baker, Pop. 647
Baker County SD 300/PK-12
PO Box 40, 229-734-5346
Dr. Torrance Choates, supt. Fax 734-3064
bck12.baker.k12.ga.us/
Baker County S 300/PK-12
260 GA Highway 37 SW, 229-734-5274
Dr. Torrance Choates, prin. Fax 734-3071

Norcross, Gwinnett, Pop. 8,915
Gwinnett County SD
Supt. — See Suwanee
Gwinnett InterVention Education Ctr West 200/Alt
5550 Peachtree Industrial 30071 770-246-5300
Todd Marschke, prin. Fax 246-5348
Meadowcreek HS 3,100/9-12
4455 Steve Reynolds Blvd 30093 770-381-9680
Tommy Welch, prin. Fax 806-2230
Norcross HS 3,600/9-12
5300 Spalding Dr 30092 770-448-3674
William Bishop, prin. Fax 447-2664

Summerour MS 1,400/6-8
321 Price Pl 30071 770-448-3045
Dorothy Parker-Jarrett, prin. Fax 417-2476

Ashworth College Post-Sec.
6625 the Corners Pkwy # 500 30092 770-729-8400
Everest Institute Post-Sec.
1750 Beaver Ruin Rd Ste 500 30093 770-921-1085
Greater Atlanta Christian S 1,900/PK-12
1575 Indian Trail Lilburn 30093 770-243-2000
Dr. David Fincher, pres. Fax 243-2268
Professional Career Development Inst Post-Sec.
6625 the Corners Pkey # 500 30092 800-957-5412
Torch and the Sword Christian Academy PK-12
100 Pinnacle Way #190 30071 678-691-3164
Jenny Hong, prin. Fax 557-0582
Wesleyan S 1,100/K-12
5405 Spalding Dr 30092 770-448-7640
Chris Cleveland, hdmstr. Fax 448-3699

Norman Park, Colquitt, Pop. 956
Colquitt County SD
Supt. — See Moultrie
Colquitt County HS 1,700/10-12
105 Darbyshire Rd 31771 229-890-6141
Stephanie Terrell, prin. Fax 890-6166

Oakwood, Hall, Pop. 3,904
Hall County SD
Supt. — See Gainesville
West Hall HS 1,100/9-12
5500 McEver Rd 30566 770-967-9826
Scott Justus, prin. Fax 967-4864
West Hall MS 900/6-8
5470 McEver Rd 30566 770-967-4871
Rodney Stephens, prin. Fax 967-4874

Lanier Technical College Post-Sec.
2990 Landrum Education Dr 30566 770-531-6300

Ocilla, Irwin, Pop. 3,380
Irwin County SD 1,800/PK-12
PO Box 225 31774 229-468-7485
Dr. Thad Clayton, supt. Fax 468-7220
www.irwin.k12.ga.us/
Irwin County HS 400/9-12
149 Chieftain Cir 31774 229-468-9421
Kerry Billingsley, prin. Fax 468-9423
Irwin County MS 400/6-8
149 Chieftain Cir 31774 229-468-5517
Edd Cunningham, prin. Fax 468-3134

Oglethorpe, Macon, Pop. 1,323
Macon County SD 1,600/PK-12
31 Buck Creek Bypass Rd 31068 478-472-8188
Dr. D. Ray Hill, supt. Fax 472-2042
www.macon.k12.ga.us/
Macon County MS 400/6-8
400 St Hwy 128 31068 478-472-7045
Amanda Gorham, prin. Fax 472-2549
Other Schools – See Montezuma

Oxford, Newton, Pop. 2,073

Providence Classical Christian S 100/PK-12
252 Byrd Rd 30054 770-788-6618

Peachtree City, Fayette, Pop. 33,616
Fayette County SD
Supt. — See Fayetteville
Booth MS 1,200/6-8
250 S Peachtree Pkwy 30269 770-631-3240
Steve Greene, prin. Fax 631-3245
McIntosh HS 1,700/9-12
201 Walt Banks Rd 30269 770-631-3232
Lisa Fine, prin. Fax 631-3278

Peachtree Crnrs, Gwinnett
Gwinnett County SD
Supt. — See Suwanee
Pinckneyville MS 1,300/6-8
5440 W Jones Bridge Rd, 770-263-0860
Marci Sledge, prin. Fax 447-2617

Pearson, Atkinson, Pop. 2,082
Atkinson County SD 1,800/PK-12
98 Roberts Ave E 31642 912-422-7373
Bob Brown, supt. Fax 422-7369
www.atkinson.k12.ga.us
Atkinson County HS 500/9-12
145 Rebel Ln 31642 912-422-3267
Shane Miller, prin. Fax 422-7889
Atkinson County MS 400/6-8
145 Rebel Ln 31642 912-422-3267
Anthony Davis, prin. Fax 422-3348

Pelham, Mitchell, Pop. 3,877
Pelham CSD 1,500/PK-12
203 Mathewson Ave SW 31779 229-294-8715
Floyd Fort, supt. Fax 294-2760
www.pelham-city.k12.ga.us
Pelham City HS 500/9-12
720 Barrow Ave SW 31779 229-294-8623
Dr. Russ Chesser, prin. Fax 294-6069
Pelham City MS 300/6-8
209 Mathewson Ave SW 31779 229-294-6063
John Hamilton, prin. Fax 294-6046

Pembroke, Bryan, Pop. 2,165
Bryan County SD
Supt. — See Black Creek
Bryan County MS 500/6-8
600 Payne Dr 31321 912-626-5050
Dr. Michael Tinney, prin. Fax 653-2705
Byran County HS 500/9-12
1234 Camellia Dr 31321 912-626-5060
Crystal Morales, prin. Fax 653-2858

Perry, Houston, Pop. 13,635
Houston County SD 26,900/PK-12
PO Box 1850 31069 478-988-6200
Dr. Mark Scott, supt. Fax 988-6259
www.hcbe.net

Perry HS 1,300/9-12
1307 North Ave 31069 478-988-6298
Wesley Martin, prin. Fax 988-6381
Perry MS 900/6-8
495 Perry Pkwy 31069 478-988-6285
Thomas Moore, prin. Fax 988-6345
Other Schools – See Bonaire, Centerville, Kathleen, Warner Robins

---

Westfield S 600/PK-12
2005 US Highway 41 S 31069 478-987-0547
William Carroll, hdmstr. Fax 987-7379

Pinehurst, Dooly, Pop. 452
Dooly County SD
Supt. — See Vienna
Dooly County MS 300/6-8
11949 US Highway 41 31070 229-645-3421
Dr. Kelvin Butts, prin. Fax 645-3840

Fullington Academy 300/PK-12
PO Box B 31070 229-645-3383

Pooler, Chatham, Pop. 18,668
Savannah-Chatham County SD
Supt. — See Savannah
West Chatham MS 1,000/6-8
800 Pine Barren Rd 31322 912-395-3650
Julian Childers, prin. Fax 201-7688

Portal, Bulloch, Pop. 637
Bulloch County SD
Supt. — See Statesboro
Portal MSHS 400/6-12
27245 US Highway 80 W 30450 912-842-8360
Patrick Hill, prin. Fax 865-5659

Port Wentworth, Chatham, Pop. 5,224
Savannah-Chatham County SD
Supt. — See Savannah
Rice Creek S 3-8
100 Mulberry Ave 31407 912-395-4100
Dr. Troy Brown, prin. Fax 201-5068

Powder Springs, Cobb, Pop. 13,580
Cobb County SD
Supt. — See Marietta
Hillgrove HS 2,200/9-12
4165 Luther Ward Rd 30127 678-331-3961
Christian Suttle, prin. Fax 331-8128
Lovinggood MS 1,400/6-8
3825 Luther Ward Rd 30127 678-331-3015
Angela Stewart, prin. Fax 331-3016
McEachern HS 2,300/9-12
2400 New Macland Rd 30127 770-222-3710
Regina Montgomery, prin. Fax 222-3712
Tapp MS 800/6-8
3900 Macedonia Rd 30127 770-222-3758
Dr. Tony Wilcher, prin. Fax 222-3760

Paulding County SD
Supt. — See Dallas
Dobbins MS 800/6-8
637 Williams Lake Rd 30127 770-443-4835
Cartess Ross, prin. Fax 439-1672

Powder Springs Beauty College Post-Sec.
4114 Austell Powder Springs 30127 770-439-9432
Praise Academy 300/PK-12
4052 Hiram Lithia Springs 30127 770-943-2484
Joe White M.Ed., admin. Fax 943-9458

Quitman, Brooks, Pop. 3,809
Brooks County SD 2,200/PK-12
1081 Barwick Rd 31643 229-263-7531
Owen Clemons, supt. Fax 263-5206
www.brookscountyschools.com/
Brooks County HS 600/9-12
1801 Moultrie Hwy 31643 229-263-8923
Dr. Elena Ponder, prin. Fax 263-7049
Brooks County MS 500/6-8
2171 Moultrie Hwy 31643 229-263-7521
Djana Goss, prin. Fax 263-9038

Rabun Gap, Rabun

Rabun Gap-Nacoochee S 300/5-12
339 Nacoochee Dr 30568 706-746-7467
Dr. Anthony Sgro, head sch Fax 746-2594

Reidsville, Tattnall, Pop. 4,920
Tattnall County SD 3,500/PK-12
PO Box 157 30453 912-557-4726
Dr. Gina Williams, supt. Fax 557-3036
www.tattnallschools.org
Reidsville MS 300/6-8
148 W Brazell St 30453 912-557-3993
Gwenda Johnson, prin. Fax 557-4124
Tattnall County HS 900/9-12
1 Battle Creek Warrior Blvd 30453 912-557-4374
Glenn Stewart, prin. Fax 557-4542
Other Schools – See Glennville

Rex, Clayton
Clayton County SD
Supt. — See Jonesboro
Adamson MS 600/6-8
3187 Rex Rd 30273 770-968-2925
Chuck Wilkerson, prin. Fax 968-2949
Rex Mill MS 1,100/6-8
6380 Evans Dr 30273 770-474-0702
Dr. Caryn Turner, prin. Fax 474-5812

Richmond Hill, Bryan, Pop. 8,989
Bryan County SD
Supt. — See Black Creek
Richmond Hill HS 1,800/9-12
1 Wildcat Dr 31324 912-459-5151
Debi McNeal, prin. Fax 756-4958
Richmond Hill MS 1,500/6-8
503 Warren Hill Rd 31324 912-459-5130
Dr. William McGrath, prin. Fax 756-5369

Rincon, Effingham, Pop. 8,590
Effingham County SD
Supt. — See Springfield
Ebenezer MS 800/6-8
1100 Ebenezer Rd 31326 912-754-7757
Amie Dickerson, prin. Fax 754-4012

Ringgold, Catoosa, Pop. 3,500
Catoosa County SD 10,700/PK-12
PO Box 130 30736 706-965-2297
Denia Reese, supt. Fax 965-8913
www.catoosa.k12.ga.us
Heritage HS 1,300/9-12
3960 Poplar Springs Rd 30736 706-937-6464
Ronnie Bradford, prin. Fax 937-6477
Heritage MS 1,000/6-8
4005 Poplar Springs Rd 30736 706-937-3568
Chris Lusk, prin. Fax 937-2483
Ringgold HS 1,000/9-12
29 Tiger Trl 30736 706-935-2254
J.R. Jones, prin. Fax 965-8910
Ringgold MS 800/6-8
217 Tiger Trl 30736 706-935-3381
Jeff Fricks, prin. Fax 965-8908
Other Schools – See Fort Oglethorpe, Rossville

Riverdale, Clayton, Pop. 14,852
Clayton County SD
Supt. — See Jonesboro
Drew HS 1,600/9-12
6237 Garden Walk Blvd 30274 770-472-2820
Gary Townsend, prin. Fax 472-2825
Riverdale HS 1,400/9-12
160 Roberts Dr 30274 770-473-2905
Jamille Miller-Brown, prin. Fax 473-2913
Riverdale MS 700/6-8
400 Roberts Dr 30274 770-994-4045
Adrian Courtland, prin. Fax 994-4467
Sequoyah MS 900/6-8
95 Valley Hill Rd SW 30274 770-515-7524
Fax 515-7540

Southern Regional Medical Center Post-Sec.
11 Upper Riverdale Rd SW 30274 770-991-8053

Roberta, Crawford, Pop. 993
Crawford County SD 1,800/PK-12
PO Box 8 31078 478-836-3131
Brent Lowe, supt. Fax 836-3114
crawfordcounty.schoolinsites.com
Crawford County HS 500/9-12
400 E Agency St 31078 478-836-3126
Mike Campbell, prin. Fax 836-4853
Crawford County MS 400/6-8
401 Lowe Rd 31078 478-836-3181
Dr. Anthony English, prin. Fax 836-3795

Rochelle, Wilcox, Pop. 1,171
Wilcox County SD
Supt. — See Abbeville
Wilcox County HS 300/9-12
186 7th Ave 31079 229-365-7231
Chad Davis, prin. Fax 365-7461
Wilcox County MS 300/6-8
114 7th Ave 31079 229-365-2331
Chad Davis, prin. Fax 365-2641

Rockmart, Polk, Pop. 4,119
Polk County SD
Supt. — See Cedartown
Rockmart HS 900/9-12
990 Cartersville Hwy 30153 770-684-5432
Wesley Cupp, prin. Fax 684-4768
Rockmart MS 700/6-8
60 Knox Mountain Rd 30153 678-757-1479
Robyn Teems, prin. Fax 757-9868

Georgia Northwestern Technical College Post-Sec.
466 Brock Rd 30153 770-684-5696

Rock Spring, Walker

Georgia Northwestern Technical College Post-Sec.
265 Bicentennial Trl 30739 706-764-3510

Rocky Face, Whitfield
Whitfield County SD
Supt. — See Dalton
Westside MS 500/6-8
580 Lafayette Rd 30740 706-673-2611
Angela Hargis, prin. Fax 673-5349

Rome, Floyd, Pop. 35,635
Floyd County SD 9,800/PK-12
600 Riverside Pkwy NE 30161 706-234-1031
Dr. John Jackson, supt. Fax 236-1824
www.floydboe.net
Armuchee HS 600/9-12
4203 Martha Berry Hwy NW 30165 706-236-1886
Dr. James Burris, prin. Fax 802-6757
Coosa HS 700/9-12
4454 Alabama Hwy NW 30165 706-236-1870
Trevor Hubbard, prin. Fax 290-8142
Coosa MS 600/6-8
212 Eagle Dr NW 30165 706-236-1856
Vondell Ringer, prin. Fax 802-6766
Model HS 700/9-12
3252 Calhoun Rd NE 30161 706-236-1895
Scott Savage, prin. Fax 802-6750
Model MS 500/6-8
164 Barron Rd NE 30161 706-290-8150
Steve Turrentine, prin. Fax 802-6775
Other Schools – See Armuchee, Lindale

Rome CSD 5,800/PK-12
508 E 2nd St 30161 706-236-5050
Louis Byars, supt. Fax 802-4311
www.rcs.rome.ga.us
Rome HS 1,600/9-12
1000 Veterans Memorial NE 30161 706-235-9653
Dr. Phillip Brown Ph.D., prin. Fax 236-5078
Rome MS 900/7-8
1020 Veterans Memorial NE 30161 706-235-4695
Greg Christian, prin. Fax 234-5903
Rome Transitional Academy Alt
1162 Spider Webb Dr SE 30161 706-802-4326
Jennifer Perkins, prin. Fax 802-4327

Darlington S 800/PK-12
1014 Cave Spring Rd SW 30161 706-235-6051
Brent Bell, hdmstr. Fax 232-3600
Georgia Highlands College Post-Sec.
3175 Cedartown Hwy SE 30161 706-802-5000
Georgia Northwestern Technical College Post-Sec.
1 Maurice Culberson Dr SW 30161 706-295-6963
Shorter University Post-Sec.
315 Shorter Ave SW 30165 800-868-6980
Unity Christian S 400/PK-12
2960 New Calhoun Hwy NE 30161 706-292-0700
Eric Munn, head sch Fax 292-0772

Rossville, Walker, Pop. 4,039
Catoosa County SD
Supt. — See Ringgold
Lakeview MS 700/6-8
416 Cross St 30741 706-866-1040
Steve McClure, prin. Fax 861-6644

Walker County SD
Supt. — See La Fayette
Ridgeland HS 1,300/9-12
2478 Happy Valley Rd 30741 706-820-9361
Glen Brown, prin. Fax 820-1342
Rossville MS 600/6-8
316 Bull Dog Trl 30741 706-820-0638
Jason Pelham, prin. Fax 820-0696

Roswell, Fulton, Pop. 86,448
Fulton County SD
Supt. — See Atlanta
Centennial HS 1,900/9-12
9310 Scott Rd 30076 770-650-4230
Kibbey Crumbley, prin. Fax 650-4250
Crabapple MS 900/6-8
10700 Crabapple Rd 30075 470-254-4520
Rako Morrissey, prin. Fax 254-4524
Elkins Pointe MS 1,100/6-8
11290 Elkins Rd 30076 470-254-2892
Kindra Smith, prin. Fax 254-2898
Roswell HS 2,200/9-12
11595 King Rd 30075 470-254-4500
Jerome Huff, prin. Fax 254-4509

Blessed Trinity Catholic HS 1,000/9-12
11320 Woodstock Rd 30075 678-277-9083
Brian Marks, prin. Fax 277-9756
Chrysalis Experiential Academy 100/5-12
10 Mansell Ct E Ste 500 30076 404-513-9914
Fellowship Christian S 700/PK-12
10965 Woodstock Rd 30075 770-993-1650
Kathy Teston, admin. Fax 993-9262
St. Francis Day S 900/PK-12
9375 Willeo Rd 30075 770-641-8257
Strayer University Post-Sec.
100 Mansell Ct E 30076 770-650-3000

Saint Marys, Camden, Pop. 16,595
Camden County SD
Supt. — See Kingsland
Saint Marys MS 1,000/6-8
205 Martha Dr 31558 912-882-8626
Michael Wooden, prin. Fax 882-5473

Saint Simons Island, Glynn, Pop. 12,646

Frederica Academy 400/PK-12
200 Murray Way 31522 912-638-9981
John Thomas, head sch Fax 638-1442

Sandersville, Washington, Pop. 5,844
Washington County SD 3,100/PK-12
PO Box 716 31082 478-552-3981
Dr. Donna Hinton, supt. Fax 552-3128
www.washington.k12.ga.us/
Elder MS 600/6-8
902 Linton Rd 31082 478-552-2007
Dr. Darryl Gilbert, prin. Fax 552-7388
Washington County Alternative S Alt
446 Riddleville Rd 31082 478-553-1243
Vicki Harden, prin. Fax 553-1245
Washington County HS 900/9-12
420 Riddleville Rd 31082 478-552-2324
Dr. Allen Gray, prin. Fax 552-3140

Brentwood S 400/PK-12
PO Box 955 31082 478-552-5136
Anne Brantley, head sch Fax 552-2947
Oconee Fall Line Technical College Post-Sec.
1189 Deepstep Rd 31082 478-553-2050

Sandy Springs, Fulton, Pop. 91,346
Fulton County SD
Supt. — See Atlanta
North Springs Charter HS 1,600/9-12
7447 Roswell Rd 30328 770-551-2490
Michael Hanson, prin. Fax 551-2498
Ridgeview Charter MS 1,100/6-8
5340 S Trimble Rd, 404-843-7710
Oliver Blackwell, prin. Fax 847-3292
Riverwood International Charter HS 1,700/9-12
5900 Raider Dr 30328 470-254-1980
Robert Shaw, prin. Fax 254-8709
Sandy Springs MS 900/6-8
8750 Pride Pl 30350 470-254-4970
Charles Gardner, prin. Fax 254-3334

Gwinnett College - Sandy Springs Post-Sec.
6690 Roswell Rd Ste 2200 30328 770-457-2021

Savannah, Chatham, Pop. 133,567
Savannah-Chatham County SD 37,100/PK-12
208 Bull St 31401 912-395-5600
Dr. Thomas Lockamy, supt. Fax 201-9073
www.savannah.chatham.k12.ga.us/
Beach HS 900/9-12
3001 Hopkins St 31405 912-395-5330
Derrick Muhammad, prin. Fax 201-5322
Building Bridges Academy HS Alt
402 Market St 31408 912-395-2540
Marcus Scott, admin. Fax 201-5065
Building Bridges Academy MS Alt
100 Priscilla D Pkwy 31408 912-395-6780
Keith Groeper, admin.
Coastal MS 800/6-8
4595 US Highway 80 E 31410 912-395-3950
Allison Schuster-Jones, prin. Fax 898-3951
DeRenne MS 700/6-8
1009 Clinch St 31405 912-395-5900
Carol Mobley, prin. Fax 201-5903
Groves HS 700/9-12
100 Priscilla D Thomas Way 31408 912-395-2520
Timothy Cox, prin. Fax 201-5840
Hubert MS 500/6-8
768 Grant St 31401 912-395-5235
Wilhelmenia Manning, prin. Fax 201-5238
Islands HS 900/9-12
170 Whitemarsh Island Rd 31410 912-395-2000
Kerry Coursey, prin.
Jenkins HS 1,000/9-12
1800 E De Renne Ave 31406 912-395-6300
Heather Handy, prin. Fax 303-6331
Johnson HS 900/9-12
3012 Sunset Blvd 31404 912-395-6400
Bernadette Ball-Oliver, prin. Fax 395-6418
Mercer MS 500/6-8
201 Rommel Ave 31408 912-395-6700
Horace Magwood, prin. Fax 201-5979
Myers MS 700/6-8
2025 E 52nd St 31404 912-395-6600
Ericka Washington, prin. Fax 303-6604
Savannah Arts Academy 800/9-12
500 Washington Ave 31405 912-395-5000
Gif Lockley, prin. Fax 201-4160
Savannah Early College HS 100/9-12
400 Pennsylvania Ave 31404 912-395-5050
Caroline Gordon-Jelks, admin. Fax 201-7585
School of Liberal Studies 700/9-12
400 Pennsylvania Ave 31404 912-395-5050
Tammy Broadnax, prin. Fax 201-5054
Southwest MS 900/6-8
6030 Ogeechee Rd 31419 912-395-3540
Craig Daughtry, prin. Fax 201-5831
STEM Academy 600/6-8
207 E Montgomery Xrd 31406 912-395-3500
Peter Ulrich, prin. Fax 201-4161
Windsor Forest HS 1,100/9-12
12419 Largo Dr 31419 912-395-3400
Derrick Butler, prin. Fax 961-3422
Woodville-Tompkins Tech & Career HS Vo/Tech
151 Coach Joe Turner St 31408 912-395-6750
Alfred McGuire, prin. Fax 965-6768
Other Schools – See Bloomingdale, Pooler, Port Wentworth

Armstrong Atlantic State University Post-Sec.
11935 Abercorn St 31419 912-344-2576
Benedictine Military S 300/9-12
6502 Seawright Dr 31406 912-644-7000
Rev. Frank Ziemkiewicz, hdmstr. Fax 236-3527
Bethesda Academy 100/6-12
PO Box 13039 31416 912-351-2055
Megan Kicklighter, prin. Fax 351-2062
Bible Baptist S 300/PK-12
4700 Skidaway Rd 31404 912-352-3067
Kathy Hodges, admin. Fax 352-9830
Calvary Day S 700/PK-12
4625 Waters Ave 31404 912-644-5080
Habersham S 100/PK-12
505 E 54th St 31405 912-509-0540
Memorial Day S 300/PK-12
6500 Habersham St 31405 912-352-4535
Michael Harper, hdmstr. Fax 352-4536
Mercer University Post-Sec.
4700 Waters Ave 31404
Providence Christian S 200/PK-12
401 Tibet Ave 31406 912-335-7976
Paula Cook, hdmstr. Fax 335-7981
Ramah SDA Junior Academy 200/PK-10
3400 Florance St 31405 912-233-3101
St. Andrew's S 400/PK-12
601 Penn Waller Rd 31410 912-897-4941
Dr. Kelley Waldron, hdmstr. Fax 897-4943
St. Vincent's Academy 300/9-12
207 E Liberty St 31401 912-236-5508
Mary Anne Hogan, prin. Fax 236-7877
Savannah Christian Preparatory S 1,300/PK-12
PO Box 2848 31402 912-234-1653
Chris Harmon, hdmstr. Fax 234-0491
Savannah College of Art & Design Post-Sec.
PO Box 3146 31402 912-525-5100
Savannah Country Day S 900/PK-12
824 Stillwood Dr 31419 912-925-8800
Kef Wilson, head sch Fax 920-7800
Savannah State University Post-Sec.
3219 College St 31404 912-358-4778
Savannah Technical College Post-Sec.
5717 White Bluff Rd 31405 912-443-5700
South University Post-Sec.
709 Mall Blvd 31406 912-201-8000
Veritas Academy 100/PK-12
PO Box 8332 31412 912-238-1222
Scott Taylor, hdmstr. Fax 234-0566
Virginia College Post-Sec.
14045 Abercorn St Ste 1503 31419 912-721-5600

Scottdale, DeKalb, Pop. 10,220

Fugees Academy, PO Box 388 30079 100/6-12
Luma Mufleh, dir. 678-358-0547

Senoia, Coweta, Pop. 3,245
Coweta County SD
Supt. — See Newnan
East Coweta MS 700/6-8
6291 Highway 16 30276 770-599-6607
Dr. Schwanda Jackson, prin. Fax 599-1051

Sharpsburg, Coweta, Pop. 336
Coweta County SD
Supt. — See Newnan

East Coweta HS 2,900/9-12
400 McCollum Sharpsburg Rd 30277 770-254-2850
Steve Allen, prin. Fax 254-2857
Lee MS 1,000/6-8
370 Willis Rd 30277 770-251-1547
Dr. Cindy Bennett, prin. Fax 253-8381

Central Christian S 100/K-12
3613 Highway 34 E 30277 770-252-1234
Trinity Christian S of Sharpsburg 1,000/PK-12
8817 Highway 54 W 30277 770-251-6770
Dean Demos, hdmstr. Fax 251-6714

Siloam, Greene, Pop. 278

Greene Academy 200/PK-12
PO Box 109 30665 706-467-2147
Robert Bradley, head sch Fax 467-2147

Smyrna, Cobb, Pop. 49,900
Cobb County SD
Supt. — See Marietta
Campbell HS 2,400/9-12
5265 Ward St SE 30080 678-842-6850
Dr. Jeanne Walker, prin. Fax 842-6852
Campbell MS 1,300/6-8
3295 Atlanta Rd SE 30080 678-842-6873
Jonathan Tanner, prin. Fax 842-6875
Griffin MS 1,200/6-8
4010 King Springs Rd SE 30082 678-842-6917
Paul Gillihan, prin. Fax 842-6919

Medix School Post-Sec.
2108 Cobb Pkwy SE 30080 770-980-0002

Snellville, Gwinnett, Pop. 17,762
Gwinnett County SD
Supt. — See Suwanee
Brookwood HS 3,400/9-12
1255 Dogwood Rd 30078 770-972-7642
William Ford, prin. Fax 978-5075
Shiloh HS 2,200/9-12
4210 Shiloh Rd 30039 770-972-8471
Dr. Danyel Dollard, prin. Fax 736-4345
Shiloh MS 1,900/6-8
4285 Shiloh Rd 30039 770-972-3224
Dr. Eli Welch, prin. Fax 736-4563
Snellville MS 900/6-8
3155 Pate Rd 30078 770-972-1530
Katise Menchan, prin. Fax 736-4444
South Gwinnett HS 2,400/9-12
2288 Main St E 30078 770-972-4840
Monique Lee, prin. Fax 736-4329

Social Circle, Walton, Pop. 4,199
Social Circle CSD 1,700/PK-12
147 Alcova Dr 30025 770-464-2731
Dr. Todd McGhee, supt. Fax 464-4920
www.socialcircleschools.com/
Social Circle HS 500/9-12
154 Alcova Dr 30025 770-464-2611
Dr. Carrie Ann Booher, prin. Fax 464-2612
Social Circle MS 400/6-8
154 Alcova Dr 30025 770-464-1932
Cappy Douglass, prin. Fax 464-2612

Soperton, Treutlen, Pop. 3,093
Treutlen County SD 1,200/PK-12
5040 S Third St 30457 912-529-7101
Dr. Cheryl Conley, supt. Fax 529-4226
www.treutlen.k12.ga.us
Treutlen MSHS 600/6-12
7892 GA Highway 29 30457 912-529-7131
Christopher Watkins, prin. Fax 529-6121

Sparks, Cook, Pop. 2,024
Cook County SD
Supt. — See Adel
Cook MS 700/6-8
1601 N Elm St 31647 229-549-5999
Russell Meadows, prin. Fax 549-5986

Sparta, Hancock, Pop. 1,390
Hancock County SD 1,000/PK-12
11311 GA Highway 15 31087 706-444-5775
Dr. Charles Culver, supt. Fax 444-7026
www.hancockcountyschools.net/
Hancock Central HS 300/9-12
11311 GA Highway 15 31087 706-444-7009
Dr. Tanger Ward, prin. Fax 444-9918
Hancock Central MS 200/6-8
11311 GA Highway 15 31087 706-444-6652
Anthony Webb, prin. Fax 444-4344

Springfield, Effingham, Pop. 2,815
Effingham County SD 11,500/PK-12
405 N Ash St 31329 912-754-6491
Dr. Randy Shearouse, supt. Fax 754-7033
www.effingham.k12.ga.us
Effingham County HS 1,900/9-12
1589 GA Highway 119 S 31329 912-754-6404
Billy Hughes, prin. Fax 754-6893
Other Schools – See Guyton, Rincon

Statenville, Echols, Pop. 1,016
Echols County SD 800/PK-12
216 US Highway 129 N 31648 229-559-5734
Lance Heard, supt. Fax 559-0484
www.echols.k12.ga.us
Echols County HS 200/9-12
PO Box 40 31648 229-559-5437
Dave Rosser, prin. Fax 559-3491

Statesboro, Bulloch, Pop. 27,883
Bulloch County SD 9,900/PK-12
150 Williams Rd Ste A 30458 912-212-8500
Charles Wilson, supt. Fax 212-8529
www.bulloch.k12.ga.us
James MS 600/6-8
18809 US Highway 80 W 30458 912-212-8820
Mike Yawn, prin. Fax 489-5916
Langston Chapel MS 700/6-8
156 Langston Chapel Rd 30458 912-212-8720
Dr. Evelyn Gamble-Hilton, prin. Fax 681-6416
Statesboro HS 1,500/9-12
10 Lester Rd 30458 912-212-8860
Dr. Ken LeCain, prin. Fax 489-5965
Transitions Learning Center Alt
150 Williams Rd Ste B 30458 912-212-8610
Tim Rountree, admin. Fax 489-9978
Other Schools – See Brooklet, Portal

Bulloch Academy 500/PK-12
873 Westside Rd 30458 912-764-6297
Georgia Southern University Post-Sec.
PO Box 8024 30460 912-478-5391
Ogeechee Technical College Post-Sec.
1 Joseph E Kennedy Blvd 30458 912-681-5500
Trinity Christian S 200/PK-12
571 E Main St 30461 912-489-1375
David Lattner, hdmstr. Fax 764-3136

Statham, Barrow, Pop. 2,353
Barrow County SD
Supt. — See Winder
Bear Creek MS 700/6-8
228 Jefferson St 30666 770-725-5575
Dr. Jennifer Wood, prin. Fax 725-7656

Stillmore, Emanuel, Pop. 530

Emanuel Academy 200/PK-12
PO Box 400 30464 912-562-4405
Emeriel Hubbard, hdmstr. Fax 562-3465

Stockbridge, Henry, Pop. 24,827
Henry County SD
Supt. — See Mc Donough
Austin Road MS 800/6-8
100 Austin Rd 30281 770-507-5407
Gabriel Wiley, prin. Fax 507-5413
Stockbridge HS 1,400/9-12
1151 Old Conyers Rd 30281 770-474-8747
Eric Watson, prin. Fax 474-4727
Stockbridge MS 600/6-8
533 Old Conyers Rd 30281 770-474-5710
Purvis Jackson, prin. Fax 507-8406
Woodland HS 1,400/9-12
800 Moseley Dr 30281 770-389-2784
Dr. Shannon Ellis, prin. Fax 389-2790
Woodland MS 700/6-8
820 Moseley Dr 30281 770-389-2774
Legena Williams, prin. Fax 389-2780

Rockdale County SD
Supt. — See Conyers
Davis MS 900/6-8
3375 E Fairview Rd SW 30281 770-388-5675
Randy Goerner, prin. Fax 388-5676

Community Christian S 900/PK-12
2001 Jodeco Rd 30281 678-432-0191
Frederick Banke, hdmstr. Fax 914-1217
DeVry University Post-Sec.
675 Southcrest Pkwy Ste 100 30281 678-284-4700

Stone Mountain, DeKalb, Pop. 5,717
DeKalb County SD 98,000/PK-12
1701 Mountain Industrial Bl 30083 678-676-1200
Dr. R. Stephen Green, supt. Fax 676-0785
www.dekalbschoolsga.org
Andrews HS 700/Alt
1701 Mountain Industrial 30083 678-676-2602
Merlon Jones, prin. Fax 676-2610
Champion MS 800/6-8
5265 Mimosa Dr 30083 678-875-1502
Antoine Rhodes, prin. Fax 875-1510
DeKalb Alternative S 100/Alt
5855 Memorial Dr 30083 678-676-2302
Margie Smith, prin. Fax 676-2310
DeKalb Early College Academy 300/9-12
1701 Mountain Industrial Bl 30083 678-875-2402
Edward Conner, dir.
Freedom MS 1,100/6-8
505 S Hairston Rd 30088 678-874-8702
Dr. Marchell Boston, prin. Fax 874-8710
Redan HS 1,100/9-12
5247 Redan Rd 30088 678-676-3602
Janice Boger, prin. Fax 676-3610
Stephenson HS 1,600/9-12
701 Stephenson Rd 30087 678-676-4202
Michael Jones, prin. Fax 676-4210
Stephenson MS 1,000/6-8
922 Stephenson Rd 30087 678-676-4402
Carolyn Williams, prin. Fax 676-4410
Stone Mountain HS 1,100/9-12
4555 Central Dr 30083 678-676-6302
Dr. James Jones, prin. Fax 676-6310
Stone Mountain MS 1,000/6-8
4301 Sarr Pkwy 30083 678-676-4802
Dr. Vincent Hinton, prin. Fax 676-4810
Other Schools – See Atlanta, Avondale Estates, Chamblee, Clarkston, Decatur, Doraville, Dunwoody, Ellenwood, Lithonia, Tucker

Pro Way Hair School Post-Sec.
5684 Memorial Dr 30083 404-299-5156

Suches, Union
Union County SD
Supt. — See Blairsville
Woody Gap S 100/K-12
2331 State Highway 60 30572 706-747-2401
Sheila Collins, prin. Fax 747-1419

Sugar Hill, Gwinnett, Pop. 18,185
Gwinnett County SD
Supt. — See Suwanee
Lanier HS 1,600/9-12
918 Buford Hwy 30518 678-765-4040
Dr. Reuben Gresham, prin. Fax 765-4049
Lanier MS 1,400/6-8
6482 Suwanee Dam Rd 30518 770-945-8419
Todd Hamilton, prin. Fax 271-5108
North Gwinnett MS 2,000/6-8
170 Peachtree Industrial Bl 30518 678-745-2300
Wanda Law, prin. Fax 745-2348

Summerville, Chattooga, Pop. 4,440
Chattooga County SD 2,800/PK-12
33 Middle School Rd 30747 706-857-3447
Jimmy Lenderman, supt. Fax 857-3440
chattooga.schoolfusion.us
Chattooga CrossRoads Academy 50/Alt
989 Highway 114 30747 706-857-1112
Barry Peppers, prin. Fax 857-6644
Chattooga HS 800/9-12
989 Highway 114 30747 706-857-2402
Jeff Martin, prin. Fax 857-2565
Summerville MS 400/6-8
200 Middle School Rd 30747 706-857-2444
Kevin Muskett, prin. Fax 857-7769

Suwanee, Gwinnett, Pop. 15,041
Forsyth County SD
Supt. — See Cumming
Lambert HS 2,600/9-12
805 Nichols Rd 30024 678-965-5050
Dr. Gary Davison, prin. Fax 965-5051
Riverwatch MS 1,400/6-8
610 James Burgess Rd 30024 678-455-7311
Kathy Carpenter, prin. Fax 455-7316

Gwinnett County SD 170,400/PK-12
437 Old Peachtree Rd NW 30024 678-301-6000
J. Alvin Wilbanks, supt. Fax 301-6030
www.gwinnett.k12.ga.us/
Collins Hill HS 3,100/9-12
50 Taylor Rd 30024 770-682-4100
Kerensa Wing, prin. Fax 682-4105
Northbrook MS 6-8
1221 Northbrook Pkwy 30024 678-407-7140
Dr. Keith Thompson, prin. Fax 407-7157
North Gwinnett HS 2,600/9-12
20 Level Creek Rd 30024 770-945-9558
Nathan Ballantine, prin. Fax 271-5185
Peachtree Ridge HS 3,200/9-12
1555 Old Peachtree Rd NW 30024 678-957-3100
Dr. Jeff Matthews, prin. Fax 957-3108
Other Schools – See Buford, Dacula, Duluth, Grayson, Hoschton, Lawrenceville, Lilburn, Loganville, Norcross, Peachtree Crnrs, Snellville, Sugar Hill

Friendship Christian S 200/PK-12
3160 Old Atlanta Rd 30024 678-845-0418
Dr. Rick Johnson Ph.D., head sch Fax 845-0417

Swainsboro, Emanuel, Pop. 7,222
Emanuel County SD 4,000/PK-12
PO Box 130 30401 478-237-6674
Dr. Kevin A. Judy, supt. Fax 419-1102
www.emanuel.k12.ga.us
Swainsboro HS 800/9-12
689 S Main St 30401 478-237-2267
Dr. Denise Warnock, prin. Fax 419-1134
Swainsboro MS 600/6-8
200 Tiger Trl 30401 478-237-8047
Dr. Willie Gibson, prin. Fax 419-1148
Other Schools – See Twin City

East Georgia State College Post-Sec.
131 College Cir 30401 478-289-2000
Swainsboro Technical College Post-Sec.
346 Kite Rd 30401 478-289-2200

Sylvania, Screven, Pop. 2,925
Screven County SD 2,400/PK-12
PO Box 1668 30467 912-451-2000
William Bland, supt. Fax 451-2001
www.screven.k12.ga.us
Screven County HS 700/9-12
110 Halcyondale Rd 30467 912-451-2300
Brian Scott, prin. Fax 451-2301
Screven County MS 500/6-8
126 Friendship Rd 30467 912-451-2200
Dr. Bobby Costlow, prin. Fax 451-2201

Sylvester, Worth, Pop. 6,122
Worth County SD 3,400/PK-12
103 Eldridge St 31791 229-776-8600
Kay Mathews, supt. Fax 776-8603
www.worthschools.net
Worth County Comprehensive HS 900/9-12
406 W King St 31791 229-776-8625
Fax 776-8614
Worth County MS 800/6-8
1305 N Isabella St 31791 229-776-8620
Tiffany Sevier, prin. Fax 776-8624

Talbotton, Talbot, Pop. 965
Talbot County SD 500/PK-12
PO Box 308 31827 706-665-8528
Dr. Jack Catrett, supt. Fax 665-3620
www.talbot.k12.ga.us/
Central S 500/PK-12
PO Box 308 31827 706-665-8577
Jake Golden, prin. Fax 665-3946

Tallapoosa, Haralson, Pop. 3,111
Haralson County SD 3,600/PK-12
299 Robertson Ave 30176 770-574-2500
Jerry Bell, supt. Fax 574-2225
www.haralson.k12.ga.us
Haralson County HS 1,100/9-12
1655 Georgia Highway 120 30176 770-574-7647
Topher Byrnes, prin. Fax 574-7648
Haralson County MS 800/6-8
2633 Georgia Highway 120 30176 770-646-8600
Dr. Brian Ridley, prin. Fax 646-0108

Tallulah Falls, Rabun, Pop. 164

Tallulah Falls S 300/5-12
PO Box 10 30573 706-754-0400
Larry Peevy, head sch Fax 754-3595

Temple, Paulding, Pop. 4,145
Carroll County SD
Supt. — See Carrollton
Temple HS 600/9-12
589 Sage St 30179 770-562-3218
Tim Gribben, prin. Fax 562-1510

Temple MS 500/6-8
275 Rainey Rd 30179 770-562-6001
Gail Parmer, prin. Fax 562-6002
Villa Rica MS 500/6-8
614 Tumlin Lake Rd 30179 770-459-0407
Greta Jackson, prin. Fax 459-5496

Thomaston, Upson, Pop. 9,037
Thomaston-Upson County SD 4,200/PK-12
205 Civic Center Dr 30286 706-647-9621
Dr. Maggie Shook, supt. Fax 647-7154
www.upson.k12.ga.us
Upson-Lee Alternative S Alt
300 Adams St 30286 706-647-5738
Cristina Cunningham, prin. Fax 646-3160
Upson-Lee HS 1,300/9-12
268 Knight Trl 30286 706-647-8171
Tracy Caldwell, prin. Fax 646-9380
Upson-Lee MS 1,100/6-8
101 Holston Dr 30286 706-647-6256
Rhonda Gulley, prin. Fax 647-0011

Thomasville, Thomas, Pop. 18,212
Thomas County SD 5,600/PK-12
200 N Pinetree Blvd 31792 229-225-4380
Dr. George Kornegay, supt. Fax 225-5012
www.thomas.k12.ga.us
Renaissance Center Alt
200 N Pinetree Blvd 31792 229-227-3222
Sharon Monroe, prin. Fax 225-3223
Thomas County Central HS 1,400/9-12
4686 US Highway 84 Byp W 31792 229-225-5050
Trista Jones, prin. Fax 227-2422
Thomas County MS 1,700/5-8
4681 US Highway 84 Byp W 31792 229-225-4394
Jamie Thompson, prin. Fax 225-4378

Thomasville CSD 3,000/PK-12
404 N Broad St Ste 3 31792 229-225-2600
Sabrina Boykins-Everett, supt. Fax 226-6997
www.tcitys.org
MacIntyre Park MS 600/6-8
117 Glenwood Dr 31792 229-225-2628
Tina McBride, prin. Fax 225-3502
Scholars Academy 6-12
820 E Washington St 31792 229-228-3397
Dr. Dale Graham, dir. Fax 225-3525
Thomasville HS 800/9-12
315 S Hansell St 31792 229-225-2634
Todd Mobley, prin. Fax 225-2663

Brookwood S 500/PK-12
301 Cardinal Ridge Rd 31792 229-226-8070
Dr. Randolph Watts, hdmstr. Fax 227-0326
Southwest Georgia Technical College Post-Sec.
15689 US Highway 19 N 31792 229-225-4096
Thomas University Post-Sec.
1501 Millpond Rd 31792 229-226-1621

Thomson, McDuffie, Pop. 6,688
McDuffie County SD 4,300/PK-12
716 Lee St 30824 706-986-4000
Dr. Mychele Rhodes, supt. Fax 986-4001
www.mcduffie.k12.ga.us
McDuffie Achievement Center Alt
511 Main St 30824 706-986-4070
Steve Strouble, prin. Fax 595-4733
Thomson HS 1,200/9-12
1160 White Oak Rd 30824 706-986-4200
Carla Shelton, prin. Fax 986-4201
Thomson-McDuffie MS 1,000/6-8
1191 White Oak Rd 30824 706-986-4300
Anita Cummings, prin. Fax 986-4301

Tifton, Tift, Pop. 16,154
Tift County SD 7,500/PK-12
PO Box 389 31793 229-387-2400
Patrick Atwater, supt. Fax 386-1020
www.tiftschools.com
Eighth Street MS 1,200/7-8
700 8th St W 31794 229-387-2445
Dr. Chad Stone, prin. Fax 386-1036
Sixth Street Academy Alt
805 6th St W 31794 229-387-2485
Tom Mark, dir. Fax 386-1066
Tift County HS 1,600/10-12
1 Blue Devil Way 31794 229-387-2475
Kim Seigler, prin. Fax 386-1022
Tift County HS Northeast Campus 500/9-9
3021 Fulwood Rd 31794 229-387-2450
Scott Haskins, prin. Fax 386-1038

Abraham Baldwin Agriculture College Post-Sec.
2802 Moore Hwy 31793 229-391-5001
Moultrie Technical College Post-Sec.
52 Tech Dr 31794 229-391-2600

Tiger, Rabun, Pop. 402
Rabun County SD 2,300/PK-12
963 Tiger Connector 30576 706-212-4350
Melissa Williams, supt. Fax 782-6224
www.rabun.k12.ga.us
Rabun County HS 700/9-12
230 Wildcat Hill Dr 30576 706-782-4526
Jonathan Gibson, prin. Fax 782-7550
Rabun County MS 400/7-8
95 Wildcat Pride Way 30576 706-782-5470
Vicki Tyler, prin. Fax 782-4520

Toccoa, Stephens, Pop. 8,279
Stephens County SD 2,500/PK-12
191 Big A School Rd 30577 706-886-9415
Bryan Dorsey, supt. Fax 886-3882
www.stephens.k12.ga.us
Stephens County HS 1,100/9-12
323 Indian Trl 30577 706-886-6825
Sandy Steele, prin. Fax 886-8765
Stephens County MS 900/5-8
1315 Rose Ln 30577 706-886-2880
Joel Strickland, prin. Fax 886-2882

North Georgia Technical College Post-Sec.
8989 Highway 17 30577 706-779-8100

Toccoa Falls, Stephens

Toccoa Falls College Post-Sec.
107 Kincaid Dr, Toccoa GA 30577 706-886-6831

Trenton, Dade, Pop. 2,264
Dade County SD 2,200/PK-12
PO Box 188 30752 706-657-4361
Dr. Jan Harris, supt. Fax 657-4572
www.dadecountyschools.org
Dade County HS 600/9-12
300 Tradition Ln 30752 706-657-7517
Josh Ingle, prin. Fax 657-4854
Dade MS 500/6-8
250 Pace Dr 30752 706-657-6491
Jamison Griffin, prin. Fax 657-3055

Trion, Chattooga, Pop. 1,797
Trion CSD 1,400/PK-12
239 Simmons St 30753 706-734-2363
Dr. Phil Williams, supt. Fax 734-3397
www.trionschools.org/
Trion HS 400/9-12
919 Allgood St Ste 3 30753 706-734-7316
Bryan Edge, prin. Fax 734-7692
Trion MS 300/6-8
919 Allgood St Ste 2 30753 706-734-7433
Scott Crabbe, prin. Fax 734-7517

Tucker, DeKalb, Pop. 26,961
DeKalb County SD
Supt. — See Stone Mountain
Tucker HS 1,800/9-12
5036 Lavista Rd 30084 678-874-3702
James Jackson, prin. Fax 874-3746
Tucker MS 1,200/6-8
2160 Idlewood Rd 30084 678-875-0902
Dr. Kathy Cunningham, prin. Fax 875-0910

Le Cordon Bleu College of Culinary Arts Post-Sec.
1927 Lakeside Pkwy 30084 770-938-4711

Tunnel Hill, Whitfield, Pop. 854
Whitfield County SD
Supt. — See Dalton
Northwest Whitfield County HS 1,300/9-12
1651 Tunnel Hill Varnell Rd 30755 706-516-2200
Britt Adams, prin. Fax 673-7098

Twin City, Emanuel, Pop. 1,730
Emanuel County SD
Supt. — See Swainsboro
Emanuel County Institute 600/6-12
PO Box 218 30471 478-763-2673
Barry Joiner, prin. Fax 763-3834

Tyrone, Fayette, Pop. 6,701
Fayette County SD
Supt. — See Fayetteville
Flat Rock MS 800/6-8
325 Jenkins Rd 30290 770-969-2830
Jade Bolton, prin. Fax 969-2835
Sandy Creek HS 1,200/9-12
360 Jenkins Rd 30290 770-969-2840
Robert Hunter, prin. Fax 969-2838

Valdosta, Lowndes, Pop. 53,506
Lowndes County SD 10,900/PK-12
1592 Norman Dr 31601 229-245-2250
Wes Taylor, supt. Fax 245-2255
www.lowndes.k12.ga.us
Lowndes HS 3,000/9-12
1606 Norman Dr 31601 229-245-2260
LeAnne McCall, prin. Fax 245-2468
Lowndes MS 900/6-8
2379 Copeland Rd 31601 229-245-2280
Bill Haskin, prin. Fax 245-2470
Mathis Learning Center 400/Alt
1500 Lankford Dr 31601 229-245-2271
Dr. Derald Jones, dir. Fax 259-2273
Pine Grove MS 700/6-8
4159 River Rd 31605 229-219-3234
Ivy Smith, prin. Fax 219-3233
Other Schools – See Hahira

Valdosta CSD 8,200/PK-12
PO Box 5407 31603 229-333-8500
Dr. William Todd Cason, supt. Fax 247-7757
www.gocats.org
Horne Learning Center 200/Alt
PO Box 5407 31603 229-333-8597
K. Alan Hose, prin. Fax 333-0313
Newbern MS 800/6-8
PO Box 5407 31603 229-333-8566
Rick Thomas, prin. Fax 245-5655
Valdosta Early College Academy 6-12
PO Box 5407 31603 229-671-8455
Dr. Mae McKinney, prin. Fax 247-7689
Valdosta HS 2,000/9-12
PO Box 5407 31603 229-333-8540
Dr. Janice Richardson, prin. Fax 333-8584
Valdosta MS 900/6-8
PO Box 5407 31603 229-333-8555
Beth DeLoach, prin. Fax 245-5656

Georgia Christian S 200/PK-12
4359 Dasher Rd 31601 229-559-5131
Highland Christian Academy 200/K-12
4023 Pine Grove Rd 31605 229-245-8111
Ron Kooy, prin. Fax 245-8110
Open Bible Christian S 300/PK-12
3992 N Oak Street Ext 31605 229-244-6694
Valdosta State University Post-Sec.
1500 N Patterson St 31698 229-333-5800
Wiregrass Georgia Technical College Post-Sec.
4089 Val Tech Rd 31602 229-333-2100

Vidalia, Toombs, Pop. 10,364
Vidalia CSD 2,700/PK-12
301 Adams St 30474 912-537-3088
Dr. J. Garrett Wilcox, supt. Fax 538-0938
www.vidaliacity.schoolinsites.com

Trippe MS 600/6-8
2200 McIntosh St 30474 912-537-3813
Sandy Reid, prin. Fax 537-3223
Vidalia Comprehensive HS 800/9-12
1001 North St W 30474 912-537-7931
John Sharpe, prin. Fax 537-3006

Southeastern Technical College Post-Sec.
3001 E 1st St 30474 912-538-3100
Vidalia Heritage Academy 100/PK-12
PO Box 2005 30475 912-537-6679
Jeff McCormick, admin. Fax 226-3495

Vienna, Dooly, Pop. 3,989
Dooly County SD 1,400/PK-12
202 E Cotton St 31092 229-268-4761
Julie Harrelson, supt. Fax 268-6148
www.doolyschools.org
Dooly County HS 400/9-12
715 N 3rd St 31092 229-268-8181
Dr. Ed Mashburn, prin. Fax 268-1916
Other Schools – See Pinehurst

Villa Rica, Carroll, Pop. 13,578
Carroll County SD
Supt. — See Carrollton
Bay Springs MS 800/6-8
122 Bay Springs Rd 30180 770-459-2098
Marti Stephens, prin. Fax 459-2097
Villa Rica HS 1,600/9-12
600 Rocky Branch Rd 30180 770-459-5185
Glen Harding, prin. Fax 459-2119

Waco, Haralson, Pop. 513

West Georgia Technical College Post-Sec.
176 Murphy Campus Blvd 30182 770-537-6000

Waleska, Cherokee, Pop. 623

Reinhardt University Post-Sec.
7300 Reinhardt Cir 30183 770-720-5600

Warner Robins, Houston, Pop. 64,686
Houston County SD
Supt. — See Perry
Edge Academy, 400 Elberta Rd 31093 Alt
Shirley Randall, admin. 478-929-7801
Feagin Mill MS 800/6-8
1200 Feagin Mill Rd 31088 478-953-0430
Dr. Jesse Davis, prin. Fax 953-0438
Houston County Crossroads Center Alt
215 Scott Blvd 31088 478-929-7828
Dr. Ronnie Walker, prin. Fax 929-7118
Houston County HS 1,700/9-12
920 GA Highway 96 31088 478-988-6340
Dr. Douglas Rizer, prin. Fax 988-6341
Huntington MS 800/6-8
206 Wellborn Rd 31088 478-542-2240
Dr. Gwen Taylor, prin. Fax 542-2247
Northside HS 1,800/9-12
926 Green St 31093 478-929-7858
Dr. Greg Peavy, prin. Fax 929-7813
Northside MS 700/6-8
500 Johnson Rd 31093 478-929-7845
Jan Melnick, prin. Fax 929-7124
Warner Robins HS 1,700/9-12
401 S Davis Dr 31088 478-929-7877
Chris McCook, prin. Fax 929-7769
Warner Robins MS 800/6-8
425 Mary Ln 31088 478-929-7832
Brett Wallace, prin. Fax 929-7834

Central Geogia Technical College Post-Sec.
80 Cohen Walker Dr 31088 478-988-6800

Warrenton, Warren, Pop. 1,925
Warren County SD 700/PK-12
PO Box 228 30828 706-465-3383
Carole Carey, supt. Fax 465-9141
www.warren.k12.ga.us/
Warren County HS 100/9-12
1253 Atlanta Hwy 30828 706-465-3742
Trevor Roberson, prin. Fax 465-0901
Warren County MS 100/6-8
1253 Atlanta Hwy 30828 706-465-3742
Shauna Andrews, prin. Fax 465-0901

Briarwood Academy 300/PK-12
4859 Thomson Hwy 30828 706-595-5641
Clayton Parish M.Ed., hdmstr. Fax 595-0097

Washington, Wilkes, Pop. 4,057
Wilkes County SD 1,700/PK-12
313 N Alexander Ave Ste A 30673 706-678-2718
Dr. Rosemary Caddell, supt. Fax 678-3799
www.wilkes.k12.ga.us
Washington-Wilkes Comprehensive HS 500/9-12
1182 Tignall Rd 30673 706-678-2426
Robert Wheeler, prin. Fax 678-2628
Washington-Wilkes MS 400/6-8
1180 Tignall Rd 30673 706-678-7131
Deleki Lee, prin. Fax 678-3546

Watkinsville, Oconee, Pop. 2,786
Oconee County SD 6,700/K-12
PO Box 146 30677 706-769-5130
Dr. Jason Branch, supt. Fax 769-3500
www.oconeeschools.org/
Oconee County HS 1,000/9-12
2721 Hog Mountain Rd 30677 706-769-6655
Ben Wiggins, prin. Fax 310-2003
Oconee County MS 800/6-8
1101 Mars Hill Rd 30677 706-769-3575
Keith Carter, prin. Fax 310-2001
Other Schools – See Bogart

Westminster Christian Academy 300/PK-12
PO Box 388 30677 706-769-9372
Jared Clark, head sch Fax 769-2050

Waycross, Ware, Pop. 14,397
Ware County SD — 5,700/PK-12
1301 Bailey St 31501 — 912-283-8656
Jim LeBrun, supt. — Fax 283-8698
www.ware.k12.ga.us
Ware County HS — 1,500/9-12
700 Victory Dr 31503 — 912-287-2351
Bert Smith, prin. — Fax 287-2358
Ware County Learning Center — Alt
950 New Mexico Ave 31503 — 912-490-1055
Harold McClain, prin. — Fax 284-2054
Ware County MS — 700/6-8
2301 Cherokee St 31503 — 912-287-2341
Dr. Darlene Tanner, prin. — Fax 287-2353
Waycross MS — 600/6-8
700 Central Ave 31501 — 912-287-2333
David Hitt, prin. — Fax 287-2352

Okefenokee Technical College — Post-Sec.
1701 Carswell Ave 31503 — 912-287-6584
South Georgia State College — Post-Sec.
2001 S Georgia Pkwy W 31503 — 912-449-7600
Southside Christian S — 100/PK-12
3439 Knight Ave 31503 — 912-285-5438

Waynesboro, Burke, Pop. 5,700
Burke County SD — 4,400/PK-12
789 Burke Veterans Pkwy 30830 — 706-554-5101
Rudy Falana, supt. — Fax 554-8051
www.burke.k12.ga.us
Burke County Academy of Success — Alt
PO Box 1005 30830 — 706-554-8046
Dr. Chiquita Brady, prin. — Fax 554-8081
Burke County HS — 1,100/9-12
1057 Burke Veterans Pkwy 30830 — 706-554-6691
Dr. Kaveous Preston, prin. — Fax 554-8070
Burke County MS — 1,000/6-8
356 Southside Dr 30830 — 706-554-3532
Dr. Mona Reynolds, prin. — Fax 554-8063

Burke Academy — 400/PK-12
PO Box 787 30830 — 706-554-4479
Faith Christian Academy — 100/PK-12
726 GA Highway 24 S 30830 — 706-554-1577
Amy Grubb, prin. — Fax 554-2566

West Point, Troup, Pop. 3,435

Point University — Post-Sec.
507 W 10th St 31833 — 706-385-1000

White, Bartow, Pop. 658
Bartow County SD
Supt. — See Cartersville
Cass HS — 1,600/9-12
1000 Colonel Way NE 30184 — 770-606-5845
Mike Nelson, prin. — Fax 606-5467

Williamson, Pike, Pop. 334

CrossPointe Christian Academy — 100/PK-12
5224 Hollonville Rd 30292 — 770-412-6000
Kim Rogers, head sch

Winder, Barrow, Pop. 13,757
Barrow County SD — 12,900/PK-12
179 W Athens St 30680 — 770-867-4527
Dr. Chris McMichael, supt. — Fax 867-4540
www.barrow.k12.ga.us
Apalachee HS — 1,600/9-12
940 Haymon Morris Rd 30680 — 770-586-5111
Jennifer Martin, prin. — Fax 307-3726
Haymon-Morris MS — 700/6-8
1008 Haymon Morris Rd 30680 — 678-963-0602
Dr. James Bowen, prin. — Fax 867-1854
Russell MS — 800/6-8
364 W Candler St 30680 — 770-867-8181
Paul DeFoor, prin. — Fax 868-1215
Sims Academy of Innovation & Technology — Vo/Tech
985 Austin Rd 30680 — 770-867-7467
Dr. Douglas Blackwell, prin.
Westside MS — 700/6-8
240 Matthews School Rd 30680 — 770-307-2972
Dr. Brad Bowling, prin. — Fax 307-2976
Winder-Barrow HS — 1,800/9-12
272 N 5th Ave 30680 — 770-867-4519
Dr. Al Darby, prin. — Fax 867-6412
Other Schools – See Bethlehem, Statham

Winston, Douglas
Douglas County SD
Supt. — See Douglasville
Mason Creek MS — 800/6-8
7777 Mason Creek Rd 30187 — 770-651-2500
Eric Collins, prin. — Fax 920-4278

Woodbury, Meriwether, Pop. 960

Flint River Academy — 300/PK-12
PO Box 247 30293 — 706-553-2541
Tommy Amoroso, head sch — Fax 553-9777

Woodstock, Cherokee, Pop. 23,245
Cherokee County SD
Supt. — See Canton
Booth MS — 1,600/6-8
6550 Putnam Ford Dr 30189 — 770-721-5500
Dawn Weinbaum, prin.
Etowah HS — 2,400/9-12
6565 Putnam Ford Dr 30189 — 770-721-3120
Keith Ball, prin. — Fax 926-4157
Mill Creek MS — 1,200/6-8
442 Arnold Mill Rd 30188 — 770-721-6400
Dr. Kerry Martin, prin. — Fax 926-5439
Polaris Evening Program — 200/Alt
6565 Putnam Ford Dr 30189 — 770-721-3100
Dr. Curt Ashley, admin. — Fax 592-3509
River Ridge HS — 1,500/9-12
400 Arnold Mill Rd 30188 — 770-721-6500
Darrell Herring, prin. — Fax 721-6590
Woodstock HS — 2,000/9-12
2010 Towne Lake Hills S Dr 30189 — 770-721-3000
Mark Smith, prin. — Fax 592-3509
Woodstock MS — 1,100/6-8
2000 Towne Lake Hills S Dr 30189 — 770-721-3060
David Childress, prin. — Fax 591-8054

Cherokee Christian S — 400/K-12
3075 Trickum Rd 30188 — 678-494-5464
Michael Lee, supt. — Fax 592-4881
Lyndon Academy — 200/K-12
485 Toonigh Rd 30188 — 770-926-0166
Linda Murdock, hdmstr. — Fax 874-8686

Wrens, Jefferson, Pop. 2,160
Jefferson County SD
Supt. — See Louisville
Wrens MS — 300/6-8
PO Box 585 30833 — 706-547-6580
Julia Wells, prin. — Fax 547-6224

Wrightsville, Johnson, Pop. 2,174
Johnson County SD — 1,100/PK-12
PO Box 110 31096 — 478-864-3302
Rebecca Thomas, supt. — Fax 864-4053
www.johnson.k12.ga.us/
Johnson County HS — 300/9-12
150 Trojan Way 31096 — 478-864-2222
Elaine Merritt, prin. — Fax 864-4054
Johnson County MS — 300/6-8
150 Trojan Way 31096 — 478-864-2222
Elaine Merritt, prin. — Fax 864-4054

Young Harris, Towns, Pop. 891

Young Harris College — Post-Sec.
PO Box 68 30582 — 706-379-3111

Zebulon, Pike, Pop. 1,154
Pike County SD — 3,400/PK-12
PO Box 386 30295 — 770-567-8489
Dr. Michael Duncan, supt. — Fax 567-8349
www.pike.k12.ga.us/
Pike County HS — 1,100/9-12
331 Pirate Dr 30295 — 770-567-8770
Michael Maddox, prin. — Fax 567-3303
Pike County MS — 800/6-8
406 Hughley Rd 30295 — 770-567-3353
Dr. Vickie Smith, prin. — Fax 567-5054

HAWAII

HAWAII DEPARTMENT OF EDUCATION
PO Box 2360, Honolulu 96804-2360
Telephone 808-586-3230
Fax 808-586-3234
Website doe.k12.hi.us

Superintendent of Education   Kathryn Matayoshi

HAWAII BOARD OF EDUCATION
PO Box 2360, Honolulu 96804-2360

Chairperson   Lance Mizumoto

PUBLIC, PRIVATE AND CATHOLIC SECONDARY SCHOOLS

Aiea, Honolulu, Pop. 7,258
Hawaii SD
Supt. — See Honolulu
Aiea HS 1,100/9-12
98-1276 Ulune St 96701 808-483-7300
Kim Sanders, prin. Fax 483-7303
Aiea IS 600/7-8
99-600 Kulawea St 96701 808-483-7230
Tom Kurashige, prin. Fax 483-7235

Calvary Chapel Christian S 100/PK-12
98-1016 Komo Mai Dr 96701 808-524-0846
Rev. Edwin Arcalas, dir. Fax 275-5193

Ewa Beach, Honolulu, Pop. 10,071
Hawaii SD
Supt. — See Honolulu
Campbell HS 2,900/9-12
91-980 North Rd 96706 808-689-1200
Naomi Takamari, prin. Fax 689-1242
Ewa Makai MS 800/7-8
91-6291 Kapolei Pkwy 96706 808-687-9500
Edward Oshiro, prin. Fax 685-2052
Ilima IS 900/7-8
91-884 Fort Weaver Rd 96706 808-687-9300
Christopher Bonilla, prin. Fax 689-1258

Friendship Christian S 300/PK-12
91-1207 Renton Rd 96706 808-681-8838
James Reid, pres. Fax 681-5383
Lanakila Baptist HS 100/7-12
91-1219 Renton Rd 96706 808-681-3146
Rick Denham, prin. Fax 681-0704

Hana, Maui, Pop. 446
Hawaii SD
Supt. — See Honolulu
Hana S 300/K-12
PO Box 128 96713 808-248-4815
Richard Paul, prin. Fax 248-4819

Hilo, Hawaii, Pop. 26,125
Hawaii SD
Supt. — See Honolulu
Hilo HS 1,200/9-12
556 Waianuenue Ave 96720 808-974-4021
Robert Dircks, prin. Fax 974-4036
Hilo IS 500/7-8
587 Waianuenue Ave 96720 808-974-4955
Heather Dansdill, prin. Fax 974-6184
Waiakea HS 1,200/9-12
155 W Kawili St 96720 808-974-4888
Kelcy Koga, prin. Fax 974-4880
Waiakea IS 900/6-8
200 W Puainako St 96720 808-981-7231
Lisa Souza, prin. Fax 981-7237
Hilo Community S Adult
155 W Kawili St # P27 96720 808-974-4100
Chad Okinaka, prin. Fax 974-6170

Hawaii College or Oriental Medicine Post-Sec.
93 Banyan Dr Rm 504 96720 808-981-2790
Hawaii Community College Post-Sec.
200 W Kawili St 96720 808-934-2500
St. Joseph JSHS 100/7-12
1000 Ululani St 96720 808-935-4936
Llewellyn Young Ed.D., prin. Fax 969-9019
University of Hawaii at Hilo Post-Sec.
200 W Kawili St 96720 808-974-7414

Honokaa, Hawaii, Pop. 1,529
Hawaii SD
Supt. — See Honolulu
Honoka'a HS 700/7-12
45-527 Pakalana St 96727 808-775-8800
Rachelle Matsumura, prin. Fax 775-8803

Honolulu, Honolulu, Pop. 378,155
Hawaii SD 186,100/PK-12
PO Box 2360 96804 808-586-3230
Kathryn Matayoshi, supt. Fax 586-3234
www.hawaiipublicschools.org
Aliamanu MS 700/7-8
3271 Salt Lake Blvd 96818 808-421-4100
Robert Eggleston, prin. Fax 421-4103
Central MS 400/6-8
1302 Queen Emma St 96813 808-587-4400
Cindy Yun-Kim, prin. Fax 587-4409
Dole MS 800/6-8
1803 Kamehameha IV Rd 96819 808-832-3340
Mavis Tasaka, prin. Fax 832-3349
Farrington HS 2,400/9-12
1564 N King St 96817 808-832-3600
Alfredo Carganilla, prin. Fax 832-3587
Jarrett MS 300/6-8
1903 Palolo Ave 96816 808-733-4888
Reid Kuba, prin. Fax 733-4894
Kaimuki HS 800/9-12
2705 Kaimuki Ave 96816 808-733-4900
Wade Araki, prin. Fax 733-4929
Kaimuki MS 1,000/6-8
631 18th Ave 96816 808-733-4800
Frank Fernandes, prin. Fax 733-4810
Kaiser HS 1,200/9-12
511 Lunalilo Home Rd 96825 808-394-1200
Justin Mew, prin. Fax 394-1201
Kalakaua MS 1,000/6-8
821 Kalihi St 96819 808-832-3130
Lorelei Aiwohi, prin. Fax 832-3140
Kalani HS 1,300/9-12
4680 Kalanianaole Hwy 96821 808-377-7744
Mitchell Otani, prin. Fax 377-2483
Kawananakoa MS 900/6-8
49 Funchal St 96813 808-587-4430
Ann Sugibayashi, prin. Fax 587-4443
Kula Kaiapuni O Anuenue S 400/K-12
2528 10th Ave 96816 808-733-8465
Glen Miyasato, prin. Fax 733-8467
McKinley HS 1,700/9-12
1039 S King St 96814 808-594-0400
Ron Okamura, prin. Fax 594-0407
Moanalua HS 2,000/9-12
2825 Ala Ilima St 96818 808-837-8455
Robin Martin, prin. Fax 831-7919
Moanalua MS 800/7-8
1289 Mahiole St 96819 808-831-7850
Lisa Nagamine, prin. Fax 831-7859
Niu Valley MS 900/6-8
310 Halemaumau St 96821 808-377-2440
Sean Tajima, prin. Fax 377-2444
Radford HS 1,300/9-12
4361 Salt Lake Blvd 96818 808-421-4200
James Sunday, prin. Fax 421-4210
Roosevelt HS 1,400/9-12
1120 Nehoa St 96822 808-531-9500
Sean Wong, prin. Fax 587-4637
Stevenson MS 700/6-8
1202 Prospect St 96822 808-587-4520
Linell Dilwith, prin. Fax 587-4523
Washington MS 800/6-8
1633 S King St 96826 808-973-0177
Michael Harano, prin. Fax 973-0181
Farrington Community S Adult
1101 Kalihi St 96819 808-832-3595
Kenneth Furukawa, prin. Fax 832-3598
McKinley Community S Adult
634 Pensacola St Ste 216 96814 808-594-0540
Helen Sanpei, prin. Fax 594-0544
Moanalua Community S Adult
2825 Ala Ilima St Ste A 96818 808-837-8466
Lance Jyo, prin. Fax 831-7926
Other Schools – See Aiea, Ewa Beach, Hana, Hilo, Honokaa, Hoolehua, Kahuku, Kahului, Kailua, Kailua Kona, Kaneohe, Kapaa, Kapaau, Kapolei, Keaau, Kealakekua, Kihei, Lahaina, Lanai City, Laupahoehoe, Lihue, Makawao, Mililani, Pahala, Pahoa, Pearl City, Wahiawa, Waialua, Waianae, Wailuku, Waimea, Waipahu

---

Argosy University/Hawaii Post-Sec.
1001 Bishop St Ste 400 96813 808-536-5555
Assets S 400/K-12
1 Ohana Nui Way 96818 808-423-1356
Paul Singer, head sch Fax 422-1920
Babel University Professional School Post-Sec.
1833 Kalakaua Ave 96815 808-946-3773
Chaminade University of Honolulu Post-Sec.
3140 Waialae Ave 96816 808-735-4711
Christian Academy 400/PK-12
3400 Moanalua Rd 96819 808-836-0233
E. Rebecca Ducatt, prin. Fax 836-4415
Damien Memorial S 400/6-12
1401 Houghtailing St 96817 808-841-0195
Wes Porter, pres. Fax 847-1401
Hawaiian Mission Academy 100/9-12
1438 Pensacola St 96822 808-536-2207
Hawaii Baptist Academy 200/7-8
420 Wyllie St 96817 808-595-6302
Ronald Shiira, pres.
Hawaii Baptist Academy 500/9-12
420 Wyllie St 96817 808-595-6301
Ronald Shiira, pres. Fax 595-6354
Hawaii Institute of Hair Design Post-Sec.
1128 Nuuanu Ave Ste 102 96817 808-533-6596
Hawaii Pacific University Post-Sec.
1164 Bishop St 96813 808-544-0200
Hawaii School for the Deaf and the Blind Post-Sec.
3440 Leahi Ave 96815 808-733-4999
Hawaii Tokai International College Post-Sec.
2241 Kapiolani Blvd 96826 808-983-4100
Heald College Post-Sec.
1500 Kapiolani Blvd 96814 808-955-1500
Honolulu Community College Post-Sec.
874 Dillingham Blvd 96817 808-845-9211
Honolulu Waldorf HS 100/9-12
5257 Kalanianaole Hwy 96821 808-735-9311
Dr. Jocelyn Demirbag, dir. Fax 373-4982
Institute of Clinical Acupuncture Post-Sec.
100 N Beretania St Ste 203B 96817 808-521-2288
Iolani S 1,900/K-12
563 Kamoku St 96826 808-949-5355
Dr. Timothy Cottrell Ph.D., head sch Fax 943-2297
Kaimuki Christian S 300/PK-12
1117 Koko Head Ave 96816 808-732-1781
Dr. Mark Gallagher, prin. Fax 735-1354
Kamehameha S - Kapalama Campus 3,200/K-12
1887 Makuakane St 96817 808-842-8211
Debbie Lindsey, head sch Fax 842-8411
Kapiolani Community College Post-Sec.
4303 Diamond Head Rd 96816 808-734-9000
La Pietra - Hawaii S for Girls 200/6-12
2933 Poni Moi Rd 96815 808-922-2744
Mahina Hugo, head sch Fax 923-4514
Lutheran HS of Hawaii 100/6-12
1404 University Ave 96822 808-949-5302
Fax 947-3701
Maryknoll S 600/K-12
1526 Alexander St 96822 808-952-7200
Shawna Tong, prin. Fax 952-7201
Medical Assisting School of Hawaii Post-Sec.
33 S King St Ste 223 96813 808-524-3363
Mid-Pacific Institute 1,500/PK-12
2445 Kaala St 96822 808-973-5000
Dr. Paul Turnbull Ph.D., pres. Fax 973-5099
New Hope Christian College - Hawaii Post-Sec.
290 Sand Island Access Rd 96819 808-853-1040
Pacific Buddhist Academy 100/9-12
1710 Pali Hwy 96813 808-532-2649
Josh Hernandez Morse, head sch Fax 522-7395
Punahou S 3,700/K-12
1601 Punahou St 96822 808-944-5711
Dr. James Scott, pres. Fax 944-5762
Remington College Post-Sec.
1111 Bishop St Ste 400 96813 808-942-1000
Sacred Hearts Academy 1,100/PK-12
3253 Waialae Ave 96816 808-734-5058
Betty White, head sch Fax 737-7867
St. Andrew's S 400/PK-12
224 Queen Emma Sq 96813 808-536-6102
Dr. Ruth Fletcher, head sch Fax 538-1035
St. Francis S 300/PK-12
2707 Pamoa Rd 96822 808-988-4111
Sr. Joan of Arc Souza, prin. Fax 988-5497
St. Louis S 600/K-12
3142 Waialae Ave 96816 808-739-7777
Glenn Medeiros Ed.D., pres. Fax 739-4853
Travel Institute of the Pacific Post-Sec.
1314 S King St Ste 1164 96814 808-591-2708
University of Hawaii at Manoa Post-Sec.
2500 Campus Rd 96822 808-956-8111
World Medicine Institute Post-Sec.
1073 Hind Iuka Dr 96821 808-373-2849

Hoolehua, Maui
Hawaii SD
Supt. — See Honolulu
Moloka'i HS 300/9-12
PO Box 158 96729 808-567-6950
Stan Hao, prin. Fax 567-6960
Moloka'i MS 200/7-8
PO Box 443 96729 808-567-6940
Dawn Mains, prin. Fax 567-6939

Kahuku, Honolulu, Pop. 995
Hawaii SD
Supt. — See Honolulu
Kahuku JSHS 1,500/7-12
56-490 Kamehameha Hwy 96731 808-293-8950
Pauline Masaniai, prin. Fax 293-8960

Kahului, Maui, Pop. 18,567
Hawaii SD
Supt. — See Honolulu

Maui HS 1,900/9-12
660 Lono Ave 96732 808-873-3000
Bruce Anderson, prin. Fax 873-3010
Maui Waena IS 1,100/6-8
795 Onehee Ave 96732 808-873-3070
Jamie Yap, prin. Fax 873-3066
Maui Community S for Adults Adult
179 W Kaahumanu Ave 96732 808-873-3082
Kurt Ginoza, prin. Fax 873-3046

Maui College Post-Sec.
310 W Kaahumanu Ave 96732 808-984-3500

Kailua, Honolulu, Pop. 26,779
Hawaii SD
Supt. — See Honolulu
Kailua HS 800/9-12
451 Ulumanu Dr 96734 808-266-7900
Francine Honda, prin. Fax 266-7915
Kailua IS 700/7-8
145 S Kainalu Dr 96734 808-263-1500
Lisa DeLong, prin. Fax 266-7984
Kalaheo HS 900/9-12
730 Iliaina St 96734 808-254-7900
Susan Hummel, prin. Fax 254-7907
Olomana JSHS 100/7-12
42-522 Kalanianaole Hwy 96734 808-266-7866
Stacey Oshio, prin. Fax 266-7873
Windward School for Adults Adult
730 Iliaina St 96734 808-254-7955
John Vannatta, prin. Fax 254-7958

Le Jardin Academy 800/PK-12
917 Kalanianaole Hwy 96734 808-261-0707
D.J. Condon, head sch Fax 262-9339
Trinity Christian S 300/PK-12
875 Auloa Rd 96734 808-262-8501
Stephen Sprague, hdmstr. Fax 261-3916

Kailua Kona, Hawaii, Pop. 7,780
Hawaii SD
Supt. — See Honolulu
Kealakehe HS 1,400/9-12
74-5000 Puohulihuli St 96740 808-327-4300
Wilfred Murakami, prin. Fax 327-4307
Kealakehe IS 700/6-8
74-5062 Onipaa St 96740 808-327-4314
Joyce Crisafi, prin. Fax 327-4315
Kona Community S Adult
74-5000 Puohulihuli St 96740 808-327-4692
John Vannatta, prin. Fax 327-4693

Makua Lani Christian Academy 100/8-12
74-4966 Kealakaa St 96740 808-329-4898
Thaddea Pitts, prin. Fax 329-5898
Mauna Loa Helicopter Post-Sec.
73-310 UU St 96740 808-334-0234

Kamuela, Hawaii, Pop. 5,972

Hawaii Preparatory Academy 600/K-12
65-1692 Kohala Mountain Rd 96743 808-885-7321
Robert McKendry, head sch Fax 881-4003
Parker S 300/K-12
65-1224 Lindsey Rd 96743 808-885-7933
Carl Sturges Ph.D., hdmstr. Fax 885-6233

Kaneohe, Honolulu, Pop. 22,238
Hawaii SD
Supt. — See Honolulu
Castle HS 1,200/9-12
45-386 Kaneohe Bay Dr 96744 808-233-5600
Bernadette Tyrell, prin. Fax 233-5623
King IS 600/7-8
46-155 Kamehameha Hwy 96744 808-233-5727
Wendy Matsuzaki, prin. Fax 233-5747

Koolau Baptist Academy 200/K-12
PO Box 1642 96744 808-233-2900
Windward Community College Post-Sec.
45-720 Keaahala Rd 96744 808-235-7400

Kapaa, Kauai, Pop. 7,352
Hawaii SD
Supt. — See Honolulu
Kapa'a HS 1,000/9-12
4695 Mailihuna Rd 96746 808-821-4400
Daniel Hamada, prin. Fax 821-4420
Kapa'a MS 600/6-8
4867 Olohena Rd 96746 808-821-4460
Nathan Aiwohi, prin. Fax 821-6967

Kapaau, Hawaii, Pop. 1,135
Hawaii SD
Supt. — See Honolulu
Kohala HS 300/9-12
54-3611 Akoni Pule Hwy 96755 808-889-7117
Janette Snelling, prin. Fax 889-7120
Kohala MS 200/6-8
PO Box 777 96755 808-889-7119
Alan Brown, prin. Fax 889-7121

Kapolei, Honolulu, Pop. 8,781
Hawaii SD
Supt. — See Honolulu
Kapolei HS 2,000/9-12
91-5007 Kapolei Pkwy 96707 808-692-8200
Elden Esmeralda, prin. Fax 692-8255
Kapolei MS 1,500/6-8
91-5335 Kapolei Pkwy 96707 808-693-7025
Bruce Naguwa, prin. Fax 693-7030

American Renaissance Academy 100/K-12
PO Box 75357 96707 808-682-7337
Dr. Kelly Tanizaki, head sch Fax 682-7336
Island Pacific Academy 700/K-12
909 Haumea St 96707 808-674-3523
Gerald Teramae, head sch Fax 674-3575
University of Hawaii - West Oahu Post-Sec.
91-1001 Farrington Hwy 96707 808-689-2800

Keaau, Hawaii, Pop. 1,591
Hawaii SD
Supt. — See Honolulu
Kea'au HS 800/9-12
16-725 Keaau Pahoa Rd 96749 808-982-4220
Dean Cevallos, prin. Fax 982-4224
Kea'au MS 600/6-8
16-565 Keaau Pahoa Rd 96749 808-982-4200
Elna Gomes, prin. Fax 982-4219

Christian Liberty S 300/PK-12
16-675 Milo St 96749 808-966-8445
Troy Rimel, dir. Fax 966-8866
Kamehameha S - Hawaii Campus 1,100/K-12
16-716 Volcano Rd 96749 808-982-0000
Monica Naeole-Wong Ed.D., hdmstr. Fax 982-0010

Kealakekua, Hawaii, Pop. 1,317
Hawaii SD
Supt. — See Honolulu
Konawaena HS 700/9-12
81-1043 Konawaena School Rd 96750 808-323-4500
Shawn Suzuki, prin. Fax 323-4515
Konawaena MS 600/6-8
81-1045 Konawaena School Rd 96750 808-323-4566
Teddy Burgess, prin. Fax 323-4574

Kihei, Maui, Pop. 16,763
Hawaii SD
Supt. — See Honolulu
Lokelani IS 600/6-8
1401 Liloa Dr 96753 808-875-6800
Donna Whitford, prin. Fax 875-6835

Koloa, Kauai, Pop. 1,524

Kahili Adventist S K-12
2-4035 Kaumualii Hwy 96756 808-742-9294

Kula, Maui, Pop. 5,082

Haleakala Waldorf S 200/PK-12
4160 Lower Kula Rd 96790 808-878-2511
Kelly Brewer, admin. Fax 878-3341

Lahaina, Maui, Pop. 8,745
Hawaii SD
Supt. — See Honolulu
Lahaina IS 600/6-8
871 Lahainaluna Rd 96761 808-662-3965
Stacy Bookland, prin. Fax 662-3968
Lahainaluna HS 1,000/9-12
980 Lahainaluna Rd 96761 808-662-4000
Emily DeCosta, prin. Fax 662-3997

Maui Preparatory Academy 200/PK-12
PO Box 186 96767 808-665-9966
Dr. Jonathan Silver Ph.D., head sch Fax 665-1075

Laie, Honolulu, Pop. 2,912

Brigham Young University Post-Sec.
55-220 Kulanui St 96762 808-675-3211

Lanai City, Maui, Pop. 2,317
Hawaii SD
Supt. — See Honolulu
Lanai S 600/K-12
PO Box 630630 96763 808-565-7900
Elton Kinoshita, prin. Fax 565-7904

Laupahoehoe, Hawaii, Pop. 416
Hawaii SD
Supt. — See Honolulu
Laupahoehoe Community Public Charter S 50/9-12
PO Box 189 96764 808-962-2200
Nely Caberto, prin. Fax 962-2202

Lihue, Kauai, Pop. 4,702
Hawaii SD
Supt. — See Honolulu
Kamakahelei MS 900/6-8
4431 Nuhou St 96766 808-241-3200
Debra Badua, prin. Fax 241-3210
Kaua'i HS 1,200/9-12
3577 Lala Rd 96766 808-274-3160
Anne Kane, prin. Fax 274-3170
Kauai Community S for Adults Adult
3607A Lala Rd Ste P-12 96766 808-274-3390
Helen Sanpei, prin. Fax 274-3393

Island S 400/PK-12
3-1875 Kaumualii Hwy 96766 808-246-0233
L. Shannon Graves M.Ed., head sch Fax 245-6053
Kauai Community College Post-Sec.
3-1901 Kaumualii Hwy 96766 808-245-8311

Makawao, Maui, Pop. 4,664
Hawaii SD
Supt. — See Honolulu
Kalama IS 800/6-8
120 Makani Rd 96768 808-573-8735
John Costales, prin. Fax 573-8748
Kekaulike HS 1,000/9-12
121 Kula Hwy 96768 808-573-8710
Mark Elliott, prin. Fax 573-2231

Seabury Hall 400/6-12
480 Olinda Rd 96768 808-572-7235
Sarah Bakhiet, head sch Fax 572-7196

Mililani, Honolulu, Pop. 19,872
Hawaii SD
Supt. — See Honolulu
Mililani HS 2,500/9-12
95-1200 Meheula Pkwy 96789 808-627-7747
Fred Murphy, prin. Fax 627-7375
Mililani MS 1,700/6-8
95-1140 Lehiwa Dr 96789 808-626-7355
Elynne Chung, prin. Fax 626-7358

Hanalani S 700/PK-12
94-294 Anania Dr 96789 808-625-0737
Mark Sugimoto, head sch Fax 625-0691

Pahala, Hawaii, Pop. 832
Hawaii SD
Supt. — See Honolulu
Ka'u HS & Pahala ES 500/K-12
963150 Pikake St 96777 808-313-4100
Sharon Beck, prin. Fax 928-2092

Pahoa, Hawaii, Pop. 606
Hawaii SD
Supt. — See Honolulu
Pahoa JSHS 700/7-12
15-3038 Puna Rd 96778 808-313-4300
Darlene Bee, prin. Fax 965-2153

Paia, Maui, Pop. 1,965

Todd Memorial Christian S 200/PK-12
519 Baldwin Ave 96779 808-579-9237
Carolyn Moore, prin. Fax 579-9449

Pearl City, Honolulu, Pop. 36,969
Hawaii SD
Supt. — See Honolulu
Highlands IS 900/7-8
1460 Hoolaulea St 96782 808-453-6480
Amy Martinson, prin. Fax 453-6484
Pearl City HS 1,700/9-12
2100 Hookiekie St 96782 808-454-5500
Aaron Tominaga, prin. Fax 453-6521

Leeward Community College Post-Sec.
96-045 Ala Ike St 96782 808-455-0011

Pukalani, Maui, Pop. 4,987

Kamehameha Schools Maui 1,000/K-12
275 Aapueo Pkwy 808-572-3300
Kula Gaughen-Haili, hdmstr. Fax 572-3150

Wahiawa, Honolulu, Pop. 11,315
Hawaii SD
Supt. — See Honolulu
Leilehua HS 1,800/9-12
1515 California Ave 96786 808-305-3000
Jason Nakamoto, prin. Fax 622-6554
Wahiawa MS 800/6-8
275 Rose St 96786 808-622-6500
Ursula Kawaguchi, prin. Fax 622-6506
Wheeler MS 800/6-8
2 Wheeler Army Airfield 96786 808-622-6525
Brenda Vierra-Chun, prin. Fax 622-6529
Wahiawa Community S Adult
1515 California Ave 96786 808-305-3200
Wanelle Kaneshiro-Erdman, prin. Fax 621-7765

Ho'ala S 100/K-12
1067 California Ave Ste A 96786 808-621-1898

Waialua, Honolulu, Pop. 2,839
Hawaii SD
Supt. — See Honolulu
Waialua JSHS 600/7-12
67-160 Farrington Hwy 96791 808-637-8200
Avis Nanbu, prin. Fax 637-8209

Waianae, Honolulu, Pop. 4,907
Hawaii SD
Supt. — See Honolulu
Nanakuli JSHS 1,000/7-12
89-980 Nanakuli Ave 96792 808-668-5823
Darin Pilialoha, prin. Fax 668-5828
Wai'anae HS 1,800/9-12
85-251 Farrington Hwy 96792 808-697-9400
Disa Hauge, prin. Fax 697-7018
Wai'anae IS 900/7-8
85-626 Farrington Hwy 96792 808-697-7121
Raechelle Fabrao, prin. Fax 697-7124

Wailuku, Maui, Pop. 10,085
Hawaii SD
Supt. — See Honolulu
Baldwin HS 1,500/9-12
1650 Kaahumanu Ave 96793 808-984-5656
Catherine Kilborn, prin. Fax 984-5674
Iao IS 900/6-8
260 S Market St 96793 808-984-5610
Norma Barroga, prin. Fax 984-5617

St. Anthony MSHS 100/6-12
1618 Lower Main St 96793 808-244-4190
Betsey Gunderson, head sch Fax 242-8081

Waimea, Kauai, Pop. 1,080
Hawaii SD
Supt. — See Honolulu
Niihau S 50/K-12
PO Box 339 96796 808-338-6800
Nely Caberto, prin. Fax 338-6807
Waimea Canyon MS 400/6-8
PO Box 518 96796 808-338-6830
Melissa Speetjens, prin. Fax 338-6832
Waimea HS 600/9-12
PO Box 339 96796 808-338-6800
Mahina Anguay, prin. Fax 338-6807

Waipahu, Honolulu, Pop. 28,747
Hawaii SD
Supt. — See Honolulu
Waipahu HS 2,400/9-12
94-1211 Farrington Hwy 96797 808-528-9555
Keith Hayashi, prin. Fax 675-0257
Waipahu IS 1,300/7-8
94-455 Farrington Hwy 96797 808-675-0177
Randell Dunn, prin. Fax 675-0181
Waipahu Community S Adult
94-1211 Farrington Hwy 96797 808-528-9577
John Vannatta, prin. Fax 675-0259

IDAHO

IDAHO DEPARTMENT OF EDUCATION
PO Box 83720, Boise 83720-0003
Telephone 208-332-6800
Fax 208-334-2228
Website http://www.sde.idaho.gov

Superintendent of Public Instruction Sherry Ybarra

IDAHO BOARD OF EDUCATION
PO Box 83720, Boise 83720-0003

President Emma Atchley

PUBLIC, PRIVATE AND CATHOLIC SECONDARY SCHOOLS

Aberdeen, Bingham, Pop. 1,945
Aberdeen SD 58 — 800/PK-12
PO Box 610 83210 — 208-397-4113
Jane Ward, supt. — Fax 397-4114
aberdeen58.org/
Aberdeen HS — 200/9-12
PO Box 610 83210 — 208-397-4152
Travis Pincock, prin. — Fax 397-4439
Aberdeen MS — 200/6-8
PO Box 610 83210 — 208-397-3280
Ann Mennear, prin. — Fax 397-3281

American Falls, Power, Pop. 4,393
American Falls JSD 381 — 1,500/PK-12
827 Fort Hall Ave 83211 — 208-226-5173
Dr. Ron Bolinger, supt. — Fax 226-5754
www.sd381.k12.id.us
American Falls Academy — 50/Alt
598 Lincoln St 83211 — 208-226-5008
Cliff Hart, prin. — Fax 226-3194
American Falls HS — 400/9-12
2966 S Frontage Rd 83211 — 208-226-2531
Travis Hansen, prin. — Fax 226-5853
Thomas MS — 300/6-8
355 Bannock Ave 83211 — 208-226-5203
Randy Jensen, prin. — Fax 226-5274

Ammon, Bonneville, Pop. 13,621
Bonneville JSD 93
Supt. — See Idaho Falls
Hillcrest HS — 1,400/9-12
2800 Owen St 83406 — 208-525-4429
Doug McLaren, prin. — Fax 525-4437
Sandcreek MS — 800/7-8
2955 Owen St 83406 — 208-525-4416
Yvonne Thurber, prin. — Fax 525-4438

Arco, Butte, Pop. 974
Butte County JSD 111 — 400/PK-12
PO Box 89 83213 — 208-690-3410
Joel Wilson, supt. — Fax 527-8950
www.butteschooldistrict.org
Butte County HS — 100/9-12
PO Box 655 83213 — 208-690-3430
Robert Chambers, prin. — Fax 527-8246
Butte County MS — 100/6-8
PO Box 695 83213 — 208-690-3430
Robert Chambers, prin. — Fax 527-8246

Arimo, Bannock, Pop. 334
Marsh Valley JSD 21 — 1,300/PK-12
PO Box 180 83214 — 208-254-3306
Marvin Hansen, supt. — Fax 254-9243
www.mvsd21.org
Marsh Valley Alternative S — 50/Alt
12655 S Old Highway 91 83214 — 208-254-3711
Mike Welch, admin. — Fax 254-9230
Marsh Valley HS — 400/9-12
12655 S Old Highway 91 83214 — 208-254-3711
Mike Welch, prin. — Fax 254-9230
Marsh Valley MS — 200/7-8
12805 S Old Highway 91 83214 — 208-254-3260
Jason Brower, prin. — Fax 254-3631

Ashton, Fremont, Pop. 1,114
Fremont County JSD 215
Supt. — See Saint Anthony
North Fremont JSHS — 300/6-12
3581 E 1300 N 83420 — 208-652-7468
Drex Hathaway, prin. — Fax 652-7784

Bancroft, Caribou, Pop. 366
North Gem SD 149 — 200/PK-12
PO Box 70 83217 — 208-648-7848
Curry Donaldson, supt. — Fax 648-7895
www.sd149.com
North Gem JSHS — 100/7-12
PO Box 70 83217 — 208-648-7848
Curry Donaldson, admin. — Fax 648-7895

Blackfoot, Bingham, Pop. 11,732
Blackfoot SD 55 — 4,100/PK-12
270 E Bridge St 83221 — 208-785-8800
Brian Kress, supt. — Fax 785-8809
www.d55.k12.id.us
Blackfoot HS — 1,100/9-12
870 S Fisher Ave 83221 — 208-785-8810
Roger Thomas, prin. — Fax 785-2329
Independence Alternative HS — 200/Alt
155 E Francis St 83221 — 208-785-8825
Mark Kartchner, prin. — Fax 785-8893
Mountain View MS — 600/7-8
645 Mitchell Ln 83221 — 208-785-8820
Wes Jensen, prin. — Fax 785-8823

Snake River SD 52 — 1,800/PK-12
103 S 900 W 83221 — 208-684-3001
David Kerns, supt. — Fax 684-3003
www.snakeriver.org
Snake River HS — 500/9-12
922 W Highway 39 83221 — 208-684-3061
Ray Carter, prin. — Fax 684-3074
Snake River JHS — 300/7-8
918 W Highway 39 83221 — 208-684-3018
Bryce Salmon, prin. — Fax 684-3047

Bliss, Gooding, Pop. 316
Bliss JSD 234 — 100/K-12
PO Box 115 83314 — 208-352-4445
Kevin Lancaster, supt. — Fax 352-1954
www.bliss234.org
Bliss S — 100/K-12
PO Box 115 83314 — 208-352-4445
Kevin Lancaster, prin. — Fax 352-1954

Boise, Ada, Pop. 200,322
ISD of Boise City — 27,000/PK-12
8169 W Victory Rd 83709 — 208-854-4000
Dr. Don Coberly, supt. — Fax 854-4003
www.boiseschools.org
Boise SHS — 1,500/10-12
1010 W Washington St 83702 — 208-854-4270
Robb Thompson, prin. — Fax 854-4271
Borah SHS — 1,500/10-12
6001 W Cassia St 83709 — 208-854-4370
Tim Standlee, prin. — Fax 854-4371
Capital SHS — 1,400/10-12
8055 W Goddard Rd 83704 — 208-854-4490
Sandy Winters, prin. — Fax 854-4491
Church HS — 900/Alt
8051 W Salt Creek Dr 83709 — 208-854-5650
Derek Gardner, prin. — Fax 854-5651
East JHS — 600/7-9
5600 E Warm Springs Ave 83716 — 208-854-4730
David Greene, prin. — Fax 854-4731
Fairmont JHS — 700/7-9
2121 N Cole Rd 83704 — 208-854-4790
Brian Walker, prin. — Fax 854-4791
Hillside JHS — 600/7-9
3536 W Hill Rd 83703 — 208-854-5120
Nate Dennis, prin. — Fax 854-5121
Les Bois JHS — 600/7-9
4150 E Grand Forest Dr 83716 — 208-854-5340
Rich Clements, prin. — Fax 854-5341
North JHS — 900/7-9
1105 N 13th St 83702 — 208-854-5740
Jeff Roberts, prin. — Fax 854-5741
Professional Technical Education Center — Vo/Tech
8201 W Victory Rd 83709 — 208-854-5810
Dr. Irene Westrick, prin. — Fax 854-5811
Riverglen JHS — 700/7-9
6801 Gary Ln 83714 — 208-854-5910
Deb Watts, prin. — Fax 854-5911
South JHS — 700/7-9
3101 W Cassia St 83705 — 208-854-6110
Jeff Hultberg, prin. — Fax 854-6111
Timberline SHS — 1,100/10-12
701 E Boise Ave 83706 — 208-854-6230
Ted Hettinga, prin. — Fax 854-6232
Treasure Valley Math & Science Center — 50/7-12
6801 Gary Ln 83714 — 208-854-6800
Dr. Holly MacLean, admin. — Fax 854-6801
West JHS — 900/7-9
8371 W Salt Creek Dr 83709 — 208-854-6450
Janet Cherry, prin. — Fax 854-6451
Boise Evening S — Adult
8051 W Salt Creek Dr 83709 — 208-854-6700
Jeff Lamping, admin. — Fax 854-5676

West Ada SD
Supt. — See Meridian
Centennial HS — 1,700/9-12
12400 W Mcmillan Rd 83713 — 208-855-4250
Michael Farris, prin. — Fax 855-4273
Lake Hazel MS — 1,400/6-8
11625 W La Grange St 83709 — 208-855-4375
Scot Montoya, prin. — Fax 855-4399
Scott MS — 1,000/6-8
13600 W Mcmillan Rd 83713 — 208-350-4060
Linda Ventura, prin. — Fax 350-4074

Bishop Kelly HS — 700/9-12
7009 W Franklin Rd 83709 — 208-375-6010
Mike Caldwell M.Ed., prin. — Fax 375-3626
Boise Bible College — Post-Sec.
8695 W Marigold St 83714 — 800-893-7755
Boise State University — Post-Sec.
1910 University Dr 83725 — 208-426-1000
Carrington College — Post-Sec.
1122 N Liberty St 83704 — 877-206-2106
Milan Institute — Post-Sec.
8590 W Fairview Ave 83704 — 208-672-9500
Riverstone International School — 300/PK-12
5521 E Warm Springs Ave 83716 — 208-424-5000
Bob Carignan, head sch — Fax 424-0033
St. Alphonsus Regional Medical Center — Post-Sec.
1055 N Curtis Rd 83706 — 208-378-2000
Stevens-Henager College — Post-Sec.
1444 S Entertainment Ave 83709 — 208-336-7671

Bonners Ferry, Boundary, Pop. 2,493
Boundary County SD 101 — 1,500/PK-12
7188 Oak St 83805 — 208-267-3146
Gary Pflueger, supt. — Fax 267-7217
www.bcsd101.com
Bonners Ferry HS — 500/9-12
6485 Tamarack Ln 83805 — 208-267-3149
Kevin Dinning, prin. — Fax 267-5171
Boundary County MS — 300/6-8
6577 Main St Ste 100 83805 — 208-267-5852
David Miles, prin. — Fax 267-8099

Bruneau, Owyhee
Bruneau-Grand View JSD 365 — 300/PK-12
39678 State Highway 78 83604 — 208-834-2260
Dennis Wilson, supt. — Fax 834-2516
www.sd365.us
Rimrock JSHS — 200/6-12
39678 State Highway 78 83604 — 208-834-2260
Dennis Wilson, prin. — Fax 834-2516

Buhl, Twin Falls, Pop. 4,067
Buhl JSD 412 — 1,300/PK-12
920 Main St 83316 — 208-543-6436
Ronald Anthony, supt. — Fax 543-6360
www.buhlschools.org
Buhl HS — 300/9-12
1 Indian Territory 83316 — 208-543-8262
Ryan Bowman, prin. — Fax 543-8705
Buhl MS — 300/6-8
525 Sawtooth Ave 83316 — 208-543-8292
Suzanne Wilkin, prin. — Fax 543-5137

Burley, Cassia, Pop. 10,210
Cassia County JSD 151 — 5,500/PK-12
3650 Overland Ave 83318 — 208-878-6600
Dr. Gaylen Smyer Ph.D., supt. — Fax 878-4231
www.cassiaschools.org
Burley HS — 800/9-12
2100 Park Ave 83318 — 208-878-6606
Levi Power, prin. — Fax 878-6647
Burley JHS — 500/7-8
700 W 16th St 83318 — 208-878-6613
Steve Copmann, prin. — Fax 878-6624
Cassia JSHS — 100/Alt
1010 W 17th St 83318 — 208-878-6630
Lauri Heward, prin. — Fax 878-0822
Cassia Regional Technical Center — Vo/Tech
1143 W 16th St 83318 — 208-878-6610
Curtis Richins, prin. — Fax 878-6641
Other Schools – See Declo, Malta, Oakley

Caldwell, Canyon, Pop. 45,339
Caldwell SD 132 — 6,300/K-12
1502 Fillmore St 83605 — 208-455-3300
Dr. N. Shalene French, supt. — Fax 455-3302
www.caldwellschools.org
Caldwell HS — 1,300/9-12
3401 S Indiana Ave 83605 — 208-455-3304
Anita Wilson, prin. — Fax 455-3256
Canyon Springs Alternative HS — 400/Alt
516 N 11th Ave 83605 — 208-455-3325
Monica White, prin. — Fax 455-3341
Jefferson MS — 700/6-8
3311 S 10th Ave 83605 — 208-455-3309
Moss Strong, prin. — Fax 459-6773

Syringa MS 700/6-8
1100 Willow St 83605 208-455-3305
Shay Swan, prin. Fax 455-3353

Vallivue SD 139 9,500/PK-12
5207 S Montana Ave 83607 208-454-0445
Dr. Pat Charlton, supt. Fax 454-0293
www.vallivue.org
Rivervue Academy 100/Alt
21985 Dixie River Rd 83607 208-454-8899
Mary Ann VandeBrake, prin. Fax 454-8261
Vallivue Academy 200/Alt
6123 Timbre Pl 83607 208-455-1917
Mark Layne, prin. Fax 455-3567
Vallivue HS 1,800/9-12
1407 E Homedale Rd 83607 208-454-9253
Dick Brulotte, prin. Fax 459-7114
Vallivue MS 800/6-8
16412 S 10th Ave 83607 208-454-1426
Brian Lee, prin. Fax 454-7846
Other Schools – See Nampa

Gem State Academy 100/9-12
16115 S Montana Ave 83607 208-459-1627
Marvin Thorman, prin. Fax 454-9079
The College of Idaho Post-Sec.
2112 Cleveland Blvd 83605 208-459-5011

Cambridge, Washington, Pop. 325
Cambridge JSD 432 100/PK-12
PO Box 39 83610 208-257-3321
Ed Schumacher, supt. Fax 257-3323
www.cambridge432.org/
Cambridge MSHS 100/6-12
PO Box 39 83610 208-257-3311
Ed Schumacher, supt. Fax 257-3323

Carey, Blaine, Pop. 598
Blaine County SD 61
Supt. — See Hailey
Carey S 200/K-12
20 Panther Ln 83320 208-823-4391
John Peck, prin. Fax 823-4310

Cascade, Valley, Pop. 926
Cascade SD 422 300/PK-12
PO Box 291 83611 208-630-6057
Pal Sartori, supt. Fax 382-3797
www.cascadeschools.org
Cascade JSHS 100/7-12
PO Box 291 83611 208-630-6057
Joni Stevenson, prin. Fax 382-3797

Castleford, Twin Falls, Pop. 224
Castleford JSD 417 300/PK-12
500 Main St 83321 208-537-6511
Lyle Bayley, supt. Fax 537-6855
www.castlefordschools.com
Castleford S 300/PK-12
500 Main St 83321 208-537-6511
Lyle Bayley, supt. Fax 537-6855

Challis, Custer, Pop. 1,066
Challis JSD 181 400/K-12
PO Box 304 83226 208-879-4231
Peter McPherson, supt. Fax 879-5473
www.d181.k12.id.us
Challis JSHS 200/7-12
PO Box 304 83226 208-879-2255
Russ Bradshaw, prin. Fax 879-5801

Chubbuck, Bannock, Pop. 13,624

The School of Hairstyling Post-Sec.
141 E Chubbuck Rd 83202 208-232-9170

Clark Fork, Bonner, Pop. 519
Lake Pend Oreille SD 84
Supt. — See Ponderay
Clark Fork JSHS 100/7-12
PO Box 129 83811 208-255-7177
Phil Kemink, prin. Fax 266-1692

Coeur d Alene, Kootenai, Pop. 43,078
Coeur D'Alene SD 271 10,400/PK-12
1400 N Northwood Center Ct 83814 208-664-8241
Matthew Handelman, supt. Fax 664-1748
www.cdaschools.org
Canfield MS 800/6-8
1800 E Dalton Ave 83815 208-664-9188
Nick Lilyquist, prin. Fax 769-2951
Coeur D'Alene HS 1,400/9-12
5530 N 4th St 83815 208-667-4507
Troy Schueller, prin. Fax 664-5785
Lake City HS 1,600/9-12
6101 N Ramsey Rd 83815 208-769-0769
Deanne Clifford, prin. Fax 769-2944
Lakes Magnet MS 600/6-8
930 N 15th St 83814 208-667-4544
Jeff Bengtson, prin. Fax 769-7400
Venture HS 200/Alt
1619 N 9th St 83814 208-667-7460
Teresa Kaiser, prin. Fax 765-2299
Woodland MS 900/6-8
2101 W St Michelle 83815 208-667-5996
David Serwat, prin. Fax 667-5997

Lake City Junior Academy 200/PK-10
111 E Locust Ave 83814 208-667-0877
Adam Weeks, prin. Fax 665-1462
North Idaho College Post-Sec.
1000 W Garden Ave 83814 208-769-3300
The Headmasters School of Hair Design Post-Sec.
317 Coeur DAlene Lake Dr 83814 208-664-0541

Cottonwood, Idaho, Pop. 891
Cottonwood JSD 242 400/PK-12
PO Box 158 83522 208-962-3971
Rene' Forsmann, supt. Fax 962-7780
www.sd242.org
Prairie JSHS 200/7-12
PO Box 540 83522 208-962-3901
Carrie Nygaard, prin. Fax 962-7702

Summit Academy 100/PK-12
PO Box 427 83522 208-962-5650
James Hickel, prin. Fax 962-7129

Council, Adams, Pop. 826
Council SD 13 200/PK-12
PO Box 468 83612 208-253-4217
Murray Dalgleish, supt. Fax 253-4297
www.csd13.org/
Council JSHS 100/7-12
PO Box 468 83612 208-253-4217
Murray Dalgleish, supt. Fax 253-4297

Craigmont, Lewis, Pop. 493
Highland JSD 305 200/PK-12
PO Box 130 83523 208-924-5211
Brad Baumberger M.Ed., supt. Fax 924-5614
www.sd305.org
Highland S 200/PK-12
PO Box 130 83523 208-924-5211
Dr. Sarah Hatfield, prin. Fax 924-5614

Culdesac, Nez Perce, Pop. 380
Culdesac JSD 342 100/PK-12
600 Culdesac Ave 83524 208-843-5413
Alan Felgenhauer, supt. Fax 843-2719
pass.culsch.org
Culdesac S 100/PK-12
600 Culdesac Ave 83524 208-843-5413
Chase Woodford, prin. Fax 843-2719

Dayton, Franklin, Pop. 454
West Side JSD 202 700/PK-12
PO Box 39 83232 208-747-3502
Spencer Barzee, supt. Fax 747-3705
www.wssd.k12.id.us
Beutler MS 100/6-8
626 N Westside Hwy 83232 208-747-3303
Spencer Barzee, prin. Fax 747-3637
West Side HS 200/9-12
PO Box 39 83232 208-747-3411
Tyler Telford, prin. Fax 747-3990

Deary, Latah, Pop. 490
Whitepine JSD 288 200/K-12
PO Box 249 83823 208-877-1408
Dennis Coulter, supt. Fax 877-1570
www.sd288.k12.id.us
Deary S 200/4-12
PO Box 9 83823 208-877-1151
Doug Henderson, prin. Fax 877-1366

Declo, Cassia, Pop. 341
Cassia County JSD 151
Supt. — See Burley
Declo HS 300/9-12
505 E Main St 83323 208-654-2030
Roland Bott, prin. Fax 654-2404
Declo JHS 300/6-8
205 E Main St 83323 208-654-9960
Scott Muir, prin. Fax 654-2070

Dietrich, Lincoln, Pop. 330
Dietrich SD 314 300/PK-12
406 N Park St 83324 208-544-2158
Ben Hardcastle, supt. Fax 544-2832
www.sd314.k12.id.us
Dietrich S 300/PK-12
406 N Park St 83324 208-544-2158
Stefanie Shaw, prin. Fax 544-2832

Driggs, Teton, Pop. 1,636
Teton County SD 401 1,700/K-12
PO Box 775 83422 208-228-5923
Monte Woolstenhulme, supt. Fax 354-2250
tsd401.org
Basin JSHS Alt
510 N 1st E 83422 208-354-4800
Fax 354-2250
Teton HS 500/9-12
555 E Ross Ave 83422 208-228-5924
Frank Mello, prin. Fax 354-2907
Teton MS 400/6-8
935 N 5th E 83422 208-228-5925
Brian Ashton, prin. Fax 354-8685

Dubois, Clark, Pop. 673
Clark County SD 161 200/PK-12
PO Box 237 83423 208-374-5215
Daniel Lantis, supt. Fax 374-5234
www.clarkcountyschools161.org/
Clark County JSHS 100/6-12
PO Box 237 83423 208-374-5215
Daniel Lantis, supt. Fax 374-5234

Eagle, Ada, Pop. 19,545
West Ada SD
Supt. — See Meridian
Eagle Academy 200/Alt
100 S Academy Ave 83616 208-350-4220
James Buschine, prin. Fax 350-4234
Eagle HS 1,700/9-12
574 Park Ln 83616 208-350-4235
Terry Beck, prin. Fax 350-4254
Eagle MS 1,300/6-8
1000 W Floating Feather Rd 83616 208-350-4255
Tony Nelson, prin. Fax 350-4269
Idaho Fine Arts Academy 6-12
3467 W Flint Dr 83616 208-350-4420
Christian Housel, prin. Fax 350-4429

Emmett, Gem, Pop. 6,420
Emmett ISD 221 2,500/K-12
400 S Pine St 83617 208-365-6301
Wayne Rush, supt. Fax 365-2961
emmettschools.org
Black Canyon Alternative HS 100/Alt
400 S Pine St Ste 2 83617 208-365-5552
Stephen Joyner, prin. Fax 365-5085
Emmett HS 500/9-12
721 W 12th St 83617 208-365-6323
Wade Carter, prin. Fax 365-6100
Emmett MS 600/5-8
301 E 4th St 83617 208-365-2921
Larry Parks, prin. Fax 365-2427

Fairfield, Camas, Pop. 404
Camas County SD 121 200/K-12
610 Soldier Rd 83327 208-764-2625
Jim Cobble, supt. Fax 764-9218
www.camascountyschools.org/
Camas County HS 50/9-12
610 Soldier Rd 83327 208-764-2472
Jeff Rast, prin. Fax 764-2018

Filer, Twin Falls, Pop. 2,469
Filer SD 413 1,500/PK-12
700B Stevens Ave 83328 208-326-5981
Dr. John Graham, supt. Fax 326-3350
www.filer.k12.id.us
Filer HS 400/9-12
3915 Wildcat Way 83328 208-326-5944
Leon Madsen, prin. Fax 326-3419
Filer MS 300/7-8
299 Highway 30 83328 208-326-5906
Shane Hild, prin. Fax 326-3385

Firth, Bingham, Pop. 462
Firth SD 59 800/PK-12
319 Lincoln St 83236 208-346-6815
Sid Tubbs, supt. Fax 346-6814
www.firthschools.org
Firth HS 200/9-12
329 Lincoln St 83236 208-346-6812
Jeff Gee, prin. Fax 346-6987
Firth MS 200/5-8
410 Roosevelt St 83236 208-346-6240
David Mecham, prin. Fax 346-4306

Fruitland, Payette, Pop. 4,599
Fruitland SD 373 1,700/PK-12
PO Box A 83619 208-452-3595
Teresa Fabricius, supt. Fax 452-6430
www.fruitlandschools.org
Fruitland HS 500/9-12
PO Box A 83619 208-452-4411
Mike Fitch, prin. Fax 452-4485
Fruitland MS 400/6-8
PO Box A 83619 208-452-3350
Shane Burrup, prin. Fax 452-4063
Fruitland Preparatory Academy 50/Alt
PO Box A 83619 208-452-3360
Gayle VanWeerdhuizen, admin.

Garden Valley, Boise, Pop. 390
Garden Valley SD 71 200/PK-12
PO Box 710 83622 208-462-3756
Gregory Alexander, supt. Fax 462-3570
www.gvsd.net
Garden Valley S 200/PK-12
PO Box 710 83622 208-462-3756
Gregory Alexander, supt. Fax 462-3570

Genesee, Latah, Pop. 930
Genesee JSD 282 300/K-12
PO Box 98 83832 208-285-1161
Wendy Moore, supt. Fax 285-1495
www.sd282.org/
Genesee S 300/K-12
PO Box 98 83832 208-285-1161
Kelly Caldwell, prin. Fax 285-1495

Glenns Ferry, Elmore, Pop. 1,301
Glenns Ferry JSD 192 500/PK-12
800 Old Highway 30 83623 208-366-7436
Cody Fisher, supt. Fax 366-7455
www.glennsferryschools.org/
Glenns Ferry HS 100/9-12
639 N Bannock St 83623 208-366-7434
Cody Fisher, prin. Fax 366-2056
Glenns Ferry MS 100/6-8
639 N Bannock St 83623 208-366-7438
Rob Spriggs, prin. Fax 366-2056

Gooding, Gooding, Pop. 3,514
Gooding JSD 231 1,200/PK-12
507 Idaho St 83330 208-934-4321
Spencer Larsen, supt. Fax 934-4403
www.goodingschools.org
Gooding HS 300/9-12
1050 7th Ave W 83330 208-934-4831
Douglas Owen, prin. Fax 934-4347
Gooding MS 300/6-8
1047 7th Ave W 83330 208-934-8443
Chad Avery, prin. Fax 934-4898

Idaho State School for the Deaf/Blind Post-Sec.
1450 Main St 83330 208-934-4457

Grace, Caribou, Pop. 908
Grace JSD 148 400/PK-12
PO Box 347 83241 208-425-3984
Jamie Holyoak, supt. Fax 425-3809
www.sd148.org/
Grace JSHS 200/7-12
PO Box 348 83241 208-425-3731
Stephen Brady, prin. Fax 425-3063

Grangeville, Idaho, Pop. 3,096
Mountain View SD 244 1,200/PK-12
714 Jefferson St 83530 208-983-0990
Kent Stokes, supt. Fax 983-1245
www.sd244.org
Grangeville HS 300/9-12
910 S D St 83530 208-983-0580
Steve Higgins, prin. Fax 983-3786
Other Schools – See Kooskia

Greenleaf, Canyon, Pop. 835

Greenleaf Friends Academy 200/PK-12
PO Box 368 83626 208-459-6346
Ron Emry M.Ed., prin. Fax 459-7700

Hagerman, Gooding, Pop. 864
Hagerman JSD 233 400/K-12
324 N 2nd Ave 83332 208-837-6344
Eric Anderson, supt. Fax 837-6380
www.hagerman.k12.id.us
Hagerman JSHS 200/7-12
150 Lake St W 83332 208-837-4572
Mark Kress, prin. Fax 837-6502

Hailey, Blaine, Pop. 7,880
Blaine County SD 61 3,300/K-12
118 W Bullion St 83333 208-578-5000
Dr. GwenCarol Holmes, supt. Fax 578-5110
www.blaineschools.org/
Silver Creek HS 100/Alt
1060 Fox Acres Rd Ste 1000 83333 208-578-5060
Mike Glenn, admin. Fax 578-5160
Wood River HS 800/9-12
1250 Fox Acres Rd 83333 208-578-5020
John Pearce, prin. Fax 578-5120
Wood River MS 700/6-8
900 N 2nd Ave 83333 208-578-5030
Fritz Peters, prin. Fax 578-5130
Other Schools – See Carey

Hansen, Twin Falls, Pop. 1,129
Hansen SD 415 400/PK-12
550 Main St S 83334 208-423-6387
Kristin Beck, supt. Fax 423-6808
www.hansen.k12.id.us
Hansen JSHS 200/7-12
550 Main St S 83334 208-423-5593
Kayla Kelly, prin. Fax 423-6808

Harrison, Kootenai, Pop. 203
Kootenai SD 274 200/K-12
13030 E Ogara Rd 83833 208-689-3631
Lynette Ferguson, supt. Fax 689-3641
www.ksd-id.schoolloop.com
Kootenai JSHS 100/6-12
13030 E Ogara Rd 83833 208-689-3311
Tim Schultz, prin. Fax 689-9072

Hayden, Kootenai, Pop. 13,034

North Idaho Christian S 200/1-12
251 W Miles Ave 83835 208-772-7546
Cal Booth, admin. Fax 719-3000

Hazelton, Jerome, Pop. 738
Valley SD 262 600/PK-12
882 Valley Rd 83335 208-829-5333
Arlyn Bodily, supt. Fax 829-5548
www.valleyvikings.org
Valley S 600/PK-12
882 Valley Rd 83335 208-829-5353
Brian Hardy, admin. Fax 829-5548

Heyburn, Minidoka, Pop. 3,058
Minidoka County JSD 331
Supt. — See Rupert
Mt. Harrison JSHS 300/Alt
1431 17th St 83336 208-436-6252
Kelly Arritt, prin. Fax 436-4746

Homedale, Owyhee, Pop. 2,586
Homedale JSD 370 1,200/K-12
116 E Owyhee Ave 83628 208-337-4611
Rob Sauer, supt. Fax 337-4911
www.homedaleschools.org
Homedale HS 300/9-12
203 E Idaho Ave 83628 208-337-4613
Matt Holtry, prin. Fax 337-4933
Homedale MS 400/5-8
3437 Johnstone Rd 83628 208-337-5780
Amy Winters, prin. Fax 337-5782

Horseshoe Bend, Boise, Pop. 696
Horseshoe Bend SD 73 300/PK-12
398 School Dr 83629 208-793-2225
Dennis Chesnut, supt. Fax 793-2449
www.hsbschools.org
Horseshoe Bend MSHS 100/7-12
398 School Dr 83629 208-793-2225
Dennis Chesnut, admin. Fax 793-2449

Idaho City, Boise, Pop. 473
Basin SD 72 400/PK-12
PO Box 227 83631 208-392-4183
John McFarlane, supt. Fax 392-9954
www.idahocityschools.net
Idaho City MSHS 200/7-12
PO Box 227 83631 208-392-4183
John McFarlane, prin. Fax 392-9954

Idaho Falls, Bonneville, Pop. 55,872
Bonneville JSD 93 10,900/PK-12
3497 N Ammon Rd 83401 208-525-4400
Dr. Charles Shackett, supt. Fax 529-0104
www.d93schools.org
Bonneville HS 1,300/9-12
3165 E Iona Rd 83401 208-525-4406
Heath Jackson, prin. Fax 523-7014
Lincoln HS 300/Alt
3175 E Lincoln Rd 83401 208-525-4445
Lance Miller, prin. Fax 525-4446
Rocky Mountain MS 800/7-8
3443 N Ammon Rd 83401 208-525-4403
Jason Lords, prin. Fax 525-4469
Technical Careers HS Vo/Tech
3497 N Ammon Rd 83401 208-525-4433
Lyndon Oswald, prin. Fax 525-4434
Other Schools – See Ammon

Idaho Falls SD 91 10,500/PK-12
690 John Adams Pkwy 83401 208-525-7500
George Boland, supt. Fax 525-7596
www.d91.k12.id.us
Compass Academy 400/9-12
955 Garfield St 83401 208-525-7720
Matthew Bertasso, dir. Fax 525-7732
Eagle Rock MS 800/7-8
2020 Pancheri Dr 83402 208-525-7700
Matt Hancock, prin. Fax 525-7703
Eastern Idaho Professional Technical HS Vo/Tech
690 John Adams Pkwy 83401 208-525-7549
Bobbi Crosser Finlayson, coord. Fax 525-7640
Emerson Alternative HS 200/Alt
335 5th St 83401 208-524-7800
Robin Busch, prin. Fax 525-7795
Idaho Falls HS 1,300/9-12
601 S Holmes Ave 83401 208-525-7740
Bob Devine, prin. Fax 525-7768
Skyline HS 1,200/9-12
1767 Blue Sky Dr 83402 208-525-7770
Aaron Jarnagin, prin. Fax 525-7778
Taylorview MS 800/7-8
350 Castlerock Ln 83404 208-524-7850
Kathy Smith, prin. Fax 524-7851

Eastern Idaho Technical College Post-Sec.
1600 S 25th E 83404 208-524-3000
Stevens-Henager College Post-Sec.
901 Pier View Dr Ste 105 83402 208-522-0887
Watersprings S 500/PK-12
4250 S 25th E 83404 208-542-6250
Katheryn King, prin. Fax 441-6806

Jerome, Jerome, Pop. 10,745
Jerome JSD 261 3,800/PK-12
125 4th Ave W 83338 208-324-2392
Dale Layne, supt. Fax 324-7609
www.jeromeschools.org
Jerome HS 1,000/9-12
104 Tiger Dr 83338 208-324-8137
Nathan Tracy, prin. Fax 324-1266
Jerome MS 900/6-8
520 10th Ave W 83338 208-324-8134
Ryan Ellsworth, prin. Fax 324-7458
Northside Alternative JSHS 50/Alt
125 4th Ave W 83338 208-324-8137
Dale Layne, prin. Fax 324-1266

Juliaetta, Latah, Pop. 565
Kendrick JSD 283 300/PK-12
305 4th St 83535 208-289-4211
Dr. Lindsay Park Ph.D., supt. Fax 289-4201
www.dist283.org/
Other Schools – See Kendrick

Kamiah, Lewis, Pop. 1,246
Kamiah JSD 304 500/PK-12
1102 Hill St 83536 208-935-2991
Fred Mercer, supt. Fax 935-4005
www.kamiah.org/
Kamiah HS 100/9-12
1102 Hill St 83536 208-935-4067
Peggy Flerchinger, prin. Fax 935-4068
Kamiah MS 200/4-8
1102 Hill St 83536 208-935-4040
Jim Engledow, prin. Fax 935-4041

Kellogg, Shoshone, Pop. 2,083
Kellogg JSD 391 1,000/K-12
800 Bunker Ave 83837 208-784-1348
Woody Woodford, supt. Fax 786-3331
www.kelloggschools.org
Kellogg HS 400/9-12
2 Jacobs Gulch Rd 83837 208-784-1371
Curt Bayer, prin. Fax 783-0741
Kellogg MS 300/6-8
810 Bunker Ave 83837 208-784-1311
Jan Bayer, prin. Fax 784-0134

Kendrick, Latah, Pop. 297
Kendrick JSD 283
Supt. — See Juliaetta
Kendrick JSHS 100/7-12
2001 Highway 3 83537 208-289-4202
Steven Kirkland, prin. Fax 289-4213

Kimberly, Twin Falls, Pop. 3,233
Kimberly SD 414 1,700/K-12
141 Center St W 83341 208-423-4170
Luke Schroeder, supt. Fax 423-6155
www.kimberly.edu/
Kimberly HS 500/9-12
141 Center St W 83341 208-423-4170
Lisa Senecal, prin. Fax 423-5181
Kimberly MS 400/6-8
141 Center St W 83341 208-423-4170
Mathew Schvaneveldt, prin. Fax 423-6155

Kooskia, Idaho, Pop. 590
Mountain View SD 244
Supt. — See Grangeville
Clearwater Valley JSHS 200/6-12
PO Box 130 83539 208-926-4511
Randall Miskin, prin. Fax 926-4807

Kuna, Ada, Pop. 14,851
Kuna JSD 3 5,200/PK-12
711 E Porter St 83634 208-922-1000
Wendy Johnson, supt. Fax 922-5646
www.kunaschools.org
Initial Point HS 100/Alt
1080 N Ten Mile Rd 83634 208-472-9721
Lora Seabaugh, prin. Fax 472-9730
Kuna HS 1,300/9-12
637 E Deer Flat Rd 83634 208-955-0200
Brian Graves, prin. Fax 922-2178
Kuna MS 800/7-8
1360 Boise St 83634 208-922-1002
Deb McGrath, prin. Fax 922-1030

Lapwai, Nez Perce, Pop. 1,098
Lapwai SD 341 500/PK-12
404 S Main St 83540 208-843-2622
Dr. David Aiken, supt. Fax 843-7746
www.lapwai.org
Lapwai JSHS 200/6-12
404 S Main St 83540 208-843-2241
D'Lisa Pinkham, prin. Fax 843-5289

Leadore, Lemhi, Pop. 105
South Lemhi SD 292 100/PK-12
PO Box 119 83464 208-768-2441
Michael Jacobson, supt. Fax 768-2797
www.leadoreschool.org
Leadore S 100/PK-12
PO Box 119 83464 208-768-2441
Michael Jacobson, prin. Fax 768-2797

Lewiston, Nez Perce, Pop. 31,213
Lewiston ISD 1 5,000/PK-12
3317 12th St 83501 208-748-3000
Dr. Robert Donaldson, supt. Fax 748-3059
www.lewistonschools.net
Jenifer JHS 600/7-9
1213 16th St 83501 208-748-3300
JoAnne Greear, prin. Fax 748-3349
Lewiston SHS 1,000/10-12
1114 9th Ave 83501 208-748-3100
Kevin Driskill, prin. Fax 748-3149
Sacajawea JHS 600/7-9
3610 12th St 83501 208-748-3400
Phil Uhlorn, prin. Fax 748-3449
Tammany Alternative Learning Center 200/Alt
1982 Tammany Creek Rd 83501 208-748-3270
Greg Kramasz, admin. Fax 748-3299

Confluence Christian HS 50/9-12
PO Box 1852 83501 208-731-6320
Ross Carlton, prin.
Lewis-Clark State College Post-Sec.
500 8th Ave 83501 208-792-5272
Mr. Leon's School of Hair Design Post-Sec.
205 10th St 83501 208-743-6822
The Headmasters School of Hair Design Post-Sec.
602 Main St 83501 208-743-1512

Mc Call, Valley, Pop. 2,959
McCall-Donnelly JSD 421 1,100/PK-12
120 Idaho St 83638 208-634-2161
Jim Foudy, supt. Fax 634-4075
www.mdsd.org
Heartland Alternative S 50/Alt
124 Idaho St 83638 208-634-3686
David Pickard, prin. Fax 634-1512
McCall-Donnelly HS 300/9-12
401 N Mission St 83638 208-634-2218
Tim Thomas, prin. Fax 634-7505
Payette Lakes MS 200/6-8
111 S Samson Trl 83638 208-634-5994
Susan Buescher, prin. Fax 634-5231

Mackay, Custer, Pop. 515
Mackay JSD 182 200/PK-12
PO Box 390 83251 208-588-2896
Leigh Patterson, supt. Fax 588-2269
mackayschools.org
Mackay JSHS 100/7-12
PO Box 390 83251 208-588-2262
Leigh Patterson, prin. Fax 588-2549

Malad City, Oneida, Pop. 2,070
Oneida County SD 351 900/PK-12
25 E 50 S Ste A 83252 208-534-6080
Dr. Rich Moore, supt. Fax 534-6080
www.oneidaschooldistrict.org
Malad HS 300/9-12
181 Jenkins Ave 83252 208-497-2588
Rob O'Neal, prin. Fax 497-2588
Malad MS 200/6-8
175 Jenkins Ave 83252 208-497-5877
Sheldon Vaughan, prin. Fax 497-5877
Oneida Alternative HS 50/Alt
300 W 450 N 83252 208-497-5877
Terri Sorensen, prin. Fax 497-5877

Malta, Cassia, Pop. 193
Cassia County JSD 151
Supt. — See Burley
Raft River JSHS 100/7-12
PO Box 68 83342 208-645-2220
Eric Boden, prin. Fax 645-2640

Marsing, Owyhee, Pop. 1,018
Marsing JSD 363 900/K-12
PO Box 340 83639 208-896-4111
Norm Stewart, supt. Fax 896-4790
www.marsingschools.org/
Marsing HS 200/9-12
PO Box 340 83639 208-896-4111
Tim Little, prin. Fax 896-4457
Marsing MS 200/6-8
PO Box 340 83639 208-896-4111
Nick Ketterling, prin. Fax 896-5128

Melba, Canyon, Pop. 503
Melba JSD 136 800/PK-12
PO Box 185 83641 208-495-1141
Andy Grover, supt. Fax 495-1142
www.melbaschools.org
Melba JSHS 400/7-12
PO Box 185 83641 208-495-2221
Eric Forsgren, prin. Fax 495-2188

Menan, Jefferson, Pop. 728
Jefferson County JSD 251
Supt. — See Rigby
Jefferson HS 100/Alt
529 N 3470 E 83434 208-754-4550
Eric Jensen, prin. Fax 754-4581

Meridian, Ada, Pop. 73,335
West Ada SD 36,800/PK-12
1303 E Central Dr 83642 208-855-4500
Dr. Mary Ann Ranells, supt. Fax 350-5962
www.westada.org
Central Academy 200/Alt
6075 N Locust Grove Rd, 208-855-4325
Donell McNeal, prin. Fax 855-4324
Crossroads MS 200/Alt
650 N Nola Rd 83642 208-855-4275
Karen Harr, prin. Fax 855-4284
Heritage MS 1,100/6-8
4990 N Meridian Rd, 208-350-4130
Susan McInerney, prin. Fax 350-4139
Lewis & Clark MS 1,100/6-8
4141 E Pine Ave 83642 208-350-4270
Kelly Davies, prin. Fax 350-4284
Meridian Academy 200/Alt
2311 E Lanark St 83642 208-855-4315
Dustin Barrett, prin. Fax 855-4326
Meridian HS 1,500/9-12
1900 W Pine Ave 83642 208-350-4160
Jill Lillenkamp, prin. Fax 350-4178
Meridian MS 1,000/6-8
1507 W 8th St 83642 208-855-4225
Lisa Austin, prin. Fax 855-4248

Mountain View HS 2,200/9-12
2000 S Millenium Way 83642 208-855-4050
Aaron Maybon, prin. Fax 855-4074
Pathways MS 100/Alt
1855 E Heritage Park Ln, 208-350-4040
Dr. Eric Eschen, prin. Fax 350-4059
Rebound School of Opportunity 100/Alt
1450 E Watertower St 83642 208-350-5232
Mike Hanneman, prin. Fax 350-5179
Renaissance HS 700/9-12
1307 E Central Dr 83642 208-350-4380
Dr. Shana Hawkins, prin. Fax 350-4399
Rocky Mountain HS 2,100/9-12
5450 N Linder Rd, 208-350-4340
Mike Hirano, prin. Fax 350-4369
Sawtooth MS 1,000/6-8
3730 N Linder Rd, 208-855-4200
Kevin Leishman, prin. Fax 855-4224
Victory MS 6-8
920 W Kodiak Dr 83642 208-350-4443
Brett Heller, prin. Fax 350-4444
Other Schools – See Boise, Eagle

Ambrose S 400/K-12
6100 N Locust Grove Rd, 208-323-3888
Kirk VanderLeest, hdmstr. Fax 672-0522
Broadview College Post-Sec.
2750 E Gala St 83642 208-577-2900
Cole Valley Christian S 300/7-12
200 E Carlton Ave 83642 208-947-1212
Brad Carr, supt. Fax 898-9290
Covenant Academy 50/K-12
2400 E Fairview Ave 83642 208-377-2385
David Barrett, admin. Fax 377-8061
Northwest Lineman College Post-Sec.
7600 S Meridian Rd 83642 208-888-4817
Sheridan Academy 50/6-12
2273 E Gala St Ste 120 83642 208-331-2044

Middleton, Canyon, Pop. 5,406
Middleton SD 134 3,700/PK-12
5 S 3rd Ave W 83644 208-585-3027
Dr. Rich Bauscher, supt. Fax 585-3028
www.msd134.org
ATLAS S 100/Alt
200 S 4th Ave W 83644 208-585-3027
Christine McMillan, hdmstr. Fax 585-3028
Middleton HS 1,100/9-12
1538 Emmett Rd 83644 208-585-6657
Mike Williams, prin. Fax 585-3362
Middleton MS 900/6-8
511 W Main St 83644 208-585-3251
Andrew Horning, prin. Fax 585-2098

Midvale, Washington, Pop. 169
Midvale SD 433 100/K-12
PO Box 130 83645 208-355-2234
James Warren, supt. Fax 355-2347
www.midvalerangers.org
Midvale Alternative S 50/Alt
PO Box 130 83645 208-355-2234
KyLee Morris, prin. Fax 355-2347
Midvale S 100/K-12
PO Box 130 83645 208-355-2234
James Warren, prin. Fax 355-2347

Montpelier, Bear Lake, Pop. 2,578
Bear Lake County SD 33
Supt. — See Paris
Bear Lake HS 300/9-12
330 Boise St 83254 208-847-0294
Luke Kelsey, prin. Fax 847-0144
Bear Lake MS 300/6-8
633 Washington St 83254 208-847-2255
Dr. Steve Heeder, prin. Fax 847-3626

Moscow, Latah, Pop. 23,195
Moscow SD 281 2,400/PK-12
650 N Cleveland St 83843 208-882-1120
Greg Bailey, supt. Fax 883-4440
www.msd281.org
Moscow HS 800/9-12
402 E 5th St 83843 208-882-2591
Erik Perryman, prin. Fax 892-1136
Moscow MS 600/6-8
1410 E D St 83843 208-882-3577
Kevin Hill, prin. Fax 892-1182
Paradise Creek Regional HS 50/Alt
1314 S Main St 83843 208-882-3687
William Marineau, prin. Fax 882-6815

Logos S 400/PK-12
110 Baker St 83843 208-882-1226
Mr. Leon's School of Hair Design Post-Sec.
618 S Main St 83843 208-882-2923
New Saint Andrews College Post-Sec.
PO Box 9025 83843 208-882-1566
University of Idaho Post-Sec.
PO Box 444264 83844 208-885-6111

Mountain Home, Elmore, Pop. 13,628
Mountain Home SD 193 3,400/PK-12
PO Box 1390 83647 208-587-2580
James Gilbert, supt. Fax 587-9896
www.mtnhomesd.org
Bennett Mountain HS 100/Alt
560 E Jackson St 83647 208-587-3837
Stehvn Tesar, prin. Fax 587-2564
Mountain Home JHS 300/8-9
1600 E 6th S 83647 208-587-2590
Sam Gunderson, prin. Fax 587-2597
Mountain Home SHS 700/10-12
300 S 11th E 83647 208-587-2570
Jeff Johnson, prin. Fax 587-2579

Mullan, Shoshone, Pop. 674
Mullan SD 392 100/K-12
PO Box 71 83846 208-744-1118
Robin Stanley, supt. Fax 744-1119
www.mullanschools.com
Mullan JSHS 50/7-12
PO Box 71 83846 208-744-1126
Tom Durbin, prin. Fax 744-1128

Murtaugh, Twin Falls, Pop. 114
Murtaugh JSD 418 200/PK-12
PO Box 117 83344 208-432-5451
Michele Capps, supt. Fax 432-5477
www.murtaugh.k12.id.us/
Murtaugh HS 100/9-12
PO Box 117 83344 208-432-5451
Adam Johnson, prin. Fax 432-5477
Murtaugh MS 100/6-8
PO Box 117 83344 208-432-5451
Adam Johnson, prin. Fax 432-5477

Nampa, Canyon, Pop. 79,667
Nampa SD 131 15,400/PK-12
619 S Canyon St 83686 208-468-4600
David Peterson, supt. Fax 468-4638
www.nsd131.org/
Columbia HS 1,300/9-12
301 S Happy Valley Rd 83687 208-498-0571
Cory Woolstenhulme, prin. Fax 498-0573
East Valley MS 1,000/6-8
4085 E Greenhurst Rd 83686 208-468-4760
Matt Crist, admin. Fax 468-4762
Gateways Alternative S Alt
94 N Canyon St 83651 208-498-0557
Cyndi Cook, prin. Fax 468-2834
Lone Star MS 900/6-8
11055 Lone Star Rd 83651 208-468-4745
Greg Heideman, prin. Fax 468-2828
Nampa HS 1,500/9-12
203 Lake Lowell Ave 83686 208-498-0551
Diana Molino, prin. Fax 468-2829
Skyview HS 1,300/9-12
1303 E Greenhurst Rd 83686 208-498-0561
William Barber, prin. Fax 468-2833
South MS 900/6-8
229 W Greenhurst Rd 83686 208-468-4740
Stuart Vickers, prin. Fax 468-2826
Union HS 200/Alt
506 Fletcher Dr 83686 208-498-0559
Carleen Schnitker, prin. Fax 468-2832
West MS 700/6-8
28 S Midland Blvd 83651 208-468-4750
Stefanie Duby, prin. Fax 468-2809

Vallivue SD 139
Supt. — See Caldwell
Ridgevue HS 1,300/9-12
18800 Madison Rd 83687 208-453-4480
Julie Yamamoto Ph.D., admin.
Sage Valley MS 900/6-8
18070 Santa Ana Ave 83687 208-468-4919
Sean Smith, prin. Fax 468-4904

Calvary Chapel Christian S 100/PK-12
1210 N Middleton Rd 83651 208-467-9114
College of Western Idaho Post-Sec.
5500 Opportunity Dr 83687 208-562-3000
Milan Institute Post-Sec.
1021 W Hemingway Blvd 83651 208-461-0616
Nampa Christian HS 200/6-12
11920 W Flamingo Ave 83651 208-466-8451
Dr. Greg Wiles Ed.D., supt. Fax 475-1741
Northwest Nazarene University Post-Sec.
623 S University Blvd 83686 208-467-8011
Razzle Dazzle College of Hair Design Post-Sec.
721 E Roosevelt Ave 83686 208-465-7660

New Meadows, Adams, Pop. 492
Meadows Valley SD 11 200/PK-12
PO Box F 83654 208-347-2411
Mike Howard, supt. Fax 347-2624
www.mvsd11.org
Meadows Valley S 200/PK-12
PO Box F 83654 208-347-2118
Mike Howard, supt. Fax 347-2624

New Plymouth, Payette, Pop. 1,508
New Plymouth SD 372 1,000/PK-12
103 SE Avenue 83655 208-278-5740
Kevin Barker, supt. Fax 278-3069
npschoolsidaho.wordpress.com
New Plymouth HS 300/9-12
207 S Plymouth Ave 83655 208-278-5311
Clete Edmunson, prin. Fax 278-5313
New Plymouth MS 200/6-8
4400 SW 2nd Ave 83655 208-278-5788
Sean King, prin. Fax 278-3773

Nezperce, Lewis, Pop. 463
Nezperce JSD 302 100/PK-12
PO Box 279 83543 208-937-2551
Dennis Kachelmier, supt. Fax 937-2136
www.nezpercesd.us/
Nezperce S 100/PK-12
PO Box 279 83543 208-937-2551
Les Wells, prin. Fax 937-2136

Notus, Canyon, Pop. 520
Notus SD 135 400/K-12
PO Box 256 83656 208-459-7442
Craig Woods, supt. Fax 453-1027
www.notusschools.org
Notus JSHS 200/7-12
PO Box 256 83656 208-459-4633
Craig Woods, prin. Fax 459-6304

Oakley, Cassia, Pop. 762
Cassia County JSD 151
Supt. — See Burley
Oakley JSHS 200/7-12
455 W Main St 83346 208-862-3328
Michael Corbett, prin. Fax 862-3330

Oldtown, Bonner, Pop. 183

House of the Lord Christian Academy 100/PK-12
754 Silver Birch Ln 83822 208-437-2184
Candace Craddick, prin. Fax 437-0441

Orofino, Clearwater, Pop. 3,071
Orofino JSD 171 900/PK-12
1051 Michigan Ave 83544 208-476-5593
Robert Vian, supt. Fax 476-7293
www.sd171.k12.id.us
Orofino HS 400/7-12
300 Dunlap Rd 83544 208-476-5557
Dan Hull, prin. Fax 476-0147
Other Schools – See Weippe

Paris, Bear Lake, Pop. 510
Bear Lake County SD 33 1,100/PK-12
PO Box 300 83261 208-945-2891
Dr. Gary Brogan, supt. Fax 945-2893
blsd.net
Other Schools – See Montpelier

Parma, Canyon, Pop. 1,955
Parma SD 137 1,100/K-12
805 E McConnell Ave 83660 208-722-5115
Jim Norton, supt. Fax 722-7937
www.parmaschools.org
Parma HS 300/9-12
137 Panther Way 83660 208-722-5115
David Carson, prin. Fax 722-7153
Parma MS 300/5-8
905 E McConnell Ave 83660 208-722-5115
Peggy Sharkey, prin. Fax 722-6913

Paul, Minidoka, Pop. 1,146
Minidoka County JSD 331
Supt. — See Rupert
West Minico MS 400/6-8
155 S 600 W 83347 208-438-5018
Tim Perrigot, prin. Fax 438-8513

Payette, Payette, Pop. 7,244
Payette JSD 371 1,600/PK-12
20 N 12th St 83661 208-642-9366
Pauline King, supt. Fax 642-9006
www.payetteschools.org/
McCain MS 400/6-8
400 N Iowa Ave 83661 208-642-4122
Rick Hale, prin. Fax 642-2171
Payette HS 400/9-12
1500 6th Ave S 83661 208-642-3327
Mark Heleker, prin. Fax 642-3368

Plummer, Benewah, Pop. 956
Plummer/Worley JSD 44 300/PK-12
PO Box 130 83851 208-686-1621
Judi Sharrett, supt. Fax 686-2108
www.pwsd44.com
Lakeside JSHS 100/7-12
PO Box 130 83851 208-686-1937
Jennifer Hall, prin. Fax 686-2207

Pocatello, Bannock, Pop. 53,083
Pocatello/Chubbuck SD 25 12,500/PK-12
3115 Pole Line Rd 83201 208-232-3563
Dr. Douglas Howell, supt. Fax 235-3280
www.sd25.us
Alameda MS 6-8
3115 Pole Line Rd 83201 208-235-6800
Brandon Vaughan, prin. Fax 235-6801
Century HS 1,200/9-12
7801 W Diamond Back Dr 83204 208-478-6863
Sheryl Brockett, prin. Fax 478-6870
Franklin MS 800/6-8
2271 E Terry St 83201 208-233-5590
Patrick Vereecken, prin. Fax 233-1024
Hawthorne MS 800/6-8
1025 W Eldredge Rd 83201 208-237-1680
Dr. Heidi Kessler, prin. Fax 237-1682
Highland HS 1,400/9-12
1800 Bench Rd 83201 208-237-1300
Brad Wallace, prin. Fax 237-1350
Irving MS 600/6-8
911 N Grant Ave 83204 208-232-3039
Tonya Wilkes, prin. Fax 232-0379
New Horizon HS 200/Alt
955 W Alameda Rd 83201 208-237-2233
Amy Myers, prin. Fax 238-3635
Pocatello HS 1,100/9-12
325 N Arthur Ave 83204 208-233-2056
Lisa Delonas, prin. Fax 232-0365

Idaho State University Post-Sec.
921 S 8th Ave 83209 208-282-0211

Ponderay, Bonner, Pop. 1,102
Lake Pend Oreille SD 84 3,800/PK-12
901 N Triangle Dr 83852 208-263-2184
Shawn Woodward, supt. Fax 263-5053
www.lposd.org/
Other Schools – See Clark Fork, Sandpoint

Post Falls, Kootenai, Pop. 26,948
Post Falls SD 273 5,800/PK-12
PO Box 40 83877 208-773-1658
Jerry Keane, supt. Fax 773-3218
www.pfsd.com
New Vision Alternative S 200/Alt
PO Box 40 83877 208-773-3541
Dawn Mackesy, prin. Fax 773-3542
Post Falls HS 1,400/9-12
PO Box 40 83877 208-773-0581
Chris Sensel, prin. Fax 773-0587
Post Falls MS 700/6-8
PO Box 40 83877 208-773-7554
Brad Harmon, prin. Fax 773-0884
River City MS 600/6-8
PO Box 40 83877 208-457-0933
Michael Yovetich, prin. Fax 457-1673

American Institute of Clinical Massage Post-Sec.
4365 E Inverness Dr 83854 208-773-5890
Classical Christian Academy 200/PK-12
2289 W Seltice Way 83854 208-777-4400
Genesis Preparatory Academy 100/K-12
PO Box 1237 83877 208-691-0712
Chris Finch, prin. Fax 777-8853

Potlatch, Latah, Pop. 786
Potlatch SD 285 500/K-12
130 6th St 83855 208-875-0327
Jeffrey A. Cirka, supt. Fax 875-1028
www.potlatchschools.org

Potlatch JSHS 200/7-12
130 6th St 83855 208-875-1231
Cheryl Riedinger, prin. Fax 875-1028

Preston, Franklin, Pop. 5,154
Preston JSD 201 2,600/PK-12
105 E 2nd S 83263 208-852-0283
Marc Gee, supt. Fax 852-3976
www.prestonidahoschools.org
Franklin County HS 100/Alt
11 S 1st W 83263 208-852-2272
Ken Gifford, prin. Fax 852-2282
Preston HS 700/9-12
151 E 2nd S 83263 208-852-0280
Jeff Lords, prin. Fax 852-0080
Preston JHS 600/6-8
450 E 800 S 83263 208-852-0751
Curtis Jenson, prin. Fax 852-3510

Priest River, Bonner, Pop. 1,684
West Bonner County SD 83 1,300/PK-12
134 Main St 83856 208-448-4439
Paul Anselmo, supt. Fax 448-4629
www.sd83.org
PREP Alternative HS 50/Alt
134 Main St 83856 208-448-1405
Leoni Johnson, prin. Fax 448-0630
Priest River JHS 200/7-8
5709 Highway 2 83856 208-448-1118
Leoni Johnson, prin. Fax 448-1119
Priest River Lamanna HS 400/9-12
596 Highway 57 83856 208-448-1211
Joe Kren, prin. Fax 448-1212

Rathdrum, Kootenai, Pop. 6,685
Lakeland SD 272 4,200/PK-12
PO Box 39 83858 208-687-0431
Becky Meyer, supt. Fax 687-1884
web.lakeland272.org
Kootenai Technical Education Center Vo/Tech
6838 W Lancaster Rd 83858 208-712-4733
Colby Mattilla, prin. Fax 712-6004
Lakeland HS 700/9-12
PO Box 69 83858 208-687-0181
Trent Derrick, prin. Fax 687-1313
Lakeland JHS 400/7-8
PO Box 98 83858 208-687-0661
Georgeanne Griffith, prin. Fax 687-1510
Mountain View Alternative HS 100/Alt
PO Box 39 83858 208-687-0025
Paul Uzzi, admin. Fax 687-2843
Other Schools – See Spirit Lake

Rexburg, Madison, Pop. 25,087
Madison SD 321 5,400/PK-12
PO Box 830 83440 208-359-3300
Dr. Geoffrey Thomas, supt. Fax 359-3345
www.d321.k12.id.us
Central HS 100/Alt
379 S 2nd E 83440 208-359-2337
Rodger Hampton M.Ed., prin. Fax 359-2521
Madison Academy 50/Alt
379 S 2nd E 83440 208-359-2337
Rodger Hampton M.Ed., admin. Fax 359-2521
Madison JHS 1,200/7-9
134 Madison Ave 83440 208-359-3310
Rex Fullmer M.Ed., prin. Fax 372-0105
Madison SHS 1,100/10-12
2300 University Blvd 83440 208-359-3305
Mike Bennett M.Ed., prin. Fax 359-3346

Brigham Young University - Idaho Post-Sec.
525 S Center St 83460 208-496-1411

Richfield, Lincoln, Pop. 478
Richfield SD 316 200/PK-12
555 N Tiger Dr 83349 208-487-2241
Mike Smith, supt. Fax 487-2240
sites.google.com/site/richfieldtigers
Richfield S 200/PK-12
555 N Tiger Dr 83349 208-487-2790
Kevin Case, prin. Fax 487-2055

Rigby, Jefferson, Pop. 3,876
Jefferson County JSD 251 4,100/K-12
3850 E 300 N 83442 208-745-6693
Lisa Sherick, supt. Fax 745-0848
www.sd251.org
Rigby HS 900/9-12
3833 Rigby High Ln 83442 208-745-7704
Bryan Lords, prin. Fax 745-7707
Rigby MS 300/6-8
290 N 3800 E 83442 208-745-6674
Sherry Simmons, prin. Fax 745-6675
Other Schools – See Menan

Riggins, Idaho, Pop. 415
Salmon River JSD 243 100/PK-12
PO Box 872 83549 208-630-6027
Jim Doramus, supt. Fax 630-6026
www.jsd243.org
Salmon River JSHS 100/6-12
PO Box 872 83549 208-630-6025
Jim Doramus, supt. Fax 630-6026

Ririe, Jefferson, Pop. 653
Ririe JSD 252 500/PK-12
PO Box 508 83443 208-538-7482
Chad Williams, supt. Fax 538-7363
www.ririeschools.org
Ririe JSHS 200/7-12
PO Box 568 83443 208-538-7311
Chad Williams, prin. Fax 538-7860

Rockland, Power, Pop. 294
Rockland SD 382 200/K-12
PO Box 119 83271 208-548-2221
Chester Bradshaw, supt. Fax 548-2224
www.rbulldogs.org
Rockland S 200/K-12
PO Box 119 83271 208-548-2221
Chester Bradshaw, prin. Fax 548-2224

Rupert, Minidoka, Pop. 5,482
Minidoka County JSD 331 4,200/K-12
310 10th St 83350 208-436-4727
Dr. Kenneth Cox, supt. Fax 436-6593
www.minidokaschools.org
East Minico MS 500/6-8
1805 H St 83350 208-436-3178
Bryan McKinney, prin. Fax 436-3235
Minico HS 1,000/9-12
292 W 100 S 83350 208-436-4721
Suzette Miller, prin. Fax 436-3266
Other Schools – See Heyburn, Paul

Saint Anthony, Fremont, Pop. 3,512
Fremont County JSD 215 2,200/PK-12
945 W 1st N 83445 208-624-7542
Dr. Garry Parker, supt. Fax 624-3385
www.sd215.net
South Fremont HS 400/9-12
855 N Bridge St 83445 208-624-3416
Larry Bennett, prin. Fax 624-4898
South Fremont JHS 400/6-8
550 N 1st W 83445 208-624-7880
David Marotz, prin. Fax 624-4386
Other Schools – See Ashton

Saint Maries, Benewah, Pop. 2,361
Saint Maries JSD 41 1,000/PK-12
PO Box 384 83861 208-245-2579
John Cordell, supt. Fax 245-3970
www.sd41.org
Saint Maries Community Education Center 50/Alt
422 Hells Gulch Rd 83861 208-245-2152
John Cordell, prin. Fax 245-0212
Saint Maries HS 300/9-12
424 Hells Gulch Rd 83861 208-245-2142
John Cordell, prin. Fax 245-5650
Saint Maries MS 200/6-8
1315 W Jefferson Ave 83861 208-245-3495
Jeffrey Andersen, prin. Fax 245-0506

Saint Maries Christian S 50/3-8
201 N 8th St Ste 11 83861 208-245-2274

Salmon, Lemhi, Pop. 3,067
Salmon SD 291 600/PK-12
907 Sharkey St 83467 208-756-4271
Chris Born, supt. Fax 756-6695
www.salmonschools.com
Salmon Alternative HS 50/Alt
1501 S Bean Ln 83467 208-756-6277
Jenny McKenna, prin. Fax 756-6695
Salmon JSHS 300/6-12
401 S Warpath 83467 208-756-2415
Jenny McKenna, prin. Fax 756-3484

Sandpoint, Bonner, Pop. 7,221
Lake Pend Oreille SD 84
Supt. — See Ponderay
Lake Pend Oreille Alternative HS 100/Alt
1005 N Boyer Ave 83864 208-263-6121
Geoffrey Penrose, prin. Fax 265-5734
Sandpoint HS 1,000/9-12
410 S Division Ave 83864 208-263-3034
Tom Albertson, prin. Fax 263-5321
Sandpoint MS 500/7-8
310 S Division Ave 83864 208-265-4169
Casey McLaughlin, prin. Fax 263-5525

Shelley, Bingham, Pop. 4,332
Shelley JSD 60 2,200/PK-12
545 Seminary Ave 83274 208-357-3411
Dr. Bryan Jolley, supt. Fax 357-5741
www.shelleyschools.org
Hobbs MS 300/7-8
350 E Pine St 83274 208-357-7667
Dale Clark, prin. Fax 357-3003
Shelley HS 600/9-12
570 W Fir St 83274 208-357-7400
Eric Lords, prin. Fax 357-5585

Shoshone, Lincoln, Pop. 1,444
Shoshone JSD 312 400/PK-12
61 E Highway 24 83352 208-886-2381
Dr. Rob Waite, supt. Fax 886-2038
www.shoshonesd.org
Shoshone JSHS 100/6-12
61 E Highway 24 83352 208-886-2381
Kelly Chapman, prin. Fax 886-2742

Soda Springs, Caribou, Pop. 3,009
Soda Springs JSD 150 900/K-12
250 E 2nd S 83276 208-547-3371
Dr. Molly Stein, supt. Fax 547-4878
www.sodaschools.org
Soda Springs HS 200/9-12
300 E 1st N 83276 208-547-4308
Robert Daniel, prin. Fax 547-3327
Tigert MS 300/5-8
250 E 2nd S Ste B 83276 208-547-4922
Debra Daniels, prin. Fax 547-2619

Spirit Lake, Kootenai, Pop. 1,910
Lakeland SD 272
Supt. — See Rathdrum
Timberlake HS 500/9-12
PO Box 909 83869 208-623-6303
Kurt Hoffman, prin. Fax 623-6203
Timberlake JHS 300/7-8
PO Box 1080 83869 208-623-2582
Chris McDougall, prin. Fax 623-2750

Sugar City, Madison, Pop. 1,499
Sugar-Salem JSD 322 1,600/PK-12
PO Box 150 83448 208-356-8802
Alan Dunn, supt. Fax 356-7237
www.sugarsalem.org
Sugar-Salem HS 500/9-12
1 S Digger Dr 83448 208-356-0274
Jared Jenks, prin. Fax 359-3167
Sugar-Salem JHS 200/7-8
PO Box 180 83448 208-356-4437
Kevin Schultz, prin. Fax 358-9717
Valley View Alt HS 50/Alt
25 N Cutler Ave 83448 208-356-6845
Jay Miller, prin. Fax 356-3167

Sun Valley, Blaine, Pop. 1,392

Community S 300/PK-12
PO Box 2118 83353 208-622-3955
Ben Pettit, head sch Fax 622-3962

Terreton, Jefferson
West Jefferson SD 253 500/PK-12
1256 E 1500 N 83450 208-663-4542
Dwight Richins, supt. Fax 663-4543
www.wjsd.org
West Jefferson HS 200/9-12
1260 E 1500 N 83450 208-663-4391
David McDonald, prin. Fax 663-4390

Troy, Latah, Pop. 841
Troy SD 287 300/K-12
PO Box 280 83871 208-835-3791
Dr. Christy Castro, supt. Fax 835-3790
www.sd287.k12.id.us
Troy JSHS 200/7-12
101 Trojan Dr 83871 208-835-2361
Brad Malm, prin. Fax 835-2441

Twin Falls, Twin Falls, Pop. 43,303
Twin Falls SD 411 9,900/PK-12
201 Main Ave W 83301 208-733-6900
Wiley Dobbs, supt. Fax 733-6987
www.tfsd.k12.id.us
Canyon Ridge HS 1,200/9-12
300 N College Rd W 83301 208-732-7555
Kasey Teske, prin. Fax 732-7556
Magic Valley HS 300/Alt
512 Main Ave N 83301 208-733-8823
Roger Keller, prin. Fax 733-8505
O'Leary JHS 900/6-8
2350 Elizabeth Blvd 83301 208-733-2155
Keelie Campbell, prin. Fax 733-8666
Stuart JHS 900/6-8
644 Caswell Ave W 83301 208-733-4875
Amy McBride, prin. Fax 733-4949
Twin Falls HS 1,100/9-12
1615 Filer Ave E 83301 208-733-6551
Dan Vogt, prin. Fax 733-8192

College of Southern Idaho Post-Sec.
PO Box 1238 83303 208-733-9554
Lighthouse Christian S 300/PK-12
960 Eastland Dr 83301 208-737-1425
Kevin Newbry, supt. Fax 737-4671
Mr. Juan's College of Hair Design Post-Sec.
586 Blue Lakes Blvd N 83301 208-733-7777
Twin Falls Christian Academy 100/K-12
798 Eastland Dr N 83301 208-733-1452
Brent Walker, prin. Fax 734-1417

Wallace, Shoshone, Pop. 769
Wallace SD 393 500/PK-12
405 7th St 83873 208-753-4515
Dr. Robert Ranells, supt. Fax 753-4151
www.wsd393.org/
Wallace JSHS 300/7-12
1 Miners Aly 83873 208-753-5315
Don Almquist, prin. Fax 753-7105

Weippe, Clearwater, Pop. 439
Orofino JSD 171
Supt. — See Orofino
Timberline S 100/PK-12
22869 Highway 11 83553 208-435-4411
Jason Hunter, prin. Fax 435-4846

Weiser, Washington, Pop. 5,415
Weiser SD 431 1,600/PK-12
925 Pioneer Rd 83672 208-414-0616
Wil Overgaard, supt. Fax 414-1265
www.weiserschools.org
Indianhead Academy 50/Alt
2235 Paddock Rd 83672 208-707-6500
Larry Goto, prin.
Weiser HS 500/9-12
690 W Indianhead Rd 83672 208-414-2595
David Davies, prin. Fax 414-1795
Weiser MS 400/6-8
320 E Galloway Ave 83672 208-414-2620
Tim Erhard, prin. Fax 414-2094

Wendell, Gooding, Pop. 2,752
Wendell SD 232 1,200/PK-12
PO Box 300 83355 208-536-2418
Greg Lowe, supt. Fax 536-2629
www.wendellschools.org
Wendell HS 300/9-12
850 E Main St 83355 208-536-2100
Jon Goss, prin. Fax 536-2124
Wendell MS 400/5-8
920 E Main St 83355 208-536-5531
Jennifer Cook, prin. Fax 536-5957

Wilder, Canyon, Pop. 1,528
Wilder SD 133 400/PK-12
210 A Ave 83676 208-482-6228
Jeff Dillon, supt. Fax 482-6980
www.wilderschools.org
Wilder MSHS 200/6-12
419 Huff Rd 83676 208-482-6229
Tim Jensen, prin. Fax 482-7421

ILLINOIS

ILLINOIS DEPARTMENT OF EDUCATION
100 N 1st St, Springfield 62777-0002
Telephone 866-262-6663
Fax 217-524-8585
Website http://www.isbe.net

Superintendent of Education Dr. Tony Smith

ILLINOIS BOARD OF EDUCATION
100 N 1st St, Springfield 62777-0002

Chairperson James Meeks

REGIONAL OFFICES OF EDUCATION (ROE)

Adam/Brwn/Cass/Morgn/Pik/Sctt ROE
Deborah Niederhauser, supt. 217-277-2080
507 Vermont St, Quincy 62301 Fax 277-2092
www.wc4.org

Alxndr/Jcksn/Pulsk/Prry/Union ROE
Donna Boros, supt., 1001 Walnut St 618-687-7290
Murphysboro 62966 Fax 687-7296
www.roe30.org

Bond/Christn/Effingham/Fayette/Mtgmy ROE
Julie Wollerman, supt. 618-283-5011
300 S 7th St, Vandalia 62471 Fax 283-5013
www.roe3.org

Boone/Winnebago ROE
Dr. Lori Fanello, supt. 815-636-3060
300 Heart Blvd, Loves Park 61111 Fax 636-3069
www.bwroe.org

Bureau/Henry/Stark ROE
Angie Zarvell, supt. 309-936-7890
107 S State St, Atkinson 61235 Fax 936-1111
www.bhsroe.org

Calhoun/Greene/Jersey/Macoupin ROE
Michelle Mueller, supt. 217-854-4016
225 E Nicholas St, Carlinville 62626 Fax 854-2032
www.roe40.com

Carroll/Jo Daviess/Stephenson ROE
Aaron Mercier, supt. 815-599-1408
27 S State Ave Ste 101 Fax 297-9032
Freeport 61032
www.roe8.com

Champaign/Ford ROE
Jane Quinlan, supt. 217-893-3219
200 S Fredrick St, Rantoul 61866 Fax 893-0024
www.roe9.k12.il.us/

Clay/Crawford/Jspr/Lwrnce/Rchlnd ROE
Monte Newlin, supt. 618-392-4631
103 W Main St Ste 23, Olney 62450 Fax 392-3993
www.roe12.net

Clintn/Jeffrsn/Marin/Washngtn ROE
Keri Jo Garrett, supt. 618-594-2432
930 Fairfax St Ste B, Carlyle 62231 Fax 594-7192
www.roe13.k12.il.us

Clk/Cls/Cumb/Dglas/Edg/Mlt/Shlb ROE
Dr. Bobbi Mattingly, supt. 217-348-0151
730 7th St, Charleston 61920 Fax 348-0171
www.roe11.k12.il.us/

DeKalb ROE
Amanda Christensen, supt. 815-217-0460
2500 N Annie Glidden Rd Fax 217-0467
DeKalb 60115
www.dekalbcounty.org/roe

DeWitt/Livingston/Logan/McLean ROE
Mark Jontry, supt. 309-888-5120
200 W Front St Ste 500 Fax 862-0420
Bloomington 61701
www.roe17.org

Dupage ROE
Darlene Ruscitti, supt. 630-407-5800
421 N County Farm Rd Fax 407-5801
Wheaton 60187
www.dupage.k12.il.us/

Edwds/Gtn/Hdn/Pope/Sln/Wbsh/Wyn/Wt ROE
Lawrence Fillingim, supt. 618-253-5581
512 N Main St, Harrisburg 62946 Fax 252-8472
www.roe20.org

Franklin-Johnson-Massac-Williamson ROE
Matt Donkin, supt. 618-438-9711
202 W Main St, Benton 62812 Fax 435-2861
www.roe21.org

Grundy/Kendall ROE
Christopher Mehochko, supt. 815-941-3247
1320 Union St, Morris 60450 Fax 942-5384
www.roe24.org

Hancck/Fultn/Schuylr/McDonogh ROE
John Meixner, supt. 309-837-4821
130 S Lafayette St Ste 200 Fax 837-2887
Macomb 61455
www.roe26.net

Henderson/Knox/Mercer/Warren ROE
Jodi Scott, supt. 309-734-6822
105 N E St Ste 1, Monmouth 61462 Fax 734-2452
www.roe33.net

Iroquois/Kankakee ROE
Greg Murphy, supt. 815-937-2950
189 E Court St Ste 600 Fax 937-2921
Kankakee 60901
www.i-kan.org

Kane ROE
Patricia Dal Santo, supt. 630-232-5955
28 N 1st St Ste 201, Geneva 60134 Fax 208-5115
www.kaneroe.org/

Lake ROE
Dr. Roycealee Wood, supt. 847-543-7833
800 Lancer Ln Ste E128 Fax 543-7832
Grayslake 60030
www.lake.k12.il.us

LaSalle/Marshall/Putnam ROE
Christopher Dvorak, supt. 815-434-0780
119 W Madison St, Ottawa 61350 Fax 434-2453
www.roe35.org

Lee/Ogle/Whiteside ROE
Robert Sondgeroth, supt. 815-625-2054
1001 W 23rd St, Sterling 61081 Fax 625-1625
www.roe47.org

Macon/Piatt ROE 39
Matthew Snyder, supt. 217-872-3721
1690 Huston Dr, Decatur 62526 Fax 872-0239
www.maconpiattroe.com/

Madison County ROE
Dr. Robert Daiber, supt. 618-296-4530
157 N Main St, Edwardsville 62025 Fax 692-7018
www.roe41.org

Mason-Tazewell-Woodford ROE
Patrick Durley, supt. 309-477-2290
414 Court St Ste 100, Pekin 61554 Fax 347-3735
www.roe53.net

McHenry ROE
Leslie Schermerhorn, supt. 815-334-4475
2200 N Seminary Ave Fax 338-0475
Woodstock 60098
www.mchenryroe.org/

Menard/Sangamon ROE
Jeff Vose, supt. 217-753-6620
200 S 9th St Ste 303 Fax 535-3166
Springfield 62701
www.roe51.org

Monroe-Randolph ROE
Kelton Davis, supt. 618-939-5650
107 E Mill St, Waterloo 62298 Fax 939-5332
www.roe45.org

North Cook Intermediate Service Center
Dr. Bruce Brown, dir. 847-824-8300
2340 S River Rd Fax 824-1033
Des Plaines 60018
www.ncisc.org

Peoria ROE
Gerald Brookhart, supt. 309-672-6906
324 Main St Ste 401, Peoria 61602 Fax 672-6053
www.co.peoria.il.us/roe

Rock Island ROE
Tammy Muerhoff, supt. 309-736-1111
3430 Avenue of the Cities Fax 736-1127
Moline 61265
www.riroe.com/

Saint Clair ROE
Susan Sarfaty, supt. 618-825-3900
1000 S Illinois St, Belleville 62220 Fax 825-3999
www.stclair.k12.il.us/

South Cook Intermediate Service Center
Dr. Vanessa Kinder, supt. 708-754-6600
253 W Joe Orr Rd Fax 754-8687
Chicago Heights 60411
www.s-cook.org

Vermilion ROE
Cheryl Reifsteck, supt. 217-431-2668
200 S College St Ste B Fax 431-2671
Danville 61832
www.roe54.k12.il.us/

West Suburb Intermediate Service Center
Kay Poyner Brown, dir. 708-449-4284
4413 Roosevelt Rd Ste 104 Fax 449-4288
Hillside 60162
www.west40.org

Will ROE
Shawn Walsh, supt. 815-740-8360
702 W Maple St, New Lenox 60451 Fax 740-4788
www.willroe.org

PUBLIC, PRIVATE AND CATHOLIC SECONDARY SCHOOLS

Abingdon, Knox, Pop. 3,272
Abingdon-Avon CUSD 276 800/PK-12
401 W Latimer St 61410 309-462-2301
Don Daily, supt. Fax 462-3870
www.d276.net
Abingdon-Avon HS 200/9-12
600 W Martin St 61410 309-462-2338
Shane Gordon, prin. Fax 462-2492
Other Schools – See Avon

Addison, DuPage, Pop. 36,491
Addison SD 4 4,200/PK-8
222 N JF Kennedy Dr 60101 630-458-2500
John Langton, supt. Fax 628-8829
www.asd4.org
Indian Trail JHS 1,400/6-8
222 N JF Kennedy Dr Frnt 1 60101 630-458-2600
Craig Bennett, prin. Fax 628-2841

DAOES
301 S Swift Rd 60101 630-691-7590
Michael Zimmerman, dir. Fax 691-7592
www.tcdupage.org
Technology Center of Dupage Vo/Tech
301 S Swift Rd Ste B 60101 630-620-8770
Steven Carr, prin. Fax 691-7592

DuPage HSD 88 3,900/9-12
2 Friendship Plz 60101 630-530-3981
Dr. Scott Helton, supt. Fax 832-0198
www.dupage88.net/
Addison Trail HS 2,000/9-12
213 N Lombard Rd 60101 630-628-3300
Michael Bolden, prin. Fax 628-0177
Other Schools – See Villa Park

Chamberlain College of Nursing Post-Sec.
1221 N Swift Rd 60101 630-953-3680
DeVry University Post-Sec.
1221 N Swift Rd 60101 630-953-1300

Albion, Edwards, Pop. 1,965
Edwards County CUSD 1 1,000/PK-12
361 W Main St Ste 100 62806 618-445-2814
David Cowger, supt. Fax 445-2272
www.edwardscountyschools.org
Edwards County HS 300/9-12
361 W Main St 62806 618-445-2325
Preston Nelson, prin. Fax 445-3154

Aledo, Mercer, Pop. 3,626
Mercer County SD 404 1,400/PK-12
1002 SW 6th St 61231 309-582-2238
Scott Petrie, supt. Fax 582-7428
www.mercerschools.org
Mercer County HS 400/9-12
1500 S College Ave 61231 309-582-2223
Stacey Day, prin. Fax 582-5920
Other Schools – See Joy

Alexander, Morgan
Franklin CUSD 1 — 300/PK-12
PO Box 140 62601 — 217-478-3011
Andy Stremlau, supt. — Fax 478-4921
www.franklinhigh.com
Other Schools – See Franklin

Algonquin, McHenry, Pop. 29,616
CUSD 300 — 19,100/PK-12
2550 Harnish Dr 60102 — 847-551-8300
Fred Heid, supt. — Fax 551-8413
www.d300.org
Algonquin MS — 500/6-8
520 Longwood Dr 60102 — 847-658-2545
Andrew Reincke, prin. — Fax 658-2547
Jacobs HS — 2,200/9-12
2601 Bunker Hill Dr 60102 — 847-658-2500
Barb Valle, prin. — Fax 658-3203
Other Schools – See Carpentersville, Hampshire, West Dundee

Consolidated SD 158 — 9,200/PK-12
650 Academic Dr 60102 — 847-659-6158
Dr. John Burkey, supt. — Fax 659-6125
www.district158.org/
Heineman MS — 900/6-8
725 Academic Dr 60102 — 847-659-4300
Jake Litchfield, prin. — Fax 659-4320
Other Schools – See Huntley, Lake in the Hills

Alsip, Cook, Pop. 19,017
Alsip-Hazelgreen-Oaklawn SD 126 — 1,500/K-8
11900 S Kostner Ave 60803 — 708-389-1900
Craig Gwaltney, supt. — Fax 396-3793
www.dist126.org
Prairie JHS — 300/7-8
11910 S Kostner Ave 60803 — 708-371-3080
Maureen Paulmeyer, prin. — Fax 396-3798

Atwood Heights SD 125 — 700/PK-8
12150 S Hamlin Ave 60803 — 708-371-0080
Dr. Thomas Livingston, supt. — Fax 371-7847
www.ahsd125.org
Hamlin Upper Grade Center — 200/6-8
12150 S Hamlin Ave 60803 — 708-597-1550
Dr. Lisa West, prin. — Fax 396-0515

Altamont, Effingham, Pop. 2,313
Altamont CUSD 10 — 800/PK-12
7 S Ewing St 62411 — 618-483-6195
Jeff Fritchtnitch, supt. — Fax 483-6303
www.altamontschools.org
Altamont HS — 300/9-12
7 S Ewing St 62411 — 618-483-6194
Jerry Tkachuk, prin. — Fax 483-5399

Alton, Madison, Pop. 26,887
Alton CUSD 11 — 5,000/PK-12
PO Box 9028 62002 — 618-474-2600
Mark Cappel, supt. — Fax 463-2126
www.altonschools.org
Alton HS — 2,000/9-12
4200 Humbert Rd 62002 — 618-474-2700
Mike Bellm, prin. — Fax 463-2000
Alton MS — 1,400/6-8
2200 College Ave 62002 — 618-474-2200
Cindy Inman, prin. — Fax 463-2127

CALC Institute of Technology — Post-Sec.
200 N Center Dr Ste A 62002 — 618-474-0616
Marquette HS — 400/9-12
219 E 4th St 62002 — 618-463-0580
Michael Slaughter, prin. — Fax 465-4029
Mississippi Valley Christian S — 100/PK-12
2009 Seminary St 62002 — 618-462-1071
Jerry Fair, prin. — Fax 462-9877
St. Mary MS — 100/6-8
1015 Milton Rd 62002 — 618-465-9719
Judy Kulp, prin. — Fax 465-9726

Amboy, Lee, Pop. 2,480
Amboy CUSD 272 — 700/K-12
11 E Hawley St 61310 — 815-857-2164
Jeff Thake, supt. — Fax 857-4434
www.amboy.net/
Amboy HS — 200/9-12
11 E Hawley St 61310 — 815-857-3632
Joshua Nichols, prin. — Fax 857-3631
Amboy JHS — 200/5-8
140 S Appleton Ave 61310 — 815-857-3528
Joyce Schamberger, prin. — Fax 857-4603

Anna, Union, Pop. 4,407
Anna CCSD 37 — 700/PK-8
301 S Green St 62906 — 618-833-6812
Charles Goforth, supt. — Fax 833-3205
anna37.com/
Anna JHS — 300/5-8
301 S Green St 62906 — 618-833-6415
Mark Laster, prin. — Fax 833-6535

Anna-Jonesboro Community HSD 81 — 500/9-12
608 S Main St 62906 — 618-833-8421
Rob Wright, supt. — Fax 833-4239
aj81.net
Anna-Jonesboro HS — 500/9-12
608 S Main St 62906 — 618-833-8502
Brett Detering, prin. — Fax 833-5931

Annawan, Henry, Pop. 875
Annawan CUSD 226 — 400/PK-12
501 W South St 61234 — 309-935-6781
Joseph Buresh, supt. — Fax 935-6065
www.annawan226.org
Annawan HS — 100/9-12
501 W South St 61234 — 309-935-6781
Wayne Brau, prin. — Fax 935-6065

Antioch, Lake, Pop. 14,166
Antioch CCSD 34 — 3,000/PK-8
964 Spafford St 60002 — 847-838-8400
Dr. Jay Marino, supt. — Fax 838-8404
www.antioch34.com
Antioch Upper Grade S — 1,000/6-8
800 Highview Dr 60002 — 847-838-8310
Joe Koeune, prin. — Fax 838-8304

Community HSD 117
Supt. — See Lake Villa
Antioch Community HS — 1,300/9-12
1133 Main St 60002 — 847-395-1421
Bradford Hubbard, prin. — Fax 395-2435

Arcola, Douglas, Pop. 2,899
Arcola CUSD 306 — 800/PK-12
351 W Washington St 61910 — 217-268-4963
Thomas Mulligan, supt. — Fax 268-3809
www.arcola.k12.il.us
Arcola JSHS — 300/7-12
351 W Washington St 61910 — 217-268-4962
Lisa Sigrist, prin. — Fax 268-4483

Pleasant View S — 50/K-12
184 N County Road 300E 61910 — 217-268-3886
Allen Miller, admin.

Argenta, Macon, Pop. 935
Argenta-Oreana CUSD 1 — 1,000/PK-12
PO Box 440 62501 — 217-795-2313
Damian Jones, supt. — Fax 795-2174
www.argenta-oreana.org/
Argenta-Oreana HS — 300/9-12
PO Box 469 62501 — 217-795-4821
Sean German, prin. — Fax 795-4550
Argenta-Oreana MS — 200/6-8
PO Box 439 62501 — 217-795-2163
Patrick Blair, prin. — Fax 795-4502

Arlington Heights, Cook, Pop. 74,142
Arlington Heights SD 25 — 5,300/PK-8
1200 S Dunton Ave 60005 — 847-758-4900
Dr. Lori Bein, supt. — Fax 758-4907
www.sd25.org
South MS — 900/6-8
400 S Highland Ave 60005 — 847-398-4250
Piper Boston, prin. — Fax 394-6260
Thomas MS — 900/6-8
1430 N Belmont Ave 60004 — 847-398-4260
Brian Kaye, prin. — Fax 394-6843

CCSD 59 — 6,800/PK-8
2123 S Arlington Heights Rd 60005 — 847-593-4300
Dr. Art Fessler, supt. — Fax 593-4409
www.ccsd59.org
Other Schools – See Des Plaines, Elk Grove Village, Mount Prospect

Township HSD 214 — 11,800/9-12
2121 S Goebbert Rd 60005 — 847-718-7600
David Schuler Ph.D., supt. — Fax 718-7609
www.d214.org
Academy at Forest View — 100/Alt
2121 S Goebbert Rd 60005 — 847-718-7771
Kara Kendrick, dir. — Fax 718-7773
Hersey HS — 2,000/9-12
1900 E Thomas St 60004 — 847-718-4800
Gordon Sisson, prin. — Fax 718-4817
Vanguard S — 100/Alt
2121 S Goebbert Rd 60005 — 847-718-7888
Kate Kraft, dir. — Fax 718-7869
Other Schools – See Buffalo Grove, Elk Grove Village, Mount Prospect, Rolling Meadows, Wheeling

---

Christian Liberty Academy — 400/PK-12
502 W Euclid Ave 60004 — 847-259-4444
Thad Bennett, hdmstr. — Fax 259-9972
Northwest Community Hospital — Post-Sec.
800 W Central Rd 60005 — 847-618-1000
Robert Morris University — Post-Sec.
2123 S Goebbert Rd 60005 — 800-762-5960
St. Viator HS — 1,000/9-12
1213 E Oakton St 60004 — 847-392-4050
Eileen Manno, prin. — Fax 392-4329

Armstrong, Vermilion
Armstrong Twp. HSD 225 — 100/9-12
PO Box 37 61812 — 217-569-2122
Bill Mulvaney, supt. — Fax 569-2171
www.armstrong.k12.il.us
Armstrong HS — 100/9-12
PO Box 37 61812 — 217-569-2122
Darren Loschen, prin. — Fax 569-2171

Arthur, Douglas, Pop. 2,280
Arthur CUSD 305 — 1,100/PK-12
301 E Columbia St 61911 — 217-543-2511
Kenneth Schwengel, supt. — Fax 543-2210
www.cusd305.org
Arthur-Lovington-Atwood-Hammond HS — 200/9-12
301 E Columbia St 61911 — 217-543-2146
Steffanie Seegmiller, prin. — Fax 543-2174

Arthur Christian S — 100/PK-12
1710 State Highway 133 61911 — 217-543-2397
Greg Mast, prin. — Fax 543-3781

Ashkum, Iroquois, Pop. 755
Central CUSD 4 — 1,100/PK-12
PO Box 158 60911 — 815-698-2212
Tonya Evans, supt. — Fax 694-2844
www.clifton-u4.k12.il.us
Other Schools – See Clifton

Ashland, Cass, Pop. 1,324
A-C Central CUSD 262 — 400/PK-12
PO Box 260 62612 — 217-476-8112
Timothy Page, supt. — Fax 476-8100
a-ccentral.com
A-C Central HS — 100/9-12
PO Box 260 62612 — 217-476-3312
Steve Groll, prin. — Fax 476-3312
A-C Central MS — 200/5-8
PO Box 260 62612 — 217-476-3313
Steve Groll, prin. — Fax 476-3730

Ashton, Lee, Pop. 967
Ashton-Franklin Center CUSD 275 — 400/PK-12
611 Western Ave 61006 — 815-453-7461
John Zick, supt. — Fax 453-7462
www.afcschools.net
Ashton-Franklin Center JSHS — 200/7-12
611 Western Ave 61006 — 815-453-7461
Tammy Harvey, prin. — Fax 453-7462

Assumption, Christian, Pop. 1,158
Central A & M CUSD 21 — 800/PK-12
105 N College St 62510 — 217-226-4042
Dr. DeAnn Heck, supt. — Fax 226-4133
camraiders.com
Central A & M MS — 200/6-8
404 Colegrove St 62510 — 217-226-4241
Ryan Scott, prin. — Fax 226-4442
Other Schools – See Moweaqua

Astoria, Fulton, Pop. 1,131
Astoria CUSD 1 — 400/PK-12
402 N Jefferson St 61501 — 309-329-2156
Don Willett, supt. — Fax 329-2214
www.astoria.fulton.k12.il.us
Astoria HS — 100/9-12
402 N Jefferson St 61501 — 309-329-2156
Don Willett, prin. — Fax 329-2246
Astoria JHS — 100/6-8
402 N Jefferson St 61501 — 309-329-2158
Dave Crouse, prin. — Fax 329-2963

Athens, Menard, Pop. 1,956
Athens CUSD 213 — 1,000/PK-12
1 Warrior Way 62613 — 217-636-8761
Dr. Scott Laird, supt. — Fax 636-8851
www.athens-213.org
Athens HS — 300/9-12
1 Warrior Way 62613 — 217-636-8314
Bill Reed, prin. — Fax 636-8851
Athens JHS — 100/7-8
1 Warrior Way 62613 — 217-636-8380
Matt Rhoades, prin. — Fax 636-8851

Menard/Sangamon ROE
Supt. — See Springfield
Salt Creek Academy — Alt
30819 Fancy Prairie Ave 62613 — 217-566-3841
Del Sutter, prin. — Fax 566-3653

Auburn, Sangamon, Pop. 4,722
Auburn CUSD 10 — 1,400/PK-12
606 W North St 62615 — 217-438-6164
Darren Root, supt. — Fax 438-6483
www.auburn.k12.il.us
Auburn HS — 400/9-12
511 N 7th St 62615 — 217-438-6817
Nathan Essex, prin. — Fax 438-6153
Other Schools – See Divernon

Augusta, Hancock, Pop. 586
Southeastern CUSD 337 — 500/PK-12
PO Box 215 62311 — 217-392-2172
Todd Fox, supt. — Fax 392-2174
www.southeastern337.com/
Southeastern JSHS — 200/7-12
PO Box 155 62311 — 217-392-2125
Cyle Rigg, prin. — Fax 392-2229

Aurora, Kane, Pop. 194,432
Aurora East Unit SD 131 — 14,700/PK-12
417 5th St 60505 — 630-299-5550
Dr. Mark McDonald, supt. — Fax 299-5500
www.d131.org
Cowherd MS — 1,000/6-8
441 N Farnsworth Ave 60505 — 630-299-5900
Crystal England, prin. — Fax 299-5901
East HS — 3,500/9-12
500 Tomcat Ln 60505 — 630-299-8000
Anthony Crespo, prin. — Fax 299-8199
Rodgers Magnet Academy — 400/3-8
157 N Root St 60505 — 630-299-7175
Angela Rowley, prin.
Simmons MS — 1,000/6-8
1130 Sheffer Rd 60505 — 630-299-4150
Mechelle Patterson, prin. — Fax 299-4151
Waldo MS — 900/6-8
56 Jackson St 60505 — 630-299-8400
Sandra Katula, prin. — Fax 299-8401

Aurora West Unit SD 129 — 12,800/PK-12
1877 W Downer Pl 60506 — 630-301-5000
Dr. Jeff Craig, supt. — Fax 844-5710
www.sd129.org/
Herget MS — 700/6-8
1550 Deerpath Rd 60506 — 630-301-5006
Cindy Larry, prin. — Fax 301-5222
Jefferson MS — 800/6-8
1151 Plum St 60506 — 630-301-5009
Shawn Munos, prin. — Fax 844-5711
Success Academy Blackhawk Campus — Alt
1720 N Randall Rd 60506 — 630-301-5355
Elroy Phillips, prin. — Fax 264-3376
Washington MS — 800/6-8
231 S Constitution Dr 60506 — 630-301-5017
Dr. Brett Burton, prin. — Fax 844-5712
West Aurora HS — 3,700/9-12
1201 W New York St 60506 — 630-301-5600
Dr. Chuck Hiscock, prin. — Fax 844-4505
Other Schools – See North Aurora

CUSD 308
Supt. — See Oswego
Bednarcik JHS — 600/6-8
3025 Heggs Rd, — 630-636-2500
Dr. Sharon Alexander, prin. — Fax 636-2591

Indian Prairie CUSD 204 28,600/PK-12
780 Shoreline Dr 60504 630-375-3000
Dr. Karen Sullivan, supt. Fax 375-3009
ipsdweb.ipsd.org
Fischer MS 1,000/6-8
1305 Long Grove Dr 60504 630-375-3100
Jennifer Nonnemacher, prin. Fax 375-3101
Granger MS 1,100/6-8
2721 Stonebridge Blvd, 630-375-1010
Laurie Fiorenza, prin. Fax 375-1110
Indian Plains HS 100/Alt
1322 N Eola Rd, 630-375-3375
Cecilia Tobin, prin. Fax 375-3361
Metea Valley HS 2,600/9-12
1801 N Eola Rd, 630-375-5900
Dr. Darrell Echols, prin. Fax 375-5901
Still MS 900/6-8
787 Meadowridge Dr 60504 630-375-3900
Kimberly Cornish, prin. Fax 375-3901
Waubonsie Valley HS 2,600/9-12
2590 Ogden Ave 60504 630-375-3300
Jason Stipp, prin. Fax 375-3326
Other Schools – See Naperville

John C. Dunham STEM Partnership SD 3-8
405 S Gladstone Ave 60506 630-947-1240
Arin Carter, dir.
www.stem.aurora.edu
Dunham STEM Partnership S 3-8
405 S Gladstone Ave 60506 630-947-1240
Arin Carter, dir.

Aurora Central Catholic HS 600/9-12
1255 N Edgelawn Dr 60506 630-907-0095
Rev. F. William Etheredge, admin. Fax 907-1076
Aurora Christian S 600/PK-12
2255 Sullivan Rd 60506 630-892-1551
Collette House, supt. Fax 892-1692
Aurora University Post-Sec.
347 S Gladstone Ave 60506 630-892-6431
Marmion Academy 500/9-12
1000 Butterfield Rd, 630-897-6936
Anthony Tinerella, head sch Fax 897-7086
Rasmussen College Post-Sec.
2363 Sequoia Dr Ste 131 60506 630-888-3500
Robert Morris University Post-Sec.
905 Meridian Lake Dr 60504 800-762-5960
Rosary HS 400/9-12
901 N Edgelawn Dr 60506 630-896-0831
Sr. Ann Brummel, prin. Fax 896-8372

Avon, Fulton, Pop. 778
Abingdon-Avon CUSD 276
Supt. — See Abingdon
Abingdon-Avon MS 100/6-8
320 E Woods St 61415 309-465-3621
Chad Cox, prin. Fax 465-7194

Barrington, Cook, Pop. 10,188
Barrington CUSD 220 8,800/PK-12
310 James St 60010 847-381-6300
Dr. Brian Harris, supt. Fax 381-6337
www.barrington220.org
Barrington HS 3,000/9-12
616 W Main St 60010 847-381-1400
Steve McWilliams, prin. Fax 304-3937
Barrington MS Prairie Campus 1,100/6-8
40 E Dundee Rd 60010 847-304-3990
Travis Lobbins, prin. Fax 304-3986
Barrington MS Station Campus 1,000/6-8
215 Eastern Ave 60010 847-756-6400
Dr. Craig Winkelman, prin. Fax 842-1343

Barry, Pike, Pop. 1,297
Western CUSD 12 600/PK-12
401 McDonough St 62312 217-335-2323
Terry Robertson, supt. Fax 335-2212
www.westerncusd12.org
Western HS 100/9-12
401 McDonough St 62312 217-335-2323
Constance Thomas, prin. Fax 335-2211
Other Schools – See Kinderhook

Bartlett, Cook, Pop. 40,574
SD U-46
Supt. — See Elgin
Bartlett HS 2,600/9-12
701 W Schick Rd 60103 630-372-4700
Mike Demovsky, prin. Fax 372-4682
Eastview MS 900/7-8
321 N Oak Ave 60103 630-213-5550
Donald Donner, prin. Fax 213-5563

Bartonville, Peoria, Pop. 6,361
Limestone Community HSD 310 1,000/9-12
4201 Airport Rd 61607 309-697-6271
Dr. Allan Gresham, supt. Fax 697-9635
www.limestone.k12.il.us
Limestone Community HS 1,000/9-12
4201 Airport Rd 61607 309-697-6271
Jeri Look, prin. Fax 697-9635

Oak Grove SD 68 300/PK-8
4812 Pfeiffer Rd 61607 309-697-3367
Loren Baele, supt. Fax 633-2381
www.og68.org
Oak Grove West JHS 100/5-8
6018 W Lancaster Rd 61607 309-697-0621
Rachel Baughman, prin. Fax 697-0721

Batavia, Kane, Pop. 25,733
Batavia Unit SD 101 6,100/PK-12
335 W Wilson St 60510 630-937-8800
Dr. Lisa Hichens, supt. Fax 937-8801
www.bps101.net
Batavia HS 1,900/9-12
1200 Main St 60510 630-937-8600
Dr. JoAnne Smith, prin. Fax 937-8601
Rotolo MS 1,500/6-8
1501 S Raddant Rd 60510 630-937-8700
Bryan Zwemke, prin. Fax 937-8701

Beach Park, Lake, Pop. 13,341
Beach Park CCSD 3 2,300/PK-8
11315 W Wadsworth Rd 60099 847-599-5070
Dr. Nancy Wagner, supt. Fax 263-2133
www.bpd3.org
Beach Park MS 800/6-8
40667 N Green Bay Rd 60099 847-596-5860
John Fredrickson, prin. Fax 731-2402

Beardstown, Cass, Pop. 6,084
Beardstown CUSD 15 1,400/PK-12
500 E 15th St 62618 217-323-3099
Ron Gilbert, supt. Fax 323-5190
www.beardstown.com
Beardstown JSHS 800/5-12
500 E 15th St 62618 217-323-3665
Scott Riddle, prin. Fax 323-3667

Bedford Park, Cook, Pop. 575

Fox College Post-Sec.
6640 S Cicero Ave 60638 708-444-4500

Beecher, Will, Pop. 4,314
Beecher CUSD 200U 1,000/K-12
PO Box 338 60401 708-946-2266
Jeffrey McCartney, supt. Fax 946-3404
www.beecher200u.org/
Beecher HS 400/9-12
PO Box 338 60401 708-946-2266
Nathan Schilling, prin. Fax 946-3403
Beecher JHS 200/6-8
101 E Church Rd 60401 708-946-3412
Michael Meyer, prin. Fax 946-2763

Belleville, Saint Clair, Pop. 43,276
Belleville SD 118 3,700/PK-8
105 W A St 62220 618-233-2830
Matt Klosterman, supt. Fax 233-8355
www.belleville118.org
Central JHS 400/7-8
1801 Central School Rd 62220 618-233-5377
Rocky Horrighs, prin. Fax 233-5440
West JHS 300/7-8
840 Royal Heights Rd 62226 618-234-8200
Gustavo Cotto, prin. Fax 234-8220

Belleville Township HSD 201 4,900/9-12
920 N Illinois St 62220 618-222-8200
Dr. Jeff Dosier, supt. Fax 233-7586
bths201.org/
Belleville HS East 2,600/9-12
2555 West Blvd 62221 618-222-3700
Jason Karstens, prin. Fax 222-3799
Belleville HS West 2,200/9-12
4063 Frank Scott Pkwy W 62223 618-222-7500
Rich Mertens, prin. Fax 235-2484
Belleville Night/Alternative S 100/Alt
4063 Frank Scott Pkwy W 62223 618-222-7660
Andrea Gannon, admin. Fax 235-2484

Harmony Emge SD 175 900/PK-8
7401 Westchester Dr 62223 618-397-8444
Dr. Pam Leonard, supt. Fax 397-8446
www.harmony175.org/
Emge JHS 200/7-8
7401 Westchester Dr 62223 618-397-6557
Matt Graham, prin. Fax 397-3011

Whiteside SD 115 1,400/PK-8
111 Warrior Way 62221 618-239-0000
Peggy Burke, supt. Fax 239-9240
www.wssd115.org
Whiteside MS 600/5-8
111 Warrior Way 62221 618-239-0000
Monica Laurent, prin. Fax 239-9240

Althoff Catholic HS 400/9-12
5401 W Main St 62226 618-235-1100
David Harris, prin. Fax 235-9535
Alvareita's College of Cosmetology Post-Sec.
5400 W Main St 62226 618-257-9193
French Academy 200/PK-12
219 W Main St 62220 618-233-7542
St. Elizabeth Hospital Post-Sec.
211 S 3rd St 62220 618-234-2120
Southwestern Illinois College Post-Sec.
2500 Carlyle Ave 62221 618-235-2700

Bellwood, Cook, Pop. 18,875
Bellwood SD 88 2,300/PK-8
640 Eastern Ave 60104 708-344-9344
Rosemary Hendricks, supt. Fax 344-9416
sd88.org
Roosevelt MS 500/6-8
2500 Oak St 60104 708-544-3318
Mark Holder, prin. Fax 544-0192

Belvidere, Boone, Pop. 25,242
Belvidere CUSD 100 8,100/PK-12
1201 5th Ave 61008 815-544-8513
Daniel Woestman, supt. Fax 544-8513
www.district100.com
Belvidere Central MS 1,000/6-8
8787 Beloit Rd 61008 815-544-0190
Nicole Difford, prin. Fax 544-1128
Belvidere HS 1,200/9-12
1500 East Ave 61008 815-547-6345
William Lewis, prin. Fax 547-7304
Belvidere North HS 1,400/9-12
9393 Beloit Rd 61008 815-544-2636
Marc Eckmann, prin. Fax 547-2916
Belvidere South MS 900/6-8
919 E 6th St 61008 815-544-3175
Ben Commore, prin. Fax 544-2780

Bement, Piatt, Pop. 1,710
Bement CUSD 5 400/PK-12
201 S Champaign St 61813 217-678-4200
Sheila Greenwood, supt. Fax 678-4251
www.bement.k12.il.us
Bement HS 100/9-12
201 S Champaign St 61813 217-678-4200
Douglas Kepley, prin. Fax 678-4251
Bement MS 100/6-8
201 S Champaign St 61813 217-678-4200
Douglas Kepley, prin. Fax 678-4251

Bensenville, DuPage, Pop. 18,131
Bensenville SD 2 1,800/PK-8
210 S Church Rd 60106 630-766-5940
Dr. James Stelter Ed.D., supt. Fax 766-6099
www.bsd2.org
Blackhawk MS 700/6-8
250 S Church Rd 60106 630-766-2601
Perry Finch, prin. Fax 766-7612

Fenton Community HSD 100 1,500/9-12
1000 W Green St 60106 630-860-6257
Dr. Gayle Wahlin, supt. Fax 766-3178
www.fenton100.org
Fenton HS 1,500/9-12
1000 W Green St 60106 630-766-2500
James Ongtengco, prin. Fax 766-3178

Robert Morris University Post-Sec.
1000 Tower Ln # 200 60106 630-787-7800

Benson, Woodford, Pop. 423
Roanoke-Benson CUSD 60
Supt. — See Roanoke
Roanoke-Benson JHS 200/5-8
PO Box 137 61516 309-394-2233
John Streit, prin. Fax 394-2612

Benton, Franklin, Pop. 7,012
Benton CCSD 47 1,200/PK-8
1000 Forrest St 62812 618-439-3136
Dr. Jay Goble, supt. Fax 435-4840
www.benton47.org/
Benton MS 400/5-8
1000 Forrest St 62812 618-438-4011
Tammy McCollum, prin. Fax 435-2152

Benton Consolidated HSD 103 600/9-12
511 E Main St 62812 618-439-6415
Dr. Aaron Mattox, supt. Fax 438-8091
www.bentonhighschool.org
Benton Consolidated HS 600/9-12
511 E Main St 62812 618-439-3103
Mark Miller, prin. Fax 438-2915

Berkeley, Cook, Pop. 5,108
Berkeley SD 87 2,700/PK-8
1200 N Wolf Rd 60163 708-449-3350
Dr. Terri Bresnahan, supt. Fax 547-3341
www.berkeley87.org
MacArthur MS 500/6-8
1310 N Wolf Rd 60163 708-449-3185
Dr. Kermit Blakley, prin. Fax 649-3780
Other Schools – See Northlake

Berwyn, Cook, Pop. 56,069
Berwyn North SD 98 3,400/PK-8
6633 16th St 60402 708-484-6200
Dr. Carmen Ayala, supt. Fax 795-2482
www.bn98.org
Lincoln MS 1,100/6-8
6432 16th St 60402 708-795-2475
Michelle Smith, prin. Fax 795-2880

Berwyn South SD 100 3,900/PK-8
3401 Gunderson Ave 60402 708-795-2300
Mary Havis, supt. Fax 795-2317
www.bsd100.org
Freedom MS 600/6-8
3016 Ridgeland Ave 60402 708-795-5800
James Calabrese, prin. Fax 795-5806
Heritage MS 500/6-8
6850 31st St 60402 708-749-6110
Allison Boutet, prin. Fax 749-6124

J. S. Morton HSD 201
Supt. — See Cicero
Morton West HS 3,400/9-12
2400 Home Ave 60402 708-780-4100
Josh McMahon, prin. Fax 222-5903

Bethalto, Madison, Pop. 9,426
Bethalto CUSD 8 2,500/PK-12
610 Texas Blvd 62010 618-377-7200
Dr. Jill Griffin, supt. Fax 377-2845
www.bethalto.org
Civic Memorial HS 700/9-12
200 School St 62010 618-377-7220
Aaron Kilpatrick, prin. Fax 377-7001
Trimpe MS 600/6-8
910 2nd St 62010 618-377-7240
Dr. Kelly McClain, prin. Fax 377-7218

Bethany, Moultrie, Pop. 1,345
Okaw Valley CUSD 302 600/PK-12
PO Box 97 61914 217-665-3232
Kent Stauder, supt. Fax 665-3601
www.okawvalley.org
Okaw Valley HS 200/9-12
PO Box 249 61914 217-665-3631
Matthew Shoaff, prin. Fax 665-3863
Other Schools – See Findlay

Biggsville, Henderson, Pop. 300
West Central CUSD 235 900/PK-12
1514 US Route 34 61418 309-627-2371
Paula Markey, supt. Fax 627-2453
www.wc235.k12.il.us
West Central HS 300/9-12
1514 US Route 34 61418 309-627-2377
Ben Rees, prin. Fax 627-2120
Other Schools – See Stronghurst

Big Rock, Kane, Pop. 710
Hinckley-Big Rock CUSD 429
Supt. — See Hinckley

Hinckley-Big Rock MS 200/6-8
PO Box 247 60511 630-556-4180
Jeff Strouss, prin. Fax 556-4181

Bismarck, Vermilion, Pop. 578
Bismarck-Henning CUSD 1 800/PK-12
PO Box 350 61814 217-759-7261
Scott Watson, supt. Fax 759-7942
www.bismarck.k12.il.us
Bismarck-Henning HS 300/9-12
PO Box 350 61814 217-759-7291
Brent Rademacher, prin. Fax 759-7815
Bismarck-Henning JHS 300/5-8
PO Box 350 61814 217-759-7301
Rusty Campbell, prin. Fax 759-7313

Bloomingdale, DuPage, Pop. 21,714
Bloomingdale SD 13 1,200/PK-8
164 Euclid Ave 60108 630-893-9590
Dr. Jon Bartelt, supt. Fax 893-1818
www.sd13.org
Westfield MS 400/6-8
149 Fairfield Way 60108 630-529-6211
Stefan Larsson, prin. Fax 893-9336

CCSD 93 3,800/PK-8
230 Covington Dr 60108 630-893-9393
William Shields Ed.D., supt. Fax 539-3450
www.ccsd93.com
Stratford MS 600/6-8
251 Butterfield Dr 60108 630-980-9898
Patrick Dawson, prin. Fax 980-9914
Other Schools – See Carol Stream

Pivot Point International Academy Post-Sec.
144 E Lake St Ste C 60108 847-985-5900

Bloomington, McLean, Pop. 74,597
Bloomington SD 87 5,600/PK-12
300 E Monroe St 61701 309-827-6031
Dr. Barry Reilly, supt. Fax 827-5717
www.district87.org
Bloomington HS 1,400/9-12
1202 E Locust St 61701 309-828-5201
Tim Moore, prin. Fax 829-1078
Bloomington JHS 1,200/6-8
901 Colton Ave 61701 309-827-0086
Sherri Thomas, prin. Fax 829-0084

McLean County Unit SD 5
Supt. — See Normal
Evans JHS 700/6-8
2901 Morrissey Dr 61704 309-557-4406
Trevor Chapman, prin. Fax 557-4507

McLean/Dewitt Regional Vocational System
PO Box 5187 61702 309-829-8671
Tom Frazier, supt.
Bloomington Area Career Center Vo/Tech
PO Box 5187 61702 309-829-8671
Tom Frazier, dir. Fax 828-3546

Central Catholic HS 400/9-12
1201 Airport Rd 61704 309-661-7000
Sean Foster, prin. Fax 661-7010
Cornerstone Christian Academy 400/PK-12
PO Box 1608 61702 309-662-9900
Doug Pavey, head sch Fax 662-9904
Hairmasters Institute of Cosmetology Post-Sec.
506 S McClun St 61701 309-827-6971
Illinois Wesleyan University Post-Sec.
1312 Park St 61701 309-556-1000

Blue Island, Cook, Pop. 23,417
Community HSD 218
Supt. — See Oak Lawn
Eisenhower HS 1,800/9-12
12700 Sacramento Ave 60406 708-597-6300
Erik Briseno, prin. Fax 597-9958

Cook County SD 130 3,800/PK-8
12300 Greenwood Ave 60406 708-385-6800
Dr. Tina Halliman, supt. Fax 385-8467
www.district130.org/
Kerr MS 400/6-8
12915 Maple Ave 60406 708-385-5959
Bridgette McNeal, prin. Fax 371-6812
Veterans Memorial MS 400/6-8
12320 Greenwood Ave 60406 708-489-6630
Kiwana Sanders, prin. Fax 489-3522
Other Schools – See Crestwood

Cannella School of Hair Design Post-Sec.
12840 Western Ave 60406 708-388-4949

Bluffs, Scott, Pop. 708
Scott-Morgan CUSD 2 200/PK-12
PO Box 230 62621 217-754-3351
Kevin Blankenship, supt. Fax 754-3908
www.bluffs-school.com/
Bluffs HS 100/9-12
PO Box 230 62621 217-754-3815
Joseph Kuhlmann, prin. Fax 754-3908
Bluffs JHS 50/6-8
PO Box 230 62621 217-754-3815
Joseph Kuhlmann, prin. Fax 754-3908

Bluford, Jefferson, Pop. 685
Bluford Unit SD 318 400/K-12
901 6th St 62814 618-732-8242
John Ashby, supt. Fax 732-6114
www.busd318.org
Webber HS 100/9-12
PO Box 110 62814 618-732-6121
Brock Harris, prin. Fax 732-8784

Bolingbrook, Will, Pop. 71,637
Valley View CUSD 365U
Supt. — See Romeoville
Addams MS 700/6-8
905 Lily Cache Ln 60440 630-759-7200
Teresa Burrell, prin. Fax 759-6362

Bolingbrook HS 3,600/9-12
365 Raider Way 60440 630-759-6400
Dr. Jason Pascavage, prin. Fax 759-2650
Brooks MS 1,200/6-8
350 Blair Ln 60440 630-759-6340
Dr. Keith Wood, prin. Fax 759-6360
Humphrey MS 700/6-8
777 Falconridge Way 60440 630-972-9240
Dan Laverty, prin. Fax 739-8521

Bourbonnais, Kankakee, Pop. 18,268
Bourbonnais ESD 53 2,200/PK-8
281 W John Casey Rd 60914 815-929-5100
Daniel R. Hollowell Ed.D., supt. Fax 939-0481
www.besd53.org
Bourbonnais Upper Grade Center 500/7-8
200 W John Casey Rd 60914 815-929-5200
Jeffrey Gindy, prin. Fax 935-7849

Kankakee Area Career Center
PO Box 570 60914 815-939-4971
Don Fay, dir. Fax 939-7598
www.kacc-il.org
Kankakee Area Career Center Vo/Tech
PO Box 570 60914 815-939-4971
Bosa Goodale, prin. Fax 939-7598

Olivet Nazarene University Post-Sec.
1 University Ave 60914 815-939-5011

Bradford, Stark, Pop. 767
Bradford CUSD 1 200/PK-8
345 Silver St 61421 309-897-4441
Chad Gripp, supt. Fax 897-8361
bradfordschool.net
Bradford JHS 100/6-8
115 High St 61421 309-897-2801
Chad Gripp, admin. Fax 897-4451

Bradley, Kankakee, Pop. 15,644
Bradley SD 61 1,600/PK-8
111 N Crosswell Ave 60915 815-933-3371
Dr. Scott Goselin M.Ed., supt. Fax 939-6601
www.bradleyschools.com/
Bradley Central MS 500/6-8
260 N Wabash Ave 60915 815-939-3564
Mark Kohl, prin. Fax 939-6603

Bradley-Bourbonnais Comm. HSD 307 2,000/9-12
700 W North St 60915 815-937-3707
Dr. Scott Wakeley, supt. Fax 937-0156
www.bbchs.org
Bradley-Bourbonnais Community HS 2,000/9-12
700 W North St 60915 815-937-3707
Dr. Brian Wright, prin. Fax 937-0156

Paul Mitchell The School Post-Sec.
605 E North St 60915 815-932-5049

Braidwood, Will, Pop. 6,143
Reed-Custer CUSD 255U 1,600/PK-12
255 S Comet Dr 60408 815-458-2307
Mark Mitchell, supt. Fax 458-4106
www.rc255.net
Reed-Custer HS 500/9-12
249 S Comet Dr 60408 815-458-2166
Tim Ricketts, prin. Fax 458-4138
Reed-Custer MS 400/6-8
407 S Comet Dr 60408 815-458-2868
Shane Trager, prin. Fax 458-4118

Breese, Clinton, Pop. 4,414
Central Community HSD 71 500/9-12
7740 Old US Highway 50 62230 618-526-4510
Kevin Meyer, supt. Fax 526-2521
www.centralcougars.org
Central Community HS 500/9-12
7740 Old US Highway 50 62230 618-526-4578
B. Kent Jones, prin. Fax 526-7647

Mater Dei HS 500/9-12
900 Mater Dei Dr 62230 618-526-7216
Dennis Litteken, prin. Fax 526-8310

Bridgeport, Lawrence, Pop. 1,874
Red Hill CUSD 10 1,000/PK-12
1250 Judy Ave 62417 618-945-2061
Jakie Walker, supt. Fax 945-7607
redhill.cusd10.org
Red Hill JSHS 400/7-12
908 Church St 62417 618-945-2521
Clarence Gross, prin. Fax 945-7151

Bridgeview, Cook, Pop. 16,102

AQSA S 200/PK-12
7361 W 92nd St 60455 708-598-2700
Northwestern Business College Post-Sec.
7725 S Harlem Ave 60455 888-205-2283
Universal S 600/PK-12
7350 W 93rd St 60455 708-599-4100

Brighton, Macoupin, Pop. 2,236
Southwestern CUSD 9 1,000/PK-12
PO Box 728 62012 618-372-3813
Mark Skertich, supt. Fax 372-4681
www.piasabirds.net
Other Schools – See Piasa

Brimfield, Peoria, Pop. 851
Brimfield CUSD 309 700/PK-12
PO Box 380 61517 309-446-3378
Robert Richardson, supt. Fax 446-3716
www.brimfield309.com/
Brimfield HS 200/9-12
PO Box 380 61517 309-446-3349
Robert Richardson, prin. Fax 446-3716

Broadlands, Champaign, Pop. 347
Heritage CUSD 8
Supt. — See Homer

Heritage HS 200/9-12
PO Box 260 61816 217-834-3392
Thomas Davis, prin. Fax 834-3016

Brookfield, Cook, Pop. 18,709
Brookfield Lagrange Park SD 95 1,100/K-8
3524 Maple Ave 60513 708-485-0606
Dr. Mark Kuzniewski, supt. Fax 485-8066
www.district95.org
Gross MS 400/6-8
3524 Maple Ave 60513 708-485-0600
Kevin Nicholson, prin. Fax 485-0638

Brownstown, Fayette, Pop. 753
Brownstown CUSD 201 300/PK-12
421 S College Ave 62418 618-427-3355
Adam Bussard, supt. Fax 427-3704
www.bcusd201.com
Brownstown JSHS 100/7-12
421 S College Ave 62418 618-427-3839
Michael Shackelford, prin. Fax 427-3704

Brussels, Calhoun, Pop. 140
Brussels CUSD 42 100/K-12
PO Box 128 62013 618-883-2131
Dr. Mark Martin, supt. Fax 883-2514
Brussels HS 100/7-12
PO Box 128 62013 618-883-2131
Alex Pulido, prin. Fax 883-2514

Buckley, Iroquois, Pop. 593

Christ Lutheran HS 50/9-12
PO Box 8 60918 217-394-2547
Sandy Spitz, dir. Fax 394-2097

Buda, Bureau, Pop. 531
Bureau Valley CUSD 340
Supt. — See Manlius
Bureau Valley South S 300/3-8
PO Box 277 61314 309-895-2037
Kristal LeRette, prin. Fax 895-2200

Buffalo, Sangamon, Pop. 499
Tri-City CUSD 1 600/PK-12
324 W Charles St 62515 217-364-4811
Jill Larson, supt. Fax 364-4896
www.tricityschools.org
Tri-City HS 200/9-12
324 W Charles St 62515 217-364-4530
Christy Kindel, prin. Fax 364-4812
Tri-City JHS 100/6-8
324 W Charles St 62515 217-364-4530
Christy Kindel, prin. Fax 364-4812

Buffalo Grove, Cook, Pop. 40,915
Aptakisic-Tripp CCSD 102 2,100/PK-8
1231 Weiland Rd 60089 847-353-5660
Dr. Lori Wilcox, supt. Fax 634-5334
www.d102.org
Aptakisic JHS 500/7-8
1231 Weiland Rd 60089 847-353-5500
Eli Rogers, prin. Fax 634-5347

Kildeer Countryside CCSD 96 3,100/PK-8
1050 Ivy Hall Ln 60089 847-459-4260
Julie Schmidt, supt. Fax 459-2344
www.kcsd96.org
Twin Groves MS 500/6-8
2600 N Buffalo Grove Rd 60089 847-821-8946
Jessica Barnes, prin. Fax 821-8949
Other Schools – See Long Grove

Township HSD 214
Supt. — See Arlington Heights
Buffalo Grove HS 1,900/9-12
1100 W Dundee Rd 60089 847-718-4000
Jeff Wardle, prin. Fax 718-4122

Wheeling CCSD 21
Supt. — See Wheeling
Cooper MS 700/6-8
1050 Plum Grove Cir 60089 847-520-2750
Robert Gurney, prin. Fax 419-3071

Bunker Hill, Macoupin, Pop. 1,760
Bunker Hill CUSD 8 500/PK-12
504 E Warren St 62014 618-585-3116
Dr. Victor Buehler, supt. Fax 585-3212
bhschools.wordpress.com
Bunker Hill HS 200/8-12
314 S Meissner St 62014 618-585-3232
Matthew Smith, prin. Fax 585-3241

Burbank, Cook, Pop. 28,566
Burbank SD 111 3,400/PK-8
7600 Central Ave 60459 708-496-0500
Dr. Franzy Fleck, supt. Fax 496-0510
www.bsd111.org
Liberty JHS 800/7-8
5900 W 81st St 60459 708-952-3255
Mark Antkiewicz, prin. Fax 229-0659

Reavis Township HSD 220 1,800/9-12
6034 W 77th St 60459 708-599-7200
Dr. Daniel Riordan, supt. Fax 599-8751
www.reavisd220.org
Reavis HS 1,800/9-12
6034 W 77th St 60459 708-599-7200
Dr. Daniel Riordan, prin. Fax 599-8751

Queen of Peace HS 400/9-12
7659 Linder Ave 60459 708-458-7600
Hedi Belkaoui, prin. Fax 458-5734
St. Laurence HS 600/9-12
5556 W 77th St 60459 708-458-6900
Jim Muting, prin. Fax 458-7898

Burlington, Kane, Pop. 618
Central CUSD 301 3,600/PK-12
PO Box 396 60109 847-464-6005
Dr. Todd Stirn, supt. Fax 464-6021
www.burlington.k12.il.us

Central HS 1,100/9-12
PO Box 68 60109 847-464-6030
Chris Testone, prin. Fax 464-6039
Central MS 300/8-8
PO Box 397 60109 847-464-6000
Carie Walter, prin. Fax 464-0233

Burr Ridge, DuPage, Pop. 10,371
CCSD 180 600/PK-8
15W451 91st St 60527 630-734-6600
Dr. Thomas Schneider, supt. Fax 325-6450
www.ccsd180.org
Burr Ridge MS 300/5-8
15W451 91st St 60527 630-325-5454
Julie Bartell, prin. Fax 325-6450

Gower SD 62
Supt. — See Willowbrook
Gower MS 400/5-8
7941 S Madison St 60527 630-323-8275
Tracy Murphy, prin. Fax 323-2055

Pleasantdale SD 107 800/PK-8
7450 Wolf Rd 60527 708-784-2013
Dr. David Palzet, supt. Fax 246-0161
www.d107.org
Pleasantdale MS 300/5-8
7450 Wolf Rd 60527 708-246-3210
John Glimco, prin. Fax 352-0092

Everest College Post-Sec.
6880 N Frontage Rd 60527 630-920-1102

Bushnell, McDonough, Pop. 3,074
Bushnell-Prairie City CUSD 170 800/PK-12
845 Walnut St 61422 309-772-9461
Kathy Dinger, supt. Fax 772-9462
bpcschools.org
Bushnell-Prairie City HS 200/9-12
845 Walnut St 61422 309-772-2113
Dawna Daily, prin. Fax 772-2104
Bushnell-Prairie City JHS 200/6-8
847 Walnut St 61422 309-772-3123
Mike Snowden, prin. Fax 772-2666

Byron, Ogle, Pop. 3,700
Byron CUSD 226 1,500/PK-12
696 N Colfax St 61010 815-234-5491
Dr. James Hammack, supt. Fax 234-4106
www.byron226.org
Byron HS 500/9-12
696 N Colfax St 61010 815-234-5491
Jay Mullens, prin. Fax 234-2045
Byron MS 400/6-8
850 N Colfax St 61010 815-234-5491
Zack Ettelbrick, prin. Fax 234-4225

Cahokia, Saint Clair, Pop. 14,938
Cahokia CUSD 187 3,600/K-12
1700 Jerome Ln 62206 618-332-3700
Arthur Ryan, supt. Fax 332-3706
www.cusd187.org
Cahokia HS 1,000/9-12
800 Range Ln 62206 618-332-3730
Kevin Bement, prin. Fax 332-3747
8th Grade Academy 200/8-8
1900 Mousette Ln 62206 618-332-5900
Melissa Rebmann, prin. Fax 332-3725

Cairo, Alexander, Pop. 2,772
Cairo Unit SD 1 500/PK-12
4201 Sycamore St 62914 618-734-4102
Dr. Andrea Evers, supt. Fax 734-4047
www.cairoschooldistrict1.com
Cairo JSHS 200/6-12
4201 Sycamore St 62914 618-734-2187
Dr. Lisa Thomas, prin. Fax 734-2189

Calumet City, Cook, Pop. 36,556
Calumet City SD 155 1,100/K-8
540 Superior Ave 60409 708-862-7665
Dr. Troy Paraday, supt. Fax 868-7555
www.calumetcity155.org/
Wentworth JHS 400/6-8
560 Superior Ave 60409 708-862-0750
Ermetra Olawumi, prin. Fax 862-1194

Dolton SD 149 3,000/PK-8
292 Torrence Ave 60409 708-868-7861
Dr. Shelly Davis-Jones, supt. Fax 868-7850
www.schooldistrict149.org/
Creative Communications Academy 200/7-8
1650 Pulaski Rd 60409 708-868-7585
Gerald Scott, prin. Fax 868-7589
School of Fine Arts 200/7-8
1650 Pulaski Rd 60409 708-868-7565
Dellnora Winters, prin. Fax 868-7589
STEM Academy 200/7-8
1650 Pulaski Rd 60409 708-868-7595
Michael Steele, prin. Fax 868-7589

Hoover-Schrum Memorial SD 157 900/PK-8
1255 Superior Ave 60409 708-868-7500
Dr. Michele Morris, supt. Fax 868-7511
www.hsdist157.org
Schrum Memorial MS 300/6-8
485 165th St 60409 708-862-4236
Dr. Shernita Mays, prin. Fax 862-4580

Thornton Fractional Township HSD 215 3,400/9-12
1601 Wentworth Ave 60409 708-585-2321
Dr. Creg Williams, supt. Fax 585-2317
www.tfd215.org/
Center for Academics & Technology Vo/Tech
1605 Wentworth Ave 60409 708-585-2353
Kent Farlow, prin. Fax 585-2356
Thornton Fractional North HS 1,600/9-12
755 Pulaski Rd 60409 708-585-1000
Dr. Dwayne Evans, prin. Fax 585-1010
Other Schools – See Lansing

Westwood College Post-Sec.
80 River Oaks Ctr Ste 111 60409 708-832-1988

Calumet Park, Cook, Pop. 7,781
Calumet Public SD 132 1,200/PK-8
1440 W Vermont Ave 60827 708-388-8920
Dr. Elizabeth Reynolds, supt. Fax 388-2138
www.sd132.org
Calumet MS 400/6-8
1440 W Vermont Ave 60827 708-388-8820
Andrea Delaney, prin. Fax 388-8557

Cambridge, Henry, Pop. 2,137
Cambridge CUSD 227 500/PK-12
300 S West St 61238 309-937-2144
Thomas Akers, supt. Fax 937-5128
www.district227.org
Cambridge Community JSHS 200/7-12
300 S West St 61238 309-937-2051
Robert Reagan, prin. Fax 937-5128

Campbell Hill, Jackson, Pop. 333
Trico CUSD 176 900/PK-12
PO Box 220 62916 618-426-1111
Larry Lovel, supt. Fax 426-3625
www.trico176.org
Trico HS 300/9-12
PO Box 336 62916 618-426-1111
Mike Denault, prin. Fax 426-3701
Trico JHS 200/6-8
PO Box 335 62916 618-426-1111
Ronald Coleman, prin. Fax 426-3712

Camp Point, Adams, Pop. 1,120
Central CUSD 3 800/K-12
2110 Highway 94 N 62320 217-593-7116
Martin Cook, supt. Fax 593-7026
www.cusd3.com/
Central HS 300/9-12
2110 Highway 94 N 62320 217-593-7731
Jeff Waggener, prin. Fax 593-7025
Central JHS 300/5-8
2110 Highway 94 N 62320 217-593-7741
Erica Smith, prin. Fax 593-7028

Canton, Fulton, Pop. 14,563
Canton Union SD 66 2,600/PK-12
20 W Walnut St 61520 309-647-9411
Rolf Sivertsen, supt. Fax 649-5036
www.cantonusd.org
Canton HS 700/9-12
1001 N Main St 61520 309-647-1820
Jennifer Watts, prin. Fax 649-5039
Ingersoll MS 800/5-8
1605 E Ash St 61520 309-647-6951
Wayne Krus, prin. Fax 647-6959

Hancck/Fultn/Schuylr/McDonogh ROE
Supt. — See Macomb
Spoon River Academy Alt
23235 N County 22 61520 309-226-5090
Barb Schoonover, prin.

Graham Hospital Post-Sec.
210 W Walnut St 61520 309-647-4086
Spoon River College Post-Sec.
23235 N County Highway 22 61520 309-647-4645

Carbondale, Jackson, Pop. 25,058
Carbondale Community HSD 165 1,100/9-12
330 S Giant City Rd 62902 618-457-4722
Stephen Murphy, supt. Fax 457-3353
www.cchs165.jacksn.k12.il.us/
Carbondale Community HS 1,100/9-12
1301 E Walnut St 62901 618-457-3371
Daniel Booth, prin. Fax 549-1686

Carbondale ESD 95 1,500/PK-8
925 S Giant City Rd 62902 618-457-3591
Michael Shimshak, supt. Fax 457-2043
www.ces95.org
Carbondale MS 400/6-8
1150 E Grand Ave 62901 618-457-2174
Marilynn Ross, prin. Fax 457-2176

Southern Illinois University Post-Sec.
1263 Lincoln Dr 62901 618-453-2121
Trinity Christian S 100/PK-12
1218 W Freeman St 62901 618-529-3733
Chris Hottensen, prin. Fax 549-8252

Carlinville, Macoupin, Pop. 5,852
Carlinville CUSD 1 1,500/PK-12
829 W Main St 62626 217-854-9823
Mike Kelly, supt. Fax 854-2777
www.cusd1.com
Carlinville HS 400/9-12
829 W Main St 62626 217-854-3104
Patrick Drew, prin. Fax 854-5260
Carlinville MS 300/6-8
110 Illinois Ave 62626 217-854-3106
Roy Kulenkamp, prin. Fax 854-4503

Blackburn College Post-Sec.
700 College Ave 62626 217-854-3231

Carlyle, Clinton, Pop. 3,259
Carlyle CUSD 1 1,200/PK-12
1400 13th St 62231 618-594-8283
Joe Novsek, supt. Fax 594-8285
www.carlyle.k12.il.us
Carlyle HS 400/9-12
1461 12th St 62231 618-594-2453
Joe Wilkerson, prin. Fax 594-8286
Carlyle JHS 400/5-8
1631 12th St 62231 618-594-8292
Dustin Bilbruck, prin. Fax 594-8294

Clintn/Jeffrsn/Marin/Washngtn ROE 50/
930 Fairfax St Ste B 62231 618-594-2432
Keri Jo Garrett, supt. Fax 594-7192
www.roe13.k12.il.us
Other Schools – See Centralia

Carmi, White, Pop. 5,196
Carmi-White County CUSD 5 1,400/PK-12
211 W Robinson St 62821 618-382-2341
Brad Lee, supt. Fax 384-3207
www.carmischools.org
Carmi-White County HS 400/9-12
800 W Main St 62821 618-382-4661
Jarrod Newell, prin. Fax 382-2453
Carmi-White County JHS 200/7-8
800 W Main St 62821 618-382-4661
Bart King, prin. Fax 382-2453

Carol Stream, DuPage, Pop. 38,894
CCSD 93
Supt. — See Bloomingdale
Stream MS 600/6-8
283 El Paso Ln 60188 630-462-8940
Peter LaChance, prin. Fax 462-9224

Glenbard Township HSD 87
Supt. — See Glen Ellyn
Glenbard North HS 2,400/9-12
990 Kuhn Rd 60188 630-653-7000
Dr. John Mensik, prin. Fax 653-7259

Carpentersville, Kane, Pop. 37,150
CUSD 300
Supt. — See Algonquin
Carpentersville MS 800/6-8
100 Cleveland Ave 60110 847-426-1380
Asia Gurney, prin. Fax 426-1404
Dundee-Crown HS 2,500/9-12
1500 Kings Rd 60110 847-426-1415
Devon Larosa, prin. Fax 426-1245
Oak Ridge S 50/Alt
300 Cleveland Ave 60110 847-426-4052
Stacy Wilkinson, prin. Fax 426-4474

Carrier Mills, Saline, Pop. 1,618
Carrier Mills-Stonefort CUSD 2 400/PK-12
7071 US 45 S 62917 618-994-2392
Bryce K. Jerrell, supt. Fax 994-2929
Carrier Mills-Stonefort HS 100/9-12
PO Box 217 62917 618-994-2392
Bryce K. Jerrell, prin. Fax 994-2929

Carrollton, Greene, Pop. 2,475
Carrollton CUSD 1 600/PK-12
950A 3rd St 62016 217-942-5314
Dr. Kerry Cox, supt. Fax 942-9259
www.c-hawks.net
Carrollton HS 200/9-12
950 3rd St 62016 217-942-6913
Leslee Frazier, prin. Fax 942-6835

Carterville, Williamson, Pop. 5,368
Carterville CUSD 5 2,100/PK-12
306 Virginia Ave 62918 618-985-4826
Keith Liddell, supt. Fax 985-2041
www.cartervillelions.com
Carterville HS 600/9-12
1415 W Grand Ave 62918 618-985-2940
Todd Rogers, prin. Fax 985-2741
Carterville JHS 300/7-8
816 S Division St 62918 618-985-2940
Jeff Hartford, prin. Fax 985-2492

John A. Logan College Post-Sec.
700 Logan College Dr 62918 618-985-3741

Carthage, Hancock, Pop. 2,577
Carthage ESD 317 400/PK-8
210 S Adams St 62321 217-357-3922
Vicki Hardy, supt. Fax 357-6793
www.cesd317.org
Carthage MS 200/5-8
210 S Adams St 62321 217-357-3914
Jerry Butcher, prin. Fax 357-3755

Hancck/Fultn/Schuylr/McDonogh ROE
Supt. — See Macomb
Hancock County Academy 50/Alt
553 Main St 62321 217-575-3226

Illini West HSD 307 400/9-12
600 Miller St 62321 217-357-9607
Kim Schilson, supt. Fax 357-9609
www.illiniwest.org
Illini West HS 400/9-12
600 Miller St 62321 217-357-2136
Scott Schneider, prin. Fax 357-3569

Cary, McHenry, Pop. 17,990
Cary CCSD 26 2,500/PK-8
2115 Crystal Lake Rd 60013 224-357-5100
Brian Coleman, supt. Fax 639-3898
www.cary26.org
Cary JHS 1,000/6-8
2109 Crystal Lake Rd 60013 224-357-5150
Linda Goeglein, prin. Fax 516-5507

Community HSD 155
Supt. — See Crystal Lake
Cary-Grove HS 1,800/9-12
2208 3 Oaks Rd 60013 847-639-3825
Jay Sargeant, prin. Fax 639-3873

Trinity Oaks Christian Academy 200/PK-12
233 Trinity Oaks Way 60013 847-462-5971
Dr. Paul Wrobbel, head sch Fax 462-5972

Casey, Clark, Pop. 2,756
Casey-Westfield CUSD C4 900/PK-12
502 E Delaware Ave 62420 217-932-2184
Dee Scott, supt. Fax 932-5553
www.caseywestfield.org

Casey-Westfield JSHS 400/7-12
306 E Edgar Ave 62420 217-932-2175
James Sullivan, prin. Fax 932-2004

Catlin, Vermilion, Pop. 2,025
Salt Fork CUSD 512
Supt. — See Sidell
Salt Fork HS 200/9-12
701 W Vermilion St 61817 217-427-5331
Darin Chambliss, prin. Fax 427-2468

Centralia, Marion, Pop. 12,732
Centralia HSD 200 900/9-12
2100 E Calumet St 62801 618-532-7391
Chuck Lane, supt. Fax 532-8952
www.centraliahs.org
Centralia HS 900/9-12
2100 E Calumet St 62801 618-532-7391
Reid Shipley, prin. Fax 532-8952

Centralia SD 135 1,300/PK-8
400 S Elm St 62801 618-532-1907
Craig Clark, supt. Fax 532-4986
www.ccs135.com
Centralia JHS 500/5-8
900 S Pine St 62801 618-533-7130
Tron Young, prin. Fax 533-7123

Clintn/Jeffrsn/Marin/Washngtn ROE
Supt. — See Carlyle
Alternative Learning Academy 50/Alt
1000 E 3rd St 62801 618-533-3935
Brad Weathers, dir. Fax 533-3936

Christ Our Rock Lutheran HS 100/9-12
9545 Shattuc Rd 62801 618-226-3315
Don Duensing, prin. Fax 226-3312
Kaskaskia College Post-Sec.
27210 College Rd 62801 618-545-3000

Cerro Gordo, Piatt, Pop. 1,398
Cerro Gordo CUSD 100 400/PK-12
PO Box 79 61818 217-763-5221
Brett Robinson, supt. Fax 763-6562
www.cgbroncos.org
Cerro Gordo JSHS 200/7-12
PO Box 79 61818 217-763-2711
Steve Cline, prin. Fax 763-6287

Chadwick, Carroll, Pop. 548
Chadwick-Milledgeville CUSD 399 500/PK-12
15 School St 61014 815-684-5191
Timothy Schurman, supt. Fax 684-5241
www.dist399.net
Chadwick JHS 100/6-8
19 School St 61014 815-684-5191
Timothy Schurman, prin. Fax 684-5241
Other Schools – See Milledgeville

Champaign, Champaign, Pop. 78,771
Champaign CUSD 4 9,600/PK-12
703 S New St 61820 217-351-3800
Dr. Judy Wiegand, supt. Fax 352-3590
www.champaignschools.org
Centennial HS 1,400/9-12
913 Crescent Dr 61821 217-351-3951
Gregory Johnson, prin. Fax 351-3730
Central HS 1,200/9-12
610 W University Ave 61820 217-351-3911
Joe Williams, prin. Fax 351-3919
Edison MS 700/6-8
306 W Green St 61820 217-351-3771
Angela Schoonover, prin. Fax 355-2564
Franklin MS 600/6-8
817 N Harris Ave 61820 217-351-3819
Sara Sanders, prin. Fax 351-3729
Jefferson MS 700/6-8
1115 Crescent Dr 61821 217-351-3790
Angelica Franklin, prin. Fax 351-3754
Novak Academy 50/Alt
815 N Randolph St 61820 217-352-4328
Danielle Cook, prin. Fax 352-7292

High School of St. Thomas More 300/9-12
3901 N Mattis Ave 61822 217-352-7210
Jason Schreder, prin. Fax 352-7213
Judah Christian S 500/PK-12
908 N Prospect Ave 61820 217-359-1701
Mike Chitty, admin. Fax 359-0214
Parkland College Post-Sec.
2400 W Bradley Ave 61821 217-351-2200

Channahon, Will, Pop. 12,437
Channahon SD 17 1,400/PK-8
24920 S Sage St 60410 815-467-4315
Nicholas Henkle, supt. Fax 467-4343
csd17.org
Channahon JHS 400/7-8
24917 W Sioux Dr 60410 815-467-4314
Dr. Chad Uphoff, prin. Fax 467-2188

Minooka Community HSD 111 2,500/9-12
26655 W Eames St 60410 815-467-2557
Dr. Kenneth Lee, supt. Fax 467-9733
www.mchs.net
Minooka Community HS South Campus 1,300/9-10
26655 W Eames St 60410 815-521-4001
Ron Kiesewetter, prin. Fax 467-6120
Other Schools – See Minooka

Families of Faith Christian Academy 100/PK-12
PO Box 277 60410 815-521-1381
Karen Blan, admin. Fax 467-4476

Charleston, Coles, Pop. 21,496
Charleston CUSD 1 2,700/PK-12
410 W Polk Ave 61920 217-639-1000
Jim Littleford, supt. Fax 639-1005
www.charleston.k12.il.us
Charleston HS 800/9-12
1615 Lincoln Ave 61920 217-639-5000
Trevor Doughty, prin. Fax 639-5005
Charleston MS 400/7-8
920 Smith Dr 61920 217-639-6000
Chad Burgett, prin. Fax 639-6005

Eastern Illinois University Post-Sec.
600 Lincoln Ave 61920 217-581-5000

Chatham, Sangamon, Pop. 11,317
Ball Chatham CUSD 5 4,600/PK-12
201 W Mulberry St 62629 217-483-2416
Dr. Douglas A Wood, supt. Fax 483-2940
www.chathamschools.org
Glenwood HS 1,400/9-12
1501 E Plummer Blvd 62629 217-483-2424
Jim Lee, prin. Fax 483-5402
Glenwood MS 700/7-8
595 Chatham Rd 62629 217-483-2481
Christina Root, prin. Fax 483-4940

Chester, Randolph, Pop. 8,526
Chester CUSD 139 1,000/PK-12
1940 Swanwick St 62233 618-826-4509
Rick Goodman, supt. Fax 826-4500
www.chester139.com
Chester HS 300/9-12
1901 Swanwick St 62233 618-826-2302
Dr. Sarah Gass, prin. Fax 826-3723

Chicago, Cook, Pop. 2,654,865
City of Chicago SD 299 406,100/PK-12
42 W Madison St 60602 773-553-1000
Forrest Claypool, supt. Fax 535-1502
www.cps.edu
Air Force Academy HS 400/9-12
3630 S Wells St 60609 773-535-1590
Yashika Eggleston, prin. Fax 535-1847
Albany Park Multicultural MS 300/7-8
4929 N Sawyer Ave 60625 773-534-5108
Hiliana Araceli Leon, prin. Fax 534-5178
Alcott College Prep 300/9-12
2957 N Hoyne Ave 60618 773-534-5970
Elias Estrada, prin. Fax 534-5971
Amundsen HS 1,200/9-12
5110 N Damen Ave 60625 773-534-2320
Anna Pavichevich, prin. Fax 534-2330
Back of the Yards IB HS 300/9-12
2111 W 47th St 60609 773-535-7320
Patricia Barrera Brekke, prin. Fax 535-6880
Banner West Academy HS 300/Alt
819 N Leamington Ave 60651 773-854-1188
Eric Carlton, prin. Fax 854-1196
Bogan Computer Tech HS 1,100/9-12
3939 W 79th St 60652 773-535-2180
Alahrie Aziz-Sims, prin. Fax 535-2165
Bowen HS 400/9-12
2710 E 89th St 60617 773-535-7650
Nia Abdullah, prin. Fax 535-6489
Bronzeville Scholastic Academy 500/9-12
4934 S Wabash Ave 60615 773-535-1150
Stephanie Glover-Douglas, prin. Fax 535-1228
Brooks College Prep Academy 800/9-12
250 E 111th St 60628 773-535-9930
Shannae Jackson, prin. Fax 535-9939
Camelot Safe Academy 50/Alt
7877 S Coles Ave 60649 773-902-2487
Joseph Haley, prin. Fax 902-7961
Camelot Safe Garfield HS 50/Alt
230 N Kolmar Ave 60624 773-417-2045
Carmen Knott, prin. Fax 417-2198
Camelot Safe HS 50/Alt
7877 S Coles Ave 60649 773-902-2487
Joseph Haley, prin. Fax 902-7961
Carver Military Academy 500/9-12
13100 S Doty Ave 60827 773-535-5250
Steven Rouse, prin. Fax 535-5037
Castellanos MS 600/4-8
2524 S Central Park Ave 60623 773-534-1620
Virginia Jimenez, prin. Fax 534-1611
Chicago Academy HS 500/9-12
3400 N Austin Ave 60634 773-534-0146
David Gilligan, prin. Fax 534-0192
Chicago Excel Academy HS 300/Alt
1257 W 111th St 60643 773-629-8379
Tyree Booker, prin. Fax 629-8736
Chicago HS for Agricultural Sciences 600/9-12
3857 W 111th St 60655 773-535-2500
William Hook, prin. Fax 535-2507
Chicago HS for the Arts 600/9-12
2714 W Augusta Blvd 60622 773-534-9710
Mike Wang, prin. Fax 534-9720
Chicago Military Academy 400/9-12
3519 S Giles Ave 60653 773-534-9750
Octavio Kasas, prin. Fax 534-9760
Chicago Technology Academy 400/9-12
1301 W 14th St 60608 773-534-7755
Linnea Garrett, prin. Fax 534-7757
Chicago Vocational Career Academy Vo/Tech
2100 E 87th St 60617 773-535-6100
Douglas Maclin, prin. Fax 535-6975
Clark Academic Prep HS 500/9-12
5101 W Harrison St 60644 773-534-6250
Charles Anderson, prin. Fax 534-6292
Clemente Community Academy 700/9-12
1147 N Western Ave 60622 773-534-4000
Marcey Sorensen, prin. Fax 534-4012
Collins Academy HS 400/9-12
1313 S Sacramento Dr 60623 773-534-1840
LeKenya Sanders-Sharpe, prin. Fax 542-6471
Community Services West Academy Vo/Tech
8 W Root St 60609 312-809-3511
Bertha Buchanan, prin. Fax 281-0221
Corliss HS 500/9-12
821 E 103rd St 60628 773-535-5115
Leonard Harris, prin. Fax 535-5511
Crane Medical Preparatory HS 100/9-12
2245 W Jackson Blvd 60612 773-534-7600
Fareeda Jahaan Shabazz, prin. Fax 534-7612
Curie Metropolitan HS 2,900/9-12
4959 S Archer Ave 60632 773-535-2100
Allison Tingwall, prin. Fax 535-2049
DeVry Advantage Academy 200/11-12
3300 N Campbell Ave 60618 773-697-2216
Carolyn Eggert, prin. Fax 327-4262
Disney II Magnet HS 200/7-12
3900 N Lawndale Ave 60618 773-534-5010
Kathleen Speth, prin. Fax 534-5199
Douglass Academy 300/9-12
543 N Waller Ave 60644 773-534-6176
Vanessa Perry, prin. Fax 534-6172
Dunbar Vocational Career Academy Vo/Tech
3000 S King Dr 60616 773-534-9000
Gerald Morrow, prin. Fax 534-9250
Dyett Academic Center 50/Alt
555 E 51st St 60615 773-535-1825
Beulah McLoyd, prin. Fax 535-1037
Evergreen Academy MS 400/6-8
3537 S Paulina St 60609 773-535-4836
Marian Strok, prin. Fax 535-4853
Excel Acadamy-Englewood HS 200/9-12
7141 S Morgan St 60621 773-669-1476
Melvin Berry, prin.
Excel Academy - Southwest 100/9-12
7014 S Washtenaw Ave 60629 773-424-0721
Jamal Tillery, prin. Fax 424-0746
Farragut Career Academy Vo/Tech
2345 S Christiana Ave 60623 773-534-1300
Tonya Hammaker, prin. Fax 534-1336
Fenger Academy HS 400/9-12
11220 S Wallace St 60628 773-535-5430
Richard Smith, prin. Fax 535-5444
Field ES 300/5-8
7019 N Ashland Blvd 60626 773-534-2030
Adrian Dobbins, prin. Fax 534-2189
Foreman College and Career Academy 1,400/9-12
3235 N Leclaire Ave 60641 773-534-3400
Wayne Issa, prin. Fax 534-3684
Gage Park HS 600/9-12
5630 S Rockwell St 60629 773-535-9230
Brian Metcalf, prin. Fax 535-9411
Gary ES 1,200/PK-PK, 3-
3740 W 31st St 60623 773-534-1455
Alberto Juarez, prin. Fax 534-1435
Goode STEM Academy 500/9-12
7651 S Homan Ave 60652 773-535-7875
Armando Rodriguez, prin. Fax 535-7877
Hancock College Prep HS 900/9-12
4034 W 56th St 60629 773-535-2410
Dr. Karen Boran, prin. Fax 535-2434
Harlan Community Academy HS 900/7-12
9652 S Michigan Ave 60628 773-535-5400
Ramona Fannings, prin. Fax 535-5061
Harper HS 500/9-12
6520 S Wood St 60636 773-535-9150
Leonetta Sanders, prin. Fax 535-9090
Hernandez MS for Advancement of Sciences 900/6-8
3510 W 55th St 60632 773-535-8850
Debra Fritz-Fanning, prin. Fax 535-8851
Hirsch Metro HS 200/9-12
7740 S Ingleside Ave 60619 773-535-3100
Larry Varn, prin. Fax 535-3240
Hope College Prep HS 400/9-12
5515 S Lowe Ave 60621 773-535-3160
Michael Durr, prin. Fax 535-3444
Hubbard HS 1,600/9-12
6200 S Hamlin Ave 60629 773-535-2200
Nancy Wiley, prin. Fax 535-2218
Hyde Park Academy HS 900/9-12
6220 S Stony Island Ave 60637 773-535-0880
Antonio Ross, prin. Fax 535-0633
Infinity Math Science & Tech HS 400/9-12
3120 S Kostner Ave 60623 773-535-4225
Charles Smith, prin. Fax 535-4270
Jefferson Alternative S 200/Alt
1100 S Hamilton Ave 60612 312-433-7110
Judith Gibbs, prin. Fax 433-4442
Johnson - Brainerd HS 100/Alt
8908 S Ashland Ave 60620 773-239-2037
Sandra Smith, dir. Fax 239-2084
Johnson - Englewood HS 100/Alt
845 W 69th St 60621 773-962-9256
Veriner James, dir. Fax 969-9995
Johnson - Humboldt Park HS 100/Alt
2421 W Division St 60622 773-276-0620
Kisha Lang, dir. Fax 276-0692
Johnson - North Lawndale HS 100/Alt
3222 W Roosevelt Rd 60624 773-826-1136
John Shenberger, prin. Fax 826-1180
Johnson - Roseland HS 100/Alt
10928 S Halsted Ave 60628 773-468-1480
Raashida Washington, dir. Fax 468-1507
Jones College Prep HS 1,100/9-12
700 S State St 60605 773-534-8600
Dr. Joseph Powers, prin. Fax 534-8625
Juarez Community Academy 1,700/9-12
2150 S Laflin St 60608 773-534-7030
Juan Ocon, prin. Fax 534-7058
Julian HS 1,000/9-12
10330 S Elizabeth St 60643 773-535-5170
Myron Hester, prin. Fax 535-5230
Kelly HS 2,400/9-12
4136 S California Ave 60632 773-535-4900
Dr. Lisa Bucciarelli-Carlos, prin. Fax 535-4841
Kelvyn Park HS 900/7-12
4343 W Wrightwood Ave 60639 773-534-4200
Allyson Fox-Crump, prin. Fax 534-4507
Kennedy HS 1,500/9-12
6325 W 56th St 60638 773-535-2325
George Szkapiak, prin. Fax 535-2485
Kenwood Academy HS 1,800/7-12
5015 S Blackstone Ave 60615 773-535-1350
Gregory Jones, prin. Fax 535-1360
King College Prep HS 800/9-12
4445 S Drexel Blvd 60653 773-535-1180
David Narain, prin. Fax 535-1658

Lake View HS 1,400/9-12
4015 N Ashland Ave 60613 773-534-5440
Paul Karafiol, prin. Fax 534-5585
Lane Tech HS 4,100/7-12
2501 W Addison St 60618 773-534-5400
Brian Tennison, prin. Fax 534-5544
Lincoln Park HS 2,200/9-12
2001 N Orchard St 60614 773-534-8130
Michael Boraz, prin. Fax 534-8218
Lindblom Math & Science Academy 1,200/7-12
6130 S Wolcott Ave 60636 773-535-9300
Wayne Bevis, prin. Fax 535-9314
Madero MS 300/6-8
3202 W 28th St 60623 773-535-4466
Jose Illanes, prin. Fax 535-4469
Manley Career Academy Vo/Tech
2935 W Polk St 60612 773-534-6900
Trista Harper, prin. Fax 534-6924
Marine Leadership Academy - Ames 500/7-12
1920 N Hamlin Ave 60647 773-534-4970
Erin Galfer, prin. Fax 534-4975
Marshall Metro HS 600/9-12
3250 W Adams St 60624 773-534-6455
Falilat Shokunbi, prin. Fax 534-6409
Marshall MS 300/7-8
3900 N Lawndale Ave 60618 773-534-5200
Januario Gutierrez, prin. Fax 534-5292
Mather HS 1,600/9-12
5835 N Lincoln Ave 60659 773-534-2350
Christie Jones, prin. Fax 534-2424
Morgan Park HS 1,400/7-12
1744 W Pryor Ave 60643 773-535-2550
Carolyn Epps, prin. Fax 535-2706
Multicultural Academy of Scholarship 300/9-12
3120 S Kostner Ave 60623 773-535-4242
James Clarke, prin. Fax 535-4273
North-Grand HS 900/9-12
4338 W Wabansia Ave 60639 773-534-8520
Emily Feltes, prin. Fax 534-8535
Northside College Prep HS 1,100/9-12
5501 N Kedzie Ave 60625 773-534-3954
Kelly Mest, prin. Fax 534-3964
Northwest MS 700/6-8
5252 W Palmer St 60639 773-534-3250
Margaret Byrne, prin. Fax 534-3251
Ogden International HS 800/6-12
1250 W Erie St, 773-534-0866
Dr. Michael Beyer, prin. Fax 534-0869
Ombudsman - Northwest HS 100/Alt
7500 N Harlem Ave 60631 708-669-7828
Lyntina Lampley, prin. Fax 669-7829
Ombudsman - South HS 500/Alt
6057 S Western Ave 60636 773-498-5085
Sue Fila, prin. Fax 424-7291
Ombudsman - West HS 400/Alt
2401 W Congress Pkwy 60612 312-243-1550
Dr. Samuel Brown, prin. Fax 243-1562
Orr Academy HS 800/9-12
730 N Pulaski Rd 60624 773-534-6500
Shanele Andrews, prin. Fax 534-6504
Pathways in Education - Ashburn 300/Alt
3284 W 87th St 60652 773-434-6300
Andrew Morgan, prin. Fax 434-6301
Pathways in Education - Avondale 200/Alt
3100 W Belmont Ave 60618 773-588-5007
Andrew Morgan, prin. Fax 588-5009
Pathways in Education - Brighton Park 300/Alt
3124 W 47th St 60632 773-579-1220
Andrew Morgan, prin. Fax 579-1224
Pathways in Education Lincoln Square Alt
4820 N Western Ave 60625 773-434-6300
Joe Zotto, prin.
Payton College Prep HS 800/9-12
1034 N Wells St 60610 773-534-0034
Timothy Devine, prin. Fax 534-0035
Peace and Education Coalition HS 100/Alt
4946 S Paulina St 60609 773-535-9023
Brigitte Lee Swenson, prin. Fax 535-9477
Phillips Academy HS 500/9-12
244 E Pershing Rd 60653 773-535-1603
Matthew Sullivan, prin. Fax 535-1605
Phoenix Military Academy 500/9-12
145 S Campbell Ave 60612 773-534-7275
Ferdinand Wipachit, prin. Fax 534-7273
Prosser Career Academy Vo/Tech
2148 N Long Ave 60639 773-534-3200
Dr. Mark Schall, prin. Fax 534-3382
Raby HS 500/9-12
3545 W Fulton Blvd 60624 773-534-6755
Femi Skanes, prin. Fax 534-6938
Richards Career Academy Vo/Tech
5009 S Laflin St 60609 773-535-4945
Durrell Anderson, prin. Fax 535-4883
Rickover Naval Academy HS 500/9-12
5900 N Glenwood Ave 60660 773-534-2890
Michael Biela, prin. Fax 534-2895
Robeson HS 400/9-12
6835 S Normal Blvd 60621 773-535-3800
Melanie Beatty-Sevier, prin. Fax 535-3620
Roosevelt HS 1,400/9-12
3436 W Wilson Ave 60625 773-534-5000
Carolyn Rownd, prin. Fax 534-5044
Schurz HS 2,400/9-12
3601 N Milwaukee Ave 60641 773-534-3420
Kathleen Valente, prin. Fax 534-3573
Senn HS 1,200/9-12
5900 N Glenwood Ave 60660 773-534-2365
Mary Beck, prin. Fax 534-2369
Shields MS 700/5-8
2611 W 48th St 60632 773-535-7115
Peter Auffant, prin. Fax 535-7296
Simeon Career Academy Vo/Tech
8147 S Vincennes Ave 60620 773-535-3200
Dr. Sheldon House, prin. Fax 535-3465
Simpson Academy for Young Women 100/Alt
1321 S Paulina St 60608 773-534-7812
Marisa Velasquez, prin. Fax 534-7819

Social Justice HS 400/9-12
3120 S Kostner Ave 60623 773-535-4300
Kathy Farr, prin. Fax 535-4271
Solorio Academy HS 1,100/9-12
5400 S Saint Louis Ave 60632 773-535-9070
Victor Iturralde, prin. Fax 535-9073
South Shore International College Prep 600/9-12
1955 E 75th St 60649 773-535-8350
Janice Elaine Wells, prin.
Spry Community Links HS 200/9-12
2400 S Marshall Blvd 60623 773-534-1997
Francisco Borras, prin. Fax 534-0354
Steinmetz College Prep HS 1,800/9-12
3030 N Mobile Ave 60634 773-534-3030
Stephen Ngo, prin. Fax 534-3151
Sullivan HS 600/9-12
6631 N Bosworth Ave 60626 773-534-2000
Chad Adams, prin. Fax 534-2141
Taft HS 3,100/7-12
6530 W Bryn Mawr Ave 60631 773-534-1000
Mark Grishaber, prin. Fax 534-1027
TEAM Englewood Academy 400/9-12
6201 S Stewart Ave 60621 773-535-3530
Michelle Russell, prin. Fax 535-3586
Tilden Career Community HS 300/9-12
4747 S Union Ave 60609 773-535-1625
Maurice Swinney, prin. Fax 535-1866
Uplift Community HS 300/9-12
900 W Wilson Ave 60640 773-534-2875
Stephanie Moore, prin. Fax 534-2876
VOISE Academy HS 300/9-12
231 N Pine Ave 60644 773-534-0660
Patricia Reynolds, prin. Fax 534-0667
Von Steuben Metro HS 1,700/9-12
5039 N Kimball Ave 60625 773-534-5100
Laura Lemone, prin. Fax 534-5210
Washington HS 1,500/9-12
3535 E 114th St 60617 773-535-5725
Kevin Gallick, prin. Fax 535-5038
Wells Community Academy HS 600/9-12
936 N Ashland Ave 60622 773-534-7010
Rituparna Raichoudhuri, prin. Fax 534-7078
Westinghouse College Prep HS 1,100/9-12
3223 W Franklin Blvd 60624 773-534-6400
Patrick McGill, prin. Fax 534-6422
Williams Prep S of Medicine 300/9-12
4934 S Wabash Ave 60615 773-535-1120
Jullanar Naselli, prin. Fax 535-1023
World Language HS 400/9-12
3120 S Kostner Ave 60623 773-535-4334
Brian Rogers, prin. Fax 254-8470
York Alternative HS 300/Alt
2700 S California Ave 60608 773-535-7021
Dr. Sharnette Sims, prin. Fax 535-7109
Young Magnet JSHS 2,200/7-12
211 S Laflin St 60607 773-534-7500
Dr. Joyce Kenner, prin. Fax 534-7261

Adler School of Professional Psychology Post-Sec.
17 N Dearborn St 60602 312-662-4000
Advocate Illinois Masonic Post-Sec.
836 W Wellington Ave 60657 773-296-8950
Advocate Trinity Hospital Post-Sec.
2320 E 93rd St 60617 773-978-2000
American Academy of Art Post-Sec.
332 S Michigan Ave Ste 3 60604 312-461-0600
American Floral Art School Post-Sec.
2519 W Altgeld St Ste 100 60647 312-922-9328
American Health Information Management Post-Sec.
233 N Michigan Ave Ste 2150 60601 312-233-1100
Argosy University/Chicago Post-Sec.
225 N Michigan Ave Ste 1300 60601 312-777-7600
ATS Institute of Technology Post-Sec.
25 E Washington St Ste 200 60602 312-214-2000
Bais Yaakov HS for Girls 200/9-12
5800 N Kimball Ave 60659 773-267-1494
Shulamis Keller, prin. Fax 267-4798
Bexley Seabury Post-Sec.
8765 W Higgins Rd 60631 773-380-6780
Bnos Rabbeinu HS 50/9-12
6237 N Whipple St 60659 773-338-3214
Tsyrl Turen, prin.
British S of Chicago 800/PK-12
814 W Eastman St, 773-506-2097
Michael Horton, prin.
Brother Rice HS 800/9-12
10001 S Pulaski Rd 60655 773-429-4300
James Antos, prin. Fax 779-5239
Cain's Barber College Post-Sec.
365 E 51st St 60615 773-536-4441
Cannella School of Hair Design Post-Sec.
9012 S Commercial Ave 60617 773-221-4700
Cannella School of Hair Design Post-Sec.
4269 S Archer Ave 60632 773-890-0412
Cannella School of Hair Design Post-Sec.
4217 W North Ave 60639 773-278-4477
Capri Beauty College Post-Sec.
2653 W 63rd St 60629 773-778-1077
Catholic Theological Union Post-Sec.
5401 S Cornell Ave 60615 773-371-5400
Chamberlain College of Nursing Post-Sec.
3300 N Campbell Ave 60618 773-961-3000
Chicago Academy for the Arts 100/9-12
1010 W Chicago Ave, 312-421-0202
Jason Patera, head sch Fax 421-3816
Chicago Hope Academy 100/9-12
2189 W Bowler St 60612 312-491-1600
Karen Pyne, head sch Fax 491-1616
Chicago Jesuit Academy 100/5-8
5058 W Jackson Blvd 60644 773-638-6103
Thomas Beckley, prin. Fax 638-6107
Chicago Sch. of Professional Psychology Post-Sec.
325 N Wells St 60654 312-329-6600
Chicago State University Post-Sec.
9501 S King Dr 60628 773-995-2000
Chicago Theological Seminary Post-Sec.
1407 E 60th St 60637 773-896-2400

Chicago Waldorf S 400/PK-12
1300 W Loyola Ave 60626 773-465-2662
Luke Goodwin, admin. Fax 465-6648
Christ the King Jesuit College Prep S 300/9-12
5088 W Jackson Blvd 60644 773-261-7505
Temple Payne, prin. Fax 261-7507
Columbia College Post-Sec.
600 S Michigan Ave 60605 312-369-1000
Computer Systems Institute Post-Sec.
29 E Madison St 60602 312-781-9292
Cook County Hospital Post-Sec.
1825 W Harrison St 60612 312-633-8533
Cornerstone Academy 9-12
1111 N Wells St Ste 403 60610 312-573-8854
Cortiva Institute-School of Massage Thpy Post-Sec.
17 N State St Fl 5 60602 312-753-7900
Coyne College Post-Sec.
330 N Green St 60607 800-999-5220
Cristo Rey Jesuit HS 500/9-12
1852 W 22nd Pl 60608 773-890-6800
Patricia Garrity, prin. Fax 890-6801
CS Academy College Prep S 100/K-12
1443 W 63rd St 60636 312-675-8691
Domonique Ziegler, admin. Fax 737-4865
De La Salle Institute - Institute Campus 1,100/9-12
3434 S Michigan Ave 60616 312-842-7355
Diane Brown, prin. Fax 842-5640
De La Salle Institute - Lourdes Campus 500/9-12
1040 W 32nd Pl 60608 773-650-6800
Diane Brown, prin. Fax 650-9723
DePaul College Prep S 400/9-12
3633 N California Ave 60618 773-539-3600
Dr. James Quaid, prin. Fax 539-9158
De Paul University Post-Sec.
1 E Jackson Blvd 60604 312-362-8000
DeVry University Post-Sec.
3300 N Campbell Ave 60618 773-929-8500
DeVry University Post-Sec.
225 W Washington St Ste 100 60606 312-372-4900
DeVry University Post-Sec.
8550 W Bryn Mawr Ave # 450 60631 773-695-1000
East-West University Post-Sec.
816 S Michigan Ave 60605 312-939-0111
Erikson Institute Post-Sec.
451 N La Salle Dr 60654 312-755-2250
Everest College Post-Sec.
7414 S Cicero Ave 60629 708-793-4600
GCE - Lab S 50/9-12
1535 N Dayton St, 312-643-0991
Eric Davis, dir. Fax 643-0975
Greater West Comm Development Project Post-Sec.
500 N Sacramento Blvd 60612 312-432-9595
Hanna Sacks Girls HS 100/9-12
3021 W Devon Ave 60659 773-338-9222
Tobie Teller, prin. Fax 338-2405
Harold S. Washington College Post-Sec.
30 E Lake St 60601 312-553-5600
Harrington College of Design Post-Sec.
200 W Madison St Lbby 2 60606 312-939-4975
Harry S. Truman College Post-Sec.
1145 W Wilson Ave 60640 773-907-4000
Holy Trinity HS 300/9-12
1443 W Division St, 773-278-4212
Marianne Lynch, prin. Fax 278-0144
Illinois Center for Broadcasting Post-Sec.
530 S State St 60605 312-884-8000
Illinois College of Optometry Post-Sec.
3241 S Michigan Ave 60616 312-225-1700
Illinois Institute of Technology Post-Sec.
3300 S Federal St 60616 312-567-3000
Illinois School of Health Careers Post-Sec.
11 E Adams St Ste 200 60603 312-913-1230
Institute for Clinical Social Work Post-Sec.
401 S State St Ste 822 60605 312-935-4232
John Marshall Law School Post-Sec.
315 S Plymouth Ct 60604 312-427-2737
Josephinum Academy 200/6-12
1501 N Oakley Blvd 60622 773-276-1261
Mary Rose Guerin, prin. Fax 292-3963
Kendall College Post-Sec.
900 N North Branch St, 888-905-3632
Kennedy-King College Post-Sec.
6301 S Halsted St 60621 773-602-5000
Latin S of Chicago 1,100/PK-12
59 W North Blvd 60610 312-582-6000
Randall Dunn, head sch Fax 582-6011
Le Cordon Bleu College of Culinary Arts Post-Sec.
361 W Chestnut St 60610 312-944-0882
Leo HS 100/9-12
7901 S Sangamon St 60620 773-224-9600
Philip Mesina, prin. Fax 224-3856
Lexington College Post-Sec.
310 S Peoria St 60607 312-226-6294
Loyola University Chicago Post-Sec.
1032 W Sheridan Rd 60660 773-274-3000
Lubavitch Girls HS 100/9-12
6350 N Whipple St 60659 773-743-7716
Kreindel Pinkus, prin. Fax 743-7735
Lubavitch Mesivta of Chicago 100/9-12
2756 W Morse Ave 60645 773-262-0430
Rabbi Moshe Perlstein, dean Fax 338-2209
Lutheran School of Theology at Chicago Post-Sec.
1100 E 55th St 60615 773-256-0700
Luther North College Preparatory HS 200/9-12
5700 W Berteau Ave 60634 773-286-3600
Wayne Wenzel, prin. Fax 286-0304
Lycee Francais de Chicago 600/PK-12
1929 W Wilson Ave 60640 773-665-0066
Eric Veteau, pres. Fax 665-1725
MacCormac College Post-Sec.
29 E Madison St 60602 312-922-1884
Malcolm X College Post-Sec.
1900 W Van Buren St 60612 312-850-7000
Marist HS 1,800/9-12
4200 W 115th St 60655 773-881-5300
Larry Tucker, prin. Fax 881-0595
McCormick Theological Seminary Post-Sec.
5460 S University Ave 60615 800-228-4687

Meadville Lombard Theological School Post-Sec.
610 S Michigan Ave 60605 773-256-3000
Midwest College of Oriental Medicine Post-Sec.
4334 N Hazel St Ste 206 60613 262-554-2010
Moody Bible Institute Post-Sec.
820 N La Salle Dr 60610 312-329-4000
Morgan Park Academy 400/PK-12
2153 W 111th St 60643 773-881-6700
Mercedes Z. Sheppard, head sch Fax 881-8409
Mother McAuley Liberal Arts HS 1,400/9-12
3737 W 99th St 60655 773-881-6500
Eileen Boyce, prin. Fax 881-6562
Mt. Carmel HS 800/9-12
6410 S Dante Ave 60637 773-324-1020
John Stimler, prin. Fax 324-9235
National Latino Education Institute Post-Sec.
2011 W Pershing Rd 60609 773-247-0707
National-Louis University Post-Sec.
122 S Michigan Ave 60603 888-658-8632
Northeastern Illinois University Post-Sec.
5500 N Saint Louis Ave 60625 773-583-4050
North Park University Post-Sec.
3225 W Foster Ave 60625 773-244-6200
North Shore SDA Jr. Academy 100/PK-12
5220 N California Ave 60625 773-769-0733
Harley Peterson, prin. Fax 769-0928
Northside Catholic Academy 100/5-8
5525 N Magnolia Ave 60640 773-271-2008
Christine Huzenis, prin. Fax 271-3101
Northwestern College Post-Sec.
4829 N Lipps Ave 60630 888-205-2283
Northwestern Memorial Hospital Post-Sec.
514 N Fairbanks 9th Floor 60611 312-926-2215
Northwestern University Post-Sec.
303 E Chicago Ave 60611 312-503-8649
Olive-Harvey College Post-Sec.
10001 S Woodlawn Ave 60628 773-291-6100
Our Lady of Tepeyac HS 200/9-12
2228 S Whipple St 60623 773-522-0023
Becca Noonan, prin. Fax 522-0508
Pacific College of Oriental Medicine Post-Sec.
65 E Wacker Pl Fl 21 60601 773-477-4822
Parker S 900/PK-12
330 W Webster Ave 60614 773-353-3000
Daniel Frank Ph.D., prin. Fax 549-4669
Providence - St. Mel S 500/PK-12
119 S Central Park Blvd 60624 773-722-4600
Jeanette DiBella, prin. Fax 722-9004
Pyramid Career Institute Post-Sec.
3051 N Lincoln Ave 60657 773-975-9898
Ravenswood Baptist Christian S 100/K-12
4437 N Seeley Ave 60625 773-561-6576
Karl Engle, prin. Fax 561-3080
Resurrection College Prep HS 600/9-12
7500 W Talcott Ave 60631 773-775-6616
Maria Hawk, prin. Fax 775-0611
Resurrection University Post-Sec.
1431 N Claremont Ave 60622 773-252-6464
Richard J. Daley College Post-Sec.
7500 S Pulaski Rd 60652 773-838-7500
Robert Morris University Post-Sec.
401 S State St 60605 312-935-6800
Roosevelt University Post-Sec.
430 S Michigan Ave 60605 312-341-3500
Rosel School of Cosmetology Post-Sec.
2446 W Devon Ave 60659 773-508-5600
Rush University Post-Sec.
600 S Paulina St # 440 60612 312-942-7100
SAE Institute - Chicago Post-Sec.
820 N Orleans St Ste 125 60610 312-300-5685
St. Augustine College Post-Sec.
1333 W Argyle St 60640 773-878-8756
St. Benedict Prep S 200/9-12
3900 N Leavitt St 60618 773-539-0066
Ericka Mickelburgh, hdmstr. Fax 539-3397
St. Francis De Sales HS 200/9-12
10155 S Ewing Ave 60617 773-731-7272
John Kimec, prin. Fax 731-7888
St. Ignatius College Prep HS 1,400/9-12
1076 W Roosevelt Rd 60608 312-421-5900
Brianna Latko, prin. Fax 421-7124
St. Mary of Providence School Post-Sec.
4200 N Austin Ave 60634 773-545-8300
St. Patrick HS 800/9-12
5900 W Belmont Ave 60634 773-282-8844
Jon Baffico, prin. Fax 282-2361
St. Rita of Cascia HS 700/9-12
7740 S Western Ave 60620 773-925-6600
Brendan Conroy, prin. Fax 925-2451
St. Xavier University Post-Sec.
3700 W 103rd St 60655 773-298-3000
Sanford-Brown College Post-Sec.
1 N State St Ste 500 60602 312-980-9200
San Miguel MS 100/6-8
1954 W 48th St 60609 773-890-1481
Thaddeus Smith, prin. Fax 254-3382
School of the Art Institute of Chicago Post-Sec.
37 S Wabash Ave 60603 312-899-5100
Shimer College Post-Sec.
3424 S State St 60616 312-235-3500
Spertus Institute for Jewish Learning Post-Sec.
610 S Michigan Ave 60605 312-322-1700
Steven Papageorge Hair Academy Post-Sec.
1113 W Belmont Ave # 15 60657 773-883-5100
Taylor Business Institute Post-Sec.
318 W Adams St Fl 5 60606 312-658-5100
Telshe HS 100/9-12
3535 W Foster Ave 60625 773-463-7738
Rabbi Shmuel Adler, dir. Fax 463-2849
Telshe Yeshiva-Chicago Post-Sec.
3535 W Foster Ave 60625 773-463-7738
The Illinois Institute of Art Post-Sec.
350 N Orleans St Lbby 136 60654 312-280-3500
Toyota Technological Inst at Chicago Post-Sec.
6045 S Kenwood Ave 60637 773-834-2500
Tribeca Flashpoint Media Arts Academy Post-Sec.
28 N Clark St Ste 500 60602 312-332-0707
University of Chicago Post-Sec.
5801 S Ellis Ave 60637 773-702-1234

University of Chicago Lab S 1,800/PK-12
1362 E 59th St 60637 773-702-9450
Beth Harris, dir. Fax 702-7455
University of Illinois at Chicago Post-Sec.
1200 W Harrison St 60607 312-996-7000
Univ. of Chicago Hospital/Roosevelt U. Post-Sec.
5841 S Maryland Ave 60637 773-702-6240
VanderCook College of Music Post-Sec.
3140 S Federal St 60616 800-448-2655
Westwood College Post-Sec.
8501 W Higgins Rd Ste 100 60631 773-380-6800
Westwood College Post-Sec.
1 N State St Ste 1000 60602 312-739-0890
Wilbur Wright College North Post-Sec.
4300 N Narragansett Ave 60634 773-777-7900
Xavier Warde S 400/4-8
751 N State St 60654 312-466-0700
Michael Kennedy, head sch Fax 337-7180
Yeshivas Meor HaTorah of Chicago 50/9-12
3635 W Devon Ave 60659 773-465-0419
Rabbi Eliyahu Millen, dean Fax 465-0520

Chicago Heights, Cook, Pop. 29,817
Bloom Township HSD 206 3,200/9-12
100 W 10th St 60411 708-755-7010
Dr. Lenell Navarre, supt. Fax 755-1149
www.sd206.org
Bloom HS 1,700/9-12
101 W 10th St 60411 708-755-1122
Krystal Thomas, prin. Fax 755-1149
Bloom Trail HS 1,500/9-12
22331 Cottage Grove Ave 60411 708-758-7000
Dr. Debra Graham, prin. Fax 758-8372
District 206 Alternative HS 100/Alt
100 W 10th St 60411 708-754-4095
Michael Campbell, prin. Fax 754-4099

Flossmoor SD 161 2,300/PK-8
41 E Elmwood Dr 60411 708-647-7000
Craig Doster, supt. Fax 754-2153
www.sd161.org
Other Schools – See Flossmoor

Park Forest SD 163
Supt. — See Park Forest
Obama S of Leadership and STEM 400/4-8
401 Concord Dr 60411 708-668-9100
Ericka Patterson, prin. Fax 283-2358

Marian Catholic HS 1,400/9-12
700 Ashland Ave 60411 708-755-7565
Steve Tortorello, prin. Fax 755-0042
Prairie State College Post-Sec.
202 S Halsted St 60411 708-709-3500

Chicago Ridge, Cook, Pop. 13,978
Chicago Ridge SD 127-5 1,500/PK-8
6135 108th St 60415 708-636-2000
Dr. Kevin B. Russell, supt. Fax 636-0916
www.crsd1275.org
Finley JHS 400/6-8
10835 Lombard Ave 60415 708-636-2005
Laura Grachan, prin. Fax 636-0045

Chillicothe, Peoria, Pop. 6,048
Illinois Valley Central Unit SD 321 1,700/PK-12
1300 W Sycamore St 61523 309-274-5418
Dr. Chad Allison, supt. Fax 274-5046
www.ivcschools.com/
Chillicothe Elementary Center & JHS 200/4-8
914 W Truitt Ave 61523 309-274-6266
Patrick Auge, prin. Fax 274-2010
Illinois Valley Central HS 700/9-12
1300 W Sycamore St 61523 309-274-5481
Kenton Bergman, prin. Fax 274-8613

Chrisman, Edgar, Pop. 1,339
Edgar County CUSD 6 300/K-12
23231 IL Highway 1 61924 217-269-2513
Dr. Steven Poznic, supt. Fax 269-3231
www.chrisman.k12.il.us
Chrisman HS 100/9-12
23231 IL Highway 1 61924 217-269-2823
Nancy Dalenberg, prin. Fax 269-2329
Chrisman-Scottland JHS 100/6-8
23231 IL Highway 1 61924 217-269-3980
Nancy Dalenberg, prin. Fax 269-3231

Christopher, Franklin, Pop. 2,363
Christopher Unit SD 99 600/PK-12
1 Bearcat Dr 62822 618-724-9461
Richard Towers, supt. Fax 724-9400
www.cpher.frnkln.k12.il.us
Christopher HS 200/9-12
1 Bearcat Dr 62822 618-724-9461
Jeff Johnston, prin. Fax 724-9400

Cicero, Cook, Pop. 83,518
Cicero SD 99 13,100/PK-8
5110 W 24th St 60804 708-863-4856
Rodolfo Hernandez, supt. Fax 652-8105
www.cicd99.edu
Unity JHS 2,700/7-8
2115 S 54th Ave 60804 708-863-8268
Donata Heppner, prin. Fax 656-5652

J. S. Morton HSD 201 8,200/9-12
5041 W 31st St 60804 708-780-2110
Dr. Michael Kuzniewski, supt. Fax 780-2111
morton201.org
Morton Alternative S 50/Alt
1874 S 54th Ave 60804 708-222-3080
Erin Kelly, prin. Fax 222-3070
Morton East HS 3,600/10-12
2423 S Austin Blvd 60804 708-780-4000
Jose Gamboa, prin. Fax 222-3090
Morton Freshman Center 1,200/9-9
1801 S 55th Ave 60804 708-863-7900
Wendy Archer, prin. Fax 863-2244
Other Schools – See Berwyn

Morton College Post-Sec.
3801 S Central Ave 60804 708-656-8000

Cisne, Wayne, Pop. 671
North Wayne CUSD 200 500/PK-12
PO Box 235 62823 618-673-2151
Julie Healy, supt. Fax 673-2152
Cisne HS 100/9-12
1456 US Highway 45 62823 618-673-2154
Kevin Bowen, prin. Fax 673-2155
Cisne MS 100/5-8
PO Box 69 62823 618-673-2156
Julie Healy, prin. Fax 673-2152

Cissna Park, Iroquois, Pop. 841
Cissna Park CUSD 6 300/K-12
511 N 2nd St 60924 815-457-2171
Dr. Daniel Hylbert, supt. Fax 457-3033
www.cissnapark.k12.il.us
Cissna Park HS 100/9-12
511 N 2nd St 60924 815-457-2171
Mark Portwood, prin. Fax 457-3033
Cissna Park JHS 100/6-8
511 N 2nd St 60924 815-457-2171
Mark Portwood, prin. Fax 457-3033

Clarendon Hills, DuPage, Pop. 8,292
CCSD 181 4,000/PK-8
115 55th St 60514 630-861-4900
Dr. Don White, supt. Fax 887-1079
www.d181.org
Clarendon Hills MS 700/6-8
301 Chicago Ave 60514 630-861-4800
Griffin Sonntag, prin. Fax 887-4267
Other Schools – See Hinsdale

Clay City, Clay, Pop. 956
Clay City CUSD 10 300/PK-12
PO Box 542 62824 618-676-1431
Cathy Croy, supt. Fax 676-1430
www.claycityschools.org
Clay City HS 100/9-12
PO Box 542 62824 618-676-1522
Ben Borries, prin. Fax 676-1481
Clay City JHS 100/6-8
PO Box 542 62824 618-676-1431
Ben Borries, prin. Fax 676-1537

Clifton, Iroquois, Pop. 1,441
Central CUSD 4
Supt. — See Ashkum
Central HS 300/9-12
1134 E 3100 North Rd 60927 815-694-2321
Marc Shaner, prin. Fax 694-2709
Nash MS 300/5-8
1134 E 3100 North Rd 60927 815-694-2323
Victoria Marquis, prin. Fax 694-2830

Clinton, DeWitt, Pop. 7,123
Clinton CUSD 15 1,200/PK-12
680 Illini Dr 61727 217-935-8321
Curt Nettles, supt. Fax 935-2300
www.cusd15.org
Clinton HS 500/9-12
1200 State Route 54 W 61727 217-935-8337
Jerry Wayne, prin. Fax 935-4029
Clinton JHS 500/6-8
701 Illini Dr 61727 217-935-2103
Drew Goebel, prin. Fax 937-1918

Coal City, Grundy, Pop. 5,546
Coal City CUSD 1 2,100/PK-12
100 S Baima St 60416 815-634-2287
Dr. Kent Bugg, supt. Fax 634-8775
www.coalcity.k12.il.us
Coal City HS 600/9-12
655 W Division St 60416 815-634-2396
Mitch Hamann, prin. Fax 634-2313
Coal City MS 500/6-8
500 S Carbon Hill Rd 60416 815-634-5039
Travis Johnson, prin. Fax 634-5049

Cobden, Union, Pop. 1,130
Cobden Unit SD 17 600/PK-12
413 N Appleknocker St 62920 618-893-2313
Edwin Shoemate, supt. Fax 893-4772
www.cobdenappleknockers.com
Cobden HS 100/9-12
413 N Appleknocker St 62920 618-893-4031
Crystal Housman, prin. Fax 893-2138
Cobden JHS 200/6-8
413 N Appleknocker St 62920 618-893-4031
Crystal Housman, prin. Fax 893-2138

Colchester, McDonough, Pop. 1,398
West Prairie CUSD 103 600/PK-12
204 S Hun St 62326 309-776-3180
Dr. Carol Kilver, supt. Fax 776-3194
www.wp103.org
West Prairie MS 200/5-8
600 S Hun St 62326 309-776-3220
Caitlin Watson, prin. Fax 776-3115
Other Schools – See Sciota

Colfax, McLean, Pop. 1,054
Ridgeview CUSD 19 500/PK-12
300 S Harrison St 61728 309-723-5111
Guy Gradert, supt. Fax 723-6395
www.ridgeview19.org
Ridgeview JSHS 200/6-12
202 E Wood St 61728 309-723-2951
Jim Campbell, prin. Fax 723-4851

Collinsville, Madison, Pop. 25,082
Collinsville CUSD 10 6,900/PK-12
201 W Clay St 62234 618-346-6350
Robert Green, supt. Fax 343-3657
www.kahoks.org
Collinsville Area Vocational Center Vo/Tech
2201 S Morrison Ave 62234 618-346-6140
Dr. Tricia Blackard, prin. Fax 343-6121

Collinsville HS 2,000/9-12
2201 S Morrison Ave 62234 618-346-6320
David Snider, prin. Fax 346-6341
Collinsville MS 1,000/7-8
9649 Collinsville Rd 62234 618-343-2100
Kimberly Jackson, prin. Fax 343-2102

Columbia, Monroe, Pop. 9,637
Columbia CUSD 4 2,100/PK-12
5 Veterans Pkwy 62236 618-281-4772
Dr. Gina Segobiano, supt. Fax 281-4570
www.columbia4.org
Columbia HS 700/9-12
77 Veterans Pkwy 62236 618-281-5001
Kevin Moore, prin. Fax 281-8081
Columbia MS 700/5-8
100 Eagle Dr 62236 618-281-4993
Brian Reeves, prin. Fax 281-4964

Concord, Morgan, Pop. 167
Triopia CUSD 27 400/PK-12
2204 Concord Arenzville Rd 62631 217-457-2283
Steve Eisenhauer, supt. Fax 457-2297
www.triopiacusd27.org/
Triopia JSHS 200/7-12
2204 Concord Arenzville Rd 62631 217-457-2281
Adam Dean, prin. Fax 457-2277

Coulterville, Randolph, Pop. 930
Coulterville Unit SD 1 200/PK-12
PO Box 396 62237 618-758-2881
Karyn Albers, supt. Fax 758-2330
Coulterville HS 100/9-12
PO Box 396 62237 618-758-2881
Brandon Taylor, prin. Fax 758-2330
Coulterville JHS 100/6-8
PO Box 396 62237 618-758-2881
Brandon Taylor, prin. Fax 758-2330

Country Club Hills, Cook, Pop. 16,299
Bremen Community HSD 228
Supt. — See Midlothian
Hillcrest HS 1,100/9-12
17401 Crawford Ave 60478 708-799-7000
Renee Simms, prin. Fax 799-0402

Country Club Hills SD 160 1,200/PK-8
4411 185th St 60478 708-957-6200
Dr. Sandra Thomas, supt. Fax 957-8686
www.cch160.org
Southwood MS 300/7-8
18635 Lee St 60478 708-957-6230
Bridgette Harris, prin. Fax 799-4033

Cowden, Shelby, Pop. 628
Cowden-Herrick Community USD 3A 400/PK-12
PO Box 188 62422 217-783-2126
Darrell Gordon, supt. Fax 783-2126
www.cowden-herrick.k12.il.us
Cowden-Herrick JSHS 200/PK-PK, 6-
PO Box 188 62422 217-783-2125
Seth Schuler, prin. Fax 783-2124

Crest Hill, Will, Pop. 20,552
Richland SD 88A 1,000/PK-8
1919 Caton Farm Rd, 815-744-7288
Dr. Michael Early, supt. Fax 744-6196
www.d88a.org
Richland JHS 400/5-8
1919 Caton Farm Rd, 815-744-6166
Dr. Kelly Whyte, prin. Fax 725-8491

Crestwood, Cook, Pop. 10,823
Cook County SD 130
Supt. — See Blue Island
Hale MS 400/6-8
5220 135th St 60445 708-385-6690
Constance Grimm-Grason, prin. Fax 385-2417

Crete, Will, Pop. 8,098
Crete-Monee CUSD 201U 4,600/PK-12
1500 S Sangamon St 60417 708-367-8300
Dr. Nathaniel Cunningham, supt. Fax 672-2698
www.cm201u.org
Crete-Monee HS 1,600/9-12
1515 W Exchange St 60417 708-367-8200
Dr. James Harden, prin. Fax 672-2888
Other Schools – See Monee, University Park

Illinois Lutheran HS 100/7-12
1610 Main St 60417 708-672-3262
Joe Archer, prin. Fax 672-0512

Creve Coeur, Tazewell, Pop. 5,361
Creve Coeur SD 76 700/PK-8
400 N Highland St 61610 309-698-3600
Tony Whiston, supt. Fax 698-9827
www.cc76.k12.il.us
Parkview JHS 300/5-8
800 Groveland St 61610 309-698-3610
Steven Johnson, prin. Fax 698-3902

Mason-Tazewell-Woodford ROE
Supt. — See Pekin
ROE 53 Academy 50/Alt
107 Riverview Dr 61610 309-698-8034
Julie Hicks, coord. Fax 698-8062

Crystal Lake, McHenry, Pop. 40,164
Community HSD 155 6,700/9-12
1 Virginia Rd 60014 815-455-8500
Johnnie Thomas, supt. Fax 459-5022
www.d155.org
Crystal Lake Central HS 1,500/9-12
45 W Franklin Ave 60014 815-459-2505
Steve Olson, prin. Fax 459-2536
Crystal Lake South HS 1,800/9-12
1200 S McHenry Ave 60014 815-455-3860
Scott Shepard, prin. Fax 455-5706
Prairie Ridge HS 1,500/9-12
6000 Dvorak Dr 60012 815-479-0404
Steven Koch, prin. Fax 459-8993
Other Schools – See Cary

Crystal Lake CCSD 47 7,800/PK-8
300 Commerce Dr 60014 815-459-6070
Kathy Hinz, supt. Fax 459-0263
www.d47.org
Beardsley MS 1,100/6-8
515 E Crystal Lake Ave 60014 815-477-5897
Cathy Alberth, prin. Fax 479-5119
Bernotas MS 1,000/6-8
170 N Oak St 60014 815-459-9210
Jeff Prickett, prin. Fax 479-5116
Lundahl MS 800/6-8
560 Nash Rd 60014 815-459-5971
Angela Compere, prin. Fax 479-5113

Prairie Grove Consolidated SD 46 800/K-8
3223 IL Route 176 60014 815-459-3023
Dr. Phil Bender, supt. Fax 356-0519
www.dist46.org/
Prairie Grove JHS 400/6-8
3225 IL Route 176 60014 815-459-3557
Martha Maggiore, prin. Fax 459-3785

Cosmetology & Spa Institute Post-Sec.
700 E Terra Cotta Ave 60014 815-455-5900
Faith Lutheran HS 100/9-12
174 S McHenry Ave 60014 815-479-9305
Chris Schoenleb, prin. Fax 479-9300
McHenry County College Post-Sec.
8900 US Highway 14 60012 815-455-3700

Cuba, Fulton, Pop. 1,288
CUSD 3 Fulton County 500/PK-12
PO Box 79 61427 309-785-5021
Brad Kenser, supt. Fax 785-5432
www.cusd3.net
Cuba HS 200/9-12
20325 N State Route 97 61427 309-785-5023
Jeff Braun, prin. Fax 785-5102
Cuba MS 100/6-8
20325 N State Route 97 61427 309-785-5023
Jeff Braun, prin. Fax 785-5102

Cullom, Livingston, Pop. 554
Tri-Point CUSD 6-J
Supt. — See Kempton
Tri-Point HS 100/9-12
PO Box 316 60929 815-689-2110
Kellee Hill, prin. Fax 689-2377

Dakota, Stephenson, Pop. 499
Dakota CUSD 201 800/PK-12
400 Campus Dr 61018 815-449-2832
Robert Prusator, supt. Fax 449-2459
www.dakota201.com
Dakota JSHS 400/7-12
300 Campus Dr 61018 815-449-2812
Eric Rankin, prin. Fax 449-2322

Danville, Vermilion, Pop. 32,053
Danville CCSD 118 5,100/PK-12
516 N Jackson St 61832 217-444-1000
Dr. Alicia Geddis, supt. Fax 444-1006
www.danville118.org
Bailey Academy Alt
502 E Main St 61832 217-477-0300
Tracy Cherry, prin. Fax 477-0399
Danville HS 1,600/9-12
202 E Fairchild St 61832 217-444-1500
Kim Norton, prin. Fax 444-1529
North Ridge MS 500/7-8
1619 N Jackson St 61832 217-444-3400
Eliza Brooks, prin. Fax 444-3488

Oakwood CUSD 76
Supt. — See Oakwood
Oakwood JHS 200/7-8
21600 N 900 East Rd 61834 217-443-2883
John Tosh, prin. Fax 776-2228

Vermilion Vocational Education Delivery
2000 E Main St 61832 217-443-8742
Nick Chatterton, dir.
www.dacc.edu/dual/college-express
College Express Vo/Tech
2000 E Main St 61832 217-443-8742
Nick Chatterton, prin.

Concept College of Cosmetology Post-Sec.
2500 Georgetown Rd 61832 217-442-9329
Danville Area Community College Post-Sec.
2000 E Main St 61832 217-443-3222
First Baptist Christian S 200/PK-12
1211 N Vermilion St 61832 217-442-2434
Robert Lazzell, prin. Fax 442-8731
Lakeview College of Nursing Post-Sec.
903 N Logan Ave 61832 217-709-0920
Schlarman Academy 500/PK-12
2112 N Vermilion St 61832 217-442-2725
Gail Lewis, prin. Fax 442-0293

Darien, DuPage, Pop. 21,762
Cass SD 63 700/PK-8
8502 Bailey Rd 60561 331-481-4000
Dr. Kerry J. Foderaro, supt. Fax 481-4001
www.cassd63.org
Cass JHS 300/5-8
8502 Bailey Rd 60561 331-481-4020
Christine Marcinkewicz, prin. Fax 481-4021

Darien SD 61 1,600/PK-8
7414 S Cass Ave 60561 630-968-7505
Dr. Robert Carlo, supt. Fax 968-0872
www.darien61.org
Eisenhower JHS 500/6-8
1410 75th St 60561 630-964-5200
Jacob Buck, prin. Fax 968-8002

Hinsdale Township HSD 86
Supt. — See Hinsdale
Hinsdale South HS 1,700/9-12
7401 Clarendon Hills Rd 60561 630-468-4000
Stephanie Palmer, prin. Fax 920-8649

Transition Center Adult
7302 Clarendon Hills Rd 60561 630-323-9673
Tammy Prentiss, coord. Fax 323-9676

Decatur, Macon, Pop. 73,849
Decatur SD 61 8,600/PK-12
101 W Cerro Gordo St 62523 217-362-3000
Bobbi Williams, supt. Fax 424-3009
www.dps61.org
Decatur MS 400/7-8
1 Educational Park 62526 217-362-3250
Deloris Brown, prin. Fax 424-3169
Eisenhower HS, 1200 S 16th St 62521 1,000/9-12
Dr. Amy Zahm, prin. 217-362-3100
Jefferson MS 500/7-8
4735 E Cantrell St 62521 217-362-3200
Nathan Sheppard, prin. Fax 424-3037
MacArthur HS 1,100/9-12
1499 W Grand Ave 62522 217-362-3151
Cordell Ingram, prin. Fax 423-4336
Phoenix Academy 50/Alt
1900 E Cleveland Ave 62521 217-424-3122
Janice Ranzy-Allen, prin. Fax 424-3092
Adult Education & Training Center Adult
300 E Eldorado St 62523 217-424-3085
Fax 424-3004

Heartland Region
1 College Park 62521 217-872-4056
Bret Hitchings, supt.
www.tech-academy.org
Heartland Technical Academy Vo/Tech
1 College Park 62521 217-872-4050
Bret Hitchings, prin.

Lutheran School Association 500/K-12
2001 E Mound Rd 62526 217-233-2000
Allison Nolen, supt. Fax 233-2000
Millikin University Post-Sec.
1184 W Main St 62522 800-373-7733
Mr. John's School of Cosmetology Post-Sec.
1745 E Eldorado St 62521 217-423-8173
Richland Community College Post-Sec.
1 College Park 62521 217-875-7200
St. Teresa HS 300/9-12
2710 N Water St 62526 217-875-2431
Dr. Ken Hendriksen, prin. Fax 875-2436

Deerfield, Lake, Pop. 18,034
Deerfield SD 109 3,100/PK-8
517 Deerfield Rd 60015 847-945-1844
Dr. Michael Lubelfeld, supt. Fax 945-1853
www.dps109.org
Caruso MS 600/6-8
1801 Montgomery Rd 60015 847-945-8430
Dr. Brian Bullis, prin. Fax 945-1963
Shepard MS 500/6-8
440 Grove Ave 60015 847-948-0620
Dr. John Filippi, prin. Fax 948-8589

Township HSD 113
Supt. — See Highland Park
Deerfield HS 1,600/9-12
1959 Waukegan Rd 60015 224-632-3000
Kathryn Anderson, prin. Fax 632-3700

Trinity International University Post-Sec.
2065 Half Day Rd 60015 847-945-8800
Zell Jewish HS 200/9-12
1095 Lake Cook Rd 60015 847-470-6700
Tony Frank, hdmstr. Fax 324-3701

DeKalb, DeKalb, Pop. 43,053
DeKalb CUSD 428 5,900/PK-12
901 S 4th St 60115 815-754-2350
Dr. Douglas Moeller, supt. Fax 758-6933
dist428.org
DeKalb HS 1,600/9-12
501 W Dresser Rd 60115 815-754-2100
Michele Albano, prin. Fax 758-0931
Huntley MS 800/6-8
1515 S 4th St 60115 815-754-2241
Dr. Thomas Kim, prin. Fax 758-6062
Rosette MS 500/6-8
650 N 1st St 60115 815-754-2226
Tim Vincent, prin. Fax 758-1097

Northern Illinois University 60115 Post-Sec.
815-753-1000

De Land, Piatt, Pop. 442
Deland-Weldon CUSD 57 200/PK-12
304 E IL Route 10 61839 217-736-2311
Jeff Asmus, supt. Fax 736-2654
www.dwschools.org
Deland-Weldon HS 100/9-12
304 E IL Route 10 61839 217-664-3314
Amanda Geary, prin. Fax 736-2654
Other Schools – See Weldon

Delavan, Tazewell, Pop. 1,679
Delavan CUSD 703 500/PK-12
907 S Locust St 61734 309-244-8283
Dr. Andrew Brooks, supt. Fax 244-7696
www.delavanschools.com
Delavan HS 100/9-12
907 S Locust St 61734 309-244-8285
Dr. Matt Gordon, prin. Fax 244-8694
Delavan JHS 100/7-8
907 S Locust St 61734 309-244-8285
Dr. Matt Gordon, prin. Fax 244-8694

De Pue, Bureau, Pop. 1,815
DePue Unit SD 103 500/PK-12
PO Box 800 61322 815-447-2121
Randall Otto, supt. Fax 447-2067
depueschools.org
DePue HS 100/9-12
PO Box 800 61322 815-447-2121
Cuauhtemoc Reyes, supt. Fax 447-2067

Des Plaines, Cook, Pop. 57,381
CCSD 59
Supt. — See Arlington Heights
Friendship JHS 700/6-8
550 Elizabeth Ln 60018 847-593-4350
Jodi Megerle, prin. Fax 593-7182

CCSD 62 4,800/PK-8
777 E Algonquin Rd 60016 847-824-1136
Dr. Floyd Williams, supt. Fax 824-0612
www.d62.org
Algonquin MS 700/6-8
767 E Algonquin Rd 60016 847-824-1205
John Swanson, prin. Fax 824-1270
Chippewa MS 700/6-8
123 N 8th Ave 60016 847-824-1503
Dr. Leah Kimmelman, prin. Fax 824-1514

East Maine SD 63 3,600/PK-8
10150 Dee Rd 60016 847-299-1900
Dr. Scott Clay, supt. Fax 299-9963
www.emsd63.org
Other Schools – See Niles

Maine Township HSD 207
Supt. — See Park Ridge
Maine West HS 2,100/9-12
1755 S Wolf Rd 60018 847-827-6176
Dr. Audrey Haugan, prin. Fax 296-4916

Oakton Community College Post-Sec.
1600 E Golf Rd 60016 847-635-1600
Willows Academy 200/6-12
1015 Rose Ave 60016 847-824-6900

Dieterich, Effingham, Pop. 615
Dieterich CUSD 30 400/K-12
PO Box 187 62424 217-925-5249
Cary Jackson, supt. Fax 925-5447
www.dieterich.k12.il.us/
Dieterich JSHS 200/7-12
PO Box 187 62424 217-925-5247
Kevin Haarman, prin. Fax 925-5447

Divernon, Sangamon, Pop. 1,159
Auburn CUSD 10
Supt. — See Auburn
Auburn JHS 300/6-8
303 E Kenney St 62530 217-628-3414
Mark Dudley, prin. Fax 628-3814

Dixmoor, Cook, Pop. 3,616
West Harvey-Dixmoor SD 147
Supt. — See Harvey
Parks MS 400/6-8
14700 Robey Ave 60426 708-371-9575
Taiyuan Banks-Tillmon, prin. Fax 371-1412

Dixon, Lee, Pop. 15,509
Dixon Unit SD 170 2,600/PK-12
1335 Franklin Grove Rd 61021 815-284-7722
Margo Empen, supt. Fax 284-8576
www.dps170.org
Dixon HS 800/9-12
300 Lincoln Statue Dr 61021 815-284-7723
Dr. Michael Grady, prin. Fax 284-4297
Reagan MS 600/6-8
620 Division St 61021 815-284-7725
Andrew Bullock, prin. Fax 284-1711

Faith Christian S 100/K-12
7571 S Ridge Rd 61021 815-652-4806
Linda Foster, prin. Fax 652-4871
Jack Mabley Development Center Post-Sec.
1120 Washington Ave 61021 815-288-8300
Sauk Valley Community College Post-Sec.
173 IL Route 2 61021 815-288-5511

Dolton, Cook, Pop. 22,862
Dolton SD 148
Supt. — See Riverdale
Lincoln JHS 200/7-8
14151 Lincoln Ave 60419 708-201-2075
Dr. Donald Parker, prin. Fax 849-3758
Roosevelt JHS 200/7-8
111 W 146th St 60419 708-201-2071
Steven Chambers, prin. Fax 849-1285

Thornton Township HSD 205
Supt. — See South Holland
Thornridge HS 1,200/9-12
15000 Cottage Grove Ave 60419 708-271-4401
James Walton, prin. Fax 271-5028

Dongola, Union, Pop. 707
Dongola Unit SD 66 200/PK-12
PO Box 190 62926 618-827-3841
Dr. Paige Maginel, supt. Fax 827-4641
dongolaschool.com
Dongola HS 100/9-12
PO Box 190 62926 618-827-3524
John Goddard, prin. Fax 827-4422
Dongola JHS 50/6-8
PO Box 190 62926 618-827-3524
John Goddard, prin. Fax 827-4422

Donovan, Iroquois, Pop. 304
Donovan CUSD 3 300/PK-12
PO Box 186 60931 815-486-7397
Lucas Schroeder, supt. Fax 486-7030
www.donovan.k12.il.us
Donovan HS 100/9-12
PO Box 186 60931 815-486-7395
Jason Bauer, admin. Fax 486-7030
Donovan JHS 50/6-8
PO Box 186 60931 815-486-7395
Jason Bauer, admin. Fax 486-7030

Downers Grove, DuPage, Pop. 47,147
Center Cass SD 66 1,000/PK-8
699 Plainfield Rd 60516 630-783-5000
Dr. Tim Arnold, supt. Fax 910-0980
www.ccsd66.org/
Lakeview JHS 400/6-8
701 Plainfield Rd 60516 630-985-2700
Paul Windsor, prin. Fax 985-1545

Community HSD 99 5,000/9-12
6301 Springside Ave 60516 630-795-7100
Dr. Henry Thiele, supt. Fax 795-7199
www.csd99.org
Downers Grove North HS 2,100/9-12
4436 Main St 60515 630-795-8400
Janice Schwarze, prin. Fax 795-8499
Downers Grove South HS 2,900/9-12
1436 Norfolk St 60516 630-795-8500
Edward Schwartz, prin. Fax 795-8599

Downers Grove SD 58 5,100/PK-8
1860 63rd St 60516 630-719-5800
Dr. Kari Cremascoli, supt. Fax 719-9857
www.dg58.org
Herrick MS 600/7-8
4435 Middaugh Ave 60515 630-719-5810
Matt Neustadt, prin. Fax 719-1628
O'Neill MS 500/7-8
635 59th St 60516 630-719-5815
Matthew Durbala, prin. Fax 719-1436

DeVry University Post-Sec.
3005 Highland Pkwy Ste 100 60515 630-515-3000
DeVry University Online Education Center Post-Sec.
3005 Highland Pkwy Ste 100 60515 630-515-3000
Marquette Manor Baptist Academy 200/PK-12
333 75th St 60516 630-964-5363
Midwestern University Post-Sec.
555 31st St 60515 630-969-4400

Downs, McLean, Pop. 986
Tri-Valley CUSD 3 1,000/PK-12
410 E Washington St 61736 309-378-2351
Dr. David Mouser, supt. Fax 378-2223
tri-valley3.org
Tri-Valley HS 300/9-12
503 E Washington St 61736 309-378-2911
Benjamin Derges, prin. Fax 378-3202
Tri-Valley MS 400/4-8
505 E Washington St 61736 309-378-3414
Doug Roberts, prin. Fax 378-3214

Dunlap, Peoria, Pop. 1,372
Dunlap CUSD 323
Supt. — See Peoria
Dunlap HS 1,200/9-12
PO Box 365 61525 309-243-7751
Scott Adreon, prin. Fax 243-9565
Dunlap MS 600/6-8
13120 N Route 91 61525 309-243-7778
Zac Chatterton, prin. Fax 243-1136
Dunlap Valley MS 300/6-8
PO Box 366 61525 309-243-1034
Jason Holmes, prin. Fax 243-9829

Dupo, Saint Clair, Pop. 4,069
Dupo CUSD 196 1,200/PK-12
600 Louisa Ave 62239 618-286-3812
Dr. Stephen Smith, supt. Fax 286-5554
www.dupo196.org
Dupo HS, 600 Louisa Ave 62239 300/9-12
Matt Hickam, prin. 618-286-3214
Dupo JHS, 600 Louisa Ave 62239 200/7-8
William Harris, prin. 618-286-3214

Du Quoin, Perry, Pop. 5,956
Du Quoin CUSD 300 1,400/PK-12
845 E Jackson St 62832 618-542-3856
Dr. Gary Kelly, supt. Fax 542-6614
www.duquoinschools.org
Du Quoin HS 400/PK-PK, 9-
500 E South St 62832 618-542-4744
Matt Hickam, prin. Fax 542-8822
Du Quoin MS 400/5-8
845 E Jackson St 62832 618-542-2646
Aaron Hill, prin. Fax 542-4373

Christian Fellowship S 100/PK-12
PO Box 227 62832 618-542-6800
Larry Bullock, admin. Fax 542-6806

Durand, Winnebago, Pop. 1,423
Durand CUSD 322 600/PK-12
200 W South St 61024 815-248-2171
Kurt Alberstett, supt. Fax 248-2599
www.durandbulldogs.com
Durand HS 200/9-12
200 W South St 61024 815-248-2171
Michael Leskowich, prin. Fax 248-2599
Durand JHS 100/7-8
200 W South St 61024 815-248-2171
Michael Leskowich, prin. Fax 248-2599

Dwight, Livingston, Pop. 4,231
Dwight Township HSD 230 300/9-12
801 S Franklin St 60420 815-584-6200
Dr. Richard Jancek, supt. Fax 584-2950
www.dwight.k12.il.us
Dwight Township HS 300/9-12
801 S Franklin St 60420 815-584-6200
Dr. Richard Jancek, supt. Fax 584-2950

Earlville, LaSalle, Pop. 1,691
Earlville CUSD 9 400/PK-12
PO Box 539 60518 815-246-8361
Rich Faivre, supt. Fax 246-8672
www.earlvillecusd9.org
Earlville HS 100/9-12
PO Box 539 60518 815-246-8361
Rich Faivre, admin. Fax 246-8672

East Alton, Madison, Pop. 6,171
East Alton SD 13 900/PK-8
210 E Saint Louis Ave 62024 618-433-2051
Virgil Moore, supt. Fax 433-2054
www.easd13.org
East Alton MS 200/6-8
1000 3rd St 62024 618-433-2201
Alyssa Smith, prin. Fax 433-2203

East Dubuque, Jo Daviess, Pop. 1,681
East Dubuque Unit SD 119 600/PK-12
100 N School Rd 61025 815-747-2111
Tori Lindeman, supt. Fax 747-3516
www.edbqhs.org
East Dubuque HS 200/7-12
200 Parklane Dr 61025 815-747-3188
Darren Sirianni, prin. Fax 747-3516

East Moline, Rock Island, Pop. 20,814
East Moline SD 37 2,800/PK-8
3451 Morton Dr 61244 309-792-2887
Kristin Humphries, supt. Fax 792-6010
www.emsd37.org
Glenview MS 1,100/5-8
3100 7th St 61244 309-755-1919
Michael Hawley, prin. Fax 752-2551

Silvis SD 34 600/PK-8
4280 4th Ave 61244 309-792-9325
Dr. Terri VandeWiele Ed.D., supt. Fax 203-1322
silvis34.net
Northeast JHS 200/6-8
4280 4th Ave 61244 309-203-1300
Jim Widdop, prin. Fax 203-1322

United Township Area Career Center
1275 Avenue of the Cities 61244 309-752-1691
Larry Shimmin, dir. Fax 752-1692
uths.net/acc
United Township Area Career Center Vo/Tech
1275 Avenue of the Cities 61244 309-752-1691
Larry Shimmin, dir. Fax 752-1692

United Township HSD 30 1,700/9-12
1275 Avenue of the Cities 61244 309-752-1633
Jay Morrow Ed.D., supt. Fax 752-1615
uths.net
United Township HS 1,700/9-12
1275 Avenue of the Cities 61244 309-752-1633
Carl Johnson, prin. Fax 752-1608

East Moline Christian S 400/PK-12
900 46th Ave 61244 309-796-1485
La' James College of Hairstyling Post-Sec.
485 Avenue of the Cities 61244 888-880-2106

East Peoria, Tazewell, Pop. 23,021
East Peoria Community HSD 309 1,100/9-12
1401 E Washington St 61611 309-694-8300
Dr. Chuck Nagel, supt. Fax 694-8322
www.ep309.org
East Peoria Community HS 1,100/9-12
1401 E Washington St 61611 309-694-8300
Dr. Chuck Nagel, supt. Fax 694-8322

East Peoria SD 86 1,700/PK-8
601 Taylor St 61611 309-427-5100
Tony Ingold, supt. Fax 698-1364
www.epd86.org
Central JHS 500/6-8
601 Taylor St 61611 309-427-5200
Dustin Schrank, prin. Fax 699-2595

Illinois Central College Post-Sec.
1 College Dr, Peoria IL 61635 309-694-5422
Midwest Technical Institute Post-Sec.
280 High Point Ln 61611 800-814-5124
Oehrlein School of Cosmetology Post-Sec.
100 Meadow Ave 61611 309-699-1561

East Saint Louis, Saint Clair, Pop. 26,776
East St. Louis SD 189 5,800/PK-12
1005 State St 62201 618-646-3000
Arthur Culver, supt. Fax 583-7186
www.estl189.com
East Saint Louis HS 1,500/9-12
4901 State St 62205 618-646-3700
Marcus Wright, prin. Fax 646-3958
Lincoln MS 600/5-8
12 S 10th St 62201 618-646-3770
Eric Harris, prin. Fax 646-3778
Mason/Clark MS 700/5-8
5510 State St 62203 618-646-3750
Keisa Garrett, prin. Fax 646-3758

Vee's School of Beauty Culture Post-Sec.
2701 State St 62205 618-274-1751

Edinburg, Christian, Pop. 1,060
Edinburg CUSD 4 300/PK-12
100 E Martin St 62531 217-623-5603
Fred Lamkey, supt. Fax 623-5604
www.ecusd4.com
Edinburg HS 100/9-12
100 E Martin St 62531 217-623-5603
Michelle Reiss, prin. Fax 623-5604
Edinburg JHS 100/7-8
100 E Martin St 62531 217-623-5603
Michelle Reiss, prin. Fax 623-5604

Edwardsville, Madison, Pop. 23,810
Edwardsville CUSD 7 7,600/PK-12
PO Box 250 62025 618-656-1182
Dr. Lynda Andre, supt. Fax 692-7423
www.ecusd7.org
Edwardsville HS 2,400/9-12
6161 Center Grove Rd 62025 618-656-7100
Dr. Dennis Cramsey, prin. Fax 655-1037
EHS South 100/Alt
6161 Center Grove Rd 62025 618-656-7100
Dr. Dennis Cramsey, admin.

Liberty MS 900/6-8
1 District Dr 62025 618-655-6800
Beth Crumbacher, prin. Fax 655-6801
Lincoln MS 800/6-8
145 West St 62025 618-656-0485
Steve Stuart, prin. Fax 659-1268

Alvareita's College of Cosmetology Post-Sec.
333 S Kansas St 62025 618-656-2593
Metro East Lutheran HS 200/9-12
6305 Center Grove Rd 62025 618-656-0043
Dr. Jay Krause, prin. Fax 656-3315
Southern Illinois Univ. Edwardsville Post-Sec.
State Route 157 62026 800-447-7483

Effingham, Effingham, Pop. 12,212
Bond/Christn/Effingham/Fayette/Mtgmy ROE
Supt. — See Vandalia
Aspire Alternative S 50/Alt
900 Edgar St 62401 217-342-2865
Amber Kidd, prin. Fax 342-9840

Effingham CUSD 40 2,500/K-12
PO Box 130 62401 217-540-1500
Mark Doan, supt. Fax 540-1510
www.effingham.k12.il.us
Effingham HS 800/9-12
1301 W Grove Ave 62401 217-540-1100
Jason Fox, prin. Fax 540-1102
Effingham JHS 500/6-8
600 S Henrietta St 62401 217-540-1300
Bill Myers, prin. Fax 540-1362

St. Anthony of Padua HS 200/9-12
304 E Roadway Ave 62401 217-342-6969
Greg Fearday, prin. Fax 342-6997

Eldorado, Saline, Pop. 4,079
Eldorado CUSD 4 1,200/PK-12
2200A Illinois Ave 62930 618-273-6394
Ryan Hobbs, supt. Fax 273-9311
www.eldorado.k12.il.us/
Eldorado HS 400/9-12
2200 Illinois Ave 62930 618-273-2881
Ryan Hobbs, prin. Fax 273-8153
Eldorado MS 200/6-8
1907 1st St 62930 618-273-8056
Billy Tippett, prin. Fax 273-2943

Elgin, Kane, Pop. 106,496
SD U-46 40,200/PK-12
355 E Chicago St 60120 847-888-5000
Tony Sanders, admin. Fax 608-4173
www.u-46.org
Abbott MS 500/7-8
949 Van St 60123 847-888-5160
Kathy Davis, prin. Fax 608-2740
Elgin HS 2,400/9-12
1200 Maroon Dr 60120 847-888-5100
Jerry Cook, prin. Fax 888-6997
Ellis MS 600/7-8
225 S Liberty St 60120 847-888-5151
Perry Hayes, prin. Fax 608-2744
Gifford Street HS 100/Alt
46 S Gifford St 60120 847-888-5000
Lourdes Baker, prin. Fax 888-5087
Kimball MS 700/7-8
451 N Mclean Blvd 60123 847-888-5290
Alan Tamburrino, prin. Fax 608-2749
Larkin HS 2,000/9-12
1475 Larkin Ave 60123 847-888-5200
Dr. Jon Tuin, prin. Fax 888-6996
Larsen MS 700/7-8
665 Dundee Ave 60120 847-888-5250
Gina Crespo, prin. Fax 888-7172
Other Schools – See Bartlett, South Elgin, Streamwood

Cannella School of Hair Design Post-Sec.
117 W Chicago St 60123 847-742-6611
Computer Systems Institute Post-Sec.
400 Airport Rd 60123 847-400-0065
DeVry University Post-Sec.
2250 Point Blvd Ste 250 60123 847-649-3980
Einstein Academy 100/PK-12
747 Davis Rd 60123 847-697-3836
Cathy Ilani, prin. Fax 697-6085
Elgin Academy 500/PK-12
350 Park St 60120 847-695-0300
Seth Hanford, hdmstr. Fax 695-5017
Elgin Community College Post-Sec.
1700 Spartan Dr 60123 847-697-1000
Harvest Christian Academy 600/PK-12
1000 N Randall Rd 60123 847-214-3500
Ollie Gibbs Ed.D., head sch Fax 214-3501
Judson University Post-Sec.
1151 N State St 60123 847-628-2500
Robert Morris University Post-Sec.
1707 N Randall Rd Ste 180 60123 800-762-5960
St. Edward Central Catholic HS 400/9-12
335 Locust St 60123 847-741-7535
Barbara Villont, prin. Fax 695-4682
Westminster Christian S 500/PK-12
2700 W Highland Ave, 847-695-0310
Steve Hall, head sch Fax 695-0135

Elizabeth, Jo Daviess, Pop. 746
Carroll/Jo Daviess/Stephenson ROE
Supt. — See Freeport
Regional Alternative Program Elizabeth 50/Alt
950 US Highway 20 W 61028 815-599-1408
Brandy Howard, coord. Fax 297-9032

Jo Daviess-Carroll Career Tech Educ Acad
950 US Highway 20 W 61028 815-858-2203
Nancy Jogerst, dir. Fax 858-2316
www.cteacademy.net
Jo Daviess-Carroll Career Tech Educ Acad Vo/Tech
950 US Highway 20 W 61028 815-858-2203
Nancy Jogerst, dir. Fax 858-2316

Elizabethtown, Hardin, Pop. 296
Hardin County CUSD 1 600/PK-12
PO Box 218 62931 618-287-2411
David Reavis, supt. Fax 287-2421
Hardin County HS 200/9-12
PO Box 218 62931 618-287-2141
Richard Ozment, prin. Fax 287-8381
Hardin County JHS 100/6-8
PO Box 218 62931 618-287-2411
Richard Ozment, prin. Fax 287-8381

Elk Grove Village, Cook, Pop. 32,640
CCSD 59
Supt. — See Arlington Heights
Grove JHS 900/6-8
777 W Elk Grove Blvd 60007 847-593-4367
John Harrington, prin. Fax 472-3001

Schaumburg CCSD 54
Supt. — See Schaumburg
Mead JHS 700/7-8
1765 Biesterfield Rd 60007 847-357-6000
David Szwed, prin. Fax 357-6001

Township HSD 214
Supt. — See Arlington Heights
Elk Grove HS 1,900/9-12
500 W Elk Grove Blvd 60007 847-718-4400
Paul Kelly, prin. Fax 718-4417

Elkville, Jackson, Pop. 899
Elverado CUSD 196 500/PK-12
PO Box 130 62932 618-568-1321
Kevin Spain, supt. Fax 568-1152
www.elv196.com
Elverado HS 100/9-12
PO Box 217 62932 618-568-1104
Jeremy Pierce, prin. Fax 568-1551
Other Schools – See Vergennes

Elmhurst, DuPage, Pop. 43,533
Elmhurst SD 205 8,400/PK-12
162 S York St 60126 630-834-4530
Dr. David Moyer, supt. Fax 617-2345
www.elmhurst205.org/
Bryan MS 700/6-8
111 W Butterfield Rd 60126 630-617-2350
Jacquie Discipio, prin. Fax 617-2232
Churchville MS 500/6-8
155 E Victory Pkwy 60126 630-832-8682
Gina Pogue Reeder, prin. Fax 617-2387
Sandburg MS 700/6-8
345 E Saint Charles Rd 60126 630-834-4534
Linda Fehrenbacher, prin. Fax 617-2380
York Community HS 2,600/9-12
355 W Saint Charles Rd 60126 630-617-2400
Erin DeLuga, prin. Fax 617-2399

Elmhurst College Post-Sec.
190 S Prospect Ave 60126 630-279-4100
I C Catholic Prep 300/9-12
217 S Cottage Hill Ave 60126 630-530-3460
Pamela Levar, prin. Fax 530-2290
Timothy Christian HS 400/9-12
1061 S Prospect Ave 60126 630-833-7575
Brad Mitchell, prin. Fax 833-9821

Elmwood, Peoria, Pop. 2,079
Elmwood CUSD 322 700/PK-12
301 W Butternut St 61529 309-742-8464
Dr. Chad Wagner, supt. Fax 742-8812
elmwood322.com
Elmwood HS 200/9-12
301 W Butternut St 61529 309-742-2851
Stan Matheny, prin. Fax 742-8350
Elmwood JHS 100/7-8
301 W Butternut St 61529 309-742-2851
Stan Matheny, prin. Fax 742-8350

Elmwood Park, Cook, Pop. 24,650
Elmwood Park CUSD 401 2,900/PK-12
8201 W Fullerton Ave 60707 708-452-7292
Dr. Kevin M. Anderson, supt. Fax 452-9504
www.epcusd401.org/
Elm MS 400/7-8
7607 W Cortland St 60707 708-452-3550
Dr. Kathleen Porreca, prin. Fax 452-0662
Elmwood Park HS 900/9-12
8201 W Fullerton Ave 60707 708-452-7272
James Jennings, prin. Fax 452-0732

El Paso, Woodford, Pop. 2,782
El Paso-Gridley CUSD 11 1,300/PK-12
97 W 5th St 61738 309-527-4410
Michael Lindy, supt. Fax 527-4040
www.unit11.org/
El Paso-Gridley HS 400/9-12
600 N Elm St 61738 309-527-4415
Brian Quam, prin. Fax 527-4411
Other Schools – See Gridley

Elsah, Jersey, Pop. 651

Principia College Post-Sec.
1 Maybeck Pl 62028 618-374-2131

Erie, Whiteside, Pop. 1,588
Erie CUSD 1 700/PK-12
520 5th Ave 61250 309-659-2239
Bradley Cox, supt. Fax 659-2230
www.ecusd.info
Erie HS 200/9-12
435 6th Ave 61250 309-659-2239
Tim McConnell, prin. Fax 659-2514
Erie MS 200/5-8
500 5th Ave 61250 309-659-2239
Keith Morgan, prin. Fax 659-7254

Eureka, Woodford, Pop. 5,225
Eureka CUSD 140 1,700/PK-12
109 W Cruger Ave 61530 309-467-3737
Robert Bardwell, supt. Fax 467-2377
www.district140.org
Eureka HS 500/9-12
200 W Cruger Ave 61530 309-467-2361
Richard Wherley, prin. Fax 467-2648
Eureka MS 500/5-8
2005 S Main St 61530 309-467-3771
Kelly Nichols, prin. Fax 467-2052

Eureka College Post-Sec.
300 E College Ave 61530 309-467-3721

Evanston, Cook, Pop. 71,880
Evanston Township HSD 202 3,000/9-12
1600 Dodge Ave 60201 847-424-7000
Dr. Eric Witherspoon, supt. Fax 424-7220
www.eths.k12.il.us
Evanston Township HS 3,000/9-12
1600 Dodge Ave 60201 847-424-7000
Marcus Campbell, prin. Fax 424-7200

Evanston/Skokie SD 65 7,600/PK-8
1500 McDaniel Ave 60201 847-859-8000
Dr. Paul Goren, supt. Fax 866-7241
www.district65.net
Chute MS 500/6-8
1400 Oakton St 60202 847-859-8600
James McHolland, prin. Fax 492-7956
Haven MS 800/6-8
2417 Prairie Ave 60201 847-859-8200
Kathleen Roberson, prin. Fax 492-9983
Nichols MS 600/6-8
800 Greenleaf St 60202 847-859-8660
Adrian Harries, prin. Fax 492-7880

Beacon Academy 50/9-12
1574 Sherman Ave 60201 224-999-1177
Jeff Bell, head sch Fax 241-3052
Garrett Evangelical Theological Seminary Post-Sec.
2121 Sheridan Rd 60201 847-866-3900
Northwestern University Post-Sec.
633 Clark St 60208 847-491-3741
Pivot Point International Post-Sec.
1560 Sherman Ave Ste 700 60201 847-866-0500
Roycemore S 300/PK-12
1200 Davis St 60201 847-866-6055
Kevin Smith, hdmstr. Fax 866-6545
St. Francis Hospital Post-Sec.
355 Ridge Ave 60202 847-492-4000

Evansville, Randolph, Pop. 690

Christ our Savior Lutheran HS 50/9-12
810 Soldiers Way 62242 618-853-7300
Matthew Foster, admin. Fax 853-7361

Evergreen Park, Cook, Pop. 19,576
Evergreen Park Community HSD 231 800/9-12
9901 S Kedzie Ave 60805 708-424-7400
Dr. James Dunlap, supt. Fax 424-7497
www.evergreenpark.org
Evergreen Park HS 800/9-12
9901 S Kedzie Ave 60805 708-424-7400
Bill Sanderson, prin. Fax 424-7497

Evergreen Park ESD 124 1,700/PK-8
2929 W 87th St 60805 708-423-0950
Robert Machak Ed.D., supt. Fax 423-4292
www.d124.org
Central MS 400/7-8
9400 S Sawyer Ave 60805 708-424-0148
Rita Sparks, prin. Fax 229-8406

Fairbury, Livingston, Pop. 3,720
Prairie Central CUSD 8 1,600/PK-12
605 N 7th St 61739 815-692-2504
Dr. John Capasso, supt. Fax 692-3195
www.prairiecentral.org
Prairie Central HS 600/9-12
411 N 7th St 61739 815-692-2355
Brad Beyers, prin. Fax 692-2438
Other Schools – See Forrest

Fairfield, Wayne, Pop. 5,118
Fairfield Community HSD 225 400/9-12
300 W King St 62837 618-842-2649
Jill Fulkerson, supt. Fax 842-4465
www.fchsmules.com
Fairfield Community HS 400/9-12
300 W King St 62837 618-842-2649
Jill Fulkerson, admin. Fax 842-5187

Fairfield SD 112 700/PK-8
806 N 1st St 62837 618-842-6501
Diana Zurliene, supt. Fax 842-2932
fairfieldcolts.com
Center Street S 300/4-8
200 W Center St 62837 618-842-2679
April Smith, prin. Fax 842-4719

Frontier Community College Post-Sec.
2 Frontier Dr 62837 618-842-3711

Fairview Heights, Saint Clair, Pop. 16,671
Grant CCSD 110 700/PK-8
10110 Old Lincoln Trl 62208 618-398-5577
Matt Stines, supt. Fax 398-5578
dist110.com
Grant MS 300/5-8
10110 Old Lincoln Trl 62208 618-397-2764
Carla Lasley, prin. Fax 397-7809

Pontiac-William Holliday SD 105 800/PK-8
400 Ashland Ave 62208 618-233-2320
Dr. Julie Brown, supt. Fax 233-0918
www.pwh105.org
Pontiac JHS 200/6-8
400 Ashland Ave 62208 618-233-6004
Joanna Luehmann, prin. Fax 233-0918

Farina, Fayette, Pop. 518
South Central CUSD 401
Supt. — See Kinmundy
South Central HS 200/9-12
800 W Washington St 62838 618-245-3363
Steve Phillips, prin. Fax 245-6165

Farmer City, DeWitt, Pop. 2,018
Blue Ridge CUSD 18 600/PK-12
411 N John St 61842 309-928-9141
Susan Wilson, supt. Fax 928-5478
www.blueridge18.org
Blue Ridge HS 200/9-12
411 N John St 61842 309-928-2622
John Lawrence, prin. Fax 928-5301
Other Schools – See Mansfield

Farmington, Fulton, Pop. 2,424
Farmington Central CUSD 265 1,400/PK-12
212 N Lightfoot Rd 61531 309-245-1000
Dr. John Asplund, supt. Fax 245-9161
www.dist265.com/
Farmington Central JHS 300/6-8
300 N Lightfoot Rd 61531 309-245-1000
Josh Piper, prin. Fax 245-9162
Farmington HS 400/9-12
310 N Lightfoot Rd 61531 309-245-1000
Brad Hulet, prin. Fax 245-9163

Findlay, Shelby, Pop. 676
Okaw Valley CUSD 302
Supt. — See Bethany
Okaw Valley MS 200/5-8
501 W Division St 62534 217-756-8521
Ross Forlines, prin. Fax 756-8599

Fisher, Champaign, Pop. 1,871
Fisher CUSD 1 600/K-12
801 S 5th St 61843 217-897-6125
Barbara Thompson, supt. Fax 897-6676
www.fisherk12.com
Fisher JSHS 300/7-12
211 W Division St 61843 217-897-1225
Tom Shallenberger, prin. Fax 897-1708

Fithian, Vermilion, Pop. 480
Oakwood CUSD 76
Supt. — See Oakwood
Oakwood HS 300/9-12
5870 US Route 150 61844 217-354-2358
Tim Lee, prin. Fax 354-2603

Flanagan, Livingston, Pop. 1,105
Flanagan-Cornell Unit SD 74 400/PK-12
202 E Falcon Hwy 61740 815-796-2233
Jerry Farris, supt. Fax 796-2856
www.fc74.org
Flanagan-Cornell HS 100/9-12
202 E Falcon Hwy 61740 815-796-2291
Brian Yoder, prin. Fax 796-2856

Flora, Clay, Pop. 5,018
Flora CUSD 35 600/PK-12
444 S Locust St 62839 618-662-2412
Joel Hackney, supt. Fax 662-4587
www.floraschools.com
Flora HS 300/9-12
600 S Locust St 62839 618-662-8316
Toby Pearce, prin. Fax 662-2725
Henson JHS 300/6-8
609 N Stanford Rd 62839 618-662-8394
Amy Leonard, prin. Fax 662-8395

Flossmoor, Cook, Pop. 9,246
Flossmoor SD 161
Supt. — See Chicago Heights
Parker JHS 900/6-8
2810 School St 60422 708-647-5400
Dr. Vickie Person, prin. Fax 799-9207

Homewood-Flossmoor Community HSD 233 2,800/9-12
999 Kedzie Ave 60422 708-799-3000
Dr. Von Mansfield, supt. Fax 799-8552
www.hfhighschool.org
Homewood-Flossmoor HS 2,800/9-12
999 Kedzie Ave 60422 708-799-3000
Dr. Von Mansfield, prin. Fax 335-6995

Ford Heights, Cook, Pop. 2,726
Ford Heights SD 169 400/PK-8
910 Woodlawn Ave 60411 708-758-1370
Dr. Gregory Jackson, supt. Fax 758-1372
www.fordheights169.org
Cottage Grove Upper Grade Center 200/5-8
800 E 14th St 60411 708-758-1400
Sharon Rivers, prin. Fax 758-0711

Forest Park, Cook, Pop. 13,818
Forest Park SD 91 900/PK-8
424 Des Plaines Ave 60130 708-366-5700
Dr. Louis Cavallo, supt. Fax 366-5761
www.forestparkschools.org
Forest Park MS 300/6-8
925 Beloit Ave 60130 708-366-5703
Joseph Pisano, prin. Fax 366-2091

Proviso Township HSD 209 4,500/9-12
8601 Roosevelt Rd 60130 708-338-5912
Dr. Jesse Rodriguez, supt. Fax 338-5999
www.pths209.org
Proviso Math & Science Academy 800/9-12
8601 Roosevelt Rd 60130 708-338-4100
Dr. Bessie Karvelas, prin. Fax 338-4199
Other Schools – See Hillside, Maywood

Forrest, Livingston, Pop. 1,217
Prairie Central CUSD 8
Supt. — See Fairbury
Prairie Central JHS 300/7-8
800 N Wood St 61741 815-657-8660
Tonya Dieken, prin. Fax 657-8677

Forreston, Ogle, Pop. 1,426
Forrestville Valley CUSD 221 700/PK-12
PO Box 665 61030 815-938-2036
Sheri Smith, supt. Fax 938-9028
www.fvvsd221.org
Forreston JSHS 400/6-12
PO Box 665 61030 815-938-2175
Travis Heinz, prin. Fax 938-2546

Forsyth, Macon, Pop. 3,456

Decatur Christian S 200/PK-12
137 S Grant St 62535 217-877-5636
Randy Grigg, supt. Fax 877-7627

Fox Lake, Lake, Pop. 10,448
Fox Lake Grade SD 114
Supt. — See Spring Grove
Stanton MS 300/5-8
101 Hawthorne Ln 60020 847-973-4200
Jeff Sefcik, prin. Fax 973-4210

Grant Community HSD 124 1,900/9-12
285 E Grand Ave 60020 847-587-2561
Dr. Christine Sefcik, supt. Fax 587-2991
www.grant.lake.k12.il.us/
Grant Community HS 1,900/9-12
285 E Grand Ave 60020 847-587-2561
Jeremy Schmidt, prin. Fax 587-2991

Fox River Grove, McHenry, Pop. 4,788
Fox River Grove SD 3 500/PK-8
403 Orchard St 60021 847-516-5100
Dr. Tim Mahaffy, supt. Fax 516-9169
www.dist3.org
Fox River Grove MS 200/5-8
401 Orchard St 60021 847-516-5105
Eric Runck, prin. Fax 516-5104

Frankfort, Will, Pop. 17,612
Frankfort CCSD 157C 2,500/PK-8
10482 Nebraska St 60423 815-469-5922
Dr. Maura Zinni, supt. Fax 469-8988
www.fsd157c.org
Hickory Creek MS 900/6-8
22150 116th Ave 60423 815-469-4474
William Seidelmann, prin. Fax 469-7930

Lincoln-Way Community HSD 210
Supt. — See New Lenox
Lincoln-Way East HS 2,200/9-12
201 Colorado Ave 60423 815-464-4000
Dr. Sharon Michalak, prin. Fax 464-4132

Summit Hill SD 161 3,300/PK-8
20100 S Spruce Dr 60423 815-464-2230
Barb Rains, supt. Fax 469-0566
www.summithill.org/
Summit Hill JHS 800/7-8
7260 W North Ave 60423 815-469-4330
Daniel Pierson, prin. Fax 464-1596

Franklin, Morgan, Pop. 598
Franklin CUSD 1
Supt. — See Alexander
Franklin JSHS 100/6-12
110 State 62638 217-675-2395
Jason Courier, prin. Fax 675-2396

Franklin Park, Cook, Pop. 18,209
Franklin Park SD 84 1,200/PK-8
2915 Maple St 60131 847-455-4230
Dr. David H. Katzin, supt. Fax 455-9094
www.d84.org
Hester JHS 400/6-8
2836 Gustav St 60131 847-455-2150
Giffen Trotter, prin. Fax 455-0945

Leyden Community HSD 212 3,400/9-12
3400 Rose St 60131 847-451-3020
Dr. Nick Polyak, supt. Fax 671-9079
www.leyden212.org
East Leyden HS 1,700/9-12
3400 Rose St 60131 847-451-3023
Jason Markey, prin. Fax 233-9928
Other Schools – See Northlake

Mannheim SD 83 2,600/PK-8
10401 Grand Ave 60131 847-455-4413
Kim Petrasek, supt. Fax 451-8290
www.d83.org/
Other Schools – See Melrose Park

Freeburg, Saint Clair, Pop. 4,312
Freeburg CCSD 70 800/PK-8
408 S Belleville St 62243 618-539-3188
Tomi Diefenbach, supt. Fax 539-5795
www.frg70.org
Freeburg ES 500/3-8
408 S Belleville St 62243 618-539-3188
Theresa Goscinski, prin. Fax 539-5795

Freeburg Community HSD 77 600/9-12
401 S Monroe St 62243 618-539-5533
Greg Frerking, supt. Fax 539-4887
www.fchs77.org/district.cfm
Freeburg HS 600/9-12
401 S Monroe St 62243 618-539-5533
Greg Frerking, prin. Fax 539-4887

Freeport, Stephenson, Pop. 24,738
Carroll/Jo Daviess/Stephenson ROE 50/
27 S State Ave Ste 101 61032 815-599-1408
Aaron Mercier, supt. Fax 297-9032
www.roe8.com
Regional Alternative Program Freeport 50/Alt
27 S State Ave 61032 815-599-1408
Brent Chrisman, prin. Fax 297-9032
Other Schools – See Elizabeth

Freeport SD 145 4,100/PK-12
501 E South St 61032 815-232-0300
Dr. Michael Schiffman, supt. Fax 235-4177
www.fsd145.org
Freeport Alternative HS 50/Alt
1330 S Locust Ave 61032 815-233-0796
Dana Dinderman, admin. Fax 232-2311
Freeport HS 1,200/9-12
701 W Moseley St 61032 815-232-0400
Dr. Beth Summers, prin. Fax 232-0629
Freeport MS 700/5-8
701 W Empire St 61032 815-232-0500
Nick Swords, prin. Fax 232-0536
Sandburg MS 500/5-8
1717 W Eby St 61032 815-232-0340
Dr. Kathy Jenkins, prin. Fax 232-1241

Aquin Central Catholic HS 200/7-12
1419 S Galena Ave 61032 815-235-3154
Rosemarie Brubaker, admin. Fax 235-3185
Highland Community College Post-Sec.
2998 W Pearl City Rd 61032 815-235-6121

Fulton, Whiteside, Pop. 3,442
River Bend CUSD 2 1,000/PK-12
1110 3rd St 61252 815-589-2711
Darryl Hogue Ed.D., supt. Fax 589-4630
www.riverbendschools.org
Fulton HS 300/9-12
1207 12th St 61252 815-589-3511
Chris Tennyson, prin. Fax 589-3412
River Bend MS 200/6-8
415 12th St 61252 815-589-2611
Kathleen Schipper, prin. Fax 589-3130

Unity Christian HS 100/7-12
711 10th St 61252 815-589-3912
Christopher Pluister, prin. Fax 589-4430

Galatia, Saline, Pop. 925
Galatia CUSD 1 400/PK-12
200 N Hickory St 62935 618-268-6371
Dr. Beth Rister, supt. Fax 268-4196
www.galatiak12.org
Galatia HS 100/9-12
200 N McKinley St 62935 618-268-4194
John Cummins, prin. Fax 268-4196
Galatia JHS 100/7-8
200 N McKinley St 62935 618-268-4194
John Cummins, prin. Fax 268-4196

Galena, Jo Daviess, Pop. 3,404
Galena Unit SD 120 800/PK-12
1206 Franklin St 61036 815-777-3086
Greg Herbst, supt. Fax 777-0303
www.gusd120.k12.il.us
Galena HS 200/9-12
1206 Franklin St 61036 815-777-0917
Elizabeth Murphy, prin. Fax 777-2089
Galena MS 200/5-8
1230 Franklin St 61036 815-777-2413
Ben Soat, prin. Fax 777-4259

Tri-State Christian S 200/PK-12
11084 W US Highway 20 61036 815-777-3800
Dr. Tad Nuce, prin. Fax 777-2991

Galesburg, Knox, Pop. 31,321
Galesburg AVC
1135 W Fremont St 61401 309-343-3733
Jeff Houston, prin. Fax 343-1305
www.gavc.weebly.com
Galesburg AVC Vo/Tech
1135 W Fremont St 61401 309-343-3733
Jeff Houston, prin. Fax 343-1305

Galesburg CUSD 205 4,600/PK-12
PO Box 1206 61402 309-343-1151
Ralph Grimm, supt. Fax 343-1319
www.galesburg205.org
Churchill JHS 500/6-8
905 Maple Ave 61401 309-973-2002
Tom Hawkins, prin. Fax 342-6384
Galesburg HS 1,300/9-12
1135 W Fremont St 61401 309-973-2001
Jeff Houston, prin. Fax 343-7122
Galesburg HS North Alt
1017 W Dayton St 61401 309-973-2003
Jason Spring, prin. Fax 343-1237
Lombard MS 500/6-8
1220 E Knox St 61401 309-973-2004
Nick Sutton, prin. Fax 342-7135

Carl Sandburg College Post-Sec.
2400 Tom L Wilson Blvd 61401 309-344-2518
Galesburg Christian S 100/PK-12
1881 E Fremont St 61401 309-343-8008
Robert Nutzhorn, admin. Fax 342-0235
Knox College Post-Sec.
2 E South St 61401 309-341-7000

Galva, Henry, Pop. 2,565
Galva CUSD 224 600/PK-12
224 Morgan Rd 61434 309-932-2108
Doug O'Riley, supt. Fax 932-8326
www.galva224.org
Galva JSHS 300/7-12
224 Morgan Rd 61434 309-932-2151
Jerry Becker, prin. Fax 932-2152

Gardner, Grundy, Pop. 1,442
Gardner-South Wilmington Twp. HSD 73 200/9-12
500 E Main St 60424 815-237-2176
Michael Perrott, supt. Fax 237-2842
www.gswhs.grundy.k12.il.us

Gardner-South Wilmington Twp. HS — 200/9-12
500 E Main St 60424 — 815-237-2176
John Engelman, prin. — Fax 237-2842

Geneseo, Henry, Pop. 6,533
Geneseo CUSD 228 — 2,600/PK-12
648 N Chicago St 61254 — 309-945-0450
Scott Kuffel, supt. — Fax 945-0445
www.dist228.org
Geneseo HS — 800/9-12
700 N State St 61254 — 309-945-0399
Michael Haugse, prin. — Fax 945-0374
Geneseo MS — 600/6-8
333 E Ogden Ave 61254 — 309-945-0599
Nathan O'Dell, prin. — Fax 945-0580

Geneva, Kane, Pop. 21,261
Geneva CUSD 304 — 5,800/PK-12
227 N 4th St 60134 — 630-463-3000
Dr. Kent Mutchler, supt. — Fax 463-3009
www.geneva304.org
Geneva Community HS — 2,000/9-12
416 McKinley Ave 60134 — 630-463-3800
Thomas Rogers, prin. — Fax 463-3809
Geneva MS North — 700/6-8
1357 Viking Dr 60134 — 630-463-3700
Lawrence Bidlack, prin. — Fax 463-3709
Geneva MS South — 700/6-8
1415 Viking Dr 60134 — 630-463-3600
Terry Bleau, prin. — Fax 463-3609

Genoa, DeKalb, Pop. 5,138
Genoa-Kingston CUSD 424 — 1,800/PK-12
980 Park Ave 60135 — 815-784-6222
Joe Burgess, supt. — Fax 784-6059
www.gkschools.org
Genoa-Kingston HS — 600/9-12
980 Park Ave 60135 — 815-784-5111
Brett McPherson, prin. — Fax 784-3124
Genoa-Kingston MS — 400/6-8
941 W Main St 60135 — 815-784-5222
Angelo Lekkas, prin. — Fax 784-4323

Georgetown, Vermilion, Pop. 3,408
Georgetown-Ridge Farm CUSD 4 — 1,100/PK-12
502 W Mulberry St 61846 — 217-662-8488
Jean Neal, supt. — Fax 662-3402
www.grf.k12.il.us
Georgetown-Ridge Farm HS — 300/9-12
500 W Mulberry St 61846 — 217-662-6716
Kevin Thomas, prin. — Fax 662-3404
Miller JHS — 300/6-8
414 W West St 61846 — 217-662-6606
Brad Russell, prin. — Fax 662-6345

Germantown Hills, Woodford, Pop. 3,399
Germantown Hills SD 69 — 800/K-8
103 Warrior Way, — 309-383-2121
Dan Mair, supt. — Fax 383-2123
ghills.metamora.k12.il.us
Germantown Hills JHS — 300/6-8
103 Warrior Way, — 309-383-2121
Dave Raffel, prin. — Fax 383-4739

Gibson City, Ford, Pop. 3,366
Gibson City-Melvin-Sibley CUSD 5 — 1,000/PK-12
307 N Sangamon Ave 60936 — 217-784-8296
Jeremy Darnell, supt. — Fax 784-8558
www.gcmsk12.org
GCMS HS — 300/9-12
815 N Church St 60936 — 217-784-4292
Christopher Garard, prin. — Fax 784-8293
GCMS MS — 300/6-8
316 E 19th St 60936 — 217-784-8731
Kyle Bieldeldt, prin. — Fax 784-8726

Gillespie, Macoupin, Pop. 3,280
Gillespie CUSD 7 — 1,300/PK-12
510 W Elm St 62033 — 217-839-2464
Joseph Tieman, supt. — Fax 839-3353
www.joomla.gcusd7.org
Gillespie HS — 400/9-12
612 Broadway St 62033 — 217-839-2114
Lori Emmons, prin. — Fax 839-4302
Gillespie MS, 412 Oregon St 62033 — 300/6-8
Jill Rosentreter, prin. — 217-839-2116

Gilman, Iroquois, Pop. 1,793
Iroquois West CUSD 10 — 1,000/PK-12
PO Box 67 60938 — 815-265-4642
Dr. Linda Dvorak, supt. — Fax 265-7008
www.iwest.k12.il.us/
Iroquois West HS — 300/9-12
PO Box 67 60938 — 815-265-4229
Joshua Houberg, prin. — Fax 265-8108
Other Schools – See Onarga

Girard, Macoupin, Pop. 2,085
North Mac CUSD 34 — 800/PK-12
525 N 3rd St 62640 — 217-627-2915
Marica Cullen, supt. — Fax 627-3519
www.northmacschools.org
North Mac IS — 100/3-8
525 N 3rd St 62640 — 217-627-2419
Dennis McMillin, prin. — Fax 627-3409
Other Schools – See Virden

Glasford, Peoria, Pop. 1,015
Illini Bluffs CUSD 327 — 900/PK-12
9611 S Hanna City Glasford 61533 — 309-389-2231
Dr. Roger Alvey, supt. — Fax 389-2251
www.illinibluffs.com
Illini Bluffs HS — 300/9-12
9611 S Hanna City Glasford 61533 — 309-389-5681
Keith Brown, prin. — Fax 389-4681
Illini Bluffs MS — 200/6-8
9611 S Hanna City Glasford 61533 — 309-389-3451
Karen Peterson, prin. — Fax 389-3454

Glen Carbon, Madison, Pop. 12,692

Gateway Legacy Christian Academy — 100/PK-12
97 Oaklawn Dr 62034 — 618-288-0452
Melissa Morrison, prin. — Fax 288-0453
McGivney Catholic HS — 9-12
7190 Bouse Rd 62034 — 618-855-9010
Mike Scholz, prin. — Fax 855-9011

Glencoe, Cook, Pop. 8,600
Glencoe SD 35 — 1,200/K-8
620 Greenwood Ave 60022 — 847-835-7800
Dr. Catherine Wang, supt. — Fax 835-7805
www.glencoeschools.org
Central S — 600/5-8
620 Greenwood Ave 60022 — 847-835-7600
Dr. Ryan Mollet, prin. — Fax 835-7605

Glendale Heights, DuPage, Pop. 33,478
Marquardt SD 15 — 2,700/PK-8
1860 Glen Ellyn Rd 60139 — 630-469-7615
Dr. Jerry O'Shea Ed.D., supt. — Fax 790-1650
www.d15.us/
Marquardt MS — 800/6-8
1912 Glen Ellyn Rd 60139 — 630-858-3850
Meredith Haugens, prin. — Fax 790-5042

Queen Bee SD 16 — 2,000/PK-8
1560 Bloomingdale Rd 60139 — 630-260-6100
Victoria Tabbert, supt. — Fax 260-6103
www.queenbee16.org
Glenside MS — 700/6-8
1560 Bloomingdale Rd 60139 — 630-260-6112
David Benson, prin. — Fax 510-8568

Glen Ellyn, DuPage, Pop. 27,048
CCSD 89 — 2,000/PK-8
22W600 Butterfield Rd 60137 — 630-469-8900
Dr. Emily Tammaru, supt. — Fax 469-8936
www.ccsd89.org
Glen Crest MS — 600/6-8
725 Sheehan Ave 60137 — 630-469-5220
Kim Price, prin. — Fax 469-5250

Glen Ellyn SD 41 — 3,600/PK-8
793 N Main St 60137 — 630-790-6400
Dr. Paul Gordon, supt. — Fax 790-1867
www.d41.org
Hadley JHS — 1,200/6-8
240 Hawthorne Blvd 60137 — 630-790-6450
Steve Diveley, prin. — Fax 790-6469

Glenbard Township HSD 87 — 8,300/9-12
596 Crescent Blvd 60137 — 630-469-9100
Dr. David Larson, supt. — Fax 469-9107
glenbard87.org/
Glenbard South HS — 1,300/9-12
23w200 Butterfield Rd 60137 — 630-469-6500
Sandra Coughlin, prin. — Fax 469-6572
Glenbard West HS — 2,300/9-12
670 Crescent Blvd 60137 — 630-469-8600
Dr. Peter Monoghan, prin. — Fax 469-8615
Other Schools – See Carol Stream, Lombard

College of DuPage — Post-Sec.
425 Fawell Blvd 60137 — 630-942-2800

Glenview, Cook, Pop. 44,009
Glenview CCSD 34 — 4,900/PK-8
1401 Greenwood Rd 60026 — 847-998-5000
Griff Powell, supt. — Fax 998-5094
www.glenview34.org
Attea MS — 900/6-8
2500 Chestnut Ave 60026 — 847-486-7700
Mark Richter, prin. — Fax 729-6251
Springman MS — 800/6-8
2701 Central Rd 60025 — 847-998-5020
Jason Kaiz, prin. — Fax 998-4032

Northfield Township HSD 225 — 4,800/9-12
3801 W Lake Ave 60026 — 847-486-4700
Dr. Michael Riggle, supt. — Fax 486-4733
www.glenbrook225.org
Glenbrook South HS — 2,700/9-12
4000 W Lake Ave 60026 — 847-486-4559
Lauren Fagel, prin. — Fax 486-4462
Glenbrook Evening HS — Adult
4000 W Lake Ave 60026 — 847-486-4709
Dr. Frank Santa, prin. — Fax 486-4733
Other Schools – See Northbrook

Glenwood, Cook, Pop. 8,797
Brookwood SD 167 — 1,200/PK-8
201 E Glenwood Dyer Rd 60425 — 708-758-5190
Dr. Valorie Moore, supt. — Fax 757-2104
www.brookwood167.org
Brookwood JHS — 300/7-8
201 E Glenwood Lansing Rd 60425 — 708-758-5252
Bethany Lindsay, prin. — Fax 758-3954

Godfrey, Madison, Pop. 17,742

Alvareita's College of Cosmetology — Post-Sec.
3048 Godfrey Rd 62035 — 618-466-8952
Lewis & Clark Community College — Post-Sec.
5800 Godfrey Rd 62035 — 618-468-7000

Golconda, Pope, Pop. 665
Pope County CUSD 1 — 600/PK-12
125 State Highway 146 W 62938 — 618-683-2301
Charles Bleyer, supt. — Fax 683-5181
www.popek12.org
Pope County HS — 200/9-12
125 State Highway 146 W 62938 — 618-683-3071
Ryan Fritch, prin. — Fax 683-9956

Goreville, Johnson, Pop. 1,046
Goreville CUSD 1 — 600/PK-12
201 S Ferne Clyffe Rd 62939 — 618-995-9831
Dr. Steve Webb, supt. — Fax 995-9832
www.gorevilleschools.com
Goreville HS — 200/9-12
201 S Ferne Clyffe Rd 62939 — 618-995-2142
Jeri Miller, prin. — Fax 995-1188

Granite City, Madison, Pop. 29,332
Granite City CUSD 9 — 4,500/PK-12
1947 Adams St 62040 — 618-451-5800
Jim Greenwald, supt. — Fax 451-6135
www.gcsd9.net
Coolidge JHS — 900/7-8
3231 Nameoki Rd 62040 — 618-451-5826
Patrick Curry, prin. — Fax 876-5154
Granite City HS — 1,900/9-12
3101 Madison Ave 62040 — 618-451-5808
Daren DePew, prin. — Fax 451-6296

Grant Park, Kankakee, Pop. 1,318
Grant Park CUSD 6 — 500/PK-12
PO Box 549 60940 — 815-465-6013
Dr. John Palan, supt. — Fax 465-2505
www.grantparkdragons.org
Grant Park HS — 200/9-12
PO Box 549 60940 — 815-465-2181
Tom Sanidas, prin. — Fax 465-2505

Granville, Putnam, Pop. 1,410
Putnam County CUSD 535 — 900/PK-12
400 E Silverspoon Ave 61326 — 815-882-2800
Carl Carlson, supt. — Fax 882-2802
www.pcschools535.org
Putnam County HS — 300/9-12
402 E Silverspoon Ave 61326 — 815-882-2800
Clay Theisinger, prin. — Fax 339-2628
Other Schools – See Mc Nabb

Grayslake, Lake, Pop. 20,539
CCSD 46 — 3,600/K-8
565 Frederick Rd 60030 — 847-223-3650
Ellen Correll, supt. — Fax 223-3695
www.d46.k12.il.us
Grayslake MS — 700/7-8
440 N Barron Blvd 60030 — 847-223-3680
Marcus Smith, prin. — Fax 223-3526

Grayslake Community HSD 127 — 3,000/9-12
400 N Lake St 60030 — 847-986-3400
Dr. Catherine Finger, supt. — Fax 231-6838
www.d127.org/
Grayslake Community HS - Central Campus — 1,400/9-12
400 N Lake St 60030 — 847-986-3300
Daniel Landry, prin. — Fax 223-8690
Grayslake Community HS - North Campus — 1,500/9-12
1925 N Route 83 60030 — 847-986-3100
Dr. James Roscoe, prin. — Fax 986-3023

Lake County HS Technology Campus
19525 W Washington St 60030 — 847-223-6681
Steve Clark, dir. — Fax 223-7363
www.techcampus.org
Lake County HS Technology Campus — Vo/Tech
19525 W Washington St 60030 — 847-223-6681
Steve Clark, dir. — Fax 223-7363

College of Lake County — Post-Sec.
19351 W Washington St 60030 — 847-543-2000
Westlake Christian Academy — 200/PK-12
275 S Lake St 60030 — 847-548-6209
Dr. Michael Healan, prin. — Fax 548-6481

Grayville, White, Pop. 1,656
Grayville CUSD 1 — 300/PK-12
728 W North St 62844 — 618-375-7114
Sarah Emery, supt. — Fax 375-5202
gcusd.com
Grayville JSHS — 100/6-12
728 W North St 62844 — 618-375-7114
Sarah Emery, prin. — Fax 375-6521

Greenfield, Greene, Pop. 1,063
Greenfield CUSD 10 — 500/PK-12
311 Mulberry St 62044 — 217-368-2447
Kevin Bowman, supt. — Fax 368-2724
www.greenfieldschools.org/
Greenfield HS — 100/9-12
502 East St 62044 — 217-368-2219
Beth Bettis, prin. — Fax 368-2230

Green Valley, Tazewell, Pop. 698
Midwest Central CUSD 191
Supt. — See Manito
Midwest Central MS — 200/6-8
121 N Church St 61534 — 309-352-2300
Kyra Fancher, prin. — Fax 352-2903

Greenview, Menard, Pop. 765
Greenview CUSD 200 — 300/PK-12
147 E Palmer St 62642 — 217-968-2295
Ryan Heavner, supt. — Fax 968-2297
www.greenviewschools.org
Greenview JSHS — 100/6-12
147 E Palmer St 62642 — 217-968-2295
Tim Turner, prin. — Fax 968-2297

Greenville, Bond, Pop. 6,851
Bond County CUSD 2 — 1,900/PK-12
1008 N Hena St 62246 — 618-664-0170
Wes Olson, supt. — Fax 664-5000
www.bccu2.org
Bond City Comm Unit 2 HS — 500/9-12
1000 E State Route 140 62246 — 618-664-1370
Wendy Porter, prin. — Fax 664-4786
Greenville JHS — 300/6-8
1200 Junior High Dr 62246 — 618-664-1226
Gary Brauns, prin. — Fax 664-5071

Greenville College — Post-Sec.
315 E College Ave 62246 — 618-664-2800

Gridley, McLean, Pop. 1,415
El Paso-Gridley CUSD 11
Supt. — See El Paso

El Paso-Gridley JHS 300/6-8
403 McLean St 61744 309-747-2156
Robby Tomlinson, prin. Fax 747-2938

Griggsville, Pike, Pop. 1,219
Griggsville-Perry CUSD 4 400/PK-12
PO Box 439 62340 217-833-2352
Dr. Janet Gladu, supt. Fax 833-2354
www.griggsvilleperry.org
Griggsville-Perry HS 100/9-12
PO Box 439 62340 217-833-2352
Jeff Bourne, prin. Fax 833-2354
Other Schools – See Perry

Gurnee, Lake, Pop. 30,557
Gurnee SD 56 2,200/PK-8
3706 Florida Ave 60031 847-336-0800
Dr. John Hutton, supt. Fax 336-1110
www.d56.org
Viking MS 600/6-8
4460 Old Grand Ave 60031 847-336-2108
Patrick Jones, prin. Fax 249-0719

Warren Township HSD 121 4,300/9-12
34090 N Almond Rd 60031 847-662-1400
John Ahlgrim, supt. Fax 548-0564
www.d121.org
Warren Township HS 2,200/9-10
500 N OPlaine Rd 60031 847-662-1400
Greg Meyer, prin. Fax 599-4848
Warren Township HS 2,100/11-12
34090 N Almond Rd 60031 847-662-1400
Patrick Keeley, prin. Fax 548-6444

Woodland CCSD 50 8,600/PK-8
1105 N Hunt Club Rd 60031 847-596-5600
Joy Swoboda, supt. Fax 856-0311
www.dist50.net
Woodland MS 2,300/6-8
7000 Washington St 60031 847-856-3400
Scott Snyder, prin. Fax 856-1306

Computer Systems Institute Post-Sec.
5330 Grand Ave 60031 847-263-4258
DeVry University Post-Sec.
1075 Tri State Pkwy Ste 800 60031 847-855-2649

Hamilton, Hancock, Pop. 2,918
Hamilton CCSD 328 600/PK-12
270 N 10th St 62341 866-332-3880
Joe Yurko, supt. Fax 847-3915
www.hhs328.com
Hamilton HS 100/9-12
1100 Keokuk St 62341 866-332-3880
Shelli Jennings, prin. Fax 847-3474
Hamilton JHS 100/7-8
1100 Keokuk St 62341 866-332-3880
Shelli Jennings, prin. Fax 847-3915

Hampshire, Kane, Pop. 5,507
CUSD 300
Supt. — See Algonquin
Hampshire HS 1,300/9-12
1600 Big Timber Rd 60140 847-792-3500
Brett Bending, prin. Fax 792-3515
Hampshire MS 900/6-8
560 S State St 60140 847-683-2522
James Szymczak, prin. Fax 683-1030

Hanover, Jo Daviess, Pop. 828
River Ridge CUSD 210 500/PK-12
4141 IL Route 84 S 61041 815-858-9005
Bradley Albrecht, supt. Fax 858-9006
www.riverridge210.org
River Ridge HS 200/9-12
4141 IL Route 84 S 61041 815-858-9005
Michael Foltz, prin. Fax 858-9006
River Ridge MS 100/6-8
4141 IL Route 84 S 61041 815-858-9005
Michael Foltz, prin. Fax 858-9006

Hanover Park, Cook, Pop. 37,237
Keeneyville SD 20 1,500/PK-8
5540 Arlington Dr E 60133 630-894-2250
Dr. Michael Connolly, supt. Fax 894-5187
www.esd20.org
Spring Wood MS 500/6-8
5540 Arlington Dr E 60133 630-893-8900
Craig Barringer, prin. Fax 894-9658

Hanover Park College of Beauty Culture Post-Sec.
1166 E Lake St 60133 630-830-6560

Hardin, Calhoun, Pop. 960
Calhoun CUSD 40 400/K-12
PO Box 387 62047 618-576-2722
Dr. Kate Sievers, supt. Fax 576-2641
www.calhoun.k12.il.us
Calhoun HS 200/9-12
PO Box 387 62047 618-576-2229
Cheri Burris, prin. Fax 576-8031

Harrisburg, Saline, Pop. 8,789
Edwds/Gtn/Hdn/Pope/Sln/Wbsh/Wyn/Wt ROE
512 N Main St 62946 618-253-5581
Lawrence Fillingim, supt. Fax 252-8472
www.roe20.org
Other Schools – See Norris City

Harrisburg CUSD 3 2,100/PK-12
40 S Main St 62946 618-253-7637
Mike Gauch, supt. Fax 253-2095
www.hbg.saline.k12.il.us
Harrisburg HS 600/9-12
333 W College St 62946 618-253-7637
Scott Dewar, prin. Fax 252-0994
Harrisburg MS 500/6-8
312 Bulldog Blvd 62946 618-253-7637
John Crabb, prin. Fax 253-2093

Southeastern Illinois College Post-Sec.
3575 College Rd 62946 618-252-5400

Hartsburg, Montgomery, Pop. 309
Hartsburg-Emden CUSD 21 200/PK-12
400 W Front St 62643 217-642-5244
Terry Wisniewski, supt. Fax 642-5333
www.hartem.org
Hartsburg-Emden JSHS 100/6-12
400 W Front St 62643 217-642-5244
Jon Leslie, prin. Fax 642-5333

Harvard, McHenry, Pop. 9,314
Harvard CUSD 50 2,500/PK-12
401 N Division St 60033 815-943-4022
Dr. Lauri Tobias, supt. Fax 943-4282
www.cusd50.org
Harvard HS 700/9-12
1103 N Jefferson St 60033 815-943-6461
Rob Zielinski, prin. Fax 943-8506
Harvard JHS 500/6-8
1301 Garfield St 60033 815-943-6466
Margaret Segersten, prin. Fax 943-8521

Harvey, Cook, Pop. 24,990
Harvey SD 152 2,300/PK-8
16001 Lincoln Ave 60426 708-333-0300
Dr. Sonya Whitaker, supt. Fax 333-0349
www.harvey152.org
Brooks MS 500/7-8
14741 Wallace St 60426 708-333-6390
Michael Allen, prin. Fax 333-3177

Thornton Township HSD 205
Supt. — See South Holland
Thornton Township HS 1,800/9-12
15001 Broadway Ave 60426 708-225-4109
Tony Ratliff, prin. Fax 225-5014

West Harvey-Dixmoor SD 147 1,300/PK-8
191 W 155th Pl 60426 708-339-9500
J. Kay Giles, supt. Fax 596-7020
www.whd147.org
Other Schools – See Dixmoor

Ingalls Memorial Hospital Post-Sec.
1 Ingalls Dr 60426 708-333-2300

Havana, Mason, Pop. 3,277
Havana CUSD 126 1,100/PK-12
501 S McKinley St 62644 309-543-3384
Mathew Plater, supt. Fax 543-3385
www.havana126.weebly.com
Havana HS 300/9-12
501 S McKinley St 62644 309-543-3337
David McKinney, prin. Fax 543-6721
Havana JHS 300/5-8
801 E Laurel Ave 62644 309-543-6677
Chris Snider, prin. Fax 543-6678

Hawthorn Woods, Lake, Pop. 7,541
Lake Zurich CUSD 95
Supt. — See Lake Zurich
Lake Zurich MS North Campus 700/6-8
95 Hubbard Ln 60047 847-719-3600
Todd Jakowitsch, prin. Fax 719-3620

Hebron, McHenry, Pop. 1,203
Alden Hebron SD 19 400/PK-12
11915 Price Rd 60034 815-648-2442
Dr. Debbie Ehlenburg, supt. Fax 648-2339
www.alden-hebron.org
Alden-Hebron HS 100/9-12
9604 Illinois St 60034 815-648-2442
Tim Hayunga, prin. Fax 648-2339
Alden-Hebron MS 100/6-8
9604 Illinois St 60034 815-648-2442
Dr. Kim Qualls, prin. Fax 648-2339

Henry, Marshall, Pop. 2,442
Henry-Senachwine CUSD 5 600/PK-12
1023 College St 61537 309-364-3614
Dr. Michael Miller, supt. Fax 364-2990
www.hscud5.org
Henry-Senachwine Consolidated HS 200/9-12
1023 College St 61537 309-364-2829
Weston Wolven, prin. Fax 364-2990

Herrin, Williamson, Pop. 12,262
Herrin CUSD 4 2,500/PK-12
500 N 10th St 62948 618-988-8024
Dr. Terry Ryker, supt. Fax 942-6998
www.herrinunit.org
Herrin HS 700/9-12
700 N 10th St 62948 618-942-6606
Jeffrey Johnson, prin. Fax 942-7562
Herrin JHS 500/6-8
700 S 14th St 62948 618-942-7461
Brad Heuring, prin. Fax 988-8821

Herscher, Kankakee, Pop. 1,577
Herscher CUSD 2 1,800/PK-12
PO Box 504 60941 815-426-2162
Dr. Richard Decman, supt. Fax 426-2872
www.hcusd2.org
Herscher HS 600/9-12
PO Box 504 60941 815-426-2103
Brad Elliot, prin. Fax 426-2957
Other Schools – See Kankakee

Heyworth, McLean, Pop. 2,807
Heyworth CUSD 4 1,000/PK-12
522 E Main St 61745 309-473-3727
Dr. Ty Wolf, supt. Fax 473-2220
www.husd4.org
Heyworth JSHS 400/7-12
308 W Cleveland St 61745 309-473-2322
Lisa Taylor, prin. Fax 473-2323

Hickory Hills, Cook, Pop. 13,836
North Palos SD 117
Supt. — See Palos Hills
Conrady JHS 1,000/6-8
7950 W 97th St 60457 708-233-4500
Andy Anderson, prin. Fax 430-8964

Highland, Madison, Pop. 9,807
Highland CUSD 5 2,800/PK-12
400 Broadway 62249 618-654-2106
Michael Sutton, supt. Fax 654-5424
www.highlandcusd5.org
Highland HS 1,000/9-12
400 Broadway 62249 618-654-7131
Dr. Karen Gauen, prin. Fax 654-6548
Highland MS 500/6-8
400 Broadway 62249 618-651-8800
Dr. Erick Baer, prin. Fax 654-1551

Highland Park, Lake, Pop. 29,398
North Shore SD 112 4,400/PK-8
1936 Green Bay Rd 60035 224-765-3000
Michael Bregy, supt. Fax 765-3083
www.nssd112.org
Edgewood MS 600/6-8
929 Edgewood Rd 60035 224-765-3200
Matt Eriksen, prin. Fax 765-3208
Elm Place MS 400/6-8
2031 Sheridan Rd 60035 224-765-3300
Heather Schumacher, prin. Fax 765-3308
Northwood JHS 500/6-8
945 North Ave 60035 224-765-3600
Sandra Arreguin, prin. Fax 765-3608

Township HSD 113 3,700/9-12
1040 Park Ave W 60035 224-765-1000
Dr. Christopher Dignam, supt. Fax 765-1060
www.dist113.org
Highland Park HS 2,100/9-12
433 Vine Ave 60035 224-765-2000
Dr. Thomas Koulentes, prin. Fax 765-2700
Other Schools – See Deerfield

Hillsboro, Montgomery, Pop. 6,176
Hillsboro CUSD 3 1,800/PK-12
1311 Vandalia Rd 62049 217-532-2942
David Powell, supt. Fax 532-3137
www.hillsboroschools.net
Hillsboro HS 500/9-12
522 E Tremont St 62049 217-532-2841
Janet Ward, prin. Fax 532-5142
Hillsboro JHS 400/6-8
909 Rountree St 62049 217-532-3742
Mark Fenske, prin. Fax 532-6211

Hillside, Cook, Pop. 8,034
Proviso Township HSD 209
Supt. — See Forest Park
Proviso West HS 2,000/9-12
4701 Harrison St 60162 708-449-6400
Oscar Hawthorne, prin. Fax 449-3636

Hinckley, DeKalb, Pop. 2,046
Hinckley-Big Rock CUSD 429 700/PK-12
700 E Lincoln Ave 60520 815-286-7578
Dr. Travis McGuire, supt. Fax 286-7577
www.hbr429.org
Hinckley-Big Rock HS 200/9-12
700 E Lincoln Ave 60520 815-286-7500
Jay Brickman, prin. Fax 286-7505
Other Schools – See Big Rock

Hines, Cook

Edward Hines Veterans Admin. Hospital Post-Sec.
PO Box 5000 60141 708-216-2153

Hinsdale, DuPage, Pop. 16,548
CCSD 181
Supt. — See Clarendon Hills
Hinsdale MS 800/6-8
100 S Garfield Ave 60521 630-861-4700
Ruben Pena, prin. Fax 655-9754

Hinsdale Township HSD 86 4,500/9-12
5500 S Grant St 60521 630-655-6100
Dr. Bruce Law, supt. Fax 325-9153
d86.hinsdale86.org
Hinsdale Central HS 2,800/9-12
5500 S Grant St 60521 630-570-8000
William Walsh, prin. Fax 887-1362
Other Schools – See Darien

Hinsdale Adventist Academy 300/PK-12
631 E Hickory St 60521 630-323-9211
Janesta Walker, prin. Fax 323-9237

Hoffman Estates, Cook, Pop. 50,808
Schaumburg CCSD 54
Supt. — See Schaumburg
Eisenhower JHS 600/7-8
800 Hassell Rd, 847-357-5500
Steve Kern, prin. Fax 357-5501

Township HSD 211
Supt. — See Palatine
Conant HS 2,400/9-12
700 E Cougar Trl, 847-755-3600
Julie Nowak, prin. Fax 755-3623
Higgins Education Center 50/Alt
1030 W Higgins Rd, 847-755-6840
Amy Friel, admin. Fax 755-6842
Hoffman Estates HS 1,900/9-12
1100 W Higgins Rd, 847-755-5600
Joshua Schumacher, prin. Fax 755-5623

Ambria College of Nursing Post-Sec.
5210 Trillium Blvd 60192 847-397-0300
Montessori Academy of North Hoffman 100/PK-12
1200 Freeman Rd 60192 847-705-1234
Dr. Molood Naghibzadeh, head sch Fax 705-0506
Valeo Academy 100/K-12
2500 Beverly Rd 60192 847-645-9300
Dunia Baca, prin. Fax 645-3986

Homer, Champaign, Pop. 1,182
Heritage CUSD 8 500/K-12
512 W 1st St 61849 217-896-2041
Thomas Davis, supt. Fax 896-2338
www.heritage.k12.il.us
Other Schools – See Broadlands

Homer Glen, Will
Homer CCSD 33C 3,400/PK-8
15733 S Bell Rd, 708-226-7600
Dr. Kara Coglianese, supt. Fax 226-7627
www.homerschools.org
Homer JHS 800/7-8
15711 S Bell Rd, 708-226-7800
Troy Mitchell, prin. Fax 226-7859

Homewood, Cook, Pop. 18,862
Homewood SD 153 1,500/PK-8
18205 Aberdeen St 60430 708-799-5661
Dr. Dale Mitchell, supt. Fax 799-1377
www.hsd153.org
Hart JHS 500/6-8
18220 Morgan St 60430 708-799-5544
Dr. Scott McAllister, prin. Fax 799-8360

Hoopeston, Vermilion, Pop. 5,322
Hoopeston Area CUSD 11 1,300/PK-12
615 E Orange St 60942 217-283-6668
Hank Hornbeck, supt. Fax 283-5431
www.hoopeston.k12.il.us
Hoopeston Area HS 400/9-12
615 E Orange St 60942 217-283-6662
Larry Maynard, prin. Fax 283-5431
Hoopeston Area MS 200/7-8
615 E Orange St 60942 217-283-6664
Anne Burton, prin. Fax 283-5431

Hume, Edgar, Pop. 377
Shiloh CUSD 1 300/PK-12
21751 N 575th St 61932 217-887-2364
Dr. Allen Hall, supt. Fax 887-2448
www.shiloh1.us
Shiloh JSHS 200/6-12
21751 N 575th St 61932 217-887-2364
Elizabeth Harbaugh, prin. Fax 887-2448

Huntley, McHenry, Pop. 23,973
Consolidated SD 158
Supt. — See Algonquin
Huntley HS 2,600/9-12
13719 Harmony Rd 60142 847-659-6600
Scott Rowe, prin. Fax 659-6620

Hutsonville, Crawford, Pop. 551
Hutsonville CUSD 1 400/PK-12
500 W Clover St 62433 618-563-4912
Julie Kraemer, supt. Fax 563-9122
hutsonvilletigers.net
Hutsonville HS 100/9-12
500 W Clover St 62433 618-563-4913
Guy Rumler, prin. Fax 563-9122

Illiopolis, Sangamon, Pop. 880
Sangamon Valley CUSD 9
Supt. — See Niantic
Sangamon Valley MS 200/6-8
341 Matilda St 62539 217-486-2241
Cody Trigg, prin. Fax 486-6038

Ina, Jefferson, Pop. 2,329
Spring Garden Community Cons SD 178
Supt. — See Mount Vernon
Spring Garden MS 100/4-8
PO Box 129 62846 618-437-5361
Tori Hartman, prin. Fax 437-5333

Rend Lake College Post-Sec.
468 N Ken Gray Pkwy 62846 618-437-5321

Ingleside, See Fox Lake
Big Hollow SD 38 1,800/PK-8
26051 W Nippersink Rd 60041 847-740-1490
Robert Gold, supt. Fax 587-2663
www.bighollow.us
Big Hollow MS 800/5-8
26051 W Nippersink Rd 60041 847-740-5322
Scott Whipple, prin. Fax 740-9021

Gavin SD 37 600/PK-8
25775 W IL Route 134 60041 847-546-2916
Dr. John Ahlemeyer, supt. Fax 546-9584
www.gavin37.org
Gavin South MS 300/5-8
25775 W IL Route 134 60041 847-546-9336
Jason Jurgaitis, prin. Fax 546-9338

Island Lake, McHenry, Pop. 7,988
Wauconda CUSD 118
Supt. — See Wauconda
Matthews MS 500/6-8
PO Box 920 60042 847-526-6210
Robert Taterka, prin. Fax 526-8918

Itasca, DuPage, Pop. 8,539
Itasca SD 10 1,000/PK-8
200 N Maple St 60143 630-773-1232
Craig Benes, supt. Fax 773-1342
www.itasca.k12.il.us
Peacock MS 300/6-8
301 E North St 60143 630-773-0335
Heidi Weeks, prin. Fax 285-7460

Environmental Technical Institute Post-Sec.
1101 W Thorndale Ave 60143 630-285-9100

Jacksonville, Morgan, Pop. 19,003
Jacksonville SD 117 3,400/PK-12
516 Jordan St 62650 217-243-9411
Steve Ptacek, supt. Fax 243-6844
www.jsd117.org
Jacksonville HS 1,000/9-12
1211 N Diamond St 62650 217-243-4384
Mike McGiles, prin. Fax 245-0445

Turner JHS 500/7-8
664 Lincoln Ave 62650 217-243-3383
Beth Brockschmidt, prin. Fax 243-3459

Illinois College Post-Sec.
1101 W College Ave 62650 217-245-3000
Illinois School for the Deaf Post-Sec.
125 S Webster Ave 62650 217-479-4200
Illinois School for Visually Impaired Post-Sec.
658 E State St 62650 217-479-4400
MacMurray College Post-Sec.
447 E College Ave 62650 217-479-7000
Mr. John's School of Cosmetology & Nails Post-Sec.
1429 S Main St 62650 217-243-1744
Routt Catholic HS 100/9-12
500 E College Ave 62650 217-243-8563
Nicholas Roscetti, prin. Fax 243-3138

Jerseyville, Jersey, Pop. 8,349
Jersey CUSD 100 2,700/PK-12
100 Lincoln Ave 62052 618-498-5561
Dr. Lori Franke-Hopkins, supt. Fax 498-5265
www.jersey100.org
Jersey Community HS 1,100/8-12
801 N State St 62052 618-498-5521
Cory Breden, prin. Fax 498-5332

Johnsburg, McHenry, Pop. 6,290
Johnsburg CUSD 12 2,000/PK-12
2222 Church St, 815-385-6916
Dr. Dan Johnson, supt. Fax 385-4715
www.johnsburg12.org
Johnsburg HS 700/9-12
2002 W Ringwood Rd, 815-385-9233
Kevin Shelton, prin. Fax 344-0451
Johnsburg JHS 500/6-8
2220 Church St, 815-385-6210
Nancy Hurckes, prin. Fax 344-7106

Johnston City, Williamson, Pop. 3,492
Johnston City CUSD 1 900/PK-12
PO Box 147 62951 618-983-8021
Kathy Clark, supt. Fax 983-6034
www.jcindians.org
Johnston City HS 300/9-12
1500 Jefferson Ave 62951 618-983-4700
Joey Ohnesorge, prin. Fax 983-6812
Washington MS 300/5-8
100 E 12th St 62951 618-983-7581
Patty Hilliard, prin. Fax 983-6409

Joliet, Will, Pop. 145,165
Joliet SD 86 11,900/PK-8
420 N Raynor Ave 60435 815-740-3196
Theresa Rouse Ed.D., supt. Fax 740-6520
www.joliet86.org
Dirksen JHS 700/6-8
203 S Midland Ave 60436 815-729-1566
Rolland Jasper, prin. Fax 744-2346
Gompers JHS 900/6-8
1501 Copperfield Ave 60432 815-727-5276
Constance Russell, prin. Fax 726-5341
Hufford JHS 1,100/6-8
1125 N Larkin Ave 60435 815-725-3540
Kyle Sartain, prin. Fax 744-5974
Washington JHS & Academy 700/6-8
402 Richards St 60433 815-727-5271
Michael Latting, prin. Fax 740-5451

Joliet Township HSD 204 6,100/9-12
300 Caterpillar Dr 60436 815-727-6970
Dr. Cheryl McCarthy, supt. Fax 727-1277
www.jths.org
Joliet Central HS 3,100/9-12
201 E Jefferson St 60432 815-727-6740
Shad Hallihan, prin. Fax 727-6824
Joliet Township Alternative HS 100/Alt
110 Collins St 60432 815-727-6810
LaTanya Harris, prin.
Joliet West HS 3,000/9-12
401 N Larkin Ave 60435 815-727-6940
Teresa Gibson, prin. Fax 744-3070

Plainfield CCSD 202
Supt. — See Plainfield
Aux Sable MS 1,000/6-8
2001 Wildspring Pkwy 60431 815-439-7092
Dr. Edward Boswell, prin. Fax 577-9476

Joliet Catholic Academy 700/9-12
1200 N Larkin Ave 60435 815-741-0500
Jeffrey Budz, prin. Fax 741-9530
Joliet Junior College Post-Sec.
1215 Houbolt Rd 60431 815-729-9020
Professional Choice Hair Design Academy Post-Sec.
2719 W Jefferson St 60435 815-741-8224
University of St. Francis Post-Sec.
500 Wilcox St 60435 800-735-7500

Joppa, Massac, Pop. 354
Joppa-Maple Grove CUSD 38 300/PK-12
PO Box 10 62953 618-543-9023
William Rogers, supt. Fax 543-9264
joppa38.com
Joppa JSHS 100/7-12
PO Box 10 62953 618-543-7589
Landon Sommer, prin. Fax 543-9264

Joy, Mercer, Pop. 416
Mercer County SD 404
Supt. — See Aledo
Mercer County JHS 200/7-8
203 N Washington St 61260 309-584-4174
Robert Reed, prin. Fax 584-4257

Junction, Gallatin, Pop. 129
Gallatin CUSD 7 800/PK-12
5175 Highway 13 62954 618-272-3821
Lucinda Schmitt, supt. Fax 272-4101

Gallatin HS 200/9-12
5175 Highway 13 62954 618-272-5141
Judy Kaegi, prin. Fax 272-4101
Gallatin JHS 200/5-8
5175 Highway 13 62954 618-272-7341
Chris Fromm, prin. Fax 272-4101

Justice, Cook, Pop. 12,733
Indian Springs SD 109 3,000/PK-8
7540 S 86th Ave 60458 708-496-8700
Dr. Jon Nebor, supt. Fax 496-8641
www.isd109.org
Wilkins JHS 600/7-8
8001 S 82nd Ave 60458 708-496-8708
Joseph Porrey, prin. Fax 728-3114

Kankakee, Kankakee, Pop. 26,896
Herscher CUSD 2
Supt. — See Herscher
Limestone MS 600/5-8
963 N 5000W Rd 60901 815-933-2243
Michelle Chavers, prin. Fax 936-4123

Kankakee SD 111 4,800/K-12
240 Warren Ave 60901 815-802-7700
Dr. Genevra A. Walters, supt. Fax 936-8944
www.k111.k12.il.us
Kankakee HS 1,200/9-12
1200 W Jeffery St 60901 815-802-5500
George Harris, prin. Fax 933-9149
Kankakee JHS 700/7-8
2250 E Crestwood St 60901 815-802-5700
Charles Hensley, prin. Fax 935-7272

Bishop McNamara Catholic S 400/7-12
550 W Brookmont Blvd 60901 815-932-7413
Terry Granger, prin. Fax 932-0926
Grace Christian Academy 200/PK-12
2499 Waldron Rd 60901 815-939-4579
Stephen Bull, prin. Fax 939-1334
Kankakee Community College Post-Sec.
100 College Dr 60901 815-802-8100
Kankakee Trinity Academy 200/PK-12
1580 Butterfield Trl 60901 815-935-8080
Brad Prairie, prin. Fax 935-0280

Kansas, Edgar, Pop. 784
Kansas CUSD 3 200/PK-12
PO Box 350 61933 217-948-5174
John Hasten, supt. Fax 948-5577
www.kansas.k12.il.us
Kansas JSHS 100/7-12
PO Box 350 61933 217-948-5175
Michael Lowery, prin. Fax 948-5577

Kempton, Ford, Pop. 229
Tri-Point CUSD 6-J 400/PK-12
PO Box 128 60946 815-253-6299
Jeff Bryan, supt. Fax 253-6298
www.tripointschools.org
Other Schools – See Cullom, Piper City

Kewanee, Henry, Pop. 12,667
Kewanee CUSD 229 1,700/PK-12
1001 N Main St 61443 309-853-3341
Christopher Sullens Ed.D., supt. Fax 852-5504
www.kcud229.org/
Central JHS 400/4-8
215 E Central Blvd 61443 309-853-4290
Jason Anderson, prin. Fax 853-3195
Kewanee HS 500/9-12
1211 E 3rd St 61443 309-853-3328
James Bryan, prin. Fax 854-0210

Wethersfield CUSD 230 600/PK-12
439 Willard St 61443 309-853-4860
Shane Kazubowski, supt. Fax 856-7976
www.geese230.com
Wethersfield JSHS 300/7-12
439 Willard St 61443 309-853-4205
Jeremiah Johnston, prin. Fax 856-7800

Kincaid, Christian, Pop. 1,483
South Fork SD 14 400/PK-12
PO Box 20 62540 217-237-4333
Ron Graham, supt. Fax 237-2245
www.southforkschools.com/
South Fork JSHS 200/6-12
PO Box 20 62540 217-237-4333
Chris Clark, prin. Fax 237-4370

Kinderhook, Pike, Pop. 216
Western CUSD 12
Supt. — See Barry
Western JHS 100/6-8
PO Box 189 62345 217-432-8324
Jerud VanDyke, prin. Fax 432-8003

Kinmundy, Marion, Pop. 794
South Central CUSD 401 700/PK-12
PO Box 189 62854 618-547-3414
Kerry Herdes, supt. Fax 547-7790
southcentralschools.org/
South Central MS 200/6-8
PO Box 40 62854 618-547-7734
Greg Grinestaff, prin. Fax 547-7441
Other Schools – See Farina

Kirkland, DeKalb, Pop. 1,732
Hiawatha CUSD 426 600/PK-12
PO Box 428 60146 815-522-6676
Theodore Hickman, supt. Fax 522-6619
www.hiawatha426.org/
Hiawatha HS 200/9-12
PO Box 428 60146 815-522-3335
Mark Zych, prin. Fax 522-9918

Knoxville, Knox, Pop. 2,888
Knoxville CUSD 202 1,100/PK-12
809 E Main St 61448 309-289-2328
Steve Wilder, supt. Fax 289-9614
www.bluebullets.org

Knoxville HS 300/9-12
600 E Main St 61448 309-289-2324
Chad Bahnks, prin. Fax 289-9466
Knoxville JHS 400/5-8
701 E Mill St 61448 309-289-4126
Daniel Powell, prin. Fax 289-4128

La Grange, Cook, Pop. 15,333
La Grange SD 105 1,400/PK-8
701 7th Ave 60525 708-482-2700
Glenn Schlichting Ph.D., supt. Fax 482-2727
www.d105.net
Gurrie MS 300/7-8
1001 S Spring Ave 60525 708-482-2720
Edmond Hood, prin. Fax 482-2724

Lyons Township HSD 204 3,900/9-12
100 S Brainard Ave 60525 708-579-6451
Dr. Timothy Kilrea, supt. Fax 579-6768
www.lths.net
Lyons Township HS North Campus 1,900/11-12
100 S Brainard Ave 60525 708-579-6300
Dr. Brian Waterman, prin. Fax 579-3187
Other Schools – See Western Springs

Lagrange Hlds, Cook
La Grange Highlands SD 106 700/PK-8
1750 W Plainfield Rd 60525 708-246-3085
Dr. Patricia Viniard, supt. Fax 246-0220
www.district106.net
Highlands MS 300/5-8
1850 W Plainfield Rd 60525 708-579-6890
Michael Papierski, prin. Fax 485-3593

La Grange Park, Cook, Pop. 13,395
La Grange SD 102 3,100/PK-8
333 N Park Rd 60526 708-482-2400
Kyle A. Schumacher Ed.D., supt. Fax 482-2402
www.dist102.k12.il.us
Park JHS 700/7-8
325 N Park Rd 60526 708-482-2500
Philip Abraham, prin. Fax 352-1170

Nazareth Academy 800/9-12
1209 W Ogden Ave 60526 708-354-0061
Deborah Tracy, prin. Fax 354-0109

La Harpe, Hancock, Pop. 1,230
La Harpe Community SD 347 200/PK-8
404 W Main St 61450 217-659-7739
Dr. Ryan Olson, supt. Fax 659-7730
www.laharpeeagles.org
La Harpe JHS 100/6-8
404 W Main St 61450 217-659-3713
Lila McKeown, prin. Fax 659-7730

Lake Bluff, Lake, Pop. 5,647
Lake Bluff ESD 65 800/PK-8
121 E Sheridan Pl 60044 847-234-9400
Dr. Jean Sophie, supt. Fax 234-9403
www.lb65.org
Lake Bluff MS 300/6-8
31 E Sheridan Pl 60044 847-234-9407
Nathan Blackmer, prin. Fax 615-9144

Lake Forest, Lake, Pop. 19,130
Lake Forest Community HSD 115 1,700/9-12
300 S Waukegan Rd 60045 847-235-9657
Michael Simeck, supt. Fax 234-2372
www.lfhs.org/
Lake Forest HS 1,700/9-12
1285 N McKinley Rd 60045 847-582-7315
Dr. Chala Holland, prin. Fax 582-7797

Lake Forest SD 67 1,900/K-8
300 S Waukegan Rd 60045 847-235-9657
Michael Simeck, supt. Fax 234-5132
www.lakeforestschools.org
Deer Path MS - West 500/7-8
155 W Deerpath 60045 847-604-7400
Renee DeVore, prin. Fax 234-2389

Lake Forest Academy 400/9-12
1500 W Kennedy Rd 60045 847-234-3210
Dr. John Strudwick, head sch Fax 615-3202
Lake Forest College Post-Sec.
555 N Sheridan Rd 60045 847-234-3100
Lake Forest Graduate Sch. of Management Post-Sec.
1905 W Field Ct 60045 847-234-5005
School of St. Mary MS 300/4-8
185 E Illinois Rd 60045 847-234-0371
Dr. Venette Biancalana, admin. Fax 234-9593
Woodlands Academy Sacred Heart 200/9-12
760 E Westleigh Rd 60045 847-234-4300
Meg Steele, head sch Fax 234-4348

Lake in the Hills, McHenry, Pop. 28,527
Consolidated SD 158
Supt. — See Algonquin
Marlowe MS 1,400/6-8
9625 Haligus Rd 60156 847-659-4700
Henry Soltesz, prin. Fax 659-4720

Lake Villa, Lake, Pop. 8,603
Community HSD 117 2,700/9-12
1625 Deep Lake Rd Ste A 60046 847-838-7100
Jim McKay, supt. Fax 395-7553
www.chsd117.org
Lakes Community HS 1,400/9-12
1600 Eagle Way 60046 847-838-7100
David Newberry, prin. Fax 395-7553
Other Schools – See Antioch

Lake Villa CCSD 41 2,400/PK-8
131 McKinley Ave 60046 847-356-2385
Dr. Lynette Zimmer, supt. Fax 356-2670
www.district41.org
Palombi MS 700/PK-PK, 7-
133 McKinley Ave 60046 847-356-2118
Victor Wight, prin. Fax 356-0833

Lake Zurich, Lake, Pop. 19,359
Lake Zurich CUSD 95 5,800/PK-12
400 S Old Rand Rd 60047 847-438-2831
Dr. Kaine Osburn, supt. Fax 438-6702
www.lz95.org
Lake Zurich HS 2,000/9-12
300 Church St 60047 847-438-5155
Kent Nightlinger, prin. Fax 438-5989
Lake Zurich MS South Campus 600/6-8
435 W Cuba Rd 60047 847-540-7070
Dave Gardner, prin. Fax 540-9438
Other Schools – See Hawthorn Woods

Quentin Road Christian S 200/PK-12
60 Quentin Rd 60047 847-438-4494
Karen Scudder, admin.

La Moille, Bureau, Pop. 722
La Moille CUSD 303 300/K-12
801 S Main St 61330 815-638-2144
Dr. Ricardo Espinoza, supt. Fax 638-2392
www.lamoilleschools.org
Allen JHS 100/4-8
801 S Main St 61330 815-638-2233
Chawn Huffaker, prin. Fax 638-2886
La Moille HS 100/9-12
801 S Main St 61330 815-638-2144
Brent Ziegler, prin. Fax 638-2392

Lanark, Carroll, Pop. 1,444
Eastland CUSD 308 600/PK-12
500 S School Dr 61046 815-493-6301
Dr. Mark Hansen, supt. Fax 493-6303
www.eastland308.com
Eastland JSHS 300/7-12
500 S School Dr 61046 815-493-6341
Monica Burkholder, prin. Fax 493-6343

Lansing, Cook, Pop. 27,924
Lansing ESD 158 2,400/PK-8
18300 Greenbay Ave 60438 708-474-6700
Cecilia Heiberger Ed.D., supt. Fax 474-9976
www.d158.net
Memorial JHS 900/6-8
2721 Ridge Rd 60438 708-474-2383
Dr. Keli Ross, prin. Fax 474-8463

Sunnybrook SD 171 1,000/PK-8
19266 Burnham Ave 60438 708-895-0750
Dr. Hughes George, supt. Fax 895-8580
www.sd171.org
Heritage MS 500/5-8
19250 Burnham Ave 60438 708-895-0790
Shalonda Randle, prin. Fax 895-8580

Thornton Fractional Township HSD 215
Supt. — See Calumet City
Thornton Fractional South HS 1,800/9-12
18500 Burnham Ave 60438 708-585-2000
Jacob Gourley, prin. Fax 585-2009

American School Post-Sec.
2200 E 170th St 60438 708-418-2800
Illiana Christian HS 600/9-12
2261 Indiana Ave 60438 708-474-0515
Peter Boonstra, prin. Fax 474-0581

La Salle, LaSalle, Pop. 9,462
La Salle ESD 122 1,000/PK-8
1165 Saint Vincents Ave 61301 815-223-0786
Brian DeBernardi, supt. Fax 223-8740
www.lasalleschools.net
Lincoln JHS 300/6-8
1165 Saint Vincents Ave 61301 815-223-0786
Jon Fox, prin. Fax 223-8740

La Salle-Peru Township HSD 120 1,300/9-12
541 Chartres St 61301 815-223-1721
Steven Wrobleski, supt. Fax 223-3444
www.lphs.net
Lasalle-Peru Area Career Center Vo/Tech
541 Chartres St 61301 815-223-2454
Dwayne Mentgen, prin. Fax 224-5066
La Salle-Peru Township HS 1,300/9-12
541 Chartres St 61301 815-223-1721
Deb Nelson, prin. Fax 223-3444

Educators of Beauty Post-Sec.
122 Wright St 61301 815-223-7326
LaSalle-Peru Christian S 100/PK-12
PO Box 1043 61301 815-223-1037
Wesley Waddle, prin.

Lawrenceville, Lawrence, Pop. 4,300
Lawrence County CUSD 20 1,200/PK-12
1802 Cedar St 62439 618-943-2326
Doug Daugherty, supt. Fax 943-4092
www.cusd20.com
Lawrenceville HS 400/9-12
2200 James St 62439 618-943-3389
Paul Higginbotham, prin. Fax 943-4925
Parkview JHS 300/6-8
1802 Cedar St 62439 618-943-2327
Jeremy Brush, prin. Fax 943-4092

Lebanon, Saint Clair, Pop. 4,302
Lebanon CUSD 9 600/PK-12
200 W Schuetz St 62254 618-537-4611
Patrick Keeney, supt. Fax 537-9588
lcusd9.org/
Lebanon HS 300/6-12
200 W Schuetz St 62254 618-537-4423
Leigh Jackson, prin. Fax 537-9588

McKendree University Post-Sec.
701 College Rd 62254 618-537-4481

Leland, LaSalle, Pop. 971
Leland CUSD 1 300/PK-12
370 N Main St 60531 815-495-3821
Jodi Moore, admin. Fax 495-4611
www.leland1.org
Leland HS 100/9-12
370 N Main St 60531 815-495-3231
Jodi Moore, admin. Fax 495-4611

Lemont, DuPage, Pop. 15,866
Lemont Township HSD 210 1,400/9-12
800 Porter St 60439 630-257-5838
Dr. Mary Ticknor, supt. Fax 257-7603
www.lhs210.net
Lemont HS 1,400/9-12
800 Porter St 60439 630-257-5838
Eric Michaelsen, prin. Fax 243-0310

Lemont-Bromberek Combined SD 113A 1,900/K-8
16100 W 127th St 60439 630-257-2286
Dr. Courtney Orzel, supt. Fax 243-3005
www.sd113a.org
Old Quarry MS 800/6-8
16100 W 127th St 60439 630-257-2286
Johnny Billingsley, prin. Fax 243-3004

Lena, Stephenson, Pop. 2,887
Lena Winslow CUSD 202 900/PK-12
401 Fremont St 61048 815-369-3100
Dr. Tom Chiles, supt. Fax 369-3102
www.le-win.net
Lena-Winslow HS 300/9-12
516 Fremont St 61048 815-369-3115
Mark Kuehl, prin. Fax 369-3165
Lena-Winslow JHS 200/6-8
517 Fremont St 61048 815-369-3114
Andrew Lobdell, prin. Fax 369-3162

Le Roy, McLean, Pop. 3,530
Le Roy CUSD 2 800/PK-12
600 E Pine St 61752 309-962-4211
Gary Tipsord, supt. Fax 962-9312
www.leroyk12.org
Le Roy HS 200/9-12
505 E Center St 61752 309-962-2911
Jeff Baughman, prin. Fax 962-8421
Le Roy JHS 100/7-8
505 E Center St 61752 309-962-2911
Jeff Baughman, prin. Fax 962-8421

Lewistown, Fulton, Pop. 2,366
Lewistown SD 97 500/PK-12
15501 E Avenue L 61542 309-547-5826
Jeanne Davis, supt. Fax 547-5235
www.cusd97.fulton.k12.il.us
Lewistown JSHS 200/7-12
15205 N State 100 Hwy 61542 309-547-2288
Clay Ginglen, prin. Fax 547-9870

Lexington, McLean, Pop. 2,036
Lexington CUSD 7 500/PK-12
100 E Wall St 61753 309-365-4141
Dwight Stricklin, supt. Fax 365-7381
www.lexington.k12.il.us
Lexington HS 100/9-12
100 E Wall St 61753 309-365-2711
Dwight Stricklin, prin. Fax 365-5032
Lexington JHS 100/6-8
100 E Wall St 61753 309-365-2711
Paul Deters, prin. Fax 365-5032

Liberty, Adams, Pop. 512
Liberty CUSD 2 700/PK-12
505 N Park St 62347 217-645-3433
Kelle Bunch, supt. Fax 645-3241
www.libertyschool.net
Liberty HS 300/7-12
505 N Park St 62347 217-645-3433
Justin Edgar, prin. Fax 645-3389

Libertyville, Lake, Pop. 20,013
Community HSD 128
Supt. — See Vernon Hills
Libertyville HS 2,000/9-12
708 W Park Ave 60048 847-327-7000
Dr. Marina Scott, prin. Fax 367-2573

Libertyville SD 70 2,500/PK-8
1381 Lake St 60048 847-362-9695
Dr. Guy Schumacher, supt. Fax 362-3003
www.d70schools.org
Highland MS 1,000/6-8
310 W Rockland Rd 60048 847-362-9020
Jon Hallmark, prin. Fax 362-0870

Lincoln, Logan, Pop. 14,271
Lincoln Community HSD 404 800/9-12
1000 Railer Way 62656 217-732-4131
Robert Bagby, supt. Fax 735-3963
www.lchsrailers.org
Lincoln Community HS 800/9-12
1000 Railer Way 62656 217-732-4131
Todd Poelker, prin. Fax 735-3963

Lincoln ESD 27 1,200/PK-8
304 8th St 62656 217-732-2522
Kent Froebe, supt. Fax 732-2198
lincoln27.homestead.com/
Lincoln JHS 400/6-8
208 Broadway St 62656 217-732-3535
Michael Workman, prin. Fax 732-2685

Lincolnland Technical Education Center
1000 Primm Rd 62656 217-732-4131
Robert Bagby, dir. Fax 735-3963
Lincolnland Technical Education Center Vo/Tech
1000 Primm Rd 62656 217-732-4131
Robert Bagby, dir. Fax 735-3963

Lincoln Christian University Post-Sec.
100 Campus View Dr 62656 217-732-3168
Lincoln College Post-Sec.
300 Keokuk St 62656 217-732-3155

Lincolnshire, Lake, Pop. 7,186
Adlai E. Stevenson HSD 125 3,800/9-12
2 Stevenson Dr 60069 847-415-4000
Dr. Eric Twadell, supt. Fax 634-0239
www.d125.org/
Stevenson HS 3,800/9-12
1 Stevenson Dr 60069 847-415-4106
Troy Gobble, prin. Fax 634-7309

Lincolnshire-Prairieview SD 103 1,700/PK-8
1370 N Riverwoods Rd 60069 847-295-4030
Dr. Scott Warren, supt. Fax 295-9196
www.d103.org
Wright JHS 800/5-8
1370 N Riverwoods Rd 60069 847-295-1560
Michelle Blackley, prin. Fax 295-7136

Lincolnwood, Cook, Pop. 12,270
Lincolnwood SD 74 1,200/PK-8
6950 N East Prairie Rd 60712 847-675-8234
Dr. Joseph F. Bailey, supt. Fax 675-4207
www.sd74.org
Lincoln Hall MS 400/6-8
6855 N Crawford Ave 60712 847-675-8240
Dr. Jean Weiss, prin. Fax 675-8124

Lindenhurst, Lake, Pop. 14,182
Millburn CCSD 24
Supt. — See Wadsworth
Millburn MS 600/6-8
640 Freedom Way 60046 847-245-1600
Jake Jorgenson, prin. Fax 265-8198

Lisle, DuPage, Pop. 21,980
Lisle CUSD 202 1,500/PK-12
5211 Center Ave 60532 630-493-8000
Keith Filipiak, supt. Fax 971-4054
www.lisle.dupage.k12.il.us/
Lisle HS 500/9-12
1800 Short St 60532 630-493-8300
Jeffery Howard, prin. Fax 968-0182
Lisle JHS 400/6-8
5207 Center Ave 60532 630-493-8200
David Kearney, prin. Fax 493-8209

Naperville CUSD 203
Supt. — See Naperville
Kennedy JHS 1,000/6-8
2929 Green Trails Dr 60532 630-420-3220
Brian Valek, prin. Fax 420-6960

Benedictine University Post-Sec.
5700 College Rd 60532 630-829-6000
Benet Academy 1,400/9-12
2200 Maple Ave 60532 630-719-2782
Stephen Marth, prin. Fax 719-2849
Universal Technical Institute Post-Sec.
2611 Corporate West Dr 60532 630-529-2662

Litchfield, Montgomery, Pop. 6,861
Litchfield CUSD 12 1,500/PK-12
1702 N State St 62056 217-324-2157
Jeffrey Strieker, supt. Fax 324-2158
www.lcusd12.org
Litchfield HS 400/9-12
1705 N State St 62056 217-324-3955
Doug Hoster, prin. Fax 324-5851
Litchfield MS 300/6-8
1701 N State St 62056 217-324-4668
Jennifer Thompson, prin. Fax 324-5693

Tri-County Beauty Academy Post-Sec.
219 N State St 62056 217-324-9062

Lockport, Will, Pop. 24,568
Lockport SD 91 700/PK-8
808 Adams St 60441 815-838-0737
Donna Gray, supt. Fax 834-4339
www.d91.net/
Kelvin Grove MS 400/4-8
808 Adams St 60441 815-838-0737
John Jennings, prin. Fax 834-4339

Lockport Township HSD 205 3,700/9-12
1323 E 7th St 60441 815-588-8100
Dr. Todd Wernet, supt. Fax 588-8109
www.lths.org
Lockport Township HS Central Campus 900/9-9
1222 S Jefferson St 60441 815-588-8200
Kerri Green, prin. Fax 588-8209
Lockport Township HS East Campus 2,800/10-12
1333 E 7th St 60441 815-588-8300
Dennis Hicks, prin. Fax 588-8309

Will County SD 92 1,700/PK-8
708 N State St 60441 815-838-8031
Dr. Peter Sullivan, supt. Fax 838-8034
www.d92.org
Oak Prairie JHS 600/6-8
15161 S Gougar Rd, 815-836-2724
Mark Murray, prin. Fax 834-2178

Lombard, DuPage, Pop. 42,433
Glenbard Township HSD 87
Supt. — See Glen Ellyn
Glenbard East HS 2,400/9-12
1014 S Main St 60148 630-627-9250
Shahe Bagdasarian, prin. Fax 627-9264

Lombard SD 44 3,100/PK-8
150 W Madison St 60148 630-827-4400
Dr. Michael Robey, supt. Fax 620-3798
www.sd44.org
Glenn Westlake MS 1,000/6-8
1514 S Main St 60148 630-827-4500
Philip Wieczorek, prin. Fax 620-3791

College Preparatory S of America 400/PK-12
331 W Madison St 60148 630-889-8000
Dr. Mohammed Taher, prin. Fax 889-8012
Illinois Center for Broadcasting Post-Sec.
455 Eisenhower Ln S Ste 200 60148 630-916-1700
Montini Catholic HS 700/9-12
19W070 16th St 60148 630-627-6930
Maryann O'Neill, prin. Fax 627-0537
National University of Health Sciences Post-Sec.
200 E Roosevelt Rd 60148 630-629-2000
Northern Seminary Post-Sec.
660 E Butterfield Rd 60148 630-620-2180

London Mills, Fulton, Pop. 391
Spoon River Valley CUSD 4 400/PK-12
35265 N IL Route 97 61544 309-778-2204
K. Scot Reynolds, supt. Fax 778-2655
www.spoon-river.k12.il.us
Spoon River Valley HS 100/9-12
35265 N IL Route 97 61544 309-778-2201
Chris Janssen, prin. Fax 778-2655
Spoon River Valley JHS 100/7-8
35265 N IL Route 97 61544 309-778-2201
Chris Janssen, prin. Fax 778-2655

Long Grove, Lake, Pop. 7,912
Kildeer Countryside CCSD 96
Supt. — See Buffalo Grove
Woodlawn MS 600/6-8
6362 Gilmer Rd 60047 847-353-8500
Greg Grana, prin. Fax 949-8237

Louisville, Clay, Pop. 1,135
North Clay CUSD 25 700/PK-12
PO Box C 62858 618-665-3358
Monty Aldrich, supt. Fax 665-3893
members.wabash.net/~northclay/
North Clay Community HS 200/9-12
PO Box 220 62858 618-665-3102
Keith Price, prin. Fax 665-4270

Lovejoy, Saint Clair, Pop. 732
Brooklyn Unit SD 188 100/PK-12
PO Box 250 62059 618-271-1014
Dr. Henrietta Young, supt. Fax 271-9108
www.lovejoy.stclair.k12.il.us
Lovejoy MS 50/6-8
PO Box 250 62059 618-271-1014
Dr. Henrietta Young, prin. Fax 271-9108
Lovejoy Technology Academy 50/9-12
PO Box 250 62059 618-271-1014
Dr. Henrietta Young, prin. Fax 271-9108

Loves Park, Winnebago, Pop. 23,555
Harlem Unit SD 122
Supt. — See Machesney Park
Harlem MS 1,100/7-8
735 Windsor Rd 61111 815-654-4510
Matthew Cascio, prin. Fax 654-4540

Lyons, Cook, Pop. 10,580
Lyons SD 103 2,400/K-8
4100 Joliet Ave 60534 708-783-4100
Dr. Carol Baker, supt. Fax 780-9725
www.sd103.com
Washington MS 800/6-8
8101 Ogden Ave 60534 708-783-4200
Christopher Cybulski, prin. Fax 780-9757

Mc Henry, McHenry, Pop. 26,740
McHenry CCSD 15 4,700/PK-8
1011 N Green St 60050 815-385-7210
R. Alan Hoffman Ed.D., supt. Fax 344-7121
www.d15.org
McHenry MS 800/6-8
2120 W Lincoln Rd 60051 815-385-2522
Mike Glover, prin. Fax 578-2101
Parkland S 800/6-8
1802 N Ringwood Rd 60050 815-385-8810
Mike Adams, prin. Fax 363-5023

McHenry Community HSD 156 2,300/9-12
4716 W Crystal Lake Rd 60050 815-385-7900
Dr. Ryan McTague, supt. Fax 344-7153
www.dist156.org
McHenry HS - East 800/9-12
1012 N Green St 60050 815-385-1145
Eric Blake, prin. Fax 363-8435
McHenry HS - West 1,500/9-12
4724 W Crystal Lake Rd 60050 815-385-7077
Marsha Potthoff, prin. Fax 363-8651

Montini MS 200/4-8
1405 N Richmond Rd 60050 815-385-1022
Michael Shukis, prin. Fax 363-7536

Machesney Park, Winnebago, Pop. 23,071
Harlem Unit SD 122 6,900/PK-12
8605 N 2nd St 61115 815-654-4500
Dr. Julie Morris, supt. Fax 654-4600
www.harlem122.org
Harlem HS 2,200/9-12
1 Huskie Cir 61115 815-654-4511
Terrell Yarbrough, prin. Fax 654-4525
Other Schools – See Loves Park

Mackinaw, Tazewell, Pop. 1,936
Deer Creek-Mackinaw CUSD 701 1,100/PK-12
401 E Fifth St 61755 309-359-8965
Scott Dearman, supt. Fax 359-5291
www.deemack.org/
Deer Creek-Mackinaw HS 300/9-12
401 E Fifth St 61755 309-359-4421
Mary Lanier, prin. Fax 359-3125

Mc Leansboro, Hamilton, Pop. 2,863
Hamilton County CUSD 10 1,200/PK-12
PO Box 369 62859 618-643-2328
Jeff Fetcho, supt. Fax 643-2015
www.unit10.com
Hamilton County JSHS 500/7-12
1 Fox Ln 62859 618-643-2328
Travis McCollum, prin. Fax 643-2307

Mc Nabb, Putnam, Pop. 278
Putnam County CUSD 535
Supt. — See Granville
Putnam County JHS 200/6-8
13183 N 350th Ave 61335 815-882-2800
Michael Olson, prin. Fax 882-2299

Macomb, McDonough, Pop. 18,862
Hanck/Fultn/Schuylr/McDonough ROE 50/
130 S Lafayette St Ste 200 61455 309-837-4821
John Meixner, supt. Fax 837-2887
www.roe26.net
Academy for Secondary Education 50/Alt
341 S Johnson St 61455 309-575-3226
Other Schools – See Canton, Carthage

Macomb CUSD 185 2,000/PK-12
323 W Washington St 61455 309-833-4161
Dr. Patrick Twomey, supt. Fax 836-2133
macomb185.org/
Macomb HS 600/9-12
1525 S Johnson St 61455 309-837-2331
John Rumley, prin. Fax 836-1034
Macomb JHS 300/7-8
1525 S Johnson St 61455 309-833-2074
Dana Isackson, prin. Fax 836-1034

McDonough District Hospital Post-Sec.
525 E Grant St 61455 309-833-4101
Western Illinois University Post-Sec.
1 University Cir 61455 309-298-1414

Macon, Macon, Pop. 1,126
Meridian CUSD 15 800/PK-12
PO Box 347 62544 217-764-5269
Daniel Brue, supt. Fax 764-5291
www.meridianhawks.net
Meridian HS 300/9-12
PO Box 380 62544 217-764-5233
Eric Hurelbrink, prin. Fax 764-5282
Meridian MS 200/6-8
PO Box 198 62544 217-764-3367
Andrew Pygott, prin. Fax 764-3902

Madison, Madison, Pop. 3,816
Madison CUSD 12 400/PK-12
602 Farrish St 62060 618-877-1712
Dr. Warletta Brookins, supt. Fax 877-2690
www.madisoncusd12.org
Madison HS 100/9-12
600 Farrish St 62060 618-876-7010
Juan Gardner, prin. Fax 877-2694
Madison JHS 100/6-8
600 Farrish St 62060 618-876-6409
Juan Gardner, prin. Fax 877-2693
Madison Student Support Center 50/Alt
1003 Farrish St 62060 618-876-6409
Rob Miller, coord. Fax 877-2693

Mahomet, Champaign, Pop. 7,188
Mahomet-Seymour CUSD 3 3,000/PK-12
PO Box 229 61853 217-586-2161
Rick Johnston, supt. Fax 586-7591
www.mscusd.org
Mahomet-Seymour HS 900/9-12
PO Box 1098 61853 217-586-4962
Shannon Cheek, prin. Fax 586-6844
Mahomet-Seymour JHS 700/6-8
PO Box 560 61853 217-586-4415
Heather Landrus, prin. Fax 586-5869

Malta, DeKalb, Pop. 1,142

Kishwaukee College Post-Sec.
21193 Malta Rd 60150 815-825-2086

Manhattan, Will, Pop. 6,984
Manhattan SD 114 1,300/PK-8
25440 S Gougar Rd 60442 815-478-6093
Russell Ragon, supt. Fax 478-7660
www.manhattan114.org
Manhattan JHS 400/6-8
15606 W Smith Rd 60442 815-478-6090
Ron Pacheco, prin. Fax 478-6094

Community Christian S 100/PK-12
22811 S Cedar Rd 60442 815-485-2379
Fax 485-2627

Manito, Mason, Pop. 1,628
Midwest Central CUSD 191 1,000/PK-12
1010 S Washington St 61546 309-968-6868
Todd Hellrigel, supt. Fax 968-7916
www.midwestcentral.org/
Midwest Central HS 300/9-12
910 S Washington St 61546 309-968-6766
Jay Blair, prin. Fax 968-6340
Other Schools – See Green Valley

Manlius, Bureau, Pop. 356
Bureau Valley CUSD 340 1,100/PK-12
PO Box 289 61338 815-445-3101
Dr. Stephen Endress, supt. Fax 445-2802
www.bv340.org
Bureau Valley HS 300/9-12
PO Box 329 61338 815-445-4004
Eric Lawson, prin. Fax 445-3017
Other Schools – See Buda

Mansfield, Piatt, Pop. 902
Blue Ridge CUSD 18
Supt. — See Farmer City
Blue Ridge IS & JHS 100/4-8
PO Box 69 61854 217-489-5201
Katie Nichols, prin. Fax 489-9051

Manteno, Kankakee, Pop. 9,119
Manteno CUSD 5 2,200/PK-12
84 N Oak St 60950 815-928-7000
Lisa Harrod, supt. Fax 468-6439
www.manteno5.org/
Manteno HS 700/9-12
443 N Maple St 60950 815-928-7100
Roger Schnitzler, prin. Fax 468-2344

Manteno MS 700/5-8
250 N Poplar St 60950 815-928-7150
David Conrad, prin. Fax 468-8082

Maple Park, Kane, Pop. 1,296
Fox Valley Career Center
47W326 Keslinger Rd 60151 630-365-5113
Dr. Rick Burchell Ed.D., dir. Fax 365-9088
www.kaneland.org/shared/fvcc
Fox Valley Career Center Vo/Tech
47W326 Keslinger Rd 60151 630-365-5113
Dr. Rick Burchell, dir. Fax 365-9088

Kaneland CUSD 302 4,600/PK-12
47W326 Keslinger Rd 60151 630-365-5111
Dr. Todd Leden, supt. Fax 365-9428
www.kaneland.org
Kaneland HS 1,300/9-12
47W326 Keslinger Rd 60151 630-365-5100
Jill Maras, prin. Fax 365-8421
Other Schools – See Sugar Grove

Marengo, McHenry, Pop. 7,571
Marengo Community HSD 154 800/9-12
110 Franks Rd 60152 815-568-6511
David Engelbrecht, supt. Fax 568-6510
www.mchs154.org
Marengo HS 800/9-12
110 Franks Rd 60152 815-568-6511
Dr. Angela Fink, prin. Fax 568-6510

Marengo-Union Consolidated ESD 165 1,100/PK-8
816 E Grant Hwy 60152 815-568-8323
Lea Damisch, supt. Fax 568-8367
www.marengo165.org
Marengo Community MS 300/6-8
816 E Grant Hwy 60152 815-568-5720
Tracy Beam, prin. Fax 568-7572

Marion, Williamson, Pop. 16,859
Crab Orchard CUSD 3 500/PK-12
19189 Bailey St 62959 618-982-2181
Derek Hutchins, supt. Fax 982-2080
www.cocusd3.org/
Crab Orchard HS 100/9-12
19189 Bailey St 62959 618-982-2181
Sy Stone, prin. Fax 982-2080

Marion CUSD 2 4,000/PK-12
1700 W Cherry St 62959 618-993-2321
Dr. Keith Oates, supt. Fax 997-0943
www.marionunit2.org
Marion HS 1,100/9-12
1501 S Carbon St 62959 618-993-8196
Dr. Keith Oates, prin. Fax 997-8749
Marion JHS 800/6-8
1609 W Main St 62959 618-997-1317
Rebecca Moss, prin. Fax 997-0477

Agape Christian HS 100/9-12
5208 Meadowland Pkwy Ste A 62959 618-997-9302
Seth Knox, prin. Fax 997-9304

Marissa, Saint Clair, Pop. 1,970
Marissa CUSD 40 600/PK-12
1 E Marissa St 62257 618-295-2313
Dr. Kevin Cogdill, supt. Fax 295-2609
www.marissa40.org
Marissa JSHS 200/7-12
300 School View Dr 62257 618-295-2393
V. Hughes, prin. Fax 295-2276

Markham, Cook, Pop. 12,287
Prairie-Hills ESD 144 2,600/PK-8
3015 W 163rd St, 708-210-2888
Dr. Kimako Patterson, supt. Fax 210-9925
phsd144.net/
Prairie-Hills JHS 1,000/6-8
3035 W 163rd St, 708-210-2860
Kenndell Smith, prin. Fax 210-9208

Maroa, Macon, Pop. 1,775
Maroa-Forsyth CUSD 2 1,200/PK-12
PO Box 738 61756 217-794-3488
Mike Williams, supt. Fax 794-3878
www.mfschools.org
Maroa-Forsyth HS 300/9-12
PO Box 738 61756 217-794-3463
Scott Adreon, prin. Fax 794-5459
Maroa-Forsyth MS 300/6-8
PO Box 738 61756 217-794-5115
Brice Stewart, prin. Fax 794-3351

Marquette Heights, Tazewell, Pop. 2,798
North Pekin & Marquette Hts SD 102 700/PK-8
51 Yates Rd 61554 309-382-2172
Byron Sondgeroth, supt. Fax 382-2122
www.dist102.org/
Georgetowne MS 200/6-8
51 Yates Rd 61554 309-382-3456
Bob Ketcham, prin. Fax 382-2122

Marshall, Clark, Pop. 3,915
Marshall CUSD 2C 1,300/PK-12
503 Pine St 62441 217-826-5912
Kevin Ross, supt. Fax 826-5170
www.marshall.k12.il.us/
Marshall HS 400/9-12
806 N 6th St 62441 217-826-2395
John Ritchey, prin. Fax 826-5511
Marshall JHS 200/7-8
806 N 6th St 62441 217-826-2812
Tony Graham, prin. Fax 826-6065

Martinsville, Clark, Pop. 1,153
Martinsville CUSD 3C 400/PK-12
PO Box K 62442 217-382-4321
Jill Rogers, supt. Fax 382-4183
www.martinsville.k12.il.us/
Martinsville JSHS 200/7-12
PO Box K 62442 217-382-4132
Jeff Thompson, prin. Fax 382-4761

Mascoutah, Saint Clair, Pop. 7,258
Mascoutah CUSD 19 3,700/PK-12
421 W Harnett St 62258 618-566-7414
Dr. Craig Fiegel, supt. Fax 448-0507
msd19.org
Mascoutah HS 1,000/9-12
1313 W Main St 62258 618-566-8523
Sandra Jouglard, prin. Fax 566-8693
Mascoutah MS 800/6-8
846 N 6th St 62258 618-566-2305
Bob Stone, prin. Fax 566-2307

Mason City, Mason, Pop. 2,332
Illini Central CUSD 189 800/PK-12
208 N West Ave 62664 217-482-5180
Mike Ward, supt. Fax 482-3121
www.illinicentral.org
Illini Central HS 200/9-12
208 N West Ave 62664 217-482-3252
Jennifer Durbin, prin. Fax 482-3323
Illini Central MS 200/6-8
208 N West Ave 62664 217-482-3252
Jennifer Durbin, prin. Fax 482-3323

Matteson, Cook, Pop. 18,630
ESD 159 1,900/PK-8
6202 Vollmer Rd 60443 708-720-1300
John Sawyer, supt. Fax 720-3218
www.dist159.com
Powell MS 700/6-8
20600 Matteson Ave 60443 708-283-9600
Kimberly Johnson, prin. Fax 283-0718

Matteson ESD 162
Supt. — See Richton Park
Huth MS 600/7-8
3718 213th Pl 60443 708-748-0470
Corey Levy, prin. Fax 503-1119

Rich Township HSD 227 3,500/9-12
20550 S Cicero Ave 60443 708-679-5800
Gregory Wright, supt. Fax 679-5740
www.rich227.org
Other Schools – See Olympia Fields, Park Forest, Richton Park

Mattoon, Coles, Pop. 18,262
Mattoon CUSD 2 3,500/K-12
1701 Charleston Ave 61938 217-238-8850
Larry Lilly, supt. Fax 238-8855
www.mattoon.k12.il.us
Mattoon HS 1,000/9-12
2521 Walnut Ave 61938 217-238-7800
Richard Stuart, prin. Fax 238-7805
Mattoon MS 800/6-8
1200 S 9th St 61938 217-238-5800
Jeremie Smith, prin. Fax 238-5805

Lake Land College Post-Sec.
5001 Lake Land Blvd 61938 217-234-5253

Maywood, Cook, Pop. 23,814
Maywood-Melrose Park-Broadview SD 89
Supt. — See Melrose Park
Irving MS 100/6-8
805 S 17th Ave 60153 708-450-2015
Michelle Hassan, prin. Fax 343-0762

Proviso Township HSD 209
Supt. — See Forest Park
Proviso East HS 1,600/9-12
807 S 1st Ave 60153 708-344-7000
Dr. Patrick Hardy, prin. Fax 344-5942

Mazon, Grundy, Pop. 1,011
Mazon-Verona-Kinsman ESD 2C 300/PK-8
1013 North St 60444 815-448-2200
Nancy Dillow, supt. Fax 448-3005
www.mvkmavericks.org
Mazon-Verona-Kinsman MS 200/5-8
1013 North St 60444 815-448-2127
Debra Paulsen, prin. Fax 448-3005

Melrose Park, Cook, Pop. 25,229
Mannheim SD 83
Supt. — See Franklin Park
Mannheim JHS 900/6-8
2600 Hyde Park Ave 60164 847-455-5020
Timothy Daley, prin. Fax 455-2038

Maywood-Melrose Park-Broadview SD 89 2,900/PK-8
906 Walton St 60160 708-450-2460
Dr. David Negron, supt. Fax 450-2461
www.maywood89.org
Stevenson MS 300/6-8
1630 N 20th Ave 60160 708-450-2053
James Parker, prin. Fax 344-1356
Other Schools – See Maywood

Everest College Post-Sec.
1101 W North Ave Ste 1 60160 708-731-4400
Lincoln College of Technology Post-Sec.
8317 W North Ave 60160 708-344-4700
Walther Christian Academy - Upper S 300/9-12
900 Chicago Ave 60160 708-344-0404
Paul Goffron, hdmstr. Fax 344-0525

Mendon, Adams, Pop. 949
CUSD 4 600/K-12
PO Box 200 62351 217-936-2111
Jane Eichman, supt. Fax 936-2643
www.cusd4.com
Unity HS 200/9-12
PO Box 200 62351 217-936-2116
William Dorethy, prin. Fax 936-2117
Unity MS 200/4-8
PO Box 200 62351 217-936-2727
Seth Klusmeyer, prin. Fax 936-2730

Mendota, LaSalle, Pop. 7,312
Mendota CCSD 289 1,200/PK-8
1806 Guiles Ave 61342 815-539-7631
Kristen School, supt. Fax 538-2927
www.mendota289.org/
Northbrook S 600/PK-PK, 5-
1804 Guiles Ave 61342 815-539-6237
Paula Daley, prin. Fax 538-3090

Mendota Township HSD 280 600/9-12
2300 W Main St 61342 815-539-7446
Jeff Prusator, supt. Fax 539-3103
mendotahs.org/
Mendota Township HS 600/9-12
2300 W Main St 61342 815-539-7446
Denise Aughenbaugh, prin. Fax 539-3103

Meredosia, Morgan, Pop. 1,040
Meredosia-Chambersburg CUSD 11 200/PK-12
PO Box 440 62665 217-584-1744
Thad Walker, supt. Fax 584-1129
www.mcsd11.net
Meredosia-Chambersburg HS 100/9-12
PO Box 440 62665 217-584-1291
Daniel Carie, prin. Fax 584-1129
Meredosia-Chambersburg JHS 50/6-8
PO Box 440 62665 217-584-1291
Daniel Carie, prin. Fax 584-1129

Merrionette Park, Cook, Pop. 1,874

Everest College Post-Sec.
11560 S Kedzie Ave 60803 708-239-0055

Metamora, Woodford, Pop. 3,585
Metamora Township HSD 122 1,000/9-12
PO Box 109 61548 309-367-4151
Randall G. Toepke, supt. Fax 367-4351
mths.metamora.k12.il.us/
Metamora Twp HS 1,000/9-12
PO Box 109 61548 309-367-4151
Randall Toepke, supt. Fax 367-4154

Metropolis, Massac, Pop. 6,368
Massac Unit SD 1 2,200/PK-12
PO Box 530 62960 618-524-9376
Dennis Smith, supt. Fax 524-4432
www.massac.org
Massac County HS 600/9-12
2841 Old Marion Rd 62960 618-524-3440
Jason Hayes, prin. Fax 524-3131
Massac JHS 300/7-8
3028 Old Marion Rd 62960 618-524-2645
Laura Walker, prin. Fax 524-2765

Midlothian, Cook, Pop. 14,581
Bremen Community HSD 228 5,100/9-12
15233 Pulaski Rd 60445 708-389-1175
Bill Kendall, supt. Fax 389-2552
www.bhsd228.com
Bremen HS 1,400/9-12
15203 Pulaski Rd 60445 708-371-3600
David Kibelkis, prin. Fax 371-7194
Other Schools – See Country Club Hills, Oak Forest, Tinley Park

Milford, Iroquois, Pop. 1,300
Milford Area SD 124 700/PK-12
PO Box 304 60953 815-889-5176
Dr. Dale Hastings, supt. Fax 889-5221
www.mpsk12.org
Milford HS 200/9-12
124 E Jones St 60953 815-889-4184
Stephen Totheroh, prin. Fax 889-4871

Millbrook, Kendall, Pop. 329
Newark CCSD 66
Supt. — See Newark
Millbrook JHS 100/5-8
8411 Fox River Dr 60536 630-553-5435
Demetra Turman, prin. Fax 553-1027

Milledgeville, Carroll, Pop. 1,027
Chadwick-Milledgeville CUSD 399
Supt. — See Chadwick
Milledgeville HS 200/9-12
100 E 8th St 61051 815-225-7141
Brian Maloy, prin. Fax 225-7847

Millstadt, Saint Clair, Pop. 3,983
Millstadt CCSD 160 800/PK-8
211 W Mill St 62260 618-476-1803
Jonathan Green, supt. Fax 476-1893
www.mccsd160.com
Millstadt Consolidated S 500/3-8
211 W Mill St 62260 618-476-1681
Sandi Pegg, prin. Fax 476-3401

Minonk, Woodford, Pop. 2,068
Fieldcrest CUSD 6 1,100/PK-12
1 Dornbush Dr 61760 309-432-2177
Dr. Dan Oakley, supt. Fax 432-3377
www.fieldcrest.k12.il.us
Fieldcrest HS 400/9-12
1 Dornbush Dr 61760 309-432-2529
William Lapp, prin. Fax 432-2064

Minooka, Grundy, Pop. 10,784
Minooka CCSD 201 4,100/PK-8
PO Box 467 60447 815-467-6121
Dr. Kris Monn, supt. Fax 467-9544
www.min201.org
Minooka JHS 900/7-8
333 W McEvilly Rd 60447 815-467-2136
Sarah Massey, prin. Fax 467-5087

Minooka Community HSD 111
Supt. — See Channahon
Minooka Community HS 1,100/11-12
301 S Wabena Ave 60447 815-467-2140
Ron Kiesewetter, prin. Fax 467-2431

Mokena, Will, Pop. 18,589
Mokena SD 159 1,700/PK-8
11244 Willow Crest Ln 60448 708-342-4900
Dr. Omar Castillo, supt. Fax 479-3143
www.mokena159.org
Mokena JHS 600/6-8
19815 Kirkstone Way 60448 708-342-4870
Dr. Michael Rolinitis, prin. Fax 479-3122

Rasmussen College Post-Sec.
8650 Spring Lake Dr 60448 815-534-3300

Moline, Rock Island, Pop. 42,701
Moline-Coal Valley CUSD 40 6,900/PK-12
1619 11th Ave 61265 309-743-1600
Lanty McGuire, supt. Fax 757-3476
www.molineschools.org
Deere MS 800/6-8
2035 11th St 61265 309-743-1622
Dr. Dusti Adrian, prin. Fax 757-3668
Moline HS 2,100/9-12
3600 Avenue of the Cities 61265 309-743-1624
Dan McGuire, prin. Fax 757-3667
Moline HS - Coolidge Campus 100/Alt
3432 Avenue of the Cities 61265 309-743-8587
Lyle Goldensoph, prin. Fax 757-3536
Wilson MS 900/6-8
1301 48th St 61265 309-743-1623
Robert Beem, prin. Fax 757-3586

Black Hawk College Post-Sec.
6600 34th Ave 61265 309-796-5000
Midwest Technical Institute Post-Sec.
3620 Avenue of the Cities 61265 800-814-5124
Quad Cities Christian S 100/7-12
4000 11th St 61265 309-762-3800
Mark Sullivan, admin. Fax 762-8150

Momence, Kankakee, Pop. 3,244
Momence CUSD 1 1,100/PK-12
400 N Pine St 60954 815-472-3501
Gary Miller, supt. Fax 472-3516
www.momence.k12.il.us
Momence HS 400/9-12
101 N Franklin St 60954 815-472-6477
Shannon Anderson, prin. Fax 472-2055
Momence JHS 300/PK-PK, 5-
801 W 2nd St 60954 815-472-4184
Jacqanai Gipson, prin. Fax 472-3517

Monee, Will, Pop. 5,063
Crete-Monee CUSD 201U
Supt. — See Crete
Monee Education Center 50/Alt
5154 Main St 60449 708-367-2660
Brian Wortel, coord. Fax 672-2764

Monmouth, Warren, Pop. 9,279
Monmouth-Roseville CUSD 238 1,800/PK-12
105 N E St 61462 309-734-4712
Edward Fletcher, supt. Fax 734-4755
www.mr238.org
Monmouth-Roseville HS 500/9-12
325 W 1st Ave 61462 309-734-5118
Jay Melton, prin. Fax 734-2918
Other Schools – See Roseville

United CUSD 304 900/PK-12
1905 100th St 61462 309-734-9413
Jeffrey Whitsitt, supt. Fax 734-0223
united.k12.il.us
United HS 300/9-12
1905 100th St 61462 309-734-9411
Amy Schmitz, prin. Fax 734-6090
United JHS 200/6-8
2140 State Highway 135 61462 309-734-8511
Joseph Nichols, prin. Fax 734-6094

Monmouth College Post-Sec.
700 E Broadway 61462 800-747-2687

Monticello, Piatt, Pop. 5,493
Monticello CUSD 25 1,600/PK-12
2 Sage Dr 61856 217-762-8511
Dr. Victor Zimmerman, supt. Fax 762-8534
www.sages.us
Monticello HS 500/9-12
1 Sage Dr 61856 217-762-8511
Tip Reedy, prin. Fax 762-7421
Monticello MS 400/6-8
2015 E Washington St 61856 217-762-8511
Jeanne Handley, prin. Fax 762-7765

Mooseheart, Kane

Mooseheart S 200/PK-12
255 W James J Davis Dr 60539 630-906-3646

Morris, Grundy, Pop. 13,509
Grundy Area Vocational Center
1002 Union St 60450 815-942-4390
Lance Copes, dir. Fax 942-6650
www.gavc-il.org
Grundy AVC Vo/Tech
1002 Union St 60450 815-942-4390
Lance Copes, dir. Fax 942-6650

Grundy/Kendall ROE 100/
1320 Union St 60450 815-941-3247
Christopher Mehochko, supt. Fax 942-5384
www.roe24.org
Premier Academy 100/Alt
7700 Ashley Rd 60450 815-416-0377
Meghan Martin, prin.

Morris Community HSD 101 900/9-12
1000 Union St 60450 815-942-1294
Dr. Patrick Halloran, supt. Fax 941-5407
www.morrishs.org
Morris Community HS 900/9-12
1000 Union St 60450 815-942-1294
Kelly Hussey, prin. Fax 941-5405

Morris SD 54 1,100/PK-8
725 School St 60450 815-942-0056
Dr. Shannon Dudek, supt. Fax 416-0581
www.morris54.org
Shabbona MS 400/5-8
54 White Oak Dr 60450 815-942-0056
Christopher Maier, prin. Fax 318-6900

Morrison, Whiteside, Pop. 4,151
Morrison CUSD 6 1,100/PK-12
643 Genesee Ave 61270 815-772-2064
Scott Vance, supt. Fax 772-4644
www.morrisonschools.org
Morrison HS 300/9-12
643 Genesee Ave 61270 815-772-4071
Kay Harwood, prin. Fax 772-4644
Morrison JHS 200/6-8
300 Academic Dr 61270 815-772-7264
Joe Robbins, prin. Fax 772-2531

Morrison Institute of Technology Post-Sec.
701 Portland Ave 61270 815-772-7218

Morrisonville, Christian, Pop. 1,053
Morrisonville CUSD 1 300/PK-12
PO Box 13 62546 217-526-4431
Gary DePatis, supt. Fax 526-4433
www.mohawks.net
Morrisonville HS 100/9-12
PO Box 13 62546 217-526-4432
Ann Little, prin. Fax 526-4452
Morrisonville JHS 50/7-8
PO Box 13 62546 217-526-4432
Ann Little, prin. Fax 526-4452

Morton, Tazewell, Pop. 16,106
Morton CUSD 709 2,800/PK-12
1050 S 4th Ave Ste 200 61550 309-263-2581
Dr. Lindsey Hall, supt. Fax 266-6320
www.mcusd709.org
Morton HS 900/9-12
350 N Illinois Ave 61550 309-266-7182
Marjorie Johnson, prin. Fax 263-2168
Morton JHS 400/7-8
225 E Jackson St 61550 309-266-6522
Lee Hoffman, prin. Fax 284-5031

Morton Grove, Cook, Pop. 22,739
Golf ESD 67 600/PK-8
9401 Waukegan Rd 60053 847-966-8200
Dr. Beth Flores, supt. Fax 966-8290
www.golf67.net
Golf MS 300/5-8
9401 Waukegan Rd 60053 847-965-3740
Karen Chvojka, prin. Fax 966-9493

Mounds, Pulaski, Pop. 797
Meridian CUSD 101 600/PK-12
1401 Mounds Rd 62964 618-342-6776
Spencer Byrd, supt. Fax 342-6856
www.meridian101.com
Meridian HS 200/7-12
1401 Mounds Rd 62964 618-342-6778
Tony Rinella, prin. Fax 342-6856

Mount Carmel, Wabash, Pop. 7,195
Wabash CUSD 348 1,500/K-12
218 W 13th St 62863 618-262-4181
Tim Buss, supt. Fax 262-7912
www.wabash348.com
Mount Carmel HS 500/9-12
201 N Pear St 62863 618-262-5104
Pat Cheesman, prin. Fax 262-8781
Mount Carmel MS 300/6-8
1520 Poplar St 62863 618-262-5699
Steven Holt, prin. Fax 263-9096

Wabash Valley College Post-Sec.
2200 College Dr 62863 618-262-8641

Mount Carroll, Carroll, Pop. 1,702
West Carroll CUSD 314 1,100/PK-12
642 S East St 61053 815-734-3374
Adam Brumbaugh, supt. Fax 244-0211
www.wc314.org/
West Carroll MS 300/5-8
633 S East St 61053 815-244-2002
Julie Katzenberger, prin. Fax 244-1051
Other Schools – See Savanna

Mount Morris, Ogle, Pop. 2,953
Oregon CUSD 220
Supt. — See Oregon
Rahn JHS 200/7-8
105 W Brayton Rd 61054 815-734-5300
Kip Crandall, prin. Fax 734-7129

Mount Olive, Macoupin, Pop. 2,093
Mount Olive CUSD 5 500/PK-12
804 W Main St 62069 217-999-7831
Patrick Murphy, supt. Fax 999-2150
www.mtoliveschools.org
Mount Olive HS 200/9-12
804 W Main St 62069 217-999-4231
Jonathan Baumberger, prin. Fax 999-4302

Mount Prospect, Cook, Pop. 53,352
CCSD 59
Supt. — See Arlington Heights
Holmes JHS 500/6-8
1900 W Lonnquist Blvd 60056 847-593-4390
Rob Bowers, prin. Fax 593-7386

Mount Prospect SD 57 2,200/PK-8
701 W Gregory St 60056 847-394-7300
Dr. Elaine Aumiller, supt. Fax 394-7311
www.d57.org
Lincoln MS 700/6-8
700 W Lincoln St 60056 847-394-7350
Paul Suminski, prin. Fax 394-7358

River Trails SD 26 1,300/PK-8
1900 E Kensington Rd 60056 847-297-4120
Dane Delli Ph.D., supt. Fax 297-4124
www.rtsd26.org
River Trails MS 500/6-8
1000 N Wolf Rd 60056 847-298-1750
Keir Rogers, prin. Fax 298-2639

Township HSD 214
Supt. — See Arlington Heights
Prospect HS 2,100/9-12
801 W Kensington Rd 60056 847-718-5200
Michelle Dowling, prin. Fax 718-5216

Christian Life College Post-Sec.
400 E Gregory St 60056 847-259-1840

Mount Pulaski, Logan, Pop. 1,560
Mount Pulaski CUSD 23 500/PK-12
119 N Garden St Ste 2 62548 217-792-7222
Todd Hamm, supt. Fax 792-5551
www.mtpulaski.k12.il.us
Mount Pulaski HS 200/9-12
206 S Spring St 62548 217-792-3209
Terry Morgan, prin. Fax 792-3248

Mount Sterling, Brown, Pop. 2,006
Brown County CUSD 1 800/PK-12
503 NW Cross St 62353 217-773-3359
Vicki Phillips, supt. Fax 773-2121
www.bchornets.com/
Brown County HS 200/9-12
500 E Main St 62353 217-773-3345
Pollee Craven, prin. Fax 773-2128
Brown County MS 200/5-8
504 E Main St 62353 217-773-9152
Karen Jirjis, prin. Fax 773-9121

Mount Vernon, Jefferson, Pop. 14,904
Mount Vernon Area Vocational Center
320 S 7th St 62864 618-246-5602
Robert Knutson, dir. Fax 244-8049
Mount Vernon Area Vocational Center Vo/Tech
320 S 7th St 62864 618-246-5602
Robert Knutson, dir. Fax 244-8049

Mount Vernon CSD 80 1,700/PK-8
2710 North St 62864 618-244-8080
Fax 244-8082
www.mtv80.org
Casey MS 400/6-8
1829 Broadway St 62864 618-244-8060
Mary McGreer, prin. Fax 244-8014

Mount Vernon Township HSD 201 1,200/9-12
11101 N Wells Bypass 62864 618-244-3700
Dr. Michael Smith, supt. Fax 244-3047
www.mvths.org
Mount Vernon HS 1,200/9-12
11101 N Wells Bypass 62864 618-244-3700
Rowdy Fatheree, prin. Fax 244-8047

Spring Garden Community Cons SD 178 100/K-8
14975 E Bakerville Rd 62864 618-244-8070
Stuart Parks, supt. Fax 244-8071
springgarden178.weebly.com
Other Schools – See Ina

DuQuoin Beauty College Post-Sec.
212 S 20th St 62864 618-542-9777

Mount Zion, Macon, Pop. 5,766
Mount Zion CUSD 3 2,400/PK-12
455 Elm St 62549 217-864-2366
Dr. Travis Roundcount, supt. Fax 864-2200
www.mtzion.k12.il.us
Mount Zion HS 700/9-12
305 S Henderson St 62549 217-864-2363
Cheryl Warner, prin. Fax 864-5815
Mount Zion JHS 400/7-8
315 S Henderson St 62549 217-864-2369
Julie Marquardt, prin. Fax 864-6829

Moweaqua, Shelby, Pop. 1,822
Central A & M CUSD 21
Supt. — See Assumption
Central A & M HS 300/9-12
229 E Pine St 62550 217-768-3866
Charles Brown, prin. Fax 768-3797

Mulberry Grove, Bond, Pop. 626
Mulberry Grove CUSD 1 300/PK-12
801 W Wall St 62262 618-326-8812
Brad Turner, supt. Fax 326-8482
www.mgschools.com
Mulberry Grove JSHS 100/6-12
801 W Wall St 62262 618-326-8221
Brad Turner, prin. Fax 326-8482

Mundelein, Lake, Pop. 30,630
Diamond Lake SD 76 1,100/PK-8
500 Acorn Ln 60060 847-566-9221
Dr. Bhavna Sharma-Lewis, supt. Fax 566-5689
www.d76.lake.k12.il.us/
West Oak MS 400/5-8
500 Acorn Ln 60060 847-566-9220
Christopher Willeford, prin. Fax 970-3534

Fremont SD 79 2,200/PK-8
28855 N Fremont Center Rd 60060 847-566-0169
Dr. Jill Gildea, supt. Fax 566-7280
www.fsd79.org
Fremont MS 700/6-8
28871 N Fremont Center Rd 60060 847-566-9384
Pam Motsenbocker, prin. Fax 566-7805

Mundelein Consolidated HSD 120 2,100/9-12
1350 W Hawley St 60060 847-949-2200
Dr. Kevin Myers Ph.D., supt. Fax 949-4756
www.d120.org/
Mundelein Consolidated HS 2,100/9-12
1350 W Hawley St 60060 847-949-2200
Dr. Kevin Myers, supt. Fax 949-0599

Mundelein ESD 75 2,000/PK-8
470 N Lake St 60060 847-949-2700
Dr. Andy Henrikson, supt. Fax 949-2727
www.district75.org
Sandburg MS 600/PK-PK, 6-
855 W Hawley St 60060 847-949-2707
Mark Pilut, prin. Fax 949-2716

Carmel HS 1,400/9-12
1 Carmel Pkwy 60060 847-566-3000
Mark Ostap, prin. Fax 566-8465
University of St. Mary of the Lake Post-Sec.
1000 E Maple Ave 60060 847-566-6401

Murphysboro, Jackson, Pop. 7,754
Alxndr/Jcksn/Pulsk/Prry/Union ROE 50/
1001 Walnut St 62966 618-687-7290
Donna Boros, supt. Fax 687-7296
www.roe30.org
Cope Alternative S 50/Alt
1725B Shomaker Dr 62966 618-684-2913
David Brauer, prin.

Murphysboro CUSD 186 1,500/K-12
593 Ava Rd 62966 618-684-3781
Christopher Grode, supt. Fax 684-2465
www.cusd186.org
Murphysboro HS 600/9-12
50 Blackwood Dr 62966 618-687-2336
Tony Wilson, prin. Fax 687-3532
Murphysboro MS 500/6-8
2125 Spruce St 62966 618-684-3041
Jeff Keener, prin. Fax 687-1042

Naperville, DuPage, Pop. 138,897
Indian Prairie CUSD 204
Supt. — See Aurora
Crone MS 1,200/6-8
4020 111th St 60564 630-428-5600
Melissa Couch, prin. Fax 428-5601
Gregory MS 900/6-8
2621 Springdale Cir 60564 630-428-6300
Stephen Severson, prin. Fax 428-6301
Hill MS 800/6-8
1836 Brookdale Rd 60563 630-428-6200
Michael Dutdut, prin. Fax 428-6201
Neuqua Valley HS 3,800/9-12
2360 95th St 60564 630-428-6000
Dr. Robert McBride, prin. Fax 428-6026
Scullen MS 1,100/6-8
2815 Mistflower Ln 60564 630-428-7000
James Seput, prin. Fax 428-7001

Naperville CUSD 203 17,100/PK-12
203 W Hillside Rd 60540 630-420-6300
Dan Bridges, supt. Fax 420-1066
www.naperville203.org
Jefferson JHS 900/6-8
1525 N Loomis St 60563 630-420-6307
Megan Ptak, prin. Fax 420-6930
Lincoln JHS 900/6-8
1320 Olympus Dr 60565 630-420-6370
Patrick Gaskin, prin. Fax 637-4582
Madison JHS 700/6-8
1000 River Oak Dr 60565 630-420-4257
Erin Anderson, prin. Fax 420-6402
Naperville Central HS 2,900/9-12
440 Aurora Ave 60540 630-420-6420
William Wiesbrook, prin. Fax 369-6247
Naperville North HS 3,000/9-12
899 N Mill St 60563 630-420-6484
Stefanie Posey, prin. Fax 420-4255
Washington JHS 600/5-8
201 N Washington St 60540 630-420-6390
Jon Vogel, prin. Fax 420-6474
Other Schools – See Lisle

Covenant Classical S 100/K-11
1852 95th St 60564 630-983-7500
Sharon Weldy, prin.
DeVry University Post-Sec.
2056 Westings Ave Ste 40 60563 630-428-9086
Naperville Christian Academy 50/PK-12
1451 Raymond Dr Ste 200 60563 630-637-9622
Rebecca Ruff, dir. Fax 355-1828
North Central College Post-Sec.
30 N Brainard St 60540 630-637-5100

Nashville, Washington, Pop. 3,221
Nashville Community HSD 99 400/9-12
1300 S Mill St 62263 618-327-8286
Ernie Fowler, supt. Fax 327-4512
www.county.washington.k12.il.us
Nashville Community HS 400/9-12
1300 S Mill St 62263 618-327-8286
Brian Pasero, prin. Fax 327-4512

Neoga, Cumberland, Pop. 1,622
Neoga CUSD 3 500/PK-12
PO Box 280 62447 217-895-2201
Dr. Elizabeth Pressler, supt. Fax 895-3476
www.neoga.k12.il.us
Neoga JSHS 200/6-12
PO Box 280 62447 217-895-2205
Carol Smith, prin. Fax 895-3957

Newark, Kendall, Pop. 984
Newark CCSD 66 200/K-8
503 Chicago Rd 60541 815-695-5143
Dr. Diane Cepela, supt. Fax 695-5776
www.newarkdistrict66.org
Other Schools – See Millbrook

Newark Community HSD 18 200/9-12
413 Chicago Rd 60541 815-695-5164
Amy Smith, supt. Fax 695-5752
www.newarkhs.k12.il.us
Newark Community HS 200/9-12
413 Chicago Rd 60541 815-695-5164
Jim Still, prin. Fax 695-5752

New Athens, Saint Clair, Pop. 2,032
New Athens CUSD 60 500/PK-12
501 Hanft St 62264 618-475-2174
Brian Karraker, supt. Fax 475-2176
www.na60.org
New Athens HS 200/9-12
501 Hanft St 62264 618-475-2173
Dan Lehman, prin. Fax 475-2176
New Athens JHS 100/6-8
501 Hanft St 62264 618-475-2172
Jim Marlow, prin. Fax 475-2176

New Berlin, Sangamon, Pop. 1,336
New Berlin CUSD 16 900/PK-12
600 N Cedar St 62670 217-488-2040
Adam Ehrman, supt. Fax 488-2043
www.pretzelpride.com
New Berlin HS 200/9-12
PO Box 230 62670 217-488-6012
Hattie Doyle, prin. Fax 488-3207
New Berlin JHS 200/6-8
PO Box 230 62670 217-488-6011
Megan Doerfler, prin. Fax 488-3207

New Lenox, Will, Pop. 24,189
Lincoln-Way Community HSD 210 5,300/9-12
1801 E Lincoln Hwy 60451 815-462-2100
Dr. R. Scott Tingley, supt. Fax 462-2519
www.lw210.org
Lincoln-Way Central HS 1,900/9-12
1801 E Lincoln Hwy 60451 815-462-2100
Dr. Steven Provis, prin. Fax 485-7648
Lincoln Way West HS 1,300/9-12
21701 Gougar Rd 60451 815-717-3500
Dr. Monica Schmitt, prin. Fax 717-3509
Other Schools – See Frankfort

New Lenox SD 122 5,400/K-8
102 S Cedar Rd 60451 815-485-2169
Dr. Margaret Manville, supt. Fax 485-2236
www.nlsd122.org
Liberty JHS 700/7-8
151 Lenox St 60451 815-462-7951
Shane Street, prin. Fax 462-0672
Martino JHS 600/7-8
731 E Joliet Hwy 60451 815-485-7593
Dr. Bonnie Groen, prin. Fax 485-9578

Providence Catholic HS 1,200/9-12
1800 W Lincoln Hwy 60451 815-717-3179
Dr. John Harper, prin. Fax 485-2709

Newton, Jasper, Pop. 2,823
Jasper County CUSD 1 1,400/PK-12
609 S Lafayette St 62448 618-783-8459
Andrew D. Johnson, supt. Fax 783-3679
www.cusd1.jasper.k12.il.us
Jasper County JHS 200/7-8
1104 W Jourdan St 62448 618-783-4202
Travis Wyatt, prin. Fax 783-4257
Newton Community HS 500/9-12
201 West End Ave 62448 618-783-2303
Beth Probst, prin. Fax 783-3783

Niantic, Macon, Pop. 703
Sangamon Valley CUSD 9 700/PK-12
PO Box 200 62551 217-668-2338
Robert Meadows, supt. Fax 668-2406
www.sangamonvalley.org
Sangamon Valley HS 200/9-12
PO Box 200 62551 217-668-2392
Jonathon Field, prin. Fax 668-2221
Other Schools – See Illiopolis

Niles, Cook, Pop. 29,272
East Maine SD 63
Supt. — See Des Plaines
Gemini JHS 800/7-8
8955 N Greenwood Ave 60714 847-827-1181
Dr. Rene Carranza, prin. Fax 827-3499

Park Ridge-Niles CCSD 64
Supt. — See Park Ridge
Emerson MS 800/6-8
8101 N Cumberland Ave 60714 847-318-8110
Dr. Jim Morrison, prin. Fax 318-8701

Logos Christian Academy 200/PK-12
7280 N Caldwell Ave 60714 847-647-9456
Larry Murg, prin. Fax 647-7916
Niles School of Cosmetology Post-Sec.
8057 N Milwaukee Ave 60714 847-965-8061
Northridge Preparatory S 300/6-12
8320 W Ballard Rd 60714 847-375-0600
John Kestler, prin. Fax 375-0606
Notre Dame College Prep S 800/9-12
7655 W Dempster St 60714 847-965-2900
Daniel Tully, pres. Fax 965-2975

Nokomis, Montgomery, Pop. 2,240
Nokomis CUSD 22 700/PK-12
511 Oberle St 62075 217-563-7311
Dr. Scott Doerr, supt. Fax 563-2549
www.nokomis.k12.il.us
Nokomis JSHS 300/6-12
511 Oberle St 62075 217-563-2014
Rachelle McDowell, prin. Fax 563-2671

Normal, McLean, Pop. 51,379
ISU Lab SD 1,000/PK-12
ISU Campus Box 5300 61790 309-438-8542
Dr. Jeffrey Hill, supt. Fax 438-3813
www.uhigh.ilstu.edu/labschool/unitwide.html
University HS 600/9-12
ISU Campus Box 7100 61790 309-438-8542
Dr. Jeffrey Hill, prin. Fax 438-5198

McLean County Unit SD 5 13,500/PK-12
1809 Hovey Ave 61761 309-557-4000
Dr. Mark Daniel, supt. Fax 557-4501
www.unit5.org
Chiddix JHS 700/6-8
300 S Walnut St 61761 309-557-4405
Jim Allen, prin. Fax 557-4506
Field Vocational Training Center Vo/Tech
412 E Cypress St 61761 309-557-4440
Jane Collins, coord. Fax 557-4534
Kingsley JHS 900/6-8
303 Kingsley St 61761 309-557-4407
Shelly Erickson, prin. Fax 557-4508
Normal Community HS 1,900/9-12
3900 E Raab Rd 61761 309-557-4401
David Bollmann, prin. Fax 557-4502
Normal Community West HS 1,600/9-12
501 N Parkside Rd 61761 309-557-4402
David Johnson, prin. Fax 557-4503
Parkside JHS 700/6-8
101 N Parkside Rd 61761 309-557-4408
Dan Lamboley, prin. Fax 557-4509
Other Schools – See Bloomington

Calvary Christian Academy 300/PK-12
1017 N School St 61761 309-452-7912
Mike Sturgill, head sch Fax 451-0033
Heartland Community College Post-Sec.
1500 W Raab Rd 61761 309-268-8000
Illinois State University Post-Sec.
Campus Box 4000 61790 309-438-2111

Norridge, Cook, Pop. 14,463
Ridgewood Community HSD 234 800/9-12
7500 W Montrose Ave 60706 708-456-4242
Dr. Jennifer Kelsall, supt. Fax 456-8238
www.ridgenet.org
Ridgewood Community HS 800/9-12
7500 W Montrose Ave 60706 708-456-4242
Christopher Uhle, prin. Fax 456-8238

Norris City, White, Pop. 1,272
Edwds/Gtn/Hdn/Pope/Sln/Wbsh/Wyn/Wt ROE
Supt. — See Harrisburg
Learning Alternative Branch S Alt
308 Powell St 62869 618-387-0107
Jim Taylor, prin. Fax 387-0109

Norris City-Omaha-Enfield CUSD 3 800/PK-12
PO Box 399 62869 618-378-3222
Matthew Vollman, supt. Fax 378-3286
www.ncoecusd.white.k12.il.us
Norris City-Omaha-Enfield HS 200/9-12
PO Box 399 62869 618-378-3312
Todd Haley, prin. Fax 378-3364

North Aurora, Kane, Pop. 16,455
Aurora West Unit SD 129
Supt. — See Aurora
Jewel MS 700/6-8
1501 Waterford Rd 60542 630-301-5010
Dr. Greg Scalia, prin. Fax 907-3161

Everest College Post-Sec.
150 S Lincolnway Ste 100 60542 630-896-2140

Northbrook, Cook, Pop. 32,798
Northbrook ESD 27 1,200/PK-8
1250 Sanders Rd 60062 847-498-2610
Dr. David Kroeze, supt. Fax 498-5916
www.nb27.org
Wood Oaks JHS 400/6-8
1250 Sanders Rd 60062 847-272-1900
Robert McElligott, prin. Fax 480-4834

Northbrook SD 28 1,600/PK-8
1475 Maple Ave 60062 847-498-7900
Dr. Larry Hewitt, supt. Fax 498-7970
www.northbrook28.net
Northbrook JHS 600/6-8
1475 Maple Ave 60062 847-498-7920
Scott Meek, prin. Fax 656-1712

Northbrook/Glenview SD 30 1,100/K-8
2374 Shermer Rd 60062 847-498-4190
Dr. Brian Wegley, supt. Fax 498-8981
www.district30.org
Maple S 400/6-8
2370 Shermer Rd 60062 847-400-8900
Dr. Nathan Carter, prin. Fax 272-0979

Northfield Township HSD 225
Supt. — See Glenview
Glenbrook North HS 2,100/9-12
2300 Shermer Rd 60062 847-509-2400
Dr. John Finan, prin. Fax 509-2411

West Northfield SD 31 900/K-8
3131 Techny Rd 60062 847-272-6880
Dr. Alexandra Nicholson, supt. Fax 272-4818
www.district31.net/
Field MS 300/6-8
2055 Landwehr Rd 60062 847-272-6884
Erin Murphy, prin. Fax 272-1050

North Chicago, Lake, Pop. 31,474
North Chicago SD 187 2,500/PK-12
2000 Lewis Ave 60064 847-689-8150
Dr. Ben Martindale, supt. Fax 689-6328
d187.org
Neal Math Science Academy 600/6-8
1905 Argonne Dr 60064 847-689-6313
Victorene King, prin. Fax 689-6332

North Chicago Community HS 800/9-12
1717 17th St 60064 847-578-7400
Venessa Simmons-Woods, prin. Fax 689-7473

R. Franklin University of Medicine Post-Sec.
3333 Green Bay Rd 60064 847-578-3000

Northfield, Cook, Pop. 5,375
New Trier Township HSD 203 4,200/9-12
7 Happ Rd 60093 847-446-7000
Dr. Linda Yonke, supt. Fax 446-0874
www.newtrier.k12.il.us
New Trier Township HS -Northfield Campus 1,000/9-9
7 Happ Rd 60093 847-446-7000
Paul Waechtler, prin. Fax 784-7500
Other Schools – See Winnetka

Sunset Ridge SD 29 500/K-8
525 Sunset Ridge Rd 60093 847-881-9456
Dr. Edward Stange, supt.
www.sunsetridge29.net
Sunset Ridge MS 300/4-8
525 Sunset Ridge Rd 60093 847-881-9400
Dr. Ivy Sukenik, prin.

Christian Heritage Academy 500/PK-12
315 Waukegan Rd 60093 847-446-5252
Dr. David Roth, admin. Fax 446-5267

Northlake, Cook, Pop. 12,227
Berkeley SD 87
Supt. — See Berkeley
Northlake MS 400/6-8
202 S Lakewood Ave 60164 708-449-3195
Dr. Sunil Mody, prin. Fax 547-2548

Leyden Community HSD 212
Supt. — See Franklin Park
West Leyden HS 1,700/9-12
1000 N Wolf Rd 60164 847-451-3154
Dr. Tatiana Bonuma, prin. Fax 451-3180

Oak Brook, DuPage, Pop. 7,720
Butler SD 53 500/PK-8
2801 York Rd 60523 630-573-2887
Dr. Heidi Wennstrom, supt. Fax 573-5374
www.butler53.com
Butler JHS 200/6-8
2801 York Rd 60523 630-573-2760
Amy Read, prin. Fax 573-1725

Hair Professionals Acad of Cosmetology Post-Sec.
1200 Harger Rd Ste 100 60523 630-653-6630
PCCTI Healthcare Post-Sec.
2625 Butterfield Rd #102E 60523 630-705-9999

Oakbrook Terrace, DuPage, Pop. 2,106

John Hancock University Post-Sec.
1 Mid America Plz Ste 130 60181 877-355-4762

Oak Forest, Cook, Pop. 27,551
Arbor Park SD 145 1,500/PK-8
17301 Central Ave 60452 708-687-8040
Dr. Andrea Sala, supt. Fax 687-9498
www.arbor145.org
Arbor Park MS 600/5-8
17303 Central Ave 60452 708-687-5330
Ronald Murabito, prin. Fax 535-4527

Bremen Community HSD 228
Supt. — See Midlothian
Oak Forest HS 1,400/9-12
15201 Central Ave 60452 708-687-0500
Dr. Brad Sikora, prin. Fax 687-0594

Forest Ridge SD 142 1,600/PK-8
15000 Laramie Ave 60452 708-687-3334
Dr. Paul McDermott, supt. Fax 687-2970
www.d142.org
Hille MS 500/6-8
5800 151st St 60452 708-687-5550
John Orth, prin. Fax 687-8569

Capri Beauty College Post-Sec.
15815 Rob Roy Dr 60452 708-687-3020
John Amico's School of Hair Design Post-Sec.
15301 Cicero Ave 60452 708-687-7800

Oakland, Coles, Pop. 873
Oakland CUSD 5 300/PK-12
310 Teeter St 61943 217-346-2555
Lance Landeck, supt. Fax 346-2267
www.oak.k12.il.us
Oakland HS 100/9-12
310 Teeter St 61943 217-346-2118
Adam Clapp, prin. Fax 346-2267

Oak Lawn, Cook, Pop. 55,942
Community HSD 218 5,500/9-12
10701 Kilpatrick Ave 60453 708-424-2000
Dr. Ty Harting, supt. Fax 424-6389
www.chsd218.org
Richards HS 1,700/9-12
10601 Central Ave 60453 708-499-2550
Mike Jacobson, prin. Fax 499-6941
Other Schools – See Blue Island, Palos Heights, Robbins

Oak Lawn Community HSD 229 1,800/9-12
9400 Southwest Hwy 60453 708-424-5200
Dr. Michael Riordan, supt. Fax 424-5297
www.olchs.org
Oak Lawn Community HS 1,800/9-12
9400 Southwest Hwy 60453 708-424-5200
Dr. Jeana Lietz, prin. Fax 424-5263

Oak Lawn-Hometown SD 123 3,000/PK-8
4201 W 93rd St 60453 708-423-0150
Dr. Paul Enderle, supt. Fax 423-0160
www.d123.org/
Oak Lawn-Hometown MS 1,000/6-8
5345 W 99th St 60453 708-499-6400
Kristin Simpkins, prin. Fax 499-7684

Ridgeland SD 122 2,400/PK-8
6500 W 95th St 60453 708-599-5550
Julie Shellberg, supt. Fax 599-5626
www.ridgeland122.com
Simmons MS 700/6-8
6450 W 95th St 60453 708-599-8540
Tracy Flood, prin. Fax 599-8015

Cameo Beauty Academy Post-Sec.
9714 S Cicero Ave 60453 708-636-4660
South Side Baptist S 100/PK-12
5220 W 105th St 60453 708-425-3435
Robert Burckart, prin. Fax 425-9016

Oak Park, Cook, Pop. 50,159
Oak Park ESD 97 5,800/PK-8
260 Madison St 60302 708-524-3000
Dr. Carol Kelley, supt. Fax 524-3019
www.op97.org
Brooks MS 900/6-8
325 S Kenilworth Ave 60302 708-524-3050
LeeAndra Khan, prin. Fax 524-3036
Julian MS 900/6-8
416 S Ridgeland Ave 60302 708-524-3040
Dr. Todd Fitzgerald, prin. Fax 524-3035

Oak Park-River Forest SD 200 3,200/9-12
201 N Scoville Ave 60302 708-383-0700
Dr. Joylynn Pruitt, supt. Fax 434-3917
www.oprfhs.org
Oak Park-River Forest HS 3,200/9-12
201 N Scoville Ave 60302 708-383-0700
Nathaniel Rouse, prin. Fax 434-3917

Fenwick HS 1,200/9-12
505 Washington Blvd 60302 708-386-0127
Peter Groom, prin. Fax 386-3052

Oakwood, Vermilion, Pop. 1,576
Oakwood CUSD 76 1,000/PK-12
12190 US Route 150 61858 217-446-6081
Gary Lewis, supt. Fax 446-6218
www.oakwood.k12.il.us
Other Schools – See Danville, Fithian

Oblong, Crawford, Pop. 1,457
Oblong CUSD 4 600/PK-12
PO Box 40 62449 618-592-3933
Jeffery Patchett, supt. Fax 592-3427
www.oblongschools.net
Oblong HS 200/9-12
700 S Range St 62449 618-592-4235
Jeffery Patchett, prin. Fax 592-3540

Odin, Marion, Pop. 1,064
Odin SD 722 300/PK-12
102 S Merritt St 62870 618-775-8266
Jeffrey Humes, supt. Fax 775-8268
www.odinpublicschools.org
Odin HS 100/9-12
102 S Merritt St 62870 618-775-8266
Sam Alli, prin. Fax 775-8268

O Fallon, Saint Clair, Pop. 27,465
Central SD 104 600/PK-8
309 Hartman Ln 62269 618-632-6336
John Bute, supt. Fax 632-0263
www.central104.org
Arthur MS 200/5-8
160 Saint Ellen Mine Rd 62269 618-632-6336
Jered Weh, prin. Fax 622-8691

O'Fallon CCSD 90 3,400/PK-8
118 E Washington St 62269 618-632-3666
Carrie Hruby, supt. Fax 632-7864
www.of90.net/pages/O_Fallon_C_C_School_District_9
Carriel JHS 700/6-8
450 N 7 Hills Rd 62269 618-632-3666
Ellen Hays, prin. Fax 622-2940
Fulton JHS 500/6-8
307 Kyle Rd 62269 618-628-0090
Joi Wills, prin. Fax 624-9390

O'Fallon Township HSD 203 2,500/9-12
600 S Smiley St 62269 618-632-3507
Dr. Darcy Benway, supt. Fax 632-9730
www.oths.k12.il.us/
O'Fallon HS - Milburn 600/9-9
650 Milburn School Rd 62269 618-622-9647
Richard Bickel, prin. Fax 622-9630
O'Fallon HS - Smiley 1,900/10-12
600 S Smiley St 62269 618-632-3507
Richard Bickel, prin. Fax 206-2468

First Baptist Academy 200/K-12
1111 E Highway 50 62269 618-726-6040
Jackye Biehl, admin. Fax 632-8029

Oglesby, LaSalle, Pop. 3,742
Oglesby ESD 125 600/PK-8
755 Bennett Ave 61348 815-883-9297
Michael Pillion, supt. Fax 883-3568
www.ops125.net
Washington MS 100/6-8
212 W Walnut St 61348 815-883-3517
Cindy Pozzi, prin. Fax 883-9282

Illinois Valley Community College Post-Sec.
815 N Orlando Smith St 61348 815-224-2720

Ohio, Bureau, Pop. 504
Ohio Community HSD 505 50/9-12
PO Box 478 61349 815-376-4414
Jennifer Hamilton, supt. Fax 376-2102
www.bhsroe.org
Ohio Community HS 50/9-12
PO Box 478 61349 815-376-4414
Jason Wilt, prin. Fax 376-2102

Okawville, Washington, Pop. 1,424
West Washington County CUSD 10 600/PK-12
PO Box 27 62271 618-243-6454
Scott Fuhrhop, supt. Fax 243-6454
www.okawville-k12.org
Okawville JSHS 300/7-12
400 S Hanover St 62271 618-243-5201
Keith Senior, prin. Fax 243-6110

Olney, Richland, Pop. 9,020
Richland County CUSD 1 2,100/PK-12
1100 E Laurel St 62450 618-395-2324
Larry Bussard, supt. Fax 392-4147
www.rccu1.net
Richland County HS 600/9-12
1200 E Laurel St 62450 618-393-2191
Chad LeCrone, prin. Fax 395-1256
Richland County MS 400/6-8
1099 N Van St 62450 618-395-4372
Cris Edwards, prin. Fax 392-3399

Olney Central College Post-Sec.
305 N West St 62450 618-395-7777

Olympia Fields, Cook, Pop. 4,901
Rich Township HSD 227
Supt. — See Matteson
Rich Central HS 1,300/9-12
3600 W 203rd St 60461 708-679-5600
Venesa Woods, prin. Fax 679-5632

Onarga, Iroquois, Pop. 1,354
Iroquois West CUSD 10
Supt. — See Gilman
Iroquois West MS 200/6-8
303 N Evergreen St 60955 815-268-4355
Duane Ehmen, prin. Fax 268-7608

Oneida, Knox, Pop. 697
ROWVA CUSD 208 700/PK-12
PO Box 69 61467 309-483-3711
Joe Sornberger, supt. Fax 483-6123
www.rowva.k12.il.us
ROWVA HS 200/9-12
PO Box 69 61467 309-483-6371
Joe Peters, prin. Fax 483-8223
ROWVA JHS 100/7-8
PO Box 69 61467 309-483-6376
Fax 483-6378

Orangeville, Stephenson, Pop. 784
Orangeville CUSD 203 400/PK-12
201 S Orange St 61060 815-789-4289
Dr. Doug DeSchepper, supt. Fax 789-4709
www.orangevillecusd.com/
Orangeville HS 100/9-12
201 S Orange St 61060 815-789-4289
Andrew Janecke, prin. Fax 789-4709
Orangeville JHS 100/6-8
201 S Orange St 61060 815-789-4289
Andrew Janecke, prin. Fax 789-4709

Oregon, Ogle, Pop. 3,686
Oregon CUSD 220 1,400/PK-12
206 S 10th St 61061 815-732-5300
Thomas Mahoney, supt. Fax 732-2187
www.ocusd.net
Oregon HS 500/9-12
210 S 10th St 61061 815-732-5300
Andrew Nelson, prin. Fax 732-3361
Other Schools – See Mount Morris

Orion, Henry, Pop. 1,846
Orion CUSD 223 1,100/PK-12
PO Box 189 61273 309-526-3388
Joseph Blessman, supt. Fax 526-3711
orionschools.us/
Orion HS 300/9-12
PO Box 39 61273 309-526-3361
Nathan DeBaillie, prin. Fax 526-3854
Orion MS 300/6-8
PO Box 129 61273 309-526-3392
Scott Briney, prin. Fax 526-3872

Orland Hills, Cook, Pop. 7,042
Consolidated HSD 230
Supt. — See Orland Park
Andrew HS 2,100/9-12
9001 171st St, 708-342-5800
Robert Nolting, prin. Fax 532-7383

Orland Park, Cook, Pop. 56,112
Consolidated HSD 230 7,800/9-12
15100 S 94th Ave 60462 708-745-5203
Dr. James Gay, supt. Fax 349-2105
www.d230.org
Sandburg HS 3,300/9-12
13300 S La Grange Rd 60462 708-671-3100
Deborah Baker, prin. Fax 361-9714
Other Schools – See Orland Hills, Palos Hills

Orland SD 135 5,000/K-8
15100 S 94th Ave 60462 708-364-3306
Dr. D.J. Skogsberg, supt. Fax 873-6479
www.orland135.org
Century JHS 800/6-8
10801 W 159th St 60467 708-364-3500
Brian Horn, prin. Fax 349-5840
Jerling JHS 600/6-8
8851 W 151st St 60462 708-364-3700
Kevin Brown, prin. Fax 873-6457

Orland JHS 500/6-8
14855 West Ave 60462 708-364-4200
Linda Kane, prin. Fax 349-5843

Robert Morris University Post-Sec.
43 Orland Square Dr 60462 800-762-5960

Oswego, Kendall, Pop. 29,822
CUSD 308 17,500/PK-12
4175 State Route 71 60543 630-636-3080
Dr. John W. Sparlin, supt. Fax 636-3688
www.sd308.org
Oswego East HS 2,100/9-12
1525 Harvey Rd 60543 630-636-2200
Scott Savage, prin. Fax 636-2454
Oswego HS 2,600/9-12
4250 State Route 71 60543 630-636-2000
Mike Wayne, prin. Fax 636-2199
Plank JHS 900/6-8
510 Secretariat Ln 60543 630-551-9400
James Martin, prin. Fax 551-9691
Thompson JHS 1,000/6-8
440 Boulder Hill Pass 60543 630-636-2600
Shannon Lueders, prin. Fax 636-2691
Traughber JHS 1,000/6-8
570 Colchester Dr 60543 630-636-2700
Tarah Fowler, prin. Fax 636-2791
Other Schools – See Aurora, Plainfield

Hair Professionals School of Cosmetology Post-Sec.
PO Box 40 60543 630-554-2266

Ottawa, LaSalle, Pop. 18,544
Ottawa ESD 141 2,100/PK-8
320 W Main St 61350 815-433-1133
Cleve Threadgill, supt. Fax 433-1888
www.oes141.org
Shepherd MS 500/7-8
701 E McKinley Rd 61350 815-434-7925
Gary Windy, prin. Fax 433-9447

Ottawa Township HSD 140 1,400/9-12
211 E Main St 61350 815-433-1323
Michael Cushing, supt. Fax 433-1338
www.ottawahigh.com
Ottawa Township HS 1,400/9-12
211 E Main St 61350 815-433-1323
Patrick Leonard, prin. Fax 433-1338

Marquette Academy 400/PK-12
1000 Paul St 61350 815-433-0125
Brooke Rick, prin. Fax 433-2632

Palatine, Cook, Pop. 67,495
Palatine CCSD 15 12,500/PK-8
580 N 1st Bank Dr 60067 847-963-3000
Scott Thompson Ed.D., supt. Fax 963-3200
www.ccsd15.net
Sundling JHS 700/7-8
1100 N Smith St 60067 847-963-3700
Jason Dietz, prin. Fax 963-3706
Winston Campus JHS 800/7-8
120 N Babcock Dr 60074 847-963-7400
Matt Warren, prin. Fax 963-7508
Other Schools – See Rolling Meadows

Township HSD 211 12,100/9-12
1750 S Roselle Rd 60067 847-755-6600
Dr. Daniel Cates, supt. Fax 755-6810
adc.d211.org
District 211 North Campus 50/Alt
335 E Illinois Ave 60067 847-755-6700
Francesca Anderson, admin. Fax 755-6858
Fremd HS 2,700/9-12
1000 S Quentin Rd 60067 847-755-2600
Kurt Tenopir, prin. Fax 755-2623
Palatine HS 2,700/9-12
1111 N Rohlwing Rd 60074 847-755-1600
Gary Steiger, prin. Fax 755-1623
Other Schools – See Hoffman Estates, Schaumburg

William Rainey Harper College Post-Sec.
1200 W Algonquin Rd 60067 847-925-6000

Palestine, Crawford, Pop. 1,359
Palestine CUSD 3 300/PK-12
100 S Main St 62451 618-586-2713
Chris Long, supt. Fax 586-2905
www.palestine-pioneers.net
Palestine HS 100/9-12
102 N Main St 62451 618-586-2712
Tangi Waldrop, dean Fax 586-5328

Palmyra, Macoupin, Pop. 692
Northwestern CUSD 2 300/PK-12
30953 Route 111 62674 217-436-2210
Patrick Bowman, supt. Fax 436-2701
www.northwestern.k12.il.us
Northwestern HS 100/9-12
30889 Route 111 62674 217-436-2011
Brandi Maxedon, prin. Fax 436-9112
Northwestern JHS 100/7-8
30889 Route 111 62674 217-436-2011
Brandi Maxedon, prin. Fax 436-9112

Palos Heights, Cook, Pop. 12,393
Community HSD 218
Supt. — See Oak Lawn
Shepard HS 1,800/9-12
13049 S Ridgeland Ave 60463 708-371-1111
Greg Walder, prin. Fax 371-7688

Palos Heights SD 128 800/PK-8
12809 S McVickers Ave 60463 708-597-9040
Dr. Dawn Green, supt. Fax 597-9089
www.palos128.org
Independence JHS 200/6-8
6610 W Highland Dr 60463 708-448-0737
Kevin Kirk, prin. Fax 448-0179

Chicago Christian HS 400/9-12
12001 S Oak Park Ave 60463 708-388-7650
Sue Tameling, prin. Fax 388-0154
Trinity Christian College Post-Sec.
6601 W College Dr 60463 708-597-3000

Palos Hills, Cook, Pop. 17,273
Consolidated HSD 230
Supt. — See Orland Park
Stagg HS 2,400/9-12
8015 W 111th St 60465 708-974-7400
Eric Olsen, prin. Fax 974-0803

North Palos SD 117 3,200/PK-8
7825 W 103rd St 60465 708-598-5500
Dr. Jeannie Stachowiak, supt. Fax 598-5539
www.npd117.net/
Other Schools – See Hickory Hills

Hair Professionals Career College Post-Sec.
10321 S Roberts Rd 60465 708-430-1755
Moraine Valley Community College Post-Sec.
9000 W College Pkwy 60465 708-974-4300

Palos Park, Cook, Pop. 4,788
Palos CCSD 118 1,900/PK-8
8800 W 119th St 60464 708-448-4800
Dr. Anthony Scarsella, supt. Fax 448-4880
www.palos118.org
Palos South MS 600/6-8
13100 S 82nd Ave 60464 708-448-5971
Stuart Wrzesinski, prin. Fax 448-0754

Pana, Christian, Pop. 5,807
Pana CUSD 8 1,100/PK-12
PO Box 377 62557 217-562-1500
Dr. David Lett, supt. Fax 562-1501
www.panaschools.com
Pana HS 400/9-12
PO Box 377 62557 217-562-6600
Gayle McRoberts, prin. Fax 562-6714
Pana JHS 200/6-8
PO Box 377 62557 217-562-6500
Juletta Ellis, prin. Fax 562-6712

Paris, Edgar, Pop. 8,761
Paris CUSD 4 500/PK-8
15601 US Highway 150 61944 217-465-5391
Lorraine Bailey, supt. Fax 466-1225
www.crestwood.k12.il.us
Crestwood JHS 200/6-8
15601 US Highway 150 61944 217-465-5391
Danette Young, prin. Fax 466-1225

Paris-Union SD 95 1,600/PK-12
300 S Eads Ave 61944 217-465-8448
Jeremy Larson, supt. Fax 463-2243
www.paris95.k12.il.us
Mayo MS 300/6-8
310 E Wood St 61944 217-466-3050
Jeremy Larson, prin. Fax 466-3905
Paris Cooperative HS 600/9-12
14040 E 1200th Rd 61944 217-466-1175
Dave Meister, dir. Fax 466-1903

Park Forest, Cook, Pop. 21,337
Park Forest SD 163 1,400/PK-8
242 S Orchard Dr 60466 708-668-9400
Dr. Joyce Carmine, supt. Fax 748-9359
www.sd163.com
Obama S of Technology and the Arts 500/4-8
215 Wilson St 60466 708-668-9600
Cheryl Muench, prin. Fax 503-2297
Other Schools – See Chicago Heights

Rich Township HSD 227
Supt. — See Matteson
Rich East Campus HS 1,100/9-12
300 Sauk Trl 60466 708-679-6100
Dr. Sherrie Birts, prin. Fax 679-7330

Park Ridge, Cook, Pop. 37,078
Maine Township HSD 207 6,300/9-12
1177 S Dee Rd 60068 847-696-3600
Dr. Kenneth Wallace, supt. Fax 696-3254
www.maine207.org
Frost Academy 50/Alt
1177 S Dee Rd 60068 847-292-6521
Edward Pieczynski, dir. Fax 692-8132
Maine East HS 1,800/9-12
2601 Dempster St 60068 847-825-4484
Dr. Michael Pressler, prin. Fax 825-1636
Maine South HS 2,400/9-12
1111 S Dee Rd 60068 847-825-7711
Shawn Messmer, prin. Fax 825-0677
Other Schools – See Des Plaines

Park Ridge-Niles CCSD 64 4,400/PK-8
164 S Prospect Ave 60068 847-318-4300
Dr. Laurie Heinz, supt. Fax 318-4351
www.d64.org
Lincoln MS 700/6-8
200 S Lincoln Ave 60068 847-318-4215
Dr. Anthony Murray, prin. Fax 318-4210
Other Schools – See Niles

Patoka, Marion, Pop. 584
Patoka CUSD 100 300/PK-12
1220 Kinoka Rd 62875 618-432-5440
David Rademacher, supt. Fax 432-5306
pcusd100.sharpschool.net
Patoka HS 100/9-12
1220 Kinoka Rd 62875 618-432-5440
Bryan Rainey, prin. Fax 432-5306
Patoka JHS 50/7-8
1220 Kinoka Rd 62875 618-432-5200
Bryan Rainey, prin. Fax 432-5306

Pawnee, Sangamon, Pop. 2,672
Pawnee CUSD 11 600/PK-12
810 4th St 62558 217-625-2471
Gary Alexander, supt. Fax 625-2251
www.pawneeschools.com/
Pawnee JSHS 300/7-12
810 4th St 62558 217-625-2471
Tim Kratochvil, prin. Fax 625-2251

Paw Paw, Lee, Pop. 862
Paw Paw CUSD 271 200/K-12
PO Box 508 61353 815-627-2841
Stan Adcock, supt. Fax 627-2971
www.2paws.net
Paw Paw JSHS 100/6-12
PO Box 37 61353 815-627-2671
Chuck Schneider, prin. Fax 627-8481

Paxton, Ford, Pop. 4,437
Paxton-Buckley-Loda CUSD 10 1,400/PK-12
PO Box 50 60957 217-379-3314
Clifford McClure, supt. Fax 379-2862
pblunit10.com
Paxton-Buckley-Loda HS 400/9-12
PO Box 50 60957 217-379-4331
Travis Duley, prin. Fax 379-2491
Paxton-Buckley-Loda JHS 300/6-8
PO Box 50 60957 217-379-9202
Josh Didier, prin. Fax 379-9169

Payson, Adams, Pop. 1,023
Payson CUSD 1 500/PK-12
406 W State St 62360 217-656-3323
Donna Veile, supt. Fax 656-4042
www.cusd1.org
Seymour JSHS 200/7-12
420 W Brainard St 62360 217-656-3355
Dawn VanCamp, prin. Fax 656-3584

Pearl City, Stephenson, Pop. 832
Pearl City CUSD 200 500/PK-12
PO Box 9 61062 815-443-2715
Timothy Thill, supt. Fax 443-2237
www.pcwolves.net/
Pearl City HS 200/9-12
PO Box 9 61062 815-443-2715
Kelly Mandrell, prin. Fax 443-2237
Pearl City JHS 100/7-8
PO Box 9 61062 815-443-2715
Kelly Mandrell, prin. Fax 443-2237

Pecatonica, Winnebago, Pop. 2,172
Pecatonica CUSD 321 900/PK-12
PO Box 419 61063 815-239-1639
William Faller, supt. Fax 239-2125
www.pecschools.com/
Pecatonica Community MS 300/5-8
PO Box 419 61063 815-239-2612
Timothy King, prin. Fax 239-1274
Pecatonica HS 300/9-12
PO Box 419 61063 815-239-2611
Todd France, prin. Fax 239-9128

Pekin, Tazewell, Pop. 33,678
Mason-Tazewell-Woodford ROE 50/
414 Court St Ste 100 61554 309-477-2290
Patrick Durley, supt. Fax 347-3735
www.roe53.net
Other Schools – See Creve Coeur

Pekin Community HSD 303 2,000/9-12
320 Stadium Dr 61554 309-477-4222
Dr. Danielle Owens, supt. Fax 477-4376
www.pekinhigh.net
Pekin Community HS 2,000/9-12
1903 Court St 61554 309-347-4101
Amy Hubner, prin. Fax 477-4377

Pekin SD 108 3,700/PK-8
501 Washington St 61554 309-477-4700
Dr. Bill Link, supt. Fax 477-4701
www.pekin.net
Broadmoor JHS 400/7-8
501 Maywood Ave 61554 309-477-4731
Ty Goss, prin. Fax 477-4739
Edison JHS 400/7-8
1400 Earl St 61554 309-477-4732
Bill Heisel, prin. Fax 477-4738

Faith Baptist Christian S 100/PK-12
1501 Howard Ct 61554 309-347-6178
Rev. Shawn Haynie, prin. Fax 347-8716

Peoria, Peoria, Pop. 111,234
Dunlap CUSD 323 4,200/PK-12
3020 W Willow Knolls Dr 61614 309-691-3955
Dr. Lisa Parker, supt. Fax 691-6764
www.dunlapcusd.net
Other Schools – See Dunlap

Norwood ESD 63 400/PK-8
6521 W Farmington Rd 61604 309-676-3523
David Black, supt. Fax 676-6099
www.norwood63.org
Norwood MS 200/5-8
6521 W Farmington Rd 61604 309-676-3683
Joel Kilgus, prin. Fax 676-6099

Peoria SD 150 13,500/PK-12
3202 N Wisconsin Ave 61603 309-672-6768
Sharon Desmoulin-Kherat, supt. Fax 672-6708
www.psd150.org
Bills MS 200/5-8
6001 N Frostwood Pkwy 61615 309-693-4437
Laura Rodgers, prin. Fax 693-4438
Knoxville Center for Student Success 100/Alt
2628 N Knoxville Ave 61604 309-439-0000
Eric Thomas, prin. Fax 282-0007
Lindbergh MS 400/5-8
6327 N Sheridan Rd 61614 309-693-4427
Susan Malahy, prin. Fax 693-0499

Manual Academy 800/8-12
811 S Griswold St 61605 309-672-6600
Heather Young, prin. Fax 672-6605
Peoria HS 1,200/9-12
1615 N North St 61604 309-672-6630
Annette Coleman, prin. Fax 685-5803
Richwoods HS 1,400/9-12
6301 N University St 61614 309-693-4400
Brett Elliott, prin. Fax 693-4414
Rolling Acres MS 300/5-8
5617 N Merrimac Ave 61614 309-689-1100
Michael Barber, prin. Fax 693-4423
Sterling MS 300/5-8
2315 N Sterling Ave 61604 309-672-6557
Joe Gallo, prin. Fax 681-8286
Von Steuben MS 400/5-8
801 E Forrest Hill Ave 61603 309-672-6561
Thomas Ryan, prin. Fax 685-7631
Washington Gifted MS 300/5-8
3706 N Grand Blvd 61614 309-672-6563
David Poehls, prin. Fax 672-6564
Woodruff Career & Technical Center Vo/Tech
1800 NE Perry Ave 61603 309-672-6665
Cindy Janovitz, prin. Fax 282-5260
Other Schools – See West Peoria

Pleasant Valley SD 62 500/PK-8
3314 W Richwoods Blvd 61604 309-679-0634
Dr. Allen Johnson, supt. Fax 674-0165
www.pv62.com
Pleasant Valley MS 300/PK-K, 5-8
3314 W Richwoods Blvd 61604 309-679-0634
Dr. Allen Johnson, admin. Fax 679-0652

Bradley University Post-Sec.
1501 W Bradley Ave 61625 309-676-7611
Daarul Uloom Islamic S 200/PK-10
4125 W Charter Oak Rd 61615 309-691-9089
Mona Rustom, prin.
Methodist College Post-Sec.
415 NE Saint Mark Ct 61603 309-672-5513
Midstate College Post-Sec.
411 W Northmoor Rd 61614 309-692-4092
Peoria Christian S 900/PK-12
3506 N California Ave 61603 309-686-4500
Becky Gardner, admin. Fax 686-2569
Peoria Notre Dame HS 800/9-12
5105 N Sheridan Rd 61614 309-691-8741
Randy Simmons, prin. Fax 691-0875
Robert Morris University Post-Sec.
211 Fulton St 61602 800-762-5960
St. Francis Medical Center Post-Sec.
530 NE Glen Oak Ave 61637 309-655-2000
St. Francis Medical Ctr. Coll./Nursing Post-Sec.
511 NE Greenleaf St 61603 309-655-2201

Peoria Heights, Peoria, Pop. 5,986
Peoria Heights CUSD 325 800/PK-12
500 E Glen Ave 61616 309-686-8800
Eric Heath, supt. Fax 686-8801
www.phcusd325.net
Peoria Heights HS 200/9-12
508 E Glen Ave 61616 309-686-8803
Joseph Stoner, prin. Fax 686-8808

Peoria Christian S - Monroe 300/5-8
3725 N Monroe Ave 61616 309-681-0500
Thomas Schlich, prin. Fax 807-3353

Peotone, Will, Pop. 4,103
Peotone CUSD 207U 1,400/PK-12
212 W Wilson St 60468 708-258-0991
Steve Stein, supt. Fax 258-0994
www.peotoneschools.org
Peotone HS 600/9-12
605 W North St 60468 708-258-3236
Tyler Hesh, prin. Fax 258-6991
Peotone JHS 400/6-8
1 Blue Devil Dr 60468 708-258-3246
Scott Wenzel, prin. Fax 258-6669

Perry, Pike, Pop. 397
Griggsville-Perry CUSD 4
Supt. — See Griggsville
Griggsville-Perry MS 100/5-8
PO Box 98 62362 217-236-9161
Carl Spath, prin. Fax 236-7221

Peru, LaSalle, Pop. 10,189
Peru ESD 124 700/PK-8
1800 Church St 61354 815-223-0486
Mark Cross, supt. Fax 223-0490
www.perued.net
Parkside MS 400/5-8
1800 Church St 61354 815-223-7723
Lori Madden, prin. Fax 223-0285

St. Bede Academy 300/9-12
24 W US Highway 6 61354 815-223-3140
Michelle Mershon, prin. Fax 223-8580

Petersburg, Menard, Pop. 2,232
PORTA CUSD 202 1,100/PK-12
PO Box 202 62675 217-632-3803
Matthew Brue, supt. Fax 632-3221
www.porta202.org
PORTA HS 300/9-12
PO Box 202 62675 217-632-3216
Darren Hartry, prin. Fax 632-5446
PORTA JHS 200/7-8
PO Box 202 62675 217-632-3219
Amy McMahan, prin. Fax 632-5448

Phoenix, Cook, Pop. 1,934
South Holland SD 151
Supt. — See South Holland
Coolidge MS 500/6-8
15500 7th Ave 60426 708-339-5300
Patricia Payne, prin. Fax 339-5327

Piasa, Macoupin
Southwestern CUSD 9
Supt. — See Brighton
Southwestern HS 500/9-12
PO Box 100 62079 618-729-3211
Mark Bearley, prin. Fax 729-4276
Southwestern MS 300/7-8
PO Box 70 62079 618-729-3217
Scott Hopkins, prin. Fax 729-9231

Pinckneyville, Perry, Pop. 5,604
Pinckneyville Community HSD 101 400/9-12
600 E Water St 62274 618-357-5013
Keith Hagene, supt. Fax 357-6045
www.pchspanthers.com
Pinckneyville Community HS 400/9-12
600 E Water St 62274 618-357-5013
Dustin Foutch, prin. Fax 357-6045

Pinckneyville SD 50 600/PK-8
301 W Mulberry St 62274 618-357-9096
Tim O'Leary, supt. Fax 357-8731
www.p50.perry.k12.il.us
Pinckneyville MS 300/5-8
700 E Water St 62274 618-357-2724
Mark Rohlfing, prin.

Piper City, Ford, Pop. 823
Tri-Point CUSD 6-J
Supt. — See Kempton
Tri-Point MS 200/K-K, 4-8
PO Box 158 60959 815-686-2247
Jay Bennett, prin. Fax 686-2663

Pittsfield, Pike, Pop. 4,559
Pikeland CUSD 10 1,300/PK-12
512 S Madison St 62363 217-285-2147
Paula Hawley, supt. Fax 285-5059
www.pikeland.net
Pikeland Community S 600/3-8
601 Piper Ln 62363 217-285-9462
Lisa Jockisch, prin. Fax 285-9551
Pittsfield HS 300/9-12
201 E Higbee St 62363 217-285-6888
Angie Greger, prin. Fax 285-9583

Plainfield, Will, Pop. 38,856
CUSD 308
Supt. — See Oswego
Murphy JHS 600/6-8
26923 W Grande Park Blvd, 630-608-5100
Brent Anderson, prin. Fax 608-5191

Plainfield CCSD 202 28,400/PK-12
15732 S Howard St 60544 815-577-4000
Dr. Ronald Abrell, supt. Fax 436-7824
www.psd202.org
Drauden Point MS 900/6-8
1911 Drauden Rd, 815-577-4900
Patrick Flynn, prin. Fax 439-9385
Heritage Grove MS 900/6-8
12425 S Van Dyke Rd, 815-439-4810
Shannon Miller, prin. Fax 436-4661
Indian Trail MS 800/6-8
14723 S Eastern Ave 60544 815-436-6128
Dr. Christian Rivara, prin. Fax 436-7536
Jones MS 900/6-8
15320 W Wallin Dr 60544 815-267-3600
Thomas Novinski, prin. Fax 439-7201
Kennedy MS 1,200/6-8
12350 Essington Rd, 815-439-8024
Amandeep Hundal, prin. Fax 254-7375
Plainfield Academy 200/Alt
23930 W Lockport St 60544 815-439-5521
Tod Schnowske, prin. Fax 439-7014
Plainfield Central HS 2,100/9-12
24120 W Fort Beggs Dr 60544 815-436-3200
Dave Stephens, prin. Fax 439-2882
Plainfield East HS 2,000/9-12
12001 S Naperville Rd, 815-577-0324
Joseph O'Brien, prin. Fax 577-0979
Plainfield North HS 2,100/9-12
12005 S 248th Ave, 815-609-8506
Ross Draper, prin. Fax 254-6138
Plainfield South HS 2,500/9-12
7800 Caton Farm Rd, 815-439-5555
Robert Yanello, prin. Fax 436-5108
Timber Ridge MS 1,100/6-8
2101 S Bronk Rd, 815-439-3410
Dean Kariotakis, prin. Fax 439-3412
Other Schools – See Joliet

Troy CCSD 30C 4,500/PK-8
5800 Theodore Dr, 815-577-6760
Todd Koehl Ph.D., supt. Fax 577-3795
troywebs.troy30c.org
Troy MS 1,000/7-8
5800 Theodore Dr, 815-230-9920
Renee Marski, prin. Fax 577-2867

Plano, Kendall, Pop. 10,709
Plano CUSD 88 2,300/PK-12
800 S Hale St 60545 630-552-8978
Dr. Hector Garcia, supt. Fax 552-8548
www.plano88.org/
Plano HS 600/9-12
704 W Abe St 60545 630-552-3178
Eric Benson, prin. Fax 552-8824
Plano MS 300/7-8
804 S Hale St 60545 630-552-3608
Mark Heller, prin. Fax 552-3802

Pleasant Hill, Pike, Pop. 964
Pleasant Hill CUSD 3 300/PK-12
PO Box 277 62366 217-734-2311
Donald Peebles, supt. Fax 734-2629
www.phwolves.com
Pleasant Hill HS 100/9-12
PO Box 277 62366 217-734-2311
Donald Peebles, prin. Fax 734-2725

Pleasant Plains, Sangamon, Pop. 790
Pleasant Plains CUSD 8 1,300/PK-12
PO Box 20 62677 217-626-1041
Matt Runge, supt. Fax 626-1082
www.ppcusd8.org
Pleasant Plains HS 400/9-12
PO Box 320 62677 217-626-1044
Luke Brooks, prin. Fax 626-1667
Pleasant Plains MS 400/5-8
2455 N Farmingdale Rd 62677 217-626-1061
Ben Theilen, prin. Fax 626-2272

Polo, Ogle, Pop. 2,326
Polo CUSD 222 600/PK-12
100 S Union Ave 61064 815-946-3815
Christopher Rademacher, supt. Fax 946-2493
polo222.org
Aplington MS 100/6-8
610 E Mason St 61064 815-946-2519
Mark Downey, prin. Fax 946-2537
Polo Community HS 200/9-12
100 S Union Ave 61064 815-946-3314
Andy Faivre, prin. Fax 946-2493

Pontiac, Livingston, Pop. 11,777
Livingston Area Career Center
1100 E Indiana Ave 61764 815-842-2557
Tera Graves, dir. Fax 842-1005
www.lacc.k12.il.us
Livingston Area Career Center Vo/Tech
1100 E Indiana Ave 61764 815-842-2557
Tera Graves, dir. Fax 842-1005

Pontiac CCSD 429 1,300/PK-8
117 W Livingston St 61764 815-842-1533
Brian Dukes, supt. Fax 844-5773
www.pontiac429.org
Pontiac JHS 400/6-8
600 N Morrow St 61764 815-842-4343
Brian Hensley, prin. Fax 844-6230

Pontiac Township HSD 90 700/9-12
1100 E Indiana Ave 61764 815-844-6113
Jon Kilgore, supt. Fax 844-6116
www.pontiac90.org
Pontiac HS 700/9-12
1100 E Indiana Ave 61764 815-844-6113
Eric Bohm, prin. Fax 844-6116

Poplar Grove, Boone, Pop. 4,959
North Boone CUSD 200 1,600/K-12
6248 N Boone School Rd 61065 815-765-3322
Dr. Michael Greenlee, supt. Fax 765-2053
www.nbcusd.org
North Boone HS 500/9-12
17823 Poplar Grove Rd 61065 815-765-3311
Jacob Hubert, prin. Fax 765-3316
North Boone MS 300/7-8
17641 Poplar Grove Rd 61065 815-765-9274
Jamison Pearce, prin. Fax 765-9275

Port Byron, Rock Island, Pop. 1,628
Riverdale CUSD 100 1,100/PK-12
9624 256th St N 61275 309-523-3184
Ronald Jacobs, supt. Fax 523-3550
riverdaleschools.org
Riverdale HS 300/9-12
9622 256th St N 61275 309-523-3181
Rick Dwyer, prin. Fax 523-2885
Riverdale MS 300/6-8
9822 256th St N 61275 309-523-3131
James Jennings, prin. Fax 523-3934

Posen, Cook, Pop. 5,912
Posen-Robbins ESD 143-5 1,700/PK-8
14025 S Harrison Ave 60469 708-388-7200
Dr. Anthony Edison Ed.D., supt. Fax 388-3868
www.prsd1435.org
Other Schools – See Robbins

Princeton, Bureau, Pop. 7,583
Princeton ESD 115 700/PK-8
506 E Dover Rd 61356 815-875-3162
Tim Smith, supt. Fax 875-3101
www.princeton115schools.org
Logan JHS 400/5-8
302 W Central Ave 61356 815-875-6415
Amanda Carr, prin. Fax 872-0034

Princeton HSD 500 500/9-12
103 S Euclid Ave 61356 815-875-3308
Kirk Haring, supt. Fax 875-8525
www.phs-il.org
Princeton HS 500/9-12
103 S Euclid Ave 61356 815-875-3308
Andy Berlinski, prin. Fax 875-8525

Princeville, Peoria, Pop. 1,723
Princeville CUSD 326 800/PK-12
909 N Town Ave 61559 309-385-2213
Shannon Duling, supt. Fax 385-1823
www.princeville326.org/
Princeville HS 200/9-12
302 Cordis Ave 61559 309-385-4660
Richard Thole, prin. Fax 385-1110

Prophetstown, Whiteside, Pop. 2,069
Prophetstown-Lyndon-Tampico CUSD 3 900/PK-12
79 Grove St 61277 815-537-5101
Chad Colmone, supt. Fax 537-5102
plt3.org
PLT MS 200/6-8
38 Ferry St 61277 815-537-5084
Steven Kastorff, prin. Fax 537-5085
Prophetstown HS 300/9-12
310 W Riverside Dr 61277 815-537-5161
Josh Johnson, prin. Fax 537-5102

Prospect Heights, Cook, Pop. 16,131
Prospect Heights SD 23 1,500/PK-8
700 N Schoenbeck Rd 60070 847-870-3850
Dr. Deb Wilson, supt. Fax 870-3896
www.d23.org/

MacArthur MS 500/6-8
700 N Schoenbeck Rd 60070 847-870-3879
Steven Lee, prin. Fax 870-3881

Quincy, Adams, Pop. 39,738
Quincy Area Vocational Technical Center
219 Baldwin Dr 62301 217-224-3775
Mark Pfleiger, dir. Fax 221-4800
www.qps.org/qavtc/
Quincy Area Vocational Technical Center Vo/Tech
219 Baldwin Dr 62301 217-224-3775
Mark Pfleiger, dir. Fax 221-4800

Quincy SD 172 5,900/PK-12
1416 Maine St 62301 217-223-8700
Roy Webb, supt. Fax 228-7162
www.qps.org
Quincy HS 1,300/9-12
3322 Maine St 62301 217-224-3770
Danielle Arnold, prin. Fax 228-7149
Quincy JHS 900/6-8
100 S 14th St 62301 217-222-3073
Dan Sparrow, prin. Fax 228-7185

Blessing Hospital Post-Sec.
PO Box 7005 62305 217-223-8400
Blessing-Rieman College of Nursing Post-Sec.
PO Box 7005 62305 217-228-5520
Gem City College Post-Sec.
700 State St 62301 217-222-0391
John Wood Community College Post-Sec.
1301 S 48th St 62305 217-224-6500
Quincy Christian S 100/PK-12
PO Box 3643 62305 217-223-5698
Paul Lamm, admin. Fax 223-5724
Quincy Notre Dame HS 400/9-12
1400 S 11th St 62301 217-223-2479
Mark McDowell, prin. Fax 223-0023
Quincy University Post-Sec.
1800 College Ave 62301 217-222-8020
Vatterott College Post-Sec.
3609 N Marx Dr 62305 217-224-0600

Ramsey, Fayette, Pop. 1,024
Ramsey CUSD 204 500/PK-12
702 W 6th St 62080 618-423-2335
Melissa Ritter, supt. Fax 423-2314
www.ramsey.fayette.k12.il.us
Ramsey HS 100/9-12
702 W 6th St 62080 618-423-2333
Ginger Edwards, prin. Fax 423-1275

Rantoul, Champaign, Pop. 12,421
Rantoul CSD 137 1,600/PK-8
400 E Wabash Ave 61866 217-893-4171
Michelle Ramage, supt. Fax 892-4313
www.rcs137.org
Eater JHS, 400 E Wabash Ave 61866 500/6-8
Ryan Green, prin. 217-892-2115

Rantoul Township HSD 193 800/9-12
200 S Sheldon St 61866 217-892-2151
Scott Amerio, supt. Fax 892-4442
www.rths.k12.il.us
Rantoul Township HS 800/9-12
200 S Sheldon St 61866 217-892-2151
Todd Wilson, prin. Fax 892-4442

Raymond, Montgomery, Pop. 996
Panhandle CUSD 2 400/PK-12
509 N Prairie St 62560 217-229-4215
Aaron Hopper, supt. Fax 229-4216
www.panhandleschools.com
Lincolnwood HS 100/9-12
507 N Prairie St 62560 217-229-4237
Kendal Elvidge, prin. Fax 229-3005
Lincolnwood JHS 100/6-8
507 N Prairie St 62560 217-229-4237
Kendal Elvidge, prin. Fax 229-3005

Red Bud, Randolph, Pop. 3,675
Red Bud CUSD 132 1,000/PK-12
815 Locust St 62278 618-282-3507
Jonathan Tallman, supt. Fax 282-6151
www.redbud132.org
Red Bud HS 400/9-12
815 Locust St 62278 618-282-3826
Rob Pipher, prin. Fax 282-6828

Richmond, McHenry, Pop. 1,854
Nippersink SD 2 1,300/PK-8
4213 US Highway 12 60071 815-678-4242
Dr. Dan Oest, supt. Fax 675-0413
www.nippersinkdistrict2.org
Nippersink MS 500/6-8
10006 N Main St 60071 815-678-7129
Tim Molitor, prin. Fax 678-7210

Richmond-Burton Community HSD 157 800/9-12
4213 US Highway 12 60071 815-678-4525
Dr. Dan Oest, supt. Fax 678-4324
www.rbchs.com
Richmond-Burton HS 800/9-12
8311 IL Route 31 60071 815-678-4525
Tom Lind, prin. Fax 678-4324

Richton Park, Cook, Pop. 13,324
Matteson ESD 162 3,000/PK-8
4601 Sauk Trl 60471 708-748-0100
Dr. Blondean Davis, supt. Fax 748-7302
www.sd162.org
Other Schools – See Matteson

Rich Township HSD 227
Supt. — See Matteson
Rich South Campus HS 1,100/9-12
5000 Sauk Trl 60471 708-679-3000
Jennifer Bednarczyk, prin. Fax 679-3168

Riverdale, Cook, Pop. 13,395
Dolton SD 148 2,300/PK-8
114 W 144th St 60827 708-841-2290
Dr. Saundra R. Mickles, supt. Fax 841-5048
www.district148.net
Washington JHS 100/7-8
13900 S School St 60827 708-201-2078
Dorothy Jeter, prin. Fax 201-2148
Other Schools – See Dolton

River Forest, Cook, Pop. 10,962
River Forest SD 90 1,400/PK-8
7776 Lake St 60305 708-771-8282
Edward Condon Ph.D., supt. Fax 771-8291
www.district90.org/
Roosevelt JHS 700/5-8
7560 Oak Ave 60305 708-366-9230
Larry Garstki, prin. Fax 771-3962

Concordia University Chicago Post-Sec.
7400 Augusta St 60305 708-209-3100
Dominican University Post-Sec.
7900 Division St 60305 708-366-2490
Trinity HS 500/9-12
7574 Division St 60305 708-771-8383
Dr. Noreen Powers, prin. Fax 488-2014

River Grove, Cook, Pop. 10,116

Guerin College Preparatory HS 500/9-12
8001 Belmont Ave 60171 708-453-6233
Karen Booth, prin. Fax 453-6296
Triton College Post-Sec.
2000 5th Ave 60171 708-456-0300

Riverside, Cook, Pop. 8,771
Riverside Brookfield Township HSD 208 1,500/9-12
160 Ridgewood Rd 60546 708-442-7500
Dr. Kevin Skinkis, supt. Fax 447-5570
www.rbhs208.net
Riverside Brookfield Township HS 1,500/9-12
160 Ridgewood Rd 60546 708-442-7500
Kristin Smetana, prin. Fax 442-7840

Riverside SD 96 1,600/PK-8
63 Woodside Rd 60546 708-447-5007
Martha Ryan-Toye, supt. Fax 447-3252
www.district96.org
Hauser JHS 600/6-8
65 Woodside Rd 60546 708-447-3896
April Mahy, prin. Fax 447-5180

Riverton, Sangamon, Pop. 3,413
Riverton CUSD 14 1,400/PK-12
PO Box 1010 62561 217-629-6009
Dr. Lance Thurman, supt. Fax 629-6008
www.rivertonschools.org
Riverton HS 400/9-12
PO Box 560 62561 217-629-6003
Matt Moore, prin. Fax 629-6020
Riverton MS 400/5-8
PO Box 530 62561 217-629-6002
Chris Koerwitz, prin. Fax 629-6017

Roanoke, Woodford, Pop. 2,057
Roanoke-Benson CUSD 60 600/PK-12
PO Box 320 61561 309-923-8921
Rohn Peterson, supt. Fax 923-7508
www.rb60.com/
Roanoke-Benson HS 200/9-12
PO Box 320 61561 309-923-8401
Michael Tresnak, prin. Fax 923-7508
Other Schools – See Benson

Linn Mennonite Christian S 50/K-12
1594 County Road 1700 N 61561 309-923-5641
Matthew Kennell, pres.

Robbins, Cook, Pop. 5,299
Community HSD 218
Supt. — See Oak Lawn
Delta Learning Center 200/Alt
3940 W Midlothian Tpke 60472 708-371-1880
Joe Fowler, prin. Fax 371-4782

Posen-Robbins ESD 143-5
Supt. — See Posen
Kellar JHS 500/6-8
14123 S Lydia Ave 60472 708-388-7201
Dr. Monica Spence, prin. Fax 388-6177

Robinson, Crawford, Pop. 7,621
Robinson CUSD 2 1,600/PK-12
PO Box 190 62454 618-544-7511
Josh Quick, supt. Fax 544-9284
www.robinsonschools.com/
Nuttall MS 300/6-8
PO Box 190 62454 618-544-8618
Craig Beals, prin. Fax 544-8618
Robinson HS 500/9-12
PO Box 190 62454 618-544-9510
Victoria McDonald, prin. Fax 544-7921

Lincoln Trail College Post-Sec.
11220 State Highway 1 62454 618-544-8657

Rochelle, Ogle, Pop. 9,466
Rochelle CCSD 231 1,700/PK-8
444 N 8th St 61068 815-562-6363
Todd Prusator, supt. Fax 562-5500
www.d231.rochelle.net
Rochelle MS 500/6-8
111 School Ave 61068 815-562-7997
Tony Doyle, prin. Fax 562-8527

Rochelle Township HSD 212 900/9-12
1401 Flagg Rd 61068 815-562-4161
Richard Craven, supt. Fax 562-6693
www.rths.rochelle.net/
Rochelle Township HS 900/9-12
1401 Flagg Rd 61068 815-562-4161
Jason Harper, prin. Fax 562-6693

Rochester, Sangamon, Pop. 3,622
Rochester CUSD 3A 2,300/PK-12
4 Rocket Dr 62563 217-498-6210
Dr. Thomas Bertrand, supt. Fax 498-8045
www.rochester3a.net
Rochester HS 700/9-12
1 Rocket Dr 62563 217-498-9761
Brent Ashbaugh, prin. Fax 498-9825
Rochester JHS 400/7-8
3 Rocket Dr 62563 217-498-9761
Kim Poole, prin. Fax 498-6204

Rock Falls, Whiteside, Pop. 9,103
Rock Falls ESD 13 1,100/PK-8
602 4th Ave 61071 815-626-2604
Dan Arickx, supt. Fax 626-2627
www.rfsd13.org
Rock Falls MS 300/6-8
1701 12th Ave 61071 815-626-2626
Kyle Ackman, prin. Fax 626-3198

Rock Falls Township HSD 301 700/9-12
101 12th Ave 61071 815-625-3886
Ron McCord, supt. Fax 625-3889
www.wside.k12.il.us/rfhs
Rock Falls Township HS 700/9-12
101 12th Ave 61071 815-625-3886
Mike Berentes, prin. Fax 625-3889

Rockford, Winnebago, Pop. 148,827
Rockford SD 205 26,200/PK-12
501 7th St 61104 815-966-3000
Dr. Ehren Jarrett, supt. Fax 966-3193
www.rps205.com
Auburn HS 1,800/9-12
5110 Auburn St 61101 815-966-3300
Janice Hawkins, prin. Fax 966-3911
Eisenhower MS 800/6-8
3525 Spring Creek Rd 61107 815-229-2450
Jeff Carlson, prin. Fax 229-2456
Flinn MS 1,100/6-8
2525 Ohio Pkwy 61108 815-229-2800
Randy Bay, prin. Fax 229-2894
Guilford HS 1,800/9-12
5620 Spring Creek Rd 61114 815-654-4870
Jennifer Lawrence, prin. Fax 654-4901
Jefferson HS 1,800/9-12
4145 Samuelson Rd 61109 815-874-9536
Don Rundall, prin. Fax 921-0306
Kennedy MS 700/6-8
520 N Pierpont Ave 61101 815-654-4880
Renneth Richardson, prin. Fax 654-4874
Lincoln MS 700/6-8
1500 Charles St 61104 815-229-2400
Jim Parker, prin. Fax 229-2420
Marshall S 600/4-8
4664 N Rockton Ave 61103 815-490-5400
Jessica Powell, prin. Fax 490-5405
Rockford East HS 1,900/9-12
2929 Charles St 61108 815-229-2100
Peter Verona, prin. Fax 229-2113
Rockford Environmental Science Academy 1,000/6-8
1800 Ogilby Rd 61102 815-489-5509
Ben Stover, prin. Fax 966-5360
Roosevelt Community Education Center 300/Alt
978 Haskell Ave 61103 815-966-3265
Morgan Gallagher, prin. Fax 966-3105
West MS 800/6-8
1900 N Rockton Ave 61103 815-966-3200
Maurice Davis, prin. Fax 966-3216

Berean Baptist Christian S 200/PK-12
5626 Safford Rd 61101 815-962-4841
Douglas Swanson, admin. Fax 962-4851
Boylan Central Catholic HS 1,200/9-12
4000 Saint Francis Dr 61103 815-877-0531
Jerry Kerrigan, prin. Fax 877-2544
Christian Life Schools 700/PK-12
5950 Spring Creek Rd 61114 815-877-5749
Michael Hoekstra, prin. Fax 877-4358
Educators of Beauty Post-Sec.
2601B N Mulford Rd 61114 815-639-9200
Keith Country Day S 300/PK-12
1 Jacoby Pl 61107 815-399-8823
Dr. Debra Dimke, hdmstr. Fax 399-2470
North Love Christian S 200/PK-12
5301 E Riverside Blvd 61114 815-877-6021
Tony Cotelleso, admin. Fax 877-6076
Our Lady of the Sacred Heart Academy 50/5-12
3218 11th St 61109 815-399-3021
Lou Bageanis, prin.
Rasmussen College Post-Sec.
6000 E State St Fl 4 61108 815-316-4800
Rockford Career College Post-Sec.
1130 S Alpine Rd Ste 100 61108 815-965-8616
Rockford Christian S 1,200/PK-12
1401 N Bell School Rd 61107 815-391-8000
Randy Taylor, supt. Fax 391-8004
Rockford IQRA S 200/PK-12
5925 Darlene Dr 61109 815-397-6899
Huda Ghazal, prin. Fax 397-1681
Rockford Lutheran JSHS 600/6-12
3411 N Alpine Rd 61114 815-877-9551
Don Kortze, prin. Fax 636-4429
Rockford Memorial Hospital Post-Sec.
2400 N Rockton Ave 61103 815-971-5000
Rockford University Post-Sec.
5050 E State St 61108 815-226-4000
Rock Valley College Post-Sec.
3301 N Mulford Rd 61114 815-921-7821
St. Anthony College of Nursing Post-Sec.
5658 E State St 61108 815-395-5091

St. Anthony Medical Center Post-Sec.
5666 E State St 61108 815-226-2000
Spectrum S 200/PK-12
2909 N Main St 61103 815-877-1600
Christine Klekamp, dir. Fax 877-1685
Swedish-American Hospital Post-Sec.
1401 E State St 61104 815-968-4400

Rock Island, Rock Island, Pop. 37,879
Rock Island-Milan SD 41 6,600/PK-12
2101 6th Ave 61201 309-793-5900
Dr. Michael Oberhaus, supt. Fax 793-5905
rockislandschools.org
Edison JHS 400/7-8
4141 9th St 61201 309-793-5920
Christi Thigpen, prin. Fax 793-5919
Marshall Center 100/Alt
600 11th Ave 61201 309-793-5924
Phillip Ambrose, prin. Fax 793-5979
Rock Island HS 1,700/9-12
1400 25th Ave 61201 309-793-5950
Eric Moore, prin. Fax 793-9866
Washington JHS 500/7-8
3300 18th Ave 61201 309-793-5915
Kristin Allen, prin. Fax 793-5917

Alleman HS 500/9-12
1103 40th St 61201 309-786-7793
David Hobin, prin. Fax 786-7834
Augustana College Post-Sec.
639 38th St 61201 309-794-7000
Trinity College of Nursing Post-Sec.
2122 25th Ave 61201 309-779-7700

Rockton, Winnebago, Pop. 7,573
Hononegah Community HSD 207 2,100/9-12
307 Salem St 61072 815-624-5010
Dr. Lynn Gibson, supt. Fax 624-5029
www.hononegah.org
Hononegah Community HS 2,100/9-12
307 Salem St 61072 815-624-5005
Eric Flohr, prin. Fax 624-5025

Rockton SD 140 1,500/PK-8
1050 E Union St 61072 815-624-7143
Glenn Terry, supt. Fax 624-4640
rockton140.org
Mack MS 500/6-8
11810 Old River Rd 61072 815-624-2611
Autumn Czizek, prin. Fax 624-5900

Rolling Meadows, Cook, Pop. 23,765
Palatine CCSD 15
Supt. — See Palatine
Plum Grove JHS 800/7-8
2600 Plum Grove Rd 60008 847-963-7600
Kerry Wilson Ed.D., prin. Fax 963-7606
Sandburg JHS 600/7-8
2600 Martin Ln 60008 847-963-7800
Douglas Harter, prin. Fax 963-7806

Township HSD 214
Supt. — See Arlington Heights
Rolling Meadows HS 1,800/9-12
2901 Central Rd 60008 847-718-5600
Eileen Hart, prin. Fax 718-5617
Young Adult Program 100/Alt
2901 Central Rd 60008 847-718-5787
Dan Williams, dir. Fax 718-5617

Northwest Suburban College Post-Sec.
5999 New Wilke Rd Ste 400 60008 847-290-6425

Romeoville, Will, Pop. 38,967
Valley View CUSD 365U 17,500/PK-12
755 Dalhart Ave 60446 815-886-2700
Dr. James Mitchem, supt. Fax 886-7294
www.vvsd.org/
Lukancic MS 600/6-8
725 W Normantown Rd 60446 815-886-2216
Tricia Rollerson, prin. Fax 886-2264
Martinez MS 800/6-8
590 Belmont Dr 60446 815-886-6100
Sarah DeDonato, prin. Fax 886-7264
Romeoville HS 1,800/9-12
100 N Independence Blvd 60446 815-886-1800
Derek Kinder, prin. Fax 886-7272
Other Schools – See Bolingbrook

Wilco Area Career Center
500 Wilco Blvd 60446 815-838-6941
Katrina Plese, dir. Fax 838-1163
www.wilco.k12.il.us
Wilco Area Career Center Vo/Tech
500 Wilco Blvd 60446 815-838-6941
Katrina Plese, dir. Fax 838-1163

Illinois Welding School Post-Sec.
1315 Enterprise Dr Ste E 60446 630-679-0566
Lewis University Post-Sec.
1 University Pkwy 60446 815-838-0500
Rasmussen College Post-Sec.
1400 W Normantown Rd 60446 815-306-2600
Romeoville Christian Academy 100/PK-12
301 W Normantown Rd 60446 815-886-4850
Mark Widmer, prin.

Roscoe, Winnebago, Pop. 10,602
Kinnikinnick CCSD 131 1,900/PK-8
5410 Pine Ln 61073 815-623-2837
Keli Freedlund, supt. Fax 623-9285
www.kinn131.org
Roscoe MS 700/6-8
6121 Elevator Rd 61073 815-623-2837
Julie Cropp, prin. Fax 623-7604

Roselle, DuPage, Pop. 22,408
Lake Park Community HSD 108 2,800/9-12
590 Medinah Rd 60172 630-529-4500
Dr. Lynne Panega, supt. Fax 295-5414
www.lphs.org
Lake Park HS East Campus 1,400/9-10
600 Medinah Rd 60172 630-529-4500
John Gouriotis, prin. Fax 295-5212
Lake Park HS West Campus 1,400/11-12
500 W Bryn Mawr Ave 60172 630-595-5322
John Gouriotis, prin. Fax 351-2932

Medinah SD 11 700/K-8
700 E Granville Ave 60172 630-893-3737
Dr. John Butts, supt. Fax 893-4947
www.medinah11.org
Medinah MS 200/6-8
700 E Granville Ave 60172 630-893-3838
George Gouriotis, prin. Fax 893-5198

Roselle SD 12 700/K-8
100 E Walnut St 60172 630-529-2091
Dr. M. Kaczkowski, supt. Fax 529-2467
www.sd12.org
Roselle MS 300/6-8
500 S Park St 60172 630-529-1600
Kathleen Schneiter, prin. Fax 529-1882

Roseville, Warren, Pop. 986
Monmouth-Roseville CUSD 238
Supt. — See Monmouth
Monmouth-Roseville JHS 200/7-8
200 E Gossett St 61473 309-426-2682
Donald Farr, prin. Fax 426-2303

Round Lake, Lake, Pop. 17,862
Round Lake Area SD 116 7,500/PK-12
884 W Nippersink Rd 60073 847-270-9000
Dr. Constance Collins, supt. Fax 546-3538
www.rlas-116.org
Magee MS 700/6-8
500 N Cedar Lake Rd 60073 847-546-8800
Dr. Lisa Steffen, prin. Fax 740-3836
Round Lake HS 2,100/9-12
800 High School Dr 60073 847-270-9300
Dr. Donn Mendoza, prin. Fax 546-5872
Other Schools – See Round Lake Heights

Round Lake Heights, Lake, Pop. 2,629
Round Lake Area SD 116
Supt. — See Round Lake
Round Lake MS 1,000/6-8
2000 Lotus Dr 60073 847-270-9400
David Higgs, prin. Fax 270-9419

Roxana, Madison, Pop. 1,531
Roxana CUSD 1 1,500/PK-12
401 Chaffer Ave 62084 618-254-7544
Debra Kreutztrager, supt. Fax 254-7547
www.roxanaschools.org
Roxana HS 500/9-12
401 Chaffer Ave 62084 618-254-7553
Jason Dandurand, prin. Fax 254-7580
Roxana JHS 400/6-8
401 Chaffer Ave 62084 618-254-7560
Steve Mayerhofer, prin. Fax 254-8107

Royal, Champaign, Pop. 293
Prairieview-Ogden CCSD 197 200/K-8
PO Box 27 61871 217-583-3300
Victor White Ed.D., supt. Fax 583-3391
www.pvo.k12.il.us/
Other Schools – See Thomasboro

Rushville, Schuyler, Pop. 3,179
Schuyler-Industry CUSD 5 1,200/PK-12
740 Maple Ave 62681 217-322-4311
Beau Fretueg, supt. Fax 322-4398
www.sid5.com/
Rushville-Industry HS 400/9-12
730 N Congress St 62681 217-322-4311
Brad Gooding, prin. Fax 322-2844
Schuyler-Industry MS 400/5-8
750 N Congress St 62681 217-322-4311
Jim Shepherd, prin. Fax 322-3938

Saint Anne, Kankakee, Pop. 1,243
Saint Anne Community HSD 302 200/9-12
PO Box 630 60964 815-422-5022
Charles Stegall, supt. Fax 422-5023
www.sachs302.org
Saint Anne Community HS 200/9-12
PO Box 630 60964 815-427-8141
Ramie Kolitwenzew, prin. Fax 427-8609

Saint Charles, Kane, Pop. 32,580
Saint Charles CUSD 303 13,300/PK-12
201 S 7th St 60174 331-228-2000
Dr. Donald Schlomann, supt. Fax 228-2001
www.d303.org
Haines MS 1,100/6-8
305 S 9th St 60174 331-228-3100
Pamela Jensen, prin. Fax 228-3101
Saint Charles East HS 2,500/9-12
1020 Dunham Rd 60174 331-228-4000
Charlie Kyle, prin. Fax 228-4001
Saint Charles North HS 2,000/9-12
255 Red Gate Rd 60175 331-228-4400
Audra Christenson, prin. Fax 228-4401
Thompson MS 900/6-8
705 W Main St 60174 331-228-3400
Timothy Loversky, prin. Fax 228-3401
Wredling MS 1,300/6-8
1200 Dunham Rd 60174 331-228-3400
Steve Morrill, prin. Fax 228-3401

Saint Elmo, Fayette, Pop. 1,414
Saint Elmo CUSD 202 500/PK-12
1200 N Walnut St 62458 618-829-3264
Deborah Philpot, supt. Fax 829-5161
www.stelmo.org
Saint Elmo HS 100/9-12
300 W 12th St 62458 618-829-3227
Brian Garrard, prin. Fax 829-5161
Saint Elmo JHS 100/7-8
300 W 12th St 62458 618-829-3227
Brian Garrard, prin. Fax 829-5161

Saint Jacob, Madison, Pop. 1,092
Triad CUSD 2
Supt. — See Troy
Triad MS 800/6-8
9539 US Highway 40 62281 618-644-5511
Matt Noyes, prin. Fax 644-9435

Saint Joseph, Champaign, Pop. 3,931
Saint Joseph CCSD 169 900/PK-8
PO Box 409 61873 217-469-2291
Todd Pence, supt. Fax 469-8906
www.stjoe.k12.il.us
Saint Joseph MS 400/5-8
PO Box 409 61873 217-469-2334
Chris Graham, prin. Fax 469-2537

Saint Joseph-Ogden Community HSD 305 500/9-12
PO Box 890 61873 217-469-2586
Brian Brooks, supt.
www.sjo.k12.il.us
Saint Joseph-Ogden HS 500/9-12
PO Box 890 61873 217-469-2332
Gary Page, prin. Fax 469-8290

Salem, Marion, Pop. 7,393
Salem Community HSD 600 800/9-12
1200 N Broadway Ave 62881 618-548-0727
Brad Detering, supt. Fax 548-8021
www.salemhigh.com
Salem Community HS 800/9-12
1200 N Broadway Ave 62881 618-548-0727
John Boles, prin. Fax 548-8021

Salem SD 111 1,100/PK-8
1300 Hawthorn Rd 62881 618-548-7702
Leslie Foppe, supt. Fax 548-7714
www.salem111.com
Franklin Park MS 600/PK-PK, 4-
1325 N Franklin St 62881 618-548-7704
Matt Sturgeon, prin. Fax 548-7712

Sandoval, Marion, Pop. 1,257
Sandoval CUSD 501 500/PK-12
859 W Missouri Ave 62882 618-247-3233
Dr. Jennifer Garrison, supt. Fax 247-3243
www.sandoval501.org
Sandoval HS 100/9-12
859 W Missouri Ave 62882 618-247-3361
Annie Gray, prin. Fax 247-3235
Sandoval JHS 100/7-8
859 W Missouri Ave 62882 618-247-3361
Annie Gray, prin. Fax 247-3235

Sandwich, DeKalb, Pop. 7,330
Indian Valley Vocational Center
600 Lions Rd 60548 815-786-9873
Joe Barbic, dir. Fax 786-6928
www.ivvc.net
Indian Valley Vocational Center Vo/Tech
600 Lions Rd 60548 815-786-9873
Joe Barbic, dir. Fax 786-6928

Sandwich CUSD 430 2,200/PK-12
720 S Wells St 60548 815-786-2187
Rick Schmitt, supt. Fax 786-6229
www.sandwich430.org
Sandwich Community HS 700/9-12
515 Lions Rd 60548 815-786-2157
Tom Sodaro, prin. Fax 786-2632
Sandwich MS 500/6-8
600 S Wells St 60548 815-786-2138
B.J. Richardson, prin. Fax 786-6606

Sauk Village, Cook, Pop. 10,221
CCSD 168 1,500/PK-8
21899 Torrence Ave 60411 708-758-1610
Dr. Donna Leak, supt. Fax 758-5929
www.d168.org
Rickover JHS 500/6-8
22151 Torrence Ave 60411 708-758-1900
Chantel Bullock, prin. Fax 758-1601

Savanna, Carroll, Pop. 3,017
West Carroll CUSD 314
Supt. — See Mount Carroll
West Carroll HS 400/9-12
500 Cragmoor St 61074 815-273-7715
Jeff Utsinger, prin. Fax 273-7819

Scales Mound, Jo Daviess, Pop. 373
Scales Mound CUSD 211 200/PK-12
210 Main St 61075 815-845-2215
William Caron, supt. Fax 845-2238
www.scalesmound.net
Scales Mound HS 100/9-12
210 Main St 61075 815-845-2215
Dr. Matthew Wiederholt, prin. Fax 845-2238
Scales Mound JHS 50/6-8
210 Main St 61075 815-845-2215
Dr. Matthew Wiederholt, prin. Fax 845-2238

Schaumburg, Cook, Pop. 72,713
Schaumburg CCSD 54 13,900/PK-8
524 E Schaumburg Rd 60194 847-357-5000
Andrew DuRoss, supt. Fax 357-5152
www.sd54.org
Addams JHS 700/7-8
700 S Springinsguth Rd 60193 847-357-5900
Chris Bingen, prin. Fax 357-5901
Frost JHS 600/7-8
320 W Wise Rd 60193 847-357-6800
Scott Ross, prin. Fax 357-6801
Keller JHS 500/7-8
820 Bode Rd 60194 847-357-6500
Heather Wilson, prin. Fax 357-6501
Other Schools – See Elk Grove Village, Hoffman Estates

Township HSD 211
Supt. — See Palatine
Schaumburg HS 2,300/9-12
1100 W Schaumburg Rd 60194 847-755-4600
Timothy Little, prin. Fax 755-4623

American Intercontinental Univ Online — Post-Sec.
231 N Martingale Rd Fl 6 60173 — 877-701-3800
Argosy University/Schaumburg — Post-Sec.
999 N Plaza Dr Ste 111 60173 — 847-969-4900
DeVry University — Post-Sec.
1051 Perimeter Dr Fl 9 60173 — 847-330-0040
Lake Forest Graduate Sch. of Management — Post-Sec.
1300 E Woodfield Rd Ste 600 60173 — 847-234-5005
Robert Morris University — Post-Sec.
1000 E Woodfield Rd 60173 — 800-225-1520
Roosevelt University — Post-Sec.
1400 N Roosevelt Blvd 60173 — 847-619-7300
Schaumburg Christian S — 1,200/PK-12
200 N Roselle Rd 60194 — 847-885-3230
The Illinois Institute of Art — Post-Sec.
1000 N Plaza Dr Ste 100 60173 — 847-619-3450

Schiller Park, Cook, Pop. 11,679
Schiller Park SD 81 — 1,400/PK-8
9760 Soreng Ave 60176 — 847-671-1816
Dr. Kimberly Boryszewski, supt. — Fax 671-1872
www.sd81.org
Lincoln MS — 400/6-8
9750 Soreng Ave 60176 — 847-678-2916
Constance Stavrou, prin. — Fax 678-4059

Sciota, McDonough, Pop. 61
West Prairie CUSD 103
Supt. — See Colchester
West Prairie HS — 200/9-12
18575 E 800th St 61475 — 309-456-3750
Scott Sullivan, prin. — Fax 456-3997

Seneca, LaSalle, Pop. 2,330
Seneca CCSD 170 — 500/PK-8
174 Oak St 61360 — 815-357-8744
Eric Misener, supt. — Fax 357-1516
www.sgs170.org
Seneca MS South Campus — 200/5-8
174 Oak St 61360 — 815-357-8744
Shane Severson, prin. — Fax 357-1078

Seneca Township HSD 160 — 500/9-12
PO Box 20 61360 — 815-357-5000
Dr. Jim Carlson, supt. — Fax 357-5050
www.senecahs.org
Seneca HS — 500/9-12
PO Box 20 61360 — 815-357-5000
Marty Voiles, prin. — Fax 357-5050

Serena, LaSalle
Serena CUSD 2 — 700/K-12
PO Box 107 60549 — 815-496-2850
Marty Felesena, supt. — Fax 496-6630
www.unit2.net
Serena Community HS — 200/9-12
PO Box 107 60549 — 815-496-2361
Steve Hanson, prin. — Fax 496-2987

Sesser, Franklin, Pop. 1,900
Sesser-Valier CUSD 196 — 700/PK-12
4626 State Highway 154 62884 — 618-625-5105
Dr. Jason D. Henry, supt. — Fax 625-6696
sv196.org
Sesser-Valier HS — 200/9-12
4626 State Highway 154 62884 — 618-625-5105
Natalie Page, prin. — Fax 625-6696
Sesser-Valier JHS — 200/6-8
4626 State Highway 154 62884 — 618-625-5105
Judy L. Logsdon, prin. — Fax 625-3040

Shabbona, DeKalb, Pop. 921
Indian Creek CUSD 425 — 600/PK-12
506 S Shabbona Rd 60550 — 815-824-2197
Chad Willis, supt. — Fax 824-2199
www.indiancreekschools.org
Indian Creek HS — 200/9-12
506 S Shabbona Rd 60550 — 815-824-2197
Sarah Montgomery, prin. — Fax 824-2199
Other Schools – See Waterman

Shelbyville, Shelby, Pop. 4,676
Shelbyville CUSD 4 — 1,200/PK-12
720 W Main St 62565 — 217-774-4626
Denise Bence, supt. — Fax 774-2521
www.shelbyville.k12.il.us/
Moulton MS — 400/4-8
1101 W North 6th St 62565 — 217-774-2169
Russell Tomblin, prin. — Fax 774-3042
Shelbyville HS — 400/9-12
1001 W North 6th St 62565 — 217-774-3926
Shane Schuricht, prin. — Fax 774-5836

Sherrard, Mercer, Pop. 637
Sherrard CUSD 200 — 1,600/PK-12
PO Box 369 61281 — 309-593-4075
Dr. Samuel Light, supt. — Fax 593-4078
www.sherrard.us
Sherrard HS — 500/9-12
4701 176th Ave 61281 — 309-593-2175
Timothy Wernentin, prin. — Fax 593-2775
Sherrard JHS — 300/7-8
4701 176th Ave 61281 — 309-593-2135
Richard Basala, prin. — Fax 593-2143

Shiloh, Saint Clair, Pop. 12,229
Shiloh Village SD 85 — 600/PK-8
125 Diamond Ct 62269 — 618-632-7434
Dale Sauer, supt. — Fax 632-8343
www.shiloh.stclair.k12.il.us
Shiloh MS — 300/5-8
1 Wildcat Xing 62269 — 618-632-7434
Jeff Alt, prin. — Fax 622-9350

Sidell, Vermilion, Pop. 607
Salt Fork CUSD 512 — 700/PK-12
7087 N 600 East Rd 61876 — 217-288-9306
Dr. Phil Harrison, supt. — Fax 288-9393
www.saltfork.k12.il.us
Salt Fork JHS — 100/6-8
7087 N 600 East Rd 61876 — 217-288-9394
Brian Allensworth, prin. — Fax 288-9393

Other Schools – See Catlin

Skokie, Cook, Pop. 62,756
Niles Township HSD 219 — 4,800/9-12
7700 Gross Point Rd 60077 — 847-626-3000
Dr. Steven Isoye, supt. — Fax 626-3090
www.niles219.org
Niles Central S — 50/Alt
7700 Gross Point Rd 60077 — 847-626-3120
Dr. Anne Hellmer, dir. — Fax 626-3080
Niles North HS — 2,200/9-12
9800 Lawler Ave 60077 — 847-626-2000
James Edwards, prin. — Fax 626-3424
Niles West HS — 2,600/9-12
5701 Oakton St 60077 — 847-626-2500
Dr. Jason Ness, prin. — Fax 626-3700

Skokie SD 68 — 1,800/PK-8
9440 Kenton Ave 60076 — 847-676-9000
Dr. James Garwood, supt. — Fax 676-9232
www.skokie68.org
Old Orchard JHS — 600/PK-PK, 6-
9310 Kenton Ave 60076 — 847-676-9010
Robyn Huemmer, prin. — Fax 676-3827

Skokie SD 69 — 1,700/PK-8
5050 Madison St 60077 — 847-675-7666
Margaret Clauson, supt. — Fax 675-7675
www.skokie69.net
Lincoln JHS — 600/6-8
7839 Lincoln Ave 60077 — 847-676-3545
Lorenzo Cervantes, prin. — Fax 676-3595

Skokie SD 73-5 — 1,000/PK-8
8000 E Prairie Rd 60076 — 847-324-0509
Kate Donegan, supt. — Fax 673-1282
www.sd735.org
McCracken MS — 300/6-8
8000 E Prairie Rd 60076 — 847-673-1220
Allison Stein, prin. — Fax 673-1282

Computer Systems Institute — Post-Sec.
8930 Gross Point Rd 60077 — 847-967-5030
Everest College — Post-Sec.
9811 Woods Dr Ste 200 60077 — 847-470-0277
Fasman Yeshiva HS — 100/9-12
7135 Carpenter Rd 60077 — 847-982-2500
Hebrew Theological College — Post-Sec.
7135 Carpenter Rd 60077 — 847-982-2500
Ida Crown Jewish Academy — 300/9-12
8233 Central Park Ave 60076 — 773-973-1450
Rabbi Leonard Matanky, dean — Fax 973-6131
Knowledge Systems Institute — Post-Sec.
3420 Main St 60076 — 847-679-3135
Zarem/Golde ORT Technical Institute — Post-Sec.
5440 Fargo Ave 60077 — 847-324-5588

Somonauk, DeKalb, Pop. 1,867
Somonauk CUSD 432 — 800/PK-12
501 W Market St 60552 — 815-498-2314
Jay Streicher, supt. — Fax 498-9523
www.somonauk.net
Somonauk HS — 300/9-12
501 W Market St 60552 — 815-498-2314
Laura Hatch, prin. — Fax 498-9841
Somonauk MS — 300/5-8
510 W Lasalle St 60552 — 815-498-1866
Justin Snider, prin. — Fax 498-1647

South Beloit, Winnebago, Pop. 7,705
Prairie Hill CCSD 133 — 800/K-8
6605 Prairie Hill Rd 61080 — 815-389-3957
Wes Heiar, supt. — Fax 389-6107
www.prairiehill.org
Willowbrook MS — 400/5-8
6605 Prairie Hill Rd 61080 — 815-389-3957
Steve Heidel, prin. — Fax 389-6107

South Beloit CUSD 320 — 1,000/PK-12
850 Hayes Ave 61080 — 815-389-3478
Scott Fisher, supt. — Fax 389-3477
www.sbsobos.org/
South Beloit HS — 300/9-12
245 Prairie Hill Rd 61080 — 815-389-9004
Clint Czizek, prin. — Fax 389-9268
South Beloit JHS — 200/7-8
840 Blackhawk Blvd 61080 — 815-389-1421
Michael McCoy, prin. — Fax 389-8811

South Elgin, Kane, Pop. 21,549
SD U-46
Supt. — See Elgin
Kenyon Woods MS — 1,000/7-8
1515 Raymond St 60177 — 847-289-6685
Lisa Olsem, prin. — Fax 628-6166
South Elgin HS — 2,700/9-12
760 E Main St 60177 — 847-289-3760
Brian Moran, prin. — Fax 888-7014

South Holland, Cook, Pop. 21,729
South Holland SD 150 — 700/PK-8
848 E 170th St 60473 — 708-339-4240
Dr. Jerry Jordan, supt. — Fax 339-4244
www.sd150.org
McKinley JHS — 300/4-8
16949 Cottage Grove Ave 60473 — 708-339-8500
Jerome Ferrell, prin. — Fax 331-5805

South Holland SD 151 — 1,500/PK-8
525 E 162nd St 60473 — 708-339-1516
Dr. Teresa D. Hill, supt. — Fax 331-7600
www.shsd151.org
Other Schools – See Phoenix

Thornton Township HSD 205 — 4,900/9-12
465 E 170th St 60473 — 708-225-4000
Leotis Swopes Ed.D., supt. — Fax 225-4004
www.district205.net
Thornwood HS — 1,900/9-12
17101 S Park Ave 60473 — 708-225-4701
Dennis Willis, prin. — Fax 225-5033
Other Schools – See Dolton, Harvey

South Suburban College of Cook County — Post-Sec.
15800 State St 60473 — 708-596-2000

South Roxana, Madison, Pop. 2,033

Bethel Christian Academy — 100/PK-12
PO Box 87207 62087 — 618-254-0188
Tera Brasel, prin. — Fax 254-2067

Sparland, Marshall, Pop. 403
Midland CUSD 7
Supt. — See Varna
Midland MS — 200/5-8
901 Hilltop Dr 61565 — 309-469-3131
Adam Janssen, prin. — Fax 469-5701

Sparta, Randolph, Pop. 4,242
Sparta CUSD 140 — 900/PK-12
203B Dean Ave 62286 — 618-443-5331
Dr. Larry Beattie, supt. — Fax 443-2023
www.sparta.k12.il.us
Sparta HS — 400/9-12
205 W Hood St 62286 — 618-443-4341
R. Scott Beckley, prin. — Fax 443-5059

Springfield, Sangamon, Pop. 113,193
Capital Area Career Center
2201 Toronto Rd Ste B, — 217-529-5431
Jodi Ferriell, dir. — Fax 529-7861
capital.tec.il.us
Capital Area Career Center — Vo/Tech
2201 Toronto Rd Ste B, — 217-529-5431
Molly Uhe, prin. — Fax 529-7861

Menard/Sangamon ROE
200 S 9th St Ste 303 62701 — 217-753-6620
Jeff Vose, supt. — Fax 535-3166
www.roe51.org
Sangamon County Learning Academy — Alt
2201 Toronto Rd, — 217-529-3390
Julie Sullivan, prin.
Other Schools – See Athens

Springfield SD 186 — 14,900/PK-12
1900 W Monroe St 62704 — 217-525-3000
Jennifer Gill, supt. — Fax 525-3005
www.sps186.org/
Douglas S — 50/Alt
444 W Reynolds St 62702 — 217-525-4400
Kari Borders, prin. — Fax 525-4401
Franklin MS — 800/6-8
1200 Outer Park Dr 62704 — 217-787-3006
Tod Davis, prin. — Fax 525-7937
Grant MS — 600/6-8
1800 W Monroe St 62704 — 217-525-3170
Cindy Baugher, prin. — Fax 525-3390
Jefferson MS — 600/6-8
3001 S Allis St 62703 — 217-585-5810
Karen Stapleton-Crump, prin. — Fax 525-3293
Lanphier HS — 1,200/9-12
1300 N 11th St 62702 — 217-525-3080
Artie Doss, prin. — Fax 525-3084
Lee S — 200/PK-12
1201 Bunn Ave 62703 — 217-585-5828
Nathan Kochanowski, prin. — Fax 535-2755
Lincoln Magnet MS — 300/6-8
300 S 11th St 62703 — 217-525-3236
Nichole Heyen, prin. — Fax 525-3294
Springfield HS — 1,400/9-12
101 S Lewis St 62704 — 217-525-3100
Lisa Leardi, prin. — Fax 525-3122
Springfield Learning Academy — 100/Alt
101 E Laurel St 62704 — 217-525-3358
Reiko Hurd, prin. — Fax 525-3090
Springfield Southeast HS — 1,400/9-12
2350 E Ash St 62703 — 217-525-3130
Jason Wind, prin. — Fax 525-3139
Washington MS — 700/6-8
2300 E Jackson St 62703 — 217-525-3182
Vincent Turner, prin. — Fax 525-3319
Lawrence Education Center — Adult
101 E Laurel St 62704 — 217-525-3144
Kathi Lee, prin. — Fax 525-3090

Calvary Academy — 300/PK-12
1730 W Jefferson St 62702 — 217-546-5987
Dr. Jay Hinckley, prin. — Fax 321-1063
Lincoln Land Community College — Post-Sec.
PO Box 19256 62794 — 217-786-2200
Lutheran HS — 200/9-12
3500 W Washington St, — 217-546-6363
Glenn Rollins, prin. — Fax 546-6489
Midwest Technical Institute — Post-Sec.
2731 N Farmers Market Rd 62707 — 800-814-5124
Robert Morris University — Post-Sec.
3101 Montvale Dr 62704 — 800-762-5960
Sacred Heart-Griffin HS — 800/9-12
1200 W Washington St 62702 — 217-787-1595
Sr. Katherine O'Connor, prin. — Fax 787-9856
St. John's College — Post-Sec.
729 E Carpenter St 62702 — 217-525-5628
St. John's Hospital — Post-Sec.
800 E Carpenter St 62769 — 217-544-6464
University of Illinois at Springfield — Post-Sec.
1 University Plz 62703 — 217-206-6600

Spring Grove, McHenry, Pop. 5,732
Fox Lake Grade SD 114 — 800/PK-8
29067 W Grass Lake Rd 60081 — 847-973-4114
John Donnellan, supt. — Fax 973-4010
www.foxlake114.org
Other Schools – See Fox Lake

Spring Valley, Bureau, Pop. 5,488
Hall HSD 502 — 400/9-12
800 W Erie St 61362 — 815-664-4500
Michael Struna, supt. — Fax 664-2300
www.hallhighschool.org

Hall HS 400/9-12
800 W Erie St 61362 815-664-2100
Michael Struna, prin. Fax 664-2300

Stanford, McLean, Pop. 590
Olympia CUSD 16 1,800/PK-12
903 E 800 North Rd 61774 309-379-6011
Dr. Andrew S. Wise, supt. Fax 379-2328
www.olympia.org
Olympia HS 600/9-12
7832 N 100 East Rd 61774 309-379-5911
Dr. Ed Jodlowski, prin. Fax 379-2583
Olympia MS 400/6-8
911 E 800 North Rd 61774 309-379-5941
Andrew Walsh, prin. Fax 379-5411

Staunton, Macoupin, Pop. 5,081
Staunton CUSD 6 1,200/PK-12
801 N Deneen St 62088 618-635-2962
Dan Cox, supt. Fax 635-2994
www.stauntonschools.org
Staunton HS 400/9-12
801 N Deneen St 62088 618-635-3838
Brett Allen, prin. Fax 635-2834
Staunton JHS 300/6-8
801 N Deneen St 62088 618-635-3831
Nancy Werden, prin. Fax 635-4637

Steeleville, Randolph, Pop. 2,076
Steeleville CUSD 138 400/PK-12
609 S Sparta St 62288 618-965-3469
Dr. Stephanie Mulholland, supt. Fax 965-3433
www.steeleville138.org
Steeleville HS 100/9-12
701 S Sparta St 62288 618-965-3432
Jennifer Haertling, prin. Fax 965-3433

Steger, Will, Pop. 9,382
Steger SD 194 800/PK-8
3753 Park Ave 60475 708-755-0022
Dr. Patricia Hahto, supt. Fax 755-9512
www.sd194.org
Columbia Central MS 500/5-8
94 Richton Rd 60475 708-755-0021
Mike Smith, prin. Fax 755-1877

Sterling, Whiteside, Pop. 15,098
Sterling CUSD 5 3,300/PK-12
410 E Le Fevre Rd 61081 815-626-5050
Tad Everett, supt. Fax 622-4113
www.sterlingpublicschools.org
Challand MS 700/6-8
1700 6th Ave 61081 815-626-3300
Matt Birdsley, prin. Fax 622-4173
Sterling HS 1,000/9-12
1608 4th Ave 61081 815-625-6800
Jason Austin, prin. Fax 622-4157

Whiteside Area Career Center
1608 5th Ave 61081 815-626-5810
Kim Purvis, supt.
Whiteside Area Career Center Vo/Tech
1608 5th Ave 61081 815-626-5810
Kim Purvis, prin.

Educators of Beauty Post-Sec.
211 E 3rd St 61081 815-625-0247
Newman Central Catholic HS 300/9-12
1101 W 23rd St 61081 815-625-0500
Kathleen Howard, prin. Fax 625-8444

Stillman Valley, Ogle, Pop. 1,114
Meridian CUSD 223 1,800/PK-12
207 W Main St 61084 815-645-2230
Dr. Phillip Caposey, supt. Fax 645-4325
www.meridian223.org
Meridian JHS 400/6-8
207 W Main St 61084 815-645-2230
Jill Davis, prin. Fax 645-8181
Stillman Valley HS 600/9-12
425 S Pine St 61084 815-645-2230
Leslie Showers, prin. Fax 645-8145

Stockton, Jo Daviess, Pop. 1,848
Stockton CUSD 206 600/PK-12
540 N Rush St 61085 815-947-3391
Dr. David Gilliland, supt. Fax 947-2673
www.stocktonschools.com
Stockton HS 200/9-12
540 N Rush St 61085 815-947-3323
Dr. David Gilliland, prin. Fax 947-2673
Stockton MS 200/5-8
500 N Rush St 61085 815-947-3702
Brad Fox, prin. Fax 947-2114

Strasburg, Shelby, Pop. 465
Stewardson-Strasburg CUSD 5A 300/PK-12
2806 E 600 North Rd 62465 217-682-3355
Dr. Michele Lindenmeyer, supt. Fax 682-3305
www.stew-stras.org
Stewardson-Strasburg JSHS 100/7-12
2806 E 600 North Rd 62465 217-682-3355
Justin Deters, prin. Fax 682-3305

Streamwood, Cook, Pop. 39,124
SD U-46
Supt. — See Elgin
Canton MS 600/7-8
1100 Sunset Cir 60107 630-213-5525
Jeff Smith, prin. Fax 213-5709
Streamwood HS 2,000/9-12
701 W Schaumburg Rd 60107 630-213-5500
Ariel Correa, prin. Fax 483-5909
Tefft MS 900/7-8
1100 Shirley Ave 60107 630-213-5535
Lavonne Smiley, prin. Fax 213-5646

Streator, LaSalle, Pop. 13,509
Streator ESD 44 1,800/PK-8
1520 N Bloomington St 61364 815-672-2926
Matthew Wilkinson, supt. Fax 673-2032
www.ses44.net/
Northlawn JHS 800/5-8
202 E 1st St 61364 815-672-4558
Keri Jancek, prin. Fax 672-8109

Streator Twp. HSD 40 900/9-12
202 W Lincoln Ave 61364 815-672-0545
Matt Seaton, supt. Fax 673-3637
www.streatorhs.org
Streator Twp. HS 900/9-12
202 W Lincoln Ave 61364 815-672-0545
Amy Mascal, prin. Fax 673-3637

Woodland CUSD 5 500/PK-12
5800 E 3000 North Rd 61364 815-672-5974
Ryan McGuckin, supt. Fax 673-1630
www.woodland5.com
Woodland HS 100/9-12
5800 E 3000 North Rd 61364 815-672-2900
Debra Derby, prin.

Stronghurst, Henderson, Pop. 875
West Central CUSD 235
Supt. — See Biggsville
West Central MS 200/6-8
PO Box 179 61480 309-924-1681
Julia Burns, prin. Fax 924-1122

Sugar Grove, Kane, Pop. 8,881
Kaneland CUSD 302
Supt. — See Maple Park
Harter MS 1,100/6-8
1601 N Esker Dr 60554 630-466-8400
Brian Faulkner, prin. Fax 466-1999

Waubonsee Community College Post-Sec.
Route 47 at Waubonsee Dr 60554 630-466-7900

Sullivan, Moultrie, Pop. 4,417
Sullivan CUSD 300 1,100/PK-12
725 N Main St 61951 217-728-8341
Brad Tuttle, supt. Fax 728-4139
home.sullivan.k12.il.us
Sullivan HS 300/9-12
725 N Main St 61951 217-728-8311
Erik Young, prin. Fax 728-4139
Sullivan MS 200/6-8
713 N Main St 61951 217-728-8381
Ted Walk, prin. Fax 728-4139

Summit, Cook
Summit SD 104 1,900/PK-8
6021 S 74th Ave 60501 708-458-0505
Dr. Troy J. Whalen, supt. Fax 458-0532
www.sd104.us
Heritage MS 500/6-8
6021 S 74th Ave 60501 708-458-7590
Robert Bassett, prin. Fax 728-3111

Summit Argo, Cook, Pop. 10,942
Argo Community HSD 217 1,800/9-12
7329 W 63rd St 60501 708-728-3200
Dr. Kevin O'Mara, supt. Fax 728-3155
www.argohs.net
Argo Community HS 1,800/9-12
7329 W 63rd St 60501 708-728-3200
Dr. Christopher Covino, prin. Fax 728-3155

Swansea, Saint Clair, Pop. 13,123
Wolf Branch SD 113 900/K-8
410 Huntwood Rd 62226 618-277-2100
Scott Harres, supt. Fax 235-2376
www.wbsd113.org
Wolf Branch MS 400/5-8
410 Huntwood Rd 62226 618-277-2100
Jennifer Poirot, dean Fax 277-5461

Sycamore, DeKalb, Pop. 17,257
Sycamore CUSD 427 3,700/PK-12
245 W Exchange St Ste 1 60178 815-899-8100
Kathy Countryman, supt. Fax 899-8110
www.syc427.org
Sycamore HS 1,200/9-12
427 Spartan Trl 60178 815-899-8160
Tim Carlson, prin. Fax 899-8166
Sycamore MS 900/6-8
150 Maplewood Dr 60178 815-899-8170
Jim Cleven, prin. Fax 899-8177

Cornerstone Christian Academy 300/PK-12
355 N Cross St 60178 815-895-8522
Tom Olmstead, admin. Fax 895-8717
Hair Professionals Career College Post-Sec.
2245 Gateway Dr 60178 815-756-3596

Table Grove, Fulton, Pop. 410
V I T CUSD 2 400/PK-12
1502 E US Highway 136 61482 309-758-5138
Michael Curry, supt. Fax 758-5298
www.vit2.org
V I T HS 100/9-12
1500 E US Highway 136 61482 309-758-5136
Tracey Korsmeyer, prin. Fax 758-5126
V I T JHS 50/7-8
1500 E US Highway 136 61482 309-758-5136
Tracey Korsmeyer, prin. Fax 758-5126

Tamms, Alexander, Pop. 620
Egyptian CUSD 5 500/PK-12
20023 Diswood Rd 62988 618-776-5306
Brad Misner, supt. Fax 776-5122
www.egyptianschool.com
Egyptian HS 100/9-12
20023 Diswood Rd 62988 618-776-5251
Bret Gowin, prin. Fax 776-5122
Egyptian JHS 100/6-8
20023 Diswood Rd 62988 618-776-5251
Bret Gowin, prin. Fax 776-5122

Five County Regional Vocational System
130 Washington Ave 62988 618-747-2703
Jerry Ohlau, dir. Fax 747-2872
Five County Regional Vocational Center Vo/Tech
130 Washington Ave 62988 618-747-2703
Jerry Ohlau, dir. Fax 747-2872

Taylor Ridge, Rock Island
Rockridge CUSD 300 1,100/PK-12
14110 134th Ave W 61284 309-793-8001
Perry Miller, supt. Fax 795-1719
rockridgeschools.org
Rockridge HS 400/9-12
14110 134th Ave W 61284 309-793-8020
Katy Hasson, prin. Fax 795-1763
Rockridge JHS 300/6-8
14110 134th Ave W 61284 309-793-8040
Katy Hasson, prin. Fax 795-9823

Taylorville, Christian, Pop. 11,116
Taylorville CUSD 3 2,600/PK-12
512 W Spresser St 62568 217-824-4951
Dr. Greggory Fuerstenau, supt. Fax 824-5157
www.taylorvilleschools.com
Taylorville HS 800/9-12
815 W Springfield Rd 62568 217-824-2268
Matthew Hutchison, prin. Fax 824-3352
Taylorville JHS 800/5-8
120 E Bidwell St 62568 217-824-4924
Kirk Kettelkamp, prin. Fax 824-7180

Teutopolis, Effingham, Pop. 1,530
Teutopolis CUSD 50 1,100/PK-12
PO Box 607 62467 217-857-3535
William Fritcher, supt. Fax 857-6265
www.teutopolisschools.org/
Teutopolis HS 400/9-12
801 W Main St 62467 217-857-3139
Greg Beck, prin. Fax 857-3473
Teutopolis JHS 200/7-8
904 W Water St 62467 217-857-6678
Patrick Drees, prin. Fax 857-6051

Thomasboro, Champaign, Pop. 1,098
Prairieview-Ogden CCSD 197
Supt. — See Royal
Prairieview-Ogden JHS 100/7-8
2499 County Road 2100 E 61878 217-694-4122
Steve Fiscus, prin. Fax 694-4123

Thompsonville, Franklin, Pop. 542
Thompsonville CUSD 174 300/K-12
21191 Shawneetown Rd 62890 618-627-2446
Chris Grant, supt. Fax 627-2302
thompsonville.il.schoolwebpages.com/
Thompsonville HS 100/9-12
21191 Shawneetown Rd 62890 618-627-2301
Chris Grant, prin. Fax 627-2302

Thompsonville Christian Junior Academy 50/K-10
PO Box 53 62890 618-627-2065
Evelyn Hainey, prin. Fax 627-2065

Tinley Park, Cook, Pop. 56,069
Bremen Community HSD 228
Supt. — See Midlothian
Tinley Park HS 1,200/9-12
6111 175th St 60477 708-532-1900
Theresa Nolan, prin. Fax 532-4332

CCSD 146 2,400/PK-8
6611 171st St 60477 708-614-4500
Dr. Jeff Stawick, supt. Fax 614-8992
www.district146.org
Central MS 700/6-8
18146 Oak Park Ave 60477 708-614-4510
Randy Fortin, prin. Fax 614-7271

Kirby SD 140 3,600/PK-8
16931 Grissom Dr 60477 708-532-6462
Julia Mikulich, supt. Fax 532-1512
www.ksd140.org
Grissom MS 600/6-8
17000 80th Ave 60477 708-429-3030
Deborah Broadwell, prin. Fax 532-8529
Prairie View MS 600/6-8
8500 175th St, 708-532-8540
Meghan Maurer, prin. Fax 532-8544

DeVry University Post-Sec.
18624 W Creek Dr 60477 708-342-3300
Fox College Post-Sec.
18020 Oak Park Ave 60477 708-444-4500
Paul Mitchell The School Post-Sec.
18454 W Creek Dr 60477 708-478-6907

Toledo, Cumberland, Pop. 1,235
Cumberland CUSD 77 1,000/PK-12
1496 Illinois Route 121 62468 217-923-3132
Todd Butler, supt. Fax 923-3132
www.cumberland.k12.il.us
Cumberland HS 300/9-12
1496 Illinois Route 121 62468 217-923-3133
Kevin Maynard, prin. Fax 923-5514
Cumberland MS 300/5-8
1496 Illinois Route 121 62468 217-923-3135
Stacy Keyser, prin. Fax 923-5449

Tolono, Champaign, Pop. 3,389
Tolono CUSD 7 1,700/PK-12
PO Box 720 61880 217-485-6510
Andrew Larson, supt. Fax 485-3091
www.unitsevenschools.com
Unity HS 500/9-12
1127 County Road 800 N 61880 217-485-6230
Phil Morrison, prin. Fax 485-6220
Unity JHS 400/6-8
1121 County Road 800 N 61880 217-485-6735
Laura Fitzgerald, prin. Fax 485-3218

Toulon, Stark, Pop. 1,289
Stark County CUSD 100
Supt. — See Wyoming
Stark County HS 300/9-12
PO Box 419 61483 309-286-4451
William Lamb, prin. Fax 286-3321
Stark County JHS, PO Box 659 61483 200/6-8
William Lamb, prin. 309-286-3451

Tremont, Tazewell, Pop. 2,212
Tremont CUSD 702 1,000/PK-12
400 W Pearl St 61568 309-925-3461
Jeff Hinman, supt. Fax 925-5817
www.tremont702.net
Tremont HS 300/9-12
400 W Pearl St 61568 309-925-2051
Sean Berry, prin. Fax 925-5817
Tremont MS 300/5-8
400 W Pearl St 61568 309-925-3823
Jeremy Garrett, prin. Fax 925-5817

Trenton, Clinton, Pop. 2,693
Wesclin CUSD 3 1,100/PK-12
699 Wesclin Rd 62293 618-224-7583
Jennifer Filyaw, supt. Fax 588-9106
www.wesclin.org
Wesclin HS 400/9-12
699 Wesclin Rd 62293 618-224-7341
John Isenhower, prin. Fax 588-9106
Wesclin MS 200/4-8
10003 State Route 160 62293 618-224-7355
Roger Freeze, prin. Fax 224-7085

Troy, Madison, Pop. 9,707
Triad CUSD 2 3,600/PK-12
203 E Throp St 62294 618-667-5400
Leigh Lewis, supt. Fax 667-8854
www.tcusd2.org
Triad HS 1,200/9-12
703 E US Highway 40 62294 618-667-5409
Dr. Rodney Winslow, prin. Fax 667-8853
Other Schools – See Saint Jacob

Tuscola, Douglas, Pop. 4,425
Tuscola CUSD 301 1,000/PK-12
409 S Prairie St 61953 217-253-4241
Michael Smith, supt. Fax 253-4522
www.tuscola.k12.il.us/
East Prairie JHS 300/5-8
409 S Prairie St 61953 217-253-2828
Carol Munson, prin. Fax 253-3236
Tuscola HS 300/9-12
500 S Prairie St 61953 217-253-2377
Brad Allen, prin. Fax 253-4861

Ullin, Pulaski, Pop. 448
Century CUSD 100 400/K-12
4721 Shawnee College Rd 62992 618-845-3447
Leslie Varble, supt. Fax 845-3476
www.centuryschooldistrict100.com/
Century JSHS 200/6-12
4721 Shawnee College Rd 62992 618-845-3518
Leslie Varble, prin. Fax 845-3476

Shawnee Community College Post-Sec.
8364 Shawnee College Rd 62992 618-634-3200

Union, McHenry, Pop. 576
McHenry ROE
Supt. — See Woodstock
Evergreen Academy 50/Alt
6506 National St 60180 815-923-2789
Cheryl Horn, prin. Fax 923-4450

University Park, Will, Pop. 6,997
Crete-Monee CUSD 201U
Supt. — See Crete
Crete-Monee MS 800/6-8
635 Olmstead Ln, 708-367-2400
Kokona Chrisos, prin. Fax 672-2777

Governors State University Post-Sec.
1 University Pkwy, 708-534-5000

Urbana, Champaign, Pop. 39,989
University of IL Lab S 300/8-12
1212 W Springfield Ave 61801 217-333-2870
Dr. Jeffrey Wakington, supt.
University of Illinois HS 300/8-12
1212 W Springfield Ave 61801 217-333-2870
Susan Kovacs, dir.

Urbana SD 116 4,300/PK-12
PO Box 3039 61803 217-384-3636
Dr. Donald Owen Ed.D., supt. Fax 337-4973
www.usd116.org
Urbana HS 1,000/9-12
1002 S Race St 61801 217-384-3505
Matthew Stark, prin. Fax 384-3532
Urbana MS 900/6-8
1201 S Vine St 61801 217-384-3685
Scott Woods, prin. Fax 367-3156

Concept College of Cosmetology Post-Sec.
129 N Race St 61801 217-344-7550
Kingswood S 50/K-12
PO Box 834 61803 217-344-5540
Marsh Jones, hdmstr. Fax 344-5535
University of Illinois Post-Sec.
901 W Illinois St 61801 217-333-1000

Utica, LaSalle, Pop. 1,346
Waltham Community CESD 185 200/K-8
946 N 33rd Rd 61373 815-667-4790
Kristine Eager, supt. Fax 667-4462
www.wesd185.org
Waltham North S 200/3-8
946 N 33rd Rd 61373 815-667-4417
Kristine Eager, admin. Fax 667-4462

Valmeyer, Monroe, Pop. 1,250
Valmeyer CUSD 3 500/PK-12
300 S Cedar Bluff Dr 62295 618-935-2100
Eric Frankford, supt. Fax 935-2108
www.valmeyerk12.org
Valmeyer HS 100/9-12
300 S Cedar Bluff Dr 62295 618-935-2100
Eric Frankford, prin. Fax 935-2108
Valmeyer JHS 100/6-8
300 S Cedar Bluff Dr 62295 618-939-2100
Teena Riechmann, prin. Fax 939-2108

Vandalia, Fayette, Pop. 6,969
Bond/Christn/Effingham/Fayette/Mtgmy ROE 100/
300 S 7th St 62471 618-283-5011
Julie Wollerman, supt. Fax 283-5013
www.roe3.org
New Approach Alternative HS 50/Alt
1500 W Jefferson St 62471 618-283-9311
Laura Benhoff, prin. Fax 283-9339
Other Schools – See Effingham

Okaw Area Vocational Center
1109 N 8th St 62471 618-283-5150
Dian Keil, supt. Fax 283-2014
www.vcs.fayette.k12.il.us/OKAW
Okaw Area Vocational Center Vo/Tech
1109 N 8th St 62471 618-283-5150
Nick Casey, dir. Fax 283-2014

Vandalia CUSD 203 1,100/PK-12
1109 N 8th St 62471 618-283-4525
Rich Well, supt. Fax 283-4107
www.vcs.fayette.k12.il.us/
Vandalia Community HS 500/9-12
1109 N 8th St 62471 618-283-5155
Randy Protz, prin. Fax 283-9855
Vandalia JHS 500/4-8
1011 W Fletcher St 62471 618-283-5151
Brian Kern, prin. Fax 283-8165

Varna, Marshall, Pop. 382
Midland CUSD 7 700/PK-12
1830 State Route 17 61375 309-469-2061
Bill Wrenn, supt. Fax 463-2685
midland-7.info
Midland HS 200/9-12
1830 State Route 17 61375 309-463-2095
Jeremy Gauwitz, prin. Fax 463-2630
Other Schools – See Sparland

Vergennes, Jackson, Pop. 291
Elverado CUSD 196
Supt. — See Elkville
Elverado JHS 100/6-8
PO Box 35 62994 618-684-3527
Belinda Conner, prin. Fax 687-3363

Vernon Hills, Lake, Pop. 24,688
Community HSD 128 3,300/9-12
50 Lakeview Pkwy Ste 101 60061 847-247-4500
Dr. Prentiss Lea, supt. Fax 247-4543
www.d128.org/
Vernon Hills HS 1,300/9-12
145 Lakeview Pkwy 60061 847-932-2000
Dr. Jon Guillaume, prin. Fax 932-2049
Other Schools – See Libertyville

Hawthorn CCSD 73 4,000/K-8
841 W End Ct 60061 847-990-4200
Nicholas Brown, supt. Fax 367-3290
www.hawthorn73.org
Hawthorn MS North 600/6-8
201 W Hawthorn Pkwy 60061 847-990-4400
Robert Collins, prin. Fax 367-8124
Hawthorn MS South 700/6-8
600 N Aspen Dr 60061 847-990-4100
Robert Natale, prin. Fax 816-9259

Vienna, Johnson, Pop. 1,414
Vienna HSD 133 300/9-12
601 N 1st St 62995 618-658-4461
Joshua W. Stafford, supt. Fax 658-9727
www.viennahighschool.com
Vienna HS 300/9-12
601 N 1st St 62995 618-658-4461
John R. Griffin, dean Fax 658-2122

Villa Grove, Douglas, Pop. 2,492
Villa Grove CUSD 302 600/PK-12
400 N Sycamore St 61956 217-832-2261
Norm Tracy, supt. Fax 832-8615
www.vg302.org
Villa Grove HS 200/9-12
400 N Sycamore St 61956 217-832-2321
Stephen Killion, prin. Fax 832-8689
Villa Grove JHS 100/7-8
400 N Sycamore St 61956 217-832-2261
Stephen Killion, prin. Fax 832-8615

Villa Park, DuPage, Pop. 21,596
DuPage County SD 45 3,400/PK-8
255 W Vermont St 60181 630-516-7700
Anthony Palmisano, supt. Fax 530-1624
www.d45.org
Jackson MS 700/6-8
301 W Jackson St 60181 630-516-7600
James Doyle, prin. Fax 530-6271
Jefferson MS 400/6-8
255 W Vermont St 60181 630-516-7800
Raul Gaston, prin. Fax 993-6348

DuPage HSD 88
Supt. — See Addison
Willowbrook HS 2,000/9-12
1250 S Ardmore Ave 60181 630-530-3400
Daniel Krause, prin. Fax 530-3401

Salt Creek SD 48 500/PK-8
1110 S Villa Ave 60181 630-279-8400
Dr. John Correll, supt. Fax 279-6167
www.saltcreek48.org
Albright MS 200/5-8
1110 S Villa Ave 60181 630-279-6160
Scott Jackson, prin. Fax 279-1614

Cannella School of Hair Design Post-Sec.
617 W North Ave 60181 630-833-6118
Islamic Foundation S 700/PK-12
300 W Highridge Rd 60181 630-941-8800
Omar Qureshi, dir. Fax 941-8804
Ms. Robert's Academy of Beauty Culture Post-Sec.
17 E Park Blvd 60181 630-941-3880

Virden, Macoupin, Pop. 3,404
North Mac CUSD 34
Supt. — See Girard
North Mac HS 400/9-12
231 W Fortune St 62690 217-965-4127
Rob Horn, prin. Fax 965-4006

Virginia, Cass, Pop. 1,600
Virginia CUSD 64 200/PK-12
651 S Morgan St 62691 217-452-3085
Brent ODaniell, supt. Fax 452-3088
virginia64.com
Virginia JSHS 100/6-12
651 S Morgan St 62691 217-452-3087
Aaron Llewellyn, prin. Fax 452-3088

Wadsworth, Lake, Pop. 3,763
Millburn CCSD 24 1,400/PK-8
18550 W Millburn Rd 60083 847-356-8331
Dr. Jason Lind, supt. Fax 356-9722
www.millburn24.net/
Other Schools – See Lindenhurst

Waltonville, Jefferson, Pop. 432
Waltonville CUSD 1 400/PK-12
804 W Knob St 62894 618-279-7211
Alan Estes, supt. Fax 279-3291
www.wcusd1.org
Waltonville HS 100/9-12
804 W Knob St 62894 618-279-7211
Alan Estes, admin. Fax 279-3291

Warren, Jo Daviess, Pop. 1,421
Warren CUSD 205 400/PK-12
311 S Water St 61087 815-745-2653
Shawn Teske, supt. Fax 745-2037
www.205warren.net
Warren JSHS 200/6-12
311 S Water St 61087 815-745-2641
Steve Rickert, prin. Fax 745-2654

Warrensburg, Macon, Pop. 1,195
Warrensburg-Latham CUSD 11 1,000/PK-12
430 W North St 62573 217-672-3514
Dr. Kristen Kendrick-Weikle, supt. Fax 672-8468
www.wl.k12.il.us
Warrensburg-Latham HS 300/9-12
427 W North St 62573 217-672-3531
Ken Hatcher, prin. Fax 672-3261
Warrensburg-Latham MS 200/6-8
425 W North St 62573 217-672-3321
Paul Hoffman, prin. Fax 672-3770

Warrenville, DuPage, Pop. 12,933
CUSD 200
Supt. — See Wheaton
Hubble MS 800/6-8
3S600 Herrick Rd 60555 630-821-7900
Dr. Jon Pilkington, prin. Fax 821-7901

Carmel Montessori Academy 50/PK-12
3S238 State Route 59 60555 630-393-2995
Jacob LaFranzo, admin.

Warsaw, Hancock, Pop. 1,585
Warsaw CUSD 316 400/PK-12
340 S 11th St 62379 217-256-4282
Bob Gound, supt. Fax 256-4282
warsawschool.com
Warsaw HS, 340 S 11th St 62379 200/9-12
Brad Froman, prin. 217-256-4281

Washburn, Marshall, Pop. 1,146
Lowpoint-Washburn CUSD 21 400/PK-12
PO Box 580 61570 309-248-7522
Parker Deitrich, supt. Fax 248-7518
www.lwdistrict21.com
Lowpoint-Washburn JSHS 200/7-12
PO Box 580 61570 309-248-7521
Mark Zulz, prin. Fax 248-7410

Washington, Tazewell, Pop. 14,931
Central SD 51 1,300/PK-8
1301 Eagle Ave 61571 309-444-3943
Dale Heidbreder, supt. Fax 444-9898
www.central51.net
Central IS 700/4-8
1301 Eagle Ave 61571 309-444-3943
Brian Hoelscher, prin. Fax 444-3414

District 50 Schools 800/PK-8
304 E Almond Dr 61571 309-745-8914
Dr. Chad Allaman, supt. Fax 745-5417
www.d50schools.com
Manor MS, 1014 School St 61571 400/4-8
Angela Ludlum, prin. 309-745-3921

Washington Community HSD 308 1,200/9-12
115 Bondurant St 61571 309-444-7704
Dr. Kyle Freeman, supt. Fax 444-5767
www.wacohi.net
Washington Comm HS 1,200/9-12
115 Bondurant St 61571 309-444-3167
Dr. Kyle Freeman, admin. Fax 444-5767

Washington SD 52 — 1,000/PK-8
303 Jackson St 61571 — 309-444-4182
Patreak Minasian, supt. — Fax 444-8538
www.d52schools.com
Washington MS — 400/5-8
1100 N Main St 61571 — 309-444-3361
Daniel Foehrkolb, prin. — Fax 444-3941

Waterloo, Monroe, Pop. 9,722
Waterloo CUSD 5 — 2,700/PK-12
302 Bellefontaine Dr 62298 — 618-939-3453
Brian Charron, supt. — Fax 939-4578
www.wcusd5.net
Waterloo HS — 900/9-12
505 E Bulldog 62298 — 618-939-3455
Lori Costello, prin. — Fax 939-5180
Waterloo JHS — 600/6-8
200 Bellefontaine Dr 62298 — 618-939-3457
Nick Schwartz, prin. — Fax 939-1383

Gibault Catholic HS — 200/9-12
501 Columbia Ave 62298 — 618-939-3883
Russell Hart, prin. — Fax 939-7215

Waterman, DeKalb, Pop. 1,482
Indian Creek CUSD 425
Supt. — See Shabbona
Indian Creek MS — 200/5-8
425 S Elm St 60556 — 815-264-7712
Steven Simpson, prin. — Fax 264-7826

Watseka, Iroquois, Pop. 5,192
Iroquois County CUSD 9 — 900/PK-12
1411 W Lafayette St 60970 — 815-432-4931
James Bunting, supt. — Fax 432-6889
www.watseka-u9.k12.il.us
Raymond MS — 200/5-8
101 W Mulberry St 60970 — 815-432-2115
Bradley Welch, prin. — Fax 432-6896
Watseka Community HS — 300/9-12
138 S Belmont Ave 60970 — 815-432-2486
Carolyn Short, prin. — Fax 432-5578

Wauconda, Lake, Pop. 13,421
Wauconda CUSD 118 — 4,500/PK-12
555 N Main St 60084 — 847-526-7690
Dr. Daniel J. Coles, supt. — Fax 526-1019
www.d118.org
Wauconda HS — 1,300/9-12
555 N Main St 60084 — 847-526-6611
Daniel Klett, prin. — Fax 487-3595
Wauconda MS — 500/6-8
215 Slocum Lake Rd 60084 — 847-526-2122
Daniel Stoller, prin. — Fax 487-3597
Other Schools – See Island Lake

Frassati Academy — 6-8
316 W Mill St 60084 — 847-487-5600
Tammy Kleckner, prin. — Fax 487-5611

Waukegan, Lake, Pop. 87,117
Waukegan CUSD 60 — 16,700/PK-12
1201 N Sheridan Rd 60085 — 224-303-1000
Theresa Plascencia, supt.
www.wps60.org
Abbott MS — 800/6-8
1319 Washington St 60085 — 224-303-2360
Timothy Bryner, prin. — Fax 399-8512
Benny MS — 600/6-8
1401 Montesano Ave 60087 — 224-303-2460
Shanie Keelean, prin. — Fax 399-8524
Jefferson MS — 900/6-8
600 S Lewis Ave 60085 — 224-303-2560
Dr. Chaun Johnson, prin. — Fax 399-8516
Juarez MS — 800/6-8
201 N Butrick St 60085 — 224-303-2660
Nelson Campos, prin. — Fax 399-8506
Waukegan Alternative S — 100/Alt
1020 Glen Rock Ave 60085 — 224-303-2860
Grant Flink, dir. — Fax 399-8520
Waukegan HS — 4,400/9-12
2325 Brookside Ave 60085 — 224-303-3000
Brian Riegler, prin. — Fax 399-8542
Webster MS — 700/6-8
930 New York St 60085 — 224-303-2760
Yvonne Brown, prin. — Fax 399-8540

Cristo Rey St. Martin College Prep HS — 200/9-12
515 S Martin Luther King Jr 60085 — 847-623-5500
Michael Odiotti, prin. — Fax 623-5604
Lake County Baptist S — 200/PK-12
1550 W Yorkhouse Rd 60087 — 847-623-7600
Timothy Kowach, prin. — Fax 623-2085
Robert Morris University — Post-Sec.
1507 S Waukegan Rd 60085 — 800-762-5960

Waverly, Morgan, Pop. 1,296
Waverly CUSD 6 — 300/PK-12
201 N Miller St 62692 — 217-435-8121
Dustin Day, supt. — Fax 435-3431
www.waverlyscotties.com
Waverly HS — 100/7-12
201 N Miller St 62692 — 217-435-2211
Tamara Hermes, prin. — Fax 435-3431

Wayne City, Wayne, Pop. 1,023
Wayne City CUSD 100 — 500/PK-12
302 Mill St 62895 — 618-895-3103
Jeff Mitchell, supt. — Fax 895-2331
www.waynecity100.org
Wayne City JSHS — 200/7-12
302 Mill St 62895 — 618-895-3103
Tony Richardson, prin. — Fax 895-2331

Weldon, DeWitt, Pop. 425
Deland-Weldon CUSD 57
Supt. — See De Land
Deland-Weldon MS — 50/7-8
2311 N 300 East Rd 61882 — 217-736-2401
Amanda Geary, prin. — Fax 736-2654

Westchester, Cook, Pop. 16,532
Westchester SD 92-5 — 1,200/K-8
9981 Canterbury St 60154 — 708-450-2700
Michael Dziallo, supt. — Fax 450-2718
www.sd925.org
Westchester MS — 400/6-8
1620 Norfolk Ave 60154 — 708-450-2735
Gregory Leban, prin. — Fax 450-2752

St. Joseph HS — 800/9-12
10900 W Cermak Rd 60154 — 708-562-4433
Ronald Hoover, prin. — Fax 562-4459

West Chicago, DuPage, Pop. 26,802
Benjamin SD 25 — 700/PK-8
28W250 Saint Charles Rd 60185 — 630-876-7800
Dr. Philip Ehrhardt, supt. — Fax 876-3325
www.bendist25.org
Benjamin MS — 300/5-8
28W300 Saint Charles Rd 60185 — 630-876-7820
Michael Fitzgerald, prin. — Fax 231-3886

Community HSD 94 — 2,000/9-12
326 Joliet St 60185 — 630-876-6200
Dr. Douglas Domeracki, supt. — Fax 876-6241
www.d94.org
Community HS — 2,000/9-12
326 Joliet St 60185 — 630-876-6200
Dr. Moses Cheng, prin. — Fax 876-6241

West Chicago ESD 33 — 4,400/PK-8
312 E Forest Ave 60185 — 630-293-6000
Dr. Charles Johns, supt. — Fax 293-6088
www.wego33.org
Leman MS — 1,300/6-8
238 E Hazel St 60185 — 630-293-6060
Marc Campbell, prin. — Fax 562-2586

Central Medical Education — Post-Sec.
550 E Washington St 60185 — 630-682-1600
Wheaton Academy — 600/9-12
900 Prince Crossing Rd 60185 — 630-562-7500
Dr. Gene Frost, head sch — Fax 231-0842

West Dundee, Kane
CUSD 300
Supt. — See Algonquin
Dundee MS — 1,000/6-8
4200 W Main St 60118 — 847-426-1485
Jeff Herb, prin. — Fax 426-4008

Hair Professionals Academy — Post-Sec.
825 Village Quarter Rd # B 60118 — 847-836-5900

Western Springs, Cook, Pop. 12,882
Lyons Township HSD 204
Supt. — See La Grange
Lyons Township HS South Campus — 2,000/9-10
4900 Willow Springs Rd 60558 — 708-579-6500
Dr. Brian Waterman, prin. — Fax 588-7473

Western Springs SD 101 — 1,500/PK-8
4225 Wolf Rd 60558 — 708-246-3700
Dr. Brian Barnhart, supt. — Fax 482-2581
www.d101.org
McClure JHS — 500/6-8
4225 Wolf Rd 60558 — 708-246-7590
F. Daniel Chick, prin. — Fax 246-4370

West Frankfort, Franklin, Pop. 8,100
Frankfort CUSD 168 — 1,900/PK-12
900 N Cherry St 62896 — 618-937-2421
Gregory Goins, supt. — Fax 932-2025
www.wfschools.org
Central JHS — 300/7-8
1600 E 9th St 62896 — 618-937-2444
Charley Cass, prin. — Fax 937-2445
Frankfort Community HS — 600/9-12
601 E Main St 62896 — 618-932-3126
Bethany Shaw, prin. — Fax 932-6515

Westmont, DuPage, Pop. 24,243
CUSD 201 — 1,400/PK-12
133 S Grant St 60559 — 630-468-8000
Kevin Carey, supt. — Fax 969-9022
www.cusd201.org
Westmont HS — 500/9-12
909 Oakwood Dr 60559 — 630-468-8100
Jack Baldermann, prin. — Fax 654-2758
Westmont JHS — 400/6-8
944 Oakwood Dr 60559 — 630-468-8200
John Jonak, prin. — Fax 654-2203

Maercker SD 60 — 1,300/PK-8
1 S Cass Ave Ste 202 60559 — 630-515-4840
Sean Nugent, supt. — Fax 515-4845
www.maercker.org
Other Schools – See Willowbrook

West Peoria, Peoria, Pop. 4,328
Peoria SD 150
Supt. — See Peoria
Coolidge MS — 400/5-8
2708 W Rohmann Ave 61604 — 309-672-6506
Mervyn Swanson, prin. — Fax 673-7605

Westville, Vermilion, Pop. 3,171
Westville CUSD 2 — 1,300/PK-12
125 W Ellsworth St 61883 — 217-267-3141
Dr. Seth Miller, supt. — Fax 267-3144
www.westville.k12.il.us
Westville HS — 400/9-12
918 N State St 61883 — 217-267-2183
Guy Goodlove, prin. — Fax 267-7593
Westville JHS — 200/7-8
412 Moses Ave 61883 — 217-267-2185
Jared Ellison, prin. — Fax 267-3621

Wheaton, DuPage, Pop. 51,936
CUSD 200 — 13,100/PK-12
130 W Park Ave 60189 — 630-682-2002
Dr. Jeff Schuler, supt. — Fax 682-2227
www.cusd200.org
Edison MS — 700/6-8
1125 S Wheaton Ave 60189 — 630-682-2050
Rachel Bednar, prin. — Fax 682-2337
Franklin MS — 700/6-8
211 E Franklin St 60187 — 630-682-2060
David Bendis, prin. — Fax 682-2340
Monroe MS — 800/6-8
1855 Manchester Rd 60187 — 630-682-2285
Bryan Buck, prin. — Fax 682-2331
Wheaton North HS — 2,100/9-12
701 W Thomas Rd 60187 — 630-784-7300
Matt Biscan, prin. — Fax 682-2158
Wheaton/Warrenville South HS — 2,100/9-12
1920 S Wiesbrook Rd 60189 — 630-784-7200
Dave Claypool, prin. — Fax 682-2042
Other Schools – See Warrenville

Clapham S, PO Box 209 60187 — 100/PK-12
Kathy Bailey, admin. — 630-547-5125
St. Francis HS — 800/9-12
2130 W Roosevelt Rd 60187 — 630-668-5800
Raeann Huhn, prin. — Fax 668-5893
Wheaton College — Post-Sec.
501 College Ave 60187 — 630-752-5000

Wheeling, Cook, Pop. 37,130
Township HSD 214
Supt. — See Arlington Heights
Wheeling HS — 1,800/9-12
900 S Elmhurst Rd 60090 — 847-718-7000
Angela Sisi, prin. — Fax 718-7007

Wheeling CCSD 21 — 6,800/PK-8
999 W Dundee Rd 60090 — 847-537-8270
Dr. Kate Hyland, supt. — Fax 520-2848
www.ccsd21.org
Holmes MS — 800/6-8
221 S Wolf Rd 60090 — 847-520-2790
Martin Hopkins, prin. — Fax 419-3073
London MS — 700/6-8
1001 W Dundee Rd 60090 — 847-520-2745
Luis Correa, prin. — Fax 520-2842
Other Schools – See Buffalo Grove

Chicago Professional Center — Post-Sec.
500 Harvester Ct Ste 6 60090 — 847-215-8203
SOLEX College — Post-Sec.
350 E Dundee Rd 60090 — 847-229-9595
Worsham College of Mortuary Science — Post-Sec.
495 Northgate Pkwy 60090 — 847-808-8444

White Hall, Greene, Pop. 2,509
North Greene Unit SD 3 — 900/PK-12
250 E Sherman St 62092 — 217-374-2842
Lawrence Coultas, supt. — Fax 374-2849
www.northgreene.com
North Greene JSHS — 400/7-12
546 N Main St 62092 — 217-374-2131
Keppen Clanton, prin. — Fax 374-2132

Williamsfield, Knox, Pop. 574
Williamsfield CUSD 210 — 300/PK-12
325 W Kentucky Ave 61489 — 309-639-2219
Tim Farquer, supt. — Fax 639-2618
www.billtown.org
Williamsfield HS — 100/9-12
325 W Kentucky Ave 61489 — 309-639-2216
Zack Binder, prin.
Williamsfield MS — 100/6-8
325 W Kentucky Ave 61489 — 309-639-2216
Zack Binder, prin.

Williamsville, Sangamon, Pop. 1,465
Williamsville CUSD 15 — 1,500/PK-12
800 S Walnut St 62693 — 217-566-2014
Don Beard, supt. — Fax 566-2183
www.wcusd15.org
Williamsville HS — 500/9-12
900 S Walnut St 62693 — 217-566-3361
Doug Furlow, prin. — Fax 566-3792
Williamsville JHS — 300/6-8
500 S Walnut St 62693 — 217-566-3600
Clay Shoufler, prin. — Fax 566-2475

Willowbrook, DuPage, Pop. 8,420
Gower SD 62 — 900/PK-8
7700 Clarendon Hills Rd 60527 — 630-986-5383
Dr. Victor Simon, supt. — Fax 323-3074
www.gower62.com
Other Schools – See Burr Ridge

Maercker SD 60
Supt. — See Westmont
Westview Hills MS — 400/6-8
630 65th St 60527 — 630-515-4830
Amber Quirk, prin. — Fax 515-4835

Wilmette, Cook, Pop. 26,500
Avoca SD 37 — 700/PK-8
2921 Illinois Rd 60091 — 847-251-3587
Kevin Jauch, supt. — Fax 251-7742
avoca37.org
Murphy MS — 300/PK-PK, 6-
2921 Illinois Rd 60091 — 847-251-3617
Matthew Palcer, prin. — Fax 251-4179

Wilmette SD 39 — 3,700/PK-8
615 Locust Rd 60091 — 847-256-2450
Ray Lechner, supt. — Fax 256-1920
www.wilmette39.org
Wilmette JHS — 800/7-8
620 Locust Rd 60091 — 847-256-7280
Kelly Jackson, prin. — Fax 256-0204

Loyola Academy 2,100/9-12
1100 Laramie Ave 60091 847-256-1100
Kathryn Baal Ph.D., prin. Fax 853-4512
Regina Dominican HS 300/9-12
701 Locust Rd 60091 847-256-7660
Meg Bigane, prin. Fax 256-3726

Wilmington, Will, Pop. 5,660
Wilmington CUSD 209U 1,500/PK-12
209U Wildcat Ct 60481 815-926-1751
Dr. Matthew Swick, supt. Fax 926-1692
www.wilmington.will.k12.il.us
Wilmington HS 500/9-12
209 Wildcat Ct 60481 815-926-1752
Scott Maupin, prin. Fax 926-1691
Wilmington MS 300/6-8
715 S Joliet St 60481 815-476-2189
Adam Spicer, prin. Fax 476-1941

Winchester, Scott, Pop. 1,579
Winchester CUSD 1 700/PK-12
149 S Elm St 62694 217-742-3175
David Roberts, supt. Fax 742-3312
www.winchesterschools.net
Winchester HS, 200 W Cross St 62694 200/9-12
Dennis Vortman, prin. 217-742-3151

Windsor, Shelby, Pop. 1,177
Windsor CUSD 1 400/PK-12
1424 Minnesota Ave 61957 217-459-2636
Gavin Sronce, supt. Fax 459-2661
www.windsor.k12.il.us
Windsor JSHS 200/7-12
1424 Minnesota Ave 61957 217-459-2636
Erik Van Hoveln, prin. Fax 459-2794

Winfield, DuPage, Pop. 8,924
Winfield SD 34 300/PK-8
0S150 Winfield Rd 60190 630-909-4900
Dr. Gwynne Kell, supt. Fax 260-2382
www.winfield34.org/
Winfield Central S 200/3-8
0S150 Park St 60190 630-909-4960
Dawn Reinke, prin. Fax 933-9236

Winnebago, Winnebago, Pop. 3,067
Winnebago CUSD 323 1,500/PK-12
304 E McNair Rd 61088 815-335-2456
Scott Bloomquist, supt. Fax 335-7574
www.winnebagoschools.org
Winnebago HS 500/9-12
200 E McNair Rd 61088 815-335-2336
Ronald Gruber, prin. Fax 335-7548
Winnebago MS 300/6-8
407 N Elida St 61088 815-335-2364
Catherine Finley, prin. Fax 335-1437

Winnetka, Cook, Pop. 12,045
New Trier Township HSD 203
Supt. — See Northfield
New Trier Township HS - Winnetka Campus 3,100/10-12
385 Winnetka Ave 60093 847-446-7000
Denise Dubravec, prin. Fax 835-9851

Winnetka SD 36 1,800/K-8
1235 Oak St 60093 847-446-9400
Trisha Kocanda, supt. Fax 446-9408
www.winnetka36.org
Washburne MS 400/7-8
515 Hibbard Rd 60093 847-446-5892
Dave Kanne, prin. Fax 446-1380

Hadley School for the Blind Post-Sec.
700 Elm St 60093 847-446-8111
Music Center of the North Shore Post-Sec.
300 Green Bay Rd 60093 847-446-3822
North Shore Country Day S 500/PK-12
310 Green Bay Rd 60093 847-446-0674
Dr. Thomas Flemma, head sch Fax 446-0675

Winthrop Harbor, Lake, Pop. 6,595
Winthrop Harbor SD 1 600/K-8
500 North Ave 60096 847-731-3085
Patricia Goodwin, supt. Fax 731-3156
www.whsd1.org
North Prairie JHS 300/5-8
500 North Ave 60096 847-731-3089
Carrie Nottingham, prin. Fax 731-3152

Wolf Lake, Union
Shawnee CUSD 84 200/PK-12
3365 N State Route 3 62998 618-833-5709
Shelly Clover-Hill, supt. Fax 833-4171
www.shawneedistrict84.com/
Shawnee JSHS 100/6-12
3365 N State Route 3 62998 618-833-5307
Mike Hanson, prin. Fax 833-5468

Wood Dale, DuPage, Pop. 13,602
Wood Dale SD 7 1,200/PK-8
543 N Wood Dale Rd 60191 630-595-9510
Dr. John Corbett, supt. Fax 595-5625
www.wd7.org
Wood Dale JHS 400/6-8
655 N Wood Dale Rd 60191 630-766-6210
Shelly Skarzynski, prin. Fax 766-1839

Woodhull, Henry, Pop. 803
Alwood CUSD 225 400/PK-12
301 E 5th Ave 61490 309-334-2719
Shannon Bumann, supt. Fax 334-2925
www.alwood.net
Alwood MSHS 200/6-12
301 E 5th Ave 61490 309-334-2102
David Mills, prin. Fax 334-2632

Woodlawn, Jefferson, Pop. 691
Woodlawn Unit SD 209 500/PK-12
300 N Central St 62898 618-735-2631
David Larkin, supt. Fax 735-2032
www.woodlawnschools.org
Woodlawn HS 200/9-12
300 N Central St 62898 618-735-2631
Eric Helbig, prin. Fax 735-2032

Woodridge, DuPage, Pop. 34,058
Woodridge SD 68 3,000/PK-8
7925 Janes Ave 60517 630-985-7925
Dr. Cathy Skinner, supt. Fax 910-2060
www.woodridge68.org
Jefferson JHS 600/7-8
7200 Janes Ave 60517 630-852-8010
Dr. William Schmidt, prin. Fax 969-7168

Westwood College Post-Sec.
7155 Janes Ave 60517 630-434-7655

Wood River, Madison, Pop. 10,543
East Alton-Wood River Community HSD 14 500/9-12
777 N Wood River Ave 62095 618-254-3151
Dr. John Pearson, supt. Fax 254-9113
www.eawr.net
East Alton-Wood River HS 500/9-12
777 N Wood River Ave 62095 618-254-3151
Leigh Robinson, prin. Fax 254-9113

Wood River-Hartford ESD 15 700/PK-8
501 E Lorena Ave 62095 618-254-0607
Patrick Anderson Ph.D., supt. Fax 254-9048
www.wrh15.org/
Lewis-Clark JHS 200/6-8
501 E Lorena Ave 62095 618-254-4355
Heather Johnson, prin. Fax 254-7600

Woodstock, McHenry, Pop. 24,445
McHenry ROE 50/
2200 N Seminary Ave 60098 815-334-4475
Leslie Schermerhorn, supt. Fax 338-0475
www.mchenryroe.org/
Other Schools – See Union

Woodstock CUSD 200 6,500/PK-12
227 W Judd St 60098 815-338-8200
Michael Moan Ed.D., supt. Fax 338-2005
www.woodstockschools.org/
Creekside MS 800/6-8
3201 Hercules Rd 60098 815-337-5200
Michael Wheatley, prin. Fax 206-0476
Northwood MS 600/6-8
2121 N Seminary Ave 60098 815-338-4900
Jeremy Schaaf, prin. Fax 337-2150
Woodstock HS 1,000/9-12
501 W South St 60098 815-338-4370
Justin Smith Ed.D., prin. Fax 334-0811
Woodstock North HS 900/9-12
3000 Raffel Rd 60098 815-334-2100
Darlea Livengood, prin. Fax 334-2101

Marian Central Catholic HS 700/9-12
1001 McHenry Ave 60098 815-338-4220
Debra Novy, prin. Fax 338-4253

Worth, Cook, Pop. 10,649
Worth SD 127 1,100/PK-8
11218 S Ridgeland Ave 60482 708-448-2800
Dr. Rita Wojtylewski, supt. Fax 448-6215
www.worthschools.org
Worth JHS 300/6-8
11151 S New England Ave 60482 708-448-2803
Joseph Zampillo, prin. Fax 448-6155

Wyoming, Stark, Pop. 1,418
Stark County CUSD 100 800/PK-12
300 W Van Buren St 61491 309-695-6123
Jerry Klooster, supt.
www.stark100.com
Other Schools – See Toulon

Yorkville, Kendall, Pop. 16,715
Yorkville CUSD 115 5,200/PK-12
PO Box 579 60560 630-553-4382
Dr. Tim Shimp, supt. Fax 553-4398
www.y115.org
Yorkville HS 1,200/10-12
797 Game Farm Rd 60560 630-553-4380
David Travis, prin. Fax 553-4397
Yorkville HS Academy 9-9
702 Game Farm Rd 60560 630-553-4385
David Travis, prin. Fax 553-4592
Yorkville MS 900/7-8
920 Prairie Crossing Dr 60560 630-553-4544
Lisa Adler, prin. Fax 553-5181

Parkview Christian Academy 200/PK-12
201 W Center St 60560 630-553-5158
Deborah Benson, supt. Fax 553-3370

Zeigler, Franklin, Pop. 1,781
Zeigler-Royalton CUSD 188 600/PK-12
PO Box 38 62999 618-596-5841
George Wilkerson, supt. Fax 596-6789
www.zr188.org
Zeigler-Royalton HS 200/9-12
PO Box 38 62999 618-596-5841
Quent Hamilton, prin. Fax 596-6789
Zeigler-Royalton JHS 100/7-8
PO Box 87 62999 618-596-2121
Leigh Bailey, prin. Fax 596-2075

Zion, Lake, Pop. 23,535
Zion ESD 6 2,800/PK-8
2200 Bethesda Blvd 60099 847-872-5455
Dr. Keely Roberts, supt. Fax 746-1280
www.zion6.com
Zion Central JHS 600/7-8
1716 27th St 60099 847-746-1431
Tanya Housing, prin. Fax 746-9750

Zion-Benton Township HSD 126 2,700/9-12
3901 21st St 60099 847-731-9300
Dr. Chris Clark, supt. Fax 731-4441
www.zbths.org
New Tech High @ Zion-Benton East 400/9-12
1634 23rd St 60099 847-731-9800
David Frusher, prin. Fax 746-5428
Zion-Benton Township HS 2,300/9-12
3901 21st St 60099 847-731-9300
Chris Pawelczyk, prin. Fax 731-4408

INDIANA

INDIANA DEPARTMENT OF EDUCATION
151 W Ohio St Ste X, Indianapolis 46204
Telephone 317-232-6610
Fax 317-232-8004
Website http://www.doe.in.gov

Superintendent of Public Instruction Dr. Jennifer McCormick

INDIANA BOARD OF EDUCATION
200 W Washington St Ste 229, Indianapolis 46204-2731

Chairperson Glenda Ritz

EDUCATIONAL SERVICE CENTERS (ESC)

Central Indiana ESC
Dr. Kevin M. Caress, dir. 317-759-5555
6036 Lakeside Blvd Bldg A
Indianapolis 46278
www.ciesc.k12.in.us

East Central ESC
Larry John, dir., 1601 Indiana Ave 765-825-1247
Connersville 47331 Fax 825-2532
www.ecesc.k12.in.us/

Northern Indiana ESC
Ted Chittum, dir. 574-254-0111
56535 Magnetic Dr Fax 254-0148
Mishawaka 46545
www.niesc.k12.in.us/

Northwest Indiana ESC
Edward Schoenfelt, dir. 219-926-5555
48 W 900 N, Chesterton 46304 Fax 926-5553
www.nwiesc.k12.in.us/

Region 8 ESC
Joshua Wenning, dir. 260-423-0030
1027 W Rudisill Blvd Ste D1 Fax 423-0031
Fort Wayne 46807
www.r8esc.k12.in.us/

Southern Indiana ESC
Judy Bueckert, dir. 812-482-6641
1102 Tree Lane Dr, Jasper 47546 Fax 482-6652
www.siec.k12.in.us/

Wabash Valley ESC
Dr. Dennis Cahill, dir. 765-463-1589
3061 Benton St Fax 463-1580
West Lafayette 47906
www.esc5.k12.in.us/

West Central ESC
Valerie Buchanan, dir. 765-653-2727
PO Box 21, Greencastle 46135 Fax 653-7897
www.wciesc.k12.in.us/

William E. Wilson ESC
Dr. Phil Partenheimer, dir. 812-256-8000
PO Box 217, Charlestown 47111 Fax 256-8012
www.wesc.k12.in.us/

PUBLIC, PRIVATE AND CATHOLIC SECONDARY SCHOOLS

Akron, Kosciusko, Pop. 1,159
Tippecanoe Valley SC 2,000/K-12
8343 S State Road 19 46910 574-598-2759
Brett Boggs, supt. Fax 598-2773
www.tvsc.k12.in.us
Tippecanoe Valley HS 700/9-12
8345 S State Road 19 46910 574-598-2100
Dr. Michael Bendicsen, prin. Fax 598-2177
Tippecanoe Valley MS 500/6-8
11303 W 800 S 46910 574-598-2200
Scott Backus, prin. Fax 598-2266

Albion, Noble, Pop. 2,325
Central Noble Community SC 1,000/K-12
200 E Main St 46701 260-636-2175
Alan Middleton, supt. Fax 636-7918
www.centralnoble.k12.in.us
Central Noble JSHS 400/6-12
401 E Highland St 46701 260-636-2117
Geoff Brose, prin. Fax 636-2791

Alexandria, Madison, Pop. 5,088
Alexandria Community SC 1,600/PK-12
202 E Washington St 46001 765-724-4496
Melissa Brisco, supt. Fax 724-5049
www.alex.k12.in.us
Alexandria-Monroe JSHS 700/7-12
1 Burden Ct 46001 765-724-4413
Thomas Johns, prin. Fax 724-5041

Anderson, Madison, Pop. 54,768
Anderson Community SC 6,700/PK-12
1600 Hillcrest Ave 46011 765-641-2000
Terry Thompson, supt. Fax 641-2080
www.acsc.net
Anderson HS 1,900/9-12
4610 S Madison Ave 46013 765-641-2037
Eric Davis, prin. Fax 641-2041
D26 Career Center Vo/Tech
325 W 38th St 46013 765-641-2046
Kelly Durr, dir. Fax 641-2041
Highland MS 1,500/6-8
2108 E 200 N 46012 765-641-2059
David Tijerina, prin. Fax 641-2064

Frankton-Lapel Community SD 3,000/PK-12
7916 W 300 N 46011 765-734-1261
Bobby Fields, supt. Fax 734-1129
www.flcs.k12.in.us/
Other Schools – See Frankton, Lapel

Anderson Christian S 200/PK-12
5401 S Madison Ave 46013 765-649-0123
Thomas Snell, admin. Fax 649-3844
Anderson University Post-Sec.
1100 E 5th St 46012 765-649-9071
Apex School of Beauty Culture Post-Sec.
333 Jackson St 46016 765-642-7560
Harrison College Post-Sec.
140 E 53rd St 46013 765-644-7514
Indiana Christian Academy 100/PK-12
432 W 300 N 46012 765-643-7884
Kevin Plew, prin. Fax 683-4200
Liberty Christian HS 300/7-12
2323 Columbus Ave 46016 765-644-7774
Stacy Scott, prin. Fax 644-7779

Angola, Steuben, Pop. 8,487
Metropolitan SD of Steuben County 3,000/K-12
400 S Martha St 46703 260-665-2854
Dr. Brent Wilson, supt. Fax 665-9155
www.msdsteuben.k12.in.us
Angola HS 900/9-12
350 S John McBride Ave 46703 260-665-2186
Travis Heavin, prin. Fax 665-7012
Angola MS 700/6-8
1350 E Maumee St 46703 260-665-9581
Ann Rice, prin. Fax 665-9583

Trine University Post-Sec.
1 University Ave 46703 260-665-4100

Arcadia, Hamilton, Pop. 1,652
Hamilton Heights SC 2,300/PK-12
PO Box 469 46030 317-984-3538
Dr. Derek Arrowood, supt. Fax 984-3042
www.hhschuskies.org
Hamilton Heights HS 700/9-12
PO Box 379 46030 317-984-3551
Jarrod Mason, prin. Fax 984-3554
Hamilton Heights MS 500/6-8
PO Box 609 46030 317-984-3588
Bret Bailey, prin. Fax 984-3231

Argos, Marshall, Pop. 1,665
Argos Community SD 600/PK-12
410 N First St 46501 574-892-5139
Michele Riise, supt. Fax 892-6527
www.argos.k12.in.us/
Argos Community JSHS 300/7-12
500 Yearick St 46501 574-892-5137
Nick Medich, prin. Fax 892-6527

Attica, Fountain, Pop. 3,214
Attica Consolidated SC 800/PK-12
205 E Sycamore St 47918 765-762-7000
Derek Marshall, supt. Fax 762-7007
www.attica.k12.in.us
Attica JSHS 400/7-12
211 E Sycamore St 47918 765-762-7000
Johnathan Hoke, prin. Fax 762-7017

Auburn, DeKalb, Pop. 12,632

Lakewood Park Christian S 500/PK-12
5555 County Road 29 46706 260-925-1393
Dr. Ed Yoder, supt. Fax 925-5010

Aurora, Dearborn, Pop. 3,721
South Dearborn Community SC 2,700/PK-12
6109 Squire Pl 47001 812-926-2090
Dr. John Mehrle, supt. Fax 926-4216
www.sdcsc.k12.in.us
South Dearborn HS 900/9-12
5770 Highlander Pl 47001 812-926-2090
Brad Stoneking, prin. Fax 926-4162
South Dearborn MS 500/7-8
5850 Squire Pl 47001 812-926-2090
Jason Cheek, prin. Fax 926-2149

Austin, Scott, Pop. 4,251
Scott County SD 1 1,300/K-12
PO Box 9 47102 812-794-8750
Robert Anderson, supt. Fax 794-8765
www.scsd1.com/
Austin HS 400/9-12
401 S Highway 31 47102 812-794-8730
Sherman Smith, prin. Fax 794-8739
Austin MS 300/6-8
401 S Highway 31 47102 812-794-8740
David Deaton, prin. Fax 794-8739

Avon, Hendricks, Pop. 12,177
Avon Community SC 8,800/K-12
7203 E US Highway 36 46123 317-544-6000
Dr. Margaret Hoernemann, supt. Fax 544-6001
www.avon-schools.org
Avon HS 2,600/9-12
7575 E County Road 150 S 46123 317-544-5000
Matt Shockley, prin. Fax 544-5001
Avon MS North 700/7-8
1251 N Dan Jones Rd 46123 317-544-5500
Susan Green, prin. Fax 544-5501
Avon MS South 800/7-8
7199 E US Highway 36 46123 317-544-5700
Dan Chapin, prin. Fax 544-5701

Bainbridge, Putnam, Pop. 737
North Putnam Community SD 1,600/PK-12
PO Box 169 46105 765-522-6218
Daniel Noel Ed.D., supt. Fax 522-3562
www.nputnam.k12.in.us
Other Schools – See Greencastle, Roachdale

Batesville, Franklin, Pop. 6,459
Batesville Community SC 2,200/PK-12
PO Box 121 47006 812-934-2194
Bill Narwold, supt. Fax 933-0833
www.batesvilleinschools.com
Batesville HS 700/9-12
1 Bulldog Blvd 47006 812-934-4384
Andy Allen, prin. Fax 934-5964
Batesville MS 500/6-8
201 N Mulberry St 47006 812-934-5175
Dave Strouse, prin. Fax 933-0834

Bedford, Lawrence, Pop. 13,252
North Lawrence Community SD 5,100/PK-12
PO Box 729 47421 812-279-3521
Gary Conner, supt. Fax 275-1577
www.nlcs.k12.in.us
Bedford MS 600/6-8
1501 N St 47421 812-279-9781
David Schlegel, prin. Fax 277-3218
Bedford-North Lawrence HS 1,600/9-12
595 Stars Blvd 47421 812-279-9756
Daniel Dyke, prin. Fax 279-9304
North Lawrence Career Ctr Vo/Tech
258 BNL Dr 47421 812-279-3561
Glenn Weil, dir. Fax 275-1578
Shawswick MS 200/6-8
71 Shawswick School Rd 47421 812-275-6121
James Pentzer, prin. Fax 275-3458
Other Schools – See Oolitic

Beech Grove, Marion, Pop. 13,930
Beech Grove CSD 2,900/PK-12
5334 Hornet Ave 46107 317-788-4481
Dr. Paul Kaiser, supt. Fax 782-4065
www.bgcs.k12.in.us
Beech Grove HS 800/9-12
5330 Hornet Ave 46107 317-786-1447
Elizabeth Walters, prin. Fax 781-2920
Beech Grove MS 500/7-8
1248 Buffalo St 46107 317-784-6649
Thomas Gearhart, prin. Fax 781-2926

St. Francis Hospital Center Post-Sec.
1600 Albany St 46107 317-783-8220

Berne, Adams, Pop. 3,972
South Adams SD 1,300/PK-12
1075 Starfire Way 46711 260-589-3133
Scott Litwiller, supt. Fax 589-2065
www.southadams.k12.in.us
South Adams HS 400/9-12
1000 Parkway St 46711 260-589-3131
Trent Lehman, prin. Fax 589-3042
South Adams MS 300/6-8
1212 Starfire Way 46711 260-589-1102
Jeff Rich, prin. Fax 589-2112

Bicknell, Knox, Pop. 2,893
North Knox SC 1,300/K-12
11110 N State Road 159 47512 812-735-4434
Darrel Bobe, supt. Fax 328-6262
www.nknox.k12.in.us
North Knox JSHS 600/7-12
10890 N State Road 159 47512 812-735-2990
Matt Sandefer, prin. Fax 328-2155

Bloomfield, Greene, Pop. 2,386
Bloomfield SD 900/K-12
PO Box 266 47424 812-384-4507
Doug Rose, supt. Fax 384-0172
www.bsd.k12.in.us
Bloomfield JSHS 400/7-12
PO Box 266 47424 812-384-4550
David Dean, prin. Fax 384-1422

Eastern Greene SD 1,300/PK-12
1471 N State Road 43 47424 812-825-5722
Ted Baechtold, supt. Fax 825-9413
www.egreene.k12.in.us/
Eastern Greene HS 400/9-12
11064 E State Road 54 47424 812-825-5621
Doug Lewis, prin. Fax 825-6661
Eastern Greene MS 400/5-8
10503 E State Road 54 47424 812-825-5010
Dennis Massengill, prin. Fax 825-7386

Bloomington, Monroe, Pop. 78,128
Monroe County Community SC 10,900/PK-12
315 E North Dr 47401 812-330-7700
Judith DeMuth Ed.D., supt. Fax 330-7813
www.mccsc.edu
Academy of Science & Entrepreneurship 100/9-12
444 S Patterson Dr 47403 812-330-2480
Jessica Willis, prin. Fax 330-2481
Batchelor MS 500/7-8
900 W Gordon Pike 47403 812-330-7763
Eric Gilpin, prin. Fax 330-7766
Bloomington Graduation S 100/Alt
705 W Coolidge Dr 47403 812-330-7708
Eric Jackson, dir. Fax 330-2433
Bloomington HS North 1,500/9-12
3901 N Kinser Pike 47404 812-330-7724
Jeffry Henderson, prin. Fax 330-7805
Bloomington HS South 1,700/9-12
1965 S Walnut St 47401 812-330-7714
Mark Fletcher, prin. Fax 330-7810
Hoosier Hills Career Center Vo/Tech
3070 N Prow Rd 47404 812-330-7730
Alan Dafoe, dir. Fax 330-7807
Jackson Creek MS 600/7-8
3980 S Sare Rd 47401 812-330-2451
David Pillar, prin. Fax 330-2457
Tri-North MS 600/7-8
1000 W 15th St 47404 812-330-7745
Dr. Gale Hill, prin. Fax 330-7799
Broadview Learning Center Adult
705 W Coolidge Dr 47403 812-330-7731
Robert Moore, dir. Fax 330-7789

Bloomington Hospital Post-Sec.
PO Box 1149 47402 812-336-6821
Covenant Christian S 100/K-12
4000 E Moores Creek Rd 47401 812-287-8833
Rob Akers, head sch Fax 333-2445
Hair Arts Academy Post-Sec.
1681 N College Ave 47404 812-339-1117
Harmony S 200/PK-12
PO Box 1787 47402 812-334-8349
Steve Bonchek, dir. Fax 333-3435
Indiana University Post-Sec.
107 S Indiana Ave 47405 812-855-4848
Ivy Tech Community College - Bloomington Post-Sec.
200 N Daniels Way 47404 812-332-1559
Lighthouse Christian Academy 200/K-12
1201 W That Rd 47403 812-824-2000
Joyce Huck B.A., prin. Fax 824-2017

Bluffton, Wells, Pop. 9,806
Bluffton-Harrison Metropolitan SD 1,500/PK-12
805 E Harrison Rd 46714 260-824-2620
Wayne Barker, supt. Fax 824-6011
www.bhmsd.org
Bluffton-Harrison MS 400/5-8
1500 Stogdill Rd 46714 260-824-3536
Claire Paul, prin. Fax 824-6014
Bluffton HS 400/9-12
1 Tiger Trl 46714 260-824-3724
Steve Baker, prin. Fax 824-6001

Boone Grove, Porter
Porter Township SC
Supt. — See Valparaiso
Boone Grove MS 400/6-8
325 W 550 S 46302 219-464-4828
Robert Lichtenberger, prin. Fax 465-0999

Boonville, Warrick, Pop. 6,171
Warrick County SC 9,900/K-12
PO Box 809 47601 812-897-0400
Brad Schneider, supt. Fax 897-6033
www.warrick.k12.in.us/
Boonville HS 900/9-12
300 N 1st St 47601 812-897-4701
Mike Whitten, prin. Fax 897-6061
Boonville MS 700/6-8
555 N Yankeetown Rd 47601 812-897-1420
Abbie Redmon, prin. Fax 897-6584
Other Schools – See Lynnville, Newburgh

Borden, Clark, Pop. 799
West Clark Community SC
Supt. — See Sellersburg
Borden JSHS 300/7-12
PO Box 260 47106 812-967-2087
Lisa Nale, prin. Fax 967-2086

Bourbon, Marshall, Pop. 1,801
Triton SC 1,000/K-12
100 Triton Dr 46504 574-342-2255
Donna Burroughs, supt. Fax 342-8165
www.triton.k12.in.us/
Triton JSHS 500/7-12
300 Triton Dr 46504 574-342-6505
Robert Ross, prin. Fax 342-8175

Brazil, Clay, Pop. 7,835
Clay Community SD 4,400/PK-12
1013 S Forest Ave 47834 812-443-4461
Jeffery Fritz, supt. Fax 442-0849
www.clay.k12.in.us
North Clay MS 800/6-8
3450 W State Road 340 47834 812-448-1530
Robert Boltinghouse, prin. Fax 442-0608
Northview HS 1,100/9-12
3150 W State Road 340 47834 812-448-2661
Christopher Mauk, prin. Fax 446-2647
Other Schools – See Clay City

Bremen, Marshall, Pop. 4,550
Bremen Public SD 1,500/K-12
512 W Grant St 46506 574-546-3929
Dr. James White, supt. Fax 546-6303
www.bps.k12.in.us
Bremen HS 500/9-12
511 W Grant St 46506 574-546-3511
Bruce Jennings, prin. Fax 546-5477

Brookville, Franklin, Pop. 2,579
Franklin County Community SC 2,800/PK-12
225 E 10th St 47012 765-647-4128
Dr. Debbie Howell, supt. Fax 647-2417
www.fccsc.k12.in.us
Brookville MS 400/5-8
9092 Wildcat Ln 47012 765-647-6040
Christopher Bundy, prin. Fax 647-4960
Franklin County HS 900/9-12
1 Wildcat Ln 47012 765-647-4101
Keith Isaacs, prin. Fax 647-2732

Brownsburg, Hendricks, Pop. 20,984
Brownsburg Community SC 8,000/PK-12
310 S Stadium Dr 46112 317-852-5726
Jim Snapp, supt. Fax 852-1015
www.brownsburg.k12.in.us
Brownsburg East MS 1,200/6-8
1250 Airport Rd 46112 317-852-2386
Shane Hacker, prin. Fax 852-1023
Brownsburg HS 2,400/9-12
1000 S Odell St 46112 317-852-2258
Bret Daghe, prin. Fax 852-1490
Brownsburg West MS 800/6-8
1555 S Odell St 46112 317-852-3143
Laurie Johnson, prin. Fax 858-4100
Harris Academy Alt
725 S Green St Ste A 46112 317-852-1010
Lynn Lodwick, dir. Fax 852-1012

Bethesda Christian S 400/PK-12
7950 N County Road 650 E 46112 317-858-2820
Don Criss, supt. Fax 858-2819
Midwest Technical Institute Post-Sec.
544 Pitt Rd 46112 317-456-7410

Brownstown, Jackson, Pop. 2,921
Brownstown Central Community SC 1,700/PK-12
608 W Commerce St 47220 812-358-4271
Greg Walker, supt. Fax 358-5303
www.btownccs.k12.in.us
Brownstown Central HS 600/9-12
500 N Elm St 47220 812-358-3453
Joseph Sheffer, prin. Fax 358-5318
Brownstown Central MS 400/6-8
520 W Walnut St 47220 812-358-4947
Doug McClure, prin. Fax 358-3940

Bunker Hill, Miami, Pop. 866
Maconaquah SC 2,300/PK-12
7932 S Strawtown Pike 46914 765-689-9131
Dr. Douglas Arnold, supt. Fax 689-0995
www.maconaquah.k12.in.us
Maconaquah HS 700/9-12
256 E 800 S 46914 765-689-9131
Chad Carlson, prin. Fax 689-9528
Maconaquah MS 500/6-8
594 E 800 S 46914 765-689-9131
Craig Jernagan, prin. Fax 689-9360

Butler, DeKalb, Pop. 2,658
DeKalb County Eastern Community SD 1,400/K-12
300 E Washington St 46721 260-868-2125
Dr. Jeffrey Stephens, supt. Fax 868-2562
www.dekalbeastern.com
Eastside JSHS 600/7-12
603 E Green St 46721 260-868-2186
Larry Yoder, prin. Fax 868-5773

Cambridge City, Wayne, Pop. 1,861
Western Wayne SD
Supt. — See Pershing
Lincoln HS 300/9-12
205 E Parkway Dr 47327 765-478-5916
Jason Bodnar, prin. Fax 478-3262
Lincoln MS 300/6-8
205 E Parkway Dr 47327 765-478-5840
Jason Bodnar, prin. Fax 478-3265

Campbellsburg, Washington, Pop. 579
West Washington SC 800/PK-12
8026 W Batt Rd 47108 812-755-4996
Keith Nance, supt. Fax 755-4843
www.wwcs.k12.in.us
West Washington JSHS 400/7-12
8028 W Batts Rd 47108 812-755-4996
Mary Knapp, prin. Fax 755-4460

Cannelton, Perry, Pop. 1,540
Cannelton CSD 200/PK-12
109 S 3rd St Ste A 47520 812-547-2637
Alva Sibbitt, supt. Fax 547-4142
www.cannelton.k12.in.us
Cannelton JSHS 100/6-12
109 S 3rd St 47520 812-547-3296
Brian Garrett, prin. Fax 548-2288

Carmel, Hamilton, Pop. 77,695
Carmel Clay SD 15,900/PK-12
5201 E Main St 46033 317-844-9961
Dr. Nicholas D. Wahl, supt. Fax 844-9965
www.ccs.k12.in.us
Carmel HS 4,800/9-12
520 E Main St 46032 317-846-7721
John Williams, prin. Fax 571-4066
Carmel MS 1,200/6-8
300 S Guilford Rd 46032 317-846-7331
Lila Jay, prin. Fax 571-4067
Clay MS 1,200/6-8
5150 E 126th St 46033 317-844-7251
Todd Crosby, prin. Fax 571-4020
Creekside MS 1,500/6-8
3525 W 126th St 46032 317-733-6420
Tom Harmas, prin. Fax 733-6422

Coram Deo Academy 100/K-12
651 W Main St 46032 317-844-4224
Kent Welch, head sch
University HS of Indiana 300/9-12
2825 W 116th St 46032 317-733-4475
Charles Webster, head sch Fax 733-4484

Castleton, Marion, Pop. 36

Kaye Beauty College Post-Sec.
6346 E 82nd St 46250 317-576-0224

Cayuga, Vermillion, Pop. 1,146
North Vermillion Community SC 700/K-12
5551 N Falcon Dr 47928 765-492-4033
Daniel Nelson, supt. Fax 492-7001
www.nvc.k12.in.us
North Vermillion JSHS 400/7-12
5555 N Falcon Dr 47928 765-492-3364
Jayne Ann Virostko, prin. Fax 492-7006

Cedar Lake, Lake, Pop. 11,431
Hanover Community SC 2,100/K-12
PO Box 645 46303 219-374-3500
Thomas Taylor, supt. Fax 374-4411
www.hanover.k12.in.us
Hanover Central HS 700/9-12
10120 W 133rd Ave 46303 219-374-3800
Mary Ann West, prin. Fax 374-4408
Hanover Central MS 500/6-8
10631 W 141st Ave 46303 219-374-3900
Tony Hiatt, prin. Fax 374-8926

Centerville, Wayne, Pop. 2,522
Centerville-Abington Community SD 1,800/PK-12
115 W South St 47330 765-855-3475
Philip Stevenson, supt. Fax 855-2524
www.centerville.k12.in.us
Centerville-Abington JHS 300/7-8
509 Willow Grove Rd 47330 765-855-5113
Rick Schauss, prin. Fax 855-5207
Centerville HS 500/9-12
507 Willow Grove Rd 47330 765-855-3481
Mikel McCoy, prin. Fax 855-3484

Chalmers, White, Pop. 504
Frontier SC 700/K-12
PO Box 809 47929 219-984-5009
Dan Sichting, supt. Fax 984-5022
www.frontier.k12.in.us
Frontier JSHS 300/7-12
1 Falcon Dr 47929 219-984-5437
Jeff Hettinger, prin. Fax 984-5360

Charlestown, Clark, Pop. 7,449
Greater Clark County SD
Supt. — See Jeffersonville
Charlestown HS 700/9-12
1 Pirate Pl 47111 812-256-3328
Mark Laughner, prin. Fax 256-7274
Charlestown MS 500/6-8
8804 High Jackson Rd 47111 812-256-6363
Karen Wesely, prin. Fax 256-7282

Charlottesville, Hancock
Eastern Hancock County Community SC 1,100/K-12
10370 E County Road 250 N 46117 317-467-0064
Dr. Vicki McGuire, supt. Fax 936-5516
www.easternhancock.org
Eastern Hancock HS 400/9-12
10320 E County Road 250 N 46117 317-936-5595
David Pfaff, prin. Fax 936-5050
Eastern Hancock MS 300/6-8
10380 E County Road 250 N 46117 317-936-5324
David Pfaff, prin. Fax 936-5050

Chesterton, Porter, Pop. 12,902
Duneland SC 5,900/K-12
601 W Morgan Ave 46304 219-983-3600
Dr. David Pruis, supt. Fax 983-3614
www.duneland.k12.in.us
Chesterton HS 2,000/9-12
2125 S 11th St 46304 219-983-3730
Jeff Van Drie, prin. Fax 983-3775
Chesterton MS 1,000/7-8
651 W Morgan Ave 46304 219-983-3776
Mike Megyesi, prin. Fax 983-3798

Churubusco, Whitley, Pop. 1,774
Smith-Green Community SD 1,200/PK-12
222 W Tulley St 46723 260-693-2007
Galen Mast, supt. Fax 693-6434
www.sgcs.k12.in.us/
Churubusco JSHS 700/6-12
1 Eagle Dr 46723 260-693-2131
Jim Folland, prin. Fax 693-3673

Cicero, Hamilton, Pop. 4,762

Indiana Academy 100/9-12
24815 State Road 19 46034 317-984-3575
Steve Baughman M.Ed., prin. Fax 984-5081

Clarksville, Clark, Pop. 21,221
Clarksville Community SC 1,400/PK-12
200 Ettel Ln 47129 812-282-7753
Dr. Kim Knott, supt. Fax 282-7754
www.ccsc.k12.in.us/
Clarksville HS 400/9-12
800 Dr Dot Lewis Dr 47129 812-282-8231
Adrienne Goldman, prin. Fax 282-8234
Clarksville MS 400/5-8
101 Ettel Ln 47129 812-282-8235
Nikki Bullington, prin. Fax 280-5004

Our Lady of Providence JSHS 500/7-12
707 Providence Way 47129 812-945-2538
Melinda Ernstberger, prin. Fax 981-2538
PJ's College of Cosmetology Post-Sec.
1414 Blackiston Mill Rd 47129 812-282-0459

Clay City, Clay, Pop. 856
Clay Community SD
Supt. — See Brazil
Clay City JSHS 400/7-12
601 Lankford St 47841 812-939-2154
Jeff Bell, prin. Fax 939-3170

Clayton, Hendricks, Pop. 965
Mill Creek Community SC 1,500/PK-12
6631 S County Road 200 W 46118 317-539-9200
Jim Diagostino, supt. Fax 303-1811
www.mccsc.k12.in.us/
Cascade HS 500/9-12
6565 S County Road 200 W 46118 317-539-9315
Jon Acton, prin. Fax 303-1905
Cascade MS 400/6-8
6423 S County Road 200 W 46118 317-539-9285
Eric Sieferman, prin. Fax 303-1907

Clinton, Vermillion, Pop. 4,826
South Vermillion Community SC 1,800/PK-12
PO Box 387 47842 765-832-2426
David Chapman, supt. Fax 832-7391
www.svcs.k12.in.us
South Vermillion HS 500/9-12
770 Wildcat Dr 47842 765-832-3551
Don Harman, prin. Fax 832-5310
South Vermillion MS 400/6-8
900 Wildcat Dr 47842 765-832-7727
Angela Harris, prin. Fax 832-5316

Cloverdale, Putnam, Pop. 2,143
Cloverdale Community SD 1,200/PK-12
310 E Logan St 46120 765-795-4664
Greg Linton, supt. Fax 795-5166
www.cloverdale.k12.in.us
Cloverdale HS 400/9-12
205 E Market St 46120 765-795-4203
Sonny Stoltz, prin. Fax 795-4381
Cloverdale MS 400/5-8
312 E Logan St 46120 765-795-2900
Stacey Baugh, prin. Fax 795-2901

Columbia City, Whitley, Pop. 8,635
Whitley County Consolidated SD 4,000/PK-12
107 N Walnut St 46725 260-244-5772
Dr. Patricia O'Connor, supt. Fax 244-4590
www.wccsonline.com
Columbia City HS 1,100/9-12
600 N Whitley St 46725 260-244-6136
Jennifer Reiff, prin. Fax 244-7326
Eagle Tech Academy 400/9-12
107 N Walnut St 46725 260-244-5707
Braden Mullett, admin. Fax 248-4403
Indian Springs MS 800/6-8
1692 S State Road 9 46725 260-244-5148
Jan Boylen, prin. Fax 244-4710

Columbus, Bartholomew, Pop. 43,281
Bartholomew Consolidated SC 11,500/PK-12
1200 Central Ave 47201 812-376-4220
Dr. Jim Roberts Ed.D., supt. Fax 376-4486
www.bcsc.k12.in.us
Central MS 800/7-8
725 7th St 47201 812-376-4287
Randall Gratz, prin. Fax 376-4511
Columbus Area Career Connection Vo/Tech
1400 25th St 47201 812-376-4240
Gene Hack, dir. Fax 376-4699
Columbus East HS 1,500/9-12
230 S Marr Rd 47201 812-376-4369
Mark Newell, prin. Fax 376-4358
Columbus North HS 2,000/9-12
1400 25th St 47201 812-376-4432
David Clark, prin. Fax 376-4291
Columbus Signature Acad - NewTech 9-12
2205 25th St 47201 812-376-4595
Mike Reed, prin. Fax 376-4599
McDowell Educational Center Alt
2700 McKinley Ave 47201 812-376-4451
Andrea Quick, dir. Fax 376-4512
Northside MS 900/7-8
1400 27th St 47201 812-376-4405
Amy Dixon, prin. Fax 376-4479

Columbus Christian S 200/PK-12
3170 Indiana Ave 47201 812-372-3780
Rev. Kendall Wildey, admin. Fax 372-3878
Columbus Regional Hospital Post-Sec.
2400 17th St 47201 812-376-5439
Harrison College Post-Sec.
2222 Poshard Dr 47203 812-379-9000
Ivy Tech Community College - Columbus Post-Sec.
4475 Central Ave 47203 812-372-9925

Connersville, Fayette, Pop. 13,304
Fayette County SC 3,800/PK-12
1401 Spartan Dr 47331 765-825-2178
Dr. Russell Hodges, supt. Fax 825-8060
www.fayette.k12.in.us
Connersville HS 1,100/9-12
1100 Spartan Dr 47331 765-825-1151
Randal Judd, prin. Fax 825-0777
Connersville MS 600/7-8
1900 N Grand Ave 47331 765-825-1139
Beth Denham, prin. Fax 827-4346
Whitewater Career Center Vo/Tech
1300 Spartan Dr 47331 765-825-0521
Steven Dungan, dir. Fax 827-0836

Converse, Miami, Pop. 1,252
Oak Hill United SC 1,600/K-12
PO Box 550 46919 765-395-3341
Joel Martin, supt. Fax 395-3343
www.ohusc.k12.in.us
Oak Hill HS 500/9-12
7756 W Delphi Pike Ste 27 46919 765-384-4381
Michael McDivitt, prin. Fax 384-5414
Oak Hill JHS 300/7-8
7760 W Delphi Pike Ste 27 46919 765-384-4385
Greg Perkins, prin. Fax 384-4386

Corydon, Harrison, Pop. 3,080
South Harrison Community SD 3,100/K-12
315 S Harrison Dr 47112 812-738-2168
Dr. Mark Eastridge, supt. Fax 738-2158
www.shcsc.k12.in.us/
Corydon Central HS 700/9-12
375 Country Club Rd 47112 812-738-4181
Keith Marshall, prin. Fax 738-1145
Corydon Central JHS 400/7-8
377 Country Club Rd 47112 812-738-4184
Mark Black, prin. Fax 738-5752
Other Schools – See Elizabeth

Covington, Fountain, Pop. 2,619
Covington Community SC 1,000/PK-12
601 Market St 47932 765-793-4877
Kirk Booe M.S., supt. Fax 793-5209
www.covington.k12.in.us/
Covington Community HS 300/9-12
1017 6th St 47932 765-793-2286
Philip Cunningham, prin. Fax 793-5200
Covington MS 200/6-8
514 Railroad St 47932 765-793-4451
Steve Reynolds, prin. Fax 793-5217

Crawfordsville, Montgomery, Pop. 15,708
Crawfordsville Community SD 1,900/PK-12
1000 Fairview Ave 47933 765-362-2342
Scott Bowling, supt. Fax 364-3237
www.cville.k12.in.us
Crawfordsville HS 600/9-12
1 W Athenian Dr 47933 765-362-2340
Gregory Hunt, prin. Fax 364-3200
Crawfordsville MS 6-8
705 Wallace Ave 47933 765-362-2992
Brent Bokhart, prin. Fax 364-3212

North Montgomery Community SC 2,000/PK-12
480 W 580 N 47933 765-359-2112
Dr. Colleen Moran, supt. Fax 359-2111
www.nm.k12.in.us/
North Montgomery HS 600/9-12
5945 N US Highway 231 47933 765-362-5140
Michael Cox, prin. Fax 362-6710
Northridge MS 500/6-8
482 W 580 N 47933 765-364-1071
Benjamin Moore, prin. Fax 362-7985

South Montgomery Community SC 1,600/K-12
6425 US 231 S 47933 765-866-0203
Dr. Shawn Greiner, supt. Fax 866-0736
www.southmont.k12.in.us
Southmont HS 500/9-12
6425 S US Highway 231 47933 765-866-0350
Mike Tricker, prin. Fax 866-2044
Southmont JHS 300/7-8
6460 S US Highway 231 47933 765-866-2023
Anna Roth, prin. Fax 866-2045

Wabash College Post-Sec.
301 W Wabash Ave 47933 765-361-6100

Crothersville, Jackson, Pop. 1,577
Crothersville Community SD 500/K-12
201 S Preston St 47229 812-793-2601
Dr. Terry Goodin, supt. Fax 793-3004
www.crothersville.k12.in.us
Crothersville JSHS 300/6-12
109 N Preston St 47229 812-793-2051
David Schill, prin. Fax 793-3004

Crown Point, Lake, Pop. 27,010
Crown Point Community SC 8,000/PK-12
200 E North St 46307 219-663-3371
Dr. Teresa Eineman, supt. Fax 662-3414
www.cps.k12.in.us
Colonel John Wheeler MS 900/6-8
401 W Joliet St 46307 219-663-2173
Timothy Vassar, prin. Fax 662-4378
Crown Point HS 2,700/9-12
1500 S Main St 46307 219-663-4885
Chip Pettit, prin. Fax 662-5661
Taft MS 900/6-8
1000 S Main St 46307 219-663-1507
Michael Hazen, prin. Fax 662-4349

St. Anthony School of Echocardiography Post-Sec.
1201 S Main St 46307 219-757-6132

Culver, Marshall, Pop. 1,330
Culver Community SC 700/K-12
700 School St 46511 574-842-3364
Charles Kitchell, supt. Fax 842-4615
www.culver.k12.in.us
Culver Community MSHS 300/7-12
701 School St 46511 574-842-3391
Brett Berndt, prin. Fax 842-3392

.Culver Academies 800/9-12
1300 Academy Rd 46511 574-842-7000
Jim Power, head sch Fax 842-8161

Daleville, Delaware, Pop. 1,631
Daleville Community SD 800/K-12
14300 W 2nd St 47334 765-378-3329
Paul Garrison M.S., supt. Fax 378-3649
www.daleville.k12.in.us
Daleville JSHS 400/7-12
8400 S Bronco Dr 47334 765-378-3371
Eric Douglas M.A., prin. Fax 378-4076

Danville, Hendricks, Pop. 8,895
Danville Community SC 2,600/PK-12
200 Warrior Way 46122 317-745-2212
Dr. Tracey Shafer, supt. Fax 745-3924
www.danville.k12.in.us
Central Normal Campus Alt
49 N Wayne St 46122 317-745-7942
James Bryant, dir. Fax 745-3886
Danville Community HS 800/9-12
100 Warrior Way 46122 317-745-6431
Paul Hamann, prin. Fax 745-3908
Danville Community MS 800/5-8
1425 W Lincoln St 46122 317-745-5491
Marsha Webster, prin. Fax 745-3949

Decatur, Adams, Pop. 9,334
North Adams Community SD 1,800/PK-12
625 Stadium Dr 46733 260-724-7146
Brent Lehman, supt. Fax 724-4777
www.nadams.k12.in.us
Bellmont HS 700/9-12
1000 E North Adams Dr 46733 260-724-7121
Kimberly Harsh, prin. Fax 724-7826
Bellmont MS 500/5-8
1200 E North Adams Dr 46733 260-724-3137
Scott Miller, prin. Fax 724-4495

Delphi, Carroll, Pop. 2,860
Delphi Community SC 1,500/PK-12
501 Armory Rd 46923 765-564-2100
Greg Briles, supt. Fax 564-6919
www.delphi.k12.in.us/
Delphi Community HS 500/9-12
301 Armory Rd 46923 765-564-3481
Ann-Marie Circle, prin. Fax 564-3260
Delphi Community MS 300/6-8
401 Armory Rd 46923 765-564-3411
Sarah Tislow, prin. Fax 564-2135

Demotte, Jasper, Pop. 3,774

Covenant Christian HS 100/9-12
PO Box 430 46310 219-987-7651
Clarence Oudman, admin. Fax 987-3721

Denver, Miami, Pop. 480
North Miami Community SD 1,000/K-12
394 E 900 N 46926 765-985-3891
Nicholas Eccles, supt. Fax 985-3904
www.nmcs.k12.in.us/
North Miami MSHS 500/7-12
570 E 900 N 46926 765-985-2931
Fax 985-2056

Donaldson, Marshall

Ancilla College Post-Sec.
PO Box 1 46513 574-936-8898

Dubois, Dubois, Pop. 488
Northeast Dubois County SC 1,000/PK-12
5379 E Main St 47527 812-678-2781
William Hochgesang, supt. Fax 678-4418
www.nedubois.k12.in.us
Dubois MS 300/5-8
4550 N 4th St 47527 812-678-2181
Ryan Case, prin. Fax 678-2282

Northeast Dubois HS 300/9-12
4711 N Dubois Rd NE 47527 812-678-2251
Rick Gladish, prin. Fax 678-3991

Dugger, Sullivan, Pop. 917
Dugger Union Community School Corp K-12
7356 E County Road 50 S 47848 812-648-7109
Ross Martin, supt. Fax 648-7112
www.duggerunionschools.org
Dugger Union Community S K-12
7356 E County Road 50 S 47848 812-648-7109
Ross Martin, prin. Fax 648-7112

Dunkirk, Jay, Pop. 2,346
Jay SC
Supt. — See Portland
West Jay MS 300/6-8
140 E Highland Ave 47336 765-768-7648
Mike Crull, prin. Fax 768-6152

Dyer, Lake, Pop. 16,198
Lake Central SC
Supt. — See Saint John
Kahler MS 1,000/5-8
600 Joliet St 46311 219-865-3535
Ken Newton, prin. Fax 865-4428

Heritage Christian HS 50/9-12
10790 Calumet Ave 46311 219-558-2660
Ralph Medema, admin. Fax 558-2664
Mid-America Reformed Seminary Post-Sec.
229 Seminary Dr 46311 219-864-2400

East Chicago, Lake, Pop. 29,444
School City of East Chicago 4,000/PK-12
1401 E 144th St 46312 219-391-4100
Dr. Paige McNulty, supt. Fax 391-4126
www.scec.k12.in.us
Block MS 300/7-8
2700 Cardinal Dr 46312 219-391-4084
Dee Etta Wright, prin. Fax 391-4282
East Chicago Central HS 1,200/9-12
1100 W Columbus Dr 46312 219-391-4000
Shaunna Finley, prin. Fax 391-4049

Edinburgh, Johnson, Pop. 4,440
Edinburgh Community SC 900/PK-12
202 Keeley St 46124 812-526-2681
Dr. William A. Glentzer, supt. Fax 526-0271
www.ecsc.k12.in.us
Edinburgh Community HS 300/9-12
300 Keeley St 46124 812-526-5501
Kevin Rockey, prin. Fax 526-3439
Edinburgh Community MS 200/6-8
300 Keeley St 46124 812-526-3418
Kevin Rockey, prin. Fax 526-3439

Elizabeth, Harrison, Pop. 161
South Harrison Community SD
Supt. — See Corydon
South Central JSHS 400/6-12
6675 E Highway 11 SE 47117 812-969-2941
David Beaver, prin. Fax 969-3019

Elkhart, Elkhart, Pop. 49,305
Baugo Community SD 1,900/K-12
29125 County Road 22 46517 574-293-8583
James DuBois, supt. Fax 294-2171
www.baugo.org/
Jimtown HS 600/9-12
59021 County Road 3 46517 574-295-2343
Jeffrey Ziegler, prin. Fax 294-2171
Jimtown JHS 300/7-8
58903 County Road 3 46517 574-294-6586
Michael Stout, prin. Fax 294-8557

Concord Community SD 5,200/K-12
59040 Minuteman Way 46517 574-875-5161
John Trout, supt. Fax 875-8762
www.concord.k12.in.us
Concord Community HS 1,600/9-12
59117 Minuteman Way 46517 574-875-6524
M. Greg Dettinger, prin. Fax 875-8580
Concord JHS 900/7-8
59397 County Road 11 46517 574-875-5122
Rob Zook, prin. Fax 875-1089

Elkhart Community SD 13,000/PK-12
2720 California Rd 46514 574-262-5500
Dr. Robert Haworth, supt. Fax 262-5733
www.elkhart.k12.in.us
Elkhart Area Career Ctr Vo/Tech
2424 California Rd 46514 574-262-5650
Dr. David Benak, dir. Fax 262-5801
Elkhart Central HS 1,800/9-12
1 Blazer Blvd 46516 574-295-4700
Frank Serge, prin. Fax 295-4712
Elkhart Memorial HS 1,800/9-12
2608 California Rd 46514 574-262-5600
Cary Anderson, prin. Fax 262-5625
Moran MS 600/7-8
200 W Lusher Ave 46517 574-295-4805
Cynthia Bonner, prin. Fax 295-4807
North Side MS 600/7-8
300 Lawrence St 46514 574-262-5570
Sara Jackowiak, prin. Fax 262-5573
West Side MS 600/7-8
101 S Nappanee St 46514 574-295-4815
Kristie Stutsman, prin. Fax 295-4812

Anabaptist Mennonite Biblical Seminary Post-Sec.
3003 Benham Ave 46517 800-964-2627
Elkhart Christian Academy 400/PK-12
25943 County Road 22 46517 574-293-1609
Sue Alberts, supt. Fax 293-3238
Harrison College Post-Sec.
56075 Parkway Ave 46516 574-522-0397

Ellettsville, Monroe, Pop. 6,255
Richland-Bean Blossom Community SC 2,800/PK-12
600 Edgewood Dr 47429 812-876-7100
Dr. Mike Wilcox, supt. Fax 876-7020
www.rbbcsc.k12.in.us/
Edgewood HS 800/9-12
601 S Edgewood Dr 47429 812-876-2277
Dirk Ackerman, prin. Fax 876-9163
Edgewood JHS 600/6-8
851 W Edgewood Dr 47429 812-876-2005
Rod Hite, prin. Fax 876-8985

Elnora, Daviess, Pop. 631
North Daviess Community SD 1,200/K-12
5494 E State Road 58 47529 812-636-8000
Robert Bell, supt. Fax 636-7546
www.ndaviess.k12.in.us
North Daviess JSHS 500/7-12
5494 E State Road 58 47529 812-636-8000
Jed Jerrels, prin. Fax 636-7255

Elwood, Madison, Pop. 8,510
Elwood Community SC 1,300/PK-12
1306 N Anderson St 46036 765-552-9861
Dr. Christopher Daughtry, supt. Fax 552-8088
www.elwood.k12.in.us
Elwood JSHS 500/7-12
1137 N 19th St 46036 765-552-9854
David Retherford, prin. Fax 552-1044
Hinds Career Center Vo/Tech
1105 N 19th St 46036 765-552-9881
James Pearson, dir. Fax 552-2021

Eminence, Morgan
Eminence Community SC 400/PK-12
PO Box 135 46125 765-528-2101
Jeff Gibboney, supt. Fax 528-2262
www.eminence.k12.in.us
Eminence JSHS 200/6-12
PO Box 105 46125 765-528-2222
Corey Scott, prin. Fax 528-2276

Evansville, Vanderburgh, Pop. 114,065
Evansville-Vanderburgh SC 22,800/PK-12
951 Walnut St 47713 812-435-8453
Dr. David Smith, supt. Fax 435-8421
www.evscschools.com/
Academy for Innovative Studies 500/Alt
3013 N 1st Ave 47710 812-435-8316
Kristine Eichholz, prin. Fax 435-8517
Bosse HS 800/9-12
1300 Washington Ave 47714 812-477-1661
Sheila Huff, prin. Fax 474-6976
Central HS 1,200/9-12
5400 N 1st Ave 47710 812-435-8292
Andrea Campbell, prin. Fax 435-8515
Harrison HS 1,000/9-12
211 Fielding Rd 47715 812-477-1046
Elizabeth Wells, prin. Fax 474-4125
Helfrich Park MS 600/6-8
2603 W Maryland St 47712 812-435-8246
Cory Herrin, prin. Fax 435-8249
McGary MS 300/6-8
1535 Joyce Ave 47714 812-476-3035
Dale Naylor, prin. Fax 474-6919
New Tech Institute 300/9-12
1901 Lynch Rd 47711 812-435-0967
Christpher Gibson, prin. Fax 435-8568
North HS 1,500/9-12
15331 Highway 41 N 47725 812-435-8283
John Skinner, prin. Fax 435-8349
North JHS 900/7-8
15325 Highway 41 N 47725 812-435-0975
Aaron Huff, prin. Fax 435-8887
Perry Heights MS 400/6-8
5800 Hogue Rd 47712 812-435-8326
Jeanette Lindauer, prin. Fax 435-8363
Plaza Park MS 700/6-8
7301 Lincoln Ave 47715 812-476-4971
Shane Browder, prin. Fax 474-6922
Reitz HS 1,300/9-12
350 Dreier Blvd 47712 812-435-8206
Beth Carnahan, prin. Fax 435-8217
Southern IN Career and Technical Center Vo/Tech
1901 Lynch Rd 47711 812-435-8438
David St. Clair, prin. Fax 435-8366
Thompkins MS 700/6-8
1300 W Mill Rd 47710 812-435-8323
Nichole Alcorn, prin. Fax 435-8588
Washington MS 400/6-8
1801 Washington Ave 47714 812-477-8983
Michele Branson, prin. Fax 474-6930

Evansville Day S 50/PK-12
3400 N Green River Rd 47715 812-476-3039
Jarin Jaffee, head sch Fax 476-4061
Harrison College Post-Sec.
4601 Theatre Dr 47715 812-476-6000
Ivy Tech Community College - Southwest Post-Sec.
3501 N 1st Ave 47710 812-426-2865
Mater Dei HS 500/9-12
1300 Harmony Way 47720 812-426-2258
Darin Knight, prin. Fax 421-5717
Reitz Memorial HS 800/9-12
1500 Lincoln Ave 47714 812-476-4973
Marie Williams, prin. Fax 474-2942
Roger's Academy of Hair Design Post-Sec.
2903 Mount Vernon Ave 47712 812-429-0110
University of Evansville Post-Sec.
1800 Lincoln Ave 47714 812-488-2000
University of Southern Indiana Post-Sec.
8600 University Blvd 47712 812-464-8600
Westside Catholic S St. Boniface Campus 100/6-8
2031 W Michigan St 47712 812-422-1014
Tracey Unfried, prin. Fax 422-1057

Fairland, Shelby, Pop. 314
Northwestern Cons SD of Shelby County 1,400/PK-12
4920 W 600 N 46126 317-835-7461
Chris Hoke, supt. Fax 835-4441
www.nwshelbyschools.org
Triton Central HS 500/9-12
4774 W 600 N 46126 317-835-3000
Cary Chandler, prin. Fax 480-1887
Triton Central MS 400/5-8
4740 W 600 N 46126 317-835-3006
Bobby Thompson, prin. Fax 835-3008

Fairmount, Grant, Pop. 2,932
Madison-Grant United SC 1,100/PK-12
11580 S E 00 W 46928 765-948-4143
Dr. Scott Deetz Ph.D., supt. Fax 948-4150
www.mgusc.k12.in.us
Madison-Grant JSHS 400/7-12
11700 S E 00 W 46928 765-948-4141
Chris Smedley, prin. Fax 948-4874

Farmersburg, Sullivan, Pop. 1,110
Northeast SC
Supt. — See Hymera
North Central HS 300/9-12
910 E County Road 975 N 47850 812-397-2132
Monty Kirk, prin. Fax 397-2133

Ferdinand, Dubois, Pop. 2,150
Southeast Dubois County SC 1,400/PK-12
432 E 15th St 47532 812-817-0900
Richard Allen, supt. Fax 367-1075
www.sedubois.k12.in.us
Forest Park JSHS 600/7-12
1440 Michigan St 47532 812-817-0900
Jamie Pund, prin. Fax 367-1172

Fishers, Hamilton, Pop. 75,207
Hamilton Southeastern SD 20,100/K-12
13485 Cumberland Rd 46038 317-594-4100
Dr. Allen Bourff, supt. Fax 594-4109
www.hse.k12.in.us
Fall Creek JHS 7-8
12001 Olio Rd, 317-594-4390
Kim Lippe, prin. Fax 594-4399
Fishers HS 2,700/9-12
13000 Promise Rd 46038 317-915-4290
Jason Urban, prin. Fax 915-4299
Fishers JHS 1,100/7-8
13257 Cumberland Rd 46038 317-594-4150
Crystal Thorpe, prin. Fax 594-4159
Hamilton Southeastern HS 3,000/9-12
13910 E 126th St, 317-594-4190
Matt Kegley, prin. Fax 594-4199
Hamilton Southeastern Intermediate JHS 1,200/5-8
12278 Cyntheanne Rd, 317-594-4120
Tim Mankin, prin. Fax 594-4129
Riverside JHS 1,000/7-8
10910 Eller Rd 46038 317-915-4280
Rob Huesing, prin. Fax 915-4289

Flora, Carroll, Pop. 2,010
Carroll Consolidated SC 1,100/PK-12
2 S 3rd St 46929 574-967-4113
John Sayers, supt. Fax 967-3831
www.carroll.k12.in.us/
Carroll JSHS 500/7-12
2362 E State Road 18 46929 574-967-4157
Tiffany Myers, prin. Fax 967-4027

Floyds Knobs, Floyd
New Albany Floyd County Consolidated SD
Supt. — See New Albany
Floyd Central HS 1,700/9-12
6575 Old Vincennes Rd 47119 812-542-8504
Dr. Rob Willman, prin. Fax 542-4795

Fort Branch, Gibson, Pop. 2,743
South Gibson SC 2,000/K-12
1029 W 650 S 47648 812-753-4230
Dr. Stacey Humbaugh, supt. Fax 753-4081
www.sgibson.k12.in.us
Gibson Southern HS 700/9-12
3499 W 800 S 47648 812-753-3011
Scott Reid, prin. Fax 753-4862

Fortville, Hancock, Pop. 3,887
Mt. Vernon Community SC 3,500/PK-12
1806 W State Road 234 46040 317-485-3100
Dr. Shane Robbins, admin. Fax 485-3113
www.mvcsc.k12.in.us
8th Grade Academy 300/8-8
8112 N 200 W 46040 317-485-3131
Scott Shipley, prin. Fax 482-0027
Mt. Vernon HS 1,100/9-12
8112 N 200 W 46040 317-485-3131
Greg Roach, prin. Fax 485-3154

Fort Wayne, Allen, Pop. 246,159
East Allen County SD
Supt. — See New Haven
East Allen University 200/9-12
6501 Wayne Trce 46816 260-446-0240
Doug Hicks, prin. Fax 446-0249
Harding JHS 300/7-8
6501 Wayne Trce 46816 260-446-0240
Danielle Newman, prin. Fax 446-0249

Fort Wayne Community SD 30,300/PK-12
1200 S Clinton St 46802 260-467-1000
Dr. Wendy Robinson, supt. Fax 467-1980
fortwayneschools.org
Anthis Career Center Vo/Tech
1200 Barr St 46802 260-467-1010
Larry Gerardot, prin. Fax 425-7609
Blackhawk MS 900/6-8
7200 E State Blvd 46815 260-467-4885
Kara Froning, prin. Fax 467-4943
Jefferson MS 700/6-8
5303 Wheelock Rd 46835 260-467-4825
Jeff King, prin. Fax 467-4883

Kekionga MS 500/6-8
2929 Engle Rd 46809 260-467-6600
Robin Peterman, prin. Fax 467-6658
Lakeside MS 500/6-8
2100 Lake Ave 46805 260-467-8625
Alan Jones, prin. Fax 467-8672
Lane MS 500/6-8
4901 Vance Ave 46815 260-467-4400
Mark Bailey, prin. Fax 467-4437
Memorial Park MS 700/6-8
2200 Maumee Ave 46803 260-467-5300
Tim Rayl, prin. Fax 467-5298
Miami MS 800/6-8
8100 Amherst Dr 46819 260-467-8560
Adam Swinford, prin. Fax 467-8606
Northrop HS 2,200/9-12
7001 Coldwater Rd 46825 260-467-2300
Kevin Simmons, prin. Fax 467-2301
North Side HS 1,700/9-12
475 E State Blvd 46805 260-467-2800
Chad Hissong, prin. Fax 467-2690
Northwood MS 700/6-8
1201 E Washington Center Rd 46825 260-467-2930
Austin Couch, prin. Fax 467-2987
Portage MS 500/6-8
3521 Taylor St 46802 260-467-4500
Michael Christner, prin. Fax 467-4497
Shawnee MS 900/6-8
1000 E Cook Rd 46825 260-467-6525
Matt Schiebel, prin. Fax 467-6527
Snider HS 1,800/9-12
4600 Fairlawn Pass 46815 260-467-4600
Nicole Chisley, prin. Fax 467-4729
South Side HS 1,400/9-12
3601 S Calhoun St 46807 260-467-2600
Carlton Mable, prin. Fax 467-2663
Ward Education Center Alt
3501 Warsaw St 46806 260-467-4570
Gradlin Pruitt, prin. Fax 467-5497
Wayne HS 1,400/9-12
9100 Winchester Rd 46819 260-467-6400
John Houser, prin. Fax 467-6490

Metro SD of Southwest Allen County 7,000/K-12
4824 Homestead Rd 46814 260-431-2051
Dr. Philip Downs, supt. Fax 431-2063
www.sacs.k12.in.us
Homestead HS 2,300/9-12
4310 Homestead Rd 46814 260-431-2200
Park Ginder, prin. Fax 431-2299
Summit MS 700/6-8
4509 Homestead Rd 46814 260-431-2502
Josh St. John, prin. Fax 431-2599
Woodside MS 1,000/6-8
2310 W Hamilton Rd S 46814 260-431-2701
Jerry Schillinger, prin. Fax 431-2799

Northwest Allen County SD 6,900/PK-12
13119 Coldwater Rd 46845 260-637-3155
Christopher Himsel, supt. Fax 637-8355
www.nacs.k12.in.us/
Allen County Youth Services Center 50/Alt
11805 Lima Rd 46818 260-449-3561
Sam DiPrimio, admin. Fax 449-7943
Carroll Freshman Center 500/9-9
3905 Carroll Rd 46818 260-338-5360
Tanya Pickett, admin. Fax 637-5868
Carroll HS 1,600/10-12
3701 Carroll Rd 46818 260-637-3161
Brandon Bitting, prin. Fax 637-8356
Carroll MS 900/6-8
4027 Hathaway Rd 46818 260-637-5159
Brandon Basham, prin. Fax 637-5478
Maple Creek MS 800/6-8
425 Union Chapel Rd 46845 260-338-0802
Bill Toler, prin. Fax 338-0369

Bishop Dwenger HS 1,000/9-12
1300 E Washington Center Rd 46825 260-496-4700
Jason Schiffli, prin. Fax 496-4702
Bishop Luers HS 600/9-12
333 E Paulding Rd 46816 260-456-1261
Tiffany Albertson, prin. Fax 456-1262
Blackhawk Christian S 700/PK-12
7400 E State Blvd 46815 260-493-7400
Linda Pearson, admin. Fax 749-8527
Canterbury S 900/PK-12
3210 Smith Rd 46804 260-436-0746
William Ennist, hdmstr. Fax 436-5137
Concordia Lutheran HS 700/9-12
1601 Saint Joe River Dr 46805 260-797-8495
Patrick Frerking, head sch Fax 797-8495
Concordia Theological Seminary Post-Sec.
6600 N Clinton St 46825 260-452-2100
Fort Wayne School of Radiography Post-Sec.
700 Broadway 46802 260-425-3990
Harrison College Post-Sec.
6413 N Clinton St 46825 260-471-7667
Indiana Tech Post-Sec.
1600 E Washington Blvd 46803 260-422-5561
Indiana Univ-Purdue Univ at Fort Wayne Post-Sec.
2101 E Coliseum Blvd 46805 260-481-6100
International Business College Post-Sec.
5699 Coventry Ln 46804 260-459-4500
Ivy Tech Community College - Northeast Post-Sec.
3800 N Anthony Blvd 46805 260-482-9171
MedTech College Post-Sec.
7230 Engle Rd Ste 200 46804 260-436-3272
National College Post-Sec.
6131 N Clinton St 46825 260-483-1605
Ravenscroft Beauty College Post-Sec.
6110 Stellhorn Rd 46815 260-486-8868
Rudae's School of Beauty Culture Post-Sec.
5317 Coldwater Rd 46825 260-483-2466
The Masters of Cosmetology College Post-Sec.
1732 Bluffton Rd 46809 260-747-6667
University of St. Francis Post-Sec.
2701 Spring St 46808 260-399-7999

Fountain City, Wayne, Pop. 783
Northeastern Wayne SD 1,000/PK-12
PO Box 406 47341 765-847-2821
Laura Blessing, supt. Fax 847-5355
www.nws.k12.in.us
Northeastern HS 400/9-12
7295 N US Highway 27 47341 765-847-2591
Steve Angel, prin. Fax 847-2875
Northeastern MS 6-8
7295 N US Highway 27 47341 765-847-2591
Dawn Sonsini, prin. Fax 847-2875

Fowler, Benton, Pop. 2,292
Benton Community SC 1,900/PK-12
PO Box 512 47944 765-884-0850
Gregg Hoover, supt. Fax 884-1614
www.benton.k12.in.us
Other Schools – See Oxford

Francesville, Pulaski, Pop. 873
West Central SC 900/K-12
PO Box 578 47946 219-567-9161
Don Street, supt. Fax 567-9761
www.wcsc.k12.in.us
West Central HS 300/9-12
1852 S US Highway 421 47946 219-567-9119
Pat Culp, prin. Fax 567-2597
West Central MS 200/6-8
1850 S US Highway 421 47946 219-567-2534
Pat Culp, prin. Fax 567-9535

Frankfort, Clinton, Pop. 16,300
Clinton Prairie SC 1,100/K-12
4431 W Old State Road 28 46041 765-659-1339
John Sampson, supt. Fax 659-5305
www.clintonprairie.com
Clinton Prairie JSHS 500/7-12
2400 S County Road 450 W 46041 765-659-3305
Amanda Whitlock, prin. Fax 659-3205

Frankfort Community SC 3,200/PK-12
2400 E Wabash St 46041 765-654-5585
Donald DeWeese, supt. Fax 659-6220
www.frankfortschools.org
Frankfort HS 800/9-12
1 S Maish Rd 46041 765-654-8545
Steve Edwards, prin. Fax 654-9224
Frankfort MS 800/6-8
329 N Maish Rd 46041 765-659-3321
Kelly Berenda, prin. Fax 659-6260

Franklin, Johnson, Pop. 23,366
Franklin Community SC 5,000/PK-12
998 Grizzly Cub Dr 46131 317-738-5800
David Clendening, supt. Fax 738-5812
www.franklinschools.org
Franklin Community HS 1,700/9-12
2600 Cumberland Dr 46131 317-738-5700
Leah Wooldridge, prin. Fax 738-5703
Franklin Community MS 800/7-8
625 Grizzly Cub Dr 46131 317-346-8400
Steve Ahaus, prin. Fax 346-8411

Franklin College Post-Sec.
101 Branigin Blvd 46131 317-738-8000

Frankton, Madison, Pop. 1,842
Frankton-Lapel Community SD
Supt. — See Anderson
Frankton JSHS 700/7-12
610 E Clyde St 46044 765-754-7879
Greg Granger, prin. Fax 754-8594

Fremont, Steuben, Pop. 2,131
Fremont Community SD 1,000/K-12
PO Box 665 46737 260-495-5005
Dr. William Stitt, supt. Fax 495-9798
fremontschoolsin.com
Fremont HS 300/9-12
PO Box 655 46737 260-495-9876
Mark Sherbondy, prin. Fax 495-1838
Fremont MS 300/5-8
PO Box 770 46737 260-495-6100
Mark Fowerbaugh, prin. Fax 495-7301

French Lick, Orange, Pop. 1,754
Springs Valley Community SC 900/K-12
498 S Larry Bird Blvd 47432 812-936-4474
Anthony Whitaker, supt. Fax 936-9392
www.svalley.k12.in.us
Springs Valley Community JSHS 500/6-12
326 S Larry Bird Blvd 47432 812-936-9984
James Bush, prin. Fax 936-9266

Fulton, Fulton, Pop. 332
Caston SC 800/K-12
PO Box 8 46931 574-857-2035
Lucinda Douglass, supt. Fax 857-6035
www.caston.k12.in.us/
Caston JSHS 400/7-12
PO Box 128 46931 574-857-3505
Chuck Evans, prin. Fax 857-6795

Garrett, DeKalb, Pop. 6,210
Garrett-Keyser-Butler Community SD 1,800/K-12
801 E Houston St 46738 260-357-3185
Tonya Weaver, supt. Fax 357-4565
www.gkb.k12.in.us
Garrett HS 600/9-12
801 E Houston St 46738 260-357-4114
Matthew Smith, prin. Fax 357-5000
Garrett MS 400/6-8
801 E Houston St 46738 260-357-5745
Lucas Fielden, prin. Fax 357-3575

Gary, Lake, Pop. 78,995
Gary Community SC 6,500/PK-12
1988 Polk St 46407 219-881-5401
Dr. Cheryl Pruitt, supt. Fax 881-4102
www.garycsc.k12.in.us

Gary Career Center Vo/Tech
1800 E 35th Ave 46409 219-962-7571
Gershon Jackson, prin. Fax 962-6269
New Tech S Vo/Tech
1800 E 35th Ave 46409 219-963-2901
Dr. Vanessa Nichols, prin. Fax 963-2937
West Side Leadership Academy 1,100/7-12
900 Gerry St 46406 219-413-9870
Terrance Little, prin. Fax 977-2168
Wirt/Emerson Visual Performing Arts JSHS 600/5-12
210 N Grand Blvd 46403 219-321-8555
Mary Ward, prin. Fax 938-7517

Lake Ridge New Tech SC 1,900/K-12
6111 W Ridge Rd 46408 219-838-1819
Dr. Sharon Johnson-Shirley, supt. Fax 989-7802
www.lakeridge.k12.in.us
Calumet New Tech HS 600/9-12
3900 Calhoun St 46408 219-838-6990
Cynthia Mose-Trevino, prin. Fax 989-7849
Lake Ridge New Tech MS 400/6-8
3601 W 41st Ave 46408 219-980-0730
Greg Mikulich, prin. Fax 980-0731

Indiana University Northwest Post-Sec.
3400 Broadway 46408 219-980-6500
Ivy Tech Community College - Northwest Post-Sec.
1440 E 35th Ave 46409 219-981-1111

Gas City, Grant, Pop. 5,872
Mississinewa Community SC 2,500/PK-12
424 E South A St 46933 765-674-8528
Tab McKenzie, supt. Fax 674-8529
www.olemiss.k12.in.us
Baskett MS 600/6-8
125 N Broadway St 46933 765-674-8536
Jamie Eckstein, prin. Fax 677-4452
Mississinewa HS 800/9-12
1 Indian Trail Dr 46933 765-674-2248
Steve Quaderer, prin. Fax 677-4424

Gaston, Delaware, Pop. 858
Wes-Del Community SD 900/K-12
10290 N County Road 600 W 47342 765-358-4006
Michael Bush, supt. Fax 358-4065
www.wes-del.k12.in.us
Wes-Del MSHS 500/6-12
10000 N County Road 600 W 47342 765-358-4091
Kyle Mealy, prin. Fax 358-3514

Georgetown, Floyd, Pop. 2,851
New Albany Floyd County Consolidated SD
Supt. — See New Albany
Highland Hills MS 1,500/5-8
3492 Edwardsville Galena Rd 47122 812-542-8501
Steve Griffin, prin. Fax 542-4792

Goshen, Elkhart, Pop. 31,231
Fairfield Community SD 2,100/K-12
67240 County Road 31 46528 574-831-2188
Steve Thalheimer, supt. Fax 831-5698
www.fairfield.k12.in.us
Fairfield JSHS 900/7-12
67530 US Highway 33 46526 574-831-2184
Amy Bertram, prin. Fax 831-2187

Goshen Community SD 6,500/PK-12
613 E Purl St 46526 574-533-8631
Dr. Diane Woodworth, supt. Fax 533-2505
www.goshenschools.org/
Goshen HS 1,800/9-12
401 Lincolnway E 46526 574-533-8651
Dr. Barry Younghans, prin. Fax 534-1567
Goshen MS 1,500/6-8
1216 S Indiana Ave 46526 574-533-0391
Lori Shreiner, prin. Fax 534-3042

Bethany Christian S 300/4-12
2904 S Main St 46526 574-534-2567
Hank Willems, prin. Fax 533-0150
Clinton Christian S 100/PK-12
61763 County Road 35 46528 574-642-3940
Matt Blosser, admin. Fax 642-3674
Goshen College Post-Sec.
1700 S Main St 46526 574-535-7000

Granger, Saint Joseph, Pop. 29,968
Penn-Harris-Madison SC
Supt. — See Mishawaka
Discovery MS 900/6-8
10050 Brummitt Rd 46530 574-674-6010
Sheryll Harper, prin. Fax 679-4214

Granger Christian S 200/PK-12
52025 Gumwood Rd 46530 574-272-5815
Mark Wever, lead tchr. Fax 968-2664

Greencastle, Putnam, Pop. 10,164
Greencastle Community SC 2,000/PK-12
PO Box 480 46135 765-653-9771
Jeffrey Hubble, supt. Fax 653-1282
www.greencastle.k12.in.us
Greencastle HS 600/9-12
910 E Washington St 46135 765-653-9711
Russell Hesler, prin. Fax 653-4773
Greencastle MS 500/6-8
400 Percy L Julian Dr 46135 765-653-9774
Scott Wetlz, prin. Fax 653-5381

North Putnam Community SD
Supt. — See Bainbridge
Area 30 Career Center Vo/Tech
1 N Calbert Way 46135 765-653-3515
Lora Busch, dir. Fax 653-6110

South Putnam Community SD 900/K-12
3999 S US Highway 231 46135 765-653-3119
Bruce Bernhardt, supt. Fax 653-7476
www.sputnam.k12.in.us
South Putnam MSHS 400/6-12
1780 E US Highway 40 46135 765-653-3148
Michael Schimpf, prin. Fax 653-3149

DePauw University Post-Sec.
PO Box 37 46135 765-658-4800

Greenfield, Hancock, Pop. 20,372
Greenfield-Central Community SD 4,600/PK-12
110 W North St 46140 317-462-4434
Dr. Harold Olin, supt. Fax 467-4227
www.gcsc.k12.in.us
Greenfield-Central HS 1,500/9-12
810 N Broadway St 46140 317-462-9211
Steven Bryant, prin. Fax 467-6723
Greenfield Central JHS 800/7-8
1440 N Franklin St 46140 317-477-4616
Dan Jack, prin. Fax 477-4617

Hancock Memorial Hospital Post-Sec.
801 N State St 46140 317-462-0457
PJ's College of Cosmetology Post-Sec.
1400 W Main St 46140 317-462-9239

Greensburg, Decatur, Pop. 11,380
Decatur County Community SD 2,100/PK-12
2020 N Montgomery Rd 47240 812-663-4595
Johnny Budd, supt. Fax 663-4168
www.decaturco.k12.in.us
North Decatur JSHS 500/7-12
3172 N State Road 3 47240 812-663-4204
Charlie McCoy, prin. Fax 663-9606
South Decatur JSHS 500/7-12
8885 S State Road 3 47240 812-591-3330
Jim Jameson, prin. Fax 591-3331

Greensburg Community SC 2,300/K-12
1312 W Westridge Pkwy 47240 812-663-4774
Tom Hunter, supt. Fax 663-5713
www.greensburg.k12.in.us
Greensburg Community HS 700/9-12
1000 E Central Ave 47240 812-663-7176
Grant Peters, prin. Fax 663-8911
Greensburg Community JHS 600/6-8
505 E Central Ave 47240 812-663-7523
Matt Clifford, prin. Fax 663-9425

Greentown, Howard, Pop. 2,402
Eastern Howard SC 1,100/K-12
221 W Main St Ste 1 46936 765-628-3391
Dr. Tracy Caddell Ed.D., supt. Fax 628-5017
www.eastern.k12.in.us
Eastern HS 500/9-12
421 S Harrison St 46936 765-628-3333
Keith Richie Ed.D., prin. Fax 628-5021
Eastern MS 6-8
421 S Harrison St 46936 765-628-5030
Lindsey Brown, prin. Fax 628-5031

Greenwood, Johnson, Pop. 48,867
Center Grove Community SC 7,700/K-12
4800 W Stones Crossing Rd 46143 317-881-9326
Dr. Richard Arkanoff, supt. Fax 881-0241
www.centergrove.k12.in.us
Center Grove HS 2,400/9-12
2717 S Morgantown Rd 46143 317-881-0581
Doug Bird, prin. Fax 885-4509
Center Grove MS Central 1,000/6-8
4900 W Stones Crossing Rd 46143 317-882-9391
Craig Smith, prin. Fax 885-4534
Center Grove MS North 900/6-8
202 N Morgantown Rd 46142 317-885-8800
Scott Johnson, prin. Fax 885-3388

Central Nine Career Center SD
1999 US Highway 31 S 46143 317-888-4401
Nicole Otte, dir. Fax 865-8670
www.central9.k12.in.us
Central Nine Career Center Vo/Tech
1999 US Highway 31 S 46143 317-888-4401
Nicole Otte, dir. Fax 885-8670

Clark-Pleasant Community SC
Supt. — See Whiteland
Clark Pleasant MS 1,000/6-8
1354 E Worthsville Rd 46143 317-535-7121
Tim Rinehold, prin. Fax 535-2064

Greenwood Community SC 3,800/PK-12
605 W Smith Valley Rd 46142 317-889-4060
Dr. Kent DeKoninck, supt. Fax 889-4068
gws.k12.in.us
Greenwood Community HS 1,100/9-12
615 W Smith Valley Rd 46142 317-889-4000
Todd Garrison, prin. Fax 889-4039
Greenwood MS 900/6-8
523 S Madison Ave 46142 317-889-4040
Chris Sutton, prin. Fax 889-4044

Greenwood Christian Academy 400/PK-12
835 W Worthsville Rd 46143 317-215-5300
MedTech College Post-Sec.
1500 American Way 46143 317-534-0322

Griffith, Lake, Pop. 16,641
Griffith Public SD 2,400/PK-12
PO Box 749 46319 219-924-4250
Dr. Peter Morikis, supt. Fax 922-5933
www.griffith.k12.in.us
Griffith HS 800/9-12
600 N Wiggs St 46319 219-924-4281
Brian Orkis, prin. Fax 922-5920
Griffith MS 400/7-8
600 N Raymond St 46319 219-924-4280
Dustin Nelson, prin. Fax 922-5927

Hagerstown, Wayne, Pop. 1,765
Nettle Creek SC 1,100/PK-12
297 E Northmarket St 47346 765-489-4543
Dr. William Doering, supt. Fax 489-4914
nettlecreekschools.com
Hagerstown JSHS 500/7-12
701 Baker Rd 47346 765-489-4511
Mark Childs, prin. Fax 489-4333

Hamilton, DeKalb, Pop. 1,521
Hamilton Community SD 400/K-12
903 S Wayne St 46742 260-488-2513
Dr. Nicole Singer, supt. Fax 488-2348
www.hcs.k12.in.us
Hamilton Community JSHS 200/7-12
903 S Wayne St 46742 260-488-2161
Chris Gerbers, prin. Fax 488-3149

Hamlet, Starke, Pop. 787
Oregon-Davis SC 600/PK-12
5998 N 750 E 46532 574-867-2111
Dr. Donald Harman, supt. Fax 867-8191
www.od.k12.in.us
Oregon-Davis JSHS 300/7-12
5990 N 750 E 46532 574-867-4561
Timothy Pletcher, prin. Fax 867-2481

Hammond, Lake, Pop. 79,563
Hammond CSD 13,400/PK-12
41 Williams St 46320 219-933-2400
Dr. Walter Watkins, supt. Fax 933-2495
www.hammond.k12.in.us
Area Career Center Vo/Tech
5727 Sohl Ave 46320 219-933-2428
Scott Miller, prin. Fax 554-4570
Eggers MS 700/6-8
5825 Blaine Ave 46320 219-933-2449
Rhoderick Poats, prin. Fax 554-4575
Gavit MSHS 1,500/6-12
1670 175th St 46324 219-989-7328
Michelle Ondas, prin. Fax 554-4573
Hammond HS 800/9-12
5926 Calumet Ave 46320 219-933-2442
Johnny Goodlow, prin. Fax 933-1688
Morton HS 1,200/9-12
6915 Grand Ave 46323 219-989-7316
Kenneth Easton, prin. Fax 554-4574
Scott MS 800/6-8
3635 173rd St 46323 219-989-7340
Colleen Bergren, prin. Fax 554-4576
Other Schools – See Whiting

Bishop Noll Institute 500/9-12
1519 Hoffman St 46327 219-932-9058
Craig Stafford, prin. Fax 853-1736
Brightwood College Post-Sec.
7833 Indianapolis Blvd 46324 219-844-0100
Purdue University Calumet Post-Sec.
2200 169th St 46323 219-989-2400
St. Margaret Hospital Post-Sec.
5454 Hohman Ave 46320 219-932-2300

Hanover, Jefferson, Pop. 3,496
Southwestern-Jefferson County Cons SC 1,300/PK-12
239 S Main Cross St 47243 812-866-6250
Trevor Jones, supt. Fax 866-6256
www.swjcs.us
Southwestern HS 400/9-12
167 S Main Cross St 47243 812-866-6230
Jeff Bates, prin. Fax 866-6233
Southwestern MS 300/6-8
167 S Main Cross St 47243 812-866-6220
Jason Watson, prin. Fax 866-4680

Hanover College Post-Sec.
PO Box 108 47243 812-866-7000

Hartford City, Blackford, Pop. 6,115
Blackford County SD 1,800/PK-12
668 W 200 S 47348 765-348-7550
Dr. Scot Croner, supt. Fax 348-7552
www.bcs.k12.in.us
Blackford HS 500/9-12
2392 N State Road 3 47348 765-348-7560
Scott Shimer, prin. Fax 348-7568
Blackford JHS 300/7-8
800 W Van Cleve St 47348 765-348-7590
Melissa Blossom, prin. Fax 348-7593

Hebron, Porter, Pop. 3,695
Metro SD of Boone Township 1,200/K-12
307 S Main St 46341 219-996-4771
Dr. Nathan H. Kleefisch, supt. Fax 996-5777
www.hebronschools.k12.in.us/
Hebron HS 300/9-12
509 S Main St 46341 219-996-4771
Mark Lutze, prin. Fax 996-5777
Hebron MS 300/6-8
307 S Main St 46341 219-996-4771
Jeff Brooks, prin. Fax 996-5777

Henryville, Clark, Pop. 1,892
West Clark Community SC
Supt. — See Sellersburg
Henryville JSHS 500/7-12
213 N Ferguson St 47126 812-294-1455
Troy Albert, prin. Fax 294-4276

Highland, Lake, Pop. 23,446
Town of Highland SD 3,200/K-12
9145 Kennedy Ave 46322 219-924-7400
Brian J. Smith, supt. Fax 922-5637
www.highland.k12.in.us
Highland HS 1,200/9-12
9135 Erie St 46322 219-922-5610
Patrick Weil, prin. Fax 922-5636
Highland MS 800/6-8
2941 41st St 46322 219-922-5620
Terry Mucha, prin. Fax 922-2270

Creative Hair Styling Academy Post-Sec.
2549 Highway Ave 46322 219-838-2004

Hobart, Lake, Pop. 28,672
Hobart CSD 4,100/PK-12
32 E 7th St 46342 219-942-8885
Dr. Peggy Buffington, supt. Fax 942-0081
www.hobart.k12.in.us
Hobart HS 1,300/9-12
2211 E 10th St 46342 219-942-8521
Angela Patrick, prin. Fax 942-3326
Hobart MS 1,000/6-8
36 E 8th St 46342 219-942-8541
Nikki Neeley, prin. Fax 947-7194

River Forest Community SC 1,000/K-12
3250 Michigan St 46342 219-962-2909
Dr. Steven Disney, supt. Fax 962-4951
www.rfcsc.k12.in.us
River Forest HS 400/9-12
3300 Indiana St 46342 219-962-7551
Dr. Alexander Brandon, prin. Fax 962-8338
River Forest MS 100/6-8
3300 Indiana St 46342 219-962-7751
Randall Horka, prin. Fax 962-8338

College of Court Reporting Post-Sec.
111 W 10th St Ste 111 46342 866-294-3974

Hope, Bartholomew, Pop. 2,080
Flat Rock-Hawcreek SC 900/PK-12
9423 N State Road 9 47246 812-546-4922
Shawn Price, supt. Fax 546-5617
www.flatrock.k12.in.us
Hauser JSHS 400/7-12
9273 N State Road 9 47246 812-546-4421
James Mayer, prin. Fax 546-2005

Howe, Lagrange, Pop. 791

Howe Military Academy 100/7-12
PO Box 240 46746 260-562-2131
Angela Lehmer, hdmstr. Fax 562-3678

Huntingburg, Dubois, Pop. 6,020
Southwest Dubois County SC 1,800/PK-12
113 N Jackson St 47542 812-683-3971
Mike Eineman, supt. Fax 683-2752
www.swdubois.k12.in.us
Southridge HS 500/9-12
1110 S Main St 47542 812-683-2272
Chad Sickbert, prin. Fax 683-2010
Southridge MS 400/6-8
1112 S Main St 47542 812-683-3372
Kelly Murphy, prin. Fax 683-2817

Huntington, Huntington, Pop. 17,196
Huntington County Community SC 5,900/K-12
2485 Waterworks Rd 46750 260-356-8312
Randy Harris, supt. Fax 358-2222
www.hccsc.k12.in.us
Crestview MS 600/6-8
1151 W 500 N 46750 260-356-6210
Shane Grove, prin. Fax 358-2232
Huntington North HS 1,700/9-12
450 MacGahan St 46750 260-356-6104
Russ Degitz, prin. Fax 358-2210
Riverview MS 700/6-8
2465 Waterworks Rd 46750 260-356-0910
Curt Crago, prin. Fax 358-2243

Huntington University Post-Sec.
2303 College Ave 46750 260-356-6000

Hymera, Sullivan, Pop. 795
Northeast SC 800/PK-12
PO Box 493 47855 812-383-5761
Dr. Mark Baker, supt. Fax 383-4591
www.nesc.k12.in.us/
Other Schools – See Farmersburg, Shelburn

Indianapolis, Marion, Pop. 800,178
Franklin Township Community SC 9,100/PK-12
6141 S Franklin Rd 46259 317-862-2411
Dr. Flora Reichanadter, supt. Fax 862-7238
www.ftcsc.k12.in.us
Franklin Central HS 2,500/9-12
6215 S Franklin Rd 46259 317-862-6646
Kevin Koers, prin. Fax 862-7262
Franklin Township MS East 1,200/6-8
10440 Indian Creek Rd S 46259 317-803-8100
Chase Huotari, prin. Fax 803-8199
Franklin Township MS West 900/6-8
7620 E Edgewood Ave 46239 317-862-2446
Matthew Vandermark, prin. Fax 862-7271

Indianapolis SD 25,800/PK-12
120 E Walnut St 46204 317-226-4000
Dr. Lewis Ferebee, supt. Fax 226-4936
www.myips.org
Arlington Community HS 7-12
4825 N Arlington Ave 46226 317-226-2345
Stanley Law, prin.
Arsenal Technical HS 2,100/9-12
1500 E Michigan St 46201 317-693-5300
Julie Blakehorn, admin. Fax 226-3932
Attucks Medical Magnet HS 400/6-12
1140 Dr Martin Luther King 46202 317-226-2800
Stephanie Nixon, prin. Fax 226-3495
Broad Ripple HS for Arts & Humanities 500/6-12
1115 Broad Ripple Ave 46220 317-693-5700
Michael Akers, prin. Fax 226-3783
Harshman Magnet MS 400/7-8
1501 E 10th St 46201 317-226-4101
James Larkin, prin. Fax 226-3444
IPS Career Technology Center Vo/Tech
725 N Oriental St 46202 317-693-5430
Ben Carter, dir. Fax 226-3709

Key Learning Community S 100/K-12
777 S White River Pkwy W Dr 46221 317-226-4992
Michael Akers, prin. Fax 226-3049
Marshall Community HS 600/7-12
10101 E 38th St 46235 317-693-5460
Ashauna Short, prin. Fax 226-3718
Northwest HS 800/7-12
5525 W 34th St 46224 317-693-5600
Michelle Britian - Watts, prin. Fax 226-3409
Shortridge HS 400/9-12
3401 N Meridian St 46208 317-226-2810
Shane O'Day, prin. Fax 226-3725
Washington Community HS 500/7-12
2215 W Washington St 46222 317-693-5555
Emily Butler, prin. Fax 226-3273

Metro SD of Decatur Township 6,100/PK-12
5275 Kentucky Ave 46221 317-856-5265
Nathan Davis Ed.D., admin. Fax 856-2156
www.msddecatur.k12.in.us
Decatur Central HS 1,800/9-12
5251 Kentucky Ave 46221 317-856-5288
Scott DeFreese, prin. Fax 856-2157
Decatur MS 900/7-8
5108 S High School Rd 46221 317-856-5274
Kyle Barrentine, prin. Fax 856-2163

Metro SD of Pike Township 11,000/PK-12
6901 Zionsville Rd 46268 317-293-0393
Nathaniel Jones, supt. Fax 297-7896
www.pike.k12.in.us
Guion Creek MS 900/6-8
4401 W 52nd St 46254 317-293-4549
Maggie Bishop, prin. Fax 298-2794
Lincoln MS 800/6-8
5353 W 71st St 46268 317-291-9499
Dan Kuznik, prin. Fax 297-1673
New Augusta Public Academy North 800/6-8
6450 Rodebaugh Rd 46268 317-388-7700
Kim Mills, prin. Fax 388-7786
Pike Freshman Center 800/9-9
6801 Zionsville Rd 46268 317-347-8600
Troy Inman, prin. Fax 347-8555
Pike HS 2,200/10-12
5401 W 71st St 46268 317-291-5250
Troy Inman, prin. Fax 328-7239
Pike Prep Academy Alt
7140 Waldemar Dr 46268 317-347-8352
Roy Dobbs, prin. Fax 298-0681

Metro SD of Warren Township 12,400/PK-12
975 N Post Rd 46219 317-869-4300
Dr. Dena Cushenberry, supt. Fax 869-4399
www.warren.k12.in.us
Creston MS 600/7-8
10925 Prospect St 46239 317-532-6800
Chad Reedy, prin. Fax 532-6899
Raymond Park MS 600/7-8
8575 E Raymond St 46239 317-532-8900
Dr. John Kleine, prin. Fax 532-8999
Renaissance S 300/Alt
8931 E 30th St 46219 317-532-2975
Masimba Taylor, dir. Fax 532-2951
Stonybrook MS 600/7-8
11300 Stony Brook Dr 46229 317-532-8800
Pam Griffin, prin. Fax 532-8899
Walker Career Center Vo/Tech
9651 E 21st St 46229 317-532-6150
Dr. Steven Rogers, dir. Fax 532-6199
Warren Central HS 3,600/9-12
9500 E 16th St 46229 317-532-6200
Rich Shepler, prin. Fax 532-6459

Metropolitan SD of Lawrence Township 14,900/PK-12
6501 Sunnyside Rd 46236 317-423-8200
Dr. Shawn Smith, supt. Fax 543-3534
www.ltschools.org/
Belzer MS 1,100/7-8
7555 E 56th St 46226 317-964-6200
Andrew Harsha, prin. Fax 543-3355
Fall Creek Valley MS 1,100/7-8
9701 E 63rd St 46236 317-964-6600
Kathryn Luessow, prin. Fax 823-5497
Lawrence Central HS 2,300/9-12
7300 E 56th St 46226 317-964-7400
Rocco Valadez, prin. Fax 543-3348
Lawrence North HS 2,300/9-12
7802 Hague Rd 46256 317-964-7700
Brett Crousore, prin. Fax 576-6406
McKenzie Ctr for Innovation & Technology Vo/Tech
7250 E 75th St 46256 317-964-8000
Frank Svarczkopf, prin. Fax 849-2546

Metropolitan SD of Washington Township 11,200/PK-12
8550 Woodfield Crossing 46240 317-845-9400
Dr. Nikki Woodson, supt. Fax 205-3384
www.msdwt.k12.in.us
Eastwood MS 800/6-8
4401 E 62nd St 46220 317-259-5401
Sean Taylor, prin. Fax 259-5407
Light Career Center Vo/Tech
1901 E 86th St 46240 317-259-5265
Shawn Wright-Browner, dir. Fax 259-5298
North Central HS 3,400/9-12
1801 E 86th St 46240 317-259-5301
Bryant Branigan, prin. Fax 259-5369
Northview MS 800/6-8
8401 Westfield Blvd 46240 317-259-5421
Matt Kaiser, prin. Fax 259-5431
Westlane MS 900/6-8
1301 W 73rd St 46260 317-259-5412
Bill Pitcock, prin. Fax 259-5409

Metropolitan SD of Wayne Township 16,000/PK-12
1220 S High School Rd 46241 317-988-8600
Jeffrey Butts Ph.D., supt. Fax 243-5744
www.wayne.k12.in.us
Area 31 Career Center Vo/Tech
1200 N Girls School Rd 46214 317-988-7230
Patrick Biggerstaff, prin. Fax 988-7298
Chapel Hill 7th & 8th Grade Center 1,200/7-8
7320 W 10th St 46214 317-988-8800
Sheri Patterson, prin. Fax 988-8949
Davis 9th Grade Center 1,200/9-9
1150 N Girls School Rd 46214 317-988-7500
Steve Samuel, prin. Fax 484-3124
Davis HS 3,100/10-12
1200 N Girls School Rd 46214 317-988-7000
Sandra Squire, prin. Fax 988-7311
Davis University HS 400/10-12
1155 S High School Rd 46241 317-988-7800
Rebecca Daugherty, prin. Fax 243-5683
Lynhurst 7th & 8th Grade Center 1,200/7-8
2805 S Lynhurst Dr 46241 317-988-8100
Dan Wilson, prin. Fax 243-5532

Perry Township SD 14,600/PK-12
6548 Orinoco Ave 46227 317-789-3700
Dr. Thomas Little, supt. Fax 789-3709
www.msdpt.k12.in.us
Perry Meridian HS 2,200/9-12
401 W Meridian School Rd 46217 317-789-4400
Rolland Abraham, prin. Fax 789-4479
Perry Meridian MS 1,100/7-8
202 W Meridian School Rd 46217 317-789-4100
Jonathan Romine, prin. Fax 865-2710
Southport HS 2,100/9-12
971 E Banta Rd 46227 317-789-4800
Brian Knight, prin. Fax 780-4325
Southport MS 1,000/7-8
5715 S Keystone Ave 46227 317-789-4600
Stephanie Quinlan, prin. Fax 780-4302

American College of Education Post-Sec.
101 W Ohio St Ste 1200 46204 800-280-0307
Art Institute of Indianapolis Post-Sec.
3500 Depauw Blvd 46268 317-613-4800
Aviation Institute of Maintenance Post-Sec.
7251 W McCarty St 46241 317-243-4519
Bishop Chatard HS 700/9-12
5885 Crittenden Ave 46220 317-251-1451
Rick Wagner, prin. Fax 251-3648
Brebeuf Jesuit Prep S 800/9-12
2801 W 86th St 46268 317-524-7128
Greg VanSlambrook, prin. Fax 524-7148
Brightwood College Post-Sec.
4200 S East St 46227 317-782-0315
Butler University Post-Sec.
4600 Sunset Ave 46208 317-940-8000
Calvary Christian S 200/PK-12
3639 S Keystone Ave 46227 317-789-8710
Charles Barcus, admin. Fax 789-8718
Cardinal Ritter JSHS 600/7-12
3360 W 30th St 46222 317-924-4333
Matthew Hollowell, prin. Fax 927-7929
Cathedral HS 1,300/9-12
5225 E 56th St 46226 317-968-7337
David Worland, prin. Fax 543-5050
Central Christian Academy 200/PK-12
2565 Villa Ave 46203 317-788-1587
Daniel Pride, head sch Fax 781-4758
Chamberlain College of Nursing Post-Sec.
9100 Keystone Xing 46240 317-816-7335
Christian Theological Seminary Post-Sec.
1000 W 42nd St 46208 317-924-1331
Colonial Christian S 200/PK-12
8140 Union Chapel Rd 46240 317-253-0649
Dr. Kevin Suiter, admin. Fax 254-2840
Community Hospital of Indianapolis Post-Sec.
1500 N Ritter Ave 46219 317-355-5529
Covenant Christian HS 300/9-12
7525 W 21st St 46214 317-390-0202
Andy Goodwin, prin. Fax 390-6823
Crosspointe Christian Academy 200/PK-12
220 Country Club Rd 46234 317-271-1600
Rev. Brent Floyd, admin. Fax 209-8227
Crossroads Bible College Post-Sec.
601 N Shortridge Rd 46219 317-789-8255
DeVry University Post-Sec.
9100 Keystone Xing Ste 100 46240 317-581-8854
Empire Beauty School Post-Sec.
3810 E Southport Rd 46237 317-781-0959
Fortis College Post-Sec.
9001 Wesleyan Rd Ste 101 46268 317-808-4800
Franklin University Post-Sec.
8415 Allison Pointe Ste 400 46250 319-429-3100
Harrison College Post-Sec.
550 E Washington St 46204 317-447-6200
Harrison College Post-Sec.
6300 Technology Center Dr 46278 317-873-6500
Harrison College Post-Sec.
8150 Brookville Rd 46239 317-375-8000
Harrison College - Online Post-Sec.
500 N Meridian St Ste 500 46204 317-217-6815
Heritage Christian S 1,400/PK-12
6401 E 75th St 46250 317-849-3441
Jeff Freeman, admin. Fax 594-5863
Horizon Christian S 300/PK-12
7702 Indian Lake Rd 46236 317-823-4538
Michael Slack, head sch Fax 823-2396
Indiana School for the Deaf Post-Sec.
1200 E 42nd St 46205 317-924-4374
Indiana State School for the Blind Post-Sec.
7725 N College Ave 46240 317-253-1481
Indiana University School of Allied Hlth Post-Sec.
1140 W Michigan St 46202 317-274-4702
Indiana Univ-Purdue Univ at Indianapolis Post-Sec.
355 Lansing St 46202 317-274-5555
International Business College Post-Sec.
7205 Shadeland Sta 46256 317-813-2300
International S of Indiana 600/PK-12
4330 Michigan Rd 46208 317-923-1951
David Garner, hdmstr. Fax 923-1910
Ivy Tech Community College - Central IN Post-Sec.
50 W Fall Creek Pkwy N Dr 46208 317-921-4800
Kaplan University Post-Sec.
9000 Keystone Crossing #800 46240 317-208-5311
Lincoln College of Technology Post-Sec.
7225 Winton Dr # 128 46268 317-632-5553
Lutheran HS 200/9-12
5555 S Arlington Ave 46237 317-787-5474
Michael Brandt, head sch Fax 787-2794
Marian University Post-Sec.
3200 Cold Spring Rd 46222 317-955-6000
Martin University Post-Sec.
PO Box 18567 46218 317-543-3235
MedTech College Post-Sec.
6612 E 75th St Ste 300 46250 317-845-0100
Methodist Hosp/Clarian Health Partners Post-Sec.
PO Box 1367 46206 317-929-5900
National College Post-Sec.
6060 Castleway West Dr 46250 317-578-7353
Park Tudor S 1,000/PK-12
7200 N College Ave 46240 317-415-2700
Gareth Vaughan, head sch Fax 254-2714
Providence Cristo Rey HS 100/9-12
75 N Belleview Pl 46222 317-860-1000
Brian Dinkins, prin.
Reppert School of Auctioneering Post-Sec.
6851 Madison Ave 46227 317-300-1075
Roncalli HS 1,100/9-12
3300 Prague Rd 46227 317-787-8277
Charles Weisenbach, prin. Fax 788-4095
Scecina Memorial HS 300/9-12
5000 Nowland Ave 46201 317-356-6377
John Hegarty, prin. Fax 322-4287
Suburban Christian S 100/PK-12
722 E County Line Rd 46227 317-888-3366
Jeremy Wilhelm, prin. Fax 884-4025
TCM International Institute Post-Sec.
PO Box 24560 46224 317-299-0333
The Chef's Academy Post-Sec.
644 E Washington St 46204 800-919-2500
Trinity Christian S 100/K-12
440 Saint Peter St 46201 317-631-3194
Sharon Ragan, prin. Fax 631-7230
University of Indianapolis Post-Sec.
1400 E Hanna Ave 46227 317-788-3368

Jasonville, Greene, Pop. 2,204
Metro SD Shakamak 800/K-12
9233 Shakamak School Rd 47438 812-665-3550
Mike Mogan, supt. Fax 665-5001
www.shakamak.k12.in.us/
Shakamak JSHS 400/7-12
9233 Shakamak School Rd 47438 812-665-3550
Dennis Moody, prin. Fax 665-5001

Jasper, Dubois, Pop. 14,939
Greater Jasper Consolidated SD 3,200/PK-12
1520 Saint Charles St 47546 812-482-1801
Dr. Tracy Lorey, supt. Fax 482-3388
www.gjcs.k12.in.us
Jasper HS 1,100/9-12
1600 Saint Charles St 47546 812-482-6050
Brian Wilson, prin. Fax 634-3971
Jasper MS 800/6-8
3600 N Portersville Rd 47546 812-482-6454
David Hubster, prin. Fax 482-6457

Holy Trinity S 200/3-8
990 Church Ave 47546 812-482-5050
Tyler Lemen, prin. Fax 481-9909

Jeffersonville, Clark, Pop. 43,626
Greater Clark County SD 10,500/PK-12
2112 Utica Sellersburg Rd 47130 812-283-0701
Dr. Andrew Melin, supt. Fax 288-4804
www.gcs.k12.in.us
Clark County MSHS 100/6-12
2710 E 10th St 47130 812-288-4837
Jeff Griffith, prin. Fax 288-4829
Corden Porter S 100/Alt
630 Meigs Ave 47130 812-288-4891
Donna Daily, prin. Fax 288-4843
Jeffersonville HS 2,000/9-12
2315 Allison Ln 47130 812-282-6601
Julie Straight, prin. Fax 288-4812
Parkview MS 800/6-8
1600 Brigman Ave 47130 812-288-4844
Amy Hasselbring, prin. Fax 288-2849
River Valley MS 900/6-8
2220 Veterans Pkwy 47130 812-288-4848
Michelle Dyer, prin. Fax 288-4851
Other Schools – See Charlestown, New Washington

Mid-America College of Funeral Service Post-Sec.
3111 Hamburg Pike 47130 812-288-8878
Ottawa University Post-Sec.
287 Quartermaster Ct 47130 812-280-7271

Jonesboro, Grant, Pop. 1,733

King's Academy 100/K-12
1201 S Water St 46938 765-674-1722
Tony Miner, hdmstr. Fax 674-7322

Kendallville, Noble, Pop. 9,716
East Noble SC 3,800/PK-12
126 W Rush St 46755 260-347-2502
Ann Linson, supt. Fax 347-0111
www.eastnoble.net
Alternative Learning Center Alt
702 Dowling St 46755 260-349-0814
Belinda Justus, dir. Fax 347-1242
East Noble HS 1,200/9-12
901 Garden St 46755 260-347-2032
Kathy Longenbaugh, prin. Fax 347-2362
East Noble MS 600/7-8
401 E Diamond St 46755 260-347-0100
Andrew Deming, prin. Fax 347-7168

Kentland, Newton, Pop. 1,729
South Newton SC — 900/PK-12
13232 S 50 E 47951 — 219-474-5184
Kenneth Rudnick, supt. — Fax 474-6966
www.newton.k12.in.us/
South Newton HS — 300/9-12
13102 S 50 E 47951 — 219-474-5167
Charles Huckstep, prin. — Fax 474-6592
South Newton MS — 200/6-8
13100 S 50 E 47951 — 219-474-5167
Tansey Mulligan, prin. — Fax 474-3624

Knightstown, Henry, Pop. 2,153
C.A. Beard Memorial SC — 1,000/K-12
8139 W US Highway 40 46148 — 765-345-5101
Jediah Behny, supt. — Fax 345-5103
www.cabeard.k12.in.us
Knightstown HS — 400/9-12
8149 W US Highway 40 46148 — 765-345-5153
Scott Ritchie, prin. — Fax 345-7977
Knightstown IS — 400/4-8
1 Panther Trl 46148 — 765-345-5455
K. Gardner, prin. — Fax 345-5523

Knox, Starke, Pop. 3,653
Knox Community SC — 2,000/PK-12
2 Redskin Trl 46534 — 574-772-1600
A.J. Gappa, supt. — Fax 772-1608
www.knox.k12.in.us
Knox Community HS — 600/9-12
1 Redskin Trl 46534 — 574-772-1670
Dr. Elizabeth Ratliff, prin. — Fax 772-1681
Knox Community MS — 500/6-8
901 S Main St 46534 — 574-772-1654
David Miller, prin. — Fax 772-1664

Kokomo, Howard, Pop. 44,079
Kokomo SC — 6,800/PK-12
PO Box 2188 46904 — 765-455-8000
Dr. Jeff Hauswald, supt. — Fax 455-8018
www.kokomo.k12.in.us
Bon Air MS Technology Academy — 300/6-8
2796 N Apperson Way 46901 — 765-454-7025
Amanda Landrum, prin. — Fax 454-7034
Central Middle (KEY) International S — 400/6-8
303 E Superior St 46901 — 765-454-7000
Holly Herrera, prin. — Fax 454-7007
International Program — 10-12
303 E Superior St 46901 — 765-454-7000
Dr. Heidi Gutwein, dir.
Kokomo Area Career Center — Vo/Tech
2415 S Berkley Rd 46902 — 765-455-8021
Jonathan Schuck, prin. — Fax 454-7014
Kokomo HS — 1,900/9-12
2501 S Berkley Rd 46902 — 765-455-8040
Angela Blessing, prin. — Fax 455-8060
Maple Crest Middle STEM S — 600/6-8
2727 S Washington St 46902 — 765-455-8085
Thomas Hughes, prin. — Fax 455-8062
McKinley Alternative S — Alt
1217 W Carter St 46901 — 765-454-7080
Idowu Ikudabo, coord. — Fax 454-7081
Twilight Alternative HS — Alt
2501 S Berkley Rd 46902 — 765-454-8040
Rick Hagenow, dir.

Northwestern SC — 1,700/K-12
3075 N Washington St 46901 — 765-452-3060
Ryan Snoddy, supt. — Fax 452-3065
nwsc.k12.in.us
Northwestern HS — 600/9-12
3431 N 400 W 46901 — 765-454-2332
Kristen Bilkey, prin. — Fax 454-2333
Northwestern MS — 300/7-8
3431 N 400 W 46901 — 765-454-2323
Brett Davis, prin. — Fax 457-2324

Taylor Community SC — 1,100/PK-12
3750 E 300 S 46902 — 765-453-3035
Chris Smith, supt. — Fax 455-8531
www.taylor.k12.in.us
Taylor HS — 400/9-12
3794 E 300 S 46902 — 765-453-1101
Eric Hartman, prin. — Fax 455-5163
Taylor MS — 300/6-8
3794 E 300 S 46902 — 765-455-5186
Heather Hord, prin. — Fax 455-5157

Indiana University at Kokomo — Post-Sec.
2300 S Washington St 46902 — 765-453-2000
Ivy Tech Community College - Kokomo — Post-Sec.
PO Box 1373 46903 — 765-459-0561
Rudae's School of Beauty Culture — Post-Sec.
208 W Jefferson St 46901 — 765-459-4197
St. Joseph Hospital & Health Center — Post-Sec.
1907 W Sycamore St 46901 — 765-452-5611

Kouts, Porter, Pop. 1,870
East Porter County SC — 2,500/K-12
PO Box 370 46347 — 219-766-2214
Dr. Rod Gardin, supt. — Fax 766-2885
www.eastporter.k12.in.us
Kouts MSHS — 500/6-12
PO Box 699 46347 — 219-766-2231
Thomas Stoner, prin. — Fax 766-3763
Other Schools – See Valparaiso

La Crosse, LaPorte, Pop. 550
Tri Township School Corp
Supt. — See Wanatah
La Crosse HS — 100/9-12
PO Box 360 46348 — 219-754-2461
Aaron Owney, prin. — Fax 754-2511

Lafayette, Tippecanoe, Pop. 65,793
Lafayette SC — 7,500/K-12
2300 Cason St 47904 — 765-771-6000
Les Huddle, supt. — Fax 771-6049
www.lsc.k12.in.us
Jefferson HS — 1,900/9-12
1801 S 18th St 47905 — 765-772-4700
Mark Preston, prin. — Fax 772-4713
Lafayette Tecumseh JHS — 1,000/7-8
2101 S 18th St 47905 — 765-772-4750
Brandon Hawkins, prin. — Fax 772-4763
Oakland HS — 100/9-12
1100 Elizabeth St 47904 — 765-807-8550
David Walker, prin. — Fax 807-8551

Tippecanoe SC — 12,300/K-12
21 Elston Rd 47909 — 765-474-2481
Dr. Scott Hanback, supt. — Fax 474-0533
www.tsc.k12.in.us
East Tipp MS — 500/6-8
7501 E 300 N 47905 — 765-589-3566
Shaad Buss, prin. — Fax 589-3129
McCutcheon HS — 1,800/9-12
4951 Old US Highway 231 S 47909 — 765-474-1488
John Beeker, prin. — Fax 477-9710
Southwestern MS — 400/6-8
2100 W 800 S 47909 — 765-538-3025
Karen Shuman, prin. — Fax 538-2877
Wainwright MS — 300/6-8
7501 E 700 S 47905 — 765-269-8350
Dr. Neal McCutcheon, prin. — Fax 269-8359
Wea Ridge MS — 700/6-8
4410 S 150 E 47909 — 765-471-2164
Fred Roop, prin. — Fax 474-5347
Other Schools – See West Lafayette

Central Catholic JSHS — 400/7-12
2410 S 9th St 47909 — 765-474-2496
Neil Wagner, prin. — Fax 474-8752
Faith Christian S — 700/PK-12
5526 State Road 26 E 47905 — 765-447-2727
Scott Grass, supt. — Fax 449-3737
Harrison College — Post-Sec.
4705 Meijer Ct 47905 — 765-447-9550
Ivy Tech Community College - Lafayette — Post-Sec.
PO Box 6299 47903 — 765-269-5000
Lafayette Beauty Academy — Post-Sec.
833 Ferry St 47901 — 765-742-0068
St. Elizabeth School of Nursing — Post-Sec.
1508 Tippecanoe St 47904 — 765-423-6400

Lagrange, Lagrange, Pop. 2,609
Lakeland SC — 2,200/K-12
825 E 075 N 46761 — 260-499-2400
Dr. Eva Merkel, supt. — Fax 463-4800
www.lakeland.k12.in.us
Lakeland HS — 700/9-12
805 E 075 N 46761 — 260-499-2470
Anthony Harl, prin. — Fax 463-4058
Lakeland MS — 500/6-8
1055 E 075 N 46761 — 260-499-2480
Bradley Targgart, prin. — Fax 463-2648

Prairie Heights Community SC — 1,400/K-12
305 S 1150 E 46761 — 260-351-3214
Jeff Reed, supt. — Fax 351-3614
www.ph.k12.in.us/
Prairie Heights HS — 500/9-12
245 S 1150 E 46761 — 260-351-3214
Jeremy Swander, prin. — Fax 351-3848
Prairie Heights MS — 400/5-8
395 S 1150 E 46761 — 260-351-2334
Andy Arndt, prin. — Fax 351-2334

Lake Station, Lake, Pop. 12,350
Lake Station Community SD — 1,500/K-12
2500 Pike St 46405 — 219-962-1159
Dr. Tom Cripliver, supt. — Fax 962-4011
www.lakes.k12.in.us
Edison JSHS — 600/7-12
3304 Parkside Ave 46405 — 219-962-8531
Christine Pepa, prin. — Fax 962-2064

Lakeville, Saint Joseph, Pop. 778
Union-North United SC — 1,100/K-12
22601 Tyler Rd 46536 — 574-784-8141
Mitchell Mawhorter, supt. — Fax 784-2181
www.unorth.k12.in.us
Laville JSHS — 500/7-12
69969 US Highway 31 46536 — 574-784-3151
Nathan McKeand, prin. — Fax 784-8695

Lanesville, Harrison, Pop. 557
Lanesville Community SC — 700/K-12
2725 Crestview Ave NE 47136 — 812-952-2555
Steve Morris, supt. — Fax 952-3762
www.lanesville.k12.in.us/
Lanesville JSHS — 300/7-12
2725 Crestview Ave NE 47136 — 812-952-2555
Steve Morris, prin. — Fax 952-3762

Lapel, Madison, Pop. 2,035
Frankton-Lapel Community SD
Supt. — See Anderson
Lapel HS — 500/9-12
1850 S 900 W 46051 — 765-534-3036
Chad Kemerly, prin. — Fax 203-9943
Lapel MS — 300/6-8
2883 S State Road 13 46051 — 765-534-3137
Bill Chase, prin. — Fax 203-9937

La Porte, LaPorte, Pop. 21,655
La Porte Community SC — 6,400/K-12
1921 A St 46350 — 219-362-7056
Mark Francesconi, supt. — Fax 324-9347
www.lpcsc.k12.in.us
Boston MS — 700/6-8
1000 Harrison St 46350 — 219-326-6930
Deborah Carter, prin. — Fax 324-7108
Kesling MS — 800/6-8
306 E 18th St 46350 — 219-362-7507
Bill Wilmsen, prin. — Fax 324-5712
La Porte HS — 2,000/9-12
602 F St 46350 — 219-362-3102
Benjamin Tonagel, prin. — Fax 324-2142

La Lumiere S — 200/9-12
PO Box 5005 46352 — 219-326-7450
Adam Kronk, head sch — Fax 326-3185

Larwill, Whitley, Pop. 280
Whitko Community SC — 1,600/K-12
710 N State Road 5 Ste B 46764 — 260-327-3677
Steven Clason, supt. — Fax 327-3238
www.whitko.org
Whitko MS — 400/6-8
710 N State Road 5 46764 — 260-327-3603
Dr. Eugene Sweeney, prin. — Fax 327-3805
Other Schools – See South Whitley

Lawrenceburg, Dearborn, Pop. 4,938
Lawrenceburg Community SC — 2,000/K-12
300 Tiger Blvd 47025 — 812-537-7200
Karl Galey, supt. — Fax 537-0759
www.lburg.k12.in.us
Greendale MS — 500/6-8
200 Tiger Blvd 47025 — 812-537-7259
Jayme Herbert, prin. — Fax 537-6385
Lawrenceburg HS — 600/9-12
100 Tiger Blvd 47025 — 812-537-7219
Bill Snyder, prin. — Fax 537-7221

Lebanon, Boone, Pop. 15,595
Lebanon Community SC — 3,500/K-12
1810 N Grant St 46052 — 765-482-0380
Dr. Robert Taylor, supt. — Fax 483-3053
www.leb.k12.in.us/
Lebanon HS — 1,000/9-12
510 Essex Dr 46052 — 765-482-0400
Kevin O'Rourke, prin. — Fax 483-3040
Lebanon MS — 800/6-8
1800 N Grant St 46052 — 765-482-3400
Doyle Dunshee, prin. — Fax 483-3049

Leo, Allen
East Allen County SD
Supt. — See New Haven
Leo JSHS — 1,300/7-12
14600 Amstutz Rd 46765 — 260-446-0180
Dr. Neal Brown, prin. — Fax 446-0189

Leopold, Perry
Perry Central Community SC — 1,200/PK-12
18677 Old State Road 37 47551 — 812-843-5576
Mary Roberson, supt. — Fax 843-4746
www.pccs.k12.in.us/
Perry Central JSHS — 500/7-12
18677 Old State Road 37 47551 — 812-843-5121
Seth Clark, prin. — Fax 843-4198

Liberty, Union, Pop. 2,110
Union County/College Corner JSD — 1,200/K-12
107 S Layman St 47353 — 765-458-7471
Dr. Zach Rozelle, supt. — Fax 458-5647
www.uc.k12.in.us/
Union County HS — 500/9-12
410 Patriot Blvd 47353 — 765-458-5136
Connie Rosenberger, prin. — Fax 458-6315
Union County MS — 300/6-8
488 E State Road 44 47353 — 765-458-7438
Ronald Ross, prin. — Fax 458-6041

Ligonier, Noble, Pop. 4,376
West Noble SC — 2,500/K-12
5050 N US Highway 33 46767 — 260-894-3191
Dr. Dennis VanDuyne Ph.D., supt. — Fax 894-3260
westnoble.k12.in.us/
West Noble HS — 700/9-12
5094 N US Highway 33 46767 — 260-894-3191
Dr. Greg Baker, prin. — Fax 894-4708
West Noble MS — 800/5-8
5194 N US Highway 33 46767 — 260-894-3191
Melanie Tijerina, prin. — Fax 894-4703

Lincoln City, Spencer
North Spencer County SC — 2,000/PK-12
PO Box 316 47552 — 812-937-2400
Daniel Scherry, supt. — Fax 937-7187
www.nspencer.k12.in.us
Heritage Hills HS — 600/9-12
3644 E County Road 1600 N 47552 — 812-937-4472
Nick Alcorn, prin. — Fax 937-4878
Heritage Hills MS — 300/7-8
PO Box 1777 47552 — 812-937-4472
Chad Schnieders, prin. — Fax 937-4327

Linton, Greene, Pop. 5,354
Linton-Stockton SC — 1,400/K-12
801 1st St NE 47441 — 812-847-6020
Nick Karazsia, supt. — Fax 847-8659
www.lssc.k12.in.us/
Linton-Stockton HS — 300/9-12
10 H St NE 47441 — 812-847-6024
Nathan Moore, prin. — Fax 847-6037
Linton-Stockton MS — 300/6-8
109 I St NE 47441 — 812-847-6022
Jeff Sparks, prin. — Fax 847-6032

Lizton, Hendricks, Pop. 481
North West Hendricks SD — 1,900/PK-12
PO Box 70 46149 — 317-994-4100
Richard King, supt. — Fax 994-5963
www.hendricks.k12.in.us/
Tri-West HS — 600/9-12
7883 N State Road 39 46149 — 317-994-4000
Adam Benner, prin. — Fax 994-5106
Tri-West MS — 500/6-8
555 W US Highway 136 46149 — 317-994-4200
Ryan Nickoli, prin. — Fax 994-4230

Logansport, Cass, Pop. 18,151
Logansport Community SC — 4,200/PK-12
2829 George St 46947 — 574-722-2911
Michele Starkey, supt. — Fax 753-0143
www.lcsc.k12.in.us

Century Career Center Vo/Tech
2500 Hopper St 46947 574-722-3811
James Little, dir. Fax 753-7649
Columbia MS 500/6-8
1300 N 3rd St 46947 574-753-3797
Greg Grostefon, prin. Fax 753-6159
Lincoln MS 500/6-8
2901 Usher St 46947 574-753-7115
Jeff Canady, prin. Fax 753-5826
Logansport Community HS 1,200/9-12
1 Berry Ln 46947 574-753-0441
Matt Jones, prin. Fax 753-3688

Loogootee, Martin, Pop. 2,735
Loogootee Community SC 800/K-12
PO Box 282 47553 812-295-2595
Chip Mehaffey, supt. Fax 295-5595
www.loogootee.k12.in.us/
Loogootee HS 300/9-12
201 Brooks Ave 47553 812-295-3254
Andrea Huff, prin. Fax 295-3694
Loogootee MS 100/5-8
201 Brooks Ave 47553 812-295-3254
Lacey Wade, prin. Fax 295-3694

Lowell, Lake, Pop. 9,196
Tri-Creek SC 3,400/K-12
19290 Cline Ave 46356 219-696-6661
Dr. Debra K. Howe, supt. Fax 696-2150
www.tricreek.k12.in.us
Lowell HS 1,200/9-12
2051 E Commercial Ave 46356 219-696-7733
Lori Pavell, prin. Fax 696-0042
Lowell MS 900/6-8
19250 Cline St 46356 219-696-7701
Rebecca Pavich, prin. Fax 690-2620

Lynn, Randolph, Pop. 1,088
Randolph Southern SC 500/K-12
1 Rebel Dr 47355 765-874-1181
Donnie Bowsman, supt. Fax 874-1298
www.rssc.k12.in.us
Randolph Southern JSHS 300/7-12
2 Rebel Dr 47355 765-874-2541
Donald Knotts, prin. Fax 874-2660

Lynnville, Warrick, Pop. 881
Warrick County SC
Supt. — See Boonville
Tecumseh HS 300/9-12
5244 W State Route 68 47619 812-922-3237
Josh Susott, prin. Fax 922-3608
Tecumseh MS 200/6-8
5300 W State Road 68 47619 812-922-0122
Keith Paige, prin.

Madison, Jefferson, Pop. 11,775
Madison Consolidated SD 3,000/K-12
2421 Wilson Ave 47250 812-274-8001
Dr. Ginger Bolinger, supt. Fax 274-8507
www.madison.k12.in.us
Madison Consolidated HS 1,000/9-12
743 Clifty Dr 47250 812-274-8002
Kevin Yancey, prin. Fax 274-8788
Madison Consolidated JHS 700/6-8
701 8th St 47250 812-274-8003
Jill Mires, prin. Fax 274-8403

Christian Academy of Madison 100/PK-12
477 W Hutchinson Ln 47250 812-273-5000
Anna Gosman, admin. Fax 265-0700
Ivy Tech Community College - Southeast Post-Sec.
590 Ivy Tech Dr 47250 812-265-2580
King's Daughter's Hospital Post-Sec.
PO Box 447 47250 812-265-5211
Shawe Memorial JSHS 200/7-12
201 W State St 47250 812-273-2150
Steve Hesse, prin. Fax 273-8975

Marengo, Crawford, Pop. 809
Crawford County Community SC 1,000/PK-12
5805 E Administration Rd 47140 812-365-2135
Woodrow DeRossett, supt. Fax 365-2783
www.cccs.k12.in.us/
Carwford County MS 50/6-8
177 S 2nd St 47140 812-365-2116
Amy Belcher, prin. Fax 365-2814
Crawford County HS 500/9-12
1130 S State Road 66 47140 812-365-2125
Brandon Johnson, prin. Fax 365-2127

Marion, Grant, Pop. 29,023
Eastbrook Community SC 1,600/K-12
560 S 900 E 46953 765-664-0624
Brett Garrett, supt. Fax 664-0626
eastbrook.k12.in.us
Eastbrook HS 600/9-12
560 S 900 E 46953 765-664-1214
Patrick McLaughlin, prin. Fax 664-1216
Eastbrook JHS 300/7-8
560 S 900 E 46953 765-668-7136
Elizabeth Duckwall, prin. Fax 668-7137

Marion Community SD 3,700/PK-12
750 W 26th St 46953 765-662-2546
Brad Lindsay, supt. Fax 651-2043
www.marion.k12.in.us
Marion HS 1,100/9-12
750 W 26th St 46953 765-664-9051
Keith Burke, prin. Fax 662-0383
Marion Regional Career Center Vo/Tech
750 W 26th St 46953 765-664-9051
Michael Ripperger, dir.
McCulloch JHS 500/7-8
3528 S Washington St 46953 765-674-6917
Melissa Pogue, prin. Fax 674-8943

Indiana Wesleyan University Post-Sec.
4201 S Washington St 46953 765-674-6901

Lakeview Christian S 300/PK-12
5316 S Western Ave 46953 765-677-4266
Dr. Douglas Ballinger, admin. Fax 677-4269

Marshall, Parke, Pop. 323
North Central Parke Community SC 1,300/K-12
1497 E State Road 47 47859 765-597-2750
Dr. Thomas Rohr, supt. Fax 597-2755
www.ncp.k12.in.us
Turkey Run JSHS 300/7-12
1551 E State Road 47 47859 765-597-2700
Scott Schulz, prin. Fax 597-4202
Other Schools – See Rockville

Martinsville, Morgan, Pop. 11,701
Metro SD of Martinsville 4,300/PK-12
389 E Jackson St 46151 765-342-6641
Dr. Michele Moore, supt. Fax 342-6877
www.msdmartinsville.org
Hammons S 50/Alt
389 E Jackson St 46151 765-342-0120
Melody Bentley, lead tchr. Fax 349-5256
Martinsville HS 1,600/9-12
1360 E Gray St 46151 765-342-5571
Nicholas Sears, prin. Fax 349-5256
Wooden MS 400/7-8
109 E Garfield Ave 46151 765-342-6628
Eric Bowlen, prin. Fax 349-5232

Tabernacle Christian S 100/PK-12
2189 Burton Ln 46151 765-342-0501
Kenny Roll, prin. Fax 342-0502

Medora, Jackson, Pop. 677
Medora Community SC 200/PK-12
PO Box 369 47260 812-966-2210
Roger Bane, supt. Fax 966-2217
www.medorahornets.org/
Medora JSHS 100/7-12
PO Box 248 47260 812-966-2201
Austin Absher, prin. Fax 966-2209

Merrillville, Lake, Pop. 34,497
Merrillville Community SC 6,700/K-12
6701 Delaware St 46410 219-650-5300
Dr. Mark B. Sperling, supt. Fax 650-5320
www.mvsc.k12.in.us
Merrillville HS 2,300/9-12
276 E 68th Pl 46410 219-650-5307
Michael Krutz, prin. Fax 650-5391
Pierce MS 1,100/7-8
199 E 70th Ave 46410 219-650-5308
Christine Kibler-Wheeler, prin. Fax 650-5483

Andrean HS 600/9-12
5959 Broadway 46410 219-887-5281
Richard Piwowarski, prin. Fax 981-5072
DeVry University Post-Sec.
1000 E 80th Pl Ste 222N 46410 219-736-7440
Merrillville Beauty College Post-Sec.
48 W 67th Pl 46410 219-769-2232
Success School Post-Sec.
8101 Polo Club Dr 46410 219-736-9999

Michigan City, LaPorte, Pop. 30,502
Michigan City Area SD 4,900/K-12
408 S Carroll Ave 46360 219-873-2000
Dr. Barbara Eason-Watkins, supt. Fax 873-2072
www.mcas.k12.in.us
Barker MS 300/7-8
319 Barker Rd 46360 219-873-2057
Karen Puchalski, prin. Fax 873-3099
Krueger MS 300/7-8
2001 Springland Ave 46360 219-873-2061
Vera Jones, prin. Fax 873-2063
Michigan City HS 1,700/9-12
8466 W Pahs Rd 46360 219-873-2044
Bonnie Manuel, prin. Fax 873-2055
Smith Area Career Center Vo/Tech
817 Lafayette St 46360 219-873-2120
Audra Peterson, dir. Fax 873-2068

Lakeshore Medical Lab Training Programs Post-Sec.
402 Franklin St 46360 219-872-7032
Marquette Catholic HS 200/9-12
306 W 10th St 46360 219-873-1325
James White, prin. Fax 873-1327

Michigantown, Clinton, Pop. 463
Clinton Central SC 1,000/K-12
PO Box 118 46057 765-249-2515
Dr. Jeffery Studebaker, supt. Fax 249-2504
www.clinton.k12.in.us/
Clinton Central JSHS 500/7-12
PO Box 178 46057 765-249-2255
Wendy Haag, prin. Fax 249-0214

Middlebury, Elkhart, Pop. 3,377
Middlebury Community SD 4,400/K-12
56853 Northridge Dr 46540 574-825-9425
Jane Allen, supt. Fax 825-9426
www.mcsin-k12.org/
Northridge HS 1,300/9-12
56779 Northridge Dr 46540 574-825-2142
Andrew Wood, prin. Fax 825-1473
Northridge MS 1,000/6-8
56691 Northridge Dr 46540 574-825-9531
Robby Goodman, prin. Fax 825-9154

Middletown, Henry, Pop. 2,295
Shenandoah SC 1,400/PK-12
5100 N Raider Rd 47356 765-354-2266
Ron Green, supt. Fax 354-2274
www.shenandoah.k12.in.us/
Shenandoah HS 500/9-12
7354 W US Highway 36 47356 765-354-6640
Jacob Wiese, prin. Fax 354-3110

Shenandoah MS 300/6-8
5156 N Raider Rd 47356 765-354-6638
Greg Allen, prin. Fax 354-3120

Milan, Ripley, Pop. 1,874
Milan Community SC 1,200/K-12
412 E Carr St 47031 812-654-2365
Paul Ketcham M.S., supt. Fax 654-2441
www.milan.k12.in.us
Milan HS 400/9-12
609 N Warpath Dr 47031 812-654-3096
Ryan Langferman, prin. Fax 654-2368
Milan MS 300/6-8
609 N Warpath Dr 47031 812-654-1616
Patrick Murphy, prin. Fax 654-2368

Mishawaka, Saint Joseph, Pop. 46,961
Penn-Harris-Madison SC 10,300/K-12
55900 Bittersweet Rd 46545 574-259-7941
Dr. Jerry Thacker, supt. Fax 258-9547
www.phmschools.org
Grissom MS 600/6-8
13881 Kern Rd 46544 574-633-4061
Nathan Boyd, prin. Fax 633-2134
Penn HS 3,300/9-12
56100 Bittersweet Rd 46545 574-259-7961
Steve Hope, prin. Fax 258-9543
Schmucker MS 1,000/6-8
56045 Bittersweet Rd 46545 574-259-5661
Sean Galiher, prin. Fax 259-0807
Other Schools – See Granger

School City of Mishawaka 5,000/K-12
1402 S Main St 46544 574-254-4500
Dr. A. Dean Speicher, supt. Fax 254-4585
www.mishawaka.k12.in.us
Mishawaka HS 1,500/9-12
1202 Lincolnway E 46544 574-254-7300
Jerome Calderone, prin. Fax 254-7481
Young MS 700/7-8
1801 N Main St 46545 574-254-3600
C. Mike Fisher, prin. Fax 258-3021

Bais Yaakov HS of Indiana 50/9-12
206 W 8th St 46544 574-257-0689
Dena Gewirtz, admin. Fax 255-7553
Bethel College Post-Sec.
1001 Bethel Cir 46545 574-807-7000
Marian HS 700/9-12
1311 S Logan St 46544 574-259-5257
Mark Kirzeder, prin. Fax 258-7668

Mitchell, Lawrence, Pop. 4,315
Mitchell Community SD 1,700/PK-12
441 N 8th St 47446 812-849-4481
Dr. Steve Phillips, supt. Fax 849-2133
www.mitchell.k12.in.us
Mitchell HS 600/9-12
1000 W Bishop Blvd 47446 812-849-3663
Sean Vandeventer, prin. Fax 849-5368
Mitchell JHS 400/6-8
1010 W Bishop Blvd 47446 812-849-3747
Jennifer Caruso, prin. Fax 849-5841

Modoc, Randolph, Pop. 190
Union SC 400/K-12
8707 W US Highway 36 47358 765-853-5464
Alan Hayne, supt. Fax 853-5070
www.usc.k12.in.us
Union JSHS 200/7-12
8707 W US Highway 36 47358 765-853-5421
Allen Hayne, prin. Fax 853-6057

Monon, White, Pop. 1,750
North White SC 600/K-12
402 E Broadway St 47959 219-253-6618
Dr. Teresa L. Gremaux, supt. Fax 253-6488
www.nwhite.k12.in.us/
North White MSHS 400/6-12
305 E Broadway St 47959 219-253-6638
Anthony Cassel, prin. Fax 253-7004

Monroe, Adams, Pop. 839
Adams Central Community SD 1,200/K-12
222 W Washington St 46772 260-692-6193
Dr. Lori M. Stiglitz, supt. Fax 692-6198
www.accs.k12.in.us/
Adams Central HS 400/9-12
222 W Washington St 46772 260-692-6151
Jeff McCullough, prin. Fax 692-6192
Adams Central MS 300/6-8
222 W Washington St 46772 260-692-6151
Chad Smekens, prin. Fax 692-6192

Monroeville, Allen, Pop. 1,229
East Allen County SD
Supt. — See New Haven
Heritage JSHS 800/7-12
13608 Monroeville Rd 46773 260-446-0140
Matt Widenhoefer, prin. Fax 446-0146

Monrovia, Morgan, Pop. 1,058
Monroe-Gregg SD 1,500/PK-12
135 S Chestnut St 46157 317-996-3720
Dr. William Roberson, supt. Fax 996-2977
www.m-gsd.org/
Monrovia HS 500/9-12
205 S Chestnut St 46157 317-996-2259
Mike Springer, prin. Fax 996-3519
Monrovia MS 400/6-8
215 S Chestnut St 46157 317-996-2352
Micah Elliott, prin. Fax 996-3429

Montezuma, Parke, Pop. 1,013
Southwest Parke Community SC 1,000/K-12
4851 S Coxville Rd 47862 765-569-2073
Dr. Philip Harrison, supt. Fax 569-0309
www.swparke.k12.in.us
Riverton Parke JSHS 500/7-12
4907 S Coxville Rd 47862 765-569-2045
Kyle Kersey, prin. Fax 569-2047

Montgomery, Daviess, Pop. 341
Barr-Reeve Community SD 800/K-12
PO Box 97 47558 812-486-3220
Travis Madison, supt. Fax 486-3509
www.barr.k12.in.us
Barr-Reeve MSHS 400/6-12
PO Box 129 47558 812-486-3265
Jeff Doyle, prin. Fax 486-2829

Monticello, White, Pop. 5,324
Twin Lakes SC 2,400/PK-12
565 S Main St 47960 574-583-7211
Michael Galvin, supt. Fax 583-2679
www.tlschools.com
Roosevelt MS 600/6-8
721 W Broadway St 47960 574-583-5552
Rod Coffing, prin. Fax 583-3675
Twin Lakes HS 700/9-12
300 S 3rd St 47960 574-583-7108
Michael Kelley, prin. Fax 583-2679

Mooresville, Morgan, Pop. 9,219
Mooresville Consolidated SC 4,600/PK-12
11 W Carlisle St 46158 317-831-0950
Dr. David Marcotte, supt. Fax 831-9202
www.mooresvilleschools.org
Hadley MS 700/7-8
200 W Carlisle St 46158 317-831-9208
Jacob Allen, prin. Fax 831-9249
Mooresville HS 1,400/9-12
550 N Indiana St 46158 317-831-9203
Brian Disney, prin. Fax 831-9206

Morocco, Newton, Pop. 1,125
North Newton SC 1,400/K-12
PO Box 8 47963 219-285-2228
Destin Haas, supt. Fax 285-2708
www.nn.k12.in.us/
North Newton JSHS 700/7-12
1641 W 250 N 47963 219-285-2252
Jason Hostetler, prin. Fax 285-2881

Morristown, Shelby, Pop. 1,211
Shelby Eastern SD
Supt. — See Shelbyville
Morristown JSHS 300/6-12
PO Box 960 46161 765-763-1221
Ken Howell, prin. Fax 763-7170

Mount Summit, Henry, Pop. 346
Blue River Valley SD 600/PK-12
PO Box 217 47361 765-836-4816
Eric Creviston, supt. Fax 836-4817
www.brv.k12.in.us
Other Schools – See New Castle

Mount Vernon, Posey, Pop. 6,543
Metro SD of Mt. Vernon 2,200/PK-12
1000 W 4th St 47620 812-838-4471
Dr. Tom Kopatich, supt. Fax 833-5179
www.mvschool.org
Mount Vernon HS 800/9-12
700 Harriett St 47620 812-838-4356
Tom Russell, prin. Fax 833-2099
Mount Vernon JHS 500/6-8
701 Tile Factory Rd 47620 812-833-2077
Chad Rodgers, prin. Fax 833-2083

Muncie, Delaware, Pop. 68,179
Cowan Community SC 800/K-12
9401 S Nottingham St 47302 765-289-4866
Dennis Chambers, supt. Fax 284-0315
www.cowan.k12.in.us
Cowan JSHS 400/7-12
9401 S Nottingham St 47302 765-289-7128
Patrick Bloom, prin. Fax 741-5954

Delaware Community SC 2,600/K-12
9750 N Williamson Rd 47303 765-284-5074
Reece Mann, supt. Fax 284-5259
www.delcomschools.org
Delta HS 800/9-12
3400 E State Road 28 47303 765-288-5597
Christopher Conley, prin. Fax 288-8498
Delta MS 600/6-8
9800 N County Rd 200 E 47303 765-747-0869
Kelly Brown, prin. Fax 213-2131

Muncie Community SD 5,800/K-12
2501 N Oakwood Ave 47304 765-747-5211
Dr. Steven Baule, supt. Fax 747-5341
www.muncie.k12.in.us
Muncie Area Career Center Vo/Tech
2500 N Elgin St 47303 765-747-5250
JoAnn McCowan, dir. Fax 747-5455
Muncie Central HS 900/9-12
801 N Walnut St 47305 765-747-5260
Chris Walker, prin. Fax 747-5314
Muncie Southside MS 1,000/6-8
1601 E 26th St 47302 765-747-5320
Kelli Turner, prin. Fax 747-5325
Northside MS 700/6-8
2400 W Bethel Ave 47304 765-747-5290
Jackie Samuels, prin. Fax 751-0616

University Schools, Supt. — None
Dr. William Sharp, supt.
Burris Laboratory S 600/K-12
2201 W University Ave 47306 765-285-1131
Dawn Miller, prin. Fax 285-8620
IN Academy for Science Math & Humanities 300/10-12
301 N Talley Ave 47303 765-285-7457
Dr. Jeffrey Smith, prin. Fax 285-2777

Ball Memorial Hospital Post-Sec.
2401 W University Ave 47303 765-747-3393
Ball State University Post-Sec.
2000 W University Ave 47306 765-289-1241
Heritage Hall Christian S 200/PK-12
6401 W River Rd 47304 765-289-6371
Ivy Tech Community College - East Centrl Post-Sec.
4301 S Cowan Rd 47302 765-289-2291
PJ's College of Cosmetology Post-Sec.
3100 W Kilgore Ave 47304 765-289-6144

Munster, Lake, Pop. 23,303
Town of Munster SD 4,100/K-12
8616 Columbia Ave 46321 219-836-9111
Dr. Jeffrey Hendrix, supt. Fax 836-3215
www.munster.k12.in.us
Munster HS 1,500/9-12
8808 Columbia Ave 46321 219-836-3200
Michael Wells, prin. Fax 836-3203
Wright MS 1,000/6-8
8650 Columbia Ave 46321 219-836-6260
Timothy Sopko, prin. Fax 836-0501

Nappanee, Elkhart, Pop. 6,570
Wa-Nee Community SD 3,000/K-12
1300 N Main St 46550 574-773-3131
Joe Sabo, supt. Fax 773-5593
www.wanee.org
Northwood HS 800/9-12
2101 N Main St 46550 574-773-4127
David Maugel, prin. Fax 773-4099
Other Schools – See Wakarusa

Nashville, Brown, Pop. 795
Brown County SC 2,100/PK-12
PO Box 38 47448 812-988-6601
Dr. Laura Hammack, supt. Fax 988-5403
www.brownco.k12.in.us
Brown County HS 700/9-12
PO Box 68 47448 812-988-6606
Shane Killinger, prin. Fax 988-5422
Brown County JHS 400/7-8
PO Box 578 47448 812-988-6605
Brian Garman, prin. Fax 988-5415

New Albany, Floyd, Pop. 35,385
New Albany Floyd County Consolidated SD 11,300/PK-12
PO Box 1087 47151 812-949-4200
Dr. Bruce Hibbard, supt. Fax 949-6900
www.nafcs.k12.in.us
Hazelwood MS 1,000/5-8
1021 Hazelwood Ave 47150 812-542-8502
Jessica Waters, prin. Fax 542-4793
New Albany HS 2,000/9-12
1020 Vincennes St 47150 812-542-8506
Janet Page, prin. Fax 542-4797
Prosser Career Education Center Vo/Tech
4202 Charlestown Rd 47150 812-542-8508
Cathy Wheeler, prin. Fax 542-4799
Scribner MS 900/5-8
910 Old Vincennes Rd 47150 812-542-8503
Keith Bush, prin. Fax 542-4794
Other Schools – See Floyds Knobs, Georgetown

Christian Academy of Indiana 700/PK-12
1000 Academy Dr 47150 812-944-6200
Darin Long, prin. Fax 944-6903
Indiana University Southeast Post-Sec.
4201 Grant Line Rd 47150 812-941-2333

Newburgh, Warrick, Pop. 3,276
Warrick County SC
Supt. — See Boonville
Castle HS 1,900/9-12
3344 State Route 261 47630 812-853-3331
Doug Gresham, prin. Fax 853-9886
Castle North MS 800/6-8
2800 State Route 261 47630 812-853-7347
John Bertram, prin. Fax 858-1089
Castle South MS 700/6-8
3711 Casey Rd 47630 812-490-7930
Jim Hood, prin. Fax 490-7925
Warrick Education Center Alt
3199 State Route 261 47630 812-858-4309
Drew Gerth, prin. Fax 858-3420

Newburgh Christian S 50/PK-12
4156 State Road 261 47630 812-842-0455

New Carlisle, Saint Joseph, Pop. 1,830
New Prairie United SC 2,900/K-12
5327 N Cougar Rd 46552 574-654-7273
Dr. Paul White, supt. Fax 654-7274
www.npusc.k12.in.us
New Prairie HS 900/9-12
5333 N Cougar Rd 46552 574-654-7271
Jennifer Sass, prin. Fax 654-3390
New Prairie MS 700/6-8
5325 N Cougar Rd 46552 574-654-3070
Janet Scott, prin. Fax 654-7009

New Castle, Henry, Pop. 17,809
Blue River Valley SD
Supt. — See Mount Summit
Blue River Valley JSHS 300/7-12
4741 N Hillsboro Rd 47362 765-836-4811
Adam Perdue, prin. Fax 836-3255

New Castle Community SC 3,400/K-12
322 Elliott Ave 47362 765-521-7201
Stephen Fisher, supt. Fax 521-7268
www.nccsc.k12.in.us
New Castle Chrysler HS 1,100/9-12
801 Parkview Dr 47362 765-593-6670
Christopher Walker, prin. Fax 593-6585
New Castle MS 600/7-8
601 Parkview Dr 47362 765-521-7230
Jaci Hadsell, prin. Fax 521-7269

New Haven, Allen, Pop. 14,574
East Allen County SD 8,800/PK-12
1240 State Road 930 E 46774 260-446-0100
Dr. Kenneth Folks, supt. Fax 446-0107
www.eacs.k12.in.us
East Allen Alternative S Alt
800 Homestead Dr 46774 260-446-0260
Jeff Kline, prin. Fax 446-0263
New Haven HS 1,000/9-12
1300 Green Rd 46774 260-446-0220
Anna Murphy, prin. Fax 446-0228
New Haven MS 500/6-8
900 Prospect Ave 46774 260-446-0230
Chad Houser, prin. Fax 446-0236
Other Schools – See Fort Wayne, Leo, Monroeville, Woodburn

New Palestine, Hancock, Pop. 2,034
Southern Hancock County Community SC 3,300/PK-12
PO Box 508 46163 317-861-4463
Dr. Lisa Lantrip, supt. Fax 861-2142
corp.newpal.k12.in.us/
Doe Creek MS 500/7-8
PO Box 478 46163 317-861-4487
James Voelz, prin. Fax 861-2136
New Palestine HS 1,100/9-12
PO Box 448 46163 317-861-4417
Keith Fessler, prin. Fax 861-2125

New Washington, Clark, Pop. 563
Greater Clark County SD
Supt. — See Jeffersonville
New Washington MSHS 500/6-12
226 N Highway 62 47162 812-293-3368
Ben Ledbetter, prin. Fax 293-5803

Noblesville, Hamilton, Pop. 51,089
Noblesville SD 9,800/PK-12
18025 River Rd, 317-773-3171
Dr. Beth Niedermeyer, supt. Fax 773-7845
www.noblesvilleschools.org
Noblesville East MS 1,000/6-8
1625 Field Dr 46060 317-773-0782
Ryan Rich, prin. Fax 776-6261
Noblesville HS 2,600/9-12
18111 Cumberland Rd 46060 317-773-4680
Jeff Bryant, prin. Fax 776-6289
Noblesville West MS 1,300/6-8
19900 Hague Rd, 317-776-7792
Stacey Swan, prin. Fax 776-7797

Kaye Beauty College Post-Sec.
1111 S 10th St 46060 317-773-6189
St. Theodore Guerin HS 700/9-12
15300 N Gray Rd, 317-582-0120
James McNeany, prin. Fax 582-0140

North Judson, Starke, Pop. 1,752
North Judson-San Pierre SC 900/K-12
801 Campbell Dr 46366 574-896-2155
Dr. Annette Zupin, supt. Fax 896-2156
www.njsp.k12.in.us
North Judson-San Pierre JSHS 400/7-12
1 Bluejay Dr 46366 574-896-2158
James Polite, prin. Fax 896-3945

North Manchester, Wabash, Pop. 6,040
Manchester Community SD 1,600/K-12
404 W 9th St 46962 260-982-7518
Dr. Bill Reichhart, supt. Fax 982-4583
www.mcs.k12.in.us
Manchester JSHS 700/7-12
1 Squire Dr 46962 260-982-2196
Nancy Alspaugh, prin. Fax 982-1034

Manchester University Post-Sec.
604 E College Ave 46962 260-982-5000

North Vernon, Jennings, Pop. 6,629
Jennings County SC 4,600/K-12
34 W Main St 47265 812-346-4483
Dr. Terry Sargent, supt. Fax 346-4490
www.jcsc.org
Jennings County HS 1,500/9-12
800 W Walnut St 47265 812-346-5588
Tom Black, prin. Fax 346-4232
Jennings County MS 700/7-8
820 W Walnut St 47265 812-346-4940
George Grubbs, prin. Fax 346-4497

Notre Dame, Saint Joseph, Pop. 5,766

Holy Cross College Post-Sec.
PO Box 308 46556 574-239-8377
St. Mary's College 46556 Post-Sec.
574-284-4000
University of Notre Dame Post-Sec.
220 Main Building 46556 574-631-5000

Oakland City, Gibson, Pop. 2,406
East Gibson SC 900/PK-12
941 S Franklin St 47660 812-749-4755
Dr. Henry Brewster, supt. Fax 749-3343
www.egsc.k12.in.us
Wood Memorial HS 300/9-12
943 S Franklin St 47660 812-749-4757
Kevin Smith, prin. Fax 749-3512
Wood Memorial JHS 100/7-8
945A S Franklin St 47660 812-749-4715
Kevin Smith, prin. Fax 749-4988

Oakland City University Post-Sec.
138 N Lucretia St 47660 812-749-4781

Oldenburg, Franklin, Pop. 669

Oldenburg Academy 200/9-12
1 Twister Cir 47036 812-934-4440
Brian McFee, prin. Fax 934-4838

Oolitic, Lawrence, Pop. 1,177
North Lawrence Community SD
Supt. — See Bedford

Oolitic MS 300/6-8
903 Hoosier Ave 47451 812-275-7551
Steve Underwood, prin. Fax 277-3219

Orleans, Orange, Pop. 2,135
Orleans Community SD 900/K-12
173 Marley St 47452 812-865-2688
Gary McClintic, supt. Fax 865-3428
www.orleans.k12.in.us/
Orleans JSHS 400/7-12
200 W Wilson St 47452 812-865-2688
Chris Stevens, prin. Fax 865-3532

Osgood, Ripley, Pop. 1,609
Jac-Cen-Del Community SC 900/PK-12
723 N Buckeye St 47037 812-689-4114
Timothy W. Taylor, supt. Fax 689-7423
www.jaccendel.k12.in.us
Jac-Cen-Del MSHS 400/7-12
4586 N US Highway 421 47037 812-689-4643
Daryl Werner, prin. Fax 689-0152

Ossian, Wells, Pop. 3,255
Northern Wells Community SD 2,400/PK-12
312 N Jefferson St 46777 260-622-4125
Dr. Scott Mills, supt. Fax 622-7893
www.nwcs.k12.in.us
Norwell HS 800/9-12
1100 E US Highway 224 46777 260-543-2213
Mark Misch, prin. Fax 543-2591
Norwell MS 500/6-8
1100 E US Highway 224 46777 260-543-2218
Tim Wilson, prin. Fax 543-2510

Oxford, Benton, Pop. 1,155
Benton Community SC
Supt. — See Fowler
Benton Central JSHS 900/7-12
4241 E 300 S 47971 765-884-1600
Corey Robb, prin. Fax 884-8445

Paoli, Orange, Pop. 3,640
Lost River Career Cooperative SD
600 Elm St Ste 1 47454 812-723-4818
David Embree, supt. Fax 723-4822
Lost River Career Cooperative S Vo/Tech
600 Elm St Ste 1 47454 812-723-4818
David Embree, prin. Fax 723-4822

Paoli Community SC 1,600/PK-12
501 Elm St 47454 812-723-4717
Casey Brewster, supt. Fax 723-5100
www.paoli.k12.in.us
Paoli JSHS 700/7-12
501 Elm St 47454 812-723-3905
Chad Johnson, prin. Fax 723-4459

Parker City, Randolph, Pop. 1,400
Monroe Central SC 1,000/K-12
1918 N 1000 W 47368 765-468-6868
Adrian Moulton, supt. Fax 468-6578
www.monroecentral.org
Monroe Central JSHS 500/7-12
1878 N 1000 W 47368 765-468-7545
Scott Ritchie, prin. Fax 468-8878

Pekin, Washington, Pop. 1,385
East Washington SC 1,500/K-12
1050 N Eastern School Rd 47165 812-967-3926
Fax 967-5797
www.ewsc.k12.in.us
Eastern HS 500/9-12
1100 N Eastern School Rd 47165 812-967-3931
Darin Farris, prin. Fax 967-5767
East Washington MS 500/5-8
1100 N Eastern School Rd 47165 812-967-5000
Amber Sater, prin. Fax 967-5737

Pendleton, Madison, Pop. 4,212
South Madison Community SC 4,500/PK-12
203 S Heritage Way 46064 765-778-2152
Joseph Buck, supt. Fax 778-8207
www.smadison.k12.in.us
Pendleton Heights HS 1,300/9-12
1 Arabian Dr 46064 765-778-2161
Mark Hall, prin. Fax 778-0605
Pendleton Heights MS 800/7-8
7450 S 300 W 46064 765-778-2139
Daniel Joyce, prin. Fax 778-0557

Pershing, Wayne, Pop. 406
Western Wayne SD 1,000/PK-12
PO Box 217 47370 765-478-5375
Dr. Robert Mahon, supt. Fax 478-4577
www.wwayne.k12.in.us
Other Schools – See Cambridge City

Peru, Miami, Pop. 11,168
Peru Community SC 2,200/PK-12
35 W 3rd St 46970 765-473-3081
Sam Watkins Ed.D., supt. Fax 472-5129
www.peru.k12.in.us
KEYS Academy Alt
19 Park Dr 46970 765-472-5150
Kristy Eddy, dir. Fax 472-5157
Peru HS 600/9-12
401 N Broadway 46970 765-472-3301
Jason Cary, prin. Fax 472-5148
Peru JHS 400/7-8
30 Daniel St 46970 765-473-3084
Sheri Spiker, prin. Fax 473-4007

Petersburg, Pike, Pop. 2,365
Pike County SC 1,800/PK-12
211 S 12th St 47567 812-354-8731
Suzanne Blake, supt. Fax 354-7138
www.pcsc.k12.in.us
Pike Central HS 600/9-12
1810 E State Road 56 47567 812-354-8478
Chad Whitehead, prin. Fax 789-2992

Pike Central MS 500/6-8
1814 E State Road 56 47567 812-354-8478
Chad Whitehead, prin. Fax 354-9559

Plainfield, Hendricks, Pop. 27,200
Plainfield Community SC 5,100/PK-12
985 Longfellow Ln 46168 317-839-2578
Scott Olinger, supt. Fax 838-3664
www.plainfield.k12.in.us
Plainfield Community MS 1,300/6-8
709 Stafford Rd 46168 317-838-3966
Jerry Goldsberry, prin. Fax 838-3965
Plainfield HS 1,500/9-12
1 Red Pride Dr 46168 317-839-7711
Melvin Siefert, prin. Fax 838-3671

PJ's College of Cosmetology Post-Sec.
2026 Stafford Rd 46168 317-839-2761

Plymouth, Marshall, Pop. 9,894
Plymouth Community SC 3,700/PK-12
611 Berkley St 46563 574-936-3115
Daniel Tyree, supt. Fax 936-3160
www.plymouth.k12.in.us/
Lincoln JHS 600/7-8
220 N Liberty St 46563 574-936-3113
Reid Gault, prin. Fax 936-3574
Plymouth HS 1,100/9-12
1 Big Red Dr 46563 574-936-2178
Jim Condon, prin. Fax 936-4842

Poneto, Wells, Pop. 166
Southern Wells Community SD 900/K-12
9120 S 300 W 46781 765-728-5537
Steve Darnell, supt. Fax 728-8124
www.swraiders.com
Southern Wells JSHS 400/7-12
9120 S 300 W 46781 765-728-5534
Chad Yencer, prin. Fax 728-8124

Portage, Porter, Pop. 36,264
Portage Township SD 8,000/K-12
6240 US Highway 6 46368 219-762-6511
Dr. Richard Weigel, supt. Fax 762-3263
www.portage.k12.in.us
Fegely MS 800/6-8
5384 Stone Ave 46368 219-763-8150
Tom Martin, prin. Fax 763-8157
Portage HS 2,600/9-12
6450 US Highway 6 46368 219-763-8100
Max Gill, prin. Fax 764-6062
Willowcreek MS 1,100/6-8
5962 Central Ave 46368 219-763-8090
Michelle Stewart, prin. Fax 762-3455

Portage Christian S 200/K-12
3040 Arlene St 46368 219-762-8962
Larry Pender, supt. Fax 763-9931

Portland, Jay, Pop. 6,162
Jay SC 3,500/PK-12
1976 W Tyson Rd 47371 260-726-9341
Bradley DeRome, supt. Fax 726-4959
www.jayschools.k12.in.us
East Jay MS 600/6-8
225 E Water St 47371 260-726-9371
Lee Newman, prin. Fax 726-2383
Jay County HS 1,100/9-12
2072 W State Road 67 47371 260-726-9306
Chad Dodd, prin. Fax 726-9760
Other Schools – See Dunkirk

Poseyville, Posey, Pop. 1,039
Metro SD of North Posey County 1,400/PK-12
101 N Church St 47633 812-874-2243
Dr. Todd Camp, supt. Fax 874-8806
www.northposey.k12.in.us/
North Posey HS 500/9-12
5900 High School Rd 47633 812-673-4242
Dr. Scott Strieter, prin. Fax 673-6616
North Posey JHS 200/7-8
5800 High School Rd 47633 812-673-4244
Steve Kavanaugh, prin. Fax 673-6622

Princeton, Gibson, Pop. 8,390
North Gibson SC 1,900/PK-12
1104 N Embree St 47670 812-385-4851
Dr. Brian Harmon, supt. Fax 386-1531
www.ngsc.k12.in.us
Princeton Community HS 600/9-12
1101 N Main St 47670 812-385-2591
Steve Hauger, prin. Fax 386-1535
Princeton Community MS 500/6-8
1106 N Embree St 47670 812-385-2020
Noah Velthouse, prin. Fax 386-6746

Ramsey, Harrison
North Harrison Community SC 2,200/PK-12
1260 Highway 64 NW 47166 812-347-2407
D. John Thomas, supt. Fax 347-2870
www.nhcs.k12.in.us
North Harrison HS 600/9-12
1070 Highway 64 NW 47166 812-347-2741
Stephen Hatton, prin. Fax 347-2875
North Harrison MS 500/6-8
1180 Highway 64 NW 47166 812-347-2421
Nathan Freed, prin. Fax 347-2835

Rensselaer, Jasper, Pop. 5,800
Rensselaer Central SC 1,700/PK-12
900 E Washington St 47978 219-866-7822
Ned Speicher, supt. Fax 866-8360
www.rensselaerschools.org
Rensselaer Central HS 500/9-12
1106 E Grace St 47978 219-866-5175
Andrew Jones, prin. Fax 866-5135
Rensselaer Central MS 400/6-8
1106 E Bomber Dr 47978 219-866-4661
Eric Huffman, prin. Fax 866-2103

St. Joseph's College Post-Sec.
PO Box 870 47978 219-866-6000

Richmond, Wayne, Pop. 35,381
Richmond Community SC 5,300/PK-12
300 Hub Etchison Pkwy 47374 765-973-3300
Todd Terrill, supt. Fax 973-3417
www.rcs.k12.in.us
Community Youth Services 100/Alt
315 NW 3rd St 47374 765-973-3430
Rachel Etherington, prin. Fax 973-3715
Hibberd Building Alt
900 S L St 47374 765-973-3488
Fax 973-3703
Richmond HS 1,500/9-12
380 Hub Etchison Pkwy 47374 765-973-3424
Rae Woolpy, prin. Fax 973-3716
Test IS 700/5-8
33 S 22nd St 47374 765-973-3412
Stacy Mopps, prin. Fax 973-3712
Worth IS 700/5-8
222 NW 7th St 47374 765-973-3495
Richard Bryant, prin. Fax 973-3703
Richmond Adult Education Center Adult
302 N 7th St 47374 765-973-3486
Rusty Hensley, prin. Fax 975-1825

Bethany Theological Seminary Post-Sec.
615 National Rd W 47374 800-287-8822
David Demuth Institute of Cosmetology Post-Sec.
1301 S 8th Pl 47374 765-935-7964
Earlham Coll. & Earlham Sch. of Religion Post-Sec.
801 National Rd W 47374 765-983-1200
Indiana University East Post-Sec.
2325 Chester Blvd 47374 765-973-8200
Ivy Tech Community College - Richmond Post-Sec.
2357 Chester Blvd 47374 765-966-2656
PJ's College of Cosmetology Post-Sec.
115 N 9th St 47374 765-962-3005
Reid Hospital & Health Care Services Post-Sec.
1401 Chester Blvd 47374 765-983-3167
Seton Catholic JSHS 100/7-12
233 S 5th St 47374 765-965-6956
Rick Ruhl, prin. Fax 935-9930

Rising Sun, Ohio, Pop. 2,292
Rising Sun-Ohio County Community SD 800/K-12
110 S Henrietta St 47040 812-438-2655
Branden Roeder, supt. Fax 438-4636
www.risingsun.k12.in.us
Rising Sun HS 200/9-12
210 S Henrietta St 47040 812-438-2652
Noel Bostic, prin. Fax 438-2431

Roachdale, Putnam, Pop. 922
North Putnam Community SD
Supt. — See Bainbridge
North Putnam HS 500/9-12
8869 N County Road 250 E 46172 765-522-6282
Jason Chew, prin. Fax 522-2862
North Putnam MS 400/6-8
8905 N County Road 250 E 46172 765-522-2900
Scott Miller, prin. Fax 522-2863

Rochester, Fulton, Pop. 6,144
Rochester Community SC 1,900/PK-12
PO Box 108 46975 574-223-2159
Jana Vance, supt. Fax 223-4909
www.zebras.net
Rochester Community HS 500/9-12
PO Box 108 46975 574-223-2176
Adam Strasser, prin. Fax 223-3401
Rochester Community MS 400/6-8
PO Box 108 46975 574-223-2280
Oscar Haughs, prin. Fax 223-1531

Rockport, Spencer, Pop. 2,241
South Spencer County SC 1,300/PK-12
321 S 5th St 47635 812-649-2591
Dr. Richard Rutherford, supt. Fax 649-4249
www.sspencer.k12.in.us
South Spencer HS 500/9-12
1142 N Orchard Rd 47635 812-649-9157
Angela Gladish, prin. Fax 649-2214
South Spencer MS 300/6-8
1298 N Orchard Rd 47635 812-649-2203
Scot French, prin. Fax 649-9630

Rockville, Parke, Pop. 2,594
North Central Parke Community SC
Supt. — See Marshall
Rockville JSHS 400/7-12
506 N Beadle St 47872 765-569-5686
Dwight Ashley, prin. Fax 569-1047

Rolling Prairie, LaPorte, Pop. 580

Sacred Heart Apostolic S 50/7-12
PO Box 7 46371 219-778-4596

Rossville, Clinton, Pop. 1,638
Rossville Consolidated SD 700/K-12
PO Box 11 46065 765-379-2990
Dr. James Hanna, supt. Fax 379-3014
www.rcsd.k12.in.us
Rossville MSHS 300/6-12
PO Box 530 46065 765-379-2551
Michael Gick, prin. Fax 379-2556

Royal Center, Cass, Pop. 854
Pioneer Regional SC 900/K-12
PO Box 577 46978 574-643-2605
Dr. David Bess, supt. Fax 643-9977
www.pioneer.k12.in.us/
Pioneer JSHS 500/7-12
PO Box 547 46978 574-643-3145
Jeremy Tucker, prin. Fax 643-2020

Rushville, Rush, Pop. 6,250
Rush County SD 2,500/PK-12
330 W 8th St 46173 765-932-4186
Matthew Vance, supt. Fax 938-1608
rcs.rushville.k12.in.us/
Rush MS 400/7-8
1601 N Sexton St 46173 765-932-2968
Maria Peek, prin. Fax 938-2011
Rushville Consolidated HS 800/9-12
1201 Lions Path 46173 765-932-3901
Robert Hadley, prin. Fax 932-4051

Russiaville, Howard, Pop. 1,087
Western SC 2,600/K-12
2600 S 600 W 46979 765-883-5576
Randy McCracken, supt. Fax 883-7946
www.western.k12.in.us
Western HS 800/9-12
2600 S 600 W 46979 765-883-5541
Rick Davis, prin. Fax 883-4522
Western MS 700/6-8
2600 S 600 W 46979 765-883-5566
Tracy Horrell, prin. Fax 883-4531

Saint John, Lake, Pop. 14,717
Lake Central SC 9,700/PK-12
8260 Wicker Ave 46373 219-365-8507
Dr. Lawrence Veracco, supt. Fax 365-6406
www.lcsc.us
Clark MS 1,100/5-8
8915 W 93rd Ave 46373 219-365-9203
Scott Graber, prin. Fax 365-9348
Lake Central HS 3,200/9-12
8400 Wicker Ave 46373 219-365-8551
Sean Begley, prin. Fax 365-7156
Other Schools – See Dyer, Schererville

Saint Leon, Franklin, Pop. 670
Sunman-Dearborn Community SC 3,400/K-12
1 Trojan Pl Ste B, Brookville IN 47012 812-623-2291
Dr. Andrew Jackson, supt. Fax 623-3341
www.sunmandearborn.k12.in.us
East Central HS 1,300/9-12
1 Trojan Pl Ste A, Brookville IN 47012 812-576-4811
Beverly Ester, prin. Fax 576-2047
Sunman-Dearborn MS 600/6-8
8356 Schuman Rd, Brookville IN 47012 812-576-3500
Matt Maple, prin. Fax 576-3506

Saint Mary of the Woods, Vigo, Pop. 793

St. Mary-of-the-Woods College Post-Sec.
1 St Mary of Woods Coll 47876 812-535-5151

Saint Meinrad, Spencer, Pop. 700

St. Meinrad School of Theology Post-Sec.
200 Hill Dr 47577 812-357-6611

Salem, Washington, Pop. 6,263
Salem Community SD 1,500/K-12
500 N Harrison St 47167 812-883-4437
Dr. D. Lynn Reed, supt. Fax 883-1031
www.salemschools.com/
Salem HS 600/9-12
700 N Harrison St 47167 812-883-3904
Derek Smith, prin. Fax 883-3905
Salem MS 400/6-8
1001 N Harrison St 47167 812-883-3808
Ray Oppel, prin. Fax 883-8049

Schererville, Lake, Pop. 28,917
Lake Central SC
Supt. — See Saint John
Grimmer MS 900/5-8
225 W 77th Ave 46375 219-865-6985
John Alessia, prin. Fax 865-4423

Don Roberts Beauty Academy Post-Sec.
152 E US Highway 30 46375 219-864-1600

Scottsburg, Scott, Pop. 6,707
Scott County SD 2 2,700/PK-12
375 E Mcclain Ave 47170 812-752-8946
Dr. Marc Slaton, supt. Fax 752-8951
www.scsd2.k12.in.us/
Scottsburg HS 800/9-12
500 S Gardner St 47170 812-752-8927
Ric Manns, prin. Fax 752-6207
Scottsburg MS 600/6-8
425 S 3rd St 47170 812-752-8926
Kristin Nass, prin. Fax 752-8864

Sellersburg, Clark, Pop. 6,055
West Clark Community SC 4,700/PK-12
601 Renz Ave 47172 812-246-3375
Dr. Chad Schenck, supt. Fax 246-9731
www.wclark.k12.in.us
Silver Creek HS 800/9-12
557 Renz Ave 47172 812-246-3391
Michael Crabtree, prin. Fax 246-8184
Silver Creek MS 700/6-8
495 N Indiana Ave 47172 812-246-4421
Al Eckert, prin. Fax 246-7430
West Clark Education Center Alt
206 N New Albany St 47172 812-248-7130
Tate Enlow, dir. Fax 246-7439
Other Schools – See Borden, Henryville

Ivy Tech Community College - Southern Post-Sec.
8204 Highway 311 47172 812-246-3301

Selma, Delaware, Pop. 856
Liberty-Perry Community SC 1,100/K-12
PO Box 337 47383 765-282-5615
Bryan Rausch, supt. Fax 281-3733
www.libertyperry.org
Selma MS 300/6-8
10501 E County Road 167 S 47383 765-288-7242
Dennis Thompson, prin. Fax 281-3727
Wapahani HS 400/9-12
10401 E County Road 167 S 47383 765-289-7323
Dr. Mark Fahey, prin. Fax 281-3724

Seymour, Jackson, Pop. 17,275
Seymour Community SD 4,300/PK-12
1638 S Walnut St 47274 812-522-3340
Robert Hooker, supt. Fax 522-8031
www.scsc.k12.in.us
Seymour HS 1,200/9-12
1350 W 2nd St 47274 812-522-4384
Greg Prange, prin. Fax 523-2347
Seymour MS 1,000/6-8
920 N Obrien St 47274 812-522-5453
J.B. Royer, prin. Fax 523-8134

Trinity Lutheran HS 100/9-12
7120 N County Road 875 E 47274 812-524-8547
Benjamin Stellwagen, prin. Fax 524-8523

Sharpsville, Tipton, Pop. 600
Tri-Central Community School Corporation 900/PK-12
4774 N 200 W 46068 765-963-2585
Dave Driggs, supt. Fax 963-3042
www.tccs.k12.in.us
Tri Central MSHS 500/6-12
2115 W 500 N 46068 765-963-2560
Adam Long, prin. Fax 963-6844

Shelburn, Sullivan, Pop. 1,220
Northeast SC
Supt. — See Hymera
Northeast MS 200/6-8
620 N Washington St 47879 812-397-5390
J.T. Roberts, prin. Fax 397-2886

Shelbyville, Shelby, Pop. 18,951
Shelby Eastern SD 1,300/PK-12
2451 N 600 E 46176 765-544-2246
Dr. Robert Evans, supt. Fax 544-2247
www.ses.k12.in.us
Other Schools – See Morristown, Waldron

Shelbyville Central SD 4,000/PK-12
803 Saint Joseph St 46176 317-392-2505
Dr. David Adams, supt. Fax 392-5737
www.shelbycs.k12.in.us
Shelbyville HS 1,100/9-12
2003 S Miller St 46176 317-398-9731
Kathleen Miltz, prin. Fax 392-5709
Shelbyville MS 900/6-8
1200 W McKay Rd 46176 317-392-2551
Ryan Mikus, prin. Fax 392-5713

Southwestern Cons SD of Shelby County 600/K-12
3406 W 600 S 46176 317-729-5746
Dr. Paula Maurer, supt. Fax 729-5330
www.swshelby.k12.in.us
Southwestern JSHS 300/7-12
3406 W 600 S 46176 317-729-5122
Curtis Chase, prin. Fax 729-2424

Sheridan, Hamilton, Pop. 2,630
Sheridan Community SD 1,100/PK-12
24795 Hinesley Rd 46069 317-758-4172
Dr. David Mundy, supt. Fax 758-6248
www.scs.k12.in.us/
Sheridan HS 300/9-12
24185 Hinesley Rd 46069 317-758-4431
Jane Newblom, prin. Fax 758-2406
Sheridan MS 200/6-8
3030 W 246th St 46069 317-758-6780
Jane Newblom, prin. Fax 758-2435

Shoals, Martin, Pop. 746
Shoals Community SC 600/PK-12
11741 Ironton Rd 47581 812-247-2060
Candace Roush, supt. Fax 247-2278
shoals.k12.in.us/
Shoals Community JSHS 300/7-12
7900 US Highway 50 47581 812-247-2090
Kindra Hovis, prin. Fax 247-2056

South Bend, Saint Joseph, Pop. 97,691
South Bend Community SC 18,900/PK-12
215 S Saint Joseph St 46601 574-283-8000
Dr. Kenneth Spells, supt. Fax 283-8143
www.sbcsc.k12.in.us
Adams HS 1,800/9-12
808 S Twyckenham Dr 46615 574-283-7700
James Seitz, prin. Fax 283-7704
Brown Intermediate Center 400/4-8
737 Beale St 46616 574-287-9680
Joseph Somers, prin. Fax 283-5581
Clay HS 1,300/9-12
19131 Darden Rd 46637 574-243-7000
Mansour Eid, prin. Fax 243-7005
Clay Intermediate Center 500/5-8
52900 Lily Rd 46637 574-243-7145
Frances Beard, prin. Fax 243-7151
CTE Vo/Tech
3206 Sugar Maple Bus Ct 46628 574-283-7505
Laura Marzotto, dir. Fax 283-7549
Dickinson Intermediate Fine Arts Academy 600/5-8
4404 Elwood Ave 46628 574-283-7625
Thomas Sims, prin. Fax 283-7633
Edison Intermediate Center 500/5-8
2701 Eisenhower Ave 46615 574-283-8900
Keith Lewis, prin. Fax 283-8903
Greene Intermediate Center 300/5-8
24702 Roosevelt Rd 46614 574-283-7900
Fax 283-7903
Jackson Intermediate Center 600/5-8
5001 Miami St 46614 574-231-5600
Gretchen McEndarfer, prin. Fax 231-5605
Jefferson Traditional S 600/5-8
528 S Eddy St 46617 574-283-8700
Carmen Williams, prin. Fax 283-8703
LaSalle Intermediate Academy 900/5-8
2701 Elwood Ave 46628 574-283-7500
Fax 283-7513
Marshall Intermediate Center 500/5-8
1433 Byron Dr 46614 574-231-5801
Tiana Batiste-Waddell, prin. Fax 231-5804
Navarre Intermediate Center 700/5-8
4702 Ford St 46619 574-283-7345
Matthew Emery, prin. Fax 283-7351
Riley HS 1,200/9-12
1902 Fellows St 46613 574-283-8400
Francois Bayingana, prin. Fax 283-8405
Rise Up Academy 200/Alt
19010 Adams Rd 46637 574-243-7300
Terry Moore, prin. Fax 243-7303
Washington HS 1,100/9-12
4747 W Washington St 46619 574-283-7200
Byron Sanders, prin. Fax 283-7205

Community Baptist Christian S 200/PK-12
5715 Miami St 46614 574-291-3620
Matt Fenton, admin. Fax 291-3648
Indiana University South Bend Post-Sec.
PO Box 7111 46634 574-520-4872
Ivy Tech Community College North Central Post-Sec.
220 Dean Johnson Blvd 46601 574-289-7001
National College Post-Sec.
1030 E Jefferson Blvd 46617 574-307-7100
Purdue University-College of Technology Post-Sec.
PO Box 7111 46634 574-520-4180
Radiological Technologies University-VT Post-Sec.
100 E Wayne St Ste 140 46601 574-232-2408
St. Joseph HS 800/9-12
435 N Notre Dame Ave 46617 574-233-6137
Susan Richter, prin. Fax 232-3482
Trinity S at Greenlawn 200/7-12
107 S Greenlawn Ave 46617 574-287-5590
John A. Lee, head sch Fax 236-6628

South Whitley, Whitley, Pop. 1,743
Whitko Community SC
Supt. — See Larwill
Whitko HS 600/9-12
1 Big Blue Ave 46787 260-723-5146
John Snyder, prin. Fax 723-4724

Speedway, Marion, Pop. 11,556
Town of Speedway SD 1,700/PK-12
5335 W 25th St 46224 317-244-0236
Kenneth Hull, supt. Fax 486-4843
www.speedwayschools.org
Speedway HS 500/9-12
5357 W 25th St 46224 317-244-7238
Kyle Trebley, prin. Fax 486-4838
Speedway JHS 200/7-8
5151 W 14th St 46224 317-244-3359
John Dizney, prin. Fax 486-4845

Spencer, Owen, Pop. 2,205
Spencer-Owen Community SD 2,700/PK-12
205 E Hillside Ave 47460 812-829-2233
Dr. Chad Briggs, supt. Fax 829-6614
www.socs.k12.in.us
Owen Valley HS 800/9-12
622 W State Highway 46 47460 812-829-2266
Rhonda Schafer, prin. Fax 829-6605
Owen Valley MS 400/7-8
626 W State Highway 46 47460 812-829-2249
Aaron LaGrange, prin. Fax 829-6635

Straughn, Henry, Pop. 222
South Henry SC 800/K-12
6972 S State Road 103 47387 765-987-7882
Wesley Hammond, supt. Fax 987-7589
www.shenry.k12.in.us/
Tri JSHS 400/7-12
6972 S State Road 103 47387 765-987-7988
Tony Benson, prin. Fax 987-8446

Sullivan, Sullivan, Pop. 4,203
Southwest SC 1,800/PK-12
110 N Main St 47882 812-268-6311
Chris Stitzle, supt. Fax 268-6312
www.swest.k12.in.us/
Sullivan HS 500/9-12
902 N Section St 47882 812-268-6301
Dr. Tara Jenkins, prin. Fax 268-6303
Sullivan MS 300/6-8
415 W Frakes St 47882 812-268-4000
Dustin Hitt, prin. Fax 268-5368

Switz City, Greene, Pop. 291
White River Valley SD 500/PK-12
PO Box 1470 47465 812-659-1424
Robert Hacker, supt. Fax 659-2278
www.wrv.k12.in.us
WRV JSHS 200/7-12
PO Box 1470 47465 812-659-2274
LeAnne Kelley, prin. Fax 659-2283

Syracuse, Kosciusko, Pop. 2,781
Wawasee Community SC 3,100/PK-12
1 Warrior Path Bldg 2 46567 574-457-3188
Dr. Thomas Edington, supt. Fax 457-4962
www.wawasee.k12.in.us/
Wawasee HS 900/9-12
1 Warrior Path Bldg 1 46567 574-457-3147
Michael Schmidt, prin. Fax 457-4364
Wawasee MS 500/6-8
9850 N State Road 13 46567 574-457-8839
Susan Mishler, prin. Fax 457-3575

Tell City, Perry, Pop. 7,212
Tell City-Troy Township SC 1,500/PK-12
837 17th St 47586 812-547-3300
John Scioldo, supt. Fax 547-9704
www.tellcity.k12.in.us

Tell City JSHS 600/7-12
900 12th St 47586 812-547-3131
Brad Ramsey, prin. Fax 547-9705

Terre Haute, Vigo, Pop. 59,043
Vigo County SC 15,500/PK-12
PO Box 3703 47803 812-462-4011
Daniel Tanoos, supt. Fax 462-4115
www.vigoschools.org/
Honey Creek MS 800/6-8
6601 S Carlisle St 47802 812-462-4372
Nolan Cox, prin. Fax 462-4367
McLean Alternative HS 100/Alt
961 Lafayette Ave 47804 812-462-4330
Jeannie Conley, prin. Fax 462-4017
Otter Creek MS 900/6-8
4801 N Lafayette St 47805 812-462-4391
Sarah Gore, prin. Fax 462-4388
Scott MS 500/6-8
1000 Grant St 47802 812-462-4381
Scotia Brown, prin. Fax 462-4370
Terre Haute North Vigo HS 1,900/9-12
3434 Maple Ave 47804 812-462-4312
Robin Smith, prin. Fax 462-4204
Terre Haute South Vigo HS 1,800/9-12
3737 S 7th St 47802 812-462-4252
Dr. Tammy Rowshandel, prin. Fax 462-4408
Washington Alternative HS 50/Alt
3707 S 7th St 47802 812-462-4252
Tammy Rowshandel, prin. Fax 462-4066
Wilson MS 900/6-8
301 S 25th St 47803 812-462-4396
Susan Mardis, prin. Fax 232-2217
Other Schools – See West Terre Haute

Harrison College Post-Sec.
1378 S State Road 46 47803 812-877-2100
Indiana State University Post-Sec.
200 N 7th St 47809 812-237-6311
Ivy Tech Community College Wabash Valley Post-Sec.
8000 S Education Dr 47802 812-299-1121
Rose-Hulman Institute of Technology Post-Sec.
5500 Wabash Ave 47803 812-877-1511
Terre Haute Adventist S 50/K-10
900 S 29th St 47803 812-232-1339

Thorntown, Boone, Pop. 1,514
Western Boone County Community SD 1,800/PK-12
1201 N State Road 75 46071 765-482-6333
Rob Ramey, supt. Fax 482-0890
www.weboschools.org
Western Boone JSHS 800/7-12
1205 N State Road 75 46071 765-482-6143
Brent Miller, prin. Fax 482-6146

Tipton, Tipton, Pop. 5,058
Tipton Community SC 1,700/K-12
1051 S Main St 46072 765-675-2147
Kevin Emsweller, supt. Fax 675-3857
www.tcsc.k12.in.us
Tipton HS 600/9-12
619 S Main St 46072 765-675-7431
Joe Rushton, prin. Fax 675-9519
Tipton MS 400/6-8
817 S Main St 46072 765-675-7521
Shayne Clark, prin. Fax 675-9027

Topeka, Lagrange, Pop. 1,128
Westview SC 2,300/K-12
1545 S 600 W 46571 260-768-4404
Dr. Randall Zimmerly, supt. Fax 768-7368
www.westview.k12.in.us
Westview JSHS 800/7-12
1635 S 600 W 46571 260-768-4146
Rich Cory, prin. Fax 768-7611

Trafalgar, Johnson, Pop. 1,089
Nineveh-Hensley-Jackson United SC 1,800/PK-12
802 S Indian Creek Dr 46181 317-878-2100
Dr. Tim Edsell, supt. Fax 878-5765
www.nhj.k12.in.us
Indian Creek HS 600/9-12
803 W Indian Creek Dr 46181 317-878-2110
Luke Skobel, prin. Fax 878-2112
Indian Creek MS 500/6-8
801 W Indian Creek Dr 46181 317-878-2130
Sean Zachery, prin. Fax 878-2149

Union City, Randolph, Pop. 3,547
Randolph Eastern SC 900/PK-12
731 N Plum St 47390 765-964-4994
Lisa Smith, supt. Fax 964-6590
www.resc.k12.in.us/
Union City Community JSHS 400/7-12
603 N Walnut St 47390 765-964-4840
Aaron Black, prin. Fax 964-3775

Union Mills, LaPorte
South Central Community SC 900/K-12
9808 S 600 W 46382 219-767-2263
Linda Wiltfong, supt. Fax 767-2260
www.scentral.k12.in.us/
South Central JSHS 500/7-12
9808 S 600 W 46382 219-767-2266
Sandra Wood, prin. Fax 767-2260

Upland, Grant, Pop. 3,790

Taylor University Post-Sec.
236 W Reade Ave 46989 800-882-3456

Valparaiso, Porter, Pop. 31,160
East Porter County SC
Supt. — See Kouts
Morgan Township MSHS 400/6-12
299 S State Road 49 46383 219-462-5883
Chris George, prin. Fax 462-4014
Washington Township MSHS 500/6-12
381 E State Road 2 46383 219-464-3598
Sue Lipinski, prin. Fax 462-3372

Porter Township SC 1,500/K-12
248 S 500 W 46385 219-477-4933
Dr. Stacey Schmidt, supt. Fax 477-4834
www.ptsc.k12.in.us
Boone Grove HS 500/9-12
260 S 500 W 46385 219-306-8600
Clay Corman, prin. Fax 306-8659
Other Schools – See Boone Grove

Union Township SC 1,500/K-12
599 W 300 N Ste A 46385 219-759-2531
John Hunter, supt. Fax 759-3250
www.union.k12.in.us
Union Township MS 400/6-8
599 W 300 N 46385 219-759-2562
Jerry Lasky, prin. Fax 759-4359
Wheeler HS 500/9-12
587 W 300 N 46385 219-759-2561
Donald Gandy, prin. Fax 759-5602

Valparaiso Community SD 6,400/K-12
3801 Campbell St 46385 219-531-3000
Dr. E. Ric Frataccia Ed.D., supt. Fax 531-3009
www.valpo.k12.in.us
Franklin MS 900/6-8
605 Campbell St 46385 219-531-3020
Christopher Fields, prin. Fax 531-3026
Jefferson MS 700/6-8
1600 Roosevelt Rd 46383 219-531-3140
Elizabeth Krutz, prin. Fax 531-3146
Porter County Career Ctr Vo/Tech
1005 Franklin St 46383 219-531-3170
Jon Groth, prin. Fax 531-3173
Valparaiso HS 2,100/9-12
2727 Campbell St 46385 219-531-3070
Dr. Reid Amones, prin. Fax 531-3076

Don Roberts Beauty School Post-Sec.
1354 Lincolnway 46385 219-462-5189
Porter Memorial Hospital Post-Sec.
814 Laporte Ave 46383 219-465-4883
South Haven Christian S 100/PK-12
786 Juniper Rd 46385 219-759-5313
Michael Owney, prin. Fax 759-1577
Valparaiso University 46383 Post-Sec.
219-464-5000
Victory Christian Academy 300/PK-12
3805 LaPorte Ave 46383 219-548-8803
Anthony Clymer, admin. Fax 548-7413

Veedersburg, Fountain, Pop. 2,156
Southeast Fountain SC 1,200/K-12
744 E US Highway 136 47987 765-294-2254
Doug Allison, supt. Fax 294-3200
www.sefschools.org/
Fountain Central JSHS 600/7-12
750 E US Highway 136 47987 765-294-2206
Bill Chestnut, prin. Fax 294-3204

Versailles, Ripley, Pop. 2,089
South Ripley Community SC 1,200/K-12
PO Box 690 47042 812-689-6282
Robert D. Moorhead, supt. Fax 689-6760
www.sripley.k12.in.us
South Ripley HS 400/9-12
1589 S Benham Rd 47042 812-689-5303
Dr. David Wintin, prin. Fax 689-6715
South Ripley JHS 200/7-8
1589 S Benham Rd 47042 812-689-0909
Destiny Rutzel, prin. Fax 689-6970

Southeastern Career SC
901 W US Highway 50 47042 812-689-5253
Bradley Street, dir. Fax 689-6977
www.sccusa.org
Southeastern Career Center Vo/Tech
901 W US Highway 50 47042 812-689-5253
Bradley Street, prin. Fax 689-6977

Vevay, Switzerland, Pop. 1,662
Switzerland County SC 1,500/PK-12
1040 W Main St 47043 812-427-2611
Michael Jones, supt. Fax 427-2044
www.switzerland.k12.in.us
Switzerland County HS 500/9-12
1020 W Main St 47043 812-427-2626
Gregg Goewert, prin. Fax 427-3445
Switzerland County MS 200/7-8
1004 W Main St 47043 812-427-3809
Sean McGarvey, prin. Fax 427-3807

Vincennes, Knox, Pop. 18,142
South Knox SC 1,200/K-12
6116 E State Road 61 47591 812-726-4440
Tim Grove, supt. Fax 743-2110
www.sknox.k12.in.us
South Knox MSHS 500/7-12
6136 E State Road 61 47591 812-726-4450
David Couchenour, prin. Fax 726-4545

Twin Rivers Career & Technical Education
PO Box 1266 47591 812-882-0801
Brandon R. Small, dir. Fax 882-0802
www.twinriversarea.org
Twin Rivers Career & Technical Education Vo/Tech
PO Box 1266 47591 812-882-0801
Brandon R. Small, dir. Fax 882-0802

Vincennes Community SC 2,700/PK-12
1712 S Quail Run Rd 47591 812-882-4844
Gregory T. Parsley, supt. Fax 885-1427
www.vcsc.k12.in.us
Clark MS 600/6-8
1926 S Richard Bauer Dr 47591 812-882-5172
Ryan Clark, prin. Fax 885-1419
Lincoln HS 800/9-12
1545 S Hart Street Rd 47591 812-882-8480
Stephen Combs, prin. Fax 885-1431

Good Samaritan Hospital Post-Sec.
520 S 7th St 47591 812-885-3195
Rivet MSHS 200/6-12
210 Barnett St 47591 812-882-6215
Janice Jones, prin. Fax 886-1939
Vincennes Beauty College Post-Sec.
12 S 2nd St 47591 812-882-1086
Vincennes University Post-Sec.
1002 N 1st St 47591 812-888-8888

Wabash, Wabash, Pop. 10,549
Heartland Career Center SD
79 S 200 W 46992 260-563-7481
Mark Hobbs, supt. Fax 563-5544
www.hcc.k12.in.us
Heartland Career Ctr Vo/Tech
79 S 200 W 46992 260-563-7481
Jon Higgins, prin. Fax 563-5544

Metro SD of Wabash County 2,100/K-12
204 N 300 W 46992 260-563-8050
Mike Keaffaber, supt. Fax 569-6836
www.msdwc.k12.in.us
Northfield JSHS 500/7-12
154 W 200 N 46992 260-563-8050
Paul Voigt, prin. Fax 569-6839
Southwood JSHS 500/7-12
564 E State Road 124 46992 260-563-8050
Andrew McDaniel, prin. Fax 569-6843
Whites JSHS 100/Alt
5233 S 50 E 46992 260-563-1150
Troy Friedersdorf, prin. Fax 563-1150

Wabash CSD 1,300/PK-12
PO Box 744 46992 260-563-2151
Jason Callahan, supt. Fax 563-2066
www.apaches.k12.in.us
Wabash HS 500/9-12
580 N Miami St 46992 260-563-4131
Kyle Wieland, prin. Fax 563-6806
Wabash MS 300/5-8
150 Colerain St 46992 260-563-4137
Scott Bumgardener, prin. Fax 569-9805

Wakarusa, Elkhart, Pop. 1,739
Wa-Nee Community SD
Supt. — See Nappanee
Northwood MS 700/6-8
PO Box 367 46573 574-862-2710
Bart Rice, prin. Fax 862-2327

Waldron, Shelby, Pop. 796
Shelby Eastern SD
Supt. — See Shelbyville
Waldron JSHS 300/6-12
PO Box 369 46182 765-525-6822
Gary Brown, prin. Fax 525-9727

Walkerton, Saint Joseph, Pop. 2,125
John Glenn SC 1,900/PK-12
101 John Glenn Dr 46574 574-586-3129
Richard Reese, supt. Fax 586-2660
www.jgsc.k12.in.us
Glenn HS 600/9-12
201 John Glenn Dr 46574 574-586-3195
William Morton, prin. Fax 586-3905
Urey MS 300/7-8
407 Washington St 46574 574-586-3184
Mark Maudlin, prin. Fax 586-3714

Walton, Cass, Pop. 1,033
Southeastern SC 1,500/K-12
100 S Main St 46994 574-626-2525
Dr. Tim Garland, supt. Fax 626-2751
www.sesc.k12.in.us
Cass JSHS 800/7-12
6422 E State Road 218 46994 574-626-2511
Shay Bonnell, prin. Fax 626-2172

Wanatah, LaPorte, Pop. 1,033
Tri Township School Corp 400/K-12
PO Box 249 46390 219-754-2461
Tim Somers, supt. Fax 754-2511
www.tritownship.k12.in.us
Other Schools – See La Crosse

Warsaw, Kosciusko, Pop. 13,362
Warsaw Community SC 7,100/PK-12
1 Administration Dr 46580 574-371-5098
David Hoffert Ed.D., supt. Fax 371-5046
www.warsaw.k12.in.us
Edgewood MS 600/7-8
900 S Union St 46580 574-371-5096
JoElla Smyth, prin. Fax 371-5010
Gateway Educational Center Alt
201 N Union St 46580 574-371-5019
Steve Ferber, prin. Fax 371-5033
Lakeview MS 600/7-8
848 E Smith St 46580 574-269-7211
Amy Sivley, prin. Fax 371-5013
Warsaw Community HS 2,100/9-12
1 Tiger Ln 46580 574-371-5099
Troy Akers, prin. Fax 371-5012

Washington, Daviess, Pop. 11,354
Washington Community SD 2,600/K-12
301 E South St 47501 812-254-5536
Dr. Dan Roach, supt. Fax 254-8346
www.wcs.k12.in.us
Washington HS 700/9-12
608 E Walnut St 47501 812-254-3860
LeAnne Kelley, prin. Fax 254-8374
Washington JHS 400/7-8
210 NE 6th St 47501 812-254-2682
Mark Arnold, prin. Fax 254-8381

Washington Catholic MSHS 100/5-12
201 NE 2nd St 47501 812-254-2050
Karie Craney, prin. Fax 254-8746

Waterloo, DeKalb, Pop. 2,205
DeKalb County Central United SC 3,700/PK-12
3326 County Road 427 46793 260-920-1011
Steven E. Teders, supt. Fax 837-7767
www.dekalbcentral.net
DeKalb HS 1,200/9-12
3424 County Road 427 46793 260-920-1012
Matthew Toth, prin. Fax 837-7841
DeKalb MS 900/6-8
3338 County Road 427 46793 260-920-1013
Kimberly Fifer, prin. Fax 837-7812

Westfield, Hamilton, Pop. 29,609
Westfield Washington SD 6,700/PK-12
1143 E 181st St 46074 317-867-8000
Sherry Grate, supt. Fax 867-0929
www.wws.k12.in.us
Westfield HS 1,900/9-12
18250 N Union St 46074 317-867-6800
Dr. Stacy McGuire, prin. Fax 867-2909
Westfield MS 1,100/7-8
345 W Hoover St 46074 317-867-6600
Ryan Haughey, prin. Fax 867-1407

West Lafayette, Tippecanoe, Pop. 29,004
Tippecanoe SC
Supt. — See Lafayette
Battle Ground MS 600/6-8
6100 N 50 W 47906 765-269-8140
Jodi Day, prin. Fax 269-8215
Harrison HS 1,700/9-12
5701 N 50 W 47906 765-463-3511
Cory Marshall, prin. Fax 463-1477
Klondike MS 400/6-8
3307 Klondike Rd 47906 765-463-2544
Christine Cannon, prin. Fax 497-9413

West Lafayette Community SC 2,200/K-12
1130 N Salisbury St 47906 765-746-1602
Dr. Rocky Killion, supt. Fax 746-1644
www.wl.k12.in.us/
West Lafayette JSHS 1,100/7-12
1105 N Grant St 47906 765-746-0400
Ronald Shriner, prin. Fax 746-0420

Purdue University Post-Sec.
610 Purdue Mall 47907 765-494-4600

West Lebanon, Warren, Pop. 721
Metro SD of Warren County
Supt. — See Williamsport
Seeger Memorial JSHS 600/7-12
1222 S State Road 263 47991 765-893-4445
Rob Beckett, prin. Fax 893-8354

West Terre Haute, Vigo, Pop. 2,213
Vigo County SC
Supt. — See Terre Haute
West Vigo HS 600/9-12
4590 W Sarah Myers Dr 47885 812-462-4282
Tom Balitewicz, prin. Fax 462-4090
West Vigo MS 500/6-8
4750 W Sarah Myers Dr 47885 812-462-4361
Julie Lautenschlager, prin. Fax 462-4358

Westville, LaPorte, Pop. 5,829
Metro SD of New Durham Township 900/K-12
207 E Valparaiso St 46391 219-785-2239
Dr. Curtiss Strietelmeier, supt. Fax 785-4584
www.westville.k12.in.us/
Westville JSHS 500/7-12
207 E Valparaiso St 46391 219-785-2531
Alissa Schnick, prin. Fax 785-2990

Purdue University North Central Post-Sec.
1401 S US Highway 421 46391 219-785-5200

Wheatfield, Jasper, Pop. 846
Kankakee Valley SC 3,500/K-12
PO Box 278 46392 219-987-4711
Aaron Case, supt. Fax 987-4710
www.kv.k12.in.us
Kankakee Valley HS 1,100/9-12
3923 W State Road 10 46392 219-956-3143
Michael Spagna, prin. Fax 956-4639
Kankakee Valley MS 800/6-8
5258 W State Road 10 46392 219-987-8810
Adam Metzger, prin. Fax 987-2540

Whiteland, Johnson, Pop. 4,117
Clark-Pleasant Community SC 5,700/PK-12
50 Center St 46184 317-535-7579
Dr. Patrick Spray, supt. Fax 535-4931
www.cpcsc.k12.in.us
Clark Pleasant Academy Alt
129 N US Highway 31 46184 317-535-3241
Lisa Morris, dir. Fax 535-0189
Whiteland Community HS 1,800/9-12
300 Main St 46184 317-535-7562
Tom Zobel, prin. Fax 535-7509
Other Schools – See Greenwood

Whitestown, Boone, Pop. 2,806
Zionsville Community SC
Supt. — See Zionsville
Zionsville West MS 900/5-8
5565 S 700 E 46075 317-873-1240
Kris Devereaux, prin. Fax 769-6909

Traders Point Christian Academy 600/PK-12
6600 S Indianapolis Rd 46075 317-769-2450
Ron Evans, head sch Fax 769-2456

Whiting, Lake, Pop. 4,948
Hammond CSD
Supt. — See Hammond
Clark MSHS 1,500/6-12
1921 Davis Ave 46394 219-659-3522
Robert Wilson, prin. Fax 554-4571

School City of Whiting 1,200/PK-12
1500 Center St 46394 219-659-0656
Cynthia Scroggins, supt. Fax 473-4008
www.whiting.k12.in.us
Whiting HS 400/9-12
1751 Oliver St 46394 219-659-0255
Julie Fregien, prin. Fax 473-1341
Whiting MS 300/6-8
1800 New York Ave 46394 219-473-1344
Erin Nolan-Higgins, prin. Fax 473-4017

Calumet College of St. Joseph Post-Sec.
2400 New York Ave 46394 219-473-7770

Williamsport, Warren, Pop. 1,888
Metro SD of Warren County 1,100/K-12
101 N Monroe St 47993 765-762-3364
Ralph Shrader, supt. Fax 762-6623
www.msdwarco.k12.in.us/
Other Schools – See West Lebanon

Winamac, Pulaski, Pop. 2,467
Eastern Pulaski Community SC 1,300/K-12
711 School Dr 46996 574-946-4010
Dan L. Foster, supt. Fax 946-4510
www.epulaski.k12.in.us/
Winamac Community HS 400/9-12
715 School Dr 46996 574-946-6151
Rick Defries, prin. Fax 946-4219
Winamac Community MS 300/6-8
715 School Dr 46996 574-946-6525
Ryan Dickinson, prin. Fax 946-4219

Winchester, Randolph, Pop. 4,890
Randolph Central SC 1,500/K-12
103 N East St 47394 765-584-1401
Dr. Gregory Hinshaw, supt. Fax 584-1403
www.rc.k12.in.us
Driver MS 400/6-8
700 N Union St 47394 765-584-4671
Thomas Osborn, prin. Fax 584-8204
Winchester Community HS 500/9-12
700 N Union St 47394 765-584-8201
Tom Osborn, prin. Fax 584-8204

Winona Lake, Kosciusko, Pop. 4,854

Grace College & Seminary Post-Sec.
200 Seminary Dr 46590 574-372-5100
Lakeland Christian Academy 100/7-12
1093 S 250 E 46590 574-267-7265
Joy Lavender, admin. Fax 267-5687

Wolcott, White, Pop. 982
Tri-County SC 800/K-12
105 N 2nd St 47995 219-279-2418
Dr. Kathy Goad, supt. Fax 279-2242
www.trico.k12.in.us
Tri-County JSHS 400/7-12
11298 W 100 S 47995 219-279-2105
Cathy Rowe, prin. Fax 279-2108

Woodburn, Allen, Pop. 1,511
East Allen County SD
Supt. — See New Haven
Woodlan JSHS 700/7-12
17215 Woodburn Rd 46797 260-446-0290
Ron Kammeyer, prin. Fax 446-0298

Yorktown, Delaware, Pop. 9,307
Yorktown Community SC 2,400/K-12
2311 S Broadway St 47396 765-759-2720
Dr. Jennifer McCormick, supt. Fax 759-7894
www.yorktown.k12.in.us
Yorktown HS 800/9-12
1100 S Tiger Dr 47396 765-759-2550
Stacey Brewer, prin. Fax 759-4040
Yorktown MS 600/6-8
8820 W Smith St 47396 765-759-2660
Heath Dudley, prin. Fax 759-3243

Zionsville, Boone, Pop. 13,972
Zionsville Community SC 6,100/PK-12
900 Mulberry St 46077 317-873-2858
Scott Robison, supt. Fax 873-8003
www.zcs.k12.in.us
Zionsville Community HS 1,800/9-12
1000 Mulberry St 46077 317-873-3355
Tim East, prin. Fax 873-8002
Zionsville MS 1,000/5-8
900 N Ford Rd 46077 317-873-2426
Sean Conner, prin. Fax 733-4001
Other Schools – See Whitestown

IOWA

IOWA DEPARTMENT OF EDUCATION
400 E 14th St, Des Moines 50319-0146
Telephone 515-281-5294
Fax 515-242-5988
Website educateiowa.gov/

Director of Education Ryan Wise

IOWA BOARD OF EDUCATION
400 E 14th St, Des Moines 50319-1004

President Charles Edwards

AREA EDUCATION AGENCIES (AEA)

AEA 267
Sam Miller, admin. 319-273-8200
3712 Cedar Heights Dr Fax 273-8229
Cedar Falls 50613
www.aea267.k12.ia.us

Grant Wood AEA 10
, 4401 6th St SW 319-399-6700
Cedar Rapids 52404 Fax 399-6457
www.aea10.k12.ia.us/

Great Prairie AEA
Dr. Jon Sheldahl, admin. 641-682-8591
2814 N Court St, Ottumwa 52501 Fax 682-9083
www.gpaea.k12.ia.us

Green Hills AEA
Dr. Lane Plugge, admin. 712-366-0503
PO Box 1109, Council Bluffs 51502 Fax 366-7772
www.ghaea.org

Heartland AEA 11
Dr. Paula Vincent, admin. 515-270-9030
6500 Corporate Dr Fax 270-5383
Johnston 50131
www.heartlandaea.org

Keystone AEA 1
Patrick Heiderscheit, admin. 563-245-1480
1400 2nd St NW, Elkader 52043 Fax 245-1484
www.aea1.k12.ia.us

Mississippi Bend AEA 9
William Decker, admin. 563-359-1371
729 21st St, Bettendorf 52722 Fax 359-5967
www.mbaea.org

Northwest AEA
Dr. Tim Grieves, admin. 800-352-9040
1520 Morningside Ave Fax 222-6123
Sioux City 51106
www.nwaea.k12.ia.us/

Prairie Lakes AEA 8
Jeff Herzberg, admin. 712-335-3588
500 NE 6th St, Pocahontas 50574 Fax 335-4600
www.plaea.org

PUBLIC, PRIVATE AND CATHOLIC SECONDARY SCHOOLS

Ackley, Hardin, Pop. 1,584
AGWSR Community SD 600/PK-12
918 4th Ave 50601 641-847-2611
Marty Jimmerson, supt. Fax 847-2612
www.agwsr.org
AGWSR HS 200/9-12
918 4th Ave 50601 641-847-2633
Marty Jimmerson, prin. Fax 847-3345

Adair, Guthrie, Pop. 778
Adair-Casey Community SD 200/PK-8
3384 Indigo Ave 50002 641-746-2241
Steve Smith, supt. Fax 746-2243
acgcschools.org
AC/GC JHS 50/7-8
3384 Indigo Ave 50002 641-746-2241
Cynthia Jensen, prin. Fax 746-2243

Adel, Dallas, Pop. 3,654
Adel DeSoto Minburn Community SD 1,600/PK-12
215 N 11th St 50003 515-993-4283
Greg Dufoe, supt. Fax 993-1921
www.admschools.org
ADM HS 500/9-12
801 Nile Kinnick Dr S 50003 515-993-4584
Lee Greibel, prin. Fax 993-3025
ADM MS 400/6-8
801 Nile Kinnick Dr S 50003 515-993-3490
Kim Timmerman, prin. Fax 993-1956

Afton, Union, Pop. 842
East Union Community SD 500/PK-12
1916 High School Dr 50830 641-347-5215
Lance Ridgely, supt. Fax 347-5514
www.east-union.k12.ia.us
East Union MSHS 200/6-12
1916 High School Dr 50830 641-347-8421
Mark Weis, prin. Fax 347-5514

Akron, Plymouth, Pop. 1,468
Akron Westfield Community SD 600/PK-12
PO Box 950 51001 712-568-2616
Randy Collins, supt. Fax 568-2997
akron-westfield.com
Akron Westfield HS 200/9-12
PO Box 950 51001 712-568-2020
Derek Briggs, prin. Fax 568-2997
Akron Westfield MS 100/6-8
PO Box 950 51001 712-568-2020
Derek Briggs, prin. Fax 568-2997

Albia, Monroe, Pop. 3,726
Albia Community SD 1,200/PK-12
701 Washington Ave E 52531 641-932-2161
Kevin Crall, supt. Fax 932-5192
www.albia.k12.ia.us
Albia HS 400/9-12
503 B Ave E 52531 641-932-2161
Richard Montgomery, prin. Fax 932-7069
Albia JHS 200/7-8
503 B Ave E 52531 641-932-2161
Richard Montgomery, prin. Fax 932-7069

Alburnett, Linn, Pop. 663
Alburnett Community SD 500/PK-12
PO Box 400 52202 319-842-2266
Dani Trimble, supt. Fax 842-2398
www.alburnettcsd.org
Alburnett JSHS 200/6-12
PO Box 400 52202 319-842-2263
Ken Kasper, prin. Fax 842-2398

Algona, Kossuth, Pop. 5,513
Algona Community SD 1,400/PK-12
600 S Hale St 50511 515-295-3528
Marty Fonley, supt. Fax 295-5166
www.algona.k12.ia.us
Algona HS 400/9-12
601 S Hale St 50511 515-295-7207
Jared Cecil, prin. Fax 295-9273
Algona MS 400/5-8
601 S Hale St 50511 515-295-7207
James Rotert, prin. Fax 295-9273

Bishop Garrigan HS 200/4-12
1224 N McCoy St 50511 515-295-3521
Christina Peterson, prin. Fax 295-7739

Alleman, Polk, Pop. 426
North Polk Community SD 1,500/PK-12
13960 NE 6th Ave 50007 515-984-3400
Dr. Dan Mart, supt. Fax 685-2002
www.northpolk.org
North Polk HS 400/9-12
13960 NE 6th Ave 50007 515-984-3400
Derrick Joel, prin. Fax 685-2004
North Polk MS 300/6-8
315 NE 141st Ave 50007 515-984-3400
Jon Richards, prin. Fax 685-3520

Allison, Butler, Pop. 1,024
North Butler Community SD 400/PK-12
PO Box 428 50602 319-267-2205
Joel Foster, supt. Fax 267-2926
www.northbutler.k12.ia.us/
Other Schools – See Greene

Alta, Buena Vista, Pop. 1,871
Alta Community SD 500/PK-12
101 W 5th St 51002 712-200-1010
Lynn Evans, supt. Fax 200-1602
www.alta.k12.ia.us
Alta-Aurelia HS 200/9-12
1009 S Main St 51002 712-200-1331
Tom Ryherd, prin. Fax 200-1602

Alton, Sioux, Pop. 1,209
MOC-Floyd Valley Community SD
Supt. — See Orange City
MOC-Floyd Valley MS 300/6-8
1104 5th Ave 51003 712-756-4128
Cam Smith, prin. Fax 756-4100

Ames, Story, Pop. 57,846
Ames Community SD 4,400/PK-12
2005 24th St 50010 515-268-6600
Dr. Tim Taylor, supt. Fax 268-6633
www.ames.k12.ia.us
Ames HS 1,300/9-12
1921 Ames High Dr 50010 515-817-0600
Spence Evans, prin. Fax 817-0627
Ames MS 900/6-8
3915 Mortensen Rd 50014 515-268-2400
Pam Stangeland, prin. Fax 268-2419

Antioch School of Church Planting Post-Sec.
2400 Oakwood Rd 50014 515-292-9694
Iowa State University 50011 Post-Sec.
515-294-4111
Professional Cosmetology Institute Post-Sec.
309 Kitty Hawk Dr 50010 515-232-7250

Anamosa, Jones, Pop. 5,484
Anamosa Community SD 1,300/PK-12
200 S Garnavillo St 52205 319-462-4321
Lisa Beames, supt. Fax 462-4322
www.anamosa.k12.ia.us
Anamosa HS 400/9-12
209 Sadie St 52205 319-462-3594
Jacqueline Lahey, prin. Fax 462-2332
Anamosa MS 400/5-8
200 S Garnavillo St 52205 319-462-3553
Linda Vaughn, prin. Fax 462-3309

Andrew, Jackson, Pop. 431
Andrew Community SD 200/PK-8
PO Box 230 52030 563-672-3221
Chris Fee, supt. Fax 672-9750
www.andrew.k12.ia.us
Andrew MS 100/6-8
PO Box 230 52030 563-672-3221
Tara Notz, prin. Fax 672-9750

Anita, Cass, Pop. 970
CAM Community SD 400/PK-12
1000 Victory Park Rd 50020 712-762-3231
Dr. Casey Berlau, supt. Fax 762-3713
www.camcougars.org
CAM HS 100/9-12
1000 Victory Park Rd 50020 712-762-3231
Dominic Giegerich, prin. Fax 762-3713
Other Schools – See Massena

Ankeny, Polk, Pop. 45,034
Ankeny Community SD 10,500/PK-12
PO Box 189 50021 515-965-9600
Dr. Bruce Kimpston, supt. Fax 965-4234
www.ankenyschools.org
Ankeny Centennial HS 1,000/10-12
2220 NW State St, 515-965-9610
Dr. Jen Lindaman, prin. Fax 964-5070
Ankeny HS 900/10-12
1155 SW Cherry St, 515-965-9630
Dr. Jeff Hawkins, prin. Fax 965-2975
Northview MS 700/8-9
1302 N Ankeny Blvd, 515-965-9700
Bev Kuehn, prin. Fax 965-9639
Southview MS 600/8-9
1020 SW Cherry St, 515-965-9635
Dan Meyer, admin. Fax 965-9223

Ankeny Christian Academy 300/PK-12
1604 W 1st St, 515-965-8114
Dr. Steve Robinson, admin. Fax 965-8210
Des Moines Area Community College Post-Sec.
2006 S Ankeny Blvd, 515-964-6200
Faith Baptist Bible College Post-Sec.
1900 NW 4th St, 515-964-0601
INSTE Bible College Post-Sec.
2302 SW 3rd St, 515-289-9200

Anthon, Woodbury, Pop. 561
Maple Valley-Anthon Oto Community SD
Supt. — See Mapleton
Maple Valley-Anthon Oto MS 100/6-8
110 W Division St 51004 712-373-5244
Jane Ellis, prin. Fax 373-5326

Aplington, Butler, Pop. 1,123
Aplington-Parkersburg Community SD
Supt. — See Parkersburg
Aplington-Parkersburg MS 200/6-8
215 10th St 50604 319-347-6621
Brian Buseman, prin. Fax 347-2395

Arlington, Fayette, Pop. 428
Starmont Community SD 600/PK-12
3202 40th St 50606 563-933-4598
Troy Heller, supt. Fax 933-2134
www.starmont.k12.ia.us
Starmont HS 200/9-12
3202 40th St 50606 563-933-2218
Marc Snavely, prin. Fax 933-2134
Starmont MS 100/6-8
3202 40th St 50606 563-933-2218
Marc Snavely, prin. Fax 933-2134

Armstrong, Emmet, Pop. 919
North Union SD 600/PK-12
600 4th Ave 50514 515-868-3542
Travis Schueller, supt. Fax 868-3550
www.northunion.k12.ia.us
North Union HS 200/9-12
PO Box 75 50514 712-868-3542
Robert Zotz, prin. Fax 868-3550
Other Schools – See Swea City

Arnolds Park, Dickinson, Pop. 1,120
Okoboji Community SD
Supt. — See Milford
Okoboji MS 300/5-8
10 W Broadway St 51331 712-332-5641
Ryan Cunningham, prin. Fax 332-7180

Atlantic, Cass, Pop. 7,038
Atlantic Community SD 1,500/PK-12
1100 Linn St 50022 712-243-4252
Mike Amstein Ed.D., supt. Fax 243-8023
www.atlanticiaschools.org/
Atlantic HS 400/9-12
1201 E 14th St 50022 712-243-5358
Heather McKay, prin. Fax 243-8007
Atlantic MS 300/6-8
1100 Linn St 50022 712-243-1330
Josh Rasmussen, prin. Fax 243-7732
Cass County Educational Opportunity Ctr 50/Alt
1209 Sunnyside Ln 50022 712-243-3535
Fax 243-2208

Audubon, Audubon, Pop. 2,169
Audubon Community SD 600/PK-12
800 3rd Ave 50025 712-563-2607
Brett Gibbs, supt. Fax 563-3607
www.audubon.k12.ia.us/
Audubon MSHS 300/5-12
800 3rd Ave 50025 712-563-2607
Eric Trager, prin. Fax 563-3607

Aurelia, Cherokee, Pop. 1,026
Aurelia Community SD 300/PK-8
PO Box 367 51005 712-434-2284
Lynn Evans, supt. Fax 434-2053
www.aurelia.k12.ia.us
Aurelia MS 200/5-8
PO Box 367 51005 712-434-5595
Jeannie Henningsen, prin. Fax 434-2053

Avoca, Pottawattamie, Pop. 1,501
AHSTW Community SD 600/PK-12
PO Box 158 51521 712-343-6364
Jesse Ulrich, supt. Fax 343-2170
www.ahstwschools.org
AHSTW HS 300/7-12
PO Box 158 51521 712-343-6364
Cynthia Phillips, prin. Fax 343-6915

Baxter, Jasper, Pop. 1,091
Baxter Community SD 400/K-12
PO Box 189 50028 641-227-3102
Todd Martin, supt. Fax 227-3217
www.baxter.k12.ia.us
Baxter JSHS 200/6-12
PO Box 189 50028 641-227-3103
Robert Luther, prin. Fax 227-3217

Bedford, Taylor, Pop. 1,430
Bedford Community SD 500/PK-12
PO Box 234 50833 712-523-2656
Joe Drake, supt. Fax 523-3166
www.bedford.k12.ia.us
Bedford MSHS 200/6-12
PO Box 234 50833 712-523-2656
Michael Irvin, prin. Fax 523-2308

Belle Plaine, Benton, Pop. 2,512
Belle Plaine Community SD 600/PK-12
707 7th St 52208 319-444-3611
Chad Straight, supt. Fax 444-3617
www.belle-plaine.k12.ia.us
Belle Plaine JSHS 200/7-12
610 13th Ave 52208 319-444-3720
Todd Werner, prin. Fax 444-4507

Bellevue, Jackson, Pop. 2,180
Bellevue Community SD 700/PK-12
1601 State St 52031 563-872-4913
Dr. Tom Meyer, supt. Fax 872-3216
www.bellevue.k12.ia.us
Bellevue MSHS 300/7-12
1601 State St 52031 563-872-4001
Jeff Recker, prin. Fax 872-3298

Marquette HS 100/PK-12
502 Franklin St 52031 563-872-3356
Geoffery Kaiser, prin. Fax 872-3285

Belmond, Wright, Pop. 2,355
Belmond-Klemme Community SD 800/PK-12
411 10th Ave NE 50421 641-444-4300
Abraham Maske, supt. Fax 444-4524
www.bkcsd.org
Belmond-Klemme Alternative S 50/Alt
411 10th Ave NE 50421 641-444-4300
Eric Dockstader, prin. Fax 444-4097
Belmond-Klemme Community JSHS 300/7-12
411 10th Ave NE 50421 641-444-4300
Eric Dockstader, prin. Fax 444-4097

Bettendorf, Scott, Pop. 32,699
Bettendorf Community SD 4,500/PK-12
PO Box 1150 52722 563-359-3681
Michael Raso, supt. Fax 359-3685
www.bettendorf.k12.ia.us
Bettendorf HS 1,500/9-12
3333 18th St 52722 563-332-7001
Jimmy Casas, prin. Fax 332-2326
Bettendorf MS 1,000/6-8
2030 Middle Rd 52722 563-359-3686
Lisa Reid, prin. Fax 359-3855
Edison Academy Alt
438 16th St 52722 563-359-9375
Tammy Chelf, coord. Fax 359-5565

Pleasant Valley Community SD 4,300/PK-12
525 Belmont Rd 52722 563-332-5550
Jim Spelhaug, supt. Fax 332-4372
www.pleasval.k12.ia.us
Other Schools – See Le Claire, Riverdale

Morning Star Academy 200/PK-12
1426 Tanglefoot Ln 52722 563-359-5700
Rob Spykstra, hdmstr. Fax 359-5737
Rivermont Collegiate 200/PK-12
1821 Sunset Dr 52722 563-359-1366
Max Roach, hdmstr. Fax 359-7576
Scott Community College Post-Sec.
500 Belmont Rd 52722 563-441-4001

Bloomfield, Davis, Pop. 2,620
Davis County Community SD 1,300/PK-12
608 S Washington St 52537 641-664-2200
Dan Maeder, supt. Fax 664-2221
www.dcmustangs.com/
Davis County HS 400/9-12
503 E Locust St 52537 641-664-2200
Jeff Graves, prin. Fax 664-1763
Davis County MS 300/5-8
500 E North St 52537 641-664-2200
Brad Nelson, prin. Fax 664-1767

Bondurant, Polk, Pop. 3,802
Bondurant-Farrar Community SD 1,100/PK-12
300 Garfield St SW 50035 515-967-7819
Dr. Richard Powers, supt. Fax 967-7847
www.bondurant.k12.ia.us/
Bondurant-Farrar HS 400/9-12
1000 Grant St N 50035 515-957-8191
Erik Garnass, prin. Fax 957-8224
Bondurant-Farrar MS 400/6-8
300 Garfield St SW 50035 515-967-3711
Mike Kramer, prin. Fax 957-9924

Boone, Boone, Pop. 12,525
Boone Community SD 2,100/PK-12
500 7th St 50036 515-433-0750
Dr. Bradley Manard, supt. Fax 433-0753
boone.k12.ia.us/
Boone HS 700/9-12
400 7th St 50036 515-433-0890
Kristopher Byam, prin. Fax 433-0989
Boone MS 600/5-8
1640 1st St 50036 515-433-0020
Scott Kelley, prin. Fax 433-0026
Futures HS 50/Alt
727 W Mamie Eisenhower Ave 50036 515-433-0885
Kristopher Byam, prin. Fax 433-0753

Des Moines Area Community College Post-Sec.
1125 Hancock Dr 50036 515-432-7203

Britt, Hancock, Pop. 2,051
West Hancock Community SD 700/PK-12
PO Box 278 50423 641-843-3833
Wayne Kronemann, supt. Fax 843-4717
www.whancock.org/
West Hancock HS 200/9-12
PO Box 278 50423 641-843-3863
Dan Peterson, prin. Fax 843-4633
Other Schools – See Kanawha

Brooklyn, Poweshiek, Pop. 1,455
Brooklyn-Guernsey-Malcom Community SD 600/PK-12
1090 Jackson St 52211 641-522-7058
Brad Hohensee, supt. Fax 522-7211
www.brooklyn.k12.ia.us
Brooklyn-Guernsey-Malcom JSHS 300/7-12
1090 Jackson St 52211 641-522-7058
Rick Radcliffe, prin. Fax 522-7211

Buffalo Center, Winnebago, Pop. 902
North Iowa Community SD 500/PK-12
111 3rd Ave NW 50424 641-562-2525
Cory Myer, supt. Fax 562-2921
www.northiowa.org
North Iowa HS 200/9-12
111 3rd Ave NW 50424 641-562-2525
Keri Bergeson, prin. Fax 562-2921
North Iowa MS 100/5-8
111 3rd Ave NW 50424 641-562-2525
Jill Schutjer, prin. Fax 562-2921

Burlington, Des Moines, Pop. 24,989
Burlington Community SD 3,800/PK-12
1429 West Ave 52601 319-753-6791
Patrick Coen, supt. Fax 753-6796
www.bcsds.org
Burlington Alternative HS 100/Alt
349 Terrace Dr 52601 319-753-5092
David Keane, prin. Fax 753-6962
Burlington Community HS 1,100/9-12
421 Terrace Dr 52601 319-753-2211
David Keane, prin. Fax 753-6634
Leopold MS 400/6-8
3075 Sunnyside Ave 52601 319-752-8390
Mark Yeoman, prin. Fax 752-8447
Stone MS 6-8
3000 Mason Rd 52601 319-752-4393
Brian Johnson, prin. Fax 752-7437

Great River Christian S 100/PK-12
426 Harrison Ave 52601 319-753-2255
Jon Frischkorn, admin. Fax 753-2030
Notre Dame HS 200/6-12
702 S Roosevelt Ave 52601 319-754-8431
Bill Maupin, prin. Fax 752-8690

Burnside, Webster
Southeast Webster-Grand Community SD 300/PK-8
PO Box 49 50521 515-359-2235
Brian Johnson, supt. Fax 359-2236
www.se-webster.k12.ia.us
Other Schools – See Dayton

Bussey, Marion, Pop. 420
Twin Cedars Community SD 400/PK-12
2204 Highway G71 50044 641-944-5241
Brian VanderSluis, supt. Fax 944-5824
www.twincedarscsd.org
Twin Cedars JSHS 200/7-12
2204 Highway G71 50044 641-944-5243
David Roby, prin. Fax 944-5225

Calmar, Winneshiek, Pop. 970
South Winneshiek Community SD 500/PK-12
PO Box 430 52132 563-562-3269
Kris Einck, supt. Fax 562-3260
www.southwinn.com
South Winneshiek HS 200/9-12
PO Box 430 52132 563-562-3269
Kris Einck, prin. Fax 562-3228
Other Schools – See Ossian

Northeast Iowa Community College Post-Sec.
PO Box 400 52132 563-562-3263

Camanche, Clinton, Pop. 4,417
Camanche Community SD 1,100/PK-12
702 13th Ave 52730 563-259-3000
Thomas Parker, supt. Fax 259-3005
www.camanche.k12.ia.us
Camanche HS 300/9-12
937 9th Ave 52730 563-259-3008
Chuck Wiebenga, prin. Fax 259-3048
Camanche MS 300/5-8
1400 9th St 52730 563-259-3014
Justin Shaffer, prin. Fax 259-3031

Carlisle, Warren, Pop. 3,818
Carlisle Community SD 2,100/PK-12
430 School St 50047 515-989-3589
Bryce Amos, supt. Fax 989-3075
carlislecsd.org
Carlisle HS 600/9-12
430 School St 50047 515-989-0831
Matthew Blackmore, prin. Fax 989-3075
Carlisle MS 500/6-8
325 Scotch Ridge Rd 50047 515-989-0833
John Elkin, prin. Fax 989-4521

Carroll, Carroll, Pop. 9,988
Carroll Community SD 1,500/PK-12
1026 N Adams St 51401 712-792-8001
Rob Cordes, supt. Fax 792-8008
www.carroll.k12.ia.us
Carroll HS 500/9-12
2809 N Grant Rd 51401 712-792-8010
Tammie McKenzie, prin. Fax 792-8118
Carroll MS 400/5-8
3203 N Grant Rd 51401 712-792-8020
Jerry Raymond, prin. Fax 792-8024

Des Moines Area Community College Post-Sec.
906 N Grant Rd 51401 712-792-1755
Kuemper Catholic HS 300/9-12
109 S Clark St 51401 712-792-3596
Pete Haefs, prin. Fax 792-8070
Kuemper Catholic MS 200/6-8
1519 N West St 51401 712-792-2123
Ted Garringer, prin. Fax 792-3365

Carson, Pottawattamie, Pop. 809
Riverside Community SD 700/PK-12
PO Box 218 51525 712-484-2212
Dr. Timothy Mitchell, supt. Fax 484-3957
www.riversideschools.org
Other Schools – See Oakland

Cascade, Dubuque, Pop. 2,146
Western Dubuque Community SD
Supt. — See Farley
Cascade JSHS 400/7-12
505 Johnson St NW 52033 563-852-3201
Greg VanderLugt, prin. Fax 852-7186

Cedar Falls, Black Hawk, Pop. 38,680
Cedar Falls Community SD 5,200/PK-12
1002 W 1st St 50613 319-553-3000
Dr. Andy Pattee, supt. Fax 277-0614
www.cfschools.org/
Cedar Falls SHS 1,100/10-12
1015 Division St 50613 319-553-2500
Jason Wedgbury, prin. Fax 277-4604
Holmes JHS 600/7-9
505 Holmes Dr 50613 319-553-2650
Jeremy Jones, prin. Fax 277-0571
Peet JHS 600/7-9
525 E Seerley Blvd 50613 319-553-2710
Bill Boevers, prin. Fax 266-8839

Kaplan University Post-Sec.
7009 Nordic Dr 50613 319-277-0220
La' James International College Post-Sec.
6322 University Ave 50613 319-277-2150
University of Northern Iowa Post-Sec.
1227 W 27th St 50614 319-273-2311
Valley Lutheran S 100/K-12
4520 Rownd St 50613 319-266-4565
Brian L'Heureux, head sch Fax 266-4054

Cedar Rapids, Linn, Pop. 122,869
Cedar Rapids Community SD 16,400/PK-12
2500 Edgewood Rd NW 52405 319-558-2000
Dr. Brad Buck, supt.
www.cr.k12.ia.us
Franklin MS, 300 20th St NE 52402 600/6-8
Lucas Ptacek, prin. 319-558-2452
Harding MS, 4801 Golf St NE 52402 800/6-8
Linda Reysack, prin. 319-558-2254
Jefferson HS, 1243 20th St SW 52404 1,500/9-12
Charles McDonnell, prin. 319-558-2435
Kennedy HS 1,700/9-12
4545 Wenig Rd NE 52402 319-558-2251
Jason Kline, prin.
McKinley MS 500/6-8
620 10th St SE 52403 319-558-2348
Jason Martinez, prin. Fax 398-2347
Metro HS, 1212 7th St SE 52401 400/Alt
Brian Galusha, prin. 319-558-2193
Polk Alternative Education Center Alt
1500 B Ave NE 52402 319-558-2475
Deb Scott, dir.
Roosevelt MS, 300 13th St NW 52405 600/6-8
Autumn Pino, prin. 319-558-2153
Taft MS, 5200 E Ave NW 52405 600/6-8
Gary Hatfield, prin. 319-558-2243
Washington HS 1,400/9-12
2205 Forest Dr SE 52403 319-558-2161
Dr. Ralph Plagman, prin.
Wilson MS, 2301 J St SW 52404 400/6-8
Andrew Eley, prin. 319-558-2156

College Community SD 5,200/PK-12
401 76th Ave SW 52404 319-848-5200
John Speer, supt. Fax 848-4019
www.prairiepride.org
Prairie HS 1,000/10-12
401 76th Ave SW 52404 319-848-5340
Erik Anderson, prin. Fax 848-5201
Prairie Point MS/9th Grade Academy 1,100/7-9
401 76th Ave SW 52404 319-848-5500
Kyle Koeppen, prin. Fax 848-5520

Capri College Post-Sec.
2945 Williams Pkwy SW 52404 319-364-1541
Cedar Valley Christian S 200/PK-12
3636 Cottage Grove Ave SE 52403 319-366-7462
Jeffrey Pospisil, prin. Fax 247-0037
Coe College Post-Sec.
1220 1st Ave NE 52402 319-399-8000
Holy Family - LaSalle MS 100/6-8
3700 1st Ave NW 52405 319-396-7792
Kimberly Graven, prin. Fax 390-6527
Kaplan University Post-Sec.
3165 Edgewood Pkwy SW 52404 319-363-0481
Kirkwood Community College Post-Sec.
PO Box 2068 52406 319-398-5411
Mercy-St. Luke's Hospital Post-Sec.
1026 A Ave NE 52402 319-369-7204
Mt. Mercy University Post-Sec.
1330 Elmhurst Dr NE 52402 319-363-8213
Regis MS 500/6-8
735 Prairie Dr NE 52402 319-363-1968
Beth Globokar, prin. Fax 247-6099
Xavier HS 800/9-12
6300 42nd St NE 52411 319-294-6635
Tom Keating, prin. Fax 294-6712

Center Point, Linn, Pop. 2,394
Center Point-Urbana Community SD 1,500/PK-12
PO Box 296 52213 319-849-1102
Matt Berninghaus, supt. Fax 849-2312
www.cpuschools.org/
Center Point-Urbana HS 400/9-12
PO Box 296 52213 319-849-1102
Rob Libolt, prin. Fax 849-2068
Center Point-Urbana MS 300/6-8
PO Box 296 52213 319-849-1102
Brent Winterhof, prin. Fax 443-2764

Centerville, Appanoose, Pop. 5,460
Centerville Community SD 1,400/PK-12
PO Box 370 52544 641-856-0601
Anthony Ryan, supt. Fax 856-0656
www.centervilleschools.org
Appanoose County Campus 50/Alt
PO Box 370 52544 641-856-0890
Roger Raum, prin.
Centerville HS 400/9-12
600 CHS Dr 52544 641-856-0813
Roger Raum, prin. Fax 856-0809
Howar JHS 200/7-8
850 S Park Ave 52544 641-856-0760
Bruce Karpen, prin. Fax 856-0761

Indian Hills Community College Post-Sec.
721 N 1st St 52544 641-856-2143

Central City, Linn, Pop. 1,249
Central City Community SD 400/PK-12
400 Barber St 52214 319-438-6181
Dr. Tim Cronin, supt. Fax 438-6110
www.central-city.k12.ia.us
Central City HS 100/9-12
400 Barber St 52214 319-438-6181
Jason McLaughlin, prin. Fax 438-6110
Central City MS 100/7-8
400 Barber St 52214 319-438-6181
Jason McLaughlin, prin. Fax 438-6110

Chariton, Lucas, Pop. 4,293
Chariton Community SD 1,300/PK-12
PO Box 738 50049 641-774-5967
Paula Wright, supt. Fax 774-8511
www.chariton.k12.ia.us/
Chariton HS 400/9-12
501 N Grand St 50049 641-774-5066
Tracy Hall, prin. Fax 774-3404
Chariton MS 300/6-8
1300 N 16th St 50049 641-774-5114
Joe Ortega, prin. Fax 774-4109

Charles City, Floyd, Pop. 7,583
Charles City Community SD 1,200/PK-12
500 N Grand Ave 50616 641-257-6500
Dr. Dan Cox, supt. Fax 257-6509
www.charlescityschools.org
Charles City HS 500/9-12
1 Comet Dr 50616 641-257-6510
Josh Johnson, prin. Fax 257-1175
Charles City MS 400/5-8
1200 1st Ave 50616 641-257-6530
Rick Gabel, prin. Fax 228-9842

Charter Oak, Crawford, Pop. 501
Charter Oak-Ute Community SD 300/PK-12
321 Main St 51439 712-678-3325
Rollie Wiebers, supt. Fax 678-3626
co-u.net
Charter Oak-Ute HS 100/9-12
321 Main St 51439 712-678-3325
Adam Eggeling, prin. Fax 678-3626
Charter Oak-Ute JHS 100/6-8
321 Main St 51439 712-678-3325
Adam Eggeling, prin. Fax 678-3626

Cherokee, Cherokee, Pop. 5,205
Cherokee Community SD 1,000/PK-12
600 W Bluff St 51012 712-225-6767
Kimberly Lingenfelter, supt. Fax 225-6769
www.ccsd.k12.ia.us/
Cherokee MS 300/5-8
206 Indian St 51012 712-225-6750
Neil Phipps, prin. Fax 225-4841
Washington HS 300/9-12
600 W Bluff St 51012 712-225-6755
Scot Aden, prin. Fax 225-6765

Churdan, Greene, Pop. 379
Paton-Churdan Community SD 200/PK-12
PO Box 157 50050 515-389-3111
Kreg Lensch, supt. Fax 389-3113
www.paton-churdan.k12.ia.us
Paton-Churdan JSHS 100/6-12
PO Box 157 50050 515-389-3111
Annie Smith, prin. Fax 389-3113

Clarence, Cedar, Pop. 966
North Cedar Community SD
Supt. — See Stanwood
North Cedar JSHS 300/7-12
PO Box 310 52216 563-452-3179
Mary Bendixen, prin. Fax 452-3972

Clarinda, Page, Pop. 5,483
Clarinda Community SD 1,200/PK-12
PO Box 59 51632 712-542-5165
Deron Stender, supt. Fax 542-3802
www.clarinda.k12.ia.us
Clarinda HS 300/9-12
PO Box 59 51632 712-542-5167
Teresa Nook, prin. Fax 542-4305
Clarinda MS 300/5-8
PO Box 59 51632 712-542-2132
Josh Porter, prin. Fax 542-5949

Iowa Western Community College Post-Sec.
923 E Washington St 51632 712-542-5117

Clarion, Wright, Pop. 2,837
Clarion-Goldfield-Dows Community SD 1,000/PK-12
319 3rd Ave NE 50525 515-532-3423
Dr. Robert Olson, supt. Fax 532-2628
www.clargold.org
Clarion-Goldfield-Dows HS 300/9-12
1111 Willow Dr 50525 515-532-2895
Erik Smith, prin. Fax 532-2897
Clarion-Goldfield-Dows MS 200/6-8
300 3rd Ave NE 50525 515-532-2412
Steve Haberman, prin. Fax 532-2741

Clarksville, Butler, Pop. 1,422
Clarksville Community SD 300/PK-12
318 N Mather St 50619 319-278-4008
Randy Strabala, supt. Fax 278-4618
www.clarksville.k12.ia.us/
Clarksville JSHS 100/7-12
318 N Mather St 50619 319-278-4273
Robert Saathoff, prin. Fax 278-4981

Clear Lake, Cerro Gordo, Pop. 7,667
Clear Lake Community SD 1,500/PK-12
1529 3rd Ave N 50428 641-357-2181
Doug Gee, supt. Fax 357-2182
www.clearlakeschools.org
Clear Lake HS 400/9-12
125 N 20th St 50428 641-357-5235
Chris Murphy, prin. Fax 357-6218
Clear Lake MS 300/6-8
1601 3rd Ave N 50428 641-357-6114
Steve Kwikkel, prin. Fax 357-8353

Clinton, Clinton, Pop. 26,311
Clinton Community SD 2,800/PK-12
1401 12th Ave N 52732 563-243-9600
Deborah Olson, supt. Fax 243-2415
www.clinton.k12.ia.us
Clinton HS 1,100/9-12
817 8th Ave S 52732 563-243-7540
John Ryan Kuch, prin. Fax 243-9612
Clinton MS, 1350 14th St NW 52732 6-8
Dan Boyd, prin. 563-243-0466

Ashford University Post-Sec.
1310 19th Ave NW 52732 866-711-1700
Clinton Community College Post-Sec.
1000 Lincoln Blvd 52732 563-244-7000
Prince of Peace Catholic S 300/PK-12
312 S 4th St 52732 563-242-1663
Nancy Peart, prin. Fax 243-8272

Clive, Polk, Pop. 15,239
West Des Moines Community SD
Supt. — See West Des Moines
Indian Hills JHS 700/7-8
9401 Indian Hills Dr 50325 515-633-4700
Shane Christensen, prin. Fax 633-4799

Colfax, Jasper, Pop. 2,079
Colfax-Mingo Community SD 700/PK-12
204 N League Rd 50054 515-674-3646
Tracy Hook, supt. Fax 674-3921
www.colfax-mingo.k12.ia.us
Colfax-Mingo JSHS 300/7-12
204 N League Rd 50054 515-674-4111
Todd Jones, prin. Fax 674-4940

College Springs, Page, Pop. 207
South Page Community SD 200/PK-12
PO Box 98 51637 712-582-3212
Gregg Cruickshank, supt. Fax 582-3217
www.southpageschools.com
South Page JSHS 100/6-12
PO Box 98 51637 712-582-3211
Denise Green, prin. Fax 582-3217

Colo, Story, Pop. 872
Colo-Nesco Comm SD 500/PK-12
PO Box 136 50056 641-377-2282
Steve Gray, supt. Fax 377-2283
www.colo-nesco.k12.ia.us
Colo-Nesco MSHS 200/5-12
PO Box 136 50056 641-377-2282
Brandon Kelley, prin. Fax 377-2283

Columbus Junction, Louisa, Pop. 1,878
Columbus Community SD 800/PK-12
1208 Colton St 52738 319-728-2911
Gary Benda, supt. Fax 728-8750
www.columbuscsd.org
Columbus Community HS 200/9-12
1004 Colton St 52738 319-728-2231
Gary Benda, prin. Fax 728-2205
Columbus Community JHS 100/6-8
1004 Colton St 52738 319-728-2233
Gary Benda, prin. Fax 728-2205

Conrad, Grundy, Pop. 1,100
BCLUW Community SD 600/K-12
PO Box 670 50621 641-366-2819
Ben Petty, supt. Fax 366-2175
www.bcluw.k12.ia.us
BCLUW HS 200/9-12
PO Box 670 50621 641-366-2810
Kristyn Kell, prin. Fax 366-2951
Other Schools – See Union

Coon Rapids, Carroll, Pop. 1,296
Coon Rapids-Bayard Community SD 400/PK-12
PO Box 297 50058 712-999-2207
Brett Gibbs, supt. Fax 999-7740
www.crbcrusaders.org
Coon Rapids-Bayard Intermediate JSHS 200/5-12
PO Box 297 50058 712-999-2208
Larry Frakes, prin. Fax 999-7740

Coralville, Johnson, Pop. 18,406
Iowa City Community SD
Supt. — See Iowa City
Northwest JHS 700/7-8
1507 8th St 52241 319-688-1060
Laura Cottrell, prin. Fax 688-1069

Corning, Adams, Pop. 1,626
Southwest Valley SD
Supt. — See Villisca
Southwest Valley HS 200/9-12
904 8th St 50841 641-322-4245
James Craig, prin. Fax 322-5149

Correctionville, Woodbury, Pop. 815
River Valley Community SD 400/PK-12
PO Box 8 51016 712-372-4420
Ken Slater, supt. Fax 372-4677
www.rvwolverines.org
River Valley JSHS 200/7-12
PO Box 8 51016 712-372-4656
Wade Riley, prin. Fax 372-4784

Corydon, Wayne, Pop. 1,578
Wayne Community SD 600/PK-12
102 N Dekalb St 50060 641-872-2184
Dave Daughton, supt. Fax 872-2091
www.wayne.k12.ia.us
Wayne Community JSHS 200/7-12
102 N Dekalb St 50060 641-872-2184
Stacy Snyder, prin. Fax 872-2091

Council Bluffs, Pottawattamie, Pop. 61,150
Council Bluffs Community SD 8,900/PK-12
300 W Broadway Ste 1600 51503 712-328-6446
Dr. Martha Bruckner, supt. Fax 328-6548
www.cb-schools.org
Jefferson HS 1,200/9-12
2501 W Broadway 51501 712-328-6493
Todd Barnett, prin. Fax 328-6497
Kanesville Alternative Learning Ctr 300/Alt
207 Scott St 51503 712-328-6510
Mike McLaughlin, prin. Fax 328-6511
Kirn MS 900/6-8
100 North Ave 51503 712-328-6454
Kerry Newman, prin. Fax 328-6554
Lincoln HS 1,300/9-12
1205 Bonham St 51503 712-328-6481
Bridgette Bellows, prin. Fax 328-6485
Tucker Career & College Center Vo/Tech
815 N 18th St 51501 712-328-6408
Cyle Forney, prin. Fax 328-6425
Wilson MS 900/6-8
715 N 21st St 51501 712-328-6476
Kim Kazmierczak, prin. Fax 328-6479

Lewis Central Community SD 3,200/PK-12
4121 Harry Langdon Blvd 51503 712-366-8202
Dr. Mark Schweer, supt. Fax 366-8315
www.lewiscentral.org/
Lewis Central HS 1,000/9-12
3504 Harry Langdon Blvd 51503 712-366-8322
Joel Beyenhof, prin. Fax 366-8340
Lewis Central MS 700/6-8
3820 Harry Langdon Blvd 51503 712-366-8251
Jim Dermody, prin. Fax 366-8324

EQ School of Hair Design Post-Sec.
536 W Broadway 51503 712-328-2613
Heartland Christian S 100/PK-12
400 Wright Rd 51501 712-322-5817
Gary Wilson, dir. Fax 322-4287
Iowa School for the Deaf Post-Sec.
3501 Harry Langdon Blvd 51503 712-366-0571
Iowa Western Community College Post-Sec.
2700 College Rd 51503 712-325-3200
Jennie Edmundson Memorial Hospital Post-Sec.
933 E Pierce St 51503 712-328-6239
St. Albert HS 300/7-12
400 Gleason Ave 51503 712-328-2316
Paul Hans, prin. Fax 328-8316

Cresco, Howard, Pop. 3,829
Howard-Winneshiek Community SD 900/PK-12
1000 Schroder Dr 52136 563-547-2762
John Carver, supt. Fax 547-5973
www.howard-winn.k12.ia.us
Crestwood Alternative S 50/Alt
1000 Schroder Dr 52136 563-547-2764
Terese Jurgensen, dir.
Crestwood HS 400/9-12
1000 Schroder Dr 52136 563-547-2764
Christopher Rogne, prin. Fax 547-4650

Total Look Sch of Cosmetology & Massage Post-Sec.
806 3rd St W 52136 563-547-3624

Creston, Union, Pop. 7,756
Creston Community SD 1,500/PK-12
801 N Elm St 50801 641-782-7028
Steve McDermott, supt. Fax 782-7020
www.crestonschools.org
Creston HS 500/9-12
601 W Townline St 50801 641-782-2116
Bill Messerole, prin. Fax 782-9502
Creston MS 300/6-8
805 Academic Ave 50801 641-782-2129
Brad Baker, prin. Fax 782-6983

Southwestern Community College Post-Sec.
1501 W Townline St 50801 641-782-7081

Dakota City, Humboldt, Pop. 834
Humboldt Community SD 1,400/PK-12
PO Box 130 50529 515-332-1330
Greg Darling, supt. Fax 332-4478
www.humboldt.k12.ia.us
Other Schools – See Humboldt

Dallas Center, Dallas, Pop. 1,610
Dallas Center-Grimes Community SD 2,600/PK-12
PO Box 512 50063 515-992-3866
Scott Grimes, supt. Fax 992-3079
dcgschools.com
Other Schools – See Grimes

Danville, Des Moines, Pop. 929
Danville Community SD 600/PK-12
419 S Main St 52623 319-392-4223
Gary DeLacy, supt. Fax 392-8390
www.danvillecsd.org
Danville JSHS 300/7-12
419 S Main St 52623 319-392-4222
John Lawrence, prin. Fax 392-8704

Davenport, Scott, Pop. 96,534
Davenport Community SD 15,400/PK-12
1606 Brady St 52803 563-445-5000
Arthur Tate, supt. Fax 445-5950
www.davenportschools.org
Central HS 1,400/9-12
1120 N Main St 52803 563-723-5400
Scott McKissick, prin. Fax 445-5952
Keystone Academy Davenport Learning Ctr 200/Alt
1002 W Kimberly Rd 52806 563-336-7650
Alvin Blocker, prin. Fax 445-5956
Mid City HS 9-12
3801 Marquette St 52806 563-336-7600
Dr. Jake Klipsch, prin. Fax 445-5955
North HS 1,000/9-12
626 W 53rd St 52806 563-723-5500
Jay Chelf, prin. Fax 445-5953
Smart IS 500/6-8
1934 W 5th St 52802 563-445-5100
Jim Caparula, prin. Fax 445-5957
Sudlow IS 700/6-8
1414 E Locust St 52803 563-445-5150
Marianne Corbin, prin. Fax 445-5958
West HS 1,900/9-12
3505 W Locust St 52804 563-723-5600
Virginia Weipert, prin. Fax 445-5954
Williams IS 700/6-8
3040 N Division St 52804 563-445-5250
Garet Egel, prin. Fax 445-5960
Wood IS 700/6-8
5701 N Division St 52806 563-445-5300
Sheri Simpson-Schultz, prin. Fax 445-5961
Other Schools – See Walcott

Assumption HS 400/9-12
1020 W Central Park Ave 52804 563-326-5313
Bridget Murphy, prin. Fax 326-3510
Capri College Post-Sec.
2540 E 53rd St 52807 563-388-6642
Hamilton Technical College Post-Sec.
1011 E 53rd St 52807 563-386-3570
Kaplan University Post-Sec.
1801 E Kimberly Rd Ste 1 52807 563-355-3500
La' James College of Hairstyling Post-Sec.
5205 N Brady St 52806 563-441-7900
Palmer College of Chiropractic Post-Sec.
1000 Brady St 52803 563-884-5000
St. Ambrose University Post-Sec.
518 W Locust St 52803 563-333-6000

Dayton, Webster, Pop. 832
Southeast Webster-Grand Community SD
Supt. — See Burnside
Southeast Valley MS 100/5-8
30850 Paragon Ave 50530 515-359-2235
Dan Fox, prin. Fax 359-2236

Decorah, Winneshiek, Pop. 8,056
Decorah Community SD 1,600/PK-12
510 Winnebago St 52101 563-382-4208
Michael Haluska, supt. Fax 387-0753
decorah.k12.ia.us/
Decorah HS 600/9-12
100 Claiborne Dr 52101 563-382-3643
Kim Sheppard, prin. Fax 382-3107
Decorah MS 500/5-8
405 Winnebago St 52101 563-382-8427
Leona Hoth, prin. Fax 387-4052

North Winneshiek Community SD 200/PK-8
3495 N Winn Rd 52101 563-735-5411
Tim Dugger, supt. Fax 735-5430
www.n-winn.k12.ia.us/
North Winneshiek MS 50/6-8
3495 N Winn Rd 52101 563-735-5411
Cheryl Miller, prin. Fax 735-5430

Luther College Post-Sec.
700 College Dr 52101 563-387-2000

Delhi, Delaware, Pop. 456
Maquoketa Valley Community SD 700/PK-12
PO Box 186 52223 563-922-9422
Doug Tuetken, supt. Fax 922-9502
www.maquoketa-v.k12.ia.us
Maquoketa Valley HS 200/9-12
PO Box 186 52223 563-922-2091
Doug Tuetken, prin. Fax 922-3026
Maquoketa Valley MS 200/6-8
PO Box 186 52223 563-922-9411
Tracy Morrison, prin. Fax 922-9502

Denison, Crawford, Pop. 8,238
Denison Community SD 2,100/K-12
819 N 16th St 51442 712-263-2176
Michael Pardun, supt. Fax 263-5233
www.denison.k12.ia.us
Denison Alternative HS 50/Alt
10 Opportunity Dr 51442 712-265-2349
Dave Wiebers, prin. Fax 265-2397
Denison HS 700/9-12
819 N 16th St 51442 712-263-3101
Dave Wiebers, prin. Fax 263-6009
Denison MS 500/6-8
1201 N 16th St 51442 712-263-9393
Scott Moran, prin. Fax 263-5418

Denver, Bremer, Pop. 1,773
Denver Community SD 800/PK-12
PO Box 384 50622 319-984-6323
Brad Laures, supt. Fax 984-5345
www.denver.k12.ia.us
Denver HS 200/9-12
PO Box 384 50622 319-984-5639
Paul Gebel, prin. Fax 984-5630
Denver MS 200/6-8
PO Box 384 50622 319-984-6041
Paul Gebel, prin. Fax 984-5630

Des Moines, Polk, Pop. 197,701
Des Moines Independent Community SD 32,900/PK-12
2323 Grand Ave 50312 515-242-7911
Thomas Ahart, supt. Fax 242-7679
www.dmschools.org
Brody MS 700/6-8
2501 Park Ave 50321 515-242-8443
Thomas Hoffman, prin. Fax 244-0927
Callanan MS 600/6-8
3010 Center St 50312 515-242-8101
Dawn Stahly, prin. Fax 242-8103
Des Moines Alternative Center Alt
1801 Grand Ave 50309 515-242-7781
Randi Oleson, prin. Fax 323-8617
Des Moines Central Campus 50/Alt
1800 Grand Ave 50309 515-242-7846
Aiddy Phomvisay, dir. Fax 242-7598
East HS 2,300/9-12
815 E 13th St 50316 515-242-7788
Morris Leslie, prin. Fax 242-7958
Goodrell MS 600/6-8
3300 E 29th St 50317 515-242-8444
Peter LeBlanc, prin. Fax 264-9057
Harding MS 700/6-8
203 E Euclid Ave 50313 515-242-8445
Joy Linquist, prin. Fax 244-3566
Hiatt MS 600/6-8
1430 E University Ave 50314 515-242-8450
Debra Chapman, prin. Fax 266-6390
Hoover HS 1,000/9-12
4800 Aurora Ave 50310 515-242-7300
Cynthia Flesch, prin. Fax 242-7308
Hoyt MS 500/6-8
2700 E 42nd St 50317 515-242-8446
Deborah Markert, prin. Fax 265-5059
Lincoln HS 2,200/9-12
2600 SW 9th St 50315 515-242-7500
Paul Williamson, prin. Fax 242-7517
Lincoln RAILS Academy 9-9
1000 Porter Ave 50315 515-242-8452
Paul Williamson, prin. Fax 323-8693
McCombs MS 700/6-8
201 County Line Rd 50320 515-242-8447
Nancy Croy, prin. Fax 287-2644
Meredith MS 700/6-8
4827 Madison Ave 50310 515-242-7250
David Johns, prin. Fax 242-8291
Merrill MS 700/6-8
5301 Grand Ave 50312 515-242-8448
Alex Hanna, prin. Fax 274-9691
North HS 1,300/9-12
501 Holcomb Ave 50313 515-242-7200
Michael Vukovich, prin. Fax 242-7319
Roosevelt HS 1,700/9-12
4419 Center St 50312 515-242-7272
Kevin Biggs, prin. Fax 242-7350
Scavo HS 300/Alt
1800 Grand Ave 50309 515-242-7589
Richard Blonigan, prin. Fax 242-7591
Weeks MS 600/6-8
901 E Park Ave 50315 515-242-8449
Audrey Rieken, prin. Fax 288-6755

Saydel Community SD 1,400/PK-12
5740 NE 14th St 50313 515-264-0866
Doug Wheeler, supt. Fax 264-0869
www.saydel.k12.ia.us
Saydel HS 500/9-12
5601 NE 7th St 50313 515-262-9325
Kevin Schulte, prin. Fax 266-8497
Woodside MS 400/5-8
5810 NE 14th St 50313 515-265-3451
Joshua Heyer, prin. Fax 265-0950

American College of Hairstyling Post-Sec.
603 E 6th St 50309 515-244-0971
Des Moines University Post-Sec.
3200 Grand Ave 50312 515-271-1400
Drake University Post-Sec.
2507 University Ave 50311 515-271-2011
Grand View Christian S 200/K-12
2905 NE 46th Ave 50317 319-777-3977
Dotty Van Hooser, prin. Fax 777-3660
Grand View University Post-Sec.
1200 Grandview Ave 50316 515-263-2800
Iowa Methodist Medical Center Post-Sec.
1200 Pleasant St 50309 515-241-6201
Iowa School of Beauty Post-Sec.
3305 70th St 50322 515-278-9939
Mercy College of Health Sciences Post-Sec.
928 6th Ave 50309 515-643-3180
Vatterott College - Des Moines Post-Sec.
7000 Fleur Dr 50321 515-309-9000

De Witt, Clinton, Pop. 5,259
Central DeWitt Community SD 1,500/PK-12
PO Box 110 52742 563-659-0700
Dr. Dan Peterson, supt. Fax 659-0707
www.central-csd.org
Central DeWitt Alternative Program 50/Alt
PO Box 110 52742 563-659-4713
George Pickup, prin. Fax 659-0714
Central DeWitt HS 500/9-12
PO Box 110 52742 563-659-0715
George Pickup, prin. Fax 659-0714
Central DeWitt MS 200/7-8
PO Box 110 52742 563-659-0735
George Pickup, prin. Fax 659-0766

Diagonal, Ringgold, Pop. 330
Diagonal Community SD 100/PK-12
403 W 2nd St 50845 641-734-5331
Karleen Stephens, supt. Fax 734-5729
www.diagonal.k12.ia.us

Diagonal JSHS 100/6-12
403 W 2nd St 50845 641-734-5331
Lorna Paxson, prin. Fax 734-5729

Dike, Grundy, Pop. 1,205
Dike-New Hartford Community SD 800/PK-12
PO Box D 50624 319-989-2552
Larry Hunt, supt. Fax 989-2735
www.dnhcsd.org
Dike-New Hartford HS 200/9-12
PO Box D 50624 319-989-2485
Irvin Laube, prin. Fax 989-2735
Other Schools – See New Hartford

Donnellson, Lee, Pop. 907
Central Lee Community SD 1,100/PK-12
2642 Highway 218 52625 319-835-9510
Andy Crozier, supt. Fax 835-3910
www.centrallee.org
Central Lee HS 300/9-12
2642 Highway 218 52625 319-835-9510
Nicole Herdrich, prin. Fax 835-5709
Central Lee MS 200/6-8
2642 Highway 218 52625 319-835-9510
Kim Ensminger, prin. Fax 835-5020

Dubuque, Dubuque, Pop. 56,421
Dubuque Community SD 10,700/PK-12
2300 Chaney Rd 52001 563-552-3000
Stan Rheingans, supt. Fax 552-3026
www.dbqschools.org
Dubuque SHS 1,600/9-12
1800 Clarke Dr 52001 563-552-5500
Dr. Daniel Johnson, prin. Fax 552-5502
Hempstead HS 1,600/9-12
3715 Pennsylvania Ave 52002 563-552-5200
Lee Kolker, prin. Fax 552-5231
Jefferson MS 600/6-8
1105 Althauser Ave 52001 563-552-4700
Kelly Molony, prin. Fax 552-4701
Roosevelt MS 1,100/6-8
2001 Radford Rd 52002 563-552-5000
Jeff Johll, prin. Fax 552-5001
Washington MS 700/6-8
51 N Grandview Ave 52001 563-552-4800
Mark Burns, prin. Fax 552-4801

Capri College Post-Sec.
395 Main St 52001 563-588-2379
Clarke University Post-Sec.
1550 Clarke Dr 52001 563-588-6300
Emmaus Bible College Post-Sec.
2570 Asbury Rd 52001 563-588-8000
Loras College Post-Sec.
1450 Alta Vista St 52001 563-588-7100
Mazzuchelli Catholic MS 400/6-8
2005 Kane St 52001 563-582-1198
Phil Bormann, prin. Fax 582-5428
University of Dubuque Post-Sec.
2000 University Ave 52001 563-589-3000
Wahlert Catholic HS 600/9-12
2005 Kane St 52001 563-583-9771
Ronald Meyers, prin. Fax 583-9775
Wartburg Theological Seminary Post-Sec.
PO Box 5004 52004 563-589-0200

Dunkerton, Black Hawk, Pop. 848
Dunkerton Community SD 500/PK-12
509 S Canfield St 50626 319-822-4295
Jim Stanton, supt. Fax 822-9456
www.dunkerton.k12.ia.us
Dunkerton JSHS 200/7-12
509 S Canfield St 50626 319-822-4295
Kory Kelchen, prin. Fax 822-9456

Dunlap, Harrison, Pop. 1,032
Boyer Valley Community SD 500/PK-12
1102 Iowa Ave 51529 712-643-5702
Doug Gee, supt. Fax 643-2279
www.boyer-valley.k12.ia.us
Boyer Valley MSHS 200/PK-PK, 6-
1102 Iowa Ave 51529 712-643-2258
Mike Weber, prin. Fax 643-2279

Durant, Cedar, Pop. 1,820
Durant Community SD 700/K-12
408 7th St 52747 563-785-4432
Duane Bennett, supt. Fax 785-4611
www.durant.k12.ia.us
Durant HS 200/9-12
408 7th St 52747 563-785-4431
Joel Diederichs, prin. Fax 785-6558
Durant MS 200/5-8
408 7th St 52747 563-785-4433
Rebecca Stineman, prin. Fax 785-6558

Dyersville, Dubuque, Pop. 4,031

Beckman Catholic HS 500/7-12
1325 9th St SE 52040 563-875-7188
Patrick Meade, prin. Fax 875-7242

Dysart, Tama, Pop. 1,367
Union Community SD
Supt. — See La Porte City
Union MS 300/6-8
PO Box 159 52224 319-476-5100
Mark Albertsen, prin. Fax 476-2385

Eagle Grove, Wright, Pop. 3,540
Eagle Grove Community SD 800/PK-12
325 N Commercial Ave 50533 515-448-4749
Jess Toliver, supt. Fax 448-3156
www.eagle-grove.k12.ia.us
Blue MS 200/5-8
1015 NW 2nd St 50533 515-448-4767
Scott Jeske, prin. Fax 448-5527
Eagle Grove HS 200/9-12
415 NW 2nd St 50533 515-448-5143
Jeff Siebersma, prin. Fax 448-3583

Earlham, Madison, Pop. 1,435
Earlham Community SD 600/K-12
PO Box 430 50072 515-758-2235
Michael Wright, supt. Fax 758-2215
home.ecsdcards.com/
Earlham HS 200/9-12
PO Box 430 50072 515-758-2235
Jennifer Knight, prin. Fax 758-2215
Earlham MS 100/7-8
PO Box 430 50072 515-758-2214
Jennifer Knight, prin. Fax 758-2215

Early, Sac, Pop. 548
Schaller-Crestland Community SD
Supt. — See Schaller
Ridge View MS 200/6-8
PO Box 377 50535 712-273-5192
Jarod Mozer, prin. Fax 273-5120

Eddyville, Wapello, Pop. 1,011
Eddyville-Blakesburg-Fremont Comm SD 900/PK-12
PO Box 429 52553 641-969-4226
Dean Cook, supt. Fax 969-4547
www.rocketsk12.org
Eddyville-Blakesburg-Fremont HS 300/9-12
1301 Berdan Ext 52553 641-969-4288
Steve Noble, prin. Fax 969-4574
Eddyville-Blakesburg-Fremont JHS 100/7-8
1301 Berdan Ext 52553 641-938-2202
Steve Noble, prin. Fax 938-2613

Edgewood, Clayton, Pop. 857
Edgewood-Colesburg Community SD 600/PK-12
PO Box 315 52042 563-928-6411
Rob Busch, supt. Fax 928-6414
www.edge-cole.k12.ia.us
Edgewood-Colesburg JSHS 300/7-12
PO Box 316 52042 563-928-6412
Dawn Voss, prin. Fax 928-6414

Eldon, Wapello, Pop. 923
Cardinal Community SD 700/PK-12
4045 Ashland Rd 52554 641-652-7531
Joel Pedersen, supt. Fax 652-3143
www.cardinalcomet.com
Cardinal MSHS 400/6-12
4045 Ashland Rd 52554 641-652-7531
Jeremy Hissem, prin. Fax 652-3143

Eldora, Hardin, Pop. 2,695
Eldora-New Providence Community SD 600/PK-12
1010 Edgington Ave 50627 641-939-5631
Jay Mathis, supt. Fax 939-3667
Eldora-New Providence HS 300/9-12
1800 24th St 50627 641-939-3421
Michael Rundall, prin. Fax 939-3423

Eldridge, Scott, Pop. 5,557
North Scott Community SD 3,000/PK-12
251 E Iowa St 52748 563-285-4819
Joe Stutting, supt. Fax 285-6075
www.north-scott.k12.ia.us
North Scott HS 900/9-12
200 S 1st St 52748 563-285-9631
Shane Knoche, prin. Fax 285-9308
North Scott JHS 500/7-8
502 S 5th St 52748 563-285-8272
John Hawley, prin. Fax 285-6045

Elgin, Fayette, Pop. 680
Valley Community SD 300/K-8
23493 Canoe Rd 52141 563-426-5501
Duane Willhite, supt. Fax 426-5502
www.valley.k12.ia.us
North Fayette Valley MS 100/7-8
23493 Canoe Rd 52141 563-426-5551
Micah Gearhart, prin. Fax 426-5502

Elkader, Clayton, Pop. 1,265
Central Community SD 500/PK-12
400 1st St NW 52043 563-245-1751
Nick Trenkamp, supt. Fax 245-1763
www.central.k12.ia.us/
Central Community JSHS 200/6-12
400 1st St NW 52043 563-245-1750
Dan Yanda, prin. Fax 245-1763

Elk Horn, Shelby, Pop. 661
Exira-Elk Horn-Kimballton Community SD 400/PK-12
PO Box 388a 51531 712-764-4616
Trevor Miller, supt. Fax 764-4626
www.exira-ehk.k12.ia.us/
Exira-Elk Horn-Kimballton HS 100/9-12
PO Box 388a 51531 712-764-4606
Trevor Miller, prin. Fax 764-4626
Other Schools – See Exira

Emmetsburg, Palo Alto, Pop. 3,872
Emmetsburg Community SD 800/PK-12
205 King St 50536 712-852-3201
Amanda Schmidt, supt. Fax 852-3338
www.e-hawks.org
Emmetsburg HS 200/9-12
205 King St 50536 712-852-2966
Mike Embrock, prin. Fax 852-3317
Emmetsburg MS 200/5-8
205 King St 50536 712-852-2892
Tracie Christensen, prin. Fax 852-3811

Iowa Lakes Community College Post-Sec.
3200 College Dr 50536 712-852-3554

Epworth, Dubuque, Pop. 1,855
Western Dubuque Community SD
Supt. — See Farley
Western Dubuque HS 800/9-12
PO Box 379 52045 563-876-3442
Dave Hoeger, prin. Fax 876-5512

Divine Word College Post-Sec.
PO Box 380 52045 563-876-3353

Essex, Page, Pop. 789
Essex Community SD 200/PK-12
111 Forbes St 51638 712-379-3117
Paul Croghan, supt. Fax 379-3200
www.ehs-ees.com/
Essex JSHS 100/6-12
111 Forbes St 51638 712-379-3115
Rob Brecht, prin. Fax 379-3200

Estherville, Emmet, Pop. 6,305
Estherville Lincoln Central Comm SD 1,200/PK-12
1814 7th Ave S 51334 712-362-2692
Tara Paul, supt. Fax 362-2410
www.estherville.k12.ia.us
Estherville Lincoln Central HS 300/9-12
1520 Central Ave 51334 712-362-2659
Brad Leonard, prin. Fax 362-2406
Estherville Lincoln Central MS 400/5-8
1430 1st Ave S 51334 712-362-2335
David McCaulley, prin. Fax 362-7822

Iowa Lakes Community College Post-Sec.
300 S 18th St 51334 712-362-7945

Evansdale, Black Hawk, Pop. 4,640
Waterloo Community SD
Supt. — See Waterloo
Bunger MS 400/6-8
157 S Roosevelt Rd 50707 319-433-2550
Rachel Savage, prin. Fax 433-2564

Everly, Clay, Pop. 602
Clay Central/Everly Community SD
Supt. — See Royal
Clay Central/Everly JSHS 200/7-12
PO Box 110 51338 712-834-2227
Curt Busch, prin. Fax 834-2193

Exira, Audubon, Pop. 839
Exira-Elk Horn-Kimballton Community SD
Supt. — See Elk Horn
Exira-Elk Horn-Kimballton MS 200/PK-K, 4-8
PO Box 335 50076 712-268-5318
Stephen Humphrey, prin. Fax 268-5319

Fairbank, Buchanan, Pop. 1,107
Wapsie Valley Community SD 800/PK-12
2535 Viking Ave 50629 319-638-6711
Jim Stanton, supt. Fax 638-7061
www.wapsievalleyschools.com
Wapsie Valley JSHS 300/7-12
2535 Viking Ave 50629 319-638-6711
Ross Bauer, prin. Fax 638-7061

Fairfield, Jefferson, Pop. 9,274
Fairfield Community SD 1,700/PK-12
403 S 20th St 52556 641-472-2655
Dr. Laurie Noll, supt. Fax 472-0269
www.fairfieldsfuture.org/
Fairfield HS 500/9-12
605 E Broadway Ave 52556 641-472-2059
Brian Stone, prin. Fax 472-4703
Fairfield MS 500/5-8
404 W Fillmore Ave 52556 641-472-5019
Laura Atwood, prin. Fax 472-5301

Maharishi S of the Age of Enlightenment 200/PK-12
804 Dr Robert Keith Wallace 52556 641-472-9400
Richard Beall Ph.D., head sch Fax 472-1211
Maharishi University of Management Post-Sec.
1000 N 4th St 52557 641-472-7000

Farley, Dubuque, Pop. 1,531
Western Dubuque Community SD 3,200/PK-12
PO Box 68 52046 563-744-3885
Rick Colpitts, supt. Fax 744-3093
www.wdbqschools.org
Drexler Middle IS 800/5-8
PO Box 279 52046 563-744-3371
Mary Jane Maher, prin. Fax 744-3711
Other Schools – See Cascade, Epworth

Seton Catholic - St. Joseph S 100/6-8
PO Box 249 52046 563-744-3290
Mary Smock, prin. Fax 744-3450

Fayette, Fayette, Pop. 1,319

Upper Iowa University Post-Sec.
PO Box 1857 52142 563-425-5200

Fontanelle, Adair, Pop. 671
Nodaway Valley Community SD
Supt. — See Greenfield
Nodaway Valley MS 200/5-8
112 S 1st St 50846 641-745-2291
Lanny Kliefoth, prin. Fax 745-3501

Forest City, Winnebago, Pop. 4,101
Forest City Community SD 1,200/PK-12
PO Box 270 50436 641-585-2323
Darwin Lehmann, supt. Fax 585-5218
www.forestcity.k12.ia.us
Forest City HS 400/9-12
206 W School St 50436 641-585-2324
Ken Baker, prin. Fax 585-3034
Forest City MS 300/6-8
216 W School St 50436 641-585-4772
Zach Dillavou, prin. Fax 585-3432

Waldorf College Post-Sec.
106 S 6th St 50436 800-292-1903

Fort Dodge, Webster, Pop. 24,736
Fort Dodge Community SD 3,200/PK-12
104 S 17th St 50501 515-576-1161
Dr. Douglas Van Zyl, supt. Fax 576-1988
www.fdschools.org

Fort Dodge HS 1,100/9-12
819 N 25th St 50501 515-955-1770
Dr. Kenneth Hayes, prin. Fax 955-3374
Willard Alternative Education HS 50/Alt
819 N 25th St 50501 515-576-7305
Dr. Kenneth Hayes, prin. Fax 576-7305

Iowa Central Community College Post-Sec.
1 Triton Cir 50501 515-576-7201
La' James International College Post-Sec.
2419 5th Ave S 50501 515-576-3119
St. Edmond HS 400/6-12
501 N 22nd St 50501 515-955-5850
Linda Mitchell, prin. Fax 955-3569

Fort Madison, Lee, Pop. 10,836
Fort Madison Community SD 2,000/PK-12
PO Box 1423 52627 319-372-7252
Erin Slater, supt. Fax 372-7255
www.fmcsd.org
Fort Madison HS 600/9-12
2001 Avenue B 52627 319-372-1862
Greg Smith, prin. Fax 372-1325
Fort Madison MS 700/4-8
502 48th St 52627 319-372-4687
Todd Dirth, prin. Fax 372-0378

Holy Trinity HS 200/7-12
2600 Avenue A 52627 319-372-2486
Michael Sheerin, prin. Fax 372-6310

Fredericksburg, Chickasaw, Pop. 923
Sumner-Fredericksburg Community SD
Supt. — See Sumner
Sumner-Fredericksburg MS 200/6-8
401 E High St 50630 563-237-5334
Jill Glenn, prin. Fax 237-6329

Garden Grove, Decatur, Pop. 208
Mormon Trail Community SD
Supt. — See Humeston
Mormon Trail JSHS 100/7-12
PO Box 177 50103 641-443-3425
Steve Hunt, prin. Fax 443-2644

Garner, Hancock, Pop. 3,097
Garner-Hayfield-Ventura Community SD 800/PK-12
PO Box 449 50438 641-923-2718
Tyler Williams, supt. Fax 923-3825
www.ghvschools.org
Garner-Hayfield-Ventura HS 400/9-12
PO Box 449 50438 641-923-2632
James Haag, prin. Fax 923-4005
Other Schools – See Ventura

Garwin, Tama, Pop. 518
GMG Community SD 500/PK-12
306 Park St 50632 641-499-2239
Ben Petty, supt. Fax 499-2159
www.garwin.k12.ia.us
GMG JSHS 200/7-12
306 Park St 50632 641-499-2005
Mark Polich, prin. Fax 499-2552

George, Lyon, Pop. 1,076
George-Little Rock Community SD 400/PK-12
PO Box 6 51237 712-475-3311
Steve Barber, supt. Fax 475-3574
george-littlerock.org
George-Little Rock HS 100/9-12
PO Box 6 51237 712-475-3311
Kevin Range, prin. Fax 475-6573
Other Schools – See Little Rock

Gilbert, Story, Pop. 1,068
Gilbert Community SD 1,400/PK-12
103 Mathews Dr 50105 515-232-3740
Lindsey Beecher, supt. Fax 827-5400
www.gilbert.k12.ia.us
Gilbert HS 400/9-12
312 Gretten St 50105 515-232-3738
Layne Billings, prin. Fax 827-1298
Gilbert MS 300/6-8
201 E Mathews Dr 50105 515-232-0540
Chris Billings, prin. Fax 827-7420

Gilbertville, Black Hawk, Pop. 708

Don Bosco HS 200/9-12
405 16th Ave 50634 319-296-1692
Rick Blackwell, prin. Fax 296-1693
Immaculate Conception S 200/3-8
311 16th Ave 50634 319-296-1089
Sharon Mayer, prin. Fax 296-3847

Gilman, Marshall, Pop. 508
East Marshall Community SD 800/PK-12
PO Box 159 50106 641-498-7481
Anthony Ryan, supt. Fax 498-2035
www.e-marshall.k12.ia.us
East Marshall MS 300/4-8
PO Box 159 50106 641-498-7483
Robert Schelp, prin. Fax 498-2180
Other Schools – See Le Grand

Glenwood, Mills, Pop. 5,209
Glenwood Community SD 2,000/PK-12
103 Central St Ste 300 51534 712-527-9034
Devin Embray, supt. Fax 527-4287
www.glenwoodschools.org
Glenwood HS 600/9-12
504 Sharp St 51534 712-527-4897
Richard Hutchinson, prin. Fax 527-9554
Glenwood MS 400/6-8
400 Sivers Rd 51534 712-527-4887
Heidi Stanley, prin. Fax 527-3411

Glidden, Carroll, Pop. 1,142
Glidden-Ralston Community SD 300/PK-12
PO Box 488 51443 712-659-3411
Kreg Lensch, supt. Fax 659-2248
www.glidden-ralston.k12.ia.us
Glidden-Ralston JSHS 200/7-12
PO Box 488 51443 712-659-2205
Dirk Troutman, prin. Fax 659-2248

Goose Lake, Clinton, Pop. 238
Northeast Community SD 800/PK-12
PO Box 66 52750 563-577-2249
Neil Gray, supt. Fax 577-2450
www.northeast.k12.ia.us
Northeast MSHS 500/6-12
PO Box 70 52750 563-577-2249
Alicia Christiansen, prin. Fax 577-2248

Gowrie, Webster, Pop. 1,027
Prairie Valley Community SD 600/PK-12
PO Box 49 50543 515-352-5575
Brian Johnson, supt. Fax 352-5573
www.prairievalley.k12.ia.us
Southeast Valley HS 300/7-12
PO Box 49 50543 515-352-3142
Jim Henrich, prin. Fax 352-3143

Graettinger, Palo Alto, Pop. 839
Graettinger-Terril Community SD 300/PK-12
PO Box 58 51342 712-859-3286
Andrew Woiwood, supt. Fax 859-3509
www.gtschools.k12.ia.us/
Graettinger-Terril MSHS 100/6-12
PO Box 58 51342 712-859-3286
Jeremy Simington, prin. Fax 859-3509

Granger, Dallas, Pop. 1,237
Woodward-Granger Community SD 1,200/PK-12
1904 State St 50109 515-999-8022
Brad Anderson, supt. Fax 999-8025
wghawks.school
Other Schools – See Woodward

Greene, Butler, Pop. 1,121
North Butler Community SD
Supt. — See Allison
North Butler JSHS 200/7-12
PO Box 190 50636 641-816-5631
Dan Huff, prin. Fax 816-5921

Greenfield, Adair, Pop. 1,975
Nodaway Valley Community SD 700/PK-12
410 NW 2nd St 50849 641-743-6127
Casey Berlau, supt. Fax 343-7173
www.nodawayvalley.org/
Nodaway Valley HS 200/9-12
410 NW 2nd St 50849 641-743-6141
Lanny Kliefoth, prin. Fax 343-7040
Other Schools – See Fontanelle

Grimes, Polk, Pop. 8,166
Dallas Center-Grimes Community SD
Supt. — See Dallas Center
Dallas Center-Grimes Community HS 500/10-12
2555 W 1st St 50111 515-986-9747
Scott Blum, prin. Fax 986-9734
Dallas Center-Grimes Meadows 400/8-9
2555 W 1st St Ste 200 50111 515-986-0105
Lori Phillips, prin. Fax 986-3155

Grinnell, Poweshiek, Pop. 9,024
Grinnell-Newburg Community SD 1,700/PK-12
1333 Sunset St 50112 641-236-2700
Dr. Janet Stutz, supt. Fax 236-2699
www.grinnell-k12.org
Grinnell Community HS 500/9-12
1333 Sunset St 50112 641-236-2720
Kevin Seney, prin. Fax 236-2692
Grinnell Community MS 500/5-8
132 East St S 50112 641-236-2750
Sara Hegg-Dunne, prin. Fax 236-2732

Grinnell College Post-Sec.
PO Box 805 50112 641-269-4000

Griswold, Cass, Pop. 1,029
Griswold Community SD 600/PK-12
PO Box 280 51535 712-778-2152
David Henrichs, supt. Fax 778-4145
www.griswoldschools.org/
Griswold MSHS 300/6-12
PO Box 280 51535 712-778-2154
Katie Elwood, prin. Fax 778-2161

Grundy Center, Grundy, Pop. 2,679
Grundy Center Community SD 500/PK-12
1301 12th St 50638 319-825-5418
Jerry Schutz, supt. Fax 825-5419
www.spartanpride.net
Grundy Center MSHS 200/5-12
1006 M Ave 50638 319-825-5449
Dr. Kristin Sheffield, prin. Fax 825-6415

Guthrie Center, Guthrie, Pop. 1,559
Guthrie Center Community SD 500/PK-12
906 School St 50115 641-332-2972
Steve Smith, supt. Fax 332-2973
www.acgcschools.org
AC/GC HS 200/9-12
906 School St 50115 641-332-2236
Shane Arp, prin. Fax 332-2973

Guttenberg, Clayton, Pop. 1,910
Clayton Ridge Community SD 800/PK-12
PO Box 520 52052 563-252-2341
Shane Wahls, supt. Fax 252-2656
www.claytonridge.k12.ia.us
Clayton Ridge HS 200/8-12
PO Box 520 52052 563-252-2342
Andy Peterson, prin. Fax 252-2656

Hampton, Franklin, Pop. 4,420
Hampton-Dumont Community SD 1,200/PK-12
601 12th Ave NE 50441 641-456-2175
Todd Lettow, supt. Fax 456-5750
www.hampton-dumont.k12.ia.us/
Hampton-Dumont HS 400/9-12
101 12th Ave NW 50441 641-456-4893
Steve Madson, prin. Fax 456-4569
Hampton-Dumont MS 400/4-8
601 12th Ave NE 50441 641-456-4735
Anthony Spradlin, prin. Fax 456-2023

Harlan, Shelby, Pop. 5,057
Harlan Community SD 1,600/PK-12
2102 Durant St 51537 712-755-2152
Justin Wagner, supt. Fax 755-7312
www.harlan.k12.ia.us
Harlan Community HS 500/9-12
2102 Durant St 51537 712-755-3101
John Connell, prin. Fax 755-7705
Harlan Community MS 400/6-8
2108 Durant St 51537 712-755-3196
Bill Mueller, prin. Fax 755-3699

Hartley, O'Brien, Pop. 1,644
Hartley-Melvin-Sanborn Community SD 600/PK-12
300 N 8th Ave W 51346 712-928-3406
Bill Thompson, supt. Fax 928-3536
www.hartley-ms.k12.ia.us
Hartley-Melvin-Sanborn HS 200/9-12
PO Box 206 51346 712-928-3406
Nathan Hemiller, prin. Fax 928-2152
Other Schools – See Sanborn

Hastings, Mills, Pop. 151
East Mills Community SD 400/PK-12
58962 380th St 51540 712-624-8700
Paul Croghan, supt. Fax 624-8279
www.emschools.org
East Mills Learning Center 50/Alt
58962 380th St 51540 712-624-8696
Paul Croghan, supt. Fax 624-8279
Other Schools – See Malvern

Hawarden, Sioux, Pop. 2,534
West Sioux Community SD 700/PK-12
1300 Falcon Dr 51023 712-551-1461
Ryan Kramer, supt. Fax 551-1367
www.westsiouxschools.org/
West Sioux HS 200/9-12
1300 Falcon Dr 51023 712-551-1181
Heidi Vasquez, prin. Fax 551-1514
West Sioux MS 200/6-8
1300 Falcon Dr 51023 712-551-1022
Heidi Vasquez, prin. Fax 551-1367

Hinton, Plymouth, Pop. 925
Hinton Community SD 700/PK-12
PO Box 128 51024 712-947-4329
Pete Stuerman, supt. Fax 947-4427
www.hintonschool.com/
Hinton HS 200/9-12
PO Box 128 51024 712-947-4328
Betty Wendt, prin. Fax 947-4427
Hinton MS 200/4-8
PO Box 128 51024 712-947-4328
Brian DeJong, prin. Fax 947-4947

Holstein, Ida, Pop. 1,384
Galva-Holstein Community SD 500/PK-12
PO Box 320 51025 712-368-4353
Jon Wiebers, supt. Fax 368-4843
www.rvraptors.org/
Ridge View HS 200/9-12
PO Box 320 51025 712-368-4353
Bret Warnke, prin. Fax 368-4843

Hubbard, Hardin, Pop. 843
Hubbard-Radcliffe Community SD 400/PK-8
PO Box 129 50122 641-864-2211
Patricia Heinz, supt. Fax 864-2422
www.hubbard.k12.ia.us
South Hardin MS 200/6-8
PO Box 129 50122 641-864-2211
Duane Harding, prin. Fax 864-2422

Hudson, Black Hawk, Pop. 2,275
Hudson Community SD 500/K-12
PO Box 240 50643 319-988-3233
Dr. Anthony Voss, supt. Fax 988-3235
hudsonpiratepride.com
Hudson JSHS 200/7-12
PO Box 240 50643 319-988-4226
Jeff Dieken, prin. Fax 988-4174

Hull, Sioux, Pop. 2,161
Boyden-Hull Community SD 600/K-12
PO Box 678 51239 712-439-2711
Steve Grond, supt. Fax 439-1419
www.boyden-hull.k12.ia.us
Boyden-Hull JSHS 300/7-12
PO Box 678 51239 712-439-2440
Dan Pottebaum, prin. Fax 439-1419

Western Christian HS 300/9-12
PO Box 658 51239 712-439-1013
Dan Barkel, prin. Fax 439-1407

Humboldt, Humboldt, Pop. 4,652
Humboldt Community SD
Supt. — See Dakota City
Humboldt HS 500/9-12
1500 Wildcat Rd 50548 515-332-1430
Lori Westhoff, prin. Fax 332-7150
Humboldt MS 400/5-8
1400 Wildcat Rd 50548 515-332-2812
Brenda Geitzenauer, prin. Fax 332-2023

Humeston, Wayne, Pop. 485
Mormon Trail Community SD 200/PK-12
PO Box 156 50123 641-877-2521
Lorna Paxson, supt. Fax 877-3400
www.mormontrailcsd.org/
Other Schools – See Garden Grove

Huxley, Story, Pop. 3,264
Ballard Community SD 1,700/PK-12
PO Box 307 50124 515-597-2811
Herman Maxey, supt. Fax 597-2965
www.ballard.k12.ia.us
Ballard Community HS 500/9-12
PO Box 307 50124 515-597-2971
John Ronca, prin. Fax 597-2964
Ballard Community MS 400/6-8
PO Box 307 50124 515-597-2815
Thomas Maher, prin. Fax 597-2818

Ida Grove, Ida, Pop. 2,129
Odebolt-Arthur/Battle Creek-Ida Grove SD 1,000/PK-12
900 John Montgomery Dr 51445 712-364-3687
Terry Kenealy, supt. Fax 364-3609
www.oabcig.org
Odebolt-Arthur/Battle Creek-Ida Grove HS 300/9-12
900 John Montgomery Dr 51445 712-364-3371
Patrick Miller, prin. Fax 364-4463
Other Schools – See Odebolt

Independence, Buchanan, Pop. 5,911
Independence Community SD 1,300/PK-12
1207 1st St W 50644 319-334-7400
Jean Peterson, supt. Fax 334-7404
www.independence.k12.ia.us/
Independence JSHS 600/7-12
700 20th Ave SW 50644 319-334-7405
John Howard, prin. Fax 332-1296

Indianola, Warren, Pop. 14,597
Indianola Community SD 3,600/PK-12
1304 E 2nd Ave 50125 515-961-9500
Art Sathoff, supt. Fax 961-9505
www.indianola.k12.ia.us
Indianola HS 1,100/9-12
1304 E 1st Ave 50125 515-961-9510
Craig Calhoun, prin. Fax 961-9519
Indianola MS 800/6-8
403 S 15th St 50125 515-961-9530
Annette Jauron, prin. Fax 961-9535

Simpson College Post-Sec.
701 N C St 50125 515-961-6251

Inwood, Lyon, Pop. 809
West Lyon Community SD 900/PK-12
1787 Iowa 182 Ave 51240 712-753-4917
Jim Hargens, supt. Fax 753-4928
www.wlwildcats.org
West Lyon HS 200/9-12
1787 Iowa 182 Ave 51240 712-753-4917
Doug Jiskoot, prin. Fax 753-4928
West Lyon JHS 100/7-8
1787 Iowa 182 Ave 51240 712-753-4917
Doug Jiskoot, prin. Fax 753-4928

Iowa City, Johnson, Pop. 66,297
Iowa City Community SD 13,100/PK-12
1725 N Dodge St 52245 319-688-1000
Stephen Murley, supt. Fax 688-1009
www.iowacityschools.org
Iowa City HS 1,500/9-12
1900 Morningside Dr 52245 319-688-1040
John Bacon, prin. Fax 688-1049
Southeast JHS 800/7-8
2501 Bradford Dr 52240 319-688-1070
Michelle Cook, prin. Fax 688-1079
Tate HS 100/Alt
1528 Mall Dr 52240 319-688-1080
Ann Browning, prin. Fax 688-1089
West HS 1,900/9-12
2901 Melrose Ave 52246 319-688-1050
Gregg Shoultz Ph.D., prin. Fax 688-1059
Other Schools – See Coralville, North Liberty

La' James International College Post-Sec.
227 E Market St 52245 319-337-2109
Regina HS 400/7-12
2150 Rochester Ave 52245 319-338-5436
Glenn Plummer, prin. Fax 887-3817
University of Iowa Post-Sec.
107 Calvin Hall 52242 319-335-3500

Iowa Falls, Hardin, Pop. 5,192
Iowa Falls Community SD 1,200/PK-12
710 North St 50126 641-648-6400
Dr. John Robbins, supt. Fax 648-6401
www.ifacadets.net
Iowa Falls - Alden HS 400/9-12
1903 Taylor Ave 50126 641-648-6440
Clyde Tarrence, prin. Fax 648-3222
Riverbend MS 200/7-8
1124 Union St 50126 641-648-6430
Jeff Burchfield, prin. Fax 648-6432

Ellsworth Community College Post-Sec.
1100 College Ave 50126 800-322-9235

Jackson Junction, Winneshiek, Pop. 58
Turkey Valley Community SD 400/PK-12
3219 Highway 24 52171 563-776-6011
Jay Jurrens, supt. Fax 776-4271
www.turkey-v.k12.ia.us
Turkey Valley JSHS 200/7-12
3219 Highway 24 52171 563-776-6011
Carol Knoll, prin. Fax 776-4271

Janesville, Bremer, Pop. 923
Janesville Consolidated SD 400/PK-12
PO Box 478 50647 319-987-2581
B.J. Meaney, supt. Fax 987-2824
www.janesville.k12.ia.us
Janesville JSHS 200/6-12
PO Box 478 50647 319-987-2581
Krista Pugh, prin. Fax 987-2824

Jefferson, Greene, Pop. 4,314
Greene County Community SD 1,000/PK-12
204 W Madison St 50129 515-386-4168
Tim Christensen, supt. Fax 386-3591
www.jefferson-scranton.k12.ia.us
Greene County HS 400/9-12
101 Ram Dr 50129 515-386-2188
Brian Phillips, prin. Fax 386-2159
Greene County MS 200/7-8
203 W Harrison St 50129 515-386-8126
Shawn Zanders, prin. Fax 386-4412

Jesup, Buchanan, Pop. 2,492
Jesup Community SD 1,000/PK-12
PO Box 287 50648 319-827-1700
Nathan Marting, supt. Fax 827-3905
www.jesup.k12.ia.us
Jesup HS 200/9-12
PO Box 287 50648 319-827-1700
Rodney Chamberlin, prin. Fax 827-3905
Jesup MS 200/5-8
PO Box 287 50648 319-827-1700
Lisa Loecher, prin. Fax 827-3905

Jewell, Hamilton, Pop. 1,204
South Hamilton Community SD 700/PK-12
315 Division St 50130 515-827-5479
Kenneth Howard, supt. Fax 827-5368
www.s-hamilton.k12.ia.us
South Hamilton MSHS 300/7-12
315 Division St 50130 515-827-5418
W. Scott Dryer, prin. Fax 827-5368

Johnston, Polk, Pop. 17,014
Johnston Community SD 6,600/PK-12
PO Box 10 50131 515-278-0470
Dr. Corey Lunn, supt. Fax 278-5884
www.johnstoncsd.org
Johnston HS 1,400/10-12
PO Box 10 50131 515-278-0449
Ryan Woods, prin. Fax 276-5795
Johnston MS 1,000/8-9
PO Box 10 50131 515-278-0476
Brent Riessen, prin. Fax 278-0130

La' James International College Post-Sec.
8805 Chambery Blvd 50131 515-278-2208

Kalona, Washington, Pop. 2,347
Mid-Prairie Community SD
Supt. — See Wellman
Mid-Prairie MS 300/6-8
713 F Ave 52247 319-656-2241
Marc Pennington, prin. Fax 656-2207

Iowa Mennonite HS 100/9-12
1421 540th St SW 52247 319-656-2586
Stephen Schrag, prin. Fax 656-2073
Shiloh University Post-Sec.
100 Shiloh Dr 52247 319-656-2447

Kanawha, Hancock, Pop. 646
West Hancock Community SD
Supt. — See Britt
West Hancock MS 200/5-8
PO Box 130 50447 641-762-3261
Ruth Verbrugge, prin. Fax 843-4717

Keokuk, Lee, Pop. 10,499
Keokuk Community SD 1,900/PK-12
1721 Franklin St 52632 319-524-1402
Tim Hood, supt. Fax 524-1114
www.keokukschools.org
Keokuk HS 600/9-12
2285 Middle Rd 52632 319-524-2542
Adam Magliari, prin. Fax 524-1784
Keokuk MS 400/6-8
2002 Orleans Ave 52632 319-524-3737
Brad McCloskey, prin. Fax 524-1511

Southeastern Community College Post-Sec.
PO Box 6007 52632 319-524-3221

Keosauqua, Van Buren, Pop. 1,003
Van Buren Community SD 600/PK-12
503 Henry St 52565 319-293-3334
Dr. Pam Ewell, supt. Fax 293-3301
www.van-buren.k12.ia.us
Van Buren Community JSHS 300/7-12
405 4th St 52565 319-293-3183
Chuck Banks, prin. Fax 293-3345

Keota, Keokuk, Pop. 998
Keota Community SD 300/PK-12
PO Box 88 52248 641-636-2189
Dennis Phelps, supt. Fax 636-3009
www.keota.k12.ia.us/
Keota JSHS 100/7-12
PO Box 88 52248 641-636-3491
Nathan Carlson, prin. Fax 636-2210

Kingsley, Plymouth, Pop. 1,392
Kingsley-Pierson Community SD 400/K-12
PO Box 520 51028 712-378-2861
Scott Bailey, supt. Fax 378-3729
www.k-pcsd.org
Kingsley-Pierson HS 100/9-12
PO Box 520 51028 712-378-2861
Scott Bailey, prin. Fax 378-3729
Other Schools – See Pierson

Knoxville, Marion, Pop. 7,242
Knoxville Community SD 1,600/PK-12
309 W Main St 50138 641-842-6551
Cassi Pearson, supt. Fax 842-2109
www.knoxville.k12.ia.us
Knoxville HS 500/9-12
1811 W Madison St 50138 641-842-2173
Tracy Wilkins, prin. Fax 842-2066
Knoxville MS 400/6-8
102 N Lincoln St 50138 641-842-3315
Brian McNeill, prin. Fax 842-5754

Lake City, Calhoun, Pop. 1,715
South Central Calhoun Community SD
Supt. — See Rockwell City
South Central Calhoun HS 300/9-12
PO Box 45 51449 712-464-7211
Randy Martin, prin. Fax 464-1012

Lake Mills, Winnebago, Pop. 2,090
Lake Mills Community SD 700/PK-12
102 S 4th Ave E 50450 641-592-0881
Chad Kohagen, supt. Fax 592-0883
www.lake-mills.org
Lake Mills HS 200/9-12
102 S 4th Ave E 50450 641-592-0893
James Scholbrock, prin. Fax 592-0883
Lake Mills MS 200/6-8
102 S 4th Ave E 50450 641-592-0894
James Scholbrock, prin. Fax 592-0883

Lake Park, Dickinson, Pop. 1,094
Harris-Lake Park Community SD 400/PK-12
PO Box 8 51347 712-832-3809
Dennis Peters, supt. Fax 832-3812
www.harris-lp.k12.ia.us
Harris-Lake Park MSHS 200/6-12
PO Box 8 51347 712-832-3809
Travis Popken, prin. Fax 832-3812

Lake View, Sac, Pop. 1,137
East Sac County SD 1,000/PK-12
PO Box 110 51450 712-665-5000
Barb Kruthoff, supt. Fax 665-5021
www.eastsac.k12.ia.us/
East Sac County HS 300/9-12
PO Box 110 51450 712-665-5001
Kevin Litterer, prin. Fax 665-5022
Other Schools – See Sac City

Lamoni, Decatur, Pop. 2,266
Lamoni Community SD 400/PK-12
202 N Walnut St 50140 641-784-3342
Chris Coffelt, supt. Fax 784-6548
lamoni.k12.ia.us
Lamoni HS 100/9-12
202 N Walnut St 50140 641-784-3351
Alan Dykens, prin. Fax 784-6548
Lamoni MS 100/6-8
202 N Walnut St 50140 641-784-7299
Alan Dykens, prin. Fax 784-6548

Graceland University Post-Sec.
1 University Pl 50140 641-784-5000

Lansing, Allamakee, Pop. 998
Eastern Allamakee Community SD 400/PK-12
569 Center St 52151 563-538-4201
Dale Crozier, supt. Fax 538-4969
www.e-allamakee.k12.ia.us/
Kee HS 100/9-12
569 Center St 52151 563-538-4201
Mary Hogan, prin. Fax 538-4969
Lansing MS 100/6-8
569 Center St 52151 563-538-4201
Mary Hogan, prin. Fax 538-4969

La Porte City, Black Hawk, Pop. 2,264
Union Community SD 1,200/PK-12
200 Adams St 50651 319-342-2674
Travis Fleshner, supt. Fax 342-2393
www.union.k12.ia.us/
Union HS 400/9-12
200 Adams St 50651 319-342-2697
Jim Cayton, prin. Fax 342-2393
Other Schools – See Dysart

Latimer, Franklin, Pop. 507
CAL Community SD 200/PK-12
1441 Gull St 50452 641-579-6087
Todd Lettow, supt. Fax 579-6408
www.cal.k12.ia.us
CAL HS 100/6-12
1441 Gull St 50452 641-579-6086
Steve Lane, prin. Fax 579-6408

Laurens, Pocahontas, Pop. 1,251
Laurens-Marathon Community SD 300/PK-12
300 W Garfield St 50554 712-841-5000
Jeff Kruse, supt. Fax 841-5010
www.laurens-marathon.k12.ia.us
Laurens-Marathon HS 100/9-12
300 W Garfield St 50554 712-841-5000
Troy Oehlertz, prin. Fax 841-5010
Laurens-Marathon MS 100/6-8
300 W Garfield St 50554 712-841-5000
Troy Oehlertz, prin. Fax 841-5010

Lawton, Woodbury, Pop. 902
Lawton-Bronson Community SD 600/PK-12
100 Tara Way 51030 712-944-5183
Randy Collins, supt. Fax 944-5568
www.lb-eagles.org
Lawton JSHS 300/7-12
100 Tara Way 51030 712-944-5181
Rachel Leavitt, prin. Fax 944-5568

Le Claire, Scott, Pop. 3,701
Pleasant Valley Community SD
Supt. — See Bettendorf

Pleasant Valley JHS 700/7-8
3501 Wisconsin St 52753 563-332-0200
Trampus Budde, prin. Fax 332-0205

Le Grand, Marshall, Pop. 933
East Marshall Community SD
Supt. — See Gilman
East Marshall HS 300/9-12
PO Box A 50142 641-479-2785
Matthew Rasmusson, prin. Fax 479-2601

Le Mars, Plymouth, Pop. 9,729
Le Mars Community SD 2,100/PK-12
940 Lincoln St SW 51031 712-546-4155
Dr. Todd Wendt, supt. Fax 546-5934
www.lemars.k12.ia.us
Individualized Learning Center 50/Alt
940 Lincoln St SW 51031 712-546-5858
Dr. Mark Iverson, prin. Fax 546-5934
Le Mars HS 600/9-12
940 Lincoln St SW 51031 712-546-4153
Dr. Mark Iverson, prin. Fax 546-9581
Le Mars MS 500/6-8
940 Lincoln St SW 51031 712-546-7022
Steve Shanks, prin. Fax 546-7024

Gehlen Catholic HS 200/7-12
709 Plymouth St NE 51031 712-546-5126
Jeff Alesch, prin. Fax 546-9384

Lenox, Taylor, Pop. 1,401
Lenox Community SD 500/PK-12
600 S Locust St 50851 641-333-2244
David Henrichs, supt. Fax 333-2247
www.lenox.k12.ia.us
Lenox JSHS 200/7-12
600 S Locust St 50851 641-333-2244
Mike Still, prin. Fax 333-2247

Leon, Decatur, Pop. 1,972
Central Decatur Community SD 800/PK-12
1201 NE Poplar St 50144 641-446-4819
Chris Coffelt, supt. Fax 446-7990
www.centraldecatur.org
Central Decatur JSHS 300/7-12
1201 NE Poplar St 50144 641-446-4816
Rudy Evertsen, prin. Fax 446-7990

Letts, Louisa, Pop. 371
Louisa-Muscatine Community SD 700/PK-12
14478 170th St 52754 319-726-3541
Mike Van Sickle, supt. Fax 726-3334
www.lmcsd.org
Louisa-Muscatine JSHS 300/7-12
14354 170th St 52754 319-726-3421
Chris Parkhurst, prin. Fax 726-3649

Liberty Center, Warren
Southeast Warren Community SD 500/PK-12
PO Box 19 50145 641-466-3510
Delane Galvin, supt. Fax 466-3525
www.se-warren.k12.ia.us
Southeast Warren JSHS 200/7-12
PO Box 19 50145 641-466-3331
Delane Galvin, prin. Fax 466-3525

Lisbon, Linn, Pop. 2,132
Lisbon Community SD 700/PK-12
PO Box 839 52253 319-455-2075
Patrick Hocking, supt. Fax 455-2733
www.lisbon.k12.ia.us
Lisbon HS 200/9-12
PO Box 839 52253 319-455-2106
Aaron Becker, prin. Fax 455-3208
Lisbon MS 100/7-8
PO Box 839 52253 319-455-2659
Aaron Becker, prin. Fax 455-2733

Little Rock, Lyon, Pop. 458
George-Little Rock Community SD
Supt. — See George
George-Little Rock MS 100/6-8
PO Box 247 51243 712-479-2771
Molly Schilling, prin. Fax 479-2770

Logan, Harrison, Pop. 1,523
Logan-Magnolia Community SD 700/PK-12
1200 N 2nd Ave 51546 712-644-2250
Tom Ridder, supt. Fax 644-2934
www.lomaschools.org
Logan-Magnolia JSHS 300/7-12
1200 N 2nd Ave 51546 712-644-2250
Christi Gochenour, prin. Fax 644-2934

Lone Tree, Johnson, Pop. 1,281
Lone Tree Community SD 500/PK-12
PO Box 520 52755 319-629-4212
Michael Reeves, supt. Fax 629-4324
www.lone-tree.k12.ia.us
Lone Tree JSHS 300/6-12
PO Box 520 52755 319-629-4610
Amber Jacque, prin. Fax 629-4324

Mc Gregor, Clayton, Pop. 856
MFL MarMac Community SD
Supt. — See Monona
MFL MarMac MS 200/4-8
PO Box 504 52157 563-873-3463
Denise Mueller, prin. Fax 873-2371

Madrid, Boone, Pop. 2,521
Madrid Community SD 600/K-12
201 N Main St 50156 515-795-1400
Brian Horn, supt. Fax 795-2121
madrid.k12.ia.us
Madrid HS 200/9-12
599 N Kennedy Ave 50156 515-795-3240
Kevin Williams, prin. Fax 795-4408
Madrid JHS 100/7-8
599 N Kennedy Ave 50156 515-795-3240
Kevin Williams, prin. Fax 795-4408

Malvern, Mills, Pop. 1,127
East Mills Community SD
Supt. — See Hastings
East Mills JSHS 200/7-12
1505 E 15th St 51551 712-624-8645
Linda Rempe, prin. Fax 624-8124

Manchester, Delaware, Pop. 5,134
West Delaware County Community SD 1,500/PK-12
701 New St 52057 563-927-3515
Dr. Kristen Rickey, supt. Fax 927-2785
www.w-delaware.k12.ia.us
West Delaware HS 500/9-12
605 New St 52057 563-927-3515
Tim Felderman, prin. Fax 927-6222
West Delaware MS 400/5-8
1101 Doctor St 52057 563-927-3515
Lisa Wunn, prin. Fax 927-9115

Manly, Worth, Pop. 1,311
Central Springs Community SD 800/PK-12
PO Box 190 50456 641-454-2211
Steve Ward, supt. Fax 454-2212
www.centralsprings.net/
Central Springs HS 300/9-12
PO Box 190 50456 641-454-2208
Ken Estes, prin. Fax 454-2212
Other Schools – See Nora Springs

Manning, Carroll, Pop. 1,493
IKM-Manning Community SD 600/PK-12
209 10th St 51455 712-655-3781
Thomas Ward, supt. Fax 655-3311
www.ikm-manning.k12.ia.us/
IKM-Manning HS 200/9-12
209 10th St 51455 712-655-3781
Brian Wall, prin. Fax 655-3311
IKM-Manning MS 200/4-8
209 10th St 51455 712-655-3761
Sharon Whitson, prin. Fax 654-9282

Manson, Calhoun, Pop. 1,685
Manson Northwest Webster Community SD 800/PK-12
PO Box 387 50563 712-469-2202
Mark Egli, supt. Fax 469-2298
www.mnwcougars.com
Manson Northwest Webster MSHS 300/7-12
1601 15th St 50563 712-469-2245
Kevin Wood, prin. Fax 469-3131

Mapleton, Monona, Pop. 1,204
Maple Valley-Anthon Oto Community SD 700/PK-12
501 S 7th St 51034 712-881-1315
Steve Oberg, supt. Fax 881-1316
www.mvaoschool.com
Maple Valley-Anthon Oto HS 200/9-12
501 S 7th St 51034 712-881-1317
Dan Dougherty, prin. Fax 881-1321
Other Schools – See Anthon

Maquoketa, Jackson, Pop. 5,978
Maquoketa Community SD 1,400/PK-12
612 S Vermont St 52060 563-652-4984
Chris Hoover, supt. Fax 652-6958
www.maquoketaschools.org
Maquoketa HS 600/9-12
600 Washington St 52060 563-652-2451
Mark Vervaecke, prin. Fax 652-5324
Maquoketa MS 300/6-8
200 E Locust St 52060 563-652-4956
Christine Snell, prin. Fax 652-6885

Marcus, Cherokee, Pop. 1,110
Marcus-Meriden-Cleghorn Community SD 300/PK-12
PO Box 667 51035 712-376-4171
Jan Brandhorst, supt. Fax 376-4302
www.mmcruroyals.org
MMCRU HS 100/9-12
PO Box 667 51035 712-376-4172
Jason Toenges, prin. Fax 376-4302

Marengo, Iowa, Pop. 2,516
Iowa Valley Community SD 600/PK-12
359 E Hilton St 52301 319-642-7714
Donita Joens, supt. Fax 642-3023
www.iowa-valley.k12.ia.us
Iowa Valley JSHS 200/7-12
359 E Hilton St 52301 319-642-3332
Shawn Kreman, prin. Fax 642-3023

Marion, Linn, Pop. 34,170
Linn-Mar Community SD 6,900/PK-12
2999 N 10th St 52302 319-447-3000
Dr. Quintin Shepherd Ph.D., supt. Fax 377-9252
www.linnmar.k12.ia.us/
Excelsior MS 900/6-8
3555 10th St 52302 319-447-3130
John Christian, prin. Fax 373-4930
Linn-Mar HS 1,900/9-12
3111 10th St 52302 319-447-3040
Dr. Jeffrey Gustason Ph.D., prin. Fax 377-0486
Oak Ridge MS 700/6-8
4901 Alburnett Rd 52302 319-447-3410
Erica Rausch, prin. Fax 373-3222

Marion ISD 2,000/PK-12
777 S 15th St 52302 319-377-4691
Joseph Chris Dyer, supt. Fax 377-4692
www.marion-isd.org
Marion HS 600/9-12
675 S 15th St 52302 319-377-9891
Greg Semler, prin. Fax 377-7621
Vernon MS 600/5-8
1350 4th Ave 52302 319-377-9401
Phillip Cochran, prin. Fax 377-7670

Marshalltown, Marshall, Pop. 27,096
Marshalltown Community SD 5,100/PK-12
1002 S 3rd Ave 50158 641-754-1000
Dr. Theron Schutte, supt. Fax 754-1003
www.marshalltown.k12.ia.us
Marshalltown HS 1,500/9-12
1602 S 2nd Ave 50158 641-754-1130
Jacquline Wyant, prin. Fax 754-1136
Miller MS 700/7-8
125 S 11th St 50158 641-754-1110
Patrick Rial, prin. Fax 754-1115

Iowa School of Beauty Post-Sec.
112 Nicholas Dr 50158 641-752-4223
Marshalltown Community College Post-Sec.
3700 S Center St 50158 641-752-7106

Martensdale, Warren, Pop. 462
Martensdale-St. Marys Community SD 600/PK-12
PO Box 350 50160 641-764-2466
Tom Wood, supt. Fax 764-2100
www.mstm.us/
Martensdale-St. Marys JSHS 300/7-12
PO Box 350 50160 641-764-2486
Josh Moser, prin. Fax 764-2100

Mason City, Cerro Gordo, Pop. 27,653
Mason City Community SD 4,000/PK-12
1515 S Pennsylvania Ave 50401 641-421-4400
Michael Penca, supt. Fax 421-4448
www.masoncityschools.org
Adams MS 600/7-8
29 S Illinois Ave 50401 641-421-4420
Jerry Siglin, prin. Fax 421-4476
Alternative HS 100/Alt
19 N Illinois Ave 50401 641-421-4426
David Ciccetti, prin. Fax 421-3362
Mason City HS 1,000/9-12
1700 4th St SE 50401 641-421-4431
Dan Long, prin. Fax 421-4523

Kaplan University Post-Sec.
2570 4th St SW 50401 641-423-2530
La' James College Post-Sec.
24 2nd St NE 50401 641-424-2161
Newman HS 200/9-12
2445 19th St SW 50401 641-423-6939
Tony Adams, prin. Fax 423-6653
North Iowa Area Community College Post-Sec.
500 College Dr 50401 641-423-1264
North Iowa Christian S 50/K-12
680 6th St SE 50401 641-423-6440
Jason Miner, prin. Fax 423-6440
North Iowa Mercy Health Center Post-Sec.
1000 4th St SW 50401 641-422-7722
World Wide College of Auctioneering Post-Sec.
PO Box 949 50402 800-423-5242

Massena, Cass, Pop. 355
CAM Community SD
Supt. — See Anita
CAM MS 100/6-8
207 E 6th St 50853 712-779-2212
Larry Hunt, prin. Fax 779-3365

Maxwell, Story, Pop. 916
Collins-Maxwell Community SD 500/PK-12
400 Metcalf St 50161 515-387-1115
Ottie Maxey, supt. Fax 387-8842
www.collins-maxwell.k12.ia.us
Collins-Maxwell MSHS 200/6-12
400 Metcalf St 50161 515-387-1115
Jordan Nelson, prin. Fax 387-8842

Mediapolis, Des Moines, Pop. 1,547
Mediapolis Community SD 800/PK-12
PO Box 358 52637 319-394-3101
Greg Ray, supt. Fax 394-3021
www.meposchools.org/
Mediapolis HS 300/9-12
PO Box 358 52637 319-394-3101
Roger Thornburg, prin. Fax 394-9198
Mediapolis MS 200/6-8
PO Box 358 52637 319-394-3101
Roger Thornburg, prin. Fax 394-9198

Melcher, Marion, Pop. 1,280
Melcher-Dallas Community SD 400/PK-12
PO Box 489 50163 641-947-3731
Randy Alger, supt. Fax 947-5002
mdcsd-ia.schoolloop.com
Melcher-Dallas HS 100/9-12
PO Box 158 50163 641-947-3731
Randy Alger, prin. Fax 947-2203
Melcher-Dallas JHS 100/6-8
PO Box 158 50163 641-947-3731
Randy Alger, prin. Fax 947-2203

Milford, Dickinson, Pop. 2,878
Okoboji Community SD 1,000/PK-12
PO Box 147 51351 712-338-4757
Todd Abrahamson, supt. Fax 338-4758
www.okoboji.k12.ia.us
Okoboji HS 300/9-12
PO Box 147 51351 712-338-2446
Brian Downing, prin. Fax 338-2550
Other Schools – See Arnolds Park

Missouri Valley, Harrison, Pop. 2,810
Missouri Valley Community SD 800/PK-12
109 E Michigan St 51555 712-642-2706
Deidre Drees, supt. Fax 642-2456
www.movalleyschools.org
Missouri Valley HS 200/9-12
605 Lincoln Hwy 51555 712-642-4149
Kristie Kruckman, prin. Fax 642-4624
Missouri Valley MS 200/6-8
607 Lincoln Hwy 51555 712-642-2707
Brent Hoesing, prin. Fax 642-3738

Mondamin, Harrison, Pop. 398
West Harrison Community SD 300/PK-12
410 Pine St 51557 712-646-2231
Lyle Schwartz, supt. Fax 646-2891
www.westharrison.org

West Harrison MSHS 200/4-12
410 Pine St 51557 712-646-2231
Fred Matlage, prin. Fax 646-2891

Monona, Clayton, Pop. 1,540
MFL MarMac Community SD 700/PK-12
PO Box 1040 52159 563-539-4795
Dr. Dale Crozier, supt. Fax 539-4913
www.mflmarmac.k12.ia.us
MFL MarMac HS 200/9-12
PO Box 1040 52159 563-539-2031
Larry Meyer, prin. Fax 539-4694
Other Schools – See Mc Gregor

Monroe, Jasper, Pop. 1,825
PCM Community SD 1,200/PK-12
PO Box 610 50170 641-259-2751
Brad Jermeland, supt. Fax 259-2753
www.pcmonroe.k12.ia.us
PCM HS 300/9-12
PO Box 610 50170 641-259-2315
Scott Bridges, prin. Fax 259-2317
Other Schools – See Prairie City

Montezuma, Poweshiek, Pop. 1,455
Montezuma Community SD 500/PK-12
PO Box 580 50171 641-623-5185
Dave Versteeg, supt. Fax 623-5733
montezuma-schools.org
Montezuma HS 200/9-12
PO Box 580 50171 641-623-5121
Brian Moretz, prin. Fax 623-5733
Montezuma JHS 100/7-8
PO Box 580 50171 641-623-5121
Brian Moretz, prin. Fax 623-5733

Monticello, Jones, Pop. 3,779
Monticello Community SD 1,100/PK-12
711 S Maple St 52310 319-465-5963
Brian Jaeger, supt. Fax 465-4092
www.monticello.k12.ia.us/
Monticello HS 300/9-12
850 E Oak St 52310 319-465-6597
Joan Young, prin. Fax 465-4253
Monticello MS 300/5-8
217 S Maple St 52310 319-465-3575
Brent Meier, prin. Fax 465-6959

Moravia, Appanoose, Pop. 658
Moravia Community SD 400/PK-12
505 N Trussell Ave 52571 641-724-3241
Brad Breon, supt. Fax 724-0629
www.moravia.k12.ia.us
Moravia JSHS 200/7-12
505 N Trussell Ave 52571 641-724-3241
Kathleen Carr, prin. Fax 724-0629

Moulton, Appanoose, Pop. 600
Moulton-Udell Community SD 200/PK-12
305 E 8th St 52572 641-642-3665
Brian VanderSluis, supt. Fax 642-3461
www.moulton-udell.k12.ia.us
Moulton-Udell JSHS 100/7-12
305 E 8th St 52572 641-642-8131
Shane Brown, prin. Fax 642-3461

Mount Ayr, Ringgold, Pop. 1,687
Mount Ayr Community SD 600/PK-12
1001 E Columbus St 50854 641-464-0500
Joe Drake, supt. Fax 464-2325
www.mtayrschools.org
Mount Ayr JSHS 300/7-12
1001 E Columbus St 50854 641-464-0510
Lynne Wallace, prin. Fax 464-2325

Mount Pleasant, Henry, Pop. 8,462
Mount Pleasant Community SD 2,000/PK-12
400 E Madison St 52641 319-385-7750
John Henriksen, supt. Fax 385-7788
www.mt-pleasant.k12.ia.us
Mount Pleasant HS 600/9-12
400 E Madison St 52641 319-385-7700
Todd Liechty, prin. Fax 385-7789
Mount Pleasant MS 500/6-8
400 E Madison St 52641 319-385-7730
Nathan Lange, prin. Fax 385-7735
WisdomQuest Education Center 50/Alt
400 E Madison St 52641 319-385-7709
Melissa Shull, prin. Fax 385-7715

Iowa Wesleyan College Post-Sec.
601 N Main St 52641 319-385-8021
Mount Pleasant Christian S 100/PK-12
1505 E Washington St 52641 319-385-8613
Tina Hill, admin. Fax 385-8415

Mount Vernon, Linn, Pop. 4,439
Mount Vernon Community SD 1,400/PK-12
525 Palisades Rd SW 52314 319-895-8845
Dr. Gary S. O'Malley, supt. Fax 895-8875
www.mountvernon.k12.ia.us
Mount Vernon HS 400/9-12
731 Palisades Rd SW 52314 319-895-8843
Steve Brand, prin. Fax 895-6185
Mount Vernon MS 400/5-8
525 Palisades Rd SW 52314 319-895-6254
Bob Haugse, prin. Fax 895-8134

Cornell College Post-Sec.
600 1st St SW 52314 319-895-4000

Moville, Woodbury, Pop. 1,596
Woodbury Central Community SD 600/PK-12
408 S 4th St 51039 712-873-3128
Doug Glackin, supt. Fax 873-3162
www.woodbury-central.k12.ia.us
Woodbury Central HS 200/9-12
408 S 4th St 51039 712-873-3128
Dan Bormann, prin. Fax 873-3162
Woodbury Central MS 100/6-8
408 S 4th St 51039 712-873-3128
Don Bormann, prin. Fax 873-3162

Murray, Clarke, Pop. 756
Murray Community SD 400/PK-12
PO Box 187 50174 641-447-2517
Alan Miller, supt. Fax 447-2313
www.murraycsd.org
Murray JSHS 200/7-12
PO Box 187 50174 641-447-2517
Tara Page, prin. Fax 447-2313

Muscatine, Muscatine, Pop. 22,599
Muscatine Community SD 5,000/PK-12
2900 Mulberry Ave 52761 563-263-7223
Dr. Jerry Riibe, supt. Fax 263-7729
www.muscatine.k12.ia.us
Central MS 600/6-8
901 Cedar St 52761 563-263-7784
Terry Hogenson, prin. Fax 263-0145
Muscatine HS 1,600/9-12
2705 Cedar St 52761 563-263-6141
Jared Smith, prin. Fax 264-1794
West MS 600/6-8
600 Kindler Ave 52761 563-263-0411
Jan Collinson, prin. Fax 263-6645

Muscatine Community College Post-Sec.
152 Colorado St 52761 563-288-6001

Nashua, Chickasaw, Pop. 1,656
Nashua-Plainfield Community SD 600/PK-12
PO Box 569 50658 641-435-4835
Randy Strabala, supt. Fax 435-4835
www.nashua-plainfield.k12.ia.us
Nashua-Plainfield JSHS 300/7-12
PO Box 569 50658 641-435-4166
Scott Striegel, prin. Fax 435-4167

Neola, Pottawattamie, Pop. 840
Tri-Center Community SD 700/PK-12
33980 310th St 51559 712-485-2257
Dr. Angie Huseman, supt. Fax 485-2411
www.tctrojans.org
Tri-Center HS 200/9-12
33980 310th St 51559 712-485-2257
Chad Harder, prin. Fax 485-2411
Tri-Center MS 200/6-8
33980 310th St 51559 712-485-2211
Chad Harder, prin. Fax 485-2402

Nevada, Story, Pop. 6,711
Nevada Community SD 1,600/PK-12
1035 15th St 50201 515-382-2783
Dr. Steven Gray, supt. Fax 382-2836
www.nevadacubs.org
Nevada HS 400/9-12
1035 15th St 50201 515-382-3521
Kody Asmus, prin. Fax 382-2935
Nevada MS 500/5-8
1035 15th St 50201 515-382-2751
Chris Schmidt, prin. Fax 382-2836

Newell, Buena Vista, Pop. 875
Newell-Fonda Community SD 300/PK-12
PO Box 297 50568 712-272-3324
Rob Olsen, supt. Fax 272-4276
www.newell-fonda.k12.ia.us
Newell-Fonda HS 100/9-12
PO Box 297 50568 712-272-3325
Alynn Coppock, prin. Fax 272-4276

New Hampton, Chickasaw, Pop. 3,557
New Hampton Community SD 1,100/PK-12
710 W Main St 50659 641-394-2134
Jay Jurrens, supt. Fax 394-2921
www.new-hampton.k12.ia.us
Education Options 50/Alt
710 W Main St 50659 641-394-2144
Sarah Updegraff, prin.
New Hampton HS 300/9-12
710 W Main St 50659 641-394-2144
Sarah Updegraff, prin. Fax 394-6046
New Hampton MS 300/5-8
206 W Main St 50659 641-394-2259
Susan Anderson, prin. Fax 394-2662

New Hartford, Butler, Pop. 512
Dike-New Hartford Community SD
Supt. — See Dike
Dike-New Hartford JHS 200/6-8
PO Box 214 50660 319-983-2206
Jerold Martinek, prin. Fax 983-2207

New London, Henry, Pop. 1,877
New London Community SD 500/PK-12
PO Box 97 52645 319-367-0512
Chad Wahls, supt. Fax 367-0513
www.new-london.k12.ia.us
New London JSHS 300/6-12
PO Box 97 52645 319-367-0500
Scott Kracht, prin. Fax 367-0501

New Sharon, Mahaska, Pop. 1,287
North Mahaska Community SD 600/PK-12
PO Box 89 50207 641-637-4187
Angela Livezey, supt. Fax 637-4559
nmwarhawks.org
North Mahaska JSHS 300/7-12
PO Box 89 50207 641-637-4187
Douglas Ray, prin. Fax 637-4559

Newton, Jasper, Pop. 15,101
Newton Community SD 2,600/PK-12
1302 1st Ave W 50208 641-792-5809
Bob Callaghan, supt. Fax 792-9159
www.newton.k12.ia.us
Berg MS 500/5-8
1900 N 5th Ave E 50208 641-792-7741
Lisa Sharp, prin. Fax 792-7779
Newton HS 800/9-12
800 E 4th St S 50208 641-792-5797
Bill Peters, prin. Fax 792-0005
WEST Academy Alternative S 100/Alt
1302 1st Ave W 50208 641-792-0335
Mike Moran, prin. Fax 792-0332

Des Moines Area Community College Post-Sec.
600 N 2nd Ave W 50208 641-791-3622

Nora Springs, Floyd, Pop. 1,424
Central Springs Community SD
Supt. — See Manly
Central Springs MS 200/4-8
PO Box 367 50458 641-749-5301
Robert Hoffman, prin. Fax 749-5898

North English, Iowa, Pop. 1,037
English Valleys Community SD 500/PK-12
PO Box 490 52316 319-664-3634
Donita Joens, supt. Fax 664-3636
www.english-valleys.k12.ia.us
English Valleys JSHS 200/7-12
PO Box 490 52316 319-664-3631
Heather Lightfoot, prin. Fax 664-3670

North Liberty, Johnson, Pop. 13,098
Iowa City Community SD
Supt. — See Iowa City
North Central JHS 500/7-8
180 Forevergreen Rd E 52317 319-688-1210
Colby Miller, prin. Fax 688-1219

Northwood, Worth, Pop. 1,968
Northwood-Kensett Community SD 600/PK-12
PO Box 289 50459 641-324-2021
Michael Crozier, supt. Fax 324-2092
www.nwood-kensett.k12.ia.us
Northwood-Kensett JSHS 200/7-12
PO Box 289 50459 641-324-2142
Keith Fritz, prin. Fax 324-2174

Norwalk, Warren, Pop. 8,841
Norwalk Community SD 2,200/PK-12
380 Wright Rd 50211 515-981-0676
Duane Magee, supt. Fax 981-0559
www.norwalk.k12.ia.us
Eastview 8/9 S 8-9
1600 North Ave 50211 515-981-9655
Dr. Jody Ratigan, prin. Fax 981-9706
Norwalk HS 600/10-12
1201 North Ave 50211 515-981-4201
Chris Basinger, prin. Fax 981-9875

Norwalk Christian Academy 50/K-12
225 North Ave 50211 515-313-7837
Kristi Ellis, admin.

Oakland, Pottawattamie, Pop. 1,517
Riverside Community SD
Supt. — See Carson
Riverside Community HS 300/7-12
PO Box 428 51560 712-482-6464
David Gute, prin. Fax 482-3074

Odebolt, Sac, Pop. 1,011
Odebolt-Arthur/Battle Creek-Ida Grove SD
Supt. — See Ida Grove
Odebolt-Arthur/Battle Creek-Ida Grove MS 100/6-8
600 S Maple St 51458 712-668-2827
Doug Mogensen, prin. Fax 668-2631

Oelwein, Fayette, Pop. 6,310
Oelwein Community SD 1,300/PK-12
307 8th Ave SE 50662 319-283-3536
Dan Diercks, supt. Fax 283-4497
www.oelwein.k12.ia.us
Oelwein HS 400/9-12
315 8th Ave SE 50662 319-283-2731
Josh Ehn, prin. Fax 283-1689
Oelwein MS 200/6-8
300 12th Ave SE 50662 319-283-3015
Mary Beth Steggall, prin. Fax 283-9813

Ogden, Boone, Pop. 2,032
Ogden Community SD 700/PK-12
PO Box 250 50212 515-275-2894
Tim Hoffman, supt. Fax 275-4537
www.ogdenschools.org
Ogden HS 200/9-12
PO Box 250 50212 515-275-4034
Jennifer Peter, prin. Fax 275-4972
Ogden MS 200/5-8
PO Box 250 50212 515-275-2912
Dave Neubauer, prin. Fax 275-2908

Onawa, Monona, Pop. 2,968
West Monona Community SD 500/PK-12
1314 15th St 51040 712-433-2043
Lyle Schwartz, supt. Fax 433-3803
www.westmonona.org
West Monona HS 200/9-12
1314 15th St 51040 712-433-2453
Tim Chesnut, prin. Fax 433-3803
West Monona MS 100/6-8
1314 15th St 51040 712-433-9098
Tim Chesnut, prin. Fax 433-1142

Orange City, Sioux, Pop. 5,966
MOC-Floyd Valley Community SD 1,400/PK-12
PO Box 257 51041 712-737-4873
Russ Adams, supt. Fax 737-8789
www.moc-fv.k12.ia.us/
MOC-Floyd Valley HS 400/9-12
615 8th St SE 51041 712-737-4871
Mike Mulder, prin. Fax 737-3933
Other Schools – See Alton

Northwestern College Post-Sec.
101 7th St SW 51041 712-707-7000

Unity Christian HS 300/9-12
216 Michigan Ave SW 51041 712-737-4114
Wayne Dykstra, prin. Fax 737-2686

Orient, Adair, Pop. 408
Orient-Macksburg Community SD 100/PK-12
PO Box 129 50858 641-337-5061
Clark Wicks, supt. Fax 337-5013
www.o-mschools.org
Orient-Macksburg Community S 100/PK-12
PO Box 129 50858 641-337-5061
Teresa Thompson, prin. Fax 337-5606

Osage, Mitchell, Pop. 3,601
Osage Community SD 1,000/PK-12
820 Sawyer Dr 50461 641-732-5381
Barbara Schwamman, supt. Fax 732-5381
www.osage.k12.ia.us
Osage HS 300/9-12
820 Sawyer Dr 50461 641-732-3102
Tim Hejhal, prin. Fax 732-3456
Osage MS 300/5-8
820 Sawyer Dr 50461 641-732-3127
Jay Marley, prin. Fax 732-5450

Osceola, Clarke, Pop. 4,887
Clarke Community SD 1,500/PK-12
802 N Jackson St 50213 641-342-4969
Steve Seid, supt. Fax 342-6101
www.clarke.k12.ia.us
Clarke Community HS 400/9-12
800 N Jackson St 50213 641-342-6505
Shane Stephens, prin. Fax 342-2213
Clarke Learning Center 50/Alt
802 N Jackson St 50213 641-342-2804
Shane Stephens, prin.
Clarke MS 200/7-8
800 N Jackson St 50213 641-342-4221
Jeff Sogard, prin. Fax 342-1528

Oskaloosa, Mahaska, Pop. 11,273
Oskaloosa Community SD 2,400/PK-12
PO Box 710 52577 641-673-8345
Russell Reiter, supt. Fax 673-8370
www.oskaloosa.k12.ia.us
Oskaloosa HS 700/9-12
1816 N 3rd St 52577 641-673-3407
Stacy Bandy, prin. Fax 672-2440
Oskaloosa MS 500/6-8
1704 N 3rd St 52577 641-673-8308
Andy Hotek, prin. Fax 673-3779

William Penn University Post-Sec.
201 Trueblood Ave 52577 800-677-9076

Ossian, Winneshiek, Pop. 842
South Winneshiek Community SD
Supt. — See Calmar
South Winneshiek MS 100/5-8
PO Box 298 52161 563-532-9365
Jason Halverson, prin. Fax 532-9855

Ottumwa, Wapello, Pop. 24,651
Ottumwa Community SD 4,500/PK-12
1112 N Van Buren Ave 52501 641-684-6596
Nicole Kooiker, supt. Fax 684-6522
www.ottumwaschools.com
Accelerated College Career Academy Alt
15260 Truman St 52501 641-683-1342
John Ohlinger, admin. Fax 684-6854
Evans MS 1,000/6-8
812 Chester Ave 52501 641-684-6511
Melissa Carson-Roark, prin. Fax 684-7386
Ottumwa HS 1,300/9-12
501 E 2nd St 52501 641-683-4444
Mark Hanson, prin. Fax 682-7528

Indian Hills Community College Post-Sec.
525 Grandview Ave 52501 641-683-5111
Iowa School of Beauty Post-Sec.
609 W 2nd St 52501 641-684-6504
Ottumwa Christian S PK-12
438 McKinley Ave 52501 641-683-9119
Arnold VanWardhuizen, prin. Fax 683-1084

Oxford, Johnson, Pop. 790
Clear Creek Amana Community SD 2,000/PK-12
PO Box 487 52322 319-828-4510
Tim Kuehl, supt. Fax 828-4743
www.ccaschools.org
Other Schools – See Tiffin

Packwood, Jefferson, Pop. 200
Pekin Community SD 600/PK-12
1062 Birch Ave 52580 319-695-3707
Dave Harper, supt. Fax 695-5130
www.pekincsd.org
Pekin HS 200/6-12
1062 Birch Ave 52580 319-695-3705
Tim Hadley, prin. Fax 661-2353

Panora, Guthrie, Pop. 1,114
Panorama Community SD 500/PK-12
PO Box 39 50216 641-755-4144
Shawn Holloway, supt. Fax 755-3008
www.panoramaschools.org
Panorama MSHS 200/6-12
PO Box 39 50216 641-755-2317
Thad Stanley, prin. Fax 755-3008

Parkersburg, Butler, Pop. 1,860
Aplington-Parkersburg Community SD 900/PK-12
610 N Johnson St 50665 319-346-1571
Jon Thompson, supt. Fax 346-1012
www.a-pcsd.net
Aplington-Parkersburg HS 300/9-12
610 N Johnson St 50665 319-346-1571
Aaron Thomas, prin. Fax 346-1012
Other Schools – See Aplington

Paullina, O'Brien, Pop. 1,052
South O'Brien Community SD 600/PK-12
PO Box 638 51046 712-949-2115
Dan Moore, supt. Fax 949-2149
www.s-obrien.k12.ia.us
South O'Brien Secondary S 300/7-12
PO Box 638 51046 712-949-3454
Steven Bruder, prin. Fax 949-3453

Pella, Marion, Pop. 10,224
Pella Community SD 2,300/PK-12
210 E University St 50219 641-628-1111
Greg Ebeling, supt. Fax 628-1116
www.pellaschools.org
Pella Community HS 700/9-12
212 E University St 50219 641-628-3870
Eric Nelson, prin. Fax 628-7402
Pella Community MS 300/7-8
613 E 13th St 50219 641-628-4784
Josh Manning, prin. Fax 628-6804

Central College Post-Sec.
812 University St 50219 641-628-9000
Pella Christian HS 300/9-12
300 Eagle Ln 50219 641-628-4440
Dan Van Kooten, prin. Fax 628-3530

Peosta, Dubuque, Pop. 1,367

Northeast Iowa Community College Post-Sec.
8342 NICC Dr 52068 563-556-5110

Perry, Dallas, Pop. 7,599
Perry Community SD 1,800/PK-12
1102 Willis Ave Ste 200 50220 515-465-4656
Lynn Ubben, supt. Fax 465-4025
www.perry.k12.ia.us/
Perry HS 600/9-12
1200 18th St 50220 515-465-3503
Dan Marburger, prin. Fax 465-5977
Perry MS 400/6-8
1200 18th St 50220 515-465-3531
Shaun Kruger, prin. Fax 465-8555

Pierson, Woodbury, Pop. 361
Kingsley-Pierson Community SD
Supt. — See Kingsley
Pierson MS 100/6-8
321 4th St 51048 712-375-5939
Robert Wiese, prin. Fax 375-5771

Pleasant Hill, Polk, Pop. 8,612
Southeast Polk Community SD 6,900/PK-12
8379 NE University Ave 50327 515-967-4294
Dirk Halupnik, supt. Fax 967-4257
www.southeastpolk.org/
Southeast Polk HS 2,000/9-12
7945 NE University Ave 50327 515-967-6631
Stephen Pettit, prin. Fax 967-5117
Southeast Polk JHS 1,000/7-8
8325 NE University Ave 50327 515-967-5509
Mike Dailey, prin. Fax 967-1676

Pleasantville, Marion, Pop. 1,681
Pleasantville Community SD 700/PK-12
415 Jones St 50225 515-848-0555
Dr. Tony Aylsworth, supt. Fax 848-0561
www.pvillecsd.org
Pleasantville HS 200/9-12
415 Jones St 50225 515-848-0541
Gary Friday, prin. Fax 848-0562
Pleasantville MS 200/6-8
415 Jones St 50225 515-848-0528
Gary Friday, prin. Fax 848-0561

Pocahontas, Pocahontas, Pop. 1,776
Pocahontas Area Community SD 500/PK-12
202 1st Ave SW 50574 712-335-4311
Joseph Kramer, supt. Fax 335-4206
www.pocahontas.k12.ia.us/
Pocahontas Area JSHS 300/7-12
205 2nd Ave NW 50574 712-335-4848
Roger Francis, prin. Fax 335-3420
Pocahontas Area Reg Learning Center 50/Alt
202 1st Ave SW 50574 712-335-5971
Roger Francis, prin.

Postville, Allamakee, Pop. 2,192
Postville Community SD 600/PK-12
PO Box 717 52162 563-864-7651
Tim Dugger, supt. Fax 864-7659
www.postville.k12.ia.us
Mott HS 200/7-12
PO Box 717 52162 563-864-7651
Brendan Knudtson, prin. Fax 864-7659

Prairie City, Jasper, Pop. 1,659
PCM Community SD
Supt. — See Monroe
PCM MS 300/6-8
PO Box 490 50228 515-994-2686
Blake Kielman, prin. Fax 994-2686

Preston, Jackson, Pop. 1,004
Easton Valley SD 400/PK-12
321 W School St 52069 563-689-4221
Chris Fee, supt. Fax 689-4222
www.eastonvalleycsd.com
Easton Valley HS 100/7-12
321 W School St 52069 563-689-4221
Tony Johnson, prin. Fax 689-4222

Redfield, Dallas, Pop. 817
West Central Valley Community SD
Supt. — See Stuart
West Central Valley MS 200/6-8
PO Box B 50233 515-833-2331
Anthony Lohse, prin. Fax 833-2629

Red Oak, Montgomery, Pop. 5,681
Red Oak Community SD 1,200/PK-12
2011 N 8th St 51566 712-623-6600
Tom Messinger, supt. Fax 623-6603
www.redoakschooldistrict.com
Red Oak HS 400/9-12
2011 N 8th St 51566 712-623-6610
Jeff Spotts, prin. Fax 623-6613
Red Oak MS 300/6-8
308 E Corning St 51566 712-623-6620
Nathan Perrien, prin. Fax 623-6626

Reinbeck, Grundy, Pop. 1,657
Gladbrook-Reinbeck Community SD 300/PK-12
300 Cedar St 50669 319-345-2712
David Hill, supt. Fax 345-2242
www.gr-rebels.net
Gladbrook-Reinbeck JSHS 200/7-12
600 Blackhawk St 50669 319-345-2921
Scot Aden, prin. Fax 345-6432

Remsen, Plymouth, Pop. 1,653
Remsen-Union Community SD 200/PK-8
511 Roosevelt Ave 51050 712-786-1101
Jan Brandhorst, supt. Fax 786-1104
www.mmcruroyals.org
MMCRU MS 100/5-8
511 Roosevelt Ave 51050 712-786-1101
Tobias Young, prin. Fax 786-1104

St. Marys HS 100/9-12
523 Madison St 51050 712-786-1433
Les Douma, prin. Fax 786-2499

Riceville, Howard, Pop. 779
Riceville Community SD 100/PK-12
912 Woodland Ave 50466 641-985-2288
Dr. Steve Nicholson, supt. Fax 985-4171
www.riceville.k12.ia.us
Riceville Community S 100/PK-12
912 Woodland Ave 50466 641-985-2288
Cory Schumann, prin. Fax 985-4171

Riverdale, Scott, Pop. 403
Pleasant Valley Community SD
Supt. — See Bettendorf
Pleasant Valley HS 1,300/9-12
604 Belmont Rd 52722 563-332-5151
Mike Zimmer, prin. Fax 332-8525

Riverside, Washington, Pop. 985
Highland Community SD 700/PK-12
1715 Vine Ave 52327 319-648-3822
Chris Armstrong, supt. Fax 648-4055
www.highland.k12.ia.us
Highland HS 200/9-12
1715 Vine Ave 52327 319-648-2891
Angela Hazelett, prin. Fax 648-3310
Highland MS 200/6-8
1715 Vine Ave 52327 319-648-5018
Angela Hazelett, prin. Fax 648-4055

Rockford, Floyd, Pop. 856
Rudd-Rockford-Marble Rock Community SD 500/PK-12
PO Box 218 50468 641-756-3610
Keith Turner, supt. Fax 756-2369
www.rockford.k12.ia.us
Rockford JSHS 200/7-12
PO Box 218 50468 641-756-3813
Keith Turner, prin. Fax 756-2369

Rock Rapids, Lyon, Pop. 2,533
Central Lyon Community SD 700/PK-12
1010 S Greene St 51246 712-472-2664
David Ackerman, supt. Fax 472-2115
www.centrallyon.org
Central Lyon HS 200/9-12
1010 S Greene St 51246 712-472-4051
David Ackerman, admin. Fax 472-2115
Central Lyon MS 100/6-8
1105 S Story St 51246 712-472-4041
Jason Engleman, prin. Fax 472-2346

Rock Valley, Sioux, Pop. 3,334
Rock Valley Community SD 800/PK-12
1712 20th Ave 51247 712-476-2701
Chad Janzen, supt. Fax 476-2125
www.rvcsd.org
Rock Valley JSHS 400/6-12
1712 20th Ave 51247 712-476-2701
Nicole Roder, prin. Fax 476-2125

Netherlands Reformed Christian S 400/K-12
712 20th Ave SE 51247 712-476-2821
Daniel Breuer, prin. Fax 476-5438

Rockwell, Cerro Gordo, Pop. 1,034
West Fork SD 600/PK-12
PO Box 60 50469 641-882-3236
Darrin Strike, supt. Fax 822-4882
www.westforkschool.org/
West Fork MS 200/5-8
PO Box 60 50469 641-822-3264
Tracy Peterson, prin. Fax 822-3273
Other Schools – See Sheffield

Rockwell City, Calhoun, Pop. 1,695
South Central Calhoun Community SD 900/PK-12
1000 Tonawanda St 50579 712-297-7341
Jeff Kruse, supt. Fax 297-7320
www.scc.k12.ia.us
South Central Calhoun MS 300/4-8
1000 Tonawanda St 50579 712-297-8111
Marc DeMoss, prin. Fax 297-7320
Other Schools – See Lake City

Roland, Story, Pop. 1,275
Roland-Story Community SD
Supt. — See Story City

Roland-Story MS 300/5-8
206 S Main St 50236 515-388-4348
Brian Town, prin. Fax 388-4435

Royal, Clay, Pop. 436
Clay Central/Everly Community SD 300/PK-12
PO Box 110 51357 712-933-2241
Dennis McClain, supt. Fax 933-2243
www.claycentraleverly.new.rschooltoday.com
Other Schools – See Everly

Ruthven, Palo Alto, Pop. 734
Ruthven-Ayrshire Community SD 200/PK-12
PO Box 159 51358 712-837-5211
Andrew Woiwood, supt. Fax 837-5210
www.ruthven.k12.ia.us
Ruthven-Ayrshire JSHS 100/5-12
PO Box 159 51358 712-837-5212
Jon Josephson, prin. Fax 837-5210

Sac City, Sac, Pop. 2,191
East Sac County SD
Supt. — See Lake View
East Sac County MS 300/5-8
300 S 11th St 50583 712-662-3259
Denny Olhausen, prin. Fax 662-4323
Sac County Flex Ed Center Alt
400 S 16th St 50583 712-662-4907
Gene Coon, lead tchr. Fax 662-7602

Saint Ansgar, Mitchell, Pop. 1,101
St. Ansgar Community SD 700/PK-12
PO Box 398 50472 641-713-4681
Jody Gray, supt. Fax 713-4042
www.st-ansgar.k12.ia.us
Saint Ansgar HS 200/9-12
PO Box 398 50472 641-713-4720
Lynn Baldus, prin. Fax 713-2449
Saint Ansgar MS 100/6-8
PO Box 398 50472 641-713-4720
Lynn Baldus, prin. Fax 713-4042

Sanborn, O'Brien, Pop. 1,402
Hartley-Melvin-Sanborn Community SD
Supt. — See Hartley
Hartley-Melvin-Sanborn MS 200/5-8
PO Box 557 51248 712-930-3281
Mark Dorhout, prin. Fax 930-5414

Schaller, Sac, Pop. 764
Schaller-Crestland Community SD 400/PK-8
PO Box 249 51053 712-275-4267
Jon Wiebers, supt. Fax 275-4269
www.rvraptors.org
Other Schools – See Early

Schleswig, Crawford, Pop. 871
Schleswig Community SD 200/PK-8
PO Box 250 51461 712-676-3313
Fax 676-3539
www.schleswig.k12.ia.us
Schleswig MS 100/5-8
PO Box 250 51461 712-676-3313
David Galvin, prin. Fax 676-3539

Sergeant Bluff, Woodbury, Pop. 4,152
Sergeant Bluff-Luton Community SD 1,600/PK-12
201 Port Neal Rd 51054 712-943-4338
Rod Earleywine, supt. Fax 943-1131
www.sblschools.com
Sergeant Bluff-Luton HS 500/9-12
708 Warrior Rd 51054 712-943-5561
Jason Klingingsmith, prin. Fax 943-5887
Sergeant Bluff-Luton MS 400/6-8
208 Port Neal Rd 51054 712-943-4235
Bill McKelvey, prin. Fax 943-8780

Seymour, Wayne, Pop. 696
Seymour Community SD 300/PK-12
100 S Park Ave 52590 641-898-2291
Brad Breon, supt. Fax 898-7500
www.seymour.k12.ia.us/
Seymour JSHS 100/7-12
100 S Park Ave 52590 641-898-2291
Jamie Houser, prin. Fax 898-7500

Sheffield, Franklin, Pop. 1,165
West Fork SD
Supt. — See Rockwell
West Fork HS 200/9-12
PO Box 617 50475 641-892-4461
Clyde Tarrence, prin. Fax 892-4335

Sheldon, O'Brien, Pop. 5,156
Sheldon Community SD 1,000/PK-12
1700 E 4th St 51201 712-324-2504
Robin Spears, supt. Fax 324-5607
sheldonschools.com
Sheldon HS 300/9-12
1700 E 4th St 51201 712-324-2501
Sherrie Zeutenhorst, prin. Fax 324-5607
Sheldon MS 300/5-8
310 23rd Ave 51201 712-324-4346
Cindy Barwick, prin. Fax 324-4347

Northwest Iowa Community College Post-Sec.
603 W Park St 51201 712-324-5061

Shenandoah, Page, Pop. 5,088
Shenandoah Community SD 1,000/PK-12
304 W Nishna Rd 51601 712-246-1581
Dr. Kerri Nelson Ed.D., supt. Fax 246-3722
www.shenandoah.k12.ia.us
Shenandoah HS 300/9-12
1000 Mustang Dr 51601 712-246-4727
Sandy Hilding, prin. Fax 246-2842
Shenandoah MS 300/5-8
601 Dr Creighton Cir 51601 712-246-2520
Jason Shaffer, prin. Fax 246-2496

Sibley, Osceola, Pop. 2,785
Sibley-Ocheyedan Community SD 800/PK-12
120 11th Ave NE 51249 712-754-2533
Bill Boer, supt. Fax 754-2534
www.thegenerals.org
Sibley-Ocheyedan HS 200/9-12
120 11th Ave NE 51249 712-754-3601
Brent Town, prin. Fax 754-2534
Sibley-Ocheyedan MS 200/5-8
120 11th Ave NE 51249 712-754-2542
Fax 754-3651

Sidney, Fremont, Pop. 1,125
Sidney Community SD 400/PK-12
PO Box 609 51652 712-374-2141
Gregg Cruickshank, supt. Fax 374-2013
sidneyschools.org
Sidney JSHS 200/7-12
PO Box 609 51652 712-374-2731
Bill Huntington, prin. Fax 374-2013

Sigourney, Keokuk, Pop. 2,051
Sigourney Community SD 600/PK-12
909 E Pleasant Valley St 52591 641-622-2025
Dave Harper, supt. Fax 622-2319
www.sigourneyschools.com
Sigourney JSHS 300/7-12
907 E Pleasant Valley St 52591 641-622-2010
Shannon Webb, prin. Fax 622-2047

Sioux Center, Sioux, Pop. 7,004
Sioux Center Community SD 1,100/PK-12
550 9th St NE 51250 712-722-2985
Patrick O'Donnell, supt. Fax 722-2986
www.sioux-center.k12.ia.us
Sioux Center HS 300/9-12
550 9th St NE 51250 712-722-2981
Gary McEldowney, prin. Fax 722-2930
Sioux Center MS 300/5-8
550 9th St NE 51250 712-722-3783
Julie Schley, prin. Fax 722-3782

Dordt College Post-Sec.
498 4th Ave NE 51250 712-722-6000

Sioux City, Woodbury, Pop. 80,564
Sioux City Community SD 11,800/PK-12
627 4th St 51101 712-279-6667
Dr. Paul Gausman, supt. Fax 279-6690
www.siouxcityschools.org
East HS 1,400/9-12
5011 Mayhew Ave 51106 712-274-4000
Richard Todd, prin. Fax 274-4670
East MS 1,000/6-8
5401 Lorraine Ave 51106 712-274-4030
Dr. Michael Rogers, prin. Fax 274-4668
North HS 1,300/9-12
4200 Cheyenne Blvd 51104 712-239-7000
Ryan Dumkreiger, prin. Fax 239-8270
North MS 1,000/6-8
2101 Outer Dr N 51108 712-279-6804
Shawn Chesteen, prin. Fax 277-5941
West HS 1,200/9-12
2001 Casselman St 51103 712-279-6772
Scott Cole, prin. Fax 279-6790
West MS 900/6-8
3301 W 19th St 51103 712-279-6813
Katie Towler, prin. Fax 277-6138

Bio-Chi Institute Post-Sec.
1925 Geneva St 51103 712-252-1157
Bishop Heelan HS 500/9-12
1021 Douglas St 51105 712-252-0573
Chris Bork, prin. Fax 252-4897
Briar Cliff University Post-Sec.
3303 Rebecca St 51104 712-279-5321
Holy Cross S / Blessed Sacrament Ctr 300/3-8
3030 Jackson St 51104 712-277-4739
Michael Sweeney, prin. Fax 258-3698
Iowa School of Beauty Post-Sec.
3320 Line Dr 51106 712-274-9733
Mater Dei S - Nativity Center 100/5-8
4243 Natalia Way 51106 712-274-0268
Mary Fischer, prin. Fax 274-0377
Mercy Medical Center - Sioux City Post-Sec.
801 5th St 51101 712-279-2018
Morningside College Post-Sec.
1501 Morningside Ave 51106 712-274-5000
St. Luke's College Post-Sec.
2720 Stone Park Blvd 51104 712-279-3149
Siouxland Community Christian S 200/PK-12
6100 Morningside Ave 51106 712-276-4732
Steven Peters, supt. Fax 276-4752
Western Iowa Tech Community College Post-Sec.
4647 Stone Ave 51106 712-274-6400

Sioux Rapids, Buena Vista, Pop. 775
Sioux Central Community SD 600/PK-12
4440 US Highway 71 50585 712-283-2571
Scott Williamson, supt. Fax 283-2989
www.siouxcentral.org
Sioux Central HS 200/9-12
4440 US Highway 71 50585 712-283-2571
Jeff Scharn, prin. Fax 283-2285
Sioux Central MS 100/7-8
4440 US Highway 71 50585 712-283-2571
Jeff Scharn, prin. Fax 283-2285

Sloan, Woodbury, Pop. 970
Westwood Community SD 500/PK-12
1000 Rebel Way 51055 712-428-3355
Jay Lutt, supt. Fax 428-3246
www.wwrebels.org
Westwood JSHS 200/7-12
1000 Rebel Way 51055 712-428-3303
Matt Drees, prin. Fax 428-3246

Solon, Johnson, Pop. 2,019
Solon Community SD 1,400/PK-12
301 S Iowa St 52333 319-624-3401
Davis Eidahl, supt. Fax 624-2518
www.solon.k12.ia.us
Solon HS 500/9-12
600 W 5th St 52333 319-624-3401
Nathan Wear, prin. Fax 624-4091
Solon MS 400/5-8
313 S Iowa St 52333 319-624-3401
Mike Herdliska, prin. Fax 624-2518

Spencer, Clay, Pop. 11,130
Spencer Community SD 1,400/PK-12
PO Box 200 51301 712-262-8950
Terry Hemann, supt. Fax 262-1116
www.spenceriowaschools.com/
Spencer HS 600/9-12
PO Box 200 51301 712-262-1700
Elli Wiemers, prin. Fax 262-5704
Spencer MS 400/6-8
PO Box 200 51301 712-262-3345
Pat Hamilton, prin. Fax 264-3444

Iowa Lakes Community College Post-Sec.
1900 Grand Ave Ste B1 51301 712-262-7141

Spillville, Winneshiek, Pop. 366

C F S Consolidated S 100/4-8
PO Box 68 52168 563-562-3617
Kathryn Schmitt, prin. Fax 562-3292

Spirit Lake, Dickinson, Pop. 4,786
Spirit Lake Community SD 1,300/PK-12
2701 Hill Ave 51360 712-336-2820
Dr. David Smith Ed.D., supt. Fax 336-4641
www.spirit-lake.k12.ia.us/
Spirit Lake HS 400/9-12
2701 Hill Ave 51360 712-336-3707
Angela Olsen, prin. Fax 336-3714
Spirit Lake MS 400/5-8
2701 Hill Ave 51360 712-336-1370
Terry Bruinsma, prin. Fax 336-4758

The Faust Institute of Cosmetology Post-Sec.
1543 18th St Ste 15 51360 712-336-0512

Springville, Linn, Pop. 1,066
Springville Community SD 400/PK-12
400 Academy St 52336 319-854-6197
Pat Hocking, supt. Fax 854-6199
www.springville.k12.ia.us
Springville JSHS 200/6-12
400 Academy St 52336 319-854-6196
Nick Merritt, prin. Fax 854-7891

Stanton, Montgomery, Pop. 688
Stanton Community SD 200/K-12
PO Box 400 51573 712-829-2162
Dr. Chris Herrick, supt. Fax 829-2164
www.stantonschools.com
Stanton MSHS 100/6-12
PO Box 400 51573 712-829-2162
Kevin Blunt, prin. Fax 829-2164

Stanwood, Cedar, Pop. 676
North Cedar Community SD 600/PK-12
PO Box 247 52337 563-942-3358
John Dayton, supt. Fax 942-0014
www.north-cedarstu.org
Other Schools – See Clarence

State Center, Marshall, Pop. 1,450
West Marshall Community SD 900/PK-12
PO Box 670 50247 641-483-2660
Jacy Large, supt. Fax 483-2665
www.w-marshall.k12.ia.us
West Marshall HS 200/9-12
PO Box 670 50247 641-483-2136
Kristian Einsweiler, prin. Fax 483-2172
West Marshall MS 200/6-8
PO Box 340 50247 641-483-2165
Jeff Barry, prin. Fax 483-3095

Storm Lake, Buena Vista, Pop. 10,411
Storm Lake Community SD 2,400/PK-12
PO Box 638 50588 712-732-8060
Dr. Carl Turner Ed.D., supt. Fax 732-8063
www.slcsd.org
Storm Lake HS 700/9-12
PO Box 638 50588 712-732-8065
Beau Ruleaux, prin. Fax 732-8068
Storm Lake MS 600/5-8
PO Box 638 50588 712-732-8080
Jay Slight, prin. Fax 732-8084

Buena Vista University Post-Sec.
610 W 4th St 50588 712-749-2351
St. Mary MSHS 200/6-12
304 Seneca St 50588 712-732-4166
Cindy Cone, prin. Fax 732-4590
The Faust Institute of Cosmetology Post-Sec.
1290 Lake Ave 50588 712-732-6571

Story City, Story, Pop. 3,411
Roland-Story Community SD 1,100/PK-12
1009 Story St 50248 515-733-4301
Matt Patton, supt. Fax 733-2131
rolandstory.school
Roland-Story HS 300/9-12
1009 Story St 50248 515-733-4329
Steve Schlatter, prin. Fax 733-2131
Other Schools – See Roland

Stuart, Guthrie, Pop. 1,630
West Central Valley Community SD 900/PK-12
3299 White Pole Rd 50250 515-523-2187
Dr. David Arnold, supt. Fax 523-1166
www.wcv.k12.ia.us
West Central Valley HS 300/9-12
3299 White Pole Rd 50250 515-523-1313
Rusty Shockley, prin. Fax 523-2765
Other Schools – See Redfield

Sully, Jasper, Pop. 821
Lynnville-Sully Community SD 500/K-12
PO Box 210 50251 641-594-4445
Shane Ehresman, supt. Fax 594-2770
www.lshawks.org
Lynnville-Sully HS 200/9-12
PO Box 210 50251 641-594-4445
Shane Ehresman, prin. Fax 594-2770
Lynnville-Sully MS 100/6-8
PO Box 210 50251 641-594-4445
Teri Bowlin, prin. Fax 594-2770

Sumner, Bremer, Pop. 2,021
Sumner-Fredericksburg Community SD 900/PK-12
802 W 6th St 50674 563-578-3341
Rick Pederson, supt. Fax 578-3424
www.sfcougars.k12.ia.us
Sumner-Fredericksburg HS 200/9-12
802 W 6th St 50674 563-578-3341
Allan Eckelman, prin. Fax 578-3424
Other Schools – See Fredericksburg

Swea City, Kossuth, Pop. 535
North Union SD
Supt. — See Armstrong
North Union MS 100/6-8
PO Box 567 50590 515-272-4361
Julie Runksmeier, prin. Fax 272-4391

Tabor, Fremont, Pop. 1,036
Fremont-Mills Community SD 500/PK-12
PO Box 310 51653 712-629-2325
Dr. Christopher Herrick, supt. Fax 629-5155
www.fmtabor.org
Fremont-Mills MSHS 200/7-12
PO Box 310 51653 712-629-2325
Jeremy Christiansen, prin. Fax 629-5155

Tama, Tama, Pop. 2,803
South Tama County Community SD 1,400/PK-12
1702 Harding St 52339 641-484-4811
Mary Jones, supt. Fax 484-4861
www.s-tama.k12.ia.us/
Partnership HS 50/Alt
215 W 9th St 52339 641-484-3085
Fax 484-3924
South Tama County HS 400/9-12
1715 Harding St 52339 641-484-4345
Roy Frakes, prin. Fax 484-5152
Other Schools – See Toledo

Thornburg, Keokuk, Pop. 67
Tri-County Community SD 300/PK-12
PO Box 17 50255 641-634-2408
Dennis Phelps, supt. Fax 634-2145
www.tri-countyschools.com
Tri-County HS 100/9-12
PO Box 17 50255 641-634-2636
Clay Harrold, prin. Fax 634-2145
Tri-County JHS 50/7-8
PO Box 17 50255 641-634-2636
Clay Harrold, prin. Fax 634-2145

Tiffin, Johnson, Pop. 1,895
Clear Creek Amana Community SD
Supt. — See Oxford
Clear Creek Amana HS 600/9-12
PO Box 199 52340 319-545-2361
Mark Moody, prin. Fax 545-2863
Clear Creek Amana MS 400/6-8
PO Box 530 52340 319-545-4490
Brad Fox, prin. Fax 545-4094

Tipton, Cedar, Pop. 3,193
Tipton Community SD 1,000/PK-12
400 E 6th St 52772 563-886-6121
Dr. Marlene Johnson, supt. Fax 886-2341
www.tipton.k12.ia.us
Tipton HS 300/9-12
400 E 6th St 52772 563-886-6027
Chris Habben, prin. Fax 886-2341
Tipton MS 300/5-8
400 E 6th St 52772 563-886-6025
Sue O'Donnell, prin. Fax 886-2555

Toledo, Tama, Pop. 2,265
South Tama County Community SD
Supt. — See Tama
South Tama County MS 300/5-8
201 S Green St 52342 641-484-4121
Benjamin Adams, prin. Fax 484-2699

Traer, Tama, Pop. 1,686
North Tama County Community SD 500/K-12
605 Walnut St 50675 319-478-2265
David Hill, supt. Fax 478-2917
www.n-tama.k12.ia.us
North Tama JSHS 200/7-12
605 Walnut St 50675 319-478-2265
Paul Rea, prin. Fax 478-2917

Treynor, Pottawattamie, Pop. 919
Treynor Community SD 800/K-12
PO Box 369 51575 712-487-3414
Kevin Elwood, supt. Fax 487-3332
www.treynorschools.org
Treynor HS 200/9-12
PO Box 369 51575 712-487-3804
Gary McNeal, prin. Fax 487-3332
Treynor MS 200/6-8
PO Box 369 51575 712-487-3181
Jenny Berens, prin. Fax 487-3567

Tripoli, Bremer, Pop. 1,304
Tripoli Community SD 400/PK-12
209 8th Ave SW 50676 319-882-4202
Troy Heller, supt. Fax 882-3103
www.tripoli.k12.ia.us
Tripoli JSHS 200/6-12
209 8th Ave SW 50676 319-882-4202
Troy Heller, supt. Fax 882-3103

Troy Mills, Linn
North Linn Community SD 500/PK-12
PO Box 200 52344 319-224-3291
Chris Fenster, supt. Fax 224-3727
www.northlinncsd.org
North Linn HS 200/9-12
PO Box 200 52344 319-224-3291
Scott Beaty, prin. Fax 224-3232
North Linn MS 200/6-8
PO Box 200 52344 319-224-3291
Scott Beaty, prin. Fax 224-3232

Truro, Madison, Pop. 481
Interstate 35 Community SD 900/PK-12
PO Box 79 50257 641-765-4291
Kevin Fiene, supt. Fax 765-4593
www.i-35.k12.ia.us
Interstate 35 HS 300/9-12
PO Box 79 50257 641-765-4818
Steve Kaster, prin. Fax 765-4820
Interstate 35 MS 200/6-8
PO Box 200 50257 641-765-4908
Steve Kaster, prin. Fax 765-4905

Underwood, Pottawattamie, Pop. 909
Underwood Community SD 700/PK-12
PO Box 130 51576 712-566-2332
Edward Hawks, supt. Fax 566-2070
www.underwoodeagles.org/
Underwood HS 200/9-12
PO Box 130 51576 712-566-2703
Matt McDonough, prin. Fax 566-2712
Underwood MS 200/6-8
PO Box 130 51576 712-566-2332
Beau Jacobsen, prin. Fax 566-2070

Union, Hardin, Pop. 394
BCLUW Community SD
Supt. — See Conrad
BCLUW MS 200/5-8
704 Commercial St 50258 641-486-5371
Dirk Borgman, prin. Fax 486-5372

Urbandale, Polk, Pop. 38,851
Urbandale Community SD 4,100/PK-12
11152 Aurora Ave 50322 515-457-5000
Steve Bass, supt. Fax 457-5018
www.urbandaleschools.com
Urbandale HS 1,300/9-12
7111 Aurora Ave 50322 515-457-6800
Dr. Brian Coppess, prin. Fax 457-6810
Urbandale MS 900/6-8
7701 Aurora Ave 50322 515-457-6600
Loren DeKruyf, prin. Fax 457-6610

Des Moines Christian S 1,000/PK-12
13007 Douglas Pkwy Ste 100 50323 515-252-2480
Cade Lambert, supt. Fax 251-6911
Kaplan University Post-Sec.
4655 121st St 50323 515-727-2100

Van Horne, Benton, Pop. 678
Benton Community SD 1,200/PK-12
PO Box 70 52346 319-228-8701
Gary Zittergruen, supt. Fax 228-8254
www.benton.k12.ia.us
Benton Community HS 500/9-12
PO Box 70 52346 319-228-8701
James Bieschke, prin. Fax 228-8747
Benton Community MS 200/7-8
PO Box 70 52346 319-228-8701
Kal Goodchild, prin. Fax 228-8747

Van Meter, Dallas, Pop. 1,006
Van Meter Community SD 800/K-12
PO Box 257 50261 515-996-9960
Deron Durflinger, supt. Fax 996-2488
www.vmbulldogs.com/
Van Meter HS 400/9-12
PO Box 257 50261 515-996-2221
Deron Durflinger, prin. Fax 996-2488
Van Meter MS 200/6-8
PO Box 257 50261 515-996-2221
Adam Lamoureux, prin. Fax 996-2488

Ventura, Cerro Gordo, Pop. 712
Garner-Hayfield-Ventura Community SD
Supt. — See Garner
Garner-Hayfield-Ventura JHS 7-8
110 S Main St 50482 641-829-4484
Debra Steenhard, prin. Fax 829-3995

Victor, Iowa, Pop. 887
H-L-V Community SD 400/PK-12
402 5th St 52347 319-647-2161
Brad Hohensee, supt. Fax 647-2164
www.hlv.k12.ia.us
H-L-V JSHS 100/7-12
402 5th St 52347 319-647-2161
Cory Lahndorf, prin. Fax 647-2164

Villisca, Montgomery, Pop. 1,244
Southwest Valley SD 800/PK-12
406 E 3rd St 50864 712-826-2552
William Stone, supt. Fax 826-4072
www.southwestvalley.org
Southwest Valley MS 200/6-8
406 E 3rd St 50864 712-826-2552
Lora Top, prin. Fax 826-4072
Other Schools – See Corning

Vinton, Benton, Pop. 5,202
Vinton-Shellsburg Community SD 1,600/PK-12
1502 C Ave 52349 319-436-4728
Mary Jo Hainstock, supt. Fax 472-3889
www.vscsd.org
Vinton-Shellsburg HS 500/9-12
210 W 21st St 52349 319-436-4728
Matt Kingsbury, prin. Fax 472-5704
Vinton-Shellsburg MS 300/6-8
212 W 15th St 52349 319-436-4728
Shelly Petersen, prin. Fax 472-4014

Iowa Braille and Sight Saving School Post-Sec.
1002 G Ave 52349 319-472-5221

Walcott, Scott, Pop. 1,613
Davenport Community SD
Supt. — See Davenport
Walcott IS 400/6-8
545 E James St 52773 563-445-5200
Mike Lawler, prin. Fax 445-5959

Wapello, Louisa, Pop. 2,049
Wapello Community SD 700/PK-12
406 Mechanic St 52653 319-523-3641
Mike Peterson, supt. Fax 523-8151
www.wapello.k12.ia.us
Wapello HS 200/9-12
501 Buchanan Ave 52653 319-523-3241
Steve Bohlen, prin. Fax 523-4408
Wapello JHS 100/7-8
501 Buchanan Ave 52653 319-523-8131
Steve Bohlen, prin. Fax 523-4408

Washington, Washington, Pop. 7,169
Washington Community SD 1,700/PK-12
PO Box 926 52353 319-653-6543
Jeff Dicks, supt. Fax 653-5685
www.washington.k12.ia.us
Washington HS 500/9-12
PO Box 271 52353 319-653-2143
Erik Buchholz, prin. Fax 653-6751
Washington MS 500/6-8
PO Box 490 52353 319-653-5414
Curt Mayer, prin. Fax 653-7350

Waterloo, Black Hawk, Pop. 66,424
Waterloo Community SD 10,900/PK-12
1516 Washington St 50702 319-433-1800
Dr. Jane Lindaman, supt. Fax 433-1886
www.waterloo.k12.ia.us
Carver Academy 500/6-8
1505 Logan Ave 50703 319-433-2500
Mike Landers, prin. Fax 433-2548
Central MS 500/6-8
1350 Katoski Dr 50701 319-433-2100
Alissa Richards, prin. Fax 433-2149
East HS 1,100/9-12
214 High St 50703 319-433-2400
Marla Padget, prin. Fax 433-2498
Expo Alternative Learning Center 500/Alt
1410 Independence Ave 50703 319-433-1930
Clay Wieland, prin. Fax 433-1933
Hoover MS 800/6-8
630 Hillcrest Rd 50701 319-433-2830
Michael Fisher, prin. Fax 433-2843
West HS 1,600/9-12
425 E Ridgeway Ave 50702 319-433-2700
Andrew Miehe, prin. Fax 433-2749
Other Schools – See Evansdale

Allen College Post-Sec.
1825 Logan Ave 50703 319-226-2000
Blessed Maria Assunta Pallotta MS 6-8
3225 W 9th St 50702 319-232-6592
Tom Novotney, prin. Fax 232-6963
Capri College Post-Sec.
2323 Crossroads Blvd 50702 319-234-2600
College of Hair Design Post-Sec.
722 Water St Ste 201 50703 319-232-9995
Columbus HS 300/9-12
3231 W 9th St 50702 319-233-3358
Aaron Ferrie, prin. Fax 235-0733
Covenant Medical Center Post-Sec.
3421 W 9th St 50702 319-272-7296
Hawkeye Community College Post-Sec.
PO Box 8015 50704 319-296-2320
Waterloo Christian S 100/PK-12
1307 W Ridgeway Ave 50701 319-235-9309
Jennifer Neifer, head sch Fax 833-4780

Waukee, Dallas, Pop. 13,637
Waukee Community SD 8,200/PK-12
560 SE University Ave 50263 515-987-5161
Dr. Cindi McDonald, supt. Fax 987-2701
www.waukeeschools.org
Prairieview S 500/8-9
655 SE University Ave 50263 515-987-2770
Juley Murphy-Tiernan, prin. Fax 987-2789
Timberline S 700/8-9
2605 SE LA Grant Pkwy 50263 515-987-5161
Brady Fleming, prin. Fax 987-9051
Waukee SHS 1,500/10-12
555 SE University Ave 50263 515-987-5163
Cary Justmann, prin. Fax 987-2784

Waukon, Allamakee, Pop. 3,873
Allamakee Community SD 1,100/PK-12
1059 3rd Ave NW 52172 563-568-3409
Dave Herold, supt. Fax 568-2677
www.allamakee.k12.ia.us/
Waukon HS 400/9-12
1061 3rd Ave NW 52172 563-568-3466
Mike Hardy, prin. Fax 568-3165

Waukon MS 200/6-8
1059 3rd Ave NW 52172 563-568-6321
Jennifer Garin, prin. Fax 568-2677

Waverly, Bremer, Pop. 9,752
Waverly-Shell Rock Community SD 2,100/PK-12
1415 4th Ave SW 50677 319-352-3630
Dr. Ed Klamfoth, supt. Fax 352-5676
www.wsr.k12.ia.us
Greenview Alternative S 50/Alt
1405 4th Ave SW 50677 319-352-9273
Brady Weber, prin.
Waverly-Shell Rock HS 600/9-12
1405 4th Ave SW 50677 319-352-2087
David Fox, prin. Fax 352-2098
Waverly-Shell Rock MS 700/5-8
501 Heritage Way 50677 319-352-3632
Jeremy Langner, prin. Fax 352-5199

Wartburg College Post-Sec.
PO Box 1003 50677 319-352-8200

Wayland, Henry, Pop. 957
Waco Community SD 500/PK-12
PO Box 158 52654 319-256-6200
Jeff Dicks, supt. Fax 256-6213
www.wacocsd.org
Waco JSHS 200/7-12
PO Box 158 52654 319-256-6200
Jeff Nance, prin. Fax 256-6211

Webster City, Hamilton, Pop. 7,961
Webster City Community SD 1,600/PK-12
PO Box 10 50595 515-832-9200
Mike Sherwood, supt. Fax 832-9204
www.webster-city.k12.ia.us
Webster City HS 500/9-12
PO Box 10 50595 515-832-9210
Brent Jorth, prin. Fax 832-9215
Webster City MS 400/5-8
PO Box 10 50595 515-832-9220
Jerry Buseman, prin. Fax 832-9225

Wellman, Washington, Pop. 1,387
Mid-Prairie Community SD 1,300/PK-12
PO Box 150 52356 319-646-6093
Mark Schneider, supt. Fax 646-2093
www.mid-prairie.k12.ia.us
Alternative Learning Center 50/Alt
PO Box 150 52356 319-646-6096
Amy Shalla, prin. Fax 646-2093
Mid-Prairie HS 400/9-12
PO Box 150 52356 319-646-6091
Jay Strickland, prin. Fax 646-6097
Other Schools – See Kalona

West Bend, Palo Alto, Pop. 779
West Bend - Mallard Community SD 400/K-12
PO Box 247 50597 515-887-7821
Amanda Schmidt, supt. Fax 887-7853
www.west-bend.k12.ia.us
West Bend - Mallard HS 100/9-12
PO Box 247 50597 515-887-7831
Paul Peppmeier, prin. Fax 887-7853
West Bend - Mallard MS 100/5-8
PO Box 247 50597 515-887-7831
Paul Peppmeier, prin. Fax 887-7853

West Branch, Cedar, Pop. 2,295
West Branch Community SD 900/PK-12
148 N Oliphant St 52358 319-643-7213
Kevin Hatfield, supt. Fax 643-7122
www.west-branch.k12.ia.us
West Branch HS 300/9-12
900 W Main St 52358 319-643-7216
Shannon Bucknell, prin. Fax 643-2415
West Branch MS 300/5-8
225 N Maple St 52358 319-643-5324
Sara Oswald, prin. Fax 643-5447

Scattergood Friends S 100/9-12
1951 Delta Ave 52358 319-643-7600
Thomas Weber, head sch Fax 643-7485

West Burlington, Des Moines, Pop. 2,909
West Burlington ISD 900/PK-12
607 Ramsey St 52655 319-752-8747
David Schmitt, supt. Fax 754-9382
www.wbschools.us
West Burlington HS 300/9-12
408 W Van Weiss Blvd 52655 319-752-7138
Bruce Snodgrass, prin. Fax 754-0075
West Burlington JHS 200/6-8
408 W Van Weiss Blvd 52655 319-752-7138
Bruce Snodgrass, prin. Fax 754-0075

Southeastern Community College Post-Sec.
PO Box 180 52655 319-752-2731

West Des Moines, Polk, Pop. 55,623
West Des Moines Community SD 9,000/PK-12
3550 Mills Civic Pkwy 50265 515-633-5000
Dr. Lisa Remy, supt. Fax 633-5099
www.wdmcs.org
Stilwell JHS 700/7-8
1601 Vine St 50265 515-633-6000
Eric Boyle, prin. Fax 633-6099
Valley HS 2,000/10-12
3650 Woodland Ave 50266 515-633-4000
Tim Miller, prin. Fax 633-4099
Valley Southwoods Freshman HS 700/9-9
625 S 35th St 50265 515-633-4500
Mitch Kuhnert, prin. Fax 633-4599
Walnut Creek Alternative HS 200/Alt
1020 8th St 50265 515-633-6480
Dr. Kim Davis, prin. Fax 633-6499
Other Schools – See Clive

Dowling Catholic HS 1,400/9-12
1400 Buffalo Rd 50265 515-225-3000
Matt Meendering, prin. Fax 222-1056
Iowa Christian Academy 300/PK-12
2501 Vine St 50265 515-221-3999
Dr. Brenda Hillman, admin. Fax 225-2387

West Liberty, Muscatine, Pop. 3,704
West Liberty Community SD 1,200/PK-12
111 W 7th St 52776 319-627-2116
Steve Hanson, supt. Fax 627-2963
www.wl.k12.ia.us
West Liberty HS 300/9-12
310 W Maxson Ave 52776 319-627-2115
James Hamilton, prin. Fax 627-2046
West Liberty MS 300/6-8
203 E 7th St 52776 319-627-2118
Vicki Vernon, prin. Fax 627-2092

Westside, Crawford, Pop. 299
Ar-We-Va Community SD 200/PK-12
108 Clinton St 51467 712-663-4311
Jeff Kruse, supt. Fax 663-4312
www.ar-we-va.k12.ia.us
Westside JSHS 100/6-12
108 Clinton St 51467 712-663-4312
Rich Stoffers, prin. Fax 663-4312

West Union, Fayette, Pop. 2,464
North Fayette Community SD 800/PK-12
PO Box 73 52175 563-422-3851
Duane Willhite, supt. Fax 422-3854
www.nfvschools.com
North Fayette Valley HS 400/9-12
PO Box 73 52175 563-422-3852
Todd Wolverton, prin. Fax 422-3854

Wheatland, Clinton, Pop. 762
Calamus-Wheatland Community SD 500/PK-12
PO Box 279 52777 563-374-1292
Lonnie Luepker, supt. Fax 374-1080
www.cal-wheat.k12.ia.us
Calamus-Wheatland JSHS 300/7-12
PO Box 279 52777 563-374-1292
Christine Meyer, prin. Fax 374-1080

Whiting, Monona, Pop. 758
Whiting Community SD 200/PK-12
PO Box 295 51063 712-455-2468
Randy Collins, supt. Fax 455-2601
www.whitingcsd.org
Whiting JSHS 100/6-12
PO Box 295 51063 712-455-2468
Al Laboranti, prin. Fax 455-2601

Williamsburg, Iowa, Pop. 3,044
Williamsburg Community SD 1,200/PK-12
PO Box 120 52361 319-668-1059
Dr. Chad Garber, supt. Fax 668-9311
www.williamsburg.k12.ia.us
Williamsburg JSHS 600/7-12
PO Box 120 52361 319-668-1050
Lynell O'Connor, prin. Fax 668-9311

Wilton, Muscatine, Pop. 2,767
Wilton Community SD 800/PK-12
1002 Cypress St 52778 563-732-2035
Joe Burnett, supt. Fax 732-4121
www.wiltoncsd.org/
Wilton JSHS 300/7-12
1002 Cypress St 52778 563-732-2629
Ken Crawford, prin. Fax 732-4121

Winfield, Henry, Pop. 1,123
Winfield-Mt. Union Community SD 500/PK-12
PO Box E 52659 319-257-7700
Jeff Maeder, supt. Fax 257-7714
wmucsd.org
Winfield-Mt. Union JSHS 300/6-12
PO Box E 52659 319-257-7701
David Edwards, prin. Fax 257-7703

Winterset, Madison, Pop. 5,159
Winterset Community SD 1,800/PK-12
PO Box 30 50273 515-462-2718
Dr. Susan Meade, supt. Fax 462-2732
www.winterset.k12.ia.us
Winterset HS 500/9-12
624 Husky Dr 50273 515-462-3320
Kent Abrahamson, prin. Fax 462-2178
Winterset JHS 300/7-8
720 Husky Dr 50273 515-462-3336
Doug Hinrichs, prin. Fax 462-2178

Winthrop, Buchanan, Pop. 845
East Buchanan Community SD 600/PK-12
414 5th St N 50682 319-935-3767
Dan Fox, supt. Fax 935-3749
www.eastbuchananschools.com
East Buchanan HS 200/9-12
414 5th St N 50682 319-935-3367
Eric Dockstader, prin. Fax 935-3615
East Buchanan MS 100/6-8
414 5th St N 50682 319-935-3367
Eric Dockstader, prin. Fax 935-3615

Woodbine, Harrison, Pop. 1,455
Woodbine Community SD 500/PK-12
501 Weare St 51579 712-647-2411
Dr. Chris Anderson, supt. Fax 647-2526
sites.google.com/a/woodbine.k12.ia.us/flashy-tiger
Woodbine HS 200/7-12
501 Weare St 51579 712-647-2227
Sam Swenson, prin. Fax 647-2279

Woodward, Dallas, Pop. 1,006
Woodward-Granger Community SD
Supt. — See Granger
Woodward Academy 300/Alt
1251 334th St 50276 515-438-3481
Ryan Santi, dir. Fax 438-3489
Woodward-Granger HS 200/9-12
306 W 3rd St 50276 515-438-2115
Robert Boley, prin. Fax 438-4329
Woodward-Granger MS 200/6-8
306 W 3rd St 50276 515-438-4263
Bret Miller, prin. Fax 438-2497

Wyoming, Jones, Pop. 513
Midland Community SD 500/PK-12
PO Box 109 52362 563-488-2292
Brian Rodenberg, supt. Fax 488-2253
www.midland.k12.ia.us
Midland MSHS 200/6-12
PO Box 109 52362 563-488-2292
Carol Reilly, prin. Fax 488-2253

KANSAS

KANSAS DEPARTMENT OF EDUCATION
900 SW Jackson St, Topeka 66612-1212
Telephone 785-296-3202
Fax 785-296-7933
Website http://www.ksde.org

Commissioner of Education Randy Watson

KANSAS BOARD OF EDUCATION
120 SE 10th Ave, Topeka 66612-1103

Chairperson Jim McNiece

PUBLIC, PRIVATE AND CATHOLIC SECONDARY SCHOOLS

Abilene, Dickinson, Pop. 6,690
Abilene USD 435 — 1,700/PK-12
PO Box 639 67410 — 785-263-2630
Dr. Denise Guy, supt. — Fax 263-7610
www.abileneschools.org/
Abilene HS — 500/9-12
1300 N Cedar St 67410 — 785-263-1260
Ben Smith, prin. — Fax 263-3327
Abilene MS — 400/6-8
500 NW 14th St 67410 — 785-263-1471
Ron Wilson, prin. — Fax 263-4443

Agra, Phillips, Pop. 263
Thunder Ridge SD 110
Supt. — See Kensington
Thunder Ridge MS — 100/PK-PK, 4-
941 Kansas Ave 67621 — 785-638-2244
Beth Norris, prin. — Fax 638-2254

Allen, Lyon, Pop. 176
North Lyon County USD 251
Supt. — See Americus
Northern Heights HS — 100/9-12
1208 Highway 56 66833 — 620-528-3521
Russell Swisher, prin. — Fax 528-3392

Alma, Wabaunsee, Pop. 821
Wabaunsee USD 329 — 500/PK-12
PO Box 157 66401 — 785-765-3394
Brad Starnes, supt. — Fax 765-3624
www.usd329.com
Wabaunsee HS — 200/9-12
912 Missouri Ave 66401 — 785-765-3315
Jeff Stuewe, prin. — Fax 765-3523
Other Schools – See Paxico

Almena, Norton, Pop. 407
Northern Valley USD 212 — 200/PK-12
PO Box 217 67622 — 785-669-2445
Ken Tharman, supt. — Fax 669-2263
www.nvhuskies.org
Northern Valley HS — 100/9-12
PO Box 217 67622 — 785-669-2445
Ken Tharman, prin. — Fax 669-2263
Other Schools – See Long Island

Altamont, Labette, Pop. 1,042
Labette County USD 506 — 1,600/PK-12
PO Box 189 67330 — 620-784-5326
Dr. John Wyrick, supt. — Fax 784-5879
www.usd506.org
Labette County HS — 500/9-12
PO Box 407 67330 — 620-784-5321
Shane Holtzman, prin. — Fax 784-2682

Americus, Lyon, Pop. 875
North Lyon County USD 251 — 400/K-12
PO Box 527 66835 — 620-443-5116
Aron Dody, supt. — Fax 443-5659
www.usd251.org
Other Schools – See Allen

Andale, Sedgwick, Pop. 920
Renwick USD 267 — 1,900/PK-12
PO Box 68 67001 — 316-444-2165
Tracy Bourne, supt. — Fax 445-2241
www.usd267.com
Andale HS — 400/9-12
PO Box 28 67001 — 316-444-2607
Stan May, prin. — Fax 445-2501
Other Schools – See Garden Plain

Andover, Butler, Pop. 11,537
Andover USD 385 — 9,900/PK-12
1432 N Andover Rd 67002 — 316-218-4660
Greg Rasmussen, supt. — Fax 733-3604
www.usd385.org
Andover Central HS — 700/9-12
603 E Central Ave 67002 — 316-218-4700
Cheryl Hochhalter, prin. — Fax 266-8840
Andover Central MS — 600/6-8
903 E Central Ave 67002 — 316-218-4710
Tim Hayden, prin. — Fax 266-8878
Andover HS — 800/9-12
1744 N Andover Rd 67002 — 316-218-4600
Kristen Kuhlmann, prin. — Fax 733-3681
Andover MS — 600/6-8
1628 N Andover Rd 67002 — 316-218-4610
Deb Regier, prin. — Fax 733-4165

Anthony, Harper, Pop. 2,226
Chaparral Schools USD 361 — 800/PK-12
PO Box 486 67003 — 620-842-5183
Josh Swartz, supt. — Fax 842-5307
www.usd361.org/
Chaparral JSHS — 200/7-12
467 N State Road 14 67003 — 620-842-5155
Ken Henson, prin. — Fax 896-2927

Argonia, Sumner, Pop. 493
Argonia USD 359 — 200/PK-12
202 E Allen St 67004 — 620-435-6311
Dr. Julie McPherrron, supt. — Fax 435-6623
www.argonia359.org
Argonia JSHS — 100/6-12
202 E Allen St 67004 — 620-435-6611
Aaron Dewlen, prin. — Fax 435-6358

Arkansas City, Cowley, Pop. 11,966
Arkansas City USD 470 — 2,800/PK-12
PO Box 1028 67005 — 620-441-2000
Dr. Ron Ballard, supt. — Fax 441-2009
www.usd470.com
Arkansas City HS — 800/9-12
1200 W Radio Ln 67005 — 620-441-2010
Dr. David Zumwalt, prin. — Fax 441-2021
Arkansas City MS — 600/6-8
400 E Kansas Ave 67005 — 620-441-2030
William Pfannenstiel, prin. — Fax 441-2036

Ark City Christian Academy — 100/PK-12
PO Box 1181 67005 — 620-442-0022
Tamen Eis, prin. — Fax 442-0034
Cowley County Community College — Post-Sec.
PO Box 1147 67005 — 620-442-0430

Arma, Crawford, Pop. 1,474
Northeast USD 246 — 500/K-12
PO Box 669 66712 — 620-347-4116
Greg Gorman, supt. — Fax 347-4087
www.usd246.org
Northeast HS — 200/9-12
PO Box 669 66712 — 620-347-4115
Jason Clemensen, prin. — Fax 347-4149

Ashland, Clark, Pop. 841
Ashland USD 220 — 200/PK-12
PO Box 187 67831 — 620-635-2220
Jamie Wetig, supt. — Fax 635-2637
www.ashland.k12.ks.us
Ashland HS — 100/9-12
PO Box 187 67831 — 620-635-2814
Jamie Wetig, prin. — Fax 635-2637
Ashland JHS — 50/7-8
PO Box 187 67831 — 620-635-2814
Jamie Wetig, prin. — Fax 635-2637

Atchison, Atchison, Pop. 10,700
Atchison USD 409 — 1,700/PK-12
626 Commercial St 66002 — 913-367-4384
Dr. Susan Myers, supt. — Fax 367-2246
www.usd409.net
Atchison HS — 400/9-12
1500 Riley St 66002 — 913-367-4162
Bryon Hanson, prin. — Fax 367-0415
Atchison MS — 400/6-8
301 N 5th St 66002 — 913-367-5363
Chad Bilderback, prin. — Fax 367-1302
Central S — 50/Alt
215 N 8th St 66002 — 913-360-6540
Gerre Martin, prin. — Fax 367-2860

Benedictine College — Post-Sec.
1020 N 2nd St 66002 — 913-367-5340
Highland Community College-Technical Ctr — Post-Sec.
1501 Riley St 66002 — 913-367-6204
Maur Hill - Mount Academy — 200/9-12
1000 Green St 66002 — 913-367-5482
Monika King, prin. — Fax 367-5096
Riverbend International S — 50/6-12
1900 N 2nd St 66002 — 913-367-5199
Dr. Paul Ogle Ed.D., supt. — Fax 367-5195

Attica, Harper, Pop. 621
Attica USD 511 — 200/PK-12
PO Box 415 67009 — 620-254-7915
Dale Adams, supt. — Fax 254-7872
www.usd511.net
Attica JSHS — 50/7-12
PO Box 415 67009 — 620-254-7915
Joshua Lanning, prin. — Fax 254-7872

Atwood, Rawlins, Pop. 1,181
Rawlins County USD 105 — 300/PK-12
205 N 4th St Ste 1 67730 — 785-626-3236
Tom Dolenz, supt. — Fax 626-3083
www.usd105.org
Rawlins County JSHS — 100/7-12
100 N 8th St 67730 — 785-626-3289
Matthew Smith, prin. — Fax 626-1022

Augusta, Butler, Pop. 9,098
Augusta USD 402 — 2,300/PK-12
2345 Greyhound Dr 67010 — 316-775-5484
Dr. John Black, supt. — Fax 775-5035
www.usd402.com
Augusta HS — 600/9-12
2020 Ohio St 67010 — 316-775-5461
Donna Zerr, prin. — Fax 775-3484
Augusta MS — 500/6-8
1001 State St 67010 — 316-775-6383
Matthew Ward, prin. — Fax 775-3853

Axtell, Marshall, Pop. 393
Prairie Hills USD 113
Supt. — See Sabetha
Axtell HS — 100/9-12
504 Pine St 66403 — 785-736-2237
Larry Geist, prin. — Fax 736-2295

Baldwin City, Douglas, Pop. 4,416
Baldwin City USD 348 — 1,400/PK-12
PO Box 67 66006 — 785-594-2721
Paul Dorathy, supt. — Fax 594-3408
www.usd348.com/
Baldwin HS — 400/9-12
PO Box 67 66006 — 785-594-2725
Rob McKim, prin. — Fax 594-2858
Baldwin JHS — 300/6-8
PO Box 67 66006 — 785-594-2448
Joe Sample, prin. — Fax 594-2449

Baker University — Post-Sec.
PO Box 65 66006 — 785-594-6451

Barnes, Washington, Pop. 159
Barnes USD 223 — 500/PK-12
PO Box 188 66933 — 785-763-4231
Brian Cordel, supt. — Fax 763-4461
www.usd223.org
Other Schools – See Hanover, Linn

Basehor, Leavenworth, Pop. 4,548
Basehor-Linwood USD 458 — 2,200/K-12
PO Box 282 66007 — 913-724-1396
David Howard, supt. — Fax 724-2709
www.usd458.org
Basehor-Linwood HS — 800/9-12
2108 N 155th St 66007 — 913-724-2266
Jarred Fuhrman, prin. — Fax 724-2040
Basehor-Linwood MS — 500/6-8
15900 Conley Rd 66007 — 913-724-2976
Amy Garver, prin. — Fax 955-7074

Baxter Springs, Cherokee, Pop. 3,956
Baxter Springs USD 508 — 1,000/PK-12
1108 Military Ave 66713 — 620-856-2375
David Pendergraft, supt. — Fax 856-3943
www.usd508.org
Baxter Springs HS — 400/7-12
100 N Military Ave 66713 — 620-856-3366
Cory White, prin. — Fax 856-2918

Bel Aire, Sedgwick, Pop. 6,561
Wichita USD 259
Supt. — See Wichita
Northeast Magnet HS 600/9-12
5550 N Lycee St 67226 316-973-2300
Matt Creasman, prin. Fax 973-2307

Sunrise Christian Academy 500/PK-12
5500 E 45th St N 67220 316-744-9262
Dr. Robert Lindsted, supt. Fax 744-7449

Belle Plaine, Sumner, Pop. 1,652
Belle Plaine USD 357 600/PK-12
PO Box 760 67013 620-488-2288
Dr. James Sutton, supt. Fax 488-3517
www.usd357.org
Belle Plaine HS 200/9-12
PO Box 8 67013 620-488-2421
Judy Happy, prin. Fax 488-3536
Belle Plaine MS 200/5-8
PO Box 457 67013 620-488-2222
Morey Balzer, prin. Fax 488-3391

Belleville, Republic, Pop. 1,978
Republic County USD 109 500/K-12
PO Box 469 66935 785-527-5621
Michael Couch, supt. Fax 527-5375
www.usd109.org/
Republic County JSHS 200/6-12
PO Box 469 66935 785-527-2281
Alan Sheets, prin. Fax 527-5505

Beloit, Mitchell, Pop. 3,807
Beloit USD 273 800/PK-12
PO Box 547 67420 785-738-3261
Jeff Travis, supt. Fax 738-4103
www.usd273.org
Alternative Learning Center Alt
PO Box 506 67420 785-738-5275
Karen Niemczyk, prin. Fax 738-9967
Beloit JSHS 300/7-12
PO Box 606 67420 785-738-3593
Casey Seyfert, prin. Fax 738-5566

North Central Kansas Technical College Post-Sec.
PO Box 507 67420 785-738-2276
St. John Catholic HS 100/7-12
209 S Cherry St 67420 785-738-2942
Marcy Kee, prin. Fax 738-4462

Bennington, Ottawa, Pop. 670
Twin Valley USD 240 500/PK-12
PO Box 38 67422 785-488-3325
Fred Van Ranken, supt. Fax 488-3326
www.usd240.org
Bennington HS 100/7-12
PO Box 8 67422 785-488-3321
Curtis Nightingale, prin. Fax 488-2939
Other Schools – See Tescott

Benton, Butler, Pop. 874
Circle USD 375
Supt. — See Towanda
Circle MS 300/7-8
14697 SW 20th St 67017 316-778-1470
Brenda Young, prin. Fax 536-2249

Bird City, Cheyenne, Pop. 441
Cheylin USD 103 100/K-12
PO Box 28 67731 785-734-2341
Allaire Homburg, supt. Fax 734-2489
www.cheylin.com/
Cheylin West JSHS 100/7-12
PO Box 28 67731 785-734-2341
Allaire Homburg, prin. Fax 734-2489

Blue Rapids, Marshall, Pop. 1,010
Valley Heights USD 498
Supt. — See Waterville
Valley Heights JSHS 200/7-12
2274 6th Rd 66411 785-363-2508
Chad Kenworthy, prin. Fax 363-2072

Bonner Springs, Wyandotte, Pop. 7,122
Bonner Springs USD 204 2,500/PK-12
PO Box 435 66012 913-422-5600
Daniel Brungardt, supt. Fax 422-4193
www.usd204.net
Bonner Springs HS 700/9-12
PO Box 216 66012 913-422-5121
Rick Moulin, prin. Fax 422-7284
Clark MS 600/6-8
PO Box 336 66012 913-422-5115
Tammy DeLaRosa, prin. Fax 422-1644

Brewster, Thomas, Pop. 303
Brewster USD 314 100/PK-12
PO Box 220 67732 785-694-2236
Shea Rothchild, supt. Fax 694-2746
www.usd314.k12.ks.us
Brewster HS 50/7-12
PO Box 220 67732 785-694-2236
Shea Rothchild, prin. Fax 694-2746

Brookville, Saline, Pop. 257
Ell-Saline USD 307 500/K-12
PO Box 157 67425 785-225-6813
Jerry Minneman, supt. Fax 225-6815
www.ellsaline.org
Ell-Saline MSHS 200/7-12
414 E Anderson St 67425 785-225-6633
Doug Wilson, prin. Fax 225-6694

Bucklin, Ford, Pop. 775
Bucklin USD 459 200/PK-12
PO Box 8 67834 620-826-3828
Kelly Lampe, supt. Fax 826-3377
www.bucklinschools.com
Bucklin HS 100/5-12
PO Box 8 67834 620-826-3241
Mark Calvin, prin. Fax 826-9966

Buffalo, Wilson, Pop. 229
Altoona-Midway USD 387 200/PK-12
20584 US 75 Hwy 66717 620-537-7721
Brent Kaempfe, supt. Fax 302-2080
www.usd387.org
Altoona-Midway MSHS 100/5-12
20704 US 75 Hwy 66717 620-537-7711
Darrin Ashmore, prin. Fax 537-2641

Buhler, Reno, Pop. 1,319
Buhler USD 313 1,700/PK-12
406 W 7th St 67522 620-543-2258
Mike Berblinger, supt. Fax 543-2510
www.buhlerschools.org
Buhler HS 600/9-12
611 N Main St 67522 620-543-2255
Mike Ellegood, prin. Fax 543-2853
Other Schools – See Hutchinson

Burden, Cowley, Pop. 531
Central USD 462 300/PK-12
PO Box 128 67019 620-438-2218
Rick Shaffer, supt. Fax 438-2217
www.usd462.org
Central JSHS 100/7-12
PO Box 128 67019 620-438-2215
Shane Walter, prin. Fax 438-2217

Burlingame, Osage, Pop. 917
Burlingame USD 454 300/PK-12
100 Bloomquist Dr Ste A 66413 785-654-3328
Allen Konicek, supt. Fax 654-3570
www.usd454.net
Burlingame JSHS 200/7-12
100 Bloomquist Dr Ste A 66413 785-654-3315
Tammy Baird, prin. Fax 654-3191

Burlington, Coffey, Pop. 2,635
Burlington USD 244 900/PK-12
200 S 6th St 66839 620-364-8478
Craig Marshall, supt. Fax 364-8548
www.usd244ks.org
Burlington HS 300/9-12
830 Cross St 66839 620-364-8672
Stacy Reed, prin. Fax 364-8680
Burlington MS 300/5-8
720 Cross St 66839 620-364-2156
Matt Thomsen, prin. Fax 364-8560

Burrton, Harvey, Pop. 886
Burrton USD 369 200/PK-12
PO Box 369 67020 620-463-3840
Joan Simoneau, supt. Fax 463-2636
www.burrton.usd369.org
Burrton MSHS 100/6-12
PO Box 369 67020 620-463-3820
Tyler Hoopes, prin. Fax 463-2096

Bushton, Rice, Pop. 274
Central Plains USD 112
Supt. — See Holyrood
Central Plains MS 100/5-8
500 S Main St 67427 620-562-3596
Jane Oeser, prin. Fax 562-3248

Caldwell, Sumner, Pop. 1,059
Caldwell USD 360 300/PK-12
22 N Webb St 67022 620-845-2585
Alan Jamison, supt. Fax 845-2610
www.usd360.com
Caldwell Secondary S 100/6-12
31 N Osage St 67022 620-845-2585
Kevin Schmidt, prin. Fax 845-2534

Caney, Montgomery, Pop. 2,080
Caney Valley USD 436 800/PK-12
700 E Bullpup Blvd 67333 620-879-9200
Blake Vargas, supt. Fax 879-9209
www.caney.com
Caney Valley JSHS 400/7-12
601 E Bullpup Blvd 67333 620-879-9220
William Ellis, prin. Fax 879-9227

Canton, McPherson, Pop. 732
Canton-Galva USD 419 200/K-12
PO Box 317 67428 620-628-4901
John Denk, supt. Fax 628-4380
usd419.org
Canton-Galva JSHS 100/7-12
PO Box 275 67428 620-628-4401
Shawn Koehn, prin. Fax 628-4951

Carbondale, Osage, Pop. 1,411
Santa Fe Trail USD 434
Supt. — See Scranton
Carbondale Attendance Center 300/4-8
315 N 4th St 66414 785-836-7188
Michael Flax, prin. Fax 836-7696
Santa Fe Trail HS 300/9-12
15701 S California Rd 66414 785-665-7161
Patrick Graham, prin. Fax 665-7193

Cawker City, Mitchell, Pop. 462
Waconda USD 272 200/PK-12
PO Box 326 67430 785-781-4328
Troy Damman, supt. Fax 781-4318
www.usd272.org
Other Schools – See Downs

Cedar Vale, Chautauqua, Pop. 554
Cedar Vale USD 285 200/PK-12
PO Box 458 67024 620-758-2265
Lance Rhodd, supt. Fax 758-2647
www.cvs285.net
Cedar Vale JSHS 100/6-12
PO Box 458 67024 620-758-2791
Jackie Burdette, prin. Fax 758-2704

Centralia, Nemaha, Pop. 501
Vermillion USD 380
Supt. — See Vermillion
Centralia JSHS 100/7-12
507 John Riggins Ave 66415 785-857-3324
Larry Glatczak, prin. Fax 857-3847

Chanute, Neosho, Pop. 8,951
Chanute USD 413 1,900/PK-12
315 Chanute 35 Pkwy 66720 620-432-2500
Richard Proffitt, supt. Fax 431-6810
www.usd413.org
Chanute HS 500/9-12
1501 W 36th St 66720 620-432-2510
John Lawrence, prin. Fax 431-3020
Royster MS 400/6-8
400 W Main St 66720 620-432-2520
Lori Kiblinger, prin. Fax 431-7841

Neosho County Community College Post-Sec.
800 W 14th St 66720 620-431-2820

Chapman, Dickinson, Pop. 1,368
Chapman USD 473 1,000/K-12
PO Box 249 67431 785-922-6521
Jerry Hodson, supt. Fax 922-6446
usd473.net
Chapman HS 300/9-12
PO Box 249 67431 785-922-6561
Kevin Suther, prin. Fax 922-7162
Chapman MS 300/6-8
PO Box 249 67431 785-922-6555
Trent Horn, prin. Fax 922-6601

Chase, Rice, Pop. 461
Chase-Raymond USD 401 200/PK-12
313 E Avenue C 67524 620-938-2913
Glenna Grinstead, supt. Fax 938-2622
www.usd401.com/
Chase HS 50/9-12
313 E Avenue C 67524 620-938-2923
Brock Hampton, prin. Fax 938-2456
Raymond JHS 50/7-8
313 E Avenue C 67524 620-938-2923
Brock Hampton, prin. Fax 938-2456

Cheney, Sedgwick, Pop. 2,072
Cheney USD 268 800/PK-12
100 W 6th Ave 67025 316-542-3512
David Grover, supt. Fax 542-0326
www.cheney268.com
Cheney HS 200/9-12
100 W 6th Ave 67025 316-542-3113
Greg Rosenhagen, prin. Fax 542-3789
Cheney MS 200/6-8
100 W 6th Ave 67025 316-542-0060
Amy Wallace, prin. Fax 542-0608

Cherokee, Crawford, Pop. 696
Cherokee USD 247 500/PK-12
506 S Smelter St 66724 620-457-8350
Brad Miner, supt. Fax 457-8428
www.usd247.com
Southeast HS 200/9-12
126 W 400 Hwy 66724 620-457-8365
Larry Malle, prin. Fax 457-8389
Southeast JHS 200/5-8
206 W Magnolia St 66724 620-457-8315
Joseph Martin, prin. Fax 457-8380

Cherryvale, Montgomery, Pop. 2,326
Cherryvale USD 447 900/PK-12
618 E 4th St 67335 620-336-8130
George Owens, supt. Fax 336-8133
www.usd447.org
Cherryvale MSHS 300/7-12
700 S Carson St 67335 620-336-8100
Scott Lambdin, prin. Fax 336-8110

Chetopa, Labette, Pop. 1,068
Chetopa - St. Paul USD 505 400/PK-12
430 Elm St 67336 620-236-7244
Dr. Bobbi Williams, supt. Fax 236-4271
www.usd505.org
Chetopa HS 100/6-12
430 Elm St 67336 620-236-7244
Lonnie Moser, prin. Fax 236-4271
Other Schools – See Saint Paul

Cimarron, Gray, Pop. 2,164
Cimarron-Ensign USD 102 600/K-12
PO Box 489 67835 620-855-7743
Michael Stegman, supt. Fax 855-7745
www.cimarronschools.net
Cimarron JSHS 300/7-12
PO Box 489 67835 620-855-3323
Jara Wilson, prin. Fax 855-3219

Claflin, Barton, Pop. 637
Central Plains USD 112
Supt. — See Holyrood
Central Plains HS 100/9-12
PO Box 348 67525 620-587-3801
Toby Holmes, prin. Fax 587-3677

Clay Center, Clay, Pop. 4,283
Clay Center USD 379 1,400/K-12
PO Box 97 67432 785-632-3176
Michael Folks, supt. Fax 632-5020
www.usd379.org/
Clay Center Community HS 300/9-12
1630 9th St 67432 785-632-2131
Bud Young, prin. Fax 632-2076
Clay Center Community MS 200/6-8
935 Prospect St 67432 785-632-3232
Keith Hoffman, prin. Fax 632-6013
Other Schools – See Wakefield

Clearwater, Sedgwick, Pop. 2,443
Clearwater USD 264 1,200/PK-12
PO Box 248 67026 620-584-2091
Paul Becker, supt. Fax 584-6705
www.usd264.org

Clearwater HS 400/9-12
PO Box 248 67026 620-584-2361
Bob Mellen, prin. Fax 584-2083
Clearwater MS 200/7-8
PO Box 248 67026 620-584-2036
Kelly Bielefeld, prin. Fax 584-2199

Clyde, Cloud, Pop. 706
Clifton-Clyde USD 224 300/PK-12
616 N High St Ste 2 66938 785-446-2098
Art Baker, supt. Fax 446-3000
www.usd224.com
Clifton-Clyde HS 100/8-12
616 N High St Ste 1 66938 785-446-3444
Art Baker, prin. Fax 446-3458

Coffeyville, Montgomery, Pop. 9,654
Coffeyville USD 445 1,700/PK-12
615 Ellis St 67337 620-252-6400
Craig A. Correll Ed.D., supt. Fax 252-6807
www.cvilleschools.com
Field Kindley Memorial HS 500/9-12
1110 W 8th St 67337 620-251-9070
Travis Stalford, prin. Fax 252-6818
Horn Field Kindley Tech Academy Alt
615 Ellis St 67337 620-252-6440
Travis Stalford, prin.
Roosevelt MS 300/7-8
1000 W 8th St 67337 620-252-6420
Jeffrey Pegues, prin. Fax 252-6844
LINC, 510 W 8th St 67337 Adult
Travis Stalford, prin. 620-251-9070

Coffeyville Community College Post-Sec.
400 W 11th St 67337 620-251-7700

Colby, Thomas, Pop. 5,323
Colby USD 315 900/K-12
600 W 3rd St 67701 785-460-5000
Katina Brenn, supt. Fax 460-5050
www.colbyeagles.org
Colby HS 300/9-12
1890 S Franklin Ave 67701 785-460-5300
Troy Keiswetter, prin. Fax 460-5350
Colby MS 200/6-8
750 W 3rd St 67701 785-460-5200
Robb Ross, prin. Fax 460-5250

Colby Community College Post-Sec.
1255 S Range Ave 67701 785-462-3984
Heartland Christian S 100/PK-12
1995 W 4th St 67701 785-460-6419
Dr. Mark Gundlach, admin. Fax 460-8337

Coldwater, Comanche, Pop. 813
South Central USD 300 300/K-12
PO Box 721 67029 620-582-2181
Michael Baldwin, supt. Fax 582-2540
www.usd300ks.com
South Central HS 100/9-12
PO Box 578 67029 620-582-2158
Ty Theurer, prin. Fax 582-2535
Other Schools – See Protection

Colony, Anderson, Pop. 394
Crest USD 479 200/K-12
PO Box 305 66015 620-852-3540
Chuck Mahon, supt. Fax 852-3542
www.usd479.org
Crest HS 100/9-12
PO Box 325 66015 620-852-3521
Chuck Mahon, prin. Fax 852-3357

Columbus, Cherokee, Pop. 3,208
Columbus USD 493 1,100/PK-12
802 S Highschool Ave 66725 620-429-3661
David Carriger, supt. Fax 429-2673
www.usd493.com
Central S 400/4-8
810 S Highschool Ave 66725 620-429-3943
James Bolden, prin. Fax 429-2882
Columbus HS 300/9-12
124 S Highschool Ave 66725 620-429-3821
Tony Shearburn, prin. Fax 429-3657

Concordia, Cloud, Pop. 5,314
Concordia USD 333 1,100/PK-12
217 W 7th St 66901 785-243-3518
Quentin Breese, supt. Fax 243-8883
www.usd333.com
Concordia JSHS 400/7-12
436 W 10th St 66901 785-243-2452
Bryce Wachs, prin. Fax 243-8805

Cloud County Community College Post-Sec.
2221 Campus Dr 66901 785-243-1435

Conway Springs, Sumner, Pop. 1,251
Conway Springs USD 356 600/K-12
110 N Monnett St 67031 620-456-2961
Clay Murphy, supt. Fax 456-3173
www.usd356.org
Conway Springs HS 200/9-12
607 W Saint Louis St 67031 620-456-2963
Brent Harrell, prin. Fax 456-3314
Conway Springs MS 100/6-8
112 N Cranmer St 67031 620-456-2965
Ryan Rusco, prin. Fax 456-3313

Copeland, Gray, Pop. 310
Copeland USD 476 100/PK-8
PO Box 156 67837 620-668-5565
Jay Zehr, supt. Fax 668-5568
www.usd476.org
South Gray JHS 50/6-8
PO Box 156 67837 620-668-5565
Jay Zehr, prin. Fax 668-5568

Cottonwood Falls, Chase, Pop. 897
Chase County USD 284 400/PK-12
PO Box 569 66845 620-273-6303
Jeffrey Kohlman, supt. Fax 273-6717
www.usd284.org/
Chase County JSHS 200/7-12
600 Main St 66845 620-273-6354
Travis Githens, prin. Fax 273-8337

Council Grove, Morris, Pop. 2,159
Morris County USD 417 600/PK-12
17 Wood St 66846 620-767-5192
Doug Conwell, supt. Fax 767-5444
www.usd417.net
Council Grove JSHS 200/7-12
129 Hockaday St 66846 620-767-5149
Kelly McDiffett, prin. Fax 767-7280

Courtland, Republic, Pop. 285
Pike Valley USD 426
Supt. — See Scandia
Pike Valley JHS 100/6-8
PO Box 320 66939 785-374-4221
Mike Gritten, prin. Fax 374-4268

Cunningham, Kingman, Pop. 450
Cunningham USD 332 200/PK-12
PO Box 67 67035 620-298-3271
Robert Reed, supt. Fax 298-2562
www.usd332.org
Cunningham HS 50/7-12
PO Box 98 67035 620-298-2473
Robert Reed, prin. Fax 298-5005

Damar, Rooks, Pop. 131
Palco USD 269 50/PK-12
PO Box 38 67632 785-737-4635
Larry Lysell M.S., supt. Fax 737-4636
www.usd269.net
Other Schools – See Palco

Deerfield, Kearny, Pop. 694
Deerfield USD 216 300/PK-12
803 Beech St 67838 620-426-8516
Dr. Daniel Slack, supt. Fax 426-7890
www.usd216.org
Deerfield HS 100/9-12
803 Beech 67838 620-426-8401
Tammie Sabata, prin. Fax 426-6903
Deerfield MS 100/6-8
803 Beech 67838 620-426-7901
Tammie Sabata, prin. Fax 426-6903

Denton, Doniphan, Pop. 142
Doniphan West USD 111 200/PK-12
642 Highway 20 E 66017 785-442-3671
Mike Newman, supt. Fax 442-3289
www.usd111.org
Other Schools – See Highland

Derby, Sedgwick, Pop. 21,570
Derby USD 260 6,500/PK-12
120 E Washington St 67037 316-788-8400
Craig Wilford, supt. Fax 788-8526
www.derbyschools.com
Derby HS 1,900/9-12
920 N Rock Rd 67037 316-788-8500
Tim Hamblin, prin. Fax 788-8593
Derby MS 1,100/7-8
801 E Madison Ave 67037 316-788-8580
Clinton Shipley, prin. Fax 788-8553
Derby North MS 6-8
3100 N Rock Rd 67037 316-788-8400
Jeff Smith, prin. Fax 788-8527

De Soto, Johnson, Pop. 5,615
De Soto USD 232 7,000/PK-12
35200 W 91st St 66018 913-667-6200
Frank Harwood, supt. Fax 667-6201
www.usd232.org
De Soto HS 700/9-12
35000 W 91st St 66018 913-667-6250
Dustin Mortenson, prin. Fax 667-6251
Lexington Trails MS 300/6-8
8800 Penner Ave 66018 913-667-6260
Steve Ludwig, prin. Fax 667-6261
Other Schools – See Lenexa, Shawnee

Dexter, Cowley, Pop. 275
Dexter USD 471 100/PK-12
PO Box 97 67038 620-876-5415
K.B. Criss, supt. Fax 876-5548
www.usd471.org
Dexter JSHS 100/6-12
PO Box 97 67038 620-876-5415
K.B. Criss, prin. Fax 876-5548

Dighton, Lane, Pop. 1,017
Dighton USD 482 300/PK-12
PO Box 878 67839 620-397-2835
Dr. Kelly Arnberger, supt. Fax 397-5932
www.usd482.org
Dighton JSHS 100/7-12
PO Box 939 67839 620-397-5333
Mark Penka, prin. Fax 397-5338

Dodge City, Ford, Pop. 26,977
Dodge City USD 443 6,400/K-12
PO Box 460 67801 620-371-1070
Alan Cunningham, supt. Fax 227-1687
www.usd443.org
Comanche MS 700/6-8
1601 1st Ave 67801 620-371-1100
Marc Woofter, prin. Fax 339-4802
Dodge City HS 1,800/9-12
2201 W Ross Blvd 67801 620-227-1611
Jacque Feist, prin. Fax 227-1680
Dodge City MS 700/6-8
2000 6th Ave 67801 620-471-2100
Mike King, prin. Fax 227-1731

Dodge City Community College Post-Sec.
2501 N 14th Ave 67801 620-225-1321

Douglass, Butler, Pop. 1,675
Douglass USD 396 700/PK-12
921 E 1st St 67039 316-747-3300
Robert Reynolds, supt. Fax 747-3305
www.usd396.net/
Douglass HS 200/9-12
910 E 1st St 67039 316-747-3310
Scott Dunham, prin. Fax 747-3315
Sisk MS 200/6-8
950 E 1st St 67039 316-747-3340
Scott Dunham, prin. Fax 747-3346

Downs, Osborne, Pop. 896
Waconda USD 272
Supt. — See Cawker City
Lakeside JSHS 100/6-12
PO Box 247 67437 785-454-3332
Bob Becker, prin. Fax 454-3747

Easton, Leavenworth, Pop. 251
Easton USD 449 700/PK-12
32502 Easton Rd 66020 913-651-9740
Charles Coblentz, supt. Fax 324-5237
www.easton449.org
Pleasant Ridge HS 200/9-12
32500 Easton Rd 66020 913-651-5556
Andy Metsker, prin. Fax 254-3089
Pleasant Ridge MS 200/6-8
32504 Easton Rd 66020 913-651-5522
Amanda Brimer, prin. Fax 324-5237

Effingham, Atchison, Pop. 540
Atchison County Community USD 377 600/PK-12
PO Box 289 66023 913-833-5050
Stephen Wiseman, supt. Fax 833-5210
www.usd377.org
Atchison County Community JSHS 300/7-12
PO Box 289 66023 913-833-2240
Deanna Scherer, prin. Fax 833-5210

Elbing, Butler, Pop. 228

Berean Academy 300/PK-12
PO Box 70 67041 316-799-2211
Emir A. Ruiz Esparza M.Ed., head sch Fax 799-2601

El Dorado, Butler, Pop. 12,711
El Dorado USD 490 1,700/PK-12
124 W Central Ave 67042 316-322-4800
Sue Givens, supt. Fax 322-4801
www.eldoradoschools.org
El Dorado HS 600/9-12
401 McCollum Rd 67042 316-322-4810
Kevin House, prin. Fax 322-4811
El Dorado MS 400/6-8
440 E Wildcat Way 67042 316-322-4820
Karla King, prin. Fax 322-4821

Butler Community College Post-Sec.
901 S Haverhill Rd 67042 316-321-2222

Elkhart, Morton, Pop. 2,178
Elkhart USD 218 1,200/PK-12
PO Box 999 67950 620-697-2195
Rex Richardson, supt. Fax 697-2607
www.usd218.org
Elkhart HS 100/9-12
PO Box 999 67950 620-697-2193
Chris Hattabaugh, prin. Fax 697-4415
Elkhart MS 100/5-8
PO Box 999 67950 620-697-2197
Diane Finn, prin. Fax 697-4828
Point Rock Alternative S 50/Alt
PO Box 999 67950 620-697-1253
Antonia Villa, prin. Fax 697-4642

Ellinwood, Barton, Pop. 2,100
Ellinwood USD 355 500/K-12
300 N Schiller Ave 67526 620-564-3226
Ben Jacobs, supt. Fax 564-2206
www.usd355.org/
Ellinwood HS 100/9-12
210 E 2nd St 67526 620-564-3136
Mark Cook, prin. Fax 564-2816
Ellinwood MS 100/7-8
210 E 2nd St 67526 620-564-3136
Mark Cook, prin. Fax 564-2816

Ellis, Ellis, Pop. 2,048
Ellis USD 388 400/PK-12
PO Box 256 67637 785-726-4281
Robert Young, supt. Fax 726-4677
www.usd388.k12.ks.us
Ellis HS 100/7-12
PO Box 300 67637 785-726-3151
Corey Burton, prin. Fax 726-3169

Ellsworth, Ellsworth, Pop. 3,090
Ellsworth USD 327 600/K-12
PO Box 306 67439 785-472-5561
Dale Brungardt, supt. Fax 472-5563
www.usd327.org
Ellsworth JSHS 300/7-12
211 W 11th St 67439 785-472-4471
Ken Windholz, prin. Fax 472-8109

Elwood, Doniphan, Pop. 1,173
Riverside USD 114 700/PK-12
PO Box 49 66024 913-365-5632
Michael Newman, supt. Fax 365-5967
www.usd114.org
Riverside MS 200/6-8
PO Box 368 66024 913-365-6735
Robert Hampton, prin. Fax 365-3503
Other Schools – See Wathena

Emporia, Lyon, Pop. 24,437
Emporia USD 253 4,000/PK-12
PO Box 1008 66801 620-341-2200
Kevin Case, supt. Fax 341-2205
www.usd253.org
Emporia HS 1,100/9-12
3302 W 18th Ave 66801 620-341-2365
Dr. Britton Hart, prin. Fax 341-2376
Emporia MS 900/6-8
2300 Graphic Arts Rd 66801 620-341-2335
Wendy Baumgardner, prin. Fax 341-2341
Flint Hills Learning Center Alt
1624 Industrial Rd 66801 620-341-2251
Dr. Britton Hart, prin. Fax 343-6789

Emporia State University Post-Sec.
1200 Commercial St 66801 620-341-1200
Flint Hills Technical College Post-Sec.
3301 W 18th Ave 66801 620-343-4600

Erie, Neosho, Pop. 1,145
Erie-Galesburg USD 101 500/PK-12
PO Box 137 66733 620-244-3264
Steve Woolf, supt. Fax 244-3664
www.usd101.com
Other Schools – See Galesburg

Eskridge, Wabaunsee, Pop. 526
Mission Valley USD 330 300/PK-12
PO Box 158 66423 785-449-2282
William Clark, supt. Fax 409-6216
www.mv330.org
Mission Valley HS 9-12
12913 Mission Valley Rd 66423 866-557-6686
David Cromer, prin. Fax 409-6218
Mission Valley JHS 100/7-8
12913 Mission Valley Rd 66423 866-557-6686
Rod Hasenbank, prin. Fax 409-6218

Eudora, Douglas, Pop. 5,992
Eudora USD 491 1,600/PK-12
PO Box 500 66025 785-542-4910
Steve Splichal, supt. Fax 542-4909
www.eudoraschools.org/
Eudora - De Soto Technical Education Ctr Vo/Tech
PO Box 712 66025 785-542-4986
Ron Abel, prin. Fax 542-4970
Eudora HS 400/9-12
PO Box 712 66025 785-542-4980
Ron Abel, prin. Fax 542-4990
Eudora MS 400/6-8
PO Box 701 66025 785-542-4960
Denise Kendall, prin. Fax 542-4970

Eureka, Greenwood, Pop. 2,592
Eureka USD 389 700/PK-12
216 N Main St 67045 620-583-5588
Scott Hoyt, supt. Fax 583-8200
www.usd389.net
Eureka JSHS 300/7-12
815 N Jefferson St 67045 620-583-7428
Stacy Coulter, prin. Fax 583-8222

Everest, Brown, Pop. 283
South Brown County USD 430
Supt. — See Horton
Everest MS 200/5-8
221 S 7th St 66424 785-548-7536
Jackie Wenger, prin. Fax 548-7538

Fort Leavenworth, Leavenworth, Pop. 1,300
Ft. Leavenworth USD 207 1,900/PK-9
207 Education Way 66027 913-651-7373
Dr. Keith Mispagel, supt. Fax 758-6010
www.usd207.org
Patton JHS 400/7-9
1 Patton Cir 66027 913-651-7371
Ryan Wiebe, prin. Fax 758-6097

Fort Riley, Geary, Pop. 7,475
Geary County USD 475
Supt. — See Junction City
Fort Riley MS 700/6-8
4020 1st Division Rd 66442 785-717-4500
Heather Oentrich, prin. Fax 717-4501

Fort Scott, Bourbon, Pop. 7,870
Ft. Scott USD 234 1,900/PK-12
424 S Main St 66701 620-223-0800
Bob Beckham, supt. Fax 223-2760
www.usd234.org
Fort Scott HS 500/9-12
1005 S Main St 66701 620-223-0600
Shawn Thomas, prin. Fax 223-5368
Fort Scott MS 500/6-8
1105 E 12th St 66701 620-223-3262
Brian Weilert, prin. Fax 223-8946

Fort Scott Community College Post-Sec.
2108 Horton St 66701 620-223-2700

Fowler, Meade, Pop. 579
Fowler USD 225 200/PK-12
PO Box 170 67844 620-646-5661
Jeff Bollinger, supt. Fax 646-5713
www.usd225.org
Fowler HS 100/7-12
PO Box 140 67844 620-646-5221
Jeff Bollinger, admin. Fax 646-5295

Frankfort, Marshall, Pop. 726
Vermillion USD 380
Supt. — See Vermillion
Frankfort JSHS 100/7-12
PO Box 203 66427 785-292-4486
Dean Dalinghaus, prin. Fax 292-4636

Fredonia, Wilson, Pop. 2,433
Fredonia USD 484 500/PK-12
PO Box 539 66736 620-378-4177
Brian Smith, supt. Fax 378-4345
www.fredoniaks.com
Fredonia JSHS 200/7-12
916 Robinson St 66736 620-378-4172
Jamie Camacho, prin. Fax 378-4398

Frontenac, Crawford, Pop. 3,381
Frontenac USD 249 900/PK-12
208 S Cayuga St 66763 620-231-7551
Rick Simoncic, supt. Fax 231-1312
www.frontenac249.org
Frontenac HS 300/9-12
201 S Crawford St 66763 620-231-7550
Mike Copple, prin. Fax 231-2043
Frontenac JHS 200/6-8
208 S Cayuga St 66763 620-232-6370
Mike Martin, prin. Fax 231-1312

Galena, Cherokee, Pop. 2,973
Galena USD 499 900/PK-12
702 E 7th St 66739 620-783-4499
Dr. Brian Smith, supt. Fax 783-5547
www.usd499.org
Galena HS 200/9-12
702 E 7th St 66739 620-783-4499
Toby VanCleave, prin. Fax 783-1780
Galena MS 200/6-8
702 E 7th St 66739 620-783-4499
Lisa Scarrow, prin. Fax 783-5214

Galesburg, Neosho, Pop. 125
Erie-Galesburg USD 101
Supt. — See Erie
Galesburg MS 100/6-8
PO Box 147 66740 620-763-2470
Jared Han, prin. Fax 763-2224

Garden City, Finney, Pop. 26,301
Garden City USD 457 7,100/PK-12
1205 Fleming St 67846 620-805-7000
Dr. Steve Karlin Ed.D., supt. Fax 805-7190
www.gckschools.com
Garden City Alternate Education Center 100/Alt
1312 N 7th St 67846 620-805-8600
Mark Ronn, prin. Fax 805-8648
Garden City HS 2,000/9-12
2720 Buffalo Way Blvd 67846 620-805-5400
Steve Nordby, prin. Fax 805-5615
Good MS 800/7-8
1412 N Main St 67846 620-805-8100
Brad Springston, prin. Fax 805-8150
Henderson MS 400/Alt
2406 Fleming St 67846 620-805-8500
Jarrod Stoppel, prin. Fax 805-8598

Garden City Community College Post-Sec.
801 N Campus Dr 67846 620-276-7611

Garden Plain, Sedgwick, Pop. 838
Renwick USD 267
Supt. — See Andale
Garden Plain HS 200/9-12
PO Box 128 67050 316-531-2272
Matt Hoffman, prin. Fax 535-2727

Gardner, Johnson, Pop. 18,628
Gardner Edgerton USD 231 5,300/PK-12
PO Box 97 66030 913-856-2000
Pam Stranathan, supt. Fax 856-2069
www.usd231.com
Gardner Edgerton HS 1,400/9-12
425 N Waverly Rd 66030 913-856-2600
Mark Meyer, prin. Fax 856-2690
Pioneer Ridge MS 800/5-8
16200 S Kill Creek Rd 66030 913-856-3850
Linda Miesner, prin. Fax 856-2097
Trail Ridge MS 5-8
495 E Grand St 66030 913-856-3550
John Martin, prin. Fax 856-3552
Wheatridge MS 800/5-8
318 E Washington St 66030 913-856-2900
Carl Garrett, prin. Fax 856-2980

Garnett, Anderson, Pop. 3,385
Garnett USD 365 900/PK-12
PO Box 328 66032 785-448-6155
Donald Blome, supt. Fax 448-6157
www.usd365.org
Anderson County JSHS 500/7-12
1100 W Highway 31 66032 785-448-3115
Kenny Kellstadt, prin. Fax 448-6670

Girard, Crawford, Pop. 2,739
Girard USD 248 1,000/PK-12
415 N Summit St 66743 620-724-4325
Blaise Bauer, supt. Fax 724-8446
www.girard248.org/
Girard HS 300/9-12
415 N Summit St 66743 620-724-4326
Todd Ferguson, prin. Fax 724-6136
Girard MS 200/6-8
415 N Summit St 66743 620-724-4114
Randy Heatherly, prin. Fax 724-4610

Glasco, Cloud, Pop. 493
Southern Cloud USD 334
Supt. — See Miltonvale
Glasco HS 50/9-12
PO Box 158 67445 785-568-2291
Regina Wallace, prin. Fax 568-2239

Goddard, Sedgwick, Pop. 4,232
Goddard USD 265 5,300/K-12
PO Box 249 67052 316-794-4000
Dr. Justin Henry, supt. Fax 794-2222
www.goddardusd.com
Eisenhower HS 900/9-12
PO Box 789 67052 316-794-4190
Dr. Christie Meyer, prin. Fax 794-4191
Eisenhower MS 500/7-8
PO Box 349 67052 316-794-4150
Jerold Longabaugh, prin. Fax 794-4063
Goddard Academy 9-12
PO Box 318 67052 316-794-4142
Sean Hollas, prin. Fax 794-4143
Goddard HS 800/9-12
PO Box 189 67052 316-794-4100
Doug Bridwell, prin. Fax 794-4130
Goddard MS 400/7-8
PO Box 279 67052 316-794-4230
Lisa Hogarth, prin. Fax 794-4254

Goessel, Marion, Pop. 530
Goessel USD 411 300/K-12
PO Box 68 67053 620-367-4601
John Fast, supt. Fax 367-4603
www.usd411.org
Goessel JSHS 100/6-12
PO Box 6 67053 620-367-2242
Scott Boden, prin. Fax 367-2571

Goodland, Sherman, Pop. 4,416
Goodland USD 352 700/PK-12
PO Box 509 67735 785-890-2397
Bill Biermann, supt. Fax 890-8504
www.usd352.org
Goodland JSHS 300/6-12
PO Box 509 67735 785-890-5656
David Blochlinger, prin. Fax 890-8517

Northwest Kansas Technical College Post-Sec.
1209 Harrison St 67735 785-890-3641

Grainfield, Gove, Pop. 277
Wheatland USD 292 100/PK-12
PO Box 165 67737 785-673-4213
Gary Kraus, supt. Fax 673-4234
www.usd292.org
Wheatland HS 50/9-12
PO Box 149 67737 785-673-4223
Gary Kraus, prin. Fax 673-4234

Great Bend, Barton, Pop. 15,763
Great Bend USD 428 3,000/PK-12
201 S Patton Rd 67530 620-793-1500
Brad Reed, supt. Fax 793-1585
www.usd428.net
Great Bend HS 900/9-12
2027 Morton St 67530 620-793-1521
Tim Friess, prin. Fax 793-1537
Great Bend MS 400/7-8
1919 Harrison St 67530 620-793-1510
David Reiser, prin. Fax 793-1549

Barton County Community College Post-Sec.
245 NE 30 Rd 67530 620-792-2701

Greensburg, Kiowa, Pop. 767
Kiowa County USD 422 400/PK-12
710 S Main St 67054 620-723-2145
Glen Davis, supt. Fax 723-2705
www.usd422.org
Kiowa County HS 100/9-12
720 S Main St 67054 620-723-2164
Randy Fulton, prin. Fax 723-2019

Gridley, Coffey, Pop. 338
Le Roy-Gridley USD 245
Supt. — See Le Roy
Southern Coffey County JHS 50/6-8
PO Box 426 66852 620-836-2151
Julie Rosenquist, prin. Fax 836-4041

Grinnell, Gove, Pop. 259
Grinnell USD 291 100/K-8
PO Box 68 67738 785-824-3277
Ragena Mize, supt. Fax 824-3215
usd291.com
Grinnell MS 50/5-8
PO Box 68 67738 785-824-3277
Ragena Mize, prin. Fax 824-3215

Gypsum, Saline, Pop. 398
Southeast of Saline USD 306 700/K-12
5056 E Highway K4 67448 785-536-4291
Greg Mann, supt. Fax 536-4247
www.usd306.k12.ks.us
Southeast Saline JSHS 300/7-12
5056 E Highway K4 67448 785-536-4286
Roger Stumpf, prin. Fax 536-4292

Halstead, Harvey, Pop. 2,058
Halstead-Bentley USD 440 800/K-12
521 W 6th St 67056 316-835-2641
Thomas Alstrom, supt. Fax 835-2305
www.usd440.com
Halstead HS 200/9-12
521 W 6th St 67056 316-835-2682
Joe Gerber, prin. Fax 835-3673
Halstead MS 300/4-8
221 W 6th St 67056 316-835-2694
Amy Wagoner, prin. Fax 835-2469

Hamilton, Greenwood, Pop. 262
Hamilton USD 390 100/K-12
2596 W Rd N 66853 620-678-3244
Greg Markowitz, supt. Fax 678-3321
www.hamilton390.net
Hamilton HS 50/7-12
2596 W Rd N 66853 620-678-3651
David Kehres, prin. Fax 678-3651

Hanover, Washington, Pop. 680
Barnes USD 223
Supt. — See Barnes

Hanover HS 100/9-12
209 E North St 66945 785-337-2281
Brian Cordel, prin. Fax 337-2307

Hartford, Lyon, Pop. 364
Southern Lyon County USD 252 500/PK-12
PO Box 278 66854 620-392-5519
Dr. Michael Argabright, supt. Fax 392-5841
www.usd252.org/
Hartford JSHS 100/6-12
PO Box 218 66854 620-392-5515
Douglas Hes, prin. Fax 392-5960
Other Schools – See Olpe

Haven, Reno, Pop. 1,205
Haven USD 312 800/K-12
PO Box 130 67543 620-465-3445
Clark Wedel, supt. Fax 465-3595
www.havenschools.com
Haven HS 300/9-12
PO Box C 67543 620-465-2585
Marty Nienstedt, prin. Fax 465-7729
Haven MS 100/7-8
PO Box B 67543 620-465-2587
Marty Nienstedt, prin. Fax 465-2588

Haviland, Kiowa, Pop. 699

Barclay College Post-Sec.
607 N Kingman St 67059 620-862-5252

Hays, Ellis, Pop. 20,202
Hays USD 489 2,800/PK-12
323 W 12th St 67601 785-623-2400
John Thissen, supt. Fax 623-2409
www.usd489.com/
Hays HS 800/9-12
2300 E 13th St 67601 785-623-2600
Martin Straub, prin. Fax 623-2609
Hays MS 600/6-8
201 E 29th St 67601 785-623-2450
Craig Pallister, prin. Fax 623-2456

Fort Hays State University Post-Sec.
600 Park St 67601 785-628-4000
Hays Academy of Hair Design Post-Sec.
1214 E 27th St 67601 785-628-6624
Thomas More Prep-Marian JSHS 200/7-12
1701 Hall St 67601 785-625-6577
Chad Meitner, prin. Fax 625-3912

Haysville, Sedgwick, Pop. 10,516
Haysville USD 261 5,200/PK-12
1745 W Grand Ave 67060 316-554-2200
Dr. John Burke, supt. Fax 554-2230
www.usd261.com
Haysville HS Alt
106 Stewart Ave 67060 316-554-2231
Myron Regier, admin. Fax 554-2328
Haysville MS 600/6-8
900 W Grand Ave 67060 316-554-2251
Dr. Mike Maurer, prin. Fax 554-2258
Haysville West MS 700/6-8
1956 W Grand Ave 67060 316-554-2370
Ildo Martins, prin. Fax 554-2377
Other Schools – See Wichita

Healy, Lane, Pop. 233
Healy USD 468 100/PK-12
5006 N Dodge Rd 67850 620-398-2248
Larry Lysell, supt. Fax 398-2435
www.usd468.org
Healy JSHS 50/7-12
5006 N Dodge Rd 67850 620-398-2248
Beverly Roemer, prin. Fax 398-2435

Herington, Dickinson, Pop. 2,456
Herington USD 487 500/PK-12
19 N Broadway 67449 785-258-2263
Dr. Denis Yoder, supt. Fax 258-2982
www.heringtonschools.org
Herington HS 100/9-12
1401 N D St 67449 785-258-2261
Brandi Hendrix, prin. Fax 258-3013
Herington MS 100/6-8
1317 N D St 67449 785-258-2448
Brandi Hendrix, prin. Fax 258-3976

Hesston, Harvey, Pop. 3,645
Hesston USD 460 800/K-12
PO Box 2000 67062 620-327-4931
Ben Proctor, supt. Fax 327-7157
www.hesstonschools.org
Hesston HS 200/9-12
PO Box 2000 67062 620-327-7122
Ty Rhodes, prin. Fax 327-7138
Hesston MS 300/5-8
PO Box 2000 67062 620-327-7111
Greg Heinrichs, prin. Fax 327-7115

Hesston College Post-Sec.
PO Box 3000 67062 620-327-4221

Hiawatha, Brown, Pop. 3,067
Hiawatha USD 415 900/PK-12
PO Box 398 66434 785-742-2266
Dr. Penny Hargrove, supt. Fax 742-2301
www.hiawathaschools.org
Hiawatha HS 200/9-12
600 Red Hawk Dr 66434 785-742-3312
Andrew Gaddis, prin. Fax 742-7156
Hiawatha MS 200/5-8
307 S Morrill Ave 66434 785-742-4172
David Coufal, prin. Fax 742-1744

Highland, Doniphan, Pop. 980
Doniphan West USD 111
Supt. — See Denton
Doniphan West JSHS 100/7-12
PO Box 308 66035 785-442-3286
Chris Lackey, prin. Fax 442-3289

Highland Community College Post-Sec.
606 W Main St 66035 785-442-6000

Hill City, Graham, Pop. 1,438
Graham County USD 281 400/PK-12
PO Box 309 67642 785-421-2135
Jim Hickel, supt. Fax 421-5657
www.usd281.com
Hill City JSHS 200/7-12
PO Box 160 67642 785-421-2117
Alan Stein, prin. Fax 421-3029

Hillsboro, Marion, Pop. 2,935
Durham-Hillsboro-Lehigh USD 410 400/PK-12
416 S Date St 67063 620-947-3184
Max Heinrichs, supt. Fax 947-3475
www.usd410.net
Hillsboro MSHS 200/6-12
400 E Grand Ave 67063 620-947-3991
Clint Corby, prin. Fax 947-3251

Tabor College Post-Sec.
400 S Jefferson St 67063 620-947-3121

Hoisington, Barton, Pop. 2,656
Hoisington USD 431 800/PK-12
165 W 3rd St 67544 620-653-4134
Bill Lowry, supt. Fax 653-4073
www.usd431.net/
Hoisington HS 200/9-12
218 E 7th St 67544 620-653-2141
Joel Mason, prin. Fax 653-4164
Hoisington MS 200/5-8
360 W 11th St 67544 620-653-4951
Patricia Reinhardt, prin. Fax 653-4483

Holcomb, Finney, Pop. 2,058
Holcomb USD 363 1,000/PK-12
PO Box 8 67851 620-277-2629
Jean Rush, supt. Fax 277-2010
www.usd363.com/
Holcomb HS 200/9-12
PO Box 38 67851 620-277-2063
Rob Schneeberger, prin. Fax 277-0240
Holcomb MS 200/6-8
PO Box 89 67851 620-277-2699
Chad Krug, prin. Fax 277-2746

Holton, Jackson, Pop. 3,248
Holton USD 336 1,100/PK-12
PO Box 352 66436 785-364-3650
Dennis Stones, supt. Fax 364-3975
www.holtonks.net
Holton HS 300/9-12
901 New York Ave 66436 785-364-2181
Rod Wittmer, prin. Fax 364-5360
Holton MS 200/6-8
900 Iowa Ave 66436 785-364-2441
Michael Kimberlin, prin. Fax 364-5460

North Jackson USD 335 400/PK-12
12692 266th Rd 66436 785-364-2194
Adrianne Walsh, supt. Fax 364-4346
www.jhcobras.net
Jackson Heights MSHS 200/7-12
12719 266th Rd 66436 785-364-2195
Darren Shupe, prin. Fax 364-2487

Holyrood, Ellsworth, Pop. 439
Central Plains USD 112 600/PK-12
PO Box 168 67450 785-252-3695
Greg Clark, supt. Fax 252-3697
www.usd112.org
Other Schools – See Bushton, Claflin, Wilson

Hope, Dickinson, Pop. 357
Rural Vista USD 481
Supt. — See White City
Hope HS 50/9-12
PO Box 218 67451 785-366-7221
Mike Teeter, prin. Fax 366-7115

Horton, Brown, Pop. 1,718
South Brown County USD 430 600/PK-12
522 Central Ave 66439 785-486-2611
Dr. Steven Davies, supt. Fax 486-2496
usd430.k12.ks.us
Horton HS 200/9-12
1120 1st Ave E 66439 785-486-2151
David Norman, prin. Fax 486-2909
Other Schools – See Everest

Howard, Elk, Pop. 671
West Elk USD 282 300/PK-12
PO Box 607 67349 620-374-2113
Bert Moore, supt. Fax 374-2414
Howard West Elk S 300/PK-12
PO Box 278 67349 620-374-2147
Martin Burke, prin. Fax 374-2116

Hoxie, Sheridan, Pop. 1,186
Hoxie USD 412 400/PK-12
PO Box 348 67740 785-675-3258
James Howard, supt. Fax 675-2126
www.hoxie.org
Hoxie JSHS 100/7-12
PO Box 989 67740 785-675-3286
Gary Johnson, prin. Fax 675-2270

Hoyt, Jackson, Pop. 649
Royal Valley USD 337
Supt. — See Mayetta
Royal Valley HS 300/9-12
PO Box 128 66440 785-986-6251
James Holloman, prin. Fax 986-6479

Hugoton, Stevens, Pop. 3,876
Hugoton USD 210 1,100/PK-12
205 E 6th St 67951 620-544-4397
Adrian Howie, supt. Fax 544-7138
www.usd210.org
Hugoton HS 300/9-12
215 W 11th St 67951 620-544-4311
Melody Witt, prin. Fax 544-7392
Hugoton MS 200/7-8
115 W 11th St 67951 620-544-4341
Lance Custer, prin. Fax 544-4856

Humboldt, Allen, Pop. 1,917
Humboldt USD 258 700/PK-12
801 New York St 66748 620-473-3121
Kay Lewis, supt. Fax 473-2023
www.usd258.net
Humboldt HS 200/9-12
1020 New York St 66748 620-473-2251
John Johnson, prin. Fax 473-2086
Humboldt MS 200/6-8
1105 Bridge St 66748 620-473-3348
Stephanie Splechter, prin. Fax 473-3141
Humboldt Tech Building Vo/Tech
1116 New York St 66748 620-473-2251
John Johnson, prin. Fax 473-2086

Hutchinson, Reno, Pop. 41,132
Buhler USD 313
Supt. — See Buhler
Prairie Hills MS 400/6-8
3200 Lucille Dr 67502 620-662-6027
Todd Fredrickson, prin. Fax 694-1002

Hutchinson USD 308 4,500/PK-12
1520 N Plum St 67501 620-615-4000
Dr. Shelly Kiblinger, supt. Fax 615-4010
www.usd308.com
Hutchinson HS 1,500/9-12
810 E 13th Ave 67501 620-615-4100
Ronn Roehm, prin. Fax 615-4200
Hutchinson MS 8 400/8-8
200 W 14th Ave 67501 620-615-4800
Bruce Hurford, prin. Fax 615-4802

Nickerson USD 309 1,100/K-12
4501 W 4th Ave 67501 620-663-7141
Dr. Dawn Johnson, supt. Fax 663-7148
www.usd309ks.org
Reno Valley MS 200/7-8
1616 Wilshire Dr 67501 620-662-4573
Vince Naccarato, prin. Fax 662-6708
Other Schools – See Nickerson

Central Christian S 200/PK-12
1910 E 30th Ave 67502 620-663-2174
Tim Kuhns, supt. Fax 663-2176
Hutchinson Community College Post-Sec.
1300 N Plum St 67501 620-665-3500
Sidney's Hairdressing College Post-Sec.
200 E 3rd Ave 67501 620-662-5481
Trinity Catholic HS 300/7-12
1400 E 17th Ave 67501 620-662-5800
Joe Hammersmith, prin. Fax 662-1233

Independence, Montgomery, Pop. 9,137
Independence USD 446 2,000/K-12
517 N 10th St 67301 620-332-1800
Rusty Arnold, supt. Fax 332-1811
www.indyschools.com
Independence HS 600/9-12
1301 N 10th St 67301 620-332-1815
Mario Sherrell, prin. Fax 332-1831
Independence MS 400/6-8
300 W Locust St 67301 620-332-1836
Mark Hayward, prin. Fax 332-1841

Independence Community College Post-Sec.
1057 W College Ave 67301 620-331-4100

Ingalls, Gray, Pop. 304
Ingalls USD 477 200/PK-12
PO Box 99 67853 620-335-5136
Randy Rockhold, supt. Fax 335-5678
www.ingallsusd477.com/
Ingalls JSHS 100/6-12
PO Box 99 67853 620-335-5135
Joe Meador, prin. Fax 335-5801

Inman, McPherson, Pop. 1,343
Inman USD 448 400/PK-12
PO Box 129 67546 620-585-6441
Scott Friesen, supt. Fax 585-2797
www.usd448.com
Inman JSHS 200/7-12
PO Box 279 67546 620-585-6441
Tyler Weinbrenner, prin. Fax 585-2797

Iola, Allen, Pop. 5,562
Iola USD 257 700/PK-12
305 N Washington Ave 66749 620-365-4700
Jack Koehn, supt. Fax 365-4708
www.usd257.org
Iola HS 300/9-12
300 E Jackson Ave 66749 620-365-4715
Stacey Fager, prin. Fax 365-4730
Iola Upper MS 200/7-8
600 East St 66749 620-365-4785
Jack Stanley, prin. Fax 365-4770

Allen Community College Post-Sec.
1801 N Cottonwood St 66749 620-365-5116

Jetmore, Hodgeman, Pop. 861
Hodgeman County USD 227 300/PK-12
PO Box 398 67854 620-357-8301
Doug Chaney, supt. Fax 357-8437
www.usd227.org/

Hodgeman County HS 100/7-12
PO Box 100 67854 620-357-8378
Ron Shelton, prin. Fax 357-6563

Johnson, Stanton, Pop. 1,483
Stanton County USD 452 400/PK-12
PO Box C 67855 620-492-6226
Kim Novack, supt. Fax 492-1326
www.usd452.org
Stanton County JSHS 200/7-12
PO Box C 67855 620-492-6284
Randall Jansonius, prin. Fax 492-1326

Junction City, Geary, Pop. 21,775
Geary County USD 475 8,200/PK-12
PO Box 370 66441 785-717-4000
Dr. Corbin Witt, supt. Fax 717-4003
www.usd475.org/
Dixon Center for Innovative Studies Alt
920 W 6th St 66441 785-717-4710
Thomas Wesoloski, prin. Fax 717-4711
Freshman Success Academy 500/9-9
300 W 9th St 66441 785-717-4312
Jeff Tanner, prin.
Junction City HS 1,700/9-12
900 N Eisenhower Dr 66441 785-717-4200
Melissa Sharp, prin. Fax 717-4201
Junction City MS 1,000/6-8
700 Wildcat Ln 66441 785-717-4400
Mary Wright, prin. Fax 717-4401
Other Schools – See Fort Riley

St. Xaviers Catholic S 200/K-12
200 N Washington St 66441 785-238-2841
Shawn Augustine, prin. Fax 238-5021

Kansas City, Wyandotte, Pop. 142,097
Kansas City USD 500 20,500/PK-12
2010 N 59th St 66104 913-551-3200
Dr. Cynthia Lane, supt. Fax 551-3217
www.kckps.org
Argentine MS 600/6-8
2123 Ruby Ave 66106 913-627-6750
Jereme Brueggeman, prin. Fax 627-6783
Arrowhead MS 500/6-8
1715 N 82nd St 66112 913-627-6600
Laurie Boyd, prin. Fax 627-6654
Central MS 600/6-8
925 Ivandale St 66101 913-627-6150
Dionandre Josenberger, prin. Fax 627-6152
Coronado MS 400/6-8
1735 N 64th Ter 66102 913-627-6300
Jewell Ragsdale, prin. Fax 627-6358
Eisenhower MS 500/6-8
2901 N 72nd St 66109 913-627-6450
Samia Guess, prin. Fax 627-6455
Harmon HS 1,300/9-12
2400 Steele Rd 66106 913-627-7050
Geoff Markos, prin. Fax 627-7185
Northwest MS 700/6-8
2400 N 18th St 66104 913-627-4000
Dr. Carnest Mitchell, prin. Fax 627-4052
Rosedale MS 600/6-8
3600 Springfield St 66103 913-627-6900
Travis Helm, prin. Fax 627-6957
Schlagle HS 800/9-12
2214 N 59th St 66104 913-627-7500
Yolanda Thompson, prin. Fax 627-7555
Sumner Academy/Arts & Sciences 800/8-12
1610 N 8th St 66101 913-627-7200
Jonathan Richard, prin. Fax 627-7205
Washington HS 1,000/9-12
7340 Leavenworth Rd 66109 913-627-7800
Dr. Maritza Paul, prin. Fax 627-7850
West MS 400/6-8
2600 N 44th St 66104 913-627-6000
Elvira Randle, prin. Fax 627-6053
Wyandotte HS 1,500/9-12
2501 Minnesota Ave 66102 913-627-7600
Mary Stewart, prin. Fax 627-7700

Piper-Kansas City USD 203 1,900/PK-12
3130 N 122nd St 66109 913-721-2088
Tim Conrad, supt. Fax 721-3573
www.piperschools.com
Piper HS 600/9-12
4400 N 107th St 66109 913-721-2100
Jason Malaschak, prin. Fax 721-3867
Piper MS 400/6-8
4420 N 107th St 66109 913-721-1144
Stephen Mercer, prin. Fax 721-1526

Turner USD 202 4,000/PK-12
800 S 55th St 66106 913-288-4100
Dr. Jason Dandoy, supt. Fax 288-3401
www.turnerusd202.org/
Journey S of Choice Alt
2540 Junction Rd 66106 913-288-3690
Rena Duewel, prin. Fax 288-3691
Turner HS 1,100/9-12
2211 S 55th St 66106 913-288-3300
Alan Penrose, prin. Fax 288-3301
Turner MS 600/7-8
1312 S 55th St 66106 913-288-4000
Shannon Adams, prin. Fax 288-4001

Bishop Ward HS 300/9-12
708 N 18th St 66102 913-371-1201
Dr. Karen Hopson, prin. Fax 371-2145
Donnelly College Post-Sec.
608 N 18th St 66102 913-621-8700
Kansas City Kansas Community College Post-Sec.
7250 State Ave 66112 913-334-1100
Kansas State School for the Blind Post-Sec.
1100 State Ave 66102 913-281-3308
University of Kansas Medical Center Post-Sec.
3901 Rainbow Blvd 66160 913-588-5000

Kensington, Smith, Pop. 463
Thunder Ridge SD 110 200/PK-12
128 S Kansas St 66951 785-476-2218
Jeff Yoxall, supt. Fax 476-2258
usd110.net
Thunder Ridge HS 100/9-12
209 E Ash St 66951 785-476-2217
Jeff Yoxall, prin. Fax 476-2210
Other Schools – See Agra

Kingman, Kingman, Pop. 3,142
Kingman-Norwich USD 331 1,000/PK-12
115 N Main St 67068 620-532-3134
Dr. Robert Diepenbrock Ed.D., supt. Fax 532-3251
www.knusd331.com/
Kingman HS 200/9-12
260 W Kansas Ave 67068 620-532-3136
Andy Albright, prin. Fax 532-3027
Kingman MS 200/6-8
607 N Spruce St 67068 620-532-3186
Bill Kelley, prin. Fax 532-5137
Other Schools – See Norwich

Kiowa, Barber, Pop. 1,012
South Barber County USD 255 300/PK-12
512 Main St 67070 620-825-4115
Dr. Andi Williams, supt. Fax 825-4145
www.southbarber.com
South Barber JSHS 100/7-12
1220 N 8th St 67070 620-825-4214
Brent Shaffer, prin. Fax 825-4250

Kismet, Seward, Pop. 456
Kismet-Plains USD 483 700/PK-12
17222 Mustang Rd 67859 620-563-7103
Elton Argo, supt. Fax 563-7348
www.usd483.net
Southwestern Heights HS 200/9-12
17222 Mustang Rd 67859 620-563-7292
Dan Frisby, prin. Fax 563-7383
Southwestern Heights JHS 200/6-8
17222 Mustang Rd 67859 620-563-7100
Kurt Stanfield, prin. Fax 563-7342

La Crosse, Rush, Pop. 1,335
La Crosse USD 395 300/K-12
PO Box 778 67548 785-222-2505
Bill Keeley, supt. Fax 222-3240
www.usd395.org
La Crosse HS 100/9-12
PO Box 810 67548 785-222-2528
Kathy Keeley, prin. Fax 222-3480
La Crosse MS 50/7-8
PO Box 810 67548 785-222-3030
Kathy Keeley, prin. Fax 222-3480

LaCygne, Linn, Pop. 1,138
Prairie View USD 362 900/PK-12
13799 KS Highway 152, 913-757-2677
Rex Bollinger, supt. Fax 757-4442
www.pv362.org
Prairie View HS 300/9-12
13731 KS Highway 152, 913-757-4447
Timothy Weis, prin. Fax 757-4443
Prairie View MS 200/6-8
13667 KS Highway 152, 913-757-4497
Ken Bolt, prin. Fax 757-2728

Lakin, Kearny, Pop. 2,182
Lakin USD 215 600/PK-12
1003 W Kingman Ave 67860 620-355-6761
Mike Ward, supt. Fax 355-7317
www.usd215.org
Lakin HS 200/9-12
407 N Campbell St 67860 620-355-6411
Tim Robertson, prin. Fax 355-6460
Lakin MS 200/5-8
1201 W Kingman Ave 67860 620-355-6973
Cody Calkins, prin. Fax 355-8313

Langdon, Reno, Pop. 42
Fairfield USD 310 300/PK-12
16115 S Langdon Rd 67583 620-596-2152
Nathan Reed, supt. Fax 596-2835
www.usd310.org
Fairfield HS 100/9-12
16115 S Langdon Rd 67583 620-596-2152
Jason Briar, prin. Fax 596-2835
Fairfield MS 100/6-8
16115 S Langdon Rd 67583 620-596-2615
Jason Briar, prin. Fax 596-2835

Lansing, Leavenworth, Pop. 10,978
Lansing USD 469 2,500/PK-12
200 E Mary St 66043 913-727-1100
Dr. Darrel Stufflebeam Ed.D., supt. Fax 727-1619
www.usd469.net
Lansing HS 800/9-12
1412 147th St 66043 913-727-3357
Steve Dike, prin. Fax 727-2001
Lansing MS 600/6-8
220 Lion Ln 66043 913-727-1197
Kerry Brungardt, prin. Fax 727-1349

Larned, Pawnee, Pop. 3,979
Ft. Larned USD 495 1,000/PK-12
120 E 6th St 67550 620-285-3185
Jon Flint, supt. Fax 285-2973
www.usd495.net
Larned HS 300/9-12
815 Corse Ave 67550 620-285-2151
Troy Langdon, prin. Fax 285-7148
Larned MS 300/5-8
904 Corse Ave 67550 620-285-8430
Shane Sundahl, prin. Fax 285-8433

Lawrence, Douglas, Pop. 84,434
Lawrence USD 497 11,700/PK-12
110 McDonald Dr 66044 785-832-5000
Kyle Hayden, supt. Fax 832-5016
www.usd497.org
Lawrence Free State HS 1,600/9-12
4700 Overland Dr 66049 785-832-6050
Myron Graber, prin. Fax 832-6099
Lawrence HS 1,500/9-12
1901 Louisiana St 66046 785-832-5050
Matt Brungardt, prin. Fax 832-5066
Lawrence Liberty Memorial Central MS 400/6-8
1400 Massachusetts St 66044 785-832-5400
Jeff Harkin, prin. Fax 832-5403
Lawrence South MS 600/6-8
2734 Louisiana St 66046 785-832-5450
Jennifer Bessolo, prin. Fax 832-5453
Lawrence Southwest MS 700/6-8
2511 Inverness Dr 66047 785-832-5550
Kristen Ryan, prin. Fax 832-5554
Lawrence West MS 600/6-8
2700 Harvard Rd 66049 785-832-5500
Brad Kempf, prin. Fax 832-5504

Bishop Seabury Academy 200/6-12
4120 Clinton Pkwy 66047 785-832-1717
Dr. Don Schawang, hdmstr. Fax 832-1919
Haskell Indian Nations University Post-Sec.
155 Indian Ave 66046 785-749-8404
Pinnacle Career Institute Post-Sec.
1601 W 23rd St Ste 200 66046 785-841-9640
University of Kansas Post-Sec.
1450 Jayhawk Blvd 66045 785-864-2700
Veritas Christian S 100/K-12
256 N Michigan St 66044 785-749-0083
Kelli Huslig M.Ed., admin. Fax 749-0580

Leavenworth, Leavenworth, Pop. 33,833
Leavenworth USD 453 3,400/PK-12
PO Box 969 66048 913-684-1400
Mike Roth, supt. Fax 684-1407
www.usd453.org
Leavenworth HS 1,400/9-12
2012 10th Ave 66048 913-684-1550
Dr. Thomas Barry, prin. Fax 684-1555
Warren MS 400/6-8
PO Box 7 66048 913-684-1530
Scott Kedrowski, prin. Fax 684-1539

Immaculata HS 100/7-12
600 Shawnee St 66048 913-682-3900
Rick Geraci, prin. Fax 682-9036
University of Saint Mary Post-Sec.
4100 S 4th St 66048 913-682-5151

Leawood, Johnson, Pop. 31,391
Blue Valley USD 229
Supt. — See Overland Park
Leawood MS 500/6-8
2410 W 123rd St 66209 913-239-5300
Chris Legleiter, prin. Fax 239-5348
Prairie Star MS 600/6-8
14201 Mission Rd 66224 913-239-5600
Stacey Sperry, prin. Fax 239-5648

Lebo, Coffey, Pop. 937
Lebo-Waverly USD 243
Supt. — See Waverly
Lebo HS 100/6-12
PO Box 45 66856 620-256-6341
Duane Ford, prin. Fax 256-6342

Lenexa, Johnson, Pop. 47,046
De Soto USD 232
Supt. — See De Soto
Mill Creek MS 700/6-8
8001 Mize Blvd 66227 913-667-3512
Josh Kindler, prin. Fax 422-9229

Christ Preparatory Academy 100/K-12
15700 W 87th Street Pkwy 66219 913-831-1345
Ron Lawlor, admin. Fax 438-1402
St. James Academy 700/9-12
24505 Prairie Star Pkwy 66227 913-254-4200
Shane Rapp, prin. Fax 254-4221
The Art Institutes International Post-Sec.
8208 Melrose Dr 66214 913-217-4600

Leon, Butler, Pop. 678
Bluestem USD 205 500/PK-12
625 S Mill Rd 67074 316-742-3261
Joel Lovesee, supt. Fax 742-9265
www.usd205.com
Bluestem JSHS 300/7-12
500 S Bluestem Dr 67074 316-742-3281
Brett Mohr, prin. Fax 742-3813

Leoti, Wichita, Pop. 1,520
Leoti USD 467 400/PK-12
PO Box 967 67861 620-375-4677
Keith Higgins, supt. Fax 375-2304
www.leoti.org/
Wichita County JSHS 200/7-12
PO Box K 67861 620-375-2213
Delbert Schmidt, prin. Fax 375-4958

Le Roy, Coffey, Pop. 552
Le Roy-Gridley USD 245 200/PK-12
PO Box 278 66857 620-964-2212
Russ Mildward, supt. Fax 964-2413
usd245ks.org/
Southern Coffey County HS 100/9-12
PO Box 188 66857 620-964-2217
Russ Mildward, prin. Fax 964-2410
Other Schools – See Gridley

Liberal, Seward, Pop. 20,195
Liberal USD 480 4,200/PK-12
PO Box 949 67905 620-604-1010
Renae Hickert, supt. Fax 604-1011
www.usd480.net
Eisenhower MS 6-8
2000 N Western Ave 67901 620-604-1400
Troy McCarter, admin. Fax 604-1401

Liberal HS 1,200/9-12
1611 W 2nd St 67901 620-604-1200
Shiloh Vincent, prin. Fax 604-1201
Liberal South MS 300/7-8
950 S Grant Ave 67901 620-604-1300
Jason Diseker, prin. Fax 604-1301

Seward County Community College Post-Sec.
PO Box 1137 67905 620-624-1951

Lincoln, Lincoln, Pop. 1,283
Lincoln USD 298 400/PK-12
PO Box 289 67455 785-524-4436
Kathy Robertson, supt. Fax 524-3080
www.usd298.com
Lincoln JSHS 200/7-12
PO Box 269 67455 785-524-4193
Kenneth Huff, prin. Fax 524-5114

Lindsborg, McPherson, Pop. 3,384
Smoky Valley USD 400 1,100/PK-12
126 S Main St 67456 785-227-2981
Glen Suppes, supt. Fax 227-2982
www.smokyvalley.org/
Smoky Valley HS 300/9-12
1 Viking Blvd 67456 785-227-2909
Bill Nelson, prin. Fax 227-2900
Smoky Valley MS 300/5-8
401 N Cedar St 67456 785-227-4249
Garrett Scritchfield, prin. Fax 227-3650

Bethany College Post-Sec.
335 E Swensson Ave 67456 785-227-3311

Linn, Washington, Pop. 406
Barnes USD 223
Supt. — See Barnes
Linn HS 100/9-12
300 Parkview St 66953 785-348-5531
Tyler Ayers, prin. Fax 348-5534

Little River, Rice, Pop. 556
Little River USD 444 400/PK-12
PO Box 218 67457 620-897-6325
Brent Garrison, supt. Fax 897-6788
usd444.ss5.sharpschool.com
Little River HS 100/9-12
PO Box 8 67457 620-897-6201
Audrey Johnson, prin. Fax 897-6203
Little River JHS 100/6-8
PO Box 8 67457 620-897-6201
Audrey Johnson, prin. Fax 897-6203

Logan, Phillips, Pop. 588
Logan USD 326 200/K-12
PO Box 98 67646 785-689-7595
Michael Gower, supt. Fax 689-7517
www.logan326.net
Logan HS 100/7-12
PO Box 98 67646 785-689-7574
David Kirkendall, prin. Fax 689-7543

Long Island, Phillips, Pop. 134
Northern Valley USD 212
Supt. — See Almena
Long Island MS 100/5-8
PO Box 98 67647 785-854-7681
Marvin Gebhard, prin. Fax 854-7684

Longton, Elk, Pop. 339
Elk Valley USD 283 100/PK-12
PO Box 87 67352 620-642-2811
Jason Crawford, supt. Fax 642-6551
www.usd283.org
Elk Valley HS 100/6-12
PO Box 87 67352 620-642-2215
Jason Crawford, prin. Fax 642-3361

Lost Springs, Marion, Pop. 64
Centre USD 397 300/K-12
2382 310th St 66859 785-983-4304
Susan Beeson, supt. Fax 983-4352
www.usd397.com
Centre K-12 S 300/K-12
2374 310th St 66859 785-983-4321
Susan Beeson, prin. Fax 983-4377

Louisburg, Miami, Pop. 4,257
Louisburg USD 416 1,800/PK-12
PO Box 550 66053 913-837-1700
Dr. Brian Biermann, supt. Fax 837-1701
www.usd416.org
Louisburg HS 500/9-12
PO Box 399 66053 913-837-1720
Dr. Tammy Thomasson, prin. Fax 837-1799
Louisburg MS 400/6-8
PO Box 308 66053 913-837-1800
Michael Isaacsen, prin. Fax 837-1801

Lyndon, Osage, Pop. 1,040
Lyndon USD 421 400/PK-12
PO Box 488 66451 785-828-4413
Cheryl Cook, supt. Fax 828-3686
www.usd421.org
Lyndon HS 100/9-12
PO Box 488 66451 785-828-4911
Brad Marcotte, prin. Fax 828-4221

Lyons, Rice, Pop. 3,662
Lyons USD 405 800/PK-12
800 S Workman St 67554 620-257-5196
Bill Day, supt. Fax 257-5197
www.usd405.com
Lyons HS 200/9-12
601 E American Rd 67554 620-257-5114
Kelly Nusser, prin. Fax 257-3194
Lyons MS 200/6-8
501 E American Rd 67554 620-257-3961
Derek Carlson, prin. Fax 257-3518

Rice County Learning Ctr Alt
110 E 1st St 67554 620-257-7060
Larry Walker, dir. Fax 257-7060

Macksville, Stafford, Pop. 542
Macksville USD 351 200/PK-12
PO Box 487 67557 620-348-3415
Greg Rinehart M.Ed., supt. Fax 348-3217
www.usd351.com
Macksville MSHS 100/7-12
PO Box 307 67557 620-348-2475
Stephanie Brandyberry, prin. Fax 348-2631

Mc Louth, Jefferson, Pop. 860
Mc Louth USD 342 600/PK-12
PO Box 40 66054 913-796-2201
Steve Lilly, supt. Fax 796-6440
www.mclouth.org
Mc Louth HS 200/9-12
PO Box 40 66054 913-796-6122
Janna Davis, prin. Fax 796-6124
Mc Louth MS 100/6-8
PO Box 40 66054 913-796-6122
Janna Davis, prin. Fax 796-6124

Mc Pherson, McPherson, Pop. 12,895
Mc Pherson USD 418 2,400/PK-12
514 N Main St 67460 620-241-9400
Mark Crawford, supt. Fax 241-9410
www.mcpherson.com/418
Mc Pherson HS 700/9-12
801 E 1st St 67460 620-241-9500
Brad Plackemeier, prin. Fax 241-9506
Mc Pherson MS 600/6-8
700 E Elizabeth St 67460 620-241-9450
Brandon Simmelink, prin. Fax 241-9456

Central Christian College of Kansas Post-Sec.
PO Box 1403 67460 620-241-0723
Elyria Christian S 200/K-12
1644 Comanche Rd 67460 620-241-2994
Eric Clark, admin. Fax 241-1238
McPherson College Post-Sec.
1600 E Euclid St 67460 620-242-0400

Madison, Greenwood, Pop. 687
Madison-Virgil USD 386 300/PK-12
PO Box 398 66860 620-437-2910
Ryan Bradbury, supt. Fax 437-2916
www.usd386.net
Madison HS 100/7-12
PO Box 398 66860 620-437-2912
Ryan Bradbury, prin. Fax 437-2911

Maize, Sedgwick, Pop. 3,313
Maize USD 266 6,900/K-12
905 W Academy Ave 67101 316-722-0614
Chad Higgins, supt. Fax 722-8538
www.usd266.com
Complete HS Maize Alt
745 W Central St 67101 316-722-4790
Kristy Custer, prin. Fax 729-0621
Maize HS 1,400/9-12
11600 W 45th St N 67101 316-722-0441
Chris Botts, prin. Fax 729-7743
Maize MS 800/6-8
4600 N Maize Rd 67101 316-729-2464
Brian Thompson, prin. Fax 729-2479
Other Schools – See Wichita

Manhattan, Riley, Pop. 50,618
Manhattan-Ogden USD 383 6,400/PK-12
2031 Poyntz Ave 66502 785-587-2000
Dr. Marvin Wade, supt. Fax 587-2006
www.usd383.org
Anthony MS 500/7-8
2501 Browning Ave 66502 785-587-2890
Vickie Kline, prin. Fax 587-2899
Eisenhower MS 400/7-8
800 Walters Dr 66502 785-587-2880
Tracy Newell, prin. Fax 587-2888
Manhattan HS West/East Campus 1,900/9-12
2100 Poyntz Ave 66502 785-587-2100
Greg Hoyt, prin. Fax 587-2132

American Institute of Baking Post-Sec.
PO Box 3999 66505 785-537-4750
Crum's Beauty College Post-Sec.
512 Poyntz Ave 66502 785-776-4794
Flint Hills Christian S 100/PK-12
3905 Green Valley Rd 66502 785-776-2223
Tim McDonald, admin. Fax 776-3016
Kansas State University 66506 Post-Sec.
785-532-6250
Manhattan Area Technical College Post-Sec.
3136 Dickens Ave 66503 785-587-2800
Manhattan Christian College Post-Sec.
1415 Anderson Ave 66502 785-539-3571

Mankato, Jewell, Pop. 856
Rock Hills USD 107 300/PK-12
109 E Main St 66956 785-378-3102
Nadine Smith, supt. Fax 378-3438
www.usd107.org/
Rock Hills JSHS 100/7-12
109 E Main St 66956 785-378-3126
Sam Meyers, prin. Fax 378-3530

Marion, Marion, Pop. 1,911
Marion-Florence USD 408 500/K-12
101 N Thorp St 66861 620-382-2117
Lee Leiker, supt. Fax 382-2118
www.usd408.com
Marion HS 200/9-12
701 E Main St 66861 620-382-2168
Tod Gordon, prin. Fax 382-6021
Marion MS 100/6-8
125 S Lincoln St 66861 620-382-6070
Missy Stubenhofer, prin. Fax 382-6073

Marysville, Marshall, Pop. 3,251
Marysville USD 364 800/PK-12
211 S 10th St 66508 785-562-5308
Bill Mullins, supt. Fax 562-5309
www.usd364.org
Marysville JSHS 400/7-12
1011 Walnut St 66508 785-562-5386
Darren Schroeder, prin. Fax 562-5387

Mayetta, Jackson, Pop. 325
Royal Valley USD 337 900/PK-12
PO Box 219 66509 785-966-2246
Aaric Davis, supt. Fax 966-2490
www.rv337.com/
Royal Valley MS 300/5-8
PO Box 189 66509 785-966-2251
John Linn, prin. Fax 966-2833
Other Schools – See Hoyt

Meade, Meade, Pop. 1,700
Meade USD 226 400/PK-12
PO Box 400 67864 620-873-2081
Kenneth Harshberger, supt. Fax 873-2201
www.usd226.org/
Meade HS 100/9-12
PO Box 400 67864 620-873-2981
Scott Moshier, prin. Fax 873-2201

Medicine Lodge, Barber, Pop. 1,980
Barber County North USD 254 500/PK-12
PO Box 288 67104 620-886-3370
Mark Buck, supt. Fax 886-3640
www.usd254.org/
Medicine Lodge JSHS 200/7-12
400 W Eldorado Ave 67104 620-886-5667
Darryl Honas, prin. Fax 886-3053

Melvern, Osage, Pop. 380
Marais Des Cygnes Valley USD 456 200/K-12
PO Box 158 66510 785-549-3521
Ted Hessong, supt. Fax 549-3659
www.usd456.org
Marais Des Cygnes Valley MSHS 100/6-12
PO Box 158 66510 785-549-3313
Michelle Schulze, prin. Fax 549-3576

Meriden, Jefferson, Pop. 803
Jefferson West USD 340 900/PK-12
PO Box 267 66512 785-484-3444
A. Patton Happer, supt. Fax 484-3148
www.usd340.org
Jefferson West HS 300/9-12
PO Box 268 66512 785-484-3331
Rhonda Frakes, prin. Fax 484-2021
Jefferson West MS 300/5-8
PO Box 410 66512 785-484-2900
John Hamon, prin. Fax 484-2904

Miltonvale, Cloud, Pop. 532
Southern Cloud USD 334 200/K-12
PO Box 334 67466 785-427-3334
Roger Perkins, supt. Fax 427-2422
www.sc334.org
Miltonvale HS 50/7-12
PO Box 394 67466 785-427-3250
Roger Perkins, prin. Fax 427-3181
Other Schools – See Glasco

Minneapolis, Ottawa, Pop. 2,009
North Ottawa County USD 239 600/K-12
PO Box 257 67467 785-392-2167
Chris Vignery, supt. Fax 392-3038
www.usd239.org
Minneapolis JSHS 300/7-12
PO Box 317 67467 785-392-2113
Terry Moeckel, prin. Fax 392-2275

Minneola, Clark, Pop. 728
Minneola USD 219 300/K-12
PO Box 157 67865 620-885-4372
Mark Walker, supt. Fax 885-4509
www.usd219.org/
Minneola HS 100/9-12
PO Box 157 67865 620-885-4611
Brandon Haynes, prin. Fax 885-4509

Montezuma, Gray, Pop. 959
Montezuma USD 371 200/PK-12
PO Box 355 67867 620-846-2283
Jay Zehr, supt. Fax 846-2294
www.usd371.org
South Gray HS 100/9-12
PO Box 355 67867 620-846-2281
Tim Skinner, prin. Fax 846-2181

Moran, Allen, Pop. 543
Marmaton Valley USD 256 300/K-12
128 W Oak St 66755 620-237-4250
Kenneth McWhirter, supt. Fax 237-8872
www.usd256.org
Marmaton Valley HS 100/7-12
128 W Oak St 66755 620-237-4251
Kim Ensminger, prin. Fax 237-4576

Moscow, Stevens, Pop. 304
Moscow USD 209 200/K-12
PO Box 158 67952 620-598-2205
Stuart Moore, supt. Fax 598-2233
usd209.weebly.com
Moscow HS 100/6-12
PO Box 160 67952 620-598-2250
Tina Salmans, prin. Fax 598-2233

Mound City, Linn, Pop. 679
Jayhawk USD 346 600/PK-12
PO Box 278 66056 913-795-2247
Royce Powelson, supt. Fax 795-2185
www.usd346.org/
Jayhawk-Linn JSHS 200/7-12
PO Box D 66056 913-795-2224
Jim Dillon, prin. Fax 795-9906

Moundridge, McPherson, Pop. 1,722
Moundridge USD 423 400/K-12
PO Box K 67107 620-345-5500
George Leary, supt. Fax 345-8617
www.usd423.org
Moundridge HS 100/9-12
PO Box 610 67107 620-345-5500
Hilarie Hecox, prin. Fax 345-5218
Moundridge MS 100/5-8
PO Box 607 67107 620-345-5500
JoAnn Browne, prin. Fax 345-5307

Mulvane, Sedgwick, Pop. 5,964
Mulvane USD 263 1,800/PK-12
PO Box 130 67110 316-777-1102
Brad Rahe, supt. Fax 777-1103
www.usd263.com
Mulvane HS 600/9-12
1900 N Rock Rd 67110 316-777-1183
Jay Ensley, prin. Fax 777-2228
Mulvane MS 400/6-8
915 Westview Dr 67110 316-777-2022
Traci Becker, prin. Fax 777-4967

Natoma, Osborne, Pop. 333
Paradise USD 399 100/PK-12
PO Box 100 67651 785-885-4843
Aaron Homburg, supt. Fax 885-4523
www.usd399.com
Natoma HS 100/7-12
PO Box 100 67651 785-885-4849
Aaron Homburg, prin. Fax 885-4523

Neodesha, Wilson, Pop. 2,454
Neodesha USD 461 700/PK-12
PO Box 88 66757 620-325-2610
Don Potter, supt. Fax 325-2368
www.neodesha.k12.ks.us
Neodesha JSHS 300/7-12
1000 N 8th St 66757 620-325-3015
Daryl Pruter, prin. Fax 325-2382

Ness City, Ness, Pop. 1,441
Ness City USD 303 300/PK-12
414 E Chestnut St 67560 785-798-2210
Derek Reinhardt, supt. Fax 798-3581
www.nesscityschools.org
Ness City JSHS 200/7-12
200 N 5th St 67560 785-798-3991
Tom Flax, prin. Fax 798-3064

Newton, Harvey, Pop. 18,716
Newton USD 373 3,500/K-12
308 E 1st St 67114 316-284-6200
Dr. Deborah Hamm, supt. Fax 284-6207
usd373-ks.schoolloop.com
Chisholm MS 500/7-8
900 E 1st St 67114 316-284-6260
Bobbi Jo Grieb, prin. Fax 284-6267
Newton HS 1,000/9-12
900 W 12th St 67114 316-284-6280
Lisa Moore, prin. Fax 284-6288

Nickerson, Reno, Pop. 1,065
Nickerson USD 309
Supt. — See Hutchinson
Nickerson HS 300/9-12
305 S Nickerson St 67561 620-422-3226
Rick Blosser, prin. Fax 422-3229

North Newton, McPherson, Pop. 1,738

Bethel College Post-Sec.
300 E 27th St 67117 316-283-2500

Norton, Norton, Pop. 2,877
Norton USD 211 700/PK-12
105 E Waverly St 67654 785-877-3386
Phillip Wilson, supt. Fax 877-2030
www.usd211.org/
Norton Community HS 200/9-12
513 W Wilberforce St 67654 785-877-3338
Rudy Perez, prin. Fax 877-6940
Norton JHS 100/7-8
706 Jones Ave 67654 785-877-5851
Dustin McEwen, prin. Fax 877-3771

Norwich, Kingman, Pop. 478
Kingman-Norwich USD 331
Supt. — See Kingman
Norwich HS 100/9-12
PO Box 10 67118 620-478-2235
Wayne Morrow, prin. Fax 478-2879
Norwich MS 100/6-8
PO Box 10 67118 620-478-2235
Wayne Morrow, prin. Fax 478-2879

Oakley, Logan, Pop. 2,023
Oakley USD 274 400/PK-12
621 Center Ave Ste 103 67748 785-671-4588
Ken Bockwinkel, supt. Fax 671-3044
www.oakleyschoolsks.com/
Oakley HS 100/9-12
118 W 7th St 67748 785-671-3241
Kristy Eberle, prin. Fax 671-3743
Oakley MS 100/6-8
611 Center Ave 67748 785-671-3820
Craig Wamsley, prin. Fax 671-3010

Oberlin, Decatur, Pop. 1,774
Oberlin USD 294 400/PK-12
131 E Commercial St 67749 785-475-3805
Duane Dorshorst, supt. Fax 475-3076
www.usd294.org
Decatur Community JSHS 200/7-12
605 E Commercial St 67749 785-475-2231
Benjamin Jimenez, prin. Fax 475-2802

Olathe, Johnson, Pop. 122,644
Olathe USD 233 27,900/PK-12
PO Box 2000 66063 913-780-7000
Dr. Patricia All, supt. Fax 780-8011
www.olatheschools.com
California Trail MS 800/6-8
13775 W 133rd St 66062 913-780-7220
Mike Wiley, prin. Fax 780-7229
Chisholm Trail MS 700/6-8
16700 W 159th St 66062 913-780-7240
Mike Wolgast, prin. Fax 780-7249
Frontier Trail MS 800/6-8
15300 W 143rd St 66062 913-780-7210
Dr. Rod Smith, prin. Fax 780-7216
Indian Trail MS 700/6-8
1440 E 151st St 66062 913-780-7230
Dr. Sarah Guerrero, prin. Fax 780-7234
Mission Trail MS 6-8
1001 N Persimmon Dr 66061 913-780-7260
Rachelle Waters, prin. Fax 780-7269
Olathe Advance Technical Center Vo/Tech
611 N Nelson Rd 66061 913-780-7026
Amy Stolz, admin. Fax 780-8239
Olathe East HS 2,100/9-12
14545 W 127th St 66062 913-780-7120
Kerry Lane, prin. Fax 780-7137
Olathe North HS 2,000/9-12
600 E Prairie St 66061 913-780-7140
Jason Herman, prin. Fax 780-7837
Olathe Northwest HS 1,900/9-12
21300 College Blvd 66061 913-780-7150
Chris Zuck, prin. Fax 780-7159
Olathe South HS 2,100/9-12
1640 E 151st St 66062 913-780-7160
Clint Albers, prin. Fax 780-7170
Olathe West HS 9-12
2200 W Santa Fe St 66061
Jay Novacek, prin.
Oregon Trail MS 500/6-8
1800 W Dennis Ave 66061 913-780-7250
Anne Hawks, prin. Fax 780-7256
Pioneer Trail MS 700/6-8
15100 W 127th St 66062 913-780-7270
Elaine Carpenter, prin. Fax 780-7278
Prairie Trail MS 800/6-8
21600 W 107th St 66061 913-780-7280
Rick Sola, prin. Fax 780-7289
Santa Fe Trail MS 700/6-8
1100 N Ridgeview Rd 66061 913-780-7290
J.J. Libal, prin. Fax 780-7296

Heritage Christian Academy 7-12
16000 S Black Bob Rd 66062 913-782-3262
Rick Lukianuk, admin. Fax 397-0804
Kansas School for the Deaf Post-Sec.
450 E Park St 66061 913-791-0573
Mid-America Nazarene University Post-Sec.
2030 E College Way 66062 913-782-3750
Superior School of Hairdressing Post-Sec.
1215 E Santa Fe St 66061 913-782-4004

Olpe, Lyon, Pop. 541
Southern Lyon County USD 252
Supt. — See Hartford
Olpe JSHS 200/7-12
PO Box 206 66865 620-475-3223
Shane Clark, prin. Fax 475-3951

Onaga, Pottawatomie, Pop. 694
Onaga-Havensville-Wheaton USD 322 300/PK-12
PO Box 60 66521 785-889-4614
Adam McDaniel, supt. Fax 889-4662
www.usd322.org
Onaga HS 100/9-12
PO Box 458 66521 785-889-4251
Adam McDaniel, prin. Fax 889-4944

Osage City, Osage, Pop. 2,899
Osage City USD 420 600/K-12
520 Main St 66523 785-528-3176
Troy Hutton, supt. Fax 528-3932
www.usd420.org
Osage City HS 200/9-12
515 Ellinwood St 66523 785-528-3172
Tony Heward, prin. Fax 528-2980
Osage City MS 200/6-8
420 S 5th St 66523 785-528-3175
Tim Riemann, prin. Fax 528-2980

Osawatomie, Miami, Pop. 4,349
Osawatomie USD 367 1,300/PK-12
1200 Trojan Dr 66064 913-755-4172
Gary French, supt. Fax 755-2031
www.usd367.org/
Osawatomie HS 400/9-12
1200 Trojan Dr 66064 913-755-2191
Doug Chisam, prin. Fax 755-2645
Osawatomie MS 300/6-8
428 Pacific Ave 66064 913-755-4155
Dan Welch, prin. Fax 755-2197

Osborne, Osborne, Pop. 1,422
Osborne County USD 392 300/PK-12
213 W Adams St 67473 785-346-2145
Keith Hall, supt. Fax 346-2448
www.usd392.com
Osborne JSHS 100/7-12
219 N 2nd St 67473 785-346-2143
Tom Conway, prin. Fax 346-2331

Oskaloosa, Jefferson, Pop. 1,096
Oskaloosa USD 341 600/PK-12
404 Park St 66066 785-863-2539
Jon Pfau, supt. Fax 863-3080
www.usd341.org
Oskaloosa JSHS 300/7-12
404 Park St 66066 785-863-2281
Brent Mumford, prin. Fax 863-3106

Oswego, Labette, Pop. 1,768
Oswego USD 504 400/PK-12
PO Box 129 67356 620-795-2126
Douglas Beisel, supt. Fax 795-4871
www.usd504.org
Oswego JSHS 100/7-12
PO Box 129 67356 620-795-2125
Mike Barbo, prin. Fax 795-2130

Otis, Rush, Pop. 278
Otis-Bison USD 403 200/PK-12
PO Box 227 67565 785-387-2201
Roger W. Lowry, supt. Fax 387-2203
www.usd403.org/
Otis-Bison JSHS 100/7-12
PO Box 257 67565 785-387-2337
Mark Goodheart, prin. Fax 387-2557

Ottawa, Franklin, Pop. 12,279
Ottawa USD 290 2,400/PK-12
1404 S Ash St 66067 785-229-8010
Dr. Jeanne Stroh, supt. Fax 229-8019
www.usd290.org
Career Technology Educational Coop Vo/Tech
908 W 11th St 66067 785-229-8090
David Morford, prin. Fax 229-8099
Ottawa HS 700/9-12
1120 S Ash St 66067 785-229-8020
David Morford, prin. Fax 229-8029
Ottawa Learning Center Alt
1404 S Ash St 66067 785-229-8070
Dr. David Morford, prin. Fax 229-8079
Ottawa MS 600/6-8
1230 S Ash St 66067 785-229-8030
Derek Bland, prin. Fax 229-8039

Ottawa University Post-Sec.
1001 S Cedar St 66067 785-242-5200

Overland Park, Johnson, Pop. 169,666
Blue Valley USD 229 22,000/PK-12
PO Box 23901 66283 913-239-4000
Dr. Todd White, supt. Fax 239-4150
district.bluevalleyk12.org
Aubry Bend MS 700/6-8
12501 W 175th St 66221 913-624-2300
Diana Tate, prin. Fax 624-2348
Blue Valley Academy 100/Alt
7500 W 149th Ter 66223 913-239-4529
Valerie Jennings, prin. Fax 239-4534
Blue Valley MS 500/6-8
5001 W 163rd Ter, 913-239-5100
Roxana Rogers, prin. Fax 239-5148
Blue Valley North HS 1,500/9-12
12200 Lamar Ave 66209 913-239-3000
David Stubblefield, prin. Fax 239-3038
Blue Valley Northwest HS 1,600/9-12
13260 Switzer Rd 66213 913-239-3400
Amy Murphy Ed.D., prin. Fax 239-3555
Blue Valley Southwest HS 1,100/9-12
17600 Quivira Rd 66221 913-624-2000
Scott Roberts, prin. Fax 624-2048
Blue Valley West HS 1,400/9-12
16200 Antioch Rd, 913-239-3700
Dr. Brett Potts, prin. Fax 239-3880
Center for Advanced Professional Studies 11-12
7511 W 149th Ter 66223 913-239-5900
Chad Ralston, dir. Fax 239-5948
Harmony MS 600/6-8
10101 W 141st St 66221 913-239-5200
Sheila Albers, prin. Fax 239-5248
Lakewood MS 700/6-8
6601 Edgewater Dr 66223 913-239-5800
Steve Heinauer, prin. Fax 239-5848
Overland Trail MS 700/6-8
6201 W 133rd St 66209 913-239-5400
Shelly Nielsen, prin. Fax 239-5448
Oxford MS 600/6-8
12500 Switzer Rd 66213 913-239-5500
Linda Crosthwait, prin. Fax 239-5548
Other Schools – See Leawood, Stilwell

American Academy of Hair Design Post-Sec.
11401 W 112th Ter 66210 - -
B-Street Design School of Intl Hair Stlg Post-Sec.
10324 Mastin St 66212 913-492-4114
Cleveland Chiropractic College Post-Sec.
10850 Lowell Ave 66210 913-234-0600
Johnson County Community College Post-Sec.
12345 College Blvd 66210 913-469-8500
Kansas City College and Bible School Post-Sec.
7401 Metcalf Ave 66204 913-722-0272
LaBaron Hairdressing Academy Post-Sec.
8119 Robinson St 66204 913-642-0077
Ottawa University Post-Sec.
4370 W 109th St Ste 200 66211 913-266-8600
Overland Christian S 100/PK-12
7401 Metcalf Ave 66204 913-722-0272
Chad Pollard, admin. Fax 213-5616
Saint Paul School of Theology Post-Sec.
4370 W 109th St Ste 300 66211 913-253-5000
St. Thomas Aquinas HS 1,000/9-12
11411 Pflumm Rd 66215 913-345-1411
Craig Moss, pres. Fax 345-2319
Wright Career College Post-Sec.
10700 Metcalf Ave 66210 913-385-7700

Oxford, Sumner, Pop. 1,034
Oxford USD 358 300/PK-12
PO Box 937 67119 620-455-2227
Catherine Wilson Ed.D., supt. Fax 455-3680
www.usd358.com
Oxford JSHS 200/7-12
PO Box 970 67119 620-455-2410
Catherine Wilson Ed.D., prin. Fax 455-3741

Palco, Rooks, Pop. 275
Palco USD 269
Supt. — See Damar
Palco JSHS 50/6-12
PO Box 38 67657 785-737-4645
Roger Morris, prin. Fax 737-4646

Paola, Miami, Pop. 5,476
Paola USD 368 1,900/K-12
1115 E 303rd St 66071 913-294-8000
Judy Welter, supt. Fax 294-8001
www.usd368.org/
Paola HS 600/9-12
401 Angela St 66071 913-294-8010
Phil Bressler, prin. Fax 294-8011
Paola MS 500/6-8
405 N Hospital Dr 66071 913-294-8030
Mark Bloustine, prin. Fax 294-8031

Parsons, Labette, Pop. 10,094
Parsons USD 503 1,400/PK-12
PO Box 1056 67357 620-421-5950
Dr. Shelly Martin, supt. Fax 421-5954
www.vikingnet.net
Parsons HS 400/9-12
3030 Morton Ave 67357 620-421-3660
Matt Rogers, prin. Fax 423-8816
Parsons MS 300/6-8
2719 Main St 67357 620-421-4190
Lori Ray, prin. Fax 423-8822

Labette Community College Post-Sec.
200 S 14th St 67357 620-421-6700

Paxico, Wabaunsee, Pop. 208
Wabaunsee USD 329
Supt. — See Alma
Wabaunsee JHS 100/7-8
PO Box 128 66526 785-636-5353
Steve Oliver, prin. Fax 636-5116

Peabody, Marion, Pop. 1,179
Peabody-Burns USD 398 300/PK-12
506 N Elm St 66866 620-983-2198
Ron Traxson, supt. Fax 983-2247
www.usd398.net
Peabody-Burns JSHS 200/6-12
810 N Sycamore St 66866 620-983-2196
Ken Parry, prin. Fax 983-2773

Perry, Jefferson, Pop. 910
Perry USD 343 800/PK-12
PO Box 729 66073 785-597-5138
J.B Elliott, supt. Fax 597-2254
www.usd343.net
Perry-Lecompton HS 300/9-12
PO Box 18 66073 785-597-5124
John Luhrs, prin. Fax 597-5177
Perry-Lecompton MS 200/5-8
PO Box 31 66073 785-597-5159
Mike Maloun, prin. Fax 597-5014

Phillipsburg, Phillips, Pop. 2,555
Phillipsburg USD 325 600/PK-12
240 S 7th St 67661 785-543-5281
Mike Gower, supt. Fax 543-2271
www.usd325.com
Phillipsburg HS 200/9-12
410 S 7th St 67661 785-543-5251
Todd Bowman, prin. Fax 543-6305
Phillipsburg MS 200/5-8
647 7th St 67661 785-543-5114
Chris Look, prin. Fax 543-2934

Pittsburg, Crawford, Pop. 19,561
Pittsburg USD 250 2,900/K-12
PO Box 75 66762 620-235-3100
Destry Brown, supt. Fax 235-3106
www.usd250.org
Pittsburg HS 800/9-12
1978 E 4th St 66762 620-235-3200
Jon Bishop, prin. Fax 235-3210
Pittsburg MS 600/6-8
1310 N Broadway St 66762 620-235-3240
Terry Smith, prin. Fax 235-3248

Pittsburg State University Post-Sec.
1701 S Broadway St 66762 620-231-7000
St. Mary's Colgan HS 300/7-12
PO Box 266 66762 620-231-4690
David Stephenson, prin. Fax 231-0690

Plainville, Rooks, Pop. 1,886
Plainville USD 270 300/PK-12
203 SE Cardinal Ave 67663 785-434-4678
Gail Dunbar, supt. Fax 434-7404
www.usd270.net
Plainville HS 100/9-12
202 SE Cardinal Ave 67663 785-434-4547
Lisa Gehring, prin. Fax 434-4689

Pleasanton, Linn, Pop. 1,187
Pleasanton USD 344 400/K-12
PO Box 480 66075 913-352-8534
Travis Laver, supt. Fax 352-6588
www.usd344.org/
Pleasanton HS 200/7-12
PO Box 480 66075 913-352-8701
Mitch Shaw, prin. Fax 352-6588

Pomona, Franklin, Pop. 819
West Franklin USD 287 600/PK-12
510 E Franklin St 66076 785-566-3396
Jerry Turner, supt. Fax 566-8325
www.usd287.org
West Franklin HS 200/9-12
511 E Franklin St 66076 785-566-3392
Rick Smith, prin. Fax 566-8454
West Franklin MS 100/6-8
331 Tyler St 66076 785-566-3541
Rick Smith, prin. Fax 566-3634

Prairie Village, Johnson, Pop. 21,158

Kansas City Christian S 400/K-12
4801 W 79th St 66208 913-648-5227
Bill Glotzbach, head sch Fax 648-5269

Pratt, Pratt, Pop. 6,720
Pratt USD 382 1,100/K-12
401 S Hamilton St 67124 620-672-4500
Suzan Patton, supt. Fax 672-4509
www.usd382.com
Liberty MS 300/5-8
300 S Iuka St 67124 620-672-4530
Tony Helfrich, prin. Fax 672-4539
Pratt HS 300/9-12
400 S Hamilton St 67124 620-672-4540
Steve Blankenship, prin. Fax 672-4549

Skyline USD 438 400/PK-12
20269 W US Highway 54 67124 620-672-5651
Becca Flowers, supt. Fax 672-9377
skylineschools.org
Skyline JSHS 100/7-12
20269 W US Highway 54 67124 620-672-5651
Herb McPherson, prin. Fax 672-9377

Pratt Community College Post-Sec.
348 NE State Road 61 67124 620-672-5641

Pretty Prairie, Reno, Pop. 669
Pretty Prairie USD 311 300/PK-12
PO Box 218 67570 620-459-6241
Brad Wade, supt. Fax 459-6810
www.usd311.com
Pretty Prairie HS 100/9-12
PO Box 326 67570 620-459-6313
Randy Hendrickson, prin. Fax 459-6935
Pretty Prairie MS 100/5-8
PO Box 307 67570 620-459-6911
Randy Hendrickson, prin. Fax 459-6729

Protection, Comanche, Pop. 508
South Central USD 300
Supt. — See Coldwater
South Central MS 100/6-8
PO Box 38 67127 620-622-4545
Matt Jellison, prin. Fax 622-4844

Quinter, Gove, Pop. 912
Quinter USD 293 300/PK-12
PO Box 540 67752 785-754-2470
Linda Zeigler, supt. Fax 754-3365
www.quinterschools.org
Quinter JSHS 100/7-12
PO Box 459 67752 785-754-3660
Toby Countryman M.A., prin. Fax 754-3905

Randolph, Riley, Pop. 158
Blue Valley USD 384 200/K-12
PO Box 98 66554 785-293-5256
Brady Burton, supt. Fax 293-5607
www.usd384.org/
Blue Valley HS 100/9-12
PO Box 68 66554 785-293-5255
Marion Mazouch, prin. Fax 293-5372
Randolph MS 50/5-8
PO Box 38 66554 785-293-5253
Marion Mazouch, prin. Fax 293-5607

Ransom, Ness, Pop. 292
Western Plains USD 106 100/PK-12
100 School St 67572 785-731-2352
Dr. Jeff Jones, supt. Fax 731-2235
www.usd106.org
Western Plains HS 50/9-12
100 School St 67572 785-731-2352
Jeff Jones, prin. Fax 731-2235

Rexford, Thomas, Pop. 229
Golden Plains USD 316
Supt. — See Selden
Golden Plains HS 100/9-12
PO Box 100 67753 785-687-3265
Larry Lyder, prin. Fax 687-2285
Golden Plains MS 50/6-8
PO Box 100 67753 785-687-3265
Larry Lyder, prin. Fax 687-2285

Richmond, Franklin, Pop. 461
Central Heights USD 288 600/PK-12
3521 Ellis Rd 66080 785-869-3455
Brian Spencer, supt. Fax 869-2675
www.usd288.org
Central Heights HS 200/9-12
3521 Ellis Rd 66080 785-869-3455
Tom Horstick, prin. Fax 869-2675
Central Heights MS 100/6-8
3521 Ellis Rd 66080 785-869-3455
Buddy Welch, prin. Fax 869-2675

Riley, Riley, Pop. 930
Riley County USD 378 800/PK-12
PO Box 326 66531 785-485-4000
Cliff Williams, supt. Fax 485-2860
www.usd378.org
Riley County HS 200/9-12
PO Box 38 66531 785-485-4020
Harold Oliver, prin. Fax 485-2426

Riverton, Cherokee, Pop. 874
Riverton USD 404 800/PK-12
PO Box 290 66770 620-848-3386
Todd Berry, supt. Fax 848-9853
www.usd404.org/
Riverton HS 200/9-12
PO Box 290 66770 620-848-3388
Chad Harper, prin. Fax 848-3609
Riverton MS 200/6-8
PO Box 260 66770 620-848-3355
Zachery Martin, prin. Fax 848-3288

Roeland Park, Johnson, Pop. 6,575

Bishop Miege HS 700/9-12
5041 Reinhardt Dr 66205 913-262-2700
Randy Salisbury, prin. Fax 262-2752

Rolla, Morton, Pop. 432
Rolla USD 217 200/PK-12
PO Box 167 67954 620-593-4344
Kim Mauk, supt. Fax 593-4250
www.usd217.org
Rolla JSHS 100/6-12
PO Box 167 67954 620-593-4345
Gardell Schnable, prin. Fax 593-4204

Rosalia, Butler, Pop. 169
Flinthills USD 492 300/K-12
PO Box 188 67132 620-476-2237
Jeremy Boldra, supt. Fax 476-2253
www.usd492.org
Flinthills HS 100/9-12
806 SE Rosalia Rd 67132 620-476-2215
Bret Howard, prin. Fax 476-2244
Flinthills MS 50/7-8
806 SE Rosalia Rd 67132 620-476-2218
Larry Gawith, prin. Fax 476-2391

Rose Hill, Butler, Pop. 3,842
Rose Hill USD 394 1,700/PK-12
104 N Rose Hill Rd 67133 316-776-3300
Randal Chickadonz, supt. Fax 776-3309
www.usd394.com
Rose Hill HS 600/9-12
104 N Rose Hill Rd 67133 316-776-3360
Shannon Haydock, prin. Fax 776-3378
Rose Hill MS 400/6-8
104 N Rose Hill Rd 67133 316-776-3320
Kay Walker, prin. Fax 776-3319

Rossville, Shawnee, Pop. 1,132
Kaw Valley USD 321
Supt. — See Saint Marys
Rossville JSHS 300/7-12
PO Box 68 66533 785-584-6193
Toby McCullough, prin. Fax 584-6379

Rozel, Pawnee, Pop. 156
Pawnee Heights USD 496 700/K-12
PO Box 98 67574 620-527-4212
Daniel Binder, supt. Fax 527-4215
www.phtigers.net
Pawnee Heights S 700/K-12
PO Box 97 67574 620-527-4211
Daniel Binder, prin. Fax 527-4215

Russell, Russell, Pop. 4,436
Russell County USD 407 800/K-12
802 N Main St 67665 785-483-2173
Angela Lawrence, supt. Fax 483-2175
www.usd407.org
Ruppenthal MS 200/6-8
400 N Elm St 67665 785-483-3174
Gaylon Walter, prin. Fax 483-5386
Russell HS 300/9-12
565 E State St 67665 785-483-5631
Larry Bernard, prin. Fax 483-5636

Sabetha, Nemaha, Pop. 2,538
Prairie Hills USD 113 1,100/PK-12
1619 S US Old Highway 75 66534 785-284-2175
Todd Evans, supt. Fax 284-3739
www.usd113.org
Sabetha HS 200/9-12
1011 Blue Jay Blvd 66534 785-284-2155
Sheri Harmer, prin. Fax 284-2600
Sabetha MS 200/6-8
751 Blue Jay Blvd 66534 785-284-2151
Matthew Garber, prin. Fax 284-0061
Other Schools – See Axtell, Wetmore

Saint Francis, Cheyenne, Pop. 1,327
St. Francis Community USD 297 300/K-12
PO Box 1110 67756 785-332-8182
Robert Schiltz, supt. Fax 332-8181
www.usd297.org/
Saint Francis JSHS 100/6-12
PO Box 1110 67756 785-332-8153
David Morrow, prin. Fax 332-8177

Saint George, Pottawatomie, Pop. 611
Rock Creek USD 323
Supt. — See Westmoreland
Rock Creek JSHS 400/7-12
9355 Flush Rd 66535 785-494-8591
Eric Koppes, prin. Fax 494-8595

Saint John, Stafford, Pop. 1,281
St. John-Hudson USD 350 300/K-12
505 N Broadway St 67576 620-549-3564
Joshua P. Meyer, supt. Fax 549-3964
www.usd350.com
Saint John JSHS 200/7-12
505 N Broadway St 67576 620-549-3277
Travis Olive, prin. Fax 549-6289

Saint Marys, Pottawatomie, Pop. 2,562
Kaw Valley USD 321 1,300/PK-12
411 W Lasley St 66536 785-437-2254
Kerry Lacock, supt. Fax 437-3155
www.usd321.com
Saint Marys JSHS 300/7-12
601 E Lasley St 66536 785-437-6257
John Girodat, prin. Fax 437-3460
Other Schools – See Rossville

Saint Paul, Neosho, Pop. 622
Chetopa - St. Paul USD 505
Supt. — See Chetopa

Saint Paul HS 100/7-12
318 1st St 66771 620-449-2245
Craig Bagshaw, prin. Fax 449-8960

Salina, Saline, Pop. 46,386
Salina USD 305 7,000/PK-12
PO Box 797 67402 785-309-4700
William Hall, supt. Fax 309-4737
www.usd305.com
Lakewood MS 800/6-8
1135 E Lakewood Cir 67401 785-309-4000
Bonnie Welty, prin. Fax 309-4001
Opportunity Now Alt
219 S 3rd St 67401 785-309-5200
Jeff Hayes, coord. Fax 826-4746
Salina Central HS 1,000/9-12
650 E Crawford St 67401 785-309-3500
Nate Showman, prin. Fax 309-3501
Salina South HS 1,100/9-12
730 E Magnolia Rd 67401 785-309-3700
Curtis Stevens, prin. Fax 309-3701
Salina South MS 800/6-8
2015 Simmons St 67401 785-309-3900
Beth Morrison, prin. Fax 309-3901
Salina West Education Center Alt
501 W Cloud St 67401 785-309-4900
Rex Boley, prin.
Salina Adult Education Center Adult
2620 Centennial Rd 67401 785-309-4660
Kelly Mobray, dir. Fax 309-4669

Academy of Hair Design Post-Sec.
115 S 5th St 67401 785-825-8155
Kansas State University Post-Sec.
2310 Centennial Rd 67401 785-826-2640
Kansas Wesleyan University Post-Sec.
100 E Claflin Ave 67401 785-827-5541
Sacred Heart JSHS 300/7-12
234 E Cloud St 67401 785-827-4422
John Krajicek, prin. Fax 827-8648
St. Johns Military S 200/6-12
PO Box 5020 67402 785-823-7231
Andrew England, pres. Fax 823-2701
Salina Area Technical College Post-Sec.
2562 Centennial Rd 67401 785-309-3100
Salina Christian Academy 200/PK-12
1009 Highland Ave 67401 785-452-9929
Charlene Jackson, prin. Fax 825-2506

Satanta, Haskell, Pop. 1,111
Satanta USD 507 300/PK-12
PO Box 279 67870 620-649-2234
Dave Novack, supt. Fax 649-2668
www.usd507.org
Satanta JSHS 100/6-12
PO Box 69 67870 620-649-2611
J.D. Johnson, prin. Fax 649-2658

Scandia, Republic, Pop. 370
Pike Valley USD 426 200/K-12
PO Box 291 66966 785-335-2206
Mary Treaster, supt. Fax 335-2219
www.pikevalley.com
Pike Valley HS 100/9-12
PO Box 139 66966 785-335-2294
Jeremy Luedke, prin. Fax 335-2386
Other Schools – See Courtland

Scott City, Scott, Pop. 3,797
Scott County USD 466 900/PK-12
704 S College St 67871 620-872-7600
Jamie Rumford, supt. Fax 872-7609
www.usd466.com
Scott City HS 300/9-12
712 S Main St 67871 620-872-7620
Brad McCormick, prin. Fax 872-7629
Scott City MS 300/5-8
809 W 9th St 67871 620-872-7640
Jana Irvin, prin. Fax 872-7649

Scranton, Osage, Pop. 706
Santa Fe Trail USD 434 1,000/PK-12
104 S Burlington Ave 66537 785-793-2256
Steve Pegram, supt. Fax 793-2828
www.usd434.org
Other Schools – See Carbondale

Sedan, Chautauqua, Pop. 1,096
Chautauqua County Community USD 286 400/PK-12
302 Sherman St 67361 620-725-3187
Nathan Hinrichs, supt. Fax 725-5642
www.usd286.org
Sedan HS 200/7-12
416 E Elm St 67361 620-725-3186
Kay Hill, prin. Fax 725-3188

Sedgwick, Harvey, Pop. 1,672
Sedgwick USD 439 400/K-12
PO Box K 67135 316-772-5783
Larry Roth, supt. Fax 772-0274
www.usd439.com
Sedgwick HS 200/7-12
PO Box K 67135 316-772-5783
Mike Hilliard, prin. Fax 772-0334

Selden, Sheridan, Pop. 219
Golden Plains USD 316 200/PK-12
PO Box 199 67757 785-386-4559
Larry Lyder, supt. Fax 386-4562
usd316.k12.ks.us/
Other Schools – See Rexford

Seneca, Nemaha, Pop. 1,982
Nemaha Central USD 115 600/PK-12
318 Main St 66538 785-336-6101
Darrel Kohlman, supt. Fax 336-2268
www.usd115.org
Nemaha Central HS 200/9-12
214 N 11th St 66538 785-336-3557
Ben Scism, prin. Fax 336-3672

Sharon Springs, Wallace, Pop. 741
Wallace County USD 241 200/PK-12
521 N Main St 67758 785-852-4252
Brian McVay, supt. Fax 852-4603
www.usd241.org/
Wallace County HS 100/9-12
521 N Main St 67758 785-852-4240
Brian McVay, prin. Fax 852-4603

Shawnee, Johnson, Pop. 60,803
De Soto USD 232
Supt. — See De Soto
Mill Valley HS 1,300/9-12
5900 Monticello Rd 66226 913-422-4351
Tobie Waldeck, prin. Fax 422-4039
Monticello Trails MS 700/6-8
6100 Monticello Rd 66226 913-422-1100
Melissa Hansen, prin. Fax 422-4990

Academy of Aesthetics Arts Post-Sec.
10316 Shawnee Mission Pkwy 66203 913-962-9772
Central Baptist Theological Seminary Post-Sec.
6601 Monticello Rd 66226 800-677-2287
Maranatha Christian Academy 200/4-12
6826 Lackman Rd 66217 913-631-0637
Mark Schultze, supt. Fax 631-0899
Midland Adventist Academy 100/K-12
6915 Maurer Rd 66217 913-268-7400

Shawnee Mission, See Merriam
Shawnee Mission USD 512 27,000/PK-12
7235 Antioch Rd 66204 913-993-6200
Dr. Jim Hinson, supt. Fax 993-6247
www.smsd.org
Hocker Grove MS 800/7-8
10400 Johnson Dr 66203 913-993-0200
Ben Pretz, prin. Fax 993-0399
Horizons HS Alt
5900 Lamar Ave 66202 913-993-9500
Paul Colwell, prin. Fax 993-9599
Indian Hills MS 800/7-8
6400 Mission Rd 66208 913-993-0400
Dr. Scott Sherman, prin. Fax 993-0599
Indian Woods MS 800/7-8
9700 Woodson Dr 66207 913-993-0600
David Conrady, prin. Fax 993-0799
Shawnee Mission East HS 1,700/9-12
7500 Mission Rd 66208 913-993-6600
John McKinney, prin. Fax 993-6899
Shawnee Mission North HS 1,600/9-12
7401 Johnson Dr 66202 913-993-6900
David Tappan, prin. Fax 993-7099
Shawnee Mission Northwest HS 1,800/9-12
12701 W 67th St 66216 913-993-7200
Lisa Gruman, prin. Fax 993-7499
Shawnee Mission South HS 1,400/9-12
5800 W 107th St 66207 913-993-7500
Todd Dain, prin. Fax 993-7799
Shawnee Mission West HS 1,800/9-12
8800 W 85th St 66212 913-993-7800
Steve Loe, prin. Fax 993-8099
Trailridge MS 800/7-8
7500 Quivira Rd 66216 913-993-1000
Heath Sigg, prin. Fax 993-1199
Westridge MS 900/7-8
9300 Nieman Rd 66214 913-993-1200
Jeremy McDonnell, prin. Fax 993-1399

Silver Lake, Shawnee, Pop. 1,409
Silver Lake USD 372 700/PK-12
PO Box 39 66539 785-582-4026
Tim Hallacy, supt. Fax 582-5259
www.silverlakeschools.org/
Silver Lake JSHS 300/7-12
PO Box 39 66539 785-582-4639
Brad Womack, prin. Fax 582-4265

Smith Center, Smith, Pop. 1,647
Smith Center USD 237 400/PK-12
216 S Jefferson St 66967 785-282-6665
Ron Meitler, supt. Fax 282-6518
www.usd237.com
Smith Center JSHS 200/7-12
300 Roger Barta Way 66967 785-282-6609
Greg Koelsch, prin. Fax 282-5206

Solomon, Dickinson, Pop. 1,069
Solomon USD 393 300/PK-12
113 E 7th St 67480 785-655-2541
Justin Coup, supt. Fax 655-2505
www.usd393.net
Solomon HS 200/7-12
409 N Pine St 67480 785-655-2551
Dustin Dooley, prin. Fax 655-3011

South Haven, Sumner, Pop. 360
South Haven USD 509 200/PK-12
PO Box 229 67140 620-892-5216
Lynn Archer, supt. Fax 892-5814
www.usd509.org/
South Haven JSHS 100/6-12
PO Box 229 67140 620-892-5215
Lynn Archer, prin. Fax 892-5814

Spearville, Ford, Pop. 771
Spearville USD 381 400/K-12
PO Box 338 67876 620-385-2676
Daryl Stegman, supt. Fax 385-2614
www.usd381.org/
Spearville JSHS 200/6-12
PO Box 158 67876 620-385-2631
Patrick Crowdis, prin. Fax 385-2641

Spring Hill, Johnson, Pop. 5,340
Spring Hill USD 230 2,800/PK-12
101 E South St 66083 913-592-7200
Dr. Wayne Burke, supt. Fax 592-7270
www.usd230.org
Spring Hill HS 700/9-12
19701 S Ridgeview Rd 66083 913-592-7299
Marc Williams, prin. Fax 592-2847
Spring Hill MS 500/6-8
301 E South St 66083 913-592-7288
Rodney Sprague, prin. Fax 592-5424

Stafford, Stafford, Pop. 1,029
Stafford USD 349 200/PK-12
PO Box 400 67578 620-234-5243
Dr. Mary Jo Taylor, supt. Fax 234-6986
www.stafford349.com
Stafford MSHS 100/6-12
PO Box 370 67578 620-234-5248
Dallas Woolf, prin. Fax 234-6041

Sterling, Rice, Pop. 2,287
Sterling USD 376 500/PK-12
PO Box 188 67579 620-278-3621
Dr. Fred Dierksen, supt. Fax 278-3882
www.usd376.com
Sterling JSHS 200/7-12
308 E Washington Ave 67579 620-278-2171
Bill Anderson, prin. Fax 278-3237

Sterling College Post-Sec.
125 W Cooper St 67579 620-278-2173

Stilwell, Johnson
Blue Valley USD 229
Supt. — See Overland Park
Blue Valley HS 1,500/9-12
6001 W 159th St 66085 913-239-4800
Scott Bacon, prin. Fax 239-4835
Pleasant Ridge MS 600/6-8
9000 W 165th St 66085 913-239-5700
Phoebe Lewis, prin. Fax 239-5748

Stockton, Rooks, Pop. 1,312
Stockton USD 271 300/PK-12
201 N Cypress St 67669 785-425-6367
Shelly Swayne, supt. Fax 425-6923
www.usd271.com
Stockton HS 100/9-12
105 N Cypress St 67669 785-425-6784
Shelley Wayne, prin. Fax 425-6200

Sublette, Haskell, Pop. 1,442
Sublette USD 374 400/PK-12
PO Box 670 67877 620-675-2277
Rex Bruce, supt. Fax 675-2652
www.usd374.org/
Sublette MSHS 100/7-12
PO Box 460 67877 620-675-2232
Monty Marlin, prin. Fax 675-8347

Sylvan Grove, Lincoln, Pop. 277
Sylvan Grove USD 299 300/PK-12
504 W 4th St 67481 785-526-7175
Jude Stecklein, supt. Fax 526-7182
www.usd299.org/
Sylvan-Lucas Unified JSHS 100/7-12
504 W 4th St 67481 785-526-7175
Jeff Starkey, prin. Fax 526-7182

Syracuse, Hamilton, Pop. 1,789
Syracuse USD 494 500/PK-12
PO Box 1187 67878 620-384-7872
Kenneth Bridges, supt. Fax 384-7692
www.usd494.org
Syracuse JSHS 200/7-12
PO Box 1187 67878 620-384-7446
Paul Zuzelski, prin. Fax 384-6686

Tecumseh, Shawnee
Shawnee Heights USD 450 3,600/PK-12
4401 SE Shawnee Heights Rd 66542 785-379-5800
Dr. Martin Stessman, supt. Fax 379-5810
www.usd450.net
Shawnee Heights HS 1,100/9-12
4201 SE Shawnee Heights Rd 66542 785-379-5880
Ed West, prin. Fax 379-5967
Shawnee Heights MS 600/7-8
4335 SE Shawnee Heights Rd 66542 785-379-5830
Tim Urich, prin. Fax 379-5848

Tescott, Ottawa, Pop. 315
Twin Valley USD 240
Supt. — See Bennington
Tescott HS 100/9-12
PO Box 196 67484 785-283-4774
Steven Kimmi, prin. Fax 283-4347

Tipton, Mitchell, Pop. 210

Tipton Catholic HS 50/9-12
PO Box 146 67485 785-373-5835
Gery Hake, prin. Fax 373-5637

Tonganoxie, Leavenworth, Pop. 4,915
Tonganoxie USD 464 1,800/PK-12
330 E 24/40 Highway 66086 913-416-1400
Christopher Kleidosty, supt. Fax 416-1408
www.tong464.org
Tonganoxie HS 600/9-12
404 E 24/40 Highway 66086 913-416-1460
Mark Farrar, prin. Fax 416-1468
Tonganoxie MS 500/6-8
824 E Washington St 66086 913-416-1470
Mark Altman, prin. Fax 416-1478

Genesis Christian S 200/PK-12
PO Box 994 66086 913-845-9498
Mendy Lietzen, admin. Fax 845-9498

Topeka, Shawnee, Pop. 122,701
Auburn Washburn USD 437 7,300/PK-12
5928 SW 53rd St 66610 785-339-4000
Dr. Scott McWilliams, supt. Fax 339-4025
www.usd437.net

Pathways Learning Center Alt
4101 SW Martin Dr 66609 785-339-4270
Sean Cochran, prin. Fax 339-4275
Washburn Rural Alternative HS 1,200/Alt
5900 SW 61st St 66619 785-339-4900
Kelly Younger, prin. Fax 339-4925
Washburn Rural HS 1,800/9-12
5900 SW 61st St 66619 785-339-4100
Ed Raines, prin. Fax 339-4125
Washburn Rural MS 900/7-8
5620 SW 61st St 66619 785-339-4300
Mark Koepsel, prin. Fax 339-4325

Seaman USD 345 3,400/PK-12
901 NW Lyman Rd 66608 785-575-8600
Dr. Steve Noble, supt. Fax 575-8620
www.usd345.com
Seaman HS 1,200/9-12
4850 NW Rochester Rd 66617 785-286-8300
Michael Monaghan, prin. Fax 286-8320
Seaman MS 600/7-8
5530 NW Topeka Blvd 66617 785-286-8400
Traci Hammes, prin. Fax 286-8403

Topeka USD 501 13,500/PK-12
624 SW 24th St 66611 785-295-3000
Dr. Tiffany Anderson, supt. Fax 575-6161
www.topekapublicschools.net
Chase MS 500/6-8
2250 NE State St 66616 785-295-3840
Keith Jones, prin. Fax 575-6632
Eisenhower MS 500/6-8
3305 SE Minnesota Ave 66605 785-274-6160
Leosha Giardina, prin. Fax 274-4603
French MS 500/6-8
5257 SW 33rd St 66614 785-438-4150
Kelli Hoffman, prin. Fax 271-3609
Highland Park HS 700/9-12
2424 SE California Ave 66605 785-274-6000
Dr. Beryl New, prin. Fax 274-4896
Jardine MS 500/6-8
2600 SW 33rd St 66611 785-274-6330
Mike Haire, prin. Fax 274-4768
Landon MS 500/6-8
731 SW Fairlawn Rd 66606 785-438-4220
David Boggs, prin. Fax 271-3737
Robinson MS 400/6-8
1125 SW 14th St 66604 785-295-3770
Tammy Hazelton, prin. Fax 575-6720
Topeka HS 1,700/9-12
800 SW 10th Ave 66612 785-295-3150
Dr. Rebecca Morrisey, prin. Fax 575-6255
Topeka West HS 900/9-12
2001 SW Fairlawn Rd 66604 785-438-4000
Dustin Dick, prin. Fax 271-3497
Washburn Institute of Technology Vo/Tech
5724 SW Huntoon St 66604 785-273-7140
Dr. Clark Coco, dean Fax 273-7080
Adult Education Center Adult
5724 SW Huntoon St 66604 785-235-7690
Patricia Williamson, coord. Fax 273-7080

Baker University School of Nursing Post-Sec.
1500 SW 10th Ave 66604 888-866-4242
Bryan University Post-Sec.
1527 SW Fairlawn Rd 66604 785-272-0889
Cair Paravel Latin S 300/PK-12
635 SW Clay St 66606 785-232-3878
Melody Congdon, head sch Fax 232-0047
Community College of Cosmetology Post-Sec.
3602 SW Topeka Blvd 66611 785-267-7701
Hayden HS 500/9-12
401 SW Gage Blvd 66606 785-272-5210
James Sandstrom, prin. Fax 272-2975
Heritage Christian S 200/PK-12
2000 NW Clay St 66608 785-286-0427
Janeal Lischke, prin. Fax 286-9898
Mid West Barber College Post-Sec.
901 SW 37th St 66611 785-266-2500
Washburn Institute of Technology Post-Sec.
5724 SW Huntoon St 66604 785-273-7140
Washburn University Post-Sec.
1700 SW College Ave 66621 785-670-1010
Wichita Technical Institute - Topeka Post-Sec.
3712 SW Burlingame Rd 66609 785-354-4568

Towanda, Butler, Pop. 1,426
Circle USD 375 1,700/K-12
PO Box 9 67144 316-541-2577
James Johnson, supt. Fax 536-2249
www.usd375.org
Circle HS 500/9-12
PO Box 159 67144 316-541-2277
Todd Dreifort, prin. Fax 536-2249
Other Schools – See Benton

Troy, Doniphan, Pop. 1,001
Troy USD 429 300/PK-12
PO Box 190 66087 785-985-3950
Patrick McKernan M.S., supt. Fax 985-3688
www.troyusd.org/
Troy MSHS 200/7-12
PO Box 160 66087 785-985-3533
Josh Hevel, prin. Fax 985-3885

Tyro, Montgomery, Pop. 209

Tyro Community Christian S 100/K-12
PO Box 308 67364 620-289-4450
Terry Byrd, admin. Fax 289-4283

Udall, Cowley, Pop. 727
Udall USD 463 400/PK-12
303 S Seymour St 67146 620-782-3355
Kim Stephens, supt. Fax 782-9690
www.usd463.org/
Udall HS 100/9-12
301 W 4th St 67146 620-782-3623
Brian Rowley, prin. Fax 782-9689
Udall MS 100/6-8
301 W 4th St 67146 620-782-3623
Brian Rowley, prin. Fax 782-9689

Ulysses, Grant, Pop. 6,107
Ulysses USD 214 1,800/PK-12
111 S Baughman St 67880 620-356-3655
David Younger, supt. Fax 356-5181
www.ulysses.org
Kepley MS 400/6-8
113 N Colorado St 67880 620-356-3025
Juan Perez, prin. Fax 356-3024
Ulysses HS 500/9-12
501 N Mccall St 67880 620-356-1380
Mark Paul, prin. Fax 356-5566

Uniontown, Bourbon, Pop. 268
Uniontown USD 235 500/PK-12
601 5th St 66779 620-756-4302
Janice Hedges, supt. Fax 756-4492
www.uniontown235.org
Uniontown HS 200/7-12
601 5th St 66779 620-756-4301
Janice Hedges, prin. Fax 756-4340

Valley Center, Sedgwick, Pop. 6,673
Valley Center USD 262 2,700/PK-12
143 S Meridian Ave 67147 316-755-7000
Cory Gibson, supt. Fax 755-7001
www.usd262.net
Valley Center HS 800/9-12
9600 N Meridian Ave 67147 316-755-7070
Jamie Lewis, prin. Fax 755-7071
Valley Center MS 400/7-8
800 N Meridian Ave 67147 316-755-7060
Greg Mittman, prin. Fax 755-7061

Valley Falls, Jefferson, Pop. 1,187
Valley Falls USD 338 400/PK-12
700 Oak St 66088 785-945-3214
Loren Feldkamp, supt. Fax 945-6780
www.usd338.com
Valley Falls HS 100/9-12
601 Elm St 66088 785-945-3229
Susan Grey, prin. Fax 945-3220

Vermillion, Marshall, Pop. 108
Vermillion USD 380 600/PK-12
209 School St 66544 785-382-6216
Mischel Miller, supt. Fax 382-6213
www.usd380.com
Other Schools – See Centralia, Frankfort

Victoria, Ellis, Pop. 1,204
Victoria USD 432 300/K-12
PO Box 139 67671 785-735-9212
David Ottley, supt. Fax 735-9229
www.usd432.org/
Victoria JSHS 100/7-12
1107 10th St 67671 785-735-9211
Stuart Moeckel, prin. Fax 735-9208

Wakeeney, Trego, Pop. 1,842
WaKeeney USD 208 400/PK-12
527 Russell Ave 67672 785-743-2145
Tavis Desormiers, supt. Fax 743-2071
www.tregoeagles.com/
Trego Community HS 100/9-12
1200 Russell Ave 67672 785-743-2061
Craig Malsam, prin. Fax 743-2449

Wakefield, Clay, Pop. 948
Clay Center USD 379
Supt. — See Clay Center
Wakefield HS 100/9-12
PO Box 40 67487 785-461-5437
Thomas DeBauche, prin. Fax 461-5892

Wamego, Pottawatomie, Pop. 4,265
Wamego USD 320 1,500/PK-12
1008 8th St 66547 785-456-7643
Tim Winter, supt. Fax 456-8125
www.usd320.com
Wamego HS 400/9-12
801 Lincoln St 66547 785-456-2214
Chad Brecheisen, prin. Fax 456-7382
Wamego MS 300/6-8
1701 Kaw Valley Rd 66547 785-456-7682
Vici Jennings, prin. Fax 456-2944

Washington, Washington, Pop. 1,122
Washington County USD 108 400/PK-12
101 W College St 66968 785-325-2261
Denise O'Dea, supt. Fax 325-2771
www.usd108.org/
Washington County HS 200/7-12
101 W College St 66968 785-325-2261
Carol Whisman, prin. Fax 325-2138

Waterville, Marshall, Pop. 672
Valley Heights USD 498 400/K-12
PO Box 89 66548 785-363-2398
John Bergkamp, supt. Fax 363-2269
www.valleyheights.org/
Other Schools – See Blue Rapids

Wathena, Doniphan, Pop. 1,344
Riverside USD 114
Supt. — See Elwood
Riverside HS 200/9-12
PO Box 38 66090 785-989-4426
Robert Blair, prin. Fax 989-3317

Waverly, Coffey, Pop. 580
Lebo-Waverly USD 243 500/PK-12
PO Box 457 66871 785-733-2651
Corey Reese, supt. Fax 733-2707
www.usd243ks.org
Waverly HS 100/6-12
PO Box 8 66871 785-733-2561
Susan Brenner, prin. Fax 733-2756
Other Schools – See Lebo

Wellington, Sumner, Pop. 7,956
Wellington USD 353 1,600/K-12
PO Box 648 67152 620-326-4300
Mark Whitener, supt. Fax 326-4304
www.usd353.com/
Roosevelt Education Center Alt
201 N B St 67152 620-326-4330
Zachary Lawrence, dir. Fax 326-4332
Wellington HS 500/9-12
1700 E 16th St 67152 620-326-4310
Adam Hatfield, prin. Fax 326-4383
Wellington MS 400/6-8
605 N A St 67152 620-326-4320
Jamie Ybarra, prin. Fax 326-4390

Wellsville, Franklin, Pop. 1,818
Wellsville USD 289 800/PK-12
602 Walnut St 66092 785-883-2388
Jerald Henn, supt. Fax 883-4453
www.wellsville-usd289.org
Wellsville HS 200/9-12
602 Walnut St 66092 785-883-2057
Josh Adams, prin. Fax 883-2294
Wellsville MS 200/6-8
602 Walnut St 66092 785-883-4350
Randy Fox, prin. Fax 883-2260

Weskan, Wallace, Pop. 159
Weskan USD 242 100/PK-12
219 Coyote Blvd 67762 785-943-5222
Dave Hale, supt. Fax 943-5303
www.weskanschools.org/
Weskan JSHS 50/7-12
219 Coyote Blvd 67762 785-943-5222
Dave Hale, supt. Fax 943-5303

Westmoreland, Pottawatomie, Pop. 771
Rock Creek USD 323 900/PK-12
PO Box 70 66549 785-457-3732
Kevin Logan, supt. Fax 457-3701
www.rockcreekschools.org
Other Schools – See Saint George

Wetmore, Nemaha, Pop. 364
Prairie Hills USD 113
Supt. — See Sabetha
Wetmore HS 100/9-12
PO Box AB 66550 785-866-2860
Janelle Boden, prin. Fax 866-5450

White City, Morris, Pop. 611
Rural Vista USD 481 300/PK-12
PO Box 98 66872 785-349-2964
Ralph Blevins, supt. Fax 349-2965
www.usd481.org
White City HS 100/9-12
PO Box 8 66872 785-349-2211
Joel Kahnt, prin. Fax 349-2965
Other Schools – See Hope

Whitewater, Butler, Pop. 694
Remington-Whitewater USD 206 500/PK-12
PO Box 243 67154 316-799-2115
James Regier, supt. Fax 799-2307
www.usd206.org
Remington HS 200/9-12
8850 NW Meadowlark Rd 67154 316-799-2123
Tim Bumgarner, prin. Fax 799-2943
Remington MS 200/5-8
PO Box 99 67154 316-799-2131
Bob Friesen, prin. Fax 799-2581

Wichita, Sedgwick, Pop. 369,464
Haysville USD 261
Supt. — See Haysville
Haysville Campus HS 1,600/9-12
2100 W 55th St S 67217 316-554-2236
Myron Regier, prin. Fax 554-2241

Maize USD 266
Supt. — See Maize
Maize South HS 800/9-12
3701 N Tyler Rd 67205 316-462-8000
Dave Hickerson, prin. Fax 462-8001
Maize South MS 900/6-8
3403 N Tyler Rd 67205 316-722-0421
Gillian Macias, prin. Fax 722-4077

Wichita USD 259 47,900/PK-12
201 N Water St 67202 316-973-4000
John Allison, supt. Fax 973-4595
www.usd259.org
Allison Traditional Magnet MS 500/6-8
221 S Seneca St 67213 316-973-4800
Mitch Linn, prin. Fax 973-4810
Brooks Technology & Arts Magnet MS 600/6-8
3802 E 27th St N 67220 316-973-6450
Renee Erickson, prin. Fax 973-6581
Coleman MS 500/6-8
1544 N Governeour Rd 67206 316-973-6600
Jeff Freund, prin. Fax 973-6699
Curtis MS 700/6-8
1031 S Edgemoor St 67218 316-973-7350
Stephanie Wasko, prin. Fax 973-7410
Hadley MS 700/6-8
1101 N Dougherty Ave 67212 316-973-7800
Amy Johnson, prin. Fax 973-7816
Hamilton MS 600/6-8
1407 S Broadway Ave 67211 316-973-5350
Justin Kasel, prin. Fax 973-5360
Jardine STEM Magnet MS 400/6-8
3550 E Ross Pkwy 67210 316-973-4300
Lura Atherly, prin. Fax 973-4310
Marshall MS 500/6-8
1510 N Payne Ave 67203 316-973-9000
Ron Stubbs, prin. Fax 973-9010
Mayberry Cultural & Fine Arts Magnet MS 600/6-8
207 S Sheridan St 67213 316-973-5800
Eric Hofer-Holdeman, prin. Fax 973-5808

Mead MS 600/6-8
2601 E Skinner St 67211 316-973-8500
Toby Martin, prin. Fax 973-8503
Pleasant Valley MS 600/6-8
2220 W 29th St N 67204 316-973-8000
Victoria Manning, prin. Fax 973-8008
Robinson MS 800/6-8
328 N Oliver Ave 67208 316-973-8600
Amy Champlin, prin. Fax 973-8625
Sowers Alternative HS 100/Alt
2400 E Wassall St 67216 316-973-1600
Jackie Hultman, prin. Fax 973-1610
Stucky MS 600/6-8
4545 N Broadview Cir 67220 316-973-8400
Jennifer Sinclair, prin. Fax 973-8410
Truesdell MS 1,000/6-8
2464 S Glenn Ave 67217 316-973-3900
Terrell Davis, prin. Fax 973-3904
Wells Alternative MS 50/Alt
1221 E Galena St Ste 373 67216 316-973-7650
Darrin Ross, prin. Fax 973-7673
Wichita Alternative HS 100/Alt
1847 N Chautauqua Ave 67214 316-973-0500
Leroy Parks, prin. Fax 973-0510
Wichita East HS 2,200/9-12
2301 E Douglas Ave 67211 316-973-7200
Ken Thiessen, prin. Fax 973-7224
Wichita Heights HS 1,300/9-12
5301 N Hillside St 67219 316-973-1400
Bruce Deterding, prin. Fax 973-1410
Wichita North HS 2,100/9-12
1437 N Rochester St 67203 316-973-6300
Sherman Padgett, prin. Fax 973-6190
Wichita Northwest HS 1,400/9-12
1220 N Tyler Rd 67212 316-973-6000
Gil Alvarez, prin. Fax 973-6070
Wichita Southeast HS 1,600/9-12
2641 S 127th St E 67210 316-973-2700
Lori Doyle, prin. Fax 973-2755
Wichita South HS 1,600/9-12
701 W 33rd St S 67217 316-973-5450
Cara Ledy, prin. Fax 973-5519
Wichita West HS 1,300/9-12
820 S Osage St 67213 316-973-3600
Joel Hudson, prin. Fax 973-3657
Wilbur MS 900/6-8
340 N Tyler Rd 67212 316-973-1100
Mark Jolliffe, prin. Fax 973-1090
Other Schools – See Bel Aire

Bishop Carroll Catholic HS 1,100/9-12
8101 W Central Ave 67212 316-722-2390
Vanessa Harshberger, prin. Fax 722-6670
Classical S of Wichita 100/K-12
6355 Willowbrook St 67218 316-773-9279
Classic College of Hair Design Post-Sec.
1675 S Rock Rd Ste 101 67207 316-681-2288
Friends University Post-Sec.
2100 W University Ave 67213 316-295-5000
Independent S 500/PK-12
8317 E Douglas Ave 67207 316-686-0152
Kansas College of Chinese Medicine Post-Sec.
9235 E Harry St Bldg 200 67207 316-691-8822
Kapaun Mt. Carmel Catholic HS 900/9-12
8506 E Central Ave 67206 316-634-0315
Chris Bloomer, prin. Fax 636-2437
Newman University Post-Sec.
3100 W McCormick St 67213 316-942-4291
Old Town Barber College Post-Sec.
1211 E Douglas Ave 67211 316-264-4891
Paul Mitchell the School Post-Sec.
3242 N Rock Rd Ste 106 67226 316-630-0600
Trinity Academy 300/9-12
12345 E 21st St N 67206 316-634-0909
Matt Brewer, hdmstr. Fax 634-0928
Vatterott College Post-Sec.
8853 E 37th St N 67226 316-634-0066
Wichita Adventist Christian Academy 50/K-10
2725 S Osage Ave 67217 316-267-9472
Wichita Area Technical College Post-Sec.
4501 E 47th St S 67210 316-677-1500
Wichita Area Technical College Post-Sec.
4004 N Webb Rd 67226 316-677-9400
Wichita Area Technical College - Grove Post-Sec.
301 S Grove St 67211 316-677-9400
Wichita Collegiate S 1,000/PK-12
9115 E 13th St N 67206 316-634-0433
Tom Davis, hdmstr. Fax 634-0598
Wichita State University Post-Sec.
1845 Fairmount St 67260 316-978-3456
Wichita Technical Institute Post-Sec.
2051 S Meridian Ave 67213 316-943-2241
Wichita Technical Institute - East Post-Sec.
6130 E Central Ave 67208 316-260-1030
Wright Career College Post-Sec.
7700 E Kellogg Dr 67207 316-927-7700
Xenon International Academy Post-Sec.
3804 W Douglas Ave 67203 316-943-5516

Wilson, Ellsworth, Pop. 759
Central Plains USD 112
Supt. — See Holyrood
Wilson JSHS 100/7-12
PO Box 220 67490 785-658-2202
Kenroy Wilson, prin. Fax 658-2205

Winchester, Jefferson, Pop. 551
Jefferson County North USD 339 500/PK-12
310 5th St 66097 913-774-2000
Denise Jennings, supt. Fax 774-2027
www.usd339.net
Jefferson County North HS 100/9-12
302 5th St 66097 913-774-8515
Joe Worthington, prin. Fax 774-8535

Winfield, Cowley, Pop. 11,966
Winfield USD 465 2,000/PK-12
1407 Wheat Rd 67156 620-221-5100
Dr. J.K. Campbell, supt. Fax 221-0508
www.usd465.com
Winfield HS 700/9-12
300 Viking Blvd 67156 620-221-5160
Trenton Creeden, prin. Fax 221-5165
Winfield MS 400/6-8
130 Viking Blvd 67156 620-221-5130
David Hammer, prin. Fax 221-5147

Southwestern College Post-Sec.
100 College St 67156 620-229-6000

Winona, Logan, Pop. 161
Triplains USD 275 100/K-12
PO Box 97 67764 785-846-7869
Lamar Bergsten, supt. Fax 846-7767
triplains.weebly.com
Winona HS 50/9-12
PO Box 97 67764 785-846-7496
Lamar Bergsten, admin. Fax 846-7767

Yates Center, Woodson, Pop. 1,379
Woodson USD 366 500/PK-12
PO Box 160 66783 620-625-8804
Greg Brown, supt. Fax 625-8806
www.usd366.net
Yates Center HS 100/9-12
PO Box 160 66783 620-625-8820
Karl Hamm, prin. Fax 625-8850

KENTUCKY

KENTUCKY DEPARTMENT OF EDUCATION
500 Mero St, Frankfort 40601-1957
Telephone 502-564-4770
Fax 502-564-5680
Website http://www.education.ky.gov

Commissioner of Education Dr. Stephen Pruitt

KENTUCKY BOARD OF EDUCATION
500 Mero St Ste 1, Frankfort 40601-1957

Chairperson David Karem

PUBLIC, PRIVATE AND CATHOLIC SECONDARY SCHOOLS

Albany, Clinton, Pop. 1,999
Clinton County SD 1,700/PK-12
2353 N Highway 127 42602 606-387-6480
Charlotte Bernard, supt. Fax 387-5437
www.clinton.kyschools.us
Clinton County HS 500/9-12
65 High School Dr 42602 606-387-5569
Sheldon Harlan, prin. Fax 387-8659
Clinton County MS 500/5-8
169 Middle School Rd 42602 606-387-6466
Teresa Scott, prin. Fax 387-6469

Kentucky Tech System
Supt. — See Frankfort
Clinton County Area Technology Center Vo/Tech
151 Armstrong Honeycutt Dr 42602 606-387-6448
Stesha Flowers, prin. Fax 387-4035

Alexandria, Campbell, Pop. 8,396
Campbell County SD 4,800/PK-12
101 Orchard Ln 41001 859-635-2173
Donald Pace, supt. Fax 448-2439
www.campbell.kyschools.us/
Campbell County Day Treatment 50/Alt
51 Orchard Ln 41001 859-635-9113
Alvin Elsbernd, prin. Fax 448-2781
Campbell County HS 1,500/9-12
909 Camel Xing 41001 859-635-4161
Adam Ritter, prin. Fax 448-4886
Campbell County MS 1,100/6-8
8000 Alexandria Pike 41001 859-635-6077
Jason Smith, prin. Fax 448-4863

Kentucky Tech System
Supt. — See Frankfort
Campbell County Area Technology Center Vo/Tech
50 Orchard Ln 41001 859-635-4101
Joseph Amann, prin. Fax 635-2766

Bishop Brossart HS 400/9-12
4 Grove St 41001 859-635-2108
Dan Ridder, prin. Fax 635-2135

Ashland, Boyd, Pop. 21,270
Ashland ISD 3,000/PK-12
PO Box 3000 41105 606-327-2706
Stephen E. Gilmore, supt. Fax 327-2705
www.ashland.kyschools.us
Ashland MS 500/6-8
2800 Kansas St 41102 606-327-2727
David Greene, prin. Fax 327-2765
Blazer HS 900/9-12
1500 Blazer Blvd 41102 606-327-6040
Derek Runyon, prin. Fax 324-0517

Boyd County SD 3,400/PK-12
1104 Bob McCullough Dr 41102 606-928-4141
R. Brock Walter, supt. Fax 928-4771
www.boyd.kyschools.us
Boyd County Career & Technical Center Vo/Tech
12300 Midland Trail Rd 41102 606-928-7120
Doug Deborde, dir. Fax 928-6432
Boyd County HS 800/9-12
14375 Lions Ln 41102 606-928-7100
Thomas Holbrook, prin. Fax 928-1312
Boyd County MS 700/6-8
1226 Summitt Rd 41102 606-928-9547
Fax 928-2067
Other Schools – See Rush

Fairview ISD 800/PK-12
2201 Main St W 41102 606-324-3877
Michael Taylor, supt. Fax 324-2288
www.fairview.kyschools.us
Fairview JSHS 500/7-12
2123 Main St W 41102 606-324-9226
Eric Hale, prin. Fax 325-1486

Raceland-Worthington ISD
Supt. — See Raceland
Raceland-Worthington Campus A 50/Alt
1539 Greenup Ave 41101 606-920-2073
Marty Mills, prin. Fax 920-2075

Ashland Community and Technical College Post-Sec.
1400 College Dr 41101 606-326-2000
Holy Family S 100/PK-12
932 Winchester Ave 41101 606-324-7040
Matt Anderson, prin. Fax 324-6888
Rose Hill Christian S 200/PK-12
1001 Winslow Rd 41102 606-324-6105
Dr. Jerry Foster, prin. Fax 324-6420

Augusta, Bracken, Pop. 1,171
Augusta ISD 300/PK-12
307 Bracken St 41002 606-756-2545
Lisa McCane, supt. Fax 756-2149
www.augusta.kyschools.us
Augusta JSHS 100/7-12
207 Bracken St 41002 606-756-2105
Robin Kelsch, prin. Fax 756-3000

Barbourville, Knox, Pop. 3,119
Barbourville ISD 700/PK-12
PO Box 520 40906 606-546-3120
Kay Dixon, supt. Fax 546-3452
www.barbourvilleind.com
Barbourville Independent S 700/PK-12
PO Box 520 40906 606-546-3129
Paul Middleton, prin. Fax 546-3337

Kentucky Tech System
Supt. — See Frankfort
Knox County Area Technology Center Vo/Tech
210 Wall St 40906 606-546-5310
Ralph Halcomb, prin. Fax 546-3818

Knox County SD 4,400/PK-12
200 Daniel Boone Dr 40906 606-546-3157
Kelly Sprinkles, supt. Fax 546-2819
www.knox.kyschools.us
Knox Central HS 900/9-12
100 Panther Way 40906 606-546-9253
Tim Melton, prin. Fax 546-5684
Knox County MS 500/7-8
311 N Main St 40906 606-545-5267
Jeremy Ledford, prin. Fax 546-2161
Other Schools – See Corbin

Union College Post-Sec.
310 College St 40906 606-546-4151

Bardstown, Nelson, Pop. 11,437
Bardstown ISD 2,800/PK-12
308 N 5th St 40004 502-331-8800
Brent Holsclaw, supt. Fax 331-8830
www.bardstown.kyschools.us
Bardstown HS 600/9-12
400 N 5th St 40004 502-331-8802
Chris Pickett, prin. Fax 331-8832
Bardstown MS 500/6-8
410 N 5th St 40004 502-331-8803
Bob Blackmon, prin. Fax 331-8833

Kentucky Tech System
Supt. — See Frankfort
Nelson County Area Technology Center Vo/Tech
1060 Bloomfield Rd 40004 502-348-9096
Jeremey Booher, prin. Fax 348-9097

Nelson County SD 4,700/PK-12
288 Wildcat Ln 40004 502-349-7000
Anthony Orr, supt. Fax 349-7004
nelson.kyschools.us
Horizons Academy 50/Alt
304 Wildcat Ln 40004 502-349-7045
Penny Bradley, prin. Fax 349-7044
Nelson County HS 900/9-12
1070 Bloomfield Rd 40004 502-349-7010
Shelly Hendricks, prin. Fax 349-7017
Nelson HS 700/9-12
150 Generals Blvd 40004 502-349-4650
Wes Bradley, prin. Fax 349-4651
Old Kentucky Home MS 400/6-8
301 Wildcat Ln 40004 502-349-7040
Jesse Simpson, prin. Fax 349-7042
Other Schools – See Bloomfield

Bethlehem HS 300/9-12
309 W Stephen Foster Ave 40004 502-348-8594
Tom Hamilton, prin. Fax 349-1247

Bardwell, Carlisle, Pop. 716
Carlisle County SD 800/PK-12
4557 State Route 1377 42023 270-628-3800
Jay Simmons, supt. Fax 628-5477
www.carlisle.kyschools.us
Carlisle County HS 200/9-12
4557 State Route 1377 42023 270-628-3800
Kelli Edging, prin. Fax 628-3837
Carlisle County MS 200/6-8
4557 State Route 1377 42023 270-628-3800
DeeAnne Arant, prin. Fax 628-3974

Barlow, Ballard, Pop. 654
Ballard County SD 1,400/PK-12
3465 Paducah Rd 42024 270-665-8400
Casey Allen, supt. Fax 665-9844
www.ballard.kyschools.us
Ballard County MS 300/6-8
3565 Paducah Rd 42024 270-665-8400
Amber Parker, prin. Fax 665-5153
Ballard Memorial HS 400/9-12
3561 Paducah Rd 42024 270-665-8400
Leslee Davis, prin. Fax 665-5312

Baxter, Harlan
Harlan County SD
Supt. — See Harlan
Harlan County HS 1,100/9-12
4000 N US Highway 119 40806 606-574-2020
Edna Burkhart, prin. Fax 574-0493

Beattyville, Lee, Pop. 1,296
Kentucky Tech System
Supt. — See Frankfort
Lee County Area Technology Center Vo/Tech
PO Box B 41311 606-464-5018
Craig Herald, prin. Fax 464-0663

Lee County SD 500/K-12
PO Box 668 41311 606-464-5000
Dr. Jim Evans Ed.D., supt. Fax 464-5009
www.lee.kyschools.us
Lee County MSHS 300/6-12
599 Lee Ave 41311 606-464-5005
Debra Smith, prin. Fax 464-5014

Bedford, Trimble, Pop. 584
Trimble County SD 1,300/K-12
PO Box 275 40006 502-255-3201
Steve Miracle, supt. Fax 255-5105
www.trimble.kyschools.us
Trimble County HS 400/9-12
1029 Highway 421 N 40006 502-255-7781
Michael Slider, prin. Fax 255-5126
Trimble County MS 200/7-8
1089 Highway 421 N 40006 502-255-7361
Tracy Poe, prin. Fax 255-5102

Belfry, Pike
Kentucky Tech System
Supt. — See Frankfort
Belfry Area Technology Center Vo/Tech
PO Box 280 41514 606-353-4951
Tom Ford, prin. Fax 353-0868

Pike County SD
Supt. — See Pikeville
Belfry HS 600/9-12
PO Box 160 41514 606-237-3900
Mark Gannon, prin. Fax 237-5119
Belfry MS 500/6-8
PO Box 850 41514 606-353-9688
Jeremy Howard, prin. Fax 353-9327

Bellevue, Campbell, Pop. 5,875
Bellevue ISD 700/PK-12
219 Center St 41073 859-261-2108
Robb Smith, supt. Fax 261-1708
www.bellevue.kyschools.us

Bellevue HS 300/6-12
201 Center St 41073 859-261-2980
Dave Eckstein, prin. Fax 261-1825

Daymar College Post-Sec.
119 Fairfield Ave 41073 859-291-0800

Benton, Marshall, Pop. 4,312
Marshall County SD 4,400/PK-12
86 High School Rd 42025 270-527-8628
Trent Lovett, supt. Fax 527-0804
www.marshall.kyschools.us
Marshall County HS 1,300/9-12
416 High School Rd 42025 270-527-1453
Amy Waggoner, prin. Fax 527-0578
Marshall County Technical Center Vo/Tech
341 High School Rd 42025 270-527-8648
Stacey Bradley, dir. Fax 527-1920
South Marshall MS 200/6-8
2211 US Highway 641 S 42025 270-527-3828
Ryan Marchetti, prin. Fax 527-7616
STAR Academy 50/Alt
1308 US Highway 641 N 42025 270-252-1394
David Morris, dir. Fax 527-0804
Other Schools – See Calvert City

Christian Fellowship S 100/PK-12
1343 US Highway 68 E 42025 270-527-8377
Bill Rowley, prin. Fax 527-2872

Berea, Madison, Pop. 13,252
Berea ISD 900/PK-12
3 Pirate Pkwy 40403 859-986-8446
Mike Hogg, supt. Fax 986-1839
www.berea.kyschools.us/
Berea Community MSHS 300/6-12
1 Pirate Pkwy 40403 859-986-4911
Donna Lovell, prin. Fax 986-4640

Madison County SD
Supt. — See Richmond
Farristown MS 500/6-8
751 Farristown Industrial 40403 859-387-8600
Alicia Hunter, prin. Fax 986-3092
Foley MS 400/6-8
275 Glades Rd 40403 859-625-6140
Mark Wall, prin. Fax 986-3362
Madison Southern HS 1,200/9-12
279 Glades Rd 40403 859-625-6148
Brandon Watkins, prin. Fax 986-3092

Berea College Post-Sec.
101 Chestnut St 40403 859-985-3000

Beverly, Bell

Red Bird Christian S 200/PK-12
15420 Highway 66 40913 606-598-2416
Michael R. Hensley, head sch Fax 598-7314

Blackey, Letcher, Pop. 120
Letcher County SD
Supt. — See Whitesburg
Letcher MS 200/6-8
160 Letcher High School Dr 41804 606-633-7812
Ricky Warf, prin. Fax 633-5731

Bloomfield, Nelson, Pop. 831
Nelson County SD
Supt. — See Bardstown
Bloomfield MS 400/6-8
96 Arnold Ln 40008 502-349-7201
Traci Burke, prin. Fax 349-7203

Booneville, Owsley, Pop. 81
Owsley County SD 900/PK-12
14 Old KY 11 41314 606-593-6363
Dr. Timothy Bobrowski, supt. Fax 593-6368
www.owsley.kyschools.us
Owsley County JSHS 300/7-12
177 Shepherd Rd 41314 606-593-5185
Charles Davidson, prin. Fax 593-6312

Bowling Green, Warren, Pop. 56,664
Bowling Green ISD 4,000/PK-12
1211 Center St 42101 270-746-2200
Gary Fields, supt. Fax 746-2205
www.bgreen.kyschools.us/
Academy at 11th Street 50/Alt
877 E 11th Ave 42101 270-746-2321
Marisa Duarte, dir. Fax 746-2325
Bowling Green HS 1,200/9-12
1801 Rockingham Ave 42104 270-746-2300
William King, prin. Fax 746-2305
Bowling Green JHS 900/6-8
900 Campbell Ln 42104 270-746-2290
Cynthia West, prin. Fax 746-2295

Kentucky Tech System
Supt. — See Frankfort
Warren County Area Technology Center Vo/Tech
365 Technology Way 42101 270-746-7205
Eric Keeling, prin. Fax 746-7207

Warren County SD 13,900/PK-12
PO Box 51810 42102 270-781-5150
Rob Clayton, supt. Fax 781-2392
www.warrencountyschools.org/
Beacon Academy Alt
1022 W Main St 42104 270-842-0702
Brad Tolbert, prin.
Drakes Creek MS 600/7-8
704 Cypress Wood Ln 42104 270-843-0165
Daryl Woods, prin. Fax 782-6138
GEO International HS 9-12
1808 Loop Dr 42101 270-904-3691
Adam Hatcher, prin.
Greenwood HS 1,100/9-12
5065 Scottsville Rd 42104 270-842-3627
Greg Dunn, prin. Fax 842-2037
Jackson Academy Alt
877 Jackson St 42101 270-782-5410
Eric Wilson, prin. Fax 782-3240
Lighthouse Academy 100/Alt
877 Jackson St 42101 270-782-5410
Eric Wilson, prin. Fax 782-3240
Moss MS 500/7-8
2565 Russellville Rd 42101 270-843-0166
David Nole, prin. Fax 843-8512
South Warren HS 1,100/9-12
8140 Nashville Rd 42101 270-467-7500
Jenny Hester, prin. Fax 467-7506
South Warren MS 600/7-8
295 Richpond Rd 42104 270-467-7510
Eddy Bushelman, prin. Fax 467-7516
Warren Central HS 1,000/9-12
559 Morgantown Rd 42101 270-781-2401
Mike Stevenson, prin. Fax 781-5115
Warren East HS 900/9-12
6867 Louisville Rd 42101 270-781-1277
Nicole Clark, prin. Fax 843-2610
Warren East MS 500/7-8
7031 Louisville Rd 42101 270-843-0181
David Cloyd, prin. Fax 781-8565

Anchored Christian S 100/PK-12
1807 Cave Mill Rd 42104 270-781-9077
Bowling Green Christian Academy 100/PK-12
1730 Destiny Ln 42104 270-782-9552
Cindy Moses, admin. Fax 782-9585
Daymar College Post-Sec.
2421 Industrial Dr 42101 270-843-6750
PJs College of Cosmetology Post-Sec.
1901 Russellville Rd 42101 270-842-8149
Southcentral Kentucky Comm & Tech Coll Post-Sec.
1845 Loop St 42101 270-901-1000
Southcentral Kentucky Comm Tech College Post-Sec.
1127 Morgantown Rd 42101 270-746-7807
Western Kentucky University Post-Sec.
1906 College Heights Blvd 42101 270-745-0111

Brandenburg, Meade, Pop. 2,585
Kentucky Tech System
Supt. — See Frankfort
Meade County Area Technology Center Vo/Tech
110 Greer St 40108 270-422-3955
Faye Campbell, prin. Fax 422-3307

Meade County SD 5,100/PK-12
1155 Old Ekron Rd 40108 270-422-7500
Dr. John Millay, supt. Fax 422-5494
www.meade.kyschools.us
Meade County HS 1,600/9-12
938 Old State Rd 40108 270-422-7515
Marc Adams, prin. Fax 422-3928
Pepper MS 800/7-8
1085 Old Ekron Rd 40108 270-422-7530
Chad Butler, prin. Fax 422-5515

Brooksville, Bracken, Pop. 638
Bracken County SD 1,300/PK-12
348 W Miami St 41004 606-735-2523
Jeff Aulick, supt. Fax 735-3640
www.bracken.k12.ky.us
Bracken County HS 300/9-12
PO Box 128 41004 606-735-3153
Dennis Maines, prin. Fax 735-2549
Bracken County MS 300/6-8
167 Parsley Dr 41004 606-735-3425
Clay King, prin. Fax 735-2057

Brownsville, Edmonson, Pop. 829
Edmonson County SD 2,000/PK-12
PO Box 129 42210 270-597-2101
Patrick Waddell, supt. Fax 597-2103
www.edmonson.k12.ky.us
Edmonson County HS 600/9-12
220 Wild Cat Way 42210 270-597-2151
Tommy Hodges, prin. Fax 597-2962
Edmonson County MS 300/7-8
210 Wild Cat Way 42210 270-597-2932
Brandon Prunty, prin. Fax 597-2182

Buckhorn, Perry, Pop. 162
Perry County SD
Supt. — See Hazard
Buckhorn S 400/K-12
18392 KY Highway 28 41721 606-398-7176
Tim Wooton, prin. Fax 398-7930

Burgin, Mercer, Pop. 946
Burgin ISD 300/PK-12
PO Box B 40310 859-748-4000
Martha Collier, supt. Fax 748-4010
www.burgin.kyschools.us
Burgin S 300/PK-12
PO Box B 40310 859-748-5282
Chris LeMonds, prin. Fax 748-4002

Burkesville, Cumberland, Pop. 1,484
Cumberland County SD 1,000/K-12
PO Box 420 42717 270-864-3377
Dr. Kirk Biggerstaff, supt. Fax 864-5803
www.cland.k12.ky.us
Cumberland County HS 300/9-12
PO Box 380 42717 270-864-3451
Angela Morrison, prin. Fax 864-1284
Cumberland County MS 200/6-8
PO Box 70 42717 270-864-5818
Dr. Tim Parson, prin. Fax 864-2590

Burlington, Boone, Pop. 15,646
Boone County SD
Supt. — See Florence
Camp Ernst MS 1,000/6-8
6515 Camp Ernst Rd 41005 859-534-4000
Stephanie Hagerty, prin. Fax 534-4001

Burna, Livingston, Pop. 254
Livingston County SD
Supt. — See Smithland
Livingston County MS 200/7-8
1370 US Highway 60 E 42028 270-988-3263
Lisa Huddleston, prin. Fax 988-2518

Butler, Pendleton, Pop. 586
Pendleton County SD
Supt. — See Falmouth
Sharp MS 600/6-8
35 Wright Rd 41006 859-472-7000
David Sledd, prin. Fax 472-7011

Cadiz, Trigg, Pop. 2,498
Trigg County SD 2,100/PK-12
202 Main St 42211 270-522-6075
Travis Hamby, supt. Fax 522-7782
www.trigg.kyschools.us
Trigg County HS 600/9-12
203 Main St 42211 270-522-2200
Shannon Burcham, prin. Fax 522-2224
Trigg County MS 500/6-8
206 Lafayette St 42211 270-522-2210
Amy Breckel, prin. Fax 522-2203

Calhoun, McLean, Pop. 758
McLean County SD 1,600/K-12
PO Box 245 42327 270-273-5257
Terry Hayes, supt. Fax 273-5259
www.mclean.kyschools.us
McLean County HS 500/9-12
1859 State Route 136 E 42327 270-273-5278
Drew Taylor, prin. Fax 273-5208
McLean County MS 400/6-8
1901 State Route 136 E 42327 270-273-5191
Karen Solise, prin. Fax 273-9876

Calvert City, Marshall, Pop. 2,542
Marshall County SD
Supt. — See Benton
North Marshall MS 600/6-8
3110 US Highway 95 42029 270-395-7108
Aimee Lepisto, prin. Fax 395-5449

Campbellsville, Taylor, Pop. 8,884
Campbellsville ISD 1,100/PK-12
136 S Columbia Ave 42718 270-465-4162
Mike Deaton, supt. Fax 465-3918
www.cville.kyschools.us/
Campbellsville HS 300/9-12
230 W Main St 42718 270-465-8774
Kirby Smith, prin. Fax 789-4007
Campbellsville MS 500/4-8
230 W Main St 42718 270-465-5121
Elisha Rhodes, prin. Fax 789-3718
Eagle Academy 50/Alt
230 W Main St 42718 270-465-6337
Kirby Smith, admin. Fax 465-9777

Taylor County SD 2,100/PK-12
1209 E Broadway St 42718 270-465-5371
Roger D. Cook, supt. Fax 789-3954
www.taylor.kyschools.us
Taylor County HS 900/9-12
300 Ingram Ave 42718 270-465-4431
Laura Benningfield, prin. Fax 465-5731
Taylor County MS 600/6-8
1207 E Broadway St 42718 270-465-2877
Danita Johnson, prin. Fax 789-1753

Campbellsville University Post-Sec.
1 University Dr 42718 270-789-5000

Campton, Wolfe, Pop. 434
Wolfe County SD 1,300/K-12
PO Box 160 41301 606-668-8002
Kenny Bell, supt. Fax 668-8050
www.wolfe.kyschools.us
Wolfe County HS 300/9-12
PO Box 790 41301 606-668-8202
Greg Creech, prin. Fax 668-8250
Wolfe County MS 200/7-8
PO Box 460 41301 606-668-8152
Nick Brooks, prin. Fax 668-8100

Carlisle, Nicholas, Pop. 1,984
Nicholas County SD 1,200/PK-12
395 W Main St 40311 859-289-3770
Marty Feltner, supt. Fax 289-3777
www.nicholas.kyschools.us
Nicholas County JSHS 500/7-12
103 School Dr 40311 859-289-3780
Barbara Allison, prin. Fax 289-6429

Motif Beauty Academy Post-Sec.
225 Elderberry Dr 40311 859-745-5886

Carrollton, Carroll, Pop. 3,854
Carroll County SD 1,900/K-12
813 Hawkins St 41008 502-732-7070
Bill Hogan, supt. Fax 732-7073
www.carroll.kyschools.us
Carroll County Alternative S 50/Alt
519 Park Ave 41008 502-732-7112
Amy Sutter, lead tchr. Fax 732-7113
Carroll County HS 500/9-12
1706 Highland Ave 41008 502-732-7075
Tom Stephens, prin. Fax 732-7012
Carroll County MS 400/6-8
408 5th St 41008 502-732-7080
Dana Oak, prin. Fax 732-7107

Kentucky Tech System
Supt. — See Frankfort
Carroll County Area Technology Center Vo/Tech
1704 Highland Ave 41008 502-732-4479
Tony Jury, prin. Fax 732-4837

Christian Academy of Carrollton 100/PK-12
1703 Easter Day Rd 41008 502-732-4734
Katie Matson, admin. Fax 732-4732

Cave City, Barren, Pop. 2,196
Caverna ISD 800/PK-12
1102 N Dixie Hwy 42127 270-773-2530
Cornelius Faulkner, supt. Fax 773-2524
www.caverna.k12.ky.us
Other Schools – See Horse Cave

Cecilia, Hardin, Pop. 563
Hardin County SD
Supt. — See Elizabethtown
Central Hardin HS 1,900/9-12
3040 Leitchfield Rd 42724 270-737-6800
Tim Isaacs, prin. Fax 765-3889
West Hardin MS 600/6-8
10471 Leitchfield Rd 42724 270-862-3924
Mike Lawson, prin. Fax 862-3647

Clinton, Hickman, Pop. 1,362
Hickman County SD 800/PK-12
416 N Waterfield Dr 42031 270-653-2341
Casey Henderson, supt. Fax 653-6007
www.hickman.kyschools.us
Hickman County HS 400/7-12
301 James H Phillips Dr 42031 270-653-4044
Kevin Estes, prin. Fax 653-3200

Daymar College Post-Sec.
1171 US Highway 51 S 42031 270-653-9800

Cloverport, Breckinridge, Pop. 1,138
Cloverport ISD 400/PK-12
PO Box 37 40111 270-788-3910
Keith Haynes, supt. Fax 788-6290
www.cloverport.kyschools.us
Fraize HS 100/9-12
301 Poplar St 40111 270-788-3388
Keith Haynes, prin. Fax 788-6640
Fraize MS 100/6-8
301 Poplar St 40111 270-788-3388
Keith Haynes, prin. Fax 788-6640

Columbia, Adair, Pop. 4,378
Adair County SD 2,600/PK-12
1204 Greensburg St 42728 270-384-2476
Alan Reed, supt. Fax 384-5841
www.adair.kyschools.us
Adair County HS 700/9-12
526 Indian Dr 42728 270-384-2751
Troy Young, prin. Fax 384-6900
Adair County MS 600/6-8
322 General John Adair Dr 42728 270-384-5308
Alma Rich, prin. Fax 384-2168
Adair County Youth Development Center 50/Alt
PO Box 39 42728 270-384-0811
Tamara Smith, prin. Fax 384-2122

Lindsey Wilson College Post-Sec.
210 Lindsey Wilson St 42728 270-384-2126

Corbin, Whitley, Pop. 7,232
Corbin ISD 3,000/PK-12
108 Roy Kidd Ave 40701 606-528-1303
David Cox, supt. Fax 523-1747
www.corbinschools.org
Corbin Educational Center 50/Alt
709 Roy Kidd Ave 40701 606-523-4080
Tom Greer, admin. Fax 523-5563
Corbin HS 800/9-12
1901 Snyder St 40701 606-528-3902
John Crawford, prin. Fax 523-3627
Corbin MS 500/7-8
706 S Kentucky Ave 40701 606-523-3619
Cindy Davis, prin. Fax 523-5093

Kentucky Tech System
Supt. — See Frankfort
Corbin Area Technology Center Vo/Tech
1909 Snyder St 40701 606-528-5338
Christopher Smith, prin. Fax 528-0532

Knox County SD
Supt. — See Barbourville
Lynn Camp MSHS 500/7-12
100 N KY 830 40701 606-528-5429
Anthony Pennington, prin. Fax 528-4750

Covington, Kenton, Pop. 39,321
Covington ISD 4,100/PK-12
25 E 7th St 41011 859-392-1000
Alvin Garrison, supt. Fax 292-5970
covington.kyschools.us
Holmes HS 900/9-12
2500 Madison Ave 41014 859-655-9545
Scott Hornblower, prin. Fax 581-7259
Holmes MS 800/6-8
2500 Madison Ave 41014 859-392-1100
Sean Bohannon, prin. Fax 292-5810

Calvary Christian S 400/PK-12
5955 Taylor Mill Rd 41015 859-356-9201
Dr. Bill Dickens, admin. Fax 356-8962
Covington Catholic HS 500/9-12
1600 Dixie Hwy 41011 859-491-2247
Bob Rowe, prin. Fax 448-2242
Covington Latin HS 200/7-12
21 E 11th St 41011 859-291-7044
Jason Huther, hdmstr. Fax 291-1939
Holy Cross HS 400/9-12
3617 Church St 41015 859-431-1335
Michael Holtz, prin. Fax 655-2184

Crestview Hills, Kenton, Pop. 3,111

Thomas More College Post-Sec.
333 Thomas More Pkwy 41017 844-698-6248

Crestwood, Oldham, Pop. 4,447
Oldham County SD 11,900/PK-12
6165 W Highway 146 40014 502-241-3500
Greg Schultz, supt. Fax 241-3209
www.oldham.kyschools.us/
East Oldham MS 600/6-8
1201 E Highway 22 40014 502-222-8480
Mark Robson, prin. Fax 222-8489
South Oldham HS 1,200/9-12
5901 Veterens Memorial Pkwy 40014 502-241-6681
Jeff Griffin, prin. Fax 241-0955
South Oldham MS 700/6-8
6403 W Highway 146 40014 502-241-0320
Steve Emerson, prin. Fax 241-1438
Other Schools – See Goshen, La Grange

Jubilee Academy 100/K-12
7505 Kavanaugh Rd 40014 502-439-4400
Heather Walton, dir.
Trend Setter's Academy of Beauty Culture Post-Sec.
6539 W Highway 22 40014 502-241-0565

Cumberland, Harlan, Pop. 2,210

Southeast Kentucky Community/Tech Coll Post-Sec.
700 College Rd 40823 606-589-2145

Cynthiana, Harrison, Pop. 6,302
Harrison County SD 3,000/PK-12
308 Webster Ave 41031 859-234-7110
Andy Dotson, supt. Fax 234-8164
www.harrison.kyschools.us
Harrison County HS 900/9-12
320 Webster Ave 41031 859-234-7117
Amy Coleman, prin. Fax 234-0115
Harrison County MS 700/6-8
269 Education Dr 41031 859-234-7123
Michael McIntire, prin. Fax 234-8385

Kentucky Tech System
Supt. — See Frankfort
Harrison County Area Technology Center Vo/Tech
327 Webster Ave 41031 859-234-5286
Nicki Jones, prin. Fax 234-0658

Danville, Boyle, Pop. 15,790
Boyle County SD 2,600/PK-12
352 N Danville Byp 40422 859-236-6634
Mike LaFavers, supt. Fax 236-8624
www.boyle.kysschools.us
Boyle County Day Treatment Center 50/Alt
1637 Perryville Rd 40422 859-236-5047
LuAnn Littlefield, dir.
Boyle County HS 800/9-12
1637 Perryville Rd 40422 859-236-5047
Mark Wade, prin. Fax 236-7820
Boyle County MS 700/6-8
1651 Perryville Rd 40422 859-236-4212
Steve Karsner, prin. Fax 236-9596

Danville ISD 1,800/PK-12
152 E Martin L King Blvd 40422 859-238-1300
Dr. Keith Look, supt. Fax 238-1330
www.danvilleschools.net
Bate MS 400/6-8
460 Stanford Ave 40422 859-238-1305
Beth Lee, prin. Fax 238-1343
Danville HS 500/9-12
203 E Lexington Ave 40422 859-238-1308
Fax 936-8401

Centre College Post-Sec.
600 W Walnut St 40422 859-238-5200
Danville Christian Academy 200/PK-12
2170 Shakertown Rd 40422 859-236-2177
Debra Lucas, hdmstr. Fax 236-6759
Kentucky School for the Deaf Post-Sec.
S 2nd St 40422 859-239-7017
National College Post-Sec.
115 E Lexington Ave 40422 859-236-6991

Dawson Springs, Hopkins, Pop. 2,724
Dawson Springs ISD 600/PK-12
118 E Arcadia Ave 42408 270-797-3811
Leonard Whalen, supt. Fax 797-5201
www.dsprings.k12.ky.us
Dawson Springs HS 300/7-12
317 Eli St 42408 270-797-2957
Kevin Stockman, prin. Fax 797-5204

Dayton, Campbell, Pop. 5,244
Dayton ISD 900/PK-12
200 Clay St 41074 859-491-6565
Jay Brewer, supt. Fax 292-3995
www.dayton.kyschools.us
Dayton HS 300/7-12
200 Greendevil Ln 41074 859-292-7486
Ryan Kellinghaus, prin. Fax 261-1606

Dixon, Webster, Pop. 785
Kentucky Tech System
Supt. — See Frankfort
Webster County Area Technology Center Vo/Tech
PO Box 230 42409 270-639-5035
Lawrence Garrity, prin. Fax 639-5545

Webster County SD 2,300/PK-12
28 State Route 1340 42409 270-639-5083
Dr. Rachel Yarbrough, supt. Fax 639-0117
www.webster.kyschools.us
Webster County HS 600/9-12
1922 US Highway 41A S 42409 270-639-5092
Aaron Harrell, prin. Fax 639-0128
Webster County MS 300/7-8
1928 US Highway 41A S 42409 270-639-9496
Cyndi Boggs, prin. Fax 639-9498

Dry Ridge, Grant, Pop. 2,166
Grant County SD
Supt. — See Williamstown

Eagle Creek Academy 50/Alt
715 Warsaw Rd 41035 859-824-7706
Cody Ryan, prin. Fax 824-7067
Grant County HS 1,100/9-12
715 Warsaw Rd 41035 859-824-9739
Claudette Herald, prin. Fax 824-9756
Grant County MS 800/6-8
305 School Rd 41035 859-824-7161
John Preston, prin. Fax 824-7163

Eastern, Floyd
Floyd County SD
Supt. — See Prestonsburg
Allen Central HS 400/9-12
PO Box 139 41622 606-358-9543
Larry Begley, prin. Fax 358-9247
Allen Central MS 300/6-8
PO Box 193 41622 606-358-0110
Wes Halbert, prin. Fax 358-0112

Eddyville, Lyon, Pop. 2,514
Lyon County SD 900/K-12
217 Jenkins Rd 42038 270-388-9715
Russ Tilford, supt. Fax 388-4962
www.lyon.kyschools.us
Lyon County HS 300/9-12
209 W Fairview Ave 42038 270-388-9715
Ryan Amerson, prin. Fax 388-2296
Lyon County MS 200/6-8
111 W Fairview Ave 42038 270-388-9715
Robert Richey, prin. Fax 388-0517

Edgewood, Kenton, Pop. 8,503
Kenton County SD
Supt. — See Fort Wright
Dixie Heights HS 1,400/9-12
3010 Dixie Hwy 41017 859-341-7650
Karen Hendrix, prin. Fax 341-2531
Turkey Foot MS 1,100/6-8
3230 Turkeyfoot Rd 41017 859-341-0216
Debbie Obermeyer, prin. Fax 341-7217

St. Elizabeth Medical Center Post-Sec.
1 Medical Village Dr 41017 859-301-2170

Edmonton, Metcalfe, Pop. 1,584
Metcalfe County SD 1,300/PK-12
109 Sartin Dr 42129 270-432-3171
Dr. Benny Lile, supt. Fax 432-3170
www.metcalfe.kyschools.us
Metcalfe County HS 400/9-12
208 Randolph St 42129 270-432-2481
Kelly Bell, prin. Fax 432-2714
Metcalfe County MS 400/6-8
208 Randolph St Lot 1 42129 270-432-3359
Allen Trotter, prin. Fax 432-5828

Elizabethtown, Hardin, Pop. 27,593
Elizabethtown ISD 2,500/PK-12
219 Helm St 42701 270-765-6146
Jon Ballard, supt. Fax 765-2158
www.etown.k12.ky.us
Elizabethtown HS 800/9-12
620 N Mulberry St 42701 270-769-3381
Steve Smallwood, prin. Fax 769-2539
Stone MS 600/6-8
323 Morningside Dr 42701 270-769-6343
Jennifer Burnham, prin. Fax 769-6749
Valley View Education Center 50/Alt
701 Hawkins Dr 42701 270-769-2359
Kristin Froedge, admin. Fax 769-3860

Hardin County SD 14,700/PK-12
65 W A Jenkins Rd 42701 270-769-8800
Teresa Morgan, supt. Fax 769-8888
www.hardin.kyschools.us
Bluegrass MS 600/6-8
170 W A Jenkins Rd 42701 270-765-2658
Michael Elmore, prin. Fax 769-7935
College View Alternative S 100/Alt
521 Charlemagne Blvd 42701 270-234-5732
Robert King, prin.
Hardin Co. Early College & Career Center 300/10-12
200 University Dr 42701 270-769-7930
Dan Robbins, prin. Fax 234-5721
Hardin County HS at College View 50/Alt
521 Charlemagne Blvd 42701 270-769-8826
Wes Blair, dir.
Hardin HS 1,000/9-12
384 W A Jenkins Rd 42701 270-769-8906
Mark Wells, prin. Fax 769-8996
Other Schools – See Cecilia, Glendale, Radcliff, Vine Grove

Elizabethtown Beauty School Post-Sec.
308 N Miles St 42701 270-765-2118
Elizabethtown Community & Technical Coll Post-Sec.
600 College Street Rd 42701 270-769-2371
Trend Setter's Academy of Beauty Culture Post-Sec.
622B Westport Rd 42701 270-765-5243

Elkton, Todd, Pop. 2,020
Todd County SD 2,100/PK-12
205 Airport Rd 42220 270-265-2436
Wayne Benningfield, supt. Fax 265-5414
www.todd.kyschools.us
Todd County Central HS 500/9-12
806 S Main St 42220 270-265-2506
Jennifer Pope, prin. Fax 265-9408
Todd County MS 500/6-8
515 W Main St 42220 270-265-2511
Les Broady, prin. Fax 265-9414

Eminence, Henry, Pop. 2,433
Eminence ISD 700/PK-12
291 W Broadway St 40019 502-845-5427
Buddy Berry, supt. Fax 845-2339
www.eminence.kyschools.us

Eminence JSHS 300/6-12
254 W Broadway St 40019 502-845-5427
Angie Deckard, prin. Fax 845-1310

Erlanger, Kenton, Pop. 17,704
Erlanger-Elsmere ISD 2,200/PK-12
500 Graves Ave 41018 859-727-2009
Dr. Kathlyn Burkhardt, supt. Fax 727-5653
www.erlanger.kyschools.us
Bartlett Educational Center 50/Alt
305 Bartlett Ave 41018 859-342-2460
Chris Klosinski, prin. Fax 342-2423
Lloyd HS 500/9-12
450 Bartlett Ave 41018 859-727-1555
John Riehemann, prin. Fax 727-5912
Tichenor MS 500/6-8
305 Bartlett Ave 41018 859-727-2255
Mac Cooley, prin. Fax 342-2425

St. Henry HS 500/9-12
3755 Scheben Dr 41018 859-525-0255
David Otte, prin. Fax 525-5855

Fairdale, Jefferson, Pop. 6,563
Jefferson County SD
Supt. — See Louisville
Fairdale HS Magnet Career Academy 1,100/9-12
1001 Fairdale Rd 40118 502-485-8248
Brad Weston, prin. Fax 313-3452

Falmouth, Pendleton, Pop. 2,146
Pendleton County SD 2,400/PK-12
2525 US Highway 27 N 41040 859-654-6911
Dr. R. Anthony Strong, supt. Fax 654-6143
www.pendleton.kyschools.us
Pendleton County HS 700/9-12
2359 US Highway 27 N 41040 859-654-3355
Chad Simms, prin. Fax 654-4235
Other Schools – See Butler

Fern Creek, Jefferson, Pop. 16,406
Jefferson County SD
Supt. — See Louisville
Fern Creek Traditional HS 1,400/9-12
9115 Fern Creek Rd 40291 502-485-8251
Dr. Nathan Meyer, prin. Fax 313-3458

Flemingsburg, Fleming, Pop. 2,619
Fleming County SD 2,300/K-12
211 W Water St 41041 606-845-5851
Brian Creasman, supt. Fax 849-3158
www.fleming.kyschools.us
Fleming County HS 700/9-12
1658 Elizaville Rd 41041 606-845-6601
Stephanie Emmons, prin. Fax 845-3102
Simons MS 400/7-8
242 W Water St 41041 606-845-9331
Jesse Bacon, prin. Fax 849-2309

Florence, Boone, Pop. 29,280
Boone County SD 20,000/PK-12
8330 US Highway 42 41042 859-283-1003
Randy Poe Ed.D., supt. Fax 282-2376
www.boone.kyschools.us
Alternative Center for Education 100/Alt
99 Center St 41042 859-282-2163
Jerome Gels, prin. Fax 282-2165
Boone County HS 1,300/9-12
7056 Burlington Pike 41042 859-282-5655
Fax 282-5653
Jones MS 700/6-8
8000 Spruce Dr 41042 859-282-4610
Tony Pastura, prin. Fax 282-2364
Ockerman MS 900/6-8
8300 US Highway 42 41042 859-282-3240
Michael Poiry, prin. Fax 282-3242
Other Schools – See Burlington, Hebron, Union

Beckfield College Post-Sec.
16 Spiral Dr 41042 859-371-9393
Gateway Community & Technical College Post-Sec.
500 Technology Way 41042 859-441-4500
Hair Design School Post-Sec.
7285 Turfway Rd 41042 859-283-2690
Heritage Academy 200/PK-12
7216 US Highway 42 41042 859-525-0213
Lincoln College of Technology Post-Sec.
8095 Connector Dr 41042 859-282-9999
National College Post-Sec.
7627 Ewing Blvd 41042 859-525-6510

Fort Knox, Hardin, Pop. 9,669

Sullivan University Post-Sec.
63 Quartermaster St 40121 502-942-8500

Fort Mitchell, Kenton, Pop. 8,095
Beechwood ISD 1,300/PK-12
50 Beechwood Rd 41017 859-331-3250
Dr. Mike Stacy, supt. Fax 331-7528
www.beechwood.kyschools.us
Beechwood JSHS 600/7-12
54 Beechwood Rd 41017 859-331-1220
Alissa Ayres, prin. Fax 426-3744

Kenton County SD
Supt. — See Fort Wright
Kenton County Academies Vo/Tech
3234 Turkeyfoot Rd 41017 859-341-2266
Dr. Francis O'Hara, dir.

Fort Thomas, Campbell, Pop. 16,124
Fort Thomas ISD 2,900/PK-12
28 N Fort Thomas Ave 41075 859-781-3333
Gene Kirchner, supt. Fax 442-4016
www.fortthomas.kyschools.us
Highlands HS 900/9-12
2400 Memorial Pkwy 41075 859-781-5900
Brian Robinson, prin. Fax 441-9271
Highlands MS 700/6-8
2350 Memorial Pkwy 41075 859-441-5222
Michael Howton, prin. Fax 441-9371

Fort Wright, Kenton, Pop. 5,642
Kenton County SD 13,800/PK-12
1055 Eaton Dr 41017 859-344-8888
Dr. Terri Cox-Cruey, supt. Fax 344-1531
www.kenton.kyschools.us/
Other Schools – See Edgewood, Fort Mitchell, Independence, Taylor Mill

Frankfort, Franklin, Pop. 24,820
Frankfort ISD 800/PK-12
959 Leestown Ln 40601 502-875-8661
Dr. Houston Barber, supt. Fax 875-8663
www.frankfort.k12.ky.us
Capital City Preparatory 50/Alt
104 University Dr 40601 502-875-8650
Mike Hefling, dir. Fax 875-8652
Frankfort HS 200/9-12
328 Shelby St 40601 502-875-8655
John Lyons, prin. Fax 875-8657

Franklin County SD 6,300/PK-12
190 Kings Daughters Dr 40601 502-695-6700
Chrissy Jones, supt. Fax 695-6708
www.franklin.kyschools.us
Academy 50/Alt
400 Democrat Dr 40601 502-695-6720
Sarah Vivian, prin. Fax 695-9618
Bondurant MS 600/6-8
300 Bondurant Dr 40601 502-875-8440
Casey Sparrow, prin. Fax 875-8442
Elkhorn MS 800/6-8
1060 E Main St 40601 502-695-6740
Willie Bartley, prin. Fax 695-6745
Franklin Co. Career & Technical Center Vo/Tech
1106 E Main St 40601 502-695-6790
James Hardin, dir. Fax 695-6791
Franklin County HS 900/9-12
1100 E Main St 40601 502-695-6750
Stirling Sampson, prin. Fax 695-6755
Western Hills HS 800/9-12
100 Doctors Dr 40601 502-875-8400
Greg Roush, prin. Fax 227-4568

Kentucky Tech System
500 Mero St 40601 502-564-4286
Laura Arnold, cmmssnr. Fax 564-4800
www.kytech.ky.gov
Other Schools – See Albany, Alexandria, Barbourville, Bardstown, Beattyville, Belfry, Bowling Green, Brandenburg, Carrollton, Corbin, Cynthiana, Dixon, Glasgow, Greensburg, Greenup, Harned, Harrodsburg, Hartford, Hebron, Hickman, Hindman, Hyden, Inez, Jackson, Lancaster, Lebanon, Liberty, Mc Kee, Manchester, Martin, Mayfield, Maysville, Monticello, Morgantown, Mount Sterling, Mount Vernon, Murray, Paducah, Pikeville, Pineville, Princeton, Richmond, Russell, Russell Springs, Russellville, Shelbyville, Shepherdsville, Somerset, Stanford, Tompkinsville, West Liberty, Whitesburg, Winchester

---

Frankfort Christian Academy 300/PK-12
1349 US Highway 421 S 40601 502-695-0744
Carrie Beth Tigges, admin. Fax 695-8725
Kentucky State University Post-Sec.
400 E Main St 40601 502-597-6000

Franklin, Simpson, Pop. 8,221
Simpson County SD 2,900/PK-12
430 S College St 42134 270-586-8877
Dr. James Flynn, supt. Fax 586-2011
www.simpson.kyschools.us
Franklin Simpson HS 800/9-12
400 S College St 42134 270-586-3273
Tim Schlosser, prin. Fax 586-2021
Franklin Simpson HS West Campus 50/Alt
229 Yokley Dr 42134 270-586-2039
Crystal Bayles, prin. Fax 586-2047
Franklin Simpson MS 700/6-8
322 S College St 42134 270-586-4401
Craig Delk, prin. Fax 586-2048

Frenchburg, Menifee, Pop. 482
Menifee County SD 1,100/PK-12
PO Box 110 40322 606-768-8002
Timothy Spencer, supt. Fax 768-8050
www.menifee.kyschools.us
Menifee County Academy 50/Alt
6969 Tarr Ridge Rd 40322 606-768-8190
Steven Meadows, prin.
Menifee County HS 300/9-12
119 Indian Creek Rd 40322 606-768-8102
Steven Meadows, prin. Fax 768-8200

Fulton, Fulton, Pop. 2,370
Fulton ISD 400/PK-12
304 W State Line St 42041 270-472-1553
Dr. Tamara Smith, supt. Fax 472-6921
www.fultonind.kyschools.us
Fulton Independent HS 200/6-12
700 Stephen Beale Dr 42041 270-472-1741
Dr. R. B. Mays, prin. Fax 472-6135

Georgetown, Scott, Pop. 28,525
Scott County SD 8,900/PK-12
PO Box 578 40324 502-863-3663
Patricia Putty, supt. Fax 863-5367
www.scott.kyschools.us
Elkhorn Crossing HS 9-12
2001 Frankfort Rd 40324 502-570-4920
Michelle Nichols, prin. Fax 873-2610
Georgetown MS 500/6-8
730 S Hamilton St 40324 502-863-3805
Rhonda Schornick, prin. Fax 867-1372
Ninth Grade Center 700/9-9
1072 Cardinal Dr 40324 502-863-4635
Jonda Tippins, prin. Fax 868-0515
Royal Spring MS 800/6-8
332 Champion Way 40324 502-570-2390
Keith Griesser, prin. Fax 863-3621
Scott County Cardinal Academy Alt
1076 Cardinal Dr 40324 502-863-4057
Joretta Crowe, dir. Fax 863-4432
Scott County MS 800/6-8
1036 Cardinal Dr 40324 502-863-7202
Jennifer Sutton, prin. Fax 863-7452
Scott County SHS 1,700/10-12
1080 Cardinal Dr 40324 502-863-4131
Joe Covington, prin. Fax 867-0544

Georgetown College Post-Sec.
400 E College St 40324 502-863-8000
Providence Christian Academy 300/PK-10
172 Southgate Dr 40324 502-868-9393
Kathleen Mallory M.Ed., admin. Fax 370-4766

Glasgow, Barren, Pop. 13,692
Barren County SD 4,800/PK-12
202 W Washington St 42141 270-651-3787
Bo Matthews, supt. Fax 651-8836
www.barren.kyschools.us
Barren County HS 1,000/10-12
507 Trojan Trl 42141 270-651-6315
Brad Johnson, prin. Fax 651-9211
Barren County MS 700/7-8
555 Trojan Trl 42141 270-651-4909
Lori Downs, prin. Fax 651-5137
College Street Campus Alt
304 E College St 42141 270-629-6554
Dan Belding, dir. Fax 629-2267
Trojan Academy 9-9
505 Trojan Trl 42141 270-629-5505
Warren Cunningham, prin. Fax 629-5504

Glasgow ISD 2,000/PK-12
PO Box 1239 42142 270-651-6757
D. Sean Howard, supt. Fax 651-9791
www.glasgow.kyschools.us
Glasgow HS 500/9-12
1601 Columbia Ave 42141 270-651-8801
Keith Hale, prin. Fax 651-5189
Glasgow MS 500/6-8
105 Scottie Dr 42141 270-651-2256
Scott Jones, prin. Fax 651-3090

Kentucky Tech System
Supt. — See Frankfort
Barren County Area Technology Center Vo/Tech
491 Trojan Trl 42141 270-651-2196
Ashley Bell, prin. Fax 651-2197

Glasgow Christian Academy 200/PK-12
600 Old Cavalry Dr 42141 270-651-7729
Tracy Shaw, prin. Fax 651-6811
PJs College of Cosmetology Post-Sec.
920 Happy Valley Rd 42141 270-651-6553
Southcentral Kentucky Comm Tech College Post-Sec.
129 State Ave 42141 270-651-5373

Glendale, Hardin
Hardin County SD
Supt. — See Elizabethtown
East Hardin MS 700/6-8
129 College St 42740 270-369-7370
Brittany Nickell, prin. Fax 369-6380

Goshen, Oldham, Pop. 900
Oldham County SD
Supt. — See Crestwood
North Oldham HS 1,000/9-12
1815 S Highway 1793 40026 502-228-0158
Craig Wallace, prin. Fax 228-7735
North Oldham MS 800/6-8
1801 S Highway 1793 40026 502-228-9998
Carrie Pitsenberger, prin. Fax 228-0985

Grayson, Carter, Pop. 4,170
Carter County SD 4,700/PK-12
228 S Carol Malone Blvd 41143 606-474-6696
Ronnie Dotson, supt. Fax 474-6125
www.cartercountyschools.org
East Carter County HS 800/9-12
405 Hitchins Rd 41143 606-474-5714
Kelley Moore, prin. Fax 475-9200
East Carter MS 600/6-8
1 Spirit Ln 41143 606-474-5156
Jenny Stark, prin. Fax 474-4027
Other Schools – See Olive Hill

Kentucky Christian University Post-Sec.
100 Academic Pkwy 41143 606-474-3000

Greensburg, Green, Pop. 2,133
Green County SD 1,600/K-12
PO Box 369 42743 270-932-6601
Jim Frank, supt. Fax 932-3624
www.green.kyschools.us
Green County HS 500/9-12
PO Box 227 42743 270-932-6610
Karen Marcum, prin. Fax 932-3214
Green County MS 400/6-8
PO Box 176 42743 270-932-6615
Philip West, prin. Fax 932-7617

Kentucky Tech System
Supt. — See Frankfort
Green County Area Technology Center Vo/Tech
102 Carlisle Ave 42743 270-932-4263
LeeAnn Wall, prin. Fax 932-3072

Greenup, Greenup, Pop. 1,174
Greenup County SD 2,900/K-12
45 Musketeer Dr 41144 606-473-9819
Sherry Horsley, supt. Fax 473-5710
www.greenup.kyschools.us/
Greenup County HS 900/9-12
196 Musketeer Dr 41144 606-473-9812
Jason Smith, prin. Fax 473-7854
Other Schools – See South Shore, Wurtland

Kentucky Tech System
Supt. — See Frankfort
Greenup County Area Technology Center Vo/Tech
146 Musketeer Dr 41144 606-473-9344
Sarah Marth, prin. Fax 473-9177

Greenville, Muhlenberg, Pop. 4,256
Muhlenberg County SD
Supt. — See Powderly
Muhlenberg County Career Alternative HS 100/Alt
3875 State Route 181 N 42345 270-338-5460
Paul Moore, prin. Fax 338-4918
Muhlenberg County Career & Tech Center Vo/Tech
501 Robert Draper Way 42345 270-338-0040
Donna Bumps, prin. Fax 338-2442
Muhlenberg County HS East Campus 700/9-10
2900 State Route 176 42345 270-338-9409
Donna Bumps, prin. Fax 338-9710
Muhlenberg County HS West Campus 700/11-12
501 Robert L Draper Way 42345 270-338-0040
Donna Bumps, prin. Fax 338-2442
Muhlenberg North MS 600/6-8
1000 N Main St 42345 270-338-3550
Jerry Rager, prin. Fax 338-2911
Muhlenberg South MS 500/6-8
200 Pritchett Dr 42345 270-338-4650
Brian Lile, prin. Fax 338-0151
Renaissance Center 50/Alt
203 Airport Rd 42345 270-338-0662
Alex Watkins, prin. Fax 338-2194

Hagerhill, Johnson

Piarist S 100/6-12
PO Box 369 41222 606-789-1967
Rev. Thomas Carroll, prin. Fax 789-1968

Hardinsburg, Breckinridge, Pop. 2,302
Breckinridge County SD 2,800/PK-12
86 Airport Rd 40143 270-756-3000
Janet L. Meeks, supt. Fax 756-6888
www.breck.kyschools.us
Other Schools – See Harned

Harlan, Harlan, Pop. 1,720
Harlan County SD 4,200/PK-12
251 Ball Park Rd 40831 606-573-4330
T. Michael Howard, supt. Fax 573-5767
www.harlan.kyschools.us
Other Schools – See Baxter

Harlan ISD 800/PK-12
420 E Central St 40831 606-573-8700
Charles Morton, supt. Fax 573-8711
www.harlan-ind.k12.ky.us
Harlan MSHS 500/5-12
420 E Central St 40831 606-573-8750
Britt Lawson, prin. Fax 573-8753

Jenny Lea Academy of Cosmetology Post-Sec.
114 N Cumberland Ave 40831 606-573-9817

Harned, Breckinridge
Breckinridge County SD
Supt. — See Hardinsburg
Breckinridge County HS 900/9-12
PO Box 10 40144 270-756-3080
Nick Carter, prin. Fax 756-3090
Breckinridge County MS 600/6-8
PO Box 39 40144 270-756-3060
Jayme Knochel, prin. Fax 756-3061

Kentucky Tech System
Supt. — See Frankfort
Breckinridge County Area Technology Ctr. Vo/Tech
PO Box 68 40144 270-756-2138
Jonathan Bennett, prin. Fax 756-2878

Harrodsburg, Mercer, Pop. 8,110
Kentucky Tech System
Supt. — See Frankfort
Harrodsburg Area Technology Center Vo/Tech
661 Tapp Rd 40330 859-734-9329
Tony Webb, prin. Fax 734-3613

Mercer County SD 2,200/PK-12
530 Perryville St 40330 859-733-7000
Dennis Davis, supt. Fax 733-7004
www.mercer.kyschools.us/
Hughes Jones Harrodsburg Area Tech Ctr Vo/Tech
661 Tapp Rd 40330 859-734-9329
Tony Webb, prin. Fax 734-3613
King MS 700/6-8
937 Moberly Rd 40330 859-733-7060
Terry Gordon, prin. Fax 733-7064
Mercer Central Alternative S 50/Alt
530 Perryville St 40330 859-733-7120
Christopher Souder, dir. Fax 733-7104
Mercer County HS 600/9-12
1124 Moberly Rd 40330 859-733-7160
Malissa Hutchins, prin. Fax 733-7164

Hartford, Ohio, Pop. 2,636
Kentucky Tech System
Supt. — See Frankfort
Ohio County Area Technology Center Vo/Tech
1406 S Main St 42347 270-274-9612
Brad Sisk, prin. Fax 274-9633

Ohio County SD 4,200/PK-12
PO Box 70 42347 270-298-3249
Scott Lewis, supt. Fax 298-3886
www.ohio.kyschools.us/
Ohio County HS 1,100/9-12
1400 S Main St 42347 270-274-3366
Robby Asberry, prin. Fax 274-9482
Ohio County MS 600/7-8
1404 S Main St 42347 270-274-7893
Chip Schrader, prin. Fax 274-7320

Hawesville, Hancock, Pop. 930
Hancock County SD 1,700/PK-12
83 State Route 3543 42348 270-927-6914
Kyle Estes, supt. Fax 927-6916
www.hancock.kyschools.us
Other Schools – See Lewisport

Hazard, Perry, Pop. 4,362
Hazard ISD 900/K-12
705 Main St 41701 606-436-3911
Sandra Johnson, supt. Fax 436-2742
www.hazard.kyschools.us
Hazard HS 300/9-12
157 Bulldog Ln 41701 606-439-1318
Donald Mobelini, prin. Fax 439-2285
Hazard MS 300/5-8
325 School St 41701 606-436-4421
Kevin Combs, prin. Fax 435-0407

Knott County SD
Supt. — See Hindman
Cordia S 200/K-12
6050 Lotts Creek Rd 41701 606-785-4457
Jonathan Mullins, prin. Fax 785-4669

Perry County SD 4,000/PK-12
315 Park Ave 41701 606-439-5814
Jonathan Jett, supt. Fax 439-2512
www.perry.kyschools.us/
Perry County Central HS 900/9-12
305 Park Ave 41701 606-439-5888
Michelle Ritchie, prin. Fax 439-2825
Other Schools – See Buckhorn

Hazard Community & Technical College Post-Sec.
1 Community College Dr 41701 606-436-4282

Hebron, Boone, Pop. 5,808
Boone County SD
Supt. — See Florence
Conner HS 1,300/9-12
3310 Cougar Path 41048 859-334-4400
Tim Hitzfield, prin. Fax 334-4406
Conner MS 1,100/6-8
3300 Cougar Path 41048 859-334-4410
James Brewer, prin. Fax 334-4435

Kentucky Tech System
Supt. — See Frankfort
Boone County Area Technology Center Vo/Tech
3320 Cougar Path 41048 859-689-7855
Laura Williams, prin. Fax 689-7828

Henderson, Henderson, Pop. 28,141
Henderson County SD 7,600/PK-12
1805 2nd St 42420 270-831-5000
Marganna Stanley, supt. Fax 831-5009
www.henderson.kyschools.us
Central Academy 200/Alt
851 Center St 42420 270-831-5100
Anthony Black, prin. Fax 831-5103
Henderson County Area Technology Center Vo/Tech
2424 Zion Rd 42420 270-831-8850
Amanda Lacer, dir. Fax 831-8853
Henderson County HS 1,900/9-12
2424 Zion Rd 42420 270-831-8800
Chad Thompson, prin. Fax 831-8870
Henderson County North MS 900/6-8
1707 2nd St 42420 270-831-5060
Rebecca Johnson, prin. Fax 831-5064
Henderson County South MS 700/6-8
800 S Alves St 42420 270-831-5050
Ryan Reusch, prin. Fax 831-5058

Henderson Community College Post-Sec.
2660 S Green St 42420 270-827-1867
Pat Wilson Beauty College Post-Sec.
326 N Main St 42420 270-826-5195

Hickman, Fulton, Pop. 2,360
Fulton County SD 600/PK-12
2780 Moscow Ave 42050 270-236-3923
Aaron Collins, supt. Fax 236-2184
www.fulton.kyschools.us
Fulton County HS 200/9-12
2740 Moscow Ave 42050 270-236-3904
Ellen Murphy, prin. Fax 236-9004

Kentucky Tech System
Supt. — See Frankfort
Fulton County Area Technology Center Vo/Tech
2720 Moscow Ave 42050 270-236-2517
Terry Sullivan, prin. Fax 236-9395

Highland Heights, Campbell, Pop. 6,806

Northern Kentucky University Post-Sec.
400 Nunn Dr 41099 859-572-5100

Hi Hat, Floyd
Floyd County SD
Supt. — See Prestonsburg
South Floyd MSHS 500/6-12
299 Mt Raider Dr 41636 606-452-9600
Stacy Shannon, prin. Fax 452-2155

Hindman, Knott, Pop. 768
Kentucky Tech System
Supt. — See Frankfort
Knott County Area Technology Center Vo/Tech
1996 Highway 160 S 41822 606-785-5350
Danny Vance, prin. Fax 785-5445

Knott County SD 2,400/PK-12
1156 Hindman Byp 41822 606-785-3153
Kimberly King, supt. Fax 785-0800
www.knott.kyschools.us
Knott County Central HS 600/9-12
76 Patriot Ln 41822 606-785-3166
Bobby Pollard, prin. Fax 785-3169
Other Schools – See Hazard

Hitchins, Carter

Carter Christian Academy 50/PK-12
3547 State Highway 773 41146 606-475-1919
Nikki Lewis, prin. Fax 475-0551

Hodgenville, Larue, Pop. 3,149
LaRue County SD 2,400/PK-12
208 College St 42748 270-358-4111
Sam Sanders, supt. Fax 358-3053
www.larue.kyschools.us
LaRue County HS 700/9-12
925 S Lincoln Blvd 42748 270-358-2210
Kyle Goodlett, prin. Fax 358-9469
LaRue County MS 600/6-8
911 S Lincoln Blvd 42748 270-358-3196
Jason Detre, prin. Fax 358-3946

Hopkinsville, Christian, Pop. 30,860
Christian County SD 6,800/K-12
PO Box 609 42241 270-887-7000
Mary Ann Gemmill, supt. Fax 887-1316
www.christian.kyschools.us
Christian County Alternative Center 50/Alt
440 Lafayette Rd 42240 270-887-7380
Chris Gilkey, prin.
Christian County HS 1,300/9-12
220 Glass Ave 42240 270-887-7050
Chris Bentzel, prin. Fax 887-1294
Christian County MS 600/7-8
215 Glass Ave 42240 270-887-7070
Kevin Crider, prin. Fax 887-1189
Gateway Academy to Innovation Vo/Tech
705 N Elm St 42240 270-887-7030
Penny Knight, prin. Fax 887-1242
Hopkinsville HS 1,100/9-12
430 Koffman Dr 42240 270-887-7110
Todd Marshall, prin. Fax 887-1118
Hopkinsville MS 500/7-8
434 Koffman Dr 42240 270-887-7130
Wendy Duvall, prin. Fax 887-1234
21st Century Academy 100/Alt
210 Glass Ave 42240 270-887-7401
Debbie Upton, coord.

Heritage Christian Academy 500/PK-12
8349 Eagle Way 42240 270-885-2417
Linda Garris, hdmstr. Fax 885-0094
Hopkinsville Community College Post-Sec.
PO Box 2100 42241 270-707-3700
University Heights Academy 400/PK-12
1300 Academy Dr 42240 270-886-0254
Pam Nunn, prin. Fax 886-2716

Horse Cave, Hart, Pop. 2,268
Caverna ISD
Supt. — See Cave City
Caverna HS 200/9-12
2276 S Dixie St 42749 270-773-2828
Brad Phipps, prin. Fax 773-2825
Caverna MS 200/6-8
2278 S Dixie St 42749 270-773-4665
Barry Nesbitt, prin. Fax 773-4668

Hyden, Leslie, Pop. 362
Kentucky Tech System
Supt. — See Frankfort
Leslie County Area Technology Center Vo/Tech
PO Box 902 41749 606-672-2859
Justin Rice, prin. Fax 672-4943

Leslie County SD 1,900/PK-12
PO Box 949 41749 606-672-2397
Anthony Little, supt. Fax 672-4224
www.leslie.kyschools.us
Leslie County HS 500/9-12
PO Box 970 41749 606-672-2337
Robert Roark, prin. Fax 672-2858

Frontier Nursing University Post-Sec.
PO Box 528 41749 606-672-2312

Independence, Kenton, Pop. 24,387
Kenton County SD
Supt. — See Fort Wright
Kenton HS 1,700/9-12
11132 Madison Pike 41051 859-960-0100
John Popham, prin. Fax 960-0360
Twenhofel MS 800/6-8
11846 Taylor Mill Rd 41051 859-356-5559
Shannon Gross, prin. Fax 356-1137

Community Christian Academy 300/PK-12
11875 Taylor Mill Rd 41051 859-356-7990
Tara Bates, prin. Fax 356-7991

Inez, Martin, Pop. 715
Kentucky Tech System
Supt. — See Frankfort
Martin County Area Technology Center Vo/Tech
7900 Highway 645 41224 606-298-3879
Martha Williams, prin. Fax 298-7240

Martin County SD 2,300/PK-12
PO Box 366 41224 606-298-3572
Larry James, supt. Fax 298-4427
www.martin.kyschools.us
Clark HS 600/9-12
388 Cardinal Ln 41224 606-298-3591
Lon Laney, prin. Fax 298-5148
Other Schools – See Warfield

Irvine, Estill, Pop. 2,691
Estill County SD 2,500/PK-12
PO Box 930 40336 606-723-2181
Jeff Saylor, supt. Fax 723-6029
www.estill.kyschools.us/
Estill County HS 700/9-12
397 Engineer Rd 40336 606-723-3537
Chris Winkler, prin. Fax 723-4894
Estill County MS 500/6-8
51 Patriot Dr 40336 606-723-5136
Tim Burkhart, prin. Fax 723-2041

Jackson, Breathitt, Pop. 2,211
Breathitt County SD 2,100/PK-12
PO Box 750 41339 606-666-2491
David Gibson, supt. Fax 666-2493
www.breathitt.kyschools.us
Breathitt County HS 600/9-12
2307 Bobcat Ln 41339 606-666-7511
Derek McKnight, prin. Fax 666-7765
Cadet Leadership and Educ Alternative 50/Alt
2665 Highway 30 W 41339 606-295-2267
Dean Smith, lead tchr. Fax 295-2274
Sebastian MS 300/7-8
244 L B J Rd 41339 606-666-8894
Reggie Hamilton, prin. Fax 666-5336

Jackson ISD 400/PK-12
940 Highland Ave 41339 606-666-4979
Lonnie Morris, supt. Fax 666-4350
www.jacksonind.kyschools.us
Jackson City S 400/PK-12
940 Highland Ave 41339 606-666-5164
James Yount, prin. Fax 666-2555

Kentucky Tech System
Supt. — See Frankfort
Breathitt County Area Technology Center Vo/Tech
2303 Bobcat Ln 41339 606-666-5153
Joe Mayabb, prin. Fax 666-5394

Mt. Carmel S 100/K-12
75 Mill Creek Lawson Rd 41339 606-666-5008
David Munson, head sch Fax 666-4612
Oakdale Christian Academy 50/7-12
5801 Beattyville Rd 41339 606-666-5422
Laura Mead, prin. Fax 666-5422

Jamestown, Russell, Pop. 1,780
Russell County SD 3,100/PK-12
404 S Main St 42629 270-343-3191
Michael Ford, supt. Fax 343-3072
www.russell.kyschools.us
Other Schools – See Russell Springs

Jeffersontown, Jefferson, Pop. 25,990
Jefferson County SD
Supt. — See Louisville
Jeffersontown HS Magnet Career Academy 1,400/9-12
9600 Old Six Mile Ln 40299 502-485-8275
Matt Kingsley, prin. Fax 313-3480

Jenkins, Letcher, Pop. 2,198
Jenkins ISD 600/PK-12
PO Box 74 41537 606-832-2183
Mike Genton, supt. Fax 832-2181
www.jenkins.kyschools.us
Jenkins MSHS 300/6-12
269 Old Highway 3086 41537 606-832-2184
Eddie Whitaker, prin. Fax 832-4283

La Grange, Oldham, Pop. 7,910
Oldham County SD
Supt. — See Crestwood
Buckner Alternative HS 50/Alt
1350 N Highway 393 40031 502-222-3767
Beth Carter, prin. Fax 222-3769
Oldham County HS 1,500/9-12
1150 N Highway 393 40031 502-222-9461
Dr. Angela Newcomb Ph.D., prin. Fax 222-0558
Oldham County MS 800/6-8
4305 Brown Blvd 40031 502-222-1451
Chris Kraft, prin. Fax 222-5178

Lancaster, Garrard, Pop. 3,397
Garrard County SD 2,700/PK-12
322 W Maple Ave 40444 859-792-3018
Corey Keith, supt. Fax 792-4733
www.garrard.kyschools.us
Garrard County HS 700/9-12
599 Industry Rd 40444 859-792-2146
Kalem Gresham, prin. Fax 792-4352
Garrard MS 600/6-8
304 W Maple Ave 40444 859-792-2108
Andrew Pickerill, prin. Fax 792-9618

Kentucky Tech System
Supt. — See Frankfort
Garrard County Area Technology Center Vo/Tech
306 W Maple Ave 40444 859-792-2144
Troy Watts, prin. Fax 792-4058

Lawrenceburg, Anderson, Pop. 10,349
Anderson County SD 3,900/PK-12
1160 Bypass N 40342 502-839-3406
Sheila Mitchell, supt. Fax 839-2501
www.anderson.kyschools.us
Anderson County HS 1,200/9-12
1 Bearcat Dr 40342 502-839-5118
Chris Glass, prin. Fax 839-3486
Anderson County MS 800/6-8
1 Mustang Trl 40342 502-839-9261
Jeanna Rose, prin. Fax 839-2534

Christian Academy of Lawrenceburg 100/PK-12
126 N Main St 40342 502-839-9992
Sandra Bowman, prin. Fax 839-3728

Lebanon, Marion, Pop. 5,374
Kentucky Tech System
Supt. — See Frankfort
Marion County Area Technology Center Vo/Tech
721 E Main St 40033 270-692-3155
Christina McRay, prin. Fax 692-1357

Marion County SD 3,200/PK-12
755 E Main St 40033 270-692-3721
Taylora Schlosser, supt. Fax 692-1899
www.marion.kyschools.us
Lebanon MS 400/6-8
200 Corporate Dr 40033 270-692-3441
Christina McRay, prin. Fax 692-0266
Marion County HS 900/9-12
735 E Main St 40033 270-692-6066
Tom Brown, prin. Fax 692-6248
St. Charles MS 300/6-8
1155 Highway 327 40033 270-692-4578
Buffy Mann, prin. Fax 692-1176
Spalding Academy 50/Alt
721 E Main St 40033 270-692-0690
Eric King, dir. Fax 692-1357

Leitchfield, Grayson, Pop. 6,624
Grayson County SD 4,400/PK-12
PO Box 4009 42755 270-259-4011
Doug Robinson, supt. Fax 259-4756
www.graysoncountyschools.com
Grayson County Alternative S 50/Alt
340 School House Rd 42754 270-259-2800
Kelly Shawn Majors, dir. Fax 259-2802
Grayson County HS 1,200/9-12
340 School House Rd 42754 270-259-4078
Todd Johnston, prin. Fax 259-6131
Grayson County MS 1,000/6-8
726 John Hill Taylor Dr 42754 270-259-4175
Jim Blain, prin. Fax 259-5875
Grayson County Technology Center Vo/Tech
252 School House Rd 42754 270-259-3195
Cynthia Smith, dir. Fax 259-8082

Lewisport, Hancock, Pop. 1,650
Hancock County SD
Supt. — See Hawesville
Hancock County HS 500/9-12
80 State Route 271 S 42351 270-927-6953
Rick Lasley, prin. Fax 927-8677
Hancock County MS 400/6-8
100 State Route 271 S 42351 270-927-6255
Traci Sanders, prin. Fax 927-9895

Lexington, Fayette, Pop. 288,987
Fayette County SD 40,600/PK-12
1126 Russell Cave Rd 40505 859-381-4100
Emmanuel Caulk, supt. Fax 381-4303
www.fcps.net
Beaumont MS 1,100/6-8
2080 Georgian Way 40504 859-381-3094
Kate McAnelly, prin. Fax 381-3109
Bryan Station HS 1,800/9-12
201 Eastin Rd 40505 859-381-3308
James McMillin, prin. Fax 381-4939
Bryan Station MS 600/6-8
1865 Wickland Dr 40505 859-381-3288
Cecil Combs, prin. Fax 381-3292
Clark MS 900/6-8
3341 Clays Mill Rd 40503 859-381-3036
Jennifer Kendall, prin. Fax 381-3037
Clay HS 2,300/9-12
2100 Fontaine Rd 40502 859-381-3423
Paul Little, prin. Fax 381-3430
Crawford MS 400/6-8
1813 Charleston Dr 40505 859-381-3370
Mike Jones, prin. Fax 381-3378
Douglass HS 9-12
2000 Winchester Rd 40509 859-381-4233
Lester Diaz, prin.
Dunbar HS 2,200/9-12
1600 Man O War Blvd 40513 859-381-3546
Betsy Rains, prin. Fax 381-3560
Eastside Technical Center Vo/Tech
2208 Liberty Rd 40509 859-381-3740
Wade Stanfield, prin. Fax 381-3747
Hayes MS 1,100/6-8
260 Richardson Pl 40509 859-381-4920
Dave Hoskins, prin. Fax 381-4937
King Academy for Excellence 100/Alt
2200 Liberty Rd 40509 859-381-4040
Mark Sellers, dir. Fax 381-4031
Lafayette HS 2,000/9-12
401 Reed Ln 40503 859-381-3474
Bryne Jacobs, prin. Fax 381-3487
Learning Center at Linlee 200/Alt
475 Price Rd 40508 859-381-0597
Christopher Salyers, prin. Fax 246-1135
Leestown MS 700/6-8
2010 Leestown Rd 40511 859-381-3181
Cynthia Lawson, prin. Fax 381-3180
Lexington Traditional Magnet S 600/6-8
350 N Limestone 40508 859-381-3192
Larry Caudill, prin. Fax 381-3199
Locust Trace AgriScience Center Vo/Tech
3591 Leestown Rd 40511 859-381-3990
Anne DeMott, prin. Fax 381-3989
Morton MS 800/6-8
1225 Tates Creek Rd 40502 859-381-3533
Ronda Runyon, prin. Fax 381-3536
Opportunity Middle College 100/11-12
1126 Russell Cave Rd 40505 859-246-6379
Frank LaBoone, prin. Fax 246-6889
School for Creative and Performing Arts 300/4-8
400 Lafayette Pkwy 40503 859-381-3332
Beth Randolph, prin. Fax 381-3334
Southern MS 600/6-8
400 Wilson Downing Rd 40517 859-381-3582
Frank Coffey, prin. Fax 381-3588
Southside Technical Center Vo/Tech
1800 Harrodsburg Rd 40504 859-381-3603
Daryn Morris, prin. Fax 381-3807
Stables 50/Alt
4089 Iron Works Pike 40511 859-333-5827
Racher Baker, dir. Fax 381-4312
STEAM Academy 100/9-12
123 E Sixth St 40508 859-381-3033
Tina Stevenson, dir. Fax 381-3059
Tates Creek HS 1,800/9-12
1111 Centre Pkwy 40517 859-381-3620
Sam Meaux, prin. Fax 381-3635
Tates Creek MS 1,000/6-8
1105 Centre Pkwy 40517 859-381-3052
Eric Thornsbury, prin. Fax 381-3053
Winburn MS 600/6-8
1060 Winburn Dr 40511 859-381-3967
Whitney Allison, prin. Fax 381-3971
Woodson Academy 100/Alt
1813 Charleston Dr 40505 859-381-3933
Jaynae Boateng, dir. Fax 381-4792

Blue Grass Baptist S 200/PK-12
3743 Red River Dr 40517 859-272-1217
Bluegrass Community & Technical College Post-Sec.
470 Cooper Dr 40506 859-246-6200
Employment Solutions Coll for Tech Educ Post-Sec.
1165 Centre Pkwy Ste 120 40517 859-272-5225
Kaufman Beauty School Post-Sec.
701 E High St 40502 859-266-0693
Lexington Catholic HS 800/9-12
2250 Clays Mill Rd 40503 859-277-7183
Dr. Steve Angelucci, pres. Fax 276-5086
Lexington Christian Academy 1,600/PK-12
450 W Reynolds Rd 40503 859-422-5700
Rick Burslem, hdmstr. Fax 223-3769
Lexington Junior Academy 50/K-10
968 Lane Allen Rd 40504 859-278-0295
Lexington Theological Seminary Post-Sec.
230 Lexington Green Cir 300 40503 859-252-0361
MedTech College Post-Sec.
1648 McGrathiana Pkwy # 200 40511 859-410-2110
Montessori HS 50/9-12
620 S Broadway 40508 859-455-8064
National College Post-Sec.
2376 Sir Barton Way 40509 859-253-0621
St. Joseph's Hospital Post-Sec.
1 Saint Joseph Dr 40504 859-278-3436
Sayre S 500/PK-12
194 N Limestone 40507 859-254-1361
Stephen Manella, head sch Fax 231-0508
Spencerian College Post-Sec.
1575 Winchester Rd 40505 859-223-9608
Strayer University Post-Sec.
220 Lexington Green Cir 550 40503 859-971-4400
Sullivan University Post-Sec.
2355 Harrodsburg Rd 40504 859-276-4357
Transylvania University Post-Sec.
300 N Broadway 40508 859-233-8300
Trinity Christian Academy 400/PK-12
3900 Rapid Run Dr 40515 859-271-0079
University of Kentucky 40506 Post-Sec.
859-257-9000
Univ. of Kentucky Chandler Medical Ctr. Post-Sec.
103 Administration Plz A311 40536 859-323-5126

Liberty, Casey, Pop. 2,153
Casey County SD 2,300/PK-12
1922 N US 127 42539 606-787-6941
Marion Sowders, supt. Fax 787-5231
www.casey.kyschools.us/
Casey County HS 700/9-12
1841 E KY 70 42539 606-787-6151
Joshua Blevins, prin. Fax 787-8654
Casey County MS 400/7-8
1673 E KY 70 42539 606-787-6769
Jeff Emerson, prin. Fax 787-5337

Kentucky Tech System
Supt. — See Frankfort
Casey County Area Technology Center Vo/Tech
1723 E KY 70 42539 606-787-6241
Carmela Clark, prin. Fax 787-6243

Lick Creek, Pike, Pop. 221
Pike County SD
Supt. — See Pikeville
East Ridge HS 500/9-12
19471 Lick Mountain Rd 41540 606-835-2811
Kevin Justice, prin. Fax 835-2899

London, Laurel, Pop. 7,883
Laurel County SD 9,200/PK-12
718 N Main St 40741 606-862-4600
Doug Bennett Ed.D., supt. Fax 862-4601
www.laurel.k12.ky.us
Laurel County Center for Innovation Alt
1100 E 4th St 40741 606-862-5580
James Davis, prin.
McDaniel Learning Center 50/Alt
275 S Laurel Rd 40744 606-862-4781
Jeremy Kidd, prin. Fax 862-4782
North Laurel HS 1,400/9-12
1300 E Hal Rogers Pkwy 40741 606-862-4699
Michael Black, prin. Fax 862-4701
North Laurel MS 1,100/6-8
101 Johnson Rd 40741 606-862-4715
Steve Morris, prin. Fax 862-4717
South Laurel HS 1,200/9-12
201 S Laurel Rd 40744 606-862-4727
Harmon Hodge, prin. Fax 862-4728

South Laurel MS 1,100/6-8
223 S Laurel Rd 40744 606-862-4745
Jeffrey Reed, prin. Fax 862-4746

Lost Creek, Breathitt

Riverside Christian S 50/K-12
114 Riverside School Rd 41348 606-666-2359
Meg Plummer, prin. Fax 666-5211

Louisa, Lawrence, Pop. 2,448
Lawrence County SD 2,500/PK-12
50 Bulldog Ln 41230 606-638-9671
Robbie Fletcher, supt. Fax 638-0128
www.lawrence.kyschools.us
Lawrence County HS 600/9-12
100 Bulldog Ln 41230 606-638-9676
Christy Moore, prin. Fax 638-3227
Louisa MS 400/6-8
9 Bulldog Ln 41230 606-638-4090
Joe Cecil, prin. Fax 638-4865

Louisville, Jefferson, Pop. 248,762
Jefferson County SD 96,700/PK-12
PO Box 34020 40232 502-485-3011
Dr. Donna Hargens, supt. Fax 485-3991
www.jefferson.kyschools.us
Academy @ Shawnee 500/6-12
4001 Herman St 40212 502-485-8326
Venita Benboe, prin. Fax 313-3531
Atherton HS 1,300/9-12
3000 Dundee Rd 40205 502-485-8202
Richard Guetig, prin. Fax 313-3407
Ballard HS 2,000/9-12
6000 Brownsboro Rd 40222 502-485-8206
Staci Eddleman, prin. Fax 313-3411
Barret Traditional MS 600/6-8
2561 Grinstead Dr 40206 502-485-8207
Tom Wortham, prin. Fax 313-3412
Breckinridge Metropolitan HS 100/Alt
1128 E Broadway 40204 502-485-6678
Stuart Cripe, prin. Fax 313-3423
Brown S 700/K-12
546 S 1st St 40202 502-485-8216
Angela Parsons, prin. Fax 313-3404
Butler Traditional HS 1,700/9-12
2222 Crums Ln 40216 502-485-8220
William Allen, prin. Fax 313-3425
Carrithers MS 500/6-8
4320 Billtown Rd 40299 502-485-8224
Marcela Williams, prin. Fax 313-3429
Central HS Magnet Career Academy 1,100/9-12
1130 W Chestnut St 40203 502-485-8226
Raymond Green, prin. Fax 313-3430
Conway MS 900/6-8
6300 Terry Rd 40258 502-485-8233
Gregory Fehr, prin. Fax 313-3438
Daniels Academy 100/Alt
1960 Bashford Manor Ln 40218 502-485-8316
Don Dillard, prin. Fax 313-3506
Doss HS Magnet Career Academy 1,000/9-12
7601 Saint Andrews Church 40214 502-485-8239
Marty Pollio, prin. Fax 313-3445
DuPont Manual HS 1,900/9-12
120 W Lee St 40208 502-485-8241
Jerry Mayes, prin. Fax 313-3448
DuValle Education Center 300/Alt
3610 Bohne Ave 40211 502-485-3558
Brian Clark, admin. Fax 485-6790
Farnsley MS 1,200/6-8
3400 Lees Ln 40216 502-485-8242
Linda Hudson, prin. Fax 313-3456
Highland MS 1,200/6-8
1700 Norris Pl 40205 502-485-8266
Thomas Aberli, prin. Fax 313-3472
Iroquois HS Magnet Career Academy 1,100/9-12
4615 Taylor Blvd 40215 502-485-8269
Clay Holbrook, prin. Fax 313-3475
Jefferson County HS 300/Alt
900 S Floyd St 40203 502-485-3173
Jerry Keepers, prin. Fax 485-3671
Jefferson County Traditional MS 900/6-8
1418 Morton Ave 40204 502-485-8272
Teri Reed, prin. Fax 313-3477
Jefferson MS 900/6-8
1501 Rangeland Rd 40219 502-485-8273
Kimberly Gregory, prin. Fax 313-3541
Johnson Traditional MS 900/6-8
2509 Wilson Ave 40210 502-485-8277
Beverly Johnson, prin. Fax 313-3481
Kammerer MS 1,100/6-8
7315 Wesboro Rd 40222 502-485-8279
David Armour, prin. Fax 313-3483
Kennedy Metro MS 100/Alt
4515 Taylorsville Rd 40220 502-485-6950
Kevin Nix, prin. Fax 313-3484
Knight MS 400/6-8
9803 Blue Lick Rd 40229 502-485-8287
Catherine Gibbs, prin. Fax 313-3491
Lassiter MS 900/6-8
8200 Candleworth Dr 40214 502-485-8288
Jonathan Cesler, prin. Fax 313-3492
Liberty HS 300/Alt
3307 E Indian Trl 40213 502-485-7100
Iman Talaat, prin. Fax 313-3495
Louisville Male HS 1,800/9-12
4409 Preston Hwy 40213 502-485-8292
Jim Jury, prin. Fax 313-3499
Meyzeek MS 1,100/6-8
828 S Jackson St 40203 502-485-8299
Chris Burba, prin. Fax 313-3503
Moore Traditional MSHS 1,900/6-12
6415 Outer Loop 40228 502-485-8304
Rob Fulk, prin. Fax 313-3508
Newburg MS 1,000/6-8
4901 Exeter Ave 40218 502-485-8306
Nicole Adell, prin. Fax 313-3509
Noe MS 1,300/6-8
121 W Lee St 40208 502-485-8307
Jennifer Cave, prin. Fax 313-3511
Olmsted Academy North 600/6-8
4530 Bellevue Ave 40215 502-485-8331
Ryan Rodosky, prin. Fax 313-3514
Olmsted Academy South 700/6-8
5650 Southern Pkwy 40214 502-485-8270
Angela Allen, prin. Fax 313-3515
Phoenix S of Discovery 200/Alt
3741 Pulliam Dr 40218 502-485-7700
Ken Moeller, prin. Fax 313-3518
Pleasure Ridge Park HS Magnet Academy 1,800/9-12
5901 Greenwood Rd 40258 502-485-8311
Kimberly Salyer, prin. Fax 313-3516
Ramsey MS 900/6-8
6409 Gellhaus Ln 40299 502-485-8391
Darryl Farmer, prin. Fax 313-3520
Seneca HS Magnet Career Academy 1,500/9-12
3510 Goldsmith Ln 40220 502-485-8323
Kim Morales, prin. Fax 313-3529
Southern HS Magnet Career Academy 1,100/9-12
8620 Preston Hwy 40219 502-485-8330
Bryce Hibbard, prin. Fax 313-3535
Waggener Traditional HS 700/9-12
330 S Hubbards Ln 40207 502-485-8340
Sarah Hitchings, prin. Fax 313-3545
Western HS Early College 800/9-12
2501 Rockford Ln 40216 502-485-8344
Michael Newman, prin. Fax 313-3550
Western MS 500/6-8
2201 W Main St 40212 502-485-8345
Kymberly Rice, prin. Fax 313-3551
Westport MS 900/6-8
8100 Westport Rd 40222 502-485-8346
Jodie Zeller, prin. Fax 313-3552
Youth Performing Arts JSHS 7-12
1517 S 2nd St 40208 502-485-8355
Jerry Mayes, prin. Fax 313-3560
Other Schools – See Fairdale, Fern Creek, Jeffersontown, Middletown, Valley Station

Assumption HS 900/9-12
2170 Tyler Ln 40205 502-458-9551
Martha Tedesco, prin. Fax 454-8411
ATA College Post-Sec.
10180 Linn Station Rd #A200 40223 502-371-8383
Bellarmine University Post-Sec.
2001 Newburg Rd 40205 502-272-8131
Beth Haven Christian S 200/PK-12
5515 Johnsontown Rd 40272 502-937-3516
John Baker, head sch Fax 937-3364
Christian Academy of Louisville 1,700/PK-12
700 S English Station Rd 40245 502-244-3225
Tim Greener, supt. Fax 244-1824
Covenant Classical Academy 50/K-12
13902 Factory Ln 40245 502-243-0404
R. Lance Harris, hdmstr.
Daymar College Post-Sec.
4112 Fern Valley Rd 40219 502-495-1040
Daymar College - Online Post-Sec.
3309 Collins Ln 40245 270-926-1188
DeVry University Post-Sec.
10172 Linn Station Rd # 300 40223 502-326-2860
Evangel Christian S 200/K-12
5400 Minor Ln 40219 502-968-7744
Kevin Miller, prin. Fax 400-1906
Galen College of Nursing Post-Sec.
1031 Zorn Ave Ste 400 40207 502-410-6200
Hair Design School Post-Sec.
1049 Bardstown Rd 40204 502-459-8150
Hair Design School Post-Sec.
5120 Dixie Hwy 40216 502-447-0111
Hair Design School Post-Sec.
5314 Bardstown Rd 40291 502-499-0070
Holy Angels Academy 100/K-12
12201 Old Henry Rd 40223 502-254-9440
Joseph Norton, head sch
Holy Cross HS 200/9-12
5144 Dixie Hwy 40216 502-447-4363
Danielle Wiegandt, prin. Fax 448-1062
Immaculata Classical Academy PK-12
6010 Preston Hwy 40219 502-365-3545
Justin Fout, prin.
Jefferson Community & Technical College Post-Sec.
109 E Broadway 40202 502-213-5333
Kentucky Country Day S 1,000/PK-12
4100 Springdale Rd 40241 502-423-0440
Brad Lyman, head sch Fax 423-0445
Kentucky School for the Blind Post-Sec.
1867 Frankfort Ave 40206 502-897-1583
Louisville Bible College Post-Sec.
PO Box 91046 40291 502-231-5221
Louisville Collegiate S 700/PK-12
2427 Glenmary Ave 40204 502-479-0340
Dr. James Calleroz White, head sch Fax 454-8549
Louisville Jr. Academy 50/PK-12
2988 Newburg Rd 40205 502-452-2965
David Matthews, prin. Fax 742-0829
Louisville Presbyterian Seminary Post-Sec.
1044 Alta Vista Rd 40205 502-895-3411
Mercy Academy 600/9-12
5801 Fegenbush Ln 40228 502-671-2010
Amy Elstone, prin. Fax 491-0661
National College Post-Sec.
4205 Dixie Hwy 40216 502-447-7634
Nativity Academy at St. Boniface 100/6-8
529 E Liberty St 40202 502-855-3300
Thomas Kallay, prin. Fax 562-2192
Paul Mitchell The School Post-Sec.
156 N Hurstbourne Pkwy 40222 502-583-1018
Portland Christian S 200/K-12
8509 Westport Rd 40242 502-429-3727
Jodell Seay, dir. Fax 326-2682
Presentation Academy 300/9-12
861 S 4th St 40203 502-583-5935
Barbara Wine, prin. Fax 583-1342
Sacred Heart Academy 800/9-12
3175 Lexington Rd 40206 502-897-6097
Mary McCoy, prin. Fax 893-0120
Sacred Heart S for the Arts 200/K-12
3105 Lexington Rd 40206 502-897-1816
Dr. Anna Jo Paul, dir. Fax 896-3927
St. Francis DeSales HS 300/9-12
425 W Kenwood Dr 40214 502-368-6519
Anastasia Quirk, prin. Fax 366-6172
St. Francis S 100/PK-12
233 W Broadway 40202 502-736-1000
Alexandra Thurstone, head sch Fax 736-1049
St. Xavier HS 1,400/9-12
1609 Poplar Level Rd 40217 502-637-4712
Francisco Espinosa, prin. Fax 634-2171
Simmons College of Kentucky Post-Sec.
1018 S 7th St 40203 502-776-1443
Southern Baptist Theological Seminary Post-Sec.
2825 Lexington Rd 40280 502-897-4011
Spalding University Post-Sec.
845 S 3rd St 40203 502-585-9911
Spencerian College Post-Sec.
4627 Dixie Hwy 40216 502-447-1000
Sullivan College of Technology & Design Post-Sec.
3901 Atkinson Square Dr 40218 800-844-6528
Sullivan University Post-Sec.
3101 Bardstown Rd 40205 502-456-6505
Trend Setter's Academy of Beauty Culture Post-Sec.
7283 Dixie Hwy 40258 502-937-6816
Trend Setter's Academy of Beauty Culture Post-Sec.
8111 Preston Hwy 40219 502-962-7710
Trinity HS 1,300/9-12
4011 Shelbyville Rd 40207 502-895-9427
Daniel Zoeller, prin. Fax 895-6837
University of Louisville Post-Sec.
2301 S 3rd St 40208 502-852-5555
Valiant Christian Academy 100/PK-12
5627 New Cut Rd 40214 502-368-0080
Kristine Salvo, admin. Fax 361-5179
Valor Traditional Academy 100/K-12
11501 Schlatter Rd 40291 502-239-3345
Walden S 200/K-12
4238 Westport Rd 40207 502-893-0433
Maris Elder, head sch Fax 895-8668
Whitefield Academy 700/PK-12
7711 Fegenbush Ln 40228 502-239-2509
Gary Mounce, head sch Fax 239-3144

Ludlow, Kenton, Pop. 4,360
Ludlow ISD 900/PK-12
525 Elm St 41016 859-261-8210
Mike Borchers, supt. Fax 291-6811
www.ludlow.kyschools.us/
Ludlow HS 400/7-12
515 Elm St 41016 859-261-8211
Travis Caudill, prin. Fax 655-7536

Mc Kee, Jackson, Pop. 793
Jackson County SD 2,200/PK-12
3331 Hwy 421 S 40447 606-287-7181
Mike Smith, supt. Fax 287-8469
www.jackson.kyschools.us
Jackson County HS 600/9-12
PO Box 427 40447 606-287-7155
Keith Hays, prin. Fax 287-2123
Jackson County MS 500/6-8
PO Box 1329 40447 606-287-8351
Stephen Gabbard, prin. Fax 287-8360

Kentucky Tech System
Supt. — See Frankfort
Jackson County Area Technology Center Vo/Tech
PO Box 1509 40447 606-287-2163
Alonzo Moore, prin. Fax 287-7538

Madisonville, Hopkins, Pop. 19,131
Hopkins County SD 7,000/PK-12
320 S Seminary St 42431 270-825-6000
Deanna D. Ashby, supt. Fax 825-6072
www.hopkins.kyschools.us
Adolescent Day Treatment Center 50/Alt
110 Sugg St 42431 270-825-6059
Andy Belcher, prin. Fax 825-6053
Browning Springs MS 400/6-8
357 W Arch St 42431 270-825-6006
Jason Clark, prin. Fax 825-6009
Hophins County Career & Technology Ctr. Vo/Tech
1775 Patriot Dr 42431 270-825-6122
Pam Todd, prin.
Hopkins County Academy 50/Alt
75 S Railroad St 42431 270-825-6122
Andy Belcher, prin. Fax 906-0191
Hopkins County Central HS 900/9-12
6625 Hopkinsville Rd 42431 270-825-6133
Rick Snodgrass, prin. Fax 825-6135
Madison MS 600/6-8
510 Brown Rd 42431 270-825-6160
Timothy Roy, prin. Fax 825-6016
Madisonville North Hopkins HS 1,100/9-12
4515 Hanson Rd 42431 270-825-6017
Tommy Ransom, prin. Fax 825-6045
Other Schools – See Nortonville

Daymar College Post-Sec.
1105 National Mine Rd 42431 270-643-0312
Madisonville Community College Post-Sec.
2000 College Dr 42431 270-821-2250

Manchester, Clay, Pop. 1,245
Clay County SD 3,400/PK-12
128 Richmond Rd 40962 606-598-2168
William Sexton, supt. Fax 598-7829
www.clay.kyschools.us
Clay County HS 900/9-12
415 Clay County High Rd 40962 606-598-3737
Mike Gregory, prin. Fax 598-8976
Clay County MS 500/7-8
239 Richmond Rd 40962 606-598-1810
Steven Burchfield, prin. Fax 598-1230

Horse Creek Learning Center Alt S 50/Alt
239 Richmond Rd 40962 606-598-1601
James Hollin, dir. Fax 599-0991

Kentucky Tech System
Supt. — See Frankfort
Clay County Area Technology Center Vo/Tech
1097 N Highway 11 40962 606-598-2194
Anthony Young, prin. Fax 598-4201

Southeast School of Cosmetology Post-Sec.
PO Box 493 40962 606-598-7901

Marion, Crittenden, Pop. 3,006
Crittenden County SD 1,200/K-12
601 W Elm St 42064 270-965-3525
Vince Clark, supt. Fax 965-9064
www.crittenden.kyschools.us/
Crittenden County HS 400/9-12
519 1/2 W Gum St 42064 270-965-2248
Curtis Brown, prin. Fax 965-2797
Crittenden County MS 300/6-8
519 W Gum St 42064 270-965-5221
Tom Radivonyk, prin. Fax 965-5082

Martin, Floyd, Pop. 630
Floyd County SD
Supt. — See Prestonsburg
Renaissance Learning Center 100/Alt
PO Box 1390 41649 606-285-3634
Susan Damron, contact Fax 285-3031

Kentucky Tech System
Supt. — See Frankfort
Floyd County Area Technology Center Vo/Tech
1024 KY Route 122 41649 606-285-3088
Lenville Martin, prin. Fax 285-0274

Mayfield, Graves, Pop. 9,719
Graves County SD 4,300/PK-12
2290 State Route 121 N 42066 270-328-2656
Kim Dublin, supt. Fax 328-1561
www.graves.kyschools.us
Gateway Academy HS 50/Alt
100 E Lockridge St 42066 270-328-4979
Donna Crouch, prin. Fax 247-0051
Graves County HS 1,400/9-12
1220 Eagles Way 42066 270-674-6242
Matt Madding, prin. Fax 247-8540
Graves County MS 800/7-8
625 Jimtown Rd 42066 270-328-3670
Jonathan Miller, prin. Fax 251-3693

Kentucky Tech System
Supt. — See Frankfort
Mayfield/Graves County Area Tech Center Vo/Tech
710 Douthitt St 42066 270-247-4710
Michael Miller, prin. Fax 247-4721

Mayfield ISD 1,600/PK-12
914 E College St 42066 270-247-3868
Joe Henderson, supt. Fax 247-3854
www.mayfield.kyschools.us
Mayfield HS 400/9-12
700 Douthitt St 42066 270-247-4461
Billy Edwards, prin. Fax 247-9624
Mayfield MS 300/6-8
112 W College St 42066 270-247-7521
Kim Reed, prin. Fax 247-8297

Mid-Continent University Post-Sec.
99 E Powell Rd 42066 270-247-8521
Northside Baptist Christian S 100/PK-12
403 State Route 940 42066 270-705-2386
Emily Burge, prin. Fax 705-2386

Maysville, Mason, Pop. 8,803
Kentucky Tech System
Supt. — See Frankfort
Mason County Area Technology Center Vo/Tech
646 Kenton Station Rd 41056 606-759-7101
Jeremy McCloud, prin. Fax 759-7568

Mason County SD 2,800/PK-12
PO Box 130 41056 606-564-5563
Rick Ross, supt. Fax 564-5392
www.masoncoschools.com
Mason County HS 800/9-12
1320 US Highway 68 41056 606-564-3393
Chris O'Hearn, prin. Fax 564-5360
Mason County MS 600/6-8
420 Chenault Dr 41056 606-564-6748
Justin Moore, prin. Fax 564-5958
Mason County STEAM Academy 9-12
725 Clarks Run Rd 41056 606-759-0398
Chris O'Hearn, prin.

Maysville Community & Technical College Post-Sec.
1755 US Highway 68 41056 606-759-7141
St. Patrick S 300/PK-12
318 Limestone St 41056 606-564-5949
Fr. Michael Comer, prin. Fax 564-8795

Middlesboro, Bell, Pop. 10,068
Middlesboro ISD 1,300/PK-12
PO Box 959 40965 606-242-8800
Steve Martin, supt. Fax 242-8805
www.mboro.kyschools.us
Middlesboro HS 400/9-12
4404 W Cumberland Ave 40965 606-242-8820
Bob Bennett, prin. Fax 242-8825
Middlesboro MS 400/5-8
4400 W Cumberland Ave 40965 606-242-8880
William Jones, prin. Fax 242-8885

Middletown, Jefferson, Pop. 7,092
Jefferson County SD
Supt. — See Louisville
Crosby MS 1,400/6-8
303 Gatehouse Ln 40243 502-485-8235
Michael Kelly, prin. Fax 313-3440
Eastern HS 2,000/9-12
12400 Old Shelbyville Rd 40243 502-485-8243
Lana Kaelin, prin. Fax 313-3449

Midway, Woodford, Pop. 1,609

Midway College Post-Sec.
512 E Stephens St 40347 800-755-0031

Monticello, Wayne, Pop. 6,123
Kentucky Tech System
Supt. — See Frankfort
Wayne County Area Technology Center Vo/Tech
150 Cardinal Way 42633 606-348-8424
John Kinnett, prin. Fax 348-5090

Wayne County SD 2,900/PK-12
1025 S Main St 42633 606-348-8484
Wayne Roberts, supt. Fax 348-0734
www.wayne.kyschools.us
Lake Cumberland Youth Development Center 50/Alt
9000 Highway 1546 42633 606-348-4201
Tillie Slagle, lead tchr. Fax 348-7501
Otter Creek Academy 50/Alt
1441 Old Bethel Church Rd 42633 606-343-0203
Peggy Shearer, prin. Fax 343-0301
Wayne County HS 1,000/9-12
2 Kenny Davis Blvd 42633 606-348-5575
Justin Alley, prin. Fax 348-3458
Wayne County MS 700/6-8
95 Champion Dr 42633 606-348-6691
Melissa Gossage, prin. Fax 348-5495

Morehead, Rowan, Pop. 6,756
Rowan County SD 3,400/PK-12
121 E 2nd St 40351 606-784-8928
Marvin Moore, supt. Fax 783-1011
www.rowan.kyschools.us/
Bluegrass Discovery Academy 50/Alt
415 W Sun St 40351 606-780-9992
Dr. Ray Ginter, prin. Fax 784-6167
Morehead Youth Development Center 50/Alt
495 Forest Hills Dr 40351 606-783-8575
Paula Stafford, prin. Fax 783-8572
Rowan County MS 700/6-8
555 Viking Dr 40351 606-784-8911
Jay Padula, prin. Fax 784-5579
Rowan County SHS 900/9-12
499 Viking Dr 40351 606-784-8956
Dr. Ray Ginter, prin. Fax 784-1067

Lakeside Christian Academy 200/PK-12
2535 US Highway 60 W 40351 606-784-2751
T. W. Webb, admin. Fax 784-0056
Morehead State University Post-Sec.
150 University Blvd 40351 800-585-6781

Morganfield, Union, Pop. 3,234
Union County SD 2,400/PK-12
510 S Mart St 42437 270-389-1694
Patricia Sheffer, supt. Fax 389-9806
www.union.kyschools.us
Clements Victory Technical HS Vo/Tech
2302 US Highway 60 E 42437 270-389-2419
Holly Keeney, prin. Fax 389-9383
Union County HS 700/9-12
4464 US Highway 60 W 42437 270-389-1454
Evan Jackson, prin. Fax 389-2715
Union County Learning Academy 50/Alt
4464 US Highway 60 W 42437 270-389-3553
James Watkins, prin. Fax 389-3554
Union County MS 500/6-8
4465 US Highway 60 W 42437 270-389-0224
Jeremy Roach, prin. Fax 389-0245

Morgantown, Butler, Pop. 2,380
Butler County SD 2,200/PK-12
203 N Tyler St 42261 270-526-5624
Scott Howard, supt. Fax 526-5625
www.butlerschools.net
Butler County HS 600/9-12
1852 S Main St 42261 270-526-2204
Patrick O'Driscoll, prin. Fax 526-2268
Butler County Learning Center 50/Alt
799 Veterans Way 42261 270-526-2264
Fax 526-2305
Butler County MS 500/6-8
PO Box 10 42261 270-526-5647
Tim Freeman, prin. Fax 526-3238

Kentucky Tech System
Supt. — See Frankfort
Butler County Area Technology Center Vo/Tech
178 Academic Way Ste 400 42261 270-526-2223
Ray Hammer, prin. Fax 526-2273

Mount Olivet, Robertson, Pop. 297
Robertson County SD 400/PK-12
1762 Sardis Rd 41064 606-724-5431
Sanford Holbrook, supt. Fax 724-5921
school.robertson.k12.ky.us
Robertson County S 400/PK-12
1760 Sardis Rd 41064 606-724-5421
Jamey Johnson, prin. Fax 724-5225

Mount Sterling, Montgomery, Pop. 6,810
Kentucky Tech System
Supt. — See Frankfort
Montgomery County Area Technology Ctr Vo/Tech
682 Woodford Dr 40353 859-498-1103
Melanie Jamison, prin. Fax 498-5960

Montgomery County SD 4,900/PK-12
640 Woodford Dr 40353 859-497-8760
Matthew Thompson, supt. Fax 497-8780
www.montgomery.kyschools.us
McNabb MS 700/7-8
3570 Indian Mound Dr 40353 859-497-8770
Adam Adkins, prin. Fax 497-9683
Montgomery Co. Accelerated Academy 7-12
700 Woodford Dr 40353 859-497-8765
Robert Donaldson, prin.
Montgomery County HS 1,300/9-12
724 Woodford Dr 40353 859-497-8765
Rocky Franz, prin. Fax 497-8705
Sterling S 100/Alt
724 Woodford Dr 40353 859-497-8761
Michael Whitaker, admin. Fax 497-8780

Nu-Tek Academy of Beauty Post-Sec.
153 Evans Ave 40353 859-498-4460

Mount Vernon, Rockcastle, Pop. 2,459
Kentucky Tech System
Supt. — See Frankfort
Rockcastle County Area Technology Center Vo/Tech
1555 Lake Cumberland Rd 40456 606-256-4346
Ralph Baker, prin. Fax 256-4337

Rockcastle County SD 2,900/PK-12
245 Richmond St 40456 606-256-2125
David Pensol, supt. Fax 256-2126
www.rockcastle.kyschools.us
Rockcastle Acad for Academic Achievement 50/Alt
PO Box 1730 40456 606-256-3846
Fax 256-1027
Rockcastle County HS 800/9-12
PO Box 1410 40456 606-256-4816
Jennifer Mattingly, prin. Fax 256-3755
Rockcastle County MS 700/6-8
PO Box 1730 40456 606-256-5118
Marcus Reppert, prin. Fax 256-2622

Mount Washington, Bullitt, Pop. 9,010
Bullitt County SD
Supt. — See Shepherdsville
Bullitt East HS 1,400/9-12
11450 Highway 44 E 40047 502-869-6400
Chris Mason, prin. Fax 538-8368
Eastside MS 600/6-8
6925 Highway 44 E 40047 502-869-5000
Troy Wood, prin. Fax 538-0659
Mt. Washington MS 500/6-8
269 Water St 40047 502-869-5200
Dr. Denise Allen, prin. Fax 538-0703

Munfordville, Hart, Pop. 1,588
Hart County SD 2,300/PK-12
25 Quality St 42765 270-524-2631
Ricky Line, supt. Fax 524-2634
www.hart.kyschools.us
Hart County HS 800/9-12
1014 S Dixie Hwy 42765 270-524-9341
Greg Cecil, prin. Fax 524-3251

Murray, Calloway, Pop. 17,409
Calloway County SD 3,300/PK-12
PO Box 800 42071 270-762-7300
Tres Settle, supt. Fax 762-7310
www.calloway.kyschools.us
Alternative S 50/Alt
2003 College Farm Rd 42071 270-762-7318
Travis Anderson, prin. Fax 762-7429
Calloway County HS 900/9-12
2108 College Farm Rd 42071 270-762-7374
Randy McCallon, prin. Fax 762-7380
Calloway County MS 700/6-8
2112 College Farm Rd 42071 270-762-7355
Amy Turner, prin. Fax 762-7360

Kentucky Tech System
Supt. — See Frankfort
Murray/Calloway County Area Tech Center Vo/Tech
1800 Sycamore St 42071 270-753-1870
James Hicks, prin. Fax 759-9656

Murray ISD 1,500/PK-12
208 S 13th St 42071 270-753-4363
Bob Rogers, supt. Fax 759-4906
www.murray.kyschools.us
Murray HS 400/9-12
501 Doran Rd 42071 270-753-5202
Teresa Speed, prin. Fax 753-8391
Murray MS 600/4-8
801 Main St 42071 270-753-5125
Bob Horne, prin. Fax 753-9039

Ezell's Cosmetology School Post-Sec.
PO Box 1431 42071 270-753-4723
Murray State University Post-Sec.
102 Curris Ctr 42071 800-272-4678

Neon, Letcher, Pop. 749
Letcher County SD
Supt. — See Whitesburg
Fleming Neon MS 200/6-8
PO Box 425 41840 606-855-7864
Ronny Goins, prin. Fax 855-4485

New Castle, Henry, Pop. 887
Henry County SD 2,200/PK-12
326 S Main St 40050 502-845-8600
Tim Abrams, supt. Fax 845-8601
www.henry.kyschools.us
Henry County HS 700/9-12
1120 Eminence Rd 40050 502-845-8670
Shannon Sageser, prin. Fax 845-8671
Henry County MS 500/6-8
1124 Eminence Rd 40050 502-845-8660
Lucia Hughes, prin. Fax 845-8661

Newport, Campbell, Pop. 14,797
Newport ISD 1,800/PK-12
301 W 8th St 41071 859-292-3004
Kelly Middleton, supt. Fax 292-3073
www.newportwildcats.org/
Newport HS 400/9-12
900 E 6th St 41071 859-292-3023
Kyle Niederman, prin. Fax 292-8340
Newport MS 400/6-8
95 W 9th St 41071 859-292-3017
Tim Grayson, prin. Fax 292-3049
Newport Adult Learning Center Adult
30 W 8th St 41071 859-292-3056
Nichole Braun, coord. Fax 292-3099

Brighton Center for Employment Training Post-Sec.
601 Washington Ave Ste 140 41071 859-491-8303
Holy Trinity JHS 50/6-8
840 Washington Ave 41071 859-292-0487
James Hubbard, prin. Fax 431-8745
Newport Central Catholic HS 400/9-12
13 Carothers Rd 41071 859-292-0001
Ron Dawn, prin. Fax 292-0656

Nicholasville, Jessamine, Pop. 27,423
Jessamine County SD 8,100/PK-12
871 Wilmore Rd 40356 859-885-4179
Kathy Fields, supt. Fax 887-4811
www.jessamine.k12.ky.us
East Jessamine HS 1,100/9-12
815 Sulphur Well Pike 40356 859-885-7240
Aaron Etherington, prin. Fax 881-0161
East Jessamine MS 900/6-8
901 Union Mill Rd 40356 859-885-5561
James Botts, prin. Fax 887-1797
West Jessamine HS 1,100/9-12
2101 Wilmore Rd 40356 859-887-2421
Dr. Scott Wells, prin. Fax 887-8854
West Jessamine MS 900/6-8
1400 Wilmore Rd 40356 859-885-2244
Matt Albertson, prin. Fax 885-8078
Jessamine County Adult Education Adult
200 Computrex Dr 40356 859-887-9052
Mary Davis, prin. Fax 881-0521
Other Schools – See Wilmore

Barrett & Company School of Hair Design Post-Sec.
973 Kimberly Sq 40356 859-885-9136

Nortonville, Hopkins, Pop. 1,195
Hopkins County SD
Supt. — See Madisonville
South Hopkins MS 400/6-8
9140 Hopkinsville Rd 42442 270-825-6125
Stuart Fitch, prin. Fax 825-6085

Olive Hill, Carter, Pop. 1,580
Carter County SD
Supt. — See Grayson
Carter County Career & Technical Center Vo/Tech
15 Grahn Rd 41164 606-286-4022
Karen Tackett, prin. Fax 286-6333
West Carter County HS 600/9-12
PO Box 1479 41164 606-286-2481
John Baumgardner, prin. Fax 286-8026
West Carter County MS 500/6-8
150 Warrior Dr 41164 606-286-5354
Ryan Tomolonis, prin. Fax 286-8556

Oneida, Clay, Pop. 406

Oneida Baptist Institute 300/K-12
PO Box 67 40972 606-847-4111

Owensboro, Daviess, Pop. 55,842
Daviess County SD 11,500/PK-12
PO Box 21510 42304 270-852-7000
Owens Saylor, supt. Fax 852-7010
www.daviess.kyschools.us/
Apollo HS 1,300/9-12
2280 Tamarack Rd 42301 270-852-7100
Richard Lasley, prin. Fax 852-7110
Burns MS 800/6-8
4610 Goetz Dr 42301 270-852-7400
Dane Ferguson, prin. Fax 852-7410
College View MS 800/6-8
5061 New Hartford Rd 42303 270-852-7500
Jennifer Crume, prin. Fax 852-7510
Daviess County HS 1,600/9-12
4255 New Hartford Rd 42303 270-852-7300
Matt Mason, prin. Fax 852-7310
Daviess County MS 900/6-8
1415 E 4th St 42303 270-852-7600
Kelly Skeens, prin. Fax 852-7610
Heritage Park HS 100/Alt
3361 Buckland Sq 42301 270-852-7200
Michelle Ruckdeschel, dir. Fax 852-7210

Owensboro ISD 5,100/PK-12
450 Griffith Ave 42301 270-686-1000
Dr. Nicholas Brake, supt. Fax 684-5756
www.owensboro.kyschools.us
Gateway Academy 100/Alt
2401 McConnell Ave 42303 270-686-1120
Melissa Brown, prin. Fax 686-1036
Owensboro HS 1,100/9-12
1800 Frederica St 42301 270-686-1110
John DeLacey, prin. Fax 686-1019
Owensboro MS - North Campus 600/7-8
1300 Booth Ave 42301 270-686-1130
Cheri Smith, prin. Fax 686-1173

Brescia University Post-Sec.
717 Frederica St 42301 270-685-3131
Daymar College Post-Sec.
3361 Buckland Sq 42301 270-926-4040
Kentucky Wesleyan College Post-Sec.
3000 Frederica St 42301 270-926-3111
Mr. Jim's College of Cosmetology Post-Sec.
1240 Carter Rd 42301 270-684-3505
Owensboro Catholic HS 500/9-12
1524 W Parrish Ave 42301 270-684-3215
Gates Settle, prin. Fax 684-7050
Owensboro Catholic MS 200/7-8
2540 Christie Pl 42301 270-683-0480
David Kessler, prin. Fax 683-0495
Owensboro Community & Technical College Post-Sec.
4800 New Hartford Rd 42303 270-686-4400
Owensboro Mercy Health System Post-Sec.
811 E Parrish Ave 42303 270-688-2100

Owenton, Owen, Pop. 1,301
Owen County SD 2,000/PK-12
1600 Highway 22 E 40359 502-484-3934
Dr. Robert Stafford, supt. Fax 484-9095
www.owen.kyschools.us
Bowling MS 600/5-8
2380 Highway 22 E 40359 502-484-5701
Donette Gaines, prin. Fax 484-3044
Owen County HS 500/9-12
2340 Highway 22 E 40359 502-484-5509
Duane Kline, prin. Fax 484-0444

Owingsville, Bath, Pop. 1,507
Bath County SD 2,100/PK-12
405 W Main St 40360 606-674-6314
Harvey Tackett, supt. Fax 674-2647
www.bath.kyschools.us
Bath County HS 600/9-12
645 Chenault Dr 40360 606-674-6325
Paul Prater, prin. Fax 674-9188
Bath County MS 500/6-8
335 W Main St 40360 606-674-8165
John Slone, prin. Fax 674-2676

Paducah, McCracken, Pop. 24,294
Kentucky Tech System
Supt. — See Frankfort
Paducah Area Technology Center Vo/Tech
2400 Adams St 42003 270-443-6592
Allan Paul, prin. Fax 442-6233

McCracken County SD 6,100/PK-12
5347 Benton Rd 42003 270-538-4000
Quin Sutton, supt. Fax 538-4001
www.mccracken.kyschools.us/
Commonwealth Middle College HS 11-12
4810 Alben Barkley Dr 42001 270-534-3350
Donna Wear, prin.
Lone Oak MS 700/6-8
225 John E Robinson Dr 42001 270-538-4130
Brent Buchanan, prin. Fax 538-4131
McCracken County HS 1,900/9-12
6530 US Highway 60 W 42001 270-538-4300
Michael Ceglinski, prin. Fax 538-4301
Reidland MS 400/6-8
5351 Benton Rd 42003 270-538-4190
Randy Layne, prin. Fax 538-4191
Other Schools – See West Paducah

Paducah ISD 3,100/PK-12
PO Box 2550 42002 270-444-5600
Donald Shively, supt. Fax 444-5607
www.paducah.kyschools.us/
Paducah MS 700/6-8
342 Lone Oak Rd 42001 270-444-5710
Stacey Overlin, prin. Fax 444-5709
Paducah Tilghman HS 800/9-12
2400 Washington St 42003 270-444-5650
Arthur Davis, prin. Fax 444-5659

Community Christian Academy 200/K-12
110 Lebanon Church Rd 42003 270-554-1651
Anna Thomas, prin. Fax 554-6968
Daymar College Post-Sec.
509 S 30th St 42001 270-444-9950
St. Mary HS 200/9-12
1243 Elmdale Rd 42003 270-442-1681
Jennifer Smith, prin. Fax 442-7920
St. Mary MS 100/6-8
1243 Elmdale Rd 42003 270-442-1681
Jennifer Smith, prin. Fax 442-7920
West Kentucky Comm. & Technical College Post-Sec.
4810 Alben Barkley Dr 42001 270-554-9200

Paintsville, Johnson, Pop. 3,422
Johnson County SD 3,700/PK-12
253 N Mayo Trl 41240 606-789-2530
Thomas Salyer, supt. Fax 789-2506
www.johnson.kyschools.us/
Johnson Central HS 1,100/9-12
257 N Mayo Trl 41240 606-789-2500
Russell Halsey, prin. Fax 789-2547
Johnson County Alternative S 50/Alt
257 N Mayo Trl 41240 606-789-2077
Ben Hamilton, prin. Fax 789-2525
Johnson County MS 600/7-8
251 N Mayo Trl 41240 606-789-4133
Joey Estep, prin. Fax 789-4135

Paintsville ISD 700/PK-12
305 2nd St 41240 606-789-2654
Coy Samons, supt. Fax 789-7412
www.paintsville.kyschools.us/
Paintsville MSHS 300/7-12
225 2nd St 41240 606-789-2656
Charles McClure, prin. Fax 789-2582
Other Schools – See Prestonsburg

Paris, Bourbon, Pop. 8,356
Bourbon County SD 3,000/PK-12
3343 Lexington Rd 40361 859-987-2180
Amy Baker, supt. Fax 987-2182
www.bourbon.kyschools.us/
Bourbon County HS 900/9-12
3341 Lexington Rd 40361 859-987-2185
David Horseman, prin. Fax 987-5850
Bourbon County MS 600/6-8
3339 Lexington Rd 40361 859-987-2189
Travis Earlywine, prin. Fax 987-5854

Paris ISD 700/PK-12
310 W 7th St 40361 859-987-2160
Ken Bicknell, supt. Fax 987-6749
www.paris.kyschools.us
Paris HS 200/9-12
308 W 7th St 40361 859-987-2168
Jami Dailey, prin. Fax 987-2132
Paris MS 100/6-8
304 W 7th St 40361 859-987-2163
Jami Dailey, prin. Fax 987-2164

Park Hills, Kenton, Pop. 2,906

Notre Dame Academy 600/9-12
1699 Hilton Dr 41011 859-261-4300
Jack VonHandorf, prin. Fax 292-7722

Phelps, Pike, Pop. 888
Pike County SD
Supt. — See Pikeville
Phelps HS 300/7-12
PO Box 925 41553 606-456-3482
Mike Hamilton, prin. Fax 456-8988

Pikeville, Pike, Pop. 6,797
Kentucky Tech System
Supt. — See Frankfort
Millard Area Technology Center Vo/Tech
7925 Millard Hwy 41501 606-437-6059
Justin Trout, prin. Fax 437-0502

Pike County SD 9,000/K-12
316 S Mayo Trl 41501 606-433-9200
Kenneth Adkins, supt. Fax 432-3321
www.pike.kyschools.us
Northpoint Academy 100/Alt
5279 N Mayo Trl 41501 606-433-0181
Harold Wallace, prin. Fax 433-0626
Pike County Central HS 700/9-12
100 Winners Circle Dr 41501 606-432-4352
Fax 432-7733
Shelby Valley HS 600/9-12
125 Douglas Park 41501 606-639-0033
Greg Napier, prin. Fax 639-2074
Other Schools – See Belfry, Lick Creek, Phelps

Pikeville ISD 1,200/PK-12
148 2nd St 41501 606-432-8161
Jerry Green, supt. Fax 432-2119
www.pikeville.kyschools.us
Pikeville JSHS 600/7-12
120 Championship Dr 41501 606-432-0185
David Thomas, prin. Fax 432-2022

East Kentucky Beauty College Post-Sec.
5333 N Mayo Trl 41501 606-432-3627
National College Post-Sec.
50 National College Blvd 41501 606-478-7200
Pikeville Medical Center Post-Sec.
911 Bypass Rd 41501 606-437-3500
University of Pikeville Post-Sec.
147 Sycamore St 41501 606-218-5250

Pineville, Bell, Pop. 1,711
Bell County SD 2,800/PK-12
PO Box 340 40977 606-337-7051
Yvonne Gilliam, supt. Fax 337-1412
www.bell.kyschools.us
Bell County Alternative S 50/Alt
9828 US Highway 25 E 40977 606-337-0957
Rick Robbins, prin. Fax 337-7103
Bell County HS 800/9-12
9824 US Highway 25 E 40977 606-337-7061
Richard Gambrel, prin. Fax 337-0867

Kentucky Tech System
Supt. — See Frankfort
Bell County Area Technology Center Vo/Tech
9828 US Highway 25 E 40977 606-337-3094
David Sowders, prin. Fax 337-9053

Pineville ISD 500/PK-12
401 W Virginia Ave 40977 606-337-5701
Patrick Clore, supt. Fax 337-9983
www.pineville.kyschools.us
Pineville JSHS 200/7-12
401 W Virginia Ave 40977 606-337-5701
Bill Keyes, prin. Fax 337-3720

Clear Creek Baptist Bible College Post-Sec.
300 Clear Creek Rd 40977 606-337-3196

Pippa Passes, Knott, Pop. 530

Alice Lloyd College Post-Sec.
100 Purpose Rd 41844 606-368-6000
Buchanan S 100/K-12
100 Purpose Rd 41844 606-368-6108
Amanda Clark, dean Fax 368-6216

Powderly, Muhlenberg, Pop. 738
Muhlenberg County SD 5,300/PK-12
510 W Main St 42367 270-338-2871
Randy McCarty, supt. Fax 338-0529
www.mberg.k12.ky.us/
Other Schools – See Greenville

Prestonsburg, Floyd, Pop. 3,226
Floyd County SD 6,000/K-12
106 N Front Ave 41653 606-886-2354
Henry Webb, supt. Fax 886-8862
www.floyd.kyschools.us
Adams MS 400/6-8
2520 S Lake Dr 41653 606-886-2671
Thomas Poe, prin. Fax 886-7026

Prestonsburg HS 500/9-12
825 Blackcat Blvd 41653 606-886-2252
Jerry Butcher, prin. Fax 886-1745
Other Schools – See Eastern, Hi Hat, Martin, Stanville

Paintsville ISD
Supt. — See Paintsville
Perkins Job Corp Academy 100/Alt
478 Meadows Br 41653 606-886-1037
John Brown, prin. Fax 886-6048

Big Sandy Community & Technical College Post-Sec.
1 Bert Combs Dr 41653 606-886-3863

Princeton, Caldwell, Pop. 6,185
Caldwell County SD 2,100/PK-12
PO Box 229 42445 270-365-8000
Carrell Boyd, supt. Fax 365-5742
www.caldwell.kyschools.us/
Caldwell County HS 600/9-12
350 Beckner Ln 42445 270-365-8010
Christy Phelps, prin. Fax 365-9742
Caldwell County MS 500/6-8
440 Beckner Ln 42445 270-365-8020
Steve Smiley, prin. Fax 365-9573

Kentucky Tech System
Supt. — See Frankfort
Caldwell County Area Technology Center Vo/Tech
130 Vocational School Rd 42445 270-365-5563
Donna Wolfe, prin. Fax 365-5609

Raceland, Greenup, Pop. 2,412
Raceland-Worthington ISD 1,100/PK-12
600 Rams Blvd 41169 606-836-2144
Larry Coldiron, supt. Fax 833-5807
www.raceland.kyschools.us
Raceland-Worthington HS 500/7-12
500 Rams Blvd 41169 606-836-8221
Mickey Dixon, prin. Fax 494-2341
Other Schools – See Ashland

Radcliff, Hardin, Pop. 20,329
Hardin County SD
Supt. — See Elizabethtown
North Hardin HS 1,400/9-12
801 S Logsdon Pkwy 40160 270-351-3167
Lonnie Dennis, prin. Fax 352-4512
North MS 600/6-8
100 Trojan Way 40160 270-352-3340
Jeff Lowman, prin. Fax 352-3341

North Hardin Christian S 500/PK-12
1298 Rogersville Rd 40160 270-351-7700

Richmond, Madison, Pop. 30,594
Kentucky Tech System
Supt. — See Frankfort
Madison County Area Technology Center Vo/Tech
PO Box 809 40476 859-624-4520
Diana Gordon, prin. Fax 624-9659

Madison County SD 9,900/PK-12
PO Box 768 40476 859-624-4500
Elmer Thomas, supt. Fax 624-4508
www.madison.kyschools.us
Caudill MS 600/6-8
1428 Robert R Martin Bypass 40475 859-625-6172
Che Haselwood, prin. Fax 623-2652
Clark-Moores MS 500/6-8
1143 Berea Rd 40475 859-624-4545
Vickie Fritz, prin. Fax 624-4534
Madison Central HS 1,800/9-12
705 N 2nd St 40475 859-625-6109
Drew Muntz, prin. Fax 623-3925
Madison MS 400/6-8
101 Summit St 40475 859-624-4550
Amie Gallion, prin. Fax 624-4543
Other Schools – See Berea

Eastern Kentucky University Post-Sec.
521 Lancaster Ave 40475 859-622-1000
Kentucky Horseshoeing School Post-Sec.
3612 Lexington Rd 40475 859-575-4063
National College Post-Sec.
125 S Killarney Ln 40475 859-623-8956

Rush, Boyd
Boyd County SD
Supt. — See Ashland
Ramey-Estep HS 100/6-12
2901 Pigeon Roost Rd 41168 606-928-5801
Elizabeth Brewster, prin. Fax 928-2145

Russell, Greenup, Pop. 3,354
Kentucky Tech System
Supt. — See Frankfort
Russell Area Technology Center Vo/Tech
705 Red Devil Ln 41169 606-836-1256
David Trimble, prin. Fax 836-3784

Russell ISD 2,000/PK-12
409 Belfonte St 41169 606-836-9679
M. Sean Horne, supt. Fax 836-2865
www.russellind.kyschools.us
Russell HS 600/9-12
709 Red Devil Ln 41169 606-836-9658
Anna Chaffin, prin. Fax 836-9650
Russell MS 500/6-8
707 Red Devil Ln 41169 606-836-8135
Shawn Moore, prin. Fax 836-0614

Russell Springs, Russell, Pop. 2,403
Kentucky Tech System
Supt. — See Frankfort
Lake Cumberland Area Technology Center Vo/Tech
2330 S Highway 127 42642 270-866-6175
Jeff Adams, prin. Fax 866-2424

Russell County SD
Supt. — See Jamestown
Russell County HS 900/9-12
2166 S Highway 127 42642 270-866-3341
Shannon Williams, prin. Fax 866-8830
Russell County MS 700/6-8
2258 S Highway 127 42642 270-866-2224
Wayne Ackerman, prin. Fax 866-8679

Russellville, Logan, Pop. 6,795
Kentucky Tech System
Supt. — See Frankfort
Russellville Area Technology Center Vo/Tech
1103 W 9th St 42276 270-726-8432
Elizabeth Frogue, prin. Fax 726-6303

Logan County SD 3,600/PK-12
PO Box 417 42276 270-726-2436
Paul Mullins, supt. Fax 726-8892
www.logan.kyschools.us
Logan County HS 1,100/9-12
2200 Bowling Green Rd 42276 270-726-8454
Caycee Spears, prin. Fax 726-1108

Russellville ISD 1,000/PK-12
355 S Summer St 42276 270-726-8405
Leon Smith M.A., supt. Fax 726-4036
www.russellville.kyschools.us/
Russellville JSHS 500/6-12
1101 W 9th St 42276 270-726-8421
Kim McDaniel M.A., prin. Fax 726-3685

Daymar College Post-Sec.
206 Sam Walton Dr 42276 270-726-8311

Saint Catharine, Washington

Saint Catharine College Post-Sec.
2735 Bardstown Rd 40061 859-336-5082

Salyersville, Magoffin, Pop. 1,875
Magoffin County SD 2,300/PK-12
PO Box 109 41465 606-349-6117
Scott Helton, supt. Fax 349-3417
www.magoffin.kyschools.us
Magoffin County Career & Technical Ctr Vo/Tech
209 Hornet Dr 41465 606-349-5188
Vince Minix, dir. Fax 349-5345
Magoffin County HS 600/9-12
201 Hornet Dr 41465 606-349-2011
Chris Meadows, prin. Fax 349-5345
Whitaker MS 300/7-8
221 Hornet Dr 41465 606-349-5190
Johnnie Johnson, prin. Fax 349-5139

Sandy Hook, Elliott, Pop. 666
Elliott County SD 1,000/K-12
PO Box 767 41171 606-738-8002
Dr. C. Thomas Potter Ed.D., supt. Fax 738-8050
www.elliott.kyschools.us
Elliott County JSHS 500/7-12
PO Box 687 41171 606-738-8052
Dr. Zachary Mayse Ed.D., prin. Fax 738-8000

Scottsville, Allen, Pop. 4,154
Allen County SD 3,300/PK-12
570 Oliver St 42164 270-618-3181
Randall Jackson, supt. Fax 618-3185
www.allen.kyschools.us
Allen County Scottsville HS 800/9-12
1545 Bowling Green Rd 42164 270-622-4119
Shane Davis, prin. Fax 622-5882
Allen County Technical Center Vo/Tech
1585 Bowling Green Rd 42164 270-622-4711
Josephy Cosby, dir. Fax 622-7006
Bazzell MS 500/7-8
201 New Gallatin Rd 42164 270-622-7140
Melissa Towery, prin. Fax 622-4649

Daymar College Post-Sec.
1138 Old Gallatin Rd 42164 270-237-3577

Shelbyville, Shelby, Pop. 13,656
Kentucky Tech System
Supt. — See Frankfort
Shelby County Area Technology Center Vo/Tech
230 Rocket Ln 40065 502-633-6554
Steve Coleman, prin. Fax 633-4212

Shelby County SD 7,000/PK-12
PO Box 159 40066 502-633-2375
Dr. James Neihof, supt. Fax 633-1988
www.shelby.kyschools.us
Collins HS 1,300/8-12
801 Discovery Blvd 40065 502-647-1160
Joseph Ellison, prin. Fax 647-1161
Shelby Co. Big Picture Learning Academy 50/9-12
1361 Frankfort Rd 40065 502-633-4677
Phillip Conder, prin. Fax 633-1988
Shelby County HS 1,200/8-12
1701 Frankfort Rd 40065 502-633-2344
Margo Whisman, prin. Fax 647-0238

Cornerstone Christian Academy 200/PK-12
3850 Frankfort Rd 40065 502-633-4070
David Ladner, hdmstr. Fax 633-4605

Shepherdsville, Bullitt, Pop. 11,048
Bullitt County SD 13,300/PK-12
1040 Highway 44 E 40165 502-869-8000
Keith Davis, supt. Fax 543-3608
www.bullittschools.org
Bernheim MS 500/6-8
700 Audubon Dr 40165 502-869-4000
Katie Stephens, prin. Fax 543-5299
Bullitt Central HS 1,200/9-12
1330 Highway 44 E 40165 502-869-6000
Dr. Jim Beavers, prin. Fax 543-1797

Bullitt Lick MS 500/6-8
555 W Blue Lick Rd 40165 502-869-5400
Lee Barger, prin. Fax 543-1685
Hebron MS 400/6-8
3300 E Hebron Ln 40165 502-869-4200
Kelland Garland, prin. Fax 957-6014
North Bullitt HS 1,200/9-12
3200 E Hebron Ln 40165 502-869-6200
Chris VerDow, prin. Fax 957-6762
Riverview Opportunity Center 200/Alt
383 High School Dr 40165 502-869-6600
B.J. Ritter, prin. Fax 543-1792
Zoneton MS 500/6-8
797 Old Preston Hwy N 40165 502-869-4400
Ann Ford, prin. Fax 955-7027
Other Schools – See Mount Washington

Kentucky Tech System
Supt. — See Frankfort
Bullitt County Area Technology Center Vo/Tech
395 High School Dr 40165 502-543-7018
Angela Binkley, prin. Fax 543-1691

Little Flock Christian Academy 200/K-12
5500 N Preston Hwy 40165 502-957-7686
Rick Grice, prin. Fax 957-4122

Silver Grove, Campbell, Pop. 1,083
Silver Grove ISD 200/PK-12
PO Box 400 41085 859-441-3894
Ken Ellis, supt. Fax 441-3033
www.silvergrove.kyschools.us
Silver Grove S 200/PK-12
PO Box 444 41085 859-441-3873
Wesley Murray, prin. Fax 441-4299

Simpsonville, Shelby, Pop. 2,432

Corpus Christi Classical Academy PK-12
7010 Shelbyville Rd 40067 502-722-8090
Kathy Fehder, prin. Fax 722-8099

Smithland, Livingston, Pop. 299
Livingston County SD 1,300/PK-12
127 E Adair St 42081 270-928-2111
Victor Zimmerman, supt. Fax 928-2112
www.livingston.kyschools.us
Livingston Central HS 300/9-12
750 US Highway 60 W 42081 270-928-2065
Scott Gray, prin. Fax 928-2066
Other Schools – See Burna

Somerset, Pulaski, Pop. 11,017
Kentucky Tech System
Supt. — See Frankfort
Pulaski County Area Technology Center Vo/Tech
3865 S Highway 27 Ste 101 42501 606-678-2998
Kevin Cook, prin. Fax 678-3032

Pulaski County SD 8,700/PK-12
PO Box 1055 42502 606-679-1123
Steve Butcher, supt. Fax 679-1438
www.pulaski.net
Northern MS 800/6-8
650 Oak Leaf Ln 42503 606-678-5230
Shelly Hargis, prin. Fax 678-2729
Pulaski County Day Treatment 100/Alt
500 Chandler St 42501 606-677-9986
Tammy Roberts, admin. Fax 677-9885
Pulaski County HS 1,100/9-12
511 E University Dr 42503 606-679-1574
Rodney McAninch, prin. Fax 677-2771
Southern MS 1,000/6-8
200 Enterprise Dr 42501 606-679-6855
Brett McQueary, prin. Fax 679-2270
Southwestern HS 1,200/9-12
1765 WTLO Rd 42503 606-678-9000
Danita Ellis, prin. Fax 678-9277

Somerset ISD 1,600/PK-12
305 College St 42501 606-679-4451
Kyle Lively, supt. Fax 678-0864
www.somerset.kyschools.us
Meece MS 500/5-8
210 Barnett St 42501 606-678-5821
Calvin Rollyson, prin. Fax 678-2934
Somerset HS 500/9-12
301 College St 42501 606-678-4721
Wesley Cornett, prin. Fax 677-0087

Somerset Christian S 300/PK-12
815 Grande Central Blvd 42503 606-451-1600
John Hale, prin. Fax 677-9850
Somerset Community College Post-Sec.
808 Monticello St 42501 877-629-9722

S Portsmouth, Greenup

Harvest Christian Academy 100/K-12
PO Box 398 41174 606-932-3007
Ashley Pelfrey, admin. Fax 453-1635

South Shore, Greenup, Pop. 1,096
Greenup County SD
Supt. — See Greenup
McKell MS 300/6-8
129 Bulldog Ln 41175 606-932-3221
Nathan Sutton, prin. Fax 932-9844

Springfield, Washington, Pop. 2,454
Washington County SD 1,700/PK-12
PO Box 72 40069 859-336-5470
Dr. Robin Cochran Ed.D., supt. Fax 336-5480
www.washington.kyschools.us
Washington County HS 500/9-12
300 W US 150 Bypass 40069 859-336-5475
William Elmore, prin. Fax 336-5983

Washington County MS 200/6-8
603 Lincoln Park Rd 40069 859-336-5475
Tyler Howard, prin. Fax 336-5477

Stanford, Lincoln, Pop. 3,439
Kentucky Tech System
Supt. — See Frankfort
Lincoln County Area Technology Center Vo/Tech
422 Education Way 40484 606-365-8500
Amy Tracy, prin. Fax 365-8504

Lincoln County SD 4,000/PK-12
PO Box 265 40484 606-365-2124
Karen Hatter, supt. Fax 365-1660
www.lincoln.kyschools.us
Fort Logan Alternative JSHS 100/Alt
PO Box 265 40484 606-365-1333
Scott Montgomery, prin. Fax 365-4020
Lincoln County HS 1,100/9-12
60 Education Way 40484 606-365-9111
Fax 365-1750
Lincoln County MS 600/7-8
285 Education Way 40484 606-365-8400
Debbie Sims, prin. Fax 365-8600

Stanton, Powell, Pop. 2,713
Powell County SD 2,400/PK-12
PO Box 430 40380 606-663-3300
Michael Tate, supt. Fax 663-3303
www.powell.kyschools.us
Powell County Alternative S 50/Alt
PO Box 430 40380 606-663-3505
Kenny Rice, dir. Fax 663-3303
Powell County HS 700/9-12
700 W College Ave 40380 606-663-3320
Kendall Kearns, prin. Fax 663-3406
Powell County MS 600/6-8
770 W College Ave 40380 606-663-3308
Tiffany Anderson, prin. Fax 663-3683

Stanville, Floyd
Floyd County SD
Supt. — See Prestonsburg
Betsy Layne HS 400/9-12
554 Bobcat Blvd 41659 606-478-9138
Cassandra Akers, prin. Fax 478-3805

Stearns, McCreary, Pop. 1,397
McCreary County SD 3,000/PK-12
120 Raider Way 42647 606-376-2591
Michael Cash, supt. Fax 376-5584
www.mccreary.kyschools.us
McCreary Central Academy 50/Alt
180 Raider Way 42647 606-376-1477
Michael Cash, prin. Fax 376-1478
McCreary Central HS 800/9-12
400 Raider Way 42647 606-376-5051
Sharon Privett, prin. Fax 376-3005
McCreary County MS 500/7-8
180 Raider Way 42647 606-376-5081
Clint Taylor, prin. Fax 376-9580

Taylor Mill, Kenton, Pop. 6,506
Kenton County SD
Supt. — See Fort Wright
Scott HS 900/9-12
5400 Old Taylor Mill Rd 41015 859-356-3146
Dr. Brennon Sapp, prin. Fax 356-5516
Woodland MS 700/6-8
5399 Old Taylor Mill Rd 41015 859-356-7300
Jerry Cline, prin. Fax 356-7595

Taylorsville, Spencer, Pop. 749
Spencer County SD 2,900/PK-12
207 W Main St 40071 502-477-3250
Charles Adams, supt. Fax 477-3259
www.spencer.kyschools.us
Hillview Academy 50/Alt
PO Box 249 40071 502-477-1530
Bob Hafendorfer, prin. Fax 477-1760
Spencer County HS 800/9-12
520 Taylorsville Rd 40071 502-477-3255
Curt Haun, prin. Fax 477-3212
Spencer County MS 700/6-8
1263 Mount Washington Rd 40071 502-477-3260
Matt Mercer, prin. Fax 477-6796

Tompkinsville, Monroe, Pop. 2,360
Kentucky Tech System
Supt. — See Frankfort
Monroe County Area Technology Center Vo/Tech
757 Old Mulkey Rd 42167 270-487-8261
Jerri Rowland, prin. Fax 487-0094

Monroe County SD 1,900/PK-12
309 Emberton St 42167 270-487-5456
Amy Thompson, supt. Fax 487-5571
www.monroe.kyschools.us
Falcon Academy 50/Alt
309 Emberton St 42167 270-487-6181
Ricky Geralds, prin. Fax 487-6181
Monroe County HS 600/9-12
755 Old Mulkey Rd 42167 270-487-6217
Max Petett, prin. Fax 487-8274
Monroe County MS 400/6-8
600 S Main St 42167 270-487-9624
Jon Michael Clemmons, prin. Fax 487-9534

Union, Boone, Pop. 5,294
Boone County SD
Supt. — See Florence
Cooper HS 1,200/9-12
2855 Longbranch Rd 41091 859-384-5040
Michael Wilson, prin. Fax 384-5049
Gray MS 1,000/6-8
10400 US Highway 42 41091 859-384-5333
Todd Novak, prin. Fax 384-5318

Ryle HS 1,700/9-12
10379 US Highway 42 41091 859-384-5300
Matthew Turner, prin. Fax 384-5312

Valley Station, Jefferson, Pop. 22,840
Jefferson County SD
Supt. — See Louisville
Stuart MS 700/7-8
4603 Valley Station Rd 40272 502-485-8334
Laura Dalton, prin. Fax 313-3540
Valley Traditional HS 1,100/9-12
10200 Dixie Hwy 40272 502-485-8339
Rob Stephenson, prin. Fax 313-3544

Vanceburg, Lewis, Pop. 1,503
Lewis County SD 2,400/PK-12
PO Box 159 41179 606-796-2811
Fax 796-3081
www.lewis.kyschools.us/
Lewis County HS 700/9-12
PO Box 99 41179 606-796-2823
Jack Lykins, prin. Fax 796-3066
Lewis County MS 500/6-8
PO Box 69 41179 606-796-6228
Brenda Box, prin. Fax 796-6255
Meade Vocational Education Center Vo/Tech
PO Box 130 41179 606-796-6106
Brad Brammell, prin. Fax 796-9739

Vancleve, Breathitt

Kentucky Mountain Bible College Post-Sec.
PO Box 10 41385 606-693-5000

Versailles, Woodford, Pop. 8,423
Woodford County SD 4,100/PK-12
330 Pisgah Rd 40383 859-879-4600
D. Scott Hawkins, supt. Fax 873-1614
ilearn.woodfordschools.org/
Safe Harbor Academy 50/Alt
299 S Main St 40383 859-879-4694
Logan Culbertson, prin. Fax 873-1328
Woodford County HS 1,200/9-12
180 Frankfort St 40383 859-879-4630
Rob Akers, prin. Fax 873-7731
Woodford County MS 900/6-8
100 School House Rd 40383 859-879-4650
Tracy Bruno, prin. Fax 873-4436

Villa Hills, Kenton, Pop. 7,410

Villa Madonna Academy 7-12
2500 Amsterdam Rd 41017 859-331-6333
Pamela McQueen, prin. Fax 331-8615

Vine Grove, Hardin, Pop. 4,350
Hardin County SD
Supt. — See Elizabethtown
Alton MS 700/6-8
100 Country Club Rd 40175 270-877-2135
Jama Bennett, prin. Fax 877-6297

Walton, Boone, Pop. 3,572
Walton-Verona ISD 1,600/PK-12
16 School Rd 41094 859-485-4181
Dr. Robert Storer, supt. Fax 485-1810
wv.kyschools.us
Walton-Verona HS 500/9-12
30 School Rd 41094 859-485-7721
Joanne Estenfelder, prin. Fax 485-7739
Walton-Verona MS 500/5-8
32 School Rd 41094 859-485-7721
Eric Morwessel, prin. Fax 485-7739

Warfield, Martin, Pop. 269
Martin County SD
Supt. — See Inez
Martin County MS 500/6-8
130 Middle School Dr 41267 606-395-5900
Brent Haney, prin. Fax 395-5902

Warsaw, Gallatin, Pop. 1,574
Gallatin County SD 1,700/PK-12
75 Boardwalk 41095 859-567-2828
Travis Huber, supt. Fax 567-4528
www.gallatin.kyschools.us
Gallatin County HS 500/9-12
70 Wildcat Cir 41095 859-567-7640
Jon Jones, prin. Fax 567-8222
Gallatin County MS 400/6-8
88 Pawprint Path 41095 859-567-5860
John Ritchie, prin. Fax 567-6107
Gallatin County Wildcat Academy 50/Alt
75 Boardwalk 41095 859-567-1820

West Liberty, Morgan, Pop. 3,396
Kentucky Tech System
Supt. — See Frankfort
Morgan County Area Technology Center Vo/Tech
PO Box 249 41472 606-743-8452
Garry Harper, prin. Fax 743-8500

Morgan County SD 2,100/K-12
155 University Dr 41472 606-743-8002
Deatrah Barnett, supt. Fax 743-8050
www.morgan.kyschools.us/
Morgan County HS 600/9-12
150 Road To Success 41472 606-743-8052
Joseph Gamble, prin. Fax 743-8100
Morgan County MS 500/6-8
380 Road To Success 41472 606-743-8102
Terry Whitt, prin. Fax 743-8150

West Paducah, McCracken
McCracken County SD
Supt. — See Paducah
Heath MS 500/6-8
4330 Metropolis Lake Rd 42086 270-538-4070
Matthew Blackwell, prin. Fax 538-4071

Whitesburg, Letcher, Pop. 2,131
Kentucky Tech System
Supt. — See Frankfort
Letcher County Area Technology Center Vo/Tech
515 Cougar Dr 41858 606-633-5053
Dejah Newsom, prin. Fax 633-8084

Letcher County SD 3,200/PK-12
224 Parks St 41858 606-633-4455
Tony Sergent, supt. Fax 633-4724
www.letcher.kyschools.us
Letcher County Alternative S 50/Alt
185 Circle Dr Ste A 41858 606-633-5559
Manis Blair, lead tchr. Fax 633-2459
Letcher County Central HS 900/9-12
435 Cougar Dr 41858 606-633-2339
Gracie Maggard, prin. Fax 633-2447
Whitesburg MS 200/6-8
366 Parks St 41858 606-633-2761
Henry Frazier, prin. Fax 633-4137
Other Schools – See Blackey, Neon

Jenny Lea Academy of Cosmetology Post-Sec.
74 Parkway Plaza Loop 41858 606-633-8784

Whitesville, Daviess, Pop. 544

Trinity HS 100/9-12
10510 Main Cross St 42378 270-233-5184
Ron Williams, prin. Fax 233-9293

Williamsburg, Whitley, Pop. 5,159
Whitley County SD 4,600/PK-12
300 Main St 40769 606-549-7000
Scott Paul, supt. Fax 549-7006
www.whitley.kyschools.us
Whitley County Alternative S 50/Alt
351 Boulevard of Champions 40769 606-549-7050
Terry Huddleston, prin. Fax 549-7068
Whitley County HS 1,100/9-12
350 Boulevard Of Champions 40769 606-549-7025
Bob Lawson, prin. Fax 549-7035
Whitley County MS 700/7-8
351 Boulevard Of Champions 40769 606-549-7050
Stuart Conlin, prin. Fax 549-7055

Williamsburg ISD 900/PK-12
1000 Main St 40769 606-549-6044
Dennis Byrd, supt. Fax 549-6076
www.wburg.kyschools.us
Williamsburg S 900/PK-12
1000 Main St 40769 606-549-6044
Dr. Amon Couch, prin. Fax 549-6076

University of the Cumberlands Post-Sec.
6178 College Station Dr 40769 606-549-2200

Williamstown, Grant, Pop. 3,887
Grant County SD 3,800/K-12
820 Arnie Risen Blvd 41097 859-824-3323
Ron Livingood, supt. Fax 824-3508
www.grant.kyschools.us
Other Schools – See Dry Ridge

Williamstown ISD 900/PK-12
300 Helton St 41097 859-824-7144
Misty Middleton, supt. Fax 824-3237
www.williamstown.kyschools.us/
Williamstown HS 200/9-12
300 Helton St 41097 859-824-4421
Brandy Feagan, admin. Fax 824-4736
Williamstown JHS 200/6-8
300 Helton St 41097 859-824-4421
Brandy Feagan, prin. Fax 824-3745

Wilmore, Jessamine, Pop. 3,637
Jessamine County SD
Supt. — See Nicholasville
Jessamine Career & Technology Center Vo/Tech
881 Wilmore Rd, 859-881-8324
C. Dexter Knight, prin. Fax 887-9051
Providence S 100/Alt
210 S Lexington Ave 40390 859-887-4600
Charlanne Pook, prin. Fax 858-9586

Asbury Theological Seminary Post-Sec.
204 N Lexington Ave 40390 800-227-2879
Asbury University Post-Sec.
1 Macklem Dr 40390 859-858-3511

Winchester, Clark, Pop. 18,061
Clark County SD 4,000/PK-12
1600 W Lexington Ave 40391 859-744-4545
Paul Christy, supt. Fax 745-3935
www.clark.kyschools.us
Campbell JHS 300/7-8
620 Boone Ave 40391 859-745-5200
Dustin Howard, prin. Fax 745-2027
Clark HS 1,600/9-12
2745 Boonesboro Rd 40391 859-744-6111
David Bolen, prin. Fax 745-2418
Phoenix Academy 50/Alt
100 Vaught Rd 40391 859-744-4618
Chris Kindred, prin. Fax 745-0150

Kentucky Tech System
Supt. — See Frankfort
Clark County Area Technology Center Vo/Tech
650 Boone Ave 40391 859-744-1250
Michael Kindred, prin. Fax 744-9979

Wurtland, Greenup, Pop. 983
Greenup County SD
Supt. — See Greenup
Wurtland MS 300/6-8
700 Center St 41144 606-836-1023
Amanda Powell, prin. Fax 836-3939

LOUISIANA

LOUISIANA DEPARTMENT OF EDUCATION
PO Box 94064, Baton Rouge 70804-9064
Telephone 225-342-3602
Fax 225-342-7316
Website http://www.louisianabelieves.com

Superintendent of Education John White

LOUISIANA BOARD OF EDUCATION
PO Box 94064, Baton Rouge 70804-9064

President James Garvey

PUBLIC, PRIVATE AND CATHOLIC SECONDARY SCHOOLS

Abbeville, Vermilion, Pop. 12,038
Vermilion Parish SD 9,000/PK-12
PO Box 520 70511 337-898-5770
Jerome Puyau, supt. Fax 898-0939
www.vpsb.net
Abbeville HS 600/9-12
1305 Wildcat Dr 70510 337-893-1874
Ivy Landry, prin. Fax 893-0935
Williams MS 600/6-8
1105 Prairie Ave 70510 337-893-3943
Dana Primeaux, prin. Fax 893-5190
Other Schools – See Erath, Gueydan, Kaplan, Maurice

South Louisiana Community College Post-Sec.
1301 Clover St 70510 337-893-4984
Vermilion Catholic HS 200/9-12
425 Park Ave 70510 337-893-6636
Michael Guilbeaux, prin. Fax 898-0394

Albany, Livingston, Pop. 1,080
Livingston Parish SD
Supt. — See Livingston
Albany HS 600/9-12
29700 One Hornet Ln 70711 225-567-9319
Jill Prokop, prin. Fax 567-9162
Albany MS 600/5-8
PO Box 1210 70711 225-567-5231
Rachel Jenkins, prin. Fax 567-9177

Alexandria, Rapides, Pop. 46,974
Rapides Parish SD 22,600/PK-12
PO Box 1230 71309 318-487-0888
Nason Authement, supt. Fax 449-3167
www.rpsb.us
Alexandria HS 1,300/9-12
800 Ola St 71303 318-448-8234
Duane Urbina, prin. Fax 487-9994
Alexandria Magnet MS 500/6-8
122 Maryland Ave 71301 318-445-5343
Monte Demars, prin. Fax 442-8650
Bolton HS 600/9-12
2101 Vance Ave 71301 318-448-3628
Clovis Christman, prin. Fax 448-4329
Brame MS 900/6-8
4800 Dawn St 71301 318-443-3688
Walter Fall, prin. Fax 442-3966
Peabody Magnet HS 700/9-12
2727 Jones Ave 71302 318-448-3457
Jamie Henagan, prin. Fax 487-0771
RAPPS S 50/Alt
4645 Lincoln Rd 71302 318-448-9899
Deidra Anderson, prin. Fax 449-4774
Smith Magnet MS 500/6-8
3100 Jones Ave 71302 318-445-6241
Dr. Norvella Williams, prin. Fax 445-9255
Other Schools – See Ball, Deville, Elmer, Glenmora, Lecompte, Lena, Pineville, Tioga

---

Blue Cliff College-Alexandria Post-Sec.
1505 Metro Dr Ste 1 71301 318-445-2778
Central Louisiana Technical College Post-Sec.
4311 S MacArthur Dr 71302 318-487-5439
Grace Christian S 400/PK-12
4900 Jackson St 71303 318-445-8735
Kay Blackburn, prin. Fax 443-1034
Holy Savior Menard HS 500/7-12
4603 Coliseum Blvd 71303 318-445-8233
Joel Desselle, prin. Fax 448-8170
Louisiana State University at Alexandria Post-Sec.
8100 Highway 71 S 71302 318-445-3672
Rapides Regional Medical Center Post-Sec.
PO Box 30101 71301 318-473-3150
University Academy of Central Louisiana 200/8-12
141 Middleton Dr 71302 318-427-0123
DeEtte Loyd, dir. Fax 427-0123

Amite, Tangipahoa, Pop. 4,112
Tangipahoa Parish SD 20,000/PK-12
59656 Puleston Rd 70422 985-748-7153
Mark Kolwe, supt. Fax 748-8587
www.tangischools.org
Amite HS 500/9-12
403 S Laurel St 70422 985-748-9301
Terran Perry, prin. Fax 748-2814
West Side MS 400/5-8
401 W Oak St 70422 985-748-9073
Ashley Walker, prin. Fax 748-9225
Other Schools – See Hammond, Independence, Kentwood, Loranger, Ponchatoula, Tickfaw

---

Oak Forest Academy 700/PK-12
600 Walnut St 70422 985-748-4321
Jason Brabham, admin. Fax 748-4320

Anacoco, Vernon, Pop. 864
Vernon Parish SD
Supt. — See Leesville
Anacoco JSHS 400/7-12
4740 Port Arthur Ave 71403 337-239-3039
Towanda Willrodt, prin. Fax 238-4228

Arcadia, Bienville, Pop. 2,890
Bienville Parish SD 2,200/PK-12
PO Box 418 71001 318-263-9416
William Britt, supt. Fax 263-3100
www.bpsb.us/
Arcadia JSHS 300/6-12
967 Daniel St 71001 318-263-2264
Jeffery Sampson, prin. Fax 263-9703
Other Schools – See Castor, Gibsland, Ringgold, Saline

Archibald, Richland
Richland Parish SD
Supt. — See Rayville
Richland Career Center Vo/Tech
3768 Highway 15 71218 318-248-2465
Lee McDonald, prin. Fax 248-3525

Arnaudville, Saint Landry, Pop. 1,048
St. Landry Parish SD
Supt. — See Opelousas
Arnaudville ES 200/5-8
PO Box 770 70512 337-754-5320
Elsie Semien, prin. Fax 754-5326
Beau Chene HS 900/9-12
7076 Highway 93 70512 337-662-5815
Keith James, prin. Fax 662-3688

Athens, Claiborne, Pop. 242

Mount Olive Christian S 100/PK-12
15349 Highway 9 71003 318-258-5661

Atlanta, Winn, Pop. 159
Winn Parish SD
Supt. — See Winnfield
Atlanta S 200/PK-12
118 School Rd 71404 318-628-4613
Bridgette Bartlett, prin. Fax 628-4247

Avondale, Jefferson, Pop. 4,884
Jefferson Parish SD
Supt. — See Harvey
Ford MS 700/6-8
435 S Jamie Blvd 70094 504-436-2474
Faith Joseph, prin. Fax 436-0604
Taylor Science & Tech Academy 400/6-12
701 Church Hill Pkwy 70094 504-838-2249
Jaime Zapico, prin. Fax 436-0247

Baker, East Baton Rouge, Pop. 13,732
City of Baker SD 1,700/PK-12
14750 Plank Rd 70714 225-774-5795
Dr. Herman Brister, supt. Fax 774-5797
www.bakerschools.org
Baker HS 400/9-12
3200 Groom Rd 70714 225-775-1259
Traci Morgan, prin. Fax 775-4011
Baker MS 400/6-8
5903 Groom Rd 70714 225-775-9750
Tammy Golden, prin. Fax 775-9753

Bethany Christian S 200/PK-12
13855 Plank Rd 70714 225-774-0133
Carolyn DeSalvo, prin. Fax 774-0163

Baldwin, Saint Mary, Pop. 2,394
St. Mary Parish SD
Supt. — See Centerville
Boudreaux MS 300/6-8
18333 Highway 182 70514 337-924-7990
Magdalene Drexler, prin. Fax 924-7999
West St. Mary HS 400/9-12
PO Box 120 70514 337-924-7990
Dr. Derrick White, prin. Fax 924-7999

Ball, Rapides, Pop. 3,932
Rapides Parish SD
Supt. — See Alexandria

Tioga JHS 700/7-8
1150 Tioga Rd 71405 318-640-9412
Rebecca Pippen, prin. Fax 640-0126

Basile, Evangeline, Pop. 1,791
Evangeline Parish SD
Supt. — See Ville Platte
Basile JSHS 400/5-12
2835 2nd St 70515 337-432-5012
Tony Bertrand, prin. Fax 432-6414

Bastrop, Morehouse, Pop. 11,255
Morehouse Parish SD 2,700/PK-12
PO Box 872 71221 318-281-5784
Hazel Sellers B.A., supt. Fax 283-3456
www.mpsb.us
Bastrop HS 1,000/8-12
402 Highland Ave 71220 318-281-0194
Dr. David Nordman, prin. Fax 281-0457

Bastrop Beauty School #1 Post-Sec.
117 S Vine St 71220 318-281-8652
Prairie View Academy 300/K-12
9942 Edwin St 71220 318-281-7044

Baton Rouge, East Baton Rouge, Pop. 226,740
Central Community SD 4,400/PK-12
PO Box 78094 70837 225-262-1919
Michael Faulk, supt. Fax 262-1989
www.centralcss.org
Central HS 1,300/9-12
10200 E Brookside Dr 70818 225-261-3438
Dave Prescott, prin. Fax 261-3501
Central MS 900/6-8
12656 Sullivan Rd 70818 225-261-2237
Jason Fountain, prin. Fax 261-9973

East Baton Rouge Parish SD 40,600/PK-12
PO Box 2950 70821 225-922-5400
Warren Drake, supt. Fax 922-5499
www.ebrschools.org
Arlington Prepatory Academy 100/Alt
931 Dean Lee Dr 70820 225-766-8188
Margot Morgan-Forbes, prin. Fax 757-1276
Baton Rouge Magnet HS 1,500/9-12
2825 Government St 70806 225-383-0520
Nanette McCann, prin. Fax 344-7413
Belaire HS 1,100/9-12
12121 Tams Dr 70815 225-272-1860
Roy Walker, prin. Fax 272-3782
Broadmoor HS 1,200/9-12
10100 Goodwood Blvd 70815 225-926-1420
Shalonda Simoneaux, prin. Fax 928-5472
Broadmoor MS 400/6-8
1225 Sharp Rd 70815 225-272-0540
Daniel Edwards, prin. Fax 272-0195
Brookstown Middle Magnet Academy 6-8
4375 E Brookstown Dr 70805 225-355-6556
James Smith, prin. Fax 355-6503
Capitol MS 400/6-8
5100 Greenwell Springs Rd 70806 225-231-9292
Viola Jackson, prin. Fax 231-9291
EBR Readiness Superintendent's Academy 100/Alt
1919 Staring Ln 70810 225-757-9679
Delores Watts, prin. Fax 757-9682
Glasgow MS 700/6-8
1676 Glasgow Ave 70808 225-925-2942
Erin Howard, prin. Fax 928-3565
Glen Oaks HS 500/9-12
6650 Cedar Grove Dr 70812 225-356-4306
Ed Hunter, prin. Fax 359-6782
Greenville Alternative S at Beechwood Alt
2555 DeSoto Dr 70807 225-775-4285
Ronnie Knox, prin. Fax 356-4427
Greenville Superintendent's Academy 200/Alt
1645 N Foster Dr 70806 225-357-0139
Sherwanda Johnson, prin. Fax 356-6358
Lee HS 600/9-12
1105 Lee Dr 70808 225-924-9406
Nanette McCann, prin. Fax 924-9409
McKinley HS 1,200/9-12
800 E Mckinley St 70802 225-344-7696
Herman Brister, prin. Fax 387-5435
McKinley Magnet MS 700/6-8
1550 Eddie Robinson Sr Dr 70802 225-388-0089
Sean Joffrion, prin. Fax 387-1434
North Banks MS of Excellence 6-8
5959 Cadillac St 70811 225-357-3371
Fax 356-2665

Northdale Superintendents Academy 200/Alt
10755 Cletus Dr 70815 225-272-2036
Claudia Battley, prin. Fax 273-2125
Park Forest MS 900/6-8
3760 Aletha Dr 70814 225-275-6650
Curtis Walker, prin. Fax 275-3058
Scotlandville Magnet HS 1,300/9-12
9870 Scotland Ave 70807 225-775-3715
Tiffany Quiett, prin. Fax 774-3767
Scotlandville Pre-Engineering Academy 500/6-8
9147 Elmgrove Garden Dr 70807 225-775-0776
Shalika Scott, prin. Fax 775-2104
Sherwood MS Academic Magnet 800/6-8
1020 Marlbrook Dr 70815 225-272-3090
J. Noel, prin. Fax 273-9459
Southeast MS 800/6-8
15000 S Harrells Ferry Rd 70816 225-753-5930
Amber Boyd, prin. Fax 756-8601
Tara HS 1,000/9-12
9002 Whitehall Ave 70806 225-927-6100
Karen Triche, prin. Fax 928-0122
Westdale MS 1,200/6-8
5650 Claycut Rd 70806 225-924-1308
Jeremy Couvillon, prin. Fax 926-9929
Woodlawn HS 1,200/9-12
15755 Jefferson Hwy 70817 225-753-1200
Scott Stevens, prin. Fax 751-9269
Woodlawn MS 1,000/6-8
14939 Tiger Bend Rd 70817 225-751-0436
Shelly Colvin, prin. Fax 753-0159
Other Schools – See Pride

Southern University Lab S 500/PK-12
129 Swan St 70813 225-771-3490
Fax 771-2782
www.sulabschool.com
Southern University Lab S 500/PK-12
129 Swan St 70813 225-771-3490
Fax 771-2782

Baton Rouge Community College Post-Sec.
201 Community College Dr 70806 225-216-8000
Baton Rouge Community College Acadian Post-Sec.
3250 N Acadian Thruway E 70805 225-359-9201
Baton Rouge General Medical Center Post-Sec.
PO Box 2511 70821 225-387-7767
Baton Rouge International S 300/PK-12
5015 Auto Plex Dr 70809 225-293-4338
Baton Rouge School of Computers Post-Sec.
9352 Interline Ave 70809 225-923-2525
Brighton S 200/K-12
12108 Parkmeadow Ave 70816 225-291-2524
Camelot College Post-Sec.
2618 Wooddale Blvd # A 70805 225-928-3005
Catholic HS 1,000/8-12
855 Hearthstone Dr 70806 225-383-0397
Lisa Harvey, prin. Fax 383-0381
Christian Life Academy 600/PK-12
2037 Quail Dr 70808 225-769-6760
Linda Burley, prin. Fax 769-8068
Delta College of Arts & Technology Post-Sec.
7380 Exchange Pl 70806 225-928-7770
Diesel Driving Academy Post-Sec.
8067 Airline Hwy 70815 225-929-9990
Domestic Health Care Institute Post-Sec.
4826 Jamestown Ave 70808 225-925-5312
Dunham S 800/PK-12
11111 Roy Emerson Dr 70810 225-767-7097
Steven Eagleton, hdmstr. Fax 767-7056
Episcopal S of Baton Rouge 900/PK-12
3200 Woodland Ridge Blvd 70816 225-753-3180
Hugh McIntosh, head sch Fax 756-0507
Family Christian Academy 200/K-12
PO Box 262550 70826 225-768-3026
ITI Technical College Post-Sec.
13944 Airline Hwy 70817 225-752-4230
Lockworks Academie of Hairdressing Post-Sec.
2834 S Sherwood Forest Blvd 70816 225-295-1435
Louisiana Culinary Institute Post-Sec.
10550 Airline Hwy 70816 225-769-8820
Louisiana School for the Deaf Post-Sec.
PO Box 3074 70821 225-769-8160
Louisiana School/Visually Impaired Post-Sec.
PO Box 4328 70821 225-757-3482
Louisiana State University & A & M Coll. Post-Sec.
Louisiana State Univ 70803 225-578-3202
Louisiana State University Law Center Post-Sec.
1 E Campus Dr 70803 225-578-5292
Medical Training College Post-Sec.
10525 Plaza Americana Dr 70816 225-926-5820
MedVance Institute Post-Sec.
9255 Interline Ave 70809 225-248-1015
Our Lady of the Lake College Post-Sec.
5414 Brittany Dr 70808 225-768-1700
Our Lady of the Lake Medical Center Post-Sec.
5000 Hennessy Blvd 70808 225-769-7799
Parkview Baptist S 1,400/PK-12
5750 Parkview Church Rd 70816 225-291-2500
Dr. Don Mayes, supt. Fax 293-4135
Redemptorist HS 300/7-12
PO Box 2028 70821 225-357-0936
Dary Glueck, prin. Fax 357-4555
Remington College Post-Sec.
10551 Coursey Blvd 70816 225-236-3200
Riverdale Christian Academy 200/PK-12
2791 Oneal Ln 70816 225-753-6722
Runnels S 800/PK-12
17255 S Harrells Ferry Rd 70816 225-215-5706
Marcia Mackay M.S., head sch Fax 753-0267
St. Joseph's Academy 1,000/9-12
3015 Broussard St 70808 225-383-7207
Dr. Michele Lambert, prin. Fax 344-5714
St. Michael the Archangel HS 700/9-12
PO Box 86110 70879 225-753-9782
Ellen Lee, prin. Fax 753-0605
Southern University and A&M College Post-Sec.
Southern University 70813 225-771-4500
Virginia College Post-Sec.
9501 Cortana Pl 70815 225-236-3900

Bell City, Calcasieu
Calcasieu Parish SD
Supt. — See Lake Charles
Bell City S 600/K-12
PO Box 100 70630 337-217-4500
Reinette Guillory, prin. Fax 217-4501

Belle Chasse, Plaquemines, Pop. 12,371
Plaquemines Parish SD 4,100/PK-12
1484 Woodland Hwy 70037 504-595-6400
Denis Rousselle, supt. Fax 398-9990
www.ppsb.org
Belle Chasse HS 800/9-12
8346 Highway 23 70037 504-595-6600
Jemi Carlone, prin. Fax 393-1182
Belle Chasse MS 800/5-8
13476 Highway 23 70037 504-595-6640
Joe Williamson, prin. Fax 656-2399
Other Schools – See Braithwaite, Buras, Port Sulphur

Belle Rose, Assumption, Pop. 1,892
Assumption Parish SD
Supt. — See Napoleonville
Belle Rose MS 200/5-8
PO Box 229 70341 225-473-8917
Iris Breaux, prin. Fax 473-8429

Benton, Bossier, Pop. 1,921
Bossier Parish SD 22,000/PK-12
PO Box 2000 71006 318-549-5000
Scott Smith, supt. Fax 549-5004
www.bossierschools.org
Benton HS 900/9-12
6136 Highway 3 71006 318-549-5240
Mitch Downey, prin. Fax 549-5252
Benton MS 800/6-8
6140 Highway 3 71006 318-549-5310
Dr. Kyle Machen, prin. Fax 549-5323
Other Schools – See Bossier City, Haughton, Plain Dealing

Berwick, Saint Mary, Pop. 4,860
St. Mary Parish SD
Supt. — See Centerville
Berwick HS 500/9-12
700 Pattie Dr 70342 985-384-8450
Buffy Fegenbush, prin. Fax 384-8505
Berwick JHS 400/6-8
3955 Bourgeois Dr 70342 985-384-5664
Tim Hymel, prin. Fax 384-5663

Bogalusa, Washington, Pop. 12,052
Bogalusa City SD 1,800/PK-12
1705 Sullivan Dr 70427 985-281-2100
Willie Breaux, supt. Fax 735-8828
www.bogschools.org
Bogalusa HS 1,000/6-12
PO Box 580 70429 985-281-2180
Lesley McKinley, prin. Fax 735-9768

Ben's Ford Christian School 500/PK-12
59253 Mount Pleasant Rd 70427 985-735-0387
Northshore Technical Community College Post-Sec.
1710 Sullivan Dr 70427 985-732-6640

Bossier City, Bossier, Pop. 59,796
Bossier Parish SD
Supt. — See Benton
Airline HS 1,700/9-12
2801 Airline Dr 71111 318-549-5080
Jason Rowland, prin. Fax 549-5093
Bossier HS 600/9-12
777 Bearkat Dr 71111 318-549-6680
David Thrash, prin. Fax 549-6693
Bossier Parish S for Technology Vo/Tech
1020 Innovation Dr 71111 318-759-2900
Jayda Spillers, prin. Fax 759-2956
Butler Educational Complex 100/Alt
649 Wyche St 71111 318-549-7050
Chuck Horton, admin. Fax 549-7063
Cope MS 800/6-8
4814 Shed Rd 71111 318-549-5380
Judy Grooms, prin. Fax 549-5393
Elm Grove MS 1,000/6-8
4301 Panther Dr 71112 318-759-2400
Ross Boyett, prin. Fax 759-2409
Greenacres MS 800/6-8
2220 Airline Dr 71111 318-549-6210
Arthur James, prin. Fax 549-6223
Parkway HS 1,200/9-12
2010 Colleen St 71112 318-759-2200
Dr. Nichole Bourgeois, prin. Fax 759-2213
Rusheon MS 600/6-8
2401 Old Minden Rd 71112 318-549-6610
Judy Madden, prin. Fax 549-6623

Bossier Parish Community College Post-Sec.
6220 E Texas St 71111 318-678-6000
Pat Goins Benton Road Beauty School Post-Sec.
1701 Old Minden Rd Ste 36 71111 318-746-7674
Providence Classical Academy 500/PK-12
4525 Old Brownlee Rd 71111 318-820-9465
Virginia College Post-Sec.
2950 E Texas St Ste C 71111 318-741-8020

Bourg, Terrebonne, Pop. 2,533
Terrebonne Parish SD
Supt. — See Houma
South Terrebone HS 1,000/9-12
3879 Highway 24 70343 985-868-7850
Mark Torbert, prin. Fax 868-1691

Boutte, Saint Charles, Pop. 3,028
St. Charles Parish SD
Supt. — See Luling
Hahnville HS 1,500/9-12
200 Tiger Dr 70039 985-758-7537
Ken Oertling, prin. Fax 758-9876

Braithwaite, Plaquemines
Plaquemines Parish SD
Supt. — See Belle Chasse
Phoenix S 200/PK-12
12700 Highway 39 70040 504-595-6480
Kristie Williams, prin. Fax 333-7073

Breaux Bridge, Saint Martin, Pop. 8,038
St. Martin Parish SD 7,800/PK-12
625 Corporate Blvd 70517 337-332-2105
Dr. Lottie Beebe, supt.
www.saintmartinschools.org
Breaux Bridge HS 800/9-12
1015 Breaux Bridge Sr High 70517 337-332-3131
Louis Blanchard, prin. Fax 332-4058
Breaux Bridge JHS 200/7-8
100 Martin St 70517 337-332-2844
Denise Frederick, prin. Fax 332-4831
Other Schools – See Cecilia, Parks, Saint Martinville

Broussard, Lafayette, Pop. 8,078
Lafayette Parish SD
Supt. — See Lafayette
Broussard MS 600/5-8
1325 S Morgan Ave 70518 337-521-7870
John Mouton, prin. Fax 521-7871

Episcopal S of Acadiana 500/PK-12
1557 Smede Hwy 70518 337-365-1416
Dr. Paul Baker Ph.D., hdmstr. Fax 367-9841

Brusly, West Baton Rouge, Pop. 2,561
West Baton Rouge Parish SD
Supt. — See Port Allen
Brusly HS 600/9-12
630 Frontage Rd 70719 225-749-2815
Walt Lemoine, prin. Fax 749-8563
Brusly MS 400/6-8
601 N Kirkland St 70719 225-749-3123
Callie Kershaw, prin. Fax 749-8570

Bunkie, Avoyelles, Pop. 4,132
Avoyelles Parish SD
Supt. — See Marksville
Bunkie HS 500/7-12
435 Evergreen St 71322 318-346-6216
David Moreau, prin. Fax 346-9611

Buras, Plaquemines, Pop. 887
Plaquemines Parish SD
Supt. — See Belle Chasse
South Plaquemines HS 400/7-12
34121 Highway 23 70041 504-595-6435
John Barthelemy, prin.

Calhoun, Ouachita, Pop. 674
Ouachita Parish SD
Supt. — See Monroe
Calhoun MS 500/6-8
191 Highway 80 E 71225 318-644-5840
Buddy Canal, prin. Fax 644-5418

Calvin, Winn, Pop. 236
Winn Parish SD
Supt. — See Winnfield
Calvin S 300/PK-12
PO Box 80 71410 318-727-8784
Paula Jones, prin. Fax 727-9224

Cameron, Cameron, Pop. 399
Cameron Parish SD 1,300/PK-12
PO Box 1548 70631 337-775-5784
Charles Adkins, supt. Fax 775-5097
www.camsch.org
Johnson Bayou S 100/PK-12
6304 Gulf Beach Hwy 70631 337-569-2138
Brenda Sanders, prin. Fax 569-2673
Other Schools – See Grand Chenier, Hackberry, Lake Charles

Campti, Natchitoches, Pop. 1,035
Natchitoches Parish SD
Supt. — See Natchitoches
Lakeview JSHS 400/7-12
PO Box 200 71411 318-476-3360
William Hymes, prin. Fax 476-2851

Carencro, Lafayette, Pop. 7,438
Lafayette Parish SD
Supt. — See Lafayette
Carencro MS 600/6-8
4301 N University Ave 70520 337-521-7880
Jeffrey Janette, prin. Fax 521-7881

Castor, Bienville, Pop. 258
Bienville Parish SD
Supt. — See Arcadia
Castor S 600/PK-12
PO Box 69 71016 318-544-7271
Dr. James Guin, prin. Fax 544-9077

Cecilia, Saint Martin, Pop. 1,957
St. Martin Parish SD
Supt. — See Breaux Bridge
Cecilia HS 700/9-12
PO Box 360 70521 337-667-6221
Daniel LeBoeuf, prin. Fax 667-6795
Cecilia JHS 400/7-8
PO Box 129 70521 337-667-6226
Charee Theriot, prin. Fax 667-7352

Centerville, Saint Mary
St. Mary Parish SD 9,200/PK-12
PO Box 170 70522 337-836-9661
Leonard Armato, supt. Fax 836-5461
www.stmaryk12.net
Centerville S 600/PK-12
PO Box 59 70522 337-836-5103
Kristy Estay, prin. Fax 836-9594
Other Schools – See Baldwin, Berwick, Franklin, Morgan City, Patterson

Central, East Baton Rouge, Pop. 26,615

Central Private S 300/PK-12
12801 Centerra Ct, 225-261-3341

Chalmette, Saint Bernard, Pop. 16,314
St. Bernard Parish SD 7,000/PK-12
200 E Saint Bernard Hwy 70043 504-301-2000
Doris Voitier, supt. Fax 301-2010
www.stbernard.k12.la.us
Chalmette HS 1,700/9-12
1100 E Judge Perez Dr 70043 504-301-2600
Wayne Warner, prin. Fax 301-2610
Jackson MS 600/6-8
201 8th St 70043 504-301-1500
Montrelle Sinegar, prin. Fax 301-1510
Rowley Alternative S 100/Alt
49 Madison Ave 70043 504-301-4001
Andre Bonnaffons, prin. Fax 301-4010
Other Schools – See Meraux, Saint Bernard

Nunez Community College Post-Sec.
3710 Paris Rd 70043 504-278-6200

Chauvin, Terrebonne, Pop. 2,885
Terrebonne Parish SD
Supt. — See Houma
Lacache MS 400/5-8
5266 Highway 56 70344 985-594-3945
Mark Thibodeaux, prin. Fax 594-4128

Choudrant, Lincoln, Pop. 836
Lincoln Parish SD
Supt. — See Ruston
Choudrant HS 300/7-12
PO Box 220 71227 318-768-2542
Tony Antley, prin. Fax 768-4182

Church Point, Acadia, Pop. 4,487
Acadia Parish SD
Supt. — See Crowley
Church Point HS 500/9-12
305 E Lougarre St 70525 337-684-5472
Lee Ward Bellard, prin. Fax 684-5137
Church Point MS 300/6-8
340 W Martin Luther King Dr 70525 337-684-6381
Cheri Baggett, prin. Fax 684-0123

Clarks, Caldwell, Pop. 1,011

Old Bethel Christian Academy 100/PK-12
PO Box 95 71415 318-649-0281
Sandra Richmond, prin. Fax 649-0281

Clinton, East Feliciana, Pop. 1,628
East Feliciana Parish SD 1,800/PK-12
PO Box 397 70722 225-683-8277
Carlos Sam, supt. Fax 683-3320
www.efpsb.k12.la.us
East Feliciana MS 300/6-8
PO Box 166 70722 225-683-3321
Laron McCurry, prin. Fax 683-5115
East Feliciana Parish Enrichment Academy 50/Alt
PO Box 166 70722 225-683-8198
Ella Philson, prin. Fax 683-4900
Other Schools – See Jackson

Silliman Institute 400/PK-12
PO Box 946 70722 225-683-5383
Ann Kent, admin. Fax 683-6728

Colfax, Grant, Pop. 1,531
Grant Parish SD 3,100/PK-12
PO Box 208 71417 318-627-3274
Sheila Jackson, supt. Fax 627-5931
www.gpsb.org
Other Schools – See Dry Prong, Georgetown, Montgomery

Columbia, Caldwell, Pop. 387
Caldwell Parish SD 1,500/PK-12
PO Box 1019 71418 318-649-2689
John Gullatt, supt. Fax 649-0636
www.caldwelledu.org/
Caldwell Parish HS 400/9-12
163 Spartan Dr 71418 318-649-2750
Heath Denison, prin. Fax 649-0021
Caldwell Parish JHS 400/6-8
114 Trojan Dr 71418 318-649-2340
Kim Adams, prin. Fax 649-2341

Converse, Sabine, Pop. 416
Sabine Parish SD
Supt. — See Many
Converse S 600/PK-12
PO Box 10 71419 318-567-2673
Cindy Mary, prin. Fax 567-3400

Cottonport, Avoyelles, Pop. 1,987

Central Louisiana Technical College Post-Sec.
508 Choupique Ln 71327 318-876-2401

Coushatta, Red River, Pop. 1,958
Red River Parish SD 1,500/PK-12
PO Box 1369 71019 318-932-4081
Alison N. Hughes, supt. Fax 932-4367
www.rrbulldogs.com/
Red River HS 300/9-12
PO Box 409 71019 318-932-4913
Carroll Daniels, prin. Fax 932-5344
Red River JHS 300/6-8
915 E Carrol St 71019 318-932-5265
Mike Peter, prin. Fax 932-9959

Riverdale Academy 300/PK-12
100 Riverdale Rd 71019 318-932-5876

Covington, Saint Tammany, Pop. 8,662
St. Tammany Parish SD 37,700/PK-12
PO Box 940 70434 985-892-2276
Trey Folse, supt. Fax 898-3267
www.stpsb.org
Covington HS 1,500/9-12
73030 Lions Dr 70433 985-892-3422
Roslyn Hanson, prin. Fax 875-9699
Pitcher JHS 300/7-8
415 S Jefferson Ave 70433 985-892-3021
Raphael Tillman, prin. Fax 892-1188
Other Schools – See Folsom, Madisonville, Mandeville, Pearl River, Slidell

Archbishop Hannan HS 300/8-12
71324 Highway 1077 70433 985-249-6363
Fr. Charles Latour, prin. Fax 249-6370
Aveda Institute Post-Sec.
1355 Polders Ln 70433 985-892-9953
Christ Episcopal S 400/PK-12
80 Christwood Blvd 70433 985-871-9902
Northlake Christian S 800/PK-12
70104 Wolverine Dr 70433 985-635-0400
Monty Fontenot M.Ed., head sch Fax 893-4363
St. Paul's HS 900/8-12
917 S Jahncke Ave 70433 985-892-3200
Trevor Watkins, prin. Fax 892-4048

St. Scholastica Academy 700/8-12
PO Box 1210 70434 985-892-2540
Dr. Elizabeth Laforge, prin. Fax 893-5256

Crowley, Acadia, Pop. 13,095
Acadia Parish SD 10,100/PK-12
PO Box 309 70527 337-783-3664
John Bourque, supt. Fax 783-3761
www.acadia.k12.la.us/
Acadia Parish Alternative S 50/Alt
404 W 12th St 70526 337-783-7188
Carolla Jolivette, prin. Fax 785-0794
Crowley HS 600/9-12
263 Hensgens Rd 70526 337-783-5313
Perry Myles, prin. Fax 783-7796
Crowley MS 600/6-8
401 W Northern Ave 70526 337-783-5305
Chad Lemelle, prin. Fax 783-5338
Other Schools – See Church Point, Iota, Midland, Rayne

Acadiana Technical College Post-Sec.
1933 W Hutchinson Ave 70526 337-788-7521
Northside Christian S 300/K-12
809 E Northern Ave 70526 337-783-3620
Brandon Bergeron, prin. Fax 788-3461
Notre Dame HS 400/9-12
910 N Eastern Ave 70526 337-783-3519
Cindy Istre, prin. Fax 788-2115

Cut Off, Lafourche, Pop. 5,828
Lafourche Parish SD
Supt. — See Thibodaux
South Lafourche HS 1,100/9-12
16911 E Main St 70345 985-632-5721
Gaye Cheramie, prin. Fax 632-6723

Delcambre, Vermilion, Pop. 1,846
Iberia Parish SD
Supt. — See New Iberia
Delcambre JSHS 500/6-12
601 W Main St 70528 337-685-2595
Kimberly Messman, prin. Fax 685-6099

Delhi, Richland, Pop. 2,885
Richland Parish SD
Supt. — See Rayville
Delhi HS 200/9-12
413 Main St 71232 318-878-2235
Barbara Turner, prin. Fax 878-8967
Delhi MS 200/5-8
106 Toombs St 71232 318-878-3748
Shirley McDade, prin. Fax 878-3749

Denham Springs, Livingston, Pop. 10,120
Livingston Parish SD
Supt. — See Livingston
Denham Springs Freshman HS 600/9-9
940 N Range Ave 70726 225-665-7890
Ken Magee, prin. Fax 665-1865
Denham Springs JHS 900/6-8
401 Hatchell Ln 70726 225-665-8898
Bryan Wax, prin. Fax 665-8601
Denham Springs SHS 1,500/10-12
1000 N Range Ave 70726 225-665-8851
Kelly Jones, prin. Fax 665-4082
Juban Parc JHS 600/6-8
12470 Brown Rd 70726 225-664-1001
Jeff Frizell, prin. Fax 664-5000
Live Oak HS 1,300/9-12
36079 Hwy 16 70706 225-665-8858
Beth Jones, prin. Fax 665-8850
Southside JHS 500/6-8
26535 LA Highway 16 70726 225-664-4221
Carlos Williams, prin. Fax 664-3307

Community Christian Academy 100/PK-12
400 N River Rd 70726 225-665-5696
Denham Springs Beauty College Post-Sec.
923 Florida Ave SE 70726 225-665-6188

Dequincy, Calcasieu, Pop. 3,178
Calcasieu Parish SD
Supt. — See Lake Charles
DeQuincy HS 400/9-12
207 N Overton St 70633 337-217-4530
Craig Neal, prin. Fax 217-4531
DeQuincy MS 300/6-8
1603 W 4th St 70633 337-217-4770
Denise Doyle, prin. Fax 217-4771

Deridder, Beauregard, Pop. 10,238
Beauregard Parish SD 6,000/PK-12
PO Box 938 70634 337-463-5551
Timothy Cooley M.Ed., supt. Fax 463-6735
www.beau.k12.la.us
Beauregard Alternative Program 50/Alt
506 Martin Luther King Dr 70634 337-462-2709
Mike Greene, prin. Fax 462-2710
DeRidder HS 800/9-12
723 ONeal St 70634 337-463-3266
Harry Hooker, prin. Fax 463-9358
DeRidder JHS 600/6-8
415 N Frusha Dr 70634 337-463-9083
David Wentzel, prin. Fax 463-7696
East Beauregard HS 400/6-12
5364 Highway 113 70634 337-328-7511
Larry Hollie, prin. Fax 328-8132
Other Schools – See Longville, Merryville, Singer

Destrehan, Saint Charles, Pop. 11,371
St. Charles Parish SD
Supt. — See Luling
Destrehan HS 1,500/9-12
1 Wildcat Ln 70047 985-764-9946
Stephen Weber, prin. Fax 764-9948
Hurst MS 700/6-8
170 Road Runner Ln 70047 985-764-6367
Steven Guitterrez, prin. Fax 764-2678

Deville, Rapides, Pop. 1,751
Rapides Parish SD
Supt. — See Alexandria
Buckeye JSHS 1,100/6-12
PO Box 439 71328 318-466-5678
Doyle DeWayne Vines, prin. Fax 466-9269

Dodson, Winn, Pop. 331
Winn Parish SD
Supt. — See Winnfield
Dodson S 300/PK-12
PO Box 97 71422 318-628-2172
Mike Hearne, prin. Fax 628-7515

Donaldsonville, Ascension, Pop. 7,399
Ascension Parish SD 21,400/PK-12
1100 Webster St 70346 225-391-7000
Patrice Pujol, supt. Fax 473-7820
www.apsb.org
Donaldsonville HS 400/9-12
100 Tiger Dr 70346 225-391-7900
Marvin Evans, prin. Fax 473-4496
Lowery MS 400/6-8
2389 Highway 1 S Ste A 70346 225-391-7550
Nicole Grimes, prin. Fax 473-2514
Other Schools – See Geismar, Gonzales, Prairieville, Saint Amant

Ascension Catholic HS 200/7-12
311 Saint Vincent St 70346 225-473-9227
Sandy Pizzolato, prin. Fax 473-9235

Doyline, Webster, Pop. 803
Webster Parish SD
Supt. — See Minden
Doyline S 500/PK-12
376 College St 71023 318-745-3673
Bridget Bridges, prin. Fax 745-3695

Dry Prong, Grant, Pop. 434
Grant Parish SD
Supt. — See Colfax
Grant HS 700/9-12
17779 Highway 167 71423 318-899-3331
Amanda Morrison, prin. Fax 899-5724
Grant JHS 400/7-8
17773 Highway 167 71423 318-899-5697
Robert Smith, prin. Fax 899-7346

Dulac, Terrebonne, Pop. 1,389
Terrebonne Parish SD
Supt. — See Houma
Grand Caillou MS 300/6-8
2161 Grand Caillou Rd, 985-876-7172
Judy Gaspard, prin. Fax 876-7279

Duson, Lafayette, Pop. 1,682
Lafayette Parish SD
Supt. — See Lafayette
Judice MS 500/6-8
2645 S Fieldspan Rd 70529 337-521-7890
Sonjie Fontenot, prin. Fax 521-7891

Edgard, Saint John the Baptist, Pop. 2,428
St. John The Baptist Parish SD
Supt. — See Reserve
West St. John HS 200/8-12
PO Box 160 70049 985-497-3271
Claude Hill, prin. Fax 497-5009

Elizabeth, Allen, Pop. 531
Allen Parish SD
Supt. — See Oberlin
Elizabeth S 400/PK-12
PO Box 580 70638 318-634-5341
Keith Morgan, prin. Fax 634-5218

Elmer, Rapides
Rapides Parish SD
Supt. — See Alexandria
Oak Hill HS 400/K-12
7362 Highway 112 71424 318-793-2014
Kerry Rogers, prin. Fax 793-8589

Elton, Jefferson Davis, Pop. 1,103
Jefferson Davis Parish SD
Supt. — See Jennings
Elton JSHS 300/6-12
903 2nd St 70532 337-584-2991
Danielle Simien, prin. Fax 584-2244

Epps, West Carroll, Pop. 844
West Carroll Parish SD
Supt. — See Oak Grove
Epps S 300/PK-12
PO Box 277 71237 318-926-3624
Penny Hale, prin. Fax 926-5655

Erath, Vermilion, Pop. 2,099
Vermilion Parish SD
Supt. — See Abbeville
Erath HS 500/9-12
808 S Broadway St 70533 337-937-8451
Marc Turner, prin. Fax 937-5109
Erath MS 500/6-8
800 S Broadway St 70533 337-937-4441
Wendy Stoute, prin. Fax 937-5125

Eunice, Saint Landry, Pop. 10,256
St. Landry Parish SD
Supt. — See Opelousas
Eunice Career & Technical Education Ctr. Vo/Tech
421 S 10th St 70535 337-457-8686
Kristina Joubert, prin. Fax 457-0307
Eunice HS 700/9-12
301 S Bobcat Dr 70535 337-457-3011
Mitchell Fontenot, prin. Fax 457-3720
Eunice JHS 400/7-8
751 W Oak Ave 70535 337-457-7386
Lakesha Miller, prin. Fax 457-1764

Louisiana Academy of Beauty Post-Sec.
550 E Laurel Ave 70535 337-457-7627
Louisiana State University Eunice Post-Sec.
2048 Johnson Hwy 70535 337-457-7311
St. Edmund HS 200/7-12
351 W Magnolia Ave 70535 337-457-2592
Laurie Doucet, prin. Fax 457-2510

Evans, Vernon
Vernon Parish SD
Supt. — See Leesville
Evans S 400/PK-12
18829 Highway 111 70639 337-286-5289
Ulita Watson, prin. Fax 286-9298

Farmerville, Union, Pop. 3,818
Union Parish SD 2,100/PK-12
PO Box 308 71241 318-368-9715
Dr. George Cannon, supt. Fax 368-1012
www.unionpsd.org
Union Parish HS 600/9-12
300 Anthony St 71241 318-368-2661
David Gray, prin. Fax 368-2229
Union Parish JHS 300/7-8
606 Bernice St 71241 318-368-9235
Kristi Auger, prin. Fax 368-1989

Union Christian Academy 200/PK-12
110 W Hill St 71241 318-368-8890

Ferriday, Concordia, Pop. 3,491
Concordia Parish SD
Supt. — See Vidalia
Concordia Education Center 50/Alt
160 Kindergarten Rd 71334 318-757-3941
Lillian Franklin, prin. Fax 757-3330
Ferriday HS 300/9-12
801 EE Wallace Blvd N 71334 318-757-8626
Joyce Russ, prin. Fax 757-0763
Ferriday JHS 300/6-8
201 Martin Luther King Blvd 71334 318-757-8695
Toyua Watson, prin. Fax 757-8696

Central Louisiana Technical College Post-Sec.
PO Box 1465 71334 318-757-6501

Florien, Sabine, Pop. 616
Sabine Parish SD
Supt. — See Many
Florien S 600/PK-12
500 High School Rd 71429 318-586-3681
Eddie Jones, prin. Fax 586-3822

Folsom, Saint Tammany, Pop. 708
St. Tammany Parish SD
Supt. — See Covington
Folsom JHS 200/6-8
83055 Hay Hollow Rd 70437 985-796-3724
Sharon Garrett, prin. Fax 796-3701

Forest, West Carroll, Pop. 348
West Carroll Parish SD
Supt. — See Oak Grove
Forest S 600/PK-12
PO Box 368 71242 318-428-3672
Christy Boyte, prin. Fax 428-8875

Franklin, Saint Mary, Pop. 7,561
St. Mary Parish SD
Supt. — See Centerville
Franklin HS 400/9-12
1401 Cynthia St 70538 337-828-0143
Tybus Burdett, prin. Fax 828-0184
Franklin JHS 300/6-8
525 Morris St 70538 337-828-0855
J. Bertrand Ina, prin. Fax 828-5095
St. Mary Parish Alternative Program 100/Alt
131 Clausen Rd S 70538 337-836-9388
Harry Williams, admin. Fax 836-9397

Hanson Memorial HS 300/6-12
903 Anderson St 70538 337-828-3487
Kim Adams, prin. Fax 828-0787

Franklinton, Washington, Pop. 3,833
Washington Parish SD 5,300/PK-12
PO Box 587 70438 985-839-3436
Darrell Fairburn, supt. Fax 839-5464
www.wpsb.org
Franklinton HS 800/9-12
1 Demon Cir 70438 985-839-6781
Lisa Tanner, prin. Fax 839-9830
Franklinton JHS 700/6-8
617 Main St 70438 985-839-3501
Tiffany Hughes-Smith, prin. Fax 839-6912
Pine JSHS 600/6-12
1 Raider Dr 70438 985-848-5243
Jennifer Thomas, prin. Fax 848-9433
Other Schools – See Mount Hermon, Varnado

Bowling Green S 400/PK-12
700 Varnado St 70438 985-839-5317
Beverly Young, admin. Fax 839-5668

French Settlement, Livingston, Pop. 1,104
Livingston Parish SD
Supt. — See Livingston
French Settlement JSHS 400/7-12
15875 LA Highway 16 70733 225-698-3561
Lance Hutson, prin. Fax 698-6458

Geismar, Ascension
Ascension Parish SD
Supt. — See Donaldsonville
Dutchtown HS 2,000/9-12
13165 Highway 73 70734 225-391-6200
Carli Francois, prin. Fax 677-8191
Dutchtown MS 800/6-8
13078 Highway 73 70734 225-391-7800
Doug Walker, prin. Fax 621-2351

Georgetown, Grant, Pop. 323
Grant Parish SD
Supt. — See Colfax
Georgetown S 200/PK-12
PO Box 99 71432 318-827-5306
Carla Lasyone Ph.D., prin. Fax 827-9481

Gibsland, Bienville, Pop. 966
Bienville Parish SD
Supt. — See Arcadia
Gibsland-Coleman S 200/K-12
PO Box 70 71028 318-843-6247
Samuel Andrews, prin. Fax 843-9804

Glenmora, Rapides, Pop. 1,328
Rapides Parish SD
Supt. — See Alexandria
Glenmora HS 300/K-12
PO Box 697 71433 318-748-8145
Carrol Babb, prin. Fax 748-8146

Plainview S 300/PK-12
10935 Highway 112 71433 318-634-5944
Sonia Rasmussen, prin. Fax 634-5389

Golden Meadow, Lafourche, Pop. 2,060
Lafourche Parish SD
Supt. — See Thibodaux
Golden Meadow MS 400/6-8
630 S Bayou Dr 70357 985-475-7314
Hennessy Melancon, prin. Fax 475-6623

Gonzales, Ascension, Pop. 9,648
Ascension Parish SD
Supt. — See Donaldsonville
Central MS 700/6-8
14101 Roddy Rd 70737 225-391-6400
Monica Hills, prin. Fax 621-2682
East Ascension HS 1,800/9-12
612 E Worthy St 70737 225-391-6100
Traci McCorkle, prin. Fax 621-2397
Gonzales MS 600/6-8
1502 W Orice Roth Rd 70737 225-391-6450
Lori Charlet, prin. Fax 621-2509

Ascension Christian HS 200/7-12
14408 E A Academy Rd 70737 225-622-2800
Mark Pellegrin M.S., supt. Fax 622-2875
St. Theresa S 300/4-8
212 E New River St 70737 225-647-2803
Christine Musso, prin. Fax 647-7814

Grambling, Lincoln, Pop. 4,930

Grambling State University Post-Sec.
403 Main St 71245 318-274-3811

Grand Cane, DeSoto, Pop. 242

Central S 100/K-12
PO Box 187 71032 318-858-3319

Grand Chenier, Cameron
Cameron Parish SD
Supt. — See Cameron
South Cameron S 300/PK-12
753 Oak Grove Hwy 70643 337-542-4628
Bobbye Delaney, prin. Fax 542-4419

Grand Coteau, Saint Landry, Pop. 940

School of the Sacred Heart 500/PK-12
PO Box 310 70541 337-662-5275
Dr. Yvonne Adler, head sch Fax 662-3011

Grand Isle, Jefferson, Pop. 1,269
Jefferson Parish SD
Supt. — See Harvey
Grand Isle S 100/PK-12
PO Box 995 70358 985-787-2577
Richard Augustin, prin. Fax 787-3878

Grant, Allen
Allen Parish SD
Supt. — See Oberlin
Fairview S 400/PK-12
PO Box 216 70644 318-634-5354
Pylla Turner, prin. Fax 634-5357

Gray, Terrebonne, Pop. 5,450
Terrebonne Parish SD
Supt. — See Houma
Bourgeois HS 1,400/9-12
1 Reservation Ct 70359 985-872-3277
Matthew Hodson, prin. Fax 872-3270

Greensburg, Saint Helena, Pop. 714
St. Helena Parish SD 800/PK-12
PO Box 540 70441 225-222-4349
Dr. Kelli Joseph, supt. Fax 222-4937
www.sthpk-12.net
St. Helena College and Career Academy 300/7-12
14340 Highway 37 70441 225-222-4402
Reginald Douglas, prin. Fax 222-6986

Northshore Technical Community College Post-Sec.
PO Box 1300 70441 225-222-4251

Gretna, Jefferson, Pop. 17,467
Jefferson Parish SD
Supt. — See Harvey
Gretna MS 700/6-8
910 Gretna Blvd 70053 504-366-0120
Scott Deemer, prin. Fax 366-8807
Jefferson HS 500/9-12
17 Gretna Blvd 70053 504-363-4300
Andrew Vincent, prin. Fax 361-1114
Ruppel Academy for Advanced Studies 300/6-8
815 Huey P Long Ave 70053 504-361-8905
Emily Miller, prin. Fax 361-0792

Muslim Academy 200/1-12
440 Realty Dr 70056 504-433-1960

Gueydan, Vermilion, Pop. 1,385
Vermilion Parish SD
Supt. — See Abbeville
Gueydan HS 200/6-12
901 Main St 70542 337-536-6938
Brandy Broussard, prin. Fax 536-7000

Hackberry, Cameron, Pop. 1,258
Cameron Parish SD
Supt. — See Cameron
Hackberry S 200/PK-12
1390 School St 70645 337-762-3305
Michelle Dunham, prin. Fax 762-3304

Hammond, Tangipahoa, Pop. 19,799
Tangipahoa Parish SD
Supt. — See Amite
Hammond High Magnet S 1,400/9-12
45168 River Rd 70401 985-345-7235
Dr. Beth Moulds, prin. Fax 345-5252
Hammond Jr High Magnet S 500/7-8
111 J W Davis Dr 70403 985-345-2654
Mildred Johnson, prin. Fax 542-4215
Tangipahoa Alternative Solutions Program 100/Alt
411 E Crystal St 70401 985-542-5634
Marilyn Dunn, prin. Fax 542-9987

Compass Career College Post-Sec.
42353 Deluxe Plz Ste 20 70403 985-419-2050
North Oaks Medical Center Post-Sec.
15790 Medical Arts Dr 70403 985-543-6600
Northshore Technical Community College Post-Sec.
PO Box 489 70404 985-543-4120
St. Thomas Aquinas HS 400/9-12
14520 Voss Dr 70401 985-542-7662
Jose Becerra, prin. Fax 542-4010
Southeastern Louisiana University Post-Sec.
PO Box 784 70404 985-549-2000

Harrisonburg, Catahoula, Pop. 340
Catahoula Parish SD 1,500/PK-12
PO Box 690 71340 318-744-5727
Dr. Gwile Freeman, supt. Fax 744-9221
cpsbla.org/
Harrisonburg HS 300/K-12
PO Box 710 71340 318-744-5273
S. Floyd, prin. Fax 744-5273
Other Schools – See Jonesville, Sicily Island

Harvey, Jefferson, Pop. 20,018
Jefferson Parish SD 45,100/PK-12
501 Manhattan Blvd 70058 504-349-7600
Isaac Joseph, supt. Fax 349-7960
www.jppss.k12.la.us
Cox HS 1,000/9-12
2200 Lapalco Blvd 70058 504-367-6388
Mark Perry, prin. Fax 367-3176
West Jefferson HS 1,200/9-12
2200 8th St 70058 504-368-6055
Vanessa Brown-Lewis, prin. Fax 368-0535
Other Schools – See Avondale, Grand Isle, Gretna, Jefferson, Kenner, Lafitte, Marrero, Metairie, Terrytown, Westwego

Haughton, Bossier, Pop. 3,398
Bossier Parish SD
Supt. — See Benton
Haughton HS 1,200/9-12
210 E McKinley Ave 71037 318-549-5450
Gene Couvillion, prin. Fax 549-5470
Haughton MS 1,000/6-8
395 S Elm St 71037 318-549-5560
Waylon Bates, prin. Fax 549-5573

Haynesville, Claiborne, Pop. 2,308
Claiborne Parish SD
Supt. — See Homer
Haynesville JSHS 300/4-12
9930 Highway 79 71038 318-624-0905
Chris Brooks, prin. Fax 624-2488

Claiborne Academy 300/PK-12
6741 Highway 79 71038 318-927-2747

Holden, Livingston
Livingston Parish SD
Supt. — See Livingston
Holden S 600/K-12
30120 LA 441 Hwy 70744 225-567-9367
Paula Green, prin. Fax 567-5248

Homer, Claiborne, Pop. 3,200
Claiborne Parish SD 1,700/PK-12
PO Box 600 71040 318-927-3502
William Kennedy, supt. Fax 927-9184
www.claibornepsb.org
Homer HS 200/9-12
1008 N Main St 71040 318-927-2985
Lee Simms, prin. Fax 927-4733
Homer JHS 200/5-8
612 Pelican Dr 71040 318-927-2826
Sue Barfield, prin. Fax 927-4376
Other Schools – See Haynesville, Summerfield

Hornbeck, Vernon, Pop. 464
Vernon Parish SD
Supt. — See Leesville
Hornbeck S 400/PK-12
PO Box 9 71439 318-565-4440
Raymond Jones, prin. Fax 565-4136

Houma, Terrebonne, Pop. 33,132
Lafourche Parish SD
Supt. — See Thibodaux
Bayou Blue MS 500/5-8
196 Mazerac St 70364 985-851-1952
Andre Adams, prin. Fax 851-1849

Terrebonne Parish SD 18,400/PK-12
PO Box 5097 70361 985-876-7400
Philip Martin, supt. Fax 872-0054
www.tpsd.org
East Street Alternative S 50/Alt
609 East St 70363 985-876-1093
Tommy Salter, prin. Fax 851-7931
Ellender Memorial HS 900/9-12
3012 Patriot Dr 70363 985-868-7903
Blaise Pellegrin, prin. Fax 868-3503
Evergreen JHS 800/7-8
5000 W Main St 70360 985-876-2606
Kelly Burlette, prin. Fax 868-4395
Houma JHS 1,100/7-9
315 Saint Charles St 70360 985-872-1511
Darrell Dillard, prin. Fax 872-5121
Oaklawn JHS 500/7-8
2215 Acadian Dr 70363 985-872-2904
Charles Bergeron, prin. Fax 917-1917
Terrebonne Career & Tech HS Vo/Tech
3051 Patriot Dr 70363 985-851-1163
William Simmons, prin. Fax 851-4480
Terrebonne HS 1,000/10-12
7318 Main St 70360 985-879-3377
Julio Contreras, prin. Fax 223-2270
Bayou Cane Adult Education Adult
6484 W Main St 70360 985-876-3180
Marilyn Schwartz, coord. Fax 876-0411
Other Schools – See Bourg, Chauvin, Dulac, Gray, Montegut

Blue Cliff College-Houma — Post-Sec.
803 Barrow St 70360 — 985-601-4000
Covenant Christian Academy — 200/K-12
144 Rue Des Affaires 70364 — 985-851-7567
Jason Hutchinson M.Ed., prin. — Fax 851-1087
Houma Christian S — 400/PK-12
109 Valhi Blvd 70360 — 985-851-7423
James Champagne, prin. — Fax 872-4958
Messiah Montessori S — 100/PK-12
PO Box 20027 70360 — 985-857-8808
Dr. Jules Boquet, head sch — Fax 851-3116
Omega Institute of Cosmetology — Post-Sec.
229 S Hollywood Rd 70360 — 985-876-9334
South Louisiana Beauty College — Post-Sec.
300 Howard Ave 70363 — 985-873-8978
Vandebilt Catholic HS — 900/8-12
209 S Hollywood Rd 70360 — 985-876-2551
Yvonne Weimer, prin. — Fax 868-9774

Independence, Saint Helena, Pop. 1,638
Tangipahoa Parish SD
Supt. — See Amite
Independence HS — 500/9-12
270 Tiger Ave 70443 — 985-878-9436
Mike Stant, prin. — Fax 878-4831
Independence Middle Magnet S — 300/5-8
300 W 2nd St 70443 — 985-878-4376
Alexa Hookfin, prin. — Fax 878-4848

Iota, Acadia, Pop. 1,481
Acadia Parish SD
Supt. — See Crowley
Iota HS — 500/9-12
456 S 5th St 70543 — 337-779-2534
Dr. Cindy Abshire, prin. — Fax 779-2872
Iota MS — 300/6-8
426 S 5th St 70543 — 337-779-2536
Lee Ann Wall, prin. — Fax 779-2594

Iowa, Calcasieu, Pop. 2,909
Calcasieu Parish SD
Supt. — See Lake Charles
Iowa MSHS — 500/6-12
401 W Miller Ave 70647 — 337-217-4380
Michael Oakley, prin. — Fax 217-4381

Jackson, East Feliciana, Pop. 3,776
East Feliciana Parish SD
Supt. — See Clinton
East Feliciana HS — 400/9-12
3501 Highway 10 70748 — 225-634-5931
Curt Green, prin. — Fax 634-3207

Baton Rouge Community College Jackson — Post-Sec.
3337 Highway 10 70748 — 225-634-2636

Jeanerette, Iberia, Pop. 5,487
Iberia Parish SD
Supt. — See New Iberia
Jeanerette HS — 300/9-12
8217 E Old Spanish Trl 70544 — 337-276-6038
Linda Freeman, prin. — Fax 276-5016

Jefferson, Jefferson, Pop. 11,058
Jefferson Parish SD
Supt. — See Harvey
Martyn Alternative S — 50/Alt
1108 Shrewsbury Rd 70121 — 504-838-6933
Theresa Henderson, prin. — Fax 831-0247
Riverdale HS — 900/9-12
240 Riverdale Dr 70121 — 504-833-7288
Danielle Yunusah, prin. — Fax 340-4531
Riverdale MS — 800/6-8
3900 Jefferson Hwy 70121 — 504-828-2706
Randy Bennett, prin. — Fax 833-5125

Jena, LaSalle, Pop. 3,373
LaSalle Parish SD — 2,700/PK-12
PO Box 90 71342 — 318-992-2161
Roy Breithaupt, supt. — Fax 992-8457
www.lasallepsb.com
Jena HS — 500/9-12
PO Box 89 71342 — 318-992-5195
Glen Joiner, prin. — Fax 992-4797
Jena JHS — 400/6-8
PO Box 920 71342 — 318-992-5815
Rhonda Russell, prin. — Fax 992-6392
Other Schools – See Olla, Urania

Jennings, Jefferson Davis, Pop. 10,205
Jefferson Davis Parish SD — 5,900/PK-12
PO Box 640 70546 — 337-824-1834
Brian M. LeJeune, supt. — Fax 824-9737
www.jeffersondavis.org
Hathaway S — 500/PK-12
4040 Pine Island Hwy 70546 — 337-824-4452
Jeremy Fuselier, prin. — Fax 824-2769
Jennings HS — 900/7-12
2310 N Sherman St 70546 — 337-824-0642
Benjamin Oustalet, prin. — Fax 824-5585
West End Instructional Center — Alt
802 W Jefferson St 70546 — 337-824-9521
Kent Ray, prin. — Fax 824-9978
Other Schools – See Elton, Lacassine, Lake Arthur, Roanoke, Welsh

---

Bethel Christian S — 200/PK-12
15147 Highway 102 70546 — 337-824-0020
Chris Wales, prin. — Fax 824-0579

Jonesboro, Jackson, Pop. 4,648
Jackson Parish SD — 2,300/PK-12
PO Box 705 71251 — 318-259-4456
Wayne Alford, supt. — Fax 259-2527
www.jpsb.us/
Jonesboro-Hodge HS — 300/9-12
225 Pershing Hwy 71251 — 318-259-4138
Michael Beck, prin. — Fax 259-2701
Jonesboro-Hodge MS — 300/5-8
440 Old Winnfield Rd 71251 — 318-259-6611
Norman Amos, prin. — Fax 259-9699
Weston S — 700/PK-12
213 Highway 505 71251 — 318-259-7313
Dr. Robin Potts, prin. — Fax 259-1056
Other Schools – See Quitman

Jonesville, Catahoula, Pop. 2,258
Catahoula Parish SD
Supt. — See Harrisonburg
Block HS — 300/8-12
300 Division St 71343 — 318-339-7996
Jeffrey Odom, prin. — Fax 339-7901
Catahoula Parish Alternative S — Alt
300 Division St 71343 — 318-339-7996
Andrea Cruse, supt. — Fax 339-7901
Central S — 100/K-12
244 Larto Bayou Rd 71343 — 318-339-7574
Johnnie Adams, prin. — Fax 339-7925

Kaplan, Vermilion, Pop. 4,526
Vermilion Parish SD
Supt. — See Abbeville
Kaplan HS — 500/9-12
200 E Pirates Ln 70548 — 337-643-6385
Janet Guerrini, prin. — Fax 643-3543
Rost MS — 400/5-8
112 W 6th St 70548 — 337-643-8545
David Dupuis, prin. — Fax 643-7013

Kenner, Jefferson, Pop. 65,713
Jefferson Parish SD
Supt. — See Harvey
Bonnabel Magnet Academy HS — 1,400/9-12
2801 Bruin Dr 70065 — 504-443-4564
Dawn Kalb, prin. — Fax 443-3401
Roosevelt MS — 600/6-8
3315 Maine Ave 70065 — 504-443-1361
John Olson, prin. — Fax 443-3425

Herzing University — Post-Sec.
2500 Williams Blvd 70062 — 504-733-0074
John Jay Kenner Academy — Post-Sec.
2844 Tennessee Ave 70062 — 504-467-2951
Southwest University — Post-Sec.
2200 Veterans Memorial Blvd 70062 — 504-468-2900

Kentwood, Tangipahoa, Pop. 2,191
Tangipahoa Parish SD
Supt. — See Amite
Kentwood High Magnet S — 300/7-12
603 9th St 70444 — 985-229-2881
Rochell Bates, prin. — Fax 229-6031
Sumner HS — 500/9-12
15841 Highway 440 70444 — 985-229-8805
Walter Stuckey, prin. — Fax 229-2043
Sumner MS — 400/6-8
15649 Highway 440 70444 — 985-310-2152
Brenda Johnson, prin. — Fax 229-4257

Kilbourne, West Carroll, Pop. 412
West Carroll Parish SD
Supt. — See Oak Grove
Kilbourne S — 300/PK-12
PO Box 339 71253 — 318-428-3721
Brandon Smith, prin. — Fax 428-3860

Kinder, Allen, Pop. 2,412
Allen Parish SD
Supt. — See Oberlin
Kinder HS — 300/9-12
145 Highway 383 70648 — 337-738-2886
Charley Lemons, prin. — Fax 738-5665
Kinder MS — 400/5-8
414 N 12th St 70648 — 337-738-3223
Tracey Odom, prin. — Fax 738-3425

Labadieville, Assumption, Pop. 1,837
Assumption Parish SD
Supt. — See Napoleonville
Labadieville MS — 300/5-8
2747 Highway 1 70372 — 985-526-4227
Corey Crochet, prin. — Fax 526-4163

Lacassine, Jefferson Davis, Pop. 475
Jefferson Davis Parish SD
Supt. — See Jennings
Lacassine S — 700/PK-12
PO Box 50 70650 — 337-588-4205
Christina Fontenot, prin. — Fax 588-4283

Lafayette, Lafayette, Pop. 118,722
Lafayette Parish SD — 30,500/PK-12
PO Box 2158 70502 — 337-521-7000
Dr. Donald Aguillard, supt. — Fax 233-0977
www.lpssonline.com
Acadiana HS — 1,700/9-12
315 Rue Du Belier 70506 — 337-521-7950
David LeJeune, prin. — Fax 521-7951
Acadian MS — 400/6-8
4201 Moss St 70507 — 337-521-7840
Rollan Moore, prin. — Fax 521-7841
Alleman MS — 1,100/5-8
600 Roselawn Blvd 70503 — 337-521-7850
Jennifer Gardner, prin. — Fax 521-7851
Breaux MS — 700/6-8
1400 S Orange St 70501 — 337-521-7860
Stephen Judice, prin. — Fax 521-7861
Carencro HS — 1,100/9-12
721 W Butcher Switch Rd 70507 — 337-521-7960
Mary Qualey, prin. — Fax 521-7961
Comeaux HS — 1,900/9-12
100 W Bluebird St 70508 — 337-521-7970
Mary Zeno, prin. — Fax 521-7971
Early College Academy — 200/9-12
320 Devalcourt St 70506 — 337-521-8956
Anne Castille, prin. — Fax 262-1940
Lafayette HS — 2,400/9-12
3000 W Congress St 70506 — 337-521-7980
Dr. Donald Thornton, prin. — Fax 521-7981
Lafayette MS — 500/6-8
1301 W University Ave 70506 — 337-521-7900
Allison El Koubi, prin. — Fax 521-7901
Martin MS — 700/5-8
401 Broadmoor Blvd 70503 — 337-521-7910
Jeanne Hebert, prin. — Fax 521-7911
Moss Preparatory Program — 300/Alt
801 Mudd Ave 70501 — 337-521-7580
Jody Duhon, admin. — Fax 521-7581
Northside HS — 800/9-12
301 Dunand St 70501 — 337-521-7990
Julia Williams, prin. — Fax 521-7991
Smith Career Center — Vo/Tech
200 18th St 70501 — 337-521-7570
Alicia Caesar, prin. — Fax 521-7571
Thibodaux STEM Magnet Academy — 700/6-12
805 Teurlings Dr 70501 — 337-521-7920
Jeff Debetaz, prin. — Fax 521-7921
Other Schools – See Broussard, Carencro, Duson, Scott, Youngsville

---

Ascension Episcopal S — 700/PK-12
1030 Johnston St 70501 — 337-233-9748
Paul Quick, hdmstr. — Fax 269-9768
Blue Cliff College — Post-Sec.
120 James Comeaux Rd 70508 — 337-269-0620
Cosmetology Training Center — Post-Sec.
2516 Johnston St 70503 — 337-237-6868
Delta College of Arts & Technology — Post-Sec.
200 Republic Ave Ste F 70508 — 337-988-5455
Lafayette Christian Academy — 800/PK-12
220 Portland Ave 70507 — 337-234-9860
Lafayette General Medical Center — Post-Sec.
PO Box 52009 70505 — 337-261-7381
Lockworks Academie of Hairdressing — Post-Sec.
2922 Johnston St 70503 — 337-233-0511
Remington College — Post-Sec.
303 Rue Louis XIV 70508 — 337-981-4010
Ronnie & Dorman's School of Hair Design — Post-Sec.
201 Saint Joseph St 70506 — 337-232-1806
St. Genevieve MS — 200/5-8
91 Teurlings Dr 70501 — 337-266-5553
Julie Zaunbrecher, prin. — Fax 266-5775
St. Thomas More HS — 1,000/9-12
450 E Farrel Rd 70508 — 337-988-3700
Kelley Leger, prin. — Fax 988-2911
South Louisiana Community College — Post-Sec.
1101 Bertrand Dr 70506 — 337-521-9000
South Louisiana Community College — Post-Sec.
320 Devalcourt St 70506 — 337-521-9000
Teurlings Catholic HS — 700/9-12
139 Teurlings Dr 70501 — 337-235-5711
Michael Boyer, prin. — Fax 234-8057
Unitech Training Academy — Post-Sec.
3605 Ambassador Caffery Pky 70503 — 337-988-6764
University Medical Center — Post-Sec.
2390 W Congress St 70506 — 337-261-6004
University of Louisiana at Lafayette — Post-Sec.
104 E University Ave 70503 — 337-482-1000

Lafitte, Jefferson, Pop. 956
Jefferson Parish SD
Supt. — See Harvey
Fisher MSHS — 500/6-12
2529 Jean Lafitte Blvd 70067 — 504-689-3665
Debbie Dantin, prin. — Fax 689-7556

Lake Arthur, Jefferson Davis, Pop. 2,693
Jefferson Davis Parish SD
Supt. — See Jennings
Lake Arthur JSHS — 400/7-12
4374 Tiger Ln 70549 — 337-774-5152
Amanda Fontenot, prin. — Fax 774-2522

Lake Charles, Calcasieu, Pop. 70,438
Calcasieu Parish SD — 32,100/PK-12
PO Box 800 70602 — 337-217-4000
Karl Bruchhaus, supt. — Fax 217-4051
www.cpsb.org
Barbe HS — 1,900/9-12
2200 W McNeese St 70605 — 337-217-4460
Shannon LaFargue, prin. — Fax 217-4461
Calcasieu Parish Alternative HS — 100/Alt
745 S Shattuck St 70601 — 337-217-4290
Kenny Brown, prin. — Fax 217-4291
College Street T & I Vocational Ctr — Vo/Tech
739 E College St 70607 — 337-217-4370
Justin Mahoney, prin. — Fax 217-4371
Houston HS — 1,200/9-12
880 Sam Houston Jones Pkwy 70611 — 337-217-4480
Shannon Foolkes, prin. — Fax 217-4481
LaGrange HS — 1,000/9-12
3420 Louisiana Ave 70607 — 337-217-4960
Rico Guillory, prin. — Fax 217-4961
Lake Charles/Boston Academy — 400/9-12
1509 Enterprise Blvd 70601 — 337-217-4390
Beth Fraser, prin. — Fax 217-4391
Molo Magnet MS — 300/6-8
2300 Medora St 70601 — 337-217-4710
Shonna Anderson, prin. — Fax 217-4711
Moss Bluff MS — 1,000/6-8
297 Park Rd 70611 — 337-217-4570
Kendall Fontenot, prin. — Fax 217-4571
Oak Park MS — 500/6-8
2200 Oak Park Blvd 70601 — 337-217-4830
Martin Guillory, prin. — Fax 217-4831
STEPS HS — 9-12
3820 Bennett Johnston Ave 70615 — 337-491-2607
Matthew Rion, prin. — Fax 491-2649
Washington-Marion Magnet HS — 700/9-12
2802 Pineview St 70615 — 337-217-4540
Jackie Shelton, prin. — Fax 217-4541
Welsh MS — 1,200/6-8
1500 W Mcneese St 70605 — 337-217-4410
Bobby Jack Thompson, prin. — Fax 217-4412
White MS — 600/6-8
1000 E McNeese St 70607 — 337-217-4810
Owen Clanton, prin. — Fax 217-4811
Other Schools – See Bell City, Dequincy, Iowa, Starks, Sulphur, Vinton, Westlake

Cameron Parish SD
Supt. — See Cameron
Grand Lake S — 800/PK-12
1039 Highway 384 70607 — 337-905-2231
Holly Castile, prin. — Fax 905-2961

Covenant Grace Academy — 50/K-12
2110 E McNeese St 70607 — 337-474-2424
Marla Pennick, admin. — Fax 474-2424
Delta School of Business and Technology — Post-Sec.
517 Broad St 70601 — 337-439-5765
Hamilton Christian Academy — 300/PK-12
1415 8th St 70601 — 337-439-1178
Dr. Wayne McEntire, prin. — Fax 433-1877
Lake Charles Memorial Hospital — Post-Sec.
1701 Oak Park Blvd 70601 — 337-494-3200

McNeese State University — Post-Sec.
4205 Ryan St 70605 — 337-475-5000
St. Louis HS — 600/9-12
1620 Bank St 70601 — 337-436-7275
Christopher Fontenot, pres. — Fax 436-6792
St. Patrick's Hospital — Post-Sec.
524 S Ryan St 70601 — 337-491-7730
Sowela Technical Community College — Post-Sec.
3820 Senator Johnston Ave 70615 — 337-421-6565
Stage One - The Hair School — Post-Sec.
209 W College St 70605 — 337-474-0533

Lake Providence, East Carroll, Pop. 3,969
East Carroll Parish SD — 1,100/PK-12
PO Box 792 71254 — 318-559-2222
Dr. Voleria Millikin, supt. — Fax 559-3864
www.e-carrollschools.org
Griffin Middle Academy — 200/6-8
1205 Charles D Jones Blvd 71254 — 318-559-1395
Muriel Williams, prin. — Fax 559-0679
Trass HS — 300/9-12
700 Martin Luther King Jr 71254 — 318-559-1984
Rickey Taylor, prin. — Fax 559-5380

Briarfield Academy — 200/PK-12
301 Riddle Ln 71254 — 318-559-2360
Debra Bowers, head sch — Fax 559-2360

Laplace, Saint John the Baptist, Pop. 29,464

St. Charles Catholic HS — 400/8-12
100 Dominican Rd 70068 — 985-652-3809
Andrew Cupit, prin. — Fax 652-2609

Larose, Lafourche, Pop. 7,283
Lafourche Parish SD
Supt. — See Thibodaux
Larose-Cut Off MS — 500/6-8
13356 W Main St 70373 — 985-693-3273
Samantha Lagarde, prin. — Fax 693-3270

Lecompte, Rapides, Pop. 1,209
Rapides Parish SD
Supt. — See Alexandria
Rapides HS — 200/9-12
PO Box 770 71346 — 318-776-9371
Jeff Hickman, prin. — Fax 776-5844

Red River Academy — 100/7-12
PO Box 1255 71346 — 318-776-5655

Leesville, Vernon, Pop. 6,343
Vernon Parish SD — 8,900/PK-12
201 Belview Rd 71446 — 337-239-3401
James Williams, supt. — Fax 238-5777
www.vpsb.k12.la.us
Hicks S — 300/PK-12
1296 Hicks School Rd 71446 — 337-239-9645
Rhonda Roberts, prin. — Fax 239-6149
Leesville HS — 800/9-12
502 Berry Ave 71446 — 337-239-3464
Tammie Phillips, prin. — Fax 239-2485
Leesville JHS — 500/7-8
480 Berry Ave 71446 — 337-239-3874
Angel Williams, prin. — Fax 238-4113
Pickering JSHS — 600/7-12
180 Lebleu Rd 71446 — 337-537-1555
Dana Donaldson, prin. — Fax 537-3019
Other Schools – See Anacoco, Evans, Hornbeck, Pitkin, Rosepine, Simpson

---

Central Louisiana Technical College — Post-Sec.
15014 Lake Charles Hwy 71446 — 337-537-3135
Faith Training Christian Academy — 400/PK-12
603 E Mechanic St 71446 — 337-329-1569

Lena, Rapides
Rapides Parish SD
Supt. — See Alexandria
Northwood HS — 700/PK-12
8830 Highway 1 N 71447 — 318-793-8021
Jill Summers, prin. — Fax 793-8503

Livingston, Livingston, Pop. 1,758
Livingston Parish SD — 25,300/PK-12
PO Box 1130 70754 — 225-686-7044
John Watson, supt. — Fax 686-3052
www.lpsb.org
Doyle JSHS — 600/7-12
PO Box 160 70754 — 225-686-2318
Thomas Hodges, prin. — Fax 686-2701
Other Schools – See Albany, Denham Springs, French Settlement, Holden, Maurepas, Springfield, Walker, Watson

Livonia, Pointe Coupee, Pop. 1,418
Pointe Coupee Parish SD
Supt. — See New Roads
Livonia HS — 900/7-12
PO Box 549 70755 — 225-637-2532
Stacey Gueho, prin. — Fax 637-3024

Lockport, Lafourche, Pop. 2,549
Lafourche Parish SD
Supt. — See Thibodaux
Lockport MS — 300/6-8
720 Main St 70374 — 985-532-2597
Ashleigh Landry, prin. — Fax 532-5811

Logansport, DeSoto, Pop. 1,527
DeSoto Parish SD
Supt. — See Mansfield
Logansport S — 700/PK-12
PO Box 549 71049 — 318-697-4338
Matt LaFollette, prin. — Fax 697-1120
Stanley S — 400/PK-12
14323 Highway 84 71049 — 318-697-2664
Carolyn Phillips, prin. — Fax 697-5984

Longville, Beauregard, Pop. 621
Beauregard Parish SD
Supt. — See Deridder
South Beauregard JSHS — 800/7-12
151 Longville Church Rd 70652 — 337-725-3536
Tammy Crain, prin. — Fax 725-6222

Loranger, Tangipahoa
Tangipahoa Parish SD
Supt. — See Amite
Loranger HS — 700/9-12
19404 Hiatt St 70446 — 985-878-6271
Rhea Marrs, prin. — Fax 878-4875
Loranger MS — 700/5-8
54123 Allman St 70446 — 985-878-9455
Catherine Perry, prin. — Fax 878-4907

Loreauville, Iberia, Pop. 881
Iberia Parish SD
Supt. — See New Iberia
Loreauville JSHS — 500/7-12
PO Box 446 70552 — 337-229-4701
Karen Bashay, prin. — Fax 229-4275

Luling, Saint Charles, Pop. 11,952
St. Charles Parish SD — 9,100/PK-12
13855 River Rd 70070 — 985-785-6289
Felecia Gomez-Walker, supt. — Fax 785-1025
www.stcharles.k12.la.us
Smith MS — 300/6-8
281 Judge Edward Dufresne 70070 — 985-331-1018
Harold Blood, prin. — Fax 331-9385
Other Schools – See Boutte, Destrehan, Paradis, Saint Rose

Lutcher, Saint James, Pop. 3,521
St. James Parish SD — 3,800/PK-12
PO Box 338 70071 — 225-258-4500
P. Edward Cancienne Ph.D., supt. — Fax 869-8845
www.stjames.k12.la.us
Career & Technology Center — Vo/Tech
1410 Buddy Whitney St 70071 — 225-258-4571
Tracy Zeringue, dir. — Fax 869-7935
Lutcher HS — 1,000/7-12
1910 W Main St 70071 — 225-258-5300
Molly Stadalis, prin. — Fax 869-8872
Other Schools – See Saint James, Vacherie

Madisonville, Saint Tammany, Pop. 704
St. Tammany Parish SD
Supt. — See Covington
Madisonville JHS — 600/6-8
PO Box 850 70447 — 985-845-3355
Dwayne Kern, prin. — Fax 845-9018

Mamou, Evangeline, Pop. 3,194
Evangeline Parish SD
Supt. — See Ville Platte
Mamou JSHS — 700/5-12
1008 7th St 70554 — 337-468-5793
Liz Chatelain, prin. — Fax 468-2220

Mandeville, Saint Tammany, Pop. 11,401
St. Tammany Parish SD
Supt. — See Covington
Fontainebleau HS — 1,700/9-12
100 Bulldog Dr 70471 — 985-892-7112
Johnny Vitrano, prin. — Fax 892-9894
Fountainebleau JHS — 900/7-8
100 Hurricane Aly 70471 — 985-875-7501
Dr. Timothy Schneider, prin. — Fax 875-7650
Lakeshore HS — 1,000/9-12
1 Titan Trce 70448 — 985-624-5046
Christian Monson, prin. — Fax 624-5202
Mandeville HS — 1,800/9-12
1 Skipper Dr 70471 — 985-626-5225
Bruce Bundy, prin. — Fax 626-5298
Mandeville JHS — 700/7-8
639 Carondelet St 70448 — 985-626-4428
Mary Ann Cucchiara, prin. — Fax 674-0401
Monteleone JHS — 500/7-8
63000 Blue Marlin Dr 70448 — 985-951-8088
Sheri Jones, prin. — Fax 951-8083

Mangham, Richland, Pop. 672
Richland Parish SD
Supt. — See Rayville
Mangham HS — 300/9-12
PO Box 348 71259 — 318-248-2485
Connie Williams, prin. — Fax 248-2406
Mangham JHS — 200/6-8
810 McConnel St 71259 — 318-248-2729
Connie Williams, prin. — Fax 248-2931

Mansfield, DeSoto, Pop. 4,973
DeSoto Parish SD — 4,900/PK-12
201 Crosby St 71052 — 318-872-2836
Dr. Cade Brumley, supt. — Fax 872-1324
www.desotopsb.com
Center for Student Improvement — 50/Alt
2269 Whaley St 71052 — 318-871-0493
Toras Hill, prin. — Fax 871-0496
Mansfield HS — 400/9-12
401 Kings Hwy 71052 — 318-872-0793
Sedric Clark, prin. — Fax 872-2223
Mansfield MS — 500/5-8
1915 McArthur Dr 71052 — 318-872-1309
Grayson Collins, prin. — Fax 872-1319
Other Schools – See Logansport, Stonewall

Northwest Louisiana Technical College — Post-Sec.
943 Oxford Rd 71052 — 318-872-2243

Many, Sabine, Pop. 2,778
Sabine Parish SD — 4,300/PK-12
PO Box 1079 71449 — 318-256-9228
Dr. Sara Ebarb, supt. — Fax 256-0105
www.sabine.k12.la.us
Many HS — 300/9-12
100 Tiger Dr 71449 — 318-256-2114
Norman Booker, prin. — Fax 256-0492
Many JHS — 400/4-8
1801 Natchitoches Hwy 71449 — 318-256-3573
Madeline Owens, prin. — Fax 256-2846
Sabine Career Academy — Alt
910 W Mississippi Ave 71449 — 318-256-0582
Charlie Mason, prin. — Fax 256-5470
Other Schools – See Converse, Florien, Negreet, Noble, Pleasant Hill, Zwolle

---

Northwest Louisiana Technical College — Post-Sec.
PO Box 790 71449 — 318-256-4101

Marksville, Avoyelles, Pop. 5,505
Avoyelles Parish SD — 5,900/PK-12
221 Tunica Dr W 71351 — 318-253-5982
Blaine Dauzat, supt. — Fax 253-5178
www.avoyellespsb.com
Marksville HS — 900/7-12
407 W Bontemps St 71351 — 318-253-9356
Marvin Hall, prin. — Fax 253-4256
Other Schools – See Bunkie, Moreauville

Marrero, Jefferson, Pop. 32,762
Jefferson Parish SD
Supt. — See Harvey
Cullier Career Center — Vo/Tech
1429 Ames Blvd Ste B 70072 — 504-340-6963
Preston Gassery, prin. — Fax 341-1022
Ehret HS — 1,800/9-12
4300 Patriot St 70072 — 504-340-7651
Maria Landry, prin. — Fax 340-7295
Higgins HS — 1,400/9-12
7201 Lapalco Blvd 70072 — 504-341-2273
Randi Hindman, prin. — Fax 341-8110
Marrero MS — 800/6-8
4100 7th St 70072 — 504-341-5842
Christina Conforto, prin. — Fax 341-0004
St. Ville-Douglass Connections — 100/Alt
4300 Patriot St 70072 — 504-368-5962
Fax 362-1904
Truman MS — 800/6-8
5417 Ehret Rd 70072 — 504-341-0961
Terry Johnson, prin. — Fax 347-4497

Academy of Our Lady HS — 500/8-12
5501 Westbank Expy 70072 — 504-341-6217
Sr. Michelle Geiger, prin. — Fax 341-6229
Archbishop Shaw HS — 500/8-12
1000 Barataria Blvd 70072 — 504-340-6727
Fr. Louis Molinelli, prin. — Fax 347-9883
Conquering Word Christian Academy — 200/PK-12
812 Avenue F 70072 — 504-328-2273

Maurepas, Livingston
Livingston Parish SD
Supt. — See Livingston
Maurepas S — 400/K-12
PO Box 39 70449 — 225-695-6111
Kenny Kraft, prin. — Fax 695-3265

Maurice, Vermilion, Pop. 953
Vermilion Parish SD
Supt. — See Abbeville
North Vermilion HS — 500/9-12
11609 LA Hwy 699 70555 — 337-898-1491
Tommy Byler, prin. — Fax 893-8684
North Vermilion MS — 6-8
11609 LA Highway 699 70555 — 337-893-1583
Joan Romero, prin. — Fax 893-1585

Meraux, Saint Bernard, Pop. 5,703
St. Bernard Parish SD
Supt. — See Chalmette
Trist MS — 600/6-8
1 Pirates Cv 70075 — 504-872-9402
Denise Pritchard, prin. — Fax 872-9426

Merryville, Beauregard, Pop. 1,088
Beauregard Parish SD
Supt. — See Deridder
Merryville HS — 500/K-12
7061 Highway 110 W 70653 — 337-825-8046
Donnie Love, prin. — Fax 825-6443

Metairie, Jefferson, Pop. 136,499
Jefferson Parish SD
Supt. — See Harvey
Adams MS — 800/6-8
5525 Henican Pl 70003 — 504-887-5240
Fax 887-0173
East Jefferson HS — 1,000/9-12
400 Phlox Ave 70001 — 504-888-7171
James Kytle, prin. — Fax 888-2072
Harris MS — 800/6-8
911 Elise Ave 70003 — 504-733-0867
Otis Guichet, prin. — Fax 733-0953
Haynes Academy for Advanced Studies — 700/6-12
1416 Metairie Rd 70005 — 504-837-8300
Karla Russo, prin. — Fax 837-2110
King HS — 1,100/9-12
4301 Grace King Pl 70002 — 504-888-7334
Sharon Meggs-Hamilton, prin. — Fax 888-2082
Meisler MS — 800/6-8
3700 Cleary Ave 70002 — 504-888-5832
Semaj Allen-Raymond M.Ed., prin. — Fax 888-5855

Archbishop Chapelle HS — 900/8-12
8800 Veterans Memorial Blvd 70003 — 504-467-3105
Leila Benoit, prin. — Fax 466-3191
Archbishop Rummel HS — 800/8-12
1901 Severn Ave 70001 — 504-834-5592
Marc Milano, prin. — Fax 832-4016
Blue Cliff College — Post-Sec.
3200 Cleary Ave 70002 — 504-456-3141
Crescent City Christian S — 300/PK-12
4828 Utica St 70006 — 504-885-4700
Freddie Landry, admin. — Fax 885-4703
Ecole Classique S — 300/PK-12
5236 Glendale St 70006 — 504-887-3507
Greater New Orleans Christian Academy — K-10
5220 Irving St 70006 — 504-302-7940
Lutheran HS — 100/9-12
3864 17th St 70002 — 504-455-4062
Carol Christen, prin. — Fax 455-4453
Metairie Park Country Day S — 800/PK-12
300 Park Rd 70005 — 504-837-5204
Carolyn Chandler, hdmstr. — Fax 837-0015
Ridgewood Preparatory S — 300/PK-12
201 Pasadena Ave 70001 — 504-835-2545
St. Martin's Episcopal S — 500/PK-12
225 Green Acres Rd 70003 — 504-736-9900
Merry Sorrells, head sch — Fax 736-8800

Midland, Acadia
Acadia Parish SD
Supt. — See Crowley

Midland JSHS 300/8-12
735 S Crocker St 70559 337-783-3310
Todd Briley, prin. Fax 783-3332

Minden, Webster, Pop. 12,925
Webster Parish SD 6,600/PK-12
PO Box 520 71058 318-377-7052
Dr. Daniel Rawls, supt. Fax 377-4114
www.websterpsb.org
Minden HS 900/9-12
PO Box 838 71058 318-377-2766
Robin Tucker, prin. Fax 377-3236
Webster JHS 500/7-8
700 E Union St 71055 318-377-3847
Bewanichi Sheppard, prin. Fax 377-1943
Other Schools – See Doyline, Sarepta, Sibley, Springhill

Glenbrook S 400/K-12
1674 Country Club Cir 71055 318-377-2135
Northwest Louisiana Technical College Post-Sec.
PO Box 835 71058 318-371-3035

Monroe, Ouachita, Pop. 48,278
Monroe City SD 8,200/PK-12
PO Box 4180 71211 318-325-0601
Dr. Brent Vidrine, supt. Fax 812-3604
www.mcschools.net
Carroll Magnet HS 500/9-12
2939 Renwick St 71201 318-387-8441
Lyneta Coats, prin. Fax 361-9215
Carroll Magnet JHS 300/7-8
2913 Renwick St 71201 318-322-1683
Robert Rash, prin. Fax 322-0833
King JHS 300/7-8
3716 Nutland Rd 71202 318-387-1825
Jerry Mayhall, prin. Fax 325-4285
Lee JHS 500/7-8
1600 N 19th St 71201 318-323-1143
Dana Mullins, prin. Fax 325-5236
Neville HS 1,000/9-12
600 Forsythe Ave 71201 318-323-2237
Dr. Christella Dawson, prin. Fax 387-8774
Sherrouse S 50/Alt
300 Sherrouse Ave 71203 318-343-3258
Tammie McDaniel, prin. Fax 343-6141
Wossman HS 600/9-12
1600 Arizona Ave 71202 318-387-2932
Dr. Eric Davis, prin. Fax 322-1378

Ouachita Parish SD 20,000/PK-12
PO Box 1642 71210 318-432-5000
Dr. Don Coker, supt. Fax 432-5221
www.opsb.net
Ouachita JHS 1,000/6-8
5500 Blanks St 71203 318-345-5100
Charles Wright, prin. Fax 345-3308
Ouachita Parish HS 1,300/9-12
681 Highway 594 71203 318-343-2769
Eddie Mahoney, prin. Fax 343-9594
Richwood HS 600/9-12
5901 Highway 165 Byp 71202 318-361-0467
Dr. Sharilynn Loche, prin. Fax 361-9810
Richwood MS 500/6-8
5855 Highway 165 Byp 71202 318-432-2000
Orlando Freemont, prin. Fax 432-2049
Sterlington HS 400/9-12
233 Keystone Rd 71203 318-665-2725
Dell Ashley, prin. Fax 665-2727
Other Schools – See Calhoun, Sterlington, West Monroe

Career Technical College Post-Sec.
2319 Louisville Ave 71201 318-323-2889
Cloyd's Beauty School #2 Inc. Post-Sec.
1311 Winnsboro Rd 71202 318-322-5314
Cloyd's Beauty School #3 Inc. Post-Sec.
2514 Ferrand St 71201 318-322-5314
Geneva Academy 100/PK-12
2507 Oliver Rd 71201 318-805-0116
Louisiana Delta Community College Post-Sec.
7500 Millhaven Rd 71203 318-345-9000
Ouachita Christian S 800/PK-12
7065 Highway 165 N 71203 318-325-6000
River Oaks S 300/PK-12
600 Finks Hideaway Rd 71203 318-343-4185
St. Francis Medical Center Post-Sec.
PO Box 1901 71210 318-327-4141
St. Frederick HS 300/7-12
3300 Westminister Ave 71201 318-323-9636
Dr. Robert Webber, prin. Fax 323-7456
University of Louisiana at Monroe Post-Sec.
700 University Ave 71209 318-342-1000

Montegut, Terrebonne, Pop. 1,507
Terrebonne Parish SD
Supt. — See Houma
Montegut MS 600/5-8
138 Dolphin St 70377 985-594-5886
Jennifer Pitre, prin. Fax 594-9666

Monterey, Concordia, Pop. 437
Concordia Parish SD
Supt. — See Vidalia
Monterey S 500/PK-12
PO Box 127 71354 318-386-2214
Ralph Simmons, prin. Fax 386-7356

Montgomery, Grant, Pop. 714
Grant Parish SD
Supt. — See Colfax
Montgomery HS 200/7-12
PO Box 428 71454 318-646-2879
Patti Williams, prin. Fax 646-3926

Moreauville, Avoyelles, Pop. 900
Avoyelles Parish SD
Supt. — See Marksville
Avoyelles HS 800/7-12
287 Main St 71355 318-985-2361
Michael Rachal, prin. Fax 985-2786

Morgan City, Saint Mary, Pop. 12,212
St. Mary Parish SD
Supt. — See Centerville
Morgan City HS 700/9-12
2400 Tiger Dr 70380 985-384-1754
Milton Fabre, prin. Fax 384-7054
Morgan City JHS 600/6-8
911 Marguerite St 70380 985-384-5922
Kenneth Holmes, prin. Fax 385-4170

Central Catholic HS 200/7-12
2100 Cedar St Unit 1 70380 985-385-5372
Vic Bonnaffee, prin. Fax 385-3444
South Central Louisiana Technical Coll Post-Sec.
900 Youngs Rd 70380 985-380-2957

Mount Hermon, Washington
Washington Parish SD
Supt. — See Franklinton
Mount Hermon S 500/PK-12
36119 Highway 38 70450 985-877-4642
Jeremy Gueldner, prin. Fax 877-4710

Napoleonville, Assumption, Pop. 653
Assumption Parish SD 3,800/PK-12
4901 Highway 308 70390 985-369-7251
Earl Martinez, supt. Fax 369-2530
www.assumptionschools.com
Assumption HS 700/10-12
4880 Highway 308 70390 985-369-2956
Niles Riche, prin. Fax 369-6252
Napoleonville MS 300/5-8
4847 Highway 1 70390 985-369-6587
Shawn Preston, prin. Fax 369-6595
9th Grade Academy 300/9-9
4880 Highway 308 70390 985-369-2956
Jessica Thibodeaux, prin.
Other Schools – See Belle Rose, Labadieville, Pierre Part

Natchitoches, Natchitoches, Pop. 17,968
Louisiana S for Math Science and Arts 300/9-12
715 University Pkwy 71457 318-357-2503
Patrick Widhalm, dir. Fax 357-3189
www.lsmsa.edu
Louisiana S for Math Science and Arts 300/9-12
715 University Pkwy 71457 318-357-2503
Patrick Widhalm, dir. Fax 357-3189

Natchitoches Parish SD 6,300/PK-12
PO Box 16 71458 318-352-2358
Dale Skinner, supt. Fax 352-8138
dev.nat.k12.la.us
Jackson Technical Center 100/Alt
820 Koonce St 71457 318-357-9410
Bobby Benjamin, prin. Fax 357-8677
Natchitoches Central HS 1,400/9-12
6513 Highway 1 Byp 71457 318-352-2211
William Gordy, prin. Fax 357-8837
Natchitoches JHS 400/6-8
1621 Welch St 71457 318-238-0066
Edwin Mason, prin. Fax 238-0067
NSU Middle Lab S 200/6-8
Tec Pod Bldg NSU 71497 318-357-4509
Ben LaGrone, prin. Fax 357-4260
Other Schools – See Campti

Northwestern State University Post-Sec.
175 Sam Sibley Dr 71497 318-357-6011
Northwest Louisiana Technical College Post-Sec.
PO Box 657 71458 318-357-3162
St. Mary's S 400/PK-12
1101 E 5th St 71457 318-352-8394
Jacque Horton, prin. Fax 352-5798

Negreet, Sabine
Sabine Parish SD
Supt. — See Many
Negreet S 500/PK-12
PO Box 14 71460 318-256-2349
Chad Crow, prin. Fax 256-5868

New Iberia, Iberia, Pop. 30,160
Iberia Parish SD 13,900/PK-12
1500 Jane St 70563 337-365-2341
Dale Henderson, supt. Fax 365-6996
www.iberia.k12.la.us
Alternative Center for Education 100/Alt
500 Bank Ave 70560 337-369-3696
Maxine Jones, prin. Fax 365-5111
Anderson MS 500/7-8
1059 Anderson St 70560 337-365-3932
Dwalyn Jackson, prin. Fax 367-8285
Belle Place MS 500/7-8
4110 Loreauville Rd 70563 337-364-2141
Curtis Coquat, prin. Fax 365-9463
Iberia MS 600/7-8
613 Weeks Island Rd 70560 337-364-3927
Gleacia Morales, prin. Fax 365-9681
Iberia Parish Career Center Vo/Tech
618 Recreation Dr 70560 337-365-7231
Chris Broussard, prin. Fax 367-0875
New Iberia HS 1,700/9-12
1301 E Admiral Doyle Dr 70560 337-369-6714
Curt Landry, prin. Fax 364-6920
Westgate HS 1,100/9-12
2305 Jefferson Island Rd 70560 337-365-2431
Neely Moore, prin. Fax 364-3487
Other Schools – See Delcambre, Jeanerette, Loreauville

Assembly Christian S 300/PK-12
4219 E Admiral Doyle Dr 70560 337-364-4340
Bristow Academy Post-Sec.
1113 Vortex Dr 70560 337-364-8909
Catholic HS 800/4-12
1301 DeLasalle Dr 70560 337-364-5116
Ray Simon, prin. Fax 364-5041
Highland Baptist Christian S 500/PK-12
708 Angers St 70563 337-364-2273
Janie C. Lamothe, admin. Fax 369-6303
Neill Institute Post-Sec.
1301A W Saint Peter St 70560 337-365-6570
South Louisiana Community College Post-Sec.
609 Ember Dr 70560 337-373-0172

New Orleans, Orleans, Pop. 338,397
New Orleans Center for Creative Arts
Supt. — None
New Orleans Center for Creative Arts Vo/Tech
2800 Chartres St 70117 504-940-2850
Kyle Wedberg, pres. Fax 940-2859

Orleans Parish SD 11,700/PK-12
3520 General Degaulle Dr 70114 504-304-3520
Henderson Lewis Ph.D., supt. Fax 309-2865
opsb.us
McDonogh 35 HS 700/7-12
4000 Cadillac St 70122 504-324-7600
John Green, prin. Fax 942-0276
McMain Magnet JSHS 800/7-12
5712 S Claiborne Ave 70125 504-324-7500
Lakeysha London, prin. Fax 862-5123

Academy of the Sacred Heart HS 300/8-12
4521 Saint Charles Ave 70115 504-891-1943
Julie Boyd, prin. Fax 891-9744
Bishop McManus Academy 200/PK-12
13123 I 10 Service Rd 70128 504-246-5121
Dr. Tonilynn Tyson, prin. Fax 246-5564
Brother Martin HS 1,200/8-12
4401 Elysian Fields Ave 70122 504-283-1561
Gregory Rando, prin. Fax 286-8462
Cabrini HS 500/8-12
1400 Moss St 70119 504-482-1193
Yvonne Hrapmann, prin. Fax 483-8671
Cameron College Post-Sec.
2740 Canal St 70119 504-821-5881
De La Salle HS 400/8-12
5300 Saint Charles Ave 70115 504-895-5717
Paul Kelly, prin. Fax 895-1300
Delgado Community College Post-Sec.
615 City Park Ave 70119 504-671-5000
Dillard University Post-Sec.
2601 Gentilly Blvd 70122 504-283-8822
Eastern College of Health Vocations Post-Sec.
201 Evans Rd 70123 504-885-3353
Holy Cross MSHS 1,000/5-12
5500 Paris Ave 70122 504-942-3100
Dr. Joseph Murry, prin. Fax 286-5665
Holy Rosary HS 100/8-12
2437 Jena St 70115 504-482-7173
Cheryl Orillion, prin. Fax 482-7229
Jesuit HS 1,400/8-12
4133 Banks St 70119 504-486-6631
Peter Kernion, prin. Fax 483-3942
Louisiana State Univ. Health Sci. Center Post-Sec.
433 Bolivar St 70112 504-568-4808
Loyola University New Orleans Post-Sec.
6363 Saint Charles Ave 70118 504-865-2011
McGehee S 500/PK-12
2343 Prytania St 70130 504-561-1224
Eileen Powers, head sch Fax 525-7910
Medical Center of Louisiana/Charity Cmps Post-Sec.
1541 Tulane Ave 70112 504-568-2311
Moler Beauty College Post-Sec.
3968 Old Gentilly Rd 70126 504-282-2539
Mt. Carmel Academy 1,200/8-12
7027 Milne Blvd 70124 504-288-7626
Beth Simno, prin. Fax 288-7629
Newman S 900/PK-12
1903 Jefferson Ave 70115 504-899-5641
Dale Smith, head sch Fax 896-8597
New Orleans Baptist Theological Seminary Post-Sec.
3939 Gentilly Blvd 70126 504-282-4455
Notre Dame Seminary Post-Sec.
2901 S Carrollton Ave 70118 504-866-7426
Ochsner School of Allied Health Sciences Post-Sec.
1514 Jefferson Hwy 70121 504-842-3267
Our Lady of Holy Cross College Post-Sec.
4123 Woodland Dr 70131 504-394-7744
St. Augustine HS 900/6-12
2600 A P Tureaud Ave 70119 504-944-2424
Sean Goodwin, prin. Fax 947-7712
St. Katharine Drexel HS 300/8-12
5116 Magazine St 70115 504-899-6061
Anatalie Bachemin, prin. Fax 891-8766
St. Marys Academy 500/PK-12
6905 Chef Menteur Hwy 70126 504-245-0200
Sr. Jennie Jones, prin. Fax 245-0422
St. Marys Dominican HS 900/8-12
7701 Walmsley Ave 70125 504-865-9401
Carolyn Favre M.Ed., prin. Fax 866-5958
Southern University at New Orleans Post-Sec.
6400 Press Dr 70126 504-286-5000
Touro Infirmary Post-Sec.
1401 Foucher St 70115 504-897-8244
Tulane University Post-Sec.
6823 Saint Charles Ave 70118 504-865-5000
University of New Orleans Post-Sec.
2000 Lakeshore Dr 70148 504-280-6000
Ursuline Academy HS 400/8-12
2635 State St 70118 504-861-9150
Alice Bairnsfather, prin. Fax 861-7392
Xavier University Post-Sec.
1 Drexel Dr 70125 504-486-7411

New Roads, Pointe Coupee, Pop. 4,804
Pointe Coupee Parish SD 2,900/PK-12
PO Box 579 70760 225-638-8674
Kevin Lemoine, supt. Fax 638-3237
www.pcpsb.net
Other Schools – See Livonia

Baton Rouge Community College New Roads Post-Sec.
605 Hospital Rd 70760 225-638-8613
Catholic HS of Pointe Coupee 300/7-12
504 4th St W 70760 225-638-9313
Colleen Caillet, prin. Fax 638-6471
False River Academy 500/PK-12
201 Major Pkwy 70760 225-638-3783

Noble, Sabine, Pop. 244
Sabine Parish SD
Supt. — See Many
Ebarb S 300/PK-12
5340 Highway 482 71462 318-645-9402
Darrin Dyess, prin. Fax 645-4689

Oakdale, Allen, Pop. 7,688
Allen Parish SD
Supt. — See Oberlin
Oakdale HS 300/9-12
101 N 13th St 71463 318-335-2338
Brad Soileau, prin. Fax 335-3257
Oakdale MS 400/5-8
124 S 13th St 71463 318-335-1558
Jarrett Granger, prin. Fax 335-4690

Central Louisiana Technical College Post-Sec.
117 Highway 1152 71463 318-335-3944

Oak Grove, West Carroll, Pop. 1,714
West Carroll Parish SD 2,200/PK-12
314 E Main St 71263 318-428-2378
Richard Strong, supt. Fax 428-3775
www.wcpsb.com
Oak Grove JSHS 500/6-12
501 W Main St 71263 318-428-2308
Mike Gammill, prin. Fax 428-2311
Other Schools – See Epps, Forest, Kilbourne

Oberlin, Allen, Pop. 1,727
Allen Parish SD 4,300/PK-12
1111 W 7th Ave 70655 337-639-4311
Michael Doucet, supt. Fax 639-2346
www.allen.k12.la.us
Oberlin HS 300/7-12
PO Box D 70655 337-639-4341
Tonya Ryder, prin. Fax 639-2508
Other Schools – See Elizabeth, Grant, Kinder, Oakdale, Reeves

Olla, LaSalle, Pop. 1,375
LaSalle Parish SD
Supt. — See Jena
LaSalle HS 200/9-12
PO Box 110 71465 318-495-5165
Kara Masling, prin. Fax 495-5503

Opelousas, Saint Landry, Pop. 16,425
St. Landry Parish SD 14,200/PK-12
PO Box 310 70571 337-948-3657
Edward Brown, supt. Fax 942-0204
www.slp.k12.la.us
Magnet Academy for Cultural Arts 300/7-12
1100 Leo St 70570 337-942-6195
Karen Olivier, prin. Fax 948-6310
Magnet Academy of Biomedical Sciences 9-12
PO Box 310 70571 337-948-3657
Fax 942-0204
Northwest HS 600/9-12
3746 Highway 104 70570 337-543-2001
Gregory Campbell, prin. Fax 543-8796
Opelousas HS 900/9-12
PO Box 1269 70571 337-942-5634
Dr. Rodney Johnson, prin. Fax 942-6219
Opelousas JHS 400/7-8
730 S Market St 70570 337-942-4957
Chastity Wilson, prin. Fax 942-2659
Plaisance ES 300/5-8
3264 Highway 167 70570 337-826-3335
Larry Watson, prin. Fax 826-7062
St. Landry Accelerated Transition S 100/Alt
152 Violet Dr 70570 337-942-4761
Charles Vidrine, prin. Fax 948-9792
Other Schools – See Arnaudville, Eunice, Port Barre, Sunset, Washington

---

Family Worship Christian Acadmey 100/PK-12
PO Box 1463 70571 337-942-1563
Opelousas Catholic S 700/PK-12
428 E Prudhomme St 70570 337-942-5404
John Cavell, prin. Fax 942-5922
Opelousas School of Cosmetology Post-Sec.
529 E Vine St 70570 337-942-6147
South Louisiana Community College Post-Sec.
332 E South St 70570 337-943-1518
Westminster Christian Academy 700/PK-12
186 Westminster Dr 70570 337-948-8607
Scott Davis, head sch Fax 948-8983

Paradis, Saint Charles, Pop. 1,269
St. Charles Parish SD
Supt. — See Luling
Martin MS 800/6-8
434 South St 70080 985-758-7579
Erin Granier, prin. Fax 758-7570

Parks, Saint Martin, Pop. 645
St. Martin Parish SD
Supt. — See Breaux Bridge
Parks MS 400/5-8
1010 Saint Louis Dr Ste A 70582 337-845-4753
Dr. Wanda Phillips, prin. Fax 845-5532

Patterson, Saint Mary, Pop. 6,020
St. Mary Parish SD
Supt. — See Centerville
Patterson HS 500/9-12
2525 Main St 70392 985-395-2675
Rachael Sanders, prin. Fax 395-5453
Patterson JHS 500/4-8
1101 1st St 70392 985-395-6772
Suzanne Bergeron, prin. Fax 395-6773

Pearl River, Saint Tammany, Pop. 2,460
St. Tammany Parish SD
Supt. — See Covington
Creekside JHS 600/6-8
65434 Highway 41 70452 985-863-5882
Lisa Virga, prin. Fax 863-7658
Pearl River HS 700/9-12
39110 Rebel Ln 70452 985-863-2591
Michael Winkler, prin. Fax 863-5934

Pierre Part, Assumption, Pop. 3,145
Assumption Parish SD
Supt. — See Napoleonville
Pierre Part MS 300/5-8
3321 Highway 70 S 70339 985-252-6359
Wanda Templet, prin. Fax 252-3918

Pine Prairie, Evangeline, Pop. 1,598
Evangeline Parish SD
Supt. — See Ville Platte
Pine Prairie S 800/PK-12
PO Box 200 70576 337-599-2300
Anita West, prin. Fax 599-2003

Pineville, Rapides, Pop. 14,277
Rapides Parish SD
Supt. — See Alexandria
Pineville HS 1,400/9-12
1511 Line St 71360 318-442-8990
Dr. Karl Carpenter, prin. Fax 487-1984
Pineville JHS 700/7-8
501 Edgewood Dr 71360 318-640-0512
Dana Nolan, prin. Fax 640-9692
Rapides Training Academy 100/Alt
901 Crepe Myrtle St 71360 318-445-7017
Matt Byrnes, prin. Fax 445-5690

Louisiana College Post-Sec.
1140 College Dr 71360 318-487-7011
Pineville Beauty School Post-Sec.
1008 Main St 71360 318-445-1040

Pitkin, Vernon, Pop. 566
Vernon Parish SD
Supt. — See Leesville
Pitkin S 500/PK-12
7239 Highway 463 70656 318-358-3121
Kevin Lambright, prin. Fax 358-3580

Plain Dealing, Bossier, Pop. 996
Bossier Parish SD
Supt. — See Benton
Plain Dealing HS 300/6-12
300 E Vance St 71064 318-759-2700
Sandrina Isebaert, prin. Fax 759-2713

Plaquemine, Iberville, Pop. 7,074
Iberville Parish SD 5,000/PK-12
PO Box 151 70765 225-687-4341
Dr. P. Edward Cancienne, supt. Fax 687-5408
www.ipsb.net
Math Science & Arts Academy West Alt
57955 Saint Louis Rd 70764 225-687-6845
Elvis Cavalier, admin. Fax 687-6826
Plaquemine HS 1,300/7-12
59595 Belleview Dr 70764 225-687-6367
Chandler Smith, prin. Fax 687-4422
Other Schools – See Saint Gabriel, White Castle

Capital Area Technical College Post-Sec.
25250 Tenant Rd 70764 225-687-5500
St. John HS 200/9-12
24250 Regina St 70764 225-687-3056
Cherie Schlatre, prin. Fax 687-3530

Plaucheville, Avoyelles, Pop. 243

St. Joseph S 200/PK-12
PO Box 59 71362 318-922-3401
Bryan Runyan, prin. Fax 922-3776

Pleasant Hill, Sabine, Pop. 710
Sabine Parish SD
Supt. — See Many
Pleasant Hill S 300/PK-12
PO Box 8 71065 318-796-3670
Jarrad Rivers, prin. Fax 796-2034

Ponchatoula, Tangipahoa, Pop. 6,436
Tangipahoa Parish SD
Supt. — See Amite
Ponchatoula HS 1,800/9-12
19452 Highway 22 70454 985-386-3514
Daniel Strickland, prin. Fax 386-0011
Ponchatoula JHS 800/7-8
315 E Oak St 70454 985-370-5322
Bobby Matthews, prin. Fax 370-5327

Port Allen, West Baton Rouge, Pop. 5,131
West Baton Rouge Parish SD 3,900/PK-12
3761 Rosedale Rd 70767 225-343-8309
Wes Watts, supt. Fax 387-2101
www.wbrschools.net
Devall MS 100/5-8
11851 N River Rd 70767 225-627-4268
Laree Taylor, prin. Fax 627-4278
Port Allen HS 400/9-12
3553 Rosedale Rd 70767 225-383-1107
James Jackson, prin. Fax 344-6312
Port Allen MS 200/6-8
610 Rosedale Rd 70767 225-383-5777
Jessica Major, prin. Fax 346-5030
Other Schools – See Brusly

Port Barre, Saint Landry, Pop. 2,017
St. Landry Parish SD
Supt. — See Opelousas
Port Barre HS 500/5-12
PO Box 69 70577 337-585-7256
Timothy Villemarette, prin. Fax 585-2290

Port Sulphur, Plaquemines, Pop. 1,706
Plaquemines Parish SD
Supt. — See Belle Chasse
Plaquemines Parish Learning Center Alt
26892 Highway 23 70083 504-595-6410
John Vanison, prin. Fax 398-4366

Prairieville, Ascension, Pop. 26,585
Ascension Parish SD
Supt. — See Donaldsonville
Galvez MS 600/6-8
42018 Highway 933 70769 225-391-6350
Sandy Waguespack, prin. Fax 621-2434
Prairieville MS 900/6-8
16200 Highway 930 70769 225-391-6300
Dina Davis, prin. Fax 673-4883

Pride, East Baton Rouge
East Baton Rouge Parish SD
Supt. — See Baton Rouge
Northeast JSHS 500/7-12
13700 Pride Port Hudson Rd 70770 225-654-5808
Brandon Levatino, prin. Fax 654-5591

Quitman, Jackson, Pop. 180
Jackson Parish SD
Supt. — See Jonesboro
Quitman S 700/PK-12
PO Box 38 71268 318-259-2698
Steve Shovan, prin. Fax 259-1139

Raceland, Lafourche, Pop. 10,053
Lafourche Parish SD
Supt. — See Thibodaux
Central Lafourche HS 1,300/9-12
4820 Highway 1 70394 985-532-3319
Jarod Martin, prin. Fax 532-3822
Raceland MS 300/6-8
PO Box C 70394 985-537-5140
Hiram Bailey, prin. Fax 537-5182

Rayne, Acadia, Pop. 7,834
Acadia Parish SD
Supt. — See Crowley
Armstrong MS 400/6-8
700 Martin Luther King Blvd 70578 337-334-3377
Marshall Thibodeaux, prin. Fax 334-2681
Rayne HS 700/9-12
1016 N Polk St 70578 337-334-3691
John Prudhomme, prin. Fax 334-5568

Rayville, Richland, Pop. 3,658
Richland Parish SD 3,300/PK-12
PO Box 599 71269 318-728-5964
Sheldon Jones, supt. Fax 728-6366
www.richland.k12.la.us
Rayville HS 500/9-12
193 Highway 3048 71269 318-728-3296
Tommy Watson, prin. Fax 728-5652
Rayville JHS 200/6-8
225 Highway 3048 71269 318-728-3618
Nettie Ranel, prin. Fax 728-9374
Other Schools – See Archibald, Delhi, Mangham

Riverfield Academy 300/PK-12
115 Riverfield Dr 71269 318-728-3281
Sherri Slade, admin. Fax 728-3285

Reeves, Allen, Pop. 230
Allen Parish SD
Supt. — See Oberlin
Reeves S 300/PK-12
13770 Highway 113 70658 337-666-2414
Brenda Green, prin. Fax 666-2812

Reserve, Saint John the Baptist, Pop. 9,667
St. John The Baptist Parish SD 6,000/PK-12
PO Box AL 70084 985-536-1106
Kevin George, supt. Fax 536-1109
www.stjohn.k12.la.us
East St. John HS 1,300/9-12
1 Wildcat Dr 70084 985-536-4226
Cory Butler, prin. Fax 536-4286
St. John Alternative Program 100/Alt
1880 Highway 44 70084 985-536-4283
Orlando Watkins, prin. Fax 536-4527
Other Schools – See Edgard

Riverside Academy 800/PK-12
332 Railroad Ave 70084 985-536-4246
South Central Louisiana Technical Coll Post-Sec.
181 Regala Park Rd 70084 985-536-4418

Ringgold, Bienville, Pop. 1,471
Bienville Parish SD
Supt. — See Arcadia
Ringgold JSHS 200/6-12
4044 Bienville Rd Ste B 71068 318-894-2271
Eric Carter, prin. Fax 894-4444

River Ridge, Jefferson, Pop. 13,340

Curtis Christian S 800/PK-12
10125 Jefferson Hwy 70123 504-737-4621
J.T. Curtis, hdmstr. Fax 737-7326

Roanoke, Jefferson Davis, Pop. 537
Jefferson Davis Parish SD
Supt. — See Jennings
Welsh-Roanoke JHS 300/6-8
8150 Highway 90 70581 337-753-2317
Rae Daigle, prin. Fax 753-2245

Rosepine, Vernon, Pop. 1,651
Vernon Parish SD
Supt. — See Leesville
Rosepine JSHS 500/7-12
502 Louisiana Ave 70659 337-463-6079
Johnny Bosley, prin. Fax 462-6132

Ruston, Lincoln, Pop. 21,600
Lincoln Parish SD 5,600/PK-12
410 S Farmerville St 71270 318-255-1430
Michael Milstead, supt. Fax 255-3203
www.lincolnschools.org
Ruston HS 1,200/9-12
900 Bearcat Dr 71270 318-255-0807
Ricky Durrett, prin. Fax 251-2202
Ruston JHS 600/7-8
481 Tarbutton Rd 71270 318-251-1601
Daryl Savage, prin. Fax 254-5235
Other Schools – See Choudrant, Simsboro

Bethel Christian S 100/PK-12
2901 Winona Dr 71270 318-255-1112
Nancy Stevenson, admin. Fax 513-1113
Cedar Creek S 600/PK-12
2400 Cedar Creek Dr 71270 318-255-7707
Louisiana Tech University Post-Sec.
PO Box 3168 71272 318-257-0211
Pat Goins Ruston Beauty School Post-Sec.
213 W Alabama Ave 71270 318-255-2717

Saint Amant, Ascension
Ascension Parish SD
Supt. — See Donaldsonville
Saint Amant HS 1,900/9-12
12035 Highway 431 70774 225-391-6000
Mia Edwards, prin. Fax 621-2573
Saint Amant MS 500/6-8
44317 Highway 429 70774 225-391-6500
Christy Bourgeois, prin. Fax 621-2593

Saint Benedict, Saint Tammany

St. Joseph Seminary College Post-Sec.
75376 River Rd 70457 985-892-1800

Saint Bernard, Saint Bernard
St. Bernard Parish SD
Supt. — See Chalmette
Saint Bernard MS 300/6-8
2601 Torres Dr 70085 504-267-7878
Angela Seibert, prin. Fax 267-7886

Saint Francisville, West Feliciana, Pop. 1,749
West Feliciana Parish SD 2,200/PK-12
PO Box 1910 70775 225-635-3891
Hollis Milton, supt. Fax 635-0108
www.wfpsb.org
West Feliciana HS 600/9-12
PO Box 580 70775 225-635-4561
James Carroll, prin. Fax 635-5588
West Feliciana MS 500/6-8
PO Box 690 70775 225-635-3898
Jovanka Ganes, prin. Fax 635-6925

Saint Gabriel, Iberville, Pop. 6,621
Iberville Parish SD
Supt. — See Plaquemine
East Iberville S 600/PK-12
3285 Highway 75 70776 225-642-5410
Jillian Dotson, prin. Fax 642-9607
Math Science & Arts Academy East 300/K-12
1400 Gordon Simon LeBlanc 70776 225-642-8457
Charles Johnson, dir.

Saint James, Saint James, Pop. 827
St. James Parish SD
Supt. — See Lutcher
Saint James HS 700/7-12
PO Box 101 70086 225-258-4900
Michael Kennedy, prin. Fax 265-2455

Saint Joseph, Tensas, Pop. 1,163
Tensas Parish SD 700/PK-12
PO Box 318 71366 318-766-3269
Carol S. Johnson, supt. Fax 766-3634
www.tensaspsb.org/
Tensas HS 300/7-12
PO Box 318 71366 318-766-3585
Dena Hale, prin. Fax 766-7988

Tensas Academy 200/PK-12
PO Box 555 71366 318-766-4384

Saint Martinville, Saint Martin, Pop. 6,047
St. Martin Parish SD
Supt. — See Breaux Bridge
St. Martinville HS 700/9-12
762 N Main St 70582 337-394-3135
Michael Kreamer, prin. Fax 394-8045
St. Martinville JHS 400/6-8
7190 Main Hwy 70582 337-394-4764
Edward Boyd, prin. Fax 394-9619

Saint Rose, Saint Charles, Pop. 8,003
St. Charles Parish SD
Supt. — See Luling
Cammon MS 300/6-8
234 Pirate Dr 70087 504-467-4536
Tamika Green, prin. Fax 468-3873

Saline, Bienville, Pop. 271
Bienville Parish SD
Supt. — See Arcadia
Saline S 300/PK-12
PO Box 129 71070 318-576-3215
Scott Canady, prin. Fax 576-9068

Sarepta, Webster, Pop. 889
Webster Parish SD
Supt. — See Minden
North Webster JHS 500/6-8
6041 Highway 2 71071 318-847-4301
Cyndi Hair, prin. Fax 847-4891

Schriever, Terrebonne, Pop. 6,745

Fletcher Technical Community College Post-Sec.
1407 Highway 311 70395 985-448-7900

Scott, Lafayette, Pop. 8,472
Lafayette Parish SD
Supt. — See Lafayette
Scott MS 600/6-8
116 Marie St 70583 337-521-7930
Candy Kelly, prin. Fax 521-7931

Shreveport, Caddo, Pop. 196,498
Caddo Parish SD 35,700/PK-12
PO Box 32000 71130 318-603-6300
Dr. T. Lamar Goree, supt. Fax 631-5241
www.caddoschools.org
Bickham MS 700/6-8
7240 Old Mooringsport Rd 71107 318-929-4106
Shannon Wall, prin. Fax 929-2416
Broadmoor MS Laboratory 600/6-8
441 Atlantic Ave 71105 318-861-2403
Renata Mahoney, prin. Fax 865-4142
Byrd HS 2,300/9-12
3201 Line Ave 71104 318-869-2567
Gerald Badgley, prin. Fax 869-2253
Caddo Career/Tech Center Vo/Tech
5950 Union Ave 71108 318-636-5150
Kenneth Berg, prin. Fax 621-9138
Caddo Middle Career & Technology S 200/7-8
6310 Clift Ave 71106 318-868-2753
Dr. Grady Smith, prin. Fax 868-2755
Caddo Parish Magnet HS 1,200/9-12
1601 Viking Dr 71101 318-221-2501
Michael Ilgenfritz, prin. Fax 227-1393
Caddo Parish Magnet MS 1,300/6-8
7635 Cornelious Ln 71106 318-868-6588
Robin Debusk, prin. Fax 865-6125
Fair Park HS 700/9-12
3222 Greenwood Rd 71109 318-635-8181
Bruce Daigle, prin. Fax 631-1982
Green Oaks Performing Arts Academy 700/7-12
2550 Thomas E Howard Dr 71107 318-425-3411
Marvin Alexander, prin. Fax 425-3414
Huntington JSHS 1,100/7-12
6801 Rasberry Ln 71129 318-687-6655
Tellauance Graham, prin. Fax 687-0943
Lakeshore MS 600/7-8
1807 San Jacinto St 71109 318-635-1325
Dr. Matthew Mitchell, prin. Fax 635-1961
Northwood HS 900/9-12
5939 Old Mooringsport Rd 71107 318-929-3513
Darlene Simons, prin. Fax 929-7498
Oak Park MS 200/5-8
4331 Henry St 71109 318-635-2141
Julia Smith O'Neal, prin. Fax 636-6336
Ridgewood MS 700/6-8
2001 Ridgewood Dr 71118 318-686-0383
Scott Aymond, prin. Fax 686-0390
Shreve HS 1,300/9-12
6115 E Kings Hwy 71105 318-865-7137
Ginger Gustavson, prin. Fax 865-5041
Southwood HS 1,300/9-12
9000 Walker Rd 71118 318-686-9512
Jeff Roberts, prin. Fax 687-7588
Washington New Tech JSHS 800/7-12
2104 Milam St 71103 318-222-2186
Kristi Young, prin. Fax 226-0628
Woodlawn Leadership Academy 700/9-12
7340 Wyngate Blvd 71106 318-686-3161
Betty Jordan, prin. Fax 687-6787
Youree Drive MS 1,000/6-8
6008 Youree Dr 71105 318-868-5324
Jenifer Guerrero, prin. Fax 861-5086
Other Schools – See Vivian

Ayers Institute Post-Sec.
8820 Jewella Ave 71108 318-635-0280
Blue Cliff College Post-Sec.
8731 Park Plaza Dr 71105 318-798-6868
Calvary Baptist Academy 1,100/K-12
9333 Linwood Ave 71106 318-687-4923
Career Technical College Post-Sec.
1227 Shreveport Barksdale 71105 318-629-2889
Centenary College of Louisiana Post-Sec.
2911 Centenary Blvd 71104 318-869-5011
Diesel Driving Academy Post-Sec.
3523 Greenwood Rd 71109 318-636-6300
Evangel Christian Academy 800/PK-12
7425 Broadacres Rd 71129 318-688-7061
Guy's Academy Hair Skin and Nails Post-Sec.
1141 Shreveport Barksdale 71105 318-865-5591
Louisiana State University Post-Sec.
1 University Pl 71115 318-797-5000
Louisiana State Univ Health Sciences Ctr Post-Sec.
1501 Kings Hwy 71103 318-675-5000
Loyola College Prep S 500/9-12
921 Jordan St 71101 318-221-2675
John LeBlanc, prin. Fax 226-6334
Northwest Louisiana Technical College Post-Sec.
2010 N Market St 71107 318-676-7811
Overton Brooks VA Medical Center Post-Sec.
510 E Stoner Ave 71101 318-424-6037
Remington College Post-Sec.
2106 Bert Kouns Industrial 71118 318-671-4001
Southern University at Shreveport Post-Sec.
3050 M L King Dr 71107 318-670-6000
Word Of God Academy PK-12
2820 Summer Grove Dr 71118 318-687-9003

Sibley, Webster, Pop. 1,205
Webster Parish SD
Supt. — See Minden
Lakeside JSHS 500/7-12
9090 Highway 371 71073 318-377-2133
Johnny Rowland, prin. Fax 382-0733

Sicily Island, Catahoula, Pop. 519
Catahoula Parish SD
Supt. — See Harrisonburg
Sicily Island HS 300/PK-12
PO Box 128 71368 318-389-5337
Marguerita Krause, prin. Fax 389-5309

Simpson, Vernon, Pop. 631
Vernon Parish SD
Supt. — See Leesville
Simpson S 300/PK-12
PO Box 8 71474 337-383-7810
Lee Coriell, prin. Fax 383-7655

Simsboro, Lincoln, Pop. 828
Lincoln Parish SD
Supt. — See Ruston
Simsboro S 600/K-12
1 Tiger Dr 71275 318-247-6265
Rusty Farrar, prin. Fax 247-6276

Singer, Beauregard, Pop. 282
Beauregard Parish SD
Supt. — See Deridder
Singer HS 300/K-12
153 Highway 110 E 70660 337-463-5908
Theresa Harlow, prin. Fax 463-0199

Slidell, Saint Tammany, Pop. 26,521
St. Tammany Parish SD
Supt. — See Covington
Boyet JHS 800/7-8
59295 Rebel Dr 70461 985-643-3775
John Priola, prin. Fax 643-9470
Clearwood JHS 600/4-8
130 Clearwood Dr 70458 985-641-8200
Alan Bennett, prin. Fax 641-7122
Northshore HS 1,500/9-12
100 Panther Dr 70461 985-649-6400
Frank Jabbia, prin. Fax 649-3613
St. Tammany JHS 600/6-8
701 Cleveland Ave 70458 985-643-1592
Vincent DiCarlo, prin. Fax 643-5873
Salmen HS 1,000/9-12
300 Spartan Dr 70458 985-643-7359
Brennan McCurley, prin. Fax 645-8776
Slidell HS 1,600/9-12
1 Tiger Dr 70458 985-643-2992
William Percy, prin. Fax 649-6853
Slidell JHS 700/7-8
333 Pennsylvania Ave 70458 985-641-5914
Patrick Mackin, prin. Fax 641-6397

Academy of Creative Hair Design Post-Sec.
740 Oak Harbor Blvd 70458 985-643-2614
First Baptist Christian S 200/1-12
4141 Pontchartrain Dr 70458 985-643-3725
Mona Nelson, prin. Fax 641-9205
Pope John Paul II HS 300/8-12
1901 Jaguar Dr 70461 985-649-0914
Martha Mundine, prin. Fax 649-5494

Sorrento, Ascension, Pop. 1,385

River Parishes Community College Post-Sec.
PO Box 310 70778 225-675-8270

Springfield, Livingston, Pop. 483
Livingston Parish SD
Supt. — See Livingston
Springfield HS 400/9-12
PO Box 39 70462 225-294-3256
Spencer Harris, prin. Fax 294-4800
Springfield MS 400/5-8
PO Box 40 70462 225-294-3306
Dwayne Dykes, prin. Fax 294-3307

Springhill, Webster, Pop. 5,214
Webster Parish SD
Supt. — See Minden
North Webster HS 500/9-12
101 S Arkansas St 71075 318-539-2563
Jeff Franklin, prin. Fax 539-2569

Starks, Calcasieu, Pop. 662
Calcasieu Parish SD
Supt. — See Lake Charles
Starks S 400/PK-12
PO Box 69 70661 337-217-4820
Cary Smith, prin. Fax 217-4821

Sterlington, Ouachita, Pop. 1,568
Ouachita Parish SD
Supt. — See Monroe
Sterlington MS 300/6-8
206 High Ave 71280 318-432-2100
Marty Bumgart, prin. Fax 432-2149

Stonewall, DeSoto, Pop. 1,797
DeSoto Parish SD
Supt. — See Mansfield
North DeSoto HS 600/9-12
PO Box 430 71078 318-925-6917
Barton Weaver, prin. Fax 925-1940
North DeSoto MS 500/6-8
PO Box 310 71078 318-925-4520
Randall Simmons, prin. Fax 925-4719

Sulphur, Calcasieu, Pop. 20,056
Calcasieu Parish SD
Supt. — See Lake Charles
LeBlanc MS/Drost Special 400/6-8
1100 N Crocker St 70663 337-217-4510
Joe David, prin. Fax 217-4511
Lewis MS 900/6-8
1752 Cypress St 70663 337-217-4700
Dan Sylvest, prin. Fax 217-4701
Sulphur 9th Grade Campus 600/9-9
600 Willow Ave 70663 337-217-4440
Lee Crick, prin. Fax 217-4441
Sulphur SHS 1,300/10-12
100 Sycamore St 70663 337-217-4430
Robert Barrentine, prin. Fax 217-4434

Summerfield, Claiborne
Claiborne Parish SD
Supt. — See Homer
Summerfield S 300/PK-12
PO Box 158 71079 318-927-3621
Shane Lee, prin. Fax 927-9160

Sunset, Saint Landry, Pop. 2,868
St. Landry Parish SD
Supt. — See Opelousas
Sunset ES 400/5-8
236 Church Hill St 70584 337-662-3194
Marquet Rideau, prin. Fax 662-3478

Tallulah, Madison, Pop. 7,266
Madison Parish SD 1,200/PK-12
301 S Chestnut St 71282 318-574-3616
Benita Young, supt. Fax 574-3667
www.madisonpsb.org
Christian Acres Alternative S 100/Alt
200 Bailey St 71282 318-574-1563
Erika January, prin. Fax 574-1563
Madison Alternative S Alt
900 W Askew St 71282
Erika January, prin.
Madison HS 400/9-12
1234 Madison High Dr S 71282 318-574-3529
Glenda Douglas, prin. Fax 574-2399
Madison MS 300/7-8
1233 Madison High Dr S 71282 318-574-0933
Collins Robinson, prin. Fax 574-9199

Tallulah Academy-Delta Christian S 300/PK-12
700 Wood St 71282 318-574-2606

Terrytown, Jefferson, Pop. 22,887
Jefferson Parish SD
Supt. — See Harvey
Livaudais MS 700/6-8
925 Lamar Ave 70056 504-393-7544
Davon Hayes, prin. Fax 393-9610

Thibodaux, Lafourche, Pop. 14,384
Lafourche Parish SD 13,300/PK-12
PO Box 879 70302 985-446-5631
Dr. Jo Ann Matthews, supt. Fax 446-0801
www.lpsd.k12.la.us
East Thibodaux MS 400/6-8
802 E 7th St 70301 985-446-5616
Tanya Richard, prin. Fax 446-5610
Sixth Ward MS 300/6-8
1865 Choctaw Rd 70301 985-633-2449
Kenneth Delcambre, prin. Fax 633-7373
Thibodaux HS 1,400/8-12
1355 Tiger Dr 70301 985-447-4071
Glenn Haydel, prin. Fax 447-4077
West Thiboudaux MS 500/6-8
1111 E 12th St 70301 985-446-6889
Gregory Cook, prin. Fax 447-1777

Other Schools – See Cut Off, Golden Meadow, Houma, Larose, Lockport, Raceland

Nicholls State University Post-Sec.
906 E 1st St 70310 985-446-8111
South Central Louisiana Technical Coll Post-Sec.
1425 Tiger Dr 70301 985-447-0924
White HS 700/8-12
555 Cardinal Dr 70301 985-446-8486
Michelle Chiasson, prin. Fax 448-1275

Tickfaw, Tangipahoa, Pop. 685
Tangipahoa Parish SD
Supt. — See Amite
Nesom MS 400/6-8
14417 Highway 442 W 70466 985-345-2166
Charlotte Tillman, prin. Fax 345-3731

Tioga, Rapides
Rapides Parish SD
Supt. — See Alexandria
Tioga HS 900/9-12
PO Box 1030 71477 318-640-9661
Allen Lacombe, prin. Fax 640-9757

Urania, LaSalle, Pop. 1,308
LaSalle Parish SD
Supt. — See Jena
LaSalle JHS 200/6-8
PO Box 520 71480 318-495-3474
Stephanie Clark, prin. Fax 495-3478

Vacherie, Saint James, Pop. 2,354
St. James Parish SD
Supt. — See Lutcher
Science & Math Academy 7-12
3125 Valcour Aime St 70090 225-258-4600
Pam Bourgeois, dir. Fax 265-7093

Varnado, Washington, Pop. 1,459
Washington Parish SD
Supt. — See Franklinton
Varnado HS 400/6-12
25543 Washington St, Angie LA 70426
985-732-2025
Jennifer Beninato, prin. Fax 732-5198

Vidalia, Concordia, Pop. 4,268
Concordia Parish SD 3,700/PK-12
PO Box 950 71373 318-336-4226
Paul Nelson Ph.D., supt. Fax 336-5875
www.cpsbla.us/
Vidalia HS 500/9-12
2201 Murray Dr 71373 318-336-6231
Charles Anderson, prin. Fax 336-6233
Vidalia JHS 400/6-8
210 Gillespie St 71373 318-336-6227
Whest Shirley, prin. Fax 336-6229
Other Schools – See Ferriday, Monterey

Vidalia Beauty School Post-Sec.
208 Westside Dr 71373 318-336-2377

Ville Platte, Evangeline, Pop. 7,370
Evangeline Parish SD 6,100/PK-12
1123 Te Mamou Rd 70586 337-363-6651
Toni Hamlin, supt. Fax 363-8086
www.epsb.com/pages/Evangeline_Parish
Evangeline Central Alternative S 100/Alt
4587 Vidrine Rd 70586 337-363-6308
Dexter Brown, prin. Fax 363-6309
Ville Platte HS 900/5-12
210 W Cotton St 70586 337-363-3387
Kelli Lafleur, prin. Fax 363-7274
Other Schools – See Basile, Mamou, Pine Prairie

Christian Heritage Academy 100/PK-12
607 Prosper St 70586 337-363-7690
Sue Pomier, prin. Fax 363-7699
Sacred Heart HS 200/9-12
114 Trojan Ln 70586 337-363-1475
Dawn Shipp, prin. Fax 363-0348
South Louisiana Community College Post-Sec.
1124 Vocational Dr Ward 1 70586 337-363-2197

Vinton, Calcasieu, Pop. 3,128
Calcasieu Parish SD
Supt. — See Lake Charles
Vinton HS 300/9-12
1603 Grace Ave 70668 337-217-4400
Mitch Manuel, prin. Fax 217-4401
Vinton MS 200/6-8
900 Horridge St 70668 337-217-4720
Gena Granger, prin. Fax 217-4721

Vivian, Caddo, Pop. 3,629
Caddo Parish SD
Supt. — See Shreveport
North Caddo HS 300/9-12
201 Airport Dr 71082 318-375-3258
Annie Cherry, prin. Fax 222-8430

Walker, Livingston, Pop. 6,061
Livingston Parish SD
Supt. — See Livingston
Literacy and Technology Center 9-12
9261 Florida Blvd 70785 225-667-5268
Kim Albin, prin.
North Corbin JHS 700/6-8
32725 N Corbin Rd 70785 225-686-2038
Dennis DeLee, prin. Fax 686-2690
Pathways, 13330 Burgess Ave 70785 Alt
Lisa Kluka, prin. 225-665-6062
Pine Ridge S 50/Alt
PO Box 72 70785 225-664-4823
Tony Terry, prin. Fax 664-2984
Walker Freshman HS 400/9-9
PO Box 659 70785 225-664-0243
David Clark, prin. Fax 665-0512
Walker SHS 1,100/10-12
12646 Burgess Ave 70785 225-664-4825
Jason St. Pierre, prin. Fax 664-4321
Westside JHS 600/6-8
12615 Burgess Ave 70785 225-665-8259
Steve Link, prin. Fax 665-8283

Washington, Saint Landry, Pop. 948
St. Landry Parish SD
Supt. — See Opelousas
North Central HS 300/5-12
6579 Highway 10 70589 337-623-4239
Reginald Bush, prin. Fax 623-5360
Washington Career & Technical Center Vo/Tech
PO Box 430 70589 337-826-7360
Dr. Tracy Beard, prin. Fax 826-5264

Watson, Livingston, Pop. 1,038
Livingston Parish SD
Supt. — See Livingston
Live Oak MS 1,000/6-8
PO Box 470 70786 225-664-3211
Ryan Hodges, prin. Fax 664-1551

Welsh, Jefferson Davis, Pop. 3,178
Jefferson Davis Parish SD
Supt. — See Jennings
Welsh HS 300/9-12
306 Bourgeois St 70591 337-734-2361
Robin Primeaux, prin. Fax 734-4149

Westlake, Calcasieu, Pop. 4,510
Calcasieu Parish SD
Supt. — See Lake Charles
Arnett MS 400/6-8
400 Sulphur Ave 70669 337-217-4630
Max Caldarera, prin. Fax 217-4631
Westlake HS 500/9-12
1000 Garden Dr 70669 337-217-4950
Jason Van Metre, prin. Fax 217-4951
Westlake HS T & I Vo/Tech
2307 Jones St 70669 337-217-4375
Gary Singer, prin. Fax 217-4376

West Monroe, Ouachita, Pop. 12,872
Ouachita Parish SD
Supt. — See Monroe
Good Hope MS 700/6-8
400 Good Hope Rd 71291 318-396-9693
Twainna Calhoun, prin. Fax 397-5110
Ouachita Parish Alternative Center 100/Alt
1600 N 7th St 71291 318-323-5991
Scott Stone, prin. Fax 323-5946
Riser MS 500/6-8
100 Price Dr 71292 318-387-0567
Rodney Lloyd, prin. Fax 387-9072
West Monroe HS 2,100/9-12
201 Riggs St 71291 318-323-3771
Shelby Ainsworth, prin. Fax 388-4594
West Ouachita HS 1,100/9-12
4061 Caples Rd 71292 318-249-2117
Becky Oaks, prin. Fax 249-4774
West Ridge MS 700/6-8
6977 Cypress St 71291 318-397-8444
Jennifer Nichols, prin. Fax 397-9376
Woodlawn JHS 300/6-8
175 Woodlawn School Rd 71292 318-325-1574
Charles Dykes, prin. Fax 325-9858

Claiborne Christian S 400/PK-12
334 Laird St 71291 318-396-7968
Cloyd's Beauty School #1 Inc. Post-Sec.
603 Natchitoches St 71291 318-322-5314
Northeast Baptist S 200/PK-12
5225 I 20 Service Rd 71292 318-325-2077

Westwego, Jefferson, Pop. 8,397
Jefferson Parish SD
Supt. — See Harvey
Worley MS 800/6-8
801 Spartan Ln 70094 504-348-4964
Ira Wilson, prin. Fax 348-7057

White Castle, Iberville, Pop. 1,872
Iberville Parish SD
Supt. — See Plaquemine
White Castle HS 300/7-12
32695 Graham St 70788 225-545-3621
Charley Handy, prin. Fax 545-2964

Winnfield, Winn, Pop. 4,766
Winn Parish SD 2,400/PK-12
PO Box 430 71483 318-628-6936
Steve Bartlett, supt. Fax 628-2582
www.winnpsb.org
Winnfield HS 400/9-12
631 Thomas Mill Rd 71483 318-628-3506
Dr. Jane Griffin, prin. Fax 628-3417
Winnfield MS 400/6-8
685 Thomas Mill Rd 71483 318-628-2765
Gena Hatcher, prin. Fax 628-1838
Other Schools – See Atlanta, Calvin, Dodson

Central Louisiana Technical College Post-Sec.
5960 Highway 167 N 71483 318-628-4342

Winnsboro, Franklin, Pop. 4,862
Franklin Parish SD 3,000/PK-12
7293 Prairie Rd 71295 318-435-9046
Dr. Lanny Johnson, supt. Fax 435-3392
www.fpsb.us
Franklin Parish HS 700/9-12
1600 Glover Dr 71295 318-435-5676
Brian Gunter, prin. Fax 435-6493

Family Community Christian S 500/PK-12
2023 Highway 15 71295 318-435-4791
Franklin Academy 200/PK-12
2110 Loop Rd 71295 318-435-9520

Youngsville, Lafayette, Pop. 8,025
Lafayette Parish SD
Supt. — See Lafayette
Youngsville MS 700/6-8
600 Church St 70592 337-521-7940
Renee Nunez, prin. Fax 521-7941

Youngsville Christian S 100/PK-10
214 Church St 70592 337-856-8693
Daina Jackson, admin. Fax 856-8675

Zachary, East Baton Rouge, Pop. 14,763
Zachary Community SD 4,700/PK-12
3755 Church St 70791 225-658-4969
Scott Devillier, supt. Fax 658-5261
www.zacharyschools.org
Northwestern MS 800/7-8
5200 E Central Ave 70791 225-654-9201
Debby Brian, prin. Fax 658-2025
Zachary Career and Technical Center Vo/Tech
205 W Flonacher Rd 70791 225-658-7381
Johnathon Coats, admin. Fax 658-7385
Zachary HS 1,600/9-12
4100 Bronco Ln 70791 225-654-2776
Joe LeBlanc, prin. Fax 658-0010

Zwolle, Sabine, Pop. 1,697
Sabine Parish SD
Supt. — See Many
Zwolle JSHS 300/7-12
PO Box 188 71486 318-645-6104
Bradley McLaren, prin. Fax 645-4830

MAINE

MAINE DEPARTMENT OF EDUCATION
23 State House Sta, Augusta 04333
Telephone 207-624-6600
Fax 207-624-6700
Website http://www.maine.gov/doe/

Commissioner of Education Robert Hasson

MAINE BOARD OF EDUCATION
23 State House Sta, Augusta 04333-0023

Chairperson Martha Harris

PUBLIC, PRIVATE AND CATHOLIC SECONDARY SCHOOLS

Ashland, Aroostook, Pop. 707
RSU 32 / MSAD 32 300/PK-12
PO Box 289 04732 207-435-3661
Gehrig Johnson Ph.D., supt. Fax 435-8421
www.sad32.org
Ashland District S 300/PK-12
PO Box 369 04732 207-435-3481
Joel Hall, prin. Fax 435-6417

Auburn, Androscoggin, Pop. 22,603
Auburn SD 3,600/PK-12
PO Box 800 04212 207-784-6431
Katherine Grondin, supt. Fax 333-6628
www.auburnschl.edu
Auburn MS 500/7-8
38 Falcon Dr 04210 207-333-6654
Celena Ranger, prin. Fax 784-1359
Franklin Alternative S 100/Alt
23 High St 04210 207-782-3242
Russell Barlow, prin. Fax 783-4189
Little HS 1,000/9-12
77 Harris St 04210 207-333-6652
James Miller, prin. Fax 784-9243
Merrill Hill Alternative S 50/Alt
23 High St 04210 207-783-3242
Russell Barlow, prin.

Central Maine Community College Post-Sec.
1250 Turner St 04210 207-755-5100
St. Dominic Academy 300/7-12
121 Gracelawn Rd 04210 207-782-6911
Shelley Wheeler, prin. Fax 795-6439

Augusta, Kennebec, Pop. 18,710
Augusta SD 2,300/PK-12
40 Pierce Dr 04330 207-626-2468
James Anastasio, supt. Fax 626-2444
www.augustaschools.org/
Capitol Area Technical Center Vo/Tech
40 Pierce Dr 04330 207-626-2475
Fax 626-2498
Cony JSHS 1,000/7-12
60 Pierce Dr 04330 207-626-2460
Kim Silsby, prin. Fax 626-2541

Kaplan University Post-Sec.
14 Marketplace Dr 04330 800-987-7734
University of Maine at Augusta Post-Sec.
46 University Dr 04330 207-621-3000

Baileyville, Washington
AOS 90 - EMASS 600/PK-12
PO Box 580 04694 207-427-6913
William Braun, supt. Fax 427-3166
sites.google.com/site/aos90aos90
Woodland JSHS 200/7-12
14 First Ave 04694 207-427-3325
Thomas Vicaire, prin. Fax 427-3950
Other Schools – See Lee

Bangor, Penobscot, Pop. 32,402
Bangor SD 3,800/PK-12
73 Harlow St 04401 207-992-4152
Dr. Betsy Webb, supt. Fax 992-4163
www.bangorschools.net
Bangor HS 1,200/9-12
885 Broadway 04401 207-992-5500
Paul Butler, prin. Fax 941-6212
Cohen MS 400/6-8
304 Garland St 04401 207-941-6230
Michael Missbrenner, prin. Fax 941-6235
Doughty MS 400/6-8
143 5th St 04401 207-941-6220
Ed Hackett, prin. Fax 947-7606

Career Technical Education
Supt. — None
United Technologies Center-Region 4 Vo/Tech
200 Hogan Rd 04401 207-942-5296
Greg Miller, dir. Fax 942-0776

All Saints S - St. John Campus 100/4-8
PO Box 1749 04402 207-942-0955
Joseph Gallant, prin. Fax 942-2398
Bangor Christian S 300/PK-12
1476 Broadway 04401 207-947-7356
Dr. Jeffrey Benjamin, hdmstr. Fax 262-9528
Bapst Memorial HS 500/9-12
100 Broadway 04401 207-947-0313
Melville MacKay, head sch Fax 941-2474
Beal College Post-Sec.
99 Farm Rd 04401 207-947-4591
Eastern Maine Community College Post-Sec.
354 Hogan Rd 04401 207-974-4600
Eastern Maine Medical Center Post-Sec.
489 State St 04401 207-973-7051
Empire Beauty School Post-Sec.
639 Broadway 04401 207-942-0039
Husson University Post-Sec.
1 College Cir 04401 207-941-7000
New England School of Communications Post-Sec.
1 College Cir 04401 207-941-7176

Bar Harbor, Hancock, Pop. 2,528
AOS 91 - MDIRSS
Supt. — See Mount Desert
Mt. Desert Island HS 500/9-12
1081 Eagle Lake Rd 04609 207-288-5011
Matthew Haney, prin. Fax 288-0692

College of the Atlantic Post-Sec.
105 Eden St 04609 207-288-5015

Bath, Sagadahoc, Pop. 8,327
RSU 1 2,000/PK-12
34 Wing Farm Pkwy 04530 207-443-6601
Dr. Patrick Manuel, supt. Fax 443-8295
www.rsu1.org/
Bath MS 400/6-8
6 Old Brunswick Rd 04530 207-443-8270
Brandon Ward, prin. Fax 443-8273
Bath Regional Vocational Center Vo/Tech
800 High St 04530 207-443-8257
Julie Kenny, dir. Fax 443-8256
Morse HS 600/9-12
826 High St 04530 207-443-8250
Jay Pinkerton, prin. Fax 443-8268

Hyde S - Bath 100/9-12
616 High St 04530 207-443-5584
Laura Gauld, head sch Fax 443-1450

Belfast, Waldo, Pop. 6,555
RSU 71 1,700/PK-12
PO Box 325 04915 207-338-1960
Paul Knowles, supt. Fax 338-4597
www.rsu71.org
Belfast Area HS 500/9-12
98 Waldo Ave 04915 207-338-1790
Stephen Fitzpatrick, prin. Fax 338-6713
Howard MS 400/6-8
173 Lincolnville Ave 04915 207-338-3320
Bruce Bailey, prin. Fax 338-5588
Adult Education Adult
6B Lions Way 04915 207-338-3197
Darrell Gilman Ed.D., dir. Fax 338-2960

Bethel, Oxford
RSU 44 / MSAD 44 800/K-12
1 Parkway Ste 204 04217 207-824-2185
David Murphy Ed.D., supt. Fax 824-2725
www.sad44.org
Telstar HS 200/9-12
284 Walkers Mills Rd 04217 207-824-2136
Cheryl Lang, prin. Fax 824-7130
Telstar MS 200/6-8
284 Walkers Mills Rd 04217 207-824-2136
Mark Kenney, prin. Fax 824-0496

Gould Academy 200/9-12
PO Box 860 04217 207-824-7700
Matt Ruby, head sch Fax 824-7711

Biddeford, York, Pop. 20,950
Biddeford SD 2,500/PK-12
18 Maplewood Ave 04005 207-282-8280
Jeremy Ray, supt. Fax 284-7956
www.biddefordschooldepartment.org
Biddeford HS 800/9-12
20 Maplewood Ave 04005 207-282-1596
Jerome Sirois, prin. Fax 282-8275
Biddeford MS 600/6-8
25 Tiger Way 04005 207-282-6400
Kyle Keenan, prin. Fax 282-6040
Biddeford Regional Center of Tech Vo/Tech
10 Maplewood Ave 04005 207-282-1501
Paulette Bonneau, dir. Fax 282-7986

Heartwood College of Art Post-Sec.
2 Main St Bldg 17 Ste 223 04005 207-284-8800
University of New England Post-Sec.
11 Hills Beach Rd 04005 207-283-0171

Bingham, Somerset, Pop. 749
RSU 83 / MSAD 13 200/PK-12
PO Box 649 04920 207-672-5502
Virginia Rebar, supt. Fax 672-5502
www.sad13.org
Quimby MS 50/5-8
PO Box 649 04920 207-672-5500
Juliana Richard, prin. Fax 672-5502
Upper Kennebec Valley HS 100/9-12
PO Box 669 04920 207-672-3300
Juliana Richard, prin. Fax 672-4485

Blue Hill, Hancock, Pop. 936

Stevens Academy 300/9-12
23 Union St 04614 207-374-2808
Tim Seeley, head sch Fax 374-2982

Boothbay Harbor, Lincoln, Pop. 1,073
AOS 98 - RCSS 800/PK-12
51 Emery Ln 04538 207-633-2874
Eileen King, supt. Fax 633-5458
www.aos98schools.org
Boothbay Region HS 200/9-12
236 Townsend Ave 04538 207-633-2421
Daniel Welch, prin. Fax 633-7129

Brewer, Penobscot, Pop. 9,320
Brewer SD 1,700/PK-12
261 Center St 04412 207-989-3160
Cheri Towle, supt. Fax 989-8622
www.breweredu.org
Brewer HS 700/9-12
79 Parkway S 04412 207-989-4140
David Wall, prin. Fax 989-2657

Bridgton, Cumberland, Pop. 2,035
RSU 61 / MSAD 61 1,800/K-12
900 Portland Rd 04009 207-647-3048
Alan Smith, supt. Fax 647-5682
www.lakeregionschools.org
Other Schools – See Naples

Brunswick, Cumberland, Pop. 14,835
Brunswick SD 2,400/K-12
46 Federal St 04011 207-319-1900
Paul Perzanoski, supt. Fax 725-1700
www.brunswick.k12.me.us
Brunswick HS 900/9-12
116 Maquoit Rd 04011 207-319-1910
Shanna Crofton, prin. Fax 798-5515
Brunswick JHS 500/6-8
65 Columbia Ave 04011 207-319-1930
Walter Wallace, prin. Fax 721-0602

Career Technical Education
Supt. — None
Region 10 Technical HS Vo/Tech
68 Church Rd 04011 207-729-6622
Fax 721-0907

Bowdoin College Post-Sec.
5000 College Sta 04011 207-725-3000

Buckfield, Oxford
RSU 10
Supt. — See Dixfield
Buckfield JSHS 300/7-12
160 Morrill St 04220 207-336-2151
George Reuter, prin. Fax 336-2460

Bucksport, Hancock, Pop. 2,843
RSU 25 1,100/PK-12
62 Mechanic St 04416 207-469-7311
James Boothby, supt. Fax 469-6640
www.rsu25.org/
Bucksport HS 300/9-12
102 Broadway 04416 207-469-6650
Bill Tracy, prin. Fax 469-2081
Bucksport MS 300/5-8
100 Miles Ln 04416 207-469-6647
Joshua Tripp, prin. Fax 469-2068

Buxton, York
RSU 6 / MSAD 6 3,800/PK-12
94 Main St 04093 207-929-3831
Fax 646-9748
www.bonnyeagle.org
Bonny Eagle MS 900/6-8
92 Sokokis Trl 04093 207-929-3833
Diane Nadeau, prin. Fax 459-5150
Other Schools – See Standish

Calais, Washington, Pop. 3,074
Calais SD 600/PK-12
32 Blue Devil Hl 04619 207-454-7561
Ronald Jenkins, supt. Fax 454-2296
www.calaisschool.org
Calais MSHS 300/7-12
34 Blue Devil Hl Ste 2 04619 207-454-2591
Mary Anne Spearin, prin. Fax 454-0306
Saint Croix Regional Tech Center Vo/Tech
34 Blue Devil Hl Ste 1 04619 207-454-2581
Robert F. Moholland, admin. Fax 454-2597

Washington County Community College Post-Sec.
1 College Dr 04619 207-454-1000

Camden, Knox, Pop. 3,526
Five Town CSD 700/9-12
7 Lions Ln 04843 207-236-3358
Maria Libby, supt. Fax 236-7810
www.fivetowns.net
Other Schools – See Rockport

MSAD 28 800/K-8
7 Lions Ln 04843 207-236-3358
Maria Libby, supt. Fax 236-7810
www.fivetowns.net/sad/
Camden-Rockport MS 400/5-8
34 Knowlton St 04843 207-236-7805
Jaime Stone, prin. Fax 236-7815

Watershed S 50/9-12
32 Washington St 04843 207-230-7341

Cape Elizabeth, Cumberland, Pop. 8,854
Cape Elizabeth SD 1,700/K-12
320 Ocean House Rd 04107 207-799-2217
Howard Colter, supt. Fax 799-2914
www.cape.k12.me.us
Cape Elizabeth HS 600/9-12
345 Ocean House Rd 04107 207-799-3309
Jeffrey Shedd, prin. Fax 767-8050
Cape Elizabeth MS 500/5-8
14 Scott Dyer Rd 04107 207-799-8176
Michael Tracy, prin. Fax 767-0832

Carabaset Vly, Franklin

Carrabassett Valley Academy 100/7-12
3197 Carrabassett Dr, 207-237-2250
Kate Punderson, head sch Fax 237-2213

Caribou, Aroostook, Pop. 8,094
RSU 39 1,600/PK-12
75 Bennett Dr Ste 3 04736 207-496-6311
Timothy Doad, supt. Fax 498-3261
www.rsu39.org
Caribou HS 500/9-12
308 Sweden St 04736 207-493-4260
Travis Barnes, prin. Fax 493-4244
Caribou MS 300/6-8
21 Glenn St 04736 207-493-4240
Leland Caron, prin. Fax 493-4243
Caribou Regional Technology Center Vo/Tech
308 Sweden St Ste 1 04736 207-493-4270
Ralph Conroy, prin. Fax 493-4242
Adult Education Adult
75 Bennett Dr Ste 2 04736 207-493-4272
Dan MacDonald, dir.
Other Schools – See Limestone

Empire Beauty School Post-Sec.
30 Skyway Dr 04736 207-498-6067

Carmel, Penobscot
RSU 87 / MSAD 23 700/PK-8
44 Plymouth Rd 04419 207-848-5173
John Backus, supt. Fax 848-5196
www.rsu87.org
Caravel MS 200/5-8
520 Irish Rd 04419 207-848-3615
Mark Turner, prin. Fax 848-0884

Castine, Hancock, Pop. 1,015

Maine Maritime Academy Post-Sec.
66 Pleasant St 04420 207-326-4311

Corinth, Penobscot
RSU 64 / MSAD 64 600/PK-12
PO Box 279 04427 207-285-3334
Rhonda Sperrey, supt. Fax 285-3307
www.rsu64schools.org
Central HS 400/9-12
PO Box 370 04427 207-285-3326
Brent Slowikowski, prin. Fax 285-4342
Central MS 300/6-8
PO Box 19 04427 207-285-3177
Jonathan Perry, prin. Fax 285-4350

Cumberland Center, Cumberland, Pop. 2,477
RSU 51 / MSAD 51 1,900/K-12
PO Box 6A 04021 207-829-4800
Jeff Porter, supt. Fax 829-4802
www.msad51.org
Greely HS 700/9-12
303 Main St 04021 207-829-4805
Dan McKeone, prin. Fax 829-2256
Greely MS 6-8 500/6-8
351 Tuttle Rd 04021 207-829-4815
Mar-E Trebilcock, prin. Fax 829-4819

Danforth, Washington
RSU 84 / MSAD 14 100/PK-12
31A Houlton Rd 04424 207-448-2882
Terry A. Comeau, supt. Fax 448-7235
www.eastgrandschool.org
East Grand S 100/PK-12
31 Houlton Rd 04424 207-448-2260
Dawn Matthews, prin. Fax 448-7880

Deer Isle, Hancock
Deer Isle - Stonington Community SD 300/K-12
251 N Deer Isle Rd 04627 207-348-9100
Robert Webster, supt. Fax 348-9103
www.sedgwickschool.net/union-76-schools
Deer Isle - Stonington HS 100/9-12
251 N Deer Isle Rd 04627 207-348-2303
Todd West, prin. Fax 348-2304

Dexter, Penobscot, Pop. 2,129
AOS 94 - S46HRSD 1,200/PK-12
175 Fern Rd Ste 1 04930 207-924-6000
Kevin Jordan, supt. Fax 924-7660
www.aos94.org
Dexter HS 300/9-12
12 Abbott Hill Rd 04930 207-924-5536
Stephen Bell, prin. Fax 924-7673
Tri-County Regional Technology Center Vo/Tech
14 Abbott Hill Rd 04930 207-924-7670
Dr. Patrick O'Neill, dir. Fax 924-5539

Dixfield, Oxford, Pop. 1,056
RSU 10 2,700/PK-12
33 Nash St 04224 207-562-7254
Fax 562-7059
district.rsu10.org
Dirigo HS 300/9-12
145 Weld St 04224 207-562-4251
Mike Poulin, prin. Fax 562-6074
Dirigo MS 200/6-8
45 Middle School Dr 04224 207-562-7552
Michael Poulin, prin. Fax 562-8329
Other Schools – See Buckfield, Mexico, Rumford

Dover Foxcroft, Piscataquis, Pop. 3,077
RSU 68 / MSAD 68 700/PK-8
63 Harrison Ave Ste C 04426 207-564-6535
Robert Lucy, supt. Fax 564-3487
www.sedomocha.org
Se Do Mo Cha MS 300/5-8
63 Harrison Ave 04426 207-564-6535
Julie Kimball, prin. Fax 564-6531

Foxcroft Academy 500/9-12
975 W Main St 04426 207-564-8351
Arnold Shorey M.Ed., head sch Fax 564-8394

Dyer Brook, Aroostook
RSU 50 700/PK-12
922 Dyer Brook Rd, 207-757-8223
Todd Leroy, supt. Fax 757-8257
www.rsu50.org
Southern Aroostook Community S 300/K-12
922 Dyer Brook Rd, 207-757-8206
Jon Porter, prin. Fax 757-7313
Other Schools – See Stacyville

East Machias, Washington

Washington Academy 400/9-12
PO Box 190 04630 207-255-8301
Judson McBrine, head sch Fax 255-8303

East Millinocket, Penobscot, Pop. 1,552
East Millinocket SD 400/PK-12
45 North St 04430 207-746-3500
Dawn Pray M.Ed., supt. Fax 746-3516
eastmillinocketschools.org
Schenck HS 100/9-12
45 North St 04430 207-746-3511
Catherine Steeves M.Ed., prin. Fax 746-3516
Other Schools – See Medway

Millinocket SD 500/K-12
45 North St Ste 2 04430 207-723-6400
Frank Boynton, supt. Fax 447-6599
www.millinocketschools.org
Other Schools – See Millinocket

Easton, Aroostook
Easton SD 200/PK-12
PO Box 126 04740 207-488-7700
Roger Shaw, supt. Fax 488-2840
eastonschools.org
Easton JSHS 100/7-12
PO Box 66 04740 207-488-7702
Cameron Adams, prin. Fax 488-7707

Eastport, Washington, Pop. 1,291
AOS 77 - SCSS 600/PK-12
PO Box 190 04631 207-853-2567
Kenneth Johnson, supt. Fax 853-6260
Shead HS 100/9-12
89 High St 04631 207-853-6254
Paul Theriault, prin. Fax 853-2919

Westlawn Institute of Marine Technology Post-Sec.
16 Deep Cove Rd 04631 207-853-6600

East Waterboro, York
RSU 57 / MSAD 57
Supt. — See Waterboro
Massabesic MS 700/6-8
134 Old Alfred Rd 04030 207-247-6121
Mark Fisher, prin. Fax 247-8621

Eliot, York
RSU 35 / MSAD 35 2,300/PK-12
180 Depot Rd 03903 207-439-2438
Dr. Mary Nash, supt. Fax 439-2531
www.rsu35.org
Marshwood MS 500/6-8
626 Harold L Dow Hwy 03903 207-439-1399
Anthony Bourbon, prin. Fax 439-3504
Other Schools – See South Berwick

Ellsworth, Hancock, Pop. 7,675
Ellsworth SD 1,300/PK-12
66 Main St Ste 201 04605 207-664-7100
Daniel Higgins, supt. Fax 669-6032
www.ellsworthschools.org
Ellsworth HS 500/9-12
299 State St 04605 207-667-4722
Dan Clifford, prin. Fax 667-5027
Hancock County Technical Center Vo/Tech
112 Boggy Brook Rd 04605 207-667-9729
Amy Boles, dir. Fax 667-7138

Fairfield, Kennebec, Pop. 2,598
RSU 49 / MSAD 49 2,200/PK-12
8 School St 04937 207-453-4200
Dr. Dean Baker, supt. Fax 453-0110
www.msad49.org
Lawrence HS 700/9-12
9 School St 04937 207-453-4200
Mark Campbell, prin. Fax 453-4219
Lawrence JHS 400/7-8
7 School St 04937 207-453-4200
Roberta Hersom, prin. Fax 453-4214

Kennebec Valley Community College Post-Sec.
92 Western Ave 04937 207-453-5000

Falmouth, Cumberland, Pop. 1,834
Falmouth SD 2,100/K-12
51 Woodville Rd 04105 207-781-3200
Geoff Bruno, supt. Fax 781-5711
www.falmouthschools.org
Falmouth HS 700/9-12
74 Woodville Rd 04105 207-781-7429
Gregg Palmer, prin. Fax 781-3985
Falmouth MS 500/6-8
52 Woodville Rd 04105 207-781-3740
Janet Adams, prin. Fax 321-0108

Maine Educational Center for the Deaf Post-Sec.
Mackworth Island 04105 207-781-3165

Farmingdale, Kennebec, Pop. 1,939
RSU 2
Supt. — See Hallowell
Hall-Dale MSHS 200/6-12
111 Maple St 04344 207-622-4162
Mark Tinkham, prin. Fax 622-7515

Farmington, Franklin, Pop. 4,199
RSU 9 - Mt. Blue Regional SD 2,200/PK-12
129 Seamon Rd 04938 207-778-6571
Dr. Thomas Ward, supt. Fax 778-4160
www.mtbluersd.org/
Foster Reg Applied Tech Center Vo/Tech
129 Seamon Rd 04938 207-778-3562
Glenn Kapiloff, dir. Fax 778-3562
Mt. Blue HS 700/9-12
129 Seamon Rd 04938 207-778-3561
Bruce Mochamer, prin. Fax 778-3564
Mt. Blue MS 400/6-8
269 Middle St 04938 207-778-3511
Gary Oswald, prin. Fax 778-5810

University of Maine Farmington Post-Sec.
111 South St 04938 207-778-7050

Fort Fairfield, Aroostook, Pop. 1,799
MSAD 20 500/PK-12
28 High School Dr Ste B 04742 207-473-4455
Timothy Doak, supt. Fax 473-4095
www.msad20.org
Fort Fairfield MSHS 300/6-12
28 High School Dr Ste A 04742 207-472-3271
John Kaleta, prin. Fax 472-3281

Fort Kent, Aroostook, Pop. 2,423
MSAD 27 900/PK-12
84 Pleasant St Ste 1 04743 207-834-3189
Benjamin Sirois, supt. Fax 834-3395
www.sad27.org/
Fort Kent Community HS 300/9-12
84 Pleasant St 04743 207-834-5540
James Charette, prin. Fax 834-2723
Valley Rivers MS 100/7-8
84 Pleasant St 04743 207-834-5540
James Charette, prin. Fax 834-2723

University of Maine Fort Kent Post-Sec.
23 University Dr 04743 207-834-7500

Freeport, Cumberland, Pop. 1,447
RSU 5 1,900/PK-12
17 West St 04032 207-865-0928
Dr. Becky Foley, supt. Fax 865-2855
rsu5.org
Freeport HS 500/9-12
30 Holbrook St 04032 207-865-4706
Brian Campbell, prin. Fax 865-2900

Freeport MS 300/6-8
19 Kendall Ln 04032 207-865-6051
Raymond Grogan, prin. Fax 865-2902

Pine Tree Academy 200/PK-12
67 Pownal Rd 04032 207-865-4747
Brendan Krueger M.A., prin. Fax 865-1768

Frenchville, Aroostook
RSU 33 / MSAD 33 300/PK-12
PO Box 9 04745 207-543-7334
Dr. Fern Desjardins, supt. Fax 543-6242
www.msad33.org
St. John Valley Tech Center Vo/Tech
PO Box 509 04745 207-543-6606
David Morse, dir. Fax 543-6115
Other Schools – See Saint Agatha

Fryeburg, Oxford, Pop. 1,595
RSU 72 / MSAD 72 800/PK-8
124 Portland St 04037 207-935-2600
Jay Robinson, supt. Fax 935-3787
www.msad72.org
Ockett MS 300/6-8
25 Molly Ockett Dr 04037 207-935-2401
Emily Kirkpatrick, prin. Fax 935-4470

Fryeburg Academy 600/9-12
745 Main St 04037 207-935-2001
Erin Mayo, head sch Fax 935-4292

Gardiner, Kennebec, Pop. 5,663
MSAD 11 2,100/PK-12
150 Highland Ave 04345 207-582-5346
Patricia Hopkins, supt. Fax 582-8305
www.msad11.org
Gardiner Area HS 600/9-12
40 W Hill Rd 04345 207-582-3150
Chad Kempton, prin. Fax 582-0434
Gardiner Regional MS 500/6-8
161 Cobbossee Ave 04345 207-582-1326
Todd Sanders, prin. Fax 582-6823

Gorham, Cumberland, Pop. 6,775
Gorham SD 2,700/K-12
75 South St Ste 2 04038 207-222-1000
Heather Perry, supt. Fax 839-5003
www.gorhamschools.org/
Gorham HS 800/9-12
41 Morrill Ave 04038 207-222-1100
Brian Jandreau, prin. Fax 839-7742
Gorham MS 600/6-8
106 Weeks Rd 04038 207-222-1220
Robert Riley, prin. Fax 839-4092

Gray, Cumberland, Pop. 877
RSU 15 / MSAD 15 2,000/K-12
14 Shaker Rd 04039 207-657-3335
Dr. Craig King, supt. Fax 657-2040
www.msad15.org/
Gray-New Gloucester HS 500/9-12
10 Libby Hill Rd 04039 207-657-3323
Ted Finn, prin. Fax 657-3329
Gray-New Gloucester MS 700/5-8
31 Libby Hill Rd 04039 207-657-4994
Sherry Levesque, prin. Fax 657-5219

Greenville, Piscataquis, Pop. 1,245
Greenville SD 100/PK-12
PO Box 100 04441 207-695-3708
Jim Chasse, supt. Fax 695-3709
www.ghslakers.org
Greenville Consolidated S 100/PK-12
PO Box 100 04441 207-695-2666
Kelly MacFadyen, prin. Fax 695-4614

Guilford, Piscataquis, Pop. 885
RSU 80 / MSAD 4 700/PK-12
31 High St Ste C 04443 207-876-3444
Ann Kirkpatrick, supt. Fax 876-3446
www.sad4.org
Piscataquis Community Secondary S 300/7-12
9 Campus Dr 04443 207-876-4625
John Keane, prin. Fax 876-4628

Hallowell, Kennebec, Pop. 2,343
RSU 2 1,800/PK-12
7 Reed St 04347 207-622-6351
William Zima, supt. Fax 622-7866
www.kidsrsu.org
Other Schools – See Farmingdale, Monmouth, Richmond

Hampden, Penobscot, Pop. 4,292
RSU 22 2,100/PK-12
24 Main Rd N 04444 207-862-3255
Richard Lyons, supt. Fax 862-2789
www.rsu22.us
Hampden Academy 700/9-12
89 Western Ave 04444 207-862-3791
Leigh Larson, prin. Fax 862-4577
Reeds Brook MS 300/6-8
28A Main Rd S 04444 207-862-3540
Regan Nickels, prin. Fax 862-3551
Other Schools – See Orono, Winterport

Harrington, Washington
RSU 37 / MSAD 37 500/PK-12
1020 Sacarap Rd 04643 207-483-2734
Ronald Ramsay, supt. Fax 483-6051
www.msad37.org/
Narraguagus HS 200/7-12
1611 Main St 04643 207-483-2746
Lucille Willey, prin. Fax 483-2771

Hartland, Somerset, Pop. 799
RSU 19
Supt. — See Newport
Somerset Valley MS 200/5-8
45 Blake St 04943 207-938-4770
Don Roux, prin. Fax 938-2114

Hebron, Oxford

Hebron Academy 300/6-12
PO Box 309 04238 207-966-2100
Dan Marchetti, hdmstr. Fax 966-1111

Hermon, See Bangor
Hermon SD 1,200/PK-12
31 Billings Rd 04401 207-848-4000
Patricia Duran, supt. Fax 848-5226
www.hermon.net
Hermon HS 500/9-12
2415 Route 2 04401 207-848-4000
Brian Walsh, prin. Fax 848-5591
Hermon MS 300/5-8
29 Billings Rd 04401 207-848-4000
Gerald Kiesman, prin. Fax 848-2163

Hiram, Oxford
RSU 55 / MSAD 55 900/K-12
137 S Hiram Rd 04041 207-625-2490
Carl Landry, supt. Fax 625-7065
www.sad55.org
Sacopee Valley HS 400/9-12
115 S Hiram Rd 04041 207-625-3208
Britt Wolfe, prin. Fax 625-7869
Sacopee Valley MS 300/4-8
137 S Hiram Rd 04041 207-625-2450
Michael Lynch, prin. Fax 625-2465

Hodgdon, Aroostook
RSU 70 / MSAD 70 400/PK-12
175 Hodgdon Mills Rd 04730 207-532-3015
Scott Richardson, supt. Fax 532-2679
www.msad70.org
Hodgdon HS 200/7-12
174 Hodgdon Mills Rd 04730 207-532-2413
Mary Harbison, prin. Fax 532-4043

Holden, Penobscot
RSU 63 / MSAD 63 500/PK-8
202 Kidder Hill Rd 04429 207-843-7851
Kenneth Smith, supt. Fax 843-7295
www.edline.net/pages/rsu63
Holbrook MS 300/5-8
202 Kidder Hill Rd 04429 207-843-7769
Richard Modery, prin. Fax 843-4328

Houlton, Aroostook, Pop. 4,790
Career Technical Education
Supt. — None
Region 2 School of Applied Tech Vo/Tech
PO Box 307 04730 207-532-9541
Dave Keaton, dir. Fax 532-6975

RSU 29 / MSAD 29 1,100/PK-12
PO Box 190 04730 207-532-6555
Ellen Schneider, supt. Fax 532-6481
www.rsu29.org
Houlton MSHS 300/6-12
7 Bird St 04730 207-532-6551
Martin Bouchard, prin. Fax 532-6282

Greater Houlton Christian Academy 100/PK-12
27 School St 04730 207-532-0736
R. Thomas Zimmerman, head sch Fax 532-9553

Howland, Penobscot, Pop. 1,083
AOS 43
Supt. — See Lagrange
Hichborn MS 100/6-8
23 Cross St 04448 207-732-3113
Carol Marcinkus, prin. Fax 732-8331
Penobscot Valley HS 200/9-12
23 Cross St 04448 207-732-3111
Carol Marcinkus, prin. Fax 732-8328

Islesboro, Waldo
Islesboro School Department 100/K-12
PO Box 118 04848 207-734-2251
Patrick Phillips, supt. Fax 734-8159
ics.islesboro.k12.me.us
Islesboro Central S 100/K-12
PO Box 118 04848 207-734-2251
Heather Knight, prin. Fax 734-8159

Jackman, Somerset
RSU 82 / MSAD 12 200/K-12
606 Main St 04945 207-668-5291
Dr. William Crumley, supt. Fax 668-4482
www.sad12.com
Forest Hills Consolidated S 200/K-12
606 Main St 04945 207-668-5291
Denise Plante, prin. Fax 668-4482

Jay, Franklin
RSU 73
Supt. — See Livermore Falls
Spruce Mountain HS 500/9-12
33 Community Dr 04239 207-897-4336
Thomas Plourde, prin. Fax 897-9313
Spruce Mountain MS 400/6-8
23 Community Dr 04239 207-897-4319
Scott Albert, prin. Fax 897-3513

Jonesport, Washington
Moosabec Community SD & Union 103 200/PK-12
127 Snare Creek Ln 04649 207-497-2154
William Shuttleworth, supt. Fax 497-2703
www.union103.org
Jonesport-Beals HS 100/9-12
180 Snare Creek Ln 04649 207-497-5454
Michael Kelley, prin. Fax 497-3004

Kennebunk, York, Pop. 5,151
RSU 21 2,400/K-12
177 Alewive Rd 04043 207-985-1100
Katie Hawes, supt. Fax 985-1104
www.rsu21.net

Kennebunk HS 700/9-12
89 Fletcher St 04043 207-985-1110
Susan Cressey, prin. Fax 985-1350
Kennebunk MS 500/6-8
60 Thompson Rd 04043 207-467-8004
Jeff Rodman, prin. Fax 467-9059

Kennebunkport, York, Pop. 1,232

The Landing School Post-Sec.
PO Box 1490 04046 207-985-7976

Kents Hill, Kennebec

Kents Hill S 200/9-12
PO Box 257 04349 207-685-4914
Patrick McInerney, head sch Fax 685-9529

Kittery, York, Pop. 4,483
Kittery SD 1,100/K-12
200 Rogers Rd 03904 207-475-1334
Allyn Hutton, supt. Fax 439-5407
www.kitteryschools.com
Shapleigh MS 400/4-8
43 Stevenson Rd 03904 207-439-2572
Anne Ellis, prin. Fax 439-9958
Traip Academy 300/9-12
12 Williams Ave 03904 207-439-1121
Eric Waddell, prin. Fax 439-3789

Lagrange, Penobscot
AOS 43 1,300/PK-12
20 Howland Rd 04453 207-943-7317
Michael Wright, supt. Fax 943-5314
www.aos43.com
Other Schools – See Howland, Milo

Lee, Penobscot
AOS 90 - EMASS
Supt. — See Baileyville
Mt. Jefferson JHS 100/5-8
61 Winn Rd 04455 207-738-2866
Pamela Hamilton, prin. Fax 738-3817

Lee Academy 300/9-12
26 Winn Rd 04455 207-738-2252
W. Gus LeBlanc, hdmstr. Fax 738-2025

Lewiston, Androscoggin, Pop. 35,657
Lewiston SD 5,200/PK-12
36 Oak St 04240 207-795-4100
William T. Webster, supt. Fax 795-4177
www.lewistonpublicschools.org/
Lewiston HS 1,400/9-12
156 East Ave 04240 207-795-4190
Shawn Chabot, prin. Fax 795-4119
Lewiston MS 700/7-8
75 Central Ave 04240 207-795-4180
Jake Langlais, prin. Fax 753-1789
Lewiston Regional Technical Center Vo/Tech
156 East Ave 04240 207-795-4144
Robert Callahan, dir. Fax 795-4147

Bates College Post-Sec.
2 Andrews Rd 04240 207-786-6255
Central Maine Christian Academy 100/PK-12
390 Main St 04240 207-777-0007
Patricia St. Hilaire, admin. Fax 777-0007
College of Nursing & Health Professions Post-Sec.
70 Middle St 04240 207-795-2840
Kaplan University Post-Sec.
475 Lisbon St 04240 207-333-3300
Mr. Bernard's School of Hair Fashion Post-Sec.
711 Lisbon St 04240 207-783-7765

Limestone, Aroostook, Pop. 1,068
Maine School of Science & Mathematics 100/10-12
95 High St 04750 207-325-3303
Luke Shorty, dir. Fax 325-3340
www.mssm.org
Maine S of Science & Mathematics 100/10-12
95 High St 04750 207-325-3303
Luke Shorty, dir. Fax 325-3340

RSU 39
Supt. — See Caribou
Limestone Community S 300/PK-12
93 High St 04750 207-325-4742
Susan White, prin. Fax 325-4969

Lincoln, Penobscot, Pop. 2,837
Career Technical Education
Supt. — None
North Penobscot Tech-Region 3 Vo/Tech
35 W Broadway 04457 207-794-3004
Mary Hawkes, dir. Fax 794-8049

RSU 67 1,000/PK-12
25 Reed Dr 04457 207-794-6500
Dr. Keith Laser, supt. Fax 794-2600
www.rsu67.org
Mattanawcook Academy 400/9-12
33 Reed Dr 04457 207-794-6711
Henry Pietras, prin. Fax 794-3205
Mattanawcook JHS 300/4-8
41 School St 04457 207-794-8935
Christopher Cowing, prin. Fax 794-2601

Lisbon, See Lisbon Falls
Lisbon SD 1,300/PK-12
19 Gartley St 04250 207-353-6711
Rick Green, supt. Fax 353-3032
www.lisbonschoolsme.org
Other Schools – See Lisbon Falls

Lisbon Falls, Androscoggin, Pop. 4,031
Lisbon SD
Supt. — See Lisbon

Lisbon HS 400/9-12
2 Sugg Dr 04252 207-353-3030
Nick Gannon, prin. Fax 353-3032
Sugg MS 300/6-8
4 Sugg Dr 04252 207-353-3055
Darren Akerman, prin. Fax 353-3053

Livermore Falls, Androscoggin, Pop. 1,558
RSU 73 1,600/PK-12
9 Cedar St 04254 207-897-6722
Kenneth Healey, supt. Fax 897-2362
rsu73.com
Other Schools – See Jay

Machias, Washington, Pop. 1,257
AOS 96 - MBASS 800/PK-12
291 Court St 04654 207-255-6585
Scott Porter, supt. Fax 255-8054
www.aos96.org
Machias Memorial HS 100/9-12
1 Bulldog Ln 04654 207-255-3812
Brian Leavitt, prin. Fax 255-3093

University of Maine at Machias Post-Sec.
116 OBrien Ave 04654 207-255-1200

Madawaska, Aroostook, Pop. 2,953
Madawaska SD 500/PK-12
328 Saint Thomas St Ste 201 04756 207-728-3346
Gisele Dionne, supt. Fax 728-7823
www.madawaskaschools.org
Madawaska MSHS 200/7-12
135 7th Ave 04756 207-728-3371
Wayne Anderson, prin. Fax 728-3636

Madison, Somerset, Pop. 2,594
RSU 59 / MSAD 59 700/PK-12
205 Main St 04950 207-696-3323
Bonnie Levesque, supt. Fax 696-5631
sites.google.com/a/msad59.org/rsu59/
Madison Area Memorial HS 300/9-12
486 Main St 04950 207-696-3395
Jessica Ward, prin. Fax 696-5644
Madison JHS 200/5-8
205 Main St 04950 207-696-3381
Ryan Arnold, prin. Fax 696-5640

Mars Hill, Aroostook, Pop. 965
RSU 42 / MSAD 42 400/PK-12
PO Box 1006 04758 207-425-3771
Elaine Boulier, supt.
msad42.org
Central Aroostook JSHS 200/7-12
PO Box 310 04758 207-425-2811
Kay York, prin. Fax 429-8460

Medway, Penobscot
East Millinocket SD
Supt. — See East Millinocket
Medway MS 100/5-8
25 Middle School Dr 04460 207-746-3470
Dawn Pray M.Ed., prin. Fax 746-9435

Mexico, Oxford, Pop. 1,718
Career Technical Education
Supt. — None
Region 9 School of Applied Tech Vo/Tech
377 River Rd 04257 207-364-3764
Brenda Gammon, dir. Fax 364-2074

RSU 10
Supt. — See Dixfield
Mountain Valley MS 300/6-8
58 Highland Ter 04257 207-364-7926
Ryan Casey, prin. Fax 364-5608

Millinocket, Penobscot, Pop. 4,427
Millinocket SD
Supt. — See East Millinocket
Stearns JSHS 300/7-12
199 State St 04462 207-723-6430
Deborah Levesque, prin. Fax 723-6437

Milo, Piscataquis, Pop. 1,832
AOS 43
Supt. — See Lagrange
Penquis Valley HS 400/6-12
48 Penquis Dr 04463 207-943-7346
Jeremy Bousquet, prin. Fax 943-0940

Monmouth, Kennebec
RSU 2
Supt. — See Hallowell
Monmouth Academy 200/9-12
96 Academy Rd 04259 207-933-4416
Richard Amero, prin. Fax 933-7222
Monmouth MS 300/4-8
117 Academy Rd 04259 207-933-9002
Scott Barksdale, prin. Fax 933-7252

Mount Desert, Hancock
AOS 91 - MDIRSS 1,500/K-12
PO Box 60 04660 207-288-5049
Fax 288-5071
www.mdirss.org
Other Schools – See Bar Harbor

Naples, Cumberland, Pop. 423
RSU 61 / MSAD 61
Supt. — See Bridgton
Lake Region HS 500/9-12
1877 Roosevelt Trl 04055 207-693-6221
A. Erik Good, prin. Fax 693-4591
Lake Region MS 400/6-8
204 Kansas Rd 04055 207-647-8403
Matthew Lokken, prin. Fax 647-0991
Lake Region Vocational Center Vo/Tech
1879 Roosevelt Trl 04055 207-693-3864
Rosie Schacht, dir. Fax 647-9602

Newcastle, Lincoln, Pop. 659

Lincoln Academy 500/9-12
81 Academy Hl 04553 207-563-3596
David Sturdevant, hdmstr. Fax 563-1067

New Gloucester, Cumberland

Maine Coast Waldorf HS 50/9-12
83 Pineland Dr 04260 207-688-8989

Newport, Penobscot, Pop. 1,726
RSU 19 2,200/PK-12
PO Box 40 04953 207-368-5091
Michael Hammer, supt. Fax 368-2192
www.rsu19.org
Nokomis Regional HS 700/9-12
266 Williams Rd 04953 207-368-4354
Mary Nadeau, prin. Fax 368-3276
Sebasticook Valley MS 300/5-8
337 Williams Rd 04953 207-368-4592
Angela Brown, prin. Fax 368-4598
Other Schools – See Hartland

Norridgewock, Somerset, Pop. 1,411

Riverview Memorial S 50/K-10
201 Mercer Rd 04957 207-634-2641

North Anson, Somerset
RSU 74 / MSAD 74 700/PK-12
PO Box 219 04958 207-635-2727
Kenneth Coville, supt. Fax 635-3599
www.sad74.k12.me.us
Carrabec HS 200/9-12
PO Box 220 04958 207-635-2296
Dr. Regina Campbell, prin. Fax 635-2276

North Berwick, York, Pop. 1,596
RSU 60 / MSAD 60 2,900/K-12
PO Box 819 03906 207-676-2234
Steven Connolly, supt. Fax 676-3229
www.msad60.org
Hurd Academy, 77 High St 03906 Alt
S. Austin, prin. 207-676-2651
Noble HS 1,100/8-12
388 Somersworth Rd 03906 207-676-2843
Joseph Findlay, prin. Fax 676-2842

North Bridgton, Cumberland

Bridgton Academy 200/12-12
PO Box 292 04057 207-647-3322
Graydon Vigneau, hdmstr. Fax 514-0757

North Haven, Knox
RSU 7 / MSAD 7 100/PK-12
93 Pulpit Harbor Rd 04853 207-867-4707
Jay Bartner, supt. Fax 867-4438
www.northhavencommunityschool.org
North Haven Community S 100/PK-12
93 Pulpit Harbor Rd 04853 207-867-4707
Amy Marx, prin. Fax 867-4438

Norway, Oxford, Pop. 2,676
Career Technical Education
Supt. — None
Oxford Hills Tech-Region 11 Vo/Tech
PO Box 313 04268 207-743-7756
Shawn Lambert, dir. Fax 743-0667

Oakland, Kennebec, Pop. 2,571
RSU 18 2,900/PK-12
41 Heath St 04963 207-465-7384
Gary N. Smith, supt. Fax 465-9130
www.rsu18.org/
Messalonskee HS 800/9-12
131 Messalonskee High Dr 04963 207-465-7381
Paula Callan, prin. Fax 465-9151
Messalonskee MS 500/6-8
33 School Bus Dr 04963 207-465-2167
Mark Hatch, prin. Fax 465-9683
Other Schools – See South China

Old Orchard Beach, York, Pop. 8,527
RSU 23 700/PK-12
28 Jameson Hill Rd 04064 207-934-5751
Lloyd Crocker, supt. Fax 934-1917
www.rsu23.org
Loranger MS 300/3-8
148 Saco Ave 04064 207-934-4848
Michael Flaherty, prin. Fax 934-3712
Old Orchard Beach HS 200/9-12
40 E Emerson Cummings Blvd 04064 207-934-4461
John Suttie, prin. Fax 934-3705

Old Town, Penobscot, Pop. 7,682
RSU 34 1,500/PK-12
156 Oak St Ste 2 04468 207-827-7171
David Walker, supt. Fax 827-3922
www.rsu34.org/
Leonard MS 300/6-8
156 Oak St 04468 207-827-3900
Jennifer Cyr, prin. Fax 827-3935
Old Town HS 500/9-12
203 Stillwater Ave 04468 207-827-3910
Scott Gordon, prin. Fax 827-3918

Orono, Penobscot, Pop. 9,316
RSU 22
Supt. — See Hampden
Orono-Hampden-Old Town Adult Education Adult
14 Goodridge Dr 04473 207-866-4119

RSU 26 800/PK-12
10 Goodridge Dr 04473 207-866-7110
Michael Tracy, supt. Fax 866-4217
www.rsu26.org
Orono HS 400/9-12
14 Goodridge Dr 04473 207-866-4916
Reg Ruhlin, prin. Fax 866-7116
Orono MS 200/6-8
14 Goodridge Dr 04473 207-866-2350
Jeffrey Paul, prin. Fax 866-7111

University of Maine 04469 Post-Sec.
207-581-1110

Phillips, Franklin
RSU 58 / MSAD 58 700/PK-12
1401 Rangeley Rd 04966 207-639-2086
Susan Pratt M.Ed., supt. Fax 639-5120
www.msad58.org
Other Schools – See Salem

Pittsfield, Somerset, Pop. 3,092
RSU 53 / MSAD 53 700/PK-8
167 School St Ste A 04967 207-487-5107
Jason I. Tardy, supt. Fax 487-6310
www.msad53.org/
Warsaw MS 300/5-8
167 School St 04967 207-487-5145
Sharon Littlefield, prin. Fax 487-4511

Maine Central Institute 400/9-12
295 Main St 04967 207-487-3355
Christopher Hopkins, head sch Fax 487-3512

Poland, Androscoggin
RSU 16 1,800/PK-12
3 Aggregate Rd 04274 207-998-2727
Tina Meserve, supt. Fax 998-2753
www.rsu16.org
Poland Regional HS 500/9-12
1457 Maine St 04274 207-998-5400
Cari Medd, prin. Fax 998-5060
Whittier MS 300/7-8
1457 Maine St 04274 207-998-3462
Shawn Vincent, prin. Fax 998-3481

Portland, Cumberland, Pop. 64,466
Portland SD 7,000/PK-12
353 Cumberland Ave 04101 207-874-8100
Jeanne Crocker, supt. Fax 874-8199
www2.portlandschools.org
Casco Bay HS 300/9-12
196 Allen Ave 04103 207-874-8160
Derek Pierce, prin. Fax 797-5437
Deering HS 900/9-12
370 Stevens Ave 04103 207-874-8260
Ira Waltz, prin. Fax 874-8153
King MS 500/6-8
92 Deering Ave 04102 207-874-8140
Caitlin LeClair, prin. Fax 874-8290
Lincoln MS 500/6-8
522 Stevens Ave 04103 207-874-8145
Suellyn Santiago, prin. Fax 874-8288
Moore MS 500/6-8
171 Auburn St 04103 207-874-8150
Ben Donaldson, prin. Fax 874-8272
Portland Arts & Technology HS Vo/Tech
196 Allen Ave 04103 207-874-8165
Kevin Stilphen, dir. Fax 874-8170
Portland HS 900/9-12
284 Cumberland Ave 04101 207-874-8250
Sheila Jepson, prin. Fax 874-8248

Cheverus HS 500/9-12
267 Ocean Ave 04103 207-774-6238
Dr. John Moran, prin. Fax 774-8461
Empire Beauty School Post-Sec.
319 Marginal Way 04101 207-774-9413
Inst for Doctoral Studies in Visual Arts Post-Sec.
130 Neal St 04102 207-879-8757
Maine College of Art Post-Sec.
522 Congress St Ste 4 04101 207-775-3052
Maine Girls Academy 200/9-12
631 Stevens Ave 04103 207-797-3802
Kathryn Woodson Barr, head sch Fax 797-3804
Mercy Hospital Post-Sec.
144 State St 04101 207-879-3000
University of New England Post-Sec.
716 Stevens Ave 04103 207-797-7261
University of Southern Maine Post-Sec.
PO Box 9300 04104 207-780-4141
Waynflete S 600/PK-12
360 Spring St 04102 207-774-5721
Geoff Wagg, head sch Fax 772-4782

Presque Isle, Aroostook, Pop. 9,565
RSU 79 / MSAD 1 1,800/PK-12
PO Box 1118 04769 207-764-4101
Brian Carpenter, supt. Fax 764-4103
www.sad1.org/
Presque Isle HS 600/9-12
16 Griffin St 04769 207-764-0121
Ben Greenlaw, prin. Fax 764-7720
Presque Isle MS 400/6-8
569 Skyway St 04769 207-764-4474
Anne Blanchard, prin. Fax 768-3447
Presque Isle Regional Tech Center Vo/Tech
79 Blake St 04769 207-764-1356
Tim Prescott, prin. Fax 764-8107

Cornerstone Christian Academy 50/PK-12
PO Box 743 04769 207-768-6222
Jay Levesque, head sch Fax 768-6224
Northern Maine Community College Post-Sec.
33 Edgemont Dr 04769 207-768-2700
University of Maine at Presque Isle Post-Sec.
181 Main St 04769 207-768-9400

Rangeley, Franklin
RSU 78 200/K-12
43 Mendolia Rd 04970 207-864-3311
Dr. William Richards Ed.D., supt. Fax 864-2451
www.rangeleyschool.org
Rangeley Lakes Regional S 200/K-12
43 Mendolia Rd 04970 207-864-3311
Charles Brown, prin. Fax 864-2451

Raymond, Cumberland
RSU 14 - Windham Raymond
Supt. — See Windham
Jordan-Small MS 200/5-8
423 Webbs Mills Rd 04071 207-655-4743
Randolph Crockett, prin. Fax 655-6952
Katahdin S, 146 Plains Rd 04071 Alt
Rich Meserve, dir. 207-655-4878

Readfield, Kennebec
RSU 38 1,300/PK-12
45 Millard Harrison Dr 04355 207-685-3336
Dr. Donna H. Wolfrom, supt. Fax 685-4703
www.maranacook.org/
Maranacook Community HS 400/9-12
2250 Millard Harrison Dr 04355 207-685-4923
Dwayne Conway, prin. Fax 685-9597
Maranacook Community MS 300/6-8
2100 Millard Harrison Dr 04355 207-685-3128
Rick Hogan, prin. Fax 685-9876

Richmond, Sagadahoc, Pop. 1,737
RSU 2
Supt. — See Hallowell
Richmond MSHS 100/6-12
132 Main St 04357 207-737-4348
Steve Lavoie, prin. Fax 737-8707

Rockland, Knox, Pop. 7,144
Career Technical Education
Supt. — None
Mid-Coast School of Tech-Region 8 Vo/Tech
1 Main St 04841 207-594-2161
Elizabeth Fisher, dir. Fax 594-7506

RSU 13 1,200/PK-12
28 Lincoln St 04841 207-596-6620
John McDonald, supt. Fax 596-2004
www.rsu13.org
Oceanside HS 500/9-12
400 Broadway 04841 207-596-2010
Jennifer Curtis, prin. Fax 596-2028
Other Schools – See Thomaston

Rockport, Knox
Five Town CSD
Supt. — See Camden
Camden Hills Regional HS 700/9-12
25 Keelson Dr 04856 207-236-7800
Dr. Nick Ithomitis, prin. Fax 236-7819

Rumford, Oxford, Pop. 4,160
RSU 10
Supt. — See Dixfield
Mountain Valley HS 400/9-12
799 Hancock St 04276 207-364-4547
Matthew Gilbert, prin. Fax 364-3436

Sabattus, Androscoggin
RSU 4
Supt. — See Wales
Oak Hill MS 300/6-8
40 Ball Park Rd 04280 207-375-6961
Marco Aliberti, prin. Fax 375-8871

Saco, York, Pop. 18,250
Saco SD 1,900/K-8
90 Beach St 04072 207-284-4505
Dominic DePatsy, supt. Fax 284-5951
sacoschools.org
Saco MS 700/6-8
40 Buxton Rd 04072 207-282-4181
Brian Campbell, prin. Fax 286-1807

Thornton Academy 1,500/6-12
438 Main St 04072 207-282-3361
Rene Menard, hdmstr. Fax 282-3508

Saint Agatha, Aroostook
RSU 33 / MSAD 33
Supt. — See Frenchville
Wisdom MSHS 100/7-12
PO Box 69 04772 207-543-7717
Tammy LeBlanc, prin. Fax 543-6316

Salem, Franklin
RSU 58 / MSAD 58
Supt. — See Phillips
Mt. Abram Regional HS 300/9-12
1513 Salem Rd, 207-678-2701
Michelle Tranten, prin. Fax 678-2668

Sanford, York, Pop. 9,565
Sanford SD 3,100/K-12
917 Main St Ste 200 04073 207-324-2810
David Theoharides, supt. Fax 324-5742
www.sanford.org
Sanford HS 1,100/9-12
52 Sanford High Blvd 04073 207-324-4050
Marianne Sylvain, prin. Fax 324-3022
Sanford JHS 600/6-8
708 Main St 04073 207-324-3114
Pam Lydon, prin. Fax 490-5139
Sanford Regional Technical Center Vo/Tech
52 Sanford High Blvd 04073 207-324-2942
Kathy Sargent, dir. Fax 324-2957

Scarborough, Cumberland, Pop. 4,340
Scarborough SD 3,200/K-12
PO Box 370 04070 207-730-4100
Dr. George Entwistle, supt. Fax 730-4104
www.scarboroughschools.org
Scarborough HS 1,000/9-12
11 Municipal Dr 04074 207-730-5000
David Creech, prin. Fax 730-5007
Scarborough MS 800/6-8
21 Quentin Dr 04074 207-730-4800
Barbara Hathorn, prin. Fax 730-4804

Searsport, Waldo, Pop. 985
RSU 20 500/K-12
6 Mortland Rd 04974 207-548-6643
Chris Downing, supt. Fax 548-2310
www.rsu20.org
Searsport District HS 200/9-12
24 Mortland Rd 04974 207-548-2313
Marianne DeRaps, prin. Fax 548-2354
Searsport District MS 200/6-8
26 Mortland Rd 04974 207-548-2313
Marianne DeRaps, prin. Fax 548-2354

Skowhegan, Somerset, Pop. 6,196
RSU 54 / MSAD 54 2,700/PK-12
196 W Front St 04976 207-474-9508
Brent Colbry, supt. Fax 474-7422
www.msad54.org/
Skowhegan Area HS 800/9-12
61 Academy Cir 04976 207-474-5511
Monique Poulin, prin. Fax 474-0111
Skowhegan Area MS 500/6-8
155 Academy Cir 04976 207-474-3339
Zachary Longyear, prin. Fax 474-9588
Somerset Career & Technical Center Vo/Tech
61 Academy Cir 04976 207-474-2151
David Dorr, dir. Fax 858-4879

South Berwick, York
RSU 35 / MSAD 35
Supt. — See Eliot
Marshwood HS 700/9-12
260 Dow Hwy 03908 207-384-4500
Paul Mehlhorn, prin. Fax 384-4508

Berwick Academy 600/PK-12
31 Academy St 03908 207-384-2164
Gregory Schneider, head sch Fax 384-3332

South China, Kennebec
RSU 18
Supt. — See Oakland
China MS 200/5-8
773 Lakeview Dr 04358 207-445-1500
Lois Bowden, prin. Fax 445-3278

Erskine Academy 600/9-12
309 Windsor Rd 04358 207-445-2962
Michael McQuarrie, hdmstr. Fax 445-5520

South Paris, Oxford, Pop. 2,214
RSU 17 / MSAD 17 3,500/PK-12
232 Main St # 2 04281 207-743-8972
Rick Colpitts, supt. Fax 743-2878
www.sad17.k12.me.us/
Oxford Hills Comprehensive HS 1,100/9-12
256 Main St 04281 207-743-8914
Theodore Moccia, prin. Fax 743-5326
Oxford Hills MS 500/7-8
100 Pine St 04281 207-743-5946
Troy Eastman, prin. Fax 743-8048

South Portland, Cumberland, Pop. 24,549
South Portland SD 3,100/PK-12
130 Wescott Rd 04106 207-871-0555
Ken Kunin, supt. Fax 871-0559
www.spsd.org
Mahoney MS 300/6-8
240 Ocean St 04106 207-799-7386
Carrie Stilphen, prin. Fax 767-7731
Memorial MS 400/6-8
120 Wescott Rd 04106 207-773-5629
Megan Welter, prin. Fax 772-4597
South Portland HS 900/9-12
637 Highland Ave 04106 207-767-3266
Ryan Caron, prin. Fax 767-7713

Greater Portland Christian S 100/PK-12
1338 Broadway 04106 207-767-5123
John Bishop, head sch Fax 767-5124
Kaplan University Post-Sec.
265 Western Ave 04106 207-774-6126
Maine Medical Center Post-Sec.
SMTC Fort Rd 04106 207-767-9589
New England Bible College Post-Sec.
879 Sawyer St 04106 207-799-5979
Southern Maine Community College Post-Sec.
2 Fort Rd 04106 207-741-5500

Stacyville, Penobscot
RSU 50
Supt. — See Dyer Brook
Katahdin MSHS 200/7-12
PO Box 50, 207-365-4218
Marie Robinson, prin. Fax 365-6011

Standish, Cumberland, Pop. 464
RSU 6 / MSAD 6
Supt. — See Buxton
Bonny Eagle HS 1,200/9-12
700 Saco Rd 04084 207-929-3840
Paul Penna, prin. Fax 585-7567

St. Joseph's College of Maine Post-Sec.
278 Whites Bridge Rd 04084 207-892-6766

Sullivan, Hancock
RSU 24 900/PK-12
2165 US Hwy 1 04664 207-422-2017
Michael Eastman, supt. Fax 422-2029
www.rsu24.org
Sumner Memorial HS 300/9-12
2456 US Hwy 1 04664 207-422-3510
Ty Thurlow, prin. Fax 422-6463
RSU 24 Adult Education Adult
1888 US Highway 1 04664 207-422-4794
Ander Thebaud, dir. Fax 422-3612

Thomaston, Knox, Pop. 1,856
RSU 13
Supt. — See Rockland
Oceanside MS 100/6-8
47 Valley St 04861 207-354-2502
William Gifford, prin. Fax 354-2369

Thorndike, Waldo
RSU 3 / MSAD 3
Supt. — See Unity
Mt. View HS 500/9-12
577 Mount View Rd 04986 207-568-3255
John Yorkey, prin. Fax 568-4315
Mt. View MS 300/6-8
575 Mount View Rd 04986 207-568-7561
Quinton Donahue, prin. Fax 568-7590

Topsham, Sagadahoc, Pop. 5,854
RSU 75 / MSAD 75 2,500/K-12
50 Republic Ave 04086 207-729-9961
Bradley Smith, supt. Fax 725-9354
www.link75.org/
Mt. Ararat HS 800/9-12
73 Eagles Way 04086 207-729-2951
Donna Brunette Ph.D., prin. Fax 729-2953
Mt. Ararat MS 600/6-8
66 Republic Ave 04086 207-729-2950
Josh Ottow, prin. Fax 729-2964

Turner, Androscoggin
RSU 52 / MSAD 52 2,000/PK-12
486 Turner Ctr Rd 04282 207-225-1000
Kimberly Brandt, supt. Fax 225-5608
www.msad52.org
Leavitt Area HS 600/9-12
21 Matthews Way 04282 207-225-1100
Eben Shaw, prin. Fax 225-3978
Tripp MS 300/7-8
65 Matthews Way 04282 207-225-1070
Gail Marine, prin. Fax 225-2102

Union, Knox
RSU 40 / MSAD 40 1,800/PK-12
PO Box 701 04862 207-785-2277
Steve Nolan, supt. Fax 785-3119
www.msad40.org
Other Schools – See Waldoboro

Unity, Waldo, Pop. 459
RSU 3 / MSAD 3 1,400/PK-12
84 School St 04988 207-948-6136
Dr. Paul Austin, supt. Fax 948-6173
www.rsu3.org
Other Schools – See Thorndike

Unity College Post-Sec.
90 Quaker Hill Rd 04988 207-948-9100

Van Buren, Aroostook, Pop. 1,897
RSU 88 / MSAD 24 300/PK-12
169 Main St Ste 101 04785 207-868-2746
Dr. Timothy Kane, supt. Fax 868-5420
www.msad24.org
Van Buren District HS 100/9-12
169 Main St Ste 102 04785 207-868-5274
Dr. Timothy Kane, admin. Fax 868-3537
Van Buren Regional Technology Center Vo/Tech
169 Main St Ste 102 04785 207-868-2746
Clayton Belanger, dir. Fax 868-5420

Vinalhaven, Knox
RSU 8 / MSAD 8 200/PK-12
22 Arcola Ln 04863 207-863-4664
Bruce Mailloux, supt. Fax 863-4572
www.vinalhavenschool.org
Vinalhaven S 200/PK-12
22 Arcola Ln 04863 207-863-4800
Timothy Kane, prin. Fax 863-2035

Waldo, See Belfast
Career Technical Education
Supt. — None
Waldo County Tech Center Vo/Tech
1022 Waterville Rd 04915 207-342-5231
Kevin Michaud, dir. Fax 342-4070

Waldoboro, Lincoln, Pop. 1,207
RSU 40 / MSAD 40
Supt. — See Union
Medomak MS 300/7-8
318 Manktown Rd 04572 207-832-5028
Kate Race, prin. Fax 832-5710
Medomak Valley HS 600/9-12
320 Manktown Rd 04572 207-832-5389
Andrew Cavanaugh, prin. Fax 832-2280

Wales, Androscoggin
RSU 4 1,500/PK-12
971 Gardiner Rd 04280 207-375-4273
James Hodgkin, supt. Fax 375-2522
www.rsu4.org
Oak Hill HS 500/9-12
56 School Rd 04280 207-375-4950
Patricia Doyle, prin. Fax 375-4048
Other Schools – See Sabattus

Washburn, Aroostook, Pop. 987
RSU 45 / MSAD 45 400/PK-12
33 School St 04786 207-455-8301
Brian Carpenter, supt. Fax 455-8217
www.msad45.net
Washburn District HS 100/9-12
1359 Main St 04786 207-455-4501
Ron Ericson, prin. Fax 455-4509

Waterboro, York
RSU 57 / MSAD 57 3,200/PK-12
86 West Rd 04087 207-247-3221
Larry Malone, supt. Fax 247-3477
www.rsu57.org
Massabesic HS 1,000/9-12
88 West Rd 04087 207-247-3141
James Hand, prin. Fax 247-3146
Other Schools – See East Waterboro

Waterville, Kennebec, Pop. 15,358
AOS 92 - KVCS 3,600/PK-12
25 Messalonskee Ave 04901 207-873-4281
Eric Haley, supt. Fax 872-5531
www.aos92.org/
Mid Maine Technical Center Vo/Tech
3 Brooklyn Ave 04901 207-873-0102
Peter Hallen, dir. Fax 873-7057
Waterville HS 600/9-12
1 Brooklyn Ave 04901 207-873-2751
Brian Laramee, prin. Fax 873-7058
Waterville JHS 400/6-8
100 W River Rd 04901 207-873-2144
Carol Gilley, prin. Fax 873-5752
Other Schools – See Winslow

Colby College Post-Sec.
4000 Mayflower Hill Dr 04901 207-859-4000
Empire Beauty School Post-Sec.
251 Kennedy Memorial Dr 04901 207-873-0682
Temple Academy 200/PK-12
60 W River Rd 04901 207-873-5325
Thomas College Post-Sec.
180 W River Rd 04901 207-859-1111

Wells, York
Wells-Ogunquit Community SD 1,300/K-12
1460 Post Rd 04090 207-646-8331
James Daly, supt. Fax 646-4236
www.k12wocsd.net
Wells HS 400/9-12
200 Sanford Rd 04090 207-646-7011
Eileen Sheehy, prin. Fax 646-6964
Wells JHS 400/5-8
1470 Post Rd 04090 207-646-5142
Robert Griffin, prin. Fax 646-2899

York County Community College Post-Sec.
112 College Dr 04090 207-646-9282

Westbrook, Cumberland, Pop. 17,059
Westbrook SD 2,500/PK-12
117 Stroudwater St 04092 207-854-0800
Dr. Marc Gousse, supt. Fax 854-0809
www.westbrookschools.org
Westbrook HS 700/9-12
125 Stroudwater St 04092 207-854-0810
Jonathan Ross, prin. Fax 854-0812
Westbrook MS 800/5-8
471 Stroudwater St 04092 207-854-0830
Laurie Wood, prin. Fax 854-0858
Westbrook Regional Vocational Center Vo/Tech
125 Stroudwater St 04092 207-854-0820
Todd Fields, dir. Fax 854-0822

Windham, Cumberland, Pop. 13,020
RSU 14 - Windham Raymond 3,300/K-12
228 Windham Center Rd 04062 207-892-1800
Sanford Prince, supt. Fax 892-1805
www.rsu14.org
Windham HS 1,000/9-12
406 Gray Rd 04062 207-892-1810
Chris Howell, prin. Fax 892-1813
Windham MS 600/6-8
408 Gray Rd 04062 207-892-1820
Drew Patin, prin. Fax 892-1826
Other Schools – See Raymond

Windham Christian Academy 100/PK-12
1051 Roosevelt Trl 04062 207-892-2244
Roy Mickelson, prin. Fax 893-1289

Winslow, Kennebec, Pop. 7,626
AOS 92 - KVCS
Supt. — See Waterville
Winslow HS 500/9-12
20 Danielson St 04901 207-872-1990
Chad Bell, prin. Fax 872-1993
Winslow JHS 300/6-8
6 Danielson St 04901 207-872-1973
Jason Briggs, prin. Fax 872-1977

Winterport, Waldo, Pop. 1,327
RSU 22
Supt. — See Hampden
Wagner MS 100/5-8
19 Williams Way 04496 207-223-4309
Richard Glencross, prin. Fax 223-4325

Winthrop, Kennebec, Pop. 2,622
Winthrop SD 800/PK-12
17A Highland Ave 04364 207-377-2296
Gary Rosenthal, supt. Fax 377-2708
www.winthropschools.org
Winthrop HS 200/9-12
211 Rambler Rd 04364 207-377-2228
Keith Morin, prin. Fax 377-7486
Winthrop MS 200/6-8
400 Rambler Rd 04364 207-377-2249
Karen Criss, prin. Fax 377-3667

Wiscasset, Lincoln, Pop. 1,086
Wiscasset School Department 300/PK-12
225 Gardiner Rd 04578 207-882-4104
Dr. Heather Wilmot, supt. Fax 882-4123
www.wiscassetschools.org
Wiscasset MSHS 200/7-12
272 Gardiner Rd 04578 207-882-7722
Peg Armstrong, prin. Fax 882-8251

Yarmouth, Cumberland, Pop. 5,801
Yarmouth SD 1,500/K-12
101 McCartney St 04096 207-846-5586
Andrew Dolloff, supt. Fax 846-2339
www.yarmouthschools.org
Harrison MS 500/5-8
220 McCartney St 04096 207-846-2499
Joan Adler, prin. Fax 846-2489
Yarmouth HS 500/9-12
286 W Elm St 04096 207-846-5535
Eric Klein, prin. Fax 846-2326

North Yarmouth Academy 300/PK-12
148 Main St 04096 207-846-9051
Benjamin Jackson, head sch Fax 846-8829

York, York, Pop. 9,818
York SD 1,800/K-12
469 US Route 1 03909 207-363-3403
Dr. Debra Dunn, supt. Fax 363-5602
www.yorkschools.org
York HS 600/9-12
1 Robert Stevens Dr 03909 207-363-3621
Megan Ward, prin. Fax 363-1809
York MS 600/5-8
30 Organug Rd 03909 207-363-4214
Barbara Maling, prin. Fax 363-1815

MARYLAND

MARYLAND DEPARTMENT OF EDUCATION
200 W Baltimore St, Baltimore 21201-2595
Telephone 410-767-0600
Fax 410-333-6033
Website http://www.marylandpublicschools.org

Superintendent of Schools Karen Salmon

MARYLAND BOARD OF EDUCATION
200 W Baltimore St, Baltimore 21201-2549

President Guffrie Smith

PUBLIC, PRIVATE AND CATHOLIC SECONDARY SCHOOLS

Aberdeen, Harford, Pop. 14,190
Harford County SD
Supt. — See Bel Air
Aberdeen HS 1,400/9-12
251 Paradise Rd 21001 410-273-5500
Michael O'Brien, prin. Fax 273-5587
Aberdeen MS 1,100/6-8
111 Mount Royal Ave 21001 410-273-5510
DeAnn Webb, prin. Fax 273-5542
Alternative Education Program 100/Alt
253 Paradise Rd 21001 410-273-5594
Erica Harris, prin. Fax 273-5592

Abingdon, Harford

New Covenant Christian S 200/PK-12
128 Saint Marys Church Rd 21009 443-512-0771
Jean Armstrong, prin. Fax 569-3846

Accident, Garrett, Pop. 323
Garrett County SD
Supt. — See Oakland
Northern Garrett HS 500/9-12
86 Pride Pkwy 21520 301-746-8668
Gary Reichenbecher, prin. Fax 746-8942
Northern MS 300/6-8
371 Pride Pkwy 21520 301-746-8165
Karen DeVore, prin. Fax 746-8865

Accokeek, Prince George's, Pop. 10,314
Prince George's County SD
Supt. — See Upper Marlboro
Accokeek Academy 800/5-8
14500 Berry Rd 20607 301-203-3200
Judy Adams, prin. Fax 203-3207

Adelphi, Prince George's, Pop. 14,821
Prince George's County SD
Supt. — See Upper Marlboro
Buck Lodge MS 800/7-8
2611 Buck Lodge Rd 20783 301-431-6290
Kenneth Nance, prin. Fax 431-6294

University of Maryland University Coll Post-Sec.
3501 University Blvd E 20783 301-985-7000

Annapolis, Anne Arundel, Pop. 37,674
Anne Arundel County SD 78,600/PK-12
2644 Riva Rd 21401 410-222-5000
Dr. George Arlotto, supt. Fax 222-5602
www.aacps.org
Annapolis HS 1,700/9-12
2700 Riva Rd 21401 410-266-5240
Susan Chittim, prin. Fax 266-0687
Annapolis MS 700/6-8
1399 Forest Dr 21403 410-267-8658
Sean McElhaney, prin. Fax 267-8924
Bates MS 800/6-8
701 Chase St 21401 410-263-0270
Paul DeRoo, prin. Fax 263-0295
Broadneck HS 2,100/9-12
1265 Green Holly Dr, 410-757-1300
James Todd, prin. Fax 757-5621
Moss at Adams Academy 100/Alt
245 Clay St 21401 410-222-1639
Kellie Katzenberger, prin.
Annapolis Evening HS Adult
2700 Riva Rd 21401 410-224-2924
Patricia Suriano, admin.
Other Schools – See Arnold, Baltimore, Edgewater, Fort Meade, Gambrills, Glen Burnie, Harwood, Linthicum Heights, Lothian, Millersville, Odenton, Pasadena, Severn, Severna Park

Key S 700/PK-12
534 Hillsmere Dr 21403 410-263-9231
Matthew Nespole, hdmstr. Fax 280-5516
St. John's College Post-Sec.
PO Box 2800 21404 410-263-2371
St. Mary's HS 500/9-12
113 Duke of Gloucester St 21401 410-263-3294
Mindi Imes, prin. Fax 269-7843
United States Naval Academy Post-Sec.
121 Blake Rd 21402 410-293-4361

Arnold, Anne Arundel, Pop. 22,629
Anne Arundel County SD
Supt. — See Annapolis
Magothy River MS 700/6-8
241 Peninsula Farm Rd 21012 410-544-0926
Christopher Mirenzi, prin. Fax 544-1867
Severn River MS 800/6-8
241 Peninsula Farm Rd 21012 410-544-0922
Richard Tubman, prin. Fax 315-8006

Anne Arundel Community College Post-Sec.
101 College Pkwy 21012 410-777-2222

Baltimore, Baltimore, Pop. 609,299
Anne Arundel County SD
Supt. — See Annapolis
Brooklyn Park MS 700/6-8
200 Hammonds Ln 21225 410-636-2967
Beth Shakan, prin. Fax 636-1774

Baltimore CSD 77,600/PK-12
200 E North Ave 21202 443-984-2000
Sonja Brookins Santelise Ed.D., admin. Fax 396-8898
www.bcps.k12.md.us
Academy for College & Career Exploration 700/6-12
2801 Saint Lo Dr 21213
Dawn Strickland, prin.
Achievement Academy at Harbor City 400/9-12
2201 Pinewood Ave 21214 410-396-6241
Dave Verdi, prin.
Baltimore City College HS 1,300/9-12
3220 The Alameda 21218 410-396-6557
Cindy Harcum, prin. Fax 243-0669
Baltimore Design S 6-12
1500 Barclay St 21202 443-642-2311
Zaharah Valentine, prin.
Baltimore IT Academy 300/6-8
900 Woodbourne Ave 21212 443-642-2067
Sandy Mason, prin.
Baltimore Polytechnic Institute Vo/Tech
1400 W Cold Spring Ln 21209 410-396-7026
Jacqueline Williams, prin. Fax 235-5027
Baltimore S for the Arts 400/9-12
712 Cathedral St 21201 443-642-5165
Christopher Ford, prin.
Bard HS Early College 9-12
2801 N Dukeland St 21216 443-642-2062
Francesca Gamber, prin.
Career Academy Alt
101 W 24th St 21218 410-396-7454
Gus Herrington, prin.
Carver Voc-Tech HS Vo/Tech
2201 Pressman St 21216 410-396-0553
Shionta Somerville, prin. Fax 396-0059
Digital Harbor HS 1,400/9-12
1100 Covington St 21230 443-984-1256
Shannon Mobley, prin. Fax 539-7270
Douglass HS 900/9-12
2301 Gwynns Falls Pkwy 21217 410-396-7821
Kelvin Bridgers, prin. Fax 523-7557
Dunbar HS 900/9-12
1400 Orleans St 21231 443-642-4478
Tammy Mays, prin. Fax 545-7526
Eager Street Academy 50/Alt
401 E Eager St 21202 410-209-4091
Laura D'Anna, prin. Fax 209-4268
Edmondson-Westside HS 800/9-12
501 N Athol Ave 21229 410-396-0685
Muriel Cole-Webber, prin. Fax 545-7715
Excel Academy 300/6-12
1001 W Saratoga St 21223 410-396-1290
Tammatha Woodhouse, prin. Fax 947-7941
Forest Park HS 500/9-12
6900 Park Heights Ave 21215 410-396-0753
Monica Dailey, prin. Fax 396-0143
Franklin HS, 1201 Cambria St 21225 400/9-12
Christopher Battaglia, prin. 410-396-1373
Friendship Academy of Engring & Tech 500/6-12
2500 E Northern Pkwy 21214 443-642-5616
Tawney Manning, prin.
Jemison STEM Academy West 500/6-12
2000 Edgewood St 21216 443-642-2110
Audrey Freeman, prin. Fax 984-2774

Knowledge and Success Academy 500/6-12
2000 Edgewood St 21216 443-642-2670
Tony Edwards, prin.
Lewis HS, 6401 Pioneer Dr 21214 300/9-12
Janine Patterson, prin. 410-545-1746
Mergenthaler Vo-Tech HS Vo/Tech
3500 Hillen Rd 21218 410-396-6496
Craig Rivers, prin. Fax 243-5354
NACA Freedom and Democracy II 300/6-12
2500 E Northern Pkwy 21214 443-642-2031
Linda Johnson-Brown, prin.
National Academy Foundation HS 800/6-12
540 N Caroline St 21205 443-984-1594
Danielle Rembert, prin. Fax 837-7118
New Era Academy 400/6-12
2700 Seamon Ave 21225 443-984-2415
Sandra Simmons, prin. Fax 355-1130
Northwestern HS 600/9-12
6900 Park Heights Ave 21215 410-396-0646
Saeed Hill, prin. Fax 396-0866
Patterson HS 1,000/9-12
100 Kane St 21224 410-396-9276
Vance Benton, prin. Fax 633-0179
REACH Partnership S 400/8-12
2801 Saint Lo Dr 21213 443-642-2291
Dr. James Gresham, prin.
Renaissance Academy 300/9-12
1301 McCulloh St 21217 443-984-3164
Nikkia Rowe, prin. Fax 947-2968
Savage Institute of Visual Arts 400/9-12
1500 Harlem Ave 21217 443-396-7701
Tracey Hicks, prin.
Stadium S, 1300 Gorsuch Ave 21218 200/6-8
Shana Hall, dir. 443-984-2682
Success Academy Alt
2201 Pinewood Ave 21214 443-642-2101
Rhonda Tapper, prin.
Thomas Medical Arts Academy 400/9-12
100 N Calhoun St 21223 443-984-2831
Stephanie Farmer, prin. Fax 947-2953
Vanguard Collegiate MS 300/6-8
5000 Truesdale Rd 21206 443-642-2069
Esther Wallace, prin.
Washington MS 300/6-8
1301 McCulloh St 21217 410-396-7734
Jessica Blackmon-Stewart, prin. Fax 396-0552
Western HS 1,100/9-12
4600 Falls Rd 21209 410-396-7040
Michelle White, prin. Fax 396-7492
Youth Opportunity S Alt
1510 W Lafayette Ave 21217 410-962-1905
Ayanna McLean, prin.

Baltimore County SD
Supt. — See Towson
Arbutus MS 800/6-8
5525 Shelbourne Rd 21227 410-887-1402
Michelle Feeney, prin. Fax 536-1164
Carver Center for Arts & Technology 800/9-12
938 N York Rd 21204 410-887-2775
Karen Steele, prin. Fax 769-9114
Catonsville Center/Alternative Studies 100/Alt
901 S Rolling Rd 21228 410-887-0934
Jewell Ralph, prin. Fax 747-1789
Catonsville HS 1,700/9-12
421 Bloomsbury Ave 21228 410-887-0808
Matthew Ames, prin. Fax 747-9473
Chesapeake HS 1,000/9-12
1801 Turkey Point Rd 21221 410-887-0100
Jess Grim, prin. Fax 682-3426
Crossroads Center 200/Alt
11640 Crossroads Cir 21220 410-887-2275
John Ward, prin. Fax 887-2449
Deep Creek MS 800/6-8
1000 S Marlyn Ave 21221 410-887-0112
Thomas Baker, prin. Fax 391-6534
Dumbarton MS 1,000/6-8
300 Dumbarton Rd Ste 1 21212 410-887-3176
Susan Harris, prin. Fax 583-7020
Dundalk HS 1,300/9-12
1901 Delvale Ave 21222 410-887-7023
Kristin Anelli, prin. Fax 887-7025

Dundalk MS 500/6-8
7400 Dunmanway 21222 410-887-7018
Seth Barish, prin. Fax 887-7284
Eastern Technical HS 1,100/9-12
1100 Mace Ave 21221 410-887-0190
Christene Anderson, prin. Fax 887-0424
Golden Ring MS 600/6-8
6700 Kenwood Ave 21237 410-887-0130
Lawrence Rudolph, prin. Fax 682-6750
Holabird MS 700/6-8
1701 Delvale Ave 21222 410-887-7049
Julie Dellone, prin. Fax 887-7275
Kenwood HS 1,700/9-12
501 Stemmers Run Rd 21221 410-887-0153
Brian Powell, prin. Fax 887-6382
Lansdowne HS 1,200/9-12
3800 Hollins Ferry Rd 21227 410-887-1415
Kenneth Miller, prin. Fax 887-1461
Lansdowne MS 700/6-8
2400 Lansdowne Rd 21227 410-887-1411
Frank Dunlap, prin. Fax 887-1412
Loch Raven HS 900/9-12
1212 Cowpens Ave 21286 410-887-3525
Bonnie Lambert, prin. Fax 887-5898
Loch Raven Technical Academy 800/6-8
8101 La Salle Rd 21286 410-887-3518
Stacey Johnson, prin. Fax 821-6398
Meadowood Education Center 50/Alt
1849 Gwynn Oak Ave 21207 410-887-6888
Jewell Ralph, prin. Fax 887-6889
Middle River MS 800/6-8
800 Middle River Rd 21220 410-887-0165
Shannon Parker, prin. Fax 887-0167
Milford Mill Academy 1,500/9-12
3800 Washington Ave 21244 410-887-0660
Kyria Joseph, prin. Fax 887-0681
Northwest Academy of Health Science 600/6-8
4627 Old Court Rd 21208 410-887-0742
Dr. Katina Webster, prin. Fax 887-0670
Overlea HS 900/9-12
5401 Kenwood Ave 21206 410-887-5241
Monica Sample, prin. Fax 661-0174
Parkville MS 1,000/6-8
8711 Avondale Rd 21234 410-887-5250
Erin O'Toole-Trivas, prin. Fax 887-5315
Patapsco HS & Center for the Arts 1,400/9-12
8100 Wise Ave 21222 410-887-7060
Craig Reed, prin. Fax 887-7062
Perry Hall HS 2,100/9-12
4601 Ebenezer Rd 21236 410-887-5108
Andrew Last, prin. Fax 887-5116
Perry Hall MS 1,600/6-8
4300 Ebenezer Rd 21236 410-887-5100
Lisa Perry, prin. Fax 887-5152
Pikesville HS 900/9-12
7621 Labyrinth Rd 21208 410-887-1217
Sandra Reid, prin. Fax 486-8436
Pikesville MS 1,000/6-8
7701 Seven Mile Ln 21208 410-887-1207
Kalisha Miller, prin. Fax 887-1259
Pine Grove MS 900/6-8
9200 Old Harford Rd 21234 410-887-5270
Tina Nelson, prin. Fax 668-5237
Rosedale Center 100/Alt
7090 Golden Ring Rd 21237 410-809-0133
Paul Martin, prin. Fax 809-0473
Southwest Academy 800/6-8
6200 Johnnycake Rd 21207 410-887-0825
Karen Barnes, prin. Fax 887-0829
Sparrows Point HS 800/9-12
7400 N Point Rd 21219 410-887-7517
Emily Caster, prin. Fax 477-4311
Sparrows Point MS 500/6-8
7400 N Point Rd 21219 410-887-7524
Shannon Washington, prin. Fax 477-6953
Stemmers Run MS 700/6-8
201 Stemmers Run Rd 21221 410-887-0177
Bryan Thanner, prin. Fax 918-1787
Stricker MS 800/6-8
7855 Trappe Rd 21222 410-887-7038
Brian Wagner, prin. Fax 285-1864
Sudbrook Magnet MS 1,000/6-8
4300 Bedford Rd 21208 410-887-6720
Gordon Webb, prin. Fax 887-6737
Towson HS 1,400/9-12
69 Cedar Ave 21286 410-887-3608
Charlene Dimino, prin. Fax 583-1375
Western S of Technology 900/9-12
100 Kenwood Ave 21228 410-887-0840
Murray Parker, prin. Fax 887-1024
Windsor Mill MS 500/6-8
8300 Windsor Mill Rd 21244 410-887-0618
Harvey Chambers, prin. Fax 496-1308
Woodlawn HS 1,400/9-12
1801 Woodlawn Dr 21207 410-887-1309
Kirk Sykes, prin. Fax 887-1324
Woodlawn MS 600/6-8
3033 Saint Lukes Ln 21207 410-887-1304
Rochelle Archelus, prin. Fax 298-4352

All-State Career School Post-Sec.
2200 Broening Hwy Ste 160 21224 410-631-1818
Al-Rahmah S 300/K-12
6631 Johnnycake Rd 21244 410-719-0921
Archbishop Curley HS 600/9-12
3701 Sinclair Ln 21213 410-485-5000
Brian Kohler, prin. Fax 483-2545
Arlington Baptist S 200/PK-12
3030 N Rolling Rd 21244 410-655-9300
Dr. Mark Campbell, pres. Fax 496-3901
Bais HaMedrash & Mesivta of Baltimore Post-Sec.
6823 Old Pimlico Rd 21209 410-486-0006
Bais Hamedrash & Mesivta S of Baltimore 100/9-12
6823 Old Pimlico Rd 21209 410-486-0006
Bais Yaakov Eva Winer HS 400/9-12
6302 Smith Ave 21209 443-548-7700
Rabbi Yechezkel Zweig, prin. Fax 548-6340
Baltimore Actors Theatre Conservatory 50/K-12
300 Dumbarton Rd Ste 2 21212 410-337-8519
Dr. Walter Anderson, hdmstr. Fax 337-8582
Baltimore City Community College Post-Sec.
2901 Liberty Heights Ave 21215 410-462-8300
Baltimore Lab S 100/1-12
2220 Saint Paul St 21218 410-261-5500
Steve Buettner, head sch Fax 366-7680
Baltimore School of Massage Post-Sec.
517 Progress Dr Ste A-L 21207 410-944-8855
Baltimore Studio of Hair Design Post-Sec.
318 N Howard St 21201 410-539-1935
Baltimore-White Marsh Adventist S 50/PK-12
7427 Rossville Blvd 21237 410-663-1819
Beren HS 200/9-12
400 Mount Wilson Ln 21208 410-484-7200
Beth Tfiloh Dahan Community S 900/PK-12
3300 Old Court Rd 21208 410-486-1905
Bnos Yisroel S of Baltimore 400/PK-12
6300 Park Heights Ave 21215 443-524-3200
Boys Latin S of Maryland 600/K-12
822 W Lake Ave 21210 410-377-5192
Christopher Post, hdmstr. Fax 377-4312
Brightwood College Post-Sec.
1520 S Caton Ave 21227 410-644-6400
Broadcasting Institute of Maryland Post-Sec.
7200 Harford Rd 21234 410-254-2770
Bryn Mawr S 800/PK-12
109 W Melrose Ave 21210 410-323-8800
Maureen Walsh, hdmstr. Fax 377-8963
Calvert Hall College HS 1,200/9-12
8102 La Salle Rd 21286 410-825-4266
Charles Stembler, prin. Fax 825-6826
Catholic HS of Baltimore 300/9-12
2800 Edison Hwy 21213 410-732-6200
Sharon Johnston, prin. Fax 732-7639
Coppin State University Post-Sec.
2500 W North Ave 21216 410-951-3000
Cristo Rey Jesuit HS 9-12
420 S Chester St 21231 410-727-3255
Thomas Malone, prin. Fax 573-9898
Faith Theological Seminary Post-Sec.
529 Walker Ave 21212 410-323-6211
Fortis Institute Post-Sec.
6901 Security Blvd Ste 21 21244 410-907-8110
Friends S of Baltimore 1,000/PK-12
5114 N Charles St 21210 410-649-3200
Matthew Micciche, head sch Fax 649-3213
Gilman S 1,000/K-12
5407 Roland Ave 21210 410-323-3800
Henry Smyth, hdmstr. Fax 864-2812
Goucher College Post-Sec.
1021 Dulaney Valley Rd 21204 410-337-6000
Greater Baltimore Medical Center Post-Sec.
6701 N Charles St 21204 410-828-2121
Institute of Notre Dame 300/9-12
901 N Aisquith St 21202 410-522-7800
Christine Szala, prin. Fax 522-7810
Johns Hopkins University Post-Sec.
3400 N Charles St 21218 410-516-8000
Loyola University Maryland Post-Sec.
4501 N Charles St 21210 800-221-9107
Maryland Beauty Academy of Essex Post-Sec.
505 Eastern Blvd 21221 410-686-4477
Maryland General Hospital Post-Sec.
827 Linden Ave 21201 410-995-8600
Maryland Institute College of Art Post-Sec.
1300 W Mount Royal Ave 21217 410-669-9200
Maryland School for the Blind Post-Sec.
3501 Taylor Ave 21236
Mercy HS 400/9-12
1300 E Northern Pkwy 21239 410-433-8880
Mary Lennon, pres. Fax 323-8816
Mercy Hospital Post-Sec.
301 Saint Paul St 21202 410-332-9202
Morgan State University Post-Sec.
1700 E Cold Spring Ln 21251 443-885-3333
Mother Seton Academy 100/6-8
2215 Greenmount Ave 21218 410-563-2833
Sr. Margaret Juskelis, pres. Fax 563-7354
Mt. St. Joseph HS 1,000/9-12
4403 Frederick Ave 21229 410-644-3300
David Norton, prin. Fax 646-6221
Mt. Zion Baptist Christian S 100/PK-12
2000 E Belvedere Ave 21239 410-426-2309
Ner Israel Rabbinical College Post-Sec.
400 Mount Wilson Ln 21208 410-484-7200
North American Trade Schools Post-Sec.
6901 Security Blvd Ste 16 21244 410-298-4844
Notre Dame of Maryland University Post-Sec.
4701 N Charles St 21210 410-435-0100
Our Lady of Mt. Carmel HS 200/9-12
1706 Old Eastern Ave 21221 410-686-1023
Christopher Ashby, prin. Fax 686-2361
Park S of Baltimore 900/PK-12
2425 Old Court Rd 21208 410-339-7070
Daniel Paradis, head sch Fax 339-4125
Peabody Institute Johns Hopkins Univ. Post-Sec.
1 E Mount Vernon Pl 21202 410-234-4500
Rabbi Benjamin Steinberg MS 300/6-8
6300 Smith Ave 21209 443-548-7700
Roland Park Country S 700/PK-12
5204 Roland Ave 21210 410-323-5500
Jean Waller Brune, head sch Fax 323-2164
Rosedale Baptist S 300/PK-12
9202 Philadelphia Rd 21237 410-687-6844
Jeremy Errett, admin. Fax 687-1009
St. Frances Academy 200/9-12
501 E Chase St 21202 410-539-5794
Dr. Curtis Turner, prin. Fax 685-2650
St. Ignatius Loyola Academy 100/6-8
300 E Gittings St 21230 410-539-8268
Teresa Scott, prin. Fax 539-4821
St. Mary's Seminary & University Post-Sec.
5400 Roland Ave 21210 410-864-4000
Seton Keough HS 400/9-12
1201 S Caton Ave 21227 410-646-4444
Donna Bridickas, pres. Fax 573-0107
Sisters Academy of Baltimore 100/5-8
139 1st Ave 21227 410-242-1212
Patricia Ruppert, prin. Fax 242-5104
Sojourner-Douglass College Post-Sec.
200 N Central Ave 21202 410-276-0306
Stratford University Post-Sec.
210 S Central Ave 21202 410-752-4710
Union Memorial Hospital Post-Sec.
201 E University Pkwy 21218 410-554-2739
University of Baltimore Post-Sec.
1420 N Charles St 21201 410-837-4200
University of Maryland Baltimore Post-Sec.
620 W Lexington St 21201 410-706-3100
University of Maryland Baltimore County Post-Sec.
1000 Hilltop Cir 21250 410-455-1000
Yeshivas Chofetz Chaim - Talmudical Acad 800/PK-12
4445 Old Court Rd 21208 410-484-6600
Rabbi Yaacov Cohen, dir. Fax 484-5717

Bel Air, Harford, Pop. 9,934
Harford County SD 37,700/PK-12
102 S Hickory Ave 21014 410-838-7300
Barbara Canavan, supt. Fax 893-2478
www.hcps.org
Bel Air HS 1,700/9-12
100 Heighe St 21014 410-638-4600
Gregory Komondor, prin. Fax 638-4604
Bel Air MS 1,300/6-8
99 Idlewild St 21014 410-638-4140
Natalie Holloway, prin. Fax 638-4144
Harford Technical HS Vo/Tech
200 Thomas Run Rd 21015 410-638-3804
Charles Hagan, prin. Fax 638-3820
Patterson Mill MSHS 900/6-12
85 Patterson Mill Rd 21015 410-638-4640
Dr. Sean Abel, prin. Fax 638-4646
Southampton MS 1,300/6-8
1200 Moores Mill Rd 21014 410-638-4150
Glenn Jensen, prin. Fax 638-4305
Wright HS 1,400/9-12
1301 N Fountain Green Rd 21015 410-638-4110
Michael Thatcher, prin. Fax 638-4114
Other Schools – See Aberdeen, Edgewood, Fallston, Havre de Grace, Joppa, Pylesville

---

Harford Community College Post-Sec.
401 Thomas Run Rd 21015 443-412-2000
International Beauty School Post-Sec.
227 Archer St 21014 410-838-0845
John Carroll HS 700/9-12
703 E Churchville Rd 21014 410-879-2480
Richard O'Hara, pres. Fax 836-8514
St. Margaret MS 300/6-8
1716 E Churchville Rd Ste A 21015 410-877-9660
Madeleine Hobik, prin. Fax 420-9322

Beltsville, Prince George's, Pop. 16,294
Prince George's County SD
Supt. — See Upper Marlboro
High Point HS 2,200/9-12
3601 Powder Mill Rd 20705 301-572-6400
Nicole McClure, prin. Fax 572-6481
King MS 700/6-8
4545 Ammendale Rd 20705 301-572-0650
Robin Wiltison, prin. Fax 572-0668

Brightwood College Post-Sec.
4600 Powder Mill Rd Ste 500 20705 301-937-8448

Berlin, Worcester, Pop. 4,357
Worcester County SD
Supt. — See Newark
Decatur HS 1,300/9-12
9913 Seahawk Rd 21811 410-641-2171
Tom Zimmer, prin. Fax 641-1135
Decatur MS 600/7-8
9815 Seahawk Rd 21811 410-641-2846
Lynne Barton, prin. Fax 641-3274

Worcester Preparatory S 500/PK-12
PO Box 1006 21811 410-641-3575
Dr. Barry Tull, hdmstr. Fax 641-3586

Bethesda, Montgomery, Pop. 59,121
Montgomery County SD
Supt. — See Rockville
Bethesda-Chevy Chase HS 1,900/9-12
4301 East West Hwy 20814 240-497-6300
Dr. Donna Jones, prin. Fax 497-6306
Johnson HS 2,200/9-12
6400 Rock Spring Dr 20814 301-803-7100
Jennifer Baker, prin. Fax 571-6916
North Bethesda MS 900/6-8
8935 Bradmoor Dr 20817 301-571-3883
Alton Sumner, prin. Fax 571-3881
Pyle MS 1,400/6-8
6311 Wilson Ln 20817 301-320-6540
Christopher Nardi, prin. Fax 320-6647
Westland MS 1,200/6-8
5511 Massachusetts Ave 20816 301-320-6515
Alison Serino, prin. Fax 320-7054
Whitman HS 1,900/9-12
7100 Whittier Blvd 20817 301-320-6600
Dr. Alan Goodwin, prin. Fax 320-6594

DeVry University Post-Sec.
4550 Montgomery Ave Ste 100 20814 301-652-8477
Holton-Arms S 600/3-12
7303 River Rd 20817 301-365-5300
Susanna Jones, hdmstr. Fax 365-6085
Landon S 700/3-12
6101 Wilson Ln 20817 301-320-3200
Jim Neill, hdmstr. Fax 320-2787
Rochambeau The French International S 1,100/PK-12
9600 Forest Rd 20814 301-530-8260
Catherine Levy, head sch Fax 564-5779

Stone Ridge S of the Sacred Heart 700/1-12
9101 Rockville Pike 20814 301-657-4322
Catherine Karrels, head sch Fax 657-4393
The SANS Technology Institute Post-Sec.
8120 Woodmont Ave Ste 205 20814 301-654-7267
Washington Conservatory of Music Post-Sec.
1 Westmoreland Cir 20816 301-320-2770
Washington Waldorf S 200/PK-12
4800 Sangamore Rd 20816 301-229-6107

Bladensburg, Prince George's, Pop. 9,010
Prince George's County SD
Supt. — See Upper Marlboro
Annapolis Road Academy 100/Alt
5150 Annapolis Rd 20710 301-209-3580
Agnes Brown-Jones, prin. Fax 209-3579
Bladensburg HS 1,800/9-12
4200 57th Ave 20710 301-887-6700
BernNadette Mahoney, prin. Fax 887-6710
Community Based Classroom 100/Alt
5150 Annapolis Rd 20710 301-985-5149
Dr. Tammy Williams, prin. Fax 985-1794
International HS at Langley Park Alt
5150 Annapolis Rd 20710 301-702-3910
Carlos Beato, prin. Fax 760-3726

Elizabeth Seton HS 600/9-12
5715 Emerson St 20710 301-864-4532
Sr. Ellen Hagar, pres. Fax 864-8946

Boonsboro, Washington, Pop. 3,310
Washington County SD
Supt. — See Hagerstown
Boonsboro HS 900/9-12
10 Campus Ave 21713 301-766-8022
Dr. Sherry Hamilton, prin. Fax 432-2269
Boonsboro MS 800/6-8
1 JH Wade Dr 21713 301-766-8038
Gary Willow, prin. Fax 432-2644

Bowie, Prince George's, Pop. 52,916
Prince George's County SD
Supt. — See Upper Marlboro
Bowie HS 2,600/9-12
15200 Annapolis Rd 20715 301-805-2600
Robynne Prince, prin. Fax 805-2619
Ogle MS 900/6-8
4111 Chelmont Ln 20715 301-805-2641
Glenise Marshall, prin. Fax 805-6674
Tall Oaks HS 100/Alt
2112 Church Rd 20721 301-390-0230
Dr. Larry McCray, prin. Fax 390-0228
Tasker MS 900/6-8
4901 Collington Rd 20715 301-805-2660
Ingrid Johnson, prin. Fax 805-2663

Belair Baptist Christian Academy 50/PK-12
2801 Belair Dr 20715 301-262-0578
Dr. Gary Kohl, admin. Fax 262-0579
Bowie State University Post-Sec.
14000 Jericho Park Rd 20715 301-860-4000

Brandywine, Prince George's, Pop. 6,567
Prince George's County SD
Supt. — See Upper Marlboro
Gwynn Park HS 1,100/9-12
13800 Brandywine Rd 20613 301-372-0140
Dr. Tracie Miller, prin. Fax 372-0149
Gwynn Park MS 500/6-8
8000 Dyson Rd 20613 301-372-0120
Danielle Moore, prin. Fax 372-0119

Brooklandville, Baltimore

Maryvale Prep HS 400/6-12
11300 Falls Rd 21022 410-252-3366
Victor Shin, prin. Fax 561-1826
St. Paul's S 800/PK-12
PO Box 8100 21022 410-825-4400
David Faus, hdmstr. Fax 427-0390
St. Paul's S for Girls 400/5-12
PO Box 8000 21022 410-823-6323
Penny Evins, head sch Fax 828-7238

Brunswick, Frederick, Pop. 5,703
Frederick County SD
Supt. — See Frederick
Brunswick HS 700/9-12
101 Cummings Dr 21716 240-236-8600
Michael Dillman, prin. Fax 236-8601
Brunswick MS 600/6-8
301 Cummings Dr 21716 240-236-5400
Jay Schill, prin. Fax 236-5401

Buckeystown, Frederick, Pop. 1,012

St. John's Catholic Prep S 300/9-12
PO Box 909 21717 301-662-4210
Marc Minsker, prin. Fax 892-6877

Burtonsville, Montgomery, Pop. 8,050
Montgomery County SD
Supt. — See Rockville
Banneker MS 800/6-8
14800 Perrywood Dr 20866 301-989-5747
Dr. Otis Lee, prin. Fax 879-1032
Paint Branch HS 1,900/9-12
14121 Old Columbia Pike 20866 301-388-9900
Dr. Myriam Yarbrough, prin. Fax 989-5609

California, Saint Mary's, Pop. 11,416

Blades School of Hair Design Post-Sec.
PO Box 226 20619 301-862-9797

Callaway, Saint Mary's

King's Christian Academy 300/PK-12
20738 Point Lookout Rd 20620 301-994-3080
Kevin Fry, admin. Fax 994-3087

Cambridge, Dorchester, Pop. 12,038
Dorchester County SD 4,800/PK-12
700 Glasgow St 21613 410-228-4747
Dr. Henry Wagner, supt. Fax 228-1847
www.dcps.k12.md.us
Cambridge-South Dorchester HS 800/9-12
2475 Cambridge Beltway 21613 410-228-9224
Dave Bromwell, prin. Fax 228-0724
Dorchester Career and Technology Center Vo/Tech
2465 Cambridge Beltway 21613 410-901-6950
Kermit Hines, prin. Fax 221-8589
Maces Lane MS 500/6-8
1101 Maces Ln 21613 410-228-2111
Mike Collins, prin. Fax 221-5278
Other Schools – See Hurlock

Capitol Heights, Prince George's, Pop. 4,271
Prince George's County SD
Supt. — See Upper Marlboro
Central HS 800/9-12
200 Cabin Branch Rd 20743 301-499-7080
Keishia Wallace, prin. Fax 499-7087
Fairmont Heights HS 800/9-12
1401 Nye St 20743 301-925-1360
Torrie Walker, prin. Fax 925-1371
Walker Mill MS 700/6-8
800 Karen Blvd 20743 301-808-4055
Nicole Clifton, prin. Fax 808-4039

Maple Springs Baptist Bible Coll. & Sem. Post-Sec.
4130 Belt Rd 20743 301-736-3631

Catonsville, Baltimore, Pop. 40,573
Baltimore County SD
Supt. — See Towson
Catonsville MS 800/6-8
2301 Edmondson Ave 21228 410-887-0803
Michael Thorne, prin. Fax 887-1036

Community College of Baltimore County Post-Sec.
800 S Rolling Rd 21228 443-840-2222
Mt. de Sales Academy 500/9-12
700 Academy Rd 21228 410-744-8498
Sr. Mary Huffman, prin. Fax 747-5105

Centreville, Queen Anne's, Pop. 4,193
Queen Anne's County SD 7,600/PK-12
202 Chesterfield Ave 21617 410-758-2403
Gregory Pilewski, supt. Fax 758-8200
qacps.schoolwires.net
Centreville MS 500/6-8
231 Ruthsburg Rd 21617 410-758-0883
Amy Hudock, prin. Fax 758-4447
Queen Anne's County HS 1,100/9-12
125 Ruthsburg Rd 21617 410-758-0500
Angela Holocker, prin. Fax 758-4454
Other Schools – See Stevensville, Sudlersville

Gunston S 100/9-12
PO Box 200 21617 410-758-0620
John Lewis, hdmstr. Fax 758-0628

Cheltenham, Prince George's
Prince George's County SD
Supt. — See Upper Marlboro
Croom HS Vo/Tech
9400 Surratts Rd 20623 301-372-8846
William Henderson, prin. Fax 372-3422

Chesapeake City, Cecil, Pop. 671
Cecil County SD
Supt. — See Elkton
Bohemia Manor HS 600/9-12
2755 Augustine Herman Hwy 21915 410-885-2075
Wanita Fleury, prin. Fax 885-2485
Bohemia Manor MS 500/6-8
2757 Augustine Herman Hwy 21915 410-885-2095
Dr. Ann Little, prin. Fax 885-2485

Chestertown, Kent, Pop. 5,140
Kent County SD
Supt. — See Rock Hall
Kent County MS 400/6-8
402 E Campus Ave 21620 410-778-1771
Janice Steffy, prin. Fax 778-6541

Washington College Post-Sec.
300 Washington Ave 21620 410-778-2800

Clarksburg, Montgomery, Pop. 13,276
Montgomery County SD
Supt. — See Rockville
Clarksburg HS 2,000/9-12
22500 Wims Rd 20871 301-444-3000
Stephen Whiting, prin. Fax 444-3595
Rocky Hill MS 1,100/6-8
22401 Brick Haven Way 20871 301-353-8282
Dr. Cynthia Eldridge, prin. Fax 601-3197
Wells MS 6-8
11701 Little Seneca Pkwy 20871 301-284-4800
Barbara Woodward, prin.

Clarksville, Howard
Howard County SD
Supt. — See Ellicott City
Clarksville MS 600/6-8
6535 S Trotter Rd 21029 410-313-7057
Joelle Miller, prin. Fax 531-5105
River Hill HS 1,300/9-12
12101 Clarksville Pike 21029 410-313-7120
Kathryn McKinley, prin. Fax 313-7406

Clear Spring, Washington, Pop. 356
Washington County SD
Supt. — See Hagerstown
Clear Spring HS 500/9-12
12630 Broadfording Rd 21722 301-766-8082
Darrell Marriott, prin. Fax 842-0082
Clear Spring MS 400/6-8
12628 Broadfording Rd 21722 301-766-8094
Matthew Noll, prin. Fax 842-3826

Clinton, Prince George's, Pop. 35,163
Prince George's County SD
Supt. — See Upper Marlboro
Decatur MS 700/6-8
8200 Pinewood Dr 20735 301-449-4950
William Blake, prin. Fax 449-2105
Surrattsville HS 800/9-12
6101 Garden Dr 20735 301-599-2453
Katrina Lamont, prin. Fax 599-2565

Grace Brethren Christian S 600/PK-12
6501 Surratts Rd 20735 301-868-1600
George Hornickel, dir. Fax 868-9475

Cockeysville, Baltimore, Pop. 20,195
Baltimore County SD
Supt. — See Towson
Cockeysville MS 800/6-8
10401 Greenside Dr 21030 410-887-7626
Deborah Magness, prin. Fax 887-7628

College Park, Prince George's, Pop. 29,403

Al-Huda S PK-12
5301 Edgewood Rd 20740 301-982-2402
University of Maryland College Park Post-Sec.
20742 301-405-1000

Colora, Cecil

West Nottingham Academy 100/9-12
1079 Firetower Rd 21917 410-658-5556
Dr. Thomas Banks, head sch Fax 658-6790

Columbia, Howard, Pop. 95,623
Howard County SD
Supt. — See Ellicott City
Atholton HS 1,500/9-12
6520 Freetown Rd 21044 410-313-7065
JoAnn Hutchens, prin. Fax 313-7078
Hammond HS 1,200/9-12
8800 Guilford Rd 21046 410-313-7615
Marcy Leonard, prin. Fax 313-7632
Harper's Choice MS 500/6-8
5450 Beaverkill Rd 21044 410-313-6929
Adam Eldridge, prin. Fax 313-5612
Lake Elkhorn MS 500/6-8
6680 Cradlerock Way 21045 410-313-7600
Martin Vandenberge, prin. Fax 313-7633
Long Reach HS 1,400/9-12
6101 Old Dobbin Ln 21045 410-313-7117
Josh Wasilewski, prin. Fax 313-7422
Oakland Mills HS 1,100/9-12
9410 Kilimanjaro Rd 21045 410-313-6945
Karim Shortridge, prin. Fax 313-6948
Oakland Mills MS 400/6-8
9540 Kilimanjaro Rd 21045 410-313-6937
Katherine Orlando, prin. Fax 313-7447
Wilde Lake HS 1,200/9-12
5460 Trumpeter Rd 21044 410-313-6965
James LeMon, prin. Fax 313-6972
Wilde Lake MS 500/6-8
10481 Cross Fox Ln 21044 410-313-6957
Anne Swartz, prin. Fax 313-6963

Atholton Adventist Academy 200/PK-10
6520 Martin Rd 21044 410-740-2425
Howard Community College Post-Sec.
10901 Little Patuxent Pkwy 21044 443-518-1200
Lincoln College of Technology Post-Sec.
9325 Snowden River Pkwy 21046 410-290-7100

Cresaptown, Allegany, Pop. 4,546
Allegany County SD
Supt. — See Cumberland
Center for Career & Technical Education Vo/Tech
14211 McMullen Hwy SW 21502 301-729-6486
Candy Canan, prin. Fax 729-0661

Crisfield, Somerset, Pop. 2,671
Somerset County SD
Supt. — See Westover
Crisfield HS & Academy 300/8-12
210 N Somerset Ave 21817 410-968-0150
Chantal Russum, prin. Fax 968-1178

Crownsville, Anne Arundel, Pop. 1,733

Indian Creek S 200/9-12
1130 Anne Chambers Way 21032 410-849-5151
Richard Branson Ed.D., head sch Fax 841-2623

Cumberland, Allegany, Pop. 20,280
Allegany County SD 8,600/PK-12
PO Box 1724 21501 301-759-2000
Dr. David Cox Ed.D., supt. Fax 759-2029
www.acpsmd.org
Allegany HS 700/9-12
616 Sedgwick St 21502 301-777-8110
Michael Calhoun, prin. Fax 759-2534
Braddock MS 600/6-8
909 Holland St 21502 301-777-7990
Danny Carter, prin. Fax 777-9741
Ft. Hill HS 800/9-12
500 Greenway Ave 21502 301-777-2570
Joseph Carter, prin. Fax 777-2572
Washington MS 700/6-8
200 N Massachusetts Ave 21502 301-777-5360
Kendra Kenney, prin. Fax 777-8452

Other Schools – See Cresaptown, Frostburg, Lonaconing

Allegany College of Maryland Post-Sec.
12401 Willowbrook Rd 21502 301-784-5000
Bishop Walsh S 400/PK-12
700 Bishop Walsh Rd 21502 301-724-5360
Raymond Kiddy, prin. Fax 722-0555
Calvary Christian Academy 300/PK-12
14517 McMullen Hwy SW 21502 301-729-0791
Daniel Thompson, admin. Fax 729-1648
International Beauty School Post-Sec.
119 N Centre St 21502 301-777-3020
Lighthouse Christian Academy 100/PK-12
2020 Bedford St 21502 301-777-7375

Damascus, Montgomery, Pop. 14,848
Montgomery County SD
Supt. — See Rockville
Baker MS 500/7-8
25400 Oak Dr 20872 301-253-7010
Dr. Louise Worthington, prin. Fax 253-7020
Damascus HS 1,200/9-12
25921 Ridge Rd 20872 301-253-7030
Jennifer Webster, prin. Fax 253-7046

Darlington, Harford, Pop. 406

Harford Christian S 400/PK-12
PO Box 88 21034 410-457-5103

Denton, Caroline, Pop. 4,304
Caroline County SD 5,500/PK-12
204 Franklin St 21629 410-479-1460
John Ewald, supt. Fax 479-0108
www.cl.k12.md.us
Lockerman MS 800/6-8
410 Lockerman St 21629 410-479-2760
Lee Sutton, prin. Fax 479-3594
Other Schools – See Federalsburg, Ridgely

Dundalk, Baltimore, Pop. 61,917
Baltimore County SD
Supt. — See Towson
Sollers Point Technical HS Vo/Tech
1901 Delvale Ave 21222 410-887-7075
Michael Weglein, prin. Fax 887-7238

Easton, Talbot, Pop. 15,604
Talbot County SD 4,600/PK-12
PO Box 1029 21601 410-822-0330
Dr. Kelly Griffith, supt. Fax 820-4260
www.tcps.k12.md.us/
Easton HS 1,100/9-12
723 Mecklenburg Ave 21601 410-822-4180
David Stofa, prin. Fax 819-5814
Easton MS 800/6-8
201 Peach Blossom Ln 21601 410-822-2910
Norby Lee, prin. Fax 822-7210
Other Schools – See Saint Michaels

SS. Peter & Paul HS 200/9-12
900 High St 21601 410-822-2275
James Nemeth, prin. Fax 822-1767

Edgewater, Anne Arundel, Pop. 8,834
Anne Arundel County SD
Supt. — See Annapolis
Center of Applied Technology-South Vo/Tech
211 Central Ave E 21037 410-956-5900
Thomas Milans, prin. Fax 956-5905
Central MS 1,000/6-8
221 Central Ave E 21037 410-956-5800
Mildred Beall, prin. Fax 956-1266
South River HS 2,200/9-12
201 Central Ave E 21037 410-956-5600
William Myers, prin. Fax 956-5137
South River Evening HS Adult
201 Central Ave E 21037 410-956-0462
Rosaria Jablonski, admin. Fax 956-5919

Edgewood, Harford, Pop. 24,585
Harford County SD
Supt. — See Bel Air
Edgewood HS 1,300/9-12
2415 Willoughby Beach Rd 21040 410-612-1500
Kilo Mack, prin. Fax 612-1585
Edgewood MS 1,100/6-8
2311 Willoughby Beach Rd 21040 410-612-1518
Patrice Brown, prin. Fax 612-1523

Eldersburg, Carroll, Pop. 30,093
Carroll County SD
Supt. — See Westminster
Liberty HS 1,100/9-12
5855 Bartholow Rd 21784 410-751-3560
Kenneth Goncz, prin. Fax 751-3564

Elkridge, Howard, Pop. 15,025
Howard County SD
Supt. — See Ellicott City
Elkridge Landing MS 700/6-8
7085 Montgomery Rd 21075 410-313-5040
Gina Cash, prin. Fax 313-5045
Mayfield Woods MS 800/6-8
7950 Red Barn Way 21075 410-313-5022
Melissa Shindel, prin. Fax 313-5029

Elkton, Cecil, Pop. 14,914
Cecil County SD 15,300/PK-12
201 Booth St 21921 410-996-5400
D'Ette Devine Ed.D., supt. Fax 996-5454
www.ccps.org
Cecil County S of Technology Vo/Tech
912 Appleton Rd 21921 410-392-8879
David Dollenger, prin. Fax 392-8880
Cherry Hill MS 500/6-8
2535 Singerly Rd 21921 410-996-5020
Joseph Harbert, prin. Fax 996-5435
Elkton HS 1,100/9-12
110 James St 21921 410-996-5000
John Roush, prin. Fax 996-5646
Elkton MS 600/6-8
615 North St 21921 410-996-5010
Megan Frunzi, prin. Fax 996-5639
Other Schools – See Chesapeake City, North East, Perryville, Rising Sun

---

Tri-State Christian Academy 300/PK-12
146 Appleton Rd 21921 410-398-6444
Keith Wilson, head sch Fax 688-4847

Ellicott City, Howard, Pop. 64,049
Howard County SD 52,300/PK-12
10910 Clarksville Pike 21042 410-313-6600
Dr. Renee Foose, supt. Fax 313-6674
www.hcpss.org
Applications and Research Lab Vo/Tech
10920 Clarksville Pike 21042 410-313-6998
Karl Schindler, admin. Fax 313-7000
Bonnie Branch MS 700/6-8
4979 Ilchester Rd 21043 410-313-2580
Cherolyn Jones, prin. Fax 313-2586
Burleigh Manor MS 700/6-8
4200 Centennial Ln 21042 410-313-2507
Antoinette Roberson, prin. Fax 313-2513
Centennial HS 1,400/9-12
4300 Centennial Ln 21042 410-313-2856
Claire Hafets, prin. Fax 313-2861
Dunloggin MS 600/6-8
9129 Northfield Rd 21042 410-313-2831
Jeffrey Fink, prin. Fax 313-2530
Ellicott Mills MS 800/6-8
4445 Montgomery Rd 21043 410-313-2839
Christopher Rattay, prin. Fax 313-2845
Folly Quarter MS 500/6-8
13500 Triadelphia Rd 21042 410-313-1506
Scott Conroy, prin. Fax 313-1509
Homewood Center 100/Alt
10914 State Route 108 21042 410-313-7081
Tina Maddox, prin. Fax 313-7130
Howard HS 1,700/9-12
8700 Old Annapolis Rd 21043 410-313-2867
Nick Novak, prin. Fax 313-2870
Mt. Hebron HS 1,400/9-12
9440 Old Frederick Rd 21042 410-313-2880
Andrew Cockley, prin. Fax 313-2543
Patapsco MS 600/6-8
8885 Old Frederick Rd 21043 410-313-2848
Cynthia Dillon, prin. Fax 313-2852
Other Schools – See Clarksville, Columbia, Elkridge, Fulton, Glenelg, Glenwood, Hanover, Jessup, Laurel, Marriottsville

---

Glenelg Country S 800/PK-12
12793 Folly Quarter Rd 21042 410-531-8600
Gregory Ventre, head sch Fax 531-7363

Emmitsburg, Frederick, Pop. 2,774

Mt. St. Mary's University Post-Sec.
16300 Old Emmitsburg Rd 21727 301-447-6122

Fallston, Harford, Pop. 8,862
Harford County SD
Supt. — See Bel Air
Fallston HS 1,100/9-12
2301 Carrs Mill Rd 21047 410-638-4120
Richard Jester, prin. Fax 638-4125
Fallston MS 900/6-8
2303 Carrs Mill Rd 21047 410-638-4129
Dr. Anthony Bess, prin. Fax 638-4237

Federalsburg, Caroline, Pop. 2,672
Caroline County SD
Supt. — See Denton
Richardson HS 500/9-12
25320 Richardson Rd 21632 410-754-5575
Christal Harkowa, prin. Fax 754-3497
Richardson MS 400/6-8
25390 Richardson Rd 21632 410-754-5263
Lynn Willey, prin. Fax 754-5695

Finksburg, Carroll

Gerstell Academy 300/PK-12
2500 Old Westminster Pike 21048 410-861-3000
Dr. Lorraine Fulton, pres. Fax 861-3006

Forestville, Prince George's, Pop. 12,138
Prince George's County SD
Supt. — See Upper Marlboro
Suitland HS 1,900/9-12
5200 Silver Hill Rd 20747 301-817-0500
Nate Newman, prin. Fax 817-0515

Bishop McNamara HS 900/9-12
6800 Marlboro Pike 20747 301-735-8401
Dr. Robert Van der Waag, prin. Fax 735-0934

Fort Meade, Anne Arundel, Pop. 8,776
Anne Arundel County SD
Supt. — See Annapolis
MacArthur MS 1,000/6-8
3500 Rockenbach Rd 20755 410-674-0032
Eugene Whiting, prin. Fax 674-8021
Meade HS 2,200/9-12
1100 Clark Rd 20755 410-674-7710
John Yore, prin. Fax 551-8210
Meade MS 700/6-8
1103 26th St 20755 410-674-2355
Christine DeGuzman, prin. Fax 674-6590
Meade Evening HS Adult
1100 Clark Rd 20755 410-674-7415
Brian Gulden, admin.

Fort Washington, Prince George's, Pop. 23,036
Prince George's County SD
Supt. — See Upper Marlboro
Friendly HS 1,000/9-12
10000 Allentown Rd 20744 301-449-4900
Raynah Adams, prin. Fax 449-4911
Gourdine MS 500/6-8
8700 Allentown Rd 20744 301-449-4940
Leatriz Covington, prin. Fax 449-4948
Oxon Hill MS 600/7-8
9570 Fort Foote Rd 20744 301-749-4270
Wendell Coleman, prin. Fax 749-4286

Frederick, Frederick, Pop. 63,120
Frederick County SD 40,400/PK-12
191 S East St 21701 301-696-6820
Dr. Theresa Alban, supt. Fax 696-6823
www.fcps.org
Ballenger Creek MS 700/6-8
5525 Ballenger Creek Pike 21703 240-236-5700
Jeneen Stewart, prin. Fax 236-5701
Career and Technology Center Vo/Tech
7922 Opossumtown Pike 21702 240-236-8500
Michael Concepcion, prin. Fax 236-8501
Crestwood MS 600/6-8
7100 Foxcroft Dr 21703 240-566-9000
Jennifer Bingman, prin. Fax 566-9001
Frederick HS 1,300/9-12
650 Carroll Pkwy 21701 240-236-7000
David Franceschina, prin. Fax 236-7015
Heather Ridge S Alt
1445 Taney Ave 21702 240-236-8000
Denise Flora, prin. Fax 236-8001
Johnson HS 1,500/9-12
1501 N Market St 21701 240-236-8200
Dr. Dan Lippy, prin. Fax 236-8201
Johnson MS 500/6-8
1799 Schifferstadt Blvd 21701 240-236-4900
Neal Case, prin. Fax 236-4901
Linganore HS 1,500/9-12
12013 Old Annapolis Rd 21701 240-566-9700
Nancy Doll, prin. Fax 566-9701
Monocacy MS 800/6-8
8009 Opossumtown Pike 21702 240-236-4700
Dr. Stephanie Ware, prin. Fax 236-4701
Tuscarora HS 1,500/9-12
5312 Ballenger Creek Pike 21703 240-236-6400
Andrew Kibler, prin. Fax 236-6401
West Frederick MS 800/6-8
515 W Patrick St 21701 240-236-4000
Frank Vetter, prin. Fax 236-4050
Other Schools – See Brunswick, Ijamsville, Middletown, New Market, Thurmont, Walkersville

---

Frederick Community College Post-Sec.
7932 Opossumtown Pike 21702 301-846-2400
Hood College Post-Sec.
401 Rosemont Ave 21701 301-663-3131
Maryland School for the Deaf Post-Sec.
PO Box 250 21705
New Life Christian S 200/K-12
5909 Jefferson Pike 21703 301-663-8418
Jason Burrell, hdmstr. Fax 698-1583

Frostburg, Allegany, Pop. 8,847
Allegany County SD
Supt. — See Cumberland
Eckhart Alternative S 100/Alt
17000 National Hwy SW 21532 301-689-3483
Tonya Detrick-Grove, coord. Fax 689-2567
Mountain Ridge HS 800/9-12
100 Dr Nancy S Grasmick Ln 21532 301-689-3377
Gene Morgan, prin. Fax 689-8709

Frostburg State University Post-Sec.
101 Braddock Rd 21532 301-687-4000

Fruitland, Wicomico, Pop. 4,731
Wicomico County SD
Supt. — See Salisbury
Bennett MS 900/6-8
532 S Division St 21826 410-677-5140
Liza Hastings, prin. Fax 677-5133

Fulton, Howard, Pop. 1,957
Howard County SD
Supt. — See Ellicott City
Lime Kiln MS 600/6-8
11650 Scaggsville Rd 20759 410-880-5988
Lucy Lublin, prin. Fax 880-5996
Reservoir HS 1,500/9-12
11550 Scaggsville Rd 20759 410-888-8850
Patrick Saunderson, prin. Fax 888-8849

Gaithersburg, Montgomery, Pop. 57,995
Montgomery County SD
Supt. — See Rockville
Forest Oak MS 800/6-8
651 Saybrooke Oaks Blvd 20877 301-670-8242
Shahid Muhammad, prin. Fax 840-5322
Gaithersburg HS 2,100/9-12
101 Education Blvd 20877 301-284-4500
Dr. Christine Handy, prin. Fax 284-4701
Gaithersburg MS 500/7-8
2 Teachers Way 20877 301-840-4554
Ann Dolan Rindner, prin. Fax 840-4570
Lakelands Park MS 1,000/6-8
1200 Main St 20878 301-670-1400
Deborah Higdon, prin. Fax 670-1418
Quince Orchard HS 1,900/9-12
15800 Quince Orchard Rd 20878 301-840-4686
Carole Working, prin. Fax 840-4699
Ridgeview MS 400/7-8
16600 Raven Rock Dr 20878 301-406-1300
Daniel Garcia, prin. Fax 840-4679
Shady Grove MS 600/6-8
8100 Midcounty Hwy 20877 301-548-7540
Edward Owusu, prin. Fax 548-7535

Watkins Mill HS 1,400/9-12
10301 Apple Ridge Rd 20886 301-840-3959
Carol Goddard, prin. Fax 840-3980

Aesthetics Institutes of Cosmetology Post-Sec.
15958 Shady Grove Rd Unit C 20877 301-330-9252
Avalon S 200/K-12
200 W Diamond Ave 20877 301-963-8022
Kevin Davern, hdmstr. Fax 963-8027
Covenant Life S 300/PK-12
7503 Muncaster Mill Rd 20877 301-869-4500
Jamie Leach, hdmstr. Fax 948-4920
Sodexho Marriott Healthcare Mid-Atlantic Post-Sec.
9801 Washingtonian Blvd 20878 301-987-4127

Gambrills, Anne Arundel, Pop. 2,747
Anne Arundel County SD
Supt. — See Annapolis
Arundel HS 2,000/9-12
1001 Annapolis Rd 21054 410-674-6500
Gina Davenport, prin. Fax 672-3711
Crofton MS 1,100/6-8
2301 Davidsonville Rd 21054 410-793-0280
Nuria Williams, prin. Fax 793-0295

Germantown, Montgomery, Pop. 83,263
Montgomery County SD
Supt. — See Rockville
Clemente MS 1,100/6-8
18808 Waring Station Rd 20874 301-601-0344
Jeffrey Brown, prin. Fax 601-0370
King MS 600/6-8
13737 Wisteria Dr 20874 301-353-8080
Christopher Wynne, prin. Fax 601-0399
Kingsview MS 1,000/6-8
18909 Kingsview Rd 20874 301-601-4611
Dyan Harrison, prin. Fax 601-4610
Neelsville MS 900/6-8
11700 Neelsville Church Rd 20876 301-353-8064
Vicky Lake-Parcan, prin. Fax 353-8094
Northwest HS 2,000/9-12
13501 Richter Farm Rd 20874 301-601-4660
James D'Andrea, prin. Fax 601-4662
Seneca Valley HS 1,300/9-12
19401 Crystal Rock Dr 20874 301-353-8000
Marc Cohen, prin. Fax 353-8004

Montgomery College Post-Sec.
20200 Observation Dr 20876 240-567-7700

Glen Burnie, Anne Arundel, Pop. 65,521
Anne Arundel County SD
Supt. — See Annapolis
Corkran MS 500/6-8
7600 Quarterfield Rd 21061 410-222-6493
Adam Zetwick, prin. Fax 761-3853
Glen Burnie HS 1,900/9-12
7550 Baltimore Annapolis Bl 21060 410-761-8950
Vickie Plitt, prin. Fax 761-3711
Marley MS 800/6-8
10 Davis Ct 21060 410-761-0934
Kimberly Winterbottom, prin. Fax 761-0736
North County HS 1,900/9-12
10 1st Ave E 21061 410-222-6970
Eric Jefferson, prin. Fax 222-6976
Glen Burnie Evening HS Adult
7550 Baltimore Annapolis Bl 21060 410-761-3664
Anthony Andrione, admin. Fax 863-4531
North County Evening HS Adult
10 1st Ave E 21061 410-424-2102
Rebecca Bittman, admin.

Glencoe, Baltimore

Oldfields S 100/8-12
1500 Glencoe Rd 21152 410-472-4800
Dr. Parnell Hagerman, head sch Fax 472-3141

Glenelg, Howard
Howard County SD
Supt. — See Ellicott City
Glenelg HS 1,300/9-12
14025 Burntwoods Rd 21737 410-313-5528
David Burton, prin. Fax 313-5540

Glenwood, Howard
Howard County SD
Supt. — See Ellicott City
Glenwood MS 500/6-8
2680 Route 97 21738 410-313-5520
Robert Motley, prin. Fax 313-5534

Great Mills, Saint Mary's
St. Mary's County SD
Supt. — See Leonardtown
Great Mills HS 1,600/9-12
21130 Great Mills Rd 20634 301-863-4001
Jake Heibel, prin. Fax 863-4006

Greenbelt, Prince George's, Pop. 22,408
Prince George's County SD
Supt. — See Upper Marlboro
Greenbelt MS 1,200/6-8
6301 Breezewood Dr 20770 301-513-5040
George Covington, prin. Fax 513-5097
Roosevelt HS 2,400/9-12
7601 Hanover Pkwy 20770 301-513-5400
Reginald McNeill, prin. Fax 486-3720

Lancaster Bible College Post-Sec.
7852 Walker Dr Ste 100 20770 301-552-1400

Hagerstown, Washington, Pop. 37,853
Washington County SD 22,000/PK-12
10435 Downsville Pike 21740 301-766-2800
Dr. Clayton Wilcox, supt. Fax 766-2829
www.wcps.k12.md.us/
Antietam Academy Alt
40 W Oak Ridge Dr 21740 301-766-8447
Donald Morrow, coord. Fax 766-8479
Hicks MS 800/6-8
1321 S Potomac St 21740 301-766-8110
Deron Crawford, prin. Fax 766-8116
Ingram S for the Arts 200/9-12
7 S Potomac St 21740 301-766-8840
Rob Hovermale, prin. Fax 766-8849
Northern MS 800/6-8
701 Northern Ave 21742 301-766-8258
Beth Allshouse, prin. Fax 766-8259
North Hagerstown HS 1,300/9-12
1200 Pennsylvania Ave 21742 301-766-8238
James Aleshire, prin. Fax 733-3158
South Hagerstown HS 1,300/9-12
1101 S Potomac St 21740 301-766-8369
Jeremy Jakoby, prin. Fax 766-8474
Washington County Technical HS Vo/Tech
50 W Oak Ridge Dr 21740 301-766-8050
Jeff Stouffer, prin. Fax 797-9743
Western Heights MS 700/6-8
1300 Marshall St 21740 301-766-8403
Matthew Mauriello, prin. Fax 791-4136
Evening HS Adult
40 W Oak Ridge Dr 21740 301-766-8059
Donald Morrow, admin.
Other Schools – See Boonsboro, Clear Spring, Hancock, Smithsburg, Williamsport

---

Award Beauty School Post-Sec.
26 E Antietam St 21740 301-733-4520
Broadfording Christian Academy 300/PK-12
13535 Broadfording Church 21740 301-797-8886
William Wyand, supt. Fax 797-3155
Grace Academy 400/PK-12
13321 Cearfoss Pike 21740 301-733-2033
Dr. Mathew McIntosh, hdmstr. Fax 733-4706
Hagerstown Community College Post-Sec.
11400 Robinwood Dr 21742 240-500-2530
Heritage Academy 200/PK-12
12215 Walnut Pt W 21740 301-582-2600
Dave Hobbs, prin. Fax 582-2603
Highland View Academy 100/9-12
10100 Academy Dr 21740 301-739-8480
Erik Borges, prin. Fax 733-4770
Kaplan University Post-Sec.
18618 Crestwood Dr 21742 301-766-3600
Pittsburgh Institute of Aeronautics Post-Sec.
14516 Pennsylvania Ave 21742 800-444-1440
St. James S 200/8-12
17641 College Rd 21740 301-733-9330
Rev. D. Stuart Dunnan, hdmstr. Fax 739-1310
St. Maria Goretti HS 200/9-12
1535 Oak Hill Ave 21742 301-739-4266
Bridget Bartholomew, prin. Fax 739-4261

Hampstead, Carroll, Pop. 6,228
Carroll County SD
Supt. — See Westminster
North Carroll MS 600/6-8
2401 Hanover Pike 21074 410-751-3440
Ralph Billings, prin. Fax 751-3464
Shiloh MS 700/6-8
3675 Willow St 21074 410-386-4570
Scott Lavender, prin. Fax 386-4579

Hancock, Washington, Pop. 1,530
Washington County SD
Supt. — See Hagerstown
Hancock MSHS 300/6-12
289 W Main St 21750 301-766-8186
Rodney Gayman, prin. Fax 766-8187

Hanover, Anne Arundel
Howard County SD
Supt. — See Ellicott City
Viaduct MS 6-8
7000 Banbury Dr 21076 410-313-8711
Shiney Ann John, prin. Fax 313-8091

Harwood, Anne Arundel
Anne Arundel County SD
Supt. — See Annapolis
Southern HS 1,100/9-12
4400 Solomons Island Rd 20776 410-867-7100
Kathryn Feuerherd, prin. Fax 867-7100

Havre de Grace, Harford, Pop. 12,505
Harford County SD
Supt. — See Bel Air
Havre De Grace HS 600/9-12
700 Congress Ave 21078 410-939-6600
James Reynolds, prin. Fax 939-6667
Havre De Grace MS 500/6-8
401 Lewis Ln 21078 410-939-6608
James Johnson, prin. Fax 939-6613

Huntingtown, Calvert
Calvert County SD
Supt. — See Prince Frederick
Huntingtown HS 1,500/9-12
4125 Solomons Island Rd 20639 410-414-7036
Rick Weber, prin. Fax 535-2865
Plum Point MS 700/6-8
1475 Plum Point Rd 20639 410-550-9170
Kelley Adams, prin. Fax 286-4009

Calverton S 400/PK-12
300 Calverton School Rd 20639 410-535-0216
Daniel Rocha, hdmstr. Fax 535-6934

Hurlock, Dorchester, Pop. 2,049
Dorchester County SD
Supt. — See Cambridge
North Dorchester HS 500/9-12
5875 Cloverdale Rd 21643 410-943-4511
Lynn Sorrells, prin. Fax 943-3499
North Dorchester MS 400/6-8
5745 Cloverdale Rd 21643 410-943-3322
Leslie Tolley, prin. Fax 943-3214

Hyattsville, Prince George's, Pop. 17,068
Prince George's County SD
Supt. — See Upper Marlboro
Hyattsville MS 800/6-8
6001 42nd Ave 20781 301-209-5830
Thornton Boone, prin. Fax 209-5849
Northwestern HS 2,200/9-12
7000 Adelphi Rd 20782 301-985-1820
Elaine Murray, prin. Fax 985-1833
Orem MS 700/6-8
6100 Editors Park Dr 20782 301-853-0840
Theresa Merrifield, prin. Fax 853-0839
Northwestern Evening HS Adult
7000 Adelphi Rd 20782 301-985-1460
William Kitchings, prin. Fax 985-5749

DeMatha Catholic HS 900/9-12
4313 Madison St 20781 240-764-2200
Dr. Daniel McMahon, prin. Fax 764-2277

Ijamsville, Frederick, Pop. 350
Frederick County SD
Supt. — See Frederick
Oakdale HS 1,200/9-12
5850 Eaglehead Dr 21754 240-566-9400
Donna Clabaugh, prin. Fax 566-9401
Oakdale MS 600/6-8
5810 Oakdale School Rd 21754 240-236-5500
Mita Badshah, prin. Fax 236-5501
Urbana HS 1,500/9-12
3471 Campus Dr 21754 240-236-7600
David Kehne, prin. Fax 236-7601
Urbana MS 800/6-8
3511 Pontius Ct 21754 240-566-9200
Peter Daddone, prin. Fax 566-9201
Windsor Knolls MS 800/6-8
11150 Windsor Rd 21754 240-236-5000
Brian Vasquenza, prin. Fax 236-5001

Friends Meeting S 100/K-12
3232 Green Valley Rd 21754 301-798-0288
Mara Y. Nicastro, head sch Fax 798-0299

Indian Head, Charles, Pop. 3,706
Charles County SD
Supt. — See La Plata
Henson MS 700/6-8
3535 Livingston Rd 20640 301-375-8550
Christina Caballero, prin. Fax 375-9216
Lackey HS 1,200/9-12
3000 Chicamuxen Rd 20640 301-743-5431
Kathy Perriello, prin. Fax 743-9076
Smallwood MS 500/6-8
4990 Indian Head Hwy 20640 301-743-5422
Kathy Kiessling, prin. Fax 753-8421

Jessup, Howard, Pop. 7,088
Howard County SD
Supt. — See Ellicott City
Patuxent Valley MS 700/6-8
9151 Vollmerhausen Rd 20794 410-880-5840
Rick Robb, prin. Fax 880-5843

Joppa, Harford, Pop. 12,356
Harford County SD
Supt. — See Bel Air
Joppatowne HS 800/9-12
555 Joppa Farm Rd 21085 410-612-1510
Pamela Zeigler, prin. Fax 612-1528
Magnolia MS 700/6-8
299 Fort Hoyle Rd 21085 410-612-1525
Melissa Mickey, prin. Fax 612-1598

Kensington, Montgomery, Pop. 2,142
Montgomery County SD
Supt. — See Rockville
Einstein HS 1,700/9-12
11135 Newport Mill Rd 20895 301-929-2200
James Fernandez, prin. Fax 962-1016
Newport Mill MS 600/6-8
11311 Newport Mill Rd 20895 301-929-2244
Panagiota Tsonis, prin. Fax 929-2274

Academy of the Holy Cross 600/9-12
4920 Strathmore Ave 20895 301-942-2100
Melissa Huey-Burns, prin. Fax 929-6440
Brookewood S 100/1-12
10401 Armory Ave 20895 301-949-7997
Richard McPherson, hdmstr. Fax 949-0069

Kingsville, Baltimore, Pop. 4,276

Open Bible Christian Academy 200/PK-12
13 Open Bible Way 21087 410-593-9940
Jill Greenlee, admin. Fax 593-9942
Redeemer Classical Christian S 300/PK-12
6415 Mount Vista Rd 21087 410-592-9625
Terry Cellini, head sch Fax 817-6904

Landover, Prince George's, Pop. 22,690
Prince George's County SD
Supt. — See Upper Marlboro
Gholson MS 700/7-8
900 Nalley Rd 20785 301-883-8390
Jacqueline Marshall-Hall, prin. Fax 883-8394
Kenmoor MS 700/6-8
2500 Kenmoor Dr 20785 301-925-2300
Maha Fadli, prin. Fax 925-2317

Fortis College Post-Sec.
4351 Garden City Dr 20785 301-459-3650

Lanham Seabrook, Prince George's, Pop. 16,792
Prince George's County SD
Supt. — See Upper Marlboro

DuVal HS 1,600/9-12
9880 Good Luck Rd 20706 301-918-8600
Mark Covington, prin. Fax 918-8606
Johnson MS 1,000/6-8
5401 Barker Pl 20706 301-918-8680
Rodney McBride, prin. Fax 918-8688

Lanham Christian S 200/PK-12
8400 Good Luck Rd 20706 301-552-9102
Rev. Randy Burr, dir. Fax 552-2021

La Plata, Charles, Pop. 8,508
Charles County SD 27,300/PK-12
PO Box 2770 20646 301-932-6610
Kimberly Hill Ed.D., supt. Fax 932-6651
www.ccboe.com
La Plata HS 1,400/9-12
6035 Radio Station Rd 20646 301-934-1100
Douglass Dolan, prin. Fax 934-5657
Somers MS 900/6-8
300 Willow Ln 20646 301-934-4663
Carrie Akins, prin. Fax 934-2982
Other Schools – See Indian Head, Newburg, Pomfret, Waldorf

College of Southern Maryland Post-Sec.
PO Box 910 20646 301-934-2251

Largo, Prince George's, Pop. 10,502
Prince George's County SD
Supt. — See Upper Marlboro
Academy of Health Sciences at PGCC 300/9-12
301 Largo Rd Rm 119 20774 301-546-7247
Dr. Kathy Richard-Andrews, prin. Fax 546-5241
International HS at Largo Alt
505 Largo Rd 20774 301-702-3810
Alison Hanks-Sloan, prin. Fax 760-3673

Prince George's Community College Post-Sec.
301 Largo Rd 20774 301-336-6000

Laurel, Prince George's, Pop. 24,374
Howard County SD
Supt. — See Ellicott City
Hammond MS 500/6-8
8100 Aladdin Dr 20723 410-880-5830
Kerry Dufresne, prin. Fax 880-5837
Murray Hill MS 700/6-8
9989 Winter Sun Rd 20723 410-880-5897
Rick Wilson, prin. Fax 317-5048

Prince George's County SD
Supt. — See Upper Marlboro
Eisenhower MS 900/6-8
13725 Briarwood Dr 20708 301-497-3620
John Mangrum, prin. Fax 497-3637
Laurel HS 1,800/9-12
8000 Cherry Ln 20707 301-497-2050
Dwayne Jones, prin. Fax 497-2068

Capitol College Post-Sec.
11301 Springfield Rd 20708 800-950-1992
Maryland Univ of Integrative Health Post-Sec.
7750 Montpelier Rd 20723 410-888-9048
St. Vincent Pallotti HS 500/9-12
113 Saint Marys Pl 20707 301-725-3228
Jeffrey Palumbo, prin. Fax 776-4343

Leonardtown, Saint Mary's, Pop. 2,832
St. Mary's County SD 18,300/PK-12
23160 Moakley St 20650 301-475-5511
James Smith, supt. Fax 475-4262
www.smcps.org
Fairlead Academy II Alt
24009 Point Lookout Rd 20650 301-475-0240
Madelyn Giles, dean Fax 475-0245
Forrest Technology Center Vo/Tech
24005 Point Lookout Rd 20650 301-475-0242
Michael Egan, prin. Fax 475-0245
Leonardtown HS 1,900/9-12
23995 Point Lookout Rd 20650 301-475-0200
Mike Watson, prin. Fax 475-0204
Leonardtown MS 900/6-8
24015 Point Lookout Rd 20650 301-475-0230
Deborah Dennie, prin. Fax 475-0237
Other Schools – See Great Mills, Lexington Park, Mechanicsville, Morganza

---

St. Mary's Ryken HS 700/9-12
22600 Camp Calvert Rd 20650 301-475-2814
Rick Wood, prin. Fax 373-4195

Lexington Park, Saint Mary's, Pop. 11,085
St. Mary's County SD
Supt. — See Leonardtown
Esperanza MS 800/6-8
22790 Maple Rd 20653 301-863-4016
Jill Snyder-Mills, prin. Fax 863-4020
Fairlead Academy I Alt
20833 Great Mills Rd 20653 301-863-4090
Rebecca Cline, dean Fax 863-4013
Spring Ridge MS 1,000/6-8
19856 Three Notch Rd 20653 301-863-4031
Wendy Zimmerman, prin. Fax 863-4035

Linthicum Heights, Anne Arundel, Pop. 2,980
Anne Arundel County SD
Supt. — See Annapolis
Lindale MS 800/6-8
415 Andover Rd 21090 410-691-4344
Johnny Nash, prin. Fax 691-4359

Lonaconing, Allegany, Pop. 1,197
Allegany County SD
Supt. — See Cumberland
Westmar MS 300/6-8
16915 Lower Georges Creek 21539 301-463-5751
Stephanie Wesolowski, prin. Fax 463-2231

Lothian, Anne Arundel
Anne Arundel County SD
Supt. — See Annapolis
Southern MS 800/6-8
5235 Solomons Island Rd 20711 410-222-1659
Kevin Buckley, prin. Fax 867-0231

Lusby, Calvert, Pop. 1,786
Calvert County SD
Supt. — See Prince Frederick
Mill Creek MS 500/6-8
12200 Southern Connector 20657 410-550-9190
Beckie Bowen, prin. Fax 286-4024
Patuxent HS 1,100/9-12
12485 Southern Connector 20657 410-535-7865
Sabrina Bergen, prin. Fax 535-7875
Southern MS 500/6-8
9615 HG Trueman Rd 20657 410-535-7877
Mandy Blackmon, prin. Fax 535-7879

Lutherville, Baltimore, Pop. 6,362
Baltimore County SD
Supt. — See Towson
Ridgely MS 1,100/6-8
121 E Ridgely Rd 21093 410-887-7650
Susan Truesdell, prin. Fax 887-7834

Mc Henry, Garrett

Garrett College Post-Sec.
687 Mosser Rd 21541 301-387-3000

Manchester, Carroll, Pop. 4,742
Carroll County SD
Supt. — See Westminster
Manchester Valley HS 800/9-12
3300 Maple Grove Rd 21102 410-386-1673
Thomas Clowes, prin. Fax 386-1561

Mardela Springs, Wicomico, Pop. 336
Wicomico County SD
Supt. — See Salisbury
Mardela MSHS 700/6-12
24940 Delmar Rd 21837 410-677-5142
Amy Eskridge, prin. Fax 677-5166

Marion Station, Somerset
Somerset County SD
Supt. — See Westover
Peyton Adult & Alt Learning Ctr 200/Alt
28573 Hudson Corner Rd 21838 410-623-2385
William Johnson, prin. Fax 623-2114

Marriottsville, Howard
Howard County SD
Supt. — See Ellicott City
Marriotts Ridge HS 1,200/9-12
12100 Woodford Dr 21104 410-313-5568
Tammy Goldeison, prin. Fax 313-5574
Mount View MS 700/6-8
12101 Woodford Dr 21104 410-313-5545
Allen Cosentino, prin. Fax 313-5551

Chapelgate Christian Academy 400/PK-K, 6-1
2600 Marriottsville Rd 21104 410-442-5888
Robin Van Ness, hdmstr. Fax 419-3831

Mechanicsville, Saint Mary's, Pop. 1,477
St. Mary's County SD
Supt. — See Leonardtown
Brent MS 1,000/6-8
29675 Point Lookout Rd 20659 301-884-4635
Janet Fowler, prin. Fax 884-8937

Middletown, Frederick, Pop. 4,076
Frederick County SD
Supt. — See Frederick
Middletown HS 1,100/9-12
200 Schoolhouse Dr 21769 240-236-7400
Lee Jeffrey, prin. Fax 236-7450
Middletown MS 800/6-8
100 Martha Mason St 21769 240-236-4200
Everett Warren, prin. Fax 236-4250

Millersville, Anne Arundel
Anne Arundel County SD
Supt. — See Annapolis
Old Mill HS 2,100/9-12
600 Patriot Ln 21108 410-969-9010
Kevin Hamlin, prin. Fax 969-1620
Old Mill MS North 900/6-8
610 Patriot Ln 21108 410-969-5950
Dennis Kelly, prin. Fax 969-2612
Old Mill MS South 700/6-8
620 Patriot Ln 21108 410-969-7000
Christian Thomas, prin. Fax 969-5157

Rockbridge Academy 300/K-12
911 Generals Hwy 21108 410-923-1171
Roy Griffith, hdmstr. Fax 923-6588
Strayer University Post-Sec.
1520 Jabez Run 21108 410-923-4500

Mitchellville, Prince George's, Pop. 10,692
Prince George's County SD
Supt. — See Upper Marlboro
Just MS 600/7-8
1300 Campus Way N 20721 301-808-4040
Dr. Keary Schoen, prin. Fax 808-4050

Woodstream Christian Academy 400/PK-12
9800 Lottsford Rd 20721 301-955-1160
Bonita Bailey, dean Fax 955-1169

Monkton, Baltimore
Baltimore County SD
Supt. — See Towson
Hereford MS 900/6-8
712 Corbett Rd 21111 410-887-7902
Cathryn Walrod, prin. Fax 887-7904

Montgomery Village, Montgomery, Pop. 30,917
Montgomery County SD
Supt. — See Rockville
Montgomery Village MS 600/6-8
19300 Watkins Mill Rd 20886 301-840-4660
Dr. Edgar Malker, prin. Fax 840-6388

Living Grace Christian S 100/K-12
20300 Pleasant Ridge Dr 20886 301-840-9830
Dr. Daniel Switzer, prin. Fax 840-8005

Morganza, Saint Mary's
St. Mary's County SD
Supt. — See Leonardtown
Chopticon HS 1,600/9-12
25390 Colton Point Rd 20660 301-475-0215
Kim Summers, prin. Fax 475-0222

Mount Airy, Carroll, Pop. 9,125
Carroll County SD
Supt. — See Westminster
Mount Airy MS 700/6-8
102 Watersville Rd 21771 410-751-3554
Karl Streaker, prin. Fax 751-3556

Mount Airy Christian Academy 400/K-12
16700 Old Frederick Rd 21771 410-489-4321
Vicky Webster, head sch Fax 489-4492

Newark, Worcester, Pop. 331
Worcester County SD 6,600/PK-12
6270 Worcester Hwy 21841 410-632-5000
Jerry Wilson Ph.D., supt. Fax 632-0364
www.worcesterk12.com
Worcester Technical HS Vo/Tech
6290 Worcester Hwy 21841 410-632-5050
Caroline Bloxom, prin. Fax 632-5059
Other Schools – See Berlin, Pocomoke City, Snow Hill

Newburg, Charles
Charles County SD
Supt. — See La Plata
Piccowaxen MS 400/6-8
12834 Rock Point Rd 20664 301-934-1977
Wendell Martin, prin. Fax 934-1628

New Carrollton, Prince George's, Pop. 11,918
Prince George's County SD
Supt. — See Upper Marlboro
Carroll MS 1,000/6-8
6130 Lamont Dr 20784 301-918-8640
David Curry, prin. Fax 918-8646

Hair Academy Post-Sec.
8435 Annapolis Rd 20784 301-459-2509

New Market, Frederick, Pop. 644
Frederick County SD
Supt. — See Frederick
New Market MS 500/6-8
125 W Main St 21774 240-236-4600
Trese Suter, prin. Fax 236-4650

North Bethesda, Montgomery, Pop. 42,508

Georgetown Preparatory S 500/9-12
10900 Rockville Pike 20852 301-493-5000
John Glennon, hdmstr. Fax 493-5905

North East, Cecil, Pop. 3,496
Cecil County SD
Supt. — See Elkton
North East HS 1,000/9-12
300 Irishtown Rd 21901 410-996-6200
David Foye, prin. Fax 996-6264
North East MS 800/6-8
200 E Cecil Ave 21901 410-996-6210
Denise Sopa, prin. Fax 996-6236
Rising Sun HS 1,100/9-12
100 Tiger Dr 21901 410-658-9115
Charles Helm, prin. Fax 658-9121

Cecil College Post-Sec.
1 Seahawk Dr 21901 410-287-1000
Tome S 500/K-12
581 S Maryland Ave 21901 410-287-2050

Oakland, Garrett, Pop. 1,908
Garrett County SD 3,900/PK-12
40 S 2nd St 21550 301-334-8900
Barbara L. Baker, supt. Fax 334-7621
garrettcountyschools.org
Southern Garrett HS 700/9-12
345 Oakland Dr 21550 301-334-9447
Jim Maddy, prin. Fax 334-5085
Southern MS 500/6-8
605 Harvey Winters Dr 21550 301-334-8881
Brooks Elliott, prin. Fax 334-2315
Other Schools – See Accident

Odenton, Anne Arundel, Pop. 35,750
Anne Arundel County SD
Supt. — See Annapolis
Arundel MS 900/6-8
1179 Hammond Ln 21113 410-674-6900
George Lindley, prin. Fax 674-6593

Olney, Montgomery, Pop. 33,044
Montgomery County SD
Supt. — See Rockville
Farquhar MS 600/6-8
17017 Batchellors Forest Rd 20832 240-740-1200
Joel Beidleman, prin. Fax 774-7505
Parks MS 900/6-8
19200 Olney Mill Rd 20832 301-924-3180
Jewel Sanders, prin. Fax 924-3288

Our Lady of Good Counsel HS 1,300/9-12
17301 Old Vic Blvd 20832 240-283-3200
Thomas Campbell, prin. Fax 283-3250
Washington Christian Academy 300/K-12
16227 Batchellors Forest Rd 20832 240-390-0429
James Armistead, head sch Fax 559-0115

Owings, Calvert, Pop. 2,102
Calvert County SD
Supt. — See Prince Frederick
Northern HS 1,500/9-12
2950 Chaneyville Rd 20736 410-257-1519
Stephen Williams, prin. Fax 257-1530
Northern MS 700/6-8
2954 Chaneyville Rd 20736 410-257-1622
Jaime Webster, prin. Fax 257-1623
Windy Hill MS 700/6-8
9560 Boyds Turn Rd 20736 410-257-1560
James Kurtz, prin. Fax 257-4586

Owings Mills, Baltimore, Pop. 29,714
Baltimore County SD
Supt. — See Towson
New Town HS 900/9-12
4931 New Town Blvd 21117 410-887-1614
Kevin Whatley, prin. Fax 654-8897
Owings Mills HS 900/9-12
124 Tollgate Rd 21117 410-887-1700
Abbey Campbell, prin. Fax 581-1713

Empire Beauty School Post-Sec.
9616 Reistertown Rd Ste 105 21117 866-232-2771
Garrison Forest S 600/PK-12
300 Garrison Forest Rd 21117 410-363-1500
Kim Roberts Ph.D., hdmstr. Fax 363-8441
Jemicy S 100/9-12
11202 Garrison Forest Rd 21117 410-653-2700
Ben Shifrin, hdmstr. Fax 753-8085
McDonogh S 1,300/PK-12
8600 McDonogh Rd 21117 443-544-7000
Charles Britton, hdmstr. Fax 581-0155

Oxon Hill, Prince George's, Pop. 17,298
Prince George's County SD
Supt. — See Upper Marlboro
Oxon Hill HS 1,400/9-12
6701 Leyte Dr 20745 301-749-4300
Dr. Jean-Paul Cadet, prin. Fax 749-4320
Potomac HS 1,100/9-12
5211 Boydell Ave 20745 301-702-3900
Nathaniel Laney, prin. Fax 702-3886

Parkton, Baltimore
Baltimore County SD
Supt. — See Towson
Hereford HS 1,300/9-12
17301 York Rd 21120 410-887-1905
Louis Jira, prin. Fax 887-1944

Parkville, Baltimore, Pop. 30,034
Baltimore County SD
Supt. — See Towson
Parkville HS 1,500/9-12
2600 Putty Hill Ave 21234 410-887-5257
Maureen Astarita, prin. Fax 668-7503

Pasadena, Anne Arundel, Pop. 23,755
Anne Arundel County SD
Supt. — See Annapolis
Chesapeake Bay MS 1,100/6-8
4804 Mountain Rd 21122 410-437-2400
Michael Dunn, prin. Fax 437-9920
Chesapeake HS 1,500/9-12
4798 Mountain Rd 21122 410-255-9600
Stephen Gorski, prin. Fax 360-4364
Fox MS 900/6-8
7922 Outing Ave 21122 410-437-5512
Russell Austin, prin. Fax 360-1511
Northeast HS 1,300/9-12
1121 Duvall Hwy 21122 410-437-6400
Jason Williams, prin. Fax 437-7012

Perry Hall, Baltimore, Pop. 27,923

Perry Hall Christian S 300/PK-12
3919 Schroeder Ave 21128 410-256-4886
Steve Taylor, head sch Fax 256-5451

Perryville, Cecil, Pop. 4,257
Cecil County SD
Supt. — See Elkton
Perryville HS 800/9-12
1696 Perryville Rd 21903 410-996-6000
Justin Zimmerman, prin. Fax 996-6027
Perryville MS 600/6-8
850 Aiken Ave 21903 410-996-6010
Shawn Johnson, prin. Fax 996-6048

Pocomoke City, Worcester, Pop. 4,103
Worcester County SD
Supt. — See Newark
Pocomoke HS 300/9-12
1817 Old Virginia Rd 21851 410-632-5180
Annette Wallace, prin. Fax 632-5189
Pocomoke MS 400/4-8
800 8th St 21851 410-632-5150
Todd Hall, prin. Fax 632-5159

Pomfret, Charles, Pop. 498
Charles County SD
Supt. — See La Plata
McDonough HS 1,100/9-12
7165 Marshall Corner Rd 20675 301-934-2944
Steven Roberts, prin. Fax 753-8408
Stethem Educational Center 100/Alt
7775 Marshall Corner Rd 20675 301-753-1757
Evelyn Arnold, prin. Fax 934-0165

Poolesville, Montgomery, Pop. 4,780
Montgomery County SD
Supt. — See Rockville
Poole MS 400/6-8
17014 Tom Fox Ave 20837 301-972-7979
Robert Sinclair, prin. Fax 972-7982
Poolesville JSHS 1,200/7-12
17501 W Willard Rd 20837 301-972-7900
Deena Levine, prin. Fax 972-7943

Potomac, Montgomery, Pop. 43,827
Montgomery County SD
Supt. — See Rockville
Cabin John MS 1,000/6-8
10701 Gainsborough Rd 20854 301-469-1150
Dr. John Taylor, prin. Fax 469-1003
Churchill HS 2,100/9-12
11300 Gainsborough Rd 20854 301-469-1200
Dr. Joan Benz, prin. Fax 469-1208
Hoover MS 1,000/6-8
8810 Postoak Rd 20854 301-469-1010
Yong-Mi Kim, prin. Fax 469-1013

Bullis S 600/2-12
10601 Falls Rd 20854 301-299-8500
Dr. Gerald Boarman, hdmstr. Fax 299-9050
Connelly S of the Holy Child 300/6-12
9029 Bradley Blvd 20854 301-365-0955
Dr. Shannon Gomez, hdmstr. Fax 365-0981
German S Washington D.C. 600/PK-12
8617 Chateau Dr 20854 301-365-4400
Petra Palenzatis, head sch Fax 365-3905
Heights S 500/3-12
10400 Seven Locks Rd 20854 301-365-4300
Alvaro de Vicente, hdmstr. Fax 365-4303
McLean S 400/K-12
8224 Lochinver Ln 20854 301-299-8277
Michael Saxenian, head sch Fax 299-1639
Muslim Community S / Alim Academy 100/PK-12
7917 Montrose Rd 20854 301-340-6713
Somayyah Nahidian M.Ed., prin. Fax 340-7339
St. Andrew's Episcopal S 500/3-12
8804 Postoak Rd 20854 301-983-5200
Robert Kosasky, head sch Fax 983-4710

Prince Frederick, Calvert, Pop. 2,434
Calvert County SD 15,700/PK-12
1305 Dares Beach Rd 20678 410-535-1700
Dr. Daniel Curry, supt. Fax 535-7298
www.calvertnet.k12.md.us
Calvert HS 1,200/9-12
520 Fox Run Blvd 20678 410-535-7330
Steven Lucas, prin. Fax 535-7200
Calvert MS 600/6-8
655 Chesapeake Blvd 20678 410-550-8970
Zach Seawell, prin. Fax 286-4007
Career & Technology Academy Vo/Tech
330 Dorsey Rd 20678 410-535-7450
Mark Wilding, prin. Fax 535-7418
Other Schools – See Huntingtown, Lusby, Owings

Princess Anne, Somerset, Pop. 3,212
Somerset County SD
Supt. — See Westover
Washington HS & Academy 600/8-12
10902 Old Princess Anne Rd 21853 410-651-0480
Sidney Hankerson, prin. Fax 651-0235

University of Maryland Eastern Shore Post-Sec.
11868 Academic Oval 21853 410-651-2200

Pylesville, Harford, Pop. 684
Harford County SD
Supt. — See Bel Air
North Harford HS 1,400/9-12
211 Pylesville Rd 21132 410-638-3650
Colin Carr, prin. Fax 638-3666
North Harford MS 1,000/6-8
112 Pylesville Rd 21132 410-638-3658
Karl Wickman, prin. Fax 638-3669

Randallstown, Baltimore, Pop. 31,696
Baltimore County SD
Supt. — See Towson
Deer Park Magnet MS 1,300/6-8
9830 Winands Rd 21133 410-887-0726
Kandice Taylor, prin. Fax 887-0704
Randallstown HS 1,000/9-12
4000 Offutt Rd 21133 410-887-0748
Aubrey Brown, prin. Fax 887-0759

Reisterstown, Baltimore, Pop. 25,217
Baltimore County SD
Supt. — See Towson
Franklin HS 1,500/9-12
12000 Reisterstown Rd 21136 410-887-1119
Patrick McCusker, prin. Fax 833-4434
Franklin MS 1,300/6-8
10 Cockeys Mill Rd 21136 410-887-1114
Charlyn Maul, prin. Fax 517-2548

Maryland Beauty Academy Post-Sec.
152 Chartley Dr 21136 410-517-0442

Ridgely, Caroline, Pop. 1,595
Caroline County SD
Supt. — See Denton
Caroline Career and Technology Center Vo/Tech
10855 Central Ave 21660 410-479-0100
Eugene Smith, prin. Fax 479-1308
North Caroline HS 1,000/9-12
10990 River Rd 21660 410-479-2332
Dr. Michael Smith, prin. Fax 479-2743

Rising Sun, Cecil, Pop. 2,742
Cecil County SD
Supt. — See Elkton
Rising Sun MS 700/6-8
289 Pearl St 21911 410-658-5535
Stuart Hutchinson, prin. Fax 658-9173

Riverdale, Prince George's, Pop. 5,120
Prince George's County SD
Supt. — See Upper Marlboro
Parkdale HS 2,000/9-12
6001 Good Luck Rd 20737 301-513-5700
Tanya Washington, prin. Fax 513-5209
Wirt MS 1,000/6-8
6200 Tuckerman St 20737 301-985-1720
Rhonda Simley, prin. Fax 985-2135

Rock Hall, Kent, Pop. 1,286
Kent County SD 2,100/PK-12
5608 Boundary Ave 21661 410-778-7113
Dr. Karen Couch, supt. Fax 778-2350
www.kent.k12.md.us
Other Schools – See Chestertown, Worton

Rockville, Montgomery, Pop. 59,311
Montgomery County SD 149,200/PK-12
850 Hungerford Dr 20850 301-309-6277
Dr. Jack Smith, supt. Fax 279-3205
www.montgomeryschoolsmd.org
Blair Ewing Center Alt
14501 Avery Rd 20853 301-279-4920
Dr. Damien Ingram, prin. Fax 279-4962
Frost MS 1,200/6-8
9201 Scott Dr 20850 301-279-3949
Dr. Joey Jones, prin. Fax 279-3956
Magruder HS 1,600/9-12
5939 Muncaster Mill Rd 20855 301-840-4600
Leroy Evans, prin. Fax 840-4617
Montgomery HS 2,200/9-12
250 Richard Montgomery Dr 20852 301-610-8000
Damon Monteleone, prin. Fax 279-8428
Parkland MS 900/6-8
4610 W Frankfort Dr 20853 301-438-5700
Khanny Yang, prin. Fax 460-2699
Redland MS 500/6-8
6505 Muncaster Mill Rd 20855 301-840-4680
Everett Davis, prin. Fax 670-2231
Rockville HS 1,300/9-12
2100 Baltimore Rd 20851 301-517-8105
Billie-Jean Bensen, prin. Fax 517-8288
Tilden MS 500/7-8
11211 Old Georgetown Rd 20852 301-230-5930
Irina LaGrange, prin. Fax 230-5991
West MS 1,100/6-8
651 Great Falls Rd 20850 301-279-3979
Craig Staton, prin. Fax 517-8216
Wood MS 900/6-8
14615 Bauer Dr 20853 301-460-2150
Dr. Traci Townsend, prin. Fax 460-2104
Wootton HS 2,300/9-12
2100 Wootton Pkwy 20850 301-279-8550
Kimberly Boldon, prin. Fax 279-8569
Other Schools – See Bethesda, Burtonsville, Clarksburg, Damascus, Gaithersburg, Germantown, Kensington, Montgomery Village, Olney, Poolesville, Potomac, Sandy Spring, Silver Spring

Berman Hebrew Academy 700/PK-12
13300 Arctic Ave 20853 301-962-9400
Dr. Joshua Levisohn Ph.D., head sch Fax 962-3991
Kaplan University Post-Sec.
1390 Piccard Dr Ste 100 20850 301-258-3800
Montgomery College Post-Sec.
51 Mannakee St 20850 240-567-5000
Montrose Christian S 200/PK-12
5100 Randolph Rd 20852 301-770-5335
Dr. Ken Fentress, chncllr. Fax 881-7345
Omega Studios School of Applied Arts Post-Sec.
5609 Fishers Ln 20852 301-230-9100
School for Tomorrow 50/4-12
4511 Bestor Dr 20853 301-460-4747
Maura Kennedy, head sch
Smith Jewish Day S 700/6-12
11710 Hunters Ln 20852 301-881-1400
Rabbi Mitchel Malkus, head sch Fax 230-1986
Strayer University Post-Sec.
4 Research Pl Ste 100 20850 301-548-5500

Rosedale, Baltimore, Pop. 18,880

Community College of Baltimore County Post-Sec.
7201 Rossville Blvd 21237 443-840-2222

Saint Marys City, Saint Mary's, Pop. 3,200

St. Mary's College of Maryland Post-Sec.
18952 E Fisher Rd 20686 240-895-2000

Saint Michaels, Talbot, Pop. 1,017
Talbot County SD
Supt. — See Easton
Saint Michaels MSHS 400/7-12
200 Seymour Ave 21663 410-745-2852
Helga Einhorn, prin. Fax 745-9939

Salisbury, Wicomico, Pop. 29,461
Wicomico County SD 14,400/PK-12
PO Box 1538 21802 410-677-4400
Dr. Donna Hanlin, supt. Fax 677-4444
www.wcboe.org
Bennett HS 1,400/9-12
300 E College Ave 21804 410-677-5141
Steve Grudis, prin. Fax 677-5126
Career Technology Education Vo/Tech
1015 Beaglin Park Dr 21804 410-677-5144
Choices Academy Alt
28929 Adventist Dr 21801 410-677-5220
Christel Savage, prin. Fax 677-5225
Parkside HS 1,100/9-12
1015 Beaglin Park Dr 21804 410-677-5143
Kim Pinhey, prin. Fax 677-5104

Salisbury MS 900/6-8
607 Morris St 21801 410-677-5149
Kris Gosnell, prin. Fax 677-5122
Wicomico HS 1,000/9-12
201 Long Ave 21804 410-677-5146
Don Brady, prin. Fax 677-5151
Wicomico MS 700/6-8
635 E Main St 21804 410-677-5145
Kelley Springston, prin. Fax 677-5197
Evening HS Adult
201 Long Ave 21804 410-677-4537
David Harner, admin. Fax 677-5280
Other Schools – See Fruitland, Mardela Springs

Del-Mar-Va Beauty Academy Post-Sec.
111 Milford St 21804 410-742-7929
Salisbury Christian S 600/PK-12
807 Parker Rd 21804 410-546-0661
Lynn Franks M.A., prin. Fax 546-4674
Salisbury School 300/PK-12
6279 Hobbs Rd 21804 410-742-4464
Edwin Cowell, hdmstr. Fax 912-0896
Salisbury University Post-Sec.
1101 Camden Ave 21801 410-543-6000
Wor-Wic Community College Post-Sec.
32000 Campus Dr 21804 410-334-2800

Sandy Spring, Montgomery, Pop. 3,092
Montgomery County SD
Supt. — See Rockville
Sherwood HS 2,000/9-12
300 Olney Sandy Spring Rd 20860 301-924-3200
William Gregory, prin. Fax 924-3220

Sandy Spring Friends S 600/PK-12
16923 Norwood Rd 20860 301-774-7455
Thomas Gibian, head sch Fax 924-1115

Severn, Anne Arundel, Pop. 42,378
Anne Arundel County SD
Supt. — See Annapolis
Center of Applied Technology-North Vo/Tech
800 Stevenson Rd 21144 410-969-3100
Dan Schaffhauser, prin. Fax 696-3684

Annapolis Area Christian S 800/PK-12
109 Burns Crossing Rd 21144 410-519-5300
Rick Kempton, supt. Fax 573-6866
Archbishop Spalding HS 1,200/9-12
8080 New Cut Rd 21144 410-969-9105
Lewis VanWambeke, prin. Fax 969-1026

Severna Park, Anne Arundel, Pop. 37,032
Anne Arundel County SD
Supt. — See Annapolis
Severna Park HS 1,900/9-12
60 Robinson Rd 21146 410-544-0900
Patrick Bathras, prin. Fax 647-2978
Severna Park MS 1,400/6-8
450 Jumpers Hole Rd 21146 410-647-7900
Sharon Hansen, prin. Fax 431-5376
Severna Park Evening HS Adult
60 Robinson Rd 21146 410-544-0182
Sonja Davenport, admin.

Severn S 600/6-12
201 Water St 21146 410-647-7700
Douglas Lagarde, hdmstr. Fax 544-9455

Silver Spring, Montgomery, Pop. 69,258
Montgomery County SD
Supt. — See Rockville
Argyle MS 800/6-8
2400 Bel Pre Rd 20906 301-460-2400
James Allrich, prin. Fax 460-2423
Blair HS 2,800/9-12
51 University Blvd E 20901 301-649-2800
Renay Johnson, prin. Fax 649-2830
Blake HS 1,700/9-12
300 Norwood Rd 20905 301-879-1300
Christopher Berry, prin. Fax 879-1306
Briggs-Chaney MS 900/6-8
1901 Rainbow Dr 20905 301-989-6000
Dr. Tamitha Campbell, prin. Fax 989-6020
Eastern MS 900/6-8
300 University Blvd E 20901 301-650-6650
Casey Crouse, prin. Fax 650-6657
Edison HS of Technology Vo/Tech
12501 Dalewood Dr 20906 301-929-2175
Peter Cahall, prin. Fax 929-2177
Kennedy HS 1,600/9-12
1901 Randolph Rd 20902 301-929-2100
Joe Rubens, prin. Fax 929-2240
Key MS 900/6-8
910 Schindler Dr 20903 301-422-5600
Yolanda Stanislaus, prin. Fax 434-1375
Lee MS 700/6-8
11800 Monticello Ave 20902 301-649-8100
Kimberly Hayden Williams, prin. Fax 649-8110
Loiederman MS 800/6-8
12701 Goodhill Rd 20906 301-929-2282
Nicole Sosik, prin. Fax 962-5993
Northwood HS 1,500/9-12
919 University Blvd W 20901 301-649-8088
Mildred Charley-Greene, prin. Fax 649-8285
Silver Spring International MS 1,000/6-8
313 Wayne Ave 20910 301-650-6544
Karen Bryant, prin. Fax 562-5244
Sligo MS 400/6-8
1401 Dennis Ave 20902 301-649-8121
Cary Dimmick, prin. Fax 649-8145
Springbrook HS 1,700/9-12
201 Valley Brook Dr 20904 301-989-5700
Dr. Arthur Williams, prin. Fax 622-1875
Takoma Park MS 1,000/6-8
7611 Piney Branch Rd 20910 301-650-6444
Alicia Deeny, prin. Fax 650-6430

Wheaton HS 1,300/9-12
12401 Dalewood Dr 20906 301-929-2050
Dr. Debra Mugge, prin. Fax 929-2081
White Oak MS 700/6-8
12201 New Hampshire Ave 20904 301-989-5780
Virginia de los Santos, prin. Fax 989-5696

Barrie S 300/PK-12
13500 Layhill Rd 20906 301-576-2800
Dr. Charles Abelmann, hdmstr. Fax 576-2803
Columbia College Post-Sec.
12125 Veirs Mill Rd 20906 301-929-0565
Everest Institute Post-Sec.
8757 Georgia Ave Ste 650 20910 301-495-4400
Griggs International Academy Post-Sec.
PO Box 4437 20914 301-680-6570
Griggs University Post-Sec.
PO Box 4437 20914 301-680-6570
Holy Cross Hospital Post-Sec.
1500 Forest Glen Rd 20910 301-905-1216
Medtech College Post-Sec.
1100 Wayne Ave Ste 100 20910 301-608-2300
Montgomery Beauty School Post-Sec.
8736 Arliss St 20901 301-459-2509
Nora S 100/9-12
955 Sligo Ave 20910 301-495-6672
Dave Mullen, head sch Fax 495-7829
Siena S 100/4-12
1300 Forest Glen Rd 20901 301-244-3600
Jilly Darefsky, head sch Fax 244-3601
Yeshiva College of the Nations Capital Post-Sec.
1216 Arcola Ave 20902 301-593-2534
Yeshiva of Greater Washington - Boys Div 100/7-12
1216 Arcola Ave 20902 301-649-7077
Yeshiva of Greater Washington-Girls Div 200/7-12
2010 Linden Ln 20910 301-962-5111
Rabbi Yitzchok Merkin, hdmstr. Fax 962-8372

Smithsburg, Washington, Pop. 2,924
Washington County SD
Supt. — See Hagerstown
Smithsburg HS 800/9-12
66 N Main St 21783 301-766-8337
Michael Chilcutt, prin. Fax 824-2617
Smithsburg MS 600/6-8
68 N Main St 21783 301-766-8353
Christine Corbeil, prin. Fax 824-5147

Snow Hill, Worcester, Pop. 2,063
Worcester County SD
Supt. — See Newark
Snow Hill HS 300/9-12
305 S Church St 21863 410-632-5270
Kimberly Purvis, prin. Fax 632-5279
Snow Hill MS 400/4-8
522 Coulbourne Ln 21863 410-632-5240
Christina Welch, prin. Fax 632-5249

Spencerville, Montgomery, Pop. 1,516

Spencerville Adventist Academy 300/PK-12
2502 Spencerville Rd 20868 301-421-9101

Springdale, Prince George's, Pop. 2,957
Prince George's County SD
Supt. — See Upper Marlboro
Flowers HS 2,000/9-12
10001 Ardwick Ardmore Rd 20774 301-636-8000
Gorman Brown, prin. Fax 636-8008

Stevenson, Baltimore

St. Timothy's S 200/9-12
8400 Greenspring Ave 21153 410-486-7400
Randy Stevens, hdmstr. Fax 486-1167
Stevenson University Post-Sec.
1525 Greenspring Valley Rd 21153 410-486-7000

Stevensville, Queen Anne's, Pop. 6,708
Queen Anne's County SD
Supt. — See Centreville
Kent Island HS 1,200/9-12
900 Love Point Rd 21666 410-604-2070
John Schrecongost, prin. Fax 604-2089
Matapeake MS 400/6-8
671 Romancoke Rd 21666 410-643-7330
Dr. John Lischner, prin. Fax 643-7445
Stevensville MS 500/6-8
610 Main St 21666 410-643-3194
Kevin Kintop, prin. Fax 643-3046

Sudlersville, Queen Anne's, Pop. 476
Queen Anne's County SD
Supt. — See Centreville
Sudlersville MS 300/6-8
600 Charles St 21668 410-438-3151
Sean Kenna, prin. Fax 438-3489

Suitland, Prince George's, Pop. 25,409
Prince George's County SD
Supt. — See Upper Marlboro
Drew-Freeman MS 700/7-8
2600 Brooks Dr 20746 301-817-0900
LeTrecia Gloster, prin. Fax 817-0915
Green Valley Academy 100/Alt
2001 Shadyside Ave 20746 301-817-3100
Gordon Libby, prin. Fax 817-3176

Sykesville, Carroll, Pop. 4,375
Carroll County SD
Supt. — See Westminster
Century HS 1,100/9-12
355 Ronsdale Rd 21784 410-386-4400
Troy Barnes, prin. Fax 386-4413
Oklahoma Road MS 800/6-8
6300 Oklahoma Rd 21784 410-751-3600
Erin Brilhart, prin. Fax 751-3604

South Carroll HS 1,100/9-12
1300 W Old Liberty Rd 21784 410-751-3575
Diane Cooper, prin. Fax 751-3587
Sykesville MS 800/6-8
7301 Springfield Ave 21784 410-751-3545
Christian Roemer, prin. Fax 751-3573

Takoma Park, Montgomery, Pop. 16,094

Don Bosco Cristo Rey HS 300/9-12
1010 Larch Ave 20912 301-891-4750
Larry Savoy, prin. Fax 270-1459
Montgomery College Post-Sec.
7600 Takoma Ave 20912 240-567-5000
Takoma Academy 200/9-12
8120 Carroll Ave 20912 301-434-4700
Carla Thrower, prin. Fax 434-4814
Washington Adventist Hospital Post-Sec.
7600 Carroll Ave 20912 301-891-7600
Washington Adventist University Post-Sec.
7600 Flower Ave 20912 301-891-4000

Taneytown, Carroll, Pop. 6,558
Carroll County SD
Supt. — See Westminster
Northwest MS 500/6-8
99 Kings Dr 21787 410-751-3270
David Watkins, prin. Fax 751-3275

Temple Hills, Prince George's, Pop. 7,677
Prince George's County SD
Supt. — See Upper Marlboro
Crossland HS 1,100/9-12
6901 Temple Hill Rd 20748 301-449-4800
Theresa Moseley-Fax, prin. Fax 449-4801
Marshall MS 700/6-8
4909 Brinkley Rd 20748 301-702-7540
DeMarco Clark, prin. Fax 702-7555
Stoddert MS 600/6-8
2501 Olson St 20748 301-702-7500
Michael Gilchrist, prin. Fax 702-7515
Crossland Evening HS Adult
6901 Temple Hill Rd 20748 301-449-4994
William Kitchings, prin. Fax 449-2126

Thurmont, Frederick, Pop. 6,091
Frederick County SD
Supt. — See Frederick
Catoctin HS 1,000/9-12
14745 Sabillasville Rd 21788 240-236-8100
Bernard Quesada, prin. Fax 236-8101
Thurmont MS 600/6-8
408 E Main St 21788 240-236-5100
Jennifer Powell, prin. Fax 236-5101

Timonium, Baltimore, Pop. 9,759
Baltimore County SD
Supt. — See Towson
Dulaney HS 1,900/9-12
255 E Padonia Rd 21093 410-887-7633
Samuel Wynkoop, prin. Fax 666-8915

R. Paul Academy of Cosmetology Arts/Sci Post-Sec.
1811 York Rd Ste B 21093 410-252-4481

Towson, Baltimore, Pop. 54,024
Baltimore County SD 106,800/PK-12
6901 N Charles St 21204 410-887-4554
S. Dallas Dance Ph.D., supt. Fax 887-4309
www.bcps.org
Other Schools – See Baltimore, Catonsville, Cockeysville, Dundalk, Lutherville, Monkton, Owings Mills, Parkton, Parkville, Randallstown, Reisterstown, Timonium

---

Brightwood College Post-Sec.
803 Glen Eagles Ct 21286 410-296-5350
Concordia Prep S 300/6-12
1145 Concordia Dr 21286 410-825-2323
Alan Freeman, admin. Fax 825-2506
Loyola Blakefield HS 1,000/6-12
500 Chestnut Ave 21204 410-823-0601
Anthony Day, pres. Fax 823-5277
Medix School Post-Sec.
700 York Rd 21204 410-337-5155
Notre Dame Preparatory S 800/6-12
815 Hampton Ln 21286 410-825-0590
Laurie Jones, prin. Fax 321-4809
Towson State University Post-Sec.
8000 York Rd 21252 410-704-2000

Union Bridge, Carroll, Pop. 956
Carroll County SD
Supt. — See Westminster
Key HS 1,000/9-12
3825 Bark Hill Rd 21791 410-751-3320
John Baugher, prin. Fax 751-3325

Upper Marlboro, Prince George's, Pop. 606
Prince George's County SD 121,700/PK-12
14201 School Ln 20772 301-952-6000
Dr. Kevin Maxwell, admin. Fax 627-6576
www.pgcps.org
Douglass HS 1,000/9-12
8000 Croom Rd 20772 301-952-2400
Eddie Scott, prin. Fax 627-3377
Kettering MS 500/6-8
65 Herrington Dr 20774 301-808-4060
Amin Salaam, prin. Fax 499-3128
Largo HS 1,100/9-12
505 Largo Rd 20774 301-808-8880
Afie Mirshah-Nayar, prin. Fax 808-4066
Madison MS 800/6-8
7300 Woodyard Rd 20772 301-599-2422
Courtney King, prin. Fax 599-2562
Wise HS 2,300/9-12
12650 Brooke Ln 20772 301-780-2100
Charoscar Coleman, prin. Fax 780-2112

Other Schools – See Accokeek, Adelphi, Beltsville, Bladensburg, Bowie, Brandywine, Capitol Heights, Cheltenham, Clinton, Forestville, Fort Washington, Greenbelt, Hyattsville, Landover, Lanham Seabrook, Largo, Laurel, Mitchellville, New Carrollton, Oxon Hill, Riverdale, Springdale, Suitland, Temple Hills

---

Capitol Christian Academy 100/7-12
610 Largo Rd 20774 240-223-2467
Clinton Christian S 500/PK-12
6707 Woodyard Rd 20772 301-599-9600
Chanda Stephenson, prin. Fax 599-9603
Riverdale Baptist S 700/PK-12
1133 Largo Rd 20774 301-249-7000
Eric Harrison, head sch Fax 249-3425

Waldorf, Charles, Pop. 64,982
Charles County SD
Supt. — See La Plata
Davis MS 900/6-8
2495 Davis Rd 20603 301-638-0858
Kimberly McClarin, prin. Fax 638-3562
Hanson MS 800/6-8
3165 John Hanson Dr 20601 301-645-4520
Susan McCormick, prin. Fax 870-1182
Mattawoman MS 900/6-8
10145 Berry Rd 20603 301-645-7708
Sonia Jones, prin. Fax 638-0043
North Point HS 2,200/9-12
2500 Davis Rd 20603 301-753-1759
Michael Simms, prin. Fax 885-2347
St. Charles HS 900/9-12
5305 Piney Church Rd 20602 301-753-2090
Richard Conley, prin. Fax 396-4135
Stoddert MS 700/6-8
2040 Saint Thomas Dr 20602 301-645-1334
Kenneth Schroeck, prin. Fax 870-1183
Stone HS 1,300/9-12
3785 Leonardtown Rd 20601 301-645-2601
Chrystal Benson, prin. Fax 932-4278
Westlake HS 1,400/9-12
3300 Middletown Rd 20603 301-645-8857
Michael Meiser, prin. Fax 932-8583

Aaron's Academy of Beauty Post-Sec.
11690 Doolittle Dr 20602 301-645-3681
Grace Christian Academy of Maryland 400/PK-12
13000 Zekiah Dr 20601 301-645-0406
Dr. Lorne Wenzel, dir. Fax 645-7463

Walkersville, Frederick, Pop. 5,663
Frederick County SD
Supt. — See Frederick
Walkersville HS 1,100/9-12
81 W Frederick St 21793 240-236-7200
Tracey Franklin, prin. Fax 236-7250
Walkersville MS 800/6-8
55 W Frederick St 21793 240-236-4400
Stacey Hiltner, prin. Fax 236-4401

Westminster, Carroll, Pop. 18,162
Carroll County SD 24,800/PK-12
125 N Court St 21157 410-751-3000
Stephen Guthrie, supt. Fax 751-3030
www.carrollk12.org/
Carroll County Career & Technology Ctr Vo/Tech
1229 Washington Rd 21157 410-751-3669
William Eckles, prin. Fax 751-3677
Crossroads MS 50/Alt
45 Kate Wagner Rd 21157 410-751-3691
Bryan Wetzel, prin.
Gateway S 100/Alt
45 Kate Wagner Rd 21157 410-751-3691
Bryan Wetzel, admin. Fax 751-3687
Westminster East MS 700/6-8
121 Longwell Ave 21157 410-751-3656
James Carver, prin. Fax 751-3660
Westminster HS 1,600/9-12
1225 Washington Rd 21157 410-751-3630
Jeffrey Hopkins, prin. Fax 751-3640
Westminster West MS 900/6-8
60 Monroe St 21157 410-751-3661
Amy Gromada, prin. Fax 751-3667
Winters Mill HS 1,100/9-12
560 Gorsuch Rd 21157 410-386-1500
Eric King, prin. Fax 386-1513
Other Schools – See Eldersburg, Hampstead, Manchester, Mount Airy, Sykesville, Taneytown, Union Bridge

---

Carroll Community College Post-Sec.
1601 Washington Rd 21157 410-386-8000
McDaniel College Post-Sec.
2 College Hl 21157 410-848-7000

Westover, Somerset
Somerset County SD 3,200/PK-12
7982A Tawes Campus Dr 21871 410-651-1616
Dr. John Gaddis, supt. Fax 651-2931
www.somerset.k12.md.us
Tawes Technology & Career Center Vo/Tech
7982 Crisfield Hwy 21871 410-651-2285
Keith O'Neal, prin. Fax 651-3154
Other Schools – See Crisfield, Marion Station, Princess Anne

Holly Grove Christian S 500/PK-12
7317 Mennonite Church Rd 21871 410-957-0222
Michael Rohrer, prin. Fax 957-4250

White Plains, Charles, Pop. 3,560

Southern Maryland Christian Academy 300/PK-12
PO Box 1668 20695 301-870-2550
Matthew Gaines, dir. Fax 934-2855

Williamsport, Washington, Pop. 2,115
Washington County SD
Supt. — See Hagerstown
Springfield MS 900/6-8
334 Sunset Ave 21795 301-766-8389
Jennifer Ruppenthal, prin. Fax 766-8401
Williamsport HS 900/9-12
5 S Clifton Dr 21795 301-766-8423
Heath Wilcox, prin. Fax 223-9610

Worton, Kent, Pop. 248
Kent County SD
Supt. — See Rock Hall
Kent County HS 600/9-12
25301 Lambs Meadow Rd 21678 410-778-4540
Tracey Williams, prin. Fax 778-4266

Wye Mills, Talbot

Chesapeake College Post-Sec.
PO Box 8 21679 410-822-5400

MASSACHUSETTS

MASSACHUSETTS DEPARTMENT OF EDUCATION
75 Pleasant St, Malden 02148-4906
Telephone 781-388-3000
Fax 781-388-3770
Website http://www.doe.mass.edu

Commissioner of Education Mitchell Chester

MASSACHUSETTS BOARD OF EDUCATION
75 Pleasant St, Malden 02148-4906

Chairperson Paul Sagan

PUBLIC, PRIVATE AND CATHOLIC SECONDARY SCHOOLS

Abington, Plymouth, Pop. 15,563
Abington SD 2,000/PK-12
171 Adams St 02351 781-982-2150
Peter Schafer, supt. Fax 982-2157
www.abingtonps.org
Abington HS 500/9-12
201 Gliniewicz Way 02351 781-982-2160
Teresa Sullivan-Cruz, prin. Fax 982-0061
Frolio MS 300/7-8
1071 Washington St 02351 781-982-2170
Matthew MacCurtain, prin. Fax 982-2173

Acton, Middlesex
Acton-Boxborough Regional SD 5,800/PK-12
16 Charter Rd 01720 978-264-4700
Glenn Brand, supt. Fax 264-3340
www.abschools.org
Acton-Boxborough Regional HS 2,000/9-12
36 Charter Rd 01720 978-264-4700
JoAnn Campbell, prin. Fax 264-3345
Grey JHS 900/7-8
16 Charter Rd 01720 978-264-4700
Andrew Shen, prin. Fax 264-3343

Acushnet, Bristol, Pop. 3,170
Acushnet SD 1,000/PK-8
708 Middle Rd Ste 1 02743 508-998-0260
Stephen Donovan Ed.D., supt. Fax 998-0262
www.acushnetschools.us
Ford MS 500/5-8
708 Middle Rd 02743 508-998-0265
Fax 998-7316

Agawam, Hampden, Pop. 28,599
Agawam SD
Supt. — See Feeding Hills
Agawam HS 1,300/9-12
760 Cooper St 01001 413-821-0521
Steven Lemanski, prin. Fax 821-0536
Doering S 600/5-8
68 Main St 01001 413-789-1400
Susan Federico, prin. Fax 789-7337

Amesbury, Essex, Pop. 12,109
Amesbury SD 2,300/PK-12
5 Highland St 01913 978-388-0507
Gary S. Reese Ed.D., supt. Fax 388-8315
schools.amesburyma.gov
Amesbury HS 600/9-12
5 Highland St 01913 978-388-4800
Norman Hamond, prin. Fax 388-3393
Amesbury MS 700/5-8
220 Main St 01913 978-388-0515
Michael Curry, prin. Fax 388-1626

Sparhawk S 200/K-12
4 Noel St 01913 978-388-5354
Louise Stilphen, hdmstr. Fax 499-4303

Amherst, Hampshire, Pop. 17,824
Amherst-Pelham SD 1,500/7-12
170 Chestnut St 01002 413-362-1810
Fax 549-6108
www.arps.org
Amherst Regional HS 1,000/9-12
21 Mattoon St 01002 413-362-1700
Mark Jackson, prin. Fax 549-9704
Amherst Regional MS 500/7-8
170 Chestnut St 01002 413-362-1850
Patty Bode, prin. Fax 549-9812

Amherst College Post-Sec.
PO Box 5000 01002 413-542-2000
Hampshire College Post-Sec.
893 West St 01002 413-549-4600
University of Massachusetts 01003 Post-Sec.
413-545-0111

Andover, Essex, Pop. 8,592
Andover SD 5,900/PK-12
36 Bartlet St 01810 978-623-8501
Sheldon Berman Ed.D., supt. Fax 623-8505
www.aps1.net
Andover HS 1,800/9-12
80 Shawsheen Rd 01810 978-623-8632
Philip Conrad, prin. Fax 623-8636
Andover West MS 600/6-8
70 Shawsheen Rd 01810 978-623-8700
Rebecca Franks, prin. Fax 623-8720
Doherty MS 600/6-8
50 Bartlet St 01810 978-623-8750
Robin Wilson, prin. Fax 623-8770
Wood Hill MS 400/6-8
11 Cross St 01810 978-623-8925
Patrick Bucco, prin. Fax 623-8929

Greater Lawrence Technical SD
57 River Rd 01810 978-686-0194
John Lavoie, supt. Fax 687-6209
www.glts.net
Greater Lawrence Technical S Vo/Tech
57 River Rd 01810 978-686-0194
Elizabeth Freedman, prin. Fax 687-6209

Massachusetts School of Law at Andover Post-Sec.
500 Federal St 01810 978-681-0800
Phillips Academy 1,100/9-12
180 Main St 01810 978-749-4000
John Palfrey, head sch Fax 749-4068

Arlington, Middlesex, Pop. 41,750
Arlington SD 5,000/PK-12
869 Massachusetts Ave 02476 781-316-3523
Kathleen Bodie, supt. Fax 316-3509
www.arlington.k12.ma.us
Arlington HS 1,200/9-12
869 Massachusetts Ave 02476 781-316-3591
Matthew Janger, prin. Fax 316-3504
Ottoson MS 1,100/6-8
63 Acton St 02476 781-316-3745
Eileen Woods, prin. Fax 641-5436

Arlington Catholic HS 700/9-12
16 Medford St 02474 781-646-7770
Stephen Biagioni, prin. Fax 648-8345

Ashburnham, Worcester
Ashburnham-Westminster Regional SD 2,300/PK-12
11 Oakmont Dr 01430 978-827-1434
Dr. Gary Mazzola, supt. Fax 827-5969
www.awrsd.org
Oakmont Regional HS 700/9-12
9 Oakmont Dr 01430 978-827-5907
David Uminski, prin. Fax 827-1413
Overlook MS 600/6-8
10 Oakmont Dr 01430 978-827-1425
Philip Saisa, prin. Fax 827-1423

Cushing Academy 400/9-12
PO Box 8000 01430 978-827-7000
Christopher Torino, hdmstr. Fax 827-7500

Ashland, Middlesex, Pop. 12,066
Ashland SD 2,600/PK-12
87 W Union St 01721 508-881-0150
James Adams, supt. Fax 881-0161
www.ashland.k12.ma.us
Ashland HS 700/9-12
65 E Union St 01721 508-881-0177
Kelley St. Coeur, prin. Fax 881-0186
Ashland MS 500/6-8
87 W Union St 01721 508-881-0167
David DiGirolamo, prin. Fax 881-0169

Athol, Worcester, Pop. 8,127
Athol-Royalston SD 1,200/PK-12
1062 Pleasant St 01331 978-249-2400
Dr. Steven Meyer, supt. Fax 249-2402
www.arrsd.org
Athol HS 400/9-12
2363 Main St 01331 978-249-2435
Mitchel Aho, prin. Fax 249-7217
Athol-Royalston MS 400/5-8
1062 Pleasant St 01331 978-249-2430
Thomas Telicki, prin. Fax 249-0055

Attleboro, Bristol, Pop. 42,657
Attleboro SD 5,900/PK-12
100 Rathbun Willard Dr 02703 508-222-0012
David Sawyer, supt. Fax 223-1577
www.attleboroschools.com
Attleboro HS 1,700/9-12
100 Rathbun Willard Dr 02703 508-222-5150
William Runey, prin. Fax 223-1579
Brennan MS 600/5-8
320 Rathbun Willard Dr 02703 508-222-6260
Frederick Souza, prin. Fax 223-1555
Coelho MS 600/5-8
99 Brown St 02703 508-761-7551
Andrew Boles, prin. Fax 399-6506
Wamsutta MS 500/5-8
300 Locust St 02703 508-223-1540
Joseph Connor, prin. Fax 226-2087

Bishop Feehan HS 1,000/9-12
70 Holcott Dr 02703 508-226-6223
Sean Kane, pres. Fax 226-7696

Auburn, Worcester, Pop. 15,005
Auburn SD 2,400/K-12
5 West St 01501 508-832-7755
Maryellen Brunelle Ed.D., supt. Fax 832-7757
www.auburn.k12.ma.us
Auburn HS 600/9-12
99 Auburn St 01501 508-832-7711
Casey Handfield, prin. Fax 832-7710
Auburn MS 600/6-8
9 West St 01501 508-832-7722
Joseph Gagnon, prin. Fax 832-8655

Avon, Norfolk, Pop. 4,558
Avon SD 700/PK-12
1 Patrick Clark Dr 02322 508-588-0230
Paul Zinni, supt. Fax 559-1081
www.apps.avon.k12.ma.us
Avon MSHS 300/7-12
285 W Main St 02322 508-583-4822
Dawn Stockwell, prin. Fax 588-5501

Ayer, Middlesex, Pop. 2,780
Ayer Shirley SD 1,700/PK-12
115 Washington St 01432 978-772-8600
Dr. Mary Malone, supt. Fax 772-1863
www.asrsd.org
Ayer Shirley HS 300/9-12
141 Washington St 01432 978-772-8600
Albert Varga, prin. Fax 772-8615
Other Schools – See Shirley

Babson Park, Norfolk

Babson College Post-Sec.
231 Forest St 02457 781-235-1200

Baldwinville, Worcester, Pop. 2,008
Narragansett Regional SD 1,300/PK-12
462 Baldwinville Rd 01436 978-939-5661
Dr. Chris Casavant, supt. Fax 939-5179
www.nrsd.org
Narragansett MS 500/5-8
460 Baldwinville Rd 01436 978-393-5928
Dr. Peter Cushing, prin. Fax 939-8422
Narragansett Regional HS 400/9-12
464 Baldwinville Rd 01436 978-939-5388
Mandy Vasil, prin. Fax 939-5723

Barnstable, Barnstable, Pop. 48,854

Trinity Christian Academy 100/PK-12
979 Mary Dunn Rd 02630 508-790-0114
Ben Haskell, hdmstr. Fax 790-1293

Barre, Worcester, Pop. 998
Quabbin SD 2,400/PK-12
872 South St 01005 978-355-4668
Dr. Maureen Marshall, supt. Fax 355-6756
www.qrsd.org
Quabbin Regional HS 700/9-12
800 South St 01005 978-355-4651
Gregory Devine, prin. Fax 355-0163

Quabbin Regional MS 400/7-8
800 South St 01005 978-355-5042
Susanne Musnicki, prin. Fax 355-6104

Bedford, Middlesex, Pop. 12,996
Bedford SD 2,500/K-12
97 McMahon Rd 01730 781-275-7588
Jonathan Sills, supt. Fax 275-0885
www.bedford.k12.ma.us
Bedford HS 900/9-12
9 Mudge Way 01730 781-275-1700
Heather Galante, prin. Fax 275-6664
Glenn MS 600/6-8
99 McMahon Rd 01730 781-275-3201
Kevin Tracey, prin. Fax 275-7632

Middlesex Community College Post-Sec.
591 Springs Rd 01730 781-280-3200
National Aviation Academy of New England Post-Sec.
150 Hanscom Dr 01730 781-274-8448

Belchertown, Hampshire, Pop. 2,339
Belchertown SD 2,400/PK-12
PO Box 841 01007 413-323-0423
Karol Coffin, supt. Fax 323-0448
www.belchertownps.org
Belchertown HS 700/9-12
142 Springfield Rd 01007 413-323-9419
Christine Vigneux, prin. Fax 323-9406
Jabish Brook MS 400/7-8
62 N Washington St 01007 413-323-0433
Thomas Ruscio, prin. Fax 323-0450

Bellingham, Norfolk, Pop. 4,778
Bellingham SD 1,900/PK-12
4 Mechanic St 02019 508-883-1706
Peter Marano, supt. Fax 966-2402
www.edlinesites.net/pages/Bellingham_Public_Schools
Bellingham HS 600/8-12
60 Blackstone St 02019 508-966-3761
Lucas Giguere, prin. Fax 966-4182

Belmont, Middlesex, Pop. 24,057
Belmont SD 4,200/PK-12
644 Pleasant St 02478 617-993-5401
John Phelan, supt. Fax 993-5409
www.belmont.k12.ma.us
Belmont HS 1,200/9-12
221 Concord Ave 02478 617-993-5301
Dan Richards, prin. Fax 993-5909
Chenery MS 1,300/5-8
95 Washington St 02478 617-993-5800
Michael McAllister, prin. Fax 993-5809

Belmont Hill S 400/7-12
350 Prospect St 02478 617-484-4410
Dr. Richard Melvoin, hdmstr. Fax 484-4688
Waldorf HS of Massachusetts Bay 100/9-12
160 Lexington St 02478 617-489-6600
Mara White, admin. Fax 489-6619

Berkley, Bristol
Berkley SD 900/PK-8
21 N Main St 02779 508-822-5220
Thomas Lynch, supt. Fax 823-1772
www.berkleypublicschools.org
Berkley MS 400/5-8
21 N Main St 02779 508-884-9434
Kimberly Hebert, prin. Fax 386-1044

Beverly, Essex, Pop. 38,805
Beverly SD 4,300/PK-12
70 Balch St 01915 978-921-6100
Dr. Steven Hiersche Ed.D., supt. Fax 922-6597
www.beverlyschools.org/index2.shtm
Beverly HS 1,300/9-12
100 Sohier Rd 01915 978-921-6132
Elizabeth Taylor, prin. Fax 927-9460
Briscoe MS 900/6-8
7 Sohier Rd 01915 978-921-6103
Matthew Poska, prin. Fax 927-7781

Endicott College Post-Sec.
376 Hale St 01915 978-927-0585
Montserrat College of Art Post-Sec.
23 Essex St 01915 978-921-4242
Waring S 200/6-12
35 Standley St 01915 978-927-8793
Tim Bakland, hdmstr. Fax 921-2107

Billerica, Middlesex, Pop. 37,609
Billerica SD 5,200/K-12
365 Boston Rd 01821 978-528-7900
Tim Piwowar, supt. Fax 528-7909
www.billerica.k12.ma.us
Billerica Memorial HS 1,400/9-12
35 River St 01821 978-528-8710
Thomas Murphy, prin. Fax 528-8719
Locke MS 700/6-8
110 Allen Rd 01821 978-528-8650
Anthony Garas, prin. Fax 528-8659
Marshall MS 700/6-8
15 Floyd St 01821 978-528-8670
Michael Rossi, prin. Fax 528-8679

Shawsheen Valley Vocational Technical SD
100 Cook St 01821 978-667-2111
Timothy Broadrick, supt. Fax 663-6272
www.shawsheentech.org
Shawsheen Valley Technical HS Vo/Tech
100 Cook St 01821 978-667-2111
Dr. Robert Kanellas, prin. Fax 663-6272

Blackstone, Worcester, Pop. 8,023
Blackstone-Millville Regional SD 1,700/PK-12
175 Lincoln St 01504 508-883-4400
Allen Himmelberger, supt. Fax 883-9892
www.bmrsd.info
Blackstone-Millville Regional HS 500/9-12
175 Lincoln St 01504 508-876-0117
Michael Dudek, prin. Fax 876-1035
Hartnett MS 500/6-8
35 Federal St 01504 508-876-0190
Justin Cameron, prin. Fax 876-0198

Bolton, Worcester
Nashoba Regional SD 3,400/PK-12
50 Mechanic St 01740 978-779-0539
Brooke Clenchy, supt. Fax 779-5537
www.nrsd.net
Nashoba Regional HS 1,000/9-12
12 Green Rd 01740 978-779-2257
Parry Graham, prin. Fax 779-2720
Other Schools – See Lancaster, Stow

Boston, Suffolk, Pop. 592,375
Boston SD 54,400/PK-12
2300 Washington St 02119 617-635-9000
Tommy Chang, supt. Fax 635-9059
www.bostonpublicschools.org
Boston Arts Academy 400/9-12
174 Ipswich St 02215 617-635-6470
Anne Clark, hdmstr. Fax 635-8854
Boston Latin S 2,400/7-12
78 Avenue Louis Pasteur 02115 617-635-8895
Michael Contompasis, hdmstr. Fax 635-7883
Quincy Upper S 500/6-12
152 Arlington St 02116 617-635-8940
Richard Chang, prin. Fax 635-8945
Snowden International HS 400/9-12
150 Newbury St 02116 617-635-9989
Eugene Roundtree, hdmstr. Fax 635-9996
Boston Adult Technical Academy Adult
20 Church St 02116 617-635-1542
Benjamin Helfat, hdmstr. Fax 635-6362
Other Schools – See Brighton, Charlestown, Dorchester, East Boston, Hyde Park, Jamaica Plain, Roslindale, Roxbury, South Boston, West Roxbury

---

Bay State College Post-Sec.
122 Commonwealth Ave 02116 617-217-9000
Benjamin Franklin Inst. of Technology Post-Sec.
41 Berkeley St 02116 617-423-4630
Berklee College of Music Post-Sec.
1140 Boylston St 02215 617-266-1400
Beth Israel Healthcare Post-Sec.
330 Brookline Ave 02215 617-667-2539
Blaine The Beauty Career School Post-Sec.
30 West St 02111 617-266-2661
Boston Architectural College Post-Sec.
320 Newbury St 02115 617-262-5000
Boston Baptist College Post-Sec.
950 Metropolitan Ave 02136 617-364-3510
Boston College HS 1,600/7-12
150 William T Morrissey 02125 617-436-3900
Stephen Hughes, prin. Fax 474-5105
Boston Conservatory Post-Sec.
8 Fenway 02215 617-536-6340
Boston Trinity Academy 200/6-12
17 Hale St 02136 617-364-3700
Frank Guerra, hdmstr. Fax 364-3800
Boston University Post-Sec.
233 Bay State Rd 02215 617-353-2000
Boston University Academy 200/9-12
1 University Rd 02215 617-353-9000
Dr. Ari Betof, head sch Fax 353-8999
Brigham and Women's Hospital Post-Sec.
75 Francis St 02115 617-732-7493
British International S of Boston 300/PK-12
416 Pond St 02130 617-522-2261
Darren Nicholas, hdmstr. Fax 522-0385
Bunker Hill Community College Post-Sec.
250 Rutherford Ave 02129 617-228-2000
Cathedral HS 300/7-12
74 Union Park St 02118 617-542-2325
Dr. Oscar Santos, head sch Fax 542-1745
Children's Hospital Post-Sec.
300 Longwood Ave 02115 617-355-6433
Commonwealth S 200/9-12
151 Commonwealth Ave 02116 617-266-7525
William Wharton, head sch Fax 266-5769
Cristo Rey HS 300/9-12
100 Savin Hill Ave 02125 617-825-2580
Elizabeth Degnan, prin. Fax 825-2613
Emerson College Post-Sec.
120 Boylston St 02116 617-824-8500
Emmanuel College Post-Sec.
400 Fenway 02115 617-735-9715
Fisher College Post-Sec.
118 Beacon St 02116 617-236-8800
Massachusetts College of Art and Design Post-Sec.
621 Huntington Ave 02115 617-879-7000
MCPHS University Post-Sec.
179 Longwood Ave 02115 617-732-2800
MGH Institute of Health Professions Post-Sec.
36 1st Ave 02129 617-726-2947
New England College of Business/Finance Post-Sec.
10 High St Ste 204 02110 617-951-2350
New England College of Optometry Post-Sec.
424 Beacon St 02115 800-824-5526
New England Conservatory of Music Post-Sec.
290 Huntington Ave 02115 617-585-1100
New England Law \ Boston Post-Sec.
154 Stuart St 02116 617-451-0010
New England School of Art & Design Post-Sec.
75 Arlington St 02116 617-573-8785
New England School of Photography Post-Sec.
537 Commonwealth Ave 02215 617-437-1868
Newman Preparatory S 300/9-12
247 Marlborough St 02116 617-267-4530
Harry Lynch, hdmstr. Fax 267-7070
North Bennet Street School Post-Sec.
150 North St 02109 617-227-0155
Northeastern University Post-Sec.
360 Huntington Ave 02115 617-373-2000
St. Joseph Preparatory HS 200/9-12
617 Cambridge St 02134 617-254-8383
Thomas Nunan, head sch Fax 254-0240
School of the Museum of Fine Arts Post-Sec.
230 Fenway 02115 617-267-6100
Simmons College Post-Sec.
300 Fenway 02115 617-521-2000
Suffolk University Post-Sec.
8 Ashburton Pl 02108 617-573-8000
University of Massachusetts Boston Post-Sec.
100 William T Mrrissey Blvd 02125 617-287-5000
Urban College of Boston Post-Sec.
178 Tremont St 02111 617-348-6359
Veterans Administration Medical Center Post-Sec.
150 S Huntington Ave 02130 617-232-9500
Wentworth Institute of Technology Post-Sec.
550 Huntington Ave 02115 617-989-4590
Wheelock College Post-Sec.
200 Riverway 02215 617-879-2000
Winsor S 400/5-12
103 Pilgrim Rd 02215 617-735-9500
Dr. Sarah Pelmas, head sch Fax 912-1381

Bourne, Barnstable, Pop. 1,380
Bourne SD 2,000/PK-12
36 Sandwich Rd 02532 508-759-0660
Steven Lamarche, supt. Fax 759-1107
www.bourneps.org
Bourne HS 500/9-12
75 Waterhouse Rd 02532 508-759-0670
Amy Cetner, prin. Fax 759-0677
Bourne MS 700/5-8
77 Waterhouse Rd 02532 508-759-0690
Melissa Stafford, prin. Fax 759-0695

Upper Cape Cod Regional Vo-Tech SD
220 Sandwich Rd 02532 508-759-7711
Dr. Robert Dutch, supt. Fax 759-7208
www.uppercapetech.com
Upper Cape Cod Regional Technical S Vo/Tech
220 Sandwich Rd 02532 508-759-7711
Roger Forget, prin. Fax 759-7208

Boxford, Essex, Pop. 2,307
Masconomet SD 2,000/7-12
20 Endicott Rd 01921 978-887-2323
Kevin Lyons, supt. Fax 887-3573
www.masconomet.org
Masconomet Regional HS 1,400/9-12
20 Endicott Rd 01921 978-887-2323
Laurie Hodgdon, prin. Fax 887-7243
Masconomet Regional MS 700/7-8
20 Endicott Rd 01921 978-887-2323
Dorothy Flaherty, prin. Fax 887-1991

Boylston, Worcester
Berlin-Boylston SD 1,000/K-12
215 Main St 01505 508-869-2837
Nadine Ekstrom, supt. Fax 869-0023
www.bbrsd.org
Tahanto Regional MSHS 500/6-12
1001 Main St 01505 508-869-2333
Diane Tucceri, prin. Fax 869-0175

Bradford, See Haverhill

Bradford Christian Academy 100/1-12
97 Oxford Ave 01835 978-373-7900
Victoria Kennedy, head sch Fax 373-7977

Braintree, Norfolk, Pop. 33,800
Braintree SD 5,500/K-12
348 Pond St 02184 781-380-0130
Frank Hackett Ed.D., supt. Fax 380-0146
www.braintreeschools.org
Braintree HS 1,600/9-12
128 Town St 02184 781-848-4000
James Lee, hdmstr. Fax 380-0116
East MS 700/6-8
305 River St 02184 781-380-0170
John Sheehan, prin. Fax 848-4522
South MS 700/6-8
232 Peach St 02184 781-380-0160
Damon Rainie, prin. Fax 380-0164

Archbishop Williams HS 500/9-12
80 Independence Ave 02184 781-843-3636
Dr. Carmen Mariano, prin. Fax 843-3782
CATS Academy Boston 200/9-12
2001 Washington St 02184 857-400-9700
Steven Bliss, head sch Fax 400-9704
Thayer Academy 700/6-12
745 Washington St 02184 781-843-3580
Ted Koskores, hdmstr. Fax 843-2916

Bridgewater, Plymouth, Pop. 7,639
Bridgewater-Raynham Regional SD 5,400/PK-12
166 Mount Prospect St 02324 508-279-2140
Derek Swenson, supt. Fax 697-7012
www.bridge-rayn.org
Bridgewater MS 600/7-8
166 Mount Prospect St 02324 508-279-2100
Lynn Bastoni, prin. Fax 279-2104
Bridgewater-Raynham Regional HS 1,500/9-12
415 Center St 02324 508-697-6902
Angela Watson, prin. Fax 279-2110
Other Schools – See Raynham

Bridgewater State University Post-Sec.
131 Summer St 02325 508-531-1000

Brighton, See Boston
Boston SD
Supt. — See Boston
Another Course to College S 200/9-12
20 Warren St 02135 617-635-8865
Michele Pellam, hdmstr. Fax 635-8866

Brighton HS 1,000/9-12
25 Warren St 02135 617-635-9873
Emily Bozeman, hdmstr. Fax 635-9892
Lyon HS 100/9-12
95 Beechcroft St 02135 617-635-8351
Jean-Dominique Anoh, prin. Fax 635-8353

Bais Yaakov of Boston HS 50/9-12
PO Box 351004 02135 617-254-7547
Rabbi Tsvi Yehuda Levin, prin. Fax 254-7549
Everest Institute Post-Sec.
1505 Commonwealth Ave 02135 888-741-4270
Margolis Mesivta of Greater Boston 100/9-12
34 Sparhawk St 02135 617-779-0166
Moshe Wilhelm, prin. Fax 779-0266
Saint John's Seminary Post-Sec.
127 Lake St 02135 617-254-2610

Brockton, Plymouth, Pop. 79,948
Brockton SD 17,000/PK-12
43 Crescent St 02301 508-580-7000
Kathleen Smith, supt. Fax 580-7513
www.brocktonpublicschools.com
Ashfield MS 500/6-8
225 Coe Rd 02302 508-580-7268
Barbara Lovell, prin. Fax 580-7072
Brockton Champion HS 200/Alt
175 Warren Ave 02301 508-894-4377
Cynthia Burns, admin. Fax 894-4380
Brockton HS 4,100/9-12
470 Forest Ave 02301 508-580-7633
Michael Thomas, prin. Fax 580-7600
Douglass Academy 100/Alt
175 Warren Ave 02301 508-580-7033
Cynthia Burns, prin. Fax 580-7943
East MS 400/6-8
464 Centre St 02302 508-580-7351
Kelly Silva, prin. Fax 580-7090
Edison Academy 200/9-12
700 Belmont St 02301 508-580-7638
James Cobbs, prin. Fax 580-7987
Goddard Alternative S 100/Alt
20 Union St 02301 508-580-7203
John Lander, prin. Fax 580-7083
North MS 500/6-8
108 Oak St 02301 508-580-7371
Sean Ahern, prin. Fax 580-7088
Plouffe Academy 600/6-8
250 Crescent St 02302 508-894-4301
Michelle Nessralla, prin. Fax 894-4300
South MS 500/6-8
105 Keith Ave 02301 508-580-7311
Joseph Pomfret, prin. Fax 580-7089
West MS 600/6-8
271 West St 02301 508-580-7381
Clifford Murray, prin. Fax 580-7307
Adult Learning Center Adult
211 Crescent St 02302 508-580-7475
Kathleen Quinn, coord. Fax 580-7096

Ailano School of Cosmetology Post-Sec.
541 West St 02301 508-583-5433
Brockton Hospital Post-Sec.
680 Centre St 02302 508-941-7044
Cardinal Spellman HS 700/9-12
738 Court St 02302 508-583-6875
Paul Kelly, prin. Fax 580-1977
LaBaron Hairdressing Academy Post-Sec.
240 Liberty St 02301 508-583-1700
Lincoln Technical Institute Post-Sec.
365 Westgate Dr 02301 508-941-0730
Massasoit Community College Post-Sec.
1 Massasoit Blvd 02302 508-588-9100
Sullivan and Cogliano Training Center Post-Sec.
460 Belmont St 02301 508-584-9909
Trinity Catholic Academy - Upper Campus 200/4-8
37 Erie Ave 02302 508-583-6225
Kristin Blanchette, prin. Fax 583-6229

Brookline, Norfolk, Pop. 57,031
Brookline SD 6,800/PK-12
333 Washington St 02445 617-730-2401
Andrew Bott, supt. Fax 730-2601
www.brookline.k12.ma.us/
Brookline HS 1,800/9-12
115 Greenough St 02445 617-713-5000
Anthony Meyer, prin. Fax 713-5005
Devotion Upper S 5-8
194 Boylston St 02445
Monica Crowley, prin.

Boston Graduate Sch for Psychoanalysis Post-Sec.
1581 Beacon St 02446 617-277-3915
Dexter Southfield S 400/PK-12
20 Newton St 02445 617-522-5544
Todd Vincent, hdmstr. Fax 522-8166
Hellenic College/Holy Cross Sch Theology Post-Sec.
50 Goddard Ave 02445 617-731-3500
Maimonides S 500/K-12
34 Philbrick Rd 02445 617-232-4452
Rabbi Dov Huff, prin. Fax 566-2061
Newbury College Post-Sec.
129 Fisher Ave 02445 617-730-7000
New England Institute of Art Post-Sec.
10 Brookline Pl 02445 617-739-1700

Burlington, Middlesex, Pop. 24,055
Burlington SD 3,500/K-12
123 Cambridge St 01803 781-270-1800
Dr. Eric Conti, supt. Fax 270-1773
www.bpsk12.org
Burlington HS 1,000/9-12
123 Cambridge St 01803 781-270-1836
Mark Sullivan, prin. Fax 229-4893
Simonds MS 900/6-8
114 Winn St 01803 781-270-1781
Richard Connors, prin. Fax 229-4980

Buzzards Bay, Barnstable, Pop. 3,756

Massachusetts Maritime Academy Post-Sec.
101 Academy Dr 02532 508-830-5000

Byfield, Essex
Triton Regional SD 2,800/PK-12
112 Elm St 01922 978-465-2397
Brian Forget, supt. Fax 465-8599
www.tritonschools.org
Triton Regional HS 700/9-12
112 Elm St 01922 978-462-8171
Timothy Ruggere, prin. Fax 465-6868
Triton Regional MS 400/7-8
112 Elm St 01922 978-463-5845
Alan Macrae, prin. Fax 465-6868

Governor's Academy 400/9-12
1 Elm St 01922 978-465-1763
Dr. Peter Quimby, head sch Fax 463-9896

Cambridge, Middlesex, Pop. 100,799
Cambridge SD 6,300/PK-12
159 Thorndike St 02141 617-349-6400
Dr. Kenneth Salim, supt. Fax 349-6496
www.cpsd.us
Cambridge Rindge & Latin HS 1,700/9-12
459 Broadway 02138 617-349-6630
Damon Smith, prin. Fax 349-6749
Cambridge Street Upper S 300/6-8
158 Spring St 02141 617-349-3050
Manuel Fernandez, prin.
Putnam Avenue Upper S 200/6-8
100 Putnam Ave 02139 617-349-7780
Mirko Chardin, prin.
Rindge Avenue Upper S 300/6-8
70 Rindge Ave 02140 617-349-4060
Julie Craven, prin. Fax 349-6037
Vassal Lane Upper S 300/6-8
197 Vassal Ln 02138 617-349-6550
Daniel Coplon-Newfield, prin. Fax 349-6686

Buckingham Browne & Nichols S 1,000/PK-12
80 Gerrys Landing Rd 02138 617-800-2135
Geordie Mitchell M.Ed., admin.
Cambridge College Post-Sec.
1000 Massachusetts Ave 02138 617-868-1000
Cambridge School of Culinary Arts Post-Sec.
2020 Massachusetts Ave 02140 617-354-2020
Episcopal Divinity School Post-Sec.
99 Brattle St 02138 617-868-3450
Harvard University Post-Sec.
Massachusetts Hall 02138 617-495-1000
Hult International Business School Post-Sec.
1 Education St 02141 617-746-1990
International School of Boston 600/PK-12
45 Matignon Rd 02140 617-499-1451
Richard Ulffers, head sch Fax 499-1454
Le Cordon Bleu College of Culinary Arts Post-Sec.
215 1st St 02142 888-394-6222
Lesley University Post-Sec.
29 Everett St 02138 617-868-9600
Massachusetts Institute of Technology Post-Sec.
77 Massachusetts Ave 02139 617-253-1000
Matignon HS 400/9-12
1 Matignon Rd 02140 617-876-1212
Joseph DiSarcina, prin. Fax 661-3905
St. Paul's Choir S 50/4-8
29 Mount Auburn St 02138 617-868-8658
William McIvor, hdmstr. Fax 354-7092

Canton, Norfolk, Pop. 18,530
Blue Hills Regional Vocational SD
800 Randolph St 02021 781-828-5800
James Quaglia, supt. Fax 828-3872
www.bluehills.org
Blue Hills Regional Technical S Vo/Tech
800 Randolph St 02021 781-828-5800
Jill Rossetti, prin. Fax 828-3872

Canton SD 3,200/PK-12
960 Washington St 02021 781-821-5060
Jennifer Fischer-Mueller, supt. Fax 575-6500
www.cantonma.org
Canton HS 900/9-12
900 Washington St 02021 781-821-5050
Derek Folan, prin. Fax 821-5052
Galvin MS 800/6-8
55 Pecunit St 02021 781-821-5070
William Conard, prin. Fax 575-6509

Bay State School of Technology Post-Sec.
225 Turnpike St 02021 781-828-3434
Porter and Chester Institute Post-Sec.
5 Campanelli Cir 02021 781-830-0350

Carver, Plymouth
Carver SD 1,700/PK-12
3 Carver Square Blvd 02330 508-866-6160
Scott Knief, supt. Fax 866-2920
www.carver.org
Carver MSHS 900/6-12
60 S Meadow Rd 02330 508-866-6140
Janelle Holley, prin. Fax 866-5639

Charlemont, Franklin

Academy at Charlemont 100/7-12
1359 Route 2 E 01339 413-339-4912
Dr. Brian Bloomfield, hdmstr. Fax 339-4324

Charlestown, See Boston
Boston SD
Supt. — See Boston
Charlestown HS 900/9-12
240 Medford St 02129 617-635-9914
William Thomas, hdmstr. Fax 635-9928

Edwards MS 500/6-8
28 Walker St 02129 617-635-8516
Robert Rametti, prin. Fax 635-8522

Charlton, Worcester
Dudley-Charlton Regional SD
Supt. — See Dudley
Charlton MS 800/5-8
2 Oxford Rd 01507 508-248-1423
Dean Packard, prin. Fax 248-1418

Southern Worcester Co. Reg Vocational SD
57 Old Muggett Hill Rd 01507 508-248-5971
John Lafleche, supt. Fax 248-4747
www.baypath.net
Bay Path Regional Vocational Tech HS Vo/Tech
57 Old Muggett Hill Rd 01507 508-248-5971
Clifford Cloutier, prin. Fax 248-4747

Chatham, Barnstable, Pop. 1,395
Monomoy Regional SD 1,300/PK-12
425 Crowell Rd 02633 508-945-5130
Scott Carpenter, supt. Fax 945-5133
www.monomoy.edu/
Other Schools – See Harwich

Chelmsford, Middlesex, Pop. 33,858
Chelmsford SD 5,100/PK-12
230 North Rd 01824 978-251-5100
Dr. Jay Lang, supt. Fax 251-5110
www.chelmsford.k12.ma.us
McCarthy MS 900/5-8
250 North Rd 01824 978-251-5122
Kurt McPhee, prin. Fax 251-5130
Parker MS 700/5-8
75 Graniteville Rd 01824 978-251-5133
Dr. Jeffrey Parks, prin. Fax 251-5140
Other Schools – See North Chelmsford

Chelsea, Suffolk, Pop. 34,185
Chelsea SD 6,100/PK-12
500 Broadway 02150 617-466-4477
Mary Bourque, supt. Fax 889-8361
chelseaschools.com
Browne S 500/5-8
180 Walnut St 02150 617-466-5235
David Liebowitz, prin. Fax 889-8459
Chelsea HS 1,400/9-12
299 Everett Ave 02150 617-466-5000
Priti Johari, prin. Fax 889-8468
Clark Avenue S 600/5-8
8 Clark Ave 02150 617-466-5100
Michael Talbot, prin. Fax 889-7539
Wright Science & Technology Acad 500/5-8
180 Walnut St 02150 617-466-5240
Michelle Creamer, prin. Fax 889-8463

Everest Institute Post-Sec.
70 Everett Ave 02150 617-889-5999

Cheshire, Berkshire, Pop. 507
Adams-Cheshire Regional SD 1,400/PK-12
191 Church St 01225 413-743-2939
Robert Putnam, supt. Fax 743-4135
www.acrsd.net
Hoosac Valley HS 700/6-12
125 Savoy Rd 01225 413-743-5200
Jeremiah Ames, prin. Fax 743-8420

Chestnut Hill, See Newton

Beaver Country Day S 500/6-12
791 Hammond St 02467 617-738-2700
Peter Hutton, head sch Fax 738-2701
Boston College Post-Sec.
140 Commonwealth Ave 02467 617-552-8000
Brimmer and May S 400/PK-12
69 Middlesex Rd 02467 617-566-7462
Judy Guild, head sch Fax 734-5147
Pine Manor College Post-Sec.
400 Heath St 02467 617-731-7000

Chicopee, Hampden, Pop. 54,468
Chicopee SD 7,400/PK-12
180 Broadway St 01020 413-594-3410
Richard Rege, supt. Fax 594-3552
www.chicopeeps.org
Bellamy MS 900/6-8
314 Pendleton Ave 01020 413-594-3527
Matthew Francis, prin. Fax 594-1837
Chicopee Academy 100/Alt
12 DARE Way 01022 413-594-3449
John Leonard, prin. Fax 594-1863
Chicopee Comprehensive HS 1,400/9-12
617 Montgomery St 01020 413-594-3534
Derek Morrison, prin. Fax 594-3492
Chicopee HS 1,100/9-12
820 Front St 01020 413-594-3437
Roland Joyal, prin. Fax 594-3500
Dupont Memorial MS 6-8
650 Front St 01013 413-594-1881
Kristopher Theriault, prin. Fax 594-1897

College of Our Lady of Elms Post-Sec.
291 Springfield St 01013 413-594-2761
Pope Francis HS 9-12
134 Springfield St 01013 413-331-2480
Dr. Thomas McDowell, head sch Fax 331-2708
Porter and Chester Institute Post-Sec.
134 Dulong Cir 01022 413-593-3339

Clinton, Worcester, Pop. 7,209
Clinton SD 1,900/PK-12
150 School St 01510 978-365-4200
Terrance Ingano, supt. Fax 365-5037
clinton.k12.ma.us
Clinton HS 400/9-12
200 W Boylston St 01510 978-365-4208
James Hastings, prin. Fax 365-4237

Clinton MS 700/4-8
100 W Boylston St 01510 978-365-4220
Annmarie Sargent, prin. Fax 368-7256

Cohasset, Norfolk, Pop. 7,075
Cohasset SD 1,600/PK-12
143 Pond St 02025 781-383-6111
Louise Demas, supt. Fax 383-6507
www.cohassetk12.org
Cohasset MSHS 800/6-12
143 Pond St 02025 781-383-6100
Carolyn Connolly, prin. Fax 383-4168

Concord, Middlesex, Pop. 4,700
Concord SD 2,200/PK-8
120 Meriam Rd 01742 978-318-1500
Diana Rigby, supt. Fax 318-1537
www.concordps.org
Concord MS 700/6-8
835 Old Marlboro Rd 01742 978-318-1380
Drew Rosenshine, prin. Fax 318-1392

Concord-Carlisle SD 1,200/9-12
120 Meriam Rd 01742 978-318-1500
Diana Rigby, supt. Fax 318-1537
www.concordps.org
Concord-Carlisle HS 1,200/9-12
500 Walden St 01742 978-318-1400
Michael Mastrullo, prin. Fax 318-1435

Concord Academy 400/9-12
166 Main St 01742 978-402-2200
Richard G. Hardy, head sch Fax 402-2210
Fenn S 300/4-9
516 Monument St 01742 978-369-5800
Gerard J.G. Ward, admin. Fax 371-7520
Middlesex S 400/9-12
PO Box 9122 01742 978-369-2550
Kathleen Carroll Giles, head sch Fax 287-4759

Conway, Franklin

Conway School of Landscape Design Post-Sec.
PO Box 179 01341 413-369-4044

Dalton, Berkshire, Pop. 7,155
Central Berkshire Regional SD 1,700/PK-12
PO Box 299 01227 413-684-0320
Laurie Casna, supt. Fax 684-4088
www.cbrsd.org
Nessacus Regional MS 400/6-8
35 Fox Rd 01226 413-684-0780
John Martin, prin. Fax 684-4214
Wahconah Regional HS 600/9-12
150 Old Windsor Rd 01226 413-684-1330
James Conro, prin. Fax 684-5032

Danvers, Essex, Pop. 26,232
Danvers SD 3,600/PK-12
64 Cabot Rd 01923 978-777-4539
Lisa Dana, supt. Fax 777-8931
www.danvers.mec.edu
Danvers HS 1,000/9-12
60 Cabot Rd 01923 978-777-8925
Susan Ambrozavitch, prin. Fax 777-8931
Holten-Richmond MS 900/6-8
55 Conant St 01923 978-774-8590
Adam Federico, prin. Fax 762-8686

North Shore Community College Post-Sec.
1 Ferncroft Rd 01923 978-762-4000
St. Johns Preparatory S 1,200/9-12
72 Spring St 01923 978-774-1050
Keith Crowley Ph.D., prin. Fax 624-1315

Dedham, Norfolk, Pop. 24,346
Dedham SD 2,800/PK-12
100 Whiting Ave 02026 781-310-1100
Michael J. Welch, supt. Fax 320-0193
www.dedham.k12.ma.us
Dedham HS 800/9-12
140 Whiting Ave 02026 781-310-1100
Ron McCarthy, prin. Fax 320-8126
Dedham MS 700/6-8
70 Whiting Ave 02026 781-310-7000
Dr. Margo Fraczek, prin. Fax 461-0354

Noble And Greenough S 600/7-12
10 Campus Dr 02026 781-326-3700
Robert Henderson, hdmstr. Fax 320-1329
Ursuline Academy 400/7-12
85 Lowder St 02026 781-326-6161
Michelle Smith, prin. Fax 326-4898

Deerfield, Franklin, Pop. 620

Deerfield Academy 600/9-12
PO Box 87 01342 413-772-0241
Dr. Margarita Curtis, hdmstr. Fax 772-1129
Eaglebrook S 300/6-9
PO Box 7 01342 413-774-7411
Andrew Chase, hdmstr. Fax 774-9136

Dighton, Bristol
Bristol County Agricultural SD
135 Center St 02715 508-669-6744
Stephen Dempsey, supt. Fax 669-6747
www.bcahs.com
Bristol County Agricultural HS Vo/Tech
135 Center St 02715 508-669-6744
Aaron Polansky, prin. Fax 669-6747

Dighton-Rehoboth Regional SD
Supt. — See North Dighton
Dighton MS 400/5-8
1250R Somerset Ave 02715 508-669-4200
Richard Wheeler, prin. Fax 669-4210

Dorchester, See Boston
Boston SD
Supt. — See Boston
Boston International HS 300/9-12
100 Maxwell St 02124 617-635-9373
Thomas King, hdmstr. Fax 635-8224
Boston Latin Academy 1,700/7-12
205 Townsend St 02121 617-635-9957
Troy Henninger, hdmstr. Fax 635-6696
Burke HS 500/9-12
60 Washington St 02121 617-635-9837
Lindsa McIntyre, hdmstr. Fax 635-9852
Community Academy of Science & Health 400/9-12
11 Charles St 02122 617-635-8950
Robin Lee, prin. Fax 635-8948
Dearborn STEM Academy 300/6-12
60 Washington St 02121 617-635-8412
Lisa Gilbert-Smith, prin. Fax 635-8419
Dorchester Academy 400/9-12
11 Charles St 02122 617-635-9730
Melissa Malone Sanjeh, hdmstr. Fax 635-8847
Frederick MS 600/6-8
270 Columbia Rd 02121 617-635-1650
Pauline Lugira, prin. Fax 635-1637
Henderson Inclusion S 200/PK-12
18 Croftland Ave 02124 617-635-6365
Patricia Lampron, prin. Fax 635-6367
McCormack MS 700/6-8
315 Mount Vernon St 02125 617-635-8657
Elvis Henriquez, prin. Fax 635-9788
TechBoston Academy 1,000/6-12
9 Peacevale Rd 02124 617-635-1615
Keith Love, hdmstr. Fax 635-1622

Cross Factor Academy 200/PK-12
670 Washington St 02124 617-522-1841
Michael Dixon Ph.D., head sch Fax 524-9583
Epiphany S 100/5-8
154 Centre St 02124 617-326-0425
Rev. John Finley, head sch Fax 326-0424
Laboure College Post-Sec.
2120 Dorchester Ave 02124 617-296-8300
Mother Caroline Academy 100/4-8
515 Blue Hill Ave 02121 617-427-1177
Ed Hudner, dir. Fax 427-7788
Seton Academy 100/9-12
2220 Dorchester Ave 02124 617-296-1087
Maureen White Ph.D., prin. Fax 296-1089

Douglas, Worcester
Douglas SD 1,200/PK-12
21 Davis St 01516 508-476-7901
Norman Yvon, supt. Fax 476-3719
www.douglas.k12.ma.us/
Douglas HS 500/9-12
33 Davis St 01516 508-476-4100
Kevin Maines, prin. Fax 476-7310
Douglas MS 300/6-8
21 Davis St 01516 508-476-3332
Brian Delaney, prin. Fax 476-1604

Dover, Norfolk, Pop. 2,253
Dover-Sherborn SD 2,100/PK-12
157 Farm St 02030 508-785-0036
William McAlduff, supt. Fax 785-2239
www.doversherborn.org
Dover-Sherborn Regional HS 600/9-12
9 Junction St 02030 508-785-1730
John Smith, prin. Fax 785-8141
Dover-Sherborn Regional MS 500/6-8
155 Farm St 02030 508-785-0635
Scott Kellett, prin. Fax 785-0796

Dracut, Middlesex, Pop. 25,594
Dracut SD 3,500/PK-12
2063 Lakeview Ave 01826 978-957-2660
Steven Stone, supt. Fax 957-2682
www.dracutps.org
Dracut HS 900/9-12
1540 Lakeview Ave 01826 978-957-1500
Richard Manley, prin. Fax 957-9717
Richardson MS 600/6-8
1570 Lakeview Ave 01826 978-957-3330
Maria McGuinness, prin. Fax 957-4075

Dudley, Worcester, Pop. 3,700
Dudley-Charlton Regional SD 4,000/PK-12
68 Dudley Oxford Rd 01571 508-943-6888
Gregg Desto, supt. Fax 943-1077
www.dcrsd.org
Dudley MS 600/5-8
70 Dudley Oxford Rd 01571 508-943-2224
John Paire, prin. Fax 949-0720
Shepherd Hill Regional HS 1,100/9-12
68 Dudley Oxford Rd 01571 508-943-6700
William Chaplin, prin. Fax 943-5956
Other Schools – See Charlton

Nichols College Post-Sec.
124 Center Rd 01571 508-213-1560

Duxbury, Plymouth, Pop. 1,793
Duxbury SD 3,200/PK-12
93 Chandler St 02332 781-934-7600
Dr. Benedict Tantillo, supt. Fax 934-7644
www.duxbury.k12.ma.us
Duxbury HS 1,000/9-12
130 Saint George St 02332 781-934-7650
Andrew Stephens, prin. Fax 934-7617
Duxbury MS 800/6-8
71 Alden St 02332 781-934-7640
Blake Dalton, prin. Fax 934-7608

East Boston, See Boston
Boston SD
Supt. — See Boston
East Boston HS 1,300/9-12
86 White St 02128 617-635-9896
Phil Brangiforte, hdmstr. Fax 635-9726

East Bridgewater, Plymouth, Pop. 11,104
East Bridgewater SD 2,300/PK-12
143 Plymouth St 02333 508-378-8200
Elizabeth Legault, supt. Fax 378-8225
www.ebps.net
East Bridgewater HS 1,000/7-12
143 Plymouth St 02333 508-378-8214
Paul Vieira, prin. Fax 378-8226

East Falmouth, Barnstable, Pop. 5,768
Falmouth SD 3,500/PK-12
340 Teaticket Hwy 02536 508-548-0151
Nancy Taylor, supt. Fax 457-9032
www.falmouth.k12.ma.us
Other Schools – See Falmouth

Easthampton, Hampshire, Pop. 16,004
Easthampton SD 1,600/PK-12
50 Payson Ave Ste 200 01027 413-529-1500
Nancy Follansbee, supt. Fax 529-1567
www.epsd.us
Easthampton HS 500/9-12
70 Williston Ave 01027 413-529-1585
Kevin Burke, prin. Fax 529-1591
White Brook MS 500/5-8
200 Park St 01027 413-529-1530
Meredith Balise, prin. Fax 529-1534

Williston Northampton S 500/7-12
19 Payson Ave 01027 413-529-3000
Robert W. Hill, head sch Fax 527-9494

East Longmeadow, Hampden, Pop. 13,367
East Longmeadow SD 2,700/PK-12
180 Maple St 01028 413-525-5450
Gordon Smith, supt. Fax 525-5456
www.eastlongmeadowma.gov/schools.htm
Birchland Park MS 700/6-8
50 Hanward Hl 01028 413-525-5480
Timothy Allen Ed.D., prin. Fax 525-5320
East Longmeadow HS 900/9-12
180 Maple St 01028 413-525-5460
Gina Flanagan Ed.D., prin. Fax 525-5496

East Sandwich, Barnstable, Pop. 3,915
Sandwich SD
Supt. — See Sandwich
Sandwich HS 800/9-12
365 Quaker Meeting House Rd 02537 508-888-4900
Ellin Booras, prin. Fax 833-8392
Sandwich STEM Academy 500/7-8
365 Quaker Meeting House Rd 02537
Gilbert Newton, dir. 508-888-5300

Riverview S 100/6-12
551 Route 6A 02537 508-888-0489
Nancy Hopkins, admin. Fax 833-7001

East Walpole, Norfolk, Pop. 3,800
Walpole SD
Supt. — See Walpole
Bird MS 500/6-8
625 Washington St 02032 508-660-7226
Bridget Gough, prin. Fax 660-7229

East Weymouth, Norfolk
Weymouth SD
Supt. — See Weymouth
Chapman MS 1,000/7-8
1051 Commercial St 02189 781-337-4500
Paul Duprey, prin. Fax 340-2594

Everett, Middlesex, Pop. 38,826
Everett SD 6,900/PK-12
121 Vine St 02149 617-389-7950
Frederick Foresteire, supt. Fax 394-2408
www.everett.k12.ma.us/
Everett HS 2,000/9-12
100 Elm St 02149 617-394-2490
Erick Naumann, prin. Fax 389-5841

Pope John XXIII Central HS 300/9-12
888 Broadway 02149 617-389-0240
Thomas Mahoney, head sch Fax 389-2201

Fairhaven, Bristol, Pop. 16,132
Fairhaven SD 2,000/PK-12
128 Washington St 02719 508-979-4000
Dr. Robert Baldwin, supt. Fax 979-4149
www.fairhavenps.org
Fairhaven HS 600/9-12
12 Huttleston Ave 02719 508-979-4052
Tara Kohler, prin. Fax 979-4140
Hastings MS 400/6-8
30 School St 02719 508-979-4063
Dr. Nicholas Bettencourt, prin. Fax 979-4068

Fall River, Bristol, Pop. 86,097
Fall River SD 10,300/PK-12
417 Rock St 02720 508-675-8420
Matthew Malone Ph.D., supt. Fax 675-8462
www.fallriverschools.org
Durfee HS 2,300/9-12
360 Elsbree St 02720 508-675-8100
Maria Pontes, prin. Fax 675-8186
Kuss MS 800/6-8
52 Globe Mills Ave 02724 508-675-8335
Jennifer Copeland, prin. Fax 675-1984
Morton MS 700/6-8
1135 N Main St 02720 508-675-8340
Sheryl Patterson, prin. Fax 675-8414
Resiliency MS Alt
290 Rock St 02720 508-675-8107
Joyce Paulo, prin. Fax 675-8113
Resiliency Preparatory S 200/Alt
276 Maple St 02720 508-675-8230
Magdalana Reis, prin. Fax 235-2661

Talbot Innovation MS 800/6-8
124 Melrose St 02723 508-675-8350
Renee Lewis, prin. Fax 675-8356

Greater Fall River Vocational SD
251 Stonehaven Rd 02723 508-678-2891
Thomas Aubin, supt. Fax 679-6423
www.dimanregional.org/
Diman Regional Vocational Technical HS Vo/Tech
251 Stonehaven Rd 02723 508-678-2891
Kyle Alves, prin. Fax 679-6423

Bishop Connolly HS 300/9-12
373 Elsbree St 02720 508-676-1071
Christopher Myron, prin. Fax 676-8594
Bristol Community College Post-Sec.
777 Elsbree St 02720 508-678-2811
Rob Roy Academy Post-Sec.
260 S Main St 02721 508-672-4751
Salter School Post-Sec.
82 Hartwell St 02721 508-730-2740

Falmouth, Barnstable, Pop. 3,663
Falmouth SD
Supt. — See East Falmouth
Falmouth HS 900/9-12
874 Gifford Street Ext 02540 508-540-2200
Mary Gans, prin. Fax 548-7515
Lawrence MS 500/7-8
113 Lakeview Ave 02540 508-548-0606
Thomas Bushy, prin. Fax 457-9778

Falmouth Academy 200/7-12
7 Highfield Dr 02540 508-457-9696
Steve Duffy, head sch Fax 457-4112
National Grad. Sch. Quality Systems Mgmt Post-Sec.
186 Jones Rd 02540 508-457-1313

Feeding Hills, Hampden, Pop. 5,450
Agawam SD 4,100/PK-12
1305 Springfield St Ste 1 01030 413-821-0548
William Sapelli, supt. Fax 789-1835
www.agawampublicschools.org
Agawam JHS 600/7-8
1305 Springfield St Ste 2 01030 413-821-0561
Norman Robbins, prin. Fax 786-4240
Other Schools – See Agawam

Fiskdale, Worcester, Pop. 2,545
Tantasqua SD 1,800/7-12
320 Brookfield Rd 01518 508-347-3077
Erin Nosek, supt. Fax 347-2697
www.tantasqua.org
Tantasqua Regional HS 700/9-12
319 Brookfield Rd 01518 508-347-9301
Michael Lucas, prin. Fax 347-1061
Tantasqua Regional JHS 600/7-8
320 Brookfield Rd 01518 508-347-7381
Christopher Starczewski, prin. Fax 347-3994
Tantasqua Regional Vocational HS Vo/Tech
319 Brookfield Rd 01518 508-347-3045
Mark Wood, prin. Fax 347-1061

Fitchburg, Worcester, Pop. 39,363
Fitchburg SD 5,000/PK-12
376 South St 01420 978-345-3200
Andre Ravenelle, supt. Fax 348-2305
www.fitchburgschools.org
Fitchburg HS 1,100/9-12
140 Arnhow Farm Rd 01420 978-345-3240
Jeremy Roche, prin. Fax 348-2303
Goodrich Academy 200/Alt
111 Goodrich St 01420 978-345-3244
Raymond Dewar, prin. Fax 343-6127
Longsjo MS 500/5-8
98 Academy St 01420 978-343-2146
Craig Chalifoux, prin. Fax 348-2323
Memorial MS 700/5-8
615 Rollstone St 01420 978-345-3295
Francis Thomas, prin. Fax 343-2121

Montachusett Regional Vo/Tech HSD
1050 Westminster St 01420 978-345-9200
Dr. Sheila M. Harrity, supt. Fax 345-9165
www.montytech.net
Montachusett Reg Vocational Technical HS Vo/Tech
1050 Westminster St 01420 978-345-9200
Dr. Sheila M. Harrity, supt. Fax 348-1176

Fitchburg State University Post-Sec.
160 Pearl St 01420 978-345-2151
Henri's School of Hair Design Post-Sec.
PO Box 2244 01420 978-342-6061
Notre Dame HS 50/7-12
151 South St 01420 978-343-7635
Jeffrey Hammond, prin. Fax 343-4379
St. Bernard's HS 300/9-12
45 Harvard St 01420 978-342-3212
Robert Blanchard, admin. Fax 345-8067

Florence, See Northampton
Northampton SD
Supt. — See Northampton
Kennedy MS 600/6-8
100 Bridge Rd 01062 413-587-1489
Lesley Wilson, prin. Fax 587-1495

Foxboro, Norfolk, Pop. 5,706
Foxborough SD 2,700/PK-12
60 South St 02035 508-543-1660
Debra Spinelli, supt. Fax 543-4793
www.foxborough.k12.ma.us
Ahern MS 900/5-8
111 Mechanic St 02035 508-543-1610
Susan Abrams, prin. Fax 543-1613
Foxborough HS 900/9-12
120 South St 02035 508-543-1616
Diana Myers-Pachla, prin. Fax 698-6517

Framingham, Middlesex, Pop. 61,638
Framingham SD 8,300/PK-12
73 Mount Wayte Ave Ste 5 01702 508-626-9117
Dr. Stacy Scott Ed.D., supt. Fax 877-4240
www.framingham.k12.ma.us
Cameron MS 500/6-8
215 Elm St 01701 508-879-2290
Michelle Melick, prin. Fax 788-3560
Framingham HS 2,000/9-12
115 A St 01701 508-620-4963
Elyse Torbert, prin. Fax 877-6603
Fuller MS 500/6-8
31 Flagg Dr 01702 508-620-4956
Jose Duarte, prin. Fax 628-1308
Walsh MS 700/6-8
301 Brook St 01701 508-626-9180
Patrick Johnson, prin. Fax 877-1825

South Middlesex Regional Technical SD
750 Winter St 01702 508-416-2350
Jonathan Evans, supt. Fax 416-2342
www.keefetech.org
Keefe Technical HS Vo/Tech
750 Winter St 01702 508-416-2100
Shannon Snow, prin. Fax 416-2342

Blaine The Beauty Career School Post-Sec.
624 Worcester Rd 01702 508-370-3700
Blaine The Beauty Career School Post-Sec.
624 Worcester Rd 01702 508-370-7447
Framingham State College Post-Sec.
PO Box 9101 01701 508-620-1220
Marian HS 300/9-12
273 Union Ave 01702 508-875-7646
John Ermilio, prin. Fax 875-0838

Franklin, Norfolk, Pop. 30,893
Franklin SD 5,800/PK-12
355 E Central St 02038 508-541-5243
Dr. Maureen Sabolinski, supt. Fax 533-0321
franklindistrict.vt-s.net
Franklin HS 1,600/9-12
218 Oak St 02038 508-613-1400
Paul Peri, prin. Fax 613-1510
Mann MS 500/6-8
224 Oak St 02038 508-553-0322
Rebecca Motte, prin. Fax 541-7071
Remington MS 500/6-8
628 Washington St 02038 508-541-2130
Brian Wildeman, prin. Fax 541-2124
Sullivan MS 500/6-8
500 Lincoln St 02038 508-553-0322
Beth Wittcoff, prin. Fax 542-2109

Tri-County Regional Vocational Tech SD
147 Pond St 02038 508-528-5400
Stephen Dockray, supt. Fax 528-6074
www.tri-county.tc
Tri-County Regional Vo-Tech HS Vo/Tech
147 Pond St 02038 508-528-5400
Michael Procaccini, prin. Fax 528-6074

Dean College Post-Sec.
99 Main St 02038 508-541-1508

Gardner, Worcester, Pop. 19,860
Gardner SD 1,700/PK-12
70 Waterford St 01440 978-632-1000
Denise Clemons M.Ed., supt. Fax 632-1164
www.gardnerk12.org
Gardner Academy for Learning/Technology 100/Alt
75 E Broadway 01440 978-632-1606
Timothy McCormick, prin. Fax 632-1164
Gardner HS 600/8-12
200 Catherine St 01440 978-632-1600
Mark Pellegrino, prin. Fax 630-4040

Ralph C. Mahar Regional SD
Supt. — See Orange
Pathways Early College 50/9-12
444 Green St 01440 978-630-9480
Natalie Mercier, prin. Fax 630-9400

Mt. Wachusett Community College Post-Sec.
444 Green St 01440 978-632-6600

Georgetown, Essex
Georgetown SD 1,000/PK-12
51 North St 01833 978-352-5777
Carol Jacobs, supt. Fax 352-5778
www.georgetown-schools.org/
Georgetown MSHS 400/7-12
11 Winter St 01833 978-352-5790
Peter Lucia, prin. Fax 352-5798

Gloucester, Essex, Pop. 28,371
Gloucester SD 3,100/PK-12
2 Blackburn Dr 01930 978-281-9800
Dr. Richard Safier, supt. Fax 281-9899
www.gloucesterschools.com
Gloucester HS 900/9-12
32 Leslie O Johnson Rd 01930 978-281-9870
James Cook, prin. Fax 281-9733
O'Maley MS 700/6-8
32 Cherry St 01930 978-281-9850
Debra Lucey, prin. Fax 281-9890

Grafton, Worcester
Grafton SD 3,100/PK-12
30 Providence Rd 01519 508-839-5421
James Cummings Ed.D., supt. Fax 839-7618
www.grafton.k12.ma.us
Grafton Memorial HS 800/9-12
24 Providence Rd 01519 508-839-5425
James Pignataro, prin. Fax 839-8544
Grafton MS 500/7-8
22 Providence Rd 01519 508-839-5420
Roseanne Kurposka, prin. Fax 839-8528

Granby, Hampshire, Pop. 1,346
Granby SD 900/PK-12
387 E State St 01033 413-467-7193
Sheryl Stanton, supt. Fax 467-3909
www.granbyschoolsma.org
Granby JSHS 500/7-12
385 E State St 01033 413-467-7105
Jonathan Cavallo, prin. Fax 467-3909

MacDuffie S 200/6-12
66 School St 01033 413-255-0000
Steve Griffin, head sch Fax 467-1607

Great Barrington, Berkshire, Pop. 2,177
Berkshire Hills SD
Supt. — See Stockbridge
Monument Mountain Regional HS 600/9-12
600 Stockbridge Rd 01230 413-528-3346
Marianne Young, prin. Fax 528-9267
Monument Valley Regional MS 400/5-8
313 Monument Valley Rd 01230 413-644-2300
Ben Doren, prin. Fax 644-2394

Bard Academy at Simon's Rock 50/9-10
84 Alford Rd 01230 413-644-4400
Ian Bickford, prin. Fax 528-7365
Bard College at Simon's Rock Post-Sec.
84 Alford Rd 01230 413-644-4400

Greenfield, Franklin, Pop. 14,016
Greenfield SD 1,600/PK-12
195 Federal St # 100 01301 413-772-1300
Jordana Harper, supt. Fax 774-7940
www.gpsk12.org
Greenfield HS 500/8-12
21 Barr Ave 01301 413-772-1350
Donna Woodcock, prin. Fax 774-6204

Greenfield Community College Post-Sec.
1 College Dr 01301 413-775-1000
Stoneleigh-Burnham S 100/7-12
574 Bernardston Rd 01301 413-774-2711
Sally Mixsell, head sch Fax 772-2602

Groton, Middlesex, Pop. 1,106
Groton-Dunstable Regional SD 2,600/PK-12
PO Box 729 01450 978-448-5505
Dr. Kristan Rodriguez, supt. Fax 448-9402
www.gdrsd.org
Groton-Dunstable Regional HS 900/9-12
PO Box 730 01450 978-448-6362
Michael Woodlock, prin. Fax 448-0390
Groton-Dunstable Regional MS 900/5-8
PO Box 727 01450 978-448-6155
James Lin, prin. Fax 448-1201

Groton S 400/8-12
PO Box 991 01450 978-448-3363
Temba Maqubela, hdmstr. Fax 448-3100
Lawrence Academy 400/9-12
PO Box 992 01450 978-448-6535
Dan Scheibe, head sch Fax 448-9208

Hadley, Hampshire
Hadley SD 600/PK-12
125 Russell St 01035 413-586-0822
Anne McKenzie Ed.D., supt. Fax 582-6453
www.hadleyschools.org
Hopkins Academy 300/7-12
131 Russell St 01035 413-584-1106
Brian Beck, prin. Fax 582-6455

Hartsbrook S 300/PK-12
193 Bay Rd 01035 413-584-3198
Fax 586-9438

Hamilton, Essex
Hamilton-Wenham SD
Supt. — See Wenham
Hamilton-Wenham Regional HS 700/9-12
775 Bay Rd 01982 978-468-0400
Eric Tracy, prin. Fax 468-0241
Miles River MS 400/6-8
787 Bay Rd 01982 978-468-0362
Craig Hovey, prin. Fax 468-8454

Hampden, Hampden
Hampden-Wilbraham SD
Supt. — See Wilbraham
Burgess MS 300/5-8
85 Wilbraham Rd 01036 413-566-8950
Amy Bostian, prin. Fax 566-2163

Hanover, Plymouth, Pop. 11,912
Hanover SD 2,600/PK-12
188 Broadway 02339 781-878-0786
Matthew Ferron Ed.D., supt. Fax 871-3374
www.hanoverschools.org
Hanover HS 800/9-12
287 Cedar St 02339 781-878-5450
Matthew Paquette, prin. Fax 871-0590
Hanover MS 900/5-8
45 Whiting St 02339 781-871-1122
Daniel Birolini, prin. Fax 871-8792

South Shore Regional Vo Tech SD
476 Webster St 02339 781-878-8822
Thomas Hickey Ed.D., supt. Fax 982-0281
www.ssvotech.org
South Shore Vocational Technical HS Vo/Tech
476 Webster St 02339 781-878-8822
Margaret Dutch, prin. Fax 982-0281

Hanscom AFB, See Bedford
Lincoln SD
Supt. — See Lincoln
Hanscom MS 200/4-8
2 Eglin St 01731 781-274-0050
Erich Ledebuhr, prin. Fax 274-7329

Hanson, Plymouth, Pop. 2,089
Whitman-Hanson SD
Supt. — See Whitman
Hanson MS 500/6-8
111 Liberty St 02341 781-618-7575
William Tranter, prin. Fax 618-8815

Harvard, Worcester
Harvard SD 1,200/PK-12
39 Mass Ave 01451 978-456-4140
Linda Dwight, supt. Fax 456-8592
www.psharvard.org
Bromfield S 700/6-12
14 Mass Ave 01451 978-456-4152
Scott Hoffman, prin. Fax 456-3013

Harwich, Barnstable
Cape Cod Regional Technical HSD
351 Pleasant Lake Ave 02645 508-432-4500
Robert Sanborn, supt. Fax 432-7916
capetech.us
Cape Cod Regional Technical HS Vo/Tech
351 Pleasant Lake Ave 02645 508-432-4500
Billy Terranova, prin. Fax 430-2430

Monomoy Regional SD
Supt. — See Chatham
Monomoy Regional HS 300/8-12
75 Oak St 02645 508-430-7200
Bill Burkhead, prin.

Hatfield, Hampshire, Pop. 1,311
Hatfield SD 500/PK-12
34 School St 01038 413-247-5641
John Robert, supt. Fax 247-0201
hatfieldps.net
Smith Academy 200/7-12
34 School St 01038 413-247-5641
Andrew Berrios, prin. Fax 247-0201

Hathorne, Essex
Essex N Shore Agricultural & Tech HS
PO Box 346 01937 978-304-4700
William H. Lupini Ed.D., supt. Fax 774-6530
www.essextech.net
Essex Technical HS Vo/Tech
PO Box 346 01937 978-304-4700
Brad Morgan, prin. Fax 774-6530

Haverhill, Essex, Pop. 59,811
Haverhill SD 7,600/PK-12
4 Summer St Ste 104 01830 978-374-3400
James Scully, supt. Fax 374-3422
www.haverhill-ps.org/
Haverhill Alternative S 50/Alt
415 Primrose St 01830 978-374-3482
John DePolo, prin. Fax 372-6070
Haverhill HS 1,800/9-12
137 Monument St 01832 978-374-5700
Elizabeth Kitsos, prin. Fax 374-5705
Hunking MS 400/6-8
100 Winchester St 01835 978-374-5787
Shannon Nolan, prin. Fax 372-5890
Nettle MS 500/5-8
150 Boardman St 01830 978-374-5792
Tim Corkery, prin. Fax 374-3441
Whittier MS 500/5-8
256 Concord St 01830 978-374-5782
Brian Gill, prin. Fax 372-5999

Whittier Regional Vocational SD
115 Amesbury Line Rd 01830 978-373-4101
Maureen Lynch, supt. Fax 521-0260
www.whittiertech.org
Whittier Regional Vocational HS Vo/Tech
115 Amesbury Line Rd 01830 978-373-4101
Chris Laganas, prin. Fax 521-0260

Northern Essex Community College Post-Sec.
100 Elliott St 01830 978-556-3000
Northpoint Bible College Post-Sec.
320 S Main St 01835 978-478-3400

Hingham, Plymouth, Pop. 5,570
Hingham SD 4,200/PK-12
220 Central St 02043 781-741-1500
Dorothy Galo, supt. Fax 749-7457
www.hinghamschools.org
Hingham HS 1,100/9-12
17 Union St 02043 781-741-1560
Paula Girouard McCann, prin. Fax 741-1515
Hingham MS 1,000/6-8
1103 Main St 02043 781-741-1550
Derek Smith, prin. Fax 749-6297

Notre Dame Academy 600/9-12
1073 Main St 02043 781-749-5930
Kathleen Colin, prin. Fax 749-8366

Holbrook, Norfolk, Pop. 10,445
Holbrook SD 1,200/PK-12
245 S Franklin St 02343 781-767-1226
Dr. Patricia Lally, supt. Fax 767-1312
www.holbrook.k12.ma.us/
Holbrook JSHS 500/7-12
245 S Franklin St 02343 781-767-4616
Mary Ann DeMello, prin. Fax 767-2697

Holden, Worcester, Pop. 14,628
Wachusett Regional SD
Supt. — See Jefferson
Mountview MS 700/6-8
270 Shrewsbury St 01520 508-829-5577
Erik Githmark, prin. Fax 829-3711
Wachusett Regional HS 2,100/9-12
1401 Main St 01520 508-829-6771
William Beando, prin. Fax 829-4895

Holliston, Middlesex, Pop. 12,926
Holliston SD 2,800/PK-12
370 Hollis St 01746 508-429-0654
Bradford Jackson, supt. Fax 429-0653
www.holliston.k12.ma.us/
Adams MS 700/6-8
323 Woodland St 01746 508-429-0657
Peter Botelho, prin. Fax 429-0690
Holliston HS 800/9-12
370 Hollis St 01746 508-429-0677
Nicole Bottomley, prin. Fax 429-8225

Holyoke, Hampden, Pop. 39,370
Holyoke SD 5,600/PK-12
57 Suffolk St Ste 101 01040 413-534-2005
Dr. Stephen Zrike, supt. Fax 534-2297
www.hps.holyoke.ma.us
Dean Vocational Technical HS Vo/Tech
1045 Main St 01040 413-534-2071
Jeffrey Peterson, prin. Fax 536-9694
Holyoke HS 1,300/9-12
500 Beech St 01040 413-534-2020
Stephen Sullivan, prin. Fax 534-2098
Peck ES 400/4-8
1916 Northampton St 01040 413-534-2040
Kendra Salvador, prin. Fax 532-8563

Springfield SD
Supt. — See Springfield
Gateway to College @ HCC 50/9-12
303 Homestead Ave 01040 413-552-2176
Rhonda Jacobs, dir.

Holyoke Community College Post-Sec.
303 Homestead Ave 01040 413-538-7000

Hopedale, Worcester, Pop. 3,687
Hopedale SD 1,300/PK-12
25 Adin St 01747 508-634-2220
Karen Crebase, supt. Fax 478-1471
www.hopedaleschools.org
Hopedale JSHS 500/7-12
25 Adin St 01747 508-634-2217
Derek Atherton, prin. Fax 634-4319

Hopkinton, Middlesex, Pop. 2,531
Hopkinton SD 3,500/PK-12
89 Hayden Rowe St 01748 508-417-9360
Cathy Macleod, supt. Fax 497-9833
www.hopkinton.k12.ma.us
Hopkinton HS 1,100/9-12
90 Hayden Rowe St 01748 508-497-9820
Evan Bishop, prin. Fax 497-9829
Hopkinton MS 800/6-8
88 Hayden Rowe St 01748 508-497-9830
Alan Keller Ed.D., prin. Fax 497-9803

Hudson, Middlesex, Pop. 14,374
Hudson SD 2,900/PK-12
155 Apsley St 01749 978-567-6100
Dr. Judi Fortuna, supt. Fax 567-6123
www.hudson.k12.ma.us
Hudson JSHS 1,000/8-12
69 Brigham St 01749 978-567-6250
Brian Reagan, prin. Fax 567-6285

Hull, Plymouth, Pop. 10,097
Hull SD 1,100/PK-12
180 Harborview Rd 02045 781-925-4400
Kathleen Tyrell, supt. Fax 925-8042
www.town.hull.ma.us
Hull HS 300/9-12
180 Main St 02045 781-925-3000
Michael Devine, prin. Fax 925-3071
Memorial MS 200/6-8
81 Central Ave 02045 781-925-2040
Anthony Hrivnak, prin. Fax 925-8002

Huntington, Hampshire, Pop. 920
Gateway SD 800/PK-12
12 Littleville Rd 01050 413-685-1000
Dr. David Hopson, supt. Fax 667-8739
www.grsd.org
Gateway Regional HS 300/9-12
12 Littleville Rd 01050 413-685-1100
Jason Finnie, prin. Fax 667-5593
Gateway Regional MS 100/6-8
12 Littleville Rd 01050 413-685-1200
Jason Finnie, prin. Fax 667-5669

Hyannis, Barnstable, Pop. 14,120
Barnstable SD 5,100/PK-12
PO Box 955 02601 508-862-4953
Meg Mayo-Brown, supt. Fax 790-6454
www.barnstable.k12.ma.us
Barnstable HS 1,900/8-12
744 W Main St 02601 508-790-6445
Patrick Clark, prin. Fax 790-6430

Blaine The Beauty Career School Post-Sec.
259 North St Ste 3 02601 508-771-1680
St. John Paul II HS & St. Francis Xavier 200/K-12
120 High School Rd 02601 508-862-6336
Christopher Keavy, prin. Fax 862-6339

Hyde Park, See Boston
Boston SD
Supt. — See Boston
Boston Community Leadership Academy 500/9-12
655 Metropolitan Ave 02136 617-635-8937
Dr. Francine Locker, hdmstr. Fax 635-8942
New Mission HS 300/9-12
655 Metropolitan Ave 02136 617-635-6437
Naia Wilson, hdmstr. Fax 635-6332

Indian Orchard, See Springfield
Springfield SD
Supt. — See Springfield

Springfield Public Day HS 100/Alt
90 Berkshire St 01151 413-787-7036
Rhonda Jacobs, prin. Fax 787-6828

Ipswich, Essex, Pop. 4,128
Ipswich SD 2,000/PK-12
1 Lord Sq 01938 978-356-2935
Dr. William Hart, supt. Fax 356-0445
www.ipsk12.net
Ipswich HS 600/9-12
134 High St 01938 978-356-3137
David Dalton, prin. Fax 356-3720
Ipswich MS 500/6-8
130 High St 01938 978-356-3535
David Fabrizio, prin. Fax 412-8169

Jamaica Plain, See Boston
Boston SD
Supt. — See Boston
Community Academy 100/Alt
25 Glen Rd 02130 617-635-7734
Rayna Briceno, prin. Fax 635-7731
English HS 600/9-12
144 McBride St 02130 617-635-8979
Ligia Noriega-Murphy, prin. Fax 635-8988
Muniz Academy 200/9-12
20 Child St 02130 617-635-8198
Dr. Dania Vazquez, prin. Fax 635-7835

Nativity Prep S 4-8
39 Lamartine St 02130 617-728-0031

Jefferson, Worcester
Wachusett Regional SD 7,400/PK-12
1745 Main St 01522 508-829-1670
Dr. Darryll McCall Ed.D., supt. Fax 829-1680
www.wrsd.net
Other Schools – See Holden, Rutland, Sterling

Kingston, Plymouth, Pop. 5,491
Silver Lake Regional SD 1,800/7-12
250 Pembroke St 02364 781-585-4313
Joy Blackwood, supt. Fax 585-2994
www.slrsd.org
Silver Lake Regional HS 1,200/9-12
260 Pembroke St 02364 781-585-3844
James Mulcahy, prin. Fax 585-6544
Silver Lake Regional MS 600/7-8
256 Pembroke St 02364 781-582-3555
James Dupille, prin. Fax 582-3599

Sacred Heart HS 400/7-12
399 Bishops Hwy 02364 781-585-7511
Dr. Michael Gill, prin. Fax 396-3230

Lakeville, Plymouth
Freetown-Lakeville SD 3,000/PK-12
98 Howland Rd 02347 508-923-2000
Richard Medeiros, supt. Fax 923-0934
www.freelake.org/
Apponequet Regional HS 800/9-12
100 Howland Rd 02347 508-947-2660
Barbara Starkie, prin. Fax 946-2350
Freetown-Lakeville MS 800/6-8
96 Howland Rd 02347 508-923-3518
David Patota, prin. Fax 946-2050

Lancaster, Worcester
Nashoba Regional SD
Supt. — See Bolton
Burbank MS 200/6-8
1 Hollywood Dr 01523 978-365-4558
Laura Friend, prin. Fax 365-6882

Lawrence, Essex, Pop. 75,608
Lawrence SD 12,800/PK-12
233 Haverhill St 01840 978-975-5905
Jeffrey Riley, supt. Fax 722-8550
www.lawrence.k12.ma.us
Arlington MS 500/5-8
150 Arlington St 01841 978-975-5930
Robin Finn, prin. Fax 722-8519
Bruce S 500/3-8
135 Butler St 01841 978-975-5935
Cheryl Merz, prin. Fax 722-8521
Business Management & Finance HS 500/9-12
70-71 N Parish Rd 01843 978-946-0713
Sean McCarthy, prin. Fax 722-8501
Frost MS 500/5-8
33 Hamlet St 01843 978-722-8810
Ellen Baranowski, prin. Fax 722-8513
Guilmette MS 500/5-8
80 Bodwell St 01841 978-722-8270
Melissa Spash, prin. Fax 722-8524
Health & Human Services HS 500/9-12
70-71 N Parish Rd 01843 978-946-0735
Paul Neal, prin. Fax 722-8502
Humanities & Leadership Development HS 500/9-12
70-71 N Parish Rd 01843 978-946-0724
Juan Rodriguez, prin. Fax 722-8503
International HS 500/9-12
70-71 N Parish Rd 01843 978-946-0712
Geraldo Acosta, prin. Fax 722-8504
HS Learning Center 200/9-12
233 E Haverhill St 01841 978-975-5917
Robert Cayer, prin. Fax 722-8531
Mathematics Science & Technology HS 500/9-12
70-71 N Parish Rd 01843 978-946-0719
Fax 722-8505
Parthum MS 500/5-8
255 E Haverhill St 01841 978-691-7224
Peter Lefebre, prin. Fax 722-8536
Performing & Fine Arts HS 500/9-12
70-71 N Parish Rd 01843 978-946-0766
Juan Rodriguez, prin. Fax 722-8506
SPARK Academy 100/Alt
165 Crawford St 01843 978-975-5993
Anwar Qazilbash, dir. Fax 722-8538

Adult Learning Center — Adult
147 Haverhill St 01840 — 978-722-8110
Fax 682-1262

Bellesini Academy — 100/5-8
94 Bradford St 01840 — 978-989-0004
Julie DeFillippo, dir. — Fax 989-9404
Central Catholic HS — 1,400/9-12
300 Hampshire St 01841 — 978-682-0260
Doreen Keller, prin. — Fax 685-2707
Esperanza Academy — 100/5-8
198 Garden St 01840 — 978-686-4673
Lynne Myavec, head sch — Fax 681-1591
Notre Dame Cristo Rey HS — 300/9-12
303 Haverhill St 01840 — 978-689-8222
Delia Duran-Clark, prin. — Fax 689-8728

Lee, Berkshire, Pop. 2,028
Lee SD — 700/PK-12
300A Greylock St 01238 — 413-243-0276
Alfred Skrocki, supt. — Fax 243-4995
www.leepublicschools.net
Lee MSHS — 400/7-12
300 Greylock St 01238 — 413-243-2781
Gregg Brighenti, prin. — Fax 243-4105

Leicester, Worcester, Pop. 10,191
Leicester SD — 1,600/PK-12
1078 Main St 01524 — 508-892-7040
Dr. Judith J. Paolucci, supt. — Fax 892-7043
www.leicester.k12.ma.us/
Leicester HS — 400/9-12
174 Paxton St 01524 — 508-892-7030
Tracey Hippert, prin. — Fax 892-7034
Leicester MS — 400/6-8
70 Winslow Ave 01524 — 508-892-7055
Joyce Nelson, prin. — Fax 892-7047

Lenox, Berkshire, Pop. 1,652
Lenox SD — 800/PK-12
6 Walker St Ste 3 01240 — 413-637-5550
Timothy Lee, supt. — Fax 637-5559
www.lenoxps.org
Lenox Memorial HS — 400/6-12
197 East St 01240 — 413-637-5560
Michael Knybel, prin. — Fax 637-5564

Berkshire County Christian S — 100/PK-12
PO Box 1980 01240 — 413-637-2474
Heidi Dickerson, prin.

Leominster, Worcester, Pop. 39,624
Leominster SD — 6,200/PK-12
24 Church St 01453 — 978-534-7700
Jim Jolicoeur, supt. — Fax 534-7775
www.leominster.mec.edu/
Leominster Center Technical Education — Vo/Tech
122 Granite St 01453 — 978-534-7735
David Fiandaca, dir. — Fax 537-7934
Leominster HS — 1,100/9-12
122 Granite St 01453 — 978-534-7715
Christopher Lord, prin. — Fax 537-1765
Samoset MS — 600/6-8
100 DeCicco Dr 01453 — 978-534-7725
Colleen LeClair, prin. — Fax 466-7421
Sky View MS — 900/6-8
500 Kennedy Way 01453 — 978-534-7780
Timothy Blake, prin. — Fax 840-8600

Lexington, Middlesex, Pop. 30,568
Lexington SD — 6,600/PK-12
146 Maple St 02420 — 781-861-2580
Dr. Mary Czajkowski, supt. — Fax 863-5829
lps.lexingtonma.org
Clarke MS — 900/6-8
17 Stedman Rd 02421 — 781-861-2450
Anna Monaco, prin. — Fax 674-2043
Diamond MS — 800/6-8
99 Hancock St 02420 — 781-861-2460
Jennifer Turner, prin. — Fax 274-0174
Lexington HS — 2,000/9-12
251 Waltham St 02421 — 781-861-2320
Laura Lasa, prin. — Fax 861-2440

Minuteman Regional Vocational Tech SD
758 Marrett Rd 02421 — 781-861-6500
Dr. Edward Bouquillon, supt. — Fax 863-1747
www.minuteman.org
Minuteman Regional Technical HS — Vo/Tech
758 Marrett Rd 02421 — 781-861-6500
John Dillon, prin. — Fax 863-1747

Lexington Christian Academy — 300/6-12
48 Bartlett Ave 02420 — 781-862-7850
Timothy Russell, head sch — Fax 863-8503

Lincoln, Middlesex, Pop. 2,850
Lincoln SD — 1,300/PK-8
6 Ballfield Rd 01773 — 781-259-9400
Rebecca McFall, supt. — Fax 259-9246
www.lincnet.org/
Other Schools – See Hanscom AFB

Littleton, Middlesex, Pop. 2,867
Littleton SD — 1,600/PK-12
PO Box 1486 01460 — 978-540-2500
Kelly Clenchy, supt. — Fax 486-9581
www.littletonps.org/
Littleton HS — 400/9-12
56 King St 01460 — 978-952-2555
Dr. John Harrington, prin. — Fax 486-0758
Littleton MS — 400/6-8
55 Russell St 01460 — 978-486-8938
Cheryl Temple, prin. — Fax 952-4547

Longmeadow, Hampden, Pop. 15,594
Longmeadow SD — 2,800/PK-12
535 Bliss Rd 01106 — 413-565-4200
Dr. M. Martin O'Shea, supt. — Fax 565-4215
sites.longmeadow.k12.ma.us/www/
Glenbrook MS — 300/6-8
110 Cambridge Cir 01106 — 413-565-4250
Nikcole Allen, prin. — Fax 565-4277
Longmeadow HS — 1,000/9-12
95 Grassy Gutter Rd 01106 — 413-565-4220
Thomas Landers, prin. — Fax 565-4233
Williams MS — 400/6-8
410 Williams St 01106 — 413-565-4260
Taylor Wrye, prin. — Fax 565-4254

Bay Path College — Post-Sec.
588 Longmeadow St 01106 — 413-565-1000

Lowell, Middlesex, Pop. 102,517
Lowell SD — 14,000/PK-12
155 Merrimack St 01852 — 978-674-4320
Salah Khelfaoui Ph.D., supt. — Fax 937-7609
www.lowell.k12.ma.us
Butler MS — 600/5-8
1140 Gorham St 01852 — 978-937-8973
Teresa Soares-Pena, prin. — Fax 937-2819
Daley MS — 700/5-8
150 Fleming St 01851 — 978-937-8981
Liam Skinner, prin. — Fax 937-7610
Lowell HS — 3,000/9-12
50 Father Morissette Blvd 01852 — 978-937-8900
Brian Martin, hdmstr. — Fax 937-8902
Lowell HS Career Academy — Vo/Tech
125 Smith St 01851 — 978-970-3318
Megan O'Loughlin, dir. — Fax 275-6399
O'Connell Alternative S — Alt
21 Carter St 01852 — 978-446-7000
Michelle Butterworth, coord. — Fax 937-7656
Robinson MS — 700/5-8
110 June St 01850 — 978-937-8974
Thad King, prin. — Fax 937-8988
Stoklosa MS — 700/5-8
560 Broadway St 01854 — 978-275-6330
James Cardaci, prin. — Fax 275-6343
Sullivan MS — 700/5-8
150 Draper St 01852 — 978-937-8993
Jacqueline Paton, prin. — Fax 937-3278
Wang MS — 700/5-8
365 W Meadow Rd 01854 — 978-937-7683
Matthew Stahl, prin. — Fax 937-7680

Blaine The Beauty Career School — Post-Sec.
231 Central St 01852 — 978-459-9959
Community Christian Academy — 200/PK-12
105 Princeton Blvd 01851 — 978-453-4738
Jennifer Najem, prin. — Fax 453-1506
Lincoln Technical Institute — Post-Sec.
211 Plain St 01852 — 978-458-4800
Lowell Academy Hairstyling Institute — Post-Sec.
136 Central St 01852 — 978-453-3235
Lowell Catholic HS — 400/9-12
530 Stevens St 01851 — 978-452-1794
Maryellen DeMarco, prin. — Fax 452-5646
University of Massachusetts Lowell — Post-Sec.
1 University Ave 01854 — 978-934-4000

Ludlow, Hampden, Pop. 18,820
Ludlow SD — 2,800/PK-12
63 Chestnut St 01056 — 413-583-8372
Todd Gazda, supt. — Fax 583-5666
www.ludlowps.org
Baird MS — 600/6-8
1 Rooney Rd 01056 — 413-583-5685
Stacy Monette, prin. — Fax 583-5636
Ludlow HS — 900/9-12
500 Chapin St 01056 — 413-589-9001
Lisa Nemeth, prin. — Fax 583-5637

Jolie Hair and Beauty Academy — Post-Sec.
44 Sewall St 01056 — 413-589-0747

Lunenburg, Worcester, Pop. 1,728
Lunenburg SD — 1,100/PK-12
1025 Massachusetts Ave 01462 — 978-582-4100
Loxi Jo Calmes, supt. — Fax 582-4103
www.lunenburgschools.net/
Lunenburg HS — 400/9-12
1079 Massachusetts Ave 01462 — 978-582-4115
Brian Spadafino, prin. — Fax 582-4153
Lunenburg MS — 6-8
1079 Massachusetts Ave 01462 — 978-582-4710
Tim Santry, prin. — Fax 582-4153

Twin City Christian S — 100/PK-12
194 Electric Ave 01462 — 978-582-4901
Jana Moritz, prin. — Fax 582-4978

Lynn, Essex, Pop. 87,864
Lynn SD — 14,300/PK-12
100 Bennett St 01905 — 781-593-1680
Catherine Latham, supt. — Fax 477-7487
www.lynnschools.org/
Breed MS — 1,200/6-8
90 OCallaghan Way 01905 — 781-477-7330
Julie Louf, prin. — Fax 581-6985
Classical HS — 1,500/9-12
235 OCallaghan Way 01905 — 781-477-7404
Gene Constantino, prin. — Fax 477-7212
English HS — 1,600/9-12
50 Goodridge St 01902 — 781-477-7366
Thomas Strangie, prin. — Fax 477-7365
Fecteau-Leary JSHS — 200/7-12
33 N Common St 01902 — 781-268-3007
Maura Durgin-Scully, prin. — Fax 268-3006
Lynn Vocational Technical Institute — Vo/Tech
80 Neptune Blvd 01902 — 781-477-7431
Robert Buontempo, prin. — Fax 477-7415

Marshall MS — 1,000/6-8
100 Brookline St 01902 — 781-477-7360
Molly Cohen, prin. — Fax 477-7355
Pickering MS — 600/6-8
70 Conomo Ave 01904 — 781-477-7440
Kevin Rittershaus, prin. — Fax 477-7202

St. Mary JSHS — 600/6-12
35 Tremont St 01902 — 781-595-7885
Grace Regan, head sch — Fax 595-4471

Lynnfield, Essex, Pop. 11,472
Lynnfield SD — 2,200/PK-12
525 Salem St 01940 — 781-334-9200
Jane Tremblay, supt. — Fax 334-9209
www.lynnfield.k12.ma.us
Lynnfield HS — 600/9-12
275 Essex St 01940 — 781-334-5820
Robert Cleary, prin. — Fax 334-7207
Lynnfield MS — 800/5-8
505 Main St 01940 — 781-334-5810
Stephen Ralston, prin. — Fax 334-7203

Malden, Middlesex, Pop. 56,660
Malden SD — 6,500/PK-12
77 Salem St 02148 — 781-397-6100
Dr. Charles Grandson, supt. — Fax 397-7276
www.maldenps.org
Malden HS — 1,800/9-12
77 Salem St 02148 — 781-397-6000
Edward Lombardi, prin. — Fax 397-7224

Blaine The Beauty Career School — Post-Sec.
347 Pleasant St 02148 — 781-397-7400
Malden Catholic HS — 600/9-12
99 Crystal St 02148 — 781-322-3098
Br. Thomas Puccio, prin. — Fax 397-0573
New England Hair Academy — Post-Sec.
492 Main St # 500 02148 — 781-324-6799
Salter School — Post-Sec.
2 Florence St 02148 — 781-324-5454

Manchester, Essex, Pop. 5,286
Manchester Essex Regional SD — 1,500/PK-12
PO Box 1407 01944 — 978-526-4919
Pamela Beaudoin, supt. — Fax 526-7585
www.mersd.org
Manchester Essex Regional HS — 500/9-12
36 Lincoln St 01944 — 978-526-4412
Patricia Puglisi, prin. — Fax 526-2046
Manchester Essex Regional MS — 400/6-8
36 Lincoln St 01944 — 978-526-2022
Joanne Maino, prin. — Fax 526-2046

Mansfield, Bristol, Pop. 7,170
Mansfield SD — 4,300/K-12
2 Park Row 02048 — 508-261-7500
Zeffro Gianetti, supt. — Fax 261-7509
www.mansfieldschools.com
Mansfield HS — 1,400/9-12
250 East St 02048 — 508-261-7540
Michael Connolly, prin. — Fax 339-0259
Qualters MS — 1,100/6-8
240 East St 02048 — 508-261-7530
Suzanne Ryan, prin. — Fax 261-7535

Al-Noor Academy — 100/6-12
20 Church St 02048 — 508-261-7077

Marblehead, Essex, Pop. 19,576
Marblehead SD — 3,100/PK-12
9 Widger Rd 01945 — 781-639-3140
Maryann Perry, supt. — Fax 639-3149
www.marbleheadschools.org
Marblehead HS — 1,100/9-12
2 Humphrey St 01945 — 781-639-3100
Daniel Bauer, prin. — Fax 639-3105
Marblehead Veterans MS — 500/7-8
217 Pleasant St 01945 — 781-639-3120
Matthew Fox, prin. — Fax 639-3130

Marion, Plymouth, Pop. 1,426

Tabor Academy — 500/9-12
66 Spring St 02738 — 508-748-2000
John Quirk, head sch — Fax 291-6666

Marlborough, Middlesex, Pop. 36,087
Assabet Valley Regional Vocational SD
215 Fitchburg St 01752 — 508-485-9430
Ernest Houle, supt. — Fax 460-3472
www.assabettech.com
Assabet Valley Regional Technical HS — Vo/Tech
215 Fitchburg St 01752 — 508-485-9430
Mark Hollick, prin. — Fax 460-3472

Marlborough SD — 4,600/PK-12
17 Washington St 01752 — 508-460-3509
Maureen Greulich, supt. — Fax 485-1142
www.mps-edu.org
Hildreth S — 100/Alt
85 Sawin St 01752 — 508-460-3505
Toby Peterson, dir. — Fax 460-3746
Marlborough HS — 1,100/9-12
431 Bolton St 01752 — 508-460-3500
Charles Caliri, prin. — Fax 460-3501
Whitcomb MS — 1,400/5-8
25 Union St 01752 — 508-460-3502
Brian Daniels, prin. — Fax 460-3597

Hillside S — 100/5-9
404 Robin Hill St 01752 — 508-485-2824
David Beecher, hdmstr. — Fax 485-4420

Marshfield, Plymouth, Pop. 4,261
Marshfield SD — 4,300/PK-12
76 S River St 02050 — 781-834-5000
Jeffrey Granatino, supt. — Fax 834-5070
www.mpsd.org

Furnace Brook MS 1,100/6-8
500 Furnace St 02050 781-834-5020
Patrick Sullivan, prin. Fax 834-5899
Marshfield HS 1,300/9-12
167 Forest St 02050 781-834-5050
Robert Keuther, prin. Fax 834-5040

Mashpee, Barnstable
Mashpee SD 1,700/PK-12
150A Old Barnstable Rd 02649 508-539-1500
Brian Hyde, supt. Fax 477-5805
www.mashpee.k12.ma.us
Mashpee HS 400/9-12
500 Old Barnstable Rd 02649 508-539-3600
Mark Balestracci, prin. Fax 539-3607
Mashpee MS 300/7-8
500 Old Barnstable Rd 02649 508-539-3601
Mark Balestracci, prin. Fax 539-3603

Mattapoisett, Plymouth, Pop. 2,949
Old Rochester Regional SD 1,200/7-12
135 Marion Rd 02739 508-758-2772
Dr. Douglas White, supt. Fax 758-2802
www.oldrochester.org
Old Rochester Regional HS 700/9-12
135 Marion Rd 02739 508-758-3745
Michael Devoll, prin. Fax 758-3167
Old Rochester Regional JHS 500/7-8
133 Marion Rd 02739 508-758-4928
Kevin Brogioli, prin. Fax 758-6021

Maynard, Middlesex, Pop. 9,932
Maynard SD 1,400/PK-12
3R Tiger Dr 01754 978-897-2222
Dr. Robert Gerardi Ed.D., supt. Fax 897-4610
www.maynard.k12.ma.us
Maynard HS 400/8-12
1 Tiger Dr 01754 978-897-8891
Charles Caragianes, prin. Fax 897-6089

Medfield, Norfolk, Pop. 6,407
Medfield SD 2,700/PK-12
459 Main St Fl 3 02052 508-359-2302
Jeffrey Marsden, supt. Fax 359-9829
www.medfield.net
Blake MS 700/6-8
24 Pound St 02052 508-359-2396
Nathaniel Vaughn, prin. Fax 359-0134
Medfield HS 900/9-12
88R South St 02052 508-359-4367
Robert Parga, prin. Fax 359-2963

Montrose S 200/6-12
29 North St 02052 508-359-2423
Dr. Karen E. Bohlin Ed.D., head sch Fax 359-2597

Medford, Middlesex, Pop. 53,960
Medford SD 4,500/PK-12
489 Winthrop St 02155 781-393-2442
Roy Belson, supt. Fax 393-2322
www.medford.k12.ma.us
Andrews MS 500/6-8
3000 Mystic Valley Pkwy 02155 781-393-2228
Paul D'Alleva, prin. Fax 395-8128
Curtis-Tufts Alternative S 50/Alt
437 Main St 02155 781-393-2343
Brian Twomey, dir. Fax 393-0699
McGlynn MS 500/6-8
3004 Mystic Valley Pkwy 02155 781-393-2333
Jacob Edwards, prin. Fax 393-5462
Medford HS 1,100/9-12
489 Winthrop St 02155 781-393-2301
John Perella, prin. Fax 395-1468
Medford Vo-Tech HS Vo/Tech
489 Winthrop St 02155 781-393-2260
Heidi Riccio, dir. Fax 393-2293

Lawrence Memorial/Regis College Post-Sec.
170 Governors Ave 02155 781-306-6600
St. Clement S 200/K-12
579 Boston Ave 02155 617-393-5600
Robert Chevrier, prin. Fax 396-3230
The Elizabeth Grady School of Esthetics Post-Sec.
34 Salem St 02155 781-395-1971
Tufts University Post-Sec.
520 Boston Ave 02155 617-628-5000

Medway, Norfolk, Pop. 9,931
Medway SD 2,100/PK-12
45 Holliston St 02053 508-533-3222
Armand Pires Ph.D., supt. Fax 533-3226
www.medwayschools.org
Medway HS 800/9-12
88 Summer St 02053 508-533-3227
Timothy McCarron, prin. Fax 533-3246
Medway MS 800/5-8
45 Holliston St 02053 508-533-3230
Cari Lynne Perchase, prin. Fax 533-3257

Melrose, Middlesex, Pop. 26,480
Melrose SD 3,700/PK-12
360 Lynn Fells Pkwy 02176 781-662-2000
Cyndy Taymore, supt. Fax 979-2149
www.melroseschools.com
Melrose HS 900/9-12
360 Lynn Fells Pkwy 02176 781-979-2200
Jason Merrill, prin. Fax 979-2205
Melrose Veterans Memorial MS 900/6-8
350 Lynn Fells Pkwy 02176 781-979-2100
Brent Conway, prin. Fax 979-2104

Mendon, Worcester
Mendon-Upton Regional SD 2,400/PK-12
150 North Ave 01756 508-634-1585
Joseph Maruszczak M.Ed., supt. Fax 634-1582
www.mursd.org
Miscoe Hill S 800/5-8
148 North Ave 01756 508-634-1590
Ann Farrell, prin. Fax 634-1576

Other Schools – See Upton

Bethany Christian Academy 100/PK-12
15 Cape Rd 01756 508-634-8171
Cheri McCutchen, dir. Fax 478-4706

Methuen, Essex, Pop. 46,662
Methuen SD 6,900/PK-12
10 Ditson Pl 01844 978-722-6000
Judith Scannell, supt. Fax 722-6002
www.methuen.k12.ma.us
Methuen HS 1,700/9-12
1 Ranger Rd 01844 978-722-6040
Richard Barden, prin. Fax 722-6042

Fellowship Christian Academy 100/PK-12
1 Fellowship Way 01844 978-686-9373
Joann Spain, admin. Fax 685-7466
Presentation of Mary Academy 100/9-12
209 Lawrence St 01844 978-682-9391
Rose Maria Redman, prin. Fax 975-3595

Middleboro, Plymouth, Pop. 7,135
Middleborough SD 3,200/PK-12
30 Forest St 02346 508-946-2000
Brian Lynch, supt. Fax 946-2004
www.middleboro.k12.ma.us
Middleboro HS 800/9-12
71 E Grove St 02346 508-946-2010
Paul Branagan, prin. Fax 946-8852
Nichols MS 800/6-8
112 Tiger Dr 02346 508-946-2020
Martin Geoghegan, prin. Fax 946-2019

Milford, Worcester, Pop. 23,757
Milford SD 3,500/PK-12
31 W Fountain St 01757 508-478-1100
Kevin McIntyre Ed.D., supt. Fax 478-1459
www.milfordpublicschools.com
Milford HS 1,100/9-12
31 W Fountain St 01757 508-478-1110
Carolyn Banach, prin. Fax 478-1460
Stacy MS 600/6-8
66 School St 01757 508-478-1180
Nancy Angelini, prin. Fax 634-2370

Millbury, Worcester, Pop. 12,228
Millbury SD 1,800/PK-12
12 Martin St 01527 508-865-9501
Gregory Myers, supt. Fax 865-0888
www.millburyschools.org
Millbury JSHS 700/7-12
12 Martin St 01527 508-865-5841
Tara Bennett, prin. Fax 865-5845

Millis, Norfolk, Pop. 4,081
Millis SD 1,400/PK-12
245 Plain St 02054 508-376-7000
Nancy Gustafson, supt. Fax 376-7020
www.millisps.org
Millis HS 400/9-12
245 Plain St 02054 508-376-7010
Robert Mullaney, prin. Fax 376-7020
Millis MS 500/5-8
245 Plain St 02054 508-376-7014
Maureen Knowlton, prin. Fax 376-7020

Milton, Norfolk, Pop. 26,216
Milton SD 3,900/PK-12
25 Gile Rd 02186 617-696-4808
Mary C. Gormley, supt. Fax 696-5099
www.miltonps.org
Milton HS 1,000/PK-PK, 9-
25 Gile Rd 02186 617-696-4470
James Jette, prin. Fax 696-6990
Pierce MS 900/6-8
451 Central Ave 02186 617-696-4568
Dr. Karen Spaulding, prin. Fax 698-2238

Curry College Post-Sec.
1071 Blue Hill Ave 02186 617-333-0500
Fontbonne Academy 400/9-12
930 Brook Rd 02186 617-696-3241
Susan Degnan, head sch Fax 696-7688
Milton Academy 1,000/K-12
170 Centre St 02186 617-898-1798
Todd Bland, hdmstr. Fax 898-1700

Monson, Hampden, Pop. 2,101
Monson SD 1,200/PK-12
PO Box 159 01057 413-267-4150
Cheryl Clarke, supt. Fax 267-4163
www.monsonschools.com
Granite Valley MS 400/5-8
21 Thompson St 01057 413-267-4155
Mary Cieplik, prin. Fax 267-4624
Monson HS 300/9-12
55 Margaret St 01057 413-267-4589
William Metzger, prin. Fax 267-4157

Montague, Franklin
Gill-Montague SD
Supt. — See Turners Falls
Great Falls MS 200/6-8
224 Turnpike Rd 01351 413-863-7300
Ann Leonard, prin. Fax 863-7354
Turners Falls HS 300/9-12
222 Turnpike Rd 01351 413-863-7200
Thomas Osborn, prin. Fax 863-7353

Mount Hermon, Franklin

Northfield Mt. Hermon S 600/9-12
1 Lamplighter Way 01354 413-498-3000
Peter Fayroian, hdmstr. Fax 498-3170

Nantucket, Nantucket, Pop. 7,268
Nantucket SD 1,500/PK-12
10 Surfside Rd 02554 508-228-7285
William Cozort, supt. Fax 325-5318
www.npsk.org
Nantucket HS 500/9-12
10 Surfside Rd 02554 508-228-7280
John Buckey, prin. Fax 825-7518
Peirce MS 300/6-8
10 Surfside Rd 02554 508-228-7283
Peter Cohen, prin. Fax 325-7597

Natick, Middlesex, Pop. 30,700
Natick SD 5,300/PK-12
13 E Central St 01760 508-647-6500
Dr. Peter Sanchioni Ph.D., supt. Fax 647-6506
www.natickps.org/
Kennedy MS 700/5-8
165 Mill St 01760 508-647-6650
Andrew Zitoli, prin. Fax 647-6658
Natick HS 1,400/9-12
15 West St 01760 508-647-6600
Brian Harrigan, prin. Fax 651-7372
Wilson MS 900/5-8
22 Rutledge Rd 01760 508-647-6670
Teresa Carney, prin. Fax 647-6678

Walnut Hill S for the Arts 300/9-12
12 Highland St 01760 508-653-4312
Antonio Viva, head sch Fax 655-3726

Needham, Norfolk, Pop. 28,386
Needham SD 5,500/PK-12
1330 Highland Ave 02492 781-455-0400
Dr. Daniel Gutekanst, supt. Fax 455-0417
www.needham.k12.ma.us/
Pollard MS 900/7-8
200 Harris Ave 02492 781-455-0480
Tamatha Bibbo, prin. Fax 455-0413
Other Schools – See Needham Heights

Franklin W. Olin College of Engineering Post-Sec.
Olin Way 02492 781-292-2300
Haddad MS 200/6-8
110 May St 02492 781-449-0133
Jane Abel, head sch Fax 449-8096
St. Sebastians S 400/7-12
1191 Greendale Ave 02492 781-449-5200
William Burke, hdmstr. Fax 449-5630

Needham Heights, Norfolk
Needham SD
Supt. — See Needham
Needham HS 1,600/9-12
609 Webster St 02494 781-455-0800
Aaron Sicotte, prin. Fax 449-5111

New Bedford, Bristol, Pop. 86,721
Greater New Bedford Reg Vo/Tech HSD
1121 Ashley Blvd 02745 508-998-3321
James O'Brien, supt. Fax 995-7268
www.gnbvt.edu
Greater New Bedford Reg. Vo Tech HS Vo/Tech
1121 Ashley Blvd 02745 508-998-3321
Michael Watson, prin. Fax 995-7268

New Bedford SD 12,500/PK-12
455 County St 02740 508-997-4511
Dr. Pia Durkin Ph.D., supt. Fax 997-0298
www.newbedfordschools.org
Keith MS 800/6-8
225 Hathaway Blvd 02740 508-997-4511
Dr. Paula Bailey, prin. Fax 996-2040
New Bedford HS 2,400/9-12
230 Hathaway Blvd 02740 508-997-4511
Bernadette Coelho, hdmstr. Fax 991-7483
Normandin MS 1,000/6-8
81 Felton St 02745 508-997-4511
Stephen Farrell, prin. Fax 995-6975
Roosevelt MS 700/6-8
119 Frederick St 02744 508-997-4511
Daniel Bossolt, prin. Fax 997-1198
Trinity Day Academy 50/Alt
181 Hillman St 02740 508-997-4511
Matthew Kravitz, prin. Fax 991-7483
Whaling City Alternative S 100/Alt
455 County St 02740 508-997-4511
Arnold Chamanlal, prin.

LaBaron Hairdressing Academy Post-Sec.
281 Union St 02740 508-996-6611
Nativity Prep S 100/5-8
66 Spring St 02740 508-994-3800
Jay Goldrick, prin. Fax 994-3434
Nazarene Christian Academy 200/PK-12
764 Hathaway Rd 02740 508-992-7944
Susan Helm, prin. Fax 328-9513
Rob Roy Academy Post-Sec.
1872 Acushnet Ave 02746 508-995-8711
St. Luke's Hospital Post-Sec.
101 Page St 02740 508-997-1525
Salter School Post-Sec.
950 Kings Hwy Ste 4 02745 774-328-3500

Newburyport, Essex, Pop. 17,171
Newburyport SD 2,100/PK-12
70 Low St 01950 978-465-4456
Susan Viccaro, supt. Fax 462-3495
www.newburyport.k12.ma.us/
Newburyport HS 700/9-12
241 High St 01950 978-465-4440
Michael Parent, prin. Fax 465-2198
Nock MS 500/6-8
70 Low St 01950 978-465-4447
Lisa Furlong, prin. Fax 465-4074

Newton, Middlesex, Pop. 83,100
Newton SD
Supt. — See Newtonville

Bigelow MS 500/6-8
42 Vernon St 02458 617-552-7800
Todd Harrison, prin. Fax 552-7752
Oak Hill MS 600/6-8
130 Wheeler Rd 02459 617-559-9200
Dr. John Harutunian, prin. Fax 552-5547

Hebrew College Post-Sec.
160 Herrick Rd 02459 617-559-8600
Lasell College Post-Sec.
1844 Commonwealth Ave 02466 617-243-2000
Massachusetts School Professional Psych. Post-Sec.
1 Wells Ave 02459 617-327-6777
Mt. Alvernia HS 200/7-12
790 Centre St 02458 617-969-2260
Eileen McLaughlin, hdmstr. Fax 969-4246
New England School of Acupuncture Post-Sec.
150 California St 02458 617-558-1788
Newton Country Day S 400/5-12
785 Centre St 02458 617-244-4246
Sr. Barbara Rogers, hdmstr. Fax 965-5313

Newton Center, See Newton
Newton SD
Supt. — See Newtonville
Brown MS 700/6-8
125 Meadowbrook Rd 02459 617-559-6900
John Jordan, prin. Fax 552-7729
Newton South HS 1,800/9-12
140 Brandeis Rd 02459 617-559-6700
Joel Stembridge, prin. Fax 559-6701

Andover Newton Theological School Post-Sec.
210 Herrick Rd 02459 617-964-1100
Mt. Ida College Post-Sec.
777 Dedham St 02459 617-928-4500

Newtonville, See Newton
Newton SD 12,600/PK-12
100 Walnut St 02460 617-559-6100
David Fleishman, supt. Fax 559-6101
www.newton.k12.ma.us
Day MS 900/6-8
21 Minot Pl 02460 617-559-9100
Mark Aronson, prin. Fax 559-9103
Newton North HS 2,000/9-12
457 Walnut St 02460 617-559-6200
Henry Turner, prin. Fax 559-6204
Other Schools – See Newton, Newton Center

Norfolk, Norfolk
King Philip Regional SD 2,100/7-12
18 King St 02056 508-520-7991
Dr. Elizabeth Zielinski, supt.
www.kingphilip.org
King Philip MS 800/7-8
18 King St 02056 508-541-7324
Dr. Susan Gilson, prin. Fax 541-3467
Other Schools – See Wrentham

North Adams, Berkshire, Pop. 13,389
North Adams SD 1,500/PK-12
37 Main St Ste 200 01247 413-776-1458
Barbara Malkas, supt. Fax 776-1685
www.napsk12.org/
Drury HS 500/8-12
1130 S Church St 01247 413-662-3240
Amy Meehan, prin. Fax 662-3239

Northern Berkshire Vocational Regnl SD
70 Hodges Xrd 01247 413-663-5383
James Brosnan, supt. Fax 664-9424
www.mccanntech.org
McCann Technical S Vo/Tech
70 Hodges Xrd 01247 413-663-5383
Justin R. Kratz, prin. Fax 664-9424

C.H. McCann Technical School Post-Sec.
70 Hodges Crossroads 01247 413-663-5383
Massachusetts College of Liberal Arts Post-Sec.
375 Church St 01247 413-662-5000

Northampton, Hampshire, Pop. 27,865
Northampton SD 2,700/PK-12
212 Main St Rm 200 01060 413-587-1315
Dr. John Provost, supt. Fax 587-1318
www.northampton-k12.us/
Northampton HS 900/9-12
380 Elm St 01060 413-587-1346
Bryan Lombardi, prin. Fax 587-1374
Other Schools – See Florence

Northampton-Smith SD
80 Locust St 01060 413-587-1414
Kevin Farr, supt. Fax 587-1405
smithtech.org
Smith Vocational & Agricultural HS Vo/Tech
80 Locust St 01060 413-587-1414
Dr. Andrew Linkenhoker, prin. Fax 587-1406

Smith College 01063 Post-Sec.
413-584-2700

North Andover, Essex, Pop. 22,792
North Andover SD 4,800/PK-12
566 Main St 01845 978-794-1503
Dr. Jennifer Price, supt. Fax 794-0231
www.northandoverpublicschools.com
North Andover HS 1,400/9-12
430 Osgood St 01845 978-794-1711
Deborah Holman, prin. Fax 688-3536
North Andover MS 1,200/6-8
495 Main St 01845 978-794-1870
Joan McQuade, prin. Fax 794-3619

Brooks S 400/9-12
1160 Great Pond Rd 01845 978-725-6300
John Packard, head sch Fax 725-6215

Merrimack College Post-Sec.
315 Turnpike St 01845 978-837-5000

North Attleboro, Bristol, Pop. 16,178
North Attleborough SD 4,400/PK-12
6 Morse St 02760 508-643-2100
Suzan Cullen, supt. Fax 643-2110
www.naschools.net
North Attleboro HS 1,200/9-12
1 Wilson W Whitty Way 02760 508-643-2115
Craig Juelis, prin. Fax 643-2173
North Attleboro MS 1,200/6-8
564 Landry Ave 02760 508-643-2130
Dr. Victoria Ekk, prin. Fax 643-2134

Northborough, Worcester, Pop. 6,020
Northborough-Southborough SD
Supt. — See Southborough
Algonquin Regional HS 1,500/9-12
79 Bartlett St 01532 508-351-7010
Thomas Mead, prin. Fax 393-9226
Melican MS 600/6-8
145 Lincoln St 01532 508-351-7020
Michelle Karb, prin. Fax 351-7006

North Brookfield, Worcester, Pop. 2,236
North Brookfield SD 600/PK-12
10 New School Dr 01535 508-867-9821
Dr. Marilyn Tencza, supt. Fax 867-8148
www.nbschools.org
North Brookfield JSHS 200/7-12
10 New School Dr 01535 508-867-7131
William Evans, prin. Fax 867-3496

North Chelmsford, Middlesex
Chelmsford SD
Supt. — See Chelmsford
Chelmsford HS 1,600/9-12
200 Richardson Rd 01863 978-251-5111
Stephen Murray, prin. Fax 251-5117

North Dartmouth, Bristol, Pop. 8,000
Dartmouth SD
Supt. — See South Dartmouth
Dartmouth MS 1,000/6-8
366 Slocum Rd 02747 508-997-9333
Darren Doane, prin. Fax 999-7720

Bishop Stang HS 700/9-12
500 Slocum Rd 02747 508-996-5602
Peter Shaughnessy, prin. Fax 994-6756
University of Massachusetts Dartmouth Post-Sec.
285 Old Westport Rd 02747 508-999-8000

North Dighton, Bristol
Dighton-Rehoboth Regional SD 2,900/PK-12
2700 Regional Rd 02764 508-252-5000
Dr. Anthony C. Azar, supt. Fax 252-5024
www.drregional.org
Dighton-Rehoboth Regional HS 900/9-12
2700 Regional Rd 02764 508-252-5025
Kevin Braga, prin. Fax 252-5079
Other Schools – See Dighton, Rehoboth

North Eastham, Barnstable, Pop. 1,790
Nauset SD
Supt. — See Orleans
Nauset Regional HS 1,000/9-12
PO Box 1887 02651 508-255-1505
Eduardo MacDonald, prin. Fax 255-9701

North Easton, Bristol, Pop. 4,400
Easton SD 3,400/PK-12
PO Box 359 02356 508-230-3200
Dr. Andrew Keough, supt. Fax 238-3563
www.easton.k12.ma.us
Ames HS 1,200/9-12
100 Lothrop St 02356 508-230-3210
Wesley Paul, prin. Fax 238-7325
Easton MS 1,000/6-8
98 Columbus Ave 02356 508-230-3222
R. Luke Carroll, prin. Fax 230-3102

Stonehill College Post-Sec.
320 Washington St 02357 508-565-1000

Northfield, Franklin, Pop. 1,078
Pioneer Valley SD 1,000/PK-12
168 Main St 01360 413-498-2911
Ruth Miller, supt. Fax 498-0045
sites.google.com/a/pvrsdk12.org/pvrsdhome/
Pioneer Valley Regional JSHS 500/7-12
97 F Sumner Turner Rd 01360 413-498-2931
Jean Bacon, prin. Fax 498-0184

Redemption Christian Academy 50/PK-12
PO Box 183 01360 518-272-6679
Joan Massey, prin.

North Quincy, See Quincy
Quincy SD
Supt. — See Quincy
Atlantic MS 500/6-8
86 Hollis Ave 02171 617-984-8727
Maureen MacNeil, prin. Fax 984-8646
North Quincy HS 1,200/9-12
316 Hancock St 02171 617-984-8745
Robert Shaw, prin. Fax 984-8647

North Reading, Middlesex, Pop. 12,002
North Reading SD 2,600/PK-12
189 Park St 01864 978-664-7810
Jon Bernard, supt. Fax 664-0252
www.north-reading.k12.ma.us/
North Reading HS 800/9-12
189 Park St 01864 978-664-7800
Anthony Loprete, prin. Fax 664-7826
North Reading MS 700/6-8
189 Park St 01864 978-664-7806
Catherine O'Connell, prin. Fax 276-0679

Norton, Bristol, Pop. 1,899
Norton SD 2,600/PK-12
64 W Main St 02766 508-285-0100
Joseph Baeta, supt. Fax 285-0199
www.norton.k12.ma.us
Norton HS 700/9-12
66 W Main St 02766 508-285-0160
Megan Lafayette, prin. Fax 285-0164
Norton MS 600/6-8
215 W Main St 02766 508-285-0140
Vincent Hayward, prin. Fax 286-9457

Legacy Christian Academy 100/PK-12
1 New Taunton Ave 02766 508-952-2997
Katrina Joseph, head sch Fax 952-2977
Wheaton College Post-Sec.
26 E Main St 02766 508-286-8200

Norwell, Plymouth
Norwell SD 2,300/PK-12
322 Main St 02061 781-659-8800
Matthew Keegan, supt. Fax 659-8805
www.norwellschools.org
Norwell HS 700/9-12
18 South St 02061 781-659-8810
William Fish, prin. Fax 659-1824
Norwell MS 600/6-8
328 Main St 02061 781-659-8814
Derek Sulc, prin. Fax 659-8822

Norwood, Norfolk, Pop. 27,997
Norwood SD 3,500/PK-12
PO Box 67 02062 781-762-6804
James Hayden, supt. Fax 762-0229
www.norwood.k12.ma.us/
Coakley MS 700/6-8
PO Box 67 02062 781-762-7880
Jacqueline Mann, prin. Fax 255-5630
Norwood HS 1,000/9-12
PO Box 67 02062 781-769-2333
Jonathan Bourn, prin. Fax 762-0826

FINE Mortuary College Post-Sec.
150 Kerry Pl 02062 781-762-1211
Universal Technical Institute Post-Sec.
1 Upland Rd Ste 200 02062 781-948-2000

Oak Bluffs, Dukes
Martha's Vineyard SD
Supt. — See Vineyard Haven
Martha's Vineyard Regional HS 700/9-12
PO Box 1385 02557 508-693-1033
Sara Dingledy, prin. Fax 693-1891

Orange, Franklin, Pop. 3,955
Ralph C. Mahar Regional SD 800/7-12
PO Box 680 01364 978-544-2920
Tari Thomas, supt. Fax 544-8383
www.rcmahar.org
Mahar Regional S 700/7-12
PO Box 680 01364 978-544-2542
Scott Hemlin, prin. Fax 544-8383
Other Schools – See Gardner

Orleans, Barnstable, Pop. 1,586
Nauset SD 1,600/6-12
78 Eldridge Park Way 02653 508-255-8800
Thomas M. Conrad, supt. Fax 240-2351
www.nausetschools.org
Nauset Regional MS 600/6-8
70 S Orleans Rd 02653 508-255-0016
Dr. Maxine Minkoff, prin. Fax 240-1105
Other Schools – See North Eastham

Osterville, Barnstable, Pop. 2,911

Cape Cod Academy 300/PK-12
50 Osterville-W Barnstable 02655 508-428-5400
Thomas Trigg, head sch Fax 428-0701

Oxford, Worcester, Pop. 6,042
Oxford SD 1,500/PK-12
4 Maple Rd 01540 508-987-6050
Dr. Mark Garceau, supt. Fax 987-6054
www.oxps.org
Oxford HS 400/8-12
495 Main St 01540 508-987-6081
Ross Thibault, prin. Fax 987-6083
Project C.O.F.F.E.E. Alt
495 Main St 01540 508-987-6090
David Nugent, prin. Fax 987-6097

Palmer, Hampden, Pop. 4,069
Palmer SD 1,300/PK-12
24 Converse St Ste 1 01069 413-283-2650
Patricia Gardner, supt. Fax 283-2655
www.palmerschools.org
Palmer HS 500/8-12
4105 Main St 01069 413-283-6511
Susan North, prin. Fax 283-3476

Pathfinder Vocational-Technical SD
240 Sykes St 01069 413-283-9701
Dr. Gerald Paist, supt. Fax 284-0032
www.pathfindertech.org/
Pathfinder Reg Vocational Technical HS Vo/Tech
240 Sykes St 01069 413-283-9701
Mary Jane Rickson, prin. Fax 284-0032

Paxton, Worcester

Anna Maria College Post-Sec.
50 Sunset Ln 01612 508-849-3330

Peabody, Essex, Pop. 50,101
Peabody SD, 21 Johnson St 01960 6,100/PK-12
Herbert Levine Ph.D., supt. 978-531-1600
www.peabody.k12.ma.us/

Higgins MS 1,300/6-8
85 Perkins St 01960 978-536-4800
Todd Bucey, prin. Fax 536-4810
Peabody Veterans Memorial HS 1,800/9-12
485 Lowell St 01960 978-536-4500
Eric Buckley, prin. Fax 536-4565

Bishop Fenwick HS 600/9-12
99 Margin St 01960 978-587-8300
Br. Thomas Zoppo, admin. Fax 587-8309

Pembroke, Plymouth
Pembroke SD 3,300/PK-12
72 Pilgrim Rd 02359 781-829-0832
Erin Obey, supt. Fax 826-6957
www.edlinesites.net/pages/PembrokePS
Pembroke Community MS 600/7-8
559 School St 02359 781-293-8627
Donna McGarrigle, prin. Fax 294-0916
Pembroke HS 1,000/9-12
80 Learning Ln 02359 781-293-9281
Marc Talbot, prin. Fax 293-2812

Pepperell, Middlesex, Pop. 2,459
North Middlesex SD 3,400/PK-12
45 Main St 01463 978-597-8713
Joan Landers, supt. Fax 597-6534
nmrsd.org
Nissitissit MS 600/5-8
33 Chase Ave 01463 978-433-0114
Diane Gleason, prin. Fax 433-0118
Other Schools – See Townsend

Pittsfield, Berkshire, Pop. 43,503
Pittsfield SD 5,900/PK-12
269 1st St 01201 413-499-9512
Dr. Jason McCandless, supt. Fax 448-2643
www.pittsfield.net
Herberg MS 600/6-8
501 Pomeroy Ave 01201 413-448-9640
Gina Coleman, prin. Fax 448-9644
Pittsfield HS 1,000/9-12
300 East St 01201 413-499-9535
Matthew Bishop, prin. Fax 442-2540
Reid MS 500/6-8
950 North St 01201 413-448-9620
Linda Whitacre, prin. Fax 443-1587
Taconic HS 900/9-12
96 Valentine Rd 01201 413-448-9600
John Vosburgh, prin. Fax 499-4835

Berkshire Community College Post-Sec.
1350 West St 01201 413-499-4660
Berkshire Medical Center Post-Sec.
725 North St 01201 413-447-2144
Mildred Elley School Post-Sec.
505 East St 01201 413-499-8618
Miss Hall's S 200/9-12
PO Box 1166 01202 413-443-6401
Julia Heaton, head sch Fax 448-2994
St. Joseph Central HS 200/9-12
22 Maplewood Ave 01201 413-447-9121
Dr. Amy Gelinas, prin. Fax 443-7020

Plymouth, Plymouth, Pop. 7,138
Plymouth SD 7,700/PK-12
253 S Meadow Rd 02360 508-830-4300
Dr. Gary Maestas, supt. Fax 746-1873
www.plymouth.k12.ma.us
Plymouth Community IS 1,000/6-8
117 Long Pond Rd 02360 508-830-4450
Brian Palladino, prin. Fax 830-4464
Plymouth North HS 1,200/9-12
41 Obery St 02360 508-830-4400
Kathleen McSweeney, prin. Fax 830-4405
Plymouth South HS 1,200/9-12
490 Long Pond Rd 02360 508-224-7512
Mark Fornaciari, prin. Fax 224-6765
Plymouth South MS 800/5-8
488 Long Pond Rd 02360 508-224-2725
Steven Morgenweck, prin. Fax 224-5660

Quincy, Norfolk, Pop. 89,796
Quincy SD 9,200/PK-12
34 Coddington St 02169 617-984-8700
Dr. Richard DeCristofaro, supt. Fax 984-8965
www.quincypublicschools.com
Broad Meadows MS 300/6-8
50 Calvin Rd 02169 617-984-8723
Daniel Gilbert, prin. Fax 984-8834
Central MS 600/6-8
875 Hancock St 02170 617-984-8725
Rick DeCristofaro, prin. Fax 984-8661
Point Webster MS 400/5-8
60 Lancaster St 02169 617-984-6600
Christine Barrett, prin. Fax 984-6609
Quincy HS, 100 Coddington St 02169 1,500/9-12
Lawrence Taglieri, prin. 617-376-3355
Sterling MS 300/5-8
444 Granite St 02169 617-984-8729
John Franceschini, prin. Fax 984-8640
Other Schools – See North Quincy

Eastern Nazarene College Post-Sec.
23 E Elm Ave 02170 617-745-3000
Mansfield Beauty School Post-Sec.
200 Parkingway 02169 617-479-1090
Massachusetts School of Barbering Post-Sec.
64 Ross Way 02169 617-770-4444
Quincy College Post-Sec.
1250 Hancock St 02169 617-984-1700
Woodward S 100/6-12
1102 Hancock St 02169 617-773-5610
Carol Andrews, head sch Fax 770-1551

Randolph, Norfolk, Pop. 30,586
Randolph SD 2,900/PK-12
40 Highland Ave 02368 781-961-6205
Thomas Anderson, supt. Fax 961-6295
www.randolph.k12.ma.us
Randolph Community MS 700/6-8
225 High St 02368 781-961-6243
Thea Stovell, prin. Fax 961-6286
Randolph HS 700/9-12
70 Memorial Pkwy 02368 781-961-6220
Terry Decarbo, prin. Fax 961-6235

Raynham, Bristol, Pop. 2,100
Bridgewater-Raynham Regional SD
Supt. — See Bridgewater
Raynham MS 700/5-8
420 Titicut Rd 02767 508-977-0504
Richard Florence, prin. Fax 977-0659

Reading, Middlesex, Pop. 24,477
Reading SD 4,400/PK-12
82 Oakland Rd 01867 781-944-5800
Dr. John Doherty, supt. Fax 942-9149
reading.k12.ma.us/
Coolidge MS 400/6-8
89 Birch Meadow Dr 01867 781-942-9158
Sarah Marchant, prin. Fax 942-9118
Parker MS 600/6-8
45 Temple St 01867 781-944-1236
Richele Shankland, prin. Fax 942-9008
Reading Memorial HS 1,300/9-12
62 Oakland Rd 01867 781-944-8200
Adam Bakr, prin. Fax 942-5435

Austin Preparatory HS 700/6-12
101 Willow St 01867 781-944-4900
Dr. James Hickey, hdmstr. Fax 944-7530

Rehoboth, Bristol
Dighton-Rehoboth Regional SD
Supt. — See North Dighton
Beckwith MS 600/5-8
330R Winthrop St 02769 508-252-5080
Joseph Pirraglia, prin. Fax 252-5082

Revere, Suffolk, Pop. 50,075
Revere SD 6,800/PK-12
101 School St 02151 781-286-8226
Dr. Dianne Kelly, supt. Fax 286-8221
www.revereps.mec.edu
Anthony MS 500/6-8
107 Newhall St 02151 781-388-7520
Joanne Willett, prin. Fax 388-7521
Garfield MS 500/6-8
176 Garfield Ave 02151 781-286-8298
Samantha Meier, prin. Fax 286-3557
Revere HS 1,600/9-12
101 School St 02151 781-286-8222
Lourenco Garcia Ed.D., prin. Fax 286-8378
Rumney Marsh Academy 500/6-8
140 American Legion Hwy 02151 781-388-3500
Richard Gallucci, prin. Fax 485-8443
Seacoast HS 100/Alt
15 Everard Ave 02151 781-485-2715
Steven Magno, prin. Fax 485-2718

Rochester, Plymouth
Old Colony Reg Vocational Technical HSD
476 North Ave 02770 508-763-8011
Frank Cote, supt. Fax 763-9821
www.oldcolony.us
Old Colony Reg Vocational Tech HS Vo/Tech
476 North Ave 02770 508-763-8011
Karen Guenette, prin. Fax 763-9821

Rockland, Plymouth, Pop. 16,123
Rockland SD 2,200/K-12
34 MacKinlay Way 02370 781-878-3893
Dr. Alan Cron, supt. Fax 982-1483
rocklandschools.org
Rockland HS 600/9-12
52 MacKinlay Way 02370 781-871-0541
John Harrison, prin. Fax 878-0158
Rogers MS 700/5-8
100 Taunton Ave 02370 781-878-4341
Elizabeth Bohn, prin. Fax 871-8448

Calvary Chapel Academy 100/PK-12
PO Box 409 02370 781-871-1043
Richard Colello, hdmstr. Fax 792-3902

Rockport, Essex, Pop. 4,922
Rockport SD 1,000/PK-12
24 Jerdens Ln 01966 978-546-1200
Robert Liebow, supt. Fax 546-1205
www.rpk12.org
Rockport HS 300/9-12
24 Jerdens Ln 01966 978-546-1234
Greg Bach, prin. Fax 546-1205
Rockport MS 300/6-8
26 Jerdens Ln 01966 978-546-1250
Gregg Bach, prin. Fax 546-1205

Roslindale, See Boston
Boston SD
Supt. — See Boston
Irving MS 400/5-8
105 Cummins Hwy 02131 617-635-8072
Carmen Davis, prin. Fax 635-9363

Roxbury, See Boston
Boston SD
Supt. — See Boston
Fenway HS 300/9-12
67 Alleghany St 02120 617-635-9911
Geoffrey Walker, hdmstr. Fax 635-9204
Greater Egleston Community HS 200/9-12
80 School St 02119 617-635-6429
Julie Coles, hdmstr. Fax 635-6469

Madison Park Technical Vocational HS Vo/Tech
75 Malcolm X Blvd 02120 617-635-8970
Shawn Shackelford, hdmstr. Fax 635-9831
O'Bryant HS of Mathematics & Science 1,400/7-12
55 Malcolm X Blvd 02120 617-635-9932
Tanya Freeman-Wisdom, hdmstr. Fax 635-7769
Timilty MS 600/6-8
205 Roxbury St 02119 617-635-8109
Renee McCall, prin. Fax 635-8115

Roxbury Crossing, See Boston

Roxbury Community College Post-Sec.
1234 Columbus Ave 02120 617-427-0060

Rutland, Worcester, Pop. 2,084
Wachusett Regional SD
Supt. — See Jefferson
Central Tree MS 400/6-8
281 Main St 01543 508-886-0073
Todd Stewart, prin. Fax 886-0141

Devereux Center in Massachusetts Post-Sec.
PO Box 219 01543 508-886-4746

Salem, Essex, Pop. 40,441
Salem SD 4,300/PK-12
29 Highland Ave 01970 978-740-1212
Margarita Ruiz, supt. Fax 740-3083
www.salemk12.org
Collins MS 600/6-8
29 Highland Ave 01970 978-740-1191
Glenn Burns, prin. Fax 740-1183
Salem HS, 77 Willson St 01970 1,100/9-12
David Angeramo, prin. 978-745-9300
Salem Preparatory HS 50/Alt
Museum Place Mall 2nd Floor 01970 978-740-1171
Scott Gray, prin. Fax 740-1239

Salem State University Post-Sec.
352 Lafayette St 01970 978-542-6000

Sandwich, Barnstable, Pop. 2,933
Sandwich SD 1,900/PK-12
33 Water St 02563 508-888-1054
Dr. Pamela A. Gould, supt. Fax 888-9505
www.sandwichk12.org
Other Schools – See East Sandwich

Saugus, Essex, Pop. 26,187
Saugus SD 2,800/PK-12
23 Main St 01906 781-231-5000
David DeRousi, supt. Fax 233-9424
www.saugus.k12.ma.us
Belmonte MS 700/6-8
25 Dow St 01906 781-231-5052
Kerry Robbins, prin. Fax 233-5665
Saugus HS 700/9-12
1 Pierce Memorial Dr 01906 781-231-5027
Michael Hashem, prin. Fax 231-5030

Scituate, Plymouth, Pop. 5,135
Scituate SD 3,000/PK-12
606 Chief Justice Cushing 02066 781-545-8759
John McCarthy, supt. Fax 545-6291
www.scituate.k12.ma.us/
Gates IS 500/7-8
327 First Parish Rd 02066 781-545-8760
Ryan Lynch, prin. Fax 545-8767
Scituate HS 900/9-12
606 Chief Justice Cushing 02066 781-545-8750
Robert Wargo, prin. Fax 545-8758

Seekonk, Bristol, Pop. 13,046
Seekonk SD 2,000/PK-12
25 Water Ln 02771 508-399-5106
Arlene Bosco, supt. Fax 399-5128
seekonk.sharpschool.com/
Hurley MS 500/6-8
650 Newman Ave 02771 508-761-7570
Dr. William Whalen, prin. Fax 336-9630
Seekonk HS 600/9-12
261 Arcade Ave 02771 508-336-7272
Dr. Christopher Jones, prin. Fax 336-8535

MotoRing Technical Training Institute Post-Sec.
1241 Fall River Ave 02771 866-454-6884

Sharon, Norfolk, Pop. 5,546
Sharon SD 3,400/K-12
75 Mountain St 02067 781-784-1570
Timothy Farmer, supt. Fax 784-1573
www.sharon.k12.ma.us
Sharon HS 1,100/9-12
181 Pond St 02067 781-784-1554
Dr. Jose Libano Ed.D., prin. Fax 784-1550
Sharon MS 800/6-8
75 Mountain St 02067 781-784-1560
Kevin O'Rourke, prin. Fax 784-8432

Sheffield, Berkshire
Southern Berkshire Regional SD 800/PK-12
PO Box 339 01257 413-229-8778
David Hastings, supt. Fax 229-2913
sbrsd.org
Mount Everett Regional HS 300/7-12
PO Box 219 01257 413-229-8734
Glenn Devoti, prin. Fax 229-2044

Berkshire S 400/9-12
245 N Undermountain Rd 01257 413-229-8511
Pieter Mulder, head sch Fax 229-1010

Shelburne Falls, Franklin, Pop. 1,695
Mohawk Trail SD 1,000/PK-12
24 Ashfield Rd 01370 413-625-0192
Michael Buoniconti, supt. Fax 625-0196
www.mohawkschools.org

Mohawk Trail Regional HS 500/7-12
26 Ashfield Rd 01370 413-625-9811
Lynn Dole, prin. Fax 625-6652

Shirley, Middlesex, Pop. 1,415
Ayer Shirley SD
Supt. — See Ayer
Ayer-Shirley MS 400/6-8
1 Hospital Rd 01464 978-772-8600
Roberta Aikey, prin. Fax 425-0474

Shrewsbury, Worcester, Pop. 25,900
Shrewsbury SD 6,000/PK-12
100 Maple Ave 01545 508-841-8400
Joseph Sawyer, supt. Fax 841-8490
schools.shrewsbury-ma.gov
Oak MS 1,000/7-8
45 Oak St 01545 508-841-1200
Ann Jones, prin. Fax 841-1223
Shrewsbury HS 1,600/9-12
64 Holden St 01545 508-841-8800
Todd Bazydlo, prin. Fax 841-8858

St. John's HS 1,100/9-12
378 Main St 01545 508-842-8934
Alex Zequeira, admin. Fax 842-3670

Somerset, Bristol, Pop. 17,980
Somerset Berkley Regional SD 1,000/9-12
580 Whetstone Hill Rd 02726 508-324-3100
Jeffrey Schoonover, supt. Fax 324-3118
www.sbregional.org
Somerset Berkley Regional HS 1,000/9-12
625 County St 02726 508-324-3115
David Lanczycki, prin. Fax 324-3118

Somerset SD 1,700/PK-8
580 Whetstone Hill Rd 02726 508-324-3100
Jeffrey Schoonover, supt. Fax 324-3104
www.somersetps.com
Somerset MS 600/6-8
1141 Brayton Ave 02726 508-324-3140
Pauline Camara Ph.D., prin. Fax 324-3145

Somerville, Middlesex, Pop. 71,913
Somerville SD 4,900/PK-12
8 Bonair St 02145 617-629-5200
Mary Skipper, supt. Fax 629-5661
www.somerville.k12.ma.us
Full Circle HS 100/Alt
8 Bonair St 02145 617-629-5640
Margaret DePasquale, prin. Fax 628-6836
Next Wave JHS 50/Alt
8 Bonair St 02145 617-629-5640
Margaret DePasquale, prin. Fax 628-6837
Somerville HS 1,300/9-12
81 Highland Ave 02143 617-629-5250
John Oteri, hdmstr. Fax 629-4763

Lincoln Technical Institute Post-Sec.
5 Middlesex Ave 02145 617-776-3500

South Attleboro, See Attleboro

Dayspring Christian Academy 300/PK-12
1052 Newport Ave 02703 508-761-5552
Rev. Jason Detty, admin. Fax 761-3577

Southborough, Worcester
Northborough-Southborough SD 4,600/PK-12
53 Parkerville Rd 01772 508-486-5115
Christine Johnson, supt. Fax 486-5123
www.nsboro.k12.ma.us
Trottier MS 500/6-8
49 Parkerville Rd 01772 508-485-2400
Keith Lavoie, prin. Fax 481-1506
Other Schools – See Northborough

St. Marks S 300/9-12
25 Marlboro Rd 01772 508-786-6000
John Warren, head sch Fax 786-6109

South Boston, See Boston
Boston SD
Supt. — See Boston
Excel HS 500/9-12
95 G St 02127 617-635-9870
Stephanie Sibley, hdmstr. Fax 635-9711

Southbridge, Worcester, Pop. 13,631
Southbridge SD 1,600/PK-12
25 Cole Ave 01550 508-764-5415
Dr. Jessica Huizenga, supt. Fax 764-3181
www.southbridgepublic.org
Southbridge HS 400/9-12
132 Torrey Rd 01550 508-764-5450
Andrae Townsel, prin. Fax 318-1687
Southbridge MS, 132 Torrey Rd 01550 6-8
Rebecca Sweetman, prin. 508-764-5440

South Dartmouth, Bristol, Pop. 9,850
Dartmouth SD 3,700/PK-12
8 Bush St 02748 508-997-3391
Dr. Bonny L. Gifford, supt. Fax 991-4184
dartmouthps.schoolfusion.us/
Dartmouth HS 1,100/9-12
555 Bakerville Rd 02748 508-961-2700
John Gould, prin. Fax 910-1410
Other Schools – See North Dartmouth

South Deerfield, Franklin, Pop. 1,861
Frontier Regional SD 600/7-12
219 Christian Ln 01373 413-665-1155
Lynn M. Carey Ed.D., supt. Fax 665-8506
www.frsu38.org
Frontier Regional JSHS 600/7-12
113 N Main St 01373 413-665-2118
Darius Modestow, prin. Fax 665-1518

South Easton, Bristol
Southeastern Regional Voc Tech SD
250 Foundry St 02375 508-230-1200
Luis Lopes, supt. Fax 230-1215
www.sersd.org
Southeastern Regional Vo-Tech HS Vo/Tech
250 Foundry St 02375 508-230-1200
David Wheeler, prin. Fax 230-1224

Southeastern Technical Institute Post-Sec.
250 Foundry St 02375 508-238-1860

South Hadley, Hampshire, Pop. 5,400
South Hadley SD 1,900/PK-12
116 Main St 01075 413-538-5060
Dr. Nicholas D. Young, supt. Fax 532-6284
www.southhadleyschools.org
Smith MS 600/5-8
100 Mosier St 01075 413-538-5074
Paul Plummer, prin. Fax 538-5003
South Hadley HS 600/9-12
153 Newton St 01075 413-538-5063
Diana Bonneville, prin. Fax 532-6538

Mt. Holyoke College Post-Sec.
50 College St 01075 413-538-2000

South Hamilton, Essex, Pop. 2,750

Gordon-Conwell Theological Seminary Post-Sec.
130 Essex St 01982 978-468-7111
Pingree S 300/9-12
537 Highland St 01982 978-468-4415
Dr. Timothy Johnson, head sch Fax 468-3758

South Lancaster, Worcester, Pop. 1,842

South Lancaster Academy 300/PK-12
PO Box 1129 01561 978-368-8544
Jeffrey Lambert, prin. Fax 365-2244

Southwick, Hampden
Southwick-Tolland-Granville Regional SD 1,200/PK-12
86 Powder Mill Rd 01077 413-569-5391
Jennifer Willard, supt. Fax 569-1711
www.stgrsd.org
Southwick Regional HS 500/7-12
93 Feeding Hills Rd 01077 413-569-6171
Joseph Turmel, prin. Fax 569-4109

South Yarmouth, Barnstable, Pop. 10,789
Dennis-Yarmouth SD 2,700/PK-12
296 Station Ave 02664 508-398-7600
Carol Woodbury, supt. Fax 398-7622
www.dy-regional.k12.ma.us/
Dennis-Yarmouth Regional HS 1,000/8-12
210 Station Ave 02664 508-398-7636
Kenneth Jenks, prin. Fax 398-7635

Spencer, Worcester, Pop. 5,615
Spencer-East Brookfield SD 1,400/PK-12
306 Main St 01562 508-885-8500
Dr. N. Tracy Crowe, supt. Fax 885-8504
www.sebrsd.org
Knox Trail JHS 400/5-8
73 Ash St 01562 508-885-8550
Jodi Bourassa, prin. Fax 885-8557
Prouty HS 500/9-12
302 Main St 01562 508-885-8505
Elizabeth York, prin. Fax 885-8511

Central Mass School of Massage & Therapy Post-Sec.
200 Main St 01562 508-885-0306

Springfield, Hampden, Pop. 149,577
Springfield SD 27,600/PK-12
1550 Main St 01103 413-787-7100
Daniel Warwick, supt. Fax 787-6713
www.springfieldpublicschools.com
Balliet MS 100/Alt
111 Seymour Ave 01109 413-787-7284
Chestnut Accelerated MS North 800/6-8
355 Plainfield St 01107 413-750-2333
Jason Hynek, prin. Fax 750-2351
Chestnut Accelerated MS South 6-8
355 Plainfield St 01107 413-750-2333
Nathaniel Higgins, prin. Fax 750-2351
Chestnut Accelerated MS Talented & Gift 6-8
355 Plainfield St 01107 413-750-2333
Colleen O'Connor, prin. Fax 750-2351
Duggan S 600/6-12
1015 Wilbraham Rd 01109 413-787-7410
Michael Calvanese, prin. Fax 750-2209
Forest Park MS 700/6-8
46 Oakland St 01108 413-787-7420
Thomas Mazza, prin. Fax 787-7419
Gateway to College at STCC 50/9-12
1 Armory Sq 01105 413-755-6344
Rhonda Reddick, prin.
Kennedy MS 600/6-8
1385 Berkshire Ave 01151 413-787-7510
Sam Wolfson, prin. Fax 787-7561
Kiley MS 700/6-8
180 Cooley St 01128 413-787-7240
Christopher Sutton, prin. Fax 787-7247
Liberty Preparatory Academy 50/Alt
37 Alderman St 01108 413-750-2484
Putnam Vocational Technical HS Vo/Tech
1300 State St 01109 413-787-7424
George Johnson, prin. Fax 787-7330
South End MS, 36 Margaret St 01105 300/6-8
Cheryl Despirt, prin. 413-750-2442
Springfield Central HS 2,100/9-12
1840 Roosevelt Ave 01109 413-787-7085
Thaddeus Tokarz, prin. Fax 787-7040
Springfield Conservatory of the Arts 6-12
34 Kopernick St 01151 413-787-6914
Ryan Kelly, prin.

Springfield HS 100/Alt
37 Alderman St 01108 413-787-7285
HS of Commerce 1,300/9-12
415 State St 01105 413-787-7220
Diane Bauer, prin. Fax 787-7041
Springfield HS of Science-Tech 1,500/9-12
1250 State St 01109 413-750-2000
Sara Pragluski, prin. Fax 750-2047
Springfield Public Day MS 100/Alt
118 Alden St 01109 413-787-7261
Rhonda Jacobs, prin.
Springfield Renaissance S 700/6-12
1170 Carew St 01104 413-750-2929
Arria Coburn, prin. Fax 750-2978
STEM Middle Academy 300/6-8
60 Alton St 01109 413-787-6750
Kevin Lalime, prin. Fax 787-6952
Van Sickle Academy 1,000/6-8
1170 Carew St 01104 413-750-2887
Anna Breen, prin. Fax 750-2972
Van Sickle International Baccalaureate S 6-8
1170 Carew St 01104 413-750-2887
Daisy Roman-Davis, prin. Fax 750-2972
Adult Education Center Adult
204 Boston Rd 01109 413-787-7210
Armando Feliciano, dir.
Other Schools – See Holyoke, Indian Orchard

American International College Post-Sec.
1000 State St 01109 413-737-7000
Branford Hall Career Institute Post-Sec.
112 Industry Ave 01104 413-781-2276
Commonwealth Academy 100/6-12
1 Ames Hill Dr 01105 413-285-8976
Dr. Marcus Ware, head sch Fax 363-2874
Grace Academy 50/K-12
60 Bowles Park 01104 413-241-7305
Mansfield Beauty School Post-Sec.
266 Bridge St 01103 413-788-7575
Pioneer Valley Christian Academy 300/PK-12
965 Plumtree Rd 01119 413-782-8031
Timothy Duff, hdmstr. Fax 782-8033
Springfield College Post-Sec.
263 Alden St 01109 413-748-3000
Springfield Technical Community College Post-Sec.
PO Box 9000 01102 413-781-7822
Western New England University Post-Sec.
1215 Wilbraham Rd 01119 413-782-3111

Sterling, Worcester
Wachusett Regional SD
Supt. — See Jefferson
Chocksett MS 400/5-8
40 Boutelle Rd 01564 978-422-6552
Christopher LaBreck, prin. Fax 422-7720

Stockbridge, Berkshire
Berkshire Hills SD 1,400/PK-12
PO Box 617 01262 413-298-4017
Dr. Peter Dillon, supt. Fax 298-4672
www.bhrsd.org
Other Schools – See Great Barrington

Berkshire Waldorf HS 50/9-12
14 Pine St 01262 413-298-3800
Stephen Sagarin Ph.D., head sch Fax 298-5132

Stoneham, Middlesex, Pop. 21,118
Stoneham SD 1,900/PK-12
149 Franklin St 02180 781-279-3802
Dr. Les Olson, supt. Fax 279-3818
www.stonehamschools.org
Stoneham HS 700/9-12
149 Franklin St 02180 781-279-3810
Donna Cargill, prin. Fax 279-2070
Stoneham MS 600/5-8
101 Central St 02180 781-279-3840
Christopher Banos, prin. Fax 279-3843

Edgewood/Greater Boston Academy 200/PK-12
108 Pond St 02180 781-438-4253
Angela Watson, prin. Fax 438-6857

Stoughton, Norfolk, Pop. 27,500
Stoughton SD 3,600/PK-12
232 Pearl St 02072 781-344-4000
Marguerite C. Rizzi Ed.D., supt. Fax 344-3789
www.stoughtonschools.org/
O'Donnell MS 900/6-8
211 Cushing St 02072 781-344-7002
Matt Colantonio, prin. Fax 297-5263
Stoughton HS 1,000/9-12
232 Pearl St 02072 781-344-7001
Juliette Miller, prin. Fax 341-6041

Stow, Middlesex
Nashoba Regional SD
Supt. — See Bolton
Hale MS 300/6-8
55 Hartley Rd 01775 978-897-4788
George King, prin. Fax 897-3631

Sudbury, Middlesex
Lincoln-Sudbury SD 1,600/9-12
390 Lincoln Rd 01776 978-443-9961
Bella Wong, supt. Fax 443-8824
www.lsrhs.net
Lincoln-Sudbury Regional HS 1,600/9-12
390 Lincoln Rd 01776 978-443-9961
Bella Wong, admin. Fax 443-8824

Sudbury SD 2,900/PK-8
40 Fairbank Rd Ste C 01776 978-639-3211
Anne Wilson, supt. Fax 443-9001
www.sudbury.k12.ma.us
Curtis MS 1,000/6-8
22 Pratts Mill Rd 01776 978-443-1071
Jeff Mela, prin. Fax 443-1098

Willow Hill S 100/6-12
98 Haynes Rd 01776 978-443-2581
Marilyn G. Reid, head sch Fax 443-7560

Sutton, Worcester
Sutton SD 1,600/PK-12
383 Boston Rd 01590 508-581-1600
Theodore Friend, supt. Fax 865-6463
www.suttonschools.net/
Sutton HS 400/9-12
383 Boston Rd 01590 508-581-1640
Ted McCarthy, prin. Fax 917-0063
Sutton MS 400/6-8
383 Boston Rd 01590 508-581-1630
Gerard Goyette, prin. Fax 865-6463

Swampscott, Essex, Pop. 13,607
Swampscott SD 2,200/K-12
207 Forest Ave 01907 781-596-8800
Pamela R. H. Angelakis M.Ed., supt. Fax 599-2502
www.swampscott.k12.ma.us
Swampscott HS 700/9-12
200 Essex St 01907 781-596-8830
Robert Murphy M.Ed., prin. Fax 599-2034
Swampscott MS 700/5-8
207 Forest Ave 01907 781-596-8820
Jason Calichman M.Ed., prin. Fax 593-2126

Marian Court College Post-Sec.
35 Littles Point Rd 01907 781-595-6768

Swansea, Bristol
Swansea SD 2,100/PK-12
1 Gardners Neck Rd 02777 508-675-1195
John J. Robidoux, supt. Fax 672-1040
www.swanseaschools.org
Case HS 600/9-12
70 School St 02777 508-675-7483
Brian McCann, prin. Fax 646-4405
Case JHS 500/6-8
195 Main St 02777 508-675-0116
Robert Silveira, prin. Fax 646-4413

Taunton, Bristol, Pop. 53,462
Bristol-Plymouth Regional-Tech SD
207 Hart St 02780 508-823-5151
Alexandre Magalhaes, supt. Fax 880-7287
www.bptech.org
Bristol-Plymouth Regional Technical S Vo/Tech
207 Hart St 02780 508-823-5151
Elizabeth Sullivan, prin. Fax 822-2687

Taunton SD 7,900/PK-12
215 Harris St 02780 508-821-1100
Dr. Julie Hackett, supt. Fax 821-1177
www.tauntonschools.org
Taunton Alternative HS 100/Alt
120 Cohannet St 02780 508-844-5822
Burt Delaney, prin. Fax 227-7170
Taunton HS 2,300/8-12
50 Williams St 02780 508-821-1101
Matt Mattos, prin. Fax 821-1362

Coyle & Cassidy MSHS 600/6-12
2 Hamilton St 02780 508-823-6164
Kathleen St. Laurent, prin. Fax 823-2530
Rob Roy Academy Post-Sec.
1 School St 02780 508-822-1405

Tewksbury, Middlesex, Pop. 11,000
Tewksbury SD 3,700/PK-12
139 Pleasant St 01876 978-640-7800
Christopher Malone, supt. Fax 640-7804
www.tewksbury.k12.ma.us
Tewksbury Memorial HS 1,000/9-12
320 Pleasant St 01876 978-640-7825
Kristen Vogel, prin. Fax 640-7829
Wynn MS 700/7-8
1 Griffin Way 01876 978-640-7846
John Weir, prin. Fax 640-7850

Electrology Institute of New England Post-Sec.
1501 Main St Ste 50 01876 800-548-6339
Salter School Post-Sec.
515 Woburn St 01876 978-934-9300

Townsend, Middlesex, Pop. 1,114
North Middlesex SD
Supt. — See Pepperell
Hawthorne Brook MS 500/5-8
64 Brookline St 01469 978-597-6914
Stephen Coughlan, prin. Fax 597-0354
North Middlesex Regional HS 1,000/9-12
19 Main St 01469 978-597-8721
Isaac Taylor, prin. Fax 597-0350

Turners Falls, Franklin, Pop. 4,349
Franklin County Technical SD
82 Industrial Blvd 01376 413-863-9561
Richard Martin, supt. Fax 863-2816
www.fcts.org
Franklin County Technical HS Vo/Tech
82 Industrial Blvd 01376 413-863-9561
Shawn Rickan, prin. Fax 863-2816

Gill-Montague SD 900/PK-12
35 Crocker Ave 01376 413-863-9324
Michael Sullivan, supt. Fax 863-4560
www.gmrsd.org
Other Schools – See Montague

Hallmark Institute of Photography Post-Sec.
PO Box 308 01376 413-863-2478

Tyngsboro, Middlesex
Greater Lowell Technical HSD
250 Pawtucket Blvd 01879 978-441-4800
Roger Bourgeois, supt. Fax 441-5353
www.gltech.org
Greater Lowell Technical HS Vo/Tech
250 Pawtucket Blvd 01879 978-454-5411
Roger Bourgeois, admin. Fax 441-5353

Tyngsborough SD 1,800/PK-12
50 Norris Rd 01879 978-649-7488
Donald Ciampa, supt. Fax 649-7199
www.tyngsboroughps.org/
Tyngsborough HS 500/9-12
36 Norris Rd 01879 978-649-7571
Jeffrey Ogden, prin. Fax 649-6530
Tyngsborough MS 500/6-8
50 Norris Rd 01879 978-649-3115
Christopher Pollet, prin. Fax 649-8673

Academy of Notre Dame HS 200/9-12
180 Middlesex Rd 01879 978-649-7611
Helen Kay, prin. Fax 649-2909

Upton, Worcester, Pop. 2,982
Blackstone Valley Vocational Regional SD
65 Pleasant St 01568 508-529-7758
Dr. Michael F. Fitzpatrick, supt. Fax 529-3079
www.valleytech.k12.ma.us
Blackstone Valley Regional Voc-Tech HS Vo/Tech
65 Pleasant St 01568 508-529-7758
Anthony E. Steele, prin. Fax 529-2403

Mendon-Upton Regional SD
Supt. — See Mendon
Nipmuc Regional HS 700/9-12
90 Pleasant St 01568 508-529-2130
John Clements, prin. Fax 529-2129

Uxbridge, Worcester, Pop. 3,400
Uxbridge SD 1,900/PK-12
21 S Main St 01569 508-278-8648
Kevin Carney, supt. Fax 278-8612
uxbridgeschools.com
McCloskey MS 500/6-8
62 Capron St 01569 508-278-8634
Leanne DeMarco, prin. Fax 278-8627
Uxbridge HS 500/9-12
300 Quaker Hwy 01569 508-278-8636
Michael Rubin, prin. Fax 278-8627

Vineyard Haven, Dukes, Pop. 1,950
Martha's Vineyard SD 1,000/K-12
4 Pine St 02568 508-693-2007
Dr. Matthew D'Andrea, supt. Fax 693-3190
www.mvyps.org
Other Schools – See Oak Bluffs

Wakefield, Middlesex, Pop. 24,651
Northeast Metro Vocational SD
100 Hemlock Rd 01880 781-246-0810
David DiBarri, supt. Fax 246-4919
northeastmetrotech.com
Northeast Metro Regional Vocational HS Vo/Tech
100 Hemlock Rd 01880 781-246-0810
Carla Scuzzarella Ed.D., prin. Fax 246-4919

Wakefield SD 3,400/PK-12
60 Farm St 01880 781-246-6400
Dr. Kim Smith, supt. Fax 245-9164
www.wakefield.k12.ma.us
Galvin MS 1,100/5-8
525 Main St 01880 781-246-6410
Adam Colantuoni, prin. Fax 224-5009
Wakefield Memorial HS 1,000/9-12
60 Farm St 01880 781-246-6440
Richard Metropolis, prin. Fax 246-6324

Nazareth Academy 100/9-12
27 Cordis St 01880 781-246-7600
Phyllis Morrison, prin. Fax 246-5400

Walpole, Norfolk, Pop. 5,864
Norfolk County Agricultural SD
400 Main St 02081 508-668-0268
Dr. Tammy Quinn, supt. Fax 668-0612
www.norfolkaggie.org
Norfolk County Agricultural HS Vo/Tech
400 Main St 02081 508-668-0268
Michael Cournoyer, prin. Fax 668-0612

Walpole SD 4,000/PK-12
135 School St 02081 508-660-7200
Lincoln Lynch Ed.D., supt. Fax 668-1167
www.walpole.k12.ma.us/
Johnson MS 400/6-8
111 Robbins Rd 02081 508-660-7242
William Hahn, prin. Fax 660-7240
Walpole HS 1,200/9-12
275 Common St 02081 508-660-7257
Stephen Imbusch, prin. Fax 850-7958
Other Schools – See East Walpole

Waltham, Middlesex, Pop. 59,317
Waltham SD 5,200/PK-12
617 Lexington St 02452 781-314-5400
Drew Echelson Ed.D., supt. Fax 314-5411
www.walthampublicschools.org
Kennedy MS 500/6-8
655 Lexington St 02452 781-314-5560
John Cawley, prin. Fax 314-5571
McDevitt MS 500/6-8
75 Church St 02452 781-314-5590
Michael Sabin, prin. Fax 314-5601
Waltham HS 1,400/9-12
617 Lexington St 02452 781-314-5440
Gregory DeMeo, prin. Fax 647-0309

Bentley University Post-Sec.
175 Forest St 02452 781-891-2000
Blaine The Beauty Career School Post-Sec.
314 Moody St 02453 781-899-1500
Brandeis University Post-Sec.
415 South St 02453 781-736-2000
Center for Digital Imaging Arts at BU Post-Sec.
282 Moody St 02453 800-808-2342
Chapel Hill-Chauncy Hall S 200/9-12
785 Beaver St 02452 781-314-0800
Lance Conrad, hdmstr. Fax 894-5205
Gann Academy 300/9-12
333 Forest St 02452 781-642-6800
Rabbi Marc Baker, hdmstr. Fax 642-6805
Sodexho Marriott Services Post-Sec.
200 5th Ave 02451 800-926-7429

Ware, Hampshire, Pop. 6,031
Ware SD 1,300/PK-12
PO Box 240 01082 413-967-4271
Dr. Marlene DiLeo, supt. Fax 967-9580
www.wareps.org
Ware JSHS 500/7-12
237 West St 01082 413-967-6234
Darren Elwell, prin. Fax 967-9053

Wareham, Plymouth, Pop. 19,232
Wareham SD 2,100/PK-12
48 Marion Rd Ste 302 02571 508-291-3500
Kimberly Shaver-Hood, supt. Fax 291-3578
www.warehamps.org
Wareham Cooperative Alternative S 100/Alt
4 Viking Dr 02571 508-291-3550
Jane Fondulis, prin. Fax 291-3594
Wareham HS 600/9-12
7 Viking Dr 02571 508-291-3510
Scott Palladino, prin. Fax 291-3577
Wareham MS 800/5-8
4 Viking Dr 02571 508-291-3550
Peter Steedman, prin. Fax 291-3580

Warren, Worcester, Pop. 1,379
Quaboag Regional SD 1,100/PK-12
PO Box 1538 01083 413-436-9256
Dr. Brett Kustigian, supt. Fax 436-9738
www.quaboagrsd.org
Quaboag Regional MSHS 400/7-12
PO Box 909 01083 413-436-5991
Mary Lafreniere, prin. Fax 436-9636

Watertown, Middlesex, Pop. 30,947
Watertown SD 2,700/PK-12
30 Common St 02472 617-926-7700
Jean Fitzgerald, supt. Fax 923-1234
www.watertown.k12.ma.us
Watertown HS 700/9-12
50 Columbia St 02472 617-926-7760
Shirley Lundberg, hdmstr. Fax 926-7723
Watertown MS 500/6-8
68 Waverley Ave 02472 617-926-7783
James Carter, prin. Fax 926-5407

Cortiva Institute - Boston Post-Sec.
103 Morse St 02472 617-612-6900
Perkins School for the Blind Post-Sec.
175 N Beacon St 02472 617-972-7285

Wayland, Middlesex, Pop. 2,500
Wayland SD 2,700/K-12
PO Box 408 01778 508-358-3763
Paul Stein, supt. Fax 358-7708
www.wayland.k12.ma.us
Wayland HS 800/9-12
264 Old Connecticut Path 01778 508-358-7746
Allyson Mizoguchi, prin. Fax 358-8082
Wayland MS 700/6-8
201 Main St 01778 508-655-6670
Betsy Gavron, prin. Fax 655-2548

Webster, Worcester, Pop. 11,152
Webster SD 1,200/PK-12
PO Box 430 01570 508-943-0104
Richard Lind, supt. Fax 943-0315
www.webster-schools.org
Bartlett HS 500/9-12
52 Lake Pkwy 01570 508-943-8552
Steven Knowlton, prin. Fax 949-8274
Webster MS 300/5-8
75 Poland St 01570 508-943-1922
Jennifer Lundwall, prin. Fax 949-2648

All Saints Academy St. Louis Campus 200/5-8
48 Negus St 01570 508-943-0257
David Grenier, prin. Fax 461-9666

Wellesley, Norfolk, Pop. 27,391
Wellesley SD 5,000/PK-12
40 Kingsbury St 02481 781-446-6210
David Lussier, supt. Fax 446-6207
www.wellesley.k12.ma.us
Wellesley HS 1,400/9-12
50 Rice St 02481 781-446-6290
Jamie Chisum, prin. Fax 237-6004
Wellesley MS 1,200/6-8
50 Kingsbury St 02481 781-446-6235
Mark Ito, prin. Fax 446-6208

Dana Hall S 500/5-12
45 Dana Rd 02482 781-235-3010
Katherine L. Bradley, head sch Fax 237-5949
Massachusetts Bay Community College Post-Sec.
50 Oakland St 02481 781-239-3000
Wellesley College Post-Sec.
106 Central St 02481 781-283-1000

Wendell, Franklin

Lake Grove School-Maple Valley Post-Sec.
PO Box 767 01379 888-585-9007

Wenham, Essex, Pop. 4,212
Hamilton-Wenham SD 1,900/PK-12
5 School St 01984 978-468-5310
Dr. Michael M. Harvey, supt. Fax 468-7889
www.hwschools.net/

Other Schools – See Hamilton

Academy at Penguin Hall 9-12
36 Essex St 01984 978-468-6200
Julie Calzini, dir.
Gordon College Post-Sec.
255 Grapevine Rd 01984 978-927-2300

West Barnstable, Barnstable, Pop. 1,508

Cape Cod Community College Post-Sec.
2240 Iyannough Rd 02668 508-362-2131

Westborough, Worcester, Pop. 3,951
Westborough SD 3,600/PK-12
45 W Main St 01581 508-836-7700
Amber Bock, supt. Fax 836-7704
westborough.ma.schoolwebpages.com
Gibbons MS 600/7-8
20 Fisher St 01581 508-836-7740
John Foley, prin. Fax 836-7744
Westborough HS 1,100/9-12
90 W Main St 01581 508-836-7720
Brian Callaghan, prin. Fax 836-7723

Porter & Chester Institute Post-Sec.
129 Flanders Rd 01581 508-366-0296

West Boylston, Worcester, Pop. 6,611
West Boylston SD 900/PK-12
125 Crescent St 01583 508-835-2917
Elizabeth Schaper, supt. Fax 835-8992
www.wbschools.com
West Boylston JSHS 500/6-12
125 Crescent St 01583 508-835-4475
Christopher Fournier, prin. Fax 835-3925

Salter College Post-Sec.
184 W Boylston St 01583 508-853-1074

West Bridgewater, Plymouth
West Bridgewater SD 1,300/PK-12
2 Spring St 02379 508-894-1230
Dr. Patricia Oakley, supt. Fax 894-1232
wbridgewaterschools.org
West Bridgewater MSHS 700/7-12
155 W Center St 02379 508-894-1220
Mark Bodwell, prin. Fax 897-0537

New England Baptist Academy 100/PK-12
560 N Main St 02379 508-584-5188
Kevin Hicks, prin. Fax 584-7555

Westfield, Hampden, Pop. 40,552
Westfield SD 5,700/PK-12
94 N Elm St Ste 101 01085 413-572-6403
Stefan Czaporowski, supt. Fax 572-6518
www.schoolsofwestfield.org
North MS 700/6-8
350 Southampton Rd 01085 413-572-6441
Katie Ross, prin. Fax 572-1669
South MS 600/6-8
30 W Silver St 01085 413-568-1900
Justin Baker, prin. Fax 572-4892
Westfield HS 1,400/9-12
177 Montgomery Rd 01085 413-572-6466
Fax 572-6346
Westfield Technical Academy Vo/Tech
33 Smith Ave 01085 413-572-6533
Joseph Langone, prin. Fax 572-6542

St. Mary's Parish HS 100/9-12
27 Bartlett St 01085 413-568-5692
Nichole Nietsche, head sch Fax 562-3501
Westfield State University Post-Sec.
577 Western Ave 01085 413-572-5300

Westford, Middlesex
Nashoba Valley Technical SD
100 Littleton Rd 01886 978-692-4711
Denise Pigeon, supt. Fax 392-0570
www.nashobatech.net
Nashoba Valley Technical HS Vo/Tech
100 Littleton Rd 01886 978-692-4711
Matthew Ricard, prin. Fax 392-0570

Westford SD 5,200/PK-12
23 Depot St 01886 978-692-5560
Everett Olsen, supt. Fax 392-4497
westfordk12.us/
Blanchard MS 600/6-8
14 West St 01886 978-692-5582
Timothy Hislop, prin. Fax 692-5598
Stony Brook MS 700/6-8
9 Farmers Way 01886 978-692-2708
Christopher Chew, prin. Fax 692-5391
Westford Academy 1,600/9-12
30 Patten Rd 01886 978-692-5570
James Antonelli, prin. Fax 692-5502

Westhampton, Hampshire
Hampshire SD 800/7-12
19 Stage Rd 01027 413-527-7200
Dr. Craig Jurgensen, supt. Fax 529-9497
www.hr-k12.org/
Hampshire Regional JSHS 800/7-12
19 Stage Rd 01027 413-527-7680
Kristen Smidy, prin. Fax 527-1831

West Newbury, Essex
Pentucket SD 2,800/PK-12
22 Main St 01985 978-363-2280
Jeffrey Mulqueen, supt. Fax 363-1165
www.prsd.org
Pentucket Regional HS 800/9-12
24 Main St 01985 978-363-5507
John Seymour, prin. Fax 363-2730
Pentucket Regional MS 500/7-8
20 Main St 01985 978-363-2957
Kenneth Kelley, prin. Fax 363-2720

Weston, Middlesex, Pop. 10,200
Weston SD 2,300/PK-12
89 Wellesley St 02493 781-786-5200
Dr. Robert Tremblay, supt. Fax 786-5209
www.westonschools.org/
Weston HS 800/9-12
444 Wellesley St 02493 781-786-5800
Anthony Parker, prin. Fax 786-5829
Weston MS 500/6-8
456 Wellesley St 02493 781-786-5600
John Gibbons, prin. Fax 786-5609

Blessed John XXIII National Seminary Post-Sec.
558 South Ave 02493 781-899-5500
Cambridge S of Weston 300/9-12
45 Georgian Rd 02493 781-642-8600
Jane Moulding, hdmstr. Fax 398-8344
Regis College Post-Sec.
235 Wellesley St 02493 781-768-7000
Rivers S 500/6-12
333 Winter St 02493 781-235-9300
Edward V. Parsons, head sch Fax 239-3614

West Peabody, Essex

Covenant Christian Academy 200/PK-12
83 Pine St 01960 978-535-7100
Andrea Bergstrom, head sch Fax 535-7123

Westport, Bristol, Pop. 13,852
Westport Community SD 800/PK-12
17 Main Rd 02790 508-636-1140
Dr. Ann Marie Dargon Ed.D., supt. Fax 636-1146
www.westportschools.org
Westport JSHS 400/7-12
19 Main Rd 02790 508-636-1050
Cheryl Tutalo, prin. Fax 636-1053

West Roxbury, See Boston
Boston SD
Supt. — See Boston
Ohrenberger S 600/3-8
175 W Boundary Rd 02132 617-635-8157
Naomi Krakow, prin. Fax 635-8163
Urban Science Academy 500/9-12
1205 VFW Pkwy 02132 617-635-8930
Jeff Cook, prin. Fax 635-7895
West Roxbury Academy 600/9-12
1205 VFW Pkwy 02132 617-635-8935
Rudolph Weekes, prin. Fax 635-7912

Catholic Memorial HS 700/7-12
235 Baker St 02132 617-469-8000
Richard Chisholm, prin. Fax 325-0888
Roxbury Latin S 300/7-12
101 Saint Theresa Ave 02132 617-325-4920
Kerry Brennan, hdmstr. Fax 325-3585

West Springfield, Hampden, Pop. 27,989
West Springfield SD 3,700/PK-12
26 Central St Ste 33 01089 413-263-3290
Michael Richard M.Ed., supt. Fax 739-8748
www.wsps.org
West Springfield HS 1,200/9-12
425 Piper Rd 01089 413-263-3400
Dr. Vito Perrone, prin. Fax 781-4836
West Springfield MS 900/6-8
31 Middle School Dr 01089 413-263-3406
Peter Gillen, prin. Fax 781-0965

Kay Harvey Hairdressing Academy Post-Sec.
11 Central St 01089 413-732-7117

Westwood, Norfolk, Pop. 12,557
Westwood SD 3,200/PK-12
220 Nahatan St 02090 781-326-7500
Dr. John Antonucci, supt. Fax 326-8154
www.westwood.k12.ma.us
Thurston MS 800/6-8
850 High St 02090 781-326-7500
Allison Borchers, prin. Fax 326-2709
Westwood HS 900/9-12
200 Nahatan St 02090 781-326-7500
Sean Bevan, prin. Fax 461-8561

Xaverian Brothers HS 900/9-12
800 Clapboardtree St 02090 781-326-6392
Br. Daniel Skala, hdmstr. Fax 320-0458

Weymouth, Norfolk, Pop. 53,900
Weymouth SD 6,800/PK-12
111 Middle St 02189 781-335-1460
Jennifer Curtis-Whipple, supt. Fax 335-8777
www.weymouthschools.org
Weymouth HS 2,000/9-12
1 Wildcat Way 02190 781-337-7500
Peter Haviland, prin. Fax 340-2568
Other Schools – See East Weymouth

South Shore Christian Academy 300/PK-12
45 Broad St 02188 781-331-4340
Dr. Mark Jennings, head sch Fax 331-9956

Whitinsville, Worcester, Pop. 6,595
Northbridge SD 2,600/PK-12
87 Linwood Ave 01588 508-234-8156
Dr. Catherine Stickney, supt. Fax 234-8469
www.nps.org/
Northbridge HS 700/9-12
427 Linwood Ave 01588 508-234-6221
Michael Gauthier, prin. Fax 234-0802
Northbridge MS 800/5-8
171 Linwood Ave 01588 508-234-8718
John Zywien, prin. Fax 234-9718

Whitinsville Christian S 500/PK-12
279 Linwood Ave 01588 508-234-8211
Lance Engbers, hdmstr. Fax 234-0624

Whitman, Plymouth, Pop. 13,240
Whitman-Hanson SD 4,200/PK-12
610 Franklin St 02382 781-618-7000
Ruth Gilbert-Whitner Ed.D., supt. Fax 618-7099
www.whrsd.k12.ma.us
Whitman-Hanson Regional HS 1,200/9-12
600 Franklin St 02382 781-618-7020
Jeffrey Szymaniak, prin. Fax 618-7099
Whitman MS 600/6-8
100 Corthell Ave 02382 781-618-7035
George Ferro, prin. Fax 618-7091
Other Schools – See Hanson

Wilbraham, Hampden, Pop. 3,882
Hampden-Wilbraham SD 3,300/PK-12
621 Main St 01095 413-596-3884
Albert G. Ganem, supt. Fax 599-1328
www.hwrsd.org
Minnechaug Regional HS 1,200/9-12
621 Main St 01095 413-596-9011
Stephen Hale, prin. Fax 596-8907
Wilbraham MS 600/6-8
466 Stony Hill Rd 01095 413-596-9061
Peter Dufresne, prin. Fax 596-9382
Other Schools – See Hampden

Wilbraham & Monson Academy 400/6-12
423 Main St 01095 413-596-6811
Brian Easler, head sch Fax 599-1749

Williamstown, Berkshire, Pop. 4,791
Mt. Greylock Regional SD / S Union 71 1,200/PK-12
1781 Cold Spring Rd 01267 413-458-9582
Dr. Douglas Dias, supt. Fax 458-2856
www.wlschools.org
Mount Greylock Regional JSHS 600/7-12
1781 Cold Spring Rd 01267 413-458-9582
Mary MacDonald, prin. Fax 458-2856

Buxton S 100/9-12
291 South St 01267 413-458-3919
Peter Smith, dir. Fax 458-9427
Williams College 01267 Post-Sec.
413-597-3131

Wilmington, Middlesex, Pop. 22,011
Wilmington SD 3,500/PK-12
161 Church St 01887 978-694-6000
Sean Gallagher, supt. Fax 694-6005
wpsk12.com
Wilmington HS 900/9-12
159 Church St 01887 978-694-6060
Linda Peters, prin. Fax 694-6074
Wilmington MS 900/6-8
25 Carter Ln 01887 978-694-6080
Amy Gerade, prin. Fax 694-6085

Winchendon, Worcester, Pop. 4,143
Winchendon SD 1,300/PK-12
175 Grove St 01475 978-616-1452
Steven Haddad, supt. Fax 297-5250
www.winchendonk12.org
Murdock Academy for Success Alt
89 Ash St 01475 978-616-1690
Kris Provost, dir. Fax 297-5250
Murdock HS 300/9-12
3 Memorial Dr 01475 978-616-1653
Joshua Romano, prin. Fax 297-5250
Murdock MS 400/6-8
3 Memorial Dr 01475 978-616-1603
Joshua Romano, prin. Fax 297-5250

Winchendon S 200/9-12
172 Ash St 01475 978-297-1223
John Kerney, hdmstr. Fax 297-0911

Winchester, Middlesex, Pop. 20,931
Winchester SD 4,400/PK-12
40 Samoset Rd 01890 781-721-7004
Judith Evans, supt. Fax 721-0016
www.winchester.k12.ma.us
McCall MS 1,100/6-8
458 Main St 01890 781-721-7026
Jorge Goncalves, prin. Fax 721-0886
Winchester HS 1,200/9-12
80 Skillings Rd 01890 781-721-7020
Denise Mahoney, prin. Fax 721-7042

Winthrop, Suffolk, Pop. 18,127
Winthrop SD 2,000/PK-12
1 Metcalf Sq 02152 617-846-5500
John Macero, supt. Fax 539-0891
www.winthrop.k12.ma.us
Winthrop HS 600/9-12
400 Main St 02152 617-846-5505
Matthew Crombie, prin. Fax 539-0535
Winthrop MS, 400 Main St 02152 500/6-8
Brian Curley, prin. 617-846-5507

Woburn, Middlesex, Pop. 37,207
Woburn SD 4,800/PK-12
55 Locust St 01801 781-937-8233
Mark Donovan, supt. Fax 937-0668
www.edline.net/pages/WPS
Joyce MS 600/6-8
55 Locust St 01801 781-937-8233
Thomas Qualey, prin. Fax 937-8279
Kennedy MS 600/6-8
41 Middle St 01801 781-937-8230
Carl Nelson, prin. Fax 937-8223
Woburn Memorial HS 1,300/9-12
88 Montvale Ave 01801 781-937-8210
Jessica Callanan, prin. Fax 937-8216

Catherine Hinds Institute of Esthetics Post-Sec.
300 Wildwood Ave 01801 781-935-3344
Millenium Training Institute Post-Sec.
600 W Cummings Park # 2550 01801 888-388-9981
New England Tractor Trailer Training Sch Post-Sec.
1600 Osgood St 01815 800-333-2888
Porter & Chester Institute Post-Sec.
8 Presidential Way 01801 781-935-1108

Woods Hole, Barnstable, Pop. 767

Woods Hole Oceanographic Institution Post-Sec.
266 Woods Hole Rd 02543 508-289-2252

Worcester, Worcester, Pop. 175,487
Massachusetts Academy of Math & Science 100/11-12
85 Prescott St 01605 508-831-5859
Michael Barney, dir. Fax 831-5880
www.massacademy.org/
Massachusetts Academy of Math & Science 100/11-12
85 Prescott St 01605 508-831-5859
Michael Barney, dir. Fax 831-5880

Worcester SD 23,800/PK-12
20 Irving St 01609 508-799-3115
Maureen Binienda, supt. Fax 799-3119
worcesterschools.org
Burncoat HS 1,000/9-12
179 Burncoat St 01606 508-799-3300
William Foley, prin. Fax 799-8206
Burncoat MS 600/7-8
135 Burncoat St 01606 508-799-3390
Lisa Houlihan, prin. Fax 799-8207
Caradonio New Citizens Center Alt
1407A Main St 01603 508-799-3494
Steven Alzamora, prin. Fax 799-3222
Claremont Academy 400/7-12
15 Claremont St 01610 508-799-3077
Ricci Hall, prin. Fax 799-8202
Creamer Center Alt
120 Granite St 01604 508-799-3476
Timothy Whalen, prin. Fax 799-3459
Doherty Memorial HS 1,300/9-12
299 Highland St 01602 508-799-3270
Sally Maloney, prin. Fax 799-3276
Forest Grove MS 1,000/7-8
495 Grove St 01605 508-799-3420
Mark Williams, prin. Fax 799-8218
North HS 1,300/9-12
140 Harrington Way 01604 508-799-3370
Lisa Dyer, prin. Fax 799-8252
South Community HS 1,300/9-12
170 Apricot St 01603 508-799-3325
Diane Lynch, prin. Fax 799-8242
Sullivan MS 800/7-8
140 Apricot St 01603 508-799-3350
Dr. Josephine Robertson, prin. Fax 799-8244
University Park Campus S 200/7-12
12 Freeland St 01603 508-799-3591
Daniel St. Louis, prin. Fax 799-8159
Worcester East MS 700/7-8
420 Grafton St 01604 508-799-3430
Dr. Rose Dawkins, prin. Fax 799-8251
Worcester Technical HS Vo/Tech
1 Skyline Dr 01605 508-799-1940
Kyle Brenner, prin. Fax 799-1933

Assumption College Post-Sec.
500 Salisbury St 01609 508-767-7000
Bancroft S 500/PK-12
110 Shore Dr 01605 508-854-9227
James P. Cassidy, head sch Fax 853-7824
Bancroft School of Massage Therapy Post-Sec.
333 Shrewsbury St 01604 508-757-7923
Becker College Post-Sec.
61 Sever St 01609 508-791-9241
Clark University Post-Sec.
950 Main St 01610 508-793-7711
College of the Holy Cross Post-Sec.
1 College St 01610 508-793-2011
Hair in Motion Beauty Academy Post-Sec.
6 Park Ave 01605 508-756-6060
Holy Name Central Catholic HS 600/7-12
144 Granite St 01604 508-753-6371
Edward Reynolds, admin. Fax 831-1287
Nativity S of Worcester 5-8
67 Lincoln St 01605 508-799-0100
Sean Dillon, prin. Fax 799-3951
Notre Dame Academy 300/9-12
425 Salisbury St 01609 508-757-6200
Sr. Ann Morrison, prin. Fax 757-7200
Quinsigamond Community College Post-Sec.
670 W Boylston St 01606 508-853-2300
Rob Roy Academy Post-Sec.
150 Pleasant St 01609 508-799-2111
St. Mary HS 100/7-12
50 Richland St 01610 508-753-1170
Adam Cormier, prin. Fax 795-0560
St. Peter-Marian Central HS 600/7-12
781 Grove St 01605 508-852-5555
Christopher Cummings, admin. Fax 852-7238
University of Massachusetts Medical Sch Post-Sec.
55 Lake Ave N 01655 508-856-8989
Worcester Academy 600/6-12
81 Providence St 01604 508-754-5302
Ronald Cino, head sch Fax 792-1471
Worcester Polytechnic Institute Post-Sec.
100 Institute Rd 01609 508-831-5000
Worcester State University Post-Sec.
486 Chandler St 01602 508-929-8000

Wrentham, Norfolk
King Philip Regional SD
Supt. — See Norfolk
King Philip Regional HS 1,300/9-12
201 Franklin St 02093 508-384-1000
Dr. Lisa Mobley, prin.

MICHIGAN

MICHIGAN DEPARTMENT OF EDUCATION
608 W Allegan St, Lansing 48933-1524
Telephone 517-373-3324
Fax 517-335-4565
Website http://www.michigan.gov/mde

Superintendent of Public Instruction Brian Whiston

MICHIGAN BOARD OF EDUCATION
608 W Allegan St, Lansing 48933-1524

President John C. Austin

INTERMEDIATE SCHOOL DISTRICTS (ISD)

Allegan Area ESA
William Brown, supt. 269-512-7700
310 Thomas St, Allegan 49010 Fax 512-7701
www.alleganaesa.org/

Alpena-Montmorency-Alcona ESD
Brian Wilmot, supt. 989-354-3101
2118 US Highway 23 S Fax 356-3385
Alpena 49707
www.amaesd.org

Barry ISD
Richard Franklin, supt. 269-945-9545
535 W Woodlawn Ave Fax 945-2575
Hastings 49058
www.barryisd.org

Bay-Arenac ISD
Deborah Kadish, supt. 989-686-4410
4228 2 Mile Rd, Bay City 48706 Fax 667-3286
www.baisd.net

Berrien RESA
Dr. Kevin Ivers, supt. 269-471-7725
PO Box 364, Berrien Springs 49103 Fax 471-2941
www.berrienresa.org

Branch ISD
Joseph Lopez, supt. 517-279-5730
370 Morse St, Coldwater 49036 Fax 279-5766
www.branch-isd.org

Calhoun ISD
Terance Lunger, supt. 269-781-5141
17111 G Dr N, Marshall 49068 Fax 781-7071
www.calhounisd.org

Charlevoix-Emmet ISD
Jeffrey Crouse, supt. 231-547-9947
8568 Mercer Rd, Charlevoix 49720 Fax 547-5621
www.charemisd.org

Cheboygan-Otsego-Presque Isle ISD
Mary Vratanina, supt. 231-238-9394
6065 Learning Ln Fax 238-8551
Indian River 49749
www.copesd.org/

Clare-Gladwin RESD
Sheryl Presler, supt. 989-386-3851
4041 E Mannsiding Rd Fax 386-3238
Clare 48617
www.cgresd.net/

Clinton County RESA
Dr. Wayne Petroelje, supt. 989-224-6831
1013 S US Highway 27 Ste A Fax 224-9574
Saint Johns 48879
www.ccresa.org

C.O.O.R. ISD
Greg Bush, supt. 989-275-9555
PO Box 827, Roscommon 48653 Fax 275-5881
www.coorisd.net

Copper Country ISD
George Stockero, supt. 906-482-4250
809 Hecla St, Hancock 49930 Fax 487-5915
www.copperisd.org

Delta-Schoolcraft ISD
Doug Leisenring, supt. 906-786-9300
2525 3rd Ave S, Escanaba 49829 Fax 786-9318
www.dsisd.k12.mi.us

Dickinson-Iron ISD
Wendy Warmuth, supt. 906-779-2690
1074 Pyle Dr, Kingsford 49802 Fax 779-2669
www.diisd.org

Eastern Upper Peninsula ISD
Dr. Daniel Reattoir, supt. 906-632-3373
315 Armory Pl Fax 632-1125
Sault Sainte Marie 49783
www.eup.k12.mi.us

Eaton RESA
Cindy Anderson, supt. 517-543-5500
1790 Packard Hwy Fax 543-6633
Charlotte 48813
www.eatonresa.org

Genesee ISD
Lisa Hagel, supt. 810-591-4400
2413 W Maple Ave, Flint 48507 Fax 591-7570
www.geneseeisd.org

Gogebic-Ontonagon ISD
Bruce F. Mayle, supt. 906-575-3438
PO Box 218, Bergland 49910 Fax 575-3373
www.goisd.org/

Gratiot-Isabella RESD
Jan Amsterburg, supt. 989-875-5101
PO Box 310, Ithaca 48847 Fax 875-7531
www.giresd.net/

Hillsdale ISD
Ronna Steel, supt. 517-437-0990
310 W Bacon St, Hillsdale 49242 Fax 439-4388
www.hillsdale-isd.org

Huron ISD
Joseph Murphy, supt. 989-269-6406
1299 S Thomas Rd Ste 1 Fax 269-9218
Bad Axe 48413
www.huronisd.org

Ingham ISD
Dr. Scott Koenigsknecht, supt. 517-676-1051
2630 W Howell Rd, Mason 48854 Fax 676-4930
www.inghamisd.org

Ionia County ISD
Jason Mellema, supt. 616-527-4900
2191 Harwood Rd, Ionia 48846 Fax 527-4731
www.ioniaisd.org

Iosco RESA
Dana McGrew, supt. 989-362-3006
27 N Rempert Rd Fax 362-9076
Tawas City 48763
www.ioscoresa.net/

Jackson County ISD
Kevin Oxley, supt. 517-768-5200
6700 Browns Lake Rd Fax 787-2026
Jackson 49201
www.jcisd.org

Kalamazoo RESA
David Campbell, supt. 269-250-9200
1819 E Milham Ave, Portage 49002 Fax 250-9205
www.kresa.org

Kent ISD
Ron Caniff, supt., 2930 Knapp St NE 616-364-1333
Grand Rapids 49525 Fax 364-1488
www.kentisd.org

Lapeer County ISD
Steven Zott, supt. 810-664-5917
1996 W Oregon St, Lapeer 48446 Fax 664-1011
www.lcisd.k12.mi.us

Lenawee ISD
Mark Haag, supt. 517-265-2119
4107 N Adrian Hwy, Adrian 49221 Fax 265-9875
www.lisd.us

Lewis Cass ISD
Brent Holcomb, supt. 269-445-6204
61682 Dailey Rd, Cassopolis 49031 Fax 445-2981
www.lewiscassisd.org

Livingston ESA
R. Michael Hubert, supt. 517-546-5550
1425 W Grand River Ave Fax 546-7047
Howell 48843
www.livingstonesa.org/

Macomb ISD
Michael DeVault, supt. 586-228-3300
44001 Garfield Rd Fax 286-1523
Clinton Township 48038
www.misd.net

Manistee ISD
Jeff Jennette, supt. 231-723-4264
772 E Parkdale Ave Fax 398-3036
Manistee 49660
www.manistee.org

Marquette-Alger RESA
Deborah Veiht, supt. 906-226-5100
321 E Ohio St, Marquette 49855 Fax 226-5134
www.maresa.org

Mecosta-Osceola ISD
Dr. Curtis Finch, supt. 231-796-3543
15760 190th Ave Fax 796-3300
Big Rapids 49307
www.moisd.org

Menominee ISD
Mary Stein, supt. 906-863-5665
1201 41st Ave, Menominee 49858 Fax 863-7776
www.mc-isd.org

Midland County ESA
John Searles, supt. 989-631-5890
3917 Jefferson Ave, Midland 48640 Fax 631-4361
www.midlandesa.org

Monroe County ISD
Stephen McNew, supt. 734-242-5799
1101 S Raisinville Rd Fax 242-0567
Monroe 48161
www.monroeisd.us/

Montcalm Area ISD
Ron Simon, supt. 989-831-5261
PO Box 367, Stanton 48888 Fax 831-8727
www.maisd.com

Muskegon Area ISD
Dr. John Severson, supt. 231-777-2637
630 Harvey St, Muskegon 49442 Fax 767-7299
www.muskegonisd.org

Newaygo County RESA
Lori Clark, supt. 231-924-0381
4747 W 48th St, Fremont 49412 Fax 924-8910
www.ncresa.org

Oakland ISD
Dr. Wanda Cook-Robinson, supt. 248-209-2000
2111 Pontiac Lake Rd Fax 209-2206
Waterford 48328
www.oakland.k12.mi.us

Ottawa Area ISD
Peter Haines, supt. 616-738-8940
13565 Port Sheldon St Fax 738-8946
Holland 49424
www.oaisd.org

Saginaw ISD
Kathy Stewart, supt. 989-399-7473
6235 Gratiot Rd, Saginaw Fax 793-1571
www.sisd.cc

St. Clair County RESA
Dan DeGrow, supt. 810-364-8990
PO Box 1500, Marysville 48040 Fax 364-7474
www.sccresa.org/

St. Joseph County ISD
Barbara Marshall, supt. 269-467-5400
62445 Shimmel Rd Fax 467-4309
Centreville 49032
www.sjcisd.org

Sanilac ISD
Duane Lange Ph.D., supt. 810-648-4700
175 E Aitken Rd, Peck 48466 Fax 648-5784
www.sanilac.k12.mi.us

Shiawassee RESD
David Schulte, supt. 989-743-3471
1025 N Shiawassee St Fax 743-6477
Corunna 48817
www.sresd.org

Traverse Bay Area ISD
Michael Hill, supt. 231-922-6200
1101 Red Dr, Traverse City 49684 Fax 922-6270
www.tbaisd.org

Tuscola ISD
Eugene Pierce, supt. 989-673-2144
1385 Cleaver Rd, Caro 48723 Fax 673-5366
www.tuscolaisd.org/

Van Buren ISD
Jeffrey Mills, supt. 269-674-8091
490 S Paw Paw St Fax 674-8030
Lawrence 49064
www.vbisd.org/

Washtenaw ISD
Scott Menzel, supt. 734-994-8100
PO Box 1406, Ann Arbor 48106 Fax 994-2203
washtenawisd.org

Wayne RESA
Randy Liepa, supt. 734-334-1300
33500 Van Born Rd, Wayne 48184 Fax 334-1760
www.resa.net

West Shore ESD
Randy Howes, supt. 231-757-3716
2130 W US Highway 10 Fax 757-2406
Ludington 49431
www.wsesd.org

Wexford-Missaukee ISD
Jeff Jennette, supt. 231-876-2260
9907 E 13th St, Cadillac 49601 Fax 876-2261
www.wmisd.org

PUBLIC, PRIVATE AND CATHOLIC SECONDARY SCHOOLS

Ada, Kent
Forest Hills SD
Supt. — See Grand Rapids
Central MS 600/7-8
5810 Ada Dr SE 49301 616-493-8750
Glenn Mitcham, prin. Fax 493-8764
Eastern HS 800/9-12
2200 Pettis Ave NE 49301 616-493-8830
Steve Harvey, prin. Fax 493-8839
Eastern MS 400/7-8
2200 Pettis Ave NE 49301 616-493-8850
David Washburn, prin. Fax 493-8839

Addison, Lenawee, Pop. 592
Addison Community SD 700/K-12
219 N Comstock St 49220 517-547-6901
Steven Guerra, supt. Fax 547-3838
www.addisonschools.org
Addison HS 300/9-12
219 N Comstock St 49220 517-547-6952
Steven Guerra, supt. Fax 547-6982
Addison MS 100/6-8
219 N Comstock St 49220 517-547-6951
Julie Yeider, admin. Fax 547-6982

Adrian, Lenawee, Pop. 20,608
Adrian SD 3,000/PK-12
785 Riverside Ave Ste 1 49221 517-263-2115
Robert Behnke, supt. Fax 265-5381
www.theadrianmaples.com
Adrian HS 800/9-12
785 Riverside Ave 49221 517-263-2181
Kevin Ohrman, prin. Fax 266-4524
Adrian MS 7-8 500/7-8
615 Springbrook Ave 49221 517-263-0543
Nate Parker, prin. Fax 265-5984
McKinley Education Center 100/Alt
726 Elm St 49221 517-263-1332
Derrick Richards, coord. Fax 263-1385

Lenawee ISD 100/
4107 N Adrian Hwy 49221 517-265-2119
Mark Haag, supt. Fax 265-9875
www.lisd.us
LISD Tech Center Vo/Tech
1372 N Main St 49221 517-263-2108
Shelley Jusick, prin. Fax 263-9433

Madison SD 1,500/PK-12
3498 Treat Hwy 49221 517-263-0741
Ryan Rowe, supt. Fax 265-5635
www.madisonk12.us
Madison HS 400/9-12
3498 Treat Hwy 49221 517-263-0742
Kristin Thomas, prin. Fax 265-1848
Madison MS 400/6-8
3498 Treat Hwy 49221 517-263-0743
Brad Anschuetz, prin. Fax 265-1848

Adrian College Post-Sec.
110 S Madison St 49221 517-265-5161
Fiser's College of Cosmetology Post-Sec.
329 1/2 E Maumee St 49221 517-264-2199
Lenawee Christian S 600/PK-12
111 Wolf Creek Hwy 49221 517-265-7590
Tom Durbin, head sch Fax 266-8934
Siena Heights University Post-Sec.
1247 E Siena Heights Dr 49221 517-263-0731

Alanson, Emmet, Pop. 721
Alanson SD 300/K-12
7400 North St 49706 231-548-2261
Dean Paul, supt. Fax 548-2132
www.alansonvikings.net
Alanson HS 100/9-12
7400 North St 49706 231-548-2261
Dean Paul, admin. Fax 548-2132
Alanson MS 100/6-8
7400 North St 49706 231-548-2261
Dean Paul, admin. Fax 548-2165

Alba, Antrim, Pop. 295
Alba SD 200/PK-12
5935 Elm St 49611 231-584-2000
Douglas Tippett, supt. Fax 584-2001
www.albaschool.org/
Alba S 200/PK-12
PO Box 10 49611 231-584-2000
Rich Satterlee, supt. Fax 584-2001

Albion, Calhoun, Pop. 8,323
Marshall SD
Supt. — See Marshall
ECEC/Marshall Opportunity HS 100/Alt
14055 26 Mile Rd 49224 517-629-9421
Ben Wallace, dir. Fax 629-7534

Albion College Post-Sec.
611 E Porter St 49224 517-629-1000

Algonac, Saint Clair, Pop. 4,051
Algonac Community SD 900/PK-12
5200 Taft Rd 48001 810-794-9364
Dr. John Strycker, supt. Fax 794-0040
algonac.k12.mi.us
Algonac JSHS 600/7-12
5200 Taft Rd 48001 810-794-4911
Ryan Melrose, prin. Fax 794-8876

Allegan, Allegan, Pop. 4,893
Allegan Area ESA 100/
310 Thomas St 49010 269-512-7700
William Brown, supt. Fax 512-7701
www.alleganaesa.org/
Allegan Co. Area Technical & Educ. Ctr. Alt
2891 116th Ave 49010 269-673-3121
Linda Blankenship, dir. Fax 686-0327

Allegan SD 2,600/PK-12
550 5th St 49010 269-673-5431
Kevin Harness, supt. Fax 673-5463
www.alleganps.org/
Allegan Alternative HS 100/Alt
550 5th St 49010 269-673-5433
Laura Feffer, prin.
Allegan HS 700/9-12
1560 Lincoln Rd 49010 269-673-7002
Jim Mallard, prin. Fax 686-2486
White MS, 3300 115th Ave 49010 600/6-8
James Antoine, prin. 269-673-2241

Allendale, Ottawa, Pop. 17,229
Allendale SD 2,500/PK-12
10505 Learning Ln 49401 616-892-5570
Daniel Jonker Ed.D., supt. Fax 895-6690
www.allendale.k12.mi.us
Allendale HS 700/9-12
10760 68th Ave 49401 616-892-5585
Dan Remenap, prin. Fax 895-4280
Allendale MS 500/6-8
7161 Pleasant View Ct 49401 616-892-5595
Rocky Thompson, prin. Fax 895-9111
Allendale New Options 100/Alt
6633 Lake Michigan Dr 49401 616-892-5575
Tamika Henry, prin. Fax 892-4668

Grand Valley State University Post-Sec.
1 Campus Dr 49401 616-331-5000

Allen Park, Wayne, Pop. 27,848
Allen Park SD 3,700/K-12
9601 Vine Ave 48101 313-827-2100
Dr. John Sturock, supt. Fax 827-2151
www.apps.k12.mi.us
Allen Park HS 1,100/9-12
18401 Champaign Rd 48101 313-827-1200
Janet Wasko, prin. Fax 827-1231
Allen Park MS 900/6-8
8401 Vine Ave 48101 313-827-2200
Mark Lowe, prin. Fax 827-2251
Community S 200/Alt
14700 Moore Ave 48101 313-827-2660
Rebecca Westrate, dir. Fax 827-2661

Baker College of Allen Park Post-Sec.
4500 Enterprise Dr 48101 313-425-3700
Cabrini HS 500/9-12
15305 Wick Rd 48101 313-388-0110
James Wasukanis, prin. Fax 388-1876
Inter City Baptist S 300/K-12
4700 Allen Rd 48101 313-928-6900
Jim Hubbard Ed.D., admin. Fax 928-7310

Alma, Gratiot, Pop. 9,259
Alma SD 2,100/PK-12
1500 Pine Ave 48801 989-463-3111
Donalynn Ingersoll, supt. Fax 466-2943
www.almaschools.net
Alma HS 600/9-12
1500 Pine Ave 48801 989-463-3111
Thomas Torok, prin. Fax 463-2176
Pavlik MS 500/6-8
1700 Pine Ave 48801 989-463-3111
Wade Slavik, prin. Fax 466-7612

Gratiot-Isabella RESD
Supt. — See Ithaca
Gratiot Technical Education Center Vo/Tech
327 E Center St 48801 989-875-4832
Fax 466-9734

Alma College Post-Sec.
614 W Superior St 48801 989-463-7111

Almont, Lapeer, Pop. 2,651
Almont Community SD 1,500/K-12
4701 Howland Rd 48003 810-798-8561
Joseph Candela, supt. Fax 798-2367
www.almontschools.org
Almont HS 500/9-12
4701 Howland Rd 48003 810-798-8595
Timothy Woelkers, prin. Fax 798-7011
Almont MS 500/5-8
4624 Kidder Rd 48003 810-798-3578
Kimberly VonHiltmayer, prin. Fax 673-9349

Alpena, Alpena, Pop. 10,337
Alpena SD 3,900/K-12
2373 Gordon Rd 49707 989-358-5040
Dr. John VanWagoner, supt. Fax 358-5041
www.alpenaschools.com
ACES/Oxbow Adult/Alternative/Comm Educ 100/Alt
700 Pinecrest St 49707 989-358-5170
Michelle Cornish, dir. Fax 358-5175
Alpena HS 1,300/9-12
3303 S Third Ave 49707 989-358-5200
Matt Poli, prin. Fax 358-5205
Thunder Bay JHS 1,000/6-8
3500 S Third Ave 49707 989-358-5400
Steve Genschaw, prin. Fax 358-5499

Alpena Community College Post-Sec.
665 Johnson St 49707 989-356-9021

Ann Arbor, Washtenaw, Pop. 109,999
Ann Arbor SD 16,000/PK-12
PO Box 1188 48106 734-994-2200
Dr. Jeanice Swift, supt. Fax 994-2414
www.aaps.k12.mi.us
Clague MS 700/6-8
2616 Nixon Rd 48105 734-994-1976
Che' Carter, prin. Fax 994-1645
Community HS 500/9-12
401 N Division St 48104 734-994-2025
Marci Tuzinsky, dean Fax 994-0042
Forsythe MS 700/6-8
1655 Newport Rd 48103 734-994-1985
Jerry Morrissey, prin. Fax 994-5749
Huron HS 1,500/9-12
2727 Fuller Rd 48105 734-994-2040
Jennifer Hein, prin. Fax 994-2048
Pathways To Success Academic Campus Alt
2800 Stone School Rd 48104 734-997-1237
Tyrone Weeks, prin. Fax 997-1261
Pioneer HS 1,600/9-12
601 W Stadium Blvd 48103 734-994-2120
Tracey Lowder, prin. Fax 994-2198
Scarlett MS 500/6-8
3300 Lorraine St 48108 734-997-1220
Gerald Vazquez, prin. Fax 997-1885
Skyline HS 1,500/9-12
2552 N Maple Rd 48103 734-994-6515
Cory McElmeel, prin. Fax 994-7028
Slauson MS 800/6-8
1019 W Washington St 48103 734-994-2004
Rick Weiler, prin. Fax 994-1681
Tappan MS 700/6-8
2251 E Stadium Blvd 48104 734-994-2011
Dr. Arthur Williams, prin. Fax 997-1873

Washtenaw ISD 400/
PO Box 1406 48106 734-994-8100
Scott Menzel, supt. Fax 994-2203
washtenawisd.org
Other Schools – See Ypsilanti

Ann Arbor Academy 50/4-12
1153 Oak Valley Dr 48108 734-747-6641
Meredith Schindler M.S., dir. Fax 747-9994
Cleary University Post-Sec.
3601 Plymouth Rd 48105 800-686-1883
Concordia University Post-Sec.
4090 Geddes Rd 48105 734-995-7300
Father Gabriel Richard HS 500/9-12
4333 Whitehall Dr 48105 734-662-0496
Janie Garcia Herrera, prin. Fax 662-4133
Greenhills S 500/6-12
850 Greenhills Dr 48105 734-769-4010
Carl Pelofsky, head sch Fax 769-5029
Michigan Islamic Academy 200/PK-12
2301 Plymouth Rd 48105 734-665-8882
Sr. Fayzeh Madani, prin. Fax 665-9058
Ross Medical Education Center Post-Sec.
4741 Washtenaw Ave 48108 734-434-7320
Steiner S of Ann Arbor 100/9-12
2230 Pontiac Trl 48105 734-669-9394
Sandra Greenstone, admin. Fax 669-9396
University of Michigan-Ann Arbor Post-Sec.
1220 Student Activities Bld 48109 734-764-1817
Washtenaw Community College Post-Sec.
4800 E Huron River Dr 48105 734-973-3300

Armada, Macomb, Pop. 1,714
Armada Area SD 1,700/PK-12
74500 Burk St 48005 586-784-2112
Michael Musary, supt. Fax 784-4268
www.armadaschools.org
Armada Continuing Education Center 50/Alt
23211 Prospect Ave 48005 586-784-2400
William Zebelian, prin. Fax 784-9592
Armada HS 700/9-12
23655 Armada Center Rd 48005 586-784-2400
Phillip Jankowski, prin. Fax 784-9592
Armada MS 500/6-8
23550 Armada Center Rd 48005 586-784-2500
Todd Schafer, prin. Fax 784-8650
Macomb Academy of Arts & Sciences 100/9-12
23211 Prospect Ave 48005 586-784-2150
William Zebelian, dir. Fax 784-8688

Ashley, Gratiot, Pop. 562
Ashley Community SD 300/PK-12
PO Box 6 48806 989-847-4000
Jeffrey Rohrer, supt. Fax 847-3500
www.ashleyschools.net/
Ashley HS 100/9-12
PO Box 6 48806 989-847-2514
Traci Gavenda, prin. Fax 847-4204
Ashley MS 100/5-8
PO Box 6 48806 989-846-2514
Traci Gavenda, prin. Fax 847-4204

Athens, Calhoun, Pop. 1,000
Athens Area SD
Supt. — See East Leroy
Athens JSHS 300/6-12
300 E Holcomb St 49011 269-729-5414
Joe Huepenbecker, prin. Fax 729-9616

Atlanta, Montmorency, Pop. 815
Atlanta Community SD 300/K-12
PO Box 619 49709 989-785-4877
Donald Haskin, supt. Fax 785-2611
www.atlanta.k12.mi.us
Atlanta Community S 300/K-12
PO Box 619 49709 989-785-4877
Donald Haskin, supt. Fax 785-2611

Attica, Lapeer, Pop. 985
Lapeer County ISD
Supt. — See Lapeer
Lapeer County ISD Education Center Vo/Tech
690 N Lake Pleasant Rd 48412 810-664-1124
Dale Moore, prin. Fax 724-7600

Auburn, Bay, Pop. 2,077
Bay City SD
Supt. — See Bay City
Western HS 1,200/9-12
500 W Midland Rd 48611 989-662-4481
Judy Cox, prin. Fax 662-4413
Western MS 900/6-8
500 W Midland Rd 48611 989-662-4489
Amy Bailey, prin. Fax 662-0185

Auburn Hills, Oakland, Pop. 20,778
Avondale SD 3,400/K-12
2940 Waukegan St 48326 248-537-6000
Dr. James V. Schwarz, supt. Fax 537-6005
www.avondale.k12.mi.us
Avondale HS 1,100/9-12
2800 Waukegan St 48326 248-537-6100
Sharon Hyde, prin. Fax 537-6105
Other Schools – See Rochester Hills

Auburn Hills Christian S 200/PK-12
PO Box 214386 48321 248-373-3399
Scott Wickson, prin. Fax 409-2786
Baker College of Auburn Hills Post-Sec.
1500 University Dr 48326 248-340-0600
Oakland Christian S 700/PK-12
3075 Shimmons Rd 48326 248-373-2700
Roy Townsend, prin. Fax 373-9255
Oakland Community College Post-Sec.
2900 Featherstone Rd 48326 248-232-4100

Au Gres, Arenac, Pop. 875
Au Gres-Sims SD 500/PK-12
PO Box 648 48703 989-876-7150
Jeffrey Collier, supt. Fax 876-6752
www.ags-schools.org
Au Gres-Sims HS 200/9-12
PO Box 648 48703 989-876-7157
Chad Zeien, prin. Fax 876-4684
Au Gres-Sims MS 200/6-8
PO Box 648 48703 989-876-7157
Chad Zeien, prin. Fax 876-4684

Augusta, Kalamazoo, Pop. 868
Galesburg-Augusta Community SD
Supt. — See Galesburg
Galesburg-Augusta MS 300/5-8
750 W Van Buren St 49012 269-484-2020
Jeremy Mansfield, prin. Fax 731-4138

Bad Axe, Huron, Pop. 3,092
Bad Axe SD 1,100/K-12
200 N Barrie Rd Ste 100 48413 989-269-9938
Gregory Newland, supt. Fax 269-2739
www.badaxeps.org/
Ascent HS, 200 N Barrie Rd 48413 100/Alt
Donald Rudolph, prin. 989-269-2737
Bad Axe HS 400/8-12
200 N Barrie Rd 48413 989-269-9593
Kurt Dennis, prin. Fax 269-6947

Huron ISD 50/
1299 S Thomas Rd Ste 1 48413 989-269-6406
Joseph Murphy, supt. Fax 269-9218
www.huronisd.org
Huron Area Technical Center Vo/Tech
1160 S Van Dyke Rd 48413 989-269-9284
Clark Brock, dir. Fax 269-2844

Baldwin, Lake, Pop. 1,141
Baldwin Community SD 600/PK-12
525 4th St 49304 231-745-4791
Dr. Stiles Simmons, supt. Fax 745-3240
www.baldwin.k12.mi.us
Baldwin HS 100/9-12
525 4th St 49304 231-745-4683
Calvin Patillo, prin. Fax 745-2898
Baldwin JHS 100/7-8
525 4th St 49304 231-745-4683
Calvin Patillo, prin. Fax 745-2898

Bangor, Van Buren, Pop. 1,809
Bangor SD 1,200/K-12
801 W Arlington St 49013 269-427-6800
Dennis Paquette, supt. Fax 427-8274
www.bangorvikings.org
Bangor HS 400/9-12
801 W Arlington St 49013 269-427-6844
Wendy Tremblay, prin. Fax 427-6825
Bangor MS 400/5-8
803 W Arlington St 49013 269-427-6824
Michael Dandron, prin. Fax 427-6892

Baraga, Baraga, Pop. 1,981
Baraga Area SD 400/K-12
210 Lyons St 49908 906-353-6664
Richard Sarau, supt. Fax 353-6664
www.baragaschools.org
Baraga JSHS 300/6-12
210 Lyons St 49908 906-353-6661
Timothy Marczak, prin. Fax 353-6662

Keweenaw Bay Ojibwa Community College Post-Sec.
PO Box 519 49908 906-353-4600

Bath, Clinton, Pop. 2,052
Bath Community SD 1,000/K-12
PO Box 310 48808 517-641-6721
Jake Huffman, supt. Fax 641-6958
www.bathschools.net
Bath HS 300/9-12
PO Box 310 48808 517-641-6724
Matt Dodson, prin. Fax 641-7046
Bath MS 300/6-8
PO Box 310 48808 517-641-6781
Lorenda Jonas, prin. Fax 641-4996

Battle Creek, Calhoun, Pop. 50,321
Battle Creek SD 4,000/K-12
3 Van Buren St W 49017 269-965-9500
Kim Parker-DeVauld, supt. Fax 965-9474
www.battlecreekpublicschools.org
Battle Creek Alternative HS 100/Alt
50 W Van Buren St 49017 269-965-9500
Calvin Williams, prin.
Battle Creek Central HS 1,200/9-12
100 Van Buren St W 49017 269-965-9526
Noah Hollander, prin. Fax 660-5864
Mathematics & Science Center 300/9-12
171 Michigan Ave W 49017 269-965-9440
Susan Buckham, admin. Fax 965-9589
9th Grade Academy 400/9-9
100 Van Buren St W 49017 269-213-1742
Dr. Anita Harvey, prin. Fax 965-9567
Northwestern MS 500/6-8
176 Limit St, 269-965-9607
Timothy Reese, prin. Fax 965-9525
Other Schools – See Springfield

Calhoun ISD
Supt. — See Marshall
Calhoun Area Career Center Vo/Tech
475 Roosevelt Ave E 49017 269-968-2271
Tim Staffen, prin. Fax 968-4344

Harper Creek Community SD 2,600/K-12
7454 B Dr N 49014 269-441-6550
Rob Ridgeway, supt. Fax 962-6034
www.harpercreek.net
Harper Creek HS 800/9-12
12677 Beadle Lake Rd 49014 269-441-8450
Dennis Anthony, prin. Fax 441-2206
Harper Creek MS 800/5-8
7290 B Dr N 49014 269-441-4750
Kimberly Thayer, prin. Fax 979-4613

Lakeview SD 3,900/K-12
15 Arbor St 49015 269-565-2400
Dave Peterson, supt. Fax 565-2408
www.lakeviewspartans.org
Lakeview HS 1,300/9-12
15060 Helmer Rd S 49015 269-565-3700
Jeffrey Bohl, prin. Fax 565-3708
Lakeview MS 1,300/5-8
300 28th St S 49015 269-565-3900
Michael Norstrom, prin. Fax 565-3908

Pennfield SD 2,100/K-12
8587 Pennfield Rd 49017 269-961-9781
Tim Everett, supt. Fax 961-9799
www.pennfield.net/
Pennfield HS 600/9-12
8587 Pennfield Rd 49017 269-961-9770
Barry Duckham, prin. Fax 441-1274
Pennfield MS 600/6-8
8587 Pennfield Rd 49017 269-961-9784
Michele Herzing, prin. Fax 441-5535

Battle Creek Academy 100/K-12
480 Parkway Dr, 269-965-1278
James Davis, prin. Fax 965-3250
Calhoun Christian S 200/PK-12
20 Woodrow Ave S 49015 269-965-5560
Jeralyn Belote, prin. Fax 965-8038
Davenport University Post-Sec.
200 Van Buren St W 49017 269-968-6105
Kambly School/Developmentally Impaired Post-Sec.
1003 North Ave 49017
Kellogg Community College Post-Sec.
450 North Ave 49017 269-965-3931
Robert Miller College Post-Sec.
450 North Ave 49017 269-660-8021
St. Joseph MS 100/6-8
44 25th St N 49015 269-963-4935
Sara Myers, prin. Fax 963-0354
St. Philip Catholic Central HS 100/9-12
20 Cherry St 49017 269-963-4503
Vicky Groat, prin. Fax 963-5590
Wright Beauty Academy Post-Sec.
492 Capital Ave SW 49015 269-964-4016

Bay City, Bay, Pop. 33,947
Bangor Township SD 2,400/PK-12
3359 E Midland Rd 48706 989-684-8121
Matthew Schmidt, supt. Fax 684-6000
www.bangorschools.org
Glenn HS 900/9-12
3201 Kiesel Rd 48706 989-684-7510
Daniel Decuf, prin. Fax 684-1545
McAuliffe MS 600/6-8
3281 Kiesel Rd 48706 989-686-7640
Kevin Biskup, prin. Fax 686-7633

Bay City SD 8,100/PK-12
910 N Walnut St 48706 989-686-9700
Janet Greif, supt. Fax 686-1047
www.bcschools.net
Central HS 1,300/9-12
1624 Columbus Ave 48708 989-893-9541
Tim Marciniak, prin. Fax 893-0333
Handy MS 1,000/6-8
601 Blend St 48706 989-684-1723
Ryan Boon, prin. Fax 684-1960
Wenona HS 100/Alt
201 Woodside Ln 48708 989-895-5550
Carla Derocher, prin. Fax 895-6517
Other Schools – See Auburn

Bay-Arenac ISD
4228 2 Mile Rd 48706 989-686-4410
Deborah Kadish, supt. Fax 667-3286
www.baisd.net
Bay-Arenac ISD Career Center Vo/Tech
4155 Monitor Rd 48706 989-686-4770
Linda Englehardt, prin.

All Saints Central MSHS 300/6-12
217 S Monroe St 48708 989-892-2533
Brian Campbell, prin. Fax 892-7188
Bayshire Beauty Academy Post-Sec.
917 Saginaw St 48708 989-894-2431

Bear Lake, Manistee, Pop. 281
Bear Lake SD 300/K-12
7748 Cody St 49614 231-864-3133
Marlen Cordes, supt. Fax 864-3434
www.bearlake.k12.mi.us
Bear Lake HS 200/6-12
7748 Cody St 49614 231-864-3133
Sarah Harless, prin. Fax 864-3434

Beaver Island, Charlevoix
Beaver Island Community SD 100/K-12
37895 Kings Hwy 49782 231-448-2744
Judith Gallagher, supt. Fax 448-2919
www.beaverisland.k12.mi.us
Beaver Island Community S 100/K-12
37895 Kings Hwy 49782 231-448-2744
Judith Gallagher, prin. Fax 448-2919

Beaverton, Gladwin, Pop. 1,061
Beaverton Rural SD 700/K-12
PO Box 529 48612 989-246-3000
Susan Wooden, supt. Fax 435-7631
www.brs.cgresd.net
Beaverton JSHS 400/7-12
PO Box 529 48612 989-246-3010
Jeffrey Budge, prin. Fax 246-3366

Belding, Ionia, Pop. 5,669
Belding Area SD 2,000/PK-12
850 Hall St 48809 616-794-4700
Brent Noskey, supt. Fax 794-4730
www.bas-k12.org/
Belding HS 700/9-12
850 Hall St 48809 616-794-4900
Michael Ostrander, prin. Fax 794-4956
Belding MS 500/6-8
410 Ionia St 48809 616-794-4400
Fax 794-4420
Belding Adult and Community Education Adult
1975 Orchard St 48809 616-794-4602
Ann VanDusen, prin. Fax 794-4403

Bellaire, Antrim, Pop. 1,076
Bellaire SD 400/K-12
204 W Forrest Home Ave 49615 231-533-8141
James Emery, supt. Fax 533-6797
www.bellairepublicschools.com/
Bellaire MSHS 300/6-12
204 W Forrest Home Ave 49615 231-533-8015
James Emery, prin. Fax 533-6797

Belleville, Wayne, Pop. 3,881
Van Buren SD 5,000/PK-12
555 W Columbia Ave 48111 734-697-1016
Peter Kudlak, supt. Fax 697-6385
www.vanburenschools.net
Belleville HS 1,800/9-12
501 W Columbia Ave 48111 734-697-9133
Fax 697-6551
McBride MS 700/7-8
47097 McBride Ave 48111 734-697-9171
John Leroy, prin. Fax 697-6573

Bellevue, Eaton, Pop. 1,257
Bellevue Community SD 600/K-12
904 W Capital Ave 49021 269-763-9432
John C. Prescott, supt. Fax 763-3101
www.bellevue-schools.com/
Bellevue HS 300/6-12
576 Love Hwy 49021 269-763-9413
Sara Hendershot, prin. Fax 763-3955

Benton Harbor, Berrien, Pop. 9,796
Benton Harbor Area SD 1,200/PK-12
PO Box 1107 49023 269-605-1000
Shelly Walker Ed.D., supt. Fax 605-1043
www.bhas.org
Arts & Communications Academy 200/6-8
120 E Napier Ave 49022 269-605-1400
Fred Roseburgh, prin. Fax 605-1403
Benton Harbor HS 700/9-12
PO Box 1107 49023 269-605-1200
Fax 605-1203

Lake Michigan College Post-Sec.
2755 E Napier Ave 49022 269-927-1000

Benzonia, Benzie, Pop. 484
Benzie County Central SD 1,600/K-12
9222 Homestead Rd 49616 231-882-9653
Matthew Olson, supt. Fax 882-9121
www.benzieschools.net/
Benzie Academy Alt
7282 Hoadley Rd 49616 231-383-3386
Sarah Esper, prin.
Benzie Central HS 500/9-12
PO Box 240 49616 231-882-4497
Larry Haughn, prin. Fax 882-5699
Benzie Central MS 300/7-8
9300 Homestead Rd 49616 231-882-4498
David Clasen, prin. Fax 882-7627

Berkley, Oakland, Pop. 14,700
Berkley SD
Supt. — See Oak Park
Anderson MS 600/6-8
3205 Catalpa Dr 48072 248-837-8200
Mike Ross, prin. Fax 546-0696
Berkley HS 1,300/9-12
2325 Catalpa Dr 48072 248-837-8100
Randy Gawel, prin. Fax 544-5860

Berrien Springs, Berrien, Pop. 1,747
Berrien Springs SD 2,300/K-12
PO Box 130 49103 269-471-2891
David Eichberg, supt. Fax 471-2590
www.homeofthe shamrocks.org
Berrien Springs Discovery Academy 100/Alt
PO Box 130 49103 269-471-2593
William Bergan, prin. Fax 471-8865
Berrien Springs HS 500/9-12
PO Box 130 49103 269-471-1748
Ryan Pesce, prin. Fax 471-1511
Berrien Springs MS 400/6-8
PO Box 130 49103 269-471-2796
Mitchell Cumings, prin. Fax 471-2590

Andrews Academy 200/9-12
8833 Garland Ave 49104 269-471-3138
Jeannie Leiterman M.A., prin. Fax 471-6368

Andrews University Post-Sec.
8975 US 31 49104 269-471-7771
Griggs University Post-Sec.
8903 US Highway 31 49104 800-782-4769

Bessemer, Gogebic, Pop. 1,874
Bessemer City SD 400/PK-12
301 E Sellar St 49911 906-667-0802
David Radovich, supt. Fax 667-0318
www.bessemer.k12.mi.us
Johnston JSHS 200/7-12
100 W Lead St 49911 906-667-0413
Daniel VanderVelden, prin. Fax 667-0320

Beverly Hills, Oakland, Pop. 10,098
Birmingham SD 8,100/PK-12
31301 Evergreen Rd 48025 248-203-3000
Dr. Daniel Nerad, supt. Fax 203-3009
www.birmingham.k12.mi.us
Berkshire MS 800/6-8
21707 W 14 Mile Rd 48025 248-203-4702
Jason Clinckscale, prin. Fax 203-4802
Groves HS 1,200/9-12
20500 W 13 Mile Rd 48025 248-203-3530
Cathy Hurley, prin. Fax 203-3636
Other Schools – See Birmingham, Bloomfield Hls

Detroit Country Day MS 400/6-8
22400 Hillview Ln 48025 248-430-1677
Glen Shilling, hdmstr.
Detroit Country Day Upper S 700/9-12
22305 W 13 Mile Rd 48025 248-646-7717
Glen Shilling, hdmstr. Fax 646-2458

Big Rapids, Mecosta, Pop. 10,347
Big Rapids SD 1,800/K-12
21034 15 Mile Rd 49307 231-796-2627
Tim Haist, supt. Fax 592-0639
www.brps.org
Big Rapids HS 700/9-12
21175 15 Mile Rd 49307 231-796-7651
Ron Pincumbe, prin. Fax 592-8505
Big Rapids MS 600/5-8
500 N Warren Ave 49307 231-796-9965
Mitch Cumings, prin. Fax 592-3494
New Directions Alternative HS 100/Alt
21485 15 Mile Rd 49307 231-796-3489
Josh Easler, coord. Fax 592-0644

Mecosta-Osceola ISD 100/
15760 190th Ave 49307 231-796-3543
Dr. Curtis Finch, supt. Fax 796-3300
www.moisd.org
Mecosta-Osceola Career Center Vo/Tech
15830 190th Ave 49307 231-796-5805
Mike Miller, prin. Fax 796-0262

Ferris State University Post-Sec.
1201 S State St 49307 231-591-2000

Birch Run, Saginaw, Pop. 1,524
Birch Run Area SD 1,800/K-12
12450 Church St Ste 2 48415 989-624-9307
David Bush, supt. Fax 624-8503
www.birchrunschools.org
Birch Run Early College 11-12
12450 Church St 48415 989-624-9392
Mike Baszler, prin.
Birch Run HS 600/9-12
12450 Church St 48415 989-624-9392
Michael Baszler, prin. Fax 624-8502
Birch Run Progressive HS 100/Alt
12400 Church St 48415 989-624-9392
Mike Baszler, prin. Fax 624-8502
Greene MS 500/5-8
8225 Main St 48415 989-624-5821
Scott Preston, prin. Fax 624-8507

Birmingham, Oakland, Pop. 19,789
Birmingham SD
Supt. — See Beverly Hills
Derby MS 800/6-8
1300 Derby Rd 48009 248-203-5003
Celeste Nowacki, prin. Fax 203-4948
Seaholm HS 1,300/9-12
2436 W Lincoln St 48009 248-203-3707
Rachel Guinn, prin. Fax 203-3706

Roeper S 6-12
1051 Oakland Ave 48009 248-203-7300
David Feldman, head sch Fax 203-7310

Blanchard, Isabella
Montabella Community SD
Supt. — See Edmore
Montabella JSHS 400/7-12
1324 N County Line Rd 49310 989-427-5175
Shane Riley, prin. Fax 427-5107

Blissfield, Lenawee, Pop. 3,300
Blissfield Community SD 1,200/K-12
630 S Lane St 49228 517-486-2205
Jerry Johnson, supt. Fax 486-5701
www.blissfieldschools.us/
Blissfield HS 400/9-12
630 S Lane St 49228 517-486-2148
Steve Gfell, prin. Fax 486-4749
Blissfield MS 300/6-8
1305 Beamer Rd 49228 517-486-4420
Cris Rupp, prin. Fax 486-4758

Bloomfield Hls, Oakland, Pop. 3,811
Birmingham SD
Supt. — See Beverly Hills
Birmingham Covington S 600/3-8
1525 Covington Rd, 248-203-4425
Mark Morawski, prin. Fax 203-4433

Bloomfield Hills SD 6,600/PK-12
7273 Wing Lake Rd, 248-341-5400
Dr. Robert Glass, supt. Fax 341-5449
www.bloomfield.org
Bloomfield Hills HS 1,700/9-12
4200 Andover Rd, 248-341-5600
Charles Hollerith, prin.
Bloomfield Hills MS 700/5-8
4200 Quarton Rd, 248-341-6000
Randy English, prin. Fax 341-6099
Bowers Academy Alt
1223 E Square Lake Rd, 248-341-5985
Fax 341-5998
East Hills MS 500/5-8
2800 Kensington Rd, 248-341-6200
Jason Rubel, prin. Fax 341-6299
International Academy 1,400/9-12
1020 E Square Lake Rd, 248-341-5900
Lynne Gibson, prin. Fax 341-5959
Model Center Alt
4220 Andover Rd, 248-341-5960
Charlie Hollerith, prin. Fax 341-5999
Other Schools – See West Bloomfield

Academy of the Sacred Heart 400/PK-12
1250 Kensington Rd, 248-646-8900
Sr. Bridget Bearss, hdmstr. Fax 646-4143
Bloomfield Christian School 200/K-12
3570 Telegraph Rd, 248-499-7800
Patsy Hinton, head sch Fax 457-1520
Brother Rice HS 700/9-12
7101 Lahser Rd, 248-833-2000
Br. Tom Reidy, prin. Fax 833-2001
Cranbrook Academy of Art Post-Sec.
PO Box 801, 248-645-3300
Cranbrook S 1,700/PK-12
PO Box 801, 248-645-3000
Arlyce Seibert, dir. Fax 645-3524
Marian HS 500/9-12
7225 Lahser Rd, 248-644-1750
Sr. Lenore Pochelski, pres. Fax 644-6107

Bloomingdale, Van Buren, Pop. 446
Bloomingdale SD 1,200/K-12
PO Box 217 49026 269-521-3900
Deb Paquette, supt. Fax 521-3907
www.bdalecards.org
Bloomingdale HS 300/9-12
PO Box 217 49026 269-521-3910
Rick Reo, prin. Fax 521-3915
Bloomingdale MS 300/6-8
PO Box 217 49026 269-521-3950
Rick Reo, prin. Fax 521-3958

Boyne City, Charlevoix, Pop. 3,622
Boyne City SD 1,300/K-12
321 S Park St 49712 231-439-8190
Patrick Little M.A., supt. Fax 439-8195
www.boyne.k12.mi.us
Boyne City HS 400/9-12
1035 Boyne Ave 49712 231-439-8100
Karen Jarema M.A., prin. Fax 439-8194
Boyne City MS 400/5-8
1025 Boyne Ave 49712 231-439-8200
Mike Wilson M.A., prin. Fax 439-8233
Morgan-Shaw S 50/Alt
321 S Park St 49712 231-439-8140
Nicholas McLane, admin. Fax 439-8195

Boyne Falls, Charlevoix, Pop. 286
Boyne Falls SD 200/K-12
PO Box 356 49713 231-549-2211
Cynthia Pineda, admin. Fax 549-2922
www.boynefalls.org
Boyne Falls S 200/K-12
PO Box 356 49713 231-549-2211
Cynthia Pineda, admin. Fax 549-2922

Breckenridge, Gratiot, Pop. 1,316
Breckenridge Community SD 800/PK-12
PO Box 217 48615 989-842-3182
Kimberly Thompson, supt. Fax 842-3625
breckhuskies.org
Breckenridge AIM S 50/Alt
700 Wright St 48615 989-842-3182
Sheila Pilmore, admin. Fax 842-5761
Breckenridge HS 200/9-12
PO Box 217 48615 989-842-3182
Sheila Pilmore, prin. Fax 842-5761
Breckenridge MS 200/6-8
PO Box 217 48615 989-842-3182
Sheila Pilmore, prin. Fax 842-5761

Brethren, Manistee, Pop. 407
Kaleva Norman Dickson SD 500/K-12
4400 Highbridge Rd 49619 231-477-5353
Marlen Cordes, supt. Fax 477-5240
www.knd.k12.mi.us
Brethren HS 200/9-12
4400 Highbridge Rd 49619 231-477-5355
Jakob Veith, prin. Fax 477-5242
Brethren MS 100/7-8
4400 Highbridge Rd 49619 231-477-5354
Jakob Veith, prin. Fax 477-5351

Bridgeport, Saginaw, Pop. 6,811
Bridgeport-Spaulding Community SD 1,200/PK-12
PO Box 657 48722 989-777-1770
Carol W. Selby, supt. Fax 777-4720
www.bscs.k12.mi.us
Bridgeport HS 600/9-12
4691 Bearcat Blvd 48722 989-777-3100
John Lagalo, prin. Fax 777-6910

Bridgman, Berrien, Pop. 2,260
Bridgman SD 1,000/PK-12
9964 Gast Rd 49106 269-465-5432
Shane Peters, supt. Fax 466-0221
www.bridgmanschools.com

Bridgman HS 300/9-12
9964 Gast Rd 49106 269-465-6848
Sam Stine, prin. Fax 466-0355
Reed MS 300/5-8
10254 California 49106 269-465-5410
John Truesdell, prin. Fax 466-0393

Brighton, Livingston, Pop. 7,364
Brighton Area SD 6,000/K-12
125 S Church St 48116 810-299-4000
Greg Gray, supt. Fax 299-4092
www.brightonk12.com/
Bridge Alternative HS 100/Alt
125 S Church St 48116 810-299-4046
Colleen Deaven, admin.
Brighton HS 2,000/9-12
7878 Brighton Rd 48116 810-299-4100
Gavin Johnson, prin. Fax 299-4111
Scranton MS 1,000/7-8
8415 Maltby Rd 48116 810-299-3700
Mark Wilson, prin. Fax 299-3710

Ross Medical Education Center Post-Sec.
8110 Murphy Dr 48116 810-227-0160

Brimley, Chippewa
Brimley Area SD 500/K-12
7134 S M 221 49715 906-248-3219
Brian Reattoir, supt. Fax 248-3220
brimley.eup.k12.mi.us
Brimley HS 200/7-12
7134 S M 221 49715 906-248-3218
Brian Reattoir, prin. Fax 248-5339

Bay Mills Community College Post-Sec.
12214 W Lakeshore Dr 49715 906-248-3354

Britton, Lenawee, Pop. 584
Britton Deerfield SD 600/PK-12
201 College Ave 49229 517-451-4581
Stacy Johnson, supt. Fax 451-8595
www.bdschools.us
Britton S 500/PK-12
201 College Ave 49229 517-451-4581
John Eisley, prin. Fax 451-8595
Other Schools – See Deerfield

Bronson, Branch, Pop. 2,313
Bronson Community SD 1,300/K-12
501 E Chicago St 49028 517-369-3260
Dr. Teresa Belote, supt. Fax 369-2802
www.bronsonschools.org
Bronson JSHS 600/6-12
450 E Grant St 49028 517-369-3230
Wesley McCrea, prin. Fax 369-3506

Brooklyn, Jackson, Pop. 1,196
Columbia SD 1,000/PK-12
11775 Hewitt Rd 49230 517-592-6641
Dr. Pamela Campbell, supt. Fax 592-8090
www.myeagles.org
Columbia Central JSHS 500/7-12
11775 Hewitt Rd 49230 517-592-6634
Daniel Hyliard, prin. Fax 592-8909
Other Schools – See Clarklake

Brown City, Sanilac, Pop. 1,303
Brown City Community SD 900/PK-12
PO Box 160 48416 810-346-4700
Doug Muxlow, supt. Fax 346-3762
www.bc.k12.mi.us
Brown City JSHS 400/7-12
PO Box 160 48416 810-346-4700
Neil Kohler, prin. Fax 346-2381

Brownstown, See Flat Rock
Woodhaven-Brownstown SD
Supt. — See Woodhaven
Maple Grove Alternative HS 100/Alt
24787 Van Horn Rd 48134 734-783-3333
Matt Czajkowski, prin. Fax 783-3342
Woodhaven HS 1,200/10-12
24787 Van Horn Rd 48134 734-783-3333
Matthew Czajkowski, prin. Fax 783-3342

Buchanan, Berrien, Pop. 4,325
Buchanan Community SD 1,400/PK-12
401 W Chicago St 49107 269-695-8401
Dr. Andrea Van der Laan, supt. Fax 695-8450
www.buchananschools.com
Buchanan HS 600/8-12
401 W Chicago St 49107 269-695-8403
Stacey DeMaio, prin. Fax 695-8451

Buckley, Wexford, Pop. 683
Buckley Community SD 400/K-12
305 S 1st St 49620 231-269-3325
Laurie Walles, supt. Fax 269-3833
www.buckleyschools.com
Buckley Community S 400/K-12
305 S 1st St 49620 231-269-3325
Laurie Walles, admin. Fax 269-3833

Burr Oak, Saint Joseph, Pop. 822
Burr Oak Community SD 200/K-12
PO Box 337 49030 269-489-2213
Terry Conklin, supt. Fax 489-5198
burroakcs.org/
Burr Oak HS 100/5-12
PO Box 337 49030 269-489-5534
Robert Cary, prin. Fax 489-5198

Burton, Genesee, Pop. 29,312
Atherton Community SD 900/K-12
3354 S Genesee Rd 48519 810-591-9182
John Ploof, supt. Fax 591-1926
www.athertonschools.org
Atherton JSHS 500/7-12
3354 S Genesee Rd 48519 810-591-9184
Steven Vowles, prin. Fax 591-9180

Bendle SD 1,100/PK-12
3420 Columbine Ave 48529 810-591-2501
John Krolewski, supt. Fax 591-2210
www.bendleschools.org
Bendle HS 300/9-12
2283 E Scottwood Ave 48529 810-591-5103
Brandon Chapman, prin. Fax 591-2510
Bendle MS 300/6-8
2294 E Bristol Rd 48529 810-591-3385
Pete Gleason, prin. Fax 591-2540

Bentley Community SD 900/K-12
1170 N Belsay Rd 48509 810-591-9100
Christopher Arrington, supt. Fax 591-9102
www.bentleyschools.org
Bentley HS 200/9-12
1150 N Belsay Rd 48509 810-591-5811
Justin Dickerson, prin. Fax 591-9158
Bentley High School FUSION Academy 50/Alt
1150 N Belsay Rd 48509 810-591-9516
Brian Eddy, prin. Fax 591-9158
Bentley MS 200/6-8
1180 N Belsay Rd 48509 810-591-9043
Brian Eddy, prin. Fax 591-9166

Faithway Christian S 100/PK-12
1225 S Center Rd 48509 810-743-0055
Laura Walthers, prin. Fax 743-0033
Genesee Christian S 400/PK-12
1223 S Belsay Rd 48509 810-743-3108
Robert Buchalski, prin. Fax 743-3230
St. Thomas More Academy 100/K-12
6456 E Bristol Rd 48519 810-742-2411
Dan Le Blanc, prin. Fax 742-4803

Byron, Shiawassee, Pop. 573
Byron Area SD 1,000/PK-12
312 W Maple St 48418 810-266-4881
Tricia Murphy-Alderman, supt. Fax 266-5723
www.byron.k12.mi.us
Byron HS 400/9-12
312 W Maple St 48418 810-266-4620
Grant Hegenauer, prin. Fax 266-5010
Byron MS 200/7-8
312 W Maple St 48418 810-266-4422
Grant Hegenauer, prin. Fax 266-4151

Byron Center, Kent, Pop. 5,750
Byron Center SD 3,700/PK-12
8542 Byron Center Ave SW 49315 616-878-6100
Daniel Takens, supt. Fax 878-6120
www.bcpsk12.net
Byron Center HS 1,100/9-12
8500 Burlingame Ave SW 49315 616-878-6600
Scott Joseph, prin. Fax 878-6620
Byron Center West MS 500/7-8
8654 Homerich Ave SW 49315 616-878-6500
John Krajewski, prin. Fax 878-6520

Zion Christian S 300/PK-12
7555 Byron Center Ave SW 49315 616-878-9472
Todd Hoekstra, admin. Fax 878-9473

Cadillac, Wexford, Pop. 10,183
Cadillac Area SD 3,100/K-12
421 S Mitchell St 49601 231-876-5000
Jennifer Brown, supt. Fax 876-5021
www.cadillac.k12.mi.us
Cadillac HS 800/9-12
400 Linden St 49601 231-876-5800
Shaina Squires, prin. Fax 876-5821
Cadillac JHS 500/7-8
500 Chestnut St 49601 231-876-5700
Michael Outman, prin. Fax 876-5721
Cooley Alternative S 200/Alt
221 Granite St 49601 231-876-5900
Dave Champion, prin. Fax 876-5921

Wexford-Missaukee ISD 100/
9907 E 13th St 49601 231-876-2260
Jeff Jennette, supt. Fax 876-2261
www.wmisd.org
Wexford-Missaukee Area Career Tech Vo/Tech
9901 E 13th St 49601 231-876-2200
David Cox, dir. Fax 876-2212

Baker College of Cadillac Post-Sec.
9600 E 13th St 49601 231-876-3100
Cadillac Heritage Christian S 100/PK-12
1706 Wright St 49601 231-775-4272
William Goodwill, admin. Fax 775-2999

Caledonia, Kent, Pop. 1,496
Caledonia Community SD 4,400/PK-12
9753 Duncan Lake Ave SE 49316 616-891-8185
Randy Rodriguez, supt. Fax 891-9253
www.calschools.org
Caledonia HS 1,400/9-12
9050 Kraft Ave SE 49316 616-891-8129
Brady Lake, prin. Fax 891-7038
Duncan Lake MS 500/6-8
9757 Duncan Lake Ave SE 49316 616-891-1380
Ryan Graham, prin. Fax 891-0833
Glenmor HS 50/Alt
8948 Kraft Ave SE 49316 616-891-8236
Brady Lake, prin. Fax 891-8139
Kraft Meadows MS 500/6-8
9230 Kraft Ave SE 49316 616-891-8649
Steve Uyl, prin. Fax 891-7013

Calumet, Houghton, Pop. 716
Calumet-Laurium-Keweenaw SD 1,400/K-12
57070 Mine St 49913 906-337-0311
Darryl Pierce, supt. Fax 337-1406
clkschools.org
Calumet HS 400/9-12
57070 Mine St 49913 906-337-0311
Christopher Davidson, prin. Fax 337-5405

Horizon Alternative HS 100/Alt
57070 Mine St 49913 906-337-4611
Joel Asiala, prin. Fax 337-4614
Washington MS 300/6-8
57070 Mine St 49913 906-337-0311
Michael Steber, prin. Fax 337-5406

Camden, Hillsdale, Pop. 510
Camden-Frontier SD 500/K-12
4971 W Montgomery Rd 49232 517-368-5991
Scott Riley, supt. Fax 368-5959
www.cfss.org/
Camden Frontier HS 200/9-12
4971 W Montgomery Rd 49232 517-368-5255
Scott Riley, prin. Fax 368-5959

Canton, Wayne, Pop. 81,500
Plymouth-Canton Community SD
Supt. — See Plymouth
Canton HS 2,100/9-12
8415 N Canton Center Rd 48187 734-416-2850
Hal Heard, prin. Fax 416-7531
Discovery MS 1,000/6-8
45083 Hanford Rd 48187 734-416-2880
Terry Sawchuk, prin. Fax 416-2895
Liberty MS 6-8
46250 Cherry Hill Rd 48187 734-416-7600
James Hunter, prin. Fax 927-0576
Plymouth HS 2,100/9-12
8400 N Beck Rd 48187 734-582-5500
Cheri Steckel, prin. Fax 582-5555
Salem HS 2,000/9-12
46181 Joy Rd 48187 734-416-7800
Kim Villarosa, prin. Fax 416-7791

Michigan Institute of Aviation & Tech Post-Sec.
2955 S Haggerty Rd 48188 734-423-2100
Plymouth Christian Academy 600/PK-12
43065 Joy Rd 48187 734-459-3505
Caryn Huntsman, supt. Fax 459-9997

Capac, Saint Clair, Pop. 1,866
Capac Community SD 900/PK-12
403 N Glassford St 48014 810-395-3710
Stephen Bigelow, supt. Fax 395-4858
www.capacschools.us
Capac JSHS 400/7-12
541 N Glassford St 48014 810-395-3800
Nicole Kirby, prin. Fax 395-2427

Carleton, Monroe, Pop. 2,303
Airport Community SD 2,100/PK-12
11270 Grafton Rd 48117 734-654-2414
John Krimmel, supt. Fax 654-4014
www.airportschools.com
Airport HS 800/9-12
11330 Grafton Rd 48117 734-654-6208
Chris Lukosavich, prin. Fax 654-3005
Wagar 7/8 MS 400/7-8
11200 Grafton Rd 48117 734-654-6205
Dan Bondy, prin. Fax 654-0057
Other Schools – See Newport

Carney, Menominee, Pop. 190
Carney-Nadeau SD 200/PK-12
PO Box 68 49812 906-639-2171
Adam Cocco, supt. Fax 639-2176
www.cnps.us
Carney-Nadeau S 200/PK-12
PO Box 68 49812 906-639-2171
Adam Cocco, admin. Fax 639-2176

Caro, Tuscola, Pop. 4,185
Caro Community SD 1,800/K-12
301 N Hooper St 48723 989-673-3160
Michael Joslyn, supt. Fax 673-6248
www.carok12.org
Caro Alternative HS 100/Alt
1205 E Caro Rd 48723 989-673-6845
Kimberly Byington, prin. Fax 673-8554
Caro HS 500/9-12
301 N Hooper St 48723 989-673-3165
Stephan Clark, prin. Fax 673-8707
Caro MS 400/6-8
299 N Hooper St 48723 989-673-3167
JoAnn Nordstrom, prin. Fax 673-1225

Tuscola ISD 100/
1385 Cleaver Rd 48723 989-673-2144
Eugene Pierce, supt. Fax 673-5366
www.tuscolaisd.org/
Tuscola Technology Center Vo/Tech
1401 Cleaver Rd 48723 989-673-5300
Shawn Petri, prin. Fax 673-4228

Carson City, Montcalm, Pop. 1,086
Carson City-Crystal Area SD 900/K-12
PO Box 780 48811 989-584-3138
Kevin Murphy, supt. Fax 584-3539
www.carsoncity.k12.mi.us
Carson City-Crystal HS 300/9-12
PO Box 780 48811 989-584-3175
Duane Lyons, prin. Fax 584-3259
Carson City-Crystal Upper Elementary MS 400/4-8
PO Box 780 48811 989-584-3903
Ben Brock, prin. Fax 584-3259
Other Schools – See Crystal

Carsonville, Sanilac, Pop. 513
Carsonville-Port Sanilac SD 500/K-12
100 N Goetze Rd 48419 810-657-9393
James Stewart, supt. Fax 657-9060
www.cpsk12.us
Carsonville-Port Sanilac JSHS 200/6-12
100 N Goetze Rd 48419 810-657-9394
James Stewart, prin. Fax 657-9431
Carsonville-Pt Sanilac Acad Alt Learners 100/Alt
100 N Goetze Rd 48419 810-657-9393
Gale Travis, dir. Fax 657-9060

Casco, Saint Clair
Anchor Bay SD 6,000/PK-12
5201 County Line Rd Ste 100 48064 586-725-2861
Leonard Woodside, supt. Fax 727-9059
www.anchorbay.misd.net
Other Schools – See Fair Haven, New Baltimore

Caseville, Huron, Pop. 766
Caseville SD 100/K-12
6609 Vine St 48725 989-856-2940
Dr. Kenneth Ewald, supt. Fax 856-3095
www.caseville.k12.mi.us
Caseville S 100/K-12
6609 Vine St 48725 989-856-7192
Dr. Kenneth Ewald, prin. Fax 856-8641

Cass City, Tuscola, Pop. 2,395
Cass City SD 1,000/PK-12
4868 Seeger St 48726 989-872-2200
Jeffrey Hartel, supt. Fax 872-5015
www.casscity.k12.mi.us
Cass City JSHS 500/7-12
4868 Seeger St 48726 989-872-2148
Chad Daniels, prin. Fax 872-2068

Cassopolis, Cass, Pop. 1,687
Cassopolis SD 900/K-12
725 Center St 49031 269-445-0503
Tracy D. Hertsel, supt. Fax 445-0505
www.cassopolis.k12.mi.us
Beatty JSHS 400/7-12
22721 Diamond Cove St 49031 269-445-0540
Dave VanLue, prin. Fax 445-3112

Cedar Lake, Montcalm

Great Lakes Adventist Academy 200/9-12
PO Box 68 48812 989-427-5181
Delwin Garcia, prin. Fax 427-5027

Cedar Springs, Kent, Pop. 3,426
Cedar Springs SD 3,300/PK-12
204 E Muskegon St 49319 616-696-1204
Dr. Laura VanDuyn Ed.D., supt. Fax 696-3755
www.csredhawks.org
Cedar Springs HS 900/9-12
204 E Muskegon St 49319 616-696-1200
Ron Behrenwald, prin. Fax 696-4016
Cedar Springs MS 500/7-8
204 E Muskegon St 49319 616-696-9100
Sue Spahr, prin. Fax 696-3109
New Beginnings HS 100/Alt
204 E Muskegon St 49319 616-696-1203
Stacey Jennette, prin. Fax 696-0296

Cedarville, Mackinac
Les Cheneaux Community SD 300/K-12
PO Box 366 49719 906-484-2256
Randy Schaedig, supt. Fax 484-2072
lescheneaux.eup.k12.mi.us/site/default.aspx?PageID=1
Cedarville S 300/K-12
PO Box 366 49719 906-484-2256
Randy Schaedig, supt. Fax 484-2072

Center Line, Macomb, Pop. 8,060
Center Line SD 2,700/PK-12
26400 Arsenal 48015 586-510-2000
Eve Kaltz, supt. Fax 510-2019
www.clps.org
Center Line HS 800/9-12
26300 Arsenal 48015 586-510-2100
Andrea Szabo, prin. Fax 510-2119
Wolfe MS 600/6-8
8640 McKinley 48015 586-510-2300
Cassandra Conaton, prin. Fax 510-2319

Central Lake, Antrim, Pop. 931
Central Lake SD 400/PK-12
PO Box 128 49622 231-544-3141
Lenore Weaver, supt. Fax 544-2903
www.clps.k12.mi.us
Central Lake JSHS 200/6-12
PO Box 128 49622 231-544-5221
Michele Derenzy, prin. Fax 544-6981

Centreville, Saint Joseph, Pop. 1,388
Centreville SD 800/K-12
PO Box 158 49032 269-467-5220
Robert Kuhlman, supt. Fax 467-5214
www.cpschools.org
Centreville HS 300/9-12
PO Box 158 49032 269-467-5210
Matthew Hawkins, prin. Fax 467-5214
Centreville JHS 100/7-8
PO Box 158 49032 269-467-5210
Matthew Hawkins, prin. Fax 467-5214
Covered Bridge Alternative S 50/Alt
PO Box 158 49032 269-467-5215
Juanita Miller, prin. Fax 467-5227

Glen Oaks Community College Post-Sec.
62249 Shimmel Rd 49032 269-467-9945

Charlevoix, Charlevoix, Pop. 2,468
Charlevoix SD 1,000/PK-12
104 E Saint Marys Dr 49720 231-547-3200
Michael Ritter, supt. Fax 547-0556
www.rayder.net
Charlevoix MSHS 500/7-12
5200 Marion Center Rd 49720 231-547-3222
Suzanne Klinger, prin. Fax 547-3245

Charlotte, Eaton, Pop. 8,946
Charlotte SD 2,600/PK-12
378 State St 48813 517-541-5100
Mark Rosekrans, supt. Fax 541-5105
www.charlottenet.org
Charlotte Early Middle College 9-12
378 State St 48813 517-541-5601
Bill Barnes Ed.D., prin. Fax 541-5625

Charlotte HS 900/9-12
378 State St 48813 517-541-5600
William Barnes, prin. Fax 541-5625
Charlotte MS 400/7-8
1068 Carlisle Hwy 48813 517-541-5700
Matthew Maitland, prin. Fax 541-5705

Cheboygan, Cheboygan, Pop. 4,714
Cheboygan Area SD 1,200/K-12
PO Box 100 49721 231-627-4436
Troy Reehl, supt. Fax 627-9105
www.chebschools.org
Cheboygan Area HS 600/8-12
PO Box 100 49721 231-627-7191
Dr. Michele Ackerman, prin. Fax 627-2430
Inverness Academy Alternative Education 100/Alt
PO Box 100 49721 231-627-5613
Christopher Ackerman, dir. Fax 627-4180

Chelsea, Washtenaw, Pop. 4,865
Chelsea SD 2,400/PK-12
500 Washington St 48118 734-433-2200
Julie D. Helber Ed.D., supt. Fax 433-2218
www.chelsea.k12.mi.us
Beach MS 600/6-8
445 Mayer Dr 48118 734-433-2202
Nick Angel, prin. Fax 433-2212
Chelsea HS 800/9-12
740 N Freer Rd 48118 734-433-2201
Michael Kapolka, prin. Fax 433-2211

Chesaning, Saginaw, Pop. 2,377
Chesaning UNSD 1,500/K-12
PO Box 95 48616 989-845-7020
Mike McGough, supt. Fax 845-3722
www.chesaningschools.net
Chesaning MS 500/5-8
431 N 4th St 48616 989-845-7040
Melinda Soule, prin. Fax 845-5335
Chesaning Union HS 500/9-12
850 N 4th St 48616 989-845-2040
Kimberly Vincke, prin. Fax 845-2117

Chesterfield, Macomb
L'Anse Creuse SD
Supt. — See Clinton Township
L'Anse Creuse MS East 800/6-8
30300 Hickey Rd 48051 586-493-5200
Nina Davis, prin. Fax 493-5205

Austin Catholic HS 9-12
25925 23 Mile Rd 48051 586-200-0143
Janel Coppens, prin. Fax 408-6034

Clare, Clare, Pop. 3,061
Clare SD 1,500/K-12
201 E State St 48617 989-386-9945
Doug Fillmore, supt. Fax 386-6055
www.clare.k12.mi.us
Clare HS 500/9-12
201 E State St 48617 989-386-7789
Ed Hubel, prin. Fax 386-1236
Clare MS 500/5-8
201 E State St 48617 989-386-9979
Steve Newkirk, prin. Fax 386-4008
Pioneer HS 50/Alt
670 Ann Arbor Trl 48617 989-386-3067
Fax 386-3274

Clarklake, Jackson, Pop. 400
Columbia SD
Supt. — See Brooklyn
Columbia Options HS 100/Alt
4460 N Lake Rd 49234 517-529-9400
Lisa Klink, prin. Fax 529-4853

Clarkston, Oakland, Pop. 980
Clarkston Community SD 7,800/PK-12
6389 Clarkston Rd 48346 248-623-5400
Dr. Rod Rock, supt. Fax 623-5450
www.clarkston.k12.mi.us
Clarkston HS 1,900/10-12
6093 Flemings Lake Rd 48346 248-623-3600
Gary Kaul, prin. Fax 623-3535
Clarkston JHS 1,300/8-9
6595 Waldon Rd 48346 248-623-5600
Adam Kern, prin. Fax 623-5680
Renaissance HS 200/Alt
6558 Waldon Rd 48346 248-623-8060
Christa Fons, prin. Fax 623-4555

Oakland ISD
Supt. — See Waterford
Oakland Technical Campus NW Vo/Tech
8211 Big Lake Rd 48346 248-922-5800
Chuck Locklear, dean Fax 922-5805

Everest Collegiate HS & Academy 500/PK-12
5935 Clarkston Rd 48348 248-620-3390
Gregory Reichert, pres. Fax 620-3942

Clawson, Oakland, Pop. 11,609
Clawson SD 1,700/K-12
626 Phillips Ave 48017 248-655-4400
Monique Beels, supt. Fax 655-4422
www.clawsonschools.org
Clawson HS 600/9-12
101 John M Ave 48017 248-655-4200
Ryan Sines, prin. Fax 655-4205
Clawson MS 400/6-8
150 John M Ave 48017 248-655-4250
Adam Schihl, prin. Fax 655-4251

Climax, Kalamazoo, Pop. 761
Climax-Scotts Community SD 500/PK-12
372 S Main St 49034 269-746-2400
Douglas Newington, supt. Fax 746-4374
www.csschools.net
Climax-Scotts Alternative Education 50/Alt
372 S Main St 49034 269-746-4250
Douglas Newington, admin. Fax 746-2409
Climax-Scotts JSHS 300/6-12
372 S Main St 49034 269-746-2300
Kimberly Kirshman, prin. Fax 746-4142

Clinton, Lenawee, Pop. 2,302
Clinton Community SD 1,100/PK-12
341 E Michigan Ave 49236 517-456-6501
James Cracraft, supt. Fax 456-4324
ccsweb.clinton.k12.mi.us
Clinton HS 400/9-12
340 E Michigan Ave 49236 517-456-6511
Kevin Beazley, prin. Fax 456-2042
Clinton MS 200/6-8
100 E Franklin St 49236 517-456-6507
Eric Claus, prin. Fax 456-4997

Clinton Township, Macomb, Pop. 95,648
Chippewa Valley SD 15,300/K-12
19120 Cass Ave 48038 586-723-2000
Ron Roberts, supt. Fax 723-2001
www.chippewavalleyschools.org
Algonquin MS 600/6-8
19150 Briarwood Ln 48036 586-723-3500
Walter Kozlowski, prin. Fax 723-3501
Chippewa Valley HS 1,800/10-12
18300 19 Mile Rd 48038 586-723-2300
Dr. Jerry Davisson, prin. Fax 723-2336
Chippewa Valley Ninth Grade Center 9-9
42755 Romeo Plank Rd 48038 586-723-3100
Diane Zatkoff, prin. Fax 723-3101
International Academy of Macomb 500/9-12
42755 Romeo Plank Rd 48038 586-723-7200
Eric Sturm, prin. Fax 723-7201
Mohegan HS 100/Alt
19230 Cass Ave 48038 586-723-2080
Jim Fields, admin. Fax 723-2051
Wyandot MS 1,000/6-8
39490 Garfield Rd 48038 586-723-4200
Darleen Gauci, prin. Fax 723-4201
Other Schools – See Macomb

Clintondale Community SD 2,500/PK-12
35100 Little Mack Ave 48035 586-791-6300
Gregory Green, supt. Fax 791-6786
seatwaitingforyou.com
Clintondale Continuing Education Center 700/Alt
22280 E Price Dr 48035 586-790-2756
Kent Rivard, prin. Fax 790-7620
Clintondale HS 500/9-12
35200 Little Mack Ave 48035 586-791-6300
Meloney Cargill, prin. Fax 790-7645
Clintondale MS 400/6-8
35300 Little Mack Ave 48035 586-791-6300
Ira Hamden, prin. Fax 790-7642

L'Anse Creuse SD 10,700/PK-12
24076 Frederick Pankow Blvd 48036 586-783-6300
Dr. Jacqueline Johnston Ph.D., supt. Fax 783-6310
www.lc-ps.org
Pankow Center Vo/Tech
24600 Frederick Pankow Blvd 48036 586-783-6570
John Haas, prin. Fax 783-6577
Pellerin Center Adult
24001 Frederick Pankow Blvd 48036 586-783-6420
Jeff Glombowski, prin. Fax 783-6423
Other Schools – See Chesterfield, Harrison Township, Macomb, Mount Clemens

---

Baker College of Clinton Township Post-Sec.
34950 Little Mack Ave 48035 586-791-6610
Faith Christian S 100/PK-12
23130 Remick Dr 48036 586-783-9630
Jim Hawkins, prin. Fax 783-9628

Clio, Genesee, Pop. 2,597
Clio Area SD 3,300/K-12
430 N Mill St 48420 810-591-0500
Fletcher Spears, supt. Fax 591-0140
www.clioschools.org
Carter MS 1,000/5-8
300 Rogers Ldg 48420 810-591-0503
Neil Bedell, prin. Fax 591-8148
Clio Community HS 200/Alt
420 N Mill St 48420 810-591-4804
Neil Bedell, dir. Fax 591-8193
Clio HS 900/9-12
1 Mustang Dr 48420 810-591-1359
Mike Lytle, prin. Fax 591-8169

Coldwater, Branch, Pop. 10,680
Branch ISD 100/
370 Morse St 49036 517-279-5730
Joseph Lopez, supt. Fax 279-5766
www.branch-isd.org
Branch Area Career Center Vo/Tech
366 Morse St 49036 517-279-5721
Michael Hoffner, prin. Fax 279-5777

Coldwater Community SD 3,000/PK-12
401 Sauk River Dr 49036 517-279-5910
Terry Ann Boguth, supt. Fax 279-7651
www.coldwaterschools.org
Coldwater HS 800/9-12
275 N Fremont St 49036 517-279-5930
William Milnes, prin. Fax 278-2475
Legg MS 600/6-8
175 Green St 49036 517-279-5940
Julie Slusher, prin. Fax 279-5945

School of Creative Hair Design Post-Sec.
470 Marshall St 49036 517-279-2355

Coleman, Midland, Pop. 1,211
Coleman Community SD 700/K-12
4823 N Coleman Schools Dr 48618 989-465-6060
Jennifer McCormack, supt. Fax 465-9853
www.colemanschools.net
Coleman JSHS 300/7-12
4951 N Lewis Rd 48618 989-465-6171
John Young, prin. Fax 465-9222

Coloma, Berrien, Pop. 1,456
Coloma Community SD 900/PK-12
PO Box 550 49038 269-468-2424
Pete Bush, supt. Fax 468-2440
www.ccs.coloma.org
Coloma HS 400/9-12
PO Box 550 49038 269-468-2400
David Ehlers, prin. Fax 468-2423
Coloma JHS 100/6-8
PO Box 550 49038 269-468-2405
Peter Olsen, prin. Fax 468-2428

Colon, Saint Joseph, Pop. 1,152
Colon Community SD 600/PK-12
400 Dallas St 49040 269-386-2239
Christine Barnes, supt. Fax 432-2577
www.colonschools.org
Colon JSHS 200/7-12
400 Dallas St 49040 269-432-3231
Beth Robb, prin. Fax 432-9851

Commerce Township, Oakland, Pop. 26,955
Huron Valley SD
Supt. — See Highland
Oak Valley MS 700/6-8
4200 White Oak Trl 48382 248-684-8101
Michele Butler, prin. Fax 684-8105

Walled Lake Consolidated SD
Supt. — See Walled Lake
Central HS 1,800/9-12
1600 E Oakley Park Rd 48390 248-956-4700
Charles Morgan, prin. Fax 956-4705
Northern HS 1,600/9-12
6000 Bogie Lake Rd 48382 248-956-5300
Greg Diamond, prin. Fax 956-5305
Smart MS 1,000/6-8
8500 Commerce Rd 48382 248-956-3500
David Tucker, prin. Fax 956-3505

Comstock Park, Kent, Pop. 9,824
Comstock Park SD 2,400/PK-12
101 School St NE 49321 616-254-5001
Ethan Ebenstein, supt. Fax 784-5404
www.cppschools.com
Comstock Park HS 700/9-12
150 6 Mile Rd NE 49321 616-254-5200
Steve Gough, prin. Fax 785-9835
Mill Creek MS 500/6-8
100 Betty St NE 49321 616-254-5100
August Harju, prin. Fax 785-2464

Concord, Jackson, Pop. 1,046
Concord Community SD 700/K-12
PO Box 338 49237 517-524-8850
Dan Funston, supt. Fax 524-8613
www.concordschools.net
Concord HS 300/9-12
PO Box 338 49237 517-524-8384
Cheryl Price, prin. Fax 524-6196
Concord MS 200/6-8
PO Box 338 49237 517-524-8854
Matt Lehman, prin. Fax 524-7324

Constantine, Saint Joseph, Pop. 2,015
Constantine SD 1,400/K-12
1 Falcon Dr 49042 269-435-8900
Steve Wilson, supt. Fax 435-8980
www.constps.org
Constantine HS 400/9-12
1 Falcon Dr 49042 269-435-8920
Travis Walker, prin. Fax 435-8981
Constantine MS 300/6-8
260 W 6th St 49042 269-435-8940
Ray Bohm, prin. Fax 435-8982

Cooks, Delta
Big Bay de Noc SD 200/PK-12
8928 00.25 Rd 49817 906-644-2773
Mary Brayak, supt. Fax 644-2615
www.bigbayschool.com
Big Bay de Noc S 200/PK-12
8928 00.25 Rd 49817 906-644-2773
DeeDee Thill, prin. Fax 644-2615

Coopersville, Ottawa, Pop. 4,215
Coopersville Area SD 2,500/PK-12
198 East St 49404 616-997-3200
Ron Veldman, supt. Fax 997-3214
www.coopersvillebroncos.org/
Coopersville MS 600/6-8
198 East St 49404 616-997-3400
Ryan Pfahler, prin. Fax 997-3414
Coopersville SHS 800/9-12
198 East St 49404 616-997-3500
Brent Hadden, prin. Fax 997-3514

Corunna, Shiawassee, Pop. 3,446
Corunna SD 1,200/PK-12
124 N Shiawassee St 48817 989-743-6338
Dave Moore, supt. Fax 743-4474
www.corunna.k12.mi.us
Corunna HS 700/8-12
417 E King St 48817 989-743-3441
Leo Constine, prin. Fax 743-5901

Covert, Van Buren
Covert SD 300/PK-12
35323 M 140 Hwy 49043 269-764-3701
Dr. Bobbi Morehead, supt. Fax 764-8598
www.covertps.org
Covert HS 100/9-12
35323 M 140 Hwy 49043 269-764-3730
Yolanda Brunt, prin. Fax 764-3754
Covert MS 100/6-8
35323 M 140 Hwy 49043 269-764-3730
Yolanda Brunt, prin. Fax 764-3754

Croswell, Sanilac, Pop. 2,419
Croswell-Lexington SD 2,300/PK-12
5407 Peck Rd 48422 810-679-1000
Charles Smith, supt. Fax 679-1005
www.croslex.org

Croswell-Lexington HS 700/9-12
5461 Peck Rd 48422 810-679-1500
Kyle Wood, prin. Fax 679-1505
Croswell-Lexington MS 700/5-8
5485 Peck Rd 48422 810-679-1400
Bethany Davis, prin. Fax 679-1405
Other Schools – See Lexington

Crystal, Montcalm
Carson City-Crystal Area SD
Supt. — See Carson City
Carson City-Crystal Alternative Academy 50/Alt
217 Park St 48818 989-584-6927
Devin Pringle, prin. Fax 584-3539

Crystal Falls, Iron, Pop. 1,443
Forest Park SD 500/PK-12
801 Forest Pkwy 49920 906-214-4695
Becky Waters, supt. Fax 875-4660
www.fptrojans.org
Forest Park JSHS 300/6-12
801 Forest Pkwy 49920 906-214-4695
Lisa Olson, prin. Fax 875-4660

Custer, Mason, Pop. 279
Mason County Eastern SD 500/K-12
18 S Main St 49405 231-757-3733
Paul Shoup, supt. Fax 757-9671
mceschools.com
Mason County Eastern JSHS 200/7-12
18 S Main St 49405 231-757-3733
Paul Shoup, admin. Fax 757-9671

Dansville, Ingham, Pop. 554
Dansville SD 800/K-12
PO Box 187 48819 517-623-6120
Amy Hodgson, supt. Fax 623-6719
www.dansville.org
Dansville HS 300/9-12
PO Box 187 48819 517-623-6120
Tania Dupuis, prin. Fax 623-0127
Dansville MS 200/6-8
PO Box 187 48819 517-623-6120
Tania Dupuis, prin. Fax 623-1087

Davison, Genesee, Pop. 5,081
Davison Community SD 5,500/K-12
PO Box 319 48423 810-591-0801
Eric Lieske, supt. Fax 591-7813
www.davisonschools.org/
Alternative Education 200/Alt
1250 N Oak Rd 48423 810-591-1020
Christopher Wilson, dean Fax 591-3784
Davison HS 1,600/9-12
1250 N Oak Rd 48423 810-591-3531
Sue Kenkel, prin. Fax 591-3555
Davison MS 800/7-8
600 S Dayton St 48423 810-591-0848
Shelly Fenner-Krasny, prin. Fax 591-2754

Faith Baptist S 300/PK-12
7306 E Atherton Rd 48423 810-653-9661
Dr. Damian Ahrens, admin. Fax 658-0087

Dearborn, Wayne, Pop. 94,259
Dearborn SD 17,900/PK-12
18700 Audette St 48124 313-827-3020
Dr. Glenn Maleyko, supt. Fax 827-3137
www.dearbornschools.org
Bryant MS 800/6-8
460 N Vernon St 48128 313-827-2900
Andrew Denison, prin. Fax 827-2905
Dearborn HS 1,800/9-12
19501 Outer Dr 48124 313-827-1600
Adam Martin, prin. Fax 827-1605
Ford Early College HS 200/9-12
5101 Evergreen Rd 48128 313-317-1588
Majed Fadlallah, prin. Fax 317-2585
Ford HS 1,400/9-12
20601 Rotunda Dr 48124 313-827-1500
Scott Casebolt, prin. Fax 827-1505
Fordson HS 2,400/9-12
13800 Ford Rd 48126 313-827-1400
Heyam Alcodray, prin. Fax 827-1405
Salina IS 500/4-8
2623 Salina St 48120 313-827-6600
Jamel Lawera, prin. Fax 827-6605
Smith MS 600/6-8
23851 Yale St 48124 313-827-2800
Sean Fisher, prin. Fax 827-2805
Stout MS 800/6-8
18500 Oakwood Blvd 48124 313-827-4600
Gregory Oke, prin. Fax 827-4605
Woodworth MS 900/6-8
4951 Ternes St 48126 313-827-7100
Maysam Alie-Bazzi, prin. Fax 827-7105
Other Schools – See Dearborn Heights

Divine Child HS 800/9-12
1001 N Silvery Ln 48128 313-562-1990
Damian Hermann, prin. Fax 562-9361
Everest Institute Post-Sec.
23400 Michigan Ave Ste 200 48124 313-562-4228
Henry Ford Community College Post-Sec.
5101 Evergreen Rd 48128 313-845-9600
University of Michigan-Dearborn Post-Sec.
4901 Evergreen Rd 48128 313-593-5000

Dearborn Heights, Wayne, Pop. 56,336
Crestwood SD 3,400/PK-12
1501 N Beech Daly Rd 48127 313-278-0906
Dr. Laurine VanValkenburg, supt. Fax 278-4774
www.csdm.k12.mi.us/
Crestwood HS 1,300/9-12
1501 N Beech Daly Rd 48127 313-278-0900
John Tafelski, prin. Fax 792-0205
Riverside MS 1,100/5-8
25900 W Warren St 48127 313-274-0140
Dennis Faletti, prin. Fax 792-0201

Dearborn Heights SD 7 2,600/PK-12
20629 Annapolis St 48125 313-203-1000
John Fazer, supt. Fax 278-1413
www.district7.net
Annapolis HS 800/9-12
4650 Clippert St 48125 313-278-9870
Cheryl Howard, prin. Fax 278-1238
Best JHS 700/6-8
22201 Powers Ave 48125 313-278-6200
Melanie Ward, prin. Fax 278-2470

Dearborn SD
Supt. — See Dearborn
Berry Career Center Vo/Tech
22586 Ann Arbor Trl 48127 313-827-4800
Winifred Green, prin. Fax 827-4805
Dearborn Ctr for Math Science & Tech Alt
22586 Ann Arbor Trl 48127 313-827-2720
Winifred Green, prin. Fax 827-2725
Dearborn Magnet HS 50/9-12
22586 Ann Arbor Trl 48127 313-827-4800
Winifred Green, prin. Fax 827-4805
Adult & Community Education Adult
22586 Ann Arbor Trl 48127 313-827-1900
Julie Maconochie, coord. Fax 827-1906

Westwood Community SD 2,300/K-12
3335 S Beech Daly St 48125 313-565-1900
Sue Carnell, supt. Fax 565-3162
westwoodschools.net
Robichaud HS 400/9-12
3601 Janet St 48125 313-565-8851
Melanie Depray Learst, prin. Fax 565-0304
Westwood Alternative Education HS North Alt
23914 Ford Rd 48127 313-730-1667
Leslie Simmons, prin. Fax 565-2379
Other Schools – See Inkster

Decatur, Van Buren, Pop. 1,763
Decatur SD 900/K-12
110 Cedar St 49045 269-423-6800
Dr. Patrick Creagan, supt. Fax 423-6849
www.raiderpride.org/
Decatur HS 300/9-12
110 Cedar St 49045 269-423-6850
Matthew McLouth, prin. Fax 423-6899
Decatur MS 200/6-8
405 N Phelps St 49045 269-423-6900
Matthew McLouth, prin. Fax 423-6949

Marcellus Community SD
Supt. — See Marcellus
Volinia Outcome Base S 100/Alt
54080 Gards Prairie Rd 49045 269-782-9716
Amy Anderson, prin. Fax 782-6824

Deckerville, Sanilac, Pop. 821
Deckerville Community SD 600/K-12
2633 Black River St 48427 810-376-3615
Tricia Pawlowski, supt. Fax 376-3115
www.deckerville.k12.mi.us
Deckerville Community JSHS 300/7-12
2633 Black River St 48427 810-376-3875
Matt Connelly, prin. Fax 376-3115

Deerfield, Lenawee, Pop. 875
Britton Deerfield SD
Supt. — See Britton
Deerfield S 200/4-8
PO Box 217 49238 517-447-3015
Stacy Johnson, supt. Fax 447-3216

Delton, Barry, Pop. 851
Delton Kellogg SD 1,300/K-12
327 N Grove St 49046 269-623-1501
Carl Schoessel, supt. Fax 623-1508
dkschools.org
Delton Kellogg HS 400/9-12
10425 Panther Pride 49046 269-623-1522
Lucas Trierweiler, prin. Fax 623-1150
Delton Kellogg MS 400/5-8
6325 Delton Rd 49046 269-623-1542
April Margaritis, prin. Fax 623-1548
DK Academy Alt
10425 Panther Pride Dr 49046 269-623-1520
Sarah Nevins, admin.

De Tour Village, Chippewa, Pop. 312
De Tour Area SD 100/K-12
PO Box 429 49725 906-297-2421
Angela Reed, supt. Fax 297-3403
detour.eup.k12.mi.us
De Tour JSHS 100/7-12
PO Box 429 49725 906-297-2011
Angela Reed, supt. Fax 297-3403

Detroit, Wayne, Pop. 700,219
Detroit SD 52,800/PK-12
7321 2nd Ave Fl 14 48202 313-873-7450
Alycia Meriweather, supt. Fax 873-7433
detroitk12.org
Academy of the Americas 700/PK-10
5680 Konkel St 48210 313-596-7640
Nicholas Brown, prin. Fax 596-7652
Banks HS, 5020 Cadieux Rd 48224 100/9-12
Roslyn Fluker, prin. 313-347-7280
Breithaupt Career/Tech S Vo/Tech
9300 Hubbell St 48228 313-866-9550
Charlene Mallory, prin. Fax 866-9605
Carson S for Science & Medicine 400/9-12
571 Mack Ave 48201 313-494-1805
Charles Todd, prin. Fax 494-0992
Cass Technical HS Vo/Tech
2501 2nd Ave 48201 313-263-2000
Lisa Phillips, prin. Fax 263-2001
Clippert Academy 500/5-8
1981 McKinstry St 48209 313-849-5009
Kim Gonzalez, prin. Fax 849-5740
Cody - Academy of Public Leadership 300/9-12
18445 Cathedral St 48228 313-852-6612
Johnathon Matthews, prin. Fax 866-9266

Cody - Detroit Institute of Technology 300/9-12
18445 Cathedral St 48228 313-866-9200
Latoya Hall-King, prin. Fax 866-9266
Cody - Medicine and Community Health Acd 400/9-12
18445 Cathedral St 48228 313-866-9200
Michelle Parker, prin. Fax 866-9266
Communications & Media Arts HS 600/9-12
14771 Mansfield St 48227 313-866-9300
Donya Odom, prin. Fax 866-9304
Crockett Career/Tech S Vo/Tech
571 Mack Ave 48201 313-494-1805
Brenda Belcher, prin. Fax 494-0992
Davis Aerospace Technical HS Vo/Tech
900 Dickerson St 48215 313-822-8820
Ian Diem, prin. Fax 866-5408
Detroit Collegiate Preparatory HS 600/9-12
2200 W Grand Blvd 48208 313-623-0056
Kenyuano Jones, prin.
Detroit Intl Acad for Young Women 500/K-12
9026 Woodward Ave 48202 313-873-3050
Beverly Hibbler, prin. Fax 873-3088
Detroit Lions Alternative S 100/Alt
10101 E Canfield St 48214 313-852-9677
Cheryl White, prin. Fax 852-9676
Detroit S of Arts 500/9-12
123 Selden St 48201 313-494-6000
Delois Cooke Sprysak, prin. Fax 494-2129
Douglass Academy for Young Men 200/Alt
2001 W Warren Ave 48208 313-596-3555
Berry Greer, prin. Fax 596-3552
East English Village Preparatory Academy 1,600/9-12
5020 Cadieux Rd 48224 313-922-5600
Charlene Mallory, prin.
Fisher Magnet Upper Academy 600/5-8
15491 Maddelein St 48205 313-866-7233
Harry Coakley, prin. Fax 866-7329
Golightly Career and Technical Center Vo/Tech
900 Dickerson St 48215 313-822-8820
Nina Graves-Hicks, prin. Fax 866-3131
King HS 1,500/9-12
3200 E Lafayette St 48207 313-494-7373
Dr. Deborah Jenkins, prin. Fax 262-9140
Ludington Magnet MS 500/5-8
19501 Berg Rd 48219 313-494-7577
Allan Cosma, prin. Fax 494-7707
Osborn Academy of Mathematics 300/9-12
11600 E 7 Mile Rd 48205 313-866-0343
Dr. Dennis Myles, prin. Fax 866-0356
Osborn College Preparatory Academy 300/9-12
11600 E 7 Mile Rd 48205 313-866-0343
Senta Ray-Conley, prin. Fax 866-0356
Osborn Evergreen Acad Design & Alt Enrgy 300/9-12
11600 E 7 Mile Rd 48205 313-866-0343
Michael Barclay, prin. Fax 866-0356
Randolph Technical HS Vo/Tech
17101 Hubbell St 48235 313-494-7100
Krista McKinney-King, prin. Fax 494-7114
Renaissance HS 1,200/9-12
6565 W Outer Dr 48235 313-416-4600
Anita Williams, prin. Fax 416-4620
Western International HS 1,500/9-12
1500 Scotten St 48209 313-849-4758
Angel Garcia, prin. Fax 849-4695
West Side Academy of Alternative Ed 500/Alt
4701 McKinley St 48208 313-456-8000
Andrea Ford-Ayler, prin. Fax 456-8001
Adult Education Center East Adult
13840 Lappin St 48205 313-579-7109
Tracy Carpenter, prin.
Adult Education Center West Adult
16164 Asbury Park 48235 313-852-1089
Dedria Willis, prin.

College for Creative Studies Post-Sec.
201 E Kirby St 48202 313-664-7400
Cornerstone S 500/PK-12
6861 E Nevada St 48234 313-892-1860
Ernestine Sanders, pres. Fax 892-1861
Detroit Cristo Rey HS 200/9-12
5679 W Vernor Hwy 48209 313-843-2747
Susan Rowe, prin. Fax 843-2750
Detroit Health Department Post-Sec.
1151 Taylor St 48202 313-876-4090
DMC University Laboratories Post-Sec.
4201 Saint Antoine St 48201 313-745-3053
Dorsey School of Business Post-Sec.
18660 Ford Rd 48228 313-982-3730
Ecumenical Theological Seminary Post-Sec.
2930 Woodward Ave 48201 313-831-5200
Everest Institute Post-Sec.
300 River Place Dr Ste 1000 48207 313-567-5350
Grace Hospital Post-Sec.
6071 W Outer Dr 48235 313-966-3525
Harper Hospital Post-Sec.
3990 John R St 48201 313-745-9375
Henry Ford Hospital Post-Sec.
2799 W Grand Blvd 48202 313-876-1257
Lewis College of Business Post-Sec.
17370 Meyers Rd 48235 313-862-6300
Loyola HS 200/9-12
15325 Pinehurst St 48238 313-861-2407
Wyatt Jones, prin. Fax 861-4718
Marygrove College Post-Sec.
8425 W McNichols Rd 48221 313-927-1240
Michigan Barber School Post-Sec.
8988 Grand River Ave # 90 48204 313-894-2300
Sacred Heart Major Seminary Post-Sec.
2701 W Chicago 48206 313-883-8500
St. John's Hospital Post-Sec.
22101 Moross Rd 48236 313-343-7531
University of Detroit/Jesuit HS 900/7-12
8400 S Cambridge Ave 48221 313-862-5400
Anthony Trudel, prin. Fax 862-3299
University of Detroit Mercy Post-Sec.
4001 W McNichols Rd 48221 313-993-1000
Wayne County Community College Post-Sec.
801 W Fort St 48226 313-496-2600
Wayne State University Post-Sec.
42 W Warren Ave 48201 877-978-4636

De Witt, Clinton, Pop. 4,434
De Witt SD 3,000/K-12
PO Box 800, 517-668-3000
Dr. John Deiter, supt. Fax 668-3018
www.dewittschools.net/
De Witt HS 900/9-12
PO Box 800, 517-668-3100
Jody McKean, prin. Fax 668-3155
De Witt JHS 500/7-8
PO Box 800, 517-668-3200
Keith Cravotta, prin. Fax 668-3255

Dexter, Washtenaw, Pop. 3,976
Dexter Community SD 3,500/PK-12
7714 Ann Arbor St 48130 734-424-4100
Christopher Timmis, supt. Fax 424-4112
dexterschools.org
Dexter HS 1,200/9-12
2200 N Parker Rd 48130 734-424-4240
Kit Moran, prin. Fax 424-2747
Mill Creek MS 500/7-8
7305 Dexter Ann Arbor Rd 48130 734-424-4150
Jami Bronson, prin. Fax 424-4159

Dollar Bay, Houghton, Pop. 1,072
Dollar Bay-Tamarack City SD 300/K-12
PO Box 371 49922 906-482-5800
Dr. Jan Quarless Ph.D., supt. Fax 487-5931
www.dollarbay.k12.mi.us
Dollar Bay JSHS 200/7-12
PO Box 371 49922 906-482-5812
C. Norland, prin. Fax 487-5940

Douglas, Allegan, Pop. 1,221
Saugatuck SD 700/PK-12
PO Box 818 49406 269-857-1444
Rolfe Timmerman, supt. Fax 857-1448
www.saugatuckps.com
Other Schools – See Saugatuck

Dowagiac, Cass, Pop. 5,518
Dowagiac UNSD 2,300/K-12
243 S Front St 49047 269-782-4400
Paul Hartsig, supt. Fax 782-4418
www.dowagiacschools.org
Dowagiac MS 500/6-8
243 S Front St 49047 269-782-4440
Matthew Severin, prin. Fax 782-4449
Pathfinders Alternative/Adult Education 100/Alt
501 N Paul St 49047 269-782-4471
Kara Cox, dir. Fax 782-9748
Union HS 700/9-12
243 S Front St 49047 269-782-4420
Kelly Millin, prin. Fax 782-9518

Southwestern Michigan College Post-Sec.
58900 Cherry Grove Rd 49047 269-782-1000

Dryden, Lapeer, Pop. 947
Dryden Community SD 600/K-12
3866 Rochester Rd 48428 810-448-4090
Mary Finnigan, supt. Fax 796-3698
www.dryden.k12.mi.us
Dryden JSHS 300/7-12
3866 Rochester Rd 48428 810-796-2266
Mary Finnigan, prin. Fax 796-2510

Dundee, Monroe, Pop. 3,916
Dundee Community SD 1,400/PK-12
420 Ypsilanti St 48131 734-529-2350
Edward Manuszak, supt. Fax 529-5606
www.dundeecommunityschools.org
Dundee HS 500/9-12
130 Viking Dr 48131 734-529-7008
Bryan Schroeder, prin. Fax 529-7053
Dundee MS 400/6-8
420 Ypsilanti St 48131 734-529-2350
Aaron Carner, prin. Fax 529-7380
Riverside Academy 50/Alt
445 Toledo St 48131 734-529-3916
Tom Walentowski, dir. Fax 529-5593

Durand, Shiawassee, Pop. 3,411
Durand Area SD 1,500/PK-12
310 N Saginaw St 48429 989-288-2681
Craig McCrumb, supt. Fax 288-3553
durand.k12.mi.us/
Durand Area HS 600/8-12
9575 E Monroe Rd 48429 989-288-2684
Dave Zuehlke, prin. Fax 288-2966

East China, Saint Clair, Pop. 3,216
East China SD 4,400/K-12
1585 Meisner Rd 48054 810-676-1000
Dr. Steven Skalka, supt. Fax 676-1037
www.eastchinaschools.org
Other Schools – See Marine City, Saint Clair

East Jordan, Charlevoix, Pop. 2,312
East Jordan SD 700/K-12
PO Box 399 49727 231-536-3131
Matt Stevenson, supt. Fax 536-3310
www.ejps.org
East Jordan MSHS 300/7-12
PO Box 399 49727 231-536-2259
Kirk Baese, prin. Fax 536-3536

East Lansing, Ingham, Pop. 47,217
East Lansing SD 2,900/K-12
501 Burcham Dr 48823 517-333-7420
Dr. Robyne Thompson, supt. Fax 333-7470
www.elps.us
East Lansing HS 1,100/9-12
509 Burcham Dr 48823 517-333-7500
Coby Fletcher, prin. Fax 333-7559
MacDonald MS 500/6-8
1601 Burcham Dr 48823 517-333-7600
Amy Martin, prin. Fax 333-5098

Douglas J Educational Center Post-Sec.
331 E Grand River Ave 48823 517-351-0746
Michigan State Univ - College of Law Post-Sec.
648 N Shaw Ln Rm 368 48824 517-432-6800
Michigan State University Post-Sec.
220 Trowbridge Rd 48824 517-355-1855

East Leroy, Calhoun
Athens Area SD 600/K-12
4320 K Dr S 49051 269-729-5427
Joseph Huepenbecker, supt. Fax 729-9610
www.athensk12.org
Other Schools – See Athens

Eastpointe, Macomb, Pop. 31,538
East Detroit SD 3,700/K-12
24685 Kelly Rd 48021 586-533-3000
Dr. Ryan McLeod, supt. Fax 533-3025
www.eastdetroit.org
East Detroit HS 1,300/9-12
15501 Couzens Ave 48021 586-533-3700
Greg Roberts, prin. Fax 533-3709
Kellwood Alternative HS 200/Alt
23750 David Ave 48021 586-533-3900
Samy Chaptini, prin. Fax 533-3909
Kelly MS 900/6-8
24701 Kelly Rd 48021 586-533-3600
Fran Hobbs, prin. Fax 533-3609

Eaton Rapids, Eaton, Pop. 5,118
Eaton Rapids SD 2,500/K-12
912 Greyhound Dr 48827 517-663-8155
Dr. William DeFrance, supt. Fax 663-2236
www.erpsk12.org
Eaton Rapids HS 800/9-12
800 State St 48827 517-663-2231
Derek Lounds, prin. Fax 663-5727
Eaton Rapids MS 600/6-8
815 Greyhound Dr 48827 517-663-8151
Therese Lake, prin. Fax 663-0625
Greyhound Central Performance Academy 200/Alt
912 Greyhound Dr 48827 517-663-3510
Christien Rupp, prin. Fax 663-0626

Eau Claire, Berrien, Pop. 604
Eau Claire SD 900/K-12
6190 W Main St 49111 269-461-6947
David Gray, supt. Fax 461-0089
www.eauclaireps.com
Eau Claire Alternative HS 50/Alt
7450 Hochberger Rd 49111 269-461-6997
Shane Lausch, admin.
Eau Claire HS 200/9-12
7450 Hochberger Rd 49111 269-461-6997
Christopher Smedley, prin. Fax 461-0065
Eau Claire MS 200/6-8
7450 Hochberger Rd 49111 269-461-0083
Mike Dandron, prin. Fax 461-0082

Eben Junction, Alger
Superior Central SD 400/K-12
PO Box 148 49825 906-439-5531
William Valima, supt. Fax 439-5734
superiorcentralschools.org
Superior Central S 400/K-12
PO Box 148 49825 906-439-5532
William Valima, prin. Fax 439-5243

Ecorse, Wayne, Pop. 9,214
Ecorse SD 900/PK-12
27225 W Outer Dr 48229 313-294-4750
Thomas E. Parker, supt. Fax 294-4769
ecorse.education
Ecorse Community HS 400/8-12
27385 W Outer Dr 48229 313-294-4700
Thomas Hill, prin. Fax 294-4709
Hope Academic Academy Alt
27225 W Outer Dr 48229 313-294-4730
Kenneth McPhaul, head sch Fax 382-6534

Edmore, Montcalm, Pop. 1,174
Montabella Community SD 800/PK-12
PO Box 349 48829 989-427-5148
Shelly Millis, supt. Fax 427-3828
www.montabella.com
Other Schools – See Blanchard

Edwardsburg, Cass, Pop. 1,228
Edwardsburg SD 2,700/K-12
69410 Section St 49112 269-663-3055
Sherman Ostrander, supt. Fax 663-6485
www.edwardsburgpublicschools.org/
Edwardsburg HS 900/9-12
69410 Section St 49112 269-663-1044
Ryan Markel, prin. Fax 663-8915
Edwardsburg MS 700/6-8
69410 Section St 49112 269-663-1031
James Knoll, prin. Fax 663-8638

Elk Rapids, Antrim, Pop. 1,628
Elk Rapids SD 1,300/K-12
707 E 3rd St 49629 231-264-8692
Stephen Prissel, supt. Fax 264-6538
www.erschools.com
Cherryland MS 300/6-8
707 E 3rd St 49629 231-264-8991
Terry Starr, prin. Fax 264-9370
Elk Rapids HS 400/9-12
308 Meguzee Pt 49629 231-264-8108
Michael Travis, prin. Fax 264-0895
Sunrise Academy 50/Alt
97 Lake St 49629 231-264-5890
Jim Standerfer, prin. Fax 264-0895

Ellsworth, Antrim, Pop. 341
Ellsworth Community SD 200/PK-12
9467 Park St 49729 231-588-2544
Aaron Gaffney, supt. Fax 588-6183
www.ellsworth.k12.mi.us/
Ellsworth Community S 200/PK-12
9467 Park St 49729 231-588-2544
Aaron Gaffney, admin. Fax 588-6183

Elsie, Clinton, Pop. 962
Ovid-Elsie Area SD 1,300/PK-12
8989 E Colony Rd 48831 989-834-2271
Ryan Cunningham, supt. Fax 862-5887
www.ovidelsie.org
Ovid-Elsie HS 500/9-12
8989 E Colony Rd 48831 989-834-2271
Jason Tokar, prin. Fax 862-4463
Ovid-Elsie MS 200/6-8
8989 E Colony Rd 48831 989-834-2271
Randy Barton, prin. Fax 862-4463
Other Schools – See Ovid

Engadine, Mackinac
Engadine Consolidated SD 300/K-12
W13920 Melville St 49827 906-477-6313
Angie McArthur, supt. Fax 477-6643
www.eupschools.org
Engadine Consolidated S 300/K-12
W13920 Melville St 49827 906-477-6351
Kendra Feldhusen, prin. Fax 477-6643

Erie, Monroe
Mason Consolidated SD 1,100/PK-12
2400 Mason Eagle Dr 48133 734-848-5475
Andrew Shaw, supt. Fax 848-2516
www.eriemason.k12.mi.us
Mason HS 400/9-12
2400 Mason Eagle Dr 48133 734-848-5755
Brandon Bates, prin. Fax 848-5425
Mason MS 200/6-8
2400 Mason Eagle Dr 48133 734-848-4211
Ben Russow, prin. Fax 848-0035

Escanaba, Delta, Pop. 12,293
Escanaba Area SD 2,400/PK-12
1500 Ludington St 49829 906-786-5411
Michele Lemire, supt. Fax 786-4469
www.eskymos.com
Escanaba HS 800/9-12
500 S Lincoln Rd 49829 906-786-6521
Darci Griebel, prin. Fax 786-2166
Escanaba JHS 400/7-8
500 S Lincoln Rd 49829 906-786-6521
Jude VanDamme, prin. Fax 786-2166
Escanaba Student Success Center Alt
2525 Third Ave S 49829 906-786-9300
Dan Seder, prin. Fax 786-9318

Bay de Noc Community College Post-Sec.
2001 N Lincoln Rd 49829 906-786-5802
U.P. Academy of Hair Design Post-Sec.
1625 Sheridan Rd 49829 906-786-5750

Essexville, Bay, Pop. 3,434
Essexville-Hampton SD 1,700/K-12
303 Pine St 48732 989-894-9700
Matthew T. Cortez, supt. Fax 894-9705
www.e-hps.net
Cramer JHS 600/5-8
313 Pine St 48732 989-894-9740
Jeff Dinauer, prin. Fax 894-9720
Garber HS 600/9-12
213 Pine St 48732 989-894-9710
Fax 894-9730

Evart, Osceola, Pop. 1,857
Evart SD 900/PK-12
PO Box 917 49631 231-734-5594
Shirley Howard, supt. Fax 734-2931
www.evart.k12.mi.us/
Evart HS 300/9-12
6221 95th Ave 49631 231-734-5551
Jessica Kolenda, prin. Fax 734-4156
Evart MS 300/5-8
321 N Hemlock St 49631 231-734-4222
Jason O'Dell, prin. Fax 734-3367

Ewen, Ontonagon
Ewen-Trout Creek SD 300/K-12
14312 Airport Rd 49925 906-813-0620
Alan Tulppo, supt. Fax 813-0621
www.etc.k12.mi.us/
Ewen-Trout Creek JSHS 100/7-12
14312 Airport Rd 49925 906-813-0620
Alan Tulppo, supt. Fax 813-0621

Fairgrove, Tuscola, Pop. 559
Akron-Fairgrove SD 300/K-12
PO Box 319 48733 989-693-6163
Diane Foster, supt. Fax 693-6560
www.akronfairgrove.org
Akron-Fairgrove JSHS 200/6-12
PO Box 319 48733 989-693-6112
Andrew Beauvais, prin. Fax 693-6160

Fair Haven, Saint Clair, Pop. 1,505
Anchor Bay SD
Supt. — See Casco
Anchor Bay HS 1,900/9-12
6319 County Line Rd 48023 586-648-2525
Jack Stanton, prin. Fax 716-8306

Fairview, Oscoda
Fairview Area SD 100/K-12
1879 E Miller Rd 48621 989-848-7000
Lee Sandy, supt. Fax 848-7070
www.fairview.k12.mi.us
Fairview Area S 100/K-12
1879 E Miller Rd 48621 989-848-7009
Robert Ricketson, supt. Fax 848-7070

Farmington, Oakland, Pop. 10,133
Farmington SD 9,000/PK-12
32500 Shiawassee Rd 48336 248-489-3349
Dr. George Heitsch, supt. Fax 489-3348
www.farmington.k12.mi.us
Farmington HS 1,200/9-12
32000 Shiawassee Rd 48336 248-489-3455
Julie Kaminski, prin. Fax 489-3474
Other Schools – See Farmington Hills

Farmington Hills, Oakland, Pop. 77,980
Farmington SD
Supt. — See Farmington
East MS 900/6-8
25000 Middlebelt Rd 48336 248-489-3601
Ken Sanders, prin. Fax 489-3606
Farmington Central HS 100/Alt
30415 Shiawassee Rd 48336 248-489-3827
Dee Lacy, coord. Fax 489-3380
Harrison HS 1,200/9-12
29995 W 12 Mile Rd 48334 248-489-3499
Jim Anderson, prin. Fax 489-3514
North Farmington HS 1,300/9-12
32900 W 13 Mile Rd 48334 248-785-2005
Joe Greene, prin. Fax 855-2060
Power Upper ES 400/6-8
34740 Rhonswood St 48335 248-489-3622
Allyson Robinson, prin. Fax 489-3628
Warner Upper ES 400/6-8
30303 W 14 Mile Rd 48334 248-785-2030
Allen Archer, prin. Fax 855-0210
Farmington Community S Adult
30415 Shiawassee Rd 48336 248-489-3827
Dee Lacy, prin. Fax 489-3380

West Bloomfield SD
Supt. — See West Bloomfield
Oakland Early College S 100/9-12
27055 Orchard Lake Rd 48334 248-522-3540
Jennifer Newman, hdmstr. Fax 471-9543

Dorsey School of Business Post-Sec.
33533 W 12 Mile Rd Ste 152 48331 248-994-0133
Mercy HS 800/9-12
29300 W 11 Mile Rd 48336 248-476-8020
Carolyn Witte, prin. Fax 476-3691
Michigan Sch of Professional Psychology Post-Sec.
26811 Orchard Lake Rd 48334 248-476-1122
Oakland Community College Post-Sec.
27055 Orchard Lake Rd 48334 248-522-3400

Farwell, Clare, Pop. 865
Farwell Area SD 1,300/K-12
399 E Michigan St 48622 989-588-9917
Carl Seiter, supt. Fax 588-6440
www.farwellschools.net/
Farwell HS 400/8-12
399 E Michigan St 48622 989-588-9913
Dee Yarger, prin. Fax 588-6041
Timberland HS Alt
2655 W Ludington Dr 48622 989-588-7219
Bob First, prin.

Felch, Dickinson
North Dickinson County SD 300/K-12
W6588 State Highway M69 49831 906-542-9281
Angel Inglese, supt. Fax 542-6950
www.go-nordics.com
North Dickinson County S 300/K-12
W6588 State Highway M69 49831 906-542-9281
Angel Inglese, admin. Fax 542-6950

Fennville, Allegan, Pop. 1,373
Fennville SD 1,400/PK-12
5 Memorial Dr 49408 269-561-7331
Dirk Weeldreyer, supt. Fax 561-5792
www.fennville.org
Fennville HS 400/9-12
4 Memorial Dr 49408 269-561-7241
Jim Greydanus, prin. Fax 561-6901
Fennville MS 300/6-8
1 Memorial Dr 49408 269-561-7341
Kim Zdybel, prin. Fax 561-2143
Pearl Alternative & Adult Education Ctr 50/Alt
5 Memorial Dr 49408 269-561-2343
Mitch Overway, lead tchr. Fax 561-8630

Fenton, Genesee, Pop. 11,554
Fenton Area SD 3,400/PK-12
3100 Owen Rd 48430 810-591-4700
Adam J. Hartley, supt. Fax 591-4705
www.fentonschools.org
Fenton HS 1,200/9-12
3200 W Shiawassee Ave 48430 810-591-2600
Mark Suchowski, prin. Fax 591-2605
Schmidt MS 800/6-8
3255 Donaldson Dr 48430 810-591-7700
Heidi Ciesielski, prin. Fax 591-7705

Lake Fenton Community SD 2,000/K-12
11425 Torrey Rd 48430 810-591-4141
Wayne Wright, supt. Fax 591-9866
www.lakefentonschools.org
Lake Fenton MS 500/6-8
11425 Torrey Rd 48430 810-591-2209
Dr. Daniel Ferguson, prin. Fax 591-8475
Other Schools – See Linden

Ferndale, Oakland, Pop. 19,252
Ferndale SD 2,800/PK-12
2920 Burdette St 48220 248-586-8651
Blake Prewitt, supt. Fax 586-8655
www.ferndaleschools.org
Ferndale HS 700/9-12
881 Pinecrest Dr 48220 248-548-8600
Roger Smith, prin. Fax 586-8620
Ferndale MS 300/6-8
725 Pinecrest Dr 48220 248-541-1783
Jason Gillespie, prin. Fax 586-8834
University HS 400/9-12
2521 Bermuda St 48220 248-586-8846
Jason Beatty, admin. Fax 586-8857
Other Schools – See Oak Park

Fife Lake, Grand Traverse, Pop. 434
Forest Area Community SD 400/PK-12
7741 Shippy Rd SW 49633 231-369-4191
Joshua Rothwell M.S., supt. Fax 369-4153
www.forestarea.org
Forest Area HS 200/9-12
7741 Shippy Rd SW 49633 231-369-2884
Lisa Magee, prin. Fax 369-3646
Forest Area MS 100/4-8
7741 Shippy Rd SW 49633 231-369-2884
Lisa Magee, prin. Fax 369-3646

Flat Rock, Wayne, Pop. 9,628
Flat Rock Community SD 1,800/K-12
28639 Division St 48134 734-535-6500
Andrew Brodie, supt. Fax 535-6501
www.flatrockschools.org
Flat Rock HS 600/9-12
25600 Seneca St 48134 734-535-6600
Marc Lafayette, prin. Fax 535-6601
Simpson MS 500/6-8
24900 Meadows Ave 48134 734-535-6700
Blaine Armstrong, prin. Fax 535-6701

Flint, Genesee, Pop. 98,869
Beecher Community SD 1,400/PK-12
1020 W Coldwater Rd 48505 810-591-9200
Josha Talison Ed.D., supt. Fax 591-9851
www.beecherschools.org/
Tucker MS 400/5-8
G5159 Summit St 48505 810-591-9399
Lance Sumpter, prin. Fax 591-6190
Beecher Adult Education Adult
1020 W Coldwater Rd 48505 810-591-9824
Mark Foster, prin. Fax 591-9851
Other Schools – See Mount Morris

Carman-Ainsworth Community SD 4,400/K-12
G3475 W Court St 48532 810-591-3700
Dr. Eddie Kindle, supt. Fax 591-3323
www.carman.k12.mi.us
Atlantis Alternative S Alt
G3493 Beveridge Rd 48532 810-591-3700
Wes Mayo, coord. Fax 591-3290
Carman-Ainsworth HS 1,500/9-12
1300 N Linden Rd 48532 810-591-3240
Deborah Davis, prin. Fax 591-3215
Carman-Ainsworth MS 1,100/6-8
1409 W Maple Ave 48507 810-591-3500
Kevin Summey, prin. Fax 591-3594

Flint Community SD 5,000/PK-12
923 E Kearsley St 48503 810-760-1000
Bilal K. Tawwab, supt. Fax 760-7601
www.flintschools.org
Accelerated Learning Academy Alt
G2138 W Carpenter Rd 48505 810-767-8500
Dr. Maria Boyd-Springer, dir. Fax 760-6809
Holmes STEM Academy 400/PK-PK, 3-
6602 Oxley Dr 48504 810-760-1968
Eddie Thomas, prin. Fax 760-1624
Northwestern HS 500/10-12
G2138 W Carpenter Rd 48505 810-760-1780
Timothy Green, prin. Fax 760-6809
Southwestern Classical Academy 1,100/7-12
1420 W 12th St 48507 810-760-1400
Dana Simmons, prin. Fax 760-7772

Genesee ISD 1,000/
2413 W Maple Ave 48507 810-591-4400
Lisa Hagel, supt. Fax 591-7570
www.geneseeisd.org
Genessee Career Institute Vo/Tech
2413 W Maple Ave 48507 810-591-4462
Fax 244-1242
Mott Middle College HS 400/Alt
1401 E Court St Ste 1102 48503 810-232-8530
Margaret Green, prin. Fax 232-8660
Other Schools – See Grand Rapids

Kearsley Community SD 3,400/PK-12
4396 Underhill Dr 48506 810-591-8000
Patti Yorks, supt. Fax 591-8421
www.kearsleyschools.org
Armstrong MS 800/6-8
6161 Hopkins Rd 48506 810-591-9929
Casey Killingbeck, prin. Fax 591-9944
Kearsley HS 1,200/9-12
4302 Underhill Dr 48506 810-591-9883
Brian Wiskur, prin. Fax 591-9888

Westwood Heights SD 1,300/PK-12
3400 N Jennings Rd 48504 810-591-4341
Salli Stevens, supt.
www.hamadyhawks.net
Academy West Alternative Education 400/Alt
3400 N Jennings Rd 48504 810-591-0123
Peter Toal, prin. Fax 591-0124
Hamady Community HS 300/9-12
3223 W Carpenter Rd 48504 810-591-0890
Leslie Key, prin. Fax 591-5140
Hamady MS 200/7-8
3223 W Carpenter Rd 48504 810-591-0895
Leslie Key, prin. Fax 591-5140

Baker College of Flint Post-Sec.
1050 W Bristol Rd 48507 810-766-4000
Davenport University Post-Sec.
4318 Miller Rd 48507 810-732-9977
Flint Institute of Barbering Post-Sec.
3214 Flushing Rd 48504 810-232-4711
Hurley Medical Center Post-Sec.
701 W 8th Ave 48503 810-257-9237
Kettering University Post-Sec.
1700 University Ave 48504 810-762-9500
Mott Community College Post-Sec.
1401 E Court St 48503 810-762-0200
Powers Catholic HS 500/9-12
1505 W Court St 48503 810-591-4741
Sally Bartos, prin. Fax 591-1794
Ross Medical Education Center Post-Sec.
G3630 Miller Rd Ste D 48507 810-230-1100
University of Michigan-Flint Post-Sec.
303 E Kearsley St 48502 810-762-3300

Flushing, Genesee, Pop. 8,256
Flushing Community SD 4,100/PK-12
522 N McKinley Rd 48433 810-591-1180
Timothy Stein, supt. Fax 591-0656
www.flushingschools.org/
Flushing HS 1,300/9-12
5039 Deland Rd 48433 810-591-3770
Jason Melynchek, prin. Fax 591-0693
Flushing MS 700/7-8
8100 Carpenter Rd 48433 810-591-2800
Andrew Schmidt, prin. Fax 591-0148

Fort Gratiot, Saint Clair, Pop. 8,968
Port Huron Area SD
Supt. — See Port Huron
Fort Gratiot MS 600/6-8
3985 Keewahdin Rd 48059 810-984-6544
Alycia Shagena, prin. Fax 275-1271

Fowler, Clinton, Pop. 1,204
Fowler SD 500/PK-12
PO Box 407 48835 989-593-2296
Neil Hufnagel, supt. Fax 593-2358
www.fowlerschools.net
Fowler HS 200/9-12
PO Box 407 48835 989-593-2250
Neil Hufnagel, prin. Fax 593-2358

Fowlerville, Livingston, Pop. 2,844
Fowlerville Community SD 2,900/PK-12
7677 W Sharpe Rd Ste A 48836 517-223-6000
Wayne Roedel, supt. Fax 223-6022
www.fowlervilleschools.org
Fowlerville HS 800/9-12
7677 W Sharpe Rd Ste A 48836 517-223-6002
Bradford Lusk, prin. Fax 223-6065
Fowlerville JHS 700/6-8
7677 W Sharpe Rd Ste A 48836 517-223-6003
Myriah Lillie, prin. Fax 223-6199
Fowlerville Online Learning Academy 50/Alt
7677 W Sharpe Rd Ste A 48836 517-223-6016
Grace Damerow, admin. Fax 223-6016

Frankenmuth, Saginaw, Pop. 4,915
Frankenmuth SD 1,200/PK-12
525 E Genesee St 48734 989-652-9958
Adele Martin, supt. Fax 652-9780
www.frankenmuth.k12.mi.us/
Frankenmuth HS 500/9-12
525 E Genesee St 48734 989-652-9955
JoLynn Clark, prin. Fax 652-7253
Rittmueller MS 300/5-8
965 E Genesee St 48734 989-652-6119
Kristin Hecht, prin. Fax 652-2921

Frankfort, Benzie, Pop. 1,275
Frankfort-Elberta Area SD 500/K-12
534 11th St 49635 231-352-4641
Jeffrey Tousley, supt. Fax 352-5066
www.frankfort.k12.mi.us
Frankfort JSHS 200/7-12
534 11th St 49635 231-352-4781
Matt Stapleton, prin. Fax 352-6501

Fraser, Macomb, Pop. 14,229
Fraser SD 5,300/PK-12
33466 Garfield Rd 48026 586-439-7000
Dr. David Richards Ph.D., supt. Fax 439-7001
www.fraser.k12.mi.us/
Fraser HS 1,600/9-12
34270 Garfield Rd 48026 586-439-7200
Dr. Michael Lonze, prin. Fax 439-7201
Richards MS 900/7-8
33500 Garfield Rd 48026 586-439-7400
Huston Julian, prin. Fax 439-7401

Freeland, Saginaw, Pop. 6,900
Freeland Community SD 1,800/K-12
710 Powley Dr 48623 989-695-5527
Matthew Cairy, supt. Fax 695-5789
www.freelandschools.net
Freeland HS 600/9-12
8250 Webster Rd 48623 989-695-2586
Traci Smith, prin. Fax 695-8022
Freeland MS 300/7-8
8250 Webster Rd 48623 989-692-4032
Renee Wulff, prin. Fax 692-4034

Fremont, Newaygo, Pop. 4,037
Fremont SD 2,100/K-12
450 E Pine St 49412 231-924-2350
Ken Haggart, supt. Fax 924-5264
www.fremont.net
Fremont HS 700/9-12
5421 S Warner Ave 49412 231-924-5300
Scott Sherman, prin. Fax 924-9262
Fremont MS 500/6-8
500 Woodrow St 49412 231-924-0230
Kenneth Haggart, prin. Fax 924-9149
Quest HS 100/Alt
350 Cedar St 49412 231-924-0470
Tracy Sanchez, dir. Fax 924-9207

Newaygo County RESA 200/
4747 W 48th St 49412 231-924-0381
Lori Clark, supt. Fax 924-8910
www.ncresa.org
Newaygo County Career-Tech Center Vo/Tech
4645 W 48th St 49412 231-924-0380
Gretchen Spedowske, dir. Fax 924-7815

Fruitport, Muskegon, Pop. 1,081
Fruitport Community SD 2,800/PK-12
3255 Pontaluna Rd 49415 231-865-4100
Bob Szymoniak, supt. Fax 865-3393
www.fruitportschools.net
Fruitport Alternative HS Alt
3255 Pontaluna Rd 49415 231-865-4120
Lauren Chesney, dir. Fax 865-4105
Fruitport HS 900/9-12
357 N 6th Ave 49415 231-865-3101
Lauren Chesney, prin. Fax 865-6351

Fruitport MS 700/6-8
3113 Pontaluna Rd 49415 231-865-3128
Wendy Somers, prin. Fax 865-4086
Adult Education Adult
3255 Pontaluna Rd 49415 231-865-4130
Brenda Baker, dir. Fax 865-4046

Calvary Christian S 200/PK-12
5873 Kendra Rd 49415 231-865-2141
Thomas Kapanka, admin. Fax 865-8730

Galesburg, Kalamazoo, Pop. 1,969
Galesburg-Augusta Community SD 1,100/PK-12
1076 N 37th St 49053 269-484-2000
Dr. Dania Bazzi, supt. Fax 484-2001
www.g-aschools.org
Galesburg-Augusta HS 300/9-12
1076 N 37th St 49053 269-484-2010
Christie Robinson, prin. Fax 484-2011
Other Schools – See Augusta

Garden City, Wayne, Pop. 27,153
Garden City SD 4,300/PK-12
1333 Radcliff St 48135 734-762-8300
Derek Fisher, supt. Fax 762-8530
www.gardencityschools.com
Cambridge HS 400/Alt
28901 Cambridge St 48135 734-762-8430
Debbie Eves, prin. Fax 762-8534
Garden City HS 1,300/9-12
6500 Middlebelt Rd 48135 734-762-8350
Sharon Kollar, prin. Fax 762-8531
Garden City MS 600/7-8
1851 Radcliff St 48135 734-762-8400
Kip O'Leary, prin. Fax 762-8532

Gaylord, Otsego, Pop. 3,564
Gaylord Community SD 3,000/PK-12
615 S Elm Ave 49735 989-705-3080
Brian Pearson, supt. Fax 732-6029
www.gaylordschools.com
Gaylord HS 900/9-12
90 Livingston Blvd 49735 989-731-0969
Christopher Hodges, prin. Fax 731-2585
Gaylord MS 500/7-8
600 E 5th St 49735 989-731-0848
Gerald Belanger, prin. Fax 732-2632

St. Mary Cathedral S 300/PK-12
321 N Otsego Ave 49735 989-732-5801
Nicole Hatch, prin. Fax 732-2085

Genesee, Genesee
Genesee SD 800/PK-12
PO Box 220 48437 810-591-1650
Kevin Green, supt. Fax 591-1646
www.geneseeschools.org
Genesee JSHS 400/7-12
7347 N Genesee Rd 48437 810-591-1450
Charleen McKeever, prin. Fax 591-0302

Gibraltar, Wayne, Pop. 4,593
Gibraltar SD
Supt. — See Woodhaven
Carlson HS 1,200/9-12
30550 W Jefferson Ave 48173 734-379-7100
Jessica Shultz, prin. Fax 379-5444
Shumate MS 900/6-8
30448 W Jefferson Ave 48173 734-379-7600
Els Ferguson, prin. Fax 379-2370

Gladstone, Delta, Pop. 4,885
Gladstone Area SD 1,500/K-12
400 S 10th St 49837 906-428-2417
Dr. Jay Kulbertis, supt. Fax 789-8457
www.gladstoneschools.com
Gladstone HS 500/9-12
2100 State Highway M35 49837 906-428-9200
Brady Downey, prin. Fax 789-8312
Gladstone MS 400/6-8
300 S 10th St 49837 906-428-2295
Dave Ballard, prin. Fax 789-8404

Gladwin, Gladwin, Pop. 2,897
Gladwin Community SD 1,800/K-12
401 N Bowery Ave 48624 989-426-9255
Rick Seebeck, supt. Fax 426-5981
www.gladwinschools.net
Gladwin Community Alternative HS 50/Alt
1400 N Spring St 48624 989-426-7341
Dave Beyer, prin. Fax 426-6031
Gladwin HS 600/9-12
1400 N Spring St 48624 989-426-7341
Dave Beyer, prin. Fax 426-6031
Gladwin JHS 500/6-8
401 N Bowery Ave 48624 989-426-3808
Kaycie Soderling, prin. Fax 426-6038

Skeels Christian S 100/PK-12
3956 N M 18 48624 989-426-2054
John Shoaf, dir. Fax 426-4411

Glen Arbor, Leelanau, Pop. 228

Leelanau S 50/9-12
1 Old Homestead Rd 49636 231-334-5800
Matt Ralston, hdmstr. Fax 334-5898

Gobles, Van Buren, Pop. 803
Gobles SD 800/K-12
PO Box 412 49055 269-628-5618
Jeff Rehlander, supt. Fax 628-5306
www.gobles.org/
Gobles HS 300/9-12
PO Box 412 49055 269-628-2113
Phil McAndrew, prin. Fax 628-5306
Gobles MS 200/6-8
PO Box 412 49055 269-628-2113
Chris Miller, dean Fax 628-5306

Gobles Jr. Academy 50/K-10
32110 6th Ave 49055 269-628-2704
Thomas Coffee, prin. Fax 628-7314

Goodrich, Genesee, Pop. 1,851
Goodrich Area SD 2,000/PK-12
8029 Gale Rd 48438 810-591-2250
Michelle Imbrunone, supt. Fax 591-2550
www.goodrich.k12.mi.us
Goodrich HS 700/9-12
8029 Gale Rd 48438 810-591-2251
Brian Eddy, prin. Fax 591-2234
Goodrich MS 500/6-8
7480 Gale Rd 48438 810-591-4210
Kapeka vonKeltz, prin. Fax 636-7879

Grand Blanc, Genesee, Pop. 8,062
Grand Blanc Community SD 7,700/PK-12
11920 S Saginaw St 48439 810-591-6000
Dr. Clarence Garner, supt. Fax 591-6018
www.grandblancschools.org
Grand Blanc HS 2,000/10-12
12500 Holly Rd 48439 810-591-6638
Dr. Jennifer Hammond, prin. Fax 591-6513
Grand Blanc HS West 9-9
1 Jewett Trl 48439 810-591-6350
Jennifer Hammond, prin. Fax 591-6400
Grand Blanc MS East 1,100/6-8
6100 Perry Rd 48439 810-591-4696
Jodi Kruse, prin. Fax 591-0242
Grand Blanc MS West 1,000/6-8
1515 E Reid Rd 48439 810-591-7309
Jeff Neall, prin. Fax 591-0182

Sharps Academy of Hairstyling Post-Sec.
8166 Holly Rd 48439 810-695-6742

Grand Haven, Ottawa, Pop. 10,239
Grand Haven Area SD 6,000/PK-12
1415 S Beechtree St 49417 616-850-5000
Andrew Ingall, supt. Fax 850-5010
www.ghaps.org
Central HS 100/Alt
106 S 6th St 49417 616-850-6800
Paul Kunde, prin. Fax 850-6810
Grand Haven HS 1,900/9-12
17001 Ferris St 49417 616-850-6000
Tracy Wilson, prin. Fax 850-6010
Lakeshore MS 1,000/7-8
900 Cutler St 49417 616-850-6500
Kevin Polston, prin. Fax 850-6510

Grand Ledge, Eaton, Pop. 7,630
Grand Ledge SD 5,000/PK-12
220 Lamson St 48837 517-925-5400
Dr. Brian Metcalf, supt. Fax 925-5409
www.glcomets.net/
Grand Ledge HS 1,700/9-12
820 Spring St 48837 517-925-5815
Jill Mangrum, prin. Fax 925-5829
Hayes MS 800/7-8
12620 Nixon Rd 48837 517-925-5680
Dr. Julie Taylor, prin. Fax 925-5730

Grand Marais, Alger
Burt Township SD 50/K-12
PO Box 338 49839 906-494-2543
Heidi Homeister, supt. Fax 494-2522
grandmaraisschools.org/
Burt Township S 50/K-12
PO Box 338 49839 906-494-2521
Heidi Homeister, supt. Fax 494-2522

Grand Rapids, Kent, Pop. 182,274
East Grand Rapids SD 3,000/K-12
2915 Hall St SE 49506 616-235-3535
Dr. Sara Shubel, supt. Fax 235-6730
www.egrps.org
East Grand Rapids HS 1,000/9-12
2211 Lake Dr SE 49506 616-235-7555
Jennifer Fee, prin. Fax 235-7592
East Grand Rapids MS 700/6-8
2425 Lake Dr SE 49506 616-235-7551
Anthony Morey, prin. Fax 235-7587

Forest Hills SD 10,100/PK-12
6590 Cascade Rd SE 49546 616-493-8800
Daniel Behm, supt. Fax 493-8552
www.fhps.net
Central HS 1,300/9-12
5901 Hall St SE 49546 616-493-8700
Stephen Passinault, prin. Fax 493-8721
Northern HS 1,100/9-12
3801 Leonard St NE 49525 616-493-8600
Jon Gregory, prin. Fax 493-8644
Northern Hills MS 600/7-8
3775 Leonard St NE 49525 616-493-8650
Nancy Susterka, prin. Fax 493-8686
Other Schools – See Ada

Genesee ISD
Supt. — See Flint
Genessee Early College 200/9-12
509 N Harrison St 49502 810-591-5115
Sandra Morgan-Jones, prin. Fax 591-2503

Grand Rapids SD 14,800/PK-12
PO Box 117 49501 616-819-2000
Teresa Weatherall Neal M.Ed., supt. Fax 819-3480
www.grps.org/
Alger MS 400/6-8
921 Alger St SE 49507 616-819-6200
Roderick Wade, prin. Fax 819-6201
Burton MS 500/6-8
2133 Buchanan Ave SW 49507 616-819-2269
Lametria Johnson-Eaddy, prin. Fax 819-2282
City MSHS 700/7-12
1720 Plainfield Ave NE 49505 616-819-2380
Michael Pascoe, prin. Fax 819-2496
Frost Environmental Science Academy 500/PK-12
1460 Laughlin Dr NW 49504 616-819-2550
Greg Ramey, prin. Fax 819-2184
Grand Rapids Learning Center Alt
143 Bostwick NE 49503 616-819-2010
Grand Rapids Montessori at Central 100/9-12
421 Fountain St NE 49503 616-819-2405
Kerri Reed, prin. Fax 819-2369
Innovation Central 9-12
421 Fountain St NE 49503 616-819-2310
Mark Frost, prin. Fax 819-2369
Innovation Central 9-12
421 Fountain St NE 49503 616-819-2310
Mark Frost, prin. Fax 819-2369
Kent Vocational Options Vo/Tech
864 Crahen Ave NE 49525 616-819-2740
Laura Ochoa, prin. Fax 819-2747
Ottawa Hills HS 700/9-12
2055 Rosewood Ave SE 49506 616-819-2900
Rodney Lewis, prin. Fax 819-2877
Public Museum S 6-12
272 Pearl St NW 49504 616-819-3600
Christopher Hanks, prin.
Riverside MS 300/6-8
265 Eleanor St NE 49505 616-819-2969
William Martin, prin. Fax 819-2981
Southeast Career Pathways 100/Alt
1356 Jefferson Ave SE 49507 616-819-2666
Stephanie Davis, prin. Fax 819-2941
Union HS 1,100/9-12
1800 Tremont Blvd NW 49504 616-819-3160
Karl Nelson, prin. Fax 819-3205
University Preparatory Academy 6-12
512 Division Ave S 49503 616-819-1010
Daniel Williams, prin. Fax 819-1011
Westwood MS 400/6-8
1525 Mount Mercy Dr NW 49504 616-819-3322
Dennis Branson, prin. Fax 819-3301

Kelloggsville SD 2,100/PK-12
242 52nd St SE 49548 616-538-7460
Samuel Wright, supt. Fax 532-1597
www.kvilleps.org
54th Street Academy Alt
173 54th St SW 49548 616-531-7433
Jeremy Palmitier, dir. Fax 531-6996
Kelloggsville HS 600/9-12
23 Jean St SW 49548 616-532-1570
Kevin Simmons, prin. Fax 532-7780
Kelloggsville MS 500/6-8
4650 Division Ave S 49548 616-532-1575
James Alston, prin. Fax 532-1579

Kenowa Hills SD 3,300/PK-12
2325 4 Mile Rd NW 49544 616-784-2511
Gerald Hopkins M.Ed., supt. Fax 784-8323
khps.org
Kenowa Hills HS 1,200/9-12
3825 Hendershot Ave NW 49544 616-784-2400
Brett Zuver M.Ed., prin. Fax 647-0149
Kenowa Hills MS 700/6-8
3950 Hendershot Ave NW 49544 616-785-3225
Abby Wiseman M.Ed., prin. Fax 784-2404

Kent ISD
2930 Knapp St NE 49525 616-364-1333
Ron Caniff, supt. Fax 364-1488
www.kentisd.org
Kent Career/Technical Center Vo/Tech
1655 E Beltline Ave NE 49525 616-364-8421
John Kraus, prin. Fax 364-9140
Kent Innovation HS 9-12
1655 E Beltline Ave NE 49525 616-363-8010
Kimberly Kimber, prin. Fax 363-8030

Northview SD 3,400/PK-12
4365 Hunsberger Ave NE 49525 616-363-6861
Dr. M Korpak, supt. Fax 363-9609
www.nvps.net
Crossroads MS 500/7-8
4400 Ambrose Ave NE 49525 616-361-3430
Daniel Duba, prin. Fax 363-7868
East Campus HS 200/Alt
3801 E Beltline Ave NE 49525 616-361-7396
Derek Schmidt, prin. Fax 361-7398
Northview HS 1,200/9-12
4451 Hunsberger Ave NE 49525 616-363-4857
Mark Thomas, prin. Fax 361-3494

All Saints Academy - MS Campus 100/4-8
1110 4 Mile Rd NE 49525 616-363-7725
Abby Giroux, prin. Fax 363-3086
Aquinas College Post-Sec.
1607 Robinson Rd SE 49506 616-632-8900
Calvin College Post-Sec.
3201 Burton St SE 49546 616-526-6000
Calvin Theological Seminary Post-Sec.
3233 Burton St SE 49546 800-388-6034
Catholic Central HS 700/9-12
319 Sheldon Blvd SE 49503 616-233-5899
Greg Deja, prin. Fax 459-0257
Compass College of Cinematic Arts Post-Sec.
41 Sheldon Blvd SE 49503 616-988-1000
Cornerstone University Post-Sec.
1001 E Beltline Ave NE 49525 616-949-5300
Covenant Christian HS 200/9-12
1401 Ferndale Ave SW, 616-453-5048
Rick Noorman, prin. Fax 453-4277
Davenport University Post-Sec.
6191 Kraft Ave SE 49512 616-698-7111
Empire Beauty School Post-Sec.
1735 4 Mile Rd NE 49525 616-363-9853
Empire Beauty School Post-Sec.
455 Standale Plz NW, 616-735-9680
Everest Institute Post-Sec.
1750 Woodworth St NE 49525 616-364-8464
Grace Bible College Post-Sec.
1011 Aldon St SW 49509 616-538-2330

Grand Rapids Adventist Academy 100/K-12
1151 Oakleigh Rd NW 49504 616-791-9797
Burney Culpepper, prin. Fax 791-7242
Grand Rapids Christian HS 900/9-12
2300 Plymouth Ave SE 49506 616-574-5500
Dr. Randy Morris, prin. Fax 241-3141
Grand Rapids Christian MS 400/5-8
2036 Chesaning Dr SE 49506 616-574-6300
Ashanti Bryant, prin. Fax 574-6310
Grand Rapids Community College Post-Sec.
143 Bostwick Ave NE 49503 616-234-4000
Kuyper College Post-Sec.
3333 E Beltline Ave NE 49525 800-511-3749
Legacy Christian West Campus 200/5-8
67 68th St SW 49548 616-455-3860
Vince Bonnema M.A., admin. Fax 455-1960
NorthPointe Christian HS 400/6-12
3101 Leonard St NE 49525 616-942-0350
Todd Tolsma, head sch Fax 942-4647
Plymouth Christian HS 200/7-12
965 Plymouth Ave NE 49505 616-454-9481
James Bazen, prin. Fax 454-7243
Puritan Reformed Theological Seminary Post-Sec.
2965 Leonard St NE 49525 616-977-0599
Ross Medical Education Center Post-Sec.
4528 Breton Rd SE 49508 616-698-3075
Sacred Heart Academy 100/PK-10
1200 Dayton St SW 49504 616-459-0948
Sean Maltbie, hdmstr. Fax 459-0899
South Christian HS 700/9-12
160 68th St SW 49548 616-455-3210
George Guichelaar, prin. Fax 455-8840
Spectrum Health Post-Sec.
100 Michigan St NE 49503 616-391-1605
Taratuta School of Truck Driving Post-Sec.
2215 Oak Indstrl Dr NE #212 49505 616-742-9000
Van Andel Institute Graduate School Post-Sec.
333 Bostwick Ave NE 49503 616-234-5708
West Catholic HS 500/9-12
1801 Bristol Ave NW 49504 616-233-5900
Cynthia Kneibel, prin. Fax 453-4320

Grandville, Kent, Pop. 15,098
Grandville SD 5,600/PK-12
3839 Prairie St SW 49418 616-254-6570
Roger Bearup, supt. Fax 254-6580
www.grandville.k12.mi.us
Grandville HS 1,800/9-12
4700 Canal Ave SW 49418 616-254-6430
John Philo, prin. Fax 254-6462
Grandville MS 900/7-8
3535 Wilson Ave SW 49418 616-254-6610
John Philo, prin. Fax 254-6613

Grandville Calvin Christian HS 400/9-12
3750 Ivanrest Ave SW 49418 616-538-0990
Thelma Ensink, prin. Fax 538-9930
Grandville Calvin Christian MS 7-8
3740 Ivanrest Ave SW 49418 616-531-7400
Thelma Ensink, prin. Fax 531-7402

Grant, Newaygo, Pop. 889
Grant SD 2,000/PK-12
148 S Elder St 49327 231-834-5621
Jonathan Whan, supt. Fax 834-7146
www.grantps.net
Grant HS 600/9-12
331 E State Rd 49327 231-834-5622
Dan Simon, prin. Fax 834-8043
Grant Learning Center 100/Alt
331 E State Rd 49327 231-834-5639
Jonathan Whan, supt. Fax 834-8111
Grant MS 600/5-8
96 E 120th St 49327 231-834-5910
Lance Jones, prin. Fax 834-9029

Grass Lake, Jackson, Pop. 1,146
Grass Lake Community SD 1,200/PK-12
899 S Union St 49240 517-867-5540
Dr. Ryle Kiser, supt. Fax 522-8195
www.grasslakeschools.com
Grass Lake HS 400/9-12
11500 Warrior Trl 49240 517-867-5570
Brian Thompson, prin. Fax 522-5490
Grass Lake MS 300/6-8
1000 Grass Lake Rd 49240 517-867-5550
Jeanene Byerly, prin. Fax 522-4775

Grayling, Crawford, Pop. 1,867
Crawford AuSable SD 1,700/PK-12
1135 N Old 27 49738 989-344-3500
Joseph Powers, supt. Fax 348-6822
www.casdk12.net/
Grayling HS 500/9-12
1135 N Old 27 49738 989-344-3532
Donna Boughner, prin. Fax 348-7799
Grayling MS 400/6-8
500 Spruce St 49738 989-344-3550
Jeffrey Branch, prin. Fax 348-7045

Greenville, Montcalm, Pop. 8,316
Greenville SD 3,700/K-12
1414 Chase St 48838 616-754-3686
Linda Van Houten, supt. Fax 754-5374
www.greenville.k12.mi.us
Greenville HS 1,100/9-12
111 N Hillcrest St 48838 616-754-3681
Jeffrey Wright, prin. Fax 754-1994
Greenville MS 800/6-8
1321 Chase St 48838 616-754-9361
Leigh Acker, prin. Fax 754-2901

Grosse Ile, Wayne, Pop. 9,781
Grosse Ile Township SD 1,900/K-12
23276 E River Rd 48138 734-362-2555
Joanne Lelekatch, supt. Fax 362-2594
www.gischools.org/
Grosse Ile HS 600/9-12
7800 Grays Dr 48138 734-362-2400
Paul Szymanski, prin. Fax 362-2496
Grosse Ile MS 500/6-8
23270 E River Rd 48138 734-362-2500
Clifton Whitehouse, prin. Fax 362-2596

Grosse Pointe, Wayne, Pop. 5,336
Grosse Pointe SD 8,300/K-12
389 Saint Clair St 48230 313-432-3000
Dr. Gary Niehaus, supt. Fax 432-3002
www.gpschools.org
Brownell MS 700/6-8
260 Chalfonte Ave 48236 313-432-3900
Roger Hunwick, prin. Fax 432-3902
Grosse Pointe North HS 1,300/9-12
707 Vernier Rd 48236 313-432-3200
Kathryn Murray, prin. Fax 432-3202
Grosse Pointe South HS 1,700/9-12
11 Grosse Pointe Blvd 48236 313-432-3500
Moussa Hamka, prin. Fax 432-3502
Parcells MS 800/6-8
20600 Mack Ave 48236 313-432-4600
Daniel Hartley, prin. Fax 432-4602
Pierce MS 600/6-8
15430 Kercheval Ave 48230 313-432-4700
Chris Clark, prin. Fax 432-4702

University Liggett S 700/PK-12
1045 Cook Rd 48236 313-884-4444
Joseph P. Healey Ph.D., head sch Fax 884-1775

Gwinn, Marquette, Pop. 1,874
Gwinn Area Community SD 1,400/K-12
50 W State Highway M35 49841 906-346-9283
Thomas Jayne, supt. Fax 346-3616
www.gwinn.k12.mi.us
Gwinn HS 300/9-12
50 W State Highway M35 49841 906-346-9247
Brian Rice, prin. Fax 346-0300
Gwinn MS 200/6-8
50 W State Highway M35 49841 906-346-5914
Brian Rice, prin. Fax 346-0300

Hale, Iosco
Hale Area SD 300/K-12
200 W Main St 48739 989-728-7661
Loren Vannest, supt. Fax 728-2406
www.haleschools.net
Hale HS 200/9-12
311 N Washington 48739 989-728-3551
Michael Bowman, prin. Fax 728-9551

Hamilton, Allegan
Hamilton Community SD 2,500/PK-12
4815 136th Ave 49419 269-751-5148
David Tebo, supt. Fax 751-7116
www.hamiltonschools.us
Hamilton HS 800/9-12
4911 136th Ave 49419 269-751-5185
Tim Reeves, prin. Fax 751-7670
Hamilton MS 600/5-8
4845 136th Ave 49419 269-751-4436
Rick Frens, prin. Fax 751-8560
Other Schools – See Holland

Hamtramck, Wayne, Pop. 21,353
Hamtramck SD 2,700/PK-12
PO Box 12012 48212 313-872-9270
Thomas Niczay, supt. Fax 872-8679
www.hamtramck.k12.mi.us
Hamtramck HS 900/9-12
11410 Charest St 48212 313-892-7505
Timothy Constant, prin. Fax 892-1990
Horizon Alternative Education 100/Alt
3225 Caniff St 48212 313-893-2355
Kristen Hurt, prin. Fax 893-2294
Kosciuszko MS 300/7-8
2333 Burger St 48212 313-365-4625
Nuo Ivezaj, prin. Fax 365-4760

Hancock, Houghton, Pop. 4,572
Chassell Township SD 300/K-12
1610 Pinecrest Dr 49930 906-281-8151
Howard Parmentier, supt. Fax 281-8151
www.chassellschools.org
Chassell Township S 300/K-12
1610 Pinecrest Dr 49930 906-281-8151
Howard Parmentier, supt. Fax 281-8151

Copper Country ISD
809 Hecla St 49930 906-482-4250
George Stockero, supt. Fax 487-5915
www.copperisd.org
Career and Technical Education Vo/Tech
110 E Quincy St 49930 906-482-4250
William Rivest, prin. Fax 487-9044

Hancock SD 600/K-12
501 Campus Dr 49930 906-487-5925
Monica Healy, supt. Fax 455-2255
www.hancockpublicschools.org
Hancock MSHS 300/6-12
501 Campus Dr 49930 906-483-2540
Kipp Beaudoin, prin. Fax 483-2539

Finlandia University Post-Sec.
601 Quincy St 49930 906-482-5300

Harbor Beach, Huron, Pop. 1,671
Harbor Beach Community SD 500/PK-12
402 S 5th St 48441 989-479-3261
Lawrence Kroswek, supt. Fax 479-9881
www.hbpirates.org
Harbor Beach HS 200/9-12
402 S 5th St 48441 989-479-3261
Michael Hugan, prin. Fax 479-9881
Harbor Beach MS 100/6-8
402 S 5th St 48441 989-479-3261
Tumara Johnston, prin. Fax 479-9881

Harbor Springs, Emmet, Pop. 1,169
Harbor Springs SD 800/PK-12
800 State Rd 49740 231-526-4545
Mark Tompkins, supt. Fax 526-4544
www.harborps.org
Harbor Springs HS 300/9-12
500 N Spring St 49740 231-526-4800
Susan Jacobs, prin. Fax 526-4833
Harbor Springs MS 200/6-8
800 State Rd 49740 231-526-4700
Wil Cwikiel, prin. Fax 526-4760

Harbor Light Christian S 100/PK-12
8333 Clayton Rd 49740 231-347-7859
Ryan Coxon, admin. Fax 347-7703

Harper Woods, Wayne, Pop. 13,876
Harper Woods SD 1,500/PK-12
20225 Beaconsfield St 48225 313-245-3000
Todd Biederwolf, supt. Fax 839-1249
www.hwschools.org
Harper Woods HS 400/9-12
20225 Beaconsfield St 48225 313-245-3084
Schranda Collier, prin. Fax 371-5548
Harper Woods MS 200/7-8
20225 Beaconsfield St 48225 313-245-3000
Heath Filber, prin. Fax 839-4360
Diploma Success Community S Adult
19344 Kelly Rd 48225 313-458-8796
Lawrence Massey, prin. Fax 458-8801

Harris, Menominee
Bark River-Harris SD 700/K-12
PO Box 350 49845 906-466-9981
Jason Lockwood, supt. Fax 466-0107
www.brhschools.org/
Bark River-Harris JSHS 300/7-12
PO Box 350 49845 906-466-5321
Darren Bray, prin. Fax 466-2925

Harrison, Clare, Pop. 2,058
Harrison Community SD 1,500/K-12
PO Box 529 48625 989-539-7871
Richard T. Foote, supt. Fax 539-7491
www.harrisonschools.com/
Harrison Community Education 50/Alt
PO Box 529 48625 989-539-7194
Ryan Biller, dir. Fax 539-4314
Harrison HS 500/9-12
PO Box 529 48625 989-539-7417
Ryan Biller, prin. Fax 539-4319
Harrison MS 300/6-8
PO Box 529 48625 989-539-7194
Kelly Pieprzyk, prin. Fax 539-0460

Mid-Michigan Community College Post-Sec.
1375 S Clare Ave 48625 989-386-6622

Harrison Township, Macomb, Pop. 24,685
L'Anse Creuse SD
Supt. — See Clinton Township
L'Anse Creuse HS 1,600/9-12
38495 LAnse Creuse St 48045 586-783-6400
Stephen Czapski, prin. Fax 783-6408
L'Anse Creuse MS Central 700/6-8
38000 Reimold St 48045 586-783-6430
Andrea Glynn, prin. Fax 783-6437
L'Anse Creuse MS South 500/6-8
34641 Jefferson Ave 48045 586-493-5620
Paul Lasala, prin. Fax 493-5625

Hart, Oceana, Pop. 2,108
Hart SD 1,300/PK-12
301 Johnson St W 49420 231-873-6214
Mark Platt, supt. Fax 873-6244
www.hartschools.net
Hart HS 400/9-12
300 Johnson St W 49420 231-873-5691
Matthew McDonald, prin. Fax 873-0586
Hart MS 400/5-8
308 Johnson St W 49420 231-873-6320
Kevin Ackley, prin. Fax 873-0245

Hartford, Van Buren, Pop. 2,604
Hartford SD 1,300/PK-12
115 School St 49057 269-621-7000
Andrew Hubbard, supt. Fax 621-3887
www.hpsmi.org/
Hartford Alternative Education 100/Alt
115 School St 49057 269-621-7139
Erik Parker, prin.
Hartford HS 300/9-12
121 School St 49057 269-621-7100
David Janicki, prin. Fax 621-7160
Hartford MS 300/6-8
141 School St 49057 269-621-7200
Joel Messenger, prin. Fax 621-7260

Hartland, Livingston
Hartland Consolidated SD
Supt. — See Howell
Hartland HS 1,800/9-12
10635 Dunham Rd 48353 810-626-2200
David Minsker, prin. Fax 626-2201
Hartland MS 900/7-8
3250 Hartland Rd 48353 810-626-2400
Steve Livingway, prin. Fax 626-2401

Haslett, Ingham, Pop. 18,726
Haslett SD 2,700/K-12
5593 Franklin St 48840 517-339-8242
Steven L. Cook, supt. Fax 339-1360
www.haslett.k12.mi.us/
Haslett HS 900/9-12
5450 Marsh Rd 48840 517-339-8249
Bart Wegenke, prin. Fax 339-7353
Haslett MS 600/6-8
1535 Franklin St 48840 517-339-8233
Susan Gillings, prin. Fax 339-4837

Hastings, Barry, Pop. 7,265
Hastings Area SD 2,800/PK-12
232 W Grand St 49058 269-948-4400
Dr. Carrie Duits, supt. Fax 948-4425
www.hassk12.org
Hastings HS 900/9-12
520 W South St 49058 269-948-4409
Christopher Cooley, prin. Fax 948-8081
Hastings MS 600/6-8
232 W Grand St 49058 269-948-4404
Judy Johnson, prin. Fax 945-6101

Barry County Christian S 100/K-12
2999 McKeown Rd 49058 269-948-2151
Brandon Strong, admin. Fax 948-2795

Hazel Park, Oakland, Pop. 15,715
Hazel Park SD 2,500/PK-12
1620 E Elza Ave 48030 248-658-5200
Dr. Amy Kruppe, supt. Fax 544-5443
www.hazelparkschools.org
Hazel Park Alternative HS Alt
1620 E Elza 48030 248-658-5280
Steve Nemeckay, prin. Fax 544-5391
Hazel Park HS 800/9-12
23400 Hughes Ave 48030 248-658-5100
Fax 544-5389
Hazel Park JHS 600/6-8
22770 Highland Ave 48030 248-658-2300
Tammy Scholz, prin. Fax 586-5875
INVEST Roosevelt Alternative HS Alt
24131 S Chrysler Dr 48030 248-399-7033
Michelle Laporte, prin.
Hazel Park Adult S Adult
420 W 9 Mile Rd 48030 248-658-5600
Michelle LaPorte, prin. Fax 544-5447

Hemlock, Saginaw, Pop. 1,446
Hemlock SD 1,100/PK-12
PO Box 260 48626 989-642-5282
Donald Killingbeck, supt. Fax 642-2773
www.hemlockps.com
Hemlock Alternative S 50/Alt
PO Box 260 48626 989-642-5287
Michael Vondette, coord. Fax 642-5109
Hemlock HS 400/9-12
PO Box 260 48626 989-642-5287
Keith Green, prin. Fax 642-5109
Hemlock HS Early Middle College 11-12
PO Box 260 48626 989-642-5287
Randy Kreger, prin. Fax 642-2773
Hemlock MS 300/5-8
PO Box 260 48626 989-642-5253
Terry Keyser, prin. Fax 642-8239

Hesperia, Oceana, Pop. 932
Hesperia Community SD 1,000/K-12
PO Box 338 49421 231-854-6185
Vaughn White, supt. Fax 854-1586
www.hesp.net
Hesperia HS 300/9-12
PO Box 338 49421 231-854-6385
David LaPrairie, prin. Fax 854-6070
Hesperia MS 300/5-8
PO Box 338 49421 231-854-6475
David LaPrairie, prin. Fax 854-6096

Highland, Oakland
Huron Valley SD 9,200/PK-12
2390 S Milford Rd 48357 248-684-8000
James Baker, supt. Fax 684-8235
www.hvs.org
Harbor HS 100/Alt
5061 N Duck Lake Rd 48356 248-676-8421
Susan Gallagher, dir. Fax 676-8420
Milford HS 1,400/9-12
2380 S Milford Rd 48357 248-684-8091
Kevin McKenna, prin. Fax 684-8094
Other Schools – See Commerce Township, Milford, White Lake

Hillman, Montmorency, Pop. 696
Hillman Community SD 500/K-12
26042 M 32 S 49746 989-742-2908
Jason McElrath, supt. Fax 742-3376
www.hillmanschools.com
Hillman JSHS 200/7-12
26042 M 32 S 49746 989-742-4538
Jason McElrath, prin. Fax 742-4536

Hillsdale, Hillsdale, Pop. 8,143
Hillsdale Community SD 1,400/PK-12
30 S Norwood Ave 49242 517-437-4401
Shawn Vondra, supt. Fax 439-4194
www.hillsdaleschools.org
Davis MS 400/5-8
30 N West St 49242 517-439-4326
Erin North, prin. Fax 437-1195
Hillsdale HS 400/9-12
30 S Norwood Ave 49242 517-439-4320
Jeff Terpenning, prin. Fax 437-0377
Horizon Alternative HS 50/Alt
30 S Norwood Ave 49242 517-437-4403
Jeff Terpenning, prin. Fax 437-0377

Hillsdale ISD 100/
310 W Bacon St 49242 517-437-0990
Ronna Steel, supt. Fax 439-4388
www.hillsdale-isd.org
Workforce Development & Tech Center Vo/Tech
279 Industrial Dr 49242 517-437-3729
Kevin Leonard, dir. Fax 437-3743

Hillsdale Academy 200/K-12
1 Academy Ln 49242 517-439-8644
Dr. Kenneth Calvert, hdmstr. Fax 607-2794
Hillsdale Beauty College Post-Sec.
64 Waldron St 49242 517-437-4670
Hillsdale College Post-Sec.
33 E College St 49242 517-437-7341

Holland, Ottawa, Pop. 32,396
Hamilton Community SD
Supt. — See Hamilton
Pioneer Tech HS 50/Alt
1362 S Point Rdg 49423 616-394-1370
Joy Zomer, lead tchr.

Holland SD 3,800/PK-12
320 W 24th St 49423 616-494-2000
Dr. Brian Davis Ph.D., supt. Fax 392-8225
www.hollandpublicschools.org
Holland Early College 8-12
45 E 25th St 49423 616-494-2700
Andrea Mehall, dir. Fax 928-0581
Holland HS 1,400/8-12
600 Van Raalte Ave 49423 616-494-2200
Katie Pennington, prin. Fax 393-7534
Holland Virtual Tech HS 100/Alt
600 Van Raalte Ave 49423 616-494-2200
Tung Nguyen, dir. Fax 393-7534

Ottawa Area ISD 300/
13565 Port Sheldon St 49424 616-738-8940
Peter Haines, supt. Fax 738-8946
www.oaisd.org
Careerline Tech Center Vo/Tech
13663 Port Sheldon St 49424 616-738-8950
Dave Searles, dir. Fax 738-8956

West Ottawa SD 6,900/K-12
1138 136th Ave 49424 616-786-2050
Thomas K. Martin, supt.
www.westottawa.net
Dunes Alternative HS 50/Alt
3600 152nd Ave 49424 616-786-1100
Todd Tulgestke, prin.
Harbor Lights MS 900/6-8
1024 136th Ave 49424 616-786-1000
Dennis White, prin.
Macatawa Bay MS 700/6-8
3700 140th Ave 49424 616-786-2000
Anne Armstrong, prin.
West Ottawa HS 2,300/9-12
3685 Butternut Dr 49424 616-786-1100
Todd Tulgestke, prin.

Calvary S of Holland 7-12
6047 147th Ave 49423 616-396-0248
Martha Davis, prin.
Davenport University Post-Sec.
643 S Waverly Rd 49423 616-395-4600
Holland Christian HS 800/9-12
950 Ottawa Ave 49423 616-820-2905
Darryl De Ruiter, prin. Fax 820-2910
Holland Christian MS 200/7-8
850 Ottawa Ave 49423 616-820-3205
Dirk Hollebeek, prin. Fax 820-3210
Hope College Post-Sec.
PO Box 9000 49422 616-395-7000
Western Theological Seminary Post-Sec.
101 E 13th St 49423 616-392-8555

Holly, Oakland, Pop. 5,990
Holly Area SD 3,100/PK-12
920 Baird St 48442 248-328-3100
David M. Nuss, supt. Fax 328-3145
www.has-k12.org
Holly HS 1,200/9-12
6161 E Holly Rd 48442 248-328-3200
Peter LoFiego, prin. Fax 328-3211
Holly MS 500/6-8
14470 N Holly Rd 48442 248-328-3400
Eric Curl, prin. Fax 328-3404

Adelphian Junior Academy 50/K-10
PO Box 208 48442 248-634-9481
Nancy Danelson, prin. Fax 634-9222

Holt, Ingham, Pop. 23,336
Holt SD 5,700/PK-12
5780 Holt Rd 48842 517-694-0401
Dr. David G. Hornak, supt. Fax 694-1335
www.hpsk12.net
EdTrek Alternative Education Center 100/Alt
4610 Spahr St 48842 517-709-3148
Connie Ragnone, coord. Fax 709-3156
Holt HS 1,300/9-12
5885 Holt Rd 48842 517-694-2162
Michael Willard, prin. Fax 699-3451
Holt HS North Campus 500/12-12
5780 Holt Rd 48842 517-694-4370
Michael Willard, prin. Fax 694-8362
Holt JHS 1,000/7-8
1784 Aurelius Rd 48842 517-694-7117
Marshall Perkins, prin. Fax 694-3535

Luther HS 9-12
2418 Aurelius Rd 48842 517-694-3182
Traci Backus, supt. Fax 694-6371

Holton, Muskegon
Holton SD 800/PK-12
6500 4th St 49425 231-821-1700
Jason Kennedy, supt. Fax 821-1724
www.holtonschools.com
Holton HS 300/9-12
6477 Syers Rd 49425 231-821-1725
Adam Bayne, prin. Fax 821-1774
Holton MS 100/7-8
6477 Syers Rd 49425 231-821-1775
Adam Bayne, prin. Fax 821-1824

Homer, Calhoun, Pop. 1,660
Homer Community SD 1,100/K-12
403 S Hillsdale St 49245 517-568-4463
Scott Salow, supt. Fax 568-4468
www.homerschools.net
Homer HS 300/9-12
403 S Hillsdale St 49245 517-568-4464
Tom Salow, prin. Fax 568-7125
Homer MS 400/5-8
403 S Hillsdale St 49245 517-568-4456
Scott Salow, prin. Fax 568-7125

Hopkins, Allegan, Pop. 603
Hopkins SD 1,600/K-12
400 S Clark St 49328 269-793-7261
Gary Wood, supt. Fax 557-7919
www.hpsvikings.org
Hopkins HS 500/9-12
333 S Clark St 49328 269-793-7616
Ken Szczepanski, prin. Fax 557-7919
Hopkins MS 400/6-8
215 S Clark St 49328 269-793-7407
Scott Stockwell, prin. Fax 557-7919

Horton, Jackson
Hanover-Horton SD 1,200/K-12
10000 Moscow Rd 49246 517-563-0100
John Denney, supt. Fax 563-0150
www.hanoverhorton.org/
Hanover-Horton HS 400/9-12
10000 Moscow Rd 49246 517-563-0101
Isaac Cottrell, prin. Fax 563-0155
Hanover-Horton MS 300/6-8
10000 Moscow Rd 49246 517-563-0102
Denise Bergstrom, prin. Fax 563-9140

Houghton, Houghton, Pop. 7,574
Houghton-Portage Township SD 1,400/K-12
1603 Gundlach Rd 49931 906-482-0451
Doreen Klingbeil, supt. Fax 487-9764
www.hpts.us
Houghton Central HS 400/9-12
1603 Gundlach Rd 49931 906-482-0450
Patrick Aldrich, prin. Fax 482-5218
Houghton MS 300/6-8
1603 Gundlach Rd 49931 906-482-4871
Julie Filpus, prin. Fax 483-2566

Michigan Technological University Post-Sec.
1400 Townsend Dr 49931 906-487-1885

Houghton Lake, Roscommon, Pop. 3,390
Houghton Lake Community SD 1,400/PK-12
6001 W Houghton Lake Dr 48629 989-366-2000
Susan Tyer, supt. Fax 422-6606
www.hlcsk12.net
Houghton Lake HS 600/8-12
4433 W Houghton Lake Dr 48629 989-366-2005
John Winkler, prin. Fax 366-2071
Houghton Lake Community Education Adult
179 Cloverleaf Ln 48629 989-422-6161
Fax 366-2075

Houghton Lake Institute of Cosmetology Post-Sec.
PO Box 669 48629 - -

Howard City, Montcalm, Pop. 1,777
Tri County Area SD
Supt. — See Sand Lake
Tri County HS 700/9-12
21338 Kendaville Rd 49329 231-937-4338
Tim Goheen, prin. Fax 937-5684
Tri County MS 500/6-8
21350 Kendaville Rd 49329 231-937-4318
Steve Johnson, prin. Fax 937-6319

Howell, Livingston, Pop. 9,332
Hartland Consolidated SD 5,500/K-12
9525 E Highland Rd 48843 810-626-2100
Janet Sifferman, supt. Fax 626-2101
www.hartlandschools.us/
Hartland Alternative Education 100/Alt
9525 E Highland Rd 48843 810-626-2140
William Cain, prin. Fax 626-2101
Other Schools – See Hartland

Howell SD 7,600/K-12
411 N Highlander Way 48843 517-548-6200
Erin J. MacGregor, supt. Fax 548-6229
www.howellschools.com
Highlander Way MS 1,000/6-8
511 N Highlander Way 48843 517-548-6252
Melanie Post, prin. Fax 545-1455
Howell HS 1,900/10-12
1200 W Grand River Ave 48843 517-540-8300
Jason Schrock, prin. Fax 545-1496
Howell HS Freshman Campus 600/9-9
1400 W Grand River Ave 48843 517-548-6267
Jason Schrock, prin. Fax 545-1439
Parker MS 900/6-8
400 Wright Rd 48843 517-552-4600
Patricia Poelke, prin. Fax 552-0106

Cleary University - Livingston Campus Post-Sec.
3750 Cleary Dr 48843 800-686-1883

Hudson, Lenawee, Pop. 2,276
Hudson Area SD 900/K-12
781 N Maple Grove Ave 49247 517-448-8912
Dr. Michael Osborne Ph.D., supt. Fax 448-8570
www.hudson.k12.mi.us
Hudson Alternative HS 50/Alt
771 N Maple Grove Ave 49247 517-448-8912
Lance Horwath, prin. Fax 448-8975
Hudson Area HS 300/9-12
771 N Maple Grove Ave 49247 517-448-8912
Lance Horwath, prin. Fax 448-8975
Hudson MS 200/6-8
771 N Maple Grove Ave 49247 517-445-8912
Lance Horwath, prin. Fax 448-8975
Southern MI Ctr for Science & Industry Vo/Tech
550 E Main St 49247 517-448-1413
Dan Rogers, admin. Fax 448-1414

Hudsonville, Ottawa, Pop. 7,024
Hudsonville SD 6,200/PK-12
3886 Van Buren St 49426 616-669-1740
Dr. Nicholas Ceglarek, supt. Fax 669-4878
www.hudsonvillepublicschools.org

Baldwin Street MS — 800/6-8
3835 Baldwin St 49426 — 616-669-7750
Joel Olson, prin. — Fax 669-7755
Hudsonville Freshman Campus — 500/9-9
3370 Allen St 49426 — 616-669-1510
Matt Blood, prin.
Hudsonville HS — 1,300/10-12
5037 32nd Ave 49426 — 616-669-1500
Dave Feenstra, prin. — Fax 669-4891
Riley Street MS — 600/6-8
2745 Riley St 49426 — 616-896-1920
Bill Ross, prin. — Fax 896-1925

Hudsonville Christian MS — 300/6-8
3925 Van Buren St 49426 — 616-669-7487
Mary Broene, prin. — Fax 669-2031
Unity Christian HS — 700/9-12
5900 48th Ave 49426 — 616-669-1820
Jerry DeGroot, prin. — Fax 669-5760

Ida, Monroe
Ida SD — 1,400/K-12
3145 Prairie St 48140 — 734-269-3110
Richard Carsten, supt. — Fax 269-2294
www.idaschools.org
Ida HS — 500/9-12
3145 Prairie St 48140 — 734-269-3485
Charles Fuller, prin. — Fax 269-3495
Ida MS — 500/5-8
3143 Prairie St 48140 — 734-269-2220
Dave Eack, prin. — Fax 269-2576

Imlay City, Lapeer, Pop. 3,545
Imlay City Community SD — 2,100/PK-12
634 W Borland Rd 48444 — 810-724-2765
Dr. Stu Cameron, supt. — Fax 724-4307
www.icschools.us
Imlay City HS — 600/9-12
1001 Norlin Dr 48444 — 810-724-9810
Dr. Bill Kalmar, prin. — Fax 724-9897
Imlay City MS — 500/6-8
495 W 1st St 48444 — 810-724-9811
Patrick Brown, prin. — Fax 724-9896
Venture HS — 100/Alt
2061 S Almont Ave 48444 — 810-724-9814
Ross Gauthier, dean — Fax 724-2315

Indian River, Cheboygan, Pop. 1,930
Inland Lakes SD — 700/K-12
4363 S Straits Hwy 49749 — 231-238-6868
Mark Dombroski, supt. — Fax 238-4181
www.inlandlakes.org
Inland Lakes JSHS — 500/6-12
4363 S Straits Hwy 49749 — 231-238-6868
Melanie Allen, prin. — Fax 238-7240

Inkster, Wayne, Pop. 24,504
Westwood Community SD
Supt. — See Dearborn Heights
Tomlinson MS — 300/7-8
25912 Annapolis St 48141 — 313-565-3393
Kristen Kajoian, prin. — Fax 565-0920

Peterson-Warren Academy — 100/PK-12
PO Box 888 48141 — 313-565-5808
Angelita Crawford, lead tchr. — Fax 565-7784

Interlochen, Grand Traverse, Pop. 574

Interlochen Center for the Arts — 500/9-12
PO Box 199 49643 — 231-276-7200
Matthew Colpitts, dean — Fax 276-7885

Ionia, Ionia, Pop. 11,276
Ionia County ISD — 400/
2191 Harwood Rd 48846 — 616-527-4900
Jason Mellema, supt. — Fax 527-4731
www.ioniaisd.org
Heartlands Institute of Technology — Vo/Tech
250 E Tuttle Rd 48846 — 616-527-6540
Anne Sharkey-Scott, prin. — Fax 527-6670

Ionia SD — 3,000/PK-12
250 E Tuttle Rd 48846 — 616-527-9280
Dr. Ronald Wilson, supt. — Fax 527-8846
www.ioniaschools.org
Ionia HS — 800/9-12
250 E Tuttle Rd 48846 — 616-527-0600
Jack Manciu, prin. — Fax 527-8057
Ionia MS — 700/6-8
438 Union St 48846 — 616-527-0040
Wayne Piercefield, prin. — Fax 527-3380
Welch HS — 100/Alt
830 Harrison St 48846 — 616-527-3530
Jonathan Duley, prin. — Fax 527-8012

Iron Mountain, Dickinson, Pop. 7,523
Iron Mountain SD — 900/K-12
217 Izzo Mariucci Way 49801 — 906-779-2600
Raphael Rittenhouse, supt. — Fax 779-2676
www.imschools.org
Central MS — 200/7-8
300 W B St 49801 — 906-779-2610
Mark Herman, prin. — Fax 779-2638
IM-K Community Education — 100/Alt
800 E E St 49801 — 906-779-2660
Julie Wonders, prin. — Fax 779-2675
Iron Mountain HS — 300/9-12
300 W B St 49801 — 906-779-2610
Mark Herman, prin. — Fax 779-2638

Iron River, Iron, Pop. 2,984
West Iron County SD — 700/PK-12
601 Garfield Ave 49935 — 906-265-9218
Christopher Thomson, supt. — Fax 265-9736
www.westiron.org
West Iron County JSHS — 300/6-12
701 Garfield Ave 49935 — 906-265-5184
Michael Berutti, prin. — Fax 265-9750

Ironwood, Gogebic, Pop. 5,289
Ironwood Area SD — 400/K-12
650 E Ayer St 49938 — 906-932-0200
Timothy Kolesar, supt. — Fax 932-9915
www.ironwood.k12.mi.us/
Wright K-12 S — 400/K-12
650 E Ayer St 49938 — 906-932-0932
Denise Woodward, prin. — Fax 932-9915

Gogebic Community College — Post-Sec.
E4946 Jackson Rd 49938 — 906-932-4231

Ishpeming, Marquette, Pop. 6,339
Ishpeming SD 1 — 800/PK-12
319 E Division St 49849 — 906-485-5501
Carrie Meyer, supt. — Fax 485-1422
www.ishpemingschools.com
Ishpeming HS — 300/9-12
319 E Division St 49849 — 906-485-1066
Vicki Lempinen, prin. — Fax 485-4750
Ishpeming MS — 300/5-8
324 E Pearl St 49849 — 906-485-1066
Vicki Lempinen, prin. — Fax 485-4750

NICE Community SD — 1,200/K-12
300 S Westwood Dr 49849 — 906-485-1021
Bryan DeAugustine, supt. — Fax 485-4095
www.nice.k12.mi.us/
Westwood HS — 300/9-12
300 S Westwood Dr 49849 — 906-485-1023
David Boase, prin. — Fax 485-1530

Ithaca, Gratiot, Pop. 2,877
Gratiot-Isabella RESD
PO Box 310 48847 — 989-875-5101
Jan Amsterburg, supt. — Fax 875-7531
www.giresd.net/
Other Schools – See Alma

Ithaca SD — 1,300/PK-12
710 N Union St 48847 — 989-875-3700
Charmian Fletcher, supt. — Fax 875-4538
www.ithacaschools.net
Ithaca JSHS — 600/7-12
710 N Union St 48847 — 989-875-3373
Steven Netzley, prin. — Fax 875-2500

Jackson, Jackson, Pop. 31,900
East Jackson Community SD — 800/K-12
1404 N Sutton Rd 49202 — 517-764-2090
Steve Doerr, supt. — Fax 764-6033
www.eastjacksonschools.org
East Jackson HS — 300/9-12
1566 N Sutton Rd 49202 — 517-764-1700
Brent Cole, prin. — Fax 764-6083
East Jackson MS — 200/7-8
1566 N Sutton Rd 49202 — 517-764-6010
Brent Cole, prin. — Fax 764-6081
W-A-Y East Jackson — Alt
1404 N Sutton Rd 49202 — 517-764-2090
Brent Cole, prin. — Fax 764-6033

Jackson County ISD — 100/
6700 Browns Lake Rd 49201 — 517-768-5200
Kevin Oxley, supt. — Fax 787-2026
www.jcisd.org
Jackson Area Career Center — Vo/Tech
6800 Browns Lake Rd 49201 — 517-768-5100
Patty Horning, prin. — Fax 787-2844

Jackson SD — 4,800/K-12
522 Wildwood Ave 49201 — 517-841-2200
Jeff Beal, supt. — Fax 789-8056
www.jpsk12.org/
Fourth Street Learning Center — Alt
2400 4th St 49203 — 517-841-2313
Jeremy Patterson, prin. — Fax 768-5968
Jackson HS — 1,400/9-12
544 Wildwood Ave 49201 — 517-841-3700
Barbara Baird-Pauli, prin. — Fax 768-5910
MS at Parkside — 1,100/6-8
2400 4th St 49203 — 517-841-2300
Jeremy Patterson, prin. — Fax 768-5968
Wilson Academy — 400/Alt
310 W Morrell St 49203 — 517-841-2800
Deven Moore, prin. — Fax 783-3582

Napoleon Community SD
Supt. — See Napoleon
Ackerson Lake Community Center — 50/Alt
4126 Brooklyn Rd 49201 — 517-905-5701
Zach Kanaan, admin. — Fax 764-0265

Northwest Community SD — 2,800/PK-12
6900 Rives Junction Rd 49201 — 517-817-4700
Geoff Bontrager, supt. — Fax 569-2395
www.nwschools.org/
Northwest Alternative HS — 100/Alt
6900 Rives Junction Rd 49201 — 517-517-4702
James Upright, dir. — Fax 569-2870
Northwest HS — 900/9-12
4200 Van Horn Rd 49201 — 517-817-4701
Scott Buchler, prin. — Fax 569-2935
Northwest Kidder MS — 600/6-8
6700 Rives Junction Rd 49201 — 517-817-4703
Dan Brooks, prin. — Fax 569-2931

Vandercook Lake SD — 1,300/K-12
1000 E Golf Ave 49203 — 517-782-9044
Scott Leach, supt. — Fax 788-3690
www.vandyschools.org
Vandercook Lake JSHS — 700/6-12
1000 E Golf Ave 49203 — 517-782-8167
Mark Schonhard, prin. — Fax 782-3730

Western SD
Supt. — See Parma
Woodville Community Center — 100/Alt
3950 Catherine St 49203 — 517-841-8700
Jared Vickers, prin. — Fax 841-8807

Baker College of Jackson — Post-Sec.
2800 Springport Rd 49202 — 517-788-7800
Jackson Christian MSHS — 200/6-12
4200 Lowe Rd 49203 — 517-783-2658
Pattie Huff, prin. — Fax 783-4235
Jackson College — Post-Sec.
2111 Emmons Rd 49201 — 517-787-0800
Lumen Christi HS — 500/7-12
3483 Spring Arbor Rd 49203 — 517-787-0630
Stephanie Kristovic, prin. — Fax 787-1066

Jenison, Ottawa, Pop. 16,336
Jenison SD — 4,600/PK-12
8375 20th Ave 49428 — 616-457-8890
Thomas TenBrink, supt. — Fax 457-8898
www.jpsonline.org/
Jenison HS — 1,400/9-12
2140 Bauer Rd 49428 — 616-457-3400
Dr. Brandon Graham, prin. — Fax 457-4070
Jenison JHS — 700/7-8
8295 20th Ave 49428 — 616-457-1402
Brett Cataldo, prin. — Fax 457-8090

Johannesburg, Otsego
Johannesburg-Lewiston Area SD — 700/K-12
PO Box 69 49751 — 989-732-1773
Kathleen Makowski, supt. — Fax 732-6556
www.jlas.org
Johannesburg-Lewiston HS — 200/9-12
PO Box 69 49751 — 989-731-4420
Curt Chrencik, prin. — Fax 732-6556

Jonesville, Hillsdale, Pop. 2,240
Jonesville Community SD — 1,500/PK-12
202 Wright St 49250 — 517-849-9075
Chellie Broesamle, supt. — Fax 849-2434
www.jonesvilleschools.org
Jonesville HS — 400/9-12
460 Adrian Rd 49250 — 517-849-9934
Dustin Scharer, prin. — Fax 849-2755
Jonesville MS — 300/6-8
401 E Chicago St 49250 — 517-849-3210
Bryan Playford, prin. — Fax 849-3213
Phoenix Alternative S — 50/Alt
202 Wright St 49250 — 517-849-7304
Eric Swihart, prin. — Fax 849-3213

Kalamazoo, Kalamazoo, Pop. 71,183
Comstock SD — 2,100/PK-12
3010 Gull Rd 49048 — 269-250-8900
Todd Mora, supt. — Fax 250-8901
www.comstockps.org
Comstock Compass HS — 200/Alt
3010 Gull Rd 49048 — 269-250-8930
Jay Birchmeier, prin. — Fax 250-8931
Comstock HS — 500/9-12
2107 N 26th St 49048 — 269-250-8700
Gerielle Stewart, prin. — Fax 250-8701
Comstock Northeast MS — 500/5-8
1423 N 28th St 49048 — 269-250-8600
Kelley Howard, prin. — Fax 250-8601

Kalamazoo RESA
Supt. — See Portage
Valley Center S — 50/Alt
3122 Lake St 49048 — 269-388-9494
Fax 382-8546

Youth Opportunities Unlimited — Alt
422 E South St 49007 — 269-349-9676
Karen Carlisle, admin. — Fax 349-6852
Young Adult Program — Adult
422 E South St 49007 — 269-250-9602
Deborah Wild, prin. — Fax 250-9601

Kalamazoo SD — 12,300/K-12
1220 Howard St 49008 — 269-337-0100
Michael Rice, supt. — Fax 337-0149
www.kalamazoopublicschools.com
Alternative Learning Program — Alt
3410 Laird Ave 49008 — 269-337-0540
Tamica Frison, prin. — Fax 337-1652
Central HS — 1,600/9-12
2432 N Drake Rd 49006 — 269-337-0300
Valerie Boggan, prin. — Fax 337-0391
Hillside MS — 600/6-8
1941 Alamo Ave 49006 — 269-337-0570
Atiba McKissack, prin. — Fax 337-1618
Kalamazoo Area Math and Science Center — 9-12
600 W Vine St Ste 400 49008 — 269-337-0004
Dr. Michael Tanoff, prin.
Linden Grove MS — 800/6-8
4241 Arboretum Pkwy 49006 — 269-337-1740
Craig McCane, prin. — Fax 337-1614
Maple Magnet MS — 700/6-8
922 W Maple St 49008 — 269-337-0730
Dr. Jeffery Boggan, prin. — Fax 337-1633
Milwood Magnet MS — 700/6-8
2916 Konkle St 49001 — 269-337-0670
Craig LeSuer, prin. — Fax 337-1628
Norrix HS — 1,500/9-12
606 E Kilgore Rd 49001 — 269-337-0200
Rodney Prewitt, prin. — Fax 337-1617
Phoenix HS — 100/Alt
1411 Oakland Dr 49008 — 269-337-0760
Mark Hill, prin. — Fax 337-1756
Adult Education Program — Adult
714 S Westnedge Ave 49007 — 269-337-0422
Kim Bell, dir. — Fax 337-0490

Parchment SD
Supt. — See Parchment
Barclay Hills Education Center — Adult
1125 E Mosel Ave 49004 — 269-488-1470
Tina Maxwell, prin. — Fax 488-1480

Davenport University — Post-Sec.
4123 W Main St 49006 — 269-382-2835
Everest Institute — Post-Sec.
5177 W Main St 49009 — 269-381-9616

Heritage Christian Academy 300/PK-12
6312 Quail Run Dr 49009 269-372-1400
Randal Hadley, admin. Fax 372-6018
Kalamazoo Christian HS 300/9-12
2121 Stadium Dr 49008 269-381-2250
B.J. Huizenga, prin. Fax 381-0319
Kalamazoo College Post-Sec.
1200 Academy St 49006 269-337-7000
Kalamazoo Junior Academy 100/K-10
1601 Nichols Rd 49006 269-342-8943
Kenneth Armstrong, prin. Fax 492-1459
Kalamazoo Valley Community College Post-Sec.
PO Box 4070 49003 269-488-4400
Msgr. Hackett Catholic Prep S 300/9-12
1000 W Kilgore Rd 49008 269-381-2646
Brian Kosmerick, prin. Fax 381-3919
Western Michigan University Post-Sec.
1903 W Michigan Ave 49008 269-387-1000
West Michigan Coll of Barbering & Beauty Post-Sec.
3200 S Westnedge Ave Ste 1 49008 269-381-4424

Kalkaska, Kalkaska, Pop. 1,989
Kalkaska SD 1,600/PK-12
315 S Coral St 49646 231-258-9109
Karen Sherwood, supt. Fax 258-4474
www.kpschools.com/
Kalkaska Alternative Program 100/Alt
315 S Coral St 49646 231-258-5140
John Sattler, prin. Fax 258-4940
Kalkaska HS 400/9-12
315 S Coral St 49646 231-258-9167
John Sattler, prin. Fax 258-5188
Kalkaska MS 300/6-8
315 S Coral St 49646 231-258-4040
Staci Short, prin. Fax 258-3576

Kent City, Kent, Pop. 1,047
Kent City Community SD 1,300/PK-12
200 N Clover St 49330 616-678-7714
Mike Weiler, supt. Fax 678-4320
www.kentcityschools.org
Kent City Alternative HS 50/Alt
351 N Main St 49330 616-678-7714
Bill Crane, prin. Fax 678-4320
Kent City HS 400/9-12
351 N Main St 49330 616-678-4210
Bill Crane, prin. Fax 678-4371
Kent City MS 300/6-8
285 N Main St 49330 616-678-4214
Bill Crane, prin. Fax 678-5099

Algoma Christian S 200/PK-12
PO Box 220 49330 616-678-7480
Dr. Brian Hazeltine Ed.D., supt. Fax 678-7484

Kentwood, Kent, Pop. 47,105
Kentwood SD 8,600/PK-12
5820 Eastern Ave SE 49508 616-455-4400
Michael Zoerhoff, supt. Fax 455-4476
www.kentwoodps.org
Crestwood MS 700/6-8
2674 44th St SE 49512 616-455-1200
Donald Dahlquist, prin. Fax 455-2338
East Kentwood Freshman Campus HS 800/9-9
6170 Valley Lane Dr SE 49508 616-698-9292
Michele Siderman, prin. Fax 698-0313
East Kentwood HS 1,900/10-12
6230 Kalamazoo Ave SE 49508 616-698-6700
Omar Bakri, prin. Fax 698-2384
Pinewood MS 700/6-8
2100 60th St SE 49508 616-455-1224
Gary Harmon, prin. Fax 455-2054
Valleywood MS 500/6-8
1110 50th St SE 49508 616-538-7670
Mindy Westra, prin. Fax 538-9301
Kentwood Community Education Adult
28 60th St SE 49548 616-261-6166
Rick Hatfield, prin. Fax 261-6170

Kimball, Saint Clair, Pop. 7,247

New Life Christian Academy 200/PK-12
5517 Griswold Rd 48074 810-367-3770
Lee Ann Shimmel, admin. Fax 367-2249

Kincheloe, Chippewa
Pickford SD
Supt. — See Pickford
Consolidated Community School Services 100/Alt
4900 W Davis Ct 49788 906-495-7305
Bill Henry, prin. Fax 495-5710

Kinde, Huron, Pop. 445
North Huron SD 400/K-12
21 Main St 48445 989-874-4100
Martin Prout, supt. Fax 874-4109
www.nhuron.org
North Huron S 400/K-12
21 Main St 48445 989-874-4101
Tanya Kramer, prin. Fax 874-4129

Kingsford, Dickinson, Pop. 5,077
Breitung Township SD 1,700/PK-12
2000 W Pyle Dr 49802 906-779-2650
Craig Allen, supt. Fax 779-7703
www.kingsford.org
Kingsford HS 600/9-12
431 Hamilton Ave 49802 906-779-2670
Lyle Smithson, prin. Fax 779-2883
Kingsford MS 400/6-8
445 Hamilton Ave 49802 906-779-2680
David Holmes, prin. Fax 774-1354

Dickinson-Iron ISD 50/
1074 Pyle Dr 49802 906-779-2690
Wendy Warmuth, supt. Fax 779-2669
www.diisd.org
Dickinson-Iron Tech Educ Center Vo/Tech
300 North Blvd 49802 906-779-2697
Michael Mulligan, prin. Fax 779-2087

Kingsley, Grand Traverse, Pop. 1,450
Kingsley Area SD 1,400/K-12
402 Fenton St 49649 231-263-5261
Keith Smith, supt. Fax 263-5282
www.kingsley.k12.mi.us
Kingsley Area HS 400/9-12
402 Fenton St 49649 231-263-5262
Mike Moran, prin. Fax 263-3813
Kingsley Area MS 400/5-8
402 Fenton St 49649 231-263-5261
Karl Hartman, prin. Fax 263-4623

Kingston, Tuscola, Pop. 436
Kingston Community SD 600/PK-12
5790 State St 48741 989-683-2294
Matt Drake, supt. Fax 683-2081
www.kingstonk12.org
Kingston JSHS, 5790 State St 48741 300/7-12
Matthew Drake, supt. 989-683-2550

Laingsburg, Shiawassee, Pop. 1,260
Laingsburg Community SD 1,100/PK-12
205 S Woodhull Rd 48848 517-651-2705
Matthew Shastal, supt. Fax 651-9075
www.laingsburg.k12.mi.us/
Laingsburg HS 400/9-12
8008 Woodbury Rd 48848 517-651-5091
Brian Doepker, prin. Fax 651-9621
Laingsburg MS 300/6-8
112 High St 48848 517-651-5034
Brandon Woodworth, prin. Fax 651-6213

Lake City, Missaukee, Pop. 830
Lake City Area SD 900/K-12
PO Box 900 49651 231-839-4333
Kim Blaszak, supt. Fax 839-5219
www.lakecityschools.net
Lake City HS 300/9-12
PO Box 900 49651 231-839-4331
Tim Hejnal, prin. Fax 839-6031
Lake City MS 300/6-8
PO Box 900 49651 231-839-7163
Tim Hejnal, prin. Fax 839-6042

Lake Leelanau, Leelanau, Pop. 250

St. Mary S 200/PK-12
PO Box 340 49653 231-256-9636
Megan Glynn, prin. Fax 256-7239

Lake Linden, Houghton, Pop. 992
Lake Linden-Hubbell SD 500/K-12
601 Calumet St 49945 906-296-6211
Craig Sundblad, supt. Fax 296-0943
www.lakelinden.k12.mi.us
Lake Linden Hubbell JSHS 300/7-12
601 Calumet St 49945 906-296-6681
Craig Sundblad, prin. Fax 296-0219

Lake Odessa, Ionia, Pop. 1,980
Lakewood SD
Supt. — See Woodland
Lakewood HS 700/9-12
7223 Velte Rd 48849 616-374-8868
Jay Larner, prin. Fax 374-1477

Lake Orion, Oakland, Pop. 2,917
Lake Orion Community SD 7,300/K-12
315 N Lapeer St 48362 248-693-5400
Marion Ginopolis, supt. Fax 693-5464
www.lakeorion.k12.mi.us/
Lake Orion Community HS 2,400/9-12
495 E Scripps Rd 48360 248-693-5420
Stephen Hawley, prin. Fax 693-5459
Scripps MS 600/6-8
385 E Scripps Rd 48360 248-693-5440
Dan Haas, prin. Fax 693-5301
Waldon MS 600/6-8
2509 Waldon Rd 48360 248-391-1100
Randy Groya, prin. Fax 391-5452
Other Schools – See Oakland

Lake Orion Baptist S 100/K-12
255 E Scripps Rd 48360 248-693-6203
Tony Bryson, prin. Fax 693-6177

Lakeview, Montcalm, Pop. 988
Lakeview Community SD 1,300/PK-12
123 5th St 48850 989-352-7221
Kyle Hamlin, supt. Fax 352-8245
www.lakeviewschools.net
Lakeview HS 600/8-12
9800 Youngman Rd 48850 989-352-7221
Tom Wilcox, prin. Fax 352-6320

LAnse, Baraga, Pop. 1,920
L'Anse Area SD 600/K-12
201 N 4th St 49946 906-524-6000
Susan Tollefson, supt. Fax 524-6001
www.lanseschools.org/
L'Anse JSHS 400/6-12
201 N 4th St 49946 906-524-6000
Melissa Scroggs, prin. Fax 524-0345

Lansing, Ingham, Pop. 108,750
Lansing SD 11,700/PK-12
519 W Kalamazoo St 48933 517-755-1000
Yvonne Caamal Canul, supt. Fax 755-2009
www.lansingschools.net
Eastern HS 1,600/7-12
220 N Pennsylvania Ave 48912 517-755-1050
Donna Pohl, prin. Fax 755-1059
Everett HS 1,400/7-12
3900 Stabler St 48910 517-755-1080
Susan Cheadle-Holt, prin. Fax 755-1089
Sexton HS 900/7-12
102 Mcpherson Ave 48915 517-755-1070
Glenn Stevens, prin. Fax 755-1079
Woodcreek Achievement Center 200/Alt
4000 Woodcreek Ln 48911 517-755-1700
Broderick Williams, prin. Fax 755-1709

Waverly Community SD 2,600/PK-12
515 Snow Rd 48917 517-321-7265
Terry Urquhart, supt. Fax 321-8577
www.waverlycommunityschools.net
Waverly HS 1,000/9-12
160 Snow Rd 48917 517-323-3831
Christopher Huff, prin. Fax 323-7714
Waverly MS 400/7-8
620 Snow Rd 48917 517-321-7240
Michael Moreno, prin. Fax 321-5789

American Hotel/Lodging Educational Inst Post-Sec.
2113 N High St 48906 800-390-8399
Career Quest Learning Center Post-Sec.
3215 S Pennsylvania Ave 48910 517-318-3330
Davenport University Post-Sec.
220 E Kalamazoo St 48933 517-484-2600
Dorsey School of Business Post-Sec.
6250 S Cedar St Ste 9 48911 517-272-4018
Greater Lansing Adventist S 100/PK-10
5330 W St Joe Hwy 48917 517-321-5565
Judy Shull, prin. Fax 321-5580
Great Lakes Christian College Post-Sec.
6211 W Willow Hwy 48917 517-321-0242
Lansing Catholic Central HS 500/9-12
501 Marshall St 48912 517-267-2100
Doug Moore, prin. Fax 267-2135
Lansing Christian S 600/PK-12
3405 Belle Chase Way 48911 517-882-5779
Wendy Hofman, head sch Fax 882-5849
Lansing Community College Post-Sec.
PO Box 40010 48901 517-483-1957
New Covenant Christian S 100/PK-12
PO Box 80737 48908 517-323-8903
Fred McGlone, prin. Fax 323-0421
Ross Medical Education Center Post-Sec.
4106 W Saginaw Hwy 48917 517-703-9044
Thomas M. Cooley Law School Post-Sec.
PO Box 13038 48901 517-371-5140

Lapeer, Lapeer, Pop. 8,708
Lapeer Community SD 3,700/PK-12
250 2nd St 48446 810-667-2401
Matthew Wandrie, supt. Fax 667-2411
www.lapeerschools.org
Lapeer Community HS 100/Alt
170 Millville Rd 48446 810-667-2453
Troy Norman, dir. Fax 667-2412
Lapeer HS 800/10-12
933 S Saginaw St 48446 810-667-2418
Douglas Lindsay, prin. Fax 667-2422
Zemmer MS 200/8-9
1920 W Oregon St 48446 810-667-2413
Fax 667-2483

Lapeer County ISD 50/
1996 W Oregon St 48446 810-664-5917
Steven Zott, supt. Fax 664-1011
www.lcisd.k12.mi.us
Other Schools – See Attica

Health Enrichment Center Post-Sec.
204 E Nepessing St 48446 810-667-9453

Lathrup Village, Oakland, Pop. 3,943
Southfield SD
Supt. — See Southfield
University HS Academy 400/9-12
19301 W 12 Mile Rd 48076 248-746-4370
Marcia Williams, dean Fax 746-4374

Lawrence, Van Buren, Pop. 973
Lawrence SD 600/PK-12
650 W Saint Joseph St 49064 269-674-8233
Gretchen Gendron, supt. Fax 674-8206
www.lawrencetigers.com
Lawrence JSHS 300/7-12
650 W Saint Joseph St 49064 269-674-8232
Elizabeth Baleja, prin. Fax 674-8206

Van Buren ISD 100/
490 S Paw Paw St 49064 269-674-8091
Jeffrey Mills, supt. Fax 674-8030
www.vbisd.org/
Van Buren Technology Center Vo/Tech
250 South St 49064 269-539-5000
Scott Starkweather, prin. Fax 674-8954

Lawton, Van Buren, Pop. 1,870
Lawton Community SD 1,000/PK-12
101 Primary Way 49065 269-624-7901
Christopher Rice M.Ed., supt. Fax 624-6489
www.lawtoncs.org
Lawton Accelerated Academic Center 50/Alt
101 Primary Way 49065 269-624-7542
Tamara Webster M.Ed., admin.
Lawton HS 300/9-12
101 Primary Way 49065 269-624-7840
Tammy Wilson, prin. Fax 624-6554
Lawton MS 200/6-8
101 Primary Way 49065 269-624-7610
Tim Cerven, prin. Fax 624-5206

Leland, Leelanau, Pop. 377
Leland SD 400/K-12
PO Box 498 49654 231-256-9857
Jason Stowe, supt. Fax 256-9844
www.lelandpublicschools.com
Leland S 400/K-12
PO Box 498 49654 231-256-9857
Charles Gann, prin. Fax 256-9844

LeRoy, Osceola, Pop. 252
Pine River Area SD 900/K-12
17445 Pine River Rd 49655 231-829-3141
Matt Lukshaitis, supt. Fax 829-4410
www.pineriver.org/
Pine River Area MSHS 400/6-12
17445 Pine River Rd 49655 231-829-3841
Kim Miller, prin. Fax 829-5227

Leslie, Ingham, Pop. 1,824
Leslie SD 1,300/K-12
4141 Hull Rd 49251 517-589-8200
Jeff Manthei, supt. Fax 589-5340
www.lesliek12.net/
Leslie HS 500/9-12
4141 Hull Rd 49251 517-589-9500
Scott Powers, prin. Fax 589-5720
Leslie MS 400/5-8
400 Kimball St 49251 517-589-8218
Carol Franz, prin. Fax 589-5714

Lexington, Sanilac, Pop. 1,169
Croswell-Lexington SD
Supt. — See Croswell
Croswell-Lexington Alternative S 50/Alt
7178 Boynton St 48450 810-679-1500
Damien Pepin, admin.

Lincoln, Alcona, Pop. 335
Alcona Community SD 700/PK-12
PO Box 249 48742 989-736-6212
Shawn Thornton, supt. Fax 736-6261
www.alconaschools.net/
Alcona JSHS 400/7-12
PO Box 249 48742 989-736-8534
Daniel O'Connor, prin. Fax 736-8495

Lincoln Park, Wayne, Pop. 37,338
Lincoln Park SD 4,800/K-12
1650 Champaign Rd 48146 313-389-0200
Terry Dangerfield, supt. Fax 389-1322
www.lincolnparkpublicschools.com
Lincoln Park HS 1,400/9-12
1701 Champaign Rd 48146 313-389-0234
Jennifer Borg, prin. Fax 383-5738
Lincoln Park MS 1,100/6-8
2800 Lafayette Blvd 48146 313-389-0757
Daniel Mercer, prin. Fax 389-0761

Linden, Genesee, Pop. 3,937
Lake Fenton Community SD
Supt. — See Fenton
Lake Fenton HS 600/9-12
4070 Lahring Rd 48451 810-591-9591
Chris Belcher, prin. Fax 591-9495

Linden Community SD 2,700/PK-12
7205 Silver Lake Rd 48451 810-591-0980
Russ Ciesielski, supt. Fax 591-5587
www.lindenschools.org
Linden HS 900/9-12
7201 Silver Lake Rd 48451 810-591-0410
Darin Dreasky, prin. Fax 591-8014
Linden MS 700/6-8
15425 Lobdell Rd 48451 810-591-0710
Julie Brown, prin. Fax 591-0155

Litchfield, Hillsdale, Pop. 1,359
Litchfield Community SD 300/K-12
210 Williams St 49252 517-542-2388
Dr. Corey Helgesen Ed.D., supt. Fax 542-2580
www.lcsmi.org
Litchfield JSHS 200/6-12
210 Williams St 49252 517-542-2386
Dr. Corey Helgesen Ed.D., prin. Fax 542-2703

Livonia, Wayne, Pop. 95,640
Clarenceville SD 1,900/PK-12
20210 Middlebelt Rd 48152 248-919-0400
Paul Shepich, supt. Fax 919-0430
www.clarenceville.k12.mi.us
Clarenceville HS 600/9-12
20155 Middlebelt Rd 48152 248-919-0408
Troy Nelson, prin. Fax 919-0438
Clarenceville MS 400/6-8
20210 Middlebelt Rd 48152 248-919-0406
Stacey Lown, prin. Fax 919-0436

Livonia SD 14,400/PK-12
15125 Farmington Rd 48154 734-744-2500
Andrea Oquist, supt. Fax 744-2571
www.livoniapublicschools.org
Churchill HS 1,700/9-12
8900 Newburgh Rd 48150 734-744-2650
Keith McDonald, prin. Fax 744-2652
Emerson MS 700/7-8
29100 W Chicago St 48150 734-744-2665
Ann Owen, prin. Fax 744-2667
Franklin HS 1,700/9-12
31000 Joy Rd 48150 734-744-2655
Daniel Willenborg, prin. Fax 744-2657
Frost MS 800/7-8
14041 Stark Rd 48154 734-744-2670
Anthony Abbate, prin. Fax 744-2672
Holmes MS 800/7-8
16200 Newburgh Rd 48154 734-744-2675
Eric Stromberg, prin. Fax 744-2677
Livonia Career/Technical Center Vo/Tech
8985 Newburgh Rd 48150 734-744-2816
R. Joseph Anderson, prin. Fax 744-2817
Stevenson HS 1,900/9-12
33500 6 Mile Rd 48152 734-744-2660
Gary Harper, prin. Fax 744-2662
Other Schools – See Westland

Davenport University Post-Sec.
19499 Victor Pkwy 48152 734-943-2800
Ladywood HS 300/9-12
14680 Newburgh Rd 48154 734-591-1544
Tracey Mocon, prin. Fax 591-1545
Madonna University Post-Sec.
36600 Schoolcraft Rd 48150 734-432-5300
Schoolcraft College Post-Sec.
18600 Haggerty Rd 48152 734-462-4400

Lowell, Kent, Pop. 3,710
Lowell Area SD 3,700/K-12
300 High St 49331 616-987-2500
Gregory Pratt, supt. Fax 987-2511
www.lowellschools.com/
Lowell HS 1,200/9-12
11700 Vergennes St 49331 616-987-2900
Amy Pallo, prin. Fax 987-2911
Lowell MS 800/6-8
750 Foreman St 49331 616-987-2800
Dan VanderMeulen, prin. Fax 987-2811
Unity Alternative S 50/Alt
300 High St 49331 616-987-2524
Amy Pallo, prin. Fax 987-2511

Ludington, Mason, Pop. 7,926
Ludington Area SD 2,200/PK-12
809 E Tinkham Ave 49431 231-845-7303
Andrea D. Large, supt. Fax 843-4930
www.lasd.net
DeJonge MS 500/6-8
706 E Tinkham Ave 49431 231-845-3810
Kristi Zimmerman, prin. Fax 845-3814
Ludington HS 600/9-12
508 N Washington Ave 49431 231-845-3880
Dan Mesyar, prin. Fax 845-3881

West Shore ESD 100/
2130 W US Highway 10 49431 231-757-3716
Randy Howes, supt. Fax 757-2406
www.wsesd.org
Other Schools – See Scottville

Mc Bain, Missaukee, Pop. 651
McBain Rural Agricultural SD 700/PK-12
107 E Maple St 49657 231-825-2165
Steve Brimmer, supt. Fax 825-2119
www.mcbain.org
Mc Bain JSHS 300/7-12
107 E Maple St 49657 231-825-2412
Joel Bronkema, prin. Fax 825-2119

Northern Michigan Christian S 300/PK-12
128 S Martin St 49657 231-825-2492
Dirk Walhout, supt. Fax 825-2371

Mackinac Island, Mackinac, Pop. 466
Mackinac Island SD 100/PK-12
PO Box 340 49757 906-847-3377
David Waaso, supt. Fax 847-3773
mackinac.eup.k12.mi.us
Mackinac Island S 100/PK-12
PO Box 340 49757 906-847-3377
David Waaso, admin. Fax 847-3773

Mackinaw City, Emmet, Pop. 794
Mackinaw City SD 200/PK-12
609 W Central Ave 49701 231-436-8211
Jeffrey Curth, supt. Fax 436-5434
www.mackcity.k12.mi.us
Mackinaw City S 200/PK-12
609 W Central Ave 49701 231-436-8211
Jeffrey Curth, supt. Fax 436-5434

Macomb, Macomb, Pop. 22,714
Chippewa Valley SD
Supt. — See Clinton Township
Dakota HS 2,000/10-12
21051 21 Mile Rd 48044 586-723-2702
Paul Sibley, prin. Fax 723-2701
Dakota Ninth Grade Center 9-9
21055 21 Mile Rd 48044 586-723-3300
Kevin Koskos, prin. Fax 723-3301
Iroquois MS 1,100/6-8
48301 Romeo Plank Rd 48044 586-723-3700
Chris Gardner, prin. Fax 723-3701
Seneca MS 1,400/6-8
47200 Heydenreich Rd 48044 586-723-3900
Todd Distelrath, prin. Fax 723-3901

L'Anse Creuse SD
Supt. — See Clinton Township
L'Anse Creuse HS - North 1,800/9-12
23700 21 Mile Rd 48042 586-493-5270
Dr. Greg Dixon, prin. Fax 493-5275
L'Anse Creuse MS North 800/6-8
46201 Fairchild Rd 48042 586-493-5260
Brian Fahning, prin. Fax 493-5265

Lutheran HS North 500/9-12
16825 24 Mile Rd 48042 586-781-9151
John Reincke, prin. Fax 781-8673

Madison Heights, Oakland, Pop. 28,913
Lamphere SD 2,800/PK-12
31201 Dorchester Ave 48071 248-589-1990
Dale Steen, supt. Fax 589-2618
www.lampereschools.org
Lamphere HS 800/9-12
610 W 13 Mile Rd 48071 248-589-3943
Gregory Fuller, prin. Fax 589-0240
Page MS 600/6-8
29615 Tawas St 48071 248-589-3428
Rodney Thomas, prin. Fax 545-1870

Madison SD 1,300/K-12
26524 John R Rd 48071 248-399-7800
Valerie Martin, supt. Fax 399-2229
www.madisondistrict.org
Madison HS 400/9-12
915 E 11 Mile Rd 48071 248-548-1800
Dan Gilbertson, prin. Fax 548-9758
Madison Preparatory HS 100/Alt
25601 Couzens Ave 48071 248-543-5465
Leslie Renne-Kegebein, prin. Fax 543-9323
Wilkinson MS 300/6-8
26524 John R Rd 48071 248-399-0455
Angel Abdulahad, prin. Fax 399-1965

Bishop Foley HS 300/9-12
32000 Campbell Rd 48071 248-585-1210
Elizabeth Hubbell, prin. Fax 585-3667
Dorsey School of Business Post-Sec.
30821 Barrington St 48071 248-588-9660
Ross Medical Education Center Post-Sec.
29429 John R Rd 48071 248-548-4389

Mancelona, Antrim, Pop. 1,339
Mancelona SD 1,000/PK-12
PO Box 739 49659 231-587-9764
Jeffery DiRosa, supt. Fax 587-9500
www.mancelonaschools.org/
Mancelona HS 300/9-12
PO Box 739 49659 231-587-8551
Larry Rager, prin. Fax 587-5401
Mancelona MS 300/5-8
PO Box 739 49659 231-587-9869
Dr. Tina Frollo, prin. Fax 587-0615

Manchester, Washtenaw, Pop. 2,074
Manchester Community SD 1,100/K-12
410 City Rd 48158 734-428-9711
Cherie Vannatter, supt. Fax 428-9188
www.mcs.k12.mi.us
Manchester HS 400/9-12
20500 Dutch Dr 48158 734-428-7333
Dr. Kevin Mowrer, prin. Fax 428-0178
Manchester MS 400/5-8
710 E Main St 48158 734-428-7442
Jennifer Mayes, prin. Fax 428-9264

Manistee, Manistee, Pop. 6,070
Manistee Area SD 1,300/PK-12
550 Maple St 49660 231-723-3521
Ronald Stoneman, supt. Fax 723-1507
maps.manistee.org
Manistee MSHS 500/7-12
525 12th St 49660 231-723-2547
Julia Raddatz, prin. Fax 398-9277

Manistee Catholic Central S 200/PK-12
1200 US Highway 31 S 49660 231-723-2529
Jason Allen, prin. Fax 723-0669

Manistique, Schoolcraft, Pop. 2,986
Manistique Area SD 800/PK-12
100 N Cedar St 49854 906-341-4300
Maryann Boddy, supt. Fax 341-2374
www.manistiqueschools.org
Manistique Middle & HS 500/6-12
100 N Cedar St 49854 906-341-4300
John Shiner, prin. Fax 341-8473
Reque Alternative S Alt
100 N Cedar St 49854 906-341-4300
John Shiner, prin. Fax 341-8473

Manton, Wexford, Pop. 1,266
Manton Consolidated SD 900/K-12
105 5th St 49663 231-824-6411
Leonard Morrow, supt. Fax 824-4101
www.mantonschools.org
Manton HS 300/9-12
105 5th St 49663 231-824-6411
Char Siddall, prin. Fax 824-6114
Manton MS 300/5-8
105 5th St 49663 231-824-6401
Ryan Hiller, prin. Fax 824-4121

Maple City, Leelanau, Pop. 204
Glen Lake Community SD 800/PK-12
3375 W Burdickville Rd 49664 231-334-3061
Sander Scott, supt. Fax 334-6255
www.glenlakeschools.org
Glen Lake JSHS 400/7-12
3375 W Burdickville Rd 49664 231-334-3061
Brian Hartigan, prin. Fax 334-6295

Marcellus, Cass, Pop. 1,184
Marcellus Community SD 700/K-12
PO Box 48 49067 269-646-7655
Nanette Pauley, supt. Fax 646-2700
www.marcelluscs.org/
Marcellus JSHS 300/7-12
PO Box 48 49067 269-646-5081
Lynn Wagner, prin. Fax 646-5021
Other Schools – See Decatur

Howardsville Christian S 200/PK-12
53441 Bent Rd 49067 269-646-9367
Dave Nelson, admin. Fax 646-7006

Marine City, Saint Clair, Pop. 4,184
East China SD
Supt. — See East China
Marine City HS 600/9-12
1085 Ward St 48039 810-676-1900
Suzanne Cybulla, prin. Fax 676-1925
Marine City MS 400/6-8
6373 King Rd 48039 810-676-1201
Catherine Woolman, prin. Fax 676-1225
Riverview East HS 100/Alt
6373 King Rd 48039 810-676-1280
Nina Reznich, prin. Fax 676-1285

Cardinal Mooney HS 200/9-12
660 S Water St 48039 810-765-8825
Jason Petrella, prin. Fax 765-7164

Marion, Osceola, Pop. 863
Marion SD 500/K-12
PO Box O 49665 231-743-2486
Mort Meier, supt. Fax 743-2890
www.marion.k12.mi.us
Marion JSHS 300/6-12
PO Box O 49665 231-743-2836
John Russell, prin. Fax 743-9622

Marlette, Sanilac, Pop. 1,847
Marlette Community SD 900/PK-12
6230 Euclid St 48453 989-635-7429
Sarah Barratt, supt. Fax 635-7103
www.marletteschools.org
Marlette JSHS 500/7-12
3051 Moore St 48453 989-635-4946
Kyle Wood, prin. Fax 635-5300

Marquette, Marquette, Pop. 20,996
Marquette Area SD 3,200/PK-12
1201 W Fair Ave 49855 906-225-4200
William Saunders, supt. Fax 225-5340
www.mapsnet.org
Bothwell MS 700/6-8
1200 Tierney St 49855 906-225-4262
Dan Gannon, prin. Fax 225-4229
Marquette Alternative HS at Vandenboom 100/Alt
1175 Erie Ave 49855 906-225-4321
Andrew Crunkleton, admin. Fax 225-4312
Marquette HS 1,000/9-12
1203 W Fair Ave 49855 906-225-5353
Jonathon Young, prin. Fax 225-5370

Father Marquette MS 100/5-8
414 W College Ave 49855 906-226-7912
Michael Hedges, prin. Fax 225-9962
Marquette General Hospital Post-Sec.
420 W Magnetic St 49855 906-225-3434
Northern Michigan University Post-Sec.
1401 Presque Isle Ave 49855 906-227-1000

Marshall, Calhoun, Pop. 6,978
Calhoun ISD 200/
17111 G Dr N 49068 269-781-5141
Terance Lunger, supt. Fax 781-7071
www.calhounisd.org
Other Schools – See Battle Creek

Marshall SD 2,400/PK-12
100 E Green St 49068 269-781-1250
Dr. Randy Davis, supt. Fax 789-1813
www.marshall.k12.mi.us
Marshall HS 900/9-12
701 N Marshall Ave 49068 269-781-1252
Scott Hutchins, prin. Fax 781-5304
Marshall MS 500/6-8
100 E Green St 49068 269-781-1251
David Turner, prin. Fax 781-6621
Other Schools – See Albion

Martin, Allegan, Pop. 398
Martin SD 500/PK-12
PO Box 241 49070 269-672-7194
Dr. David Harnish, supt. Fax 672-7116
www.martinpublicschools.org
Martin JSHS 300/7-12
PO Box 241 49070 269-672-5555
Dr. David Harnish, prin. Fax 672-9263

Marysville, Saint Clair, Pop. 9,889
Marysville SD 2,700/K-12
495 E Huron Blvd 48040 810-364-7731
Dr. Shawn Wightman, supt. Fax 364-3150
www.marysvilleschools.us/
Marysville HS 800/9-12
555 E Huron Blvd 48040 810-364-7161
Bill Farnsworth, prin. Fax 364-8878
Marysville MS 600/6-8
400 Collard Dr 48040 810-364-6336
Jay Schultz, prin. Fax 364-4456

St. Clair County RESA 100/
PO Box 1500 48040 810-364-8990
Dan DeGrow, supt. Fax 364-7474
www.sccresa.org/
Career Technical Center Vo/Tech
PO Box 1500 48040 810-455-1010

Mason, Ingham, Pop. 8,111
Ingham ISD 100/
2630 W Howell Rd 48854 517-676-1051
Dr. Scott Koenigsknecht, supt. Fax 676-4930
www.inghamisd.org
Capital Area Career Center Vo/Tech
611 Hagadorn Rd 48854 517-244-1330
Jeanne Farina, prin. Fax 676-3602

Mason SD 3,100/K-12
400 S Cedar St 48854 517-676-2484
Ronald Drzewicki, supt. Fax 676-6058
www.masonk12.net
Mason HS 1,000/9-12
1001 S Barnes St 48854 517-676-9055
Lance Delbridge, prin. Fax 244-6412
Mason MS 700/6-8
235 Temple St 48854 517-676-6514
Ted Berryhill, prin. Fax 676-0287

Mattawan, Van Buren, Pop. 1,954
Mattawan Consolidated SD 3,800/K-12
56720 Murray St 49071 269-668-3361
Dr. Robin Buchler, supt. Fax 668-2372
www.mattawanschools.org
Mattawan HS 1,200/9-12
56720 Murray St 49071 269-668-3361
Tim Eastman, prin. Fax 668-8245
Mattawan MS 900/6-8
56720 Murray St 49071 269-668-3361
Chip Schuman, prin. Fax 668-3188

Mayville, Tuscola, Pop. 933
Mayville Community SD 700/PK-12
6250 Fulton St 48744 989-843-6115
Barry Markwart, supt. Fax 843-6988
www.mayville.k12.mi.us
Mayville HS 200/9-12
6250 Fulton St 48744 989-843-6115
Barry Markwart, prin. Fax 843-7208
Mayville MS 100/6-8
6210 Fulton St 48744 989-843-6115
Barry Markwart, prin. Fax 843-7209

Melvindale, Wayne, Pop. 10,396
Melvindale-Northern Allen Park SD 2,900/K-12
18530 Prospect St 48122 313-389-3300
Dr. Kimberly Soranno-Bond, supt. Fax 389-3312
www.melnap.k12.mi.us
Melvindale HS 900/9-12
18656 Prospect St 48122 313-389-3320
Jason Hanna, prin. Fax 389-2072
Strong MS 700/6-8
3303 Oakwood Blvd 48122 313-389-3330
Donald Fish, prin. Fax 389-2077

Memphis, Saint Clair, Pop. 1,172
Memphis Community SD 900/PK-12
PO Box 201 48041 810-392-2151
Nancy Thomson, supt. Fax 392-3614
www.memphisk12.org/
Memphis JSHS 500/6-12
PO Box 201 48041 810-392-2186
Brad Gudme, prin. Fax 392-2083

Mendon, Saint Joseph, Pop. 857
Mendon Community SD 600/K-12
148 Kirby Rd 49072 269-496-9940
Roger Rathburn, supt. Fax 496-8234
www.mendonschools.org
Mendon MSHS 400/6-12
148 Kirby Rd 49072 269-496-8491
Marc Kramer, prin. Fax 496-8234

Menominee, Menominee, Pop. 8,500
Menominee Area SD 1,500/PK-12
1230 13th St 49858 906-863-9951
Terri Mileski, supt. Fax 863-1171
www.menominee.k12.mi.us
Menominee HS 500/9-12
2101 18th St 49858 906-863-7814
John Mans, prin. Fax 863-8883
Menominee JHS 200/7-8
2101 18th St 49858 906-863-9929
Alison Granquist, admin. Fax 863-8883

Merrill, Saginaw, Pop. 771
Merrill Community SD 700/PK-12
431 W Alice St 48637 989-643-7261
Sarah Kettelhohn, supt. Fax 643-5570
saginawmerrill.mi.schoolwebpages.com
Merrill Alternative Education Alt
431 W Alice St 48637 989-643-7231
Todd Barraco, prin. Fax 643-7942
Merrill HS 200/9-12
431 W Alice St 48637 989-643-7231
Todd Barraco, prin. Fax 643-7942
Merrill MS 100/6-8
431 W Alice St 48637 989-643-7231
Todd Barraco, prin. Fax 643-7942

Mesick, Wexford, Pop. 390
Mesick Consolidated SD 600/K-12
PO Box 275 49668 231-885-1200
Scott Akom, supt. Fax 885-1234
www.mesick.org
Mesick JSHS 300/6-12
PO Box 275 49668 231-885-1201
Scott Morey, prin. Fax 885-2554

Michigan Center, Jackson, Pop. 4,596
Michigan Center SD 1,400/K-12
400 S State St 49254 517-764-5778
Scott Koziol, supt. Fax 764-9607
www.mccardinals.org/
Michigan Center JSHS 700/7-12
400 S State St 49254 517-764-1440
Lisa Falasco, prin. Fax 764-3346

Middleton, Gratiot
Fulton SD 1,000/PK-12
8060 Ely Hwy 48856 989-236-7300
Daymond Grifka, supt. Fax 236-7660
fultonpirates.net
Fulton Alternative Education 300/Alt
8060 Ely Hwy 48856 989-236-5130
Mike Myers, prin. Fax 236-7301
Fulton HS 200/9-12
8060 Ely Hwy 48856 989-236-7232
Paul Hungerford, prin. Fax 236-7628
Fulton MS 100/7-8
8060 Ely Hwy 48856 989-236-7232
Paul Hungerford, prin. Fax 236-7628

Middleville, Barry, Pop. 3,261
Thornapple-Kellogg SD 3,000/PK-12
10051 Green Lake Rd 49333 269-795-5521
Tom Enslen, supt. Fax 795-5401
www.tkschools.org/
Thornapple-Kellogg HS 900/9-12
3885 Bender Rd 49333 269-795-3394
Tony Petersen, prin. Fax 795-5492
Thornapple-Kellogg MS 700/6-8
10375 Green Lake Rd 49333 269-795-3349
Brian Balding, prin. Fax 795-5455

Midland, Midland, Pop. 41,135
Bullock Creek SD 1,900/K-12
1420 S Badour Rd 48640 989-631-9022
Shawn Hale, supt. Fax 631-2882
www.bcreek.k12.mi.us
Bullock Creek HS 600/9-12
1420 S Badour Rd 48640 989-631-2340
Todd Gorsuch, prin. Fax 835-5467
Bullock Creek MS 400/6-8
644 S Badour Rd 48640 989-631-9260
Curt Moses, prin. Fax 832-4018

Midland SD 7,600/K-12
600 E Carpenter St 48640 989-923-5001
Michael Sharrow, supt. Fax 923-5003
www.midlandps.org
Dow HS 1,200/9-12
3901 N Saginaw Rd 48640 989-923-5382
Dr. Steve Poole, prin. Fax 923-5301
Jefferson MS 900/6-8
800 W Chapel Ln 48640 989-923-5873
Ted Davis, prin. Fax 923-5800
Midland HS 1,400/9-12
1301 Eastlawn Dr 48642 989-923-5181
Jeff Jaster, prin. Fax 923-5100
Northeast MS 1,000/6-8
1305 E Sugnet Rd 48642 989-923-5772
Dirk DeBoer, prin. Fax 923-5780

Calvary Baptist Academy 500/PK-12
6100 Perrine Rd 48640 989-832-3341
David Warren, prin. Fax 832-7443
Davenport University Post-Sec.
3555 E Patrick Rd 48642 989-835-5588
Midland Christian S 100/PK-12
4417 W Wackerly St 48640 989-835-9881
Carianne Robbins, head sch Fax 835-5201
Northwood University Post-Sec.
4000 Whiting Dr 48640 989-837-4200

Milan, Monroe, Pop. 5,683
Milan Area SD 2,200/K-12
100 Big Red Dr 48160 734-439-5050
Bryan Girbach, supt. Fax 439-5083
www.milanareaschools.org/
Milan HS 800/9-12
200 Big Red Dr 48160 734-439-5000
Aaron Shinn, prin. Fax 439-5084
Milan MS 500/6-8
920 North St 48160 734-439-5200
Shanna Spickard, prin. Fax 439-5288

Milford, Oakland, Pop. 6,058
Huron Valley SD
Supt. — See Highland
Muir MS 800/6-8
425 George St 48381 248-684-8060
Martin Lindberg, prin. Fax 684-8068

West Highland Christian Academy 100/K-12
1116 S Hickory Ridge Rd 48380 248-887-6698
Charley Allen, head sch Fax 629-4267

Millington, Tuscola, Pop. 1,059
Millington Community SD 800/K-12
8537 Gleason St 48746 989-871-5200
Bruce Martin, supt. Fax 871-5260
www.mcsdistrict.com
Millington Accelerated Learning Center 50/Alt
8537 Gleason St 48746 989-871-5211
Roger Bearss, admin.
Millington JSHS 400/6-12
8780 Dean Dr 48746 989-871-5221
Stephen Bouvy, prin. Fax 871-5244

Mio, Oscoda, Pop. 1,791
Mio-AuSable SD 600/K-12
1110 W 8th St 48647 989-826-2401
James Gendernalik, supt. Fax 826-2415
www.miok12.net
Mio-AuSable HS 200/9-12
1110 W 8th St 48647 989-826-2481
James Gendernalik, prin. Fax 826-2416
Mio-AuSable MS 200/6-8
1110 W 8th St 48647 989-826-2481
James Gendernalik, prin. Fax 826-2416

Monroe, Monroe, Pop. 20,187
Jefferson SD 1,600/K-12
2400 N Dixie Hwy 48162 734-289-5550
Craig Haugen, supt. Fax 289-5574
www.jeffersonschools.org
Jefferson HS 700/9-12
5707 Williams Rd 48162 734-289-5555
David Vensel, prin. Fax 289-5595
Jefferson MS 300/7-8
5102 N Stoney Creek Rd 48162 734-289-5565
Sara Griffin, prin. Fax 289-5596

Monroe County ISD 800/
1101 S Raisinville Rd 48161 734-242-5799
Stephen McNew, supt. Fax 242-0567
www.monroeisd.us/
Monroe County Middle College 200/Alt
1101 S Raisinville Rd 48161 734-242-5799
Robert Krueger, prin. Fax 242-0567

Monroe SD 5,900/PK-12
PO Box 733 48161 734-265-3000
Dr. Barry Martin, supt. Fax 265-3001
www.monroe.k12.mi.us
Monroe HS 1,800/9-12
901 Herr Rd 48161 734-265-3400
Sandra Kreps, prin. Fax 265-3401
Monroe MS 900/7-8
503 Washington St 48161 734-265-4000
Cindy Flynn, prin. Fax 265-4001
Orchard Center HS 100/Alt
1750 Oak St 48161 734-265-3700
Chantele Henry, prin. Fax 265-3701

Meadow Montessori S 200/PK-12
1670 S Raisinville Rd 48161 734-241-9496
Catharine Calder, head sch Fax 241-0829
Michigan College of Beauty Post-Sec.
1020 S Monroe St 48161 734-241-8877
Monroe County Community College Post-Sec.
1555 S Raisinville Rd 48161 734-242-7300
St. Mary HS 400/9-12
108 W Elm Ave 48162 734-241-7622
Jason Linster, prin. Fax 241-9042
St. Mary MS 200/5-8
151 N Monroe St 48162 734-241-3377
Sheena Zawistowicz, prin. Fax 241-0497

Montague, Muskegon, Pop. 2,329
Montague Area SD 1,500/PK-12
4882 Stanton Blvd 49437 231-893-1515
Jeffrey Johnson, supt. Fax 894-6586
www.mapsk12.org
Chisholm MS 400/6-8
4700 Stanton Blvd 49437 231-894-5617
James Perreault, prin. Fax 894-5728
Montague HS 400/9-12
4900 Stanton Blvd 49437 231-894-2661
Kevin Kruger, prin. Fax 893-0609

Montrose, Genesee, Pop. 1,644
Montrose Community SD 1,400/PK-12
PO Box 3129 48457 810-591-8800
Dr. Edward Graham Ph.D., supt. Fax 591-7268
www.montroseschools.org
Hill-McCloy HS 400/9-12
PO Box 3129 48457 810-591-8822
Linden Bo Moore, prin. Fax 591-7281
Kuehn-Haven MS 400/5-8
PO Box 3129 48457 810-591-8832
Rhonda Barber, prin. Fax 591-7282
Montrose Choice S 100/Alt
PO Box 3129 48457 810-591-8833
Linden Bo Moore, prin. Fax 591-7289

Morenci, Lenawee, Pop. 2,192
Morenci Area SD 500/PK-12
788 Coomer St 49256 517-458-7501
Michael McAran, supt. Fax 458-7821
www.morenci.k12.mi.us
Morenci MSHS 200/5-12
788 Coomer St 49256 517-458-7502
Kimberly Irish, prin. Fax 458-7146

Morley, Mecosta, Pop. 490
Morley Stanwood Community SD 1,200/K-12
4700 Northland Dr 49336 231-856-4392
Roger Cole, supt. Fax 856-4180
www.morleystanwood.org
Morley-Stanwood HS 400/9-12
4700 Northland Dr 49336 231-856-4444
James Nelson, prin. Fax 856-7012
Morley-Stanwood MS 300/6-8
4700 Northland Dr 49336 231-856-4550
James Nelson, prin. Fax 856-0136

Morrice, Shiawassee, Pop. 914
Morrice Area SD 500/PK-12
111 E Mason 48857 517-625-3142
Scott Williams, supt. Fax 625-3866
www.morrice.k12.mi.us
Morrice JSHS 300/7-12
691 Purdy Ln 48857 517-625-3143
Scott Williams, prin. Fax 625-8935

Mount Clemens, Macomb, Pop. 15,743
L'Anse Creuse SD
Supt. — See Clinton Township
Center for Lifelong Learning Adult
33 N River Rd 48043 586-493-5680

Mount Clemens Community SD 1,200/PK-12
167 Cass Ave 48043 586-469-6100
Dr. William Pearson, supt. Fax 461-3799
www.mtcps.org
Mount Clemens HS 300/9-12
155 Cass Ave 48043 586-461-3400
Joseph Gibson, prin. Fax 469-7058
Mount Clemens MS 200/6-8
161 Cass Ave 48043 586-461-3300
Joe Gibson, prin. Fax 469-7066

Mount Morris, Genesee, Pop. 2,972
Beecher Community SD
Supt. — See Flint
Beecher HS 400/9-12
6255 Neff Rd 48458 810-591-9277
Diana Castle, prin. Fax 591-6911

Mount Morris Consolidated SD 1,800/K-12
12356 Walter St 48458 810-591-8760
Brooke Ballee-Stone, supt. Fax 591-7469
www.mtmorrisschools.org
Johnson HS 600/9-12
8041 Neff Rd 48458 810-591-2370
Andrew Lintz, prin. Fax 591-3410
Mt. Morris Education & Community Center Alt
1000 E Mount Morris St 48458 810-591-4680
Susan Carlson, prin.
Mount Morris MS 400/6-8
12356 Walter St 48458 810-591-7100
Allen Peter, prin. Fax 591-7105

Mount Pleasant, Isabella, Pop. 25,361
Beal City SD 700/PK-12
3180 W Beal City Rd 48858 989-644-3901
William Chilman, supt. Fax 644-5847
www.bealcityschools.net
Beal City JSHS 400/7-12
3180 W Beal City Rd 48858 989-644-3944
Jeffrey Jackson, prin. Fax 644-5847
Beal City South Alternative HS 50/Alt
3032 S Winn Rd 48858 989-773-9543
Jerry Ward, prin. Fax 773-9543

Mount Pleasant SD 3,300/K-12
720 N Kinney Ave 48858 989-775-2300
Michael Pung, supt. Fax 775-2309
www.mtpleasant.edzone.net
GI-TECH Vo/Tech
1155 S Elizabeth St 48858 989-775-2210
Mary Kay Voeks, dir. Fax 775-2215
Mount Pleasant HS 1,100/9-12
1155 S Elizabeth St 48858 989-775-2200
Fax 775-2209
Oasis/W-A-Y Alternative Education S 100/Alt
3480 S Isabella Rd 48858 989-775-2290
Stacie Zeien, dir. Fax 772-3165
West IS 500/7-8
440 S Bradley St 48858 989-775-2220
Dana Calkins, prin. Fax 775-2229
Mount Pleasant Comm & Adult Education Adult
3480 S Isabella Rd 48858 989-775-2370
Mary Murphy, dir. Fax 773-2374

Shepherd SD
Supt. — See Shepherd
Odyssey MSHS 100/Alt
3441 S Wise Rd 48858 989-773-9473
Michael Evans, prin. Fax 779-0429

Central Michigan University Post-Sec.
100 Warriner Hall 48859 989-774-4000
M.J. Murphy Beauty College Post-Sec.
201 W Broadway St 48858 989-772-2339
Sacred Heart Academy 200/7-12
316 E Michigan St 48858 989-772-1457
Mary Kay Yonker, prin. Fax 772-1707
Saginaw Chippewa Tribal College Post-Sec.
2274 Enterprise Dr 48858 989-775-4123

Munising, Alger, Pop. 2,289
Munising SD 700/K-12
810 State Highway M28 W 49862 906-387-2251
Pete Kelto, supt. Fax 387-5416
www.mps-up.com
Munising MSHS 400/6-12
810 State Highway M28 W 49862 906-387-2103
Peter Kelto, prin. Fax 387-5686

Muskegon, Muskegon, Pop. 37,002
Muskegon Area ISD 100/
630 Harvey St 49442 231-777-2637
Dr. John Severson, supt. Fax 767-7299
www.muskegonisd.org
Muskegon Area Career Tech Center Vo/Tech
200 Harvey St 49442 231-767-3600
Kyle Fiebig, prin. Fax 767-2692

Muskegon Heights SD 900/PK-12
2603 Leahy St 49444 231-830-3221
Steve Schiller, admin. Fax 830-3560
www.mhpsnet.org
Other Schools – See Muskegon Heights

Muskegon SD 4,300/PK-12
349 W Webster Ave 49440 231-720-2000
Jon Felske, supt. Fax 720-2050
www.muskegonpublicschools.org
MCEC 300/Alt
571 E Apple Ave 49442 231-720-2530
Brad Perkins, prin. Fax 720-2593
Muskegon HS 1,100/9-12
80 W Southern Ave 49441 231-720-2800
Bradley Perkins, prin. Fax 720-2811
Muskegon MS 600/7-8
1150 Amity Ave 49442 231-720-3000
Paul Kurdziel, prin. Fax 720-3025

Oakridge SD 1,800/PK-12
275 S Wolf Lake Rd 49442 231-788-7100
Tom Livezey, supt. Fax 788-7114
www.oakridgeschools.org
Oakridge HS 500/9-12
5493 Hall Rd 49442 231-788-7300
Jason McVoy, prin. Fax 788-7314
Oakridge MS 300/7-8
251 S Wolf Lake Rd 49442 231-788-7400
Jason McVoy, prin. Fax 788-7414

Orchard View SD 2,300/PK-12
35 S Sheridan Dr 49442 231-760-1300
Jim Nielsen, supt. Fax 760-1323
www.orchardview.org
Orchard View HS 700/9-12
16 N Quarterline Rd 49442 231-760-1400
Dan Bolhuis, prin. Fax 760-1407
Orchard View MS 600/6-8
35 S Sheridan Dr 49442 231-760-1500
Hal Holman, prin. Fax 760-1506

Reeths-Puffer SD 3,700/PK-12
991 W Giles Rd 49445 231-744-4736
Steve Edwards, supt. Fax 744-9497
www.reeths-puffer.org
Reeths-Puffer HS 1,200/9-12
1545 Roberts Rd 49445 231-744-1647
Daniel Beckeman, prin. Fax 744-4796
Other Schools – See North Muskegon

Baker College of Muskegon Post-Sec.
1903 Marquette Ave 49442 231-777-5200
Muskegon Catholic Central HS 300/7-12
1145 W Laketon Ave 49441 231-755-2201
Allison Grinnell, prin. Fax 755-8615
Muskegon Community College Post-Sec.
221 S Quarterline Rd 49442 231-773-9131
Ross Medical Education Center Post-Sec.
950 W Norton Ave 49441 231-730-9531
Western Michigan Christian HS 300/7-12
455 E Ellis Rd 49441 231-799-9644
Doug Doty, prin. Fax 798-9018

Muskegon Heights, Muskegon, Pop. 10,491
Muskegon Heights SD
Supt. — See Muskegon
Muskegon Heights Academy 300/7-12
2441 Sanford St 49444 231-830-3700
Jennifer Bouwman, prin. Fax 830-3534

Napoleon, Jackson, Pop. 1,230
Napoleon Community SD 1,400/K-12
PO Box 308 49261 517-536-8667
James Graham, supt. Fax 536-8006
www.napoleonschools.org
Napoleon HS 400/9-12
PO Box 308 49261 517-536-8667
Patrick Dillon, prin. Fax 536-8007
Napoleon MS 300/6-8
PO Box 308 49261 517-536-8667
Chris Adams, prin. Fax 536-8005
Other Schools – See Jackson

Negaunee, Marquette, Pop. 4,500
Negaunee SD 1,500/PK-12
101 S Pioneer Ave 49866 906-475-4157
Dan Skewis, supt. Fax 475-5107
www.negaunee.k12.mi.us
Negaunee HS 400/9-12
500 W Arch St 49866 906-475-7861
Mark Marana, prin. Fax 475-7989
Negaunee MS 400/5-8
102 W Case St 49866 906-475-7866
Michael McCollum, prin. Fax 475-6408

Newaygo, Newaygo, Pop. 1,944
Newaygo SD 1,600/K-12
PO Box 820 49337 231-652-6984
Dr. Peggy Mathis, supt. Fax 652-6505
www.newaygo.net
Newaygo HS 500/9-12
PO Box 820 49337 231-652-1646
Jackie Knight, prin. Fax 652-3500
Newaygo MS 500/5-8
PO Box 820 49337 231-652-1285
Brad Reyburn, prin. Fax 652-9704

New Baltimore, Macomb, Pop. 11,927
Anchor Bay SD
Supt. — See Casco
Anchor Bay MS North 1,000/6-8
52805 Ashley Dr 48047 586-725-7373
Robin Stanton, prin. Fax 725-6760
Anchor Bay MS South 500/6-8
48650 Sugarbush Rd 48047 586-949-4510
Phil Latona, prin. Fax 949-4739
Compass Pointe 100/Alt
51510 Industrial Dr 48047 586-716-7862
Robert Tidd, coord. Fax 716-7864

Newberry, Luce, Pop. 1,471
Tahquamenon Area SD 700/PK-12
700 Newberry Ave 49868 906-293-3226
Fax 293-3709
www.taschools.org
Newberry HS 300/7-12
700 Newberry Ave 49868 906-293-3243
Clifford Fossitt, prin. Fax 293-3709

New Boston, Wayne
Huron SD 2,500/K-12
32044 Huron River Dr 48164 734-782-2441
Richard Naughton, supt. Fax 783-0338
www.huronschools.org
Huron HS 900/9-12
32044 Huron River Dr 48164 734-782-1436
Donovan Rowe, prin. Fax 783-1534
Renton JHS 600/6-8
31578 Huron River Dr 48164 734-782-2483
Kurt Mrocko, prin. Fax 783-0327

New Buffalo, Berrien, Pop. 1,853
New Buffalo Area SD 600/K-12
PO Box 280 49117 269-469-6010
Dr. Jeffrey Leslie, supt. Fax 469-3315
www.nbas.org/
New Buffalo HS 200/9-12
PO Box 280 49117 269-469-6001
Craig Stafford, prin. Fax 469-2028
New Buffalo MS 100/6-8
PO Box 280 49117 269-469-6003
Wayne Butler, prin. Fax 469-6017

New Haven, Macomb, Pop. 4,447
New Haven Community SD 1,200/PK-12
PO Box 482000 48048 586-749-5123
Todd Robinson, supt. Fax 749-6307
newhaven.misd.net/
New Haven HS 300/9-12
PO Box 482000 48048 586-749-5104
Will Timmerman, prin. Fax 749-8460

New Lothrop, Shiawassee, Pop. 573
New Lothrop Area SD 900/PK-12
PO Box 339 48460 810-638-5091
Dr. Anthony Berthiaume Ph.D., supt. Fax 638-7277
www.newlothrop.k12.mi.us
New Lothrop JSHS 400/7-12
PO Box 339 48460 810-638-5054
Stephanie O'Dea, prin. Fax 638-5057

Newport, Monroe
Airport Community SD
Supt. — See Carleton
Niedermeier Center for Education 100/Alt
8400 Newport South Rd 48166 734-654-8694
Craig Freestone, dir. Fax 586-3342

Niles, Berrien, Pop. 11,170
Brandywine Community SD 1,200/PK-12
1830 S 3rd St 49120 269-684-7150
Dr. John Jarpe, supt. Fax 684-8998
www.brandywinebobcats.org
Brandywine Innovation Academy 100/Alt
1830 S 3rd St 49120 269-683-8805
Michelle Wruble, prin. Fax 684-8998
Brandywine MSHS 400/7-12
1700 Bell Rd 49120 269-683-4800
Patrick Weckel, prin. Fax 683-1186

Niles Community SD 3,600/PK-12
111 Spruce St 49120 269-683-0732
Dr. Dan Applegate Ed.D., supt. Fax 684-6337
nilesschools.schoolwires.net
Cedar Lane Alternative S 100/Alt
2301 Niles Buchanan Rd 49120 269-684-9554
John Fonash, prin. Fax 684-9555
Niles HS 600/9-12
1441 Eagle St 49120 269-683-2894
Molly Brawley, prin. Fax 684-9516
Niles New Tech Entrepreneurial Academy 300/9-12
1441 Eagle St 49120 269-683-6031
Jerry Holtgren, dir. Fax 683-1533
Ring Lardner MS 500/7-8
801 N 17th St 49120 269-683-6610
Douglas Langmeyer, prin. Fax 684-9524
Niles Adult Education Adult
111 Spruce St 49120 269-684-4480
John Fonash, dir. Fax 684-9548

North Adams, Hillsdale, Pop. 473
North Adams-Jerome SD — 300/K-12
4555 Knowles Rd 49262 — 517-287-4263
Carl Christenson, supt. — Fax 287-4722
www.najps.org
North Adams-Jerome JSHS — 200/6-12
4555 Knowles Rd 49262 — 517-287-4214
Tom George, prin. — Fax 287-4722

North Branch, Lapeer, Pop. 1,023
North Branch Area SD — 2,400/K-12
PO Box 3620 48461 — 810-688-3570
James D. Fish, supt. — Fax 688-7010
www.nbbroncos.net
North Branch HS — 800/9-12
PO Box 3620 48461 — 810-688-3001
Mark Hiltunen, prin. — Fax 688-8057
North Branch MS — 400/7-8
PO Box 3620 48461 — 810-688-4431
Cindy Howe, prin. — Fax 688-4344
Quest HS, PO Box 3620 48461 — 100/Alt
Mark Hiltunen, prin. — 810-688-3570

North Muskegon, Muskegon, Pop. 3,727
North Muskegon SD — 1,000/K-12
1600 Mills Ave 49445 — 231-719-4100
Dr. Curt Babcock, supt. — Fax 744-0739
www.nmps.net
North Muskegon HS — 300/9-12
1507 Mills Ave 49445 — 231-719-4110
Heidi Christiansen, prin. — Fax 719-4156
North Muskegon MS — 200/6-8
1507 Mills Ave 49445 — 231-719-4110
Heidi Christiansen, prin. — Fax 719-4156

Reeths-Puffer SD
Supt. — See Muskegon
Reeths-Puffer MS — 600/7-8
1911 W Giles Rd 49445 — 231-744-4721
Jennifer Anderson, prin. — Fax 744-6049

Northport, Leelanau, Pop. 512
Northport SD — 200/K-12
PO Box 188 49670 — 231-386-5153
Neil Wetherbee, supt. — Fax 386-9838
www.northportps.org
Northport S — 200/K-12
PO Box 188 49670 — 231-386-5153
Neil Wetherbee, supt. — Fax 386-9838

Northville, Oakland, Pop. 5,889
Northville SD — 7,300/K-12
501 W Main St 48167 — 248-349-3400
Mary Gallagher, supt. — Fax 347-6928
www.northvilleschools.org
Hillside MS — 1,000/6-8
775 N Center St 48167 — 248-344-8493
William Jones, prin. — Fax 334-8480
Meads Mill MS — 800/6-8
16700 Franklin Rd, — 248-344-8435
Brad O'Neill, prin. — Fax 334-1830
Northville HS — 2,300/9-12
45700 6 Mile Rd, — 248-344-8420
Anthony Koski, prin. — Fax 344-8497

Norton Shores, Muskegon, Pop. 23,577
Mona Shores SD — 3,800/K-12
121 Randall Rd 49441 — 231-780-4751
Greg Helmer, supt. — Fax 780-2099
www.monashores.net
Mona Shores HS — 1,300/9-12
1121 Seminole Rd 49441 — 231-780-4711
Jennifer Bustard, prin. — Fax 780-3634
Mona Shores MS — 900/6-8
1700 Woodside Rd 49441 — 231-759-8506
Doug Ammeraal, prin. — Fax 755-0514

Norway, Dickinson, Pop. 2,807
Norway-Vulcan Area SD — 700/PK-12
300 Section St 49870 — 906-563-9552
Louis Steigerwald, supt. — Fax 563-5169
www.norway.k12.mi.us
Norway HS — 200/9-12
300 Section St 49870 — 906-563-9542
Joseph Tinti, prin. — Fax 563-8708
Vulcan MS, 300 Section St 49870 — 200/5-8
Brad Grayvold, prin. — 906-563-9563

Novi, Oakland, Pop. 54,165
Novi Community SD — 6,300/PK-12
25345 Taft Rd 48374 — 248-449-1200
Dr. Steve Matthews, supt. — Fax 449-1219
www.novi.k12.mi.us
Novi HS — 2,000/9-12
24062 Taft Rd 48375 — 248-449-1500
Nicole Carter, prin. — Fax 449-1519
Novi MS — 1,100/7-8
49000 W 11 Mile Rd 48374 — 248-449-1600
Stephanie Schriner, prin. — Fax 449-1619
Novi Adult Education — Adult
25575 Taft Rd 48374 — 248-449-1717
Linda Cianferra, prin. — Fax 449-1719

Detroit Catholic Central HS — 1,000/9-12
27225 Wixom Rd 48374 — 248-596-3810
Fr. Dennis Noelke, prin. — Fax 596-3811
Franklin Road Christian S — 300/K-12
40800 W 13 Mile Rd 48377 — 248-668-7100
Daniel Robinson, admin. — Fax 668-7101
The Art Institute of Michigan — Post-Sec.
28125 Cabot Dr Ste 120 48377 — 248-675-3800

Oakland, Oakland
Lake Orion Community SD
Supt. — See Lake Orion
Oakview MS — 600/6-8
917 Lake George Rd 48363 — 248-693-0321
Sarah Manzo, prin. — Fax 693-5419

Oak Park, Oakland, Pop. 28,448
Berkley SD — 4,300/K-12
14700 Lincoln St 48237 — 248-837-8000
Dennis McDavid, supt. — Fax 544-5835
www.berkleyschools.org
Other Schools – See Berkley

Ferndale SD
Supt. — See Ferndale
Center for Advanced Studies & the Arts — 11-12
23561 Rosewood St 48237 — 248-586-8860
Bill James, dir. — Fax 414-6508

Oak Park SD — 4,500/PK-12
13900 Granzon St 48237 — 248-336-7700
Dr. Daveda Colbert, supt. — Fax 336-7738
www.oakparkschools.org
NOVA Discipline Academy — 100/Alt
22180 Parklawn St 48237 — 248-336-7650
Derek Faulk, admin.
Oak Park Alternative Education Center — 500/Alt
12901 Albany St 48237 — 248-291-6722
Harry Bautista, prin. — Fax 291-6724
Oak Park Freshman Institute — 500/9-9
22180 Parklawn St 48237 — 248-336-7780
Pam Vermiglio, prin. — Fax 336-7781
Oak Park Preparatory Academy — 500/7-8
22180 Parklawn St 48237 — 248-336-7780
Nickolus South, prin. — Fax 336-7738
Oak Park SHS — 1,200/10-12
13701 Oak Park Blvd 48237 — 248-336-7740
Charity Jones, prin. — Fax 336-7758

Beth Jacob School for Girls — 300/K-12
14390 W 10 Mile Rd 48237 — 248-544-9070
Lawton Career Institute — Post-Sec.
20820 Greenfield Rd 48237 — 248-569-7559
Yeshiva Gedolah of Greater Detroit — Post-Sec.
24600 Greenfield Rd 48237 — 248-968-3360
Yeshivah Gedolah HS — 100/9-12
24600 Greenfield Rd 48237 — 248-968-3360
Rabbi Mordechai Gold, prin. — Fax 968-8613

Okemos, Ingham, Pop. 20,807
Okemos SD — 4,000/K-12
4406 Okemos Rd 48864 — 517-706-5010
Catherine Ash Ph.D., supt. — Fax 349-6235
www.okemosschools.net/
Chippewa MS — 600/7-8
4000 Okemos Rd 48864 — 517-706-4800
Jody Noble, prin. — Fax 347-9824
Okemos HS — 1,300/9-12
2800 Jolly Rd 48864 — 517-706-4900
Christine Sermak, prin. — Fax 351-2850

Olivet, Eaton, Pop. 1,574
Olivet Community SD — 1,500/K-12
255 First St 49076 — 269-749-9129
Rocky Aldrich, supt. — Fax 749-9701
www.olivetschools.org
Olivet HS — 500/9-12
255 First St 49076 — 269-749-3671
Troy Waffke, prin. — Fax 749-4560
Olivet MS — 600/4-8
255 First St 49076 — 269-749-9953
Stephen Williams, prin. — Fax 749-9701

Olivet College — Post-Sec.
320 S Main St 49076 — 269-749-7000

Onaway, Presque Isle, Pop. 861
Onaway Area SD — 700/K-12
4549 M 33 49765 — 989-733-4950
Rod Fullerton, supt. — Fax 733-8612
www.onawayschools.com/
Onaway HS — 200/9-12
4549 M 33 49765 — 989-733-4800
Marty Mix, prin. — Fax 733-4899
Onaway MS — 200/6-8
4549 M 33 49765 — 989-733-4850
Marty Mix, prin. — Fax 733-4899

Onekama, Manistee, Pop. 404
Onekama Consolidated SD — 400/K-12
5016 Main St 49675 — 231-889-4251
Kevin Hughes, supt. — Fax 889-3720
ocs.manistee.org
Onekama MSHS — 300/6-12
5016 Main St 49675 — 231-889-5521
Gina Hagen, prin. — Fax 889-9567

Onsted, Lenawee, Pop. 906
Onsted Community SD — 1,500/K-12
10109 Slee Rd 49265 — 517-467-2173
Brad Hamilton, supt. — Fax 467-5600
www.onsted.k12.mi.us
Onsted HS — 500/9-12
10109 Slee Rd 49265 — 517-467-2171
Steve Head, prin. — Fax 467-5602
Onsted MS — 400/6-8
10109 Slee Rd 49265 — 517-467-2168
Michael Hoffman, prin. — Fax 467-5603

Ontonagon, Ontonagon, Pop. 1,473
Ontonagon Area SD — 400/K-12
701 Parker Ave 49953 — 906-813-0614
James Bobula, supt. — Fax 813-0615
www.oasd.k12.mi.us
Ontonagon Area S — 400/K-12
701 Parker Ave 49953 — 906-813-0614
James Bobula, admin. — Fax 813-0615

Orchard Lake, Oakland

St. Marys Preparatory HS — 500/9-12
3535 Indian Trl 48324 — 248-683-0530
Cormac Lynn, hdmstr. — Fax 683-1740
SS. Cyril and Methodius Seminary — Post-Sec.
3535 Indian Trl 48324 — 248-683-0310

Ortonville, Oakland, Pop. 1,423
Brandon SD — 2,900/PK-12
1025 S Ortonville Rd 48462 — 248-627-1800
Dr. Matthew Outlaw, supt. — Fax 627-4533
www.brandonschooldistrict.org
Brandon HS — 1,100/9-12
1025 S Ortonville Rd 48462 — 248-627-1820
Daniel Stevens, prin. — Fax 627-5628
Brandon MS — 500/7-8
609 S Ortonville Rd 48462 — 248-627-1830
Tina Chambers, prin. — Fax 627-7201

Oscoda, Iosco, Pop. 877
Oscoda Area SD — 900/K-12
PO Box 694 48750 — 989-739-2033
Scott Moore, supt. — Fax 739-2325
www.oscodaschools.org
Oscoda Area HS — 600/7-12
PO Box 694 48750 — 989-739-9121
Terence Allison, prin. — Fax 739-1688

Otisville, Genesee, Pop. 856
LakeVille Community SD — 1,400/PK-12
11107 Washburn Rd 48463 — 810-591-3980
Vickie Luoma, supt. — Fax 591-6538
www.lakevilleschools.org/
Lakeville HS — 500/9-12
11107 Washburn Rd 48463 — 810-591-4050
Mary Haslinger, prin. — Fax 591-3961
Lakeville MS — 300/6-8
11107 Washburn Rd 48463 — 810-591-3945
Kelli-Ann Fazer, prin. — Fax 591-6632

Otsego, Allegan, Pop. 3,879
Otsego SD — 2,300/PK-12
400 Sherwood St 49078 — 269-692-6066
Jeffrey Haase, supt. — Fax 692-6074
www.otsegops.org
Otsego HS — 700/9-12
550 Washington St 49078 — 269-692-6166
Herve Dardis, prin. — Fax 692-6188
Otsego MS — 600/6-8
540 Washington St 49078 — 269-692-6199
Melissa Koenig, prin. — Fax 692-6228
West Campus HS — 50/Alt
570 Washington St 49078 — 269-692-6166
Herve Dardis, prin. — Fax 692-6188

Otsego Christian Academy — 50/PK-11
247 E Allegan St 49078 — 269-694-6738
Lydia Hutchens, admin.

Ottawa Lake, Monroe
Whiteford Agricultural SD — 700/K-12
6655 Consear Rd 49267 — 734-856-1443
Valerie Orr, supt. — Fax 854-6463
www.whiteford.k12.mi.us
Whiteford HS — 200/9-12
6655 Consear Rd 49267 — 734-856-1443
Kelli Tuller, prin. — Fax 856-2564
Whiteford MS — 200/6-8
6655 Consear Rd 49267 — 734-856-1443
Kelli Tuller, prin. — Fax 856-2564

Ovid, Clinton, Pop. 1,574
Ovid-Elsie Area SD
Supt. — See Elsie
Ovid-Elsie Alternative HS — Alt
732 Mabbitt Rd 48866 — 989-834-5440
Fax 834-6108

Owendale, Huron, Pop. 236
Owendale-Gagetown Area SD — 200/K-12
7166 E Main St 48754 — 989-678-4261
Terri Falkenberg, supt. — Fax 678-4284
www.owengage.org/
Owendale-Gagetown JSHS — 100/6-12
7166 E Main St 48754 — 989-678-4141
Terri Falkenberg, prin. — Fax 678-0920

Owosso, Shiawassee, Pop. 14,957
Owosso SD — 3,300/PK-12
PO Box 340 48867 — 989-723-8131
Dr. Andrea Tuttle Ed.D., supt. — Fax 723-7777
www.owosso.k12.mi.us
Lincoln HS — 100/Alt
645 Alger Ave 48867 — 989-725-2839
Steve Irelan, prin. — Fax 729-6706
Owosso HS — 900/9-12
765 E North St 48867 — 989-723-8231
Jeff Phillips, prin. — Fax 729-5600
Owosso MS — 700/6-8
219 N Water St 48867 — 989-723-3460
Rich Collins, prin. — Fax 729-5760

Baker College of Owosso — Post-Sec.
1020 S Washington St 48867 — 989-729-3370

Oxford, Oakland, Pop. 3,399
Oxford Community SD — 5,300/PK-12
10 N Washington St 48371 — 248-969-5000
Tim Throne, supt. — Fax 969-5016
www.oxfordschools.org
Oxford Bridges HS — 100/Alt
1420 E Lakeville Rd 48371 — 248-969-1800
Aletha Vanloozen, prin. — Fax 969-1840
Oxford Crossroads Alternative S — Alt
810 James Hunt Dr 48371 — 248-969-1887
Guy Cococetta, admin.
Oxford HS — 1,500/9-12
745 N Oxford Rd 48371 — 248-969-5100
Todd Dunckley, prin. — Fax 969-5145
Oxford MS — 1,100/6-8
1420 E Lakeville Rd 48371 — 248-969-1800
Dacia Beazley, prin. — Fax 969-1840
Oxford Schools Early College — 100/9-12
10 N Washington St 48371 — 248-969-5194
Andrew Hulbert, prin. — Fax 886-9116

Painesdale, Houghton
Adams Township SD 400/K-12
PO Box 37 49955 906-482-0599
Tim Keteri, supt. Fax 487-5999
www.adams.k12.mi.us
Jeffers HS 200/7-12
PO Box 37 49955 906-482-0580
Steve Lishinski, admin. Fax 487-5999

Paradise, Chippewa
Whitefish Township Community SD 50/K-12
7221 N M 123 49768 906-492-3353
Carole Beck, supt. Fax 492-3254
whitefish.eup.k12.mi.us
Whitefish Township S 50/K-12
7221 N M 123 49768 906-492-3353
Thomas McKee, prin. Fax 492-3254

Parchment, Kalamazoo, Pop. 1,738
Parchment SD 1,700/PK-12
520 N Orient St 49004 269-488-1050
Matthew Miller, supt. Fax 488-1060
www.parchmentschools.org
Parchment HS 500/9-12
1916 E G Ave 49004 269-488-1100
George Stamas, prin. Fax 488-1110
Parchment MS 400/6-8
307 N Riverview Dr 49004 269-488-1200
Jason Misner, prin. Fax 488-1210
Other Schools – See Kalamazoo

Parma, Jackson, Pop. 755
Western SD 2,900/PK-12
1400 S Dearing Rd 49269 517-841-8100
Michael Smajda, supt. Fax 841-8801
www.wsdpanthers.org
Western HS 900/9-12
1400 S Dearing Rd 49269 517-841-8200
Susan VanRiper, prin. Fax 841-8282
Western MS 600/6-8
1400 S Dearing Rd 49269 517-841-8300
Ryan Tripp, prin. Fax 841-8803
Other Schools – See Jackson

Paw Paw, Van Buren, Pop. 3,443
Paw Paw SD 2,200/K-12
119 Johnson Rd 49079 269-657-8800
Sonia Lark, supt. Fax 657-7292
www.ppps.org
Cedar Street Comm & Family Center Alt
555 Cedar St 49079 269-657-8831
Beth Davis, prin. Fax 657-8836
Michigan Avenue Academy 100/Alt
600 E Michigan Ave 49079 269-657-8831
Jeannine Koeneke, prin. Fax 657-7411
Paw Paw HS 700/9-12
30609 E Red Arrow Hwy 49079 269-657-8840
Michael Dahlinger, prin. Fax 655-0009
Paw Paw MS 500/6-8
313 W Michigan Ave 49079 269-657-8870
Jerry McDaniel, prin. Fax 657-5011

Peck, Sanilac, Pop. 624
Peck Community SD 400/K-12
222 E Lapeer St 48466 810-378-5171
Frank Johnson, supt. Fax 378-5116
www.peck.k12.mi.us
Peck JSHS 200/7-12
222 E Lapeer St 48466 810-378-5501
Frank Johnson, prin. Fax 378-5116

Pellston, Emmet, Pop. 782
Pellston SD 600/PK-12
172 N Park St 49769 231-539-8682
Monique Dean, supt. Fax 539-8838
www.pellstonschools.org/
Pellston MSHS 300/6-12
172 N Park St 49769 231-539-8801
Enos Bacon, prin. Fax 539-8110

Pentwater, Oceana, Pop. 845
Pentwater SD 300/K-12
600 Park St 49449 231-869-4100
Scott Karaptian, supt. Fax 869-4535
www.pentwater.k12.mi.us
Pentwater S 300/K-12
600 Park St 49449 231-869-4100
Scott Karaptian, prin. Fax 869-4535

Perry, Shiawassee, Pop. 2,154
Perry SD 1,300/PK-12
2665 W Britton Rd 48872 517-625-3108
Mike Foster, supt. Fax 625-6256
www.goperry.org
Perry HS 500/9-12
2555 W Britton Rd 48872 517-625-3104
Don Beck, prin. Fax 625-0012
Perry MS 400/5-8
2775 W Britton Rd 48872 517-625-6196
Matt Schmidtfranz, prin. Fax 625-0120

Petersburg, Monroe, Pop. 1,129
Summerfield SD 700/K-12
17555 Ida West Rd 49270 734-279-1035
John Hewitt, supt. Fax 279-1448
www.summerfield.k12.mi.us
Summerfield JSHS 400/7-12
17555 Ida West Rd 49270 734-279-1012
John Hewitt, prin. Fax 279-1018

Petoskey, Emmet, Pop. 5,571
Petoskey SD 2,900/K-12
1130 Howard St 49770 231-348-2100
Dr. John Scholten Ed.D., supt. Fax 348-2342
www.petoskeyschools.org
Petoskey HS 1,000/9-12
1500 Hill St 49770 231-348-2160
Mandy Stewart, prin. Fax 348-2214
Petoskey MS 700/6-8
801 Northmen Dr 49770 231-348-2150
Jon Wilcox, prin. Fax 348-2234

North Central Michigan College Post-Sec.
1515 Howard St 49770 231-348-6600

Pickford, Chippewa
Pickford SD 400/K-12
333 S Pleasant St 49774 906-647-6285
Angela Nettleton, supt. Fax 647-3706
pickford.eup.k12.mi.us/
Pickford S 300/K-12
333 S Pleasant St 49774 906-647-4028
Angela Nettleton, prin. Fax 647-3706
Other Schools – See Kincheloe

Pigeon, Huron, Pop. 1,203
Elkton-Pigeon-Bay Port Laker SD 900/PK-12
6136 Pigeon Rd 48755 989-453-4600
W. Brian Keim, supt. Fax 453-4609
www.lakerschools.org
Laker HS 300/9-12
6136 Pigeon Rd 48755 989-453-4600
Jonathon Good, prin. Fax 453-4615
Laker MS 200/6-8
6136 Pigeon Rd 48755 989-453-4600
Jonathon Good, prin. Fax 453-4609

Pinckney, Livingston, Pop. 2,402
Pinckney Community SD 3,500/K-12
2130 E M 36 48169 810-225-3900
Richard Todd M.A., supt. Fax 225-3905
www.pinckneyschools.org
Pathfinder S 600/7-8
2100 E M 36 48169 810-225-5200
Eric Ray, prin. Fax 225-5205
Pinckney Community HS 1,400/9-12
10255 Dexter Pinckney Rd 48169 810-225-5500
April Woods, prin. Fax 225-5505

Pinconning, Bay, Pop. 1,286
Pinconning Area SD 1,300/PK-12
605 W 5th St 48650 989-308-0500
Michael Vieau, supt. Fax 879-4705
www.pasd.org/
Pinconning Area HS 500/9-12
605 W 5th St 48650 989-308-0503
Tim Hoffman, prin. Fax 879-7258
Pinconning Area MS 300/6-8
605 W 5th St 48650 989-308-0503
Tim Hoffman, prin. Fax 879-7258

Pittsford, Hillsdale
Pittsford Area SD 700/K-12
9304 Hamilton Rd 49271 517-523-3481
Deanna Edens, supt. Fax 523-3467
pittsfordk12.org
Pittsford JSHS 300/7-12
9304 Hamilton Rd 49271 517-523-3481
T.G. Cook, prin. Fax 523-2059

Plainwell, Allegan, Pop. 3,755
Plainwell Community SD 2,700/PK-12
600 School Dr 49080 269-685-5823
Matthew Montange, supt. Fax 685-1108
www.plainwellschools.org
Plainwell HS 800/9-12
684 Starr Rd 49080 269-685-9554
Dr. Jeremy Wright, prin. Fax 685-9064
Plainwell MS 600/6-8
720 Brigham St 49080 269-685-5813
Tasia Stamos, prin. Fax 685-2099
Renaissance HS 100/Alt
422 Acorn St 49080 269-685-1573
Tammy Glupker, prin. Fax 685-1564

Plymouth, Wayne, Pop. 8,997
Plymouth-Canton Community SD 16,000/PK-12
454 S Harvey St 48170 734-416-2700
Monica Merritt, supt. Fax 416-4932
www.pccsk12.com
East MS 800/6-8
1042 S Mill St 48170 734-416-4950
Scott Burek, prin. Fax 416-4949
Pioneer MS 800/6-8
46081 Ann Arbor Rd W 48170 734-416-2770
Kevin Rhein, prin. Fax 416-7569
Starkweather Academy 100/Alt
39750 Joy Rd 48170 734-416-4901
Kevin Lane, coord. Fax 416-6031
West MS 800/6-8
44401 W Ann Arbor Trl 48170 734-416-7550
Clinton Smiley, prin. Fax 416-7648
Other Schools – See Canton

Metropolitan SDA Jr Academy 50/K-10
15585 N Haggerty Rd 48170 734-420-4044
Craig Morgan, prin. Fax 420-3710
Moody Theological Seminary Post-Sec.
41550 E Ann Arbor Trl 48170 734-207-9581

Pontiac, Oakland, Pop. 57,635
Oakland ISD
Supt. — See Waterford
Oakland Technical Campus NE Vo/Tech
1371 N Perry St 48340 248-451-2700
Paul Galbenski, dean Fax 451-2720

Pontiac SD 4,400/PK-12
47200 Woodward Ave 48342 248-451-6800
Kelley Williams, supt. Fax 451-6890
www.pontiac.k12.mi.us
International Technology Academy Vo/Tech
60 Parkhurst 48342 248-451-7510
Suzanne Kavanaugh, prin. Fax 451-7536
Pontiac HS 1,000/9-12
1051 Arlene Ave 48340 248-451-7300
Burdena Johnson, prin. Fax 451-7321
Pontiac MS 1,000/7-8
1275 N Perry St 48340 248-451-8010
Shana Jackson, prin. Fax 451-8034

Dorsey School of Business Post-Sec.
440 N Telegraph Rd 48341 248-333-1814

Notre Dame Marist Acad - Middle Division 200/6-8
1300 Giddings Rd 48340 248-373-5371
Jill Mistretta, prin. Fax 373-4707
Notre Dame Preparatory HS 700/9-12
1300 Giddings Rd 48340 248-373-5300
Rev. Joseph Hindelang, prin. Fax 373-8024
Oakland County Health Division Post-Sec.
1200 N Telegraph Rd 48341 248-858-1832

Portage, Kalamazoo, Pop. 44,979
Kalamazoo RESA 300/
1819 E Milham Ave 49002 269-250-9200
David Campbell, supt. Fax 250-9205
www.kresa.org
Other Schools – See Kalamazoo

Portage SD 8,700/K-12
8107 Mustang Dr 49002 269-323-5000
Mark T. Bielang, supt. Fax 323-5001
www.portageps.org
Northern HS 1,400/9-12
1000 Idaho Ave 49024 269-323-5400
Jim French, prin. Fax 323-5490
North MS 600/6-8
5808 Oregon Ave 49024 269-323-5700
Travis Thomsen, prin. Fax 323-5790
Portage Central HS 1,400/9-12
8135 S Westnedge Ave 49002 269-323-5200
Eric Alburtus, prin. Fax 323-5290
Portage Central MS 700/6-8
8305 S Westnedge Ave 49002 269-323-5600
Chuck Haskin, prin. Fax 323-5690
Portage Community HS 200/Alt
1010 W Milham Ave 49024 269-323-6769
Clint Wagner, prin. Fax 323-6790
West MS 700/6-8
7145 Moorsbridge Rd 49024 269-323-5800
Denny Roehm, prin. Fax 323-5890

Chic University of Cosmetology Post-Sec.
6091 Constitution Blvd 49024 269-329-3333
Wright Beauty Academy Post-Sec.
6666 Lovers Ln 49002 269-321-8708

Port Huron, Saint Clair, Pop. 29,088
Port Huron Area SD 9,200/PK-12
PO Box 5013 48061 810-984-3101
James Cain, supt. Fax 984-6606
www.phasd.us
Central MS 900/6-8
200 32nd St 48060 810-984-6533
Bethany Davis, prin. Fax 272-4780
Harrison Center 200/Alt
55 15th St 48060 810-455-0029
Gloria Henry, prin. Fax 272-4783
Holland Woods MS 600/6-8
1617 Holland Ave 48060 810-984-6548
Ronnie Belle, prin. Fax 989-2713
Port Huron HS 1,300/9-12
2215 Court St 48060 810-984-2611
Michael Palmer, prin. Fax 984-6559
Port Huron Northern HS 1,200/9-12
1799 Krafft Rd 48060 810-984-2671
Charles Mossett, prin. Fax 984-2747
Other Schools – See Fort Gratiot

Baker College of Port Huron Post-Sec.
3403 Lapeer Rd 48060 810-985-7000
Port Huron Hospital Post-Sec.
1221 Pine Grove Ave 48060 810-987-5000
Ross Medical Education Center Post-Sec.
2887 Krafft Rd Ste 700 48060 810-982-0454
St. Clair County Community College Post-Sec.
PO Box 5015 48061 810-984-3881

Portland, Ionia, Pop. 3,841
Portland SD 2,000/K-12
1100 Ionia Rd 48875 517-647-4161
William Heath, supt. Fax 647-2975
portland.schooldesk.net
Portland HS 600/9-12
1100 Ionia Rd 48875 517-647-2981
Christine Rockey, prin. Fax 647-1791
Portland MS 400/6-8
745 Storz St 48875 517-647-2985
Kevin Robydek, prin. Fax 647-2820

St. Patrick S 400/PK-12
122 N West St 48875 517-647-7551
Randy Hodge, prin. Fax 647-4545

Posen, Presque Isle, Pop. 228
Posen Consolidated SD 9 200/K-12
PO Box 187 49776 989-766-2573
Michelle Wesner, supt. Fax 766-2519
www.posen.k12.mi.us
Posen Consolidated JSHS 100/7-12
PO Box 187 49776 989-766-2471
Michelle Wesner, prin. Fax 766-2519

Potterville, Eaton, Pop. 2,560
Potterville SD 900/K-12
420 N High St 48876 517-645-2662
Timothy Donahue, supt. Fax 645-0392
www.pps.k12.mi.us
Potterville HS 200/9-12
422 N High St 48876 517-645-7609
Andrew Wise, prin. Fax 645-0177
Potterville MS 300/5-8
424 N High St 48876 517-645-4777
Nathan Leale, prin. Fax 645-0091
Adult Education Adult
420 N High St 48876 517-645-4792
Julie DeRose, dir. Fax 645-0390

Powers, Menominee, Pop. 422
North Central Area SD 400/PK-12
PO Box 601 49874 906-497-5226
Bruce Tapio, supt. Fax 497-5066
www.ncajets.org

North Central JSHS 200/7-12
PO Box 601 49874 906-497-5226
Bruce Tapio, prin. Fax 497-5066

Quincy, Branch, Pop. 1,637
Quincy Community SD 1,200/PK-12
1 Educational Pkwy 49082 517-639-7141
Craig Artist, supt. Fax 639-4273
www.quincyschools.org
Quincy HS 400/9-12
18 Colfax St 49082 517-639-9245
David Spalding, prin. Fax 639-3701
Quincy MS 400/5-8
32 Fulton St 49082 517-639-4201
Joshua Haggerty, prin. Fax 639-3701

Rapid River, Delta
Rapid River SD 400/K-12
10070 US Highway 2 49878 906-474-6411
Dr. Jay Kulbertis, supt. Fax 474-9903
www.rapidriver.k12.mi.us
Rapid River JSHS 200/6-12
10070 US Highway 2 49878 906-474-6411
William Warning, prin. Fax 474-9883

Ravenna, Muskegon, Pop. 1,203
Ravenna SD 1,100/PK-12
12322 Stafford St 49451 231-853-2231
John Van Loon, supt. Fax 853-2193
www.ravennaschools.org
Ravenna HS 300/9-12
2766 S Ravenna Rd 49451 231-853-2218
Steven Anderson, prin. Fax 853-6981
Ravenna MS 300/5-8
2700 S Ravenna Rd 49451 231-853-2268
Mindy Lynch, prin. Fax 853-2629

Reading, Hillsdale, Pop. 1,073
Reading Community SD 800/K-12
PO Box 330 49274 517-283-2166
Chuck North, supt. Fax 283-3519
www.readingrangers.org
Owens JSHS 400/7-12
301 Chestnut St 49274 517-283-2142
Kurt Stump, prin. Fax 283-3758

Redford, Wayne, Pop. 51,100
Redford Union SD 2,700/K-12
17715 Brady 48240 313-242-6000
Dr. Sarena Shivers, supt. Fax 242-6025
www.redfordu.k12.mi.us
Hilbert MS 600/6-8
26440 Puritan 48239 313-242-4000
Andrew Christopherson, prin. Fax 242-4005
Redford Union HS 900/9-12
17711 Kinloch 48240 313-242-4200
Judy Nachman, prin. Fax 242-4205
Veritas Alternative Ed 100/Alt
17715 Brady 48240 313-242-3520
Katy Jain, coord. Fax 242-6060

South Redford SD 3,100/PK-12
26141 Schoolcraft 48239 313-535-4000
Brian Galdes, supt. Fax 535-1059
www.southredford.org
Pierce MS 700/6-8
25605 Orangelawn 48239 313-937-8880
Christine Hofer, prin. Fax 937-9486
SOAR Academic Institute Alt
26255 Schoolcraft 48239 313-535-4000
Matt Daly, coord. Fax 535-1059
Thurston HS 1,000/9-12
26255 Schoolcraft 48239 313-242-0600
William Simms, prin. Fax 592-0740

Concordia Lutheran S - South Campus 50/5-8
9600 Leverne 48239 313-937-2233
Judy Schwaegerle, prin. Fax 937-2233

Reed City, Osceola, Pop. 2,371
Reed City Area SD 1,500/K-12
225 W Church Ave 49677 231-832-2201
Timothy Webster, supt. Fax 832-2202
www.reedcity.k12.mi.us
Reed City HS 500/9-12
225 W Church Ave 49677 231-832-2224
Monty Price, prin. Fax 832-2501
Reed City MS 400/6-8
233 W Church Ave 49677 231-832-6174
Dean McGuire, prin. Fax 832-6180

Reese, Tuscola, Pop. 1,450
Reese SD 800/PK-12
PO Box 389 48757 989-868-9864
Keith Wetters, supt. Fax 868-9570
www.reese.k12.mi.us/
Reese HS 300/9-12
PO Box 389 48757 989-868-4191
Brian Galsterer, prin. Fax 868-4091
Reese MS 200/6-8
PO Box 389 48757 989-868-4191
Dave Hurst, prin. Fax 868-4091

Remus, Mecosta
Chippewa Hills SD 1,900/PK-12
3226 Arthur Rd 49340 989-967-2000
Dr. Michael Bob Grover, supt. Fax 967-2009
www.chsd.us
Chippewa Hills HS 600/9-12
3226 Arthur Rd 49340 989-967-2100
Michelle Newman, prin. Fax 967-2109
Chippewa Hills IS 300/5-8
3102 Arthur Rd 49340 989-967-2200
Chi Ethridge, prin. Fax 967-2209
Mosaic S 100/Alt
350 E Wheatland Ave 49340 989-967-8150
Dawn Hawley, prin. Fax 967-8385

Republic, Marquette, Pop. 565
Republic-Michigamme SD 100/PK-12
227 Maple St 49879 906-376-2277
Kevin Luokkala, supt. Fax 376-8299
r-mschool.org
Republic-Michigamme S 100/PK-12
227 Maple St 49879 906-376-2277
Kevin Luokkala, supt. Fax 376-8299

Richland, Kalamazoo, Pop. 729
Gull Lake Community SD 2,900/PK-12
11775 E D Ave 49083 269-488-5000
Christopher Rundle, supt. Fax 488-5011
www.gulllakecs.org
Gateway Academy Alt
11775 E D Ave 49083 269-548-3425
Lynette Walker, prin. Fax 548-3401
Gull Lake HS 1,000/9-12
7753 N 34th St 49083 269-488-5020
Don Eastman, prin. Fax 488-5031
Gull Lake MS 700/6-8
9550 M 89 49083 269-488-5040
Fax 488-5041

Richmond, Macomb, Pop. 5,652
Richmond Community SD 1,500/PK-12
35276 Division Rd 48062 586-727-3565
Brian Walmsley, supt. Fax 727-2098
www.richmond.k12.mi.us
Richmond HS 600/9-12
35320 Division Rd 48062 586-727-3225
Deborah Michon, prin. Fax 727-9072
Richmond MS 500/5-8
35250 Division Rd 48062 586-727-7552
Keith Bartels, prin. Fax 727-2545

River Rouge, Wayne, Pop. 7,623
River Rouge SD 1,600/K-12
1460 Coolidge Hwy 48218 313-297-9600
Derrick R. Coleman, supt. Fax 297-6525
www.riverrougeschools.org
River Rouge HS 600/9-12
1460 Coolidge Hwy 48218 313-297-9600
Michael Mokdad, prin. Fax 297-7322
Sabbath 6-8 Preparatory Academy 300/6-8
340 Frazier St 48218 313-297-9654
Brandon Cox, prin. Fax 297-5695

Riverview, Wayne, Pop. 12,365
Riverview Community SD 2,800/PK-12
13425 Colvin St Ste 1, 734-285-9660
Russell Pickell, supt. Fax 285-9822
www.riverviewschools.com
Riverview HS 900/9-12
12431 Longsdorf St, 734-285-7361
J.J. Hatzl, prin. Fax 785-6598
Seitz MS 700/6-8
17800 Kennebec St, 734-285-2043
Nicole Munoz, prin. Fax 285-6649

Detroit Business Institute Post-Sec.
19100 Fort St, 734-479-0660
Richard HS 300/9-12
15325 Pennsylvania Rd, 734-284-1875
Joseph Whalen, prin. Fax 284-9304

Rochester, Oakland, Pop. 12,556
Rochester Community SD 14,700/K-12
501 W University Dr 48307 248-726-3000
Dr. Robert Shaner, supt. Fax 726-3105
www.rochester.k12.mi.us
Other Schools – See Rochester Hills

Oakland University Post-Sec.
2200 N Squirrel Rd 48309 248-370-2100

Rochester Hills, Oakland, Pop. 69,733
Avondale SD
Supt. — See Auburn Hills
Avondale Academy 200/Alt
1435 W Auburn Rd 48309 248-537-6600
Taylor Chapman, prin. Fax 537-6605
Avondale MS 700/6-8
1445 W Auburn Rd 48309 248-537-6300
Dannon Holley, prin. Fax 537-6305

Rochester Community SD
Supt. — See Rochester
ACE Alternative S 100/Alt
1440 John R Rd 48307 248-726-5900
Susan Demeniuk, prin. Fax 726-5905
Adams HS 1,600/9-12
3200 W Tienken Rd 48306 248-726-5200
Kevin Cumming, prin. Fax 726-5205
Hart MS 1,100/6-8
6500 Sheldon Rd 48306 248-726-4500
Allison Roberts, prin. Fax 726-4505
Reuther MS 700/6-8
1430 E Auburn Rd 48307 248-726-4700
Wendy Darga, prin. Fax 726-4705
Rochester HS 1,600/9-12
180 S Livernois Rd 48307 248-726-5400
Neil Deluca, prin. Fax 726-5405
Stony Creek HS 1,600/9-12
575 E Tienken Rd 48306 248-726-5700
Cathryn Skedel Ph.D., prin. Fax 726-5705
Van Hoosen MS 800/6-8
1339 N Adams Rd 48306 248-726-4900
Dan Mooney, prin. Fax 726-4905
West MS 900/6-8
500 Old Perch Rd 48309 248-726-5000
Mike Dillon, prin. Fax 726-5005
RACE Adult
1435 W Auburn Rd 48309 248-726-5950
Sean Lively, admin. Fax 726-5955

Holy Family Regional S - South Campus 600/4-8
2633 John R Rd 48307 248-299-3798
Jon Myers, prin. Fax 299-3843

Lutheran HS Northwest 300/9-12
1000 Bagley Dr 48309 248-852-6677
Paul Looker, prin. Fax 852-2667
Rochester College Post-Sec.
800 W Avon Rd 48307 248-218-2000
Rochester Hills Christian S 300/PK-12
3300 S Livernois Rd 48307 248-852-0585
Karen Patton, prin. Fax 852-4757

Rock, Delta
Mid Peninsula SD 200/K-12
5055 Saint Nicholas 31st Rd 49880 906-359-4387
Mary Brayak, supt. Fax 359-4167
mpswolverines.com
Mid Peninsula S 200/K-12
5055 Saint Nicholas 31st Rd 49880 906-359-4390
Mary Brayak, supt. Fax 359-4167

Rockford, Kent, Pop. 5,617
Rockford SD 7,800/PK-12
350 N Main St 49341 616-863-6320
Michael Shibler Ph.D., supt. Fax 866-1911
www.rockfordschools.org
East Rockford MS 800/6-8
8615 9 Mile Rd NE 49341 616-863-6140
Mike Ramm, prin. Fax 863-6565
North Rockford MS 900/6-8
397 E Division St 49341 616-863-6300
Lissa Weidenfeller, prin. Fax 866-5998
River Valley Academy 100/Alt
350 N Main St 49341 616-863-6324
Lisa Jacobs, prin. Fax 866-1911
Rockford Freshman Center 700/9-9
4500 Kroes St NE 49341 616-863-6348
Tom Hosford, prin. Fax 866-7134
Rockford HS 1,900/10-12
4100 Kroes St NE 49341 616-863-6030
Daniel Zang, prin. Fax 866-5997

Rockwood, Wayne, Pop. 3,246
Gibraltar SD
Supt. — See Woodhaven
Downriver HS 50/Alt
33211 Mccann Rd 48173 734-379-7080
Leslie Guizzetti, prin. Fax 379-7081

Rogers City, Presque Isle, Pop. 2,809
Rogers City Area SD 600/K-12
1033 W Huron Ave Ste B 49779 989-734-9100
David O'Bryant, supt. Fax 734-7428
www.rcashurons.org
Rogers City MSHS 400/6-12
1033 W Huron Ave 49779 989-734-9170
Nicholas Hein, prin. Fax 734-2969

Romeo, Macomb, Pop. 3,511
Romeo Community SD 5,200/PK-12
316 N Main St 48065 586-752-0200
Eric Whitney, supt. Fax 752-0228
www.romeo.k12.mi.us
Romeo HS 1,700/9-12
11091 32 Mile Rd 48065 586-752-0300
Michael Kaufman, prin. Fax 752-0402
Romeo MS 600/6-8
297 Prospect St 48065 586-752-0240
Brad Martz, prin. Fax 752-0256
Other Schools – See Washington

Romulus, Wayne, Pop. 23,107
Romulus Community SD 3,000/PK-12
36540 Grant St 48174 734-532-1602
Marjie McAnally, supt. Fax 532-1611
www.romulus.net
Romulus Early College 9-12
9650 Wayne Rd 48174 734-532-1003
Flinnoia Hall, prin. Fax 532-1001
Romulus HS 1,000/9-12
9650 Wayne Rd 48174 734-532-1003
Flinnioa Hall, prin. Fax 532-1001
Romulus MS 700/6-8
37300 Wick Rd 48174 734-532-1703
Jason Salhaney, prin. Fax 532-1701

Roscommon, Roscommon, Pop. 1,048
C.O.O.R. ISD
PO Box 827 48653 989-275-9555
Greg Bush, supt. Fax 275-5881
www.coorisd.net
C.O.O.R. CTE, PO Box 827 48653 Vo/Tech
Dan Beltz, prin. 989-275-9536

Roscommon Area SD 900/PK-12
PO Box 825 48653 989-275-6600
Catherine Erickson, supt. Fax 275-8227
www.rapsk12.net
Roscommon HS 400/8-12
PO Box 825 48653 989-275-6675
Martin Ewald, prin. Fax 275-6681

Kirtland Community College Post-Sec.
10775 N Saint Helen Rd 48653 989-275-5000

Roseville, Macomb, Pop. 46,120
Roseville Community SD 4,700/K-12
18975 Church St 48066 586-445-5505
John Kment, supt. Fax 771-1772
www.rcs.misd.net
Eastland MS 300/6-8
18700 Frank St 48066 586-445-5702
Major Mickens, prin. Fax 445-5721
Roseville HS 1,600/9-12
17855 Common Rd 48066 586-445-5542
Peter Hedemark, prin. Fax 445-5654
Roseville MS 600/6-8
16250 Martin Rd 48066 586-445-5605
Jason Bettin, prin. Fax 445-5620

Dorsey School of Business Post-Sec.
31542 Gratiot Ave 48066 586-296-3225

Royal Oak, Oakland, Pop. 56,180
Oakland ISD
Supt. — See Waterford
Oakland Technical Campus SE — Vo/Tech
5055 Delemere Ave 48073 — 248-288-4020
Amy Gole, dean — Fax 288-4071

Royal Oak SD — 4,900/PK-12
800 Devillen Ave 48073 — 248-435-8400
Shawn Lewis-Lakin, supt. — Fax 435-6170
www.royaloakschools.org
Churchill Community Education Center — 100/Alt
707 Girard Ave 48073 — 248-588-5050
Melissa Hutchinson, prin. — Fax 588-2881
Royal Oak HS — 1,300/9-12
1500 Lexington Blvd 48073 — 248-435-8500
Michael Giromini, prin. — Fax 288-8733
Royal Oak MS — 1,000/6-8
709 N Washington Ave 48067 — 248-541-7100
Todd Noonan, prin. — Fax 541-0408

David Pressley School of Cosmetology — Post-Sec.
1127 S Washington Ave 48067 — 248-548-5090
Oakland Community College — Post-Sec.
739 S Washington Ave 48067 — 248-246-2400
Shrine Catholic HS & Academy — 300/7-12
3500 W 13 Mile Rd 48073 — 248-549-2925
Thomas Oppat, prin. — Fax 549-2953
William Beaumont Hospital — Post-Sec.
3601 W 13 Mile Rd 48073 — 248-551-0681

Rudyard, Chippewa
Rudyard Area SD — 700/PK-12
11185 W 2nd St 49780 — 906-478-3771
Mark Pavloski, supt. — Fax 478-3912
www.rudyard.k12.mi.us
Rudyard JSHS — 300/7-12
11185 W 2nd St 49780 — 906-478-3771
Mike DeYoung, prin. — Fax 478-4101

Saginaw, Saginaw, Pop. 50,106
Carrollton SD — 2,000/PK-12
3211 Carla Dr 48604 — 989-754-1475
Tim Wilson, supt. — Fax 754-1470
www.carrolltonpublicschools.org
Carrollton HS — 500/9-12
1235 Mapleridge Rd 48604 — 989-753-3433
Shawn Thelen, prin. — Fax 754-1041
Carrollton MS — 400/6-8
3211 Carla Dr 48604 — 989-753-9704
Marc McKenzie, prin. — Fax 754-1470
Omni Alternative HS — 200/Alt
479 Shattuck Rd 48604 — 989-753-3477
Tiffany Peterson, prin. — Fax 776-0283

Saginaw ISD — 400/
6235 Gratiot Rd, — 989-399-7473
Kathy Stewart, supt. — Fax 793-1571
www.sisd.cc
Other Schools – See University Center

Saginaw SD — 6,000/PK-12
550 Millard St 48607 — 989-399-6500
Nathaniel McClain Ph.D., supt. — Fax 399-6635
www.spsd.net
Hill HS — 900/8-12
3115 Mackinaw St 48602 — 989-399-5800
Mit Foley, prin. — Fax 399-5815
Saginaw Arts & Sciences Academy — 600/6-12
1903 N Niagara St 48602 — 989-399-5500
Priscilla Arocha-Roby, prin. — Fax 399-5515
Saginaw Career Complex — Vo/Tech
2102 Weiss St 48602 — 989-399-6150
Josh Little, prin. — Fax 399-6165
Saginaw HS — 600/8-12
3100 Webber St 48601 — 989-399-6000
Janice Davis, prin. — Fax 399-6015
Thompson MS — 500/6-8
3021 Court St 48602 — 989-399-5600
Rachel Reid, prin. — Fax 399-5615

Saginaw Township Community SD — 4,900/K-12
PO Box 6278 48608 — 989-797-1800
Douglas Trombley, supt. — Fax 797-1801
stcs.org
Heritage HS — 1,500/9-12
3465 N Center Rd 48603 — 989-799-5790
Michael Newman, prin. — Fax 799-5159
Mackinaw HS — 200/Alt
2775 Shattuck Rd 48603 — 989-799-8470
Alan Kern, prin. — Fax 797-1860
White Pine MS — 1,100/6-8
505 N Center Rd, — 989-797-1814
Pri Victoria Wandmacher, prin. — Fax 797-1859

Swan Valley SD — 1,700/K-12
8380 OHern Rd 48609 — 989-921-3701
Mat McRae, supt. — Fax 921-3705
www.swanvalley.k12.mi.us
Swan Valley Adult & Alternative Educ — 50/Alt
8400 OHern Rd 48609 — 989-921-2472
Shelley Hanson, prin. — Fax 921-2405
Swan Valley HS — 600/9-12
8400 OHern Rd 48609 — 989-921-2401
Craig Blower, prin. — Fax 921-2405
Swan Valley MS — 400/6-8
453 Van Wormer Rd 48609 — 989-921-2601
Shelly DuCharme, prin. — Fax 921-2605

Community Baptist Christian S — 100/PK-12
8331 Gratiot Rd 48609 — 989-781-2340
Douglas Jackson, prin. — Fax 781-1344
Davenport University — Post-Sec.
5300 Bay Rd 48604 — 989-799-7800
Dorsey School of Business — Post-Sec.
4390 Bay Rd 48603 — 989-249-1926
Michigan Lutheran Seminary — 200/9-12
2777 Hardin St 48602 — 989-793-1010
Rev. Joel Petermann, pres. — Fax 793-4213
Nouvel Catholic Central HS — 300/9-12
2555 Wieneke Rd 48603 — 989-791-4330
Mark Frost, prin. — Fax 797-6603
Ross Medical Education Center — Post-Sec.
4300 Fashion Square # 202 48603 — 989-791-5192
St. Mary's Medical Center — Post-Sec.
800 S Washington Ave 48601 — 989-776-8176
Valley Lutheran HS — 300/9-12
3560 McCarty Rd 48603 — 989-790-1676
Dr. John Brandt, prin. — Fax 790-1680

Saint Charles, Saginaw, Pop. 2,035
Saint Charles Community SD — 1,000/PK-12
891 W Walnut St 48655 — 989-865-9961
Michael Decker, supt. — Fax 865-6185
www.stccs.org
Saint Charles HS — 300/9-12
881 W Walnut St 48655 — 989-865-9991
Robert Paris, prin. — Fax 865-8185
Thurston MS — 200/6-8
893 W Walnut St 48655 — 989-865-9927
Shawna Groulx, prin. — Fax 865-2429

Saint Clair, Saint Clair, Pop. 5,422
East China SD
Supt. — See East China
Saint Clair HS — 900/9-12
2200 Clinton Ave 48079 — 810-676-1700
Ronald Miller, prin. — Fax 676-1725
Saint Clair MS — 600/6-8
4335 Yankee Rd 48079 — 810-676-1800
Michael Alley, prin. — Fax 676-1825

Saint Clair Shores, Macomb, Pop. 58,728
Lake Shore SD — 3,600/K-12
28850 Harper Ave 48081 — 586-285-8480
Dr. Joseph DiPonio, supt. — Fax 285-8463
www.lakeshoreschools.org
Kennedy MS — 800/6-8
23101 Masonic Blvd 48082 — 586-285-8800
Patrick Donohue, prin. — Fax 285-8804
Lake Shore HS — 1,200/9-12
22980 E 13 Mile Rd 48082 — 586-285-8900
Dr. Joseph DiPonio, prin. — Fax 285-8904
North Lake Alternative HS — 100/Alt
23340 Elmira St 48082 — 586-285-8780
Chad Johnson, prin. — Fax 285-8783
St. Clair Shores Adult & Comm Education — Adult
23055 Masonic Blvd 48082 — 586-285-8880
Gerilyn Whitfield, prin. — Fax 285-8881

Lakeview SD — 3,900/PK-12
27575 Harper Ave 48081 — 586-445-4000
Karl Paulson, supt. — Fax 445-4029
www.lakeview.misd.net
Jefferson MS — 900/6-8
27900 Rockwood St 48081 — 586-445-4130
David Lavender, prin. — Fax 445-4041
Lakeview HS — 1,400/9-12
21100 E 11 Mile Rd 48081 — 586-445-4045
Brent Case, prin. — Fax 445-4072

South Lake SD — 1,900/K-12
23101 Stadium Dr 48080 — 586-435-1600
Ted Von Hiltmayer, supt. — Fax 445-4202
www.solake.org
South Lake HS — 600/9-12
21900 E 9 Mile Rd 48080 — 586-435-1400
Robert Beato, prin. — Fax 445-4243
South Lake MS — 400/6-8
21621 California St 48080 — 586-435-1300
Michael Bruce, prin. — Fax 778-3151

Saint Ignace, Mackinac, Pop. 2,280
Saint Ignace Area SD — 600/K-12
W429 Portage St 49781 — 906-643-8145
Donald Gustafson, supt. — Fax 643-7873
stignace.eup.k12.mi.us/
Lasalle HS — 200/9-12
W443 Portage St 49781 — 906-643-8800
Gregg Fettig, prin. — Fax 643-7696

Saint Johns, Clinton, Pop. 7,721
Saint Johns SD — 3,100/K-12
501 W Sickles St 48879 — 989-227-4050
Dedrick Martin, supt. — Fax 227-4099
www.sjredwings.org
Saint Johns HS — 1,100/9-12
501 W Sickles St 48879 — 989-227-4100
Mark Palmer, prin. — Fax 227-4199
Saint Johns MS — 700/6-8
900 W Townsend Rd 48879 — 989-227-4300
Adel DiOrio, prin. — Fax 227-4399
Wilson Center — 100/Alt
101 W Cass St 48879 — 989-227-5200
Dedrick Martin, prin. — Fax 227-5299

Saint Joseph, Berrien, Pop. 8,211
Saint Joseph SD — 2,900/K-12
3275 Lincoln Ave 49085 — 269-926-3100
Ann Cardon, supt. — Fax 429-5042
www.sjschools.org/
Saint Joseph HS — 1,000/9-12
2521 Stadium Dr 49085 — 269-926-3200
Gregory Blomgren, prin. — Fax 983-1470
Upton MS — 700/6-8
800 Maiden Ln 49085 — 269-926-3400
Chad Mandarino, prin. — Fax 408-0970

Lake Michigan Catholic HS — 200/9-12
915 Pleasant St 49085 — 269-983-2511
John Berlin, prin. — Fax 983-0883
Lake Michigan Catholic MS — 100/6-8
915 Pleasant St 49085 — 269-983-2511
John Berlin, prin. — Fax 983-0883
Michigan Lutheran HS — 100/9-12
615 E Marquette Woods Rd 49085 — 269-429-7861
Matthew Herbst, prin. — Fax 429-4428
Twin City Beauty College — Post-Sec.
2600 Lincoln Ave 49085 — 269-428-2900

Saint Louis, Gratiot, Pop. 7,441
Saint Louis SD — 1,100/PK-12
113 E Saginaw St 48880 — 989-681-2545
Kristi Teall, supt. — Fax 681-5894
www.stlouisschools.net
Nurnberger MS — 200/6-8
312 Union St 48880 — 989-681-5155
Shane Brooks, prin. — Fax 681-4658
Saint Louis HS — 400/9-12
113 E Saginaw St 48880 — 989-681-2500
Jennifer McKittrick, prin. — Fax 681-4535

Saline, Washtenaw, Pop. 8,661
Saline Area SD — 5,200/PK-12
7265 N Ann Arbor St 48176 — 734-401-4000
Scot Graden, supt. — Fax 401-4098
www.salineschools.com
Saline Alternative HS — 50/Alt
7265 Saline Ann Arbor Rd 48176 — 734-401-4000
Carol Melcher, prin. — Fax 401-4098
Saline HS — 1,800/9-12
1300 Campus Pkwy 48176 — 734-401-4200
David Raft, prin. — Fax 401-4398
Saline MS — 1,200/6-8
7190 N Maple Rd 48176 — 734-401-4600
Brad Bezeau, prin. — Fax 401-4745

Washtenaw Christian Academy — 300/PK-12
7200 Moon Rd 48176 — 734-429-7733
Eric VanDerhoof, head sch — Fax 944-8343

Sand Creek, Lenawee
Sand Creek Community SD — 900/PK-12
6518 Sand Creek Hwy 49279 — 517-436-3108
Steven Laundra, supt. — Fax 436-3143
www.sc-aggies.us
Sand Creek JSHS — 500/6-12
6518 Sand Creek Hwy 49279 — 517-436-3124
Matt Benge, dean — Fax 436-3193

Sand Lake, Montcalm, Pop. 495
Tri County Area SD — 2,400/PK-12
PO Box 79 49343 — 616-636-5454
Allen Cumings M.A., supt. — Fax 636-5677
www.tricountyschools.com
Other Schools – See Howard City

Sandusky, Sanilac, Pop. 2,651
Sandusky Community SD — 900/PK-12
191 E Pinetree Ln 48471 — 810-648-3400
Mike Carmean, supt. — Fax 648-5113
www.sandusky.k12.mi.us
Sandusky JSHS — 500/7-12
191 E Pinetree Ln 48471 — 810-648-3401
Steve Carlson, prin. — Fax 648-3148

Sanford, Midland, Pop. 854
Meridian SD — 1,100/PK-12
3361 N Meridian Rd 48657 — 989-687-3200
Craig Carmoney, supt. — Fax 687-3222
www.merps.org
Meridian Early College HS — 100/9-12
3303 N Meridian Rd 48657 — 989-687-3300
Patrick Malley, prin. — Fax 687-3309
Meridian JHS — 400/5-8
3475 N Meridian Rd 48657 — 989-687-3360
Kent Boxey, prin. — Fax 687-3364

Saranac, Ionia, Pop. 1,311
Saranac Community SD — 1,000/PK-12
225 Pleasant St 48881 — 616-642-1400
Richard Geiger, supt. — Fax 642-1405
www.saranac.k12.mi.us
Saranac JSHS — 500/7-12
150 Pleasant St 48881 — 616-642-1100
Josh Leader, prin. — Fax 642-1105

Saugatuck, Allegan, Pop. 909
Saugatuck SD
Supt. — See Douglas
Saugatuck MSHS — 300/6-12
401 Elizabeth St 49453 — 269-857-2133
Dr. Timothy Travis, prin. — Fax 857-6145

Sault Sainte Marie, Chippewa, Pop. 13,362
Sault Sainte Marie Area SD — 2,400/PK-12
876 Marquette Ave 49783 — 906-635-6609
Timothy D. Hall Ed.D., supt. — Fax 635-6642
sault.eup.k12.mi.us
Malcolm HS — 100/Alt
460 W Spruce St 49783 — 906-635-6638
Sandy Sawyer, prin. — Fax 635-3836
Sault Area Career Center — Vo/Tech
904 Marquette Ave 49783 — 906-635-6652
Jo Anne Lussier, dir. — Fax 635-6641
Sault Sainte Marie Area HS — 800/9-12
904 Marquette Ave 49783 — 906-635-6605
Carl McCready, prin. — Fax 635-6641
Sault Sainte Marie MS — 500/6-8
684 Marquette Ave 49783 — 906-635-6604
Jessica Rondeau, prin. — Fax 635-3841

Lake Superior State University — Post-Sec.
650 W Easterday Ave 49783 — 906-632-6841

Schoolcraft, Kalamazoo, Pop. 1,506
Schoolcraft Community SD — 1,100/PK-12
551 E Lyons St 49087 — 269-488-7390
Dr. Wayne Stitt, supt. — Fax 488-7391
www.schoolcraftschools.org
Schoolcraft HS — 400/9-12
551 E Lyons St 49087 — 269-488-7350
Ric Seager, prin. — Fax 488-7364
Schoolcraft MS — 300/5-8
551 E Lyons St 49087 — 269-488-7300
Dave Powers, prin. — Fax 488-7303

Scottville, Mason, Pop. 1,185
Mason County Central SD — 1,400/PK-12
300 W Broadway Ave 49454 — 231-757-3713
Jeff Mount, supt. — Fax 757-5716
mccschools.org

Mason County Central HS 400/9-12
210 W Broadway Ave 49454 231-757-4748
Brad Jacobs, prin. Fax 757-9084
Mason County Central MS 300/6-8
310 W Beryl St 49454 231-757-3724
Jeff Tuka, prin. Fax 757-4820
Mason-Lake Community Educ. Consortium Adult
300 W Broadway Ave 49454 231-757-3713
Elizabeth Stark, dir. Fax 757-5716

West Shore ESD
Supt. — See Ludington
West Shore ESD Career & Technical Educ Vo/Tech
3000 N Stiles Rd 49454 231-843-5976
Lynda Matson, prin. Fax 845-7227

West Shore Community College Post-Sec.
3000 N Stiles Rd 49454 231-845-6211

Sebewaing, Huron, Pop. 1,753
Unionville-Sebewaing SD 700/PK-12
2203 Wildner Rd 48759 989-883-2360
George Rierson, supt. Fax 883-9021
www.think-usa.org
Unionville-Sebewaing HS 300/9-12
2203 Wildner Rd 48759 989-883-2534
Josh Hahn, prin. Fax 883-9739
Unionville-Sebewaing MS 200/6-8
2203 Wildner Rd 48759 989-883-3140
Josh Hahn, prin.

Shelby, Oceana, Pop. 2,029
Shelby SD 1,500/PK-12
525 N State St 49455 231-861-5211
Dan Bauer, supt. Fax 861-5416
www.shelbypublicschools.net
Shelby HS 400/9-12
641 N State St 49455 231-861-4452
Frances Schamber, prin. Fax 861-6867
Shelby MS 300/6-8
525 N State St 49455 231-861-4521
Mark Olmstead, prin. Fax 861-0415

Shelby Township, Macomb, Pop. 69,500
Utica Community SD
Supt. — See Sterling Heights
Eisenhower SHS 2,000/10-12
6500 25 Mile Rd 48316 586-797-1300
Nanette Chesney, prin. Fax 797-1301
Malow JHS 1,200/7-9
6400 25 Mile Rd 48316 586-797-3500
Brandon Manzella, prin. Fax 797-3501
Shelby JHS 1,300/7-9
51700 Van Dyke Ave 48316 586-797-3700
Lisa McDill, prin. Fax 797-3701

Shepherd, Isabella, Pop. 1,488
Shepherd SD 1,800/K-12
PO Box 219 48883 989-828-5520
Claire Bunker, supt. Fax 828-5679
www.shepherdschools.net
Shepherd HS 500/9-12
100 E Hall St 48883 989-828-6601
Joseph Passalacqua, prin. Fax 828-5452
Shepherd MS 400/6-8
150 E Hall St 48883 989-828-6601
Kelly Eckhardt, prin. Fax 828-6578
Other Schools – See Mount Pleasant

Sheridan, Montcalm, Pop. 639

Beth Haven Baptist Academy 100/PK-12
1158 W Carson City Rd 48884 989-291-0555
Kevin Crowell, prin. Fax 527-3122

Sidney, Montcalm
Montcalm Area ISD
Supt. — See Stanton
Montcalm Area Career Center Vo/Tech
1550 W Sidney Rd 48885 989-225-5708
Celena Mills, prin. Fax 225-5709

Montcalm Community College Post-Sec.
2800 College Dr 48885 989-328-2111

Southfield, Oakland, Pop. 70,027
Southfield SD 5,900/PK-12
24661 Lahser Rd 48033 248-746-8500
Dr. Lynda Wood, supt. Fax 746-8540
www.southfieldk12.org
Levey MS 300/6-8
25300 W 9 Mile Rd, 248-746-8740
Rita Teague, prin. Fax 746-8718
Southfield HS for the Arts & Technology 1,000/9-12
24675 Lahser Rd, 248-746-8600
Sonia Jackson, prin. Fax 746-8773
Southfield Regional Academic Campus Alt
21705 Evergreen Rd 48075 248-746-0012
Dwayne Eason, prin. Fax 746-0028
Other Schools – See Lathrup Village

Abcott Institute Post-Sec.
16250 Northland Dr Ste 205 48075 866-532-7699
DeVry University Post-Sec.
26999 Central Park Ste 125 48076 248-213-1610
Everest Institute Post-Sec.
21107 Lahser Rd, 248-799-9933
Farber Hebrew Day S - Yeshivat Akiv 300/PK-12
21100 W 12 Mile Rd 48076 248-386-1625
Rabbi Noam Stein, prin. Fax 386-1632
Lawrence Technological University Post-Sec.
21000 W 10 Mile Rd 48075 248-204-4000
Northwestern Technological Institute Post-Sec.
24567 Northwestern Hwy #200 48075 248-358-4006
Oakland Community College Post-Sec.
22322 Rutland Ave 48075 248-233-2700
Providence Hospital Post-Sec.
16001 W 9 Mile Rd 48075 248-424-3000
Southfield Christian S 500/PK-12
28650 Lahser Rd 48034 248-357-3660
Sue Hoffenbacher, supt. Fax 357-5271
Specs Howard School of Broadcast Arts Post-Sec.
19900 W 9 Mile Rd 48075 248-358-9000
Yeshivas Darchei Torah Girls S 300/K-12
21550 W 12 Mile Rd 48076 248-948-1080
Sharon Kahn, prin. Fax 948-1825

Southgate, Wayne, Pop. 29,584
Southgate Community SD 4,700/K-12
14600 Dix Toledo Rd 48195 734-246-4600
Leslie Hainrihar, supt. Fax 283-6791
www.sgate.k12.mi.us
Anderson HS 1,400/9-12
15475 Leroy St 48195 734-246-4611
Dr. Michelle Baker-Herring, prin. Fax 246-7840
Davidson MS 1,000/6-8
15800 Trenton Rd 48195 734-246-4628
Dennis Kemp, prin. Fax 246-7280
Asher Adult & Community Education Adult
14101 Leroy St 48195 734-246-4633
Len Samborski, dir. Fax 246-7244

Dorsey School of Business Post-Sec.
15755 Northline Rd 48195 734-285-5400

South Haven, Van Buren, Pop. 4,285
South Haven SD 2,200/PK-12
554 Green St 49090 269-637-0520
Robert Herrera, supt. Fax 637-3025
www.shps.org
Baseline MS 500/6-8
7357 Baseline Rd 49090 269-637-0530
Dr. LaTonya Gill, prin. Fax 639-9689
Career and Early College Academy Vo/Tech
125 Veterans Dr 49090 269-637-0500
Jeremy Burleson, admin. Fax 637-3025
Mohr HS 600/9-12
600 Elkenburg St 49090 269-637-0502
Jerome Sardina, prin. Fax 637-0516

South Lyon, Oakland, Pop. 11,160
South Lyon Community SD 7,400/PK-12
345 S Warren St 48178 248-573-8127
Melissa Baker, supt. Fax 437-8686
www.slcs.us
Centennial MS 900/6-8
62500 W 9 Mile Rd 48178 248-573-8600
Brian Toth, prin. Fax 486-4302
Millennium MS 900/6-8
61526 W 9 Mile Rd 48178 248-573-8200
Kelly Gallagher, prin. Fax 437-4066
South Lyon East HS 900/9-12
52200 W 10 Mile Rd 48178 248-573-8700
Dr. David Phillips, prin. Fax 486-4009
South Lyon HS 1,300/9-12
1000 N Lafayette St 48178 248-573-8150
Chad Scaling, prin. Fax 437-0233

Sparta, Kent, Pop. 4,088
Sparta Area SD 2,600/PK-12
465 S Union St 49345 616-887-8253
Gordie Nickels, supt. Fax 887-9958
www.spartaschools.org
Sparta HS 900/9-12
475 W Spartan Dr 49345 616-887-8213
Matt Spencer, prin. Fax 887-1264
Sparta MS 600/6-8
480 S State St 49345 616-887-8211
Brad Wood, prin. Fax 887-1080

Spring Arbor, Jackson, Pop. 2,850

Spring Arbor University Post-Sec.
106 E Main St 49283 517-750-1200

Springfield, Calhoun, Pop. 5,036
Battle Creek SD
Supt. — See Battle Creek
Springfield MS 500/6-8
1023 Avenue A, 269-965-9640
William Martin, prin. Fax 962-2486

Spring Lake, Ottawa, Pop. 2,288
Spring Lake SD 2,400/PK-12
345 Hammond St 49456 616-846-5500
Dennis Furton, supt. Fax 846-9830
www.springlakeschools.org
Spring Lake HS 800/9-12
16140 148th Ave 49456 616-846-5501
Mike Gilchrist, prin. Fax 847-5855
Spring Lake MS 400/7-8
345 Hammond St 49456 616-846-5502
Aaron West, prin. Fax 847-7913

Springport, Jackson, Pop. 785
Springport SD 1,000/PK-12
300 W Main St 49284 517-857-3495
Randall Cook, supt. Fax 857-4179
springportschools.net
Springport HS 300/9-12
300 W Main St 49284 517-857-3475
Tanya Newland, prin. Fax 857-4179
Springport MS 200/6-8
300 W Main St 49284 517-857-3475
Tanya Newland, prin. Fax 857-3251

Standish, Arenac, Pop. 1,487
Standish-Sterling Community SD 1,600/PK-12
3789 Wyatt Rd 48658 989-846-3670
Darren Kroczaleski, supt. Fax 846-7890
www.standish-sterling.org
Standish-Sterling Central HS 500/9-12
2401 Grove Street Rd 48658 989-846-3660
Mark Williams, prin. Fax 846-3666
Standish-Sterling MS 400/6-8
3789 Wyatt Rd 48658 989-846-4526
Gary Roper, prin. Fax 846-4529

Stanton, Montcalm, Pop. 1,397
Central Montcalm SD 1,700/PK-12
PO Box 9 48888 989-831-2000
Amy Meinhardt, supt. Fax 831-2010
www.central-montcalm.org
Central Montcalm HS 500/9-12
PO Box 9 48888 989-831-2100
C. Martin James, prin. Fax 831-2110
Central Montcalm MS 400/6-8
PO Box 9 48888 989-831-2200
Jason Johnston, prin. Fax 831-2210
Central Montcalm Learning Center Adult
PO Box 9 48888 989-831-2402
Amy Meinhardt, supt. Fax 831-2410

Montcalm Area ISD 50/
PO Box 367 48888 989-831-5261
Ron Simon, supt. Fax 831-8727
www.maisd.com
Other Schools – See Sidney

Stephenson, Menominee, Pop. 850
Stephenson Area SD 400/K-12
PO Box 509 49887 906-753-2221
Ron Kraft, supt. Fax 753-4676
www.stephenson.k12.mi.us
Stephenson JSHS 200/6-12
PO Box 529 49887 906-753-2221
Terry Proos, prin. Fax 753-2326

Sterling Heights, Macomb, Pop. 126,870
Utica Community SD 27,900/PK-12
11303 Greendale Dr 48312 586-797-1100
Christine Johns Ed.D., supt. Fax 797-1101
www.uticak12.org
Bemis JHS 1,000/7-8
12500 19 Mile Rd 48313 586-797-2500
Thomas Yaw, prin. Fax 797-2501
Davis JHS 900/7-9
11311 Plumbrook Rd 48312 586-797-2700
Brian Shepard, prin. Fax 797-2701
Ford HS 2,000/9-12
11911 Clinton River Rd 48313 586-797-1600
Ken Cucchi, prin. Fax 797-1601
Heritage JHS 500/7-9
37400 Dodge Park Rd 48312 586-797-3100
Shaun Greene-Beebe, prin. Fax 797-3101
Jeanette JHS 800/7-9
40400 Gulliver Dr 48310 586-797-3300
Jared McEvoy, prin. Fax 797-3301
Stevenson SHS 2,000/10-12
39701 Dodge Park Rd 48313 586-797-1900
Steve Pfannes, prin. Fax 797-1901
UCS Alternative Learning Center 200/Alt
7600 18 Mile Rd 48314 586-797-7000
Marc Kay, prin. Fax 797-7001
Other Schools – See Shelby Township, Utica

Warren Consolidated SD
Supt. — See Warren
Career Prep Center Vo/Tech
12200 15 Mile Rd 48312 586-825-2800
Douglas Babcock, prin. Fax 698-4177
Carleton MS 600/6-8
8900 15 Mile Rd 48312 586-825-2590
Eric Kausch, prin. Fax 698-4286
Flynn Educational Center Alt
2899 Fox Hill Dr 48310 586-825-2900
Paul Yestrepsky, dir. Fax 698-4304
Grissom MS 700/6-8
35701 Ryan Rd 48310 586-825-2560
Joseph Konal, prin. Fax 698-4313
Sterling Heights HS 1,500/9-12
12901 15 Mile Rd 48312 586-825-2700
Craig Miller, prin. Fax 698-4253

Parkway Christian S 500/PK-12
14500 Metropolitan Pkwy 48312 586-446-9900
Lila Place, head sch Fax 446-9904

Stevensville, Berrien, Pop. 1,138
Lakeshore SD 2,800/PK-12
5771 Cleveland Ave 49127 269-428-1400
Philip Freeman, admin. Fax 428-1574
www.lakeshoreschools.k12.mi.us
Lakeshore HS 900/9-12
5771 Cleveland Ave 49127 269-428-1402
Brad Brunner, prin. Fax 428-1423
Lakeshore MS 700/6-8
1459 W John Beers Rd 49127 269-428-1408
Jason Messenger, prin. Fax 428-1571

Stockbridge, Ingham, Pop. 1,207
Stockbridge Community SD 1,000/K-12
305 W Elizabeth St 49285 517-851-7188
Karl Heidrich, supt. Fax 851-8334
panthernet.net
Stockbridge HS 500/8-12
416 N Clinton St 49285 517-851-7770
Rick Cook, prin. Fax 851-9446

Sturgis, Saint Joseph, Pop. 10,748
Sturgis SD 3,300/K-12
107 W West St 49091 269-659-1500
Dr. Thomas Langdon, supt. Fax 659-1584
www.sturgisps.org/
Sturgis HS 900/9-12
216 Vinewood Ave 49091 269-659-1515
Ron Ehlers, prin. Fax 659-1532
Sturgis MS 700/6-8
1400 E Lafayette St 49091 269-659-1550
Lauri Pressly, prin. Fax 659-1553
Adult Education Center Adult
107 W West St 49091 269-659-1540
Jill Snyder, prin. Fax 659-1544

Lake Area Christian S 50/K-12
63590 Borgert Rd 49091 269-651-5135
Sharon Wickey, admin. Fax 651-8648

Suttons Bay, Leelanau, Pop. 604
Suttons Bay SD — 600/PK-12
PO Box 367 49682 — 231-271-8601
Chris Nelson, supt. — Fax 271-8691
www.suttonsbayschools.com
Suttons Bay MSHS — 300/6-12
PO Box 367 49682 — 231-271-8603
Fax 271-8671

Swartz Creek, Genesee, Pop. 5,666
Swartz Creek Community SD — 4,000/PK-12
8354 Cappy Ln 48473 — 810-591-2300
Jeff Hall Ed.D., supt. — Fax 591-2784
www.swartzcreek.org
Alternative HS — 200/Alt
8197 Miller Rd 48473 — 810-591-4380
Richard Thompson, dean — Fax 591-4348
Swartz Creek HS — 1,100/9-12
1 Dragon Dr 48473 — 810-591-1800
Jamie Johnston, prin. — Fax 591-1895
Swartz Creek MS — 900/6-8
8230 Crapo St 48473 — 810-591-1705
Kevin Klaeren, prin. — Fax 591-1712

Genesee Academy — 200/PK-12
9447 Corunna Rd 48473 — 810-250-7557
Br. Imad Tibi, prin. — Fax 250-7556

Tawas City, Iosco, Pop. 1,814
Iosco RESA
27 N Rempert Rd 48763 — 989-362-3006
Dana McGrew, supt. — Fax 362-9076
www.ioscoresa.net/
Career & Technical Education Center — Vo/Tech
27 N Rempert Rd 48763 — 989-362-3006
Ronald Stec, dir. — Fax 362-6905

Tawas Area SD — 1,100/K-12
245 W M 55 48763 — 989-984-2250
Jeffrey Hutchison, supt. — Fax 984-2253
www.tawas.net
Tawas Area HS — 400/9-12
255 W M 55 48763 — 989-984-2100
Peter Newman, prin. — Fax 984-2106
Tawas Area MS — 300/5-8
255 W M 55 48763 — 989-984-2300
Peter Newman, prin. — Fax 984-2303

Taylor, Wayne, Pop. 61,678
Taylor SD — 7,400/PK-12
23033 Northline Rd 48180 — 734-374-1200
Ben Williams, supt. — Fax 287-6083
www.taylorschools.net
Hoover MS — 500/6-8
27101 Beverly Rd 48180 — 313-295-5775
Michelle Tocco, prin. — Fax 295-8354
Kennedy HS — 1,100/9-12
13505 Kennedy Dr 48180 — 734-374-1229
Tommie Saylor, prin. — Fax 374-1676
Taylor Career & Technical Center — Vo/Tech
9601 Westlake St 48180 — 313-295-5750
Jacqueline Lancina, prin. — Fax 291-1090
Truman HS — 1,100/9-12
11211 Beech Daly Rd 48180 — 734-946-6555
Melissa Skopczynski, prin. — Fax 946-6590
West MS — 600/6-8
10575 William St 48180 — 313-295-5783
Patricia Kaechele, prin. — Fax 291-2203

Dorsey School of Business — Post-Sec.
23129 Ecorse Rd 48180 — 313-291-2177
Taylortown School of Beauty — Post-Sec.
23129 Ecorse Rd 48180 — 313-291-2177

Tecumseh, Lenawee, Pop. 8,429
Tecumseh SD — 2,800/PK-12
212 N Ottawa St 49286 — 517-424-7318
Dr. Kelly Coffin Ed.D., supt. — Fax 423-3847
tps.k12.mi.us
Tecumseh HS — 900/9-12
760 Brown St 49286 — 517-423-6008
Griff Mills, prin. — Fax 423-9644
Tecumseh MS — 900/5-8
307 N Maumee St 49286 — 517-423-1105
Rick Hilderley, prin. — Fax 423-1300

Tekonsha, Calhoun, Pop. 699
Tekonsha Community SD — 100/K-12
245 S Elm St 49092 — 517-767-4121
Jeff Kawaski, supt. — Fax 767-3465
www.tekonshaschools.org
Tekonsha JSHS — 100/K-12
245 S Elm St 49092 — 517-767-4121
Jeffrey Kawaski, admin. — Fax 767-3465

Temperance, Monroe, Pop. 8,433
Bedford SD — 4,600/K-12
1623 W Sterns Rd 48182 — 734-850-6000
Mark Kleinhans, supt. — Fax 850-6099
www.mybedford.us
Bedford HS — 1,600/9-12
8285 Jackman Rd 48182 — 734-850-6100
Andy Rousselo, prin. — Fax 850-6199
Bedford JHS — 1,100/6-8
8405 Jackman Rd 48182 — 734-850-6200
Roderick Hurley, prin. — Fax 850-6299

State Line Christian S — 300/K-12
6320 Lewis Ave 48182 — 734-847-6773
Joshua Newbold, prin. — Fax 847-4968

Three Oaks, Berrien, Pop. 1,589
River Valley SD — 500/PK-12
15480 Three Oaks Rd 49128 — 269-756-9541
William Kearney, supt. — Fax 756-6631
www.rivervalleyschools.org/
River Valley MSHS — 200/6-12
15480 Three Oaks Rd 49128 — 269-756-9541
Cynthia Ursprung, prin. — Fax 756-3007

Three Rivers, Saint Joseph, Pop. 7,541
Three Rivers Community SD — 2,800/K-12
851 6th Avenue Rd 49093 — 269-279-1100
Jean Logan, supt. — Fax 279-5584
www.trschools.org
Three Rivers HS — 700/9-12
700 6th Ave 49093 — 269-279-1120
Carrie Balk, prin. — Fax 273-8014
Three Rivers MS — 600/6-8
1101 Jefferson St 49093 — 269-279-1130
Nikki Nash, prin. — Fax 279-1139
Barrows Adult Education — Adult
416 Washington St 49093 — 269-279-9581
Scott Grace, dean — Fax 278-5103

Traverse City, Grand Traverse, Pop. 14,412
Traverse Bay Area ISD
1101 Red Dr 49684 — 231-922-6200
Michael Hill, supt. — Fax 922-6270
www.tbaisd.org
TBA Career Tech Center — Vo/Tech
880 Parsons Rd 49686 — 231-922-6273
Patrick Lamb, prin. — Fax 922-6364

Traverse City Area SD — 9,400/PK-12
412 Webster St 49686 — 231-933-1700
Paul Soma, supt. — Fax 933-1721
www.tcaps.net
Traverse City Central HS — 1,500/9-12
1150 Milliken Dr 49686 — 231-933-3500
Jesse Houghton, prin. — Fax 933-3506
Traverse City East MS — 900/6-8
1776 3 Mile Rd N 49696 — 231-933-7300
Colleen Smith, prin. — Fax 933-6998
Traverse City HS — 200/Alt
3962 3 Mile Rd N 49686 — 231-933-5860
Lance Morgan, prin. — Fax 933-5885
Traverse City West HS — 1,700/9-12
5376 N Long Lake Rd 49685 — 231-933-7500
Joe Esper, prin. — Fax 933-7506
Traverse City West MS — 1,200/6-8
3950 Silver Lake Rd 49684 — 231-933-8200
Terry Smith, prin. — Fax 933-8205

Davenport University — Post-Sec.
2200 Dendrinos Dr Ste 104 49684 — 231-995-1740
Munson Medical Center — Post-Sec.
1105 6th St 49684 — 231-935-6501
Northwestern Michigan College — Post-Sec.
1701 E Front St 49686 — 231-995-1000
St. Elizabeth Ann Seton MS — 200/6-8
1601 3 Mile Rd N 49696 — 231-932-4810
Carl Scholten, prin. — Fax 932-4814
St. Francis HS — 300/9-12
123 E Eleventh St 49684 — 231-946-8038
Erick Chittle, prin. — Fax 946-1878
Traverse City Christian S — 200/PK-12
753 Emerson Rd 49696 — 231-929-1747
Bart Den Boer, admin. — Fax 929-1831

Trenton, Wayne, Pop. 18,620
Trenton SD — 2,700/K-12
2603 Charlton Rd 48183 — 734-676-8600
Rodney Wakeham, supt. — Fax 676-4851
www.trentonschools.com
Arthurs MS — 700/6-8
4000 Marian Dr 48183 — 734-676-8700
Stephanie O'Connor, prin. — Fax 676-7364
Trenton HS — 1,000/9-12
2601 Charlton Rd 48183 — 734-692-4530
Michael Doyle Ed.D., prin. — Fax 692-4615

Troy, Oakland, Pop. 79,352
Troy SD — 12,000/K-12
4400 Livernois Rd 48098 — 248-823-4000
Dr. Richard Machesky Ed.D., supt. — Fax 823-4013
www.troy.k12.mi.us
Athens HS — 1,600/9-12
4333 John R Rd 48085 — 248-823-2900
Dr. Lara Dixon, prin. — Fax 823-2913
Baker MS — 700/6-8
1359 Torpey Dr 48083 — 248-823-4600
Dr. Audra Melton, prin. — Fax 823-4613
Boulan Park MS — 700/6-8
3570 Northfield Pkwy 48084 — 248-823-4900
Jo Kwasny, prin. — Fax 823-4913
International Academy East — 100/9-12
1291 Torpey Dr 48083 — 248-283-8300
Ryan Brinks, prin. — Fax 823-8313
Larson MS — 700/6-8
2222 E Long Lake Rd 48085 — 248-823-4800
Joseph Duda, prin. — Fax 823-4813
Smith MS — 600/6-8
5835 Donaldson Dr 48085 — 248-823-4700
Timothy Fulcher, prin. — Fax 823-4713
Troy College and Career HS — 100/Alt
201 W Square Lake Rd 48098 — 248-823-5100
Debra MacDonald-Linford, prin. — Fax 823-5113
Troy HS — 2,000/9-12
4777 Northfield Pkwy 48098 — 248-823-2700
Remo Roncone, prin. — Fax 823-2713

Bethany Christian S — 300/K-12
2601 John R Rd 48083 — 248-689-4821
Dr. Mark Wood, prin. — Fax 689-3441
Carnegie Institute — Post-Sec.
550 Stephenson Hwy Ste 100 48083 — 248-589-1078
Walsh Coll. Accountancy & Bus. Admin. — Post-Sec.
PO Box 7006 48007 — 248-689-8282

Twining, Arenac, Pop. 180
Arenac Eastern SD — 100/K-12
PO Box 98 48766 — 989-867-4234
Darren Kroczaleski, supt. — Fax 867-4241
www.arenaceastern.org
Arenac Eastern S — 100/K-12
PO Box 98 48766 — 989-867-4234
Darren Kroczaleski, supt. — Fax 867-4241

Ubly, Sanilac, Pop. 853
Ubly Community SD — 600/K-12
2020 Union St 48475 — 989-658-8202
Fax 658-2361
www.ublyschools.org
Ubly HS — 300/7-12
2020 Union St 48475 — 989-658-8202
Fax 658-2072

Union City, Branch, Pop. 1,560
Union City Community SD — 1,100/PK-12
430 Saint Joseph St 49094 — 517-741-8091
Patrick Kreger, supt. — Fax 741-5205
www.unioncityschools.org/
Union City HS — 300/9-12
430 Saint Joseph St 49094 — 517-741-8561
Christina Feneley, prin. — Fax 741-5205
Union City MS — 300/5-8
430 Saint Joseph St 49094 — 517-741-5381
Brandon Bruce, prin. — Fax 741-8513

University Center, Bay
Saginaw ISD
Supt. — See Saginaw
Great Lakes Bay Early College — 200/10-12
7400 Bay Rd 48710 — 989-964-2059
Marlene Searles, prin.

Delta College — Post-Sec.
1961 Delta Rd 48710 — 989-686-9000
Saginaw Valley State University — Post-Sec.
7400 Bay Rd 48710 — 989-964-4000

Utica, Macomb, Pop. 4,675
Utica Community SD
Supt. — See Sterling Heights
Eppler JHS — 700/7-9
45461 Brownell St 48317 — 586-797-2900
Gerard Pantano, prin. — Fax 797-2901
Utica SHS — 1,300/10-12
47255 Shelby Rd 48317 — 586-797-2200
Thomas Lietz, prin. — Fax 797-2201

Vanderbilt, Otsego, Pop. 548
Vanderbilt Area SD — 100/PK-12
947 Donovan St 49795 — 989-983-2561
Richard Heitmeyer, supt. — Fax 983-3051
www.vanderbilt.k12.mi.us
Vanderbilt Area S — 100/PK-12
947 Donovan St 49795 — 989-983-2561
Richard Heitmeyer, supt. — Fax 983-3051

Vassar, Tuscola, Pop. 2,631
Vassar SD — 1,300/PK-12
220 Athletic St 48768 — 989-823-8535
Dorothy Blackwell, supt. — Fax 823-7823
www.vassar.k12.mi.us
Vassar HS — 400/9-12
220 Athletic St 48768 — 989-823-8534
Jason Kiss, prin. — Fax 823-7823
Vassar MS — 300/6-8
220 Athletic St 48768 — 989-823-8533
Jason Kiss, prin. — Fax 823-7823
Wolverine Alternative Education — 100/Alt
1120 Commerce Dr 48768 — 989-823-9303
Charles Fabbro, prin. — Fax 823-3144

Vermontville, Eaton, Pop. 745
Maple Valley SD — 1,100/PK-12
11014 Nashville Hwy 49096 — 517-852-9699
Michelle Falcon, supt. — Fax 852-5076
mvs.k12.mi.us
Maple Valley JSHS — 500/7-12
11090 Nashville Hwy 49096 — 517-852-9275
Todd Gonser, prin. — Fax 852-2283
Maple Valley Pathways HS — 100/Alt
11090 Nashville Hwy 49096 — 517-852-2322
Duska Brumm, prin. — Fax 852-9701

Vestaburg, Montcalm
Vestaburg Community SD — 600/PK-12
7188 Avenue B 48891 — 989-268-5353
Brandon Hubbard, supt. — Fax 268-5246
www.vcs-k12.net
Vestaburg JSHS — 300/7-12
7188 Avenue B 48891 — 989-268-5343
Brandon Hubbard, prin. — Fax 268-5246

Vicksburg, Kalamazoo, Pop. 2,854
Vicksburg Community SD — 2,600/PK-12
PO Box 158 49097 — 269-321-1000
Charles Glaes, supt. — Fax 321-1055
www.vicksburgcommunityschools.org/
Vicksburg HS — 800/9-12
501 E Highway St 49097 — 269-321-1100
Keevin O'Neill, prin. — Fax 321-1155
Vicksburg MS — 600/6-8
348 E Prairie St 49097 — 269-321-1300
Matt VanDussen, prin. — Fax 321-1355
Vicksburg Pathways HS — 100/Alt
301 S Kalamazoo St 49097 — 269-321-1020
Ric Place, dir. — Fax 321-1055

Wakefield, Gogebic, Pop. 1,831
Wakefield-Marenisco SD — 300/K-12
715 Putnam St 49968 — 906-224-9421
Catherine Shamion, supt. — Fax 224-1771
www.wmschools.org
Wakefield-Marenisco S — 300/K-12
715 Putnam St 49968 — 906-224-7211
Catherine Shamion, supt. — Fax 224-1771

Waldron, Hillsdale, Pop. 534
Waldron Area SD — 100/K-12
13380 Waldron Rd 49288 — 517-286-6251
Jose Vera, supt. — Fax 286-6254
www.wassd.org
Waldron Area S — 100/K-12
13380 Waldron Rd 49288 — 517-286-6251
Jose Vera, admin. — Fax 286-6254

Walkerville, Oceana, Pop. 238
Walkerville SD 100/PK-12
145 Lathrop St 49459 231-873-4850
Michael Sweet, supt. Fax 873-5615
walkk12.org
Walkerville S 100/PK-12
145 Lathrop St 49459 231-873-4850
Michael Sweet, prin. Fax 873-5615

Walled Lake, Oakland, Pop. 6,836
Walled Lake Consolidated SD 14,600/PK-12
850 Ladd Rd Bldg D 48390 248-956-2000
Kenneth Gutman M.A., supt. Fax 956-2123
www.wlcsd.org
Geisler MS 700/6-8
46720 W Pontiac Trl 48390 248-956-2900
Sheryl Kennedy Ph.D., prin. Fax 956-2905
Western HS 1,400/9-12
600 Beck Rd 48390 248-956-4400
Joe Bell, prin. Fax 956-4405
Other Schools – See Commerce Township, West Bloomfield, Wixom

Warren, Macomb, Pop. 130,738
Fitzgerald SD 2,200/PK-12
23200 Ryan Rd 48091 586-757-1750
Barbara VanSweden, supt. Fax 758-0991
www.fitz.k12.mi.us
Chatterton MS 600/6-8
24333 Ryan Rd 48091 586-757-6650
Laurie Fournier, prin. Fax 620-6011
Fitzgerald HS 900/9-12
23200 Ryan Rd 48091 586-757-7070
Kim Cerrini, prin. Fax 620-6372

Van Dyke SD 2,700/PK-12
23500 Mac Arthur Blvd 48089 586-757-6600
Joseph Pius, supt. Fax 759-9408
www.vdps.net
Lincoln HS 700/9-12
22900 Federal Ave 48089 586-758-8307
Billie Sczepaniak, prin. Fax 758-8304
Lincoln MS 600/6-8
22500 Federal Ave 48089 586-758-8320
Lisa Williams, prin. Fax 758-8322

Warren Consolidated SD 13,700/PK-12
31300 Anita Dr 48093 888-492-7543
Dr. Robert Livernois, supt. Fax 698-4095
www.wcskids.net
Beer MS 700/6-8
3200 Martin Rd 48092 586-574-3175
Annette Lauria, prin. Fax 698-4277
Butcher Educational Center 200/Alt
27500 Cosgrove Dr 48092 586-698-4394
Dr. Catherine Neuhoff, dir. Fax 698-4397
Carter MS 800/6-8
12000 Masonic Blvd 48093 586-825-2620
Amy Hendry, prin. Fax 698-4295
Cousino HS 1,600/9-12
30333 Hoover Rd 48093 586-574-3100
Bradley Perkins, prin. Fax 698-4204
Warren-Mott HS 1,800/9-12
3131 E 12 Mile Rd 48092 586-574-3250
John Dignan, prin. Fax 698-4226
Other Schools – See Sterling Heights

Warren Woods SD 3,200/PK-12
12900 Frazho Rd 48089 586-439-4400
Stacey Denewith-Fici, supt. Fax 353-0544
www.warrenwoods.misd.net
Warren Woods Enterprise HS 100/Alt
28600 Suburban Dr 48088 586-439-4407
George Hamblin, prin. Fax 578-9474
Warren Woods MS 800/6-8
13400 E 12 Mile Rd 48088 586-439-4403
Donny Sikora, prin. Fax 574-9830
Warren Woods Tower HS 1,100/9-12
27900 Bunert Rd 48088 586-439-4402
Michael Mackenzie, prin. Fax 445-8013
Warren Woods Adult Education Adult
12900 Frazho Rd 48089 586-439-4408
Kristen Allen, prin. Fax 439-4968

Davenport University Post-Sec.
27650 Dequindre Rd 48092 586-558-8700
De La Salle Collegiate HS 800/9-12
14600 Common Rd 48088 586-778-2207
Patrick Adams, prin. Fax 778-6016
Lawton Career Institute Post-Sec.
13877 E 8 Mile Rd 48089 586-777-7344
Macomb Christian S 200/PK-12
28501 Lorraine Ave 48093 586-751-8980
Dr. Margie Baldwin, supt. Fax 751-7946
Macomb Community College Post-Sec.
14500 E 12 Mile Rd 48088 586-445-7999
Regina HS 500/9-12
13900 Masonic Blvd 48088 586-585-0500
Ann Diamond, prin. Fax 585-0507

Washington, Macomb
Romeo Community SD
Supt. — See Romeo
Powell MS 700/6-8
62100 Jewell Rd 48094 586-752-0270
Jeffrey LaPerriere, prin. Fax 752-0276
Romeo Engineering and Technology Center Vo/Tech
62300 Jewell Rd 48094 586-752-0245
Natalie Davis, admin. Fax 752-0452

Waterford, Oakland, Pop. 74,500
Oakland ISD 500/
2111 Pontiac Lake Rd 48328 248-209-2000
Dr. Wanda Cook-Robinson, supt. Fax 209-2206
www.oakland.k12.mi.us
Other Schools – See Clarkston, Pontiac, Royal Oak, Wixom

Waterford SD 9,200/PK-12
501 N Cass Lake Rd 48328 248-682-7800
Dr. Keith Wunderlich, supt. Fax 706-4888
www.wsdmi.org
Kettering HS 1,400/9-12
2800 Kettering Dr 48329 248-673-1261
Jeffrey Frankowiak, prin. Fax 673-1778
Mason MS 1,300/6-8
3835 W Walton Blvd 48329 248-674-2281
Roger Opsommer, prin. Fax 673-3718
Mott HS 1,500/9-12
1151 Scott Lake Rd 48328 248-674-4134
Jason Riggs, prin. Fax 674-2825
Pierce MS 1,000/6-8
5145 Hatchery Rd 48329 248-674-0331
Yvonne Dixon, prin. Fax 674-4222
Waterford Durant HS 200/Alt
501 N Cass Lake Rd 48328 248-674-3145
Craig Blomquist, prin. Fax 674-6320

Michigan College of Beauty Post-Sec.
5620 Dixie Hwy 48329 248-623-9494
Oakdale Academy 200/PK-12
3200 Beacham Dr 48329 248-481-9039
Paul Rumbuc, head sch
Oakland Community College Post-Sec.
7350 Cooley Lake Rd 48327 248-942-3100
Our Lady of the Lakes HS 300/6-12
5495 Dixie Hwy 48329 248-623-0340
Richard Vanden Boom, pres. Fax 623-2274

Watersmeet, Gogebic, Pop. 416
Watersmeet Township SD 200/K-12
PO Box 217 49969 906-358-4504
Gerry Pease, supt. Fax 358-4713
www.watersmeet.k12.mi.us/
Watersmeet Township S 200/K-12
PO Box 217 49969 906-358-4504
George Peterson, prin. Fax 358-4713

Watervliet, Berrien, Pop. 1,689
Watervliet SD 1,300/PK-12
450 E Red Arrow Hwy 49098 269-463-0300
Kevin Schooley, supt. Fax 463-6809
www.watervlietps.org
Watervliet HS 400/9-12
450 E Red Arrow Hwy 49098 269-463-0730
Brad Coon, prin. Fax 463-6809
Watervliet MS 300/6-8
450 E Red Arrow Hwy 49098 269-463-0780
Dave Armstrong, prin. Fax 463-6809

Grace Christian S 200/PK-12
325 N M 140 49098 269-463-5545
Todd Zimmerman, head sch Fax 463-5739

Wayland, Allegan, Pop. 3,998
Wayland UNSD 2,800/PK-12
850 E Superior St 49348 269-792-2181
Norman Taylor, supt. Fax 792-1615
waylandunion.org
Career Connections Academy Alt
870 E Superior St 49348 269-792-2254
Wayland HS 800/9-12
870 E Superior St 49348 269-792-2254
Thomas Cutler, prin. Fax 792-2116
Wayland Union MS 500/7-8
701 Wildcat Dr 49348 269-792-2306
Carolyn Whyte, prin. Fax 792-1126

Wayne, Wayne, Pop. 17,081
Wayne-Westland Community SD
Supt. — See Westland
Franklin MS 1,000/7-8
33555 Annapolis St 48184 734-419-2400
Stacy Williamson, prin. Fax 595-2401
Tinkham Alternative Education 100/Alt
3001 4th St 48184 734-419-2436
Kim Doman, dir. Fax 595-2439
Wayne Memorial HS 1,800/9-12
3001 4th St 48184 734-419-2200
Kevin Weber, prin. Fax 595-2227
Tinkham Adult and Community Education Adult
3001 4th St 48184 734-419-2427
Kim Doman, dir. Fax 595-2439

Dorsey School of Business Post-Sec.
35005 W Michigan Ave 48184 734-595-1540
Oakwood - Hospital Annapolis Center Post-Sec.
33155 Annapolis St 48184 734-467-4000

Webberville, Ingham, Pop. 1,262
Webberville Community SD 500/PK-12
309 E Grand River Rd 48892 517-521-3422
Brian Friddle, supt. Fax 521-4139
www.webbervilleschools.org
Webberville JSHS 200/6-12
309 E Grand River Rd 48892 517-521-3447
Kathy Pierman, prin. Fax 521-4740

West Bloomfield, Oakland, Pop. 67,200
Bloomfield Hills SD
Supt. — See Bloomfield Hls
West Hills MS 600/4-8
2601 Lone Pine Rd 48323 248-341-6100
Rob Durecka, prin. Fax 341-6199

Walled Lake Consolidated SD
Supt. — See Walled Lake
Walnut Creek MS 900/6-8
7601 Walnut Lake Rd 48323 248-956-2400
Fax 956-2405

West Bloomfield SD 5,600/K-12
5810 Commerce Rd 48324 248-865-6420
Dr. Gerald Hill, supt. Fax 865-6481
www.westbloomfield.k12.mi.us
Abbott MS 700/6-8
3380 Orchard Lake Rd 48324 248-865-3670
Amy Hughes, prin. Fax 865-3671
Orchard Lake MS 800/6-8
6000 Orchard Lake Rd 48322 248-865-4480
Morrison Borders, prin. Fax 865-4481
West Bloomfield HS 1,700/9-12
4925 Orchard Lake Rd 48323 248-865-6720
Patrick Watson, prin. Fax 865-6721
Other Schools – See Farmington Hills

Frankel Jewish Academy 200/9-12
6600 W Maple Rd 48322 248-592-5263
Rabbi Erin Holodnick, head sch Fax 592-0022
Michigan Jewish Institute Post-Sec.
6890 W Maple Rd 48322 248-414-6900

West Branch, Ogemaw, Pop. 2,115
West Branch-Rose City Area SD 2,000/PK-12
PO Box 308 48661 989-343-2000
Philip Mikulski, supt. Fax 343-2006
www.wbrc.k12.mi.us/
Ogemaw Heights HS 700/9-12
PO Box 308 48661 989-343-2020
Benjamin Doan, prin. Fax 343-2130
Surline MS 500/5-8
PO Box 308 48661 989-343-2140
Wendy Tuttle, prin. Fax 343-2239

Westland, Wayne, Pop. 82,217
Livonia SD
Supt. — See Livonia
Western Wayne Skill Center Vo/Tech
8075 Ritz Ave 48185 734-744-2810
Patrick Mies, prin. Fax 744-2811

Wayne-Westland Community SD 12,400/PK-12
36745 Marquette St 48185 734-419-2000
Michele A. Harmala Ph.D., supt. Fax 595-2123
www.wwcsd.net
Ford Career-Technical Center Vo/Tech
36455 Marquette St 48185 734-419-2100
Steven Kay, prin. Fax 595-2127
Glenn HS 1,900/9-12
36105 Marquette St 48185 734-419-2300
Fax 595-2338
Stevenson MS 800/7-8
38501 Palmer Rd 48186 734-419-2350
Fax 595-2692
Other Schools – See Wayne

Huron Valley Lutheran HS 100/9-12
33740 Cowan Rd 48185 734-525-0160
Daniel Schultz, prin. Fax 525-6717
Lutheran HS Westland 200/9-12
33300 Cowan Rd 48185 734-422-2090
Steven Schwecke, prin. Fax 422-8566
Manthano Christian College Post-Sec.
6420 N Newburgh Rd 48185 734-895-3280

Westphalia, Clinton, Pop. 918
Pewamo-Westphalia SD 600/PK-12
5101 S Clintonia Rd 48894 989-587-5100
Dr. Garth Cooper, supt. Fax 587-5120
www.pwschools.org
Pewamo-Westphalia MSHS 500/6-12
5101 S Clintonia Rd 48894 989-587-5100
Todd Simmons, prin. Fax 587-3550

White Cloud, Newaygo, Pop. 1,346
White Cloud SD 800/K-12
PO Box 1000 49349 231-689-6591
Barry Seabrook, supt. Fax 689-3210
www.whitecloud.net
White Cloud JSHS 300/6-12
PO Box 1001 49349 231-689-1705
Ed Canning, prin. Fax 689-3349

Whitehall, Muskegon, Pop. 2,657
Whitehall SD 2,000/PK-12
541 E Slocum St 49461 231-893-1005
Jerry McDowell, supt. Fax 894-6450
www.whitehallschools.net
Whitehall HS 600/9-12
3100 White Lake Dr 49461 231-893-1020
Dale McKenzie, prin. Fax 893-2923
Whitehall MS 500/6-8
401 S Elizabeth St 49461 231-893-1030
Joe Barron, prin. Fax 894-6844

White Lake, Oakland, Pop. 22,608
Huron Valley SD
Supt. — See Highland
International Academy West HS 9-12
1630 Bogie Lake Rd 48383 248-676-2735
Ryan Parrott, prin. Fax 676-2734
Lakeland HS 1,400/9-12
1630 Bogie Lake Rd 48383 248-676-8320
Paul Gmelin, prin. Fax 676-8330
White Lake MS 800/6-8
1450 Bogie Lake Rd 48383 248-684-8004
Patrick Borg, prin. Fax 676-8437

White Pigeon, Saint Joseph, Pop. 1,492
White Pigeon Community SD 800/K-12
410 Prairie Ave 49099 269-483-7676
Carrie Erlandson, supt. Fax 483-2256
www.wpcschools.org
White Pigeon JSHS 400/6-12
410 Prairie Ave 49099 269-483-7679
Jon Keyer, prin. Fax 483-8742

Whitmore Lake, Washtenaw, Pop. 6,301
Whitmore Lake SD 800/PK-12
8845 Main St 48189 734-449-4464
Tom DeKeyser, supt. Fax 449-5336
www.wlps.net/
Whitmore Lake HS 400/7-12
7430 Whitmore Lake Rd 48189 734-449-4461
Tom DeKeyser, prin. Fax 449-5576

Livingston Christian S 100/PK-12
8877 Main St 48189 734-878-9818
Ted Nast, admin.

Livingston Christian S 200/PK-12
8877 Main St 48189 734-878-9818
Theodore Nast, admin.

Whittemore, Iosco, Pop. 377
Whittemore-Prescott Area SD 900/PK-12
PO Box 250 48770 989-756-2500
Joseph Perrera, supt. Fax 756-2278
www.wpas.net
Whittemore-Prescott Area JSHS 300/7-12
PO Box 250 48770 989-756-2400
Bunny Miller, prin. Fax 756-3363

Williamston, Ingham, Pop. 3,766
Williamston Community SD 1,800/PK-12
418 Highland St 48895 517-655-4361
Narda Murphy, supt. Fax 655-7500
www.gowcs.net
Williamston HS 700/9-12
3939 Vanneter Rd 48895 517-655-2142
Dr. Jeffrey Thoenes, prin. Fax 655-7501
Williamston MS 400/6-8
3845 Vanneter Rd 48895 517-655-4668
Scott Martin, prin. Fax 655-7502

Wilson, Menominee, Pop. 1,391

Wilson SDA Academy 50/K-10
N13925 County Road 551 49896 906-639-2566
Emily Gibbs, prin. Fax 639-2566

Wixom, Oakland, Pop. 13,242
Oakland ISD
Supt. — See Waterford
Oakland Opportunity Academy 200/Alt
1000 Beck Rd 48393 248-668-5679
Dr. Marlana Krolicki, prin. Fax 668-5670
Oakland Technical Campus SW Vo/Tech
1000 Beck Rd 48393 248-922-5864
Alethia Barnes, dean

Walled Lake Consolidated SD
Supt. — See Walled Lake
Banks MS 800/6-8
1760 Charms Rd 48393 248-956-2200
Brad Paddock, prin. Fax 956-2205

St. Catherine of Siena Academy 9-12
28200 Napier Rd 48393 248-946-4848
Karen Ervin, prin. Fax 438-1679
Wixom Christian S 100/PK-12
620 N Wixom Rd 48393 248-624-4362
Scott Ice, admin. Fax 624-1068

Wolverine, Cheboygan, Pop. 234
Wolverine Community SD 300/K-12
PO Box 219 49799 231-525-8201
Joe Hart, supt. Fax 525-8591
wolverineschools.org
Wolverine HS 100/7-12
PO Box 219 49799 231-525-9050
Stephen Seelye, prin. Fax 525-8251

Woodhaven, Wayne, Pop. 12,674
Gibraltar SD 3,700/PK-12
19370 Vreeland Rd 48183 734-379-6350
Amy Conway, supt. Fax 379-6359
www.gibdist.net
Other Schools – See Gibraltar, Rockwood

Woodhaven-Brownstown SD 4,900/K-12
24821 Hall Rd 48183 734-783-3300
Mark Greathead, supt. Fax 783-3316
www.woodhaven.k12.mi.us
Henry MS 800/8-9
24825 Hall Rd 48183 734-362-6100
Molly Mazei, prin. Fax 362-3045
Other Schools – See Brownstown

Woodland, Barry, Pop. 422
Lakewood SD 1,400/PK-12
223 W Broadway St 48897 616-374-8043
Randy Fleenor, supt. Fax 374-8858
www.lakewoodps.org
Lakewood MS 400/5-8
8699 Brown Rd 48897 616-374-2400
Kellie Rowland, prin. Fax 374-2424
Other Schools – See Lake Odessa

Wyandotte, Wayne, Pop. 25,476
Wyandotte SD 4,500/PK-12
PO Box 130 48192 734-759-5000
Dr. Catherine Cost, supt. Fax 759-6009
www.wyandotte.org
Roosevelt HS 1,400/9-12
540 Eureka Rd 48192 734-759-5000
Thomas Kell, prin. Fax 759-5009
Wilson MS 1,000/6-8
1275 15th St 48192 734-759-5300
Carol Makuch, prin. Fax 759-5309

Wyoming, Kent, Pop. 70,258
Godfrey-Lee SD 1,900/PK-12
1324 Burton St SW 49509 616-241-4722
David Britten, supt. Fax 241-4707
www.godfrey-lee.org/
East Lee Campus 100/Alt
982 Lee St SW 49509 616-241-2661
James Jenson, prin. Fax 241-6764
Lee HS 500/9-12
1335 Lee St SW 49509 616-452-3296
Kathryn Curry, prin. Fax 241-4677
Lee MS 400/6-8
1335 Lee St SW 49509 616-452-3296
Kathryn Curry, prin. Fax 241-4677

Godwin Heights SD 2,300/K-12
15 36th St SW 49548 616-252-2090
William Fetterhoff, supt. Fax 252-2232
www.godwinschools.org
Godwin Heights HS 600/9-12
50 35th St SW 49548 616-252-2050
Chad Conklin, prin. Fax 252-2067
Godwin Heights Learning Center 100/Alt
3529 Division Ave S 49548 616-252-2040
Chad Conklin, dir. Fax 252-2043
Godwin Heights MS 600/5-8
111 36th St SE 49548 616-252-2070
Aaron Berlin, prin. Fax 252-2075

Wyoming SD 4,300/PK-12
3575 Gladiola Ave SW, 616-530-7550
Dr. Thomas Reeder, supt. Fax 530-7557
www.wyoming.k12.mi.us
Wyoming HS 1,000/10-12
1350 Prairie Pkwy SW 49509 616-530-7580
Nathan Robrahn, prin. Fax 530-7589
Wyoming JHS 1,000/7-9
2125 Wrenwood St SW, 616-530-7590
Jon Blackburn, prin. Fax 249-7673
Wyoming Community Education Center Adult
3600 Byron Center Ave SW, 616-530-7500
Adrian Lamar, dir. Fax 531-8350

Potter's House HS 100/9-12
2500 Newport St SW, 616-249-8050
Dr. Peter VandeBrake, prin. Fax 249-8555
Tri-Unity Christian HS 200/7-12
2104 44th St SW, 616-532-8827
Deb Blanker, prin. Fax 532-8701
West Michigan Lutheran HS 100/7-12
601 36th St SW 49509 616-455-2200
Robert Patrick, prin. Fax 455-2211

Yale, Saint Clair, Pop. 1,919
Yale SD 2,000/K-12
198 School Dr 48097 810-387-3231
Kenneth Nicholl, supt. Fax 387-4418
www.ypsd.us/
Yale HS 700/9-12
247 School Dr 48097 810-387-3231
Paul Flynn, prin. Fax 387-9108
Yale JHS 500/6-8
198 School Dr 48097 810-387-3231
Brad Dykstra, prin. Fax 387-9207

Ypsilanti, Washtenaw, Pop. 18,646
Lincoln Consolidated SD 4,100/PK-12
8970 Whittaker Rd 48197 734-484-7000
Sean McNatt, supt. Fax 484-1212
www.lincolnk12.org
Lincoln HS 1,200/9-12
7425 Willis Rd 48197 734-484-7004
Nicole Holden, prin. Fax 484-7012
Lincoln MS 1,000/6-8
8744 Whittaker Rd 48197 734-484-7033
Genevieve Bertsos, prin. Fax 484-7088

Washtenaw ISD
Supt. — See Ann Arbor
Washtenaw International HS 300/9-12
510 Emerick St 48198 734-994-8145
Nhu Do, prin. Fax 484-9719

Ypsilanti Community SD 4,200/PK-12
1885 Packard Rd 48197 734-221-1210
Dr. Benjamin Edmondson, supt. Fax 714-1214
www.ycschools.us
AC Tech HS 9-12
2095 Packard Rd 48197 734-221-1001
Justin Jennings, prin. Fax 221-1001
STEMM Academy 200/9-12
2095 Packard Rd 48197 734-221-1006
Christopher Johnson, prin. Fax 721-1003
Washtenaw International Middle Academy 100/6-8
510 Emerick St 48198 734-994-8145
Nhu Do, prin. Fax 484-9719
Ypsilanti Community HS 800/9-12
2095 Packard Rd 48197 734-221-1001
Cory Gildersleeve, prin. Fax 221-1003
Ypsilanti Community MS 700/6-8
235 Spencer Ln 48198 734-221-2200
Aaron Rose, prin. Fax 221-2203
Ypsilanti New Tech HS 300/9-12
2095 Packard Rd 48197 734-221-1500
Scott Snyder M.Ed., prin. Fax 221-1503
Adult Education Adult
1076 Ecorse Rd 48198 734-221-1601
Nathan Moger, dir. Fax 221-1693

Calvary Christian Academy 200/K-12
1007 Ecorse Rd 48198 734-482-1990
Cathy White, prin. Fax 484-5118
Eastern Michigan University 48197 Post-Sec.
734-487-1849

Zeeland, Ottawa, Pop. 5,407
Zeeland SD 5,900/PK-12
PO Box 110 49464 616-748-3000
Cal De Kuiper, supt. Fax 748-3035
www.zps.org/
Cityside MS 700/6-8
320 E Main Ave 49464 616-748-3200
Sarah Huizenga, prin. Fax 748-3210
Creekside MS 600/6-8
179 W Roosevelt Ave 49464 616-748-3300
C. Greshaw, prin. Fax 748-3325
Venture Academy 50/Alt
3333 96th Ave 49464 616-748-4770
Roberta Brown-Parker, dir. Fax 748-1404
Zeeland East HS 1,000/9-12
3333 96th Ave 49464 616-748-3100
J. Knoth, prin. Fax 748-3198
Zeeland West HS 900/9-12
3390 100th Ave 49464 616-748-4500
Greg Eding, prin. Fax 748-4505

MINNESOTA

MN DEPARTMENT OF EDUCATION
1500 Highway 36 W, Roseville 55113-4035
Telephone 651-582-8200
Website education.state.mn.us

Commissioner of Education Dr. Brenda Cassellius

PUBLIC, PRIVATE AND CATHOLIC SECONDARY SCHOOLS

Ada, Norman, Pop. 1,681
Ada-Borup SD 2854 500/PK-12
604 W Thorpe Ave 56510 218-784-5300
Shawn Yates, supt. Fax 784-3475
www.ada.k12.mn.us
Ada-Borup JSHS 200/7-12
604 W Thorpe Ave 56510 218-784-5300
Kelly Anderson, prin. Fax 784-3475

Adams, Mower, Pop. 779
Southland SD 500 500/K-12
203 NW 2nd St 55909 507-582-3283
Jeff Sampson, supt. Fax 582-7813
www.isd500.k12.mn.us
Southland HS 200/9-12
203 NW 2nd St 55909 507-582-3568
Scott Hall, prin. Fax 582-7813
Southland MS 100/6-8
203 NW 2nd St 55909 507-582-3568
Scott Hall, prin. Fax 582-7813

Adrian, Nobles, Pop. 1,201
Adrian SD 511 600/PK-12
PO Box 40 56110 507-483-2266
Roger Graff, supt. Fax 483-2342
www.isd511.net
Adrian HS 200/9-12
PO Box 40 56110 507-483-2232
Tim Christensen, prin. Fax 483-2375
Adrian MS 100/6-8
PO Box 40 56110 507-483-2232
Tim Christensen, prin. Fax 483-2375

Aitkin, Aitkin, Pop. 2,132
Aitkin SD 1 1,200/PK-12
306 2nd St NW 56431 218-927-2115
Bernie Novak, supt. Fax 927-4234
home.isd1.org
Aitkin Alternative S 50/Alt
306 2nd St NW 56431 218-927-3421
Chad Pederson, prin.
Aitkin HS 600/7-12
306 2nd St NW 56431 218-927-2115
Chad Pederson, prin. Fax 927-4234

Albany, Stearns, Pop. 2,533
Albany SD 745 1,400/PK-12
PO Box 40 56307 320-845-2171
Greg Johnson, supt. Fax 845-4017
www.albany.k12.mn.us
Albany JSHS 500/7-12
PO Box 40 56307 320-845-2171
Tim Wege, prin. Fax 845-4017

Albert Lea, Freeborn, Pop. 17,797
Albert Lea SD 241 3,200/PK-12
211 W Richway Dr 56007 507-379-4800
Dr. Mike Funk, supt.
www.alschools.org
Albert Lea ALC 100/Alt
2200 Riverland Dr 56007 507-369-1453
Tonya Prouty, admin. Fax 369-1460
Albert Lea HS 1,100/8-12
2000 Tiger Ln 56007 507-379-5340
Mark Grossklaus, prin. Fax 379-5498

Riverland Community College Post-Sec.
2200 Riverland Dr 56007 507-379-3300

Albertville, Wright, Pop. 6,921
Saint Michael-Albertville SD 885 4,800/PK-12
11343 50th St NE 55301 763-497-3180
Dr. Ann-Marie Foucault, supt. Fax 497-6588
www.stma.k12.mn.us
Saint Michael-Albertville MS West 900/5-8
11343 50th St NE 55301 763-497-4524
Andrew Merfeld, prin. Fax 497-6566
Other Schools – See Saint Michael

Alden, Freeborn, Pop. 654
Alden-Conger SD 242 500/PK-12
PO Box 99 56009 507-874-3240
Brian Shanks, supt. Fax 874-2747
www.alden-conger.org
Alden-Conger HS 200/7-12
PO Box 99 56009 507-874-3240
Brian Shanks, supt. Fax 874-2747

Alexandria, Douglas, Pop. 10,938
Alexandria SD 206 3,900/PK-12
PO Box 308 56308 320-762-2141
Julie Critz, supt. Fax 762-2765
www.alexandria.k12.mn.us
Alexandria Area HS 1,400/9-12
PO Box 9 56308 320-762-2142
Chad Duwenhoegger, prin. Fax 762-7749
Discovery MS 600/6-8
510 McKay Ave N 56308 320-762-7900
Matt Aker, prin. Fax 762-8347

Alexandria Technical College Post-Sec.
1601 Jefferson St 56308 320-762-0221
Northstar Christian Academy 50/9-12
PO Box 904 56308 320-219-6489
Jay Jenson, dir.

Andover, Anoka, Pop. 30,071
Anoka-Hennepin SD 11
Supt. — See Anoka
Andover HS 1,700/9-12
2115 Andover Blvd NW 55304 763-506-8400
Becky Brodeur, prin. Fax 767-3575
Oak View MS 1,400/6-8
15400 Hanson Blvd NW 55304 763-506-5600
Gary Lundeen, prin. Fax 506-5603

Legacy Christian Academy 500/PK-12
3037 Bunker Lake Blvd NW 55304 763-427-4595
Toni Johnson, coord. Fax 427-3398

Annandale, Wright, Pop. 3,201
Annandale SD 876 1,700/PK-12
PO Box 190 55302 320-274-5602
Steve Niklaus, supt. Fax 274-5978
www.annandale.k12.mn.us
Annandale HS 500/9-12
PO Box 190 55302 320-274-8208
Scot Kerbaugh, prin. Fax 274-2316
Annandale MS 400/6-8
PO Box 190 55302 320-274-8226
Tim Prom, prin. Fax 274-5978

Anoka, Anoka, Pop. 16,703
Anoka-Hennepin SD 11 37,300/PK-12
2727 N Ferry St 55303 763-506-1000
David Law, supt. Fax 506-1003
www.ahschools.us
Anoka-Hennepin Technical HS 100/Alt
1255 W Highway 10 55303 763-433-4500
Nancy Chave, prin. Fax 433-4503
Anoka HS 2,300/9-12
3939 7th Ave 55303 763-506-6200
Mike Farley, prin. Fax 506-6203
Anoka MS of the Arts - Fred Moore Campus 1,300/7-8
1523 5th Ave 55303 763-506-5000
Jerri McGonigal, prin. Fax 506-6003
Secondary Technical Education Program Vo/Tech
1353 W Highway 10 55303 763-433-4001
Jessica Lipa, dir. Fax 433-4003
Other Schools – See Andover, Blaine, Champlin, Coon Rapids

Anoka Technical College Post-Sec.
1355 W Highway 10 55303 763-576-4700

Apple Valley, Dakota, Pop. 47,792
Rosemount-Apple Valley-Eagan ISD 196
Supt. — See Rosemount
Apple Valley HS 1,700/9-12
14450 Hayes Rd 55124 952-431-8200
Michael Bolsoni, prin. Fax 431-8744
Area Learning Center 100/Alt
5840 149th St W 55124 952-431-8720
David Schmitz, coord. Fax 431-8722
Eastview HS 2,100/9-12
6200 140th St W 55124 952-431-8900
Randall Peterson, prin. Fax 431-8911
Falcon Ridge MS 1,100/6-8
12900 Johnny Cake Ridge Rd 55124 952-431-8760
Noel Mehus, prin. Fax 431-8770
School of Enviromental Studies 400/11-12
12155 Johnny Cake Ridge Rd 55124 952-431-8750
Dan Bodette, prin. Fax 431-8755
Scott Highlands MS 900/6-8
14011 Pilot Knob Rd 55124 952-423-7581
Daniel Wilharber, prin. Fax 423-7601
Valley MS - S of STEM 900/6-8
900 Garden View Dr 55124 952-431-8300
Dave McKeag, prin. Fax 431-8313

Arden Hills, Ramsey, Pop. 9,377
Mounds View SD 621
Supt. — See Shoreview
Mounds View HS 1,700/9-12
1900 Lake Valentine Rd 55112 651-621-7100
Dr. Jeff Ridlehoover, prin. Fax 621-7105

Arlington, Sibley, Pop. 2,206
Sibley East SD 2310 1,200/PK-12
PO Box 1000 55307 507-964-2292
James Amsden, supt. Fax 964-8224
www.sibleyeast.org
Sibley East SHS 300/10-12
PO Box 1000 55307 507-964-8235
Tim Schellhammer, prin. Fax 964-8245
Other Schools – See Gaylord

Ashby, Grant, Pop. 435
Ashby SD 261 300/PK-12
PO Box 30 56309 218-747-2257
Alan Niemann, supt. Fax 747-2289
www.ashby.k12.mn.us
Ashby JSHS 100/7-12
PO Box 30 56309 218-747-2257
Nate Meissner, prin. Fax 747-2289

Aurora, Saint Louis, Pop. 1,668
Mesabi East SD 2711 1,000/PK-12
601 N 1st St W 55705 218-229-3321
Gregg Allen, supt. Fax 229-3736
www.mesabieast.k12.mn.us/
Mesabi East JSHS 400/7-12
601 N 1st St W 55705 218-229-3321
Erik Erie, prin. Fax 229-3736

Austin, Mower, Pop. 24,273
Austin SD 492 4,700/PK-12
401 3rd Ave NW 55912 507-460-1900
David Krenz, supt. Fax 460-1939
www.austin.k12.mn.us
Austin Area Learning Center 100/Alt
301 3rd St NW 55912 507-460-1804
Andrea Malo, dir. Fax 460-1810
Austin HS 1,200/9-12
301 3rd St NW 55912 507-460-1800
Katie Baskin, prin. Fax 460-1810
Ellis MS 700/6-8
1700 4th Ave SE 55912 507-460-1500
Jason Senne, prin. Fax 460-1510

Pacelli JSHS 100/6-12
311 4th Ave NW 55912 507-437-3278
Laura Marreel, prin. Fax 433-5693
Riverland Community College Post-Sec.
1900 8th Ave NW 55912 507-433-0600

Babbitt, Saint Louis, Pop. 1,456
Saint Louis County ISD 2142
Supt. — See Virginia
Northeast Range S 100/PK-12
30 South Dr 55706 218-827-3101
Kelly Engman, prin. Fax 827-3103

Badger, Roseau, Pop. 364
Badger SD 676 300/PK-12
PO Box 68 56714 218-528-3201
Tom Jerome, supt. Fax 528-3366
www.badger.k12.mn.us/
Badger JSHS 100/7-12
PO Box 68 56714 218-528-3201
Thomas Jerome, prin. Fax 528-3366

Bagley, Clearwater, Pop. 1,356
Bagley SD 162 1,000/PK-12
202 Bagley Ave NW 56621 218-694-6184
Steve Cairns, supt. Fax 694-3221
www.bagley.k12.mn.us/
Bagley JSHS 400/7-12
1130 Main Ave N 56621 218-694-3120
Dave Gooch, prin. Fax 694-3225

Barnesville, Clay, Pop. 2,545
Barnesville SD 146 900/PK-12
PO Box 189 56514 218-354-2217
Scott Loeslie, supt. Fax 354-7260
www.barnesville.k12.mn.us/
Barnesville JSHS 400/7-12
PO Box 189 56514 218-354-2228
Bryan Strand, prin. Fax 354-2305

Barnum, Carlton, Pop. 583
Barnum SD 91 800/PK-12
3675 County Road 140 55707 218-389-6978
David Bottem, supt. Fax 389-3259
www.barnum.k12.mn.us
Barnum JSHS 400/7-12
3675 County Road 140 55707 218-389-3273
Brian Kazmierczak, prin. Fax 389-3259

Barrett, Grant, Pop. 415
West Central Area SD 2342 600/PK-12
301 County Road 2 56311 320-528-2650
Dr. Charles Cheney, supt. Fax 528-2279
www.westcentralareaschools.net
West Central Area Secondary S 300/5-12
301 County Road 2 56311 320-528-2520
Claire Vincent, prin. Fax 528-2609

Battle Lake, Otter Tail, Pop. 865
Battle Lake SD 542 400/K-12
402 W Summit St 56515 218-864-5215
Jeff Drake, supt. Fax 864-0919
www.battlelake.k12.mn.us/
Battle Lake JSHS 200/7-12
402 W Summit St 56515 218-864-5215
Ryan Severson, prin. Fax 864-8651

Baudette, Lake of the Woods, Pop. 1,074
Lake of the Woods SD 390 500/PK-12
PO Box 310 56623 218-634-2735
Jeff Nelson, supt. Fax 634-2467
lakeofthewoodsschool.org
Lake of the Woods JSHS 200/7-12
PO Box 310 56623 218-634-2510
Brain Novak, prin. Fax 634-2750

Baxter, Crow Wing, Pop. 7,503
Brainerd SD 181
Supt. — See Brainerd
Forestview MS 1,900/5-8
12149 Knollwood Dr 56425 218-454-6000
Jonathan Anderson, prin. Fax 454-6687

Lake Region Christian S 200/PK-12
7398 Fairview Rd 56425 218-828-1226
Steve Ogren, prin. Fax 828-1643

Becker, Sherburne, Pop. 4,467
Becker SD 726 2,800/PK-12
12000 Hancock St SE 55308 763-261-4502
Dr. Stephen Malone, supt. Fax 261-4559
www.becker.k12.mn.us
Becker HS 800/9-12
12000 Hancock St SE 55308 763-261-4501
Sandra Logrono, prin. Fax 261-4559
Becker MS 700/6-8
12000 Hancock St SE 55308 763-261-6300
Nancy Helmer, prin. Fax 261-6306

Belgrade, Stearns, Pop. 733
Belgrade-Brooten-Elrosa SD 2364 700/PK-12
PO Box 339 56312 320-254-8211
Matt Bullard, supt. Fax 254-3784
www.bbejaguars.org
Belgrade-Brooten-Elrosa JSHS 300/7-12
PO Box 339 56312 320-254-8211
Matt Bullard, prin. Fax 254-3784

Belle Plaine, Scott, Pop. 6,520
Belle Plaine SD 716 1,600/PK-12
130 S Willow St 56011 952-873-2400
Dr. Ryan Laager, supt. Fax 873-6909
www.belleplaine.k12.mn.us/
Belle Plaine HS 500/9-12
220 S Market St 56011 952-873-2403
Dave Kreft, prin. Fax 378-2420
Belle Plaine JHS 300/7-8
220 S Market St 56011 952-873-2403
Dave Kreft, prin. Fax 378-2420

Bemidji, Beltrami, Pop. 12,863
Bemidji SD 31 5,000/PK-12
502 Minnesota Ave NW 56601 218-333-3100
James Hess Ed.D., supt. Fax 333-3129
www.bemidji.k12.mn.us
Bemidji Alternative Education Center 50/Alt
502 Minnesota Ave NW 56601 218-333-3299
Tama Wesely, prin. Fax 759-3462
Bemidji HS 1,400/9-12
502 Minnesota Ave NW 56601 218-444-1600
Brian Stefanich, prin. Fax 444-1630
Bemidji MS 1,100/6-8
502 Minnesota Ave NW 56601 218-333-3215
Drew Hildenbrand, prin. Fax 333-3333
Lumberjack HS 100/Alt
502 Minnesota Ave NW 56601 218-444-1600
Brian Stefanich, prin. Fax 444-1630

Bemidji State University Post-Sec.
1500 Birchmont Dr NE 56601 218-755-2001
Northwest Technical College Post-Sec.
905 Grant Ave SE 56601 218-333-6600
Oak Hills Christian College Post-Sec.
1600 Oak Hills Rd SW 56601 218-751-8670

Benson, Swift, Pop. 3,222
Benson SD 777 700/PK-12
1400 Montana Ave 56215 320-843-2710
Dennis Laumeyer, supt. Fax 843-2262
www.benson.k12.mn.us
Benson Area Learning Center 50/Alt
1400 Montana Ave 56215 320-843-2710
Jonas Grossman, dir. Fax 843-2262
Benson HS 400/7-12
1400 Montana Ave 56215 320-843-2710
Dennis Laumeyer, prin. Fax 843-2262

Bertha, Todd, Pop. 494
Bertha-Hewitt SD 786 400/K-12
PO Box 8 56437 218-924-2500
Eric Koep, supt. Fax 924-3252
www.isd786.org
Bertha JSHS 200/7-12
PO Box 8 56437 218-924-2500
Darren Glynn, prin. Fax 924-3252

Bigfork, Itasca, Pop. 444
Grand Rapids SD 318
Supt. — See Grand Rapids
Bigfork HS 100/7-12
PO Box 228 56628 218-743-3444
Scott Patrow, prin. Fax 743-3443

Big Lake, Sherburne, Pop. 9,820
Big Lake SD 727 3,300/PK-12
501 Minnesota Ave 55309 763-262-2536
Steve Westerberg, supt. Fax 262-2539
www.biglake.k12.mn.us
Big Lake HS 900/9-12
501 Minnesota Ave 55309 763-262-2547
Bob Dockendorf, prin. Fax 262-2543
Big Lake MS 700/6-8
601 Minnesota Ave 55309 763-262-2567
Mark Ernst, prin. Fax 262-2563

Birchdale, Koochiching
South Koochiching-Rainy River ISD 363
Supt. — See Northome
Indus JSHS 100/7-12
8560 Highway 11 56629 218-634-2425
Laurie Bitter, prin. Fax 634-1334

Blackduck, Beltrami, Pop. 754
Blackduck SD 32 600/PK-12
PO Box 550 56630 218-835-5200
Mark Lundin, supt. Fax 835-4491
blackduck.k12.mn.us
Blackduck HS 300/7-12
PO Box 550 56630 218-835-5210
Joshua Grover, prin. Fax 835-5281

Blaine, Anoka, Pop. 55,728
Anoka-Hennepin SD 11
Supt. — See Anoka
Blaine HS 2,900/9-12
12555 University Ave NE 55434 763-506-6500
Jason Paske, prin. Fax 506-6503
Roosevelt MS 1,100/6-8
650 125th Ave NE 55434 763-506-5800
Greg Blodgett, prin. Fax 506-5803

Spring Lake Park SD 16
Supt. — See Spring Lake Park
Westwood MS 1,200/6-8
711 91st Ave NE 55434 763-600-5300
Tom Larson, prin. Fax 600-5313

Minnesota School of Business Post-Sec.
3680 Pheasant Ridge Dr NE 55449 763-225-8000
Rasmussen College Post-Sec.
3629 95th Ave NE 55014 763-795-4720
Regency Beauty Academy Post-Sec.
1351 113th Ave NE 55434 763-784-9102

Blooming Prairie, Steele, Pop. 1,975
Blooming Prairie SD 756 700/PK-12
202 4th Ave NW 55917 507-583-4426
Barry Olson, supt. Fax 583-7952
www.blossoms.k12.mn.us
Blooming Prairie JSHS 300/7-12
202 4th Ave NW 55917 507-583-4426
John Worke, prin. Fax 583-7952

Bloomington, Hennepin, Pop. 80,538
Bloomington SD 271 10,200/PK-12
1350 W 106th St 55431 952-681-6400
Les Fujitake, supt. Fax 681-6401
www.bloomington.k12.mn.us/
Bloomington Career and College Academy 9-12
8800 Queen Ave S 55431 952-681-6138
Gary Kressin, dir.
Jefferson HS 1,700/9-12
4001 W 102nd St 55437 952-806-7600
Jaysen Andersen, prin. Fax 806-7601
Kennedy HS 1,500/9-12
9701 Nicollet Ave S 55420 952-681-5000
Andrew Beaton, prin. Fax 681-5001
Oak Grove MS 800/6-8
1300 W 106th St 55431 952-681-6600
Brian Ingemann, prin. Fax 681-6601
Olson MS 900/6-8
4551 W 102nd St 55437 952-806-8600
Jeremy Kuhns, prin. Fax 806-8601
Valley View MS 700/6-8
8900 Portland Ave S 55420 952-681-5800
Megan Willrett, prin. Fax 681-5801

Academy College Post-Sec.
1600 W 82nd St Ste 100 55431 952-851-0066
Bethany Academy 200/K-12
4300 W 98th St 55437 952-831-8686
Nancy Johnson, head sch Fax 831-9568
Empire Beauty School Post-Sec.
9749 Lyndale Ave S 55420 952-881-8662
National American University Post-Sec.
7801 Metro Pkwy Ste 200 55425 952-356-3600
Normandale Community College Post-Sec.
9700 France Ave S 55431 952-358-8200
Northwestern Health Sciences University Post-Sec.
2501 W 84th St 55431 952-888-4777
Rasmussen College Post-Sec.
4400 W 78th St Fl 6 55435 952-545-2000

Blue Earth, Faribault, Pop. 3,328
Blue Earth Area ISD 2860 1,000/K-12
315 E 6th St 56013 507-526-3188
Evan Gough, supt. Fax 526-2432
www.blueearth.k12.mn.us
Blue Earth Area HS 400/8-12
1125 N Grove St 56013 507-526-3201
Richard Schneider, prin. Fax 526-3260

Bluffton, Otter Tail, Pop. 204

SonRise Christian S, PO Box 65 56518 50/PK-12
Cindi Wimer, admin. 218-385-3774

Braham, Isanti, Pop. 1,757
Braham SD 314 800/K-12
531 Elmhurst Ave S 55006 320-396-3313
Ken Gagner, supt. Fax 396-3068
www.braham.k12.mn.us
Braham Area JSHS 400/7-12
531 Elmhurst Ave S 55006 320-396-4444
Shawn Kuhnke, prin. Fax 396-3068

Brainerd, Crow Wing, Pop. 13,204
Brainerd SD 181 6,400/PK-12
804 Oak St 56401 218-454-6900
Laine Larson, supt. Fax 454-5549
www.isd181.org
Brainerd HS 1,900/9-12
702 S 5th St 56401 218-454-6200
Andrea Rusk, prin. Fax 824-6325
Brainerd Learning Center 100/Alt
311 10th Ave NE 56401 218-454-5400
Jessica Haapajoki, prin. Fax 454-5401
Lincoln Education Center 100/Alt
604 S 6th St 56401 218-454-6600
Nancy Anderson, admin. Fax 454-6601
Other Schools – See Baxter

Central Lakes College Post-Sec.
501 W College Dr 56401 218-855-8000

Brandon, Douglas, Pop. 489
Brandon-Evansville ISD 2908 400/PK-12
PO Box 185 56315 320-834-4084
Dean Yocum, supt. Fax 524-2228
www.b-e.k12.mn.us
Brandon-Evansville HS 100/9-12
PO Box 185 56315 320-524-2263
Tom Trisko, prin. Fax 524-2228
Other Schools – See Evansville

Breckenridge, Wilkin, Pop. 3,345
Breckenridge SD 846 600/PK-12
810 Beede Ave 56520 218-643-6822
Diane Cordes, supt. Fax 641-4035
www.breckenridge.k12.mn.us
Breckenridge HS 300/9-12
710 13th St N 56520 218-643-2694
Ivan Hirst, prin. Fax 643-5229

Brewster, Nobles, Pop. 468
Round Lake-Brewster SD 200/PK-8
PO Box 309 56119 507-842-5951
Raymond Hassing, supt. Fax 842-5365
www.rlb.mntm.org
Round Lake-Brewster MS 50/7-8
PO Box 309 56119 507-842-5951
Raymond Hassing, prin. Fax 842-5365

Brooklyn Center, Hennepin, Pop. 28,921
Brooklyn Center SD 286 2,200/PK-12
6300 Shingle Creek Pky #286 55430 763-450-3386
Mark Bonine, supt. Fax 560-2647
www.brooklyncenterschools.org
Brooklyn Center Secondary 800/6-12
6500 Humboldt Ave N 55430 763-561-2120
Carly Jarva, prin. Fax 450-3477
Other Schools – See Minneapolis

Minnesota School of Business Post-Sec.
5910 Shingle Creek Pkwy 55430 763-566-7777
National American University Post-Sec.
6200 Shingle Creek Pkwy 130 55430 763-852-7500

Brooklyn Park, Hennepin, Pop. 73,081
Osseo Area ISD 279
Supt. — See Maple Grove
Brooklyn MS 600/6-8
7377 Noble Ave N 55443 763-569-7700
Kim Monette, prin. Fax 569-7707
North View Intl Baccalaureate World MS 500/6-8
5869 69th Ave N 55429 763-585-7200
Diana Bledsoe, prin. Fax 585-7210
Osseo Area Learning Center 50/Alt
7300 Boone Ave N 55428 763-391-8890
Kristen Hauge, prin. Fax 391-8895
Park Center Intl Baccalaureate World SHS 1,300/9-12
7300 Brooklyn Blvd 55443 763-569-7600
Heather Miller-Cink, prin. Fax 569-7606

Hennepin Technical College Post-Sec.
9000 Brooklyn Blvd 55445 952-995-1300
Maranatha Christian Academy 700/PK-12
9201 75th Ave N 55428 763-488-7900
Brian Sullivan, admin. Fax 315-7294
North Hennepin Community College Post-Sec.
7411 85th Ave N 55445 763-488-0391
Rasmussen College Post-Sec.
8301 93rd Ave N 55445 763-493-4500

Browerville, Todd, Pop. 779
Browerville SD 787 400/PK-12
PO Box 185 56438 320-594-2272
Scott Vedbraaten, supt. Fax 594-8105
www.browerville.k12.mn.us/
Browerville JSHS 200/7-12
PO Box 185 56438 320-594-2272
Patrick Sutlief, prin. Fax 594-8105

Browns Valley, Traverse, Pop. 577
Browns Valley SD 801 100/PK-8
PO Box N 56219 320-695-2103
Brenda Reed, supt. Fax 695-2868
www.brownsvalley.k12.mn.us/
Browns Valley MS 50/5-8
PO Box N 56219 320-695-2103
Brenda Reed, supt. Fax 695-2868

Buffalo, Wright, Pop. 15,192
Buffalo-Hanover-Montrose SD 5,800/K-12
214 1st Ave NE 55313 763-682-5200
Scott Thielman, supt. Fax 682-8785
www.bhmschools.org
Buffalo Community MS 1,300/6-8
1300 Highway 25 N 55313 763-682-8200
Matt Lubben, prin. Fax 682-8209
Buffalo HS 1,800/9-12
877 Bison Blvd 55313 763-682-8100
Mark Mischke, prin. Fax 682-8118
Phoenix Learning Center 50/Alt
800 8th St NE 55313 763-682-8680
Kris Thompson, admin. Fax 682-8681

Buffalo Lake, Renville, Pop. 721
Buffalo Lake-Hector-Stewart SD 2159 600/PK-12
211 3rd St NE 55314 320-833-5311
David Hansen, supt. Fax 833-5311
www.blhsd.org
Other Schools – See Hector

Burnsville, Dakota, Pop. 58,440
Burnsville-Eagan-Savage ISD 191 7,600/K-12
200 River Ridge Ct 55337 952-707-2000
Dr. Joseph M. Gothard, supt. Fax 707-2002
www.isd191.org
Burnsville HS 2,000/9-12
600 Highway 13 E 55337 952-707-2100
David Helke, prin. Fax 707-2102
Metcalf MS 400/6-8
2250 Diffley Rd 55337 952-707-2400
Kelly Ronn, prin. Fax 707-2402
Nicollet MS 200/6-8
400 E 134th St 55337 952-707-2600
Renee Brandner, prin. Fax 707-2602
Other Schools – See Eagan, Savage

Southview Christian S — 100/PK-10
15304 County Road 5 55306 — 952-898-2727
Rayleen Hansen M.A., prin. — Fax 898-0457

Butterfield, Watonwan, Pop. 581
Butterfield SD 836 — 200/PK-12
PO Box 189 56120 — 507-956-2771
Sandra Novak, supt. — Fax 956-3431
butterfield.k12.mn.us
Butterfield JSHS — 100/7-12
PO Box 189 56120 — 507-956-2771
Barry Schmidt, prin. — Fax 956-3431

Byron, Olmsted, Pop. 4,841
Byron SD 531 — 1,700/PK-12
630 1st Ave SW 55920 — 507-775-2383
Jeffrey Elstad, supt. — Fax 775-2385
www.bears.byron.k12.mn.us
Byron HS — 500/9-12
1887 2nd Ave NW 55920 — 507-775-2301
Steve Willman, prin. — Fax 775-2303
Byron MS — 400/6-8
601 4th St NW 55920 — 507-775-2189
Richard Swanson, prin. — Fax 775-2825

Caledonia, Houston, Pop. 2,844
Caledonia SD 299 — 700/PK-12
511 W Main St 55921 — 507-725-3389
Benjamin Barton, supt. — Fax 725-3558
www.cps.k12.mn.us/
Caledonia Area HS — 200/9-12
825 N Warrior Ave 55921 — 507-725-3316
Mary Morem, prin. — Fax 725-3319
Caledonia Area MS — 100/6-8
825 N Warrior Ave 55921 — 507-725-3316
Mary Morem, prin. — Fax 725-3319

Cambridge, Isanti, Pop. 7,948
Cambridge-Isanti SD 911 — 5,200/PK-12
625A Main St N 55008 — 763-689-6188
Dr. Raymond Queener, supt. — Fax 689-6200
www.c-ischools.org
Cambridge-Isanti HS — 1,600/9-12
430 8th Ave NW 55008 — 763-689-6066
Brenda Damiani, prin. — Fax 689-6060
Cambridge MS — 600/6-8
31374 Xylite St NE 55008 — 763-552-6300
Charlie Burroughs, prin. — Fax 552-6399
Riverside Academy — Alt
625 Main St N 55008 — 763-552-6262
Rebecca Fuller, dir. — Fax 552-6269
Other Schools – See Isanti

Anoka-Ramsey Community College — Post-Sec.
300 Spirit River Dr S 55008 — 763-433-1100
Cambridge Christian S — 200/PK-12
2211 Old Main St S 55008 — 763-689-3806
Scott Thune, supt. — Fax 689-3807

Campbell, Wilkin, Pop. 158
Campbell-Tintah SD 852 — 100/PK-12
PO Box 8 56522 — 218-630-5311
Kyle Edgerton, supt. — Fax 630-5881
www.campbell.k12.mn.us
Campbell-Tintah S — 100/PK-12
PO Box 8 56522 — 218-630-5311
Kyle Edgerton, admin. — Fax 630-5881

Canby, Yellow Medicine, Pop. 1,782
Canby SD 891 — 500/PK-12
307 1st St W 56220 — 507-223-2001
Ryan Nielsen, supt. — Fax 223-2011
www.canbymn.org/
Canby JSHS — 300/7-12
307 1st St W 56220 — 507-223-2002
Robert Slaba, prin. — Fax 223-2012

Minnesota West Community & Tech College — Post-Sec.
1011 1st St W 56220 — 507-223-7252

Cannon Falls, Goodhue, Pop. 4,027
Cannon Falls SD 252 — 1,200/PK-12
820 Minnesota St E 55009 — 507-263-6800
Beth Giese, supt. — Fax 263-2555
www.cannonfallsschools.com
Cannon Falls Alternative Learning Center — 50/Alt
120 State St W 55009 — 507-263-6800
Tim Hodges, dir. — Fax 263-4888
Cannon Falls MSHS — 600/6-12
820 Minnesota St E 55009 — 507-263-6800
Tim Hodges, prin. — Fax 263-2555

Carlton, Carlton, Pop. 843
Carlton ISD 93 — 500/PK-12
PO Box 310 55718 — 218-384-4225
Gwen Carman, supt. — Fax 384-3543
www.carlton.k12.mn.us
Carlton JSHS — 200/6-12
PO Box 310 55718 — 218-384-4226
Craig Kotsmith, prin. — Fax 384-3607

Cass Lake, Cass, Pop. 725
Cass Lake-Bena SD 115 — 1,100/PK-12
208 Central Ave NW 56633 — 218-335-2204
Rochelle Johnson, supt. — Fax 335-2614
www.clbs.k12.mn.us
Cass Lake ALC — 100/Alt
208 Central Ave NW 56633 — 218-335-6529
Anthony Kerr, prin. — Fax 335-8826
Cass Lake-Bena HS — 200/9-12
15308 State Highway 371 NW 56633 — 218-335-2203
Bryan Hackbarth, prin. — Fax 335-7649
Cass Lake-Bena MS — 300/5-8
15314 State Highway 371 NW 56633 — 218-335-7851
Sue Chase, prin. — Fax 335-1194

Leech Lake Tribal College — Post-Sec.
PO Box 180 56633 — 218-335-4200

Center City, Chisago, Pop. 624

Hazelden Graduate School — Post-Sec.
PO Box 11 55012 — 651-213-4175

Champlin, Hennepin, Pop. 22,615
Anoka-Hennepin SD 11
Supt. — See Anoka
Champlin Park HS — 2,700/9-12
6025 109th Ave N 55316 — 763-506-6800
Michael George, prin. — Fax 506-6803
Jackson MS — 1,900/6-8
6000 109th Ave N 55316 — 763-506-5200
Thomas Hagerty, prin. — Fax 506-5203

Chanhassen, Carver, Pop. 22,622
Eastern Carver County SD 112
Supt. — See Chaska
Chanhassen HS — 1,600/9-12
2200 Lyman Blvd 55317 — 952-556-3500
Tim Dorway, prin. — Fax 556-3509

Chaska, Carver, Pop. 23,347
Eastern Carver County SD 112 — 9,200/PK-12
11 Peavey Rd 55318 — 952-556-6100
Dr. Jim Bauck, supt. — Fax 556-6109
www.district112.org/pages/112ISD
Chaska HS — 1,300/9-12
545 Pioneer Trl 55318 — 952-556-7100
Jim Bach, prin. — Fax 556-7109
Chaska MS East — 700/6-8
1600 Park Ridge Dr 55318 — 952-556-7600
Beth Holm, prin. — Fax 556-7609
Chaska MS West — 800/6-8
140 Engler Blvd 55318 — 952-556-7400
Sheryl Hough, prin. — Fax 556-7409
Integrated Arts Academy — 100/Alt
11 Peavey Rd 55318 — 952-556-6200
Tera Kaltsas, prin. — Fax 556-6109
Pioneer Ridge MS — 600/6-8
1085 Pioneer Trl 55318 — 952-556-7800
Megan Blazek, prin. — Fax 556-7809
Other Schools – See Chanhassen

Southwest Christian HS — 200/9-12
1981 Bavaria Rd 55318 — 952-556-0040
Dan Beckering, head sch — Fax 556-5567

Chatfield, Fillmore, Pop. 2,758
Chatfield SD 227 — 900/PK-12
205 Union St NE 55923 — 507-867-4210
Edward Harris, supt. — Fax 518-0704
www.chatfield.k12.mn.us
Chatfield JSHS — 400/7-12
205 Union St NE 55923 — 507-867-4210
Randy Paulson, prin. — Fax 518-0701

Chisago City, Chisago, Pop. 4,910

Chisago Lakes Baptist S — 100/PK-12
9387 Wyoming Trl 55013 — 651-257-4587

Chisholm, Saint Louis, Pop. 4,873
Chisholm SD 695 — 700/PK-12
300 3rd Ave SW 55719 — 218-254-5726
James Varichak, supt. — Fax 254-3741
www.chisholm.k12.mn.us
Chisholm HS — 300/7-12
301 4th St SW 55719 — 218-254-5726
Richard Aldrich, prin. — Fax 254-1434

Chokio, Stevens, Pop. 399
Chokio-Alberta SD 771 — 100/PK-12
PO Box 68 56221 — 320-324-7131
Dr. David Baukol, supt. — Fax 324-2731
www.chokioalberta.k12.mn.us
Chokio-Alberta S — 100/PK-12
PO Box 68 56221 — 320-324-7131
Tate Jerome, prin. — Fax 324-2731

Circle Pines, Anoka, Pop. 4,828
Centennial SD 12 — 6,300/PK-12
4707 North Rd 55014 — 763-792-6000
Brian Dietz, supt. — Fax 792-6050
www.isd12.org
Centennial ALC — 100/Alt
4203 Woodland Rd 55014 — 763-398-2960
Nick Christensen, dir. — Fax 717-4538
Centennial HS — 2,000/9-12
4757 North Rd 55014 — 763-792-5000
Tom Breuning, prin. — Fax 792-5050
Other Schools – See Lino Lakes

Clara City, Chippewa, Pop. 1,350
MACCRAY SD 2180 — 700/PK-12
PO Box 690 56222 — 320-847-2154
Brian Koslofsky, supt. — Fax 847-3239
www.maccray.k12.mn.us
MACCRAY Alternative Learning — 50/Alt
PO Box 690 56222 — 320-847-2154
Melissa Sparks, prin. — Fax 847-3239
MACCRAY JSHS — 300/7-12
PO Box 690 56222 — 320-847-2154
Melissa Sparks, prin. — Fax 847-3239

Clarissa, Todd, Pop. 674
Eagle Valley SD 2759 — 300/PK-12
PO Box 468 56440 — 218-756-3631
Dessica Veum, supt. — Fax 738-6493
www.evps.k12.mn.us
Other Schools – See Eagle Bend

Clearbrook, Clearwater, Pop. 513
Clearbrook-Gonvick SD 2311 — 400/PK-12
16770 Clearwater Lake Rd 56634 — 218-776-3112
Wayne Olson, supt. — Fax 776-3117
www.clearbrook-gonvick.k12.mn.us
Clearbrook-Gonvick JSHS — 200/7-12
16770 Clearwater Lake Rd 56634 — 218-776-3112
Jeff Burgess, prin. — Fax 776-3117

Cleveland, LeSueur, Pop. 714
Cleveland SD 391 — 300/PK-12
PO Box 310 56017 — 507-931-5953
Brian Phillips, supt. — Fax 931-9088
cleveland.k12.mn.us/
Cleveland S — 300/PK-12
PO Box 310 56017 — 507-931-5953
Scott Lusk, prin. — Fax 931-9088

Climax, Polk, Pop. 262
Climax-Shelly SD 592 — 100/PK-12
PO Box 67 56523 — 218-857-2385
Norman Baumgarn, supt. — Fax 857-3544
www.climax.k12.mn.us
Climax-Shelly S — 100/PK-12
PO Box 67 56523 — 218-857-2385
Nancy Newcomb, prin. — Fax 857-3544

Clinton, Big Stone, Pop. 449
Clinton-Graceville-Beardsley SD 2888 — 300/PK-12
PO Box 361 56225 — 320-325-5282
Phil Grant, supt. — Fax 325-5509
www.graceville.k12.mn.us
Lismore Colony S — 50/K-12
PO Box 361 56225 — 320-325-5583
Larry Mischke, prin. — Fax 325-5509
Other Schools – See Graceville

Cloquet, Carlton, Pop. 11,711
Cloquet SD 94 — 2,400/K-12
302 14th St 55720 — 218-879-6721
Ken Scarbrough, supt. — Fax 879-6724
www.isd94.org
Cloquet Area Alternative Education — 50/Alt
302 14th St 55720 — 218-879-0115
Connie Hyde, prin. — Fax 879-6941
Cloquet HS — 700/9-12
1000 18th St 55720 — 218-879-3393
Warren Peterson, prin. — Fax 879-6494
Cloquet MS — 500/6-8
509 Carlton Ave 55720 — 218-879-3328
Tom Brenner, prin. — Fax 879-4175

Fond du Lac Tribal Community College — Post-Sec.
2101 14th St 55720 — 218-879-0800

Cokato, Wright, Pop. 2,654
Dassel-Cokato SD 466 — 2,300/PK-12
4852 Reardon Ave SW 55321 — 320-286-4100
Jeff Powers, supt. — Fax 286-4101
www.dc.k12.mn.us
Dassel-Cokato Area Learning Center — 50/Alt
4852 Reardon Ave SW 55321 — 320-286-4100
Jon Nelson, dir. — Fax 286-4132
Dassel-Cokato HS — 600/9-12
4852 Reardon Ave SW 55321 — 320-286-4100
Dean Jennissen, prin. — Fax 286-4201
Dassel-Cokato MS — 700/5-8
4852 Reardon Ave SW 55321 — 320-286-4100
Alisa Johnson, prin. — Fax 286-4176

Cold Spring, Stearns, Pop. 3,975
Rocori SD 750 — 2,000/PK-12
534 5th Ave N 56320 — 320-685-4901
Scott Staska, supt. — Fax 685-4906
www.rocori.k12.mn.us/
Rocori ALC, 534 5th Ave N 56320 — 50/Alt
Mindi Jenson, admin. — 320-685-4904
Rocori HS — 700/9-12
534 5th Ave N 56320 — 320-685-8683
Mark Jenson, prin. — Fax 685-4968
Rocori MS — 500/6-8
534 5th Ave N 56320 — 320-685-3296
Mark Jenson, prin. — Fax 685-3448

Coleraine, Itasca, Pop. 1,927
Greenway SD 316
Supt. — See Marble
Greenway HS — 300/5-12
PO Box 520 55722 — 218-245-1287
Jeff Britten, prin. — Fax 245-2397

Collegeville, Stearns

St. Johns Preparatory S — 300/6-12
PO Box 4000 56321 — 320-363-3321
Pamela McCarthy, prin. — Fax 525-7737
St. John's University — Post-Sec.
PO Box 2000 56321 — 320-363-2011

Columbia Heights, Anoka, Pop. 18,748
Columbia Heights SD 13 — 3,100/PK-12
1440 49th Ave NE 55421 — 763-528-4500
Kathy Kelly, supt. — Fax 571-9203
www.colheights.k12.mn.us
Columbia Academy — 700/6-8
900 49th Ave NE 55421 — 763-586-4701
Duane Berkas, prin. — Fax 528-4707
Columbia Heights HS — 800/9-12
1400 49th Ave NE 55421 — 763-528-4600
Dan Wrobleski, prin. — Fax 571-9267

Comfrey, Brown, Pop. 378
Comfrey SD 81 — 200/K-12
305 Ochre St W 56019 — 507-877-3491
Kirsten Hutchison, supt. — Fax 877-3492
www.comfreyps.new.rschooltoday.com
Comfrey JSHS — 100/7-12
305 Ochre St W 56019 — 507-877-3491
Kirsten Hutchison, admin. — Fax 877-3492

Cook, Saint Louis, Pop. 560
Saint Louis County ISD 2142
Supt. — See Virginia
North Woods S — 300/PK-12
10248 E Olson Rd 55723 — 218-666-5221
John Vukmanich, prin. — Fax 666-5223

Coon Rapids, Anoka, Pop. 59,722
Anoka-Hennepin SD 11
Supt. — See Anoka
Anoka-Hennepin Regional HS — 200/Alt
1313 Coon Rapids Blvd NW 55433 — 763-506-7400
Nancy Chave, prin. — Fax 506-7403
Coon Rapids HS — 2,200/9-12
2340 Northdale Blvd NW 55433 — 763-506-7100
Annette Ziegler, prin. — Fax 506-7103
Coon Rapids MS — 1,200/6-8
11600 Raven St NW 55433 — 763-506-4800
Tom Shaw, prin. — Fax 506-4803
Northdale MS — 1,100/6-8
11301 Dogwood St NW 55448 — 763-506-5400
Jeff Leach, prin. — Fax 506-5403

Pathways | Adult
11238 Crooked Lake Blvd NW 55433 763-506-7600
Kathy Ferguson, prin. Fax 506-7603

Anoka-Ramsey Community College | Post-Sec.
11200 Mississippi Blvd NW 55433 763-433-1100

Cottage Grove, Washington, Pop. 33,853
South Washington County SD 833 | 17,600/PK-12
7362 E Point Douglas Rd S 55016 651-425-6300
Keith Jacobus Ph.D., supt. Fax 425-6318
www.sowashco.org
Alternative HS | 100/Alt
8400 E Point Douglas Rd S 55016 651-425-7000
Mike Mahaffey, prin. Fax 425-7015
Cottage Grove MS | 1,200/6-8
9775 Indian Blvd S 55016 651-425-6800
Elise Block, prin. Fax 425-6828
Park HS | 1,800/9-12
8040 80th St S 55016 651-425-3700
Ginger Garski, prin. Fax 425-3705
Other Schools – See Saint Paul Park, Woodbury

Cottonwood, Lyon, Pop. 1,201
Lakeview SD 2167 | 600/PK-12
PO Box 107 56229 507-423-5164
Chris Fenske, supt. Fax 423-5568
www.lakeview2167.com
Lakeview HS | 300/7-12
PO Box 107 56229 507-423-5166
Scott Hanson, prin. Fax 423-5568

Cromwell, Carlton, Pop. 231
Cromwell-Wright SD 95 | 300/PK-12
PO Box 7 55726 218-644-3737
Nathan Libbon, supt. Fax 644-3992
www.cromwellwright.k12.mn.us
Cromwell-Wright JSHS | 100/7-12
PO Box 7 55726 218-644-3716
Nathan Libbon, admin. Fax 644-3992

Crookston, Polk, Pop. 7,779
Crookston SD 593 | 1,300/PK-12
402 W Fisher Ave Ste 593 56716 218-281-5313
Chris Bates, supt. Fax 281-3505
www.crookston.k12.mn.us
Crookston HS | 500/7-12
402 W Fisher Ave 56716 218-281-2144
Eric Bubna, prin. Fax 281-4709
New Paths Area Learning Center | 100/Alt
121 E 3rd St 56716 218-281-5864
Eric Bubna, prin. Fax 281-2386

University of Minnesota Crookston | Post-Sec.
2900 University Ave 56716 218-281-6510

Crosby, Crow Wing, Pop. 2,354
Crosby-Ironton SD 182 | 1,100/PK-12
711 Poplar St 56441 218-545-8801
Dr. Jamie Skjeveland, supt. Fax 545-8836
www.ci.k12.mn.us
Crosby-Ironton JSHS | 500/7-12
711 Poplar St 56441 218-545-8802
James Christenson, prin. Fax 545-8835

Crystal, Hennepin, Pop. 21,394
Robbinsdale SD 281
Supt. — See New Hope
FAIR S Crystal | Alt
3915 Adair Ave N 55422 763-971-4500
Christina Hester, prin. Fax 971-4531

Culver, Saint Louis
Saint Louis County ISD 2142
Supt. — See Virginia
South Ridge S | 300/PK-12
8162 Swan Lake Rd 55779 218-345-6789
Andrew Bernard, prin. Fax 345-6790

Dawson, Lac qui Parle, Pop. 1,527
Dawson-Boyd SD 378 | 500/PK-12
848 Chestnut St 56232 320-769-2955
Shane Tappe, supt. Fax 769-4502
dawsonboydschools.org/
Dawson-Boyd JSHS | 200/7-12
848 Chestnut St 56232 320-769-2955
Ryan Stotesbery, prin. Fax 769-4502

Deer River, Itasca, Pop. 888
Deer River SD 317 | 900/PK-12
PO Box 307 56636 218-246-2420
Matt Grose, supt. Fax 246-8948
www.isd317.org
Deer River JSHS | 400/6-12
PO Box 307 56636 218-246-8241
Joseph Akre, prin. Fax 246-8717

Delano, Wright, Pop. 5,379
Delano SD 879 | 2,400/PK-12
700 Elm Ave E 55328 763-972-3365
Matthew Schoen, supt. Fax 972-6706
www.delano.k12.mn.us
Delano HS | 800/9-12
700 Elm Ave E 55328 763-972-3365
Dr. Steven Heil, prin. Fax 972-6706
Delano MS | 700/5-8
700 Elm Ave E 55328 763-972-3365
Barry Voight, prin. Fax 972-6876

Detroit Lakes, Becker, Pop. 8,324
Detroit Lakes SD 22 | 2,600/PK-12
PO Box 766 56502 218-847-9271
Doug Froke, supt. Fax 847-9273
www.dlschools.net/
Detroit Lakes ALC | 50/Alt
826 Summit Ave 56501 218-847-5687
Peter Sasso-Lundin, prin. Fax 847-9273
Detroit Lakes HS | 800/9-12
1301 Roosevelt Ave 56501 218-847-4491
Darren Wolf, prin. Fax 846-1797
Detroit Lakes MS | 600/6-8
510 11th Ave 56501 218-847-9228
Michael Suckert, prin. Fax 847-0057

MN State Community & Technical College | Post-Sec.
900 Highway 34 E 56501 218-846-3700

Dilworth, Clay, Pop. 3,965
Dilworth-Glyndon-Felton SD 2164 | 1,500/PK-12
PO Box 188 56529 218-477-6800
Bryan Thygeson, supt. Fax 477-6807
www.dgf.k12.mn.us
Dilworth-Glyndon-Felton MS | 300/6-8
PO Box 188 56529 218-477-6803
Heidi Critchley, prin. Fax 477-6807
Other Schools – See Glyndon

Dodge Center, Dodge, Pop. 2,647
Triton SD 2125 | 1,200/PK-12
813 W Highway St 55927 507-418-7530
Brett Joyce, supt. Fax 374-6524
www.triton.k12.mn.us
Triton HS | 300/9-12
813 W Highway St 55927 507-418-7520
Craig Schlichting, prin. Fax 374-2447
Triton MS | 300/6-8
813 W Highway St 55927 507-418-7510
Luke Lutterman, prin. Fax 633-8673

Duluth, Saint Louis, Pop. 83,742
Duluth ISD 709 | 8,200/PK-12
215 N 1st Ave E 55802 218-336-8700
William Gronseth, supt. Fax 336-8773
www.isd709.org
Area Learning Center | 200/Alt
215 N 1st Ave E 55802 218-336-8756
Adrian Norman, prin. Fax 336-8770
Denfeld HS | 1,000/9-12
401 N 44th Ave W 55807 218-336-8830
Tonya Sconiers, prin. Fax 336-8844
East HS | 1,600/9-12
301 N 40th Ave E 55804 218-336-8845
Danette Seboe, prin. Fax 336-8859
Lincoln Park MS | 500/6-8
3215 W 3rd St 55806 218-336-8880
Brenda Vatthauer, prin. Fax 336-8894
Ordean East MS | 900/6-8
2900 E 4th St 55812 218-336-8940
Gina Kleive, prin. Fax 336-8949
Adult Basic Education / GED | Adult
215 N 1st Ave E 55802 218-336-8790
Patti Fleege, admin. Fax 336-8791

College of Saint Scholastica | Post-Sec.
1200 Kenwood Ave 55811 218-723-6000
Cosmetology Careers Unlimited - Duluth | Post-Sec.
121 W Superior St 55802 218-722-7484
Duluth Business University | Post-Sec.
4724 Mike Colalillo Dr 55807 218-722-4000
Lake Superior College | Post-Sec.
2101 Trinity Rd 55811 218-733-7600
Lakeview Christian Academy | 200/PK-12
155 W Central Entrance 55811 218-723-8844
Todd Benson, admin. Fax 722-7850
Marshall S | 500/4-12
1215 Rice Lake Rd 55811 218-727-7266
Kevin Breen, head sch Fax 727-1569
University of Minnesota Duluth | Post-Sec.
1049 University Dr 55812 218-726-8000

Eagan, Dakota, Pop. 62,501
Burnsville-Eagan-Savage ISD 191
Supt. — See Burnsville
Burnsville Alternative HS | 100/Alt
2140 Diffley Rd 55122 952-707-4077
Janice Porter, prin. Fax 707-4024

Rosemount-Apple Valley-Eagan ISD 196
Supt. — See Rosemount
Black Hawk MS | 800/6-8
1540 Deerwood Dr 55122 651-683-8521
Richard Wendorff, prin. Fax 683-8527
Dakota Hills MS | 1,200/6-8
4183 Braddock Trl 55123 651-683-6800
Trevor Johnson, prin. Fax 683-6858
Eagan HS | 2,100/9-12
4185 Braddock Trl 55123 651-683-6900
Polly Reikowski, prin. Fax 683-6910

Everest Institute | Post-Sec.
1000 Blue Gentian Rd 55121 651-688-2145
Rasmussen College | Post-Sec.
3500 Federal Dr 55122 651-687-9000
Trinity S at River Ridge | 300/6-12
601 River Ridge Pkwy 55121 651-789-2890
Jon Balsbaugh, hdmstr. Fax 789-2891
Twin Cities Argosy University | Post-Sec.
1515 Central Pkwy 55121 888-844-2004

Eagle Bend, Todd, Pop. 527
Eagle Valley SD 2759
Supt. — See Clarissa
Eagle Valley JSHS | 100/7-12
PO Box 299 56446 218-756-3631
Dessica Veum, admin. Fax 738-6493

East Grand Forks, Polk, Pop. 8,422
East Grand Forks SD 595 | 1,800/PK-12
PO Box 151 56721 218-773-3494
Mike Kolness, supt. Fax 773-7408
www.egf.k12.mn.us/
Central MS | 400/6-8
PO Box 151 56721 218-773-1141
Lon Ellingson, prin. Fax 773-9112
East Grand Forks HS | 500/9-12
PO Box 151 56721 218-773-2405
Brian Loer, prin. Fax 773-3070

Northland Community & Technical College | Post-Sec.
2022 Central Ave NE 56721 218-793-2800
Sacred Heart HS | 100/7-12
122 3rd St NW 56721 218-773-0230
David Andrys, prin. Fax 773-7042

Eden Prairie, Hennepin, Pop. 59,499
Eden Prairie SD 272 | 9,100/PK-12
8100 School Rd 55344 952-975-7000
Curt Tryggestad Ph.D., supt. Fax 975-7020
www.edenpr.org
Central MS | 1,400/7-8
8025 School Rd 55344 952-975-7300
Nathan Swenson, prin. Fax 975-7320
Eden Prairie HS | 3,000/9-12
17185 Valley View Rd 55346 952-975-8000
Conn McCartan, prin. Fax 975-8020

International School of Minnesota | 400/PK-12
6385 Beach Rd 55344 952-918-1800
Christi Seiple-Cole, dir. Fax 918-1801

Eden Valley, Meeker, Pop. 1,031
Eden Valley-Watkins SD 463 | 1,000/PK-12
298 Brooks St N 55329 320-453-2900
Mark Messman, supt. Fax 453-5600
www.evw.k12.mn.us
Eden Valley Secondary S | 400/7-12
298 Brooks St N 55329 320-453-2900
Bruce Kiehn, prin. Fax 453-5600

Edgerton, Pipestone, Pop. 1,174
Edgerton SD 581 | 300/PK-12
PO Box 28 56128 507-442-7881
Keith Buckridge, supt. Fax 442-8541
www.edgertonpublic.com
Edgerton JSHS | 200/6-12
PO Box 28 56128 507-442-7881
Brian Gilbertson, prin. Fax 442-8541

Southwest Minnesota Christian HS | 100/9-12
550 W Elizabeth St 56128 507-442-4471
Darrel Ulferts, prin. Fax 442-5801

Edina, Hennepin, Pop. 47,052
Edina SD 273 | 8,500/K-12
5701 Normandale Rd 55424 952-848-3900
Ric Dressen Ed.D., supt. Fax 848-3901
www.edinaschools.org
Edina SHS | 2,000/10-12
6754 Valley View Rd 55439 952-848-3800
Bruce Locklear, prin. Fax 848-3801
South View MS | 1,300/6-9
4725 S View Ln 55424 952-848-3700
Timothy Anderson, prin. Fax 848-3701
Valley View MS | 1,400/6-9
6750 Valley View Rd 55439 952-848-3500
Shawn Dudley, prin. Fax 848-3501

DeVry University | Post-Sec.
7700 France Ave S Ste 575 55435 952-838-1860
Minneapolis Media Institute | Post-Sec.
4100 W 76th St 55435 866-701-1310

Elgin, Wabasha, Pop. 1,079
Plainview-Elgin-Millville ISD 2899
Supt. — See Plainview
Plainview-Elgin-Millville JHS | 200/7-8
70 1st St SE 55932 507-876-2521
Clark Olstad, prin. Fax 876-2110

Elk River, Sherburne, Pop. 22,557
Elk River Area SD 728 | 11,900/K-12
815 Highway 10 55330 763-241-3400
Bruce Watkins, supt. Fax 241-3407
www.isd728.org
Elk River HS | 1,700/9-12
900 School St NW 55330 763-241-3434
Terry Bizal, prin. Fax 241-3421
Salk MS | 800/6-8
11970 Highland Rd NW 55330 763-241-3455
Julie Athman, prin. Fax 241-3456
Sand Community HS | 100/Alt
1232 School St NW 55330 763-241-3530
Thomas Hoffman, prin. Fax 241-3532
VandenBerge MS | 500/6-8
948 Proctor Ave NW 55330 763-241-3450
Marcia Welch, prin. Fax 241-3552
Other Schools – See Rogers, Zimmerman

Minnesota School of Business | Post-Sec.
11500 193rd Ave NW 55330 763-367-7000

Ellsworth, Nobles, Pop. 460
Ellsworth SD 514 | 100/PK-12
PO Box 8 56129 507-967-2242
John Willey, supt. Fax 967-2588
www.ellsworth.mntm.org
Ellsworth S | 100/PK-12
PO Box 8 56129 507-967-2242
John Willey, prin. Fax 967-2588

Ely, Saint Louis, Pop. 3,405
ISD 696 | 400/PK-12
600 E Harvey St 55731 218-365-6166
Kevin Abrahamson, supt. Fax 365-6138
www.ely.k12.mn.us
Ely Memorial HS | 200/6-12
600 E Harvey St 55731 218-365-6166
Megan Anderson, prin. Fax 365-6138

Vermillion Community College | Post-Sec.
1900 E Camp St 55731 218-235-2100

Erskine, Polk, Pop. 492
Win-E-Mac SD 2609 | 400/PK-12
23130 345th St SE 56535 218-687-2236
Randy Bruer, supt. Fax 563-2902
www.win-e-mac.k12.mn.us
Win-E-Mac JSHS | 200/7-12
23130 345th St SE 56535 218-687-2236
Kevin McKeever, prin. Fax 563-2902

Esko, Carlton, Pop. 1,843
Esko SD 99 | 1,200/PK-12
PO Box 10 55733 218-879-2969
Aaron Fischer, supt. Fax 879-7490
www.esko.k12.mn.us/

Lincoln JSHS 600/7-12
PO Box 10 55733 218-879-4673
Greg Hexum, prin. Fax 879-7490

Evansville, Douglas, Pop. 609
Brandon-Evansville ISD 2908
Supt. — See Brandon
Brandon-Evansville MS 50/6-8
PO Box 40 56326 218-948-2241
Dean Yocum, prin. Fax 948-2441

Eveleth, Saint Louis, Pop. 3,636
Eveleth-Gilbert SD 2154 1,100/PK-12
801 Jones St 55734 218-744-7700
Jeff Carey, supt. Fax 744-4381
www.egschools.org
Eveleth-Gilbert SHS 300/9-12
801 Jones St 55734 218-744-7706
Angie Williams, prin. Fax 744-4381
Other Schools – See Gilbert

Mesabi Range Community & Technical Coll. Post-Sec.
PO Box 648 55734 218-741-3095

Excelsior, Hennepin, Pop. 2,144
Minnetonka SD 276
Supt. — See Minnetonka
Minnetonka West MS 1,100/6-8
6421 Hazeltine Blvd 55331 952-401-5300
Dr. Paula Hoff, prin. Fax 401-5350

Eyota, Olmsted, Pop. 1,965
Dover-Eyota SD 533 1,100/PK-12
615 South Ave SW 55934 507-545-2125
Michael Carolan, supt. Fax 545-2349
www.desch.org
Dover-Eyota HS 300/9-12
615 South Ave SW 55934 507-545-2631
Todd Rowekamp, prin. Fax 545-2218
Dover-Eyota MS 300/6-8
615 South Ave SW 55934 507-545-2631
Todd Rowekamp, prin. Fax 545-2218

Fairfax, Renville, Pop. 1,227
GFW SD 2365
Supt. — See Gibbon
GFW MS 200/5-8
300 2nd Ave SE 55332 507-426-7251
Ralph Fairchild, prin. Fax 426-7425

Prairie Lutheran MS 50/5-8
PO Box 130 55332 507-426-7755
Macord Johnson, prin. Fax 426-8372

Fairmont, Martin, Pop. 10,613
Fairmont Area SD 2752 1,700/PK-12
714 Victoria St Ste 103 56031 507-238-4234
Joseph Brown, supt. Fax 235-4050
fairmont.k12.mn.us
Fairmont JSHS 800/7-12
900 Johnson St 56031 507-238-4411
Kim Niss, prin. Fax 235-4130

Faribault, Rice, Pop. 23,011
Faribault SD 656 3,700/PK-12
710 17th St SW 55021 507-333-6000
Todd Sesker, supt. Fax 333-6050
www.faribault.k12.mn.us/
Faribault ALC 100/Alt
PO Box 618 55021 507-333-6187
Margaret Gare, dir. Fax 333-6048
Faribault HS 1,100/9-12
330 9th Ave SW 55021 507-333-6100
Jamie Bente, prin. Fax 333-6248
Faribault MS 900/6-8
704 17th St SW 55021 507-333-6300
Michael Meihak, prin. Fax 333-6400

Bethlehem Academy 300/6-12
105 3rd Ave SW 55021 507-334-3948
Thomas Donlon, prin. Fax 334-3949
Minnesota School for the Deaf Post-Sec.
615 Olof Hanson Dr 55021
Shattuck - St. Marys S 400/6-12
PO Box 218 55021 507-333-1500
Nick Stoneman, pres. Fax 333-1591
South Central College Post-Sec.
1225 3rd St SW 55021 800-422-0391

Farmington, Dakota, Pop. 20,570
Farmington SD 192 6,900/K-12
20655 Flagstaff Ave 55024 651-463-5000
Jay Haugen, supt. Fax 463-5010
www.farmington.k12.mn.us
Boeckman MS 700/6-8
800 Denmark Ave 55024 651-460-1400
Dan Miller, prin. Fax 460-1410
Dodge MS 800/6-8
4200 208th St W 55024 651-460-1500
Chris Bussmann, prin. Fax 460-1510
Farmington HS 1,900/9-12
20655 Flagstaff Ave 55024 651-252-2500
Jason Berg, prin. Fax 252-2510
Gateway Academy 3-8
4100 208th St W 55024 651-463-5004
Barb Duffrin, prin. Fax 463-5021

Christian Life Academy 200/PK-12
6300 212th St W 55024 651-463-4545
Rev. Darin Kindle, admin. Fax 463-8353

Fergus Falls, Otter Tail, Pop. 12,946
Fergus Falls SD 544 3,100/PK-12
601 Randolph Ave 56537 218-998-0544
Gerald Ness, supt. Fax 755-5000
www.isd544.org
Area Learning Center 100/Alt
340 Friberg Ave 56537 218-739-2360
Dean Monke, prin. Fax 755-5000
Kennedy HS 1,200/9-12
601 Randolph Ave 56537 218-998-0544
Dean Monke, prin. Fax 998-3947
Kennedy MS 500/6-8
601 Randolph Ave 56537 218-998-0544
Dean Monke, prin. Fax 755-5000

Hillcrest Lutheran Academy 200/7-12
610 Hillcrest Dr 56537 218-739-3371
Jeff Isaac M.Ed., prin. Fax 739-3372
Lutheran Brethren Seminary Post-Sec.
815 W Vernon Ave 56537 218-739-3375
MN State Community & Technical College Post-Sec.
1414 College Way 56537 218-736-1500

Fertile, Polk, Pop. 831
Fertile-Beltrami SD 599 400/PK-12
210 S Mill St 56540 218-945-6933
Brian Clarke, supt. Fax 945-6934
fertilebeltrami.k12.mn.us
Fertile-Beltrami JSHS 200/7-12
210 S Mill St 56540 218-945-6953
Nathaniel Messick, prin. Fax 945-6934

Finlayson, Pine, Pop. 312
East Central SD 2580 700/PK-12
61085 State Highway 23 55735 320-245-2289
Andy Almos, supt. Fax 245-5453
www.eastcentral.k12.mn.us
East Central Secondary S 300/6-12
61085 State Highway 23 55735 320-245-2289
Stef Youngberg, prin. Fax 245-2448
Other Schools – See Sandstone

Fisher, Polk, Pop. 434
Fisher SD 600 300/PK-12
313 Park Ave 56723 218-891-4105
Evan Hanson, supt. Fax 891-4251
www.fisher.k12.mn.us
Fisher JSHS 100/7-12
313 Park Ave 56723 218-891-4105
Evan Hanson, admin. Fax 891-4251

Floodwood, Saint Louis, Pop. 508
Floodwood SD 698 300/PK-12
PO Box 287 55736 218-476-2285
Dr. Rae Villebrun, supt. Fax 476-2813
www.floodwood.k12.mn.us/
Floodwood HS 100/7-12
PO Box 287 55736 218-476-2285
Dr. Rae Villebrun, prin. Fax 476-2813

Foley, Benton, Pop. 2,576
Foley SD 51 1,800/PK-12
840 Norman Ave N 56329 320-968-7175
Paul Neubauer, supt. Fax 968-8608
foley.k12.mn.us
Foley HS 500/9-12
621 Penn St 56329 320-968-7246
Shayne Kusler, prin. Fax 968-8456
Foley MS 700/4-8
840 Norman Ave N 56329 320-968-6251
Brad Kelvington, prin. Fax 968-8608

Forest Lake, Washington, Pop. 18,070
Forest Lake SD 831 6,700/PK-12
6100 210th St N 55025 651-982-8100
Dr. Linda Madsen, supt. Fax 982-8114
www.flaschools.org
Area Learning Center 100/Alt
200 4th St SW 55025 651-982-3171
Kelly Tschudy-Lafean, prin. Fax 982-3172
Century JHS 900/7-9
21395 Goodview Ave N 55025 651-982-3000
John-Paul Jacobson, prin. Fax 982-3017
Forest Lake SHS 1,400/10-12
6101 Scandia Trl N 55025 651-982-8400
Dr. Steve Massey, prin. Fax 982-8428
Southwest JHS 800/7-9
943 9th Ave SW 55025 651-982-8700
Scott Geary, prin. Fax 982-8798

Foreston, Mille Lacs, Pop. 528

Faith Christian S 100/PK-12
11818 160th Ave 56330 320-294-5501
Nathan Johnson, admin. Fax 294-5197

Fosston, Polk, Pop. 1,489
Fosston SD 601 700/PK-12
301 1st St E 56542 218-435-6335
Kevin Ricke, supt. Fax 435-1663
www.fosston.k12.mn.us
Fosston JSHS 300/7-12
301 1st St E 56542 218-435-1909
Patti Johnson, prin. Fax 435-6340

Frazee, Becker, Pop. 1,295
Frazee-Vergas SD 23 900/PK-12
305 N Lake St 56544 218-334-3181
Terry S. Karger, supt. Fax 334-3182
www.frazee.k12.mn.us/
Frazee HS 400/7-12
305 N Lake St 56544 218-334-3181
Anna Potvin, prin. Fax 334-4696

Fridley, Anoka, Pop. 26,152
Fridley SD 14 2,900/K-12
6000 Moore Lake Dr W 55432 763-502-5000
Dr. Peggy Flathmann, supt. Fax 502-5040
www.fridley.k12.mn.us
Fridley HS 900/9-12
6000 Moore Lake Dr W 55432 763-502-5600
Patty Awsumb, prin. Fax 502-5640
Fridley MS 800/5-8
6100 Moore Lake Dr W 55432 763-502-5400
Matthew Boucher, prin. Fax 502-5440
Fridley Moore Lake Area Learning Center 50/Alt
6085 7th St NE 55432 763-502-5165
Amy Cochran, prin. Fax 502-5140

Al-Amal S PK-12
1401 Gardena Ave NE 55432 763-571-8886
Audrey Zahra Williams, prin. Fax 571-1925
Calvin Christian HS 100/9-12
755 73rd Ave NE 55432 763-531-1732
Wendell Schaap, prin. Fax 531-8075

Totino-Grace HS 800/9-12
1350 Gardena Ave NE 55432 763-571-9116
Cheri Broadhead, prin. Fax 571-9118

Fulda, Murray, Pop. 1,307
Fulda SD 505 300/PK-12
410 N College Ave 56131 507-425-2514
Luther Onken, supt. Fax 425-2001
www.fps.mntm.org
Fulda JSHS 200/7-12
410 N College Ave 56131 507-425-2514
Gregg Slaathaug, prin. Fax 425-2001

Gaylord, Sibley, Pop. 2,288
Sibley East SD 2310
Supt. — See Arlington
Sibley East JHS 300/7-9
PO Box 356 55334 507-237-3315
Steve Harter, prin. Fax 237-3300

Gibbon, Sibley, Pop. 764
GFW SD 2365 800/PK-12
323 E 11th St 55335 507-834-9813
Tami Martin, supt. Fax 834-6264
www.gfw.k12.mn.us
Other Schools – See Fairfax, Winthrop

Gilbert, Saint Louis, Pop. 1,775
Eveleth-Gilbert SD 2154
Supt. — See Eveleth
Eveleth-Gilbert JHS 200/7-8
Summit St 55741 218-744-7770
Todd Griepentrog, prin. Fax 744-4381

Glencoe, McLeod, Pop. 5,593
Glencoe-Silver Lake SD 2859 1,600/PK-12
1621 16th St E 55336 320-864-2499
Chris Sonju, supt. Fax 864-6320
Glencoe-Silver Lake HS 500/9-12
1621 16th St E 55336 320-864-2400
Paul Sparby, prin. Fax 864-6475
Lincoln JHS 300/PK-PK, 7-
1621 16th St E 55336 320-864-2456
Dan Svoboda, prin. Fax 864-2475

Glenville, Freeborn, Pop. 641
Glenville-Emmons SD 2886 200/K-12
PO Box 38 56036 507-448-2889
Jerry Reshetar, supt. Fax 448-2836
www.geschools.com
Glenville-Emmons JSHS 100/7-12
230 5th St SE 56036 507-448-2889
Jeff Tietje, prin. Fax 448-2836

Glenwood, Pope, Pop. 2,537
Minnewaska SD 2149 900/PK-12
25122 State Highway 28 56334 320-239-4820
Greg Schmidt, supt. Fax 239-1360
www.minnewaska.k12.mn.us
Minnewaska Area HS 300/7-12
25122 State Highway 28 56334 320-239-4800
Cory Larson, prin. Fax 239-1362

Glyndon, Clay, Pop. 1,373
Dilworth-Glyndon-Felton SD 2164
Supt. — See Dilworth
Dilworth-Glyndon-Felton HS 400/9-12
513 Parke Ave S 56547 218-477-6804
Matt Naugle, prin. Fax 477-6808

Golden Valley, Hennepin, Pop. 19,843

Breck S 1,100/PK-12
123 Ottawa Ave N 55422 763-381-8100
Edward Kim, hdmstr. Fax 381-8288

Goodhue, Goodhue, Pop. 1,166
Goodhue SD 253 700/PK-12
510 3rd Ave 55027 651-923-4447
Michael Redmond, supt. Fax 923-4036
www.goodhue.k12.mn.us
Goodhue JSHS 300/7-12
510 3rd Ave 55027 651-923-4447
Mike Harvey, prin. Fax 923-4036

Goodridge, Pennington, Pop. 132
Goodridge SD 561 200/K-12
PO Box 195 56725 218-378-4133
Galen Clow, supt. Fax 378-4142
www.goodridge.k12.mn.us/
Goodridge JSHS 100/7-12
PO Box 195 56725 218-378-4133
Becky Carlson, prin. Fax 378-4142

Graceville, Big Stone, Pop. 577
Clinton-Graceville-Beardsley SD 2888
Supt. — See Clinton
Clinton-Graceville-Beardsley HS 200/7-12
PO Box 398 56240 320-748-7233
Larry Mischke, prin. Fax 748-7159

Granada, Martin, Pop. 302
Granada - Huntley - East Chain SD 2536 200/PK-12
PO Box 17 56039 507-447-2211
Dale Brandsoy, supt. Fax 447-2214
www.ghec.k12.mn.us
Granada - Huntley - East Chain JSHS 100/7-12
PO Box 17 56039 507-447-2211
Dale Brandsoy, supt. Fax 447-2214

Grand Marais, Cook, Pop. 1,315
Cook County SD 166 300/PK-12
101 W 5th St 55604 218-387-2271
Dr. William Crandall, supt. Fax 387-1093
www.cookcountyschools.org
Cook County MSHS 200/6-12
101 W 5th St 55604 218-387-2271
Adam Nelson, prin. Fax 387-9746

Grand Meadow, Mower, Pop. 1,132
Grand Meadow SD 495 400/PK-12
PO Box 68 55936 507-754-5318
Paul W. Besel, supt. Fax 754-5608
www.gm.k12.mn.us
Grand Meadow HS 100/9-12
PO Box 68 55936 507-754-5318
Jacob Schwarz, prin. Fax 754-5608

Grand Meadow MS 100/5-8
PO Box 68 55936 507-754-5318
Jacon Schwarz, prin. Fax 754-5608

Grand Rapids, Itasca, Pop. 10,671
Grand Rapids SD 318 4,000/PK-12
820 NW 1st Ave 55744 218-327-5700
Dr. Bruce Thomas, supt. Fax 327-5702
www.isd318.org
Elkington MS 900/5-8
1000 NE 8th Ave 55744 218-327-5800
Dan Adams, prin. Fax 327-5801
Grand Rapids Area Learning Center 100/Alt
409 SE 13th St 55744 218-999-9930
Tony Pierce, prin.
Grand Rapids HS 1,100/9-12
800 NW Conifer Dr 55744 218-327-5760
Mark Schroeder, prin. Fax 327-5761
Itaskin Education Center 50/Alt
1880 River Rd 55744 218-322-4129
Tony Pierce, prin. Fax 327-2921
Middle Area Learning Center 100/Alt
1000 NE 8th Ave 55744 218-326-5800
Dan Adams, prin. Fax 326-5701
Northland Education Center 50/Alt
510 SE 13th St 55744 218-327-2570
Tony Pierce, prin.
Other Schools – See Bigfork

Itasca Community College Post-Sec.
1851 E US Highway 169 55744 218-322-2300

Granite Falls, Yellow Medicine, Pop. 2,841
Yellow Medicine East SD 2190 600/K-12
450 9th Ave 56241 320-564-4081
Dr. Rick Clark, supt. Fax 564-4781
isd2190.org/
Yellow Medicine East HS 300/6-12
450 9th Ave 56241 320-564-4083
Ryan Luft, prin. Fax 564-4782

Minnesota West Community & Tech College Post-Sec.
1593 11th Ave 56241 320-564-5000

Greenbush, Roseau, Pop. 717
Greenbush-Middle River SD 2683 400/PK-12
PO Box 70 56726 218-782-2231
Tom Jerome, supt. Fax 782-3141
www.middleriver.k12.mn.us/
Greenbush-Middle River HS 100/9-12
PO Box 70 56726 218-782-2232
Eldon Sparby, prin. Fax 782-2165
Other Schools – See Middle River

Grove City, Meeker, Pop. 630
ACGC SD 2396 700/K-12
27250 Minnesota Highway 4 56243 320-857-2271
Sherri Broderius, supt. Fax 857-2989
www.acgc.k12.mn.us
ACGC JSHS 400/5-12
27250 Minnesota Highway 4 56243 320-857-2276
Sherri Broderius, admin. Fax 857-2937

Grygla, Marshall, Pop. 220
Grygla SD 447 200/PK-12
PO Box 18 56727 218-294-6155
Galen Clow, supt. Fax 294-6766
www.grygla.k12.mn.us/
Grygla JSHS 100/7-12
PO Box 18 56727 218-294-6155
Jamie Lunsetter, prin. Fax 294-6766

Hallock, Kittson, Pop. 976
Kittson Central SD 2171 100/PK-12
PO Box 670 56728 218-843-3682
Bob Jaszczak, supt. Fax 843-2856
www.kittson.k12.mn.us
Kittson Central S 100/PK-12
PO Box 670 56728 218-843-3682
Bob Jaszczak, prin. Fax 843-2856

Halstad, Norman, Pop. 582
Norman County West SD 2527 300/PK-12
PO Box 328 56548 218-456-2151
Shawn Yates, supt. Fax 456-2193
www.ncw.k12.mn.us
Norman County West JSHS 100/7-12
PO Box 328 56548 218-456-2151
Mary Niklaus, prin. Fax 456-2193

Hancock, Stevens, Pop. 763
Hancock SD 768 300/K-12
PO Box 367 56244 320-392-5622
Loren Hacker, supt. Fax 392-5156
hancock.k12.mn.us
Hancock JSHS 100/7-12
PO Box 367 56244 320-392-5622
Tim Pahl, prin. Fax 392-5156

Harmony, Fillmore, Pop. 1,010
Fillmore Central SD 2198
Supt. — See Preston
Fillmore Central HS 300/7-12
PO Box 599 55939 507-886-6464
Heath Olstad, prin. Fax 886-6642

Hastings, Dakota, Pop. 21,783
Hastings SD 200 4,500/K-12
1000 11th St W 55033 651-480-7000
Tim Collins, supt. Fax 480-7001
www.hastings.k12.mn.us
Hastings Area Learning Center 50/Alt
213 Ramsey St 55033 651-480-7690
Todd Levos, prin. Fax 438-9082
Hastings HS 1,500/9-12
200 General Sieben Dr 55033 651-480-7470
Mike Johnson, prin. Fax 480-7474
Hastings MS 1,400/5-8
1000 11th St W 55033 651-480-7060
Mark Zuzek, prin. Fax 480-7066

Hawley, Clay, Pop. 2,037
Hawley SD 150 1,000/K-12
PO Box 608 56549 218-483-4647
Phil Jensen, supt. Fax 483-3510
www.hawley.k12.mn.us/
Hawley JSHS 500/7-12
PO Box 608 56549 218-483-3555
Mike Martin, prin. Fax 483-4802
Spring Prairie S 50/K-12
PO Box 608 56549 218-483-3316
Chris Ellingson, prin. Fax 483-4638

Hayfield, Dodge, Pop. 1,321
Hayfield SD 203 600/K-12
9 6th Ave SE 55940 507-477-3235
Belinda Selfors, supt. Fax 477-3230
hayfield.k12.mn.us
Hayfield JSHS 300/7-12
9 6th Ave SE 55940 507-477-3235
John Howe, prin. Fax 477-3230

Hector, Renville, Pop. 1,148
Buffalo Lake-Hector-Stewart SD 2159
Supt. — See Buffalo Lake
Buffalo Lake-Hector-Stewart JSHS 300/6-12
PO Box 307 55342 320-848-2233
Sam Schroeder, prin. Fax 848-2401

Hendricks, Lincoln, Pop. 712
Hendricks SD 402 100/PK-12
PO Box 137 56136 507-275-3116
Bruce Houck, supt. Fax 275-3150
www.hendrickspublicschools.org
Hendricks S 100/PK-12
PO Box 137 56136 507-275-3115
Paul Chick, prin. Fax 275-3150

Henning, Otter Tail, Pop. 795
Henning SD 545 400/PK-12
500 School Ave 56551 218-583-2927
Dean Krogstad, supt. Fax 583-2312
www.henning.k12.mn.us
Henning JSHS 200/7-12
500 School Ave 56551 218-583-2927
Thomas Williams, prin. Fax 583-2312

Herman, Grant, Pop. 435
Herman-Norcross SD 264 100/K-12
PO Box 288 56248 320-677-2291
Rick Bleichner, supt. Fax 677-2412
herman.mn.schoolwebpages.com
Herman JSHS 50/7-12
PO Box 288 56248 320-677-2291
Rick Bleichner, prin. Fax 677-2412

Hermantown, Saint Louis, Pop. 9,290
Hermantown SD 700 1,900/PK-12
4307 Ugstad Rd 55811 218-729-9313
Kerry Juntunen, supt. Fax 729-9315
www.isd700.org
Hermantown HS 600/9-12
4335 Hawk Circle Dr 55811 218-729-8874
John Muenich, prin. Fax 729-0180
Hermantown MS 600/5-8
4289 Ugstad Rd 55811 218-729-6690
Jenny Wiese, prin. Fax 729-9890

Hibbing, Saint Louis, Pop. 16,076
Hibbing SD 701 2,400/K-12
800 E 21st St 55746 218-208-0848
Brad Johnson, supt. Fax 208-0866
www.hibbing.k12.mn.us
Hibbing HS 1,100/7-12
800 E 21st St 55746 218-208-0841
Mike Finco, prin. Fax 208-0856

Cosmetology Careers Unlimited - Hibbing Post-Sec.
2534 E Beltline 55746 218-263-8354
Hibbing Community College Post-Sec.
1515 E 25th St 55746 218-262-7200
Victory Christian Academy 100/PK-12
206 E 39th St 55746 218-262-6550
Jo Terska, admin. Fax 416-1424

Hill City, Aitkin, Pop. 617
Hill City SD 2 200/PK-12
500 Ione Ave 55748 218-697-2394
Dean Yocum, supt. Fax 697-2594
www.hillcity.k12.mn.us
Hill City JSHS 100/7-12
500 Ione Ave 55748 218-697-2394
Pat Rendle, prin. Fax 697-2594

Hills, Rock, Pop. 678
Hills-Beaver Creek SD 671 300/PK-12
PO Box 547 56138 507-962-3240
Todd Holthaus, supt. Fax 962-3238
www.hbcpatriots.com
Hills-Beaver Creek JSHS 100/6-12
PO Box 547 56138 507-962-3240
Todd Holthaus, admin. Fax 962-3238

Hinckley, Pine, Pop. 1,722
Hinckley-Finlayson SD 2165 1,000/PK-12
PO Box 308 55037 320-384-6277
Rob Prater, supt. Fax 384-6135
www.hf.k12.mn.us/
Hinckley-Finlayson HS 400/7-12
PO Box 308 55037 320-384-6132
Brian Masterson, prin. Fax 384-6135

Holdingford, Stearns, Pop. 699
Holdingford SD 738 1,000/PK-12
PO Box 250 56340 320-746-4307
Chris Swenson, supt. Fax 746-2274
www.isd738.org
Holdingford JSHS 500/7-12
PO Box 250 56340 320-746-2221
Brian Silbernick, prin. Fax 746-9959

Hopkins, Hennepin, Pop. 17,010
Hopkins SD 270 6,800/K-12
1001 Highway 7 55305 952-988-4000
John Schultz, supt. Fax 988-4020
www.hopkinsschools.org
Other Schools – See Minnetonka

Blake S 1,400/PK-12
110 Blake Rd S 55343 952-988-3400
Dr. Anne Stavney, head sch Fax 988-3455

Houston, Winona, Pop. 978
Houston SD 294 2,300/PK-12
306 W Elm St 55943 507-896-5323
Krin Abraham, supt. Fax 896-3452
www.houston.k12.mn.us
Houston JSHS 200/7-12
306 W Elm St 55943 507-896-5323
Todd Lundberg, prin. Fax 896-4665

Howard Lake, Wright, Pop. 1,947
Howard Lake-Waverly-Winsted SD 2687 1,100/PK-12
PO Box 708 55349 320-543-4646
Brad Sellner, supt. Fax 543-4630
www.hlww.k12.mn.us
Howard Lake MS 300/5-8
PO Box 708 55349 320-543-4660
Jim Schimelpfenig, prin. Fax 543-4632
Howard Lake-Waverly-Winsted HS 300/9-12
PO Box 708 55349 320-543-4600
Jason Mix, prin. Fax 543-4601

Hutchinson, McLeod, Pop. 14,005
Hutchinson SD 423 2,900/PK-12
30 Glen St NW 55350 320-587-2860
Daron VanderHeiden, supt. Fax 587-4590
www.isd423.org
Crow River ALC 50/Alt
1200 Roberts Rd SW 55350 320-587-2151
Michael Scott, prin. Fax 587-8217
Hutchinson HS 900/9-12
1200 Roberts Rd SW 55350 320-587-2151
Patrick Walsh, prin. Fax 587-8217
Hutchinson MS 700/6-8
1365 S Grade Rd SW 55350 320-587-2854
Todd Grina, prin. Fax 587-2857

Maplewood Academy 100/9-12
700 Main St N 55350 320-587-2830
Ridgewater College-Hutchinson Campus Post-Sec.
2 Century Ave SE 55350 320-234-8500

International Falls, Koochiching, Pop. 6,261
International Falls SD 361 1,000/PK-12
1515 11th St 56649 218-283-2571
Kevin Grover, supt. Fax 283-8104
www.isd361.k12.mn.us
Falls HS 500/7-12
1515 11th St 56649 218-283-2571
Tim Everson, prin. Fax 283-2384

Rainy River Community College Post-Sec.
1501 Highway 71 56649 218-285-7722

Inver Grove Heights, Dakota, Pop. 33,073
Inver Grove Heights Community ISD 199 3,700/PK-12
2990 80th St E 55076 651-306-7800
Dave Bernhardson, supt. Fax 306-7295
www.invergrove.k12.mn.us
Inver Grove Heights MS 900/6-8
8167 Cahill Ave 55076 651-306-7200
Jodi Wendel, prin. Fax 306-7152
Simley HS 1,100/9-12
2920 80th St E 55076 651-306-7000
Gerald Sakala, prin. Fax 306-7016

Inver Hills Community College Post-Sec.
2500 80th St E 55076 651-450-3000

Iron, Saint Louis, Pop. 85
Saint Louis County ISD 2142
Supt. — See Virginia
Cherry S 200/PK-12
3943 Tamminen Rd 55751 218-258-8991
Michael Johnson, prin. Fax 258-8993

Isanti, Isanti, Pop. 5,155
Cambridge-Isanti SD 911
Supt. — See Cambridge
Isanti MS 400/6-8
201 Centennial Dr 55040 763-691-8600
Randy Pauly, prin. Fax 691-8662
Minnesota Center S 100/6-8
201 Centennial Dr 55040 763-691-8676
Randy Pauly, prin. Fax 691-8677

Isle, Mille Lacs, Pop. 739
Isle SD 473 500/K-12
PO Box 25 56342 320-676-3146
Dean Kapsner, supt. Fax 676-3966
www.isle.k12.mn.us
Isle Area Learning Center 50/Alt
PO Box 25 56342 320-676-3721
Jean Novak, coord. Fax 676-3062
Isle JSHS 200/7-12
PO Box 25 56342 320-676-3101
Jeremy Schultz, prin. Fax 676-1034

Jackson, Jackson, Pop. 3,254
Jackson County Central SD 2895 1,200/PK-12
PO Box 119 56143 507-847-3608
Todd Meyer, supt. Fax 847-3078
www.jccschools.com/
Jackson County Central HS 400/9-12
PO Box 119 56143 507-847-5310
Larry Traetow, prin. Fax 847-3078
Other Schools – See Lakefield

Minnesota West Community & Tech College Post-Sec.
401 West St 56143 507-847-7920

Janesville, Waseca, Pop. 2,234
Janesville-Waldorf-Pemberton SD 2835 600/PK-12
PO Box 389 56048 507-234-5181
Bill Adams, supt. Fax 234-5796
www.jwp.k12.mn.us
Janesville-Waldorf-Pemberton HS 300/7-12
PO Box 389 56048 507-234-5181
Kevin Babcock, prin. Fax 234-5796

Jordan, Scott, Pop. 5,361
Jordan SD 717 1,800/PK-12
500 Sunset Dr 55352 952-492-6200
Matthew Helgerson, supt. Fax 492-4445
www.jordan.k12.mn.us

Jordan HS 600/9-12
600 Sunset Dr 55352 952-492-4400
Jeff Vizenor, prin. Fax 492-4425
Jordan MS 500/5-8
500 Sunset Dr 55352 952-492-2332
Ben Bakeberg, prin. Fax 492-4450

Karlstad, Kittson, Pop. 759
Tri-County SD 2358 200/PK-12
PO Box 178 56732 218-436-2261
Dave Sorgaard, supt. Fax 436-2263
www.tricounty.k12.mn.us
Tri-County HS 100/7-12
PO Box 178 56732 218-436-2374
Nick Amb, dean Fax 436-3422

Kasson, Dodge, Pop. 5,864
Kasson-Mantorville SD 204 2,100/PK-12
101 16th St NE 55944 507-634-1100
Mark D. Matuska, supt. Fax 634-6661
www.komets.k12.mn.us
Kasson-Mantorville HS 600/9-12
101 16th St NE 55944 507-634-2961
Trent Langemo, prin. Fax 634-4745
Kasson-Mantorville MS 700/5-8
1400 5th Ave NE 55944 507-634-4030
Michelle Krell, prin. Fax 634-6485

Kelliher, Beltrami, Pop. 261
Kelliher SD 36 100/PK-12
PO Box 259 56650 218-647-8286
Tim Lutz, supt. Fax 647-8660
www.kelliher.k12.mn.us
Kelliher S 100/PK-12
PO Box 259 56650 218-647-8286
Mary Lundin, admin. Fax 647-3110

Kenyon, Goodhue, Pop. 1,804
Kenyon-Wanamingo SD 2172
Supt. — See Wanamingo
Kenyon-Wanamingo HS 200/9-12
400 6th St 55946 507-789-6186
Matt Ryan, prin. Fax 789-6188
Kenyon-Wanamingo MS 100/7-8
400 6th St 55946 507-789-6186
Matt Ryan, prin. Fax 789-6188

Kerkhoven, Swift, Pop. 759
Kerkhoven-Murdock-Sunburg SD 775 600/PK-12
PO Box 168 56252 320-264-1411
Martin Heidelberger, supt. Fax 264-1410
www.kms.k12.mn.us
Kerkhoven JSHS 300/7-12
PO Box 168 56252 320-264-1412
Ted Brown, prin. Fax 264-1410

Kimball, Stearns, Pop. 750
Kimball SD 739 600/PK-12
PO Box 368 55353 320-398-5585
Jim Wagner, supt. Fax 398-5595
www.kimball.k12.mn.us/
Kimball JSHS 300/6-12
PO Box 368 55353 320-398-7700
Erik Widvey, prin. Fax 398-7733

La Crescent, Houston, Pop. 4,750
La Crescent-Hokah SD 300 1,200/PK-12
703 S 11th St 55947 507-895-4484
Ron Wilke, supt. Fax 895-8560
www.isd300.k12.mn.us
La Crescent HS 400/9-12
1301 Lancer Blvd 55947 507-895-4481
Steve Smith, prin. Fax 895-4490
La Crescent MS 300/5-8
1301 Lancer Blvd 55947 507-895-4474
Steve Smith, prin. Fax 895-8597

Lake City, Wabasha, Pop. 4,995
Lake City SD 813 1,300/PK-12
300 S Garden St 55041 651-345-2198
Erick Enger, supt. Fax 345-3709
www.lake-city.k12.mn.us
Lincoln JSHS 600/7-12
300 S Garden St 55041 651-345-4553
Greg Berge, prin. Fax 345-5894

Lake Crystal, Blue Earth, Pop. 2,527
Lake Crystal Wellcome Memorial SD 2071 800/PK-12
PO Box 160 56055 507-726-2323
Tom Farrell, supt. Fax 726-2334
www.isd2071.k12.mn.us
Lake Crystal Wellcome Memorial HS 400/6-12
PO Box 160 56055 507-726-2110
Jennifer Baumgartner, prin. Fax 726-2283

Lake Elmo, Washington, Pop. 7,919
Stillwater Area SD 834
Supt. — See Stillwater
Oak-Land JHS 800/7-9
820 Manning Ave N 55042 651-351-8500
Andy Fields, prin. Fax 351-8505

Rasmussen College Post-Sec.
8565 Eagle Point Cir 55042 651-259-6600

Lakefield, Jackson, Pop. 1,687
Jackson County Central SD 2895
Supt. — See Jackson
Jackson County Central MS 300/6-8
PO Box 338 56150 507-662-6625
Chris Naumann, prin. Fax 662-5083

Lake Park, Becker, Pop. 774
Lake Park Audubon ISD 2889 700/K-12
PO Box 479 56554 218-238-5914
Dale Hogie, supt. Fax 201-0886
www.lakeparkaudubon.com
Lake Park Audubon JSHS 300/7-12
PO Box 479 56554 218-238-5916
Kevin Ricke, prin. Fax 201-0886

Lakeville, Dakota, Pop. 54,640
Lakeville Area SD 194 10,800/K-12
8670 210th St W 55044 952-232-2000
Dr. Lisa Snyder, supt. Fax 469-6054
www.isd194.k12.mn.us
Century MS 1,000/6-8
18610 Ipava Ave 55044 952-232-2300
Christopher Endicott, prin. Fax 469-6103
Kenwood Trail MS 700/6-8
19455 Kenwood Trl 55044 952-232-3800
Kate Eisenthal, prin. Fax 469-3508
Lakeville Area Learning Center 100/Alt
20950 Howland Ave W 55044 952-232-2080
Clifford Skagen, prin. Fax 469-7171
Lakeville North HS 1,800/9-12
19600 Ipava Ave 55044 952-232-3600
Marne Berkvam, prin. Fax 469-3367
Lakeville South HS 1,800/9-12
21135 Jacquard Ave 55044 952-232-3300
John Braun, prin. Fax 469-8383
McGuire MS 900/6-8
21220 Holyoke Ave 55044 952-232-2200
Joshua Alexander, prin. Fax 469-7224

Glory Academy 50/PK-12
25170 Dodd Blvd 55044 952-985-3659
Rev. Cheryl Engelman, prin.
Minnesota School of Business Post-Sec.
17685 Juniper Path 55044 952-892-9000

Lamberton, Redwood, Pop. 817
Red Rock Central SD 2884 400/PK-12
PO Box 278 56152 507-752-7361
Bruce Olson, supt. Fax 752-6133
www.rrcnet.org/default.shtml
Red Rock Central HS 200/5-12
PO Box 278 56152 507-752-7361
Phil Goetstouwers, prin. Fax 752-6133

Lancaster, Kittson, Pop. 340
Lancaster SD 356 200/PK-12
401 Central Ave S 56735 218-762-5400
Shannon Hunstad, supt. Fax 762-5512
www.lancaster.k12.mn.us/
Lancaster JSHS 100/7-12
401 Central Ave S 56735 218-762-5400
Shannon Hunstad, admin. Fax 762-5512

Lanesboro, Fillmore, Pop. 743
Lanesboro SD 229 400/PK-12
100 Kirkwood St E 55949 507-467-2229
Matt Schultz, supt. Fax 467-3026
www.lanesboro.k12.mn.us
Lanesboro JSHS 200/7-12
100 Kirkwood St E 55949 507-467-2229
Brett Clarke, prin. Fax 467-3026

Laporte, Hubbard, Pop. 104
Laporte SD 306 300/PK-12
315 Main St W 56461 218-224-2288
Harvey Johnson, supt. Fax 224-2905
www.laporte.k12.mn.us
Laporte JSHS 100/7-12
315 Main St W 56461 218-224-2288
Kim Goodwin, prin. Fax 224-2905

Le Roy, Mower, Pop. 926
Le Roy-Ostrander SD 499 300/PK-12
PO Box 1000 55951 507-324-5743
Jeff Sampson, supt. Fax 324-5149
www.leroy.k12.mn.us
Le Roy-Ostrander JSHS 100/7-12
PO Box 1000 55951 507-324-5741
Aaron Hungerholt, prin. Fax 324-5149

Lester Prairie, McLeod, Pop. 1,714
Lester Prairie SD 424 400/PK-12
131 Hickory St N 55354 320-395-2521
Jeremy Schmidt, supt. Fax 395-4204
www.lp.k12.mn.us
Lester Prairie JSHS 200/6-12
131 Hickory St N 55354 320-395-2521
Nathaniel Boyer, prin. Fax 395-4204

Le Sueur, LeSueur, Pop. 4,019
Le Sueur-Henderson SD 2397 800/PK-12
115 1/2 N 5th St Ste 200 56058 507-665-4600
Brian Gersich, supt. Fax 665-6858
www.isd2397.org
Alternative Learning Center 50/Alt
901 Ferry St 56058 507-665-5800
Nicole Adams, prin. Fax 665-4187
Le Sueur-Henderson MSHS 300/6-12
901 Ferry St 56058 507-665-5800
Nicole Adams, prin. Fax 665-6012

Lewiston, Winona, Pop. 1,612
Lewiston-Altura SD 857 700/PK-12
100 County Road 25 55952 507-523-2191
Jeff Apse, supt. Fax 523-3460
www.lewalt.k12.mn.us
Lewiston-Altura HS 400/7-12
100 County Road 25 55952 507-523-2191
Ryan Ihrke, prin. Fax 523-2286

Lindstrom, Chisago, Pop. 4,380
Chisago Lakes SD 2144 3,400/PK-12
13750 Lake Blvd 55045 651-213-2000
Joe Thimm, supt. Fax 213-2050
chisagolakes.mn.schoolwebpages.com
Chisago Lakes HS 1,100/9-12
13750 Lake Blvd 55045 651-213-2500
David Ertl, prin. Fax 213-2550
Chisago Lakes MS 800/6-8
13750 Lake Blvd 55045 651-213-2400
Jodi Otte, prin. Fax 213-2051

Lino Lakes, Anoka, Pop. 19,895
Centennial SD 12
Supt. — See Circle Pines
Centennial MS 1,500/6-8
399 Elm St 55014 763-792-5400
Robert Stevens, prin. Fax 792-5450

Litchfield, Meeker, Pop. 6,688
Litchfield SD 465 1,400/K-12
307 E 6th St Ste 100 55355 320-693-2444
Daniel Frazier, supt. Fax 593-6528
www.litchfield.k12.mn.us
Litchfield HS 600/9-12
901 N Gilman Ave 55355 320-693-2424
Jason Michels, prin. Fax 593-3308
Litchfield MS 400/5-8
340 E 10th St 55355 320-693-2441
Beckie Simenson, prin. Fax 593-3485

Little Canada, Ramsey, Pop. 9,560
Roseville Area SD 623
Supt. — See Roseville
Roseville Area MS 900/7-8
15 County Road B2 E 55117 651-482-5280
Dr. Tyrone Brookins, prin. Fax 482-5299

Little Falls, Morrison, Pop. 8,197
Little Falls SD 482 2,400/PK-12
1001 5th Ave SE 56345 320-632-2002
Stephen Jones, supt. Fax 632-2012
www.lfalls.k12.mn.us
Little Falls Community HS 800/9-12
1001 5th Ave SE 56345 320-616-2200
Tim Bjorge, prin. Fax 616-2210
Little Falls Community MS 500/6-8
1000 1st Ave NE 56345 320-616-4200
Wade Mathers, prin. Fax 616-4210

Mary of Lourdes MS 100/5-8
205 3rd St NW 56345 320-632-6742
Maria Heymans-Becker, prin. Fax 632-3556

Littlefork, Koochiching, Pop. 646
Littlefork-Big Falls SD 362 200/PK-12
700 Main St 56653 218-278-6614
Christopher Bachmeier, supt. Fax 278-6615
www.isd362.k12.mn.us
Littlefork-Big Falls S 200/PK-12
700 Main St 56653 218-278-6614
Christopher Bachmeier, prin. Fax 278-6615

Long Lake, Hennepin, Pop. 1,729
Orono SD 278 2,800/K-12
685 N Old Crystal Bay Rd 55356 952-449-8300
Dr. Karen Orcutt, supt. Fax 449-8399
www.orono.k12.mn.us
Orono HS 900/9-12
795 N Old Crystal Bay Rd 55356 952-449-8400
Dave Benson, prin. Fax 449-8449
Orono MS 700/6-8
800 N Old Crystal Bay Rd 55356 952-449-8450
Dr. Patricia Wroten, prin. Fax 449-8453

Long Prairie, Todd, Pop. 3,383
Long Prairie-Grey Eagle SD 2753 900/PK-12
205 2nd St S 56347 320-732-2194
Jon Kringen, supt. Fax 732-3791
www.lpge.k12.mn.us/
Long Prairie-Grey Eagle HS 400/7-12
510 9th St NE 56347 320-732-2194
Paul Weinzierl, prin. Fax 732-6470

Luverne, Rock, Pop. 4,679
Luverne SD 2184 1,200/PK-12
709 N Kniss Ave 56156 507-283-8088
Craig Oftedahl, supt. Fax 283-9681
www.isd2184.net/
Luverne Alternative Program 50/Alt
709 N Kniss Ave 56156 507-283-4491
Craig Oftedahl, prin. Fax 283-9681
Luverne HS 400/9-12
709 N Kniss Ave 56156 507-283-4491
Ryan Johnson, prin. Fax 283-9681
Luverne MS 300/6-8
709 N Kniss Ave 56156 507-283-4491
Ryan Johnson, prin. Fax 283-9681

Lyle, Mower, Pop. 544
Lyle SD 497 200/PK-12
700 E 2nd St 55953 507-325-2201
Jennifer Backer, supt. Fax 325-4611
www.lyle.k12.mn.us
Lyle HS 100/7-12
700 E 2nd St 55953 507-325-2201
Nicholas Jurrens, prin. Fax 325-4611

Mabel, Fillmore, Pop. 777
Mabel-Canton SD 238 300/PK-12
316 W Fillmore 55954 507-493-5423
Jennifer Backer, supt. Fax 493-5425
www.mabelcanton.k12.mn.us/
Mabel-Canton JSHS 100/7-12
316 W Fillmore 55954 507-493-5422
Michelle Weidemann, admin. Fax 493-5425

Mc Gregor, Aitkin, Pop. 390
McGregor ISD 4 400/PK-12
PO Box 160 55760 218-768-2111
Paul Grams, supt. Fax 768-3901
www.mcgregor.k12.mn.us
McGregor JSHS 200/7-12
PO Box 160 55760 218-768-2111
Robert Staska, prin. Fax 768-3802

Madelia, Watonwan, Pop. 2,301
Madelia SD 837 500/PK-12
320 Buck Ave SE 56062 507-642-3232
Brian Grenell, supt. Fax 642-3622
www.madelia.k12.mn.us
Madelia JSHS 200/7-12
320 Buck Ave SE 56062 507-642-3232
Allan Beyer, prin. Fax 642-3622

Madison, Lac qui Parle, Pop. 1,527
Lac qui Parle Valley SD 2853 800/PK-12
2860 291st Ave 56256 320-752-4800
Renae Tostenson, supt. Fax 752-4401
www.lqpv.org
Lac qui Parle Valley HS 300/7-12
2860 291st Ave 56256 320-752-4800
Scott Sawatzky, prin. Fax 752-4401

Mahnomen, Mahnomen, Pop. 1,108
Mahnomen SD 432 600/PK-12
PO Box 319 56557 218-935-2211
Jeff Bisek, supt. Fax 935-5921
www.mahnomen.k12.mn.us/

Mahnomen Area Learning Center 50/Alt
PO Box 319 56557 218-935-2346
Sandra Haddeland, dir. Fax 935-5921
Mahnomen JSHS 300/7-12
PO Box 319 56557 218-935-2213
Kevin Hedstrom, prin. Fax 935-5921

White Earth Tribal and Community College Post-Sec.
124 1st St SW 56557 218-935-0417

Mahtomedi, Washington, Pop. 7,538
Mahtomedi SD 832 3,300/PK-12
1520 Mahtomedi Ave 55115 651-407-2000
Dr. Mark Larson, supt. Fax 407-2025
www.mahtomedi.k12.mn.us
Mahtomedi HS 1,200/9-12
8000 75th St N 55115 651-762-5800
Kathe Nickleby, prin. Fax 762-5825
Mahtomedi MS 800/6-8
8100 75th St N 55115 651-407-2200
Dr. Mike Neubeck, prin. Fax 407-2225

Mankato, Blue Earth, Pop. 38,565
Mankato SD 77 7,000/K-12
PO Box 8741 56002 507-387-1868
Sheri Allen, supt. Fax 387-4257
www.isd77.org
Central Freedom S 50/Alt
PO Box 8741 56002 507-387-2794
Kathleen Johnson, prin. Fax 387-7737
Central HS 100/Alt
PO Box 8741 56002 507-387-3047
Kathy Johnson, prin. Fax 387-7737
Mankato East HS 1,000/9-12
PO Box 8741 56002 507-387-5671
Jeff Dahline, prin. Fax 387-7927
Mankato West HS 1,200/9-12
PO Box 8741 56002 507-387-3461
Dave Lutz, prin. Fax 345-1502
Prairie Winds MS 500/6-8
PO Box 8741 56002 507-345-6625
Stephen Rustad, prin. Fax 387-2890
Other Schools – See North Mankato

Bethany Lutheran College Post-Sec.
700 Luther Dr 56001 507-344-7000
Loyola HS 200/9-12
145 Good Counsel Dr 56001 507-388-2997
Adam Bemmels, prin. Fax 388-3081
Loyola IS 200/5-8
110 N 5th St 56001 507-388-9344
Adam Bemmels, prin. Fax 388-2750
Minnesota State University Mankato Post-Sec.
309 Wigley Administrtn Ctr 56001 800-722-0544
Rasmussen College Post-Sec.
130 Saint Andrews Dr 56001 507-625-6556

Maple Grove, Hennepin, Pop. 60,235
Osseo Area ISD 279 17,400/PK-12
11200 93rd Ave N 55369 763-391-7000
Kate Maguire, supt. Fax 391-7070
www.district279.org
Maple Grove HS 1,600/9-12
9800 Fernbrook Ln N 55369 763-391-8700
Bart Becker, prin. Fax 391-8701
Maple Grove MS 1,100/6-8
7000 Hemlock Ln N 55369 763-315-7600
Lisa Hartman, prin. Fax 315-7601
Other Schools – See Brooklyn Park, Osseo

Heritage Christian Academy 500/PK-12
15655 Bass Lake Rd 55311 763-463-2200
Tonya Scott, pres. Fax 463-2299

Maple Lake, Wright, Pop. 2,037
Maple Lake SD 881 900/PK-12
200 Highway 55 E 55358 320-963-3171
Mark Redemske, supt. Fax 963-3170
www.maplelake.k12.mn.us
Maple Lake JSHS 500/7-12
200 Highway 55 E 55358 320-963-3171
David J. Hansen, prin. Fax 963-3170

Mapleton, Blue Earth, Pop. 1,738
Maple River SD 2135 1,000/PK-12
PO Box 515 56065 507-524-3918
Dan Anderson, supt. Fax 524-4882
www.isd2135.k12.mn.us/
Maple River HS 300/9-12
PO Box 515 56065 507-524-3918
Ted Simon, prin. Fax 524-4919
Maple River MS 300/6-8
PO Box 515 56065 507-524-3918
Ted Simon, prin. Fax 524-3638

Maplewood, Ramsey, Pop. 37,068
North St. Paul-Maplewood-Oakdale SD 622
Supt. — See North Saint Paul
Glenn MS 800/6-8
1560 County Road B E 55109 651-748-6300
Jill Miklausich, prin. Fax 748-6391
Harmony Learning Center 100/Alt
1961 County Road C E 55109 651-748-6200
Sue Bartling, admin. Fax 748-7486
Maplewood MS 700/6-8
2410 Holloway Ave E 55109 651-748-6500
Kevin Wolff, prin. Fax 748-6591

Hill-Murray HS 800/6-12
2625 Larpenteur Ave E 55109 651-777-1376
Jim Hansen, pres. Fax 748-2444

Marble, Itasca, Pop. 685
Greenway SD 316 700/PK-12
201 Kate St 55764 218-247-7306
David Pace, supt. Fax 245-6612
www.isd316.org
Other Schools – See Coleraine

Marshall, Lyon, Pop. 13,459
Marshall SD 413 2,300/PK-12
401 S Saratoga St 56258 507-537-6924
Scott Monson, supt. Fax 537-6931
www.marshall.k12.mn.us
Marshall HS 800/9-12
400 Tiger Dr 56258 507-537-6920
Brian Jones, prin. Fax 537-6933
Marshall MS 600/5-8
401 S Saratoga St 56258 507-537-6938
Mary Kay Thomas, prin. Fax 537-6942
MATEC 50/Alt
305 S 2nd St 56258 507-537-6210
Michelle Noriega, prin. Fax 537-7609

Southwest Minnesota State University Post-Sec.
1501 State St 56258 507-537-7678

Mayer, Carver, Pop. 1,725

Mayer Lutheran HS 200/9-12
305 5th St NE 55360 952-657-2251
Kevin Wilaby, prin. Fax 657-2344

Mazeppa, Wabasha, Pop. 837
Zumbrota-Mazeppa SD 2805 900/PK-12
343 3rd Ave NE 55956 507-732-1400
Gary Anger, supt. Fax 732-1401
www.zmschools.us/
Other Schools – See Zumbrota

Medford, Steele, Pop. 1,228
Medford ISD 763 900/PK-12
750 2nd Ave SE 55049 507-214-6300
Rick Dahlman, supt. Fax 451-6474
www.medford.k12.mn.us
Medford JSHS 400/7-12
750 2nd Ave SE 55049 507-214-6302
Chris Ovrebo, prin. Fax 451-6474

Melrose, Stearns, Pop. 3,582
Melrose SD 740 1,400/PK-12
546 5th Ave NE 56352 320-256-5160
Tom Rich, supt. Fax 256-4311
isd740org.weebly.com
Melrose HS 500/9-12
546 5th Ave NE 56352 320-256-5160
Chad Doetkott, prin. Fax 256-4639
Melrose MS 400/6-8
546 5th Ave NE 56352 320-256-5160
Robert Anerson, prin. Fax 256-4311

Menahga, Wadena, Pop. 1,296
Menahga SD 821 700/PK-12
PO Box 160 56464 218-564-4141
Kevin Wellen, supt. Fax 564-5401
www.menahga.k12.mn.us
Menahga HS 200/9-12
PO Box 160 56464 218-564-4141
Mark Frank, prin. Fax 564-5401
Menahga MS 5-8
PO Box 160 56464 218-564-4141
Ann Wothe, prin. Fax 564-4502

Mendota Heights, Dakota, Pop. 10,905
West St. Paul-Mendota Hts-Eagan SD 197 4,800/PK-12
1897 Delaware Ave 55118 651-403-7000
Dr. Nancy Allen-Mastro, supt. Fax 403-7010
www.isd197.org
Friendly Hills MS 700/5-8
701 Mendota Heights Rd 55120 651-403-7600
Chris Hiti, prin. Fax 403-7610
Sibley HS 1,400/9-12
1897 Delaware Ave 55118 651-403-7100
Dr. Ron Monson, prin. Fax 403-7110
Other Schools – See West Saint Paul

Le Cordon Bleu College of Culinary Arts Post-Sec.
1315 Mendota Heights Rd 55120 651-675-4700
St. Thomas Academy 700/7-12
949 Mendota Heights Rd 55120 651-454-4570
Matthew Mohs, hdmstr. Fax 454-4574
Sanford-Brown College Post-Sec.
1345 Mendota Heights Rd 55120 651-905-3400
Visitation S 600/PK-12
2455 Visitation Dr 55120 651-683-1700
Rene Gavic, head sch Fax 454-7144

Middle River, Marshall, Pop. 301
Greenbush-Middle River SD 2683
Supt. — See Greenbush
Greenbush-Middle River JHS 100/6-8
PO Box 130 56737 218-222-3310
Sharon Schultz, prin. Fax 222-3314

Milaca, Mille Lacs, Pop. 2,899
Milaca SD 912 1,900/PK-12
500 Highway 23 W 56353 320-982-7210
Tim Truebenbach, supt. Fax 982-7179
www.milaca.k12.mn.us/
Milaca ALC 50/Alt
305 3rd Ave NW 56353 320-982-7249
Steve Hammero, prin. Fax 982-7290
Milaca HS 800/7-12
500 Highway 23 W 56353 320-982-7206
Damian Patnode, prin. Fax 983-3566

Milroy, Redwood, Pop. 251
Milroy SD 635 100/K-8
PO Box 10 56263 507-336-2563
Wade McKittrick, supt. Fax 336-2568
www.milroy.k12.mn.us
Milroy JHS 50/7-8
PO Box 10 56263 507-336-2563
Heidi Sachariason, prin. Fax 336-2568

Minneapolis, Hennepin, Pop. 368,444
Brooklyn Center SD 286
Supt. — See Brooklyn Center
Brooklyn Center Academy Alt
5910 Shingle Creek Pkwy #1A 55430 612-450-3383
Randy Koch, prin. Fax 561-1966

Minneapolis SD 1 33,300/PK-12
1250 W Broadway Ave 55411 612-668-0000
Ed Graff, supt. Fax 668-0195
www.mpls.k12.mn.us
Anthony MS 800/6-8
5757 Irving Ave S 55419 612-668-3240
Mai Chang Vue, prin. Fax 668-3250
Anwatin MS 600/6-8
256 Upton Ave S 55405 612-668-2450
Ellen Shulman, prin. Fax 668-2460
Edison HS 700/9-12
700 22nd Ave NE 55418 612-668-1300
Eryn Warne, prin. Fax 668-1320
Field Community MS 500/5-8
4645 4th Ave S 55419 612-668-3640
VaNita Miller, prin. Fax 668-3661
Fine Arts Interdisciplinary Resource S 500/K-12
10 S 10th St 55403 612-668-1060
Sherene Judeh, prin.
Franklin MS 6-8
1501 Aldrich Ave N 55411 612-668-2600
Karon Cunningham, prin. Fax 668-2649
Henry HS 1,100/9-12
4320 Newton Ave N 55412 612-668-2000
Yusuf Abdullah, prin. Fax 668-1993
Lake Harriet Community Upper ES 600/4-8
4912 Vincent Ave S 55410 612-668-3310
Walter Schleisman, prin. Fax 668-3320
Lake Nokomis S - Keewaydin Campus 400/3-8
5209 30th Ave S 55417 612-668-4670
LaShawn Ray, prin. Fax 668-4680
Longfellow Alternative HS 100/Alt
3017 E 31st St 55406 612-668-4700
Padmini Udupa, dir. Fax 668-4710
North Academy of Arts & Communication 200/9-12
1500 James Ave N 55411 612-668-1700
Shawn Harris-Berry, prin. Fax 668-1770
Northeast MS 600/6-8
2955 Hayes St NE 55418 612-668-1500
Vernon Rowe, prin. Fax 668-1510
Olson MS 300/6-8
1607 51st Ave N 55430 612-668-1640
Steve Emerson, prin. Fax 668-1650
Ramsey MS 300/6-8
1 W 49th St 55419 612-668-4040
Erin Rathke, prin. Fax 668-4050
Roosevelt HS 800/9-12
4029 28th Ave S 55406 612-668-4800
Michael Bradley, prin. Fax 668-4810
Sanford MS 800/6-8
3524 42nd Ave S 55406 612-668-4900
Emily Palmer, prin. Fax 668-4910
South HS 1,800/9-12
3131 19th Ave S 55407 612-668-4300
Ray Aponte, prin. Fax 668-4310
Southwest HS 1,700/9-12
3414 W 47th St 55410 612-668-3030
Bill Smith, prin. Fax 668-3080
Stadium View S 50/Alt
510 Park Ave 55415 612-348-7740
Rhonda Larkin, prin. Fax 596-9989
Washburn HS 1,300/9-12
201 W 49th St 55419 612-668-3400
Rhonda Dean, prin. Fax 668-3410
Wellstone International HS 300/Alt
3328 Elliot Ave 55407 612-668-5115
Aimee Fearing, prin. Fax 668-5140
Adult Continuing Education Adult
2225 E Lake St 55407 612-668-3800
Fax 668-3805

Art Institutes International Minnesota Post-Sec.
15 S 9th St 55402 612-332-3361
Art Instruction Schools Post-Sec.
3400 Technology Dr 55418 800-801-6940
Augsburg College Post-Sec.
2211 Riverside Ave 55454 612-330-1000
Aveda Institute Post-Sec.
400 Central Ave SE 55414 612-378-7404
Bais Yaakov HS of the Twin Cities 50/9-12
4221 Sunset Blvd 55416 952-915-9117
Sarah Gibber, prin. Fax 915-9116
Bethany College of Missions Post-Sec.
6820 Auto Club Rd 55438 952-944-2121
Blake S - Northrop Campus 500/9-12
511 Kenwood Pkwy 55403 952-988-3700
Dr. Anne Stavney, head sch Fax 988-3705
Capella University Post-Sec.
225 S 6th St Fl 9 55402 888-227-3552
Cristo Rey Jesuit HS 300/9-12
2924 4th Ave S 55408 612-545-9700
Dave Mason, prin. Fax 276-0142
De La Salle HS 700/9-12
1 De La Salle Dr 55401 612-676-7600
James Benson, prin. Fax 362-9641
Dunwoody College of Technology Post-Sec.
818 Dunwoody Blvd 55403 612-374-5800
Globe University Post-Sec.
80 S 8th St Ste 51 55402 612-455-3000
Hennepin County Medical Center Post-Sec.
701 Park Ave 55415 612-347-2352
Herzing University Post-Sec.
5700 W Broadway Ave 55428 763-535-3000
Hope Academy 300/K-12
2300 Chicago Ave 55404 612-721-6294
Russell Gregg, head sch Fax 722-9048
Institute of Production and Recording Post-Sec.
300 1st Ave N Ste 500 55401 612-375-1900
Minneapolis College of Art & Design Post-Sec.
2501 Stevens Ave 55404 612-874-3700
Minneapolis Community and Tech College Post-Sec.
1501 Hennepin Ave 55403 612-659-6000
Minneapolis VA Medical Center Post-Sec.
1 Veterans Dr 55417 612-725-2000
Minnehaha Academy 400/9-12
3100 W River Pkwy 55406 612-729-8321
Dr. Donna Harris, pres. Fax 728-7787
North Central University Post-Sec.
910 Elliot Ave 55404 612-343-4400
North Memorial Medical Center Post-Sec.
3300 Oakdale Ave N 55422 763-520-5200
Sanford-Brown College Post-Sec.
5951 Earle Brown Dr 55430 763-279-2400
Summit Academy OIC Post-Sec.
935 Olson Memorial Hwy 55405 612-377-0150
University of Minnesota Twin Cities Post-Sec.
231 Pillsbury Dr SE 55455 612-625-2008
Walden University Post-Sec.
100 Washington Ave S # 900 55401 612-338-7224

Woodcrest Baptist Academy 100/PK-12
6875 University Ave NE 55432 763-571-6410
Loren Isaacs, admin. Fax 571-3978

Minneota, Lyon, Pop. 1,386
Minneota SD 414 500/K-12
PO Box 98 56264 507-872-6532
Dan Deitte, supt. Fax 872-5172
www.minneotaschools.org/
Minneota JSHS 200/7-12
PO Box 98 56264 507-872-6175
Jeremy Frie, prin. Fax 872-6494

Minnetonka, Hennepin, Pop. 48,748
Hopkins SD 270
Supt. — See Hopkins
Hopkins HS 1,700/10-12
2400 Lindbergh Dr 55305 952-988-4500
Doug Bullinger, prin. Fax 988-4716
Hopkins North JHS 1,000/7-9
10700 Cedar Lake Rd 55305 952-988-4800
Becky Melville, prin. Fax 988-4869
Hopkins West JHS 700/7-9
3830 Baker Rd 55305 952-988-4400
Shirley Gregoire, prin. Fax 988-4477

Minnetonka SD 276 9,700/K-12
5621 County Road 101 55345 952-401-5000
Dr. Dennis Peterson, supt. Fax 401-5083
www.minnetonkaschools.org
Minnetonka East MS 1,200/6-8
17000 Lake Street Ext 55345 952-401-5200
Pete Dymit, prin. Fax 401-5268
Minnetonka HS 2,900/9-12
18301 Highway 7 55345 952-401-5700
Jeff Erickson, prin. Fax 401-5709
Other Schools – See Excelsior

Minnetrista, Hennepin, Pop. 6,316
Westonka SD 277 2,200/PK-12
5901 Sunnyfield Rd E 55364 952-491-8000
Kevin Borg, supt. Fax 491-8012
www.westonka.k12.mn.us
Other Schools – See Mound

Montevideo, Chippewa, Pop. 5,317
Montevideo SD 129 1,300/PK-12
2001 William Ave 56265 320-269-8833
Dr. Luther Heller, supt. Fax 269-8834
www.montevideoschools.org
Montevideo HS 500/8-12
1501 William Ave 56265 320-269-6446
Bruce Bergeson, prin. Fax 321-8960

Montgomery, LeSueur, Pop. 2,910
Tri-City United ISD 2905 1,200/PK-12
101 2nd St NE Ste 3 56069 507-364-8100
Teri Preisler, supt. Fax 364-8103
www.tcu2905.us
Tri-City United HS 300/9-12
700 4th St NW 56069 507-364-8111
Alan Fitterer, prin. Fax 364-8410

Monticello, Wright, Pop. 12,521
Monticello SD 882 4,200/PK-12
302 Washington St 55362 763-272-2000
James Johnson, supt. Fax 272-2009
www.monticello.k12.mn.us
Monticello HS 1,200/9-12
5225 School Blvd 55362 763-272-3000
Mike Carr, prin. Fax 272-3009
Monticello MS 900/6-8
800 E Broadway St 55362 763-272-2100
Jeff Scherber, prin. Fax 272-2109
Turning Point 100/Alt
406 E 7th St 55362 763-272-3200
Joel Lundin, prin. Fax 272-3209

Moorhead, Clay, Pop. 37,202
Moorhead Area SD 152 5,600/K-12
2410 14th St S 56560 218-284-3300
Lynne Kovash Ed.D., supt. Fax 284-3333
www.moorheadschools.org/
Horizon MS 1,300/6-8
3601 12th Ave S 56560 218-284-7300
Jeremy Larson Ed.D., prin. Fax 284-7333
Moorhead HS 1,600/9-12
2300 4th Ave S 56560 218-284-2300
Dave Lawrence, prin. Fax 284-2333
Red River Area Learning Center 100/Alt
3777 34th St S 56560 218-284-2200
Deb Pender, dir. Fax 284-2233

Concordia College Post-Sec.
901 8th St S 56562 218-299-4000
Globe University Post-Sec.
2777 34th St S 56560 218-422-1000
MN State Community & Technical College Post-Sec.
1900 28th Ave S 56560 218-299-6500
Minnesota State University Moorhead Post-Sec.
1104 7th Ave S 56563 218-477-4000
Park Christian S 300/K-12
300 17th St N 56560 218-236-0500
Kent Hannestad, pres. Fax 236-7301
Rita's Moorhead Beauty College Post-Sec.
1024 Center Ave 56560 218-236-7201

Moose Lake, Carlton, Pop. 2,729
Moose Lake SD 97 600/PK-12
PO Box 489 55767 218-485-4435
Bob Indihar, supt. Fax 485-8110
www.mooselake.k12.mn.us
Moose Lake JSHS 300/7-12
PO Box 489 55767 218-485-4622
Billie Jo Steen, prin. Fax 485-8681

Mora, Kanabec, Pop. 3,511
Mora SD 332 1,700/PK-12
400 Maple Ave E 55051 320-679-6200
Craig Schultz, supt. Fax 679-6209
www.moraschools.org
Mora Alternative Learning Center 100/Alt
400 Maple Ave E 55051 320-679-6250
Karen Felger, coord.

Mora HS 700/7-12
400 Maple Ave E 55051 320-679-6220
Brent Nelson, prin. Fax 679-6238

Morgan, Redwood, Pop. 873
Cedar Mountain SD 2754 500/K-12
PO Box 188 56266 507-249-5990
Robert Tews, supt. Fax 249-3149
www.cms.mntm.org/
Cedar Mountain JSHS 300/6-12
PO Box 188 56266 507-249-5888
Rob Brandl, prin. Fax 249-3149

Morris, Stevens, Pop. 5,158
Morris SD 769 1,200/PK-12
201 S Columbia Ave 56267 320-589-4840
Richard Lahn, supt. Fax 585-2208
www.morris.k12.mn.us
Morris Area HS 500/9-12
201 S Columbia Ave 56267 320-589-4400
Bill Kehoe, prin. Fax 589-3203
Morris Area JHS 200/6-8
201 S Columbia Ave 56267 320-589-4400
Bill Kehoe, prin. Fax 589-3203

University of Minnesota Morris Post-Sec.
600 E 4th St 56267 320-589-6035

Morristown, Rice, Pop. 973
Waterville-Elysian-Morristown SD 2143
Supt. — See Waterville
Waterville-Elysian-Morristown JHS 100/7-8
PO Box 278 55052 507-685-4222
Anna Braam, prin. Fax 685-2420

Mound, Hennepin, Pop. 8,930
Westonka SD 277
Supt. — See Minnetrista
Mound-Westonka HS 800/8-12
5905 Sunnyfield Rd E 55364 952-491-8100
Mark McIlmoyle, prin. Fax 491-8103

Mounds View, Ramsey, Pop. 11,818
Mounds View SD 621
Supt. — See Shoreview
Edgewood MS 600/6-8
5100 Edgewood Dr 55112 651-621-6600
Penny Howard, prin. Fax 621-6605

Mountain Iron, Saint Louis, Pop. 2,818
Mountain Iron-Buhl SD 712 500/PK-12
5720 Marble Ave 55768 218-735-8271
John Klarich, supt. Fax 735-8244
www.mib.k12.mn.us
Mountain Iron-Buhl JSHS 200/7-12
5720 Marble Ave 55768 218-735-8271
Jim Jotter, prin. Fax 735-8217

Mountain Lake, Cottonwood, Pop. 2,081
Mountain Lake SD 173 500/PK-12
PO Box 400 56159 507-427-2325
William Strom, supt. Fax 427-3047
www.mountainlake.k12.mn.us
Mountain Lake JSHS 200/7-12
PO Box 400 56159 507-427-2325
Michelle Larson, prin. Fax 427-3047

Mountain Lake Christian S 100/PK-12
PO Box 478 56159 507-427-2010
Dr. Michael James, admin. Fax 427-3123

Nashwauk, Itasca, Pop. 964
Nashwauk-Keewatin SD 319 600/PK-12
400 2nd St 55769 218-885-1280
Lance Northey, supt.
www.isd319.org
Nashwauk-Keewatin JSHS 200/7-12
400 2nd St 55769 218-885-1280
Derek Gabardi, prin. Fax 885-2910

Nevis, Hubbard, Pop. 379
Nevis SD 308 300/PK-12
PO Box 138 56467 218-652-3500
Gregg Parks, supt. Fax 652-3505
www.nevis308.org
Nevis S 300/PK-12
PO Box 138 56467 218-652-3500
Brian Michaelson, prin. Fax 652-3505

New Brighton, Ramsey, Pop. 20,903
Mounds View SD 621
Supt. — See Shoreview
Area Learning Center 100/Alt
2574 Highway 10 55112 651-621-6200
Julie Wikelius, prin. Fax 621-6205
Highview MS 700/6-8
2300 7th St NW 55112 651-621-6700
Sheila Eller, prin. Fax 621-6705
Irondale HS 1,600/9-12
2425 Long Lake Rd 55112 651-621-6800
Amy Janecek, prin. Fax 621-6805

United Theological Seminary/Twin Cities Post-Sec.
3000 5th St NW 55112 651-633-4311

Newfolden, Marshall, Pop. 366
Marshall County Central SD 441 400/K-12
PO Box 189 56738 218-874-8530
Jeffrey Lund, supt. Fax 874-8581
www.newfolden.k12.mn.us/
Marshall County Central HS 200/7-12
PO Box 189 56738 218-874-7225
Ryan Johnson, prin. Fax 874-8581

New Hope, Hennepin, Pop. 19,669
Robbinsdale SD 281 11,800/K-12
4148 Winnetka Ave N 55427 763-504-8000
Dr. Carlton Jenkins, supt. Fax 504-8979
www.rdale.org
Robbinsdale Cooper HS 1,800/9-12
8230 47th Ave N 55428 763-504-8500
Frank Herman, prin. Fax 504-8531
Other Schools – See Crystal, Plymouth, Robbinsdale

New London, Kandiyohi, Pop. 1,247
New London-Spicer SD 345 1,400/K-12
101 4th Ave SW 56273 320-354-9001
Paul Carlson, supt. Fax 354-2252
www.nls.k12.mn.us
New London ALP 50/Alt
101 4th Ave SW 56273 320-354-2252
Kevin Acquard, prin. Fax 354-9001
New London-Spicer HS 400/9-12
101 4th Ave SW 56273 320-354-2252
Kevin Acquard, prin. Fax 354-9001
New London-Spicer MS 400/5-8
101 4th Ave SW 56273 320-354-2252
Trish Perry, prin. Fax 354-4244

New Prague, Scott, Pop. 7,228
New Prague Area SD 721 3,900/PK-12
410 Central Ave N 56071 952-758-1700
Tim Dittberner, supt. Fax 758-1799
www.npaschools.org
New Prague Alternative Learning Center 50/Alt
405 1st Ave NW 56071 952-758-1746
Lisa Ruedy-Decker, admin.
New Prague HS 1,200/9-12
221 12th St NE 56071 952-758-1200
Lonnie Seifert, prin. Fax 758-1299
New Prague MS 900/6-8
721 Central Ave N 56071 952-758-1400
Brad Gregor, prin. Fax 758-1499

New Richland, Waseca, Pop. 1,198
NRHEG SD 2168 1,000/PK-12
306 Ash Ave S 56072 507-465-3205
Dale Carlson, supt. Fax 465-8633
nrheg.k12.mn.us/pages/NRHEG
NRHEG HS 500/6-12
306 Ash Ave S 56072 507-465-3205
David Bunn, prin. Fax 465-8633

New Ulm, Brown, Pop. 13,436
New Ulm ISD 88 1,800/PK-12
414 S Payne St 56073 507-359-8414
Jeff Bertrang, supt. Fax 359-8406
www.newulm.k12.mn.us
New Ulm HS 600/9-12
1600 Oak St 56073 507-359-8420
Mark Bergmann, prin. Fax 359-8432
New Ulm MS, 414 S Payne St 56073 300/5-8
Michelle Miller, prin. 507-359-8480

Cathedral HS 200/7-12
600 N Washington St 56073 507-354-4511
Fax 354-5711
Martin Luther College Post-Sec.
1995 Luther Ct 56073 507-354-8221
Minnesota Valley Lutheran HS 200/9-12
45638 561st Ave 56073 507-354-6851
Tim Plath, prin. Fax 354-6854

New York Mills, Otter Tail, Pop. 1,166
New York Mills SD 553 700/PK-12
PO Box 218 56567 218-385-4201
Blaine Novak, supt. Fax 385-2551
www.nymills.k12.mn.us
New York Mills JSHS 300/7-12
PO Box 218 56567 218-385-4211
Michelle Young-Lecoustre, prin. Fax 385-2551

Nicollet, Nicollet, Pop. 1,085
Nicollet SD 507 100/PK-12
PO Box 108 56074 507-232-3411
Jack Eustice, supt. Fax 232-3536
www.isd507.k12.mn.us
Nicollet S 100/PK-12
PO Box 108 56074 507-232-3411
Todd Toulouse, prin. Fax 232-3536

North Branch, Chisago, Pop. 9,994
North Branch Area ISD 138 3,100/PK-12
PO Box 370 55056 651-674-1000
Dr. Deb Henton Ed.D., supt. Fax 674-1010
www.isd318.org
North Branch Area HS 1,000/9-12
PO Box 370 55056 651-674-1500
Coleman McDonough, prin. Fax 674-1510
North Branch Area Learning Center 50/Alt
PO Box 370 55056 651-674-1506
Glen Stevens, dir. Fax 674-1510
North Branch Area MS 1,000/5-8
PO Box 370 55056 651-674-1300
Todd Tetzlaff, prin. Fax 674-1310

Veritas Academy 50/K-12
34888 Kable Ave 55056 651-462-3894
Susie Brooks Ed.D., pres. Fax 462-4709

Northfield, Rice, Pop. 19,624
Northfield SD 659 3,900/K-12
1400 Division St S 55057 507-663-0600
Matt Hillmann Ph.D., supt. Fax 663-0611
northfieldschools.org
Longfellow S 100/Alt
201 Orchard St S 55057 507-645-1200
Mary Grace Hanson, admin. Fax 645-1250
Northfield Area Learning Center 100/Alt
201 Orchard St S 55057 507-645-1201
Daryl Kehler, prin. Fax 645-1250
Northfield HS 1,200/9-12
1400 Division St S 55057 507-663-0630
Joel Leer, prin. Fax 645-3455
Northfield MS 900/6-8
2200 Division St S 55057 507-663-0650
Greg Gelineau, prin. Fax 663-0660

Carleton College Post-Sec.
1 N College St 55057 507-222-4000
Laura Baker School Post-Sec.
211 Oak St 55057 507-645-8866
St. Olaf College Post-Sec.
1520 Saint Olaf Ave 55057 507-786-2222

North Mankato, Nicollet, Pop. 13,239
Mankato SD 77
Supt. — See Mankato

Dakota Meadows MS 600/6-8
1900 Howard Dr W 56003 507-387-5077
Carmen Strahan, prin. Fax 387-1119

South Central College Post-Sec.
1920 Lee Blvd 56003 507-389-7200

North Oaks, Ramsey, Pop. 4,424
Mounds View SD 621
Supt. — See Shoreview
Chippewa MS 1,000/6-8
5000 Hodgson Rd, 651-621-6400
Rob Reetz, prin. Fax 621-6405

Northome, Koochiching, Pop. 196
South Koochiching-Rainy River ISD 363 400/PK-12
PO Box 465 56661 218-897-5275
Jim Muckenhirn, supt. Fax 897-5280
www.northome.k12.mn.us
Northome JSHS 100/7-12
PO Box 465 56661 218-897-5275
Judd Wheatley, prin. Fax 897-5280
Other Schools – See Birchdale

Northrop, Martin, Pop. 227

Luther HS 100/9-12
PO Box 228 56075 507-436-5249
Paul Steinhaus, prin. Fax 436-5240

North Saint Paul, Ramsey, Pop. 11,176
North St. Paul-Maplewood-Oakdale SD 622
10,500/PK-12
2520 12th Ave E 55109 651-748-7622
Christine Osorio, supt. Fax 748-7413
www.isd622.org/
North HS 1,900/9-12
2416 11th Ave E 55109 651-748-6000
Greg Nelson, prin. Fax 748-6091
Other Schools – See Maplewood, Oakdale

Norwood Young America, Carver, Pop. 3,521
Central ISD 108 1,000/PK-12
PO Box 247 55368 952-467-7000
Brian Corlett, supt. Fax 467-7003
raiders.central.k12.mn.us
Central HS 300/9-12
PO Box 247 55368 952-467-7100
Tom Erickson, prin. Fax 467-7103
Central MS 200/6-8
PO Box 247 55368 952-467-7200
Ron Erpenbach, prin. Fax 467-7203

Oakdale, Washington, Pop. 26,751
North St. Paul-Maplewood-Oakdale SD 622
Supt. — See North Saint Paul
Skyview Community MS 800/6-8
1100 Heron Ave N 55128 651-702-8000
Joe Slavin, prin. Fax 702-8091
Tartan HS 1,700/9-12
828 Greenway Ave N 55128 651-702-8600
Ty Thompson, prin. Fax 702-8799

Ogilvie, Kanabec, Pop. 366
Ogilvie SD 333 500/PK-12
333 School Dr 56358 320-272-5000
Kathy Belsheim, supt. Fax 272-5072
www.ogilvie.k12.mn.us
Ogilvie MSHS 200/6-12
333 School Dr 56358 320-272-5000
Suzanne Davis, prin. Fax 272-5072

Okabena, Jackson, Pop. 186
Heron Lake-Okabena SD 330 300/PK-12
PO Box 97 56161 507-853-4507
Paul Bang, supt. Fax 853-4642
www.ssc.mntm.org
Heron Lake-Okabena HS 200/7-12
PO Box 97 56161 507-853-4507
Paul Bang, prin. Fax 853-4642

Oklee, Red Lake, Pop. 424
Red Lake County Central ISD 2906 400/PK-12
PO Box 100 56742 218-465-4222
Jim Guetter, supt. Fax 465-4225
www.rlcc2906.org
Red Lake County Central HS 200/7-12
PO Box 100 56742 218-796-5136
Randy Pederson, prin. Fax 796-5139

Olivia, Renville, Pop. 2,461
BOLD SD 2534 700/K-12
701 9th St S 56277 320-523-1031
John Dotson, supt. Fax 523-2399
www.bold.k12.mn.us
BOLD JSHS 400/7-12
701 9th St S 56277 320-523-1031
Brian Gauer, prin. Fax 523-5410

Onamia, Mille Lacs, Pop. 845
Onamia SD 480 600/K-12
35465 125th Ave 56359 320-532-4174
Jason Vold, supt. Fax 532-4658
www.onamia.k12.mn.us
Kokesh Area Learning Center 50/Alt
35465 125th Ave 56359 320-532-6821
Jason Vold, prin. Fax 532-4658
Onamia JSHS 300/7-12
35465 125th Ave 56359 320-532-4174
Jason Vold, prin. Fax 532-4974

Ortonville, Big Stone, Pop. 1,887
Ortonville SD 2903 300/PK-12
200 Trojan Dr 56278 320-839-6181
Jeffrey Taylor, supt. Fax 839-3708
www.ortonville.k12.mn.us
Ortonville S 300/PK-12
200 Trojan Dr 56278 320-839-6181
Jeff Taylor, supt. Fax 839-2499

Osakis, Douglas, Pop. 1,728
Osakis SD 213 700/PK-12
PO Box X 56360 320-859-2191
Joe Broderick, supt. Fax 859-2835
www.osakis.k12.mn.us
Osakis JSHS 400/5-12
PO Box X 56360 320-859-2191
Tim Roggenbuck, prin. Fax 859-2835

Osseo, Hennepin, Pop. 2,385
Osseo Area ISD 279
Supt. — See Maple Grove
Osseo HS 1,500/9-12
317 2nd Ave NW 55369 763-391-8500
Michael Lehan, prin. Fax 391-8501
Osseo MS 700/6-8
10223 93rd Ave N 55369 763-391-8800
Brian Chance, prin. Fax 391-8801

Owatonna, Steele, Pop. 25,301
Owatonna SD 761 4,700/K-12
515 W Bridge St 55060 507-444-8600
Peter Grant, supt. Fax 444-8688
www.owatonna.k12.mn.us
Owatonna Alternative Learning Ctr 100/Alt
130 E Vine St 55060 507-444-8000
Melodee Hoffner, prin.
Owatonna HS 1,500/9-12
333 E School St 55060 507-444-8800
Mark Randall, prin. Fax 444-8999
Owatonna JHS 700/7-8
500 15th St NE 55060 507-444-8700
Julie Sullivan, prin. Fax 444-8799

Parkers Prairie, Otter Tail, Pop. 1,009
Parkers Prairie ISD 547 500/PK-12
PO Box 46 56361 218-338-6011
Thomas Ames, supt. Fax 338-4077
www.isd547.com
Parkers Prairie JSHS 200/7-12
PO Box 46 56361 218-338-6011
Carey Johnson, prin. Fax 338-4077

Park Rapids, Hubbard, Pop. 3,639
Park Rapids SD 309 1,500/PK-12
301 Huntsinger Ave 56470 218-237-6500
Lance Bagstad, supt. Fax 237-6519
www.parkrapids.k12.mn.us
Century MS 400/5-8
501 Helten Ave 56470 218-237-6300
Shawn Andress, prin. Fax 237-6349
Park Rapids Area HS 400/9-12
401 Huntsinger Ave 56470 218-237-6400
Jeff Johnson, admin. Fax 237-6401

Paynesville, Stearns, Pop. 2,410
Paynesville SD 741 700/PK-12
217 W Mill St 56362 320-243-3410
Robert Huot, supt. Fax 243-7525
www.paynesvilleschools.com
Paynesville MSHS 300/6-12
795 Business 23 W 56362 320-243-3761
Lorie Floura, prin. Fax 243-4534

Pelican Rapids, Otter Tail, Pop. 2,413
Pelican Rapids SD 548 900/PK-12
PO Box 642 56572 218-863-5910
Deborah Wanek, supt. Fax 863-5915
www.pelicanrapids.k12.mn.us
Pelican Rapids Alt Learning Center 50/Alt
PO Box 642 56572 218-863-5910
Jacob Richter, prin. Fax 863-5915
Pelican Rapids JSHS 400/7-12
PO Box 642 56572 218-863-5910
Brian Korf, prin. Fax 863-5915

Pequot Lakes, Crow Wing, Pop. 2,149
Pequot Lakes SD 186 1,600/PK-12
30805 Olson St 56472 218-568-4996
Chris Lindholm, supt. Fax 568-5259
www.isd186.org
Pequot Lakes HS 500/9-12
30805 Olson St 56472 218-568-9210
Chip Rankin, prin. Fax 568-9250
Pequot Lakes MS 500/5-8
30805 Olson St 56472 218-568-9357
Michael O'Neil, prin. Fax 568-9202

Perham, Otter Tail, Pop. 2,944
Perham-Dent SD 549 1,400/PK-12
200 5th St SE 56573 218-346-4501
Mitch Anderson, supt. Fax 346-4506
www.perham.k12.mn.us
Perham Area Learning Center 50/Alt
520 1st Ave S 56573 218-346-6502
Jace Hennagir, dir. Fax 346-4506
Perham HS 500/9-12
200 5th St SE 56573 218-346-6500
Ehren Zimmerman, prin. Fax 346-6504
Prairie Wind MS 400/5-8
480 Coney St W 56573 218-346-1700
Scott Bjerke, prin. Fax 346-1704

Peterson, Fillmore, Pop. 199
Rushford-Peterson SD 239
Supt. — See Rushford
Rushford-Peterson MS 200/6-8
PO Box 8 55962 507-875-2238
Angela Shepard, prin. Fax 875-2316

Pierz, Morrison, Pop. 1,383
Pierz SD 484 1,100/PK-12
112 Kamnic St 56364 320-468-6458
George Weber, supt. Fax 468-6408
www.pierz.k12.mn.us
Healy JSHS 600/7-12
112 Kamnic St 56364 320-468-6458
Karrie Boser, prin. Fax 468-6408

Pillager, Cass, Pop. 463
Pillager SD 116 500/PK-12
323 E 2nd St 56473 218-746-2100
Michael Malmberg, supt. Fax 746-4236
www.isd116.org
Pillager HS 9-12
323 E 2nd St 56473 218-746-2113
Josh Smith, prin. Fax 746-3406
Pillager MS 100/5-8
323 E 2nd St 56473 218-746-2112
Scott Doss, prin. Fax 746-2153

Pine City, Pine, Pop. 3,072
Pine City SD 578 1,700/K-12
1400 Main St S 55063 320-629-4010
Annette Freiheit, supt. Fax 629-4070
www.pinecity.k12.mn.us
Pine City Area Learning Center 50/Alt
1400 Main St S 55063 320-629-4040
Troy Anderson, prin. Fax 629-3571
Pine City JSHS 700/7-12
1400 Main St S 55063 320-629-4112
Troy Anderson, prin. Fax 629-4105

Pine Technical College Post-Sec.
900 4th St SE 55063 320-629-5100

Pine Island, Goodhue, Pop. 3,224
Pine Island SD 255 700/PK-12
PO Box 398 55963 507-356-4849
Dr. Tammy Berg-Beniak, supt. Fax 356-8827
www.pineisland.k12.mn.us
Pine Island HS 300/5-12
PO Box 398 55963 507-356-8326
Mitchell Schiltz, prin. Fax 356-4130

Pine River, Cass, Pop. 928
Pine River-Backus SD 2174 900/PK-12
PO Box 610 56474 218-587-4720
David Endicott, supt. Fax 587-4120
www.prbschools.org
Pine River Area Learning Center 100/Alt
PO Box 610 56474 218-587-3131
Sue Peet, dir. Fax 587-3130
Pine River-Backus HS 400/7-12
PO Box 610 56474 218-587-4425
Andrew Forbort, prin. Fax 587-3108

Pipestone, Pipestone, Pop. 4,229
Pipestone Area SD 2689 1,200/PK-12
1401 7th St SW 56164 507-825-5861
Kevin Enerson, supt. Fax 825-6729
www.pas.k12.mn.us
Pipestone HS 300/9-12
1401 7th St SW 56164 507-825-5861
Cory Strasser, prin. Fax 825-6729
Pipestone MS 300/5-8
1401 7th St SW 56164 507-825-5861
Cory Strasser, prin. Fax 825-6729

Minnesota West Community & Tech College Post-Sec.
1314 N Hiawatha Ave 56164 507-825-6800

Plainview, Wabasha, Pop. 3,322
Plainview-Elgin-Millville ISD 2899 1,500/PK-12
500 W Broadway 55964 507-534-3651
Gary Kuphal, supt. Fax 534-3907
www.pem.k12.mn.us/
Plainview-Elgin-Millville HS 500/9-12
500 W Broadway 55964 507-534-3128
William Ihrke, prin. Fax 534-0174
Other Schools – See Elgin

Plymouth, Hennepin, Pop. 69,055
Robbinsdale SD 281
Supt. — See New Hope
Plymouth MS 1,300/6-8
10011 36th Ave N 55441 763-504-7100
Cheri Kulland, prin. Fax 504-7131
Robbinsdale Armstrong HS 2,000/9-12
10635 36th Ave N 55441 763-504-8800
David Dahl, prin. Fax 504-8831

Wayzata SD 284 11,200/PK-12
210 County Road 101 N 55447 763-745-5000
Dr. Chace B. Anderson, supt. Fax 745-5091
www.wayzata.k12.mn.us
Wayzata Central MS 1,100/6-8
305 Vicksburg Ln N 55447 763-745-6000
Clark Doten, prin. Fax 745-6091
Wayzata East MS 800/6-8
12000 Ridgemount Ave W 55441 763-745-6200
Paul Paetzel, prin. Fax 745-6291
Wayzata HS 3,200/9-12
4955 Peony Ln N, 763-745-6600
Scott Gengler, prin. Fax 745-6691
Other Schools – See Wayzata

Central Baptist Theological Seminary Post-Sec.
900 Forestview Ln N 55441 763-417-8250
Minnesota School of Business Post-Sec.
1455 County Road 101 N 55447 763-476-2000
Providence Academy 900/PK-12
15100 Schmidt Lake Rd, 763-258-2500
Dr. Todd Flanders, hdmstr. Fax 258-2501
West Lutheran HS 200/9-12
3350 Harbor Ln N 55447 763-509-9378
Adam Wiechmann, prin. Fax 509-0861

Preston, Fillmore, Pop. 1,314
Fillmore Central SD 2198 600/PK-12
PO Box 50 55965 507-765-3845
Richard Keith, supt. Fax 765-3636
www.fillmorecentral.k12.mn.us/
Other Schools – See Harmony

Princeton, Mille Lacs, Pop. 4,614
Princeton SD 477 3,300/PK-12
706 1st St 55371 763-389-2422
Dr. Julia Espe, supt. Fax 389-9142
www.princeton.k12.mn.us
Princeton Area Learning Center 50/Alt
1506 1st St 55371 763-389-6719
Erin Dohrmann, admin.
Princeton HS 1,000/9-12
807 8th Ave S 55371 763-389-4101
Barbara Muckenhirn, prin. Fax 389-5816
Princeton MS 800/6-8
1100 4th Ave N 55371 763-389-6704
Dan Voce, prin. Fax 389-6737

Prinsburg, Kandiyohi, Pop. 492

Central Minnesota Christian S 300/PK-12
PO Box 98 56281 320-978-8700
Peter Van Der Puy, supt. Fax 978-6797

Prior Lake, Scott, Pop. 22,273
Prior Lake - Savage Area SD 719 — 7,400/K-12
4540 Tower St SE 55372 — 952-226-0000
Teri Staloch, supt. — Fax 226-0059
www.priorlake-savage.k12.mn.us
Bridges Area Learning Center — Alt
15875 Franklin Trl SE 55372 — 952-226-0840
Dave Brown, dean — Fax 226-9724
Hidden Oaks MS — 900/6-8
15855 Fish Point Rd SE 55372 — 952-226-0700
Sasha Kuznetsov, prin. — Fax 226-0749
Twin Oaks MS — 800/6-8
15860 Fish Point Rd SE 55372 — 952-226-0500
Dr. Dan Edwards, prin. — Fax 226-0549
Other Schools – See Savage

Proctor, Saint Louis, Pop. 3,021
Proctor SD 704 — 1,800/PK-12
131 9th Ave 55810 — 218-628-4934
John Engelking, supt. — Fax 628-4937
www.proctor.k12.mn.us
Jedlicka MS — 400/6-8
131 9th Ave 55810 — 218-628-4926
Tim Rohweder, prin. — Fax 628-4932
Proctor HS — 500/9-12
131 9th Ave 55810 — 218-628-4926
Tim Rohweder, prin. — Fax 628-4931

Randolph, Dakota, Pop. 430
Randolph SD 195 — 600/PK-12
PO Box 38 55065 — 507-263-2151
Michael Kelley, supt. — Fax 645-5950
www.randolph.k12.mn.us
Randolph JSHS — 200/7-12
PO Box 38 55065 — 507-263-2151
Benjamin Fisher, prin. — Fax 645-5950

Redlake, Beltrami, Pop. 1,719
Red Lake SD 38 — 1,300/PK-12
PO Box 499 56671 — 218-679-3353
Anne Lundquist Ed.D., supt. — Fax 679-2321
www.redlake.k12.mn.us
Red Lake Alternative Learning Center — 50/Alt
PO Box 499 56671 — 218-679-3353
Jason Stanoch, prin. — Fax 679-2321
Red Lake HS — 300/9-12
PO Box 499 56671 — 218-679-3353
Jason Stanoch, prin. — Fax 679-2717
Red Lake MS — 200/6-8
PO Box 499 56671 — 218-679-2700
Mark Bensen, prin. — Fax 679-2733

Red Lake Falls, Red Lake, Pop. 1,407
Red Lake Falls SD 630 — 400/PK-12
PO Box 399 56750 — 218-253-2139
Jim Guetter, supt. — Fax 253-2135
www.redlakefalls.k12.mn.us
LaFayette JSHS — 200/7-12
PO Box 399 56750 — 218-253-2163
Brad Kennett, prin. — Fax 253-4480

Red Wing, Goodhue, Pop. 16,138
Red Wing SD 256 — 2,700/K-12
2451 Eagle Ridge Dr 55066 — 651-385-4500
Karsten Anderson, supt. — Fax 385-4510
www.rwps.org
Red Wing HS — 1,000/8-12
2451 Eagle Ridge Dr 55066 — 651-385-4600
Todd Herber, prin. — Fax 385-4610
Tower View Alternative HS — 100/Alt
154 Tower View Dr 55066 — 651-388-8963
Dr. Beth Borgen, prin. — Fax 385-8619

Minnesota State College Southeast Tech. — Post-Sec.
308 Pioneer Rd 55066 — 651-385-6300

Redwood Falls, Redwood, Pop. 5,083
Redwood Area SD 2897 — 1,100/PK-12
100 George Ramseth Dr 56283 — 507-644-3531
Rick Ellingworth, supt. — Fax 644-3057
www.redwoodareaschools.com
Redwood Valley Alternative S — Alt
100 George Ramseth Dr 56283 — 507-644-3531
Robin Beske, dir. — Fax 644-3057
Redwood Valley HS — 300/9-12
100 George Ramseth Dr 56283 — 507-644-3511
Rick Jorgenson, prin. — Fax 644-3057
Redwood Valley MS — 300/5-8
100 George Ramseth Dr 56283 — 507-644-3521
Nicole Lydick, prin. — Fax 644-3057

Remer, Cass, Pop. 366
Northland Community SD 118 — 300/PK-12
316 Main St E Rm 200 56672 — 218-566-2351
Tim Mayclin, supt. — Fax 566-2053
www.isd118.k12.mn.us
Northland HS — 200/7-12
316 Main St E Rm 300 56672 — 218-566-2352
Clayton Lindner, prin. — Fax 566-3199

Renville, Renville, Pop. 1,277
Renville County West SD 2890 — 200/K-12
PO Box 338 56284 — 320-329-8362
Michelle Mortensen, supt. — Fax 329-3271
www.rcw.k12.mn.us
Renville County West S — 200/K-12
PO Box 338 56284 — 320-329-8368
Fax 329-8191

Richfield, Hennepin, Pop. 34,223
Richfield SD 280 — 4,100/PK-12
7001 Harriet Ave 55423 — 612-798-6000
Steven Unowsky, supt. — Fax 798-6057
www.richfield.k12.mn.us
Richfield HS — 1,100/9-12
7001 Harriet Ave 55423 — 612-798-6100
Latanya Daniels, prin. — Fax 798-6127
Richfield MS — 900/6-8
7461 Oliver Ave S 55423 — 612-798-6400
Brian Zambreno, prin. — Fax 798-6427

Academy of Holy Angels — 700/9-12
6600 Nicollet Ave 55423 — 612-798-2600
Heidi Foley, prin. — Fax 798-2610
Adler Graduate School — Post-Sec.
1550 E 78th St 55423 — 612-861-7554
Blessed Trinity S - Nicollet Campus — 100/4-8
6720 Nicollet Ave 55423 — 612-869-5200
Patrick O'Keefe, prin. — Fax 767-2191
Minnesota School of Business — Post-Sec.
1401 W 76th St Ste 500 55423 — 612-861-2000

Robbinsdale, Hennepin, Pop. 13,450
Robbinsdale SD 281
Supt. — See New Hope
Robbinsdale MS — 1,300/6-8
3730 Toledo Ave N 55422 — 763-504-4800
George Nolan, prin. — Fax 504-4831

Rochester, Olmsted, Pop. 104,165
Rochester ISD 535 — 15,500/PK-12
615 7th St SW 55902 — 507-328-3000
Michael Munoz, supt. — Fax 328-4212
www.rochester.k12.mn.us
Adams MS — 1,100/6-8
1525 31st St NW 55901 — 507-328-5700
Kim McDonald, prin. — Fax 280-4726
Century HS — 1,400/9-12
2525 Viola Rd NE 55906 — 507-328-5100
Chris Fogarty, prin. — Fax 328-5045
Friedell MS — 500/6-8
1200 S Broadway 55904 — 507-328-5650
Jacque Peterson, prin. — Fax 328-5635
Kellogg MS, 503 17th St NE 55906 — 800/6-8
Eric Johnson, prin. — 507-328-5800
Marshall HS — 1,500/9-12
1510 14th St NW 55901 — 507-328-5400
Tim Limberg, prin. — Fax 328-5295
Mayo HS, 1420 11th Ave SE 55904 — 1,600/9-12
Tom Olson, prin. — 507-328-5500
Rochester Area Learning Center — 100/Alt
37 Woodlake Dr SE 55904 — 507-328-3999
Gordon Ziebart, prin.
Willow Creek MS — 1,000/6-8
2425 11th Ave SE 55904 — 507-328-5900
Nancy Denzer, prin. — Fax 328-5905
Hawthorne Adult Literacy Center — Adult
700 4th Ave SE 55904 — 507-328-4440
Nadine Holthaus, admin. — Fax 287-2643

Crossroads College — Post-Sec.
920 Mayowood Rd SW 55902 — 507-288-4563
Lourdes HS — 500/9-12
2800 19th St NW 55901 — 507-289-3991
Paul Menard, prin. — Fax 289-4008
Mayo Graduate School — Post-Sec.
200 1st St SW 55905 — 507-538-1160
Mayo Medical School — Post-Sec.
200 1st St SW 55905 — 507-538-4897
Mayo School of Health Sciences — Post-Sec.
200 1st St SW Bldg 11 55905 — 507-284-3678
Minnesota School of Business — Post-Sec.
2521 Pennington Dr NW 55901 — 507-536-9500
Rochester Community & Technical College — Post-Sec.
851 30th Ave SE 55904 — 507-285-7210
St. John the Evangelist S — 300/5-8
424 W Center St 55902 — 507-282-5248
Erin Widman, prin. — Fax 282-1343
St. Mary's Hospital/Mayo Medical Center — Post-Sec.
1216 2nd St NW 55901 — 507-255-5221
Schaeffer Academy — 400/K-12
2700 Schaeffer Ln NE 55906 — 507-286-1050
Keith E. Phillips, hdmstr. — Fax 282-3823
University of Minnesota Rochester — Post-Sec.
111 S Broadway Ste 300 55904 — 800-947-0117

Rockford, Wright, Pop. 4,215
Rockford Area ISD 883 — 1,500/PK-12
6051 Ash St 55373 — 763-477-9165
Paul Durand, supt. — Fax 477-5833
www.rockford.k12.mn.us
Rockford HS — 500/9-12
7600 County Road 50 55373 — 763-477-5846
Dr. Matthew Scheidler, prin. — Fax 477-6123
Rockford MS Center for Environmental Std — 400/5-8
6051 Ash St 55373 — 763-477-5831
Amy Denneson, prin. — Fax 477-5832

Rogers, Hennepin, Pop. 8,439
Elk River Area SD 728
Supt. — See Elk River
Rogers HS — 1,400/9-12
21000 141st Ave N 55374 — 763-274-3140
Jason Paurus, prin. — Fax 274-3141
Rogers MS — 1,000/6-8
20855 141st Ave N 55374 — 763-241-3550
Mark Huss, prin. — Fax 241-3518

Roseau, Roseau, Pop. 2,615
Roseau SD 682 — 1,200/PK-12
509 3rd St NE 56751 — 218-463-1471
Dr. Larry Guggisberg, supt. — Fax 463-3243
www.roseau.k12.mn.us
Roseau JSHS — 600/7-12
509 3rd St NE 56751 — 218-463-2770
Dave Reaves, prin. — Fax 463-3658

Rosemount, Dakota, Pop. 21,334
Rosemount-Apple Valley-Eagan ISD 196 — 26,600/PK-12
3455 153rd St W 55068 — 651-423-7700
Jane Berenz, supt. — Fax 423-7633
www.district196.org
Rosemount HS — 2,100/9-12
3335 142nd St W 55068 — 651-423-7501
John Wollersheim, prin. — Fax 423-7511
Rosemount MS — 1,200/6-8
3135 143rd St W 55068 — 651-423-7570
Mary Thompson, prin. — Fax 423-7664
Other Schools – See Apple Valley, Eagan

Dakota Co. Technical College — Post-Sec.
1300 145th St E 55068 — 651-423-8301
First Baptist S — 200/PK-12
14400 Diamond Path W 55068 — 651-423-2272
Dr. David Clear, supt. — Fax 423-8844

Roseville, Ramsey, Pop. 32,857
Roseville Area SD 623 — 7,400/K-12
1251 County Road B2 W 55113 — 651-635-1600
Dr. Aldo Sicoli, supt. — Fax 635-1659
www.isd623.org
Fairview Alternative HS — 100/Alt
1910 County Road B W 55113 — 651-604-3800
Laura Freer, prin. — Fax 604-3801
Roseville Area HS — 2,100/9-12
1240 County Road B2 W 55113 — 651-635-1660
Dr. Jenny Loeck, prin. — Fax 635-1699
Roseville Adult Learning Center — Adult
1910 W County Road B 55113 — 651-604-3554
Kristina Robertson, prin.
Other Schools – See Little Canada

American Academy of Acupuncture — Post-Sec.
1925 County Road B2 W 55113 — 651-631-0204
Concordia Academy — 300/9-12
2400 Dale St N 55113 — 651-484-8429
Dr. Tim Berner, prin. — Fax 484-0594
Minneapolis Business College — Post-Sec.
1711 County Road B W 55113 — 651-636-7406
National American University — Post-Sec.
1550 Highway 36 W 55113 — 651-855-6300

Rothsay, Wilkin, Pop. 493
Rothsay SD 850 — 100/PK-12
2040 County Road 52 56579 — 218-867-2117
Ron Bratlie, supt. — Fax 867-2376
www.rothsay.k12.mn.us
Rothsay S — 100/PK-12
2040 County Road 52 56579 — 218-867-2116
Staci Allmaras, prin. — Fax 867-2376

Royalton, Morrison, Pop. 1,237
Royalton SD 485 — 700/PK-12
120 S Hawthorn St 56373 — 320-584-4000
Dr. Jon Ellerbusch, supt. — Fax 584-4249
www.royalton.k12.mn.us
Royalton JSHS — 200/7-12
120 S Hawthorn St 56373 — 320-584-4000
Joel Swenson, prin. — Fax 584-4242

Rush City, Chisago, Pop. 3,060
Rush City SD 139 — 900/PK-12
PO Box 566 55069 — 320-358-4855
Teresa Dupre, supt. — Fax 358-1351
www.rushcity.k12.mn.us
Rush City HS — 400/7-12
PO Box 566 55069 — 320-358-4795
Brent Stavig, prin. — Fax 358-1261

Rushford, Fillmore, Pop. 1,721
Rushford-Peterson SD 239 — 700/PK-12
PO Box 627 55971 — 507-864-7785
Charles Ehler, supt. — Fax 864-2085
www.r-pschools.com
Rushford-Peterson HS — 200/9-12
PO Box 627 55971 — 507-864-7786
Jake Timm, prin. — Fax 864-2085
Other Schools – See Peterson

Russell, Lyon, Pop. 338
R T R ISD 2902
Supt. — See Tyler
R T R MS — 100/6-8
PO Box 310 56169 — 507-823-4371
Darren Baartman, admin. — Fax 823-4657

Saint Anthony, Hennepin, Pop. 8,057
Saint Anthony-New Brighton SD 282 — 1,700/PK-12
3303 33rd Ave NE 55418 — 612-706-1000
William Robert Laney, supt. — Fax 706-1020
www.stanthony.k12.mn.us
Saint Anthony MS — 400/6-8
3303 33rd Ave NE 55418 — 612-706-1032
Renee Corneille, prin. — Fax 706-1040
Saint Anthony Village HS — 700/9-12
3303 33rd Ave NE 55418 — 612-706-1102
Wayne Terry, prin. — Fax 706-1140

Saint Bonifacius, Hennepin, Pop. 2,257

Crown College — Post-Sec.
8700 College View Dr 55375 — 952-446-4100

Saint Charles, Winona, Pop. 3,695
Saint Charles SD 858 — 1,000/PK-12
600 E 6th St 55972 — 507-932-4420
Mark Roubinek, supt. — Fax 932-4700
www.scschools.net
Saint Charles HS — 400/7-12
600 E 6th St 55972 — 507-932-4420
Dr. Ben Bernard, prin. — Fax 932-4700

Saint Clair, Blue Earth, Pop. 859
Saint Clair SD 75 — 700/PK-12
PO Box 99 56080 — 507-245-3501
Tom Bruels, supt. — Fax 245-3517
www.stclair.new.rschooltoday.com
Saint Clair JSHS — 300/7-12
PO Box 99 56080 — 507-245-3027
Dustin Bosshart, prin. — Fax 245-3517

Saint Cloud, Stearns, Pop. 64,343
Saint Cloud Area SD 742 — 9,800/PK-12
1000 44th Ave N 56303 — 320-253-9333
Willie Jett, supt. — Fax 529-4343
www.isd742.org
Apollo HS — 1,300/9-12
1000 44th Ave N 56303 — 320-253-1600
Adam Holm, prin. — Fax 253-8475
McKinley Area Learning Center — 300/Alt
809 12th St N 56303 — 320-251-4963
Al Johnson, prin. — Fax 251-4173
North JHS — 800/6-8
1212 29th Ave N 56303 — 320-251-2159
Ellen Stewart, prin. — Fax 251-7350
South JHS — 1,000/6-8
1120 15th Ave S 56301 — 320-251-1322
Jason Harris, prin. — Fax 251-2911
Technical HS — 1,400/9-12
233 12th Ave S 56301 — 320-252-2231
Charles Eisenreich, prin. — Fax 252-0257

Cathedral HS 600/7-12
PO Box 1579 56302 320-251-3421
Lynn Grewing, prin. Fax 253-5576
Model College of Hair Design Post-Sec.
201 8th Ave S 56301 320-253-4222
Rasmussen College Post-Sec.
226 Park Ave S 56301 320-251-5600
Saint Cloud Christian S 200/K-12
430 3rd Ave NE 56304 320-252-8182
Jim Daniels, admin. Fax 656-9678
St. Cloud Hospital Post-Sec.
1406 6th Ave N 56303 320-255-5666
St. Cloud State University Post-Sec.
720 4th Ave S 56301 320-308-0121
St. Cloud Technical & Community College Post-Sec.
1540 Northway Dr 56303 320-308-5000

Saint Francis, Anoka, Pop. 7,077
Saint Francis SD 15 4,800/K-12
4115 Ambassador Blvd NW 55070 763-753-7040
Troy Ferguson, supt. Fax 753-4693
www.isd15.org
Crossroads S & Vocational Center 50/Alt
4111 Ambassador Blvd NW 55070 763-753-7120
Jay Powell, prin. Fax 753-1385
Saint Francis HS 1,600/9-12
3325 Bridge St NW 55070 763-213-1500
Douglas Austin, prin. Fax 213-1693
Saint Francis MS 1,100/6-8
23026 Ambassador Blvd NW 55070 763-213-8500
Bobbi Hume, prin. Fax 753-3821
Saints Academy Alt
4111 Ambassador Blvd NW 55070 763-753-7149
Scott Manni, admin.

Saint James, Watonwan, Pop. 4,579
Saint James SD 840 1,000/PK-12
PO Box 509 56081 507-375-5974
Becky Cselovszki, supt. Fax 375-7143
www.stjames.k12.mn.us
Saint James JSHS 600/6-12
1001 10th Ave N 56081 507-375-3381
Karla Beck, prin. Fax 375-4371

Saint Joseph, Stearns, Pop. 6,430

College of Saint Benedict Post-Sec.
37 College Ave S 56374 320-363-5011

Saint Louis Park, Hennepin, Pop. 43,914
Saint Louis Park SD 283 4,500/K-12
6425 W 33rd St 55426 952-928-6000
Robert Metz, supt. Fax 928-6020
www.slpschools.org
Saint Louis Park HS 1,400/9-12
6425 W 33rd St 55426 952-928-6100
Scott Meyers, prin. Fax 928-6113
Saint Louis Park MS 1,000/6-8
2025 Texas Ave S 55426 952-928-6300
Les Bork, prin. Fax 928-6383

Anthem College Post-Sec.
5100 Gamble Dr Ste 200 55416 952-417-2200
Benilde-St. Margarets HS 1,200/7-12
2501 Highway 100 S 55416 952-927-4176
Dr. Sue Skinner, prin. Fax 920-8889
Groves Academy 200/1-12
3200 Highway 100 S 55416 952-920-6377
John Alexander, head sch Fax 920-2068
Health System Minnesota/Methodist Hosp. Post-Sec.
6500 Excelsior Blvd 55426 952-993-3601

Saint Michael, Wright, Pop. 16,153
Saint Michael-Albertville SD 885
Supt. — See Albertville
Knights Academy 50/Alt
60 Central Ave W 55376 763-497-6575
Robert Driver, prin. Fax 497-6581
Saint Michael-Albertville HS 1,600/9-12
5800 Jamison Ave NE 55376 763-497-2192
Bob Driver, prin. Fax 497-6590
Saint Michael-Albertville MS East 5-8
4862 Naber Ave NE 55376 763-497-2655
Jennifer Kelly, prin. Fax 497-6591

Saint Paul, Ramsey, Pop. 275,178
Saint Paul SD 625 35,900/PK-12
360 Colborne St 55102 651-767-8100
Dr. John Thein, supt. Fax 293-8586
www.spps.org
Battle Creek MS 900/6-8
2121 N Park Dr 55119 651-293-8960
Lanisha Paddock, prin. Fax 293-8866
Central HS 2,000/9-12
275 Lexington Pkwy N 55104 651-744-4900
Mary Mackbee, prin. Fax 293-5433
Como Park HS 1,300/9-12
740 Rose Ave W 55117 651-293-8800
Theresa Neal, prin. Fax 293-8806
Creative Arts HS 100/6-12
65 Kellogg Blvd E 55101 651-292-3480
Dr. Carlondrea Hines, prin. Fax 292-3484
Farnsworth Aerospace Magnet MS 700/5-8
1000 Walsh St 55106 651-293-8880
Hamilton Bell, prin. Fax 293-8888
Harding HS 2,100/9-12
1540 6th St E 55106 651-793-4700
Doug Revsbeck, prin. Fax 293-8912
Highland Park HS 1,200/9-12
1015 Snelling Ave S 55116 651-293-8940
Dr. Winston Tucker, prin. Fax 293-8939
Highland Park MS 900/6-8
975 Snelling Ave S 55116 651-293-8950
Charlene Hoff, prin. Fax 293-8953
Humboldt HS 1,200/6-12
30 Baker St E 55107 651-293-8600
Michael Sodomka, prin. Fax 293-8605
Johnson HS 1,400/9-12
1349 Arcade St 55106 651-293-8890
Micheal Thompson, prin. Fax 293-8895
LEAP HS 200/Alt
631 Albert St N 55104 651-228-7706
Rose Santos, prin. Fax 228-7711
Linwood Monroe Arts Plus MS 600/4-8
810 Palace Ave 55102 651-293-8690
Bryan Bass, prin. Fax 293-8699
Murray MS 800/6-8
2200 Buford Ave 55108 651-293-8740
Kirk Morris, prin. Fax 293-8742
Open World Learning Community S 300/6-12
640 Humboldt Ave 55107 651-293-8670
Dave Gundale, prin. Fax 293-5308
Parks HS 200/Alt
1212 University Ave W 55104 651-744-1212
Traci Gauer, prin. Fax 744-1208
Parkway Montessori MS 400/6-8
1363 Bush Ave 55106 651-744-1000
Jocelyn Sims, prin. Fax 744-1001
Ramsey MS 700/6-8
1700 Summit Ave 55105 651-293-8860
Dr. Teresa Vibar, prin. Fax 298-1587
Washington Technology Magnet MSHS 2,100/6-12
1495 Rice St 55117 651-293-8830
Mike McCollor, prin. Fax 228-4331
Evening HS Adult
1212 University Ave W 55104 651-744-1210
Fax 744-1208

Bethel Seminary Post-Sec.
3949 Bethel Dr 55112 651-638-6288
Bethel University Post-Sec.
3900 Bethel Dr 55112 651-638-6400
Christ's Household of Faith S 200/PK-12
355 Marshall Ave 55102 651-265-3400
Vernon Harms, prin. Fax 227-9813
Concordia University-St. Paul Post-Sec.
275 Syndicate St N 55104 651-641-8278
Cretin-Derham Hall HS 1,300/9-12
550 Albert St S 55116 651-690-2443
Mona Passman, prin. Fax 696-3394
Empire Beauty School Post-Sec.
1905 Suburban Ave 55119 651-209-6930
Hamline University Post-Sec.
1536 Hewitt Ave 55104 651-523-2800
Luther Seminary Post-Sec.
2481 Como Ave 55108 800-588-4373
Macalester College Post-Sec.
1600 Grand Ave 55105 651-696-6000
McNally Smith College of Music Post-Sec.
19 Exchange St E 55101 651-291-0177
Metropolitan State University Post-Sec.
700 7th St E 55106 651-793-1300
Mounds Park Academy 600/PK-12
2051 Larpenteur Ave E 55109 651-777-2555
Dr. Bill Hudson, head sch Fax 777-8633
Northwestern College Post-Sec.
3003 Snelling Ave N 55113 651-631-5100
St. Agnes S 500/K-12
530 Lafond Ave 55103 651-925-8700
Dr. Kevin Ferdinandt, head sch Fax 925-8708
Saint Catherine University Post-Sec.
2004 Randolph Ave 55105 651-690-6000
St. Paul Academy & Summit S 600/6-12
1712 Randolph Ave 55105 651-698-2451
Bryn Roberts, head sch Fax 698-6787
St. Paul College Post-Sec.
235 Marshall Ave 55102 651-846-1600
St. Paul Preparatory S 9-12
380 Jackson St Ste 100 55101 651-288-4606
John Belpedio, prin. Fax 288-4616
University of St. Thomas Post-Sec.
2115 Summit Ave 55105 651-962-5000
William Mitchell College of Law Post-Sec.
875 Summit Ave 55105 651-227-9171

Saint Paul Park, Washington, Pop. 5,176
South Washington County SD 833
Supt. — See Cottage Grove
Oltman MS 700/6-8
1020 3rd St 55071 651-425-3500
Becky Schroeder, prin. Fax 425-3555

Hope Christian Academy 100/PK-12
920 Holley Ave Ste 2 55071 651-459-6438
Randy Krussow, prin. Fax 769-2108

Saint Peter, Nicollet, Pop. 11,009
Saint Peter SD 508 1,600/PK-12
100 Lincoln Dr 56082 507-934-5703
Dr. Paul Peterson, supt. Fax 934-2805
www.stpeterschools.org
Saint Peter MSHS 500/7-12
100 Lincoln Dr 56082 507-934-4210
Annette Engeldinger, prin. Fax 934-4783

Gustavus Adolphus College Post-Sec.
800 W College Ave 56082 507-933-8000

Sandstone, Pine, Pop. 2,776
East Central SD 2580
Supt. — See Finlayson
Crossroads Learning Center 50/Alt
130 Oriole St E Ste 2 55072 320-216-4155
Stef Youngberg, dir. Fax 216-4170

Harvest Christian S 100/PK-12
PO Box 646 55072 320-245-5330
Jack Allen, admin. Fax 245-5330

Sartell, Stearns, Pop. 15,661
Sartell-St. Stephen SD 748 3,700/K-12
212 3rd Ave N 56377 320-656-3715
Jeff Schwiebert, supt. Fax 656-3765
www.sartell.k12.mn.us
Sartell HS 1,100/9-12
748 7th St N 56377 320-656-0748
Brenda Steve, prin. Fax 656-5296
Sartell MS 1,200/5-8
627 3rd Ave N 56377 320-253-2200
Kurt Stumpf, prin. Fax 253-1403

Sauk Centre, Stearns, Pop. 4,294
Sauk Centre SD 743 1,000/PK-12
903 State Rd 56378 320-352-2284
Patrick Westby, supt. Fax 352-3404
www.isd743.k12.mn.us
Sauk Centre Secondary S 500/7-12
903 State Rd 56378 320-352-2856
Sheila Flatau, prin. Fax 352-3404

Sauk Rapids, Benton, Pop. 12,559
Sauk Rapids-Rice SD 47 4,100/PK-12
1833 Osauka Rd 56379 320-253-4703
Dr. Daniel Bittman, supt. Fax 255-1914
www.isd47.org
Sauk Rapids-Rice HS 1,200/9-12
1835 Osauka Rd 56379 320-253-4700
Erich Martens, prin. Fax 258-1717
Sauk Rapids-Rice MS 1,000/6-8
901 1st St S 56379 320-654-9073
Dr. Nate Rudolph, prin. Fax 259-8909
Hillside ECFE & ABE Adult
30 4th Ave S 56379 320-255-8910
Megan Rogholt, contact Fax 258-1197

Savage, Scott, Pop. 26,220
Burnsville-Eagan-Savage ISD 191
Supt. — See Burnsville
Eagle Ridge MS 500/6-8
13955 Glendale Rd 55378 952-707-2800
Don Leake, prin. Fax 707-2802

Prior Lake - Savage Area SD 719
Supt. — See Prior Lake
Prior Lake HS 2,400/9-12
7575 150th St W 55378 952-226-8600
Dave Lund, prin. Fax 226-8649

Sebeka, Wadena, Pop. 700
Sebeka SD 820 500/PK-12
PO Box 249 56477 218-837-5101
Dave Fjeldheim, supt. Fax 837-5967
www.sebeka.k12.mn.us
Sebeka JSHS 200/7-12
PO Box 249 56477 218-837-5101
Dave Fjeldheim, prin. Fax 837-5967

Shakopee, Scott, Pop. 36,163
Shakopee SD 720 7,600/K-12
505 Holmes St S 55379 952-496-5000
Dr. Rod Thompson, supt. Fax 496-5056
www.shakopee.k12.mn.us
East JHS 800/7-9
1137 Marschall Rd 55379 952-496-5702
Jim Miklausich, prin. Fax 496-5715
Shakopee SHS 1,500/10-12
100 17th Ave W 55379 952-496-5152
Ben Kusch, prin. Fax 496-5155
Tokata Learning Center Alt
1110 Shakopee Town Sq 55379 952-496-5982
Eric Serbus, prin. Fax 496-5985
West JHS 1,000/7-9
200 10th Ave E 55379 952-496-5752
Lori Link, prin. Fax 496-5755

Sherburn, Martin, Pop. 1,125
Martin County West SD 2448 500/K-12
105 E 5th St 56171 507-764-2330
Allison Schmidt, supt. Fax 764-2335
www.martin.k12.mn.us
Martin County West JSHS 300/7-12
16 W 5th St 56171 507-764-4661
David Traetow, prin. Fax 764-4681

Shoreview, Ramsey, Pop. 24,520
Mounds View SD 621 9,900/K-12
350 Highway 96 W 55126 651-621-6000
Chris Lennox, supt. Fax 621-6046
www.moundsviewschools.org
Other Schools – See Arden Hills, Mounds View, New Brighton, North Oaks

Silver Bay, Lake, Pop. 1,866
Lake Superior SD 381
Supt. — See Two Harbors
Kelley JSHS 200/7-12
137 Banks Blvd 55614 218-226-4437
Joe Nicklay, prin. Fax 226-4860

Slayton, Murray, Pop. 2,140
Murray County Central SD 2169 700/PK-12
2420 28th St 56172 507-836-6183
Joe W. Meyer, supt. Fax 836-6375
www.mcc.mntm.org
Murray County Central JSHS 300/7-12
2420 28th St 56172 507-836-6184
Jacob Scandrett, prin. Fax 836-6375

Sleepy Eye, Brown, Pop. 3,585
Sleepy Eye SD 84 600/PK-12
400 4th Ave SW 56085 507-794-7903
John Cselovszki, supt. Fax 794-5404
www.sleepyeyeschools.com
Sleepy Eye JSHS 300/7-12
400 4th Ave SW 56085 507-794-7904
Shane Laffen, prin. Fax 794-5404

St. Mary JSHS 200/7-12
104 Saint Marys St NW 56085 507-794-4121
Andrew Bach, prin. Fax 794-4841

South Saint Paul, Dakota, Pop. 19,660
South St. Paul SD 6 3,100/PK-12
104 5th Ave S 55075 651-457-9400
Dr. Dave Webb, supt. Fax 457-9485
www.sspps.org
Community Learning Center 100/Alt
151 6th St E 55075 651-450-9966
Nick Falde, dir. Fax 306-3666
South Saint Paul HS 1,400/6-12
700 2nd St N 55075 651-457-9408
Chuck Ochocki, prin. Fax 457-9455

Springfield, Brown, Pop. 2,141
Springfield SD 85 600/PK-12
12 Burns Ave 56087 507-723-4283
Keith Kottke, supt. Fax 723-6407
www.springfield.mntm.org/
Springfield JSHS 300/7-12
12 Burns Ave 56087 507-723-4288
Pat Moriarty, prin. Fax 723-4447

Spring Grove, Houston, Pop. 1,322
Spring Grove SD 297 400/K-12
PO Box 626 55974 507-498-3221
Rachel Udstuen, supt. Fax 498-3470
www.springgrove.k12.mn.us
Spring Grove JSHS 200/7-12
PO Box 626 55974 507-498-3223
Nancy Gulbranson, prin. Fax 498-3470

Spring Lake Park, Anoka, Pop. 6,217
Spring Lake Park SD 16 5,300/K-12
1415 81st Ave NE 55432 763-600-5000
Dr. Jeff Ronneberg, supt. Fax 600-5582
www.springlakeparkschools.org
Lighthouse S 50/1-12
7925 Able St NE 55432 763-600-5200
Mike Callahan, admin. Fax 600-5213
Spring Lake Park HS 1,400/9-12
1100 81st Ave NE 55432 763-600-5100
Jane Stevenson, prin. Fax 600-5113
Other Schools – See Blaine

Empire Beauty School Post-Sec.
8205 University Ave NE 55432 - -

Spring Valley, Fillmore, Pop. 2,458
Kingsland SD 2137 600/PK-12
705 N Section Ave 55975 507-346-7276
John McDonald, supt. Fax 346-7278
www.kingsland.k12.mn.us
Kingsland JSHS 300/7-12
705 N Section Ave 55975 507-346-7276
Jim Hecimovich, prin. Fax 346-7278

Staples, Todd, Pop. 2,930
Staples-Motley ISD 2170 800/PK-12
202 Pleasant Ave NE 56479 218-894-5400
Mary Klamm, supt. Fax 894-1828
www.isd2170.k12.mn.us/
Connections HS 50/Alt
401 Centennial Ln 56479 218-894-5400
Mike Schmidt, admin.
Staples-Motley HS 400/8-12
401 Centennial Ln 56479 218-894-2431
Michael Schmidt, prin. Fax 894-2434

Central Lakes College Post-Sec.
1830 Airport Rd 56479 218-894-5100

Stephen, Marshall, Pop. 657
Stephen-Argyle Central SD 2856 300/PK-12
PO Box 68 56757 218-478-3315
Dr. Chris Mills, supt. Fax 478-3537
www.sac.k12.mn.us/
Stephen JSHS 200/7-12
PO Box 68 56757 218-478-3314
Kevin Kuznia, prin. Fax 478-3537

Stewartville, Olmsted, Pop. 5,872
Stewartville SD 534 2,000/PK-12
301 2nd St SW 55976 507-533-1438
Dr. David Thompson, supt. Fax 533-4012
www.ssd.k12.mn.us
Stewartville HS 500/9-12
440 6th Ave SW 55976 507-533-1600
Steve Gibbs, prin. Fax 533-1490
Stewartville MS 400/6-8
440 6th Ave SW 55976 507-533-1666
Steven Gibbs, prin. Fax 533-1490

Stillwater, Washington, Pop. 17,911
Stillwater Area SD 834 8,100/K-12
1875 Greeley St S 55082 651-351-8301
Denise Pontrelli, supt. Fax 351-8380
www.stillwater.k12.mn.us
St. Croix Valley ALC 100/Alt
5640 Memorial Ave N 55082 651-351-8464
Mary Ticiu, dir. Fax 351-8465
Stillwater Area SHS 2,100/10-12
5701 Stillwater Blvd N 55082 651-351-8040
Robert Bach, prin. Fax 351-8049
Stillwater JHS 1,100/7-9
523 Marsh St W 55082 651-351-6905
Roderic VanScoy, prin. Fax 351-6999
Other Schools – See Lake Elmo

Swanville, Morrison, Pop. 348
Swanville SD 486 300/PK-12
PO Box 98 56382 320-547-5100
Gene Harthan, supt. Fax 547-2576
www.swanville.k12.mn.us/
Molly Creek ALC 50/Alt
PO Box 98 56382 320-547-9930
Michelle Peterson, lead tchr. Fax 547-2576
Swanville JSHS 100/7-12
PO Box 98 56382 320-547-5100
Sheryl Johnson, prin. Fax 547-2576

Thief River Falls, Pennington, Pop. 8,403
Thief River Falls SD 564 2,000/PK-12
230 LaBree Ave S 56701 218-681-8711
Bradley Bergstrom, supt. Fax 681-2905
www.trf.k12.mn.us
Franklin MS 400/6-8
300 Spruce Ave S 56701 218-681-8813
Bob Wayne, prin. Fax 681-4771
Lincoln HS 600/9-12
101 Knight Ave S 56701 218-681-7432
Shane Zutz, prin. Fax 681-4510
Northwest Area Learning Center 50/Alt
230 LaBree Ave S 56701 218-681-8711
Loren Leake, dir. Fax 681-4686

Northland Community & Technical College Post-Sec.
1101 Highway 1 E 56701 218-683-8800
St. John Lutheran S 50/PK-12
15671 158th St NE 56701 218-681-7753
John Folland, prin.

Tracy, Lyon, Pop. 2,129
Tracy SD 2904 800/PK-12
934 Pine St 56175 507-629-5500
Chad Anderson, supt. Fax 629-5507
www.tracy.k12.mn.us
Tracy JSHS 400/7-12
934 Pine St 56175 507-629-5500
Kathy VonDracek, prin. Fax 629-5507

Truman, Martin, Pop. 1,111
Truman SD 458 200/K-12
PO Box 276 56088 507-776-2111
Dr. Virginia Dahlstrom, supt. Fax 776-3379
www.truman.k12.mn.us
Truman JSHS 100/7-12
PO Box 276 56088 507-776-2111
Mark Nass, prin. Fax 776-3379

Twin Valley, Norman, Pop. 807
Norman County East SD 2215 300/PK-12
PO Box 420 56584 218-584-5151
Rob Nudell, supt. Fax 584-5170
www.nce.k12.mn.us
Norman County East HS 100/7-12
PO Box 420 56584 218-584-5151
Rob Nudell, prin. Fax 584-5170

Two Harbors, Lake, Pop. 3,693
Lake Superior SD 381 1,400/PK-12
1640 Highway 2 55616 218-834-8201
Dr. Bill Crandall, supt. Fax 834-8239
www.isd381.org
Two Harbors JSHS 600/6-12
1640 Highway 2 Ste 100 55616 218-834-8201
Jay Belcastro, prin. Fax 834-5513
Other Schools – See Silver Bay

Tyler, Lincoln, Pop. 1,129
R T R ISD 2902 600/PK-12
PO Box 659 56178 507-247-5913
Dick Orcutt, supt. Fax 247-3876
www.rtrschools.org
R T R HS 200/9-12
PO Box 659 56178 507-247-5911
Dan Bettin, prin. Fax 247-3876
Other Schools – See Russell

Ulen, Clay, Pop. 535
Ulen-Hitterdal SD 914 300/K-12
PO Box 389 56585 218-596-8853
Todd Cameron, supt. Fax 596-8610
www.ulenhitterdal.k12.mn.us
Ulen-Hitterdal JSHS 100/7-12
PO Box 389 56585 218-596-8853
Kent Henrickson, prin. Fax 596-8610

Underwood, Otter Tail, Pop. 340
Underwood SD 550 600/PK-12
100 Southern Ave E 56586 218-826-6101
Dr. Jeremiah Olson, supt. Fax 826-6310
www.underwood.k12.mn.us
Underwood JSHS 300/7-12
100 Southern Ave E 56586 218-826-6102
John Hamann, prin. Fax 826-6310

Upsala, Morrison, Pop. 425
Upsala SD 487 400/PK-12
PO Box 190 56384 320-573-2174
Vern Capelle, supt. Fax 573-2173
www.upsala.k12.mn.us
Upsala JSHS 200/7-12
PO Box 190 56384 320-573-2176
Vern Capelle, prin. Fax 573-2173

Verndale, Wadena, Pop. 586
Verndale SD 818 500/PK-12
411 SW Brown St 56481 218-445-5184
Paul Brownlow, supt. Fax 445-5185
www.verndale.k12.mn.us
Verndale JSHS 200/7-12
411 SW Brown St 56481 218-445-5184
Paul Brownlow, prin. Fax 445-5185

Victoria, Carver, Pop. 7,244

Holy Family HS 500/9-12
8101 Kochia Ln 55386 952-443-4659
Kathie Brown, prin. Fax 443-1822

Virginia, Saint Louis, Pop. 8,491
Saint Louis County ISD 2142 1,000/PK-12
1701 N 9th Ave 55792 218-749-8130
Steven Sallee, supt. Fax 749-8133
isd2142.net
Other Schools – See Babbitt, Cook, Culver, Iron

Virginia SD 706 1,600/PK-12
411 S 5th Ave 55792 218-742-3901
Dr. Noel Schmidt, supt. Fax 742-3960
www.vmps.org
Virginia Secondary S 700/7-12
411 S 5th Ave 55792 218-742-3916
Lisa Perkovich, prin. Fax 741-8522

Mesabi Range Community & Technical Coll. Post-Sec.
1001 Chestnut St W 55792 218-741-3095

Wabasha, Wabasha, Pop. 2,493
Wabasha-Kellogg SD 811 600/PK-12
2113 Hiawatha Dr E 55981 651-565-3559
Jim Freihammer, supt. Fax 565-2769
www.wabasha-kellogg.k12.mn.us/
Wabasha-Kellogg JSHS 300/7-12
2113 Hiawatha Dr E 55981 651-565-3559
Rob Stewart, prin. Fax 565-2769

Wabasso, Redwood, Pop. 691
Wabasso SD 640 400/PK-12
PO Box 69 56293 507-342-5114
Wade McKittrick, supt. Fax 342-5203
isd640.org
Wabasso JSHS 200/7-12
PO Box 69 56293 507-342-5114
Wade McKittrick, supt. Fax 342-5203

Waconia, Carver, Pop. 10,592
Waconia SD 110 3,300/PK-12
512 Industrial Blvd 55387 952-442-0600
Patrick Devine, supt. Fax 442-0609
www.waconia.k12.mn.us
Clearwater MS 900/6-8
1650 Community Dr 55387 952-442-0650
Shane Clausen, prin. Fax 442-0659
Waconia HS 1,100/9-12
1400 Community Dr 55387 952-442-0670
Mark Fredericksen, prin. Fax 442-0679

Wadena, Wadena, Pop. 4,023
Wadena-Deer Creek SD 2155 800/PK-12
600 Colfax Ave SW 56482 218-632-2155
Lee Westrum, supt. Fax 632-2199
www.wdc2155.k12.mn.us
Wadena-Deer Creek MSHS 400/5-12
600 Colfax Ave SW 56482 218-632-2300
Tyler Church, prin. Fax 632-2399

MN State Community & Technical College Post-Sec.
405 Colfax Ave SW 56482 218-631-7800

Waite Park, Stearns, Pop. 6,543

Minnesota School of Business Post-Sec.
1201 2nd St S 56387 320-257-2000
Regency Beauty Institute Post-Sec.
110 2nd St S 56387 320-251-0500

Walker, Cass, Pop. 910
Walker-Hackensack-Akeley SD 113 700/PK-12
PO Box 4000 56484 218-547-1311
Eric Pingrey, supt. Fax 547-4298
www.wha.k12.mn.us
Walker-Hackensack-Akeley HS 300/7-12
PO Box 4000 56484 218-547-4210
Dave Wineburner, prin. Fax 547-4297

Wanamingo, Goodhue, Pop. 1,081
Kenyon-Wanamingo SD 2172 700/PK-12
225 3rd Ave 55983 507-789-7000
Dr. Jeff Pesta, supt. Fax 789-7032
www.kw.k12.mn.us
Other Schools – See Kenyon

Warren, Marshall, Pop. 1,554
Warren-Alvarado-Oslo SD 2176 400/PK-12
224 E Bridge Ave 56762 218-745-5393
Lon Jorgensen, supt. Fax 745-5886
www.wao.k12.mn.us
Warren-Alvarado-Oslo JSHS 200/7-12
224 E Bridge Ave 56762 218-745-4646
Wade Johnson, prin. Fax 745-7658

Warroad, Roseau, Pop. 1,740
Warroad SD 690 1,000/PK-12
510 Cedar Ave NW 56763 218-386-1472
Paula Foley, supt. Fax 386-6113
www.warroad.k12.mn.us
Warroad JSHS 400/7-12
510 Cedar Ave NW 56763 218-386-1820
Craig Peterson, prin. Fax 386-1909

Waseca, Waseca, Pop. 9,257
Waseca SD 829 1,500/PK-12
501 Elm Ave E 56093 507-835-2500
Thomas Lee, supt. Fax 835-1161
www.waseca.k12.mn.us
Waseca Area Learning Center 50/Alt
501 Elm Ave E 56093 507-835-5588
JoAnn Erickson, coord. Fax 835-1724
Waseca JSHS 600/7-12
1717 2nd St NW 56093 507-835-5470
Jeanne Swanson, prin. Fax 835-1724

Watertown, Carver, Pop. 4,128
Watertown-Mayer SD 111 1,600/PK-12
1001 Highway 25 Shls NW 55388 952-955-0480
Ron Wilke, supt. Fax 955-0481
www.wm.k12.mn.us
Watertown-Mayer HS 500/9-12
1001 Highway 25 Shls NW 55388 952-955-0600
Bob Hennen, prin. Fax 955-0601
Watertown-Mayer MS 400/6-8
1001 Highway 25 Shls NW 55388 952-955-0400
Nick Guertin, prin. Fax 955-0481

Waterville, LeSueur, Pop. 1,853
Waterville-Elysian-Morristown SD 2143 900/PK-12
500 Paquin St E 56096 507-362-4432
Joel Whitehurst, supt. Fax 362-4561
www.wem.k12.mn.us/
Waterville-Elysian-Morristown HS 300/9-12
500 Paquin St E 56096 507-362-4431
John Kaplan, prin. Fax 362-4561
Other Schools – See Morristown

Waubun, Mahnomen, Pop. 324
Waubun-Ogema-White Earth SD 435 600/PK-12
PO Box 98 56589 218-473-6171
Lisa Weber, supt. Fax 473-6191
www.waubun.k12.mn.us
Waubun Alternative Learning Center 50/Alt
PO Box 98 56589 218-473-6173
Eric Martinez, dir.
Waubun JSHS 200/7-12
PO Box 98 56589 218-473-6173
Eric Martinez, prin. Fax 473-6190

Wayzata, Hennepin, Pop. 3,646
Wayzata SD 284
Supt. — See Plymouth
Wayzata West MS 700/6-8
149 Barry Ave N 55391 952-745-6400
Susan Sommerfeld, prin. Fax 745-6491

Wells, Faribault, Pop. 2,325
United South Central SD 2134 600/PK-12
PO Box 312 56097 507-553-3134
Keith Fleming, supt. Fax 553-5929
www.usc.k12.mn.us
United South Central JSHS 300/7-12
PO Box 312 56097 507-553-5819
Kelly Schlaak, prin. Fax 553-5929

Westbrook, Cottonwood, Pop. 737
Westbrook-Walnut Grove SD 2898 400/PK-12
PO Box 129 56183 507-274-5450
Loy Woelber, supt. Fax 274-6113
www.wwgschools.org
Westbrook-Walnut Grove JHHS 200/7-12
PO Box 129 56183 507-274-5450
Loy Woelber, prin. Fax 858-2329

West Saint Paul, Dakota, Pop. 19,105
West St. Paul-Mendota Hts-Eagan SD 197
Supt. — See Mendota Heights
Heritage E-STEM Magnet S 800/5-8
121 Butler Ave W 55118 651-403-7400
Karen Allen, prin. Fax 403-7410

St. Croix Lutheran MSHS 500/6-12
1200 Oakdale Ave 55118 651-455-1521
Todd Russ, pres. Fax 451-3968

Wheaton, Traverse, Pop. 1,408
Wheaton Area SD 803 400/PK-12
1700 3rd Ave S 56296 320-563-8283
Daniel Posthumus, supt. Fax 563-4218
www.wheaton.k12.mn.us
Wheaton JSHS 200/6-12
1700 3rd Ave S 56296 320-563-8282
Martin Lanter, prin. Fax 563-4218

White Bear Lake, Ramsey, Pop. 23,270
White Bear Lake Area SD 624 8,100/PK-12
4855 Bloom Ave 55110 651-407-7500
Dr. Michael Lovett, supt. Fax 407-7566
www.isd624.org
Central MS 1,000/6-8
4857 Bloom Ave 55110 651-653-2888
Timothy Schochenmaier, prin. Fax 653-2885
Sunrise Park MS 800/6-8
2399 Cedar Ave 55110 651-653-2700
Christina Pierre, prin. Fax 653-2716
White Bear Lake Area HS - North Campus 1,100/9-10
5045 Division Ave 55110 651-653-2920
Donald Bosch, prin. Fax 653-2630
White Bear Lake Area HS - South Campus 1,100/11-12
3551 McKnight Rd N 55110 651-773-6200
Timothy Wald, prin. Fax 773-6215
White Bear Lake Area Learning Center 100/Alt
2449 Orchard Ln 55110 651-773-6400
Gretchen Harriman, admin. Fax 773-6402

Century College Post-Sec.
3300 Century Ave N 55110 651-779-3200
Liberty Classical Academy 200/PK-12
3878 Highland Ave 55110 651-772-2777
Rebekah Hagstrom M.A., hdmstr. Fax 776-0393

Willmar, Kandiyohi, Pop. 19,385
Willmar SD 347 4,000/K-12
611 5th St SW 56201 320-231-8500
Dr. Jeffrey Holm, supt. Fax 231-1061
www.willmar.k12.mn.us
Willmar Area Learning Center 100/Alt
512 8th St SW 56201 320-214-6692
Linda Bahe, coord. Fax 235-5352
Willmar HS 1,200/9-12
2701 30th St NE 56201 320-231-8300
Paul Schmitz, prin. Fax 231-8460
Willmar MS 900/6-8
201 Willmar Ave SE 56201 320-214-6000
Mark Miley, prin. Fax 235-1254

Community Christian S 200/PK-12
1300 19th Ave SW 56201 320-235-0592
Steve Masseth, head sch Fax 235-0620
Rice Memorial Hospital Post-Sec.
301 Becker Ave SW 56201 320-231-4530
Ridgewater College Post-Sec.
PO Box 1097 56201 320-222-5200

Willow River, Pine, Pop. 405
Willow River SD 577 400/PK-12
PO Box 66 55795 218-372-3131
Philip Johnson, supt. Fax 372-3132
www.willowriver.k12.mn.us
Willow River JSHS 200/5-12
PO Box 66 55795 218-372-3131
Phil Johnson, prin. Fax 372-3132

Windom, Cottonwood, Pop. 4,585
Windom SD 177 1,000/K-12
PO Box 177 56101 507-831-6901
Wayne Wormstadt, supt. Fax 831-6919
www.windom.k12.mn.us
Windom Area HS 200/9-12
PO Box 177 56101 507-831-6910
Jake Tietje, prin. Fax 831-6909
Windom MS 400/4-8
PO Box 177 56101 507-831-6910
Jake Tietje, prin. Fax 831-6909

Winona, Winona, Pop. 27,243
Winona Area SD 861 3,100/PK-12
903 Gilmore Ave 55987 507-494-0861
Dr. Stephen West, supt. Fax 494-0863
www.winona.k12.mn.us
Winona ALC 100/Alt
1299 W 3rd St 55987 507-494-1460
Mark Winter, dir. Fax 494-1465
Winona HS 1,000/9-12
901 Gilmore Ave 55987 507-494-1504
Mark Anderson, prin. Fax 494-1501
Winona MS 900/5-8
1570 Homer Rd 55987 507-494-1000
Bradley Berzinski, prin. Fax 494-1002

Cotter JSHS 300/7-12
1115 W Broadway St 55987 507-453-5000
Dave Forney, prin. Fax 453-5006
Hope Lutheran HS 50/9-12
253 Liberty St 55987 507-474-7799
Rocky Sandcork, admin. Fax 452-8992
Minnesota State College Southeast Tech. Post-Sec.
PO Box 409 55987 507-453-2700
St. Mary's University of Minnesota Post-Sec.
700 Terrace Hts 55987 507-452-4430
Winona State University Post-Sec.
PO Box 5838 55987 507-457-5000

Winsted, McLeod, Pop. 2,341

Holy Trinity HS 100/7-12
PO Box 38 55395 320-485-2182
Wesley Kapping, prin. Fax 485-4283

Winthrop, Sibley, Pop. 1,386
GFW SD 2365
Supt. — See Gibbon
GFW HS 300/9-12
1001 N Cottonwood St 55396 507-647-5382
Bernardine Sauter, prin. Fax 647-4329

Woodbury, Washington, Pop. 60,529
Crosswinds Arts and Science SD 200/6-10
600 Weir Dr 55125 651-379-2600
Sue Mackert, dir. Fax 379-2690
www.crosswindsmn.org
Crosswinds Arts & Science S 200/6-10
600 Weir Dr 55125 651-379-2600
Debra Kelley, contact Fax 379-2690

South Washington County SD 833
Supt. — See Cottage Grove
East Ridge HS 1,800/9-12
4200 Pioneer Dr 55129 651-425-2300
James Smokrovich, prin. Fax 425-2305
Lake MS 1,200/6-8
3133 Pioneer Dr 55125 651-425-6400
Molly Roeske, prin. Fax 425-6428
Woodbury HS 1,800/9-12
2665 Woodlane Dr 55125 651-425-4400
Sarah Sorenson-Wagner, prin. Fax 425-4411
Woodbury MS 900/6-8
1425 School Dr 55125 651-425-4500
Kari Lopez, prin. Fax 425-4567

Globe University Post-Sec.
8089 Globe Dr 55125 651-730-5100
New Life Academy 700/PK-12
6758 Bailey Rd 55129 651-459-4121
Lynn Atkinson, head sch Fax 459-6194

Worthington, Nobles, Pop. 12,573
Worthington SD 518 2,800/PK-12
1117 Marine Ave 56187 507-372-2172
John Landgaard, supt. Fax 372-2174
www.isd518.net
Worthington Area Learning Center 100/Alt
117 11th Ave 56187 507-372-1322
Nate Hanson, prin. Fax 372-1361
Worthington HS 800/9-12
1211 Clary St 56187 507-376-6121
Josh Noble, prin. Fax 372-4304
Worthington MS 800/5-8
1401 Crailsheim Dr 56187 507-376-4174
Jeff Luke, prin. Fax 372-1424

Minnesota West Community & Tech College Post-Sec.
1450 Collegeway 56187 507-372-3400

Wrenshall, Carlton, Pop. 390
Wrenshall SD 100 300/PK-12
207 Pioneer Dr 55797 218-384-4274
Dr. Kimberly Belcastro, supt. Fax 384-4293
www.wrenshall.k12.mn.us
Wrenshall JSHS 200/7-12
207 Pioneer Dr 55797 218-384-4274
Dr. Kimberly Belcastro, prin. Fax 384-4293

Zimmerman, Sherburne, Pop. 5,145
Elk River Area SD 728
Supt. — See Elk River
Zimmerman MSHS 600/6-12
25900 4th St W 55398 763-241-3505
Marco Voce, prin. Fax 241-3506

Zumbrota, Goodhue, Pop. 3,200
Zumbrota-Mazeppa SD 2805
Supt. — See Mazeppa
Zumbrota-Mazeppa HS 300/9-12
705 Mill St 55992 507-732-7395
Dave Anderson, prin. Fax 732-4511
Zumbrota-Mazeppa MS 200/7-8
705 Mill St 55992 507-732-7395
Dave Anderson, prin. Fax 732-4511

MISSISSIPPI

MISSISSIPPI DEPARTMENT OF EDUCATION

PO Box 771, Jackson 39205-0771
Telephone 601-359-1750
Fax 601-359-3242
Website http://www.mde.k12.ms.us

Superintendent of Education Dr. Carey Wright

MISSISSIPPI BOARD OF EDUCATION

PO Box 771, Jackson 39205-0771

Chairperson Dr. John Kelly

PUBLIC, PRIVATE AND CATHOLIC SECONDARY SCHOOLS

Aberdeen, Monroe, Pop. 5,561
Aberdeen SD 1,200/PK-12
PO Box 607 39730 662-369-4682
John Mac Curlee, admin. Fax 369-0728
www.asdms.us
Aberdeen HS 400/9-12
PO Box 607 39730 662-369-8933
Cloyd Garth, prin. Fax 369-3321
Belle-Shivers MS 200/4-8
PO Box 607 39730 662-369-6241
Tami Doss, prin. Fax 319-8931

Monroe County SD
Supt. — See Amory
Monroe Co. Career and Technical Center Vo/Tech
50057 Airport Rd 39730 662-369-7845
Steve Cantrell, dir. Fax 369-9607

Ackerman, Choctaw, Pop. 1,499
Choctaw County SD 1,400/PK-12
PO Box 398 39735 662-285-4022
Stewart Beard, supt. Fax 285-4049
www.choctaw.k12.ms.us/
Choctaw County Career & Technology Ctr Vo/Tech
PO Box 775 39735 662-285-4160
Ronda Huffman, prin. Fax 285-4199
Choctaw County HS 500/7-12
393 E Main St 39735 662-285-4101
Kenny Roye, prin. Fax 285-4149

Amory, Monroe, Pop. 7,262
Amory SD 1,700/K-12
PO Box 330 38821 662-256-5991
Ken Byars, supt. Fax 256-6302
www.amoryschools.com/
Amory Career and Technical Center Vo/Tech
PO Box 330 38821 662-256-7601
David Millender, dir. Fax 256-1649
Amory HS 500/9-12
1006 Sam Haskell Cir 38821 662-256-5753
Brian Jones, prin. Fax 256-5754
Amory MS 400/6-8
700 2nd Ave N 38821 662-256-5658
Ken Goralczyk, prin. Fax 256-6304

Monroe County SD 2,200/K-12
PO Box 209 38821 662-257-2176
Scott Cantrell, supt. Fax 257-2181
www.mcsd.us
Advanced Learning Center 10-12
52251 Highway 25 S 38821 662-256-2495
Jeff Brooks, prin. Fax 256-2731
Hatley S 1,000/K-12
60286 Hatley Rd 38821 662-256-4563
Chris Kidd, prin. Fax 256-5626
Other Schools – See Aberdeen, Hamilton, Smithville

Anguilla, Sharkey, Pop. 721
South Delta SD
Supt. — See Rolling Fork
South Delta MS 200/6-8
PO Box 487 38721 662-873-6535
Mark Beechem, prin. Fax 873-6073

Arcola, Washington, Pop. 359

Deer Creek S 200/PK-12
PO Box 376 38722 662-827-5165
F. E. Allegrezza, admin. Fax 827-5128

Ashland, Benton, Pop. 566
Benton County SD 1,200/K-12
PO Box 247 38603 662-224-6252
Steve Bostick, supt. Fax 224-3607
www.benton.k12.ms.us
Ashland HS 200/9-12
PO Box 187 38603 662-224-6247
Rosie Ladd, prin. Fax 224-3614
Ashland MS 100/6-8
PO Box 368 38603 662-224-6485
Ralph Green, prin. Fax 224-3609
Benton County Career and Technical Ctr Vo/Tech
25 Industrial Rd 38603 662-224-3108
Dr. Merri Gadd, dir. Fax 224-3629
Other Schools – See Hickory Flat

Avon, Washington
Western Line SD 2,000/PK-12
PO Box 50 38723 662-335-7186
Larry Green, supt. Fax 378-2285
www.westernline.org
Riverside HS 400/7-12
PO Box 80 38723 662-335-4527
Donald Coleman, prin. Fax 334-1797
Other Schools – See Greenville

Baldwyn, Lee, Pop. 3,256
Baldwyn SD 800/K-12
107 W Main St 38824 662-365-1000
Jason McKay, supt. Fax 365-1003
www.baldwynschools.com
Baldwyn HS 200/9-12
512 N Fourth St 38824 662-365-1020
Jeff Palmer, prin. Fax 365-1028
Baldwyn MS 200/5-8
452 N Fourth St 38824 662-365-1015
Danny Ramsey, prin. Fax 365-1029

Bassfield, Jefferson Davis, Pop. 253
Jefferson Davis County SD
Supt. — See Prentiss
Bassfield JSHS 300/7-12
PO Box 370 39421 601-943-5391
Sylvia Hall, prin. Fax 943-5790

Batesville, Panola, Pop. 7,385
South Panola SD 4,400/PK-12
209 Boothe St 38606 662-563-9361
Tim Wilder, supt. Fax 563-6077
www.spsd.k12.ms.us
Batesville JHS 900/6-8
507 Tiger Dr 38606 662-563-4503
Charles Stevenson, prin. Fax 563-6038
South Panola Alternative S Alt
507 Tiger Dr 38606 662-563-3706
Patricia Gleeton, dir. Fax 563-9666
South Panola HS 1,100/9-12
601 Tiger Dr 38606 662-563-4756
Rodney Flowers, prin. Fax 563-8993

North Delta S 400/PK-12
330 Green Wave Ln 38606 662-563-4536

Bay Saint Louis, Hancock, Pop. 9,056
Bay St. Louis-Waveland SD 1,900/K-12
200 N 2nd St 39520 228-467-6621
Dr. Vikki Landry, supt. Fax 467-1230
www.bwsd.org/
Bay HS 500/9-12
750 Blue Meadow Rd 39520 228-467-6611
Dr. Amy Coyne, prin. Fax 466-0883
Bay-Waveland MS 500/6-8
600 Pine St 39520 228-463-0315
Dr. Cherie Labat, prin. Fax 463-2681

Our Lady Academy 200/7-12
222 S Beach Blvd 39520 228-467-7048
Darnell Cuevas, prin. Fax 467-1666
St. Stanislaus College Prep S 400/7-12
304 S Beach Blvd 39520 228-467-9057
Patrick McGrath, prin. Fax 466-2972

Bay Springs, Jasper, Pop. 1,763
West Jasper Consolidated SD 1,400/K-12
PO Box 610 39422 601-764-2280
Warren Woodrow, supt. Fax 764-4490
wjsd-mississippi.schoolloop.com/
Bay Springs HS 200/9-12
PO Box 389 39422 601-764-4151
Kesia Pope, prin. Fax 764-6445
Bay Springs MS 200/5-8
PO Box 587 39422 601-764-3378
Tracy Adcock, prin. Fax 764-2329
Other Schools – See Stringer

Sylva-Bay Academy 300/PK-12
PO Box J 39422 601-764-2157

Belden, Lee
Lee County SD
Supt. — See Tupelo
Improvement Center Alt
4677 Endville Rd 38826 662-842-2050
Pam Blissard, prin. Fax 620-7380

Tupelo Christian Preparatory S 500/PK-12
5440 Endville Rd 38826 662-844-8604
Ronnie Hill, hdmstr. Fax 823-6972

Belmont, Tishomingo, Pop. 2,002
Tishomingo County Special Municipal SD
Supt. — See Iuka
Belmont S 1,000/K-12
9 School Dr 38827 662-454-7924
Van Roberts, prin. Fax 454-7611

Belzoni, Humphreys, Pop. 2,229
Humphreys County SD 1,700/K-12
PO Box 678 39038 662-247-6000
Elliot Wheeler, supt. Fax 247-1578
www.humphreyscountyschools.com
Humphreys County HS 400/9-12
PO Box 658 39038 662-247-6040
Kathleen Turner, prin. Fax 247-9315
Humphreys JHS 400/6-8
PO Box 678 39038 662-247-6050
Arnesser Moore, prin. Fax 247-2212
Randle Career and Technical Ctr Vo/Tech
PO Box 672 39038 662-247-6030
Jimmie Hurst, prin. Fax 247-9313

Humphreys Academy 100/K-12
PO Box 179 39038 662-247-1572

Benoit, Bolivar, Pop. 477
West Bolivar SD
Supt. — See Rosedale
Brooks S 300/PK-12
PO Box 8 38725 662-742-3257
Barbara Flore, prin. Fax 742-3493

Benton, Yazoo

Benton Academy 200/PK-12
PO Box 308 39039 662-673-9722
Steve Flemming, hdmstr. Fax 673-9090

Biloxi, Harrison, Pop. 42,823
Biloxi Public SD 5,500/PK-12
PO Box 168 39533 228-374-1810
Arthur McMillan, supt. Fax 435-6289
www.biloxischools.net
Biloxi HS 1,500/9-12
1845 Richard Dr 39532 228-435-6105
Marcus Boudreaux, prin. Fax 435-6353
Biloxi JHS 1,200/6-8
1424 Father Ryan Ave 39530 228-435-1421
Scott Powell, prin. Fax 435-1426

Harrison County SD
Supt. — See Gulfport
D'Iberville HS 1,200/9-12
15625 Lamey Bridge Rd 39540 228-392-2678
Cheryle Broadus, prin. Fax 392-7807

Cedar Lake Christian Academy 200/PK-12
11555 Cedar Lake Rd 39532 228-392-9389
Lisa Williams, prin. Fax 396-2006
St. Patrick HS 500/7-12
18300 Saint Patrick Rd 39532 228-702-0500
J. Renee McDaniel, prin. Fax 702-0511
Virginia College Post-Sec.
920 Cedar Lake Rd 39532 228-546-9100

Blue Mountain, Tippah, Pop. 901
South Tippah SD
Supt. — See Ripley
Blue Mountain S 300/K-12
408 W Mill St 38610 662-685-4706
Tommy Ozbirn, prin. Fax 685-4706

Blue Mountain College Post-Sec.
PO Box 160 38610 662-685-4771

Blue Springs, Union, Pop. 228
Union County SD
Supt. — See New Albany
East Union S 900/PK-12
1548 Highway 9 S 38828 662-534-6920
Ray Kennedy, prin. Fax 534-6542

Bogue Chitto, Lincoln, Pop. 518
Lincoln County SD
Supt. — See Brookhaven
Bogue Chitto S 700/K-12
385 Monticello St 39629 601-734-2723
Jason Rayborn, prin. Fax 734-6020

Bolton, Hinds, Pop. 565
Hinds County SD
Supt. — See Raymond
Main Street Restart S Alt
130 Champion Hill Rd 39041 601-866-2642
Kim Davenport, prin. Fax 866-4414

Booneville, Prentiss, Pop. 8,634
Booneville SD 1,300/K-12
201 N 1st St 38829 662-728-2171
Dr. Todd English, supt. Fax 728-4940
boonevilleschools.org
Booneville HS 400/9-12
300 W George E Allen Dr # B 38829 662-728-5445
Terry King, prin. Fax 728-2953
Booneville MS 400/5-8
300 W George E Allen Dr # B 38829 662-728-5843
Brad Mixon, prin. Fax 728-2427

Prentiss County SD 2,400/K-12
PO Box 179 38829 662-728-4911
Randle Downs, supt. Fax 728-2000
www.prentiss.k12.ms.us/
Jumpertown S 300/K-12
717 Highway 4 W 38829 662-728-6378
Anthony Michael, prin. Fax 728-9420
Prentiss County Vocational Technical S Vo/Tech
302 W George E Allen Dr 38829 662-728-9259
Kim English, dir. Fax 728-9259
Thrasher S 400/K-12
167 County Road 1040 38829 662-728-5233
Jeff Boren, prin. Fax 728-8107
Other Schools – See New Site, Wheeler

Northeast Mississippi Community College Post-Sec.
101 Cunningham Blvd 38829 662-728-7751

Brandon, Rankin, Pop. 21,524
Rankin County SD 18,200/K-12
PO Box 1359 39043 601-825-5590
Dr. Susan Townsend, supt. Fax 825-2618
www.rcsd.ms
Brandon HS 1,500/9-12
3090 Highway 18 39042 601-825-2261
Dr. Charles Frazier, prin. Fax 591-1037
Brandon MS 1,200/6-8
408 S College St 39042 601-825-5998
Trey Rein, prin. Fax 825-8402
Learning Center Alt
200 School Rd 39042 601-824-0334
Patricia Corban, prin. Fax 825-2988
Other Schools – See Florence, Flowood, Pelahatchie, Puckett, Richland, Sandhill

Brookhaven, Lincoln, Pop. 12,389
Brookhaven SD 2,900/K-12
PO Box 540 39602 601-833-6661
Ray Carlock, supt. Fax 833-4154
www.brookhavenschools.org
Alexander JHS 400/7-8
713 Beauregard St 39601 601-833-7549
Patrick Hardy, prin. Fax 835-5467
Brookhaven HS 800/9-12
PO Box 532 39602 601-833-4498
David Martin, prin. Fax 823-3792
Brookhaven Technical Center Vo/Tech
325 E Court St 39601 601-833-8335
Trevor Brister, dir. Fax 835-3985
Mullins S Alt
711 Martin Luther King Dr 39601 601-833-7472
Janee Harrison, prin. Fax 823-6598

Lincoln County SD 3,100/K-12
PO Box 826 39602 601-835-0011
Mickey Myers, supt. Fax 833-3030
lcsd.k12.ms.us/
Enterprise S 800/K-12
1601 Highway 583 SE 39601 601-833-7284
Shannon Eubanks, prin. Fax 835-1261
Star S 800/K-12
1880 Highway 550 NW 39601 601-833-3473
Robin Case, prin. Fax 833-1254
West Lincoln S 800/K-12
948 Jackson Liberty Dr SW 39601 601-833-4600
Jason Case, prin. Fax 833-9909
Other Schools – See Bogue Chitto

Brookhaven Academy 500/PK-12
943 Brookway Blvd Ext 39601 601-833-4041

Brooklyn, Forrest
Forrest County Agricultural HSD
215 Old Highway 49 E 39425 601-582-4102
Billy Ellzey, supt. Fax 545-9483
www.forrestcountyahs.com
Forrest County Agricultural HS Vo/Tech
215 Old Highway 49 E 39425 601-582-4741
Charles Johnson, prin. Fax 545-9031

Bruce, Calhoun, Pop. 1,918
Calhoun County SD
Supt. — See Pittsboro
Bruce HS 400/7-12
PO Box 248 38915 662-983-3350
Michael Gillespie, prin. Fax 983-3356

Byhalia, Marshall, Pop. 1,278
Marshall County SD
Supt. — See Holly Springs
Byhalia HS 500/9-12
278 Highway 309 N 38611 662-838-2206
Ernest Smith, prin. Fax 838-2218
Byhalia MS 400/6-8
172 Highway 309 N 38611 662-838-2591
Landon Pollard, prin. Fax 838-5141

Caledonia, Lowndes, Pop. 1,021
Lowndes County SD
Supt. — See Columbus
Caledonia HS 600/9-12
111 Confederate Dr 39740 662-356-2001
Dr. Andy Stevens, prin. Fax 356-2036
Caledonia MS 500/6-8
105 Confederate Dr 39740 662-356-2042
Karen Pittman, prin. Fax 356-2045

Calhoun City, Calhoun, Pop. 1,755
Calhoun County SD
Supt. — See Pittsboro
Calhoun Career and Technical Center Vo/Tech
PO Box 1573 38916 662-628-1143
Kyle Clark, admin. Fax 628-1123
Calhoun City HS 200/9-12
PO Box 559 38916 662-628-5112
Mike Ray, prin. Fax 628-6240
Calhoun City MS 200/5-8
PO Box 1546 38916 662-628-1890
Stacia Parker, prin. Fax 628-1896

Camden, Madison
Madison County SD
Supt. — See Ridgeland
Jackson HS 300/9-12
2000 Loring Rd 39045 662-468-2531
Bertram Goodloe, prin. Fax 468-2748

Canton, Madison, Pop. 13,125
Canton SD 3,300/K-12
403 Lincoln St 39046 601-859-4110
Cassandra Williams, supt. Fax 859-4023
www.cantonschools.net
Canton Career Center Vo/Tech
487 N Union Street Ext 39046 601-859-3984
Timothy Chambers, dir. Fax 859-1115
Canton Educational Services Center Alt
529 Mace St 39046 601-859-5010
Koche Anderson, prin. Fax 859-5012
Canton HS 800/9-12
634 Finney Rd 39046 601-859-5325
Dr. Pamela Self, prin. Fax 859-2554
Nichols MS 400/6-8
529 Mace St 39046 601-859-3741
Tommy Nalls, prin. Fax 859-6561
Porter MS 300/6-8
551 Finney Rd 39046 601-407-1819
Michael Ellis, prin. Fax 407-1401

Madison County SD
Supt. — See Ridgeland
Simmons MS 200/6-8
820 Sulphur Springs Rd 39046 601-855-2406
Kelvin Griffin, prin. Fax 859-7615

Canton Academy 300/PK-12
PO Box 116 39046 601-859-5231
Ron Jurney, hdmstr. Fax 391-3274

Carriere, Pearl River
Pearl River County SD 3,000/K-12
7441 Highway 11 39426 601-798-7744
Alan Lumpkin, supt. Fax 798-3527
www.prc.k12.ms.us/
Pearl River Central Endeavor S Alt
461 Burgetown Rd 39426 601-798-6852
Nilene Quave, prin. Fax 799-4355
Pearl River Central HS 900/9-12
7407 Highway 11 39426 601-798-1986
Stacy Baudoin, prin. Fax 798-0068
Pearl River Central MS 700/6-8
7391 Highway 11 39426 601-798-5654
Dr. Lori Burkett, prin. Fax 798-2822

Carrollton, Carroll, Pop. 190
Carroll County SD 800/PK-12
PO Box 256 38917 662-237-9276
Billy Joe Ferguson, supt. Fax 237-9703
www.ccsd.ms
Other Schools – See North Carrollton

Carroll Academy 300/PK-12
PO Box 226 38917 662-237-6858

Carson, Jefferson Davis
Jefferson Davis County SD
Supt. — See Prentiss
Davis County Voc-Tech Center Vo/Tech
PO Box 70 39427 601-792-5005
John Daley, dir. Fax 792-2511

Carthage, Leake, Pop. 5,025
Leake County SD 2,900/K-12
PO Box 478 39051 601-267-4579
Billy Wilbanks, supt. Fax 267-5283
www.leakesd.org
Leake Central HS 500/9-12
704 N Jordan St 39051 601-267-7713
Bruce Burns, prin. Fax 267-3738
Leake Central JHS 500/6-8
801 Martin Luther King Dr 39051 601-267-8909
Peggy Marble, prin. Fax 267-5902
Leake County Career & Technical Center Vo/Tech
703 N West St 39051 601-267-8442
Ray New, prin. Fax 267-5150
Other Schools – See Walnut Grove

Infinity Career College Post-Sec.
305B Highway 16 W 39051 601-267-3678

Centreville, Wilkinson, Pop. 1,683
Wilkinson County SD
Supt. — See Woodville
Winans MS 300/6-8
PO Box 610 39631 601-645-0008
Eric Jackson, prin. Fax 645-0170

Centreville Academy 400/K-12
PO Box 70 39631 601-645-5912

Charleston, Tallahatchie, Pop. 2,183
East Tallahatchie Consolidated SD 1,200/PK-12
411 E Chestnut St 38921 662-647-5524
Dr. Ben Kennedy, supt. Fax 647-3720
www.etsd.k12.ms.us
Charleston HS 400/9-12
411 E Chestnut St 38921 662-647-5359
Ricky Garvin, prin. Fax 647-3724
Charleston MS 300/5-8
411 E Chestnut St 38921 662-647-2115
Greg McCord, prin. Fax 647-2380

Strider Academy 100/K-12
3698 MS Highway 32 Central 38921 662-647-5833

Clarksdale, Coahoma, Pop. 17,884
Clarksdale Municipal SD 3,000/PK-12
PO Box 1088 38614 662-627-8500
Dennis Dupree, supt. Fax 627-8542
www.cmsd.k12.ms.us/
Clarksdale HS 600/10-12
PO Box 1088 38614 662-627-8530
Dr. Manika Kemp, prin. Fax 627-8549
Higgins MS 500/7-8
PO Box 1088 38614 662-627-8550
Debra Ware, prin. Fax 627-8543
Keen Career & Technical Center Vo/Tech
PO Box 1088 38614 662-627-8580
Shirlaurence Fair, dir. Fax 627-8582
Stampley 9th Grade Academy 200/9-9
PO Box 1088 38614 662-627-8570
Herbert Smith, prin. Fax 627-7143

Coahoma Agricultural HSD 200/9-12
3240 Friars Point Rd 38614 662-621-4258
Dr. Valmadge Towner, supt. Fax 624-4315
cahs.k12.ms.us
Coahoma Agricultural HS 200/9-12
3240 Friars Point Rd 38614 662-624-8045
Milton Hardrict M.D., prin. Fax 621-4672

Coahoma County SD 1,500/K-12
PO Box 820 38614 662-624-5448
Xandra Brooks-Keys, supt. Fax 624-5512
www.coahoma.k12.ms.us
Coahoma County JSHS 500/7-12
1535 Lee Dr 38614 662-627-7378
Olenza McBride, prin. Fax 627-4516

Coahoma Community College Post-Sec.
3240 Friars Point Rd 38614 662-627-2571
Lee Academy 400/6-12
415 Lee Dr 38614 662-627-7891
Rone Walker, admin. Fax 627-7896

Cleveland, Bolivar, Pop. 12,236
Cleveland SD 3,500/PK-12
305 Merritt Dr 38732 662-843-3529
Jacquelyn Thigpen Ed.D., supt. Fax 579-3090
www.cleveland.k12.ms.us
Cleveland Career Development & Tech Ctr. Vo/Tech
601 3rd St 38732 662-843-8818
Monica Mitchell, dir. Fax 545-4612
Cleveland HS 600/9-12
300 W Sunflower Rd 38732 662-843-2460
Steven Craddock, prin. Fax 843-2455
East Side HS 300/9-12
601 Lucy Seaberry Blvd 38732 662-843-2338
Dr. Randy Grierson, prin. Fax 843-1900
Green JHS 400/7-8
305 N Bolivar Ave 38732 662-843-2456
Archie Mitchell, prin. Fax 843-6820
Smith MS 200/7-8
715 S Martin Luther King Dr 38732 662-843-4355
L'Kenna Whitehead, prin. Fax 843-7334

Bayou Academy 400/PK-12
PO Box 417 38732 662-843-3708
Delta State University Post-Sec.
1003 W Sunflower Rd 38733 662-846-3000

Clinton, Hinds, Pop. 24,956
Clinton SD 4,900/K-12
PO Box 300 39060 601-924-7533
Phillip Burchfield Ed.D., supt. Fax 924-6345
www.clintonpublicschools.com
Clinton Alternative S Alt
PO Box 300 39060 601-925-4027
Kelly Heath, prin. Fax 925-8156
Clinton Career Complex Vo/Tech
715 Lakeview Dr 39056 601-924-0247
Brett Robinson, dir. Fax 924-1168
Clinton HS 1,000/10-12
401 Arrow Dr 39056 601-924-5656
Anthony Goins, prin. Fax 924-4622
Clinton JHS 800/7-8
711 Lakeview Dr 39056 601-924-0619
Dr. Bill Hardin, prin. Fax 924-7703
Sumner Hill JHS 400/9-9
400 W Northside Dr 39056 601-924-5510
John Wallace, prin. Fax 924-4182

Clinton Christian Academy 200/PK-12
PO Box 330 39060 601-910-5990

Mississippi College Post-Sec.
200 W College St 39058 601-925-3000
Mount Salus Christian S 100/K-12
PO Box 240 39060 601-924-5863

Coffeeville, Yalobusha, Pop. 891
Coffeeville SD 600/PK-12
96 Mississippi St 38922 662-675-8941
Dr. Vivian Robinson, supt. Fax 675-5004
www.coffeevilleschools.org
Coffeeville HS 200/8-12
96 Mississippi St 38922 662-675-8904
Johnnie Dudley, prin. Fax 675-8905

Coldwater, Tate, Pop. 1,663
Tate County SD 2,900/K-12
574 Parkway St 38618 662-562-5861
Dr. Daryl Scoggin, supt. Fax 622-7402
www.tcsdms.org
Coldwater Attendence Center 500/K-12
340 Darnell St 38618 662-622-5561
Timeka Thomas, prin. Fax 622-7253
Independence HS 600/7-12
3184 Highway 305 38618 662-233-4691
Melody Carter, prin. Fax 233-2214
Senatobia/Tate Career & Technical Center Vo/Tech
165 W Central Ave 38618 662-622-5142
Kimberly Moshiach, dir. Fax 622-7005
Other Schools – See Sarah

Collins, Covington, Pop. 2,566
Covington County SD 2,900/K-12
PO Box 1269 39428 601-765-4457
Dr. Arnetta Crosby, supt. Fax 765-9402
www.cov.k12.ms.us
Carver MS 300/5-8
PO Box 757 39428 601-765-4908
Lisa Campbell, prin. Fax 765-4100
Collins HS 300/9-12
PO Box 1479 39428 601-765-3203
Brian Bagwell, prin. Fax 765-4116
Covington County Vo-Tech Center Vo/Tech
PO Box 1268 39428 601-765-9120
Cecil Easterling, dir. Fax 765-8253
Other Schools – See Mount Olive, Seminary

Collinsville, Lauderdale, Pop. 1,932
Lauderdale County SD
Supt. — See Meridian
West Lauderdale HS 600/9-12
9916 W Lauderdale Rd 39325 601-737-2277
Shane Rodgers, prin. Fax 737-2377
West Lauderdale MS 700/5-8
9916 W Lauderdale Rd 39325 601-737-8689
Glenn Boothe, prin. Fax 737-5145

Columbia, Marion, Pop. 6,495
Columbia SD 1,800/K-12
613 Bryan Ave 39429 601-736-2366
Marietta James Ed.D., supt. Fax 736-2653
www.columbiaschools.org
Columbia HS 500/9-12
1009 Broad St 39429 601-736-5334
Sheila Burbridge, prin. Fax 731-1068
Jefferson MS 400/6-8
611 Owens St 39429 601-736-2786
Raymond Powell, prin. Fax 731-3762

Marion County SD 2,100/PK-12
1010 Highway 13 N Ste 2 39429 601-736-7193
Wendy Bracey, supt. Fax 736-6274
www.marionk12.org
East Marion JSHS 300/7-12
527 E Marion School Rd 39429 601-736-3006
Percynthia Newsome, prin. Fax 736-8215
Loftin Career and Technology Ctr Vo/Tech
1140 Highway 13 S 39429 601-736-6095
Fax 731-2077
Other Schools – See Foxworth

Columbia Academy 600/K-12
1548 Highway 98 E 39429 601-736-6418

Columbus, Lowndes, Pop. 23,393
Columbus Municipal SD 4,500/PK-12
PO Box 1308 39703 662-241-7400
Dr. Philip Hickman, supt. Fax 241-7453
www.columbuscityschools.org
CMSD Alternative S Alt
924 20th St N 39701 662-241-7250
Tamela Barr, dir. Fax 241-7252
Columbus HS 1,100/9-12
215 Hemlock St 39702 662-241-7200
Lori Cargile, prin. Fax 241-7205
Columbus MS 900/6-8
175 Highway 373 39705 662-241-7300
Billie Smith, prin. Fax 241-7305
McKellar Technology Center Vo/Tech
810 N Browder St 39702 662-241-7290
Christopher Bray, dir. Fax 241-7293

Lowndes County SD 4,900/PK-12
1053 Highway 45 S 39701 662-244-5000
Lynn Wright, supt. Fax 244-5043
www.lowndes.k12.ms.us/
Lowndes County Alternative S Alt
1380 Motley Rd 39701 662-244-5060
Charles Jackson, prin. Fax 327-4857
New Hope HS 800/9-12
3419 New Hope Rd 39702 662-244-4701
Matthew Smith, prin. Fax 244-4725
New Hope MS 600/6-8
462 Center Rd 39702 662-244-4740
Sam Allison, prin. Fax 244-4758
West Lowndes HS 200/7-12
644 S Frontage Rd 39701 662-328-1369
Stefanie Jones, prin. Fax 327-3353
Other Schools – See Caledonia

Heritage Academy 500/K-12
625 Magnolia Ln 39705 662-327-5272
Mississippi University for Women Post-Sec.
1100 College St 39701 662-329-4750

Como, Panola, Pop. 1,273
North Panola SD
Supt. — See Sardis
North Panola Career & Technical Center Vo/Tech
601 Railroad St 38619 662-526-5804
Lakeldra Pride, dir. Fax 526-5868
North Panola JHS 300/6-8
526 Compress Rd 38619 662-526-5938
Valeree Ellis-Barnes, prin. Fax 526-5990

Corinth, Alcorn, Pop. 14,398
Alcorn SD 3,000/PK-12
PO Box 1420 38835 662-286-5591
Larry Mitchell, supt. Fax 286-7766
www.alcorn.k12.ms.us
Alcorn Alternative S Alt
2101 Norman Rd 38834 662-284-3359
Randy Holt, admin. Fax 284-4950
Alcorn Career & Technology Center Vo/Tech
2101 Norman Rd 38834 662-286-7727
Rodney Hopper, admin. Fax 286-5674
Biggersville JSHS 200/7-12
571 Highway 45 38834 662-286-3542
Pete Seago, admin. Fax 286-3023
Kossuth HS 400/9-12
15 County Road 604 38834 662-286-3653
Travis Smith, admin. Fax 286-3507
Kossuth MS 500/5-8
17 County Road 604 38834 662-286-7093
Samuel Roberts, admin. Fax 286-6837
Other Schools – See Glen

Corinth SD 2,600/PK-12
1204 N Harper Rd 38834 662-287-2425
Edward Lee Childress Ed.D., supt. Fax 286-1885
www.corinth.k12.ms.us
Corinth HS 600/9-12
1310 N Harper Rd 38834 662-286-1000
Dane Aube, prin. Fax 286-1003
Corinth MS 800/5-8
1000 E 5th St 38834 662-286-1261
Nathan Hall, prin. Fax 287-0296

ICS The Wright Beauty College Post-Sec.
2077 Highway 72 E Anx 38834 662-287-0944

Crystal Springs, Copiah, Pop. 5,021
Copiah County SD
Supt. — See Hazlehurst
Crystal Springs HS 400/9-12
201 Newton St 39059 601-892-4791
Bill Broadhead, prin. Fax 892-2071
Crystal Springs MS 600/4-8
2092 S Pat Harrison Dr 39059 601-892-2722
Donald Regan, prin. Fax 892-9949

Decatur, Newton, Pop. 1,826
Newton County SD 1,800/K-12
15305 Highway 15 39327 601-635-2317
J.O. Amis, supt. Fax 635-4025
www.newton.k12.ms.us
East Central Alternative S Alt
15305 Highway 15 39327 601-635-2118
Sal LaBue, prin. Fax 635-5659
Newton Co. Career and Technical Center Vo/Tech
15935 Highway 15 39327 601-635-4138
Aaron Cooley, dir. Fax 635-4024
Newton County HS 1,000/6-12
16255 Highway 503 39327 601-635-2718
Shane Phillips, prin. Fax 635-4045

East Central Community College Post-Sec.
PO Box 129 39327 601-635-2111
Newton County Academy 200/PK-12
PO Box 25 39327 601-635-2756

De Kalb, Kemper, Pop. 1,156
Kemper County SD 1,100/PK-12
PO Box 219 39328 601-743-2657
Jackie Pollock, supt. Fax 743-9297
kemper.k12.ms.us
Kemper County HS 500/7-12
PO Box 429 39328 601-743-5292
Kathi Wilson, prin. Fax 743-5952
Stennis Vocational Complex Vo/Tech
PO Box 549 39328 601-743-5226
Connie Johnson, dir. Fax 743-2351

Kemper Academy 100/PK-12
149 Walnut Ave 39328 601-743-2232

D'Iberville, Harrison, Pop. 9,203
Harrison County SD
Supt. — See Gulfport
D'Iberville MS 900/4-8
3320 Warrior Dr 39540 228-392-1746
Matthew Elias, prin. Fax 392-9948

Drew, Sunflower, Pop. 1,923
Sunflower County Consolidated SD
Supt. — See Indianola
Drew Hunter MS 100/6-8
10 Swoope Rd 38737 662-745-8940
Tony Young, prin. Fax 745-8529

North Sunflower Academy 100/K-12
148 Academy Rd 38737 662-756-4573

Durant, Holmes, Pop. 2,658
Durant SD 500/K-12
5 W Madison St 39063 662-653-3175
Glenn Carlisle, supt. Fax 653-6151
durant.k12.ms.us
Durant S 500/K-12
PO Box 669 39063 662-653-3429
Willie Dale, prin. Fax 653-3472

Ecru, Pontotoc, Pop. 882
Pontotoc County SD
Supt. — See Pontotoc
North Pontotoc HS 400/9-12
8324 Highway 15 N 38841 662-489-5612
Roger Smith, prin. Fax 489-2985

Ellisville, Jones, Pop. 4,419
Jones County SD 8,300/K-12
5204 Highway 11 N 39437 601-649-5201
Thomas Parker, supt. Fax 649-1613
www.jones.k12.ms.us/
South Jones JSHS 1,300/7-12
313 Anderson St 39437 601-477-8451
Billy Ray Jones, prin. Fax 477-3505
Other Schools – See Laurel

Jones County Junior College Post-Sec.
900 S Court St 39437 601-477-4000

Enterprise, Clarke, Pop. 526
Enterprise SD 1,000/PK-12
503 S River Rd 39330 601-659-7965
Rita Windham, supt. Fax 659-3254
www.esd.k12.ms.us/
Enterprise HS 200/9-12
501 S River Rd 39330 601-659-4435
Mike Weathers, prin. Fax 659-3274
Enterprise MS 300/5-8
105 Short St 39330 601-659-7722
Josh Perkins, prin. Fax 659-7722

Ethel, Attala, Pop. 416
Attala County SD
Supt. — See Kosciusko
Ethel JSHS 300/7-12
PO Box 340 39067 662-674-5673
James Wood, prin. Fax 674-5817

Eupora, Webster, Pop. 2,169
Webster County SD 1,700/PK-12
95 Clark Ave 39744 662-258-5921
Jack Treloar, supt. Fax 258-3134
www.webstercountyschools.org
Eupora HS 400/7-12
65 Clark Ave 39744 662-258-4041
Laci Knight, prin. Fax 258-4716
Webster County Career & Technology Ctr Vo/Tech
605 Hall Rd 39744 662-258-8206
Michael Adkins, admin. Fax 258-6769
Other Schools – See Maben

Falkner, Tippah, Pop. 510
North Tippah SD
Supt. — See Tiplersville
Falkner JSHS 300/7-12
20350 Highway 15 38629 662-837-7892
Jennifer Stroupe, prin. Fax 837-8800

Fayette, Jefferson, Pop. 1,609
Jefferson County SD 1,300/PK-12
PO Box 157 39069 601-786-3721
Vincent Turner, supt. Fax 786-8441
www.jcpsd.net
Jefferson County Career & Technical Ctr Vo/Tech
205 Industrial Park Rd 39069 601-786-3642
Cleveland Moore, dir. Fax 786-2271
Jefferson County HS 400/9-12
2277 Main St 39069 601-786-3919
Shemekia Bailey, prin. Fax 786-6002
Jefferson County JHS 200/7-8
468 Highway 33 39069 601-786-3900
David Day, prin. Fax 786-2273

Flora, Madison, Pop. 1,878

Tri-County Academy 300/PK-12
PO Box K 39071 601-879-8517
Mark Johnson, hdmstr. Fax 879-3373

Florence, Rankin, Pop. 4,112
Rankin County SD
Supt. — See Brandon
Florence HS 700/9-12
232 Highway 469 N 39073 601-845-2205
Tony Martin, prin. Fax 845-3752
Florence MS 600/6-8
PO Box 159 39073 601-845-2862
Jessica Hodges, prin. Fax 845-2114
McLaurin JSHS 500/7-12
130 Tiger Dr 39073 601-845-2247
Scott Rimes, prin. Fax 845-1170

Flowood, Rankin, Pop. 7,724
Rankin County SD
Supt. — See Brandon
Northwest Rankin HS 1,600/9-12
5805 Highway 25 39232 601-992-2242
Ben Stein, prin. Fax 992-6005
Northwest Rankin MS 900/6-8
1 Paw Print Pl 39232 601-992-1329
Shea Taylor, prin. Fax 992-1347

Hartfield Academy 400/PK-12
1240 Luckney Rd 39232 601-992-5333
David Horner, hdmstr. Fax 992-5320

Forest, Scott, Pop. 5,620
Forest Municipal SD 1,500/K-12
325 Cleveland St 39074 601-469-3250
Dr. Joseph White, supt. Fax 469-3101
www.forest.k12.ms.us/
Forest HS 400/9-12
511 Cleveland St 39074 601-469-3255
Kim Shoemaker, prin. Fax 469-8250

Hawkins MS 400/5-8
803 E Oak St 39074 601-469-1474
Nick Hillman, prin. Fax 469-8251

Scott County SD 3,900/K-12
100 E First St 39074 601-469-3861
Tony McGee, supt. Fax 469-3874
www.scott.k12.ms.us
Forest/Scott County Career & Tech Ctr Vo/Tech
521 Cleveland St 39074 601-469-2913
Timmy Fanguy, dir. Fax 469-2917
Scott Central S 1,000/K-12
2415 Old Jackson Rd 39074 601-469-4883
Patrick Henderson, prin. Fax 469-3746
Other Schools – See Lake, Morton, Sebastopol

Foxworth, Marion, Pop. 592
Marion County SD
Supt. — See Columbia
West Marion JSHS 600/7-12
2 W Marion St 39483 601-736-6381
Ellie Rich, prin. Fax 731-7937

Fulton, Itawamba, Pop. 3,914
Itawamba County SD 3,400/PK-12
605 S Cummings St 38843 662-862-2159
Michael Nanney, supt. Fax 862-4713
www.itawambacountyschools.com
Itawamba Agricultural HS 600/9-12
11900 Highway 25 S 38843 662-862-3104
Trae Wiygul, prin. Fax 862-5494
Itawamba Career & Technical Center Vo/Tech
200 Vo Tech Rd 38843 662-862-3137
Gary Hamm, prin. Fax 862-3138
Other Schools – See Mantachie, Tremont

Itawamba Community College Post-Sec.
602 W Hill St 38843 662-862-8000

Gallman, Copiah

Copiah Educational Foundation 700/PK-12
PO Box 125 39077 601-892-3770

Gautier, Jackson, Pop. 18,202
Pascagoula-Gautier SD
Supt. — See Pascagoula
Gautier HS 900/9-12
4307 Gautier Vancleave Rd 39553 228-522-8783
Al Sparkman, prin. Fax 522-8788
Gautier MS 400/7-8
1920 Graveline Rd 39553 228-522-8806
Christy Reimsnyder, prin. Fax 522-8813

Glen, Alcorn, Pop. 409
Alcorn SD
Supt. — See Corinth
Alcorn Central HS 400/9-12
8 County Road 254 38846 662-286-8720
Brandon Quinn, admin. Fax 286-8720
Alcorn Central MS 400/5-8
8A County Road 254 38846 662-286-3674
Chad Lindamood, admin. Fax 286-6712

Goodman, Holmes, Pop. 1,376

Holmes Community College Post-Sec.
PO Box 369 39079 662-472-2312

Greenville, Washington, Pop. 34,233
Greenville SD 6,000/PK-12
PO Box 1619 38702 662-334-7000
Dr. Leeson Taylor, supt. Fax 334-7021
www.gvillepublicschooldistrict.com
Coleman MS 600/6-8
400 Dr Martin L King Blvd 38701 662-334-7036
Dianne Zanders, prin. Fax 334-7040
Darling Achievement Center 50/Alt
242 S Broadway St 38701 662-334-7040
Dr. Yolonda Bankston, prin. Fax 334-7023
Greenville HS 1,200/10-12
419 E Robertshaw St 38701 662-334-7061
Xavier Hodo, prin. Fax 334-2910
Greenville Technical Center Vo/Tech
350 S Raceway Rd 38703 662-334-7170
Tarrinasha Brown-Jones, dir. Fax 334-2848
Solomon Magnet S 600/6-8
556 Bowman Blvd 38701 662-334-7052
Michael Dean, prin. Fax 334-7053
Weston 9th Grade Academy 500/9-9
901 Archer St 38701 662-334-7080
Walter McDavid, prin. Fax 334-7091

Western Line SD
Supt. — See Avon
O'Bannon HS 500/7-12
PO Box 5816 38704 662-335-2637
Derrick Cook, prin. Fax 334-1689

Delta Beauty College Post-Sec.
697 Delta Pl 38701 662-332-0587
Greenville Christian S 200/PK-12
2064 GCS Rd 38701 662-332-0946
St. Joseph Catholic S 200/7-12
1501 V F W Rd 38701 662-378-9711
Paul Artman, prin. Fax 378-3496
Washington S 700/PK-12
1605 E Reed Rd 38703 662-334-4096

Greenwood, LeFlore, Pop. 15,124
Greenwood SD 2,600/PK-12
PO Box 1497 38935 662-453-4231
Dr. Jennifer Wilson, supt. Fax 455-7409
www.greenwood.k12.ms.us/
Greenwood Career and Technical Ctr Vo/Tech
616 Sycamore Ave 38930 662-455-7414
Dr. Robie Green, dir. Fax 455-8979
Greenwood HS 700/9-12
1209 Garrard Ave 38930 662-455-7450
Dr. Kenneth Pulley, prin. Fax 455-7468
Greenwood MS 400/7-8
1200 Garrard Ave 38930 662-455-3661
Chiqueta Daniels, prin. Fax 455-5559

Leflore County SD 2,700/PK-12
1901 Highway 82 W 38930 662-453-8566
Ilean Richards, supt. Fax 459-7265
www.lefcsd.org
Elzy HS 500/9-12
604 Elzy Ave 38930 662-453-3394
Edmond Williams, prin. Fax 459-7266
Elzy JHS 400/6-8
604 Elzy Ave 38930 662-453-9677
Barren Cleark, prin. Fax 455-0139
Leflore County Career & Tech Educ Ctr Vo/Tech
PO Box 1158 38935 662-453-7706
Charles Streeter, dir. Fax 453-7733
Other Schools – See Itta Bena

Pillow Academy 800/PK-12
69601 Highway 82 W 38930 662-453-1266

Grenada, Grenada, Pop. 12,980
Grenada SD 4,100/K-12
PO Box 1940 38902 662-226-1606
Dr. David Daigneault, supt. Fax 226-7994
www.gsd.k12.ms.us/
Grenada Enrichment and Transition Center Alt
809 Tie Plant Rd 38901 662-226-3311
Dr. Tina Herrington, prin. Fax 226-8388
Grenada HS 1,100/9-12
1875 Fairground Rd 38901 662-226-8844
Jerry Williams, prin. Fax 227-6109
Grenada MS 900/6-8
28 Jones Rd 38901 662-226-5135
Marshall Whittemore, prin. Fax 227-6106
Grenada Vocational Complex Vo/Tech
2035 Jackson Ave 38901 662-226-5969
Joey Carpenter, prin. Fax 226-5992

Academy of Hair Design #1 Post-Sec.
2003B Commerce St 38901 662-226-2462
Kirk Academy 300/PK-12
PO Box 1008 38902 662-226-2791

Gulfport, Harrison, Pop. 66,180
Gulfport SD 6,300/K-12
2001 Pass Rd 39501 228-865-4600
Glen East, supt. Fax 865-1918
www.gulfportschools.org/
Bayou View MS 800/6-8
212 43rd St 39507 228-865-4633
Jonathan Dill, prin. Fax 867-1967
Gulfport Central MS 600/6-8
1310 42nd Ave 39501 228-870-1035
Dr. Mike Battle, prin. Fax 870-1041
Gulfport HS 1,500/9-12
100 Perry St 39507 228-896-7525
Michael Lindsey, prin. Fax 896-8281
Gulfport Vocational Annex S Vo/Tech
100 Perry St 39507 228-896-6011
David Fava, dir. Fax 896-7686
Learning Center Alt
1215 Church St 39507 228-897-6045
Tim Bellipanni, prin. Fax 897-6053

Harrison County SD 14,100/K-12
11072 Highway 49 39503 228-539-6500
Roy Gill, supt. Fax 539-6507
www.harrison.k12.ms.us/
Harrison Central HS 1,500/9-12
15600 School Rd 39503 228-832-2610
Averie Bush, prin. Fax 832-7433
Harrison County Alternative S Alt
11072 Highway 49 39503 228-539-5956
Fax 539-5959
Harrison County Vocational Complex Vo/Tech
15600 School Rd 39503 228-832-6652
Libby White, prin. Fax 539-5965
North Gulfport MS 500/7-8
4715 Illinois Ave 39501 228-864-5326
Kelly Fuller, prin. Fax 863-9649
West Harrison HS 1,000/9-12
10399 County Farm Rd 39503 228-539-8900
Dana Trochessett, prin. Fax 539-8910
Other Schools – See Biloxi, D'Iberville

Blue Cliff College Post-Sec.
12251 Bernard Pkwy 39503 228-896-9727
Chris' Beauty College Post-Sec.
1265 Pass Rd 39501 228-864-2920
Christian Collegiate Academy 300/PK-12
12200 Dedeaux Rd 39503 228-832-4585
Infinity Career College Post-Sec.
319 Pass Rd 39507 228-864-4663
Miller-Motte Technical College Post-Sec.
12121 Highway 49 39503 228-273-3400

Guntown, Lee, Pop. 2,042
Lee County SD
Supt. — See Tupelo
Guntown MS 800/6-8
1539 Main St 38849 662-348-8800
Casey Dye, prin. Fax 348-8810

Hamilton, Monroe, Pop. 450
Monroe County SD
Supt. — See Amory
Hamilton S 700/K-12
40201 Hamilton Rd 39746 662-343-8307
Tim Dickerson, prin. Fax 343-5813

Hattiesburg, Forrest, Pop. 45,409
Forrest County SD 2,400/K-12
400 Forrest St 39401 601-545-6055
Brian Freeman, supt. Fax 545-6054
www.forrest.k12.ms.us/
North Forrest JSHS 400/7-12
693 Eatonville Rd 39401 601-545-9304
Jennifer Riels, prin. Fax 545-9318

Hattiesburg SD 3,700/PK-12
PO Box 1569 39403 601-582-5078
Dr. Robert Williams, supt. Fax 582-6666
www.hattiesburgpsd.com
Bethune Alternative Center Alt
610 Dumas Ave 39401 601-584-6311
C. Jermaine Brown, prin. Fax 583-7322
Burger MS 600/7-8
174 WSF Tatum Drive Ext 39401 601-582-0536
Tonsa Vaughn, prin. Fax 582-0572
Hattiesburg HS 1,100/9-12
301 Hutchinson Ave 39401 601-544-0811
Dexter Jordan, prin. Fax 544-8946

Lamar County SD
Supt. — See Purvis
Oak Grove HS 1,600/9-12
5198 Old Highway 11 39402 601-264-7232
Helen Price, prin. Fax 264-0160
Oak Grove MS 1,300/6-8
2543 Old Highway 24 39402 601-264-4634
Patrick Gray, prin. Fax 264-2822

Antonelli College Post-Sec.
1500 N 31st Ave 39401 601-583-4100
Forrest General Hospital Post-Sec.
6051 U S Highway 49 39401 601-288-4201
Hattiesburg Radiology Group Post-Sec.
5000 W 4th St 39402 601-288-4241
Presbyterian Christian S 1,000/PK-12
221 Bonhomie Rd 39401 601-582-4956
Sacred Heart S 700/PK-12
608 Southern Ave 39401 601-583-8683
Brian McCrory, prin. Fax 583-8684
University of Southern Mississippi Post-Sec.
118 College Dr 39406 601-266-1000
William Carey University Post-Sec.
498 Tuscan Ave 39401 601-318-6051

Hazlehurst, Copiah, Pop. 3,977
Copiah County SD 2,800/K-12
254 W Gallatin St 39083 601-894-1341
Rickey Clopton, supt. Fax 894-2634
www.copiah.ms/
Other Schools – See Crystal Springs, Wesson

Hazlehurst CSD 1,500/PK-12
119 Robert McDaniel Dr 39083 601-894-1152
Lisa Davis, supt. Fax 894-3170
www.hazlehurst.k12.ms.us
Hazlehurst HS 400/9-12
101 S Haley St 39083 601-894-2489
Jeffery Mumford, prin. Fax 894-3120
Hazlehurst MS 300/6-8
112 School Dr 39083 601-894-3463
Kristi Harris, prin. Fax 894-5939

Heidelberg, Jasper, Pop. 716
East Jasper Consolidated SD 900/K-12
PO Box E 39439 601-787-3281
Dr. Nadene Arrington, supt. Fax 787-3410
www.eastjasper.k12.ms.us
Heidelberg HS 300/9-12
PO Box M 39439 601-787-3414
Bufus Ellis, prin. Fax 787-3416
Heidelberg JHS 100/7-8
PO Box M 39439 601-787-3665
Edna Burrage, prin. Fax 787-3045

Heidelberg Academy 200/PK-12
PO Box Q 39439 601-787-4589

Hernando, DeSoto, Pop. 13,952
DeSoto County SD 32,200/PK-12
5 E South St 38632 662-429-5271
Corey Uselton, supt. Fax 429-4198
www.desotocountyschools.org
Hernando HS 1,100/9-12
805 Dilworth Ln 38632 662-429-4170
Freddie Joseph, prin. Fax 429-6269
Hernando MS 900/6-8
700 Dilworth Ln 38632 662-429-4154
Rob Chase, prin. Fax 429-4189
Other Schools – See Horn Lake, Lake Cormorant, Olive Branch, Southaven

Hickory Flat, Benton, Pop. 592
Benton County SD
Supt. — See Ashland
Hickory Flat S 600/K-12
26 Rebel Dr 38633 662-333-7731
Roger Browning, prin. Fax 333-4127

Hollandale, Washington, Pop. 2,691
Hollandale SD 600/K-12
PO Box 128 38748 662-827-2276
Angela Johnson, supt. Fax 827-5261
www.hollandalesd.org
Simmons JSHS 300/7-12
PO Box 428 38748 662-827-2228
Shiquita Brown, prin. Fax 827-2231

Holly Springs, Marshall, Pop. 7,662
Holly Springs SD 1,400/PK-12
840 Highway 178 E 38635 662-252-2183
Dr. Irene Walton Turnage, supt. Fax 252-7718
www.hssd.k12.ms.us
Holly Springs Career & Technical Center Vo/Tech
410 E Falconer Ave 38635 662-252-2071
Cravin Turnage, dir. Fax 252-7719

Holly Springs HS 400/9-12
165 N Walthall St 38635 662-252-4371
Marcus Autry, prin. Fax 252-7720
Holly Springs JHS 200/7-8
325 E Falconer Ave 38635 662-252-7737
Letashia White, prin. Fax 252-7751

Marshall County SD 3,300/K-12
122 S Spring St 38635 662-252-4271
Carrie Skelton, supt. Fax 252-5129
www.marshallcountysd.org/
Byers HS 200/9-12
4178 Highway 72 38635 662-851-7826
Charles Lesure, prin. Fax 851-4027
Byers MS 200/6-8
4178 Highway 72 38635 662-851-7826
James Kimbrough, prin. Fax 851-4915
Other Schools – See Byhalia, Potts Camp

Infinity Career College Post-Sec.
960 Highway 4 E 38635 662-252-2600
Marshall Academy 300/PK-12
100 Academy Dr 38635 662-252-3449
Barrett Donahoe, hdmstr. Fax 252-4510
Rust College Post-Sec.
150 Rust Ave 38635 662-252-8000

Horn Lake, DeSoto, Pop. 25,611
DeSoto County SD
Supt. — See Hernando
Desoto County Alternative Center Alt
6870 Center St E 38637 662-253-0017
Jay Baird, prin. Fax 253-0013
DeSoto County Career Tech West Vo/Tech
1005 Kuykendall Kn 38637 662-996-5268
Paul Chrestman, prin. Fax 253-0382
Horn Lake HS 1,400/9-12
3360 Church Rd 38637 662-393-5273
Andy Orr, prin. Fax 393-5275
Horn Lake MS 1,000/6-8
6125 Hurt Rd 38637 662-393-7443
Nick Toungett, prin. Fax 342-5039

Delta Technical College Post-Sec.
6550 Interstate Dr # D 38637 662-280-1443

Houlka, Chickasaw, Pop. 621
Chickasaw County SD 500/PK-12
PO Box 480 38850 662-568-3333
Dr. Betsy Collums, supt. Fax 568-2993
chickasaw.k12.ms.us/
Houlka S 500/PK-12
510 Griffin Ave 38850 662-568-2772
Seth Burt, prin. Fax 568-7931

Houston, Chickasaw, Pop. 3,580
Houston SD 1,800/K-12
PO Box 351 38851 662-456-3332
Tony Cook, supt. Fax 456-5259
www.houston.k12.ms.us
Houston HS 500/9-12
PO Box 568 38851 662-456-3320
Jason Cook, prin. Fax 456-3527
Houston MS 400/6-8
PO Box 192 38851 662-456-5174
John Ellison, prin. Fax 456-2254

Indianola, Sunflower, Pop. 10,634
Sunflower County Consolidated SD 4,100/K-12
PO Box 70 38751 662-887-4919
Dr. Debra Dace, supt. Fax 887-7051
www.sunflower.k12.ms.us
Gentry HS 500/10-12
801 BB King Rd 38751 662-884-1240
Randy Ball, prin. Fax 887-7410
Indianola Academic Achievement Center Alt
300 Jefferson St 38751 662-884-1278
Brenda Singleton, prin. Fax 887-3038
Indianola Career & Technical Center Vo/Tech
801 BB King Rd 38751 662-884-6000
Rosalind Johnson, dir. Fax 887-7087
Merritt MS 500/7-9
705 Kinlock Rd 38751 662-884-1270
Demond Radcliff, prin. Fax 887-5247
Other Schools – See Drew, Inverness, Moorhead, Ruleville

Indianola Academy 500/PK-12
PO Box 967 38751 662-887-2025
Restoration Ministries Christian Academy 100/PK-12
PO Box 1001 38751 662-887-2040
Vivian Jenkins, prin. Fax 887-2040

Inverness, Sunflower, Pop. 1,017
Sunflower County Consolidated SD
Supt. — See Indianola
Ruleville Central HS 400/9-12
PO Box 228 38753 662-756-4757
Dr. Cassandra Winters, prin. Fax 265-0027

Itta Bena, LeFlore, Pop. 2,046
Leflore County SD
Supt. — See Greenwood
Leflore County HS 500/7-12
PO Box 564 38941 662-254-7762
Cassandra Hart, prin. Fax 254-7530

Mississippi Valley State University Post-Sec.
14000 Highway 82 W 38941 662-254-9041

Iuka, Tishomingo, Pop. 2,992
Tishomingo County Special Municipal SD 3,200/K-12
1620 Paul Edmondson Dr 38852 662-423-3206
Christie Holly, supt. Fax 424-9820
www.tcsk12.com
Iuka MS 300/5-8
507 W Quitman St 38852 662-423-3316
Monica Moss, prin. Fax 423-2426
Tishomingo County HS 600/9-12
701 Highway 72 38852 662-423-7300
Jackie Beals, prin. Fax 423-7307
Other Schools – See Belmont, Tishomingo

Jackson, Hinds, Pop. 172,074
Jackson SD 28,700/PK-12
PO Box 2338 39225 601-960-8700
Dr. Cedrick Gray, supt. Fax 960-8713
www.jackson.k12.ms.us
Bailey APAC MS 600/6-8
1900 N State St 39202 601-960-5343
Christi Hollingshead, prin. Fax 592-2496
Blackburn MS 500/6-8
1311 W Pearl St 39203 601-960-5329
Dr. Valerie Bradley, prin. Fax 360-2601
Brinkley MS 400/6-8
3535 Albermarle Rd 39213 601-987-3573
Larry Armstrong, prin. Fax 987-3746
Callaway HS 1,100/9-12
601 Beasley Rd 39206 601-987-3535
William Trammell, prin. Fax 987-3729
Capital City Alternative S Alt
2221 Boling St 39213 601-713-2376
Dr. Falanda Addison-Ross, prin. Fax 987-3727
Cardozo MS 600/6-8
3180 McDowell Road Ext 39204 601-346-5635
Eliza Lee, prin. Fax 373-0286
Chastain MS 700/6-8
4650 Manhattan Rd 39206 601-987-3550
Anthony Moore, prin. Fax 987-4930
Forest Hill HS 1,100/9-12
2607 Raymond Rd 39212 601-371-4313
Tommy Nalls, prin. Fax 371-4379
Hardy MS 600/6-8
545 Ellis Ave 39209 601-960-5362
Vertis Holmes, prin. Fax 360-2686
Hill HS 1,200/9-12
2185 Coach Fred Harris St 39204 601-960-5354
Tanyatemeika Mason, prin. Fax 360-2625
Jackson Career Development Center Vo/Tech
2703 First Ave 39209 601-960-5322
Dr. Brenda Jackson, prin. Fax 960-5411
Kirksey MS, 5677 Highland Dr 39206 300/6-8
Quita Ware, prin. 601-987-8360
Lanier HS 800/9-12
833 Maple St 39203 601-960-5369
Eric Johnson, prin. Fax 960-4047
Murrah HS 1,500/9-12
1400 Murrah Dr 39202 601-960-5380
Kennieth Green, prin. Fax 360-2622
Northwest Jackson MS 300/6-8
7020 Highway 49 N 39213 601-987-3609
Denese Sutton, prin. Fax 987-4975
Peeples MS 500/6-8
2940 Belvedere Dr 39212 601-346-5660
Dr. Kerry Gray, prin. Fax 371-4722
Powell MS 500/6-8
3655 Livingston Rd 39213 601-987-3580
Justin Green, prin. Fax 987-3583
Provine HS 1,100/9-12
2400 Robinson St 39209 601-960-5393
Laketia Marshall-Thomas, prin. Fax 360-2606
Rowan MS 200/6-8
136 E Ash St 39202 601-960-5349
Dr. Shimelle Mayers, prin. Fax 960-4046
Siwell Road MS 600/6-8
1983 N Siwell Rd 39209 601-923-2550
Marnetta McIntyre, prin. Fax 923-2570
Whitten MS 500/6-8
210 Daniel Lake Blvd 39212 601-371-4309
Victor Ellis, prin. Fax 371-4728
Wingfield HS 900/9-12
1985 Scanlon Dr 39204 601-371-4350
Dr. Willie Killins, prin. Fax 371-4734

Academy of Hair Design #3 Post-Sec.
1815 Terry Rd 39204 601-372-9800
Antonelli College Post-Sec.
2323 Lakeland Dr 39232 601-362-9991
Belhaven University Post-Sec.
1500 Peachtree St 39202 601-968-5940
Christ Missionary & Industrial S 200/PK-12
3910 Main St 39213 601-366-6413
Education Center S 200/K-12
PO Box 55509 39296 601-982-2812
Healthcare Institute of Jackson Post-Sec.
405 Briarwood Dr Ste 110 39206 601-956-3940
Hillcrest Christian S 500/K-12
4060 S Siwell Rd 39212 601-372-0149
Jackson Academy 1,200/PK-12
PO Box 14978 39236 601-362-9676
Dr. Pat Taylor, hdmstr. Fax 364-5722
Jackson Preparatory S 800/6-12
3100 Lakeland Dr 39232 601-939-8611
Jason Walton Ph.D., head sch Fax 936-4068
Jackson State University Post-Sec.
1440 J R Lynch St 39217 601-979-2100
Magnolia College of Cosmetology Post-Sec.
4725 I 55 N 39206 601-362-6940
Millsaps College Post-Sec.
1701 N State St 39210 601-974-1000
Mississippi Baptist Medical Center Post-Sec.
1225 N State St 39202 601-968-5130
Mississippi School for the Blind Post-Sec.
1252 Eastover Dr 39211 601-984-8000
Mississippi School for the Deaf Post-Sec.
1253 Eastover Dr 39211 601-984-8001
Reformed Theological Seminary Post-Sec.
5422 Clinton Blvd 39209 601-923-1600
St. Dominic-Jackson Memorial Hospital Post-Sec.
969 Lakeland Dr 39216 601-364-6935
Traxler School of Hair Post-Sec.
2845 Suncrest Dr 39212 601-371-0226
University of Mississippi Medical Center Post-Sec.
2500 N State St 39216 601-984-1000
Virginia College Post-Sec.
5841 Ridgewood Rd 39211 601-977-0960
Wesley Biblical Seminary Post-Sec.
787 E Northside Dr 39206 601-366-8880

Kilmichael, Montgomery, Pop. 698
Montgomery County SD
Supt. — See Winona
Montgomery County HS 100/7-12
PO Box 278 39747 662-262-5535
Lewis Zeigler, prin. Fax 262-4218

Kiln, Hancock, Pop. 2,194
Hancock County SD 4,900/K-12
17304 Highway 603 39556 228-255-0376
Alan Dedeaux, supt. Fax 255-0378
www.hancock.k12.ms.us
Hancock County Career Technical Center Vo/Tech
7180 Stennis Airport Rd 39556 228-467-3568
Dr. Rick Saucier, dir. Fax 466-4944
Hancock HS 1,200/9-12
7084 Stennis Airport Rd 39556 228-467-2251
Tara Ladner, prin. Fax 467-2689
Hancock MS 1,100/6-8
7070 Stennis Airport Rd 39556 228-467-1889
Dr. Jessical Taylor, prin. Fax 467-2812

Kosciusko, Attala, Pop. 7,358
Attala County SD 1,100/PK-12
100 Courthouse Ste 3 39090 662-289-2801
Bryan Weaver, supt. Fax 289-2804
www.attala.k12.ms.us/
Kosciusko-Attala County Voc Complex Vo/Tech
450 Highway 12 E 39090 662-289-2689
Tony Holder, dir. Fax 289-2701
Other Schools – See Ethel, Sallis

Kosciusko SSD 2,300/K-12
229 W Washington St 39090 662-289-4771
Gina Rogers Smith, supt. Fax 289-1177
www.ksd.k12.ms.us/
Kosciusko HS 600/9-12
229 W Washington St 39090 662-289-2424
Cory Blaylock, prin. Fax 289-8767
Kosciusko JHS 500/6-8
229 W Washington St 39090 662-289-3737
Jackie McElwain, prin. Fax 289-1177

Lake, Newton, Pop. 321
Scott County SD
Supt. — See Forest
Lake HS 200/9-12
24442 Highway 80 39092 601-775-3248
Lee Killen, prin. Fax 775-3861
Lake MS 200/5-8
1770 E Scott Rd 39092 601-775-3614
Nancy Butler, prin. Fax 775-8830

Lake Cormorant, DeSoto
DeSoto County SD
Supt. — See Hernando
Lake Cormorant HS 900/9-12
10201 Star Landing Rd 38641 662-996-3060
Rhonda Guice, prin. Fax 996-2520
Lake Cormorant MS 800/6-8
3203 Wilson Mill Rd 38641 662-781-0778
Jeff Morgan, prin. Fax 781-0688

Laurel, Jones, Pop. 18,408
Jones County SD
Supt. — See Ellisville
Jones County Career & Tech Center Vo/Tech
2409 Moose Dr 39440 601-425-2378
Patsy Reon, prin. Fax 425-2349
Northeast Jones JSHS 1,000/7-12
68 Northeast Dr 39443 601-425-2347
Cooper Pope, prin. Fax 649-1736
West Jones JSHS 1,300/7-12
254 Springhill Rd 39443 601-729-8144
Lynn Lyon, prin. Fax 729-8148

Laurel SD 3,100/PK-12
PO Box 288 39441 601-649-6391
Dr. Chuck Benigno, supt. Fax 649-6398
www.laurelschools.org
Laurel HS 800/9-12
1100 W 12th St 39440 601-649-4145
Jeannine Agee, prin. Fax 426-2347
Laurel MS 700/6-8
1600 Grandview Dr 39440 601-428-5312
Leah McCullum, prin. Fax 426-6775

Laurel Christian S 500/PK-12
PO Box 8425 39441 601-649-4190
Mississippi College of Beauty Culture Post-Sec.
732 Sawmill Rd 39440 601-428-7127
Southeastern Baptist College Post-Sec.
4229 Highway 15 N 39440 601-426-6346

Leakesville, Greene, Pop. 893
Greene County SD 2,100/PK-12
PO Box 1329 39451 601-394-2364
Charles Breland, supt. Fax 394-5542
www.greene.k12.ms.us
Greene County HS 600/9-12
4336 High School Rd 39451 601-394-5290
Scott Bray, prin. Fax 394-4878
Greene County Vo-Tech Complex Vo/Tech
173 Vo Tech Rd 39451 601-394-2973
Dr. Tom Wallace, dir. Fax 394-5953
Leakesville JHS 400/5-8
PO Box 1299 39451 601-394-2495
Monica Edwards, prin. Fax 394-5690

Learned, Hinds, Pop. 92

Rebul Academy 100/PK-12
5257 Learned Rd 39154 601-885-6802

Leland, Washington, Pop. 4,449
Leland SD 900/PK-12
408 4th St 38756 662-686-5000
Rev. Jessie King, supt. Fax 686-5029
lelandschooldistrict.schoolinsites.com
Leland HS 300/9-12
404 E 3rd St 38756 662-686-5020
Melvin Brown, prin. Fax 686-5027
Leland MS 300/5-8
200 Milam St 38756 662-686-5017
Susie Williams, prin. Fax 686-5042
Leland Vocational Center Vo/Tech
E Deer Creek Dr 38756 662-686-5025
Kermit McAdory, dir. Fax 686-5024

Lexington, Holmes, Pop. 1,722
Holmes County SD 1,900/PK-12
PO Box 630 39095 662-834-2175
Dr. Angel Meeks, supt. Fax 834-9060
www.holmes.k12.ms.us
Holmes County Career & Technical Center Vo/Tech
77 Kickernick St 39095 662-834-3052
Dr. Reginald Barnes, dir. Fax 834-3053
Holmes County Central HS 400/9-12
9479 Brozville Rd 39095 662-834-2172
George Jackson, prin. Fax 834-2709
Other Schools – See Tchula

Central Holmes Christian S 300/PK-12
130 Robert E Lee Dr 39095 662-834-3011

Liberty, Amite, Pop. 726
Amite County SD' 1,000/K-12
PO Box 378 39645 601-657-4361
Scotty Whittington, supt. Fax 657-4291
www.amite.k12.ms.us/
Amite County HS 400/7-12
PO Box 328 39645 601-657-8920
Celdric McDowell, prin. Fax 657-4044
Amite County Vocational Educational S Vo/Tech
PO Box 770 39645 601-657-8081
Augustus Russ, dir. Fax 657-8098

Amite School Center 200/K-12
PO Box 354 39645 601-657-8896

Long Beach, Harrison, Pop. 14,545
Long Beach SD 3,100/K-12
19148 Commission Rd 39560 228-864-1146
Dr. Jay Smith, supt. Fax 863-3196
www.lbsdk12.com
Long Beach HS 800/9-12
300 E Old Pass Rd 39560 228-863-6945
Vivian Robinson, prin. Fax 864-8961
Long Beach MS 600/7-8
204 N Cleveland Ave 39560 228-864-3370
Dr. Tim Holland, prin. Fax 867-1789

Lorman, Jefferson

Alcorn State University Post-Sec.
1000 Alcorn Dr 39096 601-877-6100

Louisville, Winston, Pop. 6,587
Louisville Municipal SD 2,800/PK-12
PO Box 909 39339 662-773-3411
Ken McMullan, supt. Fax 773-4013
louisville.k12.ms.us/
Eiland MS 400/6-8
508 Camille Ave 39339 662-773-9001
Jawana Young, prin. Fax 773-4016
Louisville HS 500/9-12
200 Ivy Ave 39339 662-773-3431
Hilute Hudson, prin. Fax 773-4017
Waiya S 500/K-12
13937 Highway 397 39339 662-773-6770
Belinda Swart, prin. Fax 773-6764
Winston-Louisville Career & Tech Center Vo/Tech
204 Ivy Ave 39339 662-773-6152
James Webb, dir. Fax 773-9572
Other Schools – See Noxapater

Grace Christian S 100/PK-12
173 McLeod Rd 39339 662-773-8524
Gale Gregory, hdmstr. Fax 773-4308
Winston Academy 500/PK-12
PO Box 545 39339 662-773-3569

Lucedale, George, Pop. 2,907
George County SD 4,100/PK-12
5152 Main St 39452 601-947-6993
Pam Touchard, supt. Fax 947-8805
www.gcsd.us
George County HS 1,100/9-12
9284 Old 63 S 39452 601-947-3116
Wade Whitney, prin. Fax 947-1076
George County MS 700/7-8
330 Church St 39452 601-947-3106
Kiley Hughes, prin. Fax 947-6004

Lumberton, Lamar, Pop. 2,065
Lumberton SD 600/K-12
107 E 10th Ave 39455 601-796-2441
Dr. Linda Smith, supt. Fax 796-2051
www.lumberton.k12.ms.us/
Lumberton HS 200/9-12
7920 U S Highway 11 39455 601-796-2451
John Barnes, prin. Fax 796-7907

Bass Memorial Academy 100/9-12
6433 U S Highway 11 39455 601-794-8561

Maben, Webster, Pop. 864
Webster County SD
Supt. — See Eupora
East Webster HS 400/7-12
195 Old Cumberland Rd 39750 662-263-5321
Bill Brand, prin. Fax 263-4518

Mc Comb, Pike, Pop. 12,696
McComb SD 2,900/PK-12
PO Box 868 39649 601-684-4661
Cederick Ellis Ph.D., supt. Fax 249-4732
www.mccomb.k12.ms.us
Business & Technology Complex Vo/Tech
1003 Virginia Ave 39648 601-684-5288
Robert Biggs, dir. Fax 249-2454
Denman JHS 400/7-8
1211 Louisiana Ave 39648 601-684-2387
James Brown, prin. Fax 249-3564
McComb HS 700/9-12
310 7th St 39648 601-684-5678
Robert Lamkin, prin. Fax 249-4737

Parklane Academy 900/K-12
1115 Parklane Dr 39648 601-684-8113
SW Mississippi Regional Medical Center Post-Sec.
PO Box 1307 39649 601-249-1807

Macon, Noxubee, Pop. 2,760
Noxubee County SD 1,800/PK-12
PO Box 540 39341 662-726-4527
Roger Liddell Ed.D., supt. Fax 726-2809
www.noxcnty.k12.ms.us
Liddell MS 300/5-8
PO Box 229 39341 662-726-4880
D.J. Ward, prin. Fax 726-5044
Noxubee County Career & Technical Center Vo/Tech
13002 Highway 45 39341 662-726-4225
Dr. Annie Snow, dir. Fax 726-2804
Noxubee County HS 500/9-12
PO Box 490 39341 662-726-4428
James Covington, prin. Fax 726-5048

Central Academy 100/PK-12
PO Box 231 39341 662-726-4817

Madden, Leake

Leake Academy 600/PK-12
PO Box 128 39109 601-267-4461

Madison, Madison, Pop. 23,961
Madison County SD
Supt. — See Ridgeland
Germantown HS 900/9-12
200 Calhoun Pkwy 39110 601-859-6150
Wesley Quick, prin. Fax 859-6075
Germantown MS 700/6-8
202 Calhoun Pkwy 39110 601-859-0376
Chris Perritt, prin. Fax 859-1302
Madison Central HS 1,300/10-12
1417 Highland Colony Pkwy 39110 601-856-7121
Austin Brown, prin. Fax 853-2712
Madison County Academic Options Center Alt
300 Industrial Dr S 39110 601-859-0367
Brent Cofield, prin. Fax 859-0374
Madison County Career & Tech Center Vo/Tech
142 Calhoun Pkwy 39110 601-859-6847
Aimee Brown, dir. Fax 859-0372
Madison MS 1,300/6-8
1365 Mannsdale Rd 39110 601-605-4171
Leatha Phillips, prin. Fax 853-2254
Scott S 400/9-9
200 Crawford St 39110 601-605-0054
Sean Brewer, prin. Fax 898-5017

Madison Ridgeland Academy 900/PK-12
7601 Old Canton Rd 39110 601-856-4455
St. Joseph Catholic S 500/7-12
PO Box 2027 39130 601-898-4800
Doug Jones, prin. Fax 898-4689

Magee, Simpson, Pop. 4,347
Simpson County SD
Supt. — See Mendenhall
Magee HS 500/9-12
501 Choctaw St E 39111 601-849-2263
Pete Howell, prin. Fax 849-6201
Magee MS 600/5-8
413 Choctaw St E Ste 100 39111 601-849-3334
Dr. Rasheda Bell, prin. Fax 849-6130
Simpson County Achievement Center Alt
177 Simpson Highway 149 39111 601-849-6135
Dr. Roma Morris, prin. Fax 849-6137

Magnolia, Pike, Pop. 2,410
South Pike SD 1,800/K-12
250 W Bay St 39652 601-783-0430
Dr. Johnnie Vick, supt. Fax 783-6733
www.southpike.org
South Pike Career & Technical Center Vo/Tech
252 W Bay St 39652 601-783-0438
Billy Passman, dir. Fax 783-3491
South Pike HS 500/9-12
205 W Myrtle St 39652 601-783-0420
LeDwayne Harris, prin. Fax 783-4179
South Pike JHS 300/7-8
222 W Myrtle St 39652 601-783-0425
Warren Eyster, prin. Fax 783-2272

Mantachie, Itawamba, Pop. 1,139
Itawamba County SD
Supt. — See Fulton
Mantachie HS 400/7-12
PO Box 38 38855 662-282-4276
Millie Wood, prin. Fax 282-4270

Marks, Quitman, Pop. 1,725
Quitman County SD 1,200/K-12
PO Box E 38646 662-326-7046
Evelyn W. Jossell, supt. Fax 326-3694
qcschools.com
Palmer HS 300/9-12
PO Box 350 38646 662-326-5191
Walter Atkins, prin. Fax 326-8918
Quitman County Career Technical Center Vo/Tech
PO Box 117 38646 662-326-8427
Cynthia Washington, dir. Fax 326-8430
Quitman County MS 400/5-8
PO Box 290 38646 662-326-6871
Phelton C. Moss, prin. Fax 326-6300

Delta Academy 200/PK-12
PO Box 70 38646 662-326-8164

Meadville, Franklin, Pop. 448
Franklin County SD 1,200/PK-12
PO Box 605 39653 601-384-2340
Chris Kent, supt. Fax 384-2393
www.franklincountyschoolsms.com
Franklin County Career & Technical Ctr Vo/Tech
PO Box 155 39653 601-384-5889
Terry Moffett, prin. Fax 384-5578
Franklin County HS 400/9-12
PO Box 666 39653 601-384-2965
Marion Bilbo, prin. Fax 384-2498
Franklin County MS 200/7-8
236 Edison St S 39653 601-384-2441
Lisa Storey, prin. Fax 384-2085

Mendenhall, Simpson, Pop. 2,477
Simpson County SD 4,100/K-12
111 Education Ln 39114 601-847-8000
Greg Paes, supt. Fax 847-8001
www.simpson.k12.ms.us
Mendenhall HS 600/9-12
207 Circle Dr 39114 601-847-2411
Robert Sanders, prin. Fax 847-8002
Mendenhall JHS 500/5-8
733 Dixie Ave 39114 601-847-2296
Kirby Craft, prin. Fax 847-7175
Simpson County Technical Center Vo/Tech
3415 Simpson Highway 49 39114 601-847-4000
Dr. George Huffman, dir. Fax 847-8011
Other Schools – See Magee

Simpson County Academy 500/K-12
124 Academy Cir 39114 601-847-1394

Meridian, Lauderdale, Pop. 40,816
Lauderdale County SD 6,700/PK-12
PO Box 5498 39302 601-693-1683
Randy Hodges, supt. Fax 485-1748
www.lauderdale.k12.ms.us
Clarkdale HS 300/9-12
7000 Highway 145 39301 601-693-4463
Ken Hardy, prin. Fax 693-6329
Clarkdale MS 300/5-8
7000 Highway 145 39301 601-693-4463
Dr. Angie McHenry, prin. Fax 483-6329
Northeast Lauderdale HS 600/9-12
702 Briarwood Rd 39305 601-679-8523
Steve Nelson, prin. Fax 679-7515
Northeast MS 700/5-8
7763 Highway 39 39305 601-483-3532
Tim Moore, prin. Fax 485-0846
Southeast HS 400/9-12
2362 Long Creek Rd 39301 601-483-5501
Tim Moore, prin. Fax 483-6347
Southeast MS 400/5-8
2535 Old Highway 19 SE 39301 601-485-5751
Marcus Irby, prin. Fax 485-2302
Other Schools – See Collinsville

Meridian SD 6,000/PK-12
1019 25th Ave 39301 601-483-6271
Dr. Amy Carter, supt. Fax 484-4917
www.mpsd.k12.ms.us
Carver MS 400/6-8
900 44th Ave 39307 601-484-4482
Tommy Branch, prin. Fax 484-3011
Collins Career & Tech Center Vo/Tech
2640 24th Ave 39305 601-483-3331
Rob Smith, dir. Fax 484-5173
Magnolia MS 400/6-8
1350 24th St 39301 601-484-4060
Angela McQuarley, prin. Fax 484-5179
Meridian HS 1,500/9-12
2320 32nd St 39305 601-482-3191
Victor Hubbard, prin. Fax 483-5502
Northwest MS 500/6-8
4400 32nd St 39307 601-484-4094
Justus Booth, prin. Fax 484-5180

Final Touch Beauty School Post-Sec.
5700 N Hills St 39307 601-485-7733
Lamar S 500/PK-12
544 Lindley Rd 39305 601-482-1345
Meridian Community College Post-Sec.
910 Highway 19 N 39307 601-483-8241
Russell Christian Academy 400/PK-12
1844D Highway 11 And 80 39301 601-484-5888

Mississippi State, Oktibbeha, Pop. 3,939

Mississippi State University Post-Sec.
PO Box J 39762 662-325-2323

Mize, Smith, Pop. 339
Smith County SD
Supt. — See Raleigh
Mize S 800/K-12
PO Box 187 39116 601-733-2242
Chuck Jones, prin. Fax 733-9649

Monticello, Lawrence, Pop. 1,561
Lawrence County SD 2,200/K-12
346 Thomas E Jolly Dr W 39654 601-587-2506
Tammy Fairburn, supt. Fax 587-2221
www.lawrence.k12.ms.us
Lawrence County HS 600/9-12
PO Box 488 39654 601-587-4910
Darrell Turner, prin. Fax 587-5001

Lawrence County Technology & Career Ctr Vo/Tech
PO Box 578 39654 601-587-9346
Cindy Williamson, dir. Fax 587-2980
Paige MS 400/5-8
1570 W Broad St 39654 601-587-2128
Cassie Bridges, prin. Fax 587-7178

Mooreville, Lee, Pop. 646
Lee County SD
Supt. — See Tupelo
Mooreville HS 400/9-12
PO Box 60 38857 662-842-6859
Lee Bruce, prin. Fax 841-5988
Mooreville MS 400/6-8
PO Box 180 38857 662-680-4894
Roman Doty, prin. Fax 680-4896

Moorhead, Sunflower, Pop. 2,399
Sunflower County Consolidated SD
Supt. — See Indianola
Moorhead MS 100/6-8
PO Box 749 38761 662-246-5680
Tanya Rodges, prin. Fax 246-5080

Mississippi Delta Community College Post-Sec.
PO Box 668 38761 662-246-6322

Morton, Scott, Pop. 3,416
Scott County SD
Supt. — See Forest
Jack Upper MS 500/5-8
PO Box 500 39117 601-732-6977
Miles Porter, prin. Fax 732-2242
Morton HS 400/9-12
238 E Fourth Ave 39117 601-732-6210
Scott Wells, prin. Fax 732-8086

Moss Point, Jackson, Pop. 13,562
Jackson County SD
Supt. — See Vancleave
East Central HS 800/9-12
21700 Slider Rd 39562 228-588-7000
James Hughey, prin. Fax 588-7045
East Central MS 600/6-8
5404 Hurley Wade Rd 39562 228-588-7009
Monique Farrington, prin. Fax 588-7043

Moss Point SD 2,200/PK-12
4924 Church St 39563 228-475-4558
Shannon Vincent Ph.D., supt. Fax 474-3302
www.mosspointschools.org/
Career & Technical Center Vo/Tech
4924 Church St 39563 228-475-1455
Dr. Durand Payton, dir.
Magnolia MS 600/6-8
4924 Church St 39563 228-475-1429
Susan Stachowski, prin. Fax 475-2684
Moss Point Alternative Learning Center Alt
4924 Church St 39563 228-475-3543
Searcy Kay, prin. Fax 474-3395
Moss Point HS 700/9-12
4924 Church St 39563 228-475-5721
Joe Griffin, prin. Fax 475-5074

Mound Bayou, Bolivar, Pop. 1,532
North Bolivar Consolidated SD 1,200/K-12
201 Green St 38762 662-741-2555
Linda Robinson, supt. Fax 741-2726
www.nbcsd.k12.ms.us
Kennedy Memorial HS 300/7-12
204 N Edwards Ave 38762 662-741-2510
Shawneequa Beal, prin. Fax 741-2246
Other Schools – See Shelby

Mount Olive, Covington, Pop. 971
Covington County SD
Supt. — See Collins
Mt. Olive S 400/K-12
PO Box 309 39119 601-797-3939
O'Tonya Walker, prin. Fax 797-3980

Myrtle, Union, Pop. 482
Union County SD
Supt. — See New Albany
Myrtle S 700/PK-12
1008 Hawk Ave 38650 662-988-2416
Nancy Yates, prin. Fax 988-2001
West Union S 600/PK-12
1610 State Road 30 W 38650 662-534-6745
Russell Taylor, prin. Fax 534-6716

Natchez, Adams, Pop. 15,630
Natchez-Adams SD 4,000/PK-12
10 Homochitto St 39120 601-445-2800
Dr. Fred Butcher, supt. Fax 445-2818
www.natchez.k12.ms.us
Fallin Career & Technology Center Vo/Tech
315 Sgt Prentiss Dr 39120 601-445-2902
Daisy West, dir. Fax 445-2967
Morgantown Arts Academy 200/6-8
101 Cottage Home Dr 39120 601-445-2917
Tawanna Thornton, admin. Fax 445-2912
Morgantown College Prep 100/6-8
101 Cottage Home Dr 39120 601-445-2917
Shamekia Isaac, admin. Fax 445-2912
Natchez Early College 100/9-10
319 Sgt Prentiss Dr 39120 601-445-2865
Kesha Campbell, admin. Fax 445-2870
Natchez Freshman Academy 300/9-9
208 Lynda Lee Dr 39120 601-445-2941
Tracey Myers, admin. Fax 445-2498
Natchez HS 700/10-12
319 Sgt Prentiss Dr 39120 601-445-2864
Ernest Fields, prin. Fax 445-2870

Adams County Christian S 400/PK-12
300 Chinquapin Ln 39120 601-442-1422
Cathedral S 700/PK-12
701 N Dr ML King Jr St 39120 601-442-2531
Patrick Sanguinetti, prin. Fax 442-0960

Copiah-Lincoln Community College Post-Sec.
11 Co Lin Cir 39120 601-442-9111
Trinity Episcopal Day S 300/PK-12
1 Mallan G Morgan Dr 39120 601-442-5424
Fr. Paul Andersen, hdmstr. Fax 442-3216

Nettleton, Itawamba, Pop. 1,982
Nettleton SD 1,200/K-12
PO Box 409 38858 662-963-2151
Michael Cates, supt. Fax 963-7407
www.nettletonschools.com/
Nettleton HS 300/9-12
PO Box 409 38858 662-963-2306
Jeff Credille, prin. Fax 963-7407
Nettleton JHS 200/6-8
PO Box 409 38858 662-963-7400
Ray Weeks, prin. Fax 963-1525

New Albany, Union, Pop. 7,897
New Albany SD 2,100/PK-12
301 State Highway 15 N 38652 662-534-1800
Jackie Ford, supt. Fax 534-3608
www.newalbany.k12.ms.us
New Albany HS 600/9-12
201 State Highway 15 N 38652 662-534-1805
Lance Evans, prin. Fax 534-1817
New Albany MS 500/6-8
400 Apple St 38652 662-534-1820
Damon Ladner Ph.D., prin. Fax 534-1819
New Albany/S. Tippah/Union Co. Alt S Alt
915 Denmill Rd 38652 662-538-4100
Minerva Graham, dir. Fax 538-4102
New Albany Vocational Complex Vo/Tech
203 State Highway 15 N 38652 662-534-1810
John Ferrell, dir. Fax 534-1811

Union County SD 2,800/PK-12
PO Box 939 38652 662-534-1960
Ken Basil, supt. Fax 534-1961
www.union.k12.ms.us
Ingomar S 700/PK-12
1384 County Road 101 38652 662-534-2680
Mark Grubbs, prin. Fax 534-3624
Other Schools – See Blue Springs, Myrtle

New Augusta, Perry, Pop. 638
Perry County SD 1,200/K-12
PO Box 137 39462 601-964-3211
Dr. Scott Dearman, supt. Fax 964-8204
www.perry.k12.ms.us/
Perry Central HS 300/9-12
9899 Highway 98 39462 601-964-3235
Titus Hines, prin. Fax 964-8273
Perry County Vocational Tech Center Vo/Tech
PO Box 138 39462 601-964-8282
Dale Goodin, admin. Fax 964-8562

New Site, Prentiss
Prentiss County SD
Supt. — See Booneville
New Site HS 300/9-12
1020 Highway 4 E 38859 662-728-5205
Ronald Clark, prin. Fax 728-1965

Newton, Newton, Pop. 3,349
Newton Municipal SD 900/K-12
205 School St 39345 601-683-2451
Dr. Virginia Young, supt. Fax 683-7131
www.nmsd.k12.ms.us
Newton HS 300/9-12
PO Box 150 39345 601-683-2232
Shernise Wilson, prin. Fax 683-6808
Pilate MS 200/6-8
521 E Church St 39345 601-683-3926
Melanie Hamrick, prin. Fax 683-7139

North Carrollton, Carroll, Pop. 470
Carroll County SD
Supt. — See Carrollton
George HS 300/6-12
PO Box 398 38947 662-237-4701
Coretta Green, prin. Fax 237-4522

Noxapater, Winston, Pop. 468
Louisville Municipal SD
Supt. — See Louisville
Noxapater S 400/K-12
220 W Alice St 39346 662-724-4241
Chet Wilkes, prin. Fax 724-4240

Ocean Springs, Jackson, Pop. 17,087
Jackson County SD
Supt. — See Vancleave
St. Martin HS 1,200/9-12
11300 Yellow Jacket Rd 39564 228-875-8418
Dina Holland, prin. Fax 875-8426
St. Martin MS 1,000/6-8
10800 Yellow Jacket Rd 39564 228-818-4833
Stephanie Gruich, prin. Fax 818-0198

Ocean Springs SD 5,700/K-12
PO Box 7002 39566 228-875-7706
Dr. Bonita Coleman, supt. Fax 875-7708
oceansprings.schooldesk.net
Keys Alternative Education Center Alt
PO Box 7002 39566 228-872-0031
Kelly Long, dir. Fax 875-7745
Ocean Springs HS 1,700/9-12
PO Box 7002 39566 228-875-0333
Vickie Tiblier, prin. Fax 875-7404
Ocean Springs MS 900/7-8
PO Box 7002 39566 228-872-6210
Adelle Register, prin. Fax 872-9850

Day Spa Career College Post-Sec.
3900 Bienville Blvd 39564 228-875-4809

Okolona, Chickasaw, Pop. 2,664
Okolona SSD 700/K-12
411 W Main St 38860 662-447-2353
Dexter Green, supt. Fax 447-9955
okolona.k12.ms.us
Okolona JSHS 400/5-12
404 Dr Howard Gunn St 38860 662-447-2362
Christopher Hill, prin. Fax 447-3306

Olive Branch, DeSoto, Pop. 33,067
DeSoto County SD
Supt. — See Hernando
Center Hill HS 900/9-12
13250 Kirk Rd 38654 662-890-2490
Doug Payne, prin. Fax 890-2458
Center Hill MS 800/6-8
8756 Forest Hill Irene Ln 38654 662-892-6800
Jacob Stripling, prin. Fax 892-6810
Desoto County Career Tech East Vo/Tech
8890 Deerfield Dr 38654 662-893-0855
Beth Turner, prin. Fax 893-0853
Lewisburg HS 800/9-12
1755 Craft Rd 38654 662-890-6708
Chris Fleming, prin. Fax 890-6202
Lewisburg MS 700/6-8
1711 Craft Rd 38654 662-892-5050
Brad Meadows, prin. Fax 892-5060
Olive Branch HS 1,100/9-12
9366 E Sandidge Rd 38654 662-893-3344
Allyson Killough, prin. Fax 893-3353
Olive Branch MS 800/6-8
6530 Blocker St 38654 662-895-4610
Jerry Floate, prin. Fax 895-7358

DeSoto County Academy 400/PK-12
100 Academy Dr 38654 662-895-6385
Mildred Waters, prin.

Oxford, Lafayette, Pop. 18,701
Lafayette County SD 2,700/PK-12
100 Commodore Dr 38655 662-234-3271
Dr. Adam Pugh, supt. Fax 236-3019
www.gocommodores.org
Lafayette HS 700/9-12
160 Commodore Dr 38655 662-234-3614
Glenn Kitchens, prin. Fax 234-3856
Lafayette MS 600/6-8
102 Commodore Dr 38655 662-234-1664
Chad Chism, prin. Fax 232-8736

Oxford SD 2,700/PK-12
224 Bramlett Blvd 38655 662-234-3541
Brian Harvey, supt. Fax 232-2862
www.oxfordsd.org
Oxford HS 1,000/9-12
101 Charger Loop 38655 662-234-1562
W. Bradley Roberson, prin. Fax 232-1862
Oxford Learning Center Alt
399 N 5th St 38655 662-234-3588
Kathy Howington, prin. Fax 236-1052
Oxford MS 600/7-8
222 Bramlett Blvd 38655 662-234-2288
Audra Rester, prin. Fax 236-7337

Regents S of Oxford 200/PK-12
14 County Road 130 38655 662-232-1945

Pascagoula, Jackson, Pop. 22,125
Pascagoula-Gautier SD 6,900/K-12
PO Box 250 39568 228-938-6491
Wayne Rodolfich, supt. Fax 938-6528
www.pgsd.ms
College & Career Technical Institute Vo/Tech
2602 Market St 39567 228-938-6579
Thomas Brooks, dir. Fax 938-6597
Colmer MS 600/7-8
3112 Eden St 39581 228-938-6473
Dr. Myrick Nicks, prin. Fax 938-6593
Opportunity Center Alt
1520 Tucker Ave 39567 228-938-6222
Lisa Rex, prin. Fax 938-6210
Pascagoula HS 1,000/9-12
1716 Tucker Ave 39567 228-938-6443
Anthony Herbert, prin. Fax 938-6445
Other Schools – See Gautier

Resurrection Catholic MSHS 200/7-12
520 Watts Ave 39567 228-762-3353
Noah Hamilton, prin. Fax 769-1226

Pass Christian, Harrison, Pop. 4,509
Pass Christian SD 1,900/K-12
6457 Kiln Delisle Rd 39571 228-255-6200
Carla Evers Ph.D., supt. Fax 255-6204
www.pc.k12.ms.us
Pass Christian HS 500/9-12
720 W North St 39571 228-452-2008
Robyn Killebrew, prin. Fax 452-6128
Pass Christian MS 500/6-8
280 W Second St 39571 228-452-5220
Joe Nelson, prin. Fax 452-9616

Pearl, Rankin, Pop. 24,692
Pearl SD 4,000/K-12
3375 Highway 80 E 39208 601-932-7921
Dr. Raymond Morgigno, supt. Fax 932-7929
www.pearl.k12.ms.us/
Pearl HS 1,100/9-12
500 Pirates Cv 39208 601-932-7931
Chris Chism, prin. Fax 932-7992
Pearl JHS 900/6-8
200 Mary Ann Dr 39208 601-932-7952
Dr. Jessica Broome, prin. Fax 932-7998

Academy of Hair Design #4 Post-Sec.
3167 Highway 80 E 39208 601-939-4441

Park Place Christian Academy 400/PK-12
201 Park Place Dr 39208 601-939-6229
Ted Poore, head sch Fax 939-3276

Pelahatchie, Rankin, Pop. 1,321
Rankin County SD
Supt. — See Brandon
Pelahatchie JSHS 300/7-12
PO Box 569 39145 601-854-8135
Dr. Bryan Marshall, prin. Fax 854-8638

East Rankin Academy 800/PK-12
PO Box 509 39145 601-854-5691
Dan Boyce, hdmstr. Fax 854-5893

Perkinston, Stone

Mississippi Gulf Coast Community College Post-Sec.
PO Box 548 39573 601-928-5211

Petal, Forrest, Pop. 10,310
Petal SD 4,000/K-12
115 E Central Ave 39465 601-545-3002
Dr. Matthew L. Dillon, supt. Fax 584-4700
www.petalschools.com
Petal HS 1,200/9-12
1145 Highway 42 39465 601-583-3538
Steven Hampton, prin. Fax 545-1229
Petal MS 700/7-8
203 Highway 42 39465 601-584-6301
Michael Hogan, prin. Fax 584-4716

Pheba, Clay

Hebron Christian S 100/PK-12
6230 Henryville Rd 39755 662-494-7513

Philadelphia, Neshoba, Pop. 7,347
Neshoba County SD 3,200/K-12
401 E Beacon St Ste 102 39350 601-656-3752
Joe Killens, supt. Fax 656-3789
www.neshoba.k12.ms.us/
Neshoba Central HS 900/9-12
1125 Golf Course Rd 39350 601-656-3654
John Bowen, prin. Fax 656-1588
Neshoba Central MS 800/6-8
1000 Saint Francis Dr 39350 601-656-4636
Dr. Kenyon Barron, prin. Fax 389-2989

Philadelphia SD 1,100/K-12
248 Byrd Ave N 39350 601-656-2955
Lisa Hull, supt. Fax 656-3141
www.phillytornadoes.com
Philadelphia HS 300/9-12
248 Byrd Ave N 39350 601-656-2672
Michael Tardy, prin. Fax 656-2273
Philadelphia MS 200/7-8
248 Byrd Ave N 39350 601-656-6439
Stacie Collins, prin. Fax 656-5328

Picayune, Pearl River, Pop. 10,684
Picayune SD 3,400/K-12
706 Goodyear Blvd 39466 601-798-3230
Dean Shaw, supt. Fax 798-1742
www.pcu.k12.ms.us/
Picayune JHS 600/7-8
702 Goodyear Blvd 39466 601-798-5449
James Williams, prin. Fax 799-4715
Picayune Memorial HS 900/9-12
800 Fifth Ave 39466 601-798-1380
Kent Kirkland, prin. Fax 798-4705
PMHS Career & Technology Center Vo/Tech
600 Goodyear Blvd 39466 601-798-7601
Fax 799-4711

Piney Woods, Rankin

Piney Woods S 100/9-12
PO Box 57 39148 601-845-2214

Pittsboro, Calhoun, Pop. 200
Calhoun County SD 2,500/PK-12
119 W Main St 38951 662-412-3152
Mike Moore, supt. Fax 412-3157
www.calhoun.k12.ms.us/
Other Schools – See Bruce, Calhoun City, Vardaman

Calhoun Academy 200/PK-12
10 County Road 406 38951 662-412-2084

Plantersville, Lee, Pop. 1,140
Lee County SD
Supt. — See Tupelo
Plantersville MS 300/5-8
PO Box 129 38862 662-842-4690
Rodney Spears, prin. Fax 791-0491

Pontotoc, Pontotoc, Pop. 5,537
Pontotoc CSD 2,300/K-12
140 Education Dr 38863 662-489-3336
Dr. Michelle Bivens, supt. Fax 489-7932
www.pontotoc.k12.ms.us
Pontotoc HS 600/9-12
123 N Main St 38863 662-489-1275
Paul Henry, prin. Fax 489-5255
Pontotoc JHS 300/7-8
132 N Main St 38863 662-489-8360
Phil Webb, prin. Fax 489-8947

Pontotoc County SD 3,200/PK-12
354 Center Ridge Dr 38863 662-489-3932
Brock Puckett, supt. Fax 489-2940
www.pcsd.ms
Pontotoc Ridge Career & Technolog Center Vo/Tech
354 Ridge Dr 38863 662-489-1826
Phil Ryan, dir. Fax 489-0704
South Pontotoc HS 400/9-12
1523 S Pontotoc Rd 38863 662-489-5925
Tim West, prin. Fax 489-8598
South Pontotoc MS 400/6-8
1523 S Pontotoc Rd 38863 662-489-5925
Jimmy Flake, prin. Fax 489-6252
Other Schools – See Ecru

Poplarville, Pearl River, Pop. 2,824
Poplarville SSD 1,900/PK-12
302 Julia St 39470 601-795-8477
Carl Merritt, supt. Fax 795-0712
www.poplarvilleschools.org/
Poplarville Career Development Center Vo/Tech
9 Career Center Cir 39470 601-795-8343
Marlene Cole, prin. Fax 795-1353
Poplarville HS 600/9-12
1 Hornet Dr 39470 601-795-8424
Jonathan Will, prin. Fax 795-1345
Poplarville MS 500/6-8
6 Spirit Dr 39470 601-795-1350
Heidi Dillon, prin. Fax 795-1351

Pearl River Community College Post-Sec.
101 Highway 11 N 39470 601-403-1000

Port Gibson, Claiborne, Pop. 1,561
Claiborne County SD 1,600/PK-12
404 Market St 39150 601-437-4232
Dr. Cardell Williams Ph.D., supt. Fax 437-3036
www.claiborne.k12.ms.us/
Clairborne Co. Voc Educational Complex Vo/Tech
PO Box 47 39150 601-437-3800
Norma Thompson-Lewis, dir. Fax 437-3099
Port Gibson HS 400/9-12
159 Old Highway 18 39150 601-437-4190
Myron Franklin, prin. Fax 437-3803
Port Gibson MS 400/6-8
PO Box 567 39150 601-437-4251
Marvin Harvey, prin. Fax 437-3099

Potts Camp, Marshall, Pop. 520
Marshall County SD
Supt. — See Holly Springs
Potts Camp HS 200/9-12
7050 Church Ave 38659 662-333-6354
Luke Tentoni, prin. Fax 333-7023
Potts Camp MS 200/4-8
7050 Church Ave 38659 662-333-6354
Tana Miller, prin.

Prentiss, Jefferson Davis, Pop. 1,069
Jefferson Davis County SD 1,600/K-12
PO Box 1197 39474 601-792-4267
Will Russell, supt. Fax 792-2251
www.jdcsd.com
Prentiss JSHS 400/7-12
PO Box 1168 39474 601-792-4646
Willie Armstrong, prin. Fax 792-8149
Other Schools – See Bassfield, Carson

Prentiss Christian S 300/K-12
PO Box 1287 39474 601-792-8549

Puckett, Rankin, Pop. 315
Rankin County SD
Supt. — See Brandon
Puckett HS 300/7-12
PO Box 40 39151 601-825-5742
Robert Crain, prin. Fax 825-9838

Purvis, Lamar, Pop. 2,145
Lamar County SD 9,400/PK-12
PO Box 609 39475 601-794-1030
Tess Smith, supt. Fax 794-1012
www.lamarcountyschools.org
Jefferson-Todd Alternative Education Ctr Alt
PO Box 609 39475 601-794-1097
Bryan Stewart, prin. Fax 794-1070
Lamar County Center for Technical Educ Vo/Tech
41 College Dr 39475 601-794-8298
Tina Byrd, prin. Fax 794-5475
Purvis HS 600/9-12
PO Box 1089 39475 601-794-6221
Brad Skeen, prin. Fax 794-1036
Purvis MS 400/6-8
PO Box 549 39475 601-794-1068
Frank Bunnell, prin. Fax 794-1037
Other Schools – See Hattiesburg, Sumrall

Lamar Christian S 300/PK-12
PO Box 880 39475 601-794-0016
United Christian Academy 50/4-9
48 Azalea Trl 39475 601-520-1113
Callison Richardson, head sch

Quitman, Clarke, Pop. 2,307
Quitman SD 2,000/PK-12
104 E Franklin St 39355 601-776-2186
Dr. Donna H. Boone Ph.D., supt. Fax 776-1051
www.quitmanschools.org
Clarke County Vocational Center Vo/Tech
910 N Archusa Ave 39355 601-776-5219
Mark Hudson, dir. Fax 776-5219
Quitman HS 500/9-12
210 S Jackson Ave 39355 601-776-3341
Howard Savage, prin. Fax 776-6136
Quitman JHS 500/6-8
501 W Lynda St 39355 601-776-6243
Amy Johnson, prin. Fax 776-1288

Raleigh, Smith, Pop. 1,457
Smith County SD 2,800/K-12
PO Box 308 39153 601-782-4296
Jimmy Hancock, supt. Fax 782-9895
smithcountyschools.net
Raleigh HS 500/7-12
491 Magnolia Dr 39153 601-782-4261
Randy McIntyre, prin. Fax 782-4359
Smith County Career Center Vo/Tech
469 Magnolia Dr 39153 601-782-4211
Hollis Blackwell, dir. Fax 782-9842

Other Schools – See Mize, Taylorsville

Raymond, Hinds, Pop. 1,915
Hinds County SD 6,200/PK-12
13192 Highway 18 39154 601-857-5222
Dr. Delesicia Martin, supt. Fax 857-8548
www.hinds.k12.ms.us/
Carver MS 200/6-8
PO Box 47 39154 601-857-5006
Deborah Newman, prin. Fax 857-4935
Hinds County Career Center Vo/Tech
PO Box 789 39154 601-857-3680
Patricia Ashmore, prin. Fax 857-2212
Raymond HS 600/9-12
14050 Highway 18 39154 601-857-8016
Lorenza Grimes, prin. Fax 857-2007
Other Schools – See Bolton, Terry

Central Hinds Academy 400/K-12
2894 Raymond Bolton Rd 39154 601-857-5568
Hinds Community College Post-Sec.
PO Box 1100 39154 601-857-5261

Richland, Rankin, Pop. 6,844
Rankin County SD
Supt. — See Brandon
Richland HS 900/7-12
1202 Highway 49 S 39218 601-939-5144
Richard Sutton, prin. Fax 939-7631

Richton, Perry, Pop. 1,058
Richton SD 700/K-12
PO Box 568 39476 601-788-6581
James Clay Anglin, supt. Fax 788-9391
www.richtonschools.com
Richton JSHS 400/7-12
PO Box 568 39476 601-788-9608
Patrick Lee, prin. Fax 788-6390

Ridgeland, Madison, Pop. 23,769
Madison County SD 12,600/PK-12
476 Highland Colony Pkwy 39157 601-879-3000
Dr. Ronnie McGehee, supt. Fax 879-3039
www.madison-schools.com/
Olde Towne MS 700/6-8
210 Sunnybrook Rd 39157 601-898-8730
Crystal Chase, prin. Fax 853-8108
Ridgeland HS 800/9-12
586 Sunnybrook Rd 39157 601-898-5023
Tim Dowdy, prin. Fax 853-7822
Other Schools – See Camden, Canton, Madison

Delta Technical College Post-Sec.
113 Marketridge Dr 39157 601-206-5200
St. Andrew's Episcopal S 700/5-12
370 Old Agency Rd 39157 601-853-6000
Dr. George Penick, head sch Fax 853-6001

Ripley, Tippah, Pop. 5,308
South Tippah SD 2,800/K-12
402 Greenlee Dr 38663 662-837-7156
Frank Campbell, supt. Fax 837-1362
www.stippah.k12.ms.us/
Pine Grove S 600/K-12
3510A County Road 600 38663 662-837-7789
Brad Pounders, prin. Fax 837-8179
Ripley HS 500/9-12
720 S Clayton St 38663 662-837-7583
George Buchanan, prin. Fax 837-0118
Ripley MS 600/5-8
718 S Clayton St 38663 662-837-7959
James Storey, prin. Fax 837-0251
Tippah Career & Technology Center Vo/Tech
PO Box 533 38663 662-837-9798
Tony Elliott, dir. Fax 837-8833
Other Schools – See Blue Mountain

Foster's Cosmetology College Post-Sec.
PO Box 66 38663 662-837-9334

Rolling Fork, Sharkey, Pop. 2,129
South Delta SD 900/PK-12
PO Box 219 39159 662-873-4302
Sammie Ivy, supt. Fax 873-6114
www.southdelta.k12.ms.us/
South Delta HS 300/9-12
303 Parkway Ave 39159 662-873-4308
Eddwin Smith, prin. Fax 873-6106
South Delta Vocational S Vo/Tech
285 Maple St 39159 662-873-2029
Beverly Wilson, prin. Fax 873-4194
Other Schools – See Anguilla

Sharkey Issaquena Academy 200/K-12
272 Academy Dr 39159 662-873-4241

Rosedale, Bolivar, Pop. 1,864
West Bolivar SD 1,500/PK-12
PO Box 189 38769 662-759-3525
James Waldington, supt. Fax 759-6795
wbcsdk12.org
Barnes Vocational Center Vo/Tech
PO Box 160 38769 662-759-3791
Kandice Jernigan, dir. Fax 759-6795
West Bolivar HS 200/9-12
PO Box 398 38769 662-759-3346
Joseph Griffin, prin. Fax 759-0039
West Bolivar MS 200/5-8
PO Box 159 38769 662-759-3743
Dr. Nehru Brown, prin. Fax 759-6795
Other Schools – See Benoit, Shaw

Ruleville, Sunflower, Pop. 2,980
Sunflower County Consolidated SD
Supt. — See Indianola
Ruleville MS 200/6-8
250 Oscar St 38771 662-756-4698
Tommy Molden, prin. Fax 756-4902

Sallis, Attala, Pop. 134
Attala County SD
Supt. — See Kosciusko
Mc Adams JSHS 200/7-12
6315 Attala Road 4167 39160 662-289-3838
Jackie Sandifer, prin. Fax 289-7181

Saltillo, Lee, Pop. 4,701
Lee County SD
Supt. — See Tupelo
Saltillo HS 1,000/9-12
PO Box 460 38866 662-869-5466
Tim DeVaughn, prin. Fax 869-7229

Sandhill, Rankin
Rankin County SD
Supt. — See Brandon
Pisgah HS 400/7-12
PO Box 70 39161 601-829-2825
Craig Yates, prin. Fax 829-1753

Sarah, Tate
Tate County SD
Supt. — See Coldwater
Strayhorn HS 400/7-12
86 Mustang Dr 38665 662-562-9246
Aundrea Taylor, prin. Fax 562-9249

Sardis, Panola, Pop. 1,686
North Panola SD 1,500/PK-12
470 Highway 51 N 38666 662-487-2305
Cedric Richardson, supt. Fax 487-2050
www.northpanolaschools.org
North Panola HS 400/9-12
500 Highway 51 N 38666 662-487-1070
Braxton Stowe, prin. Fax 487-2052
Other Schools – See Como

Scooba, Kemper, Pop. 727

East Mississippi Community College Post-Sec.
PO Box 158 39358 662-476-8442

Sebastopol, Scott, Pop. 272
Scott County SD
Supt. — See Forest
Sebastopol Attendance Center 600/K-12
PO Box 86 39359 601-625-8654
Kaleb Smith, prin. Fax 625-9426

Seminary, Covington, Pop. 314
Covington County SD
Supt. — See Collins
Seminary HS 400/9-12
PO Box 34 39479 601-722-3220
Jonathan Chancelor, prin. Fax 722-9543
Seminary MS 400/5-8
PO Box 34 39479 601-722-4510
Caprice Smalley, prin. Fax 722-0232

Senatobia, Tate, Pop. 8,076
Senatobia Municipal SD 1,800/K-12
104 McKie St 38668 662-562-4897
Jay Foster, supt. Fax 562-4996
www.senatobiaschools.com
Senatobia JSHS 700/7-12
221 Warrior Dr 38668 662-562-4230
Ben Stigler, prin. Fax 562-6659
Tate County Career Technical Center Vo/Tech
403 W Gilmore St 38668 662-562-5193
Fax 562-4996

Infinity Career College Post-Sec.
562 W Main St Ste B 38668 662-562-8010
Magnolia Heights S 600/PK-12
1 Chiefs Dr 38668 662-562-4491
Dr. Marvin Lishman Ph.D., admin. Fax 562-0386
Northwest Mississippi Community College Post-Sec.
4975 Highway 51 N 38668 662-562-3200

Shannon, Lee, Pop. 1,726
Lee County SD
Supt. — See Tupelo
Shannon HS 500/9-12
PO Box 8 38868 662-767-9566
Bill Rosenthal, prin. Fax 767-2847
Shannon MS 300/6-8
PO Box 349 38868 662-767-3986
Barry Woods, prin. Fax 767-9981

Shaw, Bolivar, Pop. 1,947
West Bolivar SD
Supt. — See Rosedale
Shaw HS 200/9-12
PO Box 510 38773 662-754-2611
L'Kenna Whitehead, prin. Fax 754-4418

Shelby, Bolivar, Pop. 2,225
North Bolivar Consolidated SD
Supt. — See Mound Bayou
Broad Street HS 200/9-12
PO Box 149 38774 662-398-4040
Ramona Myles, prin. Fax 398-5900
Shelby MS 200/5-8
PO Box 28 38774 662-398-4020
Sonya DeBose, prin. Fax 398-4039

Smithville, Monroe, Pop. 930
Monroe County SD
Supt. — See Amory
Smithville S 600/K-12
60017 Highway 23 38870 662-651-4276
Chad O'Brian, prin. Fax 651-4163

Southaven, DeSoto, Pop. 48,244
DeSoto County SD
Supt. — See Hernando
Desoto Central HS 1,600/9-12
2911 Central Pkwy 38672 662-536-3612
Cliff Johnston, prin. Fax 536-3622
Desoto Central MS 1,200/6-8
2611 Central Pkwy 38672 662-349-6660
Duane Case, prin. Fax 349-1045
Southaven HS 1,900/9-12
735 Rasco Rd W 38671 662-393-9300
Shane Jones, prin. Fax 996-1574
Southaven MS 1,600/6-8
899 Rasco Rd W 38671 662-280-0422
Levi Williams, prin. Fax 280-3613

Northpoint Christian S 1,100/PK-12
7400 Getwell Rd 38672 662-349-3096
David Manley, pres. Fax 349-4962

Starkville, Oktibbeha, Pop. 23,580
Starkville-Oktibbeha SD 3,900/K-12
401 Greensboro St 39759 662-324-4050
Dr. Lewis Holloway, supt. Fax 324-4068
www.starkvillesd.com
Armstrong MS 1,000/6-8
303 McKee St 39759 662-324-4070
Timothy Bourne, prin. Fax 324-4075
Millsaps Career & Tech Center Vo/Tech
803 Louisville St 39759 662-324-4170
Dr. Lenora Hogan, dir. Fax 324-4103
Overstreet S Alt
307 S Jackson St 39759 662-324-4090
Lisa Thompson, dir. Fax 324-4162
Starkville HS 1,200/9-12
603 Yellow Jacket Dr 39759 662-324-4130
Sean McDonnall, prin. Fax 324-4128

Starkville Academy 700/PK-12
505 Academy Rd 39759 662-323-7814
Jeremy Nicholas, head sch Fax 323-5480
Starkville Christian S 200/PK-12
303 Lynn Ln 39759 662-323-7453
Rev. Randall Witbeck, prin. Fax 323-7571

Steens, Lowndes

Columbus Christian Academy 300/PK-12
6405 Military Rd 39766 662-328-7888
Terry Walters, prin. Fax 328-7750

Stringer, Jasper
West Jasper Consolidated SD
Supt. — See Bay Springs
Stringer S 600/K-12
PO Box 1068 39481 601-428-5508
Jay Arrington, prin. Fax 426-6760

Summit, Pike, Pop. 1,702
North Pike SD 2,400/K-12
1036 Jaguar Trl 39666 601-276-2216
Dennis Penton, supt. Fax 276-3666
npsd.k12.ms.us/
North Pike HS 700/9-12
1022 Jaguar Trl 39666 601-276-2175
Scott Hallmark, prin. Fax 276-2720
North Pike MS 800/5-8
2034 Highway 44 NE 39666 601-684-3283
Allen Barron, prin. Fax 684-3269

Southwest Mississippi Community College Post-Sec.
1156 College Dr 39666 601-276-2000

Sumner, Tallahatchie, Pop. 316
West Tallahatchie SD
Supt. — See Webb
North Delta Alternative S Alt
300 Jennings St 38957 662-375-8392
Sherry T. Ellington, prin. Fax 375-0069

Sumrall, Lamar, Pop. 1,412
Lamar County SD
Supt. — See Purvis
Sumrall HS 500/9-12
PO Box 187 39482 601-758-4730
Sheila Kribbs, prin. Fax 758-0512
Sumrall MS 400/6-8
1217 Highway 42 39482 601-758-4416
Terry Smith, prin. Fax 758-4148

Taylorsville, Smith, Pop. 1,344
Smith County SD
Supt. — See Raleigh
Taylorsville HS 400/6-12
PO Box 8 39168 601-785-6942
Jeff Duvall, prin. Fax 785-9711

Tchula, Holmes, Pop. 2,088
Holmes County SD
Supt. — See Lexington
Holmes County Learning Center Alt
PO Box 387 39169 662-235-5637
Fax 235-5639

Terry, Hinds, Pop. 1,052
Hinds County SD
Supt. — See Raymond
Byram MS 1,000/6-8
2009 Byram Bulldog Blvd 39170 601-372-4597
Benjamin Lundy, prin. Fax 346-2383
Terry HS 1,300/9-12
235 W Beasley St 39170 601-878-5905
Roy Balentine, prin. Fax 878-2782

Tiplersville, Tippah
North Tippah SD 1,300/K-12
PO Box 65 38674 662-223-4384
Junior Wooten, supt. Fax 223-5379
www.ntippah.k12.ms.us
Other Schools – See Falkner, Walnut

Tishomingo, Tishomingo, Pop. 335
Tishomingo County Special Municipal SD
Supt. — See Iuka
Tishomingo County Alternative S Alt
1419 Highway 25 38873 662-438-6864
Fax 438-7115
Tishomingo County Vocational Center Vo/Tech
PO Box 890, 662-438-6689
John Taylor, dir. Fax 438-6777

Tougaloo, Hinds

Tougaloo College Post-Sec.
500 W County Line Rd 39174 601-977-7700

Tremont, Itawamba, Pop. 462
Itawamba County SD
Supt. — See Fulton
Tremont Attendance Center 300/K-12
320 School Loop Dr 38876 662-652-3391
Dawn Rogers, prin. Fax 652-3994

Tunica, Tunica, Pop. 1,021
Tunica County SD 2,400/PK-12
PO Box 758 38676 662-363-2811
Dr. Margie Pulley, supt. Fax 363-3061
www.tunicak12.org
Rosa Fort HS 600/9-12
PO Box 997 38676 662-363-1343
Valarie Davis, prin. Fax 363-4222
TCS Alternative S Alt
PO Box 997 38676 662-363-1343
Willie Bolden, prin. Fax 363-4222
Tunica MS 500/6-8
PO Box 967 38676 662-363-4224
Angela Ellington, prin. Fax 357-1058
Williams Career and Technical Ctr Vo/Tech
PO Box 2618 38676 662-363-2051
Dianne Daley, dir. Fax 363-2052

Tunica Academy 200/PK-12
PO Box 966 38676 662-363-1051

Tupelo, Lee, Pop. 34,140
Lee County SD 7,100/K-12
PO Box 832 38802 662-841-9144
Jimmy Weeks, supt. Fax 680-6012
www.leecountyschools.us/
Other Schools – See Belden, Guntown, Mooreville, Plantersville, Saltillo, Shannon

Tupelo SD 7,200/PK-12
PO Box 557 38802 662-841-8850
Dr. Gearl Loden, supt. Fax 841-8887
www.tupeloschools.com/
Tupelo HS 2,000/9-12
4125 Golden Wave Dr 38801 662-841-8970
Jason Harris, prin. Fax 841-8987
Tupelo MS 1,100/7-8
1009 Varsity Dr 38801 662-840-8780
Dr. Brock English, prin. Fax 840-1831

Creations College of Cosmetology Post-Sec.
PO Box 2635 38803 662-844-9264
North Mississippi Medical Center Post-Sec.
830 S Gloster St 38801 662-841-3136

Tylertown, Walthall, Pop. 1,598
Walthall County SD 1,900/K-12
814 Morse Ave 39667 601-876-3401
Wade Carney, supt. Fax 876-6982
www.wcsd.k12.ms.us
Dexter S 200/K-12
927 Highway 48 E 39667 601-876-3985
Allen Dyess, prin. Fax 876-5410
Salem S 500/K-12
881 Highway 27 N 39667 601-876-2580
Charles Boyd, prin. Fax 876-4155
Tylertown JSHS 700/7-12
204 High School Rd 39667 601-876-3370
Dr. Ronald Morgan, prin. Fax 876-3122
Walthall County Career & Tech Center Vo/Tech
803 Ball Ave 39667 601-222-1500
Elizabeth Cowart, dir. Fax 222-1506

Union, Newton, Pop. 1,954
Union SD 1,000/PK-12
PO Box 445 39365 601-774-9579
Lundy Brantley, supt. Fax 774-0600
www.unioncity.k12.ms.us/
Union HS 300/9-12
101 Forest St 39365 601-774-8257
Brett Rigby, prin. Fax 774-9600
Union MS 300/5-8
115 James St 39365 601-774-5303
Tyler Hansford, prin. Fax 774-9607

University, Lafayette, Pop. 4,155

University of Mississippi Post-Sec.
PO Box 1848 38677 662-915-7211

Vancleave, Jackson, Pop. 5,787
Jackson County SD 9,300/K-12
PO Box 5069 39565 228-826-1757
Dr. Barry Amacker, supt. Fax 826-3393
www.jcsd.k12.ms.us/
Jackson County Technology Center Vo/Tech
12425 Highway 57 39565 228-826-5944
Dr. Jerry Morgan, dir. Fax 826-4209
Vancleave HS 700/9-12
12424 Highway 57 39565 228-826-4701
John Mundy, prin. Fax 826-5066
Vancleave MS 600/6-8
4725 Bull Dog Ln 39565 228-826-5902
Rhett Ladner, prin. Fax 826-1421
Other Schools – See Moss Point, Ocean Springs

Vardaman, Calhoun, Pop. 1,309
Calhoun County SD
Supt. — See Pittsboro

Vardaman HS 300/7-12
106 WB Gregg Dr 38878 662-682-7574
Porter Casey, prin. Fax 682-7743

Vicksburg, Warren, Pop. 23,676
Vicksburg Warren SD 8,200/PK-12
1500 Mission 66 39180 601-638-5122
Chad Shealy, supt. Fax 631-2819
www.vwsd.k12.ms.us/
Academy of Innovation 7-8
1315 Grove St 39183 601-636-2539
Jason McKellar, prin. Fax 631-2856
River City Early College 9-12
755 Hwy 27 S 39180 601-636-2914
Tammy Burris, prin.
Vicksburg HS 1,000/9-12
3701 Drummond St 39180 601-636-2914
Deowarski McDonald, prin. Fax 631-2885
Vicksburg JHS 600/7-8
1533 Baldwin Ferry Rd 39180 601-636-1966
LeAndrew Drake, prin. Fax 631-2830
Warren Central HS 1,200/9-12
1000 Highway 27 39180 601-638-3372
Eric Green, prin. Fax 631-2937
Warren Central JHS 700/7-8
1630 Baldwin Ferry Rd 39180 601-638-3981
Dr. Cedric Magee, prin. Fax 631-2839

Porters Chapel Academy 200/K-12
3460 Porters Chapel Rd 39180 601-638-3733
Vicksburg Catholic S - St. Aloysius 300/7-12
1900 Grove St 39183 601-636-2256
Dr. Buddy Strickland, prin. Fax 631-0430

Victoria, Marshall

Friendship Christian Academy PK-12
184 Friendship Rd 38679 662-838-4000
Brenda Scherff B.S., admin. Fax 838-4001

Walnut, Tippah, Pop. 762
North Tippah SD
Supt. — See Tiplersville
Walnut S 500/K-12
280 Commerce Ave 38683 662-223-6471
Joe McCoy, prin. Fax 223-5275

Walnut Grove, Leake, Pop. 1,907
Leake County SD
Supt. — See Carthage
Leake County HS 300/7-12
PO Box 159 39189 601-253-2393
Sammie McLaurin, prin. Fax 253-0100

Water Valley, Yalobusha, Pop. 3,370
Water Valley SD 1,200/K-12
PO Box 788 38965 662-473-1203
Dr. Michael McInnis, supt. Fax 473-1225
www.wvsd.k12.ms.us
Water Valley JSHS 500/7-12
PO Box 647 38965 662-473-2468
Drew Pitcock, prin. Fax 473-1444

Waynesboro, Wayne, Pop. 4,998
Wayne County SD 3,300/K-12
810 Chickasawhay St 39367 601-735-4871
Bobby Jones, supt. Fax 735-4872
www.wayne.k12.ms.us
Wayne County Career and Technical Center Vo/Tech
800 Collins St 39367 601-735-5036
Bobby Jones, prin. Fax 735-6326
Wayne County HS 1,000/9-12
1325 Azalea Dr 39367 601-735-2851
Dr. Cathy Davis, prin. Fax 735-1389
Waynesboro MS 500/5-8
155 Wayne St 39367 601-735-3159
Shronda Turner, prin. Fax 735-6316

Wayne Academy 300/K-12
46 Joe Jordan Dr 39367 601-735-2921

Webb, Tallahatchie, Pop. 557
West Tallahatchie SD 800/K-12
PO Box 129 38966 662-375-9291
Christopher Furdge, supt. Fax 375-9294
www.wtsd.k12.ms.us
West Tallahatchie HS 300/7-12
PO Box 130 38966 662-375-8829
Robert Skipper, prin. Fax 375-7402
Other Schools – See Sumner

Wesson, Copiah, Pop. 1,907
Copiah County SD
Supt. — See Hazlehurst
Wesson S 1,100/K-12
1048 Grove St 39191 601-643-2221
Marilyn Phillips, prin. Fax 643-2458

Copiah-Lincoln Community College Post-Sec.
PO Box 649 39191 601-643-5101

West Point, Clay, Pop. 11,257
West Point SD 3,300/K-12
PO Box 656 39773 662-494-4242
Burnell McDonald, supt. Fax 494-8605
www.westpoint.k12.ms.us/
Fifth Street JHS 500/7-8
418 5th St 39773 662-494-2191
Richard Bryant, prin. Fax 494-2432
West Point Career and Technology Center Vo/Tech
1253 E Church Hill Rd 39773 662-494-6176
Fax 495-2426
West Point HS 900/9-12
90 S Eshman Ave 39773 662-494-5083
Jermaine Taylor, prin. Fax 494-0969

Gibson's Barber & Beauty College Post-Sec.
PO Box 990 39773 662-494-5444
Oak Hill Academy 400/PK-12
1682 N Eshman Ave 39773 662-494-5043
Dr. Cathy Davis, hdmstr. Fax 494-0487

Wheeler, Prentiss
Prentiss County SD
Supt. — See Booneville
Wheeler S 500/K-12
318 County Road 5011 38880 662-365-2629
Todd Swinney, prin. Fax 365-2535

Wiggins, Stone, Pop. 4,345
Stone County SD 2,600/K-12
214 Critz St N 39577 601-928-7247
Inita Owen, supt. Fax 928-5122
www.stone.k12.ms.us
Stone HS 700/9-12
400 Border Ave E 39577 601-928-5492
Adam Stone, prin. Fax 928-6874
Stone MS 700/6-8
532 Central Ave E 39577 601-928-4876
Leslie Cudd, prin. Fax 928-6440

Winona, Montgomery, Pop. 5,020
Montgomery County SD 300/K-12
PO Box 687 38967 662-283-4533
Michael Hood, supt. Fax 283-4584
www.mcsdms.net
Other Schools – See Kilmichael

Winona SD 1,100/PK-12
218 Fairground St 38967 662-283-3731
Dr. Teresa Jackson, supt. Fax 283-1003
www.winonaschools.net
Winona Career and Technical Center Vo/Tech
300 N Applegate St 38967 662-283-3601
Lance VanHorn, prin. Fax 283-9807
Winona HS 500/7-12
301 Fairground St 38967 662-283-1244
Charlie Parkerson, prin. Fax 283-4267

Winona Christian S 300/PK-12
1014 S Applegate St 38967 662-283-1169

Woodville, Wilkinson, Pop. 1,088
Wilkinson County SD 1,300/PK-12
PO Box 785 39669 601-888-3582
Kimberly Jackson, supt. Fax 888-3133
wilkinsoncounty.schoolinsites.com/
King Vocational Complex Vo/Tech
PO Box 1193 39669 601-888-4394
Derek Morgan, dir. Fax 888-3936
Wilkinson County HS 300/9-12
522 Pinckneyville Rd 39669 601-888-4228
Edward Reed, prin. Fax 888-4736
Other Schools – See Centreville

Wilkinson County Christian Academy 300/K-12
2420 US Highway 61 S 39669 601-888-4313

Yazoo City, Yazoo, Pop. 11,345
Yazoo City Municipal SD 2,200/PK-12
1133 Calhoun Ave 39194 662-746-2125
Dr. Darron Edwards, supt. Fax 746-9210
www.yazoocity.k12.ms.us/
Summers Vocational Center Vo/Tech
1825 Dr Martin Luther King 39194 662-746-7642
Terri Felton, dir. Fax 746-0991
Woolfolk MS 500/5-8
209 E Fifth St 39194 662-746-2904
Torrey Hampton Ed.D., prin. Fax 746-8609
Yazoo City Alternative S Alt
1318 Grand Ave 39194 662-746-0985
Ethel Luckett, prin.
Yazoo City HS 600/9-12
1825 Dr Martin Luther King 39194 662-746-2378
Michael Johnson, prin. Fax 746-3779

Yazoo County SD 1,700/K-12
94 Panther Dr 39194 662-746-4672
Rebecca Fisher, supt. Fax 746-9270
www.yazoo.k12.ms.us
Yazoo County HS 500/9-12
191 Panther Dr 39194 662-746-1492
Jana Bardwell, prin. Fax 746-1593
Yazoo County MS 400/6-8
116 Panther Dr 39194 662-746-1596
Virginia Ables, prin. Fax 746-1616

Manchester Academy 400/PK-12
2132 Gordon Ave 39194 662-746-5913

MISSOURI

MISSOURI DEPARTMENT OF EDUCATION
PO Box 480, Jefferson City 65102-0480
Telephone 573-751-4212
Fax 573-751-1179
Website http://www.dese.mo.gov

Commissioner of Education Dr. Margie Vandeven

MISSOURI BOARD OF EDUCATION
PO Box 480, Jefferson City 65102-0480

President Charles Shields

PUBLIC, PRIVATE AND CATHOLIC SECONDARY SCHOOLS

Adrian, Bates, Pop. 1,663
Adrian R-III SD 700/PK-12
PO Box 98 64720 816-297-2710
Don Lile, supt. Fax 297-2980
www.adrian.k12.mo.us
Adrian JSHS 400/6-12
PO Box 98 64720 816-297-4460
Abe Lewis, prin. Fax 297-4598

Advance, Stoddard, Pop. 1,340
Advance R-IV SD 400/PK-12
201 E School St 63730 573-722-3581
Shannon Garner, supt. Fax 722-9886
www.advance.k12.mo.us
Advance JSHS 200/7-12
201 E School St 63730 573-722-3584
Gena Sitton, prin. Fax 722-5479

Albany, Gentry, Pop. 1,720
Albany R-III SD 500/PK-12
101 W Jefferson St 64402 660-726-3911
Erin Oligschlaeger, supt. Fax 726-5841
www.albany.k12.mo.us
Albany HS 100/9-12
101 W Jefferson St 64402 660-726-3912
Sarah Barmann-Smith, prin. Fax 726-5841
Albany MS 100/6-8
101 W Jefferson St 64402 660-726-3912
Sarah Barmann-Smith, prin. Fax 726-5841

Alma, Lafayette, Pop. 395
Santa Fe R-X SD 400/K-12
PO Box 197 64001 660-674-2238
Derek Lark, supt. Fax 674-2239
santafechiefs.k12.mo.us
Santa Fe HS 200/7-12
PO Box 197 64001 660-674-2236
Tom Burton, prin. Fax 674-2760

Alton, Oregon, Pop. 847
Alton R-IV SD 700/K-12
RR 2 Box 2180 65606 417-778-7216
Dr. Eric Allen, supt. Fax 778-6394
www.alton.k12.mo.us/
Alton HS 300/7-12
RR 2 Box 2180 65606 417-778-7215
Joby Steele, prin. Fax 778-7851

Amoret, Bates, Pop. 185
Miami R-I SD 200/K-12
7638 NW State Route J 64722 660-267-3480
Dr. Steven Beckett, supt. Fax 267-3630
www.miamir1.net
Miami JSHS 100/7-12
7638 NW State Route J 64722 660-267-3484
Dr. Daniel Johnson, prin. Fax 267-3630

Anderson, McDonald, Pop. 1,900
McDonald County R-I SD 3,800/PK-12
100 Mustang Dr 64831 417-845-3321
Dr. Mark Stanton, supt. Fax 845-6972
mcdonaldr1.net
Anderson MS 200/7-8
135 Mustang Dr 64831 417-845-1805
Ken Anders, prin. Fax 845-7406
McDonald County HS 1,100/9-12
100 Mustang Dr 64831 417-845-3322
Greg Leach, prin. Fax 845-8467
Other Schools – See Noel, Pineville

Annapolis, Iron, Pop. 343
South Iron R-I SD 300/PK-12
210 School St 63620 573-598-4241
Donald Wakefield, supt. Fax 598-4210
www.sipanthers.k12.mo.us
South Iron JSHS 100/7-12
210 School St 63620 573-598-4241
Joseph Jackson, prin. Fax 598-4210

Appleton City, Saint Clair, Pop. 1,108
Appleton City R-II SD 300/PK-12
408 W 4th St 64724 660-476-2161
Ryan Middleton Ed.D., supt. Fax 476-5564
www.appletoncity.k12.mo.us
Appleton City HS 200/6-12
408 W 4th St 64724 660-476-2118
James Gurney, prin. Fax 476-5564

Archie, Cass, Pop. 1,157
Archie R-V SD 500/PK-12
302 W State Route A 64725 816-293-5312
Jeffrey Kramer, supt. Fax 293-5712
www.archie.k12.mo.us
Archie JSHS 300/6-12
302 W State Route A 64725 816-293-5312
Coy Dalton, prin. Fax 293-5712

Arnold, Jefferson, Pop. 20,546
Fox C-6 SD 11,700/PK-12
745 Jeffco Blvd 63010 636-296-8000
Dr. Jim Wipke, supt. Fax 282-5170
www.fox.k12.mo.us
Fox HS 1,800/9-12
751 Jeffco Blvd 63010 636-296-5210
Dr. Ryan Sherp, prin. Fax 282-6980
Fox MS 500/7-8
743 Jeffco Blvd 63010 636-296-5077
Aaron Wilken, prin. Fax 282-5171
Ridgewood MS 500/7-8
1401 Ridgewood School Rd 63010 636-282-1459
Jamie Cavato, prin. Fax 282-5193
Other Schools – See Barnhart, Imperial

Metro Business College Post-Sec.
2132 Tenbrook Rd 63010 636-296-9300

Ash Grove, Greene, Pop. 1,452
Ash Grove R-IV SD 700/PK-12
100 N Maple Ln 65604 417-751-2534
Dr. Aaron Gerla, supt. Fax 751-2283
www.ashgrove.k12.mo.us
Ash Grove JSHS 400/7-12
100 N Maple Ln 65604 417-751-2330
Christopher Thompson, prin. Fax 751-2889

Ashland, Boone, Pop. 3,660
Southern Boone County R-I SD 1,600/PK-12
PO Box 168 65010 573-657-2147
Christopher Felmlee, supt. Fax 657-5513
ashland.k12.mo.us
Southern Boone County HS 500/9-12
PO Box 168 65010 573-657-2144
Dale Van Deven, prin. Fax 657-9035
Southern Boone County MS 400/6-8
PO Box 168 65010 573-657-2146
Kevin Kiley, prin. Fax 657-5519

Atlanta, Macon, Pop. 377
Atlanta C-3 SD 200/K-12
600 S Atterberry St 63530 660-239-4212
William Perkins, supt. Fax 239-4205
www.atlanta.k12.mo.us/
Atlanta JSHS 100/7-12
600 S Atterberry St 63530 660-239-4211
Josh Brummit, prin. Fax 239-4205

Aurora, Lawrence, Pop. 7,398
Aurora R-VIII SD 2,100/PK-12
201 S Madison Ave 65605 417-678-3373
Dr. Travis Shaw, supt. Fax 678-4043
www.aurorar8.org
Aurora HS 600/9-12
305 W Prospect St 65605 417-678-3355
Patrick Rapert, prin. Fax 678-2905
Aurora JHS 400/7-8
500 W Olive St 65605 417-678-3630
Dr. Allison Murphy-Pope, prin. Fax 678-2487

Ava, Douglas, Pop. 2,954
Ava R-I SD 1,400/PK-12
PO Box 338 65608 417-683-4717
Dr. Jason Dial, supt. Fax 683-6329
www.avaschools.k12.mo.us/
Ava HS 400/9-12
PO Box 338 65608 417-683-5747
Teresa Nash, prin. Fax 683-2306
Ava MS 400/5-8
PO Box 338 65608 417-683-3835
Marcella Swatosh, prin. Fax 683-9101

Bakersfield, Ozark, Pop. 240
Bakersfield R-IV SD 400/PK-12
PO Box 38 65609 417-284-7333
Dr. Amy Britt, supt. Fax 284-7335
www.bakersfield.k12.mo.us
Bakersfield JSHS 200/6-12
PO Box 38 65609 417-284-7333
Doyne Byrd, prin. Fax 284-7335

Ballwin, Saint Louis, Pop. 29,903
Parkway C-2 SD
Supt. — See Chesterfield
Parkway South HS 1,700/9-12
801 Hanna Rd 63021 314-415-7700
Dr. Patrice Aitch, prin. Fax 415-7712
Parkway West HS 1,200/9-12
14653 Clayton Rd 63011 314-415-7500
Dr. Jeremy Mitchell, prin. Fax 415-7534

Rockwood R-VI SD
Supt. — See Eureka
Lafayette HS 2,000/9-12
17050 Clayton Rd 63011 636-733-4100
Dr. John Shaughnessy, prin. Fax 458-7219
Selvidge MS 700/6-8
235 New Ballwin Rd 63021 636-207-2622
Dr. Michael Anselmo, prin. Fax 207-2632

Al-Salam Day S 300/PK-12
519 Weidman Rd 63011 636-394-8986
Dr. Abdul-Mun'im Jitmoud Ed.D., prin. Fax 207-8549
Grabber School of Hair Design Post-Sec.
14557 Manchester Rd 63011 636-227-4440

Barnard, Nodaway, Pop. 221
South Nodaway County R-IV SD 200/PK-12
209 Morehouse St 64423 660-652-3221
Johnnie Silkett, supt. Fax 652-3411
www.southnodaway.k12.mo.us
South Nodaway JSHS 100/7-12
209 Morehouse St 64423 660-652-3727
Fax 652-3411

Barnhart, Jefferson, Pop. 5,631
Fox C-6 SD
Supt. — See Arnold
Antonia MS 400/6-8
6798 Saint Lukes Church Rd 63012 636-282-6970
Joe Willis, prin. Fax 282-6971

Bell City, Stoddard, Pop. 438
Bell City R-II SD 200/K-12
25254 Walnut St 63735 573-733-4444
Matthew Asher, supt. Fax 733-4114
www.bellcity.k12.mo.us/
Bell City JSHS 100/7-12
25254 Walnut St 63735 573-733-4444
Lincoln Scherer, prin. Fax 733-4114

Belle, Maries, Pop. 1,518
Maries County R-II SD 800/K-12
PO Box 819 65013 573-859-3800
Dr. Patrick Call, supt. Fax 859-3883
www.mariesr2.org
Belle HS 200/9-12
PO Box 819 65013 573-859-6114
Danielle Tuepker, prin. Fax 859-6122
Other Schools – See Bland

Belton, Cass, Pop. 22,497
Belton SD 124 4,700/PK-12
110 W Walnut St 64012 816-489-7000
Dr. Andrew Underwood, supt. Fax 489-7005
www.beltonschools.org
Belton HS 1,000/10-12
801 W North Ave 64012 816-489-7500
Phil Clark, prin. Fax 489-7505
Belton MS/Freshman Center 700/7-9
107 Pirate Pkwy 64012 816-348-1040
Dr. Jean Selby, prin. Fax 348-1595

Heartland Christian S 100/PK-12
810 S Cedar St 64012 816-331-1000
Claire Baker, prin. Fax 322-2782

Benton, Scott, Pop. 855
Scott County R-IV SD 1,000/PK-12
4035 State Highway 77 63736 573-545-3541
Fara Jones, supt. Fax 545-3929
sites.google.com/a/kellyhawks.org/kellyhawks
Kelly HS 300/9-12
4035 State Highway 77 63736 573-545-3541
Dan Hecht, prin. Fax 545-4485
Scott County MS 200/6-8
4035 State Highway 77 63736 573-545-3541
Kari Bickings, prin. Fax 545-4386

Berkeley, Saint Louis, Pop. 8,830
Ferguson-Florissant R-II SD
Supt. — See Florissant
Berkeley MS 300/6-8
8300 Frost Ave 63134 314-524-3883
Demetrius Adams, prin. Fax 524-3885

Vatterott College - NorthPark Post-Sec.
8580 Evans Ave 63134 314-264-1000

Bernie, Stoddard, Pop. 1,930
Bernie R-XIII SD 500/PK-12
516 W Main Ave 63822 573-293-5333
Dustin Hicks, supt. Fax 293-5731
www.bernie.k12.mo.us
Bernie JSHS 200/7-12
516 W Main Ave 63822 573-293-5334
Lucas McKinnis, prin. Fax 293-5334

Bethany, Harrison, Pop. 3,262
South Harrison County R-II SD 700/PK-12
PO Box 445 64424 660-425-8044
Dennis Eastin, supt. Fax 425-7050
www.shr2.k12.mo.us
North Central Career Center Vo/Tech
PO Box 445 64424 660-425-2196
Erik Coffey, dir. Fax 425-2197
South Harrison County R-II HS 200/9-12
PO Box 445 64424 660-425-8051
Mark Forster, prin. Fax 425-7447
South Harrison County R-II MS 6-8
PO Box 445 64424 660-425-7467
Shane Jones, prin. Fax 425-7469

Bevier, Macon, Pop. 711
Bevier C-4 SD 200/K-12
400 Bloomington St 63532 660-773-6611
Joan Patrick, supt. Fax 773-6955
bevierc-4.com
Bevier HS 100/9-12
400 Bloomington St 63532 660-773-5213
Jason Martie, prin. Fax 773-6964

Billings, Christian, Pop. 1,023
Billings R-IV SD 400/PK-12
118 W Mount Vernon Rd 65610 417-744-2623
Cynthia Brandt, supt. Fax 744-4545
www.billings.k12.mo.us
Billings HS 200/7-12
118 W Mount Vernon Rd 65610 417-744-2551
Jennifer Wilson, prin. Fax 744-4545

Bismarck, Saint Francois, Pop. 1,531
Bismarck R-V SD 500/PK-12
PO Box 257 63624 573-734-6111
Charles Hasty, supt. Fax 734-2957
www.bismarckr5.org
Bismarck JSHS 200/6-12
PO Box 257 63624 573-734-6111
Jason King, prin. Fax 734-2957

Black, Reynolds
Lesterville R-IV SD
Supt. — See Lesterville
Lesterville Ranch Campus 50/Alt
525 County Road 816 63625 573-269-4207
Mary Balderas, prin. Fax 269-4277

Bland, Gasconade, Pop. 534
Maries County R-II SD
Supt. — See Belle
Maries County MS 300/5-8
PO Box 10 65014 573-646-3912
Kristin Williams, prin. Fax 646-3148

Bloomfield, Stoddard, Pop. 1,925
Bloomfield R-XIV SD 700/PK-12
505 Court St 63825 573-568-4564
Toni Hill, supt. Fax 568-4565
www.bps14.org
Bloomfield HS 200/9-12
505 Court St 63825 573-568-2146
Jason Karnes, prin. Fax 568-2147
Bloomfield MS 200/6-8
505 Court St 63825 573-568-4283
Louis Bell, prin. Fax 568-4286

Blue Eye, Stone, Pop. 163
Blue Eye R-V SD 700/PK-12
PO Box 105 65611 417-779-5332
Dan Ray, supt. Fax 779-2151
www.blueeye.k12.mo.us
Blue Eye HS 200/9-12
PO Box 105 65611 417-779-5331
Ben Johnson, prin. Fax 779-2151
Blue Eye MS 200/5-8
PO Box 105 65611 417-779-4299
Roger Cavener, prin. Fax 779-4526

Blue Springs, Jackson, Pop. 51,123
Blue Springs R-IV SD 14,400/K-12
1801 NW Vesper St 64015 816-224-1300
Dr. James Finley, supt. Fax 224-1310
www.bssd.net
Blue Springs Freshman Center 1,200/9-9
2103 NW Vesper St 64015 816-874-3440
Brandon Martin, prin. Fax 224-1344
Blue Springs HS 1,800/10-12
2000 NW Ashton Dr 64015 816-874-3400
Robert Jerome, prin. Fax 229-1025
Blue Springs South HS 1,500/10-12
1200 SE Adams Dairy Pkwy 64014 816-874-3500
Dr. Charles Belt, prin. Fax 224-1324
Brittany Hill MS 900/6-8
2701 NW 1st St 64014 816-874-3470
Dallas Truex, prin. Fax 224-1704
Kinder MS 800/6-8
3930 S R D Mize Rd 64015 816-874-3560
Steve Goddard, prin. Fax 224-1309
Moreland Ridge MS 1,000/6-8
900 SW Bishop Dr 64015 816-874-3540
Kevin Grover, prin. Fax 224-1805
Valley View HS Alt
5000 NW Valley View Rd 64015 816-874-3750
Charles Weber, prin. Fax 224-1374
Other Schools – See Lees Summit

House of Heavilin Beauty College Post-Sec.
2000 SW State Route 7 64014 816-229-9000
Plaza Heights Christian Academy 200/PK-12
1500 SW Clark Rd 64015 816-228-0670
Chuck Lawson, admin. Fax 229-4092

Bolivar, Polk, Pop. 10,153
Bolivar R-I SD 2,800/PK-12
524 W Madison St 65613 417-326-5291
Dr. Jason Dial, supt. Fax 326-3562
www.bolivarschools.org
Bolivar HS 800/9-12
1401 Highway D 65613 417-326-5228
Dr. David Geurin, prin. Fax 326-4325
Bolivar MS 600/6-8
604 W Jackson St 65613 417-326-3811
Dr. Tim Garber, prin. Fax 326-8277

Bolivar Technical College Post-Sec.
2001 W Broadway St Ste 2 65613 417-777-5062
Southwest Baptist University Post-Sec.
1600 University Ave 65613 417-328-5281

Bonne Terre, Saint Francois, Pop. 6,797
North St. Francois County R-I SD 3,200/PK-12
300 Berry Rd 63628 573-431-3300
Dr. Yancy Poorman, supt. Fax 358-2377
www.ncsd.k12.mo.us/
North County HS 900/9-12
7151 Raider Rd 63628 573-431-3300
Lance Sprenkel, prin. Fax 358-0021
Unitec Career Center Vo/Tech
7163 Raider Rd 63628 573-358-2271
Larry Kekec, dir. Fax 358-3577
Other Schools – See Desloge

Boonville, Cooper, Pop. 8,135
Boonville R-I SD 1,500/K-12
736 Main St 65233 660-882-7474
Dr. Mark Ficken, supt. Fax 882-5721
www.boonville.k12.mo.us/
Boonslick Technical Education Center Vo/Tech
1694 W Ashley Rd 65233 660-882-5306
Cody Bashore, dir. Fax 882-3269
Boonville HS 500/9-12
1690 W Ashley Rd 65233 660-882-7426
Timothy Edwards, prin. Fax 882-3368
Elliott MS 300/6-8
700 Main St 65233 660-882-6649
Frederick Smith, prin. Fax 882-8646

Bosworth, Carroll, Pop. 302
Bosworth R-V SD 100/PK-12
102 E Eldridge St 64623 660-534-7311
Lachrissa Smith, supt. Fax 534-7409
www.bosworthr-v.k12.mo.us/
Bosworth JSHS 50/7-12
102 E Eldridge St 64623 660-534-7311
Natalie Ikenberry, prin. Fax 534-7409

Bourbon, Crawford, Pop. 1,624
Crawford County R-I SD 1,000/PK-12
1444 S Old Highway 66 65441 573-732-4426
Patricia L. Thompson, supt. Fax 732-4545
www.warhawks.k12.mo.us
Bourbon HS 300/9-12
1500 S Old Highway 66 65441 573-732-5615
Dena Smith, prin. Fax 732-4407
Bourbon MS 300/5-8
363 Jost St 65441 573-732-4424
Brian Witt, prin. Fax 732-4425

Bowling Green, Pike, Pop. 5,265
Bowling Green R-I SD 1,300/K-12
700 W Adams St 63334 573-324-5441
J.W. Brandt, supt. Fax 324-2439
www.bgschools.k12.mo.us
Bowling Green HS 400/9-12
700 W Adams St 63334 573-324-5341
Brock Bailey, prin. Fax 324-3011
Bowling Green MS 300/6-8
700 W Adams St 63334 573-324-2181
David Koogler, prin. Fax 324-3292

Bradleyville, Taney, Pop. 84
Bradleyville R-I SD 200/PK-12
PO Box 20 65614 417-796-2288
Scott Ewing, supt. Fax 796-2289
Bradleyville JSHS 100/7-12
PO Box 20 65614 417-796-2288
Gina Norwine, prin. Fax 796-2289

Branson, Taney, Pop. 10,302
Branson R-IV SD 4,600/PK-12
1756 Bee Creek Rd 65616 417-334-6541
Dr. Brad Swofford, supt. Fax 332-2510
www.branson.k12.mo.us
Branson HS 1,400/9-12
935 Buchanan Rd 65616 417-334-6511
Jack Harris, prin. Fax 335-4889
Branson JHS 700/7-8
263 Buccaneer Dr 65616 417-334-3087
Bryan Bronn, prin. Fax 336-3913

Brashear, Adair, Pop. 264
Adair County R-II SD 200/K-12
205 W Dewey St 63533 660-323-5272
Shelly Shipman, supt. Fax 323-5250
brashear.k12.mo.us
Adair County R-II HS 100/7-12
205 W Dewey St 63533 660-323-5272
Brent Doolin, prin. Fax 323-5250

Braymer, Caldwell, Pop. 864
Braymer C-4 SD 300/PK-12
400 Bobcat Ave 64624 660-645-2284
Don Regan, supt. Fax 645-2780
www.braymerbobcats.org
Braymer JSHS 100/7-12
400 Bobcat Ave 64624 660-645-2284
Mitchel Barnes, prin. Fax 645-2780

Breckenridge, Caldwell, Pop. 364
Breckenridge R-I SD 100/PK-12
400 W Colfax St 64625 660-644-5715
Brent Skinner, supt. Fax 644-5710
Breckenridge HS 50/7-12
400 W Colfax St 64625 660-644-5715
Brent Skinner, prin. Fax 644-5710

Brentwood, Saint Louis, Pop. 7,905
Brentwood SD 800/PK-12
1201 Hanley Industrial Ct 63144 314-962-4507
David Faulkner, supt. Fax 962-7302
www.brentwoodmoschools.org
Brentwood HS 200/9-12
2221 High School Dr 63144 314-962-3837
Dr. Edward M. Johnson, prin. Fax 963-3166
Brentwood MS 200/6-8
9127 White Ave 63144 314-962-8238
Dr. Andrew Loiterstein, prin. Fax 968-8724

Missouri College Post-Sec.
1405 S Hanley Rd 63144 314-768-7800

Brighton, Polk
Pleasant Hope R-VI SD
Supt. — See Pleasant Hope
Pleasant Hope Ranch S 100/4-12
5545 N Highway 13 65617 417-376-3000
Brent Dunning, dir. Fax 376-3575

Bronaugh, Vernon, Pop. 241
Bronaugh R-VII SD 200/PK-12
527 E 6th St 64728 417-922-3211
Dr. David Copeland, supt. Fax 922-3308
www.bronaughschools.net
Bronaugh JSHS 100/7-12
527 E 6th St 64728 417-922-3211
Jordan Dickey, prin. Fax 922-3308

Brookfield, Linn, Pop. 4,463
Brookfield R-III SD 1,100/PK-12
124A N Pershing Dr 64628 660-258-7443
Dr. Kyle Collins, supt. Fax 258-4711
www.brookfield.k12.mo.us
Brookfield HS 300/9-12
124 N Pershing Dr 64628 660-258-7242
Carey Smith, prin. Fax 258-2871
Brookfield MS 300/5-8
126 N Pershing Dr 64628 660-258-7335
Melinda Wilbeck, prin. Fax 258-3064
Linn County Area Career Tech Center Vo/Tech
122 N Pershing Dr 64628 660-258-2682
Carey Smith, dir. Fax 258-3875

Broseley, Butler
Twin Rivers R-X SD 1,000/K-12
PO Box 146 63932 573-328-4321
Jeremy Siebert, supt. Fax 328-1070
www.tr10.us
Twin Rivers HS 300/9-12
PO Box 146 63932 573-328-4730
Misty Lovelace, prin. Fax 328-1511

Brunswick, Chariton, Pop. 841
Brunswick R-II SD 300/PK-12
1008 County Rd 65236 660-548-3550
Robert Kottman, supt. Fax 548-3029
www.brunswick.k12.mo.us
Brunswick JSHS 100/7-12
1008 County Rd 65236 660-548-3771
Cara Engelbrecht, prin. Fax 548-3072

Bucklin, Linn, Pop. 465
Bucklin R-II SD 100/PK-12
26832 Highway 129 64631 660-695-3555
Stephen Coulson, supt. Fax 695-3345
www.bucklin.k12.mo.us/
Bucklin R-II S 100/PK-12
26832 Highway 129 64631 660-695-3225
Nicole Head, prin. Fax 695-3345

Buffalo, Dallas, Pop. 3,038
Dallas County R-I SD 1,600/K-12
309 W Commercial St 65622 417-345-2222
Dr. Tim Ryan, supt. Fax 345-8446
www.bisonpride.us
Buffalo HS 500/9-12
500 W Main St 65622 417-345-2223
Keith White, prin. Fax 345-8495
Buffalo MS 500/5-8
926 Truman 65622 417-345-2335
Jeremie akins, prin. Fax 345-5968
Other Schools – See Louisburg

Bunceton, Cooper, Pop. 348
Cooper County R-IV SD 100/K-12
500 E Main St 65237 660-427-5347
John Thompson, supt. Fax 427-5348
www.bunceton.k12.mo.us
Bunceton JSHS 100/7-12
500 E Main St 65237 660-427-5415
Amanda Frost, prin. Fax 427-5348

Bunker, Reynolds, Pop. 405
Bunker R-III SD 200/K-12
PO Box 365 63629 573-689-2507
John Eaton, supt. Fax 689-1268
www.bunkerr3.k12.mo.us/
Bunker JSHS 100/7-12
PO Box 365 63629 573-689-2211
Melissa Nash, prin. Fax 689-2011

Burlington Junction, Nodaway, Pop. 533
West Nodaway R-I SD 300/PK-12
PO Box 260 64428 660-725-4613
Shannon Nolte, supt. Fax 725-4300
www.wnrockets.com/
West Nodaway JSHS 100/6-12
PO Box 260 64428 660-725-3317
Roger Johnson, prin. Fax 725-4300

Butler, Bates, Pop. 4,155
Ballard R-II SD 100/K-12
10247 NE State Route 18 64730 816-297-2656
John Siebeneck, supt. Fax 297-4002
www.ballardr2.net
Ballard JSHS 100/7-12
10247 NE State Route 18 64730 816-297-2656
Eric Hon, prin. Fax 297-4002

Butler R-V SD 1,000/PK-12
420 S Fulton St 64730 660-679-0653
Darin Carter, supt. Fax 200-3010
www.butlerr5.org/
Butler JSHS 400/7-12
420 S Fulton St 64730 660-679-6121
Heath Oates, prin. Fax 679-4378

Cabool, Texas, Pop. 2,104
Cabool R-IV SD 700/PK-12
1025 Rogers Ave 65689 417-962-3153
Robin Ritchie, supt. Fax 962-5043
www.cabool.k12.mo.us
Cabool HS 200/9-12
1025 Rogers Ave 65689 417-962-3153
Brad Shockley, prin. Fax 962-5663
Cabool MS 300/5-8
1025 Rogers Ave 65689 417-962-3153
Cheryl Manning, prin. Fax 962-5043

Cadet, Washington
Kingston SD K-14 700/K-12
10047 Diamond Rd 63630 573-438-4982
Alex McCaul, supt. Fax 438-8813
www.kingston.k12.mo.us
Kingston HS 200/9-12
10047 Diamond Rd 63630 573-438-4982
Levi Rawson, prin. Fax 438-1212
Kingston MS 200/6-8
10047 Diamond Rd 63630 573-438-4982
Levi Rawson, prin. Fax 438-1212

Cainsville, Harrison, Pop. 285
Cainsville R-I SD 100/PK-12
PO Box 108 64632 660-893-5213
Richard Smith, supt. Fax 893-5713
cainsville.k12.mo.us
Cainsville JSHS 50/7-12
PO Box 108 64632 660-893-5214
Bill Pottorff, prin. Fax 893-5713

Cairo, Randolph, Pop. 287
Northeast Randolph County R-IV SD 400/PK-12
301 W Martin St 65239 660-263-2788
Darren Rapert, supt. Fax 263-5735
www.ner4schools.org
Northeast JSHS 200/6-12
301 W Martin St 65239 660-263-2788
Greg Taylor, prin. Fax 263-5735

Caledonia, Washington, Pop. 130
Valley R-VI SD 300/K-12
1 Viking Dr 63631 573-779-3446
Brad Crocker, supt. Fax 779-3505
www.valleyschooldistrict.org
Valley JSHS 200/7-12
1 Viking Dr 63631 573-779-3515
Michael Silvy, prin. Fax 779-3346

Calhoun, Henry, Pop. 463
Calhoun R-VIII SD 100/PK-12
409 S College St 65323 660-694-3422
Ronald Hay, supt. Fax 694-3501
calhoun.k12.mo.us
Calhoun JSHS 100/7-12
409 S College St 65323 660-694-3412
Christopher Calhoun, prin. Fax 694-3941

California, Moniteau, Pop. 4,221
Moniteau County R-I SD 1,300/PK-12
211 S Owen St Ste B 65018 573-796-2145
Dwight Sanders, supt. Fax 796-6123
www.californiak12.org/
California HS 400/9-12
1501 W Buchanan St 65018 573-796-4911
Sean Kirksey, prin. Fax 796-4503
California MS 300/6-8
211 S Owen St 65018 573-796-2146
Matt Abernathy, prin. Fax 796-8257

Camdenton, Camden, Pop. 3,647
Camdenton R-III SD 4,300/PK-12
PO Box 1409 65020 573-346-9213
Dr. Tim Hadfield, supt. Fax 346-9211
camdentonschools.schoolwires.net/
Camdenton HS 1,300/9-12
PO Box 1409 65020 573-346-9232
Brett Thompson, prin. Fax 346-9238
Camdenton MS 600/7-8
PO Box 1409 65020 573-346-9257
Matt Stacey, prin. Fax 346-9288
Lake Career & Technical Center Vo/Tech
PO Box 1409 65020 573-346-9260
Jackie Jenkins, dir. Fax 346-9284

Cameron, Clinton, Pop. 9,834
Cameron R-I SD 1,400/PK-12
423 N Chestnut St 64429 816-632-2170
Dr. Matt Robinson, supt. Fax 632-2612
www.cameron.k12.mo.us
Cameron HS 500/9-12
1022 S Chestnut St 64429 816-882-1036
Wiegers Mark, prin. Fax 882-1037
Cameron Veterans MS 400/6-8
1015 S Park 64429 816-882-1042
Tiffani Collins, prin. Fax 882-1043

Campbell, Dunklin, Pop. 1,968
Campbell R-II SD 700/PK-12
801 S State Highway 53 63933 573-246-2133
Jay Thornton, supt. Fax 246-3212
www.campbell.k12.mo.us
Campbell JSHS 300/7-12
801 S State Highway 53 63933 573-246-2576
Daren Ellsworth, prin. Fax 246-2890

Canton, Lewis, Pop. 2,342
Canton R-V SD 500/PK-12
200 S 4th St 63435 573-288-5216
W.A. Anderson, supt. Fax 288-5442
www.canton.k12.mo.us
Canton JSHS 200/7-12
200 S 4th St 63435 573-288-5216
Jesse Uhlmeyer, prin. Fax 288-5442

Culver-Stockton College Post-Sec.
1 College Hl 63435 573-288-6000

Cape Girardeau, Cape Girardeau, Pop. 37,082
Cape Girardeau SD 63 4,300/PK-12
301 N Clark St 63701 573-335-1867
Dr. James Welker, supt. Fax 335-1820
www.capetigers.com
Cape Girardeau Career & Technology Ctr Vo/Tech
1080 S Silver Springs Rd 63703 573-334-0826
Rich Payne, dir. Fax 334-5930
Central Academy Alt
301 N Spring St 63701 573-335-5939
Scott McMullen, admin. Fax 335-6041
Central HS 1,200/9-12
1000 S Silver Springs Rd 63703 573-335-8228
Chris Kase, prin. Fax 334-1114
Central JHS 600/7-8
205 Caruthers St 63701 573-334-2923
Carla Fee, prin. Fax 332-8746

Cape Girardeau Career & Technical School Post-Sec.
1080 S Silver Springs Rd 63703 573-334-0826
Eagle Ridge Christian S 200/PK-12
4210 State Highway K 63701 573-339-1335
Janice Margrabe, admin. Fax 339-1390
Metro Business College Post-Sec.
1732 N Kings Highway St 63701 573-334-9181
Notre Dame Regional HS 600/9-12
265 Notre Dame Dr 63701 573-335-6772
Br. David Migliorino, prin. Fax 335-3458
Southeast Hospital College of Nursing Post-Sec.
2001 William St # 2 63703 573-334-6825
Southeast Missouri State University Post-Sec.
1 University Plz 63701 573-651-2000

Cardwell, Dunklin, Pop. 704
Southland C-9 SD 400/PK-12
500 S Main St 63829 573-654-3574
Kim Campbell, supt. Fax 654-3575
southland.k12.mo.us
Southland JSHS 200/7-12
500 S Main St 63829 573-654-3531
Johnny McMinn, prin. Fax 654-3534

Carl Junction, Jasper, Pop. 7,264
Carl Junction R-I SD 3,400/PK-12
206 S Roney St 64834 417-649-7026
Dr. Phillip Cook, supt. Fax 649-6594
www.cjr1.org
Carl Junction HS 1,000/9-12
206 S Roney St 64834 417-649-7081
David Pyle, prin. Fax 649-5791
Carl Junction JHS 500/7-8
206 S Roney St 64834 417-649-7246
Scott Sawyer, prin. Fax 649-0022
Other Schools – See Joplin

Carrollton, Carroll, Pop. 3,737
Carrollton R-VII SD 900/PK-12
103 E 9th St 64633 660-542-2769
Dr. Jon Oetinger, supt. Fax 542-3416
www.trojans.k12.mo.us/
Carrollton Area Career Center Vo/Tech
305 E 10th St 64633 660-542-0000
David Reinke, dir. Fax 542-0600
Carrollton HS 300/9-12
300 E 9th St 64633 660-542-1276
Todd Park, prin. Fax 542-1903
Carrollton MS 300/5-8
300 E 9th St 64633 660-542-3472
Brent Dobbins, prin. Fax 542-3169

Carthage, Jasper, Pop. 14,047
Carthage R-IX SD 4,600/PK-12
710 Lyon St 64836 417-359-7000
Dr. Sean Smith, supt. Fax 359-7004
www.carthagetigers.org
Carthage HS 1,200/9-12
2600 S River St 64836 417-359-7020
Matt Huntley, prin. Fax 359-7037
Carthage JHS 700/7-8
714 S Main St 64836 417-359-7050
Jenny Bogle, prin. Fax 359-7057
Carthage Technical Center North Campus Vo/Tech
609 S River St 64836 417-359-7095
Gregg Wolf, dir. Fax 359-7419
Carthage Technical Center South Campus Vo/Tech
1100 E Airport Dr 64836 417-359-7026
Wolf Gregg, dir. Fax 359-7098

Caruthersville, Pemiscot, Pop. 6,073
Caruthersville SD 18 1,200/PK-12
1711 Ward Ave 63830 573-333-6100
J.J. Bullington, supt. Fax 333-6108
www.cps18.org
Caruthersville HS 300/9-12
1708 Ward Ave 63830 573-333-6110
Dr. Claire Jackson, prin. Fax 333-6117
Caruthersville MS 300/6-8
1705 Ward Ave 63830 573-333-6120
Stephanie McGraw, prin. Fax 333-1835

Cassville, Barry, Pop. 3,224
Cassville R-IV SD 1,900/PK-12
1501 Main St 65625 417-847-2221
Dr. Richard Asbill, supt. Fax 847-4009
cassville.k12.mo.us/
Cassville HS 600/9-12
1501 Main St 65625 417-847-3137
Jeff Swadley, prin. Fax 847-5111
Cassville MS 400/6-8
1501 Main St 65625 417-847-3136
Jimmie Barton, prin. Fax 847-3156

Cedar Hill, Jefferson, Pop. 1,703
Northwest R-I SD
Supt. — See High Ridge
Northwest HS 2,000/9-12
6005 Cedar Hill Rd 63016 636-274-0555
Brad Snell, prin. Fax 274-2076

Center, Ralls, Pop. 502
Ralls County R-II SD 800/PK-12
21622 Highway 19 63436 573-267-3397
Dr. Tara Lewis, supt. Fax 267-3538
rallsr2.k12.mo.us
Twain HS 200/9-12
21622 Highway 19 63436 573-267-3397
Clark Howell, prin. Fax 267-3538
Twain JHS 200/6-8
21622 Highway 19 63436 573-267-3397
Delores Woodhurst, prin. Fax 267-3538

Centerview, Johnson, Pop. 266
Johnson County R-VII SD 500/PK-12
92 NW State Route 58 64019 660-656-3316
Brett Gray, supt. Fax 656-3633
www.crestridge.org
Crest Ridge HS 200/7-12
92 NW State Route 58 64019 660-656-3391
James Frank, prin. Fax 656-3633

Centralia, Boone, Pop. 3,976
Centralia R-VI SD 1,400/PK-12
1399 E Highway 22 Ste B 65240 573-682-3561
Darin Ford, supt. Fax 682-2181
www.centralia.k12.mo.us
Boren MS 300/6-8
110 N Jefferson St 65240 573-682-2617
Nathan Gordon, prin. Fax 682-1500
Centralia HS 400/9-12
849 S Jefferson St 65240 573-682-3508
Matt Smith, prin. Fax 682-2749

Sunnydale Adventist Academy 100/9-12
6818 Audrain Road 9139 65240 573-682-2164

Chadwick, Christian
Chadwick R-I SD 200/PK-12
PO Box 274 65629 417-634-3588
Dana Comstock, supt. Fax 634-2668
www.chadwick.k12.mo.us/
Chadwick JSHS 100/7-12
PO Box 274 65629 417-634-3588
David Aldrich, contact Fax 634-4040

Chaffee, Scott, Pop. 2,925
Chaffee R-II SD 600/PK-12
517 W Yoakum Ave 63740 573-887-3532
Ken Latham, supt. Fax 887-3926
chaffee.k12.mo.us
Chaffee JSHS 300/7-12
517 W Yoakum Ave 63740 573-887-3226
Brad Blackman, prin. Fax 887-3926

Chamois, Osage, Pop. 395
Osage County R-I SD 200/PK-12
614 S Poplar St 65024 573-763-5666
Lyle Best, supt. Fax 763-5686
www.chamois.k12.mo.us
Chamois JSHS 100/7-12
614 S Poplar St 65024 573-763-5393
Bradley Strobel, prin. Fax 763-5686

Charleston, Mississippi, Pop. 5,882
Charleston R-I SD 1,000/PK-12
PO Box 39 63834 573-683-3776
Dr. Tammy Lupardus, supt. Fax 683-2909
charleston.k12.mo.us
Charleston HS 300/9-12
PO Box 39 63834 573-683-3761
Kathy Browning, prin. Fax 683-2907
Charleston MS 200/6-8
PO Box 39 63834 573-683-3346
Sarah Spain, prin. Fax 683-2930

Chesterfield, Saint Louis, Pop. 46,860
Parkway C-2 SD 17,200/PK-12
455 N Woods Mill Rd 63017 314-415-8100
Dr. Keith Marty, supt. Fax 415-8009
www.parkwayschools.net
Parkway Central HS 1,300/9-12
369 N Woods Mill Rd 63017 314-415-7900
Tim McCarthy, prin. Fax 415-7913
Parkway Central MS 900/6-8
471 N Woods Mill Rd 63017 314-415-7800
Dr. Michael Baugus, prin. Fax 415-7834
Parkway West MS 900/6-8
2312 Baxter Rd 63017 314-415-7400
Anne Miller, prin. Fax 415-7409
Other Schools – See Ballwin, Creve Coeur, Manchester

Rockwood R-VI SD
Supt. — See Eureka
Marquette HS 2,300/9-12
2351 Clarkson Rd 63017 636-891-6000
Dr. Greg Mathison, prin. Fax 537-4319

Barat Academy 200/9-12
17815 Wild Horse Creek Rd 63005 636-300-5500
Debra Watson, pres. Fax 300-5501
Logan College of Chiropractic Post-Sec.
1851 Schoettler Rd 63017 800-533-9210
Missouri Torah Institute 50/9-12
1809 Clarkson Rd 63017 636-778-1897
Rabbi Dovid Goldman, prin. Fax 778-1899
St. Joseph's Institute for the Deaf Post-Sec.
1809 Clarkson Rd 63017 636-532-3211
Westminster Christian Academy 900/7-12
800 Maryville Centre Dr 63017 314-997-2900
Tim Hall, head sch Fax 997-2903

Chilhowee, Johnson, Pop. 315
Chilhowee R-IV SD 100/PK-12
101 SW State Route 2 64733 660-678-2511
Troy Marnholtz, supt. Fax 678-5711
www.chilhowee.k12.mo.us
Chilhowee JSHS 100/7-12
101 SW State Route 2 64733 660-678-4511
John Murphy, prin. Fax 678-5711

Chillicothe, Livingston, Pop. 9,375
Chillicothe R-II SD 1,900/K-12
PO Box 530 64601 660-646-4566
Dr. Roger Barnes, supt. Fax 646-6508
www.chillicotheschools.org/
Chillicothe HS 600/9-12
2801 Hornet Rd 64601 660-646-0700
Brian Sherrow, prin. Fax 646-7106
Chillicothe MS 400/6-8
1529 Calhoun St 64601 660-646-1916
Steve Haley, prin. Fax 646-5065
Grand River Tech S Vo/Tech
1200 Fair St 64601 660-646-3414
Jayme Caughron, prin. Fax 646-3568

Chillicothe Beauty Academy Post-Sec.
505 Elm St 64601 660-646-4198

Clarksville, Pike, Pop. 436
Pike County R-III SD 500/PK-12
28176 Highway WW 63336 573-242-3546
Mark Harvey, supt. Fax 485-2393
www.cloptonhawks.com
Clopton JSHS 200/7-12
28176 Highway WW 63336 573-242-3546
Larry Lagemann, prin. Fax 485-2393
Other Schools – See Eolia

Clarkton, Dunklin, Pop. 1,265
Clarkton C-4 SD 300/PK-12
PO Box 637 63837 573-448-3712
Delane Beckwith, supt. Fax 448-5182
www.clarktonschools.org/
Clarkton JSHS 200/7-12
PO Box 637 63837 573-448-3712
Dustin Ferguson, prin. Fax 448-3226

Clayton, Saint Louis, Pop. 15,572
Clayton SD 2,700/PK-12
2 Mark Twain Cir 63105 314-854-6000
Dr. Sean Doherty, supt. Fax 854-6093
www.claytonschools.net
Clayton HS 900/9-12
1 Mark Twain Cir 63105 314-854-6600
Dr. Dan Gutchewsky, prin. Fax 854-6793
Wydown MS 600/6-8
6500 Wydown Blvd 63105 314-854-6400
Dr. Jamie Jordan, prin. Fax 854-6491

Cleveland, Cass, Pop. 645
Midway R-I SD 400/K-12
5801 E State Route 2 64734 816-250-2994
Gordon Myers, supt. Fax 899-2823
www.midwayk12.net
Midway JSHS 200/7-12
5801 E State Route 2 64734 816-250-2994
Doug Dahman, prin. Fax 899-2823

Clever, Christian, Pop. 2,109
Clever R-V SD 500/PK-12
103 S Public Ave 65631 417-743-4800
Steve Carvajal, supt. Fax 743-4802
www.cleverbluejays.org
Clever HS 300/9-12
6800 State Highway 14 W 65631 417-743-4830
Joe Casey, prin. Fax 743-4832

Clifton Hill, Randolph, Pop. 111
Westran R-I SD
Supt. — See Huntsville
Westran MS 200/6-8
622 Harlan St 65244 660-261-4511
Mike Aulbur, prin. Fax 261-4292

Climax Springs, Camden, Pop. 124
Climax Springs R-IV SD 200/PK-12
571 Climax Ave 65324 573-347-3905
Nathan Barb, supt. Fax 347-9931
www.csprings.k12.mo.us
Climax Springs JSHS 100/7-12
571 Climax Ave 65324 573-347-2351
Caleb Petet, prin. Fax 347-2394

Clinton, Henry, Pop. 8,864
Clinton SD 124 1,800/PK-12
701 S 8th St 64735 660-885-2237
Dr. Adam Willard, supt. Fax 885-7033
clinton.k12.mo.us
Clinton HS 600/9-12
701 S 8th St 64735 660-885-2247
Jarrod Steffens, prin. Fax 885-2012
Clinton MS 400/6-8
701 S 8th St 64735 660-885-3353
Ashlee Cochran, prin. Fax 885-4826
Clinton Technical S Vo/Tech
701 S 8th St 64735 660-885-6101
Jacob Fowler, dir. Fax 885-6789

Cole Camp, Benton, Pop. 1,108
Cole Camp R-I SD 700/PK-12
500 S Keeney St 65325 660-668-4427
Dr. Tim Roling, supt. Fax 668-4703
colecamp.schoolwires.net
Cole Camp HS 300/9-12
500 S Keeney St 65325 660-668-3751
Brandon Harding, prin. Fax 668-4703
Cole Camp MS 200/5-8
500 S Keeney St 65325 660-668-3502
Tyler Clark, prin. Fax 668-4703

Columbia, Boone, Pop. 105,254
Columbia SD 93 17,600/PK-12
1818 W Worley St 65203 573-214-3400
Dr. Peter Stiepleman, supt. Fax 214-3401
www.cpsk12.org
Battle HS 1,100/9-12
7575 E Saint Charles Rd 65202 573-214-3300
Dr. Kim Presko, prin. Fax 214-3301
Columbia Area Career Ctr Vo/Tech
4203 S Providence Rd 65203 573-214-3800
Randy Gooch, dir. Fax 214-3801
Douglass HS 100/Alt
310 N Providence Rd 65203 573-214-3680
Dr. Eryca Neville, prin. Fax 214-3681
Gentry MS 800/6-8
4200 Bethel St 65203 573-214-3240
Dr. Jeff Beiswinger, prin. Fax 214-3241
Hickman HS 1,800/9-12
1104 N Providence Rd 65203 573-214-3000
Eric Johnson, prin. Fax 214-3057
Jefferson MS 500/6-8
713 Rogers St 65201 573-214-3210
Dr. Greg Caine, prin. Fax 214-3211
Lange MS 700/6-8
2201 Smiley Ln 65202 573-214-3250
Dr. Bernard Solomon, prin. Fax 214-3251
Oakland MS 500/6-8
3405 Oakland Pl 65202 573-214-3220
Helen Porter, prin. Fax 214-3221
Rock Bridge HS 2,000/9-12
4303 S Providence Rd 65203 573-214-3100
Dr. Jennifer Rukstad, prin. Fax 214-3109
Smithton MS 700/6-8
3600 W Worley St 65203 573-214-3260
Edward Schumaker, prin. Fax 214-3261
West MS 600/6-8
401 Clinkscales Rd 65203 573-214-3230
Dr. Connie Dewey, prin. Fax 214-3231

Bryan University Post-Sec.
3215 Lemone Industrial Blvd 65201 573-777-5550
Christian Fellowship S 300/PK-12
4600 Christian Fellowship 65203 573-445-8565
Dr. Rick Mueller, admin. Fax 445-8564
Columbia Beauty Academy Post-Sec.
503 E Nifong Blvd 65201 573-445-6611
Columbia College Post-Sec.
1001 Rogers St 65216 573-875-8700
Columbia Independent S 400/PK-12
1801 N Stadium Blvd 65202 573-777-9250
Adam Dube, head sch Fax 777-9251
Jerry's School of Hairstyling Post-Sec.
1001 Royal Birkdale Dr 65203 573-449-7527
Stephens College Post-Sec.
1200 E Broadway 65215 800-876-7207
Tolton HS 9-12
3351 E Gans Rd 65201 573-445-7700
Bernie Naumann, pres. Fax 445-7703
University of Missouri Post-Sec.
228 Jesse Hall 65211 573-882-2121

Conception, Nodaway, Pop. 209

Conception Seminary College Post-Sec.
PO Box 502 64433 660-944-3105

Conception Junction, Nodaway, Pop. 198
Jefferson C-123 SD 100/PK-12
37614 US Highway 136 64434 660-944-2316
Tim Jermain, supt. Fax 944-2315
Jefferson JSHS 100/7-12
37614 US Highway 136 64434 660-944-2316
Tim Jermain, supt. Fax 944-2315

Concordia, Lafayette, Pop. 2,425
Concordia R-II SD 500/PK-12
PO Box 879 64020 660-463-7235
Mary Beth Scherer, supt. Fax 463-1326
www.concordia.k12.mo.us
Concordia JSHS 200/7-12
PO Box 879 64020 660-463-2246
Lucas Lewis, prin. Fax 463-4081

St. Paul Lutheran HS 200/9-12
PO Box 719 64020 660-463-2238
Rev. Paul Mehl, dir. Fax 463-7621

Conway, Laclede, Pop. 768
Laclede County R-I SD 700/K-12
726 W Jefferson Ave 65632 417-589-2951
Mark Hedger, supt. Fax 589-3202
www.lacledecountyr1.com
Conway HS 300/7-12
726 W Jefferson Ave 65632 417-589-2941
Ricky Lowrance, prin. Fax 589-2500

Cooter, Pemiscot, Pop. 468
Cooter R-IV SD 300/K-12
PO Box 218 63839 573-695-3312
Clay Snider, supt. Fax 695-3073
cooter.k12.mo.us
Cooter JSHS 200/7-12
PO Box 218 63839 573-695-4972
Josh Teeter, prin. Fax 695-3073

Cottleville, Saint Charles, Pop. 3,037

Patsy & Rob's Academy of Beauty Post-Sec.
5065 Highway N 63304 636-447-0650
St. Charles Community College Post-Sec.
4601 Mid Rivers Mall Dr 63376 636-922-8000

Craig, Holt, Pop. 248
Craig R-III SD 50/K-12
402 N Ward St 64437 660-683-5351
Michael Leach, supt. Fax 683-5769
www.craigr3school.com
Craig R-III S 50/K-12
402 N Ward St 64437 660-683-5431
Jennifer Dyer, prin. Fax 683-5769

Crane, Stone, Pop. 1,443
Crane R-III SD 700/PK-12
PO Box 405 65633 417-723-5300
Dr. Chris Johnson, supt. Fax 723-5551
www.crane.k12.mo.us
Crane HS 300/7-12
PO Box 405 65633 417-723-5300
Grant Stock, prin. Fax 723-8598

Creighton, Cass, Pop. 347
Sherwood Cass R-VIII SD 900/PK-12
PO Box 98 64739 660-499-2834
Dr. Tim Gallagher, supt. Fax 499-2624
sites.google.com/a/sherwoodk12.net/sherwood/home
Sherwood HS 300/9-12
PO Box 98 64739 660-499-2239
William Stackhouse, prin. Fax 499-2258
Sherwood MS 200/6-8
PO Box 98 64739 660-499-2239
Brenda Koch, prin. Fax 499-2585

Creve Coeur, Saint Louis, Pop. 17,490
Parkway C-2 SD
Supt. — See Chesterfield
Fern Ridge HS 100/Alt
13157 N Olive Spur Rd 63141 314-415-6900
Michelle Howren, coord. Fax 415-6912
Parkway Northeast MS 900/6-8
181 Coeur De Ville Dr 63141 314-415-7100
Kashina Bell, prin. Fax 415-7113
Parkway North HS 1,400/9-12
12860 Fee Fee Rd, Saint Louis MO 63146
314-415-7600
Dr. Jenny Marquart, prin. Fax 415-7614

Crocker, Pulaski, Pop. 1,094
Crocker R-II SD 600/PK-12
PO Box 488 65452 573-736-5000
Gary Doerhoff, supt. Fax 736-5924
www.crockerschools.org
Crocker JSHS 200/7-12
PO Box 488 65452 573-736-5000
Heath Waters, prin. Fax 736-2801

Crystal City, Jefferson, Pop. 4,757
Crystal City SD 47 500/K-12
1100 Mississippi Ave 63019 636-937-4411
Philip Harrison, supt. Fax 937-2512
www.crystal.k12.mo.us/
Crystal City HS 200/9-12
1100 Mississippi Ave 63019 636-937-2005
Matthew Holdinghausen, prin. Fax 937-2075

National Academy of Beauty Arts Post-Sec.
137 Twin City Mall 63019 636-931-7100

Cuba, Crawford, Pop. 3,311
Crawford County R-II SD 1,500/K-12
1 Wildcat Pride Dr 65453 573-885-2534
Jon Earnhart, supt. Fax 885-3900
www.cuba.k12.mo.us/
Cuba HS 400/9-12
1 Wildcat Pride Dr 65453 573-885-2534
Geoffrey Neill, prin. Fax 885-7726
Cuba MS 500/5-8
1 Wildcat Pride Dr 65453 573-885-2534
Marie Shoemaker, prin. Fax 885-6278

Curryville, Pike, Pop. 217

Pike County Christian S 50/K-12
PO Box 96 63339 573-324-2700
Frank Welch, admin. Fax 324-2700

Dadeville, Dade, Pop. 228
Dadeville R-II SD 100/K-12
PO Box 188 65635 417-995-2201
Matt Bushey, supt. Fax 995-2110
bearcats.dadeville.k12.mo.us
Dadeville JSHS 100/6-12
PO Box 188 65635 417-995-2201
Cassy Farmer, prin. Fax 995-2110

Dearborn, Platte, Pop. 488
North Platte County R-I SD 500/PK-12
212 W 6th St 64439 816-450-3511
Karl Matt, supt. Fax 992-8727
www.nppanthers.org
North Platte HS 200/9-12
212 W 6th St 64439 816-450-3344
Michelle Johnson, prin. Fax 992-8955
North Platte JHS, 212 W 6th St 64439 100/6-8
Michelle Johnson, prin. 816-450-3350

Deepwater, Henry, Pop. 430
Lakeland R-III SD 400/PK-12
12530 Lakeland School Dr 64740 417-644-2223
Mitch Towne, supt. Fax 644-2316
www.lakeland.k12.mo.us
Lakeland JSHS 200/7-12
12530 Lakeland School Dr 64740 417-644-2223
Adam Collins, prin. Fax 644-2316

Deering, Pemiscot, Pop. 130
Delta C-7 SD 200/K-12
PO Box 297 63840 573-757-6648
Kenny Copley, supt. Fax 757-9691
www.deltac7.k12.mo.us
Delta C-7 JSHS 100/7-12
PO Box 297 63840 573-757-6611
Nathan Baker, prin. Fax 757-9691

De Kalb, Buchanan, Pop. 219
Buchanan County R-IV SD 300/PK-12
702 Main St 64440 816-685-3160
Travis Dittemore, supt. Fax 685-3203
www.bcr4.k12.mo.us/
De Kalb JSHS 100/7-12
702 Main St 64440 816-685-3211
Brian Hansen, prin. Fax 685-3156

Delta, Cape Girardeau, Pop. 421
Delta R-V SD 300/PK-12
PO Box 787 63744 573-794-2500
Dr. Mellisa Heath, supt. Fax 794-2504
www.deltar5schools.com
Delta JSHS 100/7-12
PO Box 787 63744 573-794-2511
James Gloth, prin. Fax 794-2504

Desloge, Saint Francois, Pop. 4,987
North St. Francois County R-I SD
Supt. — See Bonne Terre
North County MS 500/7-8
406 E Chestnut St 63601 573-431-3300
Brenda Hampton, prin. Fax 431-5203

De Soto, Jefferson, Pop. 6,303
Desoto SD 73 3,100/PK-12
610 Vineland School Rd 63020 636-586-1000
Dr. Josh Isaacson, supt. Fax 586-1009
www.desoto.k12.mo.us
De Soto HS 900/9-12
815 Amvets Dr 63020 636-586-1050
Mike Rickermann, prin. Fax 586-1059
De Soto JHS 500/7-8
731 Amvets Dr 63020 636-586-1030
Alex Mahn, prin. Fax 586-1039

Dexter, Stoddard, Pop. 7,773
Dexter R-XI SD 2,100/PK-12
1031 Brown Pilot Ln 63841 573-614-1000
Mitchell D. Wood, supt. Fax 614-1002
dexter.k12.mo.us/
Dexter HS 600/9-12
1101 W Grant St 63841 573-614-1030
Dan Pollock, prin. Fax 614-1032
Hill MS 500/6-8
1107 Brown Pilot Ln 63841 573-614-1010
Scott Kruse, prin. Fax 614-1012

Diamond, Newton, Pop. 880
Diamond R-IV SD 800/K-12
PO Box 68 64840 417-325-5186
Steve Hubbard, supt. Fax 325-5338
www.diamondwildcats.org/
Diamond HS 300/9-12
PO Box 68 64840 417-325-5188
Don Epps, prin. Fax 325-5331
Diamond MS 300/5-8
PO Box 68 64840 417-325-5336
Chris Gold, prin. Fax 325-5333

Dixon, Pulaski, Pop. 1,508
Dixon R-I SD 1,100/PK-12
106 W 4th St 65459 573-759-7163
Duane Doyle, supt. Fax 759-2506
www.dixonr1.com
Dixon HS 300/9-12
106 W 4th St 65459 573-759-7163
Brian Foerster, prin. Fax 759-3625
Dixon MS 200/6-8
106 W 4th St 65459 573-759-7163
Mark Parker, prin. Fax 759-6627

Doniphan, Ripley, Pop. 1,976
Doniphan R-I SD 1,500/PK-12
309 Pine St 63935 573-996-3667
Dr. Jennifer Snyder, supt. Fax 996-5865
www.doniphanr1.k12.mo.us
Current River Career Center Vo/Tech
301 E Spring St 63935 573-996-3667
Dustin Braschler, dir. Fax 996-7838
Doniphan HS 500/9-12
5 Ball Park Rd 63935 573-996-3667
Mike Jones, prin. Fax 996-3739
Doniphan MS 400/5-8
651 E Summit St 63935 573-996-3667
Dr. Fish James, prin. Fax 996-4525

Dora, Ozark
Dora R-III SD 300/PK-12
613 County Road 379 65637 417-261-2346
Steve Richards, supt. Fax 261-2673
www.dora.org
Dora JSHS 200/7-12
613 County Road 379 65637 417-261-2263
Rick Luna, prin. Fax 261-2673

Drexel, Bates, Pop. 952
Drexel R-IV SD 300/K-12
PO Box 860 64742 816-657-4715
Terry Mayfield, supt. Fax 657-4798
www.drexel.k12.mo.us
Drexel HS 200/7-12
PO Box 860 64742 816-619-2287
Dennis Bolton, prin. Fax 657-4798

Eagleville, Harrison, Pop. 315
North Harrison R-III SD 300/PK-12
12023 Fir St 64442 660-867-5222
Rick Johnson, supt. Fax 867-5263
www.nhr3.net
North Harrison County JSHS 100/7-12
12023 Fir St 64442 660-867-5221
Mike Schmidli, prin. Fax 867-5263

Earth City, Saint Louis

Everest College Post-Sec.
3420 Rider Trl S 63045 314-739-7333
Midwest Institute - Earth City Post-Sec.
4260 Shoreline Dr 63045 314-344-4440

Easton, Buchanan, Pop. 228
East Buchanan County C-1 SD
Supt. — See Gower
East Buchanan MS 200/6-8
301 N County Park Rd 64443 816-473-2451
David Elms, prin. Fax 473-2604

East Prairie, Mississippi, Pop. 3,146
East Prairie R-II SD 1,200/PK-12
PO Box 10 63845 573-649-3562
C.A. Counts, supt. Fax 649-5455
eastprairie.org/
East Prairie HS 300/9-12
PO Box 10 63845 573-649-3564
Jamie Johnson, prin. Fax 649-3208
East Prairie JHS 200/7-8
210 E Washington St 63845 573-649-9368
Amanda Dean, prin. Fax 649-9370

Edina, Knox, Pop. 1,171
Knox County R-I SD 500/PK-12
55701 State Hwy 6 63537 660-397-2228
Andy Turgeon, supt. Fax 397-3998
www.knox.k12.mo.us/
Knox County JSHS 300/6-12
55701 State Hwy 6 63537 660-397-2231
Brian Brown, prin. Fax 397-3282

Eldon, Miller, Pop. 4,478
Eldon R-I SD 2,000/PK-12
112 S Pine St 65026 573-392-8000
Matt Davis, supt. Fax 392-8080
eldonmustangs.org
Eldon Career Center Vo/Tech
112 S Pine St 65026 573-392-8060
Kelli Engelbrecht, dir. Fax 392-9154
Eldon HS 600/9-12
101 S Pine St 65026 573-392-8010
Kristina Harwood, prin. Fax 392-5057
Eldon MS 300/7-8
1400 N Grand Ave 65026 573-392-8020
Shaun Fischer, prin. Fax 392-9151

El Dorado Springs, Cedar, Pop. 3,534
El Dorado Springs R-II SD 1,200/PK-12
901 S Grand Ave 64744 417-876-3112
Mark Koca, supt. Fax 876-2128
www.eldo.k12.mo.us/
El Dorado Springs HS 400/9-12
901 S Grand Ave 64744 417-876-3112
David Hedrick, prin. Fax 876-2128
El Dorado Springs MS 300/6-8
901 S Grand Ave 64744 417-876-3112
Brad Steward, prin. Fax 876-2128

El Dorado Christian S 100/PK-12
1600 S Ohio St 64744 417-876-2201
Amy Castor, prin. Fax 876-4913

Ellington, Reynolds, Pop. 979
Southern Reynolds County R-II SD 500/PK-12
1 School St 63638 573-663-3591
Dr. Mike Redlich, supt. Fax 663-2412
www.ellington.k12.mo.us
Southern Reynolds County HS 200/7-12
1 School St 63638 573-663-2291
Dr. Jannifer Johnson, prin. Fax 663-2155

Ellisville, Saint Louis, Pop. 9,012
Rockwood R-VI SD
Supt. — See Eureka
Crestview MS 1,200/6-8
16025 Clayton Rd 63011 636-207-2520
Gary Jansen, prin. Fax 207-2529

Ellsinore, Carter, Pop. 444
East Carter County R-II SD 700/PK-12
24 S Herren Ave 63937 573-322-5625
Dr. Richard Sullivan, supt. Fax 322-8586
www.ecarter.k12.mo.us
East Carter County R-II HS 200/9-12
24 S Herren Ave 63937 573-322-5653
Veronica Hollis, prin. Fax 322-5720
East Carter County R-II MS 200/6-8
24 S Herren Ave 63937 573-322-5420
Theresa Kearbey, prin. Fax 322-5420

Elsberry, Lincoln, Pop. 1,898
Elsberry R-II SD 800/PK-12
PO Box 106 63343 573-898-5554
Dr. Tim Reller, supt. Fax 898-3140
www.elsberryschools.com
Cannon MS 300/5-8
PO Box 106 63343 573-898-5554
Jason Miller, prin. Fax 898-5825
Elsberry HS 200/9-12
PO Box 106 63343 573-898-5554
Michael Boedeker, prin. Fax 898-9132

Eminence, Shannon, Pop. 585
Eminence R-I SD 300/PK-12
PO Box 730 65466 573-226-3252
Charles James, supt. Fax 226-3250
www.redwingsk12.org
Eminence JSHS 100/7-12
PO Box 730 65466 573-226-3252
James McBride, prin. Fax 226-3211

Eolia, Pike, Pop. 513
Pike County R-III SD
Supt. — See Clarksville
Pike-Lincoln Technical Center Vo/Tech
342 Vo Tech Rd 63344 573-485-2900
Martin Hanley, dir. Fax 485-2388

Essex, Stoddard, Pop. 469
Richland R-I SD 200/K-12
24456 State Highway 114 63846 573-283-5332
Frank Killian, supt. Fax 283-5798
www.richland.k12.mo.us/
Richland JSHS 100/7-12
24456 State Highway 114 63846 573-283-5332
Cynthia Rhodes, prin. Fax 283-5798

Eugene, Cole, Pop. 159
Cole County R-V SD 600/PK-12
14803 Highway 17 65032 573-498-4000
Dawna Burrow, supt. Fax 498-4090
www.coler-v.k12.mo.us
Eugene JSHS 300/7-12
14803 Highway 17 65032 573-498-4001
Brian Dickerson, prin. Fax 498-4091

Eureka, Saint Louis, Pop. 10,033
Rockwood R-VI SD 21,900/PK-12
111 E North St 63025 636-733-2000
Dr. Eric Knost, supt. Fax 938-2251
www.rsdmo.org
Eureka HS 1,900/9-12
4525 Highway 109 63025 636-733-3100
Charles Crouther, prin. Fax 938-2411
Individualized Learning Center Alt
500 N Central Ave 63025 636-733-2100
Matthew Dieckhaus, admin. Fax 938-2346
Other Schools – See Ballwin, Chesterfield, Ellisville, Fenton, Glencoe

Everton, Dade, Pop. 310
Everton R-III SD 100/K-12
211 E School St 65646 417-535-2221
Dr. Karl Janson, supt. Fax 535-4105
www.evertontigers.org
Everton MSHS 50/6-12
211 E School St 65646 417-535-2221
Heather Harden, prin. Fax 535-4105

Excelsior Springs, Clay, Pop. 10,839
Excelsior Springs SD 40 2,800/PK-12
300 W Broadway St 64024 816-630-9200
Dr. David Lawrence, supt. Fax 630-9203
www.essd40.com
Excelsior Springs Career Ctr Vo/Tech
PO Box 248 64024 816-630-9240
Dr. Chris Lake, dir. Fax 630-9245
Excelsior Springs HS 800/9-12
PO Box 248 64024 816-630-9210
John Newell, prin. Fax 630-9227
Excelsior Springs MS 600/6-8
PO Box 248 64024 816-630-9230
Mark Bullimore, prin. Fax 630-9236
Excelsior Springs Technical HS 50/Alt
PO Box 248 64024 816-630-5501
Tom Mayfield, prin. Fax 637-1806

Martinez School of Cosmetology Post-Sec.
248 1/2 E Broadway St 64024 816-630-3900

Exeter, Barry, Pop. 762
Exeter R-VI SD 300/K-12
101 Locust St 65647 417-835-2922
Dr. Ernest Raney, supt. Fax 835-3201
www.exeter.k12.mo.us/
Exeter HS 100/9-12
101 Locust St 65647 417-835-3745
Robert Taylor, prin. Fax 835-3201

Fairfax, Atchison, Pop. 634
Fairfax R-III SD 100/PK-12
500 E Main St 64446 660-686-2421
Dr. Michael Garrett, supt. Fax 686-2848
www.fairfaxk12mo.us/
Fairfax JSHS 100/7-12
500 E Main St 64446 660-686-2851
Dustin Barnes, prin. Fax 686-3436

Fair Grove, Greene, Pop. 1,384
Fair Grove R-X SD 1,100/PK-12
132 N Main St 65648 417-759-2233
Mike Bell, supt. Fax 759-7150
www.fairgrove.k12.mo.us
Fair Grove HS 400/9-12
132 N Main St 65648 417-759-2554
Chris Stallings, prin. Fax 759-7685
Fair Grove MS 300/5-8
132 N Main St 65648 417-759-2556
Marc Green, prin. Fax 759-9053

Fair Play, Polk, Pop. 467
Fair Play R-II SD 400/PK-12
301 N Walnut St 65649 417-654-2231
Renee Sagaser, supt. Fax 654-5028
www.fairplay.k12.mo.us/
Fair Play JSHS 200/7-12
301 N Walnut St 65649 417-654-2232
Randy Lightfoot, prin. Fax 654-3503

Farmington, Saint Francois, Pop. 16,061
Farmington R-VII SD 4,000/PK-12
PO Box 570 63640 573-701-1300
Matthew R. Ruble, supt. Fax 701-1309
www.fsdknights.com
Farmington HS 1,200/9-12
1 Black Knight Dr 63640 573-701-1310
Dr. Nathan Hostetler, prin. Fax 701-1329
Farmington MS 600/7-8
506 S Fleming St 63640 573-701-1330
Dr. Dorothy Winslow, prin. Fax 701-1339
Midwest Learning Center 50/Alt
PO Box 570 63640 573-701-1395
Jerry Will, lead tchr. Fax 701-1388

Mineral Area Regional Medical Center Post-Sec.
1212 Weber Rd 63640 573-756-4581
National Academy of Beauty Arts Post-Sec.
670 Walton Dr 63640 573-756-2730
St. Paul Lutheran HS 50/9-12
4337 Showplace Dr 63640 573-756-1099
Andy Sherril, prin.

Faucett, Buchanan
Mid-Buchanan County R-V SD 700/K-12
3221 SE State Route H 64448 816-238-1646
John James, supt. Fax 238-4150
www.midbuchanan.k12.mo.us
Mid-Buchanan JSHS 300/7-12
3221 SE State Route H 64448 816-238-1646
Dave Rapp, prin. Fax 238-2484

Fayette, Howard, Pop. 2,632
Fayette R-III SD 500/PK-12
705 Lucky St 65248 660-248-2153
Dr. Tamara Kimball, supt. Fax 248-3702
www.fayette.k12.mo.us/
Fayette HS 200/9-12
510 N Cleveland St 65248 660-248-2124
Jeff Jacques, prin. Fax 248-2120

Central Methodist University Post-Sec.
411 Central Methodist Sq 65248 660-248-3391

Fenton, Saint Louis, Pop. 3,976
Rockwood R-VI SD
Supt. — See Eureka
Rockwood South MS 1,000/6-8
1628 Hawkins Rd 63026 636-861-7723
Laurie Birkenmeier, prin. Fax 861-7730
Rockwood Summit HS 1,300/9-12
1780 Hawkins Rd 63026 636-891-6800
Dr. Renee Trotier, prin. Fax 861-7717

Anthem College Post-Sec.
645 Gravois Bluffs Blvd 63026 888-852-7272
Heritage Classical Christian Academy 50/5-12
1694 Smizer Station Rd 63026 636-394-8063
Jason Wood, hdmstr.
Midwest Institute Post-Sec.
964 S Highway Dr 63026 314-965-8363
St. Louis College of Health Careers Post-Sec.
1297 N Highway Dr 63026 636-529-0000

Ferguson, Saint Louis, Pop. 20,785

St. Louis Community College Post-Sec.
3400 Pershall Rd 63135 314-513-4200

Festus, Jefferson, Pop. 11,379
Festus R-VI SD 3,000/K-12
1515 Midmeadow Ln 63028 636-937-4920
Dr. Link Luttrell, supt. Fax 937-8525
www.festus.k12.mo.us
Festus HS 900/9-12
501 Westwind Dr 63028 636-937-5410
Diana Allen, prin. Fax 937-8048
Festus MS 400/7-8
1717 W Main St 63028 636-937-5417
Tina Thebeau, prin. Fax 937-4171

Jefferson County R-VII SD 1,000/PK-12
1250 Dooling Hollow Rd 63028 636-937-7940
Clint D. Johnston, supt. Fax 937-9189
www.jr7.k12.mo.us/
Danby-Rush Tower MS 200/6-8
1250 Dooling Hollow Rd 63028 636-937-9188
Cynthia Holdinghausen, prin. Fax 937-9189
Jefferson County HS 300/9-12
7 Blue Jay Way 63028 636-933-6900
David Haug, prin. Fax 933-2663

St. Pius X HS 300/9-12
1030 Saint Pius Dr 63028 636-931-7488
Karen DeCosty, prin. Fax 931-3519

Florissant, Saint Louis, Pop. 50,980
Ferguson-Florissant R-II SD 12,200/PK-12
1005 Waterford Dr 63033 314-506-9000
Dr. Joseph Davis, supt. Fax 506-9010
www.fergflor.org
Cross Keys MS 900/7-8
14205 Cougar Dr 63033 314-506-9700
Christopher Clark, prin. Fax 506-9701
McCluer HS 1,300/9-12
1896 S New Florissant Rd 63031 314-506-9400
Cedric Gerald, prin. Fax 506-9401
McCluer North HS 1,800/9-12
705 Waterford Dr 63033 314-506-9200
Dr. Andrew Croley, prin. Fax 506-9201
Student Support Center 200/Alt
1555 Derhake Rd 63033 314-839-5959
Mark Weller, prin. Fax 839-7536
Other Schools – See Berkeley, Saint Louis

Hazelwood SD 18,400/PK-12
15955 New Halls Ferry Rd 63031 314-953-5000
Dr. Nettie Collins-Hart, supt. Fax 953-5085
www.hazelwoodschools.org
Hazelwood Central HS 2,000/9-12
15875 New Halls Ferry Rd 63031 314-953-5400
Audrey Lee, prin. Fax 953-5413
Hazelwood Central MS 700/6-8
13450 Old Jamestown Rd 63033 314-953-7400
Steve Richards, prin. Fax 953-7413
Hazelwood North MS 800/6-8
4420 Vaile Ave 63034 314-953-7500
Crystal Reiter, prin. Fax 953-7513
Hazelwood Northwest MS 800/6-8
1605 Shackelford Rd 63031 314-953-5500
Nicole Huffman, prin. Fax 953-5513
Other Schools – See Hazelwood, Saint Louis

Special SD of St. Louis County
Supt. — See Saint Louis
North Technical HS Vo/Tech
1700 Derhake Rd 63033 314-989-7600
James Hieger, prin. Fax 989-7665

North County Christian S 300/PK-12
845 Dunn Rd 63031 314-972-6227
Dr. Greg Clark, supt. Fax 972-6220
St. Louis Christian College Post-Sec.
1360 Grandview Dr 63033 314-837-6777
Urshan Graduate School of Theology Post-Sec.
704 Howdershell Rd 63031 314-921-9290

Fordland, Webster, Pop. 792
Fordland R-III SD 600/PK-12
1230 School St 65652 417-738-2296
Chris Ford, supt. Fax 767-4483
www.fordland.k12.mo.us
Fordland HS 200/9-12
1248 School St 65652 417-738-2212
Doug Fields, prin. Fax 767-2240
Fordland MS 100/6-8
1230 School St 65652 417-738-2119
Doug Fields, prin. Fax 767-4483

Forsyth, Taney, Pop. 2,219
Forsyth R-III SD 1,200/PK-12
PO Box 187 65653 417-546-6384
Dr. Jeff Mingus, supt. Fax 546-2204
www.forsythpanthers.org
Forsyth HS 400/9-12
PO Box 187 65653 417-546-6383
Christian Meier, prin. Fax 546-5987
Forsyth MS 400/5-8
PO Box 187 65653 417-546-6382
Dr. Sandra Goss, prin. Fax 546-6943

Fredericktown, Madison, Pop. 3,947
Fredericktown R-I SD 1,900/PK-12
704 E Highway 72 63645 573-783-2570
Brett Reutzel, supt. Fax 783-7045
www.fpsk12.org/
Fredericktown HS 600/9-12
805 E Highway 72 63645 573-783-3628
Shannon Henson, prin. Fax 783-8224
Fredericktown MS 400/6-8
805A E Highway 72 63645 573-783-6555
Kenneth Lunsford, prin. Fax 783-8079

Fulton, Callaway, Pop. 12,513
Fulton SD 58 2,200/K-12
2 Hornet Dr 65251 573-590-8000
Dr. Jacque Cowherd, supt. Fax 590-8090
www.fulton58.org
Fulton HS 600/9-12
1 Hornet Dr 65251 573-590-8100
Chris Mincher, prin. Fax 590-8190
Fulton MS 500/6-8
403 E 10th St 65251 573-590-8200
Beth Houf, prin. Fax 590-8290

Kingdom Christian Academy 200/PK-12
650 E 8th St 65251 573-642-2117
Kevin Browne, admin. Fax 642-2022
Missouri School for the Deaf Post-Sec.
505 E 5th St 65251 573-592-4000
Westminister College Post-Sec.
501 Westminster Ave 65251 573-642-3361
William Woods University Post-Sec.
1 University Ave 65251 573-642-2251

Gainesville, Ozark, Pop. 761
Gainesville R-V SD 700/PK-12
422 Bulldog Dr 65655 417-679-4200
Joe Donley, supt. Fax 679-4270
gainesville.mo.schoolwebpages.com
Gainesville HS 300/7-12
422 Bulldog Dr 65655 417-679-4200
Aaron Dalton, prin. Fax 679-4270

Galena, Stone, Pop. 437
Galena R-II SD 500/PK-12
PO Box 286 65656 417-357-6027
Dr. Daniel Humble, supt. Fax 357-0058
www.galena.k12.mo.us/
Galena JSHS 200/7-12
PO Box 286 65656 417-357-6618
Bob Baker, prin. Fax 357-8444

Gallatin, Daviess, Pop. 1,762
Gallatin R-V SD 500/PK-12
602 S Olive St 64640 660-663-2171
Dr. Bryan Copple, supt. Fax 663-2559
gallatin.k12.mo.us
Gallatin HS 200/9-12
602 S Olive St 64640 660-663-2171
Brent Burke, prin. Fax 663-2559
Gallatin MS 5-8
600 S Olive St 64640 660-663-2172
Tiffany Otto, prin. Fax 663-2559

Galt, Grundy, Pop. 246
Grundy County R-V SD 200/K-12
PO Box 6 64641 660-673-6511
Robert Deaver, supt. Fax 673-6523
Grundy County JSHS 100/7-12
PO Box 6 64641 660-673-6511
Randy Huffman, prin. Fax 673-6523

Garden City, Cass, Pop. 1,626

Training Center Christian S 50/PK-12
PO Box 200 64747 816-773-8367
Judy Williams, supt. Fax 862-6052

Gideon, New Madrid, Pop. 1,088
Gideon SD 37 300/PK-12
PO Box 227 63848 573-448-3911
James Breece, supt. Fax 448-5197
gideon.k12.mo.us/
Gideon JSHS 100/7-12
PO Box 227 63848 573-448-3471
Keenan Buchanan, prin. Fax 448-3868

Gilman City, Daviess, Pop. 381
Gilman City R-IV SD 100/PK-12
141 Lindsey Ave 64642 660-876-5221
Roger Alley, supt. Fax 876-5553
www.gilman.k12.mo.us
Gilman City JSHS 100/7-12
141 Lindsey Ave 64642 660-876-5221
Brent Mitchell, prin. Fax 876-5553

Gladstone, Clay, Pop. 24,544
North Kansas City SD 74
Supt. — See Kansas City
Antioch MS 900/6-8
2100 NE 65th St 64118 816-321-5260
Dr. Stephanie Schnoebelen, prin. Fax 321-5261

Paris II Educational Center Post-Sec.
6840 N Oak Trfy 64118 816-468-6666

Glasgow, Howard, Pop. 1,085
Glasgow SD 300/PK-12
860 Randolph St 65254 660-338-2012
Michael Reynolds, supt. Fax 338-2610
Glasgow JSHS 200/7-12
860 Randolph St 65254 660-338-2012
Sonya Fuemmeler, prin. Fax 338-2610

Glencoe, Saint Louis
Rockwood R-VI SD
Supt. — See Eureka
LaSalle Springs MS 900/6-8
3300 Highway 109 63038 636-938-2425
Deborah Brandt, prin. Fax 938-2434
Rockwood Valley MS 800/6-8
1220 Babler Park Dr 63038 636-458-7324
Dr. Karen Hedrick, prin. Fax 458-7325
Wildwood MS 800/6-8
17401 Manchester Rd 63038 636-458-7360
Dr. Allison Klouse, prin. Fax 458-7372

Golden City, Barton, Pop. 757
Golden City R-III SD 200/PK-12
1208 Walnut St 64748 417-537-4900
Steven Brigham, supt. Fax 537-8717
Golden City JSHS 100/7-12
1208 Walnut St 64748 417-537-8311
Jason Kramer, prin. Fax 537-8717

Gower, Buchanan, Pop. 1,511
East Buchanan County C-1 SD 700/K-12
100 Smith St 64454 816-424-6466
Paul Mensching, supt. Fax 424-3511
www.ebs.k12.mo.us/
East Buchanan HS 200/9-12
100 Smith St 64454 816-424-6460
Douglas Miller, prin. Fax 424-6410
Other Schools – See Easton

Graham, Nodaway, Pop. 171
Nodaway-Holt R-VII SD 200/PK-12
318 S Taylor St 64455 660-939-2137
Karma Coleman, supt. Fax 939-2200
www.nodholt.k12.mo.us
Nodaway-Holt JSHS 100/7-12
318 S Taylor St 64455 660-939-2135
Ethan Sickels, prin. Fax 939-2201

Grain Valley, Jackson, Pop. 12,604
Grain Valley R-V SD 4,000/PK-12
PO Box 304 64029 816-847-5006
Dr. Roy Moss Ph.D., supt. Fax 229-4831
www.gvr5.net
Grain Valley HS 1,000/9-12
PO Box 304 64029 816-847-5000
Dr. Jeremy Plowman Ph.D., prin. Fax 847-5002
Grain Valley North MS 300/6-8
PO Box 304 64029 816-994-4800
Theresa Nelson, prin. Fax 994-4899
Grain Valley South MS 600/6-8
PO Box 304 64029 816-229-3499
Jim Myers, prin. Fax 847-5017

Granby, Newton, Pop. 2,075
East Newton County R-VI SD 1,500/PK-12
22808 E Highway 86 64844 417-472-6231
Todd McCrackin, supt. Fax 472-3500
www.eastnewton.org
East Newton HS 500/9-12
22876 E Highway 86 64844 417-472-6238
Scott Charlton, prin. Fax 472-7129

Grandview, Jackson, Pop. 23,651
Grandview C-4 SD 4,100/PK-12
13015 10th St 64030 816-316-5000
Kenny Rodrequez, supt. Fax 316-5050
www.grandviewc4.net
C.A.I.R. Alt
1001 Main St 64030 816-316-5150
Derek Jordan, prin. Fax 316-5995
Grandview HS 1,200/9-12
2300 High Grove Rd 64030 816-316-5800
Jennifer Price, prin. Fax 316-5898
Grandview MS 600/6-8
12650 Manchester Ave 64030 816-316-5600
Jacqueline Spencer, prin. Fax 316-5699

Grandview Christian S 100/K-12
12340 Grandview Rd 64030 816-767-8630

Grant City, Worth, Pop. 858
Worth County R-III SD 300/PK-12
510 East Ave 64456 660-564-3389
Matt Martz, supt. Fax 564-2193
wc.k12.mo.us
Worth County JSHS 200/7-12
510 East Ave 64456 660-564-2218
Jonathan Adwell, prin. Fax 564-2193

Green City, Sullivan, Pop. 647
Green City R-I SD 300/PK-12
301 N East St 63545 660-874-4128
Tennille Banner, supt. Fax 874-4515
www.greencity.k12.mo.us/
Green City JSHS 100/7-12
301 N East St 63545 660-874-4127
Cindy Roberts, prin. Fax 874-5010

Greenfield, Dade, Pop. 1,342
Greenfield R-IV SD 400/PK-12
410 College St 65661 417-637-5321
Jeffery Davis, supt. Fax 637-5805
www.greenfieldwildcats.org
Greenfield JSHS 200/7-12
410 College St 65661 417-637-5328
John Hinsley, prin. Fax 637-5805

Green Ridge, Pettis, Pop. 466
Green Ridge R-VIII SD 400/K-12
PO Box 70 65332 660-527-3315
Cara Easter, supt. Fax 527-3299
greenridge.k12.mo.us
Green Ridge JSHS 200/7-12
PO Box 70 65332 660-527-3315
Rodney Edington, prin. Fax 527-3299

Greenville, Wayne, Pop. 503
Greenville R-II SD 800/PK-12
PO Box 320 63944 573-224-3844
Dr. Todd Porter, supt. Fax 224-3412
bears.k12.mo.us
Greenville HS 200/9-12
PO Box 320 63944 573-224-3618
Rick Clubb, prin. Fax 224-3580
Greenville JHS 100/7-8
PO Box 320 63944 573-224-3833
Rick Clubb, prin. Fax 224-3580

Hale, Carroll, Pop. 409
Hale R-I SD 200/PK-12
PO Box 248 64643 660-565-2417
Clinton Heussner, supt. Fax 565-2418
haleschooldistrict.com
Hale JSHS 100/7-12
PO Box 248 64643 660-565-2417
Hollie Burnside, prin. Fax 565-2418

Half Way, Polk, Pop. 165
Halfway R-III SD 300/K-12
2150 Highway 32 65663 417-445-2351
Tim Boatwright, supt. Fax 445-2026
www.halfwayschools.org
Halfway JSHS 100/7-12
2150 Highway 32 65663 417-445-2211
Lance Roweton, prin. Fax 445-3330

Hallsville, Boone, Pop. 1,463
Hallsville R-IV SD 1,400/PK-12
421 Hwy 124 E 65255 573-696-5512
John Downs, supt. Fax 696-3606
www.hallsville.org/
Hallsville HS 400/9-12
421 Hwy 124 E 65255 573-696-5512
Scott Daly, prin. Fax 696-1482
Hallsville MS 300/6-8
421 Hwy 124 E 65255 573-696-5512
Clinton Hague, prin. Fax 696-7238

Hamilton, Caldwell, Pop. 1,790
Hamilton R-II SD 700/PK-12
PO Box 130 64644 816-583-2134
Troy Ford, supt. Fax 583-2139
www.hamilton.k12.mo.us/
Hamilton MS 200/6-8
PO Box 130 64644 816-583-2173
Dave Richman, prin. Fax 583-2686
Penney HS 200/9-12
PO Box 130 64644 816-583-2136
Tim Schieber, prin. Fax 583-2319

Hannibal, Marion, Pop. 17,465
Hannibal SD 60 3,600/PK-12
4650 McMasters Ave 63401 573-221-1258
Susan Johnson, supt. Fax 221-2994
www.hannibal.k12.mo.us
Hannibal Career & Technical Center Vo/Tech
4550 McMasters Ave 63401 573-221-4430
Roger McGregor, dir. Fax 221-7971
Hannibal HS 1,000/9-12
4500 Mcmasters Ave 63401 573-221-2733
Ted Sampson, prin. Fax 221-9511
Hannibal MS 800/6-8
4700 Mcmasters Ave 63401 573-221-5840
Matt Nimmo, prin. Fax 221-7779

Hannibal Area Voc. Technical School Post-Sec.
4550 McMasters Ave 63401 573-221-4430
Hannibal-LaGrange University Post-Sec.
2800 Palmyra Rd 63401 573-221-3675

Hardin, Ray, Pop. 565
Hardin-Central C-2 SD 300/PK-12
PO Box 548 64035 660-398-4394
Trey Cavanah, supt. Fax 398-4396
www.hardin-central.org
Hardin-Central JSHS 100/7-12
PO Box 548 64035 660-398-4394
Phyllis Stanley, prin. Fax 398-4396

Harrisburg, Boone, Pop. 260
Harrisburg R-VIII SD 500/K-12
1000 S Harris St 65256 573-875-5604
Lynn Proctor, supt. Fax 875-8877
www.harrisburg.k12.mo.us
Harrisburg HS 200/9-12
801 S Harris St 65256 573-875-5602
Steve Combs, prin. Fax 443-1559
Harrisburg MS 100/6-8
233 S Harris St 65256 573-817-5857
Kyle Fisher, prin. Fax 875-8936

Harrisonville, Cass, Pop. 9,864
Harrisonville R-IX SD 2,700/PK-12
503 S Lexington St 64701 816-380-2727
Frank Dahman, supt. Fax 380-3134
www.harrisonvilleschools.org
Cass Career Center Vo/Tech
1600 E Elm St 64701 816-380-3253
Jeanette Miller, dir. Fax 884-3179
Harrisonville HS 900/9-12
1504 E Elm St 64701 816-380-3273
Jason Eggers, prin. Fax 380-5853
Harrisonville MS 600/6-8
601 S Highland Dr 64701 816-380-7654
Chris Grantham, prin. Fax 884-5733

Harrisonville Christian S West Campus 100/5-8
1202 S Commercial St 64701 816-884-6499
Al Sancken, prin. Fax 887-2093

Hartville, Wright, Pop. 610
Hartville R-II SD 700/PK-12
PO Box 460 65667 417-741-7676
Mark Piper, supt. Fax 741-7746
www.hartville.k12.mo.us
Hartville JSHS 300/7-12
PO Box 460 65667 417-741-7676
Scott Keith, prin. Fax 741-7746

Hayti, Pemiscot, Pop. 2,893
Hayti R-II SD 800/PK-12
PO Box 469 63851 573-359-6500
Jackie Johnson, supt. Fax 359-6502
haytir2.com
Hayti HS 300/9-12
PO Box 469 63851 573-359-6500
Melanie Tipton, prin. Fax 359-6504
Wallace MS 200/5-8
PO Box 469 63851 573-359-6500
Twanna Jones, prin. Fax 359-6254

Pemiscot County Special SD 573-359-0021
1317 State Highway 84 63851 Fax 359-6525
Doug White, supt.
Pemiscot County Career & Tech Center Vo/Tech
1317 State Highway 84 63851 573-359-2601
Brock Crowley, dir. Fax 359-1317

Hazelwood, Saint Louis, Pop. 25,088
Hazelwood SD
Supt. — See Florissant
Hazelwood West HS 2,200/9-12
1 Wildcat Ln 63042 314-953-5800
Dennis Newell, prin. Fax 953-5813
Hazelwood West MS 800/6-8
12834 Missouri Bottom Rd 63042 314-953-5800
Lisa Ostrowski, prin. Fax 953-5813

Herculaneum, Jefferson, Pop. 3,429
Dunklin R-V SD 1,700/K-12
497 Joachim Ave 63048 636-479-5200
Stan Stratton, supt. Fax 479-6208
www.dunklin.k12.mo.us
Herculaneum HS 400/9-12
1 Black Cat Dr 63048 636-479-5200
Dr. John Crabtree, prin. Fax 479-2050
Senn-Thomas MS 300/6-8
200 Senn Tomas Dr 63048 636-479-5200
Brian Johnson, prin. Fax 479-7219

Hermann, Gasconade, Pop. 2,399
Gasconade County R-I SD 1,000/K-12
170 Blue Pride Dr 65041 573-486-2116
Dr. Tracey Hankins, supt. Fax 486-3032
www.hermann.k12.mo.us
Hermann HS 300/9-12
176 Bearcat Xing 65041 573-486-5425
Gary Leimkuehler, prin. Fax 486-3058
Hermann MS 300/4-8
164 Blue Pride Dr 65041 573-486-3121
Nicole Buschmann, prin. Fax 486-5106

Hermitage, Hickory, Pop. 457
Hermitage R-IV SD 300/PK-12
PO Box 327 65668 417-745-6418
William Vest, supt. Fax 745-6475
www.hermitage.k12.mo.us/
Hermitage HS 100/9-12
PO Box 327 65668 417-745-6417
Krissy Friedman, prin. Fax 745-6475
Hermitage MS 100/6-8
PO Box 327 65668 417-745-6417
Krissy Friedman, prin. Fax 745-6475

Higbee, Randolph, Pop. 552
Higbee R-VIII SD 200/K-12
PO Box 128 65257 660-456-7277
Darrell Treece, supt. Fax 456-7278
www.higbeeschool.com/
Higbee JSHS 100/7-12
PO Box 128 65257 660-456-7206
Christopher Stockhorst, prin. Fax 456-7207

Higginsville, Lafayette, Pop. 4,706
Lafayette County C-1 SD 1,000/PK-12
805 W 31st St 64037 660-584-3631
David Figg, supt. Fax 584-2622
www.huskers.k12.mo.us
Lafayette County HS 300/9-12
807a W 31st St 64037 660-584-3661
Todd Whitney, prin. Fax 584-8666
Lafayette County MS 200/6-8
807b W 31st St 64037 660-584-7161
Jove Stickel, prin. Fax 584-6080

Highlandville, Christian, Pop. 898
Spokane R-VII SD 800/PK-12
167 Kentling Ave 65669 417-443-2200
Daryl Bernskoetter, supt. Fax 443-2205
www.spokane.k12.mo.us
Other Schools – See Spokane

High Ridge, Jefferson, Pop. 4,270
Northwest R-I SD 6,600/PK-12
2843 Community Ln 63049 636-677-3473
Dr. Paul Ziegler, supt. Fax 677-5480
www.northwestschools.net
Woodridge MS 600/6-8
2109 Gravois Rd 63049 636-677-3577
Shannon Umfleet, prin. Fax 677-5581
Other Schools – See Cedar Hill, House Springs

Hillsboro, Jefferson, Pop. 2,784
Grandview R-II SD 800/K-12
11470 State Road C 63050 636-944-3941
Matt Zoph, supt. Fax 944-5239
www.grandviewr2.com
Grandview HS 300/9-12
11470 State Road C 63050 636-944-3390
Andy Arbeitman, prin. Fax 944-3515
Grandview MS 200/6-8
11470 State Road C 63050 636-944-3931
Allen Davis, prin. Fax 944-5239

Hillsboro R-III SD 3,500/K-12
5 Ridgewood Dr 63050 636-789-0060
Aaron Cornman Ph.D., supt. Fax 789-3216
www.hsdr3.org
Hillsboro Alternative S 50/Alt
10486 Business 21 63050 636-789-0000
Fax 789-2773
Hillsboro HS 1,200/9-12
123 Leon Hall Pkwy 63050 636-789-0010
Cathleen Freeman, prin. Fax 789-3211
Hillsboro JHS 500/7-8
12 Hawk Dr 63050 636-789-0020
Heath Allison, prin. Fax 789-3212

Christian Outreach S 50/PK-12
4450 Outreach Dr 63050 636-797-3466
Steve Miller, prin.
Jefferson College Post-Sec.
1000 Viking Dr 63050 636-797-3000

Holcomb, Dunklin, Pop. 633
Holcomb R-III SD 600/PK-12
PO Box 190 63852 573-792-3113
Dr. Ashley McMillian, supt. Fax 792-3118
www.holcombschools.com
Holcomb JSHS 300/7-12
PO Box 190 63852 573-792-3362
Matthew Hodges, prin. Fax 792-3631

Holden, Johnson, Pop. 2,201
Holden R-III SD 1,300/PK-12
1612 S Main St 64040 816-732-5568
Wade Schroeder, supt. Fax 732-4336
www.holdenschools.org
Holden HS 400/9-12
1901 S Main St 64040 816-732-5523
Ginger Jones, prin. Fax 732-4142
Holden MS 300/6-8
301 Eagle Dr 64040 816-732-4125
Dr. Mike Hough, prin. Fax 732-2009

Hollister, Taney, Pop. 4,346
Hollister R-V SD 1,500/PK-12
1914 State Highway BB 65672 417-243-4005
Dr. Brian Wilson, supt. Fax 334-2663
www.hollister.k12.mo.us/
Hollister HS 500/9-12
2112 State Highway BB 65672 417-243-4045
Travis Graham, prin. Fax 334-2240
Hollister MS 300/6-8
1798 State Highway BB 65672 417-243-4035
Shawn Page, prin. Fax 334-6482

Trinity Christian Academy 100/PK-12
119 Myrtle Ave 65672 417-334-7084
Holly Gregory, prin. Fax 334-1794

Hopkins, Nodaway, Pop. 530
North Nodaway County R-VI SD 300/PK-12
705 E Barnard St 64461 660-778-3411
James Simmelink, supt. Fax 778-3210
www.nnr6.org/
North Nodaway County JSHS 100/6-12
705 E Barnard St 64461 660-778-3315
Timothy Conn, prin. Fax 778-3210

Hornersville, Dunklin, Pop. 654
Senath-Hornersville C-8 SD
Supt. — See Senath
Senath-Hornersville MS 200/5-8
601 School St 63855 573-737-2455
Jared Gurley, prin. Fax 737-2456

House Springs, Jefferson
Northwest R-I SD
Supt. — See High Ridge
Valley MS 800/6-8
4300 Gravois Rd 63051 636-671-3470
Dayle Burgdorf, prin. Fax 671-0948

Houston, Texas, Pop. 2,038
Houston R-I SD 1,000/PK-12
423 W Pine St 65483 417-967-3024
Dr. Allen Moss, supt. Fax 967-4887
www.houston.k12.mo.us
Houston HS 400/9-12
423 W Pine St 65483 417-967-3024
Amy Smith, prin. Fax 967-3669
Houston MS 200/6-8
423 W Pine St 65483 417-967-3024
Amber Stephens, prin. Fax 967-5481

Texas County Techical College Post-Sec.
6915 Highway 63 65483 417-967-5466

Hughesville, Pettis, Pop. 182
Pettis County R-V SD 300/K-12
16215 Highway H 65334 660-827-0772
Dr. Cody Hirschi, supt. Fax 827-7162
www.northwest.k12.mo.us
Northwest JSHS 200/7-12
16215 Highway H 65334 660-827-0774
David Dawson, prin. Fax 827-7162

Humansville, Polk, Pop. 1,030
Humansville R-IV SD 300/PK-12
300 N Oak St 65674 417-754-2535
Tammy Erwin, supt. Fax 754-8565
www.humansville.k12.mo.us
Humansville HS 100/9-12
300 N Oak St 65674 417-754-2219
Steve Gallivan, prin. Fax 754-8565
Humansville MS 6-8
300 N Oak St 65674 417-754-2119
Colleena Frazier, admin. Fax 754-8565

Hume, Bates, Pop. 331
Hume R-VIII SD 200/PK-12
9163 SW 2nd St 64752 660-643-7411
David Quick, supt. Fax 643-7506
www.humer8.k12.mo.us
Hume JSHS 100/7-12
9163 SW 2nd St 64752 660-643-7411
Scott Morrsion, prin. Fax 643-7506

Huntsville, Randolph, Pop. 1,540
Westran R-I SD 700/PK-12
228 Huntsville Ave 65259 660-277-4429
Dr. Kelly Shelby, supt. Fax 277-4420
westran.k12.mo.us/
Westran HS 200/9-12
601 Hornet Ln 65259 660-277-4415
Michael Nagel, prin. Fax 277-4644
Other Schools – See Clifton Hill

Hurley, Stone, Pop. 177
Hurley R-I SD 200/K-12
PO Box 248 65675 417-369-3271
Dr. Doug Arnold, supt. Fax 369-2212
www.hurley.k12.mo.us/
Hurley JSHS 100/6-12
PO Box 248 65675 417-369-3271
Joey Little, prin. Fax 369-2202

Iberia, Miller, Pop. 730
Iberia R-V SD 700/PK-12
201 Pemberton Dr 65486 573-793-6818
Lyndel Whittle, supt. Fax 793-6821
www.iberia.k12.mo.us/
Iberia HS 300/7-12
201 Pemberton Dr 65486 573-793-2228
Tara Luttrell, prin. Fax 793-2946

Imperial, Jefferson, Pop. 4,673
Fox C-6 SD
Supt. — See Arnold
Seckman HS 1,800/9-12
2800 Seckman Rd 63052 636-282-1485
Todd Scott, prin. Fax 282-5177
Seckman MS 500/7-8
2840 Seckman Rd 63052 636-296-5707
Dr. Tammy Cardona, prin. Fax 296-5707

Windsor C-1 SD 2,900/K-12
6208 US Highway 61 67 63052 636-464-4400
Joel Holland Ed.D., supt. Fax 464-4454
windsor.k12.mo.us
Windsor HS 900/9-12
6208 US Highway 61 67 63052 636-464-4429
David Gilmore, prin. Fax 464-4456
Windsor MS 700/6-8
6208 US Highway 61 67 63052 636-464-4417
Karl Shininger, prin. Fax 464-4473

Independence, Jackson, Pop. 113,065
Fort Osage R-I SD 5,000/PK-12
2101 N Twyman Rd 64058 816-650-7000
Jason Snodgrass, supt. Fax 650-3888
www.fortosage.net
Career & Technology Center Vo/Tech
2101 N Twyman Rd 64058 816-650-7180
Mike Pantleo, dir. Fax 650-7195
Ft. Osage HS 1,500/9-12
2101 N Twyman Rd 64058 816-650-7030
Scott Moore, prin. Fax 650-7088
Lewis and Clark Academy Alt
2101 N Twyman Rd 64058 816-650-7708
Kim Hawley, prin. Fax 650-7712
Osage Trail MS 800/7-8
2101 N Twyman Rd 64058 816-650-7151
Robbie Shepherd, prin. Fax 650-7152

Independence SD 30 13,600/PK-12
201 N Forest Ave 64050 816-521-5300
Dr. Dale Herl, supt. Fax 521-5680
www.isdschools.org
Bingham MS 400/7-8
1716 S Speck Rd 64057 816-521-5490
Brett Playter, prin. Fax 521-5631
Chrisman HS 1,500/9-12
1223 N Noland Rd 64050 816-521-5355
Mike Becker, prin. Fax 521-5606
Independence Academy 100/Alt
600 W Mechanic Ave 64050 816-521-5505
Rebecca Bressman, prin. Fax 521-5613
Nowlin MS 800/6-8
2800 S Hardy Ave 64052 816-521-5380
Cristin Nowak, prin. Fax 521-5633
Pioneer Ridge MS 500/7-8
1656 S Speck Rd 64057 816-521-5385
Michael Estes, prin. Fax 521-5630
Truman HS 1,600/9-12
3301 S Noland Rd 64055 816-521-5350
Pam Boatright, prin. Fax 521-5604
Van Horn HS 700/9-12
1109 S Arlington Ave 64053 816-521-5360
Randy Maglinger, prin. Fax 521-5610

Graceland University Post-Sec.
1401 W Truman Rd 64050 816-833-0524
Independence College of Cosmetology Post-Sec.
815 W 23rd St 64055 816-252-4247
Metropolitan Community Coll - Blue River Post-Sec.
20301 E State Route 78 64057 816-604-6500
National American University Post-Sec.
3620 Arrowhead Ave 64057 816-353-4554

Ironton, Iron, Pop. 1,442
Arcadia Valley R-II SD 1,000/PK-12
750 Park Dr 63650 573-546-9700
Jim Carver Ed.D., supt. Fax 546-7314
www.avr2.org
Arcadia Valley Career Tech Vo/Tech
650 Park Dr 63650 573-546-9700
Steve Pursley, dir. Fax 546-6956
Arcadia Valley HS 400/9-12
520 Park Dr 63650 573-546-9700
Rebecca Amelunke, prin. Fax 546-3934
Arcadia Valley MS 300/5-8
550 Park Dr 63650 573-546-9700
Kent Huddleston, prin. Fax 546-7304

Jackson, Cape Girardeau, Pop. 13,577
Jackson R-II SD 4,700/PK-12
614 E Adams St 63755 573-243-9501
Dr. John Link, supt. Fax 243-9503
www.jacksonr2schools.com
Hawkins JHS 700/8-9
210 N West Ln 63755 573-243-9533
Cory Crosnoe, prin. Fax 243-9584
Jackson SHS 1,100/10-12
315 S Missouri St 63755 573-243-9513
Seth Harrell, prin. Fax 243-9524

Saxony Lutheran HS 200/9-12
2004 Saxony Ln 63755 573-204-7555
Mark Ruark, prin. Fax 204-7445

Jameson, Daviess, Pop. 124
North Daviess R-III SD 100/PK-12
413 E 2nd St 64647 660-828-4123
Daniel Street, supt. Fax 828-4122
www.northdaviess.org
North Daviess JSHS 50/7-12
413 E 2nd St 64647 660-828-4123
Tim Harding, prin. Fax 828-4122

Jamesport, Daviess, Pop. 506
Tri-County R-VII SD 100/K-12
904 W Auberry Grv 64648 660-684-6118
David Probasco, supt. Fax 684-6218
Tri-County HS 100/7-12
904 W Auberry Grv 64648 660-684-6116
Tinna Croy, prin. Fax 684-6218

Jamestown, Moniteau, Pop. 378
Jamestown C-1 SD 200/K-12
222 School St 65046 660-849-2141
Ellen Ash, supt. Fax 849-2600
www.jamestown.k12.mo.us
Jamestown C-I JSHS 100/7-12
222 School St 65046 660-849-2141
Steven McDannold, prin. Fax 849-2600

Jasper, Jasper, Pop. 913
Jasper County R-V SD 500/K-12
201 W Mercer St 64755 417-394-2416
Kathy Fall, supt. Fax 394-2394
www.jasper.k12.mo.us/
Jasper County JSHS 200/7-12
201 W Mercer St 64755 417-394-2511
Christina Hess, prin. Fax 394-9977

Jefferson City, Cole, Pop. 42,185
Jefferson City SD 9,100/PK-12
315 E Dunklin St 65101 573-659-3000
Larry Linthacum, supt. Fax 659-3807
www.jcschools.us
Jefferson City HS 1,900/10-12
609 Union St 65101 573-659-3050
Dr. James Robert, prin. Fax 659-3153
Jefferson MS 1,000/6-8
1201 Fairgrounds Rd 65109 573-659-3250
Bray David, prin. Fax 659-3259
Lewis and Clark MS 900/6-8
325 Lewis and Clark Dr 65101 573-659-3200
Sherri Thomas, prin. Fax 659-3209
Nichols Career Center Vo/Tech
605 Union St 65101 573-659-3100
Sharon Longan, dir. Fax 659-3154
Simonsen Ninth Grade Center 700/9-9
501 E Miller St 65101 573-659-3125
Ben Meldrum, admin. Fax 659-7362

Helias Catholic HS 800/9-12
1305 Swifts Hwy 65109 573-635-6139
Kenya Fuemmeler, prin. Fax 635-5615
Lincoln University Post-Sec.
820 Chestnut St 65101 573-681-5000
Merrell Univ of Beauty Arts & Science Post-Sec.
1101 Southwest Blvd Ste R 65109 573-635-4433
Metro Business College Post-Sec.
210 El Mercado Plz 65109 573-635-6600
Nichols Career Center Post-Sec.
605 Union St 65101 573-659-3100

Jennings, Saint Louis, Pop. 14,545
Jennings SD 2,500/PK-12
2559 Dorwood Dr 63136 314-653-8000
Dr. Art McCoy, supt. Fax 653-8030
www.jenningsk12.org
Jennings HS 700/9-12
8850 Cozens Ave 63136 314-653-8100
Dr. Rhonda Key, prin. Fax 653-8102
Jennings JHS 400/7-8
8831 Cozens Ave 63136 314-653-8150
Melba Davis, prin. Fax 653-8168

Joplin, Jasper, Pop. 48,394
Carl Junction R-I SD
Supt. — See Carl Junction
Carl Junction Satellite 50/Alt
1999 Snowberry Ln 64804 417-347-7895
Cynthia Jackson, dir. Fax 649-7895

Joplin SD 7,700/PK-12
PO Box 128 64802 417-625-5200
Dr. Norm Ridder, supt. Fax 625-5210
www.joplinschools.org
East MS 500/6-8
PO Box 128 64802 417-625-5280
Jason Cravens, prin. Fax 625-5284
Franklin Tech S Vo/Tech
PO Box 128 64802 417-625-5260
David Rockers, dir. Fax 625-5266
Joplin HS 2,100/9-12
PO Box 128 64802 417-625-5230
Brandon Eggleston, prin. Fax 625-5238
North MS 600/6-8
PO Box 128 64802 417-625-5270
Matthew Harding, prin. Fax 625-5273
South MS 700/6-8
PO Box 128 64802 417-625-5250
Stephen Gilbreth, prin. Fax 625-5256

College Heights Christian S 500/PK-12
4311 Newman Rd 64801 417-782-4114
Nelson Horton, supt. Fax 659-9092
Franklin Technology - MSSU Post-Sec.
3950 Newman Rd 64801 417-659-4400
Jefferson Independent Day S 300/PK-12
3401 Newman Rd 64801 417-781-5124
Ben Parsons, head sch Fax 781-1949
McAuley Catholic HS 100/9-12
930 S Pearl Ave 64801 417-624-9320
Gene Koester, prin. Fax 626-8334
Missouri Southern State University Post-Sec.
3950 Newman Rd 64801 417-625-9300
New Dimensions School of Hair Design Post-Sec.
705 Illinois Ave Ste 12 64801 417-782-2875
Ozark Christian College Post-Sec.
1111 N Main St 64801 417-626-1234
St. John's Regional Medical Center Post-Sec.
2727 Mc Clelland Blvd 64804 417-781-2727
St. Peter MS 100/6-8
931 Byers Ave 64801 417-624-5605
Gene Koester, prin. Fax 624-6254
Vatterott College - Joplin Post-Sec.
809 Illinois Ave 64801 417-781-5633
Wichita Technical Institute - Joplin Post-Sec.
1715 N Range Line Rd 64801 417-206-9115

Kahoka, Clark, Pop. 2,063
Clark County R-I SD 1,000/PK-12
427 W Chestnut St 63445 660-727-2377
Ritchie Kracht, supt. Fax 727-2035
www.clarkcounty.k12.mo.us/
Clark County HS 300/9-12
680 E Main St 63445 660-727-2205
Jason Harper, prin. Fax 727-2245
Clark County MS 200/6-8
384 N Jefferson St 63445 660-727-3319
Jason Church, prin. Fax 727-3363

Shiloh Christian S 50/K-12
RR 1 Box 68A 63445 573-853-4430
Ken Penfield, admin. Fax 853-4432

Kansas City, Jackson, Pop. 447,224

Center SD 58 — 2,600/PK-12
8701 Holmes Rd 64131 — 816-349-3300
Dr. Sharon Nibbelink, supt. — Fax 349-3431
www.center.k12.mo.us
Center Alternative S — Alt
8434 Paseo Blvd 64131 — 816-349-3440
Kristian Foster, prin. — Fax 349-3667
Center HS — 700/9-12
8715 Holmes Rd 64131 — 816-349-3330
Sharon Ahuna, prin. — Fax 349-3427
Center MS — 500/6-8
326 E 103rd St 64114 — 816-612-4000
Linda Williams, prin. — Fax 612-4053

Hickman Mills C-I SD — 4,800/PK-12
9000 Old Santa Fe Rd 64138 — 816-316-7000
Dr. Dennis Carpenter, supt. — Fax 316-7020
www.hickmanmills.org
Hickman Mills Freshman Center — 500/9-9
9010 Old Santa Fe Rd 64138 — 816-316-7300
Venita Truman, prin. — Fax 316-8009
Ruskin HS — 1,100/10-12
7000 E 111th St Ste 46 64134 — 816-316-7400
Dawn Smith, prin. — Fax 316-7475
Smith-Hale MS — 500/7-8
8925 Longview Rd 64134 — 816-316-7700
Daniel Weakley, prin. — Fax 316-7704

Kansas City SD 33 — 12,600/PK-12
2901 Troost Ave 64109 — 816-418-7000
Dr. Mark Bedell, supt. — Fax 418-7766
www.kcpublicschools.org
Central Academy of Excellence — 400/9-12
3221 Indiana Ave 64128 — 816-418-2000
Anthony Madry, prin. — Fax 418-2027
Central MS — 7-8
3611 E Linwood Blvd 64128 — 816-418-7000
Dr. Cynthia Johnson, prin.
East HS — 700/9-12
1924 Van Brunt Blvd 64127 — 816-418-3125
Jeffrey Spaletta, prin. — Fax 418-3130
Lincoln College Prep HS — 900/6-12
2111 Woodland Ave 64108 — 816-418-3000
Steve Evans, prin. — Fax 418-3015
Manual Career & Tech Center — Vo/Tech
1215 E Truman Rd 64106 — 816-418-5200
Rashawn Caruthers, prin. — Fax 418-5220
Northeast HS — 600/9-12
415 Van Brunt Blvd 64124 — 816-418-3300
Douglas Bolden, prin. — Fax 418-3310
Northeast MS — 7-8
4904 Independence Ave 64124 — 816-418-7000
Jessica Bassett, prin.
Paseo Academy of Fine & Performing Arts — 500/7-12
4747 Flora Ave 64110 — 816-418-2275
Dennis Walker, prin. — Fax 418-2300
Southeast HS — 400/7-12
3500 E Meyer Blvd 64132 — 816-418-1078
Dr. Jason Whitt, prin.
Success Academy at Anderson — Alt
1601 Forest Ave 64108 — 816-418-5300
Robert Lee, prin. — Fax 418-5323

North Kansas City SD 74 — 19,600/PK-12
2000 NE 46th St 64116 — 816-321-5000
Dr. Dan Clemens, supt. — Fax 321-5005
www.nkcschools.org
Career & Technical Education — Vo/Tech
1950 NE 46th St 64116 — 816-321-6425
Dr. Renee Freers, dir.
Eastgate MS — 700/6-8
4700 NE Parvin Rd 64117 — 816-321-5270
Dr. Chris McCann, prin. — Fax 321-5271
Maple Park MS — 800/6-8
5300 N Bennington Ave 64119 — 816-321-5280
Brian Van Batavia, prin. — Fax 321-5281
New Mark MS — 1,100/6-8
515 NE 106th St 64155 — 816-321-5290
Terri Sherry, prin. — Fax 321-5291
Northgate MS — 800/6-8
2117 NE 48th St 64118 — 816-321-5300
P.J. McGinnis, prin. — Fax 321-5301
Oak Park HS — 1,400/9-12
825 NE 79th Ter 64118 — 816-321-5320
Christopher Sartain, prin. — Fax 321-5321
Staley HS — 1,400/9-12
2800 NE Shoal Creek Pkwy 64156 — 816-321-5330
Clark Mershon, prin. — Fax 321-5331
Winnetonka HS — 1,300/9-12
5815 NE 48th St 64119 — 816-321-5340
Matt Lindsey, prin. — Fax 321-5341
Other Schools – See Gladstone, North Kansas City

Park Hill SD — 10,700/PK-12
7703 NW Barry Rd 64153 — 816-359-4000
Dr. Jeanette Cowherd, supt. — Fax 359-4049
www.parkhill.k12.mo.us
Congress MS — 900/7-8
8150 N Congress Ave 64152 — 816-359-4230
Dr. Timothy Todd, prin. — Fax 359-4219
Jones Education Center — 50/Alt
7642 N Green Hills Rd 64151 — 816-359-4510
Dr. Lance Miller, prin. — Fax 359-4519
Lakeview MS — 800/7-8
6720 NW 64th St 64151 — 816-359-4220
Larry Smith, prin. — Fax 359-4229
Park Hill HS — 1,700/9-12
7701 NW Barry Rd 64153 — 816-359-4110
Dr. J. Bradford Kincheloe, prin. — Fax 359-4119
Other Schools – See Riverside

Platte County R-III SD
Supt. — See Platte City
Barry S — 400/5-8
2001 NW 87th Ter 64154 — 816-436-9623
Merri Beth Means, prin. — Fax 468-6046

Raytown C-2 SD
Supt. — See Raytown
Raytown MS — 800/6-8
4900 Pittman Rd 64133 — 816-268-7360
Dr. Georgetta May, prin. — Fax 268-7365

Achieve Test Prep — Post-Sec.
2300 Main St Fl 9 64108 — 816-399-4556
Anthem College — Post-Sec.
9001 State Line Rd 64114 — 888-852-7272
ARAMARK Healthcare Support Services SW — Post-Sec.
1000 Carondelet Dr 64114 — 816-943-2146
Archbishop O'Hara HS — 400/9-12
9001 James A Reed Rd 64138 — 816-763-4800
John O'Connor, prin. — Fax 763-0156
Aviation Institute of Maintenance — Post-Sec.
4100 Raytown Rd 64129 — 816-753-9920
Avila University — Post-Sec.
11901 Wornall Rd 64145 — 816-942-8400
Barstow S — 700/PK-12
11511 State Line Rd 64114 — 816-942-3255
Shane Foster, head sch — Fax 942-3227
Blue Ridge Christian S — 200/PK-12
15701 Calvary Rd 64147 — 816-358-0950
Kathleen Reynolds, supt.
Calvary Bible College & Theological Sem — Post-Sec.
15800 Calvary Rd 64147 — 816-322-0110
City Vision College — Post-Sec.
3101 Troost Ave Ste 200 64109 — 816-960-2008
Concorde Career College — Post-Sec.
3239 Broadway St 64111 — 816-531-5223
Cristo Rey Kansas City HS — 400/9-12
211 W Linwood Blvd 64111 — 816-457-6044
Kathleen Hanlon Ph.D., pres. — Fax 457-6046
DeVry University — Post-Sec.
1310 E 104th St 64131 — 816-943-7300
Everest College — Post-Sec.
1740 W 92nd St 64114 — 816-423-8600
Faith Christian Academy — 300/K-12
3500 NE Prather Rd 64116 — 816-455-3513
Grantham University — Post-Sec.
7200 NW 86th St 64153 — 800-955-2527
House of Heavilin Beauty College — Post-Sec.
5720 Troost Ave 64110 — 816-523-2471
Islamic S of Greater Kansas City — 300/PK-12
8505 E 99th St 64134 — 816-763-0322
Kansas City Art Institute — Post-Sec.
4415 Warwick Blvd 64111 — 816-472-4852
KC Univ. of Medicine and Biosciences — Post-Sec.
1750 Independence Ave 64106 — 816-654-7000
L'Ecole Culinaire — Post-Sec.
310 Ward Pkwy 64112 — 866-205-2521
Lutheran HS of Kansas City — 100/9-12
12411 Wornall Rd 64145 — 816-241-5478
Dr. Cary Stelmachowicz Ed.D., admin. — Fax 876-2069
Metropolitan Comm College - Penn Valley — Post-Sec.
3201 Southwest Traffic Way 64111 — 816-604-5000
Metropolitan Community Coll - Bus & Tech — Post-Sec.
1775 Universal Ave 64120 — 816-604-1000
Metropolitan Community Coll-Maple Woods — Post-Sec.
2601 NE Barry Rd 64156 — 816-604-3000
Midwestern Baptist Theological Seminary — Post-Sec.
5001 N Oak Trfy 64118 — 816-414-3700
Nazarene Theological Seminary — Post-Sec.
1700 E Meyer Blvd 64131 — 816-268-5400
Northland Christian S — 200/PK-12
4214 NW Cookingham Rd 64164 — 816-548-2222
Richard Rice, prin. — Fax 533-6914
Notre Dame de Sion HS — 400/9-12
10631 Wornall Rd 64114 — 816-942-3282
Natalie McDonough, prin. — Fax 942-4052
Pembroke Hill S - Ward Pkwy Campus — 700/6-12
400 W 51st St 64112 — 816-936-1200
Dr. Steven J. Bellis, head sch — Fax 936-1208
Pinnacle Career Institute — Post-Sec.
10301 Hickman Mills Dr #100 64137 — 816-331-5700
Pinnacle Career Institute — Post-Sec.
11500 N Ambassador Dr # 221 64153 — 816-270-5300
Research College of Nursing — Post-Sec.
2525 E Meyer Blvd 64132 — 816-995-2800
Research Medical Center — Post-Sec.
2316 E Meyer Blvd 64132 — 816-276-4101
Rockhurst HS — 1,100/9-12
9301 State Line Rd 64114 — 816-363-2036
Gregory Harkness, prin. — Fax 363-3764
Rockhurst University — Post-Sec.
1100 Rockhurst Rd 64110 — 816-501-4000
St. Luke's College of Health Sciences — Post-Sec.
624 Westport Rd 64111 — 816-932-6700
St. Paul School of Theology — Post-Sec.
5123 E Truman Rd 64127 — 816-483-9600
St. Pius X HS — 400/9-12
1500 NE 42nd Ter 64116 — 816-453-3450
Joseph Monachino, prin. — Fax 452-7099
St. Teresa Academy — 600/9-12
5600 Main St 64113 — 816-501-0011
Barbara McCormick M.S., prin. — Fax 523-0232
Strayer University — Post-Sec.
10450 Holmes Rd Ste 100 64131 — 816-489-4500
Truman Medical Center — Post-Sec.
2301 Holmes St 64108 — 816-556-3153
University of Missouri - Kansas City — Post-Sec.
5100 Rockhill Rd 64110 — 816-235-1000
Vatterott College - Kansas City — Post-Sec.
4131 N Corrington Ave 64117 — 816-861-1000
Whitefield Academy — 200/PK-12
8929 Holmes 64131 — 816-444-3567
Dr. Quentin Johnston Ph.D., hdmstr. — Fax 822-8405

Kearney, Clay, Pop. 8,257

Kearney R-I SD — 3,600/K-12
1002 S Jefferson St 64060 — 816-628-4116
Dr. William Nicely, supt. — Fax 628-4074
www.ksdr1.net
Kearney HS — 900/10-12
715 E 19th St 64060 — 816-628-4585
David Schwarzenbach, prin. — Fax 628-3383
Kearney JHS — 600/8-9
2215 S Campus St 64060 — 816-628-2650
Andy Gustafson, prin. — Fax 628-1938

Kennett, Dunklin, Pop. 10,740

Kennett SD 39 — 2,200/PK-12
510 College Ave 63857 — 573-717-1100
Chris Wilson, supt. — Fax 717-1016
www.kennett.k12.mo.us
Kennett Career & Technology Center — Vo/Tech
1400 W Washington St 63857 — 573-717-1123
Terry Bruce, dir. — Fax 717-1386
Kennett HS — 600/9-12
1400 W Washington St 63857 — 573-717-1120
Richard Leeker, prin. — Fax 717-1016
Kennett MS — 500/6-8
510 College Ave 63857 — 573-717-1105
Ward Billings, prin. — Fax 717-1106

Keytesville, Chariton, Pop. 471

Keytesville R-III SD — 100/PK-12
27247 Highway 5 65261 — 660-288-3787
Josh Shoemaker, supt. — Fax 288-3110
keytesville.k12.mo.us
Keytesville R-III HS — 100/7-12
27247 Highway 5 65261 — 660-288-3767
Vicki Enyart, prin. — Fax 288-3110

King City, Gentry, Pop. 1,004

King City R-I SD — 300/PK-12
PO Box 189 64463 — 660-535-4319
Danny Johnson, supt. — Fax 535-4765
www.kingcityschools.org
King City JSHS — 100/7-12
PO Box 189 64463 — 660-535-4319
Dottie Stoll, prin. — Fax 535-4765

Kingdom City, Callaway, Pop. 127

North Callaway County R-I SD — 1,100/PK-12
2690 Thunderbird Dr 65262 — 573-386-2214
Dr. Bryan Thomsen, supt. — Fax 386-2169
nc.k12.mo.us
North Callaway HS — 400/9-12
2700 Thunderbird Dr 65262 — 573-386-2211
Brian Jobe, prin. — Fax 386-2403

Kingsville, Johnson, Pop. 264

Kingsville R-I SD — 100/K-12
PO Box 7 64061 — 816-597-3422
Kevin Coleman, supt. — Fax 597-3702
kingsville.k12.mo.us
Kingsville S — 100/K-12
PO Box 7 64061 — 816-597-3422
Lorna Warren, prin. — Fax 597-3702

Kirbyville, Taney, Pop. 203

Kirbyville R-VI SD — 300/K-8
6225 E State Highway 76 65679 — 417-337-8913
Carless Osbourn, supt. — Fax 348-0794
www.kirbyville.k12.mo.us/
Kirbyville MS — 200/4-8
6225 E State Highway 76 65679 — 417-348-0444
Amy Burton, prin. — Fax 348-0525

Kirksville, Adair, Pop. 17,170

Kirksville R-III SD — 2,600/PK-12
1901 E Hamilton St 63501 — 660-665-7774
Dr. Damon Kizzire, supt. — Fax 626-1448
www.kirksville.k12.mo.us
Kirksville Area Technical Center — Vo/Tech
1103 Cottage Grove Ave 63501 — 660-665-2865
Sheryl Ferguson, prin. — Fax 626-1477
Kirksville HS — 800/9-12
1300 Cottage Grove Ave 63501 — 660-665-4631
Randy Mikel, prin. — Fax 626-1439
Matthew MS — 500/6-8
1515 Cottage Grove Ave 63501 — 660-665-3793
Dr. Michael Mitchell, prin. — Fax 626-1418

Kirksville Coll. of Osteopathic Medicine — Post-Sec.
800 W Jefferson St 63501 — 660-626-2237
School of Health Management — Post-Sec.
800 W Jefferson St 63501 — 877-626-5577
Still Univ MO Sch of Dentistry & Oral Hl — Post-Sec.
800 W Jefferson St 63501 — 866-626-2878
Truman State University — Post-Sec.
100 E Normal Ave 63501 — 660-785-4000

Kirkwood, Saint Louis, Pop. 27,112

Kirkwood R-VII SD — 5,900/PK-12
11289 Manchester Rd 63122 — 314-213-6101
Dr. Tom Williams, supt. — Fax 984-0002
www.kirkwoodschools.org
Kirkwood HS — 1,800/9-12
801 W Essex Ave 63122 — 314-213-6110
Dr. Michael Havener, prin. — Fax 984-4412
Nipher MS — 600/6-8
700 S Kirkwood Rd 63122 — 314-213-6180
Laura Havener, prin. — Fax 213-6178
North Kirkwood MS — 600/6-8
11287 Manchester Rd 63122 — 314-213-6170
Tim Cochran, prin. — Fax 213-6177

St. Louis Community College - Meramec — Post-Sec.
11333 Big Bend Rd 63122 — 314-984-7500

Knob Noster, Johnson, Pop. 2,592

Knob Noster R-VIII SD — 1,500/PK-12
401 E Wimer St 65336 — 660-563-3186
Dr. Jerrod Wheeler, supt. — Fax 563-3026
www.knobnoster.k12.mo.us
Knob Noster HS — 300/9-12
504 S Washington Ave 65336 — 660-563-2283
Connie Morris, prin. — Fax 563-3384
Knob Noster MS — 400/5-8
211 E Wimer St 65336 — 660-563-2260
Shelby Scarbrough, prin. — Fax 563-3274

Koshkonong, Oregon, Pop. 200
Oregon-Howell R-III SD 200/K-12
100 School St 65692 417-867-5601
Seth Bryant, supt. Fax 867-3757
Koshkonong HS 100/9-12
100 School St 65692 417-867-5601
David Miller, prin. Fax 867-3757

Laddonia, Audrain, Pop. 512
Community R-VI SD 300/PK-12
35063 Highway BB 63352 855-708-7567
Cheryl Mack, supt. Fax 492-6268
www.cr6.net/
Community HS 200/6-12
35063 Highway BB 63352 855-708-7567
Bob Curtis, prin. Fax 492-6407

Lake Ozark, Camden, Pop. 1,563
School of the Osage R-II SD 1,900/PK-12
PO Box 1960 65049 573-365-4091
Dr. Brent Depee', supt. Fax 365-5748
www.osageschools.org
Other Schools – See Osage Beach

Lake Saint Louis, Saint Charles, Pop. 14,381
Wentzville R-IV SD
Supt. — See Wentzville
Liberty HS 300/9-12
2275 Sommers Rd 63367 636-561-0075
Edgar Nelson, prin. Fax 561-0058

Lamar, Barton, Pop. 4,398
Lamar R-I SD 1,300/PK-12
202 W 7th St 64759 417-682-3527
Dr. Zach Harris, supt. Fax 682-6013
www.lamar.k12.mo.us
Lamar Career & Technical Center Vo/Tech
202 W 7th St 64759 417-682-3384
Dr. Scott Nolting, dir. Fax 682-3420
Lamar HS 400/9-12
202 W 7th St 64759 417-682-5571
Jennifer Beem, prin. Fax 681-0328
Lamar MS 300/6-8
202 W 7th St 64759 417-682-3548
Alan Ray, prin. Fax 682-4409

La Monte, Pettis, Pop. 1,113
La Monte R-IV SD 400/PK-12
301 S Washington St 65337 660-347-5439
Dr. Randal E. Bagby, supt. Fax 347-5467
lamonte.k12.mo.us/
La Monte JSHS 200/7-12
301 S Washington St 65337 660-347-5439
Lacy Warren, prin. Fax 347-5467

La Plata, Macon, Pop. 1,336
La Plata R-II SD 300/PK-12
201 W Moore St 63549 660-332-7001
Dr. Craig Noah, supt. Fax 332-7929
laplata.k12.mo.us
La Plata JSHS 200/7-12
201 W Moore St 63549 660-332-7001
Andy Jackson, prin. Fax 332-7656

Laquey, Pulaski
Laquey R-V SD 700/PK-12
PO Box 130 65534 573-765-3716
Dr. Randy Caffey, supt. Fax 765-4052
www.laquey.k12.mo.us/
Laquey R-V HS 200/9-12
PO Box 130 65534 573-765-4051
Eric Shaw, prin. Fax 765-5608
Laquey R-V MS 200/6-8
PO Box 130 65534 573-765-3129
Nicole Hanson, prin. Fax 765-4086

Lathrop, Clinton, Pop. 2,052
Lathrop R-II SD 900/K-12
700 East St 64465 816-528-7500
Chris Fine, supt. Fax 528-7514
lathropschools.com
Lathrop HS 300/9-12
102 N School Dr 64465 816-528-7400
Robert Bowers, prin. Fax 528-7456
Lathrop MS 200/6-8
612 Center St 64465 816-528-7600
Andy McNeely, prin. Fax 528-7646

Lawson, Ray, Pop. 2,441
Lawson R-XIV SD 1,200/PK-12
PO Box 157 64062 816-580-7277
Roger Schmitz, supt. Fax 296-7723
lawsoncardinals.org
Lawson HS 400/9-12
PO Box 157 64062 816-580-7270
Scott Harrold, prin. Fax 296-3048
Lawson MS 400/5-8
PO Box 157 64062 816-580-7279
Tammy Dunn, prin. Fax 296-3164

Leadwood, Saint Francois, Pop. 1,274
West St. Francois County R-IV SD 1,000/PK-12
1124 Main St 63653 573-562-7535
Stacy Stevens, supt. Fax 562-7510
westco.k12.mo.us/
Other Schools – See Park Hills

Lebanon, Laclede, Pop. 14,144
Lebanon R-III SD 4,700/PK-12
1310 E Route 66 65536 417-532-9141
David Schmitz, supt. Fax 532-9492
www.lebanon.k12.mo.us
Hillcrest Education Center 300/Alt
301 Hoover St 65536 417-532-4681
Scott Williamson, dir. Fax 533-3801
Lebanon MS 600/6-8
2700 Buzz Pride Dr 65536 417-532-9121
Tom Merriott, prin. Fax 533-3805
Lebanon SHS 1,400/9-12
777 Brice St 65536 417-532-9144
Kevin Lowery, prin. Fax 532-3386
Lebanon Technology Career Center Vo/Tech
757 Brice St 65536 417-532-5494
Keith Davis, dir. Fax 532-4510

Lees Summit, Jackson, Pop. 89,308
Blue Springs R-IV SD
Supt. — See Blue Springs
Delta Woods MS 700/6-8
4401 NE Lakewood Way 64064 816-874-3580
Steven Cook, prin. Fax 795-5839

Lee's Summit R-VII SD 17,900/PK-12
301 NE Tudor Rd 64086 816-986-1000
Dr. David Benson, supt. Fax 986-1170
www.lsr7.org
Campbell MS 900/7-8
1201 NE Colbern Rd 64086 816-986-3175
Dr. Sherri Lewis, prin. Fax 986-3245
Lee's Summit HS 1,900/9-12
400 SE Blue Pkwy 64063 816-986-2000
Dr. John Faulkenberry, prin. Fax 986-2095
Lee's Summit North HS 1,900/9-12
901 NE Douglas St 64086 816-986-3000
Dr. Jeff Meisenheimer, prin. Fax 986-3170
Lee's Summit West HS 1,900/9-12
2600 SW Ward Rd 64082 816-986-4000
Dr. David Sharp, prin. Fax 986-4115
Pleasant Lea MS 900/7-8
630 SW Persels Rd 64081 816-986-1175
Janette Miller, prin. Fax 986-1225
Summit Lakes MS 1,000/7-8
3500 SW Windemere Dr 64082 816-986-1375
Dr. David Carlson, prin. Fax 986-1435
Summit Ridge Academy Alt
2620 SW Ward Rd 64082 816-986-4120
Burt Whaley, prin. Fax 986-4135
Summit Technology Academy Vo/Tech
777 NW Blue Pkwy 64086 816-524-3366
Elaine Metcalf, prin. Fax 524-1436

Metropolitan Community Coll - Longview Post-Sec.
500 SW Longview Rd 64081 816-604-2000
Summit Christian Academy 700/PK-12
1500 SW Jefferson St 64081 816-525-1480
Linda Harrelson, head sch Fax 525-5402

Leeton, Johnson, Pop. 557
Leeton R-X SD 400/PK-12
500 N Main St 64761 660-653-2301
Susan Crooks, supt. Fax 653-4315
www.leeton.k12.mo.us/
Leeton HS 100/9-12
500 N Main St 64761 660-653-4314
Bryan Himes, prin. Fax 653-4315
Leeton MS 100/6-8
500 N Main St 64761 660-653-4314
Bryan Himes, prin. Fax 653-4315

Leopold, Bollinger
Leopold R-III SD 200/K-12
PO Box 39 63760 573-238-2211
Keenan Kinder, supt. Fax 238-9868
www.leopold.k12.mo.us
Leopold JSHS 100/7-12
PO Box 39 63760 573-238-2211
Matt Britt, prin. Fax 238-9868

Lesterville, Reynolds
Lesterville R-IV SD 300/PK-12
PO Box 120 63654 573-637-2201
James Watts, supt. Fax 637-2279
www.lesterville.k12.mo.us/
Lesterville JSHS 100/7-12
PO Box 120 63654 573-637-2201
James Watts, prin. Fax 637-2279
Other Schools – See Black

Lewistown, Lewis, Pop. 532
Lewis County C-1 SD 1,000/PK-12
21504 State Highway 6 63452 573-209-3217
John French, supt. Fax 209-3318
www.lewis.k12.mo.us
Highland JSHS 500/7-12
21504 State Highway 6 63452 573-209-3215
Alan Koch, prin. Fax 209-3469

Lexington, Lafayette, Pop. 4,541
Lexington R-V SD 900/PK-12
2323 High School Dr Ste A 64067 660-259-4369
Dr. Dan Hoehn, supt. Fax 259-4992
www.lexington.k12.mo.us
Lexington HS 200/9-12
2309 Aull Ln 64067 660-259-4391
Moore Travis, prin. Fax 259-2166
Lexington MS 300/5-8
1111 S 24th St 64067 660-259-4611
Cory LaBoube, prin. Fax 259-2538
Lex La-Ray Tech Ctr Vo/Tech
2323 High School Dr 64067 660-259-2264
Sarrah Morgan, dir. Fax 259-6262

Wentworth Military Academy Post-Sec.
1880 Washington Ave 64067 800-962-7682
Wentworth Military Academy 100/9-12
1880 Washington Ave 64067 660-259-2221
Col. Michael Lierman, pres. Fax 259-2064

Liberal, Barton, Pop. 739
Liberal R-II SD 500/PK-12
PO Box 38 64762 417-843-5115
William Harvey, supt. Fax 843-6698
www.liberal.k12.mo.us/
Liberal HS 200/9-12
PO Box 38 64762 417-843-2125
Margaret Ruddick, prin. Fax 843-2403
Liberal MS 100/6-8
PO Box 38 64762 417-843-6033
Rachel Miller, prin. Fax 843-2403

Liberty, Clay, Pop. 28,451
Liberty SD 53 11,800/PK-12
8 Victory Ln 64068 816-736-5300
Dr. Jeremy Tucker, supt. Fax 736-5306
www.liberty.k12.mo.us
Discovery MS 600/6-8
800 Midjay Dr 64068 816-736-7300
Dr. Julie Moore, prin. Fax 736-7306
Heritage MS 700/6-8
600 W Kansas St 64068 816-736-5380
Scott Carr, prin. Fax 736-5384
Liberty Academy Alt
8 Victory Ln 64068 816-736-5470
Dr. Melissa Norris, dir. Fax 736-5471
Liberty HS 1,800/9-12
200 Blue Jay Dr 64068 816-736-5340
April Adams, prin. Fax 736-5345
Liberty MS 700/6-8
1500 S Withers Rd 64068 816-736-5410
Katherine Lawson, prin. Fax 736-5415
Liberty North HS 1,400/9-12
1000 NE 104th St 64068 816-736-5500
Martin Jacobs, prin. Fax 736-5535
South Valley MS 600/6-8
1000 Midjay Dr 64068 816-736-7180
Jill Mullen, prin. Fax 736-7185

William Jewell College Post-Sec.
500 College Hl 64068 816-781-7700

Licking, Texas, Pop. 3,111
Licking R-VIII SD 900/PK-12
125 College Ave 65542 573-674-2911
Dr. John Hood, supt. Fax 674-4064
www.licking.k12.mo.us/
Licking JSHS 400/7-12
125 College Ave 65542 573-674-2711
Grant Crow, prin. Fax 674-2142

Lincoln, Benton, Pop. 1,178
Lincoln R-II SD 500/K-12
PO Box 39 65338 660-547-3514
Kevin Smith, supt. Fax 547-3729
www.lincoln.k12.mo.us/
Lincoln JSHS 200/7-12
PO Box 39 65338 660-547-3514
Marc Spunaugle, prin. Fax 547-3729

Linn, Osage, Pop. 1,447
Osage County R-II SD 600/PK-12
141 Wildcat Dr 65051 573-897-4200
Dr. Lenice Basham, supt. Fax 897-3768
www.linn.k12.mo.us
Linn JSHS 300/6-12
141 Wildcat Dr 65051 573-897-4216
Dr. Melinda Aholt, prin. Fax 897-4570

Linn State Technical College Post-Sec.
1 Technology Dr 65051 573-897-5000

Lockwood, Dade, Pop. 928
Lockwood R-I SD 300/PK-12
400 W 4th St 65682 417-232-4513
Bill Rogers, supt. Fax 232-4187
www.lockwoodschools.org/
Lockwood HS 100/9-12
400 W 4th St 65682 417-232-4513
Clay Lasater, prin. Fax 232-4187

Lone Jack, Jackson, Pop. 1,030
Lone Jack C-6 SD 600/PK-12
313 S Bynum Rd 64070 816-697-3539
Bryan Prewitt, supt. Fax 566-3128
www.lonejackc6.net
Lone Jack JSHS 300/7-12
313 S Bynum Rd 64070 816-697-2215
Matthew Tarwater, prin. Fax 566-3128

Louisburg, Dallas, Pop. 116
Dallas County R-I SD
Supt. — See Buffalo
Dallas County Career Center Vo/Tech
PO Box 100 65685 417-752-3491
Debby Dryer, admin. Fax 752-3493

Louisiana, Pike, Pop. 3,291
Louisiana R-II SD 700/PK-12
3321 Georgia St 63353 573-754-4261
Dr. Todd Smith, supt. Fax 754-4319
louisianarii.org
Louisiana HS 200/9-12
3321 Georgia St 63353 573-754-6181
Derrick Branstetter, prin. Fax 754-5964
Louisiana MS 200/6-8
3321 Georgia St 63353 573-754-5340
Chuck Tophinke, prin. Fax 754-5377

Ludlow, Livingston, Pop. 131
Southwest Livingston County R-I SD 200/PK-12
4944 Highway DD 64656 660-738-4433
Cinthia Barnes, supt. Fax 738-4441
www.southwestr1.org/
Southwest Livingston County JSHS 100/7-12
4944 Highway DD 64656 660-738-4433
Michele Rex, prin. Fax 738-4115

Macks Creek, Camden, Pop. 238
Macks Creek R-V SD 400/PK-12
245 State Rd N 65786 573-363-5909
Joshua Phillips, supt. Fax 363-5981
www.mcreek.k12.mo.us
Macks Creek JSHS 100/7-12
245 State Rd N 65786 573-363-5911
Doug Kempker, prin. Fax 363-5981

Macon, Macon, Pop. 5,339
Macon County R-I SD 1,400/PK-12
702 N Missouri St 63552 660-385-5719
Dr. Scott Jarvis, supt. Fax 385-7179
www.macon.k12.mo.us

Family Literacy Center Alt
204 Crescent Dr 63552 660-385-2061
Shandra Clark, dir. Fax 385-5893
Macon Area Vocational Technical S Vo/Tech
702 N Missouri St 63552 660-385-2158
Peter Claas, dir. Fax 385-3667
Macon County HS 500/9-12
702 N Missouri St 63552 660-385-5748
Jeffrey Haley, prin. Fax 385-2746
Macon County MS 300/6-8
702 N Missouri St 63552 660-385-2189
Bruce Weimer, prin. Fax 385-7230

Madison, Monroe, Pop. 551
Madison C-3 SD 200/PK-12
309 S Thomas St 65263 660-291-5115
Lesa Rapert, supt. Fax 291-5006
www.madison.k12.mo.us
Madison JSHS 100/7-12
309 S Thomas St 65263 660-291-4515
Shane Stocks, prin. Fax 291-5006

Malden, Dunklin, Pop. 4,199
Malden R-I SD 900/PK-12
505 Burkhart St 63863 573-276-5794
Kenneth Cook, supt. Fax 276-5796
www.malden.k12.mo.us/
Malden JSHS 400/7-12
505 Burkhart St 63863 573-276-4546
Josh Blaylock, prin. Fax 276-4548

Malta Bend, Saline, Pop. 249
Malta Bend R-V SD 100/K-12
PO Box 10 65339 660-595-2371
John Angelhow, supt. Fax 595-2430
mbtigers.weebly.com
Malta Bend JSHS 50/7-12
PO Box 10 65339 660-595-2371
Angelhow John, prin. Fax 595-2430

Manchester, Saint Louis, Pop. 17,723
Parkway C-2 SD
Supt. — See Chesterfield
Parkway South MS 600/6-8
760 Woods Mill Rd 63011 314-415-7200
Amy Branson, prin. Fax 415-7213
Parkway Southwest MS 700/6-8
701 Wren Ave 63021 314-415-7300
Dr. Craig Maxwell, prin. Fax 415-7334

Kennedy HS 300/9-12
500 Woods Mill Rd 63011 636-227-5900
Patty McMullen-Hellwig, prin. Fax 227-0298

Mansfield, Wright, Pop. 1,287
Mansfield R-IV SD 700/PK-12
316 W Ohio St 65704 417-924-8458
Dr. Nathan Moore, supt. Fax 924-3427
www.mansfieldschool.net
Mansfield HS 200/9-12
315 W Ohio St 65704 417-924-3236
Richard Wylie, prin. Fax 924-8789
Mansfield JHS 200/6-8
316 W Ohio St 65704 417-924-8625
Dr. Gary Greene, prin. Fax 924-8789

Maplewood, Saint Louis, Pop. 7,766
Maplewood Richmond Heights SD 1,300/PK-12
7539 Manchester Rd 63143 314-644-4400
Karen I. Hall, supt. Fax 781-3160
www.mrhschools.net
Maplewood Richmond Heights HS 300/9-12
7539 Manchester Rd 63143 314-644-4401
Kevin Grawer, prin. Fax 644-3681
Maplewood Richmond Heights MS 100/7-8
7539 Manchester Rd 63143 314-644-4406
Dr. Dittrich Michael, prin. Fax 781-4629

Marble Hill, Bollinger, Pop. 1,464
Woodland R-IV SD 900/K-12
RR 5 Box 3210 63764 573-238-3343
Daniel Schlief, supt. Fax 238-2153
www.woodland.k12.mo.us/
Woodland HS 300/9-12
RR 5 Box 3210 63764 573-238-2663
Shawn Kinder, prin. Fax 238-0186
Woodland MS 300/5-8
RR 5 Box 3210 63764 573-238-2656
Brian Hukel, prin. Fax 238-0133

Marceline, Linn, Pop. 2,210
Marceline R-V SD 600/PK-12
400 E Santa Fe Ave 64658 660-376-3371
Dr. Gabe Edgar Ed.D., supt. Fax 376-6001
www.marcelineschools.org
Marceline HS 200/9-12
314 E Santa Fe Ave 64658 660-376-2411
Matt Finch, prin. Fax 376-6016
Marceline MS 100/6-8
314 E Santa Fe Ave 64658 660-376-2411
Matt Finch, prin. Fax 376-6016

Marionville, Lawrence, Pop. 2,171
Marionville R-IX SD 700/PK-12
PO Box 409 65705 417-258-7755
Dr. Larry Brown, supt. Fax 258-2564
www.marionville.us/
Marionville HS 200/9-12
PO Box 409 65705 417-258-2521
Mark Estep, prin. Fax 258-7637
Marionville MS 200/6-8
PO Box 409 65705 417-258-2531
Shane Moseman, prin. Fax 258-2564

Marquand, Madison, Pop. 203
Marquand-Zion R-VI SD 200/K-12
205 E Morley 63655 573-783-3388
Scott Blake, supt. Fax 783-3067
mz.k12.mo.us
Marquand-Zion JSHS 100/7-12
205 E Morley 63655 573-783-3388
Sabrina Doublin, prin. Fax 783-3067

Marshall, Saline, Pop. 12,591
Marshall SD 2,400/K-12
860 W Vest St 65340 660-886-7414
Dr. Carol Maher, supt. Fax 886-5641
www.marshallschools.com/
Bueker MS 700/5-8
565 S Odell Ave 65340 660-886-6833
Lance Tobin, prin. Fax 886-7529
Marshall HS 800/9-12
805 S Miami Ave 65340 660-886-2244
Jim Heinzler, prin. Fax 886-2669
Saline County Career Center Vo/Tech
900 W Vest St 65340 660-886-6958
Mitchell Holder, dir. Fax 886-3092

Missouri Valley College Post-Sec.
500 E College St 65340 660-831-4000

Marshfield, Webster, Pop. 6,529
Marshfield R-I SD 3,100/PK-12
170 State Highway DD 65706 417-859-2120
Alan Thomas, supt. Fax 859-2193
www.mjays.us
Marshfield HS 900/9-12
370 State Highway DD 65706 417-859-2120
Jeff Curley, prin. Fax 859-7756
Marshfield JHS 700/6-8
660 N Locust St 65706 417-859-2120
Doug Summers, prin. Fax 859-4970

Maryland Heights, Saint Louis, Pop. 26,834
Pattonville R-3 SD
Supt. — See Saint Ann
Pattonville Heights MS 500/6-8
195 Fee Fee Rd 63043 314-213-8033
Scot Mosher, prin. Fax 213-8633
Pattonville HS 1,800/9-12
2497 Creve Coeur Mill Rd 63043 314-213-8051
Joe Dobrinic Ed.D., prin. Fax 213-8651

Anthem College Post-Sec.
13723 Riverport Dr Ste 103 63043 888-852-7272

Maryville, Nodaway, Pop. 11,837
Maryville R-II SD 1,500/PK-12
1429 S Munn Ave 64468 660-562-3255
Becky Albrecht, supt. Fax 562-4113
www.maryville.k12.mo.us/
Maryville HS 500/9-12
1503 S Munn Ave 64468 660-562-3511
Thom Alvarez, prin. Fax 562-4822
Maryville MS 400/5-8
525 W South Hills Dr 64468 660-562-3244
Kevin Pitts, prin. Fax 562-4138
Northwest Technical S Vo/Tech
1515 S Munn Ave 64468 660-562-3022
Jeremy Ingraham, dir. Fax 562-2010

Northwest Missouri State University Post-Sec.
800 University Dr 64468 660-562-1212

Maysville, DeKalb, Pop. 1,100
Maysville R-I SD 600/K-12
PO Box 68 64469 816-449-2308
Robert Smith, supt. Fax 449-5678
www.maysville.k12.mo.us
Maysville JSHS 300/7-12
PO Box 68 64469 816-449-2154
Alan Hutchcraft, prin. Fax 449-5610

Meadville, Linn, Pop. 461
Meadville R-IV SD 200/K-12
PO Box 217 64659 660-938-4111
Ron Holcer, supt. Fax 938-4100
Meadville JSHS 100/7-12
PO Box 217 64659 660-938-4112
Ronald Holcer, prin. Fax 938-4100

Memphis, Scotland, Pop. 1,807
Scotland County R-I SD 600/PK-12
438 W Lovers Ln 63555 660-465-8531
Ryan Bergeson, supt. Fax 465-8636
scotland.k12.mo.us/
Scotland County JSHS 300/7-12
606 W Lovers Ln 63555 660-465-8901
Kirk Stott, prin. Fax 465-7715

Mendon, Chariton, Pop. 171
Northwestern R-I SD 200/PK-12
PO Box 43 64660 660-272-3201
Ron Garber, supt. Fax 272-3419
www.northwestern.k12.mo.us
Northwestern HS 100/7-12
PO Box 43 64660 660-272-3201
Eric Hoyt, prin. Fax 272-3738

Mercer, Mercer, Pop. 315
North Mercer County R-III SD 200/PK-12
PO Box 648 64661 660-382-4214
Dan Owens, supt. Fax 382-4239
www.northmercer.k12.mo.us
Mercer JSHS 100/7-12
PO Box 648 64661 660-382-4214
Kim Palmer, prin. Fax 382-4239

Mexico, Audrain, Pop. 11,278
Mexico SD 59 2,400/PK-12
2101 Lakeview Rd 65265 573-581-3773
Kevin Freeman, supt. Fax 581-1794
www.mexicoschools.net
Hart Career Center Vo/Tech
905 N Wade St 65265 573-581-5684
Chris Denham, dir. Fax 581-7084
Mexico Education Center Alt
905 N Wade St 65265 573-581-5529
Chris Denham, dir. Fax 581-1794
Mexico HS 700/9-12
639 N Wade St 65265 573-581-4296
Dr. Terry Robinson, prin. Fax 581-3788
Mexico MS 500/6-8
1200 W Boulevard St 65265 573-581-4664
Deb Haag, prin. Fax 581-8440

Missouri Military Academy 200/7-12
204 N Grand St 65265 573-581-1776
Charles McGeorge, pres. Fax 581-0081

Milan, Sullivan, Pop. 1,949
Milan C-2 SD 700/PK-12
373 S Market St 63556 660-265-4414
Dr. Ben Yocom, supt. Fax 265-4315
www.milan.k12.mo.us/
Milan HS 200/9-12
373 S Market St 63556 660-265-4415
Michael Hostetter, prin. Fax 265-4315
Milan MS 200/5-8
373 S Market St 63556 660-265-4421
Erik Logan, prin. Fax 265-4315

Miller, Lawrence, Pop. 697
Miller R-II SD 500/PK-12
110 W 6th St 65707 417-452-3515
Dr. Dustin Storm, supt. Fax 452-2709
www.millerschools.org
Miller JSHS 200/7-12
110 W 6th St 65707 417-452-3271
Charles Marcum, prin. Fax 452-2310

Round Grove Christian Academy 100/PK-12
877 Highway UU 65707 417-452-2324
Tammy McCanless, admin. Fax 452-2573

Moberly, Randolph, Pop. 13,647
Moberly SD 2,300/K-12
926 Kwix Rd 65270 660-269-2600
Dr. Matthew S. Miller, supt. Fax 269-2611
moberly.k12.mo.us
Moberly Area Technical Center Vo/Tech
1623 Gratz Brown St 65270 660-269-2690
Sam Richardson, dir. Fax 269-2692
Moberly HS 800/9-12
1625 Gratz Brown St 65270 660-269-2660
Zach McMains, prin. Fax 263-5977
Moberly MS 500/6-8
920 Kwix Rd 65270 660-269-2680
Wes Land, prin. Fax 269-8519
North Central Regional Alternative S Alt
200 Porter St 65270 660-269-8800
Debbie Young, dir. Fax 269-8576

Central Christian College of the Bible Post-Sec.
911 E Urbandale Dr 65270 660-263-3900
Moberly Area Community College Post-Sec.
101 College Ave 65270 660-263-4110

Mokane, Callaway, Pop. 182
South Callaway County R-II SD 800/PK-12
10135 State Road C 65059 573-676-5225
Kevin Hillman, supt. Fax 676-5134
www.sc.k12.mo.us/
South Callaway HS 300/9-12
10135 State Road C 65059 573-676-5225
Heather Helsel, prin. Fax 676-5132
South Callaway MS 200/6-8
10135 State Road C 65059 573-676-5216
Gary Bonsall, prin. Fax 676-5347

Monett, Barry, Pop. 8,746
Monett R-I SD 2,300/PK-12
900 E Scott St 65708 417-235-7422
Dr. Brad Hanson, supt. Fax 235-1415
monett.schoolfusion.us/
Monett HS 700/9-12
1 David Sippy Dr 65708 417-235-5445
David Williams, prin. Fax 235-7884
Monett MS 400/7-8
710 9th St 65708 417-235-6228
Dr. Jonathan Apostol, prin. Fax 235-3278
Scott Regional Tech Center Vo/Tech
2 David Sippy Dr 65708 417-235-7022
David Miller, dir. Fax 235-8270

Monroe City, Monroe, Pop. 2,481
Monroe City R-I SD 700/PK-12
401 US Highway 24 36 E 63456 573-735-4631
Tracy Bottoms, supt. Fax 735-2413
monroe.k12.mo.us
Monroe City MS 200/5-8
430 N Washington St 63456 573-735-4742
Troy Patterson, prin. Fax 735-2413
Monroe City R-I HS 200/9-12
401 US Highway 24 36 E 63456 573-735-4626
Ryan Watson, prin. Fax 735-2413

Montgomery City, Montgomery, Pop. 2,792
Montgomery County R-II SD 1,300/PK-12
418 N Highway 19 63361 573-564-2278
Michael Gray, supt. Fax 782-8700
www.mc-wildcats.org
Montgomery County HS 400/9-12
394 N Highway 19 63361 573-564-2278
Chris Redmon, prin. Fax 782-8701
Montgomery County MS 300/6-8
418 N Highway 19 63361 573-564-2278
Chris Parker, prin. Fax 782-8702

Montrose, Henry, Pop. 383
Montrose R-XIV SD 100/K-12
307 E 2nd St 64770 660-693-4812
Denise Fast, supt. Fax 693-4594
www.montrose.k12.mo.us
Montrose R-XIV HS 50/9-12
307 E 2nd St 64770 660-693-4812
Denise Fast, supt. Fax 693-4594

Morrisville, Polk, Pop. 377
Marion C. Early R-V SD 600/PK-12
5309 S Main Ave 65710 417-376-2255
Dr. Eric Kurre, supt. Fax 376-3243
www.mceonline.net
Early HS 200/9-12
5309 S Main Ave 65710 417-376-2216
Dr. Joel Carey, prin. Fax 376-7622
Early JHS 100/6-8
5309 S Main Ave 65710 417-376-2216
Dr. Joel Carey, prin. Fax 376-7622

Moscow Mills, Lincoln, Pop. 2,430
Lincoln County R-III SD
Supt. — See Troy
Ninth Grade Center 500/9-9
80 Elm Tree Rd 63362 636-366-4450
Dr. Chris Chaney, prin. Fax 366-4451
Troy South MS 800/6-8
200 S Campus Rd 63362 636-462-5125
Amy Salvo Ed.D., prin. Fax 462-5126

Mound City, Holt, Pop. 1,154
Mound City R-II SD 200/PK-12
708 Nebraska St 64470 660-442-3737
Kenneth Eaton, supt. Fax 442-5941
mndcty.k12.mo.us
Mound City HS 100/9-12
708 Nebraska St 64470 660-442-5429
Korey Miles, prin. Fax 442-3154

Mountain Grove, Wright, Pop. 4,721
Mountain Grove R-III SD 1,400/K-12
PO Box 806 65711 417-926-3177
Jim Dickey, supt. Fax 926-4564
www.mg.k12.mo.us
Mountain Grove HS 400/9-12
PO Box 806 65711 417-926-3177
Marcia Stumpff, prin. Fax 926-1702
Mountain Grove MS 400/5-8
PO Box 806 65711 417-926-3177
Lori Golden, prin. Fax 926-1673
Ozark Mountain Technical Center Vo/Tech
PO Box 806 65711 417-926-3177
J.T. Hale, dir. Fax 926-6858

Mountain View, Howell, Pop. 2,694
Mountain View-Birch Tree R-III SD 1,200/PK-12
1054 Old Highway 60 65548 417-934-5408
Dr. Don Christensen, supt. Fax 934-5404
mvbt.k12.mo.us
Liberty HS 400/9-12
1054 Old Highway 60 65548 417-934-2020
John Daniels, prin. Fax 934-1329
Liberty MS 300/6-8
1054 Old Highway 60 65548 417-934-2020
Ryan Chowning, prin. Fax 934-1329

Mount Vernon, Lawrence, Pop. 4,491
Mt. Vernon R-V SD 1,400/K-12
731 S Landrum St 65712 417-466-7573
Scott Cook, supt. Fax 466-7058
www.mtvernon.k12.mo.us
Mount Vernon HS 500/9-12
400 W Highway 174 65712 417-466-7526
Dr. Josh Ladd, prin. Fax 466-4307
Mount Vernon MS 300/6-8
731 S Landrum St 65712 417-466-3137
Robert Senninger, prin. Fax 466-7058

Myrtle, Oregon
Couch R-I SD 200/PK-12
RR 91 Box 1187 65778 417-938-4211
Sherry McMasters, supt. Fax 938-4267
www.couch.k12.mo.us/
Couch JSHS 100/7-12
RR 91 Box 1187 65778 417-938-4212
Pamela Smith, prin. Fax 938-4267

Naylor, Ripley, Pop. 602
Naylor R-II SD 400/K-12
101 Batten St 63953 573-399-2505
Terry Arnold, supt. Fax 399-2874
naylor.k12.mo.us
Naylor JSHS 200/7-12
RR 2 Box 512 63953 573-399-2506
Christopher White, prin. Fax 399-2388

Neelyville, Butler, Pop. 467
Neelyville R-IV SD 600/PK-12
PO Box 8 63954 573-989-3813
Bradley Hagood, supt. Fax 989-3434
www.neelyville.k12.mo.us
Neelyville JSHS 300/7-12
PO Box 8 63954 573-989-3815
Justin Dobbins, prin. Fax 989-6322

Neosho, Newton, Pop. 11,282
Neosho R-V SD 4,300/PK-12
418 Fairground Rd 64850 417-451-8600
Dan Decker, supt. Fax 451-8604
www.neoshosd.org
Neosho HS 1,300/9-12
511 S Neosho Blvd 64850 417-451-8670
Darren Cook, prin. Fax 451-8605
Neosho JHS 300/7-8
511 S Neosho Blvd 64850 417-451-8660
Dr. Jenifer Cryer, prin. Fax 451-8687

Crowder College Post-Sec.
601 Laclede Ave 64850 417-451-3223
Neosho Beauty College Post-Sec.
116 N Wood St 64850 417-451-7216
Neosho Christian S 100/PK-12
903 W South St 64850 417-451-1941
Ozark Christian Academy 50/K-12
PO Box 786 64850 417-451-1100
Joyce Prihoda, prin. Fax 451-2059

Nevada, Vernon, Pop. 8,266
Nevada R-V SD 2,600/PK-12
811 W Hickory St 64772 417-448-2000
Dr. Tyson Beshore, supt. Fax 448-2006
www.nevada.k12.mo.us
Nevada HS 800/9-12
800 W Hickory St 64772 417-448-2020
Gerald Whalen, prin. Fax 448-1923
Nevada MS 600/6-8
900 N Olive St 64772 417-448-2040
Geoff Stewart, prin. Fax 448-2048
Nevada Regional Tech-Center Vo/Tech
900 W Ashland St 64772 417-448-2090
Dr. Phillip Witt, dir. Fax 448-2092

Cottey College Post-Sec.
1000 W Austin Blvd 64772 417-667-8181

Newark, Knox, Pop. 88

Heartland Christian College Post-Sec.
500 New Creation Rd N 63458 660-284-4800

New Bloomfield, Callaway, Pop. 652
New Bloomfield R-III SD 600/PK-12
307 Redwood Dr 65063 573-491-3700
David Tramel, supt. Fax 491-3696
www.nb.k12.mo.us
New Bloomfield JSHS 300/7-12
307 Redwood Dr 65063 573-491-3700
Jeremy Davidson, prin. Fax 491-3696

Newburg, Phelps, Pop. 466
Newburg R-II SD 500/PK-12
PO Box C 65550 573-762-9653
Dr. Lynne Reed, supt. Fax 762-3040
www.newburg.k12.mo.us
Newburg JSHS 200/7-12
PO Box C 65550 573-762-2331
Steve Guffey, prin. Fax 762-0140

New Cambria, Macon, Pop. 195
Macon County R-IV SD 100/K-12
PO Box 70 63558 660-226-5615
John Dunham, supt. Fax 226-5618
www.mcr4.k12.mo.us/
Macon County JSHS 100/7-12
PO Box 70 63558 660-226-5615
Zach Bruner, prin. Fax 226-5618

New Franklin, Howard, Pop. 1,064
New Franklin R-I SD 500/PK-12
412 W Broadway 65274 660-848-2141
Dr. David Haggard, supt. Fax 848-2226
www.nfranklin.k12.mo.us/
New Franklin MSHS 200/6-12
412 W Broadway 65274 660-848-2314
Benji Dorson, prin. Fax 848-3071

New Haven, Franklin, Pop. 2,057
New Haven SD 500/K-12
100 Park Dr 63068 573-237-3231
Josh Hoener, supt. Fax 237-5959
www.newhavenschools.org
New Haven HS 200/9-12
100 Park Dr 63068 573-237-2629
Chip Stutzman, prin. Fax 237-5959
New Haven MS 100/7-8
100 Park Dr 63068 573-237-2900
Chip Stutzman, prin. Fax 237-5959

New Madrid, New Madrid, Pop. 3,072
New Madrid County R-I SD 1,500/PK-12
310 US Highway 61 63869 573-688-2161
Dr. Sam Duncan, supt. Fax 688-2169
www.newmadridco.k12.mo.us/
Central HS 400/9-12
310 US Highway 61 63869 573-688-2165
Gerald Murphy, prin. Fax 688-2169
Central MS 300/6-8
308 US Highway 61 63869 573-688-2176
Thomas Drummond, prin. Fax 688-2245
New Madrid R-I Tech Skills Center Vo/Tech
310 US Highway 61 63869 573-688-2161
John Garner, dir. Fax 688-2169

Newtown, Sullivan, Pop. 178
Newtown-Harris R-III SD 100/PK-12
306 N Main St 64667 660-794-2245
Kimberly Johnson, supt. Fax 794-2730
www.nhtigers.k12.mo.us/
Newtown-Harris JSHS 50/7-12
306 N Main St 64667 660-794-2245
Misty Foster, prin. Fax 794-2730

Niangua, Webster, Pop. 404
Niangua R-V SD 300/PK-12
301 Rumsey St 65713 417-473-6101
Thomas Bransfield, supt. Fax 473-1056
www.nianguaschools.com
Niangua JSHS 100/7-12
301 Rumsey St 65713 417-473-6101
Thomas Bransfield, prin. Fax 473-1056

Nixa, Christian, Pop. 18,653
Nixa SD 5,900/PK-12
301 S Main St 65714 417-875-5400
Dr. Stephen Kleinsmith, supt. Fax 449-3190
www.nixapublicschools.net
Nixa HS 1,700/9-12
514 S Nicholas Rd 65714 417-724-3500
Mark McGehee, prin. Fax 724-3515
Nixa JHS 900/7-8
205 North St 65714 417-875-5430
Dr. Lori Wilson, prin. Fax 875-5426
SCORE Learning Center Alt
1398 W Mount Vernon St 65714 417-724-4080
Cheryl Huson, prin. Fax 724-4088

Noel, McDonald, Pop. 1,745
McDonald County R-I SD
Supt. — See Anderson
Noel ES 400/3-8
318 Sulphur St 64854 417-475-3302
Samantha Buckridge, prin. Fax 475-6516

Norborne, Carroll, Pop. 697
Norborne R-VIII SD 200/PK-12
PO Box 192 64668 660-593-3319
Troy Lentz, supt. Fax 593-3657
www.norborneschools.com
Norborne HS 100/6-12
PO Box 192 64668 660-593-3319
Jennifer Courtney, prin. Fax 593-3657

Normandy, Saint Louis, Pop. 4,907
Normandy Schools Collaborative
Supt. — See Saint Louis
Normandy MS 400/7-8
7855 Natural Bridge Rd 63121 314-493-0500
Andrew Miller, prin. Fax 493-0560

North Kansas City, Clay, Pop. 4,094
North Kansas City SD 74
Supt. — See Kansas City
North Kansas City HS 1,500/9-12
620 E 23rd Ave 64116 816-321-5310
Dr. Dan Wartick, prin. Fax 321-5311

North Kansas City Hospital Post-Sec.
2800 Clay Edwards Dr 64116 816-691-2000

Norwood, Wright, Pop. 654
Norwood R-I SD 500/PK-12
675 N Hawk St 65717 417-746-4101
Shannon Crain, supt. Fax 746-9950
www.norwood.k12.mo.us/
Norwood HS 200/7-12
675 N Hawk St 65717 417-746-4101
Kevin Johnson, prin. Fax 746-9950

Novinger, Adair, Pop. 454
Adair County R-I SD 300/K-12
600 Rombauer Ave 63559 660-488-6411
Rick Roberts, supt. Fax 488-5400
www.novinger.k12.mo.us
Adair County JSHS 100/7-12
600 Rombauer Ave 63559 660-488-6411
Robin Daniels, prin. Fax 488-5400

Oak Grove, Jackson, Pop. 7,672
Oak Grove R-VI SD 2,000/PK-12
601 SE 12th St 64075 816-690-4156
Freddie Doherty, supt. Fax 690-3031
www.oakgrove.k12.mo.us
Oak Grove HS 600/9-12
605 SE 12th St 64075 816-690-4152
Adam Salmon, prin. Fax 690-5666
Oak Grove MS 500/6-8
401 SE 12th St 64075 816-690-4154
Tracy Kemp, prin. Fax 690-3976

Oak Ridge, Cape Girardeau, Pop. 236
Oak Ridge R-VI SD 400/K-12
PO Box 10 63769 573-266-3218
Dr. Adrian Eftink, supt. Fax 266-0133
www.oakridger6schools.com
Oak Ridge JSHS 100/7-12
PO Box 10 63769 573-266-3630
Allan Horrell, prin. Fax 266-0133

Odessa, Lafayette, Pop. 5,180
Odessa R-VII SD 2,100/K-12
701 S 3rd St 64076 816-633-5316
Robert Brinkley, supt. Fax 633-8582
www.odessa.k12.mo.us/
Odessa HS 700/9-12
713 S 3rd St 64076 816-633-5533
Buffie McConville, prin. Fax 633-7506
Odessa MS 500/6-8
607 S 5th St 64076 816-633-1500
Kendra Malizzi, prin. Fax 633-7101

O Fallon, Saint Charles, Pop. 77,920
Ft. Zumwalt R-II SD 18,500/K-12
555 E Terra Ln 63366 636-240-2072
Dr. Bernard DuBray, supt. Fax 272-1059
www.fz.k12.mo.us
Fort Zumwalt Hope HS 100/Alt
307 W Pitman St 63366 636-379-5300
Ryan Bishop, prin. Fax 379-5909
Ft. Zumwalt North HS 1,400/9-12
1230 Tom Ginnever Ave 63366 636-272-4447
Joe Sutton, prin. Fax 272-6124
Ft. Zumwalt North MS 1,000/6-8
210 Virgil St 63366 636-281-2356
Dr. Damon Burkhart, prin. Fax 281-0005
Ft. Zumwalt West HS 2,000/9-12
1251 Turtle Creek Dr 63366 636-379-0300
Neil Berry, prin. Fax 281-0202
Ft. Zumwalt West MS 1,400/6-8
150 Waterford Crossing Dr, 636-272-6690
Dan Mcquerrey, prin. Fax 272-6361
Other Schools – See Saint Peters

Wentzville R-IV SD
Supt. — See Wentzville
Frontier MS 900/6-8
9233 Highway DD, 636-625-1026
Jeri LaBrot, prin. Fax 625-1094

Living Word Christian MSHS 500/6-12
1145 Tom Ginnever Ave 63366 636-978-1680
Keith Currivean, supt. Fax 978-5024
St. Dominic HS 700/9-12
31 Saint Dominic Dr 63366 636-240-8303
Janet Eaton, prin. Fax 240-9884

Oran, Scott, Pop. 1,284
Oran R-III SD 400/K-12
PO Box 250 63771 573-262-2330
Blane Keel, supt. Fax 262-2330
www.oran.k12.mo.us
Oran HS 200/7-12
PO Box 250 63771 573-262-3345
Adam Friga, prin. Fax 262-2289

Oregon, Holt, Pop. 851
South Holt County R-I SD 300/PK-12
201 S Barbour St 64473 660-446-2282
Bob Ottman, supt. Fax 446-2312
www.southholtr1.com
South Holt County JSHS 100/7-12
201 S Barbour St 64473 660-446-3454
Rachel Peek, prin. Fax 446-2312

Orrick, Ray, Pop. 827
Orrick R-XI SD 400/PK-12
100 Kirkham St 64077 816-770-0094
Aerin O'Dell, supt. Fax 496-3829
www.orrick.k12.mo.us
Orrick JSHS 200/7-12
100 Kirkham St 64077 816-770-3327
Scott Archibald, prin. Fax 496-3829

Osage Beach, Miller, Pop. 4,299
School of the Osage R-II SD
Supt. — See Lake Ozark
Osage HS 600/9-12
636 Highway 42 65065 573-348-0115
Mike Williams, prin. Fax 348-9774
Osage MS 400/6-8
635 Highway 42 65065 573-552-8326
Tony Slack, prin. Fax 552-8322

Osborn, DeKalb, Pop. 422
Osborn R-0 SD 100/K-12
275 Clinton Ave 64474 816-675-2217
Richard Goin, supt. Fax 675-2222
www.osbornwildcats.org
Osborn JSHS 100/7-12
275 Clinton Ave 64474 816-675-2217
Derek Brady, prin. Fax 675-2222

Osceola, Saint Clair, Pop. 924
Osceola SD 500/PK-12
76 SE Highway WW 64776 417-646-8143
Danny Dewitt, supt. Fax 646-8075
www.osceola.k12.mo.us
Osceola JSHS 200/7-12
76 SE Highway WW 64776 417-646-8144
Dustin Schubert, prin. Fax 646-8549

Otterville, Cooper, Pop. 446
Otterville R-VI SD 200/K-12
101 W Georgetown St 65348 660-366-4391
Kim Oelrichs, supt. Fax 366-4293
www.ottervillervi.k12.mo.us
Otterville JSHS 100/7-12
101 W Georgetown St 65348 660-366-4391
Kim Oelrichs, admin. Fax 366-4293

Overland, Saint Louis, Pop. 15,614
Ritenour SD
Supt. — See Saint Louis
Ritenour HS 1,900/9-12
9100 Saint Charles Rock Rd 63114 314-493-6105
Shane Hopper, prin. Fax 429-6725
Ritenour MS 700/6-8
2500 Marshall Ave 63114 314-493-6250
Brian Rich, prin. Fax 429-6726

Owensville, Gasconade, Pop. 2,647
Gasconade County R-II SD 1,900/PK-12
PO Box 536 65066 573-437-2177
Dr. Chuck Garner, supt. Fax 437-5808
www.owensville.k12.mo.us
Owensville HS 600/9-12
PO Box 536 65066 573-437-2174
Cindy Hawkins, prin. Fax 437-7174
Owensville MS 400/6-8
PO Box 536 65066 573-437-2172
Teresa Schulte, prin. Fax 437-6704

Ozark, Christian, Pop. 17,472
Ozark R-VI SD 4,500/K-12
PO Box 166 65721 417-582-5900
Dr. Kevin Patterson, supt. Fax 582-5960
www.ozark.k12.mo.us
Ozark HS 1,500/9-12
PO Box 166 65721 417-582-5901
Dr. Sam Taylor, prin. Fax 582-5944
Ozark JHS 400/8-8
PO Box 166 65721 417-582-4701
Jim Hubbard, prin. Fax 582-4714

Pacific, Franklin, Pop. 6,911
Meramec Valley R-III SD 3,400/PK-12
126 N Payne St 63069 636-271-1400
Dr. Ed Hillhouse, supt. Fax 271-1406
www.mvr3.k12.mo.us/
Pacific HS 1,000/9-12
425 Indian Warpath Dr 63069 636-271-1414
Tom Sauvage, prin. Fax 271-1420
Riverbend S 300/8-8
2085 Highway N 63069 636-271-1481
David Quanz, prin. Fax 271-1485

Palmyra, Marion, Pop. 3,541
Palmyra R-I SD 1,100/K-12
PO Box 151 63461 573-769-2066
Eric Churchwell, supt. Fax 769-4218
www.palmyra.k12.mo.us
Palmyra HS 400/9-12
PO Box 151 63461 573-769-2067
Jared Pontius, prin. Fax 769-1013
Palmyra MS 400/5-8
PO Box 151 63461 573-769-2174
Michael Kirt Malone, prin. Fax 769-4227

Paris, Monroe, Pop. 1,208
Paris R-II SD 400/PK-12
740 Cleveland St 65275 660-327-4112
Aaron Vitt, supt. Fax 327-4290
paris.k12.mo.us/site/
Paris HS 100/9-12
25686 Business Highway 24 65275 660-327-4111
Chris Willingham, prin. Fax 327-6220
Paris JHS 100/7-8
25678 Business Highway 24 65275 660-327-4563
Chris Willingham, prin. Fax 327-4782

Park Hills, Saint Francois, Pop. 8,642
Central R-III SD 2,100/PK-12
200 High St 63601 573-431-2616
Dr. Desmond Mayberry, supt. Fax 431-2107
www.centralr3.org
Central HS 500/9-12
116 Rebel Dr 63601 573-431-2616
Brad Coleman, prin. Fax 431-0700
Central MS 500/6-8
801 Columbia St 63601 573-431-2616
Mike Harlow, prin. Fax 431-5393

West St. Francois County R-IV SD
Supt. — See Leadwood
West County HS 300/9-12
768 Highway M 63601 573-562-7521
Eric Moyers, prin. Fax 562-7554
West County MS 200/6-8
728 Highway M 63601 573-562-7544
Kevin Coffman, prin. Fax 562-2714

Mineral Area College Post-Sec.
PO Box 1000 63601 573-431-4593

Parkville, Platte, Pop. 5,415

Park University Post-Sec.
8700 NW River Park Dr 64152 816-741-2000

Patton, Bollinger
Meadow Heights R-II SD 500/K-12
RR 5 Box 2365 63662 573-866-0060
Dr. John D. Wiggans, supt. Fax 866-3240
Meadow Heights JSHS 200/7-12
RR 5 Box 2365 63662 573-866-2924
Mitchell Nanney, prin. Fax 866-2219

Pattonsburg, Daviess, Pop. 346
Pattonsburg R-II SD 200/PK-12
PO Box 200 64670 660-367-2111
Scott Ireland, supt. Fax 367-4205
www.pattonsburg.k12.mo.us
Pattonsburg JSHS 100/6-12
PO Box 200 64670 660-367-2111
Chris Hodge, prin. Fax 367-4205

Peculiar, Cass, Pop. 4,532
Raymore-Peculiar R-II SD 6,600/PK-12
PO Box 789 64078 816-892-1300
Dr. Kari Monsees, supt. Fax 892-1380
www.raypec.k12.mo.us
Raymore-Peculiar Academy 400/Alt
PO Box 789 64078 816-892-1530
Jim Brown, prin. Fax 892-1529
Raymore-Peculiar HS 1,900/9-12
PO Box 789 64078 816-892-1400
Steven Miller, prin. Fax 892-1401
Other Schools – See Raymore

Perryville, Perry, Pop. 8,127
Perry County SD 32 2,300/K-12
326 College St 63775 573-547-7500
Andrew Comstock, supt. Fax 547-8572
www.perryville.k12.mo.us
Perry County MS 700/5-8
326 College St 63775 573-547-7500
Stephen Phillips, prin. Fax 547-1962
Perryville Area Career Center Vo/Tech
326 College St 63775 573-547-7500
Craig Hayden, dir. Fax 517-0396
Perryville HS 700/9-12
326 College St 63775 573-547-7500
Jeff Steffens, prin. Fax 517-0592

St. Vincent JSHS 200/7-12
210 S Waters St 63775 573-547-4300
Dr. Patricia Hensley, head sch Fax 547-1722

Philadelphia, Marion
Marion County R-II SD 200/PK-12
2905 Highway D 63463 573-439-5913
Dianna Hoenes, supt. Fax 439-5914
www.marion.k12.mo.us/
Marion County JSHS 100/7-12
2905 Highway D 63463 573-439-5913
Dianna Hoenes, supt. Fax 439-5914

Piedmont, Wayne, Pop. 1,960
Clearwater R-I SD 1,000/PK-12
RR 4 Box 1004 63957 573-223-7426
Deborah Hand, supt. Fax 223-2932
cwtigers.net
Clearwater HS 300/9-12
RR 4 Box 1004 63957 573-223-4524
Teresa Smith, prin. Fax 223-3208
Clearwater MS 300/5-8
RR 4 Box 1004 63957 573-223-7724
Michael Keller, prin. Fax 223-3117

Pierce City, Lawrence, Pop. 1,276
Pierce City R-VI SD 700/PK-12
300 N Myrtle St 65723 417-476-2555
Dr. Russell Moreland, supt. Fax 476-5213
www.pcschools.net
Pierce City HS 200/9-12
300 N Myrtle St 65723 417-476-2515
Steve Garner, prin. Fax 476-3516
Pierce City MS 100/5-8
300 N Myrtle St 65723 417-476-2842
Charity Rakoski, prin. Fax 476-5405

Pilot Grove, Cooper, Pop. 759
Pilot Grove C-4 SD 300/PK-12
107 School St 65276 660-834-6915
Ashley Groepper, supt. Fax 834-6925
www.pilotgrove.k12.mo.us
Pilot Grove HS 100/9-12
107 School St 65276 660-834-4415
Randall Glenn, prin. Fax 834-4401
Pilot Grove MS 50/7-8
107 School St 65276 660-834-4415
Randall Glenn, prin. Fax 834-4401

Pineville, McDonald, Pop. 780
McDonald County R-I SD
Supt. — See Anderson
Pineville ES 200/3-8
202 E 8th St 64856 417-223-4346
Tamra Kester, prin. Fax 223-4195

Plato, Texas, Pop. 109
Plato R-V SD 600/PK-12
PO Box A 65552 417-458-3333
Kim Hawk, supt. Fax 458-4706
www.plato.k12.mo.us/
Plato HS 300/6-12
PO Box A 65552 417-458-4980
Justin Copley, prin. Fax 458-4706

Platte City, Platte, Pop. 4,565
Platte County R-III SD 3,000/PK-12
998 Platte Falls Rd 64079 816-858-5420
Dr. Mike Reik, supt. Fax 858-5593
www.plattecountyschooldistrict.com/
Northland Career Center Vo/Tech
1801 Branch St 64079 816-858-5505
Brian Noller, dir. Fax 858-3278
Platte City MS 600/6-8
900 Pirate Dr 64079 816-858-2036
Dr. Chris Miller, prin. Fax 858-3748
Platte County HS 1,100/9-12
1501 Branch St 64079 816-858-2822
Dr. Chad Sayre, prin. Fax 858-5140
Other Schools – See Kansas City

Plattsburg, Clinton, Pop. 2,263
Clinton County R-III SD 700/PK-12
800 W Frost St 64477 816-539-2183
Dr. Sandy Steggall, supt. Fax 539-2412
ccr3.k12.mo.us
Clinton County R-III MS 200/6-8
800 W Frost St 64477 816-539-3920
Brandon Burns, prin. Fax 539-2412
Plattsburg HS 200/9-12
800 W Frost St 64477 816-539-2184
Ryan Beatty, prin. Fax 539-3315

Pleasant Hill, Cass, Pop. 7,996
Pleasant Hill R-III SD 2,100/PK-12
318 Cedar St 64080 816-540-3161
Dr. Wesley Townsend, supt. Fax 540-5135
www.pleasanthillschools.com
Pleasant Hill HS 700/9-12
1 Rooster Way 64080 816-540-3111
Dr. Paul Canaan, prin. Fax 987-6084
Pleasant Hill MS 300/7-8
1301 E Myrtle St 64080 816-540-2149
Greg Reeves, prin. Fax 987-2017

Pleasant Hope, Polk, Pop. 604
Pleasant Hope R-VI SD 1,000/PK-12
PO Box 387 65725 417-267-2850
Kelly Lowe, supt. Fax 267-4373
www.phr6.org
Pleasant Hope HS 300/9-12
PO Box 387 65725 417-267-2271
Brent Offerdahl, prin. Fax 267-5007
Pleasant Hope MS 300/5-8
PO Box 387 65725 417-267-7701
Allison Dishman, prin. Fax 267-9221
Other Schools – See Brighton

Point Lookout, Taney

College of the Ozarks Post-Sec.
PO Box 17 65726 417-334-6411
School of the Ozarks 300/K-12
PO Box 17 65726 417-690-2325

Polo, Caldwell, Pop. 552
Polo R-VII SD 400/K-12
300 W School St 64671 660-354-2326
Donald Wilburn, supt. Fax 354-2910
polo.k12.mo.us/
Polo HS 100/9-12
300 W School St 64671 660-354-2524
Kyle Ross, prin. Fax 354-2738
Polo MS 100/5-8
300 W School St 64671 660-354-2200
Monica Palmer, prin. Fax 354-3162

Poplar Bluff, Butler, Pop. 16,562
Poplar Bluff R-I SD 4,800/PK-12
1110 N Westwood Blvd 63901 573-785-7751
Scott Dill, supt. Fax 785-0336
www.poplarbluffschools.net
Poplar Bluff HS 1,300/9-12
3209 Oak Grove Rd 63901 573-785-6471
Michael Kiehne, prin. Fax 785-6471
Poplar Bluff JHS 800/7-8
550 N Westwood Blvd 63901 573-785-5602
Bob Case, prin. Fax 785-5004
Technical Career Center Vo/Tech
3203 Oak Grove Rd 63901 573-785-2248
Charles Kinsey, dir. Fax 785-4168

Three Rivers Community College Post-Sec.
2080 Three Rivers Blvd 63901 573-840-9600

Portageville, New Madrid, Pop. 3,162
Portageville SD 800/PK-12
904 King Ave 63873 573-379-3855
Michael Allred, supt. Fax 379-5817
www.portageville.k12.mo.us
Portageville HS 200/9-12
904 King Ave 63873 573-379-3819
Jeff Bullock, prin. Fax 379-5817
Portageville MS 200/6-8
902 King Ave 63873 573-379-3853
Barry Branscum, prin. Fax 379-5817

Potosi, Washington, Pop. 2,627
Potosi R-III SD 2,400/PK-12
400 N Mine St 63664 573-438-5485
Dr. Shawn McCue, supt. Fax 438-5487
www.potosir3.org/
Evans MS 400/7-8
303 S Lead St 63664 573-438-2101
Brice Wilson, prin. Fax 438-4635
Potosi HS 700/9-12
1 Trojan Dr 63664 573-438-2156
Angela Schlosser, prin. Fax 438-2269

Prairie Home, Cooper, Pop. 279
Prairie Home R-V SD 200/K-12
301 Highway 87 65068 660-841-5296
David Heeb, supt. Fax 841-5513
www.prairiehome.k12.mo.us
Prairie Home HS 100/7-12
301 Highway 87 65068 660-841-5296
Patrick Tray, prin. Fax 841-5513

Princeton, Mercer, Pop. 1,164
Princeton R-V SD 400/PK-12
1008 E Coleman St 64673 660-748-3490
Jerry Girdner, supt. Fax 748-3212
www.tigertown.k12.mo.us
Princeton JSHS 200/7-12
1008 E Coleman St 64673 660-748-3490
Tamie Miller, prin. Fax 748-4018

Purdin, Linn, Pop. 189
Linn County R-I SD 100/PK-12
PO Box 130 64674 660-244-5045
Ryan Livingston, supt. Fax 244-5025
www.linnr1.k12.mo.us
Linn County R-1 S 100/PK-12
PO Box 130 64674 660-244-5035
Candi Gray, prin. Fax 244-5025

Purdy, Barry, Pop. 1,081
Purdy R-II SD 700/K-12
PO Box 248 65734 417-442-3216
Dr. Steven Chancellor, supt. Fax 442-3963
www.purdyk12.com
Purdy HS 200/9-12
PO Box 248 65734 417-442-3215
Matthew Gower, prin. Fax 442-3632
Purdy MS 200/5-8
PO Box 248 65734 417-442-7066
Janet Boys, prin. Fax 442-7067

Puxico, Stoddard, Pop. 867
Puxico R-VIII SD 800/PK-12
481 N Bedford St 63960 573-222-3762
Dr. Kyle Dare, supt. Fax 222-3137
www.puxico.k12.mo.us
Mingo/Puxico Technical HS Vo/Tech
481 N Bedford St 63960 573-222-2675
Jason Hill, prin. Fax 222-3137
Puxico HS 200/9-12
481 N Bedford St 63960 573-222-3175
Cindy Crabb, prin. Fax 222-2375
Puxico JHS 200/6-8
481 N Bedford St 63960 573-222-3058
Jason Hill, prin. Fax 222-6373

Queen City, Schuyler, Pop. 595
Schuyler County R-I SD 600/PK-12
21701 N Highway 63 63561 660-766-2204
Robert Amen, supt. Fax 766-2400
www.schuyler.k12.mo.us
Schuyler County R-I HS 300/7-12
21701 N Highway 63 63561 660-766-2424
Kyle Windy, prin. Fax 766-2646

Ravenwood, Nodaway, Pop. 439
Northeast Nodaway County R-V SD 200/PK-12
PO Box 206 64479 660-937-3112
Jeff Mehlenbacher Ed.D., supt. Fax 937-3110
nen.k12.mo.us
Northeast Nodaway HS 100/7-12
PO Box 206 64479 660-937-3125
Ken Grove, prin. Fax 937-3110

Raymore, Cass, Pop. 18,776
Raymore-Peculiar R-II SD
Supt. — See Peculiar
Raymore-Peculiar East MS 1,000/7-8
17509 E State Route 58 64083 816-388-4000
David Mitchell, prin. Fax 388-4001

House of Heavilin Beauty College Post-Sec.
800 W Foxwood Dr 64083 816-767-8000

Raytown, Jackson, Pop. 28,561
Raytown C-2 SD 8,900/PK-12
6608 Raytown Rd 64133 816-268-7000
Dr. Allan Markley, supt. Fax 268-7019
www.raytownschools.org/
Herndon Career Center Vo/Tech
11501 E State Route 350 64138 816-268-7140
Cheryl Reichert, dir. Fax 268-7149
Raytown Alternative S Alt
10750 E State Route 350 64138 816-268-7180
Lori Forte, prin. Fax 268-7185
Raytown Central MS 600/6-8
10601 E 59th St 64133 816-268-7050
Dr. Jaime Sadich, prin. Fax 268-7055
Raytown HS 1,500/9-12
6019 Blue Ridge Blvd 64133 816-268-7300
Dr. Chad Bruton, prin. Fax 268-7315
Raytown South HS 1,200/9-12
8211 Sterling Ave 64138 816-268-7330
Dr. Kevin Overfelt, prin. Fax 268-7345
Raytown South MS 600/6-8
8401 E 83rd St 64138 816-268-7380
Carl Calcara, prin. Fax 268-7385
Other Schools – See Kansas City

Reeds Spring, Stone, Pop. 896
Reeds Spring R-IV SD 1,900/PK-12
20281 State Highway 413 65737 417-272-8173
Dr. Michael Mason, supt. Fax 272-8656
www.rs-wolves.com
Gibson Technical Center Vo/Tech
386 W State Highway 76 65737 417-272-3271
Nick Thieman, dir. Fax 272-1529
New Horizons Alternative S Alt
386 W State Highway 76 65737 417-272-3271
Nick Thieman, dir. Fax 272-1529
Reeds Spring HS 600/9-12
20277 State Highway 413 65737 417-272-8171
Dr. Isaac Sooter, prin. Fax 272-1481
Reeds Spring MS 300/7-8
21016 Main St 65737 417-272-8245
Travis Kite, prin. Fax 272-8490

Republic, Greene, Pop. 14,495
Republic R-III SD 4,800/PK-12
518 N Hampton Ave 65738 417-732-3605
Chance Wistrom, supt. Fax 732-3609
www.republicschools.org
Republic HS 1,300/9-12
4370 S Repmo Dr 65738 417-732-3650
Tyler Overstreet Ed.D., prin. Fax 732-3659
Republic MS 1,100/6-8
1 Tiger Dr 65738 417-732-3640
Tonia Herbold, prin. Fax 732-3649

Rich Hill, Bates, Pop. 1,356
Rich Hill R-IV SD 400/K-12
703 N 3rd St 64779 417-395-2418
Jeff Blackford, supt. Fax 395-2407
www.richhill.k12.mo.us/
Rich Hill HS 200/7-12
703 N 3rd St 64779 417-395-4191
Brian Gillis, prin. Fax 395-2407

Richland, Pulaski, Pop. 1,803
Richland R-IV SD 600/PK-12
714 E Jefferson Ave 65556 573-765-3241
Doug Smith, supt. Fax 765-5552
www.richlandbears.us
Richland HS 200/9-12
714 E Jefferson Ave 65556 573-765-3711
Pamela Dawson, prin. Fax 765-5552
Richland JHS 100/7-8
714 E Jefferson Ave 65556 573-765-3711
Pamela Dawson, prin. Fax 765-5552

Richmond, Ray, Pop. 5,691
Richmond R-XVI SD 1,600/PK-12
1017 E Main St 64085 816-776-6912
Dr. Mike Aytes, supt. Fax 776-5554
richmond.k12.mo.us
Richmond HS 500/9-12
451 E South St 64085 816-776-2226
John Parker, prin. Fax 776-8748
Richmond MS 400/6-8
715 S Wellington St 64085 816-776-5841
Jana Fleckenstine, prin. Fax 776-2788

Ridgeway, Harrison, Pop. 462
Ridgeway R-V SD 100/PK-12
305 Main St 64481 660-872-6813
Brenda Dougan, supt. Fax 872-6230
Ridgeway JSHS 50/7-12
305 Main St 64481 660-872-6813
Kristi Weldon, prin. Fax 872-6230

Risco, New Madrid, Pop. 338
Risco R-II SD 200/K-12
PO Box 17 63874 573-396-5568
Amy Baker, supt. Fax 396-5503
www.risco.k12.mo.us/
Risco JSHS 100/7-12
PO Box 17 63874 573-396-5568
Craig Earnheart, prin. Fax 396-5503

Riverside, Platte, Pop. 2,836
Park Hill SD
Supt. — See Kansas City
Park Hill South HS 1,600/9-12
4500 NW River Park Dr 64150 816-359-4120
Dr. Dale Longenecker, prin. Fax 359-4129

Rock Port, Atchison, Pop. 1,303
Rock Port R-II SD 300/K-12
600 S Nebraska St 64482 660-744-6298
Craig Walker, supt. Fax 744-5539
rockport.k12.mo.us
Rock Port JSHS 200/7-12
600 S Nebraska St 64482 660-744-6296
Jonnie Kemerling, prin. Fax 744-5539

Rogersville, Greene, Pop. 3,000
Logan-Rogersville R-VIII SD 2,400/PK-12
100 E Front St 65742 417-753-2891
Dr. Shawn B. Randles, supt. Fax 753-3063
logrog.net/
Logan-Rogersville HS 700/9-12
4700 S State Highway 125 65742 417-753-2813
Dr. Teresa McKenzie, prin. Fax 753-3960
Logan-Rogersville MS 400/7-8
8225 E Farm Road 174 65742 417-753-2896
Dr. Toby Kite, prin. Fax 753-3182

Rolla, Phelps, Pop. 19,067
Rolla SD 31 4,100/PK-12
500A Forum Dr 65401 573-458-0100
Dr. Aaron Zalis, supt. Fax 458-0105
rolla.k12.mo.us
Rolla JHS 600/8-9
1360 Soest Rd 65401 573-458-0130
Monica Fulton, prin. Fax 458-0135
Rolla SHS 900/10-12
900 Bulldog Run 65401 573-458-0140
Dr. Jim Pritchett, prin. Fax 458-0147
Rolla Technical Center Vo/Tech
500 Forum Dr 65401 573-458-0160
Keith McCarthy, dir. Fax 458-0164
Rolla Technical Institute Vo/Tech
1304 E 10th St 65401 573-458-0150
Lucas Chapman, dir. Fax 458-0155

Metro Business College Post-Sec.
1202 E State Route 72 65401 573-364-8464
Missouri University of Science & Tech Post-Sec.
1870 Miner Cir 65409 573-341-4111
Salem College of Hairstyling Post-Sec.
1051 Kingshighway St Ste 1 65401 573-368-3136

Rosendale, Andrew, Pop. 143
North Andrew County R-VI SD 400/K-12
9120 Highway 48 64483 816-567-2965
Jim Shultz, supt. Fax 567-2096
northandrew.org
North Andrew HS 100/9-12
9120 Highway 48 64483 816-567-2525
Jason Tolen, prin. Fax 567-2096
North Andrew MS 100/6-8
9120 Highway 48 64483 816-567-2525
Jason Tolen, prin. Fax 567-2096

Russellville, Cole, Pop. 799
Cole County R-I SD 600/PK-12
13600 Route C 65074 573-782-3534
Perry Gorrell, supt. Fax 782-3545
www.cole.k12.mo.us
Cole County R-I HS 200/9-12
13600 Route C 65074 573-782-3313
Chris Mitchell, prin. Fax 782-3262
Cole County R-I MS 100/6-8
13600 Route C 65074 573-782-4915
Elaine Buschjost, prin. Fax 782-3775

Saint Albans, Franklin

Fulton S at St. Albans 100/PK-12
PO Box 78 63073 636-458-6688

Saint Ann, Saint Louis, Pop. 12,679
Pattonville R-3 SD 5,700/PK-12
11097 Saint Charles Rock Rd 63074 314-213-8500
Dr. Michael Fulton, supt. Fax 213-8601
psdr3.org
Holman MS 600/6-8
11055 Saint Charles Rock Rd 63074 314-213-8032
Sarah Moran, prin. Fax 213-8632
Other Schools – See Maryland Heights

Ritenour SD
Supt. — See Saint Louis
Hoech MS 700/6-8
3312 Ashby Rd 63074 314-493-6200
Dr. Terrance Peterson, prin. Fax 426-3837

American Trade School Post-Sec.
3925 Industrial Dr 63074 314-423-1900
Patsy & Rob's Academy of Beauty Post-Sec.
18 Northwest Plz 63074 314-298-8808

Saint Charles, Saint Charles, Pop. 64,512
Francis Howell R-III SD 20,100/PK-12
4545 Central School Rd 63304 636-851-4000
Dr. Mary Hendricks-Harris, supt. Fax 851-4093
www.fhsdschools.org
Barnwell MS 900/6-8
1035 Jungs Station Rd 63303 636-851-4100
David Eckhoff, prin. Fax 851-4095
Heritage Landing Alternative Program Alt
1400 Gettysburg Lndg 63303 636-851-5300
Anthony Haan, prin. Fax 851-4130
Hollenbeck MS 600/6-8
4555 Central School Rd 63304 636-851-5400
Woody Borgschulte, prin. Fax 851-4132
Howell Central HS 1,900/9-12
5199 Highway N 63304 636-851-4600
Dr. Sonny Arnel, prin. Fax 851-4111
Howell HS 2,000/9-12
7001 S Highway 94 63304 636-851-4700
Dave Wedlock, prin. Fax 851-4116
Howell North HS 1,900/9-12
2549 Hackmann Rd 63303 636-851-4900
Andrew Downs, prin. Fax 851-6199
Howell Union HS 100/Alt
1405 Highway D 63304 636-851-5000
Rob Gaugh, prin. Fax 851-4127
Saeger MS 800/6-8
5201 Highway N 63304 636-851-5600
Krisandar Worley, prin. Fax 851-4138
Other Schools – See Weldon Spring

Orchard Farm R-V SD 1,600/PK-12
3489 Boshertown Rd 63301 636-925-5400
Dr. Thomas Muzzey, supt. Fax 925-0340
www.ofsd.k12.mo.us
Orchard Farm HS 500/9-12
2175 Highway V 63301 636-250-5400
Brian Smith, prin. Fax 250-5425
Orchard Farm MS 400/6-8
2195 Highway V 63301 636-250-5300
Keith Klostermann, prin. Fax 250-5306

St. Charles R-VI SD 5,100/PK-12
400 N 6th St 63301 636-443-4000
Dr. Jeff Marion, supt. Fax 443-4001
www.stcharlessd.org
Hardin MS 800/7-8
1950 Elm St 63301 636-443-4300
Dr. Ed Gettemeier, prin. Fax 443-4301
Lewis & Clark Career Center Vo/Tech
2400 Zumbehl Rd 63301 636-443-4950
Dr. Andrew Stewart, dir. Fax 443-4951
St. Charles HS 800/9-12
725 N Kingshighway St 63301 636-443-4100
Jeff Walker, prin. Fax 443-4101
St. Charles West HS 700/9-12
3601 Droste Rd 63301 636-443-4200
Dr. Kim Fitterling, prin. Fax 443-4201
Success Campus Alternative S Alt
1600 Waverly St 63301 636-443-4890
Dr. Christine Jarus, prin. Fax 443-4891

Duchesne HS 500/9-12
2550 Elm St 63301 636-946-6767
Fritz Long, prin. Fax 946-6267
Lewis & Clark Career Center Post-Sec.
2400 Zumbehl Rd 63301 636-443-4950
Lindenwood University Post-Sec.
209 S Kingshighway St 63301 636-949-2000
Missouri Tech Post-Sec.
1690 Country Club Dr 63303 636-573-9300
The Art Institute of Saint Louis Post-Sec.
1520 S 5th St Ste 107 63303 636-688-3010
Vatterott College - St. Charles Post-Sec.
3550 W Clay St 63301 636-940-4100

Saint Clair, Franklin, Pop. 4,665
St. Clair R-XIII SD 2,300/K-12
905 Bardot St 63077 636-629-3500
Kyle Kruse, supt. Fax 629-4466
www.stcmo.org
Saint Clair HS 800/9-12
1015 High School Dr 63077 636-629-3500
Jenny Davis, prin. Fax 629-1979
Saint Clair JHS 500/6-8
925 High School Dr 63077 636-629-3500
Eric Lause, prin. Fax 629-1363

Sainte Genevieve, Sainte Genevieve, Pop. 4,356
St. Genevieve County R-II SD 1,900/PK-12
375 N 5th St 63670 573-883-4500
Jeffrey Lindsey, supt. Fax 883-5957
www.sgdragons.org
Sainte Genevieve HS 600/9-12
715 Washington St 63670 573-883-4500
Chris Hoehne, prin. Fax 883-5957
Sainte Genevieve MS 400/6-8
211 N 5th St 63670 573-883-4500
Paul Taylor, prin. Fax 883-5957

Valle Catholic HS 100/9-12
40 N 4th St 63670 573-883-7496
Paul Hinman, prin. Fax 883-9142

Saint Elizabeth, Miller, Pop. 334
St. Elizabeth R-IV SD 100/PK-12
PO Box 68 65075 573-493-2246
Toni Taylor, supt. Fax 493-2380
www.ste.k12.mo.us
Saint Elizabeth S 100/PK-12
PO Box 68 65075 573-493-2246
Crintina Irwin, prin. Fax 493-2380

Saint James, Phelps, Pop. 4,150
St. James R-I SD 1,800/PK-12
122 E Scioto St 65559 573-265-2300
Dr. Merlyn Johnson, supt. Fax 265-6126
www.stjschools.org/
St. James HS 500/9-12
101 E Scioto St 65559 573-265-2300
Jo Stammers, prin. Fax 265-3652
St. James MS 400/6-8
1 Tiger Dr 65559 573-265-2300
Kaaren Lepper, prin. Fax 265-6302

Saint John, Saint Louis, Pop. 6,331
Ritenour SD
Supt. — See Saint Louis
Ritenour Adult Learning Center Adult
8762 Saint Charles Rock Rd 63114 314-426-7900
Fax 429-4348

Saint Joseph, Buchanan, Pop. 74,914
St. Joseph SD 11,300/PK-12
925 Felix St 64501 816-671-4000
Dr. Robert Newhart, supt. Fax 671-4470
www.sjsd.k12.mo.us
Benton HS 800/9-12
5655 S 4th St 64504 816-671-4030
Beery Johnson, prin. Fax 671-4036
Bode MS 500/7-8
720 N Noyes Blvd 64506 816-671-4050
Roberta Dias, prin. Fax 671-4473
Central HS 1,700/9-12
2602 Edmond St 64501 816-671-4080
Deborah Stephens, prin. Fax 671-4474
Colgan Alternative Resource Center 300/Alt
3510 Frederick Ave 64506 816-671-4072
Jeremy Burright, dir. Fax 671-4022
Hillyard Technical Center Vo/Tech
3434 Faraon St 64506 816-671-4170
Dennis Merritt, dir. Fax 671-4479
Lafayette HS 800/9-12
412 E Highland Ave 64505 816-671-4220
Dr. Tyran Sumy, prin. Fax 671-4480
Robidoux MS 400/7-8
4212 Saint Joseph Ave 64505 816-671-4350
Mark Weis, prin. Fax 671-4487
Spring Garden MS 400/7-8
5802 S 22nd St 64503 816-671-4380
Dr. Lara Gilpin, prin. Fax 671-4489
Truman MS 500/7-8
3227 Olive St Ste 45 64507 816-671-4400
Jason Callaway, prin. Fax 671-4491
Webster Learning Center Alt
1211 N 18th St 64501 816-671-4020
Fax 671-4471

American Business and Technology Univ Post-Sec.
1018 W Saint Maartens Dr 64506 816-279-7000
Bishop Le Blond HS 200/9-12
3529 Frederick Ave 64506 816-279-1629
Jeff Sullivan, prin. Fax 279-5488
Hosanna Christian S 50/K-12
17290 US HIghway 71 64505 816-324-2000
Missouri Western State University Post-Sec.
4525 Downs Dr 64507 816-271-4200
St. Joseph Christian S 300/PK-12
5401 Gene Field Rd 64506 816-279-1555
Dr. Jason Tindol, supt. Fax 279-4574
Vatterott College - Saint Joseph Post-Sec.
3709 N Belt Hwy 64506 816-558-7500

Saint Louis, Saint Louis, Pop. 312,138
Affton SD 101 2,400/PK-12
8701 MacKenzie Rd 63123 314-638-8770
Dr. Steve Brotherton, supt. Fax 631-2548
www.afftonschools.net
Affton HS 800/9-12
8309 MacKenzie Rd 63123 314-638-6330
Dr. Vince Powell, prin. Fax 633-5990
Rogers MS 500/6-8
7550 MacKenzie Rd 63123 314-351-9679
Jason Buck, prin. Fax 351-6381

Bayless SD 1,600/PK-12
4530 Weber Rd 63123 314-256-8600
Ronald J. Tucker, supt. Fax 544-6315
baylessk12.org
Bayless HS 500/9-12
4532 Weber Rd 63123 314-256-8660
Patrick McEvoy, prin. Fax 544-6315
Bayless JHS 400/6-8
4530 Weber Rd 63123 314-256-8690
Doug Harness, prin. Fax 544-6315

Ferguson-Florissant R-II SD
Supt. — See Florissant
Ferguson MS 600/7-8
701 January Ave 63135 314-506-9600
Dr. Katherine Chambers, prin. Fax 506-9601
McCluer South - Berkeley HS 600/9-12
201 Brotherton Ln 63135 314-506-9800
Steven Lawler, prin. Fax 506-9801

Hancock Place SD 1,500/PK-12
9417 S Broadway 63125 314-544-1300
Dr. Kevin Carl, supt. Fax 631-3752
hancock.k12.mo.us
Hancock Place HS 400/9-12
229 W Ripa Ave 63125 314-544-1200
Dr. Shelly Vogler, prin. Fax 544-6427
Hancock Place MS 300/6-8
243 W Ripa Ave 63125 314-544-6423
Thomas Dittrich, prin. Fax 544-6470

Hazelwood SD
Supt. — See Florissant
Hazelwood East HS 1,400/9-12
11300 Dunn Rd 63138 314-953-5600
Yolander Pittman, prin. Fax 953-5613
Hazelwood East MS 500/6-8
1865 Dunn Rd 63138 314-953-5700
Dr. Irma Moore, prin. Fax 953-5713
Hazelwood Southeast MS 700/6-8
918 Prigge Rd 63138 314-953-7700
Chauncey Granger, prin. Fax 953-7713

Ladue SD 4,100/PK-12
9703 Conway Rd 63124 314-994-7080
Dr. Donna Jahnke, supt. Fax 994-0441
www.ladueschools.net
Ladue MS 1,000/6-8
9701 Conway Rd 63124 314-993-3900
Greg Baber, prin. Fax 997-8736
Watkins HS 1,300/9-12
1201 S Warson Rd 63124 314-993-6447
Brad Griffith, prin. Fax 994-1467

Lindbergh SD 6,000/PK-12
4900 S Lindbergh Blvd 63126 314-729-2480
Dr. Jim Simpson, supt. Fax 729-2482
www.lindberghschools.ws/
Lindbergh HS 2,000/9-12
5000 S Lindbergh Blvd 63126 314-729-2410
Dr. Eric Cochran, prin. Fax 729-2412
Sperreng MS 700/6-8
12111 Tesson Ferry Rd 63128 314-729-2420
Mark Eggers, prin. Fax 729-2422
Truman MS 700/6-8
12225 Eddie and Park Rd 63127 314-729-2470
Michael Straatman, prin. Fax 729-2472

Mehlville R-IX SD 11,100/PK-12
3120 Lemay Ferry Rd 63125 314-467-5000
Dr. Chris Gaines, supt. Fax 467-5099
www.mehlvilleschooldistrict.com
Bernard MS 700/6-8
1054 Forder Rd 63129 314-467-6600
Lori Sullivan, prin. Fax 467-6699
Buerkle MS 600/6-8
623 Buckley Rd 63125 314-467-6800
Jim Kern, prin. Fax 467-6899
Mehlville HS 1,800/9-12
3200 Lemay Ferry Rd 63125 314-467-6000
Dr. Denise Swanger, prin. Fax 467-6099
Oakville HS 1,700/9-12
5557 Milburn Rd 63129 314-467-7000
Jan Kellerman, prin. Fax 467-7099
Oakville MS 600/6-8
5950 Telegraph Rd 63129 314-467-7400
Mike Salsman, prin. Fax 467-7499
Washington MS 600/6-8
5165 Ambs Rd 63128 314-467-7600
Adam Smith, prin. Fax 467-7699

Normandy Schools Collaborative 2,500/PK-12
3855 Lucas and Hunt Rd 63121 314-493-0400
Dr. Charles Pearson, supt. Fax 493-0475
www.normandysc.org
Normandy HS 600/9-12
6701 Saint Charles Rock Rd 63133 314-493-0600
Derrick Mitchell, prin. Fax 493-0668
Other Schools – See Normandy

Ritenour SD 6,400/PK-12
2420 Woodson Rd 63114 314-493-6010
Dr. Christopher Kilbride, supt. Fax 426-7144
www.ritenour.k12.mo.us
Other Schools – See Overland, Saint Ann, Saint John

Riverview Gardens SD 5,000/PK-12
1370 Northumberland Dr 63137 314-869-2505
Dr. Scott Spurgeon, supt. Fax 388-6002
www.rgsd.k12.mo.us
Central MS 600/6-8
9800 Patricia Barkalow Dr 63137 314-867-2603
Lakena Curtis, prin. Fax 388-6028
Riverview Gardens HS 1,000/9-12
1218 Shepley Dr 63137 314-869-4700
Darius Kirk, prin. Fax 388-6020
Westview MS 600/6-8
1950 Nemnich Rd 63136 314-867-0410
Valeska Hill, prin. Fax 388-6055

Special SD of St. Louis County 2,500/10-12
12110 Clayton Rd 63131 314-989-8100
Don Bohannon, supt. Fax 989-8440
www.ssdmo.org/
South Technical HS Vo/Tech
12721 W Watson Rd 63127 314-989-7400
Jacob Lohse, prin. Fax 989-7503
Other Schools – See Florissant

St. Louis City SD 26,300/PK-12
801 N 11th St 63101 314-231-3720
Dr. Kelvin Adams, supt. Fax 345-2661
www.slps.org/
Busch MS of Character & Athletics 300/6-8
5910 Clifton Ave 63109 314-352-1043
Robert Lescher, prin. Fax 244-1729
Carnahan HS of the Future 400/9-12
4041 S Broadway 63118 314-457-0582
Rene Racette, prin. Fax 457-9741
Carr Lane Visual & Performing Art MS 600/6-8
1004 N Jefferson Ave 63106 314-231-0413
Barrett Taylor, prin. Fax 244-1733
Central Visual and Performing Arts HS 400/9-12
3125 S Kingshighway Blvd 63139 314-771-2772
Dr. Kacy Seals, prin. Fax 771-0135
Cleveland NJROTC Academy 300/9-12
4939 Kemper Ave 63139 314-776-1301
Victoria Shearing, prin. Fax 244-1747
Collegiate S of Medicine and Bioscience 9-12
1547 S Theresa Ave 63104 314-696-2290
Frederick Steele, prin. Fax 244-1790
Compton-Drew ILC MS 500/6-8
5130 Oakland Ave 63110 314-652-9282
Nicole Holland, prin. Fax 244-1756
Fanning MS Community Education Center 400/6-8
3417 Grace Ave 63116 314-772-1038
June Berry, prin. Fax 244-1766
Fresh Start Academy Alt
4248 Cottage Ave 63113 314-531-2220
Fax 244-1930
Gateway MST Prep S 600/6-8
1200 N Jefferson Ave 63106 314-241-2295
Nakia King, prin. Fax 241-7698
Gateway STEM HS 1,200/9-12
5101 McRee Ave 63110 314-776-3300
Steven Clay, prin. Fax 776-8267
Langston MS 300/6-8
5511 Wabada Ave 63112 314-383-2908
Lanetra Thomas, prin. Fax 385-4632
Long MS Community Education Center 200/6-8
5028 Morganford Rd 63116 314-481-3440
Brenda Smith, prin. Fax 481-7329
McKinley Classical Junior Academy 200/6-8
2156 Russell Blvd 63104 314-773-0027
Steven Warmack, prin. Fax 771-9749
McKinley Classical Leadership Academy 200/9-12
2156 Russell Blvd 63104 314-773-0027
Stephen Warmack, prin. Fax 244-1834
Metro Academic & Classical HS 300/9-12
4015 McPherson Ave 63108 314-534-3894
Wilfred Moore Ph.D., prin. Fax 531-4894
Miller Career Academy Vo/Tech
1000 N Grand Blvd 63106 314-371-0394
Michael Brown, prin. Fax 371-1311
Northwest Academy of Law 400/9-12
5140 Riverview Blvd 63120 314-385-4774
Valerie Carter-Thomas, prin. Fax 385-3651
Nottingham CAJT Vo/Tech
4915 Donovan Ave 63109 314-481-4095
Kimberly Long, prin. Fax 244-1730
Roosevelt HS 800/9-12
3230 Hartford St 63118 314-776-6040
Crystal Gale, prin. Fax 244-1861
Soldan International Studies HS 600/9-12
918 Union Blvd 63108 314-367-9222
Dr. Thomas Cason, prin. Fax 367-1898
Sumner Magnet HS 600/9-12
4248 Cottage Ave 63113 314-371-1048
Michael Triplett, prin. Fax 531-9852
Vashon HS 900/9-12
3035 Cass Ave 63106 314-533-9487
Debra Powell, prin. Fax 533-7540

Yeatman-Liddell MS 400/7-9
4265 Athlone Ave 63115 314-261-8132
Dr. Leslie Bonner, prin. Fax 389-4613

Webster Groves SD
Supt. — See Webster Groves
Hixson MS 700/7-8
630 S Elm Ave 63119 314-963-6450
Dr. Stacie Smith, prin. Fax 918-4624

Achieve Test Prep Post-Sec.
1810 Craig Rd Ste 213 63146 314-288-0702
Aquinas Institute of Theology Post-Sec.
23 S Spring Ave 63108 314-256-8800
Bishop DuBourg HS 500/9-12
5850 Eichelberger St 63109 314-832-3030
Dr. Bridget Timoney, prin. Fax 832-0529
Block Yeshiva HS 50/9-12
1146 N Warson Rd 63132 314-872-8701
Brookes Bible Institute Post-Sec.
3465 S Grand Blvd 63118 314-773-0083
Burroughs S 600/7-12
755 S Price Rd 63124 314-993-4040
Andy Abbott, head sch Fax 993-6458
Cardinal Ritter College Prep HS 300/9-12
701 N Spring Ave 63108 314-446-5500
Michael Blackshear, prin. Fax 446-5570
Chamberlain College of Nursing Post-Sec.
11830 Westline Indtrl # 106 63146 314-991-6200
Chaminade College Preparatory S 800/6-12
425 S Lindbergh Blvd 63131 314-993-4400
Philip Rone, prin. Fax 993-4403
Christian Academy of Greater St. Louis 100/PK-12
11050 N Warson Rd 63114 314-429-7070
Christian Brothers College HS 900/9-12
1850 De La Salle Dr 63141 314-985-6100
Timothy Seymour, prin. Fax 985-6115
Concordia Seminary Post-Sec.
801 Seminary Pl 63105 314-505-7000
Cor Jesu Academy 600/9-12
10230 Gravois Rd 63123 314-842-1546
Veronica Beato, prin. Fax 842-6061
Court Reporting Institute Post-Sec.
7730 Carondelet Ave Ste 400 63105 888-208-6780
Covenant Theological Seminary Post-Sec.
12330 Conway Rd 63141 800-264-8064
Crossroads College Preparatory S 200/7-12
500 De Baliviere Ave 63112 314-367-8085
Dr. Jason Heisserer, head sch Fax 367-9711
De Smet Jesuit HS 1,000/9-12
233 N New Ballas Rd 63141 314-567-3500
Trevor Bonat, prin. Fax 567-1519
DeVry University Post-Sec.
11830 Westline Indstrl #100 63146 866-831-3882
DVA Medical Center Post-Sec.
1 Jefferson Barracks Rd 63125 314-894-6631
Elaine Steven Beauty College Post-Sec.
10420 W Florissant Ave 63136 314-868-8196
ex'treme Institute by Nelly Post-Sec.
800 N 3rd St 63102 888-669-0633
Fontbonne University Post-Sec.
6800 Wydown Blvd 63105 314-862-3456
Goldfarb School of Nursing Barnes-Jewish Post-Sec.
4483 Duncan Ave 63110 314-454-7055
Harris-Stowe State University Post-Sec.
3026 Laclede Ave 63103 314-340-3300
Healing Arts Center Post-Sec.
10073 Manchester Rd Ste 100 63122 314-647-8080
Hickey College Post-Sec.
940 W Port Plz Ste 101 63146 314-434-2212
IHM Health of EMS Post-Sec.
2500 Abbott Pl 63143 314-768-1234
IHM Health Studies Center Post-Sec.
3663 Lindell Blvd 63108 314-768-1000
Incarnate Word Academy 400/9-12
2788 Normandy Dr 63121 314-725-5850
Dr. Molly Grumich, prin. Fax 725-2308
Jefferson S 100/7-12
4100 S Lindbergh Blvd 63127 314-843-4151
Dr. Elizabeth Holekamp, head sch Fax 843-3527
Kaplan University Post-Sec.
1807 Park 270 Dr 63146 314-205-7900
Kenrick School of Theology Post-Sec.
5200 Glennon Dr 63119 314-792-6100
L'Ecole Culinaire Post-Sec.
9811 S 40 Dr 63124 314-587-2433
Logos S 100/6-12
9137 Old Bonhomme Rd 63132 314-997-7002
Dr. Kathleen Boyd-Fenger, head sch Fax 997-6848
Loyola Academy 100/6-8
3851 Washington Blvd 63108 314-531-9091
Paul Bozdech, prin. Fax 531-3603
Lutheran HS North 300/9-12
5401 Lucas and Hunt Rd 63121 314-389-3100
Tim Brackman, prin. Fax 389-3103
Lutheran HS South 500/9-12
9515 Tesson Ferry Rd 63123 314-631-1400
Brian Ryherd, prin. Fax 631-7762
Lutheran School of Nursing Post-Sec.
3547 S Jefferson Ave 63118 314-577-5850
Marian MS 100/5-8
4130 Wyoming St 63116 314-771-7674
Sr. Sarah Heger, prin. Fax 771-7679
Mary Institute/St. Louis Country Day S 1,200/PK-12
101 N Warson Rd 63124 314-995-7367
Lisa Lyle, head sch
Maryville University of St. Louis Post-Sec.
650 Maryville University Dr 63141 314-529-9300
Miller Bais Yaakov HS 50/9-12
700 North and South Rd 63130 314-863-9230
Tova Greenblatt, prin. Fax 863-3856
Missouri Baptist University Post-Sec.
1 College Park Dr 63141 314-434-1115
Missouri School for the Blind Post-Sec.
3815 Magnolia Ave 63110 314-776-4320
National Academy of Beauty Arts Post-Sec.
157 Concord Plz 63128 314-842-3616

Nerinx Hall HS 600/9-12
530 E Lockwood Ave 63119 314-968-1505
Jane Kosash, prin. Fax 968-0604
Notre Dame HS 200/9-12
320 E Ripa Ave 63125 314-544-1015
Amy Bush, prin. Fax 544-8003
Parks College of St. Louis University Post-Sec.
3450 Lindell Blvd 63103 314-977-8203
Principia S 500/PK-12
13201 Clayton Rd 63131 314-434-2100
Travis Brantingham, prin. Fax 275-3583
Providence Classical Christian Academy 100/K-12
5293 S Lindbergh Blvd 63126 314-842-6846
Ranken Technical College Post-Sec.
4431 Finney Ave 63113 314-371-0236
Rosati-Kain HS 400/9-12
4389 Lindell Blvd 63108 314-533-8513
Dr. Elizabeth Goodwin, prin. Fax 533-1618
St. John Vianney HS 600/9-12
1311 S Kirkwood Rd 63122 314-965-4853
Kevin Walsh, prin. Fax 965-1950
St. Joseph's Academy 600/9-12
2307 S Lindbergh Blvd 63131 314-394-4300
Dr. Jennifer Sudekom, prin. Fax 965-9114
St. Louis College of Health Careers Post-Sec.
909 S Taylor Ave 63110 314-652-0300
St. Louis College of Pharmacy Post-Sec.
4588 Parkview Pl 63110 314-367-8700
St. Louis Community College- Forest Park Post-Sec.
5600 Oakland Ave 63110 314-644-9100
St. Louis Hair Academy Post-Sec.
3701 Kossuth Ave 63107 314-533-3125
St. Louis Priory S 400/7-12
500 S Mason Rd 63141 314-434-3690
Fr. Gregory Mohrmann, hdmstr. Fax 576-7088
St. Louis University Post-Sec.
221 N Grand Blvd 63103 800-758-3678
St. Louis University HS 1,100/9-12
4970 Oakland Ave 63110 314-531-0330
Craig Hannick, prin. Fax 531-3441
St. Mary's HS 300/9-12
4701 S Grand Blvd 63111 314-481-8400
Kevin Hacker, prin. Fax 481-3670
Stevens Institute of Business & Arts Post-Sec.
1521 Washington Ave 63103 800-871-0949
Strayer University Post-Sec.
1600 S Brentwood Blvd # 300 63144 314-817-9100
Tower Grove Christian S 200/PK-12
4257 Magnolia Ave 63110 314-776-6473
Michael Gregory, admin. Fax 776-4867
Trinity Catholic HS 300/9-12
1720 Redman Rd 63138 314-741-1333
Kristen Shipp, prin. Fax 741-1335
University of Missouri - Saint Louis Post-Sec.
1 University Blvd 63121 314-516-5000
Ursuline Academy 600/9-12
341 S Sappington Rd 63122 314-984-2800
Dr. Mark Michalski, prin. Fax 966-3396
Villa Duchesne/Oak Hill JSHS 400/7-12
801 S Spoede Rd 63131 314-432-2021
Sr. Donna Collins, prin. Fax 432-0199
Visitation Academy 600/PK-12
3020 N Ballas Rd 63131 314-625-9100
Dan Hildebrand, head sch Fax 432-7210
Washington University in St. Louis Post-Sec.
1 Brookings Dr 63130 314-935-5000
Webster University Post-Sec.
470 E Lockwood Ave 63119 314-968-6900
Westminster Christian Academy K-12
10900 Ladue Rd 63141 314-997-2900
Whitfield S 400/6-12
175 S Mason Rd 63141 314-434-5141
John Delautre, head sch Fax 434-6193

Saint Peters, Saint Charles, Pop. 51,692
Ft. Zumwalt R-II SD
Supt. — See O Fallon
DuBray MS 900/6-8
100 DuBray Dr 63376 636-279-7979
Michael Anderson, prin. Fax 278-4749
Ft. Zumwalt East HS 1,300/9-12
600 First Executive Ave 63376 636-477-2400
Brian Bishop, prin. Fax 926-3345
Ft. Zumwalt South HS 1,400/9-12
8050 Mexico Rd 63376 636-978-1212
Dr. Kevin Keltner, prin. Fax 980-1745
Ft. Zumwalt South MS 1,000/6-8
300 Knaust Rd 63376 636-281-0776
Dr. Monte Massey, prin. Fax 281-0006

Le Cordon Bleu College of Culinary Arts Post-Sec.
7898 Veterans Memorial Pkwy 63376 866-863-2061
Lutheran HS of St. Charles County 300/9-12
5100 Mexico Rd 63376 636-928-5100
Jon Bernhardt, prin. Fax 928-8451

Salem, Dent, Pop. 4,859
Salem R-80 SD 1,200/PK-12
1409 W Rolla Rd 65560 573-729-6642
John McColloch, supt. Fax 729-8493
www.salem.k12.mo.us/
Salem HS 600/9-12
1400 Tiger Pride Dr 65560 573-729-6642
Charles Anderson, prin. Fax 729-7408
Salem MS 200/6-8
1400 Tiger Pride Dr 65560 573-729-6642
Kerry Roberts, prin. Fax 729-2720

Salisbury, Chariton, Pop. 1,601
Salisbury R-IV SD 400/K-12
1000 S Maple Ave 65281 660-388-6699
Troy Clawson, supt. Fax 388-6753
www.salisbury.k12.mo.us/
Salisbury JSHS 200/7-12
1000 S Maple Ave 65281 660-388-6442
Justin Yates, prin. Fax 388-5651

Sarcoxie, Jasper, Pop. 1,304
Sarcoxie R-II SD 700/K-12
101 S 17th St 64862 417-548-3134
Dr. Kevin Goddard, supt. Fax 548-6165
www.sarcoxie.k12.mo.us/
Sarcoxie JSHS 400/6-12
101 S 17th St 64862 417-548-2153
Philip Lewis, prin. Fax 548-7193

Savannah, Andrew, Pop. 5,020
Savannah R-III SD 2,300/K-12
408 W Market St 64485 816-324-3144
Dr. David Brax, supt. Fax 324-5594
www.savannahr3.com
Savannah HS 700/9-12
701 State Route E 64485 816-324-3128
Dr. Robert Sigrist, prin. Fax 324-6536
Savannah MS 600/6-8
10500 State Route T 64485 816-324-3126
Clint Howren, prin. Fax 324-6397

Scott City, Scott, Pop. 4,518
Scott City R-I SD 800/PK-12
3000 Main St 63780 573-264-2381
Brian Lee, supt. Fax 264-2206
scschools.k12.mo.us/
Scott City HS 300/9-12
3000 Main St 63780 573-264-2138
Michael Johnson, prin. Fax 264-2608
Scott City MS 200/5-8
3000 Main St 63780 573-264-2139
Michael Umfleet, prin. Fax 264-2599

Sedalia, Pettis, Pop. 20,824
Sedalia SD 200 4,200/PK-12
2806 Matthew Dr 65301 660-829-6450
Bradley Pollitt, supt. Fax 827-8938
www.sedalia200.org
Smith-Cotton HS 1,000/9-12
2010 Tiger Pride Blvd 65301 660-851-5300
Wade Norton, prin. Fax 851-5393
Smith-Cotton JHS 700/6-8
312 E Broadway Blvd 65301 660-829-6300
Jason Curry, prin. Fax 829-6409

American College of Hair Design Post-Sec.
125 Duke Rd 65301 660-827-3295
Sacred Heart S 100/PK-12
416 W 3rd St 65301 660-827-3800
Dr. Gary Manning, prin. Fax 827-3806
State Fair Community College Post-Sec.
3201 W 16th St 65301 660-530-5800

Senath, Dunklin, Pop. 1,752
Senath-Hornersville C-8 SD 900/PK-12
PO Box 370 63876 573-738-2669
Chad Morgan, supt. Fax 738-9845
www.shs.k12.mo.us/
Senath-Hornersville HS 200/9-12
PO Box 370 63876 573-738-2661
Brett Gibson, prin. Fax 738-3481
Other Schools – See Hornersville

Seneca, Newton, Pop. 2,214
Seneca R-VII SD 1,500/PK-12
914 Frisco St 64865 417-776-3426
Jim Cummins, supt. Fax 776-2177
www.senecar7.com
Seneca HS 500/9-12
914 Frisco St 64865 417-776-3926
Richie Fretwell, prin. Fax 776-1878
Seneca JHS 200/7-8
914 Frisco St 64865 417-776-3911
John Whitehead, prin. Fax 776-2673

Seymour, Webster, Pop. 1,885
Seymour R-II SD 800/PK-12
416 E Clinton Ave 65746 417-935-2287
Bruce Denney, supt. Fax 935-4060
www.seymourschool.net
Seymour HS 200/9-12
625 E Clinton Ave 65746 417-935-4508
Wilbanks Brian, prin. Fax 935-4539
Seymour MS 200/6-8
501 E Clinton Ave 65746 417-935-4626
Brian Bell, prin. Fax 935-2848

Victory Academy 100/PK-12
PO Box 309 65746 417-935-2315
Teresa Bruffett, admin. Fax 935-2316

Shelbina, Shelby, Pop. 1,695
Shelby County R-IV SD 600/PK-12
4154 Highway 36 63468 573-588-4961
Tim Maddex, supt. Fax 588-2490
www.cardinals.k12.mo.us
South Shelby MSHS 200/6-12
4154 Highway 36 63468 573-588-4163
Deacon Windsor, prin. Fax 588-2490

Shelbyville, Shelby, Pop. 547
North Shelby SD 300/PK-12
3071 Highway 15 63469 573-633-2410
Kim Gaines, supt. Fax 633-2138
www.nshelby.k12.mo.us
North Shelby JSHS 100/7-12
3071 Highway 15 63469 573-633-2410
Kerri Greenwell, prin. Fax 633-2138

Sheldon, Vernon, Pop. 525
Sheldon R-VIII SD 200/PK-12
100 E Gene Lathrop Dr 64784 417-884-5113
Jason Irwin, supt. Fax 884-5331
www.sheldon.k12.mo.us
Sheldon JSHS 100/7-12
100 E Gene Lathrop Dr 64784 417-884-5111
Jason Irwin, admin. Fax 884-5331

Sikeston, Scott, Pop. 16,008
Scott County Central SD 400/PK-12
20794 US Highway 61 63801 573-471-2686
Alvin McFerren, supt. Fax 471-2029
scottcentral.k12.mo.us
Scott County Central JSHS 200/7-12
20794 US Highway 61 63801 573-471-2001
John-Mark Jones M.Ed., prin. Fax 471-2004

Sikeston R-6 SD 3,400/K-12
1002 Virginia St 63801 573-472-2581
Thomas Williams, supt. Fax 472-2584
www.sikeston.k12.mo.us
Sikeston 7th and 8th Grade Center 500/7-8
1002 Virginia St 63801 573-471-1720
Frank Staple, prin. Fax 472-8884
Sikeston Career & Technology Center Vo/Tech
1002 Virginia St 63801 573-471-5442
Chad King, dir. Fax 472-8861
Sikeston HS 1,000/9-12
1002 Virginia St 63801 573-472-8850
Steve Bays, prin. Fax 472-8857

Christian Academy 100/PK-12
103 E Kathleen St 63801 573-481-0216
Kevin Self, admin. Fax 481-9485

Silex, Lincoln, Pop. 187
Silex R-I SD 300/K-12
PO Box 46 63377 573-384-5227
Elaine Henderson, supt. Fax 384-5996
www.silex.k12.mo.us
Silex JSHS 200/6-12
PO Box 46 63377 573-384-5227
Dr. Tom Moore, prin. Fax 384-5996

Slater, Saline, Pop. 1,827
Slater SD 400/PK-12
515 Elm St 65349 660-529-2278
Debbie Gonzalez, supt. Fax 529-2279
www.slaterpublicschools.net
Slater HS 100/9-12
515 Elm St 65349 660-529-2278
Dr. Jessica Clements, prin. Fax 529-2279

Smithton, Pettis, Pop. 561
Smithton R-VI SD 400/PK-12
505 S Myrtle Ave 65350 660-343-5316
Matt Teeter Ed.D., supt. Fax 343-5389
smithton.k12.mo.us
Smithton HS 200/9-12
505 S Myrtle Ave 65350 660-343-5318
Jonathan Petersen M.S., prin. Fax 343-5389
Smithton MS 5-8
505 S Myrtle Ave 65350 660-343-5316
Brandon Wallace, prin. Fax 343-5389

Smithville, Clay, Pop. 8,290
Smithville R-II SD 2,500/PK-12
655 S Commercial Ave 64089 816-532-0406
Dr. Todd Schuetz, supt. Fax 532-4192
www.smithvilleschooldistrict.net
Smithville HS 800/9-12
645 S Commercial Ave 64089 816-532-0405
Dr. Mike Bartig, prin. Fax 532-4193
Smithville MS 600/6-8
675 S Commercial Ave 64089 816-532-1122
Tod Winterboer, prin. Fax 532-3210

Sparta, Christian, Pop. 1,734
Sparta R-III SD 800/PK-12
PO Box 160 65753 417-634-4284
Dr. Jeffrey Hyatt, supt. Fax 634-3156
www.sparta.k12.mo.us/
Sparta HS 200/9-12
PO Box 160 65753 417-634-3224
Michael Wright, prin. Fax 634-0091
Sparta MS 200/5-8
PO Box 160 65753 417-634-5518
Rocky Valentine, prin. Fax 634-3426

Spokane, Christian, Pop. 175
Spokane R-VII SD
Supt. — See Highlandville
Spokane HS 200/9-12
PO Box 218 65754 417-443-3502
Chris Kohl, prin. Fax 443-7714
Spokane MS 200/6-8
PO Box 220 65754 417-443-3506
Pamila Rowe, prin. Fax 443-2069

Springfield, Greene, Pop. 154,799
Springfield R-XII SD 25,500/PK-12
1359 E Saint Louis St 65802 417-523-0000
Dr. John Jungmann, supt. Fax 523-0391
www.springfieldpublicschoolsmo.org/
Carver MS 800/6-8
3325 W Battlefield St 65807 417-523-6800
Dr. Dana Powers, prin. Fax 523-6895
Central HS 1,800/6-12
423 E Central St 65802 417-523-9600
Lisa Anderson, prin. Fax 523-9695
Cherokee MS 800/6-8
420 E Farm Road 182 65810 417-523-7200
William Powers, prin. Fax 523-7295
Glendale HS 1,200/9-12
2727 S Ingram Mill Rd 65804 417-523-8900
Dr. Natalie Cauldwell, prin. Fax 523-8995
Hickory Hills MS 500/6-8
4650 E State Highway YY 65802 417-523-7100
Sarah Odom, prin. Fax 523-7195
Hillcrest HS 1,000/9-12
3319 N Grant Ave 65803 417-523-8000
Garry Moore, prin. Fax 523-8095
Jarrett MS 500/6-8
840 S Jefferson Ave 65806 417-523-6600
Rob Kroll, prin. Fax 523-6695
Kickapoo HS 1,800/9-12
3710 S Jefferson Ave 65807 417-523-8500
Kelly Allison, prin. Fax 523-8595
OTC Middle College Alt
1001 E Chestnut Expy 65802 417-447-7500
Jackie Jenkins, prin.
Parkview HS 1,400/9-12
516 W Meadowmere St 65807 417-523-9200
Eric Ramsey, prin. Fax 523-9295
Pershing MS 700/6-8
2120 S Ventura Ave 65804 417-523-2400
Dr. Pam Holmes, prin. Fax 523-2495
Pipkin MS 600/6-8
1215 N Boonville Ave 65802 417-523-6000
Rebecca Ash, prin. Fax 523-6195
Pleasant View MS 400/6-8
2210 E State Highway AA 65803 417-523-2100
Joshua Groves, prin. Fax 523-2395
Reed MS 600/6-8
2000 N Lyon Ave 65803 417-523-6300
Dr. Debbie Grega, prin. Fax 523-6395
Study Alternative Center Alt
2343 W Olive St 65802 417-523-6400
Justin Dickenson, coord.
Westport MS 400/6-8
415 S Golden Ave 65802 417-523-3100
Jeff Wilcox, prin. Fax 523-3195

Baptist Bible College Post-Sec.
628 E Kearney St 65803 800-228-5754
Bryan University Post-Sec.
4255 S Nature Center Way 65804 417-862-5700
Cox College Post-Sec.
1423 N Jefferson Ave 65802 417-269-3401
Drury University Post-Sec.
900 N Benton Ave 65802 417-873-7879
Evangel University Post-Sec.
1111 N Glenstone Ave 65802 417-865-2811
Everest College Post-Sec.
1010 W Sunshine St 65807 417-864-7220
Global University Post-Sec.
1211 S Glenstone Ave 65804 417-862-9533
Grace Classical Academy 200/PK-12
2436 E Cherry St 65802 417-877-7910
Greenwood Laboratory S 400/K-12
901 S National Ave, 417-836-5124
Dr. Janice Duncan, dir. Fax 836-8449
Missouri College of Cosmetology North Post-Sec.
2555 W Kearney St 65803 417-866-2786
Missouri State University Post-Sec.
901 S National Ave, 417-836-5000
New Covenant Academy 300/PK-12
3304 S Cox Ave 65807 417-887-9848
Matthew Searson M.A., admin. Fax 887-2419
Ozarks Technical Community College Post-Sec.
1001 E Chestnut Expy 65802 417-447-7500
Professional Massage Training Center Post-Sec.
229 E Commercial St 65803 417-863-7682
Rockbridge Seminary Post-Sec.
3111 E Battlefield St 65804 866-931-4300
St. John's Regional Health Center Post-Sec.
1235 E Cherokee St 65804 417-885-2845
St. John's School of Nursing Post-Sec.
4431 S Fremont Ave 65804 417-885-2098
School of Professional Psychology Post-Sec.
2885 W Battlefield St 65807 417-823-3477
Southwest Baptist University Post-Sec.
4431 S Fremont Ave 65804 417-820-2069
Springfield Catholic HS 300/9-12
2340 S Eastgate Ave 65809 417-887-8817
Jeanne Skahan, prin. Fax 885-1165
Springfield SDA Junior Academy 50/K-10
704 S Belview Ave 65802 417-862-0833
Judi Thompson, prin.
Summit Prep S of Southwest Missouri 100/PK-12
2155 W Chesterfield Blvd 65807 417-869-8077
Rob Gronniger, head sch Fax 869-8087
Vatterott College - Springfield Post-Sec.
3850 S Campbell Ave 65807 417-831-8116

Stanberry, Gentry, Pop. 1,181
Stanberry R-II SD 300/PK-12
610 N Park St 64489 660-783-2136
Brian Garner, supt. Fax 783-2177
www.sr2.k12.mo.us
Stanberry JSHS 200/7-12
610 N Park St 64489 660-783-2163
Lisa Craig, prin. Fax 783-2177

Steele, Pemiscot, Pop. 2,134
South Pemiscot County R-V SD 700/PK-12
611 Beasley Rd 63877 573-695-4426
Chris Moore, supt. Fax 695-4427
www.southpemiscot.com
South Pemiscot HS 300/7-12
611 Beasley Rd 63877 573-695-3342
Glenn Carter, prin. Fax 695-7461

Steelville, Crawford, Pop. 1,631
Steelville R-III SD 900/PK-12
PO Box 339 65565 573-775-2175
Mike Whittaker, supt. Fax 775-2179
steelville.k12.mo.us
Steelville HS 300/9-12
PO Box 339 65565 573-775-2144
Steven Vetter, prin. Fax 775-5050
Steelville MS 300/5-8
PO Box 339 65565 573-775-2176
Curtis Finley, prin. Fax 775-2591

Stewartsville, DeKalb, Pop. 741
Stewartsville C-2 SD 200/K-12
902 Buchanan St 64490 816-669-3792
Jay Albright, supt. Fax 669-8125
www.stewartsville.k12.mo.us
Stewartsville JSHS 100/7-12
902 Buchanan St 64490 816-669-3258
Avery Williamson, prin. Fax 669-8125

Stockton, Cedar, Pop. 1,789
Stockton R-I SD 1,000/K-12
PO Box 190 65785 417-276-5143
Shannon Snow, supt. Fax 276-3765
www.stockton.k12.mo.us/
Stockton HS 300/9-12
PO Box 190 65785 417-276-8806
Michael Postlewait, prin. Fax 276-8584
Stockton MS 300/5-8
PO Box 190 65785 417-276-5141
Robert Bolte, prin. Fax 276-6389

Stoutland, Laclede, Pop. 192
Stoutland R-II SD 500/PK-12
7584 State Road T 65567 417-286-3711
Eric Cooley, supt. Fax 286-3153
www.stoutlandschools.com
Stoutland JSHS 200/7-12
7584 State Road T 65567 417-286-3711
Tami Bobbitt, prin. Fax 286-3981

Stover, Morgan, Pop. 1,079
Morgan County R-I SD 600/PK-12
701 N Oak St 65078 573-377-2217
Dr. Matt Unger, supt. Fax 377-2211
mcr1.us/
Morgan County R-I HS 300/7-12
701 N Oak St 65078 573-377-2218
Michael Marriott, prin. Fax 377-2952

Strafford, Greene, Pop. 2,311
Strafford R-VI SD 1,100/K-12
201 W McCabe St 65757 417-736-7000
John Collins, supt. Fax 736-7016
straffordschools.net
Strafford HS 400/9-12
201 W McCabe St 65757 417-736-7000
Brett Soden, prin. Fax 736-7020
Strafford MS 300/6-8
211 W McCabe St 65757 417-736-7000
Marcia Chadwell, prin. Fax 736-7019

Sturgeon, Boone, Pop. 864
Sturgeon R-V SD 500/PK-12
210 W Patton St 65284 573-687-3515
Shawn Schultz, supt. Fax 687-2116
www.sturgeon.k12.mo.us/
Sturgeon HS 100/9-12
210 W Patton St 65284 573-687-3512
Becky Shafer, prin. Fax 687-3441
Sturgeon MS 100/5-8
210 W Patton St 65284 573-687-2155
Brandee Brown, prin. Fax 687-1226

Sullivan, Franklin, Pop. 7,019
Sullivan SD 2,300/PK-12
138 Taylor St 63080 573-468-5171
Dr. Thomas Allen, supt. Fax 468-7720
www.sullivaneagles.org
Sullivan HS 700/9-12
1073 E Vine St 63080 573-468-5181
Dr. Jennifer Schmidt, prin. Fax 860-3524
Sullivan MS 500/6-8
1156 Elmont Rd 63080 573-468-5191
Kim Dill, prin. Fax 860-2326

Summersville, Texas, Pop. 492
Summersville R-II SD 400/PK-12
PO Box 198 65571 417-932-4045
Rick Stark, supt. Fax 932-5360
www.sville.k12.mo.us
Summersville JSHS 200/7-12
PO Box 198 65571 417-932-4929
Jon Johnson, prin. Fax 932-4178

Sunset Hills, Saint Louis, Pop. 8,388

Vatterott College - Sunset Hills Post-Sec.
12900 Maurer Industrial Dr 63127 314-843-4200

Sweet Springs, Saline, Pop. 1,457
Sweet Springs R-VII SD 500/PK-12
600 E Marshall St 65351 660-335-4860
Donna Wright, supt. Fax 335-4378
sweetsprings.k12.mo.us/
Sweet Springs JSHS 200/7-12
600 E Marshall St 65351 660-335-6341
Josh Hume, prin. Fax 335-6379

Tarkio, Atchison, Pop. 1,576
Tarkio R-I SD 300/K-12
312 S 11th St 64491 660-736-4161
Rob Dowis, supt. Fax 736-4546
tarkio.k12.mo.us
Tarkio JSHS 100/7-12
312 S 11th St 64491 660-736-4118
Carrie Livengood, prin. Fax 736-4546

Thayer, Oregon, Pop. 2,197
Thayer R-II SD 700/PK-12
401 E Walnut St 65791 417-264-4600
Tonya Woods, supt. Fax 264-4608
thayer.k12.mo.us/
Thayer JSHS 300/7-12
401 E Walnut St 65791 417-264-4600
Marc Pitts, prin. Fax 264-4608

Theodosia, Ozark, Pop. 239
Lutie R-VI SD 100/K-12
5802 US Highway 160 65761 417-273-4274
Scot Young, supt. Fax 273-4171
lutieschool.org
Lutie JSHS 100/6-12
5802 US Highway 160 65761 417-273-4274
Scot Young, prin. Fax 273-4171

Tina, Carroll, Pop. 154
Tina-Avalon R-II SD 200/PK-12
11896 Highway 65 64682 660-622-4211
Jana Holcer, supt. Fax 622-4210
tinaavalon.k12.mo.us/

Tina-Avalon JSHS 100/7-12
11896 Highway 65 64682 660-622-4212
Shelly Rex, prin. Fax 622-4210

Tipton, Moniteau, Pop. 3,237
Tipton R-VI SD 600/K-12
305 US Highway 50 E 65081 660-433-5520
Daniel Williams, supt. Fax 433-5241
tipton.k12.mo.us
Tipton HS 300/7-12
305 US Highway 50 E 65081 660-433-5528
Ellen Allee, prin. Fax 433-2419

Trenton, Grundy, Pop. 5,941
Trenton R-IX SD 1,200/K-12
1607 Normal St 64683 660-359-3994
Daniel Wiebers, supt. Fax 359-3995
www.trentonr9.k12.mo.us/
Trenton HS 400/9-12
1415 Oklahoma Ave 64683 660-359-2291
Ron Franklin, prin. Fax 359-4073
Trenton MS 400/5-8
1417 Oklahoma Ave 64683 660-359-4328
Daniel Gott, prin. Fax 359-6554

North Central Missouri College Post-Sec.
1301 Main St 64683 660-359-3948

Troy, Lincoln, Pop. 10,315
Lincoln County R-III SD 6,900/PK-12
951 W College St 63379 636-462-6098
Dr. Mark S. Penny Ed.D., supt. Fax 462-6099
www.troy.k12.mo.us
Buchanan HS 1,400/10-12
1190 Old Cap Au Gris Rd 63379 636-462-5148
Dr. Jerry Raines, prin. Fax 462-5149
New Horizons HS Alt
41 Clonts Field Dr 63379 636-462-4967
Barb Hatcher, prin. Fax 462-4968
Troy MS 1,500/6-8
713 W College St 63379 636-462-4937
Dr. Briscoe Kelly, prin. Fax 462-4938
Other Schools – See Moscow Mills

Tuscumbia, Miller, Pop. 203
Miller County R-III SD 200/K-12
PO Box 1 65082 573-369-2375
Jason Price, supt. Fax 369-2833
www.tuscumbialions.k12.mo.us
Tuscumbia HS 100/9-12
PO Box 1 65082 573-369-2375
Randy Gum, prin. Fax 369-2833

Union, Franklin, Pop. 10,024
Union R-XI SD 3,100/K-12
PO Box 440 63084 636-583-8626
Dr. Steve Weinhold, supt. Fax 583-2403
union.k12.mo.us
Union HS 900/9-12
PO Box 440 63084 636-583-2513
Amy Kain, prin. Fax 583-4203
Union MS 400/7-8
PO Box 440 63084 636-583-5855
Ty Crain, prin. Fax 583-6156

East Central College Post-Sec.
1964 Prairie Dell Rd 63084 636-584-6500

Union Star, DeKalb, Pop. 430
Union Star R-II SD 100/K-12
6132 NW State Route Z 64494 816-593-2294
Rick Calloway, supt. Fax 593-4427
www.usr2.com
Union Star JSHS 100/6-12
6132 NW State Route Z 64494 816-593-2294
Chris Turpin, prin. Fax 593-4427

Unionville, Putnam, Pop. 1,843
Putnam County R-I SD 700/PK-12
803 S 20th St 63565 660-947-3361
Dr. Heath Halley Ed.D., supt. Fax 947-2912
www.putnamcountyr1.net
Putnam County R-1 HS 200/9-12
803 S 20th St 63565 660-947-2481
Jeremy Watt, prin. Fax 947-2912
Putnam County R-1 MS 200/6-8
802 S 18th St 63565 660-947-3237
Andrew Garber, prin. Fax 947-2912

University City, Saint Louis, Pop. 34,413
School District of University City 3,100/PK-12
8136 Groby Rd 63130 314-290-4000
Sharonica Hardin-Bartley Ph.D., supt.
www.ucityschools.org
Brittany Woods MS 700/6-8
8125 Groby Rd 63130 314-290-4280
Elliott Shostak, prin. Fax 997-1786
Lieberman Learning Center Alt
8136 Groby Rd 63130 314-290-4330
Chris Blumenhorst, prin. Fax 432-4478
University City HS 800/9-12
7401 Balson Ave 63130 314-290-4100
Susan Hill, prin. Fax 290-4120

Urbana, Hickory, Pop. 412
Hickory County R-I SD 500/K-12
RR 1 Box 838 65767 417-993-4241
Dr. Mark Beem, supt. Fax 993-4269
www.skylineschools.info
Skyline HS 200/7-12
RR 1 Box 838 65767 417-993-4226
Randall Dougherty, prin. Fax 993-5947

Valley Park, Saint Louis, Pop. 6,786
Valley Park SD 1,000/PK-12
1 Main St 63088 636-923-3500
Dr. David Knes, supt. Fax 861-1002
www.vp.k12.mo.us
Valley Park HS 300/9-12
1 Main St 63088 636-923-3613
Dr. Matthew Bailey, prin. Fax 225-0542
Valley Park MS 200/6-8
1 Main St 63088 636-923-3624
Kelly Muzzey, prin. Fax 225-1529

Van Buren, Carter, Pop. 813
Van Buren R-I SD 500/PK-12
PO Box 550 63965 573-323-4281
Sonia Kuessner, supt. Fax 323-4297
www.vanburen.k12.mo.us
Van Buren HS 200/7-12
PO Box 550 63965 573-323-4295
Mark Wood, prin. Fax 323-4295

Vandalia, Audrain, Pop. 3,832
Van-Far R-I SD 600/PK-12
2200 W US Highway 54 63382 573-594-6111
Stephen Hunter, supt. Fax 594-2878
www.vf.k12.mo.us
Van-Far JSHS 200/7-12
2200 W US Highway 54 63382 573-594-6442
Kimberlee Pafford, prin. Fax 594-3054

Verona, Lawrence, Pop. 608
Verona R-VII SD 400/K-12
PO Box 7 65769 417-498-2274
Tony L. Simmons, supt. Fax 498-6590
verona.k12.mo.us
Verona JSHS 200/7-12
PO Box 7 65769 417-498-6775
Terry Winton, prin. Fax 498-6045

Versailles, Morgan, Pop. 2,421
Morgan County R-II SD 1,500/PK-12
913 W Newton St 65084 573-378-4231
Dr. Joyce Ryerson, supt. Fax 378-5714
www.mcr2.k12.mo.us/
Morgan County HS 500/9-12
913 W Newton St 65084 573-378-4697
Chris Marshall, prin. Fax 378-2704
Morgan County MS 300/6-8
913 W Newton St 65084 573-378-5432
Travis Troyer, prin. Fax 378-6610

Viburnum, Iron, Pop. 688
Iron County C-4 SD 400/K-12
35 Highway 49 65566 573-244-5422
Dr. Tim Hager, supt. Fax 244-5424
www.ironc4.k12.mo.us
Viburnum JSHS 200/7-12
35 Highway 49 65566 573-244-5521
Clay LaRue, prin. Fax 244-3410

Vienna, Maries, Pop. 605
Maries County R-I SD 500/PK-12
PO Box 218 65582 573-422-3304
Joseph Dunlap, supt. Fax 422-3185
www.mariesr1.k12.mo.us
Vienna HS 300/7-12
PO Box 218 65582 573-422-3363
Ian Murray, prin. Fax 422-3185

Villa Ridge, Franklin, Pop. 2,605

Crosspoint Christian S 100/PK-12
PO Box 100 63089 636-742-5380
Bob Templeton, admin. Fax 742-5917

Walker, Vernon, Pop. 266
Northeast Vernon County R-I SD 200/PK-12
216 E Leslie Ave 64790 417-465-2221
Charles Naas, supt. Fax 465-2388
www.nevcknights.org
Northeast Vernon County R-I HS 100/7-12
216 E Leslie Ave 64790 417-465-2221
Chris Hudson, prin. Fax 465-2388

Walnut Grove, Greene, Pop. 659
Walnut Grove R-V SD 300/K-12
PO Box 187 65770 417-788-2543
Gwenda Barton, supt. Fax 788-1254
www.wgtigers.com
Walnut Grove JSHS 100/7-12
PO Box 187 65770 417-788-2543
Rory Henry, prin. Fax 788-1254

Wardell, Pemiscot, Pop. 423
North Pemiscot County R-I SD 300/K-12
PO Box 38 63879 573-628-3471
Terry Hamilton, supt. Fax 628-3472
www.northpem.k12.mo.us
North Pemiscot County JSHS 100/6-12
PO Box 38 63879 573-628-3465
Bill Hoffmann, prin. Fax 628-3418

Wardsville, Cole, Pop. 1,489
Blair Oaks R-II SD 1,200/K-12
6124 Falcon Ln 65101 573-636-2020
Dr. James Jones, supt. Fax 636-2202
www.blairoaks.k12.mo.us
Blair Oaks HS 400/9-12
6124 Falcon Ln 65101 573-635-8514
Gary Verslues, prin. Fax 635-6327
Blair Oaks MS 300/5-8
6124 Falcon Ln 65101 573-634-2053
Julia Gampher, prin. Fax 636-3509

Warrensburg, Johnson, Pop. 18,253
Warrensburg R-VI SD 3,300/PK-12
PO Box 638 64093 660-747-7823
Dr. Scott Patrick, supt. Fax 747-9615
www.warrensburgr6.org
Reese S Alt
301 W Market St 64093 660-747-2496
Leslie Brown, dir. Fax 747-2579
Warrensburg Area Career Center Vo/Tech
205 S Ridgeview Dr 64093 660-747-2283
Rusty Sproat, dir. Fax 747-3778
Warrensburg HS 1,000/9-12
1411 S Ridgeview Dr 64093 660-747-2262
Simone Dillingham, prin. Fax 747-8731
Warrensburg MS 700/6-8
640 E Gay St 64093 660-747-5612
Jim Elliott, prin. Fax 747-8779

University of Central Missouri Post-Sec.
PO Box 800 64093 660-543-4111

Warrenton, Warren, Pop. 7,746
Warren County R-III SD 3,200/PK-12
385 W Veterans Memorial Pky 63383 636-456-6901
Dr. James Chandler, supt. Fax 456-7687
www.warrencor3.org
Black Hawk MS 700/6-8
300 Kuhl Ave 63383 636-456-6903
Lisa Pirrung, prin. Fax 456-1445
Warrenton HS 1,000/9-12
803 Pinckney St 63383 636-456-6902
Nicholas Heggemann, prin. Fax 456-5771

Warsaw, Benton, Pop. 2,107
Warsaw R-IX SD 1,300/PK-12
PO Box 248 65355 660-438-7120
Dr. Shawn Poyser, supt. Fax 438-5028
www.warsaw.k12.mo.us
Boise MS 300/6-8
PO Box 1750 65355 660-438-9079
Dr. Eric Findley, prin. Fax 438-2209
Warsaw HS 400/9-12
PO Box 248 65355 660-438-7351
Randy Luebbert, prin. Fax 438-3749

Washburn, Barry, Pop. 418
Southwest R-V SD 800/PK-12
529 E Pineville Rd 65772 417-826-5410
Tosha Tilford, supt. Fax 826-5603
www.swr5.net
Southwest HS 200/9-12
529 E Pineville Rd 65772 417-826-5413
Eric Roller, prin. Fax 826-5603
Southwest MS 200/5-8
529 E Pineville Rd 65772 417-826-5050
Beverly Bonner, prin. Fax 826-5603

Washington, Franklin, Pop. 13,819
Washington SD 4,000/PK-12
220 Locust St 63090 636-231-2000
Dr. Lori VanLeer, supt. Fax 239-3315
www.washington.k12.mo.us
Four Rivers Career Center Vo/Tech
1978 Image Dr 63090 636-231-2100
Andy Robinson, dir. Fax 239-0791
Washington HS 1,400/9-12
600 Blue Jay Dr 63090 636-231-2200
Dr. Kelle McCallum, prin. Fax 231-2165
Washington MS 600/7-8
401 E 14th St 63090 636-231-2300
Ron Millheiser, prin. Fax 231-2305

St. Francis Borgia Regional HS 500/9-12
1000 Borgia Dr 63090 636-239-7871
Rob Struckhoff, prin. Fax 239-1198

Waynesville, Pulaski, Pop. 4,531
Waynesville R-VI SD 6,200/PK-12
200 Fleetwood Dr 65583 573-842-2097
Dr. Brian Henry, supt. Fax 433-2967
www.waynesville.k12.mo.us
Waynesville Career Center Vo/Tech
400 GW Ln 65583 573-842-2500
Dr. Traci Pattison, dir. Fax 842-2402
Waynesville HS 1,700/9-12
200 GW Ln 65583 573-842-2400
Courtney Long, prin. Fax 842-2401
Waynesville MS 900/7-8
1001 Historic 66 W 65583 573-842-2550
Michele Sumter, prin. Fax 842-2559

Central College of Cosmetology Post-Sec.
PO Box 463 65583 573-336-3888

Weaubleau, Hickory, Pop. 411
Weaubleau R-III SD 300/PK-12
509 N Center St 65774 417-428-3668
Eric Wilken, supt. Fax 428-3004
www.weaubleau.k12.mo.us/
Weaubleau HS 200/7-12
509 N Center St 65774 417-428-3368
Rodney Delmont, prin. Fax 428-3004

Webb City, Jasper, Pop. 10,693
Webb City R-VII SD 4,100/PK-12
411 N Madison St 64870 417-673-6000
Anthony Rossetti, supt. Fax 673-6007
www.wcr7.org
Webb City HS 1,200/9-12
621 N Madison St 64870 417-673-6010
Tim Davied, prin. Fax 673-6017
Webb City JHS 600/7-8
807 W 1st St 64870 417-673-6030
Angie Broadus, prin. Fax 673-6037

Webster Groves, Saint Louis, Pop. 22,645
Webster Groves SD 4,600/PK-12
400 E Lockwood Ave 63119 314-961-1233
Dr. John Simpson, supt. Fax 963-6411
www.webster.k12.mo.us
Webster Groves HS 1,300/9-12
100 Selma Ave 63119 314-963-6400
Dr. Jon Clark, prin. Fax 963-6483
Other Schools – See Saint Louis

Eden Theological Seminary Post-Sec.
475 E Lockwood Ave 63119 314-961-3627
Holy Cross Academy Annunciation S 50/6-8
16 W Glendale Rd 63119 314-961-7712
Janet Dolan, prin. Fax 961-2157

Weldon Spring, Saint Charles, Pop. 5,401
Francis Howell R-III SD
Supt. — See Saint Charles
Bryan MS 900/6-8
605 Independence Rd 63304 636-851-5800
Suzanne Chester, prin. Fax 851-6208
Howell MS 800/6-8
825 OFallon Rd 63304 636-851-4800
Ted Huff, prin. Fax 851-4121

Wellington, Lafayette, Pop. 797
Wellington-Napoleon R-IX SD 400/K-12
800 Highway 131 64097 816-934-2531
MIndy Hampton, supt. Fax 934-8649
www.wntigers.net
Wellington-Napoleon JSHS 200/6-12
800 Highway 131 64097 816-240-2621
Matt Hakes, prin. Fax 934-8649

Wellsville, Montgomery, Pop. 1,206
Wellsville Middletown R-I SD 400/PK-12
900 Burlington St 63384 573-684-2428
Pete Nasir, supt. Fax 684-2018
wmr1.k12.mo.us/
Wellsville-Middleton JSHS 200/7-12
900 Burlington St 63384 573-684-2017
Darin Sehlke, prin. Fax 684-2018

Wentzville, Saint Charles, Pop. 28,539
Wentzville R-IV SD 14,500/K-12
1 Campus Dr 63385 636-327-3800
Dr. Curtis Cain, supt. Fax 327-8611
www.wentzville.k12.mo.us
Holt HS 1,700/9-12
600 Campus Dr 63385 636-327-3876
Shane Schlueter, prin. Fax 327-3953
Timberland HS 2,000/9-12
559 E Highway N 63385 636-327-3988
Kyle Lindquist, prin. Fax 327-3922
Wentzville MS 1,200/6-8
405 Campus Dr 63385 636-327-3815
Dr. Kelly Mantz, prin. Fax 327-3954
Wentzville South MS 1,200/6-8
561 E Highway N 63385 636-327-3928
Scott Swift, prin. Fax 327-3955
Other Schools – See Lake Saint Louis, O Fallon

Midwest University Post-Sec.
851 Parr Rd 63385 636-327-4645

Weston, Platte, Pop. 1,614
West Platte County R-II SD 600/PK-12
1103 Washington St 64098 816-640-2236
Dr. John Rinehart, supt. Fax 386-2104
www.wpsd.net
West Platte County JSHS 300/7-12
935 Washington St 64098 816-640-2292
Vince Matlick, prin. Fax 386-2293

Westphalia, Osage, Pop. 382
Osage County R-III SD 800/K-12
PO Box 37 65085 573-455-2375
Chuck Woody, supt. Fax 455-9884
www.fatimacomets.org
Fatima JSHS 500/7-12
PO Box 37 65085 573-455-2550
Jeff Buthod, prin. Fax 455-9884

West Plains, Howell, Pop. 11,780
West Plains R-VII SD 2,600/PK-12
305 Valley View Dr 65775 417-256-6150
Dr. John Mulford, supt. Fax 256-8616
wpr7.schoolwires.net
South Central Career Center Vo/Tech
407 W Thornburgh St 65775 417-256-6152
Jim Laughary, dir. Fax 256-5786
West Plains HS 1,100/9-12
602 E Olden St 65775 417-256-6150
Jack Randolph, prin. Fax 256-8908
West Plains MS 500/5-8
730 E Olden St 65775 417-256-6150
Dr. Wesley Davis, prin. Fax 256-8907

Missouri State University - West Plains Post-Sec.
128 Garfield Ave 65775 417-255-7255
Ozarks Christian Academy 100/PK-12
PO Box 1620 65775 417-255-1622

Wheatland, Hickory, Pop. 358
Wheatland R-II SD 300/PK-12
PO Box 68 65779 417-282-6433
Tim Judd, supt. Fax 282-5733
sites.google.com/a/wheatland.k12.mo.us/district/
Wheatland JSHS 100/7-12
PO Box 68 65779 417-282-5833
Matt Gunter, prin. Fax 282-5733

Wheaton, Barry, Pop. 680
Wheaton R-III SD 400/PK-12
PO Box 249 64874 417-652-3914
Dr. Lance Massey, supt. Fax 652-7355
www.wheatonbulldogs.org/
Wheaton JSHS 200/7-12
PO Box 249 64874 417-652-7249
Traci Mitchell, prin. Fax 652-7355

Wildwood, Saint Louis, Pop. 35,007

Living Water Academy 100/PK-10
17770 Mueller Rd 63038 636-821-2308
Thomas Keller, head sch Fax 821-1709
Saint Louis Community College - Wildwood Post-Sec.
2645 Generations Dr 63040 636-422-2000

Willard, Greene, Pop. 5,200
Willard R-II SD 4,400/PK-12
500 Kime St 65781 417-742-2584
Dr. Kent Medlin, supt. Fax 742-2586
www.willardschools.net
Willard HS 1,300/9-12
515 E Jackson St 65781 417-742-3524
Curt Graves, prin. Fax 742-3667
Willard MS 700/7-8
205 S Miller Rd 65781 417-742-2588
Amy Sims, prin. Fax 742-3505

Willow Springs, Howell, Pop. 2,140
Willow Springs R-IV SD 1,400/PK-12
215 W 4th St 65793 417-469-3260
Derrick Hutsell, supt. Fax 469-5127
www.willowspringsschool.com/
Willow Springs HS 400/9-12
215 W 4th St 65793 417-469-2114
Jimalee James, prin. Fax 469-2507
Willow Springs MS 400/5-8
215 W 4th St 65793 417-469-3211
Philip Pietroburgo, prin. Fax 469-1229

Windsor, Henry, Pop. 2,866
Henry County R-I SD 700/PK-12
210 North St 65360 660-647-3533
Dr. Kristee Lorenz, supt. Fax 647-2711
henrycountyr1.k12.mo.us
Windsor JSHS 300/7-12
210 North St 65360 660-647-3106
William Johnston, prin. Fax 647-3218

Winfield, Lincoln, Pop. 1,383
Winfield R-IV SD 1,500/K-12
701 W Elm St 63389 636-668-8188
Nancy Baker, supt. Fax 668-8641
www.winfield.k12.mo.us
Winfield HS 500/9-12
701 W Elm St 63389 636-668-8130
Eric Alderson, prin. Fax 566-6455
Winfield MS 300/6-8
701 W Elm St 63389 636-668-8001
Tom McCracken, prin. Fax 668-6044

Winona, Shannon, Pop. 1,311
Winona R-III SD 500/PK-12
PO Box 248 65588 573-325-8101
Scott Lindsey, supt. Fax 325-8447
www.winonar3.org
Winona HS 100/9-12
PO Box 248 65588 573-325-8101
Gilbert Miley, prin. Fax 325-4700

Winston, Daviess, Pop. 258
Winston R-VI SD 200/PK-12
PO Box 38 64689 660-749-5331
Brian Robinson, supt. Fax 749-5432
www.winston.k12.mo.us
Winston JSHS 100/7-12
PO Box 38 64689 660-749-5456
Chris Gagnon, prin. Fax 749-5432

Wright City, Warren, Pop. 3,037
Wright City R-II SD 1,600/PK-12
90 Bell Rd 63390 636-745-7200
Dr. David Buck, supt. Fax 745-3613
www.wrightcity.k12.mo.us/
Wright City HS 400/9-12
520 Westwoods Rd 63390 636-745-7500
Shawn Brown, prin. Fax 745-7518
Wright City MS 300/6-8
100 Bell Rd 63390 636-745-7300
Douglas Smith, prin. Fax 745-7304

Liberty Christian Academy 100/PK-12
PO Box 514 63390 636-745-0388
Beverly Wilgus, admin. Fax 745-0390

Zalma, Bollinger, Pop. 122
Zalma R-V SD 200/K-12
HC 2 Box 184 63787 573-722-5504
Gerard Vandeven, supt. Fax 722-9870
zalma.k12.mo.us
Zalma JSHS 100/7-12
HC 2 Box 184 63787 573-722-3320
Elaine Lasher, prin. Fax 722-9870

MONTANA

MONTANA OFFICE OF PUBLIC INSTRUCTION
PO Box 202501, Helena 59620-2501
Telephone 406-444-3095
Fax 406-444-2893
Website opi.mt.gov

State Superintendent of Public Instruction Elsie Arntzen

MONTANA BOARD OF EDUCATION
PO Box 200601, Helena 59620-0601

Chairperson Sharon Carroll

COUNTY SUPERINTENDENTS OF SCHOOLS

Beaverhead County Office of Education
Linda Marsh, supt. 406-683-3737
2 S Pacific St Ste 7, Dillon 59725 Fax 683-3769
Big Horn County Office of Education
Vicki Gale, supt. 406-665-9820
PO Box 908, Hardin 59034 Fax 665-9823
Blaine County Office of Education
Kelly Mills, supt. 406-357-3270
PO Box 819, Chinook 59523 Fax 357-2199
Broadwater County Office of Education
Douglas Ellis, supt. 406-266-9215
515 Broadway St, Townsend 59644 Fax 266-3674
Carbon County Office of Education
Jane Swanson-Webb, supt. 406-446-1301
PO Box 116, Red Lodge 59068 Fax 446-9155
Carter County Office of Education
Tracey Walker, supt. 406-775-8714
PO Box 352, Ekalaka 59324 Fax 775-8703
Cascade County Office of Education
Patricia Boyle, supt. 406-454-6776
121 4th St N Ste 1A Fax 454-6778
Great Falls 59401
www.cascadecountymt.gov
Chouteau County Office of Education
Mary Lou Tweet, supt. 406-622-3242
PO Box 459, Fort Benton 59442 Fax 622-3028
Custer County Office of Education
Doug Ellingson, supt. 406-874-3421
1010 Main St, Miles City 59301 Fax 874-3452
Daniels County Office of Education
Joan Bjarko, supt. 406-487-2651
PO Box 67, Scobey 59263 Fax 487-5432
Dawson County Office of Education
Steve Engebretson, supt. 406-377-3963
207 W Bell St, Glendive 59330 Fax 377-2022
Deer Lodge County Office of Education
Michael O'Rourke, supt. 406-563-9178
800 Main St, Anaconda 59711 Fax 563-5476
Fallon County Office of Education
Don Dilworth, supt. 406-778-8158
PO Box 846, Baker 59313 Fax 778-2048
Fergus County Office of Education
Rhonda Long, supt. 406-535-3136
712 W Main St, Lewistown 59457 Fax 535-2819
Flathead County Office of Education
Jack Eggensperger, supt. 406-758-5720
935 1st Ave W, Kalispell 59901 Fax 758-5850
Gallatin County Office of Education
Laura Axtman, supt. 406-582-3090
311 W Main St Rm 107 Fax 582-3093
Bozeman 59715
Garfield County Office of Education
Jessica McWilliams, supt. 406-557-6115
PO Box 28, Jordan 59337 Fax 557-6115
Glacier County Office of Education
Darryl Omsberg, supt. 406-873-2295
1210 E Main St, Cut Bank 59427 Fax 873-9103
www.glaciercountygov.com
Golden Valley County Office of Education
Craig Mattheis, supt. 406-568-2342
107 Kemp St, Ryegate 59074 Fax 568-2428

Granite County Office of Education
Vicki Harding, supt. 406-859-9831
PO Box 9, Philipsburg 59858 Fax 859-3817
Hill County Office of Education
Diane McLean, supt. 406-265-5481
315 4th St, Havre 59501 Fax 265-5487
Jefferson County Office of Education
Garry Pace, supt. 406-225-4114
PO Box H, Boulder 59632 Fax 225-4149
Judith Basin County Office of Education
Julie Anderson Peevey, supt. 406-566-2277
PO Box 307, Stanford 59479 Fax 566-2211
Lake County Office of Education
Carolyn Hall, supt. 406-883-7262
106 4th Ave E, Polson 59860 Fax 883-7283
www.lakemt.gov/
Lewis & Clark County Office of Education
Katrina Chaney, supt. 406-447-8344
316 N Park Ave Ste 221 Fax 447-8398
Helena 59623
www.lccountymt.gov/education
Liberty County Office of Education
Kathy Armstrong, supt. 406-759-5216
PO Box 684, Chester 59522 Fax 759-5996
Lincoln County Office of Education
Nancy Trotter-Higgins, supt. 406-283-2401
512 California Ave, Libby 59923 Fax 293-7760
Madison County Office of Education
Pam Birkeland, supt. 406-843-4280
PO Box 247, Virginia City 59755 Fax 843-5388
McCone County Office of Education
Nita Crockett, supt. 406-485-3590
PO Box 180, Circle 59215 Fax 485-2689
Meagher County Office of Education
Helen Hanson, supt., PO Box 429 406-547-3388
White Sulphur Springs 59645
Mineral County Office of Education
Mary Yarnall, supt. 406-822-3529
PO Box 100, Superior 59872 Fax 822-3579
Missoula County Office of Education
Erin Lipkind, supt. 406-258-3349
438 W Spruce St, Missoula 59802 Fax 258-3973
Musselshell County Office of Education
Kathryn Pfister, supt. 406-323-1470
506 Main St, Roundup 59072 Fax 323-3303
Park County Office of Education
Jo Newhall, supt. 406-222-4148
414 E Callender St Fax 222-4199
Livingston 59047
Petroleum County Office of Education
Pamela Bevis, supt. 406-429-5551
PO Box 226, Winnett 59087 Fax 429-6328
Phillips County Office of Education
Vivian Taylor, supt. 406-654-2010
PO Box 138, Malta 59538 Fax 654-3333
Pondera County Office of Education
Lynn Utterback, supt. 406-271-4055
20 4th Ave SW Ste 307 Fax 271-4070
Conrad 59425
Powder River County Office of Education
Molly Lloyd, supt. 406-436-2488
PO Box 718, Broadus 59317 Fax 436-2151

Powell County Office of Education
Jules Waber, supt. 406-846-9719
409 Missouri Ave Fax 846-3891
Deer Lodge 59722
Prairie County Office of Education
Jamie Smith, supt. 406-635-5577
PO Box 566, Terry 59349 Fax 635-5576
Ravalli County Office of Education
Regina Plettenberg, supt. 406-375-6551
215 S 4th St Ste B, Hamilton 59840 Fax 375-6554
Richland County Office of Education
Gail Anne Staffanson, supt. 406-433-1608
201 W Main St, Sidney 59270 Fax 433-3731
Roosevelt County Office of Education
Jeri Toavs, supt. 406-653-6266
400 2nd Ave S, Wolf Point 59201 Fax 653-6203
Rosebud County Office of Education
Joby Parker, supt. 406-346-2537
PO Box 407, Forsyth 59327 Fax 346-7319
Sanders County Office of Education
Carol Turk, supt. 406-826-4288
PO Box 519, Plains 59859 Fax 826-4299
Sheridan County Office of Education
June Johnson, supt. 406-765-3403
100 W Laurel Ave Fax 765-2609
Plentywood 59254
www.co.sheridan.mt.us
Silver Bow County Office of Education
Cathy Maloney, supt. 406-497-6215
155 W Granite St, Butte 59701 Fax 497-6328
Stillwater County Office of Education
Judy Martin, supt. 406-322-8057
PO Box 1139, Columbus 59019 Fax 322-1118
Sweet Grass County Office of Education
Susan Metcalf, supt. 406-932-5147
PO Box 1310, Big Timber 59011 Fax 932-5112
Teton County Office of Education
Cathy Sessions, supt. 406-466-2907
PO Box 610, Choteau 59422 Fax 466-2138
tetoncomt.org/supofschools
Toole County Office of Education
Boyd Jackson, supt. 406-424-8322
226 1st St S, Shelby 59474 Fax 424-8321
toolecountymt.gov
Treasure County Office of Education
Tamara Kimball, supt. 406-342-5545
PO Box 429, Hysham 59038 Fax 342-5445
Valley County Office of Education
Lynne Nyquist, supt. 406-228-6226
501 Court Sq Ste 2 Fax 228-9027
Glasgow 59230
Wheatland County Office of Education
Susan Beley, supt. 406-632-4816
PO Box 637, Harlowton 59036 Fax 632-4873
Wibaux County Office of Education
Patricia Zinda, supt. 406-796-2481
PO Box 199, Wibaux 59353 Fax 796-2625
Yellowstone County Office of Education
Sherry Long, supt. 406-256-6933
217 N 27th St, Billings 59101 Fax 256-6930
www.co.yellowstone.mt.gov/

PUBLIC, PRIVATE AND CATHOLIC SECONDARY SCHOOLS

Absarokee, Stillwater, Pop. 1,134
Absarokee SD 300/PK-12
327 S Woodard Ave 59001 406-328-4583
Dustin Sturm, supt. Fax 328-4077
www.absarokee.k12.mt.us/
Absarokee HS 100/9-12
327 S Woodard Ave 59001 406-328-4583
Dustin Sturm, prin. Fax 328-4077
Absarokee MS 50/7-8
327 S Woodard Ave 59001 406-328-4583
Dustin Sturm, prin. Fax 328-4077

Alberton, Mineral, Pop. 415
Alberton SD 100/PK-12
PO Box 330 59820 406-722-4413
Clay Acker, supt. Fax 722-3040
Alberton HS 50/9-12
PO Box 330 59820 406-722-3381
Kyle Fisher, prin. Fax 722-3040
Alberton MS 50/7-8
PO Box 330 59820 406-722-4413
Kyle Fisher, prin. Fax 722-3040

Anaconda, Deer Lodge, Pop. 9,095
Anaconda SD 1,100/PK-12
1410 W Park Ave 59711 406-563-6361
Dr. Gerry Nolan, supt. Fax 563-7763
www.anacondaschools.org/
Anaconda HS 300/9-12
1410 W Park Ave 59711 406-563-6361
Shawn Hansen, prin. Fax 563-5260
Moodry JHS 200/7-8
219 E 3rd St 59711 406-563-6242
Tammy Hurley, prin. Fax 563-5093

Arlee, Lake, Pop. 605
Arlee SD 400/K-12
72220 Fyant St 59821 406-726-3216
Dave Whitesell, supt. Fax 360-8531
www.arleeschools.org
Arlee HS 100/9-12
72220 Fyant St 59821 406-726-3216
James Taylor, prin. Fax 726-3940
Arlee JHS 100/7-8
72220 Fyant St 59821 406-726-3216
James Taylor, prin. Fax 726-3940

Ashland, Rosebud, Pop. 799
Ashland ESD 100/PK-8
PO Box 17 59003 406-784-2568
Steve Henderson, supt. Fax 784-6138
www.ashlandpublicschool.com
Ashland MS 50/7-8
PO Box 17 59003 406-784-2568
Kathryn Piller, prin. Fax 784-6138

St. Labre Catholic HS 100/9-12
PO Box 216 59003 406-784-4564
Trivian Rides The Bear, prin. Fax 784-4565
St. Labre Catholic MS 200/5-8
PO Box 216 59003 406-784-4567
Jack Gion, prin. Fax 784-4565

Augusta, Lewis and Clark, Pop. 305
Augusta SD 100/PK-12
PO Box 307 59410 406-562-3384
Matt Genger, supt. Fax 562-3898
Augusta HS 50/9-12
PO Box 307 59410 406-562-3384
Matt Genger, prin. Fax 562-3898
Augusta MS 50/7-8
PO Box 307 59410 406-562-3384
Matt Genger, prin. Fax 562-3898

Bainville, Roosevelt, Pop. 202
Bainville SD 200/PK-12
PO Box 177 59212 406-769-2321
Renee Rasmussen, supt. Fax 769-3291
www.bainvilleschool.k12.mt.us
Bainville HS 50/9-12
PO Box 177 59212 406-769-2321
Rhiannon Beery, prin. Fax 769-3291
Bainville MS 50/7-8
PO Box 177 59212 406-769-2321
Rhiannon Beery, prin. Fax 769-3291

Baker, Fallon, Pop. 1,723
Baker SD 400/PK-12
PO Box 659 59313 406-778-3574
Jon Wrzesinski, supt. Fax 778-2785
www.baker.k12.mt.us
Baker HS 100/9-12
PO Box 659 59313 406-778-3329
David Breitbach, prin. Fax 778-2785
Baker MS 100/7-8
PO Box 659 59313 406-778-3329
David Breitbach, prin. Fax 778-2785

Belfry, Carbon, Pop. 215
Belfry SD 50/PK-12
PO Box 210 59008 406-664-3319
Jason Olson, supt. Fax 664-3274
belfrybats.org
Belfry HS 50/9-12
PO Box 210 59008 406-664-3319
Jason Olson, prin. Fax 664-3274
Belfry MS 50/7-8
PO Box 210 59008 406-664-3319
Jason Olson, prin. Fax 664-3274

Belgrade, Gallatin, Pop. 7,233
Belgrade SD 2,700/PK-12
PO Box 166 59714 406-924-2006
Leland Stocker, supt. Fax 388-0122
www.bsd44.org
Belgrade HS 900/9-12
303 N Hoffman St 59714 406-924-2545
Paul Lamb, prin. Fax 388-4633
Belgrade MS 900/5-8
410 Triple Crown St 59714 406-924-2258
Julie Mickolio, prin. Fax 388-8894

Belt, Cascade, Pop. 585
Belt SD 300/PK-12
PO Box 197 59412 406-277-3351
Kathleen Prody, supt. Fax 277-4466
www.beltschool.com
Belt HS 100/9-12
PO Box 197 59412 406-277-3351
Kyle Paulson, prin. Fax 277-4466
Belt MS 50/6-8
PO Box 197 59412 406-277-3351
Kyle Paulson, prin. Fax 277-4466

Bigfork, Flathead, Pop. 4,196
Bigfork SD 800/K-12
PO Box 188 59911 406-837-7400
Matt Jensen, supt. Fax 837-7407
www.bigforkschools.org
Bigfork HS 300/9-12
PO Box 188 59911 406-837-7420
Alan Robbins, prin. Fax 837-7245
Bigfork MS 100/7-8
PO Box 188 59911 406-837-7412
Brenda Clarke, prin. Fax 837-7438

Swan River ESD 100/K-8
1205 Swan Hwy 59911 406-837-4528
Marc Bunker, prin. Fax 837-4055
www.swanriverschool.org
Swan River MS 50/7-8
1205 Swan Hwy 59911 406-837-4528
Marc Bunker, prin. Fax 837-4055

Big Sandy, Chouteau, Pop. 583
Big Sandy SD 200/PK-12
PO Box 570 59520 406-378-2502
Brad Moore, supt. Fax 378-2275
www.bigsandy.k12.mt.us
Big Sandy HS 50/9-12
PO Box 570 59520 406-378-2502
Brad Moore, prin. Fax 378-2275
Big Sandy JHS 50/7-8
PO Box 570 59520 406-378-2502
Brad Moore, prin. Fax 378-2275

Big Sky, Gallatin, Pop. 2,277
Big Sky SD
Supt. — See Gallatin Gateway
Lone Peak HS 100/9-12
PO Box 161280 59716 406-995-4281
Alexander Ide, prin. Fax 995-2161

Big Sky Discovery Academy 50/PK-12
PO Box 161548 59716 406-993-2008
Nettie Breuner, dir.

Big Timber, Sweet Grass, Pop. 1,599
Big Timber ESD 300/PK-8
PO Box 887 59011 406-932-5939
Mark Ketcham, supt. Fax 932-4069
www.bigtimber-gs.k12.mt.us
Big Timber MS 100/7-8
PO Box 887 59011 406-932-5939
Mark Ketcham, prin. Fax 932-4069

Sweet Grass County HSD 200/9-12
PO Box 886 59011 406-932-5993
Alvin Buerkle, supt. Fax 932-5982
www.sgchs.com/
Sweet Grass County HS 200/9-12
PO Box 886 59011 406-932-5993
Matt Kleinsasser, prin. Fax 932-5982

Billings, Yellowstone, Pop. 101,668
Billings SD 16,400/PK-12
415 N 30th St 59101 406-281-5065
Terry Bouck, supt. Fax 281-6179
www.billingsschools.org/
Billings HS 1,700/9-12
425 Grand Ave 59101 406-281-5400
Jeff Uhren, prin. Fax 281-6174
Billings West HS 1,900/9-12
2201 Saint Johns Ave 59102 406-281-5600
David Cobb, prin. Fax 655-3100
Career Center Vo/Tech
3723 Central Ave 59102 406-281-5340
Scott Anderson, dir. Fax 655-3096
Castle Rock MS 800/7-8
1441 Governors Blvd 59105 406-281-5800
O'Shean Moran, prin. Fax 254-1116
James MS 700/6-8
1200 30th St W 59102 406-281-6100
Kim Verschoot, prin. Fax 281-6178
Lewis & Clark MS 700/6-8
1315 Lewis Ave 59102 406-281-5900
Jody Sulser, prin. Fax 281-6177
Medicine Crow MS 6-8
900 Barrett Rd 59105 406-281-8600
Nikki Hofmann, prin.
Riverside MS 600/6-8
3700 Madison Ave 59101 406-281-6000
Kevin Kirkman, prin. Fax 255-3534
Skyview HS 1,500/9-12
1775 High Sierra Blvd 59105 406-281-5200
Debra Black, prin. Fax 255-3507
Steele MS 59101 6-8
Adult & Basic Education Adult
415 N 30th St 59101 406-281-5001
Barb Gustafson, dir. Fax 281-6827

Canyon Creek ESD 200/PK-8
3139 Duck Creek Rd 59101 406-656-4471
Brent Lipp, supt. Fax 655-1031
www.canyoncreekschool.org
Canyon Creek MS 50/7-8
3139 Duck Creek Rd 59101 406-656-4471
Brent Lipp, prin. Fax 655-1031

Elder Grove ESD 400/K-8
1532 S 64th St W 59106 406-656-2893
Justin Klebe, supt. Fax 651-4346
www.eldergrove.k12.mt.us/
Elder Grove MS 100/6-8
1532 S 64th St W 59106 406-656-2893
Nathan Schmitz, prin. Fax 651-4346

Elysian ESD 200/PK-8
6416 Elysian Rd 59101 406-656-4101
Bob Whalen, supt. Fax 656-9941
elysianschool.org
Elysian MS 50/7-8
6416 Elysian Rd 59101 406-656-4101
Luke Shelton, prin. Fax 656-9941

Lockwood ESD 1,200/PK-8
1932 US Highway 87 E 59101 406-252-6022
Tobin Novasio, supt. Fax 259-2502
www.lockwoodschool.org/
Lockwood MS 400/6-8
1932 US Highway 87 E 59101 406-259-0154
Gordon Klasna, prin. Fax 259-3832

Billings Central Catholic HS 300/9-12
3 Broadwater Ave 59101 406-245-6651
Sheldon Hanser, prin. Fax 259-3124
Billings Christian S 100/PK-12
4519 Grand Ave 59106 406-656-9484
Diann Floth, head sch Fax 655-4880
City College MSU Billings Post-Sec.
3803 Central Ave 59102 406-247-3000
Montana State University - Billings Post-Sec.
1500 University Dr 59101 406-657-2011
Rocky Mountain College Post-Sec.
1511 Poly Dr 59102 800-877-6259
SAGE Technical Service Truck Driving Sch Post-Sec.
3044 Hesper Rd 59102 800-545-4546
St. Francis Upper S 200/6-8
205 N 32nd St 59101 406-259-5037
Jim Stanton, prin. Fax 259-7981
St. Vincent's Hospital & Health Center Post-Sec.
PO Box 35200 59107 406-657-7102

Bonner, Missoula, Pop. 1,669
Bonner ESD 400/PK-8
PO Box 1004 59823 406-258-6151
James Howard, supt. Fax 258-6153
www.bonner.k12.mt.us
Bonner MS 100/7-8
PO Box 1004 59823 406-258-6151
James Howard, prin. Fax 258-6153

Potomac ESD 100/PK-8
29750 Potomac Rd 59823 406-244-5581
Fax 244-5840
www.potomacschoolmontana.us/
Potomac MS 50/7-8
29750 Potomac Rd 59823 406-244-5581
Angie Williams, prin. Fax 244-5840

Boulder, Jefferson, Pop. 1,141
Boulder ESD 200/PK-8
PO Box 1346 59632 406-225-3316
Maria Pace, supt. Fax 225-9218
www.bgs.k12.mt.us/
Boulder MS 100/7-8
PO Box 1346 59632 406-225-3316
Maria Pace, prin. Fax 225-9218

Jefferson HSD 200/9-12
PO Box 838 59632 406-225-3740
Tim Norbeck, supt. Fax 225-3289
www.jhs.k12.mt.us
Jefferson HS 200/9-12
PO Box 838 59632 406-225-3317
Greg Leidle, prin. Fax 225-3289

Box Elder, Hill, Pop. 80
Box Elder SD 400/PK-12
PO Box 205 59521 406-352-4195
Thom Peck, supt. Fax 352-3830
www.boxelder.k12.mt.us
Box Elder HS 100/9-12
PO Box 205 59521 406-352-4195
Melanie Jenkins, prin. Fax 352-3830
Box Elder MS 100/7-8
PO Box 205 59521 406-352-4195
Melanie Jenkins, prin. Fax 352-3830

Rocky Boy SD 600/PK-12
81 Mission Taylor Rd 59521 406-395-4291
Voyd St. Pierre, supt. Fax 395-4829
www.rockyboy.k12.mt.us
Rocky Boy HS 100/9-12
81 Mission Taylor Rd 59521 406-395-4270
Deborah Lamere, prin. Fax 395-4829
Rocky Boy MS 100/7-8
81 Mission Taylor Rd 59521 406-395-4270
Lewis Reese, prin. Fax 395-4829

Stone Child College Post-Sec.
8294 Upper Box Elder Rd 59521 406-395-4875

Bozeman, Gallatin, Pop. 36,568
Anderson ESD 200/PK-8
10040 Cottonwood Rd 59718 406-587-1305
Scott McDowell, supt. Fax 587-2501
www.andersonmt.org/
Anderson MS 50/7-8
10040 Cottonwood Rd 59718 406-587-1305
Scott McDowell, prin. Fax 587-2501

Bozeman SD 5,600/PK-12
404 W Main St 59715 406-522-6000
Robert Watson, supt. Fax 522-6065
www.bsd7.org
Bozeman HS 2,000/9-12
205 N 11th Ave 59715 406-522-6200
Kevin Conwell, prin. Fax 522-6222
Chief Joseph MS 700/6-8
4255 Kimberwicke St 59718 406-522-6300
Brian Ayers, prin. Fax 522-6306
Sacajawea MS 600/6-8
3525 S 3rd Rd 59715 406-522-6470
Gordon Grissom, prin. Fax 522-6474

LaMotte ESD 100/K-8
841 Bear Canyon Rd 59715 406-586-2838
Fax 585-8626
www.lamotteschool.com
LaMotte MS 50/7-8
841 Bear Canyon Rd 59715 406-586-2838
LeeAnn Burke, prin. Fax 585-8626

Monforton ESD 300/PK-8
6001 Monforton School Rd 59718 406-586-1557
Darren Strauch, supt. Fax 587-5049
www.monfortonschool.org/
Monforton MS 100/7-8
6001 Monforton School Rd 59718 406-586-1557
Darren Strauch, supt. Fax 587-5049

Academy of Cosmetology Post-Sec.
133 W Mendenhall St 59715 406-587-1265
Headwaters Academy 50/6-8
418 W Garfield St 59715 406-585-9997
Heritage Christian S 200/K-12
4310 Durston Rd 59718 406-587-9311
Gerry Goede M.S., admin. Fax 587-1838
Montana Bible College Post-Sec.
3625 S 19th Ave 59718 406-586-3585
Montana State University Post-Sec.
PO Box 172190 59717 406-994-0211
Mt. Ellis Academy 100/9-12
3641 Bozeman Trail Rd 59715 406-587-5178
Michael Lee, prin. Fax 587-5170
Petra Academy 100/PK-12
4720 Classical Way 59718 406-582-8165
Craig Dunham, hdmstr. Fax 556-8777

Bridger, Carbon, Pop. 700
Bridger SD 200/PK-12
429 W Park Ave 59014 406-662-3588
Bill Phillips, supt. Fax 662-3520
www.bridgerscouts.org
Bridger HS 100/9-12
429 W Park Ave 59014 406-662-3533
Jim Goltz, prin. Fax 662-3076
Bridger MS 50/7-8
106 N 4th St 59014 406-662-3588
Jim Goltz, prin. Fax 662-3520

Broadus, Powder River, Pop. 457
Broadus SD 200/PK-12
PO Box 500 59317 406-436-2658
Jim Hansen, supt. Fax 436-2660
www.broadus.net/
Powder River County District HS 100/7-12
PO Box 500 59317 406-436-2658
Rosalie Lunby, prin. Fax 436-2660

Broadview, Yellowstone, Pop. 191
Broadview SD 200/PK-12
PO Box 147 59015 406-667-2337
Gary Fisher, supt. Fax 667-2195
www.broadviewschools.org
Broadview HS 100/9-12
PO Box 147 59015 406-667-2337
Gary fisher, supt. Fax 667-2195
Broadview MS 50/7-8
PO Box 147 59015 406-667-2337
Gary Fisher, supt. Fax 667-2195

Brockton, Roosevelt, Pop. 255
Brockton SD 100/PK-12
PO Box 198 59213 406-786-3311
Teresa McMakin, supt. Fax 786-3377
www.brockton.k12.mt.us/
Brockton HS 50/9-12
PO Box 198 59213 406-786-3311
Fax 786-3377
Gilligan MS 50/7-8
PO Box 198 59213 406-786-3311
Francis LaBounty, prin. Fax 786-3377

Browning, Glacier, Pop. 998
Browning SD 2,000/PK-12
PO Box 610 59417 406-338-2715
John P. Rouse, supt. Fax 338-3200
www.bps.k12.mt.us
Browning HS 500/9-12
PO Box 610 59417 406-338-2745
Shawn Clark, prin. Fax 338-2844
Browning MS 300/7-8
PO Box 610 59417 406-338-2725
Julie Hayes, prin. Fax 338-5320

Blackfeet Community College Post-Sec.
PO Box 819 59417 406-338-5441
De LaSalle Blackfeet S 100/4-8
PO Box 1489 59417 406-338-5290
Br. Dale Mooney, pres. Fax 338-7900

Butte, Silver Bow, Pop. 32,958
Butte SD 4,300/PK-12
111 N Montana St 59701 406-533-2500
Judy Jonart, supt. Fax 533-2526
www.butte.k12.mt.us
Butte HS 1,300/9-12
401 S Wyoming St 59701 406-533-2200
John Metz, prin. Fax 533-2277
East MS 600/7-8
2600 Grand Ave 59701 406-533-2600
Larry Driscoll, prin. Fax 533-2670

Butte Academy of Beauty Culture Post-Sec.
303 W Park St 59701 406-723-8565
Butte Central HS 100/9-12
9 S Idaho St 59701 406-782-6761
Kevin St. John, prin. Fax 723-3873
Highlands College of Montana Tech Post-Sec.
25 Basin Creek Rd 59701 406-496-3707
Montana Tech of the University of MT Post-Sec.
1300 W Park St 59701 406-496-4101

Cascade, Cascade, Pop. 673
Cascade SD 300/K-12
PO Box 529 59421 406-468-9383
Justin Barnes, supt. Fax 468-2212
www.cascade.k12.mt.us
Cascade HS 100/9-12
PO Box 529 59421 406-468-2267
Kevin Sukut, prin. Fax 468-2212
Cascade JHS 50/7-8
PO Box 529 59421 406-468-2267
Kevin Sukut, prin. Fax 468-2212

Charlo, Lake, Pop. 328
Charlo SD 300/K-12
PO Box 10 59824 406-644-2206
Steve Love, supt. Fax 644-2400
www.charlo.k12.mt.us
Charlo HS 100/9-12
PO Box 10 59824 406-644-2206
Bonnie Perry, prin. Fax 644-2400
Charlo MS 50/7-8
PO Box 10 59824 406-644-2206
Bonnie Perry, prin. Fax 644-2400

Chester, Liberty, Pop. 830
Chester-Joplin-Inverness SD 200/PK-12
PO Box 550 59522 406-759-5945
Francis LaBounty, supt. Fax 759-5867
www.cji.k12.mt.us
Chester-Joplin-Inverness HS 100/9-12
PO Box 550 59522 406-759-5108
Rita Chvilicek, prin. Fax 759-5867
Chester-Joplin-Inverness MS 50/7-8
PO Box 550 59522 406-759-5108
Rita Chvilicek, prin. Fax 759-5867

Chinook, Blaine, Pop. 1,183
Chinook SD 400/PK-12
PO Box 1059 59523 406-357-2236
Darin Hannum, supt. Fax 357-2238
www.chinookschools.org
Chinook HS 100/9-12
PO Box 1059 59523 406-357-2236
Matt Molyneaux, prin. Fax 357-2238
Chinook MS 50/7-8
PO Box 1059 59523 406-357-2237
Matt Molyneaux, prin. Fax 357-2238

Choteau, Teton, Pop. 1,646
Choteau SD 400/PK-12
204 7th Ave NW 59422 406-466-5303
Chuck Gameon, supt. Fax 466-5305
www.choteauschools.net
Choteau HS 100/9-12
204 7th Ave NW 59422 406-466-5303
Dave Jamison, prin. Fax 466-5305
Choteau MS 50/7-8
204 7th Ave NW 59422 406-466-5303
Dave Jamison, prin. Fax 466-5305

Circle, McCone, Pop. 606
Circle SD 200/PK-12
PO Box 99 59215 406-485-3600
Willie Thibault, supt. Fax 485-2332
circleschools.k12.mt.us
Circle HS 100/9-12
PO Box 99 59215 406-485-3600
Willie Thibault, prin. Fax 485-2332
Redwater MS 50/7-8
PO Box 99 59215 406-485-2140
Craig Widhalm, prin. Fax 485-2332

Clancy, Jefferson, Pop. 1,638
Clancy ESD 200/PK-8
PO Box 209 59634 406-933-5575
Dave Selvig, supt. Fax 933-5715
www.clancyschool.org
Clancy MS 50/7-8
PO Box 209 59634 406-933-5575
Dave Selvig, prin. Fax 933-5715

Montana City ESD 400/K-8
11 McClellan Creek Rd 59634 406-442-6779
Tony Kloker, supt. Fax 443-8875
montanacity.schoolwires.com
Montana City MS 200/6-8
11 McClellan Creek Rd 59634 406-442-6779
Daryl Mikesell, prin. Fax 443-8875

Clinton, Missoula, Pop. 1,018
Clinton ESD 200/PK-8
PO Box 250 59825 406-825-3113
Tom Stack, supt. Fax 825-3114
www.clintoncougars.com
Clinton MS 50/7-8
PO Box 250 59825 406-825-3113
Tom Stack, prin. Fax 825-3114

Clyde Park, Park, Pop. 288
Shields Valley SD 200/PK-12
PO Box 40 59018 406-578-2535
Randy Russell, supt. Fax 578-2176
www.shieldsvalleyschools.org/
Shields Valley HS 100/9-12
405 1st St E 59018 406-686-4621
Greg Sager, prin. Fax 686-4937
Shields Valley MS 50/7-8
405 1st St E 59018 406-686-4621
Greg Sager, prin. Fax 686-4937

Colstrip, Rosebud, Pop. 2,118
Colstrip SD 600/PK-12
PO Box 159 59323 406-748-4699
Bob Lewandowski, supt. Fax 748-2268
colstrippublicschools.org
Brattin MS 100/6-8
PO Box 159 59323 406-748-4699
Pax Haslem, prin. Fax 748-3143
Colstrip HS 200/9-12
PO Box 159 59323 406-748-4699
Mark Ator, prin. Fax 748-2517

Columbia Falls, Flathead, Pop. 4,562
Columbia Falls SD 2,100/K-12
PO Box 1259 59912 406-892-6550
Steve Bradshaw, supt. Fax 892-6552
www.cfmtschools.net
Columbia Falls HS 700/9-12
PO Box 1259 59912 406-892-6500
Scott Gaiser, prin. Fax 892-6583
Columbia Falls JHS 500/6-8
PO Box 1259 59912 406-892-6530
Dave Wick, prin. Fax 892-6528

Deer Park ESD 100/PK-8
2105 Middle Rd 59912 406-892-5388
Fax 892-3504
sites.google.com/a/deerparkedu.org/panthers/
Deer Park MS 50/7-8
2105 Middle Rd 59912 406-892-5388
Dan Block, prin. Fax 892-3504

Columbus, Stillwater, Pop. 1,857
Columbus SD 700/PK-12
433 N 3rd St 59019 406-322-5373
Jeff Bermes, supt. Fax 322-5028
www.columbus.k12.mt.us
Columbus HS 200/9-12
433 N 3rd St 59019 406-322-5373
George McKay, prin. Fax 322-5028
Columbus MS 200/6-8
415 N 3rd St 59019 406-322-5375
Ron Osborne, prin. Fax 322-5376

Conrad, Pondera, Pop. 2,522
Conrad SD 500/PK-12
215 S Maryland St 59425 406-278-5521
Sharyl Allen, supt. Fax 278-3630
www.conradschools.org
Conrad HS 200/9-12
308 S Illinois St 59425 406-278-3285
Ken Larson, prin. Fax 278-3806
Utterback MS 50/4-8
24 2nd Ave SW 59425 406-278-3227
Danele Dyer, prin. Fax 278-3228

Corvallis, Ravalli, Pop. 945
Corvallis SD 1,300/PK-12
PO Box 700 59828 406-961-4211
Tim Johnson, supt. Fax 961-5144
www.corvallis.k12.mt.us
Corvallis HS 400/9-12
PO Box 700 59828 406-961-3201
Jason Wirt, prin. Fax 961-4894
Corvallis JHS 200/7-8
PO Box 700 59828 406-961-3007
Rich Durgin, prin. Fax 961-5144

Crow Agency, Big Horn, Pop. 1,597

Little Big Horn College Post-Sec.
PO Box 370 59022 406-638-3100

Culbertson, Roosevelt, Pop. 690
Culbertson SD 300/PK-12
PO Box 459 59218 406-787-6246
Larry Crowder, supt. Fax 787-6244
www.culbertsonschool.com
Culbertson HS 100/9-12
PO Box 459 59218 406-787-6241
Mike Olson, prin. Fax 787-6244
Culbertson MS 50/7-8
PO Box 459 59218 406-787-6241
Mike Olson, prin. Fax 787-6244

Custer, Yellowstone, Pop. 158
Custer SD 100/K-12
PO Box 69 59024 406-856-4117
Dr. David Perkins, supt. Fax 856-4206
www.custerschools.org
Custer HS 50/9-12
PO Box 69 59024 406-856-4117
Dr. David Perkins, supt. Fax 856-4206
Custer MS 50/7-8
PO Box 69 59024 406-856-4117
Dr. David Perkins, supt. Fax 856-4206

Cut Bank, Glacier, Pop. 2,736
Cut Bank SD 700/PK-12
101 3rd Ave SE 59427 406-873-2229
Wade Johnson, supt. Fax 873-4691
www.cutbankschools.net
Cut Bank HS 200/9-12
101 3rd Ave SE 59427 406-873-5629
Peter Hamilton, prin. Fax 873-4691
Cut Bank MS 200/6-8
101 3rd Ave SE 59427 406-873-4421
Gail Hofstad, prin. Fax 873-4691

Darby, Ravalli, Pop. 697
Darby SD 300/PK-12
209 School Dr 59829 406-821-1314
Loyd Rennaker, supt. Fax 821-4977
www.darby.k12.mt.us/
Darby HS 100/9-12
209 School Dr 59829 406-821-3252
J.P. McCrossin, prin. Fax 821-4977
Darby MS 100/7-8
209 School Dr 59829 406-821-3252
J.P. McCrossin, prin. Fax 821-4977

Deer Lodge, Powell, Pop. 3,077
Deer Lodge ESD 400/PK-8
444 Montana Ave 59722 406-846-1553
Rodney Simpson, supt. Fax 846-1599
Duvall MS 100/7-8
444 Montana Ave 59722 406-846-1684
Rick Chrisman, prin. Fax 846-1599

Powell County HSD 200/9-12
709 Missouri Ave 59722 406-846-2757
Rick Duncan, supt. Fax 846-2759
www.pchs.dl.k12.mt.us
Powell County HS 200/9-12
709 Missouri Ave 59722 406-846-2757
Kerry Glisson, prin. Fax 846-2759

Denton, Fergus, Pop. 253
Denton SD 100/K-12
PO Box 1048 59430 406-567-2270
Gerald Krenzke, supt. Fax 567-2559
www.denton.k12.mt.us/
Denton HS 50/9-12
PO Box 1048 59430 406-567-2270
Gerald Krenzke, admin. Fax 567-2559
Denton JHS 50/7-8
PO Box 1048 59430 406-567-2270
Gerald Krenzke, admin. Fax 567-2559

Dillon, Beaverhead, Pop. 4,039
Beaverhead County HSD 300/9-12
104 N Pacific St 59725 406-683-2361
Gary Haverfield, supt. Fax 683-5263
bchsmt.schoolwires.com
Beaverhead County HS 300/9-12
104 N Pacific St 59725 406-683-2361
Megan Conrow, prin. Fax 683-5263

Dillon ESD 700/PK-8
22 Cottom Dr 59725 406-683-4311
Glen Johnson, supt. Fax 683-4312
www.dillonelem.k12.mt.us/
Dillon MS 200/6-8
14 Cottom Dr 59725 406-683-2368
Randy Shipman, prin. Fax 683-2369

University of Montana Western — Post-Sec.
710 S Atlantic St 59725 — 406-683-7331

Dixon, Sanders, Pop. 184

Dixon ESD — 50/PK-8
PO Box 10 59831 — 406-246-3566
Crista Anderson, admin. — Fax 246-3379
www.dixonschool.org

Dixon MS — 50/7-8
PO Box 10 59831 — 406-246-3566
Crista Anderson, prin. — Fax 246-3379

Dodson, Phillips, Pop. 121

Dodson SD — 100/PK-12
PO Box 278 59524 — 406-383-4361
Gary Weitz, supt. — Fax 383-4489
www.dodson.k12.mt.us

Dodson HS — 50/9-12
PO Box 278 59524 — 406-383-4361
Gary Weitz, supt. — Fax 383-4489

Dodson MS — 50/7-8
PO Box 278 59524 — 406-383-4362
Gary Weitz, supt. — Fax 383-4489

Drummond, Granite, Pop. 304

Drummond SD — 200/K-12
PO Box 349 59832 — 406-288-3281
Bryan Kott, supt. — Fax 288-3299

Drummond HS — 100/9-12
PO Box 349 59832 — 406-288-3281
Bryan Kott, prin. — Fax 288-3299

Drummond MS — 50/7-8
PO Box 349 59832 — 406-288-3281
Bryan Kott, prin. — Fax 288-3299

Dutton, Teton, Pop. 311

Dutton/Brady SD — 200/PK-12
101 2nd St NE 59433 — 406-476-3424
D.K. Brooks, supt. — Fax 476-3342
duttonbradyps.schoolwires.net

Dutton/Brady HS — 50/9-12
101 2nd St NE 59433 — 406-476-3424
D.K. Brooks, prin. — Fax 476-3342

Dutton/Brady MS — 50/7-8
101 2nd St NE 59433 — 406-476-3424
D.K. Brooks, prin. — Fax 476-3342

East Helena, Lewis and Clark, Pop. 1,919

East Helena ESD — 1,200/PK-8
PO Box 1280 59635 — 406-227-7700
Ron Whitmoyer, supt. — Fax 227-5534
www.ehps.k12.mt.us

East Valley MS — 400/6-8
PO Box 1280 59635 — 406-227-7740
Dan Rispens, prin. — Fax 227-9730

Helena Christian S — 200/PK-12
3384 Canyon Ferry Rd 59635 — 406-442-3821
Ted Clark, supt. — Fax 442-0341

Ekalaka, Carter, Pop. 327

Ekalaka SD — 100/PK-12
PO Box 458 59324 — 406-775-8765
Daniel Schrock, supt. — Fax 775-8766
www.ekalaka.net

Carter County HS — 50/9-12
PO Box 458 59324 — 406-775-8767
Daniel Schrock, prin. — Fax 775-8766

Ekalaka MS — 50/7-8
PO Box 458 59324 — 406-775-8767
Daniel Schrock, prin. — Fax 775-8766

Ennis, Madison, Pop. 828

Ennis SD — 300/PK-12
PO Box 517 59729 — 406-682-4258
Casey Clasna, supt. — Fax 682-7751
www.ennisschools.org

Ennis HS — 100/9-12
PO Box 517 59729 — 406-682-4258
Richard Borden, prin. — Fax 682-7751

Ennis MS — 100/7-8
PO Box 517 59729 — 406-682-4237
Brian Hilton, prin. — Fax 682-7752

Eureka, Lincoln, Pop. 1,015

Eureka SD — 700/PK-12
PO Box 2000 59917 — 406-297-5650
Jim Mepham, supt. — Fax 297-2644
www.lchigh.net

Eureka MS — 200/5-8
PO Box 2000 59917 — 406-297-5600
Trevor Utter, prin. — Fax 297-5653

Lincoln County HS — 300/9-12
PO Box 2000 59917 — 406-297-5700
Joel Graves, prin. — Fax 297-5714

Fairfield, Teton, Pop. 690

Fairfield SD — 300/K-12
PO Box 399 59436 — 406-467-2103
Les Meyer, supt. — Fax 467-2554
www.fairfield.k12.mt.us/

Fairfield HS — 100/9-12
PO Box 399 59436 — 406-467-2528
Dustin Gordon, prin. — Fax 467-2554

Fairfield MS — 50/7-8
PO Box 399 59436 — 406-467-2425
Dustin Gordon, prin. — Fax 467-2554

Greenfield ESD — 100/PK-8
590 Mt Highway 431 59436 — 406-467-2433
Fax 467-3138

Greenfield MS — 50/7-8
590 Mt Highway 431 59436 — 406-467-2433
Paul Wilson, prin. — Fax 467-3138

Fairview, Richland, Pop. 832

Fairview SD — 300/PK-12
PO Box 467 59221 — 406-742-5265
Luke Kloker, supt. — Fax 742-3336
fschool.org

Fairview HS — 100/9-12
PO Box 467 59221 — 406-742-5265
Rick Miller, prin. — Fax 742-3336

Fairview MS — 50/7-8
PO Box 467 59221 — 406-742-5265
Mark Thompson, prin. — Fax 742-8265

Florence, Ravalli, Pop. 755

Florence-Carlton SD — 800/PK-12
5602 Old US Highway 93 59833 — 406-273-6751
Bud Scully, supt.
www.florence.k12.mt.us

Florence-Carlton HS — 300/9-12
5602 Old US Highway 93 59833 — 406-273-6301
Audrey Backus, prin. — Fax 273-2643

Florence-Carlton MS — 100/7-8
5602 Old US Highway 93 59833 — 406-273-0587
Audrey Backus, prin. — Fax 273-0545

Forsyth, Rosebud, Pop. 1,757

Forsyth SD — 400/PK-12
PO Box 319 59327 — 406-346-2796
Dinny Bennett, supt. — Fax 346-7455
www.forsyth.k12.mt.us

Forsyth HS — 100/9-12
PO Box 319 59327 — 406-346-2796
Shelly Weight, prin. — Fax 346-9219

Forsyth JHS — 100/7-8
PO Box 319 59327 — 406-346-2796
Shelly Weight, prin. — Fax 346-9219

Fort Benton, Chouteau, Pop. 1,439

Ft. Benton SD — 300/PK-12
PO Box 399 59442 — 406-622-5691
Jory Thompson, supt. — Fax 622-3305
fortbentonschools.weebly.com

Fort Benton HS — 100/9-12
PO Box 399 59442 — 406-622-3213
Jory Thompson, admin. — Fax 622-5691

Fort Benton JHS — 50/7-8
PO Box 399 59442 — 406-622-3213
Rusty Bowers, prin. — Fax 622-5691

Frazer, Valley, Pop. 360

Frazer SD — 100/PK-12
PO Box 488 59225 — 406-695-2241
Carroll Decoteau, supt. — Fax 695-2243
www.frazer.k12.mt.us

Frazer HS — 50/9-12
PO Box 488 59225 — 406-695-2241
Carroll DeCoteau, admin. — Fax 695-2243

Frazer MS — 50/7-8
PO Box 488 59225 — 406-695-2241
Carroll DeCoteau, admin. — Fax 695-2243

Frenchtown, Missoula, Pop. 1,780

Frenchtown SD — 1,200/PK-12
PO Box 117 59834 — 406-626-2600
Randy Cline, supt. — Fax 626-2605
www.ftsd.org

Frenchtown HS — 400/9-12
PO Box 117 59834 — 406-626-2670
Jacob Haynes, prin. — Fax 626-2676

Frenchtown MS — 200/7-8
PO Box 117 59834 — 406-626-2650
Mark McMurray, prin. — Fax 626-2654

Froid, Roosevelt, Pop. 181

Froid SD — 100/K-12
PO Box 218 59226 — 406-766-2343
Ken Taylor, supt. — Fax 766-2206

Froid HS — 50/9-12
PO Box 218 59226 — 406-766-2342
Ken Taylor, admin. — Fax 766-2206

Froid MS — 50/7-8
PO Box 218 59226 — 406-766-2342
Ken Taylor, admin. — Fax 766-2206

Fromberg, Carbon, Pop. 437

Fromberg SD — 100/PK-12
319 School St 59029 — 406-668-7611
Teri Harris, supt. — Fax 668-7669
frombergpublicschools.com

Fromberg HS — 50/9-12
319 School St 59029 — 406-668-7315
Teri Harris, admin. — Fax 668-7669

Fromberg MS — 50/7-8
319 School St 59029 — 406-668-7315
Teri Harris, admin. — Fax 668-7669

Gallatin Gateway, Gallatin, Pop. 845

Big Sky SD — 200/PK-12
45465 Gallatin Rd 59730 — 406-995-4281
Dr. Dustin Shipman, supt. — Fax 995-2161
www.bssd72.org

Ophir MS — 100/5-8
45465 Gallatin Rd 59730 — 406-995-4281
Alexander Ide, prin. — Fax 995-2161

Other Schools – See Big Sky

Gallatin Gateway ESD — 200/PK-8
PO Box 265 59730 — 406-763-4415
Travis Anderson, supt. — Fax 763-4886
www.gallatingatewayschool.com

Gallatin Gateway MS — 50/7-8
PO Box 265 59730 — 406-763-4415
Travis Anderson, prin. — Fax 763-4886

Gardiner, Park, Pop. 871

Gardiner SD — 200/PK-12
510 Stone St 59030 — 406-848-7261
J.T. Stroder, supt. — Fax 848-0606
www.gardinerpublicschools.org

Gardiner HS — 100/9-12
510 Stone St 59030 — 406-848-7261
Mike Baer, prin. — Fax 848-9489

Gardiner MS — 50/7-8
510 Stone St 59030 — 406-848-7563
Mike Baer, prin. — Fax 848-9489

Geraldine, Chouteau, Pop. 255

Geraldine SD — 100/PK-12
PO Box 347 59446 — 406-737-4371
Aaron Skogen, supt. — Fax 737-4478
www.geraldine.k12.mt.us/

Geraldine HS — 50/9-12
PO Box 347 59446 — 406-737-4371
Aaron Skogen, prin. — Fax 737-4478

Geraldine MS — 50/7-8
PO Box 347 59446 — 406-737-4371
Aaron Skogen, prin. — Fax 737-4478

Geyser, Judith Basin, Pop. 87

Geyser SD 58 — 100/PK-12
PO Box 70 59447 — 406-735-4368
Dale Bernard, supt. — Fax 735-4452
www.geyser.k12.mt.us

Geyser HS — 50/9-12
PO Box 70 59447 — 406-735-4368
Dale Bernard, admin. — Fax 735-4452

Geyser MS — 50/7-8
PO Box 70 59447 — 406-735-4368
Dale Bernard, admin. — Fax 735-4452

Glasgow, Valley, Pop. 3,170

Glasgow SD — 600/PK-12
PO Box 28 59230 — 406-228-2406
Robert Connors, supt. — Fax 228-2407
www.glasgow.k12.mt.us/

Glasgow HS — 300/9-12
PO Box 28 59230 — 406-228-2485
Brett Huntsman, prin. — Fax 228-4061

Glasgow MS — 100/6-8
PO Box 28 59230 — 406-228-2485
Michael Zoanni, prin. — Fax 228-4061

Glendive, Dawson, Pop. 4,857

Glendive SD — 1,200/PK-12
PO Box 701 59330 — 406-377-5293
Ross Farber, supt. — Fax 377-6212
www.glendiveschools.com

Dawson County HS — 300/9-12
PO Box 701 59330 — 406-377-5265
Wade Murphy, prin. — Fax 377-8206

Washington MS — 300/6-8
PO Box 701 59330 — 406-377-2356
Mark Goyette, prin. — Fax 377-2357

Dawson Community College — Post-Sec.
300 College Dr 59330 — 406-377-3396

Grass Range, Fergus, Pop. 109

Grass Range SD #27 — 100/PK-12
PO Box 58 59032 — 406-428-2122
Joe Gaylord, supt. — Fax 428-2235
www.grps.k12.mt.us

Grass Range HS — 50/9-12
PO Box 58 59032 — 406-428-2341
Joe Gaylord, supt. — Fax 428-2235

Grass Range MS — 50/7-8
PO Box 58 59032 — 406-428-2122
Joe Gaylord, supt. — Fax 428-2235

Great Falls, Cascade, Pop. 56,542

Great Falls SD — 10,400/PK-12
PO Box 2429 59403 — 406-268-6001
Tammy Lacey, supt. — Fax 268-6002
www.gfps.k12.mt.us

East MS — 700/7-8
4040 Central Ave 59405 — 406-268-6500
Paul Furthmyre, prin. — Fax 268-6524

Great Falls HS — 1,500/9-12
1900 2nd Ave S 59405 — 406-268-6250
Heather Hoyer, prin. — Fax 268-6256

North MS — 700/7-8
2601 8th St NE 59404 — 406-268-6525
Brad Barringer, prin. — Fax 268-6575

Paris Gibson Education Center — 300/Alt
2400 Central Ave 59401 — 406-268-6600
Drew Uecker, prin. — Fax 268-6603

Russell HS — 1,500/9-12
228 17th Ave NW 59404 — 406-268-6100
Kerry Parsons, prin. — Fax 268-6109

Benefits Health Care-West Campus — Post-Sec.
PO Box 5013 59403 — 406-727-3333

Dahl's College of Beauty — Post-Sec.
718 Central Ave 59401 — 406-454-3453

Foothills Community Christian S — 200/PK-12
2210 5th Ave N 59401 — 406-452-5276
David Culpepper, head sch — Fax 452-8606

Great Falls Central Catholic HS — 100/9-12
2800 18th Ave S 59405 — 406-216-3344
Vickie Donisthorpe, prin. — Fax 216-3343

Great Falls College Montana State Univ — Post-Sec.
2100 16th Ave S 59405 — 406-771-4300

Montana School for the Deaf and Blind — Post-Sec.
3911 Central Ave 59405 — 406-771-6000

University of Great Falls — Post-Sec.
1301 20th St S 59405 — 800-856-9544

Hamilton, Ravalli, Pop. 4,256

Hamilton SD — 1,500/PK-12
217 Daly Ave 59840 — 406-363-2280
Tom Korst, supt. — Fax 363-1843
www.hsd3.org

Hamilton HS — 500/9-12
327 Fairgrounds Rd 59840 — 406-375-6060
Dan Kimzey, prin. — Fax 375-6076

Hamilton MS — 400/6-8
209 S 5th St 59840 — 406-363-2121
Marlin Lewis, prin. — Fax 363-7032

Hardin, Big Horn, Pop. 3,345

Hardin SD 17-H & 1 — 1,900/PK-12
401 Park Rd 59034 — 406-665-9300
Dennis Gerke, supt. — Fax 665-9338
www.hardin.k12.mt.us

Hardin HS 400/9-12
702 N Terry Ave 59034 406-665-6300
Rob Hankins, prin. Fax 665-1909
Hardin MS 400/6-8
611 5th St W 59034 406-665-6350
Scott Brokaw, prin. Fax 665-1409

Harlem, Blaine, Pop. 770
Harlem SD 600/PK-12
PO Box 339 59526 406-353-2289
Sean Smith, supt. Fax 353-2674
www.harlem-hs.k12.mt.us
Harlem HS 200/9-12
PO Box 339 59526 406-353-2287
Doug Komrosky, prin. Fax 353-2339
Harlem MS 100/7-8
PO Box 339 59526 406-353-2287
Doug Komrosky, prin. Fax 353-2339

Aaniiih Nakoda College Post-Sec.
PO Box 159 59526 406-353-2607

Harlowton, Wheatland, Pop. 971
Harlowton SD 300/PK-12
PO Box 288 59036 406-632-4822
Andrew Begger, supt. Fax 632-4416
www.harlowton.k12.mt.us
Harlowton HS 100/9-12
PO Box 288 59036 406-632-4324
Gregg Wasson, prin. Fax 632-4416
Hillcrest MS 50/7-8
PO Box 288 59036 406-632-4361
Gregg Wasson, prin. Fax 632-4416

Harrison, Madison, Pop. 137
Harrison SD 100/K-12
PO Box 7 59735 406-685-3428
Fred Hofman, supt. Fax 685-3420
sites.google.com/a/harrison.k12.mt.us/hhswildcats/
Harrison HS 50/9-12
PO Box 7 59735 406-685-3428
Fred Hofman, admin. Fax 685-3430
Harrison MS 50/7-8
PO Box 7 59735 406-685-3428
Fred Hofman, admin. Fax 685-3430

Havre, Hill, Pop. 8,979
Havre SD 2,000/K-12
PO Box 7791 59501 406-265-4356
Andy Carlson, supt. Fax 265-8460
www.havre.k12.mt.us/
Havre HS 600/9-12
PO Box 7791 59501 406-265-6731
Michael Haugen, prin. Fax 265-3217
Havre MS 500/6-8
1441 11th St W 59501 406-265-9613
Dustin Kraske, prin. Fax 265-4414

Montana State University - Northern Post-Sec.
PO Box 7751 59501 406-265-3700

Hays, Blaine, Pop. 831
Hays-Lodge Pole SD 200/PK-12
PO Box 110 59527 406-673-3120
Margaret Campbell, supt. Fax 673-3415
Hays-Lodge Pole HS 100/9-12
PO Box 110 59527 406-673-3120
Amy Snow, prin. Fax 673-3415
Hays-Lodge Pole MS 50/7-8
PO Box 110 59527 406-673-3120
Amy Snow, prin. Fax 673-3274

Heart Butte, Pondera, Pop. 576
Heart Butte SD 200/PK-12
PO Box 259 59448 406-338-3344
Vern Folley, supt. Fax 338-5832
www.heartbutteschool.com
Heart Butte HS 50/9-12
PO Box 259 59448 406-338-3344
Steven Schwartz, prin. Fax 338-5832
Heart Butte MS 50/7-8
PO Box 259 59448 406-338-2200
Steven Schwartz, prin. Fax 338-5832

Helena, Lewis and Clark, Pop. 27,530
Helena SD 8,000/PK-12
55 S Rodney St 59601 406-324-2001
George Copps, supt. Fax 324-2035
helenaschools.org
Anderson MS 1,000/6-8
1200 Knight St 59601 406-324-2800
Bruce Campbell, prin. Fax 324-2801
Capital HS 1,300/9-12
100 Valley Dr 59601 406-324-2500
Brett Zanto, prin. Fax 324-2501
Helena HS 1,600/9-12
1300 Billings Ave 59601 406-324-2200
Steve Thennis, prin. Fax 324-2201
Helena MS 700/6-8
1025 N Rodney St 59601 406-324-1000
Josh McKay, prin. Fax 324-1001
Project for Alternative Learning Alt
815 Front St 59601 406-324-1630
Stephanie Thennis, prin. Fax 324-1631

Carroll College Post-Sec.
1601 N Benton Ave 59625 406-447-4300
Helena College University of Montana Post-Sec.
1115 N Roberts St 59601 406-447-6900
St. Andrew's S 200/K-12
PO Box 231 59624 406-449-3201
Donna Smillie, prin. Fax 449-0129

Highwood, Chouteau, Pop. 174
Highwood SD 100/PK-12
160 West St S 59450 406-733-2081
Jane Suberg, supt. Fax 733-2671
www.highwood.k12.mt.us
Highwood HS 50/9-12
160 West St S 59450 406-733-2081
Jane Suberg, admin. Fax 733-2671
Highwood MS 50/6-8
160 West St S 59450 406-733-2081
Jane Suberg, admin. Fax 733-2671

Hinsdale, Valley, Pop. 212
Hinsdale SD 100/PK-12
PO Box 398 59241 406-364-2314
Ed Sugg, supt. Fax 364-2205
www.hinsdale.k12.mt.us
Hinsdale HS 50/9-12
PO Box 398 59241 406-364-2314
Julie Gaffney, admin. Fax 364-2205
Hinsdale MS 50/7-8
PO Box 398 59241 406-364-2314
Julie Gaffney, admin. Fax 364-2205

Hobson, Judith Basin, Pop. 215
Hobson SD 100/PK-12
PO Box 410 59452 406-423-5483
Tim Tharp, supt. Fax 423-5260
www.hobson.k12.mt.us/
Hobson HS 50/9-12
PO Box 410 59452 406-423-5483
Fax 423-5260
Hobson MS 50/7-8
PO Box 410 59452 406-423-5483
Tim Tharp, prin. Fax 423-5260

Hot Springs, Sanders, Pop. 493
Hot Springs SD 200/PK-12
PO Box 1005 59845 406-741-3285
Dr. Mike Perry, supt. Fax 741-3287
Hot Springs HS 100/9-12
PO Box 1005 59845 406-741-2962
Kelly Moore, prin. Fax 741-3287
Hot Springs MS 50/7-8
301 Broadway St 59845 406-741-2962
Kelly Moore, prin. Fax 741-3287

Hysham, Treasure, Pop. 299
Hysham SD 100/PK-12
PO Box 272 59038 406-342-5237
Larry Fink, supt. Fax 342-5257
www.hysham.k12.mt.us
Hysham HS 50/9-12
PO Box 272 59038 406-342-5237
Larry Fink, admin. Fax 342-5257
Hysham MS 50/7-8
PO Box 272 59038 406-342-5237
Larry Fink, admin. Fax 342-5257

Joliet, Carbon, Pop. 592
Joliet SD 400/PK-12
PO Box 590 59041 406-962-3541
Allison B. Evertz M.Ed., supt. Fax 962-3958
www.jolietschools.org/
Joliet HS 100/9-12
PO Box 590 59041 406-962-3541
Marilyn Vukonich, prin. Fax 962-3958
Joliet MS 100/7-8
PO Box 590 59041 406-962-3541
Marilyn Vukonich, prin. Fax 962-3958

Jordan, Garfield, Pop. 342
Jordan SD 200/PK-12
PO Box 409 59337 406-557-2259
Nathan Olson, supt. Fax 557-2778
jordanpublicschools.org
Garfield County HS 100/9-12
PO Box 409 59337 406-557-2259
Nathan Olson, prin. Fax 557-2778
Jordan MS 50/7-8
PO Box 409 59337 406-557-2259
Nathan Olson, prin. Fax 557-2778

Judith Gap, Wheatland, Pop. 125
Judith Gap SD 50/PK-12
PO Box 67 59453 406-473-2211
Annette Hart, supt. Fax 473-2250
www.judithgap.k12.mt.us/
Judith Gap HS 50/9-12
PO Box 67 59453 406-473-2211
Annette Hart, supt. Fax 473-2250
Judith Gap MS 50/7-8
PO Box 67 59453 406-473-2211
Annette Hart, supt. Fax 473-2250

Kalispell, Flathead, Pop. 19,453
Cayuse Prairie ESD 200/PK-8
897 Lake Blaine Rd 59901 406-756-4560
Amy Piazzola, supt. Fax 756-4570
cayuseprairie.com
Cayuse Prairie MS 50/7-8
897 Lake Blaine Rd 59901 406-756-4560
Amy Piazzola, prin. Fax 756-4570

Evergreen SD 600/PK-8
18 W Evergreen Dr 59901 406-751-1111
Dr. Laurie Barron, supt. Fax 752-2307
www.evergreensd50.com
Evergreen JHS 200/5-8
18 W Evergreen Dr 59901 406-751-1131
Kim Anderson, prin. Fax 751-1134

Fair-Mont-Egan ESD 200/PK-8
797 Fairmont Rd 59901 406-755-7072
Christine Anthony, admin. Fax 755-7077
www.fmemontana.net
Fair-Mont-Egan MS 50/7-8
797 Fairmont Rd 59901 406-755-7072
Christine Anthony, prin. Fax 755-7077

Helena Flats SD 15 200/K-8
1000 Helena Flats Rd 59901 406-257-2301
Dan Anderson, supt. Fax 257-2304
helenaflats.org
Helena Flats MS 50/7-8
1000 Helena Flats Rd 59901 406-257-2301
Dan Anderson, prin. Fax 257-2304

Kalispell SD 6,000/PK-12
233 1st Ave E 59901 406-751-3400
Mark Flatau, supt. Fax 751-3416
www.sd5.k12.mt.us
Flathead HS 1,500/9-12
644 4th Ave W 59901 406-751-3500
Peter Fusaro, prin. Fax 751-3505
Glacier HS 1,300/9-12
375 Wolfpack Way 59901 406-758-8600
Callie Langohr, prin. Fax 758-8602
Kalispell MS 1,100/6-8
205 Northwest Ln 59901 406-751-3800
Tryg Johnson, prin. Fax 751-3805
Linderman Education Center 200/Alt
124 3rd Ave E 59901 406-751-3990
Jodie Barber, prin. Fax 751-3930

Smith Valley ESD 200/K-8
2901 US Highway 2 W 59901 406-756-4535
Fax 756-4534
www.smithvalleyschool.org
Smith Valley MS 50/7-8
2901 US Highway 2 W 59901 406-756-4535
Laili Komenda, prin. Fax 756-4534

West Valley ESD 500/PK-8
2290 Farm To Market Rd 59901 406-755-7239
Cal Ketchum, supt. Fax 755-7300
www.westvalleyschool.com
West Valley MS 200/6-8
2290 Farm To Market Rd 59901 406-755-7239
Tina Blair, prin. Fax 755-7300

Flathead Valley Community College Post-Sec.
777 Grandview Dr 59901 406-756-3822
Stillwater Christian S 300/PK-12
255 FFA Dr 59901 406-752-4400
Daniel Makowski, head sch Fax 755-4061

Kila, Flathead, Pop. 375
Kila ESD 200/PK-8
PO Box 40 59920 406-257-2428
Fax 755-6663
www.kilaschool.com/
Kila MS 50/7-8
PO Box 40 59920 406-257-2428
Jason Christy, prin. Fax 755-6663

Lambert, Richland
Lambert SD 100/PK-12
PO Box 260 59243 406-774-3333
Sean Beddow, supt. Fax 774-3335
lps.schoolwires.net
Lambert HS 50/9-12
PO Box 260 59243 406-774-3333
Kara Triplett, admin. Fax 774-3335
Lambert MS 50/7-8
PO Box 260 59243 406-774-3333
Kara Triplett, admin. Fax 774-3335

Lame Deer, Rosebud, Pop. 2,025
Lame Deer SD 500/PK-12
PO Box 96 59043 406-477-6305
Gerald Chouinard, supt. Fax 477-6535
www.lamedeer.k12.mt.us/
Lame Deer HS 100/9-12
PO Box 96 59043 406-477-8900
Steve Ewing, prin. Fax 477-8906
Lame Deer MS 100/7-8
PO Box 96 59043 406-477-8900
Steve Ewing, prin. Fax 477-8906

Chief Dull Knife College Post-Sec.
PO Box 98 59043 406-477-6215

Laurel, Yellowstone, Pop. 6,588
Laurel SD 2,000/K-12
410 Colorado Ave 59044 406-628-8623
Linda Filpula, supt. Fax 628-8625
www.laurel.k12.mt.us
Laurel HS 600/9-12
203 E 8th St 59044 406-628-7911
Edward Norman, prin. Fax 628-3558
Laurel MS 600/5-8
725 Washington Ave 59044 406-628-6919
Patrick Cates, prin. Fax 628-3350

Lavina, Golden Valley, Pop. 177
Lavina SD 100/PK-12
PO Box 290 59046 406-636-2761
Duane Walker, supt. Fax 636-4911
www.lavinapublicschools.com
Lavina HS 50/9-12
PO Box 290 59046 406-636-2761
Duane Walker, prin. Fax 636-4911
Lavina MS 50/7-8
PO Box 290 59046 406-636-2761
Duane Walker, prin. Fax 636-4911

Lewistown, Fergus, Pop. 5,800
Lewistown SD 800/K-12
215 7th Ave S 59457 406-535-8777
Jason Butcher, supt. Fax 535-7292
www.lewistown.k12.mt.us
Fergus HS 300/9-12
215 7th Ave S 59457 406-535-2321
Jeff Elliott, prin. Fax 535-3835
Lewistown JHS 200/7-8
215 7th Ave S 59457 406-535-5419
Tim Majerus, prin. Fax 535-2300

Libby, Lincoln, Pop. 2,579
Libby SD 1,000/PK-12
724 Louisiana Ave 59923 406-293-8811
Craig Barringer, supt. Fax 293-8812
www.libbyschools.org
Libby MSHS 300/7-12
150 Education Way 59923 406-293-8802
Ruth VanWorth-Rogers, prin. Fax 293-3927

Kootenai Valley Christian S 100/PK-12
1024 Montana Ave 59923 406-293-2303
Ruthanne Dolezal, admin. Fax 293-2303

Lima, Beaverhead, Pop. 213
Lima SD 100/PK-12
PO Box 186 59739 406-276-3571
Brian Rayburn, supt. Fax 276-3495
www.limaschoolmt.org
Lima HS 50/9-12
PO Box 186 59739 406-276-3571
Brian Rayburn, prin. Fax 276-3495
Lima JHS 50/7-8
PO Box 186 59739 406-276-3571
Brian Rayburn, prin. Fax 276-3495

Lincoln, Lewis and Clark, Pop. 993
Lincoln SD 100/PK-12
PO Box 39 59639 406-362-4201
Carla Anderson, supt. Fax 362-4030
www.lincolnlynx.com
Lincoln HS 100/9-12
PO Box 39 59639 406-362-4201
Carla Anderson, prin. Fax 362-4030
Lincoln MS 50/7-8
PO Box 39 59639 406-362-4201
Carla Anderson, prin. Fax 362-4030

Livingston, Park, Pop. 6,921
Arrowhead ESD 75 50/PK-8
1489 E River Rd 59047 406-222-4148
Jo Newhall, supt. Fax 222-4199
www.arrowheadk8.org
Arrowhead MS 50/7-8
1489 E River Rd 59047 406-333-4359
Leah Shannon, lead tchr. Fax 333-4975

Livingston SD 1,400/K-12
132 S B St 59047 406-222-0861
Don Viegut Ph.D., supt. Fax 222-7323
www.livingston.k12.mt.us
Park HS 500/9-12
102 View Vista Dr 59047 406-222-0448
Lynne Scalia, prin. Fax 222-9404
Sleeping Giant MS 400/6-8
301 View Vista Dr 59047 406-222-3292
Lisa Rosburg, prin. Fax 222-3512

Pine Creek ESD 50/PK-8
2575 E River Rd 59047 406-581-8446
Kimberly DeBruycker, supt. Fax 222-0059
pinecreekschool.com
Pine Creek MS 50/7-8
2575 E River Rd 59047 406-222-0059
Monte Silk, lead tchr. Fax 222-0059

Summit Christian Academy 50/K-12
PO Box 403 59047 406-823-9155
Bob Brown, admin. Fax 308-7203

Lodge Grass, Big Horn, Pop. 414
Lodge Grass SD 300/PK-12
PO Box 810 59050 406-639-2304
Victoria Falls Down M.Ed., supt. Fax 639-2388
www.lodgegrass.k12.mt.us
Lodge Grass HS 100/9-12
PO Box 810 59050 406-639-2702
Curtis Brien M.Ed., prin. Fax 639-2066
Lodge Grass MS 50/7-8
PO Box 810 59050 406-639-2702
Curtis Brien M.Ed., prin. Fax 639-2066

Lolo, Missoula, Pop. 3,815
Lolo ESD 600/PK-8
11395 US Highway 93 S 59847 406-273-0451
Dr. Michael Magone, supt. Fax 273-2628
www.lolo.k12.mt.us
Lolo MS 200/5-8
11395 US Highway 93 S 59847 406-273-6141
Dale Olinger M.Ed., prin. Fax 273-2628

Woodman ESD 50/K-8
18470 Highway 12 W 59847 406-273-6770
Fax 273-6659
www.woodmanschool.org
Woodman MS 50/7-8
18470 Highway 12 W 59847 406-273-6770
Charis Jacobson, lead tchr. Fax 273-6659

Lustre, Valley

Lustre Christian HS 50/9-12
294 Lustre Rd 59225 406-392-5735
Wes Young, admin. Fax 392-5765

Malta, Phillips, Pop. 1,893
Malta SD 500/PK-12
PO Box 670 59538 406-654-1871
Kris Kuehn, supt. Fax 654-2205
www.malta.k12.mt.us/
Malta HS 200/9-12
PO Box 670 59538 406-654-2002
Scott King, prin. Fax 654-2226
Malta JHS 100/6-8
PO Box 670 59538 406-654-2225
Shawn Bleth, prin. Fax 654-2226

Manhattan, Gallatin, Pop. 1,493
Manhattan SD 600/PK-12
PO Box 425 59741 406-284-6460
Scott Chauvet, supt. Fax 284-6853
manhattan.schoolwires.com
Manhattan HS 200/9-12
PO Box 425 59741 406-284-3341
Neil Harvey, prin. Fax 284-3104
Manhattan MS 100/7-8
PO Box 425 59741 406-284-3250
Scott Schumacher, prin. Fax 284-4122

Manhattan Christian S 300/PK-12
8000 Churchill Rd 59741 406-282-7261
Patrick DeJong, supt. Fax 282-7701

Marion, Flathead, Pop. 853
Marion ESD 100/K-8
205 Gopher Ln 59925 406-854-2333
Cherie Stobie, prin. Fax 854-2690
www.marionschoolmt.com
Marion MS 50/7-8
205 Gopher Ln 59925 406-854-2333
Cherie Stobie, prin. Fax 854-2690

Medicine Lake, Sheridan, Pop. 215
Medicine Lake SD 100/PK-12
PO Box 265 59247 406-789-2211
Tiffani Anderson, supt. Fax 789-2213
www.medicinelake.k12.mt.us/
Medicine Lake HS 50/9-12
PO Box 265 59247 406-789-2211
Tiffani Anderson, supt. Fax 789-2213
Medicine Lake MS 50/7-8
PO Box 265 59247 406-789-2211
Tiffani Anderson, supt. Fax 789-2213

Melstone, Musselshell, Pop. 96
Melstone SD 100/PK-12
PO Box 97 59054 406-358-2352
Kelly Haaland, supt. Fax 358-2346
Melstone HS 50/9-12
PO Box 97 59054 406-358-2352
Kelly Haaland, prin. Fax 358-2346
Melstone MS 50/7-8
PO Box 97 59054 406-358-2352
Kelly Haaland, prin. Fax 358-2346

Miles City, Custer, Pop. 8,282
Miles City SD 1,500/PK-12
1604 Main St 59301 406-234-3840
Keith Campbell, supt. Fax 234-3147
www.milescity.k12.mt.us
Custer County District HS 500/9-12
20 S Center Ave 59301 406-234-4920
Beez Lucero, prin. Fax 234-4923
Washington MS 200/7-8
210 N 9th St 59301 406-234-2084
Derrick Tvedt, prin. Fax 234-7403

Miles Community College Post-Sec.
2715 Dickinson St 59301 406-874-6100

Missoula, Missoula, Pop. 65,061
DeSmet ESD 100/K-8
6355 Padre Ln 59808 406-549-4994
Shawn Clark, admin. Fax 549-6731
www.desmet.k12.mt.us
DeSmet MS 50/7-8
6355 Padre Ln 59808 406-549-4994
Shawn Clark, prin. Fax 549-6731

Hellgate ESD 1,800/PK-8
2385 Flynn Ln 59808 406-728-5626
Dr. Doug Reisig, supt. Fax 728-5636
www.hellgate.k12.mt.us
Hellgate MS 400/6-8
2385 Flynn Ln 59808 406-721-2452
Jamie Courville, prin. Fax 728-0967

Missoula SD 1 8,600/K-12
215 S 6th St W 59801 406-728-2400
Mark Thane, supt. Fax 542-4009
www.mcpsmt.org
Big Sky HS 1,100/9-12
3100 South Ave W 59804 406-728-2401
Natalie Jaeger, prin. Fax 549-4616
Hellgate HS 1,200/9-12
900 S Higgins Ave 59801 406-728-2402
Judson Miller, prin. Fax 728-2496
Meadow Hill MS 500/6-8
4210 S Reserve St 59803 406-542-4045
Christina Stevens, prin. Fax 721-4418
Porter MS 500/6-8
2510 W Central Ave 59804 406-542-4060
Lisa Hendrix, prin. Fax 542-4098
Sentinel HS 1,200/9-12
901 South Ave W 59801 406-728-2403
Ted Fuller, prin. Fax 329-5959
Washington MS 600/6-8
645 W Central Ave 59801 406-542-4085
Craig Henkel, prin. Fax 721-7346
Willard Alternative Learning Center Alt
901 S 6th St W 59801 406-542-4073
Kevin Ritchlin, prin. Fax 327-6965
Other Schools – See Seeley Lake

Target Range ESD 500/PK-8
4095 South Ave W 59804 406-549-9239
Dr. Corey Austin, supt. Fax 728-8841
www.target.k12.mt.us
Target Range MS 200/6-8
4095 South Ave W 59804 406-549-9239
Barbara Droessler, prin. Fax 728-8841

Loyola Sacred Heart HS 200/9-12
320 Edith St 59801 406-549-6101
Jeremy Beck, prin. Fax 542-1432

Missoula College University of Montana Post-Sec.
909 South Ave W 59801 406-243-7882
Modern Beauty School Post-Sec.
2700 Paxson St Ste G 59801 406-721-1800
St. Patrick Hospital Post-Sec.
PO Box 4587 59806 406-543-7271
University of Montana Post-Sec.
32 Campus Dr 59812 406-243-0211
Valley Christian S 200/PK-12
2526 Sunset Ln 59804 406-549-0482
Anthony Baugher, head sch Fax 549-5047

Moore, Fergus, Pop. 188
Moore SD 100/PK-12
509 Highland Ave 59464 406-374-2231
Denise Chrest, supt. Fax 374-2490
www.moore.k12.mt.us
Moore HS 50/9-12
509 Highland Ave 59464 406-374-2231
Denise Chrest, admin. Fax 374-2490
Moore MS 50/7-8
509 Highland Ave 59464 406-374-2231
Denise Chrest, admin. Fax 374-2490

Nashua, Valley, Pop. 284
Nashua SD 100/PK-12
PO Box 170 59248 406-746-3411
William Clter, supt. Fax 746-3458
www.nashua.k12.mt.us
Nashua HS 50/9-12
PO Box 170 59248 406-746-3411
William Colter, supt. Fax 746-3458
Nashua MS 50/7-8
PO Box 170 59248 406-746-3411
William Colter, supt. Fax 746-3458

Noxon, Sanders, Pop. 210
Noxon SD 200/PK-12
300 Noxon Ave 59853 406-847-2922
Thad Kaiser, supt. Fax 847-8684
noxonschools.com
Noxon HS 100/9-12
300 Noxon Ave 59853 406-847-2442
Rik Rewerts, prin. Fax 847-2232
Noxon MS 50/7-8
300 Noxon Ave 59853 406-847-2442
Rik Rewerts, prin. Fax 847-2232

Opheim, Valley, Pop. 83
Opheim SD 50/PK-12
PO Box 108 59250 406-762-3214
Tony Warren, supt. Fax 762-3348
sites.google.com/site/opheimschool/Home
Opheim HS 50/9-12
PO Box 108 59250 406-762-3214
Tony Warren, prin. Fax 762-3348
Opheim MS 50/7-8
PO Box 108 59250 406-762-3214
Tony Warren, prin. Fax 762-3348

Pablo, Lake, Pop. 2,090

Salish Kootenai College Post-Sec.
PO Box 70 59855 406-275-4800

Park City, Stillwater, Pop. 973
Park City SD 300/PK-12
PO Box 278 59063 406-633-2406
Dan Grabowska, supt. Fax 633-2913
parkcityschools.org
Park City HS 100/9-12
PO Box 278 59063 406-633-2350
Jared Delaney, prin. Fax 633-2913
Park City MS 50/7-8
PO Box 278 59063 406-633-2350
Jared Delaney, prin. Fax 633-2913

Philipsburg, Granite, Pop. 808
Philipsburg SD 200/PK-12
PO Box 400 59858 406-859-3232
Mike Cutler, supt. Fax 859-3674
pburg.k12.mt.us
Granite HS 100/9-12
PO Box 400 59858 406-859-3232
Mike Cutler, prin. Fax 859-3674
Philipsburg MS 50/7-8
PO Box 400 59858 406-859-3232
Mike Cutler, prin. Fax 859-3674

Plains, Sanders, Pop. 1,024
Plains SD 400/PK-12
PO Box 549 59859 406-826-8600
Thomas Chisholm, supt. Fax 826-4439
www.plainsschools.net/
Plains HS 100/9-12
PO Box 549 59859 406-826-8600
Kevin Meredith, prin. Fax 826-4439
Plains MS 50/7-8
PO Box 549 59859 406-826-8600
Kevin Meredith, prin. Fax 826-4439

Plentywood, Sheridan, Pop. 1,706
Plentywood SD 400/PK-12
100 E Laurel Ave 59254 406-765-1803
Matt Torix, supt. Fax 765-1175
www.plentywood.k12.mt.us/
Plentywood HS 100/9-12
100 E Laurel Ave 59254 406-765-1803
James Russell, prin. Fax 765-1195
Plentywood MS 100/7-8
100 E Laurel Ave 59254 406-765-1803
Rob Pedersen, prin. Fax 765-1195

Plevna, Fallon, Pop. 160
Plevna SD 100/PK-12
PO Box 158 59344 406-772-5666
Jule Walker, supt. Fax 772-5548
www.plevna.k12.mt.us/
Plevna HS 50/9-12
PO Box 158 59344 406-772-5666
Jule Walker, lead tchr. Fax 772-5548

Plevna MS 50/7-8
PO Box 158 59344 406-772-5666
Jule Walker, lead tchr. Fax 772-5548

Polson, Lake, Pop. 4,155
Polson SD 1,700/PK-12
111 4th Ave E 59860 406-883-6355
Rex Weltz, supt. Fax 883-6345
www.polson.k12.mt.us
Polson HS 500/9-12
1712 2nd St W 59860 406-883-6351
Scott Wilson, prin. Fax 883-6330
Polson MS 300/7-8
1602 2nd St W 59860 406-883-6335
Tom Digiallonardo, prin. Fax 883-6334

Mission Valley Christian Academy 100/K-12
38907 Mt Highway 35 59860 406-883-6858
Chris Bumgarner, dir. Fax 883-6858

Poplar, Roosevelt, Pop. 787
Poplar SD 700/PK-12
PO Box 458 59255 406-768-6602
James Baldwin, supt. Fax 768-6800
www.poplar.k12.mt.us
Poplar HS 200/9-12
PO Box 458 59255 406-768-6830
Dwain Haggard, prin. Fax 768-6803
Poplar JHS 100/5-8
PO Box 458 59255 406-768-6730
David Allen, prin. Fax 768-6802

Fort Peck Community College Post-Sec.
PO Box 398 59255 406-768-6300

Power, Teton, Pop. 174
Power SD 100/PK-12
PO Box 155 59468 406-463-2251
Loren Dunk, supt. Fax 463-2360
www.power.k12.mt.us/
Power HS 100/9-12
PO Box 155 59468 406-463-2251
Loren Dunk, prin. Fax 463-2360
Power MS 50/7-8
PO Box 155 59468 406-463-2251
Loren Dunk, prin. Fax 463-2360

Pryor, Big Horn, Pop. 610
Pryor SD 100/PK-12
PO Box 229 59066 406-259-7329
D McGee, supt. Fax 245-8938
Plenty Coups HS 100/9-12
PO Box 229 59066 406-259-7329
Dan McGee, prin. Fax 245-8938
Pryor MS 50/7-8
PO Box 229 59066 406-259-7329
Dan McGee, prin. Fax 245-8938

Ramsay, Silver Bow
Ramsay ESD 100/K-8
PO Box 105 59748 406-782-5470
Maury Cook, admin. Fax 723-8905
Ramsay MS 50/7-8
PO Box 105 59748 406-782-5470
Maury Cook, prin. Fax 723-8905

Rapelje, Stillwater
Rapelje SD 50/K-12
PO Box 89 59067 406-663-2215
Jerry Thompson, supt. Fax 663-2299
www.rapelje.k12.mt.us/
Rapelje HS 50/9-12
PO Box 89 59067 406-663-2215
Jerry Thompson, admin. Fax 663-2299
Rapelje MS 50/7-8
PO Box 89 59067 406-663-2215
Jerry Thompson, admin. Fax 663-2299

Red Lodge, Carbon, Pop. 2,091
Red Lodge SD 500/PK-12
PO Box 1090 59068 406-446-2110
John Fitzgerald, supt. Fax 446-2037
redlodge.schoolwires.com/
Red Lodge HS 200/9-12
PO Box 1090 59068 406-446-1903
Rex Ternan, prin. Fax 446-3953
Roosevelt JHS 100/6-8
PO Box 1090 59068 406-446-2110
Jason Reimer, prin. Fax 446-3975

Reed Point, Stillwater, Pop. 186
Reed Point SD 100/K-12
PO Box 338 59069 406-326-2245
Michael Ehinger, supt. Fax 326-2339
www.reedpoint.k12.mt.us/
Reed Point HS 50/9-12
PO Box 338 59069 406-326-2245
Michael Ehinger, supt. Fax 326-2339
Reed Point MS 50/7-8
PO Box 338 59069 406-326-2245
Michael Ehinger, supt. Fax 326-2339

Richey, Dawson, Pop. 177
Richey SD 100/PK-12
PO Box 60 59259 406-773-5523
Maureen Simonson, supt. Fax 773-5554
www.richey.k12.mt.us/
Richey HS 50/9-12
PO Box 60 59259 406-773-5523
Maureen Simonson, prin. Fax 773-5554
Richey MS 50/7-8
PO Box 60 59259 406-773-5680
Maureen Simonson, prin. Fax 773-5554

Roberts, Carbon, Pop. 354
Roberts SD 100/K-12
PO Box 78 59070 406-445-2421
Alexander Ator, supt. Fax 445-2506
www.roberts.k12.mt.us
Roberts HS 50/9-12
PO Box 78 59070 406-445-2421
Alex Ator, prin. Fax 445-2506
Roberts MS 50/7-8
PO Box 78 59070 406-445-2421
Alex Ator, prin. Fax 445-2506

Ronan, Lake, Pop. 1,691
Ronan SD 1,500/PK-12
421 Andrew St NW 59864 406-676-3390
Mark J. Johnston, supt. Fax 676-3392
www.ronank12.edu/
Ronan HS 400/9-12
421 Andrew St NW 59864 406-676-3390
Kevin Kenelty, prin. Fax 676-3330
Ronan MS 400/5-8
421 Andrew St NW 59864 406-676-3390
Sandra Beal, prin. Fax 676-2852

Rosebud, Rosebud, Pop. 111
Rosebud SD 100/PK-12
PO Box 38 59347 406-347-5353
Michael Silverman, supt. Fax 347-5544
www.rhs12.com
Rosebud HS 50/9-12
PO Box 38 59347 406-347-5353
Michael Silverman, prin. Fax 347-5544
Rosebud MS 50/7-8
PO Box 38 59347 406-347-5353
Michael Silverman, prin. Fax 347-5544

Roundup, Musselshell, Pop. 1,766
Roundup SD 600/PK-12
700 3rd St W 59072 406-323-1507
Chad Sealey, supt. Fax 323-1927
www.roundup.k12.mt.us
Roundup HS 200/9-12
525 6th Ave W 59072 406-323-2402
Dana Quenzer, prin. Fax 323-1583
Roundup JHS 100/7-8
525 6th Ave W 59072 406-323-2402
Dana Quenzer, prin. Fax 323-1583

Roy, Fergus, Pop. 108
Roy SD 50/K-12
PO Box 9 59471 406-464-2511
Steve Picard, supt. Fax 464-2561
www.roy.k12.mt.us
Roy HS 50/9-12
PO Box 9 59471 406-464-2511
Steve Picard, prin. Fax 464-2561
Roy MS 50/7-8
PO Box 9 59471 406-464-2511
Steve Picard, prin. Fax 464-2561

Rudyard, Hill, Pop. 252
North Star SD 200/PK-12
PO Box 129 59540 406-355-4481
Bart Hawkins, supt. Fax 355-4532
www.northstar.k12.mt.us
North Star HS 100/9-12
PO Box 129 59540 406-355-4481
Bart Hawkins, prin. Fax 355-4532
North Star MS 50/7-8
PO Box 129 59540 406-355-4481
Bart Hawkins, prin. Fax 355-4532

Ryegate, Golden Valley, Pop. 241
Ryegate SD 50/K-12
PO Box 129 59074 406-568-2211
Park A. Hook, supt. Fax 568-2528
Ryegate HS 50/9-12
PO Box 129 59074 406-568-2211
Park A. Hook, supt. Fax 568-2528
Ryegate MS 50/7-8
PO Box 129 59074 406-568-2211
Park A. Hook, supt. Fax 568-2528

Saco, Phillips, Pop. 189
Saco SD 100/PK-12
PO Box 298 59261 406-527-3531
Wade Sundby, supt. Fax 527-3479
www.sacoschools.k12.mt.us
Saco HS 50/9-12
PO Box 298 59261 406-527-3531
Gordon Hahn, lead tchr. Fax 527-3479
Saco MS 50/7-8
PO Box 298 59261 406-527-3531
Gordon Hahn, lead tchr. Fax 527-3479

Saint Ignatius, Lake, Pop. 774
St. Ignatius SD 500/PK-12
PO Box 1540 59865 406-745-3811
Jason Sargent, supt. Fax 745-4421
www.stignatiusschools.org
St. Ignatius HS 100/9-12
PO Box 1540 59865 406-745-3811
Shawn Hendrickson, prin. Fax 745-4060
St. Ignatius MS 100/6-8
PO Box 1540 59865 406-745-3811
Shawn Hendrickson, prin. Fax 745-4060

Saint Regis, Mineral, Pop. 301
Saint Regis SD 200/PK-12
PO Box 280 59866 406-649-2311
Joe Steele, supt. Fax 649-2271
sites.google.com/a/stregis.k12.mt.us/stregisschool/
Saint Regis HS 50/9-12
PO Box 280 59866 406-649-2311
Shaun Ball, prin. Fax 649-2788
Saint Regis MS 50/7-8
PO Box 280 59866 406-649-2311
Shaun Ball, prin. Fax 649-2788

Sand Coulee, Cascade, Pop. 209
Centerville SD 300/PK-12
PO Box 100 59472 406-736-5123
John McGee, supt. Fax 736-5210
www.centerville.k12.mt.us/
Centerville HS 100/9-12
PO Box 100 59472 406-736-5167
Michael Taylor, prin. Fax 736-5210
Centerville MS 50/7-8
PO Box 100 59472 406-736-5167
Michael Taylor, prin. Fax 736-5210

Savage, Richland
Savage SD 100/PK-12
PO Box 110 59262 406-776-2317
Lynne Peterson, supt. Fax 776-2260
www.savagepublicschool.com
Savage HS 50/9-12
PO Box 110 59262 406-776-2317
Lynne Peterson, admin. Fax 776-2260
Savage MS 50/7-8
PO Box 110 59262 406-776-2317
Lynne Peterson, prin. Fax 776-2260

Scobey, Daniels, Pop. 996
Scobey SD 300/PK-12
PO Box 10 59263 406-487-2202
Dan Schmidt, supt. Fax 487-2204
www.scobeyschools.com
Scobey HS 100/9-12
PO Box 10 59263 406-487-2202
Dan Schmidt, prin. Fax 487-2204
Scobey MS 50/7-8
PO Box 10 59263 406-487-2202
Dan Schmidt, prin. Fax 487-2204

Seeley Lake, Missoula, Pop. 1,625
Missoula SD 1
Supt. — See Missoula
Seeley-Swan HS 100/9-12
PO Box 416 59868 406-677-2224
Kathleen Pecora, prin. Fax 677-2949

Seeley Lake ESD 34 200/PK-8
PO Box 840 59868 406-677-2265
Chris Stout, supt. Fax 677-2264
www.sleonline.org
Seeley Lake MS 50/7-8
PO Box 840 59868 406-677-2265
Chris Stout, prin. Fax 677-2264

Shelby, Toole, Pop. 3,316
Shelby SD 400/PK-12
1010 Oilfield Ave 59474 406-434-2622
Elliott Crump, supt. Fax 434-2959
www.shelbypublicschools.org/
Shelby HS 100/9-12
1001 Valley St 59474 406-424-8910
Phil French, prin. Fax 434-7273
Shelby MS 100/7-8
1001 Valley St 59474 406-424-8910
Phil French, prin. Fax 434-7273

Shepherd, Yellowstone, Pop. 501
Shepherd SD 800/PK-12
PO Box 8 59079 406-373-5461
Dan Jamieson, supt. Fax 373-5284
www.shepherd.k12.mt.us/
Shepherd HS 300/9-12
PO Box 8 59079 406-373-5300
Kenneth Poepping, prin. Fax 373-5342
Shepherd MS 100/6-8
PO Box 8 59079 406-373-5873
Richard Hash, prin. Fax 373-5648

Sheridan, Madison, Pop. 623
Sheridan SD 200/K-12
PO Box 586 59749 406-842-5302
Micheal Wetherbee, supt. Fax 842-5391
www.sheridan.k12.mt.us/
Sheridan HS 100/9-12
PO Box 586 59749 406-842-5401
Micheal Wetherbee, prin. Fax 842-5856
Sheridan MS 50/7-8
PO Box 586 59749 406-842-5302
Micheal Wetherbee, prin. Fax 842-5391

Sidney, Richland, Pop. 5,107
Sidney SD 1,000/PK-12
200 3rd Ave SE 59270 406-433-4080
Dr. Daniel Farr Ed.D., supt. Fax 433-4358
www.sidney.k12.mt.us/
Sidney HS 400/9-12
200 3rd Ave SE 59270 406-433-2330
Susan Andersen, prin. Fax 433-2481
Sidney MS 300/6-8
200 3rd Ave SE 59270 406-433-4050
Kelly Johnson, prin. Fax 433-4052

Simms, Cascade, Pop. 343
Sun River Valley SD 200/PK-12
PO Box 380 59477 406-264-5110
Dave Marzolf, supt. Fax 264-5189
www.srvs.k12.mt.us
Simms HS 100/6-12
PO Box 380 59477 406-264-5110
Luke Mckinley, prin. Fax 264-5189

Somers, Flathead, Pop. 1,095
Somers ESD 600/PK-8
315 School Addition Rd 59932 406-857-3301
Joseph Price, supt. Fax 857-3144
www.somersdist29.org
Somers MS 200/6-8
315 School Addition Rd 59932 406-857-3661
Rose McIntyre, prin. Fax 857-3144

Stanford, Judith Basin, Pop. 400
Stanford SD 100/PK-12
PO Box 506 59479 406-566-2265
Tim Dolphay, supt. Fax 566-2772
www.stanford.k12.mt.us/
Stanford HS 50/9-12
PO Box 506 59479 406-566-2265
Tim Dolphay, supt. Fax 566-2772

Stanford MS — 50/7-8
PO Box 506 59479 — 406-566-2265
Tim Dolphay, prin. — Fax 566-2772

Stevensville, Ravalli, Pop. 1,781
Lone Rock ESD — 300/PK-8
1112 Three Mile Creek Rd 59870 — 406-777-3314
Michael Williams, supt. — Fax 777-2770
www.lonerockschool.org/
Lone Rock MS — 100/7-8
1112 Three Mile Creek Rd 59870 — 406-777-3314
Carrie Kouba, prin. — Fax 777-2770

Stevensville SD — 800/K-12
300 Park St 59870 — 406-777-5481
Dr. Bob Moore, supt. — Fax 258-1246
www.stevensvilleschool.net/
Stevensville HS — 400/9-12
300 Park St 59870 — 406-777-5481
Brian Gum, prin. — Fax 258-1243
Stevensville MS — 100/4-8
300 Park St 59870 — 406-777-5533
Tracey Rogstad, prin. — Fax 258-1242

Sunburst, Toole, Pop. 361
Sunburst SD 2 — 200/K-12
PO Box 710 59482 — 406-937-2811
M. Christina Barbachano, supt. — Fax 937-2828
www.sunburstschools.net/
Sunburst HS — 100/9-12
PO Box 710 59482 — 406-937-2811
M. Christina Barbachano, prin. — Fax 937-2828
Sunburst MS — 50/7-8
PO Box 710 59482 — 406-937-2816
M. Christina Barbachano, prin. — Fax 937-4444

Superior, Mineral, Pop. 795
Superior SD — 300/PK-12
PO Box 400 59872 — 406-822-3600
Scott Kinney, supt. — Fax 822-3601
www.superior.k12.mt.us
Superior HS — 100/9-12
PO Box 400 59872 — 406-822-4851
Chris Clairmont, prin. — Fax 822-4396
Superior MS — 50/7-8
PO Box 400 59872 — 406-822-4851
Chris Clairmont, prin. — Fax 822-4396

Terry, Prairie, Pop. 589
Terry SD — 100/PK-12
PO Box 187 59349 — 406-635-5533
Tammi Masters, supt. — Fax 635-5705
www.terry.k12.mt.us/
Terry HS — 50/9-12
PO Box 187 59349 — 406-635-5533
Tammi Masters, prin. — Fax 635-5705
Terry MS — 50/7-8
PO Box 187 59349 — 406-635-5595
Tammi Masters, prin. — Fax 635-5705

Thompson Falls, Sanders, Pop. 1,286
Thompson Falls SD — 500/PK-12
206 Haley Ave 59873 — 406-827-3323
Jason Slater, supt. — Fax 827-3020
www.thompsonfalls.net
Thompson Falls HS — 200/9-12
206 Haley Ave 59873 — 406-827-3561
Don Jensen, prin. — Fax 827-9463
Thompson Falls MS — 100/7-8
206 Haley Ave 59873 — 406-827-3593
Len Dorscher, prin. — Fax 827-0306

Three Forks, Gallatin, Pop. 1,859
Three Forks SD — 500/PK-12
212 E Neal St 59752 — 406-285-3224
Dr. Robert DoBell, supt. — Fax 285-3503
www.tfschools.com
Three Forks HS — 200/9-12
210 E Neal St 59752 — 406-285-3224
Justin Helvik, prin. — Fax 285-3503
Three Forks MS — 100/7-8
210 E Neal St 59752 — 406-285-3224
Justin Helvik, prin. — Fax 285-3503

Townsend, Broadwater, Pop. 1,847
Townsend SD — 600/PK-12
201 N Spruce St 59644 — 406-441-3454
Erik Wilkerson, supt. — Fax 441-3457
townsendps.schoolwires.com
Broadwater HS — 200/9-12
201 N Spruce St 59644 — 406-441-3430
Sheri Heavrin, prin. — Fax 441-3466
Townsend MS — 100/7-8
201 N Spruce St 59644 — 406-441-3431
Brad Racht, prin. — Fax 441-3475

Trout Creek, Sanders, Pop. 235
Trout Creek SD — 50/PK-8
4 School Ln 59874 — 406-827-3629
Debbie Phillips, admin. — Fax 827-4185
www.troutcreekeagles.org
Trout Creek MS — 50/7-8
4 School Ln 59874 — 406-827-3629
Debbie Phillips, prin. — Fax 827-4185

Troy, Lincoln, Pop. 913
Troy SD — 400/PK-12
PO Box 867 59935 — 406-295-4606
Dr. Jacob Francom, supt. — Fax 295-4802
troymtk-12.us/
Troy HS — 100/9-12
PO Box 867 59935 — 406-295-4520
Dr. Jacob Francom, prin. — Fax 295-5371
Troy MS — 100/7-8
PO Box 867 59935 — 406-295-4520
Dr. Jacob Francom, prin. — Fax 295-5371

Turner, Blaine, Pop. 56
Turner SD — 100/K-12
PO Box 40 59542 — 406-379-2315
Russ McKenna, supt. — Fax 379-2398
turner.k12.mt.us
Turner HS — 50/9-12
PO Box 40 59542 — 406-379-2219
Russ McKenna, supt. — Fax 379-2398
Turner MS — 50/7-8
PO Box 40 59542 — 406-379-2219
Russ McKenna, supt. — Fax 379-2398

Twin Bridges, Madison, Pop. 367
Twin Bridges SD — 200/PK-12
PO Box 419 59754 — 406-684-5657
Chad Johnson, supt. — Fax 684-5458
www.twinbridges.k12.mt.us
Twin Bridges HS — 100/9-12
PO Box 419 59754 — 406-684-5657
Chad Johnson, prin. — Fax 684-5458
Twin Bridges MS — 50/7-8
PO Box 419 59754 — 406-684-5613
Tammy Demien, prin. — Fax 684-5458

Ulm, Cascade, Pop. 714
Ulm ESD — 100/PK-8
PO Box 189 59485 — 406-866-3313
Lyndsey Green, supt. — Fax 866-3209
www.ulmschools.com
Ulm MS — 50/7-8
PO Box 189 59485 — 406-866-3313
Lyndsey Green, prin. — Fax 866-3209

Valier, Pondera, Pop. 489
Valier SD — 200/PK-12
PO Box 528 59486 — 406-279-3613
Julie Gaffney, supt. — Fax 279-3212
sites.google.com/a/valier.k12.mt.us/homepage/
Valier HS — 50/9-12
PO Box 528 59486 — 406-279-3613
Julie Gaffney, prin. — Fax 279-3764
Valier MS — 50/7-8
PO Box 508 59486 — 406-279-3314
Julie Gaffney, prin. — Fax 279-3510

Vaughn, Cascade, Pop. 628
Vaughn ESD — 100/PK-8
PO Box 279 59487 — 406-965-2231
Jan Cahill, supt. — Fax 965-3703
www.vaughnschool.com
Vaughn MS — 50/7-8
PO Box 279 59487 — 406-965-2231
Jan Cahill, admin. — Fax 965-3703

Victor, Ravalli, Pop. 724
Victor SD — 400/PK-12
425 4th Ave 59875 — 406-642-3221
Lance Pearson, supt. — Fax 642-3446
www.victor.k12.mt.us/
Victor HS — 100/9-12
425 4th Ave 59875 — 406-642-3221
Lance Pearson, prin. — Fax 642-3446
Victor MS — 100/6-8
425 4th Ave 59875 — 406-642-3221
Danny Johnston, prin. — Fax 642-3446

Westby, Sheridan, Pop. 166
Westby SD — 100/PK-12
PO Box 109 59275 — 406-385-2225
Tony Holecek, supt. — Fax 385-2430
www.westbyschool.k12.mt.us/
Westby HS — 50/9-12
PO Box 109 59275 — 406-385-2225
Tony Holecek, prin. — Fax 385-2430
Westby MS — 50/7-8
PO Box 109 59275 — 406-385-2225
Tony Holecek, prin. — Fax 385-2430

West Yellowstone, Gallatin, Pop. 1,235
West Yellowstone SD — 300/PK-12
PO Box 460 59758 — 406-646-7617
Kevin Flanagan, supt. — Fax 646-7232
www.westyellowstone.k12.mt.us
West Yellowstone HS — 100/9-12
PO Box 460 59758 — 406-646-7617
Brian Smith, prin. — Fax 646-7232
West Yellowstone MS — 50/7-8
PO Box 460 59758 — 406-646-7617
Brian Smith, prin. — Fax 646-7232

Whitefish, Flathead, Pop. 6,250
Olney-Bissell ESD — 100/PK-8
5955 Farm To Market Rd 59937 — 406-862-2828
Fax 862-2838
www.olneybissellschool.com
Bissell MS — 50/7-8
5955 Farm to Market Rd 59937 — 406-862-2828
Trevor Dahlman, prin. — Fax 862-2838

Whitefish SD — 1,600/PK-12
600 2nd St E 59937 — 406-862-8640
Heather Davis Schmidt, supt. — Fax 862-1507
whitefishschools.com
Whitefish HS — 500/9-12
600 2nd St E 59937 — 406-862-8600
Kerry Drown, prin. — Fax 862-2586
Whitefish Independent HS — Alt
600 2nd St E 59937 — 406-862-8688
Kerry Drown, prin. — Fax 862-8689
Whitefish MS — 500/5-8
600 2nd St E 59937 — 406-862-8650
Josh Branstetter, prin. — Fax 862-8664

Whitefish Christian Academy — 100/PK-10
820 Ashar Ave 59937 — 406-862-5875
George Bristol, hdmstr. — Fax 862-3515

Whitehall, Jefferson, Pop. 1,005
Whitehall SD — 400/PK-12
PO Box 1109 59759 — 406-287-3455
John Sullivan, supt. — Fax 287-3843
whitehall.schoolwires.com/
Whitehall HS — 100/9-12
PO Box 1109 59759 — 406-287-3862
Hannah Nieskens, prin. — Fax 287-3843
Whitehall JHS — 100/7-8
PO Box 1109 59759 — 406-287-3882
Britt McLean, prin. — Fax 287-5508

White Sulphur Springs, Meagher, Pop. 922
White Sulphur Springs SD — 200/PK-12
PO Box C 59645 — 406-547-3751
Larry Markuson, supt. — Fax 547-3922
www.whitesulphur.k12.mt.us/
White Sulphur Springs HS — 100/9-12
PO Box C 59645 — 406-547-3351
Jacqueline Boyd, prin. — Fax 547-2407
White Sulphur Springs MS — 50/7-8
PO Box C 59645 — 406-547-3351
Jacqueline Boyd, prin. — Fax 547-2407

Whitewater, Phillips, Pop. 62
Whitewater SD — 100/PK-12
PO Box 46 59544 — 406-674-5418
Darin Cummings, supt. — Fax 674-5460
www.whitewater.k12.mt.us
Whitewater HS — 50/9-12
PO Box 46 59544 — 406-674-5417
Darin Cummings, prin. — Fax 674-5460
Whitewater MS — 50/7-8
PO Box 46 59544 — 406-674-5417
Darin Cummings, prin. — Fax 674-5460

Wibaux, Wibaux, Pop. 582
Wibaux SD — 200/PK-12
121 F St N 59353 — 406-796-2474
Terry Quintus, supt. — Fax 796-2259
wibauxschools.net
Wibaux HS — 100/9-12
121 F St N 59353 — 406-795-2474
Terry Quintus, prin. — Fax 795-2259
Wibaux JHS — 50/7-8
121 F St N 59353 — 406-796-2474
Janet Huisman, prin. — Fax 796-2259

Willow Creek, Gallatin, Pop. 206
Willow Creek SD — 100/PK-12
PO Box 189 59760 — 406-285-6991
Bonnie Lower, supt. — Fax 285-6923
www.willowcreek.k12.mt.us
Willow Creek HS — 50/9-12
PO Box 189 59760 — 406-285-6991
Bonnie Lower, prin. — Fax 285-6923
Willow Creek MS — 50/7-8
PO Box 189 59760 — 406-285-6991
Bonnie Lower, prin. — Fax 285-6923

Winifred, Fergus, Pop. 207
Winifred SD — 50/PK-12
PO Box 109 59489 — 406-462-5420
Chad Fordyce, supt. — Fax 462-5477
www.winifred.k12.mt.us
Winifred S — 50/PK-12
PO Box 109 59489 — 406-462-5420
Kelli Carlson, prin. — Fax 462-5477

Winnett, Petroleum, Pop. 182
Winnett SD — 100/PK-12
PO Box 167 59087 — 406-429-2251
Walt Stevens, supt. — Fax 429-7631
Winnett HS — 50/9-12
PO Box 167 59087 — 406-429-2251
Walt Stevens, admin. — Fax 429-7631
Winnett MS — 50/7-8
PO Box 167 59087 — 406-429-2251
Walt Stevens, admin. — Fax 429-7631

Wolf Point, Roosevelt, Pop. 2,478
Frontier ESD — 100/PK-8
6996 Roy St 59201 — 406-653-7083
Christine Eggar, supt. — Fax 653-2508
www.wolfpoint.k12.mt.us
Frontier MS — 50/7-8
6996 Roy St 59201 — 406-653-2501
Jeff Whitmus, admin. — Fax 653-2508

Wolf Point SD — 900/PK-12
213 6th Ave S 59201 — 406-653-5540
Robert Osborne, supt. — Fax 653-1881
wolfpoint.k12.mt.us
Wolf Point HS — 200/9-12
213 6th Ave S 59201 — 406-653-1200
Kim Hanks, prin. — Fax 653-3104
Wolf Point JHS — 100/7-8
213 6th Ave S 59201 — 406-653-1200
Kim Hanks, prin. — Fax 653-3104

Worden, Yellowstone, Pop. 573
Huntley Project SD — 800/PK-12
1477 Ash St 59088 — 406-967-2540
Wes Coy, supt. — Fax 967-3059
www.huntley.k12.mt.us/
Huntley Project HS — 300/9-12
2436 N 15th Rd 59088 — 406-967-2540
Mark Wandle, prin. — Fax 967-2589
Huntley Project MS — 100/7-8
2436 N 15th Rd 59088 — 406-967-2540
Frank Hollowell, prin. — Fax 967-3054

Wyola, Big Horn, Pop. 212
Wyola ESD — 100/PK-8
PO Box 66 59089 — 406-343-2722
Linda Brien, supt. — Fax 343-5901
www.wyola.k12.mt.us
Wyola MS — 50/7-8
PO Box 66 59089 — 406-343-2722
Linda Brien, prin. — Fax 343-5901

NEBRASKA

NEBRASKA DEPARTMENT OF EDUCATION
PO Box 94987, Lincoln 68509-4987
Telephone 402-471-2295
Fax 402-471-0117
Website http://www.education.ne.gov/

Commissioner of Education Dr. Matthew Blomstedt

NEBRASKA BOARD OF EDUCATION
PO Box 94987, Lincoln 68509-4987

President Rachel Wise

EDUCATIONAL SERVICE UNITS (ESU)

ESU 1
Robert Uhing, admin. 402-287-2061
211 10th St, Wakefield 68784 Fax 287-2065
www.esu1.org/

ESU 2
Dr. Ted DeTurk Ed.D., admin. 402-721-7710
PO Box 649, Fremont 68026 Fax 721-7712
www.esu2.org/

ESU 3
Dr. Dan Schnoes, admin. 402-597-4800
6949 S 110th St, La Vista 68128 Fax 597-4808
www2.esu3.org/esu3/

ESU 4
Jon Fisher, admin. 402-274-4354
919 16th St, Auburn 68305 Fax 274-4356
www.esu4.org

ESU 5
Dr. Brenda McNiff, admin. 402-223-5277
900 W Court St, Beatrice 68310 Fax 223-5279
www.esu5.org

ESU 6
Dr. Dan Shoemake, admin. 800-327-0091
210 5th St, Milford 68405 Fax 761-3279
www.esu6.org

ESU 7
Larianne Polk, admin. 402-564-5753
2657 44th Ave, Columbus 68601 Fax 563-1121
ww2.esu7.org

ESU 8
Bill Mowinkel, admin. 402-887-5041
PO Box 89, Neligh 68756 Fax 887-4604
www.esu8.org

ESU 9
Dr. Kraig Lofquist, admin. 402-463-5611
1117 E South St, Hastings 68901 Fax 463-9555
home.site.esu9.org

ESU 10
Wayne Bell, admin. 308-237-5927
PO Box 850, Kearney 68848 Fax 237-5920
www.esu10.org/

ESU 11
Paul Tedesco, admin. 308-995-6585
PO Box 858, Holdrege 68949 Fax 995-6587
www.esu11.org

ESU 13
Dr. Jeff West, admin. 308-635-3696
4215 Avenue I, Scottsbluff 69361 Fax 635-0680
www.esu13.org

ESU 15 308-334-5160
, PO Box 398, Trenton 69044 Fax 334-5581
www.esu15.org

ESU 16
Margene Beatty, admin. 308-284-8481
PO Box 915, Ogallala 69153 Fax 284-8483
www.blogesu16.org

ESU 17
Geraldine Erickson, admin. 402-387-1420
207 N Main St, Ainsworth 69210 Fax 387-1028
www.esu17.org

ESU 18
Steve Joel Ed.D., supt. 402-436-1000
PO Box 82889, Lincoln 68501 Fax 436-1620
www.lps.org

ESU 19
Dr. Julia Allen, admin. 531-299-9463
3215 Cuming St, Omaha 68131
esu19.org

PUBLIC, PRIVATE AND CATHOLIC SECONDARY SCHOOLS

Adams, Gage, Pop. 572
Freeman SD 400/PK-12
PO Box 259 68301 402-988-2525
Randy Page, supt. Fax 988-3475
www.freemanpublicschools.org/
Freeman JSHS 200/7-12
PO Box 259 68301 402-988-2525
Bob Michl, prin. Fax 988-3475

Ainsworth, Brown, Pop. 1,710
Ainsworth SD 500/PK-12
PO Box 65 69210 402-387-2333
Darrell Peterson, supt. Fax 387-0525
www.ainsworthschools.org
Ainsworth HS 200/9-12
PO Box 65 69210 402-387-2082
Bill Lentz, prin. Fax 387-0525
Ainsworth MS 100/5-8
PO Box 65 69210 402-387-2082
Sarah Williams, prin. Fax 387-0525

Albion, Boone, Pop. 1,646
Boone Central SD 500/K-12
PO Box 391 68620 402-395-2134
Cory Worrell, supt. Fax 395-2137
sites.google.com/a/boonecentral.esu7.org/bcscardina ls
Boone Central HS 200/9-12
PO Box 391 68620 402-395-2134
Erik Kravig, prin. Fax 395-2137
Other Schools – See Petersburg

Allen, Dixon, Pop. 375
Allen Consolidated SD 200/K-12
PO Box 190 68710 402-635-2484
Michael Pattee, supt. Fax 635-2331
www.allenschools.org/
Allen JSHS 100/7-12
PO Box 190 68710 402-635-2484
Lana Oswald, prin. Fax 635-2331

Alliance, Box Butte, Pop. 8,339
Alliance SD 1,400/PK-12
1604 Sweetwater Ave 69301 308-762-5475
Dr. Troy Unzicker, supt. Fax 762-8249
apschools.schoolfusion.us
Alliance HS 500/9-12
1604 Sweetwater Ave 69301 308-762-3359
George Clear, prin. Fax 762-7683
Alliance MS 300/6-8
1604 Sweetwater Ave 69301 308-762-3079
Troy Mach, prin. Fax 762-7302

Western Nebraska Community College Post-Sec.
1750 Sweetwater Ave 69301 308-763-2000

Alma, Harlan, Pop. 1,129
Alma SD 300/K-12
PO Box 170 68920 308-928-2131
Jon Davis, supt. Fax 928-2763
almacardinals.org
Alma JSHS 100/7-12
PO Box 170 68920 308-928-2131
Galen Kronhofman, prin. Fax 928-2763

Amherst, Buffalo, Pop. 248
Amherst SD 300/K-12
PO Box 8 68812 308-826-3131
Tom Moore, supt. Fax 826-4865
amherst.k12.ne.us/
Amherst JSHS 100/7-12
PO Box 8 68812 308-826-3131
Roger Thomsen, prin. Fax 826-4865

Ansley, Custer, Pop. 440
Ansley SD 200/PK-12
PO Box 370 68814 308-935-1121
Dave Mroczek, supt. Fax 935-9103
ansleynebraska.org
Ansley JSHS 100/7-12
PO Box 370 68814 308-935-1121
Lance Bristol, prin. Fax 935-9103

Arapahoe, Furnas, Pop. 1,013
Arapahoe SD 300/K-12
PO Box 360 68922 308-962-5458
Dr. George Griffith, supt. Fax 962-7481
Arapahoe HS 100/7-12
PO Box 360 68922 308-962-5458
Bob Braithwait, prin. Fax 962-7481

Arcadia, Valley, Pop. 309
Arcadia SD 100/PK-12
PO Box 248 68815 308-789-6522
Jess Underwood Ed.D., supt. Fax 789-6214
www.arcadiapublicschools.org/
Arcadia JSHS 100/7-12
PO Box 248 68815 308-789-6522
Jess Underwood Ed.D., admin. Fax 789-6214

Arlington, Washington, Pop. 1,239
Arlington SD 600/K-12
PO Box 580 68002 402-478-4173
Lynn Johnson, supt. Fax 478-4176
www.apseagles.org
Arlington JSHS 300/7-12
PO Box 580 68002 402-478-4171
Aaron Pfingsten, prin. Fax 478-4176

Arnold, Custer, Pop. 592
Arnold SD 100/K-12
PO Box 399 69120 308-848-2226
Dawn Lewis, supt. Fax 848-2201
blog.arnold.k12.ne.us
Arnold JSHS 50/7-12
PO Box 399 69120 308-848-2226
Joel Morgan, prin. Fax 848-2201

Arthur, Arthur, Pop. 117
Arthur County SD 100/K-12
PO Box 145 69121 308-764-2253
Barry Schaeffer, supt. Fax 764-2206
www.arthurcountywolves.org
Arthur County JSHS 50/7-12
PO Box 145 69121 308-764-2253
Barry Schaeffer, supt. Fax 764-2206

Ashland, Saunders, Pop. 2,429
Ashland-Greenwood SD 900/PK-12
1842 Furnas St 68003 402-944-2128
Jason Libal, supt. Fax 944-3310
www.agps.org/
Ashland-Greenwood HS 300/9-12
1842 Furnas St 68003 402-944-2114
Brad Jacobsen, prin. Fax 944-2116
Ashland-Greenwood MS 200/6-8
1842 Furnas St 68003 402-944-2114
Brad Jacobsen, prin. Fax 944-2116

Atkinson, Holt, Pop. 1,242
West Holt SD 400/K-12
PO Box 457 68713 402-925-2848
Paul Pistulka, supt. Fax 925-2177
www.westholtps.org
West Holt HS 200/7-12
PO Box 457 68713 402-925-2848
Kevin Young, prin. Fax 925-2177

Auburn, Nemaha, Pop. 3,425
Auburn SD 800/PK-12
1713 J St 68305 402-274-4830
Kevin Reiman, supt. Fax 274-5227
www.auburnpublicschools.org
Auburn HS 200/9-12
1713 J St 68305 402-274-4328
Vernon Golladay, prin. Fax 274-5434
Auburn MS 200/6-8
1829 Central Ave 68305 402-274-4027
Vernon Golladay, prin. Fax 274-4147

Aurora, Hamilton, Pop. 4,447
Aurora SD 1,200/PK-12
300 L St 68818 402-694-6923
Damon McDonald, supt. Fax 694-5097
aurorahuskies.us
Aurora HS 400/9-12
300 L St 68818 402-694-6968
Douglas Kittle, prin. Fax 694-2573
Aurora MS 300/6-8
300 L St 68818 402-694-6915
Kenneth Thiele, prin. Fax 694-3815

Axtell, Kearney, Pop. 718
Axtell Community SD 200/K-12
PO Box 97 68924 308-743-2415
Steven Wickham, supt. Fax 743-2417
www.axtellwildcats.org
Axtell HS 100/9-12
PO Box 97 68924 308-743-2415
Bill Gilbreath, prin. Fax 743-2417
Axtell MS 100/6-8
PO Box 97 68924 308-743-2415
Bill Gilbreath, prin. Fax 743-2417

Bancroft, Cuming, Pop. 482
Bancroft-Rosalie SD 200/K-12
PO Box 129 68004 402-648-3336
Jon Cerny, supt. Fax 648-3338
www.bancroft-rosalie.org
Bancroft JSHS 100/7-12
PO Box 129 68004 402-648-3336
Mike Sjuts, prin. Fax 648-3338

Bartlett, Wheeler, Pop. 117
Wheeler Central SD 100/PK-12
PO Box 68 68622 308-654-3273
Rodney Olson, supt. Fax 654-3237
www.wbroncs.org
Wheeler Central JSHS 50/7-12
PO Box 68 68622 308-654-3273
Jay Johnson, prin. Fax 654-3237

Bartley, Red Willow, Pop. 282
Southwest SD 179 300/PK-12
PO Box 187 69020 308-692-3223
Robert Porter, supt. Fax 692-3221
www.swpschools.org/
Southwest JSHS 100/7-12
PO Box 187 69020 308-692-3223
Matt Springer, prin. Fax 692-3221

Bassett, Rock, Pop. 618
Rock County SD 200/K-12
PO Box 448 68714 402-684-3411
Thomas Becker, supt. Fax 684-3671
www.rockcountyschools.org
Rock County HS 100/7-12
PO Box 448 68714 402-684-3411
Steve Camp, prin. Fax 684-3671

Battle Creek, Madison, Pop. 1,202
Battle Creek SD 400/K-12
PO Box 100 68715 402-675-6905
Jay Bellar, supt. Fax 675-1038
bcps.esu8.org/
Battle Creek JSHS 200/7-12
PO Box 100 68715 402-675-3705
Jeff Heimes, prin. Fax 675-1038

Bayard, Morrill, Pop. 1,198
Bayard SD 400/PK-12
PO Box 607 69334 308-586-1325
Travis Miller, supt. Fax 586-1638
www.bayardpublicschools.org/
Bayard JSHS 200/7-12
PO Box 607 69334 308-586-1700
Thomas Perlinski, prin. Fax 586-1638

Beatrice, Gage, Pop. 12,303
Beatrice SD 2,200/PK-12
320 N 5th St 68310 402-223-1500
Pat Nauroth, supt. Fax 223-1509
www.beatricepublicschools.org
Beatrice HS 600/9-12
600 Orange Blvd 68310 402-223-1515
Jason Sutter, prin. Fax 223-1510
Beatrice MS 500/6-8
215 N 5th St 68310 402-223-1545
John Jarosh, prin. Fax 223-1547
Compass Learning Community Alt
2920 Court St 68310 402-223-1500

Joseph's College of Beauty Post-Sec.
618 Court St 68310 402-223-3588
Southeast Community College Post-Sec.
4771 W Scott Rd 68310 402-228-3468

Bellevue, Sarpy, Pop. 48,571
Bellevue SD 9,900/PK-12
2600 Arboretum Dr 68005 402-293-4000
Dr. Jeff Rippe, supt. Fax 293-5002
www.bellevuepublicschools.org
Bellevue East HS 1,500/9-12
1401 High School Dr 68005 402-293-4150
Dr. Jeffrey Wagner, prin. Fax 293-4259
Bellevue West HS 1,600/9-12
1501 Thurston Ave 68123 402-293-4040
Kevin Rohlfs, prin. Fax 293-4149
Fontenelle MS 500/7-8
701 Kayleen Dr 68005 402-293-4360
Doug Schaefer, prin. Fax 293-4450
Lewis & Clark MS 500/7-8
13502 S 38th St 68123 402-898-8760
Dr. Mike Smith, prin. Fax 898-9018
Mission MS 400/7-8
2202 Washington St 68005 402-293-4260
Dr. Jenny Powell, prin. Fax 293-4350

Bellevue University Post-Sec.
1000 Galvin Rd S 68005 402-293-2000
Cornerstone Christian S 9-12
16405 Clay St 68123 402-291-2260
Teri Lynn Schrag, admin.
Gross HS 400/9-12
7700 S 43rd St 68147 402-734-2000
John Schultz, prin. Fax 734-4270

Benkelman, Dundy, Pop. 937
Dundy County-Stratton SD 300/PK-12
PO Box 586 69021 308-423-2738
James Kent, supt. Fax 423-2711
www.dcstigers.org
Dundy County Stratton JSHS 100/7-12
PO Box 586 69021 308-423-2738
Adam Fette, prin. Fax 423-2711

Bennington, Douglas, Pop. 1,439
Bennington SD 1,700/K-12
PO Box 309 68007 402-238-3044
Dr. Terry Haack, supt. Fax 238-2185
www.benningtonschools.org
Bennington JSHS 600/7-12
PO Box 309 68007 402-238-2447
Matthew Blomenkamp, prin. Fax 238-2950

Bertrand, Phelps, Pop. 742
Bertrand SD 300/K-12
PO Box 278 68927 308-472-3427
Dr. Dennis Shipp, supt. Fax 472-3429
bertrandvikings.org
Bertrand JSHS 100/7-12
PO Box 278 68927 308-472-3427
Shaun Kidder, prin. Fax 472-3429

Big Springs, Deuel, Pop. 393
South Platte SD 200/K-12
PO Box 457 69122 308-889-3674
David Spencer, supt. Fax 889-3523
www.southplatteschools.com
South Platte HS 100/7-12
PO Box 457 69122 308-889-3622
Seth Ford, prin. Fax 889-3523

Blair, Washington, Pop. 7,886
Blair Community SD 2,100/PK-12
PO Box 288 68008 402-426-2610
Rex Pfeil, supt. Fax 426-3110
www.blairschools.org/
Blair HS 700/9-12
PO Box 288 68008 402-426-4941
Thomas Anderson, prin. Fax 426-4949
Otte Blair MS 600/6-8
PO Box 288 68008 402-426-3678
Chris Stogdill, prin. Fax 426-1788

Bloomfield, Knox, Pop. 1,011
Bloomfield SD 200/PK-12
PO Box 308 68718 402-373-4800
Shane Alexander, supt. Fax 373-2712
www.bloomfieldschools.net
Bloomfield JSHS 100/7-12
PO Box 308 68718 402-373-4800
Shane Alexander, prin. Fax 373-2712

Blue Hill, Webster, Pop. 925
Blue Hill SD 300/K-12
PO Box 217 68930 402-756-2085
Joel Ruybalid, supt. Fax 756-2086
www.bluehillschools.org
Blue Hill JSHS 200/7-12
PO Box 217 68930 402-756-3043
Patrick Moore, prin. Fax 756-3044

Boys Town, Douglas, Pop. 727

Boys Town HS 300/9-12
13727 Flanagan Blvd 68010 402-498-1800
Mary Anderson, supt. Fax 498-3246

Brady, Lincoln, Pop. 425
Brady SD 200/K-12
PO Box 68 69123 308-584-3317
James McGown, supt. Fax 584-3725
www.bradyschools.org
Brady JSHS 100/7-12
PO Box 68 69123 308-584-3317
Matt Gordon, prin. Fax 584-3725

Brainard, Butler, Pop. 330
East Butler SD 300/K-12
PO Box 36 68626 402-545-2081
Sam Stecher, supt. Fax 545-2023
www.ebutlertigers.org
Brainard JSHS 200/7-12
PO Box 36 68626 402-545-2081
Michael Eldridge, prin. Fax 545-2023

Bridgeport, Morrill, Pop. 1,536
Bridgeport SD 63 500/K-12
PO Box 430 69336 308-262-1470
Chuck Lambert, supt. Fax 262-1284
www.bridgeportschools.org
Bridgeport JSHS 200/7-12
PO Box 430 69336 308-262-0346
Dustin Favinger, prin. Fax 262-1284

Broken Bow, Custer, Pop. 3,500
Broken Bow SD 700/PK-12
323 N 7th Ave 68822 308-872-6821
Tom Bailey, supt. Fax 872-2751
www.bbps.org
Broken Bow HS 200/9-12
323 N 7th Ave 68822 308-872-2475
Rusty Kluender, prin. Fax 872-6296
Broken Bow MS 100/6-8
323 N 7th Ave 68822 308-872-6441
Rusty Kluender, prin. Fax 872-2528

Bruning, Thayer, Pop. 279
Bruning-Davenport USD
Supt. — See Davenport
Bruning-Davenport HS 100/9-12
PO Box 70 68322 402-353-4685
Erik Sokol, prin. Fax 353-4445

Burwell, Garfield, Pop. 1,207
Burwell SD 400/PK-12
PO Box 670 68823 308-346-4150
Daniel Bird, supt. Fax 346-5430
www.burwellpublicschools.org
Burwell JSHS 200/7-12
PO Box 670 68823 308-346-4150
David Owen, prin. Fax 346-5430

Cairo, Hall, Pop. 780
Centura SD 500/PK-12
PO Box 430 68824 308-485-4258
Julie Otero, supt. Fax 485-4780
centuraps.org
Centura JSHS 200/7-12
PO Box 430 68824 308-485-4258
Tammy Holcomb, prin. Fax 485-4780

Callaway, Custer, Pop. 533
Callaway SD 200/K-12
PO Box 280 68825 308-836-2272
Dawn Lewis, supt. Fax 836-2771
callawaypublicschools.org
Callaway JSHS 100/7-12
PO Box 280 68825 308-836-2272
Heath Birkel, prin. Fax 836-2771

Cambridge, Furnas, Pop. 1,055
Cambridge SD 300/K-12
PO Box 100 69022 308-697-3322
Gregory Shepard, supt. Fax 697-4880
cambridge.k12.ne.us
Cambridge JSHS 200/7-12
PO Box 100 69022 308-697-3322
Jarod Albers, prin. Fax 697-4880
Cambridge MS 7-8
PO Box 100 69022 308-697-3322
Jarod Albers, prin. Fax 697-4180

Cedar Bluffs, Saunders, Pop. 604
Cedar Bluffs SD 200/PK-12
PO Box 66 68015 402-628-2060
Harlan Ptomey, supt. Fax 628-2108
www.cedarbluffsschools.org/
Cedar Bluffs HS 100/9-12
PO Box 66 68015 402-628-2080
Kevin Janssen, prin. Fax 628-2108
Cedar Bluffs MS 50/6-8
PO Box 66 68015 402-628-2080
Kevin Janssen, admin. Fax 628-2108

Cedar Rapids, Boone, Pop. 382
Riverside SD
Supt. — See Spalding
Cedar Rapids MSHS 50/6-12
408 W Dayton St 68627 308-358-0640
Christopher Kuncl, prin. Fax 358-0211

Central City, Merrick, Pop. 2,899
Central City SD 700/PK-12
PO Box 57 68826 308-946-3055
Jeff Jensen, supt. Fax 946-3149
www.centralcityschoolsne.org
Central City HS 200/9-12
PO Box 57 68826 308-946-3086
Shawn McDiffett, prin. Fax 946-2954
Central City MS 200/5-8
PO Box 57 68826 308-946-3056
Holee Hanke, prin. Fax 946-2124

Nebraska Christian S 200/PK-12
1847 Inskip Ave 68826 308-946-3836
Joshua Cumpston, admin. Fax 946-3837

Chadron, Dawes, Pop. 5,665
Chadron SD 900/K-12
602 E 10th St 69337 308-432-0700
Dr. Caroline Winchester, supt. Fax 432-0702
www.chadronschools.org/
Chadron HS 300/9-12
901 Cedar St 69337 308-432-0707
Jerry Mack, prin. Fax 432-0723
Chadron MS 300/5-8
551 E 6th St 69337 308-432-0708
Nichlas Dressel, prin. Fax 432-0720

Chadron State College Post-Sec.
1000 Main St 69337 308-432-6000

Chambers, Holt, Pop. 268
Chambers SD 100/K-12
PO Box 218 68725 402-482-5233
Justin Frederick, supt. Fax 482-5234
chambers.esu8.org/
Chambers JSHS 100/7-12
PO Box 218 68725 402-482-5233
Justin Frederick, prin. Fax 482-5234

Chappell, Deuel, Pop. 921
Creek Valley SD 300/K-12
PO Box 608 69129 308-874-2911
Ron Howard, supt. Fax 874-2602
creekvalleystorm.com
Creek Valley HS 100/9-12
PO Box 608 69129 308-874-3310
Patrick Ningen, prin. Fax 874-2604
Other Schools – See Lodgepole

Clarks, Merrick, Pop. 363
High Plains Community SD
Supt. — See Polk
High Plains MS 100/6-8
PO Box 205 68628 308-548-2216
Karyee LeSuer, prin. Fax 548-2120

Clarkson, Colfax, Pop. 655
Clarkson SD 100/PK-12
PO Box 140 68629 402-892-3454
Rich Lemburg, supt. Fax 892-3455
www.clarksonpublicschools.org
Clarkson S 100/PK-12
PO Box 140 68629 402-892-3454
Rich Lemburg, admin. Fax 892-3455

Clearwater, Antelope, Pop. 413
Nebraska USD 1
Supt. — See Orchard
Clearwater/Orchard S 100/PK-12
PO Box 38 68726 402-485-2505
Mike Sanne, prin. Fax 485-2634

Cody, Cherry, Pop. 150
Cody-Kilgore SD 100/PK-12
PO Box 216 69211 402-823-4190
Adam Lambert, supt. Fax 823-4275
www.cody-kilgore.com
Cody-Kilgore JSHS 100/6-12
PO Box 216 69211 402-823-4190
Adam Lambert, prin. Fax 823-4275

Coleridge, Cedar, Pop. 470
Laurel-Concord-Coleridge SD
Supt. — See Laurel

Laurel-Concord-Coleridge MS 100/5-8
PO Box 37 68727 402-283-4844
Tim Vanderheiden, prin. Fax 283-4508

Columbus, Platte, Pop. 21,922
Columbus SD 3,600/K-12
PO Box 947 68602 402-563-7000
Dr. Troy Loeffelholz, supt. Fax 563-7005
www.columbuspublicschools.org
Columbus HS 1,100/9-12
2200 26th St 68601 402-563-7050
Steve Woodside, prin. Fax 563-7058
Columbus MS 800/6-8
2410 16th St 68601 402-563-7060
Amy Haynes, prin. Fax 563-7068

Lakeview Community SD 600/K-12
3744 83rd St 68601 402-563-2345
Dr. Aaron Plas, supt. Fax 564-5209
www.lakeviewcs.esu7.org
Lakeview JSHS 300/7-12
3744 83rd St 68601 402-563-2345
Steve Borer, prin. Fax 564-5209

Central Community College Post-Sec.
PO Box 1027 68602 402-564-7132
Scotus Central Catholic JSHS 400/7-12
1554 18th Ave 68601 402-564-7165
Jeff Ohnoutka, pres. Fax 564-6004

Cook, Johnson, Pop. 316
Johnson County Central SD
Supt. — See Tecumseh
Johnson County Central MS 100/6-8
PO Box 255 68329 402-864-4181
Rich Bacon, prin. Fax 864-2074

Cozad, Dawson, Pop. 3,959
Cozad Community SD 900/PK-12
1910 Meridian Ave 69130 308-784-2745
Joel Applegate, supt. Fax 217-4504
www.cozadschools.net
Cozad Alternative Education Center Alt
1910 Meridian Ave 69130 308-784-2745
Bill Beckenhauer, admin. Fax 217-4504
Cozad HS 300/9-12
1710 Meridian Ave 69130 308-784-2744
William Beckenhauer, prin. Fax 217-4505
Cozad MS 200/6-8
1810 Meridian Ave 69130 308-784-2746
Brian Regelin, prin. Fax 217-4506

Crawford, Dawes, Pop. 968
Crawford SD 200/PK-12
908 5th St 69339 308-665-1537
Ted Classen, supt. Fax 665-1909
www.cpsrams.org
Crawford JSHS 100/7-12
908 5th St 69339 308-665-1531
Christopher Geary, prin. Fax 665-1483

Creighton, Knox, Pop. 1,135
Creighton SD 200/K-12
PO Box 10 68729 402-358-3663
Stephanie Petersen, supt. Fax 358-3804
www.creightonpublicschools.org
Creighton Community JSHS 200/4-12
PO Box 10 68729 402-358-3663
Ryon Nilson, prin. Fax 358-3804

Crete, Saline, Pop. 6,858
Crete SD 1,800/PK-12
920 Linden Ave 68333 402-826-5855
Dr. Mike Waters, supt. Fax 826-5120
www.creteschools.com
Crete HS 500/9-12
920 Linden Ave 68333 402-826-5811
Tim Conway, prin. Fax 826-2701
Crete MS 500/5-8
920 Linden Ave 68333 402-826-5844
Steve Teget, prin. Fax 381-0223

Doane College Post-Sec.
1014 Boswell Ave 68333 402-826-2161

Crofton, Knox, Pop. 722
Crofton Community SD 300/K-12
PO Box 429 68730 402-388-2440
Corey Dahl, supt. Fax 388-4265
www.croftonschools.org
Crofton JSHS 200/7-12
PO Box 429 68730 402-388-2440
Johnnie Ostermeyer, prin. Fax 388-4265

Curtis, Frontier, Pop. 926
Medicine Valley SD 200/K-12
PO Box 9 69025 308-367-4106
Alan Garey, supt. Fax 367-4108
www.mvraiders.org/
Medicine Valley JSHS 100/7-12
PO Box 9 69025 308-367-4106
Steven Gleisberg, prin. Fax 367-4108

University of Nebraska NE Coll of Tech Post-Sec.
404 E 7th St 69025 308-367-4124

Dalton, Cheyenne, Pop. 312
Leyton SD 200/K-12
PO Box 297 69131 308-377-2303
Gregory Brenner, supt. Fax 377-2304
www.leytonwarriors.org
Leyton HS 100/9-12
PO Box 297 69131 308-377-2303
Lance Howitt, prin. Fax 377-2304

Davenport, Thayer, Pop. 289
Bruning-Davenport USD 200/PK-12
PO Box 190 68335 402-364-2225
Dr. Trudy Clark, supt. Fax 364-2477
www.bruningdavenport.org/
Bruning-Davenport MS 50/5-8
PO Box 190 68335 402-364-2225
Erik Sokol, prin. Fax 364-2477
Other Schools – See Bruning

David City, Butler, Pop. 2,884
David City SD 700/PK-12
750 D St 68632 402-367-4590
Chad Denker, supt. Fax 367-3479
www.davidcitypublicschools.org/
David City JSHS 300/7-12
750 D St 68632 402-367-3187
Cortney Couch, prin. Fax 367-3479

Aquinas HS 300/6-12
PO Box 149 68632 402-367-3175
David McMahon, prin. Fax 367-3176

Daykin, Jefferson, Pop. 166
Meridian SD 200/K-12
PO Box 190 68338 402-446-7265
Randall Kort, supt. Fax 446-7246
www.meridianmustangs.org
Meridian JSHS 100/7-12
PO Box 190 68338 402-446-7265
Harold Scott, prin. Fax 446-7246

Deshler, Thayer, Pop. 745
Deshler SD 200/K-12
PO Box 547 68340 402-365-7272
Dr. Al Meier, supt. Fax 365-7560
www.deshlerpublicschools.org
Deshler JSHS 100/7-12
PO Box 547 68340 402-365-7272
Josh Weber, prin. Fax 365-7560

De Witt, Saline, Pop. 509
Tri County SD 400/K-12
72520 Highway 103 68341 402-683-2037
Randy Schlueter, supt. Fax 683-2116
www.tricountyschools.org
Tri County JSHS 200/7-12
72520 Highway 103 68341 402-683-2015
Matthew Uher, prin. Fax 683-2116

Doniphan, Hall, Pop. 824
Doniphan-Trumbull SD 500/K-12
PO Box 300 68832 402-845-2282
Kirk Russell, supt. Fax 845-6688
www.dtcardinals.org
Doniphan-Trumbull JSHS 200/7-12
PO Box 300 68832 402-845-6531
Brent Breckner, prin. Fax 845-6688

Dorchester, Saline, Pop. 580
Dorchester SD 200/K-12
PO Box 7 68343 402-946-2781
Daryl Schrunk, supt. Fax 946-6271
www.dorchesterschool.org
Dorchester JSHS 100/7-12
PO Box 7 68343 402-946-2781
Daryl Schrunk, admin. Fax 946-6271

Dunning, Blaine, Pop. 103
Sandhills SD 100/K-12
PO Box 29 68833 308-538-2224
Dale Hafer, supt. Fax 538-2228
blog.sandhills.k12.ne.us/
Dunning JSHS 100/7-12
PO Box 29 68833 308-538-2224
Dale Hafer, prin. Fax 538-2228

Elba, Howard, Pop. 212
Elba SD 100/PK-12
PO Box 100 68835 308-863-2228
William Porter, supt. Fax 863-2329
www.elba.k12.ne.us
Elba JSHS 50/7-12
PO Box 100 68835 308-863-2228
William Porter, supt. Fax 863-2329

Elgin, Antelope, Pop. 656
Elgin SD 200/PK-12
PO Box 399 68636 402-843-2455
Daniel Polk, supt. Fax 843-2475
www.elgineagles.org
Elgin HS 100/7-12
PO Box 399 68636 402-843-2457
Greg Wemhoff, prin. Fax 843-2475

Pope John XXIII Central Catholic HS 100/7-12
PO Box 179 68636 402-843-5325
Betty Getzfred, prin. Fax 843-2297

Elkhorn, Douglas, Pop. 8,192
Elkhorn SD 6,900/PK-12
20650 Glenn St 68022 402-289-2579
Steve Baker, supt. Fax 289-2585
www.elkhornweb.org/
Elkhorn HS 800/9-12
1401 Veterans Dr 68022 402-289-4239
Dan Radicia, prin. Fax 289-4383
Elkhorn MS 700/6-8
3200 N 207th Plz 68022 402-289-2428
Deb Garrison, prin. Fax 289-1639
Elkhorn Valley View MS 500/6-8
1313 S 208th St 68022 402-289-0362
Chad Soupir, prin.
Other Schools – See Omaha

Mt. Michael Benedictine HS 200/9-12
22520 Mount Michael Rd 68022 402-289-2541
Dr. David Peters, head sch Fax 289-4539

Elm Creek, Buffalo, Pop. 896
Elm Creek SD 300/PK-12
PO Box 490 68836 308-856-4300
Tom Reeser, supt. Fax 856-4907
elmcreekschools.org
Elm Creek JSHS 100/7-12
PO Box 490 68836 308-856-4300
Jason Sullivan, prin. Fax 856-4907

Elwood, Gosper, Pop. 693
Elwood SD 200/K-12
PO Box 107 68937 308-785-2491
Daren Hatch, supt. Fax 785-2322
elwood.k12.ne.us
Elwood JSHS 100/7-12
PO Box 107 68937 308-785-2491
Kyle Hemmerling, prin. Fax 785-2322

Emerson, Dakota, Pop. 834
Emerson-Hubbard SD 300/PK-12
PO Box 9 68733 402-695-2621
Lindsey Burback, supt. Fax 695-2622
www.emersonhubbardschools.org
Emerson-Hubbard JSHS 100/7-12
PO Box 9 68733 402-695-2636
Dustin Nielsen, prin. Fax 695-2637

Eustis, Frontier, Pop. 399
Eustis-Farnam SD 200/K-12
PO Box 9 69028 308-486-3991
Steve Sampy, supt. Fax 486-5350
www.efknights.org
Eustis-Farnam HS 100/7-12
PO Box 9 69028 308-486-3991
Nick Hodge, prin. Fax 486-5659

Ewing, Holt, Pop. 385
Ewing SD 100/K-12
PO Box 98 68735 402-626-7235
Ted Hillman, supt. Fax 626-7236
ewing.ne.schoolwebpages.com
Ewing JSHS 100/7-12
PO Box 98 68735 402-626-7235
Greg Appleby, prin. Fax 626-7236

Exeter, Fillmore, Pop. 589
Exeter-Milligan SD 200/PK-12
PO Box 139 68351 402-266-5911
Paul Sheffield, supt. Fax 266-4811
www.emwolves.org/
Exeter-Milligan JSHS 100/7-12
PO Box 139 68351 402-266-5911
Paul Sheffield, prin. Fax 266-4811

Fairbury, Jefferson, Pop. 3,893
Fairbury SD 900/PK-12
703 K St 68352 402-729-6104
Stephen Grizzle, supt. Fax 729-6392
www.fairburyjeffs.org
Fairbury JSHS 400/7-12
1501 9th St 68352 402-729-6116
Nicholas Kroon, prin. Fax 729-6275

Fairfield, Clay, Pop. 385
South Central Nebraska Unified SD 500/PK-12
30671 Highway 14 68938 402-726-2151
Dr. Randall Gilson, supt. Fax 726-2208
www.southcentralunified.org
Sandy Creek JSHS 100/7-12
30671 Highway 14 68938 402-726-2151
Jason Searle, prin. Fax 726-2208
Other Schools – See Nelson

Fairmont, Fillmore, Pop. 560
Fillmore Central SD
Supt. — See Geneva
Fillmore Central MS 200/5-8
PO Box 157 68354 402-268-3411
Steven Adkisson, prin. Fax 268-3491

Falls City, Richardson, Pop. 4,224
Falls City SD 800/PK-12
PO Box 129 68355 402-245-2825
Dr. Tim Heckenlively, supt. Fax 245-2022
www.fctigers.org/
Falls City HS 300/9-12
1400 Fulton St 68355 402-245-2116
Gale Dunkhas, prin. Fax 245-5050
Falls City MS 200/6-8
PO Box 129 68355 402-245-3455
Rick Johnson, prin. Fax 245-2022

Sacred Heart S 200/K-12
1820 Fulton St 68355 402-245-4151
Doug Goltz, prin. Fax 245-5217

Firth, Lancaster, Pop. 580
Norris SD 160 2,200/PK-12
25211 S 68th St 68358 402-791-0000
Dr. John Skretta, supt. Fax 791-0025
www.norris160.org
Norris HS 700/9-12
25211 S 68th St 68358 402-791-0010
Ryan Ruhl, prin. Fax 791-0027
Norris MS 500/5-8
25211 S 68th St 68358 402-791-0020
Mary Jo Leininger, prin. Fax 791-0029

Fort Calhoun, Washington, Pop. 895
Fort Calhoun SD 600/K-12
5876 County Rd P43 68023 402-468-5591
Dr. Donald Johnson, supt. Fax 468-5593
www.fortcalhounschools.org
Fort Calhoun JSHS 300/7-12
5876 County Rd P43 68023 402-468-5591
Jerry Green, prin. Fax 468-5593

Franklin, Franklin, Pop. 993
Franklin SD 300/K-12
1001 M St 68939 308-425-6283
Dr. Candace Conradt, supt. Fax 425-6553
fpsflyers.org
Franklin JSHS 200/7-12
1001 M St 68939 308-425-6283
Adam Boettcher, prin. Fax 425-6553

Fremont, Dodge, Pop. 26,088
Fremont SD 4,700/PK-12
130 E 9th St 68025 402-727-3000
Mark Shepard, supt. Fax 727-3002
www.fpsweb.org
Fremont HS 1,400/9-12
1750 N Lincoln Ave 68025 402-727-3050
Chuck Story, prin. Fax 727-3033
Fremont Learning Center 100/Alt
130 E 9th St 68025 402-727-3180
Lea Adler, lead tchr. Fax 727-3085
Fremont MS 700/7-8
540 Johnson Rd 68025 402-727-3100
LaVonna Emmanuel, prin. Fax 727-3963

Archbishop Bergan JSHS 200/7-12
545 E 4th St 68025 402-721-9683
Dan Koenig, prin. Fax 721-5366
Midland University Post-Sec.
900 N Clarkson St 68025 800-642-8382

Friend, Saline, Pop. 1,022
Friend SD 300/PK-12
PO Box 67 68359 402-947-2781
David Kraus, supt. Fax 947-2026
www.friendbulldogs.org
Friend JSHS 100/7-12
PO Box 67 68359 402-947-2781
Ben Dempsey, prin. Fax 947-2026

Fullerton, Nance, Pop. 1,303
Fullerton SD 300/K-12
PO Box 520 68638 308-536-2431
Jeffrey Anderson, supt. Fax 536-2432
www.fullertonpublicschools.org
Fullerton HS 100/9-12
PO Box 520 68638 308-536-2431
Joshua Rathje, prin. Fax 536-2432

Geneva, Fillmore, Pop. 2,199
Fillmore Central SD 500/K-12
1410 L St 68361 402-759-4955
Mark Norvell, supt. Fax 759-4038
www.fillmorecentral.org
Fillmore Central HS 200/9-12
1410 L St 68361 402-759-3141
James Rose, prin. Fax 759-4038
Other Schools – See Fairmont

Genoa, Nance, Pop. 992
Twin River SD 400/K-12
PO Box 640 68640 402-993-2274
Dr. John M. Weidner, supt. Fax 993-7718
www.twinriverschools.org
Twin River JSHS 200/7-12
PO Box 640 68640 402-993-2911
Terry Gray, prin. Fax 993-7718

Gering, Scotts Bluff, Pop. 8,397
Gering SD 2,000/PK-12
1519 10th St 69341 308-436-3125
Bob Hastings, supt. Fax 436-4301
www.geringschools.net
Gering Freshman Academy 9-9
800 Q St 69341 308-436-4255
Eldon Hubbard, prin.
Gering JHS 300/7-8
800 Q St 69341 308-436-3123
Dora Olivares, prin. Fax 436-6010
Gering SHS 500/10-12
1500 U St 69341 308-436-3121
Eldon Hubbard, prin. Fax 436-4214

Gibbon, Buffalo, Pop. 1,809
Gibbon SD 600/PK-12
PO Box 790 68840 308-468-6555
Larry Witt, supt. Fax 468-5164
www.gibbonpublic.org
Gibbon JSHS 200/7-12
PO Box 790 68840 308-468-5721
Troy Lurz, prin. Fax 468-5164

Giltner, Hamilton, Pop. 348
Giltner SD 200/K-12
PO Box 160 68841 402-849-2238
Larry Lambert, supt. Fax 849-2440
www.giltner.k12.ne.us
Giltner JSHS 100/7-12
PO Box 160 68841 402-849-2238
Kurt Polt, prin. Fax 849-2440

Gordon, Sheridan, Pop. 1,571
Gordon-Rushville SD 700/PK-12
PO Box 530 69343 308-282-1322
Lori Liggett, supt. Fax 282-2207
www.grmustangs.org
Gordon-Rushville HS 200/9-12
PO Box 530 69343 308-282-1322
Nathan Livingston, prin. Fax 282-2207
Other Schools – See Rushville

Gothenburg, Dawson, Pop. 3,547
Gothenburg SD 900/K-12
1322 Avenue I 69138 308-537-3651
Michael Teahon, supt. Fax 537-3965
www.gothenburgswedes.org
Gothenburg JSHS 400/7-12
1322 Avenue I 69138 308-537-3651
Randy Evans, prin. Fax 537-3965

Grand Island, Hall, Pop. 47,867
Grand Island SD 9,500/PK-12
PO Box 4904 68802 308-385-5900
Dr. Tawana Grover, supt. Fax 385-5949
www.gips.org
Barr MS 800/6-8
602 W Stolley Park Rd 68801 308-385-5875
Brian Kort, prin. Fax 385-5880
Career Pathways Institute Vo/Tech
1215 S Adams St 68801 308-385-5601
Dan Phillips, coord. Fax 385-5697
Grand Island HS 2,300/9-12
2124 N Lafayette Ave 68803 308-385-5950
Jeff Gilbertson, prin. Fax 385-5966
Success Academy Alt
1912 N Lafayette Ave 68803 308-385-5885
Dr. Kenneth Defrank, dir. Fax 385-5608
Walnut MS 900/6-8
1600 N Custer Ave 68803 308-385-5990
Rod Foley, prin. Fax 385-5992
Westridge MS 400/6-8
4111 W 13th St 68803 308-385-5886
Brad Wolfe, prin. Fax 385-5003

Northwest SD 1,500/PK-12
2710 N North Rd 68803 308-385-6398
Matthew Fisher, supt. Fax 385-6393
www.ginorthwest.org
Northwest HS 800/9-12
2710 N North Rd 68803 308-385-6394
Tim Krupicka, prin. Fax 385-6393

Central Catholic MSHS 300/6-12
1200 Ruby Ave 68803 308-384-2440
Steve Osborn, prin. Fax 389-3274
Central Community College Post-Sec.
PO Box 4903 68802 308-398-4222
Heartland Lutheran HS 100/9-12
3900 W Husker Hwy 68803 308-385-3900
Timothy Leech, prin. Fax 381-7415
Joseph's College of Beauty Post-Sec.
305 W 3rd St 68801 308-381-8848

Grant, Perkins, Pop. 1,163
Perkins County SD 400/K-12
PO Box 829 69140 308-352-4735
Phillip Picquet, supt. Fax 352-4769
www.perkinscountyschools.org
Perkins County JSHS 100/6-12
PO Box 829 69140 308-352-4735
Dean Friedel, prin. Fax 352-4769

Perkins County Christian S 50/K-10
PO Box 322 69140 308-352-8309
Jarret Malmkar, pres. Fax 352-4505

Greeley, Greeley, Pop. 461
Central Valley SD 100/PK-12
PO Box 160 68842 308-428-3145
Amy Malander, supt. Fax 428-5395
www.centralvps.org
Central Valley JSHS 50/7-12
PO Box 160 68842 308-428-3145
Todd Beck, prin. Fax 428-5395

Gretna, Sarpy, Pop. 4,403
Gretna SD 3,700/PK-12
11717 S 216th St 68028 402-332-3265
Dr. Kevin Riley, supt. Fax 332-5833
www.gretnadragons.org
Gretna HS 800/9-12
11717 S 216th St 68028 402-332-3936
Roger Miller, prin. Fax 332-4119
Gretna MS 800/6-8
11717 S 216th St 68028 402-332-3048
Harvey Birky, prin. Fax 332-2931

Hampton, Hamilton, Pop. 420
Hampton SD 200/PK-12
458 5th St 68843 402-725-3117
Holly Herzberg, supt. Fax 725-3334
www.hamptonhawks.us
Hampton JSHS 100/7-12
458 5th St 68843 402-725-3116
Tim Huls, prin. Fax 725-3334

Harrisburg, Banner, Pop. 96
Banner County SD 100/PK-12
PO Box 5 69345 308-436-5263
Lana Sides, supt. Fax 436-5252
www.bannercountyschool.org
Banner County JSHS 100/7-12
PO Box 5 69345 308-436-5263
Charles Jones, prin. Fax 436-5252

Harrison, Sioux, Pop. 247
Sioux County SD 100/K-12
PO Box 38 69346 308-668-2415
Dr. Brett Gies, supt. Fax 668-2260
www.siouxcountyschools.org
Sioux County HS 50/9-12
PO Box 38 69346 308-668-2415
Barry Swisher, prin. Fax 668-2260

Hartington, Cedar, Pop. 1,550
Hartington - Newcastle SD 300/PK-12
PO Box 75 68739 402-254-3947
Adrian Johnson, supt. Fax 254-3945
hartington.esu1.org
Hartington - Newcastle JSHS 100/7-12
PO Box 75 68739 402-254-3947
Corey Uldrich, prin. Fax 254-3945

Cedar Catholic JSHS 200/7-12
PO Box 15 68739 402-254-3906
Terry Kathol, prin. Fax 254-3976

Harvard, Clay, Pop. 1,002
Harvard SD 300/K-12
PO Box 100 68944 402-772-2171
Michael Derr, supt. Fax 772-2204
www.harvardcardinals.org
Harvard JSHS 200/6-12
PO Box 100 68944 402-772-2171
Neil Riley, prin. Fax 772-2204

Hastings, Adams, Pop. 24,622
Adams Central SD 800/K-12
PO Box 1088 68902 402-463-3285
Shawn Scott, supt. Fax 463-6344
adamscentral.us
Adams Central JSHS 500/7-12
PO Box 1088 68902 402-463-3285
David Barrett, prin. Fax 463-6344

Hastings SD 3,300/PK-12
1924 W A St 68901 402-461-7500
Craig Kautz, supt. Fax 461-7509
www.hastingspublicschools.org
Hastings HS 1,000/9-12
1100 W 14th St 68901 402-461-7550
Thomas Szlanda, prin. Fax 461-7535
Hastings MS 800/6-8
201 N Marian Rd 68901 402-461-7520
David Essink, prin. Fax 461-7650

Central Community College Post-Sec.
PO Box 1024 68902 402-463-9811
Hastings College Post-Sec.
PO Box 269 68902 402-463-2402
Joseph's College of Beauty Post-Sec.
828 W 2nd St 68901 402-463-1357
Mary Lanning Healthcare Radiology Sch Post-Sec.
715 N Saint Joseph Ave 68901 402-461-5177

St. Cecilia MSHS 300/6-12
521 N Kansas Ave 68901 402-462-2105
Sandy VanCura, prin. Fax 462-2106

Hayes Center, Hayes, Pop. 214
Hayes Center SD 100/K-12
PO Box 8 69032 308-286-5600
Philip Mahan, supt. Fax 286-5629
www.hccardinals.org
Hayes Center JSHS 50/7-12
PO Box 8 69032 308-286-5600
Tony Primavera, prin. Fax 286-5629

Hay Springs, Sheridan, Pop. 560
Hay Springs SD 200/PK-12
PO Box 280 69347 308-638-4434
Jason Cline, supt. Fax 915-5126
hshawks.com
Hay Springs HS 50/9-12
PO Box 280 69347 308-638-4434
Jason Cline, admin. Fax 915-5126
Hay Springs MS 50/6-8
PO Box 280 69347 308-638-4434
Jason Cline, prin. Fax 915-5126

Hebron, Thayer, Pop. 1,566
Thayer Central Community SD 300/PK-12
PO Box 9 68370 402-768-6117
Drew Harris, supt. Fax 768-6110
www.thayercentral.org/
Thayer Central HS 200/7-12
PO Box 9 68370 402-768-6117
Tom Kiburz, prin. Fax 768-6110

Hemingford, Box Butte, Pop. 793
Hemingford SD 400/K-12
PO Box 217 69348 308-487-3328
Casper Ningen, supt. Fax 487-5215
www.hemingfordschools.org
Hemingford JSHS 200/7-12
PO Box 217 69348 308-487-3328
Peggy Foster, prin. Fax 487-5215

Henderson, York, Pop. 988
Heartland Community SD 300/K-12
1501 Front St 68371 402-723-4434
Brad Best, supt. Fax 723-4431
www.heartlandschools.org/
Heartland Community JSHS 100/7-12
1501 Front St 68371 402-723-4434
Tim Carr, prin. Fax 723-4431

Hershey, Lincoln, Pop. 650
Hershey SD 600/PK-12
PO Box 369 69143 308-368-5572
Jane Davis, supt. Fax 368-5570
www.hpspanthers.org
Hershey JSHS 300/7-12
PO Box 369 69143 308-368-5573
Jeff Steinbeck, prin. Fax 368-5571

Hildreth, Franklin, Pop. 376
Wilcox-Hildreth SD
Supt. — See Wilcox
Wilcox-Hildreth MS 50/6-8
613 Nelson St 68947 308-938-2415
Justin Patterson, prin. Fax 938-5335

Holdrege, Phelps, Pop. 5,459
Holdrege SD, PO Box 2002 68949 1,100/K-12
Todd Hilyard, supt. 308-995-8663
www.holdregedusters.org
Holdrege HS, PO Box 2002 68949 300/9-12
Robert Drews, prin. 308-995-6558
Holdrege MS, PO Box 2002 68949 400/5-8
Angie Girard, prin. 308-995-5421

Homer, Dakota, Pop. 542
Homer Community SD 400/PK-12
PO Box 340 68030 402-698-2377
Cheryll Malcom, supt. Fax 698-2379
www.homerknights.org
Homer JSHS 200/7-12
PO Box 340 68030 402-698-2377
Randy Pirner, prin. Fax 698-2379

Hooper, Dodge, Pop. 820
Logan View SD 300/K-12
2163 County Road G 68031 402-654-3317
Jeremy Klein, supt. Fax 654-3699
www.loganview.org/
Logan View JSHS 200/7-12
2163 County Road G 68031 402-654-3317
Rochelle Clausen, prin. Fax 654-3699

Howells, Colfax, Pop. 557
Howells-Dodge Consolidated SD 200/PK-12
PO Box 159 68641 402-986-1621
Jeffrey Walburn Ed.D., supt. Fax 986-1261
www.howellsdodgeschools.org
Howells JSHS 100/7-12
PO Box 159 68641 402-986-1621
Mark Ernst B.S., prin. Fax 986-1261

Humboldt, Richardson, Pop. 874
Humboldt Table Rock Steinauer SD 70 300/PK-12
810 Central Ave 68376 402-862-2235
Sherri Edmundson, supt. Fax 862-3135
www.htrstitans.com
Humboldt Table Rock Steinauer HS 100/9-12
810 Central Ave 68376 402-862-2151
Lisa Othmer, prin. Fax 862-2152
Other Schools – See Table Rock

Humphrey, Platte, Pop. 758
Humphrey SD 67 200/PK-12
PO Box 278 68642 402-923-1230
Greg Sjuts, supt. Fax 923-1235
www.humphrey.esu7.org
Humphrey JSHS 100/7-12
PO Box 278 68642 402-923-1230
Brice King, prin. Fax 923-1235

St. Francis S 200/PK-12
PO Box 277 68642 402-923-0818
Fax 923-1590

Hyannis, Grant, Pop. 178
Hyannis Area SD 200/K-12
PO Box 286 69350 308-458-2202
Fax 458-2227
www.disteleven.org
Hyannis JSHS 100/7-12
PO Box 286 69350 308-458-2202
Bruce Parish, prin. Fax 458-2227

Imperial, Chase, Pop. 2,057
Chase County SD 600/K-12
PO Box 577 69033 308-882-4304
Joseph Lefdal, supt. Fax 882-5629
chasecountyschools.org
Chase County HS 200/9-12
PO Box 577 69033 308-882-4304
Chad Scheel, prin. Fax 882-5629
Chase County MS 200/5-8
PO Box 577 69033 308-882-4304
Chad Scheel, prin. Fax 882-5629

Johnson, Nemaha, Pop. 325
Johnson-Brock SD 300/K-12
PO Box 186 68378 402-868-5235
Jeff Koehler, supt. Fax 868-4785
www.johnsonbrock.esu6.org/
Johnson JSHS 100/7-12
PO Box 186 68378 402-868-5235
Lucus Dalinghaus, prin. Fax 868-4785

Kearney, Buffalo, Pop. 30,426
Kearney SD 5,300/PK-12
310 W 24th St 68845 308-698-8000
Kent Edwards, supt. Fax 698-8001
www.kearneypublicschools.org
Horizon MS 500/6-8
915 W 35th St 68845 308-698-8120
Kipp Petersen, prin. Fax 698-8143
Kearney HS 1,400/9-12
2702 W 11th St 68845 308-698-8060
Dr. Jay Dostal, prin. Fax 698-8061
Sunrise MS 500/6-8
4611 N Ave 68847 308-698-8150
Jeff Ganz, prin. Fax 698-8152

Joseph's of Kearney Sch of Hair Design Post-Sec.
2213 Central Ave 68847 308-234-6594
Kearney Catholic HS 300/6-12
PO Box 1866 68848 308-234-2610
Terrence Torson, prin. Fax 234-4986
University of Nebraska at Kearney Post-Sec.
905 W 25th St 68849 308-865-8526

Kenesaw, Adams, Pop. 876
Kenesaw SD 200/K-12
PO Box 129 68956 402-752-3215
Robby Thompson, supt. Fax 752-3579
www.kenesawschools.org/
Kenesaw JSHS 100/7-12
PO Box 129 68956 402-752-3215
Rodney Richardson, prin. Fax 752-3579

Kimball, Kimball, Pop. 2,447
Kimball SD 500/PK-12
901 S Nadine St 69145 308-235-2188
Marshall Lewis, supt. Fax 235-3269
kimball.k12.ne.us/
Kimball JSHS 200/7-12
901 S Nadine St 69145 308-235-4861
Eugene Hanks, prin. Fax 235-4128

Laurel, Cedar, Pop. 959
Laurel-Concord-Coleridge SD 300/K-12
PO Box 8 68745 402-256-3133
Randall Klooz, supt. Fax 256-9465
www.lccschool.org
Laurel-Concord-Coleridge HS 100/7-12
PO Box 8 68745 402-256-3731
Jay Vance, prin. Fax 256-9468
Other Schools – See Coleridge

La Vista, Sarpy, Pop. 15,366
Papillion La Vista Community SD
Supt. — See Papillion
La Vista MS 800/7-8
7900 Edgewood Blvd 68128 402-898-0436
Dr. Patricia Zalesky, prin. Fax 898-0442

Leigh, Colfax, Pop. 404
Leigh Community SD 200/K-12
PO Box 98 68643 402-487-3301
Dr. Michael Montgomery Ed.D., supt. Fax 487-3341
www.leighcommunityschools.org
Leigh JSHS 100/7-12
PO Box 98 68643 402-487-2228
Troy Holmberg M.Ed., prin. Fax 487-2607

Lewiston, Pawnee, Pop. 68
Lewiston SD 200/K-12
306 Tiger Ave 68380 402-865-4675
Rick Kentfield, supt. Fax 865-4875
www.lewistonschool.org/
Lewiston JSHS 100/7-12
306 Tiger Ave 68380 402-865-4675
Fred Ivey, prin. Fax 865-4875

Lexington, Dawson, Pop. 10,140
Lexington SD 2,900/PK-12
PO Box 890 68850 308-324-4681
John Hakonson Ed.D., supt. Fax 324-2528
www.lexschools.org
Lexington HS 800/9-12
705 W 13th St 68850 308-324-4691
Kyle Hoehner, prin. Fax 324-7224
Lexington MS 600/6-8
1100 N Washington St 68850 308-324-2349
Scott West, prin. Fax 324-6612

Lincoln, Lancaster, Pop. 251,784
Lincoln SD 37,300/PK-12
PO Box 82889 68501 402-436-1000
Stephen Joel Ed.D., supt. Fax 436-1084
www.lps.org/
Arts & Humanities Focus Program 9-12
643 S 25th St 68510 402-436-1785
Dr. Pat Hunter-Pirtle, prin. Fax 458-3281
Bryan Community S 100/Alt
300 S 48th St 68510 402-436-1308
Tanner Penrod, prin. Fax 458-3208
Career Academy, 8800 O St 68520 Vo/Tech
Dr. Dan Hohensee, dir. 402-436-1316
Culler MS 700/6-8
5201 Vine St 68504 402-436-1210
Gary Czapla, prin. Fax 458-3210
Dawes MS 400/6-8
5130 Colfax Ave 68504 402-436-1211
Angela Plugge, prin. Fax 458-3211
Goodrich MS 700/6-8
4600 Lewis Ave 68521 402-436-1213
Kelly Schrad, prin. Fax 458-3213
Irving MS 800/6-8
2745 S 22nd St 68502 402-436-1214
Jason Shanahan, prin. Fax 458-3214
Lefler MS 600/6-8
1100 S 48th St 68510 402-436-1215
Jessie Carlson, prin. Fax 458-3215
Lincoln East HS 1,500/9-12
1000 S 70th St 68510 402-436-1302
Susan Cassata, prin. Fax 436-1325
Lincoln HS 1,600/9-12
2229 J St 68510 402-436-1301
Mark Larson, prin. Fax 458-1540
Lincoln Northeast HS 1,500/9-12
2635 N 63rd St 68507 402-436-1303
Kurt Glathar, prin. Fax 436-1345
Lincoln North Star HS 2,000/9-12
5801 N 33rd St 68504 402-436-1305
Dr. Vann Price, prin. Fax 436-1054
Lincoln Southeast HS 2,000/9-12
2930 S 37th St 68506 402-436-1304
Brent Toalson, prin. Fax 436-1357
Lincoln Southwest HS 1,800/9-12
7001 S 14th St 68512 402-436-1306
Mike Gillotti, prin. Fax 436-1085
Lux MS 1,000/6-8
7800 High St 68506 402-436-1220
Duane Dohmen, prin. Fax 458-3292
Mickle MS 600/6-8
2500 N 67th St 68507 402-436-1216
Gene Thompson, prin. Fax 458-3216
Moore MS 6-8
8700 Yankee Woods Dr 68501 402-436-1225
Gary Czapla, prin.
Nuernberger Education Center Alt
1801 S 40th St 68506 402-436-1255
Jaime Boedeker, prin. Fax 458-3272
Park MS 800/6-8
855 S 8th St 68508 402-436-1212
Ryan Zabawa, prin. Fax 458-3212
Pound MS 800/6-8
4740 S 45th St 68516 402-436-1217
Dr. Christopher Deibler, prin. Fax 458-3217
Schoo MS 800/6-8
700 Penrose Dr 68521 402-436-1222
Bill Schulenberg, prin. Fax 458-3222
Science Focus Program 9-12
1222 S 27th St 68502 402-436-1780
Dr. Pat Hunter-Pirtle, prin. Fax 458-3280
Scott MS 1,000/6-8
2200 Pine Lake Rd 68512 402-436-1218
Dave Knudsen, prin. Fax 458-3218

Bryan College of Health Sciences Post-Sec.
5035 Everett St 68506 402-481-3801
College of Hair Design Post-Sec.
304 S 11th St 68508 402-477-4040
College of Hair Design - East Post-Sec.
9000 Andermatt Dr 68526 402-477-4040
College View Academy 200/PK-12
5240 Calvert St 68506 402-483-1181
Brian Carlson, prin. Fax 483-5574
Joseph's College of Beauty Post-Sec.
2637 O St 68510 402-435-2333
Kaplan University Post-Sec.
1821 K St 68508 402-474-5315
Lincoln Christian S 600/PK-12
5801 S 84th St 68516 402-488-8888
Rodney Zach, admin. Fax 486-4527
Lincoln Lutheran MSHS 400/6-12
1100 N 56th St 68504 402-467-5404
Scott Ernstmeyer, dir. Fax 467-5405
Myotherapy Institute Post-Sec.
4001 Pioneer Woods Dr 68506 402-421-7410
Nebraska Wesleyan University Post-Sec.
5000 Saint Paul Ave 68504 402-466-2371
Parkview Christian S 200/PK-12
4400 N 1st St 68521 402-474-5820
Marty Hughes, admin. Fax 474-5830
Pius X HS 1,100/9-12
6000 A St 68510 402-488-0931
Thomas Korta, prin. Fax 488-1061
Southeast Community College Post-Sec.
8800 O St 68520 402-471-3333
Union College Post-Sec.
3800 S 48th St 68506 402-486-2600
University of Nebraska Post-Sec.
14th & R Sts 68588 402-472-7211

Lindsay, Platte, Pop. 253

Holy Family S 100/PK-12
PO Box 158 68644 402-428-3455
Andy Bishop, prin. Fax 428-3231

Litchfield, Sherman, Pop. 262
Litchfield SD 100/PK-12
PO Box 167 68852 308-446-2244
Dr. Scott Maline, supt. Fax 446-2244
litchfieldpublicschools.org
Litchfield JSHS 100/7-12
PO Box 167 68852 308-446-2244
Wade Finley, prin. Fax 446-2244

Lodgepole, Cheyenne, Pop. 315
Creek Valley SD
Supt. — See Chappell
Creek Valley MS 100/5-8
PO Box 158 69149 308-483-5252
Tessa Fraass, prin. Fax 483-5251

Loomis, Phelps, Pop. 377
Loomis SD 200/K-12
PO Box 250 68958 308-876-2111
Nicole Hardwick, supt. Fax 876-2372
loomiswolves.org
Loomis JSHS 100/7-12
PO Box 250 68958 308-876-2111
Sam Dunn, prin. Fax 876-2372

Louisville, Cass, Pop. 1,086
Louisville SD 500/K-12
PO Box 489 68037 402-234-3585
Andrew Farber, supt. Fax 234-2141
www.lpslions.org
Louisville HS 200/9-12
PO Box 489 68037 402-234-3585
Brett Schwartz, prin. Fax 234-2141
Louisville MS 100/6-8
PO Box 489 68037 402-234-3585
Brett Schwartz, prin. Fax 234-2141

Loup City, Sherman, Pop. 1,023
Loup City SD 300/K-12
PO Box 628 68853 308-745-0120
Blake Dahlberg, supt. Fax 745-0130
blog.loupcity.k12.ne.us
Loup City HS 100/7-12
PO Box 628 68853 308-745-0548
Blake Dahlberg, prin. Fax 745-0130

Lynch, Boyd, Pop. 241
Lynch SD 100/K-12
PO Box 98 68746 402-569-2081
Ted Hillman, supt. Fax 569-2091
lynch.esu8.org
Lynch JSHS 50/7-12
PO Box 98 68746 402-569-2081
Ted Hillman, admin. Fax 569-2091

Lyons, Burt, Pop. 845
Lyons-Decatur Northeast SD 200/PK-12
PO Box 526 68038 402-687-2363
Fred Hansen, supt. Fax 687-2472
www.lyonsdecaturschools.org/
Northeast JSHS 100/7-12
PO Box 526 68038 402-687-2349
Derek Lahm, prin. Fax 687-2472

Mc Cook, Red Willow, Pop. 7,616
Mc Cook SD 1,500/PK-12
700 W 7th St 69001 308-345-2510
Grant Norgaard, supt. Fax 345-2511
www.mccookbison.org/
Mc Cook HS 500/9-12
600 W 7th St 69001 308-345-5422
Jeff Gross, prin. Fax 345-5477
Mc Cook JHS 300/6-8
800 W 7th St 69001 308-345-6940
Chad Lyons, prin. Fax 345-6941
Mc Cook Learning Center 50/Alt
404 W 7th St 69001 308-345-5631
Jeff Gross, prin. Fax 345-6134

McCook Community College Post-Sec.
1205 E 3rd St 69001 308-345-8100

Mc Cool Junction, York, Pop. 409
Mc Cool Junction SD 300/K-12
PO Box 278 68401 402-724-2231
Curtis Cogswell, supt. Fax 724-2232
www.mccool.esu6.org/
Mc Cool Junction JSHS 100/7-12
PO Box 278 68401 402-724-2231
Dade McDonald, prin. Fax 724-2232

Macy, Thurston, Pop. 1,021
UMO N HO N Nation SD 400/PK-12
PO Box 280 68039 402-837-5622
Stacie Hardy, supt. Fax 837-5245
www.unpsk-12.org
UMO N HO N Nation HS 100/9-12
PO Box 280 68039 402-837-5622
Broderick Steed, prin. Fax 837-5245
UMO N HO N Nation MS 100/6-8
PO Box 280 68039 402-837-5622
Broderick Steed, prin. Fax 837-5245

Nebraska Indian Community College Post-Sec.
PO Box 428 68039 402-494-2311

Madison, Madison, Pop. 2,422
Madison SD 600/PK-12
PO Box 450 68748 402-454-3336
Alan Ehlers, supt. Fax 454-2238
madison.esu8.org/
Madison HS 200/9-12
PO Box 450 68748 402-454-3336
Jim Crilly, prin. Fax 454-2238
Madison MS 100/6-8
PO Box 450 68748 402-454-3336
Andrew Offner, prin. Fax 454-2238

Malcolm, Lancaster, Pop. 378
Malcolm SD 500/K-12
10004 NW 112th St 68402 402-796-2151
Ryan Terwilliger, supt. Fax 796-2178
www.malcolmschools.org
Malcolm JSHS 300/7-12
10002 NW 112th St 68402 402-796-2151
Greg Adams, prin. Fax 796-2189

Maxwell, Lincoln, Pop. 309
Maxwell SD 200/K-12
PO Box 188 69151 308-582-4585
Todd Rhodes, supt. Fax 582-4584
www.maxwellschools.org
Maxwell JSHS 100/7-12
PO Box 188 69151 308-582-4585
Dr. Jason Lavaley, prin. Fax 582-4584

Maywood, Frontier, Pop. 257
Maywood SD 200/K-12
PO Box 46 69038 308-362-4223
Cynthia Huff, supt. Fax 362-4454
www.maywoodtigers.org

Maywood JSHS 100/7-12
PO Box 46 69038 308-362-4223
Jason Brown, prin. Fax 362-4454

Mead, Saunders, Pop. 567
Mead SD 200/K-12
PO Box 158 68041 402-624-2745
Dr. Dale Rawson, supt. Fax 624-2001
www.meadpublicschools.org/
Mead JSHS 100/7-12
PO Box 158 68041 402-624-3435
P.J. Quinn, prin. Fax 624-2069

Merna, Custer, Pop. 361
Anselmo-Merna SD 100/K-12
PO Box 68 68856 308-643-2224
Jason Mundorf, supt. Fax 643-2243
a-mps.fesdev.org/
Anselmo-Merna S 100/K-12
PO Box 68 68856 308-643-2224
Darrin Max, prin. Fax 643-2243

Milford, Seward, Pop. 2,066
Milford SD 700/PK-12
PO Box C 68405 402-761-3321
Kevin Wingard, supt. Fax 761-3322
www.milfordpublicschools.org/
Milford JSHS 300/7-12
PO Box C 68405 402-761-2525
Brandon Mowinkel, prin. Fax 761-2663

Southeast Community College Post-Sec.
600 State St 68405 402-761-2131

Minatare, Scotts Bluff, Pop. 808
Minatare SD 200/PK-12
PO Box 425 69356 308-783-1232
Tim Cody, supt. Fax 783-1050
www.edline.net/pages/Minatare_Public_Schools
Minatare JSHS 100/7-12
PO Box 425 69356 308-783-1733
Kyle Metzger, prin. Fax 783-2982

Minden, Kearney, Pop. 2,907
Minden SD 800/PK-12
PO Box 301 68959 308-832-2440
Melissa Wheelock, supt. Fax 832-2567
minden.k12.ne.us
Jones MS 300/4-8
PO Box 301 68959 308-832-2338
John Osgood, prin. Fax 832-3236
Minden HS 200/9-12
PO Box 301 68959 308-832-2254
Don Hosick, prin. Fax 832-1892

Mitchell, Scotts Bluff, Pop. 1,691
Mitchell SD 700/PK-12
1819 19th Ave 69357 308-623-1707
Katherine Urbanek, supt. Fax 623-1330
www.mpstigers.com
Mitchell JSHS 300/7-12
1819 19th Ave 69357 308-623-1707
Heath Peters, prin. Fax 623-1330

Morrill, Scotts Bluff, Pop. 916
Morrill SD 400/PK-12
PO Box 486 69358 308-247-3414
Joseph Sherwood, supt. Fax 247-2196
www.mpslions.org
Morrill JSHS 100/7-12
PO Box 486 69358 308-247-2149
Tom Peacock, prin. Fax 247-2196

Mullen, Hooker, Pop. 506
Mullen SD 200/K-12
PO Box 127 69152 308-546-2223
Mark Sievering, supt. Fax 546-2209
www.mullenpublicschools.org
Mullen JSHS 100/7-12
PO Box 127 69152 308-546-2223
Michael Kvanvig, prin. Fax 546-2209

Murdock, Cass, Pop. 236
Elmwood-Murdock SD 400/PK-12
300 Wyoming St 68407 402-867-2341
Daniel Novak, supt. Fax 867-2009
www.elm.esu3.org
Elmwood-Murdock JSHS 200/7-12
300 Wyoming St 68407 402-867-2341
Tim Allemang, prin. Fax 867-2009

Murray, Cass, Pop. 456
Conestoga SD 600/PK-12
PO Box 184 68409 402-235-2992
Beth Johnsen, supt. Fax 227-2992
www.conestogacougars.org/
Conestoga JSHS 300/7-12
PO Box 40 68409 402-235-2271
David Friedli, prin. Fax 235-2421

Nebraska City, Otoe, Pop. 7,192
Nebraska City SD 1,400/PK-12
215 N 12th St 68410 402-873-6033
Dr. Jeffrey Edwards, supt. Fax 873-6030
www.nebcityps.org
Nebraska City HS 400/9-12
141 Steinhart Park Rd 68410 402-873-3360
Brian Hoover, prin. Fax 873-3831
Nebraska City MS 300/6-8
909 1st Corso 68410 402-873-5591
Craig Taylor, prin. Fax 873-5641

Lourdes Central S 200/PK-12
412 2nd Ave 68410 402-873-6154
Curt Feilmeier, prin. Fax 873-3154
Nebraska School for Visually Handicapped Post-Sec.
PO Box 129 68410

Neligh, Antelope, Pop. 1,591
Neligh-Oakdale SD 400/PK-12
PO Box 149 68756 402-887-4166
Scott Gregory, supt. Fax 887-5322
www.nelighoakdaleschools.com
Neligh-Oakdale JSHS 200/7-12
PO Box 149 68756 402-887-4166
George Loofe, prin. Fax 887-5322

Nelson, Nuckolls, Pop. 480
South Central Nebraska Unified SD
Supt. — See Fairfield
Lawrence/Nelson JSHS 100/7-12
PO Box 368 68961 402-225-3371
Dana Epley, prin. Fax 225-5431

Newman Grove, Madison, Pop. 715
Newman Grove SD 100/K-12
PO Box 370 68758 402-447-2721
Mikal Shalikow, supt. Fax 447-2445
newman.esu8.org
Newman Grove JSHS 100/7-12
PO Box 370 68758 402-447-6294
Darrell Barnes, prin. Fax 447-2445

Niobrara, Knox, Pop. 360
Niobrara SD 200/K-12
PO Box 310 68760 402-857-3323
Margaret Sandoz, supt. Fax 857-3877
www.niobraraschools.org
Niobrara JSHS 100/5-12
PO Box 310 68760 402-857-3322
Angie Guenther, prin. Fax 857-3716

Santee SD 100/PK-12
206 Frazier Ave E 68760 402-857-2741
Carol Rempp, supt. Fax 857-2743
www.santeeschools.org
Santee HS 50/7-12
206 Frazier Ave E 68760 402-857-2741
Tony Hoffman, prin. Fax 857-2743

Norfolk, Madison, Pop. 23,882
Norfolk SD 4,200/PK-12
PO Box 139 68702 402-644-2500
Jami Jo Thompson, supt. Fax 644-2506
www.norfolkpublicschools.org/
Alternatives for Success 50/Alt
PO Box 139 68702 402-379-7565
Jake Luhr, prin.
Norfolk JHS 600/7-8
PO Box 139 68702 402-644-2516
Jennifer Robinson, prin. Fax 644-2519
Norfolk SHS 1,300/9-12
PO Box 139 68702 402-644-2529
Jason Luhr, prin. Fax 644-2538

Joseph's College of Beauty Post-Sec.
202 W Madison Ave 68701 402-371-3358
Lutheran HS Northeast 100/9-12
2010 N 37th St 68701 402-379-3040
Daniel Sievert, prin. Fax 379-8340
Norfolk Catholic JSHS 300/7-12
2300 W Madison Ave 68701 402-371-2784
Jeff Bellar, prin. Fax 379-2929
Northeast Community College Post-Sec.
PO Box 469 68702 402-371-2020

North Bend, Dodge, Pop. 1,172
North Bend Central SD 600/K-12
PO Box 160 68649 402-652-3268
Dan Endorf, supt. Fax 652-8348
www.nbtigers.org
North Bend Central JSHS 300/7-12
PO Box 160 68649 402-652-3268
Brenda Petersen, prin. Fax 652-8348

North Platte, Lincoln, Pop. 24,455
North Platte SD 3,700/PK-12
PO Box 1557 69103 308-535-7100
Dr. Ron Hanson, supt. Fax 535-5300
www.nppsd.org
Adams MS 400/7-8
1200 McDonald Rd 69101 308-535-7112
Dan Helberg, prin. Fax 535-5309
Learning Center 50/Alt
1400 N Madison Ave 69101 308-535-5311
James Ayres, prin. Fax 535-5311
North Platte HS 1,200/9-12
1220 W 2nd St 69101 308-535-7105
James Ayres, prin. Fax 535-7111

Joseph's College of Beauty Post-Sec.
1620 E 4th St 69101 308-532-4664
Mid-Plains Community College Post-Sec.
601 W State Farm Rd 69101 308-535-3600
North Platte Community College Post-Sec.
1101 Halligan Dr 69101 308-535-3600
St. Patrick MSHS 200/7-12
PO Box 970 69103 308-532-1874
Kevin Dodson, admin. Fax 532-8015

Oakland, Burt, Pop. 1,227
Oakland Craig SD 500/PK-12
309 N Davis Ave 68045 402-685-5661
Jeffery Smith, supt. Fax 685-5697
www.ocknights.org
Oakland Craig HS 100/9-12
309 N Davis Ave 68045 402-685-5661
Rusty Droescher, prin. Fax 685-5697
Oakland Craig JHS 100/7-8
309 N Davis Ave 68045 402-685-5661
Rusty Droescher, prin. Fax 685-5697

Odell, Gage, Pop. 299
Diller-Odell SD 200/K-12
PO Box 188 68415 402-766-4171
Michael Meyerle, supt. Fax 766-4211
www.dillerodell.org
Diller-Odell JSHS 100/7-12
PO Box 188 68415 402-766-4210
Christopher Prososki, prin. Fax 766-4211

Ogallala, Keith, Pop. 4,669
Ogallala SD 500/PK-12
801 E O St 69153 308-284-4060
Michael L. Apple, supt. Fax 284-3981
www.opsd.org/
Ogallala HS 300/9-12
602 E G St 69153 308-284-4029
Greg Pavlik, prin. Fax 284-3869

Omaha, Douglas, Pop. 399,005
Elkhorn SD
Supt. — See Elkhorn
Elkhorn Grandview MS 6-8
17801 Grand Ave 68116 402-289-9399
Mike Tomjack, prin. Fax 289-9499
Elkhorn Ridge MS 400/6-8
17880 Marcy St 68118 402-334-9302
Kevin Riggert, prin. Fax 334-9378
Elkhorn South HS 1,000/9-12
20303 Blue Sage Pkwy 68130 402-289-0616
Mark Kalvoda, prin. Fax 289-1523

Millard SD 23,100/PK-12
5606 S 147th St 68137 402-715-8200
Dr. James Sutfin, supt. Fax 715-8409
www.mpsomaha.org
Andersen MS 900/6-8
15404 Adams St 68137 402-715-8440
Jeff Alfrey, prin. Fax 715-8410
Beadle MS 1,200/6-8
18201 Jefferson St 68135 402-715-6100
John Southworth, prin. Fax 715-6140
Horizon HS 100/Alt
5300 George B Lake Pkwy, 402-715-8470
Angie Craft, prin. Fax 715-6196
Kiewit MS 900/6-8
15650 Howard St 68118 402-715-1470
Marshall Smith, prin. Fax 715-1490
Millard Central MS 800/6-8
12801 L St 68137 402-715-8225
Beth Fink, prin. Fax 715-8574
Millard North HS 2,500/9-12
1010 S 144th St 68154 402-715-1365
Brian Begley, prin. Fax 715-1336
Millard North MS 800/6-8
2828 S 139th St 68144 402-715-1280
Scott Ingwerson, prin. Fax 715-1275
Millard South HS 2,100/9-12
14905 Q St 68137 402-715-8268
Heidi Weaver, prin. Fax 715-6160
Millard West HS 2,400/9-12
5710 S 176th Ave 68135 402-715-6000
Greg Tiemann, prin. Fax 715-6060
Russell MS 900/6-8
5304 S 172nd St 68135 402-715-8500
Teresa Perkins, prin. Fax 715-8368

Omaha SD 48,800/PK-12
3215 Cuming St 68131 402-557-2222
Mark Evans, supt. Fax 557-2019
www.ops.org
Benson Magnet HS 1,300/9-12
5120 Maple St 68104 402-557-3000
Anita Harkins, prin. Fax 557-3039
Beveridge Magnet MS 700/7-8
1616 S 120th St 68144 402-557-4000
Dr. David Lavender, prin. Fax 557-4009
Blackburn Alternative S Alt
2606 Hamilton St 68131 402-344-3385
Jodi Pesek, dir. Fax 344-3724
Bryan HS 1,700/9-12
4700 Giles Rd 68157 402-557-3100
Robert Aranda, prin. Fax 557-3139
Bryan MS 800/7-8
8210 S 42nd St 68147 402-557-4100
Darren Rasmussen, prin. Fax 557-4129
Buffet Magnet MS 700/5-8
14101 Larimore Ave 68164 402-561-6160
Dr. Rony Ortega, prin. Fax 561-6170
Burke HS 2,200/9-12
12200 Burke Blvd 68154 402-557-3200
Dr. Steven Scraggs, prin. Fax 557-3239
Career Center, 3230 Burt St 68131 Vo/Tech
Jeremy Cowley, dir. 402-299-0330
Central HS 2,600/9-12
124 N 20th St 68102 402-557-3300
Dr. Ed Bennett, prin. Fax 557-3339
Davis MS 400/6-8
8050 N 129th Ave 68142 402-561-6130
Dan Bartels, prin. Fax 933-9131
Hale MS 300/7-8
6143 Whitmore St 68152 402-557-4200
Darin Williams, prin. Fax 557-4229
Integrated Learning Alt
3030 Spaulding St 68111 402-344-7895
Sandra Bender, dir. Fax 344-0548
King Science/Tech Magnet MS 300/5-8
3720 Florence Blvd 68110 402-557-3720
Maria Buckner, prin. Fax 557-4459
Lewis & Clark MS 700/7-8
6901 Burt St 68132 402-557-4300
Dr. Lisa Sterba, prin. Fax 557-4309
Marrs Magnet MS 700/5-8
5619 S 19th St 68107 402-557-4400
Bryan Dunne, prin. Fax 557-4429
McMillan Magnet MS 500/7-8
3802 Redick Ave 68112 402-557-4500
Dr. Jeaneen Talbott, prin. Fax 557-4509
Monroe MS 500/7-8
5105 Bedford Ave 68104 402-557-4600
Boris Moore, prin. Fax 557-4609
Morton Magnet MS 600/5-8
4606 Terrace Dr 68134 402-557-4700
Sherri Wehr, prin. Fax 557-4709
Norris MS 800/7-8
2235 S 46th St 68106 402-557-4800
Dr. David Alati, prin. Fax 557-4809
Omaha North Magnet HS 1,800/9-12
4410 N 36th St 68111 402-557-3400
Gene Haynes, prin. Fax 557-3439
Omaha Northwest Magnet HS 1,400/9-12
8204 Crown Point Ave 68134 402-557-3500
Thomas Lee, prin. Fax 557-3539
Omaha South Magnet HS 2,400/9-12
4519 S 24th St 68107 402-557-3600
Ruben Cano, prin. Fax 557-3639
Parrish S Alt
4469 Farnam St 68131 402-554-8460
Andrew Karmazin, dir. Fax 554-1639
Adult HS, 3230 Burt St 68131 Adult
Jacqueline Washington, dir. 531-299-9394

Westside Community SD 6,200/PK-12
909 S 76th St 68114 402-390-2100
Dr. Blane McCann Ph.D., supt. Fax 390-2120
www.westside66.org
Westside HS 1,900/9-12
8701 Pacific St 68114 402-343-2600
Jay Opperman, prin. Fax 343-2608
Westside HS West Campus Alt
3534 S 108th St 68144 402-390-8214
Jenni Allen, admin.
Westside MS 900/7-8
8601 Arbor St 68124 402-390-6464
Russ Olsen, prin. Fax 390-6454

Alegent Health School of Radiologic Tech Post-Sec.
7500 Mercy Rd 68124 402-398-5527
Bishop Clarkson Memorial Hospital Post-Sec.
4350 Dewey Ave 68105 402-552-3203
Brownell-Talbot S 500/PK-12
400 N Happy Hollow Blvd 68132 402-556-3772
Dr. Kristi Gibbs, head sch Fax 553-2994
Capitol School of Hairstyling - West Post-Sec.
10803 John Galt Blvd 68137 402-333-3329
Clarkson College Post-Sec.
101 S 42nd St 68131 402-552-3100
College of Saint Mary Post-Sec.
7000 Mercy Rd 68106 402-399-2400
Concordia Lutheran JSHS 300/6-12
15656 Fort St 68116 402-445-4000
Matthew Korte, prin. Fax 965-9310
Creighton Preparatory S 1,000/9-12
7400 Western Ave 68114 402-393-1190
Jim Bopp, prin. Fax 393-0260
Creighton University Post-Sec.
2500 California Plz 68178 402-280-2700
Duchesne Academy 300/9-12
3601 Burt St 68131 402-558-3800
Laura Hickman Ed.D., prin. Fax 558-0051
Grace University Post-Sec.
1311 S 9th St 68108 402-449-2800
Immanuel Medical Center Post-Sec.
6901 N 72nd St 68122 402-572-2270
Jesuit Academy 100/4-8
2311 N 22nd St 68110 402-346-4464
Troy Wharton, prin. Fax 341-1817
Kaplan University Post-Sec.
5425 N 103rd St 68134 402-431-6100
Marian HS 700/9-12
7400 Military Ave 68134 402-571-2618
Susan Sullivan, prin. Fax 571-2978
Mercy HS 400/9-12
1501 S 48th St 68106 402-553-9424
Sarah Regan, prin. Fax 553-0394
Metropolitan Community College Post-Sec.
PO Box 3777 68103 402-738-4500
Metropolitan Community College- Ft Omaha Post-Sec.
PO Box 3777 68103 402-457-2700
Metropolitan Community Coll- Elkhorn Vly Post-Sec.
PO Box 3777 68103 402-289-1200
Montessori International S of the Plains 50/7-12
7001 Oak St 68106 402-614-9074
Nebraska Methodist College Post-Sec.
720 N 87th St 68114 402-354-7000
Omaha Christian Academy 300/PK-12
10244 Wiesman Dr 68134 402-399-9565
Dr. Victor Fordyce Ed.D., supt. Fax 399-0248
Omaha School of Massage Therapy Post-Sec.
9748 Park Dr 68127 402-331-3694
Roncalli HS 400/9-12
6401 Sorensen Pkwy 68152 402-571-7670
Dania Freudenburg, prin. Fax 571-3216
Skutt Catholic HS 700/9-12
3131 S 156th St 68130 402-333-0818
Rob Meyers, prin. Fax 333-1790
The Creative Center Post-Sec.
10850 Emmet St 68164 402-898-1000
Universal College of Healing Arts Post-Sec.
8702 N 30th St 68112 402-556-4456
University of Nebraska Medical Center Post-Sec.
987020 Nebraska Medical Ctr 68198 402-559-4000
University of Nebraska Omaha Post-Sec.
6001 Dodge St 68182 402-554-2800
Vatterott College - Omaha Post-Sec.
11818 I St 68137 402-891-9411
Wright Career College Post-Sec.
3000 S 84th St 68124 913-381-2577
Xenon International Academy Post-Sec.
8516 Park Dr 68127 402-393-2933

O Neill, Holt, Pop. 3,676
O'Neill SD 700/PK-12
PO Box 230 68763 402-336-3775
Amy Shane, supt. Fax 336-4890
www.oneillpublicschools.org
O'Neill JSHS 300/7-12
PO Box 230 68763 402-336-1544
Corey Fisher, prin. Fax 336-1105

St. Mary S 300/PK-12
300 N 4th St 68763 402-336-4455
Cody Havranek, prin. Fax 336-1281

Orchard, Antelope, Pop. 377
Nebraska USD 1 200/PK-12
PO Box 248 68764 402-893-2068
Dale Martin, supt. Fax 893-2065
neunified1.esu8.org/
Other Schools – See Clearwater, Verdigre

Ord, Valley, Pop. 2,094
Ord SD 500/K-12
320 N 19th St 68862 308-728-5013
Jason Alexander, supt. Fax 728-5108
www.ordps.org
Ord JSHS 300/7-12
1800 K St 68862 308-728-3241
Mark Hagge, prin. Fax 728-5108

Osceola, Polk, Pop. 874
Osceola SD 200/K-12
PO Box 198 68651 402-747-3121
Steve Rinehart, supt. Fax 747-3041
www.osceolaschools.org
Osceola HS 100/9-12
PO Box 198 68651 402-747-3121
Dale Maynard, prin. Fax 747-3041
Osceola MS 100/6-8
PO Box 198 68651 402-747-3121
Dale Maynard, prin. Fax 747-3041

Oshkosh, Garden, Pop. 869
Garden County SD 200/PK-12
PO Box 230 69154 308-772-3242
Dr. Paula Sissel, supt. Fax 772-3039
www.gardencountyschools.org/
Garden County JSHS 100/7-12
PO Box 230 69154 308-772-3242
Jason Spady, prin. Fax 772-3039

Osmond, Pierce, Pop. 774
Osmond SD 200/K-12
PO Box 458 68765 402-748-3777
David Hamm, supt. Fax 748-3210
www.osmondtigers.org
Osmond JSHS 100/7-12
PO Box 458 68765 402-748-3777
Michael Brown, prin. Fax 748-3210

Overton, Dawson, Pop. 592
Overton SD 300/PK-12
PO Box 310 68863 308-987-2424
Mark Aten, supt. Fax 987-2349
www.overtoneagles.org
Overton JSHS 100/7-12
PO Box 310 68863 308-987-2424
Brian Fleischman, prin. Fax 987-2349

Oxford, Furnas, Pop. 773
Southern Valley SD 400/K-12
43739 Highway 89 68967 308-868-2222
Darren Tobey, supt. Fax 868-2223
sites.google.com/a/sveagles.org/southern-valley
Southern Valley JSHS 200/7-12
43739 Highway 89 68967 308-868-2222
Brendan Calahan, prin. Fax 868-2223

Palmer, Merrick, Pop. 470
Palmer SD 300/PK-12
PO Box 248 68864 308-894-3065
Dr. Joel Bohlken, supt. Fax 894-8245
www.palmertigers.org
Palmer JSHS 100/7-12
PO Box 248 68864 308-894-3065
Greg Morris, prin. Fax 894-8245

Palmyra, Otoe, Pop. 536
Palmyra OR 1 SD 400/K-12
PO Box 130 68418 402-780-5327
Robert Hanger, supt. Fax 780-5328
www.district or1.org/
Palmyra JSHS 200/7-12
PO Box 130 68418 402-780-5327
David Bottrell, prin. Fax 780-5328

Papillion, Sarpy, Pop. 18,478
Papillion La Vista Community SD 10,900/PK-12
420 S Washington St 68046 402-537-6200
Dr. Andrew Rikli, supt. Fax 537-6216
www.paplv.org
Ideal S Alt
1104 Applewood Dr 68046 402-898-0485
Russ Wiederholt, prin. Fax 898-0486
Liberty MS, 10820 Wittmuss Dr 68046 7-8
Brent Holder, prin. 402-537-6200
Papillion-La Vista HS 1,600/9-12
402 E Centennial Rd 68046 402-898-0400
Jerry Kalina, prin. Fax 898-0415
Papillion-La Vista South HS 1,700/9-12
10799 Highway 370 68046 402-829-4600
Jeff Johnson, prin. Fax 827-1330
Papillion MS 800/7-8
423 S Washington St 68046 402-898-0424
Tim Johnson, prin. Fax 898-0430
Other Schools – See La Vista

Nebraska Christian College Post-Sec.
12550 S 114th St 68046 402-935-9400

Pawnee City, Pawnee, Pop. 861
Pawnee City SD 300/K-12
PO Box 393 68420 402-852-2988
Brian Rottinghaus, supt. Fax 852-2993
www.pawneecityschool.com
Pawnee City JSHS 100/7-12
PO Box 393 68420 402-852-2988
Donald Jacobs, prin. Fax 852-2993

Paxton, Keith, Pop. 521
Paxton Consolidated SD 200/K-12
PO Box 368 69155 308-239-4283
Delbert Dack, supt. Fax 239-4359
www.paxtonschools.org
Paxton JSHS 100/7-12
PO Box 368 69155 308-239-4283
Sheri Chittenden, prin. Fax 239-4359

Pender, Thurston, Pop. 991
Pender SD 400/PK-12
609 Whitney St 68047 402-385-3244
Jason Dolliver, supt. Fax 385-3342
www.penderschools.org/
Pender JSHS 200/7-12
609 Whitney St 68047 402-385-3244
Eric Miller, prin. Fax 385-3342

Peru, Nemaha, Pop. 853

Peru State College Post-Sec.
PO Box 10 68421 402-872-3815

Petersburg, Boone, Pop. 329
Boone Central SD
Supt. — See Albion
Boone Central MS 100/6-8
PO Box 240 68652 402-386-5302
Jimmy Feeney, prin. Fax 386-5464

Pierce, Pierce, Pop. 1,757
Pierce SD 600/K-12
201 N Sunset St 68767 402-329-4677
Kendall Steffensen, supt. Fax 329-4678
www.piercepublic.org/
Pierce JSHS 300/7-12
201 N Sunset St 68767 402-329-6217
Mark Brahmer, prin. Fax 329-4678

Pilger, Stanton, Pop. 343
Wisner-Pilger SD
Supt. — See Wisner
Wisner-Pilger MS 100/7-8
350 E 2nd St 68768 402-396-3566
Mark Porter, prin. Fax 396-3566

Plainview, Pierce, Pop. 1,240
Plainview SD 300/K-12
PO Box 638 68769 402-582-4993
Darren Arlt, supt. Fax 582-4665
www.plainviewschools.org/
Plainview JSHS 200/7-12
PO Box 638 68769 402-582-4991
Patty Novicki, prin. Fax 582-4665

Plattsmouth, Cass, Pop. 6,376
Plattsmouth SD 1,800/PK-12
1912 E Highway 34 68048 402-296-3361
Dr. Richard E. Hasty, supt. Fax 296-3361
www.pcsd.org
Plattsmouth HS 500/9-12
1912 E Highway 34 68048 402-296-3322
Jeffery Wiles, prin. Fax 296-3342
Plattsmouth MS 500/5-8
1912 E Highway 34 68048 402-296-3174
Mark Smith, prin. Fax 296-2910

Pleasanton, Buffalo, Pop. 340
Pleasanton SD 300/PK-12
PO Box 190 68866 308-388-2041
Jeff Vetter, supt. Fax 388-2041
pleasantonbulldogs.org
Pleasanton JSHS 100/7-12
PO Box 190 68866 308-388-2041
James Westland, prin. Fax 388-5502

Polk, Polk, Pop. 321
High Plains Community SD 200/K-12
PO Box 29 68654 402-765-2271
Brian Tonniges, supt. Fax 765-2272
www.hpcstorm.org
High Plains HS 100/9-12
PO Box 29 68654 402-765-3331
Cameron Hudson, prin. Fax 765-3332
Other Schools – See Clarks

Ponca, Dixon, Pop. 947
Ponca SD 400/K-12
PO Box 568 68770 402-755-5700
Joan Reznicek, supt. Fax 755-5773
www.poncaschool.org
Ponca JSHS 200/7-12
PO Box 568 68770 402-755-5701
Michelle Rinas, prin. Fax 755-5773

Potter, Cheyenne, Pop. 337
Potter-Dix SD 200/K-12
PO Box 189 69156 308-879-4434
Michael Williams, supt. Fax 879-4566
www.pdcoyotes.org
Potter-Dix JSHS 100/7-12
PO Box 189 69156 308-879-4434
Jane Brown, prin. Fax 879-4566

Ralston, Douglas, Pop. 5,872
Ralston SD 3,100/PK-12
8545 Park Dr 68127 402-331-4700
Dr. Mark Adler, supt. Fax 331-4843
www.ralstonschools.org/
Ralston HS 1,000/9-12
8969 Park Dr 68127 402-331-7373
Jesse Tvrdy, prin. Fax 898-3511
Ralston MS 500/7-8
8202 Lakeview St 68127 402-331-4701
Andy Parizek, prin. Fax 331-5376

Randolph, Cedar, Pop. 943
Randolph SD 45 200/PK-12
PO Box 755 68771 402-337-0252
Jeffrey Hoesing, supt. Fax 337-0235
www.randolphpublic.org/
Randolph JSHS 100/7-12
PO Box 755 68771 402-337-0252
Dennis Bazata, prin. Fax 337-0235

Ravenna, Buffalo, Pop. 1,347
Ravenna SD 500/PK-12
PO Box 8400 68869 308-452-3249
Dr. Ken Schroeder, supt. Fax 452-3172
www.ravennabluejays.org
Ravenna JSHS 200/7-12
PO Box 8400 68869 308-452-3249
Brad Kjar, prin. Fax 452-3172

Raymond, Lancaster, Pop. 163
Raymond Central SD 500/K-12
1800 W Agnew Rd 68428 402-785-2615
Paul Hull, supt. Fax 785-2097
www.rcentral.org
Raymond JSHS 300/7-12
1800 W Agnew Rd 68428 402-785-2685
Kolin Haecker, prin. Fax 785-7070

Red Cloud, Webster, Pop. 1,006
Red Cloud Community SD 200/K-12
334 N Cherry St 68970 402-746-3413
Brian Hof, supt. Fax 746-3690
www.redcloud.k12.ne.us/
Washington JSHS 100/7-12
121 W 7th Ave 68970 402-746-2818
Jason Heldt, prin. Fax 746-2817

Rising City, Butler, Pop. 373
Shelby-Rising City SD
Supt. — See Shelby

Shelby-Rising City MS 100/6-8
PO Box 160 68658 402-542-2216
William Curry, prin. Fax 542-2265

Roseland, Adams, Pop. 235
Silver Lake SD 200/K-12
PO Box 8 68973 402-756-6611
Mel Crowe, supt. Fax 756-6613
www.silverlakemustangs.org
Silver Lake JSHS 100/7-12
PO Box 8 68973 402-756-6611
Terry Bauer, prin. Fax 756-6613

Rushville, Sheridan, Pop. 866
Gordon-Rushville SD
Supt. — See Gordon
Gordon-Rushville MS 200/6-8
PO Box 590 69360 308-327-2491
Matt Stetson, prin. Fax 327-2504

Saint Edward, Boone, Pop. 704
Saint Edward SD 100/K-12
PO Box C 68660 402-678-2282
Kevin Lyons, supt. Fax 678-2284
stedwardpublicschool.ne.schoolinsites.com
Saint Edward JSHS 100/7-12
PO Box C 68660 402-678-2282
Kevin Lyons, prin. Fax 678-2284

Saint Paul, Howard, Pop. 2,270
Saint Paul SD 600/K-12
PO Box 325 68873 308-754-4433
John Poppert, supt. Fax 754-5374
www.stpaulpublicschools.org
Saint Paul JSHS 200/7-12
PO Box 325 68873 308-754-4433
Jennifer Hagen, prin. Fax 754-5374

Sargent, Custer, Pop. 524
Sargent SD 200/K-12
PO Box 366 68874 308-527-4119
Wayne Ruppert, supt. Fax 527-3332
sargentpublicschools.org
Sargent JSHS 100/7-12
PO Box 366 68874 308-527-4119
Cory Grint, prin. Fax 527-3332

Schuyler, Colfax, Pop. 6,165
Schuyler Community SD 1,800/PK-12
401 Adam St 68661 402-352-2421
Dr. Daniel Hoesing, supt. Fax 352-5552
schuylercommunityschools.org
Schuyler Central HS 500/9-12
401 Adam St 68661 402-352-3527
Stephen Grammer, prin. Fax 352-5552
Schuyler MS 300/6-8
200 W 10th St 68661 402-352-5514
Michelle Burton, prin. Fax 352-2644

Scottsbluff, Scotts Bluff, Pop. 14,885
Scottsbluff SD 3,100/PK-12
1722 1st Ave 69361 308-635-6200
Rick Myles, supt. Fax 635-6217
www.sbps.net
Bluffs MS 700/6-8
23rd and Broadway 69361 308-635-6270
Bert Wright, prin. Fax 635-6271
Scottsbluff HS 800/9-12
313 E 27th St 69361 308-635-6230
Michael Halley, prin. Fax 635-6240

Regional West Medical Center Post-Sec.
4021 Avenue B 69361 308-635-3711
Western Nebraska Community College Post-Sec.
1601 E 27th St 69361 308-635-3606

Scribner, Dodge, Pop. 841
Scribner-Snyder SD 200/K-12
PO Box L 68057 402-664-2568
Ginger Meyer, supt. Fax 664-2708
www.sstrojans.org
Scribner-Snyder JSHS 100/7-12
PO Box L 68057 402-664-2567
Brad Stithem, prin. Fax 664-2407

Seward, Seward, Pop. 6,883
Seward SD 1,400/PK-12
410 South St 68434 402-643-2941
Greg Barnes, supt. Fax 643-4986
www.sewardpublicschools.org
Seward HS 500/9-12
532 Northern Heights Dr 68434 402-643-2988
Scott Axt, prin. Fax 643-2599
Seward MS 400/5-8
2401 Karol Kay Blvd 68434 402-643-2986
Kirk Gottschalk, prin. Fax 643-6686

Concordia University Post-Sec.
800 N Columbia Ave 68434 402-643-3651
Saint Gregory the Great Seminary Post-Sec.
800 Fletcher Rd 68434 402-643-4052

Shelby, Polk, Pop. 707
Shelby-Rising City SD 400/PK-12
PO Box 218 68662 402-527-5946
Chester Kay, supt. Fax 527-5133
www.shelby.esu7.org
Shelby-Rising City HS 100/9-12
PO Box 218 68662 402-527-5946
William Curry, prin. Fax 527-5133
Other Schools – See Rising City

Shelton, Buffalo, Pop. 1,053
Shelton SD 300/K-12
PO Box 610 68876 308-647-6742
Brian Gegg, supt. Fax 647-5233
www.shelton.k12.ne.us
Shelton JSHS 100/7-12
PO Box 610 68876 308-647-5459
Jeremy Wieseler, prin. Fax 647-5233

Shickley, Fillmore, Pop. 338
Shickley SD 50/PK-12
PO Box 407 68436 402-627-3375
Bryce Jorgenson, supt. Fax 627-2003
www.shickleypublicschool.com
Shickley S 50/PK-12
PO Box 407 68436 402-627-3375
Derek Ippensen, prin. Fax 627-2003

Sidney, Cheyenne, Pop. 6,700
Sidney SD 1,100/PK-12
1101 21st Ave 69162 308-254-5855
Jay Ehler, supt. Fax 254-5756
www.sidneyraiders.org
Sidney HS 300/9-12
1101 21st Ave 69162 308-254-5893
Chris Arent, prin. Fax 254-5992
Sidney MS 200/7-8
1101 21st Ave 69162 308-254-5853
Brandon Ross, prin. Fax 254-1130

Western Nebraska Community College Post-Sec.
371 College Dr 69162 308-254-5450

South Sioux City, Dakota, Pop. 13,178
South Sioux City SD 3,700/K-12
PO Box 158 68776 402-494-2425
Dr. Vernon Fisher, supt. Fax 494-3916
www.ssccardinals.org
South Sioux City HS 1,200/9-12
3301 G St 68776 402-494-2433
Odell Santos, prin. Fax 494-2464
South Sioux City MS 800/6-8
3625 G St 68776 402-494-3061
Tom McGuire, prin. Fax 494-8427

Spalding, Greeley, Pop. 485
Riverside SD 100/PK-12
124 S Ash St 68665 308-358-0640
Dr. Joan Carraher, supt. Fax 358-0211
www.riversideps.org
Other Schools – See Cedar Rapids

Spalding Academy 100/K-12
PO Box 310 68665 308-497-2103
Amy McKay, prin. Fax 497-2105

Spencer, Boyd, Pop. 452
West Boyd SD 200/K-12
PO Box 109 68777 402-589-1333
Merrell Nelsen, supt. Fax 589-2041
www.westboyd.com
West Boyd - Spencer Attendance Center 100/5-12
PO Box 109 68777 402-589-1333
Mark Koch, prin. Fax 589-1142

Springfield, Sarpy, Pop. 1,494
Springfield Platteview Community SD 1,100/PK-12
14801 S 108th St 68059 402-592-1300
Brett Richards, supt. Fax 597-8551
www.springfieldplatteview.org
Platteview Central JHS 200/7-8
14801 S 108th St 68059 402-339-5052
Darin Johnson, prin. Fax 339-3166
Platteview HS 300/9-12
14801 S 108th St 68059 402-339-3606
Ronald Alexander, prin. Fax 339-3751

Springview, Keya Paha, Pop. 242
Keya Paha County SD 100/K-12
PO Box 219 68778 402-497-3501
Charlie Curnyn, supt. Fax 497-4321
keyapahacountyschools.org/
Keya Paha County HS 50/7-12
PO Box 219 68778 402-497-3501
Lucas Wroblewski, prin. Fax 497-4321

Stanton, Stanton, Pop. 1,562
Stanton Community SD 500/K-12
PO Box 749 68779 402-439-2233
Michael J. Sieh Ed.D., supt. Fax 439-2270
www.scs-ne.org/
Stanton MSHS 200/7-12
PO Box 749 68779 402-439-2250
David Cunningham, prin. Fax 439-2270

Stapleton, Logan, Pop. 305
Stapleton SD 200/PK-12
PO Box 128 69163 308-636-2252
Clayton Waddle, supt. Fax 636-2618
www.stapletonschools.org
Stapleton JSHS 100/7-12
PO Box 128 69163 308-636-2252
Clayton Waddle, prin. Fax 636-2618

Sterling, Johnson, Pop. 476
Sterling SD 200/K-12
PO Box 39 68443 402-866-4761
Ryan Knippelmeyer, supt. Fax 866-4771
www.sterlingjets.org
Sterling HS 100/9-12
PO Box 39 68443 402-866-4761
Ryun Theobald, prin. Fax 866-4771
Sterling MS 50/6-8
PO Box 39 68443 402-866-4761
Ryun Theobald, prin. Fax 866-4771

Stromsburg, Polk, Pop. 1,155
Cross County Community SD 300/PK-12
PO Box 525 68666 402-764-5521
Brent Hollinger, supt. Fax 764-8294
crosscountyschools.org
Cross County MSHS 100/6-12
PO Box 525 68666 402-764-5521
Bobby Kelley, prin. Fax 764-8294

Stuart, Holt, Pop. 586
Stuart SD 200/PK-12
PO Box 99 68780 402-924-3302
Robert Hanzlik, supt. Fax 924-3676
www.stuartbroncos.org
Stuart JSHS 100/7-12
PO Box 99 68780 402-924-3302
Robert Hanzlik, prin. Fax 924-3676

Sumner, Dawson, Pop. 234
Sumner-Eddyville-Miller SD 200/K-12
PO Box 126 68878 308-752-2925
Kevin Finkey, supt. Fax 752-2600
www.semmustangs.org
SEM JSHS 100/7-12
PO Box 126 68878 308-752-2925
William Schmidt, supt. Fax 752-2600

Superior, Nuckolls, Pop. 1,929
Superior SD 500/PK-12
PO Box 288 68978 402-879-3258
Charles Isom, supt. Fax 879-3022
Superior JSHS 200/7-12
PO Box 288 68978 402-879-3257
Robert Cook, prin. Fax 879-3022

Sutherland, Lincoln, Pop. 1,283
Sutherland SD 300/PK-12
PO Box 217 69165 308-386-4656
Dan Keyser, supt. Fax 386-2426
www.spssailors.org/
Sutherland JSHS 200/7-12
PO Box 217 69165 308-386-4656
Dustin Mitchell, prin. Fax 386-2426

Sutton, Clay, Pop. 1,500
Sutton SD 400/PK-12
PO Box 590 68979 402-773-5569
Dana Wiseman, supt. Fax 773-5578
www.suttonpublicschool.org
Sutton JSHS 200/7-12
PO Box 590 68979 402-773-4303
Brandy Thompson, prin. Fax 773-5578

Syracuse, Otoe, Pop. 1,933
Syracuse-Dunbar-Avoca SD 700/PK-12
PO Box P 68446 402-269-2381
Bradley Buller, supt. Fax 269-3028
www.sdarockets.org
Syracuse HS 200/9-12
PO Box P 68446 402-269-2381
Kyle Rohrig, prin. Fax 269-3028
Syracuse MS 300/4-8
PO Box P 68446 402-269-2388
Tim Farley, prin. Fax 269-2402

Table Rock, Pawnee, Pop. 267
Humboldt Table Rock Steinauer SD 70
Supt. — See Humboldt
Humboldt Table Rock Steinauer MS 100/6-8
608 State St 68447 402-862-2151
Lisa Othmer, prin. Fax 862-2152

Taylor, Loup, Pop. 190
Loup County SD 100/K-12
PO Box 170 68879 308-942-6115
Wayne Ruppert, supt. Fax 942-6248
blog.loupcounty.k12.ne.us/school/
Loup County JSHS 50/7-12
PO Box 170 68879 308-942-6115
Ken Sheets, prin. Fax 942-6248

Tecumseh, Johnson, Pop. 1,665
Johnson County Central SD 600/PK-12
PO Box 338 68450 402-335-3320
Jack Moles, supt. Fax 335-3346
www.jccentral.org
Johnson County Central HS 200/9-12
PO Box 338 68450 402-335-3328
Rick Lester, prin. Fax 335-3346
Other Schools – See Cook

Tekamah, Burt, Pop. 1,725
Tekamah-Herman SD 600/PK-12
112 N 13th St 68061 402-374-2157
Dan Gross, supt. Fax 374-2155
www.tekamah.esu2.org
Tekamah JSHS 200/7-12
112 N 13th St 68061 402-374-2156
Tom Borders, prin. Fax 374-2155

Thedford, Thomas, Pop. 188
Thedford SD 100/PK-12
PO Box 248 69166 308-645-2230
Henry Eggert, supt. Fax 645-2618
thedfordschools.org/thedfordschools.org/Thedford_Home
Thedford HS 50/7-12
PO Box 248 69166 308-645-2614
Jim York, prin. Fax 645-2618

Tilden, Madison, Pop. 942
Elkhorn Valley SD 300/PK-12
PO Box 430 68781 402-368-5301
Keith Leckron, supt. Fax 368-5338
www.elkhornvalleyschools.org
Elkhorn Valley JSHS 100/7-12
PO Box 430 68781 402-368-5301
Darin Hahne, prin. Fax 368-5338

Trenton, Hitchcock, Pop. 557
Hitchcock County SD 300/PK-12
PO Box 368 69044 308-334-5575
Robert Sattler, supt. Fax 334-5381
www.hcfalcons.org
Hitchcock County HS 100/7-12
PO Box 368 69044 308-334-5575
Robert Sattler, prin. Fax 334-5381

Tryon, McPherson, Pop. 153
McPherson County SD 100/K-12
PO Box 38 69167 308-587-2262
Lorrie Miller, supt. Fax 587-2571
www.mcstryon.org
McPherson County HS 50/8-12
PO Box 38 69167 308-587-2262
Debra Brownfield, prin. Fax 587-2571

Utica, Seward, Pop. 859
Centennial SD 500/PK-12
PO Box 187 68456 402-534-2291
Tim DeWaard, supt. Fax 534-2291
www.centennialbroncos.org
Centennial JSHS 200/7-12
PO Box 187 68456 402-534-2321
Colin Bargen, prin. Fax 534-2291

Valentine, Cherry, Pop. 2,652
Valentine SD 600/K-12
431 N Green St 69201 402-376-1780
Jamie Isom, supt. Fax 376-2736
www.valentinecommunityschools.org/
Valentine HS 200/9-12
431 N Green St 69201 402-376-2730
Andy Cronin, prin. Fax 376-2736
Valentine MS 100/6-8
239 N Wood St 69201 402-376-3367
Jeff Sayer, prin. Fax 376-3386

Valley, Douglas, Pop. 1,851
Douglas County West Community SD 700/K-12
PO Box 378 68064 402-359-2583
Melissa Poloncic, supt. Fax 359-4371
www.dcwest.org/
Douglas County West HS 300/9-12
PO Box 378 68064 402-359-2121
Jim Knott, prin. Fax 359-2893
Other Schools – See Waterloo

Verdigre, Knox, Pop. 565
Nebraska USD 1
Supt. — See Orchard
Verdigre S 100/PK-12
201 S 3rd St 68783 402-668-2275
Chuck Kucera, prin. Fax 668-2276

Waco, York, Pop. 233

Nebraska Evangelical Lutheran HS 100/9-12
203 Kendall St 68460 402-728-5236
Mark Otte, admin. Fax 728-5433

Wahoo, Saunders, Pop. 4,441
Wahoo SD 1,000/PK-12
2201 N Locust St 68066 402-443-3051
Brandon Lavaley, supt. Fax 443-4731
www.wahooschools.org
Wahoo HS 300/9-12
2201 N Locust St 68066 402-443-4332
Jarred Royal, prin. Fax 443-4731
Wahoo MS 200/6-8
2201 N Locust St 68066 402-443-3101
Marc Kaminski, prin. Fax 443-4731

Bishop Neumann Central HS 300/7-12
202 S Linden St 68066 402-443-4151
Fr. Jeremy Hazuka, prin. Fax 443-5551

Wakefield, Dixon, Pop. 1,440
Wakefield SD 400/PK-12
PO Box 330 68784 402-287-2012
Mark Bejot, supt. Fax 287-2014
www.wakefieldschools.org/
Wakefield JSHS 200/7-12
PO Box 330 68784 402-287-2012
Jason Heitz, prin. Fax 287-2014

Wallace, Lincoln, Pop. 360
Wallace SD 65 R 200/K-12
151 N Wallace Rd 69169 308-387-4323
Thomas Sandberg, supt. Fax 387-4322
whs.esu16.org
Wallace JSHS 100/7-12
151 N Wallace Rd 69169 308-387-4323
Dana Reinke, prin. Fax 387-4322

Walthill, Thurston, Pop. 761
Walthill SD 300/K-12
PO Box 3C 68067 402-846-5432
Ed Stansberry, supt. Fax 846-5029
walthweb.esu1.org
Walthill JSHS 100/7-12
PO Box 3C 68067 402-846-5432
Ed Ross, prin. Fax 846-5029

Waterloo, Douglas, Pop. 837
Douglas County West Community SD
Supt. — See Valley
Douglas County West MS 200/5-8
800 N Front St 68069 402-779-2646
Jeremy Travis, prin. Fax 779-2534

Wauneta, Chase, Pop. 575
Wauneta-Palisade SD 200/K-12
PO Box 368 69045 308-394-5700
Randy Geier, supt. Fax 394-5962
www.waunetapalisadeschools.org
Wauneta-Palisade HS 50/9-12
PO Box 368 69045 308-394-5650
Joseph Frecks, prin. Fax 394-5962
Wauneta Palisade MS 50/7-8
PO Box 368 69045 308-394-5650
Joseph Frecks, prin. Fax 394-5962

Wausa, Knox, Pop. 629
Wausa SD 200/K-12
PO Box 159 68786 402-586-2255
Bradley Hoesing, supt. Fax 586-2406
wausaweb.esu1.org
Wausa HS 100/9-12
PO Box 159 68786 402-586-2255
Bradley Hoesing, prin. Fax 586-2406

Waverly, Lancaster, Pop. 3,253
Waverly SD 145 1,900/K-12
PO Box 426 68462 402-786-2321
Dr. Bill Heimann, supt. Fax 786-2799
www.district145.org
Waverly HS 600/9-12
PO Box 426 68462 402-786-2765
Ryan Ricenbaw, prin. Fax 786-2799
Waverly MS 400/6-8
PO Box 426 68462 402-786-2348
Ross Ricenbaw, prin. Fax 786-2782

Wayne, Wayne, Pop. 5,585
Wayne SD 700/PK-12
611 W 7th St 68787 402-375-3150
Mark Lenihan, supt. Fax 375-5251
www.wayneschools.org
Wayne JSHS 300/7-12
611 W 7th St 68787 402-375-3150
Mark Hanson, prin. Fax 375-5251

Wayne State College Post-Sec.
1111 Main St 68787 402-375-7000

Weeping Water, Cass, Pop. 1,042
Weeping Water SD 300/PK-12
PO Box 206 68463 402-267-2445
Dr. Ken Heinz Ed.D., supt. Fax 267-5217
www.weepingwaterps.org/
Weeping Water HS 100/9-12
PO Box 206 68463 402-267-2445
Gary Wockenfuss, prin. Fax 267-5217
Weeping Water MS 6-8
PO Box 206 68463 402-267-2445
Gary Wockenfuss, prin. Fax 267-5217

West Point, Cuming, Pop. 3,356
West Point SD 600/PK-12
1200 E Washington St 68788 402-372-5860
Bill McAllister, supt. Fax 372-5458
www.wpcadets.org
West Point-Beemer JSHS 300/5-12
1200 E Washington St 68788 402-372-5546
Daniel Weddle, prin. Fax 372-2252

Guardian Angels/Central Catholic HS 200/7-12
419 E Decatur St 68788 402-372-5326
Kate Hagemann, prin. Fax 372-5327

Wilber, Saline, Pop. 1,843
Wilber-Clatonia SD 600/PK-12
PO Box 487 68465 402-821-2266
Ray Collins, supt. Fax 821-3013
www.wilber-clatonia.org
Wilber-Clatonia JSHS 200/7-12
PO Box 487 68465 402-821-2508
Mark Fritch, prin. Fax 821-3013

Wilcox, Kearney, Pop. 354
Wilcox-Hildreth SD 200/K-12
PO Box 190 68982 308-478-5265
Dan Ingwersen, supt. Fax 478-5260
whfalcons.org
Wilcox-Hildreth HS 100/9-12
PO Box 190 68982 308-478-5265
Justin Patterson, prin. Fax 478-5260
Other Schools – See Hildreth

Winnebago, Thurston, Pop. 756
Winnebago SD 500/K-12
PO Box KK 68071 402-878-2224
Dan Fehringer, supt. Fax 878-2472
winnebago.esu1.org
Winnebago HS 100/7-12
PO Box KK 68071 402-878-2224
Lori Tremayne, prin. Fax 878-2472

Little Priest Tribal College Post-Sec.
PO Box 270 68071 402-878-2380

Winside, Wayne, Pop. 419
Winside SD 200/PK-12
203 Crawford Ave 68790 402-286-4466
Michael Shoff, supt. Fax 286-4466
www.winsidewildcats.org
Winside JSHS 100/7-12
203 Crawford Ave 68790 402-286-4465
Sarah Remm, prin. Fax 286-4466

Wisner, Cuming, Pop. 1,154
Wisner-Pilger SD 400/K-12
PO Box 580 68791 402-529-3249
Chad Boyer, supt. Fax 529-3477
www.wisnerpilger.org
Wisner HS 200/9-12
PO Box 580 68791 402-529-3249
Christopher Uttecht, prin. Fax 529-3477
Other Schools – See Pilger

Wood River, Hall, Pop. 1,319
Wood River Rural SD 500/K-12
PO Box 518 68883 308-583-2249
Dr. James Haley Ed.D., supt. Fax 583-2395
www.woodriver.k12.ne.us/
Wood River Rural HS 100/9-12
PO Box 518 68883 308-583-2249
Terry Zessin, prin. Fax 583-2395
Wood River Rural MS 100/6-8
PO Box 518 68883 308-583-2249
Terry Zessin, prin. Fax 583-2395

Wymore, Gage, Pop. 1,431
Southern SD 1 400/K-12
PO Box 237 68466 402-645-3326
Gene Haddix, supt. Fax 645-8049
www.southernschools.org
Southern JSHS 200/7-12
PO Box 237 68466 402-645-3326
Jeff Murphy, prin. Fax 645-8049

Wynot, Cedar, Pop. 165
Wynot SD 200/K-12
PO Box 157 68792 402-357-2121
Jeff Messersmith, supt. Fax 357-2524
www.wynotpublicschools.org
Wynot HS 100/9-12
PO Box 157 68792 402-357-2121
Richard Higgins, prin. Fax 357-2524
Wynot MS 50/5-8
PO Box 157 68792 402-357-2121
Richard Higgins, prin. Fax 357-2524

York, York, Pop. 7,673
York SD 1,200/PK-12
1715 N Delaware Ave 68467 402-362-6655
Dr. Mike Lucas, supt. Fax 362-6943
www.yorkpublic.org/
York HS 400/9-12
1005 Duke Dr 68467 402-362-6655
Mitch Bartholomew, prin. Fax 362-2994
York MS 300/6-8
1730 N Delaware Ave 68467 402-362-6655
Kenny Loosvelt, prin. Fax 362-6831

York College Post-Sec.
1125 E 8th St 68467 402-363-5600

Yutan, Saunders, Pop. 1,169
Yutan SD 400/K-12
1200 2nd St 68073 402-625-2243
Stanford Hendricks, supt. Fax 625-2812
www.yutanpublicschools.com
Yutan JSHS 200/7-12
1200 2nd St 68073 402-625-2241
Timothy McNamara, prin. Fax 625-2812

NEVADA

NEVADA DEPARTMENT OF EDUCATION
700 E Fifth St, Carson City 89701-5096
Telephone 775-687-9200
Fax 775-687-9101
Website http://www.doe.nv.gov/

Superintendent of Instruction Steve Canavero

NEVADA BOARD OF EDUCATION
700 E Fifth St, Carson City 89701-5096

President Elaine Wynn

PUBLIC, PRIVATE AND CATHOLIC SECONDARY SCHOOLS

Alamo, Lincoln, Pop. 1,045
Lincoln County SD
Supt. — See Panaca
Pahranagat Valley JSHS 100/6-12
PO Box 298 89001 775-725-3321
Mike Strong, prin. Fax 725-3334

Austin, Lander, Pop. 191
Lander County SD
Supt. — See Battle Mountain
Austin S 50/K-12
PO Box 160 89310 775-964-2467
Michelle Caramella, lead tchr. Fax 964-1206

Battle Mountain, Lander, Pop. 3,594
Lander County SD 800/PK-12
PO Box 1300 89820 775-635-2886
Jim Squibb, supt. Fax 635-5347
www.lander.k12.nv.us
Battle Mountain HS 300/9-12
PO Box 1330 89820 775-635-5436
Russel Klein, prin. Fax 635-5459
Lemaire JHS 100/6-8
PO Box 1360 89820 775-635-8114
Dr. Toby Melver, prin. Fax 635-8803
Other Schools – See Austin

Beatty, Nye, Pop. 983
Nye County SD
Supt. — See Tonopah
Beatty HS 100/9-12
PO Box 806 89003 775-553-2595
Rob Williams, prin. Fax 553-2887

Boulder City, Clark, Pop. 14,662
Clark County SD
Supt. — See Las Vegas
Boulder City HS 600/9-12
1101 5th St 89005 702-799-8200
Amy Wagner, prin. Fax 799-8230
Garrett MS 500/6-8
1200 Avenue G 89005 702-799-8290
Jamey Hood, prin. Fax 799-8252

Caliente, Lincoln, Pop. 1,102
Lincoln County SD
Supt. — See Panaca
Bastian HS 100/7-12
PO Box 1088 89008 775-726-8250
Cody Christensen, prin. Fax 726-3371

Carlin, Elko, Pop. 2,339
Elko County SD
Supt. — See Elko
Carlin S 100/K-12
PO Box 730 89822 775-754-6317
Janice Alexander, prin. Fax 754-2175

Carson City, Carson City, Pop. 54,098
Carson City SD 7,500/K-12
PO Box 603 89702 775-283-2000
Richard Stokes, supt. Fax 283-2090
www.carsoncityschools.com
Carson HS 2,200/9-12
1111 N Saliman Rd 89701 775-283-1600
Tasha Fuson, prin. Fax 283-1790
Carson MS 1,100/6-8
1140 W King St 89703 775-283-2800
Dan Sadler, prin. Fax 283-2890
Eagle Valley MS 600/6-8
4151 E Fifth St 89701 775-283-2600
Lee Conley, prin. Fax 283-2690
Pioneer HS 200/Alt
202 Corbett St 89706 775-283-1300
Jason Zona, prin. Fax 283-1390

Carson City Beauty Academy Post-Sec.
1851 S Roop St Ste 100 89701 775-885-9853
Sierra Lutheran HS 100/9-12
3601 Romans Rd 89705 775-267-1921
Rev. Juls Clausen, prin. Fax 267-6580
Western Nevada College Post-Sec.
2201 W College Pkwy 89703 775-445-3000

Dayton, Lyon, Pop. 8,727
Lyon County SD
Supt. — See Yerington
Dayton HS 700/9-12
335 Dayton Valley Rd 89403 775-246-6240
Steve Henderson, prin. Fax 246-6245
Dayton IS 400/7-8
315 Dayton Valley Rd 89403 775-246-6250
Kevin Kranjcec, prin. Fax 246-6253

Dyer, Esmeralda, Pop. 249

Deep Springs College Post-Sec.
HC 72 Box 45001 89010 760-872-2000

Elko, Elko, Pop. 17,970
Elko County SD 8,800/K-12
PO Box 1012 89803 775-738-5196
Jeff Zander, supt. Fax 738-5857
www.ecsdnv.net
Adobe MS 600/7-8
3375 Jennings Way 89801 775-738-3375
Colby Corbitt, prin. Fax 738-3860
Elko HS 1,300/9-12
987 College Ave 89801 775-738-7281
Tim Wickersham, prin. Fax 738-9616
Adult HS Adult
PO Box 1012 89803 775-753-2233
Jack French, dir. Fax 753-2257
Other Schools – See Carlin, Jackpot, Owyhee, Spring Creek, Wells, West Wendover

---

Great Basin College Post-Sec.
1500 College Pkwy 89801 775-738-8493

Ely, White Pine, Pop. 4,185
White Pine County SD 1,300/K-12
1135 Avenue C 89301 775-289-4851
Adam Young, supt. Fax 289-3999
www.whitepine.k12.nv.us
White Pine HS 400/9-12
1800 Bobcat Dr 89301 775-289-4811
Rebecca Murdock, prin. Fax 289-1542
White Pine MS 300/6-8
844 Aultman St 89301 775-289-4841
Susan Jensen, prin. Fax 289-1565
Other Schools – See Lund

Eureka, Eureka, Pop. 600
Eureka County SD 200/PK-12
PO Box 249 89316 775-237-5373
Dan Wold, supt. Fax 237-5014
www.eureka.k12.nv.us
Eureka County JSHS 100/7-12
PO Box 237 89316 775-237-5361
Dave Pyle, prin. Fax 237-5113

Fallon, Churchill, Pop. 8,201
Churchill County SD 2,500/PK-12
690 S Maine St 89406 775-423-0462
Dr. Sandra Sheldon, supt. Fax 423-9581
www.churchill.k12.nv.us
Churchill County HS 1,200/9-12
1222 S Taylor St 89406 775-423-2181
Kevin Lords, prin. Fax 423-8968
Churchill County MS 800/6-8
650 S Maine St 89406 775-423-7701
Scott Meihack, prin. Fax 423-8010

Fernley, Lyon, Pop. 18,657
Lyon County SD
Supt. — See Yerington
Fernley HS 900/9-12
1300 US Highway 95A S 89408 775-575-3400
Kent Jones, prin. Fax 575-3406
Silverland MS 500/7-8
1100 Jasmine Ln 89408 775-575-1575
Ryan Cross, prin. Fax 575-1566
Fernley Adult Education Center Adult
1300 US Highway 95A S 89408 775-575-3409
Carol King, coord. Fax 575-3399

Gabbs, Nye, Pop. 259
Nye County SD
Supt. — See Tonopah
Gabbs S 50/PK-12
PO Box 147 89409 775-285-2692
David Dispensa, prin. Fax 285-2381

Gardnerville, Douglas, Pop. 5,526
Douglas County SD
Supt. — See Minden
Carson Valley MS 500/6-8
1477 US Highway 395 N 89410 775-782-2265
Bob Been, prin. Fax 782-7341
Pau-Wa-Lu MS 400/6-8
701 Long Valley Rd, 775-265-6100
David Whittemore, prin. Fax 265-1653

Gerlach, Washoe, Pop. 206
Washoe County SD
Supt. — See Reno
Gerlach S 50/K-12
555 E Sunset Blvd 89412 775-557-2326
Rick Taylor, prin. Fax 557-2587

Hawthorne, Mineral, Pop. 3,168
Mineral County SD 500/PK-12
PO Box 1540 89415 775-945-2403
Walter Hackford, supt. Fax 945-3709
www.mineral.k12.nv.us
Hawthorne JHS 100/7-8
PO Box 938 89415 775-945-3332
Jeff Wales, prin. Fax 945-3371
Mineral County HS 100/9-12
PO Box 938 89415 775-945-3332
Jeff Wales, prin. Fax 945-3371

Henderson, Clark, Pop. 247,241
Clark County SD
Supt. — See Las Vegas
Basic Academy of International Studies 2,200/9-12
400 Palo Verde Dr 89015 702-799-8000
David Bechtel, prin. Fax 799-8966
Brown JHS 900/6-8
307 Cannes St 89015 702-799-8900
Wendy Phelps, prin. Fax 799-3511
Burkholder MS 800/6-8
355 W Van Wagenen St 89015 702-799-8080
Greg Hunter, prin. Fax 799-8088
College of Southern Nevada HS-South 100/11-12
700 College Dr, 702-651-3080
Barbara Collins, prin. Fax 651-3075
Coronado HS 3,100/9-12
1001 Coronado Center Dr 89052 702-799-6800
Mike Piccininni, prin. Fax 799-6839
Foothill HS 2,800/9-12
800 College Dr, 702-799-3500
Lisa Burkhead, prin. Fax 799-3524
Greenspun JHS 1,400/6-8
140 N Valle Verde Dr 89074 702-799-0920
Jacqueline Carducci, prin. Fax 799-0925
Green Valley HS 3,000/9-12
460 N Arroyo Grande Blvd 89014 702-799-0950
Kent Roberts, prin. Fax 799-0717
Liberty HS 2,500/9-12
3700 Liberty Heights Ave 89052 702-799-2270
Derek Bellow, prin. Fax 799-6858
Mannion MS 1,600/6-8
155 E Paradise Hills Dr, 702-799-3020
David Erbach, prin. Fax 799-3501
Miller MS 1,700/6-8
2400 Cozy Hill Cir 89052 702-799-2260
Nicole Lehman-Donadio, prin. Fax 799-1309
Webb MS 1,800/6-8
2200 Reunion Ave 89052 702-799-1305
Paula Naegle, prin. Fax 799-1310
White MS 1,400/6-8
1661 Galleria Dr 89014 702-799-0777
Andrea Katona, prin. Fax 799-7690

American Heritage Academy 100/PK-12
2100 Olympic Ave 89014 702-949-5614
Calvary Chapel Green Vlly Christian Acad 100/K-12
2615 W Horizon Ridge Pkwy 89052 702-456-2422
Bill Adams, prin. Fax 456-2515
DeVry University Post-Sec.
2490 Paseo Verde Pkwy #150 89074 702-933-9700
Euphoria Inst of Beauty Arts & Sciences Post-Sec.
11041 S Eastern Ave Ste 112 89052 702-932-8111
Everest College Post-Sec.
170 N Stephanie St 89074 702-567-1920
Green Valley Christian S 600/PK-12
711 Valle Verde Ct 89014 702-454-4056
Stephanie Smith, prin. Fax 454-6275
Henderson International S 400/PK-12
1165 Sandy Ridge Ave 89052 702-818-2100
Seth Ahlborn, hdmstr. Fax 616-2065
Lake Mead Christian Academy 600/PK-12
540 E Lake Mead Pkwy 89015 702-565-5831
Gayle Blakeley, admin. Fax 566-6206
Nevada State College Post-Sec.
1125 Nevada State Dr, 702-992-2000

Roseman University of Health Sciences Post-Sec.
11 Sunset Way 89014 702-990-4433
Sanford-Brown College Post-Sec.
2495 Village View Dr 89074 702-990-0150
The Art Institute of Las Vegas Post-Sec.
2350 Corporate Cir 89074 702-369-9944

Incline Village, Washoe, Pop. 8,627
Washoe County SD
Supt. — See Reno
Incline HS 300/9-12
499 Village Blvd 89451 775-832-4260
Leslie Hermann, prin. Fax 832-4208
Incline MS 200/6-8
931 Southwood Blvd 89451 775-832-4220
Sharon Kennedy, prin. Fax 832-4210

Sierra Nevada College-Lake Tahoe Post-Sec.
999 Tahoe Blvd 89451 775-831-1314

Indian Springs, Clark, Pop. 947
Clark County SD
Supt. — See Las Vegas
Indian Springs S 100/K-12
PO Box 1088 89018 702-799-0932
Brian Wiseman, prin. Fax 879-3142

Jackpot, Elko, Pop. 1,175
Elko County SD
Supt. — See Elko
Jackpot S 100/K-12
PO Box 463 89825 775-755-2374
Brian Messmer, prin. Fax 755-2291

Las Vegas, Clark, Pop. 562,567
Clark County SD 310,300/PK-12
5100 W Sahara Ave 89146 702-799-5000
Pat Skorkowsky, supt. Fax 799-5125
www.ccsd.net
Advanced Technologies Academy 1,100/9-12
2501 Vegas Dr 89106 702-799-7870
Jonathan Synold, prin. Fax 799-0656
Arbor View HS 2,800/9-12
7500 Whispering Sands Dr 89131 702-799-6660
Kevin McPartlin, prin. Fax 799-6669
Bailey MS 1,200/6-8
2500 N Hollywood Blvd 89156 702-799-4811
Gregory Cole, prin. Fax 799-4807
Becker MS 1,300/6-8
9151 Pinewood Hills Dr 89134 702-799-4460
Amy Smith, prin. Fax 799-4470
Bonanza HS 2,000/9-12
6665 Del Rey Ave 89146 702-799-4000
Joseph Petrie, prin. Fax 799-4078
Brinley MS 900/6-8
2480 Maverick St 89108 702-799-4550
Brett Booth, prin. Fax 799-4549
Burk Horizon/Southwest Sunset HS 200/Alt
4560 W Harmon Ave 89103 702-799-8150
Gina Piccolo, prin. Fax 799-1207
Cadwallader MS 1,500/6-8
7775 Elkhorn Rd 89131 702-799-6692
Mindi Martinez, prin. Fax 799-4536
Canarelli MS 1,900/6-8
7808 S Torrey Pines Dr 89139 702-799-1340
Monica Lang, prin. Fax 799-5715
Cannon JHS 900/6-8
5850 Euclid St 89120 702-799-5600
Warren McKay, prin. Fax 799-5644
Cashman MS 1,600/6-8
4622 W Desert Inn Rd 89102 702-799-5880
Misti Taton, prin. Fax 799-5947
Centennial HS 3,000/9-12
10200 Centennial Pkwy 89149 702-799-3440
Trent Day, prin. Fax 799-3443
Chaparral HS 2,200/9-12
3850 Annie Oakley Dr 89121 702-799-7580
Lolo James, prin. Fax 799-0776
Cimarron-Memorial HS 2,300/9-12
2301 N Tenaya Way 89128 702-799-4400
Lori Sarabyn, prin. Fax 799-4425
Clark HS 3,000/9-12
4291 Pennwood Ave 89102 702-799-5800
Jillyn Pendleton, prin. Fax 799-5813
College of Southern Nevada HS-West 200/11-12
6375 W Charleston Blvd 89146 702-651-5030
Barbara Collins, prin. Fax 651-5035
Cortney JHS 1,300/6-8
5301 E Hacienda Ave 89122 702-799-2400
David Rose, prin. Fax 799-2407
Cowan Behavior JSHS 100/Alt
5300 E Russell Rd 89122 702-799-6380
Belinda Marentic, prin. Fax 799-6388
Cowan Sunset Southeast High School 100/Alt
5300 E Russell Rd 89122 702-799-6370
Anita Williams, prin. Fax 799-6377
Del Sol HS 1,800/9-12
3100 E Patrick Ln 89120 702-799-6830
Gregory Misel, prin. Fax 799-2235
Desert Oasis HS 2,300/9-12
6600 W Erie Ave 89141 702-799-6881
Arthur Adams, prin. Fax 799-6888
Desert Pines HS 2,200/9-12
3800 Harris Ave 89110 702-799-2196
Isaac Stein, prin. Fax 799-2198
Durango HS 2,300/9-12
7100 W Dewey Dr 89113 702-799-5850
Nathan Miller, prin. Fax 799-5855
East Career & Technical Academy Vo/Tech
6705 Vegas Valley Dr 89142 702-799-8888
Darlin Delgado, prin. Fax 799-8899
Eldorado HS 1,800/9-12
1139 Linn Ln 89110 702-799-7200
David Wilson, prin. Fax 799-7255
Escobedo MS 1,200/6-8
9501 Echelon Point Dr 89149 702-799-4560
Stefanie Machin, prin. Fax 799-4568
Faiss MS 1,400/6-8
9525 W Maule Ave 89148 702-799-6850
Fax 799-6852
Fertitta MS 1,500/6-8
9905 W Mesa Vista Ave 89148 702-799-1900
Cailin Ellis, prin. Fax 799-5688
Fremont Professional Development MS 900/6-8
1100 E Saint Louis Ave 89104 702-799-5558
Ann Schiller, prin. Fax 799-5566
Garside JHS 1,200/6-8
300 S Torrey Pines Dr 89107 702-799-4245
Scarlett Perryman, prin. Fax 799-4296
Gibson MS 1,200/6-8
3900 W Washington Ave 89107 702-799-4700
Jennifer Jaeger, prin. Fax 799-4705
Global Community HS 200/Alt
3801 E Washington Ave 89110 702-799-8850
Gerald Bustamante, prin. Fax 799-8898
Guinn MS 800/6-8
4150 S Torrey Pines Dr 89103 702-799-5900
Georgia Taton, prin. Fax 799-5905
Harney MS 1,800/6-8
1580 S Hollywood Blvd 89142 702-799-3240
Susan Echols, prin. Fax 799-3286
Hyde Park MS 1,700/6-8
900 Hinson St 89107 702-799-4260
Anna Belknap, prin. Fax 799-0348
Johnson JHS 1,200/6-8
7701 Ducharme Ave 89145 702-799-4480
George Anas, prin. Fax 799-4497
Keller MS 1,300/6-8
301 N Fogg St 89110 702-799-3220
Debbie Brockett, prin. Fax 799-3226
Knudson MS 1,300/6-8
2400 Atlantic St 89104 702-799-7470
Monica Cortez, prin. Fax 799-0157
Las Vegas Academy of the Arts 1,700/9-12
315 S 7th St 89101 702-799-7800
Scott Walker, prin. Fax 799-7807
Las Vegas HS 3,000/9-12
6500 E Sahara Ave 89142 702-799-0180
Debbie Brockett, prin. Fax 799-0192
Lawrence JHS 1,500/6-8
4410 S Juliano Rd 89147 702-799-2540
Bevelyn Smothers, prin. Fax 799-2563
Leavitt MS 1,500/6-8
4701 Quadrel St 89129 702-799-4699
Keith Wipperman, prin. Fax 799-4528
Lied MS 1,200/6-8
5350 W Tropical Pkwy 89130 702-799-4620
Kelly O'Rourke, prin. Fax 799-4626
Mack MS 1,400/6-8
4250 Karen Ave 89121 702-799-2005
Roxanne Kelley, prin. Fax 799-2412
Martin MS 1,500/6-8
200 N 28th St 89101 702-799-7922
Mary Hafner, prin. Fax 799-7959
Molasky JHS 1,300/6-8
7801 W Gilmore Ave 89129 702-799-3400
Spencer Beals, prin. Fax 799-3407
Monaco MS 1,300/6-8
1870 N Lamont St 89115 702-799-3670
Lisa Medina, prin. Fax 799-3202
Morris Sunset E HS 100/Alt
1905 Atlantic St 89104 702-799-8880
Stacey White, prin. Fax 799-8898
Northwest Career & Technical Academy 1,800/9-12
8200 W Tropical Pkwy 89149 702-799-4640
Tina Statucki, prin. Fax 799-4644
O'Callaghan MS 1,400/6-8
1450 Radwick Dr 89110 702-799-7340
Scott Fligor, prin. Fax 799-8870
Orr MS 900/6-8
1562 E Katie Ave 89119 702-799-5573
George Leavens, prin. Fax 799-0297
Palo Verde HS 2,900/9-12
333 S Pavilion Center Dr 89144 702-799-1450
Darren Sweikert, prin. Fax 799-1455
Peterson Academic Center 50/Alt
10250 Centennial Pkwy 89149 702-799-6610
Michael Sharapan, prin. Fax 799-6604
Rancho HS 3,100/9-12
1900 Searles Ave 89101 702-799-7000
James Kuzma, prin. Fax 799-8316
Robison MS 1,100/6-8
825 Marion Dr 89110 702-799-7300
Fax 799-7302
Rogich MS 1,800/6-8
235 N Pavilion Center Dr 89144 702-799-6040
Susan Harrison, prin. Fax 799-6094
Saville MS 1,500/6-8
8101 N Torrey Pines Dr 89131 702-799-3460
Sean Davis, prin. Fax 799-4511
Sawyer MS 1,300/6-8
5450 Redwood St 89118 702-799-5980
Gregory Mingo, prin. Fax 799-5969
Schofield MS 1,300/6-8
8625 Spencer St 89123 702-799-2290
Terri Knepp, prin. Fax 799-5717
Shadow Ridge HS 2,500/9-12
5050 Brent Ln 89131 702-799-6699
Travis Warnick, prin. Fax 799-4698
Sierra Vista HS 2,300/9-12
8100 W Robindale Rd 89113 702-799-6820
John Anzalone, prin. Fax 799-6847
Silverado HS 2,200/9-12
1650 Silver Hawk Ave 89123 702-799-5790
Robert Mars, prin. Fax 799-5744
Silvestri JHS 1,600/6-8
1055 E Silverado Ranch Blvd, 702-799-2240
Merry Sillitoe, prin. Fax 799-2247
South Academic Center 100/Alt
1905 Atlantic St 89104 702-799-2070
Fax 799-2089
Southeast Career Tech Academy Vo/Tech
5710 Mountain Vista St 89120 702-799-7500
Kerry Pope, prin. Fax 799-2007
Southwest Career & Tech Academy Vo/Tech
7050 W Shelbourne Ave 89113 702-799-5766
Donna Levy, prin. Fax 799-5751
Spring Mountain JSHS 100/Alt
PO Box 252 89125 702-455-5555
Daniel Triana, prin. Fax 382-6035
Spring Valley HS 1,900/9-12
3750 S Buffalo Dr 89147 702-799-2580
Tam Larnerd, prin. Fax 799-1288
Sunrise Mountain HS 2,500/9-12
2575 Los Feliz St 89156 702-799-7207
Julia Llapur, prin. Fax 799-7212
Tarkanian MS 1,600/6-8
5800 W Pyle Ave 89141 702-799-6801
Eric Johnson, prin. Fax 799-6805
Valley HS 2,800/9-12
2839 Burnham Ave, 702-799-5450
Ramona Esparza, prin. Fax 799-1074
Veterans Tribute Career Technical Acad 700/9-12
2531 Vegas Dr 89106 702-799-4710
Tammy Bofelli, prin. Fax 799-4722
Von Tobel MS 1,100/6-8
2436 N Pecos Rd 89115 702-799-7280
Jaime Ditto, prin. Fax 799-7286
West Career & Technical Academy 1,400/9-12
11945 W Charleston Blvd 89135 702-799-4340
Amy Dockter-Rozar, prin. Fax 799-4355
Western HS 2,500/9-12
4601 W Bonanza Rd 89107 702-799-4080
Fax 799-4104
West Prep S 1,300/K-12
2050 Saphire Stone Ave 89106 702-799-3120
Danny Eichelberger, prin. Fax 799-1858
Woodbury MS 900/6-8
3875 E Harmon Ave 89121 702-799-7660
Greg Snelling, prin. Fax 799-0805
Other Schools – See Boulder City, Henderson, Indian Springs, Laughlin, Mesquite, North Las Vegas, Overton, Sandy Valley

---

Academy of Hair Design Post-Sec.
5191 W Charleston Blvd #150 89146 702-878-1185
Adelson Educational Campus 500/PK-12
9700 Hillpointe Rd 89134 702-255-4500
Rabbi Joyce Raynor, head sch Fax 255-7232
American Institute of Medical Sonography Post-Sec.
5450 W Sahara Ave Ste 320 89146 702-369-4216
Anthem Institute Post-Sec.
2320 S Rancho Dr 89102 702-385-6700
Associated Pathologist Laboratories Post-Sec.
4230 Burnham Ave 89119 702-733-7866
Bishop Gorman HS 1,300/9-12
5959 S Hualapai Way 89148 702-732-1945
Kevin Kiefer, prin. Fax 732-2856
Brightwood College Post-Sec.
3535 W Sahara Ave 89102 702-368-2338
Calvary Chapel Christian S 600/PK-12
7175 W Oquendo Rd 89113 702-248-8879
Rick Martin Ed.D., supt. Fax 220-8694
Carrington College Post-Sec.
5740 S Eastern Ave Ste 140 89119 702-514-3236
College of Southern Nevada Post-Sec.
6375 W Charleston Blvd 89146 702-651-5000
Desert Torah Academy 200/PK-12
1312 Vista Dr 89102 702-259-1000
Euphoria Inst of Beauty Arts & Sciences Post-Sec.
9340 W Sahara Ave Ste 205 89117 702-341-8111
Faith Lutheran MSHS 1,400/6-12
2015 S Hualapai Way 89117 702-804-4400
Dr. Steven Buuck Ph.D., admin. Fax 804-4488
Institute of Professional Careers Post-Sec.
4472 S Eastern Ave 89119 702-734-9900
Le Cordon Bleu College of Culinary Arts Post-Sec.
1451 Center Crossing Rd 89144 702-365-7690
Liberty Baptist Academy 200/K-12
6501 W Lake Mead Blvd 89108 702-647-4522
John Shorer, admin. Fax 647-8083
Marinello School of Beauty Post-Sec.
5001 E Bonanza Rd Ste 110 89110 702-796-6200
Meadows S 900/PK-12
8601 Scholar Ln 89128 702-254-1610
Jeremy Gregersen, head sch Fax 254-2452
Montessori Visions Academy PK-12
1905 E Warm Springs 89119 702-451-9801
Mountain View Christian S 300/PK-12
3900 E Bonanza Rd 89110 702-452-1300
Dr. Crystal McClanahan, supt. Fax 452-9006
Northwest Career College Post-Sec.
7398 Smoke Ranch Rd 89128 702-254-7577
Pima Medical Institute Post-Sec.
3333 E Flamingo Rd 89121 702-458-9650
Southern Nevada Univ of Cosmetology Post-Sec.
3315 E Russell Rd Ste A4 89120 702-458-6333
Spring Valley Christian Academy 50/K-12
7570 Peace Way 89147 702-873-3216
Trinity International S 100/6-12
4141 Meadows Ln 89107 702-732-3957
Maria Cochrane, admin. Fax 784-0192
University of Nevada Las Vegas Post-Sec.
4505 S Maryland Pkwy 89154 702-895-3011
Word of Life Christian Academy 300/PK-12
3520 N Buffalo Dr 89129 702-645-1180
Rev. Kelly Marchello, prin. Fax 396-0293

Laughlin, Clark, Pop. 7,092
Clark County SD
Supt. — See Las Vegas
Laughlin MSHS 400/6-12
1900 Cougar Dr 89029 702-298-1996
Dawn Estes, prin. Fax 298-5493

Lovelock, Pershing, Pop. 1,824
Pershing County SD 700/K-12
PO Box 389 89419 775-273-7819
Russell Fecht, supt. Fax 273-2668
www.pershing.k12.nv.us
Pershing County HS 200/9-12
PO Box 990 89419 775-273-2625
Thomas R. Brooks, prin. Fax 273-2163
Pershing County MS 200/6-8
PO Box 1020 89419 775-273-1200
Cindy Plummer, prin. Fax 273-3191

Lund, White Pine, Pop. 277
White Pine County SD
Supt. — See Ely
Lund JSHS 50/7-12
PO Box 129 89317 775-238-5200
Robert Bischoff, prin. Fax 238-0208

Mc Dermitt, Humboldt, Pop. 172
Humboldt County SD
Supt. — See Winnemucca
Mc Dermitt JSHS 50/7-12
PO Box 98 89421 775-532-8761
Doc Welter, prin. Fax 532-8017

Mesquite, Clark, Pop. 15,069
Clark County SD
Supt. — See Las Vegas
Hughes MS 600/6-8
550 Hafen Ln 89027 702-346-3250
Maurice Perkins, prin. Fax 346-3095
Virgin Valley HS 700/9-12
820 Valley View Dr 89027 702-346-2780
Clifford Hughes, prin. Fax 346-7265

Minden, Douglas, Pop. 2,948
Douglas County SD 5,100/K-12
1638 Mono Ave 89423 775-782-5134
Teri White, supt. Fax 782-8562
www.dcsd.k12.nv.us
ASPIRE Academy 100/Alt
1680 Bently Pkwy S 89423 775-392-1475
Michelle Trujillo, prin.
Douglas HS 1,200/9-12
1670 State Route 88 89423 775-782-5136
Marty Swisher, prin. Fax 782-7039
Other Schools – See Gardnerville, Zephyr Cove

North Las Vegas, Clark, Pop. 207,375
Clark County SD
Supt. — See Las Vegas
Bridger MS 1,400/6-8
2505 N Bruce St 89030 702-799-7185
Deanna Jaskolski, prin. Fax 799-7074
Canyon Springs HS 2,700/9-12
350 E Alexander Rd 89032 702-799-1870
Ronnie Guerzon, prin. Fax 799-1876
Cheyenne HS 2,100/9-12
3200 W Alexander Rd 89032 702-799-4830
Zachary Robbins, prin. Fax 799-4856
College of Southern Nevada HS-East 100/11-12
3200 E Cheyenne Ave 89030 702-651-4070
Barbara Collins, prin. Fax 651-4627
Cram MS 1,600/6-8
1900 W Deer Springs Way 89084 702-799-7020
Gary Bugash, prin. Fax 799-8346
Findlay MS 1,500/6-8
333 W Tropical Pkwy 89031 702-799-3160
Brenda Caszatt, prin. Fax 799-3169
Johnston MS 1,400/6-8
5855 Lawrence St, 702-799-7001
Demetrius Johnson, prin. Fax 799-7010
Legacy HS 2,800/9-12
150 W Deer Springs Way 89084 702-799-1777
Kenneth Sobaszek, prin. Fax 799-1701
Mojave HS 2,200/9-12
5302 Goldfield St 89031 702-799-0432
Antonio Rael, prin. Fax 799-0437
Sedway MS 1,500/6-8
3465 Engelstad St 89032 702-799-3880
Chareece Sheppard, prin. Fax 799-1785
Smith MS 900/6-8
1301 E Tonopah Ave 89030 702-799-7080
Henry Rodda, prin. Fax 799-7195
Swainston MS 1,100/6-8
3500 W Gilmore Ave 89032 702-799-4860
Lori Desiderato, prin. Fax 799-4806
Desert Rose Adult HS Adult
444 W Brooks Ave 89030 702-799-6240
Janice Polley-Augente, prin. Fax 799-0397

American Institute of Trucking Post-Sec.
4020 E Lone Mountain Rd, 702-508-9659
University Baptist Academy 100/K-12
3770 W Washburn Rd 89031 702-732-3385

Overton, Clark
Clark County SD
Supt. — See Las Vegas
Lyon MS 400/6-8
179 S Andersen St 89040 702-397-8610
Kenneth Paul, prin. Fax 397-2754
Moapa Valley HS 500/9-12
PO Box 278 89040 702-397-2611
Hal Mortensen, prin. Fax 397-2892

Owyhee, Elko, Pop. 941
Elko County SD
Supt. — See Elko
Owyhee S 100/K-12
PO Box 100 89832 775-757-3400
Steve Cook, prin. Fax 757-3663

Pahrump, Nye, Pop. 35,299
Nye County SD
Supt. — See Tonopah
Clarke MS 900/6-8
4201 N Blagg Rd 89060 775-727-5546
Tim Wombaker, prin. Fax 727-7104
Pahrump Valley HS 1,300/9-12
501 E Calvada Blvd 89048 775-727-7737
Chris Brockman, prin. Fax 727-7722
Pathways Innovative Education 100/Alt
484 West St 89048 775-751-6822
Shelly Pierson, prin. Fax 751-6829

Panaca, Lincoln, Pop. 955
Lincoln County SD 900/PK-12
PO Box 118 89042 775-728-8000
Pam Teel, supt. Fax 728-4435
lcsdnv.com
Lincoln County HS 200/9-12
PO Box 268 89042 775-728-4481
Marty Soderborg, prin. Fax 728-4484
Meadow Valley MS 100/7-8
PO Box 567 89042 775-728-4655
Cody Christensen, prin. Fax 728-4302
Other Schools – See Alamo, Caliente

Reno, Washoe, Pop. 217,361
State Supported Schools
Supt. — None
Davidson Academy of Nevada 100/5-12
PO Box 9119 89507 775-682-5800
Colleen Harsin, dir. Fax 682-5801

Washoe County SD 63,900/PK-12
PO Box 30425 89520 775-348-0200
Traci Davis, supt. Fax 348-0304
www.washoeschools.net
Academy of Arts Careers and Technology Vo/Tech
380 Edison Way 89502 775-327-3920
Josh Reddig, prin. Fax 861-4415
Billinghurst MS 700/7-8
6685 Chesterfield Ln 89523 775-746-5870
Sheri-Lyn Cutler, prin. Fax 746-5875
Clayton Pre-AP Academy 600/7-8
1295 Wyoming Ave 89503 775-746-5860
Bruce Meissner, prin. Fax 746-5864
Cold Springs MS 700/5-8
18235 Cody Ct, 775-677-5433
Roberta Duval, prin. Fax 677-5439
Damonte Ranch HS 1,600/9-12
10500 Rio Wrangler Pkwy, 775-851-5656
Denise Hausauer, prin. Fax 851-5663
Depoali MS 1,100/6-8
9300 Wilbur May Pkwy, 775-852-6700
Joye Ancina, prin. Fax 852-6701
Galena HS 1,300/9-12
3600 Butch Cassidy Dr 89511 775-851-5630
Tom Brown, prin. Fax 851-5607
Hug HS 1,300/9-12
2880 Sutro St 89512 775-333-5300
Lauren Ford-Baxter, prin. Fax 333-5312
McQueen HS 1,900/9-12
6055 Lancer St 89523 775-746-5880
Sue Denning, prin. Fax 747-6883
North Valleys HS 2,100/9-12
1470 E Golden Valley Rd 89506 775-677-5499
Jeana Curtis, prin. Fax 677-5497
O'Brien STEM Academy 700/7-8
10500 Stead Blvd 89506 775-677-5420
Mary Basso, prin. Fax 677-5423
Pine MS 900/7-8
4800 Neil Rd 89502 775-689-2550
Brad Boudreau, prin. Fax 689-2539
Reno HS 1,600/9-12
395 Booth St 89509 775-333-5050
Kris Hackbusch, prin. Fax 333-5058
Swope MS 700/7-8
901 Keele Dr 89509 775-333-5330
Desiree Mandeville, prin. Fax 333-5083
Traner MS 600/7-8
1700 Carville Dr 89512 775-333-5130
Tiffany McMaster, prin. Fax 333-5135
Truckee Meadows Community College HS 200/11-12
7000 Dandini Blvd 89512 775-674-7660
Melissa Olsen, admin. Fax 674-7931
Vaughn MS 600/7-8
1200 Bresson Ave 89502 775-333-5160
Dr. Victoria Roybal, prin. Fax 333-5118
Washoe Innovations HS 400/Alt
777 W 2nd St 89503 775-333-5150
Taylor Harper, prin. Fax 333-5122
Washoe Inspire Academy 100/Alt
1155 Corporate Blvd 89502 775-857-3181
Richard Johnston-Salter, admin. Fax 857-3182
Wooster HS 1,700/9-12
1331 E Plumb Ln 89502 775-333-5100
Leah Keuscher, prin. Fax 333-5108
RISE Academy Adult
1301 Cordone Ave 89502 775-337-9939
Victor Sherbondy, dir. Fax 333-5324
Other Schools – See Gerlach, Incline Village, Sparks

Bishop Manogue Catholic HS 600/9-12
110 Bishop Manogue Dr 89511 775-336-6000
Brianne Thoreson, prin. Fax 336-6015
Carrington College Post-Sec.
5580 Kietzke Ln 89511 775-335-1714
Church Academy 50/1-12
1205 N McCarran Blvd 89512 775-329-5848
Dan Moriarty, admin. Fax 329-3360
Sage Ridge S 200/5-12
2515 Crossbow Ct 89511 775-852-6222
Norman Colb, head sch Fax 852-6228
Sierra Nevada HS 600/9-12
14175 Mount Charleston St 89506 775-789-0951
Truckee Meadows Community College Post-Sec.
7000 Dandini Blvd 89512 775-673-7000
University of Nevada Reno Post-Sec.
1664 N Virginia St 89557 775-784-1110

Round Mountain, Nye
Nye County SD
Supt. — See Tonopah
Round Mountain JSHS 100/6-12
PO Box 1427 89045 775-377-2690
James Fitch, prin. Fax 377-1239

Sandy Valley, Clark, Pop. 1,978
Clark County SD
Supt. — See Las Vegas
Sandy Valley S 100/K-12
HC 31 Box 111 89019 702-799-0935
Fax 723-1802

Silver Springs, Lyon, Pop. 5,112
Lyon County SD
Supt. — See Yerington
Silver Stage HS 300/9-12
3755 W Spruce Ave 89429 775-577-5071
Patrick Peters, prin. Fax 577-5079

Smith, Lyon, Pop. 1,033
Lyon County SD
Supt. — See Yerington
Smith Valley S 200/K-12
20 Day Ln 89430 775-465-2332
Kathy Bomba-Edgerton, prin. Fax 465-2681

Sparks, Washoe, Pop. 87,304
Washoe County SD
Supt. — See Reno
Dilworth MS 600/7-8
255 Prater Way 89431 775-353-5740
Laura Petersen, prin. Fax 353-5584
Mendive MS 1,000/7-8
1900 Whitewood Dr 89434 775-353-5990
Brandon Bringhurst, prin. Fax 353-5994
Reed HS 2,000/9-12
1350 Baring Blvd 89434 775-353-5700
Josh Rosenbloom, prin. Fax 353-5708
Shaw MS 1,000/7-8
600 Eagle Canyon Dr, 775-425-7777
Gina Leonhard, prin. Fax 425-7779
Spanish Springs HS 2,300/9-12
1065 Eagle Canyon Dr, 775-425-7733
Tammy Hart, prin. Fax 425-7735
Sparks HS 1,200/9-12
820 15th St 89431 775-353-5550
Kevin Carroll, prin. Fax 353-5514
Sparks MS 700/7-8
2275 18th St 89431 775-353-5770
Stacey Ting-Senini, prin. Fax 353-5585

Career College of Northern Nevada Post-Sec.
1421 Pullman Dr 89434 775-856-2266
Excel Christian S 100/PK-12
850 Baring Blvd 89434 775-356-9995
Lisa Cross, admin. Fax 356-9527
Milan Institute Post-Sec.
950 Industrial Way 89431 775-348-7200

Spring Creek, Elko, Pop. 12,111
Elko County SD
Supt. — See Elko
Spring Creek HS 900/9-12
14550 Lamoille Hwy 89815 775-753-5575
Keith Walz, prin. Fax 753-5956
Spring Creek MS 700/6-8
14650 Lamoille Hwy 89815 775-777-1688
Tim Giere, prin. Fax 777-1738

Tonopah, Nye, Pop. 2,418
Nye County SD 4,800/PK-12
PO Box 113 89049 775-482-6258
Dale Norton, supt. Fax 482-8573
www.nye.k12.nv.us
Tonopah HS 100/9-12
PO Box 1349 89049 775-482-3698
James Fossett, prin. Fax 482-3635
Other Schools – See Beatty, Gabbs, Pahrump, Round Mountain

Virginia City, Storey, Pop. 832
Storey County SD 400/PK-12
PO Box C 89440 775-847-0983
Dr. Robert Slaby, supt. Fax 847-0989
www.storey.k12.nv.us
Virginia City HS 100/9-12
PO Box C 89440 775-847-0992
Patrick Beckwith, prin. Fax 847-0994
Virginia City MS 100/6-8
PO Box C 89440 775-847-0980
Todd Hess, prin. Fax 847-0913

Wells, Elko, Pop. 1,257
Elko County SD
Supt. — See Elko
Wells S 100/K-12
PO Box 338 89835 775-752-3837
Chris McAnany, prin. Fax 752-2470

West Wendover, Elko, Pop. 4,333
Elko County SD
Supt. — See Elko
West Wendover JSHS 300/7-12
PO Box 3830 89883 775-664-3940
Craig Kyllonen, prin. Fax 664-3944

Winnemucca, Humboldt, Pop. 7,277
Humboldt County SD 3,400/K-12
310 E 4th St 89445 775-623-8100
Dr. David Jensen, supt. Fax 623-8102
www.hcsdnv.com
Lowry HS 900/9-12
5375 Kluncy Canyon Rd 89445 775-623-8130
Ray Parks, prin. Fax 623-8185
Winnemucca JHS 500/7-8
451 Reinhart St 89445 775-623-8120
Janet Kennedy, prin. Fax 623-8208
Other Schools – See Mc Dermitt

Yerington, Lyon, Pop. 2,993
Lyon County SD 8,100/PK-12
25 E Goldfield Ave 89447 775-463-6800
Wayne Workman, supt. Fax 463-6808
www.lyoncsd.org
Yerington HS 400/9-12
114 Pearl St 89447 775-463-6822
Duane Mattice, prin. Fax 463-6828
Yerington IS 400/5-8
215 Pearl St 89447 775-463-6833
Sean Moyle, prin. Fax 463-6840
Other Schools – See Dayton, Fernley, Silver Springs, Smith

Zephyr Cove, Douglas, Pop. 557
Douglas County SD
Supt. — See Minden
Whittell HS 200/7-12
PO Box 677 89448 775-588-2446
Crespin Esquivel, prin. Fax 588-2443

NEW HAMPSHIRE

NEW HAMPSHIRE DEPT. OF EDUCATION
101 Pleasant St, Concord 03301-3860
Telephone 603-271-3494
Fax 603-271-1953
Website http://www.education.nh.gov/

Commissioner of Education Virginia Barry

NEW HAMPSHIRE BOARD OF EDUCATION
101 Pleasant St, Concord 03301-3860

Chairperson Tom Raffio

SCHOOL ADMINISTRATIVE UNITS (SAU)

SAU 1
Kimberly Saunders, supt. 603-924-3336
106 Hancock Rd Fax 924-6707
Peterborough 03458
convalsd.net

SAU 2
Mary Moriarty, supt. 603-279-7947
103 Main St Ste 2, Meredith 03253 Fax 279-3044
www.sau2.k12.nh.us/

SAU 3
Corinne Cascadden, supt. 603-752-6500
183 Hillside Ave, Berlin 03570 Fax 752-2528
www.sau3.org/

SAU 4
Stacy Buckley, supt. 603-744-5555
20 N Main St, Bristol 03222 Fax 744-6659
www.sau4.org

SAU 5
Dr. James Morse, supt. 603-868-5100
36 Coe Dr, Durham 03824 Fax 868-6668
www.orcsd.org

SAU 6
Dr. Middleton McGoodwin Ed.D., supt. 603-543-4200
165 Broad St, Claremont 03743 Fax 543-4244
www.sau6.org

SAU 7
Bruce Beasley, supt. 603-237-5571
21 Academy St, Colebrook 03576 Fax 237-5126
www.sau7.org

SAU 8
Terri Forsten, supt. 603-225-0811
38 Liberty St, Concord 03301 Fax 226-2187
www.sau8.org

SAU 9
Kevin Richard, supt. 603-447-8368
176A Main St, Conway 03818 Fax 447-8497
www.sau9.org

SAU 10
Dr. Laura Nelson, supt. 603-432-1210
18 S Main St, Derry 03038 Fax 432-1264
www.sau10.org

SAU 11
Dr. Elaine Arbour, supt. 603-516-6800
61 Locust St Ste 409, Dover 03820 Fax 516-6809
www.dover.k12.nh.us

SAU 12
Dr. Nathan Greenberg, supt. 603-432-6920
268C Mammoth Rd Fax 425-1049
Londonderry 03053
www.londonderry.org

SAU 13
Louis Goscinski, supt. 603-323-5088
881A Tamworth Rd Fax 323-5093
Tamworth 03886
sau13.weebly.com

SAU 14
Valerie McKenney, supt. 603-679-5402
213 Main St, Epping 03042 Fax 679-1237
www.sau14.org

SAU 15
Dr. Charles Littlefield, supt. 603-622-3731
90 Farmer Rd, Hooksett 03106 Fax 669-4352
www.sau15.net

SAU 16
Michael Morgan, supt. 603-775-8653
30 Linden St, Exeter 03833 Fax 775-8673
www.sau16.org/

SAU 17
Dr. Brian Blake, supt. 603-642-3688
178 Main St, Kingston 03848 Fax 642-7885
web.sau17.org

SAU 18
Daniel LeGallo, supt. 603-934-3108
119 Central St, Franklin 03235 Fax 934-3462
www.franklin.k12.nh.us

SAU 19
Brian Balke, supt. 603-497-4818
11 School St, Goffstown 03045 Fax 497-8425
www.goffstown.k12.nh.us

SAU 20
Paul Bousquet, supt. 603-466-3632
123 Main St, Gorham 03581 Fax 466-3870
www.sau20.org/

SAU 21
Robert Sullivan Ed.D., supt. 603-926-8992
2 Alumni Dr, Hampton 03842 Fax 926-5157
www.sau21.org/sau

SAU 23
Laurie Melanson, supt. 603-787-2113
2975 Dartmouth College Hwy Fax 787-2118
North Haverhill 03774
www.sau23.org

SAU 24
Dr. Lorraine Tacconi-Moore, supt. 603-428-3269
258 Western Ave, Henniker 03242 Fax 428-6545
www.sau24.org

SAU 25
Eric McGee, supt. 603-472-3755
103 County Rd, Bedford 03110 Fax 472-2567
www.sau25.net/

SAU 26
Marjorie Chiafery, supt. 603-424-6200
36 McElwain St, Merrimack 03054 Fax 424-6229
www.merrimack.k12.nh.us

SAU 27
James O'Neill, supt. 603-578-3570
1 Highlander Ct, Litchfield 03052 Fax 578-1267
www.litchfieldsd.org

SAU 28
Dr. Amanda Lecaroz, supt. 603-635-1145
59A Marsh Rd, Pelham 03076 Fax 635-1283
www.pelhamsd.org

SAU 29
Robert Malay, supt. 603-357-9002
193 Maple Ave, Keene 03431 Fax 357-9012
www.sau29.org

SAU 30
Dr. Brendan Minnihan, supt. 603-524-5710
PO Box 309, Laconia 03247 Fax 528-8442
laconiaschools.weebly.com

SAU 31
Meredith Nadeau, supt. 603-659-5020
186A Main St, Newmarket 03857 Fax 659-5022
www.newmarket.k12.nh.us

SAU 32
Frank Perotti, supt. 603-469-3442
92 Bonner Rd, Meriden 03770 Fax 469-3985
www.plainfieldschool.org

SAU 33
Ellen Small, supt. 603-895-4299
43 Harriman Hill Rd Fax 895-0147
Raymond 03077
www.sau33.com

SAU 34
Dr. Robert Hassett, supt. 603-464-4466
PO Box 2190, Deering 03244 Fax 464-4053
www.hdsd.org

SAU 35
Pierre Couture, supt. 603-444-3925
260 Cottage St Ste C Fax 444-6299
Littleton 03561
www.sau35.k12.nh.us

SAU 36
Marion Anastasia, supt. 603-837-9363
14 King Sq, Whitefield 03598 Fax 837-2326
www.sau36.org

SAU 37
Dr. Bolgen Vargas, supt. 603-624-6300
195 McGregor St Ste 201 Fax 624-6337
Manchester 03102
www.mansd.org

SAU 39
Peter Warburton, supt. 603-673-2690
PO Box 849, Amherst 03031 Fax 672-1786
www.sau39.org

SAU 40
Robert Marquis, supt. 603-673-2202
100 West St, Milford 03055 Fax 673-2237
milfordk12.org

SAU 41
Andrew Corey, supt. 603-324-5999
4 Lund Ln, Hollis 03049 Fax 465-3933
www.sau41.org

SAU 42
Cornelia Brown, supt. 603-966-1000
PO Box 687, Nashua 03061 Fax 594-4350
www.nashua.edu

SAU 43
Dr. Cynthia Gallagher, supt. 603-865-9701
247 N Main St, Newport 03773 Fax 865-9707
www.sau43.org

SAU 44
Robert Gadomski, supt. 603-942-1290
23 Mountain Ave Unit A Fax 942-1295
Northwood 03261
www.sau44.org

SAU 45
Susan Noyes M.Ed., supt. 603-476-5247
PO Box 419 Fax 476-8009
Moultonborough 03254
sau45.org

SAU 46
Mark MacLean, supt. 603-753-6561
105 Community Dr Fax 753-6023
Penacook 03303
sau46.mvsd.k12.nh.us

SAU 47
Reuben Duncan, supt. 603-532-8100
81 Fitzgerald Dr Unit 2 Fax 532-8165
Jaffrey 03452
www.sau47.org

SAU 48
Mark Halloran, supt. 603-536-1254
47 Old Ward Bridge Rd Fax 536-3545
Plymouth 03264
sau48.org

SAU 49
Kathleen Cuddy-Egbert, supt. 603-569-1658
PO Box 190, Wolfeboro Falls 03896 Fax 569-6983
www.govwentworth.k12.nh.us

SAU 50
Salvatore Petralia, supt. 603-422-9572
48 Post Rd, Greenland 03840 Fax 422-9575
www.sau50.org

SAU 51
Dr. John Freeman, supt. 603-435-5526
23 Oneida St Unit 1 Fax 435-5331
Pittsfield 03263
www.pittsfieldnhschools.org

SAU 52
Stephen Zadravec, supt. 603-431-5080
1 Junkins Ave Unit 402 Fax 431-6753
Portsmouth 03801
www.cityofportsmouth.com/school/

SAU 53
Dr. Gail E. Paludi, supt. 603-485-5188
267 Pembroke St, Pembroke 03275 Fax 485-9529
www.sau53.org

SAU 54
Michael Hopkins, supt. 603-332-3678
150 Wakefield St Ste 8 Fax 335-7367
Rochester 03867
www.rochesterschools.com

SAU 55
Dr. Earl Metzler, supt. 603-382-6119
30 Greenough Rd, Plaistow 03865 Fax 382-3334
www.timberlane.net/sau/

SAU 56
Jeni Mosca, supt. 603-692-4450
51 W High St, Somersworth 03878 Fax 692-9100
www.sau56.org

SAU 57
Michael Delahanty, supt. 603-893-7040
38 Geremonty Dr, Salem 03079 Fax 893-7080
www.sau57.org

SAU 58
Michael Kelley, supt. 603-636-1437
15 Preble St, Groveton 03582 Fax 636-6102
www.sau58.org

SAU 59
Dr. Tammy Davis, supt. 603-286-4116
433 W Main St, Northfield 03276 Fax 286-7402
www.winnisquam.k12.nh.us/Sau/index.htm

SAU 60
Lorraine Landry, supt. 603-835-0006
159 East St, Charlestown 03603 Fax 835-0007
www.sau60.org

SAU 61
Ruth Vaughn, supt. 603-755-2627
60 Charles St, Farmington 03835 Fax 755-9334
www.sau61.org

SAU 62
Patrick Andrew, supt. — 603-632-5563
PO Box 789, Enfield 03748 — Fax 632-4181
www.mascoma.k12.nh.us

SAU 63
Bryan Lane, supt., 192 Forest Rd — 603-654-8088
Lyndeborough 03082 — Fax 654-6691
www.sau63.org

SAU 64
Earl Sussman, supt. — 603-652-0262
18 Commerce Way, Milton 03851 — Fax 652-0250
www.sau64.org

SAU 65
Winfried Feneberg, supt. — 603-526-2051
114 Cougar Ct, New London 03257 — Fax 526-2145
www.kearsarge.org

SAU 66
Steven Chamberlin, supt. — 603-746-5186
204 Maple St, Contoocook 03229 — Fax 746-5714
www.hopkintonschools.org

SAU 67
Dr. Dean Cascadden, supt. — 603-224-4728
32 White Rock Hill Rd, Bow 03304 — Fax 224-4111
www.bownet.org

SAU 68
Judith McGann, supt. — 603-745-2051
PO Box 846, Lincoln 03251 — Fax 745-2352
www.lin-wood.org

SAU 70
Franklyn Bass, supt. — 603-643-6050
41 Lebanon St Ste 2 — Fax 643-3073
Hanover 03755
www.sau70.org/

SAU 71
Dr. Michele Munson, supt. — 603-863-2420
29 School Rd, Lempster 03605 — Fax 863-2451
www.sau71.org

SAU 72
Dr. Pamela Stiles, supt. — 603-875-7890
252 Suncook Valley Rd — Fax 875-0391
Alton 03809
www.myacs.org/domain/8

SAU 73
Kirk Beitler, supt. — 603-527-9215
2 Belknap Mountain Rd — Fax 527-9216
Gilford 03249
www.sau73.org/

SAU 74
Gail Kushner, supt. — 603-664-2715
572 Calef Hwy, Barrington 03825 — Fax 664-2609
www.sau74.org

SAU 75
Jacqueline Guillette, supt. — 603-863-9689
300 Route 10 S, Grantham 03753 — Fax 863-9684
www.gvshawks.org/sau-75

SAU 76
Dr. Michael Harris, supt. — 603-795-4431
PO Box 117, Lyme 03768 — Fax 795-9407
www.lymeschool.org

SAU 77
Susan Hodgdon, admin. — 603-638-2800
PO Box 130, Monroe 03771 — Fax 638-2031
www.monroeschool77.com

SAU 78
Dr. Michael Harris, supt. — 603-353-2170
10 School Dr, Orford 03777 — Fax 353-2189

SAU 79
John Fauci, supt. — 603-267-9097
9 Currier Hill Rd, Gilmanton 03237 — Fax 267-9498
www.sau79.org

SAU 80
Michael Tursi, supt. — 603-267-9223
58 School St, Belmont 03220 — Fax 267-9225
www.sau80.org

SAU 81
Dr. Phyllis Schlichter, supt. — 603-886-1235
20 Library St, Hudson 03051 — Fax 886-1236
www.sau81.org

SAU 82
Dr. Darrell Lockwood, supt. — 603-887-1401
22 Murphy Dr, Chester 03036 — Fax 887-4961
www.chesteracademy.org

SAU 83
Dr. Betsey Cox-Buteau, supt. — 603-895-6903
432 Main St, Fremont 03044 — Fax 895-6905
www.sau83.org

SAU 84
Dr. Steven Nilhas, supt. — 603-444-5215
65 Maple St, Littleton 03561 — Fax 444-3015
www.littletonschools.org/

SAU 85
Russell Holden, supt. — 603-763-4627
70 Lower Main St, Sunapee 03782 — Fax 763-4718
www.sunapeeschools.org

SAU 86
Dr. Brian Cochrane, supt. — 603-435-1510
PO Box 250 — Fax 435-1511
Center Barnstead 03225
www.barnstead.k12.nh.us/sau-86.html

SAU 87
Ruthann Goguen, supt. — 603-721-0160
16 School St, Greenville 03048 — Fax 721-0175
www.sau.mascenic.org

SAU 88
Joanne Roberts, supt. — 603-790-8500
20 Seminary Hl — Fax 790-8310
West Lebanon 03784
www.sau88.net

SAU 89
Kristen Kivela, supt. — 603-878-2962
13 Darling Hill Rd, Mason 03048 — Fax 878-3439
mason.sau89.org

SAU 90
Kathleen Murphy, supt. — 603-926-4560
6 Marston Way, Hampton 03842 — Fax 926-5070
www.sau90.org/

SAU 91
Kenneth Dassau, supt. — 603-209-3315
1 Village Rd, Surry 03431

SAU 92
Wayne Woolridge, supt. — 603-336-5728
PO Box 27, Hinsdale 03451 — Fax 336-5731
www.hnhsd.org

SAU 93
Lisa Witte, supt. — 603-352-6955
600 Old Homestead Hwy — Fax 358-6708
Swanzey 03446
www.mrsd.org

SAU 94
James Lewis, supt. — 603-239-8061
PO Box 46, Winchester 03470 — Fax 239-7593
www.wnhsd.org

SAU 95
Richard Langlois, supt. — 603-425-1976
19 Haverhill Rd, Windham 03087 — Fax 425-1719
www.sau95.org

SAU 96
Kenneth Dassau, supt. — 603-209-3315
PO Box 111, Sullivan 03445

SAU 97
Kathleen Vizard, supt. — 603-356-5535
91 Samuel Hale Dr — Fax 356-5535
Hales Location 03860

SAU 98
Jennifer Fish, supt. — 603-246-3321
136 County Farm Rd — Fax 246-8117
West Stewartstown 03597

SAU 201
David Smith, hdmstr. — 603-942-5531
907 1st NH Tpke — Fax 942-7537
Northwood 03261
www.coebrown.org

SAU 202
Griffin Morse, hdmstr. — 603-437-5200
5 Pinkerton St, Derry 03038 — Fax 432-5328
www.pinkertonacademy.net

SAU 301
Robert Cullison, supt. — 603-875-8600
242 Suncook Valley Rd — Fax 875-8200
Alton 03809
www.pmhschool.com

PUBLIC, PRIVATE AND CATHOLIC SECONDARY SCHOOLS

Allenstown, Merrimack
Allenstown SD
Supt. — See Pembroke
Dupont MS — 100/5-8
10 1/2 School St 03275 — 603-485-4474
Mark Dangora, prin. — Fax 485-1806

Alstead, Cheshire
Fall Mountain Regional SD
Supt. — See Langdon
Vilas MS — 100/5-8
82 Mechanic St 03602 — 603-835-6351
Gail Rowe, prin. — Fax 835-2052

Alton, Belknap, Pop. 499
Prospect Mountain SD — 500/9-12
242 Suncook Valley Rd 03809 — 603-875-3800
Robert L. Cullison M.Ed., supt. — Fax 875-8200
www.pmhschool.com
Prospect Mountain HS — 500/9-12
242 Suncook Valley Rd 03809 — 603-875-3800
James Fitzpatrick, prin. — Fax 875-8200

Amherst, Hillsborough, Pop. 612
Amherst SD — 1,400/K-8
PO Box 849 03031 — 603-673-2690
Peter Warburton, supt. — Fax 672-1786
www.sau39.org
Amherst MS — 700/5-8
PO Box 966 03031 — 603-673-8944
Porter Dodge, prin. — Fax 673-6774

Souhegan Cooperative SD — 800/9-12
PO Box 849 03031 — 603-673-2690
Peter Warburton, supt. — Fax 672-1786
www.sau39.org
Souhegan Cooperative HS — 800/9-12
PO Box 1152 03031 — 603-673-9940
Rob Scully, prin. — Fax 673-0318

Andover, Merrimack

Proctor Academy — 400/9-12
PO Box 500 03216 — 603-735-6000
Michael Henriques, head sch — Fax 735-5129

Antrim, Hillsborough, Pop. 1,376
Contoocook Valley SD
Supt. — See Peterborough
Great Brook MS — 300/5-8
16 School St 03440 — 603-588-6630
James Elder, prin. — Fax 588-3207

Barrington, Strafford
Barrington SD — 1,000/PK-8
572 Calef Hwy 03825 — 603-664-2715
Gail Kushner, supt. — Fax 664-2609
www.sau74.org
Barrington MS — 400/5-8
51 Haley Dr 03825 — 603-664-2127
Terrence Leatherman, prin. — Fax 664-5739

Bedford, Hillsborough
Bedford SD — 4,400/PK-12
103 County Rd 03110 — 603-472-3755
Eric McGee, supt. — Fax 472-2567
www.sau25.net/
Bedford HS — 1,400/9-12
47 Nashua Rd Unit B 03110 — 603-310-9000
William Hagen, prin. — Fax 472-3024
Lurgio MS — 800/7-8
47 Nashua Rd Unit A 03110 — 603-310-9100
Edward Joyce, prin. — Fax 472-5090

Michael's School of Hair Design — Post-Sec.
79 S River Rd Ste 6 03110 — 603-668-4300

Belmont, Belknap, Pop. 1,272
Shaker Regional SD — 1,400/PK-12
58 School St 03220 — 603-267-9223
Michael Tursi, supt. — Fax 267-9225
www.sau80.org
Belmont HS — 400/9-12
255 Seavey Rd 03220 — 603-267-6525
David Williams, prin. — Fax 267-5962
Belmont MS — 400/5-8
38 School St 03220 — 603-267-9220
Aaron Pope, prin. — Fax 267-9228

Berlin, Coos, Pop. 9,890
Berlin SD — 1,300/K-12
183 Hillside Ave 03570 — 603-752-6500
Corinne Cascadden, supt. — Fax 752-2528
www.sau3.org/
Berlin HS — 400/9-12
550 Willard St 03570 — 603-752-4122
Kevin Carpenter, prin. — Fax 752-8566
Berlin MS — 300/6-8
200 State St 03570 — 603-752-5311
Tammy Fauteux, prin. — Fax 752-8580
Berlin Regional Vocational Center — Vo/Tech
550 Willard St 03570 — 603-752-4122
Roland Pinette, coord. — Fax 752-8566

White Mountains Community College — Post-Sec.
2020 Riverside Dr 03570 — 603-752-1113

Bethlehem, Grafton, Pop. 962
Profile SD
Supt. — See Littleton
Profile HS — 200/9-12
691 Profile Rd 03574 — 603-823-7411
Benjamin Jellison, prin. — Fax 823-7490
Profile JHS — 100/7-8
691 Profile Rd 03574 — 603-823-7411
Benjamin Jellison, prin. — Fax 823-7490

White Mountain S — 100/9-12
371 W Farm Rd 03574 — 603-444-2928
Dr. Timothy Breen Ph.D., head sch — Fax 444-1258

Bow, Merrimack
Bow SD — 1,600/PK-12
55 Falcon Way 03304 — 603-224-4728
Dr. Dean Cascadden, supt. — Fax 224-4111
www.bownet.org
Bow HS — 500/9-12
55 Falcon Way 03304 — 603-228-2210
Dr. John House-Myers, prin. — Fax 228-2212
Bow Memorial S — 500/5-8
20 Bow Center Rd 03304 — 603-225-3212
Adam Osburn, prin. — Fax 228-2228

Bristol, Grafton, Pop. 1,657
Newfound Area SD — 1,200/PK-12
20 N Main St 03222 — 603-744-5555
Stacy Buckley, supt. — Fax 744-6659
www.sau4.org
Newfound Memorial MS — 300/6-8
155 N Main St 03222 — 603-744-8162
Jay Lewis, prin. — Fax 744-8037
Newfound Regional HS — 400/9-12
150 Newfound Rd 03222 — 603-744-6006
Paul Hoiriis, prin. — Fax 744-2526

Canaan, Grafton, Pop. 511
Mascoma Valley Regional SD
Supt. — See Enfield
Indian River S — 400/5-8
45 Royal Rd 03741 — 603-632-4357
Kevin Towle, prin. — Fax 632-4262
Mascoma Valley Regional HS — 400/9-12
27 Royal Rd 03741 — 603-632-4308
James Collins, prin. — Fax 632-5419

Cardigan Mountain S — 200/6-9
62 Alumni Dr 03741 — 603-523-4321
Christopher Day, head sch — Fax 523-7227

Candia, Rockingham

Remington HS 50/9-12
PO Box 473 03034 603-483-5664
Jeffrey Philbrick, hdmstr. Fax 483-4811

Charlestown, Sullivan, Pop. 1,173
Fall Mountain Regional SD
Supt. — See Langdon
Charlestown MS 100/6-8
307 Main St 03603 603-826-7711
Paula Southard-Stevens, prin. Fax 826-3102

Claremont, Sullivan, Pop. 13,132
Claremont SD 1,800/PK-12
165 Broad St 03743 603-543-4200
Dr. Middleton McGoodwin Ed.D., supt. Fax 543-4244
www.sau6.org
Claremont MS 400/6-8
107 South St 03743 603-543-4250
Paulette Fitzgerald, prin. Fax 543-4289
Stevens HS 500/9-12
175 Broad St 03743 603-543-4220
Patricia Barry, prin. Fax 542-2805
Sugar River Valley Regional Tech Ctr Vo/Tech
111 South St 03743 603-543-4291
Joel Schneid, dir. Fax 543-4296

Claremont Christian Academy 100/K-12
97 Maple Ave 03743 603-542-8759
Mark Pomeroy, dir. Fax 542-8759
River Valley Community College Post-Sec.
1 College Dr 03743 603-542-7744

Colebrook, Coos, Pop. 1,376
Colebrook SD 400/PK-12
21 Academy St 03576 603-237-5571
Bruce Beasley, supt. Fax 237-5126
www.sau7.org
Colebrook Academy 100/9-12
13 Academy St 03576 603-237-4280
Mark Fiorentino, prin. Fax 237-5717

Pittsburg SD 100/PK-12
21 Academy St 03576 603-237-5571
Bruce Beasley, supt. Fax 237-5126
www.sau7.org
Other Schools – See Pittsburg

Concord, Merrimack, Pop. 41,988
Concord SD 4,800/PK-12
38 Liberty St 03301 603-225-0811
Terri Forsten, supt. Fax 226-2187
www.sau8.org
Concord HS 1,700/9-12
170 Warren St 03301 603-225-0800
Tom Sica, prin. Fax 223-2054
Concord Regional Technical Center Vo/Tech
170 Warren St 03301 603-225-0800
Steve Rothenberg, admin. Fax 223-2050
Rundlett MS 1,000/6-8
144 South St 03301 603-225-0862
James McCollum, prin. Fax 226-3288

Bishop Brady HS 400/9-12
25 Columbus Ave 03301 603-224-7418
Andrea Elliot, prin. Fax 228-6664
Concord Academy of Hair Design Post-Sec.
20 S Main St 03301 603-224-2211
Concord Christian Academy 200/PK-12
37 Regional Dr 03301 603-228-8888
Dr. David Johnson, hdmstr. Fax 226-9696
Granite State College Post-Sec.
25 Hall St 03301 603-228-3000
NHTI - Concord's Community College Post-Sec.
31 College Dr 03301 603-271-6484
St. Paul's S, 325 Pleasant St 03301 500/9-12
Michael Hirschfeld, head sch 603-229-4600
Trinity Christian S 200/PK-12
80 Clinton St 03301 603-225-5410
Michael Kingsley, prin. Fax 225-3235
University of New Hampshire Sch of Law Post-Sec.
2 White St 03301 603-228-1541

Contoocook, Merrimack, Pop. 1,432
Hopkinton SD 900/PK-12
204 Maple St 03229 603-746-5186
Steven Chamberlin, supt. Fax 746-5714
www.hopkintonschools.org
Hopkinton HS 300/9-12
297 Park Ave 03229 603-746-4167
Christopher Kelley, prin. Fax 746-5109
Hopkinton MS 100/7-8
297 Park Ave 03229 603-746-4167
Christopher Kelley, prin. Fax 746-5109

Conway, Carroll, Pop. 1,799
Conway SD 1,800/K-12
176A Main St 03818 603-447-8368
Kevin Richard, supt. Fax 447-8497
www.sau9.org
Kennett MS 300/7-8
176 Main St 03818 603-447-6364
Richard Biche, prin. Fax 447-6842
Other Schools – See North Conway

Deering, Hillsborough
Hillsboro-Deering Cooperative SD 1,200/PK-12
78 School St 03244 603-464-4466
Dr. Robert Hassett, supt. Fax 464-4053
www.hdsd.org
Other Schools – See Hillsborough

Derry, Rockingham, Pop. 21,640
Derry Cooperative SD 3,600/PK-8
18 S Main St 03038 603-432-1210
Dr. Laura Nelson, supt. Fax 432-1264
www.sau10.org
Hood MS 700/6-8
5 Hood Rd 03038 603-432-1224
Austin Garofalo, prin. Fax 432-1227
West Running Brook MS 600/6-8
1 W Running Brook Ln 03038 603-432-1250
Leslie Saucier, prin. Fax 432-1243

Pinkerton Academy 3,000/9-12
5 Pinkerton St 03038 603-437-5200
Griffin Morse, hdmstr. Fax 432-5328
www.pinkertonacademy.org
Pinkerton Academy 3,000/9-12
5 Pinkerton St 03038 603-437-5200
Griffin Morse, hdmstr. Fax 432-5328

Dover, Strafford, Pop. 29,321
Dover SD 4,000/PK-12
61 Locust St Ste 409 03820 603-516-6800
Dr. Elaine Arbour, supt. Fax 516-6809
www.dover.k12.nh.us
Dover HS 1,300/9-12
25 Alumni Dr 03820 603-516-6900
Peter Driscoll, prin. Fax 516-6926
Dover MS 1,100/5-8
16 Daley Dr 03820 603-516-7200
Kimberly Lyndes, prin. Fax 516-5747
Dover Regional Career Technical Center Vo/Tech
25 Alumni Dr 03820 603-516-6978
Louise Paradis, dir. Fax 516-6975

Portsmouth Christian Academy 600/PK-12
20 Seaborne Dr 03820 603-742-3617
Dr. John Engstrom, head sch Fax 750-0490
St. Thomas Aquinas HS 600/9-12
197 Dover Point Rd 03820 603-742-3206
Kevin Collins, prin. Fax 749-7822

Dublin, Cheshire

Dublin S 100/9-12
PO Box 522 03444 603-563-8584
Bradford Bates, head sch Fax 563-7121

Durham, Strafford, Pop. 10,187
Oyster River Cooperative SD 2,000/K-12
36 Coe Dr 03824 603-868-5100
Dr. James Morse Ed.D., supt. Fax 868-6668
www.orcsd.org
Oyster River HS 700/9-12
55 Coe Dr 03824 603-868-2375
Suzanne Filippone, prin. Fax 868-2049
Oyster River MS 700/5-8
1 Coe Dr 03824 603-868-2155
Jay Richard, prin. Fax 868-3469

University of New Hampshire Post-Sec.
105 Main St 03824 603-862-1234

Enfield, Grafton, Pop. 1,510
Mascoma Valley Regional SD 1,200/PK-12
PO Box 789 03748 603-632-5563
Patrick Andrew, supt. Fax 632-4181
sites.google.com/a/mvrsd.org/home/
Other Schools – See Canaan

Epping, Rockingham, Pop. 1,654
Epping SD 1,000/PK-12
213 Main St 03042 603-679-5402
Valerie McKenney, supt. Fax 679-1237
www.sau14.org
Epping HS 300/9-12
21 Academy St 03042 603-679-5472
Dorothy Mohr, prin. Fax 679-2966
Epping MS 200/6-8
33 Prescott Rd 03042 603-679-2544
Brian Ernest, prin. Fax 679-5514

Exeter, Rockingham, Pop. 9,087
Exeter Region Cooperative SD 3,100/6-12
30 Linden St 03833 603-775-8653
Michael Morgan, supt. Fax 775-8673
www.sau16.org/
Exeter HS 1,700/9-12
1 Blue Hawk Dr 03833 603-775-8400
James Tremblay, prin. Fax 395-2499
Seacoast School of Tech Vo/Tech
40 Linden St 03833 603-775-8461
Margaret Callahan, prin. Fax 775-8983
Other Schools – See Stratham

Phillips Exeter Academy 1,000/9-12
20 Main St 03833 603-772-4311
Lisa MacFarlane, prin. Fax 777-4384

Farmington, Strafford, Pop. 3,815
Farmington SD 1,200/PK-12
60 Charles St 03835 603-755-2627
Ruth Vaughn, supt. Fax 755-9334
www.sau61.org
Farmington HS 400/9-12
40 Thayer Dr 03835 603-755-2811
Matthew Jozokos, prin. Fax 755-3252
Wilson Memorial MS 400/4-8
51 School St 03835 603-755-2181
Jessica Richardson, prin. Fax 755-9473

Franklin, Merrimack, Pop. 8,346
Franklin SD 1,100/PK-12
119 Central St 03235 603-934-3108
Daniel LeGallo, supt. Fax 934-3462
www.sau18.org
Franklin HS 400/9-12
119 Central St 03235 603-934-5441
Carrie Charette, prin. Fax 934-7445
Franklin MS 300/4-8
200 Sanborn St 03235 603-934-5828
Kevin Barbour, prin. Fax 934-2432

Gilford, Belknap
Gilford SD 1,200/K-12
2 Belknap Mountain Rd 03249 603-527-9215
Kirk Beitler, supt. Fax 527-9216
www.sau73.org/
Gilford HS 500/9-12
88 Alvah Wilson Rd 03249 603-524-7135
Anthony Sperazzo, prin. Fax 524-3867
Gilford MS 300/5-8
72 Alvah Wilson Rd 03249 603-527-2460
Peter Sawyer, prin. Fax 527-2461

Goffstown, Hillsborough, Pop. 14,621
Goffstown SD 2,900/PK-12
11 School St 03045 603-497-4818
Brian Balke, supt. Fax 497-8425
www.goffstown.k12.nh.us
Goffstown HS 1,200/9-12
27 Wallace Rd 03045 603-497-4841
Frank McBride, prin. Fax 497-5257
Mountain View MS 900/5-8
41 Lauren Ln 03045 603-497-8288
Wendy Hastings, prin. Fax 497-4987

Gorham, Coos, Pop. 1,579
Gorham Randolph Shelburne Cooperative SD 400/K-12
123 Main St 03581 603-466-3632
Paul Bousquet, supt. Fax 466-3870
www.sau20.org/
Gorham HS 200/9-12
120 Main St 03581 603-466-2776
David Backler, prin. Fax 466-3111
Gorham MS 100/6-8
120 Main St 03581 603-466-2776
David Backler, prin. Fax 466-3111

Greenland, Rockingham
Rye SD 500/K-8
48 Post Rd 03840 603-422-9572
Salvatore Petralia, supt. Fax 422-9575
www.sau50.org
Other Schools – See Rye

Greenville, Hillsborough, Pop. 1,101
Mascenic Regional SD 1,100/PK-12
16 School St 03048 603-721-0160
Ruthann Goguen, supt. Fax 721-0175
www.sau.mascenic.org
Other Schools – See New Ipswich

Groveton, Coos, Pop. 1,110
Northumberland SD 300/K-12
15 Preble St 03582 603-636-1437
Michael Kelley, supt. Fax 636-6102
www.sau58.org
Groveton HS 200/6-12
65 State St 03582 603-636-1619
Lisa Perras, prin. Fax 636-9752

Hampstead, Rockingham
Hampstead SD
Supt. — See Plaistow
Hampstead MS 400/5-8
28 School St 03841 603-329-6743
Maria Di Nola, prin. Fax 329-4120

Hampton, Rockingham, Pop. 9,556
Hampton SD 1,200/PK-8
6 Marston Way 03842 603-926-4560
Kathleen Murphy, supt. Fax 926-5070
www.sau90.org
Hampton Academy 400/6-8
29 Academy Ave 03842 603-926-2000
David O'Connor, prin. Fax 926-1855

Seabrook SD 700/PK-8
2 Alumni Dr 03842 603-926-8992
Robert Sullivan Ed.D., supt. Fax 926-5157
www.sau21.org/sau
Other Schools – See Seabrook

Winnacunnet Cooperative SD 1,100/9-12
2 Alumni Dr 03842 603-926-8992
Robert Sullivan Ed.D., supt. Fax 926-5157
www.sau21.org/sau
Winnacunnet HS 1,100/9-12
1 Alumni Dr 03842 603-926-3395
William McGowan, prin. Fax 926-5418

Hampton Falls, Rockingham

Heronfield Academy 100/6-8
356 Exeter Rd 03844 603-772-9093
Martha Shepardson-Killam, head sch

Hanover, Grafton, Pop. 8,321
Dresden SD 1,100/6-12
41 Lebanon St Ste 2 03755 603-643-6050
Dr. Franklyn Bass, supt. Fax 643-3073
www.sau70.org/
Hanover HS 700/9-12
41 Lebanon St Ste 1 03755 603-643-3431
Justin Campbell, prin. Fax 643-0661
Richmond MS 400/6-8
63 Lyme Rd 03755 603-643-6040
Michael Lepene, prin. Fax 643-0662

Dartmouth College 03755 Post-Sec.
603-646-1110

Henniker, Merrimack, Pop. 1,723
John Stark Regional SD 700/9-12
258 Western Ave 03242 603-428-3269
Dr. Lorraine Tacconi-Moore, supt. Fax 428-6545
www.sau24.org
Other Schools – See Weare

Weare SD 1,000/PK-8
258 Western Ave 03242 603-428-3269
Dr. Lorraine Tacconi-Moore, supt. Fax 428-6545
www.sau24.org
Other Schools – See Weare

New England College Post-Sec.
98 Bridge St 03242 603-428-2211

Hillsborough, Hillsborough, Pop. 1,929
Hillsboro-Deering Cooperative SD
Supt. — See Deering
Hillsboro-Deering HS 400/9-12
12 Hillcat Dr 03244 603-464-1130
James O'Rourke, prin. Fax 464-4028
Hillsboro-Deering MS 300/6-8
6 Hillcat Dr 03244 603-464-1120
Marc Peterson, prin. Fax 464-5759

Hinsdale, Cheshire, Pop. 1,534
Hinsdale SD 500/PK-12
PO Box 27 03451 603-336-5728
Wayne Woolridge, supt. Fax 336-5731
www.hnhsd.org
Hinsdale HS 200/9-12
49 School St 03451 603-336-5984
Ann Freitag, prin. Fax 336-7497
Hinsdale MS 100/6-8
49 School St 03451 603-336-5984
Ann Freitag, prin. Fax 336-7497

Holderness, Grafton

Holderness S 300/9-12
33 Chapel Ln 03245 603-536-1257
Phillip Peck, head sch Fax 536-1267

Hollis, Hillsborough
Hollis-Brookline Cooperative SD 1,300/7-12
4 Lund Ln 03049 603-324-5999
Andrew Corey, supt. Fax 465-3933
www.sau41.org
Hollis-Brookline HS 900/9-12
24 Cavalier Ct 03049 603-465-2269
Richard Barnes, prin. Fax 465-2485
Hollis-Brookline MS 400/7-8
25 Main St 03049 603-324-5997
Robert Thompson, prin. Fax 465-7523

Hooksett, Merrimack, Pop. 4,079
Hooksett SD 1,400/PK-8
90 Farmer Rd 03106 603-622-3731
Dr. Charles Littlefield, supt. Fax 669-4352
www.sau15.net
Cawley MS 500/6-8
89 Whitehall Rd 03106 603-518-5047
Matthew Benson, prin. Fax 518-5086

Hopkinton, Merrimack

Beech Hill S, 20 Beech Hill Rd 03229 50/6-8
Rick Johnson, head sch 603-715-5129

Hudson, Hillsborough, Pop. 7,236
Hudson SD 3,900/PK-12
20 Library St 03051 603-886-1235
Dr. Phyllis Schlichter, supt. Fax 886-1236
www.sau81.org
Alvirne HS 1,400/9-12
200 Derry Rd 03051 603-886-1260
Steven Beals, prin. Fax 595-1525
Hudson Memorial MS 900/6-8
1 Memorial Dr 03051 603-886-1240
Keith Bowen, prin. Fax 883-1252
Palmer Vocational Tech Center Vo/Tech
200 Derry Rd 03051 603-886-1260
Karen Worthen, dir. Fax 595-1513

Continental Academie of Hair Design Post-Sec.
PO Box 370 03051 603-889-1614

Jaffrey, Cheshire, Pop. 2,700
Jaffrey-Rindge Cooperative SD 1,500/PK-12
81 Fitzgerald Dr Unit 2 03452 603-532-8100
Reuben Duncan, supt. Fax 532-8165
www.sau47.org
Conant HS 400/9-12
3 Conant Way 03452 603-532-8131
Lawrence Pimental, prin. Fax 532-8102
Jaffrey-Rindge MS 400/6-8
1 Conant Way 03452 603-532-8122
Robert Clark, prin. Fax 532-8124

Keene, Cheshire, Pop. 23,106
Keene SD 3,400/PK-12
193 Maple Ave 03431 603-357-9002
Robert Malay, supt. Fax 357-9012
www.sau29.org
Cheshire Career Center Vo/Tech
43 Arch St 03431 603-352-0640
Lisa Danley, prin. Fax 357-9061
Keene HS 1,400/9-12
43 Arch St 03431 603-352-0640
James Logan, prin. Fax 357-1512
Keene MS 700/6-8
167 Maple Ave 03431 603-357-9020
Dorothy Frazier, prin. Fax 357-9045

Antioch University New England Post-Sec.
40 Avon St 03431 800-553-8920
Keene Beauty Academy Post-Sec.
800 Park Ave 03431 603-357-3736
Keene State College Post-Sec.
229 Main St 03435 603-352-1909
Monadnock Waldorf S 200/PK-12
98 S Lincoln St 03431 603-357-4442
Lisa Mahar, admin. Fax 357-2955

Kingston, Rockingham
Sanborn Regional SD 1,800/PK-12
17 Danville Rd 03848 603-642-3688
Dr. Brian Blake, supt. Fax 642-7885
sau17.org
Sanborn Regional HS 700/9-12
17 Danville Rd 03848 603-642-3341
Brian Stack, prin. Fax 642-6947
Other Schools – See Newton

Laconia, Belknap, Pop. 15,741
Laconia SD 2,000/PK-12
PO Box 309 03247 603-524-5710
Brendan Minnihan, supt. Fax 528-8442
laconiaschools.weebly.com
Huot Technical Center Vo/Tech
26 Dewey St 03246 603-528-8693
David Warrender, prin. Fax 524-5711
Laconia HS 600/9-12
345 Union Ave 03246 603-524-3350
David Bartlett, prin. Fax 528-8683
Laconia MS 500/6-8
150 McGrath St 03246 603-524-4632
Dr. Alison Bryant, prin. Fax 528-8675

Empire Beauty School Post-Sec.
556 Main St 03246 603-524-8777
Laconia Christian Academy 100/PK-12
1386 Meredith Center Rd 03246 603-524-3250
Rick Duba, head sch Fax 524-3285
Lakes Region Community College Post-Sec.
379 Belmont Rd 03246 603-524-3207

Langdon, Sullivan
Fall Mountain Regional SD 1,600/PK-12
Route 12A 03602 603-835-0006
Lorraine Landry, supt. Fax 835-0007
www.sau60.org
Fall Mountain Regional HS 500/9-12
134 Fmrhs Rd 03602 603-835-6318
Richard Towne, prin. Fax 835-6254
Fall Mountain Regional Vocational Center Vo/Tech
134 Fmrhs Rd 03602 603-826-7756
Lorraine Landry, admin. Fax 835-6254
Other Schools – See Alstead, Charlestown, Walpole

Lebanon, Grafton, Pop. 12,877
Lebanon SD
Supt. — See West Lebanon
Lebanon HS 700/9-12
195 Hanover St 03766 603-448-2055
Ian Smith, prin. Fax 448-0605
Lebanon MS 400/5-8
3 Moulton Ave 03766 603-448-3056
Martha Langill, prin. Fax 448-0616

Lebanon College Post-Sec.
15 Hanover St 03766 603-448-2445
Upper Valley Teacher Institute Post-Sec.
194 Dartmouth College Hwy 03766 603-678-4888

Lincoln, Grafton, Pop. 991
Lincoln-Woodstock Cooperative SD 100/K-12
PO Box 846 03251 603-745-2051
Judith McGann, supt. Fax 745-2351
www.lin-wood.org
Lin-Wood S 100/K-12
72 Linwood Dr 03251 603-745-2214
Robert Nelson, prin. Fax 745-6797

Lisbon, Grafton, Pop. 967
Lisbon Regional SD
Supt. — See Littleton
Lisbon Regional S 100/K-12
24 Highland Ave 03585 603-838-5506
Jacqueline Daniels, prin. Fax 838-5012

Litchfield, Hillsborough
Litchfield SD 1,400/PK-12
1 Highlander Ct 03052 603-578-3570
James O'Neill, supt. Fax 578-1267
www.litchfieldsd.org
Campbell HS 500/9-12
1 Highlander Ct 03052 603-546-0300
William Lonergan, prin. Fax 546-0310
Litchfield MS 500/5-8
19 McElwain Dr 03052 603-424-0566
Thomas Lecklider, prin. Fax 424-1296

Littleton, Grafton, Pop. 4,350
Lisbon Regional SD 100/K-12
260 Cottage St Ste C 03561 603-444-3925
Pierre Couture, supt. Fax 444-6299
www.sau35.k12.nh.us
Other Schools – See Lisbon

Littleton SD 800/K-12
65 Maple St 03561 603-444-5215
Dr. Steven Nilhas, supt. Fax 444-3015
www.littletonschools.org
Bronson JHS 100/7-8
159 Oak Hill Ave 03561 603-444-5601
Joanne Melanson, prin. Fax 444-3009
Gallen Career & Technical Center Vo/Tech
140 High St 03561 603-444-5186
Alan Smith, dir. Fax 444-0167
Littleton HS 200/9-12
159 Oak Hill Ave 03561 603-444-5601
Joanne Melanson, prin. Fax 444-3009

Profile SD 300/7-12
260 Cottage St Ste C 03561 603-444-3925
Pierre Couture, supt. Fax 444-6299
www.sau35.k12.nh.us
Other Schools – See Bethlehem

Londonderry, Rockingham, Pop. 10,903
Londonderry SD 4,500/PK-12
268C Mammoth Rd 03053 603-432-6920
Dr. Nathan Greenberg, supt. Fax 425-1049
www.londonderry.org
Londonderry HS 1,600/9-12
295 Mammoth Rd 03053 603-432-6941
Jason Parent, prin. Fax 425-1022
Londonderry MS 1,100/6-8
313 Mammoth Rd 03053 603-432-6925
Richard Zacchilli, prin. Fax 432-0714

Lyndeborough, Hillsborough
Wilton-Lyndeborough Cooperative SD 400/PK-12
192 Forest Rd 03082 603-654-8088
Bryan Lane, supt. Fax 654-6691
www.sau63.org
Other Schools – See Wilton

Manchester, Hillsborough, Pop. 107,082
Manchester SD 14,700/PK-12
195 McGregor St Ste 201 03102 603-624-6300
Dr. Debra Livingston, supt. Fax 624-6337
www.mansd.org
Hillside MS 800/6-8
112 Reservoir Ave 03104 603-624-6352
Brendan McCafferty, prin. Fax 628-6049
Manchester Central HS 1,900/9-12
207 Lowell St 03104 603-624-6363
John Vaccarezza, prin. Fax 624-6376
Manchester Memorial HS 1,700/9-12
1 Crusader Way 03103 603-624-6378
Arthur Adamakos, prin. Fax 628-6009
Manchester School of Technology Vo/Tech
530 S Porter St 03103 603-624-6490
Karen Machado, prin. Fax 628-6146
Manchester West HS 1,100/9-12
9 Notre Dame Ave 03102 603-624-6384
Christopher Motika, prin. Fax 628-6153
McLaughlin MS 800/6-8
290 S Mammoth Rd 03109 603-628-6247
William Krantz, prin. Fax 628-6274
Parkside MS 700/6-8
75 Parkside Ave 03102 603-624-6356
Forrest Ransdell, prin. Fax 624-6355
Southside MS 800/6-8
140 S Jewett St 03103 603-624-6359
Jennifer Gillis, prin. Fax 624-6361

Derryfield S 400/6-12
2108 River Rd 03104 603-669-4524
Mary Halpin Carter Ph.D., head sch Fax 641-9715
Holy Family Academy 100/7-12
281 Cartier St 03102 603-644-7247
Mark Gillis, head sch Fax 644-1004
Manchester Community College Post-Sec.
1066 Front St 03102 603-206-8000
Mount Zion Christian S 100/PK-12
132 Titus Ave 03103 603-606-7930
Robert Carter, hdmstr. Fax 606-7935
New England EMS Institute Post-Sec.
1 Elliot Way 03103 603-628-2220
New Hampshire Institute of Art Post-Sec.
148 Concord St 03104 603-623-0313
St. Anselm College Post-Sec.
100 Saint Anselms Dr 03102 603-641-7000
St. Joseph Regional JHS 100/7-8
148 Belmont St 03103 603-624-4811
Denis Mailloux, prin. Fax 624-6670
Salter School of Nursing & Allied Health Post-Sec.
670 N Commercial St Ste 403 03101 603-622-8400
Southern New Hampshire University Post-Sec.
2500 N River Rd 03106 800-668-1249
Trinity HS 400/9-12
581 Bridge St 03104 603-668-2910
Denis Mailloux, prin. Fax 668-2913
University of New Hampshire Post-Sec.
400 Commercial St 03101 603-641-4321

Meredith, Belknap, Pop. 1,695
Inter-Lakes Cooperative SD 1,100/PK-12
103 Main St Ste 2 03253 603-279-7947
Mary Moriarty, supt. Fax 279-3044
www.interlakes.org/
Inter-Lakes HS 300/9-12
1 Laker Ln 03253 603-279-6162
Patricia Murphy, prin. Fax 279-5302
Inter-Lakes MS 300/5-8
1 Laker Ln 03253 603-279-5312
Everett Bennett, prin. Fax 279-5310

Meriden, Sullivan

Kimball Union Academy 300/9-12
PO Box 188 03770 603-469-2000
Michael Schafer, hdmstr. Fax 469-2033

Merrimack, Hillsborough, Pop. 22,156
Merrimack SD 3,900/PK-12
36 McElwain St 03054 603-424-6200
Marjorie Chiafery, supt. Fax 424-6229
www.merrimack.k12.nh.us
Merrimack HS 1,300/9-12
38 McElwain St 03054 603-424-6204
Kenneth Johnson, prin. Fax 424-6230
Merrimack MS 600/7-8
31 Madeline Bennett Ln 03054 603-424-6289
Adam Caragher, prin. Fax 423-1109

South Merrimack Christian Academy 300/PK-12
517 Boston Post Rd 03054 603-880-6832
Thomas More College of Liberal Arts Post-Sec.
6 Manchester St 03054 603-880-8308

Milford, Hillsborough, Pop. 8,681
Milford SD 2,600/PK-12
100 West St 03055 603-673-2202
Robert Marquis, supt. Fax 673-2237
milfordk12.org
Milford Applied Technology Center Vo/Tech
100 West St 03055 603-673-4201
Don Jalbert, dir. Fax 673-4202
Milford HS 800/9-12
100 West St 03055 603-673-4201
Bradford Craven Ph.D., prin. Fax 673-4201
Milford MS 700/6-8
33 Osgood Rd 03055 603-673-5221
Anthony DeMarco, prin. Fax 673-5221

Milton, Strafford, Pop. 560
Milton SD 600/K-12
18 Commerce Way 03851 603-652-0262
Earl Sussman, supt. Fax 652-0250
www.sau64.org
Nute HS 200/9-12
22 Elm St 03851 603-652-4591
Scott Currier, prin. Fax 652-9926
Nute JHS 100/6-8
22 Elm St 03851 603-652-4591
Scott Currier, prin. Fax 652-9926

Moultonborough, Carroll
Moultonborough SD 500/PK-12
PO Box 419 03254 603-476-5247
Susan Noyes M.Ed., supt. Fax 476-8009
sau45.org
Moultonborough Academy 100/7-8
PO Box 228 03254 603-476-5517
Andrew Coppinger, prin. Fax 476-5153
Moultonborough Academy 200/9-12
PO Box 228 03254 603-476-5517
Andrew Coppinger, prin. Fax 476-5153

Nashua, Hillsborough, Pop. 84,540
Nashua SD 11,600/PK-12
PO Box 687 03061 603-966-1000
Dr. Cornelia Brown Ph.D., supt. Fax 594-4350
www.nashua.edu
Elm Street MS 1,100/6-8
117 Elm St 03060 603-594-4322
Ian Atwell, prin. Fax 594-4370
Fairgrounds MS 700/6-8
27 Cleveland St 03060 603-594-4393
Sharon Coffey, prin. Fax 594-4355
Nashua HS North 1,700/9-12
8 Titan Way 03063 603-589-6400
Marianne Busteed, prin. Fax 589-6449
Nashua HS South 1,800/9-12
36 Riverside Dr 03062 603-589-4311
Keith Richard, prin. Fax 589-8722
Pennichuck MS 700/6-8
207 Manchester St 03064 603-594-4308
Lynne Joseph, prin. Fax 594-4413

Bishop Guertin HS 900/9-12
194 Lund Rd 03060 603-889-4107
Jason Strinste, prin. Fax 889-0701
Daniel Webster College Post-Sec.
20 University Dr 03063 800-325-6876
Nashua Catholic Regional JHS 200/7-8
6 Bartlett Ave 03064 603-883-6707
Glenda McFadden, prin. Fax 594-8955
Nashua Christian Academy 200/PK-12
55 Franklin St 03064 603-889-8892
Christine Urban, hdmstr. Fax 821-7451
Nashua Community College Post-Sec.
505 Amherst St 03063 603-882-6923
Rivier University Post-Sec.
420 S Main St 03060 603-888-1311
St. Joseph School of Nursing Post-Sec.
5 Woodward Ave 03060 603-594-2567

New Hampton, Belknap, Pop. 350

New Hampton S 300/9-12
70 Main St 03256 603-677-3400
Joe Williams, head sch Fax 677-3482

New Ipswich, Hillsborough
Mascenic Regional SD
Supt. — See Greenville
Boynton MS 300/5-8
500 Turnpike Rd 03071 603-878-4800
John MacArthur, prin. Fax 878-0525
Mascenic Regional HS 400/9-12
175 Turnpike Rd 03071 603-878-1113
John Barth, prin. Fax 878-3344

New London, Merrimack, Pop. 1,397
Kearsarge Regional SD 1,800/PK-12
114 Cougar Ct 03257 603-526-2051
Winfried Feneberg, supt.
www.kearsarge.org
Other Schools – See North Sutton

Colby-Sawyer College Post-Sec.
541 Main St 03257 603-526-3000

Newmarket, Rockingham, Pop. 5,181
Newmarket SD 800/PK-12
186A Main St 03857 603-659-5020
Dr. Meredith Nadeau, supt. Fax 659-5022
www.newmarket.k12.nh.us
Newmarket JSHS 200/6-12
213 S Main St 03857 603-659-3271
Christopher Mazzone, prin. Fax 659-1287

Newport, Sullivan, Pop. 4,688
Newport SD 1,000/PK-12
247 N Main St 03773 603-865-9701
Dr. Cynthia Gallagher, supt. Fax 865-9707
www.sau43.org
Newport HS 400/9-12
245 N Main St 03773 603-863-2414
Linda Sutton, prin. Fax 863-0887
Newport MS 100/6-8
245 N Main St 03773 603-863-2414
Linda Sutton, prin. Fax 863-0887
Sugar River Valley Reg Voc Ctr Vo/Tech
243 N Main St 03773 603-863-3759
Bonnie Akerman, dir. Fax 863-0887

Newton, Rockingham
Sanborn Regional SD
Supt. — See Kingston
Sanborn Regional MS 400/6-8
31A W Main St 03858 603-382-6226
Alexander Rutherford, prin. Fax 382-9771

North Conway, Carroll, Pop. 2,311
Conway SD
Supt. — See Conway
Kennett HS 800/9-12
409 Eagles Way 03860 603-356-4343
Cornelius Moylan, prin. Fax 356-4391
Mt. Washington Vly Career/Technical Ctr Vo/Tech
409 Eagles Way 03860 603-356-4370
Andrew Shaw, dir. Fax 356-4373

North Haverhill, Grafton
Haverhill Cooperative SD 700/PK-12
2975 Dartmouth College Hwy 03774 603-787-2113
Laurie Melanson, supt. Fax 787-2118
www.sau23.org
Haverhill Cooperative MS 300/4-8
175 Morrill Dr 03774 603-787-2100
Robert Phillips, prin. Fax 787-6117
Other Schools – See Woodsville

North Sutton, Merrimack
Kearsarge Regional SD
Supt. — See New London
Kearsarge Regional HS 500/9-12
PO Box 182 03260 603-927-4261
Robert Bennett, prin.
Kearsarge Regional MS 500/6-8
PO Box 269 03260 603-927-2100
Stephen Paterson, prin.

Northwood, Rockingham
Coe-Brown Northwood Academy 700/9-12
907 1st NH Tpke 03261 603-942-5531
David Smith, hdmstr. Fax 942-7537
www.coebrown.org
Coe-Brown Northwood Academy 700/9-12
907 1st NH Tpke 03261 603-942-5531
David Smith, hdmstr. Fax 942-7537

Orford, Grafton
Rivendell Interstate SD 500/PK-12
10 School Dr 03777 603-353-2170
Dr. Michael Harris, supt. Fax 353-2189
www.rivendellschool.org
Rivendell Academy 200/7-12
2972 Route 25A 03777 603-353-4321
Keri Gelenian, prin. Fax 353-4414

Pelham, Hillsborough
Pelham SD 2,000/PK-12
59A Marsh Rd 03076 603-635-1145
Amanda Lecaroz, supt. Fax 635-1283
www.pelhamsd.org
Pelham HS 600/9-12
85 Marsh Rd 03076 603-635-2115
Gary Dempsey, prin. Fax 635-3994
Pelham Memorial MS 500/6-8
59 Marsh Rd 03076 603-635-2321
Stacy Maghakian, prin. Fax 635-2369

Pembroke, Merrimack, Pop. 6,561
Allenstown SD 400/PK-8
267 Pembroke St 03275 603-485-5188
Dr. Gail E. Paludi, supt. Fax 485-9529
www.sau53.org
Other Schools – See Allenstown

Pembroke SD 1,600/K-12
267 Pembroke St 03275 603-485-5188
Dr. Gail E. Paludi, supt. Fax 485-9529
www.sau53.org
Pembroke Academy 900/9-12
209 Academy Rd 03275 603-485-7881
Paul Famulari, prin. Fax 485-1824
Three Rivers MS 300/5-8
243 Academy Rd 03275 603-485-9539
Jonathan Marston, prin. Fax 485-1829

Penacook, See Concord
Merrimack Valley SD 2,600/PK-12
105 Community Dr 03303 603-753-6561
Mark MacLean, supt. Fax 753-6023
www.mvsdpride.org
Merrimack Valley HS 900/9-12
106 Village St 03303 603-753-4311
David Miller, prin. Fax 753-6423
Merrimack Valley MS 600/6-8
14 Allen St 03303 603-753-6336
Kara Lamontagne, prin. Fax 753-8107

Peterborough, Hillsborough, Pop. 3,075
Contoocook Valley SD 2,400/PK-12
106 Hancock Rd 03458 603-924-3336
Kimberly Saunders, supt. Fax 924-6707
www.conval.edu
ConVal Regional HS 900/9-12
184 Hancock Rd 03458 603-924-3869
Brian Pickering, prin. Fax 924-9176
Region 14 Applied Technology Center Vo/Tech
184 Hancock Rd 03458 603-924-3869
John Reitnauer, dir. Fax 924-9176
South Meadow MS 400/5-8
108 Hancock Rd 03458 603-924-7105
Anne O'Bryant, prin. Fax 924-2064

Other Schools – See Antrim

Pittsburg, Coos
Pittsburg SD
Supt. — See Colebrook
Pittsburg HS 50/9-12
12 School St 03592 603-538-6536
Elaine Sherry, prin. Fax 538-6996

Pittsfield, Merrimack, Pop. 1,547
Pittsfield SD 500/PK-12
23 Oneida St Unit 1 03263 603-435-5526
Dr. John Freeman, supt. Fax 435-5331
www.pittsfieldnhschools.org
Pittsfield HS 200/9-12
23 Oneida St 03263 603-435-6701
Danielle Harvey, prin. Fax 435-7087
Pittsfield MS 100/7-8
23 Oneida St 03263 603-435-6701
Danielle Harvey, prin. Fax 435-7087

Plainfield, Sullivan, Pop. 204

Estabrook Christian S 50/K-10
1050 Route 12A 03781 603-675-2455

Plaistow, Rockingham
Hampstead SD 900/PK-8
30 Greenough Rd 03865 603-382-6119
Dr. Earl Metzler, supt. Fax 382-3334
www.hampstead.k12.nh.us
Other Schools – See Hampstead

Timberlane Regional SD 3,900/PK-12
30 Greenough Rd 03865 603-382-6119
Dr. Earl Metzler, supt. Fax 382-3334
www.timberlane.net/
Timberlane Regional HS 1,300/9-12
36 Greenough Rd 03865 603-382-6541
Donald Woodworth, prin. Fax 382-8086
Timberlane Regional MS 900/6-8
44 Greenough Rd 03865 603-382-7131
Michael Hogan, prin. Fax 382-2781

Plymouth, Grafton, Pop. 4,412
Pemi-Baker Regional SD 700/9-12
47 Old Ward Bridge Rd 03264 603-536-1254
Mark Halloran, supt. Fax 536-3545
www.sau48.org
Plymouth Regional HS 700/9-12
86 Old Ward Bridge Rd 03264 603-536-1444
Bruce Parsons, prin. Fax 536-9086

Plymouth State University Post-Sec.
17 High St 03264 603-535-5000

Portsmouth, Rockingham, Pop. 20,315
Portsmouth SD 2,700/PK-12
1 Junkins Ave Unit 402 03801 603-431-5080
Steve Zadravec, supt. Fax 431-6753
www.cityofportsmouth.com/school/
Portsmouth Career-Tech Center 19 Vo/Tech
50 Andrew Jarvis Dr 03801 603-436-7100
Diane Canada, dir. Fax 436-6793
Portsmouth HS 1,100/9-12
50 Andrew Jarvis Dr 03801 603-436-7100
Mary Lyons, prin. Fax 427-2320
Portsmouth MS 500/6-8
155 Parrott Ave 03801 603-436-5781
Phillip Davis, prin. Fax 427-2326

Great Bay Community College Post-Sec.
320 Corporate Dr 03801 603-427-7600
Portsmouth Beauty School of Hair Design Post-Sec.
140 Congress St 03801 603-436-7775

Raymond, Rockingham, Pop. 2,815
Raymond SD 1,400/PK-12
43 Harriman Hill Rd 03077 603-895-4299
Ellen Small M.Ed., supt. Fax 895-0147
www.sau33.com/
Gove MS 400/5-8
1 Stephen K Batchelder Pkwy 03077 603-895-3394
Robert Bickford, prin. Fax 895-9856
Raymond HS 400/9-12
45 Harriman Hill Rd 03077 603-895-6616
Steven Woodward, prin. Fax 895-1582

Rindge, Cheshire

Franklin Pierce University Post-Sec.
40 University Dr 03461 603-899-4000

Rochester, Strafford, Pop. 29,277
Rochester SD 4,400/PK-12
150 Wakefield St Ste 8 03867 603-332-3678
Michael Hopkins, supt. Fax 335-7367
www.rochesterschools.com
Carlson Academy 100/Alt
150 Wakefield St Ste 8 03867 603-332-3678
Kathy Dubois, dir. Fax 335-7367
Creteau Regional Technology Center Vo/Tech
140 Wakefield St 03867 603-332-0757
Sean Peschel, dir. Fax 335-7365
Rochester MS 900/6-8
47 Brock St 03867 603-332-4090
Adam Houghton, prin. Fax 332-9384
Spaulding HS 1,400/9-12
130 Wakefield St 03867 603-332-0757
Justin Roy, prin. Fax 330-0251

Rye, Rockingham
Rye SD
Supt. — See Greenland
Rye JHS 200/6-8
501 Washington Rd 03870 603-964-5591
Marie Soucy, prin. Fax 964-3881

Salem, Rockingham, Pop. 27,400
Salem SD 3,700/PK-12
38 Geremonty Dr 03079 603-893-7040
Dr. Michael Delahanty, supt. Fax 893-7080
www.sau57.org
Center for Career & Technical Education Vo/Tech
44 Geremonty Dr 03079 603-893-7069
Chris Dodge, prin. Fax 898-0208
Salem HS 1,400/9-12
44 Geremonty Dr 03079 603-893-7069
Tracy Collyer, prin. Fax 893-7087
Woodbury MS 900/6-8
206 Main St 03079 603-893-7055
Brad St. Laurent, prin. Fax 898-0634

Seabrook, Rockingham
Seabrook SD
Supt. — See Hampton
Seabrook MS 300/5-8
236 Walton Rd 03874 603-474-9221
Leslie Shepard, prin. Fax 474-8020

Somersworth, Strafford, Pop. 11,470
Somersworth SD 1,800/PK-12
51 W High St 03878 603-692-4450
Jeni Mosca, supt. Fax 692-9100
www.sau56.org/somersworth-school-district/home
Somersworth Career Technical Center Vo/Tech
18 Cemetery Rd 03878 603-692-2242
Katelyn Carrington, dean Fax 692-9116
Somersworth HS 600/9-12
11 Memorial Dr 03878 603-692-2431
Victor Sokul, prin. Fax 692-7326
Somersworth MS 400/6-8
7 Memorial Dr 03878 603-692-2126
Dana Hilliard, prin. Fax 692-9101

Empire Beauty School Post-Sec.
362 Route 108 03878 603-692-1515
Tri-City Christian Academy 300/PK-12
150 W High St 03878 603-692-2093
Paul Edgar, admin. Fax 692-6305

South Tamworth, Carroll

Community S 50/6-12
1164 Bunker Hill Rd 03883 603-323-7000

Stratham, Rockingham
Exeter Region Cooperative SD
Supt. — See Exeter
Cooperative MS 1,400/6-8
100 Academic Way 03885 603-775-8700
William Furbush, prin. Fax 775-0151

Sunapee, Sullivan
Sunapee SD 400/K-12
70 Lower Main St 03782 603-763-4627
Russell Holden, supt. Fax 763-4718
www.sunapeeschools.org
Sunapee HS 100/9-12
10 North Rd 03782 603-763-5615
Sean Moynihan, prin. Fax 763-3055
Sunapee MS 100/6-8
10 North Rd 03782 603-763-5615
Sean Moynihan, prin. Fax 763-3055

Mount Royal Academy 100/PK-12
PO Box 362 03782 603-763-9010
Derek Tremblay, hdmstr. Fax 763-5390

Swanzey, Cheshire
Monadnock Regional SD 1,800/PK-12
600 Old Homestead Hwy 03446 603-352-6955
Lisa Witte, supt. Fax 358-6708
www.mrsd.org
Monadnock Regional HS 600/9-12
580 Old Homestead Hwy 03446 603-352-6575
Linda Kalloger, prin. Fax 355-1209
Monadnock Regional MS 300/7-8
580 Old Homestead Hwy 03446 603-352-6575
Linda Kalloger, prin. Fax 357-6520

Tilton, Belknap, Pop. 3,081
Winnisquam Regional SD 1,500/PK-12
433 W Main St 03276 603-286-4116
Dr. Tammy Davis, supt. Fax 286-7402
www.winnisquam.k12.nh.us
Winnisquam Regional HS 500/9-12
435 W Main St 03276 603-286-4531
Tom Laliberte, prin. Fax 286-2006
Winnisquam Regional MS 300/6-8
76 Winter St 03276 603-286-7143
Robert Seaward, prin. Fax 286-7410

Tilton S 200/9-12
30 School St 03276 603-286-4342
Peter Saliba, head sch Fax 286-3137

Walpole, Cheshire, Pop. 595
Fall Mountain Regional SD
Supt. — See Langdon
Walpole MS 100/5-8
PO Box 549 03608 603-756-4728
Samuel Jacobs, prin. Fax 756-3343

Warner, Merrimack, Pop. 440

College of St. Mary Magdalen Post-Sec.
511 Kearsarge Mountain Rd 03278 603-456-2656

Weare, Hillsborough
John Stark Regional SD
Supt. — See Henniker
Stark Regional HS 700/9-12
618 N Stark Hwy 03281 603-529-7675
Christopher Corkery, prin. Fax 529-4646

Weare SD
Supt. — See Henniker
Weare MS 500/5-8
16 East Rd 03281 603-529-7555
Mark Willis, prin. Fax 529-0464

West Lebanon, See Lebanon
Lebanon SD 1,700/PK-12
20 Seminary Hl 03784 603-790-8500
Joanne Roberts, supt. Fax 790-8310
www.sau88.net
Other Schools – See Lebanon

New England School of Hair Design Post-Sec.
12 Interchange Dr 03784 603-298-5199

Whitefield, Coos, Pop. 1,128
White Mountains Regional SD 1,200/PK-12
14 King Sq 03598 603-837-9363
Dr. Marion Anastasia, supt. Fax 837-2326
www.sau36.org
White Mountains Regional HS 400/9-12
PO Box 338 03598 603-837-2528
Michael Berry, prin. Fax 837-3811
White Mountains Reg/Voc HS Vo/Tech
PO Box 338 03598 603-837-2528
Robert Scott, dir. Fax 837-3811

Wilton, Hillsborough, Pop. 1,150
Wilton-Lyndeborough Cooperative SD
Supt. — See Lyndeborough
Wilton-Lyndeborough Cooperative MSHS 200/6-12
57 School Rd 03086 603-654-6123
Brian Bagley, prin. Fax 654-2104

High Mowing S 100/9-12
222 Isaac Frye Hwy 03086 603-654-2391
Geraldine Kline, head sch Fax 654-6588

Windham, Rockingham
Windham SD 2,700/PK-12
19 Haverhill Rd 03087 603-425-1976
Richard Langlois, supt. Fax 425-1719
www.sau95.org
Windham HS 800/9-12
64 London Bridge Rd 03087 603-537-2400
Robert Dawson, prin. Fax 537-2499
Windham MS 700/6-8
112 Lowell Rd Ste A 03087 603-893-2636
Brenda Morrow, prin. Fax 870-9007

Wolfeboro, Carroll, Pop. 2,811
Governor Wentworth Regional SD 2,300/PK-12
140 Pine Hill Rd 03894 603-569-1658
Kathleen Cuddy-Egbert, supt. Fax 569-6983
www.govwentworth.k12.nh.us
Kingswood Regional HS 800/9-12
396 S Main St 03894 603-569-2055
Guy Donnelly, prin. Fax 569-8104
Kingswood Regional MS 400/7-8
404 S Main St 03894 603-569-3689
Aaron Bronson, prin. Fax 569-8113
Lakes Region Technology Center Vo/Tech
384 S Main St 03894 603-569-4361
B. Farr, prin. Fax 569-9243

Brewster Academy 400/9-12
80 Academy Dr 03894 603-569-1600
Dr. Craig Gemmell, head sch Fax 569-7199

Woodsville, Grafton, Pop. 1,115
Haverhill Cooperative SD
Supt. — See North Haverhill
Woodsville HS 300/9-12
9 High St 03785 603-747-2781
Eric Chase, prin. Fax 747-2766

NEW JERSEY

NEW JERSEY DEPARTMENT OF EDUCATION
PO Box 500, Trenton 08625
Telephone 609-292-4469
Fax 609-777-4099
Website http://www.state.nj.us/education

Commissioner of Education Kimberley Harrington

NEW JERSEY BOARD OF EDUCATION
PO Box 500, Trenton 08625-0500

President Mark Biedron

COUNTY SUPERINTENDENTS OF SCHOOLS

Atlantic County Office of Education
Dr. Richard Stepura, supt. 609-625-0004
6260 Old Harding Hwy Ste 1 Fax 625-6539
Mays Landing 08330
www.atlantic-county.org/education/
Bergen County Office of Education
Norah Peck, supt. 201-336-6875
1 Bergen County Plz Rm 350 Fax 336-6880
Hackensack 07601
Burlington County Office of Education
Todd Flora, supt. 609-265-5060
PO Box 6000, Westampton 08060 Fax 265-5922
www.co.burlington.nj.us/553/Superintendent-of-Schools
Camden County Office of Education
Dr. Lovell Pugh-Bassett, supt. 856-401-2400
PO Box 200, Blackwood 08012 Fax 401-2410
www.camdencounty.com/education
Cape May County Office of Education
Dr. Richard Stepura, supt. 609-465-1283
4 Moore Rd Fax 465-2094
Cape May Court House
www.capemaycountygov.net/
Cumberland County Office of Education
Peggy Nicolosi, supt. 856-451-0211
43 Fayette St, Bridgeton 08302 Fax 455-9523
www.co.cumberland.nj.us/
Essex County Office of Education
Joseph Zarra, supt. 973-621-2750
60 Nelson Pl, Newark 07102 Fax 621-1603

Gloucester County Office of Education
Ave Altersitz, supt. 856-686-8370
115 Budd Blvd, West Deptford Fax 686-8387
www.gloucestercountynj.gov/depts/s/sos/default.asp
Hudson County Office of Education
Monica Tone, supt. 201-369-5290
830 Bergen Ave Ste 7B Fax 369-5288
Jersey City 07306
www.hcstonline.org/main/hcdoe/Home.aspx
Hunterdon County Office of Education
Juan Torres, supt. 908-788-1414
PO Box 2900, Flemington 08822 Fax 788-1457
www.co.hunterdon.nj.us/schools.htm
Mercer County Office of Education
Dr. Laura Morana, supt. 609-588-5877
1075 Old Trenton Rd Fax 588-5878
Trenton 08690
nj.gov/counties/mercer/departments/schools/index.html
Middlesex County Office of Education
Dr. Laura Morana, supt. 732-249-2900
1460 Livingston Ave Fax 296-0683
North Brunswick 08902
Monmouth County Office of Education
Dr. Lester Richens, supt. 732-431-7810
PO Box 1264, Freehold 07728 Fax 776-7237
co.monmouth.nj.us/page.aspx?ID=172
Morris County Office of Education
Roger Jinks, supt. 973-285-8332
PO Box 900, Morristown 07963 Fax 285-8341

Ocean County Office of Education
Judith DeStefano-Anen Ed.D., supt. 732-929-2078
212 Washington St Fax 506-5336
Toms River 08753
www.co.ocean.nj.us/ocschools/
Passaic County Office of Education
Robert Davis, supt. 973-569-2110
501 River St, Paterson 07524 Fax 754-0241
www.passaiccountynj.org
Salem County Office of Education
Peggy Nicolosi, supt. 856-339-8611
110 5th St Ste 900, Salem 08079 Fax 935-6290
www.salemcountynj.gov/departments/schools/
Somerset County Office of Education
Roger Jinks, supt. 908-541-5700
PO Box 3000, Somerville 08876 Fax 722-6902
www.co.somerset.nj.us/schools/
Sussex County Office of Education
Dr. Rosalie Lamonte, supt. 973-579-6996
262 White Lake Rd, Sparta 07871 Fax 579-6476
www.sussex.nj.us/Cit-e-Access/webpage.cfm?TID=7&TPID=1560
Union County Office of Education
Dr. Kathleen Serafino, supt. 908-654-9860
300 North Ave E, Westfield 07090 Fax 654-9869
ucnj.org
Warren County Office of Education
Dr. Rosalie Lamonte, supt. 908-689-0497
1501 State Route 57 W Fax 689-1457
Washington 07882
www.co.warren.nj.us/edu.html

PUBLIC, PRIVATE AND CATHOLIC SECONDARY SCHOOLS

Aberdeen, Monmouth, Pop. 17,038
Matawan-Aberdeen Regional SD 3,700/PK-12
1 Crest Way 07747 732-705-4000
Joseph Majka J.D., supt.
www.marsd.org
Matawan Regional HS 1,000/9-12
450 Atlantic Ave 07747 732-705-5200
Michele Ruscavage, prin. Fax 566-2404
Other Schools – See Cliffwood

Monmouth County Vocational SD
Supt. — See Freehold
Aberdeen Vocational S Vo/Tech
450 Atlantic Ave 07747 732-566-5599
Denise Kebeck, prin. Fax 566-2392

Absecon, Atlantic, Pop. 8,239
Absecon CSD 800/K-8
800 Irelan Ave 08201 609-641-5375
Dr. Theresa DeFranco, supt. Fax 641-8692
www.abseconschools.org
Attales MS 300/5-8
800 Irelan Ave Ste 1 08201 609-641-5375
Steven Deo, prin. Fax 641-8692

Holy Spirit HS 600/9-12
500 S New Rd 08201 609-646-3000
Susan Dennen, prin. Fax 646-1770

Adelphia, Monmouth

Talmudical Academy of New Jersey Post-Sec.
Route 524 07710 732-431-1600
Talmudical Academy of NJ 100/9-12
PO Box 7 07710 732-431-1600

Allamuchy, Warren, Pop. 77
Allamuchy Township SD 400/PK-8
PO Box J 07820 908-852-1894
Joseph Flynn, supt. Fax 852-9816
www.aes.k12.nj.us
Allamuchy S 300/3-8
PO Box J 07820 908-852-1894
Jennifer Chickey, prin. Fax 852-9816

Allendale, Bergen, Pop. 6,407
Allendale SD 900/PK-8
100 Brookside Ave 07401 201-327-2020
Michael Barcadepone Ed.D., supt. Fax 785-9735
www.allendalek8.com
Brookside MS 500/4-8
100 Brookside Ave 07401 201-327-2020
Bruce Winkelstein, prin. Fax 825-6553

Northern Highlands Regional HSD 1,300/9-12
298 Hillside Ave 07401 201-327-8700
Scot Beckerman, supt. Fax 327-5274
www.northernhighlands.org
Northern Highlands Regional HS 1,300/9-12
298 Hillside Ave 07401 201-327-8700
Joseph Occhino, prin. Fax 327-3370

Allentown, Monmouth, Pop. 1,798
Upper Freehold Regional SD 2,300/PK-12
27 High St 08501 609-259-7292
Dr. Richard Fitzpatrick, supt. Fax 259-0881
www.ufrsd.net
Allentown HS 1,200/9-12
27 High St 08501 609-259-7292
Connie Embley, prin. Fax 259-0390
Stone Bridge MS 500/5-8
27 High St 08501 609-259-7292
Stefanie Negro, prin. Fax 208-1411

Annandale, Hunterdon, Pop. 1,653
North Hunterdon/Voorhees Regional HSD 2,900/9-12
1445 State Route 31 S 08801 908-735-2846
Jeffrey Bender, supt. Fax 735-6914
www.nhvweb.net
North Hunterdon HS 1,700/9-12
1445 State Route 31 S 08801 908-735-5191
Richard Bergacs, prin. Fax 735-6447
Other Schools – See Glen Gardner

Hunterdon Prep S 100/6-12
11 Spencer Ln 08801 908-832-7200

Asbury, Hunterdon, Pop. 273
Bethlehem Township SD 400/K-8
940 Iron Bridge Rd 08802 908-537-4044
Dr. Edward Keegan, admin. Fax 537-4309
www.btschools.org

Hoppock MS 200/6-8
280 Asbury West Portal Rd 08802 908-479-6336
Jane Smith, prin. Fax 479-1021

Asbury Park, Monmouth, Pop. 15,693
Asbury Park SD 2,000/PK-12
910 4th Ave 07712 732-776-2606
Dr. Lamont Repollet, supt. Fax 774-8067
www.asburypark.k12.nj.us
Asbury Park HS 300/9-12
1003 Sunset Ave 07712 732-776-2638
Reginald Mirthil, prin. Fax 776-3119
King MS 300/6-8
1200 Bangs Ave 07712 732-776-2559
Dr. RaShawn Adams, prin. Fax 776-7503

Monmouth County Vocational SD
Supt. — See Freehold
Culinary Education Center Vo/Tech
101 Drury Ln 07712 732-988-3299
Michael Sirianni, prin. Fax 776-8096

Atco, Camden
Winslow Township SD 4,700/PK-12
40 Cooper Folly Rd 08004 856-767-2850
Dr. H. Major Poteat, supt. Fax 767-4782
www.winslow-schools.com
Winslow Township HS 1,300/9-12
10 Cooper Folly Rd 08004 856-767-1850
Kurtis Marella, prin. Fax 767-5670
Winslow Township MS 800/7-8
30 Cooper Folly Rd 08004 856-767-7222
Stella Nwanguma, prin. Fax 767-5411

Atlantic City, Atlantic, Pop. 38,716
Atlantic City SD 7,200/PK-12
1300 Atlantic Ave 08401 609-343-7200
Paul Spaventa, supt. Fax 345-3268
www.acboe.org
Atlantic City HS 2,000/9-12
1400 N Albany Ave 08401 609-343-7300
Lina Gil, prin. Fax 343-7345

Audubon, Camden, Pop. 8,746
Audubon SD 1,500/PK-12
350 Edgewood Ave 08106 856-547-7695
Steven C. Crispin, supt. Fax 546-8550
www.audubonschools.org/

Audubon JSHS 900/7-12
350 Edgewood Ave 08106 856-547-7695
J. Robert Buchs, prin. Fax 547-4073

Avalon, Cape May, Pop. 1,326
Avalon SD 100/5-8
235 32nd St 08202 609-967-7544
Stacey Tracy, supt. Fax 967-3109
www.avesnj.org/
Avalon ES 100/5-8
235 32nd St 08202 609-967-7544
Stacey Tracy, supt. Fax 967-3109

Avenel, Middlesex, Pop. 16,588
Woodbridge Township SD
Supt. — See Woodbridge
Avenel MS 600/6-8
85 Woodbine Ave 07001 732-586-5622
Joseph Short, prin. Fax 574-0573

Barnegat, Ocean, Pop. 2,775
Barnegat Township SD 3,200/PK-12
550 Barnegat Blvd N 08005 609-698-5800
Karen Wood, supt. Fax 698-6638
www.barnegatschools.com
Barnegat HS 1,000/9-12
180 Bengal Blvd 08005 609-660-7510
Steve Nichol, prin. Fax 660-7598
Brackman MS 700/6-8
600 Barnegat Blvd N 08005 609-698-5880
John Fiorentino, prin. Fax 698-7965

Barrington, Camden, Pop. 6,884
Barrington Borough SD 600/PK-8
311 Reading Ave 08007 856-547-8467
Anthony Arcodia, supt. Fax 547-5533
www.barringtonschools.net/
Woodland MS 200/5-8
1 School Ln 08007 856-547-8402
Michael Silvestri, prin. Fax 522-1248

Castle Academy 200/PK-12
500 Clements Bridge Rd 08007 856-546-5901

Basking Ridge, Somerset, Pop. 4,000
Bernards Township SD 5,600/K-12
101 Peachtree Rd 07920 908-204-2600
Nick Markarian, supt. Fax 766-7641
www.bernardsboe.com/
Annin MS 1,300/6-8
70 Quincy Rd 07920 908-204-2610
Karen Hudock, prin. Fax 204-0244
Ridge HS 1,900/9-12
268 S Finley Ave 07920 908-204-2585
Frank Howlett, prin. Fax 204-2582

Pingry S 700/6-12
131 Martinsville Rd 07920 908-647-5555
Nathaniel Conard, hdmstr. Fax 647-3703

Bayonne, Hudson, Pop. 61,671
Bayonne SD 9,100/PK-12
669 Avenue A 07002 201-858-5800
Dr. Patricia L. McGeehan Ed.D., supt. Fax 858-6289
www.bboed.org
Bayonne HS 2,500/9-12
667 Avenue A 07002 201-858-5900
Richard Baccarella, prin. Fax 858-6263

Bayonne Hospital School of Nursing Post-Sec.
29 E 29th St 07002 201-339-9656
Marist HS 400/9-12
1241 Kennedy Blvd 07002 201-437-4544
Alice Miesnik, head sch Fax 437-6013
Yeshiva Gedola of Bayonne 100/9-12
735 Avenue C 07002 201-339-7187

Bayville, Ocean
Central Regional SD 1,900/7-12
509 Forest Hills Pkwy 08721 732-269-1100
Dr. T. Parlapanides, supt. Fax 237-8872
www.centralreg.k12.nj.us
Central Regional HS 1,300/9-12
509 Forest Hills Pkwy 08721 732-269-1100
Dr. Douglas Corbett, prin. Fax 269-7723
Central Regional MS 600/7-8
509 Forest Hills Pkwy 08721 732-269-1100
Dr. Joseph Firetto, prin. Fax 269-7723

Beachwood, Ocean, Pop. 10,934
Toms River Regional SD
Supt. — See Toms River
Toms River IS South 900/6-8
1675 Pinewald Rd 08722 732-505-3900
Paul Gluck, prin. Fax 818-7512

Belleville, Essex, Pop. 36,300
Belleville SD 4,400/PK-12
102 Passaic Ave 07109 973-450-3500
Dr. Richard Tomko, supt. Fax 450-3504
www.bellevilleschools.org
Belleville HS 1,400/9-12
100 Passaic Ave 07109 973-450-3500
Russell Pagano, prin. Fax 450-3196
Belleville MS 900/6-8
279 Washington Ave 07109 973-450-3500
Shana Wright, prin. Fax 450-5001

Eastern International College Post-Sec.
251 Washington Ave 07109 973-751-9051

Bellmawr, Camden, Pop. 11,414
Bellmawr Borough SD 1,000/PK-8
256 Anderson Ave 08031 856-931-3620
Annette Castiglione, supt. Fax 931-9326
bellmawrschools.org
Bell Oaks MS 400/5-8
256 Anderson Ave 08031 856-931-6273
Anthony Farinelli, prin. Fax 931-9326

Belmar, Monmouth, Pop. 5,731

Mesivta Keser Torah Post-Sec.
503 11th Ave 07719 732-367-4259
St. Rose HS 500/9-12
607 7th Ave 07719 732-681-2858
Sr. Kathy Nace, prin. Fax 280-2745

Belvidere, Warren, Pop. 2,652
Belvidere SD 700/K-12
809 Oxford St 07823 908-475-6600
Christopher Carrubba, supt. Fax 475-6619
www.belvideresd.org
Belvidere HS 400/9-12
809 Oxford St 07823 908-475-4025
Edward Lazzara, prin. Fax 475-1685
Oxford Street MS 200/4-8
807 Oxford St 07823 908-475-4001
Chris Karabinus, prin. Fax 475-6619

Bergenfield, Bergen, Pop. 26,177
Bergenfield SD 3,400/PK-12
225 W Clinton Ave 07621 201-385-8801
Dr. Christopher Tully, supt. Fax 384-2914
www.bergenfield.org/
Bergenfield HS 1,200/9-12
80 S Prospect Ave 07621 201-385-8600
James Fasano, prin. Fax 439-0978
Brown MS 800/6-8
130 S Washington Ave 07621 201-385-8847
Shane Biggins, prin. Fax 385-0219

Berkeley Heights, Union, Pop. 11,980
Berkeley Heights SD 2,700/PK-12
345 Plainfield Ave 07922 908-464-1718
Judith Rattner, supt. Fax 464-1728
www.bhpsnj.org/
Columbia MS 600/6-8
345 Plainfield Ave 07922 908-464-1600
Frank Geiger, prin. Fax 464-0017
Livingston HS 1,000/9-12
175 Watchung Blvd 07922 908-464-3100
Robert Nixon, prin. Fax 464-7508

Bernardsville, Somerset, Pop. 7,613
Somerset Hills SD 2,000/PK-12
25 Olcott Ave 07924 908-204-1930
Dr. Frances Wood, supt. Fax 953-0699
www.shsd.org/
Bernards HS 800/9-12
25 Olcott Ave 07924 908-204-1930
Scott Neigel, prin. Fax 766-8223
Bernardsville MS 600/5-8
141 Seney Dr 07924 908-204-1916
Gretchen Dempsey, prin. Fax 953-2184

Blackwood, Camden, Pop. 4,485
Black Horse Pike Regional SD 3,800/9-12
580 Erial Rd 08012 856-227-4106
Dr. Brian Repici, supt. Fax 227-6835
www.bhprsd.org
Highland HS 1,200/9-12
450 Erial Rd 08012 856-227-4100
Elizabeth Petitte, prin. Fax 227-3619
Other Schools – See Erial, Runnemede

Gloucester Township SD 6,500/PK-8
17 Erial Rd 08012 856-227-1400
John Bilodeau, supt. Fax 228-1422
www.gloucestertownshipschools.org
Glen Landing MS 800/6-8
85 Little Gloucester Rd 08012 856-227-3534
Suzanne Schultes, prin. Fax 228-5260
Lewis MS 700/6-8
875 Erial Rd 08012 856-227-8400
Theodore Otten, prin. Fax 228-5130
Other Schools – See Sicklerville

Camden County College Post-Sec.
PO Box 200 08012 856-227-7200

Blairstown, Warren
North Warren Regional SD 1,000/7-12
PO Box 410 07825 908-362-9342
Sarah Bilotti Ed.D., supt. Fax 362-8744
www.northwarren.org
North Warren Regional MSHS 1,000/7-12
PO Box 410 07825 908-362-8211
Susan Kappler, prin. Fax 362-7353

Blair Academy 400/9-12
PO Box 600 07825 908-362-6121
Christopher Fortunato J.D., head sch Fax 362-7945

Bloomfield, Essex, Pop. 48,200
Bloomfield Township SD 6,100/PK-12
155 Broad St 07003 973-680-8500
Salvatore Goncalves, supt. Fax 680-8274
www.bloomfield.k12.nj.us
Bloomfield HS 1,900/9-12
160 Broad St 07003 973-680-8600
Christopher Jennings, prin. Fax 680-8684
Bloomfield MS 900/7-8
60 Huck Rd 07003 973-680-8620
Alla Vayda-Manzo, prin. Fax 338-6523

Essex County Vocational Technical SD
Supt. — See Newark
Essex Co. Vocational Tech - Bloomfield Vo/Tech
209 Franklin St 07003 973-412-2226
Eric Love, prin. Fax 412-2096

Bloomfield College Post-Sec.
467 Franklin St 07003 973-748-9000
Concorde School of Hair Design Post-Sec.
15 Ward St 07003 973-680-0099

Bloomingdale, Passaic, Pop. 7,587
Bloomingdale SD 500/PK-8
225 Glenwild Ave 07403 973-838-3282
Elaine Baldwin, supt. Fax 838-8898
www.bloomingdaleschools.org
Bergen MS 300/5-8
225 Glenwild Ave 07403 973-838-4835
Frank Verducci, prin. Fax 283-1893

Bogota, Bergen, Pop. 7,987
Bogota SD 1,100/PK-12
1 Henry C Luthin Pl 07603 201-441-4800
Dr. Letizia Pantoliano, supt. Fax 489-5759
www.bogotaboe.com
Bogota JSHS 500/7-12
2 Henry C Luthin Pl 07603 201-441-4808
Damian Kennedy, prin. Fax 441-4849

Boonton, Morris, Pop. 8,097
Boonton SD 1,200/PK-12
434 Lathrop Ave 07005 973-335-9700
Robert Presuto, supt. Fax 335-8281
www.boontonschools.org
Boonton HS 600/9-12
306 Lathrop Ave 07005 973-335-9700
Jason Klebez, prin. Fax 402-5135

Bordentown, Burlington, Pop. 3,853
Bordentown Regional SD 2,400/PK-12
318 Ward Ave 08505 609-298-0025
Dr. Edward Forsthoffer, supt. Fax 298-2515
www.bordentown.k12.nj.us
Bordentown Regional HS 700/9-12
318 Ward Ave 08505 609-298-0025
Robert Walder, prin. Fax 291-0347
Bordentown Regional MS 600/6-8
50 Dunns Mill Rd 08505 609-298-0674
Joseph Slavin, prin. Fax 291-1929

Bound Brook, Somerset, Pop. 10,250
Bound Brook Borough SD 1,600/PK-12
111 W Union Ave 08805 732-652-7920
Dr. Daniel Gallagher, supt. Fax 271-9097
www.bbrook.org
Bound Brook HS 500/9-12
111 W Union Ave 08805 732-652-7950
Edward Smith, prin. Fax 356-6445
Community MS, 120 E 2nd St 08805 6-8
Dr. Joseph Santicerma, prin. 732-852-1130

Branchburg, Somerset
Branchburg Township SD 1,600/PK-8
240 Baird Rd 08876 908-722-3335
Rebecca Gensel, supt. Fax 526-6144
www.branchburg.k12.nj.us
Branchburg Central MS 600/6-8
220 Baird Rd 08876 908-526-1415
Matthew Barbosa, prin. Fax 526-7486

Raritan Valley Community College Post-Sec.
118 Larmington Rd 08876 908-526-1200

Brick, Ocean, Pop. 78,300
Brick Township SD 8,500/PK-12
101 Hendrickson Ave 08724 732-785-3000
Thomas Gialanella, supt. Fax 840-9089
www.brickschools.org/
Brick Township HS 1,400/9-12
346 Chambersbridge Rd 08723 732-262-2500
Dennis Filippone, prin. Fax 920-5907
Brick Township Memorial HS 1,700/9-12
2001 Lanes Mill Rd 08724 732-785-3090
Jennifer Joseph, prin. Fax 458-2748
Lake Riviera MS 900/6-8
171 Beaverson Blvd 08723 732-785-3000
Dr. Alyce Anderson, prin. Fax 477-0392
Veteran's Memorial MS 1,100/6-8
105 Hendrickson Ave 08724 732-785-3000
Renee Kotsianas, prin. Fax 458-9777

Ocean County Vocational SD
Supt. — See Toms River
Ocean County Voc-Tech S - Brick Vo/Tech
350 Chambersbridge Rd 08723 732-286-5670
Lynn Sauer, prin. Fax 920-0108

Capri Institute of Hair Design Post-Sec.
268 Brick Blvd 08723 732-920-3600
Star Career Academy Post-Sec.
150 Brick Blvd 08723 732-451-9710

Bridgeton, Cumberland, Pop. 24,883
Bridgeton SD 5,300/PK-12
PO Box 657 08302 856-455-8030
Dr. Thomasina Jones Ed.D., supt. Fax 455-0176
www.bridgeton.k12.nj.us/
Bridgeton HS 1,000/9-12
111 N West Ave 08302 856-455-8030
Penny Britt, prin. Fax 455-0486
ExCEL Program 6-8
398 N Pearl St 08302 856-455-8030
Isaias Garza, lead tchr. Fax 451-0328

Cumberland Regional SD 1,300/9-12
65 Love Ln 08302 856-451-9400
Steven Price, supt. Fax 455-9750
www.crhsd.org/
Cumberland Regional HS 1,300/9-12
90 Silver Lake Rd 08302 856-451-9400
Ralph Aiello, prin. Fax 455-8514

Cumberland Co. Tech. Education Center Post-Sec.
601 Bridgeton Ave 08302 856-451-9000
Devereux New Jersey Center for Autism Post-Sec.
198 Roadstown Rd 08302 856-599-6411

Bridgewater, Somerset, Pop. 36,400
Bridgewater-Raritan Regional SD
Supt. — See Martinsville

Bridgewater-Raritan HS 2,900/9-12
PO Box 6569 08807 908-231-8660
Dr. Mark Morrell, prin. Fax 231-0467
Bridgewater-Raritan MS 1,500/7-8
PO Box 6933 08807 908-231-8661
Nancy Iatesta, prin. Fax 575-0847

Somerset County Vocational SD
PO Box 6350 08807 908-526-8900
Chrys Harttraft, supt. Fax 704-0784
www.scvths.org/
Somerset County Vo-Tech HS Vo/Tech
PO Box 6350 08807 908-526-8900
Diane Ziegler, prin. Fax 704-0784

Brigantine, Atlantic, Pop. 9,281
Brigantine SD 700/PK-8
PO Box 947 08203 609-266-7671
Brian M. Pruitt, supt. Fax 266-4748
www.brigantineschools.org/
Brigantine North MS 300/5-8
PO Box 947 08203 609-266-3603
Kathleen Fox, prin. Fax 266-7062

Brookside, Morris
Mendham Township SD 700/K-8
PO Box 510 07926 973-543-7107
Dr. Salvatore Constantino, supt. Fax 543-5537
www.mendhamtwp.org
Mendham Township MS 400/5-8
PO Box 510 07926 973-543-2505
Dr. Patrick Ciccone, prin. Fax 543-0701

Budd Lake, Morris, Pop. 8,814
Mt. Olive Township SD
Supt. — See Flanders
Mt. Olive MS 1,200/6-8
160 Wolfe Rd 07828 973-691-4006
Susan Breton-Miranda, prin. Fax 691-4029

Buena, Atlantic, Pop. 4,524
Buena Regional SD 2,000/PK-12
PO Box 309 08310 856-697-0800
John DeStefano, supt. Fax 697-4963
www.buena.k12.nj.us
Buena Regional HS 700/9-12
125 Weymouth Rd 08310 856-697-2400
Moses White, prin. Fax 697-4701
Buena Regional MS 400/6-8
175 Weymouth Rd 08310 856-697-0100
Karen Santoro, prin. Fax 697-9580

Burlington, Burlington, Pop. 9,602
Burlington CSD 1,700/PK-12
518 Locust Ave 08016 609-387-5874
Dr. Patricia Doloughty, supt. Fax 386-6971
www.burlington-nj.net
Burlington City HS 700/7-12
100 Blue Devil Way 08016 609-387-5800
James Flynn, prin. Fax 387-4287

Burlington Township SD 3,900/PK-12
PO Box 428 08016 609-387-3955
Dr. Mary Ann Bell, supt. Fax 239-2192
www.burltwpsch.org
BTMS @ Springside 1,000/6-8
1600 Burlington Byp 08016 609-699-4021
Lawrence Penny, prin. Fax 699-4022
Burlington Township HS 1,300/9-12
610 Fountain Ave 08016 609-387-1713
Phillip Brownridge, prin. Fax 387-0439

Florence Township SD
Supt. — See Florence
Florence Township Memorial HS 400/9-12
1050 Cedar Ln 08016 609-499-4620
John Cogan, prin. Fax 499-3424

Doane Academy 200/PK-12
350 Riverbank 08016 609-386-3500
George Sanderson, hdmstr. Fax 386-5878
Institute of Logistical Management Post-Sec.
PO Box 427 08016 609-747-1515
Life Center Academy 300/PK-12
2045 Columbus Rd 08016 609-499-2100

Butler, Morris, Pop. 7,440
Butler SD 1,100/K-12
38 Bartholdi Ave 07405 973-492-2025
Dr. Mario Cardinale, supt. Fax 492-1016
www.butlerboe.org
Butler HS 400/9-12
38 Bartholdi Ave 07405 973-492-2000
Martin Wall, prin. Fax 492-8672
Butler MS 300/5-8
30 Pearl Pl 07405 973-492-2079
Jamie Manco, prin. Fax 492-9774

Morris County Vocational SD
Supt. — See Denville
Academy for Law & Public Safety Vo/Tech
Bartholdi Ave 07405 973-492-2000

Caldwell, Essex, Pop. 7,489
Caldwell-West Caldwell SD
Supt. — See West Caldwell
Cleveland MS 600/6-8
36 Academy Rd 07006 973-228-9115
James Brown, prin. Fax 228-7471

Caldwell College Post-Sec.
120 Bloomfield Ave 07006 973-618-3000
Mt. St. Dominic Academy 300/9-12
3 Ryerson Ave 07006 973-226-0660
Sr. Frances Sullivan, head sch Fax 226-2693

Califon, Hunterdon, Pop. 1,050
Hunterdon Co. Educational Services Comm. 100/7-12
37 Hoffmans Crossing Rd 07830 908-439-4280
Marie Kisch, supt. Fax 975-3753
www.hcesc.com

ESC Academy Tewksbury Campus 50/Alt
37 Hoffmans Crossing Rd 07830 908-439-3703
Lou Johnson, dir. Fax 439-3701

Lebanon Township SD 700/PK-8
70 Bunnvale Rd 07830 908-638-4521
Jason R. Kornegay, supt. Fax 638-5511
www.lebtwpk8.org
Woodglen MS 400/5-8
70 Bunnvale Rd 07830 908-638-4111
Michael Rubright, prin. Fax 638-8418

Tewksbury Township SD 700/PK-8
173 County Road 517 07830 908-439-2010
Monica Rowland, supt. Fax 439-2655
www.tewksburyschools.org
Old Turnpike MS 300/5-8
171 County Road 517 07830 908-439-2010
Scott Yerger, prin. Fax 439-3160

Camden, Camden, Pop. 76,282
Camden CSD 8,800/PK-12
201 N Front St 08102 856-966-2000
Paymon Rouhanifard, supt. Fax 966-2161
www.camden.k12.nj.us
Brimm Medical Arts HS 200/9-12
1626 Copewood St 08103 856-966-2500
Herbert Simons, prin. Fax 966-2489
Camden Big Picture Learning Academy 100/6-12
1875 Park Blvd 08103 856-966-5223
Timothy Jenkins, prin. Fax 541-8671
Camden HS 600/9-12
1700 Park Blvd 08103 856-966-5100
Scott Shanklin, prin. Fax 966-4756
Creative Arts Morgan Village Academy 300/6-12
990 Morgan St 08104 856-966-8955
Davida Coe-Brockington, prin. Fax 964-9759
Wilson HS 800/9-12
3100 Federal St 08105 856-966-5300
Keith Miles, prin. Fax 966-4755
Riggs Adult Learning Center Adult
1656 Kaighns Ave 08103 856-966-2000
Fax 968-6740

Cooper Hospital/Univ Medical Center Post-Sec.
1 Cooper Plz # 217 08103 856-342-2416
Our Lady of Lourdes School of Nursing Post-Sec.
1600 Haddon Ave 08103 856-757-3729
Rowan University Post-Sec.
200 N Broadway 08102 856-361-2900
Rutgers-The State University of N.J. Post-Sec.
303 Cooper St 08102 856-225-1766
West Jersey Health System Post-Sec.
1000 Atlantic Ave 08104 856-342-4600

Cape May, Cape May, Pop. 3,525
Lower Cape May Regional SD 1,400/7-12
687 Route 9 08204 609-884-3475
Chris Kobik, supt. Fax 884-0546
lcmrschooldistrict.com
Lower Cape May Regional HS 900/9-12
687 Route 9 08204 609-884-3475
Larry Ziemba, prin. Fax 884-0546
Teitelman MS 500/7-8
687 Route 9 08204 609-884-3475
Greg Lasher, prin. Fax 884-0546

Cape May Court House, Cape May, Pop. 5,227
Cape May County Technical SD
188 Crest Haven Rd, 609-380-0200
Dr. Nancy M. Hudanich, supt. Fax 465-3069
www.capemaytech.com
Cape May County Tech HS Vo/Tech
188 Crest Haven Rd, 609-380-0200
Steven Vitiello, prin. Fax 465-4504
Cape May County Tech Evening HS Adult
188 Crest Haven Rd, 609-380-0200

Dennis Township SD 500/PK-8
601 Hagan Rd, 609-861-2821
Mark Miller, supt. Fax 861-1833
dennistwpschools.org
Other Schools – See Dennisville

Middle Township SD 2,500/PK-12
216 S Main St, 609-465-1800
David Salvo, supt. Fax 463-1979
www.middletwp.k12.nj.us
Middle Township HS 800/9-12
300 E Atlantic Ave, 609-465-1852
Frank Riggitano, prin. Fax 465-3415
Middle Township MS 4 500/6-8
300 E Pacific Ave, 609-465-1834
Toni Lehmen, prin. Fax 465-5524

Burdette Tomlin Memorial Hospital Post-Sec.
2 Stone Harbor Blvd, 609-463-2180
Cape May County Technical Institute Post-Sec.
188 Crest Haven Rd, 609-465-2161

Carneys Point, Salem, Pop. 7,250
Penns Grove-Carneys Point Regional SD
Supt. — See Penns Grove
Penns Grove HS 600/9-12
334 Harding Hwy 08069 856-299-6300
Lory O'Brien, prin. Fax 299-5192

Salem County Special Services SD
Supt. — See Woodstown
Alternative S 50/Alt
SCC Davidow Hall Rm 122 08069 856-351-2238
Shawn Rebman, prin.

Salem Community College Post-Sec.
460 Hollywood Ave 08069 856-299-2100

Carteret, Middlesex, Pop. 22,279
Carteret Borough SD 3,700/PK-12
599 Roosevelt Ave 07008 732-541-8960
Kevin Ahearn, supt. Fax 541-0433
www.carteretschools.org

Carteret HS 1,000/9-12
199 Washington Ave 07008 732-541-8960
David Salvatore, prin. Fax 969-4004
Carteret MS 900/6-8
300 Carteret Ave 07008 732-541-8960
Mary Spiga, prin. Fax 541-0483

Cedar Grove, Essex, Pop. 12,053
Cedar Grove Township SD 1,700/PK-12
520 Pompton Ave 07009 973-239-1550
Michael Fetherman, supt. Fax 239-2994
www.cgschools.org
Cedar Grove HS 500/9-12
90 Rugby Rd 07009 973-239-6400
Richard Mangili, prin. Fax 857-9833
Cedar Grove Memorial MS 600/5-8
500 Ridge Rd 07009 973-239-5233
Nicholas DeCorte, prin.

Chatham, Morris, Pop. 8,814
School District of the Chathams 4,100/K-12
58 Meyersville Rd 07928 973-457-2520
Dr. Michael LaSusa, supt. Fax 457-2481
www.chatham-nj.org
Chatham HS 1,200/9-12
255 Lafayette Ave 07928 973-457-2505
Darren Groh, prin. Fax 635-8670
Chatham MS 900/6-8
480 Main St 07928 973-457-2506
Jill Gihorski, prin. Fax 457-2492

Cherry Hill, Camden, Pop. 70,100
Cherry Hill SD 10,900/K-12
PO Box 5015 08034 856-429-5600
Dr. Joseph Meloche, supt. Fax 354-1864
www.chclc.org
Beck MS 900/6-8
950 Cropwell Rd 08003 856-424-4505
Dr. Sidney Dawson, prin. Fax 424-8602
Carusi MS 900/6-8
315 Roosevelt Dr 08002 856-667-1220
John Cafagna, prin. Fax 779-0613
Cherry Hill HS - East 2,100/9-12
1750 Kresson Rd 08003 856-424-2222
Dennis Perry, prin. Fax 424-0637
Cherry Hill HS - West 1,400/9-12
2101 Chapel Ave W 08002 856-663-8006
Kwame Morton, prin. Fax 663-5746
Malberg Alternative HS 50/Alt
45 Ranoldo Ter 08034 856-427-4311
Lawyer Chapman, prin. Fax 427-0017
Rosa International MS 800/6-8
485 Browning Ln 08003 856-616-8787
George Guy, prin. Fax 616-0904

Camden Catholic HS 700/9-12
300 Cuthbert Blvd 08002 856-663-2247
Heather Crisci, prin. Fax 661-0632
Empire Beauty School Post-Sec.
2100 State Highway #38 08002 856-667-8887
Foxman Torah Institute 50/9-12
31 Maple Ave 08002 856-482-8230
Harris School of Business Post-Sec.
1 Mall Dr Ste 700 08002 856-662-5300
Kings Christian S 300/PK-12
5 Carnegie Plz 08003 856-489-6720
James Duff, admin. Fax 489-6727

Chester, Morris, Pop. 1,618
Chester SD 1,200/K-8
50 North Rd 07930 908-879-7373
Dr. Christina Van Woert, supt. Fax 879-5887
www.chester-nj.org
Black River MS 500/6-8
133 North Rd 07930 908-879-6363
Robert Mullen, prin. Fax 879-9085

West Morris Regional HSD 2,800/9-12
10 S Four Bridges Rd 07930 908-879-6404
Michael Ben-David, supt. Fax 879-8861
www.wmrhsd.org
West Morris Central HS 1,300/9-12
259 Bartley Rd 07930 908-879-5212
Stephen Ryan, prin. Fax 879-2741
Other Schools – See Mendham

Chesterfield, Burlington

Meadow View Junior Academy 50/K-12
241 Bordentown Chstrfeld Rd, 609-298-1122

Cinnaminson, Burlington, Pop. 14,583
Cinnaminson Township SD 2,300/PK-12
PO Box 224 08077 856-829-7600
Dr. Salvatore Illuzzi, supt. Fax 786-9618
www.cinnaminson.com
Cinnaminson HS 700/9-12
1197 Riverton Rd 08077 856-829-7770
Darlene Llewellyn, prin. Fax 829-7777
Cinnaminson MS 600/6-8
312 N Fork Landing Rd 08077 856-786-8012
Frank Goulburn, prin. Fax 786-1860

Clark, Union, Pop. 14,629
Clark Township SD 2,200/PK-12
365 Westfield Ave 07066 732-574-9600
Edward Grande, supt. Fax 574-1456
www.clarkschools.org
Johnson HS 800/9-12
365 Westfield Ave 07066 732-382-0910
Richard Delmonaco, prin. Fax 382-5957
Kumpf MS 500/6-8
59 Mildred Ter 07066 732-381-0400
Jennifer Feeley, prin. Fax 381-0262

Mother Seton Regional HS 300/9-12
Valley Rd 07066 732-382-1952
Joan Barron, prin. Fax 382-4725

Clayton, Gloucester, Pop. 7,923
Clayton SD — 1,400/PK-12
350 E Clinton St 08312 — 856-881-8700
David Lindenmuth, supt. — Fax 863-8196
claytonps.org
Clayton HS — 300/9-12
55 Pop Kramer Blvd 08312 — 856-881-8701
Nikolaos Koutsogiannis, prin. — Fax 863-0808
Clayton MS — 300/6-8
55 Pop Kramer Blvd 08312 — 856-881-8702
Nikolaos Koutsogiannis, prin. — Fax 863-0808

Cliffside Park, Bergen, Pop. 22,965
Cliffside Park SD — 2,500/PK-12
525 Palisade Ave 07010 — 201-313-2310
Michael Romagnino, supt. — Fax 943-7050
www.cliffsidepark.edu
Cliffside Park HS — 1,000/9-12
64 Riverview Ave 07010 — 201-313-2370
Lawrence Pinto, prin. — Fax 313-7961

Cliffwood, Monmouth, Pop. 1,500
Matawan-Aberdeen Regional SD
Supt. — See Aberdeen
Matawan Aberdeen MS — 800/6-8
469 Matawan Ave 07721 — 732-705-5400
Aaron Eyler, prin. — Fax 765-0894

Clifton, Passaic, Pop. 82,465
Clifton SD, 745 Clifton Ave 07013 — 10,300/PK-12
Richard Tardalo, supt. — 973-470-2300
www.clifton.k12.nj.us
Clifton HS — 3,100/9-12
333 Colfax Ave 07013 — 973-470-2312
Anthony Orlando, prin. — Fax 458-9290
Columbus MS — 1,200/6-8
350 Piaget Ave 07011 — 973-470-2360
Francine Parker, prin. — Fax 470-2365
Wilson MS — 1,200/6-8
1400 Van Houten Ave 07013 — 973-470-2348
Maria Caiafa-Romeo, prin. — Fax 470-2607

Garfield SD
Supt. — See Garfield
Garfield Auxiliary MSHS — 50/Alt
43 Clifton Ave 07011 — 973-272-7465
Dr. Charles Bonanno, prin. — Fax 253-5696

American Institute — Post-Sec.
346 Lexington Ave 07011 — 973-340-9500
Capri Institute of Hair Design — Post-Sec.
1595 Main Ave 07011 — 973-772-4610
Mesivta Zichron Boruch of Clifton — 100/9-12
338 Delawanna Ave 07014 — 973-779-4800
Star Career Academy — Post-Sec.
1231 Main Ave 07011 — 973-928-1700

Clinton, Hunterdon, Pop. 2,686
Clinton Township SD
Supt. — See Lebanon
Clinton Township MS — 400/7-8
34 Grayrock Rd 08809 — 908-238-9141
Judith Hammond, prin. — Fax 238-9376

Closter, Bergen, Pop. 8,270
Closter SD — 1,100/PK-8
340 Homans Ave 07624 — 201-768-3001
Joanne Newberry, supt. — Fax 768-1903
www.closterschools.org
Tenakill MS — 600/5-8
275 High St 07624 — 201-768-1332
Robert Hyman, prin. — Fax 784-0726

Collingswood, Camden, Pop. 13,647
Collingswood Borough SD — 1,800/PK-12
200 Lees Ave 08108 — 856-962-5700
Dr. Scott Oswald, supt. — Fax 962-5723
www.collingswood.k12.nj.us/
Collingswood HS — 700/9-12
424 W Collings Ave 08108 — 856-962-5701
Matthew Genna, prin. — Fax 962-5565
Collingswood MS — 300/6-8
414 W Collings Ave 08108 — 856-962-5702
Dr. John McMullin, prin. — Fax 962-5751

Colonia, Middlesex, Pop. 17,529
Woodbridge Township SD
Supt. — See Woodbridge
Colonia HS — 1,300/9-12
180 East St 07067 — 732-726-7060
Kenneth Pace, prin. — Fax 574-2575
Colonia MS — 600/6-8
100 Delaware Ave 07067 — 732-396-7000
Cynthia Lagunovich, prin. — Fax 574-0772

Colts Neck, Monmouth
Colts Neck Township SD — 1,000/PK-8
70 Conover Rd 07722 — 732-946-0055
MaryJane Garibay Ed.D., supt. — Fax 858-8583
www.coltsneckschools.org
Cedar Drive MS — 400/6-8
73 Cedar Dr 07722 — 732-946-0055
Colin Rigby, prin. — Fax 462-4108

Freehold Regional HSD
Supt. — See Englishtown
Colts Neck HS — 1,400/9-12
59 Five Points Rd 07722 — 732-761-0190
Daniel Simon, prin. — Fax 761-0193

Columbus, Burlington
Northern Burlington County Regional SD — 2,100/7-12
160 Mansfield Rd E 08022 — 609-298-3900
Dr. James Sarruda, supt. — Fax 298-3154
www.nburlington.com
Northern Burlington County Regional HS — 1,300/9-12
160 Mansfield Rd E 08022 — 609-298-3900
Sally Lopez, prin. — Fax 298-8563
Northern Burlington County Regional JHS — 800/7-8
180 Mansfield Rd E 08022 — 609-298-3900
Andrew Kearns Ed.D., prin. — Fax 291-1563

Convent Station, Morris

Academy of St. Elizabeth — 200/9-12
PO Box 297 07961 — 973-290-5202
Lynn Burek, prin. — Fax 290-5335

Cranbury, Middlesex, Pop. 2,142

Gentle Healing School of Massage — Post-Sec.
1274 S River Rd 08512 — 609-409-2700

Cranford, Union, Pop. 22,624
Cranford Township SD — 3,700/K-12
132 Thomas St 07016 — 908-709-6202
Dr. Marilyn Birnbaum, supt. — Fax 272-7735
www.cranfordschools.org
Cranford HS — 1,100/9-12
201 W End Pl 07016 — 908-709-6272
Kathleen McCabe, prin. — Fax 276-6552
Orange Avenue S — 800/3-8
901 Orange Ave 07016 — 908-709-6257
Kevin Deacon, prin. — Fax 272-3025

Union County College — Post-Sec.
1033 Springfield Ave 07016 — 908-709-7000
University of Northern New Jersey — Post-Sec.
20 Commerce Dr Ste 135 07016 — 908-603-6300

Cream Ridge, Monmouth

New Jersey United Christian Academy — 100/6-12
73 Holmes Mill Rd 08514 — 609-738-2121
Tim Costello, prin. — Fax 738-2151

Cresskill, Bergen, Pop. 8,463
Cresskill SD — 1,700/K-12
1 Lincoln Dr 07626 — 201-227-7791
Michael Burke, supt. — Fax 567-7976
www.cboek12.org
Cresskill HS — 500/9-12
1 Lincoln Dr 07626 — 201-567-7791
Alison Angrisani, prin. — Fax 567-0028
Cresskill MS — 400/6-8
1 Lincoln Dr 07626 — 201-227-7791
Alison Angrisani, prin. — Fax 567-0028

Delanco, Burlington, Pop. 3,316
Delanco Township SD — 400/K-8
1301 Burlington Ave 08075 — 856-461-1905
Joseph Mersinger, supt. — Fax 461-1627
www.delanco.com
Walnut Street MS — 100/6-8
411 Walnut St 08075 — 856-461-0874
Joseph Mersinger, admin. — Fax 461-6903

Delran, Burlington, Pop. 13,178
Delran Township SD — 2,800/PK-12
52 Hartford Rd 08075 — 856-461-6800
Dr. Brian Brotschul, supt. — Fax 461-6125
www.delranschools.org/
Delran HS — 800/9-12
50 Hartford Rd 08075 — 856-461-6100
Daniel Finkle, prin. — Fax 764-6177
Delran MS — 700/6-8
905 S Chester Ave 08075 — 856-461-8822
Wendy DeVicaris, prin. — Fax 461-0311

Holy Cross Academy — 600/9-12
5035 Route 130 08075 — 856-461-5400
Dennis Guida, prin. — Fax 461-0323

Demarest, Bergen, Pop. 4,792
Demarest SD — 700/PK-8
568 Piermont Rd 07627 — 201-768-6060
Michael Fox, supt. — Fax 767-9122
demarestsd.schoolwires.net/
Demarest MS — 300/5-8
568 Piermont Rd 07627 — 201-768-6060
Jonathon Regan, prin. — Fax 768-9122

Northern Valley Regional HSD — 2,400/9-12
162 Knickerbocker Rd 07627 — 201-768-2200
Dr. Geoffrey Gordon, supt. — Fax 768-9488
www.nvnet.org
Northern Valley Regional HS — 1,100/9-12
150 Knickerbocker Rd 07627 — 201-768-3200
James Santana, prin. — Fax 768-5438
Other Schools – See Old Tappan

Academy of the Holy Angels — 600/9-12
315 Hillside Ave 07627 — 201-768-7822
Jean Mullooly, prin. — Fax 768-6933

Dennisville, Cape May
Dennis Township SD
Supt. — See Cape May Court House
Dennis Township ES — 400/4-8
165 Academy Rd 08214 — 609-861-2821
Dr. Joseph LaRosa, prin. — Fax 861-5229

Denville, Morris, Pop. 13,812
Denville Township SD — 1,700/PK-8
400 Morris Ave Ste 279 07834 — 973-983-6530
Steven Forte, supt. — Fax 784-4778
www.denville.org
Valleyview MS — 700/6-8
320 Diamond Spring Rd 07834 — 973-983-6535
Paul Iantosca, prin. — Fax 627-0632

Morris County Vocational SD
400 E Main St 07834 — 973-627-4600
Scott Moffitt, supt. — Fax 627-6979
www.mcvts.org
Morris County School of Technology — Vo/Tech
400 E Main St 07834 — 973-627-4600
Lynne Jackson, prin. — Fax 627-4958
Other Schools – See Butler, Rockaway

Morris Catholic HS — 400/9-12
200 Morris Ave 07834 — 973-627-6660
Robert Loia, prin. — Fax 627-4351

Deptford, Gloucester
Deptford Township SD — 4,200/PK-12
2022 Good Intent Rd 08096 — 856-232-2700
Dr. Charles Ford Jr, supt. — Fax 227-7473
www.deptford.k12.nj.us
Deptford Township HS — 1,000/9-12
575 Fox Run Rd 08096 — 856-232-2713
Melvin Allen, prin. — Fax 374-9145
Other Schools – See Sewell

Dover, Morris, Pop. 17,974
Dover Town SD — 2,900/PK-12
100 Grace St 07801 — 973-989-2000
Robert Becker, supt. — Fax 989-1662
district.dover-nj.org
Dover HS — 800/9-12
100 Grace St 07801 — 973-989-2010
Robert Franks, prin. — Fax 989-1662
Dover MS — 400/7-8
302 E McFarlan St 07801 — 973-989-2040
Tawana Clarrett, prin. — Fax 361-2117

Dover Business College — Post-Sec.
1 W Blackwell St 07801 — 973-285-8400
Joe Kubert Sch of Cartoon & Graphic Arts — Post-Sec.
37 Myrtle Ave 07801 — 973-361-1327

Dumont, Bergen, Pop. 17,212
Dumont SD — 2,600/PK-12
25 Depew St 07628 — 201-387-1600
Emanuele Triggiano, supt. — Fax 387-0259
www.dumontnj.org
Dumont HS — 800/9-12
101 New Milford Ave 07628 — 201-387-3000
James Wichmann, prin. — Fax 387-8461

Dunellen, Middlesex, Pop. 7,100
Dunellen SD — 1,100/PK-12
400 High St 08812 — 732-968-3226
Gene Mosley, supt. — Fax 968-3513
www.dunellenschools.org
Dunellen HS — 300/9-12
411 1st St 08812 — 732-968-0885
Paul Lynch, prin. — Fax 968-3138
Lincoln MS — 300/6-8
400 Dunellen Ave 08812 — 732-968-0885
Robert Altmire, prin. — Fax 424-1359

East Brunswick, Middlesex, Pop. 47,400
East Brunswick Township SD — 8,100/PK-12
760 State Route 18 08816 — 732-613-6700
Victor Valeski, supt. — Fax 698-9871
www.ebnet.org
Churchill JHS — 1,300/8-9
18 Norton Rd 08816 — 732-613-6800
Mark Sutor, prin. — Fax 257-0087
East Brunswick HS — 2,200/10-12
380 Cranbury Rd 08816 — 732-613-6904
Dr. Michael Vinella, prin. — Fax 254-1938

Middlesex County Vocational SD
PO Box 1070 08816 — 732-257-3300
Brian Loughlin, supt. — Fax 257-9388
www.mcvts.net
Middlesex Co. Vocational S E Brunswick — Vo/Tech
PO Box 1070 08816 — 732-254-8700
Jeffrey Bicsko, prin. — Fax 613-9608
Other Schools – See Edison, Perth Amboy, Piscataway, Woodbridge

East Hanover, Morris, Pop. 9,926
East Hanover Township SD — 1,000/PK-8
20 School Ave 07936 — 973-887-2112
Dr. Scott Rubin, supt. — Fax 887-2773
www.easthanoverschools.org/
East Hanover MS — 400/6-8
477 Ridgedale Ave 07936 — 973-887-8810
Stacie Costello, prin. — Fax 887-5079

Hanover Park Regional HSD — 1,600/9-12
75 Mount Pleasant Ave 07936 — 973-887-0320
Carol Grossi, supt. — Fax 887-9247
www.hpreg.org
Hanover Park HS — 900/9-12
63 Mount Pleasant Ave 07936 — 973-887-0300
Thomas Callanan, prin. — Fax 515-7680
Other Schools – See Whippany

East Orange, Essex, Pop. 62,841
East Orange SD — 8,100/PK-12
199 4th Ave 07017 — 973-266-5760
Dr. Gloria Watson, supt. — Fax 678-4865
www.eastorange.k12.nj.us
East Orange Campus HS — 1,100/10-12
344 Prospect St 07017 — 973-266-7300
Dr. Jose Aviles, prin. — Fax 266-7368
East Orange Campus STEM Academy — 400/6-12
129 Renshaw Ave 07017 — 973-266-5900
Thelma Ramsey, prin. — Fax 266-3473
Fresh Start Academy — Alt
74 Halsted St 07018 — 973-266-5640
Stephen Webb, admin. — Fax 673-1374
Tyson Comm MSHS Prfrmg/Fine Arts — 700/6-12
35 Winans St 07017 — 973-414-8600
Anita Champagne, prin. — Fax 395-3888

Ahlus Sunnah S — 100/PK-12
215 N Oraton Pkwy 07017 — 973-672-4121
Best Care Training Institute — Post-Sec.
68 S Harrison St 07017 — 973-673-3900
National Career Institute — Post-Sec.
134 Evergreen Pl Fl 2 07018 — 973-678-3901

East Rutherford, Bergen, Pop. 8,757
Carlstadt-East Rutherford Regional HSD 500/9-12
120 Paterson Ave 07073 201-935-3007
Louise Clarke, supt. Fax 935-5639
www.bectonhs.org/
Becton Regional HS 500/9-12
120 Paterson Ave 07073 201-935-3007
Dario Sforza, prin. Fax 935-5639

East Rutherford SD 800/PK-8
100 Uhland St 07073 201-804-3100
Giovanni A. Giancaspro, supt. Fax 804-3131
www.erboe.net/
Faust MS 300/5-8
100 Uhland St 07073 201-804-3100
Regina Barrale, prin. Fax 804-3131

East Windsor, Mercer, Pop. 22,353
East Windsor Regional SD
Supt. — See Hightstown
Kreps MS 1,100/6-8
5 Kent Ln 08520 609-443-7767
Lori Emmerson, prin. Fax 443-8972

Eatontown, Monmouth, Pop. 12,304
Eatontown SD 500/PK-8
5 Grant Ave 07724 732-542-1055
Scott T. McCue, supt. Fax 578-0017
www.eatontown.org
Memorial MS 200/7-8
7 Grant Ave 07724 732-542-5013
Jay Medlin, prin. Fax 389-1364

Voyagers' Community S 100/PK-12
215 Broad St 07724 732-842-1660
Karen Giuffre, dir.

Edgewater Park, Burlington, Pop. 8,388
Edgewater Park Township SD 800/PK-8
25 Washington Ave 08010 609-877-2124
Dr. Roy Rakszawski, supt. Fax 877-4235
edgewaterparksd.org
Ridgeway MS 300/5-8
300 Delanco Rd 08010 609-871-3434
Ronald Trampe, prin. Fax 871-2434

Edison, Middlesex, Pop. 99,500
Edison Township SD 14,100/PK-12
312 Pierson Ave 08837 732-452-4900
Dr. Richard O'Malley, supt. Fax 452-4993
www.edison.k12.nj.us
Adams MS 800/6-8
1081 New Dover Rd 08820 732-452-2920
Joan Valentine, prin. Fax 452-2922
Edison HS 1,900/9-12
50 Boulevard of Eagles 08817 732-650-5200
Charles Ross, prin. Fax 650-5259
Hoover MS 800/6-8
174 Jackson Ave 08837 732-452-2940
Brian McGrath, prin. Fax 452-2950
Jefferson MS 700/6-8
450 Division St 08817 732-650-5290
Antoinette Emden, prin. Fax 652-5295
Stevens HS 2,100/9-12
855 Grove Ave 08820 732-452-2800
Gail Pawlikowski, prin. Fax 452-2863
Wilson MS 1,000/6-8
50 Woodrow Wilson Dr 08820 732-452-2870
Patricia Cotoia, prin. Fax 452-2876

Middlesex County Vocational SD
Supt. — See East Brunswick
Academy of Math Sci & Engineering/Tech Vo/Tech
100 Technology Dr 08837 732-452-2600
Dr. Linda Russo, prin. Fax 906-8421

Bishop George Ahr HS 900/9-12
1 Tingley Ln 08820 732-549-1108
Sr. Donna Trukowski, prin. Fax 494-2229
Middlesex County College Post-Sec.
2600 Woodbridge Ave 08837 732-548-6000
PC AGE Career Institute Post-Sec.
145 Talmadge Rd Ste 19 08817 732-287-3622
Rabbi Jacob Joseph School Post-Sec.
1 Plainfield Ave 08817 732-985-6533
Rabbi Jacob Joseph S 100/9-12
1 Plainfield Ave 08817 732-985-6533
Wardlaw-Hartridge S 400/PK-12
1295 Inman Ave 08820 908-754-1882
Andrew Webster, hdmstr. Fax 754-9678

Egg Harbor City, Atlantic, Pop. 4,134
Egg Harbor City SD 400/PK-8
730 Havana Ave 08215 609-965-1034
Adrienne Shulby, supt. Fax 965-6719
www.ehcs.k12.nj.us
Egg Harbor City Community S 200/4-8
730 Havana Ave 08215 609-965-1034
Jack Griffith, prin. Fax 965-4742

Greater Egg Harbor Regional HSD
Supt. — See Mays Landing
Cedar Creek HS 800/9-12
1701 New York Ave 08215 609-593-3560
James Reina, prin. Fax 593-3570

Pilgrim Academy 300/PK-12
PO Box 322 08215 609-965-2866
Christopher Storr, hdmstr. Fax 965-3379

Egg Harbor Township, Atlantic
Egg Harbor Township SD 7,500/PK-12
13 Swift Ave 08234 609-646-7911
Dr. Fredrick Nickles, supt. Fax 383-8749
www.eht.k12.nj.us
Alder Avenue MS 900/6-8
25 Alder Ave 08234 609-383-3366
Joseph Marinelli, prin. Fax 383-1492
Eagle Academy Alt
3517 Bargaintown Rd 08234 609-926-1235
Earl Smith, dir. Fax 926-1095
Egg Harbor Township HS 2,400/9-12
24 High School Dr 08234 609-653-0100
Terry Charlton, prin. Fax 927-8844
Fernwood Avenue MS 900/6-8
4034 Fernwood Ave 08234 609-383-3355
James Battersby, prin. Fax 383-0628

Atlantic Christian S 400/PK-12
391 Zion Rd 08234 609-653-1199
Karen Oblen, head sch Fax 653-1435
Star Career Academy Post-Sec.
3003 English Creek Ave #212 08234 609-407-2999
Trocki Hebrew Academy 50/PK-12
6814 Black Horse Pike 08234 609-383-8484

Elizabeth, Union, Pop. 122,789
Elizabeth SD 23,900/PK-12
500 N Broad St 07208 908-436-5000
Olga Hugelmeyer, supt. Fax 436-6133
www.epsnj.org
Academy of Finance 9-12
447 Richmond St 07202 908-436-6503
Dr. Megan Marx, prin.
Dwyer Technology Academy 1,000/9-12
123 Pearl St 07202 908-436-6565
Diana Pinto-Gomez, prin. Fax 436-6566
Edison Career & Technical Academy 600/9-12
625 Summer St 07202 908-436-6800
Fatimah Bey, prin. Fax 436-6780
Elizabeth HS 800/9-12
40 Morrell St 07201 908-436-5870
Michael Cummings, admin. Fax 436-5861
Halsey Health & Public Safety Academy 1,000/9-12
641 South St 07202 908-436-6600
Jeffrey Roszkowski, prin. Fax 436-6626
Hamilton Preparatory Academy 1,000/9-12
310 Cherry St 07208 908-436-6100
George Mikros, prin. Fax 436-6082
Jefferson Arts Academy 800/9-12
27 Martin Luther King Plz 07201 908-436-6767
Michael Ojeda, prin. Fax 436-6733

Benedictine Academy 200/9-12
840 N Broad St 07208 908-352-0670
James Sarto, prin. Fax 352-0698
Drake College of Business Post-Sec.
125 Broad St 07201 908-352-5509
Elizabeth General Medical Center School Post-Sec.
925 E Jersey St 07201 908-965-7390
Jewish Educational Center - Bruriah HS 400/7-12
35 North Ave 07208 908-355-4850
Rav Teitz Mesivta Academy 200/6-12
330 Elmora Ave 07208 908-355-4850
Ami Neuman, prin. Fax 355-3140
St. Mary of the Assumption HS 200/9-12
237 S Broad St 07202 908-352-4350
David Evans, prin. Fax 352-2359
Union County College Post-Sec.
40 W Jersey St Fl 8 07202 908-965-6000
Yeshivas Be'er Yitzchok Post-Sec.
1391 North Ave 07208 908-354-6057

Elmwood Park, Bergen, Pop. 19,032
Elmwood Park SD 2,400/PK-12
60 E 53rd St 07407 201-796-8700
Anthony Grieco, supt. Fax 625-6359
www.epps.org
Memorial HS 700/9-12
375 River Dr 07407 201-796-8700
David Warner, prin. Fax 625-6499
Memorial MS 500/6-8
375 River Dr 07407 201-796-8700
Corinne DiMartino, prin. Fax 625-6379

Elwood, Atlantic, Pop. 1,395
Mullica Township SD 700/PK-8
PO Box 318 08217 609-561-3868
Andrew Weber, supt. Fax 561-7133
www.mullica.k12.nj.us
Mullica Township MS 300/5-8
PO Box 318 08217 609-561-3868
Matt Mazzoni, prin. Fax 561-7133

Emerson, Bergen, Pop. 7,299
Emerson SD 1,200/PK-12
131 Main St 07630 201-262-3875
Brian Gatens, supt. Fax 599-4160
www.emersonschools.org
Emerson JSHS 600/7-12
131 Main St 07630 201-262-4447
Brian Hutchinson, prin. Fax 262-1041

Englewood, Bergen, Pop. 26,555
Englewood CSD 2,900/PK-12
274 Knickerbocker Rd 07631 201-862-6000
Robert Kravitz, supt. Fax 569-6099
www.epsd.org
Dismus MS 400/7-8
325 Tryon Ave 07631 201-862-6025
Lamarr Thomas, prin. Fax 833-9103
Morrow HS 1,000/9-12
274 Knickerbocker Rd 07631 201-862-6039
Peter Elbert, prin. Fax 833-9620

Dwight-Englewood S 900/PK-12
315 E Palisade Ave 07631 201-569-9500
Dr. Rodney DeJarnett, head sch Fax 569-1676
Englewood Hospital & Medical Center Post-Sec.
350 Engle St 07631 201-894-3002
Yeshiva Ohr Simcha of Englewood 50/9-12
101 W Forest Ave 07631 201-816-1800

Englewood Cliffs, Bergen, Pop. 5,175
Englewood Cliffs SD 500/PK-8
143 Charlotte Pl 07632 201-567-7292
Jennifer Brower, supt. Fax 567-2738
www.englewoodcliffs.org
Upper S 300/3-8
143 Charlotte Pl 07632 201-567-6151
Jennifer Brower, prin. Fax 541-8672

St. Peter's University Post-Sec.
Hudson Terrace 07632 201-761-7480

Englishtown, Monmouth, Pop. 1,825
Freehold Regional HSD 11,100/9-12
11 Pine St 07726 732-792-7300
Charles Sampson, supt. Fax 446-9126
www.frhsd.com
Manalapan HS 1,900/9-12
20 Church Ln 07726 732-792-7200
Dr. Adam Angelozzi, prin. Fax 446-4981
Other Schools – See Colts Neck, Farmingdale, Freehold, Marlboro

Manalapan-Englishtown Regional SD 4,900/PK-8
54 Main St 07726 732-786-2500
John Marciante Ph.D., supt. Fax 786-2542
www.mers.k12.nj.us
Other Schools – See Manalapan

Erial, Camden, Pop. 2,500
Black Horse Pike Regional SD
Supt. — See Blackwood
Timber Creek Regional HS 1,300/9-12
501 Jarvis Rd 08081 856-232-9703
Mae Robinson, prin. Fax 232-5267

Divers Academy International Post-Sec.
1500 Liberty Pl 08081 856-404-6100

Ewing, Mercer, Pop. 36,000
Ewing Township SD 3,400/PK-12
2099 Pennington Rd 08618 609-538-9800
Michael Nitti, supt. Fax 538-0041
www.ewing.k12.nj.us
Ewing HS 1,100/9-12
900 Parkway Ave 08618 609-538-9800
Rodney Logan Ed.D., prin. Fax 882-8172
Fisher MS 800/6-8
1325 Lower Ferry Rd 08618 609-538-9800
Barbara Brower, prin. Fax 637-9753

College of New Jersey Post-Sec.
2000 Pennington Rd 08618 609-771-1855
Villa Victoria Academy - Upper 100/9-12
376 W Upper Ferry Rd 08628 609-882-1700
Sr. Lesley Draper, prin. Fax 882-8421

Fairfield, Essex, Pop. 7,615
Essex Regional Educ Services Commission 100/6-12
369 Passaic Ave 07004 973-405-6262
Dr. Laurie Newell, supt. Fax 405-6555
www.eresc.com
Essex Campus Academy 50/Alt
369 Passaic Ave 07004 973-575-0469
David Pinkney, prin. Fax 575-0136
Other Schools – See Passaic

Fair Haven, Monmouth, Pop. 6,047
Fair Haven Borough SD 1,000/PK-8
224 Hance Rd 07704 732-747-2294
Sean McNeil, supt. Fax 747-7441
www.fairhaven.edu
Knollwood MS 600/4-8
224 Hance Rd 07704 732-747-0320
Amy Romano, prin. Fax 747-7441

Fair Lawn, Bergen, Pop. 32,055
Fair Lawn SD 4,400/PK-12
37-01 Fair Lawn Ave 07410 201-794-5500
Bruce Watson, supt. Fax 797-9296
www.fairlawnschools.org/
Fair Lawn HS 1,400/9-12
14-00 Berdan Ave 07410 201-794-5450
James Marcella, prin. Fax 794-8107
Jefferson MS 600/6-8
35-01 Morlot Ave 07410 201-703-2240
Sherrie Galofaro, prin. Fax 475-9185
Memorial MS 400/6-8
12-00 1st St 07410 201-794-5470
Scott Helfand, prin. Fax 703-2237

Artistic Academy of Hair Design Post-Sec.
21 S Broadway 07410 201-794-3502

Fairton, Cumberland, Pop. 1,193

Fairton Christian Center Academy 100/K-12
199 Fairton-Millville Rd 08320 856-455-0408
Woodson Moore, head sch Fax 455-6783

Fairview, Bergen, Pop. 13,423
Fairview SD 1,200/PK-8
130 Hamilton Ave 07022 201-943-0564
Dr. David Sleppin, supt. Fax 840-7754
www.fairviewps.org
Lincoln S 600/4-8
140 Anderson Ave 07022 201-943-0560
Lea Turro, prin. Fax 943-7154

Farmingdale, Monmouth, Pop. 1,307
Freehold Regional HSD
Supt. — See Englishtown
Howell HS 2,300/9-12
405 Squankum Yellowbrook Rd 07727732-919-2131
Jeremy Braverman, prin. Fax 919-1964

Howell Township SD 4,000/PK-8
200 Squankum Yellowbrook Rd 07727732-751-2480
Joseph Isola, supt. Fax 919-1060
www.howell.k12.nj.us
Howell Township MS North 800/6-8
501 Squankum Yellowbrook Rd 07727732-919-0095
Paul Farley, prin. Fax 919-1008
Other Schools – See Howell

Flanders, Morris, Pop. 1,200
Mt. Olive Township SD 4,400/K-12
227 US Highway 206 Ste 10 07836 973-691-4000
Larrie Reynolds Ph.D., supt. Fax 691-4022
www.mtoliveboe.org

Mt. Olive HS 1,400/9-12
18 Corey Rd 07836 973-927-2208
Kevin Stansberry, prin. Fax 927-2204
Other Schools – See Budd Lake

Flemington, Hunterdon, Pop. 4,482
Flemington-Raritan Regional SD 3,300/PK-8
50 Court St 08822 908-284-7561
Maryrose Caulfield, supt. Fax 284-7514
www.frsd.k12.nj.us/
Case MS 800/7-8
301 Case Blvd 08822 908-284-5100
Robert Castellano, prin. Fax 284-5144

Hudson County Schools of Technology
Supt. — See North Bergen
Hunterdon County Adult S Vo/Tech
8 Bartles Corner Rd Ste 2 08822 201-778-1119
Christina Shockley, dir.

Hunterdon Central Regional SD 3,000/9-12
84 State Route 31 08822 908-782-5727
Johanna S. Ruberto Ed.D., supt. Fax 284-7138
www.hcrhs.k12.nj.us
Hunterdon Central Regional HS 3,000/9-12
84 State Route 31 08822 908-782-5727
Johanna S. Ruberto Ed.D., admin. Fax 284-7138

Hunterdon County Vocational SD
8 Bartles Corner Rd Ste 2 08822 908-788-1119
Dr. Kimberly Metz, supt. Fax 806-4839
www.hcpolytech.org
Hunterdon County Polytech S - Bartles Vo/Tech
8 Bartles Corner Rd 08822 908-788-1119
Jessica Cangelosi-Hade, admin. Fax 284-1391
Hunterdon County Polytech S - Central Vo/Tech
10 Junction Rd 08822 908-284-1444
Dan Kerr, prin. Fax 284-9824

Florence, Burlington, Pop. 4,260
Florence Township SD 1,500/K-12
201 Cedar St 08518 609-499-4600
Donna Ambrosius, supt. Fax 499-9679
www.florence.k12.nj.us
Riverfront S 700/4-8
500 E Front St 08518 609-499-4647
Rosario Casiano, prin. Fax 499-8356
Other Schools – See Burlington

Florham Park, Morris, Pop. 11,496
Florham Park SD 1,000/PK-8
PO Box 39 07932 973-822-3880
Dr. Melissa Varley, supt. Fax 822-0716
www.fpks.org
Ridgedale MS 300/6-8
71 Ridgedale Ave 07932 973-822-3855
Peter Christ, prin. Fax 822-7963

Fords, Middlesex, Pop. 14,870
Woodbridge Township SD
Supt. — See Woodbridge
Fords MS 700/6-8
100 Fanning St 08863 732-596-4200
James Parry, prin. Fax 417-2159

Forked River, Ocean, Pop. 5,199
Lacey Township SD
Supt. — See Lanoka Harbor
Lacey Township MS 600/7-8
660 Denton Ave 08731 609-242-2100
Jason King, prin. Fax 242-2114

Fort Lee, Bergen, Pop. 34,777
Fort Lee SD 3,700/PK-12
2175 Lemoine Ave Fl 6 07024 201-585-4612
Kenneth Rota, supt. Fax 585-7997
www.flboe.com
Cole MS 600/7-8
467 Stillwell Ave 07024 201-585-4660
Robert Daniello, prin. Fax 585-1688
Fort Lee HS 1,000/9-12
3000 Lemoine Ave 07024 201-585-4675
Lauren Glynn, prin. Fax 585-2296

Franklin Lakes, Bergen, Pop. 10,458
Franklin Lakes SD 1,200/PK-8
490 Pulis Ave 07417 201-891-1856
Dr. Lydia Furnari, supt. Fax 891-9333
district.franklinlakes.k12.nj.us
Franklin Avenue MS 500/6-8
755 Franklin Ave 07417 201-891-0202
Joseph Keiser, prin. Fax 848-5190

Ramapo Indian Hills Regional HSD
Supt. — See Oakland
Ramapo HS 1,100/9-12
331 George St 07417 201-891-1500
Dr. Louis Moore, prin. Fax 891-6844

Franklinville, Gloucester
Delsea Regional SD 1,700/7-12
242 Fries Mill Rd 08322 856-694-0100
Dr. Piera Gravenor, supt. Fax 694-4417
www.delsearegional.us/
Delsea Regional HS 1,100/9-12
PO Box 405 08322 856-694-0100
Paul Berardelli, prin. Fax 694-2046
Delsea Regional MS 600/7-8
PO Box 405 08322 856-694-0100
Jill Bryfogle, prin. Fax 694-4417

Freehold, Monmouth, Pop. 11,870
Freehold Borough SD 1,400/PK-8
280 Park Ave 07728 732-761-2100
Rocco Tomazic Ed.D., supt. Fax 462-8954
www.freeholdboro.k12.nj.us
Freehold IS 400/6-8
280 Park Ave 07728 732-761-2156
Ronnie Dougherty, prin. Fax 761-2181

Freehold Regional HSD
Supt. — See Englishtown
Freehold HS 1,500/9-12
2 Robertsville Rd 07728 732-431-8360
Linda Jewell, prin. Fax 577-8228
Freehold Township HS 2,100/9-12
281 Elton Adelphia Rd 07728 732-431-8460
Elizabeth Higley, prin. Fax 780-5314

Freehold Township SD 4,000/PK-8
384 W Main St 07728 732-866-8400
Ross Kasun Ed.D., supt. Fax 761-1809
www.freeholdtwp.k12.nj.us/
Barkalow MS 700/6-8
498 Stillwells Corner Rd 07728 732-431-4403
John Soviero, prin. Fax 294-5560
Eisenhower MS 700/6-8
279 Burlington Rd 07728 732-431-3910
Dianne Brethauer, prin. Fax 294-7180

Monmouth County Vocational SD
PO Box 5033 07728 732-431-7942
Timothy McCorkell, supt. Fax 409-6736
www.mcvsd.org
Biotechnology HS Vo/Tech
5000 Kozloski Rd 07728 732-431-6443
Sean Meehan, prin. Fax 409-6736
Freehold Vocational S Vo/Tech
21 Robertsville Rd 07728 732-462-7570
Anthony Villane, prin. Fax 294-0569
Monmouth County Career Center Vo/Tech
1000 Kozloski Rd 07728 732-431-3773
Nathan Kraemer, prin. Fax 409-7292
Other Schools – See Aberdeen, Asbury Park, Hazlet, Highlands, Keyport, Lincroft, Long Branch, Middletown, Neptune, Tinton Falls, Wall

Frenchtown, Hunterdon, Pop. 1,362
Delaware Valley Regional HSD 900/9-12
19 Senator Stout Rd 08825 908-996-2727
Daria Wasserbach, supt. Fax 996-4527
www.dvrhs.org
Delaware Valley Regional HS 900/9-12
19 Senator Stout Rd 08825 908-996-2131
Adrienne Olcott, prin. Fax 996-6653

Galloway, Atlantic
Galloway Township SD 3,100/PK-8
101 S Reeds Rd 08205 609-748-1250
Annette Giaquinto Ed.D., supt. Fax 748-1796
www.gtps.k12.nj.us
Galloway Township MS 800/7-8
100 S Reeds Rd 08205 609-748-1250
Paula Junker, prin. Fax 748-8926

Greater Egg Harbor Regional HSD
Supt. — See Mays Landing
Absegami HS 1,500/9-12
201 S Wrangleboro Rd 08205 609-652-1372
Dr. Jeri-Lynn Vernon Ed.D., prin. Fax 652-0139

Richard Stockton College of New Jersey Post-Sec.
101 Vera King Farris Dr 08205 609-652-1776

Garfield, Bergen, Pop. 30,041
Garfield SD 4,400/PK-12
34 Outwater Ln 07026 973-340-5000
Nicholas Perrapato, supt. Fax 340-4620
www.garfield.k12.nj.us/
Garfield HS 1,000/9-12
500 Palisade Ave 07026 973-340-5010
Dora D'Amico, prin. Fax 546-8430
Garfield MS 900/6-8
175 Lanza Ave 07026 973-272-7020
Anna Sciacca, prin. Fax 340-1767
Other Schools – See Clifton

Gibbstown, Gloucester, Pop. 3,693
Greenwich Township SD 400/PK-8
415 Swedesboro Rd 08027 856-224-4920
Dr. Jennifer Foley-Hindman, supt. Fax 224-5761
www.greenwich.k12.nj.us
Nehaunsey MS 100/6-8
415 Swedesboro Rd 08027 856-224-4920
Dr. Jennifer Foley-Hindman, prin. Fax 224-5765

Gillette, Morris
Long Hill Township SD 800/PK-8
759 Valley Rd 07933 908-647-1200
Dr. Edwin Acevedo, supt. Fax 647-1200
www.longhill.org
Other Schools – See Stirling

Gladstone, Somerset, Pop. 2,086

Gill St. Bernard's S 700/PK-12
PO Box 604 07934 908-234-1611
Sid Rowell, hdmstr. Fax 234-1712

Glassboro, Gloucester, Pop. 18,158
Glassboro SD 2,100/PK-12
560 Bowe Blvd 08028 856-652-2700
Dr. Mark Silverstein, supt. Fax 881-0884
www.glassboroschools.us
Glassboro HS 600/9-12
550 Bowe Blvd 08028 856-652-2700
Dr. Danielle Sneathen, prin. Fax 307-1189
Glassboro IS 300/7-8
202 Delsea Dr N 08028 856-652-2700
Kriston Matthews, prin. Fax 881-3751

Rowan University Post-Sec.
201 Mullica Hill Rd 08028 856-256-4000

Glen Gardner, Hunterdon, Pop. 1,684
North Hunterdon/Voorhees Regional HSD
Supt. — See Annandale
Voorhees HS 1,100/9-12
256 County Road 513 08826 908-638-6116
Ronald Peterson, prin. Fax 638-8689

Glen Ridge, Essex, Pop. 7,336
Glen Ridge SD 1,900/PK-12
12 High St 07028 973-429-8302
Dirk Phillips, supt. Fax 429-5750
www.glenridge.org
Glen Ridge HS 800/7-12
200 Ridgewood Ave 07028 973-429-8303
Louis Melchor, prin. Fax 429-3531

Glen Rock, Bergen, Pop. 11,424
Glen Rock SD 2,400/K-12
620 Harristown Rd 07452 201-445-7700
Dr. Paula Valenti, supt. Fax 389-5019
www.glenrocknj.org
Glen Rock HS 700/9-12
600 Harristown Rd 07452 201-445-7700
John Arlotta, prin. Fax 389-5015
Glen Rock MS 600/6-8
400 Hamilton Ave 07452 201-445-7700
Dr. Jennifer Wirt, prin. Fax 389-5042

Gloucester City, Camden, Pop. 11,306
Gloucester City SD 1,900/PK-12
520 Cumberland St 08030 856-456-7000
Joseph Rafferty, supt. Fax 742-8815
www.gcsd.k12.nj.us
Gloucester City JSHS 700/7-12
1300 Market St 08030 856-456-7000
Sean Gorman, prin. Fax 456-2348

Gloucester Catholic HS 700/7-12
333 Ridgeway St 08030 856-456-4400
Edward Beckett, prin. Fax 456-0506
P.B. Cosmetology Education Centre Post-Sec.
110 Monmouth St 08030 856-456-4927

Great Meadows, Warren, Pop. 303
Great Meadows Regional SD 700/PK-8
PO Box 74 07838 908-637-6576
David C. Mango, supt. Fax 637-6356
www.gmrsd.com
Great Meadows Regional MS 300/6-8
273 US Highway 46 07838 908-637-4584
Israel Marmolejos, prin. Fax 637-4492

Green Brook, Somerset
Green Brook Township SD 900/PK-8
132 Jefferson Ave 08812 732-968-1171
Kevin Carroll, supt. Fax 968-1869
www.gbtps.org
Green Brook MS 400/5-8
132 Jefferson Ave 08812 732-968-1051
Dr. James Bigsby, prin. Fax 752-1086

Hackensack, Bergen, Pop. 42,163
Bergen County Vocational Technical SD
Supt. — See Paramus
Bergen County Academies Vo/Tech
200 Hackensack Ave 07601 201-343-6000
Russell Davis, prin. Fax 996-6955
Bergen Co. Adult & Continuing Education Adult
200 Hackensack Ave 07601 201-343-6000
Paul Castiglia, prin.

Hackensack SD 5,300/PK-12
191 2nd St 07601 201-646-8000
Joe Cicchelli, supt. Fax 646-7827
www.hackensackschools.org
Hackensack HS 1,800/9-12
135 1st St 07601 201-646-7900
James Montesano, prin. Fax 646-7922
Hackensack MS 1,400/5-8
360 Union St 07601 201-646-7842
Corey Jones, prin. Fax 646-7840

Academy of Massage Therapy Post-Sec.
321 Main St 07601 201-568-3220
Center for Allied Health & Nursing Educ Post-Sec.
387 Main St 07601 201-489-5836
Eastwick College Post-Sec.
250 Moore St 07601 201-488-9400
Hackensack Univ Medical Center Post-Sec.
30 Prospect Ave 07601 201-996-2000
Parisian Academy Post-Sec.
21 Passaic St 07601 201-487-2203

Hackettstown, Warren, Pop. 9,581
Hackettstown SD 1,800/PK-12
PO Box 465 07840 908-852-2800
David C. Mango, supt. Fax 852-0286
www.hackettstown.org
Hackettstown HS 900/9-12
701 Warren St 07840 908-852-8150
Matthew Scanlon, prin. Fax 852-6214
Hackettstown MS 400/5-8
500 Washington St 07840 908-852-8554
William Thompson, prin. Fax 850-6544

Centenary College Post-Sec.
400 Jefferson St 07840 908-852-1400

Haddonfield, Camden, Pop. 11,436
Haddonfield Borough SD 2,500/PK-12
1 Lincoln Ave 08033 856-429-7510
Dr. Richard Perry, supt. Fax 429-6015
www.haddonfield.k12.nj.us
Haddonfield Memorial HS 800/9-12
401 Kings Hwy E 08033 856-429-3960
Chuck Klaus, prin. Fax 795-8910
Haddonfield MS 600/6-8
5 Lincoln Ave 08033 856-429-5851
Dennis Moroldo, prin. Fax 429-2006

Paul VI HS 1,100/9-12
901 Hopkins Rd 08033 856-858-4900
Sr. Marianne McCann, prin. Fax 858-6832

Haddon Heights, Camden, Pop. 7,379
Haddon Heights SD 1,200/PK-12
316A 7th Ave 08035 856-547-1412
Michael Adams, supt. Fax 547-3868
hhsd.k12.nj.us
Haddon Heights JSHS 800/7-12
301 2nd Ave 08035 856-547-1920
Ron Corn, prin. Fax 547-6808

Baptist Regional S 200/K-12
300 Station Ave 08035 856-547-2996
Lynn Conahan, admin. Fax 547-6584

Haledon, Passaic, Pop. 8,172
Passaic County Manchester Regional HSD 900/9-12
70 Church St 07508 973-389-2820
Dr. Miguel Hernandez, supt. Fax 956-8805
www.mrhs.net
Manchester Regional HS 900/9-12
70 Church St 07508 973-389-2820
Dr. Richard Ney, prin. Fax 956-8805

Hamburg, Sussex, Pop. 3,209
Hardyston Township SD 700/PK-8
183 Wheatsworth Rd 07419 973-823-7000
Michael Ryder, supt. Fax 823-7010
www.htps.org
Hardyston MS 300/5-8
183 Wheatsworth Rd 07419 973-823-7000
Michael Ryder, prin. Fax 823-7011

Wallkill Valley Regional SD 700/9-12
10 Grumm Rd 07419 973-827-4100
David Carr, supt. Fax 827-8318
www.wallkillvrhs.org
Wallkill Valley Regional HS 700/9-12
10 Grumm Rd 07419 973-827-4100
David Carr, prin. Fax 827-8318

Hamilton, Mercer
Hamilton Township SD 11,500/PK-12
90 Park Ave 08690 609-631-4100
Thomas Ficarra, supt. Fax 631-4103
www.hamilton.k12.nj.us
Crockett MS 800/6-8
2631 Kuser Rd 08691 609-631-4149
Roger Bigos, prin. Fax 631-4116
Grice MS 900/6-8
901 Whitehorse Hamilton Sq 08610 609-631-4152
David Innocenzi, prin. Fax 631-4119
Hamilton East-Steinert HS 1,300/9-12
2900 Klockner Rd 08690 609-631-4150
Nathan Webber, prin. Fax 631-4117
Hamilton North-Nottingham HS 1,300/9-12
1055 Klockner Rd 08619 609-631-4161
Frank Ragazzo, prin. Fax 631-4129
Hamilton West-Watson HS 1,300/9-12
2720 S Clinton Ave 08610 609-631-4168
Brian Smith, prin. Fax 631-4137
Reynolds MS 1,000/6-8
2145 Yrdvll Hamilton Squ Rd 08690 609-631-4162
P. Landolfi-Collins, prin. Fax 631-4130
Accredited Evening HS Adult
90 Park Ave 08690 609-631-4100
Sylvia Zircher, prin. Fax 631-4106

Trenton Catholic Academy - Upper 200/9-12
175 Leonard Ave 08610 609-586-3705
Charles Kroekel, prin. Fax 586-6584

Hammonton, Atlantic, Pop. 14,622
Hammonton SD 3,300/PK-12
566 Old Forks Rd 08037 609-567-7000
Dr. Dan Blachford, supt. Fax 561-3567
www.hammontonps.org/
Hammonton HS 1,400/9-12
566 Old Forks Rd 08037 609-567-7000
Thomas Ramsay, prin. Fax 567-5985
Hammonton MS 800/6-8
75 N Liberty St 08037 609-567-7007
Dr. Michael Nolan, prin. Fax 561-3974

St. Joseph HS 400/9-12
328 Vine St 08037 609-561-8700
Fr. Allain Caparas, prin. Fax 561-8701

Hampton, Hunterdon, Pop. 1,385
Union Township SD 500/PK-8
165 Perryville Rd 08827 908-735-5511
Dr. Edward Hoffman Ed.D., supt. Fax 735-6657
www.uniontwpschool.org
Union Township MS 200/5-8
165 Perryville Rd 08827 908-735-5511
Frances Suchovic, prin. Fax 735-6657

Harrison, Hudson, Pop. 13,212
Harrison SD 2,000/K-12
501 Hamilton St 07029 973-483-4627
Frederick Confessore, supt. Fax 484-7484
www.harrisonschools.org
Harrison HS 700/9-12
401 Kingsland Ave 07029 973-482-5050
Matthew Weber, prin. Fax 412-8729
Washington MS 400/6-8
1 N 5th St 07029 973-483-2285
Michael Landy, prin. Fax 482-3625

Hasbrouck Heights, Bergen, Pop. 11,674
Hasbrouck Heights SD 1,800/PK-12
379 Boulevard 07604 201-288-6150
Dr. Matthew Helfant, supt. Fax 288-0289
www.hhschools.org
Hasbrouck Heights HS 600/9-12
365 Boulevard 07604 201-393-8164
Linda Simmons, prin. Fax 288-2083
Hasbrouck Heights MS 400/6-8
365 Boulevard 07604 201-393-8164
Joseph Mastropietro, prin. Fax 288-2083

Haskell, See Wanaque

Institute for Therapeutic Massage Post-Sec.
1069 Ringwood Ave Ste 315 07420 973-839-6131

Hawthorne, Passaic, Pop. 18,585
Hawthorne SD 2,200/K-12
445 Lafayette Ave 07506 973-427-1300
Richard Spirito, supt. Fax 427-1757
www.hawthorne.k12.nj.us
Hawthorne HS 600/9-12
160 Parmelee Ave 07506 973-423-6415
Daniel LaGrone, prin. Fax 423-6422
Lincoln MS 500/6-8
230 Hawthorne Ave 07506 973-423-6460
Erin Devor, prin. Fax 427-5393

Hawthorne Christian Academy 400/PK-12
2000 State Rt 208 07506 973-423-3331
David Seidman, head sch Fax 238-1718
Roman Academy of Beauty Culture Post-Sec.
431 Lafayette Ave 07506 973-423-2223

Hazlet, Monmouth, Pop. 21,976
Hazlet Township SD 3,100/PK-12
421 Middle Rd 07730 732-264-8402
Dr. Bernard Bragen, supt. Fax 264-1599
www.hazlet.org
Hazlet MS 500/7-8
1639 Union Ave 07730 732-264-0940
Christine McCoid, prin. Fax 264-0571
Raritan HS 1,000/9-12
419 Middle Rd 07730 732-264-8411
Gary Reiter, prin. Fax 264-3214

Monmouth County Vocational SD
Supt. — See Freehold
Hazlet Vocational S Vo/Tech
417 Middle Rd 07730 732-264-4995
Denise Kebeck, prin. Fax 264-3846

Hibernia, Morris, Pop. 200
Rockaway Township SD 2,300/K-8
PO Box 500 07842 973-627-8200
Dr. Greg McGann, supt. Fax 627-7968
www.rocktwp.org
Other Schools – See Rockaway

High Bridge, Hunterdon, Pop. 3,609
High Bridge SD 300/PK-8
50 Thomas St 08829 908-638-4103
Dr. Gregory Hobaugh, supt. Fax 638-4211
www.hbschools.org
High Bridge MS 100/5-8
50 Thomas St 08829 908-638-4101
Rich Kolton, prin. Fax 638-4211

Highland Park, Middlesex, Pop. 13,661
Highland Park SD 1,600/PK-12
435 Mansfield St 08904 732-572-2400
Fax 393-1174
www.hpschools.net
Highland Park HS 500/9-12
102 N 5th Ave 08904 732-572-2400
Michael Lassiter, prin. Fax 819-7041
Highland Park MS 300/6-8
330 Wayne St 08904 732-572-2400
Jennifer Minaya-Osemwegi, prin. Fax 819-7041

Reenas Bais Yaakov 100/9-12
1131 Raritan Ave 08904 732-985-5646

Highlands, Monmouth, Pop. 4,929
Henry Hudson Regional SD 300/7-12
1 Grand Tour 07732 732-872-0900
Dr. Susan Compton, supt. Fax 872-1315
www.henryhudsonreg.k12.nj.us
Hudson Regional JSHS 300/7-12
1 Grand Tour 07732 732-872-0900
Lenore Kingsmore, prin. Fax 708-1409

Monmouth County Vocational SD
Supt. — See Freehold
Marine Academy of Science & Technology Vo/Tech
305 Mast Way 07732 732-291-0995
Earl Moore, prin. Fax 291-9367

Hightstown, Mercer, Pop. 5,390
East Windsor Regional SD 5,000/PK-12
25A Leshin Ln 08520 609-443-7717
Dr. Richard Katz, supt. Fax 443-7704
www.eastwindsorregionalschools.com
Hightstown HS 1,400/9-12
25 Leshin Ln 08520 609-443-7738
Dennis Vinson, prin. Fax 443-7880
Other Schools – See East Windsor

Peddie S 600/9-12
201 S Main St 08520 609-944-7500
Peter Quinn, hdmstr. Fax 944-7901
SciCore Academy PK-12
156 Maxwell Ave 08520 609-448-8950

Hillsborough, Somerset
Hillsborough Township SD 6,900/PK-12
379 S Branch Rd 08844 908-431-6600
Dr. Jorden Schiff, supt. Fax 369-8286
www.htps.us
Hillsborough HS 2,300/9-12
466 Raider Blvd 08844 908-431-6600
Karen Bingert, prin. Fax 874-3762
Hillsborough MS 1,100/7-8
260 Triangle Rd 08844 908-431-6600
Dr. Joseph Trybulski, prin. Fax 874-3492

Hillsdale, Bergen, Pop. 10,123
Hillsdale SD 1,300/PK-8
32 Ruckman Rd 07642 201-664-4512
Dr. Jeffrey Feifer Ed.D., supt. Fax 664-9049
www.hillsdaleschools.com

White MS 600/5-8
120 Magnolia Ave 07642 201-664-0286
Donald Bergamini, prin. Fax 664-2715

Pascack Valley Regional HSD
Supt. — See Montvale
Pascack Valley HS 1,200/9-12
200 Piermont Ave 07642 201-358-7060
Thomas DeMaio, prin. Fax 358-7102

Hillside, Union, Pop. 21,044
Hillside Township SD 2,800/PK-12
195 Virginia St 07205 908-352-7664
Zende Clark, supt. Fax 282-5831
www.hillsidek12.org
Hillside HS 700/9-12
1085 Liberty Ave 07205 908-352-7664
Dr. Christine Sidwa, prin. Fax 352-4246
Krumbiegel MS 700/6-8
145 Hillside Ave 07205 908-352-7664
Dr. Christy Oliver-Hawley, prin. Fax 282-5840

Hoboken, Hudson, Pop. 49,047
Hoboken SD, 158 4th St 07030 1,700/PK-12
Dr. Christine Johnson, supt. 201-356-3600
www.hoboken.k12.nj.us
Hoboken HS 500/9-12
900 Clinton St 07030 201-356-3700
Robin Piccapietra, prin. Fax 356-3704
Hoboken MS 7-8
800 Clinton St 07030 201-356-3700
Robin Piccapietra, prin. Fax 356-3704

Cortiva Institute - Hoboken Post-Sec.
2 Hudson Pl Ste 2 07030 201-215-6440
Hudson S 200/5-12
601 Park Ave 07030 201-659-8335
Paul Perkinson, head sch Fax 222-3669
Stevens Institute of Technology Post-Sec.
Castle Point on Hudson 07030 201-216-5000

Holmdel, Monmouth
Holmdel Township SD 3,000/K-12
65 McCampbell Rd 07733 732-946-1800
Dr. Robert McGarry, supt. Fax 946-1875
www.holmdelschools.org
Holmdel HS 1,000/9-12
36 Crawfords Corner Rd 07733 732-946-1832
William Loughran, prin. Fax 946-0093
Satz MS 500/7-8
24 Crawfords Corner Rd 07733 732-946-1808
Arthur Howard, prin. Fax 834-0089

St. John Vianney HS 1,000/9-12
540A Line Rd 07733 732-739-0800
Steven DiMezza, prin. Fax 739-0824

Hopatcong, Sussex, Pop. 14,950
Hopatcong Borough SD 1,600/K-12
PO Box 1029 07843 973-398-8800
Cynthia Randina, supt. Fax 398-1961
www.hopatcongschools.org/
Hopatcong HS 500/9-12
PO Box 1029 07843 973-398-8803
Lewis Benfatti, prin. Fax 398-9048
Hopatcong MS 400/6-8
PO Box 1029 07843 973-398-8804
Emil Binotto, prin. Fax 398-4184

Hopewell, Mercer, Pop. 1,901

American Boychoir S 50/4-8
174 Lambertville Hopewell 08525 609-924-5858

Howell, Monmouth
Howell Township SD
Supt. — See Farmingdale
Howell Township MS South 700/6-8
1 Kuzminski Way 07731 732-836-1327
Dr. Robert Henig, prin. Fax 836-0698

Yeshivas Emek Hatorah 100/9-12
395 Kent Rd 07731 732-367-1289

Irvington, Essex, Pop. 60,600
Irvington Township SD 6,100/PK-12
1 University Pl 07111 973-399-6800
Dr. Neely Hackett, supt. Fax 372-3724
www.irvington.k12.nj.us
Blue Knights Academy Alt
255 Myrtle Ave 07111 973-399-6879
Hubert Chase, prin.
Irvington HS 1,200/9-12
1253 Clinton Ave 07111 973-399-6897
Mary Michailidis, prin. Fax 371-7045
Union Avenue MS 600/6-8
427 Union Ave 07111 973-399-6885
Muller Pierre, prin. Fax 371-0957
University MS 700/6-8
255 Myrtle Ave 07111 973-399-6879
Andrea Tucker, prin. Fax 351-1025

Iselin, Middlesex, Pop. 18,174
Woodbridge Township SD
Supt. — See Woodbridge
Iselin MS 700/6-8
900 Woodruff St 08830 732-602-8450
Kelly Cilento, prin. Fax 750-4861
Kennedy Memorial HS 1,400/9-12
200 Washington Ave 08830 732-602-8650
Michael Cilento, prin. Fax 634-1112

Lincoln Technical Institute Post-Sec.
675 US Highway 1 S FL 2 08830 732-548-8798
Sanford-Brown Institute Post-Sec.
675 US Highway 1 S Fl 2 08830 732-623-5740

Jackson, Ocean, Pop. 800
Jackson Township SD 8,800/PK-12
151 Don Connor Blvd 08527 732-833-4600
Dr. Stephen Genco, supt. Fax 833-4609
www.jacksonsd.org
Goetz MS 1,200/6-8
835 Patterson Rd 08527 732-833-4610
Carl Perino, prin. Fax 833-4749
Jackson Liberty HS 1,400/9-12
125 N Hope Chapel Rd 08527 732-833-4700
Maureen Butler, prin. Fax 415-7099
Jackson Memorial HS 1,700/9-12
101 Don Connor Blvd 08527 732-833-4670
Kevin DiEugenio, prin. Fax 833-4629
McAuliffe MS 900/6-8
35 S Hope Chapel Rd 08527 732-833-4701
Debra Phillips, prin. Fax 833-4729

Ocean County Vocational SD
Supt. — See Toms River
Ocean County Voc-Tech S - Jackson Vo/Tech
850 Toms River Rd 08527 732-286-5665
Lillian Zavattieri, prin. Fax 928-0490

Jamesburg, Middlesex, Pop. 5,804
Jamesburg SD 700/PK-8
13 Augusta St 08831 732-521-0303
Brian Betze, supt. Fax 521-1267
www.jamesburg.org
Breckwedel MS 200/6-8
13 Augusta St 08831 732-521-0303
Chad Donahue, prin. Fax 521-1267

Jersey City, Hudson, Pop. 239,244
Hudson County Schools of Technology
Supt. — See North Bergen
Academy of Technology Design Vo/Tech
525 Montgomery St 07302 201-631-6300
Barbara Mendolla, admin.
County Prep HS Vo/Tech
525 Montgomery St 07302 201-631-6302
Barbara Mendolla, prin.
Explore 2000 Vo/Tech
180 9th St 07302 201-631-6396
Amy Lin-Rodriguez, prin. Fax 369-5562

Jersey City SD 26,300/PK-12
346 Claremont Ave 07305 201-915-6202
Dr. Marcia Lyles, supt. Fax 915-6084
www.jcboe.org/
Academy I 400/Alt
209 Bergen Ave 07305 201-915-6500
Grace Moriarty, prin. Fax 435-9224
Conwell MS 800/6-8
107 Bright St 07302 201-946-5740
Joanna Veloz, prin. Fax 209-1293
Dickinson HS 2,000/9-12
2 Palisade Ave 07306 201-714-4400
Dr. Frederick Williams, prin. Fax 792-2292
Ferris HS 1,200/9-12
35 Colgate St 07302 201-915-6660
Jaime Morales, prin. Fax 451-6067
Infinity Institute 300/6-12
193 Old Bergen Rd 07305 201-915-1404
Treniere Dobson, prin. Fax 433-9456
Innovation HS 100/9-11
239 Bergen Ave 07305 201-915-1504
Dr. Wachera Brown, prin. Fax 369-6935
Liberty HS 200/Alt
299 Sip Ave 07306 201-714-4373
Monica Grazilla, prin. Fax 369-3714
Lincoln HS 800/9-12
60 Crescent Ave 07304 201-915-6700
Cheryl Richardson-Evans, prin. Fax 435-4493
McNair Academic HS 700/9-12
123 Coles St 07302 201-418-7618
Edward Slattery, prin. Fax 792-1498
Nolan MS 200/6-8
88 Gates Ave 07305 201-915-6570
Francine Luce, prin. Fax 369-3749
Snyder HS 800/9-12
239 Bergen Ave 07305 201-915-6600
Yvonne Waller, prin. Fax 435-5019
Williams MS 900/6-8
222 Laidlaw Ave 07306 201-714-8342
Edwin Rivera, prin. Fax 659-6457

Anthem Institute Post-Sec.
40 Journal Sq 07306 201-876-3800
Christ Hospital School of Nursing Post-Sec.
176 Palisade Ave 07306 201-795-8360
Christ Hospital School of Radiography Post-Sec.
176 Palisade Ave 07306 201-795-8246
Eastern International College Post-Sec.
684 Newark Ave 07306 201-216-9901
Hudson Catholic Regional HS 400/9-12
790 Bergen Ave 07306 201-332-5970
Richard Garibell, prin. Fax 332-6373
Hudson County Community College Post-Sec.
70 Sip Ave 07306 201-714-7100
Natural Motion Institute of Hair Design Post-Sec.
2800 John F Kennedy Blvd 07306 201-659-0303
New Jersey City University Post-Sec.
2039 John F Kennedy Blvd 07305 201-200-2000
PC AGE Career Institute Post-Sec.
2815 John F Kennedy Blvd #3 07306 201-761-0144
St. Anthony HS 200/9-12
175 8th St 07302 201-653-5143
Chad Broussard, head sch Fax 653-8120
St. Dominic Academy 500/9-12
2572 John F Kennedy Blvd 07304 201-434-5938
Sarah Degnan-Moje, head sch Fax 434-2603
St. Peter Preparatory S 1,000/9-12
144 Grand St 07302 201-434-4400
James DeAngelo, prin. Fax 547-2341
St. Peter's University Post-Sec.
2641 John F Kennedy Blvd 07306 201-761-6000
The Institute for Health Education Post-Sec.
600 Pavonia Ave Ste 1 07306 201-217-1113

Keansburg, Monmouth, Pop. 9,873
Keansburg Borough SD 1,100/PK-12
100 Palmer Pl 07734 732-787-2007
John Niesz, supt. Fax 495-6714
www.keansburg.k12.nj.us
Bolger MS 400/5-8
100 Palmer Pl 07734 732-787-2007
Joseph LaRocca, prin. Fax 495-7906
Keansburg HS 400/9-12
140 Port Monmouth Rd 07734 732-787-2007
Michelle Derpich, prin. Fax 495-5401

Kearny, Hudson, Pop. 39,579
Kearny SD 5,000/PK-12
172 Midland Ave 07032 201-955-5000
Patricia Blood, supt. Fax 955-0544
www.kearnyschools.com
Kearny HS 1,700/9-12
336 Devon St 07032 201-955-5050
Jacalyn Richardson, prin. Fax 998-9653
Lincoln MS 400/7-8
121 Beech St 07032 201-955-5095
Robert Zika, prin. Fax 997-2590

Kearny Christian Academy 100/PK-12
22 Wilson Ave 07032 201-998-0788
Helena DiSarro, admin. Fax 998-1102

Kenilworth, Union, Pop. 7,800
Kenilworth SD 1,400/PK-12
426 Boulevard 07033 908-276-5936
Dr. Thomas Tramaglini, supt. Fax 709-7315
www.kenilworthschools.com
Brearley MSHS 700/7-12
401 Monroe Ave 07033 908-931-9696
Brian Luciani, prin. Fax 931-1618

Capri Institute of Hair Design Post-Sec.
660 N Michigan Ave 07033 908-964-1330

Keyport, Monmouth, Pop. 7,124
Keyport SD 1,100/PK-12
370 Broad St 07735 732-212-6100
Dr. Lisa Savoia, supt. Fax 212-6125
www.kpsdschools.org
Keyport HS 400/9-12
351 Broad St 07735 732-212-6100
Michael Waters, prin. Fax 212-6145

Monmouth County Vocational SD
Supt. — See Freehold
Keyport Vocational S Vo/Tech
280 Atlantic St 07735 732-739-0592
Denise Kebeck, prin. Fax 739-1470

Kinnelon, Morris, Pop. 10,145
Kinnelon Borough SD 2,000/PK-12
109 Kiel Ave 07405 973-838-1418
Diane DiGiuseppe, supt. Fax 838-5527
kinnelonpublicschools.org/
Kinnelon HS 700/9-12
121 Kinnelon Rd 07405 973-838-5500
Gary Suda, prin. Fax 838-0261
Miller MS 500/6-8
117 Kiel Ave 07405 973-838-5250
Mark Mongon, prin. Fax 283-0390

Lake Hopatcong, Morris, Pop. 3,000
Jefferson Township SD 3,100/PK-12
31 State Route 181 07849 973-663-5780
Dr. Joseph Kraemer, supt. Fax 663-2790
www.jefftwp.org/
Other Schools – See Oak Ridge

Lakehurst, Ocean, Pop. 2,552
Ocean County Vocational SD
Supt. — See Toms River
Ocean County Voc-Tech S - Navy Lakehurst Vo/Tech
PO Box 1125 08733 732-286-5678
Karen Homiek, prin. Fax 657-4500
Performing Arts Academy Vo/Tech
Hangar One NAVAIR 08733 732-286-5678
Karen Homiek, prin.

Lakewood, Ocean, Pop. 53,516
Lakewood Township SD 5,400/PK-12
1771 Madison Ave Ste B 08701 732-364-2400
Laura Winters, supt. Fax 905-3687
www.lakewoodpiners.org
Lakewood HS 1,000/9-12
855 Somerset Ave 08701 732-905-3502
Marcy Marshall, prin. Fax 905-0895
Lakewood MS 1,000/6-8
755 Somerset Ave 08701 732-905-3600
Richard Goldstein, prin. Fax 905-3695

Achieve Test Prep Post-Sec.
1072 Madison Ave 08701 732-719-2353
Bais Kaila Torah Prep HS 300/9-12
PO Box 952 08701 732-370-4300
Bais Medrash Toras Chesed Post-Sec.
901 Monmouth Ave 08701 732-364-1220
Bais Shaindel HS 500/9-12
685 River Ave 08701 732-363-7074
Bais Yaakov HS 400/9-12
277 James St 08701 732-370-8200
Beth Medrash Govoha Post-Sec.
617 6th St 08701 732-367-1060
Calvary Academy 300/PK-12
1133 E County Line Rd 08701 732-363-3633
Stephanie Cruz M.Ed., prin. Fax 363-7337
Georgian Court University Post-Sec.
900 Lakewood Ave 08701 732-987-2200
Lakewood Cheder S Bais Faga 1,300/3-8
350 Courtney Rd 08701 732-370-6450
Mesivta Keren HaTorah 100/9-12
1083 Brook Rd 08701 732-942-1811
Rabbi Yitzchok Rabinowitz, prin. Fax 994-4222
Mesivta of Lakewood 400/8-12
801 W Kennedy Blvd 08701 732-367-5508
Oros Bais Yaakov 200/9-12
613 Oak St 08701 732-370-6049
Yeshiva Bais Aharon 50/9-12
1430 14th St 08701 732-367-7604
Yeshiva Chayei Olam 100/9-12
14 11th St E 08701 732-363-1267
Yeshiva Gedola Ohr HaTalmud 50/9-12
PO Box 826 08701 732-364-7062
Yeshiva Toras Chaim Post-Sec.
1027 Ridge Ave 08701 732-414-2834
Yeshiva Toras Chaim 9-12
999 Ridge Ave 08701 732-414-2834
Rabbi Mechel Gruss, pres. Fax 414-2838
Yeshiva Yesodei Hatorah Post-Sec.
2 Yesodei Ct 08701 732-370-3360

Lambertville, Hunterdon, Pop. 3,873
South Hunterdon Regional SD 900/PK-12
301 Mt Airy Harbourton Rd 08530 609-397-2060
Dr. Louis Muenker, supt. Fax 397-2366
shrsd.org
South Hunterdon Regional HS 400/7-12
301 Mt Airy Harbourton Rd 08530 609-397-2060
Jennifer MacKnight, prin. Fax 397-2366

Lanoka Harbor, Ocean
Lacey Township SD 4,100/PK-12
200 Western Blvd 08734 609-971-2000
Craig Wigley, supt. Fax 242-9406
www.laceyschools.org
Lacey Township HS 1,400/9-12
73 Haines St 08734 609-971-2020
Gregory Brandis, prin. Fax 242-0873
Other Schools – See Forked River

Laurel Springs, Camden, Pop. 1,884

Empire Beauty School Post-Sec.
1305 Blackwood Clementon Rd 08021
856-435-8100

Lawrenceville, Mercer, Pop. 3,814
Lawrence Township SD 3,900/PK-12
2565 Princeton Pike 08648 609-671-5500
Crystal Edwards Ed.D., supt. Fax 883-4225
www.ltps.org
Lawrence HS 1,200/9-12
2525 Princeton Ave 08648 609-671-5510
David Adam, prin. Fax 671-3411
Lawrence MS 600/7-8
2455 Princeton Pike 08648 609-671-5520
Mindy Milavsky, prin. Fax 671-3421

Fortis Institute Post-Sec.
2572 US Highway 1 Ste 100 08648 609-512-2560
Lawrenceville S 800/9-12
PO Box 6008 08648 609-896-0400
Steve Murray, hdmstr. Fax 895-2217
Notre Dame HS 1,300/9-12
601 Lawrence Rd 08648 609-882-7900
Mary Liz Ivins, prin. Fax 882-5723
Rider University Post-Sec.
2083 Lawrenceville Rd 08648 609-896-5000

Lebanon, Hunterdon, Pop. 1,334
Clinton Township SD 1,500/PK-8
PO Box 362 08833 908-236-7235
Dr. Gina Villani, supt. Fax 236-6358
www.ctsd.k12.nj.us
Other Schools – See Clinton

Leonardo, Monmouth, Pop. 2,725
Middletown Township SD 9,500/PK-12
834 Leonardville Rd Fl 2 07737 732-671-3850
Dr. William George, supt. Fax 615-9351
mtps.schoolwires.net
Bayshore MS 600/6-8
834 Leonardville Rd 07737 732-291-1380
Michael Scarano, prin.
Other Schools – See Middletown, Port Monmouth

Leonia, Bergen, Pop. 8,727
Leonia SD 1,700/PK-12
570 Grand Ave 07605 201-302-5200
Joanne Megargee, supt. Fax 947-4782
www.leoniaschools.org
Leonia HS 700/9-12
100 Christie Heights St 07605 201-302-5200
Dr. Edward Bertolini, prin. Fax 461-8957
Leonia MS 500/6-8
500 Broad Ave 07605 201-302-5200
Dr. Nicholas Bernice, prin. Fax 461-1510

Lincoln Park, Morris, Pop. 10,363
Lincoln Park Borough SD 900/PK-8
92 Ryerson Rd 07035 973-696-5500
James Grube, supt. Fax 696-9273
www.lincolnparkboe.org
Lincoln Park MS 400/5-8
90 Ryerson Rd 07035 973-696-5520
Michael Meyer, prin. Fax 872-8930

Lincroft, Monmouth, Pop. 6,069
Monmouth County Vocational SD
Supt. — See Freehold
High Technology HS Vo/Tech
PO Box 119 07738 732-842-8444
Kevin Bals, prin. Fax 219-9418

Brookdale Community College Post-Sec.
765 Newman Springs Rd 07738 732-224-2345
Christian Brothers Academy 1,000/9-12
850 Newman Springs Rd 07738 732-747-1959
R. Ross Fales, prin. Fax 747-1643

Linden, Union, Pop. 39,711
Linden SD 5,400/PK-12
2 E Gibbons St 07036 908-486-2800
Danny Robertozzi Ed.D., supt. Fax 486-6331
www.linden.k12.nj.us

Linden HS 1,700/9-12
121 W Saint Georges Ave 07036 908-486-5432
Yelena Horre, prin. Fax 486-3242
McManus MS 600/6-8
300 Edgewood Rd 07036 908-486-7751
Peter Fingerlin, prin. Fax 587-0607
Soehl MS 600/6-8
300 E Henry St 07036 908-486-0550
Richard Molinaro, prin. Fax 486-3478

Sinai Christian Academy 100/PK-12
2301 Grier Ave 07036 908-486-2006
Fax 925-9258
Yeshiva Gedolah Zichron Leyma Post-Sec.
1000 Orchard Ter 07036 908-587-0502

Lindenwold, Camden, Pop. 17,154
Lindenwold SD 2,300/PK-12
801 Egg Harbor Rd 08021 856-783-0276
Lori Moore, supt. Fax 435-5887
www.lindenwold.k12.nj.us/
Lindenwold HS 500/9-12
801 Egg Harbor Rd 08021 856-741-0320
Peter Brandt, prin. Fax 741-0350
Lindenwold MS 700/5-8
40 White Horse Ave 08021 856-346-3330
Kasha Giddins, prin. Fax 346-0554

Linwood, Atlantic, Pop. 6,996
Linwood CSD 800/PK-8
51 Belhaven Ave 08221 609-926-6700
Dr. Michelle Cappellutti Ed.D., supt. Fax 926-6705
www.linwoodschools.org
Belhaven MS 400/5-8
51 Belhaven Ave 08221 609-926-6700
Susan Speirs, prin. Fax 926-6705

Mainland Regional HSD 1,400/9-12
1301 Oak Ave 08221 609-927-4151
Mark Marrone, supt. Fax 927-1942
www.mainlandregional.net
Mainland Regional HS 1,400/9-12
1301 Oak Ave 08221 609-927-4151
Kevin Burns, prin. Fax 927-1942

Harris School of Business Post-Sec.
1201 New Rd Ste 226 08221 609-927-4310

Little Egg Harbor Township, Ocean, Pop. 13,333
Ocean County Vocational SD
Supt. — See Toms River
Ocean County Center for Culinary Arts Vo/Tech
261 Country Club Blvd 08087 609-296-2137
Gary MacDonald, prin.

Pinelands Regional SD 1,600/7-12
PO Box 248 08087 609-296-3106
Dr. Maryann Banks, supt. Fax 294-9519
www.prsdnj.org
Pinelands Regional HS 800/10-12
PO Box 248 08087 609-296-3106
Dr. Cheryl Stevenson, prin. Fax 296-6905
Pinelands Regional JHS 800/7-9
PO Box 248 08087 609-296-3106
F. Eric Pschorr, prin. Fax 296-2626

Little Falls, Passaic, Pop. 11,294
Little Falls Township SD 800/K-8
32 Stevens Ave 07424 973-256-1034
Dr. Tracey Marinelli, supt. Fax 256-6542
www.lfnjschools.org
Little Falls MS 1 400/5-8
32 Stevens Ave 07424 973-256-1033
Philip Ligus, prin. Fax 785-4857

Passaic Valley Regional HSD 1 1,300/9-12
100 E Main St 07424 973-890-2500
Dr. JoAnn Cardillo, supt. Fax 890-0512
www.pvhs.k12.nj.us
Passaic Valley Regional HS 1,300/9-12
100 E Main St 07424 973-890-2500
Ray Rotella, supt. Fax 890-0512

Little Silver, Monmouth, Pop. 5,876
Little Silver Borough SD 900/PK-8
124 Willow Dr 07739 732-741-2188
Dr. Carolyn Kossack, supt. Fax 741-3644
www.littlesilverschools.org
Markham Place MS 400/5-8
95 Markham Pl 07739 732-741-7112
Eric Platt, prin. Fax 741-3562

Red Bank Regional HSD 1,200/9-12
101 Ridge Rd 07739 732-842-8000
Thomas Pagano, supt. Fax 842-8504
www.rbrhs.org
Red Bank Regional HS 1,200/9-12
101 Ridge Rd 07739 732-842-8000
Risa Clay, prin. Fax 842-4868

Livingston, Essex, Pop. 27,500
Livingston SD 5,700/PK-12
11 Foxcroft Dr 07039 973-535-8000
Christina Steffner, supt. Fax 535-1254
www.livingston.org
Heritage MS 900/7-8
20 Foxcroft Dr 07039 973-535-8000
Shawn Kelly, prin. Fax 597-9492
Livingston HS 1,800/9-12
30 Robert H Harp Dr 07039 973-535-8000
Mark Stern, prin. Fax 994-4297

Kushner Yeshiva HS 200/9-12
110 S Orange Ave 07039 973-437-8000
Newark Academy 600/6-12
91 S Orange Ave 07039 973-992-7000
Donald Austin, hdmstr. Fax 992-8962
St. Barnabas Medical Center Post-Sec.
94 Old Short Hills Rd 07039 973-533-5628

Lodi, Bergen, Pop. 23,608
Lodi SD 3,200/PK-12
8 Hunter St 07644 973-778-4620
Frank Quatrone, supt. Fax 778-6393
www.lodi.k12.nj.us
Jefferson MS 700/6-8
75 1st St 07644 973-478-8662
Robert Sciolaro, prin. Fax 478-0358
Lodi HS 1,000/9-12
99 Putnam St 07644 973-478-6100
Frank D'Amico, prin. Fax 478-4012

Felician College Post-Sec.
262 S Main St 07644 201-559-6000
Immaculate Conception HS 200/9-12
258 S Main St 07644 973-773-2400
Joseph Azzolino, prin. Fax 614-0893

Logan, Gloucester
Logan Township SD 1,000/PK-8
110 School Ln 08085 856-467-5133
Patricia Haney, supt. Fax 467-9012
www.logan.k12.nj.us
Logan MS 400/6-8
110 School Ln 08085 856-467-5133
Heather Moran, prin. Fax 467-9012

Long Branch, Monmouth, Pop. 29,197
Long Branch SD 4,900/PK-12
540 Broadway 07740 732-571-2868
Michael Salvatore, supt. Fax 229-0797
www.longbranch.k12.nj.us
Long Branch HS 1,100/9-12
404 Indiana Ave 07740 732-229-7300
Vincent Muscillo, prin. Fax 229-2825
Long Branch MS 1,000/6-8
350 Indiana Ave 07740 732-229-5533
Michael Viturello, prin. Fax 229-4894

Monmouth County Vocational SD
Supt. — See Freehold
Academy of Law & Public Safety Vo/Tech
255 W End Ave 07740 732-229-3019
Joseph Diver, prin. Fax 229-5727

Ma'or Yeshiva HS for Boys 100/9-12
250 Park Ave 07740 732-222-4797
Monmouth Medical Center Post-Sec.
300 2nd Ave 07740 732-222-5200

Long Valley, Morris, Pop. 1,859
Washington Township SD 2,300/PK-8
53 W Mill Rd 07853 908-876-4172
Jeffrey Mohre, supt. Fax 876-9392
www.wtschools.org
Long Valley MS 900/6-8
51 W Mill Rd 07853 908-876-3434
Mark Ippolito, prin. Fax 876-3436

Lumberton, Burlington
Lumberton Township SD 1,400/K-8
33 Municipal Dr 08048 609-267-1406
Joseph Langowski, supt. Fax 267-0002
www.lumberton.k12.nj.us/
Lumberton MS 500/6-8
30 Dimsdale Dr 08048 609-265-0123
Pete DeFeo, prin. Fax 265-0476

Lyndhurst, Bergen, Pop. 18,262
Lyndhurst Township SD 2,100/PK-12
420 Fern Ave 07071 201-438-5683
Shauna C. DeMarco, supt. Fax 896-2118
www.lyndhurstschools.net
Jefferson S 200/4-8
336 Lake Ave 07071 201-896-2065
Joseph Vastola, prin. Fax 933-3112
Lincoln S 200/4-8
281 Ridge Rd 07071 201-438-5683
Michael Rizzo, prin. Fax 438-5786
Lyndhurst HS 700/9-12
400 Weart Ave 07071 201-896-2100
Laura Vuono, prin. Fax 896-2088
Roosevelt S 400/4-8
530 Stuyvesant Ave 07071 201-896-2068
Joseph DeCorso, prin. Fax 933-3143

Madison, Morris, Pop. 15,563
Madison SD 2,500/PK-12
359 Woodland Rd 07940 973-593-3100
Dr. Michael Rossi, supt. Fax 301-2170
www.madisonpublicschools.org
Madison HS 800/9-12
170 Ridgedale Ave 07940 973-593-3117
Greg Robertson, prin. Fax 593-3141
Madison JHS 500/6-8
160 Main St 07940 973-593-3149
David Coster, prin. Fax 966-1908

Drew University Post-Sec.
36 Madison Ave 07940 973-408-3000
Fairleigh Dickinson University Post-Sec.
285 Madison Ave 07940 973-443-8500

Mahwah, Bergen, Pop. 17,905
Mahwah Township SD 3,100/PK-12
60 Ridge Rd 07430 201-762-2400
C. Lauren Schoen, supt. Fax 529-1287
www.mahwah.k12.nj.us
Mahwah HS 1,000/9-12
50 Ridge Rd 07430 201-762-2300
John Pascale, prin. Fax 512-0949
Ramapo Ridge MS 800/6-8
150 Ridge Rd 07430 201-762-2380
Daniel Vander Molen, prin. Fax 529-6790

Lincoln Technical Institute Post-Sec.
70 McKee Dr 07430 201-529-1414
National Tax Training School Post-Sec.
PO Box 767 07430 800-914-8138

Ramapo College of New Jersey Post-Sec.
505 Ramapo Valley Rd 07430 201-684-7500

Manahawkin, Ocean, Pop. 2,289
Ocean County Vocational SD
Supt. — See Toms River
Ocean County Voc-Tech S - MATES Vo/Tech
195 Cedar Bridge Rd 08050 609-978-8439
Alison Carroll, prin. Fax 978-8540

Southern Regional SD 3,000/7-12
105 Cedar Bridge Rd 08050 609-597-9481
Craig Henry, supt. Fax 978-0298
www.srsd.net
Southern Regional HS 1,000/9-10
600 N Main St 08050 609-597-9481
Eric Wilhelm, prin. Fax 978-5375
Southern Regional HS 1,000/11-12
90 Cedar Bridge Rd 08050 609-597-9481
Eric Wilhelm, prin. Fax 978-5357
Southern Regional MS 1,000/7-8
75 Cedar Bridge Rd 08050 609-597-9481
Lorraine Airey, prin. Fax 978-8209

Manalapan, Monmouth
Manalapan-Englishtown Regional SD
Supt. — See Englishtown
Manalapan-Englishtown MS 1,200/7-8
155 Millhurst Rd 07726 732-786-2650
Robert Williams, prin. Fax 786-2660

Manasquan, Monmouth, Pop. 5,870
Manasquan SD 1,600/PK-12
169 Broad St 08736 732-528-8800
Dr. Frank Kasyan, supt. Fax 223-6286
www.manasquanschools.org
Manasquan HS 1,000/9-12
167 Broad St 08736 732-528-8820
Richard Coppola, prin. Fax 528-0316

Manchester, Ocean
Manchester Township SD
Supt. — See Whiting
Manchester Township HS 1,000/9-12
101 S Colonial Dr 08759 732-657-2121
Dennis Adams, prin. Fax 657-2781
Manchester Township MS 700/6-8
2759 Ridgeway Rd 08759 732-657-1717
Nancy Driber, prin. Fax 657-0326

Manville, Somerset, Pop. 10,188
Manville Borough SD 1,300/K-12
410 Brooks Blvd 08835 908-231-8500
Anne Facendo, supt. Fax 707-3963
www.manvilleschools.org
Batcho IS, 100 N 13th Ave 08835 300/6-8
Michael Magliacano, prin. 908-231-8521
Manville HS 400/9-12
1100 Brooks Blvd 08835 908-231-6806
Dr. James Brunn, prin. Fax 231-8532

Maple Shade, Burlington, Pop. 19,211
Maple Shade Township SD 1,900/PK-12
170 Frederick Ave 08052 856-779-1750
Beth Norcia, supt. Fax 779-1054
www.mapleshade.org
Maple Shade JSHS 700/7-12
180 Frederick Ave 08052 856-779-2880
Scott Arnauer, prin. Fax 779-8849

Maplewood, Essex, Pop. 21,756
South Orange-Maplewood SD 6,600/PK-12
525 Academy St 07040 973-762-5600
Dr. John Ramos, supt. Fax 378-9464
www.somsd.k12.nj.us
Columbia HS 1,800/9-12
17 Parker Ave 07040 973-762-5600
Elizabeth Aaron, prin. Fax 378-7607
Maplewood MS 800/6-8
7 Burnett St 07040 973-378-7660
Jerrill Adams, prin. Fax 378-5247
Other Schools – See South Orange

Margate City, Atlantic, Pop. 6,302
Margate City SD 400/PK-8
8103 Winchester Ave 08402 609-822-1686
John DiNicola, supt. Fax 822-3399
www.margateschools.org
Tighe MS 200/5-8
7804 Amherst Ave 08402 609-822-2353
Audrey Becker, prin. Fax 822-8456

Marlboro, Monmouth
Freehold Regional HSD
Supt. — See Englishtown
Marlboro HS 1,900/9-12
95 N Main St 07746 732-617-8393
Shaun Boylan, prin. Fax 972-6615

Marlboro Township SD 5,100/PK-8
1980 Township Dr 07746 732-972-2000
Dr. Eric Hibbs, supt. Fax 972-2003
www.marlboro.k12.nj.us
Marlboro MS 1,100/6-8
355 County Road 520 07746 732-972-2100
Patricia Nieliwocki, prin. Fax 972-6765
Other Schools – See Morganville

Marlton, Burlington, Pop. 9,983
Evesham Township SD 4,400/PK-8
25 S Maple Ave 08053 856-983-1800
John Scavelli, supt. Fax 983-2939
www.evesham.k12.nj.us
DeMasi MS 800/6-8
199 Evesboro Medford Rd 08053 856-988-0777
Irene Romanelli, prin. Fax 596-1571
Marlton MS 800/6-8
150 Tomlinson Mill Rd 08053 856-988-0684
Gary Hoffman, prin. Fax 988-9327

Lenape Regional HSD
Supt. — See Shamong Township
Cherokee HS 2,200/9-12
120 Tomlinson Mill Rd 08053 856-983-5140
Donna Charlesworth, prin. Fax 596-6495

Achieve Test Prep Post-Sec.
1 Eves Dr 08053 609-529-8589

Martinsville, Somerset, Pop. 11,795
Bridgewater-Raritan Regional SD 8,500/PK-12
836 Newmans Ln 08836 908-685-2777
Russell Lazovick, supt. Fax 231-8496
www.brrsd.k12.nj.us
Other Schools – See Bridgewater

Matawan, Monmouth, Pop. 8,609
Old Bridge Township SD 8,600/K-12
4207 Highway 516 07747 732-566-1000
David Cittadino, supt.
www.oldbridgeadmin.org
Old Bridge HS 2,900/9-12
4209 Highway 516 07747 732-290-3900
Vincent Sasso, prin. Fax 566-1263
Other Schools – See Old Bridge

Mays Landing, Atlantic, Pop. 2,098
Atlantic County Vocational SD
5080 Atlantic Ave 08330 609-625-2249
Dr. Philip Guenther, supt. Fax 625-2876
Atlantic County Alternative HS 100/Alt
4805 Nawakwa Blvd 08330 609-625-2249
Aaron Bullock, prin.
Atlantic County Institute of Technology Vo/Tech
5080 Atlantic Ave 08330 609-625-2249
Ronald DeFelice, prin. Fax 625-0707

Greater Egg Harbor Regional HSD 3,400/9-12
1824 Dr Dennis Foreman Dr 08330 609-625-1456
John Keenan, supt. Fax 625-0045
www.gehrhsd.net
Oakcrest HS 1,100/9-12
1824 Dr Dennis Foreman Dr 08330 609-909-2600
Joseph Carruth, prin. Fax 625-0872
Other Schools – See Egg Harbor City, Galloway

Hamilton Township SD 3,000/PK-8
1876 Dr Dennis Foreman Dr 08330 609-476-6300
Frank Vogel, supt. Fax 625-4847
www.hamiltonschools.org
Davies MS 1,000/6-8
1876 Dr Dennis Foreman Dr 08330 609-476-6242
Stephen Santilli, prin.

Atlantic Cape Community College Post-Sec.
5100 Black Horse Pike 08330 609-343-5000

Maywood, Bergen, Pop. 9,373
Maywood SD 900/PK-8
452 Maywood Ave 07607 201-845-9114
Michael Jordan, supt. Fax 845-7146
www.maywoodschools.org
Maywood Avenue MS 500/4-8
452 Maywood Ave 07607 201-845-9110
Michael Jordan, prin. Fax 291-1917

Medford, Burlington
Burlington Co. Institute of Tech SD
Supt. — See Mount Holly
Burlington Co. Institute of Technology Vo/Tech
10 Hawkin Rd 08055 609-654-0200
Mike Parker, prin. Fax 654-1081

Lenape Regional HSD
Supt. — See Shamong Township
Lenape HS 1,900/9-12
235 Hartford Rd 08055 609-654-5111
Anthony Cattani, prin. Fax 953-6779
Shawnee HS 1,600/9-12
600 Tabernacle Rd 08055 609-654-7544
Matthew Campbell, prin. Fax 654-5611

Medford Township SD 2,800/PK-8
137 Hartford Rd 08055 609-654-6416
Joseph Del Rossi Ed.D., supt. Fax 654-7436
www.medford.k12.nj.us/
Medford Township Memorial MS 700/7-8
55 Mill St 08055 609-654-7707
Shawn Ryan, prin. Fax 654-7297

Medford Lakes, Burlington, Pop. 4,117
Medford Lakes Borough SD 500/PK-8
44 Neeta Trl 08055 609-654-5155
Anthony V. Dent, supt. Fax 714-0235
www.medford-lakes.k12.nj.us
Neeta S 300/3-8
44 Neeta Trl 08055 609-654-5155
Anthony Dent, admin. Fax 953-8258

Mendham, Morris, Pop. 4,930
Mendham Borough SD 600/PK-8
12 Hilltop Rd 07945 973-543-4251
Mitzi N. Morillo, supt. Fax 543-2805
www.mendhamboro.org
Mountain View MS 300/5-8
100 Dean Rd 07945 973-543-7075
Aimee Toth, prin. Fax 543-7993

West Morris Regional HSD
Supt. — See Chester
West Morris Mendham HS 1,400/9-12
65 E Main St 07945 973-543-2501
Michael Matyas, prin. Fax 543-6950

Assumption College for Sisters Post-Sec.
350 Bernardsville Rd 07945 973-543-6528

Metuchen, Middlesex, Pop. 13,256
Metuchen SD 2,000/PK-12
16 Simpson Pl 08840 732-321-8700
Vincent Caputo, supt. Fax 321-6567
www.metuchenschools.org
Edgar MS 700/5-8
49 Brunswick Ave 08840 732-321-8770
Katherine Glutz, prin. Fax 452-0571
Metuchen HS 600/9-12
400 Grove Ave 08840 732-321-8743
Bruce Peragallo, prin. Fax 549-6415

St. Joseph HS 800/9-12
145 Plainfield Rd 08840 732-549-7600
Justin Fleetwood, prin. Fax 549-0664

Middlesex, Middlesex, Pop. 13,451
Middlesex Borough SD 2,000/PK-12
300 John F Kennedy Dr 08846 732-317-6000
Dr. Linda Madison Ed.D., supt. Fax 317-6006
www.middlesex.k12.nj.us
Mauger MS 800/4-8
Fisher Ave 08846 732-317-6000
Jason Sirna, prin. Fax 317-6002
Middlesex HS 600/9-12
300 John F Kennedy Dr 08846 732-317-6000
Joseph Sabato, prin. Fax 317-6008

Middletown, Monmouth, Pop. 24,000
Middletown Township SD
Supt. — See Leonardo
Middletown HS North 1,500/9-12
63 Tindall Rd 07748 732-706-6061
Patricia Cartier, prin. Fax 706-6067
Middletown HS South 1,400/9-12
900 Nutswamp Rd 07748 732-706-6111
Patrick Rinella, prin. Fax 706-8058
Thompson MS 900/6-8
1001 Middletown Lincroft Rd 07748 732-671-2212
Matthew Kirkpatrick, prin.

Monmouth County Vocational SD
Supt. — See Freehold
Middletown Vocational S Vo/Tech
2 Swartzel Dr 07748 732-671-0650
Joseph Diver, prin. Fax 671-7455

Mater Dei Prep HS 300/9-12
538 Church St 07748 732-671-9100
James Hauenstein, prin. Fax 671-9214

Midland Park, Bergen, Pop. 7,021
Midland Park Borough SD 1,000/PK-12
250 Prospect St 07432 201-444-1400
Dr. Marie Cirasella Ed.D., supt. Fax 444-3051
www.mpsnj.org
Midland Park JSHS 500/7-12
250 Prospect St 07432 201-444-7400
Nicholas Capuano, prin. Fax 444-0352

Millburn, Essex, Pop. 18,630
Millburn Township SD 4,900/PK-12
434 Millburn Ave 07041 973-376-3600
Dr. Christine Burton, supt. Fax 912-9396
www.millburn.org
Millburn HS, 462 Millburn Ave 07041 1,500/9-12
Dr. William Miron, prin. 973-564-7130
Millburn MS 1,100/6-8
25 Old Short Hills Rd 07041 973-379-2600
Michael Cahill, prin. Fax 912-0939

Milburn School for Hearing Handicapped Post-Sec.
Spring & Willow Sts 07041 973-376-9439

Millstone Township, Monmouth
Millstone Township SD 1,300/PK-8
5 Dawson Ct, 732-786-0950
Scott Feder, supt. Fax 792-0951
www.millstone.k12.nj.us/
Millstone Township MS 500/6-8
5 Dawson Ct, 732-786-0950
Christopher Huss, prin. Fax 786-0953

Milltown, Middlesex, Pop. 6,830
Milltown SD 600/K-8
80 Violet Ter 08850 732-214-2365
Dr. Stephanie Brown, supt. Fax 214-2376
www.milltownps.org
Kilmer S 300/4-8
21 W Church St 08850 732-214-2370
William Veit, prin. Fax 214-2378

Millville, Cumberland, Pop. 27,693
Millville SD 5,600/PK-12
PO Box 5010 08332 856-293-2000
Dr. David Gentile, supt. Fax 293-9852
mps.millvillenj.gov
Lakeside MS 1,100/6-8
2 Sharp St N 08332 856-293-2420
Dr. Spike Cook, prin. Fax 825-7588
Memorial HS 700/9-12
504 Broad St E 08332 856-327-6072
Stephanie Derose, prin. Fax 825-4480
Millville HS 1,100/9-12
200 N Wade Blvd 08332 856-327-6040
Stephanie DeRose, prin. Fax 293-1342

Monmouth Junction, Middlesex, Pop. 2,829
South Brunswick Township SD
Supt. — See North Brunswick
Crossroads North MS 1,000/6-8
635 Georges Rd 08852 732-329-4191
Mark Daniels, prin. Fax 329-1905
Crossroads South MS 1,000/6-8
195 Major Rd 08852 732-329-4633
Bonnie Capes, prin. Fax 329-1906
South Brunswick HS 2,900/9-12
750 Ridge Rd 08852 732-329-4044
Peter Varela, prin. Fax 274-1237

Noor-Ul-Iman S 500/PK-12
4137 US Highway 1 08852 732-329-1800

Monroe Township, Middlesex
Monroe Township SD 5,900/PK-12
423 Buckelew Ave 08831 732-521-2111
Dr. Michael Kozak, supt. Fax 521-2719
www.monroe.k12.nj.us
Monroe Township HS 2,000/9-12
200 Schoolhouse Rd 08831 732-521-2882
Robert Goodall, prin. Fax 521-2976
Monroe Township MS 1,400/6-8
1629 Perrineville Rd 08831 732-521-6042
Chari Chanley, prin. Fax 521-2846

Montclair, Essex, Pop. 39,200
Montclair SD 6,700/K-12
22 Valley Rd 07042 973-509-4000
Ron Bolandi, supt. Fax 509-0586
www.montclair.k12.nj.us
Glenfield MS 700/6-8
25 Maple Ave 07042 973-509-4172
Dr. Joseph Putrino, prin. Fax 509-4179
Montclair HS 2,000/9-12
100 Chestnut St 07042 973-509-4100
James Earle, prin. Fax 509-4098
Renaissance MS 300/6-8
176 N Fullerton Ave 07042 973-509-5741
Edward Wilson, prin. Fax 509-5752
Other Schools – See Upper Montclair

Eastern School of Acupuncture Post-Sec.
427 Bloomfield Ave Ste 301 07042 973-746-8717
Immaculate Conception HS 200/9-12
33 Cottage Pl 07042 973-744-7445
Michele Neves, prin. Fax 744-3926
Lacordaire Academy 100/9-12
155 Lorraine Ave 07043 973-744-1156
Brian Morgan, head sch Fax 783-9521
Montclair Kimberley Academy 400/4-8
201 Valley Rd 07042 973-746-9800
Thomas Nammack, hdmstr. Fax 509-7950
Montclair Kimberley Academy - Upper S 400/9-12
201 Valley Rd 07042 973-783-8300
Thomas Nammack, hdmstr. Fax 744-4051
Montclair State University Post-Sec.
1 Normal Ave 07043 973-655-4000
Mountainside Hospital Post-Sec.
1 Bay Ave 07042 973-429-6850

Montvale, Bergen, Pop. 7,749
Montvale SD 1,000/PK-8
47 Spring Valley Rd 07645 201-391-1662
Dr. Darren Petersen, supt. Fax 391-8935
www.montvalek8.org
Fieldstone MS 500/5-8
47 Spring Valley Rd 07645 201-391-9000
Erik Parks, prin. Fax 391-8935

Pascack Valley Regional HSD 2,000/9-12
46 Akers Ave 07645 201-358-7004
P. Erik Gundersen, supt. Fax 505-4858
www.pascack.k12.nj.us
Pascack Hills HS 800/9-12
225 W Grand Ave 07645 201-358-7020
Glenn de Marrais, prin. Fax 358-7019
Other Schools – See Hillsdale

St. Joseph Regional HS 500/9-12
40 Chestnut Ridge Rd 07645 201-391-3300
Barry Donnelly, pres. Fax 391-8073

Montville, Morris, Pop. 15,600
Montville Township SD 3,900/K-12
86 River Rd 07045 973-331-7100
Dr. Rene Rovtar, supt. Fax 316-4640
montville.net
Lazar MS 1,000/6-8
123 Changebridge Rd 07045 973-331-7100
Sharon Carr, prin. Fax 331-9279
Montville Township HS 1,300/9-12
100 Horseneck Rd 07045 973-331-7100
Douglas Sanford, prin.

Trinity Christian S 200/K-12
160 Changebridge Rd 07045 973-334-1785
Douglas Prol, head sch Fax 334-9282

Moorestown, Burlington, Pop. 13,242
Moorestown Township SD 3,900/K-12
803 N Stanwick Rd 08057 856-778-6600
Carole Butler, supt. Fax 235-0961
www.mtps.com
Allen III MS 700/7-8
801 N Stanwick Rd 08057 856-778-6620
Matthew Keith, prin. Fax 727-9309
Moorestown HS 1,400/9-12
350 Bridgeboro Rd 08057 856-778-6610
Andrew Seibel, prin. Fax 722-8983

Lincoln Technical Institute Post-Sec.
308 W Route 38 Ste 2 08057 856-722-9333
Moorestown Friends S 700/PK-12
110 E Main St 08057 856-235-2900
Laurence Van Meter, head sch Fax 235-6684

Morganville, Monmouth, Pop. 4,962
Marlboro Township SD
Supt. — See Marlboro
Marlboro Memorial MS 1,000/6-8
71 Nolan Rd 07751 732-972-7115
John Pacifico, prin. Fax 972-7118

Morris Plains, Morris, Pop. 5,456
Morris Plains SD 600/PK-8
500 Speedwell Ave 07950 973-538-1650
Mark Maire, supt. Fax 540-1983
morrisplains.schoolwires.net
Borough MS 400/3-8
500 Speedwell Ave 07950 973-538-1650
Andrew Kramar, prin. Fax 538-8367

Parsippany-Troy Hills Township SD
Supt. — See Parsippany
Parsippany Hills HS 1,100/9-12
20 Rita Dr 07950 973-682-2815
Michael DiSanto, prin. Fax 682-2855

Morristown, Morris, Pop. 18,125
Morris SD 5,000/K-12
31 Hazel St 07960 973-292-2300
Mackey Pendergrast, supt. Fax 292-2057
www.morrisschooldistrict.org
Frelinghuysen MS 1,100/6-8
10 Jean St 07960 973-292-2200
Joseph Uglialoro, prin. Fax 292-2458
Morristown HS 1,600/9-12
50 Early St 07960 973-292-2000
Mark Manning, prin. Fax 539-5573

College of Saint Elizabeth Post-Sec.
2 Convent Rd 07960 973-290-4000
Delbarton S 600/7-12
230 Mendham Rd 07960 973-538-3231
Br. Paul Diveny, hdmstr. Fax 538-8836
Morristown-Beard S 500/6-12
70 Whippany Rd 07960 973-539-3032
Peter Caldwell, hdmstr. Fax 539-1590
Morristown Memorial Hospital Post-Sec.
100 Madison Ave 07960 973-971-5177
Rabbinical College of America Post-Sec.
226 Sussex Ave 07960 973-267-9404
Villa Walsh Academy 300/7-12
455 Western Ave 07960 973-538-3680
Sr. Patricia Pompa, prin. Fax 538-6733

Mountain Lakes, Morris, Pop. 4,079
Mountain Lakes SD 1,400/K-12
400 Boulevard 07046 973-334-8280
Dr. Anne Mucci, supt. Fax 334-2316
www.mlschools.org
Briarcliff MS 300/6-8
93 Briarcliff Rd 07046 973-334-0342
Fran Schlenoff Ed.D., prin. Fax 334-6857
Mountain Lakes HS 700/9-12
96 Powerville Rd 07046 973-334-8400
Jeremy Davies, prin. Fax 334-3550

Mountainside, Union, Pop. 6,605
Mountainside SD 800/PK-8
1497 Woodacres Dr 07092 908-232-3232
Dr. Nancy Lubarsky, admin. Fax 232-1743
www.mountainsideschools.org
Deerfield ES 500/3-8
302 Central Ave 07092 908-232-8828
Kimberly Richards, prin. Fax 232-7338

Mount Arlington, Morris, Pop. 4,979
Mount Arlington SD 300/PK-8
446 Howard Blvd 07856 973-770-7140
Jane Mullins Jameson, supt. Fax 398-3614
www.mtarlingtonk8.org/
Mount Arlington MS 200/3-8
235 Howard Blvd 07856 973-398-4400
Jeffrey Grillo, prin. Fax 398-5726

Mount Ephraim, Camden, Pop. 4,636
Mount Ephraim Borough SD 400/PK-8
225 W Kings Hwy 08059 856-931-7807
Leslie Koller, supt. Fax 931-5831
mtephraimschools.org/
Kershaw MS 200/5-8
125 S Black Horse Pike 08059 856-931-1634
Michael Hunter, prin. Fax 931-5831

Mount Holly, Burlington, Pop. 10,639
Burlington Co. Institute of Tech SD
695 Woodlane Rd 08060 609-267-4226
Dr. Christopher Manno, supt. Fax 267-9788
www.bcit.cc/
Burlington Co. Institute of Tech Evening Vo/Tech
695 Woodlane Rd 08060 609-267-4226
Patrick Cruet, prin.
Burlington Co. Institute of Technology Vo/Tech
695 Woodlane Rd 08060 609-267-4226
Joseph Venuto, prin. Fax 267-3752
Other Schools – See Medford

Mount Holly Township SD 1,000/PK-8
331 Levis Dr 08060 609-267-7108
James DiDonato, supt. Fax 702-9082
www.mtholly.k12.nj.us
Holbein MS 300/6-8
333 Levis Dr 08060 609-267-7200
Carolyn McDonald, prin. Fax 702-9775

Rancocas Valley Regional HSD 1,900/9-12
520 Jacksonville Rd 08060 609-267-0830
Christopher Heilig, supt. Fax 702-0167
www.rvrhs.com/
Rancocas Valley Regional HS 1,900/9-12
520 Jacksonville Rd 08060 609-267-0830
Christopher Heilig, supt. Fax 702-0167

Burlington County Inst. of Technology Post-Sec.
695 Woodlane Rd 08060 609-267-4226

Mount Laurel, Burlington
Mount Laurel Township SD 4,000/K-8
330 Mount Laurel Rd 08054 856-235-3387
Dr. George Rafferty, supt. Fax 235-1837
www.mtlaurelschools.org
Harrington MS 900/7-8
514 Mount Laurel Rd 08054 856-234-1610
Kathleen Haines, prin. Fax 222-9754

Mullica Hill, Gloucester, Pop. 3,933
Clearview Regional HSD 2,500/7-12
420 Cedar Rd 08062 856-223-2765
John Horchak, supt. Fax 478-0409
www.clearviewregional.edu
Clearview Regional HS 1,600/9-12
625 Breakneck Rd 08062 856-223-2790
Keith Brook, prin. Fax 478-6705
Clearview Regional MS 900/7-8
595 Jefferson Rd 08062 856-223-2740
Robin Bazzel, prin. Fax 223-9068

Neptune, Monmouth, Pop. 4,773
Monmouth County Vocational SD
Supt. — See Freehold
Monmouth Co. Acad of Allied Health & Sci Vo/Tech
2325 Heck Ave 07753 732-775-0058
Paul Mucciarone, prin. Fax 775-6646

Neptune Township SD 4,200/PK-12
60 Neptune Blvd 07753 732-776-2000
Tami Crader, supt. Fax 897-7595
www.neptune.k12.nj.us/
Neptune HS 1,300/9-12
55 Neptune Blvd 07753 732-776-2200
Jennifer Joseph, prin. Fax 776-2253
Neptune MS 800/6-8
2300 Heck Ave 07753 732-776-2200
Dr. Arlene Rogo, prin. Fax 776-2254

Jersey Shore Medical Center Post-Sec.
1945 State Route 33 07753 732-776-4603

Newark, Essex, Pop. 268,973
Essex County Vocational Technical SD
60 Nelson Pl 1 North 07102 973-412-2050
Dr. James M. Pedersen, supt. Fax 412-2100
www.essextech.org
Essex Co. Vocational Tech - N 13th St Vo/Tech
300 N 13th St 07107 973-412-2203
Patricia Clark-Jeter, prin. Fax 412-2098
Essex Co. Vocational Tech - Newark Tech Vo/Tech
91 W Market St 07103 973-412-2204
Oge Denis, prin. Fax 412-2094
Other Schools – See Bloomfield, West Caldwell

Newark SD 38,100/PK-12
2 Cedar St 07102 973-733-7333
Christopher Cerf, supt. Fax 733-6834
www.nps.k12.nj.us
American History HS 400/7-12
74 Montgomery St 07103 973-733-6903
Bryan Olkowski, prin. Fax 456-7086
Arts HS 600/9-12
550 Martin Luther King Jr 07102 973-733-7391
Ricardo Pedro, prin. Fax 483-5524
Bard HS Early College 200/9-12
321 Bergen St 07103 973-733-8353
John Weinstein, prin.
Barringer Academy of Arts & Humanities 9-12
90 Parker St 07104 973-268-5106
Dr. Crystal Breedlove, prin. Fax 268-5033
Barringer S.T.E.A.M. HS 1,400/9-12
90 Parker St 07104 973-268-5125
Angela Mincy, prin. Fax 268-5322
Central HS 700/9-12
246 18th Ave 07108 973-733-6897
Sharnee Brown, prin. Fax 733-8212
Eagle Academy Alt
279 Chancellor Ave 07112 973-733-7165
Semone Morant, prin.
East Side HS 1,400/9-12
238 Van Buren St 07105 973-465-4900
Dr. Mario Santos, prin. Fax 465-4936
Fast Track Success Academy 100/Alt
200 Washington St 07102 973-733-8765
Mark Comesanas, prin.
Newark Leadership Academy 100/9-12
301 W Kinney St 07103 973-733-6773
Gabriele Kuriloff, prin.
Newark Vocational S Vo/Tech
403 S Orange Ave 07103 973-733-7018
Larry Ramkissoon, prin. Fax 792-6018
Science Park MSHS 800/7-12
260 Norfolk St 07103 973-733-8689
Kathleen Tierney, prin. Fax 733-8236
Shabazz HS 400/9-12
80 Johnson Ave 07108 973-733-6760
Damon Holmes, prin. Fax 792-6514
Technology HS Vo/Tech
187 Broadway 07104 973-481-5962
Edwin Reyes, prin. Fax 497-5786
University JSHS 600/7-12
55 Clinton Pl 07108 973-351-2010
Regina Sharpe, prin. Fax 424-4447
Weequahic HS 400/9-12
279 Chancellor Ave 07112 973-705-3900
Lisa McDonald, prin. Fax 923-4095
West Side HS 400/9-12
403 S Orange Ave 07103 973-733-6977
L. Ramkissoon, prin. Fax 733-8941

Berkeley College Post-Sec.
536 Broad St 07102 973-642-3888
Christ the King Preparatory S 300/9-12
239 Woodside Ave 07104 973-483-0033
Rev. Gregory Gebbia, prin. Fax 481-0693
Drake College of Business Post-Sec.
800 Broad St 07102 973-645-1333
Essex County College Post-Sec.
303 University Ave 07102 973-877-3000
Newark Boys Chorus S 100/4-8
1016 Broad St 07102 973-621-8900
Richard Willett, head sch Fax 621-1343
New Community Workforce Development Ctr. Post-Sec.
201 Bergen St 07103 973-824-6484
New Jersey Institute of Technology Post-Sec.
University Heights 07102 973-596-3000
New Testament S 50/PK-12
511 Orange St 07107 973-268-1310
Lisa Billow, head sch Fax 268-1310
Pillar College Post-Sec.
60 Park Pl Ste 701 07102 973-803-5000
Rutgers-The State University of N.J. Post-Sec.
249 University Ave 07102 973-353-5568
St. Benedict Preparatory S 600/7-12
520 Martin Luther King Jr 07102 973-643-4800
Rev. Edwin Leahy, hdmstr. Fax 643-6922
St. Vincent Academy 300/9-12
228 W Market St 07103 973-622-1613
Sr. June Favata, dir. Fax 622-1128
Seton Hall University School of Law Post-Sec.
1 Newark Ctr 07102 973-642-8500
Star Career Academy Post-Sec.
550 Broad St 07102 973-639-0789

New Brunswick, Middlesex, Pop. 54,229
New Brunswick SD 7,600/PK-12
PO Box 2683 08903 732-745-5300
Dr. Aubrey Johnson, supt. Fax 745-5459
www.nbpschools.net
New Brunswick HS 1,500/9-12
1000 Somerset St 08901 732-745-5300
Jorge Diaz, prin. Fax 214-1215
New Brunswick MS 1,300/6-8
1125 Livingston Ave 08901 732-745-5300
Jeremiah Clifford, prin. Fax 565-7630
Adult HS Adult
268 Baldwin St 08901 732-846-5300
Timothy Timberlake, prin. Fax 745-5325

New Brunswick Theological Seminary Post-Sec.
17 Seminary Pl 08901 732-247-5241
Rutgers-The State University of N.J. Post-Sec.
57 US Highway 1 08901 732-445-4636

New Egypt, Ocean, Pop. 2,476
Plumsted Township SD 1,400/PK-12
117 Evergreen Rd 08533 609-758-6800
Gerald North, supt. Fax 758-6808
www.newegypt.us
New Egypt HS 500/9-12
117 Evergreen Rd 08533 609-758-6800
Michael Mendes, prin. Fax 758-5683
New Egypt MS 400/6-8
115 Evergreen Rd 08533 609-758-6800
Andrea Caldes, prin. Fax 758-5538

Newfield, Gloucester, Pop. 1,534

Our Lady of Mercy Academy 100/9-12
1001 Main Rd 08344 856-697-2008
Brooke Coyle, head sch Fax 697-2887

New Milford, Bergen, Pop. 16,071
New Milford SD 1,900/K-12
145 Madison Ave 07646 201-261-2952
Michael Polizzi, supt. Fax 261-8018
www.newmilfordschools.org
New Milford HS 600/9-12
1 Snyder Cir 07646 201-262-0172
Louis Manuppelli, prin. Fax 262-4445
Owens MS 500/6-8
470 Marion Ave 07646 201-265-8661
James DeLalla, prin. Fax 265-5680

New Providence, Union, Pop. 12,002
New Providence SD 2,300/PK-12
356 Elkwood Ave 07974 908-464-9050
David Miceli Ed.D., supt. Fax 464-9041
www.npsd.k12.nj.us
New Providence HS 600/9-12
35 Pioneer Dr 07974 908-464-4700
Lauren Zirpoli, prin. Fax 464-8556
New Providence MS 400/7-8
35 Pioneer Dr 07974 908-464-9161
Jay Richter, prin. Fax 464-5927

Newton, Sussex, Pop. 7,865
Andover Regional SD 600/K-8
707 Limecrest Rd 07860 973-383-3746
Matthew L. Beck, supt. Fax 579-3972
www.andoverregional.org
Long Pond S 300/5-8
707 Limecrest Rd 07860 973-940-1234
T. Jon Sinclair, prin. Fax 579-2690

Kittatinny Regional SD 1,100/7-12
77 Halsey Rd 07860 973-383-1800
Craig Hutcheson, supt. Fax 383-6218
www.krhs.net
Kittatinny Regional JSHS 1,100/7-12
77 Halsey Rd 07860 973-383-1800
Brian Bosworth, prin. Fax 383-4392

Newton SD 1,500/PK-12
57 Trinity St 07860 973-383-1900
Dr. G. Kennedy Greene, supt. Fax 383-5378
www.newtonnj.org
Halsted Street MS 200/6-8
59 Halsted St 07860 973-383-7440
Kristi Greene, prin. Fax 383-7432
Newton HS 700/9-12
44 Ryerson Ave 07860 973-383-7573
Jeff Waldron, prin. Fax 383-1153

Sussex County Community College Post-Sec.
1 College Hill Rd 07860 973-300-2100

North Arlington, Bergen, Pop. 15,146
North Arlington SD 1,700/PK-12
222 Ridge Rd 07031 201-991-6800
Dr. Stephen Yurchak, supt. Fax 991-1656
www.narlington.k12.nj.us
North Arlington HS 500/9-12
222 Ridge Rd 07031 201-991-6800
Fax 991-0188
North Arlington MS 300/6-8
45 Beech St 07031 201-991-6800
Nicole Russo, prin. Fax 246-0703

Queen of Peace HS 500/9-12
191 Rutherford Pl 07031 201-998-8227
John Tonero, prin. Fax 998-3040

North Bergen, Hudson, Pop. 59,000
Hudson County Schools of Technology
8511 Tonnelle Ave 07047 — 201-662-6700
Frank Gargiulo, supt.
www.hcstonline.org
High Tech HS — Vo/Tech
2000 85th St 07047 — 201-662-6801
Dr. Joseph Giammarella, prin. — Fax 854-4129
Knowledge Advanced Skills — Vo/Tech
2000 85th St 07047 — 201-662-6804
Dr. Joseph Giammarella, prin.
Other Schools – See Flemington, Jersey City

North Bergen SD — 7,300/PK-12
7317 Kennedy Blvd 07047 — 201-868-1000
Dr. George Solter, supt. — Fax 295-2747
www.northbergen.k12.nj.us/
North Bergen HS — 2,400/9-12
7417 Kennedy Blvd 07047 — 201-295-2800
Paschal Tennaro, prin. — Fax 295-2873

North Brunswick, Middlesex, Pop. 37,400
North Brunswick Township SD — 5,900/PK-12
PO Box 6016 08902 — 732-289-3000
Dr. Brian Zychowski, supt. — Fax 297-8567
www.nbtschools.org
Linwood MS — 1,300/6-8
25 Linwood Pl 08902 — 732-289-3600
Roy Wilson, prin. — Fax 247-7033
North Brunswick Township HS — 1,800/9-12
98 Raider Rd 08902 — 732-289-3700
Peter Clark, prin. — Fax 821-8342

South Brunswick Township SD — 8,500/PK-12
231 Black Horse Ln 08902 — 732-297-7800
Dr. Gary McCartney, supt. — Fax 297-8456
www.sbschools.org
Other Schools – See Monmouth Junction

Anthem Institute — Post-Sec.
651 US Highway 1 08902 — 732-448-2600
DeVry University — Post-Sec.
630 US Highway 1 08902 — 732-729-3960

North Caldwell, Essex, Pop. 6,124
West Essex Regional SD — 1,600/7-12
65 W Greenbrook Rd 07006 — 973-228-1200
Barbara Longo, supt. — Fax 228-0559
www.westex.org
West Essex HS — 1,100/9-12
65 W Greenbrook Rd 07006 — 973-228-1200
Caesar Diliberto, prin. — Fax 364-1872
West Essex MS — 600/7-8
65 W Greenbrook Rd 07006 — 973-228-1200
Vee Popat, prin. — Fax 228-5852

Northfield, Atlantic, Pop. 8,484
Northfield CSD — 1,000/K-8
2000 New Rd 08225 — 609-407-4000
Pedro Bretones, supt. — Fax 646-0608
northfield.groupfusion.net
Northfield Community MS — 500/5-8
2000 New Rd 08225 — 609-407-4008
Glenn Robbins, prin. — Fax 641-2646

North Haledon, Passaic, Pop. 8,332
North Haledon SD — 700/PK-8
201 Squaw Brook Rd 07508 — 973-427-8993
Nicholas Coffaro M.A., supt. — Fax 427-4357
www.nhschools.net
High Mountain MS — 300/5-8
515 High Mountain Rd 07508 — 973-427-1220
Michele Mazzola, prin. — Fax 427-7685

Eastern Christian HS — 300/9-12
50 Oakwood Ave 07508 — 973-427-0900
Ruth Kuder, prin. — Fax 427-3716
Mary Help of Christians Academy — 200/8-12
659 Belmont Ave 07508 — 973-790-6200
Sr. Marisa DeRose, prin. — Fax 790-6125

North Plainfield, Somerset, Pop. 21,559
North Plainfield Borough SD — 2,700/PK-12
33 Mountain Ave 07060 — 908-769-6060
Dr. James McLaughlin, supt. — Fax 755-5490
www.nplainfield.org
North Plainfield HS — 1,000/9-12
34 Wilson Ave 07060 — 908-769-6000
Dr. Jerard Stephenson, prin. — Fax 769-6032
North Plainfield MS — 7-8
34 Wilson Ave 07060 — 908-769-6065
Dr. Lennox Small, prin.

Robert Fiance Beauty School — Post-Sec.
121 Watchung Ave 07060 — 908-754-4247

Nutley, Essex, Pop. 27,400
Nutley SD — 3,900/K-12
315 Franklin Ave 07110 — 973-661-8798
Dr. Julie Glazer, supt. — Fax 320-8476
www.nutleyschools.org
Nutley HS — 1,200/9-12
300 Franklin Ave 07110 — 973-661-8832
Denis Williams, prin. — Fax 661-3664
Walker MS — 600/7-8
325 Franklin Ave 07110 — 973-661-8871
Tracy Egan, prin. — Fax 661-3775

Abundant Life Academy — 400/PK-12
390 Washington Ave 07110 — 973-667-9700
John Kuebler, head sch — Fax 667-1278
Eastwick College — Post-Sec.
103 Park Ave 07110 — 973-661-0600

Oakhurst, Monmouth, Pop. 3,965
Ocean Township SD — 3,600/PK-12
163 Monmouth Rd 07755 — 732-531-5600
Dr. James Stefankiewicz, supt. — Fax 531-3874
www.oceanschools.org
Ocean Township HS — 1,200/9-12
550 W Park Ave 07755 — 732-531-5650
Dawn Kaszuba, prin. — Fax 571-4009
Other Schools – See Ocean

Oakland, Bergen, Pop. 12,608
Oakland SD — 1,600/K-8
315 Ramapo Valley Rd 07436 — 201-337-6156
Dr. Gina Coffaro, supt. — Fax 405-1237
www.oaklandschoolsnj.org
Valley MS — 600/6-8
71 Oak St 07436 — 201-337-8185
Gregg Desiderio, prin. — Fax 337-7089

Ramapo Indian Hills Regional HSD — 2,300/9-12
131 Yawpo Ave 07436 — 201-416-8100
Beverly MacKay, supt. — Fax 416-8123
www.rih.org
Indian Hills HS — 1,200/9-12
97 Yawpo Ave 07436 — 201-337-0100
Joseph Collins, prin. — Fax 337-1031
Other Schools – See Franklin Lakes

Barnstable Academy — 100/5-12
8 Wright Way 07436 — 201-651-0200

Oak Ridge, Passaic
Jefferson Township SD
Supt. — See Lake Hopatcong
Jefferson Township HS — 900/9-12
1010 Weldon Rd 07438 — 973-697-3535
Dr. Timothy Plotts, prin. — Fax 208-8409
Jefferson Township MS — 800/6-8
1000 Weldon Rd 07438 — 973-697-1980
Dr. Kelly Cooke, prin. — Fax 697-1348

Ocean, Monmouth, Pop. 26,700
Ocean Township SD
Supt. — See Oakhurst
Ocean Township IS — 1,200/5-8
1200 W Park Ave 07712 — 732-531-5630
Larry Kostula, prin. — Fax 493-1891

Concorde School of Hair Design — Post-Sec.
1458 State Route 35 07712 — 732-918-0505
Hillel Yeshiva HS — 200/9-12
1027 Deal Rd 07712 — 732-493-0420
Ilan HS — 100/9-12
1200 Roseld Ave 07712 — 732-517-1111
Hena Diamond, prin. — Fax 663-0194

Ocean City, Cape May, Pop. 11,545
Ocean City SD — 2,100/K-12
501 Atlantic Ave Ste 1 08226 — 609-399-5150
Dr. Kathleen Taylor, supt. — Fax 399-4656
www.oceancityschools.org/
Ocean City HS — 1,200/9-12
501 Atlantic Ave 08226 — 609-399-1290
Matthew Jamison, prin. — Fax 399-1966
Ocean City IS — 500/4-8
1801 Bay Ave 08226 — 609-399-5611
Geoffrey Haines, prin. — Fax 398-7089

Oceanport, Monmouth, Pop. 5,763
Oceanport Borough SD — 600/PK-8
29 Wolfhill Ave 07757 — 732-542-0683
Thomas Farrell, supt.
www.oceanport.k12.nj.us
Maple Place MS — 300/5-8
2 Maple Pl 07757 — 732-229-0267
Matthew Howell, prin. — Fax 229-0961

Old Bridge, Middlesex, Pop. 23,304
Old Bridge Township SD
Supt. — See Matawan
Salk MS — 1,000/6-8
155 W Greystone Rd 08857 — 732-360-4519
William Rezes, prin. — Fax 251-1690
Sandburg MS — 1,200/6-8
3439 Highway 516 08857 — 732-360-4400
Martha Simon, prin. — Fax 360-9676

Calvary Christian S — 300/PK-12
123 White Oak Ln 08857 — 732-479-0700
Jim Dunne, prin. — Fax 679-1948
Yeshiva Tiferes Naftoli of Central NJ — 50/9-12
8998 State Route 18 08857 — 732-952-8384

Old Tappan, Bergen, Pop. 5,680
Northern Valley Regional HSD
Supt. — See Demarest
Northern Valley Regional HS — 1,300/9-12
100 Central Ave 07675 — 201-784-1600
Bruce Sabatini, prin. — Fax 768-7724

Old Tappan SD — 800/K-8
277 Old Tappan Rd 07675 — 201-664-1421
Danielle DaGiau, supt. — Fax 664-4418
oldtappanschools.org
DeWolf MS — 400/5-8
275 Old Tappan Rd 07675 — 201-664-1475
Justin O'Neill, prin. — Fax 664-8101

Oradell, Bergen, Pop. 7,880
River Dell Regional SD
Supt. — See River Edge
River Dell Regional HS — 1,100/9-12
55 Pyle St 07649 — 201-599-7200
Lorraine Brooks, prin. — Fax 599-2294

Bergen Catholic HS — 700/9-12
1040 Oradell Ave 07649 — 201-261-1844
Timothy McElhinney, prin. — Fax 599-9507

Orange, Essex, Pop. 33,300
Orange SD — 4,300/PK-12
451 Lincoln Ave 07050 — 973-677-4000
Ronald Lee, supt. — Fax 677-0486
www.orange.k12.nj.us
Career & Innovation Academy of Orange — Vo/Tech
123 Cleveland St 07050 — 973-677-4000
Dr. Erica Stewart, prin.
Orange HS — 800/10-12
400 Lincoln Ave 07050 — 973-677-4050
Jason Belton, prin. — Fax 677-4069
Orange Preparatory Academy — 500/7-9
400 Central Ave 07050 — 973-677-4135
Aretha Malloy, prin. — Fax 677-2439

Palisades Park, Bergen, Pop. 19,390
Palisades Park SD — 1,300/PK-12
410 2nd St 07650 — 201-947-3550
Dr. Joseph Cirillo, supt. — Fax 947-4079
www.palpkschools.org
Palisades Park JSHS — 600/7-12
1 Veterans Plz 07650 — 201-941-1100
Frank Donohue, prin. — Fax 947-1280

Palmyra, Burlington, Pop. 7,223
Palmyra Borough SD — 900/PK-12
301 Delaware Ave 08065 — 856-786-9300
Brian McBride, supt. — Fax 829-9638
palmyraschools.com
Palmyra HS — 400/7-12
311 W 5th St 08065 — 856-786-9400
Kenneth Holloway, prin. — Fax 786-3014

Paramus, Bergen, Pop. 25,735
Bergen County Vocational Technical SD
540 Farview Ave 07652 — 201-343-6000
Dr. Howard Lerner, supt. — Fax 225-9182
bcts.bergen.org
Applied Technology HS — Vo/Tech
400 Paramus Rd 07652 — 201-343-6000
Andrea Sheridan, prin.
Bergen County Technical HS - Paramus — Vo/Tech
285 Pascack Rd 07652 — 201-343-6000
Carole Terrizzi, prin. — Fax 996-6935
Other Schools – See Hackensack, Teterboro

Paramus SD — 3,700/K-12
145 Spring Valley Rd 07652 — 201-261-7800
Michele Robinson, supt. — Fax 261-5861
www.paramusschools.org/ppsd/
East Brook MS — 600/5-8
190 Spring Valley Rd 07652 — 201-261-7800
Thomas LoBue, prin. — Fax 262-1541
Paramus HS — 1,300/9-12
99 E Century Rd 07652 — 201-261-7800
Raymond Kiem, prin. — Fax 261-3833
West Brook MS — 600/5-8
560 Roosevelt Blvd 07652 — 201-261-7800
Carla Alvarez, prin. — Fax 652-0376

Bergen Community College — Post-Sec.
400 Paramus Rd 07652 — 201-447-7100
Berkeley College — Post-Sec.
64 E Midland Ave 07652 — 201-967-9667
Capri Institute of Hair Design — Post-Sec.
615 Winters Ave 07652 — 201-599-0880
DeVry University — Post-Sec.
81 E State Rt 4 Ste 102 07652 — 201-556-2840
Frisch S — 600/9-12
120 W Century Rd 07652 — 201-267-9100
Lincoln Technical Institute — Post-Sec.
240 Bergen Town Ctr 07652 — 201-845-6868
Paramus Catholic HS — 1,500/9-12
425 Paramus Rd 07652 — 201-445-6465
James Vail, pres. — Fax 445-3952

Park Ridge, Bergen, Pop. 8,566
Park Ridge SD — 1,300/PK-12
85 Pascack Rd 07656 — 201-573-6000
Dr. Robert Gamper, supt. — Fax 391-6511
www.parkridge.k12.nj.us
Park Ridge HS — 600/7-12
2 Park Ave 07656 — 201-573-6000
Troy Lederman, prin. — Fax 930-4874

Parlin, Middlesex
Sayreville SD
Supt. — See South Amboy
Sayreville MS — 1,300/6-8
800 Washington Rd 08859 — 732-525-5290
Donna Jakubik, prin. — Fax 727-5621
Sayreville War Memorial HS — 1,700/9-12
820 Washington Rd 08859 — 732-525-5252
James Brown, prin. — Fax 316-0720

Parsippany, Morris, Pop. 51,000
Parsippany-Troy Hills Township SD — 6,800/PK-12
PO Box 52 07054 — 973-263-7200
Dr. Leroy Seitz, supt. — Fax 263-7230
www.pthsd.k12.nj.us
Brooklawn MS — 900/6-8
250 Beachwood Rd 07054 — 973-428-7551
Dr. Natalie Betz, prin. — Fax 781-0309
Central MS — 700/6-8
1620 US Highway 46 07054 — 973-263-7125
Mark Gray, prin. — Fax 402-1579
Parsippany HS — 1,000/9-12
309 Baldwin Rd 07054 — 973-263-7001
Dr. Denis Mulroony, prin. — Fax 263-7347
Other Schools – See Morris Plains

Anthem Institute — Post-Sec.
959 US Highway 46 07054 — 888-852-7272
Parsippany Christian S — 200/PK-12
PO Box 5365 07054 — 973-539-7012
David Detwiler, admin. — Fax 539-2527

Passaic, Passaic, Pop. 69,000
Essex Regional Educ Services Commission
Supt. — See Fairfield
Essex HS — Adult
188 1st St 07055 — 973-815-1389
Charles Johnson, prin. — Fax 815-1635

Passaic CSD 12,700/PK-12
PO Box 388 07055 973-470-5500
Pablo Munoz, supt. Fax 470-8984
www.passaicschools.org/
Lincoln MS 1,800/7-8
291 Lafayette Ave 07055 973-470-5504
Fawzi Naji, prin. Fax 470-5128
Passaic HS 2,600/9-12
170 Paulison Ave 07055 973-470-5600
Francisco Velez, prin. Fax 470-5135

Passaic Co. Education Services Comm.
Supt. — See Wayne
Hope Academy 100/Alt
266 Harrison St 07055 973-928-1509
Irene LeFebvre Ed.D., dir. Fax 928-1505

Bais Yaakov of Passaic HS 200/9-12
181 Pennington Ave 07055 973-365-0100
Baila Stern, prin. Fax 365-0570
Mesivta Tiferes Rav Zvi Aryeh Zemel 100/9-12
15 Temple Pl 07055 973-594-9001

Paterson, Passaic, Pop. 143,991
Paterson SD 23,700/PK-12
90 Delaware Ave 07503 973-321-1000
Dr. Donnie Evans, supt. Fax 321-0470
www.paterson.k12.nj.us
Bosco Technology Academy 300/7-8
764 11th Ave 07514 973-321-0580
Wendy Munoz, prin. Fax 321-0587
Eastside HS S of Culinary Arts Hosp Trsm 600/9-12
150 Park Ave 07501 973-321-2489
Edgar Nieves, prin. Fax 321-0517
Eastside HS S of Government/Public Admin 600/9-12
150 Park Ave 07501 973-321-2488
Karen Johnson, prin. Fax 321-0517
Eastside HS S of Information and Tech 600/9-12
150 Park Ave 07501 973-321-2490
Vivian Gaines, prin. Fax 321-0517
HARP Academy 300/9-12
175 Main St 07505 973-321-0560
Kelli White, admin. Fax 321-0565
International HS 500/9-12
200 Grand St 07501 973-321-2280
Robina Puryear-Castro, prin. Fax 321-2283
Kennedy HS Academy of Arch & Const Trade 500/9-12
127 Preakness Ave 07522 973-321-0504
Dewitt Evering, admin. Fax 321-0507
Kennedy HS Academy of Bus Tech Mktg 600/9-12
127 Preakness Ave 07522 973-321-0505
Pamela Powell, admin. Fax 321-0507
Kennedy HS Academy of Sci Tech Eng Math 600/9-12
127 Preakness Ave 07522 973-321-0507
Nicholas Vancheri, prin. Fax 321-0507
Kennedy HS Acad of Education & Training 9-12
127 Preakness Ave 07522 973-321-2461
Maryanne Perrotta, admin. Fax 321-0507
Morgan Academy 100/9-12
200 Grand St 07501 973-321-2540
Michael McGinley, prin. Fax 321-2283
New Roberto Clemente S 600/6-8
482 Market St 07501 973-321-0240
Hector Montes, prin. Fax 321-0247
PANTHER Academy 200/9-12
201 Memorial Dr 07505 973-321-2290
Gregg Festa, admin. Fax 321-2297
Parks HS of Fine & Performing Arts 300/9-12
413 12th Ave 07514 973-321-0520
Jalyn Lyde, prin. Fax 321-0527
Paterson City S 7 200/5-8
106 Ramsey St 07501 973-321-0070
Rebecca Cecala, prin. Fax 321-0077
Paterson City S 11 100/4-8
350 Market St 07501 973-321-0110
Carlos Ortiz, prin. Fax 321-0117
YES Academy 300/Alt
45 Smith St 07505 973-321-0570
Dr. Dorothy Douge, prin. Fax 321-0577
Silk City 2000 Academy/Adult S Adult
151 Ellison St 07505 973-321-0760
Dr. Sebastian Calabria, prin. Fax 321-0767
Other Schools – See Prospect Park

HoHoKus Sch of Trade/Technical Sciences Post-Sec.
634 Market St 07513 800-646-9353
Passaic County Community College Post-Sec.
1 College Blvd 07505 973-684-6868

Paulsboro, Gloucester, Pop. 5,820
Paulsboro SD 1,100/PK-12
662 N Delaware St 08066 856-423-2222
Dr. Laurie Bandlow, supt. Fax 423-4602
www.paulsboro.k12.nj.us
Paulsboro HS 300/9-12
670 N Delaware St 08066 856-423-2222
Paul Morina, prin. Fax 423-8915
Paulsboro JHS 200/7-8
670 N Delaware St 08066 856-423-2222
Mildred Tolbert, prin. Fax 423-8915

Pemberton, Burlington, Pop. 1,373
Pemberton Township SD 4,900/PK-12
1 Egbert St 08068 609-893-8141
Tony Trongone, supt. Fax 894-0933
www.pemberton.k12.nj.us
Fort/Newcomb MS 1,000/6-8
301 Fort Dix Rd 08068 609-893-8141
Ashley Walulak, prin. Fax 894-9287
Pemberton Township HS 1,000/9-12
148 Arneys Mount Rd 08068 609-893-8141
Eder Joseph, prin. Fax 894-0804

Burlington County College Post-Sec.
601 Pemberton Brown Mill Rd 08068 609-894-9311

Pennington, Mercer, Pop. 2,560
Hopewell Valley Regional SD 3,600/PK-12
425 S Main St 08534 609-737-4000
Dr. Thomas A. Smith, supt. Fax 737-1418
www.hvrsd.org/
Central HS 1,200/9-12
259 Pennington Titusville 08534 609-737-4003
Tana Smith, prin. Fax 737-1581
Timberlane MS 900/6-8
51 Timberlane Dr 08534 609-737-4004
Dr. Rosetta Treece, prin. Fax 737-2718

Mercer County Technical SD
Supt. — See Trenton
Sypek Center Vo/Tech
129 Bull Run Rd 08534 609-737-9785
Kimberly Schneider, prin. Fax 737-3951

Pennington S 500/6-12
112 W Delaware Ave 08534 609-737-1838
Dr. William Hawkey, hdmstr. Fax 737-2851

Pennsauken, Camden, Pop. 35,900
Camden County Technical Schools
Supt. — See Sicklerville
Camden County Technical S - Pennsauken Vo/Tech
6008 Browning Rd 08109 856-663-1040
Gregory Cappello, prin. Fax 655-8011

Pennsauken Township SD 4,600/PK-12
1695 Hylton Rd 08110 856-662-8505
Ronnie Tarchichi Ed.D., supt. Fax 663-5865
www.pennsauken.net
Pennsauken HS 1,400/9-12
800 Hylton Rd 08110 856-662-8500
Gregory Munford, prin. Fax 910-2612
Phifer MS 700/7-8
8201 Park Ave 08109 856-662-8511
Thomas Honeyman, prin. Fax 486-1422

Bishop Eustace Prep S 700/9-12
5552 Marlton Pike 08109 856-662-2160
James Beamesderfer, hdmstr. Fax 662-0025
Omega Institute Post-Sec.
7050 Kaighns Ave 08109 856-663-4299

Penns Grove, Salem, Pop. 4,982
Penns Grove-Carneys Point Regional SD 2,300/PK-12
100 Iona Ave 08069 856-299-4250
Dr. Zenaida Cobian, supt. Fax 299-5226
pgcpschools.org
Penns Grove MS 500/6-8
351 E Maple Ave 08069 856-299-0576
Dr. Luis Amberths, prin. Fax 299-4378
Other Schools – See Carneys Point

Pennsville, Salem, Pop. 11,771
Pennsville Township SD 1,700/PK-12
30 Church St 08070 856-540-6200
Dr. Michael Brodzik, supt. Fax 678-7565
www.psdnet.org/
Pennsville Memorial HS 500/9-12
110 S Broadway 08070 856-540-6220
Matthew McFarland, prin. Fax 678-2715
Pennsville MS 400/6-8
4 William Penn Ave 08070 856-540-6240
Sheila Burris, prin. Fax 678-2908

Salem County Christian Academy 200/PK-12
104 Sparks Ave 08070 856-678-9464
Mike Tardive, head sch Fax 678-3696

Perth Amboy, Middlesex, Pop. 50,388
Middlesex County Vocational SD
Supt. — See East Brunswick
Perth Amboy Vocational HS Vo/Tech
457 High St 08861 732-376-6300
Robert Fuller, prin. Fax 376-6391

Perth Amboy SD 9,800/PK-12
178 Barracks St 08861 732-376-6200
Dr. David Roman, supt. Fax 826-1644
www.paps.net
McGinnis MS 1,400/5-8
271 State St 08861 732-376-6040
Dr. Melissa Espana-Rodriguez, prin. Fax 376-6047
Perth Amboy HS 1,900/9-12
300 Eagle Ave 08861 732-376-6030
Dr. Gene Mosley, prin. Fax 376-6275
Shull MS 1,400/5-8
380 Hall Ave 08861 732-376-6060
Michael Heidelberg, prin. Fax 376-6067
Perth Amboy Adult HS Adult
178 Barracks St 08861 732-376-6240
Dr. Luis Ortega, prin. Fax 376-6245

Perth Amboy Catholic Upper S 100/4-8
500 State St 08861 732-826-1598
Sr. Mary Rebecca Piatek, prin. Fax 826-7063
Raritan Bay Medical Center Post-Sec.
530 New Brunswick Ave 08861 732-324-5232
Robert Fiance Beauty Academy Post-Sec.
312 State St 08861 732-442-6007
Universal Training Institute Post-Sec.
174 Jefferson St 08861 732-826-0155

Petersburg, See Woodbine
Upper Township SD 1,300/PK-8
525 Perry Rd 08270 609-628-3500
Vincent Palmieri, supt. Fax 628-2002
upperschools.org
Upper Township MS 500/6-8
525 Perry Rd 08270 609-628-3500
Jeffery Leek, prin. Fax 628-3506

Phillipsburg, Warren, Pop. 14,597
Lopatcong Township SD 800/PK-8
263 State Route 57 08865 908-859-0800
Rainie Roncoroni, supt. Fax 213-1339
www.lopatcongschool.org

Lopatcong MS 400/5-8
321 Stonehenge Dr 08865 908-213-2955
Jeanene Dutt, prin. Fax 213-0373

Phillipsburg SD 3,100/PK-12
445 Marshall St 08865 908-454-3400
George M. Chando, supt. Fax 213-2424
www.pburgsd.net/
Phillipsburg HS 1,600/9-12
1 Stateliner Blvd 08865 908-454-6551
Janice Trent, prin. Fax 213-2427
Phillipsburg MS 500/6-8
200 Hillcrest Blvd 08865 908-454-3400
Raffaele LaForgia, prin. Fax 213-2546

Pilesgrove, Salem
Salem County Vocational Technical SD
880 Route 45 08098 856-769-0101
John Swain, supt. Fax 769-3602
www.scvts.org/
Salem County Career & Technical HS Vo/Tech
880 Route 45 08098 856-769-0101
Jason Helder, prin. Fax 769-4214

Pine Hill, Camden, Pop. 9,944
Pine Hill Borough SD 1,800/PK-12
1003 Turnerville Rd 08021 856-783-6900
Dr. Kenneth Koczur, supt. Fax 783-2955
www.pinehill.k12.nj.us
Overbrook HS 700/9-12
1200 Turnerville Rd 08021 856-767-8000
Adam Lee, prin. Fax 767-3082
Pine Hill MS 300/6-8
1100 Turnerville Rd 08021 856-210-0200
Kathleen Klemick, prin. Fax 210-0195

Piscataway, Middlesex, Pop. 48,900
Middlesex County Vocational SD
Supt. — See East Brunswick
Piscataway Vocational HS Vo/Tech
21 Suttons Ln 08854 732-985-0717
Joseph Armstead, prin. Fax 985-7717

Piscataway Township SD 7,100/PK-12
1515 Stelton Rd 08854 732-572-2289
Teresa Rafferty, supt. Fax 777-1361
www.piscatawayschools.org/
Conackamack MS 400/6-8
5205 Witherspoon St 08854 732-699-1577
Donna White, prin. Fax 699-0118
Piscataway Township HS 2,200/9-12
100 Behmer Rd 08854 732-981-0700
Jason Lester, prin. Fax 981-1985
Quibbletown MS 500/6-8
99 Academy St 08854 732-752-0444
William Gonzalez, prin. Fax 752-5798
Schor MS 600/6-8
243 N Randolphville Rd 08854 732-752-4457
Richard Hueston, prin. Fax 424-9445

An-Noor Academy 300/PK-12
220 Centennial Ave 08854 732-667-5300
Lake Nelson SDA S 100/PK-10
555 S Randolphville Rd 08854 732-981-0626
StenoTech Career Institute Post-Sec.
262 Old New Brunswick Rd 08854 732-562-1200
Timothy Christian S 500/K-12
2008 Ethel Rd 08854 732-985-0300
Dr. Hubert Hartzler, head sch Fax 985-8008

Pitman, Gloucester, Pop. 8,890
Pitman SD 1,400/PK-12
420 Hudson Ave 08071 856-589-2145
Dr. Patrick McAleer, supt. Fax 582-5465
www.pitman.k12.nj.us
Pitman HS 400/9-12
225 Linden Ave 08071 856-589-2121
Dr. Cherie Lombardo, prin. Fax 589-8855
Pitman MS 300/6-8
138 E Holly Ave 08071 856-589-0636
Kristen Stewart, prin. Fax 589-2289

Pittsgrove, Salem
Pittsgrove Township SD 1,700/PK-12
1076 Almond Rd 08318 856-358-3094
Henry Bermann, supt. Fax 358-6020
www.pittsgrove.org
Pittsgrove Township MS 400/6-8
1082 Almond Rd 08318 856-358-8529
Priscilla Ocasio-Jimenez, prin. Fax 358-2686
Schalick HS 600/9-12
718 Centerton Rd 08318 856-358-2054
Yvette Dubois, prin. Fax 358-7063

Pittstown, Hunterdon
Alexandria Township SD 500/PK-8
557 County Road 513 08867 908-996-6811
Dr. Matthew Jennings, supt. Fax 996-7029
www.alexandriaschools.org
Alexandria MS 300/4-8
557 County Road 513 08867 908-996-6811
Joy Dominic, prin. Fax 996-7963

Plainfield, Union, Pop. 48,849
Plainfield SD 6,800/PK-12
1200 Myrtle Ave 07063 908-731-4335
Anna Belin-Pyles, supt. Fax 731-4336
www.plainfieldnjk12.org
Hubbard MS 400/6-8
661 W 8th St 07060 908-731-4320
Kwame Asante, prin. Fax 731-4315
Maxson MS 400/6-8
920 E 7th St 07062 908-731-4310
Juan Pablo Jimenez, prin. Fax 731-4306
Obama Acad for Academic & Civic Dvlpmnt 100/Alt
1200 Myrtle Ave 07063 908-731-4270
Deitria Smith-Snead, prin.
Plainfield Academy for the Arts 400/7-12
1700 W Front St 07063 908-731-4421
Angela Bento, prin.

Plainfield HS 1,300/9-12
950 Park Ave 07060 908-731-4390
Willie Worley, prin. Fax 731-4394

Koinonia Academy 200/PK-12
1040 Plainfield Ave 07060 908-668-9002
Lelia Pappas, prin. Fax 668-9883
Muhlenberg - Snyder Schools Post-Sec.
Park Avenue And Randolph Rd 07061 908-668-2400
Union County College Post-Sec.
232 E 2nd St 07060 908-412-3599

Plainsboro, Middlesex
West Windsor-Plainsboro Regional SD
Supt. — See West Windsor
Community MS 1,100/6-8
95 Grovers Mill Rd 08536 609-716-5300
Dr. Shauna Carter, prin. Fax 716-5333
West Windsor-Plainsboro HS North 1,500/9-12
90 Grovers Mill Rd 08536 609-716-5100
Jonathan Dauber, prin. Fax 716-5142

Pleasantville, Atlantic, Pop. 19,789
Pleasantville SD 3,800/PK-12
PO Box 960 08232 609-383-6800
Dr. Garnell Bailey, supt. Fax 677-8101
www.pps-nj.us/
Pleasantville HS 800/9-12
701 Mill Rd 08232 609-383-6900
Edward Bonek, prin. Fax 383-9934
Pleasantville MS 800/6-8
801 Mill Rd 08232 609-383-6800
Stephen Townsend, prin. Fax 677-0852

Shore Beauty School Post-Sec.
103 W Washington Ave 08232 609-645-3635

Point Pleasant, Ocean, Pop. 18,265
Point Pleasant Borough SD 2,900/PK-12
2100 Panther Path 08742 732-701-1900
Vincent Smith, supt. Fax 892-8403
www.pointpleasant.k12.nj.us/
Memorial MS 700/6-8
808 Laura Herbert Dr 08742 732-701-1900
Gary Floyd, prin. Fax 892-0984
Point Pleasant Borough HS 900/9-12
808 Laura Herbert Dr 08742 732-701-1900
Kurtis Karcich, prin. Fax 892-1252

Pt Pleas Bch, Ocean, Pop. 4,621
Point Pleasant Beach SD 800/PK-12
299 Cooks Ln 08742 732-899-8840
William Smith, supt. Fax 899-1730
ptbeach.com
Point Pleasant Beach HS 400/9-12
700 Trenton Ave 08742 732-899-1817
Terri King, prin. Fax 899-1145

Pompton Lakes, Passaic, Pop. 10,956
Pompton Lakes SD 1,600/K-12
237 Van Ave 07442 973-835-4334
Dr. Paul Amoroso, supt. Fax 835-1748
www.plps-k12.org
Lakeside MS 400/6-8
316 Lakeside Ave 07442 973-835-2221
Jake Herninko, prin. Fax 835-8088
Pompton Lakes HS 600/9-12
44 Lakeside Ave 07442 973-835-7100
Vincent Przybylinski, prin. Fax 835-1054

Pompton Plains, Morris
Pequannock Township SD 2,200/PK-12
538 Newark Pompton Tpke 07444 973-616-6040
Brett Charleston, supt. Fax 616-6043
www.pequannock.org
Pequannock Township HS 700/9-12
85 Sunset Rd 07444 973-616-6000
Dr. Alicia Scelso, prin. Fax 616-6029
Pequannock Valley MS 600/6-8
493 Newark Pompton Tpke 07444 973-616-6050
Richard Hayzler, prin. Fax 616-8370

Chancellor Academy 100/6-12
PO Box 338 07444 973-835-4989
Netherlands Reformed Christian S 200/PK-12
164 Jacksonville Rd 07444 973-628-7400
John VanDerBrink, prin. Fax 628-0461

Port Monmouth, Monmouth, Pop. 3,791
Middletown Township SD
Supt. — See Leonardo
Thorne MS, 70 Murphy Rd 07758 700/6-8
Thomas Olausen, prin. 732-787-1220

Port Norris, Cumberland, Pop. 1,319
Commercial Township SD 600/PK-8
1308 North Ave 08349 856-785-0840
Daniel Dooley Ed.D., supt. Fax 785-2354
www.commercial.k12.nj.us
Port Norris MS 200/6-8
6812 Brown St 08349 856-785-1611
Daniel Dooley, prin. Fax 785-2556

Pottersville, Hunterdon

Purnell S 100/9-12
PO Box 500 07979 908-439-2154
Dr. Jeffrey Beedy, head sch Fax 439-2090

Princeton, Mercer, Pop. 11,896
Princeton SD 3,400/PK-12
25 Valley Rd 08540 609-806-4220
Stephen Cochrane, supt. Fax 806-4221
www.princetonk12.org
Princeton HS 1,500/9-12
151 Moore St 08540 609-806-4280
Gary Snyder, prin. Fax 806-4281
Witherspoon MS 700/6-8
217 Walnut Ln 08540 609-806-4270
Jason Burr, prin. Fax 806-4271

Achieve Test Prep Post-Sec.
100 Overlook Ctr 08540 609-964-0772
Hun S of Princeton 600/6-12
176 Edgerstoune Rd 08540 609-921-7600
Jonathan Brougham, hdmstr.
Princeton Day S 900/PK-12
PO Box 75 08542 609-924-6700
Paul Stellato, head sch Fax 924-8944
Princeton Intl S of Mathematics & Sci 100/9-12
19 Lambert Dr 08540 609-454-5580
Princeton Theological Seminary Post-Sec.
PO Box 821 08542 609-921-8300
Princeton University 08544 Post-Sec.
609-258-3000
Raritan Valley Flying School Post-Sec.
41 Airpark Rd 08540 609-921-3100
Stuart Country Day S 400/K-12
1200 Stuart Rd 08540 609-921-2330
Dr. Patty Fagin, hdmstr. Fax 497-0784

Princeton Junction, Mercer, Pop. 2,407
West Windsor-Plainsboro Regional SD
Supt. — See West Windsor
Grover MS 1,200/6-8
10 Southfield Rd 08550 609-716-5250
Lamont Thomas, prin. Fax 716-5270

Wilberforce S 100/PK-12
99 Clarksville Rd 08550 609-924-6111
Howe Whitman, head sch Fax 924-6995

Prospect Park, Passaic, Pop. 5,739
Paterson SD
Supt. — See Paterson
Great Falls Academy 100/Alt
13 Wagaraw Blvd 07508 973-321-2390
Gerald Glisson, prin. Fax 321-2387

Rahway, Union, Pop. 26,740
Rahway SD 3,600/PK-12
1138 Kline Pl 07065 732-396-1000
Patricia Camp Ph.D., supt. Fax 396-1391
www.rahway.net
Rahway 7th & 8th Grade Academy 500/7-8
1138 Kline Pl 07065 732-396-1025
Alan Johnson, prin. Fax 396-2633
Rahway HS 1,100/9-12
1012 Madison Ave 07065 732-396-1090
John Farinella, prin. Fax 396-2630

Ramsey, Bergen, Pop. 14,315
Ramsey SD 2,900/PK-12
266 E Main St 07446 201-785-2300
Dr. Matthew Murphy Ed.D., supt. Fax 934-6623
www.ramsey.k12.nj.us
Ramsey HS 900/9-12
256 E Main St 07446 201-785-2300
Dr. Michael Thumm, prin. Fax 818-2656
Smith MS 700/6-8
2 Monroe St 07446 201-785-2313
Andrew Herre, prin. Fax 785-2320

Don Bosco Prep HS 900/9-12
492 N Franklin Tpke 07446 201-327-8003
John Stanczak, prin. Fax 327-3397
Eastwick College Post-Sec.
10 S Franklin Tpke 07446 201-327-8877

Randolph, Morris, Pop. 19,974
Randolph Township SD 4,900/PK-12
25 Schoolhouse Rd 07869 973-361-0808
Jennifer Fano, supt. Fax 361-2405
www.rtnj.org
Randolph HS 1,600/9-12
511 Millbrook Ave 07869 973-361-2400
Debbie Iosso, prin. Fax 361-1661
Randolph MS 1,300/6-8
507 Millbrook Ave 07869 973-366-8700
Dr. Dennis Copeland Ed.D., prin. Fax 361-6501

County College of Morris Post-Sec.
214 Center Grove Rd 07869 973-328-5000

Red Bank, Monmouth, Pop. 11,983
Red Bank Borough SD 1,100/PK-8
76 Branch Ave 07701 732-758-1507
Dr. Jared Rumage, supt. Fax 212-1356
www.rbb.k12.nj.us
Red Bank MS 500/4-8
101 Harding Rd 07701 732-758-1500
Maria Iozzi, prin. Fax 758-1518

Red Bank Catholic HS 1,100/9-12
112 Broad St 07701 732-747-1774
Robert Abatemarco, prin. Fax 747-1936

Richland, Atlantic

St. Augustine Prep S 700/9-12
PO Box 279 08350 856-697-2600
Fr. Donald Reilly, pres. Fax 697-8389

Ridgefield, Bergen, Pop. 10,875
Ridgefield SD 1,500/1-12
555 Chestnut St 07657 201-945-9236
Dr. Frank Romano, supt. Fax 945-7830
www.ridgefieldschools.com
Ridgefield Memorial HS 500/9-12
555 Walnut St 07657 201-945-4455
John Coviello, prin. Fax 945-3505
Slocum/Skewes ES 700/3-8
650 Prospect Ave 07657 201-943-4299
Anna Gaeta, prin. Fax 943-9527

Ridgefield Park, Bergen, Pop. 12,530
Ridgefield Park SD 1,900/PK-12
712 Lincoln Ave 07660 201-641-0800
Eric Koenig, supt. Fax 641-2203
www.rpps.net
Ridgefield Park JSHS 1,200/7-12
1 Ozzie Nelson Dr 07660 201-440-1440
James Donohue, prin. Fax 641-6861

Ridgewood, Bergen, Pop. 24,497
Ridgewood Village SD 5,600/PK-12
49 Cottage Pl 07450 201-670-2700
Dr. Daniel Fishbein, supt. Fax 670-2668
www.ridgewood.k12.nj.us
Franklin MS 700/6-8
335 N Van Dien Ave 07450 201-670-2780
Anthony Orsini, prin. Fax 670-3382
Ridgewood HS 1,700/9-12
627 E Ridgewood Ave 07450 201-670-2800
Dr. Thomas Gorman, prin. Fax 444-7008
Washington MS 700/6-8
155 Washington Pl 07450 201-670-2790
Dr. Katie Kashmanian, prin. Fax 670-3290

Valley Hospital Post-Sec.
223 N Van Dien Ave 07450 201-447-8002

Ringwood, Passaic, Pop. 11,996
Ringwood SD 1,200/K-8
121 Carletondale Rd 07456 973-962-7028
Dr. Nicholas Bernice, supt. Fax 962-9211
www.ringwoodschools.org/
Ryerson MS 400/6-8
130 Valley Rd 07456 973-962-7063
Paul Scutti, prin. Fax 962-6905

River Edge, Bergen, Pop. 11,204
River Dell Regional SD 1,600/7-12
230 Woodland Ave 07661 201-599-7200
Patrick Fletcher, supt. Fax 261-3809
www.riverdell.org/
River Dell MS 600/7-8
230 Woodland Ave 07661 201-599-7250
Richard Freedman, prin. Fax 599-2202
Other Schools – See Oradell

Riverside, Burlington, Pop. 7,974
Riverside Township SD 1,400/PK-12
112 E Washington St 08075 856-461-1255
Robin A. Ehrich, supt. Fax 461-5168
www.riverside.k12.nj.us
Riverside HS 400/9-12
112 E Washington St 08075 856-461-1255
Todd Pae, prin. Fax 461-7277
Riverside MS 300/6-8
112 E Washington St 08075 856-461-1255
Michael W. Mongon, prin. Fax 461-0182

River Vale, Bergen, Pop. 9,410
River Vale SD 1,200/K-8
609 Westwood Ave 07675 201-358-4000
Rory McCourt, supt. Fax 358-8319
www.rivervaleschools.com/
Holdrum MS 500/6-8
393 Rivervale Rd 07675 201-358-4016
James Cody, prin. Fax 358-8427

Robbinsville, Mercer, Pop. 2,974
Robbinsville SD 2,600/PK-12
155 Robbinsville Edinburg 08691 609-632-0910
Steven Mayer, supt. Fax 371-7964
www.robbinsville.k12.nj.us
Pond Road MS 900/5-8
150 Pond Rd 08691 609-632-0940
Paul Gizzo, prin. Fax 918-9011
Robbinsville HS 900/9-12
155 Robbinsville Edinburg 08691 609-632-0950
Molly Avery, prin. Fax 371-7961

Rockaway, Morris, Pop. 6,360
Morris County Vocational SD
Supt. — See Denville
Academy for Math Science & Engineering Vo/Tech
520 W Main St 07866 973-664-2301

Morris Hills Regional SD 2,700/9-12
48 Knoll Dr 07866 973-664-2291
James Jencarelli, supt. Fax 627-6588
mhrd.org
Morris Hills HS 1,200/9-12
520 W Main St 07866 973-664-2309
Todd Toriello, prin. Fax 983-7461
Morris Knolls HS 1,600/9-12
50 Knoll Dr 07866 973-664-2200
Ryan MacNaughton, prin. Fax 586-3550
Morris Hills Adult HS Adult
50 Knoll Dr 07866 973-664-2232
Scott Gambale, coord. Fax 586-3550

Rockaway Borough SD 600/PK-8
103 E Main St 07866 973-625-8600
Mark Schwarz, supt. Fax 625-7355
www.rockboro.org/
Jefferson MS, 95 E Main St 07866 400/4-8
Stephanie Bonaparte, prin. 973-625-8603

Rockaway Township SD
Supt. — See Hibernia
Copeland MS 900/6-8
100 Lake Shore Dr 07866 973-627-2465
Alfonso Gonnella, prin. Fax 983-1843

Roselle, Union, Pop. 20,670
Roselle Borough SD 2,600/PK-12
710 Locust St 07203 908-298-2040
Dr. Kevin West, supt. Fax 298-3353
www.roselleschools.org
Clark HS 700/9-12
122 E 6th Ave 07203 908-298-2004
Rashon Mickens, prin. Fax 259-0782
Wilday JHS 400/7-8
400 Brooklawn Ave 07203 908-298-2066
Dr. Josue Falaise, prin. Fax 298-2068

Roselle Catholic HS 500/9-12
350 Raritan Rd 07203 908-245-2350
Thomas Berrios, prin. Fax 241-3869

Roselle Park, Union, Pop. 13,111
Roselle Park SD 1,900/K-12
510 Chestnut St 07204 908-245-1197
Pedro Garrido, supt. Fax 245-1226
www.rpsd.org/
Roselle Park HS 600/9-12
185 W Webster Ave 07204 908-241-4550
Sarah Costa, prin. Fax 245-6609
Roselle Park MS 500/6-8
57 W Grant Ave 07204 908-245-1634
Kathleen Carlin, prin. Fax 245-7491

Rumson, Monmouth, Pop. 7,054
Rumson Borough SD 1,000/PK-8
60 Forrest Ave 07760 732-842-4747
Dr. John Bormann, supt. Fax 842-4877
www.rumsonschool.org/
Forrestdale MS 600/4-8
60 Forrest Ave 07760 732-842-0383
Jennifer Gibbons, prin. Fax 219-9458

Rumson-Fair Haven Regional HSD 900/9-12
74 Ridge Rd 07760 732-842-1597
Dr. Peter Righi, supt. Fax 741-1712
www.rumsonfairhaven.org
Rumson-Fair Haven Regional HS 900/9-12
74 Ridge Rd 07760 732-842-1597
Tracy Handerhan, prin. Fax 741-1712

Runnemede, Camden, Pop. 8,357
Black Horse Pike Regional SD
Supt. — See Blackwood
Triton HS 1,300/9-12
250 Schubert Ave 08078 856-939-4500
Melissa Sheppard, prin. Fax 939-4724

Runnemede Borough SD 800/PK-8
505 W 3rd Ave 08078 856-931-5365
Mark Iannucci, supt. Fax 931-4446
www.runnemedeschools.org/
Volz MS 500/PK-PK, 4-
505 W 3rd Ave 08078 856-931-5353
Steve Pili, prin. Fax 931-1827

Rutherford, Bergen, Pop. 17,647
Rutherford SD, 176 Park Ave 07070 2,000/PK-12
John Hurley, supt. 201-438-7675
www.rutherfordschools.org
Rutherford HS 800/9-12
56 Elliott Pl 07070 201-438-7675
Frank Morano, prin. Fax 438-7293
Union MS 200/7-8
359 Union Ave 07070 201-438-7675
Kurt Schweitzer, prin. Fax 804-8248

St. Mary HS 300/9-12
64 Chestnut St 07070 201-933-5220
Tara Brunt, prin. Fax 933-0834

Saddle Brook, Bergen, Pop. 13,296
Saddle Brook Township SD 1,600/K-12
355 Mayhill St 07663 201-843-2880
Anthony Riscica, supt. Fax 843-0216
www.saddlebrookschools.org
Saddle Brook MSHS 800/7-12
355 Mayhill St Ste 1 07663 201-843-2880
John Lawlor, prin. Fax 843-4305

Saddle River, Bergen, Pop. 3,086

Saddle River Day S 300/PK-12
147 Chestnut Ridge Rd 07458 201-327-4050
Eileen Lambert, head sch Fax 327-6161

Salem, Salem, Pop. 4,985
Salem CSD 1,200/PK-12
205 Walnut St 08079 856-935-3800
Dr. Amiot Michel, supt. Fax 935-6977
www.salemnj.org
Salem HS 300/9-12
219 Walnut St 08079 856-935-3900
John Mulhorn, prin. Fax 935-3288
Salem MS 400/3-8
51 New Market St 08079 856-935-2700
Pascale DeVilme, prin. Fax 935-2284

Scotch Plains, Union, Pop. 21,160
Scotch Plains-Fanwood SD 5,400/PK-12
2280 Evergreen Ave 07076 908-232-6161
Dr. Margaret Hayes, supt. Fax 889-1769
www.spfk12.org
Park MS 900/5-8
580 Park Ave 07076 908-322-4445
Dr. Jocelyn Dumaresq, prin. Fax 561-5929
Scotch Plains-Fanwood HS 1,600/9-12
667 Westfield Rd 07076 908-889-8600
Dr. David Heisey, prin. Fax 889-8254
Terrill MS 800/5-8
1301 Terrill Rd 07076 908-322-5215
Dr. Kevin Holloway, prin. Fax 322-6813

Union Co. Educational Services Comm SD
Supt. — See Westfield
Hillcrest Academy North Campus 100/Alt
2630 Plainfield Ave 07076 908-233-9366
John Marquet, prin. Fax 301-9093

Union County Vocational-Technical SD
1776 Raritan Rd 07076 908-889-8288
Peter A. Capodice, supt. Fax 889-4336
www.ucvts.tec.nj.us
Academy for Allied Health Sciences Vo/Tech
1776 Raritan Rd 07076 908-889-8288
Walter Smolenski, prin. Fax 889-4734
Academy for Information Technology Vo/Tech
1776 Raritan Rd 07076 908-889-8288
Colleen Gialanella, prin. Fax 889-6831
Academy for Performing Arts Vo/Tech
1776 Raritan Rd 07076 908-889-8288
Kelly Douglas-Jackson, prin. Fax 889-1666
Union County Magnet HS Vo/Tech
1776 Raritan Rd 07076 908-889-8288
Paul Rafalowski, prin. Fax 889-3196
Union County Vo-Tech HS Vo/Tech
1776 Raritan Rd 07076 908-889-8288
Jeffrey Lerner, prin. Fax 889-4399

Union Catholic Regional HS 800/9-12
1600 Martine Ave 07076 908-889-1600
Sr. Percylee Hart, prin. Fax 889-7867

Seabrook, Cumberland, Pop. 1,405
Upper Deerfield Township SD 900/PK-8
1385 Highway 77 08302 856-455-2267
Dr. Peter Koza Ed.D., supt. Fax 453-7077
www.udts.org
Woodruff MS 300/6-8
1385 Highway 77 08302 856-455-2267
Edward Regan, prin. Fax 453-7077

Secaucus, Hudson, Pop. 15,983
Secaucus SD 1,900/PK-12
PO Box 1496 07096 201-974-2000
Kenneth Knops, supt. Fax 974-1911
www.sboe.org
Secaucus HS 500/9-12
11 Millridge Rd 07094 201-974-2033
Dr. Robert Berckes, prin. Fax 974-0026
Secaucus MS 300/6-8
11 Millridge Rd 07094 201-974-2025
Robert Valente, prin. Fax 974-0275

Sewell, Gloucester
Deptford Township SD
Supt. — See Deptford
Monongahela MS 600/7-8
890 Bankbridge Rd 08080 856-415-9540
Arthur Dietz, prin. Fax 464-9284

Gloucester County Vocational SD
1360 Tanyard Rd 08080 856-468-1445
Michael Dicken, supt. Fax 468-3397
www.gcit.org
Gloucester Co. Institute of Technology Vo/Tech
1360 Tanyard Rd 08080 856-468-1445
James Dundee, prin. Fax 468-1035
Adult Regional HS Adult
1360 Tanyard Rd 08080 856-468-1445
James Dundee, prin.

Washington Township SD 7,400/PK-12
206 E Holly Ave 08080 856-589-6644
Joseph Bollendorf, supt. Fax 582-1918
www.wtps.org
Bunker Hill MS 700/6-8
372 Pitman Downer Rd 08080 856-881-7007
Dr. Joseph Vandenberg, prin. Fax 881-5414
Chestnut Ridge MS 600/6-8
641 Hurffville Crosskeys Rd 08080 856-582-3535
James Barnes, prin. Fax 589-0683
Orchard Valley MS 600/6-8
238 Pitman Downer Rd 08080 856-582-5353
Colleen McLaughlin, prin. Fax 589-0197
Washington Township HS 2,400/9-12
519 Hurffville Crosskeys Rd 08080 856-589-8500
Ann Moore, prin. Fax 218-0991

Gloucester County Christian S 400/PK-12
151 Golf Club Rd 08080 856-589-1665
Donald Netz, prin. Fax 582-4989
Gloucester County College Post-Sec.
1400 Tanyard Rd 08080 856-468-5000

Shamong Township, Burlington, Pop. 5,765
Lenape Regional HSD 6,800/9-12
93 Willow Grove Rd 08088 609-268-2000
Dr. Carol Birnbohm, supt. Fax 268-6642
www.lrhsd.org/
Other Schools – See Marlton, Medford, Tabernacle

Shamong Township SD 800/K-8
295 Indian Mills Rd 08088 609-268-0120
Christine Vespe Ed.D., supt. Fax 268-1229
www.ims.k12.nj.us
Indian Mills Memorial MS 400/5-8
295 Indian Mills Rd 08088 609-268-0440
Timothy Carroll, prin. Fax 268-1229

Sicklerville, Camden
Camden County Technical Schools
343 Berlin Cross Keys Rd 08081 856-767-7000
Patricia Fitzgerald, supt. Fax 767-3589
www.ccts.info
Camden County Technical S - Gloucester Vo/Tech
343 Berlin Cross Keys Rd 08081 856-767-7000
Bonnie Durante, prin. Fax 767-3638
Other Schools – See Pennsauken

Gloucester Township SD
Supt. — See Blackwood
Mullen MS 900/6-8
1400 Sicklerville Rd 08081 856-875-8777
Edmund Cetrullo, prin. Fax 875-0902

Technical Institute of Camden County Post-Sec.
343 Berlin Cross Keys Rd 08081 856-767-7000

Skillman, Somerset, Pop. 236
Montgomery Township SD 4,700/PK-12
1014 Route 601 08558 609-466-7600
Nancy Gartenberg, supt. Fax 466-0944
www.mtsd.k12.nj.us
Montgomery HS 1,700/9-12
1016 Route 601 08558 609-466-7602
Paul Popadiuk, prin. Fax 466-0243
Montgomery Upper MS 800/7-8
375 Burnt Hill Rd 08558 609-466-7604
Cory Delgado, prin. Fax 874-7045

Somerdale, Camden, Pop. 5,010
Sterling HSD 800/9-12
801 W Preston Ave Ste B 08083 856-784-1287
Mark Napoleon, supt. Fax 435-1530
www.sterling.k12.nj.us
Sterling HS 800/9-12
501 S Warwick Rd 08083 856-784-1333
Matthew Sheehan, prin. Fax 784-7661

Somerset, Somerset, Pop. 21,468
Franklin Township SD 7,400/PK-12
1755 Amwell Rd 08873 732-873-2400
Dr. John Ravally, supt.
www.franklinboe.org
Franklin HS 2,100/9-12
500 Elizabeth Ave 08873 732-302-4200
Thomas DiGanci, prin. Fax 302-4212
Franklin MS 1,100/7-8
415 Francis St 08873 732-249-6410
Reginald Davenport, prin. Fax 246-0770

Rutgers Preparatory S 700/PK-12
1345 Easton Ave 08873 732-545-5600
Dr. Steven Loy, hdmstr. Fax 214-1819

Somers Point, Atlantic, Pop. 10,546

Shore Memorial Hospital Post-Sec.
Shore Rd 08244 609-653-3545

Somerville, Somerset, Pop. 11,787
Somerville Borough SD 2,100/PK-12
51 W Cliff St 08876 908-218-4100
Dr. Timothy Purnell, supt. Fax 526-9668
www.somervillenjk12.org
Somerville HS 1,200/9-12
222 Davenport St 08876 908-218-4108
Gerard Foley, prin. Fax 707-0971
Somerville MS 300/6-8
51 W Cliff St 08876 908-218-4107
Georgette Boulegeris, prin. Fax 575-9526

Immaculata HS 800/9-12
240 Mountain Ave 08876 908-722-0200
Jean Kline, prin. Fax 218-7765

South Amboy, Middlesex, Pop. 8,493
Sayreville SD 5,700/K-12
150 Lincoln St 08879 732-525-5200
Dr. Richard Labbe, supt. Fax 727-5769
www.sayrevillek12.net/
Other Schools – See Parlin

South Amboy SD 900/PK-12
240 John St 08879 732-525-2100
Frank Alfano, supt. Fax 727-0730
www.sapublicschools.com
South Amboy MSHS 400/6-12
200 Gvrnr Hrold G Hffmn Plz 08879 732-316-7669
Dr. Patrick McCabe, prin. Fax 721-0054

Southampton, Burlington
Southampton Township SD 700/K-8
177 Main St 08088 609-859-2256
Michael Harris, supt. Fax 859-1542
www.southampton.k12.nj.us
Southampton Township MS 3 200/6-8
100 Warrior Way 08088 609-859-2256
Jennifer Horner, prin. Fax 801-0754

South Orange, Essex, Pop. 16,390
South Orange-Maplewood SD
Supt. — See Maplewood
South Orange MS 800/6-8
70 N Ridgewood Rd 07079 973-378-2772
Lynn Irby, prin. Fax 378-2775

Seton Hall University Post-Sec.
400 S Orange Ave 07079 973-761-9000

South Plainfield, Middlesex, Pop. 22,711
South Plainfield SD 3,400/K-12
125 Jackson Ave 07080 908-754-4620
Dr. Noreen Lishak, supt. Fax 822-2453
www.spboe.org
South Plainfield HS 1,100/9-12
200 Lake St 07080 908-754-4620
Ronnie Spring, prin. Fax 756-7659
South Plainfield MS 500/7-8
2201 Plainfield Ave 07080 908-754-4620
Roger Vroom, admin. Fax 791-1152

Avtech Institute of Technology Post-Sec.
50 Cragwood Rd Ste 350 07080 908-222-2833
Central Career School Post-Sec.
126 Corporate Blvd 07080 908-412-8600
Everest Institute Post-Sec.
5000 Hadley Rd Ste 100 07080 908-222-9300
Lincoln Technical Institute Post-Sec.
901 Hadley Rd 07080 800-305-3487

South River, Middlesex, Pop. 15,456
South River SD 2,300/PK-12
15 Montgomery St 08882 732-613-4000
Michael Pfister, supt. Fax 613-4756
www.srivernj.org
South River HS 600/9-12
11 Montgomery St 08882 732-613-4014
Kamila Buffalino, prin. Fax 613-4044
South River MS 500/6-8
3 Montgomery St 08882 732-613-4073
Lisa Wargo, prin. Fax 698-9305

Sparta, Sussex, Pop. 15,157
Sparta Township SD 3,400/PK-12
18 Mohawk Ave 07871 973-729-7886
Dennis Tobin, supt. Fax 729-0576
www.sparta.org
Sparta HS 1,200/9-12
70 W Mountain Rd 07871 973-729-6191
Janet Ferraro Ed.D., prin. Fax 729-3258

Sparta MS 800/6-8
350 Main St 07871 973-729-3151
Michael Gregory, prin. Fax 729-0573

Sussex County Technical SD
105 N Church Rd 07871 973-383-6700
Gus Modla, supt. Fax 383-4272
www.sussex.tec.nj.us
Sussex County Technical S Vo/Tech
105 N Church Rd 07871 973-383-6700
Gus Modla, prin. Fax 383-4272

Pope John XXIII HS 900/9-12
28 Andover Rd 07871 973-729-6125
Thomas Costello, prin. Fax 729-3487
Veritas Christian Academy 100/9-12
385 Houses Corner Rd 07871 973-579-6333
Sean Bevier, admin. Fax 579-6293

Spotswood, Middlesex, Pop. 8,141
Spotswood SD 1,700/PK-12
105 Summerhill Rd 08884 732-723-2200
Scott Rocco, supt. Fax 251-7666
www.spotswood.k12.nj.us
Spotswood HS 800/9-12
105 Summerhill Rd 08884 732-723-2202
Thomas Calder, prin. Fax 251-7666
Spotswood Memorial MS 300/6-8
115 Summerhill Rd 08884 732-723-2227
Christine Smith, prin. Fax 251-7666

Springfield, Union, Pop. 13,420
Springfield SD 2,200/PK-12
PO Box 210 07081 973-376-1025
Michael Davino, supt. Fax 912-9229
www.springfieldschools.com
Dayton HS 600/9-12
139 Mountain Ave 07081 973-376-1025
Dr. Norman Francis, prin. Fax 376-4570
Gaudineer MS 400/6-8
75 S Springfield Ave 07081 973-376-1025
Timothy Kielty, prin. Fax 376-3259

Stanhope, Sussex, Pop. 3,550
Byram Township SD 900/K-8
12 Mansfield Dr 07874 973-347-1047
Bryan Hensz, supt. Fax 347-9001
www.byramschools.org
Byram IS 400/5-8
12 Mansfield Dr 07874 973-347-1047
John Fritzky, prin. Fax 691-7780

Lenape Valley Regional HSD 800/9-12
PO Box 578 07874 973-347-7600
Paul DiRupo, supt. Fax 691-0164
www.lvhs.org
Lenape Valley Regional HS 800/9-12
PO Box 578 07874 973-347-7600
Thomas Claeys, prin. Fax 347-2536

Stewartsville, Warren, Pop. 346
Greenwich Township SD 800/PK-8
101 Wyndham Farm Blvd 08886 908-859-2022
Maria Eppolite, supt. Fax 859-4522
www.gtsd.net
Stewartsville MS 300/6-8
642 S Main St 08886 908-859-2023
Stephanie Snyder, prin. Fax 859-4522

Stirling, Morris
Long Hill Township SD
Supt. — See Gillette
Central MS 300/6-8
90 Central Ave 07980 908-647-2311
George Villar, prin. Fax 647-0610

Stratford, Camden, Pop. 6,903
Stratford Borough SD 800/PK-8
111 Warwick Rd 08084 856-783-2555
Thomas Attanasi, supt. Fax 784-8486
www.stratford.k12.nj.us
Yellin MS 500/4-8
111 Warwick Rd 08084 856-783-1094
David Ricci, prin. Fax 309-0304

Succasunna, Morris, Pop. 9,054
Roxbury Township SD 3,600/PK-12
42 N Hillside Ave 07876 973-584-6099
Loretta Radulic, supt. Fax 252-1434
www.roxbury.org
Eisenhower MS 600/7-8
47 Eyland Ave 07876 973-584-2973
Dominick Miller, prin. Fax 584-4529
Roxbury HS 1,400/9-12
1 Bryant Dr 07876 973-584-7699
Jeffrey Swanson, prin. Fax 584-7584

American Christian S 200/PK-12
126 S Hillside Ave 07876 973-584-6616
Kristen Brennan, head sch Fax 584-0686

Summit, Union, Pop. 21,055
Summit CSD 4,100/PK-12
14 Beekman Ter 07901 908-918-2100
Mr. June Chang, supt. Fax 273-3656
www.summit.k12.nj.us
Summit HS 1,200/9-12
125 Kent Place Blvd 07901 908-273-1494
Stacy Grimaldi, prin. Fax 273-2832
Summit MS 1,000/6-8
272 Morris Ave 07901 908-273-1190
Damen Cooper, prin. Fax 273-8320

Kent Place S 600/PK-12
42 Norwood Ave 07901 908-273-0900
Susan Bosland, head sch Fax 273-9390
Oak Knoll S of the Holy Child 600/K-12
44 Blackburn Rd 07901 908-522-8100
Timothy Saburn, head sch Fax 277-1838

Oratory Preparatory S 300/7-12
1 Beverly Rd 07901 908-273-1084
Robert Costello, head sch Fax 273-5505

Sussex, Sussex, Pop. 2,089
High Point Regional SD 1,000/9-12
299 Pidgeon Hill Rd 07461 973-875-3101
Dr. Scott D. Ripley Ed.D., supt. Fax 875-0904
www.hpregional.org
High Point Regional HS 1,000/9-12
299 Pidgeon Hill Rd 07461 973-875-3101
Jonathan Tallamy, prin. Fax 875-2756

Sussex-Wantage Regional SD 1,100/PK-8
27 Bank St 07461 973-875-3175
Robert Mooney, supt. Fax 875-7175
www.swregional.org
Sussex MS 400/6-8
10 Loomis Ave 07461 973-875-4138
Shane Schwarz, prin. Fax 875-6790

Tabernacle, Burlington
Lenape Regional HSD
Supt. — See Shamong Township
Seneca HS 1,100/9-12
110 Carranza Rd 08088 609-268-4600
Jeffrey Spector, prin. Fax 268-4635

Tabernacle Township SD 700/K-8
132 New Rd 08088 609-268-0153
Dr. John Sherry, supt. Fax 268-1006
www.tabschools.org
Olson MS 400/5-8
132 New Rd 08088 609-268-0153
Susan Grosser, prin. Fax 268-1006

Teaneck, Bergen, Pop. 39,500
Teaneck SD 3,400/PK-12
1 Merrison St 07666 201-833-5510
Vincent McHale, supt. Fax 837-9468
www.teaneckschools.org
Franklin MS 500/5-8
1315 Taft Rd 07666 201-833-5450
Natasha Pitt, prin. Fax 862-2465
Jefferson MS 500/5-8
655 Teaneck Rd 07666 201-833-5471
Angela Davis, prin. Fax 833-3983
Teaneck HS 1,300/9-12
100 Elizabeth Ave 07666 201-833-5400
Dennis Heck, prin. Fax 833-5403

Fairleigh Dickinson University Post-Sec.
1000 River Rd 07666 201-692-2000
Holy Name Hospital School of Nursing Post-Sec.
690 Teaneck Rd 07666 201-833-3005
Ma'ayanot Yeshiva HS for Girls 300/9-12
1650 Palisade Ave 07666 201-833-4307
Rachel Feldman, admin. Fax 833-0816
Torah Academy of Bergen County 300/9-12
1600 Queen Anne Rd 07666 201-837-7696

Tenafly, Bergen, Pop. 14,170
Tenafly SD 3,500/K-12
500 Tenafly Rd 07670 201-816-4500
Lynn Trager, supt. Fax 816-4521
www.tenafly.k12.nj.us
Tenafly HS 1,200/9-12
19 Columbus Dr 07670 201-816-6600
Dr. James Morrison, prin. Fax 871-9184
Tenafly MS 800/6-8
10 Sunset Ln 07670 201-816-4900
Dr. John Fabbo, prin. Fax 569-0327

Teterboro, Bergen, Pop. 61
Bergen County Vocational Technical SD
Supt. — See Paramus
Bergen County Technical HS - Teterboro Vo/Tech
504 State Rt 46 07608 201-343-6000
David Tankard, prin. Fax 996-6925

Teterboro School of Aeronautics Post-Sec.
80 Moonachie Ave 07608 201-288-6300

Tinton Falls, Monmouth, Pop. 17,575
Monmouth County Vocational SD
Supt. — See Freehold
CLASS Academy 100/Alt
537 Tinton Ave 07724 732-542-5455
Paul Christopher, prin. Fax 544-8018

Monmouth Regional HSD 1,000/9-12
1 Norman J Field Way 07724 732-542-1170
Dr. Andrew Teeple, supt. Fax 542-5815
www.monmouthregional.net
Monmouth Regional HS 1,000/9-12
1 Norman J Field Way 07724 732-542-1170
Corey Radisch, prin. Fax 542-5815

Monmouth-Ocean Ed. Serv. Comm. SD 50/6-12
900 Hope Rd, 732-695-7800
Christopher Rooney, supt.
www.moesc.org
Regional Alternative S 50/Alt
100 Tornillo Way Ste 1, 732-389-5555
Kimberly Brucale, prin. Fax 542-0302

Tinton Falls SD 1,300/K-8
658 Tinton Ave 07724 732-460-2400
John Russo, supt. Fax 542-1158
www.tfs.k12.nj.us
Tinton Falls MS 500/6-8
674 Tinton Ave 07724 732-542-0775
Mary Ehid, prin. Fax 542-8723

Ranney S 800/PK-12
235 Hope Rd 07724 732-542-4777
Dr. John Griffith, head sch Fax 544-1629
Trinity Hall 50/9-12
101 Corregidor Rd 07724 732-291-1297
Mary Sciarrillo, head sch Fax 291-2623

Toms River, Ocean, Pop. 87,576
Ocean County Vocational SD
137 Bey Lea Rd 08753 732-240-6414
William Hoey, supt. Fax 505-8929
www.ocvts.org
Ocean County Voc-Tech S - Toms River Vo/Tech
1299 Old Freehold Rd 08753 732-473-3100
Jo-Ann Price, prin. Fax 349-9788
Other Schools – See Brick, Jackson, Lakehurst, Little Egg Harbor Township, Manahawkin, Waretown

Toms River Regional SD 15,300/PK-12
1144 Hooper Ave 08753 732-505-5510
David Healy, supt. Fax 505-9330
www.trschools.com
Toms River HS - East 1,500/9-12
1225 Raider Way 08753 732-505-5666
Patrick Thomas, prin. Fax 270-0909
Toms River HS - North 2,300/9-12
1245 Old Freehold Rd 08753 732-505-5702
James Ricotta, prin. Fax 341-6249
Toms River HS - South 1,400/9-12
55 Hyers St 08753 732-505-5738
Leonard Stanziano, prin. Fax 341-1321
Toms River IS East 1,400/6-8
1519 Hooper Ave 08753 732-505-5777
Bryan Madigan, prin. Fax 286-1290
Toms River IS North 1,200/6-8
150 Intermediate North Way 08753 732-505-5800
Lynn Fronzak, prin. Fax 286-1291
Other Schools – See Beachwood

American Institution Post-Sec.
2363 Lakewood Rd 08755 973-340-9500
Donovan Catholic HS 1,000/9-12
711 Hooper Ave 08753 732-349-8801
Dr. Edward Gere, prin. Fax 349-8956
Ocean County College Post-Sec.
PO Box 2001 08754 732-255-0400

Totowa, Passaic, Pop. 10,662
Totowa SD 1,000/PK-8
10 Crews St 07512 973-956-0010
Patricia Capitelli, supt. Fax 956-9859
www.totowa.k12.nj.us
Washington Park MS 600/3-8
10 Crews St 07512 973-956-0010
Michael O'Brien, prin. Fax 389-2270

Trenton, Mercer, Pop. 83,491
Mercer County Technical SD
1085 Old Trenton Rd 08690 609-586-2129
Dr. Kimberly J. Schneider, supt. Fax 586-8966
www.mcts.edu
Assunpink Center Vo/Tech
1085 Old Trenton Rd 08690 609-586-5144
Sharon Nemeth, prin. Fax 586-1709
Health Careers Center Vo/Tech
1070 Klockner Rd 08619 609-587-7640
Sharon Nemeth, prin. Fax 587-3304
Adult Evening S Adult
1085 Old Trenton Rd 08690 609-586-5146
Mary Smith-Jones, prin. Fax 586-1709
Other Schools – See Pennington

Trenton SD 9,300/PK-12
108 N Clinton Ave 08609 609-656-4900
Lucy Feria, supt. Fax 989-2682
www.trenton.k12.nj.us
Dunn MS 800/6-8
401 Dayton St 08611 609-656-4700
Madeline Roman, prin. Fax 989-1478
Hedgepeth-Williams MS 400/6-8
301 Gladstone Ave 08629 609-656-4760
Adrienne Hill, prin. Fax 989-2544
Kilmer MS 400/6-8
1300 Stuyvesant Ave 08618 609-656-4800
Paula Bethea, prin. Fax 989-2927
Munoz-Rivera MS 500/6-8
400 N Montgomery St 08618 609-656-4840
Bernadette Trapp, prin. Fax 656-2149
Trenton Central HS - Chambers 1,800/9-12
544 Chestnut Ave 08611 609-278-7260
Hope Grant, prin. Fax 989-2940
Trenton Central HS - West 700/9-12
1001 W State St 08618 609-656-4770
Mark Hoppe, prin. Fax 989-2925
Daylight/Twilight HS Adult
501 Edgewood Ave 08618 609-656-4850
Ronald Edwards, prin. Fax 777-9490

Harris School of Business Post-Sec.
3620 Quakerbridge Rd 08619 609-586-9104
Helene Fuld Medical Center Post-Sec.
750 Brunswick Ave 08638 609-394-3174
Marie Katzenbach School for the Deaf Post-Sec.
PO Box 535 08625 609-530-3100
Mercer Medical Center Post-Sec.
PO Box 1658 08607 609-394-4050
St. Francis Medical Center Post-Sec.
601 Hamilton Ave 08629 609-599-5000
Thomas Edison State College Post-Sec.
101 W State St 08608 609-984-1100

Union, Union, Pop. 55,000
Township of Union SD 7,300/PK-12
2369 Morris Ave 07083 908-851-3000
Gregory Tatum, supt. Fax 851-9688
www.twpunionschools.org
Burnet MS 1,000/6-8
1000 Caldwell Ave 07083 908-851-6490
Raymond Salvatore, prin. Fax 687-2645
Kawameeh MS 600/6-8
490 David Ter 07083 908-851-6570
Jason Malanda, prin. Fax 687-5741
Union HS 2,300/9-12
2350 N 3rd St 07083 908-851-6500
Corey Lowery, prin. Fax 687-5204

European Academy of Cosmetology — Post-Sec.
1126 Morris Ave 07083 — 908-686-4422
Healthcare Training Institute — Post-Sec.
1969 Morris Ave 07083 — 908-851-7711
Kean University — Post-Sec.
1000 Morris Ave 07083 — 908-737-5326
Lincoln Technical Institute — Post-Sec.
2299 Vauxhall Rd 07083 — 908-964-7800

Union City, Hudson, Pop. 65,896
Union City SD — 10,700/PK-12
3912 32nd St 07087 — 201-348-5851
Silvia Abbato, supt. — Fax 330-1736
www.ucboe.us
Emerson MS — 900/6-8
318 18th St 07087 — 201-348-5900
Mike Cirone, prin. — Fax 864-2262
Marti Freshman Academy — 600/9-9
1800 Summit Ave 07087 — 201-348-5400
Rudy Baez, prin. — Fax 348-5405
Union City HS — 2,300/10-12
2500 Kennedy Blvd 07087 — 201-330-8678
Ryan Lewis, prin. — Fax 330-8736
Union Hill MS — 700/7-8
3808 Hudson Ave 07087 — 201-348-5808
Victoria Dickson, prin. — Fax 867-4205
Adult Learning Center — Adult
400 38th St 07087 — 201-348-5658
Rolando Cabana, admin. — Fax 348-5659

Learning Institute of Union City - Boys — 300/K-12
3400 New York Ave 07087 — 201-867-9107
Miftaahul Uloom Academy — 200/PK-12
501 15th St 07087 — 201-223-9920
Rising Star Academy — 100/PK-12
4613 Cottage Pl 07087 — 201-758-5590
Dr. Hala Shehadeh, prin. — Fax 758-5589

Upper Montclair, Essex, Pop. 11,116
Montclair SD
Supt. — See Montclair
Aldrin MS — 600/6-8
173 Bellevue Ave 07043 — 973-509-4220
Dr. Jill Sack, prin. — Fax 509-4218

Upper Saddle River, Bergen, Pop. 8,104
Upper Saddle River SD — 1,300/PK-8
395 W Saddle River Rd 07458 — 201-961-6500
Dr. Monica Browne, supt. — Fax 934-4923
www.usrschoolsk8.com
Cavallini MS — 500/6-8
392 W Saddle River Rd 07458 — 201-961-6400
James McCusker, prin. — Fax 236-9662

Ventnor City, Atlantic, Pop. 10,474
Ventnor City SD — 800/PK-8
400 N Lafayette Ave 08406 — 609-487-7900
Eileen Johnson, supt. — Fax 822-0150
www.veccnj.org/
Ventnor MS — 400/5-8
400 N Lafayette Ave 08406 — 609-487-7900
Robert Baker, prin. — Fax 823-4036

Vernon, Sussex
Vernon Township SD — 3,500/PK-12
PO Box 99 07462 — 973-764-2900
Arthur DiBenedetto, supt. — Fax 764-0033
www.vtsd.com
Glen Meadow MS — 600/7-8
PO Box 516 07462 — 973-764-8981
Dr. Pauline Anderson, prin. — Fax 764-3295
Vernon Township HS — 1,100/9-12
PO Box 800 07462 — 973-764-2960
Timothy Dunnigan, prin. — Fax 764-2961

Verona, Essex, Pop. 13,597
Verona SD — 2,100/K-12
121 Fairview Ave 07044 — 973-571-2029
Rui Dionisio, supt. — Fax 571-6779
www.veronaschools.org
Verona HS — 600/9-12
151 Fairview Ave 07044 — 973-571-6750
Josh Cogdill, prin. — Fax 571-6765
Whitehorne MS — 700/5-8
600 Bloomfield Ave 07044 — 973-571-6751
Yvette McNeal, prin. — Fax 571-6767

Vineland, Cumberland, Pop. 59,740
Cumberland County Technical SD
3400 College Dr 08360 — 856-451-9000
Dr. Dina Rossi Elliott, supt. — Fax 453-1118
www.cumberland.tec.nj.us
Cumberland Co. Technical Education Ctr — Vo/Tech
3400 College Dr 08360 — 856-451-9000
Greg McGraw, prin. — Fax 453-1118

Vineland CSD — 9,400/PK-12
625 E Plum St 08360 — 856-794-6700
Dr. Mary Gruccio, supt. — Fax 794-9464
www.vineland.org
Landis MS — 500/6-8
61 W Landis Ave 08360 — 856-794-6925
Melanie Beck, prin. — Fax 507-8763
Rossi MS — 500/6-8
2572 Palermo Ave 08361 — 856-794-6961
Tammy Monahan, prin. — Fax 507-8786
Veterans Memorial MS — 500/6-8
424 S Main Rd 08360 — 856-794-6918
Hope Johnson, prin. — Fax 507-8759
Vineland HS North — 1,400/9-10
3010 E Chestnut Ave 08361 — 856-794-6800
Dr. Thomas McCann, prin. — Fax 507-8781
Vineland HS South — 1,200/11-12
2880 E Chestnut Ave 08361 — 856-794-6800
Dr. Thomas McCann, prin. — Fax 507-8751
Wallace MS — 500/6-8
688 N Mill Rd 08360 — 856-362-8887
Dr. Juanita Davis, prin. — Fax 362-8980

Achieve Test Prep — Post-Sec.
313 W Landis Ave 08360 — 856-457-3881
Cumberland Christian S — 400/PK-12
1100 W Sherman Ave 08360 — 856-696-1600
Ken Howard, hdmstr. — Fax 696-0631
Cumberland County College — Post-Sec.
PO Box 1500 08362 — 856-691-8600

Voorhees, Camden, Pop. 946
Eastern Camden County Regional HSD — 2,000/9-12
PO Box 2500 08043 — 856-784-4441
Dr. Harold Melleby, supt. — Fax 627-7894
www.eccrsd.us
Eastern HS — 2,000/9-12
PO Box 2500 08043 — 856-784-4441
Robert Tull, prin. — Fax 784-1322

Voorhees Township SD — 2,900/PK-8
329 Route 73 08043 — 856-751-8446
Raymond Brosel, supt. — Fax 751-3666
www.voorhees.k12.nj.us/
Voorhees MS — 1,100/6-8
1000 Holly Oak Dr 08043 — 856-795-2025
Kristine Calabria, prin. — Fax 795-4611

Harris School of Business — Post-Sec.
401 White Horse Rd Ste 200 08043 — 856-309-3701
Rizzieri Aveda School — Post-Sec.
8200 Town Center Blvd 08043 — 856-988-8600
Trinity Preparatory S — 100/K-12
1801 S Burnt Mill Rd 08043 — 856-282-3800
Matt Williams, hdmstr.

Waldwick, Bergen, Pop. 9,513
Waldwick SD — 1,500/PK-12
155 Summit Ave 07463 — 201-445-3131
Dr. Paul Casarico, supt. — Fax 445-0584
www.waldwickschools.org
Waldwick HS — 500/9-12
155 Wyckoff Ave 07463 — 201-652-9000
Kevin Carroll, prin. — Fax 652-5053
Waldwick MS — 400/6-8
155 Wyckoff Ave 07463 — 201-652-9000
Michael Meyers, prin. — Fax 652-5053

Waldwick SDA S — 100/PK-12
70 Wyckoff Ave 07463 — 201-652-6078

Wall, Monmouth, Pop. 5,201
Monmouth County Vocational SD
Supt. — See Freehold
Communications HS of Monmouth Co. — Vo/Tech
1740 New Bedford Rd 07719 — 732-681-1010
James Gleason, prin. — Fax 681-6780

Wall Township SD — 3,700/PK-12
1620 18th Ave 07719 — 732-556-2000
Cheryl Dyer, supt. — Fax 556-2101
www.wall.k12.nj.us
Wall HS — 1,200/9-12
1630 18th Ave 07719 — 732-556-2000
Rosaleen Sirchio, prin. — Fax 556-2104
Wall IS — 900/6-8
2801 Allaire Rd 07719 — 732-556-2500
Erin Embon, prin. — Fax 556-2535

Cortiva Institute - Wall — Post-Sec.
1985 State Route 34 07719 — 732-282-0100

Wallington, Bergen, Pop. 11,200
Wallington SD — 1,100/K-12
32 Pine St 07057 — 973-777-4421
James Albro, supt. — Fax 614-9391
www.wboe.org
Wallington JSHS — 500/7-12
234 Main Ave 07057 — 973-777-0808
Fred Fromfield, prin. — Fax 777-1434

Wanaque, Passaic, Pop. 10,935
Lakeland Regional HSD — 1,000/9-12
205 Conklintown Rd 07465 — 973-835-1900
Hugh Beattie, supt. — Fax 835-2834
www.lakeland.k12.nj.us
Lakeland Regional HS — 1,000/9-12
205 Conklintown Rd 07465 — 973-835-1900
Dr. Matthew Certo, prin. — Fax 835-6369

Waretown, Ocean, Pop. 1,552
Ocean County Vocational SD
Supt. — See Toms River
Ocean County Voc-Tech S - Waretown — Vo/Tech
423 Wells Mill Rd 08758 — 609-286-5660
Thomas McInerney, prin. — Fax 693-1514

Warren, Somerset
Warren Township SD — 1,900/K-8
213 Mount Horeb Rd 07059 — 732-753-5300
Dr. Matthew Mingle, supt. — Fax 560-8801
www.warrentboe.org
Warren MS — 700/6-8
100 Old Stirling Rd 07059 — 908-753-5300
Robert Comba, prin. — Fax 753-4789

Watchung Hills Regional SD — 2,200/9-12
108 Stirling Rd 07059 — 908-647-4800
Elizabeth Jewett, supt. — Fax 647-4852
www.whrhs.org
Watchung Hills Regional HS — 2,200/9-12
108 Stirling Rd 07059 — 908-647-4800
Dr. George Alexis, prin. — Fax 647-4852

Washington, Warren, Pop. 6,336
Warren County Technical SD
1500 State Route 57 W 07882 — 908-689-0122
Robert F. Glowacky, supt. — Fax 689-9598
www.wctech.org
Warren County Technical S — Vo/Tech
1500 State Route 57 W 07882 — 908-689-0122
Robert F. Glowacky, admin. — Fax 689-7699

Warren Hills Regional HSD — 1,800/7-12
89 Bowerstown Rd 07882 — 908-689-3143
Dr. Gary Bowen, supt. — Fax 689-4814
www.warrenhills.org
Warren Hills Regional HS — 1,200/9-12
41 Jackson Valley Rd 07882 — 908-689-3050
Dennis Mack, prin. — Fax 689-9640
Warren Hills Regional MS — 600/7-8
64 Carlton Ave 07882 — 908-689-0750
Patricia Hetrick, prin. — Fax 689-3663

Good Shepherd Christian Academy — 200/PK-12
490 State Route 57 W 07882 — 908-835-1399
Cindy Weaver, admin. — Fax 835-1398
Warren County Community College — Post-Sec.
475 State Route 57 W 07882 — 908-835-9222

Washington Township, Bergen, Pop. 9,245
Westwood Regional SD — 2,600/K-12
701 Ridgewood Rd 07676 — 201-664-0880
Dr. Raymond Gonzalez, supt. — Fax 664-7642
www.wwrsd.org
Westwood Regional JSHS — 1,000/8-12
701 Ridgewood Rd 07676 — 201-664-0880
Frank Connelly, prin. — Fax 722-1542

Immaculate Heart Academy — 800/9-12
500 Van Emburgh Ave 07676 — 201-445-6800
Patricia Molloy, pres. — Fax 445-7416

Watchung, Somerset, Pop. 5,662
Watchung Borough SD — 700/PK-8
1 Dr Parenty Way 07069 — 908-755-8121
Dr. Barbara Resko, supt. — Fax 755-6946
www.watchungschools.com
Valley View MS — 300/5-8
50 Valleyview Rd 07069 — 908-755-4422
Mary Nunn, prin. — Fax 755-4035

Mt. St. Mary Academy — 400/9-12
1645 US Highway 22 07069 — 908-757-0108
Sr. Lisa Gambacorto, dir. — Fax 756-5751

Wayne, Passaic, Pop. 55,000
Passaic Co. Education Services Comm. — 100/9-12
45 Reinhardt Rd 07470 — 973-614-8585
Diana Lobosco, supt. — Fax 614-1334
www.pcesc.org
Other Schools – See Passaic

Passaic County Technical Inst SD
45 Reinhardt Rd 07470 — 973-790-6000
Diana Lobosco, supt.
www.pcti.tec.nj.us
Passaic County Technical Institute — Vo/Tech
45 Reinhardt Rd 07470 — 973-389-4259
Dr. Michael Parent, prin. — Fax 389-2049
Passaic County Adult HS — Adult
45 Reinhardt Rd 07470 — 973-389-4101
John DePalma, admin.

Wayne Township SD — 8,100/PK-12
50 Nellis Dr 07470 — 973-633-3000
Dr. Mark Toback, supt. — Fax 628-8058
www.wayneschools.com
Schuyler-Colfax MS — 700/6-8
1500 Hamburg Tpke 07470 — 973-633-3130
Aimee Toth, prin. — Fax 633-3195
Washington MS — 600/6-8
68 Lenox Rd 07470 — 973-633-3140
Jack Leonard, prin. — Fax 633-7590
Wayne Hills HS — 1,400/9-12
272 Berdan Ave 07470 — 973-317-2000
Maureen Weir, prin. — Fax 633-2589
Wayne MS — 700/6-8
201 Garside Ave 07470 — 973-389-2120
David Aulenbach, prin. — Fax 389-2130
Wayne Valley HS — 1,400/9-12
551 Valley Rd 07470 — 973-633-3067
Kenneth Palczewski, prin. — Fax 633-3082

Achieve Test Prep — Post-Sec.
40 Galesi Dr 07470 — 973-321-3217
De Paul Catholic HS — 900/9-12
1512 Alps Rd 07470 — 973-694-3702
Fr. Peter Clarke, prin. — Fax 633-5381
Fortis Institute — Post-Sec.
201 Willowbrook Blvd 07470 — 973-837-1818
Pioneer Academy — 300/K-12
164 Totowa Rd 07470 — 973-405-5169
William Paterson University — Post-Sec.
300 Pompton Rd 07470 — 973-720-2000

Weehawken, Hudson, Pop. 12,385
Weehawken Township SD — 1,300/PK-12
53 Liberty Pl 07086 — 201-422-6120
Dr. Robert Zywicki, supt.
www.weehawken.k12.nj.us
Weehawken JSHS — 500/7-12
53 Liberty Pl 07086 — 201-422-6130
Dr. Steven Spinosa, prin.

Westampton, Burlington, Pop. 60,004
Westampton Township SD — 1,000/PK-8
700 Rancocas Rd 08060 — 609-267-2053
Virginia Grossman, supt. — Fax 267-2760
www.westamptonschools.org
Westampton MS — 500/PK-PK, 5-
700 Rancocas Rd 08060 — 609-267-2722
Matthew Andris, prin. — Fax 702-9017

West Berlin, Camden, Pop. 3,000
Berlin Township SD — 600/PK-8
225 Grove Ave 08091 — 856-767-9480
Dr. Edythe Austermuhl Ed.D., supt. — Fax 767-8235
www.btwpschools.org
Eisenhower MS — 300/4-8
235 Grove Ave 08091 — 856-767-9480
Marilyn Bright, prin. — Fax 767-7992

West Caldwell, Essex, Pop. 10,422
Caldwell-West Caldwell SD 2,600/K-12
104 Gray St 07006 973-228-6979
Dr. James Heinegg, supt. Fax 228-8716
www.cwcboe.org/
Caldwell HS 800/9-12
265 Westville Ave 07006 973-228-6981
James Devlin, prin. Fax 228-1116
Other Schools – See Caldwell

Essex County Vocational Technical SD
Supt. — See Newark
Essex Co. Vocational Tech - W Caldwell Vo/Tech
620 Passaic Ave 07006 973-412-2205
Ayisha Ingram-Robinson, prin. Fax 412-2090

Essex County College Post-Sec.
730 Bloomfield Ave 07006 973-877-6590

West Deptford, Gloucester, Pop. 19,380
West Deptford Township SD 2,800/PK-12
675 Grove Rd 08066 856-848-4300
Robert Suessmuth, supt. Fax 845-5743
www.wdeptford.k12.nj.us/
West Deptford HS 900/9-12
1600 Crown Point Rd, 856-848-6110
Dr. Brian Gismondi, prin. Fax 845-5774
West Deptford MS 900/5-8
675 Grove Rd 08066 856-848-1200
Christine Trampe, prin. Fax 848-2325

Westfield, Union, Pop. 29,789
Union Co. Educational Services Comm SD 200/9-12
45 Cardinal Dr 07090 908-233-9317
Terry Foppert, supt. Fax 233-7432
www.ucesc.org/
Hillcrest Academy South Campus 100/Alt
1571 Lamberts Mill Rd 07090 908-654-8558
Dr. Jason Balsamello, prin. Fax 233-2954
Other Schools – See Scotch Plains

Westfield SD 6,100/PK-12
302 Elm St 07090 908-789-4400
Dr. Margaret Dolan, supt. Fax 789-4192
www.westfieldnjk12.org
Edison IS 800/6-8
800 Rahway Ave 07090 908-789-4470
Matthew Bolton, prin. Fax 789-1506
Roosevelt IS 700/6-8
301 Clark St 07090 908-789-4560
Stewart Carey, prin. Fax 789-4193
Westfield HS 1,800/9-12
550 Dorian Rd 07090 908-789-4500
Peter Renwick, prin. Fax 789-4230

West Long Branch, Monmouth, Pop. 8,009
Shore Regional HSD 600/9-12
132 State Route 36 07764 732-222-9300
Thomas Farrell, supt. Fax 222-8849
www.shoreregional.org
Shore Regional HS 600/9-12
132 State Route 36 07764 732-222-9300
Vincent DalliCardillo, prin. Fax 222-8849

West Long Branch SD 500/PK-8
135 Locust Ave 07764 732-222-5900
Thomas Farrell, supt. Fax 222-9325
www.wlbschools.com
Antonides S 300/5-8
135 Locust Ave 07764 732-222-5900
Dr. Michael Fiorillo, prin. Fax 222-8154

Monmouth University Post-Sec.
400 Cedar Ave 07764 732-571-3400

West Milford, Passaic, Pop. 26,600
West Milford Township SD 3,500/PK-12
46 Highlander Dr 07480 973-697-1700
Dr. Alex Anemone, supt. Fax 697-8351
www.wmtps.org
Macopin MS 600/7-8
70 Highlander Dr 07480 973-697-5691
Mary Reinhold, prin. Fax 697-0301
West Milford HS 1,200/9-12
67 Highlander Dr 07480 973-697-1701
Paul Gorski, prin. Fax 208-0912

Westmont, Camden, Pop. 5,500
Haddon Township SD 1,700/PK-12
500 Rhoads Ave 08108 856-869-7700
Bonnie J. Edwards, supt. Fax 854-7792
www.haddontwpschools.com/
Haddon Township HS 500/9-12
406 Memorial Ave 08108 856-869-7750
Gary O'Brien, prin. Fax 869-7764
Rohrer MS 400/6-8
101 MacArthur Blvd 08108 856-869-7750
Dr. Patricia Schwab, prin. Fax 869-7772

West New York, Hudson, Pop. 49,199
West New York SD 8,000/PK-12
6028 Broadway 07093 201-553-4000
Clara Brito Herrera, supt. Fax 865-2725
www.wnyschools.net
Memorial HS 1,800/9-12
5501 Park Ave 07093 201-553-4110
Scott Wohlrab, prin. Fax 864-2151
West New York MS 900/7-8
201 57th St 07093 201-563-4160
Patrick Gagliardi, prin. Fax 863-6698

Robert Fiance Beauty School Post-Sec.
5518 Bergenline Ave 07093 201-866-4000

West Orange, Essex, Pop. 45,500
West Orange SD 6,500/PK-12
179 Eagle Rock Ave 07052 973-669-5400
Jeffrey Rutzky, supt. Fax 669-1432
www.woboe.org
Liberty MS 500/7-8
1 Kelly Dr 07052 973-243-2007
Robert Klemt, prin. Fax 243-2743
Roosevelt MS 500/7-8
36 Gilbert Pl 07052 973-669-5373
Lionel Hush, prin. Fax 243-9807
West Orange HS 2,000/9-12
51 Conforti Ave 07052 973-669-5301
Hayden Moore, prin. Fax 669-1260

Golda Och Academy - Upper S 300/6-12
1418 Pleasant Valley Way 07052 973-602-3600
Adam Shapiro, head sch Fax 669-0034
Seton Hall Preparatory HS 1,000/9-12
120 Northfield Ave 07052 973-325-6624
Rev. Michael Kelly, pres. Fax 325-6652

Westville, Gloucester, Pop. 4,234

St. John of God Community Services Post-Sec.
1145 Delsea Dr 08093 856-848-4700

West Windsor, Mercer
West Windsor-Plainsboro Regional SD 9,300/PK-12
PO Box 505 08550 609-716-5000
David Aderhold Ed.D., supt. Fax 716-5012
www.ww-p.org
West Windsor-Plainsboro HS South 1,600/9-12
346 Clarksville Rd 08550 609-716-5050
Dennis Lepold, prin. Fax 716-5092
Other Schools – See Plainsboro, Princeton Junction

Mercer County Community College Post-Sec.
1200 Old Trenton Rd 08550 609-586-4800
Mercer County Community College Post-Sec.
1200 Old Trenton Rd 08550 609-586-4800

Wharton, Morris, Pop. 6,390
Wharton Borough SD 700/K-8
137 E Central Ave 07885 973-361-2592
Christopher Herdman, supt. Fax 895-2187
www.wbps.org/
MacKinnon MS 300/6-8
137 E Central Ave 07885 973-361-1253
Patrick Ketch, prin. Fax 361-4805

Whippany, Morris
Hanover Park Regional HSD
Supt. — See East Hanover
Whippany Park HS 700/9-12
165 Whippany Rd 07981 973-887-3004
Christopher Kelly, prin. Fax 887-0451

Hanover Township SD 1,500/K-8
61 Highland Ave 07981 973-515-2404
Michael Wasko, supt. Fax 540-1023
www.hanovertwpschools.com/
Memorial JHS 500/6-8
61 Highland Ave 07981 973-515-2427
Michael Wasko, prin. Fax 515-2481

Abundant Life Christian S 100/PK-12
43 S Jefferson Rd 07981 973-888-2083
Yolanda Garris, prin. Fax 463-9677

White House Station, Hunterdon, Pop. 2,066
Readington Township SD 1,800/PK-8
PO Box 807 08889 908-534-2195
Dr. Barbara Sargent, supt. Fax 349-3042
www.readington.k12.nj.us
Readington MS 700/6-8
PO Box 700 08889 908-534-2113
Sharon Moffat, prin. Fax 534-6802

Whiting, Ocean
Manchester Township SD 2,900/K-12
121 Route 539 08759 732-350-5900
David Trethaway, supt. Fax 350-0436
www.manchestertwp.org
Other Schools – See Manchester

Wildwood, Cape May, Pop. 5,246
Wildwood CSD 800/PK-12
4300 Pacific Ave 08260 609-522-7922
J. Kenyon Kummings, supt. Fax 523-1014
www.edline.net/pages/Wildwood_PSD
Wildwood HS 200/9-12
4300 Pacific Ave 08260 609-522-7922
Philip Schaffer, prin. Fax 522-7914
Wildwood MS 200/6-8
4300 Pacific Ave 08260 609-522-7922
Philip Schaffer, prin. Fax 522-7914

Wildwood Catholic HS 200/9-12
1500 Central Ave 08260 609-522-7257
Rev. Joseph Wallace, pres. Fax 522-2453

Williamstown, Gloucester, Pop. 15,255
Monroe Township SD 5,800/PK-12
75 E Academy St 08094 856-629-6400
Charles Earling, supt. Fax 262-2499
www.monroetwp.k12.nj.us
Williamstown HS 1,800/9-12
700 N Tuckahoe Rd 08094 856-262-8200
Dr. Jill DelConte, prin. Fax 262-0869
Williamstown MS 1,900/5-8
561 Clayton Rd 08094 856-629-7444
Dana Mericle, prin. Fax 875-6757

Willingboro, Burlington, Pop. 32,400
Willingboro Township SD 3,600/PK-12
440 Beverly Rancocas Rd 08046 609-835-8600
Dr. Ronald G. Taylor, supt. Fax 835-3880
www.willingboroschools.org/
Memorial MS 700/6-8
451 Van Sciver Pkwy 08046 609-835-8700
Ellis Brown, prin. Fax 835-1457
Willingboro Alternative Education Alt
56 Brooklawn Dr 08046 609-835-8950
Alicia Turner-Biddle, prin.
Willingboro HS 700/9-12
20 S John F Kennedy Way 08046 609-835-8800
Kimberly Ash, prin. Fax 835-8877

Strayer University Post-Sec.
300 Willingboro Way # 125 08046 609-835-6000

Woodbridge, Middlesex, Pop. 18,933
Middlesex County Vocational SD
Supt. — See East Brunswick
Acad for Allied Health & Biomed Science Vo/Tech
1 Convery Blvd 07095 732-634-5858
Michael Fanelli, prin. Fax 632-7073

Woodbridge Township SD 12,800/PK-12
PO Box 428 07095 732-750-3200
Dr. Robert Zega, supt. Fax 750-3493
www.woodbridge.k12.nj.us
Woodbridge HS 1,400/9-12
25 Samuel Lupo Pl 07095 732-602-8600
Glenn Lottmann, prin. Fax 602-8612
Woodbridge MS 400/6-8
525 Barron Ave 07095 732-602-8690
Dr. John Crowe, prin. Fax 855-0326
Other Schools – See Avenel, Colonia, Fords, Iselin

Achieve Test Prep Post-Sec.
1480 US Highway 9 N 07095 732-750-2321
Berkeley College Post-Sec.
430 Rahway Ave 07095 732-750-1800

Woodbury, Gloucester, Pop. 9,869
Woodbury SD 1,400/PK-12
25 N Broad St 08096 856-853-0123
Robert Goldschmidt, supt. Fax 853-0704
www.woodburysch.com
Woodbury JSHS 700/6-12
25 N Broad St 08096 856-853-0123
Jason Vivadelli, prin. Fax 853-2684

Woodbury Heights, Gloucester, Pop. 3,021
Gateway Regional SD 900/7-12
775 Tanyard Rd, 856-848-8172
Shannon Whalen Ed.D., supt. Fax 848-2049
www.gatewayhs.com
Gateway Regional MSHS 900/7-12
775 Tanyard Rd, 856-848-8200
Jeff Pierro, prin. Fax 251-9813

Woodcliff Lake, Bergen, Pop. 5,674
Woodcliff Lake SD 800/PK-8
134 Woodcliff Ave 07677 201-930-5600
Lauren Barbelet, supt. Fax 930-0488
www.woodcliff-lake.com
Woodcliff MS 300/6-8
134 Woodcliff Ave 07677 201-930-5600
Robert Lombardy, prin. Fax 391-7932

Woodland Park, Passaic
Woodland Park SD 1,000/K-8
853 McBride Ave, 973-317-7700
Dr. Michele R. Pillari, supt. Fax 317-7773
wpschools.org
Memorial MS 500/5-8
15 Memorial Dr, 973-317-7750
Charles Silverstein, prin. Fax 317-7753

Berkeley College Post-Sec.
44 Rifle Camp Rd, 973-278-5400

Wood Ridge, Bergen, Pop. 7,540
Wood-Ridge SD 800/PK-12
540 Windsor Rd 07075 201-933-6777
Nicholas Cipriano, supt. Fax 804-9204
www.wood-ridgeschools.org
Wood-Ridge JSHS 400/7-12
258 Hackensack St 07075 201-933-6777
Russell Petrocelli, prin. Fax 939-1195

Woodstown, Salem, Pop. 3,420
Salem County Special Services SD 100/6-12
PO Box 126 08098 856-769-0101
John Swain, supt. Fax 769-3202
www.scsssd.org/
Other Schools – See Carneys Point

Woodstown-Pilesgrove Regional SD 1,500/PK-12
135 East Ave 08098 856-769-0144
Thomas Coleman, supt. Fax 769-4549
www.woodstown.org
Woodstown HS 700/9-12
140 East Ave 08098 856-769-0144
Dr. Scott Hoopes, prin. Fax 769-4102
Woodstown MS 300/6-8
15 Lincoln Ave 08098 856-769-0144
Allison Pessolano, prin. Fax 769-3872

Woolwich, Gloucester
Kingsway Regional SD 2,400/7-12
213 Kings Hwy 08085 856-467-3300
Dr. James Lavender, supt. Fax 467-5382
www.krsd.org
Kingsway Regional HS 1,600/9-12
201 Kings Hwy 08085 856-467-3300
Craig Stephenson, prin. Fax 241-1932
Kingsway Regional MS 900/7-8
203 Kings Hwy 08085 856-467-3300
Brian Tonelli, prin. Fax 467-2703

Wyckoff, Bergen, Pop. 15,372
Wyckoff Township SD 2,100/PK-8
241 Morse Ave 07481 201-848-5700
Richard Kuder, supt. Fax 848-5695
www.wyckoffps.org/
Eisenhower MS 800/6-8
344 Calvin Ct 07481 201-848-5750
Christopher Iasiello, prin. Fax 848-5682

Eastern Christian MS 200/5-8
518 Sicomac Ave 07481 201-891-3663
Daniel Lazor, prin.

NEW MEXICO

NEW MEXICO PUBLIC EDUCATION DEPARTMENT
300 Don Gaspar Ave, Santa Fe 87501-2744
Telephone 505-827-5800
Fax 505-827-6696
Website http://www.sde.state.nm.us

Secretary of Education Hanna Skandara

NEW MEXICO PUBLIC EDUCATION COMMISSION
300 Don Gaspar Ave, Santa Fe 87501-2744

Chairperson Patricia Gipson

REGIONAL EDUCATION COOPS (REC) & REGIONAL CENTER COOPS (RCC)

Central REC 5
Maria Jaramillo, dir. 505-889-3412
PO Box 37440, Albuquerque 87176 Fax 889-3422
www.crecnm.org
High Plains REC 3
R. Stephen Aguirre, dir. 575-445-7090
101 N 2nd St, Raton 87740 Fax 445-7663
hprec.com
Northeast REC 4
Dr. Jim Abreu, dir. 505-426-2262
PO Box 927, Las Vegas 87701 Fax 454-1473
www.rec4.com
Northwest REC 2
Adan Delgado, dir. 575-756-1274
PO Box 113, Chama 87520 Fax 756-1278
www.nwrec2.org
Pecos Valley REC 8
David Willden, dir. 575-748-6100
PO Box 155, Artesia 88211 Fax 748-6160
www.pvrec8.com
REC 6
Scott McMath, dir. 575-562-4455
1500 S Avenue K, Portales 88130 Fax 562-4460
www.rec6.net
REC 7
Belinda Morris, dir. 575-393-0755
315 E Clinton St, Hobbs 88240 Fax 393-0249
hobbsschools.net/department/regional_education_cooperative_7
REC 9
Sean Wootton, dir. 575-257-2368
143 El Paso Rd, Ruidoso 88345 Fax 257-2141
www.rec9nm.org
Southwest REC 10
Vicki Chavez, dir. 575-546-5951
310 W Elm St, Deming 88030 Fax 546-5994
www.swrecnm.org

PUBLIC, PRIVATE AND CATHOLIC SECONDARY SCHOOLS

Alamogordo, Otero, Pop. 29,463
Alamogordo SD 6,000/PK-12
PO Box 650 88311 575-812-6000
Adrianne Salas, supt. Fax 812-6003
www.aps4kids.org
Academy Del Sol 200/10-12
PO Box 650 88311 575-812-5500
Johnnie Walker, prin. Fax 812-5503
Alamogordo HS 1,400/9-12
PO Box 650 88311 575-812-6500
George Heaton, prin. Fax 812-6503
Chaparral MS 700/6-8
PO Box 650 88311 575-812-6300
Robbi Coker, prin. Fax 812-6303
Mountain View MS 400/6-8
PO Box 650 88311 575-812-6400
Moises Cardiel, prin. Fax 812-6403
Other Schools – See Holloman AFB

Imago Dei Academy 100/K-12
1100 Michigan Ave 88310 575-434-3903
Laura King, prin.
Legacy Christian Academy 100/PK-12
3001 Thunder Rd 88310 575-434-0352
Cindy McKee, dir. Fax 434-0352
New Mexico School Visually Handicapped Post-Sec.
1900 N White Sands Blvd 88310 575-437-3505
New Mexico State University Post-Sec.
2400 Scenic Dr 88310 575-439-3600
Olympian University of Cosmetology Post-Sec.
1810 10th St 88310 575-437-2221

Albuquerque, Bernalillo, Pop. 534,167
Albuquerque SD 90,500/PK-12
PO Box 25704 87125 505-880-3700
Raquel Reedy, supt. Fax 872-8855
www.aps.edu
Adams MS 700/6-8
5401 Glenrio Rd NW 87105 505-831-0400
Modesta Hernandez, prin. Fax 836-7760
Albuquerque HS 1,700/9-12
800 Odelia Rd NE 87102 505-843-6400
Tim McCorkle, prin. Fax 848-9432
Atrisco Heritage Academy 2,400/9-12
10800 Dennis Chavez Blvd SW 87121 505-243-1458
Irene Cisneros, prin. Fax 873-1041
Career Enrichment Ctr Vo/Tech
807 Mountain Rd NE 87102 505-247-3658
Patrick Arguelles, prin. Fax 848-9421
Carter MS 1,200/6-8
8901 Bluewater Rd NW 87121 505-833-7540
Amy Mahr, prin. Fax 833-7559
Cibola HS 1,900/9-12
1510 Ellison Dr NW 87114 505-897-0110
Pam Meyer, prin. Fax 897-4251
Cleveland MS 700/6-8
6910 Natalie Ave NE 87110 505-881-9227
Susan Labarge, prin. Fax 881-9441
College and Career HS 100/9-12
525 Buena Vista Dr SE 87106 505-224-4880
Todd Resch, prin. Fax 224-4898
Del Norte HS 1,200/9-12
5323 Montgomery Blvd NE 87109 505-883-7222
Jo Sloan, prin. Fax 880-3965
Desert Ridge MS 1,000/6-8
8400 Barstow St NE 87122 505-857-9282
Kathy Alexander, prin. Fax 857-0201
Eisenhower MS 900/6-8
11001 Camero Ave NE 87111 505-292-2530
Deanne Smith, prin. Fax 291-6884
Eldorado HS 1,900/9-12
11300 Montgomery Blvd NE 87111 505-296-4871
Martin Sandoval, prin. Fax 291-6809
Freedom HS 200/Alt
5200 Cutler Ave NE 87110 505-884-6012
Esther Keeton, prin. Fax 880-3979
Garfield STEM S 300/6-8
3501 6th St NW 87107 505-344-1647
David Lynch, prin. Fax 344-6562
Grant MS 600/6-8
1111 Easterday Dr NE 87112 505-299-2113
Paul Roney, prin. Fax 291-6881
Harrison MS 900/6-8
3912 Isleta Blvd SW 87105 505-877-1279
Kevin Cummings, prin. Fax 877-6797
Hayes MS 400/6-8
1100 Texas St NE 87110 505-265-7741
Antoinette Valenzuela, prin. Fax 260-6108
Highland HS 1,500/9-12
4700 Coal Ave SE 87108 505-265-3711
Marco Harris, prin. Fax 348-8503
Hillerman MS 1,000/6-8
8101 Rainbow Blvd NW 87114 505-792-0698
Renee Salazar, prin. Fax 792-2322
Hoover MS 700/6-8
12015 Tivoli Ave NE Ste A 87111 505-298-6896
Robert Abney, prin. Fax 291-6883
Jackson MS 600/6-8
10600 Indian School Rd NE 87112 505-299-7377
Tracy Straub, prin. Fax 291-6877
Jefferson MS 900/6-8
712 Girard Blvd NE 87106 505-255-8691
Shawn Morris, prin. Fax 268-2334
Johnson MS 900/6-8
6811 Taylor Ranch Rd NW 87120 505-898-1492
Mike Bachicha, prin. Fax 898-7150
Kennedy MS 500/6-8
721 Tomasita St NE 87123 505-298-6701
Ed Bortot, prin. Fax 291-6879
La Cueva HS 1,900/9-12
7801 Wilshire Ave NE 87122 505-823-2327
Dana Lee, prin. Fax 857-0177
Madison MS 700/6-8
3501 Moon St NE 87111 505-299-4735
Andrew Legant, prin. Fax 323-9512
Manzano HS 1,800/9-12
12200 Lomas Blvd NE 87112 505-559-2200
Dr. Karen Webb, prin. Fax 291-6854
McKinley MS 500/6-8
4500 Comanche Rd NE 87110 505-881-9390
Vernon Martinez, prin. Fax 880-3968
Monroe MS 1,000/6-8
6100 Paradise Blvd NW 87114 505-897-0101
Jane Sichler, prin. Fax 897-2371
Nex+Gen Academy 300/9-12
5325 Montgomery Blvd NE 87109 505-878-6400
Amy Milazzo, prin.
Polk MS 400/6-8
2220 Raymac Rd SW 87105 505-877-6444
Michelle Armijo, prin. Fax 877-1618
Pyle MS 600/6-8
1820 Valdora Rd SW 87105 505-877-3770
Ryan Homistek, prin. Fax 873-8540
Rio Grande HS 1,600/9-12
2300 Arenal Rd SW 87105 505-873-0220
Amanda De Bell, prin. Fax 873-8523
Sandia HS 1,900/9-12
7801 Candelaria Rd NE 87110 505-294-1511
Lawrence D'Anza, prin. Fax 291-6878
School on Wheels 100/Alt
129 Hartline Ave SW 87105 505-243-2395
Lori Romero, prin. Fax 243-5180
Taylor MS 500/6-8
8200 Guadalupe Trl NW 87114 505-898-3666
Sandra Patterson, prin. Fax 897-5165
Truman MS 1,400/6-8
9400 Benavides Rd SW 87121 505-836-3030
Michele Torres, prin. Fax 836-7745
Valley HS 1,300/9-12
1505 Candelaria Rd NW 87107 505-345-9021
Anthony Griego, prin. Fax 761-8429
Van Buren MS 500/6-8
700 Louisiana Blvd SE 87108 505-268-3833
Jeri Heileman, prin. Fax 260-6104
Vision Quest Alternative MS 50/Alt
5401 Glenrio Rd NW 87105 505-352-0343
Adele Evans, prin. Fax 352-0343
Volcano Vista HS 2,200/9-12
8100 Rainbow Blvd NW 87114 505-890-0343
Valerie Atencio, prin. Fax 792-4805
Washington MS 500/6-8
1101 Park Ave SW 87102 505-764-2000
Angela Rodriguez, prin. Fax 764-2022
West Mesa HS 1,500/9-12
6701 Fortuna Rd NW 87121 505-831-6993
Mark Garcia, prin. Fax 836-7756
Wilson MS 500/6-8
1138 Cardenas Dr SE 87108 505-268-3961
Dr. Vickie Bannerman, prin. Fax 260-2000
Other Schools – See Los Ranchos, Tijeras

Albuquerque Academy 1,100/6-12
6400 Wyoming Blvd NE 87109 505-828-3200
Andrew Watson, head sch Fax 828-3320
Aveda Institute New Mexico Post-Sec.
1816 Central Ave SW 87104 505-294-5333
Bosque S 500/6-12
4000 Learning Rd NW 87120 505-898-6388
William B. Handmaker, head sch Fax 922-0392
Brookline College Post-Sec.
4201 Central Ave NW Ste J 87105 505-880-2877
Calvary Christian Academy 100/PK-12
12820 Indian School Rd NE 87112 505-842-8681
Nicole Craner, admin. Fax 292-4782
Carrington College Post-Sec.
1001 Menaul Blvd NE 87107 505-254-7777
Central New Mexico Community College Post-Sec.
525 Buena Vista Dr SE 87106 505-224-3000
DeWolff Coll of Hairstyling\Cosmetology Post-Sec.
1500 Eubank Blvd NE 87112 505-296-4100
Evangel Christian Academy 200/PK-12
4501 Montgomery Blvd NE 87109 505-883-4674
Hope Christian S 1,400/PK-12
8005 Louisiana Blvd NE 87109 505-822-8868
Tom Morris, hdmstr. Fax 822-8260

Hope Connection S — 100/6-12
4700 Eubank Blvd NE 87111 — 505-237-0844
Menaul S — 200/6-12
301 Menaul Blvd NE 87107 — 505-345-7727
Lindsey Gilbert, head sch — Fax 344-2517
National American University — Post-Sec.
4775 Indian Sch Rd NE #200 87110 — 505-348-3700
National American University — Post-Sec.
10131 Coors Blvd NW Ste I1 87114 — 800-895-9904
Olympian University of Cosmetology — Post-Sec.
6300 San Mateo Blvd NE # J 87109 — 505-765-1044
Pima Medical Institute — Post-Sec.
4400 Cutler Ave NE 87110 — 505-881-1234
Rio Grande Christian Academy — K-12
2121 Gun Club Rd 87105 — 505-877-0535
St. Pius X HS — 800/9-12
5301 Saint Josephs Dr NW 87120 — 505-831-8400
Dr. Barbara Rothweiler, prin. — Fax 831-8413
Sandia Preparatory S — 700/6-12
532 Osuna Rd NE 87113 — 505-338-3000
Bill Sinfield, head sch — Fax 338-3099
Southwest Acupuncture College — Post-Sec.
7801 Academy Rd NE 87109 — 505-888-8898
Southwestern Indian Polytechnic Inst. — Post-Sec.
9169 Coors Blvd NW 87120 — 505-346-2347
Southwest University of Visual Arts — Post-Sec.
5000 Marble Ave NE 87110 — 505-254-7575
Universal Therapeutic Massage Institute — Post-Sec.
3410 Aztec Rd NE 87107 — 505-888-0020
University of New Mexico — Post-Sec.
PO Box 4895 87196 — 505-277-0111
University of Phoenix-NM Division — Post-Sec.
5700 Pasadena Ave NE 87113 — 505-821-4800
Victory Christian S — 100/K-12
220 El Pueblo Rd NW 87114 — 505-898-3060
Glenn Frey, supt. — Fax 898-6690

Animas, Hidalgo, Pop. 225
Animas SD — 200/PK-12
PO Box 85 88020 — 575-548-2299
Loren Cushman, supt. — Fax 548-2388
www.animask12.net
Animas HS — 100/7-12
PO Box 85 88020 — 575-548-2296
Loren Cushman, prin. — Fax 548-2388

Anthony, Dona Ana, Pop. 9,342
Gadsden ISD
Supt. — See Sunland Park
Alta Vista Early College HS — 300/9-12
PO Box 70 88021 — 575-882-6400
Rosa Hood, prin. — Fax 882-6420
Desert Pride Academy — 300/Alt
PO Box 70 88021 — 575-882-0142
Don Smelser, prin. — Fax 882-4926
Gadsden HS — 1,600/9-12
6301 Highway 28 88021 — 575-882-6300
Hector Giron, prin. — Fax 882-2370
Gadsden MS — 800/7-8
1301 Washington St 88021 — 575-882-2372
Veronica Quinones, prin. — Fax 882-5227

Anton Chico, Guadalupe, Pop. 188
Santa Rosa Consolidated SD
Supt. — See Santa Rosa
Anton Chico MS — 50/6-8
PO Box 169 87711 — 575-427-6038
Sumner Price, prin. — Fax 427-4246

Artesia, Eddy, Pop. 11,178
Artesia SD — 3,800/PK-12
1106 W Quay Ave 88210 — 575-746-3585
Dr. Crit Caton, supt. — Fax 746-6232
www.bulldogs.org
Artesia HS — 700/10-12
1006 W Richardson Ave 88210 — 575-746-9816
Eric Greer, prin. — Fax 746-4365
Artesia Park JHS — 600/8-9
1508 W Cannon Ave 88210 — 575-746-9892
Cody Skinner, prin. — Fax 746-4462

Aztec, San Juan, Pop. 6,640
Aztec Municipal SD — 3,200/PK-12
1118 W Aztec Blvd 87410 — 505-334-9474
Kirk Carpenter, supt. — Fax 334-9861
www.aztecschools.com
Aztec HS — 1,000/9-12
500 E Chaco St 87410 — 505-334-9414
Warman Hall, prin. — Fax 599-4387
Koogler MS — 700/6-8
455 N Light Plant Rd 87410 — 505-334-6102
Jessica Sledzinski, prin. — Fax 599-4385
Vista Nueva HS — 50/Alt
315 S Ash St Ste 100 87410 — 505-599-4393
Rocky Torres, prin. — Fax 334-1427

Bayard, Grant, Pop. 2,310
Cobre Consolidated SD — 1,300/PK-12
PO Box 1000 88023 — 575-537-4010
Robert Mendoza, supt. — Fax 537-5455
www.cobre.k12.nm.us
Cobre HS — 300/9-12
PO Box 749 88023 — 575-537-4020
Frank Quarrell, prin. — Fax 537-5503
Snell MS — 200/7-8
PO Box 729 88023 — 575-537-4030
Patrick Abalos, prin. — Fax 537-3022

Belen, Valencia, Pop. 7,165
Belen Consolidated SD — 4,200/PK-12
520 N Main St 87002 — 505-966-1000
Max Perez, supt. — Fax 966-1050
www.beleneagles.org
Belen HS — 1,100/9-12
520 N Main St 87002 — 505-966-1300
Rodney Wright, prin. — Fax 966-1350
Belen Infinity HS — 100/Alt
520 N Main St 87002 — 505-966-1500
Mary Batista, dean — Fax 966-1550
Belen MS — 600/7-8
520 N Main St 87002 — 505-966-1600
Kim Ortiz, prin. — Fax 966-1650

Canon Christian Academy — 200/K-12
19381 Highway 314 87002 — 505-859-4041

Bernalillo, Sandoval, Pop. 8,231
Bernalillo SD — 2,700/PK-12
560 S Camino Del Pueblo 87004 — 505-867-2317
Allan Tapia, supt. — Fax 867-7850
www.bernalillo-schools.org
Bernalillo HS — 800/9-12
250 Isidora Sanchez 87004 — 505-867-2388
Keith Cowan, prin. — Fax 867-7826
Bernalillo MS — 400/6-8
485 Camino don Tomas 87004 — 505-867-3309
Jacque Mangham, prin. — Fax 867-7819

Bloomfield, San Juan, Pop. 7,953
Bloomfield SD — 3,000/PK-12
325 N Bergin Ln 87413 — 505-632-4300
Dr. Kimberly Mizell, supt. — Fax 632-4371
www.bsin.k12.nm.us
Bloomfield HS — 800/9-12
520 N 1st St 87413 — 505-634-3400
Chad Burkholder, prin. — Fax 634-3413
Brown Secondary S — 100/Alt
924 S Bloomfield Blvd 87413 — 505-634-3940
Robert Lopez, prin. — Fax 634-3950
Mesa Alta JHS — 400/7-8
329 N Bergin Ln 87413 — 505-632-8021
Adam Benavidez, prin. — Fax 634-3872

Capitan, Lincoln, Pop. 1,465
Capitan Municipal SD — 500/K-12
PO Box 278 88316 — 575-354-8500
Sean Wootton, supt. — Fax 354-8505
www.capitantigers.org
Capitan HS — 200/9-12
PO Box 278 88316 — 575-354-8550
Jimmie Mace, prin. — Fax 354-8507
Capitan MS — 100/6-8
PO Box 278 88316 — 575-354-8550
Jimmie Mace, prin. — Fax 354-8506

Carlsbad, Eddy, Pop. 25,808
Carlsbad Municipal SD — 4,600/PK-12
408 N Canyon St 88220 — 575-234-3300
Gary Perkowski, supt. — Fax 234-3367
www.carlsbadnmschools.com
Carlsbad HS — 1,700/9-12
408 N Canyon St 88220 — 575-234-3319
Mark Driskell, prin. — Fax 234-3393
Carlsbad IS @ P.R. Leyva Campus — 600/7-8
408 N Canyon St 88220 — 575-234-3318
Stephanie West, prin. — Fax 234-3452
Early College HS — 9-12
408 N Canyon St 88220 — 575-234-9415
Eric Spencer, prin.
Eddy Alternative Program — 200/Alt
408 N Canyon St 88220 — 575-234-3305
Tamara Faulk, prin. — Fax 234-3511

Eddy County Beauty College — Post-Sec.
1115 W Mermod St 88220 — 575-885-4545
New Mexico State University — Post-Sec.
1500 University Dr 88220 — 575-234-9200

Carrizozo, Lincoln, Pop. 975
Carrizozo Municipal SD — 100/PK-12
PO Box 99 88301 — 575-648-2346
Ricky Espinoza, supt. — Fax 648-2216
www.carrizozoschools.org
Carrizozo MSHS — 50/7-12
PO Box 99 88301 — 575-648-2346
Ricky Espinoza, prin. — Fax 648-3255

Casa Blanca, Cibola
Grants-Cibola County SD
Supt. — See Grants
Laguna Acoma JSHS — 300/7-12
PO Box 689 87007 — 505-552-6683
Marilyn Cheromiah, prin. — Fax 552-7184

Chaparral, Dona Ana, Pop. 14,528
Gadsden ISD
Supt. — See Sunland Park
Chaparral HS — 1,100/9-12
800 S County Line Dr, — 575-824-6700
Mark Rupcich, prin. — Fax 824-5081
Chaparral MS — 600/7-8
290 E Lisa Dr, — 575-824-4847
Marti Muela, prin. — Fax 824-4045

Cimarron, Colfax, Pop. 1,000
Cimarron Municipal SD — 400/K-12
125 N Collison Ave 87714 — 575-376-2445
Adan Estrada, supt. — Fax 376-2442
cimarronschools.org
Cimarron HS — 100/9-12
125 N Collison Ave 87714 — 575-376-2241
Letitia Martinez, prin. — Fax 376-2428
Cimarron MS — 100/5-8
125 N Collison Ave 87714 — 575-376-2512
Bonnie Lightfoot, prin. — Fax 376-2217
Other Schools – See Eagle Nest

Clayton, Union, Pop. 2,951
Clayton Municipal SD — 500/PK-12
323 S 5th St 88415 — 575-374-9611
Stacy Diller, supt. — Fax 374-9881
www.claytonschools.us
Clayton HS — 100/9-12
323 S 5th St 88415 — 575-374-2596
Don Worth, prin. — Fax 374-6012
Clayton JHS — 100/7-8
323 S 5th St 88415 — 575-374-9543
Hilary Kouhana, prin. — Fax 374-9469

Cliff, Grant, Pop. 288
Silver Consolidated SD
Supt. — See Silver City
Cliff JSHS — 100/7-12
PO Box 9 88028 — 575-535-2051
Dean Spurgeon, prin. — Fax 535-2054

Cloudcroft, Otero, Pop. 659
Cloudcroft Municipal SD — 200/PK-12
PO Box 198 88317 — 575-601-4416
Travis Dempsey, supt. — Fax 235-1668
www.cmsbears.org
Cloudcroft HS — 100/9-12
PO Box 198 88317 — 575-601-4416
Tana Daugherty, prin. — Fax 405-0833

Clovis, Curry, Pop. 36,950
Clovis Municipal SD — 8,600/PK-12
PO Box 19000 88102 — 575-769-4300
Jody Balch, supt. — Fax 769-4333
www.clovis-schools.org
Choices Alternative HS — Alt
1900 N Thornton St 88101 — 575-769-4859
Todd Morris, prin. — Fax 769-4857
Clovis Freshman Academy — 600/9-9
1400 Cameo St 88101 — 575-769-4400
John Howell, prin. — Fax 769-4403
Clovis HS — 1,600/10-12
1900 N Thornton St 88101 — 575-769-4350
Jay Brady, prin. — Fax 769-4366
Gattis MS, 5100 N Thornton St 88101 — 800/6-8
Gloria Christiansen, prin. — 575-769-4305
Marshall MS — 500/6-8
100 Commerce Way 88101 — 575-769-4410
Jennifer Longley, prin. — Fax 769-4413
Yucca MS — 600/6-8
1500 Sycamore St 88101 — 575-769-4420
Loran Hill, prin. — Fax 769-4421

Clovis Christian S — PK-12
PO Box 608 88102 — 575-935-2279
Dr. Ladona Clayton, supt. — Fax 935-2281
Clovis Community College — Post-Sec.
417 Schepps Blvd 88101 — 575-769-2811

Corona, Lincoln, Pop. 169
Corona SD — 100/PK-12
PO Box 258 88318 — 575-849-1911
Travis Lightfoot, supt. — Fax 849-2026
www.cpscardinals.org
Corona HS — 50/7-12
PO Box 258 88318 — 575-849-1911
Rick Cogdill, prin. — Fax 849-2026

Corrales, Sandoval, Pop. 8,197

Sandia View Academy — 50/9-12
65 Sandia View Ln 87048 — 505-898-0717

Crownpoint, McKinley, Pop. 2,253
Gallup-McKinley County SD
Supt. — See Gallup
Crownpoint HS — 300/9-12
PO Box 700 87313 — 505-721-1600
Ophelia Sanchez, prin. — Fax 721-1699
Crownpoint MS — 100/6-8
PO Box 1110 87313 — 505-786-5663
Michael Cubacub, prin. — Fax 721-5499

Navajo Technical College — Post-Sec.
PO Box 849 87313 — 505-786-4100

Cuba, Sandoval, Pop. 717
Cuba ISD — 500/PK-12
PO Box 70 87013 — 575-289-3211
Tony Archuleta, supt. — Fax 289-3314
cuba.k12.nm.us/
Cuba HS — 200/9-12
PO Box 70 87013 — 575-289-3211
Archie Jacquez, prin. — Fax 289-3314
Cuba MS — 100/6-8
PO Box 70 87013 — 575-289-3211
Lynn Vasquez, prin. — Fax 289-3314

Deming, Luna, Pop. 14,749
Deming SD — 5,400/PK-12
1001 S Diamond Ave 88030 — 575-546-8841
Dr. Daniel Lere, supt. — Fax 546-8517
www.demingps.org
Deming HS — 1,400/9-12
1100 S Nickel St 88030 — 575-546-2678
Janean Garney, prin. — Fax 544-0918
Red Mountain MS — 800/7-8
2100 Highway 418 SW 88030 — 575-546-0668
Robin Parnell, prin. — Fax 546-9263

Des Moines, Union, Pop. 140
Des Moines Municipal SD — 100/K-12
PO Box 38 88418 — 575-278-2611
Mark Chandler, supt. — Fax 278-2617
www.desmoines.k12.nm.us/
Des Moines JSHS — 50/7-12
PO Box 38 88418 — 575-278-2611
Kodi Sumpter, prin. — Fax 278-2617

Dexter, Chaves, Pop. 1,260
Dexter Consolidated SD — 1,000/PK-12
PO Box 159 88230 — 575-734-5420
Lesa Dodd, supt. — Fax 734-6813
www.dexterdemons.org
Dexter HS — 300/9-12
PO Box 159 88230 — 575-734-5420
Craig DeYoung, prin. — Fax 734-6709
Dexter MS — 200/6-8
PO Box 159 88230 — 575-734-5420
Chanda Crandall, prin. — Fax 734-6811

Dixon, Rio Arriba, Pop. 913

Apostolic Praise Christian Academy 50/8-12
PO Box 206 87527 505-579-4487

Dora, Roosevelt, Pop. 133
Dora Consolidated SD 200/PK-12
PO Box 327 88115 575-477-2211
Steve Barron, supt. Fax 477-2464
www.doraschools.com
Dora JSHS 100/7-12
PO Box 327 88115 575-477-2211
Brandon Hays, prin. Fax 477-2464

Dulce, Rio Arriba, Pop. 2,716
Dulce ISD 500/K-12
PO Box 547 87528 575-759-3225
Tom Savage, supt. Fax 759-3533
www.dulceschools.com
Dulce JSHS 200/7-12
PO Box 547 87528 575-759-3225
Manuel Valdez, prin. Fax 759-3533

Eagle Nest, Colfax, Pop. 289
Cimarron Municipal SD
Supt. — See Cimarron
Eagle Nest MS 100/5-8
225 Lake St 87718 575-377-6991
Fax 377-3646

Edgewood, Santa Fe, Pop. 3,663
Moriarty-Edgewood SD
Supt. — See Moriarty
Edgewood MS 300/6-8
17 Venus Rd W 87015 505-832-5880
Todd Bibiano, prin. Fax 281-7210

Elida, Roosevelt, Pop. 195
Elida Municipal SD 100/K-12
PO Box 8 88116 575-274-6211
Jim Daugherty, supt. Fax 274-6213
www.elidaschools.net/
Elida JSHS 100/7-12
PO Box 8 88116 575-274-6211
Larry Gregory, prin. Fax 274-6213

El Pueblo, San Miguel
West Las Vegas SD
Supt. — See Las Vegas
Valley MS 50/6-8
85 NM Highway 484 87560 505-426-2581
Becky Gallegos, prin. Fax 426-2582

El Rito, Rio Arriba, Pop. 781

Northern New Mexico Community College Post-Sec.
PO Box 160 87530 575-581-4110

Espanola, Rio Arriba, Pop. 10,179
Espanola SD 3,800/PK-12
1260 Industrial Park Rd 87532 505-753-2254
Eric V. Martinez, supt. Fax 747-3514
www.k12espanola.org
Espanola Valley HS 900/9-12
1260 Industrial Park Rd 87532 505-753-7357
Dr. Tom Graves, prin. Fax 753-6177
Vigil MS 500/7-8
1260 Industrial Park Rd 87532 505-753-1348
Julie Gutierrez, prin. Fax 747-3083

Northern New Mexico College Post-Sec.
921 N Paseo De Onate 87532 505-747-2100
Victory Christian Academy 50/K-12
PO Box 540 87532 505-753-0039

Estancia, Torrance, Pop. 1,626
Estancia Municipal SD 500/K-12
PO Box 68 87016 505-384-2000
Audie Brown, supt. Fax 384-2015
www.estancia.k12.nm.us
Estancia HS 200/9-12
PO Box 68 87016 505-384-2002
Martha Ward, prin. Fax 384-2015
Estancia MS 100/6-8
PO Box 68 87016 505-384-2003
Fax 384-2015

Eunice, Lea, Pop. 2,893
Eunice SD 700/PK-12
PO Box 129 88231 575-394-2524
Dwain Haynes, supt. Fax 394-3006
www.eunice.org
Caton MS 200/6-8
PO Box 129 88231 575-394-3338
Christy Boyd, prin. Fax 394-3661
Eunice HS 200/9-12
PO Box 129 88231 575-394-2332
Gary Frazier, prin. Fax 394-3140

Farmington, San Juan, Pop. 44,787
Farmington Municipal SD 10,900/PK-12
PO Box 5850 87499 505-324-9840
Dr. Eugene Schmidt, supt. Fax 599-8806
district.fms.k12.nm.us
Farmington HS 1,300/9-12
2200 N Sunset Ave 87401 505-324-0352
Tim Kienitz, prin. Fax 599-8832
Heights MS 700/6-8
3700 College Blvd 87402 505-599-8611
Nathan Pierantoni, prin. Fax 599-8673
Hermosa MS 600/6-8
1500 E 25th St 87401 505-599-8612
Mark Harris, prin. Fax 599-8681
Mesa View MS 600/6-8
4451 Wildflower Mesa Dr 87401 505-599-8622
Jay Gardenhire, prin. Fax 599-8646
Piedra Vista HS 1,400/9-12
5700 College Blvd 87402 505-599-8880
Dave Golden, prin. Fax 599-8891
Rocinante HS 200/Alt
3250 E 30th St 87402 505-599-8627
Bob Rank, prin. Fax 599-8731
Tibbetts MS 600/6-8
3500 Twin Peaks Blvd 87401 505-599-8613
Tammie Hanson, prin. Fax 599-8675

Grace Baptist Academy 100/PK-12
2200 Sullivan Ave 87401 505-325-7802
San Juan College Post-Sec.
4601 College Blvd 87402 505-326-3311

Floyd, Roosevelt, Pop. 133
Floyd Municipal SD 200/PK-12
PO Box 65 88118 575-478-2211
Damon Terry, supt. Fax 478-2811
www.floydbroncos.com
Floyd HS 100/9-12
PO Box 65 88118 575-478-2211
Damon Terry, admin. Fax 478-2811
Floyd MS 100/5-8
PO Box 65 88118 575-478-2211
Damon Terry, admin. Fax 478-2811

Fort Sumner, DeBaca, Pop. 1,008
Fort Sumner Municipal SD 300/PK-12
PO Box 387 88119 575-355-7734
Matt Moyer, supt. Fax 355-7663
www.ftsumnerk12.com
Fort Sumner HS 100/9-12
PO Box 387 88119 575-355-2231
Sharon Rowley, prin. Fax 355-7663
Fort Sumner MS 100/6-8
PO Box 387 88119 575-355-2231
Sharon Rowley, prin. Fax 355-7663

Gallina, Rio Arriba, Pop. 280
Jemez Mountain SD 200/K-12
PO Box 230 87017 575-638-5419
Dr. Manuel Medrano, supt. Fax 638-5571
www.jmsk12.com/
Coronado MSHS 100/6-12
PO Box 230 87017 575-638-5549
Donna Manuelito, prin. Fax 638-5571

Gallup, McKinley, Pop. 21,028
Gallup-McKinley County SD 11,700/PK-12
PO Box 1318 87305 505-721-1000
Frank Chiapetti, supt. Fax 721-1199
www.gmcs.k12.nm.us
Chief Manuelito MS 600/6-8
1325 Rico St 87301 505-721-5600
Steve Wargo, prin. Fax 721-5699
Gallup Central HS 200/Alt
325 Marguerite St 87301 505-721-2400
Rick Hall, prin. Fax 721-2499
Gallup HS 1,000/9-12
1055 Rico St 87301 505-721-2500
Dominic Romero, prin. Fax 721-2556
Gallup MS 400/6-8
1001 S Grandview Dr 87301 505-721-2700
Carrie Lovato, prin. Fax 721-2799
Kennedy MS 700/6-8
600 S Boardman Ave 87301 505-721-3100
Roberta Tayah, prin. Fax 721-3199
Miyamura HS 1,100/9-12
680 Boardman Dr 87301 505-721-1900
Jack McFarland, prin. Fax 721-1999
Other Schools – See Crownpoint, Navajo, Pueblo Pintado, Ramah, Thoreau, Tohatchi

University of New Mexico - Gallup Post-Sec.
705 Gurley Ave 87301 505-863-7500

Grady, Curry, Pop. 103
Grady Municipal SD 100/PK-12
PO Box 71 88120 575-357-2192
Ted Trice, supt. Fax 357-2000
www.gradyschool.com
Grady HS 50/9-12
PO Box 71 88120 575-357-2192
Michell Edwards B.S., prin. Fax 357-2000
Grady MS 50/6-8
PO Box 71 88120 575-357-2192
Michell Edwards B.S., prin. Fax 357-2000

Grants, Cibola, Pop. 9,030
Grants-Cibola County SD 3,500/PK-12
PO Box 8 87020 505-285-2600
Dr. Marc Space, supt. Fax 285-2628
www.gccs.cc/
Grants HS 900/9-12
500 Mountain Rd 87020 505-285-2651
Matt Lindsey, prin. Fax 285-2661
Los Alamitos MS 400/7-8
1100 Mount Taylor Ave 87020 505-285-2683
Joan Gilmore, prin. Fax 285-2711
Other Schools – See Casa Blanca

New Mexico State University Post-Sec.
1500 N 3rd St 87020 505-287-6678

Hagerman, Chaves, Pop. 1,250
Hagerman Municipal SD 400/PK-12
PO Box B 88232 575-752-3254
Ricky Williams, supt. Fax 752-3255
bobcat.net
Hagerman HS 100/9-12
PO Box B 88232 575-752-3283
Mark Lovas, prin. Fax 752-3306
Hagerman MS 100/6-8
PO Box B 88232 575-752-2002
Mark Lovas, prin. Fax 752-0241

Hatch, Dona Ana, Pop. 1,642
Hatch Valley SD 1,300/PK-12
PO Box 790 87937 575-267-8200
Linda Hale, supt. Fax 267-8202
www.hatchschools.net
Hatch Valley HS 400/9-12
PO Box 790 87937 575-267-8230
Tomas Lucero, prin. Fax 267-8235
Hatch Valley MS 300/6-8
PO Box 790 87937 575-267-8250
Daniel Montoya, prin. Fax 267-8255

Hobbs, Lea, Pop. 33,769
Hobbs Municipal SD 9,700/PK-12
PO Box 1030 88241 575-433-0100
T.J. Parks, supt. Fax 433-0140
www.hobbsschools.net
Freshman HS 700/9-9
1401 E Sanger St 88240 575-433-0300
Dawni Nelson, prin. Fax 433-1109
Heizer MS 700/6-8
101 E Stanolind Rd 88240 575-433-1100
Freddie Salgado, prin. Fax 433-1101
Highland MS 700/6-8
2500 N Jefferson St 88240 575-433-1200
Ron Haggerton, prin. Fax 433-1203
Hobbs HS 1,700/10-12
800 N Jefferson St 88240 575-433-0200
Zeke Kaney, prin. Fax 433-0203
Houston MS 700/6-8
300 N Houston St 88240 575-433-1300
Donna Jones, prin. Fax 433-1304

New Mexico Junior College Post-Sec.
1 Thunderbird Cir 88240 505-392-4510
University of the Southwest Post-Sec.
6610 N Lovington Hwy 88240 575-392-6561
Veritas Classical Christian Academy K-12
PO Box 2844 88241 575-942-4664
Lori Bova, admin.

Holloman AFB, Otero, Pop. 2,857
Alamogordo SD
Supt. — See Alamogordo
Holloman MS 200/6-8
381 1st St 88330 575-812-6200
Steven Starkovich, prin. Fax 812-6203

Hondo, Lincoln
Hondo Valley SD 100/K-12
PO Box 55 88336 575-653-4411
Marvin Martin, supt. Fax 653-4414
www.hondoschools.org
Hondo HS 100/7-12
PO Box 55 88336 575-653-4411
Marvin Martin, prin. Fax 653-4414

House, Quay, Pop. 68
House Municipal SD 100/K-12
PO Box 673 88121 575-279-7353
Lecil Richards, supt. Fax 279-6133
www.houseschools.net
House JSHS 50/7-12
PO Box 673 88121 575-279-7353
Lecil Richards, prin. Fax 279-6201
Learning Center Alt
PO Box 673 88121 575-279-7322
Lecil Richards, prin. Fax 279-6093

Jal, Lea, Pop. 2,030
Jal SD 400/PK-12
PO Box 1386 88252 575-395-2101
Brian Snider, supt. Fax 395-2146
www.jalnm.org
Jal JSHS 100/7-12
PO Box 1386 88252 575-395-2277
Elaine O'Neal, prin. Fax 395-3177

Jemez Pueblo, Sandoval, Pop. 1,783
Jemez Valley SD 400/PK-12
8501 Highway 4 87024 575-834-7391
Dr. Susan Wilkinson-Davis, supt. Fax 834-7394
www.jvps.org
Jemez Valley HS 100/9-12
8501 Highway 4 87024 575-834-7392
Scott Meihack, prin. Fax 834-7676
Jemez Valley MS 100/6-8
8501 Highway 4 87024 575-834-3315
Deneen Bair, prin. Fax 834-7401

Kirtland, San Juan, Pop. 7,619
Central Consolidated SD
Supt. — See Shiprock
Kirtland Central HS 800/9-12
550 Road 6100 87417 505-598-5881
Shawna Becenti, prin. Fax 598-9712
Kirtland MS 500/7-8
538 Road 6100 87417 505-598-6114
Randy Mason, prin. Fax 598-9562

Lake Arthur, Chaves, Pop. 422
Lake Arthur Municipal SD 100/PK-12
PO Box 98 88253 575-365-2000
Michael Grossman, supt. Fax 365-2002
www.la-panthers.org
Lake Arthur HS 50/9-12
PO Box 98 88253 575-365-2000
Jose Porras, prin. Fax 365-2002
Lake Arthur MS 50/6-8
PO Box 98 88253 575-365-2000
Jose Porras, prin. Fax 365-2002

Las Cruces, Dona Ana, Pop. 96,217
Las Cruces SD 24,900/PK-12
505 S Main St Ste 249 88001 575-527-5800
Dr. Greg Ewing, supt. Fax 527-5972
www.lcps.k12.nm.us
Arrowhead Park Early College HS 400/9-12
505 S Main St Ste 249 88001 575-527-9540
Jennifer Amis, prin.
Camino Real MS 700/6-8
505 S Main St Ste 249 88001 575-527-6030
Ralph Ramos, prin. Fax 527-6031

Centennial HS 1,300/9-12
505 S Main St Ste 249 88001 575-527-9330
Michael Montoya, prin. Fax 527-9331
Las Cruces HS 1,700/9-12
505 S Main St Ste 249 88001 575-527-9400
Jed Hendee, prin. Fax 527-9767
Lynn MS 800/6-8
505 S Main St Ste 249 88001 575-527-9445
Reynaldo Gomez, prin. Fax 527-9454
Mayfield HS 1,600/9-12
505 S Main St Ste 249 88001 575-527-9415
Eric Fraass, prin. Fax 527-9420
Mesa MS 600/6-8
505 S Main St Ste 249 88001 575-527-9510
Steven Rodriguez, prin. Fax 527-9511
Mesilla Valley Leadership Academy Alt
505 S Main St Ste 249 88001 575-527-6059
Toni Hull, prin.
Onate HS 1,700/9-12
505 S Main St Ste 249 88001 575-527-9430
James Schapekahm, prin. Fax 527-9444
Picacho MS 800/6-8
505 S Main St Ste 249 88001 575-527-9455
Fred Montalvo, prin. Fax 527-9459
Sierra MS 800/6-8
505 S Main St Ste 249 88001 575-527-9640
Maryester Garza, prin. Fax 527-9768
Vista MS 700/6-8
505 S Main St Ste 249 88001 575-527-9465
Mike Brewer, prin. Fax 527-9470
Zia MS 800/6-8
505 S Main St Ste 249 88001 575-527-9475
Heather Kingery, prin. Fax 527-9479
Other Schools – See Mesilla

Las Cruces Catholic S 300/PK-12
1331 N Miranda St 88005 575-526-2517
Connie Limon, prin. Fax 524-0544
Mesilla Valley Christian S 400/PK-12
3850 Stern Dr 88001 575-525-8515
Dr. John Foreman, head sch Fax 526-2713
New Mexico State Univ. Dona Ana Branch Post-Sec.
2800 Sonoma Ranch Blvd 88011 575-527-7500
New Mexico State University Post-Sec.
PO Box 30001 88003 575-646-0111
Olympian University of Cosmetology Post-Sec.
1460 Missouri Ave # 5 88001 575-523-7181
Vista College Post-Sec.
850 N Telshor Blvd Ste F 88011 866-442-4197

Las Vegas, San Miguel, Pop. 13,609
Las Vegas City SD 1,800/PK-12
901 Douglas Ave 87701 505-454-5700
Dr. Ruben Cordova, supt. Fax 454-5712
cybercardinal.com
Memorial MS 400/6-8
901 Douglas Ave 87701 505-454-5710
Monica Montoya, prin. Fax 454-2753
Robertson HS 400/9-12
901 Douglas Ave 87701 505-454-5770
Mike Yara, prin. Fax 454-2707

West Las Vegas SD 1,500/K-12
179 Bridge St 87701 505-426-2300
Christopher Gutierrez, supt. Fax 426-2318
wlvs.schooldesk.net
West Las Vegas HS 500/9-12
179 Bridge St 87701 505-426-2500
John Bustos, prin. Fax 426-2501
West Las Vegas MS 300/6-8
179 Bridge St 87701 505-426-2541
Anna Valdez, prin. Fax 426-2542
W Las Vegas Schools Family Partnership 100/Alt
179 Bridge St 87701 505-426-2535
John Bustos, prin. Fax 426-2526
Other Schools – See El Pueblo

Luna Community College Post-Sec.
366 Luna Dr 87701 505-454-2500
New Mexico Highlands University Post-Sec.
PO Box 9000 87701 505-425-7511

Logan, Quay, Pop. 1,034
Logan Municipal SD 300/PK-12
PO Box 67 88426 575-487-2252
Dennis Roch, supt. Fax 487-9479
www.loganschool.net
Logan HS 100/9-12
PO Box 67 88426 575-487-2252
Craig Terry, prin. Fax 487-9479
Logan MS 100/6-8
PO Box 67 88426 575-487-2252
Craig Terry, prin. Fax 487-9479

Lordsburg, Hidalgo, Pop. 2,787
Lordsburg Municipal SD 400/PK-12
PO Box 430 88045 575-542-9361
Randy Piper, supt. Fax 542-9364
www.lmsed.org
Dugan-Tarango MS 100/7-8
1352 Hardin St 88045 575-542-9806
Jonell Conway, prin. Fax 542-9811
Lordsburg HS 100/9-12
501 W 4th St 88045 575-542-3782
Ralph Almanzar, prin. Fax 542-3712

Los Alamos, Los Alamos, Pop. 11,762
Los Alamos SD 3,500/PK-12
PO Box 90 87544 505-663-2222
Dr. Kurt Steinhaus, supt. Fax 663-2243
www.laschools.net
Los Alamos HS 1,100/9-12
1300 Diamond Dr 87544 505-663-2510
Bradford Parker, prin. Fax 662-6846
Los Alamos MS 500/7-8
2101 Hawk Dr 87544 505-663-2375
Michael Johnson, prin. Fax 662-4270

University of New Mexico - Los Alamos Post-Sec.
4000 University Dr 87544 505-662-5919

Los Lunas, Valencia, Pop. 14,610
Los Lunas SD 8,400/PK-12
PO Box 1300 87031 505-865-9636
Dana Sanders, supt. Fax 865-7766
www.llschools.net
Century HS 100/Alt
PO Box 1300 87031 505-866-2453
Eliseo Aguirre, prin. Fax 866-8064
Los Lunas HS 1,300/9-12
PO Box 1300 87031 505-865-4646
Dan Padilla, prin. Fax 565-2847
Los Lunas MS 700/7-8
PO Box 1300 87031 505-865-7273
Lawrence Sosa, prin. Fax 865-9742
Valencia HS 1,000/9-12
PO Box 1300 87031 505-565-8755
Jason Baca, prin. Fax 565-8762
Valencia MS 500/7-8
PO Box 1300 87031 505-865-1750
Barbara Neumann, prin. Fax 866-8921

University of New Mexico - Valencia Post-Sec.
280 La Entrada Rd 87031 505-925-8500

Los Ranchos, Bernalillo
Albuquerque SD
Supt. — See Albuquerque
Taft MS 500/6-8
620 Schulte Rd NW, 505-344-4389
Steve Scully, prin. Fax 761-8440

Loving, Eddy, Pop. 1,402
Loving Municipal SD 600/PK-12
PO Box 98 88256 575-745-2000
Dr. Ann Lynn McIlroy, supt. Fax 745-2002
www.lovingschools.com
Loving HS 200/9-12
PO Box 98 88256 575-745-2000
Lee White, prin. Fax 745-2040
Loving MS 100/6-8
PO Box 98 88256 575-745-2050
Vince Taylor, prin. Fax 745-2040

Lovington, Lea, Pop. 10,904
Lovington Municipal SD 3,700/PK-12
18 W Washington Ave 88260 575-739-2200
LeAnne Gandy, supt. Fax 739-2205
www.lovingtonschools.net/
Freshman Academy 300/9-9
701 W Avenue K 88260 575-739-2260
Michael Michaleson, prin. Fax 739-2261
Lovington SHS 600/10-12
701 W Avenue K 88260 575-739-2230
Michael Michaleson, prin. Fax 739-2242
New Hope Alternative HS 100/Alt
601 N 5th St 88260 575-739-2416
John Moore, prin. Fax 739-2417
Taylor MS 500/7-8
700 S 11th St 88260 575-739-2435
Lori Brattain, prin. Fax 739-2438

Magdalena, Socorro, Pop. 910
Magdalena Municipal SD 400/PK-12
PO Box 24 87825 575-854-2241
Dr. Vannetta R. Perry, supt. Fax 854-2531
www.magdalena.k12.nm.us
Magdalena HS 100/9-12
PO Box 629 87825 575-854-8014
Leslie Clark, prin. Fax 854-2294
Magdalena MS 100/6-8
PO Box 629 87825 575-854-8014
Leslie Clark, prin. Fax 854-2294

Maxwell, Colfax, Pop. 243
Maxwell Municipal SD 100/PK-12
PO Box 275 87728 575-375-2371
Kristen Forrester, supt. Fax 375-2375
www.maxwellp12.com
Maxwell HS 50/9-12
PO Box 275 87728 575-375-2371
John Ward, prin. Fax 375-2375
Maxwell MS 50/7-8
PO Box 275 87728 575-375-2371
John Ward, prin. Fax 375-2375

Melrose, Curry, Pop. 637
Melrose SD 200/PK-12
PO Box 275 88124 575-253-4269
Jamie Widner, supt. Fax 253-4291
www.melroseschools.org
Melrose JSHS 100/7-12
PO Box 275 88124 575-253-4267
Dickie Roybal, prin. Fax 253-4291

Mesilla, Dona Ana, Pop. 2,164
Las Cruces SD
Supt. — See Las Cruces
Rio Grande Preparatory HS 200/Alt
2355 Avenida de Mesilla 88046 575-527-6058
Kathie Davis, prin. Fax 527-9736

Montezuma, San Miguel

United World College USA 200/11-12
PO Box 248 87731 505-454-4245
Dr. Mukul Kumar, pres. Fax 454-4274

Mora, Mora, Pop. 656
Mora ISD 400/K-12
PO Box 179 87732 575-387-3101
Charles Trujillo, supt. Fax 387-3111
mora.k12.nm.us
Garcia MS 100/6-8
PO Box 687 87732 575-387-3127
Paulyette Perea, prin. Fax 387-3126

Mora HS 100/9-12
PO Box 180 87732 575-387-3122
Loretta Griego, prin. Fax 387-3121

Moriarty, Torrance, Pop. 1,873
Moriarty-Edgewood SD 2,100/PK-12
PO Box 2000 87035 505-832-4471
Tom Sullivan, supt. Fax 832-4472
www.mesd.us
Moriarty HS 800/9-12
PO Box 2000 87035 505-832-4254
Robert Adams, prin. Fax 832-5989
Moriarty MS 200/6-8
PO Box 2000 87035 505-832-6200
Amanda Wilson, prin. Fax 832-5919
Other Schools – See Edgewood

Mosquero, Harding, Pop. 93
Mosquero Municipal SD 50/K-12
PO Box 258 87733 575-673-2271
Bill Ward, supt. Fax 673-2305
www.mosquero.net
Mosquero JSHS 50/7-12
PO Box 258 87733 575-673-2271
Bill Ward, prin. Fax 673-2305

Mountainair, Torrance, Pop. 908
Mountainair SD 200/PK-12
PO Box 456 87036 505-847-2333
Ron Hendrix, supt. Fax 847-2843
mps-nm.schoolloop.com
Mountainair JSHS 100/6-12
PO Box 456 87036 505-847-2211
Eliza Romero, prin. Fax 847-2298

Navajo, McKinley, Pop. 1,626
Gallup-McKinley County SD
Supt. — See Gallup
Navajo MS 100/6-8
PO Box 1287 87328 505-777-2390
Mary Ann Sherman, prin. Fax 721-5399
Navajo Pine HS 100/9-12
PO Box 1286 87328 505-777-2288
Mary Ann Sherman, prin. Fax 721-3699

Newcomb, San Juan, Pop. 335
Central Consolidated SD
Supt. — See Shiprock
Newcomb HS 200/9-12
PO Box 7927 87455 505-696-3417
Tamara Allison, prin. Fax 696-3265
Newcomb MS 200/6-8
PO Box 7927 87455 505-696-3434
Ethel Manuelito, prin. Fax 696-3430

Ojo Caliente, Taos
Mesa Vista Consolidated SD 300/PK-12
PO Box 309 87549 575-583-2645
Ernesto Valdez, supt. Fax 583-2815
www.mesavista.org
Mesa Vista MSHS 100/7-12
PO Box 50 87549 575-583-2275
Donna Giaquinto, prin. Fax 583-9133

Pecos, San Miguel, Pop. 1,378
Pecos ISD 700/PK-12
PO Box 368 87552 505-757-4700
Fred Trujillo, supt. Fax 757-8721
www.pecos.k12.nm.us
Pecos HS 200/9-12
PO Box 368 87552 505-757-4720
Simon Miera, prin. Fax 757-2772
Pecos MS 100/6-8
PO Box 368 87552 505-757-4620
Mike Lister, prin. Fax 757-2561

Penasco, Taos, Pop. 584
Penasco ISD 400/K-12
PO Box 520 87553 575-587-2502
Darlene Ulibarri, supt. Fax 587-2513
www.penascoisd.com
Penasco HS 100/9-12
PO Box 520 87553 575-587-2502
Marina Lopez, prin. Fax 587-9908
Penasco MS 100/7-8
PO Box 520 87553 575-587-2502
Marina Lopez, prin. Fax 587-9910

Portales, Roosevelt, Pop. 12,080
Portales Municipal SD 2,900/PK-12
501 S Abilene Ave 88130 575-356-7000
Johnnie S. Cain, supt. Fax 356-4377
www.portalesschools.com
Portales HS 800/9-12
201 S Knoxville St 88130 575-356-7015
Mark Gormley, prin. Fax 356-8082
Portales JHS 400/7-8
700 E 3rd St 88130 575-356-7045
Steve Harris, prin. Fax 359-0826

Eastern New Mexico University Post-Sec.
1500 S Avenue K 88130 575-562-1011

Pueblo Pintado, McKinley, Pop. 187
Gallup-McKinley County SD
Supt. — See Gallup
Tse' Yi Gai HS 100/9-12
118 Counselor Rd 87013 505-721-5500
Brian Staples, prin. Fax 721-5599

Quemado, Catron, Pop. 224
Quemado ISD 200/K-12
PO Box 128 87829 575-773-4700
David Lackey, supt. Fax 773-4717
www.quemadoschools.org
Quemado JSHS 100/7-12
PO Box 128 87829 575-773-4700
Don Goodman, prin. Fax 773-4717

Questa, Taos, Pop. 1,751
Questa ISD 300/PK-12
PO Box 440 87556 575-586-0421
Valerie Trujillo, supt. Fax 586-0531
www.qisd-nm.schoolloop.com
Questa JSHS 100/7-12
PO Box 529 87556 575-586-1604
Joyce Rock, prin. Fax 586-2282

Ramah, McKinley, Pop. 354
Gallup-McKinley County SD
Supt. — See Gallup
Ramah MSHS 200/6-12
PO Box 849 87321 505-783-4211
Lenny Ray, prin. Fax 721-3699

Ranchos de Taos, Taos, Pop. 2,481

University of New Mexico - Taos Post-Sec.
1157 County Road 110 87557 575-737-6200

Raton, Colfax, Pop. 6,809
Raton SD 600/PK-12
1550 Tiger Cir 87740 575-445-9111
Dr. M. Neil Trerhune, supt. Fax 445-5641
www.ratonschools.com
Raton HS 300/7-12
1535 Tiger Cir 87740 575-445-3541
Duncan Ware, prin. Fax 445-2237

Rehoboth, McKinley

Rehoboth Christian S 400/PK-12
PO Box 41 87322 505-863-4412
Dr. Don McGavran, supt. Fax 863-2185

Reserve, Catron, Pop. 285
Reserve ISD 100/K-12
PO Box 350 87830 575-533-6242
Bill Green, supt. Fax 533-6900
www.reserveschools.com
Reserve JSHS 100/7-12
PO Box 350 87830 575-533-6241
Cindy Shellhorn, prin. Fax 533-6900

Rio Rancho, Sandoval, Pop. 85,293
Rio Rancho SD 17,200/PK-12
500 Laser Rd NE 87124 505-896-0667
Dr. V. Sue Cleveland, supt. Fax 896-0662
www.rrps.net
Cleveland HS 2,400/9-12
4800 Laban Rd NE, 505-938-0300
Scott Affentranger, prin. Fax 338-3474
Eagle Ridge MS 800/6-8
800 Fruta Rd NE 87124 505-892-6630
Catherine Rodriguez, prin. Fax 892-6909
Independence HS 200/Alt
421 Quantum Rd NE 87124 505-338-4658
Myra Roosevelt, prin. Fax 892-9742
Lincoln MS 1,000/6-8
2287 Lema Rd SE 87124 505-892-1100
Veronica Sanders, prin. Fax 892-9728
Mountain View MS 900/6-8
4101 Montreal Loop NE, 505-867-0711
Julie Arnold, prin. Fax 867-7901
Rio Rancho HS 2,500/9-12
301 Loma Colorado Blvd NE 87124 505-896-5600
Richard Von Ancken, prin. Fax 896-5901
Rio Rancho MS 1,200/6-8
1600 Loma Colorado Blvd NE, 505-891-5335
Lynda Kitts, prin. Fax 891-1180

Gospel Light Baptist Academy 100/1-12
1500 Southern Blvd SE 87124 505-892-9463

Roswell, Chaves, Pop. 47,742
Roswell ISD 10,300/PK-12
PO Box 1437 88202 575-627-2500
Tom Burrris, supt. Fax 627-2512
www.risd.k12.nm.us
Berrendo MS 600/6-8
800 Marion Richards Rd 88201 575-627-2775
Susan Martin, prin. Fax 625-8248
Goddard HS 1,100/9-12
701 E Country Club Rd 88201 575-627-4800
Brian Luck, prin. Fax 627-4856
Mesa MS 500/6-8
1601 E Bland St 88203 575-627-2800
LaShawn Byrd, prin. Fax 625-8263
Mountain View MS 500/6-8
312 E Mountain View Rd 88203 575-627-2825
Glenda Leonard, prin. Fax 625-8260
Roswell HS 1,400/9-12
500 W Hobbs St 88203 575-637-3200
Ruben Bolanos, prin. Fax 637-3268
Sierra MS 600/6-8
615 S Sycamore Ave 88203 575-627-2850
Kevin Summers, prin. Fax 625-8283
University HS 100/Alt
25 W Martin St 88203 575-627-2750
Porter Cutrell, prin. Fax 625-8278

Aladdin Beauty College Post-Sec.
108 S Union Ave 88203 575-623-6331
Eastern New Mexico University Post-Sec.
PO Box 6000 88202 575-624-7000
Gateway Christian S 300/PK-12
PO Box 1642 88202 575-622-9710
Rick Rapp, admin. Fax 622-9739
New Mexico Military Institute Post-Sec.
101 W College Blvd 88201 575-622-6250
New Mexico Military Institute 400/9-12
101 W College Blvd 88201 575-624-8001
Valley Christian Academy 200/PK-12
1500 S Main St 88203 575-627-1500

Roy, Harding, Pop. 234
Roy Municipal SD 50/PK-12
PO Box 430 87743 575-485-2242
Bonnie Lightfoot, supt. Fax 485-2497
www.royschools.org
Roy JSHS 50/7-12
PO Box 430 87743 575-485-2242
Bonnie Lightfoot, admin. Fax 485-2497

Ruidoso, Lincoln, Pop. 7,928
Ruidoso Municipal SD 2,100/PK-12
200 Horton Cir 88345 575-630-7000
Dr. George Bickert, supt. Fax 257-4150
www.ruidososchools.org/
Ruidoso HS 600/9-12
200 Horton Cir 88345 575-630-7900
Cody Patterson, prin. Fax 258-3516
Ruidoso MS 500/6-8
200 Horton Cir 88345 575-630-7800
Anna Addis, prin. Fax 258-5809

San Jon, Quay, Pop. 209
San Jon Municipal SD 100/PK-12
PO Box 5 88434 575-576-2466
Colin Taylor, supt. Fax 576-2772
www.sanjonschools.com
San Jon HS 50/9-12
PO Box 5 88434 575-576-2466
Fax 576-2772
San Jon MS 50/6-8
PO Box 5 88434 575-576-2466
Fax 576-2772

Santa Fe, Santa Fe, Pop. 66,849

Pojoaque Valley SD 1,900/PK-12
1574 State Road 502 87506 505-455-2282
Dr. Melville Morgan, supt. Fax 455-7152
www.pvs.k12.nm.us
Pojoaque Valley HS 600/9-12
1574 State Road 502 87506 505-455-2234
Jennifer Baca, prin. Fax 455-3471
Pojoaque Valley MS 300/7-8
1574 State Road 502 87506 505-455-2238
Vera Trujillo, prin. Fax 455-3392

Santa Fe SD 13,400/PK-12
610 Alta Vista St 87505 505-467-2000
Dr. Veronica Garcia, supt. Fax 995-3300
www.sfps.info
Academy at Larragoite 100/Alt
1604 Agua Fria St 87505 505-467-1900
Dr. Cynthia Sanchez, prin. Fax 982-4432
Capital HS 1,300/9-12
4851 Paseo Del Sol 87507 505-467-1000
Channell Wilson-Segura, prin. Fax 471-4325
Capshaw MS 400/7-8
351 W Zia Rd 87505 505-467-4300
Laura Jeffery, prin. Fax 982-4431
De Vargas MS 400/7-8
1720 Llano St 87505 505-467-3300
Marc Ducharme, prin. Fax 471-3793
Early College Opportunities 9-10
2301 W Zia Rd 87505 505-467-2412
Mandela International Magnet S 50/7-8
1720 Llano St 87505 505-467-2000
Tony Gerlicz, prin. Fax 471-9287
Ortiz MS 700/6-8
4164 S Meadows Rd 87507 505-467-2300
Felicia Sena, prin. Fax 471-0610
Santa Fe HS 1,700/9-12
2100 Yucca St 87505 505-467-2400
Mary Massey, prin. Fax 471-4293

Adventist Academy of Santa Fe K-10
PO Box 28327 87592 505-954-1845
Desert Academy 200/6-12
7300 Old Santa Fe Trl 87505 505-992-8284
Terry Passalacqua, hdmstr. Fax 992-8270
Institute of American Indian Arts Post-Sec.
83 Avan NU PO 87508 505-424-2300
New Mexico School for the Deaf Post-Sec.
1060 Cerrillos Rd 87505 505-827-6739
St. John's College Post-Sec.
1160 Camino De Cruz Blanca 87505 505-984-6000
St. Michael's HS 700/7-12
100 Siringo Rd 87505 505-983-7353
Sam Govea, prin. Fax 982-8722
Santa Fe Christian Academy 200/PK-10
4601 Mission Bend 87507 505-474-8080
Bernadette Shanaberger, prin. Fax 474-8082
Santa Fe Community College Post-Sec.
6401 S Richards Ave 87508 505-428-1000
Santa Fe Preparatory S 300/7-12
1101 Camino De Cruz Blanca 87505 505-982-1829
James Leonard, hdmstr. Fax 982-2897
Santa Fe University of Art and Design Post-Sec.
1600 Saint Michaels Dr 87505 505-473-6011
Sante Fe Waldorf S 200/PK-12
26 Puesta Del Sol 87508 505-983-9727
Southwest Acupuncture College Post-Sec.
1622 Galisteo St 87505 505-438-8884
Southwestern College Post-Sec.
3960 San Felipe Rd 87507 505-471-5756

Santa Rosa, Guadalupe, Pop. 2,827
Santa Rosa Consolidated SD 600/PK-12
344 S 4th St 88435 575-472-3171
Richard Perea, supt. Fax 472-5609
www.srlions.com
Santa Rosa HS 200/9-12
717 S 3rd St 88435 575-472-3422
Martin Madrid, prin. Fax 472-3169
Santa Rosa MS 100/6-8
116 Camino de Vida 88435 575-472-3633
Julie Sanchez, prin. Fax 472-0663
Other Schools – See Anton Chico

Santa Teresa, Dona Ana, Pop. 4,240
Gadsden ISD
Supt. — See Sunland Park
Santa Teresa HS 1,300/9-12
100 Airport Rd 88008 575-589-5300
Nicholas Wohlgemuth, prin. Fax 589-5311
Santa Teresa MS 600/7-8
4800 McNutt Rd 88008 575-874-7200
Rosa Lovelace, prin. Fax 589-2780

Shiprock, San Juan, Pop. 8,162
Central Consolidated SD 6,100/PK-12
PO Box 1199 87420 505-368-4984
Fax 368-5232
www.ccsdnm.org
Career Prep HS 100/Alt
PO Box 3514 87420 505-368-4980
Stacie Gallaher, prin. Fax 368-5703
Shiprock HS 600/9-12
PO Box 3578 87420 505-368-5161
Rick Edwards, prin. Fax 368-5796
Tse' Bit'ai MS 500/6-8
PO Box 1703 87420 505-368-4741
Dr. Kaibah Begay, prin. Fax 368-5105
Other Schools – See Kirtland, Newcomb

Silver City, Grant, Pop. 10,166
Silver Consolidated SD 3,000/PK-12
2810 N Swan St 88061 575-956-2000
John Carter, supt. Fax 956-2039
www.silverschools.org
La Plata MS 600/6-8
3500 N Silver St 88061 575-956-2060
Beth Lougee, prin. Fax 956-2098
Opportunity HS 100/Alt
600 E 32nd St 88061 575-956-2140
Jason Ping, prin. Fax 956-2149
Silver HS 700/9-12
3200 N Silver St 88061 575-956-2158
Victor Oaxaca, prin. Fax 388-2927
Other Schools – See Cliff

Calvary Christian Academy 100/PK-12
PO Box 29 88062 575-388-4478
Western New Mexico University Post-Sec.
PO Box 680 88062 575-538-6011

Socorro, Socorro, Pop. 8,907
Socorro Consolidated SD 1,800/K-12
700 Franklin St 87801 575-835-0300
Dr. Randall Earwood, supt. Fax 835-1682
www.socorro.k12.nm.us/
Sarracino MS 400/6-8
1425 El Camino Real St 87801 575-835-0283
Rhonda Martinez, prin. Fax 835-0360
Socorro HS 400/9-12
1200 Michigan St 87801 575-835-0700
Susan Comiskey, admin. Fax 835-0704

New Mexico Institute Mining & Technology Post-Sec.
801 Leroy Pl 87801 575-835-5434

Springer, Colfax, Pop. 1,037
Springer Municipal SD 200/K-12
PO Box 308 87747 575-483-3432
Eddie King, supt. Fax 483-2387
www.springerschools.org
Springer HS 100/7-12
PO Box 308 87747 575-483-3464
Christina Vigil, dean Fax 483-3970

Sunland Park, Dona Ana, Pop. 14,071
Gadsden ISD 14,800/PK-12
4950 McNutt Rd 88063 575-882-6200
Efren Yturralde, supt. Fax 882-6229
www.gisd.k12.nm.us
Other Schools – See Anthony, Chaparral, Santa Teresa

International School Post-Sec.
PO Box 1919 88063 800-743-1414

Taos, Taos, Pop. 5,592
Taos Municipal SD 2,900/PK-12
310 Camino De La Placita 87571 575-758-5202
Dr. Lillian Torrez, supt. Fax 758-5250
www.taosschools.org
Taos HS 800/9-12
134 Cervantes St 87571 575-751-8000
Robert Trujillo, prin. Fax 751-8001
Taos MS 500/6-8
235 Paseo Del Canon E 87571 575-737-6000
Alfred Cordova, prin. Fax 737-6001

National College of Midwifery Post-Sec.
209 State Road 240 87571 575-758-8914

Tatum, Lea, Pop. 793
Tatum Municipal SD 300/PK-12
PO Box 685 88267 575-398-4455
Buddy Little, supt. Fax 398-8220
www.tatumschools.org
Tatum JSHS 100/7-12
PO Box 685 88267 575-398-4555
Greg Slover, prin. Fax 398-4450

Texico, Curry, Pop. 1,118
Texico Municipal SD 600/PK-12
PO Box 237 88135 575-482-3801
Robert Brown, supt. Fax 482-3650
www.texicoschools.com
Texico HS 200/9-12
PO Box 237 88135 575-482-3305
Dee Rae Timberlake, prin. Fax 482-3650
Texico MS 100/6-8
PO Box 237 88135 575-482-9520
Beth Thornton, prin. Fax 482-3650

Thoreau, McKinley, Pop. 1,831
Gallup-McKinley County SD
Supt. — See Gallup
Thoreau HS 300/9-12
PO Box 969 87323 505-721-4500
Lawrence Sena, prin. Fax 721-4599
Thoreau MS 300/6-8
PO Box 787 87323 505-721-4600
Moni Short, prin. Fax 721-4699

Tierra Amarilla, Rio Arriba, Pop. 379
Chama Valley ISD 300/PK-12
PO Box 10 87575 575-588-7285
Anthony Casados, supt. Fax 588-7860
www.chamaschools.org
Escalante MSHS 100/7-12
PO Box 157 87575 575-588-7201
Greg Marez, prin. Fax 588-7911

Tijeras, Bernalillo, Pop. 534
Albuquerque SD
Supt. — See Albuquerque
Roosevelt MS 300/6-8
11799 State Highway 14 S 87059 505-281-3316
Cee Kay Nation, prin. Fax 281-5120

Tohatchi, McKinley, Pop. 799
Gallup-McKinley County SD
Supt. — See Gallup
Tohatchi HS 300/9-12
PO Box 248 87325 505-733-2206
Craig Robinson, prin. Fax 721-4899
Tohatchi MS 200/6-8
PO Box 322 87325 505-721-4900
Anthony Morrison, prin. Fax 721-4999

Truth or Consequences, Sierra, Pop. 6,359
Truth or Consequences Municipal SD 1,300/PK-12
180 N Date St 87901 575-894-8166
Dr. Craig Cummins, supt. Fax 894-7532
www.torcschools.net
Hot Springs HS 400/9-12
180 N Date St 87901 575-894-8350
Patti Nesbitt, prin. Fax 894-0471
Truth or Consequences MS 300/6-8
180 N Date St 87901 575-894-8380
Dr. Renee Garcia, prin. Fax 894-0606

Manzano Christian S 50/K-12
1300 S Broadway St 87901 505-894-5646
Rebecca Dow, admin. Fax 894-0132

Tucumcari, Quay, Pop. 5,279
Tucumcari SD 1,000/PK-12
PO Box 1046 88401 575-461-3910
Aaron McKinney, supt. Fax 461-3554
tucumcarischools.com
Tucumcari HS 200/9-12
1001 S 7th St 88401 575-461-3830
Nicole Lesly, prin. Fax 461-3769
Tucumcari MS 200/6-8
1000 S 5th St 88401 575-461-2310
Lendy Borden, prin. Fax 461-8610

Mesalands Community College Post-Sec.
911 S 10th St 88401 575-461-4413

Tularosa, Otero, Pop. 2,782
Tularosa Municipal SD 900/K-12
504 1st St 88352 575-585-8800
Brenda Vigil, supt. Fax 585-4439
www.tularosa.k12.nm.us
Tularosa HS 300/9-12
504 1st St 88352 575-585-8866
John J. Marrujo, prin. Fax 585-8112
Tularosa MS 100/7-8
504 1st St 88352 575-585-8803
Bobbie Grace, prin. Fax 585-4739

Vaughn, Guadalupe, Pop. 444
Vaughn Municipal SD 100/PK-12
PO Box 489 88353 575-584-2283
Jack Props, supt. Fax 584-2355
www.vaughn.k12.nm.us/
Vaughn JSHS 100/7-12
PO Box 489 88353 575-584-2283
Lyndsey Padill, prin. Fax 584-2355

Wagon Mound, Mora, Pop. 312
Wagon Mound SD 100/K-12
PO Box 158 87752 575-666-3000
Sheryl Martinez, supt. Fax 666-9001
www.wm.k12.nm.us
Wagon Mound JSHS 50/7-12
PO Box 158 87752 575-666-3001
Sheryl Martinez, prin. Fax 666-9001

Zuni, McKinley, Pop. 5,857
Zuni SD 1,300/PK-12
12 Twin Buttes Dr 87327 505-782-5511
Hayes A. Lewis, supt. Fax 782-5870
www.zpsd.org
Twin Buttes HS 50/9-12
PO Box 680 87327 505-782-4446
Florence Acque, prin. Fax 782-4944
Zuni HS 300/9-12
PO Box 550 87327 505-782-4451
Donald Sparks, prin. Fax 782-5551
Zuni MS 200/6-8
PO Box E 87327 505-782-5561
Ophelia Barber, prin. Fax 782-5563

NEW YORK

NEW YORK EDUCATION DEPARTMENT
89 Washington Ave, Albany 12234-1000
Telephone 518-474-3852
Fax 518-473-4909
Website http://www.nysed.gov

Commissioner of Education MaryEllen Elia

NEW YORK BOARD OF REGENTS
89 Washington Ave, Albany 12234-1000

Chancellor Betty Rosa

BOARDS OF COOPERATIVE EDUCATIONAL SERVICES (BOCES)

Broome-Deleware-Tioga BOCES
Allen Buyck, supt. 607-766-3802
435 Glenwood Rd Fax 763-3691
Binghamton 13905
www.btboces.org/

Capital Region BOCES
Dr. Charles Dedrick, supt. 518-862-4900
900 Watervliet Shaker Rd Fax 862-4903
Albany 12205
www.capregboces.org

Cattaraugus/Allegany/Erie/Wyoming BOCES
Lynda Quick, supt. 585-376-8246
1825 Windfall Rd, Olean 14760 Fax 376-8452
www.caboces.org

Cayuga/Onondaga BOCES
William Speck, supt. 315-253-0361
1879 W Genesee Street Rd Fax 252-6493
Auburn 13021
cayboces.org

Champlain Valley Educational Services
Dr. Mark Davey, supt. 518-561-0100
PO Box 455, Plattsburgh 12901 Fax 562-1471
www.cves.org/

Ctr for Instruction Technology & Innovtn
Christopher Todd, supt. 315-963-4222
179 County Route 64 Fax 963-4475
Mexico 13114
www.oswegoboces.org

Delaware/Chenango/Madison/Otsego BOCES
, 6678 County Road 32 607-335-1233
Norwich 13815 Fax 334-9848
www.dcmoboces.com

Dutchess BOCES
Dr. Richard Hooley, supt. 845-486-4800
5 Boces Rd, Poughkeepsie 12601 Fax 486-4981
www.dcboces.org

Eastern Suffolk BOCES
Maureen Donahue-Whitley, supt. 631-687-3006
201 S Service Rd Fax 289-2529
Patchogue 11772
www.esboces.org

Erie 1 BOCES
Lynn Fusco, supt., 355 Harlem Rd 716-821-7001
West Seneca 14224 Fax 821-7242
www.erie1boces.org

Erie 2-Chautauqua-Cattaraugus BOCES
Dr. David O'Rourke, supt. 716-549-4454
8685 Erie Rd, Angola 14006 Fax 549-5181
www.e2ccb.org

Franklin-Essex-Hamilton BOCES
Stephen Shafer, supt. 518-483-6420
PO Box 28, Malone 12953 Fax 483-2178
www.fehb.org/

Genesee Valley BOCES
Kevin MacDonald, supt. 585-658-7900
80 Munson St, Le Roy 14482 Fax 344-7910
www.gvboces.org

Greater Southern Tier BOCES
James Frame, supt. 607-654-2283
9579 Vocational Dr Fax 654-2302
Painted Post 14870
www.gstboces.org

Hamilton-Fulton-Montgomery BOCES
Dr. Patrick Michel, supt. 518-736-4300
2755 State Highway 67 Fax 736-4301
Johnstown 12095
www.hfmboces.org

Herkimer-Fulton-Hamilton-Otsego BOCES
Mark Vivacqua, supt. 315-867-2023
352 Gros Blvd, Herkimer 13350 Fax 867-2002
www.herkimer-boces.org

Jefferson-Lewis-Hmltn-Hrkmr-Oneida BOCES
Stephen Todd, supt. 315-779-7010
20104 State Route 3 Fax 779-7009
Watertown 13601
www.boces.com

Madison-Oneida BOCES
Jacklin Starks, supt. 315-361-5510
PO Box 168, Verona 13478 Fax 361-5517
www.moboces.org

Monroe 1 BOCES
Daniel White, supt. 585-383-2200
41 OConnor Rd, Fairport 14450 Fax 383-6404
www.monroe.edu/

Monroe 2 BOCES
JoAnne Antonacci, supt. 585-352-2400
3599 Big Ridge Rd Fax 352-2442
Spencerport 14559
www.monroe2boces.org

Nassau BOCES
Dr. Robert Dillon, supt. 516-396-2200
PO Box 9195, Garden City 11530 Fax 997-8742
www.nassauboces.org

Oneida-Herkimer-Madison BOCES
Howard Mettelman, supt. 315-793-8561
PO Box 70, New Hartford 13413 Fax 793-8541
www.oneida-boces.org/

Onondaga-Cortland-Madison BOCES
Jody Manning, supt. 315-433-2602
PO Box 4754, Syracuse 13221 Fax 434-9347
www.ocmboces.org

Orange-Ulster BOCES
William Hecht, supt. 845-291-0100
53 Gibson Rd, Goshen 10924 Fax 291-0118
www.ouboces.org/

Orleans-Niagara BOCES
Dr. Clark Godshall, supt. 800-836-7510
4232 Shelby Basin Rd Fax 798-1317
Medina 14103
www.onboces.org

Otsego-Northern Catskills BOCES
Nicholas Savin, supt. 607-588-6291
PO Box 382, Stamford 12167 Fax 588-6098
www.oncboces.org

Putnam Northern Westchester BOCES
Dr. James Langlois, supt. 914-248-2300
200 BOCES Dr Fax 248-2308
Yorktown Heights 10598
www.pnwboces.org

Questar III BOCES
Dr. Gladys Cruz, supt. 518-477-8771
10 Empire State Blvd Fax 477-9833
Castleton on Hudson 12033
www.questar.org

Rockland BOCES
Dr. James Langlois, supt. 845-627-4701
65 Parrott Rd, West Nyack 10994 Fax 624-1764
www.rocklandboces.org/

St. Lawrence-Lewis BOCES
Thomas Burns, supt. 315-386-4504
PO Box 231, Canton 13617 Fax 386-2099
www.sllboces.org

Southern Westchester BOCES
Dr. Harold Coles, supt. 914-937-3820
17 Berkley Dr, Rye Brook 10573 Fax 937-7850
www.swboces.org

Sullivan County BOCES
Dr. Charles Khoury, supt. 845-295-4000
6 Wierk Ave, Liberty 12754 Fax 292-8694
www.scboces.org

Tompkins-Seneca-Tioga BOCES
Dr. Jeffrey Matteson, supt. 607-257-1551
555 Warren Rd, Ithaca 14850 Fax 257-2825
www.tstboces.org/

Ulster BOCES
Dr. Charles Khoury, supt. 845-255-3040
175 State Route 32 N Fax 255-7942
New Paltz 12561
www.ulsterboces.org/

Washington-Srtg-Warren-Hmltn-Essex BOCES
James Dexter, supt. 518-746-3310
1153 Burgoyne Ave Ste 2 Fax 746-3319
Fort Edward 12828
wswheboces.org

Wayne-Finger Lakes BOCES
Scott Bischoping, supt. 315-332-7284
131 Drumlin Ct, Newark 14513 Fax 332-7425
www.wflboces.org

Western Suffolk BOCES
Maureen Donahue-Whitney, admin. 631-549-4900
507 Deer Park Rd, Dix Hills 11746 Fax 623-4996
www.wsboces.org/

PUBLIC, PRIVATE AND CATHOLIC SECONDARY SCHOOLS

Accord, Ulster, Pop. 551
Rondout Valley Central SD 2,000/K-12
PO Box 9 12404 845-687-2400
Rosario Agostaro, supt. Fax 687-9577
www.rondout.k12.ny.us
Rondout Valley HS 700/9-12
PO Box 9 12404 845-687-2400
Robert Cook, prin. Fax 687-7665
Rondout Valley JHS 300/7-8
PO Box 9 12404 845-687-2400
Charles Tadduni, prin. Fax 687-8980

Adams, Jefferson, Pop. 1,752
South Jefferson Central SD
Supt. — See Adams Center
Clarke MS 400/6-8
11060 US Route 11 13605 315-232-4531
Tom O'Brien, prin. Fax 232-4620
South Jefferson HS 600/9-12
11060 US Route 11 13605 315-232-4531
Karen Denny, prin. Fax 232-3728

Adams Center, Jefferson, Pop. 1,533
South Jefferson Central SD 1,900/K-12
13180 US Route 11 13606 315-583-6104
Mary Beth Denny, supt. Fax 583-6381
www.spartanpride.org
Other Schools – See Adams

Addison, Steuben, Pop. 1,744
Addison Central SD 1,000/PK-12
7 Cleveland Dr 14801 607-359-2244
Joseph DioGuardi, supt. Fax 359-2246
www.addisoncsd.org/
Addison MSHS 400/8-12
1 Colwell St 14801 607-359-2241
Jennifer Crane, prin. Fax 359-3443

Afton, Chenango, Pop. 818
Afton Central SD 500/K-12
PO Box 5 13730 607-639-8229
Elizabeth Briggs, supt. Fax 639-1801
www.aftoncsd.org
Afton JSHS 200/6-12
PO Box 5 13730 607-639-8223
David Glover, prin. Fax 639-8257

Airmont, Rockland, Pop. 8,483

Mesifta Beth Shraga S 100/9-12
28 N Saddle River Rd, 845-356-1980
Monsey Beis Chaya Mushka 100/9-12
27 S Monsey Rd, 845-634-7400
Rabbinical College Beth Shraga Post-Sec.
28 N Saddle River Rd, 845-356-1980
Toras Chaim 50/9-12
1 Regina Rd, 845-352-9126

Akron, Erie, Pop. 2,833
Akron Central SD 1,400/K-12
47 Bloomingdale Ave 14001 716-542-5010
Kevin Shanley, supt. Fax 542-5018
www.akronschools.org

Akron HS 400/9-12
47 Bloomingdale Ave 14001 716-542-5030
Joseph Lucenti, prin. Fax 542-5018
Akron MS 400/6-8
47 Bloomingdale Ave 14001 716-542-5040
Joseph Caprio, prin. Fax 542-5018

Albany, Albany, Pop. 94,773
CSD of Albany 8,200/PK-12
1 Academy Park 12207 518-475-6000
Kimberly Wilkins Ed.D., supt. Fax 475-6009
www.albanyschools.org
Abrookin Career & Tech Center Vo/Tech
99 Kent St 12206 518-475-6400
Andrea Marques, prin. Fax 475-6402
Albany HS 2,200/9-12
700 Washington Ave 12203 518-475-6200
Dale Getto, prin. Fax 475-6202
Alternative Learning Center Alt
50 Lark St 12210 518-475-6525
Sophia Newell, prin. Fax 475-6527
Hackett MS 700/6-8
45 Delaware Ave 12202 518-475-6475
Michael Paolino, prin. Fax 475-6477
Myers MS 700/6-8
100 Elbel Ct 12209 518-475-6425
Michael Panetta, prin. Fax 475-6427
West Hill MS 7-8
395 Elk St 12206 518-475-6900
Kandie Antonetti, prin. Fax 475-6902

South Colonie Central SD 5,000/PK-12
102 Loralee Dr 12205 518-869-3576
Jonathan Buhner, supt. Fax 869-6517
www.southcolonieschools.org
Colonie Central HS 1,600/9-12
1 Raider Blvd 12205 518-459-1220
Christopher Robilotti, prin. Fax 459-8524
Lisha Kill MS 700/5-8
68 Waterman Ave 12205 518-456-2306
David Wetzel, prin. Fax 452-8165
Sand Creek MS 800/5-8
329 Sand Creek Rd 12205 518-459-1333
Thomas Nicholson, prin. Fax 459-1404

Academy of the Holy Names 300/6-12
1075 New Scotland Rd 12208 518-438-7895
Mary Anne Vigliante, head sch Fax 438-7368
Albany Academies 500/PK-12
135 Academy Rd 12208 518-429-2300
Dr. Douglas North Ph.D., head sch Fax 427-7016
Albany Academy for Girls 400/PK-12
140 Academy Rd 12208 518-429-2300
Dr. Douglas North Ph.D., head sch Fax 463-5096
Albany College of Pharmacy & Health Sci Post-Sec.
106 New Scotland Ave 12208 888-203-8010
Albany Law School Post-Sec.
80 New Scotland Ave 12208 518-445-2311
Albany Medical College Post-Sec.
47 New Scotland Ave Code 3 12208 518-262-5521
Bishop Maginn HS 100/9-12
75 Park Ave 12202 518-463-2247
Christopher Signor, prin. Fax 463-9880
Branford Hall Career Institute Post-Sec.
500 New Karner Rd 12205 518-456-4464
Bryant & Stratton College Post-Sec.
1259 Central Ave 12205 518-437-1802
Center for Natural Wellness School Post-Sec.
3 Cerone Commercial Dr 12205 518-489-4026
Christian Brothers Academy 400/6-12
12 Airline Dr 12205 518-452-9809
James Schlegel, head sch Fax 452-9804
College of Saint Rose Post-Sec.
432 Western Ave 12203 800-637-8556
Excelsior College Post-Sec.
7 Columbia Cir 12203 518-464-8500
Maimonides Hebrew Day S 100/PK-12
404 Partridge St 12208 518-453-9363
Maria College of Albany Post-Sec.
700 New Scotland Ave 12208 518-438-3111
Memorial Hospital School of Nursing Post-Sec.
600 Northern Blvd 12204 518-471-3260
Mildred Elley School Post-Sec.
855 Central Ave 12206 518-786-0855
Orlo School of Hair Design & Cosmetology Post-Sec.
232 N Allen St 12206 518-459-7832
SUNY at Albany Post-Sec.
1400 Washington Ave 12222 518-442-3300
The New School of Radio & Television Post-Sec.
7 Harriman Campus Rd 12206 518-438-7682

Albertson, Nassau, Pop. 5,037
Herricks UFD
Supt. — See New Hyde Park
Herricks MS 1,000/6-8
7 Hilldale Dr 11507 516-305-8600
Joan Keegan, prin. Fax 739-4738

Albion, Orleans, Pop. 5,876
Albion Central SD 2,000/PK-12
324 East Ave 14411 585-589-2056
Michael Bonnewell, supt. Fax 589-2059
www.albionk12.org/
Bergerson MS, 254 East Ave 14411 500/6-8
Daniel Monacelli, prin. 585-589-2020
D'Amico HS, 302 East Ave 14411 600/9-12
Matthew Peterson, prin. 585-589-2040

Alden, Erie, Pop. 2,590
Alden Central SD 1,700/K-12
13190 Park St 14004 716-937-9116
Adam Stoltman, supt. Fax 937-7132
www.aldenschools.org
Alden HS 600/9-12
13190 Park St 14004 716-937-9116
Kevin Ryan, prin. Fax 937-1740
Alden MS 400/6-8
13250 Park St 14004 716-937-9116
Steven Smith, prin. Fax 937-3563

Alexander, Genesee, Pop. 501
Alexander Central SD 900/PK-12
3314 Buffalo St 14005 585-591-1551
Kathleen Maerten, supt. Fax 591-2257
www.alexandercsd.org
Alexander MSHS 500/6-12
3314 Buffalo St 14005 585-591-1551
Shannon Whitcombe, prin. Fax 591-1098

Alexandria Bay, Jefferson, Pop. 1,066
Alexandria Central SD 600/PK-12
34 Bolton Ave 13607 315-482-9971
George Merritt, supt. Fax 482-9973
www.alexandriacentral.org
Alexandria Central JSHS 300/7-12
34 Bolton Ave 13607 315-482-5113
Joe Orobona, prin. Fax 482-9973

Alfred, Allegany, Pop. 4,085

Alfred State College Post-Sec.
10 Upper College Dr 14802 800-425-3733
Alfred University Post-Sec.
1 Saxon Dr 14802 607-871-2111

Allegany, Cattaraugus, Pop. 1,807
Allegany-Limestone Central SD 800/PK-12
3131 Five Mile Rd 14706 716-375-6600
Dr. Karen Geelan, supt. Fax 375-6629
alcsny.org
Allegany-Limestone MSHS 300/6-12
3131 Five Mile Rd 14706 716-375-6600
Cory Pecorella, prin. Fax 375-6630

Almond, Allegany, Pop. 460
Alfred-Almond Central SD 700/PK-12
6795 State Route 21 14804 607-276-6500
Richard Calkins, supt. Fax 276-6556
www.aacs.wnyric.org
Alfred-Almond JSHS 300/7-12
6795 State Route 21 14804 607-276-6555
Susan Bain-Lucey, prin. Fax 276-6556

Amenia, Dutchess, Pop. 935
Webutuck Central SD 800/PK-12
PO Box 405 12501 845-373-4100
Raymond Castellani, supt. Fax 373-4102
www.webutuckschools.org
Brooks IS 300/4-8
PO Box 405 12501 845-373-4114
Kenneth Sauer, prin. Fax 373-4126
Webutuck HS 200/9-12
PO Box 405 12501 845-373-4106
Katy McEnroe, prin. Fax 373-8529

Kildonan S 100/2-12
425 Morse Hill Rd 12501 845-373-8111
Kevin Pendergast, hdmstr. Fax 373-9793

Amherst, Erie, Pop. 45,800
Amherst Central SD 2,800/K-12
55 Kings Hwy 14226 716-362-3000
Anthony J. Panella, supt. Fax 362-3022
amherstschools.org
Amherst Central HS 800/9-12
4301 Main St 14226 716-362-8100
Gregory Pigeon, prin. Fax 836-4972
Amherst MS 700/6-8
55 Kings Hwy 14226 716-362-7100
John Griesmer, prin. Fax 836-0193

Sweet Home Central SD 3,200/PK-12
1901 Sweet Home Rd 14228 716-250-1402
Anthony Day, supt. Fax 250-1374
www.sweethomeschools.org
Sweet Home HS 1,100/9-12
1901 Sweet Home Rd 14228 716-250-1200
Andres Arroyo, prin. Fax 250-1362
Sweet Home MS 800/6-8
4150 Maple Rd 14226 716-250-1450
Marty Pizur, prin. Fax 250-1490

Daemen College Post-Sec.
4380 Main St 14226 716-839-8225

Amityville, Suffolk, Pop. 9,408
Amityville UFD, 150 Park Ave 11701 2,900/PK-12
Dr. Mary Kelly, supt. 631-565-6019
www.amityvilleufsd.org/
Amityville Memorial HS 700/10-12
250 Merrick Rd 11701 631-565-6100
Dr. Clinton Grant, prin.
Miles MS, 501 Route 110 11701 600/7-9
Edward Plaia, prin. 631-565-6200

Bethesda SDA Junior Academy 50/PK-10
76 Parkway Ave 11701 631-842-3321
Gwendolyn Wesley, prin. Fax 842-1623
Branford Hall Career Institute Post-Sec.
1100 Broadway 11701 631-608-9113
Island Drafting & Technical Institute Post-Sec.
128 Broadway 11701 631-691-8733

Amsterdam, Montgomery, Pop. 18,256
Broadalbin-Perth Central SD
Supt. — See Broadalbin
Broadalbin-Perth MS 400/6-8
1870 County Highway 107 12010 518-954-2700
Wayne Bell, prin. Fax 954-2709

Greater Amsterdam SD 3,700/PK-12
PO Box 309 12010 518-843-3180
Thomas Perillo, supt. Fax 842-0012
www.gasd.org
Amsterdam HS 1,100/9-12
140 Saratoga Ave 12010 518-843-4932
Patrick Corrigan, prin. Fax 843-5432

Lynch Literacy Academy 800/6-8
55 Brandt Pl 12010 518-843-3716
Nancy Noonan, prin. Fax 843-6287

Andes, Delaware, Pop. 250
Andes Central SD 100/PK-12
PO Box 248 13731 845-676-3167
Dr. Robert Chakar M.Ed., supt. Fax 676-3181
www.andescentralschool.org
Andes Central S 100/PK-12
PO Box 248 13731 845-676-3166
Dr. Robert Chakar M.Ed., supt. Fax 676-3181

Andover, Allegany, Pop. 1,032
Andover Central SD 300/PK-12
PO Box G 14806 607-478-8491
Lawrence Spangenburg, supt. Fax 478-8833
www.andovercsd.org/
Andover S 300/PK-12
PO Box G 14806 607-478-8491
Jon Morris, prin. Fax 478-8833

Angola, Erie, Pop. 2,096
Lake Shore Central SD 2,500/K-12
959 Beach Rd 14006 716-549-2300
James E. Przepasniak, supt. Fax 549-6407
www.lakeshorecsd.org
Lake Shore MS 600/6-8
8855 Erie Rd 14006 716-926-2400
Erich Reidell, prin. Fax 549-4374
Lake Shore SHS 800/9-12
959 Beach Rd 14006 716-926-2301
JulieAnn Hoerner, prin. Fax 549-4033

Annandale on Hudson, Dutchess

Bard College Post-Sec.
PO Box 5000 12504 845-758-6822

Ardsley, Westchester, Pop. 4,379
Ardsley UFD 2,000/K-12
500 Farm Rd 10502 914-295-5500
Dr. Lauren Allan, supt. Fax 295-5976
www.ardsleyschools.org
Ardsley HS 600/9-12
300 Farm Rd 10502 914-295-5800
Rudy Arietta, prin. Fax 295-5977
Ardsley MS 600/5-8
700 Ashford Ave 10502 914-295-5600
Dr. Jo Anne Januzzi, prin. Fax 295-5676

Argyle, Washington, Pop. 303
Argyle Central SD 500/K-12
5023 State Route 40 12809 518-638-8243
William Scott, supt. Fax 638-6373
www.argylecsd.org
Argyle Central JSHS 300/7-12
5023 State Route 40 12809 518-638-8243
Susan Passaro, prin. Fax 638-6373

Arkport, Steuben, Pop. 839
Arkport Central SD 500/K-12
35 East Ave 14807 607-295-7471
Dr. Glenn Niles, supt. Fax 295-7473
www.arkportcsd.org
Arkport Central S 500/K-12
35 East Ave 14807 607-295-7471
Caitlin Dewey, prin. Fax 295-7473

Armonk, Westchester, Pop. 4,278
Byram Hills Central SD 2,600/K-12
10 Tripp Ln 10504 914-273-4082
Dr. William Donohue, supt. Fax 273-2516
www.byramhills.org
Byram Hills HS 900/9-12
12 Tripp Ln Ste 1 10504 914-273-9200
Christopher Borsari, prin. Fax 273-2067
Crittenden MS 600/6-8
10 MacDonald Ave 10504 914-273-4250
Dr. H. Evan Powderly, prin. Fax 273-4618

Astoria, See New York
NYC Department of Education
Supt. — See New York
Academy for New Americans 100/6-8
3014 30th St 11102 718-956-4140
Betty Cartagena, prin. Fax 932-5990
IS 10 900/6-8
4511 31st Ave 11103 718-278-7054
Clemente Lopes, prin. Fax 274-1578
Baccalaureate S for Global Education 500/7-12
3412 36th Ave 11106 718-361-5275
Kelly Johnson, prin. Fax 361-5395
Long Island City HS 2,500/9-12
1430 Broadway 11106 718-545-7095
Vivian Selenikas, prin. Fax 545-2980
Sinatra HS 800/9-12
3512 35th Ave 11106 718-361-9920
Donna Finn, prin. Fax 361-9995

Empire Beauty School Post-Sec.
3815 Broadway 11103 718-726-8383
St. Demetrios Greek American S 400/4-12
3003 30th Dr 11102 718-728-1754
St. John's Prep HS 800/9-12
2121 Crescent St 11105 718-721-7200
William Higgins, prin. Fax 545-9385

Athol Springs, Erie

St. Francis HS 500/9-12
4129 Lake Shore Rd 14010 716-627-1200
Thomas Braunscheidel, prin. Fax 627-4610

Attica, Wyoming, Pop. 2,513
Attica Central SD 1,300/K-12
3338 E Main Street Rd 14011 585-591-0400
Bryce Thompson, supt. Fax 591-2681
www.atticacsd.org

Attica HS 500/9-12
3338 E Main Street Rd 14011 585-591-0400
Josh Andsley, prin. Fax 591-4484
Attica MS 400/5-8
3338 E Main Street Rd 14011 585-591-0400
Paul Clark, prin. Fax 591-4496

Auburn, Cayuga, Pop. 26,874
Auburn CSD 4,200/K-12
78 Thornton Ave 13021 315-255-8800
Jeffrey Pirozzolo, supt. Fax 255-8855
district.auburn.cnyric.org
Auburn HS 1,300/9-12
250 Lake Ave 13021 315-255-8300
Brian Morgan, prin. Fax 255-8357
Auburn JHS 600/7-8
191 Franklin St 13021 315-255-8480
David Oliver, prin. Fax 255-8495

Cayuga Community College Post-Sec.
197 Franklin St 13021 315-255-1743
Tyburn Academy of Mary Immaculate 7-12
17 Clymer St 13021 315-252-2937
Louis Massett, prin. Fax 252-4173

Aurora, Cayuga, Pop. 708
Southern Cayuga Central SD 700/PK-12
2384 State Route 34B 13026 315-364-7211
Patrick Jensen, supt. Fax 364-7863
www.southerncayuga.org
Southern Cayuga JSHS 300/7-12
2384 State Route 34B 13026 315-364-7111
Luke Carnicelli, prin. Fax 364-8207

Wells College Post-Sec.
170 Main St 13026 315-364-3264

Averill Park, Rensselaer, Pop. 1,668
Averill Park Central SD 3,000/K-12
146 Gettle Rd Ste 1 12018 518-674-7050
Dr. James D. Hoffman, supt. Fax 674-3802
www.averillpark.k12.ny.us/
Algonquin MS 700/6-8
333 NY Highway 351 12018 518-674-7100
Robert Messia, prin. Fax 674-0671
Averill Park HS 1,100/9-12
146 Gettle Rd 12018 518-674-7000
Michelle Tsao, prin. Fax 674-7046

Avoca, Steuben, Pop. 933
Avoca Central SD 400/K-12
PO Box G 14809 607-566-2221
Stephen Saxton, supt. Fax 566-2398
www.avocacsd.org/
Avoca Central S 400/K-12
PO Box G 14809 607-566-2221
Matthew Pfleegor, prin. Fax 566-8384

Avon, Livingston, Pop. 3,354
Avon Central SD 1,000/K-12
191 Clinton St 14414 585-226-2455
Dr. Aaron Johnson, supt. Fax 226-8202
www.avoncsd.org
Avon HS 300/9-12
245 Clinton St 14414 585-226-2455
Jason Shetler, prin. Fax 226-8202
Avon MS 300/5-8
191 Clinton St 14414 585-226-2455
Jennifer Miller, prin. Fax 226-8202

Babylon, Suffolk, Pop. 11,970
Babylon UFD 1,600/K-12
50 Railroad Ave 11702 631-893-7925
Linda J. Rozzi, supt. Fax 893-7935
www.babylonschools.org
Babylon JSHS 800/7-12
50 Railroad Ave 11702 631-893-7910
Al Cirone, prin. Fax 893-7936

Bainbridge, Chenango, Pop. 1,346
Bainbridge-Guilford Central SD 800/PK-12
18 Juliand St 13733 607-967-6321
Timothy R. Ryan, supt. Fax 967-4231
www.bgcsd.org
Bainbridge-Guilford HS 400/7-12
18 Juliand St 13733 607-967-6323
William Zakrajsek, prin. Fax 967-4231

Baldwin, Nassau, Pop. 23,329
Baldwin UFD 4,700/K-12
960 Hastings St 11510 516-434-6010
Dr. Shari Camhi, supt. Fax 377-9421
www.baldwinschools.org/
Baldwin HS 1,600/9-12
841 Ethel T Kloberg Dr 11510 516-434-6100
Caterina Lafergola, prin. Fax 377-9208
Baldwin MS 1,100/6-8
3211 Schreiber Pl 11510 516-434-6200
Timothy Maher, prin. Fax 377-9432

Baldwinsville, Onondaga, Pop. 7,290
Baldwinsville Central SD 5,500/K-12
29 E Oneida St 13027 315-638-6043
Matthew J. McDonald, supt. Fax 638-6041
www.bville.org
Baker HS 1,300/10-12
29 E Oneida St 13027 315-638-6008
Donald Root, prin. Fax 638-6150
Durgee JHS 1,000/8-9
29 E Oneida St 13027 315-638-6086
Bonnie VanBenschoten, prin. Fax 638-6168

Baldwinsville Christian Academy 100/PK-12
7312 Van Buren Rd 13027 315-638-1069
Dave Grey, admin. Fax 638-4207

Ballston Spa, Saratoga, Pop. 5,283
Ballston Spa Central SD 4,100/K-12
70 Malta Ave 12020 518-884-7195
Joseph Dragone Ph.D., supt. Fax 884-7101
www.bscsd.org
Ballston Spa HS 1,300/9-12
220 Ballston Ave 12020 518-884-7150
Kristi Jensen, prin. Fax 884-7199
Ballston Spa MS 1,000/6-8
210 Ballston Ave 12020 518-884-7200
Pamela Motler, prin. Fax 884-7234

John Pauls Hair Nails & Skin Care Inst Post-Sec.
2144 Saratoga Ave 12020 518-583-3700

Bardonia, Rockland, Pop. 4,047

Albertus Magnus HS 500/9-12
798 Route 304 10954 845-623-8842
Christopher Power, prin. Fax 623-0009

Barker, Niagara, Pop. 527
Barker Central SD 900/PK-12
1628 Quaker Rd 14012 716-795-3832
Dr. Roger Klatt, supt. Fax 795-3394
barkercsd.net
Barker JSHS 400/7-12
1628 Quaker Rd 14012 716-795-3201
Bradley Pritchard, prin. Fax 795-3911

Barrytown, Dutchess

Unification Theological Seminary Post-Sec.
30 Seminary Dr 12507 845-752-3000

Batavia, Genesee, Pop. 15,019
Batavia CSD 2,300/PK-12
260 State St 14020 585-343-2480
Christopher J. Dailey, supt. Fax 344-8204
www.bataviacsd.org
Batavia HS 700/9-12
260 State St 14020 585-343-2480
Scott Wilson, prin. Fax 344-8609
Batavia MS 700/5-8
96 Ross St 14020 585-343-2480
Ashley John Grillo, prin. Fax 344-8626

Continental School of Beauty Culture Post-Sec.
215 Main St 14020 585-344-0886
Genesee Community College Post-Sec.
1 College Rd 14020 585-343-0055
New York State School for the Blind Post-Sec.
2A Richmond Ave 14020
Notre Dame HS 200/9-12
73 Union St 14020 585-343-2783
Wade Bianco, prin. Fax 343-7323

Bath, Steuben, Pop. 5,678
Bath Central SD 1,600/PK-12
25 Ellas Ave 14810 607-776-3301
Joseph L. Rumsey, supt. Fax 776-5021
www.bathcsd.org
Haverling HS 500/9-12
25 Ellas Ave 14810 607-776-4107
Michael Siebert, prin. Fax 776-5021
Lyon MS 500/4-8
25 Ellas Ave 14810 607-776-2170
Jennifer D'Abbracci, prin. Fax 776-1470

Bayport, Suffolk, Pop. 8,813
Bayport-Blue Point UFD 2,400/K-12
189 Academy St 11705 631-472-7860
Vincent Butera Ed.D., supt. Fax 472-7873
www.bbpschools.org/
Bayport-Blue Point HS 800/9-12
200 Snedecor Ave 11705 631-472-7800
Dr. Gaurav Passi, prin. Fax 472-7814
Young MS 600/6-8
602 Sylvan Ave 11705 631-472-7820
Robert Haas, prin. Fax 472-7849

Bay Shore, Suffolk, Pop. 25,685
Bay Shore UFD 5,800/K-12
75 Perkal St 11706 631-968-1100
Joseph Bond, supt. Fax 968-4131
www.bayshoreschools.org
Bay Shore HS 1,900/9-12
155 3rd Ave 11706 631-968-1157
Robert Pashkin, prin. Fax 968-2332
Bay Shore MS 1,400/6-8
393 Brook Ave 11706 631-968-1210
Dr. LaQuita Outlaw, prin. Fax 968-2342

Brentwood UFD
Supt. — See Brentwood
West MS 800/6-8
2030 Udall Rd 11706 631-434-2371
Felicia Thomas-Williams, prin. Fax 242-3992

Bayside, See New York
NYC Department of Education
Supt. — See New York
Bayside HS 3,200/9-12
3224 Corporal Kennedy St 11361 718-229-7600
Michael Athy, prin. Fax 423-9566
MS 158 1,100/6-8
4635 Oceania St 11361 718-423-8100
Marie Nappi, prin. Fax 423-8135
Bell Academy 400/6-8
1825 212th St 11360 718-428-0587
David Abbott, prin. Fax 428-0237

CUNY Queensborough Community College Post-Sec.
22205 56th Ave, Oakland Gardens NY 11364
718-631-6262

Beacon, Dutchess, Pop. 15,060
Beacon CSD 3,200/PK-12
10 Education Dr 12508 845-838-6900
Ann Marie Quartironi, supt. Fax 838-6905
www.beaconcityk12.org
Beacon HS 1,000/9-12
101 Matteawan Rd 12508 845-838-6900
Dr. Joannes Sieverding, prin. Fax 838-0796
Rombout MS 700/6-8
84 Matteawan Rd 12508 845-838-6900
Brian Soltish, prin. Fax 231-0474

Beaver Falls, Lewis
Beaver River Central SD 900/K-12
9508 Artz Rd 13305 315-346-1211
Todd Green, supt. Fax 346-6775
www.brcsd.org
Beaver River HS 300/9-12
9508 Artz Rd 13305 315-346-1211
Rebecca Dunckel-King, prin. Fax 346-6775
Beaver River MS 200/6-8
9508 Artz Rd 13305 315-346-1211
Christine LaBare, prin. Fax 346-6775

Bedford, Westchester, Pop. 1,810
Bedford Central SD 4,300/K-12
632 S Bedford Rd 10506 914-241-6000
Dr. Christopher Manno, supt. Fax 241-6004
www.bcsdny.org
Fox Lane HS 1,400/9-12
PO Box 390 10506 914-241-6085
James Donnelly, prin. Fax 241-6064
Other Schools – See Mount Kisco

Rippowam Cisqua S 200/5-9
PO Box 488 10506 914-244-1250
Colm MacMahon, hdmstr. Fax 244-1245

Bedford Hills, Westchester, Pop. 2,942

Yeshiva & Mesivta Ohel Shmuel 50/9-12
165 Haines Rd Stop 1 10507 914-241-2700

Belfast, Allegany, Pop. 823
Belfast Central SD 400/PK-12
1 King St 14711 585-365-9940
Judy May, supt. Fax 365-2648
www.belfast.wnyric.org
Belfast Central S 400/PK-12
1 King St 14711 585-365-8285
Michael Roche, prin. Fax 365-2648

Belle Harbor, Queens

Mercaz Hatorah of Belle Harbor 100/9-12
505 Beach 129th St, 718-474-3064

Bellerose, Queens, Pop. 1,168
NYC Department of Education
Supt. — See New York
HS of Teaching Liberal Arts & Science 1,200/9-12
7420 Commonwealth Blvd 11426 718-736-7100
Jae Hyun-Cho, dir. Fax 736-7117

Belleville, Jefferson, Pop. 225
Belleville Henderson Central SD 500/PK-12
8372 County Route 75 13611 315-846-5826
Rick Moore, supt. Fax 846-5617
www.bhpanthers.org
Belleville Henderson Central S 500/PK-12
PO Box 158 13611 315-846-5121
Scott Storey, prin. Fax 846-5617

Bellmore, Nassau, Pop. 16,044
Bellmore-Merrick Central HSD
Supt. — See North Merrick
Grand Avenue MS 1,000/7-8
2301 Grand Ave 11710 516-992-1100
Carlo Conte, prin. Fax 679-5068
Kennedy HS 1,200/9-12
3000 Bellmore Ave 11710 516-992-1400
Lorraine Poppe, prin. Fax 826-0526
Mepham HS 1,300/9-12
2401 Camp Ave 11710 516-992-1500
Michael Harrington, prin. Fax 785-7590

Bellport, Suffolk, Pop. 2,050
South Country Central SD
Supt. — See East Patchogue
Bellport MS 1,000/6-8
35 Kreamer St 11713 631-730-1657
Dr. M. Jamal Colson, prin. Fax 286-4460

Belmont, Allegany, Pop. 950
Genesee Valley Central SD 500/PK-12
1 Jaguar Dr 14813 585-268-7900
Dr. Brian Schmitt, supt. Fax 268-7990
www.genvalley.org
Genesee Valley HS 200/7-12
1 Jaguar Dr 14813 585-268-7900
Brian LeBaron, prin. Fax 268-7990

Bemus Point, Chautauqua, Pop. 360
Bemus Point Central SD 700/PK-12
PO Box 468 14712 716-386-2375
Michael Mansfield, supt. Fax 386-2376
www.bemusptcsd.org
Maple Grove JSHS 400/6-12
PO Box 468 14712 716-386-2855
Julie Verdonik, prin. Fax 386-2376

Bergen, Genesee, Pop. 1,158
Byron-Bergen Central SD 1,000/PK-12
6917 W Bergen Rd 14416 585-494-1220
Mickey Edwards, supt. Fax 494-2613
www.bbschools.org/
Byron-Bergen JSHS 500/7-12
6917 W Bergen Rd 14416 585-494-1220
Patrick McGee, prin. Fax 494-2613

Berne, Albany
Berne-Knox-Westerlo Central SD 900/K-12
1738 Helderberg Trl 12023 518-872-1293
Dr. Timothy Mundell, supt. Fax 872-2031
www.bkwschools.org
Berne-Knox-Westerlo JSHS 400/7-12
1738 Helderberg Trl 12023 518-872-1482
Doug Kelley, prin. Fax 872-2083

Bethpage, Nassau, Pop. 16,246
Bethpage UFD 2,900/K-12
10 Cherry Ave 11714 516-644-4000
Terrence Clark, supt. Fax 931-8783
www.bethpagecommunity.com/Schools/
Bethpage HS 900/9-12
10 Cherry Ave 11714 516-644-4100
Michael Spence, prin. Fax 937-6076
Kennedy MS 700/6-8
500 Broadway 11714 516-644-4200
Kevin Fullerton, prin. Fax 937-0540

Plainedge UFD
Supt. — See North Massapequa
Plainedge MS 800/6-8
200 Stewart Ave 11714 516-992-7650
Anthony DeRiso, prin. Fax 992-7645

Briarcliffe College Post-Sec.
1055 Stewart Ave 11714 516-918-3600

Binghamton, Broome, Pop. 45,574
Binghamton CSD 5,600/PK-12
PO Box 2126 13902 607-762-8100
Dr. Tonia Thompson, supt. Fax 762-8112
www.binghamtonschools.org
Binghamton HS 1,500/9-12
31 Main St 13905 607-762-8200
Roxie Oberg, prin. Fax 762-6072
East MS 600/6-8
167 E Frederick St 13904 607-762-8300
Tim Simonds, prin. Fax 762-8398
West MS 600/6-8
W Middle Ave 13905 607-763-8400
Michael Holly, prin. Fax 763-8429

Chenango Forks Central SD 1,600/PK-12
1 Gordon Dr 13901 607-648-7543
Lloyd Peck, supt. Fax 648-7560
www.cforks.org
Chenango Forks HS 500/9-12
1 Gordon Dr 13901 607-648-7544
John Hillis, prin. Fax 648-7568
Chenango Forks MS 400/6-8
1 Gordon Dr 13901 607-648-7576
Michael Pavlovich, prin. Fax 648-2767

Chenango Valley Central SD 1,800/PK-12
221 Chenango Bridge Rd 13901 607-762-6800
David Gill, supt. Fax 762-6890
www.cvcsd.stier.org/
Chenango Valley HS 500/9-12
221 Chenango Bridge Rd 13901 607-762-6900
Terrence Heller, prin. Fax 779-4777
Chenango Valley MS 300/7-8
221 Chenango Bridge Rd 13901 607-762-6902
Eric Attleson, prin. Fax 779-4784

Binghamton University SUNY Post-Sec.
4400 Vestal Pkwy 13902 607-777-2000
Broome Community College Post-Sec.
PO Box 1017 13902 607-778-5000
Ridley-Lowell Business & Technical Inst. Post-Sec.
116 Front St 13905 607-724-2941
Seton Catholic Central HS 400/7-12
70 Seminary Ave 13905 607-723-5307
Matthew Martinkovic, prin. Fax 723-4601

Blauvelt, Rockland, Pop. 5,591
South Orangetown Central SD 3,300/K-12
160 Van Wyck Rd 10913 845-680-1050
Dr. Robert Pritchard, supt. Fax 680-1900
www.socsd.org
South Orangetown MS 800/6-8
160 Van Wyck Rd 10913 845-680-1100
Karen Tesik, prin. Fax 680-1905
Other Schools – See Orangeburg

Bloomfield, Ontario, Pop. 1,335
Bloomfield Central SD 1,000/PK-12
45 Maple Ave Ste A 14469 585-657-6121
Michael Midey, supt. Fax 657-6060
www.bloomfieldcsd.org
Bloomfield HS 300/9-12
1 Oakmount Ave 14469 585-657-6121
Daniel McAlpin, prin. Fax 657-4771
Bloomfield MS 200/6-8
1 Oakmount Ave 14469 585-657-6121
Daniel McAlpin, prin. Fax 657-4771

Bohemia, Suffolk, Pop. 10,114
Connetquot Central SD 6,200/K-12
780 Ocean Ave 11716 631-244-2215
Lynda Adams, supt. Fax 589-0683
www.ccsdli.org
Connetquot HS 2,000/9-12
190 7th St 11716 631-244-2226
Kenneth Costa, prin. Fax 244-2287
Other Schools – See Oakdale, Ronkonkoma

Branford Hall Career Institute Post-Sec.
565 Johnson Ave 11716 631-471-9100

Boiceville, Ulster
Onteora Central SD 1,400/K-12
PO Box 300 12412 845-657-6383
Victoria McLaren, supt. Fax 657-8742
onteora.schoolwires.com
Onteora HS 500/9-12
PO Box 300 12412 845-657-2373
Lance Edelman, prin. Fax 657-8430
Onteora MS 200/7-8
PO Box 300 12412 845-657-2373
Jennifer O'Connor, prin. Fax 657-7763

Bolivar, Allegany, Pop. 1,040
Bolivar-Richburg Central SD 800/PK-12
100 School St 14715 585-928-2561
Michael A. Retzlaff, supt. Fax 928-2411
www.brcs.wnyric.org
Bolivar-Richburg JSHS 400/6-12
100 School St 14715 585-928-2561
Daniel Quartley, prin. Fax 928-1368

Bolton Landing, Warren, Pop. 501
Bolton Central SD 200/PK-12
PO Box 120 12814 518-644-2400
Michael Graney, supt. Fax 644-2124
www.boltoncsd.org
Bolton Central S 200/PK-12
PO Box 120 12814 518-644-2400
Chad Shippee, prin. Fax 644-2124

Boonville, Oneida, Pop. 2,065
Adirondack Central SD 1,300/PK-12
110 Ford St 13309 315-942-9200
Edward Niznik, supt. Fax 942-5522
www.adirondackcsd.org
Adirondack HS 400/9-12
8181 State Route 294 13309 315-942-9250
Heidi Smith, prin. Fax 942-9254
Adirondack MS 300/6-8
8181 State Route 294 13309 315-942-9202
Mark Trabucco, prin. Fax 942-9211

Bradford, Schuyler
Bradford Central SD 300/PK-12
2820 State Route 226 14815 607-583-4616
John Marshall, supt. Fax 583-4013
www.bradfordcsd.org
Bradford Central S 300/PK-12
2820 State Route 226 14815 607-583-4616
Steve Kiley, prin. Fax 583-4013

Brasher Falls, Saint Lawrence, Pop. 656
Brasher Falls Central SD 1,000/PK-12
PO Box 307 13613 315-389-5131
Robert Stewart, supt. Fax 389-5245
bfcsd.org
St. Lawrence Central HS 300/9-12
PO Box 307 13613 315-389-5131
Stacy Vincent, prin. Fax 389-5245
St. Lawrence Central MS 300/5-8
PO Box 307 13613 315-389-5131
Christoper Rose, prin. Fax 389-4185

Breesport, Chemung, Pop. 625

Twin Tiers Christian Academy 100/7-12
PO Box K 14816 607-739-3619
Dr. Cary Shaw, admin. Fax 739-3619

Brentwood, Suffolk, Pop. 59,660
Brentwood UFD 17,500/PK-12
52 3rd Ave 11717 631-434-2123
Dr. Levi McIntyre, supt. Fax 273-6575
www.bufsd.org
Brentwood Freshman Center 1,200/9-9
33 Leahy Ave 11717 631-434-2541
Jerry Cheng, prin. Fax 434-2549
Brentwood SHS Ross Center 10-12
S 5th Ave 11717 631-434-2204
Richard Loeschner, prin. Fax 434-2201
Brentwood SHS Sonderling Center 3,800/10-12
2 6th Ave 11717 631-434-2204
John Callan, prin. Fax 434-2206
East MS 1,000/6-8
75 Hilltop Dr 11717 631-434-2473
Barry Mohammed, prin. Fax 434-2171
North MS 1,000/6-8
350 Wicks Rd 11717 631-434-2356
Matthew Gengler, prin. Fax 952-9249
South MS 900/6-8
785 Candlewood Rd 11717 631-434-2341
Bergre Escobores Ed.D., prin. Fax 434-2560
Other Schools – See Bay Shore

Long Island University Post-Sec.
100 2nd Ave 11717 631-273-5112
Suffolk County Community College Grant Post-Sec.
1001 Crooked Hill Rd 11717 631-851-6700

Brewster, Putnam, Pop. 2,362
Brewster Central SD 3,200/K-12
30 Farm To Market Rd 10509 845-279-8000
Dr. Timothy Conway, supt. Fax 279-3510
www.brewsterschools.org
Brewster HS 1,100/9-12
50 Foggintown Rd 10509 845-279-5051
Dr. Joseph Castagnola, prin. Fax 279-6730
Wells MS 700/6-8
570 Route 312 10509 845-279-3702
Michelle Gosh, prin. Fax 279-7634

Briarcliff Manor, Westchester, Pop. 7,748
Briarcliff Manor UFD 1,600/K-12
45 Ingham Rd 10510 914-941-8880
James Kaishian, supt. Fax 941-2177
www.briarcliffschools.org
Briarcliff Manor HS 600/9-12
444 Pleasantville Rd 10510 914-769-6299
Debora French, prin. Fax 769-2509
Briarcliff MS 400/6-8
444 Pleasantville Rd 10510 914-769-6343
Susan Howard, prin. Fax 769-6375

Bridgehampton, Suffolk, Pop. 1,736
Bridgehampton UFD 200/PK-12
PO Box 3021 11932 631-537-0271
Dr. Lois Favre, supt. Fax 537-9038
www.bridgehampton.k12.ny.us/
Bridgehampton S 200/PK-12
PO Box 3021 11932 631-537-0271
Dr. Lois Favre, prin. Fax 537-0443

Broadalbin, Fulton, Pop. 1,305
Broadalbin-Perth Central SD 1,800/PK-12
20 Pine St 12025 518-954-2500
Stephen Tomlinson, supt. Fax 954-2509
www.bpcsd.org
Broadalbin-Perth HS 600/9-12
100 Bridge St 12025 518-954-2600
Mark Brooks, prin. Fax 954-2609
Other Schools – See Amsterdam

Brockport, Monroe, Pop. 8,227
Brockport Central SD 3,500/K-12
40 Allen St 14420 585-637-1810
Lesli Myers Ed.D., supt. Fax 637-0165
www.bcs1.org
Brockport HS 1,200/9-12
40 Allen St 14420 585-637-1877
Dana Boshnack, prin. Fax 637-1867
Oliver MS 800/6-8
40 Allen St 14420 585-637-1860
Melody Martinez-Davis, prin. Fax 637-1869

Cornerstone Christian Academy 50/PK-12
60 Holley St 14420 585-637-4540
Rev. Christopher Johnson, admin. Fax 637-4518
SUNY College at Brockport Post-Sec.
350 New Campus Dr 14420 585-395-2211

Brocton, Chautauqua, Pop. 1,467
Brocton Central SD 500/K-12
138 W Main St 14716 716-792-9121
Jason Delcamp, supt. Fax 792-9965
www.broctoncsd.org
Brocton MSHS 300/6-12
138 W Main St 14716 716-792-2190
Elizabeth Antolina, prin. Fax 792-2246

Bronx, See New York
NYC Department of Education
Supt. — See New York
Academy for Language and Technology 300/9-12
1700 Macombs Rd 10453 718-731-0219
Jose Vinales, prin. Fax 731-2031
Academy for Personal Leadership 300/6-8
120 E 184th St 10468 718-220-3139
Angelo Ledda, prin. Fax 220-6018
Academy of Applied Math & Technology 300/6-8
345 Brook Ave 10454 718-292-3883
Vincent Gassetto, prin. Fax 292-4473
Academy of Public Relations 300/6-8
778 Forest Ave 10456 718-665-8866
Amy Andino-Flohr, prin. Fax 401-0051
Acad for Scholarship & Entrepreneurship 400/6-12
921 E 228th St 10466 718-696-3840
Zenobia White, prin. Fax 696-3841
Accion Academy 200/6-8
1825 Prospect Ave 10457 718-294-0514
Dr. Victor Frias, prin. Fax 294-3869
Archimedes Academy 600/6-12
456 White Plains Rd 10473 718-617-5046
Miriam Lazar, prin. Fax 617-7395
Astor Collegiate Academy 500/9-12
925 Astor Ave 10469 718-944-3418
Sandra Burgos, prin. Fax 944-3638
Baychester MS 300/6-8
3750 Baychester Ave 10466 718-547-1890
Shawn Mangar, prin. Fax 547-1895
Belmont Preparatory HS 400/9-12
500 E Fordham Rd 10458 718-733-4559
Stephen Gumbs, prin. Fax 295-3655
Blueprint MS 100/6-8
1111 Pugsley Ave 10472 718-822-2780
Tyneka Harrington, prin. Fax 822-2279
Bronck Academy 300/6-8
400 E Fordham Rd 10458 718-365-2502
Brenda Gonzalez, prin. Fax 365-3892
Bronx Academy for Software Engineering 100/9-10
2474 Crotona Ave 10458 718-733-6024
Benjamin Grossman, prin. Fax 733-6429
Bronx Academy of Health Careers 500/9-12
800 E Gun Hill Rd 10467 718-696-3340
Dawn Santiago, prin. Fax 696-3380
Bronx Aerospace Academy 400/9-12
800 E Gun Hill Rd 10467 718-696-6010
Erika Hurtado, prin. Fax 696-6030
Bronx Arena HS 200/Alt
1440 Story Ave 10473 718-860-5060
Ty Cesene, prin. Fax 860-5058
Bronx Bridges HS 300/9-12
1980 Lafayette Ave 10473 718-829-2984
Nelsie Castillo, prin. Fax 829-2987
Bronx Career and College Preparatory HS Vo/Tech
800 Home St 10456 718-542-4011
Julia Baly, prin. Fax 542-4377
Bronx Center for Science & Mathematics 500/9-12
1363 Fulton Ave 10456 718-992-7089
Edward Tom, prin. Fax 590-1052
Bronx Collaborative HS 100/9-10
100 W Mosholu Pkwy S 10468 718-543-1023
Brett Schneider, prin. Fax 543-1029
Bronx Collegiate Academy 400/9-12
240 E 172nd St 10457 718-410-4077
D. White, prin. Fax 293-9567
Bronx Community HS 200/Alt
1980 Lafayette Ave 10473 718-892-1026
Flora Greenaway, prin. Fax 892-6941
Bronx Compass HS 9-12
1980 Lafayette Ave 10473 718-828-1206
Stacy McCoy, prin.

Bronxdale HS 300/9-12
925 Astor Ave 10469 718-944-3655
Carolyne Quintana, prin. Fax 944-3662

Bronx Dance Academy 200/6-8
3617 Bainbridge Ave 10467 718-515-0410
Sandra Sanchez, prin. Fax 515-0345

Bronx Design and Construction Academy 400/9-12
333 E 151st St 10451 718-402-7690
Abigail Lovett, prin. Fax 402-4216

Bronx Early College Academy 500/6-12
250 E 164th St 10456 718-681-8287
Yvette Rivera, prin. Fax 681-8650

Bronx Engineering & Technology Academy 400/9-12
99 Terrace View Ave Rm 544 10463 718-563-6678
Karalyne Sperling, prin. Fax 741-5263

Bronx Envision Academy 200/9-12
1619 Boston Rd 10460 718-589-1590
Emily Shu, prin. Fax 589-1595

Bronx Green MS 400/6-8
2441 Wallace Ave 10467 718-325-6593
Charles Johnson, prin. Fax 325-3625

Bronx Guild HS 300/9-12
1980 Lafayette Ave 10473 718-597-1587
Sam Decker, prin. Fax 597-1371

Bronx Haven HS 100/Alt
333 E 151st St 10451 718-292-3638
Lucinda Mendez, prin. Fax 292-6065

Bronx Health Sciences HS 300/9-12
750 Baychester Ave 10475 718-862-4406
Miriam Rivas, prin. Fax 862-4410

HS for Contemporary Arts 500/9-12
800 E Gun Hill Rd 10467 718-944-5610
Pedro Cubero, prin. Fax 944-5650

HS for Energy and Technology 9-12
2474 Crotona Ave 10458 718-733-3080
Marie Guillaume, prin.

HS for Language and Innovation 200/9-12
925 Astor Ave 10469 718-944-3625
Julie Nariman, prin. Fax 944-3641

Bronx HS for Law & Community Service 400/9-12
500 E Fordham Rd 10458 718-733-5274
Michael Barakate, prin. Fax 295-3631

HS for Teaching & Professions 500/9-12
2780 Reservoir Ave 10468 718-329-7380
Roberto Hernandez, prin. Fax 365-7984

HS for Violin & Dance 400/9-12
1110 Boston Rd 10456 718-842-0687
Franklin Sim, prin. Fax 589-9849

Bronx HS for Visual Arts 500/9-12
2040 Antin Pl 10462 718-319-5160
Iris Witherspoon, prin. Fax 319-5165

Bronx HS for Writing & Communication 400/9-12
800 E Gun Hill Rd 10467 718-944-5660
Terri Grey, prin. Fax 944-5690

HS of American Studies 400/9-12
2925 Goulden Ave 10468 718-329-2144
Alessandro Weiss, prin. Fax 329-0792

Bronx HS of Business 300/9-12
240 E 172nd St 10457 718-410-4060
Ana DeJesus, prin. Fax 992-5760

HS of Computers & Technology 600/9-12
800 E Gun Hill Rd 10467 718-696-3930
Bruce Abramowitz, prin. Fax 696-3950

Bronx HS of Science 3,000/9-12
75 W 205th St 10468 718-817-7700
Jean Donahue, prin. Fax 733-7951

HS of World Cultures 300/9-12
1300 Boynton Ave 10472 718-860-8120
Dr. Ramon Namnum, prin. Fax 893-7152

IS 117 600/6-8
1865 Morris Ave 10453 718-583-7750
Delise Jones, prin. Fax 583-7658

IS 129 500/6-8
2055 Mapes Ave 10460 718-933-5976
Raymond Granda, prin. Fax 933-8132

IS 181 900/6-8
800 Baychester Ave 10475 718-904-5600
Christopher Warnock, prin. Fax 904-5620

IS 190 300/6-8
1550 Crotona Park E 10460 718-620-9423
Diana Santiago, prin. Fax 620-9927

IS 206 300/5-8
2280 Aqueduct Ave 10468 718-584-1570
David Neering, prin. Fax 584-7928

IS 219 400/6-8
3630 3rd Ave 10456 718-681-7093
Dominic Cipollone, prin. Fax 681-7324

IS 224 300/6-8
345 Brook Ave 10454 718-665-9804
Sojourner Welch, prin. Fax 665-0078

IS 229 200/6-8
275 Harlem River Park Brg 10453 718-583-6266
Dr. Ezra Matthias, prin. Fax 583-6325

IS 232 500/6-8
1700 Macombs Rd 10453 718-583-7007
Neifi Acosta, prin. Fax 583-4864

IS 254 400/6-8
2452 Washington Ave 10458 718-220-8700
Alexis Marrero, prin. Fax 220-4881

IS 303 300/6-8
1700 Macombs Rd 10453 718-583-5466
Patricia Bentley, prin. Fax 583-2463

IS 313 400/6-10
1600 Webster Ave 10457 718-583-1736
Earl Brathwaite, prin. Fax 299-5559

IS 318 300/6-8
1919 Prospect Ave 10457 718-294-8504
Sebastian Braithwaite, prin. Fax 901-0778

IS 339 600/6-8
1600 Webster Ave 10457 718-583-6767
Kim Outerbridge, prin. Fax 583-0281

Bronx International HS 400/9-12
1110 Boston Rd 10456 718-620-1053
Joaquin Vega Vargas, prin. Fax 620-1056

JHS 22 600/6-8
270 E 167th St 10456 718-681-6850
Edgar Lin, prin. Fax 681-6895

JHS 80 600/6-8
149 E Mosholu Pkwy N 10467 718-405-6300
Emmanuel Polanco, prin. Fax 405-6324

JHS 98 300/6-8
1619 Boston Rd 10460 718-589-8200
Mark Turcotte, prin. Fax 589-8179

JHS 118 1,200/6-8
577 E 179th St 10457 718-584-2330
Giulia Cox, prin. Fax 584-7763

JHS 123 500/6-8
1025 Morrison Ave 10472 718-328-2105
Richard Hallenbeck, prin. Fax 328-8561

JHS 125 400/6-8
1111 Pugsley Ave 10472 718-822-5186
Michael Collins, prin. Fax 239-3121

JHS 127 700/6-8
1560 Purdy St 10462 718-892-8600
Harry Sherman, prin. Fax 892-8300

JHS 131 700/6-8
885 Bolton Ave 10473 718-991-7490
Monique Mason, prin. Fax 328-6705

JHS 144 700/6-8
2545 Gunther Ave 10469 718-794-9749
Ellen Barrett-Kelly, prin. Fax 320-7135

JHS 145 400/5-8
1000 Teller Ave 10456 718-681-7219
Lauren Wilkins, prin. Fax 681-6913

JHS 151 300/6-8
250 E 156th St 10451 718-292-0260
Socorro Rivera, prin. Fax 292-5704

JHS 162 400/6-8
600 Saint Anns Ave 10455 718-292-0880
Deborah Sanabria, prin. Fax 292-5735

Bronx Lab S 500/9-12
800 E Gun Hill Rd 10467 718-696-3700
Sarah Marcy, prin. Fax 696-3730

Bronx Latin S 500/6-12
800 Home St 10456 718-991-6349
Annette Fiorentino, prin. Fax 991-6627

Bronx Leadership Academy 700/9-12
1710 Webster Ave 10457 718-299-4274
Ivan Yip, prin. Fax 299-4707

Bronx Leadership Academy II 400/9-12
730 Concourse Vlg W 10451 718-292-7171
R. Llobianco, prin. Fax 292-2355

Bronx Mathematics Preparatory S 300/6-8
456 White Plains Rd 10473 718-542-5063
Anya Munce, prin. Fax 542-5236

MS 101 500/6-8
2750 Lafayette Ave 10465 718-829-6372
Jared Rosoff, prin. Fax 829-6594

MS 180 800/6-8
700 Baychester Ave 10475 718-904-5650
Frank Uzzo, prin. Fax 904-5655

MS 223 400/6-8
360 E 145th St 10454 718-585-8202
Ramon Gonzalez, prin. Fax 292-7435

MS 301 200/6-8
890 Cauldwell Ave 10456 718-585-2950
Hasham Farid, prin. Fax 401-2567

MS 302 600/6-8
681 Kelly St 10455 718-292-6070
Liza Ortiz, prin. Fax 401-2958

MS 390 400/6-8
1930 Andrews Ave 10453 718-583-5501
Robert Mercedes, prin. Fax 583-5556

Bronx MSHS for Medical Science 500/6-12
240 E 172nd St 10457 718-410-4040
William Quintana, prin. Fax 992-4129

Bronx Park MS 6-8
2441 Wallace Ave 10467 718-652-6090

Bronx Regional HS 200/Alt
1010 Rev James A Polite Ave 10459 718-991-2020
Colin Thomas, prin. Fax 617-0257

Bronx River HS 100/9-12
3000 E Tremont Ave 10461 718-904-4210
Gregory Fucheck, prin. Fax 904-4209

S for Tourism and Hospitality 9-12
900 Tinton Ave 10456 718-401-4214
Brian Condon, prin.

Bronx S Law Government & Justice 800/6-12
244 E 163rd St 10451 718-410-3430
Johanie Hernandez, prin. Fax 410-3950

Bronx S of Law & Finance 400/9-12
99 Terrace View Ave Rm 804 10463 718-561-0113
Jessica Goring, prin. Fax 561-0595

Bronx S of Young Leaders 400/6-8
40 W Tremont Ave 10453 718-583-4146
Serapha Cruz, prin. Fax 583-4292

Bronx Studio S 500/6-12
928 Simpson St 10459 718-893-5158
David Vazquez, prin. Fax 893-5982

Bronx Theatre HS 400/9-12
99 Terrace View Ave Rm 716 10463 718-329-2902
William Doyle, prin. Fax 329-0433

Bronxwood Preparatory Academy 400/9-12
921 E 228th St 10466 718-696-3820
Janet Gallardo, prin. Fax 696-3821

Bronx Writing Academy 500/6-8
270 E 167th St 10456 718-293-9048
Lauren Hasson, prin. Fax 293-9748

Chaifetz Transfer HS 200/Alt
778 Forest Ave 10456 718-402-2429
Anne Fennelly, prin. Fax 402-3120

Cinema S 300/9-12
1551 E 172nd St 10472 718-620-2560
Keisha Warner, prin. Fax 620-2561

Claremont International HS 9-12
240 E 172nd St 10457 718-410-4001
Elizabeth Demchak, prin.

Clinton HS 2,700/9-12
100 W Mosholu Pkwy S 10468 718-543-1000
Santiago Taveras, prin. Fax 548-0036

Collegiate Institute of Math & Science 700/9-12
925 Astor Ave 10469 718-944-3635
Frederick Nelson, prin. Fax 652-3525

Community S for Social Justice 300/9-12
350 Gerard Ave 10451 718-402-8481
Sue-Ann Rosch, prin. Fax 402-8650

Comprehensive Model S Project-MS 327 400/6-9
1501 Jerome Ave 10452 718-294-8111
Alixandre Ricci, prin. Fax 993-2990

Cornerstone Academy for Social Action MS 200/6-8
3441 Steenwick Ave 10475 718-794-7970
Jamaal Bowman, prin. Fax 794-7981

Creston Academy 500/6-8
125 E 181st St 10453 718-367-5035
Mellissa Miller, prin. Fax 367-5176

Crotona Academy HS 100/Alt
1211 Southern Blvd 10459 718-860-5370
Patricia Williams, prin.

Crotona International HS 200/9-12
2474 Crotona Ave 10458 718-561-8701
Shweta Ratra, prin. Fax 561-8707

Cruz Bronx HS of Music 400/9-12
2780 Reservoir Ave 10468 718-329-8550
Jerrod Mabry, prin. Fax 329-8559

Curie HS 600/9-12
120 W 231st St 10463 718-432-6491
Rodney Fisher, prin. Fax 796-7051

Discovery HS 500/9-12
2780 Reservoir Ave 10468 718-733-3872
Rolando Rivera, prin. Fax 733-3621

Douglas Academy V 300/6-8
2111 Crotona Ave 10457 718-561-1617
Dena Zamore, prin. Fax 561-2184

Douglass Academy III 400/8-12
3630 3rd Ave 10456 718-538-9726
Jumel Carlos, prin. Fax 538-9796

Dreamyard Preparatory S 300/9-12
240 E 172nd St 10457 718-410-4242
Alicia Wargo, prin. Fax 410-4312

Eagle Academy for Young Men 400/9-12
4143 3rd Ave 10457 718-466-8000
Hector Velazquez, prin. Fax 466-8090

East Bronx Academy for the Future 600/6-12
1716 Southern Blvd 10460 718-861-8641
Sarah Scrogin, prin. Fax 861-8634

East Fordham Academy for the Arts 400/6-8
120 E 184th St 10468 718-220-4185
Francisco De La Cruz, prin. Fax 220-5976

Emolior Academy 200/6-8
1970 W Farms Rd 10460 718-842-2670
Derick Spaulding, prin. Fax 842-2857

English Language Learners Academy 300/9-12
99 Terrace View Ave 10463 718-220-1889
Norma Vega, prin. Fax 220-8758

Entrada Academy 300/6-8
977 Fox St 10459 718-378-1649
Jazmin Rivera-Polanco, prin. Fax 378-4707

Eximius College Preparatory Academy 400/9-12
1363 Fulton Ave 10456 718-992-7154
Jonathan Daly, prin. Fax 590-1081

Explorations Academy 400/9-12
1619 Boston Rd 10460 718-893-6173
Susana Hernandez, prin. Fax 893-6439

Fordham HS for the Arts 400/9-12
500 E Fordham Rd 10458 718-733-4656
Iris Blige, prin. Fax 295-3605

Fordham Leadership Academy 500/9-12
500 E Fordham Rd 10458 718-733-5024
Fiorella Cabrejos, prin. Fax 295-3674

Foreign Langugage Academy\Global Study 200/9-12
470 Jackson Ave 10455 718-585-4024
Leslie Chislett, prin. Fax 585-4239

Forward School of Creative Writing 300/6-8
3710 Barnes Ave 10467 718-652-0519
Magdalen Neyra, prin. Fax 652-0428

Giordano MS 800/6-8
2502 Lorillard Pl 10458 718-584-1660
Anna Maria Perrotta, prin. Fax 584-7968

Globe S for Environmental Research 300/6-8
3710 Barnes Ave 10467 718-994-1395
Marlon Williams, prin. Fax 994-1316

Hamer Freedom HS 500/9-12
1021 Jennings St 10460 718-861-0521
Jeffrey Palladino, prin. Fax 861-0619

Hamer MS 300/6-8
1001 Jennings St 10460 718-860-2707
Lorraine Chanon, prin. Fax 860-3212

Health Opportunities HS 600/9-12
350 Gerard Ave 10451 718-401-1826
Julie McHedlishvili, prin. Fax 401-1632

HERO HS 100/9-10
455 Southern Blvd 10455 718-585-8013
Kristin Garcia, prin. Fax 585-8019

Highbridge Green S 100/6-8
200 W 167th St 10452 718-410-5770
Kyle Brillante, prin. Fax 410-5779

Hostos-Lincoln Academy 500/6-12
600 Saint Anns Ave 10455 718-402-5640
Nick Paarlberg, prin. Fax 518-4321

Hunts Point S 400/6-8
730 Bryant Ave 10474 718-328-1972
Sonya Johnson, prin. Fax 328-7330

Institute for Law and Public Policy 300/9-12
1440 Story Ave 10473 718-860-5110
Grismaldy Laboy-Wilson, prin. Fax 860-5081

In-Tech Academy 1,000/6-12
2975 Tibbett Ave 10463 718-432-4300
Stephen Seltzer, prin. Fax 432-4310

International Community HS 400/9-12
345 Brook Ave 10454 718-665-4128
Berena Cabarcas, prin. Fax 665-4547

International S for Liberal Arts 500/6-12
2780 Reservoir Ave 10468 718-329-8570
Francine Cruz, prin. Fax 329-8572

KAPPA 300/5-8
3630 3rd Ave 10456 718-590-5455
Sheri Warren, prin. Fax 681-4266

KAPPA 500/9-12
500 E Fordham Rd 10458 718-933-1247
Panorea Panagiosoulis, prin. Fax 933-1568

KAPPA III S 200/6-8
2055 Mapes Ave 10460 718-561-3580
Jean Colon, prin. Fax 561-3719
Kelly HS 300/9-12
965 Longwood Ave 10459 718-860-1242
Marva Picou, prin. Fax 860-1934
Kingsbridge International HS 400/9-12
2780 Reservoir Ave 10468 718-329-8580
Ronald Foreman, prin. Fax 329-8582
Leadership Institute 200/9-12
1701 Fulton Ave 10457 718-299-7490
Marta Colon, prin.
Lehman HS 2,100/9-12
3000 E Tremont Ave 10461 718-904-4200
John Powers, prin. Fax 904-4285
Levin HS for Media & Communications 200/9-12
240 E 172nd St 10457 718-992-3709
Jacqueline Boswell, prin. Fax 992-4170
Marble Hill HS for International Studies 400/9-12
99 Terrace View Ave Rm 822 10463 718-561-0973
Kirsten Larson, prin. Fax 561-5612
Metropolitan HS 300/9-12
1180 Rev James A Polite Ave 10459 718-991-4634
Madhusudha Narayanan, prin. Fax 542-7294
Metropolitan Soundview HS 9-12
1300 Boynton Ave 10472 718-860-8240
Emarilix Lopez, prin. Fax 860-8232
Millenium Art Academy 500/9-12
1980 Lafayette Ave 10473 718-824-0978
Herman Guy, prin. Fax 824-0963
Monroe Academy for Visual Arts & Design 500/9-12
1300 Boynton Ave 10472 718-860-8160
Brendan Lyons, prin. Fax 860-8110
Morris Academy for Collaborative Studies 500/9-12
1110 Boston Rd 10456 718-542-3700
Matthew Mazzarol, prin. Fax 542-3958
Mott Hall Bronx HS 400/9-12
1595 Bathgate Ave 10457 718-466-6800
Kathryn Malloy, prin. Fax 466-6801
Mott Hall Community S 300/6-8
650 Hollywood Ave 10465 718-829-3254
Benjamin Basile, prin. Fax 829-3859
Mott Hall III 400/6-8
580 Crotona Park S 10456 718-842-6138
Jorisis Stupart, prin. Fax 842-6348
Mott Hall V 700/6-12
1551 E 172nd St 10472 718-620-8160
Peter Oroszlany, prin. Fax 620-8161
Mott Haven Community HS 9-12
455 Southern Blvd 10455 718-665-8512
Helene Spadaccini, prin.
Mott Haven Village Prep HS 300/9-12
701 Saint Anns Ave 10455 718-402-0571
Melanie Williams, prin. Fax 665-2363
Neruda Academy 300/9-12
1980 Lafayette Ave 10473 718-824-1682
David Liu, prin. Fax 824-1663
New Directions Secondary S 100/6-8
240 E 172nd St 10457 718-410-4343
James Waslawski, prin. Fax 410-4101
New Explorers HS 500/9-12
730 Concourse Vlg W 10451 718-292-4150
Lisa Luft, prin. Fax 292-5887
New Millenium Business Academy 200/6-8
1000 Teller Ave 10456 718-588-8308
Dorald Bastian, prin. Fax 681-6913
New S for Leadership and Journalism 800/6-8
120 W 231st St 10463 718-601-2869
Eduardo Mora, prin. Fax 601-2867
New World HS 400/9-12
921 E 228th St 10466 718-696-3800
Fausto Salazar, prin. Fax 696-3801
One World MS 300/6-8
3750 Baychester Ave 10466 718-515-6780
Patricia Wynne, prin. Fax 515-6785
Pan American International HS 400/9-12
1300 Boynton Ave 10472 718-991-7238
Bridgit Bye, prin. Fax 991-7872
Pantoja Preparatory Academy 500/6-12
1980 Lafayette Ave 10473 718-824-3152
Nalini Singh, prin. Fax 824-3543
Patri MS 600/6-8
2225 Webster Ave 10457 718-584-1295
Gracela Abadia, prin. Fax 584-1358
Peace & Diversity Academy 200/9-12
1180 Rev James A Polite Ave 10459 718-991-1855
Michelle Noonan, prin. Fax 991-2998
Pelham Academy of Academics 300/6-8
2441 Wallace Ave 10467 718-881-3136
Anthony Rivera, prin. Fax 881-3413
Pelham Gardens MS 6-8
2545 Gunther Ave 10469 718-794-9750
Pelham Lab HS 100/9-10
3000 E Tremont Ave 10461 718-904-5090
Jason Wagner, prin. Fax 904-5099
Pelham Preparatory Academy 500/9-12
925 Astor Ave 10469 718-944-3401
Carlos Santiago, prin. Fax 944-3479
PULSE HS 200/Alt
560 E 179th St 10457 718-294-0230
Carol Wiggins, prin. Fax 584-7809
Renaissance HS of Musical Theater 500/9-12
3000 E Tremont Ave 10461 718-430-6390
Maria Herrera, prin. Fax 430-6308
Riverdale/Kingsbridge Academy 1,400/6-12
660 W 237th St 10463 718-796-8516
Lori O'Mara, prin. Fax 796-8657
Rucker S of Community Research 300/9-12
965 Longwood Ave 10459 718-860-1053
Sharif Rucker, prin. Fax 860-1321
Schomburg Satellite Academy 200/Alt
1010 Rev James A Polite Ave 10459 718-542-2700
Marsha Vernon, prin. Fax 589-3710
School for Excellence HS 400/9-12
1110 Boston Rd 10456 718-860-1385
Carmen Brown, prin. Fax 860-4882

School for Inquiry & Social Justice 300/6-8
1025 Morrison Ave 10472 718-860-4181
Andrea Cyprys, prin. Fax 860-4163
School of Diplomacy 300/6-8
3710 Barnes Ave 10467 718-994-1028
Sean Licata, prin.
School of Performing Arts 400/6-8
977 Fox St 10459 718-589-4844
Maiysha Etienne, prin. Fax 589-7998
Schuylerville Preparatory HS 100/9-12
3000 E Tremont Ave 10461 718-904-5080
Roberto Ossorio, prin. Fax 935-4209
Science and Technology Academy 400/6-8
250 E 164th St 10456 718-293-4017
Dr. Patrick Awosogba, prin. Fax 293-7396
Smith Career and Tech HS Vo/Tech
333 E 151st St 10451 718-993-5000
Evan Schwartz, prin. Fax 292-1944
Soundview Acad for Culture & Scholarship 300/6-8
885 Bolton Ave 10473 718-991-4027
William Frackelton, prin. Fax 991-4807
South Bronx Academy for Applied Media 400/6-8
778 Forest Ave 10456 718-401-0059
Roshone Ault-Lee, prin. Fax 401-0577
South Bronx Preparatory HS 600/6-12
360 E 145th St 10454 718-292-2211
Ellen Flanagan, prin. Fax 292-2172
Theatre Arts Production Company S 600/6-12
2225 Webster Ave 10457 718-584-0832
Ron Link, prin. Fax 584-5102
Truman HS 1,900/9-12
750 Baychester Ave 10475 718-904-5400
Keri Alfano, prin. Fax 904-5502
University Heights HS 300/9-12
701 Saint Anns Ave 10455 718-292-0578
Hazel Roseboro, prin. Fax 292-4276
Urban Assembly Academy Civic Engagement 200/6-8
650 Hollywood Ave 10465 718-822-0126
Kelly Von Hoene, prin. Fax 822-1049
Urban Assembly Bronx Academy of Letters 600/6-12
339 Morris Ave 10451 718-401-4891
Brandon Cardet-Hernandez, prin. Fax 401-6626
Urban Assembly Math & Science MSHS 600/6-12
1595 Bathgate Ave 10457 718-466-7800
David Krulwich, prin. Fax 466-7801
Urban Assembly S for Careers in Sports 600/9-12
730 Concourse Vlg W 10451 718-292-7110
Johanny Garcia, prin. Fax 993-1567
Urban Assembly S Wildlife Conservation 600/6-12
2024 Mohegan Ave 10460 718-823-4130
Astrid Jacobo, prin. Fax 991-2980
Urban Institute of Mathematics 300/6-8
650 Hollywood Ave 10465 718-823-6042
Jennifer Joynt, prin. Fax 823-6347
Urban Science Academy 400/5-8
1000 Teller Ave 10456 718-588-8221
Patrick Kelly, prin. Fax 588-8263
Validus Preparatory Academy 400/9-12
1595 Bathgate Ave 10457 718-466-4000
Christopher Hibbert, prin. Fax 466-4001
West Bronx Academy for the Future 600/6-12
500 E Fordham Rd 10458 718-563-7139
Wilper Morales, prin. Fax 563-7362
Westchester Square Academy 9-12
3000 E Tremont Ave 10461 718-904-5050
Sara Dingledy, prin.
Wings Academy 500/9-12
1122 E 180th St 10460 718-597-1751
Tuwanna Williams Gray, prin. Fax 931-8366
Womans Academy of Excellence 400/9-12
456 White Plains Rd 10473 718-542-0740
Arnette Crocker, prin. Fax 542-0841
World View HS 100/9-12
100 W Mosholu Pkwy S 10468 718-601-0391
Martin Hernandez, prin. Fax 601-0821
Young Scholars Academy 300/6-8
3710 Barnes Ave 10467 718-325-5834
Jeanette Vargas, prin. Fax 325-5676
Young Womens Leadership S of the Bronx 6-8
1865 Morris Ave 10453 718-731-2590
Lemarie Laureano, prin.

Academy of Mt. St. Ursula 400/9-12
330 Bedford Park Blvd 10458 718-364-5353
Sr. Jean Marie Humphries, prin. Fax 364-2354
All Hallows HS 700/9-12
111 E 164th St 10452 718-293-4545
Sean Sullivan, prin. Fax 410-8298
Aquinas HS 600/9-12
685 E 182nd St 10457 718-367-2113
Sr. Catherine Rose Quigley, prin. Fax 295-5864
Bronx Lebanon Hospital Center Post-Sec.
1650 Grand Concourse 10457 718-518-1800
Cardinal Hayes HS 900/9-12
650 Grand Concourse 10451 718-292-6100
William Lessa, prin. Fax 292-9178
Cardinal Spellman HS 1,400/9-12
1 Cardinal Spellman Pl 10466 718-881-8000
Daniel O'Keefe, prin. Fax 515-6615
CUNY Bronx Community College Post-Sec.
2155 University Ave 10453 718-289-5100
CUNY Hostos Community College Post-Sec.
500 Grand Concourse 10451 718-518-4444
CUNY Lehman College Post-Sec.
250 Bedford Park Blvd W 10468 718-960-8000
Ethical Culture Fieldston S 400/6-12
3901 Fieldston Rd 10471 718-329-7300
Jessica Bagby, head sch Fax 329-7305
Fordham Preparatory HS 900/9-12
441 E Fordham Rd 10458 718-367-7500
Brian Carney, prin. Fax 367-7598
Fordham University Post-Sec.
441 E Fordham Rd 10458 718-817-1000
Lavelle School/Blind-Visually Impaired Post-Sec.
E 221 St & Paulding Ave 10469

Mann S 1,700/PK-12
231 W 246th St 10471 718-432-4000
Dr. Thomas M. Kelly, head sch Fax 548-2089
Monroe College Post-Sec.
2501 Jerome Ave 10468 718-933-6700
Monsignor Scanlan HS 500/9-12
915 Hutchinson River Pkwy 10465 718-430-0100
Peter Doran, prin. Fax 892-8845
Montefiore Medical Center Post-Sec.
111 E 210th St 10467 718-920-4001
Mt. St. Michael Academy 800/6-12
4300 Murdock Ave 10466 718-515-6400
Br. Steve Schlitte, prin. Fax 994-7729
New York Institute for Special Education Post-Sec.
999 Pelham Pkwy N 10469 718-519-7000
Our Saviour Lutheran S 200/PK-12
1734 Williamsbridge Rd 10461 718-792-5665
Ken Famulare, prin. Fax 409-3877
Preston HS 600/9-12
2780 Schurz Ave 10465 718-863-9134
Jane Grendell, prin. Fax 863-6125
Riverdale Country S 800/6-12
5250 Fieldston Rd 10471 718-549-8810
Dominic Randolph, hdmstr. Fax 519-2795
St. Barnabas HS 200/9-12
425 E 240th St 10470 718-325-8800
Sr. Joan Faraone, prin. Fax 325-8820
St. Catharine Academy 700/9-12
2250 Williamsbridge Rd 10469 718-882-2882
Sr. Ann Welch, prin. Fax 231-9099
St. Ignatius Academy 100/6-8
740 Manida St 10474 718-861-9084
Richard Darrell, prin. Fax 861-9096
St. Raymond Girls Academy 400/9-12
1725 Castle Hill Ave 10462 718-824-4220
Sr. Mary Ann D'Antonio, prin. Fax 829-3571
St. Raymond HS for Boys 800/9-12
2151 Saint Raymonds Ave 10462 718-824-5050
Judith Carew, prin. Fax 863-8808
Salanter Akiba Riverdale HS 500/9-12
503 W 259th St 10471 718-548-2727
SUNY Maritime College Post-Sec.
6 Pennyfield Ave 10465 718-409-7200
Veterans Affairs Medical Center Post-Sec.
130 W Kingsbridge Rd 10468 718-579-1640
Yeshiva of the Telshe Alumni Post-Sec.
4904 Independence Ave 10471 718-601-3523

Bronxville, Westchester, Pop. 6,193
Bronxville UFD 1,700/K-12
177 Pondfield Rd 10708 914-395-0500
Dr. David Quattrone, supt. Fax 337-7109
www.bronxville.k12.ny.us
Bronxville HS 500/9-12
177 Pondfield Rd 10708 914-395-0500
Ann Meyer, prin. Fax 395-0513
Bronxville MS 400/6-8
177 Pondfield Rd 10708 914-395-0500
Dr. Thomas Wilson, prin. Fax 771-6223

Concordia College Post-Sec.
171 White Plains Rd 10708 914-337-9300
Sarah Lawrence College Post-Sec.
1 Mead Way 10708 914-337-0700

Brookfield, Madison
Brookfield Central SD 200/PK-12
PO Box 60 13314 315-899-3323
James Plows, supt. Fax 899-8902
www.brookfieldcsd.org
Brookfield Central S 200/PK-12
PO Box 60 13314 315-899-3323
Carrie Smith, prin. Fax 899-8902

Brookhaven, Suffolk, Pop. 3,414
South Country Central SD
Supt. — See East Patchogue
Bellport HS 1,400/9-12
205 Beaver Dam Rd 11719 631-730-1575
Tim Hogan, prin. Fax 286-5336

Brooklyn, See New York
NYC Department of Education
Supt. — See New York
Academy for College Preparation 500/6-12
911 Flatbush Ave 11226 718-564-2566
Doris Unger, prin. Fax 564-2567
Academy for Conservation & Environment 300/9-12
6565 Flatlands Ave 11236 718-968-4101
Eugene Mazzola, prin. Fax 968-4296
Academy for Environmental Leadership 400/9-12
400 Irving Ave 11237 718-381-7100
Chantandrea Blissett, prin. Fax 628-6965
Academy for Health Careers 100/9-12
150 Albany Ave 11213 718-773-0128
Deonne Martin, prin. Fax 773-0648
Academy for Young Writers 400/9-12
1065 Elton St 11239 718-688-7230
Courtney Winkfield, prin. Fax 688-7236
Academy of Hospitality & Tourism 300/9-12
911 Flatbush Ave 11226 718-564-2580
Adam Brier, prin. Fax 564-2581
Academy of Innovative Technology 400/9-12
999 Jamaica Ave 11208 718-827-2469
Cynthia Fowlkes, prin. Fax 827-4013
Academy of Urban Planning 300/9-12
400 Irving Ave 11237 718-381-7100
Kyleema Norman, prin. Fax 418-0314
Acorn Community HS 600/9-12
561 Grand Ave 11238 718-789-2258
Andrea Piper, dir. Fax 789-2260
All City Leadership Academy 300/6-12
321 Palmetto St 11237 718-246-6500
Elvis Estevez, prin. Fax 381-9680
Arts & Media Preparatory Academy 300/9-12
905 Winthrop St 11203 718-773-3908
Deb Glauner, prin. Fax 773-7274

Aspirations Diploma Plus HS 200/Alt
1495 Herkimer St 11233 718-498-5257
Sherma Fleming, prin. Fax 498-7170

Automotive HS Vo/Tech
50 Bedford Ave 11222 718-218-9301
Catherina Lafergola, prin. Fax 599-4351

Banneker Academy 900/9-12
77 Clinton Ave 11205 718-797-3702
Adofo Muhammad, prin. Fax 797-3862

Barton HS Vo/Tech
901 Classon Ave 11225 718-636-4900
Dr. Richard Forman, prin. Fax 857-3688

Bedford Academy HS 400/9-12
1119 Bedford Ave 11216 718-398-3061
Cluny Lavache, prin. Fax 636-3819

Bedford - Stuyvesant Prep HS 100/Alt
832 Marcy Ave 11216 718-622-4310
Darryl Rascoe, prin. Fax 398-4381

Boys & Girls HS 900/9-12
1700 Fulton St 11213 718-467-1700
Michael Wiltshire, prin. Fax 221-0645

Brooklyn Academy HS 100/Alt
832 Marcy Ave 11216 718-638-4235
Charon Hall, prin. Fax 638-0051

Brooklyn Academy of Global Finance 200/9-12
125 Stuyvesant Ave 11221 718-574-3126
Dannielle Darbee, prin. Fax 574-3681

Brooklyn Acad of Science & Environment 500/9-12
883 Classon Ave 11225 718-230-6363
Veronica Peterson, prin. Fax 230-6370

Brooklyn Bridge Academy 200/Alt
6565 Flatlands Ave 11236 718-968-1689
Max Paul, prin. Fax 968-1678

Brooklyn College Academy 600/7-12
350 Coney Island Ave 11218 718-853-6184
Nick Mazzarella, prin. Fax 951-4441

Brooklyn Collegiate S 400/7-12
2021 Bergen St 11233 718-922-1145
Heather Newman, prin. Fax 922-2347

Brooklyn Community HS of Arts & Media 400/9-12
300 Willoughby Ave 11205 718-230-5748
James O'Brien, prin. Fax 230-3050

Brooklyn Democracy Academy 200/Alt
985 Rockaway Ave 11212 718-342-6348
Andrew Brown, prin. Fax 342-6708

Brooklyn Frontiers HS 200/9-12
112 Schermerhorn St 11201 718-722-4727
Alona Cohen Ph.D., prin. Fax 722-7919

Brooklyn Generation S 300/9-12
6565 Flatlands Ave 11236 718-968-4200
Lydia Bomani, prin. Fax 444-5419

HS for Civil Rights 300/9-12
400 Pennsylvania Ave 11207 718-922-6289
Michael Steele, prin. Fax 922-7253

HS for Global Citizenship 300/9-12
883 Classon Ave 11225 718-230-6300
Michelle Rochon, prin. Fax 230-6301

Brooklyn HS for Law & Technology 400/9-12
1396 Broadway 11221 718-919-1256
Vernon Johnson, prin. Fax 852-4593

HS for Medical Professions 400/9-12
1600 Rockaway Pkwy 11236 718-290-8700
Pauline O'Brien, prin. Fax 290-8705

HS for Public Service 400/9-12
600 Kingston Ave 11203 718-756-5325
Ben Shuldiner, prin. Fax 363-3206

HS for Service & Learning 400/9-12
911 Flatbush Ave 11226 718-564-2551
Peter Fabianski, prin. Fax 564-2552

Brooklyn HS for the Arts 800/9-12
345 Dean St 11217 718-855-2412
Margaret Berman, prin. Fax 852-8734

HS for Youth & Community Development 300/9-12
911 Flatbush Ave 11226 718-564-2470
Mary Prendergast, prin. Fax 564-2471

HS Innovation in Advertising 300/9-12
1600 Rockaway Pkwy 11236 718-290-8760
Adaleza Michelena, prin. Fax 290-8766

Brooklyn HS Leadership Community Service 200/Alt
300 Willoughby Ave 11205 718-638-3062
Georgia Kouriampalis, prin. Fax 638-3404

HS of Enterprise - Business & Tech 1,000/9-12
850 Grand St 11211 718-387-2800
Holger Carrillo, prin. Fax 387-2748

HS of Sports Management 300/9-12
2630 Benson Ave 11214 718-333-7650
Robin Pitts, prin. Fax 333-7675

HS of Telecommunications Arts & Tech 1,300/9-12
350 67th St 11220 718-759-3400
Xhenete Shepard, prin. Fax 759-3490

Brooklyn Institute For Liberal Arts 9-12
600 Kingston Ave 11203 718-221-1097
Ann-Marie Henry-Stephens, prin.

IS 30 400/6-8
7002 4th Ave 11209 718-491-8440
Carol Heeraman, prin. Fax 491-0071

IS 68 800/6-8
956 E 82nd St 11236 718-241-4800
Merve Williams, prin. Fax 241-5582

IS 96 700/6-8
99 Avenue P 11204 718-236-1344
Erin Lynch, prin. Fax 236-2397

IS 98 1,400/6-8
1401 Emmons Ave 11235 718-891-9005
Maria Timo, prin. Fax 646-7250

IS 136 500/6-8
4004 4th Ave 11232 718-840-1950
Eric Sackler, prin. Fax 965-9567

IS 171 800/5-8
528 Ridgewood Ave 11208 718-647-0111
Indira Mota, prin. Fax 827-5834

IS 211 700/6-8
1001 E 100th St 11236 718-251-4411
Carolyn James, prin. Fax 241-2503

IS 228 1,000/6-8
228 Avenue S 11223 718-375-7635
Dominick D'Angelo, prin. Fax 376-1209

IS 281 1,200/6-8
8787 24th Ave 11214 718-996-6706
Maria Bender, prin. Fax 996-4186

IS 285 900/6-8
5909 Beverley Rd 11203 718-451-2200
George Patterson, prin. Fax 451-0229

IS 303 600/6-8
501 West Ave 11224 718-996-0100
Carmen Amador, prin. Fax 996-3785

IS 318 1,600/6-8
101 Walton St 11206 718-782-0589
Leander Windley, prin. Fax 384-7715

IS 340 200/6-8
227 Sterling Pl 11238 718-857-5516
Jean Williams, prin. Fax 230-5479

IS 347 400/5-8
35 Starr St 11221 718-821-4248
John Barbella, prin. Fax 821-1332

IS 349 400/6-8
35 Starr St 11221 718-418-6389
Michael Loughren, prin. Fax 418-6146

IS 364 400/6-8
1426 Freeport Loop 11239 718-642-3007
Dale Kelly, prin. Fax 642-8516

IS 381 400/6-8
1599 E 22nd St 11210 718-252-0058
Mary Harrington, prin. Fax 252-0035

IS 392 300/5-8
104 Sutter Ave 11212 718-498-2491
Ingrid Joseph, prin. Fax 346-2804

Brooklyn International HS 300/9-12
49 Flatbush Avenue Ext 11201 718-643-9315
Kathleen Rucker, prin. Fax 643-9516

JHS 14 500/6-8
2424 Batchelder St 11235 718-743-0220
Teri Ahearn, prin. Fax 769-8632

JHS 50 300/6-8
183 S 3rd St 11211 718-387-4184
Benjamin Honoroff, prin. Fax 302-2320

JHS 57 200/6-8
125 Stuyvesant Ave 11221 718-574-2357
Celeste Douglas, prin. Fax 453-0577

JHS 62 1,300/6-8
700 Cortelyou Rd 11218 718-941-5450
Barry Kevorkian, prin. Fax 693-7433

JHS 78 900/6-8
1420 E 68th St 11234 718-763-4701
Anthony Cusumano, prin. Fax 251-3439

JHS 88 1,200/6-8
544 7th Ave 11215 718-788-4482
Ailene Mitchell, prin. Fax 768-0213

JHS 162 500/6-8
1390 Willoughby Ave 11237 718-821-4860
Amanda Lazerson, prin. Fax 821-1728

JHS 201 1,400/6-8
8010 12th Ave 11228 718-833-9363
Robert Ciulla, prin. Fax 836-1786

JHS 218 500/6-8
370 Fountain Ave 11208 718-647-9050
Lisa Ann Hermann, prin. Fax 827-5839

JHS 220 1,400/6-8
4812 9th Ave 11220 718-633-8200
Loretta Witek, prin. Fax 871-7466

JHS 223 900/6-8
4200 16th Ave 11204 718-438-0155
Andrew Frank, prin. Fax 871-7477

JHS 227 1,300/6-8
6500 16th Ave 11204 718-256-8218
Edwin Hernandez, prin. Fax 234-6204

JHS 234 1,900/6-8
1875 E 17th St 11229 718-645-1334
Susan Schaeffer, prin. Fax 645-7759

JHS 259 1,400/6-8
7305 Fort Hamilton Pkwy 11228 718-833-1000
Janice Geary, prin. Fax 833-3419

JHS 278 1,100/6-8
1925 Stuart St 11229 718-375-3523
Debra Garofalo, prin. Fax 998-7324

JHS 291 500/6-8
231 Palmetto St 11221 718-574-0361
Antonios Pappas, prin. Fax 574-1360

JHS 292 700/6-8
301 Vermont St 11207 718-498-6562
Evelyn Maxfield, prin. Fax 345-3327

JHS 383 900/5-8
1300 Greene Ave 11237 718-574-0390
Jeanette Smith, prin. Fax 574-1366

Brooklyn Lab S 400/9-12
999 Jamaica Ave 11208 718-235-3592
Renel Piton, prin. Fax 235-4028

Brooklyn Latin S 600/9-12
223 Graham Ave 11206 718-366-0154
Gina Mautschke, prin. Fax 381-3012

MS 35 200/6-8
272 MacDonough St 11233 718-574-2345
Jackie Charles, prin. Fax 452-1273

MS 51 1,100/6-8
350 5th Ave 11215 718-369-7603
Lenore Dileo-Berner, prin. Fax 499-4948

MS 61 800/6-8
400 Empire Blvd 11225 718-774-1002
Shannon Burton, prin. Fax 467-4335

MS 113 700/6-8
300 Adelphi St 11205 718-834-6734
Dawnique Daughtry, prin. Fax 596-2802

MS 246 600/6-8
72 Veronica Pl 11226 718-282-5230
Bently Warrington, prin. Fax 284-6429

MS 266 100/6-8
62 Park Pl 11217 718-857-2291
Glenda Esperance, prin. Fax 857-2347

MS 267 300/6-8
800 Gates Ave 11221 718-574-2318
Patricia King, prin. Fax 574-2320

MS 582 300/6-8
207 Bushwick Ave 11206 718-456-8218
Brian Walsh, prin. Fax 456-8220

MS 584 100/6-8
130 Rochester Ave 11213 718-604-1380
Kinsley Kwateng, prin. Fax 604-3784

MS 596 100/6-8
300 Willoughby Ave 11205 718-230-3273
Samantha Exantus, prin. Fax 230-0173

MS for Academic and Social Excellence 200/6-8
1224 Park Pl 11213 718-774-0105
Betsie Green, prin. Fax 774-0298

MS for Art and Philosophy 300/6-8
1084 Lenox Rd 11212 718-342-7563
Neil McNeill, prin. Fax 342-8131

MS of Marketing & Legal Studies 300/6-8
905 Winthrop St 11203 718-773-7343
Jameela Horton, prin. Fax 773-7946

Brooklyn Preparatory HS 500/9-12
257 N 6th St 11211 718-486-2550
Noah Lansner, prin. Fax 486-2505

Brooklyn S for Collaborative Studies 700/6-12
610 Henry St 11231 718-923-4700
Priscilla Chan, prin. Fax 923-4730

Brooklyn S for Global Studies 300/6-12
284 Baltic St 11201 718-694-9741
Dawn Meconi, prin. Fax 694-9745

Brooklyn School for Math and Research 200/9-12
400 Irving Ave 11237 718-381-7100
Perry Rainey, prin. Fax 381-9897

Brooklyn S for Music & Theater 400/9-12
883 Classon Ave 11225 718-230-6250
Pamela Dorcely, prin. Fax 230-6262

S of Business Finance Entrepreneurship 100/6-8
125 Stuyvesant Ave 11221 718-602-3271
Anne Malcom, prin. Fax 602-3274

Brooklyn Science and Engineering Academy 6-8
5404 Tilden Ave 11203 718-240-3790
Angela Defilippis, prin.

Brooklyn Studio Secondary S 900/6-12
8310 21st Ave 11214 718-266-5032
Andrea Ciliotta, prin. Fax 266-5093

Brooklyn Technical HS 5,500/9-12
29 Fort Greene Pl 11217 718-804-6400
Randy Asher, prin. Fax 260-9245

Brooklyn Theatre Arts HS 400/9-12
6565 Flatlands Ave 11236 718-968-1072
David Ward, prin. Fax 968-1065

Brownsville Academy HS 200/Alt
1150 E New York Ave 11212 718-778-7305
Katwona Warren, prin. Fax 778-7385

Brownsville Collaborative MS 6-8
85 Watkins St 11212 718-495-1202
Stacy Walsh, prin.

Bushwick Community HS 100/Alt
231 Palmetto St 11221 718-443-3083
Llermi Gonzalez, prin. Fax 443-4757

Bushwick HS for Social Justice 400/9-12
400 Irving Ave 11237 718-381-7100
Ana Marsh, prin. Fax 418-0192

Bushwick Leaders HS 400/9-12
797 Bushwick Ave 11221 718-919-4212
Catherine Reilly, prin. Fax 574-1103

Campos Secondary S 700/6-12
215 Heyward St 11206 718-302-7900
Eric Fraser, prin. Fax 302-7979

Carson HS for Coastal Studies 500/9-12
521 West Ave 11224 718-265-0329
Ed Wilensky, prin. Fax 372-2514

Cobble Hill S of American Studies 600/9-12
347 Baltic St 11201 718-403-9544
Annamaria Mule, prin. Fax 403-9553

Conselyea Preparatory S 500/6-8
208 N 5th St 11211 718-486-6211
Maria Masullo, prin. Fax 486-6771

Cultural Academy for Arts and Sciences 300/9-12
5800 Tilden Ave 11203 718-968-6630
Diane Varano, prin. Fax 968-6635

Cypress Hills Collegiate Preparatory S 400/9-12
999 Jamaica Ave 11208 718-647-1672
Any Yager, prin. Fax 647-6719

Dewey HS 1,900/9-12
50 Avenue X 11223 718-373-6400
Connie Hamilton, prin. Fax 266-4385

Douglas Academy IV 200/7-12
1014 Lafayette Ave 11221 718-574-2820
Elvin Crespo, prin. Fax 574-2821

Douglas Academy VII HS 300/9-12
226 Bristol St 11212 718-485-3789
Tamika Matheson, prin. Fax 922-2761

Douglass Academy VIII MS 300/6-8
1400 Pennsylvania Ave 11239 718-348-2465
Chantal Grandchamps, prin. Fax 642-4537

Eagle Academy for Young Men II 400/6-10
1137 Herkimer St 11233 718-495-0863
Rashad Meade, prin. Fax 732-2129

East Brooklyn Community HS 200/9-12
9517 Kings Hwy 11212 718-927-6880
Patrick McGillicuddy, prin. Fax 927-6885

East Flatbush Community Research S 200/6-8
905 Winthrop St 11203 718-773-3059
Daveida Daniel, prin. Fax 773-3827

East NY Family Academy 500/6-12
2057 Linden Blvd 11207 718-927-0012
Anthony Yard, prin. Fax 927-0411

East New York MS of Excellence 200/6-8
605 Shepherd Ave 11208 718-257-4061
Malik Small, prin. Fax 257-4738

Ebbets Field MS 300/6-8
46 McKeever Pl 11225 718-941-5097
Margaret Baker, prin. Fax 284-7973

EBC-HS for Public Service 500/9-12
1155 Dekalb Ave 11221 718-452-3440
Shawn Brown, prin. Fax 452-3603

Edmonds Learning Center II 100/6-8
430 Howard Ave 11233 718-467-0306
Michele Luard, prin. Fax 953-0682

El Puente Academy for Peace & Justice 200/Alt
250 Hooper St 11211 718-387-1125
Wanda Vazquez, prin. Fax 387-4229

Ericsson MS 300/6-8
424 Leonard St 11222 718-782-2527
Maria Ortega, prin. Fax 302-2319

Essence MS 100/6-8
590 Sheffield Ave 11207 718-272-8371
Jermaine Lewis, prin. Fax 272-8372

Evergreen MS for Urban Exploration 200/6-8
125 Covert St 11207 718-455-0180
Lauren Reiss, prin. Fax 455-4381

Evers Preparatory S 1,200/6-12
1186 Carroll St 11225 718-703-5400
Dr. Michael Wiltshire, prin. Fax 703-5600

Expeditionary Learning S for Comm Leader 300/9-12
2630 Benson Ave 11214 718-333-7700
David O'Hara, prin. Fax 333-7725

FDNY S for Fire & Life Safety 300/9-12
400 Pennsylvania Ave 11207 718-922-0389
James Anderson, prin. Fax 922-0593

Fort Greene Preparatory Academy 300/6-8
100 Clermont Ave 11205 718-254-9401
Paula Lettiere, prin. Fax 254-9407

Ft. Hamilton HS 4,300/9-12
8301 Shore Rd 11209 718-748-1537
Kaye Houlihan, prin. Fax 836-3955

Foundations Academy 100/9-12
70 Tompkins Ave 11206 718-302-5092
Neil Monheit, prin. Fax 599-1369

Gibran International Academy 50/8-9
362 Schermerhorn St 11217 718-237-2502
Winston Hamann, prin. Fax 488-1724

Goldstein - Sciences HS 1,100/9-12
1830 Shore Blvd 11235 718-368-8500
Scott Hughes, prin. Fax 368-8555

Gotham Professional Arts Academy 200/9-12
265 Ralph Ave 11233 718-455-0746
Alexander White, prin. Fax 574-3971

Grady Career & Tech HS Vo/Tech
25 Brighton 4th Rd 11235 718-332-5000
Tarah Montalbano, prin. Fax 332-2544

Green S Academy for Environmental Career 300/9-12
223 Graham Ave 11206 718-599-1207
Cara Tait, prin. Fax 387-7945

Highland Park Community S 6-8
528 Ridgewood Ave 11208 718-235-1785
Jamilah Seifullah, prin.

Hudde IS 900/6-8
2500 Nostrand Ave 11210 718-253-3700
Gina Votinelli, prin. Fax 253-0356

International HS at Lafayette 300/9-12
2630 Benson Ave 11214 718-333-7860
Jon Harriman, prin. Fax 333-7861

International HS at Prospect Heights 400/9-12
883 Classon Ave 11225 718-230-6333
Nedda DeCastro, prin. Fax 230-6322

It Takes a Village Academy 500/9-12
5800 Tilden Ave 11203 718-629-2307
Marina Vinitskaya, prin. Fax 629-6162

KAPPA V S, 985 Rockaway Ave 11212 200/6-8
Ronda Phillips, prin. 718-922-4690

Kingsborough Early College S 600/6-12
2630 Benson Ave 11214 718-333-7850
Tracee Murren, prin. Fax 333-7875

Liberation Diploma Plus 200/9-12
2865 W 19th St 11224 718-946-6812
April Leong, prin. Fax 946-6825

Life Academy HS for Film and Music 300/9-12
2630 Benson Ave 11214 718-333-7750
Eugenia Kelch, prin. Fax 333-7775

Lincoln HS 2,300/9-12
2800 Ocean Pkwy 11235 718-333-7400
Ari Hoogenboom, prin. Fax 946-5035

Lyons Community S 600/6-12
223 Graham Ave 11206 718-782-0918
Karen Onishi, prin. Fax 782-5283

Madiba Prep MS 6-8
1014 Lafayette Ave 11221 718-574-2804
Sharon Stephens, prin.

Madison HS 3,100/9-12
3787 Bedford Ave 11229 718-758-7200
Jodie Cohen, prin. Fax 758-7341

Mandela HS, 1700 Fulton St 11213 9-12
Tabari Bomani, prin. 718-804-6805

Math & Science Exploratory S 500/6-8
345 Dean St 11217 718-330-9328
Arin Rusch, prin. Fax 330-0944

Maxwell Career and Technical HS Vo/Tech
145 Pennsylvania Ave 11207 718-345-9100
Jocelyn Babette, prin. Fax 345-5470

McAuliffe S 900/6-8
1171 65th St 11219 718-236-3394
Justin Berman, prin. Fax 236-3638

McKinney S of the Arts 500/6-12
101 Park Ave 11205 718-834-6760
Michael Walker, prin. Fax 834-6776

Metropolitan Diploma Plus HS 100/Alt
985 Rockaway Ave 11212 718-342-6249
Meri Yallowitz, prin. Fax 342-6329

Midwood HS 3,900/9-12
2839 Bedford Ave 11210 718-724-8500
Michael McDonnell, prin. Fax 724-8515

Millennium Brooklyn HS 400/9-12
237 7th Ave 11215 718-832-4333
Kevin Conway, prin. Fax 499-2126

Mott Hall Bridges MS 200/6-8
210 Chester St 11212 718-345-6912
Nadia Lopez, prin. Fax 345-6918

Mott Hall IV, 1137 Herkimer St 11233 200/6-8
Kenya Stowe, prin. 718-485-5240

Multicultural HS 300/9-12
999 Jamaica Ave 11208 718-827-2796
Alexandra Hernandez, prin. Fax 827-3970

Murrow HS 3,900/9-12
1600 Avenue L 11230 718-258-9283
Allen Barge, prin. Fax 252-2611

New Heights MS 6-8
790 E New York Ave 11203 718-467-4501
Jessica Luciano, prin.

New Horizons S 200/6-8
317 Hoyt St 11231 718-330-9227
Noreen Mills, dir. Fax 330-9251

New Utrecht HS 3,300/9-12
1601 80th St 11214 718-232-2500
Maureen Goldfarb, prin. Fax 259-5526

New Voices S of Academic & Creative Arts 500/6-8
330 18th St 11215 718-965-0390
Frank Giordano, prin. Fax 965-0603

Olympus Academy 200/Alt
755 E 100th St 11236 718-272-1926
Bruce Gonzales, prin. Fax 272-5713

Origins HS 100/9-12
3000 Avenue X 11235 718-891-0037
John Banks, prin. Fax 891-0047

Parkside Preparatory Academy 500/6-8
655 Parkside Ave 11226 718-462-6992
Adrienne Spencer, prin. Fax 284-7717

Park Slope Collegiate S 400/6-12
237 7th Ave 11215 718-832-4300
Jill Bloomberg, prin. Fax 788-8127

Pathways in Technology Early College HS 300/9-12
150 Albany Ave 11213 718-221-1593
Rashid Davis, prin. Fax 221-1781

Performing Arts & Technology HS 400/9-12
400 Pennsylvania Ave 11207 718-922-0762
Reginald Richardson, prin. Fax 922-0953

Perkins Academy Vo/Tech
50 Bedford Ave 11222 718-388-7721
Kevin Bryant, prin. Fax 388-7793

Professional Pathways HS 100/9-12
3000 Avenue X 11235 718-332-6290
David Decamp, prin. Fax 332-6296

Progress HS 1,100/9-12
850 Grand St 11211 718-387-0228
William Jusino, prin. Fax 782-0911

Research and Service HS 100/9-12
1700 Fulton St 11213 718-804-6800
Allison Farrington, prin. Fax 804-6801

Roosevelt HS 3,100/9-12
5800 20th Ave 11204 718-621-8800
Melanie Katz, prin. Fax 232-9513

Satellite East 200/6-8
344 Monroe St 11216 718-789-4251
Kim McPherson, prin. Fax 789-4823

Satellite West MS 100/6-8
209 York St 11201 718-834-6774
Melissa Vaughan, prin. Fax 834-2979

School for Classics 300/9-12
370 Fountain Ave 11208 718-277-1069
Deborah Afanador-Soukar, prin. Fax 277-1873

School for Democracy & Leadership 300/6-12
600 Kingston Ave 11203 718-771-4865
James Olearchek, prin. Fax 771-5847

School for Human Rights 400/6-12
600 Kingston Ave 11203 718-771-4793
Michael Alexander, prin. Fax 771-4815

School for International Studies 500/6-12
284 Baltic St 11201 718-330-9390
Jillian Juman, prin. Fax 875-7522

School for Legal Studies 700/9-12
850 Grand St 11211 718-387-2800
Rosemary Vega, prin. Fax 387-3281

School of Integrated Learning 200/6-8
1224 Park Pl 11213 718-774-0362
Monique Campbell, prin. Fax 774-0521

Science and Medicine MS 400/6-8
965 E 107th St 11236 718-688-6400
Dennis Herring, prin. Fax 688-6401

Science Skills Center HS 500/9-12
49 Flatbush Avenue Ext 11201 718-243-9413
Dahilia McGregor, prin. Fax 243-9399

Science Technology & Research HS 500/6-12
911 Flatbush Ave 11226 718-564-2540
Dr. Eric Blake, prin. Fax 564-2541

Secondary S for Journalism 300/8-12
237 7th Ave 11215 718-832-4201
Marc Williams, prin. Fax 832-0273

Secondary S for Law 400/8-12
237 7th Ave 11215 718-832-4250
Oneatha Swinton, prin. Fax 499-3947

Sheepshead Bay HS 1,100/9-12
3000 Avenue X 11235 718-332-2003
John Omahoney, prin. Fax 648-9349

South Brooklyn Community HS 100/9-12
173 Conover St 11231 718-237-8902
Latoya Kittrell, dir. Fax 422-1927

Spring Creek Community S 6-12
1065 Elton St 11239 718-688-7200
Christina Koza, prin.

Stroud MS 300/6-8
750 Classon Ave 11238 718-638-3067
Tricia Delauney, prin. Fax 638-3515

Sunset Park HS 1,300/9-12
153 35th St 11232 718-840-1900
Victoria Antonini, prin. Fax 840-1925

Sunset Park Prep MS 500/6-8
4004 4th Ave 11232 718-840-1951
Jennifer Spalding, prin. Fax 965-3330

Teachers Preparatory HS 400/6-12
226 Bristol St 11212 718-498-2605
Carmen Simon, prin. Fax 345-8069

Transit Tech HS Vo/Tech
1 Wells St 11208 718-647-5204
Marlon Bynum, prin. Fax 647-4458

Twain Gifted & Talented S 1,300/6-8
2401 Neptune Ave 11224 718-266-0814
Karen Ditolla, prin. Fax 266-1693

Upper S @ PS 25 200/6-8
787 Lafayette Ave 11221 718-574-6032
Ativia Sandusky, prin. Fax 602-2357

Urban Action Academy 300/9-12
1600 Rockaway Pkwy 11236 718-290-8720
Steve Dorcely, prin. Fax 290-8721

Urban Assembly Institute Math & Science 500/6-12
283 Adams St 11201 718-260-2300
Kiri Soares, prin. Fax 260-2301

Urban Assembly S Collabortv Healthcare 9-12
999 Jamaica Ave 11208 718-277-1752
Kevin Bradley, prin.

Urban Assembly S for Criminal Justice 500/6-12
4200 16th Ave 11204 718-438-3893
Mariela Graham, prin. Fax 438-3527

Urban Assembly S for Law & Justice 500/9-12
283 Adams St 11201 718-858-1160
Suzette Dyer, prin. Fax 858-4733

Urban Assembly S for Music & Art 400/9-12
49 Flatbush Avenue Ext 11201 718-858-0249
Paul Thompson, prin. Fax 858-0492

Urban Assembly S for Urban Environment 100/6-8
70 Tompkins Ave 11206 718-599-0371
Kourtney Boyd, prin. Fax 388-0872

Victory Collegiate HS 300/9-12
6565 Flatlands Ave 11236 718-968-1530
Marcel Deans, prin. Fax 968-1526

WATCH HS 300/9-12
400 Pennsylvania Ave 11207 718-922-0650
Claudette Christie, prin. Fax 922-0709

W.E.B. DuBois Academic HS 100/9-12
402 Eastern Pkwy 11225 718-773-7765
Catherine Hartnett, prin. Fax 773-7849

West Brooklyn Community HS 200/10-12
1053 41st St 11219 718-686-1444
Gloria Rosario, prin. Fax 686-1189

Westinghouse Career & Tech HS Vo/Tech
105 Tech Pl 11201 718-625-6130
Janine Kieran, prin. Fax 596-9434

Williamsburg HS Architecture & Design 600/9-12
257 N 6th St 11211 718-388-1260
Gill Cornell, prin. Fax 486-2580

Williamsburg Preparatory S 700/9-12
257 N 6th St 11211 718-302-2306
Michael Shadrick, prin. Fax 302-3726

Young Womens Leadership S of Brooklyn 400/6-12
325 Bushwick Ave 11206 718-387-5641
Lani Lucas, prin.

Access Careers Post-Sec.
25 Elm Pl Ste 201 11201 718-643-9060

Adelphi Academy of Brooklyn 100/PK-12
8515 Ridge Blvd 11209 718-238-3308

Al-Noor S 600/PK-12
675 4th Ave 11232 718-768-7181
Abdulhakeem Alhasel, prin. Fax 768-7088

ASA Inst of Business & Computer Tech Post-Sec.
81 Willoughby St 11201 718-522-9073

Bais Brocha Stolin Karlin 500/PK-12
4314 10th Ave 11219 718-853-1222

Bais Esther S 300/PK-12
1353 50th St 11219 718-436-1234

Bais Rochel HS 900/9-12
62 Harrison Ave 11211 718-963-9287

Bais Rochel S of Boro Park 400/K-12
5301 14th Ave 11219 718-438-7822

Bais Ruchel D'Satmar 3-12
84 Sandford St 11205 718-422-0375

Bais Sarah Girls S 900/PK-12
6101 16th Ave 11204 718-871-7571

Bais Tziporah S 400/PK-12
1449 39th St 11218 718-436-8336

Bais Yaakov Academy 900/PK-12
1213 Elm Ave 11230 718-339-4747
Faigie Selengut, admin. Fax 998-5766

Bais Yaakov Adas Yereim 500/PK-12
563 Bedford Ave 11211 718-302-7500

Bais Yaakov Adas Yereim 300/PK-12
1169 43rd St 11219 718-435-5111

Bais Yaakov D'Chassidei Gur 500/PK-12
1975 51st St 11204 718-338-5600

Bais Yaakov D'Rav Meir HS 9-12
98 Lawrence Ave 11230 718-633-1232

Bay Ridge Preparatory S 400/K-12
8101 Ridge Blvd 11209 718-833-9090
Dr. Charles Fasano, head sch Fax 833-6680

Be'er Hagolah Institutes 500/K-12
671 Louisiana Ave 11239 718-642-6800

Beikvei Hatzoin S 200/PK-12
31 Division Ave 11249 718-486-6363

Beis Chaya Mushka 200/PK-12
1505 Carroll St 11213 718-756-0770

Beis Frima Chinuch Ctr 300/PK-10
1377 42nd St 11219 718-972-7666

Beit Yaakov Orot Sarah 50/9-12
1123 Avenue N 11230 718-627-3158

Belz Girls S 1,100/PK-12
600 McDonald Ave 11218 718-871-0500

Berkeley Carroll S 500/5-12
181 Lincoln Pl 11217 718-534-6550
Robert Vitalo, head sch Fax 398-3640

Beth Chana S 300/1-12
712 Bedford Ave 11206 718-935-1845

Beth HaMedrash Shaarei Yosher Post-Sec.
4102 16th Ave # 10 11204 718-854-2290

Beth Hamedrash Shaarei Yosher 100/9-12
4102 16th Ave 11204 718-854-2290

Beth Hatalmud Rabbinical College Post-Sec.
2127 82nd St 11214 718-259-2525

Beth Jacob HS 600/9-12
4420 15th Ave 11219 718-851-2255
D. Wolf, prin. Fax 435-3736

Beth Rivkah HS 500/9-12
310 Crown St 11225 718-735-0400
Bentzion Stock, dir. Fax 735-0422

Bet Medrash Gadol Ateret Post-Sec.
901 Quentin Rd 11223 347-394-1036

Bet Yaakov Ateret Torah HS 200/9-12
2166 Coney Island Ave 11223 718-382-7002

Bishop Kearney HS 600/9-12
2202 60th St 11204 718-236-6363
Elizabeth Guglielmo, prin. Fax 236-7784

Bishop Loughlin Memorial HS 700/9-12
357 Clermont Ave 11238 718-857-2700
Edward Bolan, prin. Fax 398-4227

Bnos Menachem S for Girls 600/PK-12
739 E New York Ave 11203 718-493-1100
Bnos Yaakov Educational Center 600/1-12
62 Harrison Ave 11211 718-387-7905
Bnos Yaakov Pupa 900/PK-12
1402 40th St 11218 718-851-0316
Bnos Yisroel Viznitz S 500/PK-12
12 Franklin Ave 11249 718-330-0222
Bnos Zion of Bobov 1,400/PK-12
5000 14th Ave 11219 718-438-3080
Brooklyn Amity S 200/PK-12
3867 Shore Pkwy 11235 718-891-6100
Brooklyn Friends S 800/PK-12
375 Pearl St 11201 718-852-1029
Dr. Larry Weiss, head sch Fax 643-4868
Brooklyn Hospital Post-Sec.
121 Dekalb Ave 11201 718-250-8005
Brooklyn Jesuit Prep S 100/5-8
560 Sterling Pl 11238 718-638-5884
Brian Chap, prin. Fax 228-6324
Brooklyn Law School Post-Sec.
250 Joralemon St 11201 718-625-2200
Career & Educational Consultants Post-Sec.
270 Flatbush Avenue Ext 11201 718-858-8500
Central Yeshiva Tomchei Tmimim Lubavitz Post-Sec.
841 Ocean Pkwy 11230 718-434-0784
Charles Stuart School of Locksmithing Post-Sec.
1420 Kings Hwy 11229 718-339-2640
Chatzar Hakodesh Sanz-Klausenberg 700/PK-12
945 39th St 11219 718-436-1248
Christian Heritage Academy 300/PK-12
1100 E 42nd St 11210 718-377-5682
Rev. Paul Meyerend, dir. Fax 338-9870
Congregation Khal Chasidei Skwer 300/9-12
5801 16th Ave 11204 718-633-4125
Cope Institute Post-Sec.
4006 18th Ave 11218 718-506-0500
Cristo Rey Brooklyn HS 9-12
710 E 37th St 11203 718-455-3555
Richard Reyes, prin. Fax 455-3556
CUNY Brooklyn College Post-Sec.
2900 Bedford Ave 11210 718-951-5000
CUNY Kingsborough Community College Post-Sec.
2001 Oriental Blvd 11235 718-368-5000
CUNY Medgar Evers College Post-Sec.
1650 Bedford Ave 11225 718-270-4900
CUNY New York City College of Technology Post-Sec.
300 Jay St 11201 718-260-5000
Darkei Noam Rabbinical College Post-Sec.
2822 Avenue J 11210 718-338-6464
EDP School of Computer Programming Post-Sec.
1601 Voorhies Ave 11235 718-332-6469
Educational Institute Oholei Menachem 400/9-12
417 Troy Ave 11213 718-363-0019
Elite HS 50/9-12
2115 Benson Ave 11214 718-373-0960
Followers of Jesus S 50/1-12
3065 Atlantic Ave 11208 718-235-5493
James E. Gochnauer, prin. Fax 484-1477
Fontbonne Hall Academy 500/9-12
9901 Shore Rd 11209 718-748-2244
Mary Ann Spicijaric, prin. Fax 745-3841
Fusion Academy 6-12
1 Metrotech Center N # 1004 11201 718-522-3286
Gamla College Post-Sec.
1213 Elm Ave 11230 718-339-4747
Gerer Mesivta Bais Yisroel 100/9-12
5407 16th Ave 11204 718-854-8777
Hair Design Institute at Fifth Avenue Post-Sec.
6711 5th Ave 11220 718-745-1000
Institute of Design and Construction Post-Sec.
141 Willoughby St 11201 718-855-3661
Kehilath Yakov Rabbinical Seminary Post-Sec.
638 Bedford Ave 11249 718-963-1212
Learning Institute for Beauty Sciences Post-Sec.
2384 86th St 11214 718-373-2400
Lev Bais Yaakov S 400/PK-12
3574 Nostrand Ave 11229 718-332-6000
Long Island University Post-Sec.
1 University Plz 11201 718-488-1000
Lubavitcher S Chabad 100/PK-12
841 Ocean Pkwy 11230 718-434-0795
Machon Bais Yaakov S 300/9-12
1683 42nd St 11204 718-972-7900
Machzikei Hadath Rabbinical College Post-Sec.
5407 16th Ave 11204 718-854-8777
Magen David Yeshiva HS 500/9-12
7801 Bay Pkwy 11214 718-331-4002
Rabbi Saul Zucker, prin. Fax 331-2174
Manhattan School of Computer Technology Post-Sec.
931 Coney Island Ave 11230 212-349-9768
Masores Bais Yaakov S 800/PK-12
1395 Ocean Ave 11230 718-692-2424
Shaindy Pinter, prin. Fax 692-3162
Me'orot Beit Yaakov S 50/PK-12
1123 Avenue N 11230 718-627-8758
Rabbi David Maslaton, prin. Fax 336-0149
Merkaz Bnos - Career Institute Post-Sec.
2115 Benson Ave 11214 718-234-4000
Merkaz Bnos HS 100/9-12
1400 W 6th St 11204 718-259-5600
Mesivta Bais Aron Tzvi Veretzky 100/9-12
1249 E 18th St 11230 718-258-3888
Mesivta Eastern Parkway Rabbinical Sem. Post-Sec.
510 Dahill Rd 11218 718-438-1002
Mesivta Eitz Chaim S 300/9-12
1577 48th St 11219 718-438-2018
Mesivta Imrei Yosef Spinka 400/9-12
1460 56th St 11219 718-851-1600
Mesivta Lev Bonim 100/9-12
8700 Avenue K 11236 718-444-5996
Mesivta Nachlas Yakov of Adas Yereim 100/9-12
185 Wilson St 11211 718-388-1751
Mesivta Nesivos Hatalmud 8-12
PO Box 190432 11219 718-972-0804
Rabbi Samuel Wolner, admin. Fax 972-6633
Mesivta of Manhattan Beach 50/9-11
59 W End Ave 11235 718-368-1333
Mesivta Sholom Shachne 100/9-12
129 Elmwood Ave 11230 718-252-6333
Mesivta Tiferes Elimelech S 200/9-12
4407 12th Ave 11219 718-854-3062
Mesivta Torah Vodaath Seminary Post-Sec.
425 E 9th St 11218 718-941-8000
Mesivta Yeshiva Rabbi Chaim Berlin 200/9-12
1585 Coney Island Ave 11230 718-377-8400
Rabbi Yosef Landsberg, prin. Fax 377-5883
Mirrer Yeshiva Central Institute Post-Sec.
1795 Ocean Pkwy 11223 718-645-0536
Mirrer Yeshiva Mesivta HS 200/9-12
1795 Ocean Pkwy 11223 718-375-0771
Mosdos Chasidei Square 300/K-12
1373 43rd St 11219 718-436-2550
Nazareth Regional HS 400/9-12
475 E 57th St 11203 718-763-1100
Providentia Quiles, prin. Fax 629-5382
Nefesh Academy 100/PK-12
2005 E 17th St 11229 718-627-4463
New York Methodist Hospital Post-Sec.
1401 Kings Hwy 11229 718-780-3706
Packer Collegiate Institute 1,000/PK-12
170 Joralemon St 11201 718-250-0222
Dr. Bruce L. Dennis, hdmstr. Fax 875-1363
Poly Prep Country Day S 700/5-12
9216 7th Ave 11228 718-836-9800
David Harman, hdmstr. Fax 921-5112
Polytechnic Institute of New York Univ. Post-Sec.
6 Metrotech Ctr 11201 718-260-3600
Pratt Institute Post-Sec.
200 Willoughby Ave 11205 718-636-3600
Prospect Park Bnos Leah HS 300/9-12
1604 Avenue R 11229 718-376-4400
Rabbinical Academy Mesivta Rabbi Chaim Post-Sec.
1605 Coney Island Ave 11230 718-377-0777
Rabbinical Coll. Bobovr Yeshiva Bnei Zn. Post-Sec.
1577 48th St 11219 718-438-2018
Rabbinical College Ch' San Sofer Post-Sec.
1876 50th St 11204 718-236-1171
Rabbinical College Ohr Shimon Yisroel Post-Sec.
215 Hewes St 11211 718-855-4092
Rabbinical College Ohr Yisroel Post-Sec.
8800 Seaview Ave 11236 718-633-4715
Rabbinical Seminary Adas Yereim Post-Sec.
185 Wilson St 11211 718-388-1751
Rabbinical Seminary M'Kor Chaim Post-Sec.
1571 55th St 11219 718-851-0183
St. Ann's S 1,100/PK-12
129 Pierrepont St 11201 718-522-1660
Vincent Tompkins, hdmstr. Fax 522-2599
St. Edmund Preparatory HS 700/9-12
2474 Ocean Ave 11229 718-743-6100
John Lorenzetti, prin. Fax 743-5243
St. Francis College Post-Sec.
180 Remsen St 11201 718-522-2300
St. Joseph HS 300/9-12
80 Willoughby St 11201 718-624-3618
Sr. Joan Gallagher, prin. Fax 624-2792
St. Joseph's College New York Post-Sec.
245 Clinton Ave 11205 718-940-5300
St. Saviour HS 200/9-12
588 6th St 11215 718-768-4406
Dr. Paula McKeown, prin. Fax 369-2688
Shalsheles Bais Yaakov S 100/1-12
1681 42nd St 11204 718-436-1122
Sinai Academy 50/9-12
2025 79th St 11214 718-256-7400
SUNY Downstate Medical Center Post-Sec.
450 Clarkson Ave 11203 718-270-1000
Talmudical Seminary of Bobov Post-Sec.
5120 New Utrecht Ave 11219 718-854-8700
Talmudical Seminary Oholei Torah Post-Sec.
667 Eastern Pkwy 11213 718-774-5050
Tichon Bnot Rachel HS 100/9-12
1950 E 7th St 11223 718-382-1555
Torah Academy HS of Brooklyn 50/9-12
2066 E 9th St 11223 718-339-8844
Moishe Rubin, prin. Fax 339-9701
Torah Temimah Talmudical Seminary Post-Sec.
507 Ocean Pkwy 11218 718-853-8500
United Lubavitcher Yeshiva 100/9-12
885 Eastern Pkwy 11213 718-735-6607
United Talmudical Academy 500/PK-12
82 Lee Ave 11211 718-963-9260
United Talmudical Academy 400/7-9
1346 53rd St 11219 718-438-7038
United Talmudical Seminary Post-Sec.
191 Rodney St 11211 718-963-9770
Xaverian HS 1,000/9-12
7100 Shore Rd 11209 718-836-7100
Kevin McCormack, admin. Fax 836-7114
Yeshiva and Kollel Harbotzas Torah Post-Sec.
1049 E 15th St 11230 718-692-0208
Yeshiva & Mesivta Torah Temimah 600/PK-12
555 Ocean Pkwy 11218 718-853-8500
Yeshiva Beis Meir 200/9-12
1327 38th St 11218 718-437-5844
Yeshiva Chanoch Lenaar 50/8-12
876 Eastern Pkwy 11213 718-774-8456
Yeshiva Chemdas Yisroel Kerem 200/10-12
1149 38th St 11218 718-686-5500
Yeshiva Ch'san Sofer - Mesivta M'shmuel 500/PK-12
1876 50th St 11204 718-236-1171
Yeshiva Darchai Menachem 100/4-12
432 Rutland Rd 11203 718-953-2919
Yeshiva Derech Chaim Post-Sec.
1573 39th St 11218 718-438-5476
Yeshiva Derech HaTorah 300/PK-10
2810 Nostrand Ave 11229 718-258-4441
Yeshiva Farm Settlement S 400/K-12
194 Division Ave 11211 914-387-0422
Yeshiva Gedolah Bais Yisroel Post-Sec.
2002 Avenue J 11210 718-258-7400
Yeshiva Gedolah Imrei Yosef D'Spinka Post-Sec.
1466 56th St 11219 718-851-8721
Yeshiva Gedolah of Midwood 100/11-12
1135 Ditmas Ave 11218 718-853-2400
Yeshiva Gedolah Ohr Yisrael Post-Sec.
2899 Nostrand Ave 11229 718-382-8702
Yeshiva Imrei Yoseph Spinka 200/K-12
5801 15th Ave 11219 718-851-1600
Yeshiva Karlin Stolin Post-Sec.
1818 54th St 11204 718-232-7800
Yeshiva Ketana of Bensonhurst 200/PK-10
2025 67th St 11204 718-236-4100
Yeshiva Ketana Toldos Yaakov 100/9-12
105 Heyward St 11206 718-852-0502
Yeshiva Mesivta Arugath Habosem 400/K-12
40 Lynch St 11206 718-237-4500
Yeshiva Mesivta Karlin Stolin 600/PK-12
1818 54th St 11204 718-232-7800
Yeshiva Mesivta Tiferes Yisroel S 700/K-12
1271 E 35th St 11210 718-258-9006
Yeshiva Mikdash Melech Post-Sec.
1326 Ocean Pkwy 11230 718-339-1090
Yeshiva Minchas Eluzar S 50/9-12
4706 14th Ave 11219 718-438-7633
Yeshiva Nesivos Chaim 50/9-12
221 Avenue F 11218 718-576-1421
Yeshiva of Brooklyn-Girls 700/PK-12
1470 Ocean Pkwy 11230 718-376-3775
Yeshiva of Flatbush Joel Braverman HS 600/9-12
1609 Avenue J 11230 718-377-1100
Rabbi Raymond Harari, hdmstr. Fax 258-0933
Yeshiva of Machzikai Hadas Post-Sec.
1301 47th St 11219 718-853-2442
Yeshiva of Nitra Rabbinical College Post-Sec.
194 Division Ave 11211 718-387-0422
Yeshiva R'tzahd S 400/5-8
8700 Avenue K 11236 718-444-5996
Yeshivas Boyan Tiferes Mordechai Shlomo 200/PK-12
1205 44th St 11219 718-435-6060
Yeshiva Sholom Shachna Post-Sec.
401 Elmwood Ave 11230 718-252-6333
Yeshivas Novominsk Post-Sec.
1690 60th St 11204 718-438-2727
Yeshivas Novominsk-Kol Yehuda 200/9-12
1690 60th St 11204 718-438-2727
Yeshivas Tiferes Avos 50/9-12
1960 Schenectady Ave 11234 718-252-0801
Yeshivas Vyelipol HS 100/9-12
860 E 27th St 11210 718-951-1800
Yehuda Rubin, prin. Fax 951-3414
Yeshivat Ateret Torah 1,600/PK-12
901 Quentin Rd 11223 718-375-7100
Yeshiva Tiferes Shmiel D'Aleksander 100/9-12
PO Box 190738 11219 718-633-5952
Yeshivat Ohel Torah 200/PK-12
2600 Ocean Ave 11229 718-332-2600
Yeshiva Toldos Yitzchok Bnei Mordechai 500/K-10
1413 45th St 11219 718-633-4802
Shlomo Kolodny, prin. Fax 633-1063
Yeshiva Toras Emes Kamenitz 500/PK-12
1904 Avenue N 11230 718-375-0900
Yeshivat Or Hatorah S 100/9-12
2119 Homecrest Ave 11229 718-645-4645
Yeshivat Shaare Torah Boys HS 100/9-12
1202 Avenue P 11229 718-645-6308
Yeshivat Shaare Torah Girls HS 100/9-12
1768 Ocean Ave 11230 718-382-4000
Sarah Wadler, prin. Fax 382-7999
Zvi Dov Roth Academy 100/6-12
3300 Kings Hwy 11234 718-677-5100

Brookville, Nassau, Pop. 3,435

Long Island Lutheran Middle & HS 600/6-12
131 Brookville Rd 11545 516-626-1700
Dr. Andrew Gove, head sch Fax 622-7459
Long Island University Post-Sec.
720 Northern Blvd 11548 516-299-2000

Brushton, Franklin, Pop. 466

Brushton-Moira Central SD 700/PK-12
758 County Route 7 12916 518-529-8942
Donna Andre, supt. Fax 529-6062
www.bmcsd.org
Brushton-Moira Central HS 400/7-12
758 County Route 7 12916 518-529-7342
Todd LaPage, prin. Fax 529-6062

Buffalo, Erie, Pop. 254,867

Buffalo CSD 32,500/PK-12
712 City Hall 14202 716-816-3500
Dr. Kriner Cash, supt. Fax 851-3535
www.buffaloschools.org
Public HS 195 1,000/5-12
186 E North St 14204 716-816-4230
Dr. William Kresse, prin. Fax 888-7145
Public HS 200 600/9-12
2885 Main St 14214 716-816-4250
Bert Stevenson, prin. Fax 838-7490
Public HS 204 500/9-12
370 Lafayette Ave 14213 716-816-4340
Denise Clarke, prin. Fax 888-7096
Public HS 205 800/9-12
51 Ontario St 14207 716-816-4360
Ella Dunne, prin. Fax 871-6046
Public HS 206 900/9-12
150 Southside Pkwy 14220 716-816-4828
Theresa Schuta, prin. Fax 828-4905
Public HS 212 400/9-12
320 Porter Ave 14201 716-816-4380
Florence Krieter, prin. Fax 888-7181
Public HS 301 Vo/Tech
400 Kensington Ave 14214 716-816-4450
Charlene Watson, prin. Fax 838-7546
Public HS 302 400/9-12
70 W Chippewa St 14202 716-816-3018
James Weimer, prin. Fax 851-3017
Public HS 304 1,100/9-12
256 S Elmwood Ave 14201 716-816-3888
Sabatino Cimato, prin. Fax 851-3890

Public HS 305 Vo/Tech
1500 Elmwood Ave 14207 716-816-4480
Crystal Barton, prin. Fax 897-6073
Public HS 307 400/9-12
820 Northampton St 14211 716-816-4520
Casey Young, prin. Fax 897-8130
Public HS 353 Alt
370 Lafayette Ave 14213 716-816-4340
Teena Jackson, prin.
Public HS 357 Alt
820 Northampton St 14211 716-816-4520
Michael Mogavero, prin.
Public HS 415 9-12
2885 Main St 14214 716-816-4010
Susan Doyle, prin. Fax 851-3868
Public JSHS 131 7-12
425 S Park Ave 14204 716-816-3270
Michael Mogavero, prin. Fax 851-3761
Public JSHS 197 500/5-12
101 Hertel Ave 14207 716-816-4500
Todd Miklas, prin. Fax 871-6007
Public MS 66 300/5-8
780 Parkside Ave 14216 716-816-3440
Shanie Keelean, prin. Fax 838-7448
Public MSHS 192 800/5-12
450 Masten Ave 14209 716-816-4220
Jody Covington, prin. Fax 888-7136
Public MSHS 198 500/5-12
110 14th St 14213 716-816-4300
Carlos Alvarez, prin. Fax 851-3863
Public S 156 600/5-12
319 Suffolk St 14215 716-816-4330
Michael Gruber, prin. Fax 838-7530

Kenmore-Town of Tonawanda UFSD 5,100/K-12
1500 Colvin Blvd 14223 716-874-8400
Dawn F. Mirand, supt. Fax 874-8621
www.ktufsd.org
Kenmore West HS 1,400/8-12
33 Highland Pkwy 14223 716-874-8401
Dean Johnson, prin. Fax 874-8527
Other Schools – See Tonawanda

Bishop Timon-St. Jude HS 300/9-12
601 McKinley Pkwy 14220 716-826-3610
Thomas Sullivan, prin. Fax 824-5833
Bryant & Stratton College Post-Sec.
465 Main St Ste 400 14203 716-884-9120
Buffalo Academy of the Sacred Heart 400/9-12
3860 Main St 14226 716-834-2101
Jennifer Demert, head sch Fax 834-2944
Buffalo Seminary 200/9-12
205 Bidwell Pkwy 14222 716-885-6780
Helen Marlette, head sch Fax 885-6785
Canisius College Post-Sec.
2001 Main St 14208 716-883-7000
Canisius HS 800/9-12
1180 Delaware Ave 14209 716-882-0466
Andrea Tyrpak-Endres, prin. Fax 883-1870
Continental School of Beauty Culture Post-Sec.
326 Kenmore Ave 14223 716-833-5016
Darul-Uloom Al Madania 200/PK-10
182 Sobieski St 14212 716-892-2606
D'Youville College Post-Sec.
320 Porter Ave 14201 716-829-8000
Erie Community College City Post-Sec.
121 Ellicott St 14203 716-842-2770
Medaille College Post-Sec.
18 Agassiz Cir 14214 716-880-2000
Mt. Mercy Academy 300/9-12
88 Red Jacket Pkwy 14220 716-825-8796
Margaret Staszak, prin. Fax 825-0976
Nardin Academy 500/K-12
135 Cleveland Ave 14222 716-881-6262
Rebecca Reeder, prin. Fax 881-0086
National Tractor Trailer School Post-Sec.
175 Katherine St 14210 716-849-6887
Nativity Miguel MS 100/5-8
21 Davidson Ave 14215 716-836-5188
Fr. Edward Durkin, prin. Fax 836-5189
New York Institute of Massage Post-Sec.
PO Box 645 14231 716-633-0355
Nichols S 600/5-12
1250 Amherst St 14216 716-332-6300
Bill Clough, head sch Fax 875-2169
St. Mary's School for the Deaf Post-Sec.
2253 Main St 14214
Salvatore Sch of Hospitality & Business Post-Sec.
6681 Transit Rd 14221 716-827-4300
SUNY Buffalo State College Post-Sec.
1300 Elmwood Ave 14222 716-878-4000
SUNY Educational Opportunity Center Post-Sec.
465 Washington St 14203 716-849-6725
Trocaire College Post-Sec.
360 Choate Ave 14220 716-826-1200
University at Buffalo SUNY Post-Sec.
12 Capen Hall 14260 716-645-2000
Villa Maria College of Buffalo Post-Sec.
240 Pine Ridge Rd 14225 716-896-0700

Burnt Hills, Saratoga
Burnt Hills-Ballston Lake Central SD 3,200/K-12
173 Lakehill Rd 12027 518-399-9141
Dr. Patrick McGrath, supt. Fax 399-1882
www.bhbl.org
Burnt Hills-Ballston Lake HS 1,100/9-12
88 Lake Hill Rd 12027 518-399-9141
Timothy Brunson, prin. Fax 399-4341
O'Rourke MS 700/6-8
173 Lake Hill Rd 12027 518-399-9141
Colleen Wolff, prin. Fax 384-2588

Burt, Niagara
Newfane Central SD 1,500/PK-12
6048 Godfrey Rd 14028 716-778-6850
Michael Baumann, supt. Fax 778-6852
www.newfane.wnyric.org
Other Schools – See Newfane

Cairo, Greene, Pop. 1,375
Cairo-Durham Central SD 1,000/PK-12
PO Box 780 12413 518-622-8534
Anthony Taibi, supt. Fax 622-9566
www.cairodurham.org
Cairo-Durham HS 500/9-12
PO Box 598 12413 518-622-8543
Nick Fitzgerald, prin. Fax 622-8857
Cairo-Durham MS 300/6-8
PO Box 1139 12413 518-622-0490
Nathan Farrell, prin. Fax 622-0493

Caledonia, Livingston, Pop. 2,169
Caledonia-Mumford Central SD 900/PK-12
PO Box 150 14423 585-538-3400
Robert Molisani, supt. Fax 538-3450
www.cal-mum.org
Caledonia-Mumford HS 300/9-12
PO Box 150 14423 585-538-3483
Merritt Holly, prin. Fax 538-3470
Caledonia-Mumford MS 200/6-8
PO Box 150 14423 585-538-3482
Paul Estabrooks, prin. Fax 538-3430

Cambridge, Washington, Pop. 1,844
Cambridge Central SD 900/K-12
58 S Park St 12816 518-677-8527
Vincent Canini, supt. Fax 677-3889
www.cambridgecsd.org
Cambridge HS 400/7-12
24 S Park St 12816 518-677-8527
Tammy Silvernell, prin. Fax 677-3246

Camden, Oneida, Pop. 2,211
Camden Central SD 1,900/PK-12
51 3rd St 13316 315-245-4075
Mary Lynne Szczerba, supt. Fax 245-1622
www.camdenschools.org
Camden HS 700/9-12
55 Oswego St 13316 315-245-3168
Heather Wieland, prin. Fax 245-4173
Camden MS 500/5-8
32 Union St 13316 315-245-0080
Mary Walker, prin. Fax 245-0083

Camillus, Onondaga, Pop. 1,196
West Genesee Central SD 4,800/K-12
300 Sanderson Dr 13031 315-487-4562
Dr. Christopher Brown, supt. Fax 487-2999
www.westgenesee.org
Camillus MS 500/6-8
5525 Ike Dixon Rd 13031 315-672-3159
Beth Lozier, prin. Fax 672-3309
West Genesee HS 1,600/9-12
5201 W Genesee St 13031 315-487-4592
Geoffrey Morton, prin. Fax 487-4582
West Genesee MS 700/6-8
500 Sanderson Dr 13031 315-487-4615
Stephen Dunham, prin. Fax 487-4618

Campbell, Steuben, Pop. 695
Campbell-Savona Central SD 800/PK-12
8455 County Route 125 14821 607-527-9800
Kathleen Hagenbuch, supt. Fax 527-9863
www.cscsd.org
Campbell-Savona JSHS 400/7-12
8455 County Route 125 14821 607-527-9800
Kelley Meade, prin. Fax 527-9862

Canaan, Columbia
Berkshire UFD 100/7-12
13640 State Route 22 12029 518-781-3500
Bruce Potter, supt. Fax 781-4890
www.berkshirefarm.org
Berkshire JSHS 100/Alt
13640 State Route 22 12029 518-781-3500
Michael Mitchell, prin. Fax 781-4890

Canajoharie, Montgomery, Pop. 2,208
Canajoharie Central SD 1,000/PK-12
136 Scholastic Way 13317 518-673-6302
Deborah Grimshaw, supt. Fax 673-3177
www.canajoharieschools.org
Canajoharie HS 300/9-12
136 Scholastic Way 13317 518-673-6330
Rebecca Gleason, prin. Fax 673-3177
Canajoharie MS 200/6-8
25 School District Rd 13317 518-673-6320
Mark Rauch, prin. Fax 673-5557

Canandaigua, Ontario, Pop. 10,383
Canandaigua CSD 2,900/PK-12
143 N Pearl St 14424 585-396-3700
Lynne H. Erdle, supt. Fax 396-7306
www.canandaiguaschools.org/
Canandaigua Academy 1,200/9-12
435 East St 14424 585-396-3800
Vernon Tenney, prin. Fax 396-3806
Canandaigua MS 800/6-8
215 Granger St 14424 585-396-3850
John Arthur, prin. Fax 396-3863

Finger Lakes Community College Post-Sec.
3325 Marvin Sands Dr 14424 585-394-3500

Canaseraga, Allegany, Pop. 544
Canaseraga Central SD 200/PK-12
PO Box 230 14822 607-545-6421
Chad Groff, supt. Fax 545-6265
www.ccsdny.org/
Canaseraga S 200/PK-12
PO Box 230 14822 607-545-6421
Chad Groff, supt. Fax 545-6265

Canastota, Madison, Pop. 4,723
Canastota Central SD 1,400/K-12
120 Roberts St 13032 315-697-2025
June Clarke, supt. Fax 697-6368
www.canastotacsd.org
Canastota JSHS 700/7-12
101 Roberts St 13032 315-697-2003
Jay Altobello, prin. Fax 697-6314

USC The Business College Post-Sec.
PO Box 462 13032 315-697-8200

Candor, Tioga, Pop. 840
Candor Central SD 800/K-12
PO Box 145 13743 607-659-5010
Jeffrey Kisloski, supt. Fax 659-7112
candor.org
Candor JSHS 400/7-12
PO Box 145 13743 607-659-5020
Wayne Aman, prin. Fax 659-4692

Canisteo, Steuben, Pop. 2,260
Canisteo-Greenwood Central SD 900/PK-12
84 Greenwood St 14823 607-698-4225
Jeremy Palotti, supt. Fax 698-2833
www.cg.wnyric.org
Canisteo-Greenwood HS 300/9-12
84 Greenwood St 14823 607-698-4225
Michael Wright, prin. Fax 698-9125
Canisteo-Greenwood MS 300/5-8
120 Greenwood St 14823 607-698-4225
Paul Cone, prin. Fax 698-2244

Canton, Saint Lawrence, Pop. 6,213
Canton Central SD 1,300/PK-12
99 State St 13617 315-386-8561
William Gregory, supt. Fax 386-1323
www.ccsdk12.org/
McKenney MS 400/5-8
99 State St 13617 315-386-8561
Viola Schmid-Doyle, prin. Fax 386-1323
Williams HS 400/9-12
99 State St 13617 315-386-8561
Henry D. Dominy, prin. Fax 386-1323

St. Lawrence University Post-Sec.
23 Romoda Dr 13617 315-229-5011
SUNY Canton Post-Sec.
34 Cornell Dr 13617 315-386-7011

Carle Place, Nassau, Pop. 4,914
Carle Place UFD 1,400/K-12
168 Cherry Ln 11514 516-622-6442
David J. Flatley, supt. Fax 622-6447
www.cps.k12.ny.us
Carle Place MSHS 700/7-12
168 Cherry Ln 11514 516-622-6431
Thomas DePaola, prin. Fax 622-6587

Carmel, Putnam, Pop. 4,800
Carmel Central SD
Supt. — See Patterson
Carmel HS 1,400/9-12
30 Fair St 10512 845-225-8441
Lou Riolo, prin. Fax 228-2308
Fischer MS 1,400/5-8
281 Fair St 10512 845-228-2300
John Piscitella, prin. Fax 228-2304

Carthage, Jefferson, Pop. 3,663
Carthage Central SD 3,400/K-12
25059 Woolworth St 13619 315-493-5000
Peter Turner, supt. Fax 493-5069
www.carthagecsd.org
Carthage HS 1,000/9-12
36500 State Route 26 13619 315-493-5030
Joseph Sedita, prin. Fax 493-5039
Carthage MS 1,000/5-8
21986 Cole Rd 13619 315-493-5020
Kylie Morgia, prin. Fax 493-5029

Castleton on Hudson, Rensselaer, Pop. 1,464
Schodack Central SD 900/K-12
1477 S Schodack Rd 12033 518-732-2297
Lee Bordick, supt. Fax 732-7710
www.schodack.k12.ny.us
Maple Hill HS 300/9-12
1216 Maple Hill Rd 12033 518-732-7701
Ron Agostinoni, prin. Fax 732-0494
Maple Hill MS 200/6-8
1477 S Schodack Rd 12033 518-732-7736
Jacqueline Hill, prin. Fax 732-0493

Cato, Cayuga, Pop. 516
Cato-Meridian Central SD 1,000/PK-12
2851 State Route 370 13033 315-626-3439
W. Noel Patterson, supt. Fax 626-2888
www.catomeridian.org/
Cato-Meridian HS 300/9-12
2851 State Route 370 13033 315-626-3317
Danielle Mahoney, prin. Fax 626-2551
Cato-Meridian MS 300/5-8
2851 State Route 370 13033 315-626-3319
Sean Gleason, prin. Fax 626-2327

Catskill, Greene, Pop. 3,926
Catskill Central SD 1,600/PK-12
343 W Main St 12414 518-943-4696
Annmarie Barkman, supt. Fax 943-7116
www.catskillcsd.org
Catskill HS 500/9-12
341 W Main St 12414 518-943-2300
Kerry Overbaugh, prin. Fax 943-1451
Catskill MS 300/6-8
345 W Main St 12414 518-943-5665
Cheryl Rabinowitz, prin. Fax 943-3001

Cattaraugus, Cattaraugus, Pop. 997
Cattaraugus-Little Valley Central SD 900/PK-12
25 N Franklin St 14719 716-257-5293
Dr. Sharon Huff, supt. Fax 257-5298
www.cattlv.wnyric.org
Cattaraugus-Little Valley HS 300/8-12
25 N Franklin St 14719 716-257-3483
Tony Giannicchi, prin. Fax 257-5108

Cazenovia, Madison, Pop. 2,807
Cazenovia Central SD 1,500/K-12
31 Emory Ave 13035 315-655-1317
Matthew Reilly, supt. Fax 655-1375
cazenoviacsd.com
Cazenovia JSHS 700/8-12
31 Emory Ave 13035 315-655-1314
Eric Knuth, prin. Fax 655-1371

Cazenovia College 13035 Post-Sec.
800-654-3210

Cedarhurst, Nassau, Pop. 6,500
Lawrence UFD
Supt. — See Lawrence
Lawrence HS 900/9-12
2 Reilly Rd 11516 516-295-8000
Dr. Jennifer Lagnado, prin. Fax 295-2754

Hebrew Academy of Five Towns HS 300/9-12
635 Central Ave 11516 516-569-3807
Shulamith S for Girls 500/PK-12
305 Cedarhurst Ave 11516 516-564-1500
Rabbi Perry Tirschwell, dir. Fax 977-3159

Centereach, Suffolk, Pop. 31,131
Middle Country Central SD 10,100/PK-12
8 43rd St 11720 631-285-8005
Dr. Roberta Gerold Ed.D., supt. Fax 738-2719
www.mccsd.net
Centereach HS 1,500/9-12
14 43rd St 11720 631-285-8100
Thomas Bell, prin. Fax 285-8101
Dawnwood MS 1,200/6-8
10 43rd St 11720 631-285-8200
Kristine Leonard, prin. Fax 285-8201
Selden MS 1,100/6-8
22 Jefferson Ave 11720 631-285-8400
Jonathan Singer, prin. Fax 285-8401
Other Schools – See Selden

Our Savior New American S 200/PK-12
140 Mark Tree Rd 11720 631-588-2757
Rev. Ronald Stelzer, prin. Fax 588-2617

Center Moriches, Suffolk, Pop. 7,447
Center Moriches UFD 1,600/K-12
529 Main St 11934 631-878-0052
Russell Stewart, supt. Fax 878-4326
www.cmschools.org
Center Moriches HS 600/9-12
311 Frowein Rd 11934 631-878-0092
Edward Casswell, prin. Fax 878-1796
Center Moriches MS 400/6-8
311 Frowein Rd 11934 631-878-2519
Melissa Bates, prin. Fax 878-0362

Central Islip, Suffolk, Pop. 33,583
Central Islip UFD 6,500/PK-12
50 Wheeler Rd 11722 631-348-5112
Dr. Craig Carr, supt. Fax 348-0366
www.cischools.org
Central Islip HS 1,800/9-12
85 Wheeler Rd 11722 631-348-5078
Brett MacMonigle, prin. Fax 342-0161
Mulligan MS 700/6-8
1 Broadway Ave 11722 631-348-5042
Dr. Tracy Hudson, prin. Fax 348-5164
Reed MS 500/7-8
200 Half Mile Rd 11722 631-348-5066
Dr. Michele Darby, prin. Fax 348-5159

Central Square, Oswego, Pop. 1,828
Central Square Central SD 3,900/PK-12
642 S Main St 13036 315-668-4220
Dr. Jeffrey Bryant, supt. Fax 676-4437
www.cssd.org
Central Square MS 1,000/6-8
248 US Route 11 13036 315-668-4216
Concetta Galvan, prin. Fax 668-8410
Moore HS 1,300/9-12
44 School Dr 13036 315-668-4231
Jeffrey King, prin. Fax 668-4346

Central Valley, Orange, Pop. 1,929
Monroe-Woodbury Central SD 6,900/K-12
278 Route 32 10917 845-460-6200
Elsie Rodriguez, supt. Fax 460-6080
www.mw.k12.ny.us
Monroe-Woodbury HS 2,300/9-12
155 Dunderberg Rd 10917 845-460-7000
Matthew Kravatz, prin. Fax 460-7090
Monroe-Woodbury MS 1,700/6-8
199 Dunderberg Rd 10917 845-460-6400
John Kaste, prin. Fax 460-6044

Champlain, Clinton, Pop. 1,086
Northeastern Clinton Central SD 1,300/K-12
103 State Route 276 12919 518-298-8242
Robin Garrand, supt. Fax 298-4293
www.nccscougar.org
Northeastern Clinton HS 400/9-12
103 State Route 276 12919 518-298-8638
Joshua Harrica, prin. Fax 298-4293
Northeastern Clinton MS 300/6-8
103 State Route 276 12919 518-298-8681
Thomas Brandell, prin. Fax 298-4293

Chappaqua, Westchester, Pop. 1,404
Chappaqua Central SD 4,000/K-12
PO Box 21 10514 914-238-7200
Dr. Lyn Mckay, supt. Fax 238-7231
www.ccsd.ws
Bell MS 700/5-8
50 Senter St 10514 914-238-7202
Martin Fitzgerald, prin. Fax 238-2085
Greeley HS 1,300/9-12
70 Roaring Brook Rd 10514 914-738-7201
Robert Rhodes, prin.
Seven Bridges MS 600/5-8
PO Box 22 10514 914-238-7203
Andrew Corsilia, prin. Fax 666-7306

Chateaugay, Franklin, Pop. 824
Chateaugay Central SD 500/K-12
PO Box 904 12920 518-497-6420
Loretta Fowler, supt. Fax 497-3170
www.chateaugaycsd.org
Chateaugay JSHS 200/7-12
PO Box 904 12920 518-497-6611
Lori Tourville, prin. Fax 497-3170

Chatham, Columbia, Pop. 1,720
Chatham Central SD 1,200/K-12
50 Woodbridge Ave 12037 518-392-1501
Cheryl Nuciforo, supt. Fax 392-2413
www.chathamcentralschools.com
Chatham HS 400/9-12
50 Woodbridge Ave 12037 518-392-4142
John Thorsen, prin. Fax 392-0908
Chatham MS 300/6-8
50 Woodbridge Ave 12037 518-392-1560
Amy Potter, prin. Fax 392-1559

Chaumont, Jefferson, Pop. 611
Lyme Central SD 400/PK-12
PO Box 219 13622 315-649-2417
Cammy Morrison, supt. Fax 649-2663
www.lymecsd.org
Lyme Central S 400/PK-12
PO Box 219 13622 315-649-2417
Barry Davis, prin. Fax 649-2663

Chazy, Clinton, Pop. 555
Chazy Central UFD 500/K-12
609 Miner Farm Rd 12921 518-846-7135
John Fairchild, supt. Fax 846-8322
www.chazy.org
Chazy Central Rural JSHS 200/7-12
609 Miner Farm Rd 12921 518-846-7135
John Fairchild, prin. Fax 846-8322

Cheektowaga, Erie, Pop. 74,096
Cheektowaga Central SD 1,900/PK-12
3600 Union Rd 14225 716-686-3606
Dennis Kane, supt. Fax 681-5232
www.cheektowagacentral.org
Cheektowaga Central HS 700/9-12
3600 Union Rd 14225 716-686-3602
Scott Zipp, prin. Fax 686-3619
Cheektowaga Central MS 500/6-8
3600 Union Rd 14225 716-686-3660
Gretchen Sukdola, prin. Fax 686-3669

Cheektowaga-Maryvale UFD 2,200/PK-12
1050 Maryvale Dr 14225 716-631-7407
Joseph D'Angelo, supt. Fax 635-4699
www.maryvaleufsd.org
Maryvale HS 700/9-12
1050 Maryvale Dr 14225 716-631-7481
Tom Stack, prin. Fax 631-7404
Maryvale MS 500/6-8
1050 Maryvale Dr 14225 716-631-7425
Peter Frank, prin. Fax 631-7499

Cheektowago-Sloan UFD
Supt. — See Sloan
Kennedy HS 400/9-12
305 Cayuga Creek Rd 14227 716-891-6407
Kevin Kazmierczak, prin. Fax 270-0160
Kennedy MS 300/6-8
305 Cayuga Creek Rd 14227 716-897-7300
Gretchen Cercone, prin. Fax 892-2624

Cleveland Hill UFD 1,300/PK-12
105 Mapleview Dr 14225 716-836-7200
Jon MacSwan, supt. Fax 836-0675
www.clevehill.wnyric.org/
Cleveland Hill HS 400/9-12
105 Mapleview Dr 14225 716-836-7200
Jill Sherman, prin. Fax 836-7741
Cleveland Hill MS 300/6-8
105 Mapleview Dr 14225 716-836-7200
Andrea Kersten, prin. Fax 836-7741

Cherryplain, Rensselaer
Berlin Central SD 700/PK-12
17400 Route 22 12040 518-658-2690
Dr. Stephen Young, supt. Fax 658-3822
www.berlincentral.org/
Berlin Central HS 200/9-12
17400 Route 22 12040 518-658-2515
Dr. Cathie Allain, prin. Fax 658-2535
Berlin MS 200/6-8
17400 Route 22 12040 518-658-2515
Jason Breh, prin. Fax 658-2535

Cherry Valley, Otsego, Pop. 511
Cherry Valley-Springfield Central SD 500/PK-12
PO Box 485 13320 607-264-3265
TheriJo Climenhaga, supt. Fax 264-3458
www.cvscs.org
Cherry Valley-Springfield JSHS 300/6-12
PO Box 485 13320 607-264-3265
Kevin Keane, prin. Fax 264-3458

Chester, Orange, Pop. 3,852
Chester UFD 1,000/K-12
64 Hambletonian Ave 10918 845-469-5052
Sean Michel, supt. Fax 469-2377
chesterufsd.org
Chester Academy 600/6-12
64 Hambletonian Ave 10918 845-469-2231
Denis Petrilak, prin. Fax 469-3547

Chestertown, Warren, Pop. 671
North Warren Central SD 500/PK-12
6110 State Route 8 12817 518-494-3015
Michele Gill French, supt. Fax 494-2929
www.northwarren.k12.ny.us
North Warren Central S 500/PK-12
6110 State Route 8 12817 518-494-3015
Theresa Andrew, prin. Fax 494-2323

Chestnut Ridge, Rockland, Pop. 7,763
East Ramapo Central SD
Supt. — See Spring Valley
Chestnut Ridge MS 500/7-8
892 Chestnut Ridge Rd 10977 845-577-6300
Maria Vergez, prin. Fax 426-1063

Green Meadow Waldorf S 400/PK-12
307 Hungry Hollow Rd 10977 845-356-2514

Chittenango, Madison, Pop. 5,016
Chittenango Central SD 1,500/K-12
1732 Fyler Rd 13037 315-687-2850
Michael Schiedo, supt. Fax 687-2841
www.chittenangoschools.org
Chittenango HS 700/9-12
150 Genesee St 13037 315-687-2900
Nicholas Fersch, prin. Fax 687-2924
Chittenango MS 500/5-8
1732 Fyler Rd 13037 315-687-2800
Arnold Merola, prin. Fax 687-2801

Churchville, Monroe, Pop. 1,935
Churchville-Chili Central SD 3,900/K-12
139 Fairbanks Rd 14428 585-293-1800
Loretta Orologio, supt. Fax 293-1013
www.cccsd.org
Churchville-Chili MS 1,300/5-8
139 Fairbanks Rd 14428 585-293-4541
Carl Christensen, prin. Fax 293-4516
Churchville-Chili SHS 900/10-12
5786 Buffalo Rd 14428 585-293-4540
Bill Geraci, prin. Fax 293-4508
9th Grade Academy 300/9-9
137 Fairbanks Rd 14428 585-293-4546
Mary Leach, admin. Fax 293-4521

Cicero, Onondaga
North Syracuse Central SD
Supt. — See North Syracuse
Cicero-North Syracuse SHS 2,000/10-12
6002 State Route 31 13039 315-218-4100
William LaClair, prin. Fax 218-4185

Cincinnatus, Cortland
Cincinnatus Central SD 400/K-12
2809 Cincinnatus Rd 13040 607-863-4069
Steven Hubbard, supt. Fax 863-4109
www.cc.cnyric.org/
Cincinnatus HS 200/7-12
2809 Cincinnatus Rd 13040 607-863-3200
David Phetteplace, prin. Fax 863-4559

Circleville, Orange, Pop. 1,350
Pine Bush Central SD
Supt. — See Pine Bush
Circleville MS 600/6-8
PO Box 143 10919 845-744-2031
Lisa Hankinson, prin. Fax 361-3811

Clarence, Erie, Pop. 2,634
Clarence Central SD 4,700/K-12
9625 Main St 14031 716-407-9100
Geoffrey Hicks, supt. Fax 407-9126
www.clarenceschools.org
Clarence HS 1,600/9-12
9625 Main St 14031 716-407-9020
Kenneth Smith, prin. Fax 407-9061
Clarence MS 1,200/6-8
10150 Greiner Rd 14031 716-407-9200
Robert Moore, prin. Fax 407-9229

Clayton, Jefferson, Pop. 1,959
Thousand Islands Central SD 1,000/K-12
8481 County Route 9 13624 315-686-5594
Michael Bashaw, supt. Fax 686-5511
www.1000islandsschools.org
Thousand Islands HS 300/9-12
8481 County Route 9 13624 315-686-5594
Joseph Gilfus, prin. Fax 654-5039
Thousand Islands MS 200/6-8
8487 County Route 9 13624 315-686-5594
Michael Bashaw, prin. Fax 654-5038

Clifton Park, Saratoga
Shenendehowa Central SD 9,700/K-12
5 Chelsea Pl 12065 518-881-0600
Dr. L. Oliver Robinson, supt. Fax 371-9393
www.shenet.org/
Acadia MS 800/6-8
970 Route 146 Ste 54 12065 518-881-0450
Jonathan Burns, prin. Fax 371-3981
Gowana MS 800/6-8
970 Route 146 Ste 55 12065 518-881-0460
Robin Gawrys, prin. Fax 383-1490
Koda MS 800/6-8
970 Route 146 Ste 59 12065 518-881-0470
Sean Gnat, prin. Fax 383-1532
Shenendehowa HS 3,000/9-12
970 Route 146 12065 518-881-0310
Donald Flynt, prin. Fax 383-1670

Clifton Springs, Ontario, Pop. 2,111
Phelps-Clifton Springs Central SD 1,300/K-12
1490 State Route 488 14432 315-548-6420
Jamie Farr, supt. Fax 548-6429
www.midlakes.org
Midlakes MSHS 500/7-12
1554 State Route 488 14432 315-548-6300
Frank Bai-Rossi, prin. Fax 548-6319

Climax, Greene

Grapeville Christian S 100/K-12
2416 County Route 26 12042 518-966-5037
Marianne DeDeo B.S., prin. Fax 966-5498

Clinton, Oneida, Pop. 1,917
Clinton Central SD 1,300/K-12
75 Chenango Ave 13323 315-557-2253
Dr. Stephen Grimm, supt. Fax 853-8727
www.ccs.edu
Clinton HS 400/9-12
75 Chenango Ave 13323 315-557-2233
Matthew Lee, prin. Fax 853-1424
Clinton MS 300/6-8
75 Chenango Ave 13323 315-557-2260
Shaun Carney, prin. Fax 853-8727

Hamilton College Post-Sec.
198 College Hill Rd 13323 315-859-4011

Clinton Corners, Dutchess

Upton Lake Christian S 100/K-12
PO Box 63 12514 845-266-3497
Barbara Marrine, prin. Fax 266-3828

Clintonville, Clinton
Au Sable Valley Central SD 1,200/K-12
1273 Route 9N 12924 518-834-2845
Paul Savage, supt. Fax 834-2843
www.avcs.org
Au Sable Valley HS 400/9-12
1490 Route 9N 12924 518-834-2800
Javier Perez, prin. Fax 834-2847
Au Sable Valley MS 200/7-8
1490 Route 9N 12924 518-834-2800
Philip Mero, prin. Fax 834-2847

Clyde, Wayne, Pop. 2,017
Clyde-Savannah Central SD 900/PK-12
215 Glasgow St 14433 315-902-3000
Michael Hayden, supt. Fax 923-2560
www.clydesavannah.org/
Clyde-Savannah HS 300/9-12
215 Glasgow St 14433 315-902-3050
Dr. Craig Pawlak, prin. Fax 923-7906
Clyde-Savannah MS 200/6-8
215 Glasgow St 14433 315-902-3200
Jennifer Kelly, prin. Fax 923-2560

Clymer, Chautauqua
Clymer Central SD 400/PK-12
8672 E Main St 14724 716-355-4444
Bert Lictus, supt. Fax 355-2200
www.clymercsd.org
Clymer Central S 400/PK-12
8672 E Main St 14724 716-355-4444
Edward Bailey, prin. Fax 355-4467

Cobleskill, Schoharie, Pop. 4,593
Cobleskill-Richmondville Central SD 1,800/K-12
155 Washington Ave 12043 518-234-4032
Carl Mummenthey, supt. Fax 234-7721
www.crcs.k12.ny.us
Golding MS 400/6-8
193 Golding Dr 12043 518-234-8368
Scott McDonald, prin. Fax 234-1018
Other Schools – See Richmondville

SUNY at Cobleskill Post-Sec.
State Route 7 12043 518-255-5011

Cohoes, Albany, Pop. 15,737
Cohoes CSD 1,900/K-12
7 Bevan St 12047 518-237-0100
Jennifer Spring Ed.D., supt. Fax 237-2912
www.cohoes.org
Cohoes HS 500/9-12
1 Tiger Cir 12047 518-237-9100
Joseph Rajczak, prin. Fax 238-0169
Cohoes MS 400/6-8
7 Bevan St 12047 518-237-4131
Daniel Martinelli, prin. Fax 237-2253
Page Avenue S, 21 Page Ave 12047 Alt
Erin Hill, dir. 518-237-0990

Cold Spring, Putnam, Pop. 1,981
Haldane Central SD 900/K-12
15 Craigside Dr 10516 845-265-9254
Diana Bowers, supt. Fax 265-9213
www.haldaneschool.org
Haldane HS 300/9-12
15 Craigside Dr 10516 845-265-9254
Brian Alm, prin. Fax 265-3510

Cold Spring Harbor, Suffolk, Pop. 5,024
Cold Spring Harbor Central SD 1,900/K-12
75 Goose Hill Rd 11724 631-367-5900
Judith Wilansky Ed.D., supt. Fax 367-3108
www.csh.k12.ny.us
Cold Spring Harbor JSHS 1,000/7-12
82 Turkey Ln 11724 631-367-6900
Jay Matuk, prin. Fax 692-8016

Watson School of Biological Sciences Post-Sec.
1 Bungtown Rd 11724 516-367-6890

College Point, See New York

St. Agnes Academic HS 300/9-12
1320 124th St 11356 718-353-6276
Susan Nicoletti, prin. Fax 353-6068

Colton, Saint Lawrence, Pop. 343
Colton-Pierrepont Central SD 300/PK-12
4921 State Highway 56 13625 315-262-2100
Joseph Kardash, supt. Fax 262-2644
www.cpcs.us/
Colton-Pierrepont Central S 300/PK-12
4921 State Highway 56 13625 315-262-2100
James Nee, prin. Fax 262-2644

Commack, Suffolk, Pop. 35,739
Commack UFD
Supt. — See East Northport
Commack HS, 1 Scholar Ln 11725 2,500/9-12
Leslie Boritz, prin. 631-912-2100
Commack MS 1,700/6-8
700 Vanderbilt Pkwy 11725 631-858-3500
Anthony Davidson, prin.

Long Island Business Institute Post-Sec.
6500 Jericho Tpke Ste 202 11725 631-499-7100

Congers, Rockland, Pop. 8,213

Rockland Country Day S 100/PK-12
34 Kings Hwy 10920 845-268-6802
Kimberly Morcate, head sch Fax 268-4644

Conklin, Broome
Susquehanna Valley Central SD 1,600/K-12
PO Box 200 13748 607-775-0170
Roland Doig, supt. Fax 775-4575
www.svsabers.org
Stank MS 400/6-8
PO Box 225 13748 607-775-0303
Natalie Brubaker, prin. Fax 775-9142
Susquehanna Valley HS 500/9-12
PO Box 275 13748 607-775-0304
David Daniels, prin. Fax 775-9126

Cooperstown, Otsego, Pop. 1,834
Cooperstown Central SD 900/K-12
39 Linden Ave 13326 607-547-8181
Dr. William Crankshaw, supt. Fax 547-5100
www.cooperstowncs.org
Cooperstown JSHS 400/7-12
39 Linden Ave 13326 607-547-8181
Donna Lucy, prin. Fax 547-5100

Copenhagen, Lewis, Pop. 796
Copenhagen Central SD 500/PK-12
PO Box 30 13626 315-688-4411
Scott Connell, supt. Fax 688-2001
www.ccsknights.org/
Copenhagen Central S 500/PK-12
PO Box 30 13626 315-688-4411
Nadine O'Shaughnessy, prin. Fax 688-2001

Copiague, Suffolk, Pop. 22,652
Copiague UFD 4,900/K-12
2650 Great Neck Rd 11726 631-842-4015
Dr. Kathleen Bannon, supt. Fax 841-4614
www.copiague.k12.ny.us/
Copiague MS 1,100/6-8
2650 Great Neck Rd 11726 631-842-4011
Andrew Lagnado, prin. Fax 841-4630
O'Connell - Copiague HS 1,500/9-12
1100 Dixon Ave 11726 631-842-4010
Joseph Agosta, prin. Fax 841-4642

Corfu, Genesee, Pop. 702
Pembroke Central SD 900/PK-12
PO Box 308 14036 585-599-4525
Matthew Calderon, supt. Fax 599-4213
www.pembrokecsd.org
Pembroke JSHS 500/7-12
PO Box 308 14036 585-599-4525
Dr. Nathan Work, prin. Fax 599-4213

Corinth, Saratoga, Pop. 2,505
Corinth Central SD 1,200/K-12
105 Oak St 12822 518-654-2601
Mark Stratton, supt. Fax 654-6266
www.corinthcsd.com
Corinth HS 400/9-12
105 Oak St 12822 518-654-9005
Brian Testani, prin. Fax 654-6132
Corinth MS 300/6-8
105 Oak St 12822 518-654-9005
Lisa Meade, prin. Fax 654-2129

Corning, Steuben, Pop. 10,950
Corning CSD
Supt. — See Painted Post
Corning - Painted Post HS 800/9-12
201 Cantigney St 14830 607-654-2988
Robin Sheehan, prin. Fax 654-2907
Corning - Painted Post HS Learning Ctr 50/Alt
1 Academic Dr 14830 607-962-9283
Frank Barber, prin.

Alternative S for Math & Science 100/6-8
PO Box 114 14830 607-962-0011
Linda Cole, head sch Fax 962-4866
Corning Christian Academy 200/PK-12
11 Aisne St 14830 607-962-4220
Corning Community College Post-Sec.
1 Academic Dr 14830 607-962-9011

Cornwall, Orange, Pop. 11,270
Cornwall Central SD
Supt. — See Cornwall on Hudson
Cornwall Central MS 1,100/5-8
122 Main St 12518 845-534-8009
Kate Polumbo, prin. Fax 534-7809

Cornwall on Hudson, Orange, Pop. 2,955
Cornwall Central SD 3,300/K-12
24 Idlewild Ave 12520 845-534-8009
Neal S. Miller, supt. Fax 534-9032
www.cornwallschools.com
Other Schools – See Cornwall, New Windsor

New York Military Academy 100/7-12
78 Academy Ave 12520 845-534-3710
William Beard, supt. Fax 534-7121
Storm King S 200/8-12
314 Mountain Rd 12520 845-534-7892
Jonathan Lamb, head sch Fax 534-4128

Corona, See New York
NYC Department of Education
Supt. — See New York
HS for Arts & Business 900/9-12
10525 Horace Harding Expy 11368 718-271-8383
Ana Bruakov, prin. Fax 271-7196
IS 61 2,300/6-8
9850 50th Ave 11368 718-760-3233
Joseph Lisa, prin. Fax 760-5220

Cortland, Cortland, Pop. 18,830
Cortland Enlarged CSD 2,600/K-12
1 Valley View Dr 13045 607-758-4100
Michael J. Hoose, supt. Fax 758-4128
www.cortlandschools.org
Cortland JSHS 1,200/7-12
8 Valley View Dr 13045 607-758-4100
Joseph Mack, prin. Fax 758-4119

Cortland Christian Academy 100/PK-12
15 West Rd 13045 607-756-5838
Craig Miller, head sch Fax 756-7716
SUNY College at Cortland Post-Sec.
PO Box 2000 13045 607-753-2011

Cortlandt Manor, See Peekskill
Hendrick Hudson Central SD
Supt. — See Montrose
Blue Mountain MS 600/6-8
7 Furnace Woods Rd 10567 914-257-5700
John Owens, prin. Fax 257-5701

Lakeland Central SD
Supt. — See Shrub Oak
Panas HS 1,000/9-12
300 Croton Ave 10567 914-739-2823
Keith Yi, prin. Fax 739-3545

Ohr Hameir Seminary Tifereth Israel HS 100/9-12
141 Furnace Woods Rd 10567 914-736-1500
Ohr HaMeir Theological Seminary Post-Sec.
141 Furnace Woods Rd 10567 914-736-1500

Coxsackie, Greene, Pop. 2,765
Coxsackie-Athens Central SD 1,400/K-12
24 Sunset Blvd 12051 518-731-1710
Randall Squier, supt. Fax 731-1729
www.cacsd.org
Coxsackie-Athens HS 500/9-12
24 Sunset Blvd 12051 518-731-1800
Heath Quiles, prin. Fax 731-1809
Coxsackie-Athens MS 400/5-8
24 Sunset Blvd 12051 518-731-1850
David Proper, prin. Fax 731-1859

Craryville, Columbia
Taconic Hills Central SD 1,500/PK-12
73 County Route 11A 12521 518-325-2800
Dr. Neil Howard, supt.
www.taconichills.k12.ny.us/
Taconic Hills JSHS 700/7-12
73 County Route 11A 12521 518-325-2840
James Buhrmaster, prin. Fax 325-2845

Cross River, Westchester
Katonah-Lewisboro UFD 3,000/K-12
60 N Salem Rd 10518 914-763-7000
Andrew Selesnick, supt. Fax 763-7035
www.klschooldistrict.org
Jay HS 1,200/9-12
60 N Salem Rd 10518 914-763-7200
Dr. Steven Sciliano, prin. Fax 763-7494
Jay MS 800/6-8
40 N Salem Rd 10518 914-763-7500
Rich Leprine, prin. Fax 763-7665

Croton on Hudson, Westchester, Pop. 7,883
Croton-Harmon UFD 1,700/K-12
10 Gerstein St 10520 914-271-4713
Dr. Edward Fuhrman, supt. Fax 271-8685
www.chufsd.org
Croton-Harmon HS 500/9-12
36 Old Post Rd S 10520 914-271-2147
Alan Capasso, prin. Fax 271-6643
Van Cortlandt MS 500/5-8
3 Glen Pl 10520 914-271-2191
Dr. Barbara Ulm, prin. Fax 271-6618

Crown Point, Essex
Crown Point Central SD 300/PK-12
PO Box 35 12928 518-597-4200
Shari Brannock, supt. Fax 597-4121
cpcsteam.org/
Crown Point Central S 300/PK-12
PO Box 35 12928 518-597-3285
Tara Spaulding, prin. Fax 597-4121

Cuba, Allegany, Pop. 1,561
Cuba-Rushford Central SD 800/K-12
5476 Route 305 14727 585-968-2650
Carlos Gildemeister, supt. Fax 968-2651
www.crcs.wnyric.org/
Cuba-Rushford HS 300/9-12
5476 Route 305 14727 585-968-2650
Carrie Bold, prin. Fax 968-2651
Cuba-Rushford MS 200/6-8
5476 Route 305 14727 585-968-2650
Katie Ralston, prin. Fax 968-2651

Cutchogue, Suffolk, Pop. 3,330
Mattituck-Cutchogue UFD 1,300/K-12
385 Depot Ln 11935 631-298-4242
Dr. Anne H. Smith, supt. Fax 298-8573
www.mufsd.com/cms/
Other Schools – See Mattituck

Dannemora, Clinton, Pop. 3,874
Saranac Central SD 1,500/K-12
32 Emmons St 12929 518-565-5600
Jonathan Parks, supt. Fax 565-5617
www.saranac.org

Other Schools – See Saranac

Dansville, Livingston, Pop. 4,671
Dansville Central SD 1,500/K-12
284 Main St 14437 585-335-4000
Dr. Paul Alioto, supt. Fax 335-4002
www.dansvillecsd.org
Dansville HS 700/7-12
282 Main St 14437 585-335-4010
Tom Frazier, prin. Fax 335-4080

Davenport, Delaware
Charlotte Valley Central SD 400/PK-12
15611 State Highway 23 13750 607-278-5511
James Harter, supt. Fax 278-5900
www.charlottevalleycs.org
Charlotte Valley S 400/PK-12
15611 State Highway 23 13750 607-278-5511
James Harter, supt. Fax 278-5900

Deer Park, Suffolk, Pop. 27,209
Deer Park UFD 4,300/PK-12
1881 Deer Park Ave 11729 631-274-4000
Eva Demyen, supt. Fax 242-6762
www.deerparkschools.org/
Deer Park HS 1,400/9-12
1 Falcon Pl 11729 631-274-4100
Charles Cobb, prin. Fax 254-0237
Frost MS 1,000/6-8
450 Half Hollow Rd 11729 631-274-4200
Dr. Eliana Levey, prin. Fax 242-0035

De Kalb Junction, Saint Lawrence, Pop. 515
Hermon-DeKalb Central SD 400/PK-12
709 E DeKalb Rd 13630 315-347-3442
Mark White, supt. Fax 347-3817
www.hdcsk12.org
Hermon-DeKalb Central S 400/PK-12
709 E DeKalb Rd 13630 315-347-3442
Megan Foster, prin. Fax 347-3817

Delanson, Schenectady, Pop. 371
Duanesburg Central SD 600/K-12
133 School Rd 12053 518-895-2279
Christine Crowley, supt. Fax 895-2626
www.duanesburg.org/
Duanesburg JSHS 300/7-12
163 School Rd 12053 518-895-2355
Jodi Marvin, prin. Fax 895-9971

Delhi, Delaware, Pop. 3,025
Delaware Academy Central SD at Delhi 600/K-12
2 Sheldon Dr 13753 607-746-1300
Jason D. Thomson, supt. Fax 746-6028
www.delhischools.org
Delaware Academy MSHS 200/6-12
2 Sheldon Dr 13753 607-746-1300
Laurie Alberti, prin. Fax 746-1324

SUNY Delhi Post-Sec.
2 Main St 13753 607-746-4000

Delmar, Albany, Pop. 8,360
Bethlehem Central SD 4,700/K-12
700 Delaware Ave 12054 518-439-7098
Jody Monroe, supt. Fax 475-0352
bcsd.k12.ny.us
Bethlehem Central HS 1,600/9-12
700 Delaware Ave 12054 518-439-4921
Scott Landry, prin. Fax 439-2837
Bethlehem Central MS 1,200/6-8
332 Kenwood Ave 12054 518-439-7460
Mike Klugman, prin. Fax 475-0092

Depew, Erie, Pop. 15,147
Depew UFD 1,800/K-12
5201 Transit Rd 14043 716-686-5105
Jeffrey Rabey, supt. Fax 686-5101
www.depewschools.org
Depew HS 600/9-12
5201 Transit Rd 14043 716-686-5095
Carol Townsend, prin. Fax 686-5094
Depew MS 400/6-8
5201 Transit Rd 14043 716-686-5050
James Lupini, prin. Fax 686-5057

Deposit, Delaware, Pop. 1,641
Deposit Central SD 600/PK-12
171 2nd St 13754 607-467-5380
Ed Shirkey, supt. Fax 467-5535
www.depositcsd.org/
Deposit MSHS 200/7-12
171 2nd St 13754 607-467-2197
Theresa Rajner, prin. Fax 467-5504

DeRuyter, Madison, Pop. 552
De Ruyter Central SD 400/PK-12
711 Railroad St 13052 315-852-3400
Charles Walters, supt. Fax 852-3446
www.deruytercentral.org/
De Ruyter Central JSHS 200/6-12
711 Railroad St 13052 315-852-3400
Dr. Sarah Stack Feinberg, prin. Fax 852-3404

De Witt, Onondaga, Pop. 8,244
Jamesville-DeWitt Central SD 2,900/K-12
PO Box 606 13214 315-445-8304
Dr. Alice Kendrick, supt. Fax 445-8477
www.jamesvilledewitt.org
Jamesville-DeWitt HS 900/9-12
PO Box 606 13214 315-445-8340
Paul Gasparini, prin. Fax 445-8307
Other Schools – See Jamesville

Dexter, Jefferson, Pop. 1,036
General Brown Central SD 1,500/K-12
PO Box 500 13634 315-779-2300
Cammy Morrison, supt. Fax 639-6916
www.gblions.org
Brown JSHS 700/7-12
17643 Cemetery Rd 13634 315-779-2300
Tina Heckman, prin. Fax 639-3444

Dix Hills, Suffolk, Pop. 26,364
Half Hollow Hills Central SD 8,100/K-12
525 Half Hollow Rd 11746 631-592-3000
Kelly Fallon, supt. Fax 592-3900
www.hhh.k12.ny.us
Candlewood MS 1,000/6-8
1200 Carlls Straight Path 11746 631-592-3300
Andrew Greene, prin. Fax 592-3921
Half Hollow Hills HS East 1,900/9-12
50 Vanderbilt Pkwy 11746 631-592-3100
Dr. Jeffery Woodberry, prin. Fax 592-3907
Half Hollow Hills HS West 1,400/9-12
375 Wolf Hill Rd 11746 631-592-3200
Dr. Michael Catapano, prin. Fax 592-3923
Other Schools – See Melville

Five Towns College Post-Sec.
305 N Service Rd 11746 631-656-2110
Upper Room Christian S 200/K-12
722 Deer Park Rd 11746 631-242-5359

Dobbs Ferry, Westchester, Pop. 10,650
Dobbs Ferry UFD 1,500/K-12
505 Broadway 10522 914-693-1506
Dr. Lisa Brady, supt. Fax 693-1787
www.dfsd.org
Dobbs Ferry HS 400/9-12
505 Broadway 10522 914-693-7645
John Falino, prin. Fax 693-5227
Dobbs Ferry MS 400/6-8
505 Broadway 10522 914-693-7640
Patrick Mussolini, prin. Fax 693-5229

Greenburgh-North Castle UFD 300/7-12
71 Broadway 10522 914-231-8620
Dr. Edward Placke, supt. Fax 693-8030
greenburghnorthcastleschools.com/
Other Schools – See New Windsor

Masters S 600/5-12
49 Clinton Ave 10522 914-479-6400
Laura Danforth, head sch Fax 693-1230
Mercy College Post-Sec.
555 Broadway 10522 800-637-2969

Dolgeville, Herkimer, Pop. 2,188
Dolgeville Central SD 900/PK-12
38 Slawson St 13329 315-429-3155
Christine Reynolds, supt. Fax 429-8473
www.dolgeville.org
Dolgeville Central MS 300/5-8
38 Slawson St 13329 315-429-3155
Crystal Chrisman, prin. Fax 429-8473
Green HS 300/9-12
38 Slawson St 13329 315-429-3155
Timothy Jenny, prin. Fax 429-8473

Dover Plains, Dutchess, Pop. 1,293
Dover UFD 1,400/K-12
2368 Route 22 12522 845-877-5700
Michael Tierney, supt. Fax 877-5766
www.doverschools.org
Dover HS 500/9-12
2368 Route 22 12522 845-877-5750
Eugenia Angelis, prin. Fax 877-5759
Dover MS 300/6-8
2368 Route 22 12522 845-877-5740
Patricia Rizzo, prin. Fax 877-5749

Downsville, Delaware, Pop. 606
Downsville Central SD 300/PK-12
PO Box J 13755 607-363-2100
John Evans, supt. Fax 363-2105
www.dcseagles.org
Downsville Central S 300/PK-12
PO Box J 13755 607-363-2111
Timothy McNamara, prin. Fax 363-2105

Dryden, Tompkins, Pop. 1,854
Dryden Central SD 1,600/PK-12
PO Box 88 13053 607-844-5361
Sandra Sherwood, supt. Fax 844-4733
dcsd-ny.schoolloop.com
Dryden HS 500/9-12
PO Box 88 13053 607-844-8694
John Birmingham, prin. Fax 844-9004
Dryden MS 400/6-8
PO Box 88 13053 607-844-8694
David Thon, prin. Fax 844-5174

Tompkins Cortland Community College Post-Sec.
PO Box 139 13053 607-844-8211

Dundee, Yates, Pop. 1,714
Dundee Central SD 700/PK-12
55 Water St 14837 607-243-5533
Kelly Houck, supt. Fax 243-7912
www.dundeecs.org
Dundee JSHS 400/7-12
55 Water St 14837 607-243-5534
Chris Arnold, prin. Fax 243-7912

Dunkirk, Chautauqua, Pop. 12,328
Dunkirk CSD 2,000/K-12
620 Marauder Dr 14048 716-366-9300
Gary Cerne, supt. Fax 366-9399
www.dunkirkcsd.org
Dunkirk HS 600/9-12
75 W 6th St 14048 716-366-9300
Steve O'Brien, prin. Fax 366-0321
Dunkirk MS 500/6-8
525 Eagle St 14048 716-366-9300
Joanne Russo, prin. Fax 366-9357

East Amherst, Erie
Williamsville Central SD 10,200/K-12
PO Box 5000 14051 716-626-8000
Dr. Scott Martzloff, supt. Fax 626-8089
www.williamsvillek12.org
Casey MS 700/5-8
105 Casey Rd 14051 716-626-8585
Francis McGreevy, prin. Fax 626-8562
Transit MS 1,000/5-8
8730 Transit Rd 14051 716-626-8701
Daniel Walh, prin. Fax 626-8796
Williamsville East HS 1,100/9-12
151 Paradise Rd 14051 716-626-8404
Scott Taylor, prin. Fax 626-8408
Other Schools – See Williamsville

East Aurora, Erie, Pop. 6,180
East Aurora UFD 1,800/K-12
430 Main St 14052 716-687-2302
Brian Russ, supt. Fax 652-8581
eastauroraschools.org/
East Aurora HS 600/9-12
1003 Center St 14052 716-687-2505
Dr. James Hoagland, prin. Fax 687-2552
East Aurora MS 600/5-8
430 Main St 14052 716-687-2453
Matthew Brown, prin. Fax 652-8581

Christ the King Seminary Post-Sec.
PO Box 607 14052 716-652-8900

Eastchester, Westchester, Pop. 19,285
Eastchester UFD 3,100/K-12
580 White Plains Rd 10709 914-793-6130
Dr. Walter Moran Ed.D., supt. Fax 793-9006
district.eastchesterschools.org
Eastchester HS 900/9-12
2 Stewart Pl 10709 914-793-6130
Dr. Jeffrey Capuano, prin. Fax 793-9000
Eastchester MS 700/6-8
550 White Plains Rd 10709 914-793-6130
Scott Wynne, prin. Fax 793-1699

Tuckahoe UFD 1,000/K-12
65 Siwanoy Blvd 10709 914-337-6600
Carl Albano, supt. Fax 337-3072
www.tuckahoeschools.org
Tuckahoe HS 300/9-12
65 Siwanoy Blvd 10709 914-337-5376
Bart Linehan Ed.D., prin. Fax 337-5168
Tuckahoe MS 200/6-8
65 Siwanoy Blvd 10709 914-337-5376
Dr. Ellen McDonnell, prin. Fax 337-5236

East Elmhurst, See New York
NYC Department of Education
Supt. — See New York
IS 227 1,700/5-8
3202 Junction Blvd 11369 718-335-7500
Helen Ponella, prin. Fax 779-7186

Monsignor McClancy Memorial HS 500/9-12
7106 31st Ave 11370 718-898-3800
James Castrataro, prin. Fax 898-3929

East Greenbush, Rensselaer, Pop. 4,416
East Greenbush Central SD 4,100/K-12
29 Englewood Ave 12061 518-207-2500
Angela Nagle Ph.D., supt. Fax 477-4833
www.egcsd.org
Columbia HS 1,300/9-12
962 Luther Rd 12061 518-207-2000
John Sawchuk, prin. Fax 207-2009
Goff MS 900/6-8
35 Gilligan Rd 12061 518-207-2430
Wayne Grignon, prin. Fax 477-2667

East Hampton, Suffolk, Pop. 1,079
East Hampton UFD 1,800/K-12
4 Long Ln 11937 631-329-4100
Richard Burns, supt. Fax 324-0109
www.ehufsd.org
East Hampton HS 900/9-12
2 Long Ln 11937 631-329-4130
Adam Fine, prin. Fax 329-4210
East Hampton MS 400/6-8
76 Newtown Ln 11937 631-329-4116
Dr. Charles Soriano, prin. Fax 329-4187

Ross S 300/7-12
18 Goodfriend Dr 11937 631-907-5000
Ben Bonaventura, head sch Fax 329-6830

East Meadow, Nassau, Pop. 37,572
East Meadow UFD
Supt. — See Westbury
East Meadow HS 1,600/9-12
101 Carman Ave 11554 516-228-5331
Richard Howard, prin. Fax 228-5339
Woodland MS 1,100/6-8
690 Wenwood Dr 11554 516-564-6523
James Lethbridge, prin. Fax 564-6519

East Moriches, Suffolk, Pop. 5,179
East Moriches UFD 700/K-8
9 Adelaide Ave 11940 631-878-0162
Dr. Charles Russo, supt. Fax 878-0186
emoschools.org/
East Moriches MS 300/5-8
9 Adelaide Ave 11940 631-878-0162
Michael Carlson, prin. Fax 874-0096

East Northport, Suffolk, Pop. 19,969
Commack UFD 6,900/K-12
480 Clay Pitts Rd 11731 631-912-2000
Dr. Donald James, supt. Fax 912-2240
www.commack.k12.ny.us
Other Schools – See Commack

Northport-East Northport UFD
Supt. — See Northport
East Northport MS 700/6-8
1075 5th Ave 11731 631-262-6770
Pasquale DeStefano, prin. Fax 262-6773

East Patchogue, Suffolk, Pop. 22,129
South Country Central SD 4,500/PK-12
189 N Dunton Ave 11772 631-730-1500
Dr. Joseph Giani, supt. Fax 286-6394
www.southcountry.org
Other Schools – See Bellport, Brookhaven

Victory Christian Academy 100/PK-12
1343 Montauk Hwy 11772 631-654-9284

East Rochester, Monroe, Pop. 6,434
East Rochester UFD 1,000/PK-12
222 Woodbine Ave 14445 585-248-6302
Mark Linton Ed.D., supt. Fax 586-3254
www.erschools.org
East Rochester JSHS 500/6-12
200 Woodbine Ave 14445 585-248-6350
Casey van Harssel, prin. Fax 248-6383

East Rockaway, Nassau, Pop. 9,736
East Rockaway UFD 1,200/K-12
443 Ocean Ave 11518 516-887-8300
Lisa J. Ruiz, supt. Fax 887-8308
www.eastrockawayschools.org
East Rockaway JSHS 600/7-12
443 Ocean Ave 11518 516-887-8300
Joseph Spero, prin. Fax 887-8308

East Setauket, See Setauket
Three Village Central SD
Supt. — See Stony Brook
Melville HS 1,800/10-12
380 Old Town Rd 11733 631-730-4900
Alan Baum, prin. Fax 730-4901

East Syracuse, Onondaga, Pop. 2,961
East Syracuse Minoa Central SD 3,300/PK-12
407 Fremont Rd 13057 315-434-3000
Dr. Donna DeSiato, supt. Fax 434-3020
www.esmschools.org
East Syracuse Minoa Central HS 1,100/9-12
6400 Fremont Rd 13057 315-434-3300
Grenardo Avellino, prin. Fax 434-3335
Pine Grove MS 500/7-8
6318 Fremont Rd 13057 315-434-3050
Doug Mohorter, prin. Fax 434-3070

Bishop Grimes JSHS 400/7-12
6653 Kirkville Rd 13057 315-437-0356
Brian Nolan, prin. Fax 437-0358

Eden, Erie, Pop. 3,494
Eden Central SD 1,500/PK-12
3150 Schoolview Rd 14057 716-992-3630
Sandra Anzalone, supt. Fax 992-3656
www.edencsd.org/
Eden JSHS 800/7-12
3150 Schoolview Rd 14057 716-992-3641
Jeff Cervoni, prin. Fax 992-3652

Edmeston, Otsego, Pop. 650
Edmeston Central SD 400/PK-12
PO Box 5129 13335 607-965-8931
Tracy Davison, supt. Fax 965-8942
edmestoncentralschool.net
Edmeston Central S 400/PK-12
PO Box 5129 13335 607-965-8931
Christine Nichols, prin. Fax 965-8942

Elba, Genesee, Pop. 668
Elba Central SD 400/PK-12
PO Box 370 14058 585-757-9967
Keith Palmer, supt. Fax 757-2713
www.elbacsd.org
Elba JSHS 200/7-12
PO Box 370 14058 585-757-9967
Keith Palmer, admin. Fax 757-6683

Eldred, Sullivan
Eldred Central SD 600/PK-12
PO Box 249 12732 845-456-1100
Robert M. Dufour, supt. Fax 557-3672
www.eldred.k12.ny.us/
Eldred Central JSHS 300/7-12
PO Box 249 12732 845-456-1100
Scott Krebs, prin. Fax 557-3672

Elizabethtown, Essex
Elizabethtown-Lewis Central SD 300/K-12
PO Box 158 12932 518-873-6371
Scott Osborne, supt. Fax 873-9552
elcsd.org
Elizabethtown-Lewis Central S 300/K-12
PO Box 158 12932 518-873-6371
Robert Witkiewicz, prin. Fax 873-9552

Ellenburg Depot, Clinton
Northern Adirondack Central SD 800/K-12
PO Box 164 12935 518-594-7060
Laura Marlow, supt. Fax 594-7255
www.nacs1.org/
Northern Adirondack MSHS 500/6-12
PO Box 164 12935 518-594-3962
Michael Loughman, prin. Fax 594-7255

Ellenville, Ulster, Pop. 3,954
Ellenville Central SD 1,700/PK-12
28 Maple Ave 12428 845-647-0100
Lisa Wiles, supt. Fax 647-0105
www.ecs.k12.ny.us
Ellenville HS 500/9-12
28 Maple Ave 12428 845-647-0123
Carl Pabon, prin. Fax 647-5972
Ellenville MS 400/6-8
28 Maple Ave 12428 845-647-0126
Jennifer Williams, prin. Fax 647-0230

Ellicottville, Cattaraugus, Pop. 371
Ellicottville Central SD 600/PK-12
5873 Route 219 S 14731 716-699-2368
Mark Ward, supt. Fax 699-6017
www.ellicottvillecentral.com/
Ellicottville MSHS 300/7-12
5873 Route 219 S 14731 716-699-2316
Robert Miller, prin. Fax 699-5423

Elma, Erie
Iroquois Central SD 2,200/K-12
PO Box 32 14059 716-652-3000
Douglas Scofield, supt. Fax 652-9305
www.iroquoiscsd.org
Iroquois HS 900/9-12
PO Box 32 14059 716-652-3000
Dennis Kenney, prin. Fax 995-2440
Iroquois MS 600/6-8
PO Box 32 14059 716-652-3000
Ross Esslinger, prin. Fax 995-2335

Elmhurst, See New York
NYC Department of Education
Supt. — See New York
Civic Leadership Academy 500/9-12
4510 94th St 11373 718-271-1487
Phuong Nguyen, prin. Fax 271-3408
IS 5 1,600/6-9
5040 Jacobus St 11373 718-205-6788
Kelly Nepogoda, prin. Fax 429-6518
International HS for Health Sciences 100/9-12
4801 90th St 11373 718-595-8600
Carl Finney, prin. Fax 595-8605
Maspeth HS 9-12
5440 74th St 11373 718-803-7100
Khurshid Mutakabbir, prin. Fax 803-7105
Newtown HS 2,000/9-12
4801 90th St 11373 718-595-8400
John Ficalora, prin. Fax 699-8584
Pan American International HS 400/9-12
4510 94th St 11373 718-271-3602
George Badia, prin. Fax 271-4041
VOYAGES Preparatory S 200/9-12
4510 94th St 11373 718-271-7851
Nicholas Bleiberg, prin. Fax 271-8549

Cathedral Preparatory Seminary 200/9-12
5625 92nd St 11373 718-592-6800
Richie Diaz, prin. Fax 592-5574
Jewish Institute of Queens 400/PK-12
6005 Woodhaven Blvd 11373 718-426-9369

Elmira, Chemung, Pop. 27,883
Elmira CSD 5,900/PK-12
951 Hoffman St 14905 607-735-3000
Hillary Austin, supt. Fax 735-3009
www.elmiracityschools.com
Davis Academy 800/8-9
933 Hoffman St 14905 607-735-3100
Carrie Rollins, prin. Fax 735-3109
Elmira HS 1,000/9-12
777 S Main St 14904 607-735-3200
Christopher Krantz, prin. Fax 735-3209

Arnot-Ogden Medical Center Post-Sec.
600 Roe Ave 14905 607-737-4289
Arnot-Ogden Medical Center Post-Sec.
600 Roe Ave 14905 607-737-4153
Elmira Business Institute Post-Sec.
303 N Main St 14901 800-843-1812
Elmira College Post-Sec.
1 Park Pl 14901 607-735-1800
Notre Dame HS 200/7-12
1400 Maple Ave 14904 607-734-2267
Sr. Nancy Kelly, prin. Fax 737-8903

Elmira Heights, Chemung, Pop. 4,011
Elmira Heights Central SD 1,100/K-12
2083 College Ave 14903 607-734-7114
Mary Beth Fiore, supt. Fax 734-7134
www.heightsschools.com
Cohen MS 200/6-8
100 Robinwood Ave 14903 607-734-5078
Dawn Hanrahan, prin. Fax 734-9382
Edison HS 400/9-12
2083 College Ave 14903 607-733-5604
Thomas Boyanowski, prin. Fax 737-7976

Elmont, Nassau, Pop. 32,024
Sewanhaka Central HSD
Supt. — See Floral Park
Elmont Memorial HS 1,800/7-12
555 Ridge Rd 11003 516-488-9200
Kevin Dougherty, prin. Fax 488-5560

Elmsford, Westchester, Pop. 4,549
Elmsford UFD 1,000/PK-12
98 S Goodwin Ave 10523 914-592-6632
Dr. Joseph Ricca, supt. Fax 592-2181
www.eufsd.org
Hamilton JSHS 400/7-12
98 S Goodwin Ave 10523 914-592-7311
Dr. Marc Baiocco, prin. Fax 592-2881

Elwood, Suffolk, Pop. 11,032
Elwood UFD
Supt. — See Greenlawn
Elwood/John H. Glenn HS 800/9-12
478 Elwood Rd 11731 631-266-5410
Carisa Burzynski, prin. Fax 368-5038
Elwood MS 600/6-8
478 Elwood Rd 11731 631-266-5420
Dr. Hugh Gigante, prin. Fax 266-3987

Endicott, Broome, Pop. 12,995
Union-Endicott Central SD 4,000/K-12
1100 E Main St 13760 607-757-2111
Dr. Suzanne McLeod, supt. Fax 757-2809
www.uek12.org
Snapp MS 900/6-8
101 S Loder Ave 13760 607-757-2156
Toby Riddleberger, prin. Fax 658-7117
Union-Endicott HS 1,200/9-12
1200 E Main St 13760 607-757-2181
Steven DiStefano, prin. Fax 757-2592
West S 200/K-12
1201 Union Center Maine Hwy 13760
Timothy Lowie, admin. 607-757-2149

Endwell, Broome, Pop. 11,248
Maine-Endwell Central SD 2,400/K-12
712 Farm To Market Rd 13760 607-754-1400
Jason R. Van Fossen, supt. Fax 754-1650
www.me.stier.org/
Maine-Endwell HS 800/9-12
750 Farm To Market Rd 13760 607-748-8070
Thomas Burkhardt, prin. Fax 786-8209
Maine-Endwell MS 500/6-8
1119 Farm To Market Rd 13760 607-786-8271
Richard Otis, prin. Fax 786-5137

Fabius, Onondaga, Pop. 352
Fabius-Pompey Central SD 700/K-12
1211 Mill St 13063 315-683-5301
Timothy Ryan, supt. Fax 683-5827
www.fabiuspompey.org
Fabius-Pompey MSHS 400/6-12
1211 Mill St 13063 315-683-5811
Kevin Linck, prin. Fax 683-5569

Fairport, Monroe, Pop. 5,283
Fairport Central SD 6,100/K-12
38 W Church St 14450 585-421-2000
Brett Provenzano, supt. Fax 421-3421
www.fairport.org
Brown MS 800/6-8
665 Ayrault Rd 14450 585-421-2065
David Dunn, prin. Fax 421-2136
Fairport HS 1,600/10-12
1 Dave Paddock Way 14450 585-421-2100
Robert Clark, prin. Fax 421-4645
Minerva-Deland JHS 500/9-9
140 Hulburt Rd 14450 585-421-2030
Pam Ciranni, prin. Fax 421-1985
Perrin MS 700/6-8
85 Potter Pl 14450 585-421-2080
Kevin Henchen, prin. Fax 421-2097

Falconer, Chautauqua, Pop. 2,402
Falconer Central SD 1,200/PK-12
2 East Ave N 14733 716-665-6624
Stephen Penhollow, supt. Fax 665-9265
www.falconerschools.org
Falconer MSHS 700/6-12
2 East Ave N 14733 716-665-6624
Jeffrey Jordan, prin. Fax 665-9265

Fallsburg, Sullivan
Fallsburg Central SD 1,400/PK-12
PO Box 124 12733 845-434-6800
Dr. Ivan Katz, supt. Fax 434-8346
www.fallsburgcsd.net/
Fallsburg HS 600/7-12
PO Box 124 12733 845-434-6800
Michael Williams, prin. Fax 434-0418

Farmingdale, Nassau, Pop. 8,087
Farmingdale UFD 5,900/K-12
50 Van Cott Ave 11735 516-752-6510
John Lorentz, supt.
www.farmingdaleschools.org
Farmingdale HS 1,900/9-12
150 Lincoln St 11735 516-752-6600
Glen Zakian, prin. Fax 454-6196
Howitt MS 1,400/6-8
70 Van Cott Ave 11735 516-752-6519
Luis Pena, prin. Fax 752-2004

Farmingdale State College SUNY Post-Sec.
2350 Broadhollow Rd 11735 631-420-2000

Farmingville, Suffolk, Pop. 15,238
Sachem Central SD
Supt. — See Ronkonkoma
Sachem HS East 2,400/9-12
177 Granny Rd 11738 631-716-8200
Louis Antonetti, prin. Fax 716-8207

Far Rockaway, See New York
NYC Department of Education
Supt. — See New York
Academy of Medical Technology 600/6-12
821 Bay 25th St 11691 718-471-3571
William Johnson, prin. Fax 471-0314
Douglass Academy VI HS 400/9-12
821 Bay 25th St 11691 718-471-2154
Charles Ogundimu, prin. Fax 471-2890
MS 53 300/6-8
1045 Nameoke St 11691 718-471-6900
Shawn Rux, prin. Fax 471-6955
KAPPA VI 300/6-8
821 Bay 25th St 11691 718-471-6934
Gary Dumornay, prin. Fax 471-6938
Queens HS for Info. Research & Tech. 300/9-12
821 Bay 25th St 11691 718-868-2978
Carl Manalo, prin. Fax 868-1653
Village Academy 300/6-8
1045 Nameoke St 11691 718-471-6042
Doris Lee, prin. Fax 471-6243

Beis Medrash Heichal Dovid Post-Sec.
211 Beach 17th St 11691 718-868-2300

Mesivta Chaim Shlomo S 300/9-12
211 Beach 17th St 11691 718-868-2300
Rabbi Menachem Gold, prin. Fax 868-0517
Tichon Meir Moshe S 100/9-12
613 Beach 9th St 11691 718-337-6000
Torah Academy HS for Girls 300/9-12
636 Lanett Ave 11691 718-327-1300
Yeshiva Darchei Torah S 1,600/PK-12
257 Beach 17th St 11691 718-868-2300
Rabbi Yehuda Harbater, dir. Fax 868-4450
Yeshiva of Far Rockaway Post-Sec.
802 Hicksville Rd 11691 718-327-7600
Yeshiva of Far Rockaway 200/9-12
802 Hicksville Rd 11691 718-327-7600
Rabbi Eli Goldgrab, prin. Fax 327-1430
Yeshiva Zichron Aryeh Post-Sec.
1213 Bay 25th St 11691 516-295-5700

Fayetteville, Onondaga, Pop. 4,326
Fayetteville-Manlius Central SD
Supt. — See Manlius
Wellwood MS 700/5-8
700 S Manlius St 13066 315-692-1300
Melissa Corbin, prin. Fax 692-1049

Fillmore, Allegany, Pop. 603
Fillmore Central SD 700/K-12
104 W Main St 14735 585-567-2251
Ravo Root, supt. Fax 567-2541
www.fillmorecsd.org
Fillmore Central S 700/K-12
104 W Main St 14735 585-567-2289
Michael Dodge, prin. Fax 567-2541

Fishers Island, Suffolk, Pop. 231
Fishers Island UFD 100/PK-12
78 Greenwood Rd Ste 600 06390 631-788-7444
Karen Goodwin, supt. Fax 788-5562
www.fischool.com
Fishers Island S 100/PK-12
78 Greenwood Rd Ste 600 06390 631-788-7444
Karen Goodwin, prin. Fax 788-5532

Fleetwood, See Mount Vernon

Montfort Academy 50/9-12
125 E Birch St 10552 914-699-7090
David Petrillo Ph.D., head sch Fax 699-7150

Floral Park, Nassau, Pop. 15,623
NYC Department of Education
Supt. — See New York
Altman MS 1,000/6-8
8114 257th St 11004 718-831-4000
Jeffrey Slivko, prin. Fax 831-4008

Sewanhaka Central HSD 8,100/7-12
77 Landau Ave 11001 516-488-9800
Dr. Ralph Ferrie, supt. Fax 488-7738
www.sewanhaka.k12.ny.us/
Floral Park Memorial HS 1,400/7-12
210 Locust St 11001 516-488-9300
Dr. Kathleen Sottile, prin. Fax 394-5079
Sewanhaka HS 1,600/7-12
500 Tulip Ave 11001 516-488-9600
Dr. Christopher Salinas, prin. Fax 488-9215
Other Schools – See Elmont, Franklin Square, New Hyde Park

Florida, Orange, Pop. 2,798
Florida UFD 800/K-12
PO Box 757 10921 845-651-3095
Diane Munro, supt. Fax 651-6801
www.floridaufsd.org
Seward Institute 500/6-12
PO Box 757 10921 845-651-4038
Michael Rheaume, prin. Fax 651-7166

Flushing, See New York
NYC Department of Education
Supt. — See New York
Bowne HS 3,700/9-12
6325 Main St 11367 718-263-1919
Howie Kwait, prin. Fax 575-4069
East-West S of International Studies 600/6-12
4621 Colden St 11355 718-353-0009
Benjamin Sherman, prin. Fax 353-3772
Flushing HS 2,600/9-12
3501 Union St 11354 718-888-7500
Tyee Chin, prin. Fax 886-4255
IS 25 800/6-8
3465 192nd St 11358 718-961-3480
Maryellen Beirne, prin. Fax 358-1563
IS 237 1,200/6-8
4621 Colden St 11355 718-353-6464
Judith Freidman, prin. Fax 460-6427
IS 250 300/6-8
15840 76th Rd 11366 718-591-9000
Tara Mrwik, prin. Fax 591-2340
Flushing International HS 400/9-12
14480 Barclay Ave 11355 718-463-2348
Lara Evangelista, prin. Fax 463-3514
JHS 185 1,500/6-8
14726 25th Dr 11354 718-445-3232
Theresa Mshar, prin. Fax 359-5352
JHS 189 700/6-8
14480 Barclay Ave 11355 718-359-6676
Cindy Diaz-Burgos, prin. Fax 358-0155
JHS 216 1,400/6-8
6420 175th St 11365 718-358-2005
Reginald Landeau, prin. Fax 358-2070
Harris HS 1,200/9-12
14911 Melbourne Ave 11367 718-575-5580
Anthony Barbetta, prin. Fax 575-1366
Kennedy Community HS 700/9-12
7540 Parsons Blvd 11366 718-969-5510
Beshir Abdellatif, prin. Fax 969-5524
Lewis HS 4,000/9-12
5820 Utopia Pkwy 11365 718-281-8200
David Marmor, prin. Fax 746-2017

North Queens Community HS 200/9-12
14125 77th Rd 11367 718-380-1650
Winston McCarthy, prin. Fax 380-2189
Queens Academy HS 300/10-12
13811 35th Ave 11354 718-463-3111
Shomari Akil, prin. Fax 886-5015
Queens HS for Language Studies 100/9-12
3501 Union St 11354 718-888-7530
Melanie Lee, prin. Fax 888-7526
Veritas Academy 100/9-12
3501 Union St 11354 718-888-7520
Cheryl Quatrano, prin. Fax 888-7524
World Journalism Preparatory S 600/6-12
3465 192nd St 11358 718-461-2219
Cynthia Schneider, prin. Fax 461-2633

CUNY Queens College Post-Sec.
6530 Kissena Blvd 11367 718-997-5000
Holy Cross HS 900/9-12
2620 Francis Lewis Blvd 11358 718-886-7250
Edward Burns, prin. Fax 886-7257
Long Island Business Institute Post-Sec.
13618 39th Ave 11354 718-939-5100
Mesivta Yesodei Yeshurun 100/9-12
14151 71st Ave 11367 718-261-4738
Rabbi Baruch Gopin, prin. Fax 793-1546
Mesivta Yesodei Yisroel 50/9-12
14161 71st Ave 11367 845-425-2520
New York Medical Career Training Center Post-Sec.
3609 Main St Fl 5 11354 718-460-4340
Rabbinical Seminary Chofetz Chaim HS 100/9-12
7601 147th St 11367 718-263-1445
Rabbinical Seminary of America Post-Sec.
7601 147th St 11367 718-268-4700
Vaughn College of Aeronautics and Tech Post-Sec.
8601 23rd Ave 11369 718-429-6600
Windsor S 200/7-12
3702 Main St Fl 4 11354 718-359-8300

Fonda, Montgomery, Pop. 787
Fonda-Fultonville Central SD 1,400/PK-12
PO Box 1501 12068 518-853-4415
Thomas Ciaccio, supt. Fax 853-4461
www.fondafultonvilleschools.org
Fonda-Fultonville HS 400/9-12
PO Box 1501 12068 518-853-3182
Aaron Grady, prin. Fax 853-1239
Fonda-Fultonville MS 400/5-8
PO Box 1501 12068 518-853-4747
David Zadoorian, prin. Fax 853-4498

Forest Hills, See New York
NYC Department of Education
Supt. — See New York
Forest Hills HS 3,800/9-12
6701 110th St 11375 718-268-3137
Saul Gootnick, prin. Fax 793-7850
JHS 190 1,000/6-8
6817 Austin St 11375 718-830-4970
Marilyn Grant, prin. Fax 830-3566
Metropolitan Expeditionary Learning S 200/6-12
9130 Metropolitan Ave 11375 718-286-3500
Daman McCord, prin. Fax 286-3501
Queens Metropolitan HS 400/9-12
9130 Metropolitan Ave 11375 718-286-3600
Gregory Dutton, prin. Fax 286-3601

ACE Computer Training Center Post-Sec.
10919 72nd Rd Ste 4F 11375 718-575-3223
Bramson ORT College Post-Sec.
6930 Austin St 11375 718-261-5800
Emerging Technologies Institute Post-Sec.
11616 Queens Blvd Ste 200 11375 718-261-1272
Ezra Academy 100/7-12
11945 Union Tpke 11375 718-263-5500
Sima Fish, prin. Fax 520-9424
Kew-Forest S 200/PK-12
11917 Union Tpke 11375 718-268-4667
Dr. Eric Ruoss, head sch Fax 268-9121

Forestville, Chautauqua, Pop. 686
Forestville Central SD 500/K-12
12 Water St 14062 716-965-2742
Renee Garrett, supt. Fax 965-2117
www.forestville.com
Forestville Central JSHS 300/7-12
4 Academy St 14062 716-965-2711
Daniel Grande, prin. Fax 965-2102

Fort Ann, Washington, Pop. 482
Fort Ann Central SD 400/K-12
1 Catherine St 12827 518-639-5594
Kevin Froats, supt. Fax 639-8911
www.fortannschool.org
Fort Ann S 400/K-12
1 Catherine St 12827 518-639-5594
Dan Ward, prin. Fax 639-8911

Fort Covington, Franklin
Salmon River Central SD 1,500/PK-12
637 County Route 1 12937 518-358-6610
Stanley Harper, supt. Fax 358-3492
www.srk12.org
Salmon River HS 400/9-12
637 County Route 1 12937 518-358-6620
Mike Warden, prin. Fax 358-9787
Salmon River MS 300/6-8
637 County Route 1 12937 518-358-6650
Michael Warden, prin. Fax 358-6510

Fort Edward, Washington, Pop. 3,335
Fort Edward UFD 500/PK-12
220 Broadway 12828 518-747-4594
Jeffery Ziegler, supt. Fax 747-6543
www.fortedward.org
Fort Edward S 500/PK-12
220 Broadway 12828 518-747-4529
Thomas McGurl, prin. Fax 747-6543

Hudson Falls Central SD 2,400/PK-12
1153 Burgoyne Ave 12828 518-747-2121
Linda Goewey, supt. Fax 747-0951
www.hfcsd.org
Other Schools – See Hudson Falls

Fort Plain, Montgomery, Pop. 2,284
Fort Plain Central SD 800/PK-12
25 High St 13339 518-993-4000
David Ziskin, supt. Fax 993-3393
www.fortplain.org
Fort Plain JSHS 300/7-12
1 West St 13339 518-993-4000
Deborah Larrabee, prin. Fax 993-2897

Frankfort, Herkimer, Pop. 2,561
Frankfort-Schuyler Central SD 800/K-12
605 Palmer St 13340 315-894-5083
Robert Reina, supt. Fax 895-7011
www.frankfort-schuyler.org
Frankfort-Schuyler Central MSHS 300/6-12
605 Palmer St 13340 315-895-7461
Michael Stalteri, prin. Fax 895-4032

Franklin, Delaware, Pop. 368
Franklin Central SD 300/PK-12
PO Box 888 13775 607-829-3551
Brad Zilliox, supt. Fax 829-2101
www.franklincsd.org
Franklin Central S 300/PK-12
PO Box 888 13775 607-829-3551
Julie Bergman, prin. Fax 829-2101

Franklin Square, Nassau, Pop. 28,887
Sewanhaka Central HSD
Supt. — See Floral Park
Carey HS 1,700/7-12
230 Poppy Ave 11010 516-539-9400
Christopher Fiore, prin. Fax 538-1791

Valley Stream Central HSD
Supt. — See Valley Stream
Valley Stream North HS 1,300/7-12
750 Herman Ave 11010 516-564-5510
James Bolen, prin. Fax 564-5539

Franklinville, Cattaraugus, Pop. 1,715
Franklinville Central SD 700/PK-12
31 N Main St 14737 716-676-8029
Michelle Spasiano, supt. Fax 676-8041
tbafcs.org
Franklinville JSHS 300/7-12
31 N Main St 14737 716-676-8060
Jennifer Cappelletti, prin. Fax 676-8042

Fredonia, Chautauqua, Pop. 11,103
Fredonia Central SD 1,500/PK-12
425 E Main St 14063 716-679-1581
Paul DiFonzo, supt. Fax 679-1555
www.fredonia.wnyric.org
Fredonia HS 500/9-12
425 E Main St 14063 716-679-1581
Todd Crandall, prin. Fax 672-8687
Fredonia MS 500/5-8
425 E Main St 14063 716-679-1581
Andrew Ludwig, prin. Fax 672-2686

SUNY at Fredonia Post-Sec.
280 Central Ave 14063 716-673-3111

Freeport, Nassau, Pop. 41,960
Freeport UFD 6,500/PK-12
235 N Ocean Ave 11520 516-867-5200
Dr. Kishore Kuncham, supt. Fax 623-4759
www.freeportschools.org
Dodd MS 1,000/7-8
25 Pine St 11520 516-867-5280
Johane Ligonde, prin. Fax 379-6794
Freeport HS 2,100/9-12
50 S Brookside Ave 11520 516-867-5300
Linda Carter, prin. Fax 379-7592

De LaSalle S 100/5-8
87 Pine St 11520 516-379-8660
Kathleen Boniello, prin. Fax 379-8806

Fresh Meadows, See New York
NYC Department of Education
Supt. — See New York
Queens S of Inquiry 600/6-12
15840 76th Rd 11366 718-380-6929
Meredith Inbal, prin. Fax 380-6809

St. Francis Preparatory HS 2,600/9-12
6100 Francis Lewis Blvd 11365 718-423-8810
Patrick McLaughlin, prin. Fax 504-7668

Frewsburg, Chautauqua, Pop. 1,879
Frewsburg Central SD 900/PK-12
PO Box 690 14738 716-569-7000
Stephen Vanstrom, supt. Fax 569-7050
www.frewsburgcsd.org
Frewsburg JSHS 400/7-12
PO Box 690 14738 716-569-7000
William Caldwell, prin. Fax 569-7050

Friendship, Allegany, Pop. 1,208
Friendship Central SD 400/PK-12
46 W Main St 14739 585-973-3534
Judy May, supt. Fax 973-2023
www.friendship.wnyric.org/
Friendship Central S 400/PK-12
46 W Main St 14739 585-973-3311
Judy May, supt. Fax 973-2023

Fulton, Oswego, Pop. 11,719
Fulton CSD 3,600/K-12
167 S 4th St 13069 315-593-5510
Brian Pulvino, supt. Fax 598-6351
www.fulton.cnyric.org/

Bodley HS 1,100/9-12
6 Gillard Dr 13069 315-593-5400
Donna Parkhurst, prin. Fax 593-5427
Fulton JHS 600/7-8
129 Curtis St 13069 315-593-5440
Ryan Lanigan, prin. Fax 593-5459

Gainesville, Wyoming, Pop. 228
Letchworth Central SD 900/PK-12
5550 School Rd 14066 585-493-5450
Julia Reed, supt. Fax 493-2762
www.letchworth.k12.ny.us
Letchworth HS 300/9-12
5550 School Rd 14066 585-493-2571
Matthew Wilkins, prin. Fax 493-2762
Letchworth MS 300/5-8
5550 School Rd 14066 585-493-2592
Paul Rogers, prin. Fax 493-2762

Galway, Saratoga, Pop. 200
Galway Central SD 900/K-12
5317 Sacandaga Rd 12074 518-882-1033
Shannon Shine, supt. Fax 882-5250
www.galwaycsd.org
Galway JSHS 500/7-12
5317 Sacandaga Rd 12074 518-882-1033
Michael Healey, prin. Fax 882-5250

Garden City, Nassau, Pop. 22,129
Garden City UFD 3,900/K-12
56 Cathedral Ave 11530 516-478-1000
Dr. Robert Feirsen, supt. Fax 294-8348
www.gardencity.k12.ny.us
Garden City HS 1,200/9-12
170 Rockaway Ave 11530 516-478-2000
Nanine McLaughlin, prin. Fax 294-2639
Garden City MS 900/6-8
98 Cherry Valley Ave 11530 516-478-3000
Dr. Peter Osroff, prin. Fax 294-0732

Adelphi University Post-Sec.
PO Box 701 11530 516-877-3000
Nassau Community College Post-Sec.
1 Education Dr 11530 516-572-7501
Sanford-Brown Institute Post-Sec.
711 Stewart Ave Ste 2 11530 516-247-2900
Waldorf S of Garden City 300/PK-12
225 Cambridge Ave 11530 516-742-3434
Susan Braun, admin. Fax 742-3457

Garden City Park, Nassau, Pop. 7,612
Mineola UFD
Supt. — See Mineola
Mineola HS 1,000/8-12
10 Armstrong Rd 11040 516-237-2600
Dr. Whittney Smith, prin. Fax 237-2608

Garnerville, See West Haverstraw
North Rockland Central SD 7,800/K-12
65 Chapel St 10923 845-942-3000
Ileana Eckert, supt. Fax 942-3175
www.nrcsd.org
Other Schools – See Thiells

Geneseo, Livingston, Pop. 7,881
Geneseo Central SD 900/K-12
4050 Avon Rd 14454 585-243-3450
Timothy Hayes, supt. Fax 243-9481
www.geneseocsd.org/
Geneseo MSHS 500/6-12
4050 Avon Rd 14454 585-243-3450
Michael Salatel, prin. Fax 243-9481

SUNY at Geneseo Post-Sec.
1 College Cir 14454 585-245-5000

Geneva, Ontario, Pop. 12,783
Geneva CSD 2,200/PK-12
400 W North St 14456 315-781-0400
Trina Smith Newton, supt. Fax 781-4193
www.genevacsd.org
Geneva HS 700/9-12
101 Carter Rd 14456 315-781-0402
Greg Baker, prin. Fax 781-0695
Geneva MS 500/6-8
101 Carter Rd 14456 315-781-0404
Robert Smith, prin. Fax 781-0694

Finger Lakes Health College of Nursing Post-Sec.
196 North St 14456 315-787-4000
Hobart & William Smith Colleges Post-Sec.
300 Pulteney St 14456 315-781-3000

Germantown, Columbia
Germantown Central SD 600/K-12
123 Main St 12526 518-537-6280
Susan Brown, supt. Fax 537-6283
www.germantowncsd.org
Germantown Central HS 300/7-12
123 Main St 12526 518-537-6281
Karol Harlow, prin. Fax 537-6893

Getzville, Erie, Pop. 2,300

Bryant & Stratton College Post-Sec.
3650 Millersport Hwy 14068 716-625-6300

Ghent, Columbia, Pop. 556

Hawthorne Valley Waldorf S 200/PK-12
330 County Route 21C 12075 518-672-7092
Caroline Geisler, chrpsn. Fax 672-8006

Gilbertsville, Otsego, Pop. 397
Gilbertsville-Mount Upton Central SD 400/PK-12
693 State Highway 51 13776 607-783-2207
Annette Hammond, supt. Fax 783-2254
www.gmucsd.org
Gilbertsville-Mount Upton JSHS 200/6-12
693 State Highway 51 13776 607-783-2207
Heather Wilcox, prin. Fax 783-2254

Gilboa, Schoharie
Gilboa-Conesville Central SD 300/PK-12
132 Wyckoff Rd 12076 607-588-7541
Ruth Reeve, supt. Fax 588-6820
www.gilboa-conesville.k12.ny.us/
Gilboa-Conesville Central S 300/PK-12
132 Wyckoff Rd 12076 607-588-7541
Thomas Santacrose, prin. Fax 588-6820

Glen Cove, Nassau, Pop. 26,520
Glen Cove CSD 3,200/PK-12
150 Dosoris Ln 11542 516-801-7010
Maria Rianna, supt. Fax 801-7019
www.glencove.k12.ny.us
Finley MS 700/6-8
1 Forest Ave 11542 516-801-7510
Nelson Iocolano, prin. Fax 801-7519
Glen Cove HS 1,000/9-12
150 Dosoris Ln 11542 516-801-7610
Antonio Santana, prin. Fax 801-7619

Webb Institute Post-Sec.
298 Crescent Beach Rd 11542 516-671-2213

Glendale, See New York
NYC Department of Education
Supt. — See New York
IS 119 800/6-8
7401 78th Ave 11385 718-326-8261
Dr. Jeanne Fagan, prin. Fax 456-9523

Glen Head, Nassau, Pop. 4,626
North Shore Central SD
Supt. — See Sea Cliff
North Shore HS 900/9-12
450 Glen Cove Ave 11545 516-277-7000
Albert Cousins, prin. Fax 277-7001
North Shore MS 700/6-8
505 Glen Cove Ave 11545 516-277-7300
Marc Ferris, prin. Fax 277-7301

Glens Falls, Warren, Pop. 14,415
Glens Falls CSD 2,000/PK-12
15 Quade St 12801 518-792-1212
Paul Jenkins, supt. Fax 792-1538
www.gfsd.org
Glens Falls HS 700/9-12
10 Quade St 12801 518-792-6564
Mark Stratton, prin. Fax 743-1164
Glens Falls MS 600/5-8
20 Quade St 12801 518-793-3418
Christopher Reed, prin. Fax 793-4888

Adirondack Beauty School Post-Sec.
108 Dix Ave 12801 518-745-1646
Glens Falls Hospital Post-Sec.
100 Park St 12801 518-792-3151

Gloversville, Fulton, Pop. 15,362
Gloversville CSD 2,900/PK-12
234 Lincoln St 12078 518-775-5700
Michael Vanyo, supt. Fax 725-8793
www.gesdk12.org
Gloversville HS 900/9-12
199 Lincoln St 12078 518-775-5710
Dr. Richard DeMallie, prin. Fax 773-3674
Gloversville MS 600/6-8
234 Lincoln St 12078 518-775-5720
Mark Batty, prin. Fax 773-9865

Goshen, Orange, Pop. 5,361
Goshen Central SD 2,900/K-12
227 Main St 10924 845-615-6720
Daniel Connor, supt. Fax 615-6725
www.gcsny.org
Goshen Central HS 900/9-12
222 Scotchtown Rd 10924 845-615-6100
Robert McKiernan, prin. Fax 615-6116
Hooker MS 700/6-8
41 Lincoln Ave 10924 845-615-6300
William Rolon, prin. Fax 615-6310

Burke Catholic HS 400/9-12
80 Fletcher St 10924 845-294-5481
John Dolan, prin. Fax 294-7957

Gouverneur, Saint Lawrence, Pop. 3,883
Gouverneur Central SD 1,200/PK-12
133 E Barney St 13642 315-287-4870
Lauren French, supt. Fax 287-4736
www.gcsk12.org
Gouverneur HS 500/9-12
113 E Barney St 13642 315-287-1900
Cory Wood, prin. Fax 287-7963
Gouverneur MS 400/5-8
113 E Barney St 13642 315-287-1903
Steven Coffin, prin. Fax 287-2666

Gowanda, Cattaraugus, Pop. 2,660
Gowanda Central SD 1,000/PK-12
10674 Prospect St 14070 716-532-3325
James Klubek, supt. Fax 995-2154
www.gowcsd.com
Gowanda HS 400/9-12
10674 Prospect St 14070 716-532-3325
Dr. Robert Anderson, prin. Fax 995-2108
Gowanda MS 200/7-8
10674 Prospect St 14070 716-532-3325
Robert Anderson, prin. Fax 995-2127

Grahamsville, Sullivan
Tri-Valley Central SD 1,100/PK-12
34 Moore Hill Rd 12740 845-985-2296
Thomas Palmer, supt. Fax 985-0310
www.trivalleycsd.org
Tri-Valley Secondary S 500/7-12
34 Moore Hill Rd 12740 845-985-2296
Fax 985-7903

Grand Island, Erie
Grand Island Central SD 3,000/PK-12
1100 Ransom Rd 14072 716-773-8800
Brian Graham Ed.D., supt.
www.grandislandschools.org
Connor MS 700/6-8
1100 Ransom Rd 14072 716-773-8830
John Fitzpatrick, prin. Fax 773-8983
Grand Island HS 1,000/9-12
1100 Ransom Rd 14072 716-773-8820
Daniel Quartley, prin. Fax 773-8951

Granville, Washington, Pop. 2,523
Granville Central SD 1,100/PK-12
58 Quaker St 12832 518-642-1051
Mark Bessen, supt. Fax 642-2491
www.granvillecsd.org
Granville JSHS 600/7-12
58 Quaker St 12832 518-642-1051
Camille Harrelson, prin. Fax 642-4544

Great Neck, Nassau, Pop. 9,663
Great Neck UFD 6,600/PK-12
345 Lakeville Rd 11020 516-441-4001
Dr. Teresa Prendergast, supt. Fax 441-4994
www.greatneck.k12.ny.us
Great Neck South MS 800/6-8
349 Lakeville Rd 11020 516-441-4600
Dr. James Welsch, prin. Fax 441-4690
Miller Great Neck North HS 1,000/9-12
35 Polo Rd 11023 516-441-4700
Bernard Kaplan, prin. Fax 441-4795
Sherman Great Neck North MS 700/6-8
77 Polo Rd 11023 516-441-4500
Gerald Cozine, prin. Fax 773-4841
Shine Great Neck South HS 1,200/9-12
341 Lakeville Rd 11020 516-441-4800
Susan Elliott, prin. Fax 773-8279
Village S 50/Alt
614 Middle Neck Rd 11023 516-441-4900
Stephen Goldberg, prin. Fax 441-4909

North Shore Hebrew Academy 200/6-8
26 Old Mill Rd 11023 516-487-9163
North Shore Hebrew Academy HS 9-12
400 N Service Rd 11020 516-487-2424
Dr. Daniel J. Vitow, hdmstr. Fax 487-6663

Greene, Chenango, Pop. 1,564
Greene Central SD 1,000/K-12
40 S Canal St 13778 607-656-4161
Gordie Daniels, supt. Fax 656-9362
www.greenecsd.org
Greene HS 300/9-12
40 S Canal St 13778 607-656-4161
James Walters, prin. Fax 656-8872
Greene MS 200/6-8
40 S Canal St 13778 607-656-4161
Timothy Calice, prin. Fax 656-4520

Green Island, Albany, Pop. 2,545
Green Island UFD 300/K-12
171 Hudson Ave 12183 518-273-1422
Dr. Teresa Snyder, supt. Fax 270-0818
www.greenisland.org
Heatly S 300/K-12
171 Hudson Ave 12183 518-273-1422
Erin Peteani, prin. Fax 270-0818

Greenlawn, Suffolk, Pop. 13,492
Elwood UFD 2,400/K-12
100 Kenneth Ave 11740 631-266-5400
Dr. Kenneth Bossert, supt. Fax 368-2338
www.elwood.k12.ny.us
Other Schools – See Elwood

Harborfields Central SD 3,300/K-12
2 Oldfield Rd 11740 631-754-5320
Diana Todaro, supt. Fax 261-0068
www.harborfieldscsd.net
Harborfields HS 1,100/9-12
98 Taylor Ave 11740 631-754-5360
Dr. Rory Manning, prin. Fax 754-3751
Oldfield MS 800/6-8
2 Oldfield Rd 11740 631-754-5310
Joanne Giordano, prin. Fax 754-2677

Greenport, Suffolk, Pop. 2,155
Greenport UFD 600/K-12
720 Front St 11944 631-477-1950
David Gamberg, supt. Fax 593-8951
www.gufsd.org/
Greenport JSHS 300/7-12
720 Front St 11944 631-477-1950
Gary Kalish, prin. Fax 593-8954

Greenville, Greene, Pop. 9,528
Greenville Central SD 1,200/K-12
4982 State Route 81 12083 518-966-5070
Tammy Sutherland, supt.
www.greenville.k12.ny.us
Greenville HS 400/9-12
4976 State Route 81 12083 518-966-5070
Todd Hilgendorff, prin.
Greenville MS 300/6-8
4976 State Route 81 12083 518-966-5070
Brian Reeve, prin.

Greenwich, Washington, Pop. 1,754
Greenwich Central SD 1,000/K-12
10 Gray Ave 12834 518-692-9542
Mark Fish, supt. Fax 692-9547
www.greenwichcsd.org
Greenwich JSHS 500/7-12
10 Gray Ave 12834 518-692-9542
George Niesz, prin. Fax 692-8503

Groton, Tompkins, Pop. 2,324
Groton Central SD 800/PK-12
400 Peru Rd 13073 607-898-5301
Margo Martin, supt. Fax 898-4647
www.grotoncs.org
Groton JSHS 400/6-12
400 Peru Rd 13073 607-898-5803
Laura Norris, prin. Fax 898-4555

Guilderland, Albany
Guilderland Central SD
Supt. — See Guilderland Center
Farnsworth MS 1,100/6-8
6072 State Farm Rd 12084 518-456-6010
Mary Summermatter, prin. Fax 456-3747

Guilderland Center, Albany
Guilderland Central SD 4,900/K-12
PO Box 18 12085 518-456-6200
Dr. Marie Wiles, supt. Fax 456-1152
www.guilderlandschools.org
Guilderland HS 1,700/9-12
PO Box 37 12085 518-861-8591
Thomas Lutsic, prin. Fax 861-5874
Other Schools – See Guilderland

Hadley, Saratoga, Pop. 1,003

King's S 200/PK-12
6087 State Route 9N 12835 518-654-6230

Hamburg, Erie, Pop. 9,357
Frontier Central SD 4,900/K-12
5120 Orchard Ave 14075 716-926-1700
Dr. Bret Apthorpe, supt. Fax 926-1778
www.frontier.wnyric.org
Frontier HS 1,600/9-12
4432 Bay View Rd 14075 716-926-1720
Jeffrey Sortisio, prin. Fax 646-2195
Frontier MS 1,100/6-8
2751 Amsdell Rd 14075 716-926-1730
Ryan Sikorski, prin. Fax 646-2207

Hamburg Central SD 3,700/PK-12
5305 Abbott Rd 14075 716-646-3220
Michael Cornell, supt. Fax 646-3209
www.hamburgschools.org
Hamburg HS 1,100/9-12
4111 Legion Dr 14075 716-646-3300
Michael Gallagher, prin. Fax 646-3028
Hamburg MS 900/6-8
360 Division St 14075 716-646-3250
Jennifer Giallella, prin. Fax 646-6380

Hilbert College Post-Sec.
5200 S Park Ave 14075 716-649-7900
Immaculata Academy 200/9-12
5138 S Park Ave 14075 716-649-6161
Jill Monaco, prin. Fax 646-1782

Hamilton, Madison, Pop. 4,131
Hamilton Central SD 600/PK-12
47 W Kendrick Ave 13346 315-824-6300
Anael Alston, supt. Fax 824-6314
www.hamiltoncentral.org
Hamilton JSHS 300/6-12
47 W Kendrick Ave 13346 315-824-6320
William Dowsland, prin. Fax 824-6314

Colgate University Post-Sec.
13 Oak Dr 13346 315-228-1000
New Life Christian S 100/PK-12
1528 River Rd 13346 315-824-2625
Todd Slabaugh, prin. Fax 824-5102

Hammond, Saint Lawrence, Pop. 278
Hammond Central SD 300/PK-12
PO Box 185 13646 315-324-5931
Karen Carswell, supt. Fax 324-6057
hammond.sllboces.org
Hammond Central S 300/PK-12
PO Box 185 13646 315-324-5931
Kathleen Cruikshank, prin. Fax 324-6057

Hammondsport, Steuben, Pop. 654
Hammondsport Central SD 500/K-12
8272 Main Street Ext 14840 607-569-5200
Kyle Bower, supt. Fax 569-5212
www.hammondsportcsd.org
Hammondsport JSHS 200/7-12
8272 Main Street Ext 14840 607-569-5200
Tad Rounds, prin. Fax 569-5212

Hampton Bays, Suffolk, Pop. 13,462
Hampton Bays UFD 2,000/PK-12
86 Argonne Rd E 11946 631-723-2100
Lars Clemensen, supt. Fax 723-2109
www.hbschools.us
Hampton Bays HS 600/9-12
88 Argonne Rd E 11946 631-723-2110
Chris Richardt, prin. Fax 723-2120
Hampton Bays MS 600/5-8
70 Ponquogue Ave 11946 631-723-4700
Dennis Schug, prin. Fax 723-4900

Hancock, Delaware, Pop. 1,014
Hancock Central SD 400/PK-12
67 Education Ln 13783 607-637-1301
Dr. Terrance Dougherty, supt. Fax 637-2512
hancock.stier.org
Hancock JSHS 200/5-12
67 Education Ln 13783 607-637-1306
Brenton Taylor, prin. Fax 637-2512

Hannibal, Oswego, Pop. 547
Hannibal Central SD 1,400/PK-12
928 Cayuga St 13074 315-564-8100
Christopher A. Staats, supt. Fax 564-7263
www.hannibalcsd.org
Hannibal HS 400/9-12
928 Cayuga St 13074 315-564-8130
Stephen Dunn, prin. Fax 564-7973
Kenney MS 400/5-8
928 Cayuga St 13074 315-564-8120
Shawn Morgan, prin. Fax 564-7509

Harpursville, Broome
Harpursville Central SD 800/PK-12
PO Box 147 13787 607-693-8101
Michael Rullo, supt. Fax 693-1480
www.hcs.stier.org/
Harpursville JSHS 400/7-12
PO Box 147 13787 607-693-8105
Kristine Conrow, prin. Fax 693-1480

Harrison, Westchester, Pop. 26,975
Harrison Central SD 3,500/K-12
50 Union Ave 10528 914-630-3021
Dr. Louis Wool, supt. Fax 835-5893
www.harrisoncsd.org
Harrison HS 1,000/9-12
255 Union Ave 10528 914-630-3095
Steven Siciliano, prin. Fax 835-5471
Klein MS 800/6-8
50 Union Ave 10528 914-630-3033
Scott Fried, prin. Fax 777-1346

Harrisville, Lewis, Pop. 623
Harrisville Central SD 400/PK-12
14371 Pirate Ln 13648 315-543-2707
Robert Finster, supt. Fax 543-2360
www.hcsk12.org
Harrisville JSHS 200/7-12
14371 Pirate Ln 13648 315-543-2920
Eric Luther, prin. Fax 543-2360

Hartford, Washington
Hartford Central SD 500/PK-12
4704 State Route 149 12838 518-632-5222
Andrew Cook, supt. Fax 632-5231
www.hartfordcsd.org
Hartford MSHS 300/6-12
4704 State Route 149 12838 518-632-5923
Brian George, prin. Fax 632-5231

Hartsdale, Westchester, Pop. 5,198
Greenburgh Central SD 1,800/PK-12
475 W Hartsdale Ave 10530 914-761-6000
Dr. Tahira DuPree Chase, supt. Fax 761-2354
www.greenburghcsd.org
Woodlands HS 500/9-12
475 W Hartsdale Ave 10530 914-761-6052
Matthew Smith, prin. Fax 761-6951
Woodlands MS 200/7-8
475 W Hartsdale Ave 10530 914-761-6052
Matthew Smith, prin. Fax 686-0445

Maria Regina HS 600/9-12
500 W Hartsdale Ave 10530 914-761-3300
Valerie Reidy, prin. Fax 761-0860
Solomon Schechter S of Westchester 500/6-12
555 W Hartsdale Ave 10530 914-948-8333
Michael Kay Ph.D., hdmstr. Fax 948-7979

Hastings on Hudson, Westchester, Pop. 7,663
Greenburgh-Graham UFD 300/1-12
1 S Broadway 10706 914-478-1106
Amy Goodman, supt. Fax 478-0904
www.greenburgh-graham.org
King HS 200/9-12
1 S Broadway 10706 914-478-1106
Oliver Levy, prin. Fax 478-2321

Hastings-on-Hudson UFD 1,600/K-12
27 Farragut Ave 10706 914-478-2900
Dr. Roy Montesano, supt. Fax 478-6209
www.hohschools.org
Farragut MS 500/5-8
27 Farragut Ave 10706 914-478-6230
Gail Kipper, prin. Fax 478-6314
Hastings HS 500/9-12
1 Mount Hope Blvd 10706 914-478-6250
Louis Adipietro, prin. Fax 478-7842

Hauppauge, Suffolk, Pop. 20,653
Hauppauge UFD 3,900/K-12
PO Box 6006 11788 631-265-3630
Dr. Dennis O'Hara, supt. Fax 265-9546
www.hauppauge.k12.ny.us
Hauppauge HS 1,300/9-12
PO Box 6006 11788 631-761-8302
Christine O'Connor, prin. Fax 979-0926
Hauppauge MS 900/6-8
PO Box 6006 11788 631-761-8230
Maryann Fletcher, prin. Fax 265-9546

Learning Institute for Beauty Sciences Post-Sec.
544 Route 111 11788 631-724-0440

Hempstead, Nassau, Pop. 52,895
Hempstead UFD 7,200/PK-12
185 Peninsula Blvd 11550 516-434-4000
Susan Johnson, supt. Fax 292-9471
www.hempsteadschools.org
Hempstead HS 1,900/9-12
201 President St 11550 516-434-4200
Dr. Stephen Strachan, prin. Fax 292-7770
Schultz MS 1,400/6-8
70 Greenwich St 11550 516-434-4300
Noel Rios, prin. Fax 483-2549

Uniondale UFD
Supt. — See Uniondale
Lawrence Road MS 700/6-8
50 Lawrence Rd 11550 516-918-1500
Dexter Hodge, prin. Fax 565-5023

Crescent S 200/PK-12
130 Front St 11550 516-292-1787
Sr. Iffat Ahmed, prin. Fax 292-1788
Franklin Career Institute Post-Sec.
91 N Franklin St 11550 516-481-4444
Hofstra University Post-Sec.
100 Hofstra University 11549 516-463-6600
Learning Institute for Beauty Sciences Post-Sec.
173A Fulton Ave 11550 516-483-6259
Sacred Heart Academy 900/9-12
47 Cathedral Ave 11550 516-483-7383
Sr. Joanne Forker, prin. Fax 483-1016

Henrietta, Monroe
Rush-Henrietta Central SD 5,300/K-12
2034 Lehigh Station Rd 14467 585-359-5000
Dr. J. Kenneth Graham, supt. Fax 359-5022
www.rhnet.org
Ninth Grade Academy 400/9-9
2000 Lehigh Station Rd 14467 585-359-5550
Kerry Macko, prin. Fax 359-5559
Roth MS 700/6-8
4000 E Henrietta Rd 14467 585-359-5108
Denise Zeh, prin. Fax 359-5164
Rush-Henrietta HS 1,300/10-12
1799 Lehigh Station Rd 14467 585-359-5208
Beth Patton, prin. Fax 359-5290
Vollmer Alternative Center 100/Alt
3318 E Henrietta Rd 14467 585-359-5520
Curt Diesenberg, dir. Fax 359-5523
Other Schools – See West Henrietta

Herkimer, Herkimer, Pop. 7,636
Herkimer Central SD 1,200/K-12
801 W German St 13350 315-866-2230
Robert Miller, supt. Fax 866-2234
www.herkimercsd.org
Herkimer JSHS 500/7-12
801 W German St 13350 315-866-2230
Mary Tomaso, prin. Fax 866-8595

Herkimer County Community College Post-Sec.
100 Reservoir Rd 13350 315-866-0300

Hermon, Saint Lawrence, Pop. 418
Edwards-Knox Central SD 600/PK-12
2512 County Route 24 13652 315-562-8130
George F. Merritt, supt. Fax 562-2477
www.ekcsk12.org
Edwards-Knox JSHS 300/7-12
2512 County Route 24 13652 315-562-8131
Amy Sykes, prin. Fax 562-8139

Heuvelton, Saint Lawrence, Pop. 711
Heuvelton Central SD 500/PK-12
PO Box 375 13654 315-344-2414
Susan Todd, supt. Fax 344-2349
heuvelton.schoolfusion.us
Heuvelton Central S 500/PK-12
PO Box 375 13654 315-344-2414
Jesse Coburn, prin. Fax 344-2349

Hewlett, Nassau, Pop. 6,722
Hewlett-Woodmere UFD
Supt. — See Woodmere
Hewlett HS, 60 Everit Ave 11557 1,000/9-12
Theodore Fulton, prin. 516-792-4100
Woodmere MS 700/6-8
1170 Peninsula Blvd 11557 516-792-4368
Albert Bauer, prin.

Abraham HS for Girls 300/9-12
291 Meadowview Ave 11557 516-374-7195
Helen Spirn, prin. Fax 374-2532

Hicksville, Nassau, Pop. 40,674
Hicksville UFD 5,100/PK-12
200 Division Ave 11801 516-733-2105
Dr. Carl Bonuso, supt. Fax 733-6584
www.hicksvillepublicschools.com
Hicksville HS 1,700/9-12
180 Division Ave 11801 516-733-2201
Raymond Williams, prin. Fax 733-6626
Hicksville MS 1,200/6-8
215 Jerusalem Ave 11801 516-733-2261
Mara Jorisch, prin. Fax 733-6528

Holy Trinity Diocesan HS 1,400/9-12
98 Cherry Ln 11801 516-433-2900
Gene Fennell, prin. Fax 433-2827

Highland, Ulster, Pop. 5,534
Highland Central SD 1,800/K-12
320 Pancake Hollow Rd 12528 845-691-1000
Deborah Haab, supt. Fax 691-1039
www.highland-k12.org/
Highland HS 600/9-12
320 Pancake Hollow Rd 12528 845-691-1020
Pete Harris, prin. Fax 691-1038
Highland MS 400/6-8
71 Main St 12528 845-691-1080
Daniel Seyler-Wetzel, prin. Fax 691-1083

Highland Falls, Orange, Pop. 3,773
Highland Falls Ft. Montgomery Central SD 900/PK-12
PO Box 287 10928 845-446-9575
Dr. Frank Sheboy, supt. Fax 446-3321
www.hffmcsd.org
Highland Falls IS 300/3-8
PO Box 287 10928 845-446-9575
Chris Fiorentino, prin. Fax 446-0858
O'Neill HS 500/9-12
PO Box 287 10928 845-446-9575
Louis Trombetta, prin. Fax 446-2123

Hillburn, Rockland, Pop. 844
Ramapo Central SD 4,500/K-12
45 Mountain Ave 10931 845-357-7783
Douglas Adams, supt. Fax 357-5707
www.ramapocentral.org
Other Schools – See Suffern

Hilton, Monroe, Pop. 5,826
Hilton Central SD 4,500/PK-12
225 West Ave 14468 585-392-1000
Casey Kosiorek, supt. Fax 392-1038
www.hilton.k12.ny.us
Hilton HS 1,400/9-12
400 East Ave 14468 585-392-1000
Brian Bartalo, prin. Fax 392-1052
Williams MS 700/7-8
200 School Ln 14468 585-392-1000
Tracie Czebatol, prin. Fax 392-1054

Hinsdale, Cattaraugus
Hinsdale Central SD 400/PK-12
3701 Main St 14743 716-557-2227
Larry Ljungberg, supt. Fax 557-2259
www.hinsdalebobcats.org
Hinsdale Central S 400/PK-12
3701 Main St 14743 716-557-2227
Laurie Cuddy, prin. Fax 557-2259

Holbrook, Suffolk, Pop. 26,920
Sachem Central SD
Supt. — See Ronkonkoma
Seneca MS 800/6-8
850 Main St 11741 631-471-1850
Gemma Salvia, prin. Fax 471-1849

Holland, Erie, Pop. 1,197
Holland Central SD 900/PK-12
103 Canada St 14080 716-537-8200
Cathy Fabiatos, supt. Fax 537-8203
www.holland.wnyric.org
Holland JSHS 400/7-12
103 Canada St 14080 716-537-8221
Carl Guidotti, prin. Fax 537-8233

Holland Patent, Oneida, Pop. 456
Holland Patent Central SD 1,200/PK-12
9601 Main St 13354 315-865-7200
Dr. Kathleen Davis Ed.D., supt. Fax 865-4057
www.hpschools.org
Holland Patent Central HS 500/9-12
9601 Main St 13354 315-865-8154
Russell Stevener, prin. Fax 865-4069
Holland Patent MS 300/6-8
9601 Main St 13354 315-865-8152
Lisa Gentile, prin. Fax 865-7243

Holley, Orleans, Pop. 1,790
Holley Central SD 1,200/PK-12
3800 N Main Street Rd 14470 585-638-6316
Robert D'Angelo, supt. Fax 638-7409
www.holleycsd.org
Holley JSHS 500/7-12
3800 N Main Street Rd 14470 585-638-6335
Susan Cory, prin. Fax 638-7925

Hollis, See New York
NYC Department of Education
Supt. — See New York
Cambria Heights Academy 100/9-12
18804 91st Ave 11423 718-776-2815
Melissa Menake, prin. Fax 776-2818
IS 238 1,500/6-8
8815 182nd St 11423 718-297-9821
Peter Leddy, prin. Fax 658-5288

Wang Yeshiva University HS for Girls 300/9-12
8686 Palo Alto St 11423 718-479-8550

Holtsville, Suffolk, Pop. 19,502
Sachem Central SD
Supt. — See Ronkonkoma
Sagamore MS 800/6-8
57 Division St 11742 631-696-8600
Andrew Larson, prin. Fax 696-8620

Homer, Cortland, Pop. 3,225
Homer Central SD 1,900/K-12
PO Box 500 13077 607-749-7241
Nancy Ruscio, supt. Fax 749-2312
www.homercentral.org
Homer HS 700/9-12
PO Box 500 13077 607-749-7246
Doug VanEtten, prin. Fax 749-2312
Homer JHS 500/6-8
PO Box 500 13077 607-749-1230
Tom Turck, prin. Fax 749-1238

Honeoye, Ontario, Pop. 571
Honeoye Central SD 600/K-12
PO Box 170 14471 585-229-4125
David C. Bills, supt. Fax 229-5633
www.honeoye.org
Honeoye MSHS 400/6-12
PO Box 170 14471 585-229-5171
Wayne Ackles, prin. Fax 229-4879

Honeoye Falls, Monroe, Pop. 2,631
Honeoye Falls-Lima Central SD 2,300/K-12
20 Church St 14472 585-624-7000
Gene Mancuso, supt. Fax 624-7003
www.hflcsd.org/
Honeoye Falls-Lima HS 800/9-12
83 East St 14472 585-624-7051
David Roth, prin. Fax 624-7118
Honeoye Falls-Lima MS 600/6-8
619 Quaker Meeting House Rd 14472 585-624-7100
Shawn Williams, prin. Fax 624-7121

Hoosick, Rensselaer

Hoosac S 100/8-12
PO Box 9 12089 518-686-7331
Dean Foster, hdmstr. Fax 686-3370

Hoosick Falls, Rensselaer, Pop. 3,451
Hoosick Falls Central SD 1,200/PK-12
PO Box 192 12090 518-686-7012
Kenneth Facin, supt. Fax 686-9060
www.hoosickfallscsd.org/
Hoosick Falls HS 600/7-12
PO Box 192 12090 518-686-7321
Stacy Vadney, prin. Fax 686-7452

Hopewell Junction, Dutchess, Pop. 354
Wappingers Central SD 11,100/K-12
PO Box 396 12533 845-298-5000
Jose Carrion, supt. Fax 298-5041
www.wappingersschools.org
Jay HS 2,100/9-12
2012 Route 52 12533 845-897-6700
Bonnie King, prin. Fax 897-6719
Orchard View Alternative HS 100/Alt
25 Corporate Park Dr 12533 845-298-5000
Laura DiStefano, prin. Fax 897-2083
Other Schools – See Wappingers Falls

Hornell, Steuben, Pop. 8,357
Hornell CSD 1,700/K-12
25 Pearl St 14843 607-324-1302
Douglas Wyant, supt. Fax 324-4060
www.hornellcityschools.com
Hornell JHS 300/7-8
134 Seneca St 14843 607-324-1303
Theodore Illi, prin. Fax 324-3421
Hornell SHS 500/9-12
134 Seneca St 14843 607-324-1303
Scott Carroll, prin. Fax 324-3702

St. James Mercy Hospital Post-Sec.
411 Canisteo St 14843 607-324-3900

Horseheads, Chemung, Pop. 6,375
Horseheads Central SD 4,100/PK-12
1 Raider Ln 14845 607-739-5601
Dr. Thomas J. Douglas, supt. Fax 795-2405
www.horseheadsdistrict.com/
Horseheads HS 1,300/9-12
401 Fletcher St 14845 607-795-2500
Karen Donahue, prin. Fax 795-2505
Horseheads MS 700/7-8
950 Sing Sing Rd 14845 607-739-6357
Ronald Holloway, prin. Fax 795-2525

Houghton, Allegany, Pop. 1,665

Houghton Academy 100/7-12
9790 Thayer St 14744 585-567-8115
John Nelson, head sch Fax 567-8048
Houghton College Post-Sec.
1 Willard Ave 14744 585-567-9200

Hudson, Columbia, Pop. 6,373
Hudson CSD 1,900/PK-12
215 Harry Howard Ave 12534 518-828-4360
Maria J. Suttmeier, supt. Fax 697-8777
www.hudsoncityschooldistrict.com
Columbia-Greene Partnership Academy Alt
364 Warren St 12534 518-781-3500
Dan Kalbfliesh, coord.
Hudson HS 600/9-12
215 Harry Howard Ave 12534 518-828-4132
Antonio Abitabile, prin. Fax 697-8418
Hudson JHS 300/7-8
215 Harry Howard Ave 12534 518-828-4360
Derek Reardon, prin. Fax 697-8522

Columbia-Greene Community College Post-Sec.
4400 State Route 23 12534 518-828-4181

Hudson Falls, Washington, Pop. 7,173
Hudson Falls Central SD
Supt. — See Fort Edward
Hudson Falls HS 700/9-12
80 E La Barge St 12839 518-747-2121
James Bennefield, prin. Fax 746-9033
Hudson Falls MS 500/6-8
131 Notre Dame St 12839 518-747-2121
Todd Gonyeau, prin. Fax 746-2790

Huntington, Suffolk, Pop. 17,836
Huntington UFD
Supt. — See Huntington Station
Finley MS 700/7-8
20 Greenlawn Rd 11743 631-673-2020
John Amato, prin. Fax 425-4746
Huntington HS 1,300/9-12
188 Oakwood Rd 11743 631-673-2003
Brenden Cusack, prin. Fax 425-4730

Huntington Station, Suffolk, Pop. 32,344
Huntington UFD 4,300/K-12
50 Tower St 11746 631-673-2038
James W.Polansky, supt. Fax 423-3447
www.hufsd.edu/
Other Schools – See Huntington

South Huntington UFD 5,900/K-12
60 Weston St 11746 631-812-3070
Dr. David P. Bennardo, supt. Fax 812-3075
www.shufsd.org
Stimson MS 900/7-8
401 Oakwood Rd 11746 631-812-3700
Edwin Smith, prin. Fax 812-3737
Whitman HS 1,800/9-12
301 W Hills Rd 11746 631-812-3800
John Murphy, prin. Fax 812-3838

St. Anthony HS 2,500/9-12
275 Wolf Hill Rd 11747 631-271-2020
Br. Gary Cregan, prin. Fax 547-6820

Hurley, Ulster, Pop. 3,401

Coleman HS 200/9-12
430 Hurley Ave 12443 845-338-2750
James Lyons, prin. Fax 338-0250

Hyde Park, Dutchess, Pop. 1,897
Hyde Park Central SD 3,600/K-12
PO Box 2033 12538 845-229-4000
Dr. Greer Rychcik, supt. Fax 229-4056
www.hpcsd.org
Haviland MS 900/6-8
PO Box 721 12538 845-229-4030
Eric Shaw, prin. Fax 229-2475
Other Schools – See Staatsburg on Hudson

Culinary Institute of America Post-Sec.
1946 Campus Dr 12538 845-452-9600

Ilion, Herkimer, Pop. 7,948
Central Valley Central SD 1,200/PK-12
111 Frederick St 13357 315-894-9934
Richard Hughes, supt. Fax 894-2716
www.cvalleycsd.org
Central Valley Academy 500/9-12
111 Frederick St 13357 315-895-7471
Richard Keeler, prin. Fax 894-5255
Other Schools – See Mohawk

Indian Lake, Hamilton
Indian Lake Central SD 100/PK-12
6345 Nys Route 30 12842 518-648-5024
Mark Brand, supt. Fax 648-6346
www.ilcsd.org
Indian Lake Central S 100/PK-12
6345 Nys Route 30 12842 518-648-5024
David Snide, prin. Fax 648-6346

Irvington, Westchester, Pop. 6,319
Irvington UFD 1,800/K-12
6 Dows Ln 10533 914-591-8500
Dr. Kristopher Harrison, supt. Fax 591-3064
www.irvingtonschools.org
Irvington HS 600/9-12
40 N Broadway 10533 914-591-8648
David Cohen, prin. Fax 591-6714
Irvington MS 400/6-8
40 N Broadway 10533 914-591-9494
David Sottile, prin. Fax 591-8535

Island Park, Nassau, Pop. 4,586
Island Park UFD 700/PK-8
99 Radcliffe Rd 11558 516-434-2600
Dr. Rosmarie T. Bovino, supt. Fax 431-7550
www.ips.k12.ny.us
Island Park/Lincoln Orens MS 300/PK-PK, 5-
150 Trafalgar Blvd 11558 516-434-2630
Vincent Randazzo, prin. Fax 431-7550

Islip, Suffolk, Pop. 18,391
Islip UFD 3,100/K-12
215 Main St 11751 631-650-8210
Susan Schnebel, supt. Fax 650-8218
www.islipufsd.org/
Islip HS 1,100/9-12
2508 Union Blvd 11751 631-650-8305
Michael Mosca, prin. Fax 650-8308
Islip MS 700/6-8
211 Main St 11751 631-650-8505
Dr. Timothy Martin, prin. Fax 650-8508

Islip Terrace, Suffolk, Pop. 5,327
East Islip UFD 3,200/PK-12
1 Craig B Gariepy Ave 11752 631-224-2000
John Dolan, supt. Fax 581-1617
www.eischools.org
East Islip HS 1,400/9-12
1 Redmen St 11752 631-224-2100
William Brennen, prin. Fax 581-4410
East Islip MS 900/6-8
100 Redmen St 11752 631-224-2170
Mark Bernard, prin. Fax 859-3745

Ithaca, Tompkins, Pop. 28,833
Ithaca CSD 5,400/PK-12
400 Lake St 14850 607-274-2101
Dr. Luvelle Brown, supt. Fax 274-2271
www.icsd.k12.ny.us
Boynton MS 500/6-8
1601 N Cayuga St 14850 607-274-2241
Jeffery Tomasik, prin. Fax 274-2357
De Witt MS 500/6-8
560 Warren Rd 14850 607-257-3222
Mac Knight, prin. Fax 266-3502
Ithaca HS 1,300/9-12
1401 N Cayuga St 14850 607-274-2145
Jason Trumble, prin. Fax 277-3061
Lehman Alternative Community S 300/Alt
111 Chestnut St 14850 607-274-2183
Diane Carruthers, prin. Fax 274-2351

Cornell University Post-Sec.
410 Thurston Ave 14850 607-255-2000
Ithaca College Post-Sec.
953 Danby Rd 14850 607-274-3011

Jackson Heights, See New York
NYC Department of Education
Supt. — See New York
IS 145 2,100/6-8
3334 80th St 11372 718-457-1242
Delores Beckham, prin. Fax 335-0601
IS 230 1,000/6-8
7310 34th Ave 11372 718-335-7648
Ronald Zirin, prin. Fax 335-7513

Garden S 300/PK-12
3316 79th St 11372 718-335-6363
Dr. Richard Marotta, hdmstr. Fax 565-1169
Plaza College Post-Sec.
7409 37th Ave 11372 718-779-1430

Jamaica, See New York
NYC Department of Education
Supt. — See New York
Basie MS 900/6-8
13325 Guy R Brewer Blvd 11434 718-723-6200
Omotayo Cineus, prin. Fax 527-1675
Business/Computer Applications S 200/9-12
20701 116th Ave 11411 718-978-2807
Lynne Callender, prin. Fax 978-3402
Edison Career & Tech HS Vo/Tech
16565 84th Ave 11432 718-297-6580
Moses Ojeda, prin. Fax 658-0365
Emerson S 100/6-8
10835 167th St 11433 718-657-4801
Jakub Lau, prin. Fax 657-4807
Franklin HS Finance & Info Technology 9-12
20701 116th Ave 11411 718-276-0150
Carla Theodorou, prin. Fax 276-4725
Hillcrest HS 3,200/9-12
16005 Highland Ave 11432 718-658-5407
David Morrison, prin. Fax 739-5137
Hillside Arts & Letters Academy 100/9-12
16701 Gothic Dr 11432 718-658-1249
Raquel Nolasco, prin. Fax 658-1613
Humanities & the Arts Magnet HS 500/9-12
20701 116th Ave 11411 718-978-2135
Rosemarie O'Mard, prin. Fax 978-2309
Institute for Health Professions 100/9-12
20701 116th Ave 11411 718-723-7301
Gareth Robinson, prin. Fax 723-7306
Jamaica Gateway to the Sciences 9-12
16701 Gothic Dr 11432 718-480-2689
Caren Taylor, prin. Fax 480-2697
HS for Community Leadership 100/9-12
16701 Gothic Dr 11432 718-558-9801
Carlos Borrero, prin. Fax 558-9807
HS for Law Enforcement & Public Safety 600/9-12
11625 Guy R Brewer Blvd 11434 718-977-4800
Laura Van Deren, dir. Fax 977-4802
JHS 8 600/6-8
10835 167th St 11433 718-739-6883
Angela Green, prin. Fax 526-2727
JHS 217 1,600/6-8
8505 144th St 11435 718-657-1120
Patrick Burns, prin. Fax 291-3668
Law 300/9-12
20701 116th Ave 11411 718-978-6432
Donna White, prin. Fax 978-6749
Martin HS 800/9-12
15610 Baisley Blvd 11434 718-528-2920
Rory Parnel, prin. Fax 276-1846
Math Science Research & Tech Magnet HS 400/9-12
20701 116th Ave 11411 718-978-1837
Jose Cruz, prin. Fax 978-2063
Queens Collegiate HS 600/6-12
16701 Gothic Dr 11432 718-658-4016
Jaime Dubei, prin. Fax 658-5149
Queens Gateway to the Health Sciences 800/6-12
16020 Goethals Ave 11432 718-969-3155
Judy Henry, prin. Fax 969-3552
Queens HS for Science 400/9-12
9450 159th St 11433 718-657-3181
Lenneen Gibson, prin. Fax 657-2579
Queens Satellite HS for Opportunity Alt
16202 Hillside Ave 11432 718-657-3920
Mark Melkonian, prin. Fax 658-2309
Redwood MS 6-8
13325 Guy R Brewer Blvd 11434 718-276-4540
Lisa Reiter, prin.
Voyages Prep - South Queens 100/9-12
15610 Baisley Blvd 11434 718-276-1946
Christopher Losurdo, prin. Fax 276-2784
York Early College Academy 600/6-12
10835 167th St 11433 718-262-8547
Deborah Burnett, prin. Fax 558-4257
Young Womens Leadership S 600/6-12
15091 87th Rd 11432 718-725-0402
Mala Panday, prin. Fax 725-0390

Al-Iman S 100/PK-12
8989 Van Wyck Expy 11435 718-297-6520
Allen School Post-Sec.
16318 Jamaica Ave 11432 888-620-6745
Archbishop Molloy HS 1,500/9-12
8353 Manton St 11435 718-441-2100
Darius Penikas, prin. Fax 849-8251
CUNY York College Post-Sec.
9420 Guy R Brewer Blvd 11451 718-262-2000
Jon Louis School of Beauty Post-Sec.
9114 Merrick Blvd 11432 718-658-6240
Louis Academy 900/9-12
17621 Wexford Ter 11432 718-297-2120
Sr. Kathleen McKinney, prin. Fax 739-0037
New York Automotive & Diesel Institute Post-Sec.
17818 Liberty Ave 11433 718-658-0006
St. John's University Post-Sec.
8000 Utopia Pkwy 11439 718-990-2000

Jamestown, Chautauqua, Pop. 30,116
Jamestown CSD 4,900/PK-12
197 Martin Rd 14701 716-483-4420
Tim O. Mains, supt. Fax 483-4421
www.jamestown.wnyric.org
Jamestown HS 1,400/9-12
350 E 2nd St 14701 716-483-3470
Mike McElrath Ph.D., prin. Fax 483-4399
Jefferson MS 500/5-8
195 Martin Rd 14701 716-483-4411
Carm Proctor, prin. Fax 483-4273
Persell MS 500/5-8
375 Baker St 14701 716-483-4406
Philip Cammarata, prin. Fax 483-4417
Washington MS 500/5-8
159 Buffalo St 14701 716-483-4413
Melissa Emerson, prin. Fax 483-4268

Southwestern Central SD 1,400/PK-12
600 Hunt Rd 14701 716-484-1136
Maureen Donahue, supt. Fax 484-1139
swcs.wnyric.org
Southwestern HS 500/9-12
600 Hunt Rd 14701 716-664-6273
Michael Cipolla, prin. Fax 484-1167
Southwestern MS 300/6-8
600 Hunt Rd 14701 716-664-6270
Richard Rybicki, prin. Fax 487-0855

Bethel Baptist Christian Academy 100/K-12
200 Hunt Rd 14701 716-484-7420
Mike Stormont, chrpsn. Fax 484-0087
Jamestown Business College Post-Sec.
PO Box 429 14702 716-664-5100
Jamestown Community College Post-Sec.
PO Box 20 14702 716-338-1000
Woman's Christian Assoc. Hospital Post-Sec.
207 Foote Ave 14701 716-664-8110

Jamesville, Onondaga
Jamesville-DeWitt Central SD
Supt. — See De Witt
Jamesville-DeWitt MS 900/5-8
6280 Randall Rd 13078 315-445-8360
Thomas A. Eldridge, prin. Fax 445-8421

Jasper, Steuben
Jasper-Troupsburg Central SD 500/PK-12
3769 State Route 417 14855 607-792-3675
Michael A. Mead, supt. Fax 792-3749
www.jtcsd.org
Jasper-Troupsburg JSHS 300/7-12
3769 State Route 417 14855 607-792-3675
Christopher D. Parker, prin. Fax 792-3749

Jefferson, Schoharie
Jefferson Central SD 300/K-12
1332 State Route 10 12093 607-652-7821
Brian Corey, supt. Fax 652-7806
www.jeffersoncs.org
Jefferson Central S 300/K-12
1332 State Route 10 12093 607-652-7821
Brian Corey, admin. Fax 652-7806

Jeffersonville, Sullivan, Pop. 355
Sullivan West Central SD 1,100/PK-12
PO Box 308 12748 845-482-4610
Dr. Nancy Hackett, supt. Fax 482-3022
www.swcsd.org/
Other Schools – See Lake Huntington

Jericho, Nassau, Pop. 13,391
Jericho UFD 3,000/K-12
99 Old Cedar Swamp Rd 11753 516-203-3600
Henry Grishman, supt. Fax 933-2047
www.jerichoschools.org
Jericho HS 1,200/9-12
99 Old Cedar Swamp Rd 11753 516-203-3610
Joan Rosenberg, prin. Fax 681-2895
Jericho MS 700/6-8
99 Old Cedar Swamp Rd 11753 516-203-3620
Donald Gately, prin. Fax 681-8984

Johnson City, Broome, Pop. 14,676
Johnson City Central SD 2,500/K-12
666 Reynolds Rd 13790 607-763-1230
Mary Kay Frys, supt. Fax 729-2767
www.jcschools.com
Johnson City HS 700/9-12
666 Reynolds Rd 13790 607-763-1256
Kimberly Beukema, prin. Fax 763-1211
Johnson City MS 600/6-8
601 Columbia Dr 13790 607-763-1240
Joseph Guccia, prin. Fax 763-1297

Davis College Post-Sec.
400 Riverside Dr 13790 607-729-1581
United Health Services Hospital Post-Sec.
33-57 Harrison St 13790 607-763-6000

Johnstown, Fulton, Pop. 8,615
Johnstown CSD 1,100/PK-12
1 Sir Bills Cir Ste 101 12095 518-762-4611
Robert DeLilli, supt. Fax 762-6379
www.johnstownschools.org/
Jansen Avenue S 9-12
305 Jansen Ave 12095 518-762-9119
Scott Hale, admin.
Johnstown HS 600/9-12
1 Sir Bills Cir 12095 518-762-4661
Scott Hale, prin. Fax 736-1489
Knox JHS 300/7-8
400 S Perry St 12095 518-762-3711
Michael Satterlee, prin. Fax 762-2775

Fulton-Montgomery Community College Post-Sec.
2805 State Highway 67 12095 518-736-3622

Jordan, Onondaga, Pop. 1,356
Jordan-Elbridge Central SD 1,400/PK-12
PO Box 902 13080 315-689-8500
James Froio, supt. Fax 689-0084
www.jecsd.org
Jordan-Elbridge HS 400/9-12
PO Box 901 13080 315-689-8510
Dr. David Zehner, prin. Fax 689-1985
Jordan-Elbridge MS 400/5-8
PO Box 1150 13080 315-689-8520
David Shafer, prin. Fax 689-6524

Jordanville, Herkimer

Holy Trinity Orthodox Seminary Post-Sec.
PO Box 36 13361 315-858-0945

Katonah, Westchester, Pop. 1,654

Harvey S 300/6-12
260 Jay St 10536 914-232-3161
William J. Knauer, head sch Fax 232-6034

Keene Valley, Essex
Keene Central SD 200/K-12
PO Box 67 12943 518-576-4555
Daniel Mayberry, supt. Fax 576-4599
www.keenecentralschool.org
Keene Central S 200/K-12
PO Box 67 12943 518-576-4555
Daniel Mayberry, supt. Fax 576-4599

Kendall, Orleans
Kendall Central SD 700/K-12
1932 Kendall Rd 14476 585-659-2741
Julie Christensen, supt. Fax 659-8903
www.kendallschools.org
Kendall JSHS 400/7-12
16887 Roosevelt Hwy 14476 585-659-2706
Carol D'Agostino, prin. Fax 659-8988

Kenmore, Erie, Pop. 15,148

Mt. St. Mary Academy 300/9-12
3756 Delaware Ave 14217 716-877-1358
Dawn Riggie, prin. Fax 877-0548
St. Joseph Collegiate Institute 700/9-12
845 Kenmore Ave 14223 716-874-4024
Br. Christopher Belleman, prin. Fax 874-4956

Keuka Park, Yates, Pop. 1,126

Keuka College Post-Sec.
141 Central Ave 14478 315-279-5000

Kew Garden Hills, See New York

Shaarey B'nos Chayil - Shevach HS 200/9-12
7509 Main St, 718-263-0525
Rochelle Hirtz, prin. Fax 263-3759

Kew Gardens, See New York

Yeshiva Shaar Hatorah-Grodno 100/9-12
11706 84th Ave 11418 718-846-1940
Rabbi Azriel Hoschander, prin. Fax 850-7916

Kings Park, Suffolk, Pop. 17,098
Kings Park Central SD 3,600/K-12
180 Lawrence Rd 11754 631-269-3310
Dr. Timothy Eagen, supt. Fax 269-0750
www.kpcsd.org
Kings Park HS 1,300/9-12
200 Route 25A 11754 631-269-3345
Lino Bracco, prin. Fax 269-7472
Rogers MS 900/6-8
97 Old Dock Rd 11754 631-269-3369
Carlo Spinola, prin. Fax 269-3282

Kings Point, Nassau, Pop. 4,807

United States Merchant Marine Academy Post-Sec.
300 Steamboat Rd 11024 516-726-5800

Kingston, Ulster, Pop. 22,973
Kingston CSD 5,900/PK-12
61 Crown St 12401 845-339-3000
Dr. Paul Padalino, supt. Fax 339-2249
www.kingstoncityschools.org/
Bailey MS 800/6-8
Merilina Ave Ext 12401 845-943-3940
Julie Linton, prin. Fax 338-6312
Kingston HS 1,900/9-12
403 Broadway 12401 845-331-1970
Kirk Reinhardt, prin. Fax 331-1628
Other Schools – See Lake Katrine

Gloden Hall Health Care Center Post-Sec.
Golden Hill Dr 12401 845-339-4540

Lackawanna, Erie, Pop. 17,629
Lackawanna CSD 1,700/PK-12
245 S Shore Blvd 14218 716-827-6767
Anne Spadone, supt. Fax 827-6710
www.lackawannaschools.org
Lackawanna HS 500/9-12
550 Martin Rd 14218 716-827-6727
Bruce Axelson, prin. Fax 827-6724
Lackawanna MS 200/7-8
550 Martin Rd 14218 716-827-6704
Bethany Schill, prin. Fax 827-6784

La Fargeville, Jefferson, Pop. 577
La Fargeville Central SD 600/PK-12
PO Box 138 13656 315-658-2241
Travis Hoover, supt. Fax 658-4223
www.lafargevillecsd.org
La Fargeville Central HS 300/7-12
PO Box 138 13656 315-658-2241
Steven Newcombe, prin. Fax 658-4223

La Fayette, Onondaga
La Fayette Central SD 900/PK-12
5955 US Route 20 13084 315-677-9728
Laura Lavine, supt. Fax 677-3372
www.lafayetteschools.org
Big Picture S Alt
3122 US Rt 11 N 13084 315-504-1000
Susan Osborn, prin. Fax 504-1004

La Fayette JSHS 400/7-12
3122 US Route 11 13084 315-677-3131
Jason Ryan, prin. Fax 677-5507

Lagrangeville, Dutchess
Arlington Central SD 8,500/K-12
144 Todd Hill Rd 12540 845-486-4460
Dr. Brendan Lyons, supt. Fax 486-4457
www.arlingtonschools.org
Arlington HS 3,300/9-12
1157 Route 55 12540 845-486-4860
Paul Fanuele, prin. Fax 486-4879
Lagrange MS 800/6-8
110 Stringham Rd 12540 845-486-4880
Eric Schetter, prin. Fax 486-8863
Union Vale MS 900/6-8
1657 E Noxon Rd 12540 845-223-8600
Scott Wood, prin. Fax 223-8610

Lake George, Warren, Pop. 894
Lake George Central SD 800/K-12
381 Canada St 12845 518-668-5456
Dr. Jon Hunter, supt. Fax 668-2285
www.lkgeorge.org
Lake George JSHS 400/7-12
381 Canada St 12845 518-668-5452
Francis Cocozza, prin. Fax 668-2285

Lake Grove, Suffolk, Pop. 11,039

Lake Grove School Post-Sec.
PO Box 712 11755 888-585-9007

Lake Huntington, Sullivan
Sullivan West Central SD
Supt. — See Jeffersonville
Sullivan West JSHS 600/7-12
PO Box 309 12752 845-932-8401
Mark Plescia, prin. Fax 932-8425

Lake Katrine, Ulster, Pop. 2,330
Kingston CSD
Supt. — See Kingston
Miller MS 700/6-8
65 Fording Place Rd 12449 845-943-3941
Jo Burruby, prin. Fax 382-6069

Lake Luzerne, Warren, Pop. 1,220
Hadley-Luzerne Central SD 400/PK-12
PO Box 200 12846 518-696-2378
Beecher Baker, supt. Fax 696-5884
www.hlcs.org
Hadley-Luzerne JSHS 300/6-12
PO Box 200 12846 518-696-2112
Patrick Cronin, prin. Fax 696-2356

Lake Placid, Essex, Pop. 2,496
Lake Placid Central SD 700/K-12
50 Cummings Rd 12946 518-523-2475
Dr. Roger Carania, supt. Fax 523-4971
www.lpcsd.org
Lake Placid JSHS 400/6-12
34 School St 12946 518-523-2474
Dana Wood, prin. Fax 523-2896

Mountain Lake Children's Residence Post-Sec.
386 River Rd 12946 888-585-9007
North Country S 100/4-9
4382 Cascade Rd 12946 518-523-9329
David Hochschartner, head sch Fax 523-4858
Northwood S 200/9-12
92 Northwood Rd 12946 518-523-3357
Edward Good, hdmstr. Fax 523-3405

Lake Ronkonkoma, Suffolk, Pop. 19,855
Sachem Central SD
Supt. — See Ronkonkoma
Sachem HS North 2,300/9-12
212 Smith Rd 11779 631-471-1400
Patricia Trombetta, prin. Fax 471-1408
Samoset MS 900/6-8
51 School St 11779 631-471-1700
James Horan, prin. Fax 471-1706

Lancaster, Erie, Pop. 10,243
Lancaster Central SD 5,700/K-12
177 Central Ave 14086 716-686-3201
Dr. Michael Vallely, supt. Fax 686-3350
www.lancasterschools.org
Lancaster HS 1,900/9-12
1 Forton Dr 14086 716-686-3250
Cesar Marchioli, prin. Fax 686-3347
Lancaster MS 900/7-8
148 Aurora St 14086 716-686-3220
Peter Kruszynski, prin. Fax 686-3223

St. Mary HS 400/9-12
142 Laverack Ave 14086 716-683-4824
Rebecca Kranz, prin. Fax 683-4996

Lansing, Tompkins, Pop. 3,411
Lansing Central SD 1,100/K-12
284 Ridge Rd 14882 607-533-3020
Chris Pettograsso, supt. Fax 533-3602
www.lcsd.k12.ny.us/
Lansing HS 400/9-12
300 Ridge Rd 14882 607-533-3020
Colleen Ledley, prin. Fax 533-4612
Lansing MS 300/5-8
6 Ludlowville Rd 14882 607-533-3020
Christine Rebera, prin. Fax 533-3543

Larchmont, Westchester, Pop. 5,760
Mamaroneck UFD
Supt. — See Mamaroneck
Hommocks MS 1,200/6-8
10 Hommocks Rd 10538 914-220-3300
Seth Weitzman, prin. Fax 220-3315

Latham, Albany, Pop. 10,131
North Colonie Central SD 5,300/K-12
91 Fiddlers Ln 12110 518-785-8591
D. Joseph Corr, supt. Fax 785-5504
www.northcolonie.org
Shaker HS 1,900/9-12
445 Watervliet Shaker Rd 12110 518-785-5511
Richard Murphy, prin. Fax 783-5905
Shaker JHS 900/7-8
475 Watervliet Shaker Rd 12110 518-785-1341
Dr. Russell Moore, prin. Fax 783-8877

John Paolo's Exteme Beauty Institute Post-Sec.
638 Columbia St Ext Ste 1 12110 518-783-0808

Laurelton, See New York
NYC Department of Education
Supt. — See New York
Collaborative Arts MS 500/6-8
14500 Springfield Blvd 11413 718-977-6181
Tammy Holloway, prin.
Community Voices MS 500/6-8
14500 Springfield Blvd 11413 718-977-6180
Tamra Collins, prin. Fax 977-6182

Laurens, Otsego, Pop. 259
Laurens Central SD 300/K-12
PO Box 301 13796 607-432-2050
Romona Wenck, supt. Fax 432-4388
laurenscs.org
Laurens Central S 300/K-12
PO Box 301 13796 607-432-2050
Bill Dorritie, prin. Fax 432-4388

Lawrence, Nassau, Pop. 6,454
Lawrence UFD 2,800/PK-12
PO Box 477 11559 516-295-7030
Gary Schall, supt. Fax 239-7164
www.lawrence.org
Lawrence MS 800/5-8
195 Broadway 11559 516-295-7000
Willis Perry, prin. Fax 295-7196
Other Schools – See Cedarhurst

Hebrew Academy of Five Towns Rockaway MS 300/6-8
44 Frost Ln 11559 516-569-6352
Joshua Gold, prin. Fax 569-6457
Mesivta Ateres Yaakov HS 200/9-12
131 Washington Ave 11559 516-374-6465
Rambam Mesivta 200/9-12
15 Frost Ln 11559 516-371-5824
Shor Yoshuv Rabbinical College Post-Sec.
1 Cedarlawn Ave 11559 516-239-9002

Le Roy, Genesee, Pop. 4,322
Le Roy Central SD 1,300/PK-12
2 Trigon Park 14482 585-768-8133
Kim Cox, supt. Fax 768-8929
www.leroycsd.org
Le Roy JSHS 600/7-12
9300 S Street Rd 14482 585-768-8131
Tim McArdle, prin. Fax 768-8929

Levittown, Nassau, Pop. 51,176
Island Trees UFD 2,300/K-12
74 Farmedge Rd 11756 516-520-2100
Dr. Charles Murphy, supt. Fax 520-2113
www.islandtrees.org
Island Trees HS 800/9-12
59 Straight Ln 11756 516-520-2135
Nicholas Grande, prin. Fax 520-9199
Island Trees Memorial MS 700/5-8
45 Wantagh Ave 11756 516-520-2157
Dr. Roger Bloom, prin. Fax 520-2168

Levittown UFD 7,200/K-12
150 Abbey Ln 11756 516-434-7020
Dr. Tonie McDonald, supt. Fax 520-8314
www.levittownschools.com
Division Avenue HS 1,000/9-12
120 Division Ave 11756 516-434-7150
John Coscia, prin. Fax 520-8364
MacArthur HS 1,400/9-12
3369 N Jerusalem Rd 11756 516-434-7225
Joseph Sheehan, prin. Fax 520-8466
Salk MS 900/6-8
3359 N Jerusalem Rd 11756 516-434-7350
John Zampaglione, prin. Fax 520-8479
Wisdom Lane MS 700/6-8
120 Center Ln 11756 516-434-7300
John Avena, prin. Fax 520-8380

Hunter Business School Post-Sec.
3601 Hempstead Tpke 11756 516-796-1000

Liberty, Sullivan, Pop. 4,273
Liberty Central SD 1,600/PK-12
115 Buckley St 12754 845-292-6990
Dr. William Silver Ed.D., supt. Fax 292-1164
www.libertyk12.org
Liberty HS 400/9-12
125 Buckley St 12754 845-292-5400
Jack Strassman, prin. Fax 292-7262
Liberty MS 400/5-8
145 Buckley St 12754 845-292-5400
Jack Strassman, prin. Fax 292-5691

Lido Beach, Nassau, Pop. 2,865
Long Beach CSD 3,500/K-12
235 Lido Blvd 11561 516-897-2000
David Weiss, supt. Fax 897-2107
www.lbeach.org
Long Beach HS 1,300/9-12
322 Lagoon Dr W 11561 516-897-2012
Jeffrey Myers, prin. Fax 897-2052
Long Beach MS 700/6-8
239 Lido Blvd 11561 516-897-2166
Paul Romanelli, prin. Fax 897-2145

Lima, Livingston, Pop. 2,111

Lima Christian S 200/K-12
1574 Rochester St 14485 585-624-3841
Todd Steltz, prin. Fax 624-8293

Lincolndale, Westchester, Pop. 1,500
Somers Central SD
Supt. — See Somers
Somers HS 1,100/9-12
PO Box 640 10540 914-248-8585
Mark Bayer, prin. Fax 248-8186

Ives S 100/7-11
PO Box 600 10540 914-248-7474

Lindenhurst, Suffolk, Pop. 26,920
Lindenhurst UFD 6,200/K-12
PO Box 621 11757 631-867-3000
Daniel Giordano, supt. Fax 867-3008
www.lindenhurstschools.org
Lindenhurst HS 2,100/9-12
300 Charles St 11757 631-867-3700
Christopher Gitz, prin. Fax 867-3708
Lindenhurst MS 1,400/6-8
350 S Wellwood Ave 11757 631-867-3500
Frank Naccarato, prin. Fax 867-3508

Lisbon, Saint Lawrence
Lisbon Central SD 600/PK-12
6866 County Route 10 13658 315-393-4951
Erin Woods, supt. Fax 393-7666
lisboncs.schoolwires.com
Lisbon Central S 600/PK-12
6866 County Route 10 13658 315-393-4951
Patrick Farrand, prin. Fax 393-7666

Little Falls, Herkimer, Pop. 4,870
Little Falls CSD 1,100/K-12
15 Petrie St 13365 315-823-1470
Dr. Keith Levatino, supt. Fax 823-0321
www.lfcsd.org
Little Falls HS 400/9-12
1 High School Rd 13365 315-823-1167
Bart Tooley, prin. Fax 823-1209
Little Falls MS 300/6-8
1 High School Rd 13365 315-823-4300
Brian Coleman, prin. Fax 823-3920

Little Neck, See New York
NYC Department of Education
Supt. — See New York
JHS 67 900/6-8
5160 Marathon Pkwy 11362 718-423-8138
Zoi McGrath, prin. Fax 423-8281

Liverpool, Onondaga, Pop. 2,310
Liverpool Central SD 6,500/K-12
195 Blackberry Rd 13090 315-622-7900
Dr. Mark F. Potter, supt. Fax 622-7115
www.liverpool.k12.ny.us
Chestnut Hill MS 300/7-8
204 Saslon Park Dr 13088 315-453-0245
Michael Baroody, prin. Fax 453-0278
Liverpool HS 1,600/10-12
4338 Wetzel Rd 13090 315-453-1500
Douglas Lawrence, prin. Fax 453-1246
Liverpool MS 300/7-8
720 7th St 13088 315-453-0258
Joseph Mussi, prin. Fax 453-0281
Ninth Grade Annex 9-9
4340 Wetzel Rd 13090 315-453-1275
Judy Campolieta, prin. Fax 453-1247
Soule Road MS 500/7-8
8340 Soule Rd 13090 315-453-1283
Amanda Caldwell, prin. Fax 453-1286

Bryant & Stratton College Post-Sec.
8687 Carling Rd 13090 315-652-6500
National Tractor Trailer School Post-Sec.
4650 Buckley Rd 13088 315-451-2430

Livingston Manor, Sullivan, Pop. 1,201
Livingston Manor Central SD 400/PK-12
PO Box 947 12758 845-439-4400
Dr. Deborah Fox, supt. Fax 439-4717
lmcs.k12.ny.us
Livingston Manor JSHS 200/7-12
PO Box 947 12758 845-439-4400
Sandra Johnson, prin. Fax 439-4717

Livonia, Livingston, Pop. 1,405
Livonia Central SD 1,700/PK-12
PO Box E 14487 585-346-4000
Matthew Cole, supt. Fax 346-6145
www.livoniacsd.org
Livonia HS 600/9-12
PO Box E 14487 585-346-4040
Audra Schmitt, prin. Fax 346-9605
Livonia MS 400/6-8
PO Box E 14487 585-346-4050
Chuck D'Imperio, prin. Fax 346-6835

Loch Sheldrake, Sullivan

SUNY Sullivan County Community College Post-Sec.
112 College Rd 12759 845-434-5750

Lockport, Niagara, Pop. 20,480
Lockport CSD 4,600/K-12
130 Beattie Ave 14094 716-478-4800
Michelle T. Bradley, supt. Fax 478-4863
www.lockportschools.org
Lockport HS 1,500/9-12
250 Lincoln Ave 14094 716-478-4450
Frank Movalli, prin. Fax 478-4498
Lockport HS West at Charlotte Cross Alt
319 West Ave 14094 716-478-4626
Russell Buckley, prin. Fax 478-4634

North Park JHS 700/7-8
160 Passaic Ave 14094 716-478-4700
Ryan Schoenfeld, prin. Fax 478-4705

Starpoint Central SD 2,600/K-12
4363 Mapleton Rd 14094 716-210-2352
Dr. Sean M. Croft, supt. Fax 210-2355
www.starpointcsd.org/
Starpoint HS 800/9-12
4363 Mapleton Rd 14094 716-210-2300
Gil Licata, prin. Fax 210-2334
Starpoint MS 600/6-8
4363 Mapleton Rd 14094 716-210-2200
James Bryer, prin. Fax 210-2233

Locust Valley, Nassau, Pop. 3,370
Locust Valley Central SD 2,200/K-12
22 Horse Hollow Rd 11560 516-277-5000
Dr. Anna Hunderfund, supt. Fax 277-5098
www.lvcsd.k12.ny.us/
Locust Valley HS 700/9-12
99 Horse Hollow Rd 11560 516-277-5100
Dr. Kieran McGuire, prin. Fax 277-5108
Locust Valley MS 600/6-8
99 Horse Hollow Rd 11560 516-277-5200
H. Thomas Hogan, prin. Fax 277-5208

Friends Academy 700/PK-12
270 Duck Pond Rd 11560 516-676-0393
Andrea Kelly, head sch Fax 393-4276
Portledge S 400/PK-12
355 Duck Pond Rd 11560 516-750-3100
Simon Owen-Williams, head sch Fax 674-7063

Long Beach, Nassau, Pop. 32,689

Eisman Community S 100/9-12
2 W Park Ave Ste 2 11561 516-889-2332
Mesivta of Long Beach 100/9-12
205 W Beech St 11561 516-255-4700
Rabbinical College of Long Island Post-Sec.
205 W Beech St 11561 516-255-4700

Long Island City, See New York
NYC Department of Education
Supt. — See New York
Academy for Careers in TV & Film 500/9-12
1-50 51st Ave 11101 718-609-3330
Edgar Rodriguez, prin.
Academy of American Studies 800/9-12
2804 41st Ave 11101 718-361-8786
William Bassell, prin. Fax 361-8832
Academy of Finance & Enterprise 500/9-12
3020 Thomson Ave 11101 718-389-3623
Victoria Armano, prin. Fax 389-3724
Aviation Career & Technical HS Vo/Tech
4530 36th St 11101 718-361-2032
Deno Charalambous, prin. Fax 784-8654
Bard HS Early College II 500/9-12
3020 Thomson Ave 11101 718-361-3133
Valerie Thomson, prin. Fax 361-6742
Bryant HS 2,600/9-12
4810 31st Ave 11103 718-721-5404
Namita Dwarka, prin. Fax 728-3478
Energy Tech HS 100/9-12
3641 28th St 11106 718-472-0536
Hope Barter, prin. Fax 472-0490
Hunters Point Community MS 100/6-8
150 51st Ave 11101 718-609-3300
Sarah Goodman, prin. Fax 609-3319
Information Technology HS 900/9-12
2116 44th Rd 11101 718-937-4270
Joseph Reed, dir. Fax 937-5236
International HS at Laguardia College 500/9-12
4535 Van Dam St 11101 718-392-3433
Jaclyn Valane, prin. Fax 392-3443
HS of Applied Communication 400/9-12
3020 Thomson Ave 11101 718-389-3163
Daniel Korb, prin. Fax 389-3427
IS 141 1,200/6-8
3711 21st Ave 11105 718-278-6403
Miranda Pavlou, prin. Fax 278-2884
IS 204 700/6-8
3641 28th St 11106 718-937-1463
Faye Kotzer, prin. Fax 937-7964
Middle College HS 500/9-12
4535 Van Dam St 11101 718-392-3330
Linda Siegmund, prin. Fax 392-3315
Newcomers HS 900/9-12
2801 41st Ave 11101 718-937-6005
Orlando Sarmiento, prin. Fax 937-6316
Queens Vocational HS Vo/Tech
3702 47th Ave 11101 718-937-3010
Melissa Burg, prin. Fax 392-8397
Riverview S K-12
1-50 51st Ave 11101 718-609-3320
Susan McNulty, prin. Fax 609-3322
Shanker S for Visual & Performing Arts 500/6-8
3151 21st St 11106 718-274-8316
Alexander Angueira, prin. Fax 278-6512
Wagner HS 600/7-12
4707 30th Pl 11101 718-472-5671
Stephania Vu, prin. Fax 472-9117
Young Womens Leadership S 600/6-12
2315 Newtown Ave 11102 718-267-2839
Allison Persad, prin. Fax 728-0218

Apex Technical School Post-Sec.
2402 Queens Plz S 11101 212-645-3300
Berk Trade and Business School Post-Sec.
3309 Queens Blvd Fl 2 11101 718-729-0909
CUNY LaGuardia Community College Post-Sec.
31-10 Thompson Ave 11101 718-482-7200
Evangel Christian S 500/PK-12
3921 Crescent St 11101 718-937-9600
Carolyn Marko, prin. Fax 937-1613
New York School for Medical Dental Asst. Post-Sec.
3310 Queens Blvd 11101 718-793-2330

Long Lake, Hamilton, Pop. 541
Long Lake Central SD 100/PK-12
PO Box 217 12847 518-624-2147
Dr. Donald Carlisle, supt. Fax 624-3896
www.longlakecsd.org
Long Lake Central S 100/PK-12
PO Box 217 12847 518-624-2147
Dr. Donald Carlisle, prin. Fax 624-3896

Loudonville, Albany, Pop. 10,822

Loudonville Christian S 300/PK-12
374 Loudon Rd 12211 518-434-6051
Kathryn Hills M.Ed., head sch Fax 935-2258
Siena College Post-Sec.
515 Loudon Rd 12211 518-783-2300

Lowville, Lewis, Pop. 3,442
Lowville Central SD 1,300/K-12
7668 N State St 13367 315-376-9000
Cheryl Steckly, supt. Fax 376-1933
www.lowvilleacademy.org
Lowville HS 400/9-12
7668 N State St 13367 315-376-9015
Daniel Cushing, prin. Fax 376-9016
Lowville MS 300/6-8
7668 N State St 13367 315-376-9010
Scott Exford, prin. Fax 376-9011

Lynbrook, Nassau, Pop. 19,147
Lynbrook UFD 2,800/K-12
111 Atlantic Ave 11563 516-887-0253
Melissa Burak, supt. Fax 887-3263
www.lynbrookschools.org
Lynbrook HS 900/9-12
9 Union Ave 11563 516-887-0200
Joseph Rainis, prin. Fax 887-8079
Lynbrook North MS 300/6-8
529 Merrick Rd 11563 516-887-0282
Sean Fallon, prin. Fax 887-0286
Lynbrook South MS 400/6-8
333 Union Ave 11563 516-887-0266
Caryn Blum, prin. Fax 887-0268

Lyndonville, Orleans, Pop. 823
Lyndonville Central SD 600/PK-12
PO Box 540 14098 585-765-3101
Jason Smith, supt. Fax 765-2106
www.lyndonvillecsd.org/
Webber MSHS 300/7-12
PO Box 540 14098 585-765-3162
Aaron Slack Ed.D., prin. Fax 765-3190

Lyons, Wayne, Pop. 3,527
Lyons Central SD 700/K-12
10 Clyde Rd 14489 315-946-2200
Denise Dzikowski, supt. Fax 946-2205
www.lyonscsd.org
Lyons MSHS 300/7-12
10 Clyde Rd 14489 315-946-2220
Nelson Kise, prin. Fax 946-2221

Mc Graw, Cortland, Pop. 1,031
Mc Graw Central SD 500/K-12
10 W Academy St 13101 607-836-3636
Melinda McCool, supt. Fax 836-3635
www.mcgrawschools.org
Mc Graw JSHS 300/6-12
10 W Academy St 13101 607-836-3601
Mark Dimorier, prin. Fax 836-3635

Madison, Madison, Pop. 304
Madison Central SD 500/K-12
7303 State Route 20 13402 315-893-1878
Perry Dewey, supt. Fax 893-7111
www.madisoncentralny.org
Madison Central S 500/K-12
7303 State Route 20 13402 315-893-1878
Larry Nichols, prin. Fax 893-7111

Madrid, Saint Lawrence, Pop. 751
Madrid-Waddington Central SD 700/PK-12
PO Box 67 13660 315-322-5746
Lynn Roy, supt. Fax 322-4462
www.mwcsk12.org
Madrid-Waddington JSHS 400/6-12
PO Box 67 13660 315-322-5746
Eric Burke, prin. Fax 322-4462

Mahopac, Putnam, Pop. 8,268
Mahopac Central SD 4,600/K-12
179 E Lake Blvd 10541 845-628-3415
Dennis Creedon Ed.D., supt. Fax 628-5502
www.mahopac.k12.ny.us
Mahopac HS 1,600/9-12
421 Baldwin Place Rd 10541 845-628-3256
John Augusta, prin. Fax 628-4380
Mahopac MS 1,200/6-8
425 Baldwin Place Rd 10541 845-621-1330
Vincent DiGrandi, prin. Fax 628-5847

Malone, Franklin, Pop. 5,853
Malone Central SD 2,300/PK-12
PO Box 847 12953 518-483-7800
Jerry Griffin, supt. Fax 483-3071
www.malonecsd.org
Franklin Academy HS 700/9-12
42 Huskie Ln 12953 518-483-7807
Brandon Pelkey, prin. Fax 483-7813
Malone MS 500/6-8
15 Francis St 12953 518-483-7801
James Knight, prin. Fax 483-9497

Malverne, Nassau, Pop. 8,420
Malverne UFD 1,700/K-12
301 Wicks Ln 11565 516-887-6405
Dr. James Hunderfund, supt. Fax 596-2910
www.malverne.k12.ny.us
Herber MS 400/6-8
75 Ocean Ave 11565 516-887-6444
Daniel Nehlsen, prin. Fax 596-0525
Malverne HS 500/9-12
80 Ocean Ave 11565 516-887-6420
Dr. Vincent Romano, prin. Fax 887-6479

Mamaroneck, Westchester, Pop. 18,587
Mamaroneck UFD 5,200/PK-12
1000 W Boston Post Rd 10543 914-220-3000
Dr. Robert Shaps Ed.D., supt. Fax 220-3010
www.mamkschools.org
Mamaroneck HS 1,500/9-12
1000 W Boston Post Rd 10543 914-220-3100
Elizabeth Clain, prin. Fax 220-3115
Other Schools – See Larchmont

Rye Neck UFD 1,300/K-12
310 Hornidge Rd 10543 914-777-5200
Dr. Peter Mustich, supt. Fax 777-5201
www.ryeneck.org
Rye Neck HS 400/9-12
300 Hornidge Rd 10543 914-777-5200
Dr. Barbara Ferraro, prin. Fax 777-4801
Rye Neck MS 300/5-8
300 Hornidge Rd 10543 914-777-5200
Dr. Eric Lutinski, prin. Fax 777-4701

French-American S of NY 900/PK-12
525 Fenimore Rd 10543 914-250-0400
Joel Peinado, hdmstr.
Westchester Hebrew HS 100/9-12
856 Orienta Ave 10543 914-698-0806

Manhasset, Nassau, Pop. 7,968
Manhasset UFD 3,300/K-12
200 Memorial Pl 11030 516-267-7700
Charles Cardillo, supt. Fax 627-1618
www.manhasset.k12.ny.us
Manhasset HS 1,000/9-12
200 Memorial Pl 11030 516-267-7600
Dean Schlanger, prin. Fax 627-4604
Manhasset MS 600/7-8
200 Memorial Pl 11030 516-267-7500
Dean Schlanger, prin. Fax 627-8157

Elmezzi Graduate School of Molecular Med Post-Sec.
350 Community Dr 11030 516-562-3405
St. Mary HS 700/9-12
51 Clapham Ave 11030 516-627-2711
Jonathan Kramer, prin. Fax 627-3209

Manlius, Onondaga, Pop. 4,642
Fayetteville-Manlius Central SD 4,200/K-12
8199 E Seneca Tpke 13104 315-692-1234
Dr. Craig Tice, supt. Fax 692-1227
www.fmschools.org
Eagle Hill MS 700/5-8
4645 Enders Rd 13104 315-692-1400
Maureen McCrystal, prin. Fax 692-1046
Fayetteville-Manlius HS 1,500/9-12
8201 E Seneca Tpke 13104 315-692-1900
Raymond Kilmer, prin. Fax 692-1028
Other Schools – See Fayetteville

Manorville, Suffolk, Pop. 14,172
Eastport-South Manor Central SD 3,300/K-12
149 Dayton Ave 11949 631-801-3013
Mark Nocero, supt. Fax 874-6750
www.esmonline.org
Eastport/South Manor JSHS 1,800/7-12
543 Moriches Middle Isle Rd 11949 631-801-3250
Salvatore Alaimo, prin. Fax 874-6787

Marathon, Cortland, Pop. 912
Marathon Central SD 700/PK-12
PO Box 339 13803 607-849-3117
Rebecca Stone, supt. Fax 849-3305
www.marathonschools.org/
Marathon JSHS 300/7-12
PO Box 339 13803 607-849-3251
Christopher Grethel, prin. Fax 849-3305

Marcellus, Onondaga, Pop. 1,781
Marcellus Central SD 1,700/K-12
2 Reed Pkwy 13108 315-673-6000
Dr. Judith Pastel, supt. Fax 673-1727
marcellusschools.org
Driver MS 700/4-8
2 Reed Pkwy 13108 315-673-6200
Janet O'Mara, prin. Fax 673-1727
Marcellus HS 600/9-12
1 Mustang Hl 13108 315-673-6300
John Durkee, prin. Fax 673-0312

Marcy, Oneida, Pop. 8,685
Whitesboro Central SD
Supt. — See Whitesboro
Whitesboro HS 1,000/9-12
6000 State Route 291 13403 315-266-3200
Jeff Kuhn, prin. Fax 266-3223

Margaretville, Delaware, Pop. 595
Margaretville Central SD 300/K-12
PO Box 319 12455 845-586-2647
Robert Chakar Ed.D., supt. Fax 586-2949
www.margaretvillecs.org
Margaretville Central S 300/K-12
PO Box 319 12455 845-586-2647
Colin Clark, prin. Fax 586-2949

Catskill Mountain Christian Academy 50/K-12
PO Box 26 12455 845-586-1955
Robert Engelhardt, head sch Fax 586-3492

Marion, Wayne, Pop. 1,490
Marion Central SD 800/PK-12
4034 Warner Rd 14505 315-926-2300
Donald Bavis, supt. Fax 926-5797
www.marioncs.org/
Marion JSHS 400/7-12
4034 Warner Rd 14505 315-926-4228
Nicholas Ganster, prin. Fax 926-3114

Marlboro, Ulster, Pop. 3,611
Marlboro Central SD
Supt. — See Milton
Marlboro Central HS 600/9-12
50 Cross Rd 12542 845-236-5810
Ryan Lawler, prin. Fax 236-2638
Marlboro MS 400/6-8
1375 Route 9W 12542 845-236-5840
Debra Clinton, prin. Fax 236-3634

Maspeth, See New York
NYC Department of Education
Supt. — See New York
IS 73 1,700/6-8
7002 54th Ave 11378 718-639-3817
Michael Casale, prin. Fax 429-5162

Luther S 200/6-12
6002 Maspeth Ave 11378 718-894-4000
Randal Gast, dir. Fax 894-1469

Massapequa, Nassau, Pop. 21,527
Massapequa UFD 7,400/K-12
4925 Merrick Rd 11758 516-308-5000
Lucille Iconis, supt.
www.msd.k12.ny.us
Berner MS, 50 Carman Mill Rd 11758 1,200/7-8
Jason Esposito, prin. 516-308-5700
Massapequa HS 1,900/10-12
4925 Merrick Rd 11758 516-308-5900
Patrick DiClemente, prin.
Massapequa HS Ames Campus 600/9-9
198 Baltimore Ave 11758 516-308-5800
Jordan McCaw, prin.

Plainedge UFD
Supt. — See North Massapequa
Plainedge HS 1,100/9-12
241 Wyngate Dr 11758 516-992-7550
Robert Amster, prin. Fax 992-7545

Massena, Saint Lawrence, Pop. 10,748
Massena Central SD 2,900/PK-12
84 Nightengale Ave 13662 315-764-3700
Patrick Brady, supt. Fax 764-3701
www.mcs.k12.ny.us
Leary JHS 400/7-8
84 Nightengale Ave 13662 315-764-3720
Burton Peck, prin. Fax 764-3723
Massena HS 900/9-12
84 Nightengale Ave 13662 315-764-3710
Sarah Boyce, prin. Fax 764-3719

Mastic Beach, Suffolk, Pop. 12,605
William Floyd UFD 8,700/K-12
240 Mastic Beach Rd 11951 631-874-1100
Kevin Coster, supt. Fax 281-3047
www.wfsd.k12.ny.us
Floyd HS 2,700/9-12
240 Mastic Beach Rd 11951 631-874-1699
Barbara Butler, prin. Fax 874-1540
Paca MS 900/6-8
338 Blanco Dr 11951 631-874-1414
Michele Gode, prin. Fax 874-1561
Other Schools – See Moriches

Mattituck, Suffolk, Pop. 4,155
Mattituck-Cutchogue UFD
Supt. — See Cutchogue
Mattituck-Cutchogue JSHS 800/7-12
15125 Main Rd 11952 631-298-8460
Shawn Petretti, prin. Fax 298-8544

Mayfield, Fulton, Pop. 827
Mayfield Central SD 900/PK-12
27 School St 12117 518-661-8207
Jon Peterson, supt. Fax 661-7666
www.mayfieldcsd.org
Mayfield JSHS 400/7-12
27 School St 12117 518-661-8200
Dr. Christopher Wojeski, prin. Fax 661-7666

Mayville, Chautauqua, Pop. 1,698
Chautauqua Lake Central SD 900/PK-12
100 N Erie St 14757 716-753-5808
Benjamin Spitzer, supt. Fax 753-5813
www.clake.org
Chautauqua Lake Central Secondary S 500/7-12
100 N Erie St 14757 716-753-5882
Joshua Liddell, prin. Fax 753-5886

Mechanicville, Saratoga, Pop. 5,096
Mechanicville CSD 1,400/K-12
25 Kniskern Ave 12118 518-664-5727
Dr. Michael J. McCarthy, supt. Fax 514-2101
www.mechanicville.org
Mechanicville HS 400/9-12
25 Kniskern Ave 12118 518-664-9888
Kevin Kolakowski, prin. Fax 514-2107
Mechanicville JHS 300/6-8
25 Kniskern Ave 12118 518-664-5727
Craig Forth, prin. Fax 664-5727

Augustine Classical Academy 100/K-12
7 N Main St 12118 518-541-2089

Medford, Suffolk, Pop. 23,778
Patchogue-Medford UFD
Supt. — See Patchogue
Oregon MS, 109 Oregon Ave 11763 600/6-9
Bryan Lake, prin. 631-687-6800
Patchogue-Medford HS 1,900/10-12
181 Buffalo Ave 11763 631-687-6500
Randy Rusielewicz Ed.D., prin.

Hunter Business School Post-Sec.
3247 Route 112 Ste 3 11763 631-736-7360

Medina, Orleans, Pop. 5,905
Medina Central SD 1,700/PK-12
1 Mustang Dr 14103 585-798-2700
Mark B. Kruzynski, supt. Fax 798-5676
www.medinacsd.org
Medina HS 600/8-12
2 Mustang Dr 14103 585-798-2700
Michael Cavanagh, prin. Fax 798-2787

Melville, Suffolk, Pop. 18,680
Half Hollow Hills Central SD
Supt. — See Dix Hills
West Hollow MS 1,300/6-8
250 Old East Neck Rd 11747 631-592-3400
Dr. Milton Strong, prin. Fax 592-3922

SBI Campus Post-Sec.
320 S Service Rd 11747 631-370-3300

Merrick, Nassau, Pop. 21,879
Bellmore-Merrick Central HSD
Supt. — See North Merrick
Calhoun HS 1,300/9-12
1786 State St 11566 516-992-1300
Nicole Hollings, prin. Fax 867-7390
Merrick Avenue MS 900/7-8
1870 Merrick Ave 11566 516-992-1200
Taryn Johnson, prin. Fax 867-6391

Grace Christian Academy 100/K-12
36 Smith St 11566 516-379-2223
Stephen Schultz, hdmstr. Fax 771-8063

Mexico, Oswego, Pop. 1,597
Mexico Central SD 2,100/PK-12
16 Fravor Rd Ste A 13114 315-963-8400
Sean Bruno, supt. Fax 963-5801
www.mexicocsd.org
Mexico HS 700/9-12
3338 Main St 13114 315-963-8400
Donald Root, prin. Fax 963-8887
Mexico MS 600/5-8
16 Fravor Rd 13114 315-963-8400
Kim Holliday, prin. Fax 963-3848

Middleburgh, Schoharie, Pop. 1,471
Middleburgh Central SD 600/PK-12
PO Box 606 12122 518-827-3625
Michele Weaver, supt. Fax 827-6632
www.middleburghcsd.org
Middleburgh JSHS 300/7-12
PO Box 850 12122 518-827-3600
Lorianne Petrosino, prin. Fax 827-5192

Middle Island, Suffolk, Pop. 10,280
Longwood Central SD 8,900/K-12
35 Yaphank Middle Island Rd 11953 631-345-2172
Dr. Michael Lonergan, supt. Fax 345-2166
www.longwood.k12.ny.us
Longwood HS 2,700/9-12
100 Longwood Rd 11953 631-345-9200
Scott Schuster, prin. Fax 345-9279
Longwood JHS 1,300/7-8
198 Longwood Rd 11953 631-345-2701
Adam Dewitt, prin. Fax 345-9281

Middleport, Niagara, Pop. 1,807
Royalton-Hartland Central SD 1,400/PK-12
54 State St 14105 716-735-2000
Dr. Roger Klatt, supt. Fax 735-2036
www.royhart.org
Royalton-Hartland HS 500/9-12
54 State St 14105 716-735-2000
Gary Bell, prin. Fax 735-2046
Royalton-Hartland MS 500/5-8
78 State St 14105 716-735-2000
John Fisgus, prin. Fax 735-2056

Middletown, Orange, Pop. 27,256
Middletown CSD 6,700/K-12
223 Wisner Ave 10940 845-326-1193
Dr. Kenneth Eastwood, supt. Fax 326-1225
www.middletowncityschools.org/
Middletown HS 2,100/9-12
24 Gardner Ave 10940 845-326-1600
Tracey Sorrentino, admin. Fax 326-1605
Monhagen MS 800/6-8
555 County Highway 78 10940 845-326-1700
Dominick Radogna, prin. Fax 326-1701
Twin Towers MS 800/6-8
112 Grand Ave 10940 845-326-1650
Gordon Dean, prin. Fax 326-1651

Beauty School of Middletown Post-Sec.
225 Dolson Ave Ste 100 10940 845-343-2171
Harmony Christian S 200/PK-12
1790 Route 211 E 10941 845-692-5353
Kevin Barry, admin. Fax 692-7140
SUNY Orange County Community College Post-Sec.
115 South St 10940 845-344-6222

Middle Village, See New York

Christ the King Regional HS 900/9-12
6802 Metropolitan Ave 11379 718-366-7400
Peter Mannarino, prin. Fax 366-1165

Milford, Otsego, Pop. 406
Milford Central SD 400/K-12
PO Box 237 13807 607-286-7721
Peter Livshin, supt. Fax 286-7879
www.schoolworld.milfordcentral.org
Milford Central S 400/K-12
PO Box 237 13807 607-286-3349
Teresa Glavin, prin. Fax 286-7879

Millbrook, Dutchess, Pop. 1,439
Millbrook Central SD 1,000/K-12
PO Box AA 12545 845-677-4200
Philip D'Angelo, supt. Fax 677-4206
www.millbrookcsd.org/
Millbrook HS 400/9-12
PO Box AA 12545 845-677-2510
Caroline Pidala, prin. Fax 677-2525
Millbrook MS 200/6-8
PO Box AA 12545 845-677-4210
Dr. Phyllis Amori, prin. Fax 677-6913

Millbrook S 300/9-12
131 Millbrook School Rd 12545 845-677-8261
Drew Casertano, hdmstr. Fax 677-8598

Miller Place, Suffolk, Pop. 12,218
Miller Place UFD 2,800/K-12
7 Memorial Dr 11764 631-474-2700
Dr. Marianne Cartisano, supt. Fax 474-0686
www.millerplace.k12.ny.us
Miller Place HS 900/9-12
15 Memorial Dr 11764 631-474-2723
Kevin Slavin, prin. Fax 474-1734
North Country Road MS 700/6-8
191 N Country Rd 11764 631-474-2710
Matthew Clark, prin. Fax 474-5178

Mill Neck, Nassau, Pop. 979

Mill Neck Lutheran School Post-Sec.
Frost Mill Rd B12 11765

Millwood, Westchester, Pop. 1,000

Yeshiva Kehilath Yaakov 50/12-12
PO Box 501 10546 914-782-2816

Milton, Ulster, Pop. 1,389
Marlboro Central SD 1,900/K-12
21 Milton Tpke Ste 100 12547 845-236-8000
Michael Brooks, supt. Fax 795-5904
www.marlboroschools.org
Other Schools – See Marlboro

Mineola, Nassau, Pop. 18,445
Mineola UFD 2,500/K-12
121 Jackson Ave 11501 516-237-2000
Dr. Michael Nagler, supt. Fax 237-2008
www.mineola.k12.ny.us
Other Schools – See Garden City Park

Chaminade HS 1,700/9-12
340 Jackson Ave 11501 516-742-5555
Br. Joseph Bellizzi, prin. Fax 742-1989
NY College Traditional Chinese Medicine Post-Sec.
155 1st St 11501 516-739-1545
Winthrop University Hospital Post-Sec.
259 1st St 11501 516-663-2201

Mohawk, Herkimer, Pop. 2,697
Central Valley Central SD
Supt. — See Ilion
Jarvis MS 100/5-8
28 Grove St 13407 315-866-2620
Melissa Hoskey, prin. Fax 867-2909

Monroe, Orange, Pop. 8,240
Greenwood Lake UFD 500/K-8
1247 Lakes Rd 10950 845-782-8678
Dr. Christine Ackerman, supt. Fax 782-8582
www.gwlufsd.org/
Greenwood Lake MS 300/4-8
1247 Lakes Rd 10950 845-782-8678
Dr. Matthew Lawrence, prin. Fax 782-2004

Kiryas Joel Village UFSD 50/PK-12
48 Bakertown Rd Ste 401 10950 845-782-2300
Joel Petlin, supt. Fax 782-4176
Kiryas Joel Village S 50/PK-12
1 Dinev Ct 10950 845-782-7510
Jehudah Halpern, prin. Fax 782-5849

Bnei Yoel S 300/PK-12
PO Box 255, 845-783-8036
UTA Mesivta of Kiryas Joel Post-Sec.
PO Box 2009, 845-783-9901
UTA of Kiryas Joel 5,800/K-12
PO Box 477, 845-783-5800

Monsey, Rockland, Pop. 18,318

Ateres Bais Yaakov 300/PK-12
236 Cherry Ln 10952 845-368-2200
Bais Malka Girls S of Belz 500/PK-12
PO Box 977 10952 845-354-9500
Bais Shifra Miriam S 300/K-12
PO Box 682 10952 845-356-0061
Bais Yaakov HS of Spring Valley 400/9-12
11 Smolley Dr 10952 845-356-3113
Bais Yaakov of Ramapo HS 100/9-12
16 Hershel Ter 10952 845-356-0580
Beth Medrash Meor Yitzchok Post-Sec.
65 Dykstras Way E 10952 845-426-3488
Beth Rochel School for Girls 1,000/K-12
145 Saddle River Rd 10952 845-352-5000
Bnos Yisroel Girls S of Viznitz 1,400/1-12
1 School Ter 10952 845-731-3700
Kol Yaakov Torah Center Post-Sec.
29 W Maple Ave 10952 845-425-3863
Mesivta Ziev Hatorah 50/9-12
PO Box 814 10952 845-426-6868
Ohr Somayach Monsey Post-Sec.
244 Route 306 10952 845-425-1370
Yeshiva and Kolel Bais Medrash Elyon Post-Sec.
73 Main St 10952 845-356-7064

Yeshiva Bais Binyomin 100/9-12
51 Carlton Rd 10952 845-207-0330
Nesanel Link, admin.
Yeshiva Beth David S 600/PK-12
PO Box 136 10952 845-352-3100
Yeshiva Derech Emes 50/PK-12
133 Route 59 10952 845-426-2130
Yeshiva D'Monsey Rabbinical College Post-Sec.
2 Roman Blvd 10952 845-426-3276
Yeshiva Gedolah Kesser Torah Post-Sec.
28 Cedar Ln 10952 845-406-4308
Yeshiva Gedola of South Monsey 100/9-12
260 Saddle River Rd 10952 845-356-4030
Yeshiva Ohel Torah 9-12
91 College Rd 10952 845-371-3740
Yeshiva Shaar Ephraim S 200/9-12
PO Box 253 10952 845-426-3110
Yeshivath Viznitz Post-Sec.
PO Box 446 10952 845-731-3700

Montgomery, Orange, Pop. 3,752
Valley Central SD 4,300/K-12
944 State Route 17K 12549 845-457-2400
John P. Xanthis, supt. Fax 457-4319
www.vcsd.k12.ny.us
Valley Central HS 1,500/9-12
1175 State Route 17K 12549 845-457-2400
Jayme Ginda-Baxter, prin. Fax 457-4056
Valley Central MS 1,000/6-8
1189 State Route 17K 12549 845-457-2400
Ned Hayes, prin. Fax 457-4008

Monticello, Sullivan, Pop. 6,485
Monticello Central SD 3,000/K-12
237 Forestburgh Rd 12701 845-794-7700
Tammy Mangus, supt. Fax 794-7710
www.monticelloschools.net
Kaiser MS 700/6-8
45 Breakey Ave 12701 845-796-3058
Nichole Horler, prin. Fax 796-3099
Monticello HS 900/9-12
39 Breakey Ave 12701 845-794-8840
Stephen Wilder, prin. Fax 794-8133

Montrose, Westchester, Pop. 2,689
Hendrick Hudson Central SD 2,400/K-12
61 Trolley Rd 10548 914-257-5100
Joseph Hochreiter, supt. Fax 257-5121
www.henhudschools.org/
Hendrick Hudson HS 800/9-12
2166 Albany Post Rd 10548 914-257-5800
James Mackin, prin. Fax 257-5801
Other Schools – See Cortlandt Manor

Moravia, Cayuga, Pop. 1,274
Moravia Central SD 1,000/PK-12
PO Box 1189 13118 315-497-2670
John Birmingham, supt. Fax 497-2260
www.moraviaschool.org
Moravia JSHS 500/6-12
PO Box 1189 13118 315-497-2670
Greg Jenne, prin. Fax 497-3852

Moriches, Suffolk, Pop. 2,802
William Floyd UFD
Supt. — See Mastic Beach
Floyd MS 1,000/6-8
630 Moriches Middle Island 11955 631-874-5505
Carolyn Schick, prin. Fax 878-7690

Morris, Otsego, Pop. 573
Morris Central SD 400/PK-12
PO Box 40 13808 607-263-6102
Matthew Sheldon, supt. Fax 263-2483
www.morriscsd.org
Morris Central S 400/PK-12
PO Box 40 13808 607-263-6100
Katharine Smith, prin. Fax 263-2483

Morristown, Saint Lawrence, Pop. 395
Morristown Central SD 300/PK-12
PO Box 217 13664 315-375-8814
Douglas H. McQueer, supt. Fax 375-8604
www.greenrockets.org
Morristown Central S 300/PK-12
PO Box 217 13664 315-375-8814
David L. Doe, prin. Fax 375-8604

Morrisville, Madison, Pop. 2,159
Morrisville-Eaton Central SD 700/PK-12
PO Box 990 13408 315-684-9300
Gregory Molloy, supt. Fax 684-9399
www.m-ecs.org
Morrisville-Eaton MSHS 300/6-12
PO Box 990 13408 315-684-9121
Fax 684-7033

SUNY at Morrisville Post-Sec.
PO Box 901 13408 315-684-6000

Mountain Dale, Sullivan, Pop. 200

Yeshiva Zichron Mayir 12-12
5 Ronald Tawil Way 12763 845-434-5328

Mount Kisco, Westchester, Pop. 10,701
Bedford Central SD
Supt. — See Bedford
Fox Lane MS 1,000/6-8
S Bedford Rd 10549 914-241-6126
Susan Ostrofsky, prin. Fax 241-6129

Mount Morris, Livingston, Pop. 2,942
Mount Morris Central SD 500/PK-12
30 Bonadonna Ave 14510 585-658-2568
Gregory Bump, supt. Fax 658-4814
www.mtmorriscsd.org
Mount Morris JSHS 200/7-12
30 Bonadonna Ave 14510 585-658-3333
Dr. Becky Chenaille, prin. Fax 658-4814

Mount Sinai, Suffolk, Pop. 11,989
Mount Sinai UFD 2,400/K-12
118 N Country Rd 11766 631-870-2550
Gordon Brosdal, supt. Fax 473-0905
www.mtsinai.k12.ny.us
Mount Sinai HS 800/9-12
1 Gertrude Goodman Dr 11766 631-870-2800
Robert Grable, prin. Fax 928-3668
Mount Sinai MS 800/5-8
114 N Country Rd 11766 631-870-2700
Peter Pramataris, prin. Fax 928-3129

Mount Vernon, Westchester, Pop. 64,673
Mount Vernon CSD 7,800/PK-12
165 N Columbus Ave 10553 914-358-2400
Dr. Kenneth R. Hamilton, supt. Fax 665-6077
www.mtvernoncsd.org
Davis MS 700/7-8
350 Gramatan Ave 10552 914-665-5120
Joshua Whitham, prin. Fax 665-5128
Mandela-Zollicoffer Alternative HS 100/Alt
250 Gramatan Ave 10550 914-358-2720
Ralph Burts, prin. Fax 665-5086
Mount Vernon HS 1,300/9-12
100 California Rd 10552 914-665-5300
Ronald Gonzalez, prin. Fax 665-5281
Thornton HS 700/9-12
121 S 6th Ave 10550 914-358-2740
Sharon Bradley, prin. Fax 358-2792
Turner MS 400/6-8
624 S 3rd Ave 10550 914-665-5150
Dr. Jonathan Brown, prin. Fax 665-5152

Montefiore School of Nursing Post-Sec.
53 Valentine St 10550 914-361-6472
Westchester School of Beauty Culture Post-Sec.
6 Gramatan Ave 10550 914-699-2344

Munnsville, Madison, Pop. 470
Stockbridge Valley Central SD 400/K-12
PO Box 732 13409 315-495-4400
Cindy Stocker, supt. Fax 495-4492
www.stockbridgevalley.org
Stockbridge Valley Central S 400/K-12
PO Box 732 13409 315-495-4400
Cindy Stocker, admin. Fax 495-4492

Nanuet, Rockland, Pop. 17,600
Nanuet UFD 2,200/K-12
101 Church St 10954 845-627-9888
Dr. Mark McNeill, supt. Fax 624-5338
www.nanuetsd.org
Barr MS 400/7-8
143 Church St 10954 845-627-4040
Roger Guccione, prin. Fax 624-3138
Nanuet HS 700/9-12
103 Church St 10954 845-627-9804
Dr. Vin Carella, prin. Fax 624-5520

Capri Cosmetology Learning Center Post-Sec.
251 W Route 59 10954 845-623-6339

Naples, Ontario, Pop. 1,024
Naples Central SD 700/PK-12
136 N Main St 14512 585-374-7900
Matthew Frahm, supt. Fax 374-5859
www.naplescsd.org
Naples HS 300/7-12
136 N Main St 14512 585-374-7905
Elizabeth Ashton, prin. Fax 374-5859

Nedrow, Onondaga, Pop. 2,167
Onondaga Central SD 900/PK-12
4466 S Onondaga Rd 13120 315-552-5000
Robin Price, supt. Fax 492-4650
www.ocs.cnyric.org
Onondaga JSHS 400/7-12
4479 S Onondaga Rd 13120 315-552-5020
Timothy Mumford, prin. Fax 552-5027

Nesconset, Suffolk, Pop. 13,284
Smithtown Central SD
Supt. — See Smithtown
Great Hollow MS 1,000/6-8
150 Southern Blvd 11767 631-382-2800
John Scomillio, prin. Fax 382-2807

Newark, Wayne, Pop. 8,894
Newark Central SD 2,100/PK-12
100 E Miller St Ste 5 14513 315-332-3217
Matthew Cook, supt. Fax 332-3523
www.newarkcsd.org
Newark HS 600/9-12
625 Peirson Ave 14513 315-332-3242
Thomas Roote, prin. Fax 332-3567
Newark MS 500/6-8
701 Peirson Ave 14513 315-332-3295
Teresa Prinzi, prin. Fax 332-3584

Newark Valley, Tioga, Pop. 980
Newark Valley Central SD 1,200/K-12
PO Box 547 13811 607-642-3221
Ryan Dougherty, supt. Fax 642-8821
www.nvcs.stier.org/
Newark Valley HS 500/8-12
68 Wilson Creek Rd 13811 607-642-8665
Michelle Bombard, prin. Fax 642-5292

New Berlin, Chenango, Pop. 1,014
Unadilla Valley Central SD 900/PK-12
PO Box F 13411 607-847-7500
Robert Mackey, admin. Fax 847-6924
www.uvstorm.org
Unadilla Valley Secondary S 400/6-12
PO Box F 13411 607-847-7500
Franklin Johnson, prin. Fax 847-8045

Newburgh, Orange, Pop. 28,122
Newburgh Enlarged CSD 11,900/PK-12
124 Grand St 12550 845-563-3500
Dr. Roberto Padilla, supt. Fax 563-3501
www.newburghschools.org
Newburgh Free Academy 3,300/9-12
201 Fullerton Ave 12550 845-563-5400
Matteo Doddo, prin. Fax 563-5405
Newburgh Free Academy North 700/9-12
301 Robinson Ave 12550 845-563-8400
Matteo Doddo, prin. Fax 563-8409
South MS 800/6-8
33 Monument St 12550 845-563-7000
Jessica Layne, prin. Fax 563-7019
Other Schools – See New Windsor

Cronin Presentation Academy 100/5-8
69 Bay View Ter 12550 845-567-0708
Sr. Yliana Hernandez, prin. Fax 567-0709
Mt. St. Mary College Post-Sec.
330 Powell Ave 12550 845-561-0800

New City, Rockland, Pop. 32,957
Clarkstown Central SD 8,400/K-12
62 Old Middletown Rd 10956 845-639-6418
Martin Cox, supt. Fax 639-6488
www.ccsd.edu
Clarkstown North HS 1,500/9-12
151 Congers Rd 10956 845-639-6504
Harry Leonardatos, prin. Fax 638-6916
Other Schools – See West Nyack

Mesivta Shaarei Arazim 100/9-12
900 Route 45 10956 845-426-6401
Peter Juricek, prin. Fax 940-6300

Newcomb, Essex
Newcomb Central SD 100/PK-12
PO Box 418 12852 518-582-3341
Clark Hults, supt. Fax 582-2163
www.newcombcsd.org
Newcomb Central S 100/PK-12
PO Box 418 12852 518-582-3341
Clark Hults, prin. Fax 582-2163

Newfane, Niagara, Pop. 3,772
Newfane Central SD
Supt. — See Burt
Newfane HS 600/9-12
1 Panther Dr 14108 716-778-6551
Daniel Bedette, prin. Fax 778-6578
Newfane MS 500/5-8
2700 Transit Rd 14108 716-778-6452
Thomas Adams, prin. Fax 778-6460

Newfield, Tompkins
Newfield Central SD 800/PK-12
247 Main St 14867 607-564-9955
Dr. Cheryl Thomas, supt. Fax 564-0055
www.newfieldschools.org
Newfield HS 200/9-12
247 Main St 14867 607-564-9955
Matthew Ryan, prin. Fax 564-3624
Newfield MS 200/6-8
247 Main St 14867 607-564-9955
Catherine Griggs, prin. Fax 564-3403

New Hartford, Oneida, Pop. 1,828
New Hartford Central SD 2,600/K-12
33 Oxford Rd 13413 315-624-1218
Robert Nole, supt. Fax 724-8940
www.newhartfordschools.org
New Hartford SHS 700/10-12
33 Oxford Rd 13413 315-624-1214
Mark Benson, prin. Fax 738-9209
Perry JHS 600/7-9
9499 Weston Rd 13413 315-738-9300
Keith Levatino, prin. Fax 738-9349

New Hyde Park, Nassau, Pop. 9,473
Herricks UFD 3,900/K-12
999 Herricks Rd 11040 516-305-8900
Dr. Fino Celano, supt. Fax 248-3108
www.herricks.org
Herricks HS 1,300/9-12
100 Shelter Rock Rd 11040 516-305-8700
James Ruck, prin. Fax 248-3282
Other Schools – See Albertson

Sewanhaka Central HSD
Supt. — See Floral Park
New Hyde Park Memorial HS 1,600/7-12
500 Leonard Blvd 11040 516-488-9500
Dr. Richard Faccio, prin. Fax 488-9506

New Lebanon, Columbia
New Lebanon Central SD 400/K-12
14665 State Route 22 12125 518-794-9016
Leslie Whitcomb, supt. Fax 766-5574
www.newlebanoncsd.org
New Lebanon JSHS 200/7-12
14665 State Route 22 12125 518-794-7600
Matthew Klafehn, prin. Fax 766-6265

Darrow S 100/9-12
110 Darrow Rd 12125 518-794-6000
Simon Holzapfel, head sch Fax 794-7065

New Paltz, Ulster, Pop. 6,646
New Paltz Central SD 2,200/K-12
196 Main St 12561 845-256-4020
Maria Rice, supt. Fax 256-4025
www.newpaltz.k12.ny.us
New Paltz Central HS 700/9-12
196 Main St 12561 845-256-4100
Barbara Clinton, prin. Fax 256-4109
New Paltz MS 500/6-8
196 Main St 12561 845-256-4200
Dr. Richard Wiesenthal, prin. Fax 256-4209

SUNY College at New Paltz Post-Sec.
1 Hawk Dr 12561 845-257-7869

Newport, Herkimer, Pop. 637
West Canada Valley Central SD 700/K-12
PO Box 360 13416 315-845-6800
D.J. Shepardson, supt. Fax 845-8652
www.westcanada.org
West Canada Valley JSHS 400/7-12
PO Box 360 13416 315-845-6800
Jeremy Kozak, prin. Fax 845-8652

New Rochelle, Westchester, Pop. 75,662
New Rochelle CSD 10,700/PK-12
515 North Ave 10801 914-576-4300
Dr. Brian G. Osborne, supt. Fax 632-4144
www.nred.org
Leonard MS 1,200/6-8
25 Gerada Ln 10804 914-576-4339
John Barnes, prin. Fax 576-4784
New Rochelle HS 3,400/9-12
265 Clove Rd 10801 914-576-4502
Reginald Richardson, prin. Fax 576-4284
Young MS 1,100/6-8
270 Centre Ave 10805 914-576-4360
Dr. Anthony Bongo, prin. Fax 632-2738

College of New Rochelle Post-Sec.
29 Castle Pl 10805 914-654-5000
Iona College Post-Sec.
715 North Ave 10801 914-633-2000
Iona Preparatory S 800/9-12
255 Wilmot Rd 10804 914-632-0714
Edward O'Neill, prin. Fax 632-9760
Salesian HS 500/9-12
148 E Main St 10801 914-632-0248
John Flaherty, prin. Fax 632-5426
Thornton-Donovan S 200/K-12
100 Overlook Cir 10804 914-632-8836
Ursuline HS 800/6-12
1354 North Ave 10804 914-636-3950
Carol Killebrew, prin. Fax 636-3949

New Square, Rockland, Pop. 6,907

Avir Yaakov Girl's S 1,200/K-12
15 Roosevelt Ave 10977 845-354-0874

New Windsor, Orange, Pop. 8,717
Cornwall Central SD
Supt. — See Cornwall on Hudson
Cornwall Central HS 1,100/9-12
10 Dragon Dr 12553 845-534-8009
Lynn Imperato, prin. Fax 565-2754

Greenburgh-North Castle UFD
Supt. — See Dobbs Ferry
Kaplan Career Academy 100/Alt
623 Blooming Grove Tpke 12553 845-522-8460
Anthony DiMarco, prin. Fax 522-8456

Newburgh Enlarged CSD
Supt. — See Newburgh
Heritage MS 900/6-8
405 Union Ave 12553 845-563-3750
Pedro Roman, prin. Fax 563-3759

New York, New York, Pop. 7,965,821
NYC Department of Education 940,300/PK-12
52 Chambers St 10007 718-935-2000
Carmen Farina, chncllr.
schools.nyc.gov/
Academy for Social Action 300/6-12
509 W 129th St 10027 212-543-6301
Josephine Yeboah, prin. Fax 234-8597
Academy for Software Engineering 200/9-12
40 Irving Pl 10003 – Seung Yu, prin. 212-253-3299
American Sign Language S 200/9-12
223 E 23rd St 10010 917-326-6668
Watfa Shama, prin. Fax 326-6688
Art & Design HS 1,400/9-12
231 E 56th St 10022 212-752-4340
Frances Desanctis, prin. Fax 752-4945
Baldwin S 200/Alt
351 W 18th St 10011 212-627-2812
Brady Smith, prin. Fax 627-9803
Ballet Tech / S for Dance 100/4-8
890 Broadway Fl 3 10003 212-254-1803
Roy O'Neill, prin. Fax 477-5048
Bard HS Early College 600/9-12
525 E Houston St 10002 212-995-8479
Michael Lerner, prin. Fax 777-4702
Baruch College Campus HS 400/9-12
55 E 25th St 10010 212-683-7440
Arleen Liquori, prin. Fax 683-7338
Beacon HS 1,300/9-12
530 W 44th St 10036 212-465-4230
Ruth Lacey, prin. Fax 465-4235
Bergtraum HS 1,500/9-12
411 Pearl St 10038 212-964-9610
Naima Cook, prin. Fax 732-6622
Business of Sports S 400/9-12
439 W 49th St 10019 212-246-2183
Joshua Solomon, prin. Fax 246-2913
Cascade HS 200/Alt
198 Forsyth St 10002 646-654-1261
Ezequiel Garcia, prin. Fax 654-1742
Central Park East HS 500/9-12
1573 Madison Ave 10029 212-860-5929
Bennett Lieberman, prin. Fax 860-2938
Chelsea Career & Technical Education HS Vo/Tech
131 Avenue of the Americas 10013 212-925-1080
Kimberly Bradley, prin. Fax 941-7934
Choir Academy of Harlem 200/6-12
2005 Madison Ave 10035 212-289-6227
Lennel George, prin. Fax 289-4195

City As School HS 600/Alt
16 Clarkson St 10014 212-337-6800
Alan Cheng, prin. Fax 337-6875
City College Academy of the Arts 600/6-12
4600 Broadway 10040 212-567-3164
Bernadette Drysdale, prin. Fax 567-3958
City Knoll MS, 525 W 44th St 10036 6-8
Victoria Armas, prin. 718-935-3649
Coalition S for Social Change 300/Alt
2351 1st Ave 10035 212-831-5153
John Sullivan, prin. Fax 831-5951
Collaborative Academy of Science 200/6-8
220 Henry St 10002 212-227-0762
Anthony Chianese, prin. Fax 577-9785
College Academy 500/9-12
549 Audubon Ave 10040 212-927-1841
Peter Sloman, prin. Fax 927-2388
Columbia Secondary S 700/6-12
425 W 123rd St 10027 212-666-1278
Miriam Nightengale, prin. Fax 666-3805
Community Action S - MS 258 200/6-8
154 W 93rd St 10025 212-678-5888
John Curry, prin. Fax 961-1613
Community Health Academy of the Heights 600/6-12
504 W 158th St 10032 212-342-6600
Mark House, prin.
Douglas Academy 1,500/6-12
2581 7th Ave 10039 212-491-4107
Joseph Gates, prin. Fax 491-4414
Douglass Academy II 400/6-12
215 W 114th St 10026 212-865-9260
Osei Owusu-Afriyie, prin. Fax 865-9281
East Side Community HS 700/6-12
420 E 12th St 10009 212-460-8467
Mark Federman, prin. Fax 260-9657
East Side MS 400/6-8
331 E 91st St 10128 212-360-0114
David Getz, prin. Fax 360-0121
Esperanza Preparatory Academy 200/6-8
240 E 109th St 10029 212-722-6507
Giulliano Quesada, prin. Fax 722-6717
Essex Street Academy 400/9-12
350 Grand St 10002 212-475-4773
Erin Carstensen, prin. Fax 674-2058
Facing History S 400/9-12
525 W 50th St 10019 212-757-2680
Dana Panagot, prin. Fax 757-2156
Food & Finance HS 400/9-12
525 W 50th St 10019 212-586-2943
Roger Turgeon, prin. Fax 586-4205
Forsyth Satellite Academy 9-12
198 Forsyth St 10002 212-677-8900
Ingrid Haynes, prin. Fax 260-3063
Global Learning Collaborative 500/9-12
145 W 84th St 10024 212-877-1103
Karla Chiluiza, prin. Fax 877-1138
Global Neighborhood Secondary S 100/6-8
216 E 120th St 10029 212-289-4204
Florin Purice, prin. Fax 289-4301
Global Technology Preparatory S 200/6-8
160 E 120th St 10035 212-722-1395
David Baiz, prin. Fax 722-5864
Gramercy Arts HS 600/9-12
40 Irving Pl 10003 212-253-7076
Susan DiCicco, prin. Fax 253-8095
Grange MS 6-8
500 W 138th St 10031 212-281-6184
Benjamin Lev, prin. Fax 234-4903
Green HS of Teaching 600/9-12
26 Broadway 10004 646-826-8174
Nigel Pugh, prin. Fax 826-8175
Harbor Heights MS 200/6-8
306 Fort Washington Ave 10033 212-568-6052
Monica Klehr, prin. Fax 568-7959
Harlem Renaissance HS 200/9-12
22 E 128th St 10035 212-996-3795
Nadv Ziemer, prin. Fax 996-4354
Harvest Collegiate HS 9-12
34 W 14th St 10011 212-242-3384
Catherine Burch, prin.
Health Professions & Human Services HS 1,700/9-12
345 E 15th St 10003 212-780-9175
Robert Gentile, prin. Fax 979-7261
Henry Street S for International Studies 300/6-12
220 Henry St 10002 212-406-9411
Miles Doyle, prin. Fax 406-9417
Heritage S 300/9-12
1680 Lexington Ave 10029 212-828-2858
Dyanand Sugrim, prin. Fax 828-2861
Hudson HS of Learning Technologies 500/9-12
351 W 18th St 10011 212-488-3330
Nancy Amling, prin. Fax 488-3335
Humanities Preparatory S 200/9-12
351 W 18th St 10011 212-929-4433
Jeannie Ferrari, prin. Fax 929-4445
Independence HS 300/Alt
850 10th Ave 10019 212-262-8067
Ron Smolkin, prin. Fax 262-8110
Innovation Diploma Plus 200/Alt
145 W 84th St 10024 212-724-2039
Daniel Storchan, prin. Fax 724-2765
Institute for Collaborative Education 500/6-12
345 E 15th St 10003 212-475-7972
Peter Karp, prin. Fax 475-0459
International HS at Union Square 300/9-12
40 Irving Pl 10003 212-533-2560
Vadewatie Ramsuchit, prin. Fax 228-2946
Inwood Early College for Health and Info 9-12
650 Academy St 10034 212-567-1394
Samona Tait, prin. Fax 567-1825
KAPPA IV S 200/6-8
6 Edgecombe Ave 10030 212-694-6040
Juan Vives, prin. Fax 690-8056
Kennedy-Onassis HS 700/9-12
120 W 46th St 10036 212-391-0041
Edward Demeo, prin. Fax 391-1293

La Guardia HS 2,700/9-12
100 Amsterdam Ave 10023 212-496-0700
Dr. Lisa Mars, prin. Fax 724-5748
Landmark HS 400/9-12
351 W 18th St 10011 212-647-7410
Caron Pinkus, prin. Fax 647-7416
Lazarus HS 200/Alt
100 Hester St 10002 212-925-5017
Melody Kellogg, prin. Fax 925-5920
Leadership & Public Service HS 700/9-12
90 Trinity Pl 10006 212-346-0007
Philip Santos, prin. Fax 346-0612
Legacy S for Integrated Studies 100/9-12
34 W 14th St 10011 212-645-1980
Gregory Rodrigues, prin. Fax 645-2596
Liberty HS 300/Alt
250 W 18th St 10011 212-691-0934
Rhonda Huegel, prin. Fax 727-1369
Life Science Secondary S 800/6-12
320 E 96th St 10128 212-348-1694
Kimberly Swanson, prin. Fax 348-4293
Lower East Side Prep S 500/Alt
145 Stanton St 10002 212-505-6366
Martha Polin, prin. Fax 260-0813
Lower Manhattan Arts Academy 400/9-12
350 Grand St 10002 212-505-0143
John Wenk, prin. Fax 674-8021
Lower Manhattan Community MS 400/6-8
26 Broadway 10004 646-826-8100
Kelly McGuire, prin. Fax 826-8101
Luperon HS of Science & Math 500/9-12
501 W 165th St 10032 212-928-1202
Francisca Lopez, prin. Fax 928-1309
Manhattan Academy for Arts & Language 300/9-12
111 E 33rd St 10016 212-576-0502
Siv Boletsis, prin. Fax 576-0518
Manhattan Bridges HS 600/9-12
525 W 50th St 10019 212-757-5274
Mirza Sanchez-Medina, prin. Fax 757-5411
Manhattan Business Academy 400/9-12
351 W 18th St 10011 212-647-1983
Karen Polsonetti, prin. Fax 647-1989
Manhattan Center for Science/Math 1,600/9-12
260 Pleasant Ave 10029 212-876-4639
Jose Jimenez, prin. Fax 996-5946
Manhattan Early Coll S for Advertising 9-12
411 Pearl St 10038 718-935-3477
Matthew Tossman, prin.
Manhattan/Hunter Science HS 500/9-12
122 Amsterdam Ave 10023 212-501-1235
Kevin Froner, prin. Fax 501-1171
Manhattan International HS 300/9-12
317 E 67th St, 212-517-6728
Gladys Rodriguez, prin. Fax 517-7147
Manhattan Village Academy 400/9-12
43 W 22nd St 10010 212-242-8752
Hector Geager, prin. Fax 242-7630
Marshall Academy 600/6-12
200 W 135th St 10030 212-283-8055
Sean Davenport, prin. Fax 283-8109
Marte Valle HS 400/9-12
145 Stanton St 10002 212-473-8152
Steven Aragona, prin. Fax 475-7588
Mather Building Arts & Craftsmanship HS 100/9-12
439 W 49th St 10019 212-399-3520
Larry Gabbard, prin. Fax 225-0996
McCourt HS 400/9-12
145 W 84th St 10024 212-362-2015
Danielle Salzberg, prin. Fax 362-5926
Milk HS 100/9-12
2 Astor Pl 10003 212-477-1555
Daphne Perrini, prin. Fax 674-8650
Millenium HS 600/9-12
75 Broad St 10004 212-825-9008
Colin McEvoy, prin. Fax 825-9095
Mott Hall HS 400/9-12
6 Edgecombe Ave 10030 212-694-6020
Altagracia Villalona, prin. Fax 690-5047
Mott Hall II 300/6-8
234 W 109th St 10025 212-678-2960
Marlon Lowe, prin. Fax 222-0560
Mott Hall S 300/6-8
71 Convent Ave 10027 212-281-5028
Judith De Los Santos, prin. Fax 491-3451
Murray Hill Academy 300/9-12
111 E 33rd St 10016 212-696-0195
Anita Felix, prin. Fax 696-2498
New Design HS 400/9-12
350 Grand St 10002 212-475-4148
Scott Conti, prin. Fax 674-2128
New Design MS 6-8
625 W 133rd St 10027 212-281-6339
Francesca Pisa, prin. Fax 281-6674
New Explorations Science Tech/Math S 1,700/K-12
111 Columbia St 10002 212-677-5190
Mark Berkowitz, prin. Fax 260-8124
Newton MS for Science Math Tech 300/6-8
260 Pleasant Ave 10029 212-860-6006
Lisa Nelson, prin. Fax 987-4197
HS for Arts Imagination & Inquiry 400/9-12
122 Amsterdam Ave 10023 212-799-4064
Stephen Noonan, prin. Fax 799-4171
HS for Dual Language & Asian Studies 400/9-12
350 Grand St 10002 212-475-4097
Li Yan, prin. Fax 674-1392
HS for Environmental Studies 1,300/9-12
444 W 56th St 10019 212-262-8113
Daniel Dorogusker, prin. Fax 262-0702
HS for Excellence and Innovation 200/9-12
650 Academy St 10034 212-569-1022
Tyona Washington, prin. Fax 569-1190
HS for Health Careers & Science 600/9-12
549 Audubon Ave 10040 212-927-1841
Javier Trejo, prin. Fax 927-2179
HS for Language and Diplomacy 400/9-12
40 Irving Pl 10003 212-253-2480
Amber Najmi-Shadid, prin. Fax 253-2539

HS for Law Advocacy & Community Justice 500/9-12
122 Amsterdam Ave 10023 212-501-1201
Doreen Conwell, prin. Fax 501-1195
HS for Law & Public Service 700/9-12
549 Audubon Ave 10040 212-342-6130
Nicholas Politis, prin. Fax 781-9516
HS for Math Science Engineering 500/9-12
240 Convent Ave 10031 212-281-6490
Crystal Bonds, prin. Fax 281-6918
HS for Media & Communications 500/9-12
549 Audubon Ave 10040 212-927-1841
Juan Villar, prin. Fax 927-2326
HS of Arts & Technology 600/9-12
122 Amsterdam Ave 10023 212-501-1198
Anne Geiger, prin. Fax 441-3693
HS of Economic & Finance 800/9-12
100 Trinity Pl 10006 212-346-0708
Michael Stanzione, prin. Fax 346-0712
HS of Fashion Industries 1,700/9-12
225 W 24th St 10011 212-255-1235
Daryl Blank, prin. Fax 255-4756
HS of Graphic Communication Arts 700/9-12
439 W 49th St 10019 212-245-5925
Fia Davis, prin. Fax 265-1552
HS of Hospitality Management 400/9-12
525 W 50th St 10019 212-586-1819
Matthew Corallo, prin. Fax 586-2713
IS 218 200/6-8
4600 Broadway 10040 212-567-2322
June Barnett, prin. Fax 569-7421
IS 286 200/6-8
509 W 129th St 10027 212-543-4960
Melisha Jackman, prin. Fax 694-4124
IS 289 300/6-8
201 Warren St 10282 212-571-9268
Zeynep Ozkan, prin. Fax 587-6610
IS 528 200/6-8
180 Wadsworth Ave 10033 212-740-4900
Carlos Pichardo, prin. Fax 781-7302
JHS 52 500/6-8
650 Academy St 10034 212-567-9162
Lupe Leon, prin. Fax 942-4952
JHS 54 800/6-8
103 W 107th St 10025 212-678-2861
Dr. Elana Elster, prin. Fax 316-0883
JHS 104 1,000/6-8
330 E 21st St 10010 212-674-4545
Rocco Macri, prin. Fax 477-2205
JHS 143 400/6-8
511 W 182nd St 10033 212-927-7739
Lakisha Luke, prin. Fax 781-5539
JHS 167 1,300/6-8
220 E 76th St 10021 212-535-8610
Jennifer Rehn, prin. Fax 472-9385
MS 131 400/6-8
100 Hester St 10002 212-219-1204
Phyllis Tam, prin. Fax 925-6386
MS 224 200/6-8
410 E 100th St 10029 212-860-6047
Luis Genao, prin. Fax 410-0678
MS 243 200/5-8
100 W 84th St 10024 212-799-1477
Elaine Schwartz, prin. Fax 579-9728
MS 245 The Computer S 400/6-8
100 W 77th St 10024 917-441-0873
Henry Zymeck, prin. Fax 678-5908
MS 247 200/6-8
32 W 92nd St 10025 212-799-2653
Caitlin Caldwell, prin. Fax 579-2407
MS 250 200/6-8
735 W End Ave 10025 212-866-6313
Novella Bailey, dir. Fax 678-5295
MS 255 400/6-8
319 E 19th St 10003 212-614-8785
Rhonda Perry, prin. Fax 614-0095
MS 256 200/6-8
154 W 93rd St 10025 212-222-2857
Brian Zager, prin. Fax 531-0586
MS 260 300/6-8
10 E 15th St 10003 212-695-9114
Jonathan Levin, prin. Fax 695-9611
MS 319 600/6-8
21 Jumel Pl 10032 212-923-3827
Ysidro Abreu, prin. Fax 923-3676
MS 322 400/6-8
4600 Broadway 10040 212-304-0853
Erica Zigelman, prin. Fax 567-3016
MS 324 400/6-8
21 Jumel Pl 10032 212-923-4057
Janet Heller, prin. Fax 923-4626
MS 326 300/6-8
401 W 164th St 10032 917-521-1875
Sharon Weissbrot, prin. Fax 521-1750
MS 328 300/6-8
401 W 164th St 10032 917-521-2508
Olga Quiles, prin. Fax 521-7797
NYC iSchool 400/9-12
131 Avenue of the Americas 10013 917-237-7300
Isora Bailey, prin. Fax 219-0743
NYC Lab HS for Collaborative Studies 600/9-12
333 W 17th St 10011 212-691-6119
Brooke Jackson, prin. Fax 691-2147
NYC Lab MS for Collaborative Studies 600/6-8
333 W 17th St 10011 212-691-6119
Megan Adams, prin. Fax 691-6219
NYC Museum S 500/9-12
333 W 17th St 10011 212-675-6206
Darlene Miller, dir. Fax 675-6524
Pace HS 400/9-12
100 Hester St 10002 212-334-4663
Eri Glatz, prin. Fax 334-4919
Park East HS 400/9-12
230 E 105th St 10029 212-831-1517
Kevin McCarthy, prin. Fax 348-6097
Professional Performing Arts HS 500/6-12
328 W 48th St 10036 212-247-8652
Keith Ryan, prin. Fax 247-7514

Quest to Learn S 400/6-9
351 W 18th St 10011 212-488-3645
Jennifer Rygalski, prin.
Randolph HS 1,300/9-12
443 W 135th St 10031 212-690-6800
David Fanning, prin. Fax 281-2726
Renaissance School of the Arts 200/6-8
319 E 117th St 10035 212-534-6072
Brian Bradley, prin. Fax 534-7418
Repertory Company HS for Theatre Arts 200/9-12
123 W 43rd St 10036 212-382-1875
Manuel Urena, prin. Fax 382-2306
Reynolds West Side HS 400/Alt
140 W 102nd St 10025 212-678-7300
Jean McTavish, prin. Fax 678-7380
Roosevelt HS 500/9-12
411 E 76th St 10021 212-772-1220
Demitri Saliani, prin. Fax 772-1440
Satellite Academy 300/Alt
120 W 30th St 10001 646-674-2800
Steve Zbaida, prin.
School for Global Leaders 200/6-8
145 Stanton St 10002 212-260-5375
Carry Chan, prin. Fax 260-7386
School of the Future 700/6-12
127 E 22nd St 10010 212-475-8086
Stacy Goldstein, admin. Fax 475-9273
Stuyvesant HS 3,300/9-12
345 Chambers St 10282 212-312-4800
Jie Zhang, prin. Fax 587-3874
Talent Unlimited HS 500/9-12
317 E 67th St, 212-737-1530
Linda Hamil, prin. Fax 737-2863
Technology Arts & Sciences Studio 200/6-8
185 1st Ave 10003 212-982-1836
George Morgan, prin. Fax 982-0528
Tompkins Square MS 400/6-8
600 E 6th St 10009 212-995-1430
Sonhando Estwick, prin. Fax 979-1341
Union Square Academy for Health Science 9-12
40 Irving Pl 10003 212-253-3110
Bernardo Ascona, prin.
Unity Center for Urban Technologies 300/9-12
111 E 33rd St 10016 212-576-0530
Fausto DeLaRosa, prin. Fax 576-0562
University Neighborhood HS 300/9-12
200 Monroe St 10002 212-962-4341
Elizabeth Collins, prin. Fax 267-5611
University Nieghborhood MS 100/6-8
220 Henry St 10002 212-267-5701
Laura Peynado Castro, prin. Fax 349-8224
Urban Academy Laboratory HS 100/9-12
317 E 67th St, 212-570-5284
Adam Grumbach, prin. Fax 570-5366
Urban Assembly Academy Government & Law300/9-12
350 Grand St 10002 212-505-0745
Alison Breedy, prin. Fax 674-8021
Urban Assembly for Media Studies HS 400/9-12
122 Amsterdam Ave 10023 212-501-1110
Cordelia Veve, prin. Fax 580-0156
Urban Assembly Gateway S for Technology 9-12
439 W 49th St 10019 212-246-1041
April McCoy, prin. Fax 246-2654
Urban Assembly Inst for New Technologies 100/6-8
509 W 129th St 10027 212-543-3840
Roxanne Brown, prin. Fax 690-5980
Urban Assembly Maker Academy 9-12
411 Pearl St 10038 718-935-3442
Luke Bauer, prin.
Urban Assembly New York Harbor S Vo/Tech
10 South St Slip 7 10004 212-458-0800
Jeffrey Chetirko, prin. Fax 458-0801
Urban Assembly S Design & Construction 400/9-12
525 W 50th St 10019 212-586-0981
Mathew Willoughby, prin. Fax 586-1731
Urban Assembly S for Emergency Mgmt 100/9-12
411 Pearl St 10038 212-245-4670
Rodolfo Elizondo, prin. Fax 246-4669
Urban Assembly S for Global Commerce 100/9-10
2005 Madison Ave 10035 212-831-5201
Erin Gehant, prin. Fax 831-5206
Urban Assembly S for Green Careers 400/9-12
145 W 84th St 10024 212-787-1189
Kerry Decker, prin. Fax 787-1455
Urban Assembly S for Performing Arts 400/9-12
509 W 129th St 10027 212-543-4460
Meghan McMahon, prin. Fax 234-4975
Urban Assembly S of Business 400/9-12
26 Broadway 10004 212-668-0169
Patricia Minaya, prin. Fax 668-0635
Vanguard HS 500/9-12
317 E 67th St, 212-517-5175
William Klann, prin. Fax 517-5334
Wadleigh Arts HS 500/6-12
215 W 114th St 10026 212-749-5800
Daisy Fontenez, prin. Fax 749-6463
Washington Hts. Expeditionary Learning S 700/6-12
511 W 182nd St 10033 212-781-0524
Thomas Rochowicz, prin. Fax 781-0742
West Prep Academy 200/6-8
150 W 105th St 10025 212-280-8502
Carland Washington, prin. Fax 362-2794
Yorkville East MS 6-8
1458 York Ave, 917-432-5413
Christina Riggio, prin. Fax 432-5418
Young Womens Leadership HS 500/6-12
105 E 106th St 10029 212-289-7593
Andrew Higgin, prin. Fax 289-7728
Manhattan Comprehensive Night & Day HS Adult
240 2nd Ave 10003 212-353-2010
Michael Toice, prin. Fax 353-1673

Other Schools – See Astoria, Bayside, Bellerose, Bronx, Brooklyn, Corona, East Elmhurst, Elmhurst, Far Rockaway, Floral Park, Flushing, Forest Hills, Fresh Meadows, Glendale, Hollis, Jackson Heights, Jamaica, Laurelton, Little Neck, Long Island City, Maspeth, Oakland Gardens, Ozone Park, Queens Village, Rego Park, Richmond Hill, Ridgewood, Rockaway Park, Saint Albans, South Ozone Park, Springfield Gardens, Staten Island, Whitestone, Woodside

---

ABI School of Barbering and Cosmetology Post-Sec.
252 W 29th St 10001 212-290-2289
Achieve Test Prep Post-Sec.
5 Penn Plz Ste 1975 10001 917-267-0711
AMDA College & Conservatory Post-Sec.
211 W 61st St 10023 212-787-5300
American Academy McAllister Institute Post-Sec.
619 W 54th St Fl 2 10019 212-757-1190
American Academy of Dramatic Arts Post-Sec.
120 Madison Ave 10016 800-463-8990
American University in Cairo Post-Sec.
420 5th Ave Fl 3 10018 212-730-8800
Avenues: The World S 700/PK-12
259 10th Ave 10001 212-524-9000
Dr. Robert Mattoon, head sch Fax 664-0701
Bank Street College of Education Post-Sec.
610 W 112th St 10025 212-875-4400
Barnard College Post-Sec.
3009 Broadway 10027 212-854-5262
Beekman S 100/9-12
220 E 50th St 10022 212-755-6666
George Higgins, head sch Fax 888-6085
Bellevue Hospital Center Post-Sec.
462 1st Ave 10016 212-561-4132
Berkeley College Post-Sec.
3 E 43rd St 10017 212-986-4343
Birch Wathen Lenox S 600/K-12
210 E 77th St, 212-861-0404
Frank J. Carnabuci, hdmstr. Fax 879-3388
Boricua College Post-Sec.
3755 Broadway 10032 212-694-1000
Brearley S 700/K-12
610 E 83rd St 10028 212-744-8582
Jane Fried, head sch Fax 472-8020
Browning S 400/K-12
52 E 62nd St, 212-838-6280
John Botti, head sch Fax 355-5602
Calhoun S 500/2-12
433 W End Ave 10024 212-497-6500
Steven Nelson, admin. Fax 497-6530
Cathedral HS 600/9-12
350 E 56th St 10022 212-688-1545
Maria Spagnuolo, prin. Fax 754-2024
Chapin S 700/K-12
100 E End Ave 10028 212-744-2335
Patricia Hayot Ph.D., head sch Fax 535-8138
Christie's Education Post-Sec.
11 W 42nd St Fl 8 10036 212-355-1501
Christine Valmy International School Post-Sec.
261 5th Ave 10016 212-779-7800
Collegiate S 600/K-12
260 W 78th St 10024 212-812-8500
Lee Levison, hdmstr. Fax 812-8524
Columbia Grammar & Preparatory S 1,300/PK-12
5 W 93rd St 10025 212-749-6200
Dr. Richard Soghoian, hdmstr. Fax 865-4278
Columbia University Post-Sec.
2960 Broadway 10027 212-854-1754
Connelly Center for Education 100/5-8
220 E 4th St 10009 212-982-2287
Shalonda Gutierrez, prin. Fax 982-0547
Convent of the Sacred Heart S 700/PK-12
1 E 91st St 10128 212-722-4745
Dr. Joseph Ciancaglini, head sch Fax 996-1784
Cooper Union Post-Sec.
30 Cooper Sq 10003 212-353-4100
County Univ. Sch. of Dental & Oral Surg. Post-Sec.
630 W 168th St 10032
Cristo Rey HS 400/9-12
112 E 106th St 10029 212-996-7000
William Ford, prin. Fax 427-7444
CUNY Bernard M. Baruch College Post-Sec.
1 Bernard Baruch Way 10010 646-312-1000
CUNY Borough/Manhattan Comm. College Post-Sec.
199 Chambers St 10007 212-220-8000
CUNY City College Post-Sec.
160 Convent Ave 10031 212-650-7000
CUNY Graduate Center Post-Sec.
365 5th Ave 10016 212-817-7000
CUNY Hunter College Post-Sec.
695 Park Ave, 212-772-4000
CUNY John Jay College Criminal Justice Post-Sec.
524 W 59th St 10019 212-237-8000
CUNY Stella & Charles Guttman Comm Coll Post-Sec.
50 W 40th St 10018 646-313-8000
Dalton S 1,300/K-12
108 E 89th St 10128 212-423-5200
Ellen Stein, head sch Fax 423-5259
De La Salle Academy 100/6-8
332 W 43rd St 10036 212-316-5840
Br. Brian Carty, pres. Fax 316-5998
DeVry University Post-Sec.
180 Madison Ave Ste 900 10016 212-312-4300
Dominican Academy 200/9-12
44 E 68th St, 212-744-0195
Dr. Nicole Grimes, prin. Fax 744-0375
Dwight S 800/PK-12
291 Central Park W 10024 212-724-6360
Dianne Drew, head sch Fax 874-4232
East Harlem S 200/4-8
309 E 103rd St 10029 212-876-8775
Fashion Institute of Technology Post-Sec.
227 W 27th St 10001 212-217-7999
Friends Seminary 700/K-12
222 E 16th St 10003 212-979-5030
Robert Lauder, prin. Fax 979-5034

Fusion Academy 6-12
450 Park Ave S Fl 9 10016 212-326-9522
Heather Brookman Ph.D., head sch
Fusion Academy 6-12
157 Columbus Ave 3rd Flr 10023 212-362-1014
Gateway MS 100/6-8
211 W 61st St 10023 212-777-5966
Carolyn Salzman, head sch Fax 777-5794
Gemological Institute of America Post-Sec.
270 Madison Ave Fl 2 10016 800-366-8519
General Theological Seminary Post-Sec.
440 W 21st St 10011 212-243-5150
Globe Institute of Technology Post-Sec.
500 7th Ave 10018 212-349-4330
Grace Church HS 9-12
46 Cooper Sq 10003 212-475-5610
George Davison, head sch
Hebrew Union College Post-Sec.
1 W 4th St 10012 212-674-5300
Helene Fuld College of Nursing Post-Sec.
24 E 120th St Ste 3 10035 212-616-7200
Heschel HS 300/9-12
20 W End Ave 10023 212-246-7717
Ariela Dubler, head sch Fax 246-7686
Heschel MS 100/6-8
30 W End Ave 10023 212-595-7087
Ariela Dubler, head sch Fax 489-1990
Hewitt S 500/K-12
45 E 75th St 10021 212-288-1919
Tara Kinsey, head sch Fax 472-7531
Hunter College Campus S 300/K-12
71 E 94th St 10128 212-860-1291
Lisa Siegmann, dir. Fax 722-6693
Icahn School of Medicine at Mount Sinai Post-Sec.
1 Gustave L Levy Pl 10029 212-241-6500
IDEAL S and Academy 100/PK-12
314 W 91st St 10024 212-769-1699
Dr. Tim Burns, head sch Fax 769-1698
Institute of Audio Research Post-Sec.
64 University Pl 10003 212-677-7580
Jewish Theological Seminary of America Post-Sec.
3080 Broadway 10027 212-678-8000
Juilliard School Post-Sec.
60 Lincoln Center Plz 10023 212-799-5000
Keller Graduate School Post-Sec.
120 W 45th St Fl 6 10036 212-556-0002
LaSalle Academy 300/9-12
215 E 6th St 10003 212-475-8940
Br. William Johnson, prin. Fax 529-3598
La Scuola d'Italia Guglielmo Marconi S 200/PK-12
12 E 96th St 10128 212-369-3290
Learning Institute for Beauty Sciences Post-Sec.
22 W 34th St 10001 212-695-4555
Leman Manhattan Preparatory S 500/PK-12
41 Broad St 10004 212-232-0266
Drew Alexander, head sch Fax 232-0284
Lia Schorr Inst of Cosmetic Skin Care Post-Sec.
686 Lexington Ave 10022 212-486-9541
LIM College Post-Sec.
12 E 53rd St 10022 212-752-1530
Lookstein MS 200/5-8
114 E 85th St 10028 212-774-8040
Lookstein Upper S 500/9-12
60 E 78th St, 212-774-8070
Louis Gerstner Graduate Sch Biomed Sci Post-Sec.
1275 York Ave Ste 441, 646-888-6639
Loyola HS 200/9-12
980 Park Ave 10028 212-288-3522
Dr. Kristin Ross, prin. Fax 861-1021
LREI Little Red School House & Irwin HS 400/PK-12
272 6th Ave 10014 212-477-5316
Philip Kassen, dir. Fax 677-9159
Lycee Francais De New York 1,300/PK-12
505 E 75th St 10021 212-369-1400
Sean Lynch, head sch Fax 439-4200
Lyceum Kennedy French American S 200/PK-12
225 E 43rd St 10017 212-681-1877
Dominique Velociter, head sch Fax 681-1922
Make-Up Designory Post-Sec.
375 W Broadway 10012 212-925-9250
Mandl School College of Allied Health Post-Sec.
254 W 54th St Fl 9 10019 212-247-3434
Manhattan HS for Girls 200/9-12
154 E 70th St 10021 212-737-6800
Manhattan Institute Post-Sec.
255 5th Ave 10016 347-220-8181
Manhattan Institute of Management Post-Sec.
110 William St Fl 3 10038 646-389-0947
Manhattan School of Music Post-Sec.
120 Claremont Ave 10027 212-749-2802
Marymount Manhattan College Post-Sec.
221 E 71st St 10021 212-517-0400
Marymount S 600/PK-12
1026 5th Ave 10028 212-744-4486
Concepcion Alvar, hdmstr. Fax 744-0163
Mesivta Tifereth Jerusalem of America Post-Sec.
1417 E Broadway 10002 212-964-2830
Mesivta Tifereth Jerusalem S 200/K-12
145 E Broadway 10002 212-964-2830
Rabbi Ginzberg, prin. Fax 349-5213
Metropolitan College of New York Post-Sec.
60 West St 10006 212-343-1234
Micropower Career Institute Post-Sec.
137 W 25th St 10001 212-279-2550
Mildred Elley School Post-Sec.
25 Broadway Fl 16 10004 212-380-9004
New York Academy of Art Post-Sec.
111 Franklin St 10013 212-966-0300
New York Career Institute Post-Sec.
11 Park Pl Fl 4 10007 212-962-0002
New York College of Podiatric Medicine Post-Sec.
53 E 124th St 10035 212-410-8000
New York Eye & Ear Infirmary Post-Sec.
310 E 14th St 10003 212-979-4375
New York Institute of Photography Post-Sec.
211 E 43rd St Ste 2402 10017 212-867-8260
New York Inst. of English and Business Post-Sec.
248 W 35th St 10001 212-725-9400

New York International Beauty School Post-Sec.
500 8th Ave Rm 803 10018 212-868-7171
New York Law School Post-Sec.
185 W Broadway 10013 212-431-2100
New York Presbyterian Hospital Post-Sec.
525 E 68th St, 212-746-4000
New York School of Interior Design Post-Sec.
170 E 70th St 10021 212-472-1500
New York Theological Seminary Post-Sec.
475 Riverside Dr Ste 500 10115 212-870-1211
New York University Post-Sec.
70 Washington Sq S 10012 212-998-1212
Nightingale-Bamford S 600/K-12
20 E 92nd St 10128 212-289-5020
Paul Burke, head sch Fax 876-1045
Northeastern Academy 100/9-12
532 W 215th St 10034 212-569-4800
Loris LaBorde, prin. Fax 569-6145
Notre Dame HS 300/9-12
327 W 13th St 10014 212-620-5575
Jaclyn Brilliant, prin. Fax 620-0432
Pace University Post-Sec.
1 Pace Plz 10038 212-346-1200
Pacific College of Oriental Medicine Post-Sec.
915 Broadway Fl 2 10010 212-982-3456
Phillips Beth Israel School of Nursing Post-Sec.
776 Ave of Americas Fl 4 10001 212-614-6110
Professional Business College Post-Sec.
408 Broadway Fl 2 10013 212-226-7300
Professional Children's S 200/6-12
132 W 60th St 10023 212-582-3116
Dr. James Dawson, head sch Fax 956-3295
Rabbi Isaac Elchanan Theological Sem. Post-Sec.
515 W 185th St 10033 646-592-4455
Regis HS 500/9-12
55 E 84th St 10028 212-288-1100
Dr. Gary Tocchet, prin. Fax 794-1221
Relay Graduate School of Education Post-Sec.
40 W 20th St Fl 7 10011 212-228-1888
Richard Gilder Graduate School Post-Sec.
Central Park W at 79th St 10024 212-769-5055
Rockefeller University Post-Sec.
1230 York Ave, 212-327-8000
SAE Institute of Technology Post-Sec.
218 W 18th St Fl 4 10011 212-944-9121
St. George Academy HS 100/9-12
215 E 6th St 10003 212-473-3323
Rev. Peter Shyshka, prin. Fax 534-0819
St. Jean Baptiste HS 300/9-12
173 E 75th St 10021 212-288-1645
Sr. Maria Cassano, prin. Fax 288-6540
St. Thomas Choir S 50/3-8
202 W 58th St 10019 212-247-3311
Fr. Charles Wallace, hdmstr. Fax 247-3393
St. Vincent Ferrer HS 500/9-12
151 E 65th St, 212-535-4680
Sr. Gail Morgan, prin. Fax 988-3455
St. Vincent's Hospital & Medical Center Post-Sec.
153 W 11th St 10011 212-604-7500
Sanford-Brown Institute Post-Sec.
120 E 16th St Fl 4 10003 646-313-4510
School for the Deaf Post-Sec.
225 E 23rd St 10010
School of Visual Arts Post-Sec.
209 E 23rd St 10010 212-592-2000
Sheffield School of Interior Design Post-Sec.
211 E 43rd St 10017 212-661-7270
Smith S 50/7-12
131 W 86th St 10024 212-879-6354
Sotheby's Institute of Art Post-Sec.
570 Lexington Ave Fl 6 10022 212-517-3929
Spanish-American Institute Post-Sec.
215 W 43rd St 10036 212-840-7111
Spence S, 22 E 91st St 10128 700/K-12
Bodie Brizendine, head sch 212-289-5940
Star Career Academy Post-Sec.
154 W 14th St 10011 212-675-6655
Steiner Upper S 100/7-12
15 E 78th St, 212-879-1101
Dr. William Macatee Ed.D., admin. Fax 794-1554
Stevenson S, 24 W 74th St 10023 50/6-12
Robert Cunningham, head sch 212-787-6400
Studio Jewelers Post-Sec.
32 E 31st St 10016 212-686-1944
SUNY College of Optometry Post-Sec.
33 W 42nd St 10036 212-938-4000
Swedish Institute College of Health Sci Post-Sec.
226 W 26th St Fl 5 10001 212-924-5900
Teachers College of Columbia University Post-Sec.
525 W 120th St 10027 212-678-3000
Technical Career Institute Post-Sec.
320 W 31st St 10001 212-594-4000
The Art Institute of New York City Post-Sec.
218 W 40th St Ste 232 10018 212-226-5500
The Institute of Culinary Education Post-Sec.
50 W 23rd St 10010 212-847-0711
The International Culinary Center Post-Sec.
462 Broadway 10013 888-324-2433
The King's College Post-Sec.
56 Broadway 10004 212-659-7200
The New School Post-Sec.
66 W 12th St 10011 212-229-5600
Touro College Post-Sec.
27 W 23rd St 10010 212-463-0400
Transfiguration ES 200/4-8
37 Saint James Pl 10038 212-267-9289
Dr. Patrick Taharally, prin. Fax 227-0065
Trevor Day S 400/6-12
1 W 88th St 10024 212-426-3360
Scott Reisinger, head sch Fax 873-8520
Trinity S 1,000/K-12
139 W 91st St 10024 212-932-6814
John Allman, head sch Fax 799-3417
Tri-State College of Acupuncture Post-Sec.
80 8th Ave Ste 400 10011 212-242-2255
Ultrasound Diagnostic School Post-Sec.
120 E 16th St Fl 2 10003 212-645-9116

Union Theological Seminary Post-Sec.
3041 Broadway 10027 212-662-7100
United Nations International S 1,500/K-12
2450 FDR Dr 10010 212-684-7400
Jane Camblin, dir. Fax 684-1382
Weill Cornell Medical College Post-Sec.
1300 York Ave, 212-746-5454
Wood Tobe-Coburn School Post-Sec.
8 E 40th St 10016 212-686-9040
Xavier HS 1,000/9-12
30 W 16th St 10011 212-924-7900
Michael LiVigni, hdmstr. Fax 924-0303
Yeshiva Rabbi S.R. Hirsch 400/PK-12
91 Bennett Ave 10033 212-568-6200
Diane Lanzkron, prin. Fax 928-4422
Yeshiva University Post-Sec.
500 W 185th St 10033 212-960-5400
Yeshiva University HS for Boys 300/9-12
2540 Amsterdam Ave 10033 212-960-5337
Rabbi Josh Kahn, head sch Fax 960-0027
York Prep S 300/6-12
40 W 68th St 10023 212-362-0400

New York Mills, Oneida, Pop. 3,298
New York Mills UFD 600/K-12
1 Marauder Blvd 13417 315-768-8127
Kathy Houghton, supt. Fax 768-3521
www.newyorkmills.org
New York Mills JSHS 300/7-12
1 Marauder Blvd 13417 315-768-8124
Michael Spost, prin. Fax 768-3397

Niagara Falls, Niagara, Pop. 48,343
Niagara Falls CSD 6,900/PK-12
630 66th St 14304 716-286-4253
Mark Laurrie, supt. Fax 286-4283
www.nfschools.net
Gaskill Preparatory S 500/7-8
910 Hyde Park Blvd 14301 716-278-5820
Sheila Smith, prin. Fax 278-5829
La Salle Preparatory S 500/7-8
7436 Buffalo Ave 14304 716-278-5880
James Spanbauer, prin. Fax 278-5899
Niagara Falls HS 1,900/9-12
4455 Porter Rd 14305 716-278-5800
Robert Bradley, prin. Fax 286-7964

Niagara-Wheatfield Central SD 4,100/PK-12
6700 Schultz St 14304 716-215-3003
Daniel Ljiljanich, supt. Fax 215-3039
www.nwcsd.k12.ny.us
Other Schools – See Sanborn

Cheryl Fell's School of Business Post-Sec.
2541 Military Rd 14304 716-297-2750
Niagara Catholic JSHS 100/7-12
520 66th St 14304 716-283-8771
Ronald Buggs, prin. Fax 283-8774

Niagara University, Niagara

Niagara University Post-Sec.
PO Box 2011 14109 716-285-1212

North Babylon, Suffolk, Pop. 17,252
North Babylon UFD 4,700/K-12
5 Jardine Pl 11703 631-620-7000
Glen Eschbach, supt. Fax 321-3295
www.northbabylonschools.net
Moses MS 1,100/6-8
250 Phelps Ln 11703 631-620-7300
Elizabeth Walsh-Bulger, prin. Fax 587-2619
North Babylon HS 1,500/9-12
1 Phelps Ln 11703 631-620-7100
Jonathan Klomp, prin. Fax 321-3327

North Collins, Erie, Pop. 1,203
North Collins Central SD 600/PK-12
2045 School St 14111 716-337-0101
Joan Thomas, supt. Fax 337-3457
www.northcollins.com
North Collins JSHS 300/7-12
2045 School St 14111 716-337-0101
Erich Ploetz, prin. Fax 337-3457

North Creek, Warren, Pop. 613
Johnsburg Central SD 300/K-12
165 Main St 12853 518-251-2814
Michael Markwica, supt. Fax 251-2562
www.johnsburgcsd.org
Johnsburg Central S 300/K-12
165 Main St 12853 518-251-3504
Nadeen Kearney, prin. Fax 251-2562

North Massapequa, Nassau, Pop. 17,762
Plainedge UFD 3,200/K-12
241 Wyngate Dr 11758 516-992-7455
Dr. Edward Salina, supt. Fax 992-7446
www.plainedgeschools.org
Other Schools – See Bethpage, Massapequa

North Merrick, Nassau, Pop. 12,143
Bellmore-Merrick Central HSD 5,600/7-12
1260 Meadowbrook Rd 11566 516-992-1000
John DeTommaso, supt. Fax 623-0151
www.bellmore-merrick.k12.ny.us
Other Schools – See Bellmore, Merrick

Northport, Suffolk, Pop. 7,346
Northport-East Northport UFD 5,900/K-12
PO Box 210 11768 631-262-6604
Robert L. Banzer, supt. Fax 262-6607
web.northport.k12.ny.us/
Northport HS 2,000/9-12
154 Laurel Hill Rd 11768 631-262-6652
Daniel Danbusky, prin. Fax 262-6736
Northport MS 800/6-8
11 Middleville Rd 11768 631-262-6750
Timothy Hoss, prin. Fax 262-6793
Other Schools – See East Northport

Northport VA Medical Center Post-Sec.
79 Middleville Rd 11768 631-261-4400

North Salem, Westchester
North Salem Central SD 1,200/K-12
230 June Rd 10560 914-669-5414
Dr. Kenneth Freeston, supt. Fax 669-8753
www.northsalemschools.org
North Salem MSHS 700/6-12
230 June Rd 10560 914-669-5414
Dr. Patricia Cyganovich, prin. Fax 669-5663

North Syracuse, Onondaga, Pop. 6,697
North Syracuse Central SD 9,000/PK-12
5355 W Taft Rd 13212 315-218-2100
Annette Speach, supt. Fax 218-2185
www.nscsd.org
North Syracuse JHS 1,500/8-9
5353 W Taft Rd 13212 315-218-3600
Constance Turose, prin. Fax 218-3685
Other Schools – See Cicero

North Tonawanda, Niagara, Pop. 31,199
North Tonawanda CSD 3,600/K-12
176 Walck Rd 14120 716-807-3655
Gregory Woytila, supt. Fax 807-3525
www.ntschools.org
North Tonawanda HS 1,200/9-12
405 Meadow Dr 14120 716-807-3600
James Fisher, prin. Fax 807-3639
North Tonawanda MS 600/7-8
1500 Vanderbilt Ave 14120 716-807-3700
Gregory Burgess, prin. Fax 807-3701

Christian Academy of Western New York 100/PK-12
789 Gilmore Ave 14120 716-433-1652
Patricia Poeller, admin.

Northville, Fulton, Pop. 1,084
Northville Central SD 500/PK-12
PO Box 608 12134 518-863-7000
Dr. Leslie Ford, supt. Fax 863-7011
northvillecsd.org
Northville MSHS 300/6-12
PO Box 608 12134 518-863-7000
Kyle McFarland, prin. Fax 863-7011

Norwich, Chenango, Pop. 7,042
Norwich CSD 1,900/PK-12
89 Midland Dr 13815 607-334-1600
Gerard O'Sullivan, supt. Fax 336-8652
www.norwichcsd.org
Norwich HS 600/9-12
89 Midland Dr 13815 607-334-1600
Michael Waters, prin. Fax 334-6680
Norwich MS 400/6-8
89 Midland Dr 13815 607-334-1600
Scott Ryan, prin. Fax 334-6210

Norwood, Saint Lawrence, Pop. 1,621
Norwood-Norfolk Central SD 1,000/PK-12
7852 State Highway 56 13668 315-353-6631
James Cruikshank, supt. Fax 353-2467
www.nncsk12.org/
Norwood HS 300/9-12
7852 State Highway 56 13668 315-353-6631
Robin Fetter, prin. Fax 353-2480
Norwood-Norfolk MS 300/5-8
7852 State Highway 56 13668 315-353-6631
Jon Sovay, prin.

Nunda, Livingston, Pop. 1,354
Keshequa Central SD 600/PK-12
PO Box 517 14517 585-468-2900
Thomas Kopp, supt. Fax 468-2900
www.keshequa.org
Keshequa HS 200/9-12
PO Box 517 14517 585-468-2900
Peter Reynolds, prin. Fax 468-5493
Keshequa MS 100/7-8
PO Box 517 14517 585-468-2900
Peter Reynolds, prin. Fax 468-5493

Nyack, Rockland, Pop. 6,636
Nyack UFD 2,900/K-12
13A Dickinson Ave 10960 845-353-7000
James Montesano Ed.D., supt. Fax 353-7019
www.nyackschools.com
Nyack MS 700/6-8
98 S Highland Ave 10960 845-353-7200
David Johnson, prin. Fax 353-0506
Other Schools – See Upper Nyack

Alliance Theological Seminary Post-Sec.
350 N Highland Ave 10960 845-353-2020
Nyack College Post-Sec.
1 S Boulevard 10960 845-358-1710

Oakdale, Suffolk, Pop. 7,925
Connetquot Central SD
Supt. — See Bohemia
Oakdale-Bohemia Road MS 800/6-8
60 Oakdale Bohemia Rd 11769 631-244-2268
Susanne Bailey, prin. Fax 563-6167

Dowling College Post-Sec.
150 Idle Hour Blvd 11769 631-244-3000

Oakfield, Genesee, Pop. 1,789
Oakfield-Alabama Central SD 900/PK-12
7001 Lewiston Rd 14125 585-948-5211
Mark Alexander, supt. Fax 948-9362
www.oahornets.org
Oakfield-Alabama MSHS 400/7-12
7001 Lewiston Rd 14125 585-948-5211
Lynn Muscarella, prin. Fax 948-9362

Oakland Gardens, See New York
NYC Department of Education
Supt. — See New York
Cardozo HS 3,600/9-12
5700 223rd St 11364 718-279-6500
Gerald Martori, prin. Fax 631-7880
JHS 74 1,000/6-8
6115 Oceania St 11364 718-631-6800
Anthony Armstrong, prin. Fax 631-6899

Oceanside, Nassau, Pop. 31,810
Oceanside UFD 5,600/PK-12
145 Merle Ave 11572 516-678-1215
Phyllis Harrington, supt. Fax 678-7503
www.oceansideschools.org
Castleton Academy HS 100/Alt
145 Merle Ave 11572 516-678-7593
Brendon Mitchell, prin. Fax 678-7594
Oceanside HS 1,800/9-12
3160 Skillman Ave 11572 516-678-7526
Geraldine DeCarlo, prin. Fax 678-6790
Oceanside MS 900/7-8
186 Alice Ave 11572 516-678-8518
Allison Glickman-Rogers, prin. Fax 594-2365

Hochstim School of Radiography Post-Sec.
PO Box 9007 11572 516-763-2030

Odessa, Schuyler, Pop. 582
Odessa-Montour Central SD 800/PK-12
300 College Ave 14869 607-594-3341
Christopher Wood, supt. Fax 594-3976
www.omschools.org
Odessa-Montour JSHS 300/7-12
300 College Ave 14869 607-594-3341
Almon McCarty, prin. Fax 594-3438

Ogdensburg, Saint Lawrence, Pop. 10,977
Ogdensburg CSD 1,500/PK-12
1100 State St 13669 315-393-0900
Timothy Vernsey, supt. Fax 393-2767
www.ogdensburgk12.org/
Ogdensburg Free Academy 700/7-12
1100 State St 13669 315-393-0900
Cynthia Tuttle, prin. Fax 393-7412

Old Forge, Herkimer, Pop. 747
Town of Webb UFD 300/K-12
PO Box 38 13420 315-369-3222
Rex Germer, supt. Fax 369-6216
www.towschool.org
Town of Webb S 300/K-12
PO Box 38 13420 315-369-3222
John Swick, prin. Fax 369-6216

Old Westbury, Nassau, Pop. 4,556
East Williston UFD 1,700/K-12
11 Bacon Rd 11568 516-333-1630
Dr. Elaine Kanas, supt. Fax 333-1937
www.ewsdonline.org/
Wheatley HS, 11 Bacon Rd 11568 800/8-12
Dr. Sean Feeney, prin. 516-333-7804

Westbury UFD 4,700/PK-12
2 Hitchcock Ln 11568 516-876-5016
Dr. Mary A. Lagnado, supt. Fax 876-5181
www.westburyschools.org
Westbury HS 1,300/9-12
1 Post Rd 11568 516-876-5047
Fax 876-5079
Other Schools – See Westbury

New York Institute of Technology Post-Sec.
PO Box 8000 11568 516-686-1000
SUNY College at Old Westbury Post-Sec.
PO Box 210 11568 516-876-3000

Olean, Cattaraugus, Pop. 14,023
Olean CSD 2,200/PK-12
410 W Sullivan St 14760 716-375-8001
Dr. Colleen Taggerty, supt. Fax 375-8047
www.oleanschools.org
Olean HS 800/8-12
410 W Sullivan St 14760 716-375-8010
Barbara Lias, prin. Fax 375-8048

Archbishop Walsh Academy 100/9-12
208 N 24th St 14760 585-372-8122
Thomas Manko, prin. Fax 372-6707
Continental School of Beauty Culture Post-Sec.
517 N Barry St 14760 716-372-5095
Jamestown Community College- Cattaraugus Post-Sec.
PO Box 5901 14760 716-376-7500

Olmstedville, Essex
Minerva Central SD 100/K-12
PO Box 39 12857 518-251-2000
Timothy Farrell, supt. Fax 251-2395
www.minervasd.org/
Minerva Central S 100/K-12
PO Box 39 12857 518-251-2000
Timothy Farrell, prin. Fax 251-2395

Oneida, Madison, Pop. 11,232
Oneida CSD 2,100/PK-12
PO Box 327 13421 315-363-2550
Ronald Spadafora, supt. Fax 363-6728
www.oneidacsd.org/
Oneida HS 700/9-12
560 Seneca St 13421 315-363-6901
Brian Gallagher, prin. Fax 366-0619
Other Schools – See Wampsville

Oneonta, Otsego, Pop. 13,601
Oneonta CSD 1,600/PK-12
31 Center St 13820 607-433-8200
Joseph Yelich, supt. Fax 433-8290
oneontacsd.org
Oneonta HS 500/9-12
130 East St 13820 607-433-8243
Thomas Brindley, prin. Fax 433-8204
Oneonta MS 300/7-8
130 East St 13820 607-433-8262
Colleen Lewis, prin. Fax 433-8203

Hartwick College Post-Sec.
PO Box 4020 13820 607-431-4000
Lighthouse Christian Academy 50/PK-12
12 Grove St 13820 607-432-2031
Chris Cleveland, admin. Fax 432-3403
Oneonta Community Christian S 100/PK-12
158 River St 13820 607-432-0383
Joseph Rufrano M.A., admin. Fax 436-9137
SUNY College at Oneonta Post-Sec.
108 Ravine Pkwy 13820 607-436-3500
USC The Business College Post-Sec.
17 Elm St 13820 607-432-7003

Ontario Center, Wayne
Wayne Central SD 2,300/K-12
PO Box 155 14520 315-524-1000
Dr. Mathis Calvin, supt. Fax 524-1049
www.wayne.k12.ny.us
Armstrong MS 500/6-8
PO Box 155 14520 315-524-1080
Derek Demass, prin. Fax 524-1119
Beneway HS 800/9-12
PO Box 155 14520 315-524-1050
Michael Pullen, prin. Fax 524-1079

Orangeburg, Rockland, Pop. 4,499
South Orangetown Central SD
Supt. — See Blauvelt
Tappan Zee HS 1,100/9-12
15 Dutch Hill Rd 10962 845-680-1600
Dr. Jennifer Amos, prin. Fax 680-1950

Dominican College of Blauvelt Post-Sec.
470 Western Hwy 10962 845-359-7800
Long Island University-Hudson Grad Ctr Post-Sec.
70 Route 340 10962 845-359-7200

Orchard Park, Erie, Pop. 3,209
Orchard Park Central SD
Supt. — See West Seneca
Orchard Park HS 1,500/9-12
4040 Baker Rd 14127 716-209-6242
Jonathan Wolf, prin. Fax 209-6451
Orchard Park MS 1,300/6-8
60 S Lincoln Ave 14127 716-209-6227
David Lilleck, prin. Fax 209-6338

Bryant & Stratton College Post-Sec.
200 Red Tail 14127 716-677-9500
Erie Community College South Post-Sec.
4041 Southwestern Blvd 14127 716-648-5400

Oriskany, Oneida, Pop. 1,381
Oriskany Central SD 600/K-12
PO Box 539 13424 315-768-2058
Gregory Kelahan, supt. Fax 768-1733
www.oriskanycsd.org
Oriskany JSHS 300/7-12
PO Box 539 13424 315-768-2063
Lisa Krause, prin. Fax 768-4496

Ossining, Westchester, Pop. 24,636
Ossining UFD 4,700/PK-12
190 Croton Ave 10562 914-941-7700
Raymond Sanchez, supt. Fax 941-7291
www.ossiningufsd.org/
Dorner MS 1,000/6-8
Van Cortlandt Ave 10562 914-762-5740
Regina Cellio, prin. Fax 762-5246
Ossining HS 1,300/9-12
29 S Highland Ave 10562 914-762-5760
Joshua Mandel, prin. Fax 762-4011

Oswego, Oswego, Pop. 17,912
Oswego CSD 3,700/K-12
120 E 1st St Ste 1 13126 315-341-2000
David Crisafulli, supt. Fax 341-2910
www.oswego.org
Oswego HS 1,200/9-12
2 Buccaneer Blvd 13126 315-341-2200
Heidi Sweeney, prin. Fax 341-2920
Oswego MS 600/7-8
100 Mark Fitzgibbons Dr 13126 315-341-2300
Mary Fierro, prin. Fax 341-2390

SUNY at Oswego Post-Sec.
7060 State Route 104 13126 315-312-2500

Otego, Otsego, Pop. 991
Unatego Central SD 900/K-12
2641 State Highway 7 13825 607-988-5038
Dr. David S. Richards, supt. Fax 988-1039
www.unatego.org
Unatego HS 300/9-12
2641 State Highway 7 13825 607-988-5098
Julie Lambiaso, prin. Fax 988-1050
Unatego MS 200/6-8
2641 State Highway 7 13825 607-988-5036
Patricia Hoyt, prin. Fax 988-5058

Ovid, Seneca, Pop. 592
South Seneca Central SD 700/PK-12
7263 Main St 14521 607-869-9636
Stephen Zielinski, supt. Fax 532-8540
www.southseneca.com
South Seneca HS 300/9-12
7263 Main St 14521 607-869-9636
Tim Houseknecht, prin. Fax 869-9553
South Seneca MS 200/6-8
7263 Main St 14521 607-869-9636
Tim Houseknecht, prin. Fax 532-9553

Owego, Tioga, Pop. 3,824
Owego-Apalachin Central SD 2,200/PK-12
36 Talcott St 13827 607-687-6224
Dr. William Russell, supt. Fax 687-6313
www.oacsd.org
Owego-Apalachin MS 500/5-8
3 Sheldon Guile Blvd 13827 607-687-6248
Thomas Beatty, prin. Fax 687-6593
Owego Free Academy 700/9-12
1 Sheldon Guile Blvd 13827 607-687-6230
Heath Georgia, prin. Fax 687-6244

Oxford, Chenango, Pop. 1,425
Oxford Academy & Central SD 800/PK-12
PO Box 192 13830 607-843-2025
Shawn Bissetta, supt. Fax 843-3241
www.oxac.org
Oxford Academy HS 200/9-12
PO Box 192 13830 607-843-2025
Janet Laytham, prin. Fax 843-3231
Oxford Academy MS 200/5-8
PO Box 192 13830 607-843-2025
Kathleen Hansen, prin. Fax 843-3241

Oyster Bay, Nassau, Pop. 6,598
Oyster Bay-East Norwich Central SD 1,600/PK-12
1 McCouns Ln 11771 516-624-6505
Dr. Laura Seinfeld, supt. Fax 624-6520
obenschools.org
Oyster Bay JSHS 700/7-12
150 E Main St 11771 516-624-6524
Dr. Dennis O'Hara, prin. Fax 624-6684

St. Dominic HS 400/9-12
110 Anstice St 11771 516-922-4888
Dr. Denise Smith, prin. Fax 922-4898

Ozone Park, See New York
NYC Department of Education
Supt. — See New York
Adams HS 2,800/9-12
10101 Rockaway Blvd 11417 718-322-0500
Daniel Scanlon, prin. Fax 738-9077
Goddard HS of Communication Arts & Tech. 600/9-12
13830 Lafayette St 11417 718-848-8357
Joseph Birgeles, prin. Fax 848-8579
HS for Construction Engineering & Arch 900/9-12
9406 104th St 11416 718-846-6280
Lakesha Gordon, prin. Fax 846-6283
JHS 202 1,000/6-8
13830 Lafayette St 11417 718-848-0001
William Fitzgerald, prin. Fax 848-8082
JHS 210 1,900/6-8
9311 101st Ave 11416 718-845-5942
Bonnie Butcher, prin. Fax 845-4037
MS 137 1,900/6-8
10915 98th St 11417 718-659-0471
Laura Mastrogiovanni, prin. Fax 659-4594

Painted Post, Steuben, Pop. 1,780
Corning CSD 4,000/K-12
165 Charles St 14870 607-936-3704
Michael Ginalski, supt. Fax 654-2735
www.corningareaschools.com
Corning - Painted Post MS 1,100/6-8
35 Victory Hwy 14870 607-654-2966
Richard Kimble, prin. Fax 654-2908
Other Schools – See Corning

Palmyra, Wayne, Pop. 3,491
Palmyra-Macedon Central SD 1,900/K-12
151 Hyde Pkwy 14522 315-597-3400
Dr. Robert Ike, supt. Fax 597-3898
www.palmaccsd.org
Palmyra-Macedon HS 600/9-12
151 Hyde Pkwy 14522 315-597-3400
Andrew Wahl, prin. Fax 597-3425
Palmyra-Macedon MS 400/6-8
163 Hyde Pkwy 14522 315-597-3400
Darcy Smith, prin. Fax 597-3460

East Palmyra Christian S 100/PK-12
2023 E Palmyra Port Gibson 14522 315-597-4400
Keith Vanderzwan, prin. Fax 597-9717

Panama, Chautauqua, Pop. 475
Panama Central SD 500/PK-12
41 North St 14767 716-782-2455
Bert Lictus, supt. Fax 782-4674
www.pancent.org
Panama Central S 300/7-12
41 North St 14767 716-782-2455
Stephanie Lackie, prin. Fax 782-4674

Parish, Oswego, Pop. 445
Altmar-Parish-Williamstown Central SD 1,300/PK-12
PO Box 97 13131 315-625-5251
Anita Murphy, supt. Fax 625-7952
www.apw.cnyric.org
Altmar-Parish-Williamstown JSHS 600/7-12
PO Box 97 13131 315-625-5222
Michelle Crisafulli, prin. Fax 625-4638

Parishville, Saint Lawrence, Pop. 641
Parishville-Hopkinton Central SD 500/PK-12
PO Box 187 13672 315-265-4642
Darin Saiff, supt. Fax 268-1309
phcs.neric.org
Parishville-Hopkinton JSHS 200/7-12
PO Box 187 13672 315-265-4642
Virginia Doll, prin. Fax 268-1309

Patchogue, Suffolk, Pop. 11,620
Patchogue-Medford UFD 7,100/PK-12
241 S Ocean Ave 11772 631-687-6300
Michael Hynes Ph.D., supt.
www.pmschools.org
Saxton MS 700/6-9
121 Saxton St 11772 631-687-6700
Manuel Sanzone, prin. Fax 687-6740
South Ocean MS 500/6-9
225 S Ocean Ave 11772 631-687-6600
Timothy Piciullo, prin.
Other Schools – See Medford

Briarcliffe College Post-Sec.
225 W Main St 11772 631-654-5300
St. Joseph's College New York Post-Sec.
155 W Roe Blvd 11772 631-687-5100

Patterson, Putnam
Carmel Central SD 4,300/K-12
PO Box 296 12563 845-878-2094
Andy Irvin, supt. Fax 878-2566
www.carmelschools.org
Other Schools – See Carmel

Paul Smiths, Franklin, Pop. 664

Paul Smith's College Post-Sec.
PO Box 265 12970 518-327-6227

Pavilion, Genesee, Pop. 644
Pavilion Central SD 700/PK-12
7014 Big Tree Rd 14525 585-584-3115
Kenneth Ellison, supt. Fax 584-3421
www.pavilioncsd.org
Pavilion JSHS 400/6-12
7014 Big Tree Rd 14525 585-584-3070
Dr. Sheila Eigenbrod, prin. Fax 584-3421

Pawling, Dutchess, Pop. 2,332
Pawling Central SD 1,200/K-12
515 Route 22 12564 845-855-4600
Dr. William M. Ward, supt. Fax 855-4659
www.pawlingschools.org
Pawling HS 400/9-12
30 Wagner Dr 12564 845-855-4620
Helen Callan, prin. Fax 855-4621
Pawling MS 400/5-8
80 Wagner Dr 12564 845-855-4653
Allan Lipsky, prin. Fax 855-4131

Trinity-Pawling S 300/7-12
700 Route 22 12564 845-855-3100
William Taylor, hdmstr. Fax 855-3816

Pearl River, Rockland, Pop. 15,720
Pearl River UFD 2,600/K-12
135 W Crooked Hill Rd 10965 845-620-3900
Marco Pochintesta, supt. Fax 620-3927
www.pearlriver.org
Pearl River HS 1,000/8-12
275 E Central Ave 10965 845-620-3800
Michael Murphy, prin. Fax 620-3852

Iona College Rockland Graduate Center Post-Sec.
PO Box 1522 10965 845-620-1350

Peekskill, Westchester, Pop. 22,929
Peekskill CSD 3,200/PK-12
1031 Elm St 10566 914-737-3300
Dr. David Fine, supt. Fax 737-3912
www.peekskillcsd.org
Peekskill HS 800/9-12
1072 Elm St 10566 914-737-0201
Cassandra Hyacinthe, prin. Fax 737-2550
Peekskill MS 700/6-8
212 Ringgold St 10566 914-737-4542
Jamal Lewis, prin. Fax 737-3253

Northern Westchester Sch of Hairdressing Post-Sec.
19 Bank St 10566 914-739-8400

Pelham, Westchester, Pop. 6,710
Pelham UFD 2,800/K-12
18 Franklin Pl 10803 914-738-3434
Dr. Peter Giarrizzo, supt. Fax 738-7223
www.pelhamschools.org
Pelham Memorial HS 800/9-12
575 Colonial Ave 10803 914-738-8110
Jeannine Clark, prin. Fax 738-8122
Pelham MS 700/6-8
28 Franklin Pl 10803 914-738-8190
Dr. Robert Roelle, prin. Fax 738-8132

Penfield, Monroe, Pop. 30,219
Penfield Central SD
Supt. — See Rochester
Bay Trail MS 1,100/6-8
1760 Scribner Rd 14526 585-249-6450
Winton Buddington, prin. Fax 248-0735
Penfield HS 1,400/9-12
25 High School Dr 14526 585-249-6700
Dr. Leslie Maloney Ed.D., prin. Fax 248-2810

Finney S 200/K-12
2070 Five Mile Line Rd 14526 585-387-3770
Michael VanLeeuwen, pres. Fax 387-3771

Penn Yan, Yates, Pop. 5,081
Penn Yan Central SD 1,500/PK-12
1 School Dr 14527 315-536-3371
Howard Dennis, supt. Fax 536-0068
www.pycsd.org
Penn Yan Academy 600/9-12
305 Court St 14527 315-536-4408
David Pullen, prin. Fax 536-0341
Penn Yan MS 300/6-8
515 Liberty St 14527 315-536-3366
Kelley Johnson, prin. Fax 536-7769

Perry, Wyoming, Pop. 3,633
Perry Central SD 600/PK-12
33 Watkins Ave 14530 585-237-0270
Daryl McLaughlin, supt. Fax 237-6172
www.perry.k12.ny.us
Perry JSHS 300/7-12
33 Watkins Ave 14530 585-237-0270
Rebecca Belkota, admin. Fax 237-6350

Peru, Clinton, Pop. 1,580
Peru Central SD 1,900/K-12
PO Box 68 12972 518-643-6000
Dr. Patrick Brimstein, supt. Fax 643-2043
www.perucsd.org
Peru JSHS 1,000/7-12
PO Box 68 12972 518-643-6400
Christopher Mazzella, prin. Fax 643-6438

Philadelphia, Jefferson, Pop. 1,192
Indian River Central SD 4,200/PK-12
32735 County Route 29 Ste B 13673 315-642-3441
James Kettrick, supt. Fax 642-3738
www.ircsd.org
Indian River HS 900/9-12
32925 US Route 11 13673 315-642-3427
Troy Decker, prin. Fax 642-5658
Indian River MS 900/6-8
32735 County Route 29 Ste A 13673 315-642-0125
Nancy Taylor-Schmitt, prin. Fax 642-0802

Phoenix, Oswego, Pop. 2,343
Phoenix Central SD 1,700/K-12
116 Volney St 13135 315-695-1555
Judy Belfield, supt. Fax 695-1201
www.phoenixcsd.org
Birdlebough HS 600/9-12
552 Main St 13135 315-695-1631
Gregory Molloy, prin. Fax 695-1618
Dillon MS 400/6-8
116 Volney St 13135 315-695-1521
Susan Anderson, prin. Fax 695-1523

Pine Bush, Orange, Pop. 1,744
Pine Bush Central SD 5,500/PK-12
PO Box 700 12566 845-744-2031
Joan M. Carbone, supt. Fax 744-6189
www.pinebushschools.org
Crispell MS 700/6-8
PO Box 780 12566 845-744-2031
John Boyle, prin. Fax 744-2261
Pine Bush HS 1,800/9-12
PO Box 670 12566 845-744-2031
Aaron Hopmayer, prin. Fax 744-3488
Other Schools – See Circleville

AEF Chapel Field S 100/PK-12
211 Fleury Rd 12566 845-778-1881

Pine Plains, Dutchess, Pop. 1,324
Pine Plains Central SD 900/PK-12
2829 Church St 12567 518-398-7181
Dr. Martin Handler Ed.D., supt. Fax 398-6592
www.ppcsd.org
Stissing Mountain HS 300/9-12
2829 Church St 12567 518-398-7181
Tara Grieb, prin. Fax 398-6592
Stissing Mountain MS 300/6-8
2829 Church St 12567 518-398-7181
James DiDonna, prin. Fax 398-6592

Pittsford, Monroe, Pop. 1,344
Pittsford Central SD 5,800/K-12
75 Barker Rd 14534 585-267-1000
Michael Pero, supt. Fax 267-1088
www.pittsfordschools.org
Barker Road MS 800/6-8
75 Barker Rd 14534 585-267-1800
Shana Cutaia, prin. Fax 385-5960
Calkins Road MS 700/6-8
1899 Calkins Rd 14534 585-267-1900
Joshua Walker, prin. Fax 264-0053
Pittsford-Mendon HS 1,000/9-12
472 Mendon Rd 14534 585-267-1600
Karl Thielking, prin. Fax 267-1679
Pittsford Sutherland HS 1,000/9-12
55 Sutherland St 14534 585-267-1100
Brian Weller, prin. Fax 381-7687

Plainview, Nassau, Pop. 25,853
Plainview-Old Bethpage Central SD 4,800/K-12
106 Washington Ave 11803 516-434-3000
Dr. Lorna R. Lewis, supt. Fax 937-6303
www.pobschools.org
Mattlin MS 800/5-8
100 Washington Ave 11803 516-434-3250
Christopher Donarummo, prin. Fax 937-6431
Plainview-Old Bethpage/JFK HS 1,500/9-12
50 Kennedy Dr 11803 516-434-3125
James Murray, prin. Fax 937-6433
Plainview-Old Bethpage MS 800/5-8
121 Central Park Rd 11803 516-434-3308
Alice Bowman, prin. Fax 349-4777

Plattsburgh, Clinton, Pop. 19,572
Plattsburgh CSD 1,800/PK-12
49 Broad St 12901 518-957-6002
James Short, supt. Fax 561-6605
www.plattscsd.org/
Plattsburgh HS 500/9-12
1 Clifford Dr 12901 518-561-7500
Glenn Hurlock, prin. Fax 561-1895
Stafford MS 400/6-8
15 Broad St 12901 518-563-6800
Jamie Labarge, prin. Fax 563-8520

Champlain Valley Physicians Hospital Post-Sec.
75 Beekman St 12901 518-561-2000
Seton Catholic Central JSHS 100/6-12
206 New York Rd 12903 518-561-4031
Lynn Gilbert, prin. Fax 563-1193
SUNY Clinton Community College Post-Sec.
136 Clinton Point Dr 12901 518-562-4200
SUNY College at Plattsburgh Post-Sec.
101 Broad St 12901 518-564-2000

Pleasantville, Westchester, Pop. 6,927
Pleasantville UFD 1,700/K-12
60 Romer Ave 10570 914-741-1400
Mary Fox-Alter, supt. Fax 741-1499
www.pleasantvilleschools.com
Pleasantville HS 600/9-12
60 Romer Ave 10570 914-741-1420
Joseph Palumbo, prin. Fax 741-2546
Pleasantville MS 500/5-8
40 Romer Ave 10570 914-741-1450
Vivian Ossowski, prin. Fax 741-1476

Poland, Herkimer, Pop. 505
Poland Central SD 600/PK-12
PO Box 8 13431 315-826-7900
Laura Dutton, supt. Fax 826-7516
www.polandcs.org
Poland JSHS 300/6-12
PO Box 8 13431 315-826-7900
Gregory Cuthbertson, prin. Fax 826-7516

Port Byron, Cayuga, Pop. 1,272
Port Byron Central SD 1,000/K-12
30 Maple Ave 13140 315-776-5728
Neil O'Brien, supt. Fax 776-4050
pbcschools.org
West HS 500/7-12
30 Maple Ave 13140 315-776-5728
Thomas Vaughan, prin. Fax 776-4050

Port Chester, Westchester, Pop. 28,517
Port Chester-Rye UFD 4,400/K-12
PO Box 246 10573 914-934-7900
Dr. Edward Kliszus, supt. Fax 934-0727
www.portchesterschools.org
Port Chester HS 1,300/9-12
1 Tamarack Rd 10573 914-934-7950
Dr. Mitchell Combs, prin. Fax 934-2998
Port Chester MS 1,000/6-8
113 Bowman Ave 10573 914-934-7930
Patrick Swift, prin. Fax 934-7886

Port Henry, Essex, Pop. 1,181
Moriah Central SD 700/PK-12
39 Viking Ln 12974 518-546-3301
William Larrow, supt. Fax 546-7895
www.moriahk12.org/
Moriah JSHS 300/7-12
39 Viking Ln 12974 518-546-3301
Alison Burch, prin. Fax 546-7895

Port Jefferson, Suffolk, Pop. 7,650
Port Jefferson UFD 1,200/PK-12
550 Scraggy Hill Rd 11777 631-791-4500
Dr. Kenneth Bossert, supt. Fax 476-4409
www.portjeffschools.org
Port Jefferson MS 300/6-8
350 Old Post Rd 11777 631-791-4400
Robert Neidig, prin. Fax 476-4430
Vandermuelen HS 400/9-12
350 Old Post Rd 11777 631-791-4400
Christine Austen, prin. Fax 476-4408

Port Jefferson Station, Suffolk, Pop. 7,762
Comsewogue SD 3,700/K-12
290 Norwood Ave 11776 631-474-8100
Joseph Rella, supt. Fax 474-3568
www.comsewogue.k12.ny.us
Comsewogue HS 1,200/9-12
565 Bicycle Path 11776 631-474-8178
Joseph Coniglione, prin. Fax 474-8175
Kennedy MS 900/6-8
200 Jayne Blvd 11776 631-474-8160
Michael Fama, prin. Fax 474-8176

Port Jervis, Orange, Pop. 8,515
Port Jervis CSD 2,700/K-12
9 Thompson St 12771 845-858-3100
Thomas Bongiovi, supt. Fax 856-1885
www.pjschools.org
Port Jervis HS 900/9-12
10 Route 209 12771 845-858-3100
Andrew Marotta, prin. Fax 858-2895
Port Jervis MS 500/7-8
118 E Main St 12771 845-858-3100
Jean Fazzino-Lain, prin. Fax 858-2893

Portville, Cattaraugus, Pop. 993
Portville Central SD 1,000/PK-12
PO Box 790 14770 585-933-6000
Mr. Thomas Simon, supt. Fax 933-6774
www.portville.wnyric.org/
Portville JSHS 400/7-12
PO Box 790 14770 585-933-6705
Lawrence Welty, prin. Fax 933-6774

Port Washington, Nassau, Pop. 15,596
Port Washington UFD 5,100/K-12
100 Campus Dr 11050 516-767-5000
Dr. Kathleen Mooney, supt. Fax 767-5007
www.portnet.org
Schreiber HS 1,500/9-12
101 Campus Dr 11050 516-767-5800
Ira Pernick, prin. Fax 767-5807
Weber MS 1,200/6-8
52 Campus Dr 11050 516-767-5500
Christopher Shields, prin. Fax 767-5507

Potsdam, Saint Lawrence, Pop. 9,246
Potsdam Central SD 1,300/PK-12
29 Leroy St 13676 315-265-2000
Joann Chambers, supt. Fax 265-2048
www.potsdam.k12.ny.us
Kingston MS 400/5-8
29 Leroy St 13676 315-265-2000
Mark Bennett, prin. Fax 265-8103
Potsdam HS 400/9-12
29 Leroy St 13676 315-265-2000
Alison Benedict, prin. Fax 265-8134

Clarkson University Post-Sec.
8 Clarkson Ave 13676 315-268-6400
SUNY College at Potsdam Post-Sec.
44 Pierrepont Ave 13676 315-267-2000

Pottersville, Warren, Pop. 420

Word of Life Bible Institute Post-Sec.
PO Box 129 12860 518-494-4723

Poughkeepsie, Dutchess, Pop. 31,635
Poughkeepsie CSD 4,200/PK-12
11 College Ave 12603 845-451-4900
Dr. Nicole Williams, supt. Fax 451-4955
www.poughkeepsieschools.org/
Poughkeepsie HS 1,100/9-12
70 Forbus St 12603 845-451-4850
Phee Simpson, prin. Fax 451-4853
Poughkeepsie MS 1,000/6-8
55 College Ave 12603 845-451-4800
Crystal Waterman, prin. Fax 451-4836

Spackenkill UFD 1,500/K-12
15 Croft Rd 12603 845-463-7800
Dr. Lois Powell Ed.D., supt. Fax 463-7804
www.sufsdny.org
Spackenkill HS 500/9-12
112 Spackenkill Rd 12603 845-463-7810
Steven Malkischer, prin. Fax 463-7826
Todd MS 400/6-8
11 Croft Rd 12603 845-463-7830
Dan Doherty, prin. Fax 463-7832

Dutchess Community College Post-Sec.
53 Pendell Rd 12601 845-431-8000
Faith Christian Academy 300/PK-12
25 Golf Club Ln 12601 845-462-0266
Alexander Averin, hdmstr. Fax 462-1561
Marist College Post-Sec.
3399 North Rd 12601 845-575-3000
Oakwood Friends S 100/6-12
22 Spackenkill Rd 12603 845-462-4200
Chad Cianfrani, head sch Fax 462-4251
Our Lady of Lourdes HS 700/9-12
131 Boardman Rd 12603 845-463-0400
Catherine Merryman, prin. Fax 463-0174
Poughkeepsie Day S 300/PK-12
260 Boardman Rd 12603 845-462-7600
Josie Holford, head sch Fax 462-7603
Ridley-Lowell Business & Technical Inst. Post-Sec.
26 S Hamilton St 12601 845-471-0330
Tabernacle Christian Academy 100/K-12
155 Academy St 12601 845-454-2792
Timothy Hostetter, prin. Fax 483-0926
Vassar College Post-Sec.
124 Raymond Ave 12604 845-437-7000

Prattsburgh, Steuben, Pop. 649
Prattsburgh Central SD 400/PK-12
1 Academy St 14873 607-522-3795
Jeffrey Black, supt. Fax 522-6221
www.prattsburghcsd.org/
Prattsburg Central S 400/PK-12
1 Academy St 14873 607-522-3795
Thomas Crook, supt. Fax 522-6221

Pulaski, Oswego, Pop. 2,352
Pulaski Central SD 1,100/PK-12
2 Hinman Rd 13142 315-298-5188
Brian Hartwell, supt. Fax 298-4390
www.pacs.cnyric.org
Pulaski HS 300/9-12
4624 Salina St 13142 315-298-5103
Fax 298-2371
Pulaski MS 300/6-8
4624 Salina St 13142 315-298-6001
Michael Bateson, prin. Fax 298-2371

Purchase, See Harrison

Keio Academy of New York 300/9-12
3 College Rd 10577 914-694-4825
Fumihiko Kono, hdmstr. Fax 694-4830
Long Island University Post-Sec.
735 Anderson Hill Rd 10577 914-831-2700
Manhattanville College Post-Sec.
2900 Purchase St 10577 914-694-2200
SUNY Purchase College Post-Sec.
735 Anderson Hill Rd 10577 914-251-6000

Putnam Valley, Putnam
Putnam Valley Central SD 1,800/K-12
146 Peekskill Hollow Rd 10579 845-528-8143
Dr. Frances Wills, supt. Fax 528-8386
www.pvcsd.org
Putnam Valley HS 600/9-12
146 Peekskill Hollow Rd 10579 845-526-7847
Sandra Intrieri, prin. Fax 528-4456
Putnam Valley MS 500/5-8
142 Peekskill Hollow Rd 10579 845-528-8101
Edward Hallisey, prin. Fax 528-8145

Queensbury, Warren
Queensbury UFD 3,400/K-12
429 Aviation Rd 12804 518-824-5600
Dr. Douglas Huntley, supt. Fax 793-4476
www.queensburyschool.org/
Queensbury HS 1,200/9-12
409 Aviation Rd 12804 518-824-4626
Damian Switzer, prin. Fax 824-4680
Queensbury MS 800/6-8
455 Aviation Rd 12804 518-824-3610
Michael Brannigan, prin. Fax 824-3682

SUNY Adirondack Post-Sec.
640 Bay Rd 12804 518-743-2200

Queens Village, See New York
NYC Department of Education
Supt. — See New York
Business Technology Early College HS 9-12
23017 Hillside Ave 11427 718-216-3613
Hoa Tu, prin. Fax 216-3616
Nuzzi IS 1,100/6-8
21310 92nd Ave 11428 718-465-0651
Karleen Comrie, prin. Fax 264-1246
Van Buren HS 2,100/9-12
23017 Hillside Ave 11427 718-776-4728
Sam Sochet, prin. Fax 217-6287

Randolph, Cattaraugus, Pop. 1,268
Randolph Central SD 900/PK-12
18 Main St 14772 716-358-7005
Kimberly Moritz, supt. Fax 358-7072
www.randolphcsd.org
Randolph JSHS 400/7-12
18 Main St 14772 716-358-7007
Jason Halpainy, prin. Fax 358-7072

Ravena, Albany, Pop. 3,205
Ravena-Coeymans-Selkirk Central SD 1,900/PK-12
15 Mountain Rd 12143 518-756-5200
Robert Libby, supt. Fax 767-2644
www.rcscsd.org
Ravena-Coeymans-Selkirk HS 600/9-12
2025 US Route 9W 12143 518-756-5200
Thomas Diacetis, prin. Fax 756-3534
Ravena-Coeymans-Selkirk MS 400/5-8
2025 US Route 9W 12143 518-756-5200
Pam Black, prin. Fax 756-1988

Red Creek, Wayne, Pop. 530
Red Creek Central SD 900/K-12
PO Box 190 13143 315-754-2010
David Sholes, supt. Fax 754-8169
www.rccsd.org
Red Creek HS 300/9-12
PO Box 190 13143 315-754-2040
Timothy Gaffney, prin. Fax 754-2068
Red Creek MS 200/6-8
PO Box 190 13143 315-754-2070
Matthew Vanorman, prin. Fax 754-2077

Red Hook, Dutchess, Pop. 1,942
Red Hook Central SD 2,000/K-12
9 Mill Rd 12571 845-758-2241
Paul Finch Ed.D., supt. Fax 758-3366
www.redhookcentralschools.org/
Linden Avenue MS 500/6-8
65 W Market St 12571 845-758-2241
Dr. Katie Zahedi, prin. Fax 758-0688
Red Hook HS 700/9-12
103 W Market St 12571 845-758-2241
Roy Paisley, prin. Fax 758-0482

Devereux Center in New York Post-Sec.
40 Devereux Way 12571 845-758-1899

Rego Park, See New York
NYC Department of Education
Supt. — See New York
JHS 157 1,400/6-9
6355 102nd St 11374 718-830-4910
Vincent Suraci, prin. Fax 830-4993

Metropolitan Learning Institute Post-Sec.
9777 Queens Blvd Ste 900 11374 718-897-0482
Midrash L'man Achai 100/7-12
9730 Queens Blvd 11374 718-544-4875
Rabbi Shmuel Kleinman, prin. Fax 438-6636
St. Paul's School of Nursing Post-Sec.
9777 Queens Blvd 11374 718-357-0500

Remsen, Oneida, Pop. 502
Remsen Central SD 400/PK-12
PO Box 406 13438 315-831-3797
William Crankshaw, supt. Fax 831-2172
www.remsencsd.org
Remsen JSHS 200/7-12
PO Box 406 13438 315-831-3851
Dale Turner, prin. Fax 831-2172

Rensselaer, Rensselaer, Pop. 9,055
Rensselaer CSD 1,100/PK-12
25 Van Rensselaer Dr 12144 518-465-7509
Sally Ann Shields, supt. Fax 436-0479
www.rcsd.k12.ny.us
Rensselaer JSHS 400/7-12
25 Van Rensselaer Dr 12144 518-436-8561
Karen Urbanski, prin. Fax 436-8563

Doane Stuart S 300/PK-12
199 Washington Ave 12144 518-465-5222
Pamela Clarke, head sch Fax 465-5230

Retsof, Livingston, Pop. 330
York Central SD 700/K-12
PO Box 102 14539 585-243-1730
Dr. Daniel Murray, supt. Fax 243-5269
www.yorkcsd.org/
York MSHS 300/7-12
PO Box 102 14539 585-243-1730
David Sylvester, prin. Fax 243-5269

Rhinebeck, Dutchess, Pop. 2,623
Rhinebeck Central SD 1,100/K-12
PO Box 351 12572 845-871-5520
Joseph Phelan, supt. Fax 876-4276
www.rhinebeckcsd.org/
Bulkeley MS 300/6-8
PO Box 351 12572 845-871-5500
John Kemnitzer, prin. Fax 871-5553
Rhinebeck HS 400/9-12
PO Box 351 12572 845-871-5500
Dr. Edwin Davenport, prin. Fax 876-8755

Richfield Springs, Otsego, Pop. 1,252
Richfield Springs Central SD 500/PK-12
PO Box 631 13439 315-858-0610
Tom Piatti, supt. Fax 858-2440
www.richfieldcsd.org
Richfield Springs Central S 500/PK-12
PO Box 631 13439 315-858-0610
Therijo Climenhaga, prin. Fax 858-2440

Richmond Hill, See New York
NYC Department of Education
Supt. — See New York
Epic HS - North 9-12
9425 117th St, S Richmond Hl NY 11419
David Weinberg, prin. 718-570-8230
Richmond Hill HS 2,200/9-12
8930 114th St 11418 718-846-3335
Neil Ganesh, prin. Fax 847-0980

Yeshiva Shaar HaTorah - Grodno Post-Sec.
8396 117th St 11418 718-846-1940

Richmondville, Schoharie, Pop. 910
Cobleskill-Richmondville Central SD
Supt. — See Cobleskill
Cobleskill-Richmondville HS 600/9-12
1353 State Route 7 12149 518-234-3565
Melissa Ausfeld, prin. Fax 234-1018

Ridgewood, See New York
NYC Department of Education
Supt. — See New York
Cleveland HS 1,800/9-12
2127 Himrod St 11385 718-381-9600
Denise Vittor, prin. Fax 417-8457
IS 77 1,100/6-8
976 Seneca Ave 11385 718-366-7120
Joseph Miller, prin. Fax 456-9512
IS 93 1,200/6-8
6656 Forest Ave 11385 718-821-4882
Edward Santos, prin. Fax 456-9521

Midway Paris Beauty School Post-Sec.
5440 Myrtle Ave 11385 718-418-2790

Riverdale, See New York

College of Mount Saint Vincent Post-Sec.
6301 Riverdale Ave 10471 718-405-3267
Manhattan College Post-Sec.
4513 Manhattan College Pkwy 10471 718-862-8000
Yeshiva of Telshe Alumni 100/9-12
4904 Independence Ave 10471 718-601-3523
Yeshiva Ohavei Torah of Riverdale 100/9-12
450 W 250th St 10471 718-432-2600
David Levine, prin. Fax 548-4106

Riverhead, Suffolk, Pop. 12,979
Riverhead Central SD 5,000/K-12
700 Osborn Ave 11901 631-369-6700
Nancy Carney, supt. Fax 369-6816
www.riverhead.net
Riverhead HS 1,500/9-12
700 Harrison Ave 11901 631-369-6723
Charles Regan, prin. Fax 369-5164
Riverhead MS 700/7-8
600 Harrison Ave 11901 631-369-6759
Andrea Pekar, prin. Fax 369-6829

Central Suffolk Hospital Post-Sec.
1300 Roanoke Ave 11901 631-548-6000
Long Island University Post-Sec.
121 Speonk Riverhead Rd 11901 631-287-8010
McGann-Mercy HS 500/7-12
1225 Ostrander Ave 11901 631-727-5900
Carl Semmler, prin. Fax 369-7328
Suffolk County Community College Post-Sec.
121 Speonk Riverhead Rd 11901 631-548-2500

Rochester, Monroe, Pop. 203,996
Brighton Central SD 3,500/K-12
2035 Monroe Ave 14618 585-242-5200
Dr. Kevin McGowan, supt. Fax 242-5164
www.bcsd.org
Brighton HS 1,100/9-12
1150 Winton Rd S 14618 585-242-5000
Thomas Hall, prin. Fax 242-7364
Twelve Corners MS 800/6-8
2643 Elmwood Ave 14618 585-242-5100
Rob Thomas, prin. Fax 242-2540

East Irondequoit Central SD 2,900/K-12
600 Pardee Rd 14609 585-339-1210
Susan Allen, supt. Fax 339-1219
www.eastiron.org
East Irondequoit MS 700/6-8
155 Densmore Rd 14609 585-339-1400
Lori Garsin, prin. Fax 339-1409
Eastridge HS 900/9-12
2350 E Ridge Rd 14622 585-339-1450
Mary Grow, prin. Fax 339-1459

Gates-Chili Central SD 4,100/K-12
3 Spartan Way 14624 585-247-5050
Kimberle Ward, supt. Fax 340-1072
www.gateschili.org
Gates-Chili HS 1,400/9-12
1 Spartan Way 14624 585-247-5050
Kenneth Hammel, prin. Fax 340-5518
Gates-Chili MS 1,000/6-8
2 Spartan Way 14624 585-247-5050
Dr. Lisa Buckshaw, prin. Fax 340-5532

Greece Central SD 10,400/PK-12
750 Maiden Ln 14615 585-966-2000
Kathleen Graupman, supt. Fax 581-8203
www.greececsd.org
Arcadia HS 1,100/9-12
120 Island Cottage Rd 14612 585-966-3000
Gina Larsen, prin. Fax 966-3039
Arcadia MS 800/6-8
130 Island Cottage Rd 14612 585-966-3300
Brian Lumb, prin. Fax 966-3339
Athena HS 1,200/9-12
800 Long Pond Rd 14612 585-966-4000
David Richardson, prin. Fax 966-4039
Athena MS 800/6-8
800 Long Pond Rd 14612 585-966-8800
Jason Fulkerson, prin. Fax 966-4039
Odyssey Academy 1,100/6-12
750 Maiden Ln 14615 585-966-5500
Jeffrey Green, prin. Fax 966-5539
Olympia HS 800/9-12
1139 Maiden Ln 14615 585-966-5000
Marc Fleming, prin. Fax 966-5039

Penfield Central SD 4,400/K-12
2590 Atlantic Ave 14625 585-249-5700
Dr. Thomas K. Putnam Ed.D., supt. Fax 248-8412
www.penfield.edu
Other Schools – See Penfield

Rochester CSD 28,000/PK-12
131 W Broad St 14614 585-262-8100
Dr. Bolgen Vargas, supt. Fax 262-8381
www.rcsdk12.org
All City HS 1,000/Alt
175 Martin St 14605 585-458-2110
Armando Ramirez, prin. Fax 277-0077
Charlotte HS 300/10-12
4115 Lake Ave 14612 585-663-7070
Michael Allen, prin. Fax 621-0275
East HS 1,700/6-12
1801 E Main St 14609 585-288-3130
Anibal Soler, prin. Fax 654-1066
Edison Career and Technology HS 600/9-12
655 Colfax St 14606 585-324-9700
Walter Larkin, prin.
Integrated Arts & Technology HS 400/7-12
950 Norton St 14621 585-324-3750
Kevin Klein, prin.
Leadership Academy for Young Men 300/7-12
4115 Lake Ave 14612 585-324-7760
Wakili Moore, prin.
Monroe HS 1,100/7-12
180 Ridgeway Ave 14615 585-232-1530
Vicma Ramos, prin. Fax 262-8965
Northeast College HS 400/9-12
940 Fernwood Park 14609 585-324-9273
Dr. Linus Guillory, prin.
Northwest JHS at Douglass 300/7-8
940 Fernwood Park 14609 585-324-9289
Barbara Fagan-Zelazny, prin.
Rochester Early College International HS 300/9-12
200 Genesee St 14611 585-324-9010
Sandra Jordan, prin.
School of the Arts 1,100/7-12
45 Prince St 14607 585-242-7682
Brenda Pacheco, prin. Fax 256-6580
School Without Walls Commencement Acad 300/9-12
480 Broadway 14607 585-546-6732
Idonia Owens, prin. Fax 262-8947
Vanguard Collegiate HS 400/9-12
950 Norton St 14621 585-324-3760
Bonnie Atkins, prin.
Wilson Magnet HS Commencement Academy 900/9-12
501 Genesee St 14611 585-328-3440
Uma Mehta, prin. Fax 464-6153
World of Inquiry S 58 700/K-12
200 University Ave 14605 585-325-6170
Sheelarani Webster, prin. Fax 262-8964

West Irondequoit Central SD 3,600/K-12
321 List Ave 14617 585-342-5500
Jeffrey Crane, supt. Fax 266-1556
www.westirondequoit.org
Dake JHS 600/7-8
350 Cooper Rd 14617 585-342-2140
Michelle Cramer, prin. Fax 336-3034
Irondequoit HS 1,200/9-12
260 Cooper Rd 14617 585-336-2914
Douglas Lauf, prin. Fax 336-2929

Allendale Columbia S 300/PK-12
519 Allens Creek Rd 14618 585-381-4560
Michael Gee, head sch Fax 383-1191
Aquinas Institute 900/6-12
1127 Dewey Ave 14613 585-254-2020
Theodore Mancini, prin. Fax 254-7401
Bishop Kearney HS 500/6-12
125 Kings Hwy S 14617 585-342-4000
Jason Simoni, prin. Fax 342-4694
Bryant & Stratton College Post-Sec.
854 Long Pond Rd 14612 585-720-0660
Bryant & Stratton College Post-Sec.
1225 Jeffson Rd 14623 585-292-5627
Colgate Rochester Crozer Divinity School Post-Sec.
1100 Goodman St S 14620 585-271-1320
Continental School Post-Sec.
633 Jefferson Rd 14623 585-272-8060
David Hochstein School of Music & Dance Post-Sec.
50 Plymouth Ave N 14614 585-454-4596
Everest Institute Post-Sec.
1630 Portland Ave 14621 585-266-0430
Harley S 500/PK-12
1981 Clover St 14618 585-442-1770
Ward Ghory Ed.D., head sch Fax 442-5758
McQuaid Jesuit HS 800/6-12
1800 Clinton Ave S 14618 585-473-1130
Adam Baber, prin. Fax 256-6171

Monroe Community College Post-Sec.
1000 E Henrietta Rd 14623 585-292-2000
Nativity Preparatory Academy 5-8
15 Whalin St 14620 585-271-1633
Rebecca Maloney, prin. Fax 271-1633
Nazareth College of Rochester Post-Sec.
4245 East Ave 14618 585-389-2525
Northeastern Seminary Post-Sec.
2265 Westside Dr 14624 585-594-6800
Northstar Christian Academy 300/PK-12
332 Spencerport Rd 14606 585-429-5530
Onondaga School of Therapeutic Massage Post-Sec.
302 Goodman St N Ste 200 14607 585-241-0070
Ora Academy 50/9-12
139 Winton Rd S 14610 585-271-8711
Our Lady of Mercy HS 700/6-12
1437 Blossom Rd 14610 585-288-7120
Terence Quinn, prin. Fax 288-7966
Roberts Wesleyan College Post-Sec.
2301 Westside Dr 14624 585-594-6000
Rochester General Hospital Post-Sec.
1425 Portland Ave 14621 585-338-4430
Rochester Institute of Technology Post-Sec.
1 Lomb Memorial Dr 14623 585-475-2411
Rochester School for the Deaf Post-Sec.
1545 Saint Paul St 14621 585-544-1240
St. Bernard's Sch of Theology & Ministry Post-Sec.
120 French Rd 14618 585-271-3657
St. John Fisher College Post-Sec.
3690 East Ave 14618 585-385-8000
Shear Ego Intl School of Hair Design Post-Sec.
525 Titus Ave 14617 585-342-0070
Siena Catholic Academy 300/6-8
2617 East Ave 14610 585-381-1220
Martin Kilbridge, prin. Fax 381-1223
Talmudical Institute of Upstate New York Post-Sec.
769 Park Ave 14607 585-473-2810
Talmudical Institute of Upstate New York 50/9-12
769 Park Ave 14607 585-473-2810
University of Rochester Post-Sec.
500 Joseph C Wilson Blvd 14627 585-275-2121

Rockaway Park, See New York
NYC Department of Education
Supt. — See New York
Channel View S for Research 600/6-12
10000 Beach Channel Dr 11694 718-634-1970
Denise Harper-Richards, prin. Fax 634-2896
Rockaway Collegiate HS 9-12
10000 Beach Channel Dr 11694 718-734-3290
Carol Ying, prin. Fax 634-3043
Rockaway Park HS for Environmental Sust 100/9-12
10000 Beach Channel Dr 11694 718-734-3280
Jennifer Connolly, prin. Fax 318-6176
Scholars Academy 1,300/6-12
320 Beach 104th St 11694 718-474-6918
Brian O'Connell, prin. Fax 945-8958
Waterside S for Leadership 200/6-8
190 Beach 110th St 11694 718-634-1128
Linda Munro, prin. Fax 634-1185

Rockville Centre, Nassau, Pop. 23,734
Rockville Centre UFD 3,500/K-12
128 Shepherd St 11570 516-255-8957
Dr. William H. Johnson, supt. Fax 255-8810
www.rvcschools.org
South Side HS 1,100/9-12
140 Shepherd St 11570 516-255-8944
John Murphy, prin. Fax 766-7934
South Side MS 800/6-8
67 Hillside Ave 11570 516-255-8976
Shelagh McGinn, prin. Fax 763-0914

Mercy Medical Center Post-Sec.
PO Box 9024 11571 516-705-2525
Molloy College Post-Sec.
PO Box 5002 11571 516-323-4000

Rocky Point, Suffolk, Pop. 13,836
Rocky Point UFD 3,300/K-12
90 Rocky Point Yaphank Rd 11778 631-744-1600
Dr. Michael Ring, supt. Fax 849-7557
www.rockypointschools.org
Rocky Point HS 1,100/9-12
82 Rocky Point Yaphank Rd 11778 631-744-1604
Susann Crossan, prin. Fax 591-0220
Rocky Point MS 800/6-8
76 Rocky Point Yaphank Rd 11778 631-744-1603
Scott O'Brien Ed.D., prin. Fax 886-0000

Rome, Oneida, Pop. 32,943
Rome CSD 5,400/PK-12
409 Bell Rd S 13440 315-338-6500
Jeffrey P. Simons, supt. Fax 334-7409
www.romecsd.org
Rome Free Academy 1,500/9-12
95 Dart Cir 13441 315-334-7203
Peter Blake, prin. Fax 334-7236
Strough MS 700/7-8
801 Laurel St 13440 315-338-5201
Tracy O'Rourke, prin. Fax 334-7465

New York State School for the Deaf Post-Sec.
401 Turin St 13440

Romulus, Seneca, Pop. 400
Romulus Central SD 400/PK-12
5705 State Route 96 14541 866-810-0345
Martin Rotz, supt. Fax 869-5961
www.romuluscsd.org
Romulus Central HS 200/7-12
5705 State Route 96 14541 866-810-0345
Christopher Puylara, prin. Fax 869-5961

Ronkonkoma, Suffolk, Pop. 18,816
Connetquot Central SD
Supt. — See Bohemia

Ronkonkoma MS 700/6-8
501 Peconic St 11779 631-467-6000
Charles Morea, prin. Fax 467-6003

Sachem Central SD 12,100/K-12
51 School St 11779 631-471-1336
Kenneth Graham, supt. Fax 471-1341
www.sachem.edu
Other Schools – See Farmingville, Holbrook, Holtsville, Lake Ronkonkoma

Roosevelt, Nassau, Pop. 15,891
Roosevelt UFD 3,000/PK-12
240 Denton Pl 11575 516-345-7000
Marnie Hazelton, supt. Fax 345-7326
www.rooseveltufsd.org
Roosevelt HS 800/9-12
1 Wagner Ave 11575 516-345-7200
Dr. Joan Lange, prin. Fax 345-7290
Roosevelt MS 400/7-8
335 E Clinton Ave 11575 516-345-7700
Nateasha McVea, prin. Fax 345-7791

Roscoe, Sullivan, Pop. 539
Roscoe Central SD 300/PK-12
PO Box 429 12776 607-498-4126
John Evans, supt. Fax 498-5609
www.roscoe.k12.ny.us
Roscoe Central S 300/PK-12
PO Box 429 12776 607-498-4126
Janice Phillips, prin. Fax 498-6015

Roslyn, Nassau, Pop. 2,718
Roslyn UFD 3,100/PK-12
PO Box 367 11576 516-801-5000
Gerard Dempsey, supt. Fax 801-5008
www.roslynschools.org
Other Schools – See Roslyn Heights

Roslyn Heights, Nassau, Pop. 6,383
Roslyn UFD
Supt. — See Roslyn
Roslyn HS 1,000/9-12
475 Round Hill Rd 11577 516-801-5100
Scott Andrews, prin. Fax 801-5108
Roslyn MS 800/6-8
375 Locust Ln 11577 516-801-5200
Craig Johanson, prin. Fax 801-5208

Roxbury, Delaware
Roxbury Central SD 300/PK-12
53729 State Highway 30 12474 607-326-4151
Thomas O'Brien, supt. Fax 326-4154
www.roxburycs.org
Roxbury Central S 300/PK-12
53729 State Highway 30 12474 607-326-4151
Fax 326-4154

Rushville, Ontario, Pop. 661
Marcus Whitman Central SD 1,200/K-12
4100 Baldwin Rd 14544 585-554-4848
Jeramy Clingerman, supt. Fax 554-4882
www.mwcsd.org
Whitman HS 400/9-12
4100 Baldwin Rd 14544 585-554-6441
Jennifer Taft, prin. Fax 554-5201
Whitman MS 300/6-8
4100 Baldwin Rd 14544 585-554-6442
Clayton Cole, prin. Fax 554-3414

Rye, Westchester, Pop. 15,489
Rye CSD 3,300/K-12
411 Theodore Fremd Ste 100S 10580 914-967-6100
Brian Monahan, supt. Fax 967-6957
www.ryeschools.org
Rye HS 1,000/9-12
1 Parsons St 10580 914-967-6100
Patricia Taylor, prin. Fax 967-4380
Rye MS 700/6-8
3 Parsons St 10580 914-967-6100
Dr. Ann Edwards, prin. Fax 921-6189
Rye S of Leadership Alt
324 Midland Ave 10580 914-760-1462
Jennifer Fall, dir.

Rye Country Day S 900/PK-12
Cedar St 10580 914-967-1417
Scott Nelson, hdmstr. Fax 967-1418
School of the Holy Child 300/5-12
2225 Westchester Ave 10580 914-967-5622
William Hambleton, head sch Fax 967-7210

Rye Brook, Westchester, Pop. 9,207
Blind Brook-Rye UFD 1,500/K-12
390 N Ridge St 10573 914-937-3600
Jonathan Ross Ed.D., supt. Fax 937-5871
www.blindbrook.org
Blind Brook HS 500/9-12
840 King St 10573 914-937-3600
Patricia Lambert, prin. Fax 937-4509
Blind Brook MS 400/6-8
840 King St 10573 914-937-3600
Todd Richard, prin. Fax 937-4509

Sackets Harbor, Jefferson, Pop. 1,431
Sackets Harbor Central SD 500/K-12
PO Box 290 13685 315-646-3575
Frederick Hall, supt. Fax 646-1038
www.sacketspatriots.org
Sackets Harbor Central S 500/K-12
PO Box 290 13685 315-646-3575
Jennifer Gaffney, prin. Fax 646-1038

Sag Harbor, Suffolk, Pop. 2,139
Sag Harbor UFD 1,100/PK-12
200 Jermain Ave 11963 631-725-5300
Catherine Barber-Graves, supt. Fax 725-5330
www.sagharborschools.org
Pierson MSHS 500/6-12
200 Jermain Ave 11963 631-725-5302
Jeff Nichols, prin. Fax 725-5314

Saint Albans, See New York
NYC Department of Education
Supt. — See New York
Pathways College Preparatory S 600/6-12
10989 204th St 11412 718-454-4957
Kimberly Mitchell, prin. Fax 454-4892
IS 192 500/6-8
10989 204th St 11412 718-479-5540
Harriett Diaz, prin. Fax 217-4645

Saint Bonaventure, Cattaraugus, Pop. 2,013

St. Bonaventure University Post-Sec.
3261 W State Rd 14778 716-375-2000

Saint James, Suffolk, Pop. 13,215
Smithtown Central SD
Supt. — See Smithtown
Nesaquake MS 800/6-8
479 Edgewood Ave 11780 631-382-5100
Kevin Simmons, prin. Fax 382-5107
Smithtown HS East 1,700/9-12
10 School St 11780 631-382-2700
Edwin Thompson, prin. Fax 382-2707

Knox S 100/6-12
541 Long Beach Rd 11780 631-686-1600
Kristen Tillona, head sch Fax 686-1600

Saint Johnsville, Montgomery, Pop. 1,719
Oppenheim-Ephratah-St. Jhnsvll Cntrl SD 400/PK-12
44 Center St 13452 518-568-2011
David Halloran, supt. Fax 568-2797
www.oesj.org
Oppenheim-Ephratah-St. Johnsville JSHS 100/7-12
44 Center St 13452 518-568-2011
David Slater, prin. Fax 568-2797

Saint Regis Falls, Franklin, Pop. 456
Saint Regis Falls Central SD 300/PK-12
PO Box 309 12980 518-856-9421
Alan Tessier, supt. Fax 856-0142
stregisfallscsd.org/
Saint Regis Falls S 300/PK-12
PO Box 309 12980 518-856-9421
Lorraine Childs, prin. Fax 856-0142

Salamanca, Cattaraugus, Pop. 5,605
Salamanca City Central SD 1,300/PK-12
50 Iroquois Dr 14779 716-945-2400
Robert Breidenstein, supt. Fax 945-3964
www.salamancany.org/
Salamanca JSHS 500/7-12
50 Iroquois Dr 14779 716-945-2404
Scott Cooper, prin. Fax 945-5983

Salem, Washington, Pop. 930
Salem Central SD 500/K-12
PO Box 517 12865 518-854-7855
Dr. David GLover, supt. Fax 854-3957
salemcsd.org/
Salem JSHS 200/7-12
PO Box 517 12865 518-854-7600
Jared Davis, prin. Fax 854-3957

Sanborn, Niagara, Pop. 1,620
Niagara-Wheatfield Central SD
Supt. — See Niagara Falls
Niagara-Wheatfield HS 1,300/9-12
2292 Saunders Settlement Rd 14132 716-215-3100
Tim Carter, prin. Fax 215-3125
Town MS 900/6-8
2292 Saunders Settlement Rd 14132 716-215-3150
Dr. Laura Palka, prin. Fax 215-3160

SUNY Niagara County Community College Post-Sec.
3111 Saunders Settlement Rd 14132 716-614-6200

Sandy Creek, Oswego, Pop. 769
Sandy Creek Central SD 800/PK-12
PO Box 248 13145 315-387-3445
Kyle Faulkner, supt. Fax 387-2196
www.sccs.cnyric.org/
Sandy Creek HS 200/9-12
PO Box 248 13145 315-387-3445
Maureen Shiel, prin. Fax 387-2196
Sandy Creek MS 200/6-8
PO Box 248 13145 315-387-3445
Carolyn Shirley, prin. Fax 387-2196

Saranac, Clinton
Saranac Central SD
Supt. — See Dannemora
Saranac HS 500/9-12
PO Box 8 12981 518-565-5800
Steven Grenville, prin. Fax 565-5809
Saranac MS 300/6-8
PO Box 8 12981 518-565-5700
Katie McNeil, prin. Fax 565-5706

Saranac Lake, Franklin, Pop. 5,317
Saranac Lake Central SD 1,300/K-12
79 Canaras Ave 12983 518-891-5460
Diane Fox, supt. Fax 891-5140
saranaclakecs.org
Saranac Lake HS 400/9-12
79 Canaras Ave 12983 518-891-4450
Joshua Dann, prin. Fax 891-6813
Saranac Lake MS 300/6-8
79 Canaras Ave 12983 518-891-4221
Bruce VanWeelden, prin. Fax 891-6615

SUNY North Country Community College Post-Sec.
PO Box 89 12983 518-891-2915

Saratoga Springs, Saratoga, Pop. 26,062
Saratoga Springs CSD 6,500/K-12
3 Blue Streak Blvd 12866 518-583-4700
Michael Piccirillo, supt. Fax 584-6624
www.saratogaschools.org
Maple Ave MS 1,600/6-8
515 Maple Ave 12866 518-587-4551
Dr. Jeffrey Palmer, prin. Fax 587-5759
Saratoga Springs HS 2,100/9-12
1 Blue Streak Blvd 12866 518-587-6690
Dr. Brett Miller, prin. Fax 583-1671

Saratoga Central Catholic HS 200/6-12
247 Broadway 12866 518-587-7070
Steve Lombard, prin. Fax 587-0678
Skidmore College Post-Sec.
815 N Broadway 12866 518-580-5000
SUNY Empire State College Post-Sec.
2 Union Ave 12866 518-587-2100
Waldorf S of Saratoga Springs 200/PK-12
122 Regent St 12866 518-587-0549
Anne Maguire, admin. Fax 581-1682

Saugerties, Ulster, Pop. 3,876
Saugerties Central SD 2,200/K-12
PO Box A 12477 845-247-6550
Seth Turner, supt. Fax 246-8364
www.saugerties.k12.ny.us
Saugerties JSHS 900/7-12
PO Box A 12477 845-247-6650
Thomas Averill, prin. Fax 246-4312

Woodstock Day S 200/PK-12
1430 Glasco Tpke 12477 845-246-3744
Kara Stern, head sch Fax 246-0053

Sauquoit, Oneida
Sauquoit Valley Central SD 900/K-12
2601 Oneida St 13456 315-839-6311
Ronald Wheelock, supt. Fax 839-5352
www.svcsd.org
Sauquoit Valley HS 300/9-12
2601 Oneida St 13456 315-839-6316
Zane Mahar, prin. Fax 839-6397
Sauquoit Valley MS 200/6-8
2601 Oneida St 13456 315-839-6371
Peter Madden, prin. Fax 839-6390

Sayville, Suffolk, Pop. 16,715
Sayville UFD 3,100/K-12
99 Greeley Ave 11782 631-244-6510
Dr. Walter Schartner, supt. Fax 244-6504
www.sayvilleschools.org
Sayville MS 700/6-8
291 Johnson Ave 11782 631-244-6650
Thomas Murray, prin. Fax 244-6655
Other Schools – See West Sayville

Scarsdale, Westchester, Pop. 16,786
Edgemont UFD 1,900/K-12
300 White Oak Ln 10583 914-472-7768
Dr. Victoria S. Kniewel, supt. Fax 472-6846
www.edgemont.org
Edgemont JSHS 900/7-12
200 White Oak Ln 10583 914-725-1500
Devan Ganeshananthan, prin. Fax 725-1057

Scarsdale UFD 4,800/K-12
2 Brewster Rd Ste 2 10583 914-721-2410
Dr. Thomas Hagerman, supt. Fax 722-2822
www.scarsdaleschools.k12.ny.us
Scarsdale HS 1,500/9-12
1057 Post Rd 10583 914-721-2450
Kenneth Bonamo, prin. Fax 721-2549
Scarsdale MS 1,100/6-8
134 Mamaroneck Rd 10583 914-721-2600
Michael McDermott, prin. Fax 721-2655

Schaghticoke, Rensselaer, Pop. 588
Hoosic Valley Central SD 700/K-12
2 Pleasant Ave 12154 518-753-4450
Amy Goodell, supt. Fax 753-7665
www.hoosicvalley.k12.ny.us
Hoosic Valley JSHS 400/7-12
1548 State Route 67 12154 518-753-4432
G. Michael Apostol, prin. Fax 753-7491

Schenectady, Schenectady, Pop. 59,889
Mohonasen Central SD 2,800/K-12
2072 Curry Rd 12303 518-356-8200
Dr. Kathleen Spring, supt. Fax 356-8247
www.mohonasen.org
Draper MS 700/6-8
2070 Curry Rd 12303 518-356-8350
Debra Male, prin. Fax 356-8359
Mohonasen HS 1,000/9-12
2072 Curry Rd 12303 518-356-8300
Lisa Patierne, prin. Fax 356-8309

Niskayuna Central SD 4,100/K-12
1239 Van Antwerp Rd 12309 518-377-4666
Dr. Cosimo Tangorra Ed.D., supt. Fax 377-4074
www.niskyschools.org
Iroquois MS 600/6-8
2495 Rosendale Rd 12309 518-377-2233
Vicki Wyld, prin. Fax 377-2219
Niskayuna HS 1,400/9-12
1626 Balltown Rd 12309 518-382-2511
John Rickert, prin. Fax 382-2539
Van Antwerp MS 400/6-8
2253 Story Ave 12309 518-370-1243
Luke Rakoczy, prin. Fax 370-4610

Schalmont Central SD 1,800/K-12
4 Sabre Dr 12306 518-355-9200
Carol Pallas, supt. Fax 355-9203
www.schalmont.org
Schalmont HS 600/9-12
1 Sabre Dr 12306 518-355-6110
Imran Abbasi, prin. Fax 355-8720
Schalmont MS 600/5-8
2 Sabre Dr 12306 518-355-6255
Brian Sherman, prin. Fax 355-5329

Schenectady CSD 8,400/PK-12
108 Education Dr 12303 518-370-8100
Laurence Spring, supt. Fax 370-8173
www.schenectady.k12.ny.us
Central Park MS 300/6-8
421 Elm St 12304 518-370-8250
Tamara Thorpe-Odom, prin. Fax 881-3602
Mont Pleasant MS 800/6-8
1121 Forest Rd 12303 518-370-8160
Jeffery Bennett, prin. Fax 881-3562
Oneida MS 700/6-8
1529 Oneida St 12308 518-370-8260
Tony Farina, admin. Fax 370-8277
Schenectady HS 2,600/9-12
1445 The Plaza 12308 518-881-2044
Diane Wilkinson, prin. Fax 881-3802
Steinmetz Career and Leadership Academy 9-12
880 Oakwood Ave 12303 518-881-2030
Gregory Fields, prin. Fax 881-3602

Mid-America Baptist Theological Seminary Post-Sec.
2810 Curry Rd 12303 518-355-4000
Modern Welding School Post-Sec.
1842 State St 12304 518-374-1216
Notre Dame-Bishop Gibbons HS 300/6-12
2600 Albany St 12304 518-393-3131
Peter Fusco, prin. Fax 370-3817
SUNY Schenectady County Community Coll. Post-Sec.
78 Washington Ave 12305 518-381-1200
The Belanger School of Nursing Post-Sec.
650 McClellan St 12304 518-243-4471
Troy School of Beauty Culture Post-Sec.
101 Deanna Ct 12309 518-273-7741
Union College Post-Sec.
807 Union St 12308 518-388-6000
Union Graduate College Post-Sec.
80 Nott Ter 12308 518-631-9900

Schenevus, Otsego, Pop. 543
Schenevus Central SD 300/K-12
159 Main St 12155 607-638-5530
Thomas Jennings, supt. Fax 638-5600
www.schenevuscs.org/
Schenevus Central S 300/K-12
159 Main St 12155 607-638-5881
Matthew Wendel, prin. Fax 638-5600

Schoharie, Schoharie, Pop. 912
Schoharie Central SD 800/K-12
PO Box 430 12157 518-295-6600
David Blanchard, supt. Fax 295-8178
www.schoharie.k12.ny.us
Schoharie JSHS 400/7-12
PO Box 430 12157 518-295-6601
Kevin Calacone, prin. Fax 295-8161

Schroon Lake, Essex, Pop. 817
Schroon Lake Central SD 200/PK-12
PO Box 338 12870 518-532-7164
Stephen Gratto, supt. Fax 532-0284
www.schroonschool.org
Schroon Lake Central S 200/PK-12
PO Box 338 12870 518-532-7164
Stephen Gratto, admin. Fax 532-0284

Schuylerville, Saratoga, Pop. 1,376
Schuylerville Central SD 1,700/K-12
14 Spring St 12871 518-695-3255
Ryan Sherman Ed.D., supt. Fax 695-6491
www.schuylervilleschools.org
Schuylerville HS 600/9-12
14 Spring St 12871 518-695-3255
Matthew Sickles, prin. Fax 695-3103
Schuylerville MS 400/6-8
14 Spring St 12871 518-695-3255
Mary Kate Elsworth, prin. Fax 695-6491

Scio, Allegany, Pop. 604
Scio Central SD 400/PK-12
3968 Washington St 14880 585-593-5076
Gregory L. Hardy, supt. Fax 593-3468
www.scio.wnyric.org
Scio Central S 400/PK-12
3968 Washington St 14880 585-593-5510
Dawn Race, prin. Fax 593-0653

Scotia, Schenectady, Pop. 7,607
Scotia-Glenville Central SD 2,500/K-12
900 Preddice Pkwy 12302 518-382-1215
Susan Swartz, supt. Fax 386-4336
www.sgcsd.net
Scotia-Glenville HS 800/9-12
1 Tartan Way 12302 518-382-1231
Peter Bednarek, prin. Fax 386-4303
Scotia-Glenville MS 600/6-8
10 Prestige Pkwy 12302 518-382-1263
Robert Cosmer, prin. Fax 386-4303

Mekeel Christian Academy 300/PK-12
36-38 Sacandaga Rd 12302 518-370-4272
W. Chad Bowman, head sch Fax 370-4778

Scottsville, Monroe, Pop. 1,964
Wheatland-Chili Central SD 700/K-12
13 Beckwith Ave 14546 585-889-6246
Dr. Deborah Leh, supt. Fax 889-6284
www.wheatland.k12.ny.us
Wheatland-Chili MSHS 400/6-12
940 North Rd 14546 585-889-6245
Eric Windover, prin. Fax 889-6217

Sea Cliff, Nassau, Pop. 4,948
North Shore Central SD 2,700/K-12
112 Franklin Ave 11579 516-277-7800
Dr. Edward Melnick, supt. Fax 277-7801
www.northshoreschools.org
Other Schools – See Glen Head

Seaford, Nassau, Pop. 15,154
Seaford UFD 2,300/K-12
1600 Washington Ave 11783 516-592-4000
Brian Conboy, supt. Fax 592-4049
www.seaford.k12.ny.us
Seaford HS 800/9-12
1575 Seamans Neck Rd 11783 516-592-4300
Scott Bersin, prin. Fax 592-4399
Seaford MS 500/6-8
3940 Sunset Ave 11783 516-592-4200
Dan Smith, prin. Fax 592-4299

Selden, Suffolk, Pop. 19,540
Middle Country Central SD
Supt. — See Centereach
Newfield HS 1,600/9-12
145 Marshall Dr 11784 631-285-8300
Scott Graviano, prin. Fax 285-8301

SUNY Suffolk County Community College Post-Sec.
533 College Rd 11784 631-451-4000

Seneca Falls, Seneca, Pop. 6,593
Seneca Falls Central SD 1,200/K-12
PO Box 268 13148 315-568-5500
Robert McKeveny, supt. Fax 712-0535
www.sfcs.k12.ny.us/
Mynderse Academy 400/9-12
105 Troy St 13148 315-568-5500
Andrew Doell, prin. Fax 712-0523
Seneca Falls MS 300/6-8
95 Troy St 13148 315-568-5500
Kevin Rhinehart, prin. Fax 712-0524

New York Chiropractic College Post-Sec.
2360 State Route 89 13148 315-568-3000

Setauket, Suffolk, Pop. 15,248
Three Village Central SD
Supt. — See Stony Brook
Gelinas JHS 900/7-9
25 Mud Rd 11733 631-730-4700
William Bernhard, prin. Fax 730-4706

Sharon Springs, Schoharie, Pop. 550
Sharon Springs Central SD 300/K-12
PO Box 218 13459 518-284-2266
Patterson Green, supt. Fax 284-9033
www.sharonsprings.org/
Sharon Springs Central S 300/K-12
PO Box 218 13459 518-284-2267
Patterson Green, prin. Fax 284-9075

Shelter Island, Suffolk, Pop. 1,316
Shelter Island UFD 200/K-12
PO Box 2015 11964 631-749-0302
Leonard Skuggevik, supt. Fax 749-1262
www.shelterisland.k12.ny.us
Shelter Island S 200/K-12
PO Box 2015 11964 631-749-0302
Leonard Skuggevik, supt. Fax 749-1262

Sherburne, Chenango, Pop. 1,358
Sherburne-Earlville Central SD 1,300/K-12
15 School St 13460 607-674-7300
Eric Schnabl, supt. Fax 674-9742
secsd.org
Sherburne-Earlville HS 400/9-12
13 School St 13460 607-674-7380
Julie Thompson, prin. Fax 674-7368
Sherburne-Earlville MS 300/6-8
13 School St 13460 607-674-7350
Jolene Emhof, prin. Fax 674-7392

Sherman, Chautauqua, Pop. 717
Sherman Central SD 400/PK-12
PO Box 950 14781 716-761-6122
Michael V. Ginestre, supt. Fax 761-6119
www.sherman.wnyric.org
Sherman HS 200/7-12
PO Box 950 14781 716-761-6121
Bryna Booth, prin. Fax 761-6119

Shoreham, Suffolk, Pop. 528
Shoreham-Wading River Central SD 1,800/K-12
250B Route 25A 11786 631-821-8100
Dr. Steven Cohen, admin. Fax 929-3001
www.swrschools.org
Prodell MS 600/6-8
100 Randall Rd 11786 631-821-8212
Dr. Linda Anthony, prin. Fax 821-8275
Shoreham-Wading River HS 800/9-12
250A Route 25A 11786 631-821-8264
Dan Holtzman, prin. Fax 821-8162

Shortsville, Ontario, Pop. 1,429
Manchester-Shortsville Central SD 800/PK-12
1506 State Route 21 14548 585-289-3964
Charlene Dehn, supt. Fax 289-6660
www.redjacket.org
Red Jacket HS 300/9-12
1506 State Route 21 14548 585-289-3966
Samuel Martina, prin. Fax 289-4755
Red Jacket MS 200/6-8
1506 State Route 21 14548 585-289-3967
Karen Hall, prin. Fax 289-8715

Shrub Oak, Westchester, Pop. 1,970
Lakeland Central SD 5,900/K-12
1086 E Main St 10588 914-245-1700
Dr. George Stone, supt. Fax 245-1589
www.lakelandschools.org
Lakeland HS 1,100/9-12
1349 E Main St 10588 914-528-0600
Lorrie Yurish, prin. Fax 528-0521
Other Schools – See Cortlandt Manor, Yorktown Heights

Sidney, Delaware, Pop. 3,846
Sidney Central SD 900/K-12
95 W Main St 13838 607-563-2135
William Christensen, supt. Fax 563-2386
www.sidneycsd.org
Sidney JSHS 300/7-12
95 W Main St 13838 607-561-7703
Eben Bullock, prin. Fax 563-1800

Silver Creek, Chautauqua, Pop. 2,618
Silver Creek Central SD 1,100/PK-12
1 Dickinson St 14136 716-934-2603
Todd Crandall, admin. Fax 934-7983
www.silvercreek.wnyric.org/
Silver Creek HS 300/9-12
1 Dickinson St 14136 716-934-2603
James Lauria, prin. Fax 934-2103
Silver Creek MS 200/6-8
1 Dickinson St 14136 716-934-2603
Eleanor Payne, prin. Fax 934-3760

Sinclairville, Chautauqua, Pop. 578
Cassadaga Valley Central SD 1,000/PK-12
PO Box 540 14782 716-962-5155
Charles Leichner, supt. Fax 962-5976
cvweb.wnyric.org
Cassadaga Valley MSHS 500/6-12
PO Box 540 14782 716-962-8581
Josh Gilevski, prin. Fax 962-5788

Skaneateles, Onondaga, Pop. 2,428
Skaneateles Central SD 1,500/K-12
55 East St 13152 315-291-2221
Kenneth Slentz, supt. Fax 685-0347
www.skanschools.org
Skaneateles HS 500/9-12
49 E Elizabeth St 13152 315-291-2231
Gregory Santoro, prin. Fax 291-2250
Skaneateles MS 300/6-8
35 East St 13152 315-291-2241
Gary Gerst, prin. Fax 291-2267

Slate Hill, Orange
Minisink Valley Central SD 4,000/K-12
PO Box 217 10973 845-355-5100
Brian Monahan, supt. Fax 355-5119
www.minisink.com
Minisink Valley HS 1,400/9-12
PO Box 217 10973 845-355-5150
Kenneth Hauck, prin. Fax 355-5198
Minisink Valley MS 1,000/6-8
PO Box 217 10973 845-355-5200
Michael Giardina, prin. Fax 355-5205

Sleepy Hollow, Westchester, Pop. 9,977
Tarrytown UFD 2,700/PK-12
200 N Broadway 10591 914-631-9404
Christopher Borsari, supt. Fax 332-6283
www.tufsd.org
Sleepy Hollow HS 900/9-12
210 N Broadway 10591 914-631-8838
Dr. Tracy Smith, prin. Fax 332-6219
Sleepy Hollow MS 600/6-8
210 N Broadway 10591 914-332-6275
Elizabeth Lopez, prin. Fax 332-6546

Sloan, Erie, Pop. 3,611
Cheektowaga-Sloan UFD 1,400/PK-12
166 Halstead Ave 14212 716-891-6402
Andrea Galenski, supt. Fax 891-6435
www.sloanschools.org
Other Schools – See Cheektowaga

Smithtown, Suffolk, Pop. 27,100
Smithtown Central SD 10,000/K-12
26 New York Ave 11787 631-382-2000
James J. Grossane Ed.D., supt. Fax 382-2010
www.smithtown.k12.ny.us
Accompsett MS 700/6-8
660 Meadow Rd 11787 631-382-2300
Paul McNeil, prin. Fax 382-2307
Smithtown HS West 1,700/9-12
100 Central Rd 11787 631-382-2905
John Coady, prin. Fax 382-2910
Other Schools – See Nesconset, Saint James

Smithtown Christian S 500/PK-12
1 Higbie Dr 11787 631-265-3334
Rev. Roger Erdvig M.Ed., supt. Fax 265-1079

Snyder, Erie

Park S of Buffalo 300/PK-12
4625 Harlem Rd 14226 716-839-1242
Christopher Lauricella, hdmstr. Fax 839-2014

Sodus, Wayne, Pop. 1,754
Sodus Central SD 800/PK-12
PO Box 220 14551 315-483-5201
Nelson Kise, supt. Fax 483-4755
www.soduscsd.org
Sodus JSHS 300/7-12
PO Box 220 14551 315-483-5285
Eugene Hoskins, prin. Fax 483-6168

Solvay, Onondaga, Pop. 6,416
Solvay UFD 1,500/K-12
PO Box 980 13209 315-468-1111
Lawrence Wright, supt. Fax 468-2755
www.solvayschools.org
Solvay HS 600/9-12
600 Gertrude Ave 13209 315-468-2551
Jay Tinklepaugh, prin. Fax 484-1404
Other Schools – See Syracuse

Somers, Westchester
Somers Central SD 3,300/K-12
250 Route 202 10589 914-277-2400
Dr. Raymond Blanch, supt. Fax 277-2409
www.somersschools.org/

Somers MS 800/6-8
250 Route 202 10589 914-277-3399
Jeffrey Getman, prin. Fax 277-2236
Other Schools – See Lincolndale

Kennedy HS 600/9-12
54 Route 138 10589 914-232-5061
Rev. Mark Vaillancourt Ph.D., prin. Fax 232-3416

Southampton, Suffolk, Pop. 3,057
Southampton UFD 1,600/PK-12
70 Leland Ln 11968 631-591-4500
Dr. Scott Farina, supt. Fax 287-2870
www.southamptonschools.org
Southampton HS 600/9-12
141 Narrow Ln 11968 631-591-4600
Dr. Brian Zahn, prin. Fax 283-6313
Southampton IS 400/5-8
70 Leland Ln 11968 631-591-4700
Timothy Frazier, prin. Fax 283-6899

South Dayton, Chautauqua, Pop. 607
Pine Valley Central SD 600/PK-12
7755 Route 83 14138 716-988-3293
Scott Payne, supt. Fax 988-3243
www.pval.org
Pine Valley Central JSHS 300/7-12
7827 Route 83 14138 716-988-3276
Paul Mihalko, prin. Fax 988-3139

South Fallsburg, Sullivan, Pop. 2,810

Yeshivath Zichron Moshe Post-Sec.
PO Box 580 12779 845-434-5240
Zichron Moshe S 50/PK-12
PO Box 580 12779 845-434-5240

South Glens Falls, Saratoga, Pop. 3,492
South Glens Falls Central SD 3,100/PK-12
6 Bluebird Rd 12803 518-793-9617
Michael Patton Ed.D., supt. Fax 761-0723
www.sgfcsd.org
South Glens Falls HS 1,000/9-12
42 Merritt Rd 12803 518-792-9987
Carla Biviano, prin. Fax 792-5412
Winch MS 700/6-8
99 Hudson St 12803 518-792-5891
Tim Dawkins, prin. Fax 793-9505

South Kortright, Delaware
South Kortright Central SD 400/PK-12
PO Box 113 13842 607-538-9111
Patricia Norton-White, supt. Fax 538-9205
www.skcs.org/pages/South_Kortright_Central_School
South Kortright Central S 400/PK-12
PO Box 113 13842 607-538-9111
Krislynn Dengler, prin. Fax 538-9205

Southold, Suffolk, Pop. 5,696
Southold UFD 800/K-12
PO Box 470 11971 631-765-5400
David Gamberg, supt. Fax 765-5086
www.southoldufsd.com
Southold JSHS 400/7-12
PO Box 470 11971 631-765-5081
William Galati, prin. Fax 765-5086

South Otselic, Chenango
Otselic Valley Central SD 300/K-12
PO Box 161 13155 315-653-7218
Daniel Henner, supt. Fax 653-7500
www.ovcs.org
Otselic Valley S 300/K-12
PO Box 161 13155 315-653-7218
Robert Berson, prin. Fax 653-7500

South Ozone Park, See New York
NYC Department of Education
Supt. — See New York
Epic HS - South 9-9
12110 Rockaway Blvd 11420 718-845-1290
Darius Mensah, prin.
Hawtree Creek MS 100/6-8
12110 Rockaway Blvd 11420 718-659-3792
Maureen Hussey, prin. Fax 659-3798
JHS 226 1,200/6-8
12110 Rockaway Blvd 11420 718-843-2260
Rushell White, prin. Fax 835-6317

Al-Ihsan Academy 400/PK-12
PO Box 200215 11420 718-322-3154

Sparkill, Rockland, Pop. 1,536

St. Thomas Aquinas College Post-Sec.
125 Route 340 10976 845-398-4000

Spencer, Tioga, Pop. 744
Spencer-Van Etten Central SD 900/PK-12
16 Dartts Xrd 14883 607-589-7100
Dr. Joseph Morgan, supt. Fax 589-3010
www.svecsd.org/
Spencer-Van Etten HS 300/9-12
16 Dartts Xrd 14883 607-589-7140
Melissa Jewell, prin. Fax 589-3010
Spencer-Van Etten MS 300/5-8
1 Center St 14883 607-589-7120
Eric Knolles, prin. Fax 589-3020

North Spencer Christian Academy 100/PK-12
721 Ithaca Rd 14883 607-589-6366
Dr. Guy S. Kinney, admin. Fax 589-4455

Spencerport, Monroe, Pop. 3,553
Spencerport Central SD 3,700/K-12
71 Lyell Ave 14559 585-349-5000
Michael Crumb, supt. Fax 349-5011
www.spencerportschools.org

Cosgrove MS 800/6-8
2749 Spencerport Rd 14559 585-349-5300
Ned Dale, prin. Fax 349-5346
Spencerport HS 1,300/9-12
2707 Spencerport Rd 14559 585-349-5200
Sean McCabe, prin. Fax 349-5266

Springfield Gardens, See New York
NYC Department of Education
Supt. — See New York
Carver HS for the Sciences 500/9-12
14310 Springfield Blvd 11413 718-525-6439
Dr. Janice Sutton, prin. Fax 525-6482
Excelsior Preparatory HS 500/9-12
14310 Springfield Blvd 11413 718-525-6507
Lillie Lucas, prin. Fax 525-6276
Preparatory Academy for Writers 500/6-12
14310 Springfield Blvd 11413 718-949-8405
Charles Anderson, prin. Fax 525-8495
Queens Preparatory Academy 500/9-12
14310 Springfield Blvd 11413 718-712-2304
Tashon Haywood, prin. Fax 712-3273
Queens United MS 100/6-8
22902 137th Ave 11413 718-723-3501
Richard Roder, prin. Fax 723-3507
IS 59 600/6-8
13255 Ridgedale St 11413 718-527-3501
Carleton Gordon, prin. Fax 276-1364

Spring Valley, Rockland, Pop. 30,786
East Ramapo Central SD 7,900/K-12
105 S Madison Ave 10977 845-577-6000
Dr. Joel Klein, supt. Fax 577-6168
www.eram.k12.ny.us
Ramapo HS 1,300/9-12
400 Viola Rd 10977 845-577-6400
Sherrill Murray-Lazarus, prin. Fax 426-1124
Spring Valley HS 1,100/9-12
361 W Route 59 10977 845-577-6500
Karen Pinel, prin. Fax 426-1127
Other Schools – See Chestnut Ridge, Suffern

Bais Yaakov D'Rav Hirsch 200/9-12
235 N Main St 10977 845-371-6750
Be'er Yaakov Talmudic Seminary Post-Sec.
12 Jefferson Ave 10977 845-362-3053
Bnos Esther Pupa 300/PK-12
246 N Main St 10977 845-371-1220
Sunbridge Institute Post-Sec.
285 Hungry Hollow Rd 10977 845-425-0055
United Talmudical Academy 1,700/K-12
89 S Main St 10977 845-425-0392
Yidel Spitzer, admin. Fax 352-7253
Yeshiva Avir Yaakov 3,100/PK-12
766 N Main St 10977 845-362-6600
Rabbi Eluzer Moschel, admin. Fax 354-6809
Yeshiva Bais Hachinuch 100/3-8
50A S Main St Ste 8 10977 845-354-3805
Yeshiva Degel Hatorah 300/K-12
PO Box 213 10977 845-356-4610
Yeshiva Tzoin Yosef-Pupa 400/PK-12
15 Widman Ct 10977 845-371-1220
Yeshiva Zichron Yaakov 50/9-12
720 Union Rd 10977 845-362-4990

Springville, Erie, Pop. 4,257
Springville-Griffith Inst. Central SD 1,800/K-12
307 Newman St 14141 716-592-3230
Sylvia Root, supt. Fax 592-3209
www.springvillegi.org/
Griffith Institute HS 600/9-12
290 N Buffalo St 14141 716-592-3202
Vincent Vanderlip, prin. Fax 592-3297
Griffith Institute MS 500/6-8
267 Newman St 14141 716-592-3203
Michael Retzlaff, prin. Fax 592-3268

Staatsburg on Hudson, Dutchess, Pop. 372
Hyde Park Central SD
Supt. — See Hyde Park
Roosevelt HS 1,300/9-12
156 S Cross Rd 12580 845-229-4020
Rick Pardy, prin. Fax 229-4029

Stamford, Delaware, Pop. 1,103
Stamford Central SD 300/K-12
1 River St 12167 607-652-7301
Dr. Glen Huot, supt. Fax 652-3446
www.stamfordcs.org
Stamford Central S 300/K-12
1 River St 12167 607-652-7301
Ruth Ehrets, prin. Fax 652-3446

Star Lake, Saint Lawrence, Pop. 799
Clifton-Fine Central SD 300/PK-12
11 Hall Ave 13690 315-848-3333
Regina Yeo, supt. Fax 848-3350
www.cliftonfine.org
Clifton-Fine JSHS 100/7-12
11 Hall Ave 13690 315-848-3333
Susan Shene, prin. Fax 848-3350

Staten Island, See New York
NYC Department of Education
Supt. — See New York
Concord HS 100/Alt
109 Rhine Ave 10304 718-447-1274
Christopher Anzalone, prin. Fax 442-6276
CSI HS for International Studies 500/9-12
100 Essex Dr 10314 718-370-6900
Joseph Canale, prin. Fax 370-6915
Curtis HS 2,400/9-12
105 Hamilton Ave 10301 718-390-1800
Gregory Jaenicke, prin. Fax 556-4800
Eagle Academy for Young Men 6-8
101 Warren St 10304 718-727-6201
Jermaine Cameron, prin.

Marsh Ave S for Expeditionary Learning 400/6-8
100 Essex Dr 10314 718-370-6850
Cara DeAngelo, prin. Fax 370-6860
McCown Expeditionary Learning S 500/9-12
100 Essex Dr 10314 718-370-6950
Traci Frey, prin. Fax 370-6960
McKee Career and Technical HS Vo/Tech
290 Saint Marks Pl 10301 718-420-2600
Sharon Henry, prin. Fax 981-8776
New Dorp HS 2,700/9-12
465 New Dorp Ln 10306 718-667-8686
Deirdre DeAngelis-Dales, prin. Fax 987-4889
Petrides S 1,300/K-12
715 Ocean Ter 10301 718-815-0186
Joanne Buckheit, prin. Fax 815-9638
Port Richmond HS 1,800/9-12
85 Saint Josephs Ave 10302 718-420-2100
Tim Gannon, prin. Fax 981-6203
IS 2 900/6-8
333 Midland Ave 10306 718-987-5336
Adrienne Stallone, prin. Fax 987-6937
IS 7 1,200/6-8
1270 Huguenot Ave 10312 718-697-8488
Dr. Nora DeRosa, prin. Fax 967-0809
IS 24 1,400/6-8
225 Cleveland Ave 10308 718-982-4700
Lenny Santamaria, prin. Fax 356-5834
IS 27 1,100/6-8
11 Clove Lake Pl 10310 718-981-8800
Matthew Barone, prin. Fax 815-4677
IS 34 1,100/6-8
528 Academy Ave 10307 718-477-4500
John Boyle, prin. Fax 227-4074
IS 49 800/6-8
101 Warren St 10304 718-727-6040
James DeFrancesco, prin. Fax 876-8207
IS 51 1,100/6-8
20 Houston St 10302 718-981-0502
Nicholas Mele, prin. Fax 815-3957
IS 61 1,200/6-8
445 Castleton Ave 10301 718-727-8481
Susan Tronolone, prin. Fax 447-2112
IS 72 1,200/6-8
33 Ferndale Ave 10314 718-698-5757
Peter Macellari, prin. Fax 761-5928
IS 75 1,300/6-8
455 Huguenot Ave 10312 718-356-0130
Kenneth Zapata, prin. Fax 984-5302
Staten Island Tech HS Vo/Tech
485 Clawson St 10306 718-667-3222
Mark Erlenwein, prin. Fax 987-5872
Tottenville HS 3,900/9-12
100 Luten Ave 10312 718-668-8800
Joseph Scarmato, prin. Fax 317-0962
Wagner HS 3,300/9-12
1200 Manor Rd 10314 718-698-4200
Gary Giordano, prin. Fax 698-5213

Career School of New York Post-Sec.
350 Saint Marks Pl 10301 718-420-6440
CUNY College of Staten Island Post-Sec.
2800 Victory Blvd 10314 718-982-2000
Monsignor Farrell HS 900/9-12
2900 Amboy Rd 10306 718-987-2900
Msgr. Edmund Whalen, prin. Fax 987-4241
Moore Catholic HS 600/9-12
100 Merrill Ave 10314 718-761-9200
Dr. Joseph Fusco, prin. Fax 982-7779
Notre Dame Academy 400/9-12
134 Howard Ave 10301 718-447-8878
Kathryn Jaenicke, prin. Fax 447-2926
St. John Villa Academy 500/9-12
25 Landis Ave 10305 718-442-6240
Sr. Antonia Zuffante, prin. Fax 447-6729
St. Joseph by the Sea HS 400/9-12
5150 Hylan Blvd 10312 718-984-6500
Fr. Michael Reilly, prin. Fax 984-6503
St. Joseph Hill Academy 500/9-12
850 Hylan Blvd 10305 718-447-1374
Angela Ferrando, prin. Fax 447-3041
St. Pauls School of Nursing Post-Sec.
2 Teleport Dr Ste 203 10311 718-818-6470
St. Peter's Boys HS 600/9-12
200 Clinton Ave 10301 718-447-1676
John Fodera, prin. Fax 447-4027
St. Vincent's Medical Center Post-Sec.
355 Bard Ave 10310 718-876-2413
Sisters of Charity Medical Center Post-Sec.
75 Vanderbilt Ave 10304 718-818-6470
Staten Island Academy 300/PK-12
715 Todt Hill Rd 10304 718-987-8100
Albert Cauz, head sch Fax 979-7641
Wagner College Post-Sec.
1 Campus Rd 10301 718-390-3100
Yeshiva & Mesvita of Staten Island 100/9-12
1870 Drumgoole Rd E 10309 718-356-5412

Stillwater, Saratoga, Pop. 1,707
Stillwater Central SD 1,200/PK-12
1068 Hudson Ave 12170 518-373-6100
Dr. Stan Maziejka, supt. Fax 664-9134
www.scsd.org/
Stillwater HS 400/9-12
1068 Hudson Ave 12170 518-373-6100
Mario Fernandez, prin. Fax 664-1832
Stillwater MS 300/6-8
1068 Hudson Ave 12170 518-373-6100
Patti Morris, prin. Fax 664-1832

Stone Ridge, Ulster, Pop. 1,136

SUNY Ulster Post-Sec.
491 Cottekill Rd 12484 845-687-5000

Stony Brook, Suffolk, Pop. 13,574
Three Village Central SD 6,900/K-12
100 Suffolk Ave 11790 631-730-4000
Cheryl Pedisich, supt. Fax 474-7784
www.threevillagecsd.org
Murphy JHS 900/7-9
351 Oxhead Rd 11790 631-730-4800
Vincent Vizzo, prin. Fax 730-4801
Other Schools – See East Setauket, Setauket

Stony Brook S 300/7-12
1 Chapman Pkwy 11790 631-751-1800
Joshua Crane B.D., head sch Fax 751-3449
SUNY at Stony Brook Post-Sec.
118 Administration 11794 631-632-6000

Suffern, Rockland, Pop. 10,548
East Ramapo Central SD
Supt. — See Spring Valley
Pomona MS 700/7-8
101 Pomona Rd 10901 845-577-6200
Christine Alfonso, prin. Fax 577-6245

Ramapo Central SD
Supt. — See Hillburn
Suffern HS 1,500/9-12
49 Viola Rd 10901 845-357-3800
Patrick Breen, prin. Fax 357-5035
Suffern MS 1,000/6-8
80 Hemion Rd 10901 845-357-7400
Brian Fox, prin. Fax 357-4563

Salvation Army College Officer Training Post-Sec.
201 Lafayette Ave 10901 845-368-7200
SUNY Rockland Community College Post-Sec.
145 College Rd 10901 845-574-4000
Yeshiva Ohr Reuven 100/9-12
259 Grandview Ave 10901 845-362-8362
Yeshiva Shaarei Torah 100/9-12
91 Carlton Rd W 10901 845-352-3431
Yeshiva Shaarei Torah of Rockland Post-Sec.
91 Carlton Rd W 10901 845-352-3431

Syosset, Nassau, Pop. 18,544
Syosset Central SD, 99 Pell Ln 11791 6,400/K-12
Dr. Thomas Rogers, supt. 516-364-5600
www.syossetschools.org
South Woods MS, 99 Pell Ln 11791 700/6-8
Michelle Burget, prin. 516-364-5621
Syosset HS, 70 Southwoods Rd 11791 2,200/9-12
Dr. Giovanni Durante, prin. 516-364-5675
Thompson MS, 98 Ann Dr 11791 800/6-8
James Kassebaum, prin. 516-364-5760

New York College of Health Professions Post-Sec.
6801 Jericho Tpke 11791 800-922-7337
Our Lady of Mercy Academy 500/9-12
815 Convent Rd 11791 516-921-1047
Lisa Harrison, prin. Fax 921-3634
Star Career Academy Post-Sec.
125 Michael Dr 11791 516-364-4344

Syracuse, Onondaga, Pop. 138,722
Solvay UFD
Supt. — See Solvay
Solvay MS 500/4-8
299 Bury Dr 13209 315-487-7061
Diane Hagemann, prin. Fax 484-1444

Syracuse CSD 20,100/PK-12
725 Harrison St 13210 315-435-4499
Sharon Contreras Ph.D., supt. Fax 435-4015
www.syracusecityschools.com/
Clary MS 400/6-8
100 Amidon Dr 13205 315-435-4411
Kathryne Moulton, prin. Fax 435-5832
Corcoran HS 1,400/9-12
919 Glenwood Ave 13207 315-435-4321
Jennifer King-Reese, prin. Fax 435-4024
Danforth MS 400/6-8
309 W Brighton Ave 13205 315-435-4535
Dr. Ronardo Reeves, prin. Fax 435-6208
Elmcrest S Alt
960 Salt Springs Rd 13224 315-435-6244
Debra Mastropaolo, prin. Fax 435-6246
Expeditionary Learning MS 100/6-8
4942 S Salina St 13205 315-435-6416
Kevin Burns, prin. Fax 435-4880
Fowler HS 1,300/9-12
227 Magnolia St 13204 315-435-4376
Brian Nolan, prin. Fax 435-6313
Grant MS 600/6-8
2400 Grant Blvd 13208 315-435-4433
Pamela Odom, prin. Fax 435-4856
Henninger HS 1,700/9-12
600 Robinson St 13206 315-435-4343
Robert DiFlorio, prin. Fax 435-6277
Institute of Technology at Syracuse Cntr Vo/Tech
258 E Adams St 13202 315-435-4300
Donna Formica, prin. Fax 435-5816
Lincoln MS 600/6-8
1613 James St 13203 315-435-4450
LaJuan White, prin. Fax 435-4455
Nottingham HS 1,200/9-12
3100 E Genesee St 13224 315-435-4380
David Maynard, prin. Fax 435-4177
Public Service Leadership Academy 9-12
227 Magnolia St 13204 315-435-4408
Dr. Matthew Williams, prin.
MS Alternative Program @ Shea Alt
1607 S Geddes St 13207 315-435-6226
Jim Palumbo, prin.
Westside Academy at Blodgett 400/6-8
312 Oswego St 13204 315-435-4386
Alonzo Graham, prin. Fax 435-4539
Johnson Adult & Continuing Education Ctr Adult
573 E Genesee St 13202 315-435-4135
John Dittmann, prin. Fax 435-5875

Westhill Central SD 1,800/K-12
400 Walberta Rd 13219 315-426-3218
Casey Barduhn, supt. Fax 488-6411
www.westhillschools.org/
Onondaga Hill MS 600/5-8
4860 Onondaga Rd 13215 315-426-3400
Mark Bednarski, prin. Fax 492-0156
Westhill HS 600/9-12
4501 Onondaga Blvd 13219 315-426-3100
Lee Roscoe, prin. Fax 475-0319

Bishop Ludden JSHS 300/7-12
815 Fay Rd 13219 315-468-2591
Brenda Reichert, admin. Fax 468-0097
Bryant & Stratton College Post-Sec.
953 James St 13203 315-472-6603
Christian Brothers Academy 700/7-12
6245 Randall Rd 13214 315-446-5960
Matt Keough, prin. Fax 446-3393
Crouse Hospital College of Nursing Post-Sec.
736 Irving Ave 13210 315-470-7481
Faith Heritage S 300/PK-12
3740 Midland Ave 13205 315-469-7777
Neal Capone, head sch Fax 492-7440
Le Moyne College Post-Sec.
1419 Salt Springs Rd 13214 315-445-4100
Living Word Academy 200/PK-12
6101 Court Street Rd 13206 315-437-6744
Manlius Pebble Hill S 500/PK-12
5300 Jamesville Rd 13214 315-446-2452
Jim Dunaway, head sch Fax 446-2620
Onondaga School of Therapeutic Massage Post-Sec.
719 E Genesee St 13210 315-424-1159
Phillips Hairstyling Institute Post-Sec.
709 E Genesee St 13210 315-422-9656
St. Joseph's Hospital College of Nursing Post-Sec.
206 Prospect Ave 13203 315-448-5040
SUNY College Environ. Science - Forestry Post-Sec.
1 Forestry Dr 13210 315-470-6500
SUNY Onondaga Community College Post-Sec.
4585 W Seneca Tpke 13215 315-498-2622
SUNY Upstate Medical University Post-Sec.
750 E Adams St 13210 315-464-5540
Syracuse University 13244 Post-Sec.
315-443-1870

Tannersville, Greene, Pop. 531
Hunter-Tannersville Central SD 400/PK-12
PO Box 1018 12485 518-589-5400
Dr. Patrick Sweeney, supt. Fax 589-5403
www.htcsd.org/
Tannersville MSHS 200/7-12
PO Box 1018 12485 518-589-5880
Dr. Adeline Basil, prin. Fax 589-7071

Tarrytown, Westchester, Pop. 11,035

Hackley S 800/K-12
293 Benedict Ave 10591 914-366-2642
Michael Wirtz, hdmstr. Fax 366-2636

Thiells, Rockland, Pop. 4,970
North Rockland Central SD
Supt. — See Garnerville
Fieldstone MS 1,300/7-8
100 Fieldstone Dr 10984 845-942-7900
Anthony Zollo, prin. Fax 942-7910
North Rockland HS 2,500/9-12
106 Hammond Rd 10984 845-942-3300
Michael Gill, prin. Fax 942-3365

Thornwood, Westchester, Pop. 3,718
Mount Pleasant Central SD 1,900/K-12
825 Westlake Dr 10594 914-769-5500
Dr. Susan Guiney, supt. Fax 769-3733
www.mtplcsd.org
Westlake HS 600/9-12
825 Westlake Dr 10594 914-769-8311
Keith Schenker, prin. Fax 769-0596
Westlake MS 500/6-8
825 Westlake Dr 10594 914-769-8540
Dr. Adam Bronstein, prin. Fax 769-8550

Ticonderoga, Essex, Pop. 3,342
Ticonderoga Central SD 800/K-12
5 Calkins Pl 12883 518-585-7400
Dr. John McDonald Ed.D., supt. Fax 585-2682
www.ticonderogak12.org
Ticonderoga HS 300/9-12
5 Calkins Pl 12883 518-585-7400
John Donohue, prin. Fax 585-4076
Ticonderoga MS 200/6-8
116 Alexandria Ave 12883 518-585-7400
Herbert Tedford, prin. Fax 585-2716

Tioga Center, Tioga
Tioga Central SD 1,000/K-12
PO Box 241 13845 607-687-8000
Scot Taylor, supt. Fax 687-8007
www.tiogacentral.org
Tioga HS 300/9-12
PO Box 241 13845 607-687-8001
Joshua Roe, prin. Fax 687-8010
Tioga MS 300/5-8
PO Box 241 13845 607-687-8004
Willard Cook, prin. Fax 687-6910

Tonawanda, Erie, Pop. 14,988
Kenmore-Town of Tonawanda UFSD
Supt. — See Buffalo
Kenmore East HS 900/8-12
350 Fries Rd 14150 716-874-8402
Patrick Heyden, prin. Fax 874-8443

Tonawanda CSD 1,800/PK-12
100 Hinds St 14150 716-694-7784
Dr. James Newton, supt. Fax 695-8738
www.tonawandacsd.org
Tonawanda MSHS 900/6-12
600 Fletcher St 14150 716-694-7660
Jessica Lyons, prin. Fax 743-8839

Cardinal O'Hara HS 200/9-12
39 Ohara Rd 14150 716-695-2600
Mary Holzerland, prin. Fax 692-8697
MarJon School of Beauty Culture Post-Sec.
1154 Niagara Falls Blvd 14150 716-836-6240

Troy, Rensselaer, Pop. 48,315
Brunswick Central SD 1,200/PK-12
3992 State Highway 2 12180 518-279-4600
Dr. Angelina Maloney, supt. Fax 279-1918
www.brittonkill.k12.ny.us
Tamarac MSHS 700/6-12
3992 State Highway 2 12180 518-279-4600
Richard Pogue, prin. Fax 279-3888

Lansingburgh Central SD 2,400/PK-12
576 5th Ave 12182 518-233-6850
Cynthia DeDominick, supt. Fax 235-7436
www.lansingburgh.org
Knickerbocker MS 600/6-8
320 7th Ave 12182 518-233-6811
Michael Harkin, prin. Fax 238-2518
Lansingburgh HS 800/9-12
320 7th Ave 12182 518-233-6806
Frank Macri, prin. Fax 233-6826

Troy CSD, 475 1st St 12180 4,400/PK-12
John Carmello, supt. 518-328-5052
www.troycsd.org
Public S 12, 475 1st St 12180 500/Alt
James Canfield, dir. 518-328-5083
Troy HS 1,200/9-12
1950 Burdett Ave 12180 518-328-5401
Joseph Mariano, prin. Fax 274-2341
Troy MS 800/6-8
1976 Burdett Ave 12180 518-328-5301
Brian Dunn, prin. Fax 274-8160

Catholic Central HS 500/7-12
625 7th Ave 12182 518-235-7100
Christopher Bott, prin. Fax 237-1796
La Salle Institute 400/6-12
174 Williams Rd 12180 518-283-2500
Dr. Paul Fallon, prin. Fax 283-6265
Redemption Christian Academy 100/PK-12
PO Box 753 12181 518-272-6679
Rensselaer Polytechnic Institute Post-Sec.
110 8th St 12180 518-276-6000
Samaritan Hospital School of Nursing Post-Sec.
2215 Burdett Ave 12180 518-271-3285
SUNY Hudson Valley Community College Post-Sec.
80 Vandenburgh Ave 12180 518-629-4822
The Sage Colleges Post-Sec.
65 1st St 12180 518-244-2000
Willard S 300/9-12
285 Pawling Ave 12180 518-833-1300
Dr. Susan R. Groesbeck, head sch Fax 833-1800

Trumansburg, Tompkins, Pop. 1,761
Trumansburg Central SD 1,100/K-12
100 Whig St 14886 607-387-7551
Michael McGuire, supt. Fax 387-2807
www.tburg.k12.ny.us
Dickerson HS 400/9-12
100 Whig St 14886 607-387-7551
Jon Koeng, prin. Fax 387-2807
Doig MS 300/5-8
100 Whig St 14886 607-387-7551
Joshua Hunkele, prin. Fax 387-2807

Tully, Onondaga, Pop. 852
Tully Central SD 900/K-12
20 State St 13159 315-696-6204
Robert Hughes, supt. Fax 883-1343
www.tullyschools.org
Tully JSHS 500/7-12
20 State St 13159 315-696-6235
Mary Ann Murphy, prin. Fax 696-6237

Tupper Lake, Franklin, Pop. 3,639
Tupper Lake Central SD 800/PK-12
294 Hosley Ave 12986 518-359-3371
Seth McGowan, supt. Fax 359-7862
www.tupperlakecsd.net/
Tupper Lake MSHS 400/7-12
25 Chaney Ave 12986 518-359-3322
Matthew Southwick, prin. Fax 359-7862

Turin, Lewis, Pop. 232
South Lewis Central SD 1,000/PK-12
PO Box 10 13473 315-348-2500
Douglas Premo, supt. Fax 348-2510
www.southlewis.org
South Lewis HS 300/9-12
PO Box 40 13473 315-348-2520
Chad Luther, prin. Fax 348-2510
South Lewis MS 300/5-8
PO Box 70 13473 315-348-2570
Judith Duppert, prin. Fax 348-2510

Tuxedo Park, Orange, Pop. 598
Tuxedo UFD 500/K-12
PO Box 2002 10987 845-351-4799
Nancy Teed, supt. Fax 351-5296
www.tuxedoufsd.org
Baker HS 300/7-12
PO Box 2002 10987 845-351-4786
Arthur Schouten, prin. Fax 351-4823

Uniondale, Nassau, Pop. 24,253
Uniondale UFD 6,400/PK-12
933 Goodrich St 11553 516-560-8800
Dr. William Lloyd, supt. Fax 292-2659
www.uniondaleschools.org
Turtle Hook MS 700/6-8
975 Jerusalem Ave 11553 516-918-1300
Dr. Donald Humphrey, prin. Fax 505-2533
Uniondale HS 2,100/9-12
933 Goodrich St 11553 516-560-8831
Dr. Florence Simmons, prin. Fax 564-8464
Other Schools – See Hempstead

Hebrew Academy of Nassau County 400/7-12
215 Oak St 11553 516-538-8161
Institute of Allied Medical Professions Post-Sec.
333 Earle Ovington Ste 305 11553 516-450-3110
Kellenberg Memorial HS 2,600/6-12
1400 Glenn Curtiss Blvd 11553 516-292-0200
Br. Kenneth Hoagland, prin. Fax 292-0877

Union Springs, Cayuga, Pop. 1,182
Union Springs Central SD 800/K-12
239 Cayuga St 13160 315-889-4101
Jarett Powers, supt. Fax 889-4108
www.unionspringscsd.org
Union Springs MSHS 400/7-12
239 Cayuga St 13160 315-889-4110
Charles Walker, prin. Fax 889-4118

Union Springs Academy 100/9-12
PO Box 524 13160 315-889-7314

Upper Nyack, Rockland, Pop. 2,003
Nyack UFD
Supt. — See Nyack
Nyack HS 900/9-12
360 Christian Herald Rd 10960 845-353-7100
Nicole Saieva, prin. Fax 353-7119

Utica, Oneida, Pop. 60,287
Utica CSD 9,000/K-12
106 Memorial Pkwy 13501 315-792-2210
Bruce Karam, supt. Fax 792-2200
www.uticacsd.org/
Donovan MS 700/6-8
1701 Noyes St 13502 315-792-2006
Ann Marie Palladino, prin. Fax 792-2077
Kennedy MS 600/6-8
500 Deerfield Dr E 13502 315-792-2088
Joshua Gifford, prin. Fax 792-2084
Proctor HS 2,600/9-12
1203 Hilton Ave 13501 315-368-6400
Steven Falchi, prin. Fax 223-4896

Faxton-St. Luke's Healthcare Post-Sec.
PO Box 479 13503 315-624-6136
Mohawk Valley Community College Post-Sec.
1101 Sherman Dr 13501 315-792-5400
Notre Dame JSHS 300/7-12
2 Notre Dame Ln 13502 315-724-5118
Sr. Anna Mae Collins, prin. Fax 724-9460
PrattMWP College of Art and Design Post-Sec.
310 Genesee St 13502 800-755-8920
St. Elizabeth College of Nursing Post-Sec.
2215 Genesee St 13501 315-798-8144
SUNY Institute of Technology Utica/Rome Post-Sec.
100 Seymour Rd 13502 315-792-7500
USC The Business College Post-Sec.
201 Bleecker St 13501 315-733-2300
Utica College Post-Sec.
1600 Burrstone Rd 13502 315-792-3111

Valatie, Columbia, Pop. 1,798
Ichabod Crane Central SD 1,800/K-12
PO Box 820 12184 518-758-7575
George Zini, supt. Fax 758-7579
www.ichabodcrane.org/
Crane HS 600/9-12
PO Box 820 12184 518-758-7575
Craig Shull, prin. Fax 758-2181
Crane MS 400/6-8
PO Box 820 12184 518-758-7575
Tim Farley, prin. Fax 758-1405

Valhalla, Westchester, Pop. 3,081
Valhalla UFD 1,500/K-12
316 Columbus Ave 10595 914-683-5040
Dr. Brenda Myers, supt. Fax 683-5075
www.valhallaschools.org/
Valhalla HS 500/9-12
300 Columbus Ave 10595 914-683-5014
Jonathan Thomas, prin. Fax 683-5003
Valhalla MS 400/6-8
300 Columbus Ave 10595 914-683-5011
Roberto Trigosso, prin. Fax 683-5003

New York Medical College Post-Sec.
40 Sunshine Cottage Rd 10595 914-594-4000
SUNY Westchester Community College Post-Sec.
75 Grasslands Rd 10595 914-606-6600

Valley Stream, Nassau, Pop. 36,423
Valley Stream Central HSD 4,500/7-12
1 Kent Rd 11580 516-872-5601
Dr. Bill Heidenreich, supt. Fax 872-5658
www.vschsd.org
Valley Stream Central HS 1,100/10-12
135 Fletcher Ave 11580 516-561-4410
Dr. Joseph Pompilio, prin. Fax 561-4490
Valley Stream Memorial JHS 900/7-9
320 Fletcher Ave 11580 516-872-7710
Anthony Mignella, prin. Fax 872-7711
Valley Stream South HS 1,300/7-12
150 Jedwood Pl 11581 516-791-0310
Maureen Henry, prin. Fax 791-0305
Other Schools – See Franklin Square

Business Informatics Center Post-Sec.
134 S Central Ave 11580 516-561-0050
Valley Stream Christian Academy 200/K-12
12 E Fairview Ave 11580 516-561-6122
Rev. Leslie Fowley, supt. Fax 284-7191

Van Hornesville, Herkimer
Van Hornesville-Owen D. Young Central SD 200/K-12
PO Box 125 13475 315-858-0729
Brennan Fahey, supt. Fax 858-2019
www.odyoungcsd.org
Young Central S 200/K-12
PO Box 125 13475 315-858-0729
Brennan Fahey, supt. Fax 858-2019

Verona, Oneida, Pop. 837
Vernon-Verona-Sherrill Central SD 2,000/PK-12
PO Box 128 13478 315-829-2520
Martha Group, supt. Fax 829-4949
www.vvsschools.org
Vernon-Verona-Sherrill HS 600/9-12
PO Box 128 13478 315-829-7446
Andy Brown, prin. Fax 829-4465
Vernon-Verona-Sherrill MS 300/7-8
PO Box 128 13478 315-829-7444
Carrie Hodkinson, prin. Fax 829-5966

Vestal, Broome, Pop. 5,000
Vestal Central SD 3,400/K-12
201 Main St 13850 607-757-2241
Jeffrey Ahearn, supt. Fax 757-2227
www.vestal.k12.ny.us
Vestal HS 1,100/9-12
205 Woodlawn Dr 13850 607-757-2281
Dr. Albert Penna, prin. Fax 757-2301
Vestal MS 800/6-8
600 S Benita Blvd 13850 607-757-2331
Ann Marie Loose, prin. Fax 757-2229

Elmira Business Institute Post-Sec.
4100 Vestal Rd 13850 607-729-8915
Ross Corners Christian Academy 100/PK-12
2101 Owego Rd 13850 607-748-3301
Toby Wyse, admin. Fax 748-3301

Victor, Ontario, Pop. 2,645
Victor Central SD 4,300/PK-12
953 High St 14564 585-924-3252
Dr. Dawn Santiago-Marullo, supt. Fax 742-7090
www.victorschools.org
Victor HS 1,300/9-12
953 High St 14564 585-924-3252
Yvonne O'Shea, prin. Fax 924-9536
Victor JHS 700/7-8
953 High St 14564 585-924-3252
Brian Gee, prin. Fax 924-9535

Voorheesville, Albany, Pop. 2,770
Voorheesville Central SD 1,200/K-12
432 New Salem Rd 12186 518-765-3313
Brian Hunt, supt. Fax 765-2751
vcsd.neric.org/
Bouton HS 400/9-12
432 New Salem Rd 12186 518-765-3314
Laura Schmitz, prin. Fax 765-5547
Voorheesville MS 300/6-8
432 New Salem Rd 12186 518-765-3314
Jennifer Drautz, prin. Fax 765-3842

Wallkill, Ulster, Pop. 2,258
Wallkill Central SD 3,100/K-12
PO Box 310 12589 845-895-7100
Kevin Castle, supt. Fax 895-3630
www.wallkillcsd.k12.ny.us
Borden MS 500/7-8
PO Box 310 12589 845-895-7175
Marjorie Anderson, prin. Fax 895-8036
Wallkill HS 1,100/9-12
PO Box 310 12589 845-895-7150
Michael Rydell, prin. Fax 895-8003

Walton, Delaware, Pop. 3,059
Walton Central SD 1,000/PK-12
47-49 Stockton Ave 13856 607-865-4116
Roger Clough, supt. Fax 865-8568
www.waltoncsd.org
Mack MS 200/6-8
47-49 Stockton Ave 13856 607-865-4116
Fax 865-8568
O'Neill HS 300/9-12
47-49 Stockton Ave 13856 607-865-4116
Robert Knushke, prin. Fax 865-6130

Walworth, Wayne
Gananda Central SD 1,000/K-12
1500 Dayspring Rdg 14568 315-986-3521
Dr. Shawn Van Scoy, supt. Fax 986-2003
www.gananda.org
Gananda MS 300/6-8
1500 Dayspring Rdg 14568 315-986-3521
Tracie Douglas, prin. Fax 986-1927
Gananda / Ruben A. Cirillo HS 300/9-12
1500 Dayspring Rdg 14568 315-986-3521
Matthew Mahoney, prin. Fax 986-1761

Wampsville, Madison, Pop. 531
Oneida CSD
Supt. — See Oneida
Shortell MS 300/7-8
PO Box 716 13163 315-363-1050
Todd Widrick, prin. Fax 366-0622

Wantagh, Nassau, Pop. 18,699
Wantagh UFD 3,200/K-12
3301 Beltagh Ave 11793 516-781-8000
Maureen Goldberg, supt. Fax 781-6076
www.wantaghschools.org
Wantagh HS 1,100/9-12
3297 Beltagh Ave 11793 516-679-6402
Dr. Carolyn Breivogel, prin. Fax 679-6432
Wantagh MS 800/6-8
3299 Beltagh Ave 11793 516-679-6350
Dawn Matrochano, prin. Fax 679-6311

Wappingers Falls, Dutchess, Pop. 5,339
Wappingers Central SD
Supt. — See Hopewell Junction
Ketcham HS 1,900/9-12
99 Myers Corners Rd 12590 845-298-5100
David Seipp, prin. Fax 298-5099
Van Wyck JHS 1,000/7-8
6 Hillside Lake Rd 12590 845-227-1700
Dr. Steve Shuchat, prin. Fax 227-1748
Wappingers JHS 800/7-8
30 Major MacDonald Way 12590 845-298-5200
Terrence Thompson, prin. Fax 298-5156

Warrensburg, Warren, Pop. 3,071
Warrensburg Central SD 800/K-12
103 Schroon River Rd 12885 518-623-2861
John Goralski, supt. Fax 623-2436
www.wcsd.org
Warrensburg JSHS 400/7-12
103 Schroon River Rd 12885 518-623-2862
Doug Duell, prin. Fax 623-5089

Warsaw, Wyoming, Pop. 3,438
Warsaw Central SD 900/K-12
153 W Buffalo St 14569 585-786-8000
Joseph Englebert, supt. Fax 786-8008
www.warsaw.k12.ny.us
Warsaw MSHS 500/6-12
81 W Court St 14569 585-786-8000
Richard Ellis, prin. Fax 786-3193

Warwick, Orange, Pop. 6,603
Warwick Valley Central SD 3,700/K-12
PO Box 595 10990 845-987-3000
Dr. David Leach, supt. Fax 986-1408
www.warwickvalleyschools.com
Warwick Valley HS 1,400/9-12
PO Box 595 10990 845-987-3050
Dr. Larry Washington, prin. Fax 987-8982
Warwick Valley MS 1,100/5-8
PO Box 595 10990 845-987-3100
Lisamarie Spindler, prin. Fax 986-6942

Washingtonville, Orange, Pop. 5,806
Washingtonville Central SD 4,300/PK-12
52 W Main St 10992 845-497-4000
Roy Reese, supt. Fax 496-2330
www.ws.k12.ny.us
Washingtonville HS 1,400/9-12
54 W Main St 10992 845-497-4000
Brian Connolly, prin. Fax 496-2212
Washingtonville MS 1,000/6-8
38 W Main St 10992 845-497-4000
Teresa Thompson, prin. Fax 496-2099

Waterford, Saratoga, Pop. 1,958
Waterford-Halfmoon UFD 800/K-12
125 Middletown Rd 12188 518-237-0800
Patrick Pomerville, supt. Fax 237-7335
www.whufsd.org
Waterford-Halfmoon HS 400/7-12
125 Middletown Rd 12188 518-237-0800
Christopher Scanlan, prin. Fax 237-7335

Waterloo, Seneca, Pop. 5,097
Waterloo Central SD 1,700/K-12
109 Washington St 13165 315-539-1500
Terri Bavis, supt. Fax 539-1504
www.waterloocsd.org
Waterloo HS 600/9-12
96 Stark St 13165 315-539-1550
Susan Burgess, prin. Fax 539-1536
Waterloo MS 400/6-8
65 Center St 13165 315-539-1540
Vincent Vitale, prin. Fax 539-1534

Watertown, Jefferson, Pop. 26,112
Watertown CSD 3,900/K-12
1351 Washington St 13601 315-785-3700
Terry Fralick, supt. Fax 785-6855
www.watertowncsd.org
Case MS 600/7-8
1237 Washington St 13601 315-785-3870
Terry Gonseth, prin. Fax 785-3731
Watertown HS 1,100/9-12
1335 Washington St 13601 315-785-3800
Leslie Atkinson, prin. Fax 785-3733

Faith Fellowship Christian S 200/PK-12
131 Moore Ave 13601 315-782-9342
Immaculate Heart Central JSHS 300/7-12
1316 Ives St 13601 315-788-4670
Lisa Parsons, prin. Fax 788-4672
Jefferson Community College Post-Sec.
1220 Coffeen St 13601 315-786-2200
Samaritan Medical Center Post-Sec.
830 Washington St 13601 315-785-4000

Waterville, Oneida, Pop. 1,551
Waterville Central SD 800/PK-12
381 Madison St 13480 315-841-3900
Charles Chafee, supt. Fax 841-3939
www.watervillecsd.org
Waterville JSHS 400/7-12
381 Madison St 13480 315-841-3800
Nicholas Rauch, prin. Fax 841-3838

Watervliet, Albany, Pop. 9,992
Watervliet CSD 1,300/K-12
1245 Hillside Dr 12189 518-629-3200
Dr. Lori Caplan, supt. Fax 629-3265
vliet.neric.org/
Watervliet JSHS 600/7-12
1245 Hillside Dr 12189 518-629-3300
Ryan Groat, prin. Fax 273-4772

Watkins Glen, Schuyler, Pop. 1,826
Watkins Glen Central SD 1,000/PK-12
303 12th St 14891 607-535-3220
Thomas Phillips, supt. Fax 535-4629
www.wgcsd.org
Watkins Glen Central JSHS 400/7-12
301 12th St 14891 607-535-3210
Kai D'Alleva, prin. Fax 535-3262

Waverly, Tioga, Pop. 4,388
Waverly Central SD 1,500/PK-12
15 Frederick St 14892 607-565-2841
Dr. Randy Richards, supt. Fax 565-4997
www.waverlyschools.com/
Waverly HS 500/9-12
1 Frederick St 14892 607-565-8101
Ashlee Hunt, prin. Fax 565-4997
Waverly MS 400/5-8
1 Frederick St 14892 607-565-3410
Paul Vesci, prin. Fax 565-4997

Wayland, Steuben, Pop. 1,852
Wayland-Cohocton Central SD 1,400/PK-12
2350 State Route 63 14572 585-728-2211
Michael Wetherbee, supt. Fax 728-3566
www.wccsk12.org
Wayland-Cohocton HS 400/9-12
2350 State Route 63 14572 585-728-2366
Eileen Feinman, prin. Fax 728-2425
Wayland-Cohocton MS 400/5-8
2350 State Route 63 14572 585-728-2551
Jeremy Lonneville, prin. Fax 728-3556

Webster, Monroe, Pop. 5,251
Webster Central SD 8,500/K-12
119 South Ave 14580 585-216-0000
Carmen Gumina, supt. Fax 265-6561
www.websterschools.org
Spry MS 1,000/6-8
119 South Ave 14580 585-265-6500
James Baehr, prin. Fax 265-6512
Thomas HS 1,400/9-12
800 Five Mile Line Rd 14580 585-670-8000
Glenn Widor, prin. Fax 671-1884
Webster Schroeder HS 1,400/9-12
875 Ridge Rd 14580 585-670-5000
Paul Benz, prin. Fax 671-8681
Willink MS 1,000/6-8
900 Publishers Pkwy 14580 585-670-1030
Jim Gindling, prin. Fax 671-1978

Weedsport, Cayuga, Pop. 1,803
Weedsport Central SD 800/K-12
2821 E Brutus Street Rd 13166 315-834-6637
Shaun O'Connor, supt.
www.weedsport.org
Weedsport JSHS 400/6-12
2821 E Brutus Street Rd 13166 315-834-6652
Brett Fingland, prin. Fax 834-8693

Wells, Hamilton
Wells Central SD 100/PK-12
PO Box 300 12190 518-924-6000
Thomas Sincavage, supt. Fax 924-9246
wellscsd.com/
Wells Central S 100/PK-12
PO Box 300 12190 518-924-6000
Thomas Sincavage, supt. Fax 924-9246

Wellsville, Allegany, Pop. 4,622
Wellsville Central SD 1,300/PK-12
126 W State St 14895 585-596-2170
Kimberly Mueller, supt. Fax 596-2177
www.wellsvilleschools.org
Wellsville HS 400/9-12
126 W State St 14895 585-596-2188
Jeff White, prin. Fax 596-2180
Wellsville MS 300/6-8
126 W State St 14895 585-596-2144
Mary Ellen O'Connell, prin. Fax 596-2142

West Babylon, Suffolk, Pop. 42,432
West Babylon UFD 4,100/K-12
10 Farmingdale Rd 11704 631-376-7000
Dr. Yiendhy Farrelly, supt. Fax 376-7019
www.wbschools.org
West Babylon HS 1,400/9-12
500 Great East Neck Rd 11704 631-376-7101
Dr. Ellice Vassallo, prin. Fax 376-7119
West Babylon JHS 900/6-8
200 Old Farmingdale Rd 11704 631-376-7201
Scott Payne, prin. Fax 376-7209

Commercial Driver Training School Post-Sec.
600 Patton Ave 11704 631-249-1330

Westbury, Nassau, Pop. 14,820
East Meadow UFD 7,100/K-12
718 The Plain Rd 11590 516-478-5776
Leon Campo, supt. Fax 478-5779
www.eastmeadow.k12.ny.us
Clarke HS 700/9-12
740 Edgewood Dr 11590 516-876-7451
Timothy Voels, prin. Fax 876-7416
Clarke MS 600/6-8
740 Edgewood Dr 11590 516-876-7401
Stacy Breslin, prin. Fax 876-7407
Other Schools – See East Meadow

Westbury UFD
Supt. — See Old Westbury
Westbury MS 1,000/6-8
455 Rockland St 11590 516-876-5082
David Zimbler, prin. Fax 876-5141

West Chazy, Clinton, Pop. 516
Beekmantown Central SD 1,900/PK-12
37 Eagle Way 12992 518-563-8250
Daniel W. Mannix, supt. Fax 563-8132
www.bcsdk12.org
Beekmantown HS 600/9-12
37 Eagle Way 12992 518-563-8787
Justin Gardner, prin. Fax 563-8789
Beekmantown MS 500/6-8
37 Eagle Way 12992 518-563-8690
Amy Campbell, prin. Fax 563-8691

Westfield, Chautauqua, Pop. 3,195
Westfield Central SD 700/K-12
203 E Main St 14787 716-326-2151
David Davison, supt. Fax 326-2195
www.wacs.wnyric.org/
Westfield HS 200/9-12
203 E Main St 14787 716-326-2151
Ivana Hite, prin. Fax 326-2157
Westfield MS 100/6-8
203 E Main St 14787 716-326-2151
Ivana Hite, prin. Fax 326-2157

Westhampton Beach, Suffolk, Pop. 1,702
Westhampton Beach UFD 1,800/K-12
340 Mill Rd 11978 631-288-3800
Mike Radday, supt. Fax 288-8351
www.westhamptonbeach.k12.ny.us
Westhampton Beach HS 1,000/9-12
49 Lilac Rd 11978 631-288-3800
Christopher Herr, prin. Fax 288-3915
Westhampton Beach MS 400/6-8
340 Mill Rd 11978 631-288-3800
Charisse Miller, prin. Fax 288-5496

West Hempstead, Nassau, Pop. 18,467
West Hempstead UFD 2,100/K-12
252 Chestnut St 11552 516-390-3100
Patricia Sullivan-Kriss, supt. Fax 489-1776
www.whufsd.com
West Hempstead HS 800/9-12
400 Nassau Blvd 11552 516-390-3214
Alvaro Escobar, prin. Fax 489-1769
West Hempstead MS 500/6-8
450 Nassau Blvd 11552 516-390-3160
Dina Reilly, prin. Fax 489-8946

West Henrietta, Monroe
Rush-Henrietta Central SD
Supt. — See Henrietta
Burger MS 500/6-8
639 Erie Station Rd 14586 585-359-5308
Greg Lane, prin. Fax 359-5333

West Islip, Suffolk, Pop. 28,075
West Islip UFD 4,800/K-12
100 Sherman Ave 11795 631-893-3200
Bernadette Burns, supt. Fax 893-3212
www.wi.k12.ny.us
Beach Street MS 600/6-8
17 Beach St 11795 631-893-3310
Andrew O'Farrell, prin. Fax 893-3318
Udall Road MS 600/6-8
900 Udall Rd 11795 631-893-3290
Daniel Marquardt, prin. Fax 893-3301
West Islip HS 1,600/9-12
1 Lions Path 11795 631-893-3250
Dr. Anthony Bridgeman, prin. Fax 893-3318

St. John the Baptist Diocesan HS 1,700/9-12
1170 Montauk Hwy 11795 631-587-8000
Nan Doherty, prin. Fax 587-8996

Westmoreland, Oneida, Pop. 420
Westmoreland Central SD 900/K-12
PO Box 430 13490 315-557-2614
Rocco Migliori, supt. Fax 853-4602
www.westmorelandschool.org
Westmoreland HS 300/9-12
PO Box 430 13490 315-557-2616
Joshua Saxton, prin. Fax 557-2672
Westmoreland MS 300/5-8
PO Box 430 13490 315-557-2618
Eric Coriale, prin. Fax 557-2760

West Nyack, Rockland, Pop. 3,385
Clarkstown Central SD
Supt. — See New City
Clarkstown South HS 1,400/9-12
31 Demarest Mill Rd 10994 845-624-3400
Debra Tarantino, prin. Fax 623-5470
Festa MS 2,200/6-8
30 Parrott Rd 10994 845-624-3484
Kevin Horan, prin. Fax 634-5874

West Point, Orange, Pop. 6,475

United States Military Academy Post-Sec.
646 Swift Rd 10996 845-938-4041

Westport, Essex, Pop. 508
Westport Central SD 200/K-12
25 Sisco St 12993 518-962-8244
Scott Osborne, supt. Fax 962-4571
www.westportcs.org
Westport Central S 200/K-12
25 Sisco St 12993 518-962-8244
Josh Meyer, prin. Fax 962-4571

West Sayville, Suffolk, Pop. 4,972
Sayville UFD
Supt. — See Sayville
Sayville HS 1,000/9-12
20 Brook St 11796 631-244-6600
Ronald Hoffer, prin. Fax 244-6779

West Seneca, Erie, Pop. 44,393
Orchard Park Central SD 4,900/K-12
2240 Southwestern Blvd 14224 716-209-6200
Matthew McGarrity, supt. Fax 209-6353
www.opschools.org
Other Schools – See Orchard Park

West Seneca Central SD 6,300/PK-12
675 Potters Rd 14224 716-677-3101
Dr. Mark J. Crawford, supt. Fax 677-3104
www.wscschools.org/
East MS 900/5-8
1445 Center Rd 14224 716-677-3530
Sharon Loughran, prin. Fax 674-1046
West MS 900/6-8
395 Center Rd 14224 716-677-3500
Dave Kean, prin. Fax 675-6134
West Seneca East HS 900/9-12
4760 Seneca St 14224 716-677-3300
Dr. Jonathan Cervoni, prin. Fax 677-2933
West Seneca West HS 1,300/9-12
3330 Seneca St 14224 716-677-3350
John Brinker, prin. Fax 674-3551

Continental School of Beauty Culture Post-Sec.
1050 Union Rd 14224 716-675-8205
West Seneca Christian S 100/PK-12
511 Union Rd 14224 716-674-1820
Orlando Buria Ph.D., admin. Fax 674-4894

West Valley, Cattaraugus, Pop. 518
West Valley Central SD 300/PK-12
PO Box 290 14171 716-942-3293
Eric Lawton, supt. Fax 942-3440
www.wvalley.wnyric.org
West Valley Central S 300/PK-12
PO Box 290 14171 716-942-3293
Daniel Amodeo, prin. Fax 942-3440

West Winfield, Herkimer, Pop. 820
Mount Markham CSD 1,100/K-12
500 Fairground Rd 13491 315-822-2824
Dr. Paul Berry, supt. Fax 822-6162
www.mmcsd.org
Mount Markham HS 300/9-12
500 Fairground Rd 13491 315-822-2900
Russell Kissinger, prin. Fax 822-3486
Mount Markham MS 300/5-8
500 Fairground Rd 13491 315-822-2870
Dawn Yerkie, prin. Fax 822-6125

Whitehall, Washington, Pop. 2,580
Whitehall Central SD 700/K-12
87 Buckley Rd 12887 518-499-1772
William Scott, supt. Fax 499-1759
www.railroaders.net
Whitehall JSHS 300/7-12
87 Buckley Rd 12887 518-499-1770
Mark Doody, prin. Fax 499-1759

White Plains, Westchester, Pop. 55,780
White Plains CSD 7,000/K-12
5 Homeside Ln 10605 914-422-2000
Dr. Paul Fried, supt. Fax 422-2024
www.wpcsd.k12.ny.us
White Plains HS 2,100/9-12
550 North St 10605 914-422-2182
Ellen Doherty, prin. Fax 422-2196
White Plains MS - Eastview Campus 6-8
350 Main St 10601 914-422-2223
Joseph Cloherty, prin. Fax 422-2222
White Plains MS - Highlands Campus 1,500/6-8
128 Grandview Ave 10605 914-422-2092
Ernest Spatafore, prin. Fax 422-2273

Archbishop Stepinac HS 600/9-12
950 Mamaroneck Ave 10605 914-946-4800
Paul Carty, prin. Fax 684-2591
Berkeley College Post-Sec.
99 Church St 10601 914-694-1122
Fusion Academy 6-12
701 Westchester Ave # 200E 10604 914-285-9036
German International S New York 300/PK-12
50 Partridge Rd 10605 914-948-6513
Music Conservatory of Westchester Post-Sec.
216 Central Ave 10606 914-761-3715
New York School for the Deaf Post-Sec.
555 Knollwood Rd 10603
Sanford-Brown Institute Post-Sec.
333 Westchester Ave 10604 914-874-2500
The College of Westchester Post-Sec.
325 Central Ave 10606 914-948-4442

Whitesboro, Oneida, Pop. 3,727
Whitesboro Central SD 3,200/K-12
65 Oriskany Blvd 13492 315-266-3300
David Langone, supt. Fax 768-9730
www.wboro.org
Whitesboro MS 500/7-8
75 Oriskany Blvd 13492 315-266-3100
John Egresits, prin. Fax 768-9770
Other Schools – See Marcy

Whitestone, See New York
NYC Department of Education
Supt. — See New York
JHS 194 1,000/6-8
15460 17th Ave 11357 718-746-0818
Jennifer Miller, prin. Fax 746-7618

Lincoln Technical Institute Post-Sec.
1530 Petracca Pl 11357 718-640-9800

Whitesville, Allegany
Whitesville Central SD 200/K-12
692 Main St 14897 607-356-3301
Laurie Sanders, supt. Fax 356-3598
www.whitesvillesd.org
Whitesville Central S 200/K-12
692 Main St 14897 607-356-3301
Tammy Emery, prin. Fax 356-3598

Whitney Point, Broome, Pop. 945
Whitney Point Central SD 1,500/PK-12
PO Box 249 13862 607-692-8202
Patricia Follette, supt. Fax 692-4434
www.wpcsd.org
Tioughnioga Riverside Academy 600/4-8
PO Box 249 13862 607-692-8232
Laura Chestnut, prin. Fax 692-8283
Whitney Point HS 400/9-12
PO Box 249 13862 607-692-8201
Bruce Tytler, prin. Fax 692-8256

Williamson, Wayne, Pop. 2,435
Williamson Central SD 1,100/K-12
PO Box 900 14589 315-589-9661
Dr. Gregory Macaluso, supt. Fax 589-7611
www.williamsoncentral.org
Williamson HS 300/9-12
PO Box 900 14589 315-589-9621
Kathryn Avery, prin. Fax 589-8310
Williamson MS 300/5-8
PO Box 900 14589 315-589-9665
John Fulmer, prin. Fax 589-8314

Williamsville, Erie, Pop. 5,229
Williamsville Central SD
Supt. — See East Amherst
Heim MS 700/5-8
175 Heim Rd 14221 716-626-8600
Jeffrey Jachlewski, prin. Fax 626-8626
Mill MS 900/5-8
505 Mill St 14221 716-626-8300
Michael Calandra, prin. Fax 626-8326
Williamsville North HS 1,300/9-12
1595 Hopkins Rd 14221 716-626-8505
Gary Collichio, prin. Fax 626-8597
Williamsville South HS 1,000/9-12
5950 Main St 14221 716-626-8200
Keith Boardman, prin. Fax 626-8207

Christian Central Academy 400/K-12
39 Academy St 14221 716-634-4821
Thad Gaebelein, hdmstr. Fax 634-5851
Erie Community College North Post-Sec.
6205 Main St 14221 716-634-0800
Leon Studio One School of Hair Design Post-Sec.
5221 Main St 14221 716-631-3878

Williston Park, Nassau, Pop. 7,170

Schechter S of Long Island 6-12
6 Cross St 11596 516-539-3700

Willsboro, Essex, Pop. 740
Willsboro Central SD 300/PK-12
PO Box 180 12996 518-963-4456
Stephen Broadwell, supt. Fax 963-7577
www.willsborocsd.org/
Willsboro Central S 300/PK-12
PO Box 180 12996 518-963-4456
Stephen Broadwell, prin. Fax 963-7577

Wilson, Niagara, Pop. 1,249
Wilson Central SD 1,000/K-12
PO Box 648 14172 716-751-9341
Dr. Michael Wendt, supt. Fax 751-6556
www.wilson.wnyric.org/
Wilson HS 400/9-12
PO Box 648 14172 716-751-9341
Daniel Johnson, prin. Fax 751-9597
Wilson MS 300/6-8
PO Box 648 14172 716-751-9341
Scott Benton, prin. Fax 751-9597

Windham, Greene, Pop. 359
Windham-Ashland-Jewett Central SD 300/K-12
PO Box 429 12496 518-734-3400
John Wiktorko, supt. Fax 734-6050
www.wajcs.org/
Windham-Ashland Central S 300/K-12
PO Box 429 12496 518-734-3400
David Donner, prin. Fax 734-6050

Windsor, Broome, Pop. 903
Windsor Central SD 1,700/PK-12
1191 State Route 79 13865 607-655-8216
Jason Andrews Ed.D., supt. Fax 655-3553
www.windsor-csd.org
Windsor Central HS 600/9-12
1191 State Route 79 13865 607-655-8250
Jeffrey Salasny, prin. Fax 655-3622
Windsor MS 400/6-8
213 Main St 13865 607-655-8247
Kevin Strahley, prin. Fax 655-3760

Wolcott, Wayne, Pop. 1,683
North Rose-Wolcott Central SD 1,200/PK-12
11631 Salter Colvin Rd 14590 315-594-3141
Stephan Vigliotti, supt. Fax 594-2352
www.nrwcs.org
North Rose-Wolcott HS 400/9-12
11631 Salter Colvin Rd 14590 315-594-3141
Paul Benz, prin. Fax 594-6235
North Rose-Wolcott MS 400/5-8
5957 New Hartford St 14590 315-594-3141
Mark Mathews, prin. Fax 594-3120

Woodbourne, Sullivan

HaMesivta of Ellenville 9-12
344 Hasbrouck Dr 12788 917-583-6146

Woodbury, Nassau, Pop. 8,811

Fusion Academy 6-12
260 Crossways Park Dr 11797 516-364-5414
Tiffany Belferder, head sch Fax 364-5906

Woodmere, Nassau, Pop. 17,006
Hewlett-Woodmere UFD 3,100/PK-12
1 Johnson Pl 11598 516-792-4800
Dr. Ralph Marino, supt. Fax 374-8185
www.hewlett-woodmere.net
Other Schools – See Hewlett

Davis Renov Stahler Yeshiva HS for Boys 300/9-12
700 Ibsen St 11598 516-295-7700
Lawrence Woodmere Academy 300/PK-12
336 Woodmere Blvd 11598 516-374-9000
Alan Bernstein, hdmstr. Fax 374-4707

Woodside, See New York
NYC Department of Education
Supt. — See New York
IS 125 1,700/5-8
4602 47th Ave 11377 718-937-0320
Judy Mittler, prin. Fax 361-2451

Greater New York Academy 200/9-12
4132 58th St 11377 718-639-1752
Lillian Mitchell M.Ed., prin. Fax 639-8992
Razi S 300/PK-12
5511 Queens Blvd 11377 718-779-0711

Worcester, Otsego, Pop. 1,097
Worcester Central SD 400/PK-12
198 Main St 12197 607-397-8785
William Diamond, supt. Fax 397-8464
www.worcestercs.org
Worcester Central S 400/PK-12
198 Main St 12197 607-397-8785
Jessie Westfall, prin. Fax 397-9454

Wyandanch, Suffolk, Pop. 11,382
Wyandanch UFD 2,200/PK-12
1445 Straight Path 11798 631-870-0400
Dr. Mary Jones, supt. Fax 870-0404
www.wufsd.net/
Olive MS 400/6-8
140 Garden City Ave 11798 631-870-0525
Kenya Vanterpool, prin. Fax 870-0533
Wyandanch Memorial HS 500/9-12
54 S 32nd St 11798 631-870-0450
Paul Sibblies, prin. Fax 870-0459

Yonkers, Westchester, Pop. 192,139
Yonkers CSD 25,500/PK-12
1 Larkin Ctr 10701 914-376-8000
Dr. Edwin Quezada, supt. Fax 376-8584
www.yonkerspublicschools.org
Gorton HS 1,000/9-12
100 Shonnard Pl 10703 914-376-8350
Gail Joyner-White, prin. Fax 376-8377
Lincoln HS 1,100/9-12
375 Kneeland Ave 10704 914-376-8400
Ian Sherman, prin. Fax 376-8414
Palisade Preparatory S 600/7-12
201 Palisade Ave 10703 914-376-8177
Dr. Michelle Yazurlo, prin. Fax 376-8484
Riverside HS 900/9-12
565 Warburton Ave 10701 914-376-8425
Dr. Don Solimene, prin. Fax 376-8475
Roosevelt HS - Early College Studies 700/9-12
631 Tuckahoe Rd 10710 914-376-8118
Ed DeChent, prin. Fax 779-0163
Saunders Trades & Tech HS 1,200/9-12
183 Palmer Rd 10701 914-376-8150
Steve Mazzola, prin. Fax 376-8154
Yonkers Montessori Academy 1,300/PK-12
160 Woodlawn Ave 10704 914-376-8540
Dr. Eileen Rivera-Shapiro, prin. Fax 376-8552
Yonkers MSHS 1,100/7-12
150 Rockland Ave 10705 914-376-8191
Michael Shapiro, prin. Fax 376-4856
Pathways to Success Adult
75 Riverdale Ave 10701 914-376-8600
Sanah Naber, prin. Fax 376-8605

Cochran School of Nursing Post-Sec.
967 N Broadway 10701 914-964-4296
Sacred Heart HS 400/9-12
34 Convent Ave 10703 914-965-3114
Rev. Karen Valenti-DeCecco, admin. Fax 965-4510
St. Joseph's Seminary Post-Sec.
201 Seminary Ave 10704 914-968-6200
St. Vladimir's Orthodox Theological Sem. Post-Sec.
575 Scarsdale Rd 10707 914-961-8313

Yorkshire, Cattaraugus, Pop. 1,167
Yorkshire-Pioneer Central SD 2,500/PK-12
PO Box 579 14173 716-492-9300
Ben Halsey, supt. Fax 492-9360
www.pioneerschools.org
Pioneer HS 700/9-12
PO Box 639 14173 716-492-9334
Mark Schultz, prin. Fax 492-9350
Pioneer MS 700/5-8
PO Box 619 14173 716-492-9371
Melissa Prorok, prin. Fax 492-9417

Yorktown Heights, Westchester, Pop. 1,760
Lakeland Central SD
Supt. — See Shrub Oak
Lakeland-Copper Beech MS 1,300/6-8
3401 Old Yorktown Rd 10598 914-245-1885
Robert Bergmann, prin. Fax 245-1259

Yorktown Central SD 3,500/K-12
2725 Crompond Rd 10598 914-243-8000
Dr. Ralph Napolitano, supt. Fax 243-8002
www.yorktown.org/
Strang MS 900/6-8
2701 Crompond Rd 10598 914-243-8100
Marie Horowitz, prin. Fax 243-0016
Yorktown HS 1,300/9-12
2727 Crompond Rd 10598 914-243-8050
Joseph DeGennaro, prin. Fax 245-9256

Youngstown, Niagara, Pop. 1,918
Lewiston-Porter Central SD 2,000/K-12
4061 Creek Rd 14174 716-754-8281
Paul Casseri, supt. Fax 754-2755
www.lew-port.com
Lewiston-Porter HS 700/9-12
4061 Creek Rd 14174 716-286-7262
Andrew Auer, prin. Fax 286-7852
Lewiston-Porter MS 500/6-8
4061 Creek Rd 14174 716-286-7201
Dean Ramirez, prin. Fax 286-7204

NORTH CAROLINA

NORTH CAROLINA DEPT. PUBLIC INSTRUCTION
301 N Wilmington St, Raleigh 27601-1058
Telephone 919-807-3300
Fax 919-807-3445
Website http://www.dpi.state.nc.us

Superintendent of Public Instruction Mark Johnson

NORTH CAROLINA BOARD OF EDUCATION
301 N Wilmington St, Raleigh 27601-1058

Chairperson William Cobey

PUBLIC, PRIVATE AND CATHOLIC SECONDARY SCHOOLS

Aberdeen, Moore, Pop. 6,182
Moore County SD
Supt. — See Carthage
Southern MS 800/6-8
717 Johnson St 28315 910-693-1550
Marcy Cooper, prin. Fax 693-1544

Advance, Davie, Pop. 1,117
Davie County SD
Supt. — See Mocksville
Ellis MS 500/6-8
144 William Ellis Dr 27006 336-998-2007
Leigh Walters, prin. Fax 998-6249

Ahoskie, Hertford, Pop. 4,982
Hertford County SD
Supt. — See Winton
Hertford County Early College HS 100/9-12
109 Community College Rd 27910 252-332-7788
Bryan Ruffin, prin. Fax 332-3605
Hertford County HS 700/9-12
1500 1st St W 27910 252-332-4096
James Futrell, prin. Fax 332-1689

Ahoskie Christian S 200/PK-12
500 Kiwanis St 27910 252-332-2764
Ridgecroft S 300/PK-12
PO Box 1008 27910 252-332-2964
Roanoke-Chowan Community College Post-Sec.
109 Community College Rd 27910 252-862-1200

Albemarle, Stanly, Pop. 15,632
Stanly County SD 8,300/PK-12
1000 N 1st St Ste 4 28001 704-961-3000
Bill Josey, supt. Fax 961-3099
www.stanlycountyschools.org
Albemarle HS 400/9-12
311 Park Ridge Rd 28001 704-961-3000
Douglas Kilgore, prin. Fax 961-3099
Albemarle MS 400/6-8
1811 Badin Rd 28001 704-961-3400
Beverly Pennington, prin. Fax 961-3499
Stanly Academy Learning Center 50/Alt
1121 Austin St 28001 704-961-4500
Shannon Batchelor, prin. Fax 961-4599
Stanly Early College HS 200/9-12
141 College Dr 28001 704-991-0128
Anne Faulkenberry, dean Fax 991-0109
Other Schools – See Locust, New London, Norwood, Oakboro

Stanly Community College Post-Sec.
141 College Dr 28001 704-982-0121

Andrews, Cherokee, Pop. 1,715
Cherokee County SD
Supt. — See Murphy
Andrews HS 300/9-12
50 High School Dr 28901 828-321-5415
Dr. Lisa Fletcher, prin. Fax 321-3986
Andrews MS 200/6-8
2750 Business 19 28901 828-321-5762
Julie Higdon, prin. Fax 321-2009

Angier, Harnett, Pop. 4,289
Harnett County SD
Supt. — See Lillington
Harnett Central HS 1,500/9-12
2911 Harnett Central Rd 27501 919-639-6161
Chris Mace, prin. Fax 639-3642
Harnett Central MS 1,300/6-8
2529 Harnett Central Rd 27501 919-639-6000
Linwood Smith, prin. Fax 639-9617

Apex, Wake, Pop. 36,623
Wake County SD
Supt. — See Cary
Apex Friendship HS 9-12
7801 Humie Olive Rd 27502 919-694-0500
Matt Wight, prin. Fax 694-0525
Apex HS 2,500/9-12
1501 Laura Duncan Rd 27502 919-387-2208
Dr. Diann Kearney, prin. Fax 387-3023
Apex MS 1,100/6-8
400 E Moore St 27502 919-387-2181
Allen Ellzey, prin. Fax 387-2203
Lufkin Road MS 1,000/6-8
1002 Lufkin Rd, 919-387-4465
Karen Sinders, prin. Fax 363-1095
Middle Creek HS 2,200/9-12
123 Middle Creek Park Ave, 919-773-3838
Wade Martin, prin. Fax 773-3872
Salem MS 1,200/6-8
6150 Old Jenks Rd, 919-363-1870
Elaine Hofmann, prin. Fax 363-1876
West Lake MS 1,300/6-8
4600 W Lake Rd, 919-662-2900
Anne Adkins, prin. Fax 662-2906

Arden, Buncombe
Buncombe County SD
Supt. — See Asheville
Valley Springs MS 600/6-8
224 Long Shoals Rd 28704 828-654-1785
Eddie Burchfiel, prin. Fax 654-1789

Christ S 200/8-12
500 Christ School Rd 28704 828-684-6232
Paul Krieger, hdmstr. Fax 684-2745

Asheboro, Randolph, Pop. 24,567
Asheboro CSD 4,700/PK-12
PO Box 1103 27204 336-625-5104
Dr. Terry Worrell, supt. Fax 625-9238
www.asheboro.k12.nc.us
Asheboro HS 1,200/9-12
1221 S Park St 27203 336-625-6185
Dr. Jason Saunders, prin. Fax 625-9320
North Asheboro MS 500/6-8
1861 N Asheboro School Rd 27203 336-672-1900
Candace Call, prin. Fax 672-6267
South Asheboro MS 600/6-8
523 W Walker Ave 27203 336-629-4141
Ronald Dixon, prin. Fax 629-3761

Randolph County SD 18,100/PK-12
2222 S Fayetteville St # C 27205 336-318-6100
Dr. Stephen Gainey, supt. Fax 318-6155
www.randolph.k12.nc.us
Randolph Early College HS 300/9-12
629 Industrial Park Ave 27205 336-625-1137
April Thompson, prin. Fax 625-3186
Southwestern Randolph HS 1,100/9-12
1641 Hopewell Friends Rd 27205 336-381-7747
Shon Hildreth, prin. Fax 381-7743
Southwestern Randolph MS 600/6-8
1509 Hopewell Friends Rd 27205 336-381-3900
Michael Crider, prin. Fax 381-3905
Other Schools – See Climax, Liberty, Ramseur, Randleman, Trinity

---

Fayetteville Street Christian S 200/PK-12
151 W Pritchard St 27203 336-629-1383
David Jeffreys, admin. Fax 629-0067
Neighbors Grove Christian Academy 100/PK-12
1928 N Fayetteville St 27203 336-672-1147
Randy Haithcock, admin. Fax 672-5500
Randolph Community College Post-Sec.
629 Industrial Park Ave 27205 336-633-0200

Asheville, Buncombe, Pop. 81,334
Asheville CSD 4,200/PK-12
85 Mountain St 28801 828-350-7000
Dr. Pamela Baldwin, supt. Fax 255-5131
www.ashevillecityschools.net
Asheville HS 1,000/9-12
419 Mcdowell St 28803 828-350-2500
Robyn Weinkle, prin. Fax 255-5316
Asheville MS 800/6-8
211 S French Broad Ave 28801 828-350-6200
April Dockery, prin. Fax 255-5311
School of Inquiry and Life Sciences 300/9-12
419 McDowell St 28803 828-350-2700
David Robinson, prin. Fax 255-5119

Buncombe County SD 25,500/K-12
175 Bingham Rd 28806 828-255-5921
Dr. Tony Baldwin, supt. Fax 255-5923
www.buncombe.k12.nc.us
Buncombe County Early College S 200/9-12
340 Victoria Rd 28801 828-232-4123
Dr. Donna Lanahan, prin. Fax 232-4165
Buncombe County Middle College HS 100/Alt
340 Victoria Rd 28801 828-232-4123
Dr. Donna Lanahan, prin. Fax 232-4165
Erwin HS 1,300/9-12
60 Lees Creek Rd 28806 828-232-4251
Dr. Jim Brown, prin. Fax 251-2893
Erwin MS 900/7-8
20 Erwin Hills Rd 28806 828-232-4264
Chris Thompson, prin. Fax 253-4267
Nesbitt Discovery Academy 9-10
175 Bingham Rd 28806 828-271-4521
Nathan Alison, prin. Fax 271-4525
Reynolds HS 1,400/9-12
1 Rocket Dr 28803 828-298-2500
Doris Sellers, prin. Fax 298-2002
Reynolds MS 600/6-8
2 Rocket Dr 28803 828-298-7484
Dr. Jamie Johnson, prin. Fax 298-7503
Roberson HS 1,600/9-12
250 Overlook Rd 28803 828-654-1765
Bonnie Johnston, prin. Fax 654-1768
Other Schools – See Arden, Black Mountain, Candler, Fletcher, Swannanoa, Weaverville

---

Asheville Buncombe Technical Comm. Coll. Post-Sec.
340 Victoria Rd 28801 828-254-1921
Asheville S 300/9-12
360 Asheville School Rd 28806 828-254-6345
Archibald Montgomery, head sch Fax 252-8666
Carolina Day S 700/PK-12
1345 Hendersonville Rd 28803 828-274-0757
Kirk Duncan, head sch Fax 274-0756
Daoist Traditions Coll of Chinese Med Post-Sec.
382 Montford Ave 28801 828-225-3993
Reynolds Mountain Christian Academy 100/PK-12
20 Reynolds Mountain Blvd 28804 828-645-8053
Susie Hepler, admin. Fax 645-4542
South College - Asheville Post-Sec.
140 Sweeten Creek Rd 28803 828-398-2500
Temple Baptist S 100/PK-12
985 1/2 Patton Ave 28806 828-252-3712
University of North Carolina Post-Sec.
1 University Hts 28804 828-251-6600
Warren Wilson College Post-Sec.
PO Box 9000 28815 828-298-3325

Ayden, Pitt, Pop. 4,853
Pitt County SD
Supt. — See Greenville
Ayden-Grifton HS 700/9-12
7653 NC 11 S 28513 252-746-4183
Dr. Chena Cayton, prin. Fax 746-2120
Ayden MS 400/6-8
192 3rd St 28513 252-746-3672
Dr. Jeff Theus, prin. Fax 746-9923

Bailey, Nash, Pop. 561
Nash-Rocky Mount SD
Supt. — See Nashville
Southern Nash HS 1,200/9-12
6446 Southern Nash High Rd 27807 252-451-8520
Dr. Mark Cockrell, prin. Fax 478-5953

Bakersville, Mitchell, Pop. 450
Mitchell County SD 1,900/K-12
72 Ledger School Rd 28705 828-766-2220
Chad Calhoun, supt. Fax 766-2221
www.mcsnc.org
Bowman MS 300/5-8
410 S Mitchell Ave 28705 828-766-3370
Paula Holder, prin. Fax 688-6002
Mitchell HS 500/9-12
416 Ledger School Rd 28705 828-766-3400
Mark Woody, prin. Fax 688-4847
Other Schools – See Spruce Pine

Banner Elk, Avery, Pop. 1,011

Lees-McRae College Post-Sec.
PO Box 128 28604 828-898-5241

Barco, Currituck
Currituck County SD
Supt. — See Currituck

Currituck County HS 1,000/9-12
4203 Caratoke Hwy 27917 252-453-0014
Renee Dowdy, prin. Fax 453-0017
Currituck County MS 300/6-8
4263 Caratoke Hwy 27917 252-453-2171
Dr. Matt Lutz, prin. Fax 453-0019

Battleboro, Edgecombe, Pop. 559
Edgecombe County SD
Supt. — See Tarboro
Phillips MS 200/6-8
4371 Battleboro Leggett Rd 27809 252-446-2031
Donita Gregory, prin. Fax 446-1629

Nash-Rocky Mount SD
Supt. — See Nashville
Red Oak MS 900/6-8
3170 Red Oak Battleboro Rd 27809 252-462-2000
Timothy Mudd, prin. Fax 451-5510

Bayboro, Pamlico, Pop. 1,250
Pamlico County SD 1,300/PK-12
507 Anderson Dr 28515 252-745-4171
Lisa Jackson, supt. Fax 745-4172
www.pamlico.k12.nc.us
Pamlico County HS 500/9-12
601 Main St 28515 252-745-3151
Chris Meadows, prin. Fax 745-3153
Pamlico County MS 300/6-8
15526 NC Highway 55 28515 252-745-4061
Jeremy Johnson, prin. Fax 745-5583

Bear Creek, Chatham
Chatham County SD
Supt. — See Pittsboro
Chatham Central HS 400/9-12
14950 NC 902 Hwy 27207 919-837-2251
Mitch Stensland, prin. Fax 837-2975

Beaufort, Carteret, Pop. 3,948
Carteret County SD 8,500/PK-12
107 Safrit Dr 28516 252-728-4583
Dr. Daniel Novey, supt. Fax 728-3028
www.carteretcountyschools.org
Beaufort MS 300/6-8
100 Carraway Dr 28516 252-728-4520
Dr. Cathy Tomon, prin. Fax 728-3392
East Carteret HS 600/9-12
3263 US Highway 70 E 28516 252-728-3514
Joe Poletti, prin. Fax 728-3487
Other Schools – See Morehead City, Newport, Smyrna

Belhaven, Beaufort, Pop. 1,666

Pungo Christian Academy 200/PK-12
983 W Main St 27810 252-943-2678
Marcy Morgan, head sch Fax 943-3292

Belmont, Gaston, Pop. 9,916
Gaston County SD
Supt. — See Gastonia
Belmont MS 800/6-8
110 N Central Ave 28012 704-825-9619
Susan Redmond, prin. Fax 825-6951
Cramer HS 500/9-12
101 Lakewood Rd 28012 704-866-5700
Audrey Devine, prin. Fax 825-8950
South Point HS 1,100/9-12
906 South Point Rd 28012 704-836-9612
Gary Ford, prin. Fax 825-2820

Belmont Abbey College Post-Sec.
100 Belmont Mount Holly Rd 28012 888-222-0110

Benson, Johnston, Pop. 3,270
Johnston County SD
Supt. — See Smithfield
Benson MS 400/5-8
1600 N Wall St 27504 919-894-3889
Ron Anthony, prin. Fax 894-1551
McGee's Crossroads MS 900/6-8
13353 NC Highway 210 27504 919-894-6003
Dorlisa Johnson-Cowart, prin. Fax 894-6007
West Johnston HS 1,400/9-12
5935 Raleigh Rd 27504 919-934-7333
Paula Coates, prin. Fax 934-6906

Bessemer City, Gaston, Pop. 5,262
Gaston County SD
Supt. — See Gastonia
Bessemer City HS 600/9-12
119 Yellow Jacket Rd 28016 704-836-9601
Judy Moore, prin. Fax 629-2775
Bessemer City MS 500/6-8
525 Ed Wilson Rd 28016 704-836-9602
Dr. Fran DaCanal, prin. Fax 629-4501

Community Christian Academy 100/K-12
616 Athenia Pl 28016 704-629-2391
David Ross, admin. Fax 495-6882

Bethel, Pitt, Pop. 1,573
Pitt County SD
Supt. — See Greenville
North Pitt HS 900/9-12
5659 NC Highway 11 N 27812 252-825-0054
Dr. Lionel Kato, prin. Fax 825-1310

Beulaville, Duplin, Pop. 1,278
Duplin County SD
Supt. — See Kenansville
East Duplin HS 900/9-12
394 N NC 111 Hwy 28518 910-298-4535
Scott Ballard, prin. Fax 298-2021

Biscoe, Montgomery, Pop. 1,683
Montgomery County SD
Supt. — See Troy
East MS 500/6-8
1834 US Highway 220 Alt S 27209 910-428-3278
Della Ingram, prin. Fax 428-1279

East Montgomery HS 600/9-12
157 Eagle Ln 27209 910-428-9641
Heather Seawell, prin. Fax 428-1197

Black Mountain, Buncombe, Pop. 7,683
Buncombe County SD
Supt. — See Asheville
Owen HS 800/9-12
99 Lake Eden Rd 28711 828-686-3852
Margaret Turner, prin. Fax 686-8442

Bladenboro, Bladen, Pop. 1,726
Bladen County SD
Supt. — See Elizabethtown
Bladenboro MS 400/5-8
910 S Main St 28320 910-863-3232
Randi Harrelson, prin. Fax 418-3594
West Bladen HS 800/9-12
1600 NC 410 Hwy 28320 910-862-2130
Peggy Hester, prin. Fax 897-0355

Boiling Springs, Cleveland, Pop. 4,581

Gardner-Webb University Post-Sec.
PO Box 997 28017 704-406-4000

Bolivia, Brunswick, Pop. 139
Brunswick County SD 12,500/PK-12
35 Referendum Dr NE 28422 910-253-2900
Leslie K. Tubb, supt. Fax 253-2983
www.bcswan.net
Brunswick County Academy 100/Alt
1109 Old Ocean Hwy 28422 910-754-9593
Marcia Heady, prin. Fax 754-9594
Brunswick County Early College HS 300/9-12
60 College Rd NE 28422 910-754-8565
Dr. Cheryl Skaggs, prin. Fax 754-8567
Other Schools – See Leland, Shallotte, Southport, Supply

Boone, Watauga, Pop. 16,843
Watauga County SD 4,400/PK-12
PO Box 1790 28607 828-264-7190
Dr. Scott Elliott, supt. Fax 264-7196
www.watauga.k12.nc.us
Watauga HS 1,400/9-12
300 Go Pioneers Dr 28607 828-264-2407
Marshall Gasperson, prin. Fax 264-9030

Appalachian State University Post-Sec.
Asu Sta 28608 828-262-2000

Boonville, Yadkin, Pop. 1,215
Yadkin County SD
Supt. — See Yadkinville
Starmount HS 600/9-12
2516 Longtown Rd 27011 336-468-2891
Cody Hemric, prin. Fax 468-6434
Starmount MS 400/7-8
2626 Longtown Rd 27011 336-468-6833
Rick Swaim, prin. Fax 468-6838

Bostic, Rutherford, Pop. 382
Rutherford County SD
Supt. — See Forest City
East Rutherford MS 600/6-8
259 E Church St 28018 828-245-3750
Jo Oliver, prin. Fax 245-1491

Brevard, Transylvania, Pop. 7,401
Transylvania County SD 3,600/PK-12
225 Rosenwald Ln 28712 828-884-6173
Dr. Jeff McDaris, supt. Fax 884-9524
www.tcsnc.org
Brevard HS 700/9-12
609 Country Club Rd 28712 828-884-4103
Jennifer Anderson, prin. Fax 885-7355
Brevard MS 500/6-8
400 Fisher Rd 28712 828-884-2091
Jeff Bailey, prin. Fax 883-3150
Davidson River S 100/Alt
970 Ecusta Rd 28712 828-884-9567
Donna Wilde, prin. Fax 862-5347
Other Schools – See Rosman

Brevard College Post-Sec.
1 Brevard College Dr 28712 828-883-8292

Browns Summit, Guilford
Guilford County SD
Supt. — See Greensboro
Brown Summit MS 200/6-8
4720 E NC Highway 150 27214 336-656-0432
Deborah Mott, prin. Fax 656-0439

Bryson City, Swain, Pop. 1,399
Swain County SD 2,000/PK-12
PO Box 2340 28713 828-488-3129
Sam Pattillo, supt. Fax 488-8510
www.swain.k12.nc.us
Swain County HS 600/9-12
1415 Fontana Rd 28713 828-488-2152
Mark Sale, prin. Fax 488-0523
Swain County MS 500/PK-PK, 6-
135 Arlington Ave 28713 828-488-3480
Brandon Sutton, prin. Fax 488-0949

Buies Creek, Harnett, Pop. 2,881

Campbell University Post-Sec.
PO Box 567 27506 910-893-1200

Bunn, Franklin, Pop. 340
Franklin County SD
Supt. — See Louisburg
Bunn HS 900/9-12
PO Box 146 27508 919-496-3975
Dr. Laverne Daniels, prin. Fax 496-6943
Bunn MS 700/6-8
4742 NC 39 Hwy S 27508 919-496-7700
Dr. Danielle Jones, prin. Fax 496-1404

Burgaw, Pender, Pop. 3,819
Pender County SD 9,000/PK-12
925 Penderlea Hwy 28425 910-259-2187
Dr. Terri Cobb, supt. Fax 259-0133
www.pendercountyschools.net/
Burgaw MS 200/6-8
500 S Wright St 28425 910-259-0149
Caroline Godwin, prin. Fax 259-0150
Pender Early College HS 200/8-12
100 Industrial Dr 28425 910-259-7925
Dr. Edith Skipper, prin. Fax 259-7174
Pender HS 600/9-12
5380 NC Highway 53 W 28425 910-259-0162
Christopher Madden, prin. Fax 259-0166
West Pender MS 200/6-8
10750 NC Highway 53 W 28425 910-283-5626
James Simmons, prin. Fax 283-9537
Other Schools – See Hampstead, Rocky Point

Burlington, Alamance, Pop. 49,060
Alamance-Burlington SD 22,900/PK-12
1712 Vaughn Rd 27217 336-570-6060
Dr. William Harrison, supt. Fax 570-6218
www.abss.k12.nc.us
Broadview MS 800/6-8
2229 Broadview Dr 27217 336-570-6195
Brie Butler, prin. Fax 570-6202
Career and Technical Education Center Vo/Tech
2550 Buckingham Rd 27217 336-570-6092
Darrell Thomas, prin. Fax 570-6093
Cummings HS 900/9-12
2200 N Mebane St 27217 336-570-6100
Emmet Alexander, prin. Fax 570-6107
Turrentine MS 900/6-8
1710 Edgewood Ave 27215 336-570-6150
Fredrick Sellars, prin. Fax 570-6210
Williams HS 1,200/9-12
1307 S Church St 27215 336-570-6161
Stephanie Hunt, prin. Fax 570-6214
Other Schools – See Elon, Graham, Mebane

Burlington Christian Academy 700/PK-12
621 E 6th St 27215 336-227-0288
Michael Brown, head sch Fax 570-1314
Burlington S 200/PK-12
1615 Greenwood Ter 27215 336-228-0296
Ronnie Wall, head sch Fax 226-6249

Burnsville, Yancey, Pop. 1,680
Yancey County SD 2,300/K-12
PO Box 190 28714 828-682-6101
Dr. Tony Tipton Ed.D., supt. Fax 682-7110
www.yanceync.net
Cane River MS 300/6-8
1128 Cane River School Rd 28714 828-682-2202
Miranda Elkins, prin. Fax 682-3754
East Yancey MS 300/6-8
285 Georges Fork Rd 28714 828-682-2281
Tamara Presnell, prin. Fax 682-3513
Mountain Heritage HS 700/9-12
PO Box 70 28714 828-682-6103
Kevin Huskins, prin. Fax 682-4287

Butner, Granville, Pop. 7,466
Granville County SD
Supt. — See Oxford
Butner-Stem MS 400/6-8
501 E D St 27509 919-575-9429
Lauren Curtis, prin. Fax 575-5894

Buxton, Dare, Pop. 1,259
Dare County SD
Supt. — See Nags Head
Cape Hatteras S of Coastal Studies 300/6-12
PO Box 948 27920 252-995-5730
Beth Rooks, prin. Fax 995-6161

Camden, Camden, Pop. 580
Camden County SD 1,900/PK-12
174 NC Highway 343 N 27921 252-335-0831
Melvin Hawkins, supt. Fax 331-2300
www.camden.k12.nc.us
Camden County HS 500/9-12
103 US Highway 158 W 27921 252-338-0114
Billie Berry, prin. Fax 331-6792
Camden Early College HS 200/9-12
103 US Highway 158 W Ste A 27921 252-335-7219
Amber Davis, prin. Fax 335-4219
Camden MS 300/7-8
248 Scotland Rd 27921 252-338-3349
Ernest Cooley, prin. Fax 331-2253

Cameron, Moore, Pop. 274
Moore County SD
Supt. — See Carthage
New Century MS 600/6-8
1577 Union Church Rd 28326 910-947-1301
Tracy Metcalf, prin. Fax 947-1227
Union Pines HS 1,300/9-12
1981 Union Church Rd 28326 910-947-5511
Andrew McCormick, prin. Fax 947-5117

Candler, Buncombe
Buncombe County SD
Supt. — See Asheville
Enka HS 1,300/9-12
475 Enka Lake Rd 28715 828-670-5000
Tonya Robinson, prin. Fax 670-5007
Enka MS 1,000/7-8
390 Asbury Rd 28715 828-670-5010
Leland Blankenship, prin. Fax 670-5015

Mt. Pisgah Academy 100/9-12
75 Academy Dr 28715 828-667-2535

Canton, Haywood, Pop. 4,165
Haywood County SD
Supt. — See Waynesville
Canton MS 600/6-8
60 Penland St 28716 828-646-3467
Todd Barbee, prin. Fax 646-3478

Pisgah HS 1,000/9-12
1 Black Bear Dr 28716 828-646-3440
Greg Bailey, prin. Fax 648-8618

Carrboro, Orange, Pop. 19,067
Chapel Hill-Carrboro CSD
Supt. — See Chapel Hill
Carrboro HS 900/9-12
201 Rock Haven Rd 27510 919-918-2200
LaVerne Mattocks, prin. Fax 918-2507

Carthage, Moore, Pop. 2,154
Moore County SD 13,000/PK-12
PO Box 1180 28327 910-947-2976
Robert Grimesey, supt. Fax 947-3011
www.ncmcs.org
Community Learning Center @ Pinckney 50/Alt
160 Pinckney Rd 28327 910-947-2603
Shaun Krencicki, prin. Fax 947-2404
Crain's Creek MS 400/6-8
4631 Union Church Rd 28327 910-245-3796
William Chisholm, prin. Fax 245-7312
Other Schools – See Aberdeen, Cameron, Robbins, Southern Pines, West End

Cary, Wake, Pop. 131,955
Wake County SD 153,500/PK-12
5625 Dillard Dr 27518 919-431-7400
Dr. Jim Merrill, supt.
www.wcpss.net
Cary HS 2,300/9-12
638 Walnut St 27511 919-460-3549
Jacob Bryant, prin. Fax 460-3573
Crossroads FLEX HS Alt
5651 Dillard Dr 27518 919-694-8515
Keith Richardson, prin.
Davis Drive MS 1,200/6-8
2101 Davis Dr 27519 919-387-3033
Rick Williams, prin. Fax 387-3039
East Cary MS 800/6-8
1111 SE Maynard Rd 27511 919-466-4377
Nikia Davis, prin. Fax 466-4388
Green Hope HS 2,300/9-12
2500 Carpenter Upchurch Rd 27519 919-380-3700
Karen Summers, prin. Fax 380-3712
Mills Park MS 1,700/6-8
441 Mills Park Dr 27519 919-466-1500
Robert Smith, prin. Fax 466-1522
Panther Creek HS 2,600/9-12
6770 McCrimmon Pkwy 27519 919-463-8656
Dr. Camille Hedrick, prin. Fax 463-8666
Reedy Creek MS 800/6-8
930 Reedy Creek Rd 27513 919-460-3504
Hilton Evans, prin. Fax 460-3391
West Cary MS 800/6-8
1000 Evans Rd 27513 919-460-3528
Robert James, prin. Fax 460-3540
Other Schools – See Apex, Fuquay Varina, Garner, Holly Springs, Knightdale, Raleigh, Rolesville, Wake Forest, Wendell, Zebulon

---

Cary Academy 700/6-12
1500 N Harrison Ave 27513 919-677-3873
Dr. Michael Ehrhardt Ed.D., head sch Fax 677-4002
Cary Christian S 800/K-12
1330 Old Apex Rd 27513 919-303-2560
Hopewell Academy 50/6-12
101 Preston Executive Dr 27513 919-481-2123
Miller-Motte College Post-Sec.
2205 Walnut St 27518 919-532-7171
Shepherds Theological Seminary Post-Sec.
6051 Tryon Rd 27518 919-573-5350

Cashiers, Jackson, Pop. 156
Jackson County SD
Supt. — See Sylva
Blue Ridge Early College 200/7-12
95 Bobcat Dr 28717 828-743-2646
Brent Speckhardt, prin. Fax 743-5320

Castle Hayne, New Hanover, Pop. 1,182
New Hanover County SD
Supt. — See Wilmington
Holly Shelter MS 800/6-8
3921 Roger Haynes Dr 28429 910-602-4046
Jayne Kiker, prin. Fax 602-4045
Wilmington Early College HS 200/9-12
4500 Blue Clay Rd 28429 910-362-7789
Regina Wooten, prin. Fax 362-7424

Catawba, Catawba, Pop. 599
Catawba County SD
Supt. — See Newton
Bandys HS 900/9-12
5040 E Bandys Xrd 28609 828-241-3171
Angela Williams, prin. Fax 241-9402

Cerro Gordo, Columbus, Pop. 201
Columbus County SD
Supt. — See Whiteville
West Columbus HS 500/9-12
PO Box 130 28430 910-654-6111
Jeffrey Greene, prin. Fax 654-4082

Chadbourn, Columbus, Pop. 1,832
Columbus County SD
Supt. — See Whiteville
Chadbourn MS 200/6-8
801 W Smith St 28431 910-654-4300
Michael Powell, prin. Fax 654-6809

Chapel Hill, Orange, Pop. 55,802
Chapel Hill-Carrboro CSD 12,100/PK-12
750 S Merritt Mill Rd 27516 919-967-8211
Jim Causby, supt. Fax 933-4560
www.chccs.k12.nc.us
Chapel Hill HS 1,400/9-12
1709 High School Rd 27516 919-929-2106
Sulura Jackson, prin. Fax 929-2455
East Chapel Hill HS 1,400/9-12
500 Weaver Dairy Rd 27514 919-969-2482
Eileen Tully, prin. Fax 969-2492
Grey Culbreth MS 700/6-8
225 Culbreth Rd 27516 919-929-7161
Beverly Rudolph, prin. Fax 969-2412
McDougle MS 700/6-8
900 Old Fayetteville Rd 27516 919-933-1556
Bob Bales, prin. Fax 969-2433
Phillips MS 700/6-8
606 N Estes Dr 27514 919-929-2188
Tomeka Ward-Satterfield, prin. Fax 969-2477
Phoenix Academy HS 50/Alt
750 S Merritt Mill Rd 27516 919-918-2300
John Williams, prin. Fax 933-4560
Smith MS 800/6-8
9201 Seawell School Rd 27516 919-918-2145
Stephon Goode, prin. Fax 918-2079
Other Schools – See Carrboro

Chatham County SD
Supt. — See Pittsboro
Pollard MS 600/6-8
185 Granite Mill Blvd 27516 919-969-0070
LaShonda Hester, prin.

Emerson Waldorf S 200/PK-12
6211 New Jericho Rd 27516 919-967-1858
Christina Wise, admin. Fax 967-2732
University of North Carolina 27599 Post-Sec.
919-962-2211
University of North Carolina Hospitals Post-Sec.
101 Manning Dr 27514 919-966-5111

Charlotte, Mecklenburg, Pop. 715,605
Charlotte/Mecklenburg County SD 142,700/PK-12
PO Box 30035 28230 980-343-6270
Ann Clark, supt. Fax 343-7135
www.cms.k12.nc.us/
Albemarle Road MS 1,200/6-8
6900 Democracy Dr 28212 980-343-6420
Toni Perry, prin. Fax 343-6501
Berry Academy of Technology 1,600/9-12
1430 Alleghany St 28208 980-343-5992
Terra Kennedy, prin. Fax 343-5994
Biotechnolgy Health & Public Admin @ OHS 500/9-12
4301 Sandy Porter Rd Ste E 28273 980-343-1110
Angela Bozeman, prin. Fax 343-1114
Carmel MS 1,000/6-8
5001 Camilla Dr 28226 980-343-6705
Mark Angerer, prin. Fax 343-6749
Cato Middle College HS 200/11-12
8120 Grier Rd 28215 980-343-1452
Alicisa Johnson, prin. Fax 343-1453
Charlotte Engineering Early College 9-12
9000 Robert Snyder Rd 28262 980-343-9898
Will Leach, prin. Fax 343-2517
Cochrane Collegiate Academy 1,000/6-12
6200 Starhaven Dr 28215 980-343-6460
Rachel Corn, prin. Fax 343-6521
Community House MS 1,600/6-8
9500 Community House Rd 28277 980-343-0689
Jamie Brooks, prin. Fax 343-0691
Coulwood MS 700/6-8
500 Kentberry Dr 28214 980-343-6090
Janet Moss, prin. Fax 343-6142
East Mecklenburg HS 1,800/9-12
6800 Monroe Rd 28212 980-343-6430
Richard Parker, prin. Fax 343-6437
Eastway MS 900/6-8
1501 Norland Rd 28205 980-343-6410
Mary Webb, prin. Fax 343-6406
Garinger HS 1,400/9-12
1100 Eastway Dr 28205 980-343-6450
Kelly Gwaltney, prin. Fax 343-1475
Graham MS 1,400/6-8
1800 Runnymede Ln 28211 980-343-5810
Robert Folk, prin. Fax 343-5868
Harding University HS 1,700/9-12
2001 Alleghany St 28208 980-343-6007
Eric Ward, prin. Fax 343-1767
Harper Middle College HS 11-12
315 W Hebron St 28273 980-343-0012
Brandy Nelson, prin. Fax 343-0013
Hawthorne Academy of Health Science 200/9-12
2300 W Sugar Creek Rd 28262 980-343-6011
Diann Weston, prin. Fax 343-5609
Independence HS 2,200/9-12
1967 Patriot Dr 28227 980-343-6900
David Legrand, prin. Fax 343-6907
Kell HS 2,500/9-12
10220 Ardrey Kell Rd 28277 980-343-0860
David Switzer, prin. Fax 343-0862
Kennedy MS 700/6-8
4000 Gallant Ln 28273 980-343-5540
Kevin Sudimack, prin. Fax 343-5412
King MS 900/6-8
500 Bilmark Ave 28213 980-343-0698
Jennifer Dean, prin. Fax 343-0700
Leadership & Development @ Olympic 400/9-12
4301 Sandy Porter Rd Ste C 28273 980-343-1104
Monique Hicks, prin. Fax 343-1108
Mallard Creek HS 2,300/9-12
3825 Johnston Oehler Rd 28269 980-343-1341
Kevin Garay, prin. Fax 343-1342
Martin MS 1,100/6-8
7800 IBM Dr 28262 980-343-5382
Tonya Faison, prin. Fax 343-5135
Math Engineering Tech/Science S @ OHS 500/9-12
4301 Sandy Porter Rd Ste B 28273 980-343-1101
LeDaun Pratt, prin. Fax 343-1105
McClintock MS 800/6-8
1925 Rama Rd 28212 980-343-6425
Mark McHugh, prin. Fax 343-6509
Military & Global Leadrshp Acad @ Davis K-12
3351 Griffith St 28203 980-343-0006
Ann Laszewski, prin. Fax 343-1735
Myers Park HS 2,800/9-12
2400 Colony Rd 28209 980-343-5800
Mark Bosco, prin. Fax 343-5803
Northridge MS 800/6-8
7601 The Plaza 28215 980-343-5015
Vince Golden, prin. Fax 343-5174
Northwest S of the Arts 1,000/6-12
1415 Beatties Ford Rd 28216 980-343-5500
Melody Sears, prin. Fax 343-5593
Performance Learning Center 100/Alt
2300 W Sugar Creek Rd 28262 980-343-1118
Harrison Conyers, prin. Fax 343-1117
Piedmont IB MS 1,000/6-8
1241 E 10th St 28204 980-343-5435
Jackie Barone, prin. Fax 343-5557
Providence HS 2,000/9-12
1800 Pineville Matthews Rd 28270 980-343-5390
Tracey Harrill, prin. Fax 343-3956
Quail Hollow MS 1,000/6-8
2901 Smithfield Church Rd 28210 980-343-3620
Rachael Neill, prin. Fax 343-3622
Randolph MS 1,200/6-8
4400 Water Oak Rd 28211 980-343-6700
Brian Bambauer, prin. Fax 343-6741
Ranson MS 1,100/6-8
5850 Statesville Rd 28269 980-343-6800
Erica Jordan-Thomas, prin. Fax 343-6796
Renaissance S @ Olympic 500/9-12
4301 Sandy Porter Rd Ste D 28273 980-343-1107
Tamara Hines, prin. Fax 343-1111
Ridge Road MS 1,400/6-8
7260 Highland Creek Pkwy 28269 980-344-3410
Jametta Martin-Tanner, prin. Fax 343-1835
Robinson MS 1,100/6-8
5925 Ballantyne Commons Pky 28277 980-343-6944
Mike Miliote, prin. Fax 343-6947
Sedgefield MS 700/6-8
2700 Dorchester Pl 28209 980-343-5840
Erik Turner, prin. Fax 343-5862
South Charlotte MS 900/6-8
8040 Strawberry Ln 28277 980-343-3670
Lisa Bailes, prin. Fax 343-3725
South Mecklenburg HS 2,700/9-12
8900 Park Rd 28210 980-343-3600
Dr. Maureen Furr, prin. Fax 343-3607
Southwest MS 1,400/6-8
13624 Steele Creek Rd 28273 980-343-5006
Barry Blair, prin. Fax 343-3239
TEAM HS @ Olympic 400/9-12
4301 Sandy Porter Rd Ste A 28273 980-343-1113
Erik Olejarczyk, prin. Fax 343-1102
Turning Point Academy 200/Alt
2400 Carmine St 28206 980-343-5231
Valoria Burch, prin. Fax 343-0924
Vance HS 1,700/9-12
7600 IBM Dr 28262 980-343-5284
Kit Rea, prin. Fax 343-5286
West Charlotte HS 1,700/9-12
2219 Senior Dr 28216 980-343-6060
Tamisha Barnes-Jones, prin. Fax 343-6049
West Mecklenburg HS 1,900/9-12
7400 Tuckaseegee Rd 28214 980-343-6080
Casey Jones, prin. Fax 343-6079
Whitewater MS 900/6-8
10201 Running Rapids Rd 28214 980-344-3400
Beth Thompson, prin. Fax 344-1814
Other Schools – See Cornelius, Huntersville, Matthews, Mint Hill

---

Art Institute of Charlotte Post-Sec.
2110 Water Ridge Pkwy 28217 704-357-8020
Back Creek Christian Academy 200/PK-11
1827 Back Creek Church Rd 28213 704-549-4101
Janet Ballard, head sch Fax 548-1152
Brightwood College Post-Sec.
6070 E Independence Blvd 28212 704-567-3700
Brisbane Academy Preparatory S 100/PK-12
5901 Statesville Rd 28269 704-598-5208
British International S of Charlotte 100/PK-10
7000 Endhaven Ln 28277 704-341-3236
Brookstone College of Business Post-Sec.
10125 Berkeley Place Dr 28262 704-547-8600
Carolina School of Broadcasting Post-Sec.
3435 Performance Rd 28214 704-395-9272
Carolinas College of Health Sciences Post-Sec.
PO Box 32861 28232 704-355-5043
Central Piedmont Community College Post-Sec.
PO Box 35009 28235 704-330-2722
Charlotte Catholic HS 1,400/9-12
7702 Pineville Matthews Rd 28226 704-543-1127
Kurt Telford, prin. Fax 543-1217
Charlotte Christian S 1,000/PK-12
7301 Sardis Rd 28270 704-366-5657
Barry Giller, head sch Fax 366-5678
Charlotte Country Day S 1,600/PK-12
1440 Carmel Rd 28226 704-943-4500
Mark Reed, hdmstr. Fax 943-4536
Charlotte Latin S 1,400/PK-12
9502 Providence Rd 28277 704-846-1100
Arch McIntosh, hdmstr. Fax 846-1712
Charlotte School of Law Post-Sec.
2145 Suttle Ave 28208 704-971-8500
Charlotte United Christian Academy 100/PK-12
7640 Wallace Rd 28212 704-537-0331
Dr. Hank Corcoran, head sch Fax 537-0568
Countryside Montessori S 200/1-12
9026 Mallard Creek Rd 28262 704-503-6000
Crosland S 100/K-12
5146 Parkway Plaza Blvd 28217 704-365-5490
Dr. Sean Preston, head sch Fax 365-3240
DeVry University Post-Sec.
2015 Ayrsley Town Blvd #109 28273 704-362-2345
Dudley Beauty College Post-Sec.
1950 John McDonald Ave 28216 704-392-2564
ECPI University Post-Sec.
4800 Airport Center Pkwy 28208 704-399-1010
Hairstyling Institute of Charlotte Post-Sec.
209B S Kings Dr 28204 704-334-5511
Hickory Grove Christian S 1,000/K-12
7200 E WT Harris Blvd 28215 704-531-4198
Jimmie Quesinberry, prin. Fax 531-3509
Holy Trinity Catholic MS 900/6-8
3100 Park Rd 28209 704-527-7822
Kevin Parks, prin. Fax 525-7288

Johnson & Wales University — Post-Sec.
801 W Trade St 28202 — 980-598-1000
Johnson C. Smith University — Post-Sec.
100 Beatties Ford Rd 28216 — 704-378-1000
King's College — Post-Sec.
322 Lamar Ave 28204 — 704-372-0266
Mercy School of Nursing — Post-Sec.
701 Forest Point Cir Ste B 28273 — 704-512-2010
Mountain Island Day S — 100/PK-11
1209 Little Rock Rd 28214 — 704-391-5516
Rev. Tom Winstead, head sch — Fax 391-2540
New Life Theological Seminary — Post-Sec.
3117 Whiting Ave 28205 — 704-334-6882
Northside Christian Academy — 500/PK-12
333 Jeremiah Blvd 28262 — 704-596-4074
Tony Fajardo, hdmstr. — Fax 921-1384
Presbyterian Hospital — Post-Sec.
PO Box 33549 28233 — 704-384-4141
Providence Day S — 1,500/PK-12
5800 Sardis Rd 28270 — 704-887-6000
Dr. Glyn Cowlishaw, head sch — Fax 887-7042
Queens University of Charlotte — Post-Sec.
1900 Selwyn Ave 28274 — 704-337-2200
Reformed Theological Seminary — Post-Sec.
2101 Carmel Rd 28226 — 704-366-5066
Southeastern Institute — Post-Sec.
5250 77 Center Dr Ste 100 28217 — 704-527-4979
Trinity Christian Preparatory S — 100/8-12
7516 E Independence Ste 100 28227 — 704-569-1900
Doug Corwin, head sch — Fax 569-1999
United Faith Christian Academy — 300/PK-12
8617 Providence Rd 28277 — 704-541-1742
Universal College of Beauty — Post-Sec.
1701 W Trade St 28216 — 704-333-6969
University of North Carolina — Post-Sec.
9201 University City Blvd 28223 — 704-687-2000
Victory Christian Center S — 300/PK-12
1501 Carrier Dr 28216 — 704-391-7339
Michael Pratt, prin. — Fax 391-0494

Cherryville, Gaston, Pop. 5,683
Gaston County SD
Supt. — See Gastonia
Chavis MS — 400/6-8
103 S Chavis Dr 28021 — 704-836-9606
Ryan Smith, prin. — Fax 435-6168
Cherryville HS — 600/9-12
313 Ridge Ave 28021 — 704-836-9605
Kevin Doran, prin. — Fax 435-4989

China Grove, Rowan, Pop. 3,516
Rowan-Salisbury County SD
Supt. — See Salisbury
Carson HS — 1,200/9-12
290 Kress Venture Rd 28023 — 704-855-7297
Angelo DelliSanti, prin. — Fax 857-3485
China Grove MS — 600/6-8
1013 N Main St 28023 — 704-857-7038
Ben Crawford, prin. — Fax 857-6650
South Rowan HS — 1,000/9-12
1655 Patterson St 28023 — 704-857-1161
Kelly Withers, prin. — Fax 855-1420

Chocowinity, Beaufort, Pop. 806
Beaufort County SD
Supt. — See Washington
Chocowinity MS — 400/5-8
3831 US Highway 17 S 27817 — 252-946-6191
Kimberly Gibbs, prin. — Fax 975-3812
Southside HS — 400/9-12
5700 NC Highway 33 E 27817 — 252-940-1881
Clint Johnson, prin. — Fax 940-1888

Unity Christian Academy — 100/K-12
1501 Haw Branch Rd 27817 — 252-946-5083
Jessica Crocker, admin. — Fax 946-2707

Claremont, Catawba, Pop. 1,328
Catawba County SD
Supt. — See Newton
Bunker Hill HS — 1,000/9-12
4675 Oxford School Rd 28610 — 828-241-3355
Dr. Jeff Isenhour, prin. — Fax 241-9401
Mill Creek MS — 500/7-8
1041 Shiloh Rd 28610 — 828-241-2711
Amy Rucker, prin. — Fax 241-2743
River Bend MS — 500/7-8
4670 Oxford School Rd 28610 — 828-241-2754
Chip Cathey, prin. — Fax 241-2820

Clarkton, Bladen, Pop. 821
Bladen County SD
Supt. — See Elizabethtown
Clarkton MS of Discovery — 300/6-8
PO Box 127 28433 — 910-647-6531
Stephanie Ensminger, prin. — Fax 707-0814

Clayton, Johnston, Pop. 15,821
Johnston County SD
Supt. — See Smithfield
Clayton HS — 1,500/9-12
600 S Fayetteville St 27520 — 919-553-4064
Bennett Jones, prin. — Fax 553-2563
Clayton MS — 800/6-8
490 Guy Rd 27520 — 919-553-5811
Catherine Trudell, prin. — Fax 553-6978
Cleveland HS — 1,400/9-12
1892 Polenta Rd 27520 — 919-934-2455
Kendrick Byrd, prin. — Fax 934-2414
Johnson Co Career & Tech Leadership Acad — 9-12
600 S Fayetteville St 27520 — 919-262-0740
Barretta Haynes, prin. — Fax 550-4811
Riverwood MS — 1,100/6-8
204 Athletic Club Blvd, — 919-359-2769
Kerri Evans, prin. — Fax 359-1519

LifeSpring Academy — 100/K-12
PO Box 1567, — 919-359-9959
Southside Christian S — 100/PK-12
2028 Orton Rd 27520 — 919-553-7652
Jenene Davie, prin. — Fax 553-5077

Clemmons, Forsyth, Pop. 18,375
Winston-Salem/Forsyth SD
Supt. — See Winston Salem
West Forsyth HS — 2,000/9-12
1735 Lewisville Clemmons Rd 27012 — 336-712-4400
Charles McAninch, prin. — Fax 712-4416

Climax, Guilford
Randolph County SD
Supt. — See Asheboro
Providence Grove HS — 800/9-12
5555 Mack Lineberry Rd 27233 — 336-685-0728
Dr. Brad Walston, prin. — Fax 685-0731

Clinton, Sampson, Pop. 8,488
Clinton CSD — 3,200/PK-12
300 Westover Rd 28328 — 910-592-3132
Dr. Stuart Blount, supt. — Fax 592-2011
www.clinton.k12.nc.us
Clinton HS — 800/9-12
340 Indian Town Rd 28328 — 910-592-2067
Dr. Steven Miller, prin. — Fax 299-5164
Sampson MS — 800/6-8
1201 W Elizabeth St 28328 — 910-592-3327
Greg Dirks, prin. — Fax 592-6185

Sampson County SD — 8,700/PK-12
PO Box 439 28329 — 910-592-1401
Dr. Eric Bracy, supt. — Fax 590-2445
www.sampson.k12.nc.us
Sampson Early College HS — 200/9-12
PO Box 318 28329 — 910-592-8081
Susan Westerbeek, prin. — Fax 592-8048
Union MS — 500/6-8
455 River Rd 28328 — 910-592-4547
Dr. Theresa Melenas, prin. — Fax 592-4211
Other Schools – See Dunn, Newton Grove, Roseboro, Rose Hill, Salemburg

---

Sampson Community College — Post-Sec.
PO Box 318 28329 — 910-592-8081

Clyde, Haywood, Pop. 1,216
Haywood County SD
Supt. — See Waynesville
Central Haywood HS — 100/Alt
3215 Broad St 28721 — 828-627-9944
Rodney Mashburn, prin. — Fax 627-0709
Haywood Early College HS — 100/9-12
185 Freedlander Dr 28721 — 828-565-4000
Jeff Haney, prin. — Fax 565-4074

Haywood Christian Academy — 100/PK-12
1400 Old Clyde Rd 28721 — 828-627-0229
Kelli Herbert, head sch — Fax 880-8447
Haywood Community College — Post-Sec.
185 Freedlander Dr 28721 — 828-627-4500

Columbia, Tyrrell, Pop. 886
Tyrrell County SD — 600/PK-12
PO Box 328 27925 — 252-796-1121
Dr. Will Hoffman, supt. — Fax 796-1492
www.tyrrell.k12.nc.us
Columbia Early College HS — 100/9-12
PO Box 419 27925 — 252-796-8161
Michael Yancey, prin. — Fax 796-0143
Columbia MS — 100/6-8
PO Box 839 27925 — 252-796-0369
Stephanie Horton, prin. — Fax 796-3639

Columbus, Polk, Pop. 981
Polk County SD — 2,400/PK-12
PO Box 638 28722 — 828-894-3051
Aaron Greene, supt. — Fax 894-8153
www.polkschools.org
Polk County Early College HS — 100/9-12
1545 NC 108 Hwy E 28722 — 828-894-2525
Mary Greene, dir. — Fax 894-2971
Polk County HS — 700/9-12
1681 NC 108 Hwy E 28722 — 828-894-2525
Mary Feagan, prin. — Fax 894-2093
Other Schools – See Mill Spring

Concord, Cabarrus, Pop. 77,521
Cabarrus County SD — 30,200/PK-12
PO Box 388 28026 — 704-786-6191
Dr. Chris Lowder, supt. — Fax 786-6141
www.cabarrus.k12.nc.us
Cabarrus County Opportunity S — 100/Alt
120 Marsh Ave NW 28025 — 704-793-1736
Beverly Mack, prin. — Fax 788-6158
Cabarrus Early College of Technology — 9-12
670 Concord Pkwy N 28027 — 704-260-6750
Vance Fishback, prin. — Fax 260-6759
Cabarrus-Kannapolis Early College HS — 200/9-12
1531 Trinity Church Rd 28027 — 704-260-0227
Amber Davis, prin. — Fax 260-0229
Central Cabarrus HS — 1,300/9-12
505 Highway 49 S 28025 — 704-786-0125
Andrew Crook, prin. — Fax 920-7164
Concord HS — 1,200/9-12
481 Burrage Rd NE 28025 — 704-260-6000
Dr. Adam Auerbach, prin. — Fax 260-6019
Concord MS — 900/6-8
1500 Gold Rush Dr 28025 — 704-786-4121
Carrie Tulbert, prin. — Fax 782-8632
Cox Mill HS — 1,400/9-12
1355 Cox Mill Rd 28027 — 704-788-6700
Todd Smith, prin. — Fax 788-1112
Fries MS — 600/6-9
133 Stonecrest Cir SW 28027 — 704-788-4140
Dr. Kristi Bullock, prin. — Fax 784-2086
Griffin MS — 1,100/6-9
7650 Griffins Gate Dr SW 28025 — 704-455-4700
Kristy Bullock, prin. — Fax 454-4780
Harris Road MS — 1,100/6-8
1251 Patriot Plantation 28027 — 704-782-2002
Raymond Aldridge, prin. — Fax 262-4298
Northwest Cabarrus HS — 1,100/9-12
5130 NW Cabarrus Dr 28027 — 704-788-4111
Christopher Myers, prin. — Fax 723-4114
Northwest Cabarrus MS — 900/6-8
5140 NW Cabarrus Dr 28027 — 704-788-4135
Kenna Eyster-Terrill, prin. — Fax 784-2649
Performance Learning Center — 100/Alt
133 Stonecrest Cir SW 28027 — 704-795-7074
Dr. James Williams, prin. — Fax 795-5994
Robinson HS — 1,300/9-12
300 Pitts School Rd SW 28027 — 704-788-4500
Gregory Hall, prin. — Fax 723-4352
Winkler MS — 1,000/6-9
4501 Weddington Rd NW 28027 — 704-786-2000
Michael Williams, prin. — Fax 786-2002
Other Schools – See Harrisburg, Mount Pleasant

Cabarrus College of Health Sciences — Post-Sec.
401 Medical Park Dr 28025 — 704-403-1555
Cannon S — 900/PK-12
5801 Poplar Tent Rd 28027 — 704-786-8171
Matthew Gossage, head sch — Fax 788-7779
CFA Academy — 600/PK-12
154 Warren C Coleman Blvd N 28027 — 704-793-4750
Rev. Frank Cantadore, head sch — Fax 793-4784
Covenant Classical S — 200/PK-12
3200 Patrick Henry Dr NW 28027 — 704-792-1854
Jane Dearing, head sch — Fax 792-2102
Empire Beauty School — Post-Sec.
10075 Weddington Road Ext 28027 — 800-575-5983
Hope Academy — 100/K-10
7655 Bruton Smith Blvd 28027 — 704-999-2436
Courtney Elliott, head sch — Fax 706-9160

Connelly Sprngs, Burke
Burke County SD
Supt. — See Morganton
East Burke HS — 900/9-12
3695 E Burke Blvd, — 828-397-5541
Shane Mace, prin. — Fax 397-7652
East Burke MS — 800/6-8
3519 Miller Bridge Rd, — 828-397-7446
Terry Penland, prin. — Fax 397-1086

Conover, Catawba, Pop. 8,005
Newton-Conover CSD
Supt. — See Newton
Newton-Conover MS — 700/6-8
873 Northern Dr NW 28613 — 828-464-4221
Rosanna Whisnant, prin. — Fax 464-5238

Tri-City Christian S — 200/PK-12
PO Box 1690 28613 — 828-465-0475
Keith Thomas, admin. — Fax 466-3749

Conway, Northampton, Pop. 825
Northampton County SD
Supt. — See Jackson
Conway MS — 400/5-8
400 E Main St 27820 — 252-585-0312
Mark Long, prin. — Fax 585-0335
Northampton County HS — 500/9-12
152 Hurricane Dr 27820 — 252-537-1910
Chanda Battle, prin. — Fax 537-9028

Cornelius, Mecklenburg, Pop. 24,533
Charlotte/Mecklenburg County SD
Supt. — See Charlotte
Bailey MS — 1,600/6-8
11900 Bailey Rd 28031 — 980-343-1068
Chad Thomas, prin. — Fax 343-1069
Hough HS — 2,200/9-12
12420 Bailey Rd 28031 — 980-344-0514
Dr. Laura Rosenbach, prin. — Fax 343-2215

Cramerton, Gaston, Pop. 4,105
Gaston County SD
Supt. — See Gastonia
Cramerton MS — 900/6-8
601 Cramer Mountain Rd 28032 — 704-836-9603
Bryan Denton, prin. — Fax 824-0228

Cramerton Christian Academy — 300/K-12
426 Woodlawn Ave 28032 — 704-824-2840

Creedmoor, Granville, Pop. 4,037
Granville County SD
Supt. — See Oxford
Granville Early College HS — 200/9-12
1552 South Campus Dr 27522 — 919-528-5583
Jackie Harris, prin. — Fax 528-5584
Hawley MS — 600/6-8
2173 Brassfield Rd 27522 — 919-528-0091
Frank Wiggins, prin. — Fax 528-0051
South Granville HS — 400/9-12
701 N Crescent Dr 27522 — 919-528-5532
Lisa Tusa, prin. — Fax 528-5575

Creswell, Washington, Pop. 268
Washington County SD
Supt. — See Plymouth
Creswell JSHS — 200/6-12
PO Box 188 27928 — 252-797-4766
Kevin Lloyd, prin. — Fax 797-4651

Cullowhee, Jackson, Pop. 6,135

Western Carolina University — Post-Sec.
University Dr 28723 — 828-227-7211

Currituck, Currituck
Currituck County SD — 3,900/PK-12
2958 Caratoke Hwy 27929 — 252-232-2223
Mark Stefanik, supt. — Fax 232-3655
www.currituck.k12.nc.us
Knapp Early College HS — 200/9-12
2966 Caratoke Hwy 27929 — 252-232-3107
Stephen Basnight, prin. — Fax 232-3923
Other Schools – See Barco, Moyock

Dallas, Gaston, Pop. 4,415
Gaston County SD
Supt. — See Gastonia

Friday MS 700/6-8
1221 Ratchford Dr 28034 704-922-5297
Crystal Houser, prin. Fax 922-9841
Gaston Early College HS 100/9-12
201 Highway 321 S 28034 704-922-2405
Sheila Wyont, prin. Fax 922-7456
North Gaston HS 1,100/9-12
1133 Ratchford Dr 28034 704-922-5285
George Conner, prin. Fax 922-7486

Gaston College Post-Sec.
201 Highway 321 S 28034 704-922-6200

Danbury, Stokes, Pop. 189
Stokes County SD 6,500/PK-12
PO Box 50 27016 336-593-8146
Dr. Brad Rice, supt. Fax 593-2041
www.stokes.k12.nc.us
North Stokes HS 400/9-12
1350 N Stokes School Rd 27016 336-593-8134
Nathan Rasey, prin. Fax 593-8882
Other Schools – See King, Lawsonville, Walnut Cove

Davidson, Mecklenburg, Pop. 10,776

Davidson College Post-Sec.
PO Box 7171 28035 704-894-2000
Davidson Day S 500/PK-12
750 Jetton St 28036 704-237-5200
Gene Bratek, head sch Fax 896-5535
Lake Norman Christian S 100/K-12
PO Box 4267 28036 704-987-9811
Dr. Wes Johnston, head sch Fax 896-5875

Deep Run, Lenoir
Lenoir County SD
Supt. — See Kinston
South Lenoir HS 800/9-12
3355 Old Hwy 11 28525 252-568-6161
James Saint-Amand, prin. Fax 568-6015

Delco, Columbus, Pop. 332
Columbus County SD
Supt. — See Whiteville
Acme-Delco MS 200/6-8
26133 Andrew Jackson Hwy E 28436 910-655-3200
Christy Brown, prin. Fax 655-6865

Denton, Davidson, Pop. 1,618
Davidson County SD
Supt. — See Lexington
South Davidson HS 400/9-12
14956 S NC Highway 109 27239 336-242-5700
Mike Lawson, prin. Fax 242-5702
South Davidson MS 400/6-8
14954 S NC Highway 109 27239 336-242-5705
Crystal Sexton, prin. Fax 242-5707

Denver, Lincoln, Pop. 2,276
Lincoln County SD
Supt. — See Lincolnton
East Lincoln HS 900/9-12
6471 Highway 73 28037 704-736-1860
Samantha Campbell, prin. Fax 483-6751
North Lincoln MS 700/6-8
1503 Amity Church Rd 28037 704-736-0262
Dr. Misha Rogers, prin. Fax 736-9812

Dobson, Surry, Pop. 1,569
Surry County SD 8,400/PK-12
PO Box 364 27017 336-386-8211
Dr. Travis Reeves, supt. Fax 386-4279
www.surry.k12.nc.us/
Central MS 700/6-8
PO Box 768 27017 336-386-4018
Bill Goins, prin. Fax 386-4371
Surry Central HS 800/9-12
PO Box 8 27017 336-386-8842
Celia Hodges, prin. Fax 386-4424
Surry Early College HS of Design 300/9-12
630 S Main St 27017 336-386-3621
Kevin Via, prin. Fax 386-3629
Other Schools – See Mount Airy, Pilot Mountain

Surry Community College Post-Sec.
630 S Main St 27017 336-386-8121

Drexel, Burke, Pop. 1,832
Burke County SD
Supt. — See Morganton
Hallyburton Academy 100/Alt
PO Box 3238 28619 828-437-4184
Jonathan Clontz, prin. Fax 437-0655

Dublin, Bladen, Pop. 329

Bladen Community College Post-Sec.
PO Box 266 28332 910-879-5500

Dudley, Wayne
Wayne County SD
Supt. — See Goldsboro
Brogden MS 500/5-8
3761 US 117 Alt 28333 919-705-6010
Dr. Damesha Smith, prin. Fax 705-6000
Southern Wayne HS 1,000/9-12
124 Walter Fulcher Rd 28333 919-705-6060
Dr. John Boldt, prin. Fax 731-5982

Dunn, Harnett, Pop. 9,078
Harnett County SD
Supt. — See Lillington
Coats-Erwin MS 700/6-8
2833 NC Highway 55 E 28334 910-230-0300
Lynn Herring, prin. Fax 230-0306
Dunn MS 400/6-8
1301 Meadow Lark Rd 28334 910-892-1017
Dr. Janet Doffermyre, prin. Fax 892-7923

Sampson County SD
Supt. — See Clinton
Midway MS 700/6-8
1115 Roberts Grove Church 28334 910-567-5879
Kevin Hunter, prin. Fax 567-5131

Heritage Bible College Post-Sec.
PO Box 1628 28335 910-892-3178

Durham, Durham, Pop. 223,352
Durham County SD 33,100/PK-12
PO Box 30002 27702 919-560-2000
Dr. Bert L'Homme, supt. Fax 560-2422
www.dpsnc.net
Brogden MS 700/6-8
1001 Leon St 27704 919-560-3906
Latonya Smith, prin. Fax 560-3957
Carrington MS 1,200/6-8
227 Milton Rd 27712 919-560-3916
Holly Emmanuel, prin. Fax 560-3522
City of Medicine Academy 300/9-12
301 Crutchfield St 27704 919-560-2001
Jackie Tobias, prin. Fax 477-3128
Clement Early College HS 300/9-12
1801 Fayetteville St 27707 919-560-2696
Gloria Woods-Weaks, prin. Fax 560-2698
Durham S of the Arts 1,600/6-12
401 N Duke St 27701 919-560-3926
David Hawks, prin. Fax 560-2217
Githens MS 1,000/6-8
4800 Old Chapel Hill Rd 27707 919-560-3966
Tonya Williams, prin. Fax 560-3454
Hillside HS 1,200/9-12
3727 Fayetteville St 27707 919-560-3925
Dr. William Logan, prin. Fax 560-2312
Hillside New Tech HS 300/9-12
3727 Fayetteville St 27707 919-560-9183
Tounya Wright, prin. Fax 560-3686
Holton Career & Resource Center Vo/Tech
401 N Driver St 27703 919-560-2219
Emmett Tilley, prin. Fax 237-5669
Jordan HS 1,800/9-12
6806 Garrett Rd 27707 919-560-3912
Dr. Kerry Chisnall, prin. Fax 560-2620
Lakeview S 100/Alt
3507 Dearborn Dr 27704 919-560-2520
Jeffery Dockery, prin. Fax 560-2446
Lakewood Montessori S 300/6-8
2119 Chapel Hill Rd 27707 919-560-2894
Dr. W. Renee Carmon, prin. Fax 237-7388
Lowes Grove MS 700/6-8
4418 S Alston Ave 27713 919-560-3946
Dr. Tekeisha Mitchell, prin. Fax 560-2102
Lucas MS 600/6-8
923 Snow Hill Rd 27712 919-560-3843
Michael Somers, prin. Fax 471-0072
Middle College HS at DTCC 100/11-12
1616 Cooper St Bldg Newton 27703 919-536-7203
Marcia Navarro, prin. Fax 536-7294
Neal MS 900/6-8
201 Baptist Rd 27704 919-560-3955
Michael Fuga, prin. Fax 560-3451
Northern HS 1,400/9-12
117 Tom Wilkinson Rd 27712 919-560-3956
Danny Gilfort, prin. Fax 479-3001
Performance Learning Center 200/Alt
401 N Driver St 27703 919-560-9190
Emmett Tilley, prin. Fax 560-2214
Riverside HS 1,800/9-12
3218 Rose of Sharon Rd 27712 919-560-3965
Dr. Joel County, prin. Fax 560-3798
Rogers-Herr MS 600/6-8
911 W Cornwallis Rd 27707 919-560-3970
Kecia Rogers, prin. Fax 560-2439
School for Creative Studies 300/6-12
5001 Red Mill Rd 27704 919-560-3535
Renee Price, prin. Fax 477-9189
Shepard MS 500/6-8
2401 Dakota St 27707 919-560-3938
Micah Copeland, prin. Fax 560-3945
Southern HS of Energy and Sustainability 1,000/9-12
800 Clayton Rd 27703 919-560-3968
Jerome Leathers, prin. Fax 560-2445

Apex School of Theology Post-Sec.
1701 TW Alexander Dr 27703 919-572-1625
Art Institute of Raleigh - Durham Post-Sec.
410 Blackwell St Ste 200 27701 919-317-3050
Camelot Academy 100/K-12
809 Proctor St 27707 919-688-3040
Thelma Decarlo-Glynn, dir. Fax 682-4320
Carolina Friends S 500/PK-12
4809 Friends School Rd 27705 919-383-6602
Mike Hanas, prin. Fax 383-6009
Cresset Christian Academy 200/PK-12
3707 Garrett Rd 27707 919-489-2655
Greg Hardy, admin. Fax 354-8009
Duke University 27708 Post-Sec.
919-684-8111
Durham Academy 400/5-8
3116 Academy Rd 27707 919-489-9118
Michael Ulku-Steiner, head sch Fax 489-9110
Durham Academy 400/9-12
3601 Ridge Rd 27705 919-489-6569
Michael Ulku-Steiner, head sch Fax 489-7356
Durham Technical Community College Post-Sec.
1637 E Lawson St 27703 919-536-7200
Fellowship Baptist Academy 100/PK-12
515 Southerland St 27703 919-596-9331
Liberty Christian S 200/K-12
3864 Guess Rd 27705 919-471-5522
Mt. Zion Christian Academy 200/K-12
3519 Fayetteville St 27707 919-688-4245
Peggy McIlwain, prin. Fax 688-2201
North Carolina Central University Post-Sec.
1801 Fayetteville St 27707 919-560-6100
Trinity S of Durham & Chapel Hill 500/PK-12
4011 Pickett Rd 27705 919-402-8262
Mason Goss, hdmstr. Fax 402-0762

East Bend, Yadkin, Pop. 604
Yadkin County SD
Supt. — See Yadkinville
Forbush HS 900/9-12
1525 Falcon Rd 27018 336-961-4644
Robert Kennedy, prin. Fax 961-2575
Forbush MS 500/7-8
1431 Falcon Rd 27018 336-961-6360
Kelly Kirkland, prin. Fax 961-6370

East Flat Rock, Henderson, Pop. 4,872
Henderson County SD
Supt. — See Hendersonville
East Henderson HS 900/9-12
150 Eagle Pride Dr 28726 828-697-4768
Carl Taylor, prin. Fax 698-6123
Flat Rock MS 700/6-8
191 Preston Ln 28726 828-697-4775
Jeff Roper, prin. Fax 698-6124

Eden, Rockingham, Pop. 15,244
Rockingham County SD 13,200/PK-12
511 Harrington Hwy 27288 336-627-2600
Dr. Rodney Shotwell, supt. Fax 627-2660
www.rock.k12.nc.us
Holmes MS 800/6-8
211 N Pierce St 27288 336-623-9791
Elliott Miller, prin. Fax 627-0075
Morehead HS 900/9-12
134 N Pierce St 27288 336-627-7731
Al Royster, prin. Fax 623-5462
Other Schools – See Madison, Mayodan, Reidsville, Wentworth

Edenton, Chowan, Pop. 4,952
Edenton-Chowan County SD 2,300/PK-12
PO Box 206 27932 252-482-4436
Dr. Rob Jackson, supt. Fax 482-7309
www.ecps.k12.nc.us
Holmes HS 700/9-12
PO Box 409 27932 252-482-8426
Steve Wood, prin. Fax 482-2010
Other Schools – See Tyner

Efland, Orange, Pop. 722
Orange County SD
Supt. — See Hillsborough
Gravelly Hill MS 500/6-8
4819 W Ten Rd 27243 919-245-4050
Dr. Chris Gammon, prin. Fax 245-4055

Elizabeth City, Pasquotank, Pop. 18,282
Elizabeth City/Pasquotank County SD 5,800/PK-12
1200 Halstead Blvd 27909 252-335-2981
Dr. Larry Cartner, supt. Fax 335-0974
www.ecpps.k12.nc.us
Elizabeth City MS 600/6-8
1066 Northside Rd 27909 252-335-2974
Timothy Worrell, prin. Fax 335-1751
Northeastern HS 800/9-12
963 Oak Stump Rd 27909 252-335-2932
Alton Campbell, prin. Fax 335-1005
Pasquotank County HS 700/9-12
1064 Northside Rd 27909 252-337-6880
Amy Fyffe, prin. Fax 337-6890
River Road MS 600/6-8
1701 River Rd 27909 252-333-1454
LeVar Mizelle, prin. Fax 331-1339
Trigg Community HS 100/Alt
1004 Parkview Dr 27909 252-335-1765
Ainslie Jones, prin. Fax 337-6740

Albemarle S 200/PK-12
1210 US Highway 17 S 27909 252-338-0883
Dr. Holly Glenn, hdmstr. Fax 338-1222
College of the Albemarle Post-Sec.
PO Box 2327 27906 252-335-0821
Elizabeth City State University Post-Sec.
1704 Weeksville Rd 27909 252-335-3400
Mid Atlantic Christian University Post-Sec.
715 N Poindexter St 27909 252-334-2000
Victory Christian S 200/PK-12
684 Old Hertford Hwy 27909 252-264-2011

Elizabethtown, Bladen, Pop. 3,534
Bladen County SD 5,000/PK-12
PO Box 37 28337 910-862-4136
Robert Taylor, supt. Fax 860-6170
www.bladen.k12.nc.us/
East Bladen HS 700/9-12
5600 NC Highway 87 E 28337 910-247-4610
Jason Wray, prin. Fax 818-3509
Elizabethtown MS 400/5-8
PO Box 639 28337 910-862-4071
Elizabeth Cole, prin. Fax 819-0429
Other Schools – See Bladenboro, Clarkton, Tar Heel

Elkin, Surry, Pop. 3,953
Elkin CSD 1,200/PK-12
202 W Spring St 28621 336-835-3135
Dr. Don Martin, supt. Fax 835-3376
www.elkin.k12.nc.us
Elkin HS 400/9-12
334 Elk Spur St 28621 336-835-3858
Joel Hoyle, prin. Fax 835-3253
Elkin MS 200/7-8
300 Elk Spur St 28621 336-835-3175
Cassundra Morrison, prin. Fax 835-1427

Elk Park, Avery, Pop. 449
Avery County SD
Supt. — See Newland
Cranberry MS 200/6-8
6230 N US Highway 19E 28622 828-733-2932
Matthew Bentley, prin. Fax 733-6863

Ellerbe, Richmond, Pop. 1,027
Richmond County SD
Supt. — See Hamlet
Ellerbe MS 200/6-8
128 W Ballard St 28338 910-652-3231
Melvin Ingram, prin. Fax 652-3106

Elm City, Wilson, Pop. 1,289
Wilson County SD
Supt. — See Wilson
Elm City MS 500/6-8
215 Church St E 27822 252-236-4148
Robert Pope, prin. Fax 236-3754

Elon, Alamance, Pop. 9,262
Alamance-Burlington SD
Supt. — See Burlington
Western Alamance HS 1,200/9-12
1731 N NC Highway 87 27244 336-538-6020
Todd Stephan, prin. Fax 538-6014
Western Alamance MS 900/6-8
2100 Eldon Dr 27244 336-538-6010
Gregory Holland, prin. Fax 538-6012

Elon University Post-Sec.
2700 Campus Box 27244 336-278-2000

Enfield, Halifax, Pop. 2,522
Halifax County SD
Supt. — See Halifax
Enfield MS 300/6-8
13723 NC Highway 481 27823 252-445-5455
Teicher Patterson, prin. Fax 445-3866

Erwin, Harnett, Pop. 4,318
Harnett County SD
Supt. — See Lillington
Triton HS 1,300/9-12
215 Maynard Lake Rd 28339 910-897-8121
Chip Mangum, prin. Fax 897-3148

Cape Fear Christian Academy 300/PK-12
138 Erwin Chapel Rd 28339 910-897-5423
Karen Parker, hdmstr. Fax 897-2150

Fair Bluff, Columbus, Pop. 944
Columbus County SD
Supt. — See Whiteville
Columbus Career & Coll Acad - Fair Bluff 9-12
685 Academy St 28439 910-499-0999
Nicky Hobbs, prin. Fax 649-6506

Fairmont, Robeson, Pop. 2,595
Robeson County SD
Supt. — See Lumberton
Fairgrove MS 300/4-8
1953 Fairgrove Rd 28340 910-628-8290
Hawhana Locklear, prin. Fax 628-6181
Fairmont HS 700/9-12
5419 Old Stage Rd 28340 910-628-6727
Ronald Prater, prin. Fax 628-0652
Fairmont MS 400/5-8
402 Iona St 28340 910-628-4363
Darlene Cummings, prin. Fax 628-0335

Farmville, Pitt, Pop. 4,617
Pitt County SD
Supt. — See Greenville
Farmville Central HS 800/9-12
PO Box 209 27828 252-753-5138
Brad Johnston, prin. Fax 753-7873
Farmville MS 600/6-8
3914 Grimmersburg St 27828 252-753-2116
Paul Briney, prin. Fax 753-7995

Fayetteville, Cumberland, Pop. 191,875
Cumberland County SD 51,700/PK-12
PO Box 2357 28302 910-678-2300
Dr. Frank Till, supt. Fax 678-2339
www.ccs.k12.nc.us
Abbott MS 900/6-8
590 Winding Creek Rd 28305 910-323-2201
Carla Crenshaw, prin. Fax 485-0841
Britt HS 1,900/9-12
7403 Rockfish Rd 28306 910-429-2800
Scott Pope, prin. Fax 429-2810
Byrd HS 1,200/9-12
1624 Ireland Dr 28304 910-484-8121
Dr. Zoletta Taylor, prin. Fax 323-4127
Byrd MS 700/7-8
1616 Ireland Dr 28304 910-483-3101
Meshonda Williams, prin. Fax 483-3741
Cape Fear HS 1,500/9-12
4762 Clinton Rd, 910-483-0191
Lee Spruill, prin. Fax 483-1679
Chesnutt MS 600/6-8
2121 Skibo Rd 28314 910-867-9147
Tonjai Robertson, prin. Fax 868-3695
Cross Creek Early College HS 200/9-12
1200 Murchison Rd 28301 910-672-1499
Patsy Patrick, prin. Fax 672-1590
Cumberland International Early College S 200/9-12
1200 Murchison Rd 28301 910-672-2830
Maria Pierce-Ford, prin. Fax 672-2849
Cumberland Polytechnic HS 9-12
PO Box 2357 28302 910-486-7300
Daniel Krumanocker, prin. Fax 486-7325
Griffin MS 1,000/6-8
5551 Fisher Rd 28304 910-424-7678
Tommy Dent, prin. Fax 424-7602
Howard Learning Academy 200/6-8
1608 Camden Rd 28306 910-483-5434
Allen Hines, prin. Fax 323-3159
Jeralds MS 500/6-8
2517 Ramsey St 28301 910-822-2570
Joy Williams, prin. Fax 822-1534
Lewis Chapel MS 600/6-8
2150 Skibo Rd 28314 910-864-1407
Dr. Sheldon Harvey, prin. Fax 864-8298
Massey Hill Classical HS 300/9-12
1062 Southern Ave 28306 910-485-8761
Dr. Pamela Adams-Watkins, prin. Fax 485-7950
New Century International MS 400/6-8
7455 Century Cir 28306 910-487-2001
Lavette McMillan, prin. Fax 487-2009
Pine Forest HS 1,600/9-12
525 Andrews Rd 28311 910-488-2384
David Culberth, prin. Fax 488-0790
Pine Forest MS 800/6-8
6901 Ramsey St 28311 910-488-2711
Bill Starks, prin. Fax 630-2357
Ramsey Street Alternative HS 100/Alt
117 Quincy St 28301 910-437-5829
Reggie Pinkney, prin. Fax 437-5121
Ross Classical JSHS 300/6-12
3200 Ramsey St 28301 910-488-8415
Thomas Hatch, prin. Fax 488-6209
Sanford HS 1,300/9-12
2301 Fort Bragg Rd 28303 910-484-1151
Robert Guzman, prin. Fax 484-7203
Seventy-First Classical MS 500/6-8
6830 Raeford Rd 28304 910-864-0092
Patricia Ramos, prin. Fax 487-8547
Seventy-First HS 1,600/9-12
6764 Raeford Rd 28304 910-867-3116
Myron Williams, prin. Fax 867-1445
Smith HS 1,000/9-12
1800 Seabrook Rd 28301 910-483-0153
Melody Chalmers, prin. Fax 483-7696
Westover HS 1,200/9-12
277 Bonanza Dr 28303 910-864-0190
Dr. Thomas Benson, prin. Fax 864-5924
Westover MS 800/6-8
275 Bonanza Dr 28303 910-864-0813
La'Shanda Carver-Moore, prin. Fax 864-7906
Wilkins HS 200/Alt
1429 Skibo Rd 28303 910-864-5438
Dr. Vernon Lowery, prin. Fax 868-1777
Williams MS 1,200/6-8
4644 Clinton Rd, 910-483-8222
Steven Morris, prin. Fax 483-4831
Other Schools – See Hope Mills, Spring Lake

Bal-Perazim Christian Academy 50/PK-12
4921 Bragg Blvd 28303 910-487-4220
Morris Braxton D.D.S., head sch Fax 864-3451
Berean Baptist Academy 400/PK-12
518 Glensford Dr 28314 910-868-2511
Jack Farmer, prin. Fax 868-1550
Carolina College of Biblical Studies Post-Sec.
817 S McPherson Church Rd 28303 910-323-5614
Cornerstone Christian Academy 200/PK-12
3000 Scotty Hill Rd 28303 910-867-1166
Fayetteville Academy 400/PK-12
3200 Cliffdale Rd 28303 910-868-5131
Ray Quesnel, head sch Fax 868-7351
Fayetteville Beauty College Post-Sec.
3442 Bragg Blvd 28303 910-487-0227
Fayetteville Christian S 600/PK-12
1422 Ireland Dr 28304 910-483-3905
Tammi Peters, head sch Fax 483-6966
Fayetteville State University Post-Sec.
1200 Murchison Rd 28301 910-672-1111
Fayetteville Technical Community College Post-Sec.
PO Box 35236 28303 910-678-8400
Freedom Christian Academy 300/PK-12
3130 Gillespie St 28306 910-485-7777
Paul Williams, head sch Fax 485-7757
Grace College of Divinity Post-Sec.
5117 Cliffdale Rd 28314 910-221-2224
Liberty Christian Academy 300/PK-12
6548 Rockfish Rd 28306 910-424-1205
Duncan Edge, prin. Fax 424-8049
Methodist University Post-Sec.
5400 Ramsey St 28311 910-630-7000
Miller-Motte College Post-Sec.
3725 Ramsey St 28311 910-354-1900
Mitchell's Hairstyling Academy Post-Sec.
222 Tallywood Shopping Ctr 28303 910-485-6310
Northwood Temple Academy 400/PK-12
4200 Ramsey St 28311 910-822-7711
Renee McLamb, head sch Fax 488-7299
Renaissance Classical Christian Academy 100/PK-10
6427 Cliffdale Rd 28314 910-221-0400
Ray Hendrickson, hdmstr. Fax 864-5476
Trinity Christian S of Academics 200/K-12
3727 Rosehill Rd 28311 910-488-6779
Village Christian Academy 800/K-12
908 S McPherson Church Rd 28303 910-483-5500
Dr. Gene Hales, supt. Fax 483-5335

Flat Rock, Henderson, Pop. 3,091
Henderson County SD
Supt. — See Hendersonville
Henderson County Early College HS 200/9-12
120 Alumni Way 28731 828-697-4561
Beth Caudle, prin. Fax 697-4564

Blue Ridge Community College Post-Sec.
180 W Campus Dr 28731 828-694-1700

Fletcher, Henderson, Pop. 7,049
Buncombe County SD
Supt. — See Asheville
Cane Creek MS 700/6-8
570 Lower Brush Creek Rd 28732 828-628-0824
Karen Barnhill, prin. Fax 628-9833

Fletcher Academy 200/9-12
PO Box 5440 28732 828-209-6800
Veritas Christian Academy 400/PK-12
17 Cane Creek Rd 28732 828-681-0546
Kay Belknap, hdmstr. Fax 681-0547

Forest City, Rutherford, Pop. 7,281
Rutherford County SD 8,500/PK-12
382 W Main St 28043 828-288-2200
Dr. Janet Mason, supt. Fax 288-2490
www.rcsnc.org/
Chase HS 700/9-12
1603 Chase High Rd 28043 828-245-7668
Kevin Bradley, prin. Fax 248-3584
Chase MS 700/6-8
840 Chase High Rd 28043 828-247-1044
Dr. La'Ronda Whiteside, prin. Fax 247-0551
East Rutherford HS 800/9-12
PO Box 668 28043 828-245-6424
Brad Teague, prin. Fax 247-0039
Rutherford Opportunity Center 100/Alt
140 Old Caroleen Rd 28043 828-248-5294
Tim Torvinen, prin. Fax 248-5297
Other Schools – See Bostic, Rutherfordton, Spindale

Four Oaks, Johnston, Pop. 1,883
Johnston County SD
Supt. — See Smithfield
Four Oaks MS 500/6-8
1475 Boyette Rd 27524 919-963-4022
Tol Avery, prin. Fax 963-4123
South Johnston HS 1,100/9-12
10381 US Highway 301 S 27524 919-894-3146
Dr. David Pearce, prin. Fax 894-3229

Franklin, Macon, Pop. 3,786
Macon County SD 4,300/K-12
1202 Old Murphy Rd 28734 828-524-3314
Dr. Chris Baldwin, supt. Fax 524-5938
www.macon.k12.nc.us
Franklin HS 900/9-12
100 Panther Dr 28734 828-524-6467
Barry Woody, prin. Fax 524-0684
Macon Early College HS 100/9-12
77 Siler Farm Rd 28734 828-369-7331
Mark Sutton, prin. Fax 349-9692
Macon MS 600/7-8
1345 Wells Grove Rd 28734 828-524-3766
Scot Maslin, prin. Fax 349-3900
Union Academy 100/Alt
158 Union School Rd 28734 828-369-1277
Diane Cotton, prin. Fax 524-2859
Other Schools – See Highlands, Topton

Trimont Christian Academy 200/PK-12
98 Promise Ln 28734 828-369-6756
Peter Rodewald, prin. Fax 524-0622

Franklinton, Franklin, Pop. 1,988
Franklin County SD
Supt. — See Louisburg
Franklinton HS 1,000/9-12
910 Cedar Creek Rd 27525 919-494-2332
Russell Holloman, prin. Fax 494-5140
Franklinton MS 300/6-8
3 N Main St 27525 919-494-2971
Trenton Brown, prin. Fax 494-1625

Fremont, Wayne, Pop. 1,228
Wayne County SD
Supt. — See Goldsboro
Norwayne MS 1,000/6-8
1394 Norwayne School Rd 27830 919-242-3414
Lisa Tart, prin. Fax 242-3418

Fuquay Varina, Wake, Pop. 17,531
Wake County SD
Supt. — See Cary
Fuquay-Varina HS 2,000/9-12
201 Bengal Dr 27526 919-557-2511
Jonathan Enns, prin. Fax 557-2512
Fuquay-Varina MS 800/6-8
109 N Ennis St 27526 919-557-2727
Ramey Beavers, prin. Fax 557-2754

Hilltop Christian S 300/K-12
10212 Fayetteville Rd 27526 919-552-5612
Travis Moots, prin. Fax 552-3189

Garner, Wake, Pop. 25,256
Johnston County SD
Supt. — See Smithfield
Cleveland MS 1,100/6-8
2323 Cornwallis Rd 27529 919-553-7500
Jenna Sauls-Hairr, prin. Fax 553-7798

Wake County SD
Supt. — See Cary
East Garner MS 1,300/6-8
6301 Jones Sausage Rd 27529 919-662-2339
Elena Ashburn, prin. Fax 662-2357
Garner Magnet HS 2,400/9-12
8228 Hebron Church Rd 27529 919-662-2379
Carter Hillman, prin. Fax 589-6653
North Garner MS 1,100/6-8
720 Powell Dr 27529 919-662-2434
Gregory Butler, prin. Fax 662-5637

Gaston, Northampton, Pop. 1,141
Northampton County SD
Supt. — See Jackson
Gaston MS 200/5-8
400 Broughton St 27832 252-537-1910
Monte Freeman, prin. Fax 537-9028
Northampton County Alternative S 50/Alt
4671 NC Highway 46 27832 252-537-2877
Wanda Briggs, prin. Fax 537-8706
Northampton County HS Early College 100/9-12
4671 NC Highway 46 27832 252-537-2877
Monica Edmonds, prin. Fax 537-8706

Gastonia, Gaston, Pop. 70,333
Gaston County SD 31,300/PK-12
PO Box 1397 28053 704-866-6100
Jeffrey Booker, supt. Fax 866-6321
www.gaston.k12.nc.us/
Ashbrook HS 1,500/9-12
2222 S New Hope Rd 28054 704-866-6600
Rebecca Wilson, prin. Fax 866-6203
Forestview HS 1,100/9-12
5545 Union Rd 28056 704-861-2625
Chad Carper, prin. Fax 853-3323
Grier MS 700/6-8
1622 E Garrison Blvd 28054 704-836-9604
Loretta Reed, prin. Fax 866-6116
Highland School of Technology 600/9-12
1600 N Morris St 28052 704-810-8816
Denise McLean, prin. Fax 866-6105

Huss HS 1,100/9-12
1518 Edgefield Ave 28052 704-866-6610
Brent Boone, prin. Fax 866-6103
Southwest MS 800/6-8
1 Roadrunner Dr 28052 704-866-6290
Lucretia Rice, prin. Fax 866-6293
Warlick Academy 100/Alt
1316 Spencer Mountain Rd 28054 704-824-3012
Curt Hovis, prin. Fax 824-0918
York Chester MS 400/6-8
601 S Clay St 28052 704-866-6297
Amy Holbrook, prin. Fax 866-6319
Other Schools – See Belmont, Bessemer City, Cherryville, Cramerton, Dallas, Lowell, Mount Holly, Stanley

---

Gaston Christian S 800/PK-12
1625 Lowell Bethesda Rd 28056 704-349-5020
Gaston Day S 500/PK-12
2001 Gaston Day School Rd 28056 704-864-7744
Dr. Richard Rankin, hdmstr. Fax 865-3813

Gatesville, Gates, Pop. 318
Gates County SD 1,700/PK-12
PO Box 125 27938 252-357-1113
Dr. Barry Williams, supt. Fax 357-0207
coserver.gates.k12.nc.us/
Central MS 400/6-8
362 US Highway 158 W 27938 252-357-0470
Steve Hunter, prin. Fax 357-1319
Gates County HS 500/9-12
88 US Highway 158 W 27938 252-357-0720
Jonathan Hayes, prin. Fax 357-2058

Gibsonville, Guilford, Pop. 6,318
Guilford County SD
Supt. — See Greensboro
Eastern Guilford HS 1,200/9-12
415 Peeden Dr 27249 336-449-6311
Lance Sockwell, prin. Fax 449-7392
Eastern MS 900/6-8
435 Peeden Dr 27249 336-449-4255
Christopher Tolliver, prin. Fax 449-0728

Goldsboro, Wayne, Pop. 35,562
Wayne County SD 18,600/PK-12
PO Box 1797 27533 919-731-5900
Dr. Michael Dunsmore, supt. Fax 705-6199
www.waynecountyschools.org
Dillard MS 600/5-8
1101 Devereaux St 27530 919-580-9360
Sonja Emerson, prin. Fax 736-1121
Eastern Wayne HS 1,100/9-12
1135 E New Hope Rd 27534 919-751-7120
Lee Johnson, prin. Fax 751-7107
Eastern Wayne MS 600/6-8
3518 Central Heights Rd 27534 919-751-7110
Catherine Fulcher, prin. Fax 751-7114
Goldsboro HS 500/9-12
901 Beech St 27530 919-731-5930
Robert Yelverton, prin. Fax 731-5914
Grantham MS 5-8
3093 US Highway 13 S 27530 919-689-9999
Makita Jenkins, prin.
Greenwood MS 500/5-8
3209 E Ash St 27534 919-751-7100
Rolanda Best, prin. Fax 751-7201
Rosewood HS 500/9-12
900 Rosewood Rd 27530 919-705-6050
Karen Rogers, prin. Fax 705-6055
Rosewood MS 400/6-8
541 NC 581 Hwy S 27530 919-736-5050
Brian Weeks, prin. Fax 736-5055
Wayne Early Middle College HS 200/9-12
3000 Wayne Memorial Dr 27534 919-739-7070
Freda Allen, prin. Fax 581-1011
Wayne MSHS Academy 100/Alt
801 Lionel St 27530 919-580-3608
Carole Battle, prin. Fax 731-5495
Wayne S of Engineering 400/6-12
700 N Herman St 27530 919-734-0070
Gary Hales, prin. Fax 731-0072
Other Schools – See Dudley, Fremont, Mount Olive, Pikeville, Seven Springs

---

Faith Christian Academy 300/PK-12
1200 W Grantham St 27530 919-734-8701
Mitchell's Hairstyling Academy Post-Sec.
1021 N Spence Ave 27534 919-778-8200
Wayne Christian S 500/PK-12
1201 Patetown Rd 27530 919-735-5605
Dr. Ashley Shook, admin. Fax 735-5229
Wayne Community College Post-Sec.
PO Box 8002 27533 919-735-5151
Wayne Country Day S 300/PK-12
480 Country Day Rd 27530 919-736-1045
Todd Anderson, head sch Fax 583-9493

Graham, Alamance, Pop. 13,906
Alamance-Burlington SD
Supt. — See Burlington
Alamance-Burlington Middle College HS 100/9-12
PO Box 8000 27253 336-506-4001
Bonnie Roane, prin. Fax 506-4004
Graham HS 800/9-12
903 Trollinger Rd 27253 336-570-6440
Charlotte Holmes, prin. Fax 570-6446
Graham MS 700/6-8
311 E Pine St 27253 336-570-6460
Lee Williams, prin. Fax 570-6464
Ray Street Academy 100/Alt
609 Ray St 27253 336-570-6643
Michael Bayless, prin. Fax 570-6353
Southern Alamance HS 1,500/9-12
631 Southern High School Rd 27253 336-570-6400
Teresa Faucette, prin. Fax 570-6404
Southern Alamance MS 800/6-8
771 Southern High School Rd 27253 336-570-6500
Heather Ward, prin. Fax 570-6504

Alamance Christian S 300/PK-12
PO Box 838 27253 336-578-0318
Mike Lofin, admin. Fax 578-7200
Alamance Community College Post-Sec.
PO Box 8000 27253 336-578-2002

Granite Falls, Caldwell, Pop. 4,669
Caldwell County SD
Supt. — See Lenoir
Caldwell County Gateway S 50/Alt
1889 Dudley Shoals Rd 28630 828-396-8373
Bill Schreiber, prin. Fax 396-7960
Granite Falls MS 600/6-8
90 N Main St 28630 828-396-2341
Melissa Costin, prin. Fax 396-7072

Grantsboro, Pamlico, Pop. 679

Pamlico Community College Post-Sec.
PO Box 185 28529 252-249-1851

Greensboro, Guilford, Pop. 263,264
Guilford County SD 73,500/PK-12
PO Box 880 27402 336-370-8100
Sharon Contreras Ph.D., supt. Fax 370-8299
www.gcsnc.com
Academy at Lincoln 700/4-8
1016 Lincoln St 27401 336-370-3471
Anita Stewart, prin. Fax 370-3480
Academy at Smith 200/9-12
2225 S Holden Rd 27407 336-316-5866
Lance Stokes, prin. Fax 316-5869
Allen MS 700/6-8
1108 Glendale Dr 27406 336-294-7325
Sheila Gorham, prin. Fax 294-7315
Aycock MS 600/6-8
811 Cypress St 27405 336-370-8110
Keisha Brown, prin. Fax 370-8044
Dudley HS 1,300/9-12
1200 Lincoln St 27401 336-370-8130
Rodney Wilds, prin. Fax 370-8979
Early College at Guilford 200/9-12
5608 W Friendly Ave 27410 336-316-2860
Linda Kidd, prin. Fax 316-2858
Greenboro Middle College HS 100/10-12
815 W Market St 27401 336-370-8300
Cheri Keels, prin. Fax 370-8918
Grimsley HS 1,700/9-12
801 Westover Ter 27408 336-370-8180
W. Charles Blanchard, prin. Fax 370-8194
Guilford MS 700/6-8
320 Lindley Rd 27410 336-316-5833
Patrice Brown, prin. Fax 316-5837
Hairston MS 700/6-8
3911 Naco Rd 27401 336-370-8250
Calvin Freeman, prin. Fax 370-8153
Henderson Newcomers S 200/Alt
411 Friendway Rd 27410 336-316-5883
Candice Bailey, prin. Fax 316-7092
High School Ahead Academy 100/Alt
1401 Summit Ave 27405 336-294-7640
Michelle Hayes, prin. Fax 294-7643
Jackson MS 500/6-8
2200 Ontario St 27403 336-294-7350
Katrinka Brown, prin. Fax 294-7316
Kernodle MS 900/6-8
3600 Drawbridge Pkwy 27410 336-545-3717
Thea McHam, prin. Fax 545-3714
Kiser MS 800/6-8
716 Benjamin Pkwy 27408 336-370-8240
Gerald O'Donnell, prin. Fax 370-8248
Mendenhall MS 900/6-8
205 Willoughby Blvd 27408 336-545-2000
Marshall Matson, prin. Fax 545-2004
Middle College HS @ Bennett 100/9-12
610 Gorrell St 27406 336-517-1832
Esther Coble, prin. Fax 517-2120
Middle College HS @ GTCC Greensboro 100/9-12
3505 E Wendover Ave 27405 336-375-2466
Rodney Boone, prin. Fax 375-2469
Middle College HS @ NC A&T 100/9-12
1601 E Market St 27411 336-691-0941
Marcus Gause, prin. Fax 691-0952
Middle College HS @ UNCG 200/9-12
1408 Walker Ave 27412 336-334-3662
Angela Polk-Jones, prin. Fax 334-5503
Northern HS 1,300/9-12
7101 Spencer Dixon Rd 27455 336-643-8449
William Laine, prin. Fax 644-2589
Northern MS 1,000/6-8
616 Simpson Calhoun Rd 27455 336-605-3342
Ashley Triplett, prin. Fax 643-8435
Northwest HS 2,000/9-12
5240 NW School Rd 27409 336-605-3300
Ralph Kitley, prin. Fax 605-3314
Northwest MS 1,000/6-8
5300 NW School Rd 27409 336-605-3333
Richard Thomae, prin. Fax 605-3325
Page HS 2,000/9-12
201 Alma Pinnix Dr 27405 336-370-8200
Patrice Faison, prin. Fax 370-8219
SCALE - Greensboro 50/Alt
116 Pisgah Church Rd 27455 336-545-2031
Russell Woodward, prin. Fax 545-2035
Smith HS 1,200/9-12
2407 S Holden Rd 27407 336-294-7300
Donevin Hoskins, prin. Fax 294-7313
Southeast HS 1,400/9-12
4530 SE School Rd 27406 336-674-4300
Dr. James Seagraves, prin. Fax 674-4290
Southeast MS 1,000/6-8
4825 Woody Mill Rd 27406 336-674-4280
Karen Burress, prin. Fax 674-4276
Southern HS 1,200/9-12
5700 Drake Rd 27406 336-674-4250
Debbra Kraszeski, prin. Fax 674-4254
Southern MS 800/6-8
5747 Drake Rd 27406 336-674-4266
Karen Ellis, prin. Fax 674-4278

STEM Early College at NC A&T 100/9-12
402 Laurel St 27411 336-370-8580
Jamisa Williams, prin. Fax 274-7167
Twilight HS 100/Alt
116 Pisgah Church Rd 27455 336-282-6797
Pandora Bell, prin.
Weaver Academy 300/9-12
300 S Spring St 27401 336-370-8282
Johncarlos Miller, prin. Fax 370-8287
Western HS 1,200/9-12
409 Friendway Rd 27410 336-316-5800
Pete Kashubara, prin. Fax 316-5813
Other Schools – See Browns Summit, Gibsonville, High Point, Jamestown, Mc Leansville

---

American Hebrew Academy 200/9-12
4334 Hobbs Rd 27410 336-217-7100
Glenn Drew, dir. Fax 217-7011
Bennett College Post-Sec.
900 E Washington St 27401 336-273-4431
Brookstone College of Business Post-Sec.
424 Gallimore Dairy Rd St A 27409 336-668-2627
Caldwell Academy 700/PK-12
2900 Horse Pen Creek Rd 27410 336-665-1161
Sam Cox, head sch Fax 665-1178
Carolina Graduate School of Divinity Post-Sec.
PO Box 7148 27417 336-315-8660
ECPI University Post-Sec.
7802 Airport Center Dr 27409 336-665-1400
Greensboro College Post-Sec.
815 W Market St 27401 336-272-7102
Greensboro Day S 900/PK-12
5401 Lawndale Dr 27455 336-288-8590
Mark Hale, head sch Fax 282-2905
Guilford College Post-Sec.
5800 W Friendly Ave 27410 336-316-2000
Leon's Beauty School Post-Sec.
1305 Coliseum Blvd 27403 336-274-4601
Moses H. Cone Memorial Hospital Post-Sec.
1200 N Elm St 27401 336-574-7881
New Garden Friends S 300/PK-12
1128 New Garden Rd 27410 336-299-0964
Kim Freedman, head sch Fax 346-3169
Noble Academy 100/K-12
3310 Horse Pen Creek Rd 27410 336-282-7044
Linda Hale, head sch Fax 282-2048
North Carolina A&T State University Post-Sec.
1601 E Market St 27411 336-334-7500
Shining Light Academy 200/PK-12
4530 W Wendover Ave 27409 336-299-9688
University of North Carolina Post-Sec.
PO Box 26170 27402 336-334-5000
Vandalia Christian S 700/PK-12
3919 Pleasant Garden Rd 27406 336-379-8380
Dr. Mark Weatherford, admin. Fax 379-8671
Virginia College Post-Sec.
3740 S Holden Rd 27406 336-398-5400

Greenville, Pitt, Pop. 82,822
Pitt County SD 24,000/PK-12
1717 W 5th St 27834 252-830-4200
Dr. Ethan Lenker, supt. Fax 830-4239
www.pitt.k12.nc.us/
Aycock MS 700/6-8
1325 Red Banks Rd 27858 252-756-4181
Darryl Thomas, prin. Fax 756-2408
Conley HS 1,600/9-12
2006 Worthington Rd 27858 252-756-3440
Don Marr, prin. Fax 756-3028
Eppes MS 600/6-8
1100 S Elm St 27858 252-757-2160
Charlie Langley, prin. Fax 757-2163
Hope MS 700/6-8
2995 Mills Rd 27858 252-355-7071
Jennifer Poplin, prin. Fax 355-6055
Rose HS 1,400/9-12
600 W Arlington Blvd 27834 252-321-3640
Monica Jacobson, prin. Fax 321-3653
Wellcome MS 500/6-8
3101 N Memorial Dr 27834 252-752-5938
Maurice Harris, prin. Fax 752-1685
Other Schools – See Ayden, Bethel, Farmville, Winterville

East Carolina University Post-Sec.
1000 E 5th St 27858 252-328-6131
Greenville Christian Academy 300/PK-12
1621 Greenville Blvd SW 27834 252-756-0939
Miller-Motte College Post-Sec.
1021 WH Smith Blvd Ste 102 27834 252-215-2000
Mitchell's Hairstyling Academy Post-Sec.
426 E Arlington Blvd 27858 252-756-3050
Oakwood S 300/PK-12
4000 MacGregor Downs Rd 27834 252-931-0760
Robert Peterson, hdmstr. Fax 931-0964
Pitt Community College Post-Sec.
PO Box 7007 27835 252-493-7200
St. John Paul II Catholic HS 9-12
PO Box 4431 27836 252-215-1224
Craig Conticchio, prin. Fax 225-0212
Trinity Christian S 400/PK-12
3111 Golden Rd 27858 252-758-0037

Halifax, Halifax, Pop. 232
Halifax County SD 2,900/PK-12
PO Box 468 27839 252-583-5111
Dr. Eric Cunningham, supt. Fax 583-1474
www.halifax.k12.nc.us/
Southeast Halifax HS 300/9-12
16683 NC Highway 125 27839 252-445-2027
Ann Davis, prin. Fax 445-3463
Other Schools – See Enfield, Littleton

Weldon CSD
Supt. — See Weldon
Weldon MS 300/5-8
4489 US Highway 301 27839 252-536-2571
Andre Stewart, prin. Fax 536-3485

Hallsboro, Columbus, Pop. 457
Columbus County SD
Supt. — See Whiteville
Hallsboro MS 200/6-8
89 School Rd 28442 910-646-4192
Derrick Boyd, prin. Fax 646-5072

Hamlet, Richmond, Pop. 6,381
Richmond County SD 7,800/PK-12
PO Box 1259 28345 910-582-5860
Cindy Goodman Ed.D., supt. Fax 582-7921
www.richmond.k12.nc.us
Hamlet MS 500/6-8
1406 Mcdonald Ave 28345 910-582-7903
Jim Butler, prin. Fax 582-5730
Richmond County 9th Grade Academy 500/9-9
804 County Home Rd 28345 910-582-7800
Pam Patterson, prin. Fax 582-7804
Richmond Early College HS 200/9-12
1042 W Hamlet Ave 28345 910-410-1922
Tonya Waddell, prin.
Other Schools – See Ellerbe, Rockingham

Richmond Community College Post-Sec.
PO Box 1189 28345 910-410-1700

Hampstead, Pender, Pop. 4,028
Pender County SD
Supt. — See Burgaw
Topsail HS 1,200/9-12
245 N Saint Johns Church Rd 28443 910-270-2755
Berry Simmons, prin. Fax 270-9290
Topsail MS 900/6-8
17445 US Highway 17 N 28443 910-270-2612
AnnaMaria Romero-Lehrer, prin. Fax 270-3190

Harrells, Sampson, Pop. 202

Harrells Christian Academy 400/K-12
PO Box 88 28444 910-532-4575
Kevin Kunst, hdmstr. Fax 532-2958

Harrisburg, Cabarrus, Pop. 11,315
Cabarrus County SD
Supt. — See Concord
Hickory Ridge HS 1,500/9-12
7321 Raging Ridge Rd 28075 704-454-7300
Michelle Cline, prin. Fax 454-7330
Hickory Ridge MS 1,100/6-8
7336 Raging Ridge Rd 28075 704-455-1331
Elizabeth Snyder, prin. Fax 455-1338

Charlotte Islamic Academy 200/PK-12
8810 Hickory Ridge Rd 28075 704-537-1772
Mirza Azim Beg, prin. Fax 537-1702

Havelock, Craven, Pop. 19,878
Craven County SD
Supt. — See New Bern
Early College EAST HS 200/9-12
104 Middle School Ln 28532 252-444-5194
Allan Quinn, prin. Fax 444-5129
Havelock HS 1,100/9-12
101 Webb Blvd 28532 252-444-5112
Jeffrey Murphy, prin. Fax 444-5112
Havelock MS 500/6-8
102 High School Dr 28532 252-444-5125
William Byland, prin. Fax 444-5129
Tucker Creek MS 400/6-8
200 Sermons Blvd 28532 252-444-7200
Angela Franks, prin. Fax 444-7206

Hayesville, Clay, Pop. 309
Clay County SD 1,400/PK-12
154 Yellow Jacket Dr 28904 828-389-8513
Dr. Mark Leek, supt. Fax 389-3437
www.clayschools.org/
Hayesville HS 400/9-12
205 Yellow Jacket Dr 28904 828-389-6532
Mickey Noe, prin. Fax 389-6251
Hayesville MS 500/5-8
135 School Dr 28904 828-389-9924
Dr. Cathy Andrews, prin. Fax 389-1706

Hays, Wilkes, Pop. 1,835
Wilkes County SD
Supt. — See North Wilkesboro
North Wilkes HS 700/9-12
2986 Traphill Rd 28635 336-903-4040
Lisa Joines, prin. Fax 957-4787

Henderson, Vance, Pop. 15,184
Vance County SD 7,200/PK-12
PO Box 7001 27536 252-492-2127
Dr. Anthony D. Jackson, supt. Fax 438-6119
www.vcs.k12.nc.us
Eaton-Johnson MS 700/6-8
500 N Beckford Dr 27536 252-438-5017
Dr. Brad Jones, prin. Fax 738-0250
Henderson MS 700/6-8
219 Charles St 27536 252-492-0054
Dr. John Hargrove, prin. Fax 430-8588
Northern Vance HS 900/9-12
293 Warrenton Rd 27537 252-492-6041
Andrew Markoch, prin. Fax 492-7878
Southern Vance HS 800/9-12
925 Garrett Rd 27537 252-430-6000
Stephanie Ayscue, prin. Fax 430-0308
STEM Early HS 300/6-8
293 Warrenton Rd 27537 252-738-2260
Rey Horner, prin. Fax 738-2261
Vance County Early College HS 200/9-12
PO Box 917 27536 252-738-3580
Debbie Hite, prin. Fax 438-3128
Western Vance Secondary S 100/Alt
2785 Poplar Creek Rd 27537 252-438-8407
Clarence Hicks, prin. Fax 438-4957

Crossroads Christian S 200/PK-12
PO Box 249 27536 252-431-1333
Jonathan Capps, hdmstr. Fax 431-0333
Kerr-Vance Academy 500/PK-12
700 Vance Academy Rd 27537 252-492-0018
Vance-Granville Community College Post-Sec.
PO Box 917 27536 252-492-2061
Victory Christian S 100/K-12
PO Box 592 27536 252-492-6079

Hendersonville, Henderson, Pop. 12,877
Henderson County SD 13,500/K-12
414 4th Ave W 28739 828-697-4733
Bo Caldwell, supt. Fax 697-5541
www.hendersoncountypublicschoolsnc.org
Apple Valley MS 900/6-8
43 Fruitland Rd 28792 828-697-4545
Melanie Adams, prin. Fax 698-6119
Balfour Education Center 100/Alt
2529 Asheville Hwy 28791 828-697-4629
Kent Parent, prin. Fax 698-6130
Hendersonville HS 700/9-12
1 Bearcat Blvd 28791 828-697-4802
W. Robert Wilkins, prin. Fax 698-6126
Hendersonville MS 600/6-8
825 N Whitted St 28791 828-697-4800
Luke Manuel, prin. Fax 698-6127
North Henderson HS 1,100/9-12
35 Fruitland Rd 28792 828-697-4500
John Shepard, prin. Fax 698-6129
Rugby MS 900/6-8
3345 Haywood Rd 28791 828-891-6566
Scott Moore, prin. Fax 891-6589
West Henderson HS 1,100/9-12
3600 Haywood Rd 28791 828-891-6571
Shannon Auten, prin. Fax 891-6590
Other Schools – See East Flat Rock, Flat Rock

Hertford, Perquimans, Pop. 2,119
Perquimans County SD 1,800/PK-12
PO Box 337 27944 252-426-5741
Matthew Cheeseman, supt. Fax 426-4913
www.pqschools.org
Perquimans County HS 500/9-12
PO Box 398 27944 252-426-5778
Melissa Fields, prin. Fax 426-7614
Other Schools – See Winfall

Hickory, Catawba, Pop. 39,263
Catawba County SD
Supt. — See Newton
Arndt MS 700/7-8
3350 34th Street Dr NE 28601 828-256-9545
Lee Miller, prin. Fax 256-6748
Challenger Early College HS 400/9-12
2550 US Highway 70 SE 28602 828-485-2980
Dr. Heather Benfield, prin. Fax 485-2981
St. Stephens HS 1,300/9-12
3205 34th Street Dr NE 28601 828-256-9841
Scottie Houston, prin. Fax 256-7159

Hickory CSD 4,300/PK-12
432 4th Ave SW 28602 828-322-2855
Robbie Adell Ed.D., supt. Fax 322-1834
www.hickoryschools.net
Grandview MS 500/6-8
451 Catawba Valley Blvd 28602 828-328-2289
Dr. Aaron Joplin, prin. Fax 328-2992
Hickory Career and Arts Magnet HS 200/6-12
409 8th Ave NE 28601 828-328-6738
Caroline Lovette, prin. Fax 328-8539
Hickory HS 1,000/9-12
1234 3rd St NE 28601 828-322-5860
Dr. Katherine Cater, prin. Fax 326-7101
Northview MS 600/6-8
302 28th Ave NE 28601 828-327-6300
Stephanie Dischiavi, prin. Fax 327-6367

Catawba Valley Community College Post-Sec.
2550 US Highway 70 SE 28602 828-327-7000
Hickory Christian Academy 400/K-12
3260 6th Street Dr NW 28601 828-324-5405
Lenoir-Rhyne College Post-Sec.
625 7th Ave NE 28601 828-328-1741
Tabernacle Christian S 100/PK-12
1225 29th Avenue Dr NE 28601 828-324-9936
University Christian HS 100/9-12
602 7th Ave NE 28601 828-855-2995
William Unverfehrt, prin. Fax 855-3993

Hiddenite, Alexander, Pop. 532
Alexander County SD
Supt. — See Taylorsville
East Alexander MS 700/6-8
1285 White Plains Rd 28636 828-632-7565
Dr. Lisa Harrington, prin. Fax 632-4508

Highlands, Macon, Pop. 908
Macon County SD
Supt. — See Franklin
Highlands S 400/K-12
PO Box 940 28741 828-526-2147
Brian Jetter, prin. Fax 526-0615

High Point, Guilford, Pop. 102,180
Guilford County SD
Supt. — See Greensboro
Academy at HP Central 100/9-12
700 Chestnut Dr 27262 336-885-7905
Howard Stimpson, prin. Fax 885-7927
Andrews HS 800/9-12
1920 McGuinn Dr 27265 336-819-2800
David Miller, prin. Fax 887-5585
Ferndale MS 900/6-8
701 Ferndale Blvd 27262 336-819-2855
Quincy Williams, prin. Fax 885-2854
High Point Central HS 1,400/9-12
801 Ferndale Blvd 27262 336-819-2825
Bryan Johnson, prin. Fax 819-2991
Middle College HS @ GTCC High Point 100/9-12
901 S Main St 27260 336-819-4111
Darrell Harris, prin. Fax 819-4116
Penn-Griffin School for the Arts 700/6-12
825 E Washington Dr 27260 336-819-2870
Dr. Shelley Nixon-Greene, prin. Fax 889-4841
Pruett SCALE Academy 50/Alt
900 W English Rd 27262 336-878-5380
Joseph Stone, prin. Fax 889-7625
Southwest HS 1,400/9-12
4364 Barrow Rd 27265 336-819-2970
George Alan Parker, prin. Fax 454-5175
Southwest MS 1,200/6-8
4368 Barrow Rd 27265 336-819-2985
Kerrie Douglas, prin. Fax 454-4015
Welborn Academy of Science & Technology 500/6-8
1710 McGuinn Dr 27265 336-819-2880
N. Brewington-McCormick, prin. Fax 819-2879

Hayworth Christian S 100/PK-12
1696 Westchester Dr 27262 336-882-3126
Vicki Beale, admin.
High Point Christian Academy 700/PK-12
800 Phillips Ave 27262 336-841-8702
Keith Curlee, head sch Fax 841-8850
High Point University Post-Sec.
833 Montlieu Ave 27268 336-841-9000
Laurel University Post-Sec.
1215 Eastchester Dr 27265 336-887-3000
Piedmont S 100/K-10
815 Old Mill Rd 27265 336-883-0992
Tim Montgomery, head sch Fax 883-4752
Tri-City Christian Academy 100/PK-12
8000 Clinard Farms Rd 27265 336-665-9822
Wesleyan Christian Academy 1,000/PK-12
1917 N Centennial St 27262 336-884-3333
Dr. Rob Brown, head sch Fax 884-8232
Westchester Country Day S 400/PK-12
2045 N Old Greensboro Rd 27265 336-869-2128
Cobb Atkinson, head sch Fax 869-6685

Hillsborough, Orange, Pop. 5,962
Orange County SD 7,600/K-12
200 E King St 27278 919-732-8126
Dr. Todd Wirt, supt. Fax 732-8120
www.orange.k12.nc.us
Cedar Ridge HS 1,100/9-12
1125 New Grady Brown Sch Rd 27278
919-245-4000
Heather Blackmon, prin. Fax 245-4010
Orange HS 1,300/9-12
500 Orange High School Rd 27278 919-732-6133
Eric Yarbrough, prin. Fax 644-7699
Partnership Academy S 50/Alt
1006 Storey Ln 27278 919-245-4030
Paige Marsh, prin. Fax 245-4035
Stanback MS 600/6-8
3700 NC Highway 86 S 27278 919-644-3200
Jeff Rachlin, prin. Fax 644-3226
Stanford MS 600/6-8
308 Orange High School Rd 27278 919-732-6121
Anne Purcell, prin. Fax 732-6910
Other Schools – See Efland

Hobgood, Halifax, Pop. 346

Hobgood Academy 200/PK-12
201 S Beech St 27843 252-826-4116

Holly Ridge, Onslow, Pop. 1,230
Onslow County SD
Supt. — See Jacksonville
Dixon HS 800/9-12
160 Dixon School Rd 28445 910-347-2958
Steve Clarke, prin. Fax 347-3932
Dixon MS 700/6-8
200 Dixon School Rd 28445 910-347-2738
Leigh Bizzell, prin. Fax 347-4399

Holly Springs, Wake, Pop. 24,092
Wake County SD
Supt. — See Cary
Holly Grove MS 1,400/6-8
1401 Avent Ferry Rd 27540 919-567-4177
Kenneth Proulx, prin. Fax 567-4159
Holly Ridge MS 1,200/6-8
950 Holly Springs Rd 27540 919-577-1335
Emily Mountford, prin. Fax 577-1379
Holly Springs HS 2,300/9-12
5329 Cass Holt Rd 27540 919-577-1444
Brian Pittman, prin. Fax 577-1742

Hope Mills, Cumberland, Pop. 14,573
Cumberland County SD
Supt. — See Fayetteville
Grays Creek HS 1,200/9-12
5301 Celebration Dr 28348 910-424-8589
Lisa Stewart, prin. Fax 424-7411
Grays Creek MS 1,100/6-8
5151 Celebration Dr 28348 910-483-4124
Mark Pepper, prin. Fax 483-5296
Hope Mills MS 700/6-8
4975 Cameron Rd 28348 910-425-5106
Dr. Cherie Graham, prin. Fax 423-5887
South View HS 1,800/9-12
4184 Elk Rd 28348 910-425-8181
Brian Edkins, dir. Fax 425-2962
South View MS 700/6-8
4100 Elk Rd 28348 910-424-3131
Christian Qually, prin. Fax 424-2402

Hubert, Onslow
Onslow County SD
Supt. — See Jacksonville
Onslow County Learning Center Alt
PO Box 158 28539 910-326-2305
Felicia Walton, dir. Fax 326-2208

Hudson, Caldwell, Pop. 3,744
Caldwell County SD
Supt. — See Lenoir

Caldwell County Career Center HS Vo/Tech
2857 Hickory Blvd 28638 828-759-4640
Brian Suddreth, prin. Fax 759-4672
Caldwell Early College HS 300/9-12
2859 Hickory Blvd 28638 828-759-4636
Candis Hagaman, prin. Fax 759-4666
Hudson MS 800/6-8
291 Pine Mountain Rd 28638 828-728-4281
Julia Knight, prin. Fax 726-8157
South Caldwell HS 1,600/9-12
7035 Spartan Dr 28638 828-396-2188
Chad Smith, prin. Fax 396-5929

Caldwell Community Coll. & Tech. Inst. Post-Sec.
2855 Hickory Blvd 28638 828-726-2200
Harris Chapel Christian Academy 50/PK-12
1444 Cajah Mountain Rd 28638 828-728-3721
Heritage Christian S 100/K-12
239 Mount Herman Rd 28638 828-726-0055

Huntersville, Mecklenburg, Pop. 45,893
Charlotte/Mecklenburg County SD
Supt. — See Charlotte
Alexander MS 900/6-8
12201 Hambright Rd 28078 980-343-3830
Angela Richardson, prin. Fax 343-3851
Bradley MS 1,100/6-8
13345 Beatties Ford Rd 28078 980-343-5750
Penny Presley, prin. Fax 343-5743
Hopewell HS 1,700/9-12
11530 Beatties Ford Rd 28078 980-343-5988
J. Dino Gisiano, prin. Fax 343-5990
North Mecklenburg HS 1,700/9-12
11201 Old Statesville Rd 28078 980-343-3840
Sonya McInnis, prin. Fax 343-3845

Christ the King HS 9-12
2011 Crusader Way 28078 704-799-4400
Brendan Keane, prin. Fax 799-4404
SouthLake Christian Academy 900/PK-12
13820 Hagers Ferry Rd 28078 704-949-2200
David Rowles, head sch Fax 949-2203

Indian Trail, Union, Pop. 32,854
Union County SD
Supt. — See Monroe
Porter Ridge HS 1,500/9-12
2839 Ridge Rd 28079 704-292-7662
Dr. Bashawn Harris, prin. Fax 296-9733
Porter Ridge MS 1,400/6-8
2827 Ridge Rd 28079 704-225-7555
Lee Casey, prin. Fax 226-9844
Sun Valley MS 1,300/6-8
1409 Wesley Chapel Rd 28079 704-296-3009
Vicki Merritt, prin. Fax 296-3045

Metrolina Christian Academy 1,200/PK-12
PO Box 1460 28079 704-882-3375
Richard Calloway, head sch Fax 882-0631

Iron Station, Lincoln, Pop. 736
Lincoln County SD
Supt. — See Lincolnton
East Lincoln MS 700/6-8
4137 Highway 73 28080 704-732-0761
Heather Myers, prin. Fax 732-4456

Jackson, Northampton, Pop. 512
Northampton County SD 2,100/PK-12
PO Box 158 27845 252-534-1371
Dr. Monica Smith-Woofter Ed.D., supt. Fax 534-4631
www.northampton.k12.nc.us
Other Schools – See Conway, Gaston

Jacksonville, Onslow, Pop. 67,399
Onslow County SD 25,300/PK-12
PO Box 99 28541 910-455-2211
Rick Stout, supt. Fax 455-3027
www.onslow.k12.nc.us
Hunters Creek MS 800/6-8
4040 Hunters Trl 28546 910-353-2147
Jocelyn Cassidy, prin. Fax 353-7939
Jacksonville Commons MS 800/6-8
315 Commons Dr S 28546 910-346-6888
Curtis Ehmann, prin. Fax 938-1682
Jacksonville HS 1,200/9-12
1021 Henderson Dr 28540 910-989-2048
Darin Cloninger, prin. Fax 989-2046
New Bridge MS 500/6-8
401 New Bridge St 28540 910-346-5144
Jane Dennis, prin. Fax 346-5402
Northside HS 1,000/9-12
365 Commons Dr S 28546 910-455-4868
Maria Johnson, prin. Fax 455-4987
Northwoods Park MS 500/6-8
904 Sioux Dr 28540 910-347-1202
Angela Garland, prin. Fax 347-0713
Southwest HS 700/9-12
1420 Burgaw Hwy 28540 910-455-4888
Tim Foster, prin. Fax 455-3949
Southwest MS 500/6-8
3000 Furia Dr 28540 910-455-1105
Jerome Gidrey, prin. Fax 455-4082
White Oak HS 1,100/9-12
1001 Piney Green Rd 28546 910-455-1541
Chris Barnes, prin. Fax 938-2302
Other Schools – See Holly Ridge, Hubert, Richlands, Swansboro

---

Cheveux School Hair Design and Hairport Post-Sec.
4781 Gum Branch Rd Ste 1 28540 910-455-5767
Coastal Carolina Community College Post-Sec.
444 Western Blvd 28546 910-455-1221
Jacksonville Christian Academy 300/K-12
919 Gum Branch Rd 28540 910-347-2358
Rev. Larry Haggard, admin. Fax 347-3138
Living Water Christian S 200/PK-12
3980 Gum Branch Rd 28540 910-938-7017

Miller-Motte College Post-Sec.
1291 Hargett St Ste A 28540 910-478-4300

Jamestown, Guilford, Pop. 3,331
Guilford County SD
Supt. — See Greensboro
Jamestown MS 1,200/6-8
301 Haynes Rd 27282 336-819-2100
Trent Vernon, prin. Fax 454-6734
Middle College HS @ GTCC - Jamestown 200/9-12
601 High Point Rd 27282 336-819-2957
Loretta Rowland-Kitley, prin. Fax 819-2961
Ragsdale HS 1,400/9-12
1000 Lucy Ragsdale Rd 27282 336-454-7400
James Gibson, prin. Fax 454-4001

Guilford Technical Community College Post-Sec.
PO Box 309 27282 336-334-4822

Jefferson, Ashe, Pop. 1,599
Ashe County SD 3,300/PK-12
PO Box 604 28640 336-246-7175
Phyllis Yates, supt. Fax 246-7609
www.ashe.k12.nc.us/
Other Schools – See Warrensville, West Jefferson

Kannapolis, Cabarrus, Pop. 41,850
Kannapolis CSD 5,400/PK-12
100 Denver St 28083 704-938-1131
Dr. Chip Buckwell, supt. Fax 933-6370
www.kcs.k12.nc.us
Brown HS 1,400/9-12
415 E 1st St 28083 704-932-6125
Dr. Todd Parker, prin. Fax 933-1862
Kannapolis MS 800/7-8
1445 Oakwood Ave 28081 704-932-4102
Bridgette Reese, prin. Fax 932-4104

Kenansville, Duplin, Pop. 849
Duplin County SD 9,900/PK-12
315 N Main St 28349 910-296-1521
Dr. Austin Obasohan, supt. Fax 296-1396
www.duplinschools.net
Duplin Early College HS 200/9-12
212 James Sprunt Dr 28349 910-296-1136
Selina Riley-Gurganus, prin. Fax 296-0348
Smith MS 400/6-8
PO Box 369 28349 910-296-0309
Dannie Sue Foster, prin. Fax 296-0086
Other Schools – See Beulaville, Mount Olive, Rose Hill, Teachey, Warsaw

---

James Sprunt Community College Post-Sec.
PO Box 398 28349 910-296-2400

Kenly, Johnston, Pop. 1,330
Johnston County SD
Supt. — See Smithfield
North Johnston HS 700/9-12
PO Box 339 27542 919-284-2031
David West, prin. Fax 284-6224

Kernersville, Forsyth, Pop. 22,718
Winston-Salem/Forsyth SD
Supt. — See Winston Salem
East Forsyth HS 1,800/9-12
2500 W Mountain St 27284 336-703-6735
Rodney Bass, prin. Fax 727-8546
East Forsyth MS 800/6-8
810 Bagley Rd 27284 336-703-6765
Dossie Poteat, prin. Fax 607-8531
Glenn HS 1,600/9-12
1600 Union Cross Rd 27284 336-771-4500
Brad Craddock, prin. Fax 771-4507
Kernersville MS 800/6-8
110 Brown Rd 27284 336-703-4255
Lisa Duggins, prin. Fax 996-1966
Southeast MS 1,200/6-8
1200 Old Salem Rd 27284 336-703-4219
Stephanie Gentry, prin. Fax 996-0148

Bishop McGuiness HS 500/9-12
1725 NC Highway 66 S 27284 336-564-1010
George Repass, prin. Fax 564-1060
Dudley Cosmetology University Post-Sec.
900 E Mountain St 27284 336-996-2030
Triad Baptist Christian Academy 200/PK-12
1175 S Main St 27284 336-996-7573
Dennis Roberts, admin. Fax 996-9791

Kill Devil Hills, Dare, Pop. 6,558
Dare County SD
Supt. — See Nags Head
First Flight HS 800/9-12
100 Veterans Dr 27948 252-449-7000
Tim Albert, prin. Fax 449-7004
First Flight MS 600/6-8
109 Veterans Dr 27948 252-441-8888
Dave Guiley, prin. Fax 441-7694

King, Stokes, Pop. 6,843
Stokes County SD
Supt. — See Danbury
Chestnut Grove MS 800/6-8
2185 Chestnut Grove Rd 27021 336-983-2106
David Durham, prin. Fax 983-2725
Meadowbrook Academy 100/Alt
817 Meadowbrook Dr 27021 336-985-3224
David Hicks, prin. Fax 985-3568
West Stokes HS 900/9-12
1400 Priddy Rd 27021 336-983-2099
Kevin Spainhour, prin. Fax 983-6076

Calvary Christian S 200/PK-12
748 Spainhour Rd 27021 336-983-3743

Kings Mountain, Cleveland, Pop. 10,130
Cleveland County SD
Supt. — See Shelby
Kings Mountain HS 1,300/9-12
500 Phifer Rd 28086 704-476-8330
Julie Rikard, prin. Fax 734-1723
Kings Mountain MS 700/7-8
1000 Phifer Rd 28086 704-476-8340
Dr. Anita Ware, prin. Fax 734-5615

Grace Christian Academy 100/PK-12
260 Range Rd 28086 704-734-0509

Kinston, Lenoir, Pop. 21,394
Lenoir County SD 9,300/PK-12
PO Box 729 28502 252-527-1109
Dr. Brent Williams, supt. Fax 527-6884
www.lenoir.k12.nc.us
Kinston HS 900/9-12
2601 N Queen St 28501 252-527-8067
Brian Corey, prin. Fax 527-4090
Lenoir County Learning Academy 100/Alt
2529 Cedar Dell Ln 28504 252-527-4264
Andre Whitfield, prin. Fax 527-7631
Lenoir County Early College HS 200/9-12
231 Hwy 58 S 28504 252-233-6870
Diane Heath, prin. Fax 233-6879
Rochelle MS 500/6-8
301 N Rochelle Blvd 28501 252-527-4290
Mildred Dunn, prin. Fax 527-6498
Woodington MS 700/6-8
4939 Hwy 258 S 28504 252-527-9570
Pam Heath, prin. Fax 527-3883
Other Schools – See Deep Run, La Grange

Arendell Parrott Academy 800/PK-12
PO Box 1297 28503 252-522-4222
Bert S. Bright Ed.D., hdmstr. Fax 208-0090
Bethel Christian Academy 300/PK-12
1936 Banks School Rd 28504 252-522-4636
Lenoir Community College Post-Sec.
PO Box 188 28502 252-527-6223
Lenoir Memorial Hospital Post-Sec.
100 Airport Rd 28501 252-522-7797

Knightdale, Wake, Pop. 11,083
Wake County SD
Supt. — See Cary
Knightdale HS 1,600/9-12
100 Bryan Chalk Ln 27545 919-217-5350
Dr. James Argent, prin. Fax 217-5356

La Grange, Lenoir, Pop. 2,845
Lenoir County SD
Supt. — See Kinston
Frink MS 600/6-8
102 Martin Luther King Jr 28551 252-566-3326
Elizabeth Pendleton, prin. Fax 566-4027
North Lenoir HS 900/9-12
2400 Institute Rd 28551 252-527-9184
Gil Respess, prin. Fax 527-8672

Lake Waccamaw, Columbus, Pop. 1,463
Columbus County SD
Supt. — See Whiteville
East Columbus HS 500/9-12
PO Box 401 28450 910-646-4094
Dr. Bryan Abernethy, prin. Fax 646-3779

Landis, Rowan, Pop. 3,094
Rowan-Salisbury County SD
Supt. — See Salisbury
Corriher-Lipe MS 500/6-8
214 W Rice St 28088 704-857-7946
Tonya German, prin. Fax 855-2670

Lasker, Northampton, Pop. 119

Northeast Academy 200/PK-12
210 E Church St 27845 252-539-2461

Laurel Hill, Scotland, Pop. 1,230
Scotland County SD
Supt. — See Laurinburg
Carver MS 400/6-8
18601 Fieldcrest Rd 28351 910-462-4669
Dr. Amber Alford-Watkins, prin. Fax 462-4674

Laurinburg, Scotland, Pop. 15,644
Scotland County SD 5,600/PK-12
322 S Main St 28352 910-276-1138
Dr. Ronald Hargrave, supt. Fax 277-4310
www.scotland.k12.nc.us
Scotland Early College S 200/9-12
1700 Dogwood Mile St 28352 910-277-3951
Patrick Peed, prin. Fax 277-5020
Scotland HS 1,500/9-12
1000 W Church St 28352 910-276-7370
Cory Satterfield, prin. Fax 277-4444
Shaw Academy 100/Alt
18700 Old Wire Rd 28352 910-276-0611
Latonya McLean, prin. Fax 277-4319
Spring Hill MS 400/6-8
22801 Airbase Rd 28352 910-369-0590
Brent Smith, prin. Fax 369-0595
Other Schools – See Laurel Hill

Christ the Cornerstone Academy 50/K-12
10401 McColl Rd 28352 910-277-0077
Emily Baines, prin. Fax 277-8682
St. Andrews University Post-Sec.
1700 Dogwood Mile St 28352 910-277-5555
Scotland Christian Academy 200/PK-12
10300 McColl Rd 28352 910-276-7722

Lawndale, Cleveland, Pop. 596
Cleveland County SD
Supt. — See Shelby
Burns HS 1,100/9-12
307 E Stagecoach Trl 28090 704-476-8335
Dr. Chris Blanton, prin. Fax 538-3895
Burns MS 900/6-8
215 Shady Grove Rd 28090 704-476-8223
Mickey Morehead, prin. Fax 538-3944

Lawsonville, Stokes
Stokes County SD
Supt. — See Danbury
Piney Grove MS 300/6-8
3415 Piney Grove Church Rd 27022 336-593-4000
Heather Pendleton, prin. Fax 593-4003

Leland, Brunswick, Pop. 13,291
Brunswick County SD
Supt. — See Bolivia
Leland MS 800/6-8
927 Old Fayetteville Rd NE 28451 910-371-3030
Patricia Underwood, prin. Fax 371-0647
North Brunswick HS 1,000/9-12
114 Scorpion Dr 28451 910-371-2261
Paul Price, prin. Fax 371-0879

Lenoir, Caldwell, Pop. 17,882
Caldwell County SD 12,100/PK-12
1914 Hickory Blvd SW 28645 828-728-8407
Dr. Steve Stone, supt. Fax 728-0012
www.caldwellschools.com
Gamewell MS 600/6-8
3210 Gamewell School Rd 28645 828-754-6204
Anna Crooke, prin. Fax 754-6278
Hibriten HS 800/9-12
1350 Panther Trl SE 28645 828-758-7376
David Colwell, prin. Fax 758-9708
Lenoir MS 500/6-8
1366 Wildcat Trl SE 28645 828-758-2500
Lisa Vaughn, prin. Fax 758-1570
West Caldwell HS 900/9-12
300 W Caldwell Dr 28645 828-758-5583
Andy Puhl, prin. Fax 754-2783
Other Schools – See Granite Falls, Hudson

Lewisville, Forsyth, Pop. 12,465

Forsyth Country Day S 800/PK-12
PO Box 549 27023 336-945-3151
Gardner Barrier, head sch Fax 945-2907

Lexington, Davidson, Pop. 18,479
Davidson County SD 20,000/PK-12
PO Box 2057 27293 336-249-8181
Dr. Lory Morrow, supt. Fax 249-1062
www.davidson.k12.nc.us
Central Davidson HS 1,000/9-12
2747 NC Highway 47 27292 336-357-2920
Valerie Feezor, prin. Fax 357-5175
Central Davidson MS 800/6-8
2591 NC Highway 47 27292 336-357-2310
Sloan Denny, prin. Fax 357-5965
Davidson County HS 100/Alt
2061 E Holly Grove Rd 27292 336-242-1459
Ronda Fletcher, prin. Fax 242-1465
North Davidson HS 1,500/9-12
7227 Old US Highway 52 27295 336-731-8431
Angie Kiger, prin. Fax 731-2642
North Davidson MS 800/6-8
333 Critcher Dr 27295 336-731-2331
Amy Hyatt, prin. Fax 731-2328
Tyro MS 700/6-8
2946 Michael Rd 27295 336-853-7795
Russ Snyder, prin. Fax 853-7357
West Davidson HS 800/9-12
200 Dragon Dr 27295 336-853-8082
Billy Hunt, prin. Fax 853-7315
Yadkin Valley Regional Career Academy Vo/Tech
2065 E Holly Grove Rd 27292 336-242-5820
Jonathan Brown, prin. Fax 242-5774
Other Schools – See Denton, Thomasville, Winston Salem

Lexington CSD 3,200/1-12
1010 Fair St 27292 336-242-1527
Richard Kriesky, supt. Fax 249-3206
lexcs.org
Lexington HS 700/9-12
26 Penry St 27292 336-242-1574
Monique Curry, prin. Fax 242-1285
Lexington MS 700/6-8
100 W Hemstead St 27292 336-242-1557
Sharolyn Harry-Chisholm, prin. Fax 242-1372

Davidson County Community College Post-Sec.
PO Box 1287 27293 336-249-8186
Sheets Memorial Christian S 300/PK-12
307 Holt St 27292 336-249-4224
Steven Weer, admin. Fax 249-6985
Union Grove Christian S 400/PK-12
2295 Union Grove Rd 27295 336-764-3105

Liberty, Randolph, Pop. 2,592
Randolph County SD
Supt. — See Asheboro
Northeastern Randolph MS 700/6-8
3493 Ramseur Julian Rd 27298 336-622-5808
Dana Albright-Johnson, prin. Fax 622-5868

Lillington, Harnett, Pop. 3,141
Harnett County SD 20,600/PK-12
PO Box 1029 27546 910-893-8151
Stanley Williams, supt. Fax 893-4279
www.harnett.k12.nc.us/
STAR Academy 100/Alt
PO Box 1029 27546 910-893-4072
Ron Avery, prin. Fax 893-3421
Western Harnett HS 1,400/9-12
10637 NC 27 W 27546 919-499-5113
Chris Pearson, prin. Fax 499-1537
Western Harnett MS 1,100/6-8
11135 NC 27 W 27546 919-499-4497
Walter McPherson, prin. Fax 499-1788
Other Schools – See Angier, Dunn, Erwin, Sanford, Spring Lake

Lincolnton, Lincoln, Pop. 10,295
Lincoln County SD 11,700/PK-12
PO Box 400 28093 704-732-2261
Dr. Sherry Hoyle, supt. Fax 736-4321
www.lcsnc.org
Asbury Academy 50/Alt
221 Salem Church Rd 28092 704-736-4766
Marybeth Avery, prin. Fax 736-4183
Lincoln County School of Technology Vo/Tech
1 Timken Dr 28092 704-732-4084
Dr. Cale Sain, prin. Fax 735-8292
Lincolnton HS 800/9-12
803 N Aspen St 28092 704-735-3089
Heath Belcher, prin. Fax 736-4234
Lincolnton MS 700/6-8
2361 Startown Rd 28092 704-735-1120
Dr. Dana Ayers, prin. Fax 732-6811
North Lincoln HS 1,000/9-12
2737 Lee Lawing Rd 28092 704-736-1969
Mitch Sherrill M.A., prin. Fax 736-1966
West Lincoln HS 900/9-12
172 Shoal Rd 28092 704-736-9453
Brian Clary, prin. Fax 276-2004
West Lincoln MS 700/6-8
260 Shoal Rd 28092 704-276-1760
Dr. Timothy Bean, prin. Fax 276-2293
Other Schools – See Denver, Iron Station

Littleton, Halifax, Pop. 660
Halifax County SD
Supt. — See Halifax
Northwest HS 500/9-12
8492 NC Highway 48 27850 252-586-4125
Mark Barfield, prin. Fax 586-6240

Locust, Stanly, Pop. 2,907
Stanly County SD
Supt. — See Albemarle
West Stanly MS 700/6-8
339 Running Creek Church Rd 28097 704-961-3600
Danny Poplin, prin. Fax 961-3699

Carolina Christian S 300/PK-12
PO Box 399 28097 704-888-4332
Erica Stroup, head sch Fax 888-4492

Louisburg, Franklin, Pop. 3,311
Franklin County SD 8,800/PK-12
53 West River Rd 27549 919-496-2600
Dr. Pascal Mubenga, supt. Fax 496-2104
www.fcschools.net
Franklin County Early College HS 100/9-12
8150 NC 56 Hwy 27549 919-496-1055
Erica Shoulders-Royster, prin. Fax 496-1033
Louisburg HS 500/9-12
201 Allen Ln 27549 919-496-3725
Glenn Dansky, prin. Fax 496-2505
Terrell Lane MS 500/6-8
101 Terrell Ln 27549 919-496-1855
Eric Betheil, prin. Fax 496-1370
Other Schools – See Bunn, Franklinton, Youngsville

Louisburg College Post-Sec.
501 N Main St 27549 919-496-2521

Lowell, Gaston, Pop. 3,488
Gaston County SD
Supt. — See Gastonia
Holbrook MS 700/6-8
418 S Church St 28098 704-836-9607
Jessica Steiner, prin. Fax 824-4529

Lucama, Wilson, Pop. 1,093
Wilson County SD
Supt. — See Wilson
Springfield MS 500/6-8
5551 Wiggins Mill Rd 27851 252-237-4250
Pattie Barnes, prin. Fax 239-1686

Lumber Bridge, Robeson, Pop. 94
Hoke County SD
Supt. — See Raeford
Sandy Grove MS 600/6-8
300 Chason Rd 28357 910-875-3559
Tommy Jacobs, prin. Fax 875-3632

Lumberton, Robeson, Pop. 21,026
Robeson County SD 24,100/PK-12
410 Caton Rd 28360 910-671-6000
Tommy Lowry, supt. Fax 671-6024
www.robeson.k12.nc.us
Early College HS 200/9-12
5170 N Fayetteville Rd 28360 910-737-5232
Sheila Gasque, prin. Fax 737-5231
Littlefield MS 700/4-8
9674 NC Highway 41 N 28358 910-671-6065
Kendall Hamilton, prin. Fax 671-6068
Lumberton HS 2,100/9-12
3901 Fayetteville Rd 28358 910-671-6050
Larry Obeda, prin. Fax 671-4399
Lumberton JHS 500/7-8
82 Marion Rd 28358 910-735-2108
Angela Faulkner, prin. Fax 671-4350
Robeson County Career Center Vo/Tech
1339 Hilly Branch Rd 28360 910-671-6095
Mark Smith, prin. Fax 671-6097
Other Schools – See Fairmont, Maxton, Orrum, Pembroke, Red Springs, Rowland, Saint Pauls

Antioch Christian Academy 300/K-12
5071 Old Whiteville Rd 28358 910-735-1011
Robeson Community College Post-Sec.
PO Box 1420 28359 910-272-3700

Mc Leansville, Guilford, Pop. 1,014
Guilford County SD
Supt. — See Greensboro
Northeast HS 1,000/9-12
6700 Mcleansville Rd 27301 336-375-2500
Fabby Williams, prin. Fax 375-2520
Northeast MS 900/6-8
6720 Mcleansville Rd 27301 336-375-2525
Jamie King, prin. Fax 375-2534

Madison, Rockingham, Pop. 2,190
Rockingham County SD
Supt. — See Eden
Western Rockingham MS 800/6-8
915 Ayersville Rd 27025 336-548-2168
Stephanie Wray, prin. Fax 548-1799

Maiden, Catawba, Pop. 3,281
Catawba County SD
Supt. — See Newton
Maiden HS 800/9-12
600 W Main St 28650 828-428-8197
Rob Bliss, prin. Fax 428-8341
Maiden MS 500/7-8
518 N C Ave 28650 828-428-2326
Brian Hefner, prin. Fax 428-5389

Manteo, Dare, Pop. 1,400
Dare County SD
Supt. — See Nags Head
Dare County Alternative S 50/Alt
205 N Highway 64/264 27954 252-473-3141
Teresa Twyne, prin. Fax 473-1638
Manteo HS 500/9-12
829 Wingina St 27954 252-473-5841
John Luciano, prin. Fax 473-2263
Manteo MS 400/6-8
1000 US Highway 64 and 264 27954 252-473-5549
Drew Sawyer, prin. Fax 473-2612

Marion, McDowell, Pop. 7,708
McDowell County SD 5,400/PK-12
PO Box 130 28752 828-652-4535
Mark Garrett, supt. Fax 659-2238
www.mcdowell.k12.nc.us/
Alternative Education Center Alt
176 Lukin St 28752 828-652-1040
Tracy Widmann, dir. Fax 652-9840
East McDowell MS 500/6-8
676 State St 28752 828-652-7711
Charles Gaffigan, prin. Fax 652-1469
McDowell Early College 200/9-12
54 College Dr 28752 828-659-0411
Lisa Robinson, prin. Fax 659-0469
McDowell HS 1,200/9-12
600 McDowell High Dr 28752 828-652-7920
Edwin Spivey, prin. Fax 652-1101
West McDowell MS 500/6-8
346 W McDowell Jr High Sch 28752 828-652-3390
Dr. Donna Gardner, prin. Fax 659-1964

McDowell Technical Community College Post-Sec.
54 College Dr 28752 828-652-6021
New Manna Christian S 100/K-12
PO Box 1085 28752 828-652-7729

Marshall, Madison, Pop. 859
Madison County SD 2,400/K-12
5738 US 25/70 Hwy 28753 828-649-9276
Dr. Todd Holden, supt. Fax 649-9334
www.madisonk12.net
Madison HS 600/9-12
5740 US 25/70 Hwy 28753 828-649-2876
Wesley Floyd, prin. Fax 649-0104
Madison MS 600/6-8
95 Upper Brush Creek Rd 28753 828-649-2269
Nicholas Honeycutt, prin. Fax 649-9015
Other Schools – See Mars Hill

Mars Hill, Madison, Pop. 1,829
Madison County SD
Supt. — See Marshall
Madison Early College HS 200/9-12
800 Bailey St 28754 828-689-9552
Jennifer Caldwell, prin. Fax 689-9644

Mars Hill College Post-Sec.
PO Box 370 28754 866-642-4968

Marshville, Union, Pop. 2,366
Union County SD
Supt. — See Monroe
East Union MS 800/6-8
6010 W Marshville Blvd 28103 704-290-1540
Anne Radke, prin. Fax 624-9302
Forest Hills HS 900/9-12
100 S Forest Hills School 28103 704-233-4001
Dr. Kevin Plue, prin. Fax 233-4003

Matthews, Mecklenburg, Pop. 26,705
Charlotte/Mecklenburg County SD
Supt. — See Charlotte
Butler HS 2,100/9-12
1810 Matthews Mint Hill Rd 28105 980-343-6300
John LeGrand, prin. Fax 343-6315
Crestdale MS 800/6-8
940 Sam Newell Rd 28105 980-343-5755
Kathleen Richert, prin. Fax 343-5761
Levine Middle College HS 9-12
2728 Campus Ridge Rd 28105 980-343-9437
Joseph Burch, prin. Fax 343-2432
Mint Hill MS 1,200/6-8
11501 Idlewild Rd 28105 980-343-5439
Steve Drye, prin. Fax 343-5442

Union County SD
Supt. — See Monroe
Weddington HS 1,400/9-12
4901 Weddington Rd 28104 704-708-5530
Dr. Kimberly Andrews, prin. Fax 708-6218
Weddington MS 1,200/6-8
5903 Deal Rd 28104 704-814-9772
Marcus Leake, prin. Fax 814-9775

Arborbrook Christian Academy 100/K-12
4823 Waxhaw Indian Trail Rd 28104 704-821-9952
Joy Fisk, head sch

Bible Baptist Christian S 200/PK-12
2724 Margaret Wallace Rd 28105 704-535-1694
Carmel Christian S 600/K-12
1145 Pineville Matthews Rd 28105 704-849-9723
Michael Long, head sch Fax 847-9908
Covenant Day S 800/PK-12
800 Fullwood Rd 28105 704-847-2385
Mark Davis, hdmstr. Fax 708-6137
Empire Beauty School Post-Sec.
11032 E Independence Blvd 28105 800-575-5983
Grace Academy 300/K-12
PO Box 2553 28106 704-234-0292
Southern Evangelical Seminary Post-Sec.
3000 Tilley Morris Rd 28105 704-847-5600

Maxton, Robeson, Pop. 2,397
Robeson County SD
Supt. — See Lumberton
Townsend MS 200/5-8
105 Carolina St 28364 910-844-5086
Andrea Ramsuer, prin. Fax 844-4292

Mayodan, Rockingham, Pop. 2,444
Rockingham County SD
Supt. — See Eden
McMichael HS 1,000/9-12
6845 NC Highway 135 27027 336-427-5165
Duane Whittaker, prin. Fax 427-5776

Mebane, Alamance, Pop. 11,146
Alamance-Burlington SD
Supt. — See Burlington
Eastern Alamance HS 1,200/9-12
4040 Mebane Rogers Rd 27302 919-563-5991
Dave Ebert, prin. Fax 563-6114
Hawfields MS 700/6-8
1951 S NC Highway 119 27302 919-563-5303
Greg Hook, prin. Fax 563-1351
Woodlawn MS 600/6-8
3970 Mebane Rogers Rd 27302 919-563-3222
Brian Williams, prin. Fax 563-6807

Merry Hill, Bertie

Lawrence Academy 300/PK-12
PO Box 70 27957 252-482-4748

Micro, Johnston, Pop. 438
Johnston County SD
Supt. — See Smithfield
North Johnston MS 600/6-8
PO Box 69 27555 919-284-3374
Brian Johnson, prin. Fax 284-3399

Millers Creek, Wilkes, Pop. 2,085
Wilkes County SD
Supt. — See North Wilkesboro
West Wilkes HS 700/9-12
6598 Boone Trl 28651 336-973-4503
David Johnson, prin. Fax 973-7323

Millers Creek Christian S 200/PK-12
PO Box 559 28651 336-838-2517
Roy Putman, prin. Fax 838-2546

Mill Spring, Polk
Polk County SD
Supt. — See Columbus
Polk County MS 500/6-8
321 Wolverine Trl 28756 828-894-2215
Hank Utz, prin. Fax 894-0191

Mint Hill, Mecklenburg, Pop. 22,306
Charlotte/Mecklenburg County SD
Supt. — See Charlotte
Northeast MS 800/6-8
5960 Brickstone Dr 28227 980-343-6920
Alicia McCree, prin. Fax 343-3264
Rocky River HS 1,700/9-12
10505 Clear Creek Cmmrc Dr 28227 980-344-0409
Ericia Turner, prin. Fax 343-2135

Misenheimer, Stanly, Pop. 712

Pfeiffer University Post-Sec.
48380 US Highway 52 28109 800-338-2060

Mocksville, Davie, Pop. 4,904
Davie County SD 6,400/PK-12
220 Cherry St 27028 336-751-5921
Dr. Darrin Hartness, supt. Fax 751-9013
www.davie.k12.nc.us
Central Davie Academy 50/Alt
160 Campbell Rd 27028 336-751-5712
Beth Edwards, prin. Fax 751-5719
Davie County Early College HS 200/9-12
1211 Salisbury Rd 27028 336-753-0888
Denise Absher, prin. Fax 753-1192
Davie County HS 1,800/9-12
1200 Salisbury Rd 27028 336-751-5905
Doyle Nicholson, prin. Fax 751-4597
North Davie MS 500/6-8
497 Farmington Rd 27028 336-998-5555
Mary Foster, prin. Fax 998-7233
South Davie MS 600/6-8
197 S Davie Dr 27028 336-751-5941
Melissa Lynch, prin. Fax 751-5656
Other Schools – See Advance

Monroe, Union, Pop. 32,321
Union County SD 41,300/PK-12
400 N Church St 28112 704-296-0766
Dr. Andrew Houlihan, supt. Fax 282-2171
www.ucps.k12.nc.us
Central Academy of Technology and Arts 800/9-12
600 Brewer Dr 28112 704-296-3088
Dr. Kim Fisenne, prin. Fax 296-3090
Monroe HS 900/9-12
1 High School Dr 28112 704-296-3130
Dr. Mike Harvey, prin. Fax 296-3138
Monroe MS 1,000/6-8
601 E Sunset Dr 28112 704-296-3120
Steven Wray, prin. Fax 296-3122
Parkwood HS 900/9-12
3220 Parkwood School Rd 28112 704-764-2900
Carole Alley, prin. Fax 764-2907
Parkwood MS 700/6-8
3219 Parkwood School Rd 28112 704-764-2910
Dr. Jeff Kraftson, prin. Fax 764-2914
Piedmont HS 1,200/9-12
3006 Sikes Mill Rd 28110 704-753-2810
Dr. Jonathan Tyson, prin. Fax 753-2817
Piedmont MS 1,000/6-8
2816 Sikes Mill Rd 28110 704-753-2840
Tracy Strickland, prin. Fax 753-2846
Sun Valley HS 1,300/9-12
5211 Old Charlotte Hwy 28110 704-296-3020
Dr. Shaun Poole, prin. Fax 296-3029
Union County Early College HS 300/9-12
4209A Old Charlotte Hwy 28110 704-290-1565
Dr. Stephanie McManus, prin. Fax 282-0956
Other Schools – See Indian Trail, Marshville, Matthews, Waxhaw

Shining Light Baptist Academy 100/PK-12
2541 Old Charlotte Hwy 28110 704-283-1480
Tabernacle Christian S 200/K-12
2900 Walkup Ave 28110 704-283-4395

Montreat, Buncombe, Pop. 715

Montreat College Post-Sec.
PO Box 1267 28757 800-622-6968

Mooresville, Iredell, Pop. 32,023
Iredell-Statesville SD
Supt. — See Statesville
Brawley MS 700/6-8
132 Swift Arrow Dr 28117 704-664-4430
Jimmie Dancy, prin. Fax 664-9846
Lake Norman HS 1,800/9-12
186 Doolie Rd 28117 704-799-8555
Keith Gentle, prin. Fax 799-1512
Lakeshore MS 500/6-8
244 Lakeshore School Dr 28117 704-799-0187
Brian Foster, prin. Fax 663-6431
Mount Mourne IB S 500/6-9
1431 Mecklenburg Hwy 28115 704-892-4711
Dr. Boen Nutting, prin. Fax 892-3804

Mooresville Graded SD 5,900/PK-12
305 N Main St 28115 704-658-2530
Dr. Stephen Mauney, supt. Fax 663-3005
www.mgsd.k12.nc.us
Mooresville HS 1,700/9-12
659 E Center Ave 28115 704-658-2580
Michael Royal, prin. Fax 664-4381
Mooresville MS 1,000/7-8
233 Kistler Farm Rd 28115 704-658-2720
Dr. Ayana Robinson, prin. Fax 664-5101
Woods Adv Tech / Arts Center Vo/Tech
574 W McLelland Ave 28115 704-658-2500
Devry Gibbs, prin. Fax 664-5102

Liberty Preparatory Christian Academy 100/K-12
246 Blume Rd 28117 704-660-3933
Amie Weir, admin. Fax 288-1750
NASCAR Technical Institute Post-Sec.
220 Byers Creek Rd 28117 877-201-2597
Woodlawn S 200/K-12
135 Woodlawn School Loop 28115 704-895-8653
Adam Schapiro, head sch Fax 782-1836

Moravian Falls, Wilkes, Pop. 1,870
Wilkes County SD
Supt. — See North Wilkesboro
Central Wilkes MS 700/6-8
3541 S NC Highway 16 28654 336-667-7453
Jeffrey Johnson, prin. Fax 667-5825

Morehead City, Carteret, Pop. 8,439
Carteret County SD
Supt. — See Beaufort
Bridges S 50/Alt
140 Vashti Dr 28557 252-808-3040
Dr. Mary Keel, prin. Fax 726-5245
Morehead City MS 500/6-8
400 Barbour Rd 28557 252-726-1126
Al Roberson, prin. Fax 726-4980
West Carteret HS 1,100/9-12
4700 Country Club Rd 28557 252-726-1176
Carolyn Heller, prin. Fax 726-6290

Carteret Community College Post-Sec.
3505 Arendell St 28557 252-222-6000

Morganton, Burke, Pop. 16,462
Burke County SD 13,200/PK-12
PO Box 989 28680 828-439-4312
Larry Putnam, supt. Fax 439-4314
www.burke.k12.nc.us
Burke Middle College HS 100/11-12
1001 Burkemont Ave 28655 828-448-3175
Kathy Amos, prin. Fax 442-6172
Freedom HS 1,100/9-12
511 Independence Blvd 28655 828-433-1310
Mike Swan, prin. Fax 439-8420
Johnson MS 400/6-8
701 Lenoir Rd 28655 828-430-7340
Brett Wilson, prin. Fax 430-4801
Liberty MS 600/6-8
529 Enola Rd 28655 828-437-1330
Mike Holden, prin. Fax 432-2124
Patton HS 1,000/9-12
701 Enola Rd 28655 828-433-3000
Wendi Barber, prin. Fax 433-3001
Table Rock MS 600/6-8
1585 NC 126 28655 828-437-5212
Felicia Simmons, prin. Fax 439-5702
Other Schools – See Connelly Sprngs, Drexel, Valdese

North Carolina School for the Deaf Post-Sec.
517 W Fleming Dr 28655 828-433-2971
Western Piedmont Community College Post-Sec.
1001 Burkemont Ave 28655 828-438-6000

Morrisville, Wake, Pop. 17,983

DeVry University Post-Sec.
1600 Perimeter Park Dr #100 27560 919-463-1380
The Chef's Acadmey Post-Sec.
2001 Carrington Mill Blvd 27560 919-246-9394

Mount Airy, Surry, Pop. 10,205
Mt. Airy CSD 1,700/PK-12
130 Rawley Ave 27030 336-786-8355
Dr. Kim Morrison, supt. Fax 786-7553
www.mtairy.k12.nc.us
Mount Airy HS 600/9-12
1011 N South St 27030 336-789-5147
Dr. Sandy George, prin. Fax 719-2341
Mount Airy MS 400/6-8
249 Hamburg St 27030 336-789-9021
Susan Bunch, prin. Fax 789-6074

Surry County SD
Supt. — See Dobson
Gentry MS 400/6-8
1915 W Pine St 27030 336-786-4155
Brandon Whitaker, prin. Fax 786-6863
Meadowview MS 400/6-8
1282 Mckinney Rd 27030 336-789-0276
Dr. Shelley Bryant, prin. Fax 789-0449
North Surry HS 900/9-12
2440 W Pine St 27030 336-789-5055
Paige Badgett, prin. Fax 786-8630

Northern Hospital of Surry County Post-Sec.
PO Box 1101 27030 336-719-7124

Mount Gilead, Montgomery, Pop. 1,163
Montgomery County SD
Supt. — See Troy
West MS 500/6-8
129 NC Highway 109 S 27306 910-572-9378
John McMillan, prin. Fax 572-2114
West Montgomery HS 600/9-12
147 Warrior Rd 27306 910-439-6191
Benjamin Brown, prin. Fax 439-4600

Mount Holly, Gaston, Pop. 13,424
Gaston County SD
Supt. — See Gastonia
East Gaston HS 1,200/9-12
1744 Lane Rd 28120 704-827-7251
Jennifer Reep, prin. Fax 827-5974
Mount Holly MS 800/6-8
124 S Hawthorne St 28120 704-827-4811
Jamie Peoples, prin. Fax 822-1049

Mount Olive, Wayne, Pop. 4,528
Duplin County SD
Supt. — See Kenansville
North Duplin JSHS 500/7-12
1388 W NC 403 Hwy 28365 919-658-3051
Anthony Jones, prin. Fax 658-9971

Wayne County SD
Supt. — See Goldsboro
Mount Olive MS 500/5-8
309 Wooten St 28365 919-658-7320
Tammy Keel, prin. Fax 658-7325

Mt. Olive College Post-Sec.
634 Henderson St 28365 919-658-2502

Mount Pleasant, Cabarrus, Pop. 1,645
Cabarrus County SD
Supt. — See Concord
Mount Pleasant HS 800/9-12
700 Walker Rd 28124 704-436-9321
Jon Lachance, prin. Fax 436-3179
Mount Pleasant MS 700/6-9
8325 NC Highway 49 N 28124 704-436-9302
Timothy Farra, prin. Fax 436-6112

Mount Ulla, Rowan
Rowan-Salisbury County SD
Supt. — See Salisbury
West Rowan HS 1,100/9-12
8050 NC Highway 801 28125 704-278-9233
Dr. Jamie Durant, prin. Fax 278-9733

Moyock, Currituck, Pop. 3,696
Currituck County SD
Supt. — See Currituck
Moyock MS 600/6-8
216 Survey Rd 27958 252-435-2566
Tommy Wilson, prin. Fax 435-2576

Murfreesboro, Hertford, Pop. 2,786
Hertford County SD
Supt. — See Winton
Hertford County MS 500/7-8
1850 NC Highway 11 27855 252-398-4091
Crystal Phillips, prin. Fax 398-5570

Chowan University Post-Sec.
1 University Pl 27855 252-398-6500

Murphy, Cherokee, Pop. 1,590
Cherokee County SD 3,500/PK-12
911 Andrews Rd 28906 828-837-2722
Dr. Jeana Conley, supt. Fax 837-5799
www.cherokee.k12.nc.us
Hiwassee Dam HS 200/9-12
267 Blue Eagle Cir 28906 828-644-5916
Tom Graham, prin. Fax 644-9463
Murphy HS 500/9-12
234 High School Cir 28906 828-837-2426
Boyd Shields, prin. Fax 837-2555

Murphy MS 400/6-8
65 Middle School Dr 28906 828-837-0160
Barry McClure, prin. Fax 837-5814
Oaks Academy 50/Alt
4533 Martins Creek Rd 28906 828-837-6775
Justin Clapsaddle, prin. Fax 837-7979
Tri-County Early College HS 100/9-12
21 Campus Circle 28906 828-835-4298
Alissa Cheek, prin. Fax 835-4319
Other Schools – See Andrews

Murphy Adventist Christian S 50/PK-12
1584 Old Ranger Rd 28906 828-837-5857
Tri-County Community College Post-Sec.
21 Campus Cir 28906 828-837-6810

Nags Head, Dare, Pop. 2,716
Dare County SD 5,100/PK-12
PO Box 1508 27959 252-480-8888
Dr. Sue Burgess, supt. Fax 480-8889
www.dare.k12.nc.us
Other Schools – See Buxton, Kill Devil Hills, Manteo

Nakina, Columbus
Columbus County SD
Supt. — See Whiteville
Nakina MS 200/6-8
9822 Seven Creeks Hwy 28455 910-642-8301
Wendell Duncan, prin. Fax 641-3287

Nashville, Nash, Pop. 5,285
Nash-Rocky Mount SD 15,900/PK-12
930 Eastern Ave 27856 252-459-5220
Dr. Shelton Jefferies, supt. Fax 459-6403
www.nrms.k12.nc.us
Nash Central MS 600/6-8
1638 S 1st St 27856 252-937-9065
Marquis Spell, prin. Fax 459-5297
Other Schools – See Bailey, Battleboro, Rocky Mount, Spring Hope

New Bern, Craven, Pop. 28,922
Craven County SD 14,600/PK-12
3600 Trent Rd 28562 252-514-6300
Dr. Meghan Doyle, supt. Fax 514-6351
www.cravenk12.org
Craven Early College HS 200/9-12
800 College Ct 28562 252-637-5706
Todd Bradley, prin. Fax 637-4459
Fields MS 600/6-8
2000 Dr M L King Jr Blvd 28560 252-514-6438
Thomasine Hassell, prin. Fax 514-6443
MacDonald MS 900/6-8
3127 Elizabeth Ave 28562 252-514-6450
Tabari Wallace, prin. Fax 514-6456
New Bern HS 1,700/9-12
4200 Academic Dr 28562 252-514-6400
Jerry Simmons, prin. Fax 514-6412
West Craven MS 900/6-8
515 NW Craven Middle School 28562 252-514-6488
Ashley Faulkenberry, prin. Fax 514-6491
Other Schools – See Havelock, Vanceboro

Calvary Baptist Church S 200/PK-12
PO Box 1089 28563 252-633-5410
Craven Community College Post-Sec.
800 College Ct 28562 252-638-7200
Epiphany S of Global Studies 300/K-12
2301 Trent Rd 28562 252-638-0122
Dr. Dwight Carlblom, head sch Fax 288-5723
New Bern Christian Academy 200/K-12
2911 Old Cherry Point Rd 28560 252-637-2704
Rev. Scott Coghill, prin. Fax 637-0032

Newland, Avery, Pop. 690
Avery County SD 1,700/PK-12
PO Box 1360 28657 828-733-6006
Dr. David Burleson, supt. Fax 733-8943
www.averyschools.net
Avery County HS 100/9-12
401 High School Rd 28657 828-733-0151
Todd Griffin, prin. Fax 733-1742
Avery MS 300/6-8
PO Box 729 28657 828-733-0145
Ricky Ward, prin. Fax 733-3506
Blue Ridge Academy 50/Alt
76 Old Montezuma Rd 28657 828-737-6011
Matthew Bentley, prin. Fax 737-6009
Other Schools – See Elk Park

New London, Stanly, Pop. 599
Stanly County SD
Supt. — See Albemarle
North Stanly HS 600/9-12
40206 US Highway 52 N 28127 704-961-4600
Joy Hathcock, prin. Fax 961-4699
North Stanly MS 600/6-8
36605 Old Salisbury Rd 28127 704-961-3700
Anne Watson, prin. Fax 961-3799

Newport, Carteret, Pop. 4,038
Carteret County SD
Supt. — See Beaufort
Broad Creek MS 700/6-8
2382 Highway 24 28570 252-247-3135
Sarah Weinhold, prin. Fax 247-5114
Croatan HS 900/9-12
3355 Highway 24 28570 252-393-7022
Kay Zimarino, prin. Fax 393-1223
Newport MS 500/6-8
500 E Chatham St 28570 252-223-3482
Christopher Yeomans, prin. Fax 223-4914

Gramercy Christian S 200/K-12
8170 Highway 70 28570 252-223-5199
Kirk Nielsen, hdmstr. Fax 223-2359

Newton, Catawba, Pop. 12,714
Catawba County SD 17,000/PK-12
PO Box 1010 28658 828-464-8333
Dr. Matt Stover, supt. Fax 464-0925
www.catawbaschools.net
Foard HS 1,000/9-12
3407 Plateau Rd 28658 704-462-1496
Stephen Westmoreland, prin. Fax 462-1988
Jacobs Fork MS 500/7-8
3431 Plateau Rd 28658 704-462-1827
Thomas Howell, prin. Fax 462-1600
Other Schools – See Catawba, Claremont, Hickory, Maiden

Newton-Conover CSD 3,100/PK-12
605 N Ashe Ave 28658 828-464-3191
Dr. David Stegall, supt. Fax 466-0063
www.newton-conover.org
Discovery HS 100/9-12
301 W 18th St 28658 828-466-5581
John Robinson, prin. Fax 466-5620
Newton-Conover HS 800/9-12
338 W 15th St 28658 828-465-0920
Chris Penley, prin. Fax 464-1412
Other Schools – See Conover

Newton Grove, Sampson, Pop. 561
Sampson County SD
Supt. — See Clinton
Hobbton HS 500/9-12
12201 Hobbton Hwy 28366 910-594-0242
Jennifer Daughtry, prin. Fax 594-1115
Hobbton MS 500/6-8
12081 Hobbton Hwy 28366 910-594-1420
Jeff Bradshaw, prin. Fax 594-0049
Midway HS 700/9-12
15274 Spiveys Corner Hwy 28366 910-567-6664
Monty Strickland, prin. Fax 567-5989

North Wilkesboro, Wilkes, Pop. 4,150
Wilkes County SD 10,300/PK-12
613 Cherry St 28659 336-667-1121
D. Mark Byrd, supt. Fax 667-5971
www.wilkescountyschools.org
North Wilkes MS 600/6-8
2776 Yellow Banks Rd 28659 336-903-6224
Heather Freeman, prin. Fax 696-4183
Other Schools – See Hays, Millers Creek, Moravian Falls, Ronda, Wilkesboro

Wilkes Regional Medical Center Post-Sec.
PO Box 609 28659 336-651-8433

Norwood, Stanly, Pop. 2,351
Stanly County SD
Supt. — See Albemarle
South Stanly HS 400/9-12
40488 S Stanly School Rd 28128 704-961-4100
Tanya Crisco, prin. Fax 961-4199
South Stanly MS 400/6-8
12492 Cottonville Rd 28128 704-961-5700
Damon Rhodes, prin. Fax 961-5799

Oakboro, Stanly, Pop. 1,840
Stanly County SD
Supt. — See Albemarle
West Stanly HS 800/9-12
306 E Red Cross Rd 28129 704-961-5200
Kimberly Page, prin. Fax 961-5299

Oak Ridge, Guilford, Pop. 6,114

Oak Ridge Military Academy 100/7-12
PO Box 498 27310 336-643-4131
John Haynes, pres. Fax 643-1797

Ocracoke, Hyde, Pop. 942
Hyde County SD
Supt. — See Swanquarter
Ocracoke S 200/PK-12
PO Box 189 27960 252-928-3251
Walt Padgett, prin. Fax 928-5380

Olin, Iredell
Iredell-Statesville SD
Supt. — See Statesville
North Iredell HS 1,100/9-12
156 Raider Rd 28660 704-876-4191
Teresa Hays, prin. Fax 876-3241
North Iredell MS 600/6-8
2467 Jennings Rd 28660 704-876-4802
Robert Sipes, prin. Fax 876-6190

Orrum, Robeson, Pop. 91
Robeson County SD
Supt. — See Lumberton
Orrum MS 400/5-8
PO Box 129 28369 910-628-6285
Cynthia Lewis, prin. Fax 628-8408

Oxford, Granville, Pop. 8,335
Granville County SD 7,700/PK-12
PO Box 927 27565 919-693-4613
Dr. Dorwin Howard Ed.D., supt. Fax 693-7391
www.gcs.k12.nc.us/
Center for Innovative Learning 50/Alt
3144 Webb School Rd 27565 919-690-2300
Helen Lindsey, prin. Fax 690-2301
Northern Granville MS 400/6-8
3144 Webb School Rd 27565 919-693-1483
Ashley Lewis, prin. Fax 693-1716
Potter MS 400/6-8
200 Taylor St 27565 919-693-3914
Chris Ham, prin. Fax 693-2896
Webb HS 600/9-12
3200 Webb School Rd 27565 919-693-2521
Reginald Brooks, prin. Fax 693-2589
Webb HS of Health & Life Sciences 300/9-12
3200 Webb School Rd 27565 919-693-6411
Angela Salisbury, prin. Fax 693-6079
Other Schools – See Butner, Creedmoor, Stem

Pantego, Beaufort, Pop. 178

Terra Ceia Christian S 100/K-12
4428 Christian School Rd 27860 252-943-2485
Vern Parsons, prin. Fax 944-0458

Pembroke, Robeson, Pop. 2,870
Robeson County SD
Supt. — See Lumberton
Pembroke MS 700/6-8
PO Box 1148 28372 910-522-5013
Anthony Barton, prin. Fax 522-1562
Swett HS 1,700/9-12
PO Box 1210 28372 910-521-3253
Clyde Leviner, prin. Fax 521-2956

University of North Carolina Post-Sec.
PO Box 1510 28372 910-521-6000

Pfafftown, Forsyth
Winston-Salem/Forsyth SD
Supt. — See Winston Salem
Reagan HS 1,800/9-12
3750 Transou Rd 27040 336-703-6776
Brad Royal, prin. Fax 922-1752

Pikeville, Wayne, Pop. 673
Wayne County SD
Supt. — See Goldsboro
Aycock HS 1,200/9-12
PO Box 159 27863 919-242-3400
Dr. Earl Moore, prin. Fax 242-6994

Pilot Mountain, Surry, Pop. 1,458
Surry County SD
Supt. — See Dobson
East Surry HS 600/9-12
801 W Main St 27041 336-368-2251
Lorrie Sawyers, prin. Fax 368-3035
Pilot Mountain MS 500/6-8
543 Old Westfield Rd 27041 336-368-2641
Dr. Tracey Lewis, prin. Fax 368-3935

Pinehurst, Moore, Pop. 12,981

Sandhills Community College Post-Sec.
3395 Airport Rd 28374 910-692-6185

Pinetops, Edgecombe, Pop. 1,369
Edgecombe County SD
Supt. — See Tarboro
South Edgecombe MS 400/6-8
230 Pinetops Crisp Rd 27864 252-827-5083
Amy Pearce, prin. Fax 827-2811
SouthWest Edgecombe HS 900/9-12
5912 NC 43 N 27864 252-827-5016
Craig Harris, prin. Fax 827-2815

Pinetown, Beaufort, Pop. 155
Beaufort County SD
Supt. — See Washington
Northside HS 400/9-12
7868 Free Union Church Rd 27865 252-943-6341
Charles Clark, prin. Fax 943-6344

Pittsboro, Chatham, Pop. 3,666
Chatham County SD 8,300/PK-12
PO Box 128 27312 919-542-3626
Dr. Derrick D. Jordan, supt. Fax 542-1380
www.chatham.k12.nc.us
Horton MS 400/5-8
PO Box 639 27312 919-542-2303
Valencia Toomer, prin. Fax 542-7099
Northwood HS 1,200/9-12
310 Northwood High School 27312 919-542-4181
Dr. Justin Bartholomew, prin. Fax 542-4934
Other Schools – See Bear Creek, Chapel Hill, Siler City

Haw River Christian Academy 100/PK-12
2428 Silk Hope Gum Springs 27312 919-533-4139
Larry Robinson, hdmstr.

Plymouth, Washington, Pop. 3,841
Washington County SD 1,700/PK-12
802 Washington St 27962 252-793-5171
Dr. Delilah Jackson, supt. Fax 793-5062
www.wcsnc.org
Plymouth HS 400/9-12
800 E Main St 27962 252-793-3031
Sharon Cherry, prin. Fax 793-3986
Other Schools – See Creswell, Roper

Polkton, Anson, Pop. 3,338
Anson County SD
Supt. — See Wadesboro
Anson County Early College HS 200/9-12
680 Highway 74 W 28135 704-272-5395
Carri Decker, prin. Fax 272-6155

South Piedmont Community College Post-Sec.
PO Box 126 28135 704-272-5300

Princeton, Johnston, Pop. 1,179
Johnston County SD
Supt. — See Smithfield
Princeton MSHS 900/6-12
PO Box 38 27569 919-936-5011
Jarvis Ellis, prin. Fax 936-2962

Raeford, Hoke, Pop. 4,467
Hoke County SD 8,500/PK-12
PO Box 370 28376 910-875-4106
Dr. Freddie Williamson, supt. Fax 875-3362
www.hcs.k12.nc.us
East Hoke MS 700/6-8
4702 Fayetteville Rd 28376 910-875-5048
Michelle Creammer, prin. Fax 875-9307
Hoke County HS 1,900/9-12
505 S Bethel Rd 28376 910-875-2156
Roger Edwards, prin. Fax 904-1644

SandHoke Early College HS 200/9-12
1110 E Central Ave 28376 910-878-5806
Colleen Pegram, prin. Fax 878-5807
Turlington JSHS 100/Alt
116 W Prospect Ave 28376 910-875-2583
Michael Armstrong, prin. Fax 875-3012
West Hoke MS 700/6-8
200 NC Highway 211 28376 910-875-3411
Mary McLeod, prin. Fax 875-0332
Other Schools – See Lumber Bridge

Raleigh, Wake, Pop. 395,376
Wake County SD
Supt. — See Cary
Athens Drive HS 1,900/9-12
1420 Athens Dr 27606 919-233-4050
Kathryn Chontos, prin. Fax 233-4054
Broughton HS 2,100/9-12
723 Saint Marys St 27605 919-856-7810
Stephen Mares, prin. Fax 856-7822
Carnage MS 1,200/6-8
1425 Carnage Dr 27610 919-856-7600
Pamela Johnson, prin. Fax 856-7619
Carroll MS 800/6-8
4520 Six Forks Rd 27609 919-881-1370
Elizabeth MacWilliams, prin. Fax 881-1381
Centennial MS 600/6-8
1900 Main Campus Dr 27606 919-233-4217
Katie McMillan, prin. Fax 233-4268
Daniels MS 1,100/6-8
2816 Oberlin Rd 27608 919-881-4860
Dr. Elizabeth Battle, prin. Fax 881-1418
Dillard Drive MS 1,100/6-8
5200 Dillard Dr 27606 919-233-4228
Shejuanna Rodgers, prin. Fax 854-1615
Durant Road MS 1,400/6-8
10401 Durant Rd 27614 919-870-4098
Nancy Allen, prin. Fax 518-0021
East Millbrook MS 1,000/6-8
3801 Spring Forest Rd 27616 919-850-8755
Eric Fitts, prin. Fax 850-8770
East Wake MS 900/6-8
2700 Old Milburnie Rd 27604 919-266-8500
Rebecca Beaulieu, prin. Fax 266-8506
Enloe HS 2,600/9-12
128 Clarendon Cres 27610 919-856-7918
Dr. Will Chavis, prin. Fax 856-7917
Leesville Road HS 2,200/9-12
8410 Pride Way 27613 919-870-4250
Dr. Anthony Muttillo, prin. Fax 870-4287
Leesville Road MS 1,200/6-8
8406 Pride Way 27613 919-870-4141
Cynthia Kremer, prin. Fax 870-4166
Ligon MS 1,200/6-8
706 E Lenoir St 27601 919-856-7929
Gretta Dula, prin. Fax 856-3745
Malone College & Career Academy Vo/Tech
2200 S Wilmington St 27603 919-856-8119
Dr. Ashlie Thompson, prin. Fax 856-8158
Martin MS 1,100/6-8
1701 Ridge Rd 27607 919-881-4970
Lacey Peckham, prin. Fax 881-5017
Millbrook HS 2,600/9-12
2201 Spring Forest Rd 27615 919-850-8787
Dana King, prin. Fax 850-8803
Moore Square Museums MS 500/6-8
301 S Person St 27601 919-664-5737
Dr. Jackie Jordan, prin. Fax 856-8194
Mt. Vernon MS 100/Alt
5418 Chapel Hill Rd 27607 919-233-4313
Robert Gupton, prin. Fax 233-4006
Phillips HS 200/Alt
1923 Milburnie Rd 27610 919-856-7710
Daniel Colvin, prin. Fax 856-7763
Pine Hollow MS 6-8
5365 Bartram Pl 27617 919-694-8880
Andrew Livengood, prin. Fax 589-6350
River Oaks MS 100/Alt
4700 New Bern Ave 27610 919-231-5600
Sharon Floyd, prin. Fax 231-5607
Sanderson HS 2,000/9-12
5500 Dixon Dr 27609 919-881-4800
Dr. Gregory Decker, prin. Fax 881-5006
Southeast Raleigh HS 1,700/9-12
2600 Rock Quarry Rd 27610 919-856-2800
Candis Jones, prin. Fax 856-2827
Wake Early College of Health & Sciences 300/9-12
2901 Holston Ln 27610 919-212-5800
Lisa Cummings, prin. Fax 212-5810
Wakefield HS 2,500/9-12
2200 Wakefield Pines Dr 27614 919-562-3600
Malik Bazzell, prin. Fax 562-3623
Wakefield MS 1,200/6-8
2300 Wakefield Pines Dr 27614 919-562-3500
James Sposato, prin. Fax 562-3527
Wake STEM Early College HS 200/9-12
715 Barbour Dr 27603 919-515-2255
David Schwenker, prin. Fax 515-2157
Wake Young Mens Leadership Academy 200/6-12
567 E Hargett St 27601 919-664-5644
Ian Soloman, prin. Fax 664-5657
Wake Young Womens Leadership Academy 200/6-12
303 Ashe Ave 27606 919-508-9088
Carla Jernigan-Baker, prin. Fax 508-9091
West Millbrook MS 1,000/6-8
8115 Strickland Rd 27615 919-870-4050
Kelly Aman, prin. Fax 870-4064

Cardinal Gibbons HS 1,200/9-12
1401 Edwards Mill Rd 27607 919-834-1625
Jason Curtis, prin. Fax 834-9771
ECPI University Post-Sec.
4101 Doie Cope Rd 27613 919-571-0057
Friendship Christian S 300/PK-12
5510 Falls of Neuse Rd 27609 919-872-2133
GRACE Christian HS 200/7-12
1101 Buck Jones Rd 27606 919-747-2020
Eric Bradley, head sch Fax 747-2021
Living Arts College @ Sch of Comm Arts Post-Sec.
3000 Wakefield Crossing Dr 27614 919-488-8500
Meredith College Post-Sec.
3800 Hillsborough St 27607 919-760-8600
Miller-Motte College Post-Sec.
3901 Capital Blvd Ste 151 27604 919-723-2820
Neuse Christian Academy 200/K-12
7600 Falls of Neuse Rd 27615 919-844-6496
Penny Hill, admin. Fax 861-6819
North Carolina State University Post-Sec.
PO Box 7001 27695 919-515-2011
North Raleigh Christian Academy 1,500/PK-12
7300 Perry Creek Rd 27616 919-573-7900
Dr. S.L. Sherrill, supt. Fax 573-7901
Raleigh Christian Academy 300/PK-12
2110 Trawick Rd 27604 919-872-2215
Dwight Ausley, admin. Fax 861-1000
Ravenscroft S 1,200/PK-12
7409 Falls of Neuse Rd 27615 919-847-0900
Doreen Kelly, head sch Fax 847-7952
St. Augustine's University Post-Sec.
1315 Oakwood Ave 27610 919-516-4000
St. David's S 600/PK-12
3400 White Oak Rd 27609 919-782-3331
Kevin Lockerbie, hdmstr. Fax 571-3330
St. Mary's S 200/9-12
900 Hillsborough St 27603 919-424-4000
Dr. Monica Gillespie, head sch Fax 424-4122
Shaw University Post-Sec.
118 E South St 27601 919-546-8200
Strayer University Post-Sec.
8701 Wadford Dr 27616 919-878-9900
Trinity Academy of Raleigh 400/PK-12
10224 Baileywick Rd 27613 919-786-0114
Matthew Breazeale, prin. Fax 786-0621
Wake Christian Academy 900/K-12
5500 Wake Academy Dr 27603 919-772-6264
Wake Technical Community College Post-Sec.
9101 Fayetteville Rd 27603 919-866-5000
William Peace University Post-Sec.
15 E Peace St 27604 919-508-2000
Word of God Christian Academy 200/K-12
3000 Rock Quarry Rd 27610 919-834-8200
Anesha Pittman M.Ed., prin. Fax 899-3640

Ramseur, Randolph, Pop. 1,657
Randolph County SD
Supt. — See Asheboro
Eastern Randolph HS 800/9-12
390 Eastern Randolph Rd 27316 336-824-2351
Greg Batten, prin. Fax 824-6164
Southeastern Randolph MS 700/6-8
5302 Foushee Rd 27316 336-824-6700
Gail Powers, prin. Fax 824-6705

Faith Christian S 300/PK-12
5449 Brookhaven Rd 27316 336-824-4156
Fax 824-1012

Randleman, Randolph, Pop. 4,054
Randolph County SD
Supt. — See Asheboro
Randleman HS 900/9-12
4396 Tigers Den Rd 27317 336-498-2682
Dennis Hamilton, prin. Fax 498-2609
Randleman MS 800/5-8
800 High Point St 27317 336-498-2606
Tracy Dawes, prin. Fax 498-8015

Red Springs, Robeson, Pop. 3,362
Robeson County SD
Supt. — See Lumberton
Red Springs HS 700/9-12
509 N Vance St 28377 910-843-4211
Larry Brooks, prin. Fax 843-2825
Red Springs MS 600/5-8
302 W 2nd Ave 28377 910-843-3883
Karen Brooks-Floyd, prin. Fax 843-3765

Highlander Academy 100/PK-12
200 N College St 28377 910-843-4995

Reidsville, Rockingham, Pop. 14,244
Rockingham County SD
Supt. — See Eden
Reidsville HS 800/9-12
1901 South Park Dr 27320 336-349-6361
Mary Ann Mitchell, prin. Fax 349-3205
Reidsville MS 600/6-8
1903 South Park Dr 27320 336-342-4726
Richard McGoogan, prin. Fax 342-9434
Rockingham County HS 1,100/9-12
180 High School Rd 27320 336-634-3220
Richie Weaver, prin. Fax 342-7794
Rockingham County MS 800/6-8
182 High School Rd 27320 336-616-0073
Moriah Dollarhite, prin. Fax 616-0870
S.C.O.R.E Center 50/Alt
401 Moss St 27320 336-634-3209
Curtis Gore, prin. Fax 634-3260

Community Baptist S 200/PK-12
509 Triangle Rd 27320 336-342-5991
Gene Carwile, admin. Fax 342-7180

Richlands, Onslow, Pop. 1,464
Onslow County SD
Supt. — See Jacksonville
Richlands HS 1,100/9-12
PO Box 218 28574 910-324-4191
Brad Staley, prin. Fax 324-6688
Trexler MS 900/6-8
PO Box 188 28574 910-324-4414
Lynn Jackson, prin. Fax 324-3963

Liberty Christian Academy 300/PK-12
215 Kinston Hwy 28574 910-430-0741
Cheryl Cavanaugh, head sch Fax 430-0394

Roanoke Rapids, Halifax, Pop. 15,565
Roanoke Rapids CSD 3,100/PK-12
536 Hamilton St 27870 252-519-7100
Dr. Dain Butler, supt. Fax 519-7195
www.rrgsd.org
Chaloner MS 700/6-8
2100 Virginia Ave 27870 252-519-7600
Jeff White, prin. Fax 519-7695
Roanoke Rapids HS 900/9-12
800 Hamilton St 27870 252-519-7200
Tammie Williams, prin. Fax 519-7295

Halifax Academy 400/PK-12
1400 Three Bridges Rd 27870 252-537-8527

Robbins, Moore, Pop. 1,085
Moore County SD
Supt. — See Carthage
Elise MS 200/6-8
180 W Elm St 27325 910-948-2421
Jeni Wiley, prin. Fax 948-4112
North Moore HS 600/9-12
PO Box 9 27325 910-464-3105
Jenny Purvis, prin. Fax 464-6016

Robbinsville, Graham, Pop. 615
Graham County SD 1,200/PK-12
52 Moose Branch Rd 28771 828-479-3413
Angela Knight, supt. Fax 479-9844
www.graham.k12.nc.us
Robbinsville HS 300/9-12
301 Sweetwater Rd 28771 828-479-9830
David Matheson, prin. Fax 479-9859
Robbinsville MS 200/7-8
301 Sweetwater Rd Ste B 28771 828-479-9840
Kevin White, prin. Fax 479-9847

Robersonville, Martin, Pop. 1,478
Martin County SD
Supt. — See Williamston
South Creek HS 400/9-12
21077 NC Highway 903 27871 252-795-4081
Phillip Hagen, prin. Fax 795-4187
South Creek MS 200/6-8
21230 NC Highway 903 27871 252-795-3910
Jan Wagner, prin. Fax 795-3890

Rockingham, Richmond, Pop. 9,384
Richmond County SD
Supt. — See Hamlet
Ashley Chapel Educational Center 200/Alt
377 Mizpah Rd 28379 910-997-9797
Susan Brigman, prin. Fax 997-8170
Richmond SHS 1,400/10-12
PO Box 1748 28380 910-997-9812
Keith McKenzie, prin. Fax 997-9816
Rockingham MS 700/6-8
415 Wall St 28379 910-997-9827
Dr. Wendy Jordan, prin. Fax 997-9859
Rohanen MS 300/6-8
252 School St 28379 910-997-9839
Hal Shuler, prin. Fax 997-8172

Temple Christian S 100/K-12
165 Airport Rd 28379 910-997-3179

Rockwell, Rowan, Pop. 2,077

Rockwell Christian S 100/K-12
PO Box 609 28138 704-279-8854

Rocky Mount, Edgecombe, Pop. 56,654
Edgecombe County SD
Supt. — See Tarboro
West Edgecombe MS 400/6-8
6301 Nobles Mill Pond Rd 27801 252-446-2030
Claude Archer, prin. Fax 446-1592

Nash-Rocky Mount SD
Supt. — See Nashville
Edwards MS 600/6-8
720 Edwards St 27803 252-937-9025
Chris Sivills, prin. Fax 446-5527
Nash Central HS 1,100/9-12
4279 Nash Central High Rd 27804 252-451-2860
Victor Ward, prin. Fax 451-1279
Nash-Rocky Mount Early College HS 200/9-12
530 N Old Carriage Rd 27804 252-451-2890
Jennifer Sharpe, prin. Fax 443-0068
Northern Nash HS 1,100/9-12
4230 Green Hills Rd 27804 252-937-9040
Brian Hopkins, prin. Fax 443-5448
Parker MS 300/6-8
1500 E Virginia St 27801 252-937-9060
John Milliner-Williams, prin. Fax 446-5756
Rocky Mount HS 1,300/9-12
1400 Bethlehem Rd 27803 252-937-9050
Leon Farrow, prin. Fax 443-6686
Rocky Mount MS 400/6-8
841 Nash St 27804 252-462-2010
Roderick Tillery, prin. Fax 459-5220
Tar River Academy 100/Alt
224 S Pearl St 27804 252-451-2875
Hugh Scott, prin. Fax 985-4336

Faith Christian S 400/PK-12
1333 Faith Christian Dr 27803 252-443-3700
Dr. Edward Bunn, head sch Fax 443-2456
Nash Community College Post-Sec.
522 N Old Carriage Rd 27804 252-443-4011
New Life Christian Academy 200/K-12
PO Box 8761 27804 252-443-6560
North Carolina Wesleyan College Post-Sec.
3400 N Wesleyan Blvd 27804 252-985-5100
Rocky Mount Academy 400/PK-12
1313 Avondale Ave 27803 252-443-4126
Beth Covolo, head sch Fax 937-7922

Rocky Point, Pender, Pop. 1,566
Pender County SD
Supt. — See Burgaw
Cape Fear MS 500/6-8
1886 NC Highway 133 28457 910-602-3334
Dr. Leslie Newman, prin. Fax 602-3036
Trask HS 700/9-12
14328 NC Highway 210 28457 910-602-6810
Dr. Tosha Diggs, prin. Fax 602-6662

Rolesville, Wake, Pop. 3,697
Wake County SD
Supt. — See Cary
Rolesville HS 700/9-12
1099 E Young St 27571 919-554-6303
Dhedra Lassiter, prin. Fax 554-6308
Rolesville MS 1,000/6-8
4700 Burlington Mills Rd 27571 919-570-2260
Michael Chappell, prin. Fax 570-2270

Thales Academy of Rolesville JSHS 100/6-12
1201 Granite Falls Blvd 27571 919-435-2715

Ronda, Wilkes, Pop. 410
Wilkes County SD
Supt. — See North Wilkesboro
East Wilkes HS 500/9-12
13315 Elkin Highway 268 28670 336-651-7200
Dr. Jodi Weatherman, prin. Fax 835-9298
East Wilkes MS 400/6-8
2202 Macedonia Church Rd 28670 336-651-4300
Sandra Burchette, prin. Fax 957-8734

Roper, Washington, Pop. 608
Washington County SD
Supt. — See Plymouth
Washington County Union MS 300/6-8
37 E Mill Pond Rd 27970 252-793-2835
Dianne Stokes, prin. Fax 793-4411

Roseboro, Sampson, Pop. 1,167
Sampson County SD
Supt. — See Clinton
Roseboro-Salemburg MS 400/6-8
PO Box 976 28382 910-525-4764
Shajuana Sellers, prin. Fax 525-3471

Mintz Christian Academy 100/K-12
2741 Mintz Rd 28382 910-564-6221
Joy McDowell, prin. Fax 564-6510

Rose Hill, Duplin, Pop. 1,619
Duplin County SD
Supt. — See Kenansville
Charity MS 500/6-8
PO Box 70 28458 910-289-3323
Dena Hall, prin. Fax 289-2064

Sampson County SD
Supt. — See Clinton
Union HS 600/9-12
1189 Kader Merritt Rd 28458 910-532-6300
Julie Hunter, prin. Fax 532-6350

Rosman, Transylvania, Pop. 567
Transylvania County SD
Supt. — See Brevard
Rosman HS 400/9-12
749 Pickens Hwy 28772 828-862-4284
Jason Ormsby, prin. Fax 885-5572
Rosman MS 300/6-8
2770 Old Rosman Hwy 28772 828-862-4286
Greg Carter, prin. Fax 885-5573

Rowland, Robeson, Pop. 1,020
Robeson County SD
Supt. — See Lumberton
Rowland MS 200/6-8
408 W Chapel St 28383 910-422-3983
Adrian Sincllair-Davis, prin. Fax 422-8369
South Robeson HS 500/9-12
3268 S Robeson Rd 28383 910-422-3987
Dr. Christopher Clark, prin. Fax 422-3221

Roxboro, Person, Pop. 8,217
Person County SD 4,600/PK-12
304 S Morgan St Ste 25 27573 336-599-2191
Danny Holloman, supt. Fax 599-2194
www.person.k12.nc.us
Early Coll for Innovation & Leadership 9-12
1715 College Dr 27573 336-322-2275
Shirlrona Johnson, prin. Fax 322-3024
Northern MS 500/6-8
1935 Carver Dr, 336-599-6344
Ashley Warren, prin. Fax 598-9207
Person County Learning Academy Alt
361 Virgilina Rd 27573 336-322-1021
Joan Kister, dir. Fax 322-1029
Person Early College 50/9-12
PO Box 1197 27573 336-599-1181
Shirlrona Johnson, prin.
Person HS 1,400/9-12
1010 Ridge Rd 27573 336-599-8321
Nenell Sydnor-Waugh, prin. Fax 599-6583
Southern MS 600/6-8
209 Southern Middle School 27573 336-599-6995
Dr. Jonte Hill, prin. Fax 503-0587

Piedmont Community College Post-Sec.
PO Box 1197 27573 336-599-1181

Rutherfordton, Rutherford, Pop. 4,144
Rutherford County SD
Supt. — See Forest City
R-S Central HS 900/9-12
641 US 221 Hwy N 28139 828-287-3304
Phil Rogers, prin. Fax 286-2024
R-S MS 700/6-8
545 Charlotte Rd 28139 828-286-4461
Dr. Keith Silver, prin. Fax 286-4882

Saint Pauls, Robeson, Pop. 1,997
Robeson County SD
Supt. — See Lumberton
Saint Pauls HS 900/9-12
648 N Old Stage Rd 28384 910-865-4177
Christopher Suggs, prin. Fax 865-3736
Saint Pauls MS 500/6-8
526 W Shaw St 28384 910-865-4070
Avery Brooks, prin. Fax 865-1599

Salemburg, Sampson, Pop. 427
Sampson County SD
Supt. — See Clinton
Lakewood HS 500/9-12
245 Lakewood School Rd 28385 910-525-5171
John Goode, prin. Fax 525-3344

Salisbury, Rowan, Pop. 33,082
Rowan-Salisbury County SD 20,000/PK-12
PO Box 2349 28145 704-636-7500
Lynn Moody, supt.
www.rss.k12.nc.us
East Rowan HS 1,000/9-12
175 Saint Luke Church Rd 28146 704-279-5232
Julie Erdie, prin. Fax 279-4549
Erwin MS 900/6-8
170 Saint Luke Church Rd 28146 704-279-7265
Rick Vanhoy, prin. Fax 279-7954
Henderson Independent HS 100/Alt
1215 N Main St 28144 704-639-3103
Arlisa Armond, prin. Fax 639-3118
Knox MS 600/6-8
1625 W Park Rd 28144 704-633-2922
Michael Waiksnis, prin. Fax 638-3538
Rowan County Early College S 200/9-12
PO Box 1595 28145 704-216-3873
Patrick Hosey, prin. Fax 216-2942
Salisbury HS 900/9-12
500 Lincolnton Rd 28144 704-636-1221
Luke Brown, prin. Fax 639-3029
Southeast MS 700/6-8
1570 Peeler Rd 28146 704-638-5561
Jennifer Lentz, prin. Fax 638-5719
West Rowan MS 700/6-8
5925 Statesville Blvd 28147 704-633-4775
Derek McCoy, prin. Fax 633-3157
Other Schools – See China Grove, Landis, Mount Ulla, Spencer

Catawba College Post-Sec.
2300 W Innes St 28144 800-228-2922
Hood Theological Seminary Post-Sec.
1810 Lutheran Synod Dr 28144 704-636-7611
Livingstone College Post-Sec.
701 W Monroe St 28144 704-216-6000
North Hills Christian S 300/PK-12
2970 W Innes St 28144 704-636-3005
Maria Lowder, dir. Fax 636-3597
Rowan-Cabarrus Community College Post-Sec.
1333 Jake Alexander Blvd S 28146 704-216-7222

Sanford, Lee, Pop. 27,645
Harnett County SD
Supt. — See Lillington
Highland MS 300/6-8
345 Highland School Rd 27332
Brian Graham, prin.

Lee County SD 10,100/PK-12
PO Box 1010 27331 919-774-6226
Andy Bryan Ed.D., supt. Fax 776-0443
www.lee.k12.nc.us
Bragg Street Academy 100/Alt
504 Bragg St 27330 919-775-2686
Jolanda Jordan, prin. Fax 774-1429
East Lee MS 700/6-8
1337 Broadway Rd 27332 919-776-8441
Shannon Shuey, prin. Fax 774-7451
Lee County HS 1,400/9-12
1708 Nash St 27330 919-776-7541
Steven Ross, prin. Fax 718-7170
Lee Early College 200/9-12
1105 Kelly Dr 27330 919-718-7259
Robert Biehl, prin. Fax 718-7519
SanLee MS 800/6-8
2309 Tramway Rd 27332 919-708-7227
Betsy Bridges, prin. Fax 718-2875
Southern Lee HS 1,100/9-12
2301 Tramway Rd 27332 919-718-2400
Chris Dossenbach, prin. Fax 718-2410
West Lee MS 700/6-8
3301 Wicker St 27330 919-775-7351
Melvin Marshall, prin. Fax 776-3694

Central Carolina Community College Post-Sec.
1105 Kelly Dr 27330 919-775-5401
Grace Christian S 300/K-12
PO Box 1408 27331 919-774-4415
Dr. Daniel Patton, admin. Fax 718-6777
Lee Christian S 400/PK-12
3220 Keller Andrews Rd 27330 919-708-5115
Don Payne, admin. Fax 708-6933

Selma, Johnston, Pop. 5,974
Johnston County SD
Supt. — See Smithfield
Selma MS 400/5-8
1533 US Highway 301 N 27576 919-965-2555
Chris Kennedy, prin. Fax 202-0116

Seven Springs, Wayne, Pop. 109
Wayne County SD
Supt. — See Goldsboro
Spring Creek HS 600/9-12
4340 Indian Springs Rd 28578 919-751-7160
Steve Clingan, prin. Fax 751-7202
Spring Creek MS 5-8
3579 NC Highway 111 S 28578 919-751-7125
T. Kevin Smith, prin. Fax 751-7126

Shallotte, Brunswick, Pop. 3,616
Brunswick County SD
Supt. — See Bolivia
Shallotte MS 600/6-8
225 Village Rd SW 28470 910-754-6882
Marie Laboy, prin. Fax 754-3108
West Brunswick HS 1,300/9-12
550 Whiteville Rd NW 28470 910-754-4338
Brockton Ahrens, prin. Fax 754-3110

Academy of Coastal Carolina 50/PK-12
PO Box 1988 28459 910-754-9637
Theresa Cox, head sch Fax 754-9630

Shannon, Robeson, Pop. 263

Native American Bible College Post-Sec.
PO Box 248 28386 910-843-5304

Shelby, Cleveland, Pop. 19,999
Cleveland County SD 15,600/PK-12
400 W Marion St 28150 704-476-8000
Dr. Stephen Fisher, supt. Fax 476-8300
www.clevelandcountyschools.org
Cleveland Early College HS 200/9-12
137 S Post Rd 28152 704-669-4710
Titus Hopper, prin. Fax 669-4715
Crest HS 1,200/9-12
800 Old Boiling Springs Rd 28152 704-476-8331
Holly Robinson, prin. Fax 482-1187
Crest MS 900/6-8
315 Beaver Dam Church Rd 28152 704-476-8221
Jeremy Shields, prin. Fax 487-0378
Shelby HS 800/9-12
230 E Dixon Blvd 28152 704-476-8325
David Allen, prin. Fax 487-2869
Shelby MS 500/7-8
1480 S DeKalb St 28152 704-476-8328
Dr. Dustin Bridges, prin. Fax 487-2889
Turning Point Academy 100/Alt
409 W Sumter St 28150 704-476-8399
Michelle Twiggs, prin. Fax 476-8316
Other Schools – See Kings Mountain, Lawndale

Cleveland Community College Post-Sec.
137 S Post Rd 28152 704-669-6000

Siler City, Chatham, Pop. 7,749
Chatham County SD
Supt. — See Pittsboro
Chatham MS 500/5-8
2025 S 2nd Avenue Ext 27344 919-663-2414
Chad Morgan, prin. Fax 663-2871
Chatham S of Science & Engineering 9-9
501 Martin Luther King Jr 27344 919-663-5899
Bobby Dixon, prin. Fax 663-3827
Jordan-Matthews HS 700/9-12
910 E Cardinal St 27344 919-742-2916
Tripp Crayton, prin. Fax 742-2201
SAGE Academy 100/Alt
501 M L King Jr Blvd 27344 919-663-5899
Bobby Dixon, prin. Fax 663-3827

Smithfield, Johnston, Pop. 10,815
Johnston County SD 33,900/PK-12
PO Box 1336 27577 919-934-6031
Dr. Ross Renfrow, supt. Fax 934-2586
www.johnston.k12.nc.us
Johnston County Early College Academy 200/9-12
PO Box 1336 27577 919-464-2314
Clint Eaves, prin. Fax 464-2315
Johnston County Middle College HS 100/10-12
PO Box 1336 27577 919-464-2303
Sheila Singleton, prin. Fax 464-2300
Smithfield MS 800/6-8
1455 Buffalo Rd 27577 919-934-4696
Heather Anders, prin. Fax 934-7552
Smithfield-Selma HS 1,200/9-12
700 E Booker Dairy Rd 27577 919-934-5191
Stephen Baker, prin. Fax 934-3001
South Campus Community S 50/Alt
PO Box 1336 27577 919-934-6481
Ersaleen Creech, prin. Fax 938-3555
Other Schools – See Benson, Clayton, Four Oaks, Garner, Kenly, Micro, Princeton, Selma, Wendell

---

Johnston Community College Post-Sec.
PO Box 2350 27577 919-934-3051

Smyrna, Carteret
Carteret County SD
Supt. — See Beaufort
Down East MS 200/6-8
174 Marshallberg Rd 28579 252-729-2301
Richard Paylor, admin.

Snow Hill, Greene, Pop. 1,577
Greene County SD 3,100/PK-12
301 Kingold Blvd 28580 252-747-3425
Dr. Patrick Miller, supt. Fax 747-5942
www.gcsedu.org/
Greene Central HS 900/9-12
140 School Dr 28580 252-747-3814
Patrick Greene, prin. Fax 747-5972
Greene County MS 700/6-8
485 Middle School Rd 28580 252-747-8191
Diane Blackman, prin. Fax 747-2484
Greene Early College HS 100/9-12
818 Hwy 91 28580 252-747-9044
Rodney McNeill, prin. Fax 747-9046

Southern Pines, Moore, Pop. 12,175
Moore County SD
Supt. — See Carthage
Pinecrest HS 2,100/9-12
250 Voit Gilmore Rd 28387 910-692-6554
Robert Christina, prin. Fax 692-0606

Calvary Christian S 100/PK-12
400 S Bennett St 28387 910-692-8311

O'Neal S 400/PK-12
PO Box 290 28388 910-692-6920
John Elmore, head sch Fax 692-6930
Sandhills Classical Christian S 100/PK-10
PO Box 2600 28388 910-695-1874

Southport, Brunswick, Pop. 2,791
Brunswick County SD
Supt. — See Bolivia
South Brunswick HS 1,100/9-12
280 Cougar Rd 28461 910-845-2204
Michael Hodges, prin. Fax 845-8974
South Brunswick MS 800/6-8
100 Cougar Rd 28461 910-845-2771
David Ruth, prin. Fax 845-8972

Sparta, Alleghany, Pop. 1,751
Alleghany County SD 1,500/PK-12
85 Peachtree St 28675 336-372-4345
Chad Beasley, supt. Fax 372-4204
www.alleghany.k12.nc.us
Alleghany HS 500/9-12
404 Trojan Ave 28675 336-372-4554
Scott Carter, prin. Fax 372-2680

Spencer, Rowan, Pop. 3,207
Rowan-Salisbury County SD
Supt. — See Salisbury
North Rowan HS 700/9-12
300 N Whitehead Ave 28159 704-636-4420
Fateama Fulmore, prin. Fax 639-3033
North Rowan MS 500/6-8
512 Charles St 28159 704-639-3018
Alexis Cowan, prin. Fax 639-3099

Spindale, Rutherford, Pop. 4,228
Rutherford County SD
Supt. — See Forest City
Rutherford Early College HS 200/9-12
PO Box 804 28160 828-395-4190
Jeremiah McCluney, prin. Fax 288-0285

Isothermal Community College Post-Sec.
PO Box 804 28160 828-286-3636
Word of Faith Christian S 100/K-12
207 Old Flynn Rd 28160 828-286-3772

Spring Hope, Nash, Pop. 1,294
Nash-Rocky Mount SD
Supt. — See Nashville
Southern Nash MS 900/6-8
5301 S NC Highway 581 27882 252-937-9020
Carina Bryant, prin. Fax 478-4861

Spring Lake, Cumberland, Pop. 11,305
Cumberland County SD
Supt. — See Fayetteville
Spring Lake MS 500/6-8
612 Spring Ave 28390 910-497-1175
Masa Kinsey-Shipp, prin. Fax 497-1598

Harnett County SD
Supt. — See Lillington
Overhills HS 1,700/9-12
2495 Ray Rd 28390 910-436-1436
Steve Matthews, prin. Fax 436-0413
Overhills MS 1,300/6-8
2711 Ray Rd 28390 910-436-0009
Tina Tasker, prin. Fax 436-0948

Spruce Pine, Mitchell, Pop. 2,151
Mitchell County SD
Supt. — See Bakersville
Harris MS 300/6-8
121 Harris St 28777 828-766-3340
Michael Tountasakis, prin. Fax 765-1595
Mayland Early College HS 100/9-12
200 Mayland Ln 28777 828-766-2590
Stacie Burleson, prin. Fax 766-2621

Altapass Christian S 50/PK-12
3631 Altapass Hwy 28777 828-765-0660
Mayland Community College Post-Sec.
PO Box 547 28777 828-765-7351
Tri County Christian S 50/K-12
207 Pinebridge Ave 28777 828-765-2969
Teresa Young, prin. Fax 765-0569

Stanley, Gaston, Pop. 3,517
Gaston County SD
Supt. — See Gastonia
Stanley MS 500/6-8
317 Hovis Rd 28164 704-836-9600
Rebecca Huffstetler, prin. Fax 263-0993

Stantonsburg, Wilson, Pop. 782
Wilson County SD
Supt. — See Wilson
Speight MS 400/6-8
5514 Old Stantonsburg Rd 27883 252-238-3983
Valerie Budd, prin. Fax 238-2104

Statesville, Iredell, Pop. 24,072
Iredell-Statesville SD 20,800/K-12
PO Box 911 28687 704-924-2029
Brady Johnson, supt. Fax 871-2834
www.iss.k12.nc.us
Collaborative College for Technology 200/9-12
500 W Broad St 28677 704-978-5450
Teri Hutchens, prin. Fax 878-3330
Crossroads Arts & Science Early College 300/9-12
474 N Center St 28677 704-978-0034
Alicia Eller, prin. Fax 978-0035
East Iredell MS 500/6-8
590 Chestnut Grove Rd 28625 704-872-4666
Dr. Tonya Houpe, prin. Fax 873-6602
Monticello S 100/Alt
435 Monticello Rd 28625 704-872-5297
Mark Grega, prin. Fax 924-8814
Northview IB S 400/6-9
625 N Carolina Ave 28677 704-873-7354
Sheila Jenkins, prin. Fax 873-6149
Pressly S 100/Alt
222 Knox St 28677 704-872-7606
Dr. Stacy Williams, prin. Fax 838-0839
South Iredell HS 1,400/9-12
299 Old Mountain Rd 28677 704-528-4536
Tim Ivey, prin. Fax 528-0882
Statesville HS 1,100/9-12
474 N Center St 28677 704-873-3491
Dr. Beth Bradley, prin. Fax 878-6195
Statesville MS 400/6-8
321 Clegg St 28677 704-872-2135
Kelly Campbell, prin. Fax 871-9279
West Iredell HS 900/9-12
213 Warrior Dr 28625 704-873-2181
Gordon Palmer, prin. Fax 873-0356
West Iredell MS 700/6-8
303 Watermelon Rd 28625 704-873-2887
David Ivey, prin. Fax 881-0582
Other Schools – See Mooresville, Olin, Troutman

Cornerstone Christian Academy 100/PK-12
650 Glover St 28625 704-873-0032
Crossroads Christian S of Statesville 50/K-12
1950 Salisbury Hwy 28677 704-871-1515
Anne W. Wooten, admin. Fax 871-1515
Mitchell Community College Post-Sec.
500 W Broad St 28677 704-878-3200
Southview Christian S 100/K-12
625 Wallace Springs Rd 28677 704-872-9554
Statesville Christian S 200/K-12
1210 Museum Rd 28625 704-873-9511
Mark Earwood, head sch Fax 873-0841

Stem, Granville, Pop. 446
Granville County SD
Supt. — See Oxford
Granville Central HS 600/9-12
2043 Sanders Rd 27581 919-528-5530
Brian Mathis, prin. Fax 528-5574

Sugar Grove, Watauga

Jung Tao School of Chinese Medicine Post-Sec.
207 Dale Adams Rd 28679 828-297-4181

Supply, Brunswick
Brunswick County SD
Supt. — See Bolivia
Cedar Grove MS 500/6-8
750 Grove Trl SW 28462 910-846-3400
Michael Hobbs, prin. Fax 846-3401

Brunswick Community College Post-Sec.
PO Box 30 28462 910-755-7300

Swannanoa, Buncombe, Pop. 4,465
Buncombe County SD
Supt. — See Asheville
Community HS 100/Alt
235 Old US 70 Hwy 28778 828-686-7734
Jeff Conard, prin. Fax 686-7834
Owen MS 600/6-8
730 Old US 70 Hwy 28778 828-686-7739
Heidi Von Dohlen, prin. Fax 686-7938

Asheville Christian Academy 500/PK-12
PO Box 1089 28778 828-581-2200
Dr. William George, head sch Fax 581-2218

Swanquarter, Hyde, Pop. 313
Hyde County SD 600/PK-12
PO Box 217 27885 252-926-3281
Dr. Randolph Latimore, supt. Fax 926-3083
www.hyde.k12.nc.us/
Hyde County Early College HS 200/6-12
20346 US Highway 264 27885 252-926-0221
M.D. Coleman, prin. Fax 926-0224
Other Schools – See Ocracoke

Swansboro, Onslow, Pop. 2,580
Onslow County SD
Supt. — See Jacksonville
Swansboro HS 1,100/9-12
161 Queens Creek Rd 28584 910-326-4300
Christine Andre, prin. Fax 326-1674
Swansboro MS 800/6-8
1240 W Corbett Ave 28584 910-326-3601
Helen Gross, prin. Fax 326-5848

Sylva, Jackson, Pop. 2,551
Jackson County SD 3,600/PK-12
398 Hospital Rd 28779 828-586-2311
Dr. Michael Murray, supt. Fax 586-5450
www.jcps.k12.nc.us
Jackson County Early College 100/9-12
447 College Dr 28779 828-339-4235
Rebecca Ensley, prin.
School of Alternatives 100/Alt
3770 Skyland Dr 28779 828-586-4328
Kristopher Reis, prin. Fax 586-2490
Smoky Mountain HS 800/9-12
100 Smoky Mountain Dr 28779 828-586-2177
Jake Buchanan, prin. Fax 586-2374
Other Schools – See Cashiers

Southwestern Community College Post-Sec.
447 College Dr 28779 828-339-4000

Tabor City, Columbus, Pop. 2,463
Columbus County SD
Supt. — See Whiteville
South Columbus HS 800/9-12
40 Stallion Dr 28463 910-653-4073
Adam Thompson, prin. Fax 653-9461
Tabor City MS 200/6-8
701 W 6th St 28463 910-653-3637
Dianna Bellamy, prin. Fax 653-2093

Tarboro, Edgecombe, Pop. 11,342
Edgecombe County SD 6,100/PK-12
PO Box 7128 27886 252-641-2600
John Farrelly, supt. Fax 641-5714
www.ecps.us/
Edgecombe Early College HS 100/9-12
2009 W Wilson St 27886 252-823-5166
Matt Smith, prin. Fax 823-2053
North Edgecombe HS 300/9-12
7589 NC Highway 33 NW 27886 252-823-3562
Donnell Cannon, prin. Fax 823-7847
Pattillo MS 100/6-8
PO Box 609 27886 252-823-3812
Lauren Lampron, prin. Fax 641-5706
Tarboro HS 600/9-12
1400 W Howard Ave 27886 252-823-4284
Kevin Cutler, prin. Fax 823-0862
Other Schools – See Battleboro, Pinetops, Rocky Mount

Edgecombe Community College Post-Sec.
2009 W Wilson St 27886 252-823-5166

Tar Heel, Bladen, Pop. 115
Bladen County SD
Supt. — See Elizabethtown
Tar Heel MS 300/5-8
PO Box 128 28392 910-862-2475
Kimbrie Esters, prin. Fax 878-9323

Taylorsville, Alexander, Pop. 2,066
Alexander County SD 5,400/PK-12
700 Liledoun Rd 28681 828-632-7001
Dr. Jennifer Hefner, supt. Fax 632-8862
www.alexander.k12.nc.us
Alexander Central HS 1,600/9-12
223 School Dr 28681 828-632-7063
Doug Rhoney, prin. Fax 632-5387
Alexander Early College S 100/Alt
230 Industrial Blvd 28681 828-632-8221
Jason Evans, prin.
West Alexander MS 600/6-8
85 Bulldog Ln 28681 828-495-4611
Dr. Chad Maynor, prin. Fax 495-3527
Other Schools – See Hiddenite

Teachey, Duplin, Pop. 375
Duplin County SD
Supt. — See Kenansville
Wallace-Rose Hill HS 600/9-12
602 High School Rd 28464 910-285-7501
M.D. Guthrie, prin. Fax 285-1116

Thomasville, Davidson, Pop. 26,312
Davidson County SD
Supt. — See Lexington
Brown MS 800/6-8
1140 Kendall Mill Rd 27360 336-475-8845
Christa DiBonaventura, prin. Fax 475-3842
Davidson Early College HS 100/9-12
297 DCCC Rd 27360 336-242-5686
Melissa Glover, prin. Fax 242-5688
East Davidson HS 1,000/9-12
1408 Lake Rd 27360 336-476-4814
Kemp Smith, prin. Fax 476-2982
Ledford HS 1,200/9-12
140 Jesse Green Rd 27360 336-769-9671
Chris Johnston, prin. Fax 769-0650
Ledford MS 700/6-8
3954 N NC Highway 109 27360 336-476-4816
Bruce Carroll, prin. Fax 476-1479

Thomasville CSD 2,400/PK-12
400 Turner St 27360 336-474-4200
Georgia Marshall, supt. Fax 475-0356
www.tcs.k12.nc.us
Thomasville HS 700/9-12
410 Unity St 27360 336-474-4250
Randy Duncan, prin. Fax 476-7430
Thomasville MS 500/6-8
400 Unity St 27360 336-474-4120
Kevin Leake, prin. Fax 472-5081

Topton, Macon
Macon County SD
Supt. — See Franklin
Nantahala S 100/K-12
213 Winding Stairs Rd 28781 828-321-4388
James Bryan, prin. Fax 321-4834

Trenton, Jones, Pop. 270
Jones County SD 1,200/PK-12
320 W Jones St 28585 252-448-2531
Dr. Michael Bracy, supt. Fax 448-1394
www.jonesnc.net
Jones HS 300/9-12
1490 NC Highway 58 S 28585 252-448-2451
Michael White, prin. Fax 448-1034
Jones MS 200/7-8
190 Old New Bern Rd 28585 252-448-3956
Tremaine Young, prin. Fax 448-1044

Trinity, Randolph, Pop. 6,568
Randolph County SD
Supt. — See Asheboro
Archdale-Trinity MS 900/7-8
PO Box 232 27370 336-431-2589
Todd Beane, prin. Fax 431-1809
Trinity HS 700/9-12
5746 Trinity High School Dr 27370 336-861-6870
Dr. Brian Toth, prin. Fax 861-8613
Uwharrie MS 400/6-8
1463 Pleasant Union Rd 27370 336-241-3900
Anthony Grosch, prin. Fax 241-3904
Wheatmore HS 800/9-12
3678 Finch Farm Rd 27370 336-476-1500
Eric Johnson, prin. Fax 476-1520

Troutman, Iredell, Pop. 2,323
Iredell-Statesville SD
Supt. — See Statesville

Career Academy and Technical School 50/9-12
350 Old Murdock Rd 28166 704-978-2791
Larry Rogers, prin. Fax 978-2792
Troutman MS 400/6-8
305 Rumple St 28166 704-528-5137
Bryan Paslay, prin. Fax 528-4006

Troy, Montgomery, Pop. 3,135
Montgomery County SD 4,300/PK-12
PO Box 427 27371 910-576-6511
Dr. Dale Ellis, supt. Fax 576-2044
www.montgomery.k12.nc.us
Montgomery Learning Academy 100/Alt
310 S Main St 27371 910-572-1161
Tim Addis, prin. Fax 572-2362
Other Schools – See Biscoe, Mount Gilead

Montgomery Community College Post-Sec.
1011 Page St 27371 910-576-6222
Wescare Christian Academy 100/K-12
1368 NC Hwy 134 N 27371 910-572-2270
Queen Faulkner, prin. Fax 572-2257

Tyner, Chowan
Edenton-Chowan County SD
Supt. — See Edenton
Chowan MS 500/6-8
2845 Virginia Rd 27980 252-221-4131
John Lassiter, prin. Fax 221-8033

Valdese, Burke, Pop. 4,425
Burke County SD
Supt. — See Morganton
Draughn HS 800/9-12
709 Lovelady Rd NE 28690 828-879-4200
Pat Draughn, prin. Fax 879-4201
Heritage MS 600/6-8
1951 Enon Rd 28690 828-874-0731
Heidi Bristol, prin. Fax 879-6330

Vanceboro, Craven, Pop. 972
Craven County SD
Supt. — See New Bern
West Craven HS 1,000/9-12
2600 Streets Ferry Rd 28586 252-244-3200
Randy St. Clair, prin. Fax 244-3207

Wadesboro, Anson, Pop. 5,742
Anson County SD 3,600/PK-12
320 Camden Rd 28170 704-694-4417
Michael Freeman, supt. Fax 694-7479
www.ansonschools.org/
Anson Academy 100/Alt
118 N Ashe St 28170 704-694-7447
Rodney Hyatt, prin. Fax 694-7447
Anson HS 700/9-12
96 Anson High School Rd 28170 704-694-9301
Chris Stinson, prin. Fax 694-4570
Anson MS 600/7-8
832 US Highway 52 N 28170 704-694-3945
Josh McLaurin, prin. Fax 694-5209
Anson New Technology HS 200/9-12
96 Anson High School Rd 28170 704-694-9301
Kevin Adams, prin. Fax 694-4570
Other Schools – See Polkton

Wake Forest, Wake, Pop. 29,480
Wake County SD
Supt. — See Cary
Heritage HS 1,800/9-12
1150 Forestville Rd 27587 919-570-5600
Scott Lyons, prin. Fax 570-5650
Heritage MS 1,400/6-8
3400 Rogers Rd 27587 919-562-6204
Christopher McCabe, prin. Fax 562-6227
Wake Forest HS 1,900/9-12
420 Stadium Dr 27587 919-554-8611
Patti Hamler, prin. Fax 554-8617
Wake Forest MS 1,100/6-8
1800 S Main St 27587 919-554-8440
Stacey Weddle, prin. Fax 554-8435

Southeastern Baptist Theological Sem. Post-Sec.
PO Box 1889 27588 919-761-2100

Walkertown, Forsyth, Pop. 4,605
Winston-Salem/Forsyth SD
Supt. — See Winston Salem
Walkertown HS 600/9-12
5240 Sullivantown Rd 27051 336-703-4151
Jay Jones, prin.
Walkertown MS 700/6-8
5240 Sullivantown Rd 27051 336-703-4154
Piper Hendrix, prin. Fax 595-1372

Walnut Cove, Stokes, Pop. 1,407
Stokes County SD
Supt. — See Danbury
Southeastern Stokes MS 400/6-8
1044 N Main St 27052 336-591-4371
Rhonda Jackson, prin. Fax 591-8164
South Stokes HS 700/9-12
1100 S Stokes High Dr 27052 336-994-2995
Johnna Cheek, prin. Fax 994-2608
Stokes Early College HS 100/9-12
1165 Dodgetown Rd 27052 336-593-5402
Misti Holloway, prin. Fax 593-2501

Warrensville, Ashe
Ashe County SD
Supt. — See Jefferson
Ashe County MS 500/7-8
PO Box 259 28693 336-384-3591
Dustin Farmer, prin. Fax 384-2112

Warrenton, Warren, Pop. 855
Warren County SD 2,500/PK-12
PO Box 110 27589 252-257-3184
Dr. Ray Spain, supt. Fax 257-5357
www.warrenk12nc.org/
Warren County HS 400/9-12
149 Campus Dr 27589 252-257-4413
Darrell Richardson, prin. Fax 257-1019
Warren County MS 500/6-8
118 Campus Dr 27589 252-257-3751
Noland Hicks, prin. Fax 257-4532
Warren Early College HS 100/9-12
PO Box 110 27589 252-738-3598
Tracey Neal, prin. Fax 257-5357
Warren New Tech HS 200/9-12
219 US Highway 158 Byp 27589 252-257-3767
Dr. Chandra Sledge, prin. Fax 257-1266

Warsaw, Duplin, Pop. 3,022
Duplin County SD
Supt. — See Kenansville
Kenan HS 700/9-12
1241 NC Highway 24 50 28398 910-293-4218
Michael Holton, prin. Fax 293-6744
Warsaw MS 200/6-8
738 W College St 28398 910-293-7997
Tanya Smith, prin. Fax 293-7397

Washington, Beaufort, Pop. 9,614
Beaufort County SD 7,200/PK-12
321 Smaw Rd 27889 252-946-6593
Dr. Don Phipps, supt. Fax 946-3255
www.beaufort.k12.nc.us
Beaufort County Early College HS 200/9-12
5337 US Highway 264 E 27889 252-940-6227
Emily Pake, prin. Fax 975-2752
Beaufort Co. Education Technical Center 100/Alt
820 N Bridge St 27889 252-946-5382
Betty Green, prin. Fax 946-7964
Jones MS 900/6-8
4105 Market Street Ext 27889 252-946-0874
Tracey Nixon, prin. Fax 946-7604
Washington HS 1,000/9-12
400 Slatestone Rd 27889 252-946-0858
Michael Swinson, prin. Fax 946-9633
Other Schools – See Chocowinity, Pinetown

Beaufort County Community College Post-Sec.
PO Box 1069 27889 252-946-6194

Waxhaw, Union, Pop. 9,622
Union County SD
Supt. — See Monroe
Cuthbertson HS 1,400/9-12
1400 Cuthbertson Rd 28173 704-296-0105
Dr. Kimberly Schroeder, prin. Fax 843-3565
Cuthbertson MS 1,300/6-8
1520 Cuthbertson Rd 28173 704-296-0107
Kevin Nesteruk, prin. Fax 243-1673
Marvin Ridge HS 1,500/9-12
2825 Crane Rd 28173 704-290-1520
Donna Cook, prin. Fax 243-0012
Marvin Ridge MS 1,400/6-8
2831 Crane Rd 28173 704-290-1510
Dr. Jay Jones, prin. Fax 243-0153
South Providence Alternative S 200/Alt
500 S Providence St 28173 704-290-1580
Willie Howard, prin. Fax 843-5708

Waynesville, Haywood, Pop. 9,753
Haywood County SD 7,200/PK-12
1230 N Main St 28786 828-456-2400
Anne Garrett, supt. Fax 456-2438
www.haywood.k12.nc.us
Bethel MS 300/6-8
630 Sonoma Rd 28786 828-646-3442
Shawn Parris, prin. Fax 648-6259
Tuscola HS 1,000/9-12
564 Tuscola School Rd 28786 828-456-2408
Travis Collins, prin. Fax 456-2434
Waynesville MS 900/6-8
495 Brown Ave 28786 828-456-2403
Trevor Putnam, prin. Fax 452-7905
Other Schools – See Canton, Clyde

Weaverville, Buncombe, Pop. 3,037
Buncombe County SD
Supt. — See Asheville
North Buncombe HS 1,100/9-12
890 Clarks Chapel Rd 28787 828-645-4221
Jack Evans, prin. Fax 645-4367
North Buncombe MS 600/7-8
51 N Buncombe School Rd 28787 828-645-7944
Samantha Sircey, prin. Fax 645-2509

Timbersong Academy 100/4-12
531 Upper Flat Creek Rd 28787 828-645-1919
Bryan Tomes, dir. Fax 219-7006

Weldon, Halifax, Pop. 1,616
Weldon CSD 1,200/PK-12
301 Mulberry St 27890 252-536-4821
Dr. Anitra Wells, supt. Fax 536-3062
district.weldoncityschools.org
Roanoke Valley Early College HS 200/8-12
100 College Dr Bldg 600 27890 252-536-6382
Dr. Eric Pullen, prin. Fax 536-3062
Weldon HS 200/9-12
415 County Rd 27890 252-536-4829
John Green, prin. Fax 536-0168
Other Schools – See Halifax

Halifax Community College Post-Sec.
PO Box 809 27890 252-536-4221

Wendell, Wake, Pop. 5,709
Johnston County SD
Supt. — See Smithfield
Archer Lodge MS 1,100/6-8
740 Wendell Rd 27591 919-553-0714
Ben Williams, prin. Fax 553-8540
Corinth Holders HS 1,500/9-12
6875 Applewhite Rd 27591 919-365-4306
Charles Ferrell, prin. Fax 365-4344
Wake County SD
Supt. — See Cary
East Wake HS 1,200/9-12
5101 Rolesville Rd 27591 919-365-2625
Stacey Alston, prin. Fax 365-2628
Wendell MS 1,000/6-8
3409 NC 97 Hwy 27591 919-365-1667
Robert Morrison, prin. Fax 365-1686

Wentworth, Rockingham, Pop. 2,774
Rockingham County SD
Supt. — See Eden
Rockingham County Early College HS 300/9-12
310 Wrenn Memorial Rd 27375 336-342-4261
Diane Hill, prin. Fax 349-9986

Rockingham Community College Post-Sec.
PO Box 38 27375 336-342-4261

West End, Moore
Moore County SD
Supt. — See Carthage
West Pine MS 900/6-8
144 Archie Rd 27376 910-673-1464
Doug Massengill, prin. Fax 673-1272

West Jefferson, Ashe, Pop. 1,280
Ashe County SD
Supt. — See Jefferson
Ashe County HS 1,000/9-12
PO Box 450 28694 336-846-2400
Jason Krider, prin. Fax 846-2411

Whiteville, Columbus, Pop. 5,303
Columbus County SD 6,200/PK-12
PO Box 729 28472 910-642-5168
Alan Faulk, supt. Fax 640-1010
www.columbus.k12.nc.us/
Columbus Career & College Acad - SCC 200/9-12
PO Box 151 28472 910-642-7141
Nicky Hobbs, prin. Fax 642-7693
Other Schools – See Cerro Gordo, Chadbourn, Delco, Fair Bluff, Hallsboro, Lake Waccamaw, Nakina, Tabor City

Whiteville CSD 2,300/PK-12
107 W Walter St 28472 910-642-4116
Charles Garland, supt. Fax 642-0564
www.whiteville.k12.nc.us
Central MS 500/6-8
310 S Martin Luther King Jr 28472 910-642-3546
Chris Kelly, prin. Fax 642-7484
North Whiteville Academy 50/Alt
310 S Martin Luther King Jr 28472 910-914-4161
Susan Smith, dir. Fax 914-4164
Whiteville HS 700/9-12
413 N Lee St 28472 910-914-4189
Jes Sealey, prin. Fax 914-4186

Carolina Adventist Academy 50/K-10
PO Box 1937 28472 910-640-0855
Columbus Christian Academy 200/K-12
PO Box 1100 28472 910-642-6196
Southeastern Community College Post-Sec.
PO Box 151 28472 910-642-7141

Wilkesboro, Wilkes, Pop. 3,340
Wilkes County SD
Supt. — See North Wilkesboro
West Wilkes MS 700/6-8
1677 N NC Highway 16 28697 336-651-4381
Pam Huffman, prin. Fax 973-7423
Wilkes Central HS 800/9-12
1179 Moravian Falls Rd 28697 336-667-5277
Dr. Dion Stocks, prin. Fax 667-2091
Wilkes Early College HS 200/9-12
1328 S Collegiate Dr # 800 28697 336-838-6247
Michelle Shepherd, prin. Fax 838-6198

Wilkes Community College Post-Sec.
PO Box 120 28697 336-838-6100

Williamston, Martin, Pop. 5,452
Martin County SD 3,400/PK-12
300 N Watts St 27892 252-792-1575
Dr. Chris Mansfield, supt. Fax 792-1965
martin.sharpschool.net/
Riverside HS 600/9-12
1260 Godwin Dr 27892 252-792-7881
James Guard, prin. Fax 809-4807
Riverside MS 400/6-8
2920 US Highway 17 27892 252-792-1111
Ronald Byrd, prin. Fax 792-6644
Other Schools – See Robersonville

Martin Community College Post-Sec.
1161 Kehukee Park Rd 27892 252-792-1521

Wilmington, New Hanover, Pop. 104,394
New Hanover County SD 25,600/PK-12
6410 Carolina Beach Rd 28412 910-763-5431
Dr. Tim Markley, supt. Fax 254-4479
www.nhcs.net
Ashley HS 1,700/9-12
555 Halyburton Memorial Pky 28412 910-790-2360
Patrick McCarty, prin. Fax 790-2356
Bear Early College HS 200/9-12
630 MacMillan Ave N 28403 910-350-1387
Mary Beall, prin. Fax 350-1392
Career Readiness Academy 100/Alt
3702 Princess Place Dr 28405 910-251-6161
Adrian Pearson, prin. Fax 251-6022
Hoggard HS 1,600/9-12
4305 Shipyard Blvd 28403 910-350-2072
Dr. Steve Sullivan, prin. Fax 350-2066
Laney HS 2,000/9-12
2700 N College Rd 28405 910-350-2089
Sharon Dousharm, prin. Fax 350-2083

Murray MS 900/6-8
655 Halyburton Memorial Pky 28412 910-790-2363
Philip Sutton, prin. Fax 790-2351
Myrtle Grove MS 800/6-8
901 Piner Rd 28409 910-350-2100
Sam Highsmith, prin. Fax 350-2104
New Hanover HS 1,700/9-12
1307 Market St 28401 910-251-6100
James McAdams, prin. Fax 251-6114
Noble MS 800/6-8
6520 Market St 28405 910-350-2112
Wade Smith, prin. Fax 350-2109
Roland-Grise MS 800/6-8
4412 Lake Ave 28403 910-350-2136
Dr. Charlie Broadfoot, prin. Fax 350-2133
Trask MS 800/6-8
2900 N College Rd 28405 910-350-2142
Dr. Maggie Rollison, prin. Fax 350-2144
Virgo MS 200/6-8
813 Nixon St 28401 910-251-6150
Dr. Sabrina Hill-Black, prin. Fax 251-6055
Williston MS 800/6-8
401 S 10th St 28401 910-815-6906
Ronald Villines, prin. Fax 815-6904
Other Schools – See Castle Hayne

Calvary Christian S 100/PK-10
423 N 23rd St 28405 910-343-1565
Dr. Donnie Lovette, prin. Fax 762-5847
Cape Fear Academy 600/PK-12
3900 S College Rd 28412 910-791-0287
Donald Berger, head sch Fax 791-0290
Cape Fear Community College Post-Sec.
411 N Front St 28401 910-362-7000
Coastal Christian HS 200/9-12
1150 the Kings Hwy 28409 910-395-9995
Brenda McCombie, admin. Fax 395-9901
College of Wilmington Post-Sec.
3500 Oleander Dr Ste 1111 28403 910-763-4418
Miller-Motte College Post-Sec.
5000 Market St 28405 910-392-4660
New Hanover Regional Medical Center Post-Sec.
2131 S 17th St 28401 910-343-7074
University of North Carolina Post-Sec.
601 S College Rd 28403 910-962-3000
Wilmington Christian Academy 800/PK-12
1401 N College Rd 28405 910-791-4248
Barren Nobles M.S., admin. Fax 791-4276

Wilson, Wilson, Pop. 48,488
Wilson County SD 12,400/PK-12
PO Box 2048 27894 252-399-7700
Dr. Lane Mills, supt. Fax 399-2776
www.wilsonschoolsnc.net
Beddingfield HS 800/9-12
4510 Old Stantonsburg Rd 27893 252-399-7880
F.T. Franks, prin. Fax 399-7850
Daniels Learning Center 100/Alt
723 Elvie St S 27893 252-399-7900
Leon Dupree, prin. Fax 399-7892
Darden MS 400/6-8
1665 Lipscomb Rd E 27893 252-206-4973
Jagtar Singh, prin. Fax 206-1508
Fike HS 1,200/9-12
500 Harrison Dr N 27893 252-399-7905
Mark Holley, prin. Fax 399-7893
Forest Hills MS 600/6-8
1210 Forest Hills Rd NW 27896 252-399-7913
Cheryl Baggett, prin. Fax 399-7894
Hunt HS 1,400/9-12
4559 Lamm Rd SW 27893 252-399-7930
Eddie Doll, prin. Fax 399-7897
Toisnot MS 500/6-8
1301 Corbett Ave N 27893 252-399-7973
Ronnia Cockrell, prin. Fax 399-7749
Wilson Academy of Applied Technology 100/9-12
510 Old Stantonsburg Rd 27893 252-265-4038
Krystal Cox, admin. Fax 234-0253
Wilson Early College Academy 200/9-12
PO Box 4305 27893 252-246-1418
Nelson Johnston, prin. Fax 246-1430
Other Schools – See Elm City, Lucama, Stantonsburg

Barton College Post-Sec.
PO Box 5000 27893 252-399-6300
Community Christian S 300/PK-12
5160 Packhouse Rd 27896 252-399-1376
Eastern North Carolina Sch. for the Deaf Post-Sec.
1311 US Highway 301 S 27893 252-237-2450
Greenfield S 300/PK-12
3351 NC Highway 42 W 27893 252-237-8046
Beth Peters, head sch Fax 237-1825
Mitchell's Hairstyling Academy Post-Sec.
2620 Forest Hills Rd #A 27893 252-243-3158
Wilson Christian Academy 500/PK-12
1820 Airport Blvd W 27893 252-237-8064
Wilson Community College Post-Sec.
PO Box 4305 27893 252-291-1195

Windsor, Bertie, Pop. 3,573
Bertie County SD 2,800/PK-12
PO Box 10 27983 252-794-6000
Julius Walker, supt. Fax 794-9727
www.bertie.k12.nc.us
Bertie Early College HS 100/9-12
819B Governors Rd 27983 252-794-2150
Wanda Cofield, prin. Fax 794-3407
Bertie HS 500/9-12
715 US Highway 13 N 27983 252-794-3034
Calvin Moore, prin. Fax 794-1932
Bertie MS 600/6-8
652 US Highway 13 N 27983 252-794-2143
William Peele, prin. Fax 794-4024
Bertie STEM HS 200/9-12
715 US Highway 13 N 27983 252-794-5820
Daphne Williams, prin. Fax 794-5815

Bethel Assembly Christian Academy 200/PK-12
105 Askewville Bryant St 27983 252-794-4034

Winfall, Perquimans, Pop. 587
Perquimans County SD
Supt. — See Hertford
Perquimans County MS 400/6-8
PO Box 39 27985 252-426-7355
Laura Moreland, prin. Fax 426-1424

Wingate, Union, Pop. 3,424

Wingate University Post-Sec.
220 N Camden Rd 28174 704-233-8000

Winston Salem, Forsyth, Pop. 225,143
Davidson County SD
Supt. — See Lexington
Oak Grove MS 700/6-8
1771 Hoy Long Rd 27107 336-474-8250
Dan Shamblen, prin. Fax 474-8257

Winston-Salem/Forsyth SD 53,600/PK-12
PO Box 2513 27102 336-727-2816
Dr. Beverly Emory, supt. Fax 661-6572
wsfcs.k12.nc.us
Atkins Academic & Technology HS 500/9-12
3605 Old Greensboro Rd 27101 336-703-6754
Joe Childers, prin. Fax 748-3565
Career Center Vo/Tech
910 Highland Ct 27101 336-727-8181
Chris Nichols, prin. Fax 727-7607
Carver HS 600/9-12
3545 Carver School Rd 27105 336-727-2987
Travis Taylor, prin. Fax 727-8211
Clemmons MS 900/6-8
3785 Fraternity Church Rd 27127 336-703-4217
Sandra Hunter, prin. Fax 774-4678
Early College of Forsyth County 200/9-12
2100 Silas Creek Pkwy 27103 336-757-3290
Frances Cook, prin. Fax 734-7467
Flat Rock MS, 4648 Ebert Rd 27127 900/6-8
Becky Hodges, prin. 336-703-6762
Forsyth Middle College HS 100/9-12
2100 Silas Creek Pkwy 27103 336-734-7437
William Wynn, prin.
Hanes Magnet MS 900/6-8
2355 Pleasant St 27107 336-703-4171
Robin Willard, prin. Fax 727-3207
Jefferson MS 1,300/6-8
3500 Sally Kirk Rd 27106 336-703-4222
Pam Helms, prin. Fax 774-4635
Kennedy HS 200/9-12
890 E 11th St 27101 336-703-4143
Fax 727-8559
Kingswood S 100/Alt
1001 Reynolda Rd 27104 336-703-4128
Roderick Dupree, prin.
Main Street Academy 100/Alt
2700 S Main St 27127 336-703-4185
Ronald Travis, prin. Fax 771-4706
Meadowlark MS 1,200/6-8
301 Meadowlark Dr 27106 336-703-4228
Joey Hearl, prin. Fax 922-1745
Mineral Springs MS 400/6-8
4559 Ogburn Ave 27105 336-703-6733
Debra Gladstone, prin. Fax 661-4857
Mt. Tabor HS 1,500/9-12
342 Petree Rd 27106 336-703-6700
Ed Weiss, prin. Fax 774-4606
North Forsyth HS 1,200/9-12
5705 Shattalon Dr 27105 336-661-4880
Melita Wise, prin. Fax 661-4869
Northwest MS 900/6-8
5501 Murray Rd 27106 336-703-4161
Alfreda Smith, prin. Fax 924-5128
Paisley IB Magnet MS 800/6-10
1400 Grant Ave 27105 336-703-4168
Dr. Gary Cone, prin. Fax 727-8315
Parkland HS 1,300/9-12
1600 Brewer Rd 27127 336-771-4700
Spencer Hardy, prin. Fax 771-4703
Philo-Hill Magnet MS 500/6-8
410 Haverhill St 27127 336-703-4165
Essie McCoy, prin. Fax 771-4737
Reynolds HS 1,700/9-12
301 N Hawthorne Rd 27104 336-703-4145
Leslie Alexander, prin. Fax 727-2053
Wiley Magnet MS 500/6-8
1400 W Northwest Blvd 27104 336-727-2378
Lisa Bodenheimer, prin. Fax 727-8412
Winston-Salem Preparatory Academy 400/6-12
1215 N Cameron Ave 27101 336-703-6732
Richard Watts, prin. Fax 727-2931
Other Schools – See Clemmons, Kernersville, Pfafftown, Walkertown

---

Calvary Day S 700/PK-12
5000 Country Club Rd 27104 336-765-5546
Richard Hardee, head sch Fax 714-5577
Carolina Christian College Post-Sec.
PO Box 777 27102 336-774-0900
Forsyth Technical Community College Post-Sec.
2100 Silas Creek Pkwy 27103 336-723-0371
Gospel Light Christian S 400/PK-12
4940 Gospel Light Church Rd 27101 336-722-6100
Living Arts Institute Post-Sec.
1100 S Stratford Rd 27103 336-774-7600
Piedmont Baptist College & Graduate Sch Post-Sec.
420 S Broad St 27101 336-725-8344
Salem Academy 200/9-12
500 E Salem Ave 27101 336-721-2643
Karl Sjolund, head sch Fax 917-5340
Salem Baptist Christian S 300/PK-12
429 S Broad St 27101 336-725-6113
Martha Drake, hdmstr. Fax 725-8455
Salem College Post-Sec.
601 S Church St 27101 800-327-2536
University of NC School of the Arts Post-Sec.
1533 S Main St 27127 336-770-3399
Wake Forest University Post-Sec.
1834 Wake Forest Rd 27109 336-758-5000
Winston-Salem Barber School Post-Sec.
1531 Silas Creek Pkwy 27127 336-724-1459
Winston Salem Christian S 300/PK-12
3730 University Pkwy 27106 336-759-7762
Dr. Bryan Wolfe, head sch Fax 896-7667
Winston-Salem State University Post-Sec.
601 S Mrtn Lther King Jr Dr 27110 336-750-2000
Woodland Baptist Christian S 200/PK-12
1175 Bethania Rural Hall Rd 27106 336-969-2088

Winterville, Pitt, Pop. 9,094
Pitt County SD
Supt. — See Greenville
Cox MS 800/6-8
2657 Church St 28590 252-756-3105
Norman McDuffie, prin. Fax 756-1081
Pitt County Schools Early College 100/9-12
1959 Warren Dr 28590 252-493-7821
Wynn Whittington, prin.
South Central HS 1,600/9-12
570 W Forlines Rd 28590 252-321-3232
Janarde Cannon, prin. Fax 321-7909

Christ Covenant S 200/K-12
4889 Old Tar Rd 28590 252-756-3002
Robert Lee, head sch Fax 756-4072

Winton, Hertford, Pop. 760
Hertford County SD 3,200/PK-12
PO Box 158 27986 252-358-1761
Dr. William Wright, supt. Fax 358-4745
www.hertford.k12.nc.us
Brown HS 50/Alt
102 C S Brown Dr 27986 252-358-2852
Keisha Peele, prin. Fax 358-0121
Other Schools – See Ahoskie, Murfreesboro

Yadkinville, Yadkin, Pop. 2,941
Yadkin County SD 5,700/PK-12
121 Washington St 27055 336-679-2051
Dr. Todd Martin, supt. Fax 679-4013
www.yadkin.k12.nc.us
Yadkin Early College HS 200/9-12
121 Washington St 27055 336-679-4600
Tracy Kimmer, prin. Fax 679-3210
Yadkin Success Academy 50/Alt
733 E Main St 27055 336-679-4888
Charles Garrett, prin. Fax 679-6623
Other Schools – See Boonville, East Bend

Yanceyville, Caswell, Pop. 1,971
Caswell County SD 2,800/PK-12
PO Box 160 27379 336-694-4116
Dr. Sam Shields, supt. Fax 694-5154
www.caswell.k12.nc.us/
Bartlett Yancey HS 800/9-12
PO Box 190 27379 336-694-4212
JoAnna Gwynn, prin. Fax 694-5285
Dillard MS 700/6-8
255 Hatchett Rd 27379 336-694-4941
Benjamin Gravely, prin. Fax 694-6353

Youngsville, Franklin, Pop. 1,142
Franklin County SD
Supt. — See Louisburg
Cedar Creek MS 600/6-8
2228 Cedar Creek Rd 27596 919-554-4848
James Elliott, prin. Fax 570-5143

American Institute of Applied Science Post-Sec.
100 Hunter Pl 27596 919-554-2500

Zebulon, Wake, Pop. 4,340
Wake County SD
Supt. — See Cary
Zebulon MS 600/6-8
1000 Shepard School Rd 27597 919-404-3630
Stephanie Smith, prin. Fax 404-3651

NORTH DAKOTA

NORTH DAKOTA DEPT. OF PUBLIC INSTRUCTION
600 E Boulevard Ave, Bismarck 58505-0601
Telephone 701-328-2260
Fax 701-328-2461
Website http://www.dpi.state.nd.us

Superintendent of Public Instruction Kirsten Baesler

NORTH DAKOTA BOARD OF EDUCATION
600 E Boulevard Ave, Bismarck 58505-0602

COUNTY SUPERINTENDENTS OF SCHOOLS

Adams County Office of Education
Patricia Carroll, supt. 701-567-4363
PO Box 589, Hettinger 58639 Fax 567-2910
Barnes County Office of Education
Beth Didier, supt. 701-845-6666
230 4th St NW Rm 202 Fax 845-8548
Valley City 58072
Benson County Office of Education
Lucia Jacobson, supt. 701-473-5370
PO Box 347, Minnewaukan 58351 Fax 473-5571
Billings County Office of Education 701-623-4377
, PO Box 168, Medora 58645 Fax 623-4896
Bottineau County Office of Education
Ann Monson, supt. 701-228-2035
314 5th St W Ste 11 Fax 228-3658
Bottineau 58318
Bowman County Office of Education
Lois Anderson, supt. 701-523-3665
PO Box 380, Bowman 58623 Fax 523-3428
Burke County Office of Education
Jeanine Jensen, supt. 701-377-2861
PO Box 310, Bowbells 58721 Fax 377-2020
Burleigh County Office of Education
Tamara Uselman, supt. 701-323-4074
806 N Washington St
Bismarck 58501
www.co.burleigh.nd.us
Cass County Office of Education
Mike Montplaisir, supt. 701-241-5600
PO Box 2806, Fargo 58108
www.casscountynd.gov
Cavalier County Office of Education
Lisa Gellner, supt. 701-256-2229
901 3rd St Ste 15, Langdon 58249 Fax 256-2546
Dickey County Office of Education
Tom Strand, supt. 701-349-3249
PO Box 148, Ellendale 58436 Fax 349-4639
Divide County Office of Education
Dr. Sherlock Hirning, supt. 701-965-6313
PO Box G, Crosby 58730 Fax 965-6004
www.divide-co.k12.nd.us
Dunn County Office of Education
Reinhard Hauck, supt. 701-573-4448
205 Owens St, Manning 58642 Fax 573-4444
Eddy County Office of Education
Tracy Henningsgard, supt. 701-947-2434
524 Central Ave Fax 947-2279
New Rockford 58356
Emmons County Office of Education
Rusty Plienis, supt. 701-254-4417
PO Box 776, Linton 58552 Fax 254-4802
Foster County Office of Education
Roger Schlotman, supt. 701-652-2441
PO Box 104, Carrington 58421 Fax 652-2173
Golden Valley County Office of Education
Ceil Stedman, supt. 701-872-4331
PO Box 67, Beach 58621 Fax 872-4383
www.goldenvalleycounty.org

Grand Forks County Office of Education
David Godfread, supt. 701-795-2777
5216 Chestnut St Fax 795-2770
Grand Forks 58201
Grant County Office of Education
Kelly Bachmeier, supt. 701-622-3263
210 2nd Ave W, Carson 58529 Fax 622-3717
Griggs County Office of Education
Samantha Quast, supt. 701-797-2411
PO Box 511, Cooperstown 58425 Fax 797-3587
Hettinger County Office of Education
Sheila Steiner, supt. 701-824-2500
336 Pacific Ave, Mott 58646 Fax 824-2717
Kidder County Office of Education
Angela Haverkamp, supt. 701-475-2632
PO Box 66, Steele 58482 Fax 475-2202
La Moure County Office of Education
Mike Johnson, supt. 701-883-5301
PO Box 128, LaMoure 58458 Fax 883-4240
Logan County Office of Education
Gary Schumacher, supt. 701-754-2756
PO Box 7, Napoleon 58561 Fax 754-2270
McHenry County Office of Education
Maxine Rognlien, supt. 701-537-5642
407 Main St S, Towner 58788 Fax 537-5969
www.mchenrycountynd.com
McIntosh County Office of Education
Coreen Schumacher, supt. 605-380-6813
PO Box 290, Ashley 58413 Fax 288-3671
McKenzie County Office of Education
Carol Kieson, supt. 701-444-3456
201 5th St NW Unit 503 Fax 444-4113
Watford City 58854
www.mckenziecounty.net
McLean County Office of Education
Lori Foss, supt. 701-462-8541
PO Box 1108, Washburn 58577 Fax 462-3542
Mercer County Office of Education
Gontran Langowski, supt. 701-748-3300
1021 Arthur St, Stanton 58571 Fax 748-3301
Morton County Office of Education
Dale Ekstrom, supt. 701-667-3315
210 2nd Ave NW, Mandan 58554 Fax 667-3348
www.co.morton.nd.us/
Mountrail County Office of Education
Stephanie Pappa, supt. 701-628-2145
PO Box 69, Stanley 58784 Fax 628-3975
Nelson County Office of Education
Sharon Young, supt. 701-247-2472
210 B Ave W, Lakota 58344 Fax 247-2943
Oliver County Office of Education
Judith Hintz, supt. 701-794-8721
PO Box 188, Center 58530 Fax 794-3476
Pembina County Office of Education
Linda Schlittenhard, supt. 701-265-4231
301 Dakota St W Unit 11 Fax 265-4876
Cavalier 58220

Pierce County Office of Education
Karin Fursather, supt. 701-776-5225
240 2nd St SE Ste 6, Rugby 58368 Fax 776-5707
Ramsey County Office of Education
Lisa Diseth, supt. 701-662-7023
524 4th Ave NE, Devils Lake 58301 Fax 662-7049
Ransom County Office of Education
Suzanne Anderson, supt. 701-683-6117
PO Box 112, Lisbon 58054
Renville County Office of Education
Marvin Madsen, supt. 701-756-6301
PO Box 68, Mohall 58761 Fax 756-6391
Richland County Office of Education
Harris Bailey, supt. 701-642-7702
418 2nd Ave N Ofc 15 Fax 642-7701
Wahpeton 58075
Rolette County Office of Education
Dwane Getzlaff, supt. 701-477-5665
PO Box 939, Rolla 58367 Fax 477-6339
Sargent County Office of Education
Pam Maloney, supt. 701-724-6241
355 Main St S Ste 1, Forman 58032 Fax 724-6244
Sheridan County Office of Education
Tracy Laib, supt. 701-363-2205
PO Box 439, Mc Clusky 58463 Fax 363-2953
Sioux County Office of Education
Barb Hettich, supt. 701-854-3481
PO Box L, Fort Yates 58538 Fax 854-3854
Slope County Office of Education
Jacqueline Kathrein, supt. 701-879-6277
PO Box MM, Amidon 58620 Fax 879-6278
Stark County Office of Education
Kay Haag, supt. 701-456-7630
PO Box 130, Dickinson 58602 Fax 456-7634
Steele County Office of Education
Linda Leadbetter, supt. 701-524-2110
PO Box 275, Finley 58230 Fax 524-1715
Stutsman County Office of Education
Casey Bradley, supt. 701-252-9035
511 2nd Ave SE Ste 102 Fax 251-1603
Jamestown 58401
Towner County Office of Education
Wayne Lingen, supt. 701-968-4346
PO Box 603, Cando 58324 Fax 968-4342
Traill County Office of Education
Rebecca Braaten, supt. 701-636-4458
PO Box 429, Hillsboro 58045 Fax 636-5418
Walsh County Office of Education
Kris Molde, supt. 701-352-2851
600 Cooper Ave, Grafton 58237 Fax 352-3340
Ward County Office of Education
Jodi Johnson, supt. 701-857-6495
PO Box 5005, Minot 58702 Fax 857-6424
Wells County Office of Education
Janell Rudel, supt. 701-547-3521
700 Railway St N Dept 37 Fax 547-3719
Fessenden 58438
Williams County Office of Education
Beth Innis, supt. 701-577-4580
PO Box 2047, Williston 58802 Fax 577-4535

PUBLIC, PRIVATE AND CATHOLIC SECONDARY SCHOOLS

Alexander, McKenzie, Pop. 220
Alexander SD 2 200/PK-12
PO Box 63 58831 701-828-3334
Leslie Bieber, supt. Fax 828-3134
www.alexander.k12.nd.us
Alexander HS 100/7-12
PO Box 66 58831 701-828-3335
Shannon Faller, prin. Fax 828-3134

Ashley, McIntosh, Pop. 736
Ashley SD 9 100/PK-12
703 W Main St 58413 701-288-3456
Jason Schmidt, supt. Fax 288-3457
www.ashley.k12.nd.us
Ashley HS 100/7-12
703 W Main St 58413 701-288-3456
Cary Hauth, prin. Fax 288-3457

Beach, Golden Valley, Pop. 1,013
Beach SD 3 300/K-12
PO Box 368 58621 701-872-4161
Larry Helvik, supt. Fax 872-3801
www.beach.k12.nd.us
Beach JSHS 200/7-12
PO Box 368 58621 701-872-4161
Wayne Heckaman, prin. Fax 872-3801

Belcourt, Rolette, Pop. 2,055
Belcourt SD 7 1,600/K-12
PO Box 440 58316 701-477-6471
Dr. Lana DeCoteau, supt. Fax 477-6470
www.belcourt.k12.nd.us
Turtle Mountain Community HS 600/9-12
PO Box 440 58316 701-477-6471
Melvin Laducer, prin. Fax 477-8821
Turtle Mountain Community MS 400/6-8
PO Box 440 58316 701-477-6471
Cary Morin, prin. Fax 477-3973

Turtle Mountain Community College Post-Sec.
PO Box 340 58316 701-477-7862

Belfield, Stark, Pop. 793
Belfield SD 13 200/K-12
PO Box 97 58622 701-575-4275
Wade Northrop, supt. Fax 575-8533
www.belfield.k12.nd.us/
Belfield JSHS 100/7-12
PO Box 97 58622 701-575-4275
Daren Kurle, prin. Fax 575-8533

Berthold, Ward, Pop. 449
Lewis and Clark SD 161 300/PK-12
PO Box 185 58718 701-453-3484
Brian Nelson, supt. Fax 453-3488
www.lewisandclark.k12.nd.us/

Berthold HS 100/7-12
PO Box 185 58718 701-453-3484
Margaret Person, prin. Fax 453-3488
Other Schools – See Plaza

Beulah, Mercer, Pop. 3,078
Beulah SD 27 700/K-12
204 5th St NW 58523 701-873-2237
Loren Scheer, supt. Fax 873-5273
www.beulah.k12.nd.us
Beulah HS 200/9-12
204 5th St NW 58523 701-873-2261
Kevin Hoherz, prin. Fax 873-5273
Beulah MS 200/5-8
1700 Central Ave N 58523 701-873-4325
Stacy Murschel, prin. Fax 873-2844

Binford, Griggs, Pop. 183
Midkota SD 7 100/K-12
PO Box 38 58416 701-676-2511
Les Dale, supt. Fax 676-2510
www.midkotaschools.com
Other Schools – See Glenfield

Bismarck, Burleigh, Pop. 60,375
Bismarck SD 1 11,800/PK-12
806 N Washington St 58501 701-323-4000
Tamara Uselman, supt. Fax 355-4001
www.bismarckschools.org
Bismarck Career & Technical Center Vo/Tech
1221 College Dr 58501 701-323-4340
Dale Hoerauf, prin. Fax 323-4345
Bismarck HS 1,600/9-12
800 N 8th St 58501 701-323-4800
David Wisthoff, prin. Fax 323-4805
Century HS 1,500/9-12
1000 E Century Ave 58503 701-323-4900
Steve Madler, prin. Fax 323-4905
Horizon MS 900/6-8
500 Ash Coulee Dr 58503 701-323-4550
Tabby Rabenberg, prin. Fax 323-4555
Legacy HS 300/9-12
806 N Washington St 58501 701-323-4850
Tom Schmidt, prin. Fax 323-4855
Simle MS 800/6-8
1215 N 19th St 58501 701-323-4600
Russ Riehl, prin. Fax 323-4605
South Central Alternative S 100/Alt
406 S Anderson St 58504 701-323-4520
Joe Kalvoda, prin. Fax 323-4525
Wachter MS 800/6-8
1107 S 7th St 58504 701-323-4650
Lee Ziegler, prin. Fax 323-4655
Adult Learning Center Adult
1500 Edwards Ave Rm 220 58501 701-323-4530
Dale Hoerauf, prin. Fax 323-4477

Bismarck State College Post-Sec.
PO Box 5587 58506 701-224-5400
Dakota Adventist Academy 50/9-12
15905 Sheyenne Cir 58503 701-258-9000
David Candy M.Ed., prin. Fax 258-0110
Light of Christ Academy 200/7-8
1025 N 2nd St 58501 701-223-4114
Carmen Cain, prin. Fax 223-8629
Lynnes Welding Training Post-Sec.
4329 Centurion Dr Unit 9 58504 701-751-4256
Medcenter One Health System Post-Sec.
222 N 7th St 58501 701-222-5413
Rasmussen College Post-Sec.
1701 E Century Ave 58503 701-530-9600
R.D. Hairstyling College Post-Sec.
1320 Tacoma Ave 58504 701-223-8804
St. Alexius Medical Center Post-Sec.
PO Box 5510 58506 701-224-7600
St. Marys Central HS 300/9-12
1025 N 2nd St 58501 701-223-4113
Carmen Cain, prin. Fax 223-8629
Shiloh Christian S 400/PK-12
1915 Shiloh Dr 58503 701-221-2104
Mike Dwyer, admin. Fax 224-8221
United Tribes Technical College Post-Sec.
3315 University Dr 58504 701-255-3285
University of Mary Post-Sec.
7500 University Dr 58504 701-255-7500

Bottineau, Bottineau, Pop. 2,163
Bottineau SD 1 600/K-12
301 Brander St 58318 701-228-2266
Jason Kersten, supt. Fax 228-2021
www.bottineau.k12.nd.us/
Bottineau JSHS 300/7-12
301 Brander St 58318 701-228-2266
Joel Bickford, prin. Fax 228-2021

Dakota College at Bottineau Post-Sec.
105 Simrall Blvd 58318 701-228-2277

Bowbells, Burke, Pop. 335
Bowbells SD 14 100/K-12
PO Box 279 58721 701-377-2396
Celeste Thingvold, supt. Fax 377-2399
www.bowbells.k12.nd.us
Bowbells HS 50/7-12
PO Box 279 58721 701-377-2396
Celeste Thingvold, supt. Fax 377-2399

Bowman, Bowman, Pop. 1,641
Bowman County SD 1 500/K-12
PO Box H 58623 701-523-3283
Anthony Duletski, supt. Fax 523-3849
www.bowman.k12.nd.us
Bowman HS 100/9-12
PO Box H 58623 701-523-3283
Tyler Senn, prin. Fax 523-3849

Buxton, Traill, Pop. 323
Central Valley SD 3 100/K-12
1556 Highway 81 NE 58218 701-847-2220
Jeremy Brandt, supt. Fax 847-2407
www.centralvalleynd.com
Central Valley S 100/K-12
1556 Highway 81 NE 58218 701-847-2220
Frank Justin, prin. Fax 847-2407

Cando, Towner, Pop. 1,101
North Star SD 10 300/PK-12
PO Box 489 58324 701-968-4416
Jeff Hagler, supt. Fax 968-4418
www.northstar.k12.nd.us//index.html
North Star HS 100/9-12
PO Box 489 58324 701-968-4416
Nancy Reiser, prin. Fax 968-4418

Carrington, Foster, Pop. 2,050
Carrington SD 49 500/PK-12
PO Box 48 58421 701-652-3136
Dr. Brian Duchscherer, supt. Fax 652-1243
www.carrington.k12.nd.us/
Carrington JSHS 300/7-12
PO Box 48 58421 701-652-3136
David Nowatzki, prin. Fax 652-1243

Casselton, Cass, Pop. 2,310
Central Cass SD 17 800/K-12
802 5th St N 58012 701-347-5352
Morgan Forness, supt. Fax 347-5354
www.central-cass.k12.nd.us
Central Cass HS 200/9-12
802 5th St N 58012 701-347-5352
Nikki Wixo, prin. Fax 347-5354
Central Cass MS 200/6-8
802 5th St N 58012 701-347-5352
Nikki Wixo, prin. Fax 347-5354

Cavalier, Pembina, Pop. 1,278
Cavalier SD 6 400/K-12
PO Box 410 58220 701-265-8417
Jeff Manley, supt. Fax 265-8106
www.cavalierschool.org
Cavalier HS 100/9-12
PO Box 410 58220 701-265-8417
Sandy Laxdal, prin. Fax 265-8106

Center, Oliver, Pop. 569
Center-Stanton SD 1 200/K-12
PO Box 248 58530 701-794-8778
Curt Pierce, supt. Fax 794-3659
www.center.k12.nd.us
Center-Stanton HS 100/7-12
PO Box 248 58530 701-794-8778
Tracy Peterson, prin. Fax 794-3659

Colfax, Richland, Pop. 121
Richland SD 44 300/K-12
PO Box 49 58018 701-372-3713
Tim Godfrey, supt. Fax 372-3718
www.richland.k12.nd.us
Richland JSHS 100/7-12
PO Box 49 58018 701-372-3713
Bruce Anderson, prin. Fax 372-3718

Cooperstown, Griggs, Pop. 983
Griggs County Central SD 18 200/K-12
1207 Foster Ave NE 58425 701-797-3114
Meghan Brown, supt. Fax 797-3130
www.griggs-co.k12.nd.us/
Griggs County Central HS 100/7-12
1207 Foster Ave NE 58425 701-797-3114
Meghan Brown, admin. Fax 797-3130

Crosby, Divide, Pop. 1,064
Divide County SD 1 400/PK-12
PO Box G 58730 701-965-6313
Fax 965-6004
www.divide-co.k12.nd.us
Divide County JSHS 100/7-12
PO Box G 58730 701-965-6392
Russell McKenna, prin. Fax 965-6942

Crystal, Pembina, Pop. 137
Valley-Edinburg SD 118
Supt. — See Edinburg
Valley-Edinburg ES 100/5-8
PO Box 129 58222 701-657-2163
Andrew Currie, prin. Fax 657-2150

Des Lacs, Ward, Pop. 201
United SD 7 600/PK-12
PO Box 117 58733 701-725-4334
Clarke Ranum, supt. Fax 725-4375
www.united.k12.nd.us/
Des Lacs Burlington HS 200/9-12
PO Box 117 58733 701-725-4334
Clarke Ranum, prin. Fax 725-4375

Devils Lake, Ramsey, Pop. 6,910
Devils Lake SD 1 1,500/PK-12
1601 College Dr N 58301 701-662-7640
Scott Privratsky, supt. Fax 662-7646
www.dlschools.org/
Central MS 500/5-8
325 7th St NE 58301 701-662-7664
Jared Schlenker, prin. Fax 662-7649
Devils Lake HS 500/9-12
1601 College Dr N 58301 701-662-1200
Ryan Hanson, prin. Fax 662-1208
Lake Area Career & Technology Center Vo/Tech
205 16th St NW 58301 701-662-7650
Christa Brodina, dir. Fax 662-7658

Lake Region State College Post-Sec.
1801 College Dr N 58301 701-662-1600

Dickinson, Stark, Pop. 17,565
Dickinson SD 1 3,100/PK-12
444 4th St W 58601 701-456-0002
Dr. Douglas Sullivan, supt. Fax 456-0035
www.dickinson.k12.nd.us
Dickinson HS 800/9-12
979 13th Ave W 58601 701-456-0030
Ron Dockter, prin. Fax 456-0019
Hagen JHS 500/7-8
402 4th St W 58601 701-456-0020
Marcus Lewton, prin. Fax 456-0044
Southwest Community HS Adult
1173 3rd Ave W Ste 37 58601 701-456-0042
Kristy Goodall, prin. Fax 456-0042

Dickinson State University Post-Sec.
291 Campus Dr 58601 701-483-2507
Hope Christian Academy 100/PK-12
2891 5th Ave W 58601 701-225-3919
Shane Bradley, prin. Fax 227-1464
Trinity HS 200/7-12
PO Box 1177 58602 701-483-6081
Steve Glasser, pres. Fax 483-1450

Drake, McHenry, Pop. 270
Drake SD 57 100/7-12
PO Box 256 58736 701-465-3732
Steven Heim, supt. Fax 465-3634
Drake/Anamoose HS 100/7-12
PO Box 256 58736 701-465-3732
Travis Engen, prin. Fax 465-3634

Drayton, Pembina, Pop. 819
Drayton SD 19 200/PK-12
108 S 5th St 58225 701-454-3324
Dean Ralston, supt. Fax 454-3485
www.drayton.k12.nd.us
Drayton JSHS 100/7-12
108 S 5th St 58225 701-454-3324
Jennifer Olson, prin. Fax 454-3485

Dunseith, Rolette, Pop. 742
Dunseith SD 1 400/K-12
PO Box 789 58329 701-244-0480
Pat Brenden, supt. Fax 244-5129
www.dunseith.k12.nd.us/
Dunseith HS 200/7-12
PO Box 789 58329 701-244-5249
David Sjol, prin. Fax 244-9708

Edgeley, LaMoure, Pop. 562
Edgeley SD 3 200/K-12
PO Box 37 58433 701-493-2292
Tyler Hanson, supt. Fax 493-2411
www.edgeley.k12.nd.us/
Edgeley HS 100/7-12
PO Box 37 58433 701-493-2292
Todd Kosel, prin. Fax 493-2411

Edinburg, Walsh, Pop. 192
Valley-Edinburg SD 118 200/K-12
PO Box 6 58227 701-993-8312
Mitch Jorgensen, supt. Fax 993-8313
www.edinburg.k12.nd.us
Valley-Edinburg HS 100/9-12
PO Box 6 58227 701-993-8312
Brandon Laxdal, prin. Fax 993-8313
Other Schools – See Crystal

Edmore, Ramsey, Pop. 179
Edmore SD 2 100/K-12
PO Box 188 58330 701-644-2281
Francis Schill, supt. Fax 644-2222
www.edmore.k12.nd.us
Edmore HS 50/9-12
PO Box 188 58330 701-644-2281
Diane Martinson, prin. Fax 644-2222

Elgin, Grant, Pop. 638
Elgin - New Leipzig SD 49 100/K-12
PO Box 70 58533 701-584-2374
Martin Schock, supt. Fax 584-3018
www.elgin.k12.nd.us
Grant County HS 100/7-12
PO Box 70 58533 701-584-2374
Terry Bentz, prin. Fax 584-3018

Ellendale, Dickey, Pop. 1,371
Ellendale SD 40 300/K-12
PO Box 400 58436 701-349-3232
Jeff Fastnacht, supt. Fax 349-3447
www.ellendale.k12.nd.us
Ellendale JSHS 100/7-12
PO Box 400 58436 701-349-3232
Matthew Herman, prin. Fax 349-3447

Trinity Bible College Post-Sec.
50 6th Ave S 58436 701-349-3621

Enderlin, Ransom, Pop. 884
Enderlin Area SD 24 300/K-12
410 Bluff St 58027 701-437-2240
Tom Rettig, supt. Fax 437-2242
www.enderlin.k12.nd.us/
Enderlin Area HS 200/7-12
410 Bluff St 58027 701-437-2240
Timothy Michaelson, prin. Fax 437-2242

Fairmount, Richland, Pop. 360
Fairmount SD 18 100/K-12
PO Box 228 58030 701-474-5469
Ron Stahlecker, supt. Fax 474-5862
www.fairmount.k12.nd.us/
Fairmount HS 50/7-12
PO Box 228 58030 701-474-5469
Jay Townsend, prin. Fax 474-5862

Fargo, Cass, Pop. 103,464
Fargo SD 1 11,900/K-12
415 4th St N 58102 701-446-1000
Dr. Jeff Schatz, supt. Fax 446-1200
www.fargo.k12.nd.us
Davies HS 1,200/9-12
7150 25th St S 58104 701-446-5600
Troy Cody, prin. Fax 446-5910
Discovery MS 900/6-8
1717 40th Ave S 58104 701-446-3300
Dr. Linda Davis, prin. Fax 446-3599
Eielson MS 800/6-8
1601 13th Ave S 58103 701-446-1700
Brad Larson, prin. Fax 446-1799
Fargo North HS 1,000/9-12
801 17th Ave N 58102 701-446-2400
Andrew Dahlen, prin. Fax 446-2799
Fargo South HS 1,100/9-12
1840 15th Ave S 58103 701-446-2000
Dr. Todd Bertsch, prin. Fax 446-2399
Franklin MS 700/6-8
1420 8th St N 58102 701-446-3600
John Nelson, prin. Fax 446-3899
Wilson HS 100/Alt
1305 9th Ave S 58103 701-446-2800
David Burkman, prin. Fax 446-2899
Evaluation & Training Center Adult
424 9th Ave S 58103 701-241-4858
Scott Burtsfield, dir. Fax 241-4896

Josef's School of Hair Design Post-Sec.
627 NP Ave N 58102 701-235-0011
Lynnes Welding Training Post-Sec.
2717 3rd Ave N 58102 701-373-0658
Moler Barber College of HairStyling Post-Sec.
16 8th St S 58103 701-232-6773
North Dakota State University Post-Sec.
PO Box 6050 58108 701-231-8011
Oak Grove Lutheran HS 300/6-12
124 N Terrace N 58102 701-237-0210
Darrin Roach, prin. Fax 297-1993
Rasmussen College Post-Sec.
4012 19th Ave S 58103 701-277-3889
Shanley HS 300/9-12
5600 25th St S 58104 701-893-3200
Sarah Crary, prin. Fax 893-3277
Sullivan MS 200/6-8
5600 25th St S 58104 701-893-3200
Leon Knodel, prin. Fax 893-3277

Fessenden, Wells, Pop. 475
Fessenden-Bowdon SD 25 100/PK-12
PO Box 67 58438 701-547-3296
Nancy Bollingberg, supt.
www.fessenden-bowdon.org
Fessenden-Bowdon HS 50/9-12
PO Box 67 58438 701-547-3296
Warren Strand, prin.

Finley, Steele, Pop. 440
Finley-Sharon SD 19 100/K-12
PO Box 448 58230 701-524-2420
Jeff Larson, supt. Fax 524-2588
www.finleysharonschool.com
Finley-Sharon HS 100/7-12
PO Box 448 58230 701-524-2420
Neil Race, supt. Fax 524-2588

Flasher, Morton, Pop. 229
Flasher SD 39 200/K-12
PO Box 267 58535 701-597-3355
Judy Zins, supt. Fax 597-3781
www.flasher.k12.nd.us
Flasher HS 100/7-12
PO Box 267 58535 701-597-3355
Christina Reynolds, prin. Fax 597-3781

Fordville, Walsh, Pop. 211
Fordville-Lankin SD 5 50/K-12
PO Box 127 58231 701-229-3297
Michael O'Brien, supt. Fax 229-3231
www.fordville-lankin.k12.nd.us/
Fordville Lankin HS 50/7-12
PO Box 127 58231 701-229-3297
Michael O'Brien, prin. Fax 229-3231

Forman, Sargent, Pop. 501
Sargent Central SD 6 200/PK-12
575 5th St SW 58032 701-724-3205
Michael Campbell, supt. Fax 724-3559
www.sargent.k12.nd.us
Sargent Central HS 100/7-12
575 5th St SW 58032 701-724-3205
Steve Thompson, prin. Fax 724-3559

Fort Totten, Benson, Pop. 1,233
Fort Totten SD 30 200/9-12
PO Box 239 58335 701-766-1400
Jeff Olson, supt. Fax 766-1475
Four Winds Community HS 200/9-12
PO Box 239 58335 701-766-1400
John Lohnes, prin. Fax 766-1475

Cankdeska Cikana Community College Post-Sec.
PO Box 269 58335 701-766-4415

Fort Yates, Sioux, Pop. 181
Fort Yates SD 4 200/6-8
9189 Highway 24 58538 701-854-2142
Robyn Baker, admin. Fax 854-7488
Fort Yates MS 200/6-8
9189 Highway 24 58538 701-854-3819
Tomi Kay Phillips, prin. Fax 854-7467

Sitting Bull College Post-Sec.
9299 Highway 24 58538 701-854-8000

Gackle, Logan, Pop. 308
Gackle-Streeter SD 56 100/K-12
PO Box 375 58442 701-485-3692
David Larson, supt. Fax 485-3620
www.gacklestreeter.k12.nd.us/
Gackle-Streeter HS 50/7-12
PO Box 375 58442 701-485-3692
Kurt Hayes, prin. Fax 485-3620

Garrison, McLean, Pop. 1,428
Garrison SD 51 400/PK-12
PO Box 249 58540 701-463-2818
Nicholas Klemisch, supt. Fax 463-2067
www.garrison.k12.nd.us/
Garrison JSHS 200/7-12
PO Box 249 58540 701-463-2818
Steve Dangel, prin. Fax 463-2067

Glenburn, Renville, Pop. 368
Glenburn SD 26 300/PK-12
PO Box 138 58740 701-362-7426
Jerry Erdahl, supt. Fax 362-7349
www.glenburn.k12.nd.us/
Glenburn HS 100/7-12
PO Box 138 58740 701-362-7426
Larry Derr, prin. Fax 362-7349

Glenfield, Foster, Pop. 91
Midkota SD 7
Supt. — See Binford
Midkota HS 100/7-12
PO Box 98 58443 701-785-2126
Les Dale, prin. Fax 785-2226

Glen Ullin, Morton, Pop. 794
Glen Ullin SD 48 200/K-12
PO Box 548 58631 701-348-3590
John Barry, supt. Fax 348-3084
www.glen-ullin.k12.nd.us
Glen Ullin HS 100/9-12
PO Box 548 58631 701-348-3590
Peter Remboldt, prin. Fax 348-3084

Goodrich, Sheridan, Pop. 98
Goodrich SD 16 50/K-12
PO Box 159 58444 701-884-2469
Rodney Scherbenske, supt. Fax 884-2496
Goodrich HS 50/7-12
PO Box 159 58444 701-884-2469
Rodney Scherbenske, prin. Fax 884-2496

Grafton, Walsh, Pop. 4,231
Grafton SD 3 900/K-12
1548 School Rd 58237 701-352-1930
Jack Maus, supt. Fax 352-1943
www.grafton.k12.nd.us
Grafton Central MS 300/5-8
1556 School Rd 58237 701-352-1469
Mike Kaiser, prin. Fax 352-1120
Grafton HS 300/9-12
1548 School Rd 58237 701-352-1930
Darren Albrecht, prin. Fax 352-1943
North Valley Area Career & Tech Vo/Tech
1540 School Rd 58237 701-352-3705
Michael Hanson, dir. Fax 352-3170

Grand Forks, Grand Forks, Pop. 51,662
Grand Forks SD 1 6,900/K-12
PO Box 6000 58206 701-746-2200
Dr. Larry P. Nybladh, supt. Fax 772-7739
www.gfschools.org
Central HS 1,000/9-12
115 N 4th St 58203 701-746-2375
Buck Kasowski, prin. Fax 746-2387
Community Alternative HS 100/Alt
500 Stanford Rd 58203 701-795-2777
Terry Bohan, prin. Fax 795-2770
Red River HS 1,100/9-12
2211 17th Ave S 58201 701-746-2400
Kris Arason, prin. Fax 746-2406
Schroeder MS 500/6-8
800 32nd Ave S 58201 701-746-2330
Catherine Gillach, prin. Fax 746-2332
South MS 600/6-8
1999 47th Ave S 58201 701-746-2345
Nancy Dutot, prin. Fax 746-2355
Valley MS 400/6-8
2100 5th Ave N 58203 701-746-2360
Todd Selk, prin. Fax 746-2363

Josef's School of Hair Design Post-Sec.
2011 S Washington St 58201 701-772-2728
North Dakota School for the Blind Post-Sec.
500 Stanford Rd 58203
University of North Dakota Post-Sec.
264 Centennial Dr 58202 701-777-3000

Granville, McHenry, Pop. 241
TGU SD 60
Supt. — See Towner
TGU Granville HS 100/7-12
210 6th St SW 58741 701-728-6641
Tonya Hunskor, prin. Fax 728-6386

Grenora, Williams, Pop. 241
Grenora SD 99 200/K-12
PO Box 38 58845 701-694-2711
Troy Walters, supt. Fax 694-2717
www.grenora.k12.nd.us/
Grenora HS 100/7-12
PO Box 38 58845 701-694-2711
Troy Walters, prin. Fax 694-2717

Gwinner, Sargent, Pop. 749
North Sargent SD 3 200/K-12
PO Box 289 58040 701-678-2492
Randall Cale, supt. Fax 678-2311
www.northsargent.k12.nd.us
North Sargent HS 100/7-12
PO Box 289 58040 701-678-2492
Dawn Osborn, prin. Fax 678-2311

Halliday, Dunn, Pop. 185
Halliday SD 19 50/K-12
PO Box 188 58636 701-938-4391
Myron Schweitzer, supt. Fax 938-4373
www.halliday.k12.nd.us
Halliday HS 50/7-12
PO Box 188 58636 701-938-4391
Myron Schweitzer, prin. Fax 938-4373

Hankinson, Richland, Pop. 903
Hankinson SD 8 300/K-12
PO Box 220 58041 701-242-7516
Chad Benson, supt. Fax 242-7434
www.hankinson.k12.nd.us
Hankinson HS 100/7-12
PO Box 220 58041 701-242-7138
Kent Dennis, prin. Fax 242-7434

Harvey, Wells, Pop. 1,771
Harvey SD 38 300/K-12
811 Burke Ave 58341 701-324-2265
Daniel Stutlien, supt. Fax 324-4414
www.harvey.k12.nd.us/
Harvey HS 100/7-12
200 North St E 58341 701-324-2267
Justin Stanley, prin. Fax 324-2424

Hatton, Traill, Pop. 763
Hatton Eielson SD 7 200/K-12
PO Box 200 58240 701-543-3455
Kevin Rogers, supt. Fax 543-3459
www.hattonk12.com
Hatton Eielson HS 100/7-12
PO Box 200 58240 701-543-3455
Lucas Soine, prin. Fax 543-3459

Hazelton, Emmons, Pop. 234
Hazelton-Moffit-Braddock SD 6 100/K-12
PO Box 209 58544 701-782-6231
Tracy Hanzal, supt. Fax 782-6245
www.hmb.k12.nd.us
Hazelton-Moffit-Braddock HS 50/7-12
PO Box 209 58544 701-782-6231
Tracy Hanzal, prin. Fax 782-6245

Hazen, Mercer, Pop. 2,396
Hazen SD 3 600/PK-12
PO Box 487 58545 701-748-2345
Ken Miller, supt. Fax 748-2342
www.hazen.k12.nd.us
Hazen HS 200/9-12
PO Box 487 58545 701-748-2345
Monty Mayer, prin. Fax 748-2342
Hazen JHS 100/7-8
PO Box 487 58545 701-748-6649
Ed Boger, prin. Fax 748-6650

Hebron, Morton, Pop. 732
Hebron SD 13 200/K-12
PO Box Q 58638 701-878-4442
Kevin Nelson, supt. Fax 878-4345
www.hebron.k12.nd.us/
Hebron HS 100/7-12
PO Box Q 58638 701-878-4442
Stephanie Hochhalter, prin. Fax 878-4345

Hettinger, Adams, Pop. 1,214
Hettinger SD 13 300/PK-12
PO Box 1188 58639 701-567-4502
Larry Sebastian, supt. Fax 567-5094
www.hettinger.k12.nd.us
Hettinger HS 100/7-12
PO Box 1188 58639 701-567-4502
Ryan Moser, prin. Fax 567-5094

Hillsboro, Traill, Pop. 1,587
Hillsboro SD 9 400/PK-12
PO Box 579 58045 701-636-4360
Paula Suda, supt. Fax 636-4362
www.hillsborok12.com
Hillsboro JSHS 200/7-12
PO Box 579 58045 701-636-4360
Terry Baesler, prin. Fax 636-4362

Hope, Steele, Pop. 258
Hope SD 10 100/7-12
PO Box 100 58046 701-945-2473
Hy Schlieve, supt. Fax 945-2511
www.hope-page.k12.nd.us/
Hope-Page HS 100/7-12
PO Box 100 58046 701-945-2473
Angie Zerface, prin. Fax 945-2511

Hunter, Cass, Pop. 255
Northern Cass SD 97 500/K-12
16021 18th St SE 58048 701-874-2322
Dr. Cory Steiner, supt. Fax 874-2422
www.northerncass.k12.nd.us
Northern Cass HS 200/7-12
16021 18th St SE 58048 701-874-2322
Ryan Lyson, prin. Fax 874-2422

Inkster, Grand Forks, Pop. 47
Midway SD 128 200/PK-12
3202 33rd Ave NE, 701-869-2432
Dr. Roger Abbe Ed.D., supt. Fax 869-2688
www.midwayk12.org
Midway HS 100/9-12
3202 33rd Ave NE, 701-869-2432
Ryan Baron, prin. Fax 869-2688

Jamestown, Stutsman, Pop. 15,252
Jamestown SD 1 2,100/PK-12
PO Box 269 58402 701-252-1950
Robert Lech, supt. Fax 251-2011
www.jamestown.k12.nd.us
Jamestown HS 700/9-12
PO Box 269 58402 701-952-4003
Adam Gehlhar, prin. Fax 252-8580
Jamestown MS 500/6-8
PO Box 269 58402 701-252-0317
Ryan Harty, prin. Fax 252-3310

James Valley Area Vo-Tech Center — Vo/Tech
PO Box 269 58402 — 701-252-8841
John Lynch, prin. — Fax 252-3646

University of Jamestown — Post-Sec.
6000 College Ln 58405 — 701-252-3467

Kenmare, Ward, Pop. 1,084
Kenmare SD 28 — 300/K-12
PO Box 667 58746 — 701-385-4996
Duane Mueller, supt. — Fax 385-4390
www.kenmare.k12.nd.us/
Kenmare JSHS — 100/7-12
PO Box 667 58746 — 701-385-4996
Sarah Beckedahl, prin. — Fax 385-4390

Killdeer, Dunn, Pop. 734
Killdeer SD 16 — 400/PK-12
PO Box 579 58640 — 701-764-5877
Gary Wilz, supt. — Fax 764-5648
www.killdeer.k12.nd.us
Killdeer HS — 200/7-12
PO Box 579 58640 — 701-764-5877
Karter Kleeman, prin. — Fax 764-5648

Kindred, Cass, Pop. 678
Kindred SD 2 — 700/K-12
255 Dakota St 58051 — 701-428-3177
Steven Hall, supt. — Fax 428-3149
www.kindred.k12.nd.us/
Kindred HS — 300/7-12
255 Dakota St 58051 — 701-428-3177
Kent Packer, prin. — Fax 428-3149

Kulm, LaMoure, Pop. 352
Kulm SD 7 — 100/PK-12
PO Box G 58456 — 701-647-2303
Tami Kramlich, supt. — Fax 647-2304
www.kulmschool.com
Kulm JSHS — 50/7-12
PO Box G 58456 — 701-647-2303
Justin Thorpe, prin. — Fax 647-2457

Lakota, Nelson, Pop. 665
Lakota SD 66 — 200/K-12
PO Box 388 58344 — 701-247-2992
Joseph Harder, supt. — Fax 247-2910
www.lakota.k12.nd.us
Lakota JSHS — 100/7-12
PO Box 388 58344 — 701-247-2992
Joseph Harder, prin. — Fax 247-2910

LaMoure, LaMoure, Pop. 884
La Moure SD 8 — 300/K-12
PO Box 656 58458 — 701-883-5396
Mitch Carlson, supt. — Fax 883-5144
www.lamoure.k12.nd.us/
La Moure JSHS — 100/7-12
PO Box 656 58458 — 701-883-5397
Andrew DelaBarre, prin. — Fax 883-5144

Langdon, Cavalier, Pop. 1,855
Langdon Area SD 23 — 400/PK-12
715 14th Ave 58249 — 701-256-5291
Mark Mindt, supt. — Fax 256-2606
www.langdon.k12.nd.us
Langdon Area JSHS — 200/7-12
715 14th Ave 58249 — 701-256-5291
Daryl Timian, prin. — Fax 256-2606

Larimore, Grand Forks, Pop. 1,320
Larimore SD 44 — 400/PK-12
PO Box 769 58251 — 701-343-2366
Dr. Roger Abbe, supt. — Fax 343-2908
www.larimorek12.org
Larimore JSHS — 200/7-12
PO Box 769 58251 — 701-343-2366
Kal Triplett, prin. — Fax 343-2908

Leeds, Benson, Pop. 425
Leeds SD 6 — 200/PK-12
PO Box 189 58346 — 701-466-2461
Robert Bubach, supt. — Fax 466-2422
leedsdistrict.new.rschooltoday.com
Leeds JSHS — 100/9-12
PO Box 189 58346 — 701-466-2461
Robert Bubach, prin. — Fax 466-2422

Lidgerwood, Richland, Pop. 649
Lidgerwood SD 28 — 200/PK-12
PO Box 468 58053 — 701-538-7341
Doug Jacobson, supt. — Fax 538-4483
www.lidgerwood.k12.nd.us/
Lidgerwood HS — 100/7-12
PO Box 468 58053 — 701-538-7341
Jeremy Popp, prin. — Fax 538-4483

Lignite, Burke, Pop. 154
Burke Central SD 36 — 100/K-12
PO Box 91 58752 — 701-933-2821
Sherry Lalum, supt. — Fax 933-2823
www.burkecentral.k12.nd.us
Burke Central HS — 100/7-12
PO Box 91 58752 — 701-933-2821
Erika Landro, prin. — Fax 933-2823

Linton, Emmons, Pop. 1,084
Linton SD 36 — 300/PK-12
PO Box 970 58552 — 701-254-4138
Alan Bjornson, supt. — Fax 254-4313
www.linton.k12.nd.us
Linton HS — 100/9-12
PO Box 970 58552 — 701-254-4717
Alan Bjornson, prin. — Fax 254-4313

Lisbon, Ransom, Pop. 2,132
Lisbon SD 19 — 600/K-12
PO Box 593 58054 — 701-683-4106
Steven Johnson, supt. — Fax 683-4414
www.lisbon.k12.nd.us/
Lisbon HS — 200/9-12
PO Box 593 58054 — 701-683-4106
Patrick Adair, prin. — Fax 683-4414
Lisbon MS — 200/5-8
PO Box 593 58054 — 701-683-4108
Warren Michael, prin. — Fax 683-4111

Mc Clusky, Sheridan, Pop. 368
McClusky SD 19 — 100/K-12
PO Box 499 58463 — 701-363-2470
Dr. Cheri Poitra, supt. — Fax 363-2239
www.mcclusky.k12.nd.us
McClusky JSHS — 50/7-12
PO Box 499 58463 — 701-363-2470
Daniel Klemisch, prin. — Fax 363-2239

Maddock, Benson, Pop. 380
Maddock SD 9 — 200/K-12
PO Box 398 58348 — 701-438-2531
Kimberly Anderson, supt. — Fax 438-2620
Maddock HS — 100/9-12
PO Box 398 58348 — 701-438-2531
Kim Anderson, prin. — Fax 438-2620

Mandan, Morton, Pop. 18,009
Mandan SD 1 — 3,500/K-12
901 Division St NW 58554 — 701-751-6500
Dr. Mike Bitz, supt. — Fax 751-6674
www.mandan.k12.nd.us
Brave Center Academy — 50/Alt
901 Division St NW 58554 — 701-751-6500
Perry Just, prin. — Fax 751-6674
Mandan HS — 1,000/9-12
905 8th Ave NW 58554 — 701-751-6501
Mark Andresen, prin. — Fax 751-6675
Mandan MS — 800/6-8
2901 12th Ave NW 58554 — 701-751-6502
Ryan Leingang, prin. — Fax 751-6682

Marmot SD — 100/K-12
701 16th Ave SW 58554 — 701-328-6707
Penny Veit-Hetletved, supt. — Fax 328-6651
Marmot HS, 701 16th Ave SW 58554 — 100/9-12
Michelle Pfaff, prin. — 701-667-1445

Mandaree, McKenzie, Pop. 592
Mandaree SD 36 — 200/PK-12
PO Box 488 58757 — 701-759-3311
Carolyn Bluestone, supt. — Fax 759-3112
www.mandaree.k12.nd.us
Mandaree HS — 50/9-12
PO Box 488 58757 — 701-759-3311
John Bruce, prin. — Fax 759-3112

Marion, LaMoure, Pop. 131
Litchville-Marion SD 46 — 100/PK-12
PO Box 159 58466 — 701-669-2262
Steven Larson, supt. — Fax 669-2316
www.litchville-marion.k12.nd.us/
Litchville-Marion JSHS — 100/7-12
PO Box 159 58466 — 701-669-2261
Marc Ritteman, prin. — Fax 669-2316

Max, McLean, Pop. 324
Max SD 50 — 200/K-12
PO Box 297 58759 — 701-679-2685
Pat Windish, supt. — Fax 679-2245
www.max.k12.nd.us/
Max HS — 100/7-12
PO Box 297 58759 — 701-679-2685
Robert Randel, prin. — Fax 679-2245

Mayville, Traill, Pop. 1,819
May-Port CG SD 14 — 500/K-12
900 Main St W 58257 — 701-788-2281
Michael Bradner, supt. — Fax 788-2959
www.mayportcg.com
Mayville-Portland CG HS — 200/9-12
900 Main St W 58257 — 701-788-2281
Scott Ulland, prin. — Fax 788-2959
Mayville-Portland CG MS — 100/6-8
900 Main St W 58257 — 701-788-2281
Scott Ulland, prin. — Fax 788-2959

Mayville State University — Post-Sec.
330 3rd St NE 58257 — 800-437-4104

Medina, Stutsman, Pop. 298
Medina SD 3 — 200/PK-12
PO Box 547 58467 — 701-486-3121
Brian Christopherson, supt. — Fax 486-3138
www.medina.k12.nd.us/
Medina JSHS — 100/7-12
PO Box 547 58467 — 701-486-3121
Brian Christopherson, admin. — Fax 486-3138

Milnor, Sargent, Pop. 648
Milnor SD 2 — 200/K-12
PO Box 369 58060 — 701-427-5237
Chris Larson M.Ed., supt. — Fax 427-5304
www.milnor.k12.nd.us/
Milnor HS — 100/7-12
PO Box 369 58060 — 701-427-5237
Seth Engelstad, prin. — Fax 427-5304
Sundale Colony S — 50/K-10
PO Box 369 58060 — 701-427-5237
Chelsey Pederson M.Ed., prin. — Fax 427-5304

Minnewaukan, Benson, Pop. 217
Minnewaukan SD 5 — 200/PK-12
4675 Highway 281 58351 — 701-473-5306
Jean Callahan, supt. — Fax 473-5420
www.minnewaukan.k12.nd.us
Minnewaukan S — 200/PK-12
4675 Highway 281 58351 — 701-473-5306
Jean Callahan, admin. — Fax 473-5420

Minot, Ward, Pop. 39,893
Minot SD 1 — 7,500/PK-12
215 2nd St SE 58701 — 701-857-4400
Dr. Mark Vollmer, supt. — Fax 857-4432
www.minot.k12.nd.us/
Central Campus HS — 1,000/9-10
215 1st St SE 58701 — 701-857-4660
Keith Altendorf, prin. — Fax 857-4636
Hill MS — 800/6-8
1000 6th St SW 58701 — 701-857-4477
Michael Arlien, prin. — Fax 857-4479
Magic City Campus HS — 900/11-12
1100 11th Ave SW 58701 — 701-857-4500
Scott Faul, prin. — Fax 857-4521
Ramstad MS — 600/6-8
1215 36th Ave NW 58703 — 701-857-4466
Ione Sautner, prin. — Fax 857-4464
Souris River Campus Alternative HS — 100/Alt
1510 University Ave W 58703 — 701-857-4496
Ned Strand, prin. — Fax 857-4508
Other Schools – See Minot AFB

Nedrose SD 4 — 200/K-12
6900 Highway 2 E 58701 — 701-838-5552
Charles Miller, admin. — Fax 852-6971
www.tinyurl.com/nedrose
Nedrose HS, 5705 15th Ave SE 58701 — 6-12
Matthew Norby, prin. — 701-838-5550

Bishop Ryan S — 400/PK-12
316 11th Ave NW 58703 — 701-852-4004
Darwin Routledje, prin. — Fax 839-4651
Headquarters Academy of Hair Design — Post-Sec.
108 Main St S 58701 — 701-852-8329
Minot State University — Post-Sec.
500 University Ave W 58707 — 701-858-3000
Our Redeemer's Christian S — 300/PK-12
700 16th Ave SE 58701 — 701-839-0772
Charles Strand, admin.
Trinity Medical Center — Post-Sec.
3 Burdick Expy 58701 — 701-857-5000

Minot AFB, Ward, Pop. 5,179
Minot SD 1
Supt. — See Minot
Memorial MS — 100/7-8
1 Rocket Rd 58704 — 701-727-3300
Ed Sehn, prin. — Fax 727-3303

Minto, Walsh, Pop. 603
Minto SD 20 — 200/PK-12
200 4th St 58261 — 701-248-3479
Linda Lutovsky, supt. — Fax 248-3001
www.minto.k12.nd.us
Minto HS — 100/7-12
200 4th St 58261 — 701-248-3479
Shane Robinson, prin. — Fax 248-3001

Mohall, Renville, Pop. 775
Mohall-Lansford-Sherwood SD 1 — 300/PK-12
PO Box 187 58761 — 701-756-6660
Gaillord Peltier, supt. — Fax 756-6549
www.mls.k12.nd.us
MLS - Mohall HS — 100/7-12
PO Box 187 58761 — 701-756-6660
Rob Voigt, prin. — Fax 756-6549

Montpelier, Stutsman, Pop. 87
Montpelier SD 14 — 100/PK-12
214 7th Ave 58472 — 701-489-3348
Jerry Waagen, supt. — Fax 489-3349
www.montpelier.k12.nd.us
Montpelier HS — 100/7-12
214 7th Ave 58472 — 701-489-3348
James Bear, prin. — Fax 489-3349

Mott, Hettinger, Pop. 709
Mott-Regent SD 1 — 200/K-12
205 Dakota Ave 58646 — 701-824-2795
Viola Lafontaine, supt. — Fax 824-2249
mott.nd.schoolwebpages.com
Mott / Regent HS — 100/7-12
205 Dakota Ave 58646 — 701-824-2795
Adam Hill, prin. — Fax 824-2249

Munich, Cavalier, Pop. 209
Munich SD 19 — 100/PK-12
PO Box 39 58352 — 701-682-5321
Dr. Charles Dunlop, supt. — Fax 682-5323
www.munich.k12.nd.us/
Munich HS — 50/9-12
PO Box 39 58352 — 701-682-5321
Daniel Ludvigson, prin. — Fax 682-5323

Napoleon, Logan, Pop. 791
Napoleon SD 2 — 300/K-12
PO Box 69 58561 — 701-754-2244
Richard Bjerklie, supt. — Fax 754-2233
www.napoleon.k12.nd.us/
Napoleon HS — 100/7-12
PO Box 69 58561 — 701-754-2244
Holly Randall, prin. — Fax 754-2233

Newburg, Bottineau, Pop. 110
Newburg - United SD 54 — 100/PK-12
PO Box 427 58762 — 701-272-6151
Jason Kersten, supt. — Fax 272-6117
www.newburg.k12.nd.us/
Newburg United HS — 50/7-12
PO Box 427 58762 — 701-272-6151
Bob Beaudrie, prin. — Fax 272-6117

New England, Hettinger, Pop. 588
New England SD 9 — 200/K-12
PO Box 307 58647 — 701-579-4160
Kelly Koppinger, supt. — Fax 579-4462
www.new-england.k12.nd.us
New England HS — 100/7-12
PO Box 307 58647 — 701-579-4160
Lawrence Lechler, prin. — Fax 579-4462

New Rockford, Eddy, Pop. 1,375
New Rockford-Sheyenne SD 2 300/K-12
437 1st Ave N 58356 701-947-5036
Jill Louters, supt. Fax 947-2195
www.newrockford-sheyenne.k12.nd.us
New Rockford-Sheyenne HS 200/7-12
437 1st Ave N 58356 701-947-5036
Avolt Baumbach, prin. Fax 947-2195

New Salem, Morton, Pop. 936
New Salem-Almont SD 49 300/PK-12
PO Box 378 58563 701-843-7610
Michael Severson, supt. Fax 843-7011
www.newsalem.k12.nd.us/
New Salem-Almont HS 200/7-12
PO Box 378 58563 701-843-7610
Michael Gilbertson, prin. Fax 843-7011

New Town, Mountrail, Pop. 1,853
New Town SD 1 700/K-12
PO Box 700 58763 701-627-3650
Marc Bluestone, supt. Fax 627-3689
www.new-town.k12.nd.us
New Town HS 200/9-12
PO Box 700 58763 701-627-3658
John Gartner, prin. Fax 627-3689
New Town MS 200/6-8
PO Box 700 58763 701-627-3660
Andy Decoteau, prin. Fax 627-3689

Fort Berthold Community College Post-Sec.
PO Box 490 58763 701-627-4738

Northwood, Grand Forks, Pop. 931
Northwood SD 129 200/K-12
420 Trojan Rd 58267 701-587-5221
Keith Arneson, supt. Fax 587-5423
www.northwoodk12.com
Northwood HS 100/7-12
420 Trojan Rd 58267 701-587-5221
Daniel Azure, prin. Fax 587-5423

Oakes, Dickey, Pop. 1,836
Oakes SD 41 500/PK-12
804 Main Ave 58474 701-742-3234
Joshua Johnson, supt. Fax 742-2812
www.oakes.k12.nd.us
Oakes JSHS 200/7-12
804 Main Ave 58474 701-742-3234
Dawn Osborn, prin. Fax 742-2812
Other Schools – See Wahpeton

Park River, Walsh, Pop. 1,393
Park River Area SD 8 300/K-12
PO Box 240 58270 701-284-7164
Kirk Ham, supt. Fax 284-7936
www.parkriver.k12.nd.us/
Park River HS 100/7-12
PO Box 240 58270 701-284-7164
Aaron Schramm, prin. Fax 284-7936

Parshall, Mountrail, Pop. 852
Parshall SD 3 300/PK-12
PO Box 158 58770 701-862-3129
Dr. John Weidner, supt. Fax 862-3801
www.parshall.k12.nd.us
Parshall JSHS 100/7-12
PO Box 158 58770 701-862-3129
Mark Grueneich, prin. Fax 862-3801

Pembina, Pembina, Pop. 576
North Border SD 100
Supt. — See Walhalla
North Border Pembina HS 50/9-12
155 S 3rd St 58271 701-825-6261
Lee Beattie, prin. Fax 825-6645

Petersburg, Nelson, Pop. 192
Dakota Prairie SD 1 300/K-12
PO Box 37 58272 701-345-8233
Janet Edlund, supt. Fax 345-8251
www.dakotaprairiek12nd.org
Dakota Prairie HS 100/7-12
PO Box 37 58272 701-345-8233
Jay Slade, prin. Fax 345-8251

Pingree, Stutsman, Pop. 59
Pingree-Buchanan SD 10 100/K-12
111 Lincoln Ave 58476 701-252-5563
Daren Christianson, supt. Fax 252-2245
www.pingree.k12.nd.us/
Pingree Buchanan JSHS 100/7-12
111 Lincoln Ave 58476 701-252-5563
Daren Christianson, prin. Fax 252-2245

Plaza, Mountrail, Pop. 170
Lewis and Clark SD 161
Supt. — See Berthold
North Shore Plaza S 100/PK-12
PO Box 38 58771 701-497-3734
Todd Lee, prin. Fax 497-3401

Powers Lake, Burke, Pop. 279
Powers Lake SD 27 100/K-12
PO Box 346 58773 701-464-5432
Sue Gunderson, supt. Fax 464-5435
www.powerslake.k12.nd.us
Powers Lake JSHS 50/6-12
PO Box 346 58773 701-464-5432
Seth Wisthoff, prin. Fax 464-5435

Ray, Williams, Pop. 585
Nesson SD 2 200/K-12
PO Box 564 58849 701-568-3301
Benjamin Schafer, supt. Fax 568-3302
www.ray.k12.nd.us
Ray HS 100/7-12
PO Box 564 58849 701-568-3301
Arley Larson, prin. Fax 568-3302

Richardton, Stark, Pop. 528
Richardton-Taylor SD 34 300/K-12
320 Raider Rd 58652 701-974-2111
Brent Bautz, supt. Fax 974-2161
www.richardton-taylor.k12.nd.us
Richardton-Taylor HS 100/7-12
PO Box 289 58652 701-974-2111
Dr. Misti Vogle, prin. Fax 974-2161

Rolette, Rolette, Pop. 566
Rolette SD 29 100/K-12
PO Box 97 58366 701-246-3595
Wade Sherwin, supt. Fax 246-3452
www.rolettepublicschools.com
Rolette JSHS 50/7-12
PO Box 97 58366 701-246-3595
Katie Crofutt, prin. Fax 246-3452

Rolla, Rolette, Pop. 1,226
Mt. Pleasant SD 4 300/PK-12
201 5th St NE 58367 701-477-3151
Kevin Baumgarn, supt. Fax 477-5001
www.rolla.k12.nd.us
Mt. Pleasant HS 100/7-12
201 5th St NE 58367 701-477-3151
Randy Loing, prin. Fax 477-5001

Rugby, Pierce, Pop. 2,841
Rugby SD 5 500/PK-12
1123 S Main Ave 58368 701-776-5201
Michael McNeff, supt. Fax 776-5091
www.rugby.k12.nd.us/
North Central Area Career & Tech Ctr Vo/Tech
1123 S Main Ave 58368 701-776-7208
Kathy McCracken, dir. Fax 776-5091
Rugby JSHS 300/7-12
1123 S Main Ave 58368 701-776-5201
Jared Blikre, prin. Fax 776-5091

Saint John, Rolette, Pop. 309
Saint John SD 3 400/K-12
PO Box 200 58369 701-477-5651
Donald Davis, supt. Fax 477-8195
www.stjohn.k12.nd.us
Saint John HS 100/9-12
PO Box 200 58369 701-477-5651
Charles Anderson, prin. Fax 477-8195

Saint Thomas, Pembina, Pop. 330
Saint Thomas SD 43 100/K-12
PO Box 150 58276 701-257-6424
Darren Albrecht, supt. Fax 257-6461
www.stthomas.k12.nd.us
Saint Thomas HS 50/7-12
PO Box 150 58276 701-257-6424
David Hanson, prin. Fax 257-6461

Sawyer, Ward, Pop. 354
Sawyer SD 16 100/K-12
25 1st Ave SW 58781 701-624-5167
Dr. Wayne Trottier, supt. Fax 624-5482
www.sawyer.k12.nd.us
Sawyer HS 100/7-12
25 1st Ave SW 58781 701-624-5167
Thomas Warman, prin. Fax 624-5482

Scranton, Bowman, Pop. 279
Scranton SD 33 100/K-12
PO Box 126 58653 701-275-8897
John Pretzer, supt. Fax 275-6221
www.scrantonpublicschool.homestead.com/
Scranton HS 100/7-12
PO Box 126 58653 701-275-8266
John Pretzer, prin. Fax 275-6221

Selfridge, Sioux, Pop. 151
Selfridge SD 8 100/K-12
PO Box 45 58568 701-422-3353
James Gross, supt. Fax 422-3348
www.selfridge.k12.nd.us
Selfridge HS 50/7-12
PO Box 45 58568 701-422-3353
Kristi Miller, prin. Fax 422-3348

Solen, Sioux, Pop. 73
Solen SD 3 200/K-12
PO Box 128 58570 701-445-3331
Justin Fryer, supt. Fax 445-3323
Solen HS 100/7-12
PO Box 128 58570 701-445-3331
Jeffrey Brandt, prin. Fax 445-3323

South Heart, Stark, Pop. 298
South Heart SD 9 200/PK-12
PO Box 159 58655 701-677-5671
Calvin Dean, supt. Fax 677-5616
www.southheart.k12.nd.us/
South Heart HS 100/7-12
PO Box 159 58655 701-677-5671
Scott Jung, prin. Fax 677-5616

Stanley, Mountrail, Pop. 1,448
Stanley SD 2 600/K-12
PO Box 10 58784 701-628-3811
Tim Holte, supt. Fax 628-3358
www.stanley.k12.nd.us/
Stanley JSHS 300/7-12
PO Box 10 58784 701-628-2342
Jim Swegarden, prin. Fax 628-3358

Starkweather, Ramsey, Pop. 114
Starkweather SD 44 100/PK-12
PO Box 45 58377 701-292-4381
Larry Volk, supt. Fax 292-5714
www.starkweather.k12.nd.us
Starkweather HS 50/7-12
PO Box 45 58377 701-292-4381
Lindsay Bundermann, prin. Fax 292-5714

Steele, Kidder, Pop. 715
Kidder County SD 1 400/K-12
PO Box 380 58482 701-475-2243
Rick Diegel, supt. Fax 475-2737
www.steele-dawson.k12.nd.us/
Steele-Dawson HS 200/7-12
PO Box 380 58482 701-475-2243
Darnell Schmidt, prin. Fax 475-2737
Other Schools – See Tappen

Strasburg, Emmons, Pop. 408
Strasburg SD 15 100/PK-12
PO Box 308 58573 701-336-2667
Tracy Mittleider, supt. Fax 336-7490
www.strasburg.k12.nd.us/
Strasburg JSHS 100/7-12
PO Box 308 58573 701-336-2667
Bryan Schumacher, prin. Fax 336-7490

Surrey, Ward, Pop. 914
Surrey SD 41 400/PK-12
PO Box 40 58785 701-838-1262
Terry Voiles, supt. Fax 838-8822
www.surrey.k12.nd.us
Surrey HS 200/7-12
PO Box 40 58785 701-838-3282
David Gerding, prin. Fax 838-1262

Tappen, Kidder, Pop. 197
Kidder County SD 1
Supt. — See Steele
Tappen HS 50/9-12
PO Box 127 58487 701-327-4256
Arlin Fylling, prin. Fax 327-4255

Thompson, Grand Forks, Pop. 982
Thompson SD 61 500/K-12
424 3rd St 58278 701-599-2765
John Maus, supt. Fax 599-2819
www.tps-k12.org
Thompson HS 200/7-12
424 3rd St 58278 701-599-2765
John Maus, supt. Fax 599-2819

Tioga, Williams, Pop. 1,208
Tioga SD 15 500/K-12
PO Box 279 58852 701-664-2333
Carolyn Eide, supt. Fax 664-3356
www.tioga.k12.nd.us
Tioga HS 200/7-12
PO Box 279 58852 701-664-3606
Brodie Odegaard, prin. Fax 664-3356

Tower City, Cass, Pop. 251
Maple Valley SD 4 200/K-12
PO Box 168 58071 701-749-2570
Dr. Brian Wolf, supt. Fax 749-2313
www.maple-valley.k12.nd.us/
Maple Valley HS 100/7-12
PO Box 168 58071 701-749-2570
Dr. Michael Nygaard, prin. Fax 749-2313

Towner, McHenry, Pop. 528
TGU SD 60 300/PK-12
PO Box 270 58788 701-537-5414
Debby Marshall, supt. Fax 537-5413
www.tgu.k12.nd.us
TGU Towner HS 100/7-12
PO Box 270 58788 701-537-5414
Erik Sveet, prin. Fax 537-5413
Other Schools – See Granville

Trenton, Williams
Eight Mile SD 6 200/K-12
PO Box 239 58853 701-774-8221
Darryl LaDue, supt. Fax 774-8040
www.eight-mile.k12.nd.us
Eight Mile HS 100/7-12
PO Box 239 58853 701-774-8221
Steve Morben, prin. Fax 774-8040

Turtle Lake, McLean, Pop. 570
Turtle Lake - Mercer SD 72 200/K-12
PO Box 160 58575 701-448-2365
Dick Schaffan, supt. Fax 448-2368
www.tlm.k12.nd.us/
Turtle Lake Mercer HS 100/7-12
PO Box 160 58575 701-448-2365
Sheila Schlafmann, prin. Fax 448-2368

Underwood, McLean, Pop. 762
Underwood SD 8 200/PK-12
PO Box 100 58576 701-442-3201
Brandt Dick, supt. Fax 442-3274
sites.google.com/a/underwoodschool.org/ups/
Underwood HS 100/7-12
PO Box 100 58576 701-442-3201
Lee Weisgarber, prin. Fax 442-3274

Valley City, Barnes, Pop. 6,490
Valley City SD 2 1,100/PK-12
460 Central Ave N 58072 701-845-0483
Joshua Johnson, supt. Fax 845-4109
www.valley-city.k12.nd.us
Sheyenne Valley Area Career & Tech Ctr. Vo/Tech
801 Valley Ave SE 58072 701-845-0256
Jeffrey Bopp, prin. Fax 845-0003
Valley City HS 300/9-12
460 Central Ave N 58072 701-845-0483
Kristi Brandt, prin. Fax 845-2762
Valley City JHS 200/7-8
460 Central Ave N 58072 701-845-0483
Daniel Larson, prin. Fax 845-2762

Valley City State University Post-Sec.
101 College St SW 58072 800-532-8641

Velva, McHenry, Pop. 1,077
Velva SD 1 400/K-12
PO Box 179 58790 701-338-2022
Dave Schoch, supt. Fax 338-2023
www.velva.k12.nd.us
Velva HS 200/7-12
PO Box 179 58790 701-338-2022
Kelly Mogen, prin. Fax 338-2023

Wahpeton, Richland, Pop. 7,637
Oakes SD 41
Supt. — See Oakes
SE Rgn Career & Tech-Oakes Ctr Vo/Tech
2101 9th St N 58075 701-642-8701
Dan Rood, dir. Fax 642-3811

Wahpeton SD 37 1,200/PK-12
PO Box 10 58074 701-642-6741
Rick Jacobson, supt. Fax 642-4908
www.wahpeton.k12.nd.us
SE Region Career & Tech-Wahpeton Ctr Vo/Tech
2101 9th St N 58075 701-642-8701
Dan Rood, dir. Fax 642-3811
Wahpeton HS 400/9-12
PO Box 10 58074 701-642-2604
Ned Clooten, prin. Fax 642-1330
Wahpeton MS 300/6-8
PO Box 10 58074 701-642-6687
Steve Hockert, prin. Fax 642-5622

North Dakota State College of Science Post-Sec.
800 6th St N 58076 800-342-4325

Walhalla, Pembina, Pop. 969
North Border SD 100 300/PK-12
PO Box 558 58282 701-549-3751
Dr. Paul Stremick, supt. Fax 549-3753
www.northborder.k12.nd.us
North Border Walhalla HS 100/9-12
PO Box 558 58282 701-549-3751
Tescha Bailly, prin. Fax 549-3753
Other Schools – See Pembina

Warwick, Benson, Pop. 65
Warwick SD 29 300/PK-12
210 4th Ave 58381 701-294-2561
Dean Dauphinais, supt. Fax 294-2626
www.warwick.k12.nd.us
Warwick HS 100/7-12
210 4th Ave 58381 701-294-2561
Tara Thomas, prin. Fax 294-2626

Washburn, McLean, Pop. 1,238
Washburn SD 4 300/K-12
PO Box 280 58577 701-462-3221
Brad Rinas, supt. Fax 462-3561
sites.google.com/site/washburnk12
Washburn HS 100/7-12
PO Box 280 58577 701-462-3221
Glen Weinmann, prin. Fax 462-3561

Watford City, McKenzie, Pop. 1,714
McKenzie County SD 1 1,000/K-12
PO Box 589 58854 701-444-3626
Steven Holen, supt. Fax 444-6345
www.watford-city.k12.nd.us/
Watford City JSHS 400/7-12
PO Box 589 58854 701-444-3624
Terry Vanderpan, prin. Fax 444-3612

Johnson Corners Christian Academy 50/K-12
11008 Highway 23 58854 701-675-2359
Patsy Levang, admin. Fax 675-2357

West Fargo, Cass, Pop. 25,407
West Fargo SD 6 8,500/PK-12
207 Main Ave W 58078 701-356-2000
Dr. David Flowers, supt. Fax 356-2009
www.west-fargo.k12.nd.us
Cheney MS 1,100/6-8
825 17th Ave E 58078 701-356-2090
Don Lennon, prin. Fax 356-2099
Community HS Alt
109 3rd St E 58078 701-356-2008
Dr. Thomas Gravel, prin. Fax 234-9305
Liberty MS 800/6-8
801 36th Ave E 58078 701-356-2671
Michelle Weber, prin. Fax 356-2679
Sheyenne HS 800/9-12
800 40th Ave E 58078 701-356-2160
Dr. Greg Grooters, prin. Fax 356-2169
West Fargo HS 1,400/9-12
801 9th St E 58078 701-356-2050
Dr. Jennifer Fremstad, prin. Fax 356-2060

Westhope, Bottineau, Pop. 415
Westhope SD 17 100/K-12
PO Box 406 58793 701-245-6444
John Gruenberg, supt. Fax 245-6418
www.westhope.k12.nd.us/
Westhope HS 100/7-12
PO Box 406 58793 701-245-6444
John Gruenberg, supt. Fax 245-6418

Williston, Williams, Pop. 14,321
New SD 8 200/K-8
111 7th Ave W 58801 701-572-6359
Robert Turner, supt. Fax 572-9311
www.district8.k12.nd.us/
Stoney Creek MS 50/6-8
111 7th Ave W 58801 701-572-3579
Steven Guglich, prin. Fax 572-2731

Williston SD 1 3,200/K-12
PO Box 1407 58802 701-572-1580
Dr. Viola LaFontaine, supt. Fax 572-3547
www.williston.k12.nd.us
Del Easton Alternative HS 50/Alt
PO Box 1407 58802 701-572-0967
Audrey Larson, prin.
Williston HS 1,000/9-12
PO Box 1407 58802 701-572-0967
Jason Germundson, prin. Fax 572-5449
Williston MS 400/7-8
PO Box 1407 58802 701-572-5618
Duane Noeske, prin. Fax 774-3109

Williston State College Post-Sec.
1410 University Ave 58801 701-774-4200
Williston Trinity Christian S 200/PK-12
2419 9th Ave W 58801 701-774-9056
Cory Fleck, prin. Fax 774-3158

Wilton, McLean, Pop. 705
Wilton SD 1 200/PK-12
PO Box 249 58579 701-734-6559
Barbara Kady, supt. Fax 734-6944
www.wilton.k12.nd.us
Wilton HS 100/7-12
PO Box 249 58579 701-734-6331
Andrew Jordan, prin. Fax 734-6944

Wimbledon, Barnes, Pop. 210
Barnes County North SD 7 300/PK-12
PO Box 255 58492 701-646-6202
Mark Lindahl, supt. Fax 646-6566
www.barnescountynorth.k12.nd.us/
Barnes County North HS 100/7-12
PO Box 255 58492 701-646-6202
Mark Lindahl, prin. Fax 646-6566

Wing, Burleigh, Pop. 148
Wing SD 28 100/K-12
PO Box 130 58494 701-943-2319
David Goetz, supt. Fax 943-2318
www.wing.k12.nd.us
Wing HS 50/7-12
PO Box 130 58494 701-943-2319
David Goetz, prin. Fax 943-2318

Wishek, McIntosh, Pop. 999
Wishek SD 19 200/PK-12
PO Box 247 58495 701-452-2892
Shawn Kuntz, supt. Fax 452-4273
www.wishek.k12.nd.us
Wishek JSHS 100/7-12
PO Box 247 58495 701-452-2892
Yvonne Engelhart, prin. Fax 452-4273

Wolford, Pierce, Pop. 36
Wolford SD 1 50/K-12
401 3rd Ave SW 58385 701-583-2387
Larry Zavada, supt. Fax 583-2519
www.wolford.k12.nd.us/
Wolford HS 50/7-12
401 3rd Ave SW 58385 701-583-2387
Joel Braaten, prin. Fax 583-2519

Wyndmere, Richland, Pop. 423
Wyndmere SD 42 200/K-12
PO Box 190 58081 701-439-2287
Dan Dalchow, supt. Fax 439-2804
wyndmere.schoolinsites.com
Wyndmere HS 100/7-12
PO Box 190 58081 701-439-2287
Scott Strenge, prin. Fax 439-2804

Zeeland, McIntosh, Pop. 86
Zeeland SD 4 50/K-12
PO Box 2 58581 701-423-5429
Corbley Ogren, supt. Fax 423-5465
www.zeeland.k12.nd.us/
Zeeland HS 50/7-12
PO Box 2 58581 701-423-5429
Trudy Fraase Wolf, prin. Fax 423-5465

OHIO

OHIO DEPARTMENT OF EDUCATION
25 S Front St, Columbus 43215-4183
Telephone 877-644-6338
Website http://www.ode.state.oh.us

Superintendent of Public Instruction Paolo DeMaria

OHIO BOARD OF EDUCATION
25 S Front St, Columbus 43215-4183

President Tom Gunlock

EDUCATIONAL SERVICE CENTERS (ESC)

Allen County ESC
Steve Arnold, supt. 419-222-1836
1920 Slabtown Rd, Lima 45801 Fax 224-0718
www.allencountyesc.org

Ashtabula County ESC
John Rubesich, supt. 440-576-9023
4200 State Rd, Ashtabula 44004 Fax 576-3065
www.acesc.k12.oh.us

Athens-Meigs Counties ESC
Ricky Edwards, supt. 740-797-0064
PO Box 40, Chauncey 45719 Fax 797-0070
www.athensmeigs.org

Auglaize County ESC
, 1045 Dearbaugh Ave Ste 2 419-738-3422
Wapakoneta 45895 Fax 738-1267
www.auglaizeesc.org

Brown County ESC
James Frazier, supt. 937-378-6118
9231 Hamer Rd Fax 378-4286
Georgetown 45121
brown.k12.oh.us

Butler County ESC
, 400 N Erie Hwy Ste A 513-887-3710
Hamilton 45011 Fax 887-3709
www.bcesc.org

Clark County ESC
Dan Bennett Ph.D., supt. 937-325-7671
25 W Pleasant St Fax 717-0518
Springfield 45506
www.clarkesc.org

Clermont County ESC
Jeff Weir, supt. 513-735-8300
2400 Clermont Center Dr Fax 735-8371
Batavia 45103
www.ccesc.org

Columbiana County ESC
Anna Vaughn, supt. 330-424-9591
38720 Saltwell Rd, Lisbon 44432 Fax 424-9481
www.ccesc.k12.oh.us/

Darke County ESC
Michael Gray, supt. 937-548-4915
5279 Education Dr Fax 548-8920
Greenville 45331
darkeesc.org

East Central Ohio ESC
Kevin Spears, supt., 834 E High Ave 330-308-9939
New Philadelphia 44663 Fax 422-3216
www.ecoesc.org

ESC of Central Ohio
Dr. Tom Goodney, supt. 614-445-3750
2080 Citygate Dr, Columbus 43219 Fax 445-3767
www.escco.org

ESC of Cuyahoga County
Dr. Robert Mengerink, supt. 216-524-3000
6393 Oak Tree Blvd Fax 524-3683
Independence 44131
www.esc-cc.org/

ESC of Lake Erie West
Sandra C. Frisch, supt. 419-245-4150
2275 Collingwood Blvd Fax 245-4186
Toledo 43620
www.esclakeeriewest.org

ESC of Lorain County
Greg Ring, supt. 440-324-5777
1885 Lake Ave, Elyria 44035 Fax 324-7355
www.loraincountyesc.org

ESC of Medina County
William Koran, supt. 330-723-6393
124 W Washington St Fax 723-0573
Medina 44256
www.medina-esc.org/

Fairfield County ESC
Marie Ward, supt. 740-653-3193
955 Liberty Dr, Lancaster 43130 Fax 653-4053
faircoesc.org/

Gallia-Vinton Counties ESC
Dr. Denise Shockley, supt. 740-245-0593
PO Box 178, Rio Grande 45674 Fax 245-0596
www.galliavintonesc.org

Geauga County ESC
Jennifer Felker, supt. 440-279-1700
470 Center St Bldg 2 Fax 286-7106
Chardon 44024
www.geaugaesc.org

Greene County ESC
Terry Graves-Strieter, supt. 937-767-1303
360 E Enon Rd Fax 767-1025
Yellow Springs 45387
www.greeneesc.org

Hamilton County ESC
David Distel, supt. 513-674-4200
11083 Hamilton Ave Fax 742-8339
Cincinnati 45231
www.hcesc.org

Hancock County ESC
Larry Busdeker, supt. 419-422-7525
7746 County Road 140 Fax 422-8766
Findlay 45840
hancockesc.org

Jefferson County ESC
Dr. Chuck Kokiko, supt. 740-283-3347
2023 Sunset Blvd Fax 283-2709
Steubenville 43952
www.jcesc.k12.oh.us

Knox County ESC
Timm Mackley, supt. 740-393-6767
308 Martinsburg Rd Fax 393-6812
Mount Vernon 43050
www.knoxesc.org

Lake County ESC
Dr. Brian Bontempo, supt. 440-350-2563
8221 Auburn Rd, Concord 44077 Fax 350-2566
www.esc-lc.org

Lawrence County ESC
Dr. James Payne, supt. 740-532-4223
111 S 4th St, Ironton 45638 Fax 532-7226
www.lawrencecountyesc.com

Licking County ESC
Dr. Nelson McCray, supt. 740-349-6084
145 N Quentin Rd, Newark 43055 Fax 349-6107
www.lcesc.org

Madison-Champaign ESC
Dr. Daniel Kaffenbarger, supt. 937-484-1557
2200 S US Highway 68 Fax 652-2221
Urbana 43078
www.mccesc.org

Mahoning County ESC
Dr. Ronald Iarussi, supt. 330-533-8755
7320 N Palmyra Rd Fax 533-8777
Canfield 44406
www.mahoningesc.org

Mercer County ESC
Shelly Vaughn, supt. 419-586-6628
441 E Market St, Celina 45822 Fax 586-3377
www.mercercountyesc.org

Miami County ESC
Tom Dunn, supt. 937-339-5100
2000 W Stanfield Rd, Troy 45373 Fax 339-3256
www.miami.k12.oh.us

Mid-Ohio ESC
Linda Keller, supt. 419-774-5520
890 W 4th St Ste 100 Fax 774-5523
Mansfield 44906
www.moesc.net/

Midwest Regional ESC
Heather O'Donnell, supt. 937-599-5195
121 S Opera St Fax 599-1959
Bellefontaine 43311
www.mresc.org

Montgomery County ESC
Frank DePalma, supt. 937-225-4598
200 S Keowee St, Dayton 45402 Fax 496-7426
www.mcesc.org

Muskingum Valley ESC
David Branch, supt. 740-452-4518
205 N 7th St, Zanesville 43701 Fax 455-6702
www.mvesc.org

North Central Ohio ESC
Dr. James Lahoski, supt. 419-447-2927
928 W Market St Ste A, Tiffin 44883 Fax 447-2825
www.ncoesc.org/

North Point ESC
Doug Crooks, supt. 419-627-3900
1210 E Bogart Rd, Sandusky 44870 Fax 627-3999
www.npesc.org

Northwest Ohio ESC
Kerri Gearhart, supt. 567-444-4800
205 Nolan Pkwy, Archbold 43502 Fax 444-4802
www.nwoesc.org

Ohio Valley ESC
Chris Keylor, supt. 740-439-3558
128 E 8th St, Cambridge 43725 Fax 439-0012
www.ovesc.k12.oh.us

Pickaway County ESC
Tyrus Ankrom, supt. 740-474-7529
2050 Stoneridge Dr Fax 474-7251
Circleville 43113
pickawayesc.org/

Portage County ESC
Joseph Iacano, supt. 330-297-1436
326 E Main St, Ravenna 44266 Fax 297-1113
www.portage-esc.org

Preble County ESC 937-456-1187
, 597 Hillcrest Dr, Eaton 45320 Fax 456-3253
www.preblecountyesc.org

Putnam County ESC
Dr. Jan Osborn, supt. 419-523-5951
124 Putnam Pkwy, Ottawa 45875 Fax 523-6126
www.putnamcountyesc.org

Ross-Pike Counties ESC
Steve Martin, supt. 740-702-3120
475 Western Ave Ste E Fax 702-3123
Chillicothe 45601
rpesd.org

South Central Ohio ESC
Sandy Mers, supt. 740-354-7761
522 Glenwood Ave Fax 353-1882
New Boston 45662
www.scoesc.org

Southern Ohio ESC
Beth Justice, supt. 937-382-6921
3321 Airborne Rd Fax 383-3171
Wilmington 45177
www.southernohioesc.org

Stark County ESC
Joe Chaddock, supt. 330-492-8136
2100 38th St NW, Canton 44709 Fax 492-6381
www.starkcountyesc.org

Summit County ESC
Joseph Iacano, supt. 330-945-5600
420 Washington Ave Ste 200 Fax 945-6222
Cuyahoga Falls 44221
www.cybersummit.org

Tri-County ESC
James Ritchie, supt. 330-345-6771
741 Winkler Dr, Wooster 44691 Fax 345-7622
www.youresc.k12.oh.us

Trumbull County ESC
Michael Hanshaw, supt. 330-505-2800
6000 Youngstown Warren Rd Fax 505-2814
Niles 44446
www.trumbullesc.org

Warren County ESC
Tom Isaacs, supt. 513-695-2900
1879 Deerfield Rd, Lebanon 45036 Fax 695-2961
www.warrencountyesc.com/

Western Buckeye ESC
Brian Gerber, supt. 419-399-4711
PO Box 176, Paulding 45879 Fax 399-3346
www.wbesc.org

Wood County ESC
Kyle Kanuckel, supt. 419-354-9010
1867 N Research Dr Fax 354-1146
Bowling Green 43402
www.wcesc.org/

PUBLIC, PRIVATE AND CATHOLIC SECONDARY SCHOOLS

Aberdeen, Brown, Pop. 1,615
Ripley-Union-Lewis-Huntington Local SD
Supt. — See Ripley
Ripley-Union-Lewis-Huntington MS 300/5-8
2300 Rains Eitel Rd 45101 937-795-8001
Chris Smith, prin. Fax 795-8035

Ada, Hardin, Pop. 5,849
Ada EVD 900/K-12
725 W North Ave 45810 419-634-6421
Dr. Suzanne Darmer, supt. Fax 634-0311
www.adabulldogs.org
Ada JSHS 400/7-12
725 W North Ave 45810 419-634-2746
Robin VanBuskirk, prin. Fax 634-4153

Ohio Northern University Post-Sec.
525 S Main St 45810 419-772-2000

Akron, Summit, Pop. 192,922
Akron CSD 21,000/K-12
70 N Broadway St 44308 330-761-1661
David James, supt. Fax 761-3225
www.akronschools.com
Akron Alternative Academy 300/Alt
77 W Thornton St 44311 330-761-1609
Rebecca Green-Pallotta, admin. Fax 761-1349
Akron Early College HS 300/9-12
225 S Main St 44325 330-972-6450
Cheryl Connelly, prin. Fax 972-5305
Akron Opportunity Center 100/Alt
77 W Thornton St 44311 330-761-1604
Rebecca Green-Pallotta, prin. Fax 761-1344
Buchtel HS 900/7-12
1040 Copley Rd 44320 330-761-7945
Byron Hopkins, prin. Fax 761-7947
East Community Learning Center 1,100/7-12
80 Brittain Rd 44305 330-761-7920
Vyrone Finney, prin. Fax 784-1859
Ellet HS 1,000/9-12
309 Woolf Ave 44312 330-794-4120
Michelle Marquess-Kearns, prin. Fax 794-4130
Firestone HS 1,200/9-12
470 Castle Blvd 44313 330-873-3315
Larry Johnson, prin. Fax 873-3318
Garfield HS 700/9-12
435 N Firestone Blvd 44301 330-773-6831
Frank Kalain, prin. Fax 773-3403
Hyre Community Learning Center 800/6-8
2385 Wedgewood Dr 44312 330-761-7930
Larry Bender, prin. Fax 761-7932
Innes Community Learning Center 400/6-8
1999 East Ave 44314 330-761-7900
Kathryn Rodocker, prin. Fax 848-5212
Jennings Community Learning Center 600/6-8
227 E Tallmadge Ave 44310 330-761-2002
Charles Jones, prin. Fax 761-2611
Kenmore HS 700/9-12
2140 13th St SW 44314 330-848-4141
Douglas Faris, prin. Fax 848-5270
Kent MS 500/6-8
1445 Hammel St 44306 330-773-7631
Jeannie Yost, prin. Fax 773-6442
Litchfield MS 600/6-8
470 Castle Blvd 44313 330-873-3330
Dyan Floyd, prin. Fax 873-3347
Miller South S for Visual & Perform Arts 500/4-8
1055 East Ave 44307 330-761-1765
Dawn Wilson, prin. Fax 761-1764
National Inventors Hall of Fame S - STEM 400/5-8
199 S Broadway St 44308 330-761-3195
Amanda Morgan, prin. Fax 761-5576
North HS 800/9-12
985 Gorge Blvd 44310 330-761-2665
Rachel Tecca, prin. Fax 761-2661
STEM HS 200/9-12
123 S Forge St 44308 330-761-7965
Dina Popa, prin. Fax 761-7966

Coventry Local SD 1,800/PK-12
2910 S Main St 44319 330-644-8489
Russell Chaboudy, supt. Fax 644-0159
www.coventryschools.org/
Coventry HS 700/9-12
1135 Portage Lakes Dr 44319 330-644-3004
Neal Kopp, prin. Fax 644-4222
Coventry MS 500/5-8
3257 Cormany Rd 44319 330-644-2232
Tina Norris, prin. Fax 644-0331

Manchester Local SD 1,300/K-12
6075 Manchester Rd 44319 330-882-6926
Dr. James Robinson, supt. Fax 882-0013
www.panthercountry.org
Manchester HS 500/9-12
437 W Nimisila Rd 44319 330-882-3291
James France, prin. Fax 882-5642
Manchester MS 400/5-8
760 W Nimisila Rd 44319 330-882-3812
James Miller, prin. Fax 882-2013

Springfield Local SD 2,500/PK-12
2410 Massillon Rd 44312 330-798-1111
Chuck Sincere, supt. Fax 798-1161
www.springfieldspartans.org/
Springfield HS 1,200/7-12
1880 Canton Rd 44312 330-798-1002
Shaun Morgan, prin. Fax 798-1162

Akron General Medical Center Post-Sec.
1 Akron General Ave 44307 330-846-6548
Archbishop Hoban HS 800/9-12
1 Holy Cross Blvd 44306 330-773-6658
Dr. Emily Hanson, prin. Fax 773-9100
Children's Hospital & Medical Center Post-Sec.
1 Perkins Sq 44308 330-379-8293
Cooperative Medical Technology Program Post-Sec.
1 Perkins Sq 44308 330-543-8720
Gerber Akron Beauty School Post-Sec.
1915 W Market St Ste 800 44313 330-867-6200
Herzing University Akron Post-Sec.
1600 S Arlington St Ste 100 44306 330-724-1600
Mogadore Christian Academy 50/K-12
3603 Carper Ave 44312 330-628-8482
Rob Seymour, admin. Fax 628-2677
National Institute of Massotherapy Post-Sec.
3681 Manchester Rd Ste 304 44319 330-867-1996
Ohio College of Massotherapy Post-Sec.
225 Heritage Woods Dr 44321 330-665-1084
Our Lady of the Elms MSHS 200/7-12
1375 W Exchange St 44313 330-867-0880
Dr. Cynthia Wilhite, prin. Fax 864-6488
St. Vincent-St. Mary HS 700/9-12
15 N Maple St 44303 330-253-9113
Robert Brownfield, hdmstr. Fax 996-0020
University of Akron Post-Sec.
302 Buchtel Mall 44325 330-972-7111

Albany, Athens, Pop. 825
Alexander Local SD 1,400/PK-12
6091 Ayers Rd 45710 740-698-8831
Lindy Douglas, supt. Fax 698-2038
www.alexanderschools.org/
Alexander JSHS 700/6-12
6125 School Rd 45710 740-698-8831
Frank Doudna, prin. Fax 698-3614

Alliance, Stark, Pop. 21,573
Alliance CSD 2,500/PK-12
200 Glamorgan St 44601 330-821-2100
Jeffery Talbert, supt. Fax 821-0202
www.alliancecityschools.org
Alliance HS 800/9-12
400 Glamorgan St 44601 330-829-2245
Shawn Jackson, prin. Fax 823-4920
Alliance MS 600/6-8
3205 S Union Ave 44601 330-829-2254
Jason Dixon, prin. Fax 823-0872

Marlington Local SD 2,400/K-12
10320 Moulin Ave NE 44601 330-823-7458
Joe Knoll, supt. Fax 823-7759
www.marlingtonlocal.org
Marlington HS 800/9-12
10450 Moulin Ave NE 44601 330-823-1300
Sam Pepper, prin. Fax 829-1986
Marlington MS 600/6-8
10325 Moulin Ave NE 44601 330-823-7566
Nick Evanich, prin. Fax 823-7594

Alliance Career Centre Post-Sec.
530 N Lincoln Ave 44601 330-829-2257
University of Mount Union Post-Sec.
1972 Clark Ave 44601 800-992-6682

Amanda, Fairfield, Pop. 725
Amanda-Clearcreek Local SD 1,600/K-12
328 E Main St 43102 740-969-7250
Fax 969-7620
www.amanda.k12.oh.us
Amanda-Clearcreek HS 500/9-12
328 E Main St 43102 740-969-7251
Kimberly Radulovich, prin. Fax 969-7669
Amanda-Clearcreek MS 400/6-8
328 E Main St 43102 740-969-7252
Patricia Haughn, prin. Fax 969-7638

Amherst, Lorain, Pop. 11,868
Amherst EVD 3,800/PK-12
185 Forest St 44001 440-988-4406
Steven Sayers, supt. Fax 988-4413
www.amherst.k12.oh.us
Amherst JHS 700/7-8
548 Milan Ave 44001 440-988-0324
Ryan Coleman, prin. Fax 988-0328
Steele HS 1,300/9-12
450 Washington St 44001 440-988-4433
Michael May, prin. Fax 988-5087

Andover, Ashtabula, Pop. 1,129
Pymatuning Valley Local SD 1,300/K-12
PO Box 1180 44003 440-293-6488
Mike Candela, supt. Fax 293-7654
pvschools.org
Pymatuning Valley HS 400/9-12
PO Box 1180 44003 440-293-6263
Daniel Jackson, prin. Fax 293-7214
Pymatuning Valley MS 400/5-8
PO Box 1180 44003 440-293-6981
Hendrik Wolfert, prin. Fax 293-7237

Anna, Shelby, Pop. 1,544
Anna Local SD 1,200/K-12
PO Box 169 45302 937-394-2011
Andrew Bixler, supt. Fax 394-7658
www.anna.k12.oh.us
Anna HS 300/9-12
PO Box 169 45302 937-394-2011
Rick Russell, prin. Fax 394-7658
Anna MS 300/6-8
PO Box 169 45302 937-394-2011
Cynthia Endsley, prin. Fax 394-7658

Ansonia, Darke, Pop. 1,168
Ansonia Local SD 700/K-12
PO Box 279 45303 937-337-4000
James Atchley, supt. Fax 337-9520
www.ansonia.k12.oh.us/
Ansonia HS 200/9-12
PO Box 279 45303 937-337-5591
Stephen Garman, prin. Fax 337-9520
Ansonia MS 100/7-8
PO Box 279 45303 937-337-5591
Stephen Garman, prin. Fax 337-9520

Antwerp, Paulding, Pop. 1,725
Antwerp Local SD 600/K-12
303 S Harrmann Rd 45813 419-258-5421
Martin Miller, supt. Fax 258-4041
www.antwerpschools.org
Antwerp Local HS 200/9-12
303 S Harrmann Rd 45813 419-258-5421
Michael Bute, prin. Fax 258-4041
Antwerp Local MS 200/6-8
303 S Harrmann Rd 45813 419-258-5421
Michael Bute, prin. Fax 258-4041

Apple Creek, Wayne, Pop. 1,169
Southeast Local SD 1,400/PK-12
9048 Dover Rd 44606 330-698-3001
James J. Ritchie, supt. Fax 698-5000
www.southeast.k12.oh.us
Lea MS 200/7-8
9130 Dover Rd 44606 330-698-3151
Erich Riebe, prin. Fax 698-1922
Waynedale HS 400/9-12
9050 Dover Rd 44606 330-698-3071
Richard Roth, prin. Fax 698-1432

Arcadia, Hancock, Pop. 583
Arcadia Local SD 500/K-12
19033 State Route 12 44804 419-894-6431
Bruce Kidder, supt. Fax 894-6970
www.arcadia.noacsc.org
Arcadia JSHS 200/7-12
19033 State Route 12 44804 419-894-6431
Bill Dobbins, prin. Fax 894-6970

Arcanum, Darke, Pop. 2,116
Arcanum Butler Local SD 1,100/PK-12
2011 Trojan Ave 45304 937-692-5174
John Stephens, supt. Fax 692-5959
www.arcanum-butler.k12.oh.us
Arcanum HS 300/9-12
2011 Trojan Ave 45304 937-692-5174
Jason Stephan, prin. Fax 692-8865
Butler MS 400/5-8
2011 Trojan Ave 45304 937-692-5174
Marcus Bixler, prin. Fax 692-8865

Franklin Monroe Local SD 600/K-12
8639 Oakes Rd 45304 937-947-1212
Jeffrey Patrick, supt. Fax 947-1372
www.franklin-monroe.k12.oh.us/
Franklin Monroe JSHS 300/6-12
8591 Oakes Rd 45304 937-947-1328
P.J. Burgett, prin. Fax 947-1371

Archbold, Fulton, Pop. 4,305
Archbold Area Local SD 1,200/PK-12
600 Lafayette St 43502 419-446-2728
Aaron Rex, supt. Fax 445-8536
www.archbold.k12.oh.us
Archbold HS 300/9-12
600 Lafayette St 43502 419-445-5579
Royal Short, prin. Fax 445-8536
Archbold MS 400/5-8
306 Stryker St 43502 419-446-2726
Matthew Shields, prin. Fax 445-8402

Four County Career Center SD
22900 State Route 34 43502 419-267-3331
Tim Meister, supt. Fax 267-2345
www.fourcounty.net
Four County Career Center Vo/Tech
22900 State Route 34 43502 419-267-3331
Rick Bachman, supt. Fax 267-2345

Northwest State Community College Post-Sec.
22600 State Route 34 43502 419-267-5511

Arlington, Hancock, Pop. 1,451
Arlington Local SD 600/K-12
336 S Main St 45814 419-365-5121
Kevin Haught, supt. Fax 365-1282
www.noacsc.org/hancock/ag
Arlington JSHS 300/7-12
336 S Main St 45814 419-365-5122
Nate Sorg, prin. Fax 365-1282

Ashland, Ashland, Pop. 20,088
Ashland CSD 2,500/K-12
PO Box 160 44805 419-289-1117
Douglas Marrah, supt. Fax 289-9534
www.ashlandcityschools.org/
Ashland HS 1,000/9-12
1440 King Rd 44805 419-289-7968
Thomas Marquette, prin. Fax 289-8218
Ashland MS 500/7-8
1520 King Rd 44805 419-289-7966
Matthew White, prin. Fax 289-2303

Ashland County-West Holmes JVSD
1783 State Route 60 44805 419-289-3313
Michael Parry, supt. Fax 289-3729
www.acwhcc.org
Ashland Co. - West Holmes JVS Career Ctr Vo/Tech
1783 State Route 60 44805 419-289-3313
Rodney Cheyney, prin. Fax 289-3729

Crestview Local SD 1,100/K-12
1575 State Route 96 44805 419-895-1700
L. Randall Dunlap, supt. Fax 895-1733
www.crestviewschools.net
Crestview HS 300/9-12
1575 State Route 96 44805 419-895-1700
Shannon Sprang, prin. Fax 895-3103
Crestview MS 500/4-8
1575 State Route 96 44805 419-895-1700
Eric Yetter, prin. Fax 895-1733

Mapleton Local SD 900/K-12
635 County Road 801 44805 419-945-2188
Rodney Hopton, supt. Fax 945-8133
www.mapleton.k12.oh.us/
Mapleton HS 200/9-12
1 Mountie Dr 44805 419-945-2188
Joseph Morabito, prin. Fax 945-8166
Mapleton MS 200/6-8
1 Mountie Dr 44805 419-945-2188
Corey Kline, prin. Fax 945-8167

Ashland County-West Holmes Career Center Post-Sec.
1783 State Route 60 44805 419-289-3313
Ashland University Post-Sec.
401 College Ave 44805 419-289-4142

Ashtabula, Ashtabula, Pop. 18,304
Ashtabula Area CSD 3,700/PK-12
2630 W 13th St 44004 440-992-1200
Dr. Melissa Watson, supt. Fax 992-1209
www.aacs.net
Lakeside HS 1,000/9-12
6600 Sanborn Rd 44004 440-993-2522
Donald Rapose, prin. Fax 993-2480
Lakeside JHS 500/7-8
6620 Sanborn Rd 44004 440-993-2618
Mark Potts, prin. Fax 992-2647

Buckeye Local SD 1,800/K-12
3436 Edgewood Dr 44004 440-998-4411
Patrick Colucci, supt. Fax 992-8369
www.buckeyeschools.info/
Braden MS 400/6-8
3436 Edgewood Dr 44004 440-998-0550
Bill Billington, prin.
Edgewood HS 600/9-12
2428 Blake Rd 44004 440-997-5301
Michael Notar, prin. Fax 998-6143

Kent State University at Ashtabula Post-Sec.
3300 Lake Rd W 44004 440-964-3322
St. John S 200/K-12
7911 Depot Rd 44004 440-997-5531
Scott Plescia, prin. Fax 998-1661

Ashville, Pickaway, Pop. 4,045
Teays Valley Local SD 3,700/PK-12
385 Circleville Ave 43103 740-983-5000
Robin Halley, supt. Fax 983-4158
www.tvsd.us/
Teays Valley East MS 500/6-8
655 Viking Way 43103 740-983-5000
Shannon Helser, prin. Fax 983-5037
Teays Valley HS 1,100/9-12
3887 State Route 752 43103 740-983-5000
John Keel, prin. Fax 983-5074
Other Schools – See Commercial Point

Athens, Athens, Pop. 23,284
Athens CSD
Supt. — See The Plains
Athens MS 400/7-8
51 W State St 45701 740-593-7107
Kara Bolin, prin. Fax 594-6506

Ohio University Post-Sec.
1 Ohio University 45701 740-593-1000

Attica, Seneca, Pop. 880
Seneca East Local SD 700/K-12
13343 E US Highway 224 44807 419-426-7041
Laura Kagy, supt. Fax 426-5514
www.seneca-east.k12.oh.us/
Seneca East JSHS 300/7-12
13343 E US Highway 224 44807 419-426-3312
Don Vogt, prin. Fax 426-5400

Atwater, Portage, Pop. 754
Waterloo Local SD 1,100/K-12
1464 Industry Rd 44201 330-947-2664
Shawn Braman, supt. Fax 947-2847
www.viking.portage.k12.oh.us
Waterloo HS 300/9-12
1464 Industry Rd 44201 330-947-2124
Lori Sandel, prin. Fax 947-1911
Waterloo MS 300/6-8
1464 Industry Rd 44201 330-947-0033
Aaron Walker, prin. Fax 947-4073

Aurora, Portage, Pop. 15,422
Aurora CSD 2,900/PK-12
102 E Garfield Rd 44202 330-562-6106
Pat Ciccantelli, supt. Fax 562-4892
www.aurora-schools.org
Aurora HS 1,000/9-12
109 W Pioneer Trl 44202 330-562-3501
Dr. Paul Milcetich, prin. Fax 954-2810
Harmon MS 700/6-8
130 Aurora Hudson Rd 44202 330-562-3375
Mark Abramovich, prin. Fax 562-4796

Austinburg, Ashtabula, Pop. 512

Grand River Academy 100/8-12
3042 College St 44010 440-275-2811
Tim Viands, head sch Fax 275-1825

Austintown, Mahoning, Pop. 31,500

Hair Academy Post-Sec.
6000 Mahoning Ave 44515 330-792-6504

Avon, Lorain, Pop. 20,897
Avon Local SD 3,400/PK-12
36600 Detroit Rd 44011 440-937-4680
Michael Laub, supt. Fax 937-4688
www.avonlocalschools.org
Avon HS 1,100/9-12
37545 Detroit Rd 44011 440-934-6171
Kristina Buller, prin. Fax 934-5450
Avon MS 700/6-8
3445 Long Rd 44011 440-934-3800
Dr. Craig Koehler, prin. Fax 934-3803

Avon Lake, Lorain, Pop. 22,318
Avon Lake CSD 3,700/K-12
175 Avon Belden Rd 44012 440-933-6210
Robert Scott, supt. Fax 933-6711
www.avonlakecityschools.org
Avon Lake HS 1,100/9-12
175 Avon Belden Rd 44012 440-933-6290
Dr. Brad Cocco Ph.D., prin. Fax 930-2798
Learwood MS 600/7-8
340 Lear Rd 44012 440-933-8142
Vishtasp Nuggud, prin. Fax 933-8406

Bainbridge, Ross, Pop. 838
Paint Valley Local SD 900/K-12
7454 US Highway 50 W 45612 740-634-2826
Timothy Winland, supt. Fax 634-2890
paintvalleylocalschools.org
Paint Valley HS 300/9-12
7454 US Highway 50 W 45612 740-634-3582
Casey Smith, prin. Fax 634-3518
Paint Valley MS 200/7-8
7454 US Highway 50 W 45612 740-634-3454
Lewis Ewry, prin. Fax 634-3459

Baltimore, Fairfield, Pop. 2,921
Liberty Union-Thurston Local SD 1,300/K-12
1108 S Main St 43105 740-862-4171
Todd Osborn, supt. Fax 862-2015
www.libertyunion.org
Liberty Union HS 400/9-12
500 W Washington St 43105 740-862-4107
Matt Gallatin, prin. Fax 862-4100
Liberty Union MS 400/5-8
994 S Main St 43105 740-862-4126
Tim Turner, prin. Fax 862-0239

Barberton, Summit, Pop. 25,978
Barberton CSD 3,900/K-12
479 Norton Ave 44203 330-753-1025
Patti Cleary, supt. Fax 848-0884
www.barbertonschools.org
Barberton HS 1,300/9-12
555 Barber Rd 44203 330-753-1084
Jeff Ramnytz, prin. Fax 848-5517
Barberton MS 1,200/5-8
477 4th St NW 44203 330-745-9950
Joyce Walker, prin. Fax 745-9962

Barnesville, Belmont, Pop. 4,130
Barnesville EVD 1,200/PK-12
210 W Church St 43713 740-425-3615
Angela Hannahs, supt. Fax 425-5000
www.barnesville.k12.oh.us/
Barnesville HS 300/9-12
910 Shamrock Dr 43713 740-425-3617
Micah Fuchs, prin. Fax 425-9254
Barnesville MS 400/5-8
970 Shamrock Dr 43713 740-425-3116
Julie Erwin, prin. Fax 425-9204

Olney Friends S 100/9-12
61830 Sandy Ridge Rd 43713 740-425-3655
Kenneth Hinshaw, head sch Fax 425-3202

Bascom, Seneca, Pop. 390
Hopewell-Loudon Local SD 900/K-12
PO Box 400 44809 419-937-2216
David Alvarado, supt. Fax 937-2516
www.hlschool.org
Hopewell-Loudon Local JSHS 400/7-12
PO Box 400 44809 419-937-2804
Jason Miller, prin. Fax 937-2516

Batavia, Clermont, Pop. 1,482
Batavia Local SD 2,000/PK-12
2400 Clermont Center Dr 45103 513-732-2343
Keith Millard, supt. Fax 732-3221
www.bataviaschools.org
Batavia HS 600/9-12
1 Bulldog Pl 45103 513-732-2341
Felicia Grooms, prin. Fax 732-9740
Batavia MS 500/6-8
800 Bauer Ave 45103 513-732-9534
Steve Brokamp, prin. Fax 732-3696

Clermont Northeastern Local SD 1,500/K-12
2792 US Highway 50 45103 513-625-5478
Michael Brandt, supt. Fax 625-6080
www.cneschools.org
Clermont Northeastern HS 400/9-12
5327 Hutchinson Rd 45103 513-625-1211
T.J. Glassmeyer, prin. Fax 625-3328
Clermont Northeastern MS 400/6-8
2792 US Highway 50 45103 513-625-1211
Kendra Young, prin. Fax 625-3325

West Clermont Local SD
Supt. — See Cincinnati
Amelia HS 1,100/9-12
1351 Clough Pike 45103 513-947-7400
Stephanie Walker, prin. Fax 753-2419
Amelia MS 1,000/6-8
1341 Clough Pike 45103 513-947-7500
Norbert Martini, prin. Fax 753-7851

University of Cincinnati Post-Sec.
4200 Clermont College Dr 45103 513-732-5200

Bath, Summit
Revere Local SD
Supt. — See Richfield
Revere HS 800/9-12
3420 Everett Rd 44210 330-659-6111
Phil King, prin. Fax 659-6407
Revere MS 600/6-8
PO Box 339 44210 330-666-4155
Bill Conley, prin. Fax 659-3795

Bay Village, Cuyahoga, Pop. 15,468
Bay Village CSD 2,500/K-12
377 Dover Center Rd 44140 440-617-7300
Clinton Keener, supt. Fax 617-7301
www.bayvillageschools.com
Bay HS 800/9-12
29230 Wolf Rd 44140 440-617-7400
Jason Martin, prin. Fax 617-7401
Bay MS 800/5-8
27725 Wolf Rd 44140 440-617-7600
Sean McAndrews, prin. Fax 617-7601

Beachwood, Cuyahoga, Pop. 11,798
Beachwood CSD 1,500/PK-12
24601 Fairmount Blvd 44122 216-464-2600
Robert Hardis, supt. Fax 292-2340
www.beachwoodschools.org/
Beachwood HS 600/9-12
25100 Fairmount Blvd 44122 216-831-2080
Dr. James Reed, prin. Fax 292-4169
Beachwood MS 300/6-8
2860 Richmond Rd 44122 216-831-0355
Paul Chase, prin. Fax 831-1891

Fuchs Mizrachi S 400/PK-12
26600 Shaker Blvd 44122 216-932-0220
Lauren Ginsburg, head sch Fax 932-0345

Beallsville, Monroe, Pop. 400
Switzerland of Ohio Local SD
Supt. — See Woodsfield
Beallsville JSHS 200/7-12
PO Box 262 43716 740-926-1302
Darren Cook, prin. Fax 926-1394

Beaver, Pike, Pop. 431
Eastern Local SD 800/PK-12
1170 Tile Mill Rd 45613 740-226-4851
Neil Leist, supt. Fax 226-1331
www.ep.k12.oh.us
Eastern HS 200/9-12
1170 Tile Mill Rd 45613 740-226-1544
Lance Allen, prin. Fax 226-6322
Eastern MS 200/6-8
1170 Tile Mill Rd 45613 740-226-1544
Lance Allen, prin. Fax 226-6322

Beavercreek, Greene, Pop. 44,171
Beavercreek CSD 7,500/PK-12
3040 Kemp Rd 45431 937-426-1522
Dr. Paul Otten, supt. Fax 429-7517
www.beavercreek.k12.oh.us/
Ankeney MS 800/6-8
4085 Shakertown Rd 45430 937-429-7567
Dale Wren, prin. Fax 429-7685
Beavercreek HS 2,300/9-12
2660 Dayton Xenia Rd 45434 937-429-7547
Jeffrey Jones, prin. Fax 429-7546
Other Schools – See Xenia

Bedford, Cuyahoga, Pop. 12,768
Bedford CSD 3,500/PK-12
475 Northfield Rd 44146 440-439-1500
Dr. Andrea Celico Ph.D., supt. Fax 439-4850
www.bedford.k12.oh.us
Bedford HS 1,100/9-12
481 Northfield Rd 44146 440-439-4848
Samuel Vawters, prin. Fax 439-4627
Other Schools – See Bedford Heights

Bedford Heights, Cuyahoga, Pop. 10,538
Bedford CSD
Supt. — See Bedford
Heskett MS 500/7-8
5771 Perkins Rd 44146 440-439-4450
Virginia Golden, prin. Fax 786-3572

Bellaire, Belmont, Pop. 4,190
Bellaire Local SD 1,200/K-12
340 34th St 43906 740-676-1826
Darren Jenkins Ed.D., supt. Fax 676-1826
www.bellaire.k12.oh.us
Bellaire HS 300/9-12
349 35th St 43906 740-676-3652
Katherine Anderson, prin. Fax 671-6004
Bellaire MS 400/5-8
54555 Neffs Bellaire Rd 43906 740-676-1635
Derrick McAfee, prin. Fax 676-3014

St. John Central HS 100/9-12
3625 Guernsey St 43906 740-676-4932
Kim Leonard, prin. Fax 676-4934

Bellbrook, Greene, Pop. 6,854
Bellbrook-Sugarcreek Local SD 2,500/K-12
3757 Upper Bellbrook Rd 45305 937-848-5001
Dr. Keith St. Pierre, supt. Fax 848-5018
www.sugarcreek.k12.oh.us
Bellbrook HS 800/9-12
3737 Upper Bellbrook Rd 45305 937-848-3737
Christopher Baker, prin. Fax 848-5016
Bellbrook MS 600/6-8
3600 Feedwire Rd 45305 937-848-2141
Jenness Sigman, prin. Fax 848-2152

Bellefontaine, Logan, Pop. 12,899
Bellefontaine CSD 2,500/K-12
820 Ludlow Rd 43311 937-593-9060
Brad Hall, supt. Fax 599-1346
www.bellefontaine.k12.oh.us/
Bellefontaine HS 700/9-12
555 E Lake Ave 43311 937-593-0545
Pamela Noeth, prin. Fax 593-0575
Bellefontaine MS 600/6-8
1201 Ludlow Rd 43311 937-593-9010
Lynda Holycross, prin. Fax 593-9030

Benjamin Logan Local SD 1,700/K-12
4740 County Road 26 43311 937-593-9211
David Harmon, supt. Fax 599-4059
www.benjaminlogan.org
Logan HS 500/9-12
6609 State Route 47 E 43311 937-592-1666
Mark Butler, prin. Fax 599-4061
Logan MS 500/5-8
4626 County Road 26 43311 937-599-2386
Rob Walter, prin. Fax 599-4062

Ohio Hi-Point Career Ctr SD
2280 State Route 540 43311 937-599-3010
Richard Smith, supt. Fax 599-2318
www.ohiohipoint.com
Ohio Hi-Point Career Center Vo/Tech
2280 State Route 540 43311 937-599-3010
Debbie Wortman, dir. Fax 599-2318

Calvary Christian S 200/PK-12
1140 Rush Ave 43311 937-599-6847
Paul Green, admin. Fax 599-4879

Bellevue, Huron, Pop. 8,079
Bellevue CSD 2,100/PK-12
125 North St 44811 419-484-5000
Kim Schubert, supt. Fax 483-0723
www.bellevueschools.org
Bellevue HS 600/9-12
200 Oakland Ave 44811 419-484-5070
Nate Artino, prin. Fax 483-7157
Bellevue MS 500/6-8
1035 Castalia St 44811 419-484-5060
John Bollinger, prin. Fax 484-5096

Bellville, Richland, Pop. 1,888
Clear Fork Valley Local SD 1,700/K-12
92 Hines Ave 44813 419-886-3855
Janice Wyckoff, supt. Fax 886-2237
www.clearfork.k12.oh.us
Clear Fork HS 500/9-12
987 State Route 97 E 44813 419-886-2601
Brian Brown, prin. Fax 886-4749
Clear Fork MS 400/6-8
987 State Route 97 E 44813 419-886-3111
Jennifer Klaus, prin. Fax 886-4749

Belmont, Belmont, Pop. 449
Union Local SD 1,500/PK-12
66779 Belmont Morristown Rd 43718 740-782-1978
Robert Porter, supt. Fax 782-1212
www.ulschools.com
Union Local HS 400/9-12
66779 Belmont Morristown Rd 43718 740-782-1181
Robert Mascolino, prin. Fax 782-1346
Union Local MS 300/6-8
66859 Belmont Morristown Rd 43718 740-782-1388
Robert Porter, prin. Fax 782-1474

Beloit, Mahoning, Pop. 960
West Branch Local SD 2,100/K-12
14277 S Main St 44609 330-938-9324
Dr. Timothy Saxton, supt. Fax 938-6815
www.westbranch.k12.oh.us
West Branch HS 600/9-12
14277 S Main St 44609 330-938-2183
Brian Coffee, prin. Fax 938-4444
West Branch MS 700/5-8
14409 Beloit Snodes Rd 44609 330-938-4300
Roger Kitzmiller, prin. Fax 938-4301

Belpre, Washington, Pop. 6,292
Belpre CSD 1,000/K-12
2014 Rockland Ave 45714 740-423-9511
Dwight Dunn, supt. Fax 423-3050
www.belpre.k12.oh.us
Belpre HS 400/7-12
612 3rd St 45714 740-423-3000
Dennis Eichinger, prin. Fax 423-3003

Berea, Cuyahoga, Pop. 18,699
Berea CSD 7,000/PK-12
390 Fair St 44017 216-898-8300
Michael Sheppard, supt. Fax 898-8551
www.berea.k12.oh.us
Berea-Midpark HS 1,700/10-12
165 E Bagley Rd 44017 216-898-8900
Vincenzo Ruggiero, prin. Fax 898-8558
Other Schools – See Middleburg Heights

Baldwin-Wallace University Post-Sec.
275 Eastland Rd 44017 440-826-2900

Berlin, Holmes, Pop. 892
East Holmes Local SD
Supt. — See Millersburg
Hiland JSHS 400/7-12
PO Box 275 44610 330-893-2626
Matthew Johnson, prin. Fax 893-3570

Berlin Center, Mahoning
Western Reserve Local SD 300/K-12
13850 W Akron Canfield Rd 44401 330-547-4100
Douglas McGlynn, supt. Fax 547-9302
www.westernreserve.k12.oh.us
Western Reserve S 300/K-12
13850 W Akron Canfield Rd 44401 330-547-4100
Dallas Saunders, prin. Fax 547-9302

Berlin Heights, Erie, Pop. 698
Edison Local SD
Supt. — See Milan
Edison MS 600/4-8
20 Center St 44814 419-588-2078
Cory Smith, prin. Fax 588-3212

Bethel, Clermont, Pop. 2,658
Bethel-Tate Local SD 1,600/K-12
675 W Plane St 45106 513-734-2271
Melissa Kircher, supt. Fax 734-4792
www.betheltate.org
Bethel-Tate HS 400/9-12
3420 State Route 125 45106 513-734-2271
Keith Hickman, prin. Fax 734-1355
Bethel-Tate MS 400/6-8
649 W Plane St 45106 513-734-2271
Christen Davis, prin. Fax 734-0888

U.S. Grant JVSD
718 W Plane St 45106 513-734-6222
Lisa Tuttle-Huff, supt. Fax 734-4758
www.grantcareer.com
Grant Career Center Vo/Tech
718 W Plane St 45106 513-734-6222
Barry Daulton, prin. Fax 734-4758

Beverly, Washington, Pop. 1,285
Fort Frye Local SD 900/K-12
PO Box 1149 45715 740-984-2497
Stephanie Starcher, supt. Fax 984-8784
www.fortfrye.k12.oh.us
Ft. Frye JSHS 400/7-12
PO Box 1089 45715 740-984-2376
Andrew Schob, prin. Fax 984-4361

Bexley, Franklin, Pop. 12,740
Bexley CSD 2,200/K-12
348 S Cassingham Rd 43209 614-231-7611
Dr. Michael Johnson, supt. Fax 231-8448
www.bexleyschools.org
Bexley HS 600/9-12
326 S Cassingham Rd 43209 614-231-4591
Dr. Harley Williams, prin. Fax 338-2087
Bexley MS 400/7-8
300 S Cassingham Rd 43209 614-237-4277
Dr. Harley Williams, prin. Fax 338-2090

Bidwell, Gallia
Gallia County Local SD
Supt. — See Patriot
River Valley HS 400/9-12
8785 State Route 160 45614 740-446-2926
Timothy Edwards, prin. Fax 446-7382
River Valley MS 400/6-8
8779 State Route 160 45614 740-446-8399
O. Ed Moore, prin. Fax 441-3038

Blanchester, Clinton, Pop. 4,195
Blanchester Local SD 1,700/PK-12
951 Cherry St 45107 937-783-3523
Dean D. Lynch, supt. Fax 783-2990
www.blan.org
Blanchester HS 500/9-12
953 Cherry St 45107 937-783-2461
Rick Hosler, prin. Fax 783-5666
Blanchester MS 400/6-8
955 Cherry St 45107 937-783-3642
Amy Schaljo, prin. Fax 783-3477

Bloomdale, Wood, Pop. 675
Elmwood Local SD 1,200/PK-12
7650 Jerry City Rd 44817 419-655-2583
Tony Borton, supt. Fax 655-3995
www.elmwood.k12.oh.us
Elmwood HS 300/9-12
7650 Jerry City Rd 44817 419-655-2583
Tom Bentley, prin. Fax 655-2153
Elmwood MS 400/5-8
7650 Jerry City Rd 44817 419-655-2583
Roger Frank, prin. Fax 655-2153

Bloomingdale, Jefferson, Pop. 200
Jefferson County JVSD
1509 County Road 22A 43910 740-264-5545
Dr. Todd Phillipson, supt. Fax 264-3144
www.jcjvs.k12.oh.us/district.html
Jefferson County Vocational S Vo/Tech
1509 County Road 22A 43910 740-264-5545
Dr. Todd Phillipson, supt. Fax 264-3144

Blue Ash, Hamilton, Pop. 11,860

University of Cincinnati Post-Sec.
9555 Plainfield Rd 45236 513-745-5600

Bluffton, Allen, Pop. 4,072
Bluffton EVD 1,100/K-12
102 S Jackson St 45817 419-358-5901
Gregory Denecker, supt. Fax 358-4871
www.blufftonschools.org
Bluffton HS 300/9-12
106 W College Ave 45817 419-358-7941
Michael Minnig, prin. Fax 358-6586
Bluffton MS 200/6-8
116 S Jackson St 45817 419-358-7961
Kyle Leatherman, prin. Fax 358-4871

Bluffton University Post-Sec.
1 University Dr 45817 419-358-3000

Botkins, Shelby, Pop. 1,145
Botkins Local SD 300/K-12
404 E State St 45306 937-693-4241
Jeffrey McPheron, supt. Fax 693-2557
www.botkins.k12.oh.us
Botkins S 300/K-12
404 E State St 45306 937-693-4241
Ryan Loy, prin. Fax 693-2557

Bowerston, Harrison, Pop. 397
Conotton Valley Union Local SD
Supt. — See Sherrodsville
Conotton Valley HS 200/6-12
7205 Cumberland Rd SW 44695 740-269-2711
Andrew Meister, prin. Fax 269-4405

Bowling Green, Wood, Pop. 29,467
Bowling Green CSD 3,000/PK-12
137 Clough St 43402 419-352-3576
Francis Scruci, supt. Fax 352-1701
www.bgcs.k12.oh.us
Bowling Green HS 800/9-12
530 W Poe Rd 43402 419-354-0100
Jeffrey Dever, prin. Fax 354-1839
Bowling Green MS 700/6-8
1079 Fairview Ave 43402 419-354-0200
Eric Radabaugh, prin. Fax 353-1958

Otsego Local SD 1,500/PK-12
18505 Tontogany Creek Rd 43402 419-823-4381
Adam Koch, supt. Fax 823-3035
www.otsegoknights.org
Otsego HS 400/9-12
18505 Tontogany Creek Rd 43402 419-823-4381
Kevin O'Shea, prin. Fax 823-1397
Otsego JHS 400/6-8
18505 Tontogany Creek Rd 43402 419-823-4381
Kevin Olds, prin. Fax 823-0944

Bowling Green Christian Academy 200/PK-12
1165 Haskins Rd 43402 419-354-2422
Daniel Kessler, prin. Fax 354-0232
Bowling Green State University Post-Sec.
110 McFall Ctr 43403 419-372-2531

Bradford, Darke, Pop. 1,831
Bradford EVD 500/K-12
760 Railroad Ave 45308 937-448-2770
Kenneth Miller, supt. Fax 448-2493
www.bradford.k12.oh.us
Bradford JSHS 300/6-12
750 Railroad Ave 45308 937-448-2719
Chris Abke, prin. Fax 448-2742

Brecksville, Cuyahoga, Pop. 13,500
Brecksville-Broadview Heights CSD 4,100/PK-12
6638 Mill Rd 44141 440-740-4000
Joelle Magyar, supt. Fax 740-4004
www.bbhcsd.org
Other Schools – See Broadview Heights

Cuyahoga Valley Career Ctr SD
8001 Brecksville Rd 44141 440-526-5200
Dr. Celena Roebuck, supt. Fax 746-8298
www.cvccworks.edu
Cuyahoga Valley Career Center Vo/Tech
8001 Brecksville Rd 44141 440-526-5200
Mike Hall, prin. Fax 746-8299

Stautzenberger College Post-Sec.
8001 Katherine Blvd 44141 440-838-1999

Bridgeport, Belmont, Pop. 1,773
Bridgeport EVD 800/PK-12
55781 National Rd 43912 740-635-1713
Zachary Shutler, supt. Fax 635-6003
www.bevs.k12.oh.us/
Bridgeport HS 200/9-12
55707 Industrial Dr 43912 740-635-0853
Rob Zitzelsberger, prin. Fax 635-6008
Bridgeport MS 200/5-8
55707 Industrial Dr 43912 740-635-0853
Anne Haverty, prin. Fax 635-6003

Bristolville, Trumbull
Bristol Local SD 700/K-12
PO Box 260 44402 330-889-3882
Christopher Dray, supt. Fax 889-2529
www.bristol.k12.oh.us
Bristol HS 300/7-12
PO Box 260 44402 330-889-2621
Timothy Fairfield, prin. Fax 889-2529

Broadview Heights, Cuyahoga, Pop. 19,168
Brecksville-Broadview Heights CSD
Supt. — See Brecksville
Brecksville-Broadview Heights HS 1,500/9-12
6380 Mill Rd 44147 440-740-4700
Joseph Mueller, prin. Fax 740-4704
Brecksville-Broadview Heights MS 1,000/6-8
6376 Mill Rd 44147 440-740-4400
Todd Rings, prin. Fax 740-4404

Vatterott College Post-Sec.
5025 E Royalton Rd 44147 440-526-1660

Brookfield, Trumbull
Brookfield Local SD 1,100/K-12
614 Bedford Rd SE 44403 330-448-4930
Velina Taylor, supt. Fax 448-5026
www.brookfield.k12.oh.us
Brookfield HS 300/9-12
614 Bedford Rd SE 44403 330-448-3001
John DeSantis, prin. Fax 448-8016
Brookfield MS 300/5-8
614 Bedford Rd SE 44403 330-448-3003
William Gibson, prin. Fax 448-5028

Brooklyn, Cuyahoga, Pop. 10,955
Brooklyn CSD 1,300/PK-12
9200 Biddulph Rd 44144 216-485-8100
Dr. Mark Gleichauf, supt. Fax 485-8118
www.brooklyn.k12.oh.us
Brooklyn HS 600/8-12
9200 Biddulph Rd 44144 216-485-8162
Antoinette Hostetler, prin. Fax 485-8124

Brookville, Montgomery, Pop. 5,844
Brookville Local SD 1,400/K-12
75 June Pl 45309 937-833-2181
Timothy Hopkins, supt. Fax 833-2787
www.brookvilleschools.org
Brookville HS 400/9-12
1 Blue Pride Dr 45309 937-833-6761
Christopher Bronner, prin. Fax 833-6302
Brookville IS 600/4-8
2 Blue Pride Dr 45309 937-833-6731
Erin Wheat, prin. Fax 833-6756

Brunswick, Medina, Pop. 33,855
Brunswick CSD 7,200/PK-12
3643 Center Rd 44212 330-225-7731
Michael Mayell, supt. Fax 273-0507
www.bcsoh.org
Brunswick HS 2,200/9-12
3581 Center Rd 44212 330-225-7731
Michael Draves, prin. Fax 225-0507
Edwards MS 500/6-8
1497 Pearl Rd 44212 330-225-7731
Heidi Armentrout, prin. Fax 273-0507
Visintainer MS 600/6-8
1459 Pearl Rd 44212 330-225-7731
Brian Sharosky, prin. Fax 273-0507
Willetts MS 700/6-8
1045 Hadcock Rd 44212 330-225-7731
Brian Miller, prin. Fax 273-0507

Bryan, Williams, Pop. 8,426
Bryan CSD 800/PK-12
1350 Fountain Grove Dr 43506 419-636-6973
Diana Savage, supt. Fax 633-6280
www.bryan.k12.oh.us
Bryan MSHS 500/6-12
1000 W Fountain Grove Dr 43506 419-636-4536
Mark Rairigh, prin. Fax 633-6281

Fountain City Christian S 100/K-12
120 S Beech St 43506 419-636-2333
Troy Cummins, admin. Fax 636-2888

Bucyrus, Crawford, Pop. 12,227
Bucyrus CSD 1,400/PK-12
170 Plymouth St 44820 419-562-4045
Kevin Kimmel, supt. Fax 562-3990
bucyrusschools.org
Bucyrus HS 400/9-12
900 W Perry St 44820 419-562-7721
Dr. Mark Burke, prin. Fax 562-7819
Bucyrus MS 300/6-8
455 Redman Way 44820 419-562-0003
Jay Dennison, admin. Fax 562-1773

Wynford Local SD 1,100/PK-12
3288 Holmes Center Rd 44820 419-562-7828
Frederick Fox, supt. Fax 562-7825
www.wynfordroyals.org
Wynford HS 300/9-12
3288 Holmes Center Rd 44820 419-562-7828
Jeffrey Holbrook, prin. Fax 562-7825
Wynford JHS 200/7-8
3288 Holmes Center Rd 44820 419-562-7828
Chris Solis, prin. Fax 562-7825

Burton, Geauga, Pop. 1,446
Berkshire Local SD 1,100/PK-12
PO Box 364 44021 440-834-3380
Douglas DeLong, supt.
www.berkshireschools.org
Berkshire JSHS, PO Box 365 44021 500/7-12
Stephen Reedy, prin. 440-834-3380

Kent State University-Geauga Campus Post-Sec.
14111 Claridon Troy Rd 44021 440-834-4187

Byesville, Guernsey, Pop. 2,409
Rolling Hills Local SD
Supt. — See Cambridge
Meadowbrook HS 500/9-12
58615 Marietta Rd 43723 740-685-2566
Molly Kaplet, prin. Fax 685-2797
Meadowbrook MS 400/6-8
58607 Marietta Rd 43723 740-685-2561
William Spence, admin. Fax 685-2628

Cadiz, Harrison, Pop. 3,237
Belmont-Harrison Area JVSD
Supt. — See Saint Clairsville
Harrison Career Center Vo/Tech
82500 Cadiz Jewett Rd 43907 740-942-2148
Larry Bossell, lead tchr. Fax 695-4866

Harrison Hills CSD 1,600/PK-12
730 Peppard Ave 43907 740-942-7800
Dana Snider, supt. Fax 942-7808
www.hhcsd.org/
Harrison Central JSHS 600/7-12
440 E Market St 43907 740-942-7700
Brent Ripley, prin. Fax 942-7705

Caldwell, Noble, Pop. 1,727
Caldwell EVD 800/PK-12
516 Fairground St 43724 740-732-5637
Dora Jean Bumgarner, supt. Fax 732-7303
www.caldwell.k12.oh.us
Caldwell HS, 516 Fairground St 43724 200/9-12
Devvon Dettra, prin. 740-732-5634

Caledonia, Marion, Pop. 572
River Valley Local SD 1,900/K-12
197 Brocklesby Rd 43314 740-725-5400
James Peterson, supt. Fax 725-5499
www.rivervalley.k12.oh.us
River Valley HS 500/9-12
4280 Marion Mount Gilead Rd 43314 740-725-5800
David Coleman, prin. Fax 725-5899
River Valley MS 500/6-8
4334 Marion Mount Gilead Rd 43314 740-725-5700
Donald Gliebe, prin. Fax 725-5799

Cambridge, Guernsey, Pop. 10,324
Cambridge CSD 2,100/K-12
6111 Fairdale Dr 43725 740-439-5021
Dan Coffman, supt. Fax 439-3796
www.cambridge.k12.oh.us/
Cambridge HS 600/9-12
1401 Deerpath Dr 43725 740-435-1100
Margaret Wilcox, prin. Fax 435-1101
Cambridge MS 500/6-8
1400 Deerpath Dr 43725 740-435-1140
Duane Poland, prin. Fax 435-1141

Rolling Hills Local SD 1,600/K-12
60851 Southgate Rd 43725 740-432-5370
Ryan Caldwell, supt. Fax 432-6523
www.rhcolts.org
Other Schools – See Byesville

Camden, Preble, Pop. 2,033
Preble Shawnee Local SD 1,400/PK-12
124 Bloomfield St 45311 937-452-1283
Matt Bishop, supt. Fax 452-3926
www.preble-shawnee.k12.oh.us
Preble Shawnee JSHS 600/7-12
5495 Somers Gratis Rd 45311 937-787-3541
Dianna Whitis, prin. Fax 787-3664

Campbell, Mahoning, Pop. 8,033
Campbell CSD 900/K-12
280 6th St 44405 330-799-8777
Matthew Bowen, supt. Fax 799-0875
www.campbell.k12.oh.us
Memorial HS 400/8-12
280 6th St 44405 330-799-1515
Jacquelyn Hampton, prin. Fax 799-6390

Canal Fulton, Stark, Pop. 5,390
Northwest Local SD 1,900/K-12
2309 Locust St S 44614 330-854-2291
Dr. Michael Shreffler, supt. Fax 854-3591
www.northwest.sparcc.org/
Northwest HS 600/9-12
8580 Erie Ave NW 44614 330-854-2205
Larry Tausch, prin. Fax 854-2030
Northwest MS 500/6-8
8614 Erie Ave NW 44614 330-854-3303
Gregory Ramos, prin. Fax 854-5883

Canal Winchester, Franklin, Pop. 6,995
Canal Winchester Local SD 3,600/K-12
100 Washington St 43110 614-837-4533
James Sotlar, supt. Fax 833-2165
www.cwls.us
Canal Winchester HS 1,000/9-12
300 Washington St 43110 614-833-2157
Kirk Henderson, prin. Fax 833-2163
Canal Winchester MS 900/6-8
7155 Parkview Dr 43110 614-833-2151
Kelly Zywczyk, prin. Fax 833-2173

Harvest Preparatory S 500/PK-12
PO Box 400 43110 614-382-1111
Dr. Kenneth Grunden, prin. Fax 837-9591

Canfield, Mahoning, Pop. 7,448
Canfield Local SD 2,800/K-12
100 Wadsworth St 44406 330-533-3303
Alex Geordan, supt. Fax 533-6827
www.canfieldschools.net/
Canfield HS 900/9-12
100 Cardinal Dr 44406 330-533-5507
Michael Moldovan, prin. Fax 533-1919
Canfield Village MS 900/5-8
42 Wadsworth St 44406 330-533-4019
Judd Rubin, prin. Fax 702-7064

Mahoning County Career & Technical Ctr
7300 N Palmyra Rd 44406 330-729-4000
Dr. Ronald Iarussi, supt. Fax 729-4050
www.mahoningctc.com
Mahoning County Career & Technical Ctr Vo/Tech
7300 N Palmyra Rd 44406 330-729-4000
Dr. Michael Savillie, prin. Fax 729-4015

South Range Local SD 1,200/K-12
11300 Columbiana Canfield 44406 330-549-5226
Dennis J. Dunham, supt. Fax 549-4740
www.southrange.k12.oh.us/
South Range HS 400/9-12
11300 Columbiana Canfield 44406 330-549-2163
Stephen Rohan, prin. Fax 549-4083
South Range MS 400/5-8
11300 Columbiana Canfield 44406 330-549-4071
Daniel Szolek, prin. Fax 549-4073

Canton, Stark, Pop. 69,508
Canton CSD 7,300/PK-12
305 McKinley Ave NW 44702 330-438-2500
Adrian Allison, supt. Fax 430-4230
www.ccsdistrict.org
Altitude Academy @ Crenshaw 500/6-8
2525 19th St NE 44705 330-454-7717
Tiffany Hardwick, prin. Fax 588-2120
Choices Alternative S 100/Alt
401 14th St SE 44707 330-451-3300
Shawn Monahan, prin. Fax 451-3301
College and Career Readiness Academy 600/6-8
1400 Broad Ave NW 44708 330-456-1963
Janet Peare, prin. Fax 456-8121
Compton Learning Center 50/Alt
401 14th St SE 44707 330-456-1189
James Pappas, admin. Fax 580-2404
Early College Academy @ Souers 400/6-8
2800 13th St SW 44710 330-438-2736
Amy Conn, prin. Fax 580-3540
Early College HS 9-12
231 McKinley Ave NW 44702 330-458-3950
Amy Lint-Conn, prin. Fax 458-3980
McKinley HS 1,400/9-12
2323 17th St NW 44708 330-438-2712
Corey Grubbs, prin. Fax 580-2712
STEAMM Academy @ Hartford 400/6-8
1824 3rd St SE 44707 330-453-6012
David Thompson, prin. Fax 453-5096

Canton Local SD 2,200/PK-12
4526 Ridge Ave SE 44707 330-484-8010
Stephen Milano, supt. Fax 484-8032
www.cantonlocal.org
Canton South HS 800/9-12
600 Faircrest St SE 44707 330-484-8000
Jeffrey Moore, prin. Fax 484-8013

Faircrest Memorial MS 600/5-8
616 Faircrest St SW 44706 330-484-8015
Gay Welker, prin. Fax 484-8033

Plain Local SD 6,100/K-12
901 44th St NW 44709 330-492-3500
Brent May, supt. Fax 493-5542
www.plainlocal.org/
Glenoak HS 2,000/9-12
1801 Schneider St NE 44721 330-491-3800
Michael Babics, prin. Fax 491-3801
Oakwood MS 900/7-8
2300 Schneider St NE 44721 330-491-3790
Jeanne McNeal, prin. Fax 491-3791

Aultman College Nursing and Health Sci Post-Sec.
2600 6th St SW 44710 330-363-6347
Central Catholic HS 400/9-12
4824 Tuscarawas St W 44708 330-478-2131
David Oates, prin. Fax 478-6086
Heritage Christian S 300/PK-12
2107 6th St SW 44706 330-452-8271
Karla Robinson M.Ed., admin. Fax 452-0672
Malone University Post-Sec.
2600 Cleveland Ave NW 44709 330-471-8100
National Beauty College Post-Sec.
4642 Cleveland Ave NW 44709 330-499-9444
National College Post-Sec.
4736 Dressler Rd NW 44718 330-492-5300
Timken Mercy Medical Center Post-Sec.
1320 Mercy Dr NW 44708 330-489-1001

Cardington, Morrow, Pop. 2,023
Cardington-Lincoln Local SD 1,000/K-12
121 Nichols St 43315 419-864-3691
Brian Petrie, supt. Fax 864-0946
www.cardington.k12.oh.us
Cardington-Lincoln HS 300/9-12
349 Chesterville Ave 43315 419-864-2691
Joseph Mills, prin. Fax 864-9515
Cardington-Lincoln JHS 200/7-8
349 Chesterville Ave 43315 419-864-0609
Joseph Mills, prin. Fax 864-3168

Carey, Wyandot, Pop. 3,640
Carey EVD 800/K-12
2016 Blue Devil Dr 43316 419-396-7922
Michael Wank, supt. Fax 396-3158
careyevs.schoolwires.com/
Carey JSHS 400/7-12
2016 Blue Devil Dr 43316 419-396-7638
Peter Cole, prin. Fax 396-3158

Carlisle, Warren, Pop. 4,885
Carlisle Local SD 1,600/K-12
724 Fairview Dr 45005 937-746-0710
Larry Hook, supt. Fax 746-0438
www.carlisleindians.org
Carlisle HS 500/9-12
250 Jamaica Rd 45005 937-746-4481
Bradley Potter, prin. Fax 746-6578
Chamberlain MS 400/6-8
720 Fairview Dr 45005 937-746-3227
Daniel Turner, prin. Fax 746-0519

Carroll, Fairfield, Pop. 510
Bloom-Carroll Local SD 1,800/K-12
PO Box 338 43112 614-837-6560
Lynn Landis, supt. Fax 756-4221
www.bloomcarroll.net
Bloom-Carroll HS 600/9-12
5240 Plum Rd 43112 740-756-4317
Shawn Haughn, prin. Fax 756-9525
Bloom-Carroll MS 600/5-8
PO Box 338 43112 740-756-9231
Cynthia Freeman, prin. Fax 756-7466

Eastland-Fairfield Career & Technical SD
Supt. — See Groveport
Fairfield Career Center Vo/Tech
3985 Coonpath Rd 43112 614-837-9443
Shelley Groves, dir. Fax 837-9447

Carrollton, Carroll, Pop. 3,218
Carrollton EVD 2,200/PK-12
252 3rd St NE 44615 330-627-2181
David Quattrochi, supt. Fax 627-2182
www.carrolltonschools.org
Bell-Herron MS 500/6-8
252 3rd St NE 44615 330-627-7188
Matthew Nicholas, prin. Fax 627-8429
Carrollton HS 700/9-12
252 3rd St NE 44615 330-627-2134
David Davis, prin. Fax 627-8103

Casstown, Miami, Pop. 267
Miami East Local SD 1,200/K-12
3825 N State Route 589 45312 937-335-7505
Dr. Todd Rappold, supt. Fax 335-6309
www.miamieast.k12.oh.us
Miami East HS 300/9-12
3925 N State Route 589 45312 937-335-7070
Todd Gentis, prin. Fax 440-9581
Miami East JHS 300/6-8
4025 N State Route 589 45312 937-335-5439
Allen Mack, prin. Fax 332-7927

Castalia, Erie, Pop. 846
Margaretta Local SD 1,500/PK-12
305 S Washington St 44824 419-684-5322
Dennis Mock, supt. Fax 684-9003
www.margarettaschooldistrict.com
Margaretta JSHS 600/6-12
209 Lowell St 44824 419-684-5351
Rodney Smith, prin. Fax 684-5632

Firelands Christian Academy 50/K-12
3809 Maple Ave 44824 419-684-8642
Rusty Yost, prin. Fax 684-5378

Cedarville, Greene, Pop. 3,956
Cedar Cliff Local SD 500/K-12
PO Box 45 45314 937-766-6000
Dr. Chad Mason, supt. Fax 766-4717
www.cedarcliffschools.org
Cedarville MSHS 300/7-12
PO Box 45 45314 937-766-1871
Chad Haemmerle, prin. Fax 766-5211

Cedarville University Post-Sec.
251 N Main St 45314 937-766-2211

Celina, Mercer, Pop. 10,225
Celina CSD 2,700/K-12
585 E Livingston St 45822 419-586-8300
Dr. Ken Schmiesing, supt. Fax 586-7046
www.celinaschools.org
Celina HS 900/9-12
715 E Wayne St 45822 419-586-8300
Phil Metz, prin. Fax 584-0307
Celina MS 400/7-8
615 Holly St 45822 419-586-8300
Ann Esselstein, prin. Fax 586-9166

Mercer County ESC
441 E Market St 45822 419-586-6628
Shelly Vaughn, supt. Fax 586-3377
www.mercercountyesc.org
Mercer County Alternative HS Alt
441 E Market St 45822 419-586-6722
Aaron Rose, dir.

Wright State University Post-Sec.
7600 Lake Campus Dr 45822 419-586-0300

Centerburg, Knox, Pop. 1,748
Centerburg Local SD 1,100/K-12
119 S Preston St 43011 740-625-6346
Mike Hebenthal, supt. Fax 625-9939
www.centerburgschools.org/
Centerburg HS 300/9-12
3782 Columbus Rd 43011 740-625-6055
Ryan Gallwitz, prin. Fax 625-5799
Centerburg MS 300/6-8
3782 Columbus Rd 43011 740-625-6055
Ryan Gallwitz, prin. Fax 625-5799

Centerville, Montgomery, Pop. 23,528
Centerville CSD 8,300/PK-12
111 Virginia Ave 45458 937-433-8841
Dr. Tom Henderson Ph.D., supt. Fax 438-6057
www.centerville.k12.oh.us
Centerville HS 2,800/9-12
500 E Franklin St 45459 937-439-3500
Jon Wesney, prin. Fax 439-3574
Magsig MS 600/6-8
192 W Franklin St 45459 937-433-0965
Stacey Westendorf, prin. Fax 433-5256
Tower Heights MS 500/6-8
195 N Johanna Dr 45459 937-434-0383
Clint Freese, prin. Fax 434-3033
Other Schools – See Dayton

Fortis College Post-Sec.
555 E Alex Bell Rd 45459 937-433-3410
Spring Valley Academy 300/K-12
1461 E Spring Valley Pike 45458 937-433-0790
Darren Wilkins, prin. Fax 433-0914

Chagrin Falls, Cuyahoga, Pop. 4,089
Chagrin Falls EVD 2,000/PK-12
400 E Washington St 44022 440-247-4363
Robert Hunt, supt. Fax 247-5883
www.chagrinschools.org
Chagrin Falls HS 700/9-12
400 E Washington St 44022 440-247-2072
Steven Ast, prin. Fax 247-2071
Chagrin Falls MS 300/7-8
342 E Washington St 44022 440-247-4746
Laila Discenza, prin. Fax 247-4855

Kenston Local SD 3,000/PK-12
17419 Snyder Rd 44023 440-543-9677
Nancy Santilli, supt. Fax 543-8634
www.kenstonlocal.com
Kenston HS 1,000/9-12
9500 Bainbridge Rd 44023 440-543-9821
Tom Gabram, prin. Fax 543-9021
Kenston MS 700/6-8
17425 Snyder Rd 44023 440-543-8241
Patricia Brockway, prin. Fax 543-4851

English Nanny and Governess School Post-Sec.
37 S Franklin St 44022 440-247-0600

Chardon, Geauga, Pop. 5,091
Chardon Local SD 3,000/K-12
428 North St 44024 440-285-4052
Michael Hanlon, supt. Fax 285-7229
www.chardon.k12.oh.us
Chardon HS 1,000/9-12
151 Chardon Ave 44024 440-285-4057
Douglas Murray, prin. Fax 285-9463
Chardon MS 700/6-8
424 North St 44024 440-285-4062
Douglas Higham, prin. Fax 286-0461

Notre Dame-Cathedral Latin HS 700/9-12
13000 Auburn Rd 44024 440-286-6226
Joseph Waler, prin. Fax 286-7199

Charm, Holmes
East Holmes Local SD
Supt. — See Millersburg
Wise ES, PO Box 159 44617 100/5-8
Casey Travis, prin. 330-893-2505

Chesapeake, Lawrence, Pop. 736
Chesapeake Union EVD 1,300/K-12
10183 County Road 1 45619 740-867-3135
Jerry McConnell, supt. Fax 867-3136
www.peake.k12.oh.us
Chesapeake HS 300/9-12
10181 County Road 1 45619 740-867-5958
Christopher Smith, prin. Fax 867-1130
Chesapeake MS 500/5-8
10335 County Road 1 45619 740-867-3972
Ty Johnson, prin. Fax 867-1120

Lawrence County JVSD
11627 State Route 243 45619 740-867-6641
Stephen Dodgion, supt. Fax 867-1317
www.collins-cc.edu/
Collins Career Center Vo/Tech
11627 State Route 243 45619 740-867-6641
Stephen Dodgion, supt. Fax 867-1317

Collins Career Center Post-Sec.
11627 State Route 243 45619 740-867-6641

Chesterland, Geauga, Pop. 2,498
West Geauga Local SD 2,200/K-12
8615 Cedar Rd 44026 440-729-5900
Dr. Rich Markwardt, supt. Fax 729-5939
www.westg.org
West Geauga HS 800/9-12
13401 Chillicothe Rd 44026 440-729-5950
Jay Bishop, prin. Fax 729-5959
West Geauga MS 500/6-8
8611 Cedar Rd 44026 440-729-5940
James Kish, prin. Fax 729-5909

Chillicothe, Ross, Pop. 21,171
Chillicothe CSD 2,800/K-12
425 Yoctangee Pkwy 45601 740-775-4250
Jon Saxton, supt. Fax 775-4270
www.ccsd.us/
Chillicothe HS 900/9-12
421 Yoctangee Pkwy 45601 740-702-2287
Jeffrey Fisher, prin. Fax 773-1097
Chillicothe MS Site 1 400/7-8
381 Yoctangee Pkwy 45601 740-773-2241
Matthew Ballentine, prin. Fax 774-9482

Huntington Local SD 1,200/K-12
188 Huntsman Rd 45601 740-663-5892
Peter Ruby, supt. Fax 663-6078
www.huntsmen.org
Huntington HS 300/9-12
188 Huntsman Rd 45601 740-663-2230
Nathan Caplinger, prin. Fax 663-5042
Huntington MS 300/6-8
188 Huntsman Rd 45601 740-663-6079
Alice Kellough, prin. Fax 663-6080

Pickaway-Ross County JVSD
895 Crouse Chapel Rd 45601 740-642-1200
Dennis Franks, supt. Fax 642-1399
www.pickawayross.com
Pickaway-Ross Career & Technology Center Vo/Tech
895 Crouse Chapel Rd 45601 740-642-1200
Shara Cochenour, prin. Fax 642-1399

Southeastern Local SD 1,200/K-12
2003 Lancaster Rd 45601 740-774-2003
Brian Justice, supt. Fax 774-1687
www.sepanthers.k12.oh.us/
Southeastern HS 300/9-12
2003 Lancaster Rd 45601 740-774-2003
Leonard Steyer, prin. Fax 774-1684
Southeastern MS 400/5-8
2003 Lancaster Rd 45601 740-774-2003
Zachary Pfeifer, prin. Fax 774-1684

Union-Scioto Local SD 2,200/PK-12
1565 Egypt Pike 45601 740-773-4102
Matt Thornsberry, supt. Fax 775-2852
www.unioto.org
Unioto HS 600/9-12
14193 Pleasant Valley Rd 45601 740-773-4105
James Osborne, prin. Fax 774-9158
Unioto MS 500/6-8
160 Moundsville Rd 45601 740-773-5211
Wilma Gillott, prin. Fax 772-2974

Zane Trace Local SD 1,500/K-12
946 State Route 180 45601 740-775-1355
Jerry Mowery, supt. Fax 773-0249
www.zanetrace.org
Zane Trace HS 400/9-12
946 State Route 180 45601 740-775-1809
Todd Holdren, prin. Fax 775-1301
Zane Trace MS 500/5-8
946 State Route 180 45601 740-773-5842
Bret Mavis, prin. Fax 773-9998

Daymar College Post-Sec.
1410 Industrial Dr 45601 740-774-6300
Ohio University Post-Sec.
PO Box 629 45601 740-774-7200
Recording Workshop Post-Sec.
455 Massieville Rd 45601 740-663-1000
Ross County Christian Academy 200/PK-10
2215 Egypt Pike 45601 740-772-4532
Jake Grooms, head sch Fax 422-1622

Cincinnati, Hamilton, Pop. 289,429
Cincinnati CSD, PO Box 5381 45201 31,600/PK-12
Mary Ronan, supt. 513-363-0000
www.cps-k12.org
Aiken HS - New Tech 600/7-12
5641 Belmont Ave 45224 513-363-6700
Melissa Votaw, prin. Fax 363-6720
Clark Montessori JSHS 700/7-12
3030 Erie Ave 45208 513-363-7100
Dean Blase, prin. Fax 363-7120
Dater JSHS 1,000/7-12
2146 Ferguson Rd 45238 513-363-7200
Stephen Sippel, prin. Fax 363-7220
Gamble Montessori HS 300/7-12
2700 Felicity Pl 45211 513-363-2600
Jack Jose, prin. Fax 363-2620
Hughes STEM HS 900/7-12
2515 Clifton Ave 45219 513-363-7400
Kathy Wright, prin. Fax 363-7420
Oyler S 700/PK-12
2121 Hatmaker St 45204 513-363-4100
Amy Randolph, prin. Fax 363-4120
Riverview East Academy 600/PK-12
3555 Kellogg Ave 45226 513-363-3400
Charlene Myers, prin. Fax 363-3420
School for Creative & Performing Arts 1,500/K-12
108 W Central Pkwy 45202 513-363-8000
Michael Owens, prin. Fax 363-8020
Shroder JSHS 700/7-12
5030 Duck Creek Rd 45227 513-363-6900
Larry Williams, prin. Fax 363-6920
Taft Information Technology HS 700/7-12
420 Ezzard Charles Dr 45214 513-363-8200
Michael Turner, prin. Fax 363-8220
Walnut Hills JSHS 2,500/7-12
3250 Victory Pkwy 45207 513-363-8400
Jeff Brokamp, prin. Fax 363-8420
Western Hills University HS 1,200/7-12
2144 Ferguson Rd 45238 513-363-8900
Donald Jump, prin. Fax 363-8920
Withrow University JSHS 1,300/7-12
2488 Madison Rd 45208 513-363-9200
Paul Daniels, prin. Fax 363-9220
Woodward Career Technical HS Vo/Tech
7005 Reading Rd 45237 513-363-9300
Shauna Murphy, prin. Fax 363-9320

Deer Park Community CSD 1,200/K-12
4131 Matson Ave 45236 513-891-0222
Jeff Langdon, supt. Fax 891-2930
www.deerparkcityschools.org
Deer Park JSHS 600/7-12
8351 Plainfield Rd 45236 513-891-0010
Dr. Stace Orso, prin. Fax 891-3845

Finneytown Local SD 1,400/K-12
8916 Fontainebleau Ter 45231 513-728-3700
Theresa Noe, supt. Fax 931-0986
www.finneytown.org
Finneytown Secondary Campus 700/7-12
8916 Fontainebleau Ter 45231 513-931-0712
Sally Thurman, prin. Fax 728-7230

Forest Hills Local SD 7,400/PK-12
7550 Forest Rd 45255 513-231-3600
Scot T. Prebles, supt. Fax 231-3830
www.foresthills.edu
Anderson HS 1,100/9-12
7560 Forest Rd 45255 513-232-2772
Michael Overbey, prin. Fax 232-3146
Nagel MS 1,300/7-8
1500 Nagel Rd 45255 513-474-5407
John Vander Meer, prin. Fax 474-5584
Turpin HS 1,200/9-12
2650 Bartels Rd 45244 513-232-7770
David Spencer, prin. Fax 232-9047

Great Oaks Institute of Technology
110 Great Oaks Dr 45241 513-771-8840
Harry Snyder, supt. Fax 771-6575
www.greatoaks.com/
Diamond Oaks CDC Vo/Tech
6375 Harrison Ave 45247 513-574-1300
Dan Rush, prin. Fax 574-3953
Scarlet Oaks CDC Vo/Tech
300 Scarlet Oaks Dr 45241 513-771-8810
Joe Moon, prin. Fax 771-4928
Other Schools – See Milford, Wilmington

Indian Hill EVD 1,900/K-12
6855 Drake Rd 45243 513-272-4500
Dr. Mark Miles, supt. Fax 272-4756
indianhillschools.org
Indian Hill HS 700/9-12
6865 Drake Rd 45243 513-272-4550
Dr. Antonio Shelton, prin. Fax 272-4557
Indian Hill MS 500/6-8
6845 Drake Rd 45243 513-272-4642
Bridgette Ridley, prin. Fax 272-4690

Madeira CSD 1,400/PK-12
7465 Loannes Dr 45243 513-985-6070
Kenji Matsudo, supt. Fax 985-6072
www.madeiracityschools.org
Madeira HS 400/9-12
7465 Loannes Dr 45243 513-891-8222
David Kennedy, prin. Fax 985-6089
Madeira MS 400/5-8
6612 Miami Ave 45243 513-561-5555
Tom Olson, prin. Fax 272-4145

Mariemont CSD 1,700/K-12
2 Warrior Way 45227 513-272-7500
Steven E. Estepp, supt. Fax 527-3436
www.mariemontschools.org
Mariemont HS 500/9-12
1 Warrior Way 45227 513-272-7600
Jim Renner, prin. Fax 527-5991
Mariemont JHS 300/7-8
3847 Southern Ave 45227 513-272-7300
Molly Connaughton, prin. Fax 527-3432

Mt. Healthy CSD
Supt. — See Mount Healthy
Mt. Healthy HS 700/9-12
8101 Hamilton Ave 45231 513-729-0130
Milton Folson, prin. Fax 728-4695
Mt. Healthy JHS 500/7-8
8101 Hamilton Ave 45231 513-742-0666
Michael Howton, prin. Fax 742-2797

North College Hill CSD 1,600/PK-12
1731 Goodman Ave 45239 513-931-8181
Eugene Blalock, supt. Fax 728-4774
www.nchcityschools.org
North College Hill HS 400/9-12
1620 W Galbraith Rd 45239 513-728-4783
Ann Brinkley, prin. Fax 728-4784
North College Hill MS 500/5-8
1624 W Galbraith Rd 45239 513-728-4785
Michelle Garton, prin. Fax 728-4786

Northwest Local SD 9,200/PK-12
3240 Banning Rd 45239 513-923-1000
Todd Bowling, supt. Fax 923-3644
www.nwlsd.org
Colerain HS 1,900/9-12
8801 Cheviot Rd 45251 513-385-6424
Jack Fisher, prin. Fax 741-5032
Colerain MS 600/6-8
4700 Poole Rd 45251 513-385-8490
Libby Styles, prin. Fax 385-6685
Northwest HS 900/9-12
10761 Pippin Rd 45231 513-851-7300
Susan Smith, prin. Fax 742-6376
Pleasant Run MS 700/6-8
11770 Pippin Rd 45231 513-851-2400
David Maine, prin. Fax 851-7071
White Oak MS 800/6-8
3130 Jessup Rd 45239 513-741-4300
Dustin Gehring, prin. Fax 741-0717

Oak Hills Local SD 7,800/K-12
6325 Rapid Run Rd 45233 513-574-3200
Jeffrey Brandt, supt. Fax 598-2947
ohlsd.us
Bridgetown MS 600/6-8
3900 Race Rd 45211 513-574-3511
Adam Taylor, prin. Fax 574-6689
Delhi MS 600/6-8
5280 Foley Rd 45238 513-922-8400
Scott Toon, prin. Fax 922-8472
Oak Hills HS 2,500/9-12
3200 Ebenezer Rd 45248 513-922-2300
John Stoddard, prin. Fax 922-4900
Rapid Run MS 700/6-8
6345 Rapid Run Rd 45233 513-467-0300
Travis Hunt, prin. Fax 467-0333

Princeton CSD 5,400/PK-12
3900 Cottingham Dr 45241 513-864-1000
Dr. Thomas Tucker, supt. Fax 864-1008
www.princetonschools.net
Princeton Community MS 1,200/6-8
200 Viking Way 45246 513-864-2000
Ali Moore, prin. Fax 864-2091
Princeton HS 1,400/9-12
11080 Chester Rd 45246 513-864-1500
Charles Ogdan, prin. Fax 864-1591

Sycamore Community CSD 5,300/PK-12
5959 Hagewa Dr 45242 513-686-1700
Frank Forsthoefel, supt. Fax 791-4873
www.sycamoreschools.org
Sycamore HS 1,700/9-12
7400 Cornell Rd 45242 513-686-1770
Douglas Mader, prin. Fax 489-7425
Sycamore JHS 900/7-8
5757 Cooper Rd 45242 513-686-1760
Traci Rea, prin. Fax 891-3162

West Clermont Local SD 8,000/K-12
4350 Aicholtz Rd 45245 513-943-5000
Dr. Keith Kline, supt. Fax 752-6158
www.westcler.k12.oh.us
Glen Este HS 1,200/9-12
4342 Glen Este Wthmsvlle Rd 45245 513-947-7600
Jeffrey Damadeo, prin. Fax 943-7090
Glen Este MS 900/6-8
4342 Glen Este Wthmsvlle Rd 45245 513-947-7700
Lori Crowe, prin. Fax 753-3462
Other Schools – See Batavia

Winton Woods CSD 3,600/PK-12
1215 W Kemper Rd 45240 513-619-2300
Anthony G. Smith, supt. Fax 619-2309
www.wintonwoods.org
Academy of Global Studies @ Winton Woods 200/9-12
1231 W Kemper Rd 45240 513-619-2420
Eric Martin, prin. Fax 619-2417
Winton Woods Alternative Education Alt
8 Enfield St 45218 513-619-2389
Brenda Hodges-Davis, admin.
Winton Woods HS 1,000/9-12
1231 W Kemper Rd 45240 513-619-2420
Eric Martin, prin. Fax 619-2417
Winton Woods MS 500/7-8
147 Farragut Rd 45218 513-619-2440
Doug Sanker, prin. Fax 619-2452

Aldersgate Christian Academy 100/K-12
1810 Young St 45202 513-763-6655
William Marshall, prin. Fax 763-6643
Antonelli College Post-Sec.
124 E 7th St 45202 513-241-4338
Archbishop McNicholas HS 600/9-12
6536 Beechmont Ave 45230 513-231-3500
Patricia Beckert, prin. Fax 231-1351
Art Academy of Cincinnati Post-Sec.
1212 Jackson St 45202 513-562-6262
Art Institute of Ohio - Cincinnati Post-Sec.
8845 Governors Hill Dr #100 45249 513-833-2400
Athenaeum of Ohio Post-Sec.
6616 Beechmont Ave 45230 513-231-2223
Bacon HS 400/9-12
4320 Vine St 45217 513-641-1300
Steven Schad, prin. Fax 641-0498
Beckfield College Post-Sec.
225 Pictoria Dr Ste 200 45246 513-671-1920
Christ College of Nursing & Heath Sci Post-Sec.
2139 Auburn Ave 45219 513-585-2401
Cincinnati Christian University Post-Sec.
2700 Glenway Ave 45204 513-244-8100
Cincinnati College of Mortuary Science Post-Sec.
645 W North Bend Rd 45224 888-377-8433
Cincinnati Country Day S 800/PK-12
6905 Given Rd 45243 513-561-7298
Dr. Anthony Jaccaci, hdmstr. Fax 527-7600
Cincinnati Hills Christian Academy HS 500/9-12
11525 Snider Rd 45249 513-247-0900
Randy Brunk, head sch Fax 247-0982
Cincinnati Hills Christian Academy MS 400/5-8
11300 Snider Rd 45249 513-247-0900
Randy Brunk, head sch Fax 247-9362
Cincinnati State Technical & Comm Coll Post-Sec.
3520 Central Pkwy 45223 513-569-1500
College of Mount Saint Joseph Post-Sec.
5701 Delhi Rd 45233 513-244-4200
DePaul Cristo Rey HS 100/9-12
1133 Clifton Hills Ave 45220 513-861-0600
Andrew Farfsing, prin.
DeVry University Post-Sec.
8800 Governors Hill Dr #100 45249 513-583-5000
Elder HS 900/9-12
3900 Vincent Ave 45205 513-921-3744
Kurt Ruffing, prin. Fax 921-8123
Fortis College Post-Sec.
11499 Chester Rd Ste 200 45246 513-771-2795
God's Bible School and College Post-Sec.
1810 Young St 45202 513-721-7944
Good Samaritan Coll of Nursing/Alld Hlth Post-Sec.
375 Dixmyth Ave 45220 513-862-2743
Hebrew Union College Post-Sec.
3101 Clifton Ave 45220 513-221-1875
International Academy of Hair Design Post-Sec.
8419 Colerain Ave 45239 513-741-4777
La Salle HS 700/9-12
3091 North Bend Rd 45239 513-741-3000
Aaron Marshall, prin. Fax 741-2666
Marinello-Eastern Hills Academy Post-Sec.
7681 Beechmont Ave 45255 513-231-8621
McAuley HS 600/9-12
6000 Oakwood Ave 45224 513-681-1800
Daniel Minelli, prin. Fax 681-1802
Miami Valley Christian Academy 300/PK-12
6830 School St 45244 513-272-6822
Greg Beasley, head sch Fax 272-3711
Moeller HS 900/9-12
9001 Montgomery Rd 45242 513-791-1680
Blane Collison, prin. Fax 792-3343
Moler-Hollywood Beauty Academy Post-Sec.
6142 Montgomery Rd 45213 513-621-5262
Mother of Mercy HS 500/9-12
3036 Werk Rd 45211 513-661-2740
David Mueller, prin. Fax 661-1842
National College Post-Sec.
6871 Steger Dr 45237 513-761-1291
Ohio Center for Broadcasting Post-Sec.
6703 Madison Rd 45227 513-271-6060
Purcell-Marian HS 400/9-12
2935 Hackberry St 45206 513-751-1230
Veronica Murphy, prin. Fax 751-1395
Ross Inst of Medical & Dental Technology Post-Sec.
11590 Century Blvd Ste 210 45246 513-851-8500
St. Rita School for the Deaf Post-Sec.
1720 Glendale Milford Rd 45215 513-771-7600
St. Ursula Academy 700/9-12
1339 E Mcmillan St 45206 513-961-3410
Craig Maliborski, prin. Fax 961-3856
St. Xavier HS 1,500/9-12
600 W North Bend Rd 45224 513-761-7600
Terrence Tyrrell, prin. Fax 842-1610
Seton HS 600/9-12
3901 Glenway Ave 45205 513-471-2600
Karen White, prin. Fax 471-0529
Seven Hills S 500/PK-12
5400 Red Bank Rd 45227 513-728-2400
Christopher Garten, hdmstr. Fax 728-2409
Sevenstar Academy 2,200/6-12
3630 Park 42 Dr 45241 513-612-1029
Dr. R. Mark Beadle, admin. Fax 618-3334
Summit Country Day S 1,100/PK-12
2161 Grandin Rd 45208 513-871-4700
Richard Wilson, head sch Fax 871-6558
The AIC College of Design Post-Sec.
1171 E Kemper Rd 45246 513-751-1206
Tri County Beauty College Post-Sec.
111 W Kemper Rd 45246 513-671-8340
Union Institute and University Post-Sec.
440 E McMillan St 45206 513-861-6400
University of Cincinnati Post-Sec.
2600 Clifton Ave 45220 513-556-6000
Ursuline Academy 700/9-12
5535 Pfeiffer Rd 45242 513-791-5791
Thomas Barhorst, prin. Fax 791-5802
Western Hills Sch of Beauty & Hair Dsgn. Post-Sec.
6490 Glenway Ave 45211 513-574-3818
Xavier University Post-Sec.
3800 Victory Pkwy 45207 513-745-3000

Circleville, Pickaway, Pop. 13,083
Circleville CSD 1,000/PK-12
388 Clark Dr 43113 740-474-4340
Jonathan Davis, supt. Fax 474-6600
www.circlevillecityschools.org/
Circleville HS 600/9-12
380 Clark Dr 43113 740-474-4846
Chris Thornsley, prin. Fax 474-3987
Circleville MS 500/6-8
360 Clark Dr 43113 740-474-2345
Kevin Fox, prin. Fax 477-6384

Logan Elm Local SD 2,000/PK-12
9579 Tarlton Rd 43113 740-474-7501
Tim Williams, supt. Fax 477-6525
www.loganelmschools.com/
Logan Elm HS 600/9-12
9575 Tarlton Rd 43113 740-474-7503
Nate Smith, prin. Fax 477-3592
McDowell-Exchange JHS 300/7-8
9579 Tarlton Rd 43113 740-474-7538
Marsha Waidelich, prin. Fax 474-8539

Ohio Christian University Post-Sec.
1476 Lancaster Pike 43113 740-474-8896

Clarksville, Clinton, Pop. 544
Clinton-Massie Local SD 1,900/K-12
2556 Lebanon Rd 45113 937-289-2471
Dr. Matthew Baker, supt. Fax 289-3313
www.clinton-massie.k12.oh.us
Clinton-Massie HS 500/9-12
2556 Lebanon Rd 45113 937-289-2109
Barrett Swope, prin. Fax 289-7019
Clinton-Massie MS 500/6-8
2556 Lebanon Rd 45113 937-289-2932
Barrett Swope, prin. Fax 289-8100

Clayton, Montgomery, Pop. 12,864
Miami Valley Career Technology Ctr SD
6800 Hoke Rd 45315 937-837-7781
Nicholas Weldy, supt. Fax 837-5318
www.mvctc.com
Miami Valley Career Tech Center Vo/Tech
6800 Hoke Rd 45315 937-837-7781
Fax 837-1594

Northmont CSD
Supt. — See Englewood
Northmont HS 1,500/9-12
4916 National Rd 45315 937-832-6000
George Caras, prin. Fax 832-6001
Northmont MS 800/7-8
4810 National Rd 45315 937-832-6500
Jarrod Brumbaugh, prin. Fax 832-6501

Cleveland, Cuyahoga, Pop. 388,662
Cleveland Municipal SD 35,900/PK-12
1111 Superior Ave E 44114 216-838-0000
Eric Gordon, admin. Fax 436-5144
clevelandmetroschools.org
Adams Academy 1,000/9-12
3817 Martin Luther King Jr 44105 216-491-5700
Luciana Gilmore, prin. Fax 295-4645
Addams Business Careers Center 400/8-12
2373 E 30th St 44115 216-623-8900
Elaine Gollate, prin. Fax 621-3910
Bard HS Early College 9-12
13501 Terminal Ave 44135 216-838-9704
Dumaine Williams, prin.
Cleveland Early College HS 200/9-12
2075 Stokes Blvd 44106 216-229-0200
Carol Lockhart, prin. Fax 229-0087
Cleveland HS for the Digital Arts 9-12
1440 Lakeside Ave E 44114 216-838-9650
John Buzzard, prin.
Cleveland S of Architecture & Design 300/9-12
2075 Stokes Blvd 44106 216-229-0100
Tianna Maxey, prin. Fax 229-0072
Cleveland S of Science & Medicine 400/9-12
2075 Stokes Blvd 44106 216-229-0070
Edward Weber, prin. Fax 339-3242
Cleveland S of the Arts 500/6-12
2064 Stearns Rd 44106 216-791-2496
John LePelley, prin. Fax 421-7689
Collinwood Comprehensive HS 300/12-12
15210 Saint Clair Ave 44110 216-268-6052
Mary Miller, prin. Fax 268-6057
Collinwood New Tech 9-11
15210 Saint Clair Ave 44110 216-451-8782
Maria Carlson, prin.
Design Lab-Early College @ Health Career 200/9-12
1740 E 32nd St 44114 216-621-5064
Eric Juli, prin.
E3gle Academy 9-9
13604 Christine Ave 44105 216-838-5150
Margaret Schauer, prin.
East Technical HS 500/9-12
2439 E 55th St 44104 216-838-1000
Paul Hoover, prin.
Facing History New Tech HS @ Mooney 100/9-9
3213 Montclair Ave 44109 216-838-8600
Marc Engoglia, prin. Fax 838-8610
Ginn Academy 300/9-12
655 E 162nd St 44110 216-531-4466
Nicholas Petty, prin. Fax 531-2874
Glenville HS, 650 E 113th St 44108 200/9-12
Jackie Bell, prin. 216-268-2000
Hayes HS 600/9-12
2211 W 65th St 44102 216-631-1528
Kelly Wittman, prin. Fax 634-2175
Health Career Academy - MLK Campus 300/9-12
1651 E 71st St 44103 216-431-6858
Latonia Davis, prin. Fax 431-5180
High Tech Academy 9-12
2900 Community College Ave 44115 216-987-3549
Stacy Hutchinson, prin. Fax 987-4397
Jefferson Intl Newcomers Academy 300/PK-12
3145 W 46th St 44102 216-404-5100
Marisol Burgos, prin. Fax 404-5492
Kennedy HS 400/11-12
17100 Harvard Ave 44128 216-921-1450
Michelle Kirkwood, prin. Fax 295-2455
King Career Campus 200/9-12
1651 E 71st St 44103 216-431-6858
Latonia Davis, prin. Fax 431-5180
Lincoln-West S of Global Studies 1,000/9-12
3202 W 30th St 44109 216-631-1505
Dr. Irene Javier, prin. Fax 634-2403
Marshall HS 500/11-12
3952 W 140th St 44111 216-858-6000
Angela Boie, prin. Fax 476-4458
Marshall S of Civic & Business Ldrshp 9-10
3952 W 140th St 44111 216-838-6050
Sara Kidner, prin.
Marshall S of Engineering 9-10
3952 W 140th St 44111 216-838-6100
Timothy Primus, prin.

Marshall S of Information Technology 9-10
3952 W 140th St 44111 216-838-6850
Chelsey Cook, prin.
MC2 STEM Cleveland State University 400/11-12
2124 Chester Ave 44115 216-838-8500
Feowyn MacKinnon, prin.
MC2 STEM GE Lighting S 10-10
1975 Noble Rd Bldg 336 44112 216-838-8520
Feowyn MacKinnon, head sch
MC2 STEM Great Lakes Science Center 100/9-9
601 Erieside Ave 44114 216-858-1267
Feowyn MacKinnon, prin. Fax 858-1264
Morgan S of Science 300/9-12
4016 Woodbine Ave 44113 216-281-6188
Yolanda Eiland, prin. Fax 634-2113
New Tech East @ East Technical 200/9-12
2439 E 55th St 44104 216-361-3116
Corether Johnson, prin. Fax 361-3282
New Tech West 300/9-12
11801 Worthington Ave 44111 216-281-1030
Erin Frew, prin. Fax 281-1055
PACT, 13604 Christine Ave 44105 9-12
Richard Reynolds, prin. 216-838-5200
Rhodes HS 1,300/9-12
5100 Biddulph Ave 44144 216-459-4200
Dr. Charlene Hilliard, prin. Fax 459-3133
School of One @ Nathaniel Hawthorne 300/9-12
3575 W 130th St 44111 216-659-4049
Wayne Marok, prin.
SuccessTech Academy 100/10-12
1440 Lakeside Ave E 44114 216-523-8463
Phillip Schwenk, prin. Fax 523-8464
Young Academy 300/2-12
17900 Harvard Ave 44128 216-283-5220
Karen Byron-Johnson, prin. Fax 295-3547
Other Schools – See Newburgh Heights

Benedictine HS 300/9-12
2900 Martin Luther King Jr 44104 216-421-2080
Charlene Zulandt, prin. Fax 421-0107
Bryant & Stratton College Post-Sec.
3121 Euclid Ave 44115 216-771-1700
Case Western Reserve University Post-Sec.
10900 Euclid Ave 44106 216-368-2000
Chamberlain College of Nursing Post-Sec.
6700 Euclid Ave Ste 201 44103 216-361-6005
Cleveland Central Catholic HS 500/9-12
6550 Baxter Ave 44105 216-441-4700
Sr. Allison Gusdanovic, prin. Fax 441-8353
Cleveland Clinic Center Allied Health Post-Sec.
9500 Euclid Ave 44195 216-986-4312
Cleveland Institute Dental Medical Asst. Post-Sec.
2450 Prospect Ave E 44115 216-241-2930
Cleveland Institute of Art Post-Sec.
11141 East Blvd 44106 216-421-7000
Cleveland Institute of Electronics Post-Sec.
1776 E 17th St 44114 216-781-9400
Cleveland Institute of Music Post-Sec.
11021 East Blvd 44106 216-791-5000
Cleveland State University Post-Sec.
2121 Euclid Ave 44115 216-687-2000
Cleveland Veterans Affairs Medical Ctr Post-Sec.
10701 East Blvd 44106 216-421-3028
Cuyahoga Community College Post-Sec.
2900 Community College Ave 44115 800-954-8742
Fairview General Hospital Post-Sec.
18101 Lorain Ave 44111 216-476-7000
John Carroll University Post-Sec.
1 John Carroll Blvd 44118 216-397-1886
Meridia Health System Post-Sec.
17325 Euclid Ave 44112 440-446-8260
MetroHealth Medical Center Post-Sec.
2500 Metrohealth Dr 44109 216-459-5700
Notre Dame College Post-Sec.
4545 College Rd 44121 216-381-1680
Ohio Center for Broadcasting Post-Sec.
9885 Rockside Rd Ste 160 44125 216-503-5900
Ohio Technical College Post-Sec.
1374 E 51st St 44103 216-881-1700
Remington College Post-Sec.
14445 Broadway Ave 44125 216-475-7520
St. Ignatius HS 1,500/9-12
1911 W 30th St 44113 216-651-0222
Dan Bradesca, prin. Fax 961-2564
St. Joseph Academy 700/9-12
3470 Rocky River Dr 44111 216-251-6788
Jeff Sutliff, prin. Fax 251-5809
St. Luke's Medical Center Post-Sec.
2351 E 22nd St 44115 216-368-7000
St. Martin de Porres HS 500/9-12
6111 Lausche Ave 44103 216-881-1689
Gary Sardon, prin. Fax 881-8303
Southwest General Hospital Post-Sec.
18697 Bagley Rd 44130 440-816-6801
Villa Angela-St. Joseph HS 300/9-12
18491 Lake Shore Blvd 44119 216-481-8414
David Csank, prin. Fax 486-1035

Cleveland Heights, Cuyahoga, Pop. 44,828
Cleveland Hts - University Hts CSD
Supt. — See University Heights
Monticello MS 400/6-8
3665 Monticello Blvd 44121 216-371-6520
Patrick McNichols, prin. Fax 397-5967
Roxboro MS 500/6-8
2400 Roxboro Rd 44106 216-371-7440
Denise Lackey, prin. Fax 397-3857

Beaumont HS 400/9-12
3301 N Park Blvd 44118 216-321-2954
Mary Whelan, prin. Fax 321-3947
Hebrew Academy of Cleveland 600/PK-12
1860 S Taylor Rd 44118 216-321-5838
Lutheran HS East 100/9-12
3565 Mayfield Rd 44118 216-382-6100
Chris Steinmann, prin. Fax 382-6119
Mosdos Ohr HaTorah S - Girls 400/PK-12
1700 S Taylor Rd 44118 216-321-1547

Yeshiva Derech Hatorah 200/PK-12
1508 Warrensville Center Rd 44121 216-382-6248
Rabbi Yitzchok Margareten, supt. Fax 382-4585

Cleves, Hamilton, Pop. 3,191
Three Rivers Local SD 1,400/PK-12
401 N Miami Ave 45002 513-941-6400
Craig Hockenberry, supt. Fax 941-1102
www.threeriversschools.org
Taylor HS 500/9-12
56 Cooper Ave 45002 513-467-3200
Megan Rivet, prin. Fax 467-0138
Taylor MS 5-8
56 Cooper Ave 45002 513-467-3500
Holly Simms, prin. Fax 467-0053

Clyde, Sandusky, Pop. 6,212
Clyde-Green Springs EVD 2,200/K-12
106 S Main St 43410 419-547-0588
Dennis Haft, supt. Fax 547-8644
www.clyde.k12.oh.us
Clyde HS 700/9-12
1015 Race St 43410 419-547-9511
Joe Webb, prin. Fax 547-7593
McPherson MS 600/6-8
4230 Limerick Rd 43410 419-547-9150
Brian Cannon, prin. Fax 547-9173

Coal Grove, Lawrence, Pop. 2,141
Dawson-Bryant Local SD 1,200/K-12
222 Lane St 45638 740-532-6451
Steve Easterling, supt. Fax 533-6019
db.k12.oh.us
Dawson-Bryant HS 300/9-12
1 Hornet Ln 45638 740-532-6345
Dean Mader, prin. Fax 533-6013
Dawson-Bryant MS 300/6-8
1 Hornet Ln 45638 740-533-6008
Rick Roach, prin. Fax 533-6002

Coldwater, Mercer, Pop. 4,401
Coldwater EVD 1,400/K-12
310 N 2nd St 45828 419-678-2611
Jason Wood, supt. Fax 678-3100
cw.noacsc.org
Coldwater HS 500/9-12
310 N 2nd St 45828 419-678-4821
Jason Hemmelgarn, prin. Fax 678-3100
Coldwater MS 400/5-8
310 N 2nd St 45828 419-678-3331
Dan Pohlman, prin. Fax 678-3100

Collins, Huron, Pop. 625
Western Reserve Local SD 1,100/K-12
3765 State Route 20 44826 419-660-8508
Rodge Wilson, supt. Fax 660-8429
www.western-reserve.org
Western Reserve HS 300/9-12
3841 State Route 20 44826 419-668-8470
Lisa Border, prin. Fax 663-5916
Western Reserve MS 200/7-8
3841 State Route 20 44826 419-668-1924
Lisa Border, prin. Fax 663-2521

Columbiana, Columbiana, Pop. 6,337
Columbiana EVD 1,000/PK-12
700 Columbiana Waterford Rd 44408 330-482-5352
Donald Mook, supt. Fax 482-5361
www.columbiana.k12.oh.us
Columbiana HS 300/9-12
700 Columbiana Waterford Rd 44408 330-482-3818
Lance Hostetler, prin. Fax 482-5360
South Side MS 200/5-8
720 Columbiana Waterford Rd 44408 330-482-5354
David Buzzard, prin. Fax 482-6332

Crestview Local SD 1,200/K-12
44100 Crestview Rd Ste A 44408 330-482-5526
Matthew Manley, supt. Fax 482-5367
www.crestviewlocal.k12.oh.us/
Crestview HS 400/9-12
44100 Crestview Rd Ste B 44408 330-482-4744
Lynda Dickson, prin. Fax 482-5369
Crestview MS 400/5-8
44100 Crestview Rd Ste C 44408 330-482-4648
Allison Lemaster, prin. Fax 482-5374

Heartland Christian S 300/PK-12
28 Pittsburgh St 44408 330-482-2331
Eric Hosler, admin. Fax 482-2413

Columbia Station, Lorain
Columbia Local SD 900/K-12
25796 Royalton Rd 44028 440-236-5008
Graig Bansek, supt. Fax 236-8817
www.columbia.k12.oh.us/
Columbia HS 300/9-12
14168 W River Rd 44028 440-236-5001
Sean Lynch, prin. Fax 236-3081
Columbia MS 300/5-8
13646 W River Rd 44028 440-236-5741
Andy Gibson, prin. Fax 236-9274

Columbus, Franklin, Pop. 762,045
Columbus CSD 48,500/PK-12
270 E State St 43215 614-365-5000
Dan Good Ph.D., supt. Fax 365-5689
www.ccsoh.us
Africentric Early College S 500/6-12
300 E Livingston Ave 43215 614-365-8675
William Anderson, prin. Fax 365-8908
Arts Impact MS at Everett 500/6-8
680 Jack Gibbs Blvd 43215 614-365-5558
Leon Leavell, prin. Fax 365-5561
Beechcroft HS 600/9-12
6100 Beechcroft Rd 43229 614-365-5364
Monique Jacquet, prin. Fax 365-6963
Briggs HS 1,000/9-12
2555 Briggs Rd 43223 614-365-5915
Tonya Milligan, prin. Fax 365-6964

Buckeye MS 500/6-8
2950 Parsons Ave 43207 614-365-5417
Derick Vickroy, prin. Fax 365-5895
Centennial HS 800/9-12
1441 Bethel Rd 43220 614-365-5491
Stephanie Porta, prin. Fax 365-6967
Champion MS 300/6-8
284 N 22nd St 43203 614-365-6082
Stephanie Bland, prin. Fax 365-6080
Columbus Alternative HS 700/Alt
2632 McGuffey Rd 43211 614-365-6006
Darryl Sanders, prin. Fax 365-6300
Columbus City Prep S for Boys 200/6-8
3450 Medway Ave 43213 614-365-6166
Kyle Gibson, prin. Fax 365-6164
Columbus City Prep S for Girls 400/6-8
1390 Bryden Rd 43205 614-365-6113
Stephanie Patton, prin. Fax 365-6112
Columbus Downtown HS 100/9-12
364 S 4th St 43215 614-365-2283
Cheryl Watson, dir. Fax 365-2287
Columbus Global Academy @ Brookhaven 700/6-12
4077 Karl Rd 43224 614-365-8472
Michael Sain, prin.
Columbus North International S 800/7-12
100 E Arcadia Ave 43202 614-365-4054
Kenton Lee, prin. Fax 365-8582
Dominion MS 500/6-8
330 E Dominion Blvd 43214 614-365-6020
Dorothy Flanagan, prin. Fax 365-6018
East HS 400/9-12
1500 E Broad St 43205 614-365-6096
Ernest Wood, prin. Fax 365-6966
Eastmoor Academy HS 700/9-12
417 S Weyant Ave 43213 614-365-6158
Brian Morton, prin. Fax 365-6960
Fort Hayes Arts and Academics S 700/9-12
546 Jack Gibbs Blvd 43215 614-365-6681
Milton Ruffin, prin. Fax 365-5620
Fort Hayes Career Center Vo/Tech
546 Jack Gibbs Blvd 43215 614-365-6681
Milton Ruffin, dir. Fax 365-8582
Hilltonia MS 500/6-8
2345 W Mound St 43204 614-365-5937
Joyce Albright, prin. Fax 365-8015
Independence HS 600/9-12
5175 Refugee Rd 43232 614-365-5372
Ernest West, prin. Fax 365-8286
Johnson Park MS 400/6-8
1130 S Waverly St 43227 614-365-6501
Nicole Edwards, prin. Fax 365-8698
Linden-McKinley STEM HS 600/7-12
1320 Duxberry Ave 43211 614-365-5583
Duane Bland, prin. Fax 365-6968
Marion-Franklin HS 700/9-12
1265 Koebel Rd 43207 614-365-5432
Gregory Costello, prin. Fax 365-6625
Medina MS 500/6-8
1425 Huy Rd 43224 614-365-6050
Charmaine Tinker, prin. Fax 365-8136
Mifflin HS 500/9-12
3245 Oak Spring St 43219 614-365-5466
Kimberly Normand, prin. Fax 365-6628
Mifflin MS 400/6-8
3000 Agler Rd 43219 614-365-5474
Tracey Colson, prin. Fax 365-5477
Northland HS 900/9-12
1919 Northcliff Dr 43229 614-365-5342
Jason Johnson, prin. Fax 365-6479
Ridgeview MS 500/6-8
4241 Rudy Rd 43214 614-365-5506
Natalie James, prin. Fax 365-5505
Sherwood MS 400/6-8
1400 Shady Lane Rd 43227 614-365-5393
Kevin Freeman, prin. Fax 365-8351
South HS 500/9-12
1160 Ann St 43206 614-365-5541
Edmund Baker, prin. Fax 365-5538
Walnut Ridge HS 700/9-12
4841 E Livingston Ave 43227 614-365-5400
Todd Walker, prin. Fax 365-5662
Wedgewood MS 500/6-8
3800 Briggs Rd 43228 614-365-5947
Diane Campbell, prin. Fax 365-5950
West HS 800/9-12
179 S Powell Ave 43204 614-365-5956
Lucas Cech, prin. Fax 365-6970
Westmoor MS 500/6-8
3001 Valleyview Dr 43204 614-365-5974
Paul Bailey, prin. Fax 365-6705
Whetstone HS 900/9-12
4405 Scenic Dr 43214 614-365-6060
Janet Routzong, prin. Fax 365-6971
Woodward Park MS 900/6-8
5151 Karl Rd 43229 614-365-5354
Diane Agnes, prin. Fax 365-5357
Yorktown MS 400/6-8
5600 E Livingston Ave 43232 614-365-5408
Ronnie Brown, prin. Fax 365-5411

Grandview Heights CSD 800/PK-12
1587 W 3rd Ave 43212 614-485-4015
Andy Culp, supt. Fax 481-3648
www.ghcsd.org
Edison Intermediate/Larson MS 200/4-8
1240 Oakland Ave 43212 614-481-4100
Tracie Lees, prin. Fax 481-3628
Grandview Heights HS 300/9-12
1587 W 3rd Ave 43212 614-485-4000
Ken Chaffin, prin. Fax 481-1067

Groveport Madison Local SD
Supt. — See Groveport
Groveport Madison MS North 400/6-8
5474 Sedalia Dr 43232 614-837-5508
Brandy Grieves, prin. Fax 833-2033

Hamilton Local SD 3,100/PK-12
775 Rathmell Rd 43207 614-491-8044
William J. Morrison, supt. Fax 491-8323
www.hamiltonrangers.org
Hamilton MS 500/7-8
755 Rathmell Rd 43207 614-491-8044
Jeffrey Endres, prin. Fax 491-0260
Hamilton Township HS 900/9-12
1105 Rathmell Rd 43207 614-491-8044
Dr. James Miller, prin. Fax 492-1495

Hilliard CSD 15,600/K-12
2140 Atlas St 43228 614-921-7000
John Marschhausen Ph.D., supt. Fax 921-7001
www.hilliardschools.org
Other Schools – See Hilliard

South-Western CSD
Supt. — See Grove City
Finland MS 700/7-8
1825 Finland Ave 43223 614-801-3600
Lori Balough, prin. Fax 278-6334
Franklin Heights HS 1,200/9-12
1001 Demorest Rd 43204 614-801-3200
Timothy Donahue, prin. Fax 278-6303
Norton MS 500/7-8
215 Norton Rd 43228 614-801-3700
Tresa Davis, prin. Fax 870-5528

Worthington CSD
Supt. — See Worthington
McCord MS 500/7-8
1500 Hard Rd 43235 614-450-4000
Michael Kuri, prin. Fax 883-3560
Worthington Kilbourne HS 1,200/9-12
1499 Hard Rd 43235 614-450-6400
Angie Adrean, prin. Fax 450-6560

American Inst. of Alternative Medicine Post-Sec.
6685 Doubletree Ave 43229 614-825-6255
American School of Technology Post-Sec.
2100 Morse Rd 43229 614-436-4820
Arthur James Cancer Hospital Post-Sec.
300 W 10th Ave 43210 614-293-5485
Bexley Seabury Post-Sec.
583 Sheridan Ave 43209 614-231-3095
Bishop Hartley HS 700/9-12
1285 Zettler Rd 43227 614-237-5421
Mike Winters, prin. Fax 237-3809
Bishop Ready HS 400/9-12
707 Salisbury Rd 43204 614-276-5263
Celene Seamen, prin. Fax 276-5116
Bishop Watterson HS 1,000/9-12
99 E Cooke Rd 43214 614-268-8671
Christopher Campbell, prin. Fax 268-0551
Bradford School Post-Sec.
2469 Stelzer Rd 43219 614-416-6200
Capital University Post-Sec.
1 College and Main 43209 614-236-6011
Chamberlain College of Nursing Post-Sec.
1350 Alum Creek Dr 43209 614-252-8890
Columbus College of Art and Design Post-Sec.
60 Cleveland Ave 43215 614-224-9101
Columbus School for Girls 600/PK-12
65 S Drexel Ave 43209 614-252-0781
Jennifer Ciccarelli, hdmstr. Fax 252-0571
Columbus State Community College Post-Sec.
550 E Spring St 43215 614-287-5353
Columbus Torah Academy 200/K-12
181 Noe Bixby Rd 43213 614-864-0299
Rabbi Avrohom Drandoff, head sch Fax 864-2119
Cristo Rey Columbus HS 9-12
400 E Town St 43215 614-223-9261
Dr. Cathy Thomas, prin.
DeVry University Post-Sec.
1350 Alum Creek Dr 43209 614-253-7291
DeVry University Post-Sec.
8800 Lyra Dr Ste 120 43240 614-854-7500
Felbry College School of Nursing Post-Sec.
6055 Cleveland Ave 43231 614-781-1085
Franklin University Post-Sec.
201 S Grant Ave 43215 614-797-4700
Miami-Jacobs Career College Post-Sec.
150 E Gay St Fl 15 43215 614-221-7770
Mt. Carmel College of Nursing Post-Sec.
127 S Davis Ave 43222 614-234-5800
National College Post-Sec.
5665 Forest Hills Blvd 43231 614-212-2800
Nationwide Beauty Academy Post-Sec.
5300 Westpointe Plaza Dr 43228 614-921-9109
Ohio Business College Post-Sec.
4525 Trueman Blvd 43026 800-954-4274
Ohio Center for Broadcasting Post-Sec.
5330 E Main St Ste 200 43213 614-655-5250
Ohio Dominican University Post-Sec.
1216 Sunbury Rd 43219 614-251-4500
Ohio School for the Deaf Post-Sec.
500 Morse Rd 43214
Ohio State College of Barber Styling Post-Sec.
4614 E Broad St 43213 614-868-1015
Ohio State Sch of Cosmetology Northland Post-Sec.
4390 Karl Rd 43224 614-263-1861
Ohio State School for the Blind Post-Sec.
5220 N High St 43214
Ohio State School of Cosmetology East Post-Sec.
1720 E Broad St 43203 614-868-1601
Ohio State University Post-Sec.
154 W 12th Ave 43210 614-292-6446
Ohio State University Hospitals Post-Sec.
450 W 10th Ave 43210 614-293-5555
Pontifical College Josephinum Post-Sec.
7625 N High St 43235 614-885-5585
St. Charles Preparatory S 600/9-12
2010 E Broad St 43209 614-252-6714
Jim Lower, prin. Fax 251-6800
St. Francis De Sales HS 800/9-12
4212 Karl Rd 43224 614-267-7808
Dan Garrick, prin. Fax 265-3375
Spa School Post-Sec.
5050 N High St 43214 614-888-1092

Tree of Life Christian S - Northridge 400/6-12
935 Northridge Rd 43224 614-263-2688
Dr. Todd Marrah Ph.D., supt. Fax 263-6450
Trinity Lutheran Seminary Post-Sec.
2199 E Main St 43209 614-235-4136
Valor Christian College Post-Sec.
PO Box 800 43216 800-940-9422
Wellington S 700/PK-12
3650 Reed Rd 43220 614-457-7883
Robert Brisk, head sch Fax 442-3286

Columbus Grove, Putnam, Pop. 2,103
Columbus Grove Local SD 800/K-12
201 W Cross St 45830 419-659-2639
George Verhoff, supt. Fax 659-5134
cg.noacsc.org
Columbus Grove HS 300/9-12
201 W Cross St 45830 419-659-2156
Brian Best, prin. Fax 659-5134
Columbus Grove MS 200/5-8
201 W Cross St 45830 419-659-2631
Brad Calvelage, prin. Fax 659-5134

Commercial Point, Pickaway, Pop. 1,557
Teays Valley Local SD
Supt. — See Ashville
Teays Valley West MS 400/6-8
200 Grove Run Rd 43116 740-983-5000
Michael Kauffeld, prin. Fax 983-5040

Concord, Lake
Auburn Vocational SD
8221 Auburn Rd 44077 440-357-7542
Margaret Lynch, supt. Fax 357-0310
www.auburncc.org
Auburn Career Center Vo/Tech
8140 Auburn Rd 44077 440-357-7542
Jeff Slavkovsky, prin. Fax 357-0310

Lake County ESC
8221 Auburn Rd 44077 440-350-2563
Dr. Brian Bontempo, supt. Fax 350-2566
www.esc-lc.org
Other Schools – See Eastlake

Conneaut, Ashtabula, Pop. 12,629
Conneaut Area CSD 1,700/PK-12
230 Gateway Ave Ste B 44030 440-593-7200
Lori Riley, supt. Fax 593-6253
www.cacsk12.org
Conneaut HS 500/9-12
381 Mill St 44030 440-593-7210
Timothy Neal, prin. Fax 593-6899
Conneaut MS 400/6-8
230 Gateway Ave 44030 440-593-7240
James Kennedy, prin. Fax 593-6289

Continental, Putnam, Pop. 1,147
Continental Local SD 500/K-12
5211 State Route 634 45831 419-596-3671
Danny Kissell, supt. Fax 596-3861
www.continentalpirates.org
Continental JSHS 200/7-12
5211 State Route 634 45831 419-596-3871
Danny Kissell, prin. Fax 596-2651

Convoy, Van Wert, Pop. 1,077
Crestview Local SD 800/K-12
531 E Tully St 45832 419-749-9100
Michael Estes, supt. Fax 749-4235
www.crestviewknights.com/
Crestview HS 300/9-12
531 E Tully St 45832 419-749-9100
Michael Biro, prin. Fax 749-4235
Crestview MS 100/7-8
531 E Tully St 45832 419-749-9100
David Bowen, prin. Fax 749-2484

Copley, Summit, Pop. 11,130
Copley-Fairlawn CSD 3,100/PK-12
3797 Ridgewood Rd 44321 330-664-4800
Brian Poe, supt. Fax 664-4811
www.copley-fairlawn.org
Copley-Fairlawn MS 1,000/5-8
1531 S Cleveland Massillon 44321 330-664-4875
Kathleen Ashcroft, prin. Fax 664-4912
Copley HS 1,200/9-12
3807 Ridgewood Rd 44321 330-664-4822
Michael Coury, prin. Fax 664-4951

Corning, Perry, Pop. 572
Southern Local SD 700/K-12
10397 State Route 155 SE 43730 740-394-2426
Greg Holbert, supt. Fax 394-2083
www.spsd.k12.oh.us
Miller HS 300/7-12
10397 State Route 155 SE 43730 740-394-2426
Lisa Love, prin. Fax 394-2083

Cortland, Trumbull, Pop. 7,046
Lakeview Local SD 1,800/K-12
300 Hillman Dr 44410 330-637-8741
Robert Wilson, supt. Fax 282-4260
www.lakeviewlocal.org
Lakeview HS 700/8-12
300 Hillman Dr 44410 330-637-4921
Lawrence Herrholtz, prin. Fax 638-8812

Maplewood Local SD 800/K-12
2414 Greenville Rd 44410 330-637-7506
Perry Nicholas, supt. Fax 637-6616
www.maplewood.k12.oh.us/
Maplewood HS 200/9-12
2414 Greenville Rd 44410 330-637-8466
Gordon Hitchcock, prin. Fax 637-0496
Maplewood MS 300/5-8
4174 Greenville Rd 44410 330-924-2431
Elizabeth Goerig, prin. Fax 924-5151

Mathews Local SD 600/K-12
4096 Cadwallader Sonk Rd 44410 330-637-7000
Lew Lowery, supt. Fax 637-1930
www.mathews.k12.oh.us
Other Schools – See Vienna

Coshocton, Coshocton, Pop. 11,049
Coshocton CSD 1,600/PK-12
1207 Cambridge Rd 43812 740-622-1901
Dr. David Hire, supt. Fax 623-5803
www.coshoctonredskins.com/
Coshocton JSHS 700/7-12
1205 Cambridge Rd 43812 740-622-9433
Grant Fauver, prin. Fax 623-0774

Coshocton County JVSD
23640 Airport Rd 43812 740-622-0211
Deborah Kapp-Salupo, supt. Fax 623-4651
www.coshoctoncareers.org
Coshocton County Career Center Vo/Tech
23640 Airport Rd 43812 740-622-0211
Eddie Dovenbarger, prin. Fax 623-4651

Coshocton Christian S 100/PK-12
23891 Airport Rd 43812 740-622-5052
Stanley Zurowski, prin. Fax 622-9244

Covington, Miami, Pop. 2,556
Covington EVD 800/K-12
807 Chestnut St 45318 937-473-2249
Gene Gooding, supt. Fax 473-3730
www.covington.k12.oh.us
Covington HS 200/9-12
807 Chestnut St 45318 937-473-3746
Josh Long, prin. Fax 473-3435
Covington JHS 200/7-8
807 Chestnnut St 45318 937-473-3746
Josh Long, prin. Fax 473-8189

Craig Beach, Mahoning, Pop. 1,144

TDDS Technical Institute Post-Sec.
PO Box 506 44429 330-538-2216

Crestline, Crawford, Pop. 4,534
Colonel Crawford Local SD
Supt. — See North Robinson
Crawford HS 300/9-12
5444 Crestline Rd 44827 419-562-4666
Jake Bruner, prin. Fax 562-3304
Crawford IS 200/6-8
5444 Crestline Rd 44827 419-562-7529
April Bond, prin. Fax 562-3319

Crestline EVD 600/PK-12
401 Heiser Ct 44827 419-683-3647
Noreen Mullens, supt. Fax 683-2330
www.crestline.k12.oh.us
Crestline HS 300/6-12
435 Oldfield Rd 44827 419-683-3647
Keith Strickler, prin. Fax 683-9063

Creston, Wayne, Pop. 2,138
Norwayne Local SD 1,400/PK-12
350 S Main St 44217 330-435-6382
Karen O'Hare, supt. Fax 435-4633
www.norwayne.net
Norwayne HS 400/9-12
350 S Main St 44217 330-435-6384
Douglas Zimmerly, prin. Fax 435-4633
Norwayne MS 400/6-8
350 S Main St 44217 330-435-1195
Kevin Leatherman, prin. Fax 435-4633

Crooksville, Perry, Pop. 2,512
Crooksville EVD 900/PK-12
4065 School Dr 43731 740-982-7040
Matt Sheridan, supt. Fax 982-3551
www.crooksville.k12.oh.us
Crooksville HS 300/9-12
4075 Ceramic Way 43731 740-982-7015
Kevin Smith, prin. Fax 982-3086
Crooksville MS 300/5-8
12400 Tunnel Hill Rd 43731 740-982-7010
John Toeller, prin. Fax 982-5087

Crown City, Gallia, Pop. 412
Gallia County Local SD
Supt. — See Patriot
South Gallia MSHS 200/6-12
55 Rebel Dr 45623 740-256-1054
Bray Shamblin, prin. Fax 256-6399

Cuyahoga Falls, Summit, Pop. 48,868
Cuyahoga Falls CSD 5,000/K-12
PO Box 396 44222 330-926-3800
Dr. Todd Nichols, supt. Fax 920-1074
www.cfalls.org
Bolich MS 600/6-8
2630 13th St 44223 330-926-3801
Ryan Huch, prin. Fax 920-3737
Cuyahoga Falls HS 1,600/9-12
2300 4th St 44221 330-926-3808
Allison Bogdan, prin. Fax 916-6013
Roberts MS 500/6-8
3333 Charles St 44221 330-926-3809
James Holzapfel, prin. Fax 920-3748

Cuyahoga Valley Christian Academy 900/7-12
4687 Wyoga Lake Rd 44224 330-929-0575
Dr. Matt Koons, hdmstr. Fax 929-0156
Fortis College Post-Sec.
2545 Bailey Rd 44221 330-923-9959
Walsh Jesuit HS 1,000/9-12
4550 Wyoga Lake Rd 44224 330-929-4205
Mark Hassman, prin. Fax 929-9749

Cuyahoga Heights, Cuyahoga, Pop. 635
Cuyahoga Heights Local SD 900/PK-12
4820 E 71st St 44125 216-429-5700
Thomas Evans, supt. Fax 341-3737
www.cuyhts.org

Cuyahoga Heights HS — 300/9-12
4820 E 71st St 44125 — 216-429-5707
William Young, prin. — Fax 429-5706
Cuyahoga Heights MS — 200/6-8
4840 E 71st St 44125 — 216-429-5757
William Young, prin. — Fax 429-5735

Dalton, Wayne, Pop. 1,798
Dalton Local SD — 500/PK-12
PO Box 514 44618 — 330-828-2267
James R. Saxer, supt. — Fax 828-2800
www.dalton.k12.oh.us
Dalton Local HS — 300/9-12
PO Box 514 44618 — 330-828-2261
Nathan Stutz, prin. — Fax 828-2904

Danville, Knox, Pop. 1,035
Danville Local SD — 600/K-12
PO Box 30 43014 — 740-599-6116
Dan Harper, supt. — Fax 599-5417
www.danvilleschools.org
Danville HS — 200/9-12
PO Box 30 43014 — 740-599-6116
Ed Honabarger, prin. — Fax 599-5418
Danville MS — 100/6-8
PO Box 30 43014 — 740-599-6116
Matthew Proper, dir. — Fax 599-5904

Dayton, Montgomery, Pop. 137,548
Centerville CSD
Supt. — See Centerville
Watts MS — 800/6-8
7056 McEwen Rd 45459 — 937-434-0370
Brian Miller, prin. — Fax 434-2907

Dayton CSD — 14,300/PK-12
115 S Ludlow St 45402 — 937-542-3000
Rhonda Corr, supt. — Fax 542-3188
www.dps.k12.oh.us
Belmont HS — 900/7-12
2615 Wayne Ave 45420 — 937-542-6460
Melanie Walter, prin. — Fax 542-6461
Dunbar Early College HS — 500/9-12
1400 Albritton Dr 45417 — 937-542-6760
Crystal Phillips, prin. — Fax 542-6761
Longfellow Academy — 100/Alt
245 Salem Ave 45406 — 937-542-6910
Jack Johnson, dir. — Fax 542-6911
Marshall HS — 700/9-12
4447 Hoover Ave 45417 — 937-542-6610
Sharon Goins, prin. — Fax 542-6611
Meadowdale HS — 600/7-12
3873 Whitestone Ct 45416 — 937-542-7030
Jacquelyn Pope, prin. — Fax 542-7031
Ponitz Career Center — Vo/Tech
741 Washington St 45402 — 937-542-7180
Ray Caruthers, prin. — Fax 542-7181
Stivers S for the Arts — 900/7-12
1313 E 5th St 45402 — 937-542-7380
Erin Dooley, prin. — Fax 542-7381
Wogaman MS — 300/7-8
920 McArthur Ave 45417 — 937-542-5890
Karl Perkins, prin. — Fax 542-5891
Wright Brothers MS — 500/7-8
1361 Huffman Ave 45403 — 937-542-5940
Shawna Welch, prin. — Fax 542-5941

Jefferson Township Local SD — 400/K-12
2625 S Union Rd 45417 — 937-835-5682
Dr. Richard Gates, supt. — Fax 835-5955
www.jeffersontwp.k12.oh.us/
Jefferson HS — 200/7-12
2701 S Union Rd 45417 — 937-295-5691
Walter Sledge, prin. — Fax 835-5693

Mad River Local SD — 3,900/PK-12
801 Old Harshman Rd 45431 — 937-259-6606
Chad Wyen, supt. — Fax 259-6607
www.madriverschools.org
Mad River MS — 600/7-8
1801 Harshman Rd 45424 — 937-237-4265
Laurie Plank, prin. — Fax 237-4273
Stebbins HS — 1,100/9-12
1900 Harshman Rd 45424 — 937-237-4250
Brad Holt, prin. — Fax 237-4262

Montgomery County ESC
200 S Keowee St 45402 — 937-225-4598
Frank DePalma, supt. — Fax 496-7426
www.mcesc.org
Montgomery County Learning Ctr West — Alt
3500 Kettering Blvd 45439 — 937-253-4178
Barb Savino, dir. — Fax 259-5764

Northridge Local SD — 1,700/K-12
2011 Timber Ln 45414 — 937-278-5885
David Jackson, supt. — Fax 276-8351
www.northridgeschools.org
Northridge HS — 700/7-12
2251 Timber Ln 45414 — 937-275-7469
Tim Whitestone, prin. — Fax 275-8434

Bishop Leibold Consolidated S East — 300/4-8
6666 Springboro Pike 45449 — 937-434-9343
David Timpone, prin. — Fax 436-3048
Brightwood College — Post-Sec.
2800 E River Rd 45439 — 937-294-6155
Carousel Beauty College — Post-Sec.
125 E 2nd St 45402 — 937-223-3572
Carroll HS — 800/9-12
4524 Linden Ave 45432 — 937-253-8188
Matthew Sableski, prin. — Fax 258-7001
Chaminade-Julienne HS — 600/9-12
505 S Ludlow St 45402 — 937-461-3740
John Marshall, prin. — Fax 461-6256
Creative Images-Matrix Design Academy — Post-Sec.
7535 Poe Ave 45414 — 937-454-1200
Dayton School of Medical Massage — Post-Sec.
4457 Far Hills Ave 45429 — 937-294-6994
DeVry University — Post-Sec.
3610 Pentagon Blvd Ste 100 45431 — 937-320-3200
East Dayton Christian S — 500/PK-12
999 Spinning Rd 45431 — 937-252-5400
Stacie Auvil, prin. — Fax 258-4099
International College of Broadcasting — Post-Sec.
6 S Smithville Rd 45431 — 937-258-8251
Miami-Jacobs Career College — Post-Sec.
110 N Patterson Blvd 45402 — 937-222-7337
Miami Valley Hospital — Post-Sec.
1 Wyoming St 45409 — 937-223-6192
Miami Valley S — 500/PK-12
5151 Denise Dr 45429 — 937-434-4444
Jay Scheurle, hdmstr. — Fax 434-1033
Ohio Medical Career College — Post-Sec.
1133 S E C Moses Blvd #110 45417 — 937-567-8880
Sinclair Community College — Post-Sec.
444 W 3rd St 45402 — 800-315-3000
United Theological Seminary — Post-Sec.
4501 Denlinger Rd 45426 — 937-529-2201
University of Dayton — Post-Sec.
300 College Park Ave 45469 — 937-229-1000
Wright State University — Post-Sec.
3640 Colonel Glenn Hwy 45435 — 937-775-3333

Defiance, Defiance, Pop. 16,265
Ayersville Local SD — 800/K-12
28046 Watson Rd 43512 — 419-395-1111
Don Diglia, supt. — Fax 395-9990
www.ayersville.org
Ayersville JSHS — 400/7-12
28046 Watson Rd 43512 — 419-395-1111
Jeremy Kuhlman, prin. — Fax 395-2566

Defiance CSD — 2,500/K-12
629 Arabella St 43512 — 419-782-0070
Michael Struble, supt. — Fax 782-4395
www.defiancecityschools.org
Defiance HS — 700/9-12
1755 Palmer Dr 43512 — 419-784-2777
Robert Morton, prin. — Fax 784-0102
Defiance MS — 600/6-8
629 Arabella St 43512 — 419-782-0050
Richard Peters, prin. — Fax 782-0060

Northeastern Local SD — 1,100/K-12
5921 Domersville Rd 43512 — 419-497-3461
James Roach, supt. — Fax 497-3401
www.tinora.org
Tinora HS — 300/9-12
5921 Domersville Rd 43512 — 419-497-2621
Christopher Lake, prin. — Fax 497-3401
Tinora JHS — 200/7-8
5921 Domersville Rd 43512 — 419-497-2361
G. Kent Adams, prin. — Fax 497-3401

Defiance College — Post-Sec.
701 N Clinton St 43512 — 419-784-4010

De Graff, Logan, Pop. 1,275
Riverside Local SD — 700/K-12
2096 County Road 24 S 43318 — 937-585-5981
Scott Mann, supt. — Fax 585-4599
www.riverside.k12.oh.us
Riverside JSHS — 300/7-12
2096 County Road 24 S 43318 — 937-585-5981
Kelly Kauffman, prin. — Fax 585-4599

Delaware, Delaware, Pop. 33,899
Buckeye Valley Local SD — 2,200/PK-12
679 Coover Rd 43015 — 740-369-8735
Andrew Miller, supt. — Fax 363-7654
www.buckeyevalley.k12.oh.us
Buckeye Valley HS — 700/9-12
901 Coover Rd 43015 — 740-363-1349
Jim Albanese, prin. — Fax 363-9380
Buckeye Valley MS — 800/5-8
683 Coover Rd 43015 — 740-363-6626
Brian Baker, prin. — Fax 363-4483

Delaware Area Career Center
4565 Columbus Pike 43015 — 740-548-0708
Mary Beth Freeman, supt. — Fax 548-0710
www.delawareareacc.org
Delaware Area Career Center North Campus — Vo/Tech
1610 State Route 521 43015 — 740-363-1993
Tom Marchetti, dir. — Fax 362-6461
Delaware Area Career Center South Campus — Vo/Tech
4565 Columbus Pike 43015 — 740-548-0708
Kris Lucas, prin. — Fax 548-0710

Delaware CSD — 4,500/PK-12
74 W William St 43015 — 740-833-1100
Paul Craft, supt. — Fax 833-1149
www.dcs.k12.oh.us
Dempsey MS — 800/6-8
599 Pennsylvania Ave 43015 — 740-833-1800
Dan Bartha, prin. — Fax 833-1899
Hayes HS — 1,400/9-12
289 Euclid Ave 43015 — 740-833-1010
Ric Stranges, prin. — Fax 833-1099

Delaware Christian S — 300/PK-12
45 Belle Ave 43015 — 740-363-8425
John Stubblefield, admin. — Fax 203-2117
Methodist Theological School in Ohio — Post-Sec.
3081 Columbus Pike 43015 — 740-363-1146
Ohio Wesleyan University — Post-Sec.
61 S Sandusky St 43015 — 740-368-2000

Delphos, Allen, Pop. 7,017
Delphos CSD — 1,100/K-12
234 N Jefferson St 45833 — 419-692-2509
Kevin Wolfe, supt. — Fax 692-2653
www.delphoscityschools.org
Jefferson HS — 300/9-12
901 Wildcat Ln 45833 — 419-695-1786
Chad Brinkman, prin. — Fax 692-2287
Jefferson MS — 200/6-8
227 N Jefferson St 45833 — 419-695-2523
Doug Westrick, prin. — Fax 692-2302

St. John HS — 300/9-12
515 E 2nd St 45833 — 419-692-5371
Adam Lee, prin. — Fax 879-6874

Delta, Fulton, Pop. 3,070
Pike-Delta-York Local SD — 1,300/K-12
504 Fernwood St 43515 — 419-822-3391
Ted Haselman, supt. — Fax 822-4478
www.pdys.org
Pike-Delta-York HS — 400/9-12
605 Taylor St 43515 — 419-822-8247
Kristie Reighard, prin. — Fax 822-2826
Pike-Delta-York MS — 400/5-8
1101 Panther Pride Dr 43515 — 419-822-9118
Douglas Ford, prin. — Fax 822-8490

Dennison, Tuscarawas, Pop. 2,624
Claymont CSD — 1,500/PK-12
201 N 3rd St 44621 — 740-922-5478
John Rocchi, supt. — Fax 922-7325
www.claymontschools.org
Other Schools – See Uhrichsville

Diamond, Portage
Southeast Local SD
Supt. — See Ravenna
Southeast MS — 400/6-8
8540 Tallmadge Rd 44412 — 330-654-1950
Michelle Hiser, prin. — Fax 654-9110

Dillonvale, Jefferson, Pop. 660
Buckeye Local SD — 1,900/PK-12
6899 State Route 150 43917 — 740-769-7395
Scott Celestin, supt. — Fax 769-2361
buckeye.omeresa.net/
Other Schools – See Rayland

Dola, Hardin, Pop. 136
Hardin Northern Local SD — 400/K-12
11589 State Route 81 45835 — 419-759-2331
Dr. Jeffrey Price Ed.D., supt. — Fax 759-2581
www.hardinnorthern.org
Hardin Northern JSHS — 200/7-12
11589 State Route 81 45835 — 419-759-3515
Andrew Cano, prin. — Fax 759-2581

Dover, Tuscarawas, Pop. 12,639
Dover CSD — 2,800/PK-12
219 W 6th St 44622 — 330-364-1906
Carla Birney, supt. — Fax 343-7070
www.dovertornadoes.com
Dover HS — 800/9-12
520 N Walnut St 44622 — 330-364-7148
Teresa Alberts, prin. — Fax 364-7142
Dover MS — 700/6-8
2131 N Wooster Ave 44622 — 330-364-7121
Jack Edwards, prin. — Fax 364-7127

Doylestown, Wayne, Pop. 3,018
Chippewa Local SD — 1,400/K-12
56 N Portage St 44230 — 330-658-6368
Sandy Stebly, supt. — Fax 658-5842
www.chippewa.k12.oh.us
Chippewa HS — 400/9-12
100 Valley View Rd 44230 — 330-658-2011
Shawn Braman, prin. — Fax 658-3339
Chippewa MS — 400/5-8
257 High St 44230 — 330-658-2214
Steven Watkins, prin. — Fax 658-5842

Dresden, Muskingum, Pop. 1,503
Tri-Valley Local SD — 3,000/K-12
36 E Muskingum Ave 43821 — 740-754-1442
Mark Neal, supt. — Fax 754-6400
www.tvschools.org
Tri-Valley HS — 900/9-12
46 E Muskingum Ave 43821 — 740-754-2921
Chad Shawger, prin. — Fax 754-6409
Tri-Valley MS — 500/7-8
1360 Main St 43821 — 740-754-3531
Patrick Hopkins, prin. — Fax 754-1879

Dublin, Franklin, Pop. 40,967
Dublin CSD — 14,700/PK-12
7030 Coffman Rd 43017 — 614-764-5913
Dr. Todd Hoadley, supt. — Fax 761-5856
www.dublinschools.net
Davis MS — 900/6-8
2400 Sutter Pkwy 43016 — 614-761-5820
Tracey Deagle, prin. — Fax 761-5893
Dublin Coffman HS — 1,900/9-12
6780 Coffman Rd 43017 — 614-764-5900
Mike Ulring, prin. — Fax 764-5925
Dublin Jerome HS — 1,400/9-12
8300 Hyland Croy Rd 43016 — 614-873-7377
Dustin Miller, prin. — Fax 873-7340
Dublin Scioto HS — 1,200/9-12
4000 Hard Rd 43016 — 614-717-2464
Robert Scott, prin. — Fax 717-2484
Grizzell MS — 700/6-8
8705 Avery Rd 43017 — 614-798-3569
Corinne Evans, prin. — Fax 761-6514
Karrer MS — 800/6-8
7245 Tullymore Dr 43016 — 614-873-0459
Mark Mousa, prin. — Fax 873-1492
Sells MS — 900/6-8
150 W Bridge St 43017 — 614-764-5919
Matthew Sachtleben, prin. — Fax 764-5923

Duncan Falls, Muskingum, Pop. 873
Franklin Local SD — 2,000/PK-12
PO Box 428 43734 — 740-674-5203
Sharon McDermott, supt. — Fax 674-5214
www.franklinlocalschools.org
Philo HS — 500/9-12
4000 Millers Ln 43734 — 740-674-4355
Troy Dawson, prin. — Fax 674-5202
Other Schools – See Philo

East Canton, Stark, Pop. 1,566
Osnaburg Local SD 900/PK-12
310 Browning Ct N 44730 330-488-1609
Todd Boggs, supt. Fax 488-4001
ecweb.sparcc.org
East Canton HS 300/9-12
310 Browning Ct N 44730 330-488-0316
Andrew Mangun, prin. Fax 488-4015
East Canton MS 200/6-8
310 Browning Ct N 44730 330-488-0334
Gregory Dente, prin. Fax 488-4015

East Cleveland, Cuyahoga, Pop. 17,585
East Cleveland CSD 2,500/PK-12
1843 Stanwood Rd 44112 216-268-6600
Myrna Corley, supt. Fax 268-6676
www.east-cleveland.k12.oh.us
Heritage MS 300/7-8
14410 Terrace Rd 44112 216-268-6610
Gilda Roberts, prin. Fax 268-6676
Shaw HS 900/9-12
15320 Euclid Ave 44112 216-268-6500
Diane Hunsbarger, prin. Fax 268-6676

Huron School of Nursing Post-Sec.
13951 Terrace Rd 44112 216-761-7996

Eastlake, Lake, Pop. 18,364
Lake County ESC
Supt. — See Concord
Lake Academy Alt
503 Vegas Dr 44095 440-942-7401
Bill Kermavner, dir. Fax 942-1790

Willoughby-Eastlake CSD
Supt. — See Willoughby
Eastlake MS 400/6-8
35972 Lake Shore Blvd 44095 440-942-5696
Michael Chokshi, prin. Fax 918-8973
North HS 1,300/9-12
34041 Stevens Blvd 44095 440-975-3666
Eric Frei, prin. Fax 975-3671

Bryant & Stratton College Post-Sec.
35350 Curtis Blvd Ste 100 44095 440-510-1112

East Liverpool, Columbiana, Pop. 10,871
Beaver Local SD 1,600/K-12
46088 Bell School Rd 43920 330-385-6831
Eric Lowe, supt. Fax 386-8711
www.beaver.k12.oh.us/
Beaver Local HS 600/9-12
46088 Bell School Rd 43920 330-386-8700
Thomas Cunningham, prin. Fax 386-8720
Beaver Local MS 600/5-8
46088 Bell School Rd 43920 330-386-8707
Connie Shive, prin. Fax 382-0317

East Liverpool CSD 2,200/K-12
810 W 8th St 43920 330-385-7132
Randy Taylor, supt. Fax 382-7673
www.elcsd.k12.oh.us
East Liverpool HS 600/9-12
100 Maine Blvd 43920 330-386-8750
Randy Taylor, prin. Fax 386-8753
East Liverpool JHS 300/7-8
100 Maine Blvd 43920 330-386-8750
Randy Taylor, prin. Fax 386-8753

American Spirit Academy 100/PK-12
46682 Florence St 43920 330-385-5588
Susan Mackall, hdmstr. Fax 385-1267
Kent State University-East Liverpool Post-Sec.
400 E 4th St 43920 330-385-3805
Ohio Valley College of Technology Post-Sec.
15258 State Route 170 43920 330-385-1070

East Palestine, Columbiana, Pop. 4,696
East Palestine CSD 1,100/PK-12
200 W North Ave 44413 330-426-4191
Traci Hostetler, supt. Fax 426-9592
www.myepschools.org
East Palestine HS 300/9-12
360 W Grant St 44413 330-426-9401
Chris Neifer, prin. Fax 426-5105
East Palestine MS 400/5-8
320 W Grant St 44413 330-426-9451
James Rook, prin. Fax 426-5118

Eaton, Preble, Pop. 8,276
Eaton Community SD 2,100/K-12
306 Eaton Lewisburg Rd 45320 937-456-1107
Barbara Curry, supt. Fax 472-1057
www.eaton.k12.oh.us
Eaton HS 600/9-12
600 Hillcrest Dr 45320 937-456-1141
Scott Couch, prin. Fax 456-1143
Eaton MS 500/6-8
814 Camden Rd 45320 937-456-2286
Derek Flatter, prin. Fax 456-9687

Edgerton, Williams, Pop. 1,997
Edgerton Local SD 600/PK-12
111 E River St 43517 419-298-2112
Andy Morr, supt. Fax 298-1322
www.edgerton.k12.oh.us/
Edgerton HS 300/7-12
111 E River St 43517 419-298-2331
Roger Cade, prin. Fax 298-1322

Edon, Williams, Pop. 823
Edon Northwest Local SD 500/K-12
802 W Indiana St 43518 419-272-3213
Dr. John Granger, supt. Fax 272-2240
www.edon.k12.oh.us/
Edon Northwest HS 200/7-12
802 W Indiana St 43518 419-272-3113
Anthony Stevens, prin. Fax 272-2240

Elida, Allen, Pop. 1,868
Elida Local SD 2,500/K-12
4380 Sunnydale St 45807 419-331-4155
Joel Mengerink, supt. Fax 331-1656
home.elida.k12.oh.us
Elida HS 700/9-12
401 E North St 45807 419-331-4115
Darren Sharp, prin. Fax 339-3523
Elida MS 800/5-8
4500 Sunnydale St 45807 419-331-2505
Douglas Drury, prin. Fax 331-6822

Elmore, Ottawa, Pop. 1,392
Woodmore Local SD 800/PK-12
349 Rice St 43416 419-862-1060
James Lefevre, supt. Fax 862-1951
www.woodmore.k12.oh.us
Woodmore HS 300/9-12
633 Fremont St 43416 419-862-2721
James Kieper, prin. Fax 862-3835
Other Schools – See Woodville

Elyria, Lorain, Pop. 52,588
Elyria CSD 6,400/PK-12
42101 Griswold Rd 44035 440-284-8000
Dr. Thomas Jama, supt. Fax 284-0678
www.elyriaschools.org
Eastern Heights MS 500/6-8
528 Garford Ave 44035 440-284-8015
Dr. Kimberly Benetto, prin. Fax 323-0827
Elyria HS 1,900/9-12
601 Middle Ave 44035 440-284-8300
Dr. Tim Brown, prin. Fax 323-2543
Northwood MS 500/6-8
700 Gulf Rd 44035 440-284-8016
Michael Basinski, prin. Fax 284-1546
Westwood MS 400/6-8
42350 Adelbert St 44035 440-284-8017
Theresa Lengel, prin. Fax 284-1055

Elyria Catholic HS 400/9-12
725 Gulf Rd 44035 440-365-1821
Suzanne Lester, prin. Fax 365-7536
First Baptist Christian S 100/PK-12
11400 Lagrange Rd 44035 440-458-5185
Tim Spickler, admin. Fax 458-8717
Lorain County Community College Post-Sec.
1005 Abbe Rd N 44035 440-365-5222
Open Door Christian S 500/PK-12
8287 W Ridge Rd 44035 440-322-6386
Denver Daniel, head sch Fax 284-6033

Englewood, Montgomery, Pop. 13,133
Northmont CSD 4,000/PK-12
4001 Old Salem Rd 45322 937-832-5000
Tony Thomas, supt. Fax 832-5001
www.northmontschools.com/
Other Schools – See Clayton

Enon, Clark, Pop. 2,391
Greenon Local SD 1,000/PK-12
500 S Xenia Dr 45323 937-864-1202
Bradley Silvus, supt. Fax 864-2470
www.greenon.k12.oh.us
Other Schools – See Springfield

Etna, Licking, Pop. 1,187
Southwest Licking Local SD
Supt. — See Pataskala
Watkins Memorial HS 1,100/9-12
8868 Watkins Rd SW, 740-927-3846
Mike Tanchevski, prin. Fax 964-0088
Watkins MS 900/6-8
8808 Watkins Rd SW, 740-927-5767
Ryan Brown, prin. Fax 927-2337

Euclid, Cuyahoga, Pop. 47,840
Euclid CSD 4,400/PK-12
651 E 222nd St 44123 216-261-2900
Dr. Charles Smialek, supt. Fax 261-3120
www.euclidschools.org
Euclid HS 1,900/8-12
711 E 222nd St 44123 216-797-7800
Angela Terella, prin. Fax 797-7900

Fairborn, Greene, Pop. 31,321
Fairborn CSD 4,400/PK-12
306 E Whittier Ave 45324 937-878-3961
Mark North, supt. Fax 879-8180
www.fairborn.k12.oh.us
Baker MS 900/6-8
200 Lincoln Dr 45324 937-878-4681
Deb Hauberg, prin. Fax 879-8193
Fairborn HS 1,000/9-12
900 E Dayton Yellow Springs 45324 937-879-3611
Eugene Lolli, prin. Fax 879-8190

Hondros College Post-Sec.
1810 Successful Dr 45324 937-879-1940

Fairfield, Butler, Pop. 41,547
Fairfield CSD 9,700/PK-12
4641 Bach Ln 45014 513-829-6300
Billy Smith, supt. Fax 829-0148
www.fairfieldcityschools.com
Fairfield Freshman HS 700/9-9
5050 Dixie Hwy 45014 513-829-8300
Michael Berkemeier, prin. Fax 829-4733
Fairfield MS 1,600/7-8
1111 Nilles Rd 45014 513-829-4433
Aileen Ernst, prin. Fax 829-6480
Fairfield SHS 2,100/10-12
8800 Holden Blvd 45014 513-942-2999
William Rice, prin. Fax 942-3288

Cincinnati Christian Schools - JSHS Cmps 400/7-12
7474 Morris Rd 45011 513-892-8500
Kim Stone, prin. Fax 892-0516
Moler-Hollywood Beauty Academy Post-Sec.
5951 Boymel Dr Ste S 45014 513-874-5116

Fairport Harbor, Lake, Pop. 3,058
Fairport Harbor EVD 600/K-12
329 Vine St 44077 440-354-5400
Domenic Paolo, supt. Fax 354-5426
www.fairport.k12.oh.us/
Fairport Harding JSHS 300/6-12
329 Vine St 44077 440-354-3592
Thomas Fazekas, prin. Fax 354-5426

Fairview Park, Cuyahoga, Pop. 16,640
Fairview Park CSD 1,800/PK-12
21620 Mastick Rd 44126 440-331-5500
William Wagner, supt. Fax 356-3545
www.fairviewparkschools.org
Fairview HS 600/9-12
4507 W 213th St 44126 440-356-3500
Christopher Vicha, prin. Fax 356-3529
Mayer MS 400/6-8
21200 Campus Dr 44126 440-356-3510
Raymond Mohr, prin. Fax 895-2191

Fairview Academy Post-Sec.
22610 Lorain Rd 44126 440-734-5555

Farmersville, Montgomery, Pop. 991
Valley View Local SD
Supt. — See Germantown
Valley View JHS 300/7-8
202 Jackson St 45325 937-696-2591
Nichole Thomas, prin. Fax 696-1007

Fayette, Fulton, Pop. 1,278
Fayette Local SD 400/K-12
400 E Gamble Rd 43521 419-237-2573
Erik Belcher, supt. Fax 237-3125
www.fayettesch.org
Fayette JSHS 200/7-12
400 E Gamble Rd 43521 419-237-2114
Jon Molter, prin. Fax 237-4306

Fayetteville, Brown, Pop. 329
Fayetteville-Perry Local SD 800/PK-12
551 S Apple St 45118 513-875-2423
James Brady, supt. Fax 875-2703
www.fp.k12.oh.us
Fayetteville-Perry HS 200/9-12
501 S Apple St 45118 513-875-3520
Tim Carlier, prin. Fax 875-4512
Fayetteville-Perry MS 200/6-8
521 S Apple St 45118 513-875-2829
Ryan Briggs, prin. Fax 875-4200

Felicity, Clermont, Pop. 815
Felicity-Franklin Local SD 900/PK-12
PO Box 619 45120 513-876-2113
David Gibson, supt. Fax 876-2519
www.felicityschools.org/
Felicity-Franklin Local HS 300/9-12
PO Box 619 45120 513-876-2111
Brad Ellis, prin. Fax 876-2560
Felicity-Franklin Local MS 300/5-8
PO Box 619 45120 513-876-2662
Joe Pfeffer, prin. Fax 876-2848

Findlay, Hancock, Pop. 40,536
Findlay CSD 5,800/PK-12
1100 Broad Ave 45840 419-425-8212
Edward Kurt, supt. Fax 425-8203
www.findlaycityschools.org
Donnell MS, 301 Baldwin Ave 45840 600/6-8
Don Williams, prin. 419-425-8370
Findlay HS 1,900/9-12
1200 Broad Ave 45840 419-425-8279
Craig Kupferberg, prin. Fax 427-5448
Glenwood MS 600/6-8
1715 N Main St 45840 419-425-8373
Janice Panuto, prin. Fax 427-5455
Millstream Career Center Vo/Tech
1150 Broad Ave 45840 419-425-8293
David Danoff, prin. Fax 420-7199

Hancock County ESC
7746 County Road 140 45840 419-422-7525
Larry Busdeker, supt. Fax 422-8766
hancockesc.org
Hancock Alternative Opportunity HS Alt
7746 County Road 140 45840 419-422-7525
Randy Ward, prin. Fax 422-8766

Liberty-Benton Local SD 1,300/K-12
9190 County Road 9 45840 419-422-8526
James Kanable, supt. Fax 422-5108
www.liberty-benton.org
Liberty-Benton HS 400/9-12
9190 County Road 9 45840 419-424-5351
Brenda Frankart, prin. Fax 424-5352
Liberty Benton MS 300/6-8
9190 County Road 9 45840 419-422-9166
Bruce Otley, prin. Fax 420-9237

Owens Community College Post-Sec.
3200 Bright Rd 45840 567-661-7000
University of Findlay Post-Sec.
1000 N Main St 45840 800-548-0932
Winebrenner Theological Seminary Post-Sec.
950 N Main St 45840 419-434-4200

Fort Jennings, Putnam, Pop. 485
Jennings Local SD 400/K-12
PO Box 98 45844 419-286-2238
Nicholas Langhals, supt. Fax 286-2240
www.jenningslocal.org
Fort Jennings JSHS 200/7-12
PO Box 98 45844 419-286-2238
Nicholas Langhals, prin. Fax 286-2240

Fort Loramie, Shelby, Pop. 1,478
Fort Loramie Local SD 800/K-12
PO Box 26 45845 937-295-3931
Daniel Holland, supt. Fax 295-2758
www.loramie.k12.oh.us/

Fort Loramie JSHS 400/7-12
PO Box 290 45845 937-295-3342
Kreg Hollenbacher, prin. Fax 295-2758

Fort Recovery, Mercer, Pop. 1,410
Fort Recovery Local SD 900/PK-12
PO Box 604 45846 419-375-4139
Justin Firks, supt. Fax 375-1058
www.fortrecoveryschools.org
Fort Recovery HS 300/9-12
PO Box 604 45846 419-375-4111
Marcus Overman, prin. Fax 375-2039
Fort Recovery MS 200/4-8
865 Sharpsburg Rd 45846 419-375-2815
Anthony Stahl, prin. Fax 375-4231

Fostoria, Seneca, Pop. 12,940
Fostoria CSD 1,800/PK-12
1001 Park Ave 44830 419-435-8163
Andrew Sprang, supt. Fax 436-4109
www.fostoriaschools.org/
Fostoria JSHS 700/7-12
1001 Park Ave 44830 419-436-4110
Drew Bauman, prin. Fax 436-4118

St. Wendelin S 300/PK-12
533 N Countyline St 44830 419-435-8144
Cathy Krupp, prin. Fax 436-4042

Frankfort, Ross, Pop. 1,038
Adena Local SD 1,300/PK-12
3367 County Road 550 45628 740-998-4633
John Balzer, supt. Fax 998-4632
www.adenalocalschools.com
Adena HS 400/9-12
3367 County Road 550 45628 740-998-2313
Craig Kerns, prin. Fax 998-2317
Adena MS 300/5-8
3367 County Road 550 45628 740-998-2313
Lisa Wayland, prin. Fax 998-2317

Franklin, Warren, Pop. 11,585
Franklin CSD 2,900/K-12
150 E 6th St 45005 937-746-1699
Michael Sander, supt. Fax 743-8620
www.franklincityschools.com
Franklin HS 800/9-12
750 E 4th St 45005 937-743-8610
James McFarland, prin. Fax 743-8625
Franklin JHS 500/7-8
136 E 6th St 45005 937-743-8630
Jeremy Ward, prin. Fax 743-8635

Bishop Fenwick HS 500/9-12
4855 State Route 122 45005 513-423-0723
Andrew Barczak, prin. Fax 420-8690
Middletown Christian S 500/PK-12
3011 Union Rd 45005 513-423-4542
Brian Williams, supt. Fax 261-6841

Franklin Furnace, Scioto, Pop. 1,641
Green Local SD 400/PK-12
4070 Gallia Pike 45629 740-354-9221
Jodi Armstrong, supt. Fax 355-8975
www.green.k12.oh.us
Green JSHS 200/7-12
4057 Gallia Pike 45629 740-354-9150
Joseph Emnett, prin. Fax 355-4094

Fredericktown, Knox, Pop. 2,475
Fredericktown Local SD 900/K-12
117 Columbus Rd 43019 740-694-2956
Matthew W. Chrispin, supt. Fax 694-0956
www.fredericktownschools.com
Fredericktown MSHS 300/6-12
111 Stadium Dr 43019 740-694-2726
Sam Shuman, prin. Fax 694-1294

Freeport, Harrison, Pop. 360

Antrim Mennonite S 50/K-12
20360 Cadiz Rd 43973 740-489-5161
Titus Lapp, prin.

Fremont, Sandusky, Pop. 16,145
Fremont CSD 4,100/K-12
500 W State St Ste A 43420 419-332-6454
Dr. Traci McCaudy, supt. Fax 334-5454
www.fremontschools.net
Fremont MS 1,000/6-8
1250 North St 43420 419-332-5569
Marjoe Cooper, prin. Fax 334-5494
Fremont Ross SHS 1,100/9-12
1100 North St 43420 419-332-8221
Gracy Lloyd, prin. Fax 334-5450

Vanguard-Sentinel JVSD
1306 Cedar St 43420 419-332-2626
Gregory Edinger, supt. Fax 334-4308
www.vscc.k12.oh.us/
Vanguard Career Center Vo/Tech
1306 Cedar St 43420 419-332-2626
Clay Frye, dir. Fax 334-5692
Other Schools – See Tiffin

Bishop Hoffman HS 200/7-12
702 Croghan St 43420 419-332-9947
Tim Cullen, supt. Fax 332-4945
Terra State Community College Post-Sec.
2830 Napoleon Rd 43420 419-334-8400

Gahanna, Franklin, Pop. 32,425
Gahanna-Jefferson CSD 7,100/PK-12
160 S Hamilton Rd 43230 614-471-7065
Stephen Barrett, supt. Fax 478-5568
www.gahannaschools.org
Gahanna MS East 600/6-8
730 Clotts Rd 43230 614-478-5550
Brad Barboza, prin. Fax 478-5544
Gahanna MS South 600/6-8
349 Shady Spring Dr 43230 614-337-3730
Robin Murdock, prin. Fax 337-3734
Gahanna MS West 600/6-8
350 N Stygler Rd 43230 614-478-5570
Aaron Winner, prin. Fax 337-3771
Lincoln HS 2,200/9-12
140 S Hamilton Rd 43230 614-478-5500
Robert Dodd, prin. Fax 337-3769

Columbus Academy 1,100/PK-12
4300 Cherry Bottom Rd 43230 614-475-2311
Melissa Soderberg, admin. Fax 475-0396
Everest Institute Post-Sec.
825 Tech Center Dr 43230 614-322-3414
Gahanna Christian Academy 500/PK-12
817 N Hamilton Rd 43230 614-471-9270
April Domine, supt. Fax 471-9201

Galena, Delaware, Pop. 644
Olentangy Local SD
Supt. — See Lewis Center
Berkshire MS 900/6-8
2869 S 3 Bs and K Rd 43021 740-657-5200
Carla Baker, prin. Fax 657-5299

Galion, Crawford, Pop. 10,395
Galion CSD 1,900/PK-12
470 Portland Way N 44833 419-468-3432
Dr. James Grubbs, supt. Fax 468-4333
www.galionschools.org
Galion HS 500/9-12
472 Portland Way N 44833 419-468-6500
Ronald Williams, prin. Fax 468-4333
Galion MS 500/6-8
474 Portland Way N 44833 419-468-3134
Joseph Morabito, prin. Fax 468-4333

Northmor Local SD 1,100/K-12
5247 County Road 29 44833 419-946-8861
Chad Redmon Ed.D., supt. Fax 947-6255
www.northmor.k12.oh.us
Northmor HS 500/7-12
7819 State Route 19 44833 419-946-3946
Benji Bethea, prin. Fax 947-7545

Gallipolis, Gallia, Pop. 3,534
Gallipolis CSD 2,100/PK-12
61 State 45631 740-446-3211
Roger Mace, supt. Fax 446-6433
www.gc.k12.oh.us
Alternative S 50/Alt
2855 Centenary Rd 45631 740-446-3212
Adam Clark, prin.
Gallia Academy HS 600/9-12
2855 Centenary Rd 45631 740-446-3212
Josh Donley, prin. Fax 446-3436
Gallia Academy MS 500/6-8
340 4th Ave 45631 740-446-3214
Craig Wright, prin. Fax 446-2493

Gallipolis Career College Post-Sec.
1176 Jackson Pike # 312 45631 740-446-4367
Gallipolis State Institute 45631 Post-Sec.
Ohio Valley Christian S 100/PK-12
1100 4th Ave 45631 740-446-0374
Patrick O'Donnell, admin. Fax 446-3961

Galloway, Franklin
South-Western CSD
Supt. — See Grove City
Westland HS 1,600/9-12
146 Galloway Rd 43119 614-851-7000
Steve Gehlert, prin. Fax 870-5531

Gambier, Knox, Pop. 2,300

Kenyon College Post-Sec.
1 Kenyon College 43022 740-427-5000

Garfield Heights, Cuyahoga, Pop. 28,281
Garfield Heights CSD 3,700/K-12
5640 Briarcliff Dr 44125 216-475-8100
Terrance Olszewski, supt. Fax 475-1824
www.garfieldheightscityschools.com
Garfield Heights HS 1,300/9-12
4900 Turney Rd 44125 216-662-2800
Tammy Hager, prin. Fax 271-6183
Garfield Heights MS 900/6-8
12000 Maple Leaf Dr 44125 216-475-8105
Christopher Sauer, prin. Fax 475-8146

Trinity HS 300/9-12
12425 Granger Rd 44125 216-581-1644
Linda Bacho, prin. Fax 581-9348

Garrettsville, Portage, Pop. 2,303
James A. Garfield Local SD 1,200/PK-12
10235 State Route 88 44231 330-527-4336
Ted A. Lysiak, supt. Fax 527-5941
garfield.sparcc.org/
Garfield HS 400/9-12
10233 State Route 88 44231 330-527-4341
Michael Dobran, prin. Fax 527-5636
Garfield MS 200/7-8
10231 State Route 88 44231 330-527-2151
Jennifer Mulhern, prin. Fax 527-2601

Gates Mills, Cuyahoga, Pop. 2,236

Gilmour Academy 700/PK-12
34001 Cedar Rd 44040 440-473-8090
Kathleen Kenny, head sch Fax 473-8010
Hawken S 400/9-12
PO Box 8002 44040 440-423-4446
D. Scott Looney, head sch Fax 423-2960

Geneva, Ashtabula, Pop. 6,134
Geneva CSD 2,500/PK-12
135 S Eagle St 44041 440-466-4831
Eric Kujala, supt. Fax 466-0908
www.genevaschools.org/
Geneva HS 800/9-12
1301 S Ridge Rd E 44041 440-466-4831
Douglas Wetherholt, prin. Fax 466-8547
Geneva MS 600/6-8
839 Sherman St 44041 440-466-4831
Steve Candela, prin. Fax 466-5692

Genoa, Ottawa, Pop. 2,309
Genoa Area Local SD 1,300/K-12
2810 N Genoa Clay Center Rd 43430 419-855-7741
Michael Ferguson, supt. Fax 855-4030
www.genoaschools.com
Genoa Area HS 400/9-12
2980 N Genoa Clay Center Rd 43430 419-855-7741
Cari Buehler, prin. Fax 855-7739
Genoa Area MS 300/6-8
2950 N Genoa Clay Center Rd 43430 419-855-7741
Kevin Katafias, prin. Fax 855-7784

Georgetown, Brown, Pop. 4,266
Georgetown EVD 1,000/PK-12
1043 Mount Orab Pike 45121 937-378-3730
Christopher Burrows, supt. Fax 378-2219
www.gtown.k12.oh.us/
Georgetown JSHS 400/7-12
987 Mount Orab Pike 45121 937-378-6730
Jerry Underwood, prin. Fax 378-2442

Southern Hills JVSD
9193 Hamer Rd 45121 937-378-6131
Kevin Kratzer, supt. Fax 378-4577
www.shctc.k12.oh.us
Southern Hills Career & Technical Center Vo/Tech
9193 Hamer Rd 45121 937-378-6131
Guy Hopkins, prin. Fax 378-4863

Germantown, Montgomery, Pop. 5,508
Valley View Local SD 1,900/PK-12
59 Peffley St 45327 937-855-6581
Richard Earley, supt. Fax 855-0266
www.valleyview.k12.oh.us
Valley View HS 500/9-12
6027 Frmrsvll Germantn Pike 45327 937-855-4116
Todd Kozarec, prin. Fax 855-4739
Other Schools – See Farmersville

Germantown Christian S 100/PK-12
9440 Eby Rd 45327 937-855-7334
Rhonda Jerman, prin. Fax 855-7746

Gibsonburg, Sandusky, Pop. 2,557
Gibsonburg EVD 1,100/PK-12
301 S Sunset Ave 43431 419-637-2479
Tim Murray, supt. Fax 637-3029
www.gibsonburg.k12.oh.us/
Gibsonburg HS 300/9-12
740 S Main St 43431 419-637-2873
Jim Rutter, prin. Fax 637-2873
Gibsonburg MS 200/6-8
740 S Main St 43431 419-637-2873
Jim Rutter, prin. Fax 637-2873

Girard, Trumbull, Pop. 9,767
Girard CSD 1,700/K-12
100 W Main St Ste 2 44420 330-545-2596
David Cappuzzello, supt. Fax 545-2597
www.girardcityschools.org/
Girard HS 500/9-12
1244 Shannon Rd 44420 330-545-5431
William Ryser, prin. Fax 545-5440
Girard JHS 300/7-8
1244 Shannon Rd 44420 330-545-5431
Jennifer Santangelo, prin. Fax 545-5440

Glouster, Athens, Pop. 1,756
Trimble Local SD 800/PK-12
1 Tomcat Dr 45732 740-767-4444
Scott Christman, supt. Fax 767-4901
trimble.k12.oh.us
Trimble HS 200/9-12
1 Tomcat Dr 45732 740-767-3434
Matt Curtis, prin. Fax 767-4901
Trimble MS 100/6-8
18500 Jacksonville Rd 45732 740-767-2810
Roger Nott, prin. Fax 767-9523

Gnadenhutten, Tuscarawas, Pop. 1,282
Indian Valley Local SD 1,800/K-12
PO Box 171 44629 740-254-4334
Gary Wentworth, supt. Fax 254-9271
www.ivschools.org/
Indian Valley HS 500/9-12
PO Box 130 44629 740-254-4262
Robert Clarke, prin. Fax 254-4911
Other Schools – See Tuscarawas

Goshen, Clermont
Goshen Local SD 2,700/PK-12
6694 Goshen Rd 45122 513-722-2222
Darrell Edwards, supt. Fax 722-3767
www.goshenlocalschools.org
Goshen HS 700/9-12
6707 Goshen Rd 45122 513-722-2227
Nick Inabnitt, prin. Fax 722-2247
Goshen MS 600/6-8
6692 Goshen Rd 45122 513-722-2226
Mark Edwards, prin. Fax 722-2246

Grafton, Lorain, Pop. 6,573
Midview Local SD 3,000/PK-12
13050 Durkee Rd 44044 440-748-5353
Dr. Bruce Willingham, supt. Fax 748-5395
www.midviewk12.org
Midview HS 900/9-12
38199 Capel Rd 44044 440-748-2124
Thomas Faska, prin. Fax 748-5277

Midview MS 500/7-8
12865 Grafton Rd 44044 440-748-2122
John Brown, prin. Fax 748-0411

Granville, Licking, Pop. 5,563
Granville EVD 2,500/K-12
PO Box 417 43023 740-587-8101
Jeffrey Brown, supt. Fax 683-7730
www.granvilleschools.org
Granville HS 800/9-12
248 New Burg St 43023 740-587-8105
Matt Durst, prin. Fax 587-8195
Granville MS 400/7-8
210 New Burg St 43023 740-587-8104
Lisa Sealover-Ormond, prin. Fax 587-8194

Denison University Post-Sec.
100 W College St 43023 740-587-0810
Granville Christian Academy 300/K-12
1820 Newark Granville Rd 43023 740-587-4423
Tim Barrett, supt. Fax 587-4776
Welsh Hills S 100/PK-10
2610 Newark Granville Rd 43023 740-522-2020
Michelle Lerner, head sch Fax 920-4326

Greenfield, Highland, Pop. 4,562
Greenfield EVD 2,000/K-12
200 N 5th St 45123 937-981-2152
James Wills, supt. Fax 981-4395
greenfield.k12.oh.us
Greenfield MS 500/6-8
200 N 5th St 45123 937-981-2197
Wendy Callewaert, prin. Fax 981-0417
McClain HS 500/9-12
200 N 5th St 45123 937-981-7731
Jason Potts, prin. Fax 981-4395

Greenville, Darke, Pop. 13,080
Greenville CSD 2,600/K-12
215 W 4th St 45331 937-548-3185
Douglas Fries, supt. Fax 548-6943
www.greenville.k12.oh.us
Greenville HS 900/9-12
100 Greenwave Way 45331 937-548-4188
Jeffrey Cassell, prin. Fax 548-3082
Greenville JHS 400/7-8
131 Central Ave 45331 937-548-3202
Christian Mortensen, prin. Fax 548-3315

Greenwich, Huron, Pop. 1,472
South Central Local SD 800/PK-12
3305 Greenwich Angling Rd 44837 419-752-3815
Dr. Martha Hasselbusch, supt. Fax 752-0182
www.south-central.org
South Central HS 200/9-12
3305 Greenwich Angling Rd 44837 419-752-3354
Thomas Hellickson, prin. Fax 752-6927
South Central JHS 200/5-8
3291 Greenwich Angling Rd 44837 419-752-0011
Alicia McKee, prin. Fax 752-8705

Grove City, Franklin, Pop. 34,836
South-Western CSD 20,600/PK-12
3805 Marlane Dr 43123 614-801-3000
Dr. Bill Wise, supt. Fax 871-2781
www.swcsd.us
Brookpark MS 600/7-8
2803 Southwest Blvd 43123 614-801-3500
Holly Carr, prin. Fax 871-6512
Central Crossing HS 1,700/9-12
4500 Big Run South Rd 43123 614-801-6500
Dr. Jill Burke, prin. Fax 801-6690
Grove City HS 1,900/9-12
4750 Hoover Rd 43123 614-801-3300
Bryan O'Shea, prin. Fax 871-6563
Jackson MS 600/7-8
2271 Holton Rd 43123 614-801-3800
Daniel Boland, prin. Fax 801-3818
Pleasant View MS 800/7-8
7255 Kropp Rd 43123 614-801-3900
Brett Harmon, prin. Fax 870-5530
South-Western Career Academy Vo/Tech
4750 Big Run South Rd 43123 614-801-3400
James Marion, prin. Fax 801-6138
Other Schools – See Columbus, Galloway

Grove City Christian S 600/K-12
4750 Hoover Rd 43123 614-875-3000
David Arrell, dir. Fax 875-8933
Harrison College Post-Sec.
3880 Jackpot Rd 43123 614-539-8800

Groveport, Franklin, Pop. 5,240
Eastland-Fairfield Career & Technical SD
4300 Amalgamated Pl 43125 614-836-4530
Bonnie Hopkins, supt. Fax 836-0203
www.eastland-fairfield.com
Eastland Career Center Vo/Tech
4465 S Hamilton Rd 43125 614-836-5725
Nelson Karshner, dir. Fax 836-4525
Adult Workforce Development Adult
4300 Amalgamated Pl Ste 100 43125 614-836-4541
Angela Ward, dir. Fax 836-0203
Other Schools – See Carroll

Groveport Madison Local SD 5,300/K-12
5940 Clyde Moore Dr 43125 614-492-2520
Bruce Hoover, supt. Fax 492-2532
www.gocruisers.org
Groveport Madison HS 1,300/9-12
4475 S Hamilton Rd 43125 614-836-4964
Aric Thomas, prin. Fax 836-4690
Groveport Madison MS Central 500/6-8
751 Main St 43125 614-836-4957
Neil Britton, prin. Fax 836-4999
Groveport Madison MS South 400/6-8
4400 Glendenning Dr 43125 614-836-4953
Darren Fillman, prin. Fax 836-4956
Other Schools – See Columbus

Eastland Career Center Post-Sec.
4465 S Hamilton Rd 43125 614-836-5725
Madison Christian S 500/PK-12
3565 Bixby Rd 43125 614-497-3456
Ray Kochis, prin. Fax 497-3057

Hamilton, Butler, Pop. 60,903
Butler Technology/Career Development SD
3603 Hamilton Middletown Rd 45011 513-868-1911
Jonathan Graft, supt. Fax 868-9348
www.butlertech.org
Lee Career Technology Center Vo/Tech
3603 Hamilton Middletown Rd 45011
Rick Pate, prin. 513-645-8200

Hamilton CSD 10,000/PK-12
PO Box 627 45012 513-887-5000
Tony Orr, supt. Fax 868-4473
hamiltoncityschools.com
Garfield MS 800/7-8
250 N Fair Ave 45011 513-887-5035
Brandon Stanfill, prin. Fax 887-4700
Hamilton Freshman HS 800/9-9
2260 NW Washington Blvd 45013 513-896-3400
Jeffrey Miller, prin. Fax 896-3402
Hamilton HS 1,900/10-12
1165 Eaton Ave 45013 513-868-7700
John Wilhelm, prin. Fax 887-4810
Wilson MS 700/7-8
714 Eaton Ave 45013 513-887-5170
Jonathan Szary, prin. Fax 887-5068

New Miami Local SD 700/K-12
600 Seven Mile Ave 45011 513-863-0833
Rhonda Parker, supt. Fax 863-0497
www.new-miami.k12.oh.us
New Miami HS 200/9-12
600 Seven Mile Ave 45011 513-863-4917
Trish Duebber, prin. Fax 896-3956
New Miami MS 200/6-8
600 Seven Mile Ave 45011 513-863-4917
Aileen Ernst, prin. Fax 863-3956

Ross Local SD 2,700/PK-12
3371 Hamilton Cleves Rd 45013 513-863-1253
Scott Gates, supt. Fax 863-6250
www.rossrams.com
Ross HS 800/9-12
3601 Hamilton Cleves Rd 45013 513-863-1252
Brian Martin, prin. Fax 863-8340
Ross MS 900/5-8
3425 Hamilton Cleves Rd 45013 513-863-1251
Christopher Saylor, prin. Fax 863-0066

Badin HS 500/9-12
571 Hamilton New London Rd 45013 513-863-3993
Brian Pendergest, prin. Fax 785-2844
Miami University-Hamilton Campus Post-Sec.
1601 University Blvd 45011 513-785-3000

Hamler, Henry, Pop. 573
Patrick Henry Local SD 600/PK-12
6900 State Route 18 43524 419-274-3015
Thomas L. Taylor, supt. Fax 274-1641
www.phpatriots.org
Henry HS 300/9-12
6900 State Route 18 43524 419-274-3015
Josh Biederstedt, prin. Fax 274-1641
Henry MS 300/5-8
E050 County Road 7 43524 419-274-3015
Kyle Lacy, prin. Fax 274-1641

Hammondsville, Jefferson
Edison Local SD 1,300/PK-12
14890 State Route 213 43930 330-532-3199
Bill Beattie, supt. Fax 532-2860
www.edisonlocal.k12.oh.us/
Other Schools – See Richmond

Hannibal, Monroe, Pop. 405
Switzerland of Ohio Local SD
Supt. — See Woodsfield
River HS 200/9-12
PO Box 37 43931 740-483-1358
Rob Caldwell, prin. Fax 483-2321

Hanoverton, Columbiana, Pop. 408
United Local SD 1,200/K-12
8143 State Route 9 44423 330-223-1521
Steve Viscounte, supt. Fax 223-2363
www.united.k12.oh.us
United JSHS 600/7-12
8143 State Route 9 44423 330-223-7102
William Young, prin. Fax 223-2363

Harrison, Hamilton, Pop. 9,812
Southwest Local SD 3,500/K-12
230 S Elm St 45030 513-367-4139
John Hamstra, supt. Fax 367-2287
www.southwestschools.org
Harrison HS 1,000/9-12
9860 West Rd 45030 513-367-4169
Davis Baker, prin. Fax 367-7251
Harrison MS 500/7-8
9830 West Rd 45030 513-367-4831
Christian Tracy, prin. Fax 367-0370

Harrod, Allen, Pop. 415
Allen East Local SD 1,100/PK-12
9105 Harding Hwy 45850 419-648-3333
Mel Rentschler, supt. Fax 648-5282
www.ae.k12.oh.us
Allen East HS 500/9-12
9105 Harding Hwy 45850 419-648-3333
Keith Baumgartner, prin. Fax 649-8900
Allen East MS 400/6-8
9105 Harding Hwy 45850 419-648-3333
Jarrod Wehri, prin.

Hartville, Stark, Pop. 2,894
Lake Local SD
Supt. — See Uniontown
Lake MS 800/6-8
511 Market Ave SW 44632 330-877-4290
Brian Reed, prin. Fax 877-1384

Lake Center Christian S 600/PK-12
12893 Kaufman Ave NW 44632 330-877-2049
Dr. Joseph Beeson, supt. Fax 877-2040

Haviland, Paulding, Pop. 213
Wayne Trace Local SD 900/PK-12
4915 US Route 127 45851 419-263-2415
Benjamin A. Winans, supt. Fax 263-2377
www.waynetrace.org
Wayne Trace JSHS 400/7-12
4915 US Route 127 45851 419-399-4100
Phil Noffsinger, prin. Fax 622-3037

Heath, Licking, Pop. 10,088
Heath CSD 1,600/K-12
107 Lancaster Dr 43056 740-522-2816
Trevor Thomas, supt. Fax 522-4697
www.heath.k12.oh.us
Heath HS 500/9-12
300 Licking View Dr 43056 740-788-3300
Ellis Booth, prin. Fax 788-3322
Heath MS 400/6-8
310 Licking View Dr 43056 740-788-3200
Jeffrey Hempleman, prin. Fax 788-3209

Hebron, Licking, Pop. 2,293
Lakewood Local SD 1,900/K-12
PO Box 70 43025 740-928-5878
Mary Andrews, supt. Fax 928-3152
www.lakewoodlocal.k12.oh.us/
Lakewood HS 600/9-12
PO Box 70 43025 740-928-4526
Stacey Stein, prin. Fax 928-3731
Lakewood MS 400/6-8
PO Box 70 43025 740-928-8330
Jessica Fry, prin. Fax 928-5627

Hicksville, Defiance, Pop. 3,540
Hicksville EVD 900/PK-12
958 E High St 43526 419-542-7665
Keith Countryman, supt. Fax 542-8534
www.hicksvilleschools.org/
Hicksville JSHS 400/7-12
958 E High St 43526 419-542-7636
Jeff Slattery, prin. Fax 542-8534

Highland Heights, Cuyahoga, Pop. 8,256

ATS Institute of Technology Post-Sec.
325 Alpha Park 44143 440-449-1700

Highland Hills, Cuyahoga, Pop. 1,115

Cuyahoga Community College Post-Sec.
4250 Richmond Rd 44122 800-954-8742

Hilliard, Franklin, Pop. 27,909
Hilliard CSD
Supt. — See Columbus
Hilliard Bradley HS 1,500/9-12
2800 Walker Rd 43026 614-921-7400
Mindy Mordarski, prin. Fax 921-7401
Hilliard Darby HS 1,500/9-12
4200 Leppert Rd 43026 614-921-7300
Joyce Brickley, prin. Fax 921-7301
Hilliard Davidson HS 1,700/9-12
5100 Davidson Rd 43026 614-921-7200
Aaron Cookson, prin. Fax 921-7201
Hilliard Heritage MS 800/7-8
5670 Scioto Darby Rd 43026 614-921-7500
Matthew Trombitas, prin. Fax 921-7501
Hilliard Memorial MS 800/7-8
5600 Scioto Darby Rd 43026 614-921-7600
Barry Bay, prin. Fax 921-7601
Hilliard Weaver MS 800/7-8
4600 Avery Rd 43026 614-921-7700
Craig Vroom, prin. Fax 921-7701

Hillsboro, Highland, Pop. 6,439
Hillsboro CSD 2,600/PK-12
39 Willetsville Pike 45133 937-393-3475
James Smith, supt. Fax 393-5841
www.hcs-k12.org
Hillsboro HS 800/9-12
550 US Highway 62 45133 937-393-3485
Jason Snively, prin. Fax 393-5842
Hillsboro MS 600/6-8
550 US Highway 62 45133 937-393-9877
Kathy Hoop, prin. Fax 393-5843

Hillsboro Christian Academy 100/K-12
849 S High St 45133 937-393-8422
Connie Sears, admin. Fax 393-4963
Southern State Community College Post-Sec.
100 Hobart Dr 45133 937-393-3431

Hiram, Portage, Pop. 1,376

Agape Christian Academy 50/5-12
17791 Claridon Troy Rd 44234 440-834-1705
Russell Gifford, admin. Fax 834-1708
Hiram College Post-Sec.
PO Box 67 44234 330-569-3211

Holgate, Henry, Pop. 1,102
Holgate Local SD 500/K-12
801 Joe E Brown Ave 43527 419-264-5141
Kelly Meyers, supt. Fax 264-1965
www.holgateschools.org
Holgate JSHS 200/6-12
801 Joe E Brown Ave 43527 419-264-2521
Casey Hemmelgarn, prin. Fax 264-1965

Holland, Lucas, Pop. 1,746
Springfield Local SD 3,900/K-12
6900 Hall St 43528 419-867-5600
Dr. Michael D. O'Shea, supt. Fax 867-5700
www.springfieldlocalschools.net
Springfield HS 1,000/9-12
1470 S Mccord Rd 43528 419-867-5633
Rhonda Kimmons, prin. Fax 867-5618
Springfield MS 900/6-8
7001 Madison Ave 43528 419-867-5644
Jeff Pendry, prin. Fax 867-5732

Houston, Shelby
Hardin-Houston Local SD 900/PK-12
5300 Houston Rd 45333 937-295-3010
Larry Claypool, supt. Fax 295-3737
www.houston.k12.oh.us
Houston JSHS 400/7-12
5300 Houston Rd 45333 937-295-3010
Ryan Maier, prin. Fax 295-3737

Howard, Knox, Pop. 239
East Knox Local SD 1,000/K-12
23201 Coshocton Rd 43028 740-599-7493
Stephen Larcomb, supt. Fax 599-5863
www.ekschools.com
East Knox JSHS 500/7-12
23227 Coshocton Rd 43028 740-599-7000
Alan Keesee, prin. Fax 599-2922

Hubbard, Trumbull, Pop. 7,784
Hubbard EVD 1,900/K-12
108 Orchard Ave 44425 330-534-1921
Raymond W. Soloman, supt. Fax 534-0522
www.hubbard.k12.oh.us/
Hubbard HS 600/9-12
350 Hall Ave 44425 330-534-1921
Brandilyn Yobe, prin. Fax 534-6191
Hubbard MS 600/5-8
250 Hall Ave 44425 330-534-1921
Brian Hoffman, prin. Fax 534-6191

Huber Heights, Montgomery, Pop. 36,793
Huber Heights CSD 5,900/PK-12
5954 Longford Rd 45424 937-237-6300
Susan Gunnell, supt. Fax 237-6307
www.huberheightscityschools.org/
Wayne HS 1,700/9-12
5400 Chambersburg Rd 45424 937-233-6431
Reva Cosby, prin. Fax 237-6321
Weisenborn JHS 900/7-8
6061 Troy Pike 45424 937-237-6350
Brent Carey, prin. Fax 237-7491

Carousel of Miami Valley Beauty College Post-Sec.
7809 Waynetowne Blvd 45424 937-233-8818

Hudson, Summit, Pop. 21,988
Hudson CSD 4,600/PK-12
2400 Hudson Aurora Rd 44236 330-653-1200
Phillip Herman, supt. Fax 653-1474
www.hudson.k12.oh.us
Hudson HS 1,600/9-12
2500 Hudson Aurora Rd 44236 330-653-1416
Brian Wilch, prin. Fax 653-1481
Hudson MS 1,100/6-8
77 N Oviatt St 44236 330-653-1316
Dr. Kim Cockley, prin. Fax 653-1368

Western Reserve Academy 400/9-12
115 College St 44236 330-650-4400
Christopher Burner, head sch Fax 650-9754

Hunting Valley, Cuyahoga, Pop. 696

University S 400/9-12
2785 Som Center Rd 44022 216-831-2200
Benjamin Rein, hdmstr. Fax 831-0402

Huntsburg, Geauga

Hershey Montessori S 50/7-12
11530 Madison Rd 44046 440-636-6290
Paula Leigh-Doyle, prin. Fax 636-5665

Huron, Erie, Pop. 7,058
Huron CSD 1,400/PK-12
712 Cleveland Rd E 44839 419-433-1234
Dennis Muratori, supt. Fax 433-7095
www.huronhs.com
Huron HS 500/9-12
710 Cleveland Rd W 44839 419-433-1234
Tim Lamb, prin. Fax 433-2339
McCormick JHS 200/7-8
325 Ohio St 44839 419-433-1234
Chad Carter, prin. Fax 433-8427

Bowling Green State University Post-Sec.
1 University Dr 44839 419-433-5560

Independence, Cuyahoga, Pop. 7,078
Independence Local SD 1,100/PK-12
7733 Stone Rd 44131 216-642-5850
Benjamin Hegedish, supt. Fax 642-3482
www.independence.k12.oh.us
Independence HS 400/9-12
6001 Archwood Rd 44131 216-642-5860
William McGuinness, prin. Fax 642-5886
Independence MS 300/5-8
6111 Archwood Rd 44131 216-642-5865
Kevin Jakub, prin. Fax 520-7002

Miami-Jacobs Career College Post-Sec.
6400 Rockside Rd 44131 216-834-1400

Ironton, Lawrence, Pop. 10,894
Ironton CSD 1,500/K-12
105 S 5th St 45638 740-532-4133
William Nance, supt. Fax 532-2314
www.tigertown.com
Ironton HS 400/9-12
1701 S 7th St 45638 740-532-3911
Joseph Rowe, prin. Fax 533-6027
Ironton MS 300/6-8
302 Delaware St 45638 740-532-3347
Toben Schreck, prin. Fax 532-3077

Rock Hill Local SD 1,400/PK-12
2325 County Road 26 Unit A 45638 740-532-7030
Wesley Hairston, supt. Fax 532-7043
rockhill.org
Rock Hill HS 400/9-12
2415 County Road 26 45638 740-533-7012
Glenn Hopper, prin. Fax 533-7015
Rock Hill MS 300/6-8
2171 County Road 26 45638 740-532-7026
Darrell Humphreys, prin. Fax 532-7028

Ohio University Southern Campus Post-Sec.
1804 Liberty Ave 45638 740-533-4600
St. Joseph Central HS 100/7-12
912 S 6th St 45638 740-532-0485
Paul Mollett, prin. Fax 532-3699

Irwin, Union

Rosedale Bible College Post-Sec.
2270 Rosedale Rd 43029 740-857-1311

Jackson, Jackson, Pop. 6,292
Jackson CSD 2,500/PK-12
450 Vaughn St 45640 740-286-6442
Phil Howard, supt. Fax 286-6445
www.jcs.k12.oh.us
Jackson HS 700/9-12
500 Vaughn St 45640 740-286-7575
Thad Haines, prin. Fax 286-8197
Jackson MS 600/6-8
21 Tropic St 45640 740-286-7586
Mark Broermann, prin. Fax 286-8637

Christian Life Academy 100/PK-12
10595 Chillicothe Pike 45640 740-286-1234
Melissa Boggs, admin. Fax 286-0234
Daymar College Post-Sec.
980 E Main St 45640 740-286-1554

Jackson Center, Shelby, Pop. 1,444
Jackson Center Local SD 400/PK-12
PO Box 849 45334 937-596-6053
William Reichert, supt. Fax 596-6490
www.jackson-center.k12.oh.us
Jackson Center JSHS 200/4-12
PO Box 849 45334 937-596-6149
William Reichert, prin. Fax 596-6490

Jamestown, Greene, Pop. 1,954
Greeneview Local SD 1,400/PK-12
4 S Charleston Rd 45335 937-675-2728
Isaac Seevers, supt. Fax 675-6807
www.greeneview.k12.oh.us
Greeneview MS 500/5-8
4990 Cottonville Rd 45335 937-675-9391
Mary Minear, prin. Fax 675-6866
Greenview HS 400/9-12
4710 Cottonville Rd 45335 937-675-9711
Brian Masser, prin. Fax 675-6805

Jefferson, Ashtabula, Pop. 3,086
Ashtabula County Technical & Career Ctr
1565 State Route 167 44047 440-576-6015
Dr. Jerome Brockway, supt. Fax 576-6502
atech.edu
A-Tech Vo/Tech
1565 State Route 167 44047 440-576-6015
Paul Brockett, prin. Fax 576-6502

Jefferson Area Local SD 1,700/K-12
121 S Poplar St 44047 440-576-9180
John Montanaro, supt. Fax 576-9876
www.jalsd.org
Jefferson Area HS 500/9-12
207 W Mulberry St 44047 440-576-4731
Jeremy Huber, prin. Fax 576-7344
Jefferson Area JHS 300/7-8
207 W Mulberry St 44047 440-576-1736
Richard Hoyson, prin. Fax 576-3082

Jeromesville, Ashland, Pop. 562
Hillsdale Local SD 900/K-12
485 Township Road 1902 44840 419-368-8231
Steve Dickerson, supt. Fax 368-7504
www.hillsdale.k12.oh.us/
Hillsdale HS 300/9-12
485 Township Road 1902 44840 419-368-6841
Kevin Reidy, prin. Fax 368-7504
Hillsdale MS 300/5-8
144 N High St 44840 419-368-4911
Tim Keib, prin. Fax 368-3613

Johnstown, Licking, Pop. 4,591
Johnstown-Monroe Local SD 1,600/K-12
441 S Main St 43031 740-967-6846
Dale Dickson, supt. Fax 967-1106
www.johnstown.k12.oh.us/
Adams MS 400/6-8
80 W Maple St 43031 740-967-8766
Kris Almendinger, prin. Fax 967-0051
Johnstown-Monroe HS 500/9-12
401 S Oregon St 43031 740-967-2721
Derick Busenburg, prin. Fax 967-1140

Northridge Local SD 1,200/K-12
6097 Johnstown Utica Rd 43031 740-967-6631
Dr. Chris Briggs, supt. Fax 967-5022
www.northridge.k12.oh.us
Northridge HS 400/9-12
6066 Johnstown Utica Rd 43031 740-967-6651
Amy Anderson, prin. Fax 967-6958
Northridge MS 300/6-8
6066 Johnstown Utica Rd 43031 740-967-6671
John Rathburn, prin. Fax 967-7083

Kalida, Putnam, Pop. 1,534
Kalida Local SD 600/K-12
PO Box 269 45853 419-532-3534
Karl Lammers, supt. Fax 532-2277
www.kalida.k12.oh.us
Kalida JSHS 300/5-12
PO Box 269 45853 419-532-3529
Chris Pfahler, prin. Fax 532-3582

Kansas, Sandusky, Pop. 179
Lakota Local SD 1,000/PK-12
5200 County Road 13 44841 419-986-6650
Jon Detwiler, supt. Fax 986-6651
www.lakota-sandusky.k12.oh.us
Lakota HS 300/9-12
5200 County Road 13 44841 419-986-6620
Sherry Sprow, prin. Fax 986-6621
Lakota MS 300/5-8
5200 County Road 13 44841 419-986-6630
Patrick Flanagan, prin. Fax 986-6631

Kelleys Island, Erie, Pop. 311
Kelleys Island Local SD 50/PK-12
PO Box 349 43438 419-746-2730
Phillip Thiede, supt. Fax 746-2271
www.kelleys.k12.oh.us/
Kelleys Island S 50/PK-12
PO Box 349 43438 419-746-2730
Phillip Thiede, supt. Fax 746-2271

Kent, Portage, Pop. 28,086
Kent CSD 3,300/PK-12
321 N Depeyster St 44240 330-676-7600
George Joseph, supt. Fax 677-6166
www.kentschools.net
Roosevelt HS 1,400/9-12
1400 N Mantua St 44240 330-673-9595
Dennis Love, prin. Fax 673-9217
Stanton MS 800/6-8
1175 Hudson Rd 44240 330-673-6693
Anthony Horton, prin. Fax 673-1561

Kent State University Post-Sec.
PO Box 5190 44242 330-672-3000
Northcoast Medical Training Academy Post-Sec.
1832 St Rd 59 44240 330-678-6600

Kenton, Hardin, Pop. 8,149
Kenton CSD 900/PK-12
222 W Carrol St 43326 419-673-0775
Jennifer Penczarski, supt. Fax 673-3180
www.kentoncityschools.org
Kenton HS 600/9-12
200 Harding Ave 43326 419-673-1286
Chad Thrush, prin. Fax 675-5200
Kenton MS 300/7-8
300 Oriental St 43326 419-673-1237
Kirk Cameron, prin. Fax 673-1626

Kettering, Montgomery, Pop. 55,018
Kettering CSD 7,700/PK-12
3750 Far Hills Ave 45429 937-499-1430
Scott Inskeep, supt. Fax 499-1465
www.ketteringschools.org
Kettering-Fairmont HS 2,300/9-12
3301 Shroyer Rd 45429 937-499-1601
D. Tyler Alexander, prin. Fax 499-1661
Kettering MS 1,000/6-8
3000 Glengarry Dr 45420 937-499-1550
Brian Snyder, prin. Fax 499-1598
Van Buren MS 700/6-8
3775 Shroyer Rd 45429 937-499-1800
Jeff Blakley, prin. Fax 499-1820

Archbishop Alter HS 700/9-12
940 E David Rd 45429 937-434-4434
Lourdes Lambert, prin. Fax 434-0507
Carousel Beauty College Post-Sec.
3076 Woodman Dr 45420 937-298-5752
Kettering College Post-Sec.
3737 Southern Blvd 45429 937-395-8601
National College Post-Sec.
1837 Woodman Center Dr 45420 937-299-9450
School of Advertising Art Post-Sec.
1725 E David Rd 45440 877-300-9866

Kidron, Wayne, Pop. 938

Central Christian S 300/PK-12
PO Box 9 44636 330-857-7311
Joyce Taylor, prin. Fax 857-7331

Kings Mills, Warren, Pop. 1,300
Kings Local SD 4,000/PK-12
1797 King Ave 45034 513-398-8050
Tim Ackermann, supt. Fax 229-7590
www.kingslocal.net/
Kings HS 1,200/9-12
5500 Columbia Rd 45034 513-398-8050
Doug Leist, prin. Fax 459-2941
Kings JHS 600/7-8
5620 Columbia Rd 45034 513-398-8050
Nicole Huelsman, prin. Fax 459-2951

Kinsman, Trumbull
Joseph Badger Local SD 800/PK-12
7119 State Route 7 44428 330-876-2800
Dr. David Bair, supt. Fax 876-2811
www.joseph-badger.k12.oh.us/
Badger HS 200/9-12
7119 State Route 7 44428 330-876-2820
Edwin Baldwin, prin. Fax 876-2821
Badger MS 300/5-8
7119 State Route 7 44428 330-876-2840
Steven Kochemba, prin. Fax 876-2841

Kirtland, Lake, Pop. 6,804
Kirtland Local SD 1,200/K-12
9252 Chillicothe Rd 44094 440-256-3311
William R. Wade, supt. Fax 256-3831
www.kirtlandschools.org
Kirtland HS 400/9-12
9150 Chillicothe Rd 44094 440-256-3366
Dr. Lynn Campbell, prin. Fax 256-1042
Kirtland MS 300/6-8
9152 Chillicothe Rd 44094 440-256-3358
Scott A. Amstutz, prin. Fax 256-3928

Lakeland Community College Post-Sec.
7700 Clocktower Dr 44094 440-525-7000

LaGrange, Lorain, Pop. 2,072
Keystone Local SD 1,600/K-12
531 Opportunity Way 44050 440-355-2424
Franco Gallo, supt. Fax 355-4465
www.keystonelocalschools.org/
Keystone HS 500/9-12
580 Opportunity Way 44050 440-355-2400
James Kohler, prin. Fax 355-6017
Keystone MS 400/6-8
501 Opportunity Way 44050 440-355-2200
Toni Filut, prin. Fax 355-6678

Lakeside, Ottawa, Pop. 691
Danbury Local SD 500/PK-12
9451 East Harbor Rd 43440 419-798-5185
Daniel Parent, supt. Fax 798-2260
www.danbury.k12.oh.us
Danbury HS 200/9-12
9451 East Harbor Rd 43440 419-798-4037
Joseph Miller, prin. Fax 798-2262
Danbury MS 200/5-8
9451 East Harbor Rd 43440 419-798-2258
Joseph Miller, prin. Fax 798-2259

Lakewood, Cuyahoga, Pop. 50,830
Lakewood CSD 5,600/K-12
1470 Warren Rd 44107 216-529-4000
Jeffrey Patterson, supt. Fax 228-8327
www.lakewoodcityschools.org
Garfield MS 600/6-8
13114 Detroit Ave 44107 216-529-4241
Mark Walter, prin. Fax 529-4146
Harding MS 600/6-8
16601 Madison Ave 44107 216-529-4261
Joseph Niemantsverdriet, prin. Fax 529-4708
Lakewood HS 1,700/9-12
14100 Franklin Blvd 44107 216-529-4028
Keith Ahearn, prin. Fax 529-4459

Lakewood College Post-Sec.
12900 Lake Ave Ste 3A 44107 800-517-0857
St. Edward HS 900/9-12
13500 Detroit Ave 44107 216-221-3776
Frank O'Linn, prin. Fax 221-4609
Virginia Marti College of Art & Design Post-Sec.
11724 Detroit Ave 44107 216-221-8584

Lancaster, Fairfield, Pop. 38,140
Fairfield Union Local SD 2,000/K-12
6417 Cincinnati Zanesvll NE 43130 740-536-7384
Chad Belville, supt. Fax 536-9132
www.fairfieldunion.org
Fairfield Union HS 600/9-12
6675 Cincinnati Zansvll NE 43130 740-536-7306
Brian Verde, prin. Fax 536-7911
Rushville MS 600/5-8
6409 Cincinnati Zanesvll NE 43130 740-536-7249
Chris Walton, prin. Fax 536-7211

Lancaster CSD 5,000/PK-12
345 E Mulberry St 43130 740-687-7300
Steven Wigton, supt. Fax 687-7303
www.lancaster.k12.oh.us
Ewing JHS 700/6-8
825 E Fair Ave 43130 740-687-7347
Steve Poston, prin. Fax 687-3446
Lancaster HS 1,700/9-12
1312 Granville Pike 43130 740-681-7500
Jack Greathouse, prin. Fax 681-7505
Sherman JHS 700/6-8
701 Union St 43130 740-687-7344
Scott Burre, prin. Fax 687-3443

Daymar College Post-Sec.
1579 Victor Rd NW 43130 740-687-6126
Fairfield Christian Academy 600/PK-12
1965 N Columbus St 43130 740-654-2889
Craig Carpenter, supt. Fax 654-7689
Fisher Catholic HS 300/9-12
1803 Granville Pike 43130 740-654-1231
Joseph Jasinski, pres. Fax 654-1233
Ohio University Post-Sec.
1570 Granville Pike 43130 740-654-6711

Latham, Pike
Western Local SD 500/K-12
PO Box 130 45646 740-493-3113
Brock Brewster, supt. Fax 493-2065
www.westernlocalschools.com/
Western JSHS 300/7-12
PO Box 130 45646 740-493-2514
Carrie Gast, prin. Fax 493-8513

Leavittsburg, Trumbull, Pop. 1,932
LaBrae Local SD 1,400/K-12
1001 N Leavitt Rd 44430 330-898-0800
Anthony J. Calderone, supt. Fax 898-6112
www.labrae.school
LaBrae HS 400/9-12
1001 N Leavitt Rd 44430 330-898-0800
Jeffrey Starkey, prin. Fax 898-7808
LaBrae MS 300/6-8
1001 N Leavitt Rd 44430 330-898-0800
Martin Kelly, prin. Fax 898-7808

Lebanon, Warren, Pop. 19,670
Lebanon CSD 5,000/PK-12
700 Holbrook Ave 45036 513-934-5770
Todd Yohey, supt. Fax 932-5906
www.lebanonschools.org
Lebanon HS 1,500/9-12
1916 Drake Rd 45036 513-934-5100
Scott Butler, prin. Fax 933-2150
Lebanon JHS 900/7-8
160 Miller Rd 45036 513-934-5300
Brian Dalton, prin. Fax 932-9436

Warren County ESC
1879 Deerfield Rd 45036 513-695-2900
Tom Isaacs, supt. Fax 695-2961
www.warrencountyesc.com/
Warren County Alternative S Alt
3527 N State Route 48 45036 513-695-2994
Mike Bidwell, prin. Fax 695-1836

Warren County JVSD
3525 N State Route 48 45036 513-932-5677
Margaret Hess, supt. Fax 934-0121
www.mywccc.org/
Warren County Career Center Vo/Tech
3525 N State Route 48 45036 513-932-5677
Margaret Hess, supt. Fax 932-3810
Warren Co. Career Adult Technical Center Adult
3525 N State Route 48 45036 513-932-8145
Tom Harris, dir. Fax 932-2304

Leesburg, Highland, Pop. 1,294
Fairfield Local SD 900/K-12
11611 State Route 771 45135 937-780-2221
William Garrett, supt. Fax 780-6900
www.fairfield-highland.k12.oh.us
Fairfield HS 200/9-12
11611 State Route 771 45135 937-780-2966
Stephen Hackett, prin. Fax 780-2841
Fairfield MS 300/5-8
11611 State Route 771 45135 937-780-2977
Stephen Hackett, prin. Fax 780-2841

Leetonia, Columbiana, Pop. 1,931
Leetonia EVD 700/K-12
450 Walnut St 44431 330-427-6594
Robert Mehno, supt. Fax 427-1136
www.leetonia.k12.oh.us
Leetonia HS 200/9-12
450 Walnut St 44431 330-427-2115
Troy Radinsky, prin. Fax 427-6904
Leetonia MS 200/5-8
450 Walnut St 44431 330-427-2444
Troy Radinsky, prin. Fax 427-2549

Leipsic, Putnam, Pop. 2,076
Leipsic Local SD 600/K-12
232 Oak St 45856 419-943-2165
Greg Williamson, supt. Fax 943-4331
www.lp.noacsc.org
Leipsic HS 400/6-12
232 Oak St 45856 419-943-2164
Brian Bennett, prin. Fax 943-2185

Lewisburg, Preble, Pop. 1,788
Tri-County North Local SD 800/K-12
436 N Commerce St 45338 937-962-2671
William Derringer, supt. Fax 962-4731
www.tcnschools.org
Tri-County North HS 200/9-12
436 N Commerce St 45338 937-962-2675
Joe Hoelzle, prin. Fax 833-4860
Tri-County North MS 200/6-8
530 Panther Way 45338 937-962-2631
Joe Hoelzle, prin. Fax 833-4860

Lewis Center, Delaware, Pop. 300
Olentangy Local SD 18,000/PK-12
814 Shanahan Rd Ste 100 43035 740-657-4050
Dr. Mark Raiff, supt. Fax 657-4099
www.olentangy.k12.oh.us
Olentangy HS 1,500/9-12
675 Lewis Center Rd 43035 740-657-4100
Thomas McDonnell, prin. Fax 657-4199
Olentangy Orange HS 1,500/9-12
2840 E Orange Rd 43035 740-657-5100
Kathryne McFarland, prin. Fax 657-5199
Olentangy Orange MS 900/6-8
2680 E Orange Rd 43035 740-657-5300
Scott Cunningham, prin. Fax 657-5399
Olentangy Shanahan MS 1,000/6-8
814 Shanahan Rd 43035 740-657-4300
Joshua McDaniels, prin. Fax 657-4398
Other Schools – See Galena, Powell

Lewistown, Logan, Pop. 220
Indian Lake Local SD 1,700/K-12
6210 State Route 235 N 43333 937-686-8601
Patrick O'Donnell, supt. Fax 686-8421
www.ils-k12.org
Indian Lake HS 500/9-12
6210 State Route 235 N 43333 937-686-8851
Rob Underwood, prin. Fax 686-0024
Indian Lake MS 500/5-8
8920 County Road 91 43333 937-686-8833
Melissa Mefford, prin. Fax 686-8993

Lexington, Richland, Pop. 4,768
Lexington Local SD 2,400/PK-12
103 Clever Ln 44904 419-884-2132
J. Michael Ziegelhofer, supt. Fax 884-3129
www.lexington.k12.oh.us
Lexington HS 700/9-12
103 Clever Ln 44904 419-884-1111
Jeremy Secrist, prin. Fax 884-2340
Lexington JHS 400/7-8
90 Frederick St 44904 419-884-2112
Taylor Gerhardt, prin. Fax 884-0134

Liberty Center, Henry, Pop. 1,169
Liberty Center Local SD 1,000/PK-12
PO Box 434 43532 419-533-5011
Dr. Tod Hug, supt. Fax 533-5036
www.libertycenterschools.org
Liberty Center HS 300/9-12
PO Box 434 43532 419-533-6641
Larry Black, prin. Fax 533-6108
Liberty Center MS 400/5-8
PO Box 434 43532 419-533-0020
Dr. Marcia Rozevink, admin. Fax 533-1021

Liberty Twp, Butler
Lakota Local SD 15,500/PK-12
5572 Princeton Rd 45011 513-874-5505
Robb Vogelmann, supt. Fax 644-1167
www.lakotaonline.com
Lakota East Freshman HS 9-9
7630 Bethany Rd 45044 513-588-7700
Jennifer Ulland, prin. Fax 759-2024
Lakota East HS 1,800/10-12
6840 Lakota Ln 45044 513-755-7211
Suzanna Davis, prin. Fax 759-8633
Lakota Plains JHS 700/7-8
5500 Princeton Rd 45011 513-644-1130
Kim Wade, prin. Fax 644-1135
Liberty JHS 800/7-8
7055 Dutchland Pkwy 45044 513-777-4420
Eric Bauman, prin. Fax 777-7950
Other Schools – See West Chester

Lima, Allen, Pop. 37,107
Allen County ESC
1920 Slabtown Rd 45801 419-222-1836
Steve Arnold, supt. Fax 224-0718
www.allencountyesc.org
Allen County Alternative HS Alt
1920 Slabtown Rd 45801 419-222-1836
Mitch Black, admin. Fax 222-2107

Apollo JVSD
3325 Shawnee Rd 45806 419-998-2908
Judy Wells, supt. Fax 998-2929
www.apollocareercenter.com
Apollo Career Center Vo/Tech
3325 Shawnee Rd 45806 419-998-2908
Doug Bodey, dir. Fax 998-2929

Bath Local SD 1,600/K-12
2650 Bible Rd 45801 419-221-0807
Dale Lewellen, supt. Fax 221-0983
www.bathwildcats.org
Bath HS 500/9-12
2850 Bible Rd 45801 419-221-0366
Richard Gross, prin. Fax 221-0766
Bath MS 400/6-8
2700 Bible Rd 45801 419-221-1839
Bradley Clark, prin. Fax 221-2431

Lima CSD 3,800/PK-12
755 Saint Johns Ave 45804 419-996-3400
Jill Ackerman, supt. Fax 996-3401
www.limacityschools.org
Lima HS 1,000/9-12
1 Spartan Way 45801 419-996-3000
Alison VanGorder, prin. Fax 996-3001
Lima West MS 400/7-8
503 N Cable Rd 45805 419-996-3150
Thomas Winkler, prin. Fax 996-3151

Perry Local SD 800/K-12
2770 E Breese Rd 45806 419-221-2770
Omer Schroeder, supt. Fax 224-6215
mycommodores.org
Perry HS 400/7-12
2770 E Breese Rd 45806 419-221-2773
Nicholas Weingart, prin. Fax 224-6215

Shawnee Local SD 2,500/K-12
3255 Zurmehly Rd 45806 419-998-8031
Don H. Wade, supt. Fax 998-8050
www.limashawnee.com
Shawnee HS 700/9-12
3333 Zurmehly Rd 45806 419-998-8000
Tony Cox, prin. Fax 998-8026
Shawnee MS 800/5-8
3235 Zurmehly Rd 45806 419-998-8057
Judy Gephart, prin. Fax 222-6572

Institute of Therapeutic Massage Post-Sec.
311 E Market St Fl 3 45801 419-523-9580
James A. Rhodes State Coll Post-Sec.
4240 Campus Dr 45804 419-995-8020
Liberty Christian S 50/3-12
801 Bellefontaine Ave 45801 419-229-6266
Nadine Wagner, admin. Fax 229-6266
Lima Central Catholic HS 300/9-12
720 S Cable Rd 45805 419-222-4276
Stephanie Williams, prin. Fax 222-6933
Ohio State Beauty Academy Post-Sec.
1760 N Eastown Rd 45807 419-229-7896
Ohio State University-Lima Campus Post-Sec.
4240 Campus Dr 45804 419-995-8600
Temple Christian S 200/PK-12
982 Brower Rd 45801 419-227-1644
Bruce Bowman, prin. Fax 227-6635
University of Northwestern Ohio Post-Sec.
1441 N Cable Rd 45805 419-998-3120

Lisbon, Columbiana, Pop. 2,802
Columbiana County JVSD
9364 State Route 45 44432 330-424-9561
Willard Adkins, supt. Fax 424-9719
www.ccctc.k12.oh.us/
Columbiana County Joint Vocational SHS Vo/Tech
9364 State Route 45 44432 330-424-9561
Jonathan Ludwig, prin. Fax 424-9719

Lisbon EVD 900/PK-12
317 N Market St 44432 330-424-7714
Joseph Siefke, supt. Fax 424-0135
www.lisbon.k12.oh.us/
Anderson JSHS 500/6-12
260 W Pine St 44432 330-424-3215
Keith Edenfield, prin. Fax 424-1004

Lockland, Hamilton, Pop. 3,333
Lockland Local SD 500/PK-12
210 N Cooper Ave 45215 513-563-5000
Ted Jebens, supt. Fax 563-9611
www.locklandschools.org
Lockland HS 200/9-12
249 W Forrer St 45215 513-563-5000
Bob Longworth, prin. Fax 733-0800
Lockland MS 100/7-8
249 W Forrer St 45215 513-563-5000
Bob Longworth, prin. Fax 733-0800

Lodi, Medina, Pop. 2,720
Cloverleaf Local SD 2,500/PK-12
8525 Friendsville Rd 44254 330-948-2500
Daryl Kubilus, supt. Fax 948-1034
www.cloverleaflocal.org/
Cloverleaf HS 700/9-12
8525 Friendsville Rd 44254 330-721-3526
Jamie Lormeau, prin. Fax 721-3559
Other Schools – See Seville

Logan, Hocking, Pop. 7,087
Logan-Hocking Local SD 3,900/PK-12
2019 E Front St 43138 740-385-8517
Monte Bainter, supt. Fax 385-3683
www.lhsd.k12.oh.us
Logan HS 1,100/9-12
14470 State Route 328 43138 740-385-2069
Kenneth Dille, prin. Fax 385-9564
Logan-Hocking MS 1,300/5-8
1 Middleschool Dr 43138 740-385-8764
Chad Grow, prin. Fax 385-9547

London, Madison, Pop. 9,615
London CSD 2,200/PK-12
380 Elm St 43140 740-852-5700
Dr. Louis Kramer, supt. Fax 845-3282
www.london.k12.oh.us/
London HS 500/9-12
336 Elm St 43140 740-852-5705
Chad Eisler, prin. Fax 852-3284
London MS 500/6-8
270 Keny Blvd 43140 740-852-5701
Michael Belmont, prin. Fax 845-1279

Madison-Plains Local SD 1,200/K-12
55 Linson Rd 43140 740-852-0290
Tim Dettwiller, supt. Fax 852-5895
www.mplsd.org/
Madison-Plains HS 300/9-12
800 Linson Rd 43140 740-852-0364
Matthew Unger, prin. Fax 852-3046
Madison-Plains JHS 200/6-8
803 Linson Rd 43140 740-852-1707
Dr. Matt Unger, prin. Fax 852-6351

Lorain, Lorain, Pop. 62,074
Clearview Local SD 1,700/K-12
4700 Broadway 44052 440-233-5412
Jerome M. Davis M.Ed., supt. Fax 233-6034
www.clearviewschools.org
Clearview HS 500/9-12
4700 Broadway 44052 440-233-6313
Noeleen Rothacker, prin. Fax 233-6311
Durling MS 500/5-8
100 N Ridge Rd W 44053 440-233-6869
Laura Manning, prin. Fax 233-6204

Lorain CSD 6,700/PK-12
2350 Pole Ave 44052 440-233-2271
Jeffrey Graham, supt. Fax 282-9151
www.lorainschools.org
Credit Recovery Academy 300/Alt
2321 Fairless Dr 44055 440-277-7261
Nikole Barfield-Davis, prin. Fax 277-5566
Longfellow MS 500/7-8
305 Louisiana Ave 44052 440-288-1002
Christine Miller, prin. Fax 288-1149
Lorain HS 1,800/9-12
2600 Ashland Ave 44052 440-233-2200
Robin Hopkins, prin. Fax 277-1163
New Beginnings Academy 100/Alt
307 W 7th St 44052 440-277-8157
Paul Williams, prin. Fax 277-7354
Southview MS 6-8
2321 Fairless Dr 44055 440-830-4280
Rae Bastock, prin. Fax 277-5566
Wilson MS 400/7-8
2700 Washington Ave 44052 440-246-1020
Fax 246-1016

Northern Institute of Cosmetology Post-Sec.
667 Broadway 44052 440-244-4282

Lore City, Guernsey, Pop. 322
East Guernsey Local SD
Supt. — See Old Washington
Buckeye Trail HS 200/9-12
65555 Wintergreen Rd 43755 740-489-5005
William Hartmeyer, prin. Fax 489-9839
Buckeye Trail MS 300/6-8
65553 Wintergreen Rd 43755 740-489-5100
William Hartmeyer, prin. Fax 489-9049

Loudonville, Ashland, Pop. 2,623
Loudonville-Perrysville EVD 900/PK-12
210 E Main St 44842 419-994-3912
John E. Miller M.Ed., supt. Fax 994-5528
www.lpschools.k12.oh.us
Loudonville JSHS 400/7-12
421 Campus Ave 44842 419-994-4101
John Lance, prin. Fax 994-3485

Louisville, Stark, Pop. 9,114
Louisville CSD 3,000/PK-12
407 E Main St 44641 330-875-1666
Michele Shaffer, supt. Fax 875-7603
www.leopard.sparcc.org
Louisville HS 900/9-12
1201 S Nickelplate St 44641 330-875-1438
Kenneth Faye, prin. Fax 875-7671
Louisville MS 700/6-8
1300 S Chapel St 44641 330-875-5597
Jason Orin, prin. Fax 875-7620

Good Shepherd S 50/1-12
PO Box 169 44641 330-935-0623
Rev. Gary Spencer, admin. Fax 935-0700
St. Thomas Aquinas HS 300/6-12
2121 Reno Dr 44641 330-875-1631
Frederick Schleuter, prin. Fax 875-8469

Loveland, Hamilton, Pop. 11,848
Loveland CSD 4,700/PK-12
757 S Lebanon Rd 45140 513-683-5600
Charles Hilliker Ph.D., supt. Fax 683-5697
www.lovelandschools.org/
Loveland HS 1,400/9-12
1 Tiger Trl 45140 513-683-1920
Christopher Kloesz, prin. Fax 677-7952
Loveland MS 800/7-8
801 S Lebanon Rd 45140 513-683-3100
Christopher Burke, prin. Fax 677-7986

Lowellville, Mahoning, Pop. 1,148
Lowellville Local SD 600/K-12
52 Rocket Pl 44436 330-536-6318
Dr. Eugene Thomas, supt. Fax 536-8221
www.lowellville.k12.oh.us/
Lowellville JSHS 300/7-12
52 Rocket Pl 44436 330-536-8426
Christine Sawicki, prin. Fax 536-8468

Lucas, Richland, Pop. 605
Lucas Local SD 600/PK-12
84 Lucas North Rd 44843 419-892-2338
Daniel Freund, supt. Fax 892-1138
www.lucascubs.org
Lucas HS 200/8-12
5 1st Ave 44843 419-892-2338
Eric Teague, prin. Fax 892-1138

Lucasville, Scioto, Pop. 2,738
Scioto County Career Technical Center
951 Vern Riffe Dr 45648 740-259-5522
Stan Jennings, supt. Fax 259-1553
www.sciototech.org
Scioto County Career Technical Center Vo/Tech
951 Vern Riffe Dr 45648 740-259-5522
Stan Jennings, supt. Fax 259-1553

Valley Local SD 1,000/K-12
1821 State Route 728 45648 740-259-3115
Jeffrey Rolfe, supt. Fax 259-2314
www.valleyindians.net
Valley HS 300/9-12
1821 State Route 728 45648 740-259-5551
Jane Thayer, prin. Fax 259-2314
Valley MS, 393 Indian Dr 45648 300/5-8
Aaron Franke, prin. 740-259-2651

Lynchburg, Highland, Pop. 1,486
Lynchburg-Clay Local SD 1,200/PK-12
PO Box 515 45142 937-364-2338
Brett Justice, supt. Fax 364-2339
www.lynchclay.k12.oh.us
Lynchburg-Clay HS 400/9-12
6762 State Route 134 45142 937-364-2250
Linda Hatten, prin. Fax 364-6133
Lynchburg-Clay MS 300/6-8
8250 State Route 134 45142 937-364-2811
Dr. Casey Smith, prin. Fax 364-2159

Lyndhurst, Cuyahoga, Pop. 13,838
South Euclid-Lyndhurst CSD 3,800/K-12
5044 Mayfield Rd 44124 216-691-2000
Linda Reid, supt. Fax 691-2298
www.sel.k12.oh.us
Brush HS 1,400/9-12
4875 Glenlyn Rd 44124 216-691-2065
Karl Williamson, prin. Fax 691-2064
Memorial JHS 600/7-8
1250 Professor Rd 44124 216-691-2141
Dominick Kaple, prin. Fax 691-2159

Cleveland Institute Dental Medical Asst. Post-Sec.
5564 Mayfield Rd 44124 440-473-6273
Inner State Beauty School Post-Sec.
5150 Mayfield Rd 44124 440-442-4500

Mc Arthur, Vinton, Pop. 1,685
Vinton County Local SD 2,300/PK-12
307 W High St 45651 740-596-5218
Rick Brooks, supt. Fax 596-3142
www.vinton.k12.oh.us/
Vinton County HS 600/9-12
63910 US Highway 50 45651 740-596-5258
Kevin Waddell, prin. Fax 596-3003
Vinton County MS 500/6-8
63780 Locker Plant Rd 45651 740-596-5243
Jeremy Ward, prin. Fax 596-3815

Mc Comb, Hancock, Pop. 1,624
Mc Comb Local SD 700/PK-12
328 S Todd St 45858 419-293-3979
Meri Skilliter, supt. Fax 293-2412
www.noacsc.org/hancock/mb
Mc Comb Local HS 200/9-12
328 S Todd St 45858 419-293-3853
Jeremy Herr, prin. Fax 293-3107
Mc Comb Local MS 100/7-8
328 S Todd St 45858 419-293-3855
Jeremy Herr, prin. Fax 293-2412

Mc Connelsville, Morgan, Pop. 1,738
Morgan Local SD 2,000/PK-12
PO Box 509 43756 740-962-2782
Lori Snyder-Lowe, supt. Fax 962-4931
www.mlsd.k12.oh.us/
Morgan HS 600/9-12
800 Raider Dr 43756 740-962-2944
Anita Eldridge, prin. Fax 962-6005
Morgan JHS 300/7-8
820 Junior Raider Dr 43756 740-962-2833
Timothy Hopkins, prin. Fax 962-3389

Mc Dermott, Scioto, Pop. 428
Northwest Local SD 1,600/PK-12
800 Mohawk Dr 45652 740-259-5558
Dana Pollock Ed.D., supt. Fax 259-3476
www.northwest.k12.oh.us
Northwest HS 400/9-12
914 Mohawk Dr 45652 740-259-2366
Rick Scarberry, prin. Fax 259-8544
Northwest MS 400/6-8
692 Mohawk Dr 45652 740-259-2528
Gregory Tipton, prin. Fax 259-5731

Mc Donald, Trumbull, Pop. 3,227
McDonald Local SD 800/K-12
600 Iowa Ave 44437 330-530-8051
Robert Rostan, supt. Fax 530-7041
www.mcdonald.k12.oh.us
McDonald JSHS 400/7-12
600 Iowa Ave 44437 330-530-8051
Gary Carkido, prin. Fax 530-7034

Macedonia, Summit, Pop. 11,001
Nordonia Hills CSD
Supt. — See Northfield
Nordonia HS 1,300/9-12
8006 S Bedford Rd 44056 330-468-4601
Casey Wright, prin. Fax 468-0045

Mc Guffey, Hardin, Pop. 491
Upper Scioto Valley Local SD 500/K-12
PO Box 305 45859 419-757-3231
Dennis L. Recker, supt. Fax 757-0135
usv.k12.oh.us
Upper Scioto Valley HS 200/9-12
PO Box 305 45859 419-757-3231
Craig Hurley, prin. Fax 757-0135
Upper Scioto Valley MS 100/7-8
PO Box 305 45859 419-757-3231
Craig Hurley, prin. Fax 757-0135

Madison, Lake, Pop. 3,130
Madison Local SD 3,300/PK-12
1956 Red Bird Rd 44057 440-428-2166
Angela Smith, supt. Fax 428-9379
www.madisonschools.net
Madison HS 1,000/9-12
3100 Burns Rd 44057 440-428-2161
William Fisher, prin. Fax 428-2165
Madison MS 700/6-8
6079 Middle Ridge Rd 44057 440-428-1196
Thomas Brady, prin. Fax 428-9389

Magnolia, Stark, Pop. 965
Sandy Valley Local SD 1,100/PK-12
5362 State Route 183 NE 44643 330-866-3339
David Fischer, supt. Fax 866-5238
www.sandyvalleylocal.org
Sandy Valley MSHS 500/6-12
5130 State Route 183 NE 44643 330-866-9371
Matthew Whitted, prin. Fax 866-2490

Maineville, Warren, Pop. 962
Little Miami Local SD 3,400/PK-12
7247 Zoar Rd 45039 513-899-2264
Gregory Power, supt. Fax 899-3244
www.littlemiamischools.com
Other Schools – See Morrow

Malvern, Carroll, Pop. 1,175
Brown Local SD 600/K-12
3242 Coral Rd NW 44644 330-863-1170
Connie Griffin, supt. Fax 863-1172
www.brownlocalschools.com/
Malvern HS 200/9-12
3242 Coral Rd NW 44644 330-863-1355
Scott Bowling, prin. Fax 863-1366
Malvern MS 200/6-8
3242 Coral Rd NW 44644 330-863-1355
Scott Bowling, prin. Fax 863-1366

Manchester, Adams, Pop. 1,976
Manchester Local SD 900/PK-12
130 Wayne Frye Dr 45144 937-549-4777
Dr. Charles Shreve, supt. Fax 549-4744
www.mlsd.us
Manchester HS 300/7-12
130 Wayne Frye Dr 45144 937-549-4777
James Wilkins, prin. Fax 549-2872

Mansfield, Richland, Pop. 46,379
Madison Local SD 2,600/PK-12
1379 Grace St 44905 419-589-2600
Lee Kaple, supt. Fax 589-3653
www.mlsd.net/
Madison Comprehensive HS 900/9-12
600 Esley Ln 44905 419-589-2112
Rob Peterson, prin. Fax 589-2533
Madison MS 500/5-8
1419 Grace St 44905 419-522-0471
Jonathan Muro, prin. Fax 522-1463

Mansfield CSD 3,300/PK-12
PO Box 1448 44901 419-525-6400
Brian Garverick, supt. Fax 525-6415
www.tygerpride.com
Mansfield HS 800/9-12
124 N Linden Rd 44906 419-525-6369
Jose Hernandez, prin. Fax 524-2210
Mansfield Integrated Learning Center 100/Alt
176 Hedges St 44902 419-525-6305
David Gilbert, prin. Fax 525-6387

Mansfield MS 500/7-8
124 N Linden Rd 44906 419-525-6307
Jason Goings, prin. Fax 525-6306

Mansfield Christian S 500/PK-12
500 Logan Rd 44907 419-756-5651
Dr. Cy Smith, supt. Fax 756-7470
North Central State College Post-Sec.
2441 Kenwood Cir 44906 419-755-4800
Ohio State University-Mansfield Campus Post-Sec.
1760 University Dr 44906 419-755-4011
St. Peter HS 300/7-12
104 W 1st St 44902 419-524-0979
Michael Wasiniak, prin. Fax 524-3336
Temple Christian S 200/PK-12
752 Stewart Rd N 44905 419-589-9707
Paul Baird, prin. Fax 589-7213

Mantua, Portage, Pop. 1,029
Crestwood Local SD 1,900/PK-12
11260 Bowen Rd 44255 330-357-8206
David Toth, supt. Fax 274-3710
www.crestwoodschools.org
Crestwood HS 600/9-12
10919 Main St 44255 330-357-8201
David McMahon, prin. Fax 274-3150
Crestwood MS 400/6-8
10880 John Edward Dr 44255 330-357-8202
Julie Schmidt, prin. Fax 274-3705

Maple Heights, Cuyahoga, Pop. 22,680
Maple Heights CSD 3,700/PK-12
5740 Lawn Ave 44137 216-587-6100
Dr. Charles Keenan, supt. Fax 518-2674
www.mapleschools.com/
Maple Heights HS 1,100/9-12
5445 West Blvd 44137 216-438-6400
Quarnitra Price, prin.
Milkovich MS 900/6-8
19800 Stafford Ave 44137 216-438-6000
Robert Klinar, prin. Fax 587-4523

Marengo, Morrow, Pop. 330
Highland Local SD 1,800/K-12
6506 State Route 229 43334 419-768-2206
Bill Dodds, supt. Fax 768-3115
www.highland.k12.oh.us/
Highland HS 500/9-12
1300 State Route 314 43334 419-768-3101
Nate Huffman, prin. Fax 768-3560
Highland MS 500/6-8
6506 State Route 229 43334 419-768-2781
Matthew Bradley, prin. Fax 768-2742

Maria Stein, Mercer
Marion Local SD 900/K-12
7956 State Route 119 45860 419-925-4294
Michael Pohlman, supt. Fax 925-0212
marionlocal.org
Marion Local HS 300/9-12
1901 State Route 716 45860 419-925-4597
Timothy Goodwin, prin. Fax 925-5111

Marietta, Washington, Pop. 13,848
Marietta CSD 2,700/K-12
111 Academy Dr 45750 740-374-6500
William Hampton, supt. Fax 374-6506
mariettacityschools.k12.oh.us
Marietta HS 800/9-12
208 Davis Ave 45750 740-374-6540
Chad Rinard, prin. Fax 376-2462
Marietta MS 600/6-8
242 N 7th St 45750 740-374-6530
Brittany Schob, prin. Fax 374-6531

Washington County JVSD
21740 State Route 676 45750 740-373-2766
Dennis Blatt, supt. Fax 373-9026
www.thecareercenter.net
Washington County Career Center Vo/Tech
21740 State Route 676 45750 740-373-2766
Dennis Blatt, supt. Fax 373-9026

Marietta College Post-Sec.
215 5th St 45750 740-376-4000
Memorial Hospital Post-Sec.
401 Matthew St 45750 740-374-1412
Valley Beauty School Post-Sec.
113 Wildwood Dr 45750 740-373-3617
Washington State Community College Post-Sec.
710 Colegate Dr 45750 740-374-8716

Marion, Marion, Pop. 36,113
Elgin Local SD 900/K-12
1239 Keener Rd S 43302 740-382-1101
Bruce Gast, supt. Fax 382-1672
www.elginschools.org
Elgin HS 300/9-12
1150 Keener Rd S 43302 740-223-4300
Chad Cunningham, prin. Fax 223-4310
Elgin MS 300/6-8
1200 Keener Rd S 43302 740-223-4300
Michael Malcom, prin. Fax 223-4310

Marion CSD 4,400/PK-12
420 Presidential Dr Ste B 43302 740-387-3300
Gary Barber, supt. Fax 223-4400
www.marioncityschools.org
Grant MS 1,000/6-8
420 Presidential Dr 43302 740-223-4900
Adam Kunkle, prin. Fax 223-4820
Harding HS 900/9-12
1500 Harding Hwy E 43302 740-223-4700
Forrest Trisler, prin. Fax 223-4705

Pleasant Local SD 1,200/K-12
1107 Owens Rd W 43302 740-389-4476
Dr. John Bruno, supt. Fax 389-6985
www.pleasant.treca.org
Pleasant HS 400/9-12
1101 Owens Rd W 43302 740-389-2389
Eric Holman, prin. Fax 389-3904
Pleasant MS 300/6-8
3507 Smeltzer Rd 43302 740-389-5167
Lane Warner, prin. Fax 389-5111

Tri-Rivers Career Center
2222 Marion Mount Gilead Rd 43302 740-389-4681
Charles Speelman, supt. Fax 389-2963
www.tririvers.com
Tri-Rivers Career Center Vo/Tech
2222 Marion Mount Gilead Rd 43302 740-389-4681
Larry Hickman, dir. Fax 389-2963

Marion General Hospital Post-Sec.
1000 McKinley Park Blvd 43302 740-383-8700
Marion Technical College Post-Sec.
1467 Mount Vernon Ave 43302 740-389-4636
Ohio State University at Marion Post-Sec.
1465 Mount Vernon Ave 43302 740-389-6786

Martins Ferry, Belmont, Pop. 6,765
Martins Ferry CSD 1,400/K-12
5001 Ayers Lime Stone Rd 43935 740-633-1732
Dirk Fitch, supt. Fax 633-5666
www.mfcsd.k12.oh.us
Martins Ferry HS 400/9-12
5000 Ayers Lime Stone Rd 43935 740-633-0684
Jim Fogle, prin. Fax 635-6103
Martins Ferry MS 400/5-8
5000 Ayers Lime Stone Rd 43935 740-633-9741
Michael Delatore, prin. Fax 635-6107

Speiro Academy, 500 N 5th St 43935 50/K-12
Susan Cline, prin. 740-738-0203

Marysville, Union, Pop. 21,701
Marysville EVD 5,100/K-12
1000 Edgewood Dr 43040 937-578-6100
Diane Mankins, supt. Fax 578-6113
www.marysville.k12.oh.us
Bunsold MS 900/7-8
14198 State Route 4 43040 937-578-6400
Michelle Kaffenbarger, prin. Fax 578-6413
Marysville HS 1,600/9-12
800 Amrine Mill Rd 43040 937-578-6200
Thomas Cochran, prin. Fax 578-6213
Marysville STEM Early College HS 9-12
833 N Maple St 43040 937-578-7300
Kathy McKinniss, prin. Fax 578-7313

Mason, Warren, Pop. 30,202
Mason CSD 10,300/PK-12
211 N East St 45040 513-398-0474
Dr. Gail Kist, supt. Fax 398-4554
www.masonohioschools.com
Mason HS 3,300/9-12
6100 S Mason Montgomery Rd 45040 513-398-5025
David Hyatt, prin. Fax 336-6823
Mason MS 1,800/7-8
6370 S Mason Montgomery Rd 45040 513-398-9035
Tonya Mccall, prin. Fax 459-0904

Mars Hill Academy 300/K-12
4230 Aero Dr 45040 513-770-3223
Dr. James Albritton, hdmstr. Fax 770-3443

Massillon, Stark, Pop. 31,305
Jackson Local SD 5,900/K-12
7602 Fulton Dr NW 44646 330-830-8000
Chris DiLoreto, supt. Fax 830-8008
jackson.stark.k12.oh.us
Jackson HS 2,000/9-12
7600 Fulton Dr NW 44646 330-837-3501
Jeff Kracker, prin. Fax 830-8069
Jackson Memorial MS 1,400/6-8
7355 Mudbrook St NW 44646 330-830-8034
Paul Salvino, prin. Fax 830-8068

Massillon CSD 4,100/PK-12
930 17th St NE 44646 330-830-3900
Richard Goodright, supt. Fax 830-0953
www.massillonschools.org
Massillon JHS 600/7-8
250 29th St NW 44647 330-830-3902
Vincent Lindsey, prin. Fax 830-3952
Washington HS 1,200/9-12
1 Paul E Brown Dr SE 44646 330-830-3901
Brad Warner, prin. Fax 830-1954

Perry Local SD 5,000/PK-12
4201 13th St SW 44646 330-477-8121
Scott Beatty, supt. Fax 478-6184
www.perrylocal.org
Edison MS 800/7-8
4201 13th St SW 44646 330-478-6167
Diane Kittelberger, prin. Fax 477-4612
Perry HS 1,600/9-12
3737 13th St SW 44646 330-477-3486
Jason Conrad, prin. Fax 478-6160

Stark County Area JVSD
2800 Richville Dr SE 44646 330-832-9856
Cynthia Smythe, dir. Fax 832-9850
www.drage.stark.k12.oh.us
Drage Career-Technical Center Vo/Tech
2800 Richville Dr SE 44646 330-832-9856
Daniel Murphy, dir. Fax 832-9850

Tuslaw Local SD 1,400/PK-12
1835 Manchester Ave NW 44647 330-837-7813
Melissa Marconi, supt. Fax 837-7804
www.tuslaw.sparcc.org/
Tuslaw HS 400/9-12
1847 Manchester Ave NW 44647 330-837-7800
Adam McKenzie, prin. Fax 837-6016

Tuslaw MS 500/5-8
1723 Manchester Ave NW 44647 330-837-7807
Mike Hamm, prin. Fax 837-6015

Maumee, Lucas, Pop. 14,100
Maumee CSD 2,500/PK-12
716 Askin St 43537 419-893-3200
Todd Cramer, supt. Fax 891-5387
www.maumee.k12.oh.us
Gateway MS 600/6-8
900 Gibbs St 43537 419-893-3386
Angela Rose, prin. Fax 893-2263
Maumee HS 700/9-12
1147 Saco St 43537 419-893-8778
Matthew Dick, prin. Fax 893-5621

Professional Skills Institute Post-Sec.
1505 Holland Rd 43537 419-720-6670
Stautzenberger College Post-Sec.
1796 Indian Wood Cir 43537 419-866-0261

Mayfield, Cuyahoga, Pop. 3,423
Mayfield CSD
Supt. — See Mayfield Heights
Mayfield HS 1,900/9-12
6116 Wilson Mills Rd 44143 440-995-6900
Jeffrey Legan, prin. Fax 995-6805

Mayfield Heights, Cuyahoga, Pop. 18,836
Mayfield CSD 4,500/K-12
1101 SOM Center Rd 44124 440-995-6800
Dr. Keith Kelly, supt. Fax 995-7205
www.mayfieldschools.org
CEVEC Vo/Tech
1111 Som Center Rd 44124 440-995-7450
Robert Ross, prin. Fax 646-1117
Mayfield MS 900/6-8
1123 SOM Center Rd 44124 440-995-7800
Paul Destino, prin. Fax 449-1413
Other Schools – See Mayfield

Mechanicsburg, Champaign, Pop. 1,610
Mechanicsburg EVD 900/K-12
60 High St 43044 937-834-2453
Danielle Prohaska, supt. Fax 834-3954
www.mechanicsburg.k12.oh.us
Mechanicsburg HS 300/9-12
60 High St 43044 937-834-2453
Paul Hershberger, prin. Fax 834-7103
Mechanicsburg MS, 60 High St 43044 200/6-8
Marlo Schipfer, admin. 937-834-2453

Medina, Medina, Pop. 26,154
Buckeye Local SD 2,200/PK-12
3044 Columbia Rd 44256 330-722-8257
Kent Morgan, supt. Fax 722-5793
www.buckeyeschools.org
Buckeye HS 600/9-12
3084 Columbia Rd 44256 330-722-8257
Gabriel Tudor, prin. Fax 723-5606
Buckeye JHS 400/7-8
3024 Columbia Rd 44256 330-722-8257
Daniel Flood, prin. Fax 725-2413

Highland Local SD 3,200/PK-12
3880 Ridge Rd 44256 330-239-1901
Catherine Aukerman, supt. Fax 239-2456
www.highlandschools.org
Highland HS 1,100/9-12
4150 Ridge Rd 44256 330-239-1901
Dana Addis, prin. Fax 239-7385
Highland MS 800/6-8
3880 Ridge Rd 44256 330-239-1901
Jonathan Henry, prin. Fax 239-7388

Medina CSD 7,000/PK-12
739 Weymouth Rd 44256 330-725-8831
Aaron Sable, supt. Fax 636-3006
www.medinabees.org
Claggett MS 900/6-8
420 E Union St 44256 330-636-3600
Paul Worsencroft, prin. Fax 725-9349
Evolve Academy 50/Alt
222 S Broadway St 44256 330-336-4213
Peg Hufnagel, dir.
Medina HS 2,100/9-12
777 E Union St 44256 330-636-3200
Jeffrey Harrison, prin. Fax 764-3521
Root MS 800/6-8
333 W Sturbridge Dr 44256 330-636-3500
Bryan Farson, prin. Fax 764-1471

Medina County JVSD
1101 W Liberty St 44256 330-725-8461
Steven Chrisman M.Ed., supt. Fax 725-5870
www.mcjvs.edu
Medina County Career Center Vo/Tech
1101 W Liberty St 44256 330-725-8461
Tresa Goodwin M.Ed., prin. Fax 725-5870

Hamrick School Post-Sec.
1156 Medina Rd 44256 330-239-2229
Medina County Career Center Post-Sec.
1101 W Liberty St 44256 330-725-8461

Mentor, Lake, Pop. 46,722
Mentor EVD 7,500/K-12
6451 Center St 44060 440-255-4444
Matthew Miller, supt. Fax 255-4622
www.mentorschools.net
Memorial MS 700/6-8
8979 Mentor Ave 44060 440-974-2250
Adam Dudziak, prin. Fax 974-2259
Mentor HS 2,700/9-12
6477 Center St 44060 440-974-5300
Andrew Fetchik, prin. Fax 974-5216
Ridge MS 500/6-8
7860 Johnnycake Ridge Rd 44060 440-974-5400
Ericka Blackburn, prin. Fax 974-5285

Shore MS 600/6-8
5670 Hopkins Rd 44060 440-257-8750
Douglas Baker, prin. Fax 257-8761

Brown Aveda Institute Post-Sec.
8816 Mentor Ave 44060 440-255-9494
Cleveland Institute Dental Medical Asst. Post-Sec.
5733 Hopkins Rd 44060 440-946-9530
Lake Catholic HS 800/9-12
6733 Reynolds Rd 44060 440-578-1020
Robert Kumazec, prin. Fax 974-9087

Metamora, Fulton, Pop. 623
Evergreen Local SD 1,100/K-12
14544 County Road 6 43540 419-644-3521
James Wyse, supt. Fax 644-6070
www.evergreen.k12.oh.us
Evergreen HS 300/9-12
14544 County Road 6 43540 419-644-2951
Joshua Clark, prin. Fax 644-6070
Evergreen MS 300/6-8
14544 County Road 6 43540 419-644-2331
Joseph Zabowski, prin. Fax 644-9203

Miamisburg, Montgomery, Pop. 19,876
Miamisburg CSD 5,600/PK-12
540 Park Ave 45342 937-866-3381
Dr. David Vail, supt. Fax 865-5250
www.miamisburgcityschools.org
Miamisburg HS 1,500/9-12
1860 Belvo Rd 45342 937-866-0771
Craig Morris, prin. Fax 865-5267
Miamisburg MS 1,300/6-8
8668 Miamisburg Springboro 45342 937-865-0011
Kelly Thomas, prin. Fax 865-0114

Dayton Barber College Post-Sec.
2741 Lyons Rd Ste C 45342 937-222-9101
Dayton Christian S 1,000/PK-12
9391 Washington Church Rd 45342 937-291-7201
Dr. David Rough, prin. Fax 291-7202

Middleburg Heights, Cuyahoga, Pop. 15,799
Berea CSD
Supt. — See Berea
Middleburg Heights JHS 1,600/7-9
7000 Paula Dr 44130 216-676-8400
Paul Kish, prin. Fax 676-2070

Polaris JVSD
7285 Old Oak Blvd 44130 440-891-7600
Bob Timmons, supt. Fax 243-3952
www.polaris.edu
Polaris Career Center Vo/Tech
7285 Old Oak Blvd 44130 440-891-7600
Gerald Lanning, prin. Fax 243-3952

Middlefield, Geauga, Pop. 2,651
Cardinal Local SD 1,000/K-12
PO Box 188 44062 440-632-0261
Dr. Scott J. Hunt Ed.D., supt. Fax 632-5886
www.cardinalschools.org
Cardinal HS 400/9-12
PO Box 7 44062 440-632-0261
Jeremy Hunter, prin. Fax 632-1734
Cardinal MS 300/5-8
PO Box 879 44062 440-632-0261
Dr. Jennifer Sabol, prin. Fax 632-0294

Middleport, Meigs, Pop. 2,488

Mid Valley Christian S 100/PK-12
500 N 2nd Ave 45760 740-992-6249
Melissa Dailey, admin. Fax 992-6249

Middletown, Butler, Pop. 47,397
Madison Local SD 1,300/PK-12
1324 Middletown Eaton Rd 45042 513-420-4750
Curtis Philpot, supt. Fax 420-4781
www.madisonmohawks.org/
Madison JSHS 400/7-12
5797 W Alexandria Rd 45042 513-420-4760
Justin Smith, prin. Fax 420-4914

Middletown CSD 6,200/PK-12
1 Donham Plz Fl 4 45042 513-423-0781
Samuel Ison, supt. Fax 420-4579
www.middletowncityschools.com
Middleton MS 800/7-8
1415 Girard Ave 45044 513-420-4528
Michael Valenti, prin. Fax 420-4527
Middletown HS 1,600/9-12
601 N Breiel Blvd 45042 513-420-4500
Carmela Cotter, prin. Fax 420-4648

Carousel Beauty College Post-Sec.
633 S Breiel Blvd 45044 513-422-2962
Miami University-Middletown Campus Post-Sec.
4200 N University Blvd 45042 513-727-3200
Middletown Regional Hospital Post-Sec.
PO Box 428810 45042 513-420-5100

Milan, Erie, Pop. 1,356
EHOVE JVSD
316 Mason Rd W 44846 419-499-4663
Sharon Mastroianni, supt. Fax 499-4076
www.ehove.net
EHOVE Career Center Vo/Tech
316 Mason Rd W 44846 419-499-4663
Erika Beckman, prin. Fax 499-4076

Edison Local SD 1,600/PK-12
140 S Main St 44846 419-499-3000
Thomas Roth, supt. Fax 499-4859
www.edisonchargers.org/
Edison HS 400/9-12
2603 State Route 113 E 44846 419-499-4652
Jeffrey Goodwin, prin. Fax 499-2035
Other Schools – See Berlin Heights

Milford, Clermont, Pop. 6,599
Great Oaks Institute of Technology
Supt. — See Cincinnati
Live Oaks CDC Vo/Tech
5956 Buckwheat Rd 45150 513-575-1900
Dan Cox, prin. Fax 575-0805

Milford EVD 6,600/PK-12
777 Garfield Ave 45150 513-831-1314
Nancy C. House, supt. Fax 831-3208
www.milfordschools.org
Milford HS 1,900/9-12
1 Eagles Way 45150 513-831-2990
Josh Kauffman, prin. Fax 831-9714
Milford JHS 1,000/7-8
5735 Pleasant Hill Rd 45150 513-831-1900
Rob Dunn, prin. Fax 248-3451

St. Andrew/St. Elizabeth Ann Seton S 200/6-8
555 Main St 45150 513-831-5277
Mark Wilburn, prin. Fax 831-8436

Milford Center, Union, Pop. 776
Fairbanks Local SD 1,000/K-12
11158 State Route 38 43045 937-349-3731
Robert Humble, supt. Fax 349-8885
www.fairbanks.k12.oh.us
Fairbanks HS 300/9-12
11158 State Route 38 43045 937-349-3721
Tom Montgomery, prin. Fax 349-2011
Fairbanks MS 300/6-8
11158 State Route 38 43045 937-349-6841
Thomas Montgomery, prin. Fax 349-2013

Millbury, Wood, Pop. 1,191
Lake Local SD 1,600/PK-12
28090 Lemoyne Rd 43447 419-661-6690
Jim Witt, supt. Fax 661-6678
www.lakeschools.org
Lake HS 600/8-12
28080 Lemoyne Rd 43447 419-661-6640
Lee Herman, prin. Fax 661-6650

Miller City, Putnam, Pop. 137
Miller City-New Cleveland Local SD 500/K-12
PO Box 38 45864 419-876-3172
Kerry Johnson, supt. Fax 876-3849
www.mcncschools.org
Miller City-New Cleveland HS 100/9-12
PO Box 38 45864 419-876-3173
Kerry Johnson, prin. Fax 876-2020
Miller City-New Cleveland MS 100/6-8
PO Box 38 45864 419-876-3174
Dustin Pester, prin. Fax 876-2020

Millersburg, Holmes, Pop. 2,985
East Holmes Local SD 1,800/K-12
6108 County Road 77 44654 330-893-2610
Erik Beun, supt. Fax 893-2838
www.eastholmes.k12.oh.us
Other Schools – See Berlin, Charm

West Holmes Local SD 2,400/K-12
28 W Jackson St 44654 330-674-3546
William Sterling, supt. Fax 674-6833
www.westholmes.k12.oh.us
West Holmes HS 800/9-12
10909 State Route 39 44654 330-674-6085
Aaron Kaufman, prin. Fax 674-0818
West Holmes MS 600/6-8
10901 State Route 39 44654 330-674-4761
Jeff Woods, prin. Fax 674-2311

Gospel Haven Academy 100/K-12
6871 State Route 241 44654 330-674-0752
Galen Kauffman, prin. Fax 674-0752

Millersport, Fairfield, Pop. 1,033
Walnut Township Local SD 600/K-12
11850 Lancaster St 43046 740-467-2802
Randall Cotner, supt. Fax 467-3494
www.walnuttsd.org
Millersport JSHS 300/7-12
11850 Lancaster St 43046 740-467-2929
Jeff Stought, prin. Fax 467-3494

Mineral Ridge, Trumbull, Pop. 3,840
Weathersfield Local SD 900/K-12
1334 Seaborn St 44440 330-652-0287
Damon Dohar, supt. Fax 544-7476
www.weathersfield.k12.oh.us
Mineral Ridge HS 400/7-12
1334 Seaborn St 44440 330-652-1451
Randy Cameron, prin. Fax 505-9374

Minerva, Stark, Pop. 3,671
Minerva Local SD 1,800/K-12
406 East St 44657 330-868-4332
Gary Chaddock, supt. Fax 868-4731
minerva.web1.schoolpointe.com/
Minerva HS 500/9-12
501 Almeda Ave 44657 330-868-4134
Brett Yeagley, prin. Fax 868-5973
Minerva MS 500/6-8
600 E Line St 44657 330-868-4497
Scott Cassidy, prin. Fax 868-3144

Minford, Scioto, Pop. 684
Minford Local SD 1,400/K-12
PO Box 204 45653 740-820-3896
Jeremy Litteral, supt. Fax 820-3334
www.minfordfalcons.net
Minford HS 400/9-12
PO Box 204 45653 740-820-3445
Jeffrey Pica, prin. Fax 820-4484
Minford MS 600/4-8
PO Box 204 45653 740-820-2181
Dennis Evans, prin. Fax 820-2191

Mingo Junction, Jefferson, Pop. 3,405
Indian Creek Local SD
Supt. — See Wintersville
Indian Creek MS 300/5-8
2379 Wilson Ave 43938 740-282-0834
Dr. Holly Minch-Hick, prin. Fax 282-3092

Minster, Auglaize, Pop. 2,793
Minster Local SD 900/K-12
50 E 7th St 45865 419-628-3397
Brenda Boeke, supt. Fax 628-2482
www.minsterschools.org
Minster JSHS 400/7-12
100 E 7th St 45865 419-628-2324
Michael Lee, prin. Fax 628-2495

Mogadore, Summit, Pop. 3,799
Field Local SD 2,000/K-12
2900 State Route 43 44260 330-673-2659
David Heflinger, supt. Fax 673-0270
www.fieldlocalschools.org
Field HS 600/9-12
2900 State Route 43 44260 330-673-9591
Craig Nettleton, prin. Fax 677-2520
Field MS, 1379 Saxe Rd 44260 500/6-8
Susan Blake, prin. 330-673-4176

Mogadore Local SD 700/K-12
1 S Cleveland Ave 44260 330-628-9946
Dr. Christina Dinklocker, supt. Fax 628-6661
www.mogadore.net
Mogadore JSHS 200/7-12
130 S Cleveland Ave 44260 330-628-9943
Russ Swartz, prin. Fax 628-6657

Monclova, Lucas

Monclova Christian Academy 200/K-12
7819 Monclova Rd 43542 419-866-7630
Neil Black, prin. Fax 868-1062

Monroe, Butler, Pop. 12,294
Monroe Local SD 2,500/PK-12
500 Yankee Rd 45050 513-539-2536
Dr. Philip Cagwin, supt. Fax 539-2648
www.monroelocalschools.com/
Monroe JSHS 1,000/7-12
220 Yankee Rd 45050 513-539-8471
Dr. Brian Powderly, prin. Fax 539-8474

Monroeville, Huron, Pop. 1,379
Monroeville Local SD 600/K-12
101 West St 44847 419-465-2610
G. Ralph Moore, supt. Fax 465-4263
www.monroevilleschools.org/
Monroeville JSHS 300/7-12
101 West St 44847 419-465-2531
James Kaczor, prin. Fax 465-4580

Montpelier, Williams, Pop. 4,026
Montpelier EVD 900/PK-12
PO Box 193 43543 419-485-6700
Jamison Grime, supt. Fax 485-4318
www.montpelier-k12.org
Montpelier JSHS 400/7-12
PO Box 193 43543 419-485-6703
Su Thorop, prin. Fax 485-3487

Morral, Marion, Pop. 394
Ridgedale Local SD 700/K-12
3103 Hillman Ford Rd 43337 740-382-6065
Robert Britton, supt. Fax 383-6538
www.ridgedale.k12.oh.us/
Ridgedale JSHS 400/6-12
3165 Hillman Ford Rd 43337 740-382-6065
Brian Napper, prin. Fax 387-8525

Morrow, Warren, Pop. 1,164
Little Miami Local SD
Supt. — See Maineville
Little Miami HS 1,000/9-12
3001 E US Highway 22 and 3 45152 513-899-3781
Catherine Trevathan, prin. Fax 899-4912
Little Miami JHS 600/7-8
5290 Morrow Cozaddale Rd 45152 513-899-3408
Ryan Cherry, prin. Fax 899-2048

Mount Blanchard, Hancock, Pop. 482
Riverdale Local SD 800/K-12
20613 State Route 37 45867 419-694-4994
Eric Hoffman, supt. Fax 694-6465
www.riverdale.k12.oh.us
Riverdale HS 300/9-12
20613 State Route 37 45867 419-694-2211
Dan Evans, prin. Fax 694-5008
Riverdale MS 200/6-8
20613 State Route 37 45867 419-694-2211
Dan Evans, prin. Fax 694-5008

Mount Gilead, Morrow, Pop. 3,594
Mt. Gilead EVD 1,200/PK-12
145 N Cherry St 43338 419-946-1646
Jeffrey Thompson, supt. Fax 946-3651
www.mgschools.org
Mount Gilead HS 300/9-12
338 W Park Ave 43338 419-947-6065
Debra Clauss, prin. Fax 946-3263
Mount Gilead MS 300/6-8
324 W Park Ave 43338 419-947-9517
Jon Grega, prin. Fax 947-9518

Gilead Christian S South Campus 50/6-12
3613 Township Road 115 43338 419-946-5990
Gary W. Miller, admin. Fax 946-1103

Mount Healthy, Hamilton, Pop. 5,926
Mt. Healthy CSD 3,200/K-12
7615 Harrison Ave 45231 513-729-0077
Reva Cosby, supt. Fax 728-4692
www.mthcs.org
Other Schools – See Cincinnati

Mount Orab, Brown, Pop. 3,635
Western Brown Local SD 3,100/PK-12
524 W Main St 45154 937-444-2044
Raegan White, supt. Fax 444-4303
www.wb.k12.oh.us
Mount Orab MS 800/5-8
472 W Main St 45154 937-444-2529
Sabrina Armstrong, prin. Fax 444-4268
Western Brown HS 800/9-12
476 W Main St 45154 937-444-2544
Heather Cooper, prin. Fax 444-4355

Mount Vernon, Knox, Pop. 16,729
Knox County JVSD
306 Martinsburg Rd 43050 740-397-5820
Kathy Greenich, supt. Fax 397-7040
www.knoxcc.org
Knox County Career Center Vo/Tech
306 Martinsburg Rd 43050 740-397-5820
Kathy Greenich, admin. Fax 397-7040

Mt. Vernon CSD 3,800/PK-12
300 Newark Rd 43050 740-397-7422
William Seder, supt. Fax 397-5949
www.mvcsd.us/
Mount Vernon HS 1,000/9-12
300 Martinsburg Rd 43050 740-393-5900
Kathy Kasler, prin. Fax 397-6018
Mount Vernon MS 900/6-8
298 Martinsburg Rd 43050 740-392-6867
Gary Hankins, prin. Fax 392-3369

Christian Star Academy 50/K-12
7 E Sugar St 43050 740-393-0251
Suzanne Feasel, admin. Fax 393-0067
Knox County Career Center Post-Sec.
306 Martinsburg Rd 43050 740-397-5820
Mt. Vernon Nazarene University Post-Sec.
800 Martinsburg Rd 43050 740-392-6868

Mount Victory, Hardin, Pop. 626
Ridgemont Local SD 500/PK-12
560 Taylor St W 43340 937-354-2441
Emmy Beeson, supt. Fax 354-2194
www.ridgemont.k12.oh.us
Ridgemont JSHS 200/7-12
560 Taylor St W 43340 937-354-2141
Jill Stover, prin. Fax 354-5099

Mowrystown, Highland, Pop. 359
Bright Local SD 600/PK-12
PO Box 299 45155 937-442-3114
Ted Downing, supt. Fax 442-6655
www.brightlocalschools.com
Whiteoak JSHS 200/7-12
PO Box 299 45155 937-442-2241
Brian Ruckel, prin. Fax 442-2111

Munroe Falls, Summit, Pop. 4,951
Stow-Munroe Falls CSD
Supt. — See Stow
Kimpton MS 900/7-8
380 N River Rd 44262 330-689-5288
Susan Palchesko, prin. Fax 686-4718

Napoleon, Henry, Pop. 8,677
Napoleon Area CSD 1,500/PK-12
701 Briarheath Ave Ste 108 43545 419-599-7015
Dr. Stephen R. Fogo, supt. Fax 599-7035
www.napoleonareaschools.org/
Napoleon JSHS 600/7-12
701 Briarheath Ave Ste 123 43545 419-599-1050
Ryan Wilde, prin. Fax 599-8537

Navarre, Stark, Pop. 1,939
Fairless Local SD 1,500/K-12
11885 Navarre Rd SW 44662 330-767-3577
Broc Bidlack, supt. Fax 767-3298
www.falcon.stark.k12.oh.us/
Fairless HS 400/9-12
11885 Navarre Rd SW 44662 330-767-3444
Dr. Larry Chambliss, prin. Fax 767-3447
Fairless MS 400/6-8
11836 Navarre Rd SW 44662 330-767-4293
Theodore George, prin. Fax 767-3807

Nelsonville, Athens, Pop. 5,295
Nelsonville-York CSD 1,300/PK-12
2 Buckeye Dr 45764 740-753-4441
Charles McClelland, supt. Fax 753-1968
www.nelsonvilleyork.k12.oh.us/
Nelsonville-York HS 400/9-12
1 Buckeye Dr 45764 740-753-4441
Elise Stephan, prin. Fax 753-1420
Nelsonville-York MS 200/7-8
3 Buckeye Dr 45764 740-753-4441
Thomas Taggart, prin. Fax 753-9450

Tri-County Career Center
15676 State Route 691 45764 740-753-3511
William Wittman, supt. Fax 753-5376
www.tricountyhightech.com
Tri-County Career Center Vo/Tech
15676 State Route 691 45764 740-753-3511
Connie Altier, prin. Fax 753-5132
Tri-County Career Center Adult Educ Adult
15676 State Route 691 45764 740-753-5464
Connie Altier, dir. Fax 753-5129

Hocking College Post-Sec.
3301 Hocking Pkwy 45764 740-735-3591

New Albany, Franklin, Pop. 7,553
New Albany - Plain Local SD 5,400/K-12
55 N High St 43054 614-855-2040
Michael Sawyers, supt. Fax 855-2043
www.napls.us
New Albany HS 1,300/9-12
7600 Fodor Rd 43054 614-413-8300
Dwight Carter, prin. Fax 413-8301
New Albany MS 1,200/6-8
6600 E Dublin Granville Rd 43054 614-413-8500
Donna LeBeau, prin. Fax 413-8501

Newark, Licking, Pop. 46,372
Career & Technology Educational Ctr SD
150 Price Rd 43055 740-364-2832
Joyce Malainy, supt. Fax 364-2815
www.c-tec.edu/
Career & Technology Educational Center Vo/Tech
150 Price Rd 43055 740-364-2832
Thomas Gamertsfelder, dir. Fax 364-2815

Licking Valley Local SD 2,000/K-12
1379 Licking Valley Rd 43055 740-763-3525
David Hile, supt. Fax 763-0471
www.lickingvalley.k12.oh.us/
Licking Valley HS 600/9-12
100 Hainsview Dr 43055 740-763-3721
Wes Weaver, prin. Fax 763-0847
Licking Valley MS 500/6-8
1379 Licking Valley Rd 43055 740-763-3396
Scott Beery, prin. Fax 763-2612

Newark CSD 6,200/PK-12
621 Mount Vernon Rd 43055 740-670-7000
Douglas Ute, supt. Fax 670-7009
www.newarkcityschools.org
Heritage MS 500/6-8
600 Arlington Ave 43055 740-670-7110
Brent Fickes, prin. Fax 670-7119
Liberty MS 500/6-8
1055 Evans Blvd 43055 740-670-7320
Diane Henry, prin. Fax 670-7329
Newark HS 1,500/9-12
314 Granville St 43055 740-670-7400
Thomas Bowman, prin. Fax 670-7409
Wilson MS 400/6-8
805 W Church St 43055 740-670-7120
John Davis, prin. Fax 670-7129

Central Ohio Technical College Post-Sec.
1179 University Dr 43055 740-366-9494
Newark Catholic HS 200/9-12
1 Green Wave Dr 43055 740-344-3594
Beth Hill, prin. Fax 344-0421
Ohio State University at Newark Post-Sec.
1179 University Dr 43055 740-366-3321

New Boston, Scioto, Pop. 2,223
New Boston Local SD 500/PK-12
1 Glenwood Tiger Trl 45662 740-456-4559
Melinda Burnside, supt. Fax 456-6402
www.newboston.k12.oh.us
Glenwood HS 200/7-12
1 Glenwood Tiger Trl 45662 740-456-4559
Donald Stapleton, prin. Fax 456-6402

Daymar College Post-Sec.
3879 Rhodes Ave 45662 740-456-4124

New Bremen, Auglaize, Pop. 2,950
New Bremen Local SD 800/K-12
901 E Monroe St 45869 419-629-8606
Dr. Andrea Townsend, supt. Fax 629-0115
www.newbremenschools.org
New Bremen HS 300/9-12
901 E Monroe St 45869 419-629-8606
Brian Pohl, prin. Fax 629-0115

Newburgh Heights, Cuyahoga, Pop. 2,102
Cleveland Municipal SD
Supt. — See Cleveland
Washington Park Environmental Studies 200/9-12
3875 Washington Park Blvd 44105 216-482-2671
Donald Strinka, prin. Fax 441-8038

Newbury, Geauga
Newbury Local SD 500/K-12
14775 Auburn Rd 44065 440-564-5501
Michelle Mrakovich, supt. Fax 564-9460
www.newburyschools.org/
Newbury JSHS 300/6-12
14775 Auburn Rd 44065 440-564-2281
Michael Chaffee, prin. Fax 564-9788

New Carlisle, Clark, Pop. 5,735
Tecumseh Local SD 2,600/K-12
9760 W National Rd 45344 937-845-3576
Norm Glismann, supt. Fax 845-4453
www.tecumseh.k12.oh.us
Tecumseh HS 900/9-12
9830 W National Rd 45344 937-845-4500
Ivan Gehret, prin. Fax 845-4547
Tecumseh MS 800/6-8
10000 W National Rd 45344 937-845-4465
Brian Dixon, prin. Fax 845-4484

Newcomerstown, Tuscarawas, Pop. 3,763
Newcomerstown EVD 1,000/PK-12
702 S River St 43832 740-498-8373
Jeffrey Staggs, supt. Fax 498-8375
www.nctschools.org
Newcomerstown HS 300/9-12
659 Beaver St 43832 740-498-5111
Matthew Fockler, prin. Fax 498-4994
Newcomerstown MS 200/6-8
325 W State St 43832 740-498-8151
Jason Peoples, prin. Fax 498-4991

New Concord, Muskingum, Pop. 2,459
East Muskingum Local SD 2,100/K-12
13505 John Glenn School Rd 43762 740-826-7655
Jill Sheridan, supt. Fax 826-7194
www.east-muskingum.k12.oh.us
East Muskingum MS 500/6-8
13120 John Glenn School Rd 43762 740-826-7631
Trent Cubbison, prin. Fax 826-4392
Glenn HS 600/9-12
13115 John Glenn School Rd 43762 740-826-7641
Steve Brooks, prin. Fax 826-3039

Muskingum University Post-Sec.
163 Stormont St 43762 740-826-8211

New Knoxville, Auglaize, Pop. 875
New Knoxville Local SD 300/K-12
PO Box 476 45871 419-753-2431
Kim Waterman, supt. Fax 753-2333
www.nkrangers.org
New Knoxville HS 100/7-12
PO Box 476 45871 419-753-2431
Jenny Fledderjohann, prin. Fax 753-2333

New Lebanon, Montgomery, Pop. 3,918
New Lebanon Local SD 1,100/K-12
320 S Fuls Rd 45345 937-687-1301
Dr. Greg Williams, supt. Fax 687-7321
www.newlebanonschools.org
Dixie HS 300/9-12
300 S Fuls Rd 45345 937-687-1366
Brad Wolgast, prin. Fax 687-7074
Dixie MS 300/5-8
200 S Fuls Rd 45345 937-687-3508
Aaron Smith, prin. Fax 687-7705

New Lexington, Perry, Pop. 4,679
New Lexington CSD 1,800/K-12
2549 Panther Dr 43764 740-342-4133
Casey Coffey, supt. Fax 342-6051
www.nlpanthers.org
New Lexington HS 500/9-12
2547 Panther Dr NE 43764 740-342-3528
Charles Byers, prin. Fax 342-4765
New Lexington MS 400/6-8
2549 Panther Dr NE 43764 740-342-4128
Fax 342-6071

New London, Huron, Pop. 2,415
New London Local SD 900/PK-12
2 Wildcat Dr 44851 419-929-8433
Bradley Romano, supt. Fax 929-4108
www.nlschools.org
New London HS 300/9-12
1 Wildcat Dr 44851 419-929-1586
Cosetta Adkins, prin. Fax 929-9513
New London MS 200/6-8
1 Wildcat Dr 44851 419-929-5409
Cosetta Adkins, prin. Fax 929-9513

New Madison, Darke, Pop. 886
Tri-Village Local SD 700/K-12
PO Box 31 45346 937-996-6261
Josh Sagester, supt. Fax 996-5537
www.tri-village.k12.oh.us
Tri-Village JSHS 300/7-12
PO Box 31 45346 937-996-1511
Lee Morris, prin. Fax 996-0307

New Matamoras, Washington, Pop. 879
Frontier Local SD 500/K-12
44870 State Route 7 45767 740-865-3473
Bruce Kidder, supt. Fax 865-2010
www.frontierlocalschools.com
Frontier MSHS 200/7-12
44870 State Route 7 45767 740-865-3441
William Creighton, prin. Fax 865-2011

New Middletown, Mahoning, Pop. 1,611
Springfield Local SD 1,100/K-12
PO Box 549 44442 330-542-2929
Thomas Yazvac, supt. Fax 542-9453
Springfield HS 300/9-12
11335 Youngstown Pittsburgh 44442 330-542-3626
Anthony DeFelice, prin. Fax 542-9453
Springfield IS 400/5-8
11333 Youngstown Pittsburgh 44442 330-542-3624
David Malone, prin. Fax 542-2159

New Paris, Preble, Pop. 1,607
National Trail Local SD 1,000/K-12
6940 Oxford Gettysburg Rd 45347 937-437-3333
Jeff Parker, supt. Fax 437-7865
www.nationaltrail.k12.oh.us/
National Trail HS 300/9-12
6940 Oxford Gettysburg Rd 45347 937-437-3333
Brian McKnight, prin. Fax 437-8270
National Trail MS 300/5-8
6940 Oxford Gettysburg Rd 45347 937-437-3333
Mark Wiseman, prin. Fax 437-7306

New Philadelphia, Tuscarawas, Pop. 17,008
Buckeye JVSD
545 University Dr NE 44663 330-339-2288
Bob Alsept, supt. Fax 339-5159
buckeyecareercenter.org
Buckeye Career Center Vo/Tech
545 University Dr NE 44663 330-339-2288
Jay Davis, prin. Fax 339-5159

New Philadelphia CSD 3,000/PK-12
248 Front Ave SW 44663 330-364-0600
David Brand, supt. Fax 364-9310
www.npschools.org
New Philadelphia HS 800/9-12
343 Ray Ave NW 44663 330-364-0644
Eric Jurkovic, prin. Fax 364-0633
Welty MS 700/6-8
315 4th St NW 44663 330-364-0645
Carl McCrory, prin. Fax 364-0677

Kent State University- Tuscarawas Campus Post-Sec.
330 University Dr NE 44663 330-339-3391
Tuscarawas Central Catholic HS 200/7-12
777 3rd St NE 44663 330-343-3302
Scott Power, prin. Fax 343-6388

New Richmond, Clermont, Pop. 2,535
New Richmond EVD 2,400/K-12
212 Market St 45157 513-553-2616
Adam Bird, supt. Fax 553-6431
www.nrschools.org

New Richmond HS 700/9-12
1131 Bethel New Richmond Rd 45157 513-553-3191
Mark Bailey, prin. Fax 553-2531
New Richmond MS 400/7-8
1135 Bethel New Richmond Rd 45157 513-553-3161
Courtney Lilly, prin. Fax 553-6412

New Riegel, Seneca, Pop. 248
New Riegel Local SD 400/K-12
44 N Perry St 44853 419-595-2256
Elaine Nye, supt. Fax 595-2901
newriegelschools.org
New Riegel JSHS 200/7-12
44 N Perry St 44853 419-595-2256
David Rombach, prin. Fax 595-2901

Newton Falls, Trumbull, Pop. 4,737
Newton Falls EVD 1,200/K-12
909 1/2 Milton Blvd 44444 330-872-5445
Paul Woodard, supt. Fax 872-3351
www.newton-falls.k12.oh.us/
Falls Learning Academy Alt
907 Milton Blvd 44444 330-872-5121
John Crowder, prin.
Newton Falls HS 400/9-12
907 Milton Blvd 44444 330-872-5121
John Crowder, prin. Fax 872-3351
Newton Falls JHS 200/7-8
907 1/2 Milton Blvd 44444 330-872-0695
Angellina Berilla, admin. Fax 872-8327

New Washington, Crawford, Pop. 962
Buckeye Central Local SD 700/K-12
938 S Kibler St 44854 419-492-2864
Mark Robinson, supt. Fax 492-2039
www.bcbucks.org
Buckeye Central HS 200/9-12
938 S Kibler St 44854 419-492-2266
Jay Zeiter, prin. Fax 492-2039
Buckeye Central MS 200/5-8
938 S Kibler St 44854 419-492-1035
Jay Zeiter, prin. Fax 492-2039

Niles, Trumbull, Pop. 18,878
Niles CSD 2,400/K-12
309 N Rhodes Ave 44446 330-989-5095
Ann Marie Thigpen, supt. Fax 989-5096
www.nilescityschools.org/
McKinley HS 700/9-12
616 Dragon Dr 44446 330-652-9968
Michael Guarnieri, prin. Fax 505-0755
Niles MS 600/6-8
411 Brown St 44446 330-652-5656
Samuel Reigle, prin. Fax 652-9158

ETI Technical College of Niles Post-Sec.
2076 Youngstown Warren Rd 44446 330-652-9919
Raphael's School of Beauty Culture Post-Sec.
1324 Youngstown Warren Rd 44446 330-652-1559
Victory Christian S 100/K-12
2053 Pleasant Valley Rd 44446 330-539-9827
Colleen McCullough, prin. Fax 539-9828

North Baltimore, Wood, Pop. 3,396
North Baltimore Local SD 600/PK-12
201 S Main St 45872 419-257-3531
Ryan Delaney, supt. Fax 257-2008
www.nbls.org
North Baltimore HS 200/9-12
2012 Tiger Dr 45872 419-257-3464
Dr. Bob Falkenstein Ph.D., prin. Fax 257-2008
North Baltimore MS 100/7-8
2012 Tiger Dr 45872 419-257-3464
Dr. Bob Falkenstein Ph.D., prin. Fax 257-2008

North Bloomfield, Trumbull
Bloomfield-Mespo Local SD 300/K-12
2077 Park West Rd 44450 440-685-4711
Russell McQuaide, supt. Fax 685-4751
www.bloomfield-mespo.org/
Bloomfield MSHS 100/6-12
2077 Park West Rd 44450 440-685-4711
Steven Kobus, prin. Fax 685-4751

North Canton, Stark, Pop. 17,236
North Canton CSD 4,600/PK-12
525 7th St NE 44720 330-497-5600
Jeff Wendorf, supt. Fax 497-5618
www.northcantonschools.org
Hoover HS 1,600/9-12
525 7th St NE 44720 330-497-5620
Eric Bornstine, prin. Fax 497-5606
North Canton MS 1,100/6-8
605 Fair Oaks Ave SW 44720 330-497-5635
David Eby, prin. Fax 497-5659

Kent State University Stark Campus Post-Sec.
6000 Frank Ave NW 44720 330-499-9600
Stark State College Post-Sec.
6200 Frank Ave NW 44720 330-494-6170
Walsh University Post-Sec.
2020 E Maple St 44720 330-490-7090

North Eaton, Lorain

Christian Community S 100/K-12
35716 Royalton Rd 44044 440-748-6224
Joel Brickner, hdmstr. Fax 748-1007

Northfield, Summit, Pop. 3,593
Nordonia Hills CSD 3,700/K-12
9370 Olde 8 Rd 44067 330-467-0580
Joseph Clark, supt. Fax 468-0152
www.nordoniaschools.org
Nordonia MS 600/7-8
73 Leonard Ave 44067 330-467-0584
Ryan Durr, prin. Fax 468-6719
Other Schools – See Macedonia

North Jackson, Mahoning
Jackson-Milton Local SD 800/K-12
13910 Mahoning Ave 44451 330-538-3232
Kirk Baker, supt. Fax 538-6297
www.jacksonmilton.k12.oh.us/
Jackson-Milton HS 200/9-12
13910 Mahoning Ave 44451 330-538-3308
David Vega, prin. Fax 538-0821
Jackson-Milton MS 100/7-8
13910 Mahoning Ave 44451 330-538-3308
David Vega, prin. Fax 538-0821

North Lewisburg, Union, Pop. 1,449
Triad Local SD 900/K-12
7920 Brush Lake Rd 43060 937-826-4961
Chris Piper, supt. Fax 826-3281
www.triad.k12.oh.us
Triad HS 300/9-12
8099 Brush Lake Rd 43060 937-826-3771
Kyle Huffman, prin. Fax 826-2002
Triad MS 300/5-8
7941 Brush Lake Rd 43060 937-826-3071
Duane Caudill, prin. Fax 826-1000

North Olmsted, Cuyahoga, Pop. 32,229
North Olmsted CSD 3,600/PK-12
26669 Butternut Ridge Rd 44070 440-779-3576
Michael Zalar Ph.D., supt. Fax 779-3505
www.northolmstedschools.org
North Olmsted HS 1,400/9-12
5755 Burns Rd 44070 440-779-8825
Jeffrey Stanton, prin. Fax 777-2216
North Olmsted MS 600/7-8
26855 Lorain Rd 44070 440-779-8503
Tom Dreiling, prin. Fax 779-8510

Remington College Post-Sec.
26350 Brookpark Rd 44070 440-777-2560

North Randall, Cuyahoga, Pop. 1,013

PowerSport Institute Post-Sec.
21210 Emery Rd 44128 216-587-5000

North Ridgeville, Lorain, Pop. 29,069
North Ridgeville CSD 4,100/K-12
5490 Mills Creek Ln 44039 440-327-4444
James Powell, supt. Fax 327-9774
www.nrcs.k12.oh.us
North Ridgeville HS 1,100/9-12
34600 Bainbridge Rd 44039 440-327-1992
Thomas Szendrey, prin. Fax 327-4056
North Ridgeville MS 1,000/6-8
35895 Center Ridge Rd 44039 440-353-1180
Amy Peck, prin. Fax 353-1144

Lake Ridge Academy 400/K-12
37501 Center Ridge Rd 44039 440-327-1175
Carol Klimas, pres. Fax 327-3641

North Robinson, Crawford, Pop. 201
Colonel Crawford Local SD 700/PK-12
2303 State Route 602 44827 419-562-4666
Todd Martin, supt. Fax 562-3304
www.cck12.org
Other Schools – See Crestline

North Royalton, Cuyahoga, Pop. 30,115
North Royalton CSD 4,300/1-12
6579 Royalton Rd 44133 440-237-8800
Greg Gurka, supt. Fax 582-7336
www.northroyaltonsd.org
North Royalton HS 1,600/9-12
14713 Ridge Rd 44133 440-582-7801
Sean Osborne, prin. Fax 582-7337
North Royalton MS 1,500/5-8
14709 Ridge Rd 44133 440-582-9120
Jeffrey Cicerchi, prin. Fax 582-7229

Northwood, Wood, Pop. 5,174
Northwood Local SD 900/PK-12
500 Lemoyne Rd 43619 419-691-3888
Greg Clark, supt. Fax 697-2470
www.northwoodschools.org
Northwood HS 400/7-12
700 Lemoyne Rd 43619 419-691-4651
Jason Kozina, prin. Fax 691-2846

Norton, Summit, Pop. 11,968
Norton CSD 2,600/PK-12
4128 Cleveland Massillon Rd 44203 330-825-0863
David Dunn, supt. Fax 825-0929
www.norton.k12.oh.us
Norton HS 800/9-12
4108 Cleveland Massillon Rd 44203 330-825-7300
Ryan Shanor, prin. Fax 825-4275
Norton MS 800/5-8
3390 Cleveland Massillon Rd 44203 330-825-5607
Joyce Gerber, prin. Fax 825-1461

Norwalk, Huron, Pop. 16,729
Norwalk CSD 2,800/PK-12
134 Benedict Ave 44857 419-668-2779
George Fisk, supt. Fax 663-3302
www.norwalktruckers.net
Norwalk HS 700/9-12
350 Shady Lane Dr 44857 419-660-6500
Brad Cooley, prin. Fax 668-4719
Norwalk MS 500/7-8
64 Christie Ave 44857 419-668-8370
Gary Swartz, prin. Fax 668-6622

Norwalk Catholic - St. Paul JSHS 300/7-12
93 E Main St 44857 419-668-3005
James Tokarsky, prin. Fax 668-6417

Norwood, Hamilton, Pop. 18,788
Norwood CSD 1,800/PK-12
2132 Williams Ave 45212 513-924-2500
Robert Amodio, supt. Fax 396-6420
www.norwoodschools.org
Norwood HS 500/9-12
2020 Sherman Ave 45212 513-924-2800
Bradley Winterod, prin. Fax 396-5559
Norwood MS 300/7-8
2060 Sherman Ave 45212 513-924-2700
Katherine Sabo, prin. Fax 396-5537

Oak Harbor, Ottawa, Pop. 2,732
Benton Carroll Salem Local SD 1,600/K-12
11685 W State Route 163 43449 419-898-6210
Dr. Guy Parmigian, supt. Fax 898-4303
www.bcssd.com
Oak Harbor HS 600/8-12
11661 W State Route 163 43449 419-898-6216
Cheryl Schell, prin. Fax 898-0116

Oak Hill, Jackson, Pop. 1,527
Oak Hill Union Local SD 1,300/PK-12
205 Western Ave 45656 740-682-7595
Michael A. McCoy, supt. Fax 682-6998
www.oakhill.k12.oh.us
Oak Hill MSHS 700/6-12
5063 State Route 93 45656 740-682-7055
Randall Layton, prin. Fax 682-6075

Oakwood, Paulding, Pop. 604
Oakwood CSD 2,100/PK-12
20 Rubicon Rd 45409 937-297-5332
Kyle Ramey Ed.D., supt. Fax 297-5345
www.oakwoodschools.org
Oakwood HS 700/9-12
1200 Far Hills Ave 45419 937-297-5325
Paul Waller, prin. Fax 297-5348
Oakwood JHS 400/7-8
1200 Far Hills Ave 45419 937-297-5328
Tim Badenhop, prin. Fax 297-7807

Oberlin, Lorain, Pop. 7,787
Firelands Local SD
Supt. — See South Amherst
Firelands HS 500/9-12
10643 Vermilion Rd 44074 440-965-4255
Robert Maver, prin. Fax 965-5296

Lorain County JVSD
15181 State Route 58 44074 440-774-1051
Dr. Glenn Faircloth, supt. Fax 774-2144
www.lcjvs.com/
Burton Vocational Center HS Vo/Tech
15181 State Route 58 44074 440-774-1051
Jill Petitti, prin. Fax 774-6421

Oberlin CSD 1,000/PK-12
153 N Main St 44074 440-774-1458
Dr. David H. Hall, supt. Fax 774-4492
www.oberlinschools.net
Langston MS 200/6-8
150 N Pleasant St 44074 440-775-7961
Chris Frank, prin. Fax 776-4520
Oberlin HS 300/9-12
281 N Pleasant St 44074 440-774-1295
William Baylis, prin. Fax 774-5099

Oberlin College Post-Sec.
101 N Professor St 44074 440-775-8121

Old Fort, Seneca, Pop. 185
Old Fort Local SD 400/K-12
7635 N County Rd 51 44861 419-992-4291
Stephen Anway, supt. Fax 992-4293
www.old-fort.k12.oh.us/
Old Fort JSHS 200/7-12
7635 N County Rd 51 44861 419-992-4291
Sonia Herman, prin. Fax 992-4293

Old Washington, Guernsey, Pop. 277
East Guernsey Local SD 1,000/K-12
PO Box 128 43768 740-489-5190
Adam Pittis, supt. Fax 489-9813
www.eguernsey.k12.oh.us
Other Schools – See Lore City

Olmsted Falls, Cuyahoga, Pop. 8,919
Olmsted Falls CSD 3,800/PK-12
PO Box 38010 44138 440-427-6000
Dr. Jim Lloyd, supt. Fax 427-6010
www.ofcs.net
Olmsted Falls HS 1,200/9-12
26939 Bagley Rd 44138 440-427-6100
Holly Schafer, prin. Fax 427-6110
Olmsted Falls MS 1,000/6-8
27045 Bagley Rd 44138 440-427-6200
Mark Kurz, prin. Fax 427-6210

Ontario, Richland, Pop. 6,103
Ontario Local SD 1,400/PK-12
457 Shelby Ontario Rd, 419-747-4311
Lisa Carmichael, supt. Fax 747-6859
www.ontarioschools.org
Ontario HS 500/9-12
467 Shelby Ontario Rd, 419-529-3969
Chris Smith, prin. Fax 747-6859
Ontario MS 400/6-8
447 Shelby Ontario Rd, 419-529-5507
Sue Weirich, prin. Fax 747-6859

Oregon, Lucas, Pop. 20,036
Oregon CSD 3,600/K-12
5721 Seaman Rd 43616 419-693-0661
Hal Gregory, supt. Fax 698-6016
www.oregoncityschools.org
Clay HS 1,200/9-12
5665 Seaman Rd 43616 419-693-0665
James Jurski, prin. Fax 698-6047
Fassett JHS 600/7-8
3025 Starr Ave 43616 419-693-0455
Rebecca Bihn, prin. Fax 698-6048

Cardinal Stritch HS 200/9-12
3225 Pickle Rd 43616 419-693-0465
Kevin Parkins, prin. Fax 697-2816

St. Charles Hospital | Post-Sec.
2600 Navarre Ave 43616 | 419-698-7341
Toledo Academy of Beauty Culture - East | Post-Sec.
3341 Navarre Ave 43616 | 419-693-7257

Orrville, Wayne, Pop. 8,182
Orrville CSD | 1,500/PK-12
815 N Ella St 44667 | 330-682-4651
James Ritchie, supt. | Fax 682-0073
www.orrville.k12.oh.us
Orrville HS | 400/9-12
841 N Ella St 44667 | 330-682-4661
Timothy Adams, prin. | Fax 682-4662
Orrville MS | 500/5-8
801 Mineral Springs St 44667 | 330-682-1791
David Sovacool, prin. | Fax 682-2743

Kingsway Christian S | 100/PK-12
11138 Old Lincoln Way E 44667 | 330-683-0012
Keith Fuller M.Ed., prin. | Fax 683-0017
University of Akron-Wayne College | Post-Sec.
1901 Smucker Rd 44667 | 330-683-2010

Orwell, Ashtabula, Pop. 1,614
Grand Valley Local SD | 1,300/K-12
111 W Grand Valley Ave # A 44076 | 440-437-6260
Dr. William Nye, supt. | Fax 437-1025
www.grand-valley.k12.oh.us
Grand Valley HS | 400/9-12
111 W Grand Valley Ave # C 44076 | 440-437-6260
Douglas Hitchcock, prin. | Fax 437-6254
Grand Valley MS | 400/5-8
111 W Grand Valley Ave # D 44076 | 440-437-6260
Roberta Cozad, prin. | Fax 437-6156

Ottawa, Putnam, Pop. 4,436
Ottawa-Glandorf Local SD | 1,500/K-12
630 Glendale Ave 45875 | 419-523-5261
Don Horstman, supt. | Fax 523-5978
www.ottawaglandorf.org
Ottawa-Glandorf HS | 500/9-12
630 Glendale Ave 45875 | 419-523-5702
Jayson Selgo, prin. | Fax 523-6346

Ottawa Hills, Lucas, Pop. 4,439
Ottawa Hills Local SD | 900/K-12
3600 Indian Rd, | 419-536-6371
Dr. Kevin Miller, supt. | Fax 534-5380
www.ottawahillsschools.org/
Ottawa Hills JSHS | 500/7-12
2532 Evergreen Rd, | 419-534-5376
Ben McMurray, prin. | Fax 534-5384

Ottoville, Putnam, Pop. 974
Ottoville Local SD | 400/K-12
PO Box 248 45876 | 419-453-3356
Scott Mangas, supt. | Fax 453-3367
www.ottovilleschools.org
Ottoville JSHS | 200/7-12
PO Box 248 45876 | 419-453-3358
Jon Thorbahn, prin. | Fax 453-3367

Oxford, Butler, Pop. 20,904
Talawanda CSD | 3,000/PK-12
131 W Chestnut St 45056 | 513-273-3333
Kelly Spivey, supt. | Fax 273-3113
www.talawanda.net/
Talawanda HS | 900/9-12
5301 University Park Blvd 45056 | 513-273-3200
Tom York, prin. | Fax 273-3203
Talawanda MS | 700/6-8
4030 Oxford Reily Rd 45056 | 513-273-3300
Mike Malone, prin. | Fax 273-3303

Miami University | Post-Sec.
501 E High St 45056 | 513-529-1809

Painesville, Lake, Pop. 18,851
Painesville City Local SD | 3,100/PK-12
58 Jefferson St 44077 | 440-392-5060
John Shepard, supt. | Fax 392-5089
www.pcls.net
Harvey HS | 800/9-12
200 W Walnut Ave 44077 | 440-392-5110
Van McWreath, prin. | Fax 392-5119
Heritage MS | 600/6-8
135 Cedarbrook Dr 44077 | 440-392-5250
Melissa DeAngelis, prin. | Fax 392-5259

Riverside Local SD | 4,500/K-12
585 Riverside Dr 44077 | 440-352-0668
James Kalis, supt. | Fax 639-1959
www.riversidelocalschools.com
Riverside JSHS | 1,700/8-12
585 Riverside Dr 44077 | 440-352-3341
Peter Hliatzos, prin. | Fax 352-0695

Lake Erie College | Post-Sec.
391 W Washington St 44077 | 440-296-1856

Pandora, Putnam, Pop. 1,146
Pandora-Gilboa Local SD | 500/K-12
410 Rocket Rdg 45877 | 419-384-3227
Todd Schmutz, supt. | Fax 384-3230
www.pgrockets.org
Pandora-Gilboa HS | 200/9-12
410 Rocket Rdg 45877 | 419-384-3225
Jeffrey Wise, prin. | Fax 384-3230
Pandora-Gilboa MS | 200/5-8
410 Rocket Rdg 45877 | 419-384-3225
Jodi Schroeder, prin. | Fax 384-3230

Parma, Cuyahoga, Pop. 80,516
Parma CSD | 11,100/PK-12
5311 Longwood Ave 44134 | 440-842-5300
Carl Hilling, supt. | Fax 885-8304
www.parmacityschools.org
Normandy HS | 1,400/8-12
2500 W Pleasant Valley Rd 44134 | 440-885-2400
Samuel Dickerson, prin. | Fax 885-2402
Parma HS | 1,800/8-12
6285 W 54th St 44129 | 440-885-2300
Leo Spagnola, prin. | Fax 888-0358
Other Schools – See Parma Heights

Bryant & Stratton College | Post-Sec.
12955 Snow Rd 44130 | 216-265-3151
Padua Franciscan HS | 800/9-12
6740 State Rd 44134 | 440-845-2444
David Stec, prin. | Fax 845-5710
Parma Community General Hospital | Post-Sec.
7007 Powers Blvd 44129 | 440-743-3000

Parma Heights, Cuyahoga, Pop. 20,381
Parma CSD
Supt. — See Parma
Valley Forge HS | 1,600/8-12
9999 Independence Blvd 44130 | 440-885-2330
Janine Andrzejewski, prin. | Fax 885-8412

Cuyahoga Community College | Post-Sec.
11000 W Pleasant Valley Rd 44130 | 800-954-8742
Holy Name HS | 700/9-12
6000 Queens Hwy 44130 | 440-886-0300
Shelbrey Blanc, prin. | Fax 886-1267

Pataskala, Licking, Pop. 14,629
Licking Heights Local SD | 3,700/K-12
6539 Summit Rd SW 43062 | 740-927-6926
Dr. Philip Wagner, supt. | Fax 927-9043
www.licking-heights.k12.oh.us/
Licking Heights Central MS | 900/6-8
6565 Summit Rd SW 43062 | 740-927-3365
Belinda Hohman, prin. | Fax 927-5845
Licking Heights HS | 900/9-12
4000 Mink St SW 43062 | 740-927-9046
Ken Kraemer, prin. | Fax 927-3197

Southwest Licking Local SD | 2,900/K-12
927 South St Unit A 43062 | 740-927-3941
Robert Jennell, supt. | Fax 927-4648
www.swl.k12.oh.us
Other Schools – See Etna

Liberty Christian Academy | 300/PK-12
10447 Refugee Rd SW 43062 | 740-964-2211
LaVonne McIlrath, admin. | Fax 964-2311

Patriot, Gallia
Gallia County Local SD | 1,900/PK-12
4836 State Route 325 45658 | 740-379-9085
Jude Meyers, supt. | Fax 379-9135
gallialocal.org
Other Schools – See Bidwell, Crown City

Paulding, Paulding, Pop. 3,557
Paulding EVD | 1,400/PK-12
405 N Water St 45879 | 419-399-4656
William Hanak, supt. | Fax 399-2404
www.pauldingschools.org/
Paulding HS | 400/9-12
405 N Water St 45879 | 419-399-4656
Todd Harmon, prin. | Fax 399-2404
Paulding MS | 300/6-8
405 N Water St 45879 | 419-399-4656
Chris Etzler, prin. | Fax 399-2404

Peebles, Adams, Pop. 1,762
Adams County/Ohio Valley Local SD
Supt. — See West Union
Peebles HS | 400/7-12
25719 State Route 41 45660 | 937-587-2681
Steve Appelman, prin. | Fax 587-5236

Pemberville, Wood, Pop. 1,357
Eastwood Local SD | 1,400/K-12
4800 Sugar Ridge Rd 43450 | 419-833-6411
William Welker, supt. | Fax 833-4915
www.eastwoodschools.org
Eastwood HS | 400/9-12
4900 Sugar Ridge Rd 43450 | 419-833-3611
David Riley, prin. | Fax 833-6014
Eastwood MS | 500/5-8
4800 Sugar Ridge Rd 43450 | 419-833-6011
Edward Eding, prin. | Fax 833-7454

Peninsula, Summit, Pop. 560
Woodridge Local SD | 2,000/K-12
4411 Quick Rd 44264 | 330-928-9074
Walter Davis, supt. | Fax 928-1542
www.woodridge.k12.oh.us/
Woodridge HS | 700/9-12
4440 Quick Rd 44264 | 330-929-3191
Joel Morgan, prin. | Fax 928-5036
Woodridge MS | 500/6-8
4451 Quick Rd 44264 | 330-928-7420
Jesse Hosford, prin. | Fax 928-5645

Pepper Pike, Cuyahoga, Pop. 5,884
Orange CSD | 2,100/PK-12
32000 Chagrin Blvd 44124 | 216-831-8600
Dr. Edwin Holland, supt. | Fax 831-8029
www.orangeschools.org
Brady MS | 500/6-8
32000 Chagrin Blvd 44124 | 216-831-8600
Brian Frank, prin. | Fax 839-1335
Orange HS | 700/9-12
32000 Chagrin Blvd 44124 | 216-831-8581
Dr. Paul Lucas, prin. | Fax 831-2595

Ursuline College | Post-Sec.
2550 Lander Rd 44124 | 440-449-4200

Perry, Lake, Pop. 1,647
Perry Local SD | 1,800/K-12
4325 Manchester Rd 44081 | 440-259-9200
Jack Thompson Ph.D., supt. | Fax 259-3607
www.perry-lake.org
Perry HS | 600/9-12
1 Success Blvd 44081 | 440-259-9300
Todd Porcello, prin. | Fax 259-9290
Perry MS | 600/5-8
2 Learning Ln 44081 | 440-259-9500
Robert Knisely, prin. | Fax 259-5149

Perrysburg, Wood, Pop. 20,359
Penta Career Center
9301 Buck Rd 43551 | 419-666-1120
Ron Matter, supt. | Fax 666-6049
www.pentacareercenter.org
Penta Career Center | Vo/Tech
9301 Buck Rd 43551 | 419-666-1120
Jeffrey Kurtz, prin. | Fax 666-6049

Perrysburg SD | 4,700/K-12
140 E Indiana Ave 43551 | 419-874-9131
Thomas Hosler, supt. | Fax 872-8820
www.perrysburgschools.net
Perrysburg HS | 1,300/9-12
13385 Roachton Rd 43551 | 419-874-3181
Dr. Michael Short, prin. | Fax 872-8813
Perrysburg JHS | 1,100/6-8
550 E South Boundary St 43551 | 419-874-9193
Brent Swartzmiller, prin. | Fax 872-8812

Healing Arts Institute | Post-Sec.
340 3 Meadows Dr 43551 | 419-874-4496

Pettisville, Fulton, Pop. 497
Pettisville Local SD | 500/PK-12
PO Box 53001 43553 | 419-446-2705
Dr. Stephen Switzer, supt. | Fax 445-2992
pettisvilleschools.org
Pettisville JSHS | 300/7-12
PO Box 53001 43553 | 419-446-2705
Michael Lane, prin. | Fax 445-2992

Philo, Muskingum, Pop. 726
Franklin Local SD
Supt. — See Duncan Falls
Philo JHS | 400/6-8
PO Box 178 43771 | 740-674-5210
Robert Preston, prin. | Fax 674-5217

Pickerington, Fairfield, Pop. 17,708
Pickerington Local SD | 10,200/K-12
90 N East St 43147 | 614-833-2110
Valerie Thompson Ph.D., supt. | Fax 833-2143
www.pickerington.k12.oh.us
Pickerington HS Central | 1,600/9-12
300 Opportunity Way 43147 | 614-548-1800
Stacy Tennenbaum, prin. | Fax 548-1810
Pickerington HS North | 1,600/9-12
7800 Refugee Rd 43147 | 614-830-2700
Mark Ulbrich, prin. | Fax 833-3660
Pickerington Lakeview JHS | 900/7-8
12445 Ault Rd 43147 | 614-830-2200
Pam Bertke, prin. | Fax 834-3267
Pickerington Ridgeview STEM JHS | 900/7-8
130 Hill Rd S 43147 | 614-548-1700
Eric Koch, prin. | Fax 548-1710

Piketon, Pike, Pop. 2,150
Pike County Area JVSD
PO Box 577 45661 | 740-289-2721
Eric Meredith, supt. | Fax 289-4243
www.pikectc.org
Riffe Career Technology Center | Vo/Tech
PO Box 577 45661 | 740-289-2721
Shon Tackett, dir. | Fax 289-2527

Scioto Valley Local SD | 1,300/K-12
PO Box 600 45661 | 740-289-4456
Dr. Todd Burkitt, supt. | Fax 289-3065
www.piketon.k12.oh.us/
Piketon JSHS | 600/7-12
1414 Piketon Rd 45661 | 740-289-2254
Jeffrey Reuter, prin. | Fax 289-1514

Pioneer, Williams, Pop. 1,360
North Central Local SD | 600/PK-12
400 E Baubice St 43554 | 419-737-2392
Kenneth Boyer, supt. | Fax 737-3361
www.northcentralschool.org
North Central JSHS | 200/7-12
400 E Baubice St 43554 | 419-737-2366
Timothy Rettig, prin. | Fax 737-2531

Piqua, Miami, Pop. 19,922
Piqua CSD | 2,300/K-12
719 E Ash St 45356 | 937-773-4321
Dwayne A. Thompson, supt. | Fax 778-4518
www.piqua.org
Piqua HS | 1,000/9-12
1 Indian Trl 45356 | 937-773-6314
Rob Messick, prin. | Fax 778-4514
Piqua JHS | 500/7-8
1 Tomahawk Trl 45356 | 937-778-2997
Jeff Clark, prin. | Fax 773-3574

Upper Valley JVSD
8811 Career Dr 45356 | 937-778-1980
Dr. Nancy Luce, supt. | Fax 778-0103
www.uppervalleycc.org
Upper Valley Career Center | Vo/Tech
8811 Career Dr 45356 | 937-778-1980
Jason Haak, dir. | Fax 778-4677

Edison State Community College | Post-Sec.
1973 Edison Dr 45356 | 937-778-8600

Plain City, Madison, Pop. 4,160
Jonathan Alder Local SD | 2,200/PK-12
9200 US Highway 42 S 43064 | 614-873-5621
Gary Chapman, supt. | Fax 873-8462
www.alder.k12.oh.us
Alder HS | 600/9-12
9200 US Highway 42 S 43064 | 614-873-4642
Michael Aurin, prin. | Fax 873-4252
Alder JHS | 300/7-8
6440 Kilbury Huber Rd 43064 | 614-873-4635
Jonathan Hayes, prin. | Fax 873-0845

Tolles Career & Technical Center
7877 US Highway 42 S 43064 — 614-873-4666
Kimberly Wilson, supt. — Fax 873-8761
www.tollestech.com
Tolles Career & Technical Center — Vo/Tech
7877 US Highway 42 S 43064 — 614-873-4666
Jackie Kuffel, dir. — Fax 873-6909

Shekinah Christian S — 100/K-12
10040 Lafayette Plain City 43064 — 614-873-3130
Brice Kaufmann, dir. — Fax 873-3699

Pleasant Hill, Miami, Pop. 1,191
Newton Local SD — 600/K-12
PO Box 803 45359 — 937-676-2002
Pat McBride, supt. — Fax 676-2054
www.newton.k12.oh.us/
Newton JSHS — 300/7-12
PO Box 803 45359 — 937-676-2002
Danielle Davis, prin. — Fax 676-2397

Pleasant Plain, Warren, Pop. 153

Village Christian S — 200/4-12
PO Box 48 45162 — 513-877-2125
Barry Boverie, admin. — Fax 877-2145

Plymouth, Huron, Pop. 1,844
Plymouth-Shiloh Local SD — 600/K-12
365 Sandusky St 44865 — 419-687-4733
James Metcalf, supt. — Fax 687-1541
plymouth.schoolwires.com/plymouth/site/
Plymouth HS — 200/9-12
400 Trux St 44865 — 419-687-8200
Greg Sigg, prin. — Fax 687-8175
Shiloh MS — 200/6-8
400 Trux St 44865 — 419-687-8200
Bradley Turson, prin. — Fax 687-8175

Poland, Mahoning, Pop. 2,537
Poland Local SD — 1,600/K-12
3199 Dobbins Rd 44514 — 330-757-7000
David Janofa, supt. — Fax 757-2390
www.polandbulldogs.com/
Poland MS — 400/7-8
47 College St 44514 — 330-757-7003
Mark Covell, prin. — Fax 757-2390
Poland Seminary HS — 700/9-12
3199 Dobbins Rd 44514 — 330-757-7018
Kevin Snyder, prin. — Fax 757-2390

Pomeroy, Meigs, Pop. 1,809
Meigs Local SD — 1,800/K-12
41765 Pomeroy Pike 45769 — 740-992-2153
Scot Gheen, supt. — Fax 992-7814
www.ml.k12.oh.us
Meigs HS — 500/9-12
42091 Pomeroy Pike 45769 — 740-992-2158
Travis Abbott, prin. — Fax 992-5839
Meigs MS — 400/6-8
42353 Charles Chancey Dr 45769 — 740-992-3058
Vickie Jones, prin. — Fax 992-6952

Port Clinton, Ottawa, Pop. 5,954
Port Clinton CSD — 1,700/K-12
811 Jefferson St 43452 — 419-732-2102
Patrick Adkins, supt. — Fax 734-4527
www.pccsd.net/
Port Clinton HS — 500/9-12
821 Jefferson St 43452 — 419-734-2147
Gary Steyer, prin. — Fax 734-4276
Port Clinton MS — 400/6-8
807 Jefferson St 43452 — 419-734-4448
Carrie Sanchez, prin. — Fax 734-4440

Portsmouth, Scioto, Pop. 19,655
Clay Local SD — 500/PK-12
44 Clay High St 45662 — 740-354-6645
Anthony Mantell, supt. — Fax 354-5746
clay.k12.oh.us/
Clay MSHS — 200/6-12
44 Clay High St 45662 — 740-354-6644
William Warnock, prin. — Fax 354-6105

Portsmouth CSD — 1,800/PK-12
724 Findlay St 45662 — 740-354-5663
Gary Dutey, supt. — Fax 355-4496
www.portsmouthtrojans.org
Portsmouth JSHS — 600/7-12
1225 Gallia St 45662 — 740-353-2398
Amy Hughes, prin. — Fax 354-3494

Notre Dame JSHS — 200/7-12
2220 Sunrise Ave 45662 — 740-353-2354
Thomas Walker, prin. — Fax 353-2526
Paramount Beauty Academy — Post-Sec.
PO Box 1444 45662 — 740-353-2436
Shawnee State University — Post-Sec.
940 2nd St 45662 — 740-351-4778

Powell, Delaware, Pop. 11,313
Olentangy Local SD
Supt. — See Lewis Center
Olentangy Hyatts MS — 800/6-8
6885 Sawmill Pkwy 43065 — 740-657-5400
Derrick Gilliam, prin. — Fax 657-5499
Olentangy Liberty HS — 1,800/9-12
3584 Home Rd 43065 — 740-657-4200
William Warfield, prin. — Fax 657-4299
Olentangy Liberty MS — 800/6-8
7940 Liberty Rd N 43065 — 740-657-4400
Nancy Freese, prin. — Fax 657-4499

Village Academy — 300/PK-12
284 S Liberty St 43065 — 614-841-0050
Susan Lasley, head sch — Fax 841-0501

Proctorville, Lawrence, Pop. 565
Fairland Local SD — 1,600/K-12
228 Private Drive 10010 45669 — 740-886-3100
Roni Hayes, supt. — Fax 886-7253
www.fairland.k12.oh.us
Fairland HS — 400/9-12
812 County Road 411 45669 — 740-886-3250
Chad Belville, prin. — Fax 886-6738
Fairland MS — 400/6-8
7875 County Road 107 45669 — 740-886-3200
Aaron Lewis, prin. — Fax 886-5125

Put in Bay, Ottawa, Pop. 138
Put-in-Bay Local SD — 100/K-12
PO Box 659 43456 — 419-285-3614
Steven Poe, supt. — Fax 285-2137
www.put-in-bay.k12.oh.us
Put-in-Bay JSHS — 50/7-12
PO Box 659 43456 — 419-285-3614
Steven Poe, supt. — Fax 285-2137

Racine, Meigs, Pop. 665
Southern Local SD — 700/K-12
920 Elm St 45771 — 740-949-2669
Anthony Deem, supt. — Fax 949-3309
www.southernlocalmeigs.org/
Southern HS — 200/9-12
920 Elm St 45771 — 740-949-2611
Daniel Otto, prin. — Fax 949-2456

Ravenna, Portage, Pop. 11,455
Maplewood Career Ctr SD
7075 State Route 88 44266 — 330-296-2892
Randy Griffith, supt. — Fax 296-5680
www.mwood.cc
Maplewood Career Center — Vo/Tech
7075 State Route 88 44266 — 330-296-2892
Craig Morgan, dir. — Fax 296-5680

Ravenna CSD — 2,700/PK-12
507 E Main St 44266 — 330-296-9679
Dennis Honkala, supt. — Fax 297-4158
www.ravennaschools.us
Brown MS — 600/6-8
228 S Scranton St 44266 — 330-296-3849
Jonathan Lane, prin. — Fax 297-4146
Ravenna HS — 800/9-12
6589 N Chestnut St 44266 — 330-296-3844
Beth Coleman, prin. — Fax 296-1855

Southeast Local SD — 1,400/K-12
8245 Tallmadge Rd 44266 — 330-654-5841
Robert Dunn, supt. — Fax 654-9110
www.sepirates.org
Southeast HS — 600/9-12
8423 Tallmadge Rd 44266 — 330-654-1960
David Kennedy, prin. — Fax 654-9110
Other Schools – See Diamond

Fortis College — Post-Sec.
653 Enterprise Pkwy 44266 — 330-297-7319

Rawson, Hancock, Pop. 564
Cory-Rawson Local SD — 600/PK-12
3930 County Road 26 45881 — 419-963-3415
Robert Hlasko, supt. — Fax 963-4400
cory-rawson.k12.oh.us
Cory-Rawson HS — 300/7-12
3930 County Road 26 45881 — 419-963-2611
Heath Huffman, prin. — Fax 963-4400

Rayland, Jefferson, Pop. 413
Buckeye Local SD
Supt. — See Dillonvale
Buckeye HS — 500/9-12
10692 State Route 150 43943 — 740-859-2196
Coy Sudvary, prin. — Fax 859-2857
Buckeye JHS — 300/7-8
10692 State Route 150 43943 — 740-859-2196
Jason Kovalski, prin. — Fax 859-2857

Reading, Hamilton, Pop. 10,188
Reading Community CSD — 1,600/K-12
1301 Bonnell St 45215 — 513-554-1800
Chuck LaFata, supt. — Fax 483-6754
www.readingschools.org
Reading Community HS — 400/9-12
810 E Columbia Ave 45215 — 513-733-4422
Dennis Ramsey, prin. — Fax 483-6766
Reading Community MS — 400/6-8
230 Halker Ave 45215 — 513-842-5151
Ian Frank, prin. — Fax 842-5146

Mt. Notre Dame HS — 700/9-12
711 E Columbia Ave 45215 — 513-821-3044
Judy Gerwe, head sch — Fax 821-6068

Reedsville, Meigs
Eastern Local SD — 800/K-12
50008 State Route 681 45772 — 740-667-6079
Steven Ohlinger, supt. — Fax 667-3978
www.easternlocal.com
Eastern HS — 200/9-12
38900 State Route 7 45772 — 740-985-3329
Shawn Bush, prin. — Fax 985-3778
Eastern MS — 300/5-8
38850 State Route 7 45772 — 740-985-3304
William Francis, prin. — Fax 985-4318

Reynoldsburg, Franklin, Pop. 34,685
Reynoldsburg CSD — 5,800/PK-12
7244 E Main St 43068 — 614-501-1020
Tina Thomas-Manning, supt. — Fax 501-1050
www.reyn.org/
Baldwin Road JHS — 300/7-8
2300 Baldwin Pl 43068 — 614-367-1600
Michelle Watts, prin. — Fax 367-1625
BELL Academy — 400/9-12
6699 E Livingston Ave 43068 — 614-501-4000
Danielle Bomar, prin.
ENCORE Academy — 500/9-12
8579 Summit Rd 43068 — 614-501-2300
Garry Young, prin.
eSTEM Academy — 500/9-12
8579 Summit Rd 43068 — 614-501-4000
Scott Bennett, prin.
HS2 Academy — 400/9-12
6699 E Livingston Ave 43068 — 614-501-4000
Dawn McCloud, prin. — Fax 575-3098
Waggoner Road JHS — 400/7-8
360 Waggoner Rd 43068 — 614-501-5700
Chris Brooks, prin. — Fax 501-5700

Richfield, Summit, Pop. 3,610
Revere Local SD — 2,600/PK-12
3496 Everett Rd 44286 — 330-666-4155
Matthew Montgomery, supt. — Fax 659-3127
www.revereschools.org
Other Schools – See Bath

Richmond, Jefferson, Pop. 480
Edison Local SD
Supt. — See Hammondsville
Edison HS — 400/7-12
9890 State Route 152 43944 — 740-765-4313
Matthew Morrison, prin. — Fax 765-4961

Richmond Heights, Cuyahoga, Pop. 10,347
Richmond Heights Local SD — 800/PK-12
447 Richmond Rd 44143 — 216-692-0086
Renee Willis Ph.D., supt.
www.richmondheightsschools.org
Richmond Heights MSHS — 400/7-12
447 Richmond Rd 44143 — 216-692-0094
Marnisha Brown, prin. — Fax 692-8495

Richwood, Union, Pop. 2,209
North Union Local SD — 1,500/PK-12
12920 State Route 739 43344 — 740-943-2509
Richard Baird, supt. — Fax 943-2534
www.n-union.k12.oh.us
North Union HS — 400/9-12
401 N Franklin St 43344 — 740-943-3012
Janel Chapman, prin. — Fax 943-2046
North Union MS — 400/6-8
12555 Mulvane Rd 43344 — 740-943-2369
Matt Burggraf, prin. — Fax 943-9279

Rio Grande, Gallia, Pop. 808
Gallia-Jackson-Vinton JVSD
PO Box 157 45674 — 740-245-5334
Dr. D. Kent Lewis, supt. — Fax 245-9465
bhcc.k12.oh.us/
Buckeye Hills Career Center — Vo/Tech
PO Box 157 45674 — 740-245-5334
Donald Armstrong, dir. — Fax 245-9465

University of Rio Grande — Post-Sec.
PO Box 500 45674 — 740-245-5353

Ripley, Brown, Pop. 1,713
Ripley-Union-Lewis-Huntington Local SD — 1,000/PK-12
PO Box 85 45167 — 937-392-4396
Dr. Linda Naylor, supt. — Fax 392-7003
www.ripley.k12.oh.us
Ripley-Union-Lewis-Huntington HS — 300/9-12
1317 S 2nd St 45167 — 937-392-4384
Susie Skinner, prin. — Fax 392-7017
Other Schools – See Aberdeen

Rittman, Wayne, Pop. 6,392
Rittman EVD — 1,100/K-12
100 Saurer St 44270 — 330-927-7401
James Ritchie, supt. — Fax 927-7405
www.rittman.k12.oh.us/
Rittman HS — 200/9-12
50 Saurer St 44270 — 330-927-7141
Nick Evans, prin. — Fax 927-7145
Rittman MS — 300/6-8
50 Saurer St 44270 — 330-927-7101
Keri Hamsher, prin. — Fax 927-7145

Rockford, Mercer, Pop. 1,102
Parkway Local SD — 1,100/PK-12
400 Buckeye St 45882 — 419-363-3045
Gregory Puthoff, supt. — Fax 363-2595
www.parkwayschools.org/
Parkway HS — 300/9-12
400 Buckeye St 45882 — 419-363-3045
Brian Fortkamp, prin. — Fax 363-2596
Parkway MS — 300/5-8
400 Buckeye St 45882 — 419-363-3045
Brian Woods, prin. — Fax 363-2597

Rocky River, Cuyahoga, Pop. 19,974
Rocky River CSD — 2,600/K-12
1101 Morewood Pkwy 44116 — 440-333-6000
Dr. Michael Shoaf, supt. — Fax 356-6014
www.rrcs.org
Rocky River HS — 900/9-12
20951 Detroit Rd 44116 — 440-356-6800
Rob Winton, prin. — Fax 331-2189
Rocky River MS — 600/6-8
1631 Lakeview Ave 44116 — 440-356-6870
Megan Rose, prin. — Fax 356-6881

Lutheran HS West — 400/9-12
3850 Linden Rd 44116 — 440-333-1660
Dale Wolfgram, prin. — Fax 333-1729
Magnificat HS — 800/9-12
20770 Hilliard Blvd 44116 — 440-331-1572
Marilyn Arundel, dean — Fax 331-7257

Rootstown, Portage
Rootstown Local SD — 1,200/K-12
4140 State Route 44 44272 — 330-325-9911
Andrew Hawkins, supt. — Fax 325-4105
rootstown.sparcc.org
Rootstown HS — 300/9-12
4140 State Route 44 44272 — 330-325-7911
James Conley, prin. — Fax 325-8506

Rootstown MS 300/6-8
4140 State Route 44 44272 330-325-9956
Robert Campbell, prin. Fax 325-8505

Northeastern Ohio Medical University Post-Sec.
PO Box 95 44272 800-686-2511

Rossford, Wood, Pop. 6,225
Rossford EVD 1,100/PK-12
601 Superior St 43460 419-666-2010
Daniel Creps, supt. Fax 661-2856
www.rossfordschools.org/
Rossford HS 500/9-12
701 Superior St 43460 419-666-5262
Tony Brashear, prin. Fax 661-2831
Rossford JHS 300/6-8
651 Superior St 43460 419-666-5254
Bryan Skrzyniecki, prin. Fax 661-2890

Russia, Shelby, Pop. 636
Russia Local SD 400/K-12
100 School St 45363 937-526-3156
Steven Rose, supt. Fax 526-0045
www.russiaschool.org
Russia JSHS 200/7-12
100 School St 45363 937-295-3454
Brian Hogan, prin. Fax 526-9519

Sabina, Clinton, Pop. 2,532
East Clinton Local SD 1,400/PK-12
97 Astro Way 45169 937-584-2461
Eric Magee, supt. Fax 584-2817
www.eastclinton.org
East Clinton HS 400/9-12
174 Larrick Rd 45169 937-584-2474
Kerri Matheny, prin. Fax 584-4842
East Clinton MS 300/6-8
174 Larrick Rd 45169 937-584-9267
Robbin Luck, prin. Fax 584-9558

Saint Bernard, Hamilton, Pop. 4,269
St. Bernard-Elmwood Place CSD 1,000/PK-12
105 Washington Ave 45217 513-482-7121
Dr. Mimi Webb, supt. Fax 641-0066
www.sbepschools.org
Saint Bernard-Elmwood Place JSHS 400/7-12
4615 Tower Ave 45217 513-482-7100
Alison Gates, prin. Fax 641-4878

Saint Clairsville, Belmont, Pop. 5,119
Belmont-Harrison Area JVSD
68090 Hammond Rd 43950 740-695-9130
Richard Schoene, supt. Fax 695-5340
bhccenters.com
Belmont Career Center Vo/Tech
68090 Hammond Rd 43950 740-695-9130
Frank Gregory, prin. Fax 695-5330
Other Schools – See Cadiz

St. Clairsville-Richland CSD 1,700/PK-12
108 Woodrow Ave 43950 740-695-1624
Dr. Walter Skaggs, supt. Fax 695-1627
www.stcschools.com
St. Clairsville HS 500/9-12
102 Woodrow Ave 43950 740-695-1584
Dr. Walter Skaggs, prin. Fax 695-2513
St. Clairsville MS 500/5-8
104 Woodrow Ave 43950 740-695-1591
Michael Mckeever, prin. Fax 695-2317

Belmont College Post-Sec.
120 Fox Shannon Pl 43950 740-695-9500
East Richland Christian S 100/PK-12
67888 Friends Church Rd 43950 740-695-2279
April Woods, admin. Fax 699-0562
Ohio University Post-Sec.
45425 National Rd W 43950 740-695-1720

Saint Henry, Mercer, Pop. 2,423
St. Henry Consolidated Local SD 1,000/K-12
391 E Columbus St 45883 419-678-4834
Julie Garke, supt. Fax 678-1724
sthenryschools.org
Saint Henry HS 300/9-12
391 E Columbus St 45883 419-678-4834
Eric Rosenbeck, prin. Fax 678-1724
Saint Henry MS 300/5-8
381 E Columbus St 45883 419-678-4834
Kyle Kunk, prin. Fax 678-1724

Saint Martin, Brown, Pop. 128

Chatfield College Post-Sec.
20918 State Route 251 45118 513-875-3344

Saint Marys, Auglaize, Pop. 8,208
St. Marys CSD 2,100/K-12
100 W Spring St 45885 419-394-4312
Shawn Brown, supt. Fax 394-5638
sm.k12.oh.us
St. Marys Memorial HS 700/9-12
2250 State Route 66 45885 419-394-4011
Bill Ruane, prin. Fax 394-1932
St. Marys MS 500/6-8
2250 State Route 66 45885 419-394-2112
Mary Miller, prin. Fax 394-1932

Saint Paris, Champaign, Pop. 2,056
Graham Local SD 2,000/PK-12
7790 US Highway 36 43072 937-663-4123
Kirk Koennecke, supt. Fax 663-4670
www.grahamlocalschools.org
Graham HS 500/9-12
7800 US Highway 36 43072 937-663-4127
Joe Hurst, prin. Fax 663-0396
Graham MS 500/6-8
9644 US Highway 36 43072 937-663-5339
Adam Kunkle, prin. Fax 663-4674

Salem, Columbiana, Pop. 12,168
Salem CSD 2,100/K-12
1226 E State St 44460 330-332-0316
Dr. Joseph Shivers, supt. Fax 332-8936
www.salemquakers.org
Salem HS 600/9-12
1200 E 6th St 44460 330-332-8905
Sean Kirkland, prin. Fax 332-8943
Salem JHS 300/7-8
1200 E 6th St 44460 330-332-8914
Sean Kirkland, prin. Fax 332-8923

Allegheny Wesleyan College Post-Sec.
2161 Woodsdale Rd 44460 330-337-6403
Kent State University-Salem Campus Post-Sec.
2491 State Route 45 S 44460 330-332-0361
Salem Wesleyan Academy 100/K-12
1095 Newgarden Ave 44460 330-332-4819
Dan Forrider, prin. Fax 332-4819

Salineville, Columbiana, Pop. 1,294
Southern Local SD 900/K-12
38095 State Route 39 43945 330-679-2343
John Wilson, supt. Fax 679-0193
www.southern.k12.oh.us
Southern Local JSHS 400/7-12
38095 State Route 39 43945 330-679-2305
Gerald DelBoccio, prin. Fax 679-3005

Sandusky, Erie, Pop. 24,586
Perkins Local SD 2,300/K-12
3714 Campbell St Ste B 44870 419-625-0484
Jodie Hausmann Ed.D., supt. Fax 621-2052
www.perkinsschools.org
Briar MS 500/6-8
3700 South Ave 44870 419-625-0132
Matthew Cox, prin. Fax 625-0523
Perkins HS 700/9-12
3714 Campbell St 44870 419-625-1252
Jeff Harbal, prin. Fax 621-2057

Sandusky CSD 3,300/PK-12
407 Decatur St 44870 419-626-6940
Eugene Sanders Ph.D., supt. Fax 621-2784
www.scs-k12.net
Sandusky Career Center Vo/Tech
2130 Hayes Ave 44870 419-984-1100
Nancy Hall, dir. Fax 621-2893
Sandusky Digital Academy Alt
318 Columbus Ave 44870 419-984-1060
Sherry Smith, dir.
Sandusky HS 900/9-12
2130 Hayes Ave 44870 419-984-1068
Eric Talbot, prin. Fax 621-2751
Sandusky MS 400/7-8
2130 Hayes Ave 44870 419-984-1182
Marie Prieto, prin. Fax 621-2849

Firelands Regional Medical Center Post-Sec.
1912 Hayes Ave 44870 419-557-7110
Ohio Business College Post-Sec.
5202 Timber Commons Dr 44870 419-627-8345
Sandusky Central Catholic S 600/PK-12
410 W Jefferson St 44870 419-626-1892
Dennis Antonelli, prin. Fax 621-2252

Sarahsville, Noble, Pop. 166
Noble Local SD 900/PK-12
20977 Zep Rd E 43779 740-732-2084
Daniel Leffingwell, supt. Fax 732-7669
www.gozeps.org/
Shenandoah HS 200/9-12
49346 Seneca Lake Rd 43779 740-732-2361
Justin Denius, prin. Fax 732-6479

Seaman, Adams, Pop. 934
Adams County/Ohio Valley Local SD
Supt. — See West Union
North Adams HS 500/7-12
96 Green Devil Dr 45679 937-386-2528
Matthew Young, prin. Fax 386-2888

Sebring, Mahoning, Pop. 4,362
Sebring Local SD 600/K-12
510 N 14th St 44672 330-938-6165
Toni Viscounte M.Ed., supt. Fax 938-4701
www.sebring.k12.oh.us/
McKinley JSHS 200/7-12
225 E Indiana Ave 44672 330-938-2963
Chris Corbi, prin. Fax 938-4702

Senecaville, Guernsey, Pop. 454
Mid-East Career & Technology Centers
Supt. — See Zanesville
Mid-East Career & Tech Center - Buffalo Vo/Tech
57090 Vocational Rd 43780 740-685-2516
Keith Arnold, dir. Fax 685-2518

Seven Hills, Cuyahoga, Pop. 11,709

DeVry University Post-Sec.
4141 Rockside Rd Ste 110 44131 216-328-8754
Hondros College Post-Sec.
4100 Rockside Rd 44131 216-524-1143

Seville, Medina, Pop. 2,268
Cloverleaf Local SD
Supt. — See Lodi
Cloverleaf MS 600/6-8
7500 Buffham Rd 44273 330-721-3606
Brian Madigan, prin. Fax 721-3619

Shadyside, Belmont, Pop. 3,765
Shadyside Local SD 800/PK-12
3890 Lincoln Ave 43947 740-676-3235
John Haswell, supt. Fax 676-6616
www.shadyside.k12.oh.us
Shadyside JSHS 400/7-12
3890 Lincoln Ave 43947 740-676-3235
John Haswell, prin. Fax 676-6616

Shaker Heights, Cuyahoga, Pop. 27,675
Shaker Heights CSD 5,300/PK-12
15600 Parkland Dr 44120 216-295-1400
Gregory C. Hutchings Ed.D., supt. Fax 295-4340
www.shaker.org
Shaker Heights HS 1,800/9-12
15911 Aldersyde Dr 44120 216-295-4200
Jonathan Kuehnle, prin. Fax 295-4277
Shaker Heights MS 900/7-8
20600 Shaker Blvd 44122 216-295-4100
David Glasner, prin. Fax 295-4129

Hathaway Brown S 800/PK-12
19600 N Park Blvd 44122 216-932-4214
Dr. Fran Bisselle, head sch Fax 371-1501
Laurel S 700/PK-12
1 Lyman Cir 44122 216-464-1441
Ann V. Klotz, head sch Fax 464-8995

Sharonville, Hamilton, Pop. 13,127

Miami-Jacobs Career College Post-Sec.
2 Crowne Point Ct Ste 200 45241 513-693-4400

Sheffield Lake, Lorain, Pop. 8,982
Sheffield-Sheffield Lake CSD 1,300/PK-12
1824 Harris Rd 44054 440-949-6181
Michael Cook, supt. Fax 949-4204
www.sheffield.k12.oh.us
Other Schools – See Sheffield Vlg

Northern Ohio Adventist Academy K-12
555 Kenilworth Ave 44054 440-830-2043
Leona Bange, prin.

Sheffield Vlg, Lorain
Sheffield-Sheffield Lake CSD
Supt. — See Sheffield Lake
Brookside HS 500/9-12
1662 Harris Rd 44054 440-949-4220
Brent Schremp, prin. Fax 949-4204
Brookside MS 300/7-8
1662 Harris Rd 44054 440-949-4228
Gretchen Loper, prin. Fax 949-4204

Ohio Business College Post-Sec.
5095 Waterford Dr 44035 888-514-3126

Shelby, Richland, Pop. 9,228
Pioneer Career & Technology Center
27 Ryan Rd 44875 419-347-7744
Greg Nickoli, supt. Fax 347-4977
www.pctc.k12.oh.us
Pioneer Career & Technology Center Vo/Tech
27 Ryan Rd 44875 419-347-7744
Fax 347-4977

Shelby CSD 1,800/K-12
PO Box 31 44875 419-342-3520
Tim Tarvin, supt. Fax 347-3586
www.shelbyk12.org
Shelby HS 500/9-12
1 Whippet Way 44875 419-342-5065
John Gies, prin. Fax 342-5095
Shelby MS 600/5-8
109 W Smiley Ave 44875 419-347-5451
Jeff Eichorn, prin. Fax 347-2095

Sherrodsville, Carroll, Pop. 303
Conotton Valley Union Local SD 400/PK-12
PO Box 187 44675 740-269-2000
Jerry Herman, supt. Fax 269-7901
www.cvul.org
Other Schools – See Bowerston

Sherwood, Defiance, Pop. 819
Central Local SD 1,100/K-12
6289 US Highway 127 43556 419-658-2808
Vicki L. Brunn, supt. Fax 658-4010
www.centrallocal.org
Fairview HS 300/9-12
6289 US Highway 127 43556 419-658-2378
Phil Witker, prin. Fax 658-4011
Fairview MS 300/6-8
6289 US Highway 127 43556 419-658-2331
Suzanne Geis, prin. Fax 658-4010

Sidney, Shelby, Pop. 20,551
Fairlawn Local SD 600/PK-12
18800 Johnston Rd 45365 937-492-1974
Jeffrey Hobbs, supt. Fax 492-8613
www.fairlawn.k12.oh.us
Fairlawn MSHS 300/7-12
18800 Johnston Rd 45365 937-492-5930
Rebekka Egbert, prin. Fax 492-5225

Sidney CSD 3,300/K-12
750 S 4th Ave 45365 937-497-2200
John Scheu, supt. Fax 497-2211
www.sidneycityschools.org
Sidney Alternative S 50/Alt
315 W Russell Rd 45365 937-494-2003
Clayton Westerbeck, prin. Fax 497-0010
Sidney HS 900/9-12
1215 Campbell Rd 45365 937-497-2238
Jon Geuy, prin. Fax 497-2216
Sidney MS 900/5-8
980 Fair Rd 45365 937-497-2225
Diane Voress, prin. Fax 497-2204

Christian Academy S 100/K-12
2151 W Russell Rd 45365 937-492-7556
Mary Smith, supt. Fax 492-5399
Lehman HS 200/9-12
2400 Saint Marys Rd 45365 937-498-1161
Denise Stauffer, prin. Fax 492-9877

Smithville, Wayne, Pop. 1,248
Green Local SD 1,000/K-12
PO Box 438 44677 330-669-3921
Judith Robinson, supt. Fax 669-2121
www.green-local.k12.oh.us/
Green MS 400/5-8
200 Smithie Dr 44677 330-669-3165
Jason DeMassimo, prin. Fax 669-2069
Smithville HS 300/9-12
200 Smithie Dr 44677 330-669-3165
Nathan Gaubatz, prin. Fax 669-2999

Wayne County JVSD
518 W Prospect St 44677 330-669-7000
Dr. Kip Crain, supt. Fax 669-7001
www.wayne-jvs.k12.oh.us
Wayne County Schools Career Center Vo/Tech
518 W Prospect St 44677 330-669-7000
Matt Brown, prin. Fax 669-7001

Solon, Cuyahoga, Pop. 23,009
Solon CSD 4,400/PK-12
33800 Inwood Dr 44139 440-248-1600
Joseph Regano, supt. Fax 248-7665
www.solonschools.org
Solon HS 1,700/9-12
33600 Inwood Dr 44139 440-349-6230
Erin Short, prin. Fax 349-8041
Solon MS 800/7-8
6835 Som Center Rd 44139 440-349-3848
Scott Hatteberg, prin. Fax 349-8034

South Amherst, Lorain, Pop. 1,662
Firelands Local SD 1,700/K-12
112 N Lake St 44001 440-965-5821
Dr. Michael Von Gunten, supt. Fax 986-5990
www.firelandsschools.org/
South Amherst MS 400/6-8
152 W Main St 44001 440-986-7021
Cara Gomez, prin. Fax 986-7022
Other Schools – See Oberlin

South Charleston, Clark, Pop. 1,672
Southeastern Local SD 700/PK-12
226 Clifton Rd 45368 888-627-6745
David Shea, supt. Fax 650-9129
www.sels.us
Southeastern HS 200/9-12
PO Box Z 45368 937-462-8308
P.J. Bertemes, prin. Fax 462-8394
Southeastern JHS 100/7-8
PO Box Z 45368 937-462-8308
P.J. Bertemes, prin. Fax 462-8394

Southington, Trumbull
Southington Local SD 500/PK-12
2482 State Route 534 44470 330-898-7480
Rocco Nero, supt. Fax 898-4828
www.southington.k12.oh.us/
Chalker HS 200/9-12
2482 State Route 534 44470 330-898-1781
Robert Kujala, prin. Fax 898-4828
Southington MS 200/6-8
2482 State Route 534 44470 330-898-1781
Robert Kujala, prin. Fax 898-4828

South Point, Lawrence, Pop. 3,885
South Point Local SD 1,600/K-12
302 High St 45680 740-377-4315
Mark Christian, supt. Fax 377-9735
www.southpoint.k12.oh.us
South Point HS 400/9-12
983 County Road 60 45680 740-377-4323
Benjamin Coleman, prin. Fax 377-4326
South Point MS 400/6-8
983 County Road 60 45680 740-377-4343
Mylissa Bentley, prin. Fax 377-3228

Tri-State Bible College Post-Sec.
PO Box 445 45680 740-377-2520

South Vienna, Clark, Pop. 375
Northeastern Local SD
Supt. — See Springfield
South Vienna MS 300/6-8
140 W Main St 45369 937-346-0880
Todd Justice, prin. Fax 568-4988

South Webster, Scioto, Pop. 856
Bloom-Vernon Local SD 900/PK-12
PO Box 237 45682 740-778-2281
Marc Kreischer, supt. Fax 778-2526
www.bv.k12.oh.us
South Webster JSHS 300/7-12
PO Box 100 45682 740-778-2320
Brett Roberts, prin. Fax 778-3227

Spencerville, Allen, Pop. 2,168
Spencerville Local SD 1,000/K-12
600 School St 45887 419-647-4111
Dennis Fuge, supt. Fax 647-6498
www.spencervillebearcats.com
Spencerville HS 300/9-12
2500 Wisher Dr 45887 419-647-4111
Scott Gephart, prin. Fax 647-5124
Spencerville MS 300/5-8
2500 Wisher Dr 45887 419-647-4112
Susan Wagner, prin. Fax 647-5124

Springboro, Warren, Pop. 17,124
Springboro Community CSD 5,800/K-12
1685 S Main St 45066 937-748-3960
Daniel Schroer, supt. Fax 748-3956
www.springboro.org
Springboro HS 1,600/9-12
1675 S Main St 45066 937-748-3950
Dr. Kyle Martin, prin. Fax 748-3983
Springboro JHS 1,000/7-8
1605 S Main St 45066 937-748-3953
Jonathan Franks, prin. Fax 748-3964

Miami-Jacobs Career College Post-Sec.
875 W Central Ave 45066 937-746-1830
The Academy 300/PK-12
11 Sycamore Creek Dr 45066 937-748-1991
Gina Pangalangan, prin. Fax 748-2091

Springfield, Clark, Pop. 58,259
Clark-Shawnee Local SD 1,500/PK-12
3680 Selma Rd 45502 937-328-5378
Gregg Morris, supt. Fax 328-5379
www.cslocal.org
Shawnee HS 600/9-12
1675 E Possum Rd 45502 937-325-9296
Nathan Dockter, prin. Fax 328-5389

Greenon Local SD
Supt. — See Enon
Greenon JSHS 600/7-12
3950 S Tecumseh Rd 45502 937-340-6372
Rick Newsock, prin. Fax 340-6371

Northeastern Local SD 3,400/K-12
1414 Bowman Rd 45502 937-325-7615
John Kronour, supt. Fax 328-6592
www.nelsd.org/
Kenton Ridge HS 600/9-12
4444 Middle Urbana Rd 45503 937-390-1274
John Hill, prin. Fax 390-0013
Northeastern HS 500/9-12
1480 Bowman Rd 45502 937-328-6575
Allyson Thurman, prin. Fax 328-6581
Northridge MS 500/6-8
4445 Ridgewood Rd E 45503 937-399-2852
Gary Miller, prin. Fax 342-4631
Other Schools – See South Vienna

Northwestern Local SD 1,700/PK-12
5610 Troy Rd 45502 937-964-1318
Jesse Steiner, supt. Fax 964-6019
www.northwestern.k12.oh.us
Northwestern JSHS 800/7-12
5780 Troy Rd 45502 937-964-1324
Lori Swafford, prin. Fax 964-6006

Springfield CSD 7,500/PK-12
1500 W Jefferson St 45506 937-505-2800
Robert F. Hill Ed.D., supt. Fax 505-2978
www.spr.k12.oh.us
Hayward MS 400/7-8
1700 Clifton Ave 45505 937-505-4190
Susie Samuels, prin. Fax 323-9812
Keifer Alternative Center 300/Alt
601 Selma Rd 45505 937-505-4120
Gary Cross, prin. Fax 323-8785
Roosevelt MS 400/7-8
721 E Home Rd 45503 937-505-4370
Monte Brigham, prin. Fax 342-0280
Schaefer MS 300/7-8
147 S Fostoria Ave 45505 937-505-4390
Kimberly Watkins, prin. Fax 325-8974
Springfield HS 1,700/9-12
701 E Home Rd 45503 937-342-4320
Marvin Jones, dir. Fax 342-4110

Springfield-Clark Career Technology Ctr
1901 Selma Rd 45505 937-325-7368
Rick Smith, supt. Fax 325-7452
www.scctc.org
Springfield-Clark Career Technology Ctr Vo/Tech
1901 Selma Rd 45505 937-325-7368
Chris James, dir. Fax 325-7452

Carousel Beauty College Post-Sec.
1475 Upper Valley Pike #956 45504 937-323-0277
Catholic Central ES Lagonda Campus 3-8
1200 E High St 45505 937-324-4551
Sherry Gabert, prin. Fax 327-4070
Catholic Central HS 400/9-12
1200 E High St 45505 937-325-9204
Dr. Karen Juliano, prin. Fax 328-7426
Clark State Community College Post-Sec.
PO Box 570 45501 937-325-0691
Emmanuel Christian Academy 500/PK-12
2177 Emmanuel Way 45502 937-390-3777
Dr. David Hook, supt. Fax 390-0966
Nightingale Montessori S 50/PK-12
1106 E High St 45505 937-324-0336
Maria Taylor, prin. Fax 398-0086
Wittenberg University Post-Sec.
PO Box 720 45501 937-327-6231

Steubenville, Jefferson, Pop. 18,007
Steubenville CSD 2,400/PK-12
PO Box 189 43952 740-283-3767
Melinda Young, supt. Fax 283-8930
scs.steubenville.k12.oh.us
Harding MS 700/5-8
2002 Sunset Blvd 43952 740-282-3481
Joseph Yanok, prin. Fax 283-8949
Steubenville HS 600/9-12
420 N 4th St 43952 740-282-9741
Ted Gorman, prin. Fax 283-8943

Bishop John King Mussio Central JHS 7-8
320 Westview Ave Ste 2 43952 740-346-0028
Theresa Danaher, prin. Fax 346-0070
Catholic Central HS 300/9-12
320 Westview Ave Ste 1 43952 740-264-5538
Richard Wilinski, prin. Fax 264-5443
Eastern Gateway Community College Post-Sec.
4000 Sunset Blvd 43952 740-264-5591
Franciscan University of Steubenville Post-Sec.
1235 University Blvd 43952 800-783-6220
Ohio Valley Hospital Post-Sec.
1 Ross Park Blvd 43952 740-283-7273
Trinity Medical Center East Post-Sec.
380 Summit Ave 43952 740-283-7213

Stewart, Athens, Pop. 244
Federal Hocking Local SD 1,000/PK-12
8461 State Route 144 45778 740-662-6691
Dr. George Wood, supt. Fax 662-5065
www.fedhock.com
Federal Hocking HS 300/9-12
8461 State Route 144 45778 740-662-6691
Cliff Bonner, prin. Fax 662-3805
Federal Hocking MS 100/7-8
8461 State Route 144 45778 740-662-6691
Cliff Bonner, prin. Fax 662-3805

Stow, Summit, Pop. 34,347
Stow-Munroe Falls CSD 5,300/PK-12
4350 Allen Rd 44224 330-689-5445
Thomas Bratten, supt. Fax 688-1629
www.smfschools.org
Stow-Munroe Falls HS 1,800/9-12
3227 Graham Rd 44224 330-689-5300
Jeffrey Hartmann, prin. Fax 678-3899
Other Schools – See Munroe Falls

National College Post-Sec.
3855 Fishcreek Rd 44224 330-676-1351

Strasburg, Tuscarawas, Pop. 2,588
Strasburg-Franklin Local SD 600/K-12
140 N Bodmer Ave 44680 330-878-5571
Cynthia Brown, supt. Fax 878-7900
www.strasburg.k12.oh.us/
Strasburg-Franklin HS 300/6-12
140 N Bodmer Ave 44680 330-878-5571
Adam Hall, prin. Fax 878-7900

Streetsboro, Portage, Pop. 15,768
Streetsboro CSD 2,200/PK-12
9000 Kirby Ln 44241 330-626-4900
R. Michael Daulbaugh, supt. Fax 626-8102
www.streetsboroschools.com
Streetsboro HS 600/9-12
8585 State Route 14 44241 330-626-4902
James Hogue, prin. Fax 626-8103
Streetsboro MS 300/7-8
1951 Annalane Dr 44241 330-626-4905
Vincent Suber, prin. Fax 626-8104

Strongsville, Cuyahoga, Pop. 44,134
Strongsville CSD 4,700/PK-12
18199 Cook Ave 44136 440-572-7000
Cameron Ryba, supt. Fax 572-7041
strongnet.org
Strongsville HS 2,200/9-12
20025 Lunn Rd 44149 440-572-7100
Mark Smithberger, prin. Fax 572-7107
Strongsville MS 500/7-8
13200 Pearl Rd 44136 440-572-7090
Steve Deitrick, prin. Fax 572-7094

Struthers, Mahoning, Pop. 10,554
Struthers CSD 1,900/K-12
99 Euclid Ave 44471 330-750-1061
Joseph Nohra, supt. Fax 750-5516
www.strutherscityschools.org
Struthers HS 600/9-12
111 Euclid Ave 44471 330-750-1062
Roger Day, prin. Fax 755-4525
Struthers MS 600/5-8
800 5th St 44471 330-750-1064
Peter Pirone, prin. Fax 755-4749

Stryker, Williams, Pop. 1,320
Stryker Local SD 400/K-12
400 S Defiance St 43557 419-682-6961
Nate Johnson, supt. Fax 682-2646
www.stryker.k12.oh.us
Stryker JSHS 200/7-12
400 S Defiance St 43557 419-682-4591
Dave Schultz, prin. Fax 682-3508

Sugarcreek, Tuscarawas, Pop. 2,197
Garaway Local SD 1,200/K-12
146 Dover Rd NW 44681 330-852-2421
Dr. James Millet, supt. Fax 852-2991
www.garaway.org
Garaway JSHS 600/7-12
146 Dover Rd NW 44681 330-852-4292
Ryan Taggart, prin. Fax 852-4382

Sugar Grove, Fairfield, Pop. 424
Berne Union Local SD 900/PK-12
PO Box 187 43155 740-746-8341
Richard Spindler, supt. Fax 746-9824
www.buschools.com
Berne Union HS 400/7-12
PO Box 187 43155 740-746-9956
Jon Parker, prin. Fax 746-9824

Sullivan, Ashland
Black River Local SD 1,100/PK-12
257A County Road 40 44880 419-736-3300
Chris Clark, supt. Fax 736-3308
www.blackriver.k12.oh.us/
Black River HS 300/9-12
233 County Road 40 44880 419-736-3303
Martin Yoder, prin. Fax 736-3302
Black River MS 300/6-8
257 County Road 40 44880 419-736-3304
Tammy Starkey, prin. Fax 736-3309

Sunbury, Delaware, Pop. 4,313
Big Walnut Local SD 3,400/PK-12
110 Tippett Ct 43074 740-965-3010
Angela Pollock, supt. Fax 965-4688
www.bwls.net
Big Walnut HS 900/9-12
555 S Old 3C Rd 43074 740-965-3766
Stephen Jados, prin. Fax 965-1954
Big Walnut MS 500/6-8
777 Cheshire Rd 43074 740-965-3006
Joshua Frame, prin. Fax 965-6471

Swanton, Fulton, Pop. 3,658
Swanton Local SD 1,300/K-12
108 N Main St 43558 419-826-7085
Jeffrey Schlade, supt. Fax 825-1197
www.swantonschools.org
Swanton HS 400/9-12
601 N Main St 43558 419-826-3045
Jason Longbrake, prin. Fax 826-1611
Swanton MS 300/6-8
206 Cherry St 43558 419-826-4016
Matt Smith, prin. Fax 826-5176

Sycamore, Wyandot, Pop. 857
Mohawk Local SD 1,000/PK-12
605 State Highway 231 44882 419-927-2414
Kenneth Ratliff, supt. Fax 927-2393
www.mohawklocal.org
Mohawk JSHS 400/7-12
605 State Highway 231 44882 419-927-6222
Brett Graham, prin. Fax 927-6297

Sylvania, Lucas, Pop. 18,670
Sylvania CSD 7,400/K-12
4747 N Holland Sylvania Rd 43560 419-824-8500
Scott D. Nelson, supt. Fax 824-8503
www.sylvaniaschools.org
Arbor Hills JHS 500/6-8
5334 Whiteford Rd 43560 419-824-8640
Timothy Zieroff, prin. Fax 824-8659
McCord JHS 700/6-8
4304 N McCord Rd 43560 419-824-8650
Amanda Ogren, prin. Fax 824-8619
Northview HS 1,200/9-12
5403 Silica Dr 43560 419-824-8570
Steve Swaggerty, prin. Fax 824-8698
Southview HS 1,200/9-12
7225 Sylvania Ave 43560 419-824-8580
Dave McMurray, prin. Fax 824-8678
Timberstone JHS 500/6-8
9000 Sylvania Ave 43560 419-824-8680
Mike Bader, prin. Fax 824-8690

Lourdes University Post-Sec.
6832 Convent Blvd 43560 419-885-3211
Toledo Islamic Academy 200/PK-12
5225 Alexis Rd 43560 419-882-3339
Dr. Nabila Gomaa Ph.D., prin. Fax 882-3334

Tallmadge, Summit, Pop. 17,273
Tallmadge CSD 2,400/K-12
486 East Ave 44278 330-633-3291
Jeffrey Ferguson, supt. Fax 633-5331
www.tallmadgeschools.org
Tallmadge HS 900/9-12
140 N Munroe Rd 44278 330-633-5505
Rebecca Decapua, prin. Fax 475-0567
Tallmadge MS 600/6-8
484 East Ave 44278 330-633-4994
Robert Kearns, prin. Fax 630-5984

The Plains, Athens, Pop. 2,987
Athens CSD 2,700/PK-12
25 S Plains Rd 45780 740-797-4544
Dr. Thomas J. Gibbs, supt. Fax 797-2486
www.athenscsd.org
Athens HS 700/9-12
1 High School Rd 45780 740-797-4521
David Hanning, prin. Fax 797-1421
Other Schools – See Athens

Thornville, Perry, Pop. 982
Northern Local SD 2,100/K-12
8700 Sheridan Dr 43076 740-743-1303
Thomas Perkins, supt. Fax 743-3301
nlsd.k12.oh.us
Sheridan HS 700/9-12
8725 Sheridan Dr 43076 740-743-1335
Chris King, prin. Fax 743-3311
Sheridan MS 500/6-8
8660 Sheridan Dr 43076 740-743-1315
Jay Hickman, prin. Fax 743-3319

Tiffin, Seneca, Pop. 17,722
Tiffin CSD 2,800/PK-12
244 S Monroe St 44883 419-447-2515
Dr. Vicki Wheatley Ed.D., supt. Fax 448-5202
www.tiffin.k12.oh.us
Columbian HS 800/9-12
300 S Monroe St 44883 419-447-6331
Douglas Hartenstein, prin. Fax 448-5252
Tiffin MS 700/6-8
103 Shepherd Dr 44883 419-447-3358
Robert Boes, prin. Fax 448-5250

Vanguard-Sentinel JVSD
Supt. — See Fremont
Sentinel Career Center Vo/Tech
793 E Township Road 201 44883 419-448-1212
Elissa Heal, dir. Fax 447-2544

Calvert JSHS 200/6-12
152 Madison St 44883 419-447-3844
Michael Kaucher, prin. Fax 447-2922
Heidelberg University Post-Sec.
310 E Market St 44883 419-448-2000
Tiffin Academy of Hair Design Post-Sec.
104 E Market St 44883 419-447-3117
Tiffin University Post-Sec.
155 Miami St 44883 800-968-6446

Tipp City, Miami, Pop. 9,564
Bethel Local SD 900/K-12
7490 State Route 201 45371 937-845-9414
Virginia Potter, supt. Fax 845-5007
www.bethel.k12.oh.us
Bethel HS 300/9-12
7490 State Route 201 45371 937-845-9487
Craig Vasil, prin. Fax 845-5007
Bethel MS 200/6-8
7490 State Route 201 45371 937-845-9430
Alexis Dedrick, prin. Fax 845-5007

Tipp City EVD 2,500/K-12
90 S Tippecanoe Dr 45371 937-667-8444
Dr. Gretta Kumpf, supt. Fax 667-6886
www.tippcityschools.com/
Tippecanoe HS 800/9-12
615 E Kessler Cowlesville 45371 937-667-8448
Steve Verhoff, prin. Fax 667-0912
Tippecanoe MS 600/6-8
555 N Hyatt St 45371 937-667-8454
Greg Southers, prin. Fax 667-0874

Toledo, Lucas, Pop. 278,478
ESC of Lake Erie West 100/
2275 Collingwood Blvd 43620 419-245-4150
Sandra C. Frisch, supt. Fax 245-4186
www.esclakeeriewest.org
Westwood Learning Center Alt
3939 Wrenwood Rd 43623 419-473-3442
Brittani Paszko, prin. Fax 473-3445

Toledo CSD 21,200/PK-12
1609 N Summit St 43604 419-671-0001
Dr. Romules Durant, supt. Fax 671-8425
www.tps.org
Bowsher HS 1,200/9-12
2200 Arlington Ave 43614 419-671-2000
Teri Sherwood, prin. Fax 671-2060
Jones Leadership Academy 100/7-10
430 Nebraska Ave 43604 419-671-5400
Ward Barnett, prin. Fax 671-5460
Rogers HS 800/9-12
222 McTigue Dr 43615 419-671-1000
Kelly Welch, prin. Fax 671-1060
Scott HS 500/9-12
2400 Collingwood Blvd 43620 419-671-4000
Carnel Smith, prin. Fax 671-4052
Start HS 1,500/9-12
2010 Tremainsville Rd 43613 419-671-3000
Edward Perozek, prin. Fax 671-3060
Toledo Early College HS 200/9-12
2225 Nebraska Ave 43607 419-530-3003
Dr. Karen Berman, prin. Fax 530-3040
Toledo Technology Academy Vo/Tech
3301 Upton Ave 43613 419-671-3900
Gary Thompson, prin. Fax 479-3192
Waite HS 800/9-12
301 Morrison Dr 43605 419-671-7000
Todd Deem, prin. Fax 671-7060
Woodward HS 600/9-12
701 E Central Ave 43608 419-671-6000
Jack Renz, prin. Fax 671-6050

Washington Local SD 6,800/PK-12
3505 W Lincolnshire Blvd 43606 419-473-8220
Dr. Susan Hayward, supt. Fax 473-8200
www.wls4kids.org
Career & Tech Center Vo/Tech
5719 Clegg Dr 43613 419-473-8339
Debra Heban, dir. Fax 473-8309
Jefferson JHS 500/8-8
5530 Whitmer Dr 43613 419-473-8482
Scott Scharf, prin. Fax 473-8393
Whitmer HS 2,100/9-12
5601 Clegg Dr 43613 419-473-8490
Kristine Martin, prin. Fax 473-8461

Central Catholic HS 1,000/9-12
2550 Cherry St 43608 419-255-2280
Gregory Dempsey, pres. Fax 259-2848
Davis College Post-Sec.
4747 Monroe St 43623 419-473-2700
Emmanuel Christian S 400/K-12
4607 W Laskey Rd 43623 419-885-3558
Warren Aldrich, admin. Fax 885-0139
Maumee Valley Country Day S 500/PK-12
1715 S Reynolds Rd 43614 419-381-1313
Gary Boehm, head sch Fax 381-1314
Mercy College of Ohio Post-Sec.
2221 Madison Ave 43604 419-251-1313
Notre Dame Academy 700/7-12
3535 W Sylvania Ave 43623 419-475-9359
Kimberly Grilliot, prin. Fax 725-1262
Owens Community College Post-Sec.
PO Box 10000 43699 567-661-7000
Riverside Hospital Post-Sec.
3404 W Sylvania Ave 43623 419-729-6059
St. Francis De Sales HS 600/7-12
2323 W Bancroft St 43607 419-531-1618
Eric Smola, prin. Fax 531-9740
St. John's Jesuit Academy 900/7-12
5901 Airport Hwy 43615 419-865-5743
Mike Savona, prin. Fax 861-5002
St. Ursula Academy 500/6-12
4025 Indian Rd 43606 419-531-1693
Nichole Flores, prin. Fax 534-5777
Toledo Christian S 600/PK-12
2303 Brookford Dr 43614 419-389-8700
Scott Gibson, supt. Fax 389-8703
University of Toledo Post-Sec.
2801 W Bancroft St 43606 419-530-4636

Toronto, Jefferson, Pop. 5,027
Toronto CSD 1,000/PK-12
1307 Dennis Way 43964 740-537-2456
Frederick Burns, supt. Fax 537-1102
www.torontocityschools.k12.oh.us
Toronto HS 400/6-12
1305 Dennis Way 43964 740-537-2442
Maureen Taggart, prin. Fax 537-1102

Trenton, Butler, Pop. 11,671
Edgewood CSD 3,600/PK-12
3440 Busenbark Rd 45067 513-863-4692
Simon Fussnecker, supt. Fax 867-7421
www.edgewoodschools.com
Edgewood HS 1,000/9-12
3045 Busenbark Rd 45067 513-867-6300
Adrienne Sanders, prin. Fax 867-6341
Edgewood MS 900/6-8
5005 State Route 73 45067 513-867-7425
David Slamer, prin. Fax 867-7428

Trotwood, Montgomery, Pop. 23,764
Trotwood-Madison CSD 2,500/PK-12
3594 N Snyder Rd 45426 937-854-3050
Kevin Bell, supt. Fax 854-3057
www.trotwood.k12.oh.us/
Trotwood-Madison HS 800/9-12
4440 N Union Rd 45426 937-854-4908
David White, prin. Fax 854-0594
Trotwood-Madison MS 700/5-8
4420 N Union Rd 45426 937-854-0017
Phillitia Charlton, prin. Fax 854-8433

Troy, Miami, Pop. 24,463
Troy CSD 4,300/K-12
500 N Market St 45373 937-332-6700
Eric Herman, supt. Fax 332-6771
www.troy.k12.oh.us
Troy HS 1,200/9-12
151 Staunton Rd 45373 937-332-6710
William Overla, prin. Fax 332-6738
Troy JHS 700/7-8
556 Adams St 45373 937-332-6720
Dave Dilbone, prin. Fax 332-3812

Hobart Institute of Welding Technology Post-Sec.
400 Trade Sq E 45373 800-332-9448
Miami-Jacobs Career College Post-Sec.
865 W Market St 45373 937-332-8585
Troy Christian HS 300/7-12
700 S Dorset Rd 45373 937-339-5692
Dr. Gary Wilber, supt. Fax 335-6258

Tuscarawas, Tuscarawas, Pop. 1,051
Indian Valley Local SD
Supt. — See Gnadenhutten
Indian Valley MS 500/6-8
PO Box 356 44682 740-922-4226
Brent Carter, prin. Fax 922-2493

Twinsburg, Summit, Pop. 18,443
Twinsburg CSD 4,200/PK-12
11136 Ravenna Rd 44087 330-486-2000
Kathryn Powers, supt. Fax 425-7216
www.twinsburg.k12.oh.us
Chamberlin MS 700/7-8
10270 Ravenna Rd 44087 330-486-2281
James Ries, prin. Fax 963-8313
Twinsburg HS 1,300/9-12
10084 Ravenna Rd 44087 330-486-2400
Louise Teringo, prin. Fax 405-7406

The Ohio Academy Post-Sec.
10735 Ravenna Rd Ste 3 44087 330-282-3312

Uhrichsville, Tuscarawas, Pop. 5,330
Claymont CSD
Supt. — See Dennison
Claymont HS 600/9-12
4205 Indian Hill Rd SE 44683 740-922-3471
Lisa Brown, prin. Fax 922-1031
Claymont MS 300/6-8
215 E 6th St 44683 740-922-5241
Brian Watkins, prin. Fax 922-7330

Union City, Darke, Pop. 1,628
Mississinawa Valley Local SD 700/K-12
1469 State Road 47 E 45390 937-968-5656
Douglas Dunham, supt. Fax 968-6731
www.mississinawa.k12.oh.us
Mississinawa Valley JSHS 300/7-12
10480 Staudt Rd 45390 937-968-4464
Jeffrey Winchester, prin. Fax 968-3434

Uniontown, Stark, Pop. 3,274
Green Local SD 4,200/PK-12
1755 Town Park Blvd 44685 330-896-7500
Jeffrey Miller, supt. Fax 896-7580
www.greenlocalschools.org
Green HS 1,300/9-12
1474 Boettler Rd 44685 330-896-7575
Cynthia Brown, prin. Fax 896-7550
Green MS 700/7-8
1711 Steese Rd 44685 330-896-7710
Jeff Wells, prin. Fax 896-7760

Lake Local SD 3,500/K-12
436 King Church Ave SW 44685 330-877-9383
Kevin Tobin, supt. Fax 877-4754
www.lakelocal.org
Lake HS 1,200/9-12
1025 Lake Center St SW 44685 330-877-4282
Daniel Harold, prin. Fax 877-0853
Other Schools – See Hartville

Portage Lakes JVSD
4401 Shriver Rd 44685 330-896-8200
Benjamin Moore, supt. Fax 896-8297
www.plcc.edu/
Portage Lakes Career Center Vo/Tech
4401 Shriver Rd 44685 330-896-8200
Michael Kaschak, prin. Fax 896-8297

University Heights, Cuyahoga, Pop. 13,323
Cleveland Hts - University Hts CSD 5,300/PK-12
2155 Miramar Blvd 44118 216-371-7171
Dr. Talisa Dixon, supt. Fax 397-3880
www.chuh.org
Heights HS 1,900/9-12
2181 Miramar Blvd 44118 216-371-7101
Zoraba Ross, admin. Fax 371-6506
Other Schools – See Cleveland Heights

Upper Arlington, Franklin, Pop. 33,225
Upper Arlington CSD 5,800/K-12
1950 N Mallway Dr 43221 614-487-5000
Paul Imhoff, supt. Fax 487-5012
www.uaschools.org

Hastings MS 700/6-8
1850 Hastings Ln 43220 614-487-5100
Robb Gonda, prin. Fax 487-5116
Jones MS 700/6-8
2100 Arlington Ave 43221 614-487-5080
Jason Fine, prin. Fax 487-5307
Upper Arlington HS 1,700/9-12
1650 Ridgeview Rd 43221 614-487-5200
Andrew Theado, prin. Fax 487-5238

Upper Sandusky, Wyandot, Pop. 6,540
Upper Sandusky EVD 1,600/K-12
800 N Sandusky Ave 43351 419-294-2307
Laurie Vent, supt. Fax 294-6891
www.usevs.org
Union MS 500/4-8
390 W Walker St 43351 419-294-5721
James Wheeler, prin. Fax 294-2586
Upper Sandusky HS 500/9-12
800 N Sandusky Ave 43351 419-294-2308
James Clifford, prin. Fax 294-6889

Urbana, Champaign, Pop. 11,459
Urbana CSD 2,000/K-12
711 Wood St 43078 937-653-1402
Charles Thiel, supt. Fax 652-3845
www.urbana.k12.oh.us
Urbana HS 500/9-12
500 Washington Ave 43078 937-653-1412
Kristin Mays, prin. Fax 653-1487
Urbana JHS 400/6-8
500 Washington Ave 43078 937-653-1439
Joanne Petty, prin. Fax 658-1487

Urbana University Post-Sec.
579 College Way 43078 937-484-1400

Utica, Licking, Pop. 2,106
North Fork Local SD 1,600/K-12
PO Box 497 43080 740-892-3666
Scott Hartley, supt. Fax 892-2937
www.northfork.k12.oh.us
Utica HS 400/9-12
PO Box 677 43080 740-892-2855
Mark Bowman, prin. Fax 892-2090
Utica JHS 300/7-8
PO Box 647 43080 740-892-2691
Marcia Rutherford, prin. Fax 892-2203

Van Buren, Hancock, Pop. 327
Van Buren Local SD 1,000/PK-12
217 S Main St 45889 419-299-3578
Timothy Myers, supt. Fax 299-3668
www.vbschools.net
Van Buren HS 300/9-12
217 S Main St 45889 419-299-3384
Michael Brand, prin. Fax 299-3340
Van Buren MS 200/6-8
217 S Main St 45889 419-299-3385
Jason Clark, prin. Fax 299-3340

Vandalia, Montgomery, Pop. 14,921
Vandalia-Butler CSD 2,800/PK-12
306 S Dixie Dr 45377 937-415-6400
Bradley Neavin, supt. Fax 415-6429
www.vbcsd.com
Butler HS 1,000/9-12
600 S Dixie Dr 45377 937-415-6300
Thomas Luebbe, prin. Fax 415-6457
Morton MS 700/6-8
8555 Peters Pike 45377 937-415-6600
Shannon White, prin. Fax 415-6648

Vanlue, Hancock, Pop. 358
Vanlue Local SD 300/K-12
PO Box 250 45890 419-387-7724
Traci Conley, supt. Fax 387-7722
vanlueschool.org
Vanlue JSHS 100/6-12
PO Box 250 45890 419-387-7724
Robyn Hoadley, prin. Fax 387-7722

Van Wert, Van Wert, Pop. 10,671
Lincolnview Local SD 900/K-12
15945 Middle Point Rd 45891 419-968-2226
Jeffrey Synder, supt. Fax 968-2227
www.lincolnview.k12.oh.us
Lincolnview JSHS 400/7-12
15945 Middle Point Rd 45891 419-968-2214
Brad Mendenhall, prin. Fax 968-2227
Lincolnview Marsh S 50/Alt
PO Box 150 45891 419-238-1695
Robbie Breese, prin. Fax 238-3986

Van Wert CSD 2,000/PK-12
205 W Crawford St 45891 419-238-0648
Kenneth Amstutz, supt. Fax 238-3974
vwcs.net
Van Wert HS 500/9-12
10708 State Route 118 45891 419-238-3350
Robert Priest, prin. Fax 238-0526
Van Wert MS 500/6-8
10694 State Route 118 45891 419-238-0727
Mark Bagley, prin. Fax 238-7166

Vantage JVSD
818 N Franklin St 45891 419-238-5411
Staci Kaufman, supt. Fax 238-4058
www.vantagecareercenter.com
Vantage Career Center Vo/Tech
818 N Franklin St 45891 419-238-5411
Anthony Unverferth, dir. Fax 238-4058

Vermilion, Erie, Pop. 10,413
Vermilion Local SD 1,900/K-12
1250 Sanford St 44089 440-204-1700
Philip Pempin, supt. Fax 204-1771
vermilionschools.org
Vermilion HS 800/8-12
1250 Sanford St 44089 440-204-1701
Lisa Deliz, prin. Fax 204-1781

Versailles, Darke, Pop. 2,673
Versailles EVD 1,400/K-12
PO Box 313 45380 937-526-4773
Dr. Aaron Moran, supt. Fax 526-5745
www.versailles.k12.oh.us
Versailles HS 400/9-12
PO Box 313 45380 937-526-4427
Roger McEldowney, prin. Fax 526-4356
Versailles MS 400/5-8
PO Box 313 45380 937-526-4426
Jeanne Osterfeld, prin. Fax 526-3085

Vienna, Trumbull, Pop. 1,067
Mathews Local SD
Supt. — See Cortland
Mathews JSHS 200/7-12
4429 Warren Sharon Rd 44473 330-394-1138
James Stitt, prin.

Pittsburgh Institute of Aeronautics Post-Sec.
1453 Youngstown Kingsville 44473 330-399-9992

Vincent, Washington, Pop. 337
Warren Local SD 1,400/K-12
220 Sweetapple Rd 45784 740-678-2366
Kyle Newton, supt. Fax 678-8275
www.warrenlocal.org
Warren HS 600/9-12
130 Warrior Dr 45784 740-678-2393
Benjamin Cunningham, prin. Fax 678-2783
Warren MS 400/5-8
70 Warrior Dr 45784 740-678-2395
Brent Taylor, prin. Fax 678-0118

Wadsworth, Medina, Pop. 21,350
Wadsworth CSD 4,900/PK-12
524 Broad St 44281 330-336-3571
Andrew Hill Ed.D., supt. Fax 335-1313
www.wadsworthschools.org
Wadsworth HS 1,600/9-12
625 Broad St 44281 330-335-1400
Steven Moore, prin. Fax 335-1376
Wadsworth MS 700/7-8
150 Silvercreek Rd 44281 330-335-1410
Eric Jackson, prin. Fax 336-3820

Wapakoneta, Auglaize, Pop. 9,743
Wapakoneta CSD 2,800/PK-12
1102 Gardenia Dr 45895 419-739-2900
Keith Horner, supt. Fax 739-2918
www.wapak.org/
Wapakoneta HS 800/8-12
1 Redskin Trl 45895 419-739-5200
Scott Minnig, prin. Fax 739-5305

Warren, Trumbull, Pop. 40,148
Champion Local SD 1,500/K-12
5976 Mahoning Ave NW 44483 330-847-2330
Pamela Hood, supt. Fax 847-2336
championlocal.org
Champion HS 400/9-12
5976 Mahoning Ave NW 44483 330-847-2305
John Grabowski, prin. Fax 847-2353
Champion MS 500/5-8
5435 Kuszmaul Ave NW 44483 330-847-2348
Heather Campbell, prin. Fax 847-2355

Howland Local SD 2,900/K-12
8200 South St SE 44484 330-856-8200
Kevin Spicher, supt. Fax 856-8214
www.howlandschools.com
Howland HS 900/9-12
200 Shaffer Dr NE 44484 330-856-8220
Sandra Williams, prin. Fax 856-7827
Howland MS 700/6-8
8100 South St SE 44484 330-856-8250
Stephen Kovach, prin. Fax 856-2157

Lordstown Local SD 500/K-12
1824 Salt Springs Rd W 44481 330-824-2534
Terry P. Armstrong, supt. Fax 824-2847
www.lordstown.k12.oh.us/
Lordstown JSHS 200/7-12
1824 Salt Springs Rd W 44481 330-824-2581
James Vivo, prin. Fax 824-2586

Trumbull Career & Technical Center
528 Educational Hwy NW 44483 330-847-0503
Jason Gray, supt. Fax 847-6817
www.tctchome.com
Trumbull Career & Technical Center Vo/Tech
528 Educational Hwy NW 44483 330-847-0503
Mary Flint, dir. Fax 847-0339

Warren CSD 5,100/PK-12
105 High St NE 44481 330-841-2321
Stephen Chiaro, supt. Fax 841-2434
www.warrenschools.k12.oh.us
Harding HS 1,400/9-12
860 Elm Rd NE 44483 330-841-2316
Dante Capers, prin. Fax 841-2289

Kennedy HS 300/7-12
2550 Central Parkway Ave SE 44484 330-369-1804
Joseph Kenneally, prin. Fax 369-1125
Kent State University-Trumbull Campus Post-Sec.
4314 Mahoning Ave NW 44483 330-847-0571
Trumbull Business College Post-Sec.
3200 Ridge Ave SE 44484 330-369-3200

Warrensville Heights, Cuyahoga, Pop. 13,282
Warrensville Heights CSD 1,300/PK-12
4500 Warrensville Center Rd 44128 216-865-4717
Donald J. Jolly, supt. Fax 921-5942
www.warrensville.k12.oh.us
Warrensville Heights HS 500/8-12
4270 Northfield Rd 44128 216-752-8585
Janet McDowell, prin. Fax 752-8116

Warsaw, Coshocton, Pop. 679
River View Local SD 2,000/PK-12
26496 State Route 60 43844 740-824-3521
Dalton Summers, supt. Fax 824-3760
www.river-view.k12.oh.us
River View HS 600/9-12
26496 State Route 60 43844 740-824-3522
Chuck Rinkes, prin. Fax 824-4746
River View MS 300/7-8
26546 State Route 60 43844 740-824-3523
Jerry Olinger, prin. Fax 824-5241

Washington Court House, Fayette, Pop. 13,899
Miami Trace Local SD 2,500/PK-12
3818 State Route 41 NW 43160 740-335-3010
David Lewis, supt. Fax 335-1959
miamitrace.k12.oh.us
Miami Trace HS 700/9-12
3722 State Route 41 NW 43160 740-333-4700
Robert Enochs, prin. Fax 636-2010
Miami Trace MS 600/6-8
3800 State Route 41 NW 43160 740-333-4900
Jason Binegar, prin. Fax 333-4901

Washington Court House CSD 2,200/K-12
306 Highland Ave 43160 740-335-6620
Matthew McCorkle M.Ed., supt. Fax 335-1245
www.washingtonch.k12.oh.us
Washington HS 600/9-12
400 S Elm St 43160 740-636-4221
Tracy Rose, prin. Fax 636-4261
Washington MS 500/6-8
500 S Elm St 43160 740-335-0291
Eric Wayne, prin. Fax 333-3606

Waterford, Washington, Pop. 445
Wolf Creek Local SD 600/K-12
PO Box 67 45786 740-984-2373
Douglas Baldwin M.A., supt. Fax 984-4420
www.wolfcreek.k12.oh.us
Waterford HS 200/9-12
PO Box 67 45786 740-984-2373
Suellen Coleman M.S., prin. Fax 984-4420

Wauseon, Fulton, Pop. 7,227
Wauseon EVD 1,800/K-12
126 S Fulton St 43567 419-335-6616
Larry Brown, supt. Fax 335-3978
www.wauseon.k12.oh.us
Wauseon HS 500/9-12
840 Parkview St 43567 419-335-5756
Keith Leatherman, prin. Fax 335-4228
Wauseon MS 400/6-8
940 E Oak St 43567 419-335-2701
Joe Friess, prin. Fax 335-0089

Waverly, Pike, Pop. 5,086
Waverly CSD 1,900/PK-12
1 Tiger Dr 45690 740-947-4770
Cheryl Francis, supt. Fax 947-4483
www.waverly.k12.oh.us
Waverly HS 400/9-12
1 Tiger Dr 45690 740-947-7701
Bill Hoover, prin. Fax 947-8877
Waverly JHS 500/6-8
3 Tiger Dr 45690 740-947-4527
Cynthia Houk, prin. Fax 947-8047

Pike Christian Academy 100/PK-12
400 Clough St 45690 740-947-5700
Br. Brian Roseberry, prin. Fax 947-9500

Waynesfield, Auglaize, Pop. 843
Waynesfield-Goshen Local SD 500/K-12
500 N Westminster St 45896 419-568-9100
J. Chris Pfister, supt. Fax 568-8024
www.wgschools.org
Waynesfield-Goshen Local MSHS 300/6-12
500 N Westminster St 45896 419-568-9100
Rebecca Diglia, prin. Fax 568-6282

Waynesville, Warren, Pop. 2,780
Wayne Local SD 1,500/K-12
659 Dayton Rd 45068 513-897-6971
Patrick Dubbs, supt. Fax 897-9605
www.wayne-local.com
Waynesville HS 500/9-12
735 Dayton Rd 45068 513-897-2776
Randy Gebhardt, prin. Fax 897-2713
Waynesville MS 300/6-8
723 Dayton Rd 45068 513-897-4706
Randy Gebhardt, prin. Fax 897-2083

Wellington, Lorain, Pop. 4,725
Wellington EVD 1,200/PK-12
305 Union St 44090 440-647-4286
Dennis Mock, supt. Fax 647-4806
www.wellington.k12.oh.us
McCormick MS 500/4-8
627 N Main St 44090 440-647-2342
Craig Housum, prin. Fax 647-7310
Wellington HS 400/9-12
629 N Main St 44090 440-647-3734
Tina Drake, prin. Fax 647-7318

Wellston, Jackson, Pop. 5,598
Wellston CSD 1,500/PK-12
1 E Broadway St 45692 740-384-2152
Karen Boch, supt. Fax 384-3948
www.wcs.k12.oh.us
Wellston HS 400/9-12
200 Golden Rocket Dr 45692 740-384-2162
Megan Sowers, prin. Fax 384-9581
Wellston MS 300/6-8
227 Golden Rocket Dr 45692 740-384-2251
Tyler Swackhammer, prin. Fax 384-9801

Wellsville, Columbiana, Pop. 3,433
Wellsville Local SD 800/PK-12
929 Center St 43968 330-532-2643
Richard Bereschik, supt. Fax 532-6204
www.wellsville.k12.oh.us

Wellsville JSHS 400/7-12
1 Bengal Blvd 43968 330-532-1188
Linda Rolley, prin. Fax 532-9004

West Alexandria, Preble, Pop. 1,321
Twin Valley Community Local SD 900/K-12
100 Education Dr 45381 937-839-4688
Robert O. Fischer M.Ed., supt. Fax 839-4898
www.tvs.k12.oh.us
Twin Valley South HS 300/9-12
100 Education Dr 45381 937-839-4693
Scott Cottingim, prin. Fax 839-4898
Twin Valley South MS 100/7-8
100 Education Dr 45381 937-839-4165
Scott Cottingim, prin. Fax 839-4898

West Carrollton, Montgomery, Pop. 12,886
West Carrollton CSD 3,900/PK-12
430 E Pease Ave 45449 937-859-5121
Rusty Clifford Ph.D., supt. Fax 859-5250
www.westcarrolltonschools.com
West Carrollton HS 900/9-12
5833 Student St 45449 937-859-5121
Craig Myers, prin. Fax 435-2315
West Carrollton MS 800/6-8
424 E Main St 45449 937-859-5121
Doug Mescher, prin. Fax 859-2780

West Chester, Butler
Lakota Local SD
Supt. — See Liberty Twp
Hopewell JHS 600/7-8
8200 Cox Rd 45069 513-777-2258
Jeff Rouff, prin. Fax 777-1908
Lakota Ridge JHS 600/7-8
6199 Beckett Ridge Blvd 45069 513-777-0552
Andre Gendreau, prin. Fax 777-0919
Lakota West Freshman HS 600/9-9
5050 Tylersville Rd 45069 513-874-8390
Gary Card, prin. Fax 682-4230
Lakota West HS 1,800/10-12
8940 Union Centre Blvd 45069 513-874-5699
Gary Card, prin. Fax 682-4133

Hondros College Post-Sec.
7600 Tylers Place Blvd 45069 888-466-3767

Westerville, Franklin, Pop. 35,380
Westerville CSD 14,700/PK-12
936 Eastwind Dr 43081 614-797-5700
Dr. John R. Kellogg, supt. Fax 797-5701
www.wcsoh.org
Blendon MS 700/6-8
223 S Otterbein Ave 43081 614-797-6400
Kendall Harris, prin. Fax 797-6401
Genoa MS 900/6-8
5948 S Old 3C Hwy 43082 614-797-6500
Carrie Trusley, prin. Fax 797-6501
Heritage MS 900/6-8
390 N Spring Rd 43082 614-797-6600
Joseph Kacsandi, prin. Fax 797-6601
Walnut Springs MS 900/6-8
888 E Walnut St 43081 614-797-6700
Becca Yanni, prin. Fax 797-6701
Westerville Central HS 1,600/9-12
7118 Mount Royal Ave 43082 614-797-6800
Todd Spinner, prin. Fax 797-6801
Westerville-North HS 1,400/9-12
950 County Line Rd 43081 614-797-6200
Kurt Yancey, prin. Fax 797-6201
Westerville-South HS 1,500/9-12
303 S Otterbein Ave 43081 614-797-6000
Mike Starner, prin. Fax 797-6001

Fortis College Post-Sec.
4151 Executive Pkwy Ste 120 43081 614-882-2551
Genoa Christian Academy 300/PK-12
7562 Lewis Center Rd 43082 740-965-5433
Craig Bartley, supt. Fax 965-8214
Hondros College Post-Sec.
4140 Executive Pkwy 43081 614-508-7277
Northside Christian S 200/K-12
2655 W Schrock Rd 43081 614-882-1493
John Taylor, prin.
Ohio State Cosmetology School Post-Sec.
5970 Westerville Rd 43081 614-890-3535
Otterbein University Post-Sec.
1 S Grove St 43081 614-890-3000
Worthington Christian MS 200/6-8
8225 Worthington Galena Rd 43081 614-431-8230
Tamara Evans, prin. Fax 431-8216

West Jefferson, Madison, Pop. 4,287
Jefferson Local SD 1,200/PK-12
906 W Main St 43162 614-879-7654
William Mullett, supt. Fax 879-5376
www.west-jefferson.k12.oh.us
West Jefferson HS 300/9-12
1 Roughrider Dr 43162 614-879-7681
David Metz, prin. Fax 879-5381
West Jefferson MS 300/6-8
2 Roughrider Dr 43162 614-879-8345
Deborah Omen, prin. Fax 879-5399

West Lafayette, Coshocton, Pop. 2,307
Ridgewood Local SD 1,200/PK-12
301 S Oak St 43845 740-545-6354
Michael Masloski, supt. Fax 545-6336
www.ridgewood.k12.oh.us
Ridgewood HS 500/8-12
602 Johnson St 43845 740-545-6345
Todd Stoffer, prin. Fax 545-5311

Westlake, Cuyahoga, Pop. 32,199
Westlake CSD 3,300/PK-12
24525 Hilliard Blvd 44145 440-871-7300
Scott Goggin, supt. Fax 871-6034
www.wlake.org
Burneson MS 600/7-8
2260 Dover Center Rd 44145 440-835-6340
Paul Wilson, prin. Fax 808-8964
Westlake HS 1,300/9-12
27830 Hilliard Blvd 44145 440-250-1002
Timothy Freeman, prin. Fax 835-5572

Westside Christian Academy 200/K-11
23096 Center Ridge Rd 44145 440-331-1300
Jim Whiteman, prin. Fax 331-1301

West Liberty, Champaign, Pop. 1,773
West Liberty-Salem Local SD 1,200/K-12
7208 US Highway 68 N 43357 937-465-1075
Kraig Hissong, supt. Fax 465-1095
www.wlstigers.org/
West Liberty-Salem MSHS 600/6-12
7208 US Highway 68 N 43357 937-465-1060
Greg Johnson, prin. Fax 465-1095

West Milton, Miami, Pop. 4,568
Milton-Union EVD 1,300/PK-12
7610 Milton Potsdam Rd 45383 937-884-7910
Dr. Brad Ritchey, supt. Fax 884-7911
www.milton-union.k12.oh.us
Milton-Union HS 400/9-12
7640 Milton Potsdam Rd 45383 937-884-7940
Scott Bloom, prin. Fax 884-7941
Milton-Union MS 400/6-8
7630 Milton Potsdam Rd 45383 937-884-7930
Katie Hartley, prin. Fax 884-7931

West Portsmouth, Scioto, Pop. 3,091
Washington-Nile Local SD 1,400/K-12
15332 US Highway 52 45663 740-858-1111
Jeff Stricklett, supt. Fax 858-1110
www.west.k12.oh.us
Portsmouth West HS 400/9-12
15332 US Highway 52 45663 740-858-1103
Anthony Bazler, prin. Fax 858-1110
Portsmouth West MS 500/5-8
15332 US Highway 52 Unit B 45663 740-858-6668
Christopher Jordan, prin. Fax 858-4101

West Salem, Wayne, Pop. 1,452
Northwestern Local SD 1,400/K-12
7571 N Elyria Rd 44287 419-846-3151
Jeffrey Layton, supt. Fax 846-3361
www.northwestern-wayne.k12.oh.us
Northwestern HS 400/9-12
7473 N Elyria Rd 44287 419-846-3833
Michael Burkholder, prin. Fax 846-3163
Northwestern MS 300/6-8
7569 N Elyria Rd 44287 419-846-3974
Joseph Brightbill, prin. Fax 846-3750

West Union, Adams, Pop. 3,193
Adams County/Ohio Valley Local SD 3,900/PK-12
141 Lloyd Rd 45693 937-544-5586
Richard Seas, supt. Fax 544-3720
www.ovsd.us
Ohio Valley Career & Technical Center Vo/Tech
175 Lloyd Rd 45693 937-544-2336
Jason Vesey, dir. Fax 544-5176
West Union HS 600/7-12
97 Dragon Lair Dr 45693 937-544-5553
Roger Taylor, prin. Fax 544-5361
Other Schools – See Peebles, Seaman

Adams County Christian S 100/K-12
187 Willow Dr 45693 937-544-5502
Rev. Kenneth Jones, admin. Fax 544-5503

West Unity, Williams, Pop. 1,653
Millcreek-West Unity Local SD 600/K-12
1401 W Jackson St 43570 419-924-2365
Larry E Long, supt. Fax 924-2367
www.hilltop.k12.oh.us
Hilltop HS 300/7-12
1401 W Jackson St 43570 419-924-2365
Steven J. Riley, prin. Fax 924-2367

Wheelersburg, Scioto, Pop. 6,353
Wheelersburg Local SD 1,500/PK-12
PO Box 340 45694 740-574-8484
Mark Knapp, supt. Fax 574-6134
www.wheelersburg.net
Wheelersburg HS 400/9-12
800 Pirate Dr 45694 740-574-2527
Christopher Porter, prin. Fax 574-6178
Wheelersburg MS 600/4-8
800 Pirate Dr 45694 740-574-2515
David Rucker, prin. Fax 574-9201

Whitehall, Franklin, Pop. 17,402
Whitehall CSD 3,200/PK-12
625 S Yearling Rd 43213 614-417-5000
Brian Hamler, supt. Fax 417-5023
www.wcsrams.org
Rosemore MS 700/6-8
4800 Langley Ave 43213 614-417-5200
Rochelle Rankin, prin. Fax 417-5212
Whitehall-Yearling HS 800/9-12
675 S Yearling Rd 43213 614-417-5100
Paul Smathers, prin. Fax 417-5133

Whitehouse, Lucas, Pop. 4,098
Anthony Wayne Local SD 4,300/K-12
PO Box 2487 43571 419-877-5377
Jim Fritz, supt. Fax 877-9352
www.anthonywayneschools.org
Wayne HS 1,300/9-12
5967 Finzel Rd 43571 419-877-0466
Kevin Pfefferle, prin. Fax 877-5028
Wayne JHS 800/7-8
6035 Finzel Rd 43571 419-877-5342
Brian Bocian, prin. Fax 877-4908

Wickliffe, Lake, Pop. 12,545
Wickliffe CSD 1,500/PK-12
2221 Rockefeller Rd 44092 440-943-6900
Joseph Spiccia, supt. Fax 943-7738
www.wickliffeschools.org
Wickliffe HS 500/9-12
2255 Rockefeller Rd 44092 440-944-0800
Cynthia Anderson, prin. Fax 943-7738
Wickliffe MS 500/5-8
29240 Euclid Ave 44092 440-943-3220
Dr. Bradley Leyrer, prin. Fax 943-7755

Rabbinical College of Telshe Post-Sec.
28400 Euclid Ave 44092 440-943-5300
St. Mary Seminary/Graduate Sch. Theology Post-Sec.
28700 Euclid Ave 44092 440-943-7600
Telshe HS 100/9-12
28400 Euclid Ave 44092 440-944-0299
David Klems, prin. Fax 943-5303

Wilberforce, Greene, Pop. 2,180

Central State University Post-Sec.
PO Box 1004 45384 937-376-6011
Payne Theological Seminary Post-Sec.
PO Box 474 45384 937-376-2946
Wilberforce University Post-Sec.
PO Box 1001 45384 937-376-2911

Willard, Huron, Pop. 6,140
Willard CSD 1,300/PK-12
110 S Myrtle Ave 44890 419-935-1541
Jeffrey Ritz, supt. Fax 935-8491
www.willardschools.org/
Willard MSHS 700/6-12
1 Flashes Ave 44890 419-935-0181
Mike Eicher, prin. Fax 933-6701

Celeryville Christian S 100/PK-12
4200 Broadway Rd 44890 419-935-3633
Jacob Bush, admin. Fax 933-6030

Williamsburg, Clermont, Pop. 2,468
Williamsburg Local SD 1,000/PK-12
549 W Main St Ste A 45176 513-724-3077
Matthew Earley, supt. Fax 724-1504
www.burgschools.org
Williamsburg MSHS 500/6-12
500 S 5th St 45176 513-724-2211
Heather Powell, prin. Fax 724-6577

Williamsport, Pickaway, Pop. 1,007
Westfall Local SD 1,500/PK-12
19463 Pherson Pike 43164 740-986-3671
Cara Riddel, supt. Fax 986-8375
www.westfallschools.com
Westfall HS 500/9-12
19463 Pherson Pike 43164 740-986-2911
Billy Dennis, prin. Fax 986-8897
Westfall MS 400/6-8
19545 Pherson Pike 43164 740-986-2941
Jason Fife, prin. Fax 986-8882

Willoughby, Lake, Pop. 21,949
Willoughby-Eastlake CSD 8,000/PK-12
37047 Ridge Rd 44094 440-946-5000
Stephen Thompson, supt. Fax 946-4671
www.weschools.org
South HS 1,400/9-12
5000 Shankland Rd 44094 440-975-3647
Zachary Weagley, prin. Fax 975-3645
Willoughby-Eastlake Career Academy Vo/Tech
34343 Euclid Ave 44094 440-946-7085
Susan Vargo Roseum, dir. Fax 975-3741
Willoughby MS 800/6-8
36901 Ridge Rd 44094 440-975-3600
Lawrence Keller, prin. Fax 975-3618
Other Schools – See Eastlake, Willowick

Andrews Osborne Academy 400/PK-12
38588 Mentor Ave 44094 440-942-3600
Larry Goodman Ph.D., head sch Fax 942-3660

Willoughby Hills, Lake, Pop. 9,326

Cornerstone Christian Academy 400/PK-12
2846 SOM Center Rd, 440-943-9260
Sandra Ortiz, prin. Fax 943-9262
National College Post-Sec.
27557 Chardon Rd 44092 440-944-0825

Willowick, Lake, Pop. 14,003
Willoughby-Eastlake CSD
Supt. — See Willoughby
Willowick MS 600/6-8
31500 Royalview Dr 44095 440-943-2950
Loretta Rodman, prin. Fax 943-9964

Willow Wood, Lawrence
Symmes Valley Local SD 800/K-12
14778 State Route 141 45696 740-643-2451
Jeff Saunders, supt. Fax 643-1219
www.sv.k12.oh.us
Symmes Valley HS 200/9-12
14778 State Route 141 45696 740-643-2371
Greg Bowman, prin. Fax 643-1606

Wilmington, Clinton, Pop. 12,076
Great Oaks Institute of Technology
Supt. — See Cincinnati
Laurel Oaks CDC Vo/Tech
300 Oak Dr 45177 937-382-1411
Mike Thomas, prin. Fax 383-2095

Wilmington CSD 3,000/K-12
341 S Nelson Ave 45177 937-382-1641
Ronald Sexton, supt. Fax 382-1645
www.wilmingtoncityschools.com
Borror MS 700/6-8
275 Thorne Ave 45177 937-382-7556
Jeffrey Sherby, prin. Fax 382-3295
Wilmington HS 800/9-12
300 Richardson Pl 45177 937-382-7716
Mindy McCarty-Stewart, prin. Fax 382-1139

Wilmington Christian Academy 100/K-12
642 Davids Dr 45177 937-283-6618
Matt Black, admin. Fax 283-9541
Wilmington College Post-Sec.
1870 Quaker Way 45177 937-382-6661

Winchester, Adams, Pop. 1,044
Eastern Local SD 1,300/K-12
11479 US Highway 62 45697 937-378-3981
Michele Filon, supt. Fax 695-9046
www.eb.k12.oh.us
Eastern HS 300/9-12
11557 US Highway 62 45697 937-695-0959
Jennifer Grimes, prin. Fax 695-0303
Eastern MS 300/6-8
11479 US Highway 62 45697 937-695-1249
Jordan Michael, prin. Fax 695-1299

Windham, Portage, Pop. 2,132
Windham EVD 600/PK-12
9530 Bauer Ave 44288 330-326-2711
Gregory Isler, supt. Fax 326-2134
www.windham-schools.org
Windham HS 200/9-12
9530 Bauer Ave 44288 330-326-2711
Laura Amero, prin. Fax 326-2052
Windham JHS 100/6-8
9530 Bauer Ave 44288 330-326-2711
Laura Amero, prin. Fax 326-3713

Wintersville, Jefferson, Pop. 3,879
Indian Creek Local SD 1,800/PK-12
587 Bantam Ridge Rd 43953 740-264-3502
Dr. T.C. Chappelear Ed.D., supt. Fax 266-2915
www.iclsd.org
Indian Creek HS 600/9-12
200 Park Dr 43953 740-264-1163
James Retton, prin. Fax 266-2929
Other Schools – See Mingo Junction

Jefferson County Christian S 200/PK-12
125 Fernwood Rd 43953 740-275-4326
Diane Hutchison, prin. Fax 275-4296

Woodsfield, Monroe, Pop. 2,354
Switzerland of Ohio Local SD 2,200/PK-12
304 Mill St 43793 740-472-5801
Jeffrey Greenley, supt. Fax 472-5806
www.swissohio.k12.oh.us
Monroe Central HS 300/9-12
469 Lewisville Rd 43793 740-472-0414
Thaddeus Fields, prin. Fax 472-2055
Swiss Hills Career Center Vo/Tech
46601 State Route 78 43793 740-472-0722
Marc Ring, prin. Fax 472-0367
Other Schools – See Beallsville, Hannibal

Woodville, Sandusky, Pop. 2,126
Woodmore Local SD
Supt. — See Elmore
Woodmore MS 6-8
800 W Main St 43469 419-862-1070
Kevin Ball, prin. Fax 849-2132

Wooster, Wayne, Pop. 25,513
Triway Local SD 1,700/K-12
3205 Shreve Rd 44691 330-264-9491
Nate Schindewolf, supt. Fax 262-3955
www.tccsa.net/dp/trwy
Triway HS 500/9-12
3205 Shreve Rd 44691 330-264-8685
Scott Wharton, prin. Fax 262-3955
Triway JHS 300/7-8
3145 Shreve Rd 44691 330-264-2114
Joshua Stutz, prin. Fax 264-6025

Wooster CSD 3,700/PK-12
144 N Market St 44691 330-988-1111
Dr. Michael Tefs Ed.D., supt. Fax 262-3407
www.woostercityschools.org
Boys Village S 100/Alt
3011 Akron Rd 44691 330-262-3442
Anita Jorney-Gifford, prin. Fax 202-3890
Wooster HS 1,400/8-12
515 Oldman Rd 44691 330-988-1111
Tyler Keener, prin. Fax 345-3501

College of Wooster Post-Sec.
1189 Beall Ave 44691 330-263-2000
Ohio State University-A & T Institute Post-Sec.
1328 Dover Rd 44691 330-287-1331

Worthington, Franklin, Pop. 13,300
Worthington CSD 9,500/PK-12
200 E Wilson Bridge Rd 43085 614-450-6000
Trent Bowers Ph.D., supt. Fax 883-3010
www.worthington.k12.oh.us
Kilbourne MS 400/7-8
50 E Dublin Granville Rd 43085 614-450-4200
James Gaskill, prin. Fax 883-3510
Linworth Campus Alternative Program Alt
2075 W Dublin Granville Rd 43085 614-450-6900
Chris Hasebrook, dir. Fax 883-3710
Phoenix MS 200/Alt
2341 Snouffer Rd 43085 614-450-4100
Adham Schirg, prin. Fax 883-3610
Worthington HS 1,600/9-12
300 W Dublin Granville Rd 43085 614-450-6200
Peter Scully, prin. Fax 450-6390
Worthingway MS 400/7-8
6625 Guyer St 43085 614-450-4300
Nathan Kellenberger, prin. Fax 883-3660
Other Schools – See Columbus

Worthington Christian HS 300/9-12
6670 Worthington Galena Rd 43085 614-431-8210
Dr. Scott Inboden, prin. Fax 431-8213

Wyoming, Hamilton, Pop. 8,224
Wyoming CSD 1,900/K-12
420 Springfield Pike 45215 513-206-7000
Dr. Susan Lang, supt. Fax 672-3355
www.wyomingcityschools.org
Wyoming HS 700/9-12
106 Pendery Ave 45215 513-206-7050
Ashley Whitely, prin. Fax 206-7132
Wyoming MS 600/5-8
17 Wyoming Ave 45215 513-206-7170
Tiffany Brennan, prin. Fax 206-7245

Xenia, Greene, Pop. 24,906
Beavercreek CSD
Supt. — See Beavercreek
Coy MS 1,100/6-8
1786 Dayton Xenia Rd 45385 937-429-7577
Shaun Kelly, prin. Fax 429-7686

Greene County JVSD
2960 W Enon Rd 45385 937-372-6941
David Deskins, supt. Fax 372-8283
www.greeneccc.com
Greene County Career Center Vo/Tech
2960 W Enon Rd 45385 937-426-6636
Matthew Lindley, dir. Fax 372-3125

Xenia Community SD 4,100/PK-12
819 Colorado Dr 45385 937-376-2961
Dennis Morrison, supt. Fax 372-4701
www.xenia.k12.oh.us
Warner MS 600/6-8
600 Buckskin Trl 45385 937-376-9488
Theodore Holop, prin. Fax 374-4228
Xenia HS 1,200/9-12
303 Kinsey Rd 45385 937-372-6983
Henry Jackoby, prin. Fax 374-4390

Legacy Christian Academy 400/PK-12
1101 Wesley Ave 45385 937-352-1640
Dr. Dan Bragg, supt. Fax 352-1641

Yellow Springs, Greene, Pop. 3,226
Yellow Springs EVD 700/K-12
201 S Walnut St 45387 937-767-7381
Mario Basora, supt. Fax 767-6604
www.yellow-springs.k12.oh.us/
Yellow Springs HS / McKinney MS 300/7-12
420 E Enon Rd 45387 937-767-7224
Tim Krier, prin. Fax 767-6154

Antioch University Midwest Post-Sec.
900 Dayton St 45387 937-769-1800

Youngstown, Mahoning, Pop. 65,039
Austintown Local SD 5,200/K-12
700 S Raccoon Rd 44515 330-797-3900
Vincent Colauca, supt. Fax 792-8625
www.austintown.k12.oh.us
Austintown MS 1,300/6-8
800 S Raccoon Rd 44515 330-797-3900
James Penk, prin. Fax 792-9130
Fitch HS 1,600/9-12
4560 Falcon Dr 44515 330-797-3900
Christopher Berni, prin. Fax 797-3944

Boardman Local SD 4,400/K-12
7410 Market St 44512 330-726-3404
Timothy Saxton, supt. Fax 726-3432
www.boardman.k12.oh.us
Boardman Center MS 600/5-8
7410 Market St 44512 330-726-3400
Randall Ebie, prin. Fax 726-3431
Boardman Glenwood MS 800/5-8
7635 Glenwood Ave 44512 330-726-3414
Bart Smith, prin. Fax 758-8067
Boardman HS 1,400/9-12
7777 Glenwood Ave 44512 330-758-7511
Cindy Fernback, prin. Fax 758-7515

Liberty Local SD 1,200/K-12
4115 Shady Rd 44505 330-759-0807
Stanley Watson, supt. Fax 759-1209
sites.liberty.k12.oh.us
Guy MS 300/5-8
4115 Shady Rd 44505 330-759-1733
Melissa Malone, prin. Fax 759-4507
Liberty HS 400/9-12
1 Leopard Way 44505 330-759-2301
Rocco Adduci, prin. Fax 759-4506

Youngstown CSD 5,200/PK-12
PO Box 550 44501 330-744-6900
Krishanjeev Mohip Ph.D., supt. Fax 743-1157
www.youngstown.k12.oh.us
Chaney VPA/STEM Campus 600/6-12
731 S Hazelwood Ave 44509 330-744-8822
Joseph Krumpak, prin. Fax 480-1909
East HS 800/9-11
474 Bennington Ave 44505 330-744-4005
Denise Vaclav-Danko, prin. Fax 742-6464
Programs of Promise at Wilson Alt
2725 Gibson St 44502 330-744-8002
Tod Morris, prin. Fax 788-1326
Rayen Early College MS 200/6-8
731 S Hazelwood Ave 44509 330-744-7602
Deborah DiFrancesco, prin. Fax 793-9675
Youngstown Early College HS 200/9-12
Fedor Hall 644 Elm St 44555 330-744-7923
Monica Jones, dean Fax 480-5875

Cardinal Mooney HS 600/9-12
2545 Erie St 44507 330-788-5007
Mark Vollmer, prin. Fax 788-4511
National College Post-Sec.
3487 Belmont Ave 44505 330-759-0205
St. Elizabeth Hospital Post-Sec.
PO Box 1790 44501 330-746-7211
Ursuline HS 400/9-12
750 Wick Ave 44505 330-744-4563
Matt Sammartino, prin. Fax 744-3358
Valley Christian S 500/PK-12
4401 Southern Blvd 44512 330-788-8088
Michael Pecchia, pres. Fax 788-2875
Western Reserve Care System Post-Sec.
345 Oak Hill Ave 44502 330-747-0777
Youngstown State University Post-Sec.
1 University Plz 44555 330-941-3000

Zanesville, Muskingum, Pop. 24,279
Maysville Local SD 2,100/K-12
3715 Panther Dr 43701 740-453-0754
Ruth Zitnik, supt. Fax 455-4081
www.maysville.k12.oh.us
Maysville HS 600/9-12
3725 Panther Dr 43701 740-454-7999
Jason Bunting, prin. Fax 452-9921
Maysville MS 500/6-8
3725 Panther Dr 43701 740-454-7982
Erik Winland, prin. Fax 452-9921

Mid-East Career & Technology Centers
400 Richards Rd 43701 740-454-0105
Richard Hall, supt. Fax 454-0731
www.mideastctc.org
Mid-East Career & Tech Ctr - Zanesville Vo/Tech
400 Richards Rd 43701 740-454-0101
Scott Sabino, dir. Fax 454-0723
Adult Center for Education Adult
400 Richards Rd 43701 740-455-3111
Mike Hawley, dir. Fax 455-2043
Other Schools – See Senecaville

West Muskingum Local SD 1,300/K-12
4880 West Pike 43701 740-455-4052
Dr. William Harbron Ed.D., supt. Fax 455-4063
www.westm.k12.oh.us
West Muskingum HS 400/9-12
150 Kimes Rd 43701 740-455-4050
Ray Peyton, prin. Fax 452-7648
West Muskingum MS 500/5-8
100 Kimes Rd 43701 740-455-4055
Greg Stickel, prin. Fax 455-9717

Zanesville CSD 3,300/PK-12
956 Moxahala Ave 43701 740-454-9751
Doug Baker, supt. Fax 455-4325
www.zanesville.k12.oh.us
Zanesville HS 900/9-12
1701 Blue Ave 43701 740-453-0335
Laura Tompkins, prin. Fax 455-4329
Zanesville MS 500/7-8
1429 Blue Ave 43701 740-453-0711
Jason Taylor, prin. Fax 454-7005

Bishop Rosecrans HS 200/9-12
1040 E Main St 43701 740-452-7504
Jennifer Mallett, prin. Fax 455-5080
Ohio University Post-Sec.
1425 Newark Rd 43701 740-453-0762
Valley Beauty School Post-Sec.
627 Main St 43701 740-452-6821
Zane State College Post-Sec.
1555 Newark Rd 43701 740-454-2501

Zoarville, Tuscarawas
Tuscarawas Valley Local SD 1,400/PK-12
2637 Tusky Valley Rd NE 44656 330-859-2213
Mark Murphy, supt. Fax 859-2706
www.tvtrojans.org/
Tuscarawas Valley HS 400/9-12
2637 Tusky Valley Rd NE 44656 330-859-2421
Jason Phillips, prin. Fax 859-8805
Tuscarawas Valley MS 500/5-8
2633 Tusky Valley Rd NE 44656 330-859-2427
Scott Young, prin. Fax 859-8845

OKLAHOMA

OKLAHOMA DEPARTMENT OF EDUCATION

2500 N Lincoln Blvd Rm 112, Oklahoma City 73105-4503
Telephone 405-521-3301
Fax 405-521-6205
Website sde.ok.gov/sde/

Superintendent of Public Instruction Joy Hofmeister

OKLAHOMA BOARD OF EDUCATION

2500 N Lincoln Blvd Rm 112, Oklahoma City 73105-4503

Chairperson

INTERLOCAL COOPERATIVES (IC)

Choctaw Nation IC
Kenneth Keeling, dir. 580-931-0691
PO Box 602, Durant 74702 Fax 931-0120
choctawinterlocal.org

Five Star IC
Nancy Anderson, dir. 918-225-5600
1405 E Moses St, Cushing 74023 Fax 225-3026
www.fsilc.k12.ok.us

Osage County IC
Jacque Canady, dir. 918-885-2667
207 E Main St, Hominy 74035 Fax 885-6742
www.ocic.k12.ok.us/

Seminole County IC 405-382-6121
, 630 Golf Rd, Seminole 74868 Fax 382-5254

Southeastern Oklahoma IC
Craig Wall, dir. 580-212-0831
103 NE Ave A, Idabel 74745

Tri-County IC
Michelle Taylor, dir. 580-673-2310
100 School St, Fox 73435
Fax 673-2309

PUBLIC, PRIVATE AND CATHOLIC SECONDARY SCHOOLS

Achille, Bryan, Pop. 443

Achille ISD 300/PK-12
PO Box 280 74720 580-283-3775
Richard Beene, supt. Fax 283-3787
achilleisd.org

Achille HS 100/9-12
PO Box 280 74720 580-283-3775
Dana Beene, prin. Fax 283-3524

Ada, Pontotoc, Pop. 15,623

Ada ISD 2,700/PK-12
324 W 20th St 74820 580-310-7200
Pat Harrison, supt. Fax 310-7206
www.adapss.com/

Ada JHS 600/7-9
223 W 18th St 74820 580-310-7260
Bryan Harwell, prin. Fax 310-7261

Ada SHS 500/10-12
1400 Stadium Dr 74820 580-310-7220
Jeff Maloy, prin. Fax 310-7221

Byng ISD 1,800/PK-12
500 S New Bethel Blvd 74820 580-436-3020
Todd Crabtree, supt. Fax 436-3052
www.byngschools.com

Byng JHS 300/7-9
500 S New Bethel Blvd 74820 580-310-6743
Paul Scroggins, prin. Fax 310-6741

Byng SHS 300/10-12
500 S New Bethel Blvd 74820 580-310-6732
Bubba Tamaz, prin. Fax 310-6730

Latta ISD 800/PK-12
13925 County Road 1560 74820 580-332-2092
Cliff Johnson, supt. Fax 332-3116
www.latta.k12.ok.us/

Latta HS 200/9-12
13925 County Road 1560 74820 580-332-3300
Stan Cochran, prin.

Latta MS 200/5-8
13925 County Road 1560 74820 580-332-8180
Terry Painter, prin.

OK Dept. of Voc. & Tech. Education
Supt. — None
Dr. Marcie Mack, dir.

Pontotoc Technology Center Vo/Tech
601 W 33rd St 74820 580-310-2200
David Lassiter, supt. Fax 436-0236

Vanoss ISD 400/PK-12
4665 County Road 1555 74820 580-759-2251
Marjana Tharp, supt. Fax 759-8916
www.vanoss.k12.ok.us

Vanoss HS 100/9-12
4665 County Road 1555 74820 580-759-2503
Charles Hill, prin. Fax 759-3080

Vanoss MS 100/6-8
4665 County Road 1555 74820 580-759-2623
Beth Walker, prin. Fax 759-3080

East Central University Post-Sec.
1100 E 14th St 74820 580-332-8000

Valley View Regional Hospital Post-Sec.
430 N Monte Vista St 74820 580-332-2323

Adair, Mayes, Pop. 736

Adair ISD 1,000/PK-12
PO Box 197 74330 918-785-2424
Tom Linihan, supt. Fax 785-2491
adair.k12.ok.us/APS/

Adair HS 300/9-12
PO Box 197 74330 918-785-2424
Mark Lippe, prin. Fax 785-2491

Adair MS 200/6-8
PO Box 197 74330 918-785-2425
Brad Rogers, prin. Fax 785-2491

Afton, Ottawa, Pop. 950

Afton ISD 500/PK-12
PO Box 100 74331 918-257-4470
Randy Gardner, supt. Fax 257-4846
www.aftonschools.net

Afton HS 200/9-12
PO Box 100 74331 918-257-8305
Owen Bowen, prin. Fax 257-5406

OK Dept. of Voc. & Tech. Education
Supt. — None
Dr. Marcie Mack, dir.

Northeast Tech Center Afton Campus Vo/Tech
PO Box 219 74331 918-257-8324
Paul Hocutt, dir. Fax 257-4342

Agra, Lincoln, Pop. 313

Agra ISD 400/PK-12
PO Box 279 74824 918-375-2261
Brent Meeks, supt. Fax 375-2263
www.agra.k12.ok.us/

Agra HS 100/9-12
PO Box 279 74824 918-375-2261
Tony Holt, prin. Fax 375-2260

Alex, Grady, Pop. 528

Alex ISD 300/PK-12
PO Box 188 73002 405-785-2605
Dr. Jason James, supt. Fax 785-2914
www.alex.k12.ok.us

Alex HS 100/9-12
PO Box 188 73002 405-785-2264
Doug Tolson, prin. Fax 785-9976

Aline, Alfalfa, Pop. 202

Aline-Cleo ISD 200/PK-12
PO Box 49 73716 580-463-2255
Barry Nault, supt. Fax 463-2256
www.alinecleo.k12.ok.us

Aline-Cleo Springs HS 50/9-12
PO Box 49 73716 580-463-2255
Barry Nault, prin. Fax 463-2256

Allen, Pontotoc, Pop. 878

Allen ISD 500/PK-12
PO Box 430 74825 580-857-2417
Dr. Bill Caruthers, supt. Fax 857-2636
www.allen.k12.ok.us

Allen HS 100/9-12
PO Box 430 74825 580-857-2416
Tony Wellington, prin. Fax 857-2636

Altus, Jackson, Pop. 19,118

Altus ISD 2,700/PK-12
PO Box 558 73522 580-481-2100
Roger Hill, supt. Fax 481-2129
www.altusps.com

Altus JHS 500/7-8
PO Box 558 73522 580-481-2173
Roe Worbes, prin. Fax 481-2547

Altus SHS 900/9-12
PO Box 558 73522 580-481-2167
Mark Haught, prin. Fax 481-2545

Navajo ISD 300/PK-12
15695 S County Road 210 73521 580-482-7742
Vicki Nance, supt. Fax 482-7749
www.navajo.k12.ok.us

Navajo JSHS 100/7-12
15695 S County Road 210 73521 580-482-7742
Floyd Roach, prin. Fax 482-7749

OK Dept. of Voc. & Tech. Education
Supt. — None
Dr. Marcie Mack, dir.

Southwest Technology Center Vo/Tech
711 W Tamarack Rd 73521 580-477-2250
Dale Latham, supt. Fax 477-0138

Western Oklahoma State College Post-Sec.
2801 N Main St 73521 580-477-2000

Alva, Woods, Pop. 4,829

Alva ISD 900/PK-12
418 Flynn St 73717 580-327-4823
J. Stephen Parkhurst, supt. Fax 327-2965
www.alvaschools.com

Alva HS 300/9-12
501 14th St 73717 580-327-3682
Les Potter, prin. Fax 327-4240

Alva MS 200/6-8
800 Flynn St 73717 580-327-0608
Ron Sunderland, prin. Fax 327-4255

OK Dept. of Voc. & Tech. Education
Supt. — None
Dr. Marcie Mack, dir.

Northwest Technology Center Vo/Tech
1801 11th St 73717 580-327-0344
Daren Slater, dir. Fax 327-5467

Northwestern Oklahoma State University Post-Sec.
709 Oklahoma Blvd 73717 580-327-1700

Amber, Grady, Pop. 416

Amber-Pocasset ISD 500/PK-12
PO Box 38 73004 405-224-5768
Chad Hance, supt. Fax 224-5115
www.amposchools.org

Amber-Pocasset HS 100/10-12
PO Box 38 73004 405-224-4017
Steve Spears, prin. Fax 224-5115

Amber-Pocasset JHS 100/7-9
PO Box 38 73004 405-224-4017
Steve Spears, prin. Fax 224-5115

Anadarko, Caddo, Pop. 6,230

Anadarko ISD 1,900/PK-12
1400 S Mission St 73005 405-247-6605
Cindy Hackney, supt. Fax 247-6819
www.apswarriors.com

Anadarko HS 500/9-12
1400 Warrior Dr 73005 405-247-2486
Tony Summers, prin. Fax 247-7066

Anadarko MS 400/6-8
900 W College St 73005 405-247-6671
LaVonda Bost, prin. Fax 247-3666

Antlers, Pushmataha, Pop. 2,335

Antlers ISD 900/K-12
219 NE A St 74523 580-298-5504
Cary Ammons, supt. Fax 298-4006
www.antlers.k12.ok.us

Antlers HS 300/9-12
219 NE A St 74523 580-298-2141
Bryan McNutt, prin. Fax 298-4019

Obuch MS 200/6-8
219 NE A St 74523 580-298-3308
William Neyman, prin. Fax 298-4012

OK Dept. of Voc. & Tech. Education
Supt. — None
Dr. Marcie Mack, dir.
Kiamichi Technology Center Vo/Tech
PO Box 70 74523 580-298-6354
Scott Garrett, dir. Fax 298-6412

Apache, Caddo, Pop. 1,370
Boone-Apache ISD 600/PK-12
PO Box 354 73006 580-588-3369
Don Schneberger, supt. Fax 588-3400
www.apache.k12.ok.us
Apache HS 200/9-12
PO Box 354 73006 580-588-3358
Todd Vail, prin. Fax 588-2079
Apache MS 100/6-8
PO Box 354 73006 580-588-2122
Steven Base, prin. Fax 588-3026

Arapaho, Custer, Pop. 774
Arapaho-Butler ISD 400/PK-12
PO Box 160 73620 580-323-3262
James Edelen, supt. Fax 323-5886
www.arapaho.k12.ok.us
Arapaho-Butler HS 100/9-12
PO Box 160 73620 580-323-3261
James Edelen, prin. Fax 323-5886

Ardmore, Carter, Pop. 22,734
Ardmore ISD 3,200/PK-12
PO Box 1709 73402 580-223-2483
Kim Holland, supt. Fax 226-2472
www.ardmoreschools.org
Ardmore HS 800/9-12
PO Box 1709 73402 580-226-7680
Jake Falvey, prin. Fax 221-3012
Ardmore MS 600/6-8
PO Box 1709 73402 580-223-2475
Cindy Huddleston, prin. Fax 221-3060

Dickson ISD 1,300/PK-12
4762 State Highway 199 73401 580-223-9557
Larry Case, supt. Fax 490-9152
www.dickson.k12.ok.us
Dickson HS 400/9-12
4762 State Highway 199 73401 580-226-0633
Rex Trent, prin. Fax 226-3974
Dickson MS 300/6-8
4762 State Highway 199 73401 580-223-2700
Matt Krimmer, prin. Fax 223-3972

OK Dept. of Voc. & Tech. Education
Supt. — None
Dr. Marcie Mack, dir.
Southern Oklahoma Technology Center Vo/Tech
2610 Sam Noble Pkwy 73401 580-223-2070
Dr. David Powell, supt. Fax 223-2120

Plainview ISD 1,500/PK-12
1140 S Plainview Rd 73401 580-223-6319
Karl Stricker, supt. Fax 490-3190
www.plainview.k12.ok.us/
Plainview HS 400/9-12
1140 S Plainview Rd 73401 580-223-5877
Brian Nickel, prin. Fax 490-3191
Plainview MS 300/6-8
1140 S Plainview Rd 73401 580-223-6502
Tim Parham, prin. Fax 490-3192

Ardmore Adventist Academy 50/1-10
154 Beaver Academy Rd 73401 580-223-4948
Oklahoma State Horseshoeing School Post-Sec.
4802 Dogwood Rd 73401 580-223-0064

Arkoma, LeFlore, Pop. 1,878
Arkoma ISD 400/PK-12
PO Box 349 74901 918-875-3351
John Turner Ed.D., supt. Fax 875-3780
sites.google.com/site/arkomak12/
Arkoma JSHS 100/7-12
PO Box 349 74901 918-875-3353
Cyal Walden, prin. Fax 875-3780

Arnett, Ellis, Pop. 514
Arnett ISD 200/PK-12
PO Box 317 73832 580-885-7811
Tracy Kincannon, supt. Fax 885-7922
www.arnett.k12.ok.us
Arnett HS 100/7-12
PO Box 317 73832 580-885-7285
Bob Dobrinski, prin. Fax 885-7922

Asher, Pottawatomie, Pop. 357
Asher ISD 300/PK-12
PO Box 168 74826 405-784-2332
Terry Grissom, supt. Fax 784-2306
www.asher.k12.ok.us
Asher HS 100/9-12
PO Box 168 74826 405-784-2331
Jeremy Frye, prin. Fax 784-2306

Atoka, Atoka, Pop. 2,819
Atoka ISD 800/PK-12
801 S Greathouse Dr 74525 580-889-6611
Jay Mcadams, supt. Fax 889-2513
atoka.org
Atoka HS 300/9-12
800 S Greathouse Dr 74525 580-889-3361
Ernest Michaelis, prin. Fax 889-6453
McCall MS 200/6-8
1003 W 11th St 74525 580-889-5640
Wesley Burnett, prin. Fax 889-4064

OK Dept. of Voc. & Tech. Education
Supt. — None
Dr. Marcie Mack, dir.
Kiamichi Technology Center Vo/Tech
PO Box 240 74525 580-889-7321
Elaine Gee, dir. Fax 889-5642

Tushka ISD 400/PK-12
261 W Boggy Depot Rd 74525 580-889-7355
Matthew Simpson, supt. Fax 889-6144
www.tushka.k12.ok.us
Tushka HS 200/9-12
261 W Boggy Depot Rd 74525 580-889-7355
Charles Graham, prin. Fax 889-6144

Balko, Beaver
Balko ISD, RR 1 Box 37 73931 200/PK-12
Larry Mills, supt. 580-646-3385
www.balko.k12.ok.us/
Balko HS, RR 1 Box 37 73931 50/9-12
Tammie Heathman, prin. 580-646-3385

Barnsdall, Osage, Pop. 1,134
Barnsdall ISD 400/PK-12
PO Box 629 74002 918-847-2271
Rick Loggins, supt. Fax 847-3029
www.barnsdallschools.org
Barnsdall HS, PO Box 629 74002 100/9-12
Sayra Bryant, prin. 918-847-2721
Barnsdall JHS, PO Box 629 74002 100/7-8
Sayra Bryant, prin. 918-847-2721

Bartlesville, Washington, Pop. 33,922
Bartlesville ISD 5,100/PK-12
1100 SW Jennings Ave 74003 918-336-8600
Dr. Gary Quinn, supt. Fax 337-3643
www.bps-ok.org
Bartlesville HS 800/9-12
1700 Hillcrest Dr 74003 918-336-3311
LaDonna Chancellor, prin. Fax 337-6226
Central MS 700/6-8
408 E 9th St 74003 918-336-9302
Ryan Huff, prin. Fax 337-6270
Madison MS 600/6-8
5900 Baylor Dr 74006 918-333-4444
Joseph Eidson, prin. Fax 335-6377

OK Dept. of Voc. & Tech. Education
Supt. — None
Dr. Marcie Mack, dir.
Tri-County Technology Center Vo/Tech
6101 Nowata Rd 74006 918-333-2422
Lindel Fields, supt. Fax 331-3274

Oklahoma Wesleyan University Post-Sec.
2201 Silver Lake Rd 74006 918-333-6151
Wesleyan Christian S 300/PK-12
1780 Silver Lake Rd 74006 918-333-8631
Rocky Clark, admin. Fax 333-8632

Battiest, McCurtain
Battiest ISD 300/PK-12
PO Box 199 74722 580-241-7810
Stace Ebert, supt. Fax 241-7847
www.battiest.k12.ok.us
Battiest HS 100/9-12
PO Box 199 74722 580-241-5550
Don Mullenix, prin. Fax 241-7847

Beaver, Beaver, Pop. 1,494
Beaver ISD 400/PK-12
PO Box 580 73932 580-625-3444
Scott Kinsey, supt. Fax 625-3690
www.beaver.k12.ok.us
Beaver HS 100/9-12
PO Box 580 73932 580-625-3444
Michael McVay, prin. Fax 625-3690

Beggs, Okmulgee, Pop. 1,177
Beggs ISD 1,000/PK-12
1201 W 9th St 74421 918-267-3628
Rondald Martin, supt. Fax 267-3635
www.beggs.k12.ok.us
Beggs HS 300/9-12
1201 W 9th St 74421 918-267-3625
Kristi Smith, prin. Fax 267-3624
Beggs MS 200/5-8
1201 W 9th St 74421 918-267-4916
Kenny Hurst, prin. Fax 267-4779

Bennington, Bryan, Pop. 304
Bennington ISD 300/PK-12
729 N Perry St 74723 580-847-2310
Pamela Reynolds, supt. Fax 847-2787
www.benningtonisd.org
Bennington HS 100/9-12
729 N Perry St 74723 580-847-2310
Jon Shepard, prin. Fax 847-2787

Bethany, Oklahoma, Pop. 18,252
Bethany ISD 1,700/PK-12
6721 NW 42nd St 73008 405-789-3801
Dr. Kent Shellenberger, supt. Fax 499-4606
www.bethanyschools.com/
Bethany HS 500/9-12
6721 NW 42nd St 73008 405-789-6370
Matthew Flinton, prin. Fax 499-4634
Bethany MS 400/6-8
6721 NW 42nd St 73008 405-787-3240
Trey Keoppel, prin. Fax 499-4606

Putnam City ISD
Supt. — See Oklahoma City
Western Oaks MS 700/6-8
7200 NW 23rd St 73008 405-789-4434
Meggan Wilson, prin. Fax 491-7616

Southern Nazarene University Post-Sec.
6729 NW 39th Expy 73008 405-789-6400
Southwestern Christian University Post-Sec.
PO Box 340 73008 405-789-7661

Billings, Noble, Pop. 499
Billings ISD 100/PK-12
PO Box 39 74630 580-725-3271
Rustin Clark, supt. Fax 725-3278
www.billings.k12.ok.us
Billings HS 50/9-12
PO Box 39 74630 580-725-3271
Rustin Clark, prin. Fax 725-3278

Binger, Caddo, Pop. 635
Binger-Oney ISD 400/PK-12
323 S Apache 73009 405-656-2304
Lisa King, supt. Fax 656-2267
www.binger-oney.k12.ok.us/
Binger-Oney HS 100/9-12
323 S Apache 73009 405-656-2304
Larry Milligan, prin. Fax 656-2267

Bixby, Tulsa, Pop. 19,948
Bixby ISD 5,200/PK-12
109 N Armstrong St 74008 918-366-2200
Dr. Kyle Wood, supt. Fax 366-4241
www.bixbyps.org
Bixby HS 1,100/10-12
109 N Armstrong St 74008 918-366-2234
Terry Adams, prin. Fax 366-2350
Bixby MS 800/7-8
109 N Armstrong St 74008 918-366-2201
Mike Lemon, prin. Fax 366-2337
9th Grade Center 9-9
109 N Armstrong St 74008 918-366-2200
Kate Creekmore, prin. Fax 366-4241

Blackwell, Kay, Pop. 6,745
Blackwell ISD 1,200/PK-12
201 E Blackwell Ave 74631 580-363-2570
Richard Riggs, supt. Fax 363-5513
www.blackwell.k12.ok.us
Blackwell HS 400/9-12
303 E Coolidge Ave 74631 580-363-3553
Jaylene Soulek, prin. Fax 363-2133
Blackwell MS 300/6-8
1041 S 1st St 74631 580-363-2100
Preston Kysar, prin. Fax 363-7010

Blair, Jackson, Pop. 786
Blair ISD 300/PK-12
PO Box 428 73526 580-563-2632
Jimmy Smith, supt. Fax 563-9166
www.blairschool.org
Blair HS 100/9-12
PO Box 428 73526 580-563-2486
Jimmy Smith, prin. Fax 563-9166

Blanchard, McClain, Pop. 7,360
Blanchard ISD 1,900/PK-12
211 N Tyler Ave 73010 405-485-3391
Dr. Jim Beckham, supt. Fax 485-2985
www.blanchard.k12.ok.us/
Blanchard HS 500/9-12
211 N Tyler Ave 73010 405-485-3392
Greg Jackson, prin. Fax 485-9549
Blanchard MS 400/6-8
211 N Tyler Ave 73010 405-485-3393
Larry McVay, prin. Fax 485-9103

Bridge Creek ISD 1,500/PK-12
2209 E Sooner Rd 73010 405-387-4880
David Morrow, supt. Fax 387-4882
www.bridgecreek.k12.ok.us/
Bridge Creek HS 400/9-12
2209 E Sooner Rd 73010 405-387-3981
Joe Billington, prin. Fax 387-2554
Bridge Creek MS 300/6-8
2209 E Sooner Rd 73010 405-387-9681
Kenneth Ward, prin. Fax 387-2552

Bluejacket, Craig, Pop. 318
Bluejacket ISD 200/PK-12
PO Box 29 74333 918-784-2365
Shellie Baker, supt. Fax 784-2130
www.bluejacket.k12.ok.us
Bluejacket HS 100/9-12
PO Box 29 74333 918-784-2133
Shellie Baker, prin. Fax 784-2130
Bluejacket MS, PO Box 29 74333 100/6-8
Tracy Mendez, prin. 918-784-2133

Boise City, Cimarron, Pop. 1,253
Boise City ISD 300/PK-12
PO Box 1116 73933 580-544-3110
Dr. Ira Harris Ph.D., supt. Fax 544-2972
www.boisecity.k12.ok.us/
Boise City HS, PO Box 1115 73933 100/9-12
Garrett Harland, prin. 580-544-3111
Boise City JHS 50/7-8
PO Box 1115 73933 580-544-3161
John Farmer, admin. Fax 544-2146

Bokchito, Bryan, Pop. 591
Rock Creek ISD 500/PK-12
200 E Steakley St 74726 580-295-3137
Preston Burns, supt. Fax 295-3762
www.rockcreekisd.net
Rock Creek HS 100/9-12
200 E Steakley St 74726 580-295-3761
John Cartwright, prin. Fax 295-3854

Bokoshe, LeFlore, Pop. 466
Bokoshe ISD 200/PK-12
PO Box 158 74930 918-969-2341
Dennis Shoup, supt. Fax 969-2117
www.bokosheschools.org
Bokoshe HS 50/10-12
PO Box 158 74930 918-969-2341
Dennis Shoup, prin. Fax 969-2117
Bokoshe JHS 50/7-9
PO Box 158 74930 918-969-2341
Dennis Shoup, prin. Fax 969-2117

Boswell, Choctaw, Pop. 659
Boswell ISD 400/PK-12
PO Box 839 74727 580-566-2558
Keith Edge, supt. Fax 566-2265
www.boswellschools.org/
Boswell HS 100/9-12
PO Box 839 74727 580-566-2735
Rick Grimes, prin. Fax 566-2265
Boswell MS 50/7-8
PO Box 839 74727 580-566-2735
Rick Grimes, prin. Fax 566-2265

Bowlegs, Seminole, Pop. 377
Bowlegs ISD 300/PK-12
PO Box 88 74830 405-398-4172
Tommy Eaton, supt. Fax 398-4175
www.bowlegs.k12.ok.us
Bowlegs HS 100/9-12
PO Box 88 74830 405-398-4321
Sammye Davis, prin. Fax 398-4169

Braggs, Muskogee, Pop. 242
Braggs ISD 200/PK-12
PO Box 59 74423 918-487-5265
Michael Broyles, supt. Fax 487-7171
www.braggs.k12.ok.us
Braggs HS 100/9-12
PO Box 59 74423 918-487-5265
Michael Broyles, prin. Fax 487-7171

Bristow, Creek, Pop. 3,811
Bristow ISD 1,700/PK-12
420 N Main St 74010 918-367-5555
Curtis Shelton, supt. Fax 367-5848
www.bristow.k12.ok.us
Bristow HS 500/9-12
420 N Main St 74010 918-367-2241
Brandon Poteet, prin. Fax 367-5849
Bristow MS 400/6-8
420 N Main St 74010 918-367-3551
Brian Burden, prin. Fax 367-1362

Broken Arrow, Tulsa, Pop. 94,005
Broken Arrow ISD 15,800/PK-12
701 S Main St 74012 918-259-5700
Jarod Mendenhall Ed.D., supt. Fax 258-0399
www.baschools.org/
Broken Arrow Academy Alt
412 S 9th St 74011 918-259-4600
Jack Pugh, prin. Fax 258-7531
Broken Arrow Freshman Academy 600/9-9
301 W New Orleans St 74011 918-259-4330
Margaret Coates, prin. Fax 451-1964
Broken Arrow SHS 2,300/10-12
1901 E Albany St 74012 918-259-4310
Elizabeth Burns, prin. Fax 355-3676
Centennial MS 1,000/6-8
225 E Omaha St 74012 918-259-4340
Kenneth Kinzer, prin. Fax 251-8347
Childers MS 700/6-8
301 E Tucson St 74011 918-259-4350
Stacy Replogle, prin. Fax 451-5465
Oliver MS 800/6-8
3100 W New Orleans St 74011 918-259-4590
Jill Whitaker, prin. Fax 250-8185
Oneta Ridge MS 700/6-8
6800 E Quincy Pl 74014 918-259-4360
Mickey Replogle, prin. Fax 251-8685
Sequoyah MS 500/6-8
2701 S Elm Pl 74012 918-259-4370
Beth Gilbert, prin. Fax 451-2167

OK Dept. of Voc. & Tech. Education
Supt. — None
Dr. Marcie Mack, dir.
Tulsa Tech Center Broken Arrow Campus Vo/Tech
4000 W Florence St 74011 918-828-3000
Brad Wayman, dir. Fax 828-3009

Union ISD
Supt. — See Tulsa
Union 9th Grade Center 1,200/9-9
7616 S Garnett Rd 74012 918-357-4324
John Federline, prin. Fax 357-7696
Union Eighth Grade Center 1,100/8-8
6501 S Garnett Rd 74012 918-357-4325
Michelle Cundy, prin. Fax 357-7899

Broken Arrow Beauty College Post-Sec.
400 S Elm Pl 74012 918-251-9660
Immanuel Lutheran Christian Academy 100/PK-12
400 N Aspen Ave 74012 918-251-5422
Stephen Zehnder, hdmstr. Fax 251-8365
Summit Christian Academy 500/K-12
200 E Broadway St 74012 918-251-1997
Dan Giddens, supt. Fax 251-2831

Broken Bow, McCurtain, Pop. 3,865
Broken Bow ISD 1,700/PK-12
108 W 5th St 74728 580-584-3306
Carla Ellisor, supt. Fax 584-9482
www.bbisd.org
Broken Bow HS 600/9-12
108 W 5th St 74728 580-584-3365
Luke Hanks, prin. Fax 584-2064
Rector Johnson MS 300/6-8
108 W 5th St 74728 580-584-9603
Belinda Highful, prin. Fax 584-2549

Buffalo, Harper, Pop. 1,288
Buffalo ISD 100/K-12
PO Box 130 73834 580-735-2448
Dale Spradlin, supt. Fax 735-2619
www.buffalo.k12.ok.us
Buffalo S 100/K-12
PO Box 130 73834 580-735-2448
Kenneth Horn, prin. Fax 735-2619

Bunch, Adair
Cave Springs ISD 200/PK-12
PO Box 200 74931 918-775-2364
Dr. Geary Brown Ed.D., supt. Fax 776-2052
www.cavesprings.k12.ok.us
Cave Springs HS 100/9-12
PO Box 200 74931 918-775-2364
Dr. Geary Brown Ed.D., prin. Fax 776-2052
Cave Springs MS 50/5-8
PO Box 200 74931 918-775-2364
Dr. Geary Brown Ed.D., prin. Fax 776-2052

Burlington, Alfalfa, Pop. 145
Burlington ISD 100/PK-12
PO Box 17 73722 580-431-2501
Glen Elliott, supt. Fax 431-2237
www.burlingtonschool.com/
Burlington HS 50/9-12
PO Box 17 73722 580-431-2222
Shane Feely, prin. Fax 431-2237

Burneyville, Love
Turner ISD 300/PK-12
PO Box 159 73430 580-276-1307
Burl Solie, supt. Fax 276-2006
www.turnerisd.org
Turner HS 100/9-12
PO Box 159 73430 580-276-3873
Bill Godwin, prin. Fax 276-2493

Burns Flat, Washita, Pop. 1,998
Burns Flat-Dill City ISD 700/PK-12
PO Box 129 73624 580-562-4844
Ron Hughes, supt. Fax 562-4847
www.bfdc.k12.ok.us
Burns Flat-Dill City HS 100/9-12
PO Box 129 73624 580-562-4846
Cliff McCown, prin.

OK Dept. of Voc. & Tech. Education
Supt. — None
Dr. Marcie Mack, dir.
Western Technology Center Vo/Tech
PO Box 1469 73624 580-562-3181
Hoyt Lewis, supt. Fax 562-4476

Cache, Comanche, Pop. 2,626
Cache ISD 1,700/PK-12
102 E H Ave 73527 580-429-3266
Chad Hance, supt. Fax 429-3271
www.cacheps.org
Cache HS, 102 E H Ave 73527 500/9-12
Cindy White, prin. 580-429-3214
Cache MS, 102 E H Ave 73527 200/7-8
Mitch Ange, prin. 580-429-8489

Caddo, Bryan, Pop. 914
Caddo ISD 500/PK-12
PO Box 128 74729 580-367-2208
Lee Northcutt, supt. Fax 367-2837
www.caddoisd.org
Caddo HS 100/9-12
PO Box 128 74729 580-367-2208
J.T. Busby, prin. Fax 367-2837

Calera, Bryan, Pop. 1,972
Calera ISD 700/PK-12
PO Box 386 74730 580-434-5700
Gerald Parks, supt. Fax 434-5800
www.caleraisd.k12.ok.us
Calera HS 200/9-12
PO Box 386 74730 580-434-5158
Kevin Robinson, prin. Fax 434-7842

Calumet, Canadian, Pop. 484
Calumet ISD 300/PK-12
PO Box 10 73014 405-893-2222
Keith Weldon, supt. Fax 893-8019
www.chs.k12.ok.us
Calumet HS 100/9-12
PO Box 10 73014 405-893-2222
Eric Carr, dean Fax 893-8019
Calumet JHS 50/7-8
PO Box 10 73014 405-893-2222
Eric Carr, dean Fax 893-8019

Calvin, Hughes, Pop. 277
Calvin ISD 200/PK-12
PO Box 127 74531 405-645-2411
Christopher Karch, supt. Fax 645-2384
www.calvin.k12.ok.us
Calvin HS 100/9-12
PO Box 127 74531 405-645-2411
Larry Marlow, prin. Fax 645-2384

Cameron, LeFlore, Pop. 274
Cameron ISD 300/PK-12
PO Box 190 74932 918-654-3412
Jim Caughern, supt. Fax 654-7387
www.cameronps.org
Cameron HS 100/9-12
PO Box 190 74932 918-654-3224
Curtis Curry, prin. Fax 654-3826

Canadian, Pittsburg, Pop. 206
Canadian ISD 400/PK-12
PO Box 168 74425 918-339-2705
Rodney Karch, supt. Fax 339-2393
www.canadian.k12.ok.us
Canadian HS 100/9-12
PO Box 168 74425 918-339-2705
David Smith, prin. Fax 339-2393

Caney, Atoka, Pop. 176
Caney ISD 300/PK-12
PO Box 60 74533 580-889-1996
Lori Boehme, supt. Fax 889-5033
www.caneyisd.org
Caney HS 100/9-12
PO Box 60 74533 580-889-6607
Matt Brister, prin. Fax 889-7922

Canton, Blaine, Pop. 594
Canton ISD 400/PK-12
PO Box 639 73724 580-886-3516
Carl Baker, supt. Fax 886-3501
www.canton.k12.ok.us
Canton HS 100/9-12
PO Box 639 73724 580-886-2256
Adam McPhail, prin. Fax 886-2306

Canute, Washita, Pop. 537
Canute ISD 400/PK-12
PO Box 490 73626 580-472-3295
Larry Parrish, supt. Fax 472-3187
www.canutepublicschool.com
Canute HS 100/9-12
PO Box 490 73626 580-472-3295
Kevin Merz, prin. Fax 472-3187

Carnegie, Caddo, Pop. 1,645
Carnegie ISD 600/PK-12
330 W Wildcat Dr 73015 580-654-1470
Mark Batt, supt. Fax 654-1644
www.carnegie.k12.ok.us
Carnegie HS 100/9-12
330 W Wildcat Dr 73015 580-654-1266
Jerry Hulme, prin. Fax 654-2772
Carnegie MS 100/6-8
330 W Wildcat Dr 73015 580-654-1766
Jane Nix, prin. Fax 654-2281

Carney, Lincoln, Pop. 589
Carney ISD 200/PK-12
PO Box 240 74832 405-865-2344
Alicia O'Donnell, supt. Fax 865-2345
www.carney.k12.ok.us/
Carney HS, PO Box 240 74832 100/9-12
Alicia O'Donnell, prin. 405-865-2344

Cashion, Logan, Pop. 779
Cashion ISD 400/PK-12
101 N Euclid Ave 73016 405-433-2741
Sammy Jackson, supt. Fax 433-2646
www.cashionps.org
Cashion MSHS 200/6-12
101 N Euclid Ave 73016 405-433-2575
Ryan Schenk, prin. Fax 433-2646

Catoosa, Rogers, Pop. 6,601
Catoosa SD 2,100/PK-12
2000 S Cherokee St 74015 918-266-8603
Rick Kibbe, supt. Fax 266-8647
www.catoosaps.net/
Catoosa HS 600/9-12
2000 S Cherokee St 74015 918-266-8619
Darren Peaster, prin. Fax 266-1486
Wells MS 500/6-8
2000 S Cherokee St 74015 918-266-8623
Della Parrish, prin. Fax 266-1282

Cement, Caddo, Pop. 491
Cement ISD 200/PK-12
PO Box 60 73017 405-489-3216
Daniel Pittman, supt. Fax 489-3219
www.cement.k12.ok.us
Cement HS 100/9-12
PO Box 60 73017 405-489-3216
Steve Pelzer, prin. Fax 489-3219

Chandler, Lincoln, Pop. 2,922
Chandler ISD 1,200/PK-12
901 S CHS 74834 405-258-1450
Wayland Kimble, supt. Fax 258-2657
www.chandler.k12.ok.us
Chandler HS 300/9-12
901 S CHS 74834 405-258-1269
Randy Hedge, prin. Fax 258-0071
Chandler JHS 200/7-8
901 S CHS 74834 405-258-0183
Kent Barton, prin. Fax 258-1850

Chattanooga, Comanche, Pop. 452
Chattanooga ISD 200/PK-12
PO Box 129 73528 580-597-3347
Jerry Brown, supt. Fax 597-3344
www.chatty.k12.ok.us/
Chattanooga HS 100/9-12
PO Box 129 73528 580-597-3347
James Higdon, prin. Fax 597-3344

Checotah, McIntosh, Pop. 3,060
Checotah ISD 1,600/PK-12
PO Box 289 74426 918-473-5610
Janet Blocker, supt. Fax 473-1020
www.checotah.k12.ok.us/
Checotah HS 500/9-12
PO Box 289 74426 918-473-9100
Brian Terry, prin. Fax 473-7174
Checotah MS 300/5-8
PO Box 289 74426 918-473-2239
Jason Donathan, prin. Fax 473-2532

Chelsea, Rogers, Pop. 1,729
Chelsea ISD 900/PK-12
401 Redbud Ln 74016 918-789-2528
Rich McSpadden, supt. Fax 789-3271
Chelsea HS, 401 Redbud Ln 74016 300/9-12
Howard Hill, prin. 918-789-2533
Chelsea MS, 401 Redbud Ln 74016 200/6-8
Howard Hill, prin. 918-789-2521

Cherokee, Alfalfa, Pop. 1,474
Cherokee ISD 300/PK-12
PO Box 325 73728 580-596-3391
Donna Anderson, supt. Fax 596-2319
www.cherokee.k12.ok.us
Cherokee JSHS 100/7-12
PO Box 325 73728 580-596-3391
Jeremy Hickman, prin. Fax 596-2319

Cheyenne, Roger Mills, Pop. 783
Cheyenne ISD 400/PK-12
PO Box 650 73628 580-497-3371
Robert Trammell, supt. Fax 497-3373
www.cheyenne.k12.ok.us
Cheyenne HS 100/9-12
PO Box 650 73628 580-497-3371
Whitney Moore, prin. Fax 497-3373

Chickasha, Grady, Pop. 15,287
Chickasha ISD 2,500/PK-12
900 W Choctaw Ave 73018 405-222-6500
David Cash, supt. Fax 222-6590
www.chickasha.k12.ok.us/
Chickasha HS 700/9-12
900 W Choctaw Ave 73018 405-222-6550
Michelle Pontikos, prin. Fax 222-6558
Chickasha MS 300/7-8
900 W Choctaw Ave 73018 405-222-6530
Dan Turner, prin. Fax 222-6594

OK Dept. of Voc. & Tech. Education
Supt. — None
Dr. Marcie Mack, dir.
Canadian Valley Technology Center Vo/Tech
1401 W Michigan Ave 73018 405-224-7220
Tracy Goyne, dir. Fax 222-3839

Academy of Cosmetology Post-Sec.
607 W Grand Ave 73018 405-222-2323
Caraway Christian S K-12
730 County Road 1330 73018 405-224-1998
University of Sciences & Arts of OK Post-Sec.
1727 W Alabama Ave 73018 405-224-3140

Choctaw, Oklahoma, Pop. 10,497
Choctaw-Nicoma Park ISD 5,500/PK-12
12880 NE 10th St 73020 405-769-4859
Dr. Jim McCharen, supt. Fax 769-9821
www.cnpschools.org
Choctaw HS 1,500/9-12
14300 NE 10th St 73020 405-390-8899
David Reid, prin. Fax 390-2275
Choctaw MS 700/6-8
14667 NE 3rd St 73020 405-390-2207
JeanAnn Gaona, prin. Fax 390-4439
Nicoma Park MS 600/6-8
1321 Hickman Ave 73020 405-769-3106
Brent Ingraham, prin. Fax 769-9355

OK Dept. of Voc. & Tech. Education
Supt. — None
Dr. Marcie Mack, dir.
Eastern Oklahoma County Technology Ctr Vo/Tech
4601 N Choctaw Rd 73020 405-390-9591
Dr. Terry Underwood, supt. Fax 390-9598

Life Christian Academy 200/PK-12
3200 N Choctaw Rd 73020 405-390-5081
Rodney Burchett, admin. Fax 390-5086

Chouteau, Mayes, Pop. 1,930
Chouteau-Mazie ISD 800/PK-12
PO Box 969 74337 918-476-8376
Kenny Mason, supt. Fax 476-8538
www.chouteauwildcats.com
Chouteau-Mazie HS 200/9-12
PO Box 969 74337 918-476-8334
Glen Bibelheimer, prin. Fax 476-1216
Chouteau-Mazie MS 100/6-8
PO Box 969 74337 918-476-8336
Michelle Middleton, prin. Fax 476-8306

Claremore, Rogers, Pop. 17,084
Claremore ISD 4,100/PK-12
102 W 10th St 74017 918-923-4200
Mike McClaren, supt. Fax 341-8447
www.claremore.k12.ok.us
Claremore HS 1,300/9-12
201 E Stuart Roosa Dr 74017 918-923-4211
Todd Steidley, prin. Fax 343-6331
Rogers JHS 900/6-8
1915 N Florence Ave 74017 918-923-4205
Brian Young, prin. Fax 343-6332

Justus-Tiawah SD 500/PK-8
14902 E School Rd, 918-341-3626
David Garroutte, supt. Fax 341-4920
www.justustiawah.com
Justus-Tiawah JHS North Campus 100/7-8
14902 E School Rd, 918-341-1252
David Garroutte, prin. Fax 341-4920

OK Dept. of Voc. & Tech. Education
Supt. — None
Dr. Marcie Mack, dir.
Northeast Technology Center - Claremore Vo/Tech
1901 N Highway 88 74017 918-342-8066
Rick Reimer, supt. Fax 342-9066

Sequoyah ISD 1,200/PK-12
16441 S 4180 Rd 74017 918-341-5472
Terry Saul, supt. Fax 341-5764
www.sequoyaheagles.net
Sequoyah HS 200/11-12
16401 S 4180 Rd 74017 918-341-0642
Steve Johnson, prin. Fax 343-8105
Sequoyah MS 300/6-8
16403 S 4180 Rd 74017 918-343-5105
Barry Bulman, prin. Fax 343-8109
Sequoyah Mid HS 100/9-10
16405 S 4180 Rd 74017 918-341-5537
Josh Berg, prin. Fax 343-8102

Verdigris ISD 800/PK-12
26501 S 4110 Rd, 918-266-7227
Michael Payne, supt. Fax 266-3910
vps.k12.ok.us
Verdigris JSHS 300/7-12
26501 S 4110 Rd, 918-266-2336
Greg Kelley, prin. Fax 266-0546

Claremore Beauty College Post-Sec.
200 N Cherokee Ave 74017 918-341-4370
Claremore Christian S 100/PK-12
1055 W Blue Starr Dr 74017 918-341-1765
Ryan Mullins, prin. Fax 341-1011
Rogers State University Post-Sec.
1701 W Will Rogers Blvd 74017 918-343-7777

Clayton, Pushmataha, Pop. 740
Clayton ISD 300/PK-12
329 N 1st St 74536 918-569-4492
Randall Erwin, supt. Fax 569-7757
www.clayton.k12.ok.us/
Clayton HS 100/9-12
304 N 1st 74536 918-569-4156
Bradley McNeil, prin. Fax 569-4680

Cleveland, Pawnee, Pop. 3,054
Cleveland ISD 1,700/PK-12
600 N Gilbert Ave 74020 918-358-2210
Aaron Espolt, supt. Fax 358-3071
www.clevelandtigers.com/
Cleveland HS 500/9-12
323 N Gilbert Ave 74020 918-358-2210
Dr. Alan Baker, prin. Fax 358-2141
Cleveland MS 400/6-8
322 N Gilbert Ave 74020 918-358-2210
Joe Cole, prin. Fax 358-2534

Clinton, Custer, Pop. 8,804
Clinton ISD 2,300/PK-12
PO Box 729 73601 580-323-1800
Kevin Hime, supt. Fax 323-1804
www.clintonokschools.org/
Clinton HS 600/9-12
PO Box 729 73601 580-323-1230
Kenny Stringer, prin. Fax 323-1236
Clinton MS 300/7-8
PO Box 729 73601 580-323-4228
Mark Moring, prin. Fax 323-3896

Coalgate, Coal, Pop. 1,800
Coalgate SD 700/PK-12
2 W Cedar Ave 74538 580-927-2351
Greg Davidson, supt. Fax 927-2694
www.coalgateschools.org
Byrd MS 100/7-8
2 W Cedar Ave 74538 580-927-3560
Phillip Wilkinson, prin. Fax 927-4031
Coalgate HS 200/9-12
2 W Cedar Ave 74538 580-927-2592
Kris Hall, prin. Fax 927-4020

Colbert, Bryan, Pop. 1,037
Colbert ISD 900/PK-12
PO Box 310 74733 580-296-2624
Jarvis Dobbs, supt. Fax 296-2219
www.colbert.k12.ok.us/
Colbert HS 200/9-12
PO Box 310 74733 580-296-2590
Gary Walton, prin. Fax 296-2219
Colbert MS 100/7-8
PO Box 310 74733 580-296-2590
Gary Walton, prin. Fax 296-2219

Colcord, Delaware, Pop. 719
Colcord ISD 600/PK-12
433 S Larmon 74338 918-326-4116
Bud Simmons, supt. Fax 326-4471
www.colcordschools.com
Colcord HS 200/9-12
433 S Larmon 74338 918-326-4107
Sandy Shackelford, prin. Fax 326-0035
Colcord MS 100/7-8
433 S Larmon 74338 918-326-4852
Sandy Shackelford, prin. Fax 326-4468

Coleman, Johnston
Coleman ISD 200/PK-12
PO Box 188 73432 580-937-4418
James Miller, supt. Fax 937-4615
www.coleman.k12.ok.us
Coleman HS 100/9-12
PO Box 188 73432 580-937-4418
James Miller, prin. Fax 937-4866

Collinsville, Tulsa, Pop. 5,212
Collinsville ISD 2,100/PK-12
1092 W Maple St 74021 918-371-2386
Lance West, supt. Fax 371-4285
www.collinsville.k12.ok.us
Collinsville HS 800/9-12
2400 W Broadway St 74021 918-371-3382
Jon Coleman, prin. Fax 371-6904
Collinsville MS 400/7-8
1415 W Center St 74021 918-371-2541
Dale Harp, prin. Fax 371-1302

Comanche, Stephens, Pop. 1,590
Comanche ISD 1,000/K-12
1030 Ash Ave 73529 580-439-2900
Terry Davidson, supt. Fax 439-2907
www.cpsok.org
Comanche HS 300/9-12
1030 Ash Ave 73529 580-439-2933
Steven Dunham, prin. Fax 439-2950
Comanche MS 200/6-8
1030 Ash Ave 73529 580-439-2922
Brent Crow, prin. Fax 439-2979

Commerce, Ottawa, Pop. 2,364
Commerce ISD 900/PK-12
217 Commerce St 74339 918-675-4316
Jimmy R. Haynes, supt. Fax 675-4464
www.commercetigers.net
Commerce HS 200/9-12
420 Doug Furnas Blvd 74339 918-675-4343
Jim Buttram, prin. Fax 675-4682
Commerce MS 200/6-8
500 Commerce St 74339 918-675-4101
Jack Kelley, prin. Fax 675-5353

Copan, Washington, Pop. 683
Copan ISD 900/PK-12
PO Box 429 74022 918-532-4344
Rick Ruckman, supt. Fax 532-4649
www.copan.k12.ok.us/
Copan HS 300/9-12
PO Box 429 74022 918-532-4344
Chris Tanner, prin. Fax 532-4649

Cordell, Washita, Pop. 2,865
Cordell ISD 800/PK-12
606 E 3rd St 73632 580-832-3420
Brad Overton, supt. Fax 832-1090
www.cordell.k12.ok.us
Cordell JHS 200/7-9
606 E 3rd St 73632 580-832-3420
Larry Johnson, prin. Fax 832-1091
Cordell SHS 100/10-12
606 E 3rd St 73632 580-832-3420
Larry Johnson, prin. Fax 832-1091

Corn, Washita, Pop. 497

Corn Bible Academy 100/7-12
PO Box 38 73024 580-343-2262
Curt Cloud, admin. Fax 343-2261

Council Hill, Muskogee, Pop. 140
Midway ISD 300/PK-12
PO Box 127 74428 918-474-3434
Bruce Douglas, supt. Fax 474-3636
www.midway.k12.ok.us
Midway HS 100/9-12
PO Box 127 74428 918-474-3434
Kurt Scullawl, prin. Fax 474-3900

Covington, Garfield, Pop. 512
Covington-Douglas ISD 300/PK-12
400 E Main St 73730 580-864-7481
Darren Sharp, supt. Fax 864-7644
www.c-d.k12.ok.us
Covington-Douglas HS 100/9-12
400 E Main St 73730 580-864-7482
Brian Smith, prin. Fax 864-7644

Coweta, Wagoner, Pop. 9,182
Coweta ISD 3,300/PK-12
PO Box 550 74429 918-486-6506
Jeff Holmes, supt. Fax 486-4167
www.cowetaps.com/
Coweta Intermediate HS 300/9-9
PO Box 550 74429 918-486-6103
Leslie Frazier, prin.
Coweta JHS 500/7-8
PO Box 550 74429 918-486-2127
Scott Kempenich, prin. Fax 486-7307
Coweta SHS 700/10-12
PO Box 550 74429 918-486-4474
Gary Ellis, prin. Fax 486-1062

Coyle, Logan, Pop. 317
Coyle ISD 300/PK-12
PO Box 287 73027 405-466-2242
Josh Sumrall M.Ed., supt. Fax 466-2448
www.coyle.k12.ok.us
Coyle HS 100/9-12
PO Box 287 73027 405-466-2242
Patrick Smith, prin. Fax 466-2448

Crescent, Logan, Pop. 1,340
Crescent ISD 700/PK-12
PO Box 719 73028 405-969-3738
Mickey Hart, supt. Fax 969-2003
www.crescentok.com/
Crescent HS 200/9-12
PO Box 719 73028 405-969-2545
Bart Watkins, prin. Fax 969-2003
Crescent MS 100/6-8
PO Box 719 73028 405-969-2227
Mickey Hart, prin. Fax 969-2003

Cromwell, Seminole, Pop. 270
Butner ISD 200/PK-12
PO Box 157 74837 405-944-5530
Diane Parris, supt. Fax 944-5746
Butner HS 100/9-12
PO Box 157 74837 405-944-5526
Melissa Walden, prin. Fax 944-5746

Crowder, Pittsburg, Pop. 420
Crowder ISD 500/PK-12
PO Box B 74430 918-334-3203
Robert Florenzano, supt. Fax 334-3295
www.crowder.k12.ok.us
Crowder HS, PO Box B 74430 100/9-12
Preston James, prin. 918-334-3204

Cushing, Payne, Pop. 7,369
Cushing ISD 1,600/PK-12
PO Box 1609 74023 918-225-3425
Koln Knight, supt. Fax 225-5256
cushing.k12.ok.us
Cushing HS 500/9-12
1700 E Walnut St 74023 918-225-6622
James Lauerman, prin. Fax 225-0933
Cushing MS 400/5-8
521 S Harmony Rd 74023 918-225-1311
Pat Elder, prin.

Cyril, Caddo, Pop. 1,013
Cyril ISD 300/PK-12
PO Box 449 73029 580-464-2272
Jamie Mitchell, supt. Fax 464-2445
www.cyrilschools.org
Cyril HS 100/7-12
201 W Windle Ave 73029 580-464-2272
Tim Persinger, prin. Fax 464-2445

Dale, Pottawatomie, Pop. 176
Dale ISD 700/PK-12
300 Smith Ave 74851 405-964-5558
Charles Dickinson, supt. Fax 964-5559
www.dale.k12.ok.us
Dale HS 200/9-12
300 Smith Ave 74851 405-964-5555
Ky Wilkins, prin. Fax 964-5539
Dale MS, 300 Smith Ave 74851 200/6-8
Ky Wilkins, prin. 405-964-2799

Davenport, Lincoln, Pop. 781
Davenport ISD 400/PK-12
PO Box 849 74026 918-377-2277
Daniel Acord, supt. Fax 377-2553
www.davenport.k12.ok.us/
Davenport HS 100/9-12
PO Box 849 74026 918-377-2278
Daniel Acord, admin. Fax 377-4001

Davidson, Tillman, Pop. 307
Davidson ISD 100/PK-12
PO Box 338 73530 580-568-2423
Phillip Ratcliff, supt. Fax 568-2219
www.davidson.k12.ok.us/
Davidson HS 50/9-12
PO Box 338 73530 580-568-2261
Phillip Ratcliff, prin. Fax 568-2219

Davis, Murray, Pop. 2,557
Davis ISD 1,100/PK-12
400 E Atlanta Ave 73030 580-369-2386
Todd Garrison, supt. Fax 369-3507
www.daviswolves.org
Davis HS 300/9-12
400 E Atlanta Ave 73030 580-369-5541
Rod Maynard, prin. Fax 369-3071
Davis MS 300/5-8
400 E Atlanta Ave 73030 580-369-5565
Jeff Jennings, prin. Fax 369-3289

Del City, Oklahoma, Pop. 19,870
Midwest City-Del City ISD
Supt. — See Midwest City
Del City SHS 1,400/9-12
1900 S Sunnylane Rd 73115 405-677-5777
Gina Hill, prin. Fax 671-8675
Del Crest MS 500/6-8
4731 Judy Dr 73115 405-671-8615
Michelle Parr, prin. Fax 671-8618
Kerr MS 600/6-8
2300 Linda Ln 73115 405-671-8625
Chad Collier, prin. Fax 671-8626

Christian Heritage Academy 600/PK-12
4400 SE 27th St 73115 405-672-1787
Josh Bullard, hdmstr. Fax 672-1839
Destiny Christian S 500/PK-12
3801 SE 29th St 73115 405-677-6000
Jim Howard, admin. Fax 677-6066

Depew, Creek, Pop. 440
Depew ISD 400/PK-12
PO Box 257 74028 918-324-5466
Leon Hiett, supt. Fax 324-5336
depew.k12.ok.us
Depew HS 200/9-12
PO Box 257 74028 918-324-5543
Tony Martin, prin. Fax 324-5336

Dewar, Okmulgee, Pop. 790
Dewar ISD 400/PK-12
PO Box 790 74431 918-652-9625
Todd Been, supt. Fax 652-3096
www.dewar.k12.ok.us/
Dewar HS 100/9-12
PO Box 790 74431 918-652-9625
Josh Kilhoffer, prin. Fax 652-3096
Dewar MS 100/6-8
PO Box 790 74431 918-652-9625
Josh Kilhoffer, prin. Fax 652-3096

Dewey, Washington, Pop. 3,212
Dewey ISD 1,300/PK-12
1 Bulldogger Rd 74029 918-534-2241
Dr. David Wilkins, supt. Fax 534-0149
www.deweyk12.org
Dewey HS, 1 Bulldogger Rd 74029 400/9-12
Brent Dugger, prin. 918-534-0933
Dewey MS, 1 Bulldogger Rd 74029 300/6-8
Brent Massey, prin. 918-534-0111

Dibble, McClain, Pop. 838
Dibble ISD 700/PK-12
PO Box 9 73031 405-344-6375
Chad Clanton, supt. Fax 344-6977
dibble.k12.ok.us
Dibble HS, PO Box 9 73031 200/9-12
Damon Garner, prin. 405-344-6380
Dibble MS 200/6-8
PO Box 9 73031 405-344-6380
Darlene Hayhurst, prin. Fax 344-7275

Dover, Kingfisher, Pop. 461
Dover ISD 200/PK-12
PO Box 195 73734 405-828-4206
Shannon Grimes, supt. Fax 828-7150
www.dover.k12.ok.us
Dover HS 100/9-12
PO Box 195 73734 405-828-4204
Shannon Grimes, prin. Fax 828-7150

Drummond, Garfield, Pop. 444
Drummond ISD 300/PK-12
PO Box 240 73735 580-493-2216
Mike Woods, supt. Fax 493-2273
www.drummond.k12.ok.us/
Drummond HS, PO Box 240 73735 100/9-12
Jarrod Johnson, prin. 580-493-2271

Drumright, Creek, Pop. 2,673
Drumright ISD 600/PK-12
505 W 2nd St 74030 918-352-2492
Robby Dorsey, supt. Fax 352-4430
www.drumright.k12.ok.us
Cooper MS 100/7-8
510 S Skinner Ave 74030 918-352-2318
Kevin Bilyeu, prin. Fax 352-4033
Drumright HS 200/9-12
510 S Skinner Ave 74030 918-352-2152
Judd Matthes, prin. Fax 352-9845

OK Dept. of Voc. & Tech. Education
Supt. — None
Dr. Marcie Mack, dir.
Central Tech Vo/Tech
3 Central Tech Cir 74030 918-352-2551
Fax 352-4117

Olive ISD 400/PK-12
9352 S 436th West Ave 74030 918-352-9568
Jimmy Reynolds, supt. Fax 352-4379
www.olive.k12.ok.us
Olive HS 100/9-12
9352 S 436th West Ave 74030 918-352-9568
Greg Benson, prin. Fax 352-4379

Duke, Jackson, Pop. 417
Duke ISD 200/PK-12
PO Box 160 73532 580-679-3014
Kevin Brown, supt. Fax 679-3017
www.dukeschools.com/
Duke HS, PO Box 160 73532 100/9-12
Rick Wilson, prin. 580-679-3311

Duncan, Stephens, Pop. 22,474
Duncan ISD 3,800/PK-12
PO Box 1548 73534 580-255-0686
Melonie Hau, supt. Fax 252-2453
www.duncanps.org
Duncan HS 1,000/9-12
PO Box 1548 73534 580-255-0700
Justin Smith, prin. Fax 252-2445
Duncan MS 800/6-8
PO Box 1548 73534 580-470-8106
Wade Hampton, prin. Fax 470-8743

Empire SD 400/PK-12
276803 E 1760 Rd 73533 580-252-5392
Vicki Davison, supt. Fax 252-4231
www.empireschools.org
Empire JSHS 100/7-12
276803 E 1760 Rd 73533 580-255-7515
Jodie Roberts, prin. Fax 255-2971

OK Dept. of Voc. & Tech. Education
Supt. — None
Dr. Marcie Mack, dir.
Red River Technology Center Vo/Tech
PO Box 1807 73534 580-255-2903
Dennis Loafman, supt. Fax 255-5652

Eve's College of Hairstyling Post-Sec.
PO Box 1545 73534 580-355-6620

Durant, Bryan, Pop. 14,924
Durant ISD 3,600/PK-12
1323 Waco St 74701 580-924-1276
Duane Merideth, supt. Fax 924-6019
www.durantisd.org
Durant HS 900/9-12
950 Gerlach Dr 74701 580-924-4424
Cheryl Conditt, prin. Fax 924-3642
Durant MS 500/7-8
802 W Walnut St 74701 580-924-1321
Kenny Chaffin, prin. Fax 924-8278

OK Dept. of Voc. & Tech. Education
Supt. — None
Dr. Marcie Mack, dir.
Kiamichi Technology Center Vo/Tech
810 Waldron Dr 74701 580-924-7081
Mike Goodwin, dir. Fax 924-2790

Silo ISD 700/PK-12
122 W Bourne St 74701 580-924-7000
Kate McDonald, supt. Fax 920-7988
www.siloisd.org
Silo JSHS 200/7-12
122 W Bourne St 74701 580-924-7000
Jeremy Atwood, prin. Fax 924-7045

Southeastern Oklahoma State University Post-Sec.
1405 N 4th Ave 74701 580-745-2000
Southern School of Beauty Post-Sec.
140 W Main St 74701 580-924-1049
Victory Life Academy 100/PK-12
3412 W University Blvd 74701 580-920-0850
Sarah Morrison M.Ed., hdmstr. Fax 920-9923

Eagletown, McCurtain, Pop. 515
Eagletown ISD 200/PK-12
PO Box 38 74734 580-835-2242
Brian Armstrong, supt. Fax 835-7420
www.eagletownisd.org
Eagletown HS 100/9-12
PO Box 38 74734 580-835-2242
Brian Armstrong, prin. Fax 835-7420

Earlsboro, Pottawatomie, Pop. 569
Earlsboro ISD 200/PK-12
PO Box 10 74840 405-997-5616
Mark Maloy, supt. Fax 997-3181
www.earlsboro.k12.ok.us
Earlsboro HS 100/9-12
PO Box 10 74840 405-997-5252
Ryan Friend, prin. Fax 997-3181

Edmond, Oklahoma, Pop. 78,271
Deer Creek ISD 4,900/PK-12
20701 N MacArthur Blvd, 405-348-6100
Ranet Tippens, supt. Fax 348-3049
www.deercreekschools.org
Deer Creek Freshman Academy 300/9-9
6101 NW 206th St, 405-348-5720
Melissa Jordan, prin. Fax 359-3179
Deer Creek HS 900/10-12
6101 NW 206th St, 405-348-5720
Melissa Jordan, prin. Fax 359-3179
Deer Creek MS 800/7-8
2601 NW 234th St, 405-348-4830
Kristy VanDorn, prin. Fax 359-2292

Edmond ISD 22,900/PK-12
1001 W Danforth Rd 73003 405-340-2800
Dr. Cathey Bugg, supt. Fax 340-2835
www.edmondschools.net/
Boulevard Academy Alt
215 N Boulevard 73034 405-340-2865
Mark Andrus, dir. Fax 330-6057
Central MS 800/6-8
500 E 9th St 73034 405-340-2890
Dana Renner, prin. Fax 340-3961
Cheyenne MS 1,000/6-8
1271 W Covell Rd 73003 405-340-2940
Michelle Grinsteiner, prin. Fax 330-7397
Cimarron MS 800/6-8
3701 S Bryant Ave 73013 405-340-2935
Cordell Ehrich, prin. Fax 330-3398
Edmond Memorial HS 2,100/9-12
1000 E 15th St 73013 405-340-2850
Anthony Rose, prin. Fax 340-2856
Edmond North HS 2,500/9-12
215 W Danforth Rd 73003 405-340-2875
Jason Pittenger, prin. Fax 330-7349
Edmond Santa Fe HS 2,200/9-12
1901 W 15th St 73013 405-340-2230
Jason Hayes, prin. Fax 340-2240
Sequoyah MS 1,300/6-8
1125 E Danforth Rd 73034 405-340-2900
Jason Galloway, prin. Fax 340-2909
Summit MS 1,200/6-8
1703 NW 150th St 73013 405-340-2920
Shana Perry, prin. Fax 340-2933

Mercy S Institute PK-12
14001 N Harvey Ave 73013 405-748-5500
Oklahoma Christian Academy 300/PK-12
1101 E 9th St 73034 405-844-6478
Oklahoma Christian S 900/PK-12
PO Box 509 73083 405-341-2265
Dr. Al King, hdmstr. Fax 341-4710
University of Central Oklahoma Post-Sec.
100 N University Dr 73034 405-974-2000

Eldorado, Jackson, Pop. 420
Eldorado SD I025 100/PK-12
PO Box J 73537 580-633-2219
Dr. Michael Parsons, supt. Fax 633-2316
www.eldorado.k12.ok.us/
Eldorado HS 50/9-12
PO Box J 73537 580-633-2219
Chrystal Bryant, prin. Fax 633-2316

Elgin, Comanche, Pop. 2,058
Elgin ISD 1,700/PK-12
PO Box 369 73538 580-492-3663
Nathaniel Meraz, supt. Fax 492-4084
www.elginps.org
Elgin HS 600/9-12
PO Box 369 73538 580-492-3670
Curtis Lorah, prin. Fax 492-3697
Elgin MS 600/5-8
PO Box 369 73538 580-492-3655
Melissa Hitt, prin. Fax 492-3658

Elk City, Beckham, Pop. 11,396
Elk City ISD 2,300/PK-12
222 W Broadway Ave 73644 580-225-0175
Buddy Wood, supt. Fax 225-8644
www.elkcityschools.com
EC Alternative Education Alt
222 W Broadway Ave 73644 580-333-0555
Jeff Lewallen, dir.
Elk City HS 400/10-12
222 W Broadway Ave 73644 580-225-0105
Jeff Lewallen, prin. Fax 225-1359
Elk City JHS 300/8-9
222 W Broadway Ave 73644 580-225-0476
Tammy Russell, prin. Fax 225-0208
Adult Education Adult
222 W Broadway Ave 73644 580-225-4154
Sheryl Kimball, admin.

Merritt ISD 700/PK-12
19693 E 1130 Rd 73644 580-225-5460
Jeff Daugherty, supt. Fax 225-5469
www.merritt.k12.ok.us
Merritt HS 200/9-12
19693 E 1130 Rd 73644 580-225-5460
Don Bradshaw, prin. Fax 225-5469

Elmore City, Garvin, Pop. 671
Elmore City-Pernell ISD 400/PK-12
100 N Muse Ave 73433 580-788-2565
Donny Darrow, supt. Fax 788-4665
www.ecphs.k12.ok.us

Elmore City-Pernell HS 100/7-12
100 N Muse Ave 73433 580-788-2565
Jackie Sadler, prin. Fax 788-4665

El Reno, Canadian, Pop. 16,130
El Reno ISD 2,200/PK-12
PO Box 580 73036 405-262-1703
Craig McVay, supt. Fax 262-8620
www.elrenops.org
Dale JHS 200/7-8
PO Box 580 73036 405-262-3253
Kim Landers, prin. Fax 262-8650
El Reno HS 800/9-12
PO Box 580 73036 405-262-3254
Pat Liticker, prin. Fax 262-8629

OK Dept. of Voc. & Tech. Education
Supt. — None
Dr. Marcie Mack, dir.
Canadian Valley Technology Center Vo/Tech
6505 E US Highway 66 73036 405-262-2629
Gayla Lutts, dir.

Canadian Valley Area Voc-Tech School Post-Sec.
6505 E US Highway 66 73036 405-262-2629
Redlands Community College Post-Sec.
1300 S Country Club Rd 73036 405-262-2552

Enid, Garfield, Pop. 46,752
Chisholm ISD 1,000/PK-12
305 Utah 73701 580-237-5512
Roydon Tilley, supt. Fax 234-5334
www.chisholm.k12.ok.us
Chisholm HS 300/9-12
4018 W Carrier Rd 73703 580-233-2852
Shane Dent, prin. Fax 233-9325
Chisholm MS 200/6-8
4202 W Carrier Rd 73703 580-234-0234
Crystal Szymanski, prin. Fax 234-0343

Enid ISD 7,700/PK-12
500 S Independence St 73701 580-366-7000
Dr. Darrell Floyd, supt. Fax 366-8900
www.enidpublicschools.org
Emerson MS 400/6-8
700 W Elm Ave 73701 580-366-7250
Candice Wojciechowsky, prin. Fax 249-3587
Enid HS 1,800/9-12
611 W Wabash Ave 73701 580-366-8300
Dudley Darrow, prin. Fax 366-8905
Longfellow MS 500/6-8
900 E Broadway Ave 73701 580-366-8200
Sam Robinson, prin. Fax 366-8912
Waller MS 600/6-8
2604 W Randolph Ave 73703 580-366-7900
Adam Beauchamp, prin. Fax 366-8917

OK Dept. of Voc. & Tech. Education
Supt. — None
Dr. Marcie Mack, dir.
Autry Technology Center Vo/Tech
1201 W Willow Rd 73703 580-242-2750
Brady McCullough, supt. Fax 233-8262

Enid Beauty College Post-Sec.
3905 S La Mesa Dr 73703 580-237-6677
Northern Oklahoma College Post-Sec.
PO Box 2300 73702 580-242-6300
Oklahoma Bible Academy 200/6-12
5913 W Chestnut Ave 73703 580-242-4104
Andrew Wilkins, hdmstr. Fax 242-4106
O T Autry Area Vocational Tech Center Post-Sec.
1201 W Willow Rd 73703 580-242-2750
St. Mary's Hospital Post-Sec.
305 S 5th St 73701 580-233-6100

Erick, Beckham, Pop. 1,034
Erick ISD 200/PK-12
PO Box 9 73645 580-526-3476
Jeff Kelly, supt. Fax 526-3308
www.erickps.k12.ok.us/
Erick HS 100/7-12
PO Box 9 73645 580-526-3351
Lantze Blevins, prin. Fax 526-3308

Eufaula, McIntosh, Pop. 2,615
Eufaula ISD 1,200/PK-12
1711 J M Bailey Hwy 74432 918-689-2152
Jeanette Smith, supt. Fax 689-1080
eufaula.k12.ok.us
Eufaula HS 300/9-12
1 Bell Anderson 74432 918-689-2556
Heather Combs, prin. Fax 689-1099
Eufaula MS 200/6-8
1711 J M Bailey Hwy 74432 918-689-2711
Chris Whelan, prin. Fax 689-2874

Fairfax, Osage, Pop. 1,241
Woodland SD 400/PK-12
100 N 6th St 74637 918-642-3297
Todd Kimrey, supt. Fax 642-5754
www.woodland.k12.ok.us/
Woodland HS 100/9-12
100 N 6th St 74637 918-642-3295
Rick Rogers, prin. Fax 642-5754
Other Schools – See Ralston

Fairland, Ottawa, Pop. 935
Fairland ISD 600/PK-12
202 W Washington Ave 74343 918-676-3811
Mark Alexander, supt. Fax 676-3594
www.fairlandowls.com
Fairland HS 200/9-12
202 W Washington Ave 74343 918-676-3246
Jerry Johnson, prin.
Fairland MS 100/6-8
202 W Washington Ave 74343 918-676-3246
Jerry Johnson, prin.

Fairview, Major, Pop. 2,532
Fairview ISD 700/PK-12
408 E Broadway 73737 580-227-2531
Rocky Burchfield, supt. Fax 227-2642
www.fairviewhigh.com
Chamberlain MS 100/6-8
1000 E Elm St 73737 580-227-2555
Brock Robison, prin. Fax 227-2642
Fairview HS 200/9-12
316 N 8th Ave 73737 580-227-4446
Brian Hamar, prin. Fax 227-1004

OK Dept. of Voc. & Tech. Education
Supt. — None
Dr. Marcie Mack, dir.
Northwest Technology Center Vo/Tech
801 S Vo Tech Dr 73737 580-227-3708
Colt Shaw, dir. Fax 227-2651

Fargo, Ellis, Pop. 359
Fargo-Gage SD 200/PK-12
PO Box 200 73840 580-698-2298
Mike Jones, supt. Fax 698-8019
www.fargo.k12.ok.us
Fargo HS 100/9-12
PO Box 200 73840 580-698-2298
Sherri Tune, prin. Fax 698-8019

Felt, Cimarron, Pop. 89
Felt ISD 100/PK-12
PO Box 47 73937 580-426-2220
Lewetta Hefley, supt. Fax 426-2799
www.felt.k12.ok.us
Felt HS 50/9-12
PO Box 47 73937 580-426-2220
Christopher May, prin. Fax 426-2799

Fletcher, Comanche, Pop. 1,123
Fletcher ISD 400/PK-12
PO Box 489 73541 580-549-6027
Shane Gilbreath, supt. Fax 549-6016
www.fletcherschools.org/
Fletcher JSHS, PO Box 489 73541 100/7-12
Amanda Grimes, prin. 580-549-6015

Forgan, Beaver, Pop. 539
Forgan ISD 200/PK-12
PO Box 406 73938 580-487-3366
Travis Smalts, supt. Fax 487-3368
www.forgan.k12.ok.us
Forgan HS 50/9-12
PO Box 406 73938 580-487-3366
Todd Kerr, prin. Fax 487-3368

Fort Cobb, Caddo, Pop. 599
Fort Cobb-Broxton ISD 300/PK-12
PO Box 130 73038 405-643-2336
Kyle Lierle, supt. Fax 643-2547
www.fcbmustangs.com
Fort Cobb-Broxton HS 100/9-12
PO Box 130 73038 405-643-2820
Kyle Lierle, prin. Fax 643-2547
Fort Cobb-Broxton MS 100/6-8
PO Box 130 73038 405-643-2820
James Biddy, prin. Fax 643-2547

OK Dept. of Voc. & Tech. Education
Supt. — None
Dr. Marcie Mack, dir.
Caddo-Kiowa Technology Center Vo/Tech
PO Box 190 73038 405-643-5511
Dennis Ruttman, supt. Fax 643-3014

Fort Gibson, Muskogee, Pop. 3,804
Fort Gibson ISD 1,900/PK-12
500 Ross Ave 74434 918-478-2474
Derald Glover, supt. Fax 478-8533
www.ftgibson.k12.ok.us
Fort Gibson HS 600/9-12
500 Ross Ave 74434 918-478-2452
Gary Sparks, prin. Fax 478-6244
Fort Gibson MS 400/6-8
500 Ross Ave 74434 918-478-2471
Gregory Phares, prin. Fax 478-6412

Fort Supply, Woodward, Pop. 320
Fort Supply ISD 100/PK-12
PO Box 160 73841 580-766-2611
Melva Little, supt. Fax 766-8019
www.fortsupply.k12.ok.us/
Fort Supply HS 50/9-12
PO Box 160 73841 580-766-2611
Melva Little, prin. Fax 766-8019

Fort Towson, Choctaw, Pop. 508
Fort Towson ISD 400/PK-12
PO Box 39 74735 580-873-2712
Jason Price, supt. Fax 873-1053
www.forttowson.k12.ok.us/
Fort Towson JSHS 200/7-12
PO Box 39 74735 580-873-2325
Phil Hall, prin. Fax 873-2677

Fox, Carter
Fox ISD 300/PK-12
PO Box 248 73435 580-673-2081
Brent Phelps, supt. Fax 673-2389
www.foxps.k12.ok.us
Fox HS 100/9-12
PO Box 248 73435 580-673-2082
Jason Wright, prin. Fax 673-2389

Foyil, Rogers, Pop. 287
Foyil ISD 600/PK-12
PO Box 49 74031 918-341-1113
Rod Carter, supt. Fax 341-1223
Foyil HS 100/10-12
PO Box 49 74031 918-342-1782
Lance Williams, prin. Fax 341-1223
Foyil JHS 100/7-9
PO Box 49 74031 918-342-1782
Benny Ballard, prin. Fax 341-1223

Frederick, Tillman, Pop. 3,832
Frederick ISD 600/PK-12
817 N 15th St 73542 580-335-5516
Shannon Vanderburg, supt. Fax 335-2324
www.frederickbombers.net
Frederick HS 200/9-12
817 N 15th St 73542 580-335-5521
Randy Biggs, prin. Fax 335-2634
Frederick MS 200/6-8
817 N 15th St 73542 580-335-2014
Jeremy Newton, prin. Fax 335-2763

OK Dept. of Voc. & Tech. Education
Supt. — None
Dr. Marcie Mack, dir.
Great Plains Technology Center Vo/Tech
2001 E Gladstone Ave 73542 580-335-5525
Gary Tyler, admin. Fax 335-2209

Freedom, Woods, Pop. 280
Freedom ISD 100/PK-12
PO Box 5 73842 580-621-3271
Freida Burgess, supt. Fax 621-3699
www.freedom.k12.ok.us
Freedom HS 50/9-12
PO Box 5 73842 580-621-3272
Michael Long, prin. Fax 621-3699

Gans, Sequoyah, Pop. 289
Gans ISD 400/PK-12
PO Box 70 74936 918-775-2236
Larry Calloway, supt. Fax 775-5145
www.gans.k12.ok.us
Gans HS 100/9-12
PO Box 70 74936 918-775-2236
Shawn Gillespie, prin. Fax 775-5145

Garber, Garfield, Pop. 806
Garber ISD 400/PK-12
PO Box 539 73738 580-863-2220
Jim Lamer, supt. Fax 863-2259
www.garber.k12.ok.us
Garber HS, PO Box 539 73738 100/9-12
Marc Hatton, prin. 580-863-2231

Geary, Blaine, Pop. 1,213
Geary ISD 400/PK-12
110 SW Embree Dr 73040 405-884-2411
Todd Glasgow, supt. Fax 884-2099
www.gearyschools.org
Bison Alternative Academy Alt
110 SW Embree Dr 73040 405-884-5605
Jim Shelton, dir.
Geary HS 100/9-12
110 SW Embree Dr 73040 405-884-2362
Jim Shelton, prin. Fax 884-5487
Geary MS 100/6-8
110 SW Embree Dr 73040 405-884-2362
Jim Shelton, prin. Fax 884-5487

Geronimo, Comanche, Pop. 1,179
Geronimo ISD 400/PK-12
800 W Main St 73543 580-355-3160
Bill Pascoe, supt. Fax 357-8307
www.geronimo.k12.ok.us
Geronimo HS 100/9-12
800 W Main St 73543 580-355-3160
Heath Selcer, prin. Fax 357-8307
Geronimo MS 50/7-8
800 W Main St 73543 580-355-3160
Heath Selcer, prin. Fax 357-8307

Glencoe, Payne, Pop. 577
Glencoe ISD 300/PK-12
201 E Lone Chimney Rd 74032 580-669-2261
John Lazenby, supt. Fax 669-2961
www.glencoe.k12.ok.us
Glencoe HS 100/9-12
201 E Lone Chimney Rd 74032 580-669-2261
Chad Speer, prin. Fax 669-2961

Glenpool, Tulsa, Pop. 9,951
Glenpool ISD 2,600/PK-12
PO Box 1149 74033 918-322-9500
Jerry Olansen, supt. Fax 322-1529
www.glenpool.k12.ok.us
Glenpool HS 700/9-12
PO Box 1149 74033 918-322-9500
Kim Coody, prin. Fax 322-6410
Glenpool MS 600/6-8
PO Box 1149 74033 918-322-9500
Matt Fore, prin. Fax 322-6411

Goodwell, Texas, Pop. 1,268
Goodwell ISD 200/PK-12
PO Box 580 73939 580-349-2271
Freida Burgess, supt. Fax 349-2531
www.goodwell.k12.ok.us
Goodwell HS 50/9-12
PO Box 580 73939 580-349-2271
Jason Schreiner, prin. Fax 349-2531

Yarbrough ISD 100/PK-12
RR 1 Box 31 73939 580-545-3329
Jim Wiggin, supt. Fax 545-3392
www.yarbrough.k12.ok.us/
Yarbrough HS 50/9-12
RR 1 Box 31 73939 580-545-3328
Wade Stafford, prin. Fax 545-3392

Oklahoma Panhandle State University Post-Sec.
PO Box 430 73939 580-349-2611

Gore, Sequoyah, Pop. 891
Gore ISD 500/PK-12
1200 N Highway 10 74435 918-489-5587
Lucky McCrary, supt. Fax 489-5664
www.gorepublicschools.org
Gore HS 100/9-12
1200 N Highway 10 74435 918-489-5587
Beverly Robison, prin. Fax 489-5664

Gore MS 100/6-8
1200 N Highway 10 74435 918-487-5587
Beverly Robison, prin. Fax 489-5664

Gracemont, Caddo, Pop. 298
Gracemont ISD 200/PK-12
PO Box 5 73042 405-966-2236
Mike Jones, supt. Fax 966-2395
www.gracemont.k12.ok.us
Gracemont HS 50/9-12
PO Box 5 73042 405-966-2233
Mike Jones, prin. Fax 966-2395

Grandfield, Tillman, Pop. 1,001
Grandfield ISD 300/PK-12
PO Box 639 73546 580-479-5237
James Higdon, supt. Fax 479-3381
www.grandfield.k12.ok.us/
Grandfield HS 100/9-12
PO Box 639 73546 580-479-3140
Matthew Fox, prin. Fax 479-5563

Granite, Greer, Pop. 2,034
Granite ISD 300/PK-12
PO Box 98 73547 580-535-2104
Rodney Calhoun, supt. Fax 535-2106
www.granite.k12.ok.us
Granite HS 100/9-12
PO Box 98 73547 580-535-2104
Listena Prickett, prin. Fax 535-2106

Grove, Delaware, Pop. 6,167
Grove ISD 2,600/PK-12
PO Box 450789 74345 918-786-3003
Sandy Coaly, supt. Fax 786-9365
www.ridgerunners.net
Grove HS 700/9-12
PO Box 450789 74345 918-786-2208
Renae Dozier, prin. Fax 787-5238
Grove MS 400/7-8
PO Box 450789 74345 918-786-2209
Pat Dodson, prin. Fax 786-6454

Guthrie, Logan, Pop. 9,702
Guthrie ISD 3,500/PK-12
802 E Vilas Ave 73044 405-282-8900
Dr. Mike Simpson, supt. Fax 282-5904
www.guthrieps.net
Faver Alternative S Alt
1021 E Perkins Ave 73044 405-282-5941
Gina Villalva, dir. Fax 282-5931
Guthrie HS 1,000/9-12
200 N Crooks Dr 73044 405-282-5906
Chris LeGrande, prin. Fax 282-5909
Guthrie JHS 500/7-8
705 E Oklahoma Ave 73044 405-282-5936
Robbie Rainwater, prin. Fax 282-3598

Guymon, Texas, Pop. 11,299
Guymon ISD 2,900/PK-12
PO Box 1307 73942 580-338-4340
Doug Melton, supt. Fax 338-3812
www.guymontigers.com
Central JHS 400/7-8
PO Box 1307 73942 580-338-4360
Claudia Winters, prin. Fax 338-0212
Guymon HS 800/9-12
PO Box 1307 73942 580-338-4350
Randy Williams, prin. Fax 338-0994

Haileyville, Pittsburg, Pop. 762
Haileyville ISD 400/PK-12
PO Box 29 74546 918-297-2626
Roger Hemphill, supt. Fax 297-7136
www.haileyville.k12.ok.us
Haileyville HS 100/9-12
PO Box 29 74546 918-297-2627
Brandie Kirkes, prin. Fax 297-3215

Hammon, Roger Mills, Pop. 547
Hammon ISD 300/PK-12
PO Box 279 73650 580-473-2221
Fax 473-2464
www.hammon.k12.ok.us
Hammon HS 100/9-12
PO Box 279 73650 580-473-2737
Mike Higgins, prin. Fax 473-2464

Hanna, McIntosh, Pop. 131
Hanna ISD 200/PK-12
PO Box 10 74845 918-657-2523
Richard Boatright, supt. Fax 657-2424
www.hanna.k12.ok.us
Hanna HS 200/9-12
PO Box 10 74845 918-657-2527
David Dewalt, prin. Fax 657-2424

Hardesty, Texas, Pop. 209
Hardesty ISD 100/PK-12
PO Box 129 73944 580-888-4258
Greg Faris, supt. Fax 888-4560
www.hardesty.k12.ok.us
Hardesty HS 50/9-12
PO Box 129 73944 580-888-4258
Greg Faris, prin. Fax 888-4560

Harrah, Oklahoma, Pop. 4,831
Harrah ISD 1,800/PK-12
20670 Walker St 73045 405-454-6244
Paul Blessington, supt. Fax 454-0022
www.harrahschools.com
Harrah HS 500/9-12
20370 Elm St 73045 405-454-2416
Kenneth Riddle, prin. Fax 454-6842
Harrah MS 300/6-8
20665 Walker St 73045 405-347-2700
Zane Casey, prin. Fax 454-6841

Hartshorne, Pittsburg, Pop. 1,925
Hartshorne ISD 700/PK-12
520 S 5th St 74547 918-297-2534
Mark Ichord, supt. Fax 297-2698
www.hartshorne.k12.ok.us
Hartshorne HS 200/10-12
520 S 5th St 74547 918-297-2536
Mike Reddick, prin. Fax 297-2025
Hartshorne MS 200/6-9
520 S 5th St 74547 918-297-2433
Jason Lindley, prin. Fax 297-2698

Haskell, Muskogee, Pop. 1,802
Haskell ISD 800/PK-12
900 N Ohio Ave 74436 918-482-5221
Doyle Bates, supt. Fax 482-3346
www.haskellps.org
Beavers MS 200/6-8
900 N Ohio Ave 74436 918-482-5221
Kurt Scullawl, prin. Fax 482-3346
Haskell HS 300/9-12
900 N Ohio Ave 74436 918-482-5223
Kurt Scullawl, prin. Fax 482-3346

Haworth, McCurtain, Pop. 273
Haworth ISD 500/PK-12
300 N Maple St 74740 580-245-1406
Ted Brewer, supt. Fax 245-2265
www.haworth.k12.ok.us
Haworth HS 200/9-12
300 N Maple St 74740 580-245-1406
Brandy Wall, prin. Fax 245-4913
Haworth MS 100/6-8
300 N Maple St 74740 580-245-1406
Brandy Wall, prin. Fax 245-4911

Healdton, Carter, Pop. 2,670
Healdton ISD 500/PK-12
PO Box 490 73438 580-229-0566
Terry D. Shaw, supt. Fax 229-1522
www.healdtonschools.org/
Healdton HS 200/9-12
PO Box 490 73438 580-229-0540
Justin Kana, prin. Fax 229-0557
Healdton MS 100/6-8
PO Box 490 73438 580-229-0303
Terry D. Shaw, prin. Fax 229-1475

Heavener, LeFlore, Pop. 3,279
Heavener ISD 1,100/PK-12
PO Box 698 74937 918-653-7223
Edward Wilson, supt. Fax 653-7843
www.heavenerschools.org
Heavener HS, PO Box 698 74937 300/9-12
Aaron Alexander, prin. 918-653-4307

Helena, Alfalfa, Pop. 1,366
Timberlake ISD 300/PK-12
PO Box 287 73741 580-852-3307
Mark Newton, supt. Fax 852-8019
tlakeschools.weebly.com
Timberlake HS 100/9-12
PO Box 287 73741 580-852-3281
Charlie Berg, prin. Fax 852-3280

Hennessey, Kingfisher, Pop. 2,093
Hennessey ISD 900/PK-12
604 E Oklahoma St 73742 405-853-4321
Dr. Mike Woods, supt. Fax 853-4439
www.hps.k12.ok.us
Hennessey HS 300/9-12
707 E Oklahoma St 73742 405-853-4394
Angela Avila, prin. Fax 853-4644
Hennessey MS 300/5-8
120 N Mitchell Rd 73742 405-853-4303
Stacey Schovanec, prin. Fax 853-4848

Henryetta, Okmulgee, Pop. 5,595
Henryetta ISD 1,300/PK-12
1801 W Troy Aikman Dr 74437 918-652-6523
Dwayne Noble, supt. Fax 652-6510
www.henryetta.k12.ok.us
Henryetta HS 300/9-12
1801 W Troy Aikman Dr 74437 918-652-6571
Scott Bein, prin. Fax 652-6572
Henryetta MS 300/6-8
1801 W Troy Aikman Dr 74437 918-652-6578
Brad Wion, prin. Fax 652-6506

Wilson ISD 200/PK-12
8867 Chestnut Rd 74437 918-652-3374
Andrea James, supt. Fax 652-8140
www.wpstigers.k12.ok.us
Wilson HS 100/9-12
8867 Chestnut Rd 74437 918-652-3384
Vernie Thomas, prin. Fax 650-9725

Hinton, Caddo, Pop. 3,079
Hinton ISD 700/PK-12
PO Box 1036 73047 405-542-3257
Richard Brownen, supt. Fax 542-3286
www.hintonschools.org
Hinton HS 200/9-12
PO Box 1036 73047 405-542-3235
Rennie Nickell, prin. Fax 542-3286
Hinton MS 100/6-8
PO Box 1036 73047 405-542-3235
Rennie Nickell, prin. Fax 542-3286

Hobart, Kiowa, Pop. 3,599
Hobart ISD 900/PK-12
PO Box 899 73651 580-726-5691
Cathy Hunt, supt. Fax 726-2855
www.hobart.k12.ok.us
Hobart HS, PO Box 899 73651 200/9-12
Mark Harmon, prin. 580-726-5611
Hobart MS, PO Box 899 73651 200/6-8
Kim Reed, prin. 580-726-5615

OK Dept. of Voc. & Tech. Education
Supt. — None
Dr. Marcie Mack, dir.
Western Technology Center Vo/Tech
PO Box 659 73651 580-726-8400
Jeff Ledford, dir. Fax 726-8470

Holdenville, Hughes, Pop. 5,493
Holdenville ISD 1,100/PK-12
210 Grimes Ave 74848 405-379-5483
Randy Davenport, supt. Fax 379-5874
www.holdenville.k12.ok.us
Holdenville HS 300/9-12
210 Grimes Ave 74848 405-379-3387
Shawn Richmond, prin. Fax 379-2012
Thomas MS 300/4-8
210 Grimes Ave 74848 405-379-6661
Mark Turner, prin. Fax 379-8118

Moss ISD 300/PK-12
8087 E 134 Rd 74848 405-379-2273
Gil Turpin, supt. Fax 379-2333
www.moss.k12.ok.us
Moss HS 100/9-12
8087 E 134 Rd 74848 405-379-7251
Brett Hill, prin. Fax 379-2333

Hollis, Harmon, Pop. 1,997
Hollis ISD 500/PK-12
PO Box 193 73550 580-688-3450
Jennifer Mcqueen, supt. Fax 688-2532
www.hollis.k12.ok.us
Hollis HS, PO Box 193 73550 100/9-12
Jared Robinson, prin. 580-688-2707
Hollis MS, PO Box 193 73550 100/6-8
Jared Robinson, prin. 580-688-2707

Hominy, Osage, Pop. 3,347
Hominy ISD 600/PK-12
200 S Pettit Ave 74035 918-885-6511
Doyle Edwards, supt. Fax 885-2538
www.hominy.k12.ok.us
Hominy HS 200/9-12
200 S Pettit Ave 74035 918-885-2141
Scott Harmon, prin. Fax 885-6369
Hominy MS 100/6-8
200 S Pettit Ave 74035 918-885-6253
Scott Harmon, prin. Fax 885-6369

Hooker, Texas, Pop. 1,875
Hooker ISD 600/PK-12
220 N Swem St 73945 580-652-2162
Dan Faulkner, supt. Fax 652-3118
www.hookerpublicschools.net
Hooker HS, 301 N Broadway 73945 200/9-12
Brian Stalder, prin. 580-652-2516

Howe, LeFlore, Pop. 762
Howe ISD 500/PK-12
PO Box 259 74940 918-658-3666
Scott Parks, supt. Fax 658-2233
www.howeschools.org
Howe HS 200/9-12
PO Box 259 74940 918-658-3368
Don Mcgee, prin. Fax 658-2233

Hugo, Choctaw, Pop. 4,926
Hugo ISD 1,200/PK-12
208 N 2nd St 74743 580-326-6483
Dr. Earl Dalke, supt. Fax 326-2480
www.hugoschools.com
Hugo HS 300/9-12
208 N 2nd St 74743 580-326-9648
Cory Smith, prin. Fax 326-4811
Hugo MS 200/6-8
208 N 2nd St 74743 580-326-3365
Anna Pate, prin. Fax 326-7352

OK Dept. of Voc. & Tech. Education
Supt. — None
Dr. Marcie Mack, dir.
Kiamichi Technology Center Vo/Tech
PO Box 699 74743 580-326-6491
Scott Garrett, dir. Fax 326-5696

Hulbert, Cherokee, Pop. 518
Hulbert ISD 500/PK-12
PO Box 188 74441 918-772-2501
Dr. Marilyn Dewoody, supt. Fax 772-2766
www.hulbertriders.com
Hulbert JSHS 200/7-12
PO Box 188 74441 918-772-2501
Rusty Harris, prin. Fax 772-1275

Hydro, Caddo, Pop. 947
Hydro-Eakly ISD 400/PK-12
407 E 7th St 73048 405-663-2774
Bill Derryberry, supt. Fax 663-2139
www.hydroeakly.k12.ok.us
Hydro-Eakly HS 100/9-12
407 E 7th St 73048 405-663-2246
Jeremy Bussey, prin. Fax 663-2139
Hydro-Eakly MS 100/6-8
407 E 7th St 73048 405-663-2246
Jeremy Bussey, prin. Fax 663-2139

Idabel, McCurtain, Pop. 6,641
Idabel ISD 1,200/PK-12
200 NE Ave C 74745 580-286-7639
Doug Brown, supt. Fax 286-8276
www.idabelps.org
Idabel HS 400/9-12
901 E Lincoln Rd 74745 580-286-7693
Alan Bryant, prin. Fax 286-6755
Idabel MS 200/6-8
100 NE Ave D 74745 580-286-6558
Laura Bullock, prin. Fax 286-8272

OK Dept. of Voc. & Tech. Education
Supt. — None
Dr. Marcie Mack, dir.
Kiamichi Technology Center — Vo/Tech
3205 NE Lincoln Rd 74745 — 580-286-7555
Johnnie Meredith, dir. — Fax 286-3753

Indiahoma, Comanche, Pop. 331
Indiahoma ISD — 200/PK-12
307 Chebahtah 73552 — 580-246-3448
Deanna Voegeli, supt. — Fax 246-3372
www.indiahomaps.org
Indiahoma HS — 100/9-12
307 Chebahtah 73552 — 580-246-3333
Greg Ellis, prin. — Fax 246-3372

Indianola, Pittsburg, Pop. 149
Indianola ISD — 200/PK-12
PO Box 119 74442 — 918-823-4231
Mark Baumann, supt. — Fax 823-4234
www.indianola.k12.ok.us
Indianola HS, PO Box 119 74442 — 100/9-12
Mark Baumann, prin. — 918-823-4231

Inola, Rogers, Pop. 1,643
Inola ISD — 1,400/PK-12
PO Box 1149 74036 — 918-543-2255
Dr. Kent Holbrook, supt. — Fax 543-8754
www.inola.k12.ok.us
Inola HS — 400/9-12
PO Box 789 74036 — 918-543-2404
Paul Gruenberg, prin. — Fax 543-2345
Inola MS — 400/5-8
PO Box 819 74036 — 918-543-2434
Jeff Unrau, prin. — Fax 543-6268

Jay, Delaware, Pop. 2,212
Jay ISD — 1,700/PK-12
PO Box 630 74346 — 918-253-4293
Charles Thomas, supt. — Fax 253-8970
www.jay.k12.ok.us
Jay HS — 500/9-12
PO Box 630 74346 — 918-253-4466
James Bryant, prin. — Fax 253-6249
Jay MS — 200/6-8
PO Box 630 74346 — 918-253-8510
Arlis Henegar, prin. — Fax 253-3342

Jenks, Tulsa, Pop. 16,162
Jenks ISD — 11,200/PK-12
205 E B St 74037 — 918-299-4411
Dr. Stacey Butterfield, supt. — Fax 299-9197
www.jenksps.org
Jenks Alternative Center — Alt
205 E B St 74037 — 918-299-4411
Amie Hardy, prin. — Fax 298-6640
Jenks Freshman Academy — 900/9-9
205 E B St 74037 — 918-299-4411
Judi Thorn, prin. — Fax 298-0807
Jenks HS — 2,400/10-12
205 E B St 74037 — 918-299-4411
David Beiler, prin. — Fax 298-0336
Other Schools – See Tulsa

Jenks Beauty College — Post-Sec.
535 W Main St 74037 — 918-299-0901

Jones, Oklahoma, Pop. 2,585
Jones ISD — 1,100/PK-12
9200 N Hiwassee Rd 73049 — 405-399-9215
Dr. Carl Johnson, supt. — Fax 399-9212
www.jones.k12.ok.us
Jones HS — 300/9-12
304 Dr Lee Simmons 73049 — 405-399-9122
Curtis Moses, prin. — Fax 399-9212
Jones MS — 300/6-8
16011 E Wilshire Blvd 73049 — 405-399-9114
Adam McPhail, prin. — Fax 399-6101

Kansas, Delaware, Pop. 726
Kansas ISD — 900/PK-12
PO Box 196 74347 — 918-868-2562
Jim Burgess, supt. — Fax 868-3103
www.kansasps.com/
Kansas HS — 300/9-12
PO Box 196 74347 — 918-868-3308
Phil Isom, prin. — Fax 868-3103
Kansas JHS — 200/6-8
PO Box 196 74347 — 918-868-5308
Bryon Arnold, prin. — Fax 868-5582

OK Dept. of Voc. & Tech. Education
Supt. — None
Dr. Marcie Mack, dir.
Northeast Tech Center Kansas Campus — Vo/Tech
PO Box 30 74347 — 918-868-3535
Greg Mitchell, supt. — Fax 868-3530

Kaw City, Kay, Pop. 358
Shidler ISD
Supt. — See Shidler
Shidler MS — 100/5-8
904 Washunga Dr 74641 — 580-269-2911
Janice Finton, prin. — Fax 269-2992

Kellyville, Creek, Pop. 1,083
Kellyville ISD — 1,100/PK-12
PO Box 99 74039 — 918-247-6133
Joe Pierce, supt. — Fax 247-6120
www.kellyvilleschools.org/
Kellyville HS, PO Box 99 74039 — 300/9-12
Danny Wood, prin. — 918-247-6333
Kellyville MS, PO Box 99 74039 — 200/7-8
Rod Pitts, prin. — 918-247-6134

Keota, Haskell, Pop. 531
Keota ISD — 400/PK-12
110 NE 6th St 74941 — 918-966-3950
James Eberts, supt. — Fax 966-3247
www.keota.k12.ok.us
Keota HS — 100/9-12
110 NE 6th St 74941 — 918-966-3950
Richard Reed, prin. — Fax 966-3247

Ketchum, Mayes, Pop. 396
Ketchum ISD — 600/PK-12
PO Box 720 74349 — 918-782-5091
Pete Hiseley, supt. — Fax 782-9018
www.ketchumwarriors.com
Ketchum HS — 200/9-12
PO Box 720 74349 — 918-782-4481
Joe Gramlich, prin. — Fax 782-4848
Ketchum MS — 100/6-8
PO Box 720 74349 — 918-782-3242
Jennifer Turner, prin. — Fax 782-3016

Keyes, Cimarron, Pop. 321
Keyes ISD — 100/PK-12
PO Box 47 73947 — 580-546-7231
Sherri Hitchings, supt. — Fax 546-7338
www.keyes.k12.ok.us
Keyes HS — 50/9-12
PO Box 47 73947 — 580-546-7231
Sherri Hitchings, prin. — Fax 546-7338

Kiefer, Creek, Pop. 1,550
Kiefer ISD — 700/PK-12
4600 W 151st St S 74041 — 918-321-3421
Mary Murrell, supt. — Fax 321-5216
www.kiefer.k12.ok.us/
Kiefer HS — 200/9-12
4600 W 151st St S 74041 — 918-321-3533
Sabrina Shaw, prin. — Fax 321-4443
Rongey MS — 100/7-8
4600 W 151st St S 74041 — 918-321-3533
Cory Campbell, prin. — Fax 321-4443

Kingfisher, Kingfisher, Pop. 4,523
Kingfisher SD — 1,400/PK-12
602 W Chisholm Dr 73750 — 405-375-4194
Jason Sternberger, supt. — Fax 375-5565
www.kingfisher.k12.ok.us
Kingfisher HS — 400/9-12
1500 S 13th St 73750 — 405-375-4191
Todd Overstreet, prin. — Fax 375-4456
Kingfisher MS — 400/5-8
601 S 13th St 73750 — 405-375-6607
Keith Campbell, prin. — Fax 375-6410

Kingston, Marshall, Pop. 1,514
Kingston ISD — 1,200/PK-12
PO Box 370 73439 — 580-564-9033
Ron Whipkey, supt. — Fax 564-9516
www.kingston.k12.ok.us
Kingston HS — 300/9-12
PO Box 370 73439 — 580-564-2384
Brenda Foster, prin. — Fax 564-0901
Kingston MS — 300/6-8
PO Box 370 73439 — 580-564-2996
Brian Brister, prin. — Fax 564-0902

Kinta, Haskell, Pop. 279
Kinta ISD — 200/PK-12
PO Box 219 74552 — 918-768-3338
Patricia Deville, supt. — Fax 768-3321
www.kinta.k12.ok.us
Kinta HS — 100/9-12
PO Box 219 74552 — 918-768-3338
Patricia Deville, prin. — Fax 768-3321

Kiowa, Pittsburg, Pop. 681
Kiowa ISD — 300/PK-12
PO Box 6 74553 — 918-432-5631
Rick Pool, supt. — Fax 432-5683
www.kiowa.k12.ok.us
Kiowa HS — 100/9-12
PO Box 6 74553 — 918-432-5631
Ron Slawson, prin. — Fax 432-5683

Konawa, Seminole, Pop. 1,168
Konawa ISD — 700/PK-12
701 W South St 74849 — 580-925-3244
Andy Gower, supt. — Fax 925-2146
www.konawa.k12.ok.us
Konawa HS — 200/9-12
701 W South St 74849 — 580-925-3221
Karis Reavis, prin. — Fax 925-2146
Konawa MS — 200/6-8
701 W South St 74849 — 580-925-3221
Sean Walker, prin. — Fax 925-2146

Kremlin, Garfield, Pop. 247
Kremlin-Hillsdale ISD — 200/PK-12
PO Box 198 73753 — 580-874-2284
Jim Patton M.Ed., supt. — Fax 574-4488
www.kremlin.k12.ok.us/
Kremlin-Hillsdale HS — 100/6-12
PO Box 198 73753 — 580-874-2281
Jeremy Brashears M.A., prin.

Lahoma, Garfield, Pop. 597
Cimarron ISD — 300/PK-12
PO Box 8 73754 — 580-796-2204
Robbie Burch, supt. — Fax 796-2350
www.cimarron.k12.ok.us
Cimarron HS — 100/9-12
PO Box 8 73754 — 580-796-2204
Robbie Burch, prin. — Fax 796-2350

Lamont, Grant, Pop. 412
Deer Creek-Lamont ISD — 200/PK-12
PO Box 10 74643 — 580-388-4333
Barbara Regier, supt. — Fax 388-4341
www.dcla.k12.ok.us/
Deer Creek-Lamont HS — 100/9-12
PO Box 10 74643 — 580-388-4333
Kevin Engle, prin. — Fax 388-4341

Langston, Logan, Pop. 1,691

Langston University — Post-Sec.
PO Box 1500 73050 — 405-466-2231

Laverne, Harper, Pop. 1,316
Laverne ISD — 500/PK-12
PO Box 40 73848 — 580-921-3362
Ed Thomas, supt. — Fax 921-3636
www.laverne.k12.ok.us
Laverne HS — 100/9-12
PO Box 40 73848 — 580-921-3361
Kyndra Allen, prin. — Fax 921-3936

Lawton, Comanche, Pop. 91,002
Lawton ISD — 13,400/PK-12
753 NW Fort Sill Blvd 73507 — 580-357-6900
Dr. Tom Deighan, supt. — Fax 585-6319
www.lawtonps.org
Central MS — 900/6-8
1201 NW Fort Sill Blvd 73507 — 580-355-8544
Dr. Blake Thomas, prin. — Fax 585-6452
Eisenhower HS — 1,300/9-12
5202 W Gore Blvd 73505 — 580-355-9144
Charlotte Oates, prin. — Fax 585-6329
Eisenhower MS — 900/6-8
5702 W Gore Blvd 73505 — 580-353-1040
Beverly Mattingly, prin. — Fax 585-6436
Gateway Success Center — Alt
102 E Gore Blvd 73501 — 580-353-4903
Fax 585-6479
Lawton HS — 1,700/9-12
601 NW Fort Sill Blvd 73507 — 580-355-5170
Regina Deloach, prin. — Fax 585-6433
MacArthur HS — 1,100/9-12
4402 E Gore Blvd 73501 — 580-355-5230
Rod Elam, prin. — Fax 585-6434
MacArthur MS — 700/6-8
510 NE 45th St 73507 — 580-353-5111
Regina Lambert, prin. — Fax 585-6435
Tomlinson MS — 700/6-8
702 NW Homestead Dr 73505 — 580-585-6416
Eddie Williams, prin. — Fax 585-6451

OK Dept. of Voc. & Tech. Education
Supt. — None
Dr. Marcie Mack, dir.
Great Plains Technology Center — Vo/Tech
4500 SW Lee Blvd 73505 — 580-355-6371
Dr. Tom Thomas, supt. — Fax 250-5677

Cameron University — Post-Sec.
2800 W Gore Blvd 73505 — 580-581-2200
Comanche Co. Memorial Hospital — Post-Sec.
PO Box 129 73502 — 580-355-8620
Comanche Nation College — Post-Sec.
1608 SW 9th St 73501 — 580-591-0203
Great Plains Area Voc. Tech. School — Post-Sec.
4500 SW Lee Blvd 73505 — 580-355-6371
Lawton Academy of Arts and Sciences — 100/PK-12
1911 NW 72nd St 73505 — 580-536-1900
Lawton Christian S — 500/PK-12
1 NW Crusader Dr 73505 — 580-536-6885
Platt College — Post-Sec.
112 SW 11th St 73501 — 580-355-4416

Leedey, Dewey, Pop. 416
Leedey ISD — 200/PK-12
505 E 6th St 73654 — 580-488-3424
Rusty Puffinbarger, supt. — Fax 488-3428
www.leedey.k12.ok.us
Leedey HS, 500 E 6th St 73654 — 100/9-12
Darren Danielson, prin. — 580-488-3377

LeFlore, LeFlore, Pop. 182
LeFlore ISD — 200/PK-12
PO Box 147 74942 — 918-753-2345
Lane Jackson, supt. — Fax 753-2604
www.lefloreps.k12.ok.us
LeFlore HS — 100/9-12
PO Box 147 74942 — 918-753-2345
Diana Hames, prin. — Fax 753-2604

Lexington, Cleveland, Pop. 2,050
Lexington ISD — 900/PK-12
420 NE 4th St 73051 — 405-527-7236
Ronda Bass, supt. — Fax 527-9517
www.lexington.k12.ok.us/
Lexington HS — 200/9-12
801 E Broadway St 73051 — 405-527-3810
David McLain, prin. — Fax 527-3814
Lexington MS — 200/6-8
420 NE 4th St 73051 — 405-527-7236
Jeff Hall, prin. — Fax 527-1415

Lindsay, Garvin, Pop. 2,771
Lindsay ISD — 1,200/PK-12
800 W Creek St 73052 — 405-756-3131
Dan Chapman, supt. — Fax 756-8819
www.lindsay.k12.ok.us
Lindsay HS — 300/9-12
800 W Creek St 73052 — 405-756-3132
Chuck Karpe, prin. — Fax 756-8554
Lindsay MS, 800 W Creek St 73052 — 300/6-8
Tommy Ferguson, prin. — 405-756-3133

Locust Grove, Mayes, Pop. 1,264
Locust Grove ISD — 1,500/PK-12
PO Box 399 74352 — 918-479-5243
Lori Helton, supt. — Fax 479-6468
www.lg.k12.ok.us
Locust Grove HS — 500/9-12
PO Box 399 74352 — 918-479-5247
Clint Hall, prin. — Fax 479-2743
Locust Grove MS — 300/6-8
PO Box 399 74352 — 918-479-5244
Jamie Rice, prin. — Fax 479-2930

Lone Grove, Carter, Pop. 4,751
Lone Grove ISD 1,500/PK-12
PO Box 1330 73443 580-657-3131
Meri Jayne Miller, supt. Fax 657-4355
www.lonegrove.k12.ok.us/
Lone Grove HS 400/9-12
PO Box 1330 73443 580-657-3133
Chris Sudderth, prin. Fax 657-6624
Lone Grove MS 300/6-8
PO Box 1330 73443 580-657-3132
Richie McKee, prin. Fax 657-2691

Lone Wolf, Kiowa, Pop. 435
Lone Wolf ISD 100/PK-12
PO Box 158 73655 580-846-9091
James Sutherland, supt. Fax 846-5266
lonewolfschool.com
Lone Wolf HS 50/9-12
PO Box 158 73655 580-846-9091
James Sutherland, prin. Fax 846-5266

Lookeba, Caddo, Pop. 163
Lookeba-Sickles ISD 300/PK-12
10108 County Road 1150 73053 405-457-6623
Mike Davis, supt. Fax 457-6382
www.lookeba.k12.ok.us
Lookeba-Sickles HS 100/9-12
10108 County Road 1150 73053 405-457-6621
Shirley Gathers, prin. Fax 457-6619

Luther, Oklahoma, Pop. 1,168
Luther ISD 900/PK-12
PO Box 430 73054 405-277-3233
Dr. Sheldon Buxton, supt. Fax 277-3498
www.lutherlions.org
Luther HS 300/9-12
PO Box 430 73054 405-277-3263
Jerry Martin, prin. Fax 277-3630
Luther MS 300/5-8
PO Box 430 73054 405-277-3264
Barry Gunn, prin. Fax 277-3877

McAlester, Pittsburg, Pop. 17,248
McAlester ISD 2,800/PK-12
PO Box 1027 74502 918-423-4771
Randy Hughes, supt. Fax 423-8166
www.mcalester.k12.ok.us
McAlester HS 900/9-12
PO Box 1027 74502 918-423-4776
Paula Meadows, prin. Fax 423-8689
Puterbaugh MS 400/7-8
PO Box 1027 74502 918-423-5445
Caroline Miller, prin. Fax 423-7021

OK Dept. of Voc. & Tech. Education
Supt. — None
Dr. Marcie Mack, dir.
Kiamichi Technology Center Vo/Tech
301 Kiamichi Dr 74501 918-426-0940
Angela Evans, dir. Fax 426-1626

Lakewood Christian S 200/PK-12
840 S George Nigh Expy 74501 918-426-2000
Amy Shaw, prin. Fax 302-2000

Mc Curtain, Haskell, Pop. 484
McCurtain ISD 300/PK-12
PO Box 189 74944 918-945-7237
Dart Drummonds, supt. Fax 945-7064
www.mccurtain.k12.ok.us/
McCurtain HS 100/9-12
PO Box 189 74944 918-945-7237
Perry Arnwine, prin. Fax 945-7064

Mc Loud, Pottawatomie, Pop. 3,818
McLoud ISD 1,800/PK-12
PO Box 240, 405-964-3314
Steve Stanley, supt. Fax 964-2801
www.mcloudschools.us
McLoud HS 500/9-12
PO Box 60, 405-964-3314
Leigh Todd, prin. Fax 964-3498
McLoud JHS 200/7-8
PO Box 730, 405-964-3314
Angie Drew, prin. Fax 964-7530

Macomb, Pottawatomie, Pop. 32
Macomb ISD 300/PK-12
36591 Highway 59B 74852 405-598-3892
Matthew Riggs, supt. Fax 598-8041
www.macomb.k12.ok.us
Macomb HS 100/9-12
36591 Highway 59B 74852 405-598-5420
Scott Frazier, prin. Fax 598-3295

Madill, Marshall, Pop. 3,605
Madill ISD 1,800/PK-12
601 W McArthur St 73446 580-795-3303
Jon Tuck, supt. Fax 795-3210
www.madillok.com
Madill HS 500/9-12
700 S 5th Ave 73446 580-795-3339
Andy Gower, prin. Fax 795-2657
Madill MS 400/6-8
601 W McArthur St 73446 580-795-7373
Tena Houser, prin. Fax 795-6930

Mangum, Greer, Pop. 2,935
Mangum ISD 700/PK-12
400 N Pennsylvania Ave 73554 580-782-3371
Mike Southall, supt. Fax 782-2313
www.mangum.k12.ok.us/
Mangum HS 200/9-12
301 N Oklahoma Ave 73554 580-782-3343
Travis Reese, prin. Fax 782-3265
Mangum JHS 100/7-8
400 N Oklahoma Ave 73554 580-782-2702
Barbara Gahagan, prin. Fax 782-5911

Mannford, Creek, Pop. 2,901
Mannford ISD 1,600/PK-12
136 Evans Ave 74044 918-865-4062
Dr. Steve Waldvogel, supt. Fax 865-3405
www.mannford.k12.ok.us
Mannford HS 500/9-12
220 Evans Ave 74044 918-865-3841
Tim Wright, prin. Fax 865-2813
Mannford MS 300/6-8
100 Green Valley Rd 74044 918-865-4680
Steve Anderson, prin. Fax 865-2862

Marietta, Love, Pop. 2,521
Marietta ISD 1,100/PK-12
PO Box 289 73448 580-276-9444
Chad Broughton, supt. Fax 276-4037
www.mariettaisd.org
Marietta HS 300/9-12
PO Box 289 73448 580-276-3204
Rodd Davis, prin. Fax 276-1208
Marietta MS 200/6-8
PO Box 289 73448 580-276-3886
Brandi Naylor, prin. Fax 276-1203

Marlow, Stephens, Pop. 4,444
Bray-Doyle ISD 400/PK-12
1205 S Brooks Rd 73055 580-658-5076
David Eads, supt. Fax 658-5888
www.braydoyle.k12.ok.us
Bray-Doyle HS 100/9-12
1205 S Brooks Rd 73055 580-658-5071
James Vines, prin. Fax 658-5888

Central High ISD 300/PK-12
274801 Broncho Rd 73055 580-658-6858
Bennie Newton M.Ed., supt. Fax 658-8006
www.central.k12.ok.us
Central JSHS 100/7-12
274801 Broncho Rd 73055 580-658-2929
Mark Perry M.Ed., prin. Fax 658-8010

Marlow ISD 1,400/PK-12
PO Box 73 73055 580-658-2719
George Coffman, supt. Fax 658-6455
www.marlow.k12.ok.us
Marlow HS 300/9-12
PO Box 73 73055 580-658-1516
Bryan Brantley, prin. Fax 658-2718
Marlow MS 300/6-8
PO Box 73 73055 580-658-2619
Ross Ridge, prin. Fax 658-1169

Mason, Okfuskee
Mason ISD 300/PK-12
374006 E 1000 Rd 74859 918-623-0231
Jerry Bogle, supt. Fax 623-0884
www.mason.k12.ok.us/
Mason HS 100/9-12
374006 E 1000 Rd 74859 918-623-0107
Eddie Weaver, prin. Fax 623-0147

Maud, Pottawatomie, Pop. 993
Maud ISD 300/PK-12
PO Box 130 74854 405-374-2416
Jerry McCormick, supt. Fax 374-2628
www.maud.k12.ok.us
Maud HS 100/9-12
PO Box 130 74854 405-374-2425
Darrell Reid, prin. Fax 374-2895

Maysville, Garvin, Pop. 1,159
Maysville ISD 400/PK-12
600 1st St 73057 888-806-5220
Dr. Shelly Hildebrand-Beach, supt. Fax 867-4864
maysville.k12.ok.us
Maysville HS 100/9-12
600 1st St 73057 888-806-5330
Dr. Shelly Hildebrand-Beach, prin. Fax 867-4864

Medford, Grant, Pop. 970
Medford ISD 300/PK-12
301 N Main St 73759 580-395-2392
Mickey Geurkink, supt. Fax 395-2391
www.medford.k12.ok.us/
Medford HS 100/9-12
301 N Main St 73759 580-395-2392
Micheal Thompson, prin. Fax 395-2391

Meeker, Lincoln, Pop. 1,096
Meeker ISD 900/PK-12
214 E Carl Hubbell Blvd 74855 405-788-4540
Jeffrey Pruitt, supt. Fax 279-2765
www.meeker.k12.ok.us/
Meeker HS 300/9-12
214 E Carl Hubbell Blvd 74855 405-788-4540
Mike Hedge, prin. Fax 279-2765
Meeker MS 200/6-8
214 E Carl Hubbell Blvd 74855 405-788-4540
Virgil Fowler, dean Fax 279-2765

Miami, Ottawa, Pop. 12,277
Miami ISD 1,900/PK-12
26 N Main St 74354 918-542-8455
Terry James, supt. Fax 542-1236
www.miami.k12.ok.us
Miami HS 700/9-12
2000 E Central Ave 74354 918-542-4421
Lisa Munson, prin. Fax 542-7421
Rogers MS 500/6-8
504 Goodrich Blvd 74354 918-542-5588
Justin Chase, prin. Fax 542-4400

Northeastern Oklahoma A&M College Post-Sec.
200 I St NE 74354 918-542-8441

Midwest City, Oklahoma, Pop. 51,213
Midwest City-Del City ISD 13,800/PK-12
7217 SE 15th St 73110 405-737-4461
Dr. Rick Cobb, supt. Fax 739-1615
www.mid-del.net
Albert MS 800/6-8
2515 S Post Rd 73130 405-739-1761
Cindy Anderson, prin. Fax 739-1780
Albert SHS 1,100/9-12
2009 S Post Rd 73130 405-739-1726
Kristin Goggans, prin. Fax 739-1685
Career Academy Alt
1730 Center Dr 73110 405-582-7099
Jarman MS 500/6-8
5 W MacArthur Dr 73110 405-739-1771
Lynette Brown, prin. Fax 739-1773
Midwest City SHS 1,400/9-12
213 Elm St 73110 405-739-1741
Lashonda Broiles, prin. Fax 739-1675
Monroney MS 600/6-8
7400 E Reno Ave 73110 405-739-1786
Brittany Manley, prin. Fax 739-1789
Other Schools – See Del City

OK Dept. of Voc. & Tech. Education
Supt. — None
Dr. Marcie Mack, dir.
Mid-Del Technology Center Vo/Tech
1621 Maple Dr 73110 405-739-1707
Fax 739-1716

Rose State College Post-Sec.
6420 SE 15th St 73110 405-733-7673

Milburn, Johnston, Pop. 295
Milburn ISD 200/PK-12
PO Box 429 73450 580-443-5522
Joey McBride, supt. Fax 443-5303
www.milburnps.org
Milburn HS 100/9-12
PO Box 429 73450 580-443-5522
Joey McBride, prin. Fax 443-5303

Mill Creek, Johnston, Pop. 283
Mill Creek ISD 100/PK-12
602 S Chickasaw Ave 74856 580-384-5514
Lorinda Chancellor, supt. Fax 384-3920
Mill Creek HS 50/9-12
602 S Chickasaw Ave 74856 580-384-5514
Lorinda Chancellor, prin. Fax 384-3920

Minco, Grady, Pop. 1,580
Minco ISD 600/PK-12
PO Box 428 73059 405-352-4867
Kevin Sims, supt. Fax 352-4006
www.minco.k12.ok.us
Minco HS 200/9-12
PO Box 428 73059 405-352-4377
Clint Shirley, prin. Fax 352-4006
Minco MS 100/6-8
PO Box 428 73059 405-352-4377
Troy Wittrock, prin. Fax 352-4006

Moore, Cleveland, Pop. 51,925
Moore ISD 23,000/PK-12
1500 SE 4th St 73160 405-735-4200
Dr. Robert Romines, supt. Fax 735-4392
www.mooreschools.com
Central JHS 600/7-8
400 N Broadway St 73160 405-735-4560
Tammy Baker, prin. Fax 895-7398
Highland East JHS 700/7-8
1200 SE 4th St 73160 405-735-4580
Mark Archer, prin. Fax 793-3198
Highland West JHS 600/7-8
901 N Santa Fe Ave 73160 405-735-4600
Dan Schwarz, prin. Fax 793-3218
Moore HS 2,300/9-12
300 N Eastern Ave 73160 405-735-4700
Mike Coyle, prin. Fax 793-3140
Southmoore HS 2,100/9-12
2901 S Santa Fe Ave 73160 405-735-4900
Danny Reed, prin. Fax 735-4992
Vista Academy HS Alt
224 SE 4th St 73160 405-735-4640
Dr. Sandra Ludwig, prin. Fax 793-3062
Vista Academy JHS Alt
224 SE 4th St 73160 405-735-4640
Dr. Sandra Ludwig, prin. Fax 793-3062
Other Schools – See Oklahoma City

Hillsdale Free Will Baptist College Post-Sec.
PO Box 7208 73153 405-912-9000
Platt College Post-Sec.
201 N Eastern Ave 73160 405-912-3260

Mooreland, Woodward, Pop. 1,172
Mooreland ISD 500/PK-12
PO Box 75 73852 580-994-5388
Terry Kellner M.S., supt. Fax 994-5900
www.mooreland.k12.ok.us
Mooreland HS 100/9-12
PO Box 75 73852 580-994-5426
Ron Wilson, prin. Fax 994-2344

Morris, Okmulgee, Pop. 1,388
Morris ISD 1,100/PK-12
307 S 6th St 74445 918-733-9072
James Lyons, supt. Fax 733-4205
morrisschools.net
Morris HS 300/9-12
307 S 6th St 74445 918-733-9072
Andrew Ewton, prin. Fax 733-4205
Morris MS 200/6-8
307 S 6th St 74445 918-733-9072
Monte Womack, prin. Fax 733-4205

Morrison, Noble, Pop. 700
Morrison ISD 400/PK-12
PO Box 176 73061 580-724-3341
Jay Vernon, supt. Fax 724-3004
www.morrisonps.com
Morrison HS, PO Box 176 73061 100/7-12
Shalon Reynolds, prin. 580-724-3307

Mounds, Creek, Pop. 1,107
Liberty ISD 600/PK-12
2727 E 201st St S 74047 918-366-8496
Donna Campo, supt. Fax 366-8497
libertyoc.liberty.k12.ok.us
Liberty HS, 2727 E 201st St S 74047 200/9-12
Matthew Sweet, prin. 918-366-8784

Mounds ISD 600/PK-12
PO Box 189 74047 918-827-6100
Doran Smith, supt. Fax 827-3704
www.moundsps.com
Mounds HS 200/9-12
PO Box 189 74047 918-827-6100
Stephen Sturgeon, prin. Fax 827-3705

Mountain View, Kiowa, Pop. 770
Mountain View-Gotebo ISD 300/PK-12
RR 2 Box 88 73062 580-347-2211
Sam Belcher, supt. Fax 347-2869
www.mvgschools.com
Mountain View-Gotebo HS 100/9-12
150 S 1st St 73062 580-347-2211
Linda Stephens, prin. Fax 347-2869

Moyers, Pushmataha
Moyers ISD 200/PK-12
PO Box 88 74557 580-298-5549
Donna Dudley, supt. Fax 298-2022
moyersisd.org
Moyers HS 100/9-12
PO Box 88 74557 580-298-5547
Bucky Ewton, prin. Fax 298-2022

Muldrow, Sequoyah, Pop. 3,165
Muldrow ISD 1,600/PK-12
PO Box 660 74948 918-427-7406
Ron Flanagan, supt. Fax 427-6088
www.muldrowps.org
Muldrow HS 500/9-12
PO Box 660 74948 918-427-3274
Steve Page, prin. Fax 427-1035
Muldrow MS 500/5-8
PO Box 660 74948 918-427-5421
Angela Williams, prin. Fax 427-1034

Muskogee, Muskogee, Pop. 36,324
Hilldale ISD 1,900/PK-12
500 E Smith Ferry Rd 74403 918-683-0273
Dr. Kaylin Coody, supt. Fax 683-8725
www.hilldale.k12.ok.us
Hilldale HS 500/9-12
300 E Smith Ferry Rd 74403 918-683-3253
Deborah Tennison, prin. Fax 683-0622
Hilldale MS 400/6-8
400 E Smith Ferry Rd 74403 918-683-0763
Darren Riddle, prin. Fax 683-0766

Muskogee ISD 6,100/PK-12
202 W Broadway St 74401 918-684-3700
Mike Garde, supt. Fax 684-3827
www.mpsi20.org
Muskogee HS 1,600/9-12
3200 E Shawnee Rd 74403 918-684-3750
Dawna Buck, prin. Fax 684-3751
Robertson JHS 700/7-8
402 N S St 74403 918-684-3775
Steve Barton, prin. Fax 684-3776
Rougher Alternative Academy Alt
600 Altamont St 74401 918-684-3705
Heather Jones, prin. Fax 684-3706

OK Dept. of Voc. & Tech. Education
Supt. — None
Dr. Marcie Mack, dir.
Indian Capital Technology Center Vo/Tech
2403 N 41st St E 74403 918-687-6383
Anthony Pivec, supt. Fax 687-6624

Bacone College Post-Sec.
2299 Old Bacone Rd 74403 918-683-4581
Muskogee General Hospital Post-Sec.
300 Rockefeller Dr 74401 918-682-5501
Parkview School OK School for the Blind Post-Sec.
3300 Gibson St 74403 918-682-6641
Virgil's Beauty College Post-Sec.
111 S 9th St 74401 918-682-9429

Mustang, Canadian, Pop. 16,780
Mustang ISD 10,500/PK-12
906 S Heights Dr 73064 405-376-2461
Dr. Sean McDaniel, supt. Fax 376-7333
www.mustangps.org
Mustang Education Center 400/PK-PK, 9-
906 S Heights Dr 73064 405-376-7322
Sondra Bivens, prin. Fax 376-9079
Mustang HS 2,700/9-12
906 S Heights Dr 73064 405-376-2404
Teresa Wilkerson, prin. Fax 376-7347
Mustang MS 700/7-8
906 S Heights Dr 73064 405-376-2448
Kathy Knowles, prin. Fax 376-7373
Mustang North MS 800/7-8
906 S Heights Dr 73064 405-324-2236
Christy Bradley, prin. Fax 324-2258

Mutual, Woodward, Pop. 59
Sharon-Mutual ISD 300/PK-12
210 S Maple St 73853 580-989-3210
Jeff Thompson, supt. Fax 989-3241
www.smps.k12.ok.us
Sharon-Mutual HS 100/9-12
210 S Maple St 73853 580-989-3231
Rustin Donaldson, prin. Fax 989-8019

Newcastle, McClain, Pop. 7,304
Newcastle ISD 2,000/PK-12
101 N Main St 73065 405-387-2890
Tony O'Brien, supt. Fax 387-3482
www.newcastle.k12.ok.us
Newcastle HS 500/9-12
101 N Main St 73065 405-387-4304
Rob Gilstrap, prin. Fax 387-3461
Newcastle MS 400/6-8
611 E Fox Ln 73065 405-387-3139
John Harris, prin. Fax 387-5563

Newkirk, Kay, Pop. 2,182
Newkirk ISD 800/PK-12
625 W South St 74647 580-362-2388
Brady Barnes, supt. Fax 362-3413
www.newkirk.k12.ok.us
Newkirk HS 300/9-12
221 S Main St 74647 580-362-6241
Dr. Maurisa Pruett, prin. Fax 362-6242
Newkirk MS 300/5-8
711 S Academy Ave 74647 580-362-2516
Jeff Wilson, prin. Fax 362-1150

Ninnekah, Grady, Pop. 970
Ninnekah ISD 500/PK-12
PO Box 275 73067 405-224-4092
Todd Bunch, supt. Fax 224-4096
www.ninnekah.k12.ok.us
Ninnekah HS 100/9-12
PO Box 275 73067 405-224-4299
David Pitts, prin. Fax 224-4665
Ninnekah MS 100/6-8
PO Box 275 73067 405-224-4299
Glen Shoemake, prin. Fax 224-4665

Noble, Cleveland, Pop. 6,155
Noble ISD 2,900/PK-12
111 S 4th St 73068 405-872-3452
Frank Solomon, supt. Fax 872-3271
www.nobleps.com
Inge MS 600/6-8
1201 N 8th St 73068 405-872-3495
Ronald Fulks, prin. Fax 872-8670
Noble HS 800/9-12
4601 E Etowah Rd 73068 405-872-3441
Steve Barrett, prin. Fax 872-9824

Norman, Cleveland, Pop. 105,378
Little Axe ISD 1,200/PK-12
2000 168th Ave NE 73026 405-329-7691
Jay Thomas, supt. Fax 579-2929
littleaxeps.org/
Little Axe HS 300/9-12
2000 168th Ave NE 73026 405-329-1612
Barry Thomas, prin. Fax 329-2914
Little Axe MS 300/6-8
2000 168th Ave NE 73026 405-329-2156
Dalton Griffin, prin. Fax 579-2937

Norman ISD 15,300/PK-12
131 S Flood Ave 73069 405-364-1339
Dr. Joseph Siano, supt. Fax 366-5851
www.norman.k12.ok.us
Alcott MS 700/6-8
1919 W Boyd St 73069 405-366-5845
Dr. Dana Morris, prin. Fax 447-6572
Dimensions Academy 100/Alt
1101 E Main St 73071 405-579-1880
Paul Tryggestad, prin. Fax 579-1881
Irving MS 900/6-8
125 Vicksburg Ave 73071 405-366-5941
Jonathan Atchley, prin. Fax 366-5944
Longfellow MS 700/6-8
215 N Ponca Ave 73071 405-366-5948
Carie Spannagel, prin. Fax 366-5952
Norman HS 1,900/9-12
911 W Main St 73069 405-366-5812
Dr. Scott Beck, prin. Fax 366-5945
Norman North HS 2,200/9-12
1809 Stubbeman Ave 73069 405-366-5954
Dr. Peter Liesenfeld, prin. Fax 573-3590
Whittier MS 1,100/6-8
2000 W Brooks St 73069 405-366-5956
Gayla Mears, prin. Fax 447-6562

OK Dept. of Voc. & Tech. Education
Supt. — None
Dr. Marcie Mack, dir.
Moore Norman Technology Center Vo/Tech
PO Box 4701 73070 405-364-5763
Dr. Jane Bowen, supt. Fax 217-8277

Community Christian S 700/PK-12
3002 Broce Dr 73072 405-329-2500
Hollywood Cosmetology Center Post-Sec.
1708 W Lindsey St 73069 405-364-3375
University of Oklahoma Post-Sec.
660 Parrington Oval 73019 405-325-0311

Nowata, Nowata, Pop. 3,335
Nowata ISD 1,000/PK-12
707 W Osage Ave 74048 918-273-3425
Leon Ashlock, supt. Fax 273-2105
www.npsok.org
Nowata HS 300/9-12
707 W Osage Ave 74048 918-273-2221
Bron Williams, prin. Fax 273-2105
Nowata MS 200/6-8
707 W Osage Ave 74048 918-273-1346
James Sexson, prin. Fax 273-2105

Oaks, Delaware, Pop. 277
Oaks-Mission ISD 200/PK-12
PO Box 160 74359 918-868-2183
Dr. John Sheridan, supt. Fax 868-2707
Oaks-Mission HS 100/9-12
PO Box 160 74359 918-868-2499
John Sheridan, prin. Fax 868-5012

Oilton, Creek, Pop. 965
Oilton ISD 300/PK-12
309 E Peterson St 74052 918-862-3954
Matt Posey, supt. Fax 862-3955
www.oilton.k12.ok.us
Oilton HS 100/9-12
309 E Peterson St 74052 918-862-3272
Daniel McEntire, prin. Fax 862-3763

Okarche, Kingfisher, Pop. 1,196
Okarche ISD 300/PK-12
PO Box 276 73762 405-263-7300
Robert Friesen, supt. Fax 263-7515
www.okarche.k12.ok.us
Okarche HS 100/10-12
PO Box 276 73762 405-263-7212
Robert Friesen, prin. Fax 263-7515
Okarche JHS 100/7-9
PO Box 276 73762 405-263-7212
Robert Friesen, prin. Fax 263-7515

Okay, Wagoner, Pop. 586
Okay ISD 400/PK-12
PO Box 830 74446 918-682-2548
Charles McMahan, supt. Fax 683-8331
www.okayps.org
Okay HS 100/9-12
PO Box 830 74446 918-682-0371
Mark Hayes, prin. Fax 682-7653

Okeene, Blaine, Pop. 1,187
Okeene ISD 300/PK-12
PO Box 409 73763 580-822-3268
Ron Pittman, supt. Fax 822-4123
www.okeene.k12.ok.us
Okeene JSHS 100/7-12
PO Box 409 73763 580-822-3219
Jeremy Osmus, prin. Fax 822-4123

Okemah, Okfuskee, Pop. 3,000
Okemah ISD 800/PK-12
107 W Date St 74859 918-623-1874
Tony Dean, supt. Fax 623-1203
www.okemahk12.com
Okemah HS 300/9-12
704 E Date St 74859 918-623-1874
Ronald Vick, prin. Fax 623-1884
Okemah MS 200/4-8
107 W Date St 74859 918-623-1874
Sandra Lambert, prin. Fax 623-9151

Oklahoma City, Oklahoma, Pop. 555,623
Crooked Oak ISD 1,100/PK-12
1450 S Eastern Ave 73129 405-677-5252
Brad Richards, supt. Fax 670-8070
www.crookedoak.org
Crooked Oak HS 300/9-12
1450 S Eastern Ave 73129 405-677-3452
Barbara Jaramillo, prin. Fax 670-8072
Crooked Oak MS 300/6-8
1450 S Eastern Ave 73129 405-677-5133
Dennis McCray, prin. Fax 670-2256

Millwood ISD 800/PK-12
6724 N Martin Luther King 73111 405-478-1336
Cecilia Robinson-Woods, supt. Fax 478-4698
millwood.k12.ok.us
Millwood Arts Academy 6-8
6724 N Martin Luther King 73111 405-475-1004
Candice Greene, prin. Fax 478-7134
Millwood HS 300/9-12
6718 N Martin Luther King 73111 405-475-1015
Petra Woodard, prin. Fax 478-4194

Moore ISD
Supt. — See Moore
Brink JHS 1,000/7-8
11420 S Western Ave 73170 405-735-4540
Joseph Ross, prin. Fax 692-5634
Moore West JHS 600/7-8
9400 S Pennsylvania Ave 73159 405-735-4620
Jeni Dutton, prin. Fax 692-5660
Southridge JHS 7-8
14141 S Pennsylvania 73170 405-735-4680
Melanie Smith, prin.
Westmoore HS 2,100/9-12
12613 S Western Ave 73170 405-735-4800
Mark Hunt, prin. Fax 692-5711

OK Dept. of Voc. & Tech. Education
Supt. — None
Dr. Marcie Mack, dir.
Metro Tech-Aviation Career Center Vo/Tech
5600 S MacArthur Blvd 73179 405-424-8324
Dr. Elaine Stith, supt.
Metro Tech Downtown Vo/Tech
100 N Broadway 73102 405-424-8324
Metro Tech South Bryant Campus Vo/Tech
4901 S Bryant Ave 73129 405-424-8324
Dr. Elaine Stith, supt. Fax 670-6895
Metro Tech-Springlake Campus Vo/Tech
1900 Springlake Dr 73111 405-424-8324
Dr. Elaine Stith, supt. Fax 424-8589
Tuttle-Portland Campus Vo/Tech
3500 NW 150th St 73134 405-717-7799
Dr. Tom Friedemann, supt. Fax 755-0028
Tuttle-Reno Campus Vo/Tech
7301 W Reno Ave 73127 405-717-4646
Dr. Tom Friedemann, supt.
Tuttle-Rockwell Campus Vo/Tech
12777 N Rockwell Ave 73142 405-717-7799
Dr. Tom Friedemann, supt. Fax 717-4112

Oklahoma City ISD 40,800/PK-12
900 N Klein Ave 73106 405-587-0000
Robert Neu, supt. Fax 587-0443
www.okcps.org
Belle Isle Enterprise MS 500/6-8
5904 N Villa Ave 73112 405-587-6600
Lynn Kellert, prin. Fax 587-6605
Capitol Hill HS 1,300/9-12
500 SW Grand Blvd 73109 405-587-9000
Adam Jewell, prin. Fax 587-9005
Classen S of Advanced Studies 500/6-12
1901 N Ellison Ave 73106 405-587-5400
Dr. Ashley Davis, prin. Fax 587-5405

Douglass MSHS 400/7-12
900 N Martin Luther King Av 73117 405-587-4200
Dr. Andrew Pearson, prin. Fax 587-4205
Emerson HS 500/Alt
715 N Walker Ave 73102 405-587-7900
Sheryl Kishore, prin. Fax 587-7905
Grant HS 1,600/9-12
5016 S Pennsylvania Ave 73119 405-587-2200
Greg Frederick, prin. Fax 587-2205
Jefferson MS 900/6-8
6800 S Blackwelder Ave 73159 405-587-1300
Heather Messer, prin. Fax 587-1305
Marshall MSHS 400/6-12
12201 N Portland Ave 73120 405-587-7200
Aspasia Carlson, prin. Fax 587-7205
Northeast Academy for Health Sci./Eng. 200/6-12
3100 N Kelley Ave 73111 405-587-3300
Sue Starr, prin. Fax 587-3305
Northwest Classen HS 1,100/9-12
2801 NW 27th St 73107 405-587-6300
John Wilson, prin. Fax 587-6305
Oklahoma Centennial MSHS 300/6-12
1301 NE 101st St 73131 405-587-5200
Tamie Sanders, prin. Fax 587-5205
Roosevelt MS 600/6-8
3233 SW 44th St 73119 405-587-8300
David Clark, prin. Fax 587-8305
Southeast HS 700/9-12
5401 S Shields Blvd 73129 405-587-9600
Mylissa Hall, prin. Fax 587-9605
Taft MS, 2901 NW 23rd St 73107 600/6-8
Charmaine Johnson, prin. 405-587-8000
Webster MS 800/6-8
6708 S Santa Fe Ave 73139 405-587-3900
Joey Slate, prin.
Other Schools – See Spencer

Oklahoma School of Science & Math 11-12
1141 N Lincoln Blvd 73104 405-521-6436
Dr. Frank Wang, pres. Fax 522-4586
www.ossm.edu
Oklahoma S of Science & Math 11-12
1141 N Lincoln Blvd 73104 405-521-6436
Dr. Frank Wang, pres. Fax 522-4586

Putnam City ISD 19,300/PK-12
5401 NW 40th St 73122 405-495-5200
Dr. Fred Rhodes, supt. Fax 495-8648
www.putnamcityschools.org
Cooper MS 700/6-8
8001 River Bend Blvd 73132 405-720-9887
Mark Lebsack, prin. Fax 728-5632
Hefner MS 1,100/6-8
8400 N MacArthur Blvd 73132 405-721-2411
Toye Mitchell, prin. Fax 728-5645
Mayfield MS 700/6-8
1600 N Purdue Ave 73127 405-947-8693
Tracy Sowinski, prin. Fax 948-9000
Putnam City North HS 1,900/9-12
11800 N Rockwell Ave 73162 405-722-4220
Dr. Brian Chastain, prin. Fax 721-4946
Putnam City West HS 1,600/9-12
8500 NW 23rd St 73127 405-787-1140
Buster Meeks, prin. Fax 491-7602
Other Schools – See Bethany, Warr Acres

Western Heights ISD 3,800/PK-12
8401 SW 44th St 73179 405-350-3410
Joe Kitchens, supt. Fax 745-6322
www.westernheights.k12.ok.us
Western Heights 9th Grade Center 200/9-9
8201 SW 44th St 73179 405-350-3415
James Smith, prin. Fax 261-0280
Western Heights Academy Alt
8435 SW 44th St 73179 405-350-3485
Khristi Mize, prin. Fax 745-6364
Western Heights HS 700/10-12
8201 SW 44th St 73179 405-350-3435
Paul McQueen, prin. Fax 745-6315
Western Heights MS 500/7-8
8435 SW 44th St 73179 405-350-3455
Carolyn Erickson, prin. Fax 745-6341

Academy of Classical Christian Studies 500/PK-12
1120 E Hefner Rd 73131 405-478-2077
Bishop McGuinness HS 700/9-12
801 NW 50th St 73118 405-842-6638
David Morton, prin. Fax 858-9550
Brookline College Post-Sec.
9801 Broadway Ext 73114 405-842-9400
Brown Mackie College Post-Sec.
7101 NW Expressway Ste 800 73132 405-621-8000
Casady S 900/PK-12
9500 N Pennsylvania Ave 73120 405-749-3100
Nathan Sheldon, head sch Fax 749-3214
CC's Cosmetology College Post-Sec.
4439 NW 50th St 73112 405-943-2300
Central State Beauty Academy Post-Sec.
8494 NW Expressway 73162 405-722-4499
Crossings Christian S 700/PK-12
14400 N Portland Ave 73134 405-842-8495
Paul S. MacDonald, hdmstr. Fax 767-1520
DeVry University Post-Sec.
4013 NW Expressway Ste 100 73116 405-767-9516
Heritage Hall S 900/PK-12
1800 NW 122nd St 73120 405-749-3001
Guy Bramble, hdmstr. Fax 751-7372
Metro Area Vocational Technical School Post-Sec.
1900 Springlake Dr 73111 405-424-8324
Mid-America Christian University Post-Sec.
3500 SW 119th St 73170 405-691-3800
Mt. St. Mary's HS 400/9-12
2801 S Shartel Ave 73109 405-631-8865
Talita DeNegri, prin. Fax 631-9209
Oklahoma Christian University Post-Sec.
PO Box 11000 73136 405-425-5000
Oklahoma City Community College Post-Sec.
7777 S May Ave 73159 405-682-1611
Oklahoma City University Post-Sec.
2501 N Blackwelder Ave 73106 405-208-5000
Oklahoma State University-Oklahoma City Post-Sec.
900 N Portland Ave 73107 405-947-4421
Parkview Adventist Academy 100/PK-12
4201 N Martin Luther King 73111 405-427-6525
Platt College Post-Sec.
309 S Ann Arbor Ave 73128 405-946-7799
Platt College Post-Sec.
2727 W Memorial Rd 73134 405-749-2433
Trinity S K-12
321 NW 36th St 73118 405-525-5600
Jennifer Vaught, prin. Fax 525-5602
Tuttle Vocational Technical Center Post-Sec.
12777 N Rockwell Ave 73142 405-722-7799
University Hospital of Oklahoma City Post-Sec.
PO Box 26307 73126 405-271-4000
University of Oklahoma Health Sciences Post-Sec.
1100 N Lindsay Ave 73104 405-271-4000
Wright Career College Post-Sec.
2219 W I 240 Service Rd 73159 405-681-2300

Okmulgee, Okmulgee, Pop. 11,317
OK Dept. of Voc. & Tech. Education
Supt. — None
Dr. Marcie Mack, dir.
Green Country Technology Center Vo/Tech
PO Box 1217 74447 918-758-0840
Larry Killebrew, supt. Fax 758-0422

Okmulgee ISD 1,500/PK-12
PO Box 1346 74447 918-758-2000
Renee Dove, supt. Fax 758-2088
www.okmulgeeps.com
Okmulgee HS 400/9-12
415 W 3rd St 74447 918-758-2075
Sean O'Brien, prin. Fax 758-2096
Okmulgee JHS 200/7-8
415 W 3rd St 74447 918-758-2050
Brad Ferguson, prin. Fax 758-2095

College of Muscogee Nation Post-Sec.
PO Box 917 74447 918-549-2800
Oklahoma State Univ Institute of Tech Post-Sec.
1801 E 4th St 74447 800-722-4471

Oktaha, Muskogee, Pop. 343
Oktaha ISD 800/PK-12
PO Box 9 74450 918-687-7556
Jerry Needham M.Ed., supt. Fax 687-0074
www.oktahaschool.com
Oktaha HS 200/9-12
PO Box 9 74450 918-687-3672
Chris Burt M.Ed., prin. Fax 687-8551

Olustee, Jackson, Pop. 583
Olustee ISD 200/PK-12
PO Box 70 73560 580-648-2243
Gaylene Freeman, supt. Fax 648-2501
www.olustee.k12.ok.us
Olustee HS 50/9-12
PO Box 70 73560 580-648-2243
Brent Drury, prin. Fax 648-2501

Omega, Kingfisher
Lomega ISD 200/PK-12
18319 N 2700 Rd 73764 405-729-4215
Karen Castonguay, supt. Fax 729-4666
www.lomega.k12.ok.us
Lomega HS 50/9-12
18319 N 2700 Rd 73764 405-729-4281
Karen Castonguay, prin. Fax 729-4666

OK Dept. of Voc. & Tech. Education
Supt. — None
Dr. Marcie Mack, dir.
Chisholm Trail Technology Center Vo/Tech
283 State Highway 33 73764 405-729-8324
Max Thomas, supt. Fax 729-8335

Oologah, Rogers, Pop. 1,080
Oologah-Talala ISD 1,800/PK-12
PO Box 189 74053 918-443-6000
Max Tanner, supt. Fax 443-9088
www.oologah.k12.ok.us
Oologah HS 600/9-12
PO Box 189 74053 918-443-6211
Melissa Overcash, prin. Fax 443-2418
Oologah MS 400/6-8
PO Box 189 74053 918-443-6161
Kelli Dixon, prin. Fax 443-2875

Orlando, Logan, Pop. 142
Mulhall-Orlando ISD 200/PK-12
100 E Main 73073 405-649-2000
Randy Vollmer, supt. Fax 649-2020
www.mulhall-orlando.k12.ok.us
Mulhall-Orlando HS 100/9-12
100 E Main 73073 580-455-2211
Joline Oldenburg, prin. Fax 455-8019

Owasso, Tulsa, Pop. 27,251
OK Dept. of Voc. & Tech. Education
Supt. — None
Dr. Marcie Mack, dir.
Tulsa Tech Center Owasso Campus Vo/Tech
10800 N 140th East Ave 74055 918-828-1400
Kent Inouye, dir. Fax 376-4107

Owasso ISD 9,400/PK-12
1501 N Ash St 74055 918-272-5367
Dr. Clark Ogilvie, supt. Fax 272-8111
www.owassops.org
Owasso Eighth Grade Center 800/8-8
13901 E 86th St N 74055 918-272-6274
Deirdre Hodge, prin. Fax 272-5562
Owasso HS 1,300/11-12
12901 E 86th St N 74055 918-272-5334
Matt Roberts, prin. Fax 272-8108
Owasso Mid HS 1,400/9-10
8800 N 129th East Ave 74055 918-274-3000
Matt Roberts, prin. Fax 274-3006
Owasso Ram Academy Alt
202 E Broadway St 74055 918-272-8040
Matt Roberts, prin. Fax 272-0712

Rejoice Christian S 300/PK-12
13407 E 106th St N 74055 918-516-0050
Dr. Craig Shaw, supt. Fax 516-0299

Paden, Okfuskee, Pop. 430
Paden ISD 300/PK-12
PO Box 370 74860 405-932-5053
Michelle Stiles, supt. Fax 932-4132
www.paden.k12.ok.us
Paden HS, PO Box 370 74860 100/9-12
Chris Howk, prin. 405-932-4465

Panama, LeFlore, Pop. 1,335
Panama ISD 600/PK-12
PO Box 1680 74951 918-963-2215
Grant Ralls, supt. Fax 963-4860
www.panama.k12.ok.us
Panama HS, PO Box 1680 74951 200/9-12
Richard Haynes, prin. 918-963-0409
Panama MS 100/6-8
PO Box 1680 74951 918-963-4479
James Hoffman, dean Fax 963-4493

Panola, Latimer
Panola ISD 200/PK-12
PO Box 6 74559 918-465-3298
Brad Corcoran, supt. Fax 465-3656
panolabearcats.org
Panola HS 100/9-12
PO Box 6 74559 918-465-3813
Linda Albright, prin. Fax 465-2996

Paoli, Garvin, Pop. 587
Paoli ISD 300/PK-12
PO Box 278 73074 405-484-7336
David Morris, supt. Fax 484-7268
www.paoli.k12.ok.us/
Paoli HS 100/9-12
PO Box 278 73074 405-484-7336
David Morris, prin. Fax 484-7268

Park Hill, Cherokee, Pop. 3,515
Keys ISD 900/PK-12
26622 S 520 Rd 74451 918-458-1835
Vol Woods, supt. Fax 456-1656
www.keys.k12.ok.us
Keys HS 300/9-12
26622 S 520 Rd 74451 918-458-1835
Steven Goss, prin. Fax 456-7502

Pauls Valley, Garvin, Pop. 5,834
Pauls Valley ISD 1,300/PK-12
PO Box 780 73075 405-238-6453
Mike Martin, supt. Fax 238-9178
www.paulsvalleyschools.com/
Pauls Valley HS 300/10-12
PO Box 780 73075 405-238-6497
Chris Caldwell, prin. Fax 238-1236
Pauls Valley JHS 300/7-9
PO Box 780 73075 405-238-1239
Martha Graham, prin. Fax 238-1410

Pawhuska, Osage, Pop. 3,306
Pawhuska ISD 800/PK-12
1801 McKenzie Rd 74056 918-287-1281
Dr. Landon Berry, supt. Fax 287-4461
www.pawhuskadistrict.org/
Pawhuska HS 300/8-12
621 E 15th St 74056 918-287-1266
Joel Sindelar, prin. Fax 287-1236

Pawnee, Pawnee, Pop. 2,051
Pawnee ISD 800/PK-12
615 Denver St 74058 918-762-3676
Ned Williams, supt. Fax 762-2704
www.pawnee.k12.ok.us
Pawnee HS 200/9-12
615 Denver St 74058 918-762-3676
Bobby Miller, prin. Fax 762-2704
Pawnee MS 200/6-8
605 Denver St 74058 918-762-3055
Stacy Womack, prin. Fax 762-3585

Perkins, Payne, Pop. 2,678
Perkins-Tryon ISD 1,500/PK-12
PO Box 549 74059 405-547-5703
James Ramsey, supt. Fax 547-2020
www.p-t.k12.ok.us
Perkins-Tryon HS 400/9-12
PO Box 549 74059 405-547-5724
Joe McElroy, prin. Fax 547-5760
Perkins-Tryon JHS 300/6-8
PO Box 549 74059 405-547-5715
Jerry Burnett, prin. Fax 547-5761

Perry, Noble, Pop. 4,921
Perry ISD 1,200/PK-12
900 Fir St 73077 580-336-4511
Scott Chenoweth, supt. Fax 336-5185
www.perry.k12.ok.us/
Perry HS 300/9-12
900 Fir St 73077 580-336-4415
Les Justus, prin. Fax 336-3163
Perry JHS 200/7-8
901 Elm St 73077 580-336-2265
Bryan Hall, prin. Fax 336-4211

Piedmont, Canadian, Pop. 5,527
Piedmont ISD 3,200/PK-12
713 Piedmont Rd N 73078 405-373-2311
James White, supt. Fax 373-0912
www.piedmontschools.org

Piedmont HS 800/9-12
1055 Edmond Rd NW 73078 405-373-5011
Layne Jones, prin. Fax 373-3055
Piedmont MS 500/7-8
823 2nd St NW 73078 405-373-1315
Trinity Johnson, prin. Fax 373-5006

Pittsburg, Pittsburg, Pop. 206
Pittsburg ISD 100/PK-12
PO Box 200 74560 918-432-5062
Chad Graham, supt. Fax 432-5312
www.pittsburg.k12.ok.us
Pittsburg HS, PO Box 200 74560 50/9-12
Chad Graham, prin. 918-432-5513

Pocola, LeFlore, Pop. 3,869
Pocola ISD 800/PK-12
600 E Pryor Ave 74902 918-436-2424
Lawrence Barnes, supt. Fax 436-2437
www.pocola.k12.ok.us
Pocola HS 200/9-12
603 E Pryor Ave 74902 918-436-2042
Randy Ragland, prin. Fax 436-2920
Pocola MS 200/6-8
603 E Pryor Ave 74902 918-436-2091
Mark McKenzie, prin. Fax 436-9880

Ponca City, Kay, Pop. 24,217
OK Dept. of Voc. & Tech. Education
Supt. — None
Dr. Marcie Mack, dir.
Pioneer Technology Center Vo/Tech
2101 N Ash St 74601 580-762-8336
Bruce DeMuth, supt. Fax 762-3107

Ponca City ISD 5,300/PK-12
613 E Grand Ave 74601 580-767-8000
Dr. David Pennington, supt. Fax 767-8007
www.pcps.us
East MS 400/8-8
612 E Grand Ave 74601 580-767-8010
Barbara Davis, prin. Fax 762-5301
Ponca City HS 1,500/9-12
927 N 5th St 74601 580-767-9500
Thad Dilbeck, prin. Fax 767-9515

Ponca City Beauty College Post-Sec.
122 N 1st St 74601 888-557-6709

Pond Creek, Grant, Pop. 839
Pond Creek-Hunter ISD 300/PK-12
200 E Broadway St 73766 580-532-4242
Joel Quinn, supt. Fax 532-4965
www.pondcreek-hunter.k12.ok.us
Pond Creek-Hunter HS 100/9-12
200 E Broadway St 73766 580-532-4241
Kelly Childress, prin. Fax 532-4965
Pond Creek-Hunter MS 100/5-8
200 E Broadway St 73766 580-532-4262
Jamie Ronck, prin. Fax 532-4965

Porter, Wagoner, Pop. 534
Porter Consolidated ISD 600/PK-12
PO Box 120 74454 918-483-2401
Mark Fenton, supt. Fax 483-2310
www.porter.k12.ok.us
Porter Consolidated HS 200/9-12
PO Box 120 74454 918-483-7011
Larry Shackelford, prin. Fax 483-2310

Porum, Muskogee, Pop. 622
Porum ISD 500/PK-12
PO Box 189 74455 918-484-5121
Curtis Curry, supt. Fax 484-2310
www.porum.k12.ok.us/
Porum HS 100/9-12
PO Box 189 74455 918-484-5122
Brent Pearce, prin. Fax 484-5121

Poteau, LeFlore, Pop. 8,045
OK Dept. of Voc. & Tech. Education
Supt. — None
Dr. Marcie Mack, dir.
Kiamichi Technology Center Vo/Tech
PO Box 825 74953 918-647-4525
Doug Hall, dir. Fax 647-4527

Poteau ISD 2,400/PK-12
100 Mockingbird Ln 74953 918-647-7700
Dr. Don Sjoberg, supt. Fax 647-9357
www.poteau.k12.ok.us
Kidd MS 500/6-8
100 Mockingbird Ln 74953 918-647-7741
Joe Ballard, prin. Fax 647-4286
Poteau HS 600/9-12
100 Mockingbird Ln 74953 918-647-7716
Raford Ulrich, prin. Fax 647-4383

Carl Albert State College Post-Sec.
1507 S McKenna St 74953 918-647-1200

Prague, Lincoln, Pop. 2,232
Prague ISD 1,000/K-12
3504 NBU 74864 405-567-4455
Justin Lockwood, supt. Fax 567-3095
www.prague.k12.ok.us
Prague HS 300/9-12
3504 NBU 74864 405-567-2281
Joe Jacobs, prin. Fax 567-4982
Prague MS 200/6-8
3504 NBU 74864 405-567-2281
Benny Burnett, prin. Fax 567-3095

Preston, Okmulgee
Preston ISD 500/PK-12
PO Box 40 74456 918-756-3388
Mark Hudson, supt. Fax 756-2122
www.preston.k12.ok.us/
Preston HS 100/9-12
PO Box 40 74456 918-756-8636
Pamela Snowden, prin. Fax 756-2122

Prue, Osage, Pop. 443
Prue ISD 300/PK-12
PO Box 130 74060 918-242-3351
Tom Scully, supt. Fax 242-3392
www.prue.k12.ok.us/
Prue HS 100/9-12
PO Box 130 74060 918-242-3384
Tom Scully, prin. Fax 242-3888

Pryor, Mayes, Pop. 8,842
OK Dept. of Voc. & Tech. Education
Supt. — None
Dr. Marcie Mack, dir.
Northeast Tech Center Pryor Campus Vo/Tech
PO Box 825 74362 918-825-5555
Debby Peaster, dir. Fax 825-6281

Pryor ISD 2,600/PK-12
PO Box 548 74362 918-825-1255
Don Raleigh, supt. Fax 825-3938
sites.google.com/a/pryorschools.org/pryorschools-org
Pryor HS 600/10-12
PO Box 548 74362 918-825-2340
Brad Bates, prin. Fax 825-3914
Pryor JHS 600/7-9
PO Box 548 74362 918-825-2371
Terry Gwartney, prin. Fax 825-3950

Bradford Christian S 50/K-12
2320 NE 1st St 74361 918-825-7038
Amanda Rutherford, admin. Fax 825-7037
Pryor Beauty College Post-Sec.
330 W Graham Ave 74361 918-825-2795

Purcell, McClain, Pop. 5,558
Purcell ISD 1,500/PK-12
919 1/2 N 9th Ave 73080 405-527-2146
Dr. Jason Midkiff, supt. Fax 527-6366
www.purcellps.org
Purcell HS 400/9-12
2020 N Green Ave 73080 405-527-4400
Bret Petty, prin. Fax 527-4410
Purcell JHS 300/6-8
201 Lester Ln 73080 405-527-6591
Byron Mooney, prin. Fax 527-6593

Quapaw, Ottawa, Pop. 859
Quapaw ISD 600/PK-12
305 W 1st St 74363 918-674-2501
Dr. Randy D. Darr Ed.D., supt. Fax 674-2721
www.qpswildcats.com
Quapaw HS 200/9-12
305 W 1st St 74363 918-674-2474
Tamara Bacon, prin. Fax 674-2721
Quapaw MS 100/6-8
305 W 1st St 74363 918-674-2496
Tamara Bacon, prin. Fax 674-2721

Quinton, Pittsburg, Pop. 953
Quinton ISD 500/PK-12
PO Box 670 74561 918-469-3100
Don Cox, supt. Fax 469-3308
www.quintonschools.com
Quinton HS 100/9-12
PO Box 670 74561 918-469-3309
Dane Lemons, prin. Fax 469-2310

Ralston, Pawnee, Pop. 314
Woodland SD
Supt. — See Fairfax
Woodland MS 100/5-8
6th & McKinley 74650 918-738-4286
Shelly Doshier, prin. Fax 738-4287

Ramona, Washington, Pop. 498
Caney Valley ISD 800/PK-12
PO Box 410 74061 918-536-2500
Rick Peters, supt. Fax 536-2600
www.caneyvalleyschool.org/
Caney Valley HS 200/9-12
PO Box 410 74061 918-536-3425
Debra Keil, prin. Fax 536-7105
Caney Valley MS 200/6-8
PO Box 410 74061 918-536-2705
Travis Lashbrook, prin. Fax 536-7105

Randlett, Cotton, Pop. 435
Big Pasture ISD 200/PK-12
PO Box 167 73562 580-281-3831
Danny McCuiston, supt. Fax 281-3299
www.bigpasture.org
Big Pasture HS 100/9-12
PO Box 167 73562 580-281-3276
Danny McCuiston, prin. Fax 281-3299

Rattan, Pushmataha, Pop. 299
Rattan ISD 500/PK-12
PO Box 44 74562 580-587-2546
Shari Pillow, supt. Fax 587-4000
www.rattan.k12.ok.us
Rattan JHS 100/7-8
PO Box 44 74562 580-587-2715
Neil Birchfield, prin. Fax 587-2476
Rattan SHS 100/9-12
PO Box 44 74562 580-587-2715
Neil Birchfield, prin. Fax 587-2476

Red Oak, Latimer, Pop. 508
Red Oak ISD 200/PK-12
PO Box 310 74563 918-754-2426
Bryan Deatherage, supt. Fax 754-2898
redoak.k12.ok.us
Red Oak HS 100/9-12
PO Box 310 74563 918-754-2283
Bryan Deatherage, prin. Fax 754-2898

Red Rock, Noble, Pop. 265
Frontier ISD 400/PK-12
PO Box 130 74651 580-723-4361
Tracy Kincannon, supt. Fax 723-4516
www.frontierok.com
Frontier HS 100/9-12
PO Box 130 74651 580-723-4360
Doug Sinor, prin. Fax 723-4516

Reydon, Roger Mills, Pop. 205
Reydon ISD 100/PK-12
PO Box 10 73660 580-655-4375
Phil Drouhard, supt. Fax 655-4622
www.reydon.k12.ok.us
Reydon HS, PO Box 10 73660 50/9-12
Ryan Baker, prin. 580-655-4375

Ringling, Jefferson, Pop. 968
Ringling ISD 500/PK-12
PO Box 1010 73456 580-662-2385
Kent Southward, supt. Fax 662-2683
www.ringling.k12.ok.us
Ringling HS 100/10-12
PO Box 1010 73456 580-662-2386
Barry Benson, prin. Fax 662-3323
Ringling JHS 100/7-9
PO Box 1010 73456 580-662-2386
Barry Benson, prin. Fax 662-3323

Ringwood, Major, Pop. 490
Ringwood ISD 400/PK-12
101 W 5th St 73768 580-883-2201
Wade Detrick, supt. Fax 883-2220
www.ringwood.k12.ok.us
Ringwood HS 100/9-12
101 W 5th St 73768 580-883-2201
Pete Maples, prin. Fax 883-2220

Ripley, Payne, Pop. 385
Ripley ISD 500/PK-12
PO Box 97 74062 918-372-4567
Dr. Kenny Beams, supt. Fax 372-4608
www.ripley.k12.ok.us/
Ripley HS 100/9-12
PO Box 97 74062 918-372-4245
Joshua Calavan, prin. Fax 372-4608

Roff, Pontotoc, Pop. 687
Roff ISD 400/PK-12
PO Box 157 74865 580-456-7663
Scott Morgan, supt. Fax 456-7245
www.roff.k12.ok.us
Roff HS 100/9-12
PO Box 157 74865 580-456-7252
Ead Simon, prin. Fax 456-7499

Roland, Sequoyah, Pop. 2,907
Roland ISD 1,200/PK-12
300 Ranger Blvd 74954 918-427-4601
Paul Wood, supt. Fax 427-1785
www.rolandschools.org
Roland HS 300/10-12
300 Ranger Blvd 74954 918-427-7419
Steven Barrick, prin. Fax 427-6993
Roland JHS 300/7-9
300 Ranger Blvd 74954 918-427-4631
John Speir, prin. Fax 427-0093

Rush Springs, Grady, Pop. 1,191
Rush Springs ISD 600/PK-12
PO Box 308 73082 580-476-3929
Mike Zurline, supt. Fax 476-2018
www.rushsprings.k12.ok.us
Rush Springs HS 200/9-12
PO Box 308 73082 580-476-3596
Shawn Haskins, prin. Fax 476-2018
Rush Springs MS 100/6-8
PO Box 308 73082 580-476-3447
Shawn Haskins, prin. Fax 476-2148

Ryan, Jefferson, Pop. 785
Ryan ISD 300/PK-12
1201 Washington St 73565 580-757-2308
Larry Ninman, supt. Fax 757-2609
www.ryan.k12.ok.us
Ryan HS, 1201 Washington St 73565 100/9-12
Tony Tomberlin, prin. 580-757-2296

Salina, Mayes, Pop. 1,257
Salina ISD 800/PK-12
PO Box 98 74365 918-434-5091
Tony Thomas, supt. Fax 434-5346
www.salina.k12.ok.us
Salina HS 300/9-12
PO Box 98 74365 918-434-5347
Kyle Fowler, prin. Fax 434-5537
Salina MS 200/6-8
PO Box 98 74365 918-434-5311
Debbie Cox, prin. Fax 434-5173

Sallisaw, Sequoyah, Pop. 7,974
Central ISD 500/PK-12
108089 S 4670 Rd 74955 918-775-5525
Larry Henson, supt. Fax 775-8557
www.centralps.k12.ok.us
Central HS 200/9-12
108089 S 4670 Rd 74955 918-775-5525
John Speir, prin. Fax 775-8557

OK Dept. of Voc. & Tech. Education
Supt. — None
Dr. Marcie Mack, dir.
Indian Capital Technology Center Vo/Tech
401 E Houser Blvd 74955 918-775-9119
Dr. Curtis Shumaker, dir. Fax 775-7305

Sallisaw ISD 2,000/PK-12
701 S J T Stites St 74955 918-775-5544
Scott Farmer, supt. Fax 775-1257
sallisawps.org
Sallisaw HS 600/9-12
2301 W Ruth Ave 74955 918-775-7761
Ernie Martens, prin. Fax 775-1275
Sallisaw MS 400/6-8
211 S Main St 74955 918-775-6561
Greg Cast, prin. Fax 775-1276

Sand Springs, Tulsa, Pop. 17,953
OK Dept. of Voc. & Tech. Education
Supt. — None
Dr. Marcie Mack, dir.
Tulsa Tech Center Sand Springs Campus Vo/Tech
924 E Charles Page Blvd 74063 918-828-1300
Derek Beller, dir. Fax 828-1309

Sand Springs ISD 5,300/PK-12
11 W Broadway St 74063 918-246-1400
Lloyd Snow, supt. Fax 246-1401
www.sandites.org/
Boyd MS 1,200/6-8
305 W 35th St 74063 918-246-1535
Nancy Ogle, prin. Fax 246-1544
Central 9th Grade Center 500/9-9
14 W 4th St 74063 918-246-1440
Ernie Kothe, prin. Fax 246-1446
Page Academy 100/Alt
104 W 4th St 74063 918-246-1564
Janice Marr, admin. Fax 246-1565
Page HS 1,300/10-12
500 N Adams Rd 74063 918-246-1470
Stan Trout, prin. Fax 246-1480

Sand Springs Beauty College Post-Sec.
28 E 2nd St 74063 918-245-6627

Sapulpa, Creek, Pop. 19,322
OK Dept. of Voc. & Tech. Education
Supt. — None
Dr. Marcie Mack, dir.
Central Tech Vo/Tech
1720 S Main St 74066 918-224-9300
Fax 224-3190

Sapulpa ISD 4,000/PK-12
511 E Lee Ave 74066 918-224-3400
Kevin Burr, supt. Fax 227-8347
www.sapulpaps.org
Bartlett Academy Alt
603 S Park St 74066 918-224-7958
Dr. Roger Johnson, prin. Fax 224-0049
Sapulpa JHS 600/8-9
7 S Mission St 74066 918-224-6710
Johnny Bilby, prin. Fax 227-0473
Sapulpa SHS 1,000/10-12
3 S Mission St 74066 918-224-6560
Johnny Bilby, prin. Fax 224-0174

Eagle Point Christian Academy 100/PK-12
602 S Mounds St 74066 918-227-2441
Jim Pryor, admin. Fax 248-3117

Sasakwa, Seminole, Pop. 141
Sasakwa ISD 200/PK-12
PO Box 323 74867 405-941-3250
Kyle Wilson, supt. Fax 941-3561
www.sasakwaschools.org
Sasakwa HS 100/9-12
PO Box 323 74867 405-941-3250
Brent Griffin, prin. Fax 941-3561

Savanna, Pittsburg, Pop. 629
Savanna ISD 400/PK-12
PO Box 266 74565 918-548-3777
Gary Reeder, supt. Fax 548-3836
www.savanna.k12.ok.us/
Savanna HS 200/9-12
PO Box 266 74565 918-548-3777
Brad Kellogg, prin. Fax 548-3836

Sayre, Beckham, Pop. 4,304
OK Dept. of Voc. & Tech. Education
Supt. — None
Dr. Marcie Mack, dir.
Western Technology Center Vo/Tech
2002 NE Highway 66 73662 580-928-2097
Hal Holt, dir. Fax 928-9827

Sayre ISD 800/PK-12
716 NE Highway 66 73662 580-928-5531
Todd Winn, supt. Fax 928-5538
www.sayre.k12.ok.us
Sayre HS 200/9-12
716 NE Highway 66 73662 580-928-5576
Danny Crabb, prin. Fax 928-3045
Sayre MS 200/6-8
716 NE Highway 66 73662 580-928-5578
Danny Clifton, prin. Fax 928-3045

Southwestern Oklahoma State University Post-Sec.
409 E Mississippi Ave 73662 580-928-5533

Schulter, Okmulgee, Pop. 449
Schulter ISD 200/PK-12
PO Box 203 74460 918-652-8219
Allen Callahan, supt. Fax 652-8474
www.schulter.k12.ok.us/
Schulter HS 50/9-12
PO Box 203 74460 918-652-8200
Allen Callahan, prin. Fax 652-8474

Seiling, Dewey, Pop. 824
Seiling ISD 300/PK-12
PO Box 780 73663 580-922-7383
Randy Seifried, supt. Fax 922-8019
www.seiling.k12.ok.us
Seiling JSHS 100/7-12
PO Box 780 73663 580-922-7382
Gary Baker, prin. Fax 922-8019

Seminole, Seminole, Pop. 6,934
Seminole ISD 1,500/PK-12
PO Box 1031 74818 405-382-5085
Alfred Gaches, supt. Fax 382-8281
seminole1.schooldesk.net/
Seminole HS 500/9-12
PO Box 1031 74818 405-382-1415
Steven Osborn, prin. Fax 382-1062
Seminole MS 300/7-8
PO Box 1031 74818 405-382-5065
David Dean, prin. Fax 382-8653

Strother ISD 400/PK-12
36085 EW 1140 74868 405-382-4014
Kolby Johnson, supt. Fax 382-3339
www.strother.k12.ok.us
Strother HS 100/9-12
36085 EW 1140 74868 405-382-4014
Scott Douthit, prin. Fax 382-3339

Varnum ISD 300/PK-12
11929 NS 3550 74868 405-382-1448
David Brewer, supt. Fax 382-8618
www.varnum.k12.ok.us
Varnum HS 100/9-12
11929 NS 3550 74868 405-382-1408
Kevin Romine, prin. Fax 382-8618

Seminole State College Post-Sec.
PO Box 351 74818 405-382-9950

Sentinel, Washita, Pop. 867
Sentinel ISD 300/PK-12
PO Box 640 73664 580-393-2101
Jason Goostree, supt. Fax 393-4334
www.sentinel.k12.ok.us/
Thomas HS 100/9-12
PO Box 640 73664 580-393-2112
Tony Summers, prin. Fax 393-4334

Shattuck, Ellis, Pop. 1,338
Shattuck ISD 400/PK-12
PO Box 159 73858 580-938-2586
Randy Holley, supt. Fax 938-8019
www.shattuck.k12.ok.us/
Shattuck HS 100/9-12
PO Box 159 73858 580-938-2586
Terry Conder, prin. Fax 938-8019

Shawnee, Pottawatomie, Pop. 28,106
Bethel ISD 1,300/PK-12
36000 Clearpond Rd 74801 405-273-0385
Jerry M. Johnson M.Ed., supt. Fax 273-5056
bethel.k12.ok.us
Bethel HS 400/9-12
36000 Clearpond Rd 74801 405-273-3633
Jeremy Stewart, prin. Fax 878-5571
Bethel MS 300/6-8
36000 Clearpond Rd 74801 405-273-5944
Tina Moon M.Ed., prin. Fax 273-6025

OK Dept. of Voc. & Tech. Education
Supt. — None
Dr. Marcie Mack, dir.
Cooper Technology Center Vo/Tech
1 John C Bruton Blvd 74804 405-273-7493
Marty Lewis, supt. Fax 273-4704

Shawnee ISD 4,100/PK-12
326 N Union Ave 74801 405-273-0653
Dr. April Grace, supt. Fax 273-6818
www.shawnee.k12.ok.us
Shawnee HS 1,300/9-12
1001 N Kennedy Ave 74801 405-275-3084
Matt Johnson, prin. Fax 275-9501
Shawnee MS 800/6-8
4300 N Union Ave 74804 405-273-0403
Colby Cagle, prin. Fax 275-9651
Thorpe Academy Alt
1111 N Kennedy Ave 74801 405-273-3525
Debra Watson, dir. Fax 878-1046

Family of Faith Christian S 100/K-12
PO Box 1442 74802 405-273-5331
Kathy Matthews, admin. Fax 273-8535
Family of Faith College Post-Sec.
PO Box 1805 74802 405-273-5331
Liberty Academy 300/PK-12
PO Box 1176 74802 405-273-3022
Susan Harmon, supt. Fax 273-3029
Oklahoma Baptist University Post-Sec.
500 W University St 74804 405-275-2850
St. Gregory's University Post-Sec.
1900 W MacArthur St 74804 888-784-7347
Shawnee Beauty College Post-Sec.
410 E Main St 74801 405-275-3182

Shidler, Osage, Pop. 394
Shidler ISD 300/PK-12
PO Box 85 74652 918-793-2021
John Herzig, supt. Fax 793-2061
www.shidlerpublicschools.org
Shidler HS 100/9-12
PO Box 85 74652 918-793-2461
Cory Smith, prin. Fax 793-2062
Other Schools – See Kaw City

Skiatook, Tulsa, Pop. 6,871
Skiatook ISD 2,300/PK-12
355 S Osage St 74070 918-396-1792
Rick Thomas, supt. Fax 396-1799
www.skiatookschools.org
Newman MS 600/6-8
355 S Osage St 74070 918-396-2307
Steve Cantrell Ph.D., prin. Fax 396-1799
Skiatook HS 800/9-12
355 S Osage St 74070 918-396-1790
William Parker, prin. Fax 396-1799

Hope Christian Academy 100/PK-12
612 S Broadway St 74070 918-396-4000
Kent Carver, prin. Fax 396-4009

Smithville, McCurtain, Pop. 106
Smithville ISD 300/PK-12
PO Box 8 74957 580-244-3333
Delbert McBroom, supt. Fax 244-3101
www.smithville.k12.ok.us
Smithville HS 100/9-12
PO Box 8 74957 580-244-3281
Delbert McBroom, prin. Fax 244-7277
Smithville MS 100/6-8
PO Box 8 74957 580-244-7212
Stacy Nichols, prin. Fax 244-3651

Snyder, Kiowa, Pop. 1,354
Snyder ISD 400/PK-12
PO Box 368 73566 580-569-2773
Robert Trammell, supt. Fax 569-4205
www.snyder.k12.ok.us
Snyder HS 100/9-12
PO Box 368 73566 580-569-2730
Ken McKee, prin. Fax 569-4033
Snyder MS 200/4-8
PO Box 368 73566 580-569-2691
Ryan Granger, prin. Fax 569-4657

Soper, Choctaw, Pop. 237
Soper ISD 400/PK-12
PO Box 149 74759 580-345-2757
Dr. Scotty Van Worth Ed.D., supt. Fax 345-2222
soperisd.com
Soper HS 100/9-12
PO Box 149 74759 580-345-2212
Parker Harless M.A., prin. Fax 345-2896

South Coffeyville, Nowata, Pop. 715
Oklahoma Union ISD 700/PK-12
RR 1 Box 377-7 74072 918-255-6550
Kevin Stacy, supt. Fax 255-6817
www.okunion.k12.ok.us/
Oklahoma Union HS 200/9-12
RR 1 Box 377-7 74072 918-255-6550
David Lovelace, prin. Fax 255-6817
Oklahoma Union MS 200/6-8
RR 1 Box 377-7 74072 918-255-6550
Lance Williams, prin. Fax 255-6817

South Coffeyville ISD 300/PK-12
PO Box 190 74072 918-255-6202
Clemo Haddox, supt. Fax 255-6230
www.scps.k12.ok.us
South Coffeyville HS 100/9-12
PO Box 190 74072 918-255-6087
Steve Johns, prin. Fax 255-6115

Spencer, Oklahoma, Pop. 3,660
Oklahoma City ISD
Supt. — See Oklahoma City
Rogers MS, 4000 Spencer Rd 73084 300/6-8
Jahree Herzer, prin. 405-587-4100
Star Spencer HS 400/9-12
3001 Spencer Rd 73084 405-587-8800
Chris Gardner, prin. Fax 587-8805

Sperry, Tulsa, Pop. 1,118
Sperry ISD 1,200/PK-12
400 W Main St 74073 918-288-6258
Brian Beagles Ed.D., supt. Fax 288-7067
www.sperry.k12.ok.us
Sperry HS 400/9-12
400 W Main St 74073 918-288-7213
Randy Shaw, prin. Fax 288-7230
Sperry MS 300/6-8
400 W Main St 74073 918-288-7213
Mike Juby, prin. Fax 288-7231

Cornerstone Christian Academy 100/K-12
7770 Whirlpool Dr 74073 918-274-3918
Karen Linton, prin.
Oklahoma Farriers College Post-Sec.
PO Box 788 74073 918-288-7221

Spiro, LeFlore, Pop. 2,077
OK Dept. of Voc. & Tech. Education
Supt. — None
Dr. Marcie Mack, dir.
Kiamichi Technology Center Vo/Tech
610 SW 3rd St 74959 918-962-3722
Doug Hall, dir. Fax 962-4627

Spiro ISD 1,100/K-12
600 W Broadway St 74959 918-962-2463
Don Atkinson, supt. Fax 962-2757
www.spiro.k12.ok.us
Spiro HS, 600 W Broadway St 74959 300/9-12
Larry Greenwood, prin. 918-962-2493
Spiro MS, 600 W Broadway St 74959 300/6-8
Nick Carter, prin. 918-962-2488

Springer, Carter, Pop. 636
Springer ISD 200/PK-12
16624 US Highway 77 73458 580-653-2656
Cynthia Hunter, supt. Fax 653-2666
www.springerschools.com
Springer HS 100/9-12
16624 US Highway 77 73458 580-653-2471
Russell Noland, prin.

Sterling, Comanche, Pop. 758
Sterling ISD 400/PK-12
PO Box 158 73567 580-365-4307
Julie Poteete, supt. Fax 365-4705
www.sterling.k12.ok.us/
Sterling HS 100/9-12
PO Box 158 73567 580-365-4303
Marty Curry, prin. Fax 365-4705

Stigler, Haskell, Pop. 2,525
OK Dept. of Voc. & Tech. Education
Supt. — None
Dr. Marcie Mack, dir.
Kiamichi Technology Center Vo/Tech
1410 Old Military Rd 74462 918-967-2801
April Murray, dir. Fax 967-2804

Stigler ISD 1,400/PK-12
309 NW E St 74462 918-967-2805
Monty Guthrie, supt. Fax 967-4550
www.stiglerps.com
Stigler HS 400/9-12
309 NW E St 74462 918-967-8834
David Morgan, prin. Fax 967-8974
Stigler MS 400/5-8
309 NW E St 74462 918-967-2521
Tony Gilmore, prin. Fax 967-5125

Stillwater, Payne, Pop. 43,498
OK Dept. of Voc. & Tech. Education
Supt. — None
Dr. Marcie Mack, dir.
Meridian Technology Center Vo/Tech
1312 S Sangre Rd 74074 405-377-3333
Dr. Douglas Major, supt. Fax 372-3466
Other Schools – See Ada OK, Afton OK, Altus OK, Alva OK, Antlers OK, Ardmore OK, Atoka OK, Bartlesville OK, Broken Arrow OK, Burns Flat OK, Chickasha OK, Choctaw OK, Claremore OK, Drumright OK, Duncan OK, Durant OK, El Reno OK, Enid OK, Fairview OK, Fort Cobb OK, Frederick OK, Hobart OK, Hugo OK, Idabel OK, Kansas OK, Lawton OK, McAlester OK, Midwest City OK, Muskogee OK, Norman OK, Oklahoma City OK, Okmulgee OK, Omega OK, Owasso OK, Ponca City OK, Poteau OK, Pryor OK, Sallisaw OK, Sand Springs OK, Sapulpa OK, Sayre OK, Shawnee OK, Spiro OK, Stigler OK, Stilwell OK, Tahlequah OK, Talihina OK, Tulsa OK, Wayne OK, Weatherford OK, Wetumka OK, Wilburton OK, Woodward OK, Yukon OK

Stillwater ISD 6,100/PK-12
314 S Lewis St 74074 405-533-6300
Dr. Marc Moore, supt. Fax 743-6311
www.stillwaterschools.com
Lincoln Alternative Academy Alt
215 E 12th Ave 74074 405-533-6331
Trent Swanson, prin. Fax 377-7725
Stillwater HS 1,100/10-12
1224 N Husband St 74075 405-533-6450
Uwe Gordon, prin. Fax 743-6488
Stillwater JHS 800/8-9
1900 N Skyline St 74075 405-533-6420
John Fields, prin. Fax 743-6444

Meridian Technology Center Post-Sec.
1312 S Sangre Rd 74074 405-377-3333
Northern Oklahoma College Post-Sec.
PO Box 1869 74076 405-744-2246
Oklahoma State University 74078 Post-Sec.
405-744-5000
Stillwater Beauty Academy Post-Sec.
1684 Cimarron Plz 74075 405-377-4100

Stilwell, Adair, Pop. 3,604
OK Dept. of Voc. & Tech. Education
Supt. — None
Dr. Marcie Mack, dir.
Indian Capital Technology Center Vo/Tech
RR 6 Box 3320 74960 918-696-3111
Dan Collins, dir. Fax 696-3031

Stilwell ISD 1,400/PK-12
1801 W Locust St 74960 918-696-7001
Geri Gilstrap, supt. Fax 696-2193
www.stilwellk12.org
Stilwell HS 700/9-12
1801 W Locust St 74960 918-696-7276
Ramona Ketcher, prin. Fax 696-4695
Stilwell MS 300/5-8
12 N 7th St 74960 918-696-2685
Dale Girdner, prin. Fax 696-7761

Stonewall, Pontotoc, Pop. 416
Stonewall ISD 400/PK-12
600 Highschool 74871 580-265-4241
Kevin Flowers, supt. Fax 265-4536
www.stonewall.k12.ok.us
McLish MS 100/5-8
600 Highschool 74871 580-777-2250
Jack Wofford, prin. Fax 777-2222
Stonewall HS 100/9-12
600 Highschool 74871 580-265-4242
Tamara Newberry, prin. Fax 265-4231

Stratford, Garvin, Pop. 1,461
Stratford ISD 700/PK-12
PO Box 589 74872 580-759-3615
Michael Blackburn, supt. Fax 759-2669
www.stratford.k12.ok.us
Stratford HS 200/9-12
PO Box 589 74872 580-759-2381
Paul Savage, prin. Fax 759-8913
Stratford MS 200/6-8
PO Box 589 74872 580-759-3615
Tracy Felan, prin. Fax 759-2513

Stringtown, Atoka, Pop. 364
Stringtown ISD 200/PK-12
PO Box 130 74569 580-346-7423
Tony Potts, supt. Fax 346-7726
Stringtown HS 100/9-12
PO Box 130 74569 580-346-7423
Tony Potts, prin. Fax 346-7726

Stroud, Lincoln, Pop. 2,575
Stroud ISD 800/PK-12
212 W 7th St 74079 918-968-2541
Joe Van Tuyl, supt. Fax 968-2582
www.stroud.k12.ok.us
Stroud HS 200/9-12
212 W 7th St 74079 918-968-2542
Scott Baade, prin. Fax 968-3656
Stroud MS 200/6-8
212 W 7th St 74079 918-968-2200
Betty Wages, prin. Fax 968-2391

Stuart, Hughes, Pop. 165
Stuart ISD 300/PK-12
8837 4th St 74570 918-546-2476
Tracy Blasengame, supt. Fax 546-2329
www.stuart.k12.ok.us
Stuart HS 100/9-12
8837 4th St 74570 918-546-2474
Adam Newman, prin. Fax 546-2329

Sulphur, Murray, Pop. 4,613
Sulphur ISD 1,500/PK-12
1021 W 9th St 73086 580-622-2061
Gary Jones, supt. Fax 622-6789
www.sis.sulphurk12.org
Sulphur HS 400/9-12
1021 W 9th St 73086 580-622-3174
Clete Cole, prin. Fax 622-5735
Sulphur JHS 300/6-8
1021 W 9th St 73086 580-622-4010
Dub Grisham, prin. Fax 622-3900

Oklahoma School for the Deaf Post-Sec.
1100 E Oklahoma Ave 73086 580-622-4900

Sweetwater, Roger Mills, Pop. 86
Sweetwater ISD 100/PK-12
11107 N Highway 30 73666 580-534-2272
Casey Reed, supt. Fax 534-2273
www.sweetwater.k12.ok.us/
Sweetwater HS 50/9-12
11107 N Highway 30 73666 580-534-2272
Casey Reed, prin. Fax 534-2273

Tahlequah, Cherokee, Pop. 14,483
OK Dept. of Voc. & Tech. Education
Supt. — None
Dr. Marcie Mack, dir.
Indian Capital Technology Center Vo/Tech
240 Vo Tech Dr 74464 918-456-2594
Robin Roberts, dir. Fax 456-0140

Tahlequah SD 3,300/PK-12
PO Box 517 74465 918-458-4100
Lisa Presley, supt. Fax 458-4103
www.tahlequahschools.org
Tahlequah HS 1,100/9-12
591 Pendleton St 74464 918-458-4150
Cory Slagle, prin. Fax 458-4152
Tahlequah MS 600/6-8
871 Pendleton St 74464 918-458-4140
Jaycie Smith, prin. Fax 458-4142

Academy of Salon and Spa Post-Sec.
3040 S Muskogee Ave Ste 105 74464 918-506-4071
Beauty Technical College Post-Sec.
PO Box 1506 74465 918-456-6360
Northeastern State University Post-Sec.
600 N Grand Ave 74464 918-456-5511

Talihina, Latimer, Pop. 1,013
Buffalo Valley ISD 200/PK-12
4384 SE Highway 63 74571 918-522-4426
Justin Kennedy, supt. Fax 522-4287
www.buffalovalley.k12.ok.us
Buffalo Valley HS 100/9-12
4384 SE Highway 63 74571 918-522-4803
Justin Kennedy, prin. Fax 522-4287

OK Dept. of Voc. & Tech. Education
Supt. — None
Dr. Marcie Mack, dir.
Kiamichi Technology Center Vo/Tech
13739 SE 202nd Rd 74571 918-567-2264
Larry Brooks, dir. Fax 567-3359

Talihina ISD 600/PK-12
PO Box 38 74571 918-567-2259
Jason Lockhart, supt. Fax 567-3507
www.talihina.k12.ok.us/
Talihina HS 200/9-12
PO Box 38 74571 918-567-2266
Jason Lockhart, prin. Fax 567-3507
Talihina JHS 100/7-8
PO Box 38 74571 918-567-2266
Jason Lockhart, prin. Fax 567-3507

Taloga, Dewey, Pop. 290
Taloga ISD 100/PK-12
PO Box 158 73667 580-328-5577
Darci Brown, supt. Fax 328-5237
www.taloga.k12.ok.us
Taloga HS 50/9-12
PO Box 158 73667 580-328-5586
Lora Burch, prin. Fax 328-5237

Tecumseh, Pottawatomie, Pop. 6,036
Tecumseh ISD 2,200/PK-12
1301 E Highland St 74873 405-598-3739
Tom Wilsie, supt. Fax 598-2861
www.tecumseh.k12.ok.us
Tecumseh HS 700/9-12
901 N 13th St 74873 405-598-2113
Danny Sterling, prin. Fax 598-2432
Tecumseh MS 500/6-8
315 W Park St 74873 405-598-3744
Robert Kinsey, prin. Fax 598-1948

Temple, Cotton, Pop. 952
Temple ISD 200/PK-12
PO Box 400 73568 580-342-6230
Justin Smith, supt. Fax 342-6230
www.temple.k12.ok.us/
Temple HS 100/9-12
PO Box 400 73568 580-342-6230
Justin Smith, prin. Fax 342-6230

Texhoma, Texas, Pop. 917
Texhoma ISD 200/5-12
PO Box 648 73949 580-423-7371
Tom Schroeder, supt. Fax 423-7096
www.texhoma61.net
Texhoma ES 100/5-8
PO Box 648 73949 580-423-7371
Connie Miller, prin. Fax 423-7141
Texhoma HS 100/9-12
PO Box 648 73949 580-423-7371
Connie Miller, prin. Fax 423-7096

Thackerville, Love, Pop. 429
Thackerville ISD 300/PK-12
PO Box 377 73459 580-276-2630
Greg Raper, supt. Fax 276-2638
www.thackervilleschools.org
Thackerville HS 100/9-12
PO Box 377 73459 580-276-3610
Carrie Tucker, prin. Fax 276-8314

Thomas, Custer, Pop. 1,152
Thomas-Fay-Custer Unified ISD 500/PK-12
PO Box 190 73669 580-661-3522
Rob Royalty, supt. Fax 661-3589
thomas.k12.ok.us/
Thomas-Fay-Custer HS 100/10-12
PO Box 190 73669 580-661-3522
Ray Oakes, prin. Fax 661-3589
Thomas-Fay-Custer JHS 100/7-9
PO Box 190 73669 580-661-3522
Ray Oakes, prin. Fax 661-3589

Tipton, Tillman, Pop. 830
Tipton ISD 200/K-12
PO Box 340 73570 580-667-5268
Shane Boothe, supt. Fax 667-5267
www.tiptontigers.net
Tipton HS 100/9-12
PO Box 340 73570 580-667-5268
Steve Glenn, prin. Fax 667-5478

Tishomingo, Johnston, Pop. 2,754
Tishomingo ISD 1,000/PK-12
1300 E Main St 73460 580-371-9190
Kevin Duncan, supt. Fax 371-3765
www.tishomingo.k12.ok.us/
Tishomingo HS, 1300 E Main St 73460 300/9-12
Jon Holmes, prin. 580-371-2322
Tishomingo MS, 1300 E Main St 73460 200/5-8
Charles Hook, prin. 580-371-3602

Murray State College Post-Sec.
1 Murray Campus St 73460 580-371-2371

Tonkawa, Kay, Pop. 3,131
Tonkawa ISD 600/PK-12
500 E North Ave 74653 580-628-3597
Lori Simpson, supt. Fax 628-5132
www.tonkawa.k12.ok.us/
Tonkawa JSHS 200/6-12
500 E North Ave 74653 580-628-2566
Kyle Simpson, prin. Fax 628-3646

Northern Oklahoma College Post-Sec.
PO Box 310 74653 580-628-6200

Tulsa, Tulsa, Pop. 371,916
Berryhill ISD 1,300/PK-12
3128 S 63rd West Ave 74107 918-446-1966
Mike Campbell, supt. Fax 446-6370
www.berryhillschools.org/
Berryhill HS 400/9-12
3128 S 63rd West Ave 74107 918-445-6035
Donnie Bridgeman, prin. Fax 445-6015
Berryhill MS 200/7-8
3128 S 63rd West Ave 74107 918-445-6039
Ronna Taylor, prin. Fax 445-6018

Jenks ISD
Supt. — See Jenks
Jenks MS 1,600/7-8
3019 E 101st St 74137 918-299-4411
Dr. Nick Brown, prin. Fax 298-0652

OK Dept. of Voc. & Tech. Education
Supt. — None
Dr. Marcie Mack, dir.
Tulsa Tech Center Lemley Vo/Tech
PO Box 477200 74147 918-828-1000
Randy Dean, dir. Fax 828-1009
Tulsa Tech Center Peoria Vo/Tech
PO Box 477200 74147 918-828-2000
Randy Craven, dir. Fax 828-2009
Tulsa Tech Center Riverside Campus Vo/Tech
PO Box 477200 74147 918-828-4000
Brad Hanselman, dir. Fax 828-4119

Tulsa ISD 35,600/PK-12
PO Box 470208 74147 918-746-6800
Dr. Deborah Gist, supt. Fax 746-6850
www.tulsaschools.org
Carver MS 600/6-8
624 E Oklahoma Pl 74106 918-925-1420
Melissa Woolridge, prin. Fax 925-1450
Central JSHS Fine & Performing Arts 600/7-12
3101 W Edison St 74127 918-833-8400
Jason Gilley, prin. Fax 833-8417
Clinton MS 300/6-8
2224 W 41st St 74107 918-746-8640
Michelle Brown, prin. Fax 746-8691
East Central HS 1,100/9-12
12150 E 11th St 74128 918-746-9700
Mike Crase, prin. Fax 746-9760
East Central JHS 700/7-8
12121 E 21st St 74129 918-746-9500
Joshua Regnier, prin. Fax 746-9519
Edison Preparatory MSHS 1,200/6-12
2906 E 41st St 74105 918-746-8500
Derrick Schmidt, prin. Fax 746-8511
Hale HS 1,000/9-12
6960 E 21st St 74129 918-925-1200
Dr. Sheila Riley, prin. Fax 925-1262

Hale JHS 700/7-8
2177 S 67th East Ave 74129 918-746-9260
Jody Parsons, prin. Fax 746-9291
McLain JSHS for Science & Technology 500/8-12
4929 N Peoria Ave 74126 918-833-8500
Enna Dancy, prin. Fax 833-8559
Memorial HS 1,000/9-12
5840 S Hudson Ave 74135 918-833-9600
Darin Schmidt, prin. Fax 833-9659
Memorial JHS 600/7-8
7502 E 57th St 74145 918-833-9520
Ginger Bunnell, prin. Fax 833-9551
Monroe Demonstration Academy 200/6-8
2010 E 48th St N 74130 918-833-8900
Kiana Smith, prin. Fax 833-8918
Phoenix Rising S Alt
1205 W Newton St 74127 918-833-8376
Diane Dross, dir.
Rogers JSHS 600/7-12
3909 E 5th Pl 74112 918-833-9000
Nicolette Dennis, prin. Fax 833-9065
Street S Alt
1135 S Yale Ave 74112 918-833-9800
Lori McGinnis Ed.D., dir. Fax 833-9858
Thoreau Demonstration Academy 600/6-8
7370 E 71st St 74133 918-833-9700
Audrey Doctor, prin. Fax 833-9720
TRAICE MSHS Academy 400/Alt
2740 E 41st St N 74110 918-925-1360
Elizabeth Martin, prin.
Tulsa Met JSHS 100/Alt
6201 E Virgin St 74115 918-746-9300
Michelle Butler, prin. Fax 833-9875
Washington HS 1,300/9-12
1514 E Zion St 74106 918-925-1000
Nanette Coleman, prin. Fax 928-1001
Webster HS 600/9-12
1919 W 40th St 74107 918-746-8000
Shelly Holman, prin. Fax 746-8056

Union ISD 15,500/PK-12
8506 E 61st St 74133 918-357-4321
Dr. Kirt Hartzler, supt. Fax 357-6019
www.unionps.org
Union Alternative S Alt
5656 S 129th East Ave 74134 918-357-4327
Chris Ducker, prin. Fax 357-7094
Union SHS 3,300/10-12
6636 S Mingo Rd 74133 918-357-4323
Tony Tempest, prin. Fax 357-7210
Other Schools – See Broken Arrow

Augustine Christian Academy 200/PK-12
6310 E 30th St 74114 918-832-4600
Bishop Kelley HS 800/9-12
3905 S Hudson Ave 74135 918-627-3390
Rev. Brian O'Brien, pres. Fax 664-2134
Career Point College Post-Sec.
3138 S Garnett Rd 74146 918-627-8074
Cascia Hall Preparatory S 600/6-12
2520 S Yorktown Ave 74114 918-746-2600
Roger Carter, hdmstr. Fax 746-2636
CC's Cosmetology College Post-Sec.
11630 E 21st St 74129 918-234-9444
Clary Sage College Post-Sec.
3131 S Sheridan Rd 74145 918-298-8200
Community Care College Post-Sec.
4242 S Sheridan Rd 74145 918-610-0027
Holland Hall 1,000/PK-12
5666 E 81st St 74137 918-481-1111
J.P. Culley, head sch Fax 481-1145
Lincoln Christian S 800/PK-12
1003 N 129th East Ave 74116 918-234-8863
Trandy Birch, prin. Fax 234-8864
Metro Christian Academy 1,000/PK-12
6363 S Trenton Ave 74136 918-745-9868
Mingo Valley Christian S 200/PK-12
8720 E 61st St 74133 918-294-0404
Dr. Boyd Chitwood, supt. Fax 294-0555
Oklahoma State University Post-Sec.
700 N Greenwood Ave 74106 918-594-8000
Oklahoma Technical College Post-Sec.
4444 S Sheridan Rd 74145 918-895-7500
Oral Roberts University Post-Sec.
7777 S Lewis Ave 74171 918-495-6161
OSU Center for Health Sciences Post-Sec.
1111 W 17th St 74107 918-582-1972
Peace Academy PK-12
4620 S Irvington Ave 74135 918-627-1040
Zaheer Arastu, dir.
Phillips Theological Seminary Post-Sec.
901 N Mingo Rd 74116 918-610-8303
Platt College Post-Sec.
3801 S Sheridan Rd 74145 918-663-9000
Regent Preparatory S of Oklahoma 500/PK-12
8621 S Memorial Dr 74133 918-663-1002
Andrew Shapleigh, hdmstr. Fax 663-1004
St. Francis Hospital Post-Sec.
6161 S Yale Ave 74136 918-494-1370
San Miguel MS 100/6-8
2444 E Admiral Blvd 74110 918-728-7337
John Dowdell, pres. Fax 660-2040
Spartan Coll of Aeronautics & Technology Post-Sec.
8820 E Pine St 74115 800-331-1204
Technical Institute of Cosmetology Arts Post-Sec.
822 E 6th St 74120 918-660-8828
Tulsa Adventist Academy 100/PK-10
900 S New Haven Ave 74112 918-834-1107
Tulsa Community College Post-Sec.
3727 E Apache St 74115 918-595-7000
Tulsa Community College Metro Campus Post-Sec.
909 S Boston Ave 74119 918-595-7000
Tulsa Community College Southeast Campus Post-Sec.
10300 E 81st St 74133 918-595-7000
Tulsa Community College West Campus Post-Sec.
7505 W 41st St 74107 918-595-7000
Tulsa Welding School Post-Sec.
2545 E 11th St 74104 918-587-6789
University of Oklahoma Tulsa Post-Sec.
4502 E 41st St 74135 918-660-3000
University of Tulsa Post-Sec.
800 Tucker Dr 74104 918-631-2000
Vatterott College Post-Sec.
4343 S 118th East Ave Ste A 74146 918-835-8288
Victory Christian S 1,100/PK-12
7700 S Lewis Ave 74136 918-491-7720
Dr. Dennis Demuth, supt. Fax 491-7727
Virginia College Post-Sec.
5124 S Peoria Ave 74105 918-960-5400
Wichita Technical Institute - Tulsa Post-Sec.
8421 E 61st St Ste U 74133 888-859-4564
Wright Career College Post-Sec.
4908 S Sheridan Rd 74145 918-628-7700
Wright Christian Academy 200/PK-12
11391 E Admiral Pl 74116 918-438-0922
Jeffrey L. Brown, supt. Fax 438-0700

Tupelo, Coal, Pop. 308
Tupelo ISD 300/PK-12
PO Box 239 74572 580-845-2460
Jerry Romines, supt. Fax 845-2565
www.tupelo.k12.ok.us
Tupelo HS 100/9-12
PO Box 239 74572 580-845-2381
Jeff Hiatt, prin. Fax 845-2565

Turpin, Beaver, Pop. 457
Turpin ISD 400/PK-12
PO Box 187 73950 580-778-3333
Keith Custer, supt. Fax 778-3179
www.turpinps.org
Turpin HS 100/7-12
PO Box 187 73950 580-778-3333
Gary Wallace, prin. Fax 778-3179

Tuttle, Grady, Pop. 5,837
Tuttle ISD 1,800/PK-12
PO Box 780 73089 405-381-2605
Bobby Waitman, supt. Fax 381-4008
www.tuttleschools.info/
Tuttle HS 500/9-12
PO Box 780 73089 405-381-2396
Pat Ragsdale, prin. Fax 381-4637
Tuttle MS 400/6-8
PO Box 780 73089 405-381-2062
Scott Moore, prin. Fax 381-4630

Tyrone, Texas, Pop. 753
Tyrone ISD 300/PK-12
PO Box 168 73951 580-854-6298
Josh Bell, supt. Fax 854-6474
www.tyrone.k12.ok.us/
Tyrone HS 100/9-12
PO Box 168 73951 580-854-6298
Donovan Smith, prin. Fax 854-6474

Union City, Canadian, Pop. 1,578
Union City ISD 300/PK-12
PO Box 279 73090 405-483-3531
Todd Carel, supt. Fax 483-5599
www.unioncity.k12.ok.us/
Union City HS 100/9-12
PO Box 279 73090 405-483-3531
Todd Carel, admin. Fax 483-5599

Valliant, McCurtain, Pop. 701
Valliant ISD 900/PK-12
604 E Lucas St 74764 580-933-7232
Craig Wall, supt. Fax 933-7289
www.vpsd.org
Valliant HS 300/9-12
604 E Lucas St 74764 580-933-7292
Cale Haley, prin. Fax 933-7278
Valliant MS 200/6-8
604 E Lucas St 74764 580-933-4253
Dennis Robberson, prin. Fax 933-4254

Velma, Stephens, Pop. 608
Velma-Alma ISD 400/PK-12
PO Box 8 73491 580-444-3355
Raymond Rice, supt. Fax 444-2554
www.velma-alma.k12.ok.us
Velma-Alma HS 100/6-12
PO Box 8 73491 580-444-3356
Mike Thompson, prin. Fax 444-2554

Verden, Grady, Pop. 510
Verden ISD 200/PK-12
PO Box 99 73092 405-453-7247
David Davidson, supt. Fax 453-7246
www.verdenschools.org
Verden HS 100/7-12
PO Box 99 73092 405-453-7836
David Davidson, prin. Fax 453-7246

Vian, Sequoyah, Pop. 1,346
Vian ISD 1,000/PK-12
PO Box 434 74962 918-773-5798
Victor Salcedo, supt. Fax 773-3051
www.vian.k12.ok.us
Vian HS 300/9-12
PO Box 434 74962 918-773-5475
Richard Moseley, prin. Fax 773-3051
Vian MS 200/6-8
PO Box 434 74962 918-773-8631
Marilyn Oliver, prin. Fax 773-3051

Vici, Dewey, Pop. 673
Vici ISD 300/PK-12
PO Box 60 73859 580-995-4744
Coby Nelson, supt. Fax 995-3101
www.vicischools.k12.ok.us
Vici HS 100/9-12
PO Box 60 73859 580-995-4251
Sheldon Halderman, prin. Fax 995-3101

Vinita, Craig, Pop. 5,215
Vinita ISD 1,600/PK-12
114 S Scraper St 74301 918-256-6778
Kelly Grimmett, supt. Fax 256-5617
www.vinitahornets.com
Vinita HS 500/9-12
801 N Adair St 74301 918-256-6777
Michelle Gibson, prin. Fax 256-5300
Vinita MS 300/6-8
226 N Miller St 74301 918-256-2402
Duwayne King, prin. Fax 256-5401

Ketchum Adventist Academy 50/PK-10
35369 S Highway 82 74301 918-782-2986

Wagoner, Wagoner, Pop. 7,460
Wagoner ISD 2,500/PK-12
308 NE 2nd St 74467 918-485-4046
Randy Harris, supt. Fax 485-8710
www.wagonerps.org
Lincoln Academy 200/Alt
902 Martin Luther King Blvd 74467 918-485-7615
Robert Schaefer, prin.
Wagoner HS 600/9-12
300 Bulldog Cir 74467 918-485-5553
Darlene Adair, admin. Fax 485-8886
Wagoner MS 500/6-8
500 Bulldog Cir 74467 918-485-9541
Jeremy Holmes, prin. Fax 485-4149

Walters, Cotton, Pop. 2,379
Walters ISD 700/PK-12
418 S Broadway St 73572 580-875-2568
Jimmie Dedmon, supt. Fax 875-2831
blued.org
Walters HS 200/9-12
418 S Broadway St 73572 580-875-3257
Laura Booher, prin. Fax 875-6097
Walters MS 200/6-8
418 S Broadway St 73572 580-875-3214
Fax 875-3401

Wanette, Pottawatomie, Pop. 331
Wanette ISD 200/PK-12
PO Box 161 74878 405-383-2656
Crystal Shaw, supt. Fax 383-2449
www.wanette.k12.ok.us/
Wanette HS 100/9-12
PO Box 161 74878 405-383-2254
Silvia McNeely, prin. Fax 383-2180

Wapanucka, Johnston, Pop. 399
Wapanucka ISD 200/PK-12
PO Box 188 73461 580-937-4288
Max Rowland, supt. Fax 937-4804
www.wpss.k12.ok.us
Wapanucka HS, PO Box 188 73461 100/9-12
Max Rowland, prin. 580-937-4288

Warner, Muskogee, Pop. 1,489
Warner ISD 700/PK-12
1012 5th Ave 74469 918-463-5171
David Vinson, supt. Fax 463-2542
www.warner.k12.ok.us
Warner HS 200/9-12
1012 5th Ave 74469 918-463-5172
Jeremy Jackson, prin. Fax 463-2378

Connors State College Post-Sec.
700 College Rd 74469 918-463-2931

Warr Acres, Oklahoma, Pop. 9,574
Putnam City ISD
Supt. — See Oklahoma City
Capps MS 900/6-8
4020 N Grove Ave 73122 405-787-3660
James Burnett, prin. Fax 491-7536
Putnam City Academy Alt
5604 NW 41st St Ste 300 73122 405-495-8838
Shelly Roper, prin. Fax 491-7529
Putnam City HS 1,800/9-12
5300 NW 50th St 73122 405-789-4350
Brett Bradley, prin. Fax 789-1662

Vatterott College - Oklahoma City Post-Sec.
5537 NW Expressway 73132 405-234-3600

Washington, McClain, Pop. 585
Washington ISD 1,000/PK-12
PO Box 98 73093 405-288-6190
A.J. Brewer, supt. Fax 288-6214
www.washington.k12.ok.us/
Washington HS 300/9-12
PO Box 98 73093 405-288-2354
David Crabbe, prin. Fax 288-6214
Washington MS 200/6-8
PO Box 98 73093 405-288-2428
Stuart McPherson, prin. Fax 288-6214

Watonga, Blaine, Pop. 4,947
Watonga ISD 800/PK-12
1021 N Weigle 73772 580-623-7364
Bill Seitter, supt. Fax 623-7370
www.watonga.k12.ok.us
Watonga HS 200/9-12
PO Box 310 73772 580-623-7362
David Lorenz, prin. Fax 623-8019
Watonga MS 200/6-8
PO Box 310 73772 580-623-7361
Bryan Pope, prin. Fax 623-7371

Watts, Adair, Pop. 292
Watts ISD 400/PK-12
RR 2 Box 1 74964 918-422-5311
Lisa Weaver, supt. Fax 422-5556
www.wattsschool.com
Watts HS 100/9-12
RR 2 Box 1 74964 918-422-5132
Tony Mitchell, prin. Fax 422-5556

Waukomis, Garfield, Pop. 1,254
Pioneer-Pleasant Vale ISD 600/PK-12
6520 E Wood Rd 73773 580-758-3282
Brent Koontz, supt. Fax 758-3504
www.ppv.k12.ok.us/
Pioneer-Pleasant Vale HS 200/9-12
6520 E Wood Rd 73773 580-758-3282
Tom Betchan, prin. Fax 758-1541
Pioneer-Pleasant Vale JHS 100/7-8
6520 E Wood Rd 73773 580-758-3282
Tom Betchan, prin. Fax 758-1541

Waukomis ISD 300/PK-12
PO Box 729 73773 580-758-3247
Shawn Tennyson, supt. Fax 758-3834
www.waukomis.k12.ok.us
Waukomis HS 100/6-12
PO Box 729 73773 580-758-3245
Matt Cue, prin. Fax 758-3256

Waurika, Jefferson, Pop. 1,993
Waurika ISD 300/PK-12
600 E Florida Ave 73573 580-228-3373
Roxie Terry M.Ed., supt. Fax 228-3428
www.waurikaschools.org
Waurika MSHS 100/6-12
600 E Florida Ave 73573 580-228-2341
Dale Spradlin, prin. Fax 228-3428

Wayne, McClain, Pop. 635
OK Dept. of Voc. & Tech. Education
Supt. — None
Dr. Marcie Mack, dir.
Mid-America Technology Center Vo/Tech
PO Box H 73095 405-449-3391
Dusty Ricks, supt. Fax 449-7321

Wayne ISD 500/PK-12
212 S Seifried St 73095 405-449-3646
David Powell, supt. Fax 449-7095
www.wayne.k12.ok.us
Wayne HS 200/9-12
212 S Seifried St 73095 405-449-3317
Toby Ringwald, prin. Fax 449-7095
Wayne MS 100/6-8
212 S Seifried St 73095 405-449-7047
Brandon Sharp, prin. Fax 449-7095

Waynoka, Woods, Pop. 895
Waynoka ISD 300/PK-12
2134 Lincoln St 73860 580-824-4341
Loren Tackett, supt. Fax 824-0656
www.waynoka.k12.ok.us/
Waynoka HS 100/9-12
2134 Lincoln St 73860 580-824-4341
Michael Meriwether, prin. Fax 824-0656

Weatherford, Custer, Pop. 10,475
OK Dept. of Voc. & Tech. Education
Supt. — None
Dr. Marcie Mack, dir.
Western Technology Center Vo/Tech
2605 E Main St 73096 580-774-0224
Audie Corning, dir. Fax 774-0274

Weatherford ISD 2,200/PK-12
516 N Broadway St 73096 580-772-3327
Chad Wilson, supt. Fax 774-0821
www.wpsok.org
Weatherford HS 500/9-12
1500 N Washington St 73096 580-772-3385
Mark Shadid, prin. Fax 774-1939
Weatherford MS 500/6-8
509 N Custer St 73096 580-772-2270
Steven Callen, prin. Fax 774-1981

Southwestern Oklahoma State University Post-Sec.
100 Campus Dr 73096 580-772-6611

Webbers Falls, Muskogee, Pop. 572
Webbers Falls ISD, PO Box 300 74470 300/PK-12
Dixie Swearingen Ph.D., supt. 918-464-2580
www.webbersfalls.k12.ok.us
Webbers Falls HS 100/9-12
200 S Stand Watie Blvd 74470 918-464-2334
Jim McCabe, prin. Fax 464-2313

Welch, Craig, Pop. 576
Welch ISD 300/PK-12
PO Box 189 74369 918-788-3129
Dr. Clark McKeon, supt. Fax 788-3734
welchwildcats.net
Welch HS 100/9-12
PO Box 189 74369 918-788-3129
Dr. Clark McKeon, prin. Fax 788-3734
Welch MS 100/7-8
PO Box 189 74369 918-788-3129
Kim Hall, prin. Fax 788-3734

Weleetka, Okfuskee, Pop. 906
Graham-Dustin SD 200/PK-12
116118 Highway 84 74880 918-652-8935
Rex Trent, supt. Fax 652-2422
www.graham-dustin.k12.ok.us
Graham HS 100/9-12
116118 Highway 84 74880 918-652-8935
Linda Riddle, prin. Fax 652-2422
Graham MS 50/5-8
116118 Highway 84 74880 918-652-8935
Linda Riddle, prin. Fax 652-2422

Weleetka ISD 400/PK-12
PO Box 278 74880 405-786-2203
Chris Carter, supt. Fax 786-2625
www.weleetka.k12.ok.us
Weleetka HS 100/10-12
PO Box 278 74880 405-786-2203
Rusty Johnson, prin. Fax 786-2625
Weleetka JHS, PO Box 278 74880 100/7-9
Rusty Johnson, prin. 405-786-2203

Wellston, Lincoln, Pop. 751
Wellston ISD 700/PK-12
PO Box 60 74881 405-356-2534
Dwayne Danker, supt. Fax 356-2838
www.wellstonschools.org
Wellston HS 200/9-12
PO Box 60 74881 405-356-2533
Tracy Fredman, prin. Fax 356-2838
Wellston MS 200/6-8
PO Box 60 74881 405-356-2533
Tracy Fredman, prin. Fax 356-2838

Westville, Adair, Pop. 1,479
Westville ISD 1,100/PK-12
PO Box 410 74965 918-723-3181
Terry Heustis, supt. Fax 723-3042
www.westville.k12.ok.us
Westville HS 300/10-12
PO Box 410 74965 918-723-5644
Renae Price, prin. Fax 723-3042
Westville JHS 200/7-9
PO Box 410 74965 918-723-3432
Shelly Cooper, prin. Fax 723-3042

Wetumka, Hughes, Pop. 1,171
OK Dept. of Voc. & Tech. Education
Supt. — None
Dr. Marcie Mack, dir.
Watkins Technology Center Vo/Tech
7892 Highway 9 74883 405-452-5500
Wade Walling, supt. Fax 452-3561

Wetumka ISD 500/PK-12
416 S Tiger St 74883 405-452-5150
Donna McGee, supt. Fax 452-3052
www.wetumka.k12.ok.us/
Wetumka HS 100/9-12
416 S Tiger St 74883 405-452-3291
Rodney Luellen, prin. Fax 452-5836

Wewoka, Seminole, Pop. 3,192
New Lima ISD 300/PK-12
116 Gross St 74884 405-257-5771
Gil Turpin, supt. Fax 257-3127
www.newlima.k12.ok.us
New Lima HS 100/9-12
116 Gross St 74884 405-257-5771
Rhonda Barkhimer, prin. Fax 257-2587

Wewoka ISD 800/PK-12
PO Box 870 74884 405-257-5475
Torrey Gaines, supt. Fax 257-2303
www.wps.k12.ok.us
Wewoka HS 200/9-12
PO Box 870 74884 405-257-5473
Steven Edwards, prin. Fax 257-2303
Wewoka MS 100/7-8
PO Box 870 74884 405-257-2347
Darrell Brown, prin. Fax 257-2303

Whitesboro, LeFlore, Pop. 244
Whitesboro ISD 200/PK-12
PO Box 150 74577 918-567-2556
Katie Blagg, supt. Fax 567-2842
www.whitesborops.k12.ok.us/
Whitesboro HS, PO Box 150 74577 100/9-12
Katie Blagg, prin. 918-567-2624

Wilburton, Latimer, Pop. 2,654
OK Dept. of Voc. & Tech. Education
Supt. — None
Dr. Marcie Mack, dir.
Kiamichi Technology Center Vo/Tech
PO Box 548 74578 918-465-2323
Shelley Free, supt. Fax 465-3666

Wilburton ISD 900/PK-12
1201 W Blair Ave 74578 918-465-2100
Dr. Trice Butler, supt. Fax 465-3086
wilburtondiggers.org
Wilburton HS 300/9-12
1201 W Blair Ave 74578 918-465-3125
Gary Lay, prin. Fax 465-1141
Wilburton MS 200/6-8
1201 W Blair Ave 74578 918-465-2281
Kyle Vanderburg, prin. Fax 465-3094

Eastern Oklahoma State College Post-Sec.
1301 W Main St 74578 918-465-2361

Wilson, Carter, Pop. 1,643
Wilson ISD 500/PK-12
1860 Hewitt Rd 73463 580-668-2306
Eric Smith, supt. Fax 668-2170
www.wilson.k12.ok.us
Wilson HS 200/9-12
1860 Hewitt Rd 73463 580-668-2317
Fax 668-2412

Wister, LeFlore, Pop. 1,038
Wister ISD 600/PK-12
201 Logan St 74966 918-655-7381
Rachel Pugh, supt. Fax 655-7402
www.wisterschools.org
Wister HS 200/9-12
201 Logan St 74966 918-655-7276
Albert Cole, prin. Fax 655-7402

Woodward, Woodward, Pop. 11,818
OK Dept. of Voc. & Tech. Education
Supt. — None
Dr. Marcie Mack, dir.
High Plains Technology Center Vo/Tech
3921 34th St 73801 580-256-6618
Dwight Hughes, supt. Fax 571-6190

Woodward ISD 3,000/PK-12
PO Box 668 73802 580-256-6063
Kyle Reynolds, supt. Fax 256-4391
www.woodwardps.net
Woodward HS 700/9-12
PO Box 668 73802 580-256-5329
Brad Logan, prin. Fax 256-8716
Woodward MS 600/6-8
PO Box 668 73802 580-256-7901
Sarah Hall, prin. Fax 256-8014

Woodward Beauty College Post-Sec.
502 Texas St 73801 580-256-7520

Wright City, McCurtain, Pop. 687
Wright City ISD 400/PK-12
PO Box 329 74766 580-981-2824
David Hawkins, supt. Fax 981-2115
www.wcisd.org/
Wright City HS 200/9-12
PO Box 329 74766 580-981-2558
Mike Converse, prin. Fax 981-2329
Wright City JHS 100/7-8
PO Box 329 74766 580-981-2558
Mike Converse, prin. Fax 981-2329

Wyandotte, Ottawa, Pop. 310
Wyandotte ISD 800/PK-12
PO Box 360 74370 918-678-2255
Troy Gray M.Ed., supt. Fax 678-2304
www.wyandotte.k12.ok.us
Wyandotte HS 200/9-12
PO Box 360 74370 918-678-2222
Steve Buckingham, prin. Fax 678-3906
Wyandotte MS 200/6-8
PO Box 360 74370 918-678-2222
Stacy Sloan, prin. Fax 678-3906

Wynnewood, Garvin, Pop. 2,125
Wynnewood ISD 700/PK-12
702 E Robert S Kerr Blvd 73098 405-665-2004
Raymond Cole, supt. Fax 665-5425
www.wynnewood.k12.ok.us/
Wynnewood HS 200/9-12
702 E Robert S Kerr Blvd 73098 405-665-2045
Steve Musgrove, prin.
Wynnewood MS 200/5-8
702 E Robert S Kerr Blvd 73098 405-665-4105
Kevin Lynch, prin.

Wynona, Osage, Pop. 396
Wynona ISD 100/PK-12
PO Box 700 74084 918-846-2467
Shelly Shulanberger, supt. Fax 846-2883
www.wynona.k12.ok.us
Wynona HS 50/9-12
PO Box 700 74084 918-846-2467
Dixie Hurd, prin. Fax 846-2883

Yale, Payne, Pop. 1,132
Yale ISD 500/PK-12
315 E Chicago Ave 74085 918-387-2118
Dale Bledsoe, supt. Fax 387-4243
www.yale.k12.ok.us
Yale HS 200/9-12
315 E Chicago Ave 74085 918-387-2118
Rocky Kennedy, prin. Fax 387-4243
Yale JHS 100/6-8
315 E Chicago Ave 74085 918-387-2118
Rocky Kennedy, prin. Fax 387-4243

Yukon, Canadian, Pop. 21,966
OK Dept. of Voc. & Tech. Education
Supt. — None
Dr. Marcie Mack, dir.
Canadian Valley Technology Center Vo/Tech
1000 Garth Brooks Blvd 73099 405-262-2629
Gayla Lutts, prin.
Canadian Valley Technology Center Vo/Tech
1701 S Czech Hall Rd 73099 405-345-3333
Greg Taylor, dir.

Yukon ISD 8,100/PK-12
600 Maple St 73099 405-354-2587
Dr. Jason Simeroth, supt. Fax 354-4208
www.yukonps.com
Yukon HS 2,400/9-12
1777 S Yukon Pkwy 73099 405-354-6692
Melissa Barlow, prin. Fax 354-8411
Yukon MS 1,800/6-8
801 Garth Brooks Blvd 73099 405-354-5274
Diana Lebsack, prin. Fax 354-6640

Southwest Covenant S 300/PK-12
2300 S Yukon Pkwy 73099 405-354-0772
Steve Lessman, hdmstr. Fax 350-2670
Yukon Beauty College Post-Sec.
221 W Main St 73099 405-354-3172

OREGON

OREGON DEPARTMENT OF EDUCATION
255 Capitol St NE, Salem 97310-1206
Telephone 503-947-5600
Fax 503-378-5156
Website http://www.oregon.gov/ode/Pages/default.aspx

Superintendent of Public Instruction Salam Noor

OREGON BOARD OF EDUCATION
255 Capitol St NE, Salem 97310-1300

Chairperson Miranda Summer

EDUCATION SERVICE DISTRICTS (ESD)

Clackamas ESD
Milt Dennison, supt. 503-675-4000
13455 SE 97th Ave Fax 675-4200
Clackamas 97015
www.clackesd.k12.or.us

Columbia Gorge ESD
Gary Peterson, supt. 541-298-5155
400 E Scenic Dr Ste 207 Fax 296-2965
The Dalles 97058
www.cgesd.k12.or.us

Douglas ESD
Michael Lasher, supt. 541-440-4777
1871 NE Stephens St Fax 440-4771
Roseburg 97470
www.douglasesd.k12.or.us

Grant ESD
Robert Waltenburg, supt. 541-575-1349
835 S Canyon Blvd Ste A Fax 575-3601
John Day 97845
www.grantesd.k12.or.us

Harney ESD
Charles Beck, supt. 541-573-2426
779 W Fillmore St, Burns 97720 Fax 573-1002
www.harneyesd.k12.or.us

High Desert ESD
John Rexford, supt. 541-693-5614
2804 SW 6th St, Redmond 97756 Fax 693-5601
www.hdesd.org

InterMountain ESD
Mark Mulvihill Ed.D., supt. 541-276-6616
2001 SW Nye Ave Fax 276-4252
Pendleton 97801
www.imesd.k12.or.us

Jefferson ESD
Richard Molitor, supt. 541-475-2804
295 SE Buff St, Madras 97741 Fax 475-2827
www.jcesd.k12.or.us

Lake ESD
Bob Nash, supt. 541-947-3371
357 N L St, Lakeview 97630 Fax 947-3373
www.lakeesd.k12.or.us

Lane ESD
Larry Sullivan, supt. 541-461-8200
1200 Highway 99 N, Eugene 97402 Fax 461-8298
www.lesd.k12.or.us

Linn-Benton-Lincoln ESD
Mary McKay, supt. 541-812-2600
905 4th Ave SE, Albany 97321 Fax 926-6047
www.lblesd.k12.or.us

Malheur ESD
Stephen Phillips, supt. 541-473-3138
363 A St W, Vale 97918 Fax 473-3915
www.malesd.k12.or.us

Multnomah ESD
Jim Rose, supt. 503-255-1841
PO Box 301039, Portland 97294 Fax 257-1519
www.mesd.k12.or.us

North Central ESD
Robert Waltenberg, supt. 541-384-2732
PO Box 637, Condon 97823 Fax 384-2752
www.ncesd.k12.or.us

Northwest Regional ESD
Rob Saxton, supt. 503-614-1428
5825 NE Ray Cir, Hillsboro 97124 Fax 614-1440
www.nwresd.k12.or.us

Region 18 ESD
Karen Patton, supt. 541-426-7600
107 SW 1st St Ste 105 Fax 426-3732
Enterprise 97828
www.r18esd.org

South Coast ESD
Tenneal Wetherell, supt. 541-269-1611
1350 Teakwood Ave Fax 266-4040
Coos Bay 97420
www.scesd.k12.or.us

Southern Oregon ESD
Scott Beveridge, supt. 541-776-8590
101 N Grape St, Medford 97501 Fax 779-2018
www.soesd.k12.or.us

Willamette ESD
Dave Novotney, supt. 503-588-5330
2611 Pringle Rd SE, Salem 97302 Fax 363-5787
www.wesd.org

PUBLIC, PRIVATE AND CATHOLIC SECONDARY SCHOOLS

Adel, Lake
Adel SD 21
Supt. — See Lakeview
Adel ES, PO Box 117 97620 50/4-8
Bob Nash, prin. 541-947-3371

Adrian, Malheur, Pop. 173
Adrian SD 61 200/K-12
PO Box 108 97901 541-372-2335
Gene Mills, supt. Fax 372-5380
www.adriansd.com
Adrian HS 100/9-12
PO Box 108 97901 541-372-2335
Kevin Purnell, prin. Fax 372-5380

Albany, Linn, Pop. 48,696
Greater Albany SD 8J 9,200/K-12
718 7th Ave SW 97321 541-967-4501
Jim Golden, supt. Fax 967-4587
albany.k12.or.us
Albany Options S 300/Alt
701 19th Ave SE, 541-967-4563
John Hunter, prin. Fax 924-3780
Calapooia MS 600/6-8
830 24th Ave SE, 541-967-4555
Gina Ayers, prin. Fax 924-3702
Memorial MS 600/6-8
1050 Queen Ave SW 97321 541-967-4537
Ken Gilbert, prin. Fax 924-3703
North Albany MS 500/6-8
1205 NW North Albany Rd 97321 541-967-4541
Jon Dilbone, prin. Fax 924-3704
South Albany HS 1,400/9-12
3705 Columbus St SE, 541-967-4522
Brent Belveal, prin. Fax 924-3700
Timber Ridge S 700/3-8
373 Timber Ridge St NE, 541-704-1095
Jodi Dedera, prin. Fax 704-1099
West Albany HS 1,400/9-12
1130 Queen Ave SW 97321 541-967-4545
Susie Orsborn, prin. Fax 924-3701

Linn-Benton Community College Post-Sec.
6500 Pacific Blvd SW 97321 541-917-4999

Aloha, Washington, Pop. 47,267

Life Christian S 200/PK-12
5585 SW 209th Ave, 503-259-1329
Cary Tyler, prin. Fax 649-5484

Alsea, Benton, Pop. 157
Alsea SD 7J 200/K-12
PO Box B 97324 541-487-4305
Marc Thielman, supt. Fax 487-4089
www.alsea.k12.or.us
Alsea HS 100/7-12
PO Box B 97324 541-487-4305
Marc Thielman, admin. Fax 487-4089

Amity, Yamhill, Pop. 1,569
Amity SD 4J 900/K-12
807 S Trade St 97101 503-835-2171
Jeff Clark, supt. Fax 835-5050
www.amity.k12.or.us
Amity HS 300/9-12
807 S Trade St 97101 503-835-2181
Chris Daniels, prin. Fax 835-6113
Amity MS 200/6-8
807 S Trade St 97101 503-835-0518
Dave Lund, prin. Fax 835-0418

Perrydale SD 21 500/PK-12
7445 Perrydale Rd 97101 503-835-3184
Eric Milburn, supt. Fax 835-0631
www.perrydale.k12.or.us
Perrydale JSHS 200/6-12
7445 Perrydale Rd 97101 503-835-3184
Eric Milburn, prin. Fax 835-0631

Ashland, Jackson, Pop. 19,339
Ashland SD 5 2,600/K-12
885 Siskiyou Blvd 97520 541-482-2811
Jay Hummel, supt. Fax 482-2185
www.ashland.k12.or.us
Ashland HS 1,000/9-12
201 S Mountain Ave 97520 541-482-8771
Erika Bare, prin. Fax 482-2172
Ashland MS 600/6-8
100 Walker Ave 97520 541-482-1611
Steve Retzlaff, prin. Fax 482-8112

Southern Oregon University Post-Sec.
1250 Siskiyou Blvd 97520 541-552-7672

Astoria, Clatsop, Pop. 9,193
Astoria SD 1 1,900/K-12
785 Alameda Ave 97103 503-325-6441
Craig Hoppes, supt. Fax 325-6524
www.astoria.k12.or.us
Astoria HS 600/9-12
1001 W Marine Dr 97103 503-325-3911
Lynn Jackson, prin. Fax 325-2891
Astoria MS 400/6-8
1100 Klaskanine Ave 97103 503-325-4331
Linda Berger, prin. Fax 325-3040

Knappa SD 4 500/K-12
41535 Old Highway 30 97103 503-458-5993
Paulette Johnson, supt. Fax 458-6979
www.knappa.k12.or.us
Knappa HS 100/9-12
41535 Old Highway 30 97103 503-458-6166
Terrence Smyth, prin. Fax 458-5466

Clatsop Community College Post-Sec.
1651 Lexington Ave 97103 503-325-0910

Athena, Umatilla, Pop. 1,106
Athena-Weston SD 29RJ 600/K-12
375 S 5th St 97813 541-566-3551
James Reager, supt. Fax 566-9454
www.athwest.k12.or.us
Weston-McEwen HS 200/9-12
540 E Main St 97813 541-566-3555
Rollie Marshall, prin. Fax 566-2751
Other Schools – See Weston

Aumsville, Marion, Pop. 3,437
Cascade SD 5
Supt. — See Turner
West Stayton Alternative S Alt
11463 W Stayton Rd SE 97325 503-749-8020
Matt Thatcher, prin. Fax 749-8029

Aurora, Marion, Pop. 900
North Marion SD 15 2,000/PK-12
20256 Grim Rd NE 97002 503-678-7100
Boyd Keyser, supt. Fax 678-1473
www.nmarion.k12.or.us
North Marion HS 600/9-12
20167 Grim Rd NE 97002 503-678-7123
De Ann Jenness, prin. Fax 678-7186
North Marion MS 400/6-8
20246 Grim Rd NE 97002 503-678-7118
David Sheldon, prin. Fax 678-7185

Baker City, Baker, Pop. 9,619
Baker SD 5J 1,700/K-12
2090 4th St 97814 541-524-2260
Mark Witty, supt. Fax 524-2564
www.baker.k12.or.us
Baker HS 500/9-12
2500 E St 97814 541-524-2600
Greg Mitchell, prin. Fax 524-2699
Baker MS 300/7-8
2320 Washington Ave 97814 541-524-2500
Chris Carmiencke, prin. Fax 524-2563
EAGLE CAP Innovative HS 50/Alt
2725 7th St 97814 541-524-2285
Ben Merrill, prin. Fax 359-2564

Bandon, Coos, Pop. 2,978
Bandon SD 54 700/K-12
455 9th St SW 97411 541-347-4411
Doug Ardiana, supt. Fax 347-3974
www.bandon.k12.or.us
Bandon HS 200/9-12
550 9th St SW 97411 541-347-4413
Sabrina Belletti, prin. Fax 347-3714
Harbor Lights MS 200/5-8
390 9th St SW 97411 541-347-4415
Michelle Inskeep, prin. Fax 347-1280

Banks, Washington, Pop. 1,714
Banks SD 13 1,000/K-12
12950 NW Main St 97106 503-324-8591
Jeff Leo, supt. Fax 324-6969
www.banks.k12.or.us
Banks HS 400/9-12
13050 NW Main St 97106 503-324-2281
Mark Everett, prin. Fax 324-8221
Banks MS 200/6-8
12850 NW Main St 97106 503-324-3111
Shelley Mitchell, prin. Fax 324-7441

Beaverton, Washington, Pop. 86,161
Beaverton SD 48J 39,200/K-12
16550 SW Merlo Rd, 503-356-4500
Don Grotting, supt.
www.beaverton.k12.or.us
Aloha HS 2,100/9-12
18550 SW Kinnaman Rd 97078 503-356-2760
Ken Yarnell, prin. Fax 356-2765
Arts & Communication Magnet Academy 700/6-12
11375 SW Center St 97005 503-356-3670
Michael Johnson, prin.
Beaverton HS 1,600/9-12
13000 SW 2nd St 97005 503-356-2830
Anne Erwin, prin. Fax 356-2825
Bridges Academy Alt
18640 NW Walker Rd 97006 503-356-3715
Ashley Marston, prin.
Carson Environmental MS 200/6-8
1600 NW 173rd Ave 97006 503-356-2600
Shirley Brock, prin.
Conestoga MS 900/6-8
12250 SW Conestoga Dr 97008 503-356-2580
Zan Hess, prin. Fax 356-2585
Five Oaks MS 1,100/6-8
1600 NW 173rd Ave 97006 503-356-2600
Shirley Brock, prin. Fax 356-2605
Health & Science HS 700/6-12
18640 NW Walker Rd 97006 503-356-3630
Brian Sica, prin. Fax 356-3635
Highland Park MS 800/6-8
7000 SW Wilson Ave 97008 503-356-2620
Curtis Semana, prin.
International S of Beaverton 900/6-12
17770 SW Blanton St 97078 503-356-3690
Jill O'Neill, prin. Fax 356-3695
Meadow Park MS 800/6-8
14100 SW Downing St 97006 503-356-2640
Jared Freeman, prin. Fax 356-2645
Merlo Station Community HS 200/Alt
1841 SW Merlo Dr, 503-356-3650
MaryJean Katz, prin. Fax 356-3655
Mountain View MS 800/6-8
17500 SW Farmington Rd 97007 503-356-2660
Matt Pedersen, prin. Fax 356-2665
New HS, 12500 SW 175th Ave 97007 9-12
Todd Corsetti, prin. 503-356-3500
School of Science & Technology 200/9-12
18640 NW Walker Rd 97006 503-356-3630
Brian Sica, prin. Fax 356-3655
Southridge HS 1,700/9-12
9625 SW 125th Ave 97008 503-356-2890
David Nieslanik, prin. Fax 356-2891
Whitford MS 700/6-8
7935 SW Scholls Ferry Rd 97008 503-356-2700
Brian Peerenboom, prin. Fax 356-2705
Passages Adult
1841 SW Merlo Dr, 503-259-5575
MaryJean Katz, prin. Fax 259-4220
Other Schools – See Portland

Anthem College Post-Sec.
4145 SW Watson Ave Ste 300 97005 503-646-6000
St. Stephen's Academy 200/PK-12
7275 SW Hall Blvd 97008 503-646-4617
John Breckenridge, hdmstr. Fax 459-7715
Valley Catholic HS 300/9-12
4275 SW 148th Ave 97078 503-644-3745
Doug Ierardi, prin. Fax 646-4054
Valley Catholic MS 6-8
4200 SW St Marys Dr 97078 503-626-3745
Jennifer Gfroerer, prin.

Bend, Deschutes, Pop. 74,904
Bend-LaPine Administrative SD 1 16,500/K-12
520 NW Wall St, 541-355-1000
Shay Mikalson, supt. Fax 355-1009
www.bend.k12.or.us
Bend HS 1,600/9-12
230 NE 6th St 97701 541-355-3700
Christopher Reese, prin. Fax 355-3910
Cascade MS 900/6-8
19619 Mountaineer Way 97702 541-355-7000
Stephanie Bennett, prin. Fax 355-7010
High Desert MS 800/6-8
61000 Diamondback Ln 97702 541-355-7200
Brian Moran-Crook, prin. Fax 355-7210
Marshall HS 200/Alt
1291 NE 5th St 97701 541-355-3500
Julie Linhares, prin. Fax 355-3510
Mountain View HS 1,300/9-12
2755 NE 27th St 97701 541-355-4400
Kathryn Legace, prin. Fax 355-4410
Pacific Crest MS 6-8
3030 NW Elwood Ln, 541-355-7800
Chris Boyd, prin. Fax 355-7810
Pilot Butte MS 700/6-8
1501 NE Neff Rd 97701 541-355-7400
Steven Stancliff, prin. Fax 355-7410
REALMS 100/6-8
63175 O B Riley Rd, 541-355-4900
Roger White, dir. Fax 355-4910
Sky View MS 800/6-8
63555 18th St 97701 541-355-7600
Scott Olszewski, prin. Fax 355-7610
Summit HS 1,400/9-12
2855 NW Clearwater Dr, 541-355-4000
Alice Dewittie, prin. Fax 355-4210
Other Schools – See La Pine

Cascades Academy 200/PK-12
19860 Tumalo Reservoir Rd, 541-382-0699
Julie Amberg, head sch Fax 382-0225
Central Oregon Community College Post-Sec.
2600 NW College Way 97701 541-383-7700
Phagans' Central Oregon Beauty College Post-Sec.
1310 NE Cushing Dr 97701 541-382-6171
Trinity Lutheran S 300/PK-12
2550 NE Butler Market Rd 97701 541-382-1850
Hanne Krause, prin. Fax 382-1850

Boardman, Morrow, Pop. 3,160
Morrow SD 1
Supt. — See Heppner
Riverside JSHS 400/7-12
210 NE Boardman Ave 97818 541-481-2525
Marie Shimer, prin. Fax 481-2047

Bonanza, Klamath, Pop. 407
Klamath County SD
Supt. — See Klamath Falls
Bonanza S 200/K-12
PO Box 128 97623 541-545-6581
Art Ochoa, prin. Fax 545-1719

Boring, Clackamas
Oregon Trail SD 46
Supt. — See Sandy
Boring MS 400/6-8
27801 SE Dee St 97009 503-668-9393
Tim Werner, prin. Fax 668-5291

Brookings, Curry, Pop. 6,146
Brookings-Harbor SD 17C 1,600/K-12
629 Easy St 97415 541-469-7443
Sean Gallagher, supt. Fax 463-6599
www.brookings.k12.or.us
Azalea MS 400/6-8
629 Easy St 97415 541-469-7427
Nicole Medrano, prin. Fax 469-7080
Brookings-Harbor HS 500/9-12
629 Easy St 97415 541-469-2108
Lisa Dion, prin. Fax 469-0176

Brookings Harbor Christian S 100/PK-11
PO Box 5809 97415 541-469-6478
Kari Schultz, dir. Fax 412-7242

Brooks, Marion, Pop. 395

Willamette Valley Christian S 200/PK-12
9075 Pueblo Ave NE 97305 503-393-5236
Debbie Tipton, prin. Fax 485-8203

Burns, Harney, Pop. 2,728
Harney County SD 3 800/K-12
550 N Court Ave 97720 541-573-6811
Steve Quick, supt. Fax 573-7557
www.burnsschools.k12.or.us
Burns Alternative S 50/Alt
550 N Court Ave 97720 541-573-8198
Steven Jones, dir. Fax 573-7557
Burns HS 200/9-12
1100 Oregon Ave 97720 541-573-2044
David Goetz, prin. Fax 573-5456
Other Schools – See Hines

Canby, Clackamas, Pop. 15,520
Canby SD 86 4,700/K-12
1130 S Ivy St 97013 503-266-7861
Samuel Goodall, supt. Fax 266-0022
www.canby.k12.or.us
Baker Prairie MS 600/7-8
1859 SE Township Rd 97013 503-263-7170
Jennifer Turner, prin. Fax 263-7189
Canby HS 1,500/9-12
721 SW 4th Ave 97013 503-263-7200
Greg Dinse, prin. Fax 263-7211

Canyon City, Grant, Pop. 694
Grant SD 3 600/K-12
401 N Canyon City Blvd 97820 541-575-1280
Curt Shelley, supt. Fax 575-3614
www.grantesd.k12.or.us
Other Schools – See John Day

Canyonville, Douglas, Pop. 1,804

Canyonville Christian Academy 100/9-12
PO Box 1100 97417 541-839-4401
Daron Patton, prin. Fax 839-6228

Cave Junction, Josephine, Pop. 1,818
Three Rivers SD
Supt. — See Grants Pass
Byrne MS 300/5-8
101 S Junction Ave 97523 541-592-2163
Scott Polen, prin. Fax 592-4851
Illinois Valley HS 400/9-12
625 E River St 97523 541-592-2116
Tanner Smith, prin. Fax 592-4853

Central Point, Jackson, Pop. 16,683
Central Point SD 6 4,400/K-12
300 Ash St 97502 541-494-6200
Samantha Steele, supt. Fax 664-1637
www.district6.org
Crater Acad of Health & Public Service 500/9-12
655 N 3rd St 97502 541-494-6300
Julie Howland, prin. Fax 494-6286
Crater Renaissance Academy 500/9-12
655 N 3rd St 97502 541-494-6300
Adrienne Hillman, prin. Fax 494-6286
Crater S of Business Innovation Science 500/9-12
655 N 3rd St 97502 541-494-6300
Tiffany Slaughter, prin. Fax 494-6286
Scenic MS 800/6-8
1955 Scenic Ave 97502 541-494-6400
Brad Eaton, prin. Fax 664-8534
Other Schools – See Gold Hill

Chiloquin, Klamath, Pop. 678
Klamath County SD
Supt. — See Klamath Falls
Chiloquin JSHS 200/7-12
PO Box 397 97624 541-783-2321
Denise Brumels, prin. Fax 783-2792

Christmas Valley, Lake

Solid Rock Christian S 50/K-12
PO Box 745 97641 541-576-2895
Dr. Megan Eide, prin. Fax 576-3554

Clackamas, Clackamas, Pop. 2,578
North Clackamas SD 12
Supt. — See Milwaukie
Clackamas HS 2,300/9-12
14486 SE 122nd Ave 97015 503-353-5800
Christine Garcia, prin. Fax 353-5815
Rock Creek MS 800/6-8
14897 SE Parklane Dr 97015 503-353-5680
John Brooks, prin. Fax 353-5695

Northwest College of Hair Design Post-Sec.
8307 SE Monterey Ave 97086 503-659-2834
Pioneer Pacific College Post-Sec.
8800 SE Sunnyside Rd 97015 503-654-8000
Spring Mountain Christian Academy PK-12
12152 SE Mather Rd 97015 503-454-0319
Dr. Hanna Grishkevich Ph.D., prin. Fax 286-0473

Clatskanie, Columbia, Pop. 1,681
Clatskanie SD 6J 700/K-12
PO Box 678 97016 503-728-0587
Dr. Lloyd Hartley, supt. Fax 728-0608
www.csd.k12.or.us
Clatskanie MSHS 400/7-12
PO Box 68 97016 503-728-2146
Amy McNeil, prin. Fax 728-4632

Cloverdale, Tillamook, Pop. 245
Nestucca Valley SD 101 500/K-12
PO Box 99 97112 503-392-4892
David Phelps, supt. Fax 392-9061
www.nestucca.k12.or.us
Nestucca JSHS 200/7-12
PO Box 38 97112 503-392-3194
David Phelps, prin. Fax 392-3724

Colton, Clackamas
Colton SD 53 600/K-12
30429 S Grays Hill Rd 97017 503-824-3535
Jay Kosik, supt. Fax 824-3530
www.colton.k12.or.us
Colton HS 200/9-12
30205 S Wall St 97017 503-824-2311
Tori Hazelton, prin. Fax 824-2312
Colton MS 100/6-8
21580 S Schieffer Rd 97017 503-824-2319
Susan Inman, prin. Fax 824-2309

Condon, Gilliam, Pop. 677
Condon SD 25J 100/K-12
210 E Bayard St 97823 541-384-2441
Robert Waltenburg, supt. Fax 384-2504
www.condon.k12.or.us
Condon HS 50/9-12
210 E Bayard St 97823 541-384-2441
Michelle Geer, prin. Fax 384-2504

Coos Bay, Coos, Pop. 15,210
Coos Bay SD 9 3,000/K-12
1255 Hemlock Ave 97420 541-267-3104
Bryan Trendell, supt. Fax 269-5366
www.cbd9.net
Destinations S 100/Alt
1255 Hemlock Ave 97420 541-267-1485
Dale Inskeep, prin. Fax 266-7314
Harding Learning Center Alt
1255 Hemlock Ave 97420 541-267-1485
Dale Inskeep, prin. Fax 266-7314
Marshfield HS 1,000/8-12
1255 Hemlock Ave 97420 541-267-1405
Travis Howard, prin. Fax 269-0161

Southwestern Oregon Community College Post-Sec.
1988 Newmark Ave 97420 541-888-2525

Coquille, Coos, Pop. 3,760
Coquille SD 8 — 400/PK-12
1366 N Gould St 97423 — 541-396-2181
Tim Sweeney, supt. — Fax 396-5015
www.coquille.k12.or.us
Coquille JSHS — 300/7-12
499 W Central Blvd 97423 — 541-396-2163
Jeff Philley, prin. — Fax 396-4635
Winter Lakes S — 50/Alt
180 N Baxter St 97423 — 541-824-0115
Tony Jones, prin. — Fax 824-0116

Corbett, Multnomah
Corbett SD 39 — 900/K-12
35800 E Historic Colmb Riv 97019 — 503-261-4211
Dr. Randy Trani, supt. — Fax 695-3641
corbett.k12.or.us
Corbett HS — 200/9-12
35800 E Historic Colmb Riv 97019 — 503-261-4226
Dr. Phillip Pearson, prin. — Fax 695-3641
Corbett MS — 200/6-8
35800 E Historic Colmb Riv 97019 — 503-261-4226
Randy Trani, prin. — Fax 695-3641

Corvallis, Benton, Pop. 52,340
Corvallis SD 509J — 6,400/K-12
PO Box 3509J 97339 — 541-757-5811
Ryan Noss, supt. — Fax 757-5703
www.csd509j.net/
Cheldelin MS — 500/6-8
987 NE Conifer Blvd 97330 — 541-757-5971
Darren Bland, prin. — Fax 757-4596
Corvallis HS — 1,300/9-12
1400 NW Buchanan Ave 97330 — 541-757-5871
Matt Boring, prin. — Fax 757-5875
Crescent Valley HS — 1,000/9-12
4444 NW Highland Dr 97330 — 541-757-5801
Steve Kunke, prin. — Fax 757-4522
Pauling MS — 700/6-8
1111 NW Cleveland Ave 97330 — 541-757-5961
Alicia Ward-Satey, prin. — Fax 757-4598

Oregon State University 97333 — Post-Sec.
541-737-1000
Phagans' Beauty College — Post-Sec.
1565 SW 53rd St 97333 — 541-753-6466
Santiam Christian S — 600/PK-12
7220 NE Arnold Ave 97330 — 541-745-5524
Lance Villers, supt. — Fax 745-6338

Cottage Grove, Lane, Pop. 9,371
South Lane SD 45J3 — 2,900/K-12
PO Box 218 97424 — 541-942-3381
Dr. Krista Parent, supt. — Fax 942-8098
www.slane.k12.or.us
Cottage Grove HS — 800/9-12
1375 S River Rd 97424 — 541-942-3391
Iton Udosenata, prin. — Fax 942-7492
Kennedy Alternative HS — 100/Alt
PO Box 218 97424 — 541-942-1962
Mike Ingman, prin. — Fax 942-3672
Lincoln MS — 500/6-8
1565 S 4th St 97424 — 541-942-3316
Jeremy Smith, prin. — Fax 942-9801

Crane, Harney, Pop. 128
Harney County UNHSD 1J — 100/9-12
PO Box 828 97732 — 541-493-2641
Matthew Hawley, supt. — Fax 493-2051
cranehighschool.org
Crane Union HS — 100/9-12
PO Box 828 97732 — 541-493-2641
Matthew Hawley, prin. — Fax 493-2051

Creswell, Lane, Pop. 4,867
Creswell SD 40 — 1,300/K-12
998 A St 97426 — 541-895-6000
Todd Hamilton, supt. — Fax 895-6019
www.creswell.k12.or.us
Creswell HS — 400/9-12
33390 Nieblock Ln 97426 — 541-895-6020
Andy Bracco, prin. — Fax 895-6089
Creswell MS — 300/6-8
655 W Oregon Ave 97426 — 541-895-6090
Shirley Burrus, prin. — Fax 895-6139

Creswell Christian S — 100/PK-12
PO Box 217 97426 — 541-895-4622
Rebecca Lake, admin. — Fax 895-4622

Culver, Jefferson, Pop. 1,338
Culver SD 4 — 700/K-12
PO Box 259 97734 — 541-546-2541
Stefanie Garber, supt. — Fax 546-7517
www.culver.k12.or.us/
Culver HS — 200/9-12
PO Box 259 97734 — 541-546-2251
Tim Fields, prin. — Fax 546-2201
Culver MS — 200/6-8
PO Box 259 97734 — 541-546-3090
Brad Kudlac, prin. — Fax 546-2137

Dallas, Polk, Pop. 14,264
Dallas SD 2 — 3,200/K-12
111 SW Ash St 97338 — 503-623-5594
Dr. Michelle Johnstone, supt. — Fax 623-5597
www.dallas.k12.or.us
Dallas HS — 1,000/9-12
1250 SE Holman Ave 97338 — 503-623-8336
Steve Spencer, prin. — Fax 623-4669
LaCreole MS — 700/6-8
701 SE Lacreole Dr 97338 — 503-623-6662
Jamie Richardson, prin. — Fax 623-8477

Damascus, Clackamas, Pop. 10,286
Gresham-Barlow SD 10J
Supt. — See Gresham
Damascus MS — 200/6-8
14151 SE 242nd Ave, — 503-658-3171
Lori Walter, prin. — Fax 658-6275

Damascus Christian S — 200/K-12
14251 SE Rust Way, — 503-658-4100
Zachary Davidson, prin. — Fax 658-5827

Days Creek, Douglas, Pop. 264

Milo Adventist Academy — 100/9-12
PO Box 278 97429 — 541-825-3200

Dayton, Yamhill, Pop. 2,476
Dayton SD 8 — 1,000/K-12
PO Box 219 97114 — 503-864-2215
Janelle Beers, supt. — Fax 864-3927
daytonk12.org
Dayton HS — 300/9-12
801 Ferry St 97114 — 503-864-2273
Jami Fluke, prin. — Fax 864-2932
Dayton JHS — 200/6-8
801 Ferry St 97114 — 503-864-2246
Jami Fluke, prin. — Fax 864-2932

Dayville, Grant, Pop. 148
Dayville SD 16J — 100/PK-12
PO Box C 97825 — 541-987-2412
Kathryn Hedrick, supt. — Fax 987-2155
www.dayvilleschools.com
Dayville S — 100/PK-12
PO Box C 97825 — 541-987-2412
Kathryn Hedrick, prin. — Fax 987-2155

Dillard, Douglas
Winston-Dillard SD 116
Supt. — See Winston
Dillard Alternative HS — 50/Alt
165 Dyke Rd 97432 — 541-679-3023
Brenyl Swanson, prin. — Fax 784-2620

Drain, Douglas, Pop. 1,120
North Douglas SD 22 — 300/K-12
PO Box 428 97435 — 541-836-2223
John Lahley, supt. — Fax 836-7558
www.northdouglas.k12.or.us
North Douglas HS — 100/9-12
PO Box 488 97435 — 541-836-2222
Scott Yakovich, prin. — Fax 836-2387

Dufur, Wasco, Pop. 590
Dufur SD 29 — 300/K-12
802 NE 5th St 97021 — 541-467-2509
Jack Henderson, supt. — Fax 467-2589
www.dufur.k12.or.us
Dufur S — 300/K-12
802 NE 5th St 97021 — 541-467-2509
Leo Baptiste, prin. — Fax 467-2589

Eagle Point, Jackson, Pop. 8,245
Jackson County SD 9 — 3,600/PK-12
PO Box 548 97524 — 541-830-6551
Cynda Rickert, supt. — Fax 830-6550
www.eaglepnt.k12.or.us
Eagle Point HS — 1,100/9-12
PO Box 198 97524 — 541-830-1300
Jenn Whitehead, prin. — Fax 830-6682
Eagle Point MS — 500/6-8
PO Box 218 97524 — 541-830-1250
Joni Parsons, prin. — Fax 830-6086
Other Schools – See White City

Echo, Umatilla, Pop. 686
Echo SD 5 — 300/PK-12
600 E Gerone St 97826 — 541-376-8436
Raymon Smith, supt. — Fax 376-8473
www.echo.k12.or.us
Echo S — 300/PK-12
600 E Gerone St 97826 — 541-376-8436
Raymon Smith, prin. — Fax 376-8473

Elgin, Union, Pop. 1,678
Elgin SD 23 — 400/PK-12
PO Box 68 97827 — 541-437-1211
Dianne Greif, supt. — Fax 437-1231
www.elgin.k12.or.us
Elgin HS — 100/9-12
PO Box 68 97827 — 541-437-2021
Robert Shell, prin. — Fax 437-8212

Elmira, Lane
Fern Ridge SD 28J — 1,500/K-12
88834 Territorial Rd 97437 — 541-935-2253
Gary Carpenter, supt. — Fax 935-8222
www.fernridge.k12.or.us
Elmira HS — 500/9-12
24936 Fir Grove Ln 97437 — 541-935-8200
Gary Carpenter, prin. — Fax 935-8205
Fern Ridge MS — 300/6-8
88831 Territorial Rd 97437 — 541-935-8230
Peter Barsotti, prin. — Fax 935-8234

Enterprise, Wallowa, Pop. 1,904
Enterprise SD 21 — 400/K-12
201 SE 4th St 97828 — 541-426-3193
Erika Pinkerton, supt. — Fax 426-3504
www.enterprise.k12.or.us
Enterprise HS — 200/7-12
201 SE 4th St 97828 — 541-426-3193
Blake Carlsen, prin. — Fax 426-3504

Enterprise SDA S — 50/K-10
PO Box N 97828 — 541-426-8339

Estacada, Clackamas, Pop. 2,646
Estacada SD 108 — 2,400/K-12
255 NE 6th Ave 97023 — 503-630-6871
Marla Stephenson, supt. — Fax 630-8513
www.estacada.k12.or.us
Estacada HS — 600/9-12
355 NE 6th Ave 97023 — 503-630-8515
Ryan Carpenter, prin. — Fax 630-8699
Estacada MS — 300/6-8
500 NE Main St 97023 — 503-630-8516
Kristin Turnquist, prin. — Fax 630-8693

Eugene, Lane, Pop. 149,658
Bethel SD 52 — 5,600/K-12
4640 Barger Dr 97402 — 541-689-3280
Chris Parra, supt. — Fax 689-0719
www.bethel.k12.or.us
Cascade MS — 300/6-8
1525 Echo Hollow Rd 97402 — 541-689-0641
Natalie Oliver, prin. — Fax 689-9622
Kalapuya HS — 100/Alt
1200 N Terry St 97402 — 541-607-9853
Kee Zublin, prin. — Fax 607-9857
Shasta MS — 500/6-8
4656 Barger Dr 97402 — 541-688-9611
Brady Cottle, prin. — Fax 689-9382
Willamette HS — 1,600/9-12
1801 Echo Hollow Rd 97402 — 541-689-0731
Mindy LeRoux, prin. — Fax 689-7119

Crow-Applegate-Lorane SD 66 — 300/K-12
85955 Territorial Hwy 97402 — 541-935-2100
Aaron Brown, supt. — Fax 935-6107
www.cal.k12.or.us
Crow MSHS — 100/7-12
25863 Crow Rd 97402 — 541-935-2227
Marci Haro, prin. — Fax 935-6829

Eugene SD 4J — 16,400/K-12
200 N Monroe St 97402 — 541-790-7700
Dr. Gustavo Balderas, supt. — Fax 790-7711
www.4j.lane.edu
Arts and Technology Academy at Jefferson — 300/6-8
1650 W 22nd Ave 97405 — 541-790-5700
Linda O'Shea, prin. — Fax 790-5705
Churchill HS — 1,100/9-12
1850 Bailey Hill Rd 97405 — 541-790-5100
Greg Borgerding, prin. — Fax 790-5110
Eugene College and Career Options — Alt
4000 E 30th Ave 97405 — 541-463-3930
Molly Gillette, prin. — Fax 463-3937
Family MS — 6-8
1650 W 22nd Ave 97405 — 541-790-5705
Linda O'Shea, prin. — Fax 790-5705
International HS Churchill Campus — Alt
1850 Bailey Hill Rd 97405 — 541-790-5225
Jessica Schabtach, prin. — Fax 790-5110
International HS Sheldon Campus — Alt
2455 Willakenzie Rd 97401 — 541-790-6636
Jessica Schabtach, prin. — Fax 790-6605
International HS South Eugene Campus — Alt
400 E 19th Ave 97401 — 541-790-8030
Jessica Schabtach, prin. — Fax 790-8005
Kelly MS — 400/6-8
850 Howard Ave 97404 — 541-790-4740
Juan Cuadros, prin. — Fax 790-4746
Kennedy MS — 500/6-8
2200 Bailey Hill Rd 97405 — 541-790-5500
Charlie Smith, prin. — Fax 790-5505
Madison MS — 500/6-8
875 Wilkes Dr 97404 — 541-790-4300
Scott Marsh, prin. — Fax 790-4320
Monroe MS — 500/6-8
2800 Bailey Ln 97401 — 541-790-6300
Mike Johnson, prin. — Fax 790-6305
North Eugene HS — 1,000/9-12
200 Silver Ln 97404 — 541-790-4500
Casandra Kamens, prin. — Fax 790-4440
Roosevelt MS — 600/6-8
500 E 24th Ave 97405 — 541-790-8500
Chris Mitchell, prin. — Fax 790-8505
Sheldon HS — 1,500/9-12
2455 Willakenzie Rd 97401 — 541-790-6600
Bob Bolden, prin. — Fax 790-6605
South Eugene HS — 1,400/9-12
400 E 19th Ave 97401 — 541-790-8000
Andy Dey, prin. — Fax 790-8005
Spencer Butte MS — 500/6-8
500 E 43rd Ave 97405 — 541-790-8300
Tasha Katsuda, prin. — Fax 790-8305
Young MS — 500/6-8
2555 Gilham Rd 97408 — 541-790-6400
Jericho Dunn, prin. — Fax 790-6456

Gutenberg College — Post-Sec.
1883 University St 97403 — 541-683-5141
Lane Community College — Post-Sec.
4000 E 30th Ave 97405 — 541-463-3000
Marist HS — 500/9-12
1900 Kingsley Rd 97401 — 541-686-2234
Stacey Baker, prin. — Fax 342-6451
New Hope Christian College — Post-Sec.
2155 Bailey Hill Rd 97405 — 541-485-1780
Northwest Christian University — Post-Sec.
828 E 11th Ave 97401 — 541-343-1641
Oak Hill S — 100/K-12
86397 Eldon Schafer Dr 97405 — 541-744-0954
Robert Sarkisian, head sch — Fax 741-6968
University of Oregon — Post-Sec.
1217 University of Oregon 97403 — 541-346-1000
Wellsprings Friends S — 100/9-12
3590 W 18th Ave 97402 — 541-686-1223
Dennis Hoerner Ph.D., head sch — Fax 687-1493

Fairview, Multnomah, Pop. 8,478
Reynolds SD 7 — 11,600/PK-12
1204 NE 201st Ave 97024 — 503-661-7200
Linda Florence, supt. — Fax 667-6932
www.reynolds.k12.or.us
Reynolds MS — 1,000/6-8
1200 NE 201st Ave 97024 — 503-665-8166
Stacy Talus, prin. — Fax 262-3796
Reynolds Learning Academy — Adult
20234 NE Halsey St 97024 — 503-667-4673
Erin Ferguson, prin. — Fax 667-0530
Other Schools – See Portland, Troutdale

Falls City, Polk, Pop. 925
Falls City SD 57 — 200/K-12
111 N Main St 97344 — 503-787-3521
Jack Thompson, supt. — Fax 787-5805
www.fallscityschools.org/

Falls City HS 100/9-12
111 N Main St 97344 503-787-3521
Jack Thompson, admin. Fax 787-1507

Finn Rock, Lane
McKenzie SD 68 200/K-12
51187 Blue River Dr, Vida OR 97488 541-822-3338
Jim Thomas, supt. Fax 822-8014
www.mckenzie.k12.or.us
McKenzie HS 100/9-12
51187 Blue River Dr, Vida OR 97488 541-822-3313
Lane Tompkins, prin. Fax 822-8014

Florence, Lane, Pop. 8,201
Siuslaw SD 97J 1,300/K-12
2111 Oak St 97439 541-997-2651
Ethel Angal, supt. Fax 997-6748
www.siuslaw.k12.or.us
Siuslaw HS 400/9-12
2975 Oak St 97439 541-997-3448
Kerri Tatum, prin. Fax 997-4160
Siuslaw MS 300/6-8
2525 Oak St 97439 541-997-8241
Andrew Grzeskowiak, prin. Fax 997-4161

Forest Grove, Washington, Pop. 20,448
Forest Grove SD 15 5,900/PK-12
1728 Main St 97116 503-357-6171
Dr. Yvonne Curtis, supt. Fax 359-2520
www.fgsd.k12.or.us
Armstrong MS 800/7-8
1777 Mountain View Ln 97116 503-359-2465
Brandon Hundley, prin. Fax 359-2560
Community Alternative Learning Center Alt
2701 Taylor Way 97116 503-359-2413
Jessica Pierce, prin.
Forest Grove HS 1,900/9-12
1401 Nichols Ln 97116 503-359-2432
Karen O'Neill, prin. Fax 359-2521

Pacific University Post-Sec.
2043 College Way 97116 800-677-6712

Gaston, Washington, Pop. 631
Gaston SD 511J 500/K-12
PO Box 68 97119 503-985-0210
Susy McKenzie, supt. Fax 985-3366
www.gaston.k12.or.us
Gaston JSHS 300/7-12
PO Box 68 97119 503-985-7516
Christine Collins, prin. Fax 985-3279

Gervais, Marion, Pop. 2,415
Gervais SD 1 1,100/PK-12
PO Box 100 97026 503-792-3803
Matt Henry, supt. Fax 792-3809
www.gervais.k12.or.us
Brown Academy 100/Alt
PO Box 100 97026 503-792-3830
Kim Kellison, prin. Fax 792-3809
Gervais HS 300/9-12
PO Box 195 97026 503-792-3656
Mike Solem, prin. Fax 792-3770
Gervais MS 200/6-8
PO Box 176 97026 503-792-3626
Ann O'Connell, prin. Fax 792-3770

Gilchrist, Klamath
Klamath County SD
Supt. — See Klamath Falls
Gilchrist S 100/K-12
PO Box 668 97737 541-433-2295
Steve Prock, prin. Fax 433-2688

Gladstone, Clackamas, Pop. 11,109
Gladstone SD 115 2,100/PK-12
17789 Webster Rd 97027 503-655-2777
Bob Stewart, supt. Fax 655-5201
www.gladstone.k12.or.us
Gladstone HS 700/9-12
18800 Portland Ave 97027 503-655-2544
Kevin Taylor, prin. Fax 655-0320
Kraxberger MS 500/6-8
17777 Webster Rd 97027 503-655-3636
John Olson, prin. Fax 650-2596

Grace Christian S 100/PK-12
6460 Glen Echo Ave 97027 503-655-3074
Michael Thompson, prin. Fax 655-1702

Glide, Douglas, Pop. 1,756
Glide SD 12 600/K-12
301 Glide Loop Dr 97443 541-496-3521
Mike Narkiewicz, supt. Fax 496-4300
www.glide.k12.or.us
Glide HS 200/9-12
18990 N Umpqua Hwy 97443 541-496-3554
Kristina Haug, prin. Fax 496-4304
Glide MS 100/7-8
18990 N Umpqua Hwy 97443 541-496-3516
Kristina Haug, prin. Fax 496-4302

Gold Beach, Curry, Pop. 2,158
Central Curry SD 1 500/K-12
29516 Ellensburg Ave 97444 541-247-2003
Roy Durfee, supt. Fax 247-9717
www.ccsd.k12.or.us
Gold Beach HS 200/9-12
29516 Ellensburg Ave 97444 541-247-6647
Roy Durfee, prin. Fax 247-4557

Gold Hill, Jackson, Pop. 1,181
Central Point SD 6
Supt. — See Central Point
Hanby MS 200/6-8
806 6th Ave N 97525 541-494-6800
Scott Dippel, prin. Fax 855-1120

Grants Pass, Josephine, Pop. 33,499
Grants Pass SD 7 5,700/K-12
725 NE Dean Dr 97526 541-474-5700
Kirk Kolb, supt. Fax 474-5705
www.grantspass.k12.or.us
Grants Pass HS 1,800/9-12
830 NE 9th St 97526 541-474-5710
Ryan Thompson, prin. Fax 474-5717
Grants Pass HS - Gladiola Campus Alt
1137 SE Gladiola Dr 97526 541-474-5790
Kelly Marval, admin. Fax 474-0098
North MS 700/6-8
1725 NW Highland Ave 97526 541-474-5740
Tommy Blanchard, prin. Fax 474-5739
South MS 600/6-8
350 W Harbeck Rd 97527 541-474-5750
Jeff Weiss, prin. Fax 474-9742

Three Rivers SD 4,800/K-12
8550 New Hope Rd 97527 541-862-3111
Dave Valenzuela, supt. Fax 862-3119
www.threerivers.k12.or.us
Fleming MS 400/6-8
6001 Monument Dr 97526 541-476-8284
Sidney Hobgood, prin. Fax 471-2458
Hidden Valley HS 700/9-12
651 Murphy Creek Rd 97527 541-862-2124
Daye Stone, prin. Fax 862-2872
Lincoln Savage MS 400/6-8
8551 New Hope Rd 97527 541-862-2171
Mark Higgins, prin. Fax 862-2713
North Valley HS 600/9-12
6741 Monument Dr 97526 541-479-3388
Dennis Misner, prin. Fax 471-2462
Other Schools – See Cave Junction, Merlin

Brighton Academy 100/PK-12
1121 NE 7th St 97526 541-474-6865
New Hope Christian S 200/PK-12
5961 New Hope Rd 97527 541-476-4588
Ernest Stone, admin. Fax 474-7626
Phagans' Grants Pass College of Beauty Post-Sec.
304 NE Agness Ave Ste F 97526 541-479-6678
Rogue Community College Post-Sec.
3345 Redwood Hwy 97527 541-956-7500

Gresham, Multnomah, Pop. 101,317
Centennial SD 28J
Supt. — See Portland
Centennial HS 1,800/9-12
3505 SE 182nd Ave 97030 503-762-6180
Mairi Scott-Aguirre, prin. Fax 661-5296

Gresham-Barlow SD 10J 11,900/PK-12
1331 NW Eastman Pkwy 97030 503-261-4550
Jim Schlachter, supt. Fax 261-4552
www.gresham.k12.or.us
Barlow HS 1,700/9-12
5105 SE 302nd Ave 97080 503-258-4850
Bruce Schmidt, prin. Fax 258-4840
Clear Creek MS 700/6-8
219 NE 219th Ave 97030 503-492-6700
David Atherton, prin. Fax 492-6707
Gresham HS 1,700/9-12
1200 N Main Ave 97030 503-674-5500
Michael Schaefer, prin. Fax 674-5549
McCarty MS 600/6-8
1400 SE 5th St 97080 503-665-0148
John George, prin. Fax 669-1892
Russell MS 800/6-8
3625 SE Powell Valley Rd 97080 503-667-6900
Rolland Hayden, prin. Fax 492-6708
Springwater Trail HS 200/9-12
1440 SE Fleming Ave 97080 503-261-4600
Ryan Blaszak, prin. Fax 261-4630
West Orient MS 400/6-8
29805 SE Orient Dr 97080 503-663-3323
Elise Cantanese, prin. Fax 663-2504
Other Schools – See Damascus

Multnomah ESD
Supt. — See Portland
Alpha HS 100/Alt
876 NE 8th St 97030 503-262-4050
Peter Kane, prin. Fax 262-4065

Mt. Hood Community College Post-Sec.
26000 SE Stark St 97030 503-491-6422
Phonics Phactory 300/PK-10
PO Box 2128 97030 503-661-5632
Rev. Brian Mayer, admin. Fax 907-5827

Halsey, Linn, Pop. 874
Central Linn SD 552 700/K-12
PO Box 200 97348 541-369-2813
Brian Gardner, supt. Fax 369-3439
www.centrallinn.k12.or.us
Central Linn HS 300/7-12
32433 Highway 228 97348 541-369-2811
Jon Zwemke, prin. Fax 369-3455

Happy Valley, Clackamas, Pop. 13,434
North Clackamas SD 12
Supt. — See Milwaukie
Happy Valley MS 1,000/6-8
13865 SE King Rd Ste B, 503-353-1920
Emily Behunin, prin. Fax 353-1935

Phagans' School of Hair Design Post-Sec.
11860 SE 82nd Ave # K-217, 503-652-2668

Harrisburg, Linn, Pop. 3,472
Harrisburg SD 7 900/K-12
PO Box 208 97446 541-995-6626
Bryan Starr, supt. Fax 995-3453
www.harrisburg.k12.or.us
Harrisburg HS 300/9-12
PO Box 209 97446 541-995-6626
Steve Atkinson, prin. Fax 995-6697
Harrisburg MS 200/6-8
PO Box 317 97446 541-995-6551
Darci Stuller, prin. Fax 995-5120

Harris S 100/PK-12
PO Box 347 97446 541-995-6444
Lifegate Christian International S 50/6-12
21211 Coburg Rd 97446 541-689-5847
Donna Wickwire, prin. Fax 689-6028

Helix, Umatilla, Pop. 175
Helix SD 1 200/K-12
PO Box 398 97835 541-457-2175
Darrick Cope, supt. Fax 457-2481
www.helix.k12.or.us
Helix S 200/K-12
PO Box 398 97835 541-457-2175
Darrick Cope, prin. Fax 457-2481

Heppner, Morrow, Pop. 1,251
Morrow SD 1 2,200/K-12
PO Box 100 97836 541-676-9128
Dirk Dirksen, supt. Fax 676-5742
www.morrow.k12.or.us
Heppner JSHS 200/7-12
PO Box 67 97836 541-676-9138
Matt Combe, prin. Fax 676-5836
Other Schools – See Boardman, Irrigon

Hermiston, Umatilla, Pop. 16,457
Hermiston SD 8 5,200/K-12
305 SW 11th St 97838 541-667-6000
Dr. Fred Maiocco, supt. Fax 667-6050
www.hermiston.k12.or.us
Hermiston HS 1,400/9-12
600 S 1st St 97838 541-667-6100
Tom Spoo, prin. Fax 667-6150
Innovative Learning Center 100/Alt
581 S 1st St 97838 541-667-6100
Tom Spoo, prin. Fax 667-6153
Larive MS 700/6-8
1497 SW 9th St 97838 541-667-6200
Stacie Roberts, prin. Fax 667-6250
Sandstone MS 500/6-8
400 NE 10th St 97838 541-667-6300
Lori Mills, prin. Fax 667-6350

Hillsboro, Washington, Pop. 88,100
Hillsboro SD 1J 20,800/K-12
3083 NE 49th Pl 97124 503-844-1500
Mike Scott, supt. Fax 844-1540
www.hsd.k12.or.us
Brown MS 800/7-8
1505 SW Cornelius Pass Rd 97123 503-844-1070
Roger Will, prin. Fax 844-1071
Century HS 1,700/9-12
2000 SE Century Blvd 97123 503-844-1800
Martha Guise, prin. Fax 844-1825
Evergreen MS 800/7-8
29850 NW Evergreen Rd 97124 503-844-1400
Otis Gulley, prin. Fax 844-1402
Glencoe HS 1,600/9-12
2700 NW Glencoe Rd 97124 503-844-1900
Claudia Ruf, prin. Fax 844-1949
Hillsboro HS 1,400/9-12
3285 SE Rood Bridge Rd 97123 503-844-1980
Lou Bailey, prin. Fax 844-1999
Liberty HS 1,500/9-12
21945 NW Wagon Way 97124 503-844-1250
Greg Timmons, prin. Fax 844-1299
Miller Education Center 50/Alt
440 SE Oak St 97123 503-844-1680
Gregg O'Mara, prin. Fax 844-1684
Miller Education Center 100/Alt
215 SE 6th Ave 97123 503-844-1000
Gregg O'Mara, prin. Fax 844-1019
Poynter MS 700/7-8
1535 NE Grant St 97124 503-844-1580
Jon Pede, prin. Fax 844-1583
South Meadows MS 800/7-8
4690 SE Davis Rd 97123 503-844-1220
Mary Mendez, prin. Fax 844-1221

Airman Proficiency Center Post-Sec.
3565 NE Cornell Rd 97124 503-648-2831
Faith Bible Christian HS 100/9-12
2299 SE 45th Ave 97123 503-681-8254
Kevin Rex, supt. Fax 681-9274

Hines, Harney, Pop. 1,525
Harney County SD 3
Supt. — See Burns
Hines MS 200/6-8
PO Box 38 97738 541-573-6436
David Robinson, prin. Fax 573-7255

Hood River, Hood River, Pop. 7,008
Hood River County SD 4,000/K-12
1011 Eugene St 97031 541-386-2511
Dan Goldman, supt. Fax 387-5099
www.hoodriver.k12.or.us
Hood River MS 500/6-8
1602 May St 97031 541-386-2114
Brent Emmons, prin. Fax 387-5070
Hood River Valley HS 1,300/9-12
1220 Indian Creek Rd 97031 541-386-4500
Rich Polkinghorn, prin. Fax 386-2400
Wy'East MS 500/6-8
3000 Wyeast Rd 97031 541-354-1548
Sarah Braman-Smith, prin. Fax 354-5120

Horizon Christian S 200/PK-12
700 Pacific Ave 97031 541-387-3200
Ken Block, supt. Fax 387-3651
Mid-Columbia Adventist Academy 50/K-10
1100 22nd St 97031 541-386-3187

Huntington, Baker, Pop. 429
Huntington SD 16J 100/K-12
520 3rd St E 97907 541-869-2204
Scott Bullock, supt. Fax 869-2444
www.huntington.k12.or.us/
Huntington S 100/K-12
520 3rd St E 97907 541-869-2204
Scott Bullock, admin. Fax 869-2444

Independence, Polk, Pop. 8,352
Central SD 13J 3,100/K-12
750 S 5th St 97351 503-838-0030
Buzz Brazeau, supt. Fax 838-0033
www.central.k12.or.us
Central HS 900/9-12
1530 Monmouth St 97351 503-838-0480
Buzz Brazeau, prin. Fax 838-0483
Talmadge MS 700/6-8
51 S 16th St 97351 503-606-2252
Perry LaBounty, prin. Fax 606-2436

Irrigon, Morrow, Pop. 1,788
Morrow SD 1
Supt. — See Heppner
Irrigon JSHS 400/7-12
315 E Wyoming Ave 97844 541-922-5551
Ryan Keefauver, prin. Fax 922-5558
Morrow Education Center 100/Alt
240 W Columbia Ln 97844 541-922-4004
Craig Bensen, dir. Fax 922-4122

Jasper, Lane

Laurelwood Academy 50/9-12
PO Box 2072 97438 541-726-8340
Stephen Henton, prin. Fax 726-8380

Jefferson, Marion, Pop. 3,013
Jefferson SD 14J 900/K-12
1328 N 2nd St 97352 541-327-3337
Kent Klewitz, supt. Fax 327-2960
www.jefferson.k12.or.us
Jefferson HS 300/9-12
2200 Talbot Rd SE 97352 541-327-3337
Cathy Emmert, prin. Fax 327-1867
Jefferson MS 200/6-8
1344 N 2nd St 97352 541-327-3337
Dan Fritz, prin. Fax 327-7762

John Day, Grant, Pop. 1,713
Grant SD 3
Supt. — See Canyon City
Grant Union JSHS 300/7-12
911 S Canyon Blvd 97845 541-575-1799
Ryan Gerry, prin. Fax 575-2754

Jordan Valley, Malheur, Pop. 179
Jordan Valley SD 3 100/K-12
PO Box 99 97910 541-586-2213
Rusty Bengoa, supt. Fax 586-2568
www.jordanvalley.k12.or.us
Jordan Valley HS 50/7-12
PO Box 99 97910 541-586-2213
Rusty Bengoa, supt. Fax 586-2569

Junction City, Lane, Pop. 5,249
Junction City SD 69 1,700/K-12
325 Maple St 97448 541-998-6311
Dr. Kathleen Rodden-Nord, supt. Fax 998-3926
www.junctioncity.k12.or.us
Junction City HS 600/9-12
1135 W 6th Ave 97448 541-998-2343
Malcolm McRae, prin. Fax 998-6303
Oaklea MS 500/5-8
1515 Rose St 97448 541-998-3381
Brian Young, prin. Fax 998-3383

Keizer, Marion, Pop. 35,273
Salem-Keizer SD 24J
Supt. — See Salem
Claggett Creek MS 900/6-8
1810 Alder Dr NE 97303 503-399-3701
Rob Schoepper, prin. Fax 399-3708
McNary HS 2,100/9-12
595 Chemawa Rd N 97303 503-399-3233
Erik Jespersen, prin. Fax 391-4025
Whiteaker MS 800/6-8
1605 Lockhaven Dr NE 97303 503-399-3224
Julia DeWitt, prin. Fax 375-7872

Klamath Falls, Klamath, Pop. 20,019
Klamath County SD 5,800/K-12
10501 Washburn Way 97603 541-883-5000
Greg Thede, supt. Fax 883-6677
www.kcsd.k12.or.us
Brixner JHS 300/7-8
4727 Homedale Rd 97603 541-883-5025
Leslie Garrett, prin. Fax 883-5019
Falcon Heights Academy 100/Alt
8205 Highway 39 97603 541-883-6699
Laura Blair, prin. Fax 273-8763
Henley HS 700/9-12
8245 Highway 39 97603 541-883-5040
Jack Lee, prin. Fax 883-6663
Henley MS 300/7-8
7925 Highway 39 97603 541-883-5050
Kristine Creed, prin. Fax 883-5012
Mazama HS 700/9-12
3009 Summers Ln 97603 541-883-5024
Steve Morosin, prin. Fax 883-5044
Other Schools – See Bonanza, Chiloquin, Gilchrist, Merrill

Klamath Falls CSD 3,000/K-12
1336 Avalon St 97603 541-883-4700
Dr. Paul Hillyer, supt. Fax 850-2766
www.kfalls.k12.or.us
Klamath Learning Center Alt
2856 Eberlein St 97603 541-883-4719
Tonie Kellom, dir. Fax 885-4281
Klamath Union HS 700/9-12
1300 Monclaire St 97601 541-883-4710
Charlene Herron, prin. Fax 885-4276
Ponderosa JHS 700/6-8
2554 Main St 97601 541-883-4740
Daymond Monteith, prin. Fax 885-4286

College of Cosmetology Post-Sec.
357 E Main St 97601 541-882-6644
Hosanna Christian S 300/PK-12
5000 Hosanna Way 97603 541-882-7732
Don Wonsley, admin. Fax 882-6940
Klamath Community College Post-Sec.
7390 S 6th St 97603 541-882-3521
Oregon Institute of Technology Post-Sec.
3201 Campus Dr 97601 541-885-1000
Triad S 200/PK-12
2450 Summers Ln 97603 541-885-7940
Gary Weldon, head sch Fax 885-7945

La Grande, Union, Pop. 12,606
La Grande SD 1 2,200/K-12
1305 N Willow St 97850 541-663-3202
Larry Glaze, supt. Fax 663-3223
www.lagrandesd.org
La Grande HS 600/9-12
708 K Ave 97850 541-663-3301
Brett Baxter, prin. Fax 663-3313
La Grande MS 500/6-8
1108 4th St 97850 541-663-3421
Kyle McKinney, prin. Fax 663-3422

Eastern Oregon University Post-Sec.
1 University Blvd 97850 541-962-3672

Lake Oswego, Clackamas, Pop. 35,589
Lake Oswego SD 7J 6,800/K-12
PO Box 70 97034 503-534-2000
Dr. Heather Beck, supt. Fax 534-2030
www.loswego.k12.or.us
Lake Oswego HS 1,300/9-12
PO Box 310 97034 503-534-2313
Rollin Dickinson, prin. Fax 534-2327
Lake Oswego JHS 900/6-8
2500 Country Club Rd 97034 503-534-2335
Sara Deboy, prin. Fax 534-2341
Lakeridge HS 1,200/9-12
PO Box 739 97034 503-534-2319
Jennifer Schiele, prin. Fax 534-2392
Lakeridge JHS 800/6-8
4700 Jean Rd 97035 503-534-2343
Kurt Schultz, prin. Fax 534-2276

Lakeview, Lake, Pop. 2,216
Adel SD 21 50/4-8
357 N L St 97630 541-947-5418
Bob Nash, admin. Fax 947-3373
www.lakeesd.k12.or.us
Other Schools – See Adel

Lake County SD 7 700/K-12
1341 S 1st St 97630 541-947-3347
Will Cahill, supt. Fax 947-3386
www.lakeview.k12.or.us
Daly MS 100/7-8
906 S 3rd St 97630 541-947-2287
Jesse Hamilton, prin. Fax 947-3506
Lakeview HS 200/9-12
906 S 3rd St 97630 541-947-2287
Jesse Hamilton, prin. Fax 947-3601

La Pine, Deschutes, Pop. 1,617
Bend-LaPine Administrative SD 1
Supt. — See Bend
La Pine HS 500/9-12
51633 Coach Rd 97739 541-355-8400
Matt Montgomery, prin. Fax 355-8410
La Pine MS 300/6-8
16360 1st St 97739 541-355-8200
Robi Phinney, prin. Fax 355-8210

Lebanon, Linn, Pop. 15,042
Lebanon Community SD 9 4,200/K-12
485 S 5th St 97355 541-451-8511
Rob Hess, supt. Fax 259-6857
www.lebanon.k12.or.us
Lebanon HS 1,300/9-12
1700 S 5th St 97355 541-451-8555
Brad Shreve, prin. Fax 451-8550
Seven Oak MS 500/6-8
550 Cascade Dr 97355 541-451-8416
Wayne Raposa, prin. Fax 451-8431

East Linn Christian Academy 300/PK-12
36883 Victory Dr 97355 541-259-2324
Janelle Detweiler M.Ed., supt. Fax 244-9334

Lincoln City, Lincoln, Pop. 7,723
Lincoln County SD
Supt. — See Newport
Taft HS 600/7-12
3780 SE Spy Glass Ridge Dr 97367 541-996-2115
Majalise Tolan, prin. Fax 996-4335

Lincoln City Seventh-day Adventist S 100/1-12
2126 NE Surf Ave 97367 541-994-5181
Karie MacPhee, prin. Fax 994-5181

Long Creek, Grant, Pop. 191
Long Creek SD 17 50/PK-12
PO Box 429 97856 541-421-3896
Bill Delong, supt. Fax 421-3012
www.longcreekschool.com
Long Creek S 50/PK-12
PO Box 429 97856 541-421-3896
Bill Delong, prin. Fax 421-3012

Lowell, Lane, Pop. 983
Lowell SD 71 300/K-12
65 S Pioneer St 97452 541-937-8405
Dr. Walt Hanline, supt. Fax 937-2112
www.lowell.k12.or.us
Lowell JSHS 100/7-12
65 S Pioneer St 97452 541-937-2124
Kay Graham, prin. Fax 937-2112

Mc Minnville, Yamhill, Pop. 31,337
McMinnville SD 40 6,600/K-12
1500 NE Baker St 97128 503-565-4000
Maryalice Russell, supt. Fax 565-4043
www.msd.k12.or.us
Duniway MS 800/6-8
575 NW Michelbook Ln 97128 503-565-4400
Hilary Brittan, prin. Fax 565-4414
McMinnville HS 2,000/9-12
615 NE 15th St 97128 503-565-4200
Tony Vicknair, prin. Fax 565-4244
Patton MS 800/6-8
1175 NE 19th St 97128 503-565-4500
Brian Crain, prin. Fax 565-4515

Linfield College Post-Sec.
900 SE Baker St 97128 503-883-2200

Madras, Jefferson, Pop. 5,846
Jefferson County SD 509J 3,100/K-12
445 SE Buff St 97741 541-475-6192
Dr. Rick Molitor, supt. Fax 475-6856
www.jcsd.k12.or.us
Bridges Career and Technical HS 200/Alt
410 SW 4th St 97741 541-475-4820
Caron Smith, admin. Fax 475-9409
Jefferson County MS 600/6-8
1180 SE Kemper Way 97741 541-475-7253
Simon White, prin. Fax 475-4825
Madras HS 800/9-12
390 SE 10th St 97741 541-475-7265
Mark Neffendorf, prin. Fax 475-7744

Mapleton, Lane
Mapleton SD 32 200/K-12
10868 E Mapleton Rd 97453 541-268-4312
Jodi O'Mara, supt. Fax 268-4632
www.mapleton.k12.or.us
Mapleton MSHS 100/7-12
10868 E Mapleton Rd 97453 541-268-4322
Brenda Moyer, prin. Fax 268-4632

Marcola, Lane
Marcola SD 79J 200/K-12
PO Box 820 97454 541-933-2512
Bill Watkins, supt. Fax 933-2338
www.marcola.k12.or.us
Mohawk MSHS 100/6-12
38300 Wendling Rd 97454 541-933-2512
Bill Watkins, prin. Fax 933-2338

Marylhurst, Clackamas

Marylhurst University Post-Sec.
PO Box 261 97036 503-636-8141

Maupin, Wasco, Pop. 405
South Wasco County SD 1 200/PK-12
PO Box 346 97037 541-395-2645
Ryan Wraught, supt. Fax 395-2679
www.swasco.net
South Wasco County HS 100/7-12
PO Box 347 97037 541-395-2225
Lynn Cowdrey, prin. Fax 395-2223

Medford, Jackson, Pop. 72,448
Medford SD 549C 13,400/K-12
815 S Oakdale Ave 97501 541-842-3636
Brian Shumate, supt. Fax 842-1087
www.medford.k12.or.us
Central Medford HS 200/Alt
815 S Oakdale Ave 97501 541-842-3669
Amy Herbst, prin. Fax 842-1990
Hedrick MS 900/7-8
1501 E Jackson St 97504 541-842-3700
Beth Anderson, prin. Fax 842-1548
McLoughlin MS 900/7-8
320 W 2nd St 97501 541-842-3720
Linda White, prin. Fax 842-1652
North Medford HS 1,700/9-12
1900 N Keene Way Dr 97504 541-842-3670
Dan Smith, prin. Fax 842-5206
South Medford HS 1,800/9-12
1551 Cunningham Ave 97501 541-842-3680
Damian Crowson, prin. Fax 842-1513

Abdill Career College Post-Sec.
843 E Main St Ste 203 97504 541-779-8384
Cascade Christian HS 400/6-12
855 Chevy Way 97504 541-772-0606
Devon Rickabaugh, prin. Fax 608-1369
Phagans' Medford Beauty School Post-Sec.
2320 Poplar Dr 97504 541-772-6155
Rogue Valley Adventist Academy 100/K-12
3675 S Stage Rd 97501 541-773-2988
Ann Campbell, prin. Fax 779-7575
St. Mary's HS 400/6-12
816 Black Oak Dr 97504 541-773-7877
Jim Meyer, pres. Fax 772-8973

Merlin, Josephine, Pop. 1,565
Three Rivers SD
Supt. — See Grants Pass
Merlin Alternative Center Alt
345 Merlin Rd 97532 541-476-2524
Mike Herzog, admin. Fax 476-6899

Merrill, Klamath, Pop. 817
Klamath County SD
Supt. — See Klamath Falls

Lost River JSHS 200/7-12
23330 Highway 50 97633 541-798-5666
Jamie Ongman, prin. Fax 798-5072

Mill City, Linn, Pop. 1,789
Santiam Canyon SD 129J 300/K-12
PO Box 197 97360 503-897-2321
Todd Miller, supt.
www.santiam.k12.or.us
Santiam JSHS 200/7-12
PO Box 199 97360 503-897-2311
David Plotts, prin. Fax 897-3154

Milton Freewater, Umatilla, Pop. 6,982
Milton-Freewater USD 7 1,200/K-12
1020 S Mill St 97862 541-938-3551
Dr. Robert Clark, supt. Fax 938-6704
www.miltfree.k12.or.us
Central MS 400/6-8
306 SW 2nd Ave 97862 541-938-5504
Tim Sprenger, prin. Fax 938-6615
McLoughlin HS 500/9-12
120 S Main St 97862 541-938-5591
Mindi Vaughan, prin. Fax 938-5593

Milwaukie, Clackamas, Pop. 19,622
North Clackamas SD 12 16,700/K-12
12400 SE Freeman Way 97222 503-353-6000
Matt Utterback, supt. Fax 353-6007
www.nclack.k12.or.us
Alder Creek MS 1,000/6-8
13801 SE Webster Rd 97267 503-353-5700
Alyson Brant, prin. Fax 353-5715
Milwaukie HS 1,100/9-12
11300 SE 23rd Ave 97222 503-353-5830
Mark Pinder, prin. Fax 353-5845
New Urban HS 200/Alt
1901 SE Oak Grove Blvd 97267 503-353-5925
Noah Hurd, prin. Fax 353-5928
Putnam HS 1,200/9-12
4950 SE Roethe Rd 97267 503-353-5860
Kathleen Walsh, prin. Fax 353-5875
Rowe MS 900/6-8
3606 SE Lake Rd 97222 503-353-5725
Greg Harris, prin. Fax 353-5740
Sabin-Schellenberg Professional-Tech Ctr Vo/Tech
14211 SE Johnson Rd 97267 503-353-5900
Karen Phillips, prin. Fax 353-5915
Other Schools – See Clackamas, Happy Valley

LaSalle College Prep HS 600/9-12
11999 SE Fuller Rd 97222 503-353-1432
Andrew Kuffner, prin.
National Coll of Technical Instruction Post-Sec.
9800 SE McBrod Ave 97222 971-236-9231
Portland Waldorf S 300/PK-12
2300 SE Harrison St 97222 503-654-2200

Mitchell, Wheeler, Pop. 123
Mitchell SD 55 100/K-12
PO Box 247 97750 541-462-3311
Nancy Moon, supt. Fax 462-3849
www.mitchell.k12.or.us
Mitchell S 100/K-12
PO Box 247 97750 541-462-3311
Tim Wilson, prin. Fax 462-3849

Molalla, Clackamas, Pop. 7,927
Molalla River SD 35 2,700/K-12
PO Box 188 97038 503-829-2359
Tony Mann, supt. Fax 829-5540
www.molallariv.k12.or.us
Molalla HS 700/9-12
PO Box 309 97038 503-829-2355
Randy Dalton, prin. Fax 829-5680
Molalla River MS 500/6-8
PO Box 225 97038 503-829-6133
Mike Nelson, prin. Fax 829-5680

Country Christian S 200/K-12
16975 S Highway 211 97038 503-829-5503

Monmouth, Polk, Pop. 9,171

Mid Valley Christian Academy 100/PK-12
1483 N 16th St 97361 503-838-2818
Gaye Stewart, admin.
Western Oregon University Post-Sec.
345 Monmouth Ave N 97361 503-838-8000

Monroe, Benton, Pop. 601
Monroe SD 1J 500/K-12
365 N 5th St 97456 541-847-6292
Fax 847-6290
www.monroe.k12.or.us
Monroe HS 100/9-12
365 N 5th St 97456 541-847-5161
Bill Crowson, prin. Fax 847-6161

Monument, Grant, Pop. 127
Monument SD 8 50/PK-12
PO Box 127 97864 541-934-2646
Earl Pettit, supt. Fax 934-2005
www.grantesd.k12.or.us/Monument
Monument S 50/PK-12
PO Box 127 97864 541-934-2646
Earl Pettit, admin. Fax 934-2005

Moro, Sherman, Pop. 321
Sherman County SD 200/K-12
65912 High School Loop 97039 541-565-3500
Wes Owens, supt. Fax 565-3319
shermancountyschooldistrict.weebly.com
Sherman JSHS 100/7-12
65912 High School Loop 97039 541-565-3500
Bill Blevins, prin. Fax 565-3319

Mount Angel, Marion, Pop. 3,231
Mt. Angel SD 91 700/K-12
PO Box 1129 97362 503-845-2345
Troy Stoops, supt. Fax 845-2789
www.masd91.org
Kennedy HS 200/9-12
890 E Marquam St 97362 503-845-6128
Sean Aker, prin. Fax 845-9586
Mount Angel MS 200/6-8
460 E Marquam St 97362 503-845-6137
Jennifer McCallum, prin. Fax 845-2856

Myrtle Creek, Douglas, Pop. 3,296
South Umpqua SD 19 1,500/K-12
558 Chadwick Ln 97457 541-863-3115
Jim Howard, supt. Fax 863-5212
www.susd.k12.or.us
Coffenberry MS 300/6-8
591 Rice St 97457 541-863-3104
Douglas Park, prin. Fax 863-5187
South Umpqua HS 400/9-12
501 Chadwick Ln 97457 541-863-3118
Kristi McGree, prin. Fax 863-5486

Myrtle Point, Coos, Pop. 2,411
Myrtle Point SD 41 600/PK-12
413 C St 97458 541-572-1220
Bruce Shull, supt. Fax 572-5401
www.mpsd.k12.or.us
Myrtle Point JSHS 300/7-12
717 4th St 97458 541-572-1270
Ken Smith, prin. Fax 572-5221

Newberg, Yamhill, Pop. 21,511
Newberg SD 29J 5,200/K-12
714 E 6th St 97132 503-554-5000
Dr. Kym LeBlanc-Esparza, supt. Fax 538-4374
www.newberg.k12.or.us
Catalyst S Alt
1421 Deborah Rd 97132 503-554-4492
Bill Rogers, prin. Fax 554-4521
Chehalem Valley MS 700/6-8
403 W Foothills Dr 97132 503-554-4600
Karen Pugsley, prin. Fax 537-3239
Mountain View MS 600/6-8
2015 N Emery Dr 97132 503-554-4500
Michele Paton, prin. Fax 537-3337
Newberg HS 1,600/9-12
2400 Douglas Ave 97132 503-554-4525
Kyle Laier, prin. Fax 554-4440

Country Faith Christian Academy 50/3-12
26155 NE Bell Rd 97132
Jolaine Davis, prin.
George Fox University Post-Sec.
414 N Meridian St 97132 503-538-8383
Lewis Academy 100/PK-12
PO Box 3250 97132 503-538-0114
Michael Wenger, admin. Fax 538-4113
Veritas S 200/K-12
401 Mission Dr 97132 503-538-1962

Newport, Lincoln, Pop. 9,688
Lincoln County SD 3,500/K-12
PO Box 1110 97365 541-265-9211
Steve Boynton, supt. Fax 265-0511
www.lincoln.k12.or.us
Newport HS 600/9-12
322 NE Eads St 97365 541-265-9281
Jon Zagel, prin. Fax 574-2228
Newport MS 100/6-8
825 NE 7th St 97365 541-265-6601
Aaron Belloni, prin. Fax 265-6493
Other Schools – See Lincoln City, Toledo, Waldport

Phagans' Newport Academy of Cosmetology Post-Sec.
158 E Olive St 97365 541-265-3083

North Bend, Coos, Pop. 9,275
North Bend SD 13 3,900/K-12
1913 Meade St 97459 541-756-2521
Bill Yester, supt. Fax 756-1313
www.nbend.k12.or.us
North Bend HS 500/9-12
2323 Pacific St 97459 541-756-8328
Bill Lucero, prin. Fax 756-6945
North Bend MS 300/6-8
1500 16th St 97459 541-756-8341
Marci Stadiem, prin. Fax 756-6460

Kingsview Christian S 100/PK-12
1850 Clark St 97459 541-756-1411
Dr. Michael Myers, supt. Fax 756-0105

Nyssa, Malheur, Pop. 3,244
Nyssa SD 26 1,200/K-12
804 Adrian Blvd 97913 541-372-2275
Jana Iverson, supt. Fax 372-2204
www.nyssa.k12.or.us
Nyssa Alternative S 50/Alt
804 Adrian Blvd 97913 541-372-2275
Jana Iverson, admin. Fax 372-2204
Nyssa HS 300/9-12
824 Adrian Blvd 97913 541-372-2287
Ryan Swearingen, prin. Fax 372-5634
Nyssa MS 300/6-8
101 S 11th St 97913 541-372-3891
Luke Cleaver, prin. Fax 372-3260

Oakland, Douglas, Pop. 890
Oakland SD 1 500/K-12
PO Box 390 97462 541-459-4341
Nanette Hagen, supt. Fax 459-4120
www.oakland.k12.or.us
Lincoln MS 200/5-8
PO Box 420 97462 541-459-3407
Diana Sweeden, prin. Fax 459-9167
Oakland HS 200/9-12
PO Box 479 97462 541-459-2597
Jeff Clark, prin. Fax 459-4765

Oakridge, Lane, Pop. 3,091
Oakridge SD 76 500/K-12
76499 Rose St 97463 541-782-2813
Dr. Donald Kordosky, supt. Fax 782-2982
www.oakridge.k12.or.us
Oakridge HS 200/9-12
47997 W 1st St 97463 541-782-2231
Tamara Skordahl, prin. Fax 782-4692
Oakridge JHS 100/7-8
76486 Rose St 97463 541-782-2731
Tamara Skordahl, prin. Fax 782-4647

Ontario, Malheur, Pop. 11,152
Ontario SD 8C 2,400/K-12
195 SW 3rd Ave 97914 541-889-5374
Nicole Albisu, supt. Fax 889-8553
www.ontario.k12.or.us
Ontario HS 700/9-12
1115 W Idaho Ave 97914 541-889-5309
Jodi Elizondo, prin. Fax 889-8117
Ontario MS 400/7-8
573 SW 2nd Ave 97914 541-889-5377
Lisa Estrada, prin. Fax 881-0060

Treasure Valley Christian S 100/PK-12
386 N Verde Dr 97914 541-889-4662
Fran Renk, prin. Fax 889-9199
Treasure Valley Community College Post-Sec.
650 College Blvd 97914 541-881-8822

Oregon City, Clackamas, Pop. 30,976
Oregon City SD 62 8,000/K-12
PO Box 2110 97045 503-785-8000
Larry Didway, supt. Fax 657-2492
www.orecity.k12.or.us
Gardiner MS 800/6-8
180 Ethel St 97045 503-785-8200
Kelly Schmidt, prin. Fax 650-5482
Ogden MS 900/6-8
14133 Donovan Rd 97045 503-785-8300
Peter Danner, prin. Fax 657-2508
Oregon City HS 2,200/9-12
19761 Beavercreek Rd 97045 503-785-8900
Tom Lovell, prin. Fax 785-8578

Clackamas Community College Post-Sec.
19600 Molalla Ave 97045 503-594-6000
North Clackamas Christian S 200/PK-12
19575 Sebastian Way 97045 503-655-5961
Tim Tutty, admin. Fax 655-4875

Pendleton, Umatilla, Pop. 16,180
Pendleton SD 16 2,900/PK-12
107 NW 10th St 97801 541-276-6711
Andy Kovach, supt. Fax 278-3208
www.pendleton.k12.or.us
Hawthorne Alternative HS Alt
1207 SW Frazer Ave 97801 541-966-3378
Curt Thompson, prin. Fax 966-3291
Pendleton HS 900/9-12
1800 NW Carden Ave 97801 541-966-3804
Dan Greenough, prin. Fax 966-3813
Sunridge MS 700/6-8
700 SW Runnion Ave 97801 541-276-4560
David Williams, prin. Fax 276-4724

Blue Mountain Community College Post-Sec.
PO Box 100 97801 541-276-1260
Harris Junior Academy 100/PK-10
3121 SW Hailey Ave 97801 541-276-0615
Shannon Whidden, admin. Fax 276-3465

Philomath, Benton, Pop. 4,445
Philomath SD 17J 1,500/K-12
1620 Applegate St 97370 541-929-3169
Melissa Goff, supt. Fax 929-3991
www.philomath.k12.or.us
Philomath HS 500/9-12
2054 Applegate St 97370 541-929-3211
Ken Ball, prin. Fax 929-3244
Philomath MS 300/6-8
2021 Chapel Dr 97370 541-929-3167
Steve Bell, prin. Fax 929-3180

Phoenix, Jackson, Pop. 4,376
Phoenix-Talent SD 4 2,700/K-12
PO Box 698 97535 541-535-1517
Teresa Sayre, supt. Fax 535-3928
www.phoenix.k12.or.us
Phoenix HS 800/9-12
PO Box 697 97535 541-535-1526
Dr. Don Rugraff, prin. Fax 535-7511
Other Schools – See Talent

Pilot Rock, Umatilla, Pop. 1,457
Pilot Rock SD 2 400/K-12
PO Box BB 97868 541-443-8291
Steve Staniak, supt. Fax 443-8000
www.pilotrock.k12.or.us
Pilot Rock JSHS 200/7-12
PO Box BB 97868 541-443-2671
Anna Tester, prin. Fax 443-2120

Pleasant Hill, Lane
Pleasant Hill SD 1 800/K-12
36386 Highway 58 97455 541-746-9646
Tony Scurto, supt. Fax 746-2537
www.pleasanthill.k12.or.us
Pleasant Hill HS 400/6-12
36386 Highway 58 97455 541-747-4541
Randy Fisher, prin. Fax 744-3351

Emerald Christian Academy 100/K-12
35582 Zephyr Way 97455 541-746-1708

Portland, Multnomah, Pop. 557,791
Beaverton SD 48J
Supt. — See Beaverton

Cedar Park MS 1,000/6-8
11100 SW Park Way 97225 503-356-2560
Shannon Anderson, prin. Fax 356-2565
Early College HS 11-12
17705 NW Springville Rd 97229 971-722-7473
Drew Cronk, admin. Fax 722-7553
Stoller MS 1,300/6-8
14141 NW Laidlaw Rd 97229 503-356-2680
Florence Richey, prin. Fax 356-2685
Sunset HS 2,000/9-12
13840 NW Cornell Rd 97229 503-356-2960
John Huelskamp, prin. Fax 356-2955
Westview HS 2,500/9-12
4200 NW 185th Ave 97229 503-356-3020
Jon Franco, prin. Fax 356-3025

Centennial SD 28J 6,100/K-12
18135 SE Brooklyn St 97236 503-760-7990
Dr. Paul Coakley, supt. Fax 762-3689
csd28j.org
Centennial MS 1,000/7-8
17650 SE Brooklyn St 97236 503-762-3206
Rise' Hawley, prin. Fax 762-3236
Centennial Park S 100/Alt
17630 SE Main St 97233 503-762-3202
Ajai Huja, prin. Fax 760-1651
Other Schools – See Gresham

David Douglas SD 40 11,000/PK-12
11300 NE Halsey St 97220 503-252-2900
Ken Richardson, supt. Fax 261-8208
www.ddouglas.k12.or.us
Douglas HS 3,200/9-12
1001 SE 135th Ave 97233 503-261-8300
John Bier, prin. Fax 261-8399
Fir Ridge Campus 200/Alt
11215 SE Market St 97216 503-256-6530
Joy O'Renick, prin. Fax 261-8433
Light MS 800/6-8
10800 SE Washington St 97216 503-256-6511
Doug Pease, prin. Fax 261-8423
Ott MS 700/6-8
12500 SE Ramona St 97236 503-256-6510
James Johnston, prin. Fax 261-8403
Russell MS 900/6-8
3955 SE 112th Ave 97266 503-256-6519
Andy Long, prin. Fax 761-7246

Multnomah ESD 300/
PO Box 301039 97294 503-255-1841
Jim Rose, supt. Fax 257-1519
www.mesd.k12.or.us
Helensview HS 200/Alt
8678 NE Sumner St 97220 503-262-4150
Kris Persson, prin. Fax 255-1767
Other Schools – See Gresham

Parkrose SD 3 3,300/K-12
10636 NE Prescott St 97220 503-408-2100
Dr. Karen Fischer Gray, supt. Fax 408-2140
www.parkrose.k12.or.us
Parkrose HS 1,000/9-12
12003 NE Shaver St 97220 503-408-2600
Molly Ouche, prin. Fax 408-2739
Parkrose MS 800/6-8
11800 NE Shaver St 97220 503-408-2700
Annette Sweeney, prin. Fax 408-2998

Portland SD 1J 44,900/PK-12
PO Box 3107 97208 503-916-2000
Robert McKean, supt. Fax 916-3107
www.pps.net
Alliance HS 200/9-12
4039 NE Alberta Ct 97211 503-916-5747
Lorna Fast Buffalo Horse, prin. Fax 916-2680
Alliance HS @ Benson 11-12
546 NE 12th Ave 97232 503-916-6486
Lorna Fast Buffalo Horse, prin. Fax 916-2696
Beaumont MS 600/6-8
4043 NE Fremont St 97212 503-916-5610
Harriette Vimegnon, prin. Fax 916-2609
Benson Polytechnic HS Vo/Tech
546 NE 12th Ave 97232 503-916-5100
Curtis Wilson, prin. Fax 916-2690
Cleary ES @ Fernwood Campus 4-8
1915 NE 33rd Ave 97212 503-916-6480
John Ferraro, prin. Fax 916-2626
Cleveland HS 1,500/9-12
3400 SE 26th Ave 97202 503-916-5120
Tammy O'Neill, prin. Fax 916-2692
Da Vinci Arts MS 500/6-8
2508 NE Everett St 97232 503-916-5356
Fred Locke, prin. Fax 916-2721
Franklin HS 1,500/9-12
3905 SE 91st Ave 97266 503-916-5140
Juanita Valder, prin. Fax 916-2694
George MS 400/6-8
10000 N Burr Ave 97203 503-916-6262
Lavert Robertson, prin. Fax 916-2627
Grant HS 1,500/9-12
2245 NE 36th Ave 97212 503-916-5160
Carol Campbell, prin. Fax 916-2695
Gray MS 500/6-8
5505 SW 23rd Ave, 503-916-5676
Beth Madison, prin. Fax 916-2629
Hosford International MS 600/6-8
2303 SE 28th Pl 97214 503-916-5640
Kristyn Westphal, prin. Fax 916-2637
Jackson MS 500/6-8
10625 SW 35th Ave 97219 503-916-5680
Kevin Crotchett, prin. Fax 916-2640
Jefferson HS 500/9-12
5210 N Kerby Ave 97217 503-916-5180
Margaret Calvert, prin. Fax 916-2698
Lane MS 500/6-8
7200 SE 60th Ave 97206 503-916-6355
Jeandre Carbone, prin. Fax 916-2648
Lincoln HS 1,600/9-12
1600 SW Salmon St 97205 503-916-5200
Peyton Chapman, prin. Fax 916-2700

Madison HS 1,100/9-12
2735 NE 82nd Ave 97220 503-916-5220
Petra Callin, prin. Fax 916-2702
Metropolitan Learning Center S 400/Alt
2033 NW Glisan St 97209 503-916-5737
Pamela Joyner, prin. Fax 916-2658
Mt. Tabor MS 600/6-8
5800 SE Ash St 97215 503-916-5646
Anh Nguyen-Johnson, prin. Fax 916-2659
Ockley Green MS 300/5-8
6031 N Montana Ave 97217 503-916-5660
Rene Acevedo, prin. Fax 916-2661
PISA @ Benson 9-12
546 NE 12th Ave 97232 503-916-5252
Paige Kelsey, prin.
Roosevelt HS 900/9-12
6941 N Central St 97203 503-916-5260
Filip Hristic, prin. Fax 916-2704
Sellwood MS 500/6-8
8300 SE 15th Ave 97202 503-916-5656
Brian Anderson, prin. Fax 916-2672
West Sylvan MS 900/6-8
8111 SW West Slope Dr 97225 503-916-5690
Cherie Kinnersley, prin. Fax 916-2681
Wilson HS 1,200/9-12
1151 SW Vermont St 97219 503-916-5280
Brian Chatard, prin. Fax 916-2705
Portland Evening & Summer Scholars Adult
546 NE 12th Ave 97232 503-916-5720
Fax 916-2691

Reynolds SD 7
Supt. — See Fairview
Lee MS 800/6-8
1121 NE 172nd Ave 97230 503-255-5686
Dan Kimbrow, prin. Fax 328-0439

Riverdale SD 51J 600/K-12
11733 SW Breyman Ave 97219 503-262-4840
Terry Brandon, supt. Fax 262-4841
www.riverdaleschool.com
Riverdale HS 200/9-12
9727 SW Terwilliger Blvd 97219 503-262-4844
Paula Robinson, prin. Fax 262-4845

American College of Healthcare Sciences Post-Sec.
5940 SW Hood Ave, 800-487-8839
Art Institute of Portland Post-Sec.
1122 NW Davis St 97209 503-228-6528
Beau Monde College Acad of Cosmetology Post-Sec.
525 SW 12th Ave 97205 503-252-7444
Beau Monde College of Hair Design Post-Sec.
1221 SW 12th Ave 97205 503-226-7355
Birthingway College of Midwifery Post-Sec.
12113 SE Foster Rd 97266 503-760-3131
Catlin Gabel S 700/PK-12
8825 SW Barnes Rd 97225 503-297-1894
Timothy Bazemore, head sch Fax 297-0139
Central Catholic HS 800/9-12
2401 SE Stark St 97214 503-235-3138
John Garrow, prin. Fax 233-0073
City Christian S 400/PK-12
9200 NE Fremont St 97220 503-252-5207
Columbia Christian S 200/PK-12
413 NE 91st Ave 97220 503-252-8577
Ami Vensel, prin. Fax 252-2108
Concorde Career Institute Post-Sec.
1425 NE Irving St Ste 300 97232 503-281-4181
Concordia University Post-Sec.
2811 NE Holman St 97211 503-288-9371
De La Salle North HS 300/9-12
7528 N Fenwick Ave 97217 503-285-9385
Tim Joy, prin. Fax 285-9546
DeVry University Post-Sec.
9755 SW Barnes Rd Ste 150 97225 503-296-7468
Everest College Post-Sec.
425 SW Washington St 97204 503-222-3225
Heald College Post-Sec.
6035 NE 78th Ct 97218 503-229-0492
ISMET/OIA PK-12
10330 SW Scholls Ferry Rd 97223 503-579-6621
Jesuit HS 1,200/9-12
9000 SW Beaverton Hillsdale 97225 503-291-5417
Paul Hogan, prin. Fax 291-5464
Le Cordon Bleu College of Culinary Arts Post-Sec.
600 SW 10th Ave Ste 500 97205 503-223-2245
Lewis and Clark College Post-Sec.
0615 SW Palatine Hill Rd 97219 503-768-7000
Linfield College Post-Sec.
2255 NW Northrup St 97210 503-413-8481
Maayan Torah Day S 100/PK-12
2900 SW Peaceful Ln, 971-245-5568
Multnomah University Post-Sec.
8435 NE Glisan St 97220 503-255-0332
National College of Natural Medicine Post-Sec.
049 SW Porter St 97201 503-552-1555
Oregon College of Art and Craft Post-Sec.
8245 SW Barnes Rd 97225 503-297-5544
Oregon College of Oriental Medicine Post-Sec.
75 NW Couch St 97209 503-253-3443
Oregon Culinary Institute Post-Sec.
1701 SW Jefferson St 97201 503-961-6200
Oregon Episcopal S 800/PK-12
6300 SW Nicol Rd 97223 503-246-7771
Mo Copeland, head sch Fax 293-1105
Oregon Health & Science University Post-Sec.
3181 SW Sam Jackson Park Rd,
503-494-8311
Pacific Crest Community S 100/6-12
116 NE 29th Ave 97232 503-234-2826
Pacific Northwest College of Art Post-Sec.
1241 NW Johnson St 97209 503-226-4391
Phagans' School of Hair Design Post-Sec.
1542 NE Weidler St 97232 503-239-0838
Portland Adventist Academy 200/9-12
1500 SE 96th Ave 97216 503-255-8372
Portland Christian JSHS 300/6-12
12425 NE San Rafael St 97230 503-256-3960
Sherri James, prin. Fax 256-2773

Portland Community College Post-Sec.
PO Box 19000 97280 971-722-6111
Portland State University Post-Sec.
PO Box 751 97207 503-725-3000
Reed College Post-Sec.
3203 SE Woodstock Blvd 97202 503-771-1112
St. Andrew Nativity S 100/6-8
4925 NE 9th Ave 97211 503-335-9600
Michael Chambers, prin. Fax 335-9494
St. Mary's Academy 600/9-12
1615 SW 5th Ave 97201 503-228-8306
Kelli Clark, prin. Fax 223-0995
St. Vincent Hospital & Medical Center Post-Sec.
9205 SW Barnes Rd 97225 503-216-3031
Sumner College Post-Sec.
8909 SW Barbur Blvd 97219 503-223-5100
University of Portland Post-Sec.
5000 N Willamette Blvd 97203 503-943-8000
University of Western States Post-Sec.
2900 NE 132nd Ave 97230 503-256-3180
Veterans Administration Medical Center Post-Sec.
PO Box 1034 97207 503-220-8262
Walla Walla University School of Nursing Post-Sec.
10345 SE Market St 97216 503-251-6115
Warner Pacific College Post-Sec.
2219 SE 68th Ave 97215 503-517-1000
Western Seminary Post-Sec.
5511 SE Hawthorne Blvd 97215 503-517-1800

Port Orford, Curry, Pop. 1,095
Port Orford-Langlois SD 2CJ 200/K-12
PO Box 8 97465 541-366-2111
Steve Perkins, supt. Fax 332-0190
www.2cj.com
Other Schools – See Sixes

Powers, Coos, Pop. 625
Powers SD 31 100/K-12
PO Box 479 97466 541-439-2291
Matt Shorb, supt. Fax 439-2875
www.powers.k12.or.us
Powers HS 100/7-12
PO Box 479 97466 541-439-2291
Matt Shorb, prin. Fax 439-2875

Prairie City, Grant, Pop. 882
Prairie City SD 4 100/K-12
PO Box 345 97869 541-820-3314
Julie Gurczynski, supt. Fax 820-4352
www.grantesd.k12.or.us/Prairie-City/
Prairie City S 100/K-12
PO Box 345 97869 541-820-3314
Julie Gurczynski, prin. Fax 820-4352

Prineville, Crook, Pop. 9,076
Crook County SD 2,700/K-12
471 NE Ochoco Plaza Dr 97754 541-447-5664
Dr. Duane Yecha, supt. Fax 447-3645
www.crookcounty.k12.or.us
Crook County HS 800/9-12
1100 SE Lynn Blvd 97754 541-416-6900
Michelle Jonas, prin. Fax 416-6907
Crook County MS 600/6-8
100 NE Knowledge St 97754 541-447-6283
Kurt Sloper, prin. Fax 447-3293
Pioneer Alternative HS 100/Alt
297 NE Holly St 97754 541-447-1268
Michelle Jonas, prin. Fax 447-1862

High Desert Christian Academy 100/PK-12
839 S Main St 97754 541-416-0114
Maggie Hale, admin. Fax 416-0330

Rainier, Columbia, Pop. 1,842
Rainier SD 13 1,000/K-12
28168 Old Rainier Rd 97048 503-556-3777
R. Michael Carter, supt. Fax 556-3778
www.rainier.k12.or.us
Rainier JSHS 500/7-12
28170 Old Rainier Rd 97048 503-556-4215
Graden Blue, prin. Fax 556-1120

Redmond, Deschutes, Pop. 25,592
Redmond SD 2J 7,100/PK-12
145 SE Salmon Dr 97756 541-923-5437
Mike McIntosh, supt. Fax 923-5142
www.redmondschools.org
Brown Education Center 100/Alt
850 SW Antler Ave 97756 541-923-4868
Karen Mitchell, coord. Fax 923-4867
Gregory MS 600/6-8
1220 NW Upas Ave 97756 541-526-6440
Tracie Renwick, prin. Fax 526-6441
Obsidian MS 600/6-8
1335 SW Obsidian Ave 97756 541-923-4900
Tami Nakamura, prin. Fax 923-6509
Redmond HS 1,000/9-12
675 SW Rimrock Way 97756 541-923-4800
Paul Nolan, prin. Fax 548-0809
Ridgeview HS 800/9-12
4555 SW Elkhorn Ave 97756 541-504-3600
Lee Loving, prin. Fax 504-3601

Central Christian S 300/PK-12
2731 SW Airport Way 97756 541-548-7803
Elisa Carlson, head sch Fax 548-2801

Riddle, Douglas, Pop. 1,134
Riddle SD 70 300/K-12
PO Box 45 97469 541-874-3131
Dave Gianotti, supt. Fax 874-2345
www.riddle.k12.or.us
Riddle JSHS, PO Box 45 97469 200/7-12
William Starkweather, prin. 541-874-2251

Rockaway, Tillamook, Pop. 1,282
Neah-Kah-Nie SD 56 800/K-12
PO Box 28 97136 503-355-2222
Paul Erlebach, supt. Fax 355-3434
www.nknsd.org

Neah-Kah-Nie HS 200/9-12
24705 Highway 101 N 97136 503-355-2272
Heidi Buckmaster, prin. Fax 355-8200
Neah-Kah-Nie MS 200/6-8
25111 Highway 101 N 97136 503-355-2990
Leo Lawyer, prin. Fax 355-8514

Rogue River, Jackson, Pop. 2,091
Rogue River SD 35 800/K-12
PO Box 1045 97537 541-582-3235
Paul Young, supt. Fax 582-1600
www.rogueriver.k12.or.us
Rogue River JSHS 400/7-12
PO Box 1045 97537 541-582-3297
Jamie Wright, prin. Fax 582-6005

Roseburg, Douglas, Pop. 20,494
Douglas County SD 4 6,000/PK-12
1419 NW Valley View Dr, 541-440-4015
Gerry Washburn, supt. Fax 440-4003
www.roseburg.k12.or.us
Fremont MS 700/6-8
850 W Keady Ct, 541-440-4055
Ben Bentea, prin. Fax 440-4060
Lane MS 700/6-8
2153 NE Vine St 97470 541-440-4104
Bill Bartlett, prin. Fax 440-4100
Roseburg HS 1,800/9-12
400 W Harvard Ave 97470 541-440-4142
Jill Weber, prin. Fax 440-8296

Geneva Academy 100/K-12
PO Box 1154 97470 541-637-7500
Brian Turner, hdmstr.
Roseburg Beauty College Post-Sec.
700 SE Stephens St 97470 541-673-5533
Umpqua Community College Post-Sec.
PO Box 967 97470 541-440-4600
Umpqua Valley Christian S 100/PK-12
18585 Dixonville Rd 97470 541-679-4964
Adam Armstrong, head sch Fax 679-1881

Saint Benedict, Marion, Pop. 55

Mt. Angel Seminary Post-Sec.
1 Abbey Dr 97373 503-845-3951

Saint Helens, Columbia, Pop. 12,364
Saint Helens SD 502 3,200/K-12
474 N 16th St 97051 503-397-3085
Scot Stockwell, supt. Fax 397-1907
www.sthelens.k12.or.us
Columbia County Education Campus 100/Alt
474 N 16th St 97051 503-366-3207
Colleen Grogan, dir. Fax 397-2723
Saint Helens HS 1,000/9-12
2375 Gable Rd 97051 503-397-1900
B.G. Aguirre, prin. Fax 397-1828
Saint Helens MS 500/7-8
354 N 15th St 97051 503-366-7300
Carol Dowsett, prin. Fax 366-7306

Saint Paul, Marion, Pop. 420
St. Paul SD 45 300/PK-12
20449 Main St NE 97137 503-633-2541
Joseph Wehrli, supt. Fax 633-2540
www.stpaul.k12.or.us
Saint Paul JSHS 100/7-12
20449 Main St NE 97137 503-633-2541
Tony Smith, prin. Fax 633-2540

Salem, Marion, Pop. 148,676
Salem-Keizer SD 24J 40,300/PK-12
PO Box 12024 97309 503-399-3000
Christy Perry, supt. Fax 399-5579
www.salkeiz.k12.or.us
Crossler MS 700/6-8
1155 Davis Rd S 97306 503-399-3444
Kristine Walton, prin. Fax 391-4005
Early College HS 200/Alt
4071 Winema Pl NE Ste 50 97305 503-365-4800
Jay Weeks, prin. Fax 365-4802
Houck MS 1,000/6-8
1155 Connecticut St SE, 503-399-3446
Mark Thompson, prin. Fax 391-4167
Judson MS 900/6-8
4512 Jones Rd SE 97302 503-399-3201
Alicia Kruska, prin. Fax 391-4041
Leslie MS 800/6-8
3850 Pringle Rd SE 97302 503-399-3206
Denny McCarthy, prin. Fax 399-3479
McKay HS 2,100/9-12
2440 Lancaster Dr NE 97305 503-399-3080
Sara LeRoy, prin. Fax 375-7807
North Salem HS 1,800/9-12
765 14th St NE 97301 503-399-3241
Cynthia Richardson, prin. Fax 375-7808
Parrish MS 700/6-8
802 Capitol St NE 97301 503-399-3210
Dustin Purnell, prin. Fax 391-4004
Roberts HS 500/Alt
3620 State St 97301 503-399-5550
Jay Weeks, prin. Fax 391-4075
South Salem HS 1,900/9-12
1910 Church St SE 97302 503-399-3252
Lara Tiffin, prin. Fax 375-7805
Sprague HS 1,600/9-12
2373 Kuebler Rd S 97302 503-399-3261
Craig Swanson, prin. Fax 391-4046
Stephens MS 1,000/6-8
4962 Hayesville Dr NE 97305 503-399-3442
Jennie Madland, prin. Fax 391-4079
Straub MS 700/6-8
1920 Wilmington Ave NW 97304 503-399-2030
Laura Perez, prin. Fax 399-2032
Waldo MS 900/6-8
2805 Lansing Ave NE 97301 503-399-3215
Tricia Nelson, prin. Fax 391-4070
Walker MS 500/6-8
1075 8th St NW 97304 503-399-3220
Aaron Persons, prin. Fax 399-5540
West Salem HS 1,700/9-12
1776 Titan Dr NW 97304 503-399-5533
Ken Phillips, prin. Fax 584-5004
Other Schools – See Keizer

Abiqua Academy 200/PK-12
6974 Bates Rd S 97306 503-399-9020
Academy of Hair Design Post-Sec.
305 Court St NE 97301 503-585-8122
Blanchet S 400/6-12
4373 Market St NE 97301 503-391-2639
Brian Heinze, prin. Fax 399-1259
Chemeketa Community College Post-Sec.
PO Box 14007 97309 503-399-5000
College of Hair Design Careers Post-Sec.
1684 Clay St NE 97301 503-588-5888
Corban University Post-Sec.
5000 Deer Park Dr SE, 503-581-8600
Institute of Technology Post-Sec.
4700 Silverton Rd NE 97305 877-887-8007
Livingstone Adventist Academy 200/PK-12
5771 Fruitland Rd NE, 503-363-9408
Oregon State School for the Deaf Post-Sec.
999 Locust St NE 97301
Phagans' School of Beauty Post-Sec.
622 Lancaster Dr NE 97301 503-363-6800
Salem Academy 700/PK-12
942 Lancaster Dr NE 97301 503-378-1219
Jeff Williamson, supt. Fax 375-3522
Western Mennonite S 200/6-12
9045 Wallace Rd NW 97304 503-363-2000
Robby Gilliam, head sch Fax 370-9455
Willamette University Post-Sec.
900 State St 97301 503-370-6300

Sandy, Clackamas, Pop. 9,279
Oregon Trail SD 46 4,100/K-12
PO Box 547 97055 503-668-5541
Aaron Bayer, supt. Fax 668-7906
www.oregontrailschools.com
Cedar Ridge MS 400/6-8
17225 Smith Ave 97055 503-668-8067
Nicole Johnston, prin. Fax 668-3977
Sandy HS 1,400/9-12
37400 Bell St 97055 503-668-8011
Kim Ball, prin. Fax 668-7646
Other Schools – See Boring

Scappoose, Columbia, Pop. 6,380
Scappoose SD 1J 2,300/K-12
33589 High School Way 97056 971-200-8000
Stephen Jupe, supt. Fax 543-7011
www.scappoose.k12.or.us
Scappoose HS 700/9-12
33700 High School Way 97056 971-200-8005
Jim Jones, prin. Fax 200-8000
Scappoose MS 400/7-8
52265 Columbia River Hwy 97056 503-543-7163
Ron Alley, prin. Fax 543-7917

Scio, Linn, Pop. 809
Scio SD 95 4,200/K-12
38875 NW 1st Ave 97374 503-394-3261
Gary Tempel, supt. Fax 394-3920
www.scio.k12.or.us
Scio HS 300/9-12
38875 NW 1st Ave 97374 503-394-3276
Patrick Dutcher, prin. Fax 394-3236
Scio MS 200/6-8
38875 NW 1st Ave 97374 503-394-3271
Greg Nolan, prin. Fax 394-4042

Seaside, Clatsop, Pop. 6,285
Jewell SD 8 100/PK-12
83874 Highway 103 97138 503-755-2451
Alice Hunsaker, supt. Fax 755-0616
www.jewell.k12.or.us
Jewell S 100/PK-12
83874 Highway 103 97138 503-755-2451
Mike Scott, prin. Fax 755-0616

Seaside SD 10 1,500/K-12
1801 S Franklin St 97138 503-738-5591
Dr. Sheila Roley, supt. Fax 738-3471
www.seaside.k12.or.us
Broadway MS 400/6-8
1120 Broadway St 97138 503-738-5560
Robert Rusk, prin. Fax 738-3900
Seaside HS 500/9-12
1901 N Holladay Dr 97138 503-738-5586
Jeff Roberts, prin. Fax 738-5589

Sheridan, Yamhill, Pop. 5,880
Sheridan SD 48J 1,000/K-12
435 S Bridge St 97378 971-261-6959
Dr. Steven Sugg, supt. Fax 843-3505
www.sheridan.k12.or.us
Sheridan HS 200/9-12
433 S Bridge St 97378 971-261-6970
Dean Rech, admin. Fax 843-3466

Delphian S 200/K-12
20950 SW Rock Creek Rd 97378 503-843-3521
Trevor Ott, hdmstr. Fax 843-4158

Sherwood, Washington, Pop. 17,504
Sherwood SD 88J 5,100/PK-12
23295 SW Main St 97140 503-825-5000
Dr. Heather Cordie, supt. Fax 825-5001
www.sherwood.k12.or.us
Laurel Ridge MS 500/6-8
21416 SW Copper Ter 97140 503-825-5800
Brian Bailey, prin. Fax 825-5801
Sherwood HS 1,500/9-12
16956 SW Meinecke Rd 97140 503-825-5500
Ken Bell, prin. Fax 825-5501
Sherwood MS 700/6-8
21970 SW Sherwood Blvd 97140 503-825-5400
Marianne Funderhide, prin. Fax 825-5401

Silver Lake, Lake, Pop. 147
North Lake SD 14 200/PK-12
57566 Fort Rock Rd 97638 541-576-2121
Dave Kerr, supt. Fax 576-2705
www.nlake.k12.or.us/
North Lake S 200/PK-12
57566 Fort Rock Rd 97638 541-576-2121
Dave Kerr, admin. Fax 576-2705

Silverton, Marion, Pop. 9,064
Silver Falls SD 4J 3,300/K-12
802 Schlador St 97381 503-873-5303
Andy Bellando, supt. Fax 873-2936
silverfallsschools.org
Silverton HS 1,300/9-12
1456 Pine St 97381 503-873-6331
Justin Lieuallen, prin. Fax 873-8606
Silverton MS 7-8
714 Schlador St 97381 503-873-5317
Nancy Griffith, prin. Fax 873-7108

Sisters, Deschutes, Pop. 2,007
Sisters SD 6 1,100/K-12
525 E Cascade Ave 97759 541-549-8521
Curtiss Scholl, supt. Fax 549-8951
www.sisters.k12.or.us
Sisters HS 500/9-12
1700 W McKinney Butte Rd 97759 541-549-4045
Joe Hosang, prin. Fax 549-4051
Sisters MS 400/5-8
15200 McKenzie Hwy 97759 541-549-2099
Marshall Jackson, prin. Fax 549-2098

Sixes, Curry
Port Orford-Langlois SD 2CJ
Supt. — See Port Orford
Pacific HS 100/9-12
45525 Highway 101 97476 541-348-2293
Krista Nieraeth, prin. Fax 348-2389

Spray, Wheeler, Pop. 157
Spray SD 1 50/PK-12
PO Box 230 97874 541-468-2226
Phil Starkey, supt. Fax 468-2630
www.spray.k12.or.us
Spray S 50/PK-12
PO Box 230 97874 541-468-2226
Phil Starkey, prin. Fax 468-2630

Springfield, Lane, Pop. 57,056
Springfield SD 19 10,500/K-12
525 Mill St 97477 541-747-3331
Susan Rieke-Smith Ed.D., supt. Fax 726-3312
www.springfield.k12.or.us
Briggs MS 500/6-8
2355 Yolanda Ave 97477 541-744-6350
Jeff Mather, prin. Fax 744-6354
Gateways HS 100/9-12
665 Main St 97477 541-744-8862
Paul Weill, prin. Fax 744-8863
Hamlin MS 600/6-8
326 Centennial Blvd 97477 541-744-6356
Kevin Wright, prin. Fax 744-6360
Springfield HS 1,400/9-12
875 7th St 97477 541-744-4700
Jose da Silva, prin. Fax 744-4875
Stewart MS 600/6-8
900 S 32nd St 97478 541-988-2520
Jeff Fuller, prin. Fax 988-2530
Thurston HS 1,400/9-12
333 58th St 97478 541-744-5000
Chad Towe, prin. Fax 744-5029
Thurston MS 600/6-8
6300 Thurston Rd 97478 541-744-6368
Brandi Starck, prin. Fax 744-6372

Pioneer Pacific College Post-Sec.
3800 Sports Way 97477 541-684-4644
Springfield College of Beauty Post-Sec.
307 Q St 97477 541-746-4473

Stanfield, Umatilla, Pop. 1,997
Stanfield SD 61 500/K-12
1120 N Main St 97875 541-449-8766
Shelley Liscom, supt. Fax 449-8768
www.stanfield.k12.or.us
Stanfield Secondary S 200/6-12
1120 N Main St 97875 541-449-3851
Beth Burton, prin. Fax 449-8751

Stayton, Marion, Pop. 7,435
North Santiam SD 29J 2,400/K-12
1155 N 3rd Ave 97383 503-769-6924
Andrew Gardner, supt. Fax 769-3578
www.nsantiam.k12.or.us
Stayton HS 700/9-12
757 W Locust St 97383 503-769-2171
Alan Kirby, prin. Fax 769-6050
Stayton Intermediate / MS 600/4-8
1021 Shaff Rd 97383 503-769-2198
Michael Proctor, prin. Fax 769-9524

Regis HS 200/9-12
550 W Regis St 97383 503-769-2159
Rick Schindler, prin. Fax 769-1706

Sutherlin, Douglas, Pop. 7,596
Sutherlin SD 130 1,400/K-12
531 E Central Ave 97479 541-459-2228
Terry Prestianni, supt. Fax 459-2484
www.sutherlin.k12.or.us
Sutherlin HS 400/9-12
500 E Fourth Ave 97479 541-459-9551
Justin Huntley, prin. Fax 459-4887
Sutherlin MS 200/7-8
649 E Fourth Ave 97479 541-459-2668
Jon Martz, prin. Fax 459-2047

Sweet Home, Linn, Pop. 8,693
Sweet Home SD 55 2,400/K-12
1920 Long St 97386 541-367-7126
Tom Yahraes, supt. Fax 367-7105
www.sweethome.k12.or.us
Sweet Home HS 800/9-12
1641 Long St 97386 541-367-7142
Ralph Brown, prin. Fax 367-7196
Sweet Home JHS 300/7-8
880 22nd Ave 97386 541-367-7187
Colleen Henry, prin. Fax 367-7107

Talent, Jackson, Pop. 5,873
Phoenix-Talent SD 4
Supt. — See Phoenix
Talent MS 600/6-8
PO Box 359 97540 541-535-1552
Aaron Santi, prin. Fax 535-7532

The Dalles, Wasco, Pop. 13,258
North Wasco County SD 21 3,000/K-12
3632 W 10th St 97058 541-506-3420
Candy Armstrong, supt. Fax 298-6018
www.nwasco.k12.or.us
The Dalles HS 900/9-12
220 E 10th St 97058 541-506-3400
Nick Nelson, prin. Fax 298-4964
The Dalles MS 600/6-8
1100 E 12th St 97058 541-506-3380
Sandy Harris, prin. Fax 298-1942
Wahtonka Community S Alt
3601 W 10th St 97058 541-506-3410
Brian Goodwin, admin.

Columbia Gorge Community College Post-Sec.
400 E Scenic Dr 97058 541-506-6000

Tigard, Washington, Pop. 46,005
Tigard-Tualatin SD 23J 12,600/K-12
6960 SW Sandburg St 97223 503-431-4000
Ernest Brown, supt. Fax 431-4047
www.ttsdschools.org
Durham Center 100/Alt
8040 SW Durham Rd 97224 503-431-4580
Andy McFarlane, dir. Fax 431-4590
Fowler MS 800/6-8
10865 SW Walnut St 97223 503-431-5000
Dan Busch, prin. Fax 431-5010
Tigard HS 2,000/9-12
9000 SW Durham Rd 97224 503-431-5400
Andy Van Fleet, prin. Fax 431-5410
Twality MS 1,000/6-8
14650 SW 97th Ave 97224 503-431-5200
Carol Kinch, prin. Fax 431-5210
Other Schools – See Tualatin

Everest Institute Post-Sec.
9600 SW Oak St Fl 4 97223 503-892-8100
Phagans' Tigard Beauty School Post-Sec.
8820 SW Center St 97223 503-639-6107
Westside Christian HS 200/9-12
8200 SW Pfaffle St 97223 503-697-4711
Dr. Debi Miller, head sch Fax 697-4605

Tillamook, Tillamook, Pop. 4,782
Tillamook SD 9 2,000/K-12
2510 1st St 97141 503-842-4414
Randy Schild, supt. Fax 842-6854
www.tillamook.k12.or.us
Tillamook HS 600/9-12
2605 12th St 97141 503-842-2566
Greg English, prin. Fax 842-1340
Tillamook JHS 300/7-8
3906 Alder Ln 97141 503-842-7531
Melissa Radcliffe, prin. Fax 842-1349
Trask River HS 50/Alt
6700 Officers Row 97141 503-842-2565
Jerry Dorland, prin. Fax 842-4918
Wilson River S Alt
2510 1st St 97141 503-842-7538
Rachel Sip, prin. Fax 842-1378

Tillamook Bay Community College Post-Sec.
4301 3rd St 97141 503-842-8222

Toledo, Lincoln, Pop. 3,349
Lincoln County SD
Supt. — See Newport
Toledo JSHS 300/7-12
1800 NE Sturdevant Rd 97391 541-336-5104
Clint Raever, prin. Fax 336-2970

Troutdale, Multnomah, Pop. 15,404
Reynolds SD 7
Supt. — See Fairview
Morey MS 600/6-8
2801 SW Lucas Ave 97060 503-491-1935
Tanya Pruett, prin. Fax 491-0245
Reynolds HS 2,800/9-12
1698 SW Cherry Park Rd 97060 503-667-3186
Wade Bakley, prin. Fax 669-0776

Tualatin, Washington, Pop. 25,026
Tigard-Tualatin SD 23J
Supt. — See Tigard
Hazelbrook MS 1,000/6-8
11300 SW Hazelbrook Rd 97062 503-431-5100
Eric Nesse, prin. Fax 431-5110
Tualatin HS 1,800/9-12
22300 SW Boones Ferry Rd 97062 503-431-5600
Darin Barnard, prin. Fax 431-5610

West Linn-Wilsonville SD 3J 9,100/PK-12
22210 SW Stafford Rd 97062 503-673-7000
Dr. Kathy Ludwig, supt. Fax 673-7001
www.wlwv.k12.or.us
Athey Creek MS 600/6-8
2900 SW Borland Rd 97062 503-673-7400
Joel Sebastian, prin. Fax 638-8302
Other Schools – See West Linn, Wilsonville

Horizon Christian HS 100/9-12
PO Box 2690 97062 503-612-6521
Bill Smethurst, prin. Fax 783-2361
Northwest College of Hair Design Post-Sec.
8345 SW Nyberg St 97062 503-218-2265

Turner, Marion, Pop. 1,825
Cascade SD 5 2,200/K-12
10226 Marion Rd SE 97392 503-749-8010
Darin Drill, supt. Fax 749-8019
www.cascade.k12.or.us
Cascade HS 700/9-12
10226 Marion Rd SE 97392 503-749-8020
Matt Thatcher, prin. Fax 749-8029
Cascade JHS 500/6-8
10226 Marion Rd SE 97392 503-749-8030
Peter Rasmussen, prin. Fax 749-8039
Other Schools – See Aumsville

Crosshill Christian S 200/PK-12
2707 Maranatha Ct SE 97392 503-391-9082
Adam Kronberger, supt. Fax 378-0507

Ukiah, Umatilla, Pop. 181
Ukiah SD 80R 50/K-12
PO Box 218 97880 541-427-3731
Dan Korber, supt. Fax 427-3730
www.ukiah.k12.or.us
Ukiah S 50/K-12
PO Box 218 97880 541-427-3731
Dan Korber, supt. Fax 427-3730

Umatilla, Umatilla, Pop. 6,845
Umatilla SD 6R 1,300/K-12
1001 6th St 97882 541-922-6500
Heidi Sipe, supt. Fax 922-6507
www.umatilla.k12.or.us
Brownell MS 300/6-8
1300 7th St 97882 541-922-6625
Liz Durant, prin. Fax 922-6507
Umatilla HS 400/9-12
1400 7th St 97882 541-922-6525
Bob Lorence, prin. Fax 922-6599

Union, Union, Pop. 2,065
Union SD 5 300/K-12
PO Box K 97883 541-562-5166
Carter Wells, supt. Fax 562-8116
www.union.k12.or.us
Union JSHS 200/7-12
PO Box 908 97883 541-562-5166
Carter Wells, prin. Fax 562-8116

Vale, Malheur, Pop. 1,833
Vale SD 84 900/K-12
403 E St W 97918 541-473-0201
Scott Linenberger, supt. Fax 473-3294
www.vale.k12.or.us
Vale HS 300/9-12
505 Viking Dr 97918 541-473-0290
Mary Jo Sharp, prin. Fax 473-2364
Vale MS 100/7-8
403 E St W 97918 541-473-0241
Jeri Schaffeld, prin. Fax 473-3293

Vernonia, Columbia, Pop. 2,091
Vernonia SD 47J 600/K-12
1201 Texas Ave 97064 503-429-5891
Aaron Miller, supt. Fax 429-7742
www.vernonia.k12.or.us/
Vernonia HS 200/9-12
1000 Missouri Ave 97064 503-429-1333
Nate Underwood, prin. Fax 429-0588
Vernonia MS 100/6-8
1000 Missouri Ave 97064 503-429-1333
Nate Underwood, prin. Fax 429-0588

Waldport, Lincoln, Pop. 1,936
Lincoln County SD
Supt. — See Newport
Waldport HS 200/7-12
PO Box 370 97394 541-563-3243
Diana MacKenzie, prin. Fax 563-4145

Wallowa, Wallowa, Pop. 785
Wallowa SD 12 200/K-12
PO Box 425 97885 541-886-2061
Bret Uptmor, supt. Fax 886-7355
www.wallowa.k12.or.us/
Wallowa JSHS 100/7-12
PO Box 425 97885 541-886-2951
David Howe, prin. Fax 886-7355

Warrenton, Clatsop, Pop. 4,827
Warrenton-Hammond SD 30 900/K-12
820 SW Cedar Ave 97146 503-861-2281
Mark Jeffery, supt. Fax 861-2911
www.warrentonschools.com
Warrenton HS 200/9-12
1700 S Main Ave 97146 503-861-3317
Rod Heyen, prin. Fax 861-2997

West Linn, Clackamas, Pop. 24,356
West Linn-Wilsonville SD 3J
Supt. — See Tualatin
Rosemont Ridge MS 700/6-8
20001 Salamo Rd 97068 503-673-7550
Debi Briggs-Crispin, prin. Fax 657-8720
West Linn HS 1,600/9-12
5464 W A St 97068 503-673-7800
Kevin Mills, prin. Fax 657-8710

Weston, Umatilla, Pop. 646
Athena-Weston SD 29RJ
Supt. — See Athena
Weston MS 200/4-8
PO Box 188 97886 541-566-3548
Ann Vescio, prin. Fax 566-2326

White City, Jackson, Pop. 7,814
Jackson County SD 9
Supt. — See Eagle Point
White Mountain MS 400/6-8
550 Wilson Way 97503 541-830-6315
Karina Rizo, prin. Fax 830-6751

Willamina, Yamhill, Pop. 1,910
Willamina SD 30J 800/K-12
PO Box 1000 97396 503-876-4525
Carrie Zimbrick, supt. Fax 876-3610
www.willamina.k12.or.us
Willamina HS 200/9-12
PO Box 1000 97396 503-876-2545
Tim France, prin. Fax 876-2511
Willamina MS 100/7-8
PO Box 1000 97396 503-876-2545
Tim France, prin. Fax 876-2511

Wilsonville, Clackamas, Pop. 18,997
West Linn-Wilsonville SD 3J
Supt. — See Tualatin
Arts and Technology HS 100/PK-PK, 9-
29796 SW Town Center Loop E 97070 503-673-7375
Saskia Dresler, prin. Fax 570-8720
Wilsonville HS 1,200/9-12
6800 SW Wilsonville Rd 97070 503-673-7600
Dan Schumaker, prin. Fax 682-0917
Wood MS 700/6-8
11055 SW Wilsonville Rd 97070 503-673-7500
Jim Severson, prin. Fax 682-9109

Pioneer Pacific College Post-Sec.
27501 SW Parkway Ave 97070 503-682-3903

Winston, Douglas, Pop. 5,205
Winston-Dillard SD 116 1,500/K-12
620 NW Elwood Dr 97496 541-679-3000
Kevin Miller, supt. Fax 679-4819
www.wdsd.org
Douglas HS 500/9-12
1381 NW Douglas Blvd 97496 541-679-3001
Brenyl Swanson, prin. Fax 679-7284
Winston MS 200/7-8
330 SE Thompson Ave 97496 541-679-3002
David Welker, prin. Fax 679-3026
Other Schools – See Dillard

Woodburn, Marion, Pop. 23,765
Woodburn SD 103 5,700/PK-12
1390 Meridian Dr 97071 503-981-9555
Chuck Ransom, supt. Fax 981-8018
www.woodburnsd.org
Academy of International Studies 300/9-12
1785 N Front St 97071 503-980-6100
Victor Vergara, prin. Fax 981-2629
French Prairie MS 600/6-8
1025 N Boones Ferry Rd 97071 971-983-3550
Ricardo Marquez, prin. Fax 981-2724
Valor MS 600/6-8
450 Parr Rd 97071 503-981-2750
Danny Nanez, prin. Fax 981-2790
Wellness Business and Sports S 300/9-12
1785 N Front St 97071 503-980-6150
Eric Swenson, prin. Fax 981-2621
Woodburn Acad Art Science & Technology 400/9-12
1785 N Front St 97071 503-980-6200
Geri Federico, prin. Fax 980-6209
Woodburn Arts and Communication Academy 400/9-12
1785 N Front St 97071 503-980-6250
Greg Baisch, prin. Fax 980-6255
Woodburn Success HS 200/Alt
610 Young St 97071 503-980-6185
Jennifer Dixon, prin. Fax 982-8372

Yamhill, Yamhill, Pop. 999
Yamhill-Carlton SD 1 1,200/K-12
120 N Larch 97148 503-852-6980
Charan Cline, supt. Fax 662-4931
www.ycsd.k12.or.us
Yamhill-Carlton HS 400/9-12
275 N Maple St 97148 503-852-7600
Greg Neuman, prin. Fax 662-3220
Yamhill-Carlton IS 300/5-8
310 E Main St 97148 503-852-7680
Michael Fisher, prin. Fax 662-4079

Yoncalla, Douglas, Pop. 1,008
Yoncalla SD 32 200/K-12
PO Box 568 97499 541-849-2782
Jan Zarate, supt. Fax 849-2190
www.yoncalla.k12.or.us
Yoncalla HS 100/7-12
PO Box 568 97499 541-849-2175
Brian Berry, prin. Fax 849-2669

PENNSYLVANIA

PENNSYLVANIA DEPARTMENT OF EDUCATION
333 Market St Fl 9, Harrisburg 17101-2215
Telephone 717-783-6788
Fax 717-787-7222
Website http://www.education.state.pa.us

Secretary of Education Pedro Rivera

PENNSYLVANIA BOARD OF EDUCATION
333 Market St Fl 10, Harrisburg 17101-2210

Chairperson Larry Wittig

INTERMEDIATE UNITS (IU)

Allegheny IU 3
Dr. Linda Hippert, dir. 412-394-5700
475 E Waterfront Dr Fax 394-5706
Homestead 15120
www.aiu3.net/
Appalachia IU 8
Dr. Thomas Butler, dir. 814-940-0223
4500 6th Ave, Altoona 16602 Fax 949-0984
www.iu08.org/
ARIN IU 28
James Wagner, dir. 724-463-5300
2895 W Pike Rd, Indiana 15701 Fax 463-5315
www.iu28.org
Beaver Valley IU 27
Eric Rosendale, dir. 724-774-7800
147 Poplar Ave, Monaca 15061 Fax 774-4751
www.bviu.org/
Berks County IU 14
Dr. Jill Hackman, dir. 610-987-2248
PO Box 16050, Reading 19612 Fax 987-8400
www.berksiu.org
BLaST IU 17
William Martens, dir. 570-323-8561
PO Box 3609, Williamsport 17701 Fax 323-1738
www.iu17.org
Bucks County IU 22
Dr. Mark Hoffman, dir. 800-770-4822
705 N Shady Retreat Rd Fax 340-1964
Doylestown 18901
www.bucksiu.org
Capital Area IU 15
Cindy Mortzfeldt, dir. 717-732-8400
55 Miller St, Enola 17025 Fax 732-8421
www.caiu.org
Carbon-Lehigh IU 21
Elaine Eib Ed.D., dir. 610-769-4111
4210 Independence Dr Fax 769-1290
Schnecksville 18078
www.cliu.org

Central IU 10
Dr. Hugh Dwyer, dir. 814-342-0884
345 Link Rd, West Decatur 16878 Fax 342-5137
www.ciu10.com
Central Susquehanna IU 16
Dr. Kevin Singer, dir. 570-523-1155
90 Lawton Ln, Milton 17847 Fax 524-7104
www.csiu.org/
Chester County IU 24
Joseph Lubitsky, dir. 484-237-5000
455 Boot Rd, Downingtown 19335 Fax 237-5154
www.cciu.org/
IU 1
Charles Mahoney, dir. 724-938-3241
1 Intermediate Unit Dr Fax 938-6665
Coal Center 15423
www.iu1.k12.pa.us/
Colonial IU 20
Dr. Charlene Brennan, dir. 610-252-5550
6 Danforth Dr, Easton 18045 Fax 252-5740
www.ciu20.org
Delaware County IU 25
Maria Edelberg Ed.D., dir. 610-938-9000
200 Yale Ave, Morton 19070 Fax 938-9887
www.dciu.org/
Lancaster-Lebanon IU 13
Dr. Brian Barnhart, dir. 717-606-1600
1020 New Holland Ave
Lancaster 17601
www.iu13.org
Lincoln IU 12
Dr. LeeAnn Zeroth, dir. 717-624-4616
PO Box 70, New Oxford 17350 Fax 624-6519
www.iu12.org
Luzerne IU 18
Dr. Anthony Grieco, dir. 570-287-9681
368 Tioga Ave, Kingston 18704 Fax 287-5721
www.liu18.org/
Midwestern IU 4
Dr. Wayde Killmeyer, dir. 724-458-6700
453 Maple St, Grove City 16127 Fax 458-5083
www.miu4.k12.pa.us/

Montgomery County IU 23
Dr. John George, dir. 610-539-8550
1605 W Main St Ste B Fax 539-5973
Norristown 19403
www.mciu.org
Northeastern Educational IU 19
Bob McTiernan, dir. 570-876-9200
1200 Line St, Archbald 18403 Fax 876-8660
www.iu19.org
Northwest Tri-County IU 5
Dr. Frederick Johnson, dir. 814-734-5610
252 Waterford St, Edinboro 16412 Fax 734-5806
www.iu5.org/
Philadelphia IU 26
Dr. William Hite, dir. 215-400-4000
440 N Broad St, Philadelphia 19130
www.phila.k12.pa.us/
Pittsburgh/Mt. Oliver IU 2
Dr. Linda Lane, dir. 412-224-4580
1305 Muriel St, Pittsburgh 15203 Fax 224-4583
www.pmoiu2.k12.pa.us/
Riverview IU 6
Jeff Brown, dir. 814-226-7103
270 Mayfield Rd, Clarion 16214 Fax 226-4850
www.riu6.org/
Schuylkill IU 29
Dr. Diane Niederriter, dir. 570-544-9131
PO Box 130, Mar Lin 17951 Fax 544-6412
www.iu29.org/
Seneca Highlands IU 9
Don Wismar, dir. 814-887-5512
PO Box 1566, Smethport 16749 Fax 887-2157
www.iu9.org
Tuscarora IU 11
Dr. Kendra Trail, dir. 717-899-7143
2527 US Highway 522 S
Mc Veytown 17051
www.tiu11.org
Westmoreland IU 7
Dr. Jason Conway, dir. 724-836-2460
102 Equity Dr, Greensburg 15601 Fax 836-1747
wiu.k12.pa.us/

PUBLIC, PRIVATE AND CATHOLIC SECONDARY SCHOOLS

Abington, Montgomery, Pop. 56,600
Abington SD 7,600/K-12
970 Highland Ave 19001 215-884-4700
Amy Sichel Ph.D., supt. Fax 881-2545
www.abington.k12.pa.us
Abington JHS 1,700/7-9
2056 Susquehanna Rd 19001 215-884-4700
Dr. Mark Pellico, prin. Fax 885-0293
Abington SHS 1,700/10-12
900 Highland Ave 19001 215-884-4700
Angelo Berrios, prin. Fax 886-1871

Abington Memorial Hospital Post-Sec.
1200 Old York Rd 19001 215-576-2000
Penn State Abington Post-Sec.
1600 Woodland Rd 19001 215-881-7300

Albion, Erie, Pop. 1,497
Northwestern SD 1,500/K-12
100 Harthan Way 16401 814-756-9400
Dr. Karen Downie, supt. Fax 756-9414
www.nwsd.org
Northwestern HS 500/9-12
200 Harthan Way 16401 814-756-9400
Daniel Shreve, prin. Fax 756-9411
Northwestern MS 300/6-8
150 Harthan Way 16401 814-756-9400
Greg Lehman, prin. Fax 756-9415

Alexandria, Huntingdon, Pop. 344
Juniata Valley SD 800/K-12
PO Box 318 16611 814-669-9150
Michael Zinobile, supt. Fax 669-4492
www.jvhornets.com
Juniata Valley JSHS 400/7-12
PO Box 318 16611 814-669-4401
Michael Estep, prin. Fax 669-4421

Aliquippa, Beaver, Pop. 9,176
Aliquippa SD 1,200/K-12
800 21st St 15001 724-857-7500
David Wytiaz, supt. Fax 857-3404
www.quipsd.org
Aliquippa JSHS 500/7-12
800 21st St 15001 724-857-7500
Alvin Gipson, prin. Fax 857-7560

Hopewell Area SD 2,200/K-12
2354 Brodhead Rd 15001 724-375-6691
Dr. Charles Reina, supt. Fax 375-0942
www.hopewell.k12.pa.us
Hopewell HS 800/9-12
1215 Longvue Ave 15001 724-378-8565
Michael Allison, prin. Fax 378-4952
Hopewell JHS 700/5-8
2354 Brodhead Rd 15001 724-375-6691
Edward Katkich, prin. Fax 378-2594

Allentown, Lehigh, Pop. 115,413
Allentown CSD 16,400/PK-12
PO Box 328 18105 484-765-4000
Dr. C. Russ Mayo, supt. Fax 765-4239
www.allentownsd.org/
Allen HS 2,600/9-12
126 N 17th St 18104 484-765-5000
Luke Shafnisky, prin. Fax 765-5010
Building 21 HS, 265 Lehigh St 18102 9-9
Janice Mathesz, prin. 484-765-4400
Dieruff HS 1,700/9-12
815 N Irving St 18109 484-765-5500
Susan Bocian, prin. Fax 765-5512
Harrison-Morton MS 800/6-8
137 N 2nd St 18101 484-765-5700
Daria Custer, prin. Fax 765-5715

Raub MS 900/6-8
102 S Saint Cloud St 18104 484-765-5300
Susan Elliott, prin. Fax 765-5310
South Mountain MS 1,100/6-8
709 W Emaus Ave 18103 484-765-4300
Frank Derrick, prin. Fax 765-4310
Trexler MS 900/6-8
851 N 15th St 18102 484-765-4600
Steve Serensits, prin. Fax 765-4610

Parkland SD 9,200/K-12
1210 Springhouse Rd 18104 610-351-5503
Richard Sniscak, supt. Fax 351-5509
www.parklandsd.org
Parkland HS 3,100/9-12
2700 N Cedar Crest Blvd 18104 610-351-5600
James Moniz, prin. Fax 351-5656
Springhouse MS 1,200/6-8
1200 Springhouse Rd 18104 610-351-5700
Michelle Minotti, prin. Fax 351-5748
Other Schools – See Orefield

Salisbury Township SD 1,600/K-12
1140 Salisbury Rd 18103 610-797-2062
Dr. Randy Ziegenfuss, supt. Fax 791-9983
www.stsd.org
Salisbury HS 600/9-12
500 E Montgomery St 18103 610-797-4107
Heather Morningstar, prin. Fax 797-1972
Salisbury MS 400/6-8
3301 Devonshire Rd 18103 610-791-0830
Ken Parliman, prin. Fax 797-9648

Allentown Central Catholic HS 800/9-12
301 N 4th St 18102 610-437-4601
Blair Tiger, prin. Fax 437-6760

Allentown School of Cosmetology Post-Sec.
1921 Union Blvd 18109 610-437-4626
Blackstone Career Institute Post-Sec.
PO Box 3717 18106 610-871-0031
Cedar Crest College Post-Sec.
100 College Dr 18104 610-437-4471
Intl Academy of Medical Reflexology Post-Sec.
1701 Union Blvd 18109 267-424-4549
Lehigh Valley Christian HS 100/9-12
3436 Winchester Rd 18104 610-351-9144
Robert Walsh, head sch Fax 351-9187
Lehigh Valley Hospital & Health Network Post-Sec.
PO Box 7017 18105 610-402-2556
Lincoln Technical Institute Post-Sec.
5151 W Tilghman St 18104 610-398-5300
McCann School of Business & Technology Post-Sec.
2200 N Irving St 18109 484-223-4600
Muhlenberg College Post-Sec.
2400 Chew St 18104 484-664-3100
Sacred Heart Hospital Post-Sec.
421 Chew St 18102 610-776-4745
Welder Training & Testing Institute Post-Sec.
729 E Highland St 18109 610-437-9720

Allison Park, Allegheny, Pop. 21,377
Area Vocational Technical School
Supt. — None
Beattie Career Center Vo/Tech
9600 Babcock Blvd 15101 412-366-2800
Eric Heasley, prin. Fax 366-9600

Hampton Township SD 3,000/K-12
4591 School Dr 15101 412-486-6000
Dr. Michael Loughead, supt.
www.ht-sd.org
Hampton HS 1,100/9-12
2929 McCully Rd 15101 412-492-6376
Dr. Marguerite Imbarlina, prin. Fax 486-7050
Hampton MS 700/6-8
4589 School Dr 15101 412-492-6356
Marlynn Lux, prin. Fax 487-7544

Altoona, Blair, Pop. 45,425
Altoona Area SD 7,600/K-12
1415 6th Ave 16602 814-946-8211
John Kopicki, supt. Fax 946-8226
www.aasdcat.com/aasd/
Altoona Area JHS 1,900/7-9
1400 7th Ave 16602 814-381-7500
Lori Mangan, prin. Fax 381-7501
Altoona Area SHS 1,700/10-12
1415 6th Ave 16602 814-946-8273
Patricia Burlingame, prin. Fax 946-8272
Kimmel Alternative S 50/Alt
900 S Jaggard St 16602 814-946-8246
Paul Hasson, prin. Fax 946-8402

Area Vocational Technical School
Supt. — None
Greater Altoona CTC Vo/Tech
1500 4th Ave 16602 814-946-8450
Dr. Donna Miller, prin. Fax 946-8351

Altoona Beauty School Post-Sec.
1528 Valley View Blvd 16602 814-942-3141
Altoona Hospital Post-Sec.
620 Howard Ave 16601 814-946-2223
Bishop Guilfoyle Catholic HS 300/9-12
2400 Pleasant Valley Blvd 16602 814-944-4014
Joan Donnelly, prin. Fax 944-8695
Great Commission S 100/PK-12
1100 6th Ave 16602 814-942-9710
Kimberly Salyards, supt. Fax 942-7147
Holy Trinity Catholic MS 300/5-8
5519 6th Ave 16602 814-942-7835
Elaine Spencer, prin. Fax 942-1095
Penn State Altoona Post-Sec.
3000 Ivyside Park 16601 814-949-5000
Pruonto's Hair Design Institute Post-Sec.
705 12th St 16602 814-944-4494
South Hills School of Business & Tech. Post-Sec.
541 58th St 16602 814-944-6134
YTI Career Institute Post-Sec.
2900 Fairway Dr 16602 814-944-5643

Alverton, Westmoreland
Southmoreland SD
Supt. — See Scottdale
Southmoreland HS 600/9-12
PO Box A 15612 724-887-2010
Dan Krofcheck, prin. Fax 887-2980

Ambler, Montgomery, Pop. 6,216
Wissahickon SD 4,400/K-12
601 Knight Rd 19002 215-619-8000
Dr. James Crisfield, supt. Fax 619-8002
wsdweb.org
Wissahickon HS 1,400/9-12
521 Houston Rd 19002 215-619-8112
Dr. Lynne Blair, prin. Fax 619-8113
Wissahickon MS 1,000/6-8
500 Houston Rd 19002 215-619-8110
Elizabeth Bauer, prin. Fax 619-8111

Ambler Beauty Academy Post-Sec.
50 E Butler Ave 19002 215-643-5994

Ambridge, Beaver, Pop. 6,737
Ambridge Area SD 2,600/K-12
901 Duss Ave 15003 724-266-2833
Dr. Joseph Dimperio, supt. Fax 266-3981
www.ambridge.k12.pa.us
Ambridge Area HS 800/9-12
909 Duss Ave 15003 724-266-2833
Janice Zupsic, prin. Fax 266-5056
Other Schools – See Freedom

Trinity School for Ministry Post-Sec.
311 11th St 15003 724-266-3838

Annville, Lebanon, Pop. 4,714
Annville-Cleona SD 1,200/K-12
520 S White Oak St 17003 717-867-7600
Dr. Cheryl A. Potteiger, supt. Fax 867-7610
www.acschools.org
Annville-Cleona JSHS 500/7-12
500 S White Oak St 17003 717-867-7700
David Wright, prin. Fax 867-7712

Lebanon Valley College Post-Sec.
101 N College Ave 17003 717-867-6100

Apollo, Armstrong, Pop. 1,610
Apollo-Ridge SD 1,300/K-12
1825 State Route 56 15613 724-478-6000
Dr. Matthew E. Curci, supt. Fax 478-1149
www.apolloridge.com/
Other Schools – See Spring Church

Archbald, Lackawanna, Pop. 6,931
Valley View SD 2,500/K-12
1 Columbus Dr 18403 570-876-5080
Donald Kanavy, supt. Fax 876-6365
www.valleyviewsd.org/
Valley View HS 800/9-12
1 Columbus Dr 18403 570-876-4110
Peter Chapla, prin. Fax 803-0217
Valley View MS 600/6-8
1 Columbus Dr 18403 570-876-6461
Craig Sweeney, prin. Fax 803-0276

Ardmore, Montgomery, Pop. 12,170
Lower Merion SD 7,800/K-12
301 E Montgomery Ave 19003 610-645-1800
Robert Copeland, supt. Fax 645-9772
www.lmsd.org
Lower Merion HS 1,300/9-12
315 E Montgomery Ave 19003 610-645-1810
Sean Hughes, prin. Fax 645-9657
Other Schools – See Bala Cynwyd, Narberth, Rosemont

Armagh, Indiana, Pop. 121
United SD 1,100/PK-12
10780 Route 56 Hwy E 15920 814-446-5615
Dr. Barbara Parkins, supt. Fax 446-6615
www.unitedsd.net/
United JSHS 500/7-12
10780 Route 56 Hwy E 15920 814-446-5615
Michael Worthington, prin. Fax 446-6615

Ashland, Schuylkill, Pop. 2,790
North Schuylkill SD 1,900/K-12
15 Academy Ln 17921 570-874-0466
Dr. Robert Ackell, supt. Fax 874-3334
www.northschuylkill.net
North Schuylkill JSHS 900/7-12
15 Academy Ln 17921 570-874-0495
Ken Roseberry, prin. Fax 874-1531

Aston, Delaware
Area Vocational Technical School
Supt. — None
Delaware County Technical HS Aston Vo/Tech
100 Crozerville Rd 19014 610-459-3050
Christopher Moritzen, prin.

Chichester SD 3,300/K-12
401 Cherry Tree Rd 19014 610-485-6881
Dr. Kathleen Sherman, supt. Fax 485-3086
www.chichestersd.org
Other Schools – See Boothwyn

Penn-Delco SD 3,400/K-12
2821 Concord Rd 19014 610-497-6300
Dr. George Steinhoff, supt. Fax 497-1798
www.pdsd.org
Northley MS 800/6-8
2801 Concord Rd 19014 610-497-6300
Lanny Blair, prin. Fax 497-5737
Sun Valley HS 1,100/9-12
2881 Pancoast Ave 19014 610-497-6300
Pete Donaghy, prin. Fax 497-2863

Neumann University Post-Sec.
1 Neumann Dr 19014 610-459-0905

Atglen, Chester, Pop. 1,387
Octorara Area SD 2,500/K-12
228 Highland Rd Ste 1 19310 610-593-8238
Dr. Thomas Newcome, supt. Fax 593-6425
www.octorara.k12.pa.us
Octorara Area HS 800/9-12
226 Highland Rd 19310 610-593-8238
Scott Rohrer, prin. Fax 593-4945
Octorara Area JHS 400/7-8
228 Highland Rd 19310 610-593-8238
Dr. Scott Rohrer, prin. Fax 593-5185

Athens, Bradford, Pop. 3,332
Athens Area SD 1,900/PK-12
401 W Frederick St 18810 570-888-7766
Craig Stage, supt. Fax 882-6250
www.athensasd.org
Athens Area HS 700/9-12
401 W Frederick St 18810 570-888-7766
Corey Mosher, prin. Fax 888-4038
Rowe MS 200/6-8
116 W Pine St Ste 1 18810 570-888-7766
Peter Henning, prin. Fax 888-9536

Austin, Potter, Pop. 562
Austin Area SD 200/PK-12
138 Costello Ave 16720 814-647-8603
Jerome Sasala, supt. Fax 647-8869
www.austinsd.net
Austin Area HS 100/7-12
138 Costello Ave 16720 814-647-8603
Jerome Sasala, prin. Fax 647-8869

Avella, Washington, Pop. 795
Avella Area SD 600/K-12
1000 Avella Rd 15312 724-356-2218
Cyril Walther, supt. Fax 356-2207
www.avella.k12.pa.us
Avella Area JSHS 300/7-12
1000 Avella Rd 15312 724-356-2216
Sheryl Wright-Brown, prin. Fax 356-7905

Avis, Clinton, Pop. 1,476

Walnut Street Christian S 200/PK-12
PO Box 616 17721 570-753-3400
Tim Longnecker, prin. Fax 753-5728

Baden, Beaver, Pop. 4,097

Quigley HS 100/9-12
200 Quigley Dr 15005 724-869-2188
Rita McCormick, prin. Fax 869-3091

Bala Cynwyd, Montgomery, Pop. 8,000
Lower Merion SD
Supt. — See Ardmore
Bala Cynwyd MS 900/6-8
510 Bryn Mawr Ave 19004 610-645-1480
Jason Potten, prin. Fax 664-2798

Kosloff Torah Academy HS 100/9-12
50 Montgomery Ave 19004 610-660-5010
Barry Lichtenstein, prin. Fax 667-5005

Bangor, Northampton, Pop. 5,192
Bangor Area SD 3,000/K-12
123 Five Points Richmond Rd 18013 610-588-2163
Dr. Frank J. DeFelice, supt. Fax 599-7040
www.bangor.k12.pa.us
Bangor Area HS 1,000/9-12
187 Five Points Richmond Rd 18013 610-599-7011
Tami Gary, prin. Fax 599-7043
Bangor Area MS 500/7-8
401 Five Points Richmond Rd 18013 610-599-7012
Allison Tucker, prin. Fax 599-7045

Bartonsville, Monroe
Area Vocational Technical School
Supt. — None
Monroe Career & Tech Institute Vo/Tech
194 Laurel Lake Rd 18321 570-629-2001
Adam Lazarchak, dir. Fax 629-9698

Beaver, Beaver, Pop. 4,471
Beaver Area SD 2,000/K-12
1300 5th St 15009 724-774-4021
Dr. Carrie Rowe, supt. Fax 774-8770
www.basd.k12.pa.us
Beaver Area HS 600/9-12
1 Gypsy Glenn Rd 15009 724-774-0251
Steve Wellendorf, prin. Fax 774-3926
Beaver Area MS 300/7-8
Gypsy Glen Rd 15009 724-774-0253
Jeff Beltz, prin. Fax 774-3926

Medical Center of Beaver County Post-Sec.
1000 Dutch Ridge Rd 15009 724-728-7000

Beaver Falls, Beaver, Pop. 8,590
Big Beaver Falls Area SD 1,700/K-12
1503 8th Ave 15010 724-843-3420
Dr. Donna Nugent, supt. Fax 843-2360
www.tigerweb.org
Beaver Falls Area HS 500/9-12
1701 8th Ave 15010 724-843-7470
Mary Beth Leeman, prin. Fax 843-0892
Beaver Falls MS 400/6-8
1601 8th Ave 15010 724-846-5470
Thomas House, prin. Fax 846-2579

Blackhawk SD 2,000/K-12
500 Blackhawk Rd 15010 724-846-6600
Dr. Robert Postupac, supt. Fax 846-2021
www.bsd.k12.pa.us
Blackhawk HS 800/9-12
500 Blackhawk Rd 15010 724-846-9600
Scott Nelson, prin. Fax 891-7113
Highland MS 600/5-8
402 Shenango Rd 15010 724-843-1700
Amy Anderson, prin. Fax 843-0934

Beaver County Christian HS 9-12
510 37th St 15010 724-843-3002
Doug Carson, prin. Fax 843-5224
Beaver Falls Beauty Academy Post-Sec.
720 13th St 15010 724-843-7700
Geneva College Post-Sec.
3200 College Ave 15010 724-846-5100

Bedford, Bedford, Pop. 2,806
Bedford Area SD 1,900/K-12
330 E John St 15522 814-623-4290
Dr. Allen Sell, supt. Fax 623-4299
www.bedford.k12.pa.us
Bedford HS 600/9-12
330 E John St 15522 814-623-4250
Kyle Kane, prin. Fax 623-4265
Bedford MS 500/6-8
440 E Watson St 15522 814-623-4200
Kevin Windows, prin. Fax 623-4214

Bellefonte, Centre, Pop. 6,107
Bellefonte Area SD 2,700/K-12
318 N Allegheny St 16823 814-355-4814
Dr. Michelle Saylor, supt. Fax 353-5342
www.basd.net
Bellefonte Area HS 800/9-12
830 E Bishop St 16823 814-355-4833
Jennifer Brown, prin. Fax 353-5320
Bellefonte Area MS 600/6-8
100 N School St 16823 814-355-5466
Sommer Garman, prin. Fax 353-5350

Belle Vernon, Fayette, Pop. 1,081
Belle Vernon Area SD 2,400/K-12
270 Crest Ave 15012 724-808-2500
Dr. John Wilkinson, supt. Fax 929-5598
www.bellevernonarea.net/bvasd/site/default.asp
Belle Vernon Area HS 900/9-12
425 Crest Ave 15012 724-808-2500
Jason Boone, prin.
Belle Vernon Area MS 200/7-8
500 Perry Ave 15012 724-808-2500
Greg Zborovancik, prin.

Belleville, Mifflin, Pop. 1,819

Belleville Mennonite S 200/PK-12
4105 Front Mountain Rd 17004 717-935-2184
Starla Fogleman, supt. Fax 935-5641

Bellwood, Blair, Pop. 1,814
Bellwood-Antis SD 1,300/K-12
300 Martin St 16617 814-742-2271
Dr. Thomas McInroy, supt. Fax 742-9049
moss.blwd.k12.pa.us
Bellwood-Antis HS 400/9-12
400 Martin St 16617 814-742-2274
Richard Schreier, prin. Fax 742-9817
Bellwood-Antis MS 400/5-8
400 Martin St 16617 814-742-2273
Donald Wagner, prin. Fax 742-9817

Bensalem, Bucks, Pop. 59,700
Bensalem Township SD 6,300/K-12
3000 Donallen Dr 19020 215-750-2800
Dr. Samuel Lee, supt. Fax 359-0181
www.bensalemsd.org/
Bensalem HS 1,900/9-12
4319 Hulmeville Rd 19020 215-750-2800
William J. Ferrara, prin. Fax 244-2970
Shafer MS 600/7-8
3333 Hulmeville Rd 19020 215-750-2800
William Incollingo, prin. Fax 244-2964
Snyder MS 400/7-8
3330 Hulmeville Rd 19020 215-750-2800
Dr. Thomas Evert, prin. Fax 244-2851

Everest Institute Post-Sec.
3050 Tillman Dr 19020 267-223-2900
Holy Ghost Prep S 500/9-12
2429 Bristol Pike 19020 215-639-2102
Jeff Danilak, prin. Fax 639-4225

Bentleyville, Washington, Pop. 2,539
Bentworth SD 1,200/K-12
150 Bearcat Dr 15314 724-239-2861
Scott Martin, supt. Fax 239-2865
bentworth.org
Bentworth HS 400/9-12
75 Bearcat Dr 15314 724-239-5911
Keith Konyk, prin. Fax 239-4010
Bentworth MS 400/5-8
563 Lincoln Ave 15314 724-239-4431
David Schreiber, prin. Fax 239-5889

Benton, Columbia, Pop. 821
Benton Area SD 700/K-12
600 Green Acres Rd 17814 570-925-6651
Dr. Brian Cooper, supt. Fax 925-6973
www.bentonsd.k12.pa.us/
Benton Area MSHS 300/7-12
400 Park St 17814 570-925-2651
Coleen Genovese, prin. Fax 925-0956

Berlin, Somerset, Pop. 2,084
Berlin Brothersvalley SD 800/K-12
1025 Main St 15530 814-267-4621
Dwayne Northcraft, supt. Fax 267-6060
www.bbsd.com/
Berlin Brothersvalley HS 300/9-12
1025 Main St 15530 814-267-4622
Brian Thompson, prin. Fax 267-6060
Berlin Brothersvalley MS 300/5-8
1025 Main St 15530 814-267-6931
Martin Mudry, prin. Fax 267-6060

Bernville, Berks, Pop. 942
Tulpehocken Area SD
Supt. — See Bethel
Tulpehocken Area JSHS 700/7-12
430 New Schaefferstown Rd 19506 610-488-6286
Andrew Netznik, prin. Fax 488-7976

Berwick, Columbia, Pop. 10,321
Berwick Area SD 2,900/K-12
500 Line St 18603 570-759-6400
Wayne Brookhart, supt. Fax 759-6439
www.berwicksd.org
Berwick Area HS 800/9-12
1100 Fowler Ave 18603 570-759-6400
Robert Croop, prin. Fax 759-6466
Berwick Area MS 700/6-8
1100 Evergreen Dr 18603 570-759-6400
Christopher Rivera, prin. Fax 759-7978

Berwyn, Chester, Pop. 3,583
Tredyffrin-Easttown SD
Supt. — See Wayne
Conestoga HS 2,100/9-12
200 Irish Rd 19312 610-240-1000
Dr. Amy Meisinger, prin. Fax 240-1055
Tredyffrin-Easttown MS 1,100/5-8
801 Conestoga Rd 19312 610-240-1200
Mark Cataldi, prin. Fax 240-1225

Bessemer, Lawrence, Pop. 1,097
Mohawk Area SD 1,500/K-12
PO Box 25 16112 724-667-7723
Michael Leitera, supt. Fax 667-0602
www.mohawk.k12.pa.us
Mohawk JSHS 700/7-12
PO Box 25 16112 724-667-7782
Raymond Omer, prin. Fax 667-0602

Bethel, Berks, Pop. 495
Tulpehocken Area SD 1,400/K-12
27 Rehrersburg Rd 19507 717-933-4611
Dr. Robert Schultz, supt. Fax 933-9724
www.tulpehocken.org
Other Schools – See Bernville

Bethel Dunkard Brethren Church S 1,300/K-12
5450 Four Point Rd 19507 717-933-5510
Dale Eberly, prin. Fax 933-5510

Bethel Park, Allegheny, Pop. 32,035
Bethel Park SD 4,500/K-12
301 Church Rd 15102 412-854-8402
Dr. Joseph W. Pasquerilla, supt. Fax 854-8430
www.bpsd.org
Bethel Park HS 1,600/9-12
309 Church Rd 15102 412-854-8581
Dr. Zeb Jansante, prin. Fax 854-8552
Independence MS 700/7-8
2807 Bethel Church Rd 15102 412-854-8677
David Muench, prin. Fax 854-8732

Hillcrest Christian Academy 200/PK-12
2500 Bethel Church Rd 15102 412-854-4040
Alan Ciechanowski, prin. Fax 854-4051

Bethlehem, Northampton, Pop. 73,573
Area Vocational Technical School
Supt. — None
Bethlehem AVTS Vo/Tech
3300 Chester Ave 18020 610-866-8013
Brian Williams, dir. Fax 866-6124

Bethlehem Area SD 13,800/K-12
1516 Sycamore St 18017 610-861-0500
Dr. Joseph J. Roy, supt. Fax 807-5599
www.beth.k12.pa.us
Broughal MS 500/6-8
114 W Morton St 18015 610-866-5041
Dr. Detrick McGriff, prin. Fax 807-5909
East Hills MS 1,100/6-8
2005 Chester Rd 18017 610-867-0541
David Horvath, prin. Fax 807-5941
Freedom HS 1,800/9-12
3149 Chester Ave 18020 610-867-5843
Michael LaPorta, prin. Fax 867-7360
Liberty HS 2,800/9-12
1115 Linden St 18018 610-691-7200
Harrison Bailey, prin. Fax 691-0741
Nitschmann MS 800/6-8
909 W Union Blvd 18018 610-866-5781
Peter Mayes, prin. Fax 866-1435
Northeast MS 800/6-8
1170 Fernwood St 18018 610-868-8581
Joseph Rahs, prin. Fax 807-5997

Bethlehem Catholic HS 800/9-12
2133 Madison Ave 18017 610-866-0791
John Petruzzelli M.Ed., prin. Fax 866-4429
International Inst Restorative Practices Post-Sec.
PO Box 229 18016 610-807-9221
Lehigh University Post-Sec.
27 Memorial Dr W 18015 610-758-3000
Moravian Academy MS 200/6-8
11 W Market St 18018 610-866-6677
George N. King, hdmstr. Fax 866-6337
Moravian Academy - Upper S 300/9-12
4313 Green Pond Rd 18020 610-691-1600
Jeff Zemsky, hdmstr. Fax 691-3354
Moravian College Post-Sec.
1200 Main St 18018 610-861-1300
Moravian Theological Seminary Post-Sec.
60 W Locust St 18018 610-861-1516
Northampton Community College Post-Sec.
3835 Green Pond Rd 18020 610-861-5300
St. Luke's Hospital Post-Sec.
801 Ostrum St 18015 610-954-3400
Triangle Tech Post-Sec.
3184 Airport Rd 18017 610-266-2910

Biglerville, Adams, Pop. 1,195
Upper Adams SD 1,600/K-12
PO Box 847 17307 717-677-7191
Fax 677-9807
upperadams.org
Biglerville HS 500/9-12
161 N Main St 17307 717-677-7191
Richard Sterner, prin. Fax 677-0142
Upper Adams MS 300/7-8
161 N Main St 17307 717-677-7191
David Zinn, prin. Fax 677-0219

Birdsboro, Berks, Pop. 5,083
Daniel Boone Area SD
Supt. — See Douglassville
Boone Area HS 1,100/9-12
PO Box 450 19508 610-582-6100
Preston McKnight, prin. Fax 582-5400

Berks Christian S 100/PK-12
926 Philadelphia Ter 19508 610-582-1000
Philip Warner, admin. Fax 404-0126

Blairsville, Indiana, Pop. 3,366
Blairsville-Saltsburg SD 1,700/PK-12
102 School Ln 15717 724-459-5500
Tammy Whitfield Ed.D., supt. Fax 459-9209
www.b-ssd.org
Blairsville HS 300/9-12
100 School Ln 15717 724-459-8882
Allan Berkhimer, prin. Fax 459-3392
Blairsville MS 200/6-8
104 School Ln 15717 724-459-8880
Allan Berkhimer, prin. Fax 459-0213
Other Schools – See Saltsburg

WyoTech - Blairsville Post-Sec.
500 Innovation Dr 15717 724-459-9500

Bloomsburg, Columbia, Pop. 14,675
Area Vocational Technical School
Supt. — None
Columbia-Montour AVTS Vo/Tech
5050 Sweppenheiser Dr 17815 570-784-8040
Dave Bacher, dir. Fax 784-3565

Bloomsburg Area SD 1,600/K-12
728 E 5th St 17815 570-784-5000
Dr. Cosmas Curry, supt. Fax 387-8832
bloomsburgasd.schoolwires.com
Bloomsburg Area HS 400/9-12
1200 Railroad St 17815 570-784-6100
Daniel Bonomo M.Ed., prin. Fax 387-3492
Bloomsburg Area MS 400/6-8
1100 Railroad St 17815 570-784-9100
Marc Freeman, prin. Fax 387-3491

Central Columbia SD 1,800/K-12
4777 Old Berwick Rd 17815 570-784-2850
Harry Mathias, supt. Fax 387-0192
www.ccsd.cc
Central Columbia HS 500/9-12
4777 Old Berwick Rd 17815 570-784-2850
Jeffrey Groshek, prin. Fax 784-0863
Central Columbia MS 600/5-8
4777 Old Berwick Rd 17815 570-784-2850
Chad Heintzelman, prin. Fax 784-4935

Bloomsburg University of Pennsylvania Post-Sec.
400 E 2nd St 17815 570-389-4000
Columbia County Christian S 200/PK-12
123 Schoolhouse Rd 17815 570-784-2977
Daniel Thompson, head sch Fax 784-1755

Blossburg, Tioga, Pop. 1,532
Southern Tioga SD 1,600/K-12
241 Main St 16912 570-638-2183
Sam Rotella, supt. Fax 638-3512
www.southerntioga.org
Other Schools – See Liberty, Mansfield

Blue Bell, Montgomery, Pop. 6,001

Montgomery County Community College Post-Sec.
340 Dekalb Pike 19422 215-641-6300
Reformed Episcopal Seminary Post-Sec.
826 2nd Ave 19422 610-292-9852

Boalsburg, Centre, Pop. 3,655

St. Joseph's Catholic Academy 9-12
901 Boalsburg Pike 16827 814-808-6118
Christopher Chirieleison, prin. Fax 808-6170

Boiling Springs, Cumberland, Pop. 3,185
South Middleton SD 2,100/K-12
4 Forge Rd 17007 717-258-6484
Dr. Alan Moyer, supt. Fax 258-1214
www.smsd.us
Boiling Springs HS 700/9-12
4 Forge Rd 17007 717-258-6484
Joel Hain, prin. Fax 258-5014
Yellow Breeches MS 500/6-8
4 Forge Rd 17007 717-258-6484
Dr. Jesse White, prin. Fax 258-0301

Boothwyn, Delaware, Pop. 4,830
Chichester SD
Supt. — See Aston
Chichester HS 1,000/9-12
3333 Chichester Ave 19061 610-485-6881
Michael Stankavage, prin. Fax 485-6510
Chichester MS 1,000/5-8
925 Meetinghouse Rd 19061 610-485-6881
Stacie Hardy, prin. Fax 494-3064

Boswell, Somerset, Pop. 1,262
North Star SD 1,200/PK-12
1200 Morris Ave 15531 814-629-5631
Louis M. Lepley, supt. Fax 629-6181
www.nscougars.com
North Star HS 400/9-12
400 Ohio St 15531 814-629-6651
Thaddeus Kiesnowski, prin. Fax 629-9346
Other Schools – See Stoystown

Boyertown, Berks, Pop. 4,017
Boyertown Area SD 7,100/K-12
911 Montgomery Ave 19512 610-367-6031
Dr. Richard Faidley, supt. Fax 369-7620
www.boyertownasd.org
Boyertown Area JHS West 900/7-9
380 S Madison St 19512 610-369-7471
Gregory Galtere, prin. Fax 369-7476
Boyertown Area SHS 1,600/10-12
120 N Monroe St 19512 610-369-7435
Brett Cooper, prin. Fax 369-7359
Other Schools – See Gilbertsville

Bradford, McKean, Pop. 8,658
Bradford Area SD 2,600/PK-12
PO Box 375 16701 814-362-3841
Katharine Pude, supt. Fax 362-2552
www.bradfordareaschools.org
Bradford Area HS 800/9-12
81 Interstate Pkwy 16701 814-362-3845
David Ray, prin. Fax 362-1765
Fretz MS 600/6-8
140 Lorana Ave 16701 814-362-3500
Tina Slaven, prin. Fax 362-1812

Bradford Regional Medical Center Post-Sec.
116 Interstate Pkwy 16701 814-362-8292
University of Pittsburgh at Bradford Post-Sec.
300 Campus Dr 16701 814-362-7500

Bridgeville, Allegheny, Pop. 5,046
Chartiers Valley SD
Supt. — See Pittsburgh

Chartiers Valley HS 1,100/9-12
50 Thoms Run Rd 15017 412-429-2241
Valerie Keys, prin. Fax 276-5808
Chartiers Valley MS 700/6-8
50 Thoms Run Rd 15017 412-429-2223
Adrienne Floro, prin. Fax 429-2226

Bristol, Bucks, Pop. 9,494
Bristol Borough SD 900/PK-12
1776 Farragut Ave 19007 215-781-1000
Dr. Thomas Shaffer, supt. Fax 781-1012
www.bbsd.org
Bristol HS, 1801 Wilson Ave 19007 300/9-12
Dr. Thomas Shaffer, prin. 215-781-1000

Bristol Township SD
Supt. — See Levittown
Roosevelt MS 500/7-8
1001 New Rodgers Rd 19007 267-599-2300
Kevin Boles, prin. Fax 599-2349

Pennco Tech Post-Sec.
3815 Otter St 19007 215-785-0111

Brockway, Jefferson, Pop. 2,057
Brockway Area SD 1,000/K-12
40 North St 15824 814-265-8411
Daniel Hawkins, supt. Fax 265-8498
www.brockway.k12.pa.us/
Brockway Area JSHS 400/7-12
100 Alexander St 15824 814-265-8414
Mark Dippold, prin. Fax 265-8413

Brodheadsville, Monroe, Pop. 1,776
Pleasant Valley SD 4,900/K-12
2233 Route 115 Ste 100 18322 570-402-1000
Carole Geary, supt. Fax 992-7275
www.pvbears.org
Pleasant Valley HS 1,900/9-12
1671 Route 209 18322 570-402-1000
John Gress, prin. Fax 992-7733
Pleasant Valley MS 900/7-8
2233 Route 115 18322 570-402-1000
Rocco Seiler, prin. Fax 992-6968

Brookhaven, Delaware, Pop. 7,890
Chester-Upland SD
Supt. — See Chester
Toby Farms IS 500/4-8
201 Bridgewater Rd 19015 610-447-3815
R. Victoria Pressley, prin. Fax 499-3814

Christian Academy 400/K-12
4301 Chandler Dr 19015 610-872-5100
Dr. Timothy Sierer, hdmstr. Fax 876-2173

Brookville, Jefferson, Pop. 3,884
Brookville Area SD 1,600/K-12
PO Box 479 15825 814-849-1100
Dr. Robin Fillman, supt. Fax 849-6842
www.basd.us
Brookville Area JSHS 700/7-12
PO Box 479 15825 814-849-1106
Robert Rocco, prin. Fax 849-1117

Broomall, Delaware, Pop. 10,688
Area Vocational Technical School
Supt. — None
Delaware County Technical HS - Marple Vo/Tech
85 N Malin Rd 19008 610-423-7000
Dr. Philip Lachimia, dir.

Marple Newtown SD
Supt. — See Newtown Square
Paxon Hollow MS 800/6-8
815 Paxon Hollow Rd 19008 610-359-4320
Stephen Subers Ed.D., prin. Fax 353-4061

Brightwood Career Institute Post-Sec.
1991 Sproul Rd Ste 42 19008 610-353-7630

Brownstown, Lancaster, Pop. 741
Area Vocational Technical School
Supt. — None
Lancaster County CTC-Brownstown Vo/Tech
PO Box 519 17508 717-859-5100
Margaret Roth, prin. Fax 859-4529

Brownsville, Fayette, Pop. 2,220
Brownsville Area SD 900/K-12
5 Falcon Dr 15417 724-785-2021
Dr. Philip Savini, supt. Fax 785-6988
www.basd.org
Brownsville Area HS 500/9-12
1 Falcon Dr 15417 724-785-8200
Jason Kushak, prin. Fax 785-8930
Brownsville Area MS 400/6-8
3 Falcon Dr 15417 724-785-2155
Vincent Nesser, prin. Fax 785-2502

Bryn Athyn, Montgomery, Pop. 1,347

Academy of the New Church-Boys S 100/9-12
PO Box 707 19009 267-502-2500
Jeremy Irwin M.Ed., prin. Fax 502-2617
Academy of the New Church Girls S 100/9-12
PO Box 707 19009 267-502-2556
Kira Schadegg, prin. Fax 502-2617
Bryn Athyn College Post-Sec.
PO Box 462 19009 267-502-6000

Bryn Mawr, Montgomery, Pop. 3,647

American College Post-Sec.
270 S Bryn Mawr Ave 19010 610-526-1000
Baldwin S 600/PK-12
701 Montgomery Ave 19010 610-525-2700
Marisa Porges Ph.D., head sch Fax 525-7534
Barrack Hebrew Academy 300/6-12
272 S Bryn Mawr Ave 19010 610-922-2300
Sharon Levin, head sch Fax 922-2301

Bryn Mawr College Post-Sec.
101 N Merion Ave 19010 610-526-5000
Country Day S of the Sacred Heart 300/PK-12
480 S Bryn Mawr Ave 19010 610-527-3915
Deirdre Cryor, head sch Fax 527-0942
Harcum College Post-Sec.
750 Montgomery Ave 19010 610-525-4100
Shipley S 800/PK-12
814 Yarrow St 19010 610-525-4300
Dr. Steven Piltch, hdmstr. Fax 525-5082

Burgettstown, Washington, Pop. 1,365
Burgettstown Area SD 1,200/K-12
100 Bavington Rd 15021 724-947-8136
Dr. James Walsh, supt. Fax 947-8143
www.burgettstown.k12.pa.us
Burgettstown MSHS 700/6-12
104 Bavington Rd 15021 724-947-8100
Brian Fadden, prin. Fax 947-3325

Tri State Christian Academy 100/PK-12
750 Steubenville Pike 15021 724-947-8722
John Massey, prin. Fax 947-0821

Butler, Butler, Pop. 13,451
Area Vocational Technical School
Supt. — None
Butler County AVTS Vo/Tech
210 Campus Ln 16001 724-282-0735
Regina Hiler, prin. Fax 282-7448

Butler Area SD 5,500/K-12
110 Campus Ln 16001 724-287-8721
Dr. Dale Lumley, supt. Fax 287-1802
www.basdk12.org
Butler Area Intermediate HS 600/7-9
551 Fairground Hill Rd 16001 724-287-8721
John Wyllie, prin. Fax 287-5457
Butler Area SHS 1,200/10-12
120 Campus Ln 16001 724-287-8721
Jeffery Schnur, prin. Fax 287-1596

Butler Beauty School Post-Sec.
233 S Main St 16001 724-287-0708
Butler County Community College Post-Sec.
107 College Dr 16002 724-287-8711
First Baptist Christian S 100/PK-12
221 New Castle St 16001 724-287-1188
Dan Gwilt, prin. Fax 287-6934

Cairnbrook, Somerset, Pop. 520
Shade-Central CSD 500/K-12
203 McGregor Ave 15924 814-754-4648
John Krupper, supt. Fax 754-5848
www.shade.k12.pa.us
Shade JSHS 200/7-12
203 McGregor Ave 15924 814-754-4648
Sean Wechtenhiser, prin.

California, Washington, Pop. 6,712

California University of Pennsylvania Post-Sec.
250 University Ave 15419 724-938-4000

Cambridge Springs, Crawford, Pop. 2,577
PENNCREST SD
Supt. — See Saegertown
Cambridge Springs JSHS 500/7-12
641 Venango Ave 16403 814-398-4631
David Nuhfer, prin. Fax 398-8343

Camp Hill, Cumberland, Pop. 7,766
Camp Hill SD 1,300/K-12
2627 Chestnut St 17011 717-901-2401
Dr. David Reeder, supt. Fax 901-2421
www.camphillsd.k12.pa.us
Camp Hill HS 400/9-12
100 S 24th St 17011 717-901-2500
Mark Ziegler, prin. Fax 901-2614
Camp Hill MS 300/6-8
2401 Chestnut St 17011 717-901-2450
Leslee DeLong, prin. Fax 901-2573

West Shore SD
Supt. — See Lewisberry
Allen MS 500/6-8
4225 Gettysburg Rd 17011 717-901-9552
Tara Lingle, prin. Fax 901-8201
Cedar Cliff HS 1,300/9-12
1301 Carlisle Rd 17011 717-737-8654
Dr. Kevin Fillgrove, prin. Fax 737-0874

Holy Spirit Hospital Post-Sec.
505 N 21st St 17011 717-763-2106
Trinity HS 600/9-12
3601 Simpson Ferry Rd 17011 717-761-1116
Joseph Gressock, prin. Fax 761-7309

Canonsburg, Washington, Pop. 8,707
Area Vocational Technical School
Supt. — None
Western Area CTC Vo/Tech
688 Western Ave 15317 724-746-2890
Dr. Dennis McCarthy, prin. Fax 746-0817

Canon-McMillan SD 5,000/K-12
1 N Jefferson Ave 15317 724-746-2940
Michael Daniels, supt. Fax 746-9184
www.cmsd.k12.pa.us
Canon-McMillan HS 1,500/9-12
314 Elm Street Ext 15317 724-745-1400
Dave Helinski, prin. Fax 745-2258
Canonsburg MS 800/7-8
25 E College St 15317 724-745-9030
Greg Taranto, prin. Fax 873-5230

Canton, Bradford, Pop. 1,948
Canton Area SD 1,000/K-12
509 E Main St 17724 570-673-3191
Eric Briggs, supt. Fax 673-3680
www.canton.k12.pa.us

Canton JSHS 400/7-12
509 E Main St 17724 570-673-5134
Craig Coleman, prin. Fax 673-5566

Carbondale, Lackawanna, Pop. 8,778
Carbondale Area SD 1,600/PK-12
101 Brooklyn St 18407 570-282-2507
David Cerra, supt. Fax 282-6988
www.ca.k12.pa.us
Carbondale Area JSHS 700/7-12
101 Brooklyn St 18407 570-282-4500
Joseph Farrell, prin. Fax 282-3394

Carlisle, Cumberland, Pop. 18,109
Carlisle Area SD 4,900/K-12
540 W North St 17013 717-240-6800
John W. Friend, supt. Fax 240-6898
www.carlisleschools.org
Carlisle HS 1,500/9-12
540 W North St 17013 717-240-6800
Jay Rauscher, prin. Fax 240-7145
Lamberton MS 600/6-8
540 W North St 17013 717-240-6800
Keith Colestock, prin. Fax 240-2066
Wilson MS 600/6-8
540 W North St 17013 717-240-6800
Colleen Friend, prin. Fax 240-2050

Carlisle Christian Academy 100/K-12
1412 Holly Pike, 717-249-3692
James Koser, admin. Fax 240-0644
Dickinson College Post-Sec.
PO Box 1773 17013 717-243-5121
McCann School of Business & Technology Post-Sec.
346 York Rd 17013 714-218-3400

Carmichaels, Greene, Pop. 473
Carmichaels Area SD 1,100/PK-12
300 W Greene St 15320 724-966-5045
John Menhart, supt. Fax 966-8793
www.carmarea.org
Carmichaels Area HS 400/9-12
215 N Vine St 15320 724-966-5045
Lisa Zdravecky, prin. Fax 966-5556
Carmichaels Area MS 200/6-8
300 W Greene St 15320 724-966-5045
Ron Gallagher, prin. Fax 966-5556

Carnegie, Allegheny, Pop. 7,765
Carlynton SD 1,400/K-12
435 Kings Hwy 15106 412-429-8400
Dr. Gary D. Peiffer, supt. Fax 429-2502
www.carlynton.k12.pa.us
Carlynton JSHS 700/7-12
435 Kings Hwy 15106 412-429-2500
Michael Loughren, prin. Fax 429-2508

Catasauqua, Lehigh, Pop. 6,277
Catasauqua Area SD 1,500/K-12
201 N 14th St 18032 610-264-5571
Robert Spengler, supt. Fax 264-5618
www.cattysd.org
Catasauqua MS 500/5-8
850 Pine St 18032 610-264-4341
Melissa Inselmann, prin. Fax 264-5458
Other Schools – See Northampton

Catawissa, Columbia, Pop. 1,525
Southern Columbia Area SD 1,400/K-12
800 Southern Dr 17820 570-356-2331
Paul Caputo, supt. Fax 356-2892
www.scasd.us
Southern Columbia Area HS 400/9-12
812 Southern Dr 17820 570-356-3450
James Becker, prin. Fax 356-2835
Southern Columbia Area MS 500/5-8
810 Southern Dr 17820 570-356-3400
Angela Farronato, prin. Fax 356-2835

Center Valley, Lehigh
Southern Lehigh SD 2,900/K-12
5775 Main St 18034 610-282-3121
Dr. Leah M. Christman, supt. Fax 282-0193
www.slsd.org
Southern Lehigh HS 1,100/9-12
5800 Main St Unit 1 18034 610-282-1421
Christine Siegfried, prin. Fax 282-2965
Southern Lehigh MS 500/7-8
3715 Preston Ln 18034 610-282-3700
Dr. Edward Donahue, prin. Fax 282-2963

Achieve Test Prep Post-Sec.
3477 Corporate Pkwy 18034 610-628-0912
DeSales University Post-Sec.
2755 Station Ave 18034 610-282-1100
Penn State Lehigh Valley Post-Sec.
2809 Saucon Valley Rd 18034 610-285-5000

Chalfont, Bucks, Pop. 3,976
Central Bucks SD
Supt. — See Doylestown
Unami MS 900/7-9
160 Moyer Rd 18914 267-893-3400
Christina Lang, prin. Fax 893-5820

Chambersburg, Franklin, Pop. 19,639
Area Vocational Technical School
Supt. — None
Franklin County CTC Vo/Tech
2463 Loop Rd, 717-263-9033
James Duffey, dir. Fax 263-6568

Chambersburg Area SD 8,800/K-12
435 Stanley Ave 17201 717-263-9281
Dr. Joseph Padasak, supt. Fax 261-3321
casdonline.org
Career Magnet S 400/9-12
2459 Loop Rd, 717-261-5656
Mark Long, admin. Fax 261-5658
Chambersburg Area MS North 1,000/6-8
1957 Scotland Ave 17201 717-261-3366
Kurt Widmann, prin. Fax 261-3379

Chambersburg Area MS South — 1,000/6-8
1151 E McKinley St 17201 — 717-261-3385
Melissa Cashdollar, prin. — Fax 261-3401
Chambersburg Area SHS — 2,100/9-12
511 S 6th St 17201 — 717-261-3322
Burdette Chapel, prin. — Fax 263-6532

Cumberland Valley Christian S — 400/PK-12
600 Miller St 17201 — 717-264-3266
Dr. Wilford Rathel, admin. — Fax 264-0416
Montessori Academy of Chambersburg — 100/PK-12
875 Ragged Edge Rd, — 717-261-1110
Michelle D'Antonio, head sch — Fax 267-3626
Shalom Christian Academy — 400/PK-12
126 Social Island Rd, — 717-375-2223
Angie Petersheim, admin. — Fax 375-2224
Wilson College — Post-Sec.
1015 Philadelphia Ave 17201 — 717-264-4141

Charleroi, Washington, Pop. 4,003
Area Vocational Technical School
Supt. — None
Mon Valley CTC — Vo/Tech
5 Guttman Blvd 15022 — 724-489-9581
Neil Henehan, dir. — Fax 489-0711

Charleroi Area SD — 1,600/K-12
125 Fecsen Dr 15022 — 724-483-3509
Edward Zelich, supt. — Fax 483-3776
www.charleroisd.org
Charleroi Area HS — 500/9-12
100 Fecsen Dr 15022 — 724-483-3573
Dr. Patricia Mason, prin. — Fax 483-2294
Charleroi Area MS — 400/6-8
100 Fecsen Dr 15022 — 724-483-3600
Adam Brewer, prin. — Fax 489-9128

Chester, Delaware, Pop. 33,256
Chester-Upland SD — 2,900/PK-12
232 W 9th St 19013 — 610-447-3600
Gregory Shannon M.Ed., supt. — Fax 447-3616
www.chesteruplandsd.org/
Chester HS — 800/9-12
232 W 9th St 19013 — 610-447-3700
Constance McAlister, prin. — Fax 447-3682
STEM at Showalter — 700/7-12
1100 W 10th St 19013 — 610-477-3650
Anthony Womack, prin.
Other Schools – See Brookhaven

Widener University — Post-Sec.
1 University Pl 19013 — 610-499-4000

Cheswick, Allegheny, Pop. 1,738
Allegheny Valley SD — 1,000/K-12
300 Pearl Ave 15024 — 724-274-5300
Patrick M. Graczyk, supt. — Fax 274-8040
www.avsdweb.org
Other Schools – See Springdale

Deer Lakes SD — 2,000/K-12
19 E Union Rd 15024 — 724-265-5300
Dr. Janell Logue-Belden, supt. — Fax 265-5025
www.deerlakes.net
Deer Lakes HS — 600/9-12
163 E Union Rd 15024 — 724-265-5320
Pat Baughman, prin. — Fax 265-3970
Deer Lakes MS — 400/6-8
17 E Union Rd 15024 — 724-265-5310
David Campos, prin. — Fax 265-3711

Cheswick Christian Academy — 200/K-12
1407 Pittsburgh St 15024 — 724-274-4846

Cheyney, Delaware

Cheyney University of Pennsylvania — Post-Sec.
PO Box 200 19319 — 610-399-2275

Clairton, Allegheny, Pop. 6,590
Clairton CSD — 800/K-12
502 Mitchell Ave 15025 — 412-233-7090
Dr. Ginny Hunt, supt. — Fax 233-4755
www.ccsdbears.org
Clairton MSHS — 400/6-12
501 Waddell Ave 15025 — 412-233-9200
Thomas McCloskey, prin. — Fax 233-3243

Clarion, Clarion, Pop. 5,178
Clarion Area SD — 800/K-12
221 Liberty St 16214 — 814-226-6110
Dr. Michael Stahlman, supt. — Fax 226-9292
www.clarion-schools.com
Clarion Area JSHS — 400/7-12
219 Liberty St 16214 — 814-226-8112
John Kimmel, prin. — Fax 226-9004

Clarion University of Pennsylvania — Post-Sec.
840 Wood St 16214 — 814-393-2000

Clarks Green, Lackawanna, Pop. 1,470

Abington Christian Academy — 100/PK-12
413 Layton Rd 18411 — 570-586-5270
Janet Wells M.Ed., admin. — Fax 587-4648

Clarks Summit, Lackawanna, Pop. 5,073
Abington Heights SD — 3,300/K-12
200 E Grove St 18411 — 570-586-2511
Michael Mahon, supt. — Fax 586-1756
www.ahsd.org
Abington Heights HS — 1,100/9-12
222 Noble Rd 18411 — 570-585-5300
Dr. Pamela Murray, prin. — Fax 586-9093
Abington Heights MS — 1,000/5-8
1555 Newton Ransom Blvd 18411 — 570-586-1281
Dr. Michael Elia, prin. — Fax 586-6361

Baptist Bible College and Seminary — Post-Sec.
538 Venard Rd 18411 — 570-586-2400

Claysburg, Blair, Pop. 1,606
Claysburg-Kimmel SD — 900/K-12
531 Bedford St 16625 — 814-239-5141
Royce Boyd, supt. — Fax 239-5896
www.cksdbulldogs.com
Claysburg-Kimmel JSHS — 400/7-12
531 Bedford St 16625 — 814-239-5141
Stephen Puskar, prin. — Fax 239-8949

Claysville, Washington, Pop. 815
McGuffey SD — 1,800/K-12
90 McGuffey Dr 15323 — 724-948-3731
Dr. Erica Kolat, supt. — Fax 948-3769
www.mcguffey.k12.pa.us
McGuffey HS — 600/9-12
86 McGuffey Dr 15323 — 724-948-3328
Mark Bonus, prin. — Fax 948-3344
McGuffey MS — 400/6-8
86 McGuffey Dr 15323 — 724-948-3323
Michael Wilson, prin. — Fax 948-2413

Clearfield, Clearfield, Pop. 6,141
Area Vocational Technical School
Supt. — None
Clearfield County CTC — Vo/Tech
1620 River Rd 16830 — 814-765-5308
Elizabeth Frankhouser, dir. — Fax 765-5474

Clearfield Area SD — 1,400/K-12
PO Box 710 16830 — 814-765-5511
Terry Struble, supt. — Fax 765-5515
www.clearfield.org
Clearfield Area JSHS — 800/7-12
PO Box 910 16830 — 814-765-2401
Tim Janocko, prin. — Fax 765-2405

Clearfield Alliance Christian S — 200/K-12
56 Alliance Rd 16830 — 814-765-0216
Victoria Albert, prin. — Fax 765-8846
Clearfield Beauty Academy — Post-Sec.
22 N 3rd St 16830 — 814-765-2022
Clearfield Hospital — Post-Sec.
PO Box 992 16830 — 814-768-2496
Lock Haven University-Clearfield Campus — Post-Sec.
201 University Dr 16830 — 814-768-3405

Clymer, Indiana, Pop. 1,351
Penns Manor Area SD — 800/PK-12
6003 Route 553 Hwy 15728 — 724-254-2666
Daren Johnston, supt. — Fax 254-3418
www.pennsmanor.org
Penns Manor Area JSHS — 400/6-12
6003 Route 553 Hwy 15728 — 724-254-2666
Michelle Dolges, prin. — Fax 254-3417

Coal Center, Washington, Pop. 134
California Area SD — 800/K-12
11 Trojan Way Ste 100 15423 — 724-785-5800
Michael S. Sears, supt. — Fax 785-4866
www.calsd.org/
California Area HS — 300/9-12
11 Trojan Way 15423 — 724-785-5800
Leigh Ann Folmar, prin. — Fax 785-8860
California Area MS — 200/5-8
40 Trojan Way 15423 — 724-785-5800
Raymond Huffman, prin. — Fax 785-5458

Coal Township, Northumberland, Pop. 9,922
Area Vocational Technical School
Supt. — None
Northumberland County AVTS — Vo/Tech
1700 W Montgomery St 17866 — 570-644-0304
James Monaghan, admin.

Shamokin Area SD — 1,600/PK-12
2000 W State St 17866 — 570-648-5752
James Zack, supt. — Fax 648-2592
www.indians.k12.pa.us/
Shamokin Area JSHS — 700/7-12
2000 W State St 17866 — 570-648-5731
Chris Venna, prin.

Our Lady of Lourdes Regional S — 300/PK-12
2001 Clinton Ave 17866 — 570-644-0375
Martin McCarthy, admin. — Fax 644-7655

Coatesville, Chester, Pop. 12,560
Coatesville Area SD
Supt. — See Thorndale
Coatesville Area 9-10 Center — 1,200/9-10
1425 E Lincoln Hwy 19320 — 610-383-3735
Brian Chenger, prin. — Fax 383-3723
Coatesville Area SHS — 1,000/11-12
1445 E Lincoln Hwy 19320 — 610-383-3730
Robert Fisher, prin. — Fax 383-3725
North Brandywine MS — 500/6-8
256 Reeceville Rd 19320 — 610-383-3745
Chamise Taylor, prin. — Fax 383-3749
Scott MS — 500/6-8
800 Olive St 19320 — 610-383-6946
Dr. Denise Ray, prin. — Fax 383-7110
South Brandywine MS — 700/6-8
600 Doe Run Rd 19320 — 610-383-3750
Michelle Snyder, prin. — Fax 383-3754

Brandywine Hospital — Post-Sec.
201 Reeceville Rd 19320 — 610-383-9000

Cochranton, Crawford, Pop. 1,126
Crawford Central SD
Supt. — See Meadville
Cochranton JSHS — 500/7-12
PO Box 127 16314 — 814-425-7421
Donald Wigton, prin. — Fax 425-2071

Collegeville, Montgomery, Pop. 4,996
Perkiomen Valley SD — 5,800/K-12
3 Iron Bridge Dr 19426 — 610-489-8506
Dr. Clifford Rogers, supt. — Fax 489-2974
www.pvsd.org
Perkiomen Valley East MS — 800/6-8
100 Kagey Rd 19426 — 610-409-8580
Dr. Seamus Clune, prin. — Fax 489-8851
Perkiomen Valley HS — 1,800/9-12
509 Gravel Pike 19426 — 610-489-1230
Cyndi Lewis, prin. — Fax 489-1921
Other Schools – See Zieglerville

Ursinus College — Post-Sec.
PO Box 1000 19426 — 610-409-3000
Valley Forge Baptist Academy — 200/K-12
616 S Trappe Rd 19426 — 610-792-1884
Lois Rall, admin. — Fax 948-6423

Columbia, Lancaster, Pop. 10,150
Columbia Borough SD — 1,000/K-12
200 N 5th St 17512 — 717-684-2283
Dr. Carol Powell, supt. — Fax 681-2220
www.columbia.k12.pa.us
Columbia HS — 300/9-12
901 Ironville Pike 17512 — 717-684-7500
Maura Meiser, prin. — Fax 681-2219
Columbia MS Hill Campus — 7-8
901 Ironville Pike 17512 — 717-684-7500
Jodie Parkinson, prin.

Commodore, Indiana, Pop. 325
Purchase Line SD — 1,000/K-12
16559 Route 286 Hwy E 15729 — 724-254-4312
Joseph Bradley, supt. — Fax 254-1621
www.plsd.k12.pa.us/
Purchase Line JSHS — 500/7-12
16559 Route 286 Hwy E 15729 — 724-254-4312
James Price, prin. — Fax 254-2306

Confluence, Somerset, Pop. 758
Turkeyfoot Valley Area SD — 400/K-12
172 Turkeyfoot Rd 15424 — 814-395-3621
Jeffrey Malaspino, supt. — Fax 395-3366
www.turkeyfoot.k12.pa.us
Turkeyfoot Valley Area JSHS — 200/7-12
172 Turkeyfoot Rd 15424 — 814-395-3622
Richard Berkley, prin. — Fax 395-3366

Conneaut Lake, Crawford, Pop. 646
Conneaut SD
Supt. — See Linesville
Conneaut Lake MS — 100/5-8
10331 US Highway 6 16316 — 814-382-5315
Joel Wentling, prin. — Fax 382-0165

Conneautville, Crawford, Pop. 765
Conneaut SD
Supt. — See Linesville
Conneaut Valley MS — 100/5-8
22154 State Highway 18 16406 — 814-587-2091
Kevin Burns, prin. — Fax 587-2094

Connellsville, Fayette, Pop. 7,510
Area Vocational Technical School
Supt. — None
Connellsville Area CTC — Vo/Tech
720 Locust St 15425 — 724-626-0236
Kevin O'Donnell, dir.

Connellsville Area SD — 4,400/K-12
732 Rockridge Rd 15425 — 724-628-3300
Philip Martell, supt. — Fax 628-9002
www.casdfalcons.org
Connellsville Area HS — 1,200/9-12
201 Falcon Dr 15425 — 724-628-1350
Nicholas Bosnic, prin. — Fax 628-0280
Connellsville JHS — 800/7-8
710 Locust St 15425 — 724-628-8910
Charles Michael, prin. — Fax 628-9293

Geibel Catholic JSHS — 200/7-12
611 E Crawford Ave 15425 — 724-628-5600
Patricia Nickler, prin. — Fax 626-5700

Coraopolis, Allegheny, Pop. 5,475
Cornell SD — 600/K-12
1099 Maple Street Ext 15108 — 412-264-5010
Aaron Thomas, supt. — Fax 264-1445
www.cornell.k12.pa.us
Cornell JSHS — 300/7-12
1099 Maple Street Ext 15108 — 412-264-5010
Doug Szokoly, prin. — Fax 264-1445

Montour SD
Supt. — See Mc Kees Rocks
Williams MS — 900/5-8
Porters Hollow Rd 15108 — 412-771-8802
Dominic Salpeck, prin. — Fax 771-3772

Our Lady of Sacred Heart HS — 400/9-12
1504 Woodcrest Ave 15108 — 412-264-5140
Tim Plocinik, prin. — Fax 264-4143

Corry, Erie, Pop. 6,515
Corry Area SD — 1,400/PK-12
540 E Pleasant St 16407 — 814-664-4677
Fax 664-9645
www.corrysd.net
Career & Technical Center — Vo/Tech
534 E Pleasant St 16407 — 814-664-4677
Susan Barra, dir. — Fax 663-0722
Corry Area HS — 700/9-12
534 E Pleasant St 16407 — 814-665-8297
Kelly Cragg, prin. — Fax 664-3650
Corry Area MS — 300/6-8
534 E Pleasant St 16407 — 814-665-8297
Gail Swank, prin. — Fax 664-3650

Coudersport, Potter, Pop. 2,519
Coudersport Area SD — 800/K-12
698 Dwight St 16915 — 814-274-9480
Stephen M. Mongillo, supt. — Fax 274-7551
www.coudyschools.net
Coudersport Area JSHS — 400/7-12
698 Dwight St 16915 — 814-274-8500
Steve Mongillo, prin. — Fax 274-8053

Cranberry Township, Butler

Cardinal Wuerl North Catholic HS 200/9-12
1617 Route 228 16066 412-321-4823
Luke Crawford, prin. Fax 776-2287

Cresson, Cambria, Pop. 1,702
Penn Cambria SD 1,700/PK-12
201 6th St 16630 814-886-8121
William Marshall, supt. Fax 886-4809
www.pcam.org
Penn Cambria HS 500/9-12
401 Linden Ave 16630 814-886-8188
James Abbott, prin. Fax 884-3977
Other Schools – See Gallitzin

Mount Aloysius College Post-Sec.
7373 Admiral Peary Hwy 16630 814-886-4131

Curwensville, Clearfield, Pop. 2,529
Curwensville Area SD 1,100/K-12
650 Beech St 16833 814-236-1101
Ronald Matchock, supt. Fax 236-1103
www.curwensville.org
Curwensville Area JSHS 500/7-12
650 Beech St 16833 814-236-1100
William Hayward, prin. Fax 236-2392

Dallas, Luzerne, Pop. 2,782
Dallas SD 2,700/K-12
PO Box 2000 18612 570-674-7221
Dr. Thomas Duffy, supt. Fax 674-7295
www.dallassd.com/
Dallas HS 900/9-12
PO Box 2000 18612 570-674-7230
Jason Rushmer, prin. Fax 674-6843
Dallas MS 700/6-8
PO Box 2000 18612 570-674-7245
Jeffrey Shaffer, prin. Fax 674-7219

Lake-Lehman SD 1,900/K-12
1237 Market St 18612 570-675-2165
James McGovern, supt. Fax 675-7657
www.lake-lehman.k12.pa.us
Other Schools – See Lehman

Misericordia University Post-Sec.
301 Lake St 18612 570-674-6400

Dallastown, York, Pop. 3,985
Dallastown Area SD 6,000/K-12
700 New School Ln 17313 717-244-4021
Dr. Ronald Dyer, supt. Fax 894-0583
www.dallastown.net
Dallastown Area HS 1,800/9-12
700 New School Ln 17313 717-244-4021
Dr. Kevin Duckworth, prin. Fax 223-7505
Dallastown Area MS 1,000/7-8
700 New School Ln 17313 717-244-4021
Chad Bumsted, prin. Fax 233-9796

Danville, Montour, Pop. 4,646
Danville Area SD 2,300/K-12
600 Walnut St 17821 570-271-3268
Cheryl Latorre, supt. Fax 275-7712
www.danville.k12.pa.us
Danville Area HS 600/9-12
600 Walnut St 17821 570-271-3268
Chris Johns, prin. Fax 275-5463
Danville Area MS 500/6-8
120 Northumberland St 17821 570-271-3268
Charles Smargiassi, prin. Fax 284-4943

Geisinger Medical Center Post-Sec.
100 N Academy Ave 17822 570-271-5200

Darby, Delaware, Pop. 10,364
William Penn SD
Supt. — See Lansdowne
Penn Wood MS 800/7-8
121 Summit St 19023 610-586-1804
Brian Wilson, prin. Fax 586-7372

Davidsville, Somerset, Pop. 1,129
Conemaugh Township Area SD 1,000/K-12
PO Box 407 15928 814-479-7575
Thomas Kakabar, supt. Fax 479-2620
www.ctasd.org
Conemaugh Township Area MSHS 500/6-12
PO Box 407 15928 814-479-4014
James Foster, prin. Fax 479-2038

Denver, Lancaster, Pop. 3,812
Cocalico SD 3,100/PK-12
PO Box 800 17517 717-336-1413
Dr. Bruce Sensenig, supt. Fax 336-1415
www.cocalico.org/
Cocalico HS 1,000/9-12
PO Box 800 17517 717-336-1423
Christopher Irvine, prin. Fax 336-1418
Cocalico MS 700/6-8
PO Box 800 17517 717-336-1471
Dr. Stephen Melnyk, prin. Fax 336-1482

Gehmans Mennonite S 100/K-12
650 Gehman School Rd 17517 717-484-4222
Michael Burkholder, prin. Fax 484-4222

Derry, Westmoreland, Pop. 2,670
Derry Area SD 2,200/K-12
982 N Chestnut Street Ext 15627 724-694-1401
Cheryl Walters, supt. Fax 694-1429
derryasd.schoolwires.com/Page/1
Derry Area HS 700/9-12
988 N Chestnut Street Ext 15627 724-694-2780
Gregory Ferencak, prin. Fax 694-1482
Derry Area MS 500/6-8
994 N Chestnut Street Ext 15627 724-694-8231
Lisa Dubich, prin. Fax 694-0288

Devon, Chester, Pop. 1,486

Devon Preparatory S 300/6-12
363 N Valley Forge Rd 19333 610-688-7337
Francisco Aisa, hdmstr. Fax 688-2409

Dickson City, Lackawanna, Pop. 5,996

McCann School of Business & Technology Post-Sec.
2227 Scranton Carbondale 18519 570-969-4330

Dillsburg, York, Pop. 2,514
Northern York County SD 3,100/K-12
149 S Baltimore St 17019 717-432-8691
Dr. Eric Eshbach, supt. Fax 432-1421
www.northernpolarbears.com
Northern HS 1,000/9-12
653 S Baltimore St 17019 717-432-8691
Matthew LaBuda, prin. Fax 432-0375
Northern MS 700/6-8
655 S Baltimore St 17019 717-432-8691
Sylvia Murray, prin. Fax 432-5889

Dingmans Ferry, Pike
Delaware Valley SD
Supt. — See Milford
Dingman-Delaware MS 700/6-8
1365 Route 739 18328 570-296-3140
James Mitchell, prin. Fax 296-3170

East Stroudsburg Area SD
Supt. — See East Stroudsburg
East Stroudsburg HS North 1,100/9-12
279 Timberwolf Dr 18328 570-588-4420
Stephen Zall, prin. Fax 588-4421
Lehman IS 800/6-8
257 Timberwolf Dr 18328 570-588-4410
Robert Dilliplane, prin. Fax 588-4411

Donegal, Westmoreland, Pop. 120

Champion Christian S 100/PK-PK, 5-
1076 Kings Way 15628 724-593-9200
Dr. D. Merle Skinner, dir. Fax 593-9210

Douglassville, Berks, Pop. 444
Daniel Boone Area SD 2,900/K-12
2144 Weavertown Rd 19518 610-582-6140
Dr. Robert Hurley, supt. Fax 689-6215
www.dboone.org
Boone Area MS 900/6-8
1845 Weavertown Rd 19518 610-689-6300
Jenny Rexrode, prin. Fax 689-6306
Other Schools – See Birdsboro

Dover, York, Pop. 1,967
Dover Area SD 3,500/K-12
101 Edgeway Rd 17315 717-292-3671
Ken Cherry, supt. Fax 292-9659
www.doversd.org/
Dover Area HS 1,000/9-12
46 W Canal St 17315 717-292-8066
William Rickard, prin. Fax 292-7303
Dover Area IS 600/7-8
4500 Intermediate Ave 17315 717-292-8067
Dr. Philip Livelsberger, prin. Fax 292-9849

Downingtown, Chester, Pop. 7,678
Area Vocational Technical School
Supt. — None
Technical College HS - Brandywine Campus Vo/Tech
443 Boot Rd 19335 484-593-5100
Seth Schram, prin.

Downingtown Area SD 11,100/K-12
540 Trestle Pl 19335 610-269-8460
Lawrence Mussoline Ph.D., supt. Fax 873-1404
www.dasd.org
Downingtown HS - West Campus 1,500/9-12
445 Manor Ave 19335 610-269-4400
Kurt Barker, prin. Fax 269-1801
Downingtown MS 900/7-8
115 Rock Raymond Rd 19335 610-518-0685
Dr. Nick Indeglio, prin. Fax 518-0685
Downingtown STEM Academy 800/9-12
335 Manor Ave 19335 610-269-8460
Arthur Campbell, prin.
Other Schools – See Exton

Bishop Shanahan HS 1,200/9-12
220 Woodbine Rd 19335 610-518-1300
Michael McCardle, prin. Fax 343-6220

Doylestown, Bucks, Pop. 8,255
Central Bucks SD 19,600/K-12
20 Weldon Dr 18901 267-893-2000
Dr. David Weitzel, supt. Fax 893-5800
www.cbsd.org
Central Bucks SHS - East 1,600/10-12
2804 Holicong Rd, 267-893-2300
Abram Lucabaugh, prin. Fax 794-5446
Central Bucks SHS - West 1,500/10-12
375 W Court St 18901 267-893-2500
Jason Bucher, prin. Fax 348-9832
Holicong MS 1,200/7-9
2900 Holicong Rd, 267-893-2700
Kevin Shillingford, prin. Fax 893-5816
Lenape MS 900/7-9
313 W State St 18901 267-893-2800
Timothy Donovan, prin. Fax 345-4699
Tohickon MS 1,000/7-9
5051 Old Easton Rd, 267-893-3300
Kevin Marton, prin. Fax 893-5819
Other Schools – See Chalfont, Warrington

Delaware Valley College Post-Sec.
700 E Butler Ave 18901 215-345-1500

Dresher, Montgomery
Upper Dublin SD
Supt. — See Maple Glen

Sandy Run MS 1,000/6-8
520 Twining Rd 19025 215-576-3280
Dr. Jill Clark, prin. Fax 572-3886

Drexel Hill, Delaware, Pop. 27,609
Upper Darby SD 12,200/K-12
4611 Bond Ave 19026 610-789-7200
Dr. Richard Dunlap, supt. Fax 789-8671
www.upperdarbysd.org
Drexel Hill MS, 3001 State Rd 19026 1,300/6-8
Frank Salerno, prin. 610-853-4580
Upper Darby HS 3,600/9-12
601 N Lansdowne Ave 19026 610-622-7000
Edward Roth, prin. Fax 622-7844
Other Schools – See Upper Darby

Bonner/Prendergast HS 1,300/9-12
403 N Lansdowne Ave 19026 610-259-0280
Dr. Tracey Rush, prin. Fax 259-1630

Du Bois, Clearfield, Pop. 7,711
Du Bois Area SD 3,800/K-12
500 Liberty Blvd 15801 814-371-2700
J. Mark Heckman, supt. Fax 371-2544
www.dasd.k12.pa.us
Du Bois Area HS 1,100/9-12
425 Orient Ave 15801 814-371-8111
Jeffrey Vizza, prin. Fax 371-3928
Du Bois Area MS 900/6-8
404 Liberty Blvd 15801 814-375-8770
Wendy Benton, prin. Fax 375-8775

Du Bois Area Catholic HS 200/9-12
PO Box 567 15801 814-371-3060
Dawn Bressler, prin. Fax 371-3215
Du Bois Area Catholic MS 100/6-8
PO Box 567 15801 814-371-3060
Dawn Bressler, prin. Fax 371-3215
DuBois Business College Post-Sec.
1 Beaver Dr 15801 814-371-6920
DuBois Christian S 100/PK-12
197 Eastern Ave 15801 814-371-7395
Mark Montgomery M.Ed., admin. Fax 371-7399
Penn State Du Bois Post-Sec.
1 College Place 15801 814-375-4700
PA Academy of Cosmetic Arts & Sciences Post-Sec.
19 N Brady St 15801 814-371-4151
Triangle Tech Post-Sec.
PO Box 551 15801 814-371-2090

Duke Center, McKean
Otto-Eldred SD 700/PK-12
143 Sweitzer Dr 16729 814-817-1380
Matthew D. Splain, supt. Fax 966-3911
www.ottoeldred.org
Otto-Eldred JSHS 300/7-12
143 Sweitzer Dr 16729 814-817-1380
Harley D. Ramsey, prin. Fax 966-3911

Duncannon, Perry, Pop. 1,503
Susquenita SD 1,700/K-12
1725 Schoolhouse Rd 17020 717-957-6000
Kent R. Smith, supt. Fax 957-2463
www.susq.k12.pa.us/
Susquenita HS 500/9-12
309 Schoolhouse Rd 17020 717-957-6000
Craig Funk, prin. Fax 957-1792
Susquenita MS 500/5-8
200 Susquenita Dr 17020 717-957-6000
William Quigley, prin. Fax 957-6022

Dunmore, Lackawanna, Pop. 13,930
Dunmore SD 1,600/K-12
300 W Warren St 18512 570-343-2110
Richard McDonald, supt. Fax 343-1458
www.dunmoreschooldistrict.net/
Dunmore HS 500/9-12
300 W Warren St 18512 570-346-2043
Matthew Quinn, prin. Fax 343-5923
Dunmore MS 300/7-8
300 W Warren St 18512 570-207-9590
Matthew Quinn, prin. Fax 346-5923

Holy Cross HS 500/9-12
501 E Drinker St 18512 570-346-7541
Ben Tolerico, prin. Fax 348-1070
Penn State Worthington Scranton Post-Sec.
120 Ridgeview Dr 18512 570-963-2500

Eagleville, Montgomery, Pop. 4,719
Methacton SD 5,000/K-12
1001 Kriebel Mill Rd 19403 610-489-5000
Dr. David Zerbe, supt. Fax 489-5019
www.methacton.org
Arcola IS 800/7-8
4001 Eagleville Rd Ste A 19403 610-489-5000
Amy Mangano, prin. Fax 831-5317
Methacton HS 1,700/9-12
1005 Kriebel Mill Rd 19403 610-489-5000
Judith Landis, prin. Fax 489-8165

East Greenville, Montgomery, Pop. 2,902
Upper Perkiomen SD
Supt. — See Pennsburg
Upper Perkiomen MS 700/6-8
510 Jefferson St 18041 215-679-6288
Duane Wickard, prin. Fax 679-3091

Easton, Northampton, Pop. 25,861
Area Vocational Technical School
Supt. — None
Career Institute of Technology Vo/Tech
5335 Kesslersville Rd 18040 610-258-2857
Dr. Ronald Roth, dir.

Easton Area SD 8,700/K-12
1801 Bushkill Dr 18040 610-250-2400
John Reinhart, supt. Fax 923-8954
www.eastonsd.org
Easton Area Academy Alt
2035 Edgewood Ave 18045 610-829-5700
Kyle Geiger, dean Fax 829-5708
Easton Area HS 2,600/9-12
2601 William Penn Hwy 18045 610-250-2481
Michael Koch, prin. Fax 250-2483
Easton Area MS 7/8 1,300/7-8
1010 Echo Trl 18040 610-250-2460
Dr. Charlene Symia, prin. Fax 250-2613

Wilson Area SD 2,200/K-12
2040 Washington Blvd 18042 484-373-6000
Douglas Wagner, supt. Fax 258-6421
www.wilsonareasd.org
Wilson Area HS 700/9-12
424 Warrior Ln 18042 484-373-6030
John Martuscelli, prin. Fax 258-8831
Wilson Area IS 700/5-8
2400 Firmstone St 18042 484-373-6110
Anthony Tarsi, prin. Fax 258-4014

Bethlehem Christian S Calvary Campus 50/5-8
5300 Green Pond Rd 18045 610-365-8176
Carol Aversa, prin. Fax 365-8407
Lafayette College Post-Sec.
730 High St 18042 610-330-5000
Notre Dame HS 600/9-12
3417 Church Rd 18045 610-868-1431
Mario Lucrezi, prin. Fax 868-6710

East Stroudsburg, Monroe, Pop. 9,606
East Stroudsburg Area SD 7,300/K-12
50 Vine St 18301 570-424-8500
Dr. William Riker, supt. Fax 424-5646
www.esasd.net
East Stroudsburg HS South 1,400/9-12
279 N Courtland St 18301 570-424-8471
Michael Catrillo, prin. Fax 420-8338
Lambert IS 1,000/6-8
2000 Milford Rd 18301 570-424-8430
Heather Piperato, prin. Fax 476-0464
Other Schools – See Dingmans Ferry

East Stroudsburg University of PA Post-Sec.
200 Prospect St 18301 570-422-3211
Notre Dame HS 200/6-12
60 Spangenburg Ave 18301 570-421-0466
Jeffrey Lyons, prin. Fax 476-0629

Ebensburg, Cambria, Pop. 3,337
Area Vocational Technical School
Supt. — None
Admiral Peary AVTS Vo/Tech
948 Ben Franklin Hwy 15931 814-472-6490
Ken Jubas, dir. Fax 472-6494

Central Cambria SD 1,700/K-12
208 Schoolhouse Rd 15931 814-472-8870
Vincent DiLeo Ed.D., supt. Fax 472-9695
www.cencam.org
Central Cambria HS 500/9-12
204 Schoolhouse Rd 15931 814-472-8860
Kimberly McDermott, prin. Fax 472-8886
Central Cambria MS 400/6-8
206 Schoolhouse Rd 15931 814-472-6505
Christopher Santini, prin. Fax 472-4187

Bishop Carroll Catholic HS 200/9-12
728 Ben Franklin Hwy 15931 814-472-7500
Lorie Ratchford, prin. Fax 472-8020
Pennsylvania Institute of Taxidermy Post-Sec.
118 Industrial Park Rd 15931 814-472-4510

Edinboro, Erie, Pop. 6,330
General McLane SD 2,200/K-12
11771 Edinboro Rd 16412 814-273-1033
Richard Scaletta, supt. Fax 273-1030
www.generalmclane.org
McLane HS 800/9-12
11761 Edinboro Rd 16412 814-273-1033
Daniel Mennow, prin. Fax 273-1035
Parker MS 700/5-8
11781 Edinboro Rd 16412 814-273-1033
John Hansen, prin. Fax 273-1038

Edinboro University of Pennsylvania Post-Sec.
219 Meadville St 16444 814-732-2000

Elizabeth, Allegheny, Pop. 1,455
Elizabeth Forward SD 2,300/K-12
401 Rock Run Rd 15037 412-896-2312
Dr. Bart Rocco, supt. Fax 751-9483
www.efsd.net
Elizabeth Forward HS 800/9-12
1000 Weigles Hill Rd 15037 412-896-2349
Michael Routh, prin. Fax 384-2030
Elizabeth Forward MS 600/6-8
401 Rock Run Rd 15037 412-896-2335
Trisha Martell, prin. Fax 751-6669

Elizabethtown, Lancaster, Pop. 11,397
Elizabethtown Area SD 3,900/K-12
600 E High St 17022 717-367-1521
Dr. Michele Balliet, supt. Fax 367-1920
www.etownschools.org
Elizabethtown Area HS 1,200/9-12
600 E High St 17022 717-367-1533
Daniel Serfass, prin. Fax 367-4149
Elizabethtown Area MS 600/7-8
600 E High St 17022 717-361-7525
Dr. Nathan Frank, prin. Fax 361-2597

Elizabethtown College Post-Sec.
1 Alpha Dr 17022 717-361-1000

Mt. Calvary Christian S 300/PK-12
629 Holly St 17022 717-367-1649
Dr. Daniel Sheard, hdmstr. Fax 367-5672

Elizabethville, Dauphin, Pop. 1,493
Upper Dauphin Area SD
Supt. — See Lykens
Upper Dauphin Area HS 400/9-12
220 N Church St 17023 717-362-8181
Dermot Garrett, prin. Fax 362-8088

Elkins Park, Montgomery, Pop. 4,700
Cheltenham Township SD 4,600/K-12
2000 Ashbourne Rd 19027 215-886-9500
Dr. Wagner Marseille, supt. Fax 884-3029
www.cheltenham.org
Other Schools – See Philadelphia, Wyncote

Medical College Hospitals Post-Sec.
60 Township Line Rd 19027 215-663-6150
Salus University Post-Sec.
8360 Old York Rd 19027 215-780-1400

Elkland, Tioga, Pop. 1,798
Northern Tioga SD 2,100/K-12
110 Ellison Rd 16920 814-258-5642
Dr. Diane Barnes, supt. Fax 258-7083
www.ntiogasd.org
Other Schools – See Tioga, Westfield

Elliottsburg, Perry
West Perry SD 2,500/PK-12
2606 Shermans Valley Rd 17024 717-789-3934
Dr. Michael O'Brien, supt. Fax 789-4997
www.westperry.org
West Perry HS 800/9-12
2608 Shermans Valley Rd 17024 717-789-3931
Christopher Rahn, prin. Fax 789-2110
West Perry MS 600/6-8
2620 Shermans Valley Rd 17024 717-789-3012
Renee LeDonne, prin. Fax 789-3393

Ellwood City, Lawrence, Pop. 7,833
Ellwood City Area SD 1,800/K-12
501 Crescent Ave 16117 724-752-1591
Joseph Mancini, supt. Fax 752-8556
www.ellwood.k12.pa.us
Lincoln JSHS 900/7-12
501 Crescent Ave 16117 724-752-1591
Kirk Lape, prin. Fax 752-8556

Riverside Beaver County SD 1,500/PK-12
318 Country Club Dr 16117 724-758-7512
Dr. David Anney, supt. Fax 758-2070
www.riverside.k12.pa.us
Riverside HS 500/9-12
300 Country Club Dr 16117 724-758-7512
Michael Brooks, prin. Fax 758-7519
Riverside MS 400/6-8
302 Country Club Dr 16117 724-758-7512
Alicia Dwyer, prin. Fax 758-0919

Elverson, Chester, Pop. 1,218
Twin Valley SD 3,400/K-12
4851 N Twin Valley Rd 19520 610-286-8611
Dr. Robert Pleis, supt. Fax 286-8608
www.tvsd.org
Twin Valley HS 1,000/9-12
4897 N Twin Valley Rd 19520 610-286-8600
William Clements, prin. Fax 286-8604
Twin Valley MS 1,100/5-8
770 Clymer Hill Rd 19520 610-286-8660
Dr. Gerald Catagnus, prin. Fax 286-8662

Emmaus, Lehigh, Pop. 11,070
East Penn SD 8,100/K-12
800 Pine St 18049 610-966-8300
Michael Schilder Ed.D., supt. Fax 966-8339
new.eastpennsd.org
Emmaus HS 2,600/9-12
500 N Macungie St 18049 610-966-1651
David Piperato, prin.
Other Schools – See Macungie

Emporium, Cameron, Pop. 2,061
Cameron County SD 600/K-12
601 Woodland Ave 15834 814-486-4000
Dr. Keith Wolfe, supt. Fax 486-4006
www.camcosd.org
Cameron County JSHS 300/7-12
601 Woodland Ave 15834 814-486-4000
Amy Schwab, prin. Fax 486-4003

Emsworth, Allegheny, Pop. 2,403

Holy Family Academy 9-12
8235 Ohio River Blvd 15202 412-307-0230
Lisa Abel-Palmieri, head sch

Enola, Cumberland, Pop. 5,946
East Pennsboro Area SD 2,700/K-12
890 Valley St 17025 717-732-3601
Dr. Jay Burkhart, supt. Fax 732-8927
www.epasd.k12.pa.us
East Pennsboro Area HS 800/9-12
425 W Shady Ln 17025 717-732-0723
Craig Robbins, prin. Fax 732-8932
East Pennsboro Area MS 900/5-8
529 N Enola Dr 17025 717-732-0771
Michael Sim, prin. Fax 732-8948

Ephrata, Lancaster, Pop. 13,209
Ephrata Area SD 4,200/K-12
803 Oak Blvd 17522 717-721-1400
Dr. Brian Troop, supt. Fax 721-1514
www.easdpa.org
Ephrata HS 1,300/9-12
803 Oak Blvd 17522 717-721-1478
Scott Galen, prin. Fax 721-1129
Ephrata MS 600/7-8
957 Hammon Ave 17522 717-721-1468
Kevin Deemer, prin. Fax 721-1469

Ephrata Mennonite S 200/K-10
598 Stevens Rd 17522 717-738-4266
Joshua Good, prin. Fax 738-1644
Pleasant Valley Mennonite S 100/K-12
144 Pleasant Valley Rd 17522 717-738-1833
Larry Weaver, prin. Fax 738-3941

Erdenheim, Montgomery
Springfield Township SD
Supt. — See Oreland
Springfield Township HS 600/9-12
1801 Paper Mill Rd 19038 215-233-6030
Dr. Charles Rittenhouse, prin. Fax 233-0691

Antonelli Institute Post-Sec.
300 Montgomery Ave 19038 215-836-2222
Philadelphia-Montgomery Christian Acad 300/K-12
35 Hillcrest Rd 19038 215-233-0782
Donald Beebe, hdmstr. Fax 233-0829

Erie, Erie, Pop. 98,321
Area Vocational Technical School
Supt. — None
Erie County Technical S Vo/Tech
8500 Oliver Rd 16509 814-464-8600
Joseph Tarasovich, prin. Fax 464-8625

Erie CSD 11,700/PK-12
148 W 21st St 16502 814-874-6000
Dr. Jay Badams, supt. Fax 874-6010
eriesd.org
Central Career and Technical S Vo/Tech
3325 Cherry St 16508 814-874-6200
Pamela Mackowski, prin. Fax 874-6207
East HS 1,000/9-12
1001 Atkins St 16503 814-874-6400
Jill Crable, prin. Fax 874-6407
Northwest Pennsylvania Collegiate Acad 800/9-12
2825 State St 16508 814-874-6300
James Vieira, dean Fax 874-6307
Roosevelt MS 600/6-8
3325 Cherry St 16508 814-874-6800
Teresa Szumigala, prin. Fax 874-6807
Vincent HS 700/9-12
1330 W 8th St 16502 814-874-6500
Scherry Prater, prin. Fax 874-6507
Wilson MS 800/6-8
718 E 28th St 16504 814-874-6600
Donald Orlando, prin. Fax 874-6607

Iroquois SD, 800 Tyndall Ave 16511 1,200/K-12
Shane S. Murray, supt. 814-899-7643
www.iroquoissd.org
Iroquois JSHS 600/7-12
4301 Main St 16511 814-899-7643
Fax 898-4105

Millcreek Township SD 7,200/PK-12
3740 W 26th St 16506 814-835-5300
William Hall, supt. Fax 835-5307
www.mtsd.org
McDowell Intermediate HS 1,200/9-10
3320 Caughey Rd 16506 814-835-5487
Dr. Timothy Stoops, prin. Fax 835-5417
McDowell SHS 1,200/11-12
3580 W 38th St 16506 814-835-5403
Timothy Rankin, prin. Fax 836-6810
Westlake MS 700/PK-PK, 6-
4330 W Lake Rd 16505 814-835-5750
Marty Kaverman, prin. Fax 835-5770
Wilson MS 600/6-8
901 W 54th St 16509 814-835-5500
Terry Costello, prin. Fax 835-5542
Other Schools – See Fairview

Wattsburg Area SD 1,400/K-12
10782 Wattsburg Rd 16509 814-824-3400
Kenneth Berlin, supt. Fax 824-5200
www.wattsburg.org/
Seneca HS 500/9-12
10770 Wattsburg Rd 16509 814-824-3400
Keith Miller, prin. Fax 825-2262
Wattsburg Area MS 400/5-8
10774 Wattsburg Rd 16509 814-824-3400
Christopher Paris, prin. Fax 825-6337

Bethel Christian S of Erie 100/PK-12
1781 W 38th St 16508 814-868-2365
Kathe Gleason, admin. Fax 864-7674
Cathedral Preparatory HS 500/9-12
225 W 9th St 16501 814-453-7737
Jim Smith, prin. Fax 453-6180
Erie Business Center Post-Sec.
246 W 9th St 16501 814-456-7504
Erie First Christian Academy 300/PK-12
8150 Oliver Rd 16509 814-866-6979
John Richardson, supt. Fax 866-5829
Erie Institute of Technology Post-Sec.
940 Millcreek Mall 16565 814-868-9900
Gannon University Post-Sec.
109 University Sq 16541 814-871-7000
Great Lakes Institute of Technology Post-Sec.
5100 Peach St 16509 814-864-6666
Lake Erie College\Osteopathic Medicine Post-Sec.
1858 W Grandview Blvd 16509 814-866-6641
Mercyhurst Prep S 600/9-12
538 E Grandview Blvd 16504 814-824-2210
Deborah Laughlin, prin. Fax 824-3638
Mercyhurst University Post-Sec.
501 E 38th St 16546 814-824-2000
Northwest Regional Technology Institute Post-Sec.
3104 State St 16508 814-455-4446
Penn State Erie The Behrend College Post-Sec.
4701 College Dr 16563 814-898-6000
Toni & Guy Hairdressing Academy Post-Sec.
930 Peach St 16501 800-775-4187
Triangle Tech Post-Sec.
2000 Liberty St 16502 814-453-6016
Tri-State Business Institute Post-Sec.
5757 W 26th St 16506 814-838-7673

Villa Maria Academy 300/9-12
2403 W 8th St 16505 814-838-2061
Brenda Karlinchak, prin. Fax 836-0881

Essington, Delaware

All-State Career School Post-Sec.
50 W Powhattan Ave 19029 610-362-1124

Everett, Bedford, Pop. 1,810
Area Vocational Technical School
Supt. — None
Bedford County Technical Center Vo/Tech
195 Pennknoll Rd 15537 814-623-2760
David DiPasquale, prin. Fax 623-7234

Everett Area SD 1,300/K-12
427 E South St 15537 814-652-9114
Dr. Danny Webb, supt. Fax 652-6191
www.everett.k12.pa.us
Everett Area HS 500/9-12
1 Renaissance Cir 15537 814-652-9114
Christina Ramsey, prin. Fax 652-0107
Everett Area MS 300/6-8
1 Renaissance Cir 15537 814-652-9114
Laurie Criswell, prin. Fax 652-0107

Foundations Christian Academy 50/PK-12
377 Upper Snake Spring Rd 15537 814-623-2840
Amy Will M.A., admin. Fax 623-4864

Exeter, Luzerne, Pop. 5,622
Wyoming Area SD 1,500/K-12
252 Memorial St 18643 570-655-2836
Janet Serino, supt. Fax 883-1280
www.wyomingarea.org
Wyoming Area Secondary Center 1,100/7-12
20 Memorial St 18643 570-655-2836
Vito Quaglia, prin. Fax 883-1280

Exton, Chester, Pop. 4,742
Downingtown Area SD
Supt. — See Downingtown
Downingtown HS - East Campus 1,600/9-12
50 Devon Dr 19341 610-363-6400
Paul Hurley, prin. Fax 903-1047
Lionville MS 1,100/7-8
550 W Uwchlan Ave 19341 610-524-6300
Jonathan Ross, prin. Fax 524-0152

Automotive Training Center Post-Sec.
114 Pickering Way 19341 610-363-6716
Church Farm S 200/7-12
1001 E Lincoln Hwy 19341 610-363-7500
Rev. Edmund Sherrill, head sch Fax 363-5367
Universal Technical Institute Post-Sec.
750 Pennsylvania Dr 19341 877-884-3986

Factoryville, Wyoming, Pop. 1,146
Lackawanna Trail SD 1,100/K-12
PO Box 85 18419 570-945-5184
Matthew Rakauskas, supt. Fax 945-3154
www.ltsd.org
Lackawanna Trail JSHS 500/7-12
PO Box 85 18419 570-945-5181
Dr. Mark Murphy Ph.D., prin. Fax 945-3832

Fairfield, Adams, Pop. 504
Fairfield Area SD 1,100/K-12
4840 Fairfield Rd 17320 717-642-8228
Karen Kugler, supt. Fax 642-2036
www.fairfieldpaschools.org/
Fairfield Area HS 400/9-12
4840 Fairfield Rd 17320 717-642-2004
Brian McDowell, prin. Fax 642-2029
Fairfield Area MS 400/5-8
4840 Fairfield Rd 17320 717-642-2005
Patricia Weber, prin. Fax 642-2030

Fairless Hills, Bucks, Pop. 8,316
Area Vocational Technical School
Supt. — None
Bucks County Technical HS Vo/Tech
610 Wistar Rd 19030 215-949-1700
Dr. Leon Poeske, dir.

Bristol Township SD
Supt. — See Levittown
Armstrong MS 500/7-8
475 Wistar Rd 19030 215-945-4940
Edward Dayton, prin. Fax 945-1664

Pennsbury SD
Supt. — See Fallsington
Pennsbury HS East 3,200/9-12
705 Hood Blvd 19030 215-949-6700
Shawn Neely, prin. Fax 949-3896
Pennsbury HS West 9-12
608 S Olds Blvd 19030 215-949-6780
Lisa Becker, prin. Fax 949-6857

Conwell-Egan HS 600/9-12
611 Wistar Rd 19030 215-945-6200
Dr. Marion Mann, prin. Fax 945-6206

Fairview, Erie, Pop. 2,337
Fairview SD 1,600/K-12
7466 McCray Rd 16415 814-474-2600
Erik Kincade, supt. Fax 474-5497
www.fairviewschools.org
Fairview HS 500/9-12
7460 McCray Rd 16415 814-474-2600
Dale Lewis, prin. Fax 474-1367
Fairview MS 500/5-8
4967 Avonia Rd 16415 814-474-2600
Steve Ferringer, prin. Fax 474-1640

Millcreek Township SD
Supt. — See Erie
Walnut Creek MS 500/PK-PK, 6-
5901 Sterrettania Rd 16415 814-835-5700
Marcie Morgan, prin. Fax 835-5720

Fallsington, Bucks
Pennsbury SD 10,200/K-12
134 Yardley Ave 19054 215-428-4100
Dr. William Gretzula, supt. Fax 295-8912
www.pennsbury.k12.pa.us
Other Schools – See Fairless Hills, Yardley

Farrell, Mercer, Pop. 4,855
Farrell Area SD 800/K-12
1600 Roemer Blvd 16121 724-346-6585
Dr. Lora Adams-King, supt. Fax 346-0223
www.farrellareaschools.com
Farrell Area MSHS 300/7-12
1700 Roemer Blvd 16121 724-346-6585
Matthew Fowler, prin. Fax 346-2381

Fawn Grove, York, Pop. 449
South Eastern SD 2,800/PK-12
377 Main St 17321 717-382-4843
Dr. Rona Kaufmann, supt. Fax 382-4769
www.sesdweb.net/
Kennard-Dale HS 800/9-12
393 Main St 17321 717-382-4871
Heather Venne, prin. Fax 382-4869
South Eastern MS 400/7-8
375 Main St 17321 717-382-4851
Jon Horton, prin. Fax 382-9033

Feasterville, Bucks, Pop. 3,026
Neshaminy SD
Supt. — See Langhorne
Poquessing MS 600/6-8
300 Heights Ln 19053 215-809-6210
Joann Holland, prin.

Bucks County School of Beauty Culture Post-Sec.
1761 Bustleton Pike 19053 215-322-0666

Finleyville, Washington, Pop. 453
Ringgold SD
Supt. — See New Eagle
Ringgold MS 700/6-8
6023 State Route 88 15332 724-348-7154
Mark Alberta, prin. Fax 348-8839

Fishertown, Bedford
Chestnut Ridge SD 1,300/PK-12
3281 Valley Rd 15539 814-839-4195
Mark J. Kudlawiec, supt. Fax 839-2088
www.crsd.k12.pa.us
Other Schools – See New Paris

Fleetwood, Berks, Pop. 4,046
Fleetwood Area SD 2,600/K-12
801 N Richmond St 19522 610-944-9598
Dr. Paul Eaken, supt. Fax 944-9408
www.fleetwoodasd.org
Fleetwood Area HS 900/9-12
803 N Richmond St 19522 610-944-7656
Stephen Herman, prin. Fax 944-6952
Fleetwood Area MS 800/5-8
407 N Richmond St 19522 610-944-7634
Gangi Cucciuffo, prin. Fax 944-5307

Flinton, Cambria
Glendale SD 800/K-12
1466 Beaver Valley Rd 16640 814-687-3402
Edward DiSabato, supt. Fax 687-3341
www.gsd1.org
Glendale JSHS 400/7-12
1466 Beaver Valley Rd 16640 814-687-4261
Richard Stackhouse, prin. Fax 687-4718

Flourtown, Montgomery, Pop. 4,474

Mount St. Joseph Academy 600/9-12
120 W Wissahickon Ave 19031 215-233-3177
Dr. Judith Caviston, prin. Fax 233-4734

Folcroft, Delaware, Pop. 6,473
Area Vocational Technical School
Supt. — None
Delaware County Technical HS - Folcroft Vo/Tech
701 Henderson Blvd N 19032 610-583-7620
Ryan Coughlin, prin. Fax 583-6537

Southeast Delco SD 4,100/K-12
1560 Delmar Dr 19032 610-522-4300
Dr. Stephen D. Butz, supt. Fax 461-4874
www.sedelco.org
Other Schools – See Sharon Hill

Folsom, Delaware, Pop. 8,224
Ridley SD 5,500/K-12
901 Morton Ave 19033 610-534-1900
Lee Ann Wentzel, supt. Fax 534-2335
www.ridleysd.org/
Ridley HS 1,900/9-12
901 Morton Ave 19033 610-237-8034
Dr. Kenneth Acker, prin. Fax 237-9641
Other Schools – See Ridley Park

Ford City, Armstrong, Pop. 2,961
Area Vocational Technical School
Supt. — None
Lenape Tech Vo/Tech
2215 Chaplin Ave 16226 724-763-7116
Dawn Kocher-Taylor, dir.

Forest City, Susquehanna, Pop. 1,887
Forest City Regional SD 800/PK-12
100 Susquehanna St 18421 570-785-2400
Dr. Jessica Aquilina, supt. Fax 785-9557
www.fcrsd.org
Forest City Regional JSHS 400/7-12
100 Susquehanna St 18421 570-785-2400
Peter Jordan, prin. Fax 785-3785

Fort Washington, Montgomery, Pop. 5,372
Upper Dublin SD
Supt. — See Maple Glen

Upper Dublin HS 1,400/9-12
800 Loch Alsh Ave 19034 215-643-8900
Robert Schultz M.Ed., prin. Fax 643-8898

DeVry University Post-Sec.
1140 Virginia Dr 19034 215-591-5700
Germantown Academy 1,100/PK-12
340 Morris Rd 19034 215-646-3300
James Connor, head sch Fax 646-1216

Forty Fort, Luzerne, Pop. 4,182

Fortis Institute Post-Sec.
166 Slocum St 18704 570-288-8400

Foxburg, Clarion, Pop. 183
Allegheny-Clarion Valley SD 700/K-12
PO Box 100 16036 724-659-5820
David McDeavitt, supt. Fax 659-2963
www.acvsd.org/
Allegheny-Clarion Valley JSHS 400/7-12
PO Box 345 16036 724-659-4661
William Jordan, prin. Fax 659-4774

Frackville, Schuylkill, Pop. 3,786
Area Vocational Technical School
Supt. — None
Schuylkill Technology Center - North Vo/Tech
101 Technology Dr 17931 570-874-1034
Jeff Sweda, admin. Fax 874-4028

Franklin, Venango, Pop. 6,385
Franklin Area SD 1,900/K-12
702 Liberty St 16323 814-432-8917
Dr. Pamela Dye, supt. Fax 437-5754
www.fasd.k12.pa.us/
Franklin Area HS 600/9-12
246 Pone Ln 16323 814-432-2121
Gary Canfora, prin. Fax 432-5031
Franklin Area MS 300/7-8
246 Pone Ln 16323 814-432-2224
Christina Cohlhepp, prin. Fax 437-1491

Valley Grove SD 900/K-12
429 Wiley Ave 16323 814-432-4919
Jeffrey Clark, supt. Fax 437-1243
www.vgsd.org/
Rocky Grove JSHS 400/7-12
403 Rocky Grove Ave 16323 814-437-3759
Matthew LaVerde, prin. Fax 437-1062

Fredericksburg, Lebanon, Pop. 1,345
Northern Lebanon SD
Supt. — See Jonestown
Northern Lebanon HS 700/9-12
PO Box 100 17026 717-865-2117
Joshua Kuehner, prin. Fax 865-7818
Northern Lebanon MS 400/6-8
PO Box 100 17026 717-865-2117
Bradly Reist, prin. Fax 865-5835

Fredericktown, Washington, Pop. 397
Bethlehem-Center SD 1,300/K-12
194 Crawford Rd 15333 724-267-4910
Linda Marcolini, supt. Fax 267-4904
www.bc.k12.pa.us
Bethlehem-Center HS 400/9-12
179 Crawford Rd 15333 724-267-4944
Aaron Cornell, prin. Fax 267-4907
Bethlehem-Center MS 300/6-8
136 Crawford Rd 15333 724-267-4935
Amanda Kinneer, prin. Fax 267-4937

Freedom, Beaver, Pop. 1,529
Ambridge Area SD
Supt. — See Ambridge
Ambridge Area JHS 400/7-8
401 1st St 15042 724-266-2833
Shaun Cooke, prin. Fax 869-5321

Freedom Area SD 1,200/K-12
1702 School St 15042 724-775-5464
Dr. Jeffrey Fuller, supt. Fax 775-7434
www.freedomareaschools.org
Freedom Area HS 500/9-12
1190 Bulldog Dr 15042 724-775-7400
William Deal, prin. Fax 775-7753
Freedom Area MS 200/5-8
1702 School St 15042 724-775-7641
Ryan Smith, prin. Fax 775-7748

Freeland, Luzerne, Pop. 3,500

MMI Prep S 200/6-12
154 Centre St 18224 570-636-1108
D. Scott Wiggins, head sch Fax 636-0742

Freeport, Armstrong, Pop. 1,775
Freeport Area SD
Supt. — See Sarver
Freeport Area MS 300/6-8
325 4th St 16229 724-295-9020
Donald Dell, prin. Fax 295-4630

Friedens, Somerset, Pop. 1,520
Shanksville-Stonycreek SD 300/PK-12
1325 Corner Stone Rd 15541 814-267-6499
Samuel Romesberg, supt. Fax 267-4372
www.sssd.com
Other Schools – See Shanksville

Galeton, Potter, Pop. 1,134
Galeton Area SD 400/PK-12
27 Bridge St 16922 814-435-6571
Alanna Huck, supt. Fax 435-6981
gasd.net
Galeton Area S 400/PK-12
27 Bridge St 16922 814-435-6571
Alanna Huck, supt. Fax 435-6981

Gallitzin, Cambria, Pop. 1,656
Penn Cambria SD
Supt. — See Cresson

Penn Cambria MS 500/5-8
401 Division St 16641 814-886-4181
Jeff Baird, prin. Fax 886-9308

Geigertown, Berks

High Point Baptist Academy 200/K-12
PO Box 188 19523 610-286-5942
Brad Feldmeier, admin. Fax 286-7525

Gettysburg, Adams, Pop. 7,466
Gettysburg Area SD 3,000/K-12
900 Biglerville Rd 17325 717-334-6254
Dr. Larry Redding, supt. Fax 334-5220
www.gettysburg.k12.pa.us
Gettysburg Area HS 1,000/9-12
1130 Old Harrisburg Rd 17325 717-334-6254
Mark Blanchard, prin. Fax 337-4439
Gettysburg Area MS 700/6-8
37 Lefever St 17325 717-334-6254
Elwood Strait, prin. Fax 334-6999

Adams County Christian Academy 50/PK-12
1865 Biglerville Rd 17325 717-334-9177
Rhonda Fertich, prin. Fax 334-7691
Freedom Christian S 100/PK-12
3185 York Rd 17325 717-624-3884
Karen Trout, prin. Fax 624-1562
Gettysburg College Post-Sec.
300 N Washington St 17325 717-337-6300
Lutheran Theological Seminary Post-Sec.
61 Seminary Rdg 17325 717-334-6286

Gibsonia, Allegheny, Pop. 2,710
Pine-Richland SD 4,600/K-12
702 Warrendale Rd 15044 724-625-7773
Dr. Brian Miller, supt. Fax 625-1490
www.pinerichland.org
Pine-Richland HS 1,500/9-12
700 Warrendale Rd 15044 724-625-4444
Nancy Bowman, prin. Fax 625-4640
Pine-Richland MS 800/7-8
100 Logan Rd 15044 724-625-3111
Dr. David Kristofic, prin. Fax 625-3144

Aquinas Academy 300/K-12
2308 W Hardies Rd 15044 724-444-0722
Leslie Mitros, hdmstr. Fax 444-0750

Gilbertsville, Montgomery, Pop. 4,774
Boyertown Area SD
Supt. — See Boyertown
Boyertown Area JHS East 900/7-9
2020 Big Rd 19525 610-754-9550
Andrew Ruppert, prin. Fax 754-9567

Girard, Erie, Pop. 3,073
Girard SD 1,800/PK-12
1203 Lake St 16417 814-774-5666
Dr. James Tracy, supt. Fax 774-4220
www.girardsd.org
Girard HS 600/9-12
1135 Lake St 16417 814-774-5607
Gregg McClelland, prin. Fax 774-2239
Rice Avenue MS 500/5-8
1100 Rice Ave 16417 814-774-5604
David Koma, prin. Fax 774-5259

Glen Mills, Delaware
Garnet Valley SD, 80 Station Rd 19342 4,800/K-12
Dr. Marc Bertrando, supt. 610-579-7300
www.garnetvalleyschools.com/
Garnet Valley HS 1,500/9-12
552 Smithbridge Rd 19342 610-579-7745
Dr. Janet Girolami, prin.
Garnet Valley MS 1,200/6-8
601 Smithbridge Rd 19342 610-579-5100
Dr. Kenneth Acker, prin.

Glen Rock, York, Pop. 1,997
Southern York County SD 3,100/K-12
PO Box 128 17327 717-235-4811
Dr. Sandra Lemmon, supt. Fax 235-0863
www.syc.k12.pa.us
Southern MS 500/7-8
PO Box 128 17327 717-235-4811
Dr. Len Reppert, prin. Fax 227-9681
Susquehannock HS 900/9-12
PO Box 128 17327 717-235-4811
Dr. Kevin Molin, prin. Fax 227-1951

Glenshaw, Allegheny, Pop. 8,914
Shaler Area SD 4,600/K-12
1800 Mount Royal Blvd 15116 412-492-1200
Dr. Victor Morrone, supt. Fax 492-1293
www.sasd.k12.pa.us
Shaler Area MS 700/7-8
1810 Mount Royal Blvd 15116 412-492-1200
Martin Martynuska, prin. Fax 492-1237
Other Schools – See Pittsburgh

Glenside, Montgomery, Pop. 8,249

Arcadia University Post-Sec.
450 S Easton Rd 19038 215-572-2900
LaSalle College HS 1,100/9-12
8605 Cheltenham Ave 19038 215-233-2911
Michael O'Toole, prin. Fax 233-1418
Princeton Information Technology Center Post-Sec.
140 S Easton Rd 19038 215-576-5650
Won Institute of Graduate Studies Post-Sec.
137 S Easton Rd 19038 215-884-8942

Greencastle, Franklin, Pop. 3,946
Greencastle-Antrim SD 3,000/K-12
500 Leitersburg St 17225 717-597-3226
Jolinda Wilson, supt. Fax 597-2180
www.gcasd.org
Greencastle-Antrim HS 900/9-12
300 S Ridge Ave 17225 717-597-3226
Edward Rife, prin. Fax 597-2912
Greencastle-Antrim MS 700/6-8
370 S Ridge Ave 17225 717-597-3226
Mark Herman, prin. Fax 597-6468

Shady Grove Mennonite S 200/1-10
1442 Buchanan Trl E 17225 717-597-0843
Wilmer Eby, prin.

Greensboro, Greene, Pop. 254
Southeastern Greene SD 600/K-12
1000 Mapletown Rd 15338 724-943-3630
Rich Pekar, supt. Fax 943-3052
www.segsd.org
Mapletown JSHS 300/7-12
1000 Mapletown Rd 15338 724-943-3401
Bart Donley, prin. Fax 943-4769

Greensburg, Westmoreland, Pop. 14,523
Greensburg Salem SD 2,900/K-12
1 Academy Hill Pl 15601 724-832-2901
Dr. Eileen Amato, supt. Fax 832-2968
www.greensburgsalem.org
Greensburg Salem HS 900/9-12
65 Mennel Dr 15601 724-832-2960
David Zilli, prin. Fax 832-2922
Greensburg Salem MS 600/6-8
301 N Main St 15601 724-832-2930
Adam Jones, prin. Fax 832-2937

Hempfield Area SD 5,900/K-12
4347 State Route 136 15601 724-834-2590
Dr. Barbara J. Marin, supt. Fax 850-2298
www.hasdpa.net
Harrold MS 400/6-8
1368 Middletown Rd 15601 724-850-2301
Jason Lochner, prin. Fax 850-2302
Hempfield Area HS 1,900/9-12
4345 State Route 136 15601 724-834-9000
Kathy Charlton, prin. Fax 850-2090
Wendover MS 500/6-8
425 Wendover Jr High Rd 15601 724-838-4070
Deanna Mikesic, prin. Fax 838-4071
Other Schools – See Irwin

Education and Technology Institute Post-Sec.
219 Donohoe Rd 15601 724-836-2395
Greensburg Central Catholic JSHS 500/7-12
911 Armory Dr 15601 724-834-0310
Benjamin Althof, prin. Fax 834-2472
Seton Hill University Post-Sec.
Seton Hill Dr 15601 724-834-2200
Triangle Tech Post-Sec.
222 E Pittsburgh St # A 15601 724-832-1050
University of Pittsburgh Post-Sec.
150 Finoli Dr 15601 724-837-7040
Westmoreland Christian Academy 100/PK-12
538 Rugh St 15601 724-853-8308
Jordan Tomson, prin. Fax 836-7472

Greenville, Mercer, Pop. 5,850
Greenville Area SD 1,400/K-12
9 Donation Rd 16125 724-588-2500
Mark Ferrara, supt. Fax 588-5024
www.greenville.k12.pa.us
Greenville JSHS 700/7-12
9 Donation Rd 16125 724-588-2500
Brian Tokar, prin. Fax 588-4397

Reynolds SD 1,100/PK-12
531 Reynolds Rd 16125 724-646-5501
Joseph Neuch, supt. Fax 646-5505
www.reynolds.k12.pa.us
Reynolds JSHS 600/7-12
531 Reynolds Rd 16125 724-646-5701
Scott Shearer, prin. Fax 646-5705

Living Word Christian S 100/K-12
12 N Diamond St 16125 724-373-8336
Jan Chapin, admin. Fax 588-8742
Thiel College Post-Sec.
75 College Ave 16125 724-589-2000

Grove City, Mercer, Pop. 8,236
Grove City Area SD 2,100/K-12
511 Highland Ave 16127 724-458-6733
Jeffrey Finch, supt. Fax 458-5868
www.grovecity.k12.pa.us
Grove City Area HS 700/9-12
511 Highland Ave 16127 724-458-5456
Dr. RaeLin Howard, prin. Fax 450-0678
Grove City Area MS 500/6-8
100 Middle School Dr 16127 724-458-8040
Larry Connelly, prin. Fax 450-0780

Grove City College Post-Sec.
100 Campus Dr 16127 724-458-2000

Guys Mills, Crawford, Pop. 121
PENNCREST SD
Supt. — See Saegertown
Maplewood JSHS 600/7-12
30383 Guys Mills Rd 16327 814-789-3666
Kenneth Wolfarth, prin. Fax 789-2409

Faith Builders Christian S 100/1-12
28527 Guys Mills Rd 16327 814-789-2303
Gerald Miller, admin. Fax 789-3396

Gwynedd Valley, Montgomery

Gwynedd-Mercy Academy 400/9-12
PO Box 902 19437 215-646-8815
Sr. Patricia Flynn, prin. Fax 646-4361
Gwynedd-Mercy University Post-Sec.
PO Box 901 19437 215-646-7300

Hadley, Mercer
Commodore Perry SD 500/K-12
3002 Perry Hwy 16130 724-253-3255
Kim Zippie, supt. Fax 253-3467
www.cppanthers.org/CPWeb.htm
Perry JSHS 200/7-12
3002 Perry Hwy 16130 724-253-2232
Doug Mays, prin. Fax 253-3467

Halifax, Dauphin, Pop. 814
Halifax Area SD 1,100/PK-12
3940 Peters Mountain Rd 17032 717-896-3416
Dr. Michele Orner, supt. Fax 896-3976
www.hasd.us
Halifax Area HS 300/9-12
3940 Peters Mountain Rd 17032 717-896-3416
David Hatfield, prin. Fax 896-3976
Halifax Area MS 300/6-8
3940 Peters Mountain Rd 17032 717-896-3416
Rick Ansel, prin. Fax 896-3976

Hamburg, Berks, Pop. 4,259
Hamburg Area SD 2,300/K-12
Windsor St 19526 610-562-2241
Dr. Richard Mextorf, supt. Fax 562-2634
www.hasdhawks.org
Hamburg Area HS 700/9-12
701 Windsor St 19526 610-562-3861
Christopher Spohn, prin. Fax 561-3394
Hamburg Area MS 600/6-8
Windsor St 19526 610-562-3990
Geno McGorry, prin. Fax 562-1425

Blue Mountain Academy 200/9-12
2363 Mountain Rd 19526 484-662-7000
David Morgan, prin. Fax 662-7001

Hanover, York, Pop. 15,077
Hanover Public SD 1,700/K-12
403 Moul Ave 17331 717-637-9000
Dr. John Scola, supt. Fax 630-4617
www.hanoverpublic.org
Hanover HS 500/9-12
401 Moul Ave 17331 717-637-9000
Catherine Houck, prin. Fax 630-4634
Hanover MS 500/5-8
300 Keagy Ave 17331 717-637-9000
Mark Hershner, prin. Fax 630-4632

South Western SD 4,100/K-12
225 Bowman Rd 17331 717-632-2500
Dr. Barbara Rupp, supt. Fax 632-7993
www.swsd.k12.pa.us/
Markle IS 1,000/6-8
225 Bowman Rd Ste 1 17331 717-633-4840
Dr. Daniel Hartman, prin. Fax 633-7073
South Western HS 1,200/9-12
200 Bowman Rd 17331 717-633-4807
Dr. Judy Berryman, prin. Fax 633-4819

Empire Beauty School Post-Sec.
1000 Carlisle St 17331 717-633-6201
St. Joseph MS 100/6-8
5125 Grandview Rd 17331 717-632-0118
Susan Mummert, prin. Fax 632-0030

Hanover Twp, Lehigh
Hanover Area SD 2,000/K-12
1600 Sans Souci Pkwy 18706 570-831-2300
Andrew Kuhl, supt. Fax 831-2322
www.hanoverarea.org
Hanover Area JSHS 900/7-12
1600 Sans Souci Pkwy 18706 570-831-2300
Daniel Malloy, prin. Fax 831-2316

Harborcreek, Erie
Harbor Creek SD 2,000/K-12
6375 Buffalo Rd 16421 814-897-2100
Kelly Hess, supt. Fax 897-2142
www.hcsd.iu5.org
Harbor Creek HS 600/9-12
6375 Buffalo Rd 16421 814-897-2100
Pamela Chodubski, prin. Fax 897-2136
Harbor Creek JHS 300/7-8
6375 Buffalo Rd 16421 814-897-2100
Andrew Krahe, prin. Fax 897-2121

Harleysville, Montgomery, Pop. 9,178
Souderton Area SD
Supt. — See Souderton
Indian Valley MS 800/6-8
130 Maple Ave 19438 215-256-8896
Dr. Dale Burkhard, prin. Fax 256-1288

Harmony, Butler, Pop. 882
Seneca Valley SD 7,200/K-12
124 Seneca School Rd 16037 724-452-6040
Dr. Tracy Vitale, supt. Fax 452-6105
www.svsd.net/
Seneca Valley Intermediate HS 1,200/9-10
126 Seneca School Rd 16037 724-452-6040
Matthew Delp, prin. Fax 452-3718
Seneca Valley MS 1,200/7-8
122 Seneca School Rd 16037 724-452-6040
Robert Ceh, prin. Fax 452-0331
Seneca Valley SHS 1,100/11-12
128 Seneca School Rd 16037 724-452-6040
Mark Korcinsky, prin. Fax 452-8357

Harrisburg, Dauphin, Pop. 47,794
Area Vocational Technical School
Supt. — None
Dauphin County Technical S Vo/Tech
6001 Locust Ln 17109 717-652-3170
Dr. Peggy Grimm, prin. Fax 652-9326

Other Schools – See Allison Park PA, Altoona PA, Aston PA, Bartonsville PA, Bethlehem PA, Bloomsburg PA, Broomall PA, Brownstown PA, Butler PA, Canonsburg PA, Chambersburg PA, Charleroi PA, Clearfield PA, Coal Township PA, Connellsville PA, Downingtown PA, Easton PA, Ebensburg PA, Erie PA, Everett PA, Fairless Hills PA, Folcroft PA, Ford City PA, Frackville PA, Hazle Township PA, Hughesville PA, Indiana PA, Jamison PA, Jefferson Hills PA, Jim Thorpe PA, Johnstown PA, Kingston PA, Lansdale PA, Latrobe PA, Lebanon PA, Leesport PA, Lewistown PA, Limerick PA, Mc Connellsburg PA, Mc Keesport PA, Mar Lin PA, Meadville PA, Mechanicsburg PA, Mercer PA, Mill Creek PA, Mill Hall PA, Monaca PA, Monroeville PA, Mount Joy PA, New Berlin PA, New Castle PA, New Kensington PA, New Stanton PA, Oakdale PA, Oil City PA, Oley PA, Perkasie PA, Philadelphia PA, Phoenixville PA, Pleasant Gap PA, Plymouth Meeting PA, Port Allegany PA, Pottsville PA, Reading PA, Reynoldsville PA, Schnecksville PA, Scranton PA, Shippenville PA, Somerset PA, Springville PA, Towanda PA, Uniontown PA, Warren PA, Waynesburg PA, West Grove PA, Wilkes Barre PA, Willow Grove PA, Willow Street PA, York PA

Central Dauphin SD 10,800/K-12
600 Rutherford Rd 17109 717-545-4703
Dr. Carol Johnson, supt. Fax 657-4999
www.cdschools.org
Central Dauphin East HS 1,400/9-12
626 Rutherford Rd 17109 717-541-1662
Dr. Jesse Rawls, prin. Fax 545-7139
Central Dauphin East MS 700/6-8
628 Rutherford Rd 17109 717-545-4703
Christine Miller, prin. Fax 657-4987
Central Dauphin HS 1,700/9-12
437 Piketown Rd 17112 717-703-5360
Ken Miller, prin. Fax 703-5730
Central Dauphin MS 700/6-8
4600 Locust Ln 17109 717-540-4606
Jeffrey Matzner, prin. Fax 214-5055
Linglestown MS 700/6-8
1200 N Mountain Rd 17112 717-657-3060
Mickey Termin, prin. Fax 657-0537
Other Schools – See Steelton

Harrisburg City SD 4,800/K-12
1601 State St 17103 717-703-4000
Dr. Sybil Knight-Burney, supt. Fax 703-4115
www.hbgsd.k12.pa.us
Camp Curtin Academy 400/5-8
2900 N 6th St 17110 717-703-4200
Portia Slaughter, prin. Fax 703-4225
Harrisburg HS 1,100/9-12
2451 Market St 17103 717-703-4300
Eugene Spells, prin. Fax 703-4333
Marshall Math Science Academy 200/5-8
301 Hale Ave 17104 717-703-1400
Marisol Craig, prin. Fax 703-1420
Rowland Academy 800/5-8
1842 Derry St 17104 717-703-4500
Roma Benjamin, prin. Fax 703-4520
Sci-Tech HS 400/9-12
215 Market St 17101 717-703-1900
Sieta Achampong, dir. Fax 703-1915

Susquehanna Township SD 2,800/K-12
2579 Interstate Dr 17110 717-657-5100
Dr. Tod F. Kline Ed.D., supt. Fax 724-1851
www.hannasd.org
Susquehanna Township HS 900/9-12
3500 Elmerton Ave 17109 717-657-5117
Keith Still, prin. Fax 657-5146
Susquehanna Township MS 700/6-8
801 Wood St 17109 717-657-5125
Kenneth R. Edwards, prin. Fax 657-9841

Bishop McDevitt HS 700/9-12
1 Crusader Way 17111 717-236-7973
Sr. Mary Anne Bednar, prin. Fax 234-1270
Brightwood Career Institute Post-Sec.
5650 Derry St 17111 717-564-4112
Covenant Christian Academy 200/PK-12
1982 Locust Ln 17109 717-540-9885
Dr. David Sonju Ph.D., hdmstr. Fax 540-7176
Empire Beauty School Post-Sec.
3941 Jonestown Rd 17109 717-652-8500
Harrisburg Area Community College Post-Sec.
1 Hacc Dr 17110 717-780-2300
Harrisburg Christian S 300/K-12
2000 Blue Mountain Pkwy 17112 717-545-3728
Philip G. Puleo, hdmstr. Fax 545-9370
Harrisburg University of Science & Tech Post-Sec.
326 Market St 17101 717-901-5100
Keystone Technical Institute Post-Sec.
2301 Academy Dr 17112 717-545-4747
Widener University School of Law Post-Sec.
PO Box 69380 17106 717-541-3900

Harrison City, Westmoreland, Pop. 134
Penn-Trafford SD 4,000/K-12
PO Box 530 15636 724-744-4496
Dr. Matthew Harris, supt. Fax 744-4016
www.penntrafford.org
Penn-Trafford HS 1,400/9-12
3381 Route 130 15636 724-744-4471
Tony Aquilio, prin. Fax 744-1214
Other Schools – See Jeannette, Trafford

Hatboro, Montgomery, Pop. 7,268
Upper Moreland Township SD
Supt. — See Willow Grove
Upper Moreland MS 700/6-8
4000 Orangemans Rd 19040 215-674-4185
Joseph Waters Ed.D., prin. Fax 956-1906

Hatfield, Montgomery, Pop. 3,211
North Penn SD
Supt. — See Lansdale
Northbridge S Alt
2374 N Penn Rd 19440 215-412-4009
Kyle Hassler, prin. Fax 853-1627
Pennfield MS 800/7-9
726 Forty Foot Rd 19440 215-368-9600
Dr. Barbara Galloway, prin. Fax 368-9791

Biblical Theological Seminary Post-Sec.
200 N Main St 19440 800-235-4021

Haverford, Montgomery, Pop. 6,000

Haverford College Post-Sec.
370 Lancaster Ave 19041 610-896-1000
Haverford S 1,000/PK-12
450 Lancaster Ave 19041 610-642-3020
Dr. John Nagl, hdmstr. Fax 649-4898

Havertown, Delaware, Pop. 30,000
Haverford Township SD 5,800/K-12
50 E Eagle Rd 19083 610-853-5900
Dr. Maureen Reusche, supt. Fax 853-5942
www.haverford.k12.pa.us
Haverford HS 1,700/9-12
200 Mill Rd 19083 610-853-5900
Fax 853-5952
Haverford MS 1,300/6-8
1701 Darby Rd 19083 610-853-5900
Daniel Horan, prin. Fax 853-5937

Hawley, Pike, Pop. 1,191
Wallenpaupack Area SD 3,400/K-12
2552 Route 6 18428 570-226-4557
Michael Silsby, supt. Fax 226-0638
www.wallenpaupack.org/
Hawley Center 100/Alt
500 Academy St 18428 570-226-4557
Fax 251-3010
Wallenpaupack Area HS 1,200/9-12
2552 Route 6 18428 570-226-4557
Jay Starnes, prin. Fax 251-3153
Wallenpaupack Area MS 800/6-8
139 Atlantic Ave 18428 570-226-4557
Keith Gunuskey, prin. Fax 251-3165

Hazleton, Luzerne, Pop. 25,114
Hazleton Area SD
Supt. — See Hazle Township
Hazleton S 1,000/3-8
700 N Wyoming St 18201 570-459-3221
Maureen DeRose, prin. Fax 501-8433

Academy of Hair Design Post-Sec.
1057 N Church St # A 18202 570-784-1020
Immanuel Christian S 100/K-12
725 N Locust St 18201 570-459-1111
Kelly Knowlden, head sch Fax 459-6920
McCann School of Business & Technology Post-Sec.
370 Maplewood Dr 18202 570-454-6172
Penn State Hazleton Post-Sec.
76 University Dr 18202 570-450-3000

Hazle Township, Luzerne
Area Vocational Technical School
Supt. — None
Hazleton Area Career Center Vo/Tech
1451 W 23rd St, 570-459-3221
Lori Herman, prin. Fax 459-3181

Hazleton Area SD 10,500/PK-12
1515 W 23rd St 18202 570-459-3111
Dr. Craig Butler, supt. Fax 459-3118
www.hasdk12.org
Hazleton Area HS 3,200/9-12
1601 W 23rd St, 570-459-3221
Rocco Petrone, prin. Fax 459-3242
Other Schools – See Hazleton

Hegins, Schuylkill, Pop. 805
Tri-Valley SD
Supt. — See Valley View
Tri-Valley JSHS 400/7-12
155 E Main St 17938 570-682-3125
Charles Hall, prin. Fax 682-9873

Hellertown, Northampton, Pop. 5,840
Saucon Valley SD 2,100/K-12
2097 Polk Valley Rd 18055 610-838-7026
Monica McHale-Small, supt. Fax 838-6419
www.svpanthers.org
Saucon Valley HS 700/9-12
2100 Polk Valley Rd 18055 610-838-7001
Eric Kahler, prin. Fax 838-2365
Saucon Valley MS 600/5-8
2095 Polk Valley Rd 18055 610-838-7071
Pamela Bernardo, prin. Fax 838-7473

Herminie, Westmoreland, Pop. 785
Yough SD 2,200/K-12
915 Lowber Rd 15637 724-446-7272
Dr. Janet Sardon, supt. Fax 446-5017
www.youghsd.net
Yough HS 700/9-12
919 Lowber Rd 15637 724-446-5520
Earl Thompson, prin. Fax 446-6008
Other Schools – See Ruffs Dale

Hermitage, Mercer, Pop. 16,014
Hermitage SD 2,000/K-12
411 N Hermitage Rd 16148 724-981-8750
Dr. Daniel Bell, supt. Fax 981-5080
www.hermitage.k12.pa.us
Hickory HS 800/8-12
640 N Hermitage Rd 16148 724-981-8750
Dr. Chris Gill, prin. Fax 347-4558

Kennedy Catholic HS 300/9-12
2120 Shenango Valley Fwy 16148 724-346-5531
William Lyon, hdmstr. Fax 346-3011
Kennedy Catholic MS 100/6-8
2120 Shenango Valley Fwy 16148 724-346-5531
William Lyon, hdmstr. Fax 346-3011

Herndon, Northumberland, Pop. 322
Line Mountain SD 1,200/K-12
185 Line Mountain Rd 17830 570-758-2640
David Campbell, supt. Fax 758-2842
www.linemountain.com
Line Mountain HS 400/9-12
187 Line Mountain Rd 17830 570-758-2011
Jeffrey Roadcap, prin. Fax 758-1514
Line Mountain MS 400/5-8
187 Line Mountain Rd 17830 570-758-2011
Jeffrey Roadcap, prin.

Hershey, Dauphin, Pop. 13,934
Derry Township SD 3,500/K-12
PO Box 898 17033 717-534-2501
Joseph McFarland, supt. Fax 533-4357
www.hershey.k12.pa.us
Hershey HS 1,200/9-12
PO Box 898 17033 717-531-2244
Dale Reimann Ed.D., prin. Fax 534-2684
Hershey MS 800/6-8
PO Box 898 17033 717-531-2222
Erick Valentin, prin. Fax 531-2245

Hershey S 1,800/PK-12
PO Box 830 17033 717-520-2000
Peter Gurt, pres. Fax 520-2002
M. Hershey Medical Center Coll of Med. Post-Sec.
500 University Dr 17033 717-531-8521

Hilltown, Bucks

St. Agnes-Sacred Heart MS 100/4-8
PO Box 31 18927 215-822-9174
Margaret Graham, prin. Fax 822-7942

Holland, Bucks, Pop. 5,300
Council Rock SD
Supt. — See Newtown
Council Rock HS South 2,100/9-12
2002 Rock Way 18966 215-944-1100
Al Funk, prin. Fax 944-1145
Holland MS 500/7-8
400 E Holland Rd 18966 215-944-2700
Daniel Greenland, prin. Fax 944-2789

Villa Joseph Marie HS 400/9-12
1180 Holland Rd 18966 215-357-8810
Lauren Carr, prin. Fax 357-2477

Hollidaysburg, Blair, Pop. 5,745
Hollidaysburg Area SD 3,400/K-12
405 Clark St 16648 814-696-4454
Dr. Robert Gildea, supt. Fax 695-2315
www.tigerwires.com
Hollidaysburg Area JHS 800/7-9
1000 Hewit St 16648 814-695-4426
Edward Barton, prin. Fax 696-2959
Hollidaysburg Area SHS 800/10-12
1500 N Montgomery St 16648 814-695-4416
Dr. Maureen Letcher, prin. Fax 696-2958

Hollsopple, Somerset

Johnstown Christian S 200/PK-12
125 Christian School Rd 15935 814-288-2588
Dr. Kathy Keafer, admin. Fax 288-1447

Homer City, Indiana, Pop. 1,691
Homer-Center SD 900/K-12
65 Wildcat Ln 15748 724-479-8080
Dr. Charles Koren, supt. Fax 479-3967
homercenter.org/
Homer-Center JSHS 400/7-12
70 Wildcat Ln 15748 724-479-8026
Jody Rainey, prin. Fax 479-4236

Honesdale, Wayne, Pop. 4,431
Wayne Highlands SD 2,700/K-12
474 Grove St 18431 570-253-4661
Gregory Frigoletto, supt. Fax 253-9409
www.whsdk12.com
Honesdale HS 900/9-12
459 Terrace St 18431 570-253-2046
Christopher Pietraszewsk, prin. Fax 253-1502
Wayne Highlands MS 500/6-8
482 Grove St 18431 570-253-5900
Peter Jordan, prin. Fax 253-5259

Hookstown, Beaver, Pop. 144
South Side Area SD 1,100/PK-12
4949 Route 151 15050 724-573-9581
Tamara Adams, supt. Fax 573-0414
www.sssd.k12.pa.us
South Side HS 400/9-12
4949 Route 151 15050 724-573-9581
Anthony Paull, prin. Fax 573-0449
South Side MS 300/6-8
4949 Route 151 15050 724-573-9581
Samuel Adams, prin. Fax 573-0449

Horsham, Montgomery, Pop. 14,608
Hatboro-Horsham SD 4,700/K-12
229 Meetinghouse Rd 19044 215-420-5000
Dr. Curtis Griffin, supt. Fax 420-5262
www.hatboro-horsham.org
Hatboro-Horsham HS 1,600/9-12
899 Horsham Rd 19044 215-420-5500
Dennis Williams, prin. Fax 420-5613
Keith Valley MS 1,200/6-8
227 Meetinghouse Rd 19044 215-420-5050
Jonathan Kircher, prin. Fax 420-5291

Houston, Washington, Pop. 1,253
Chartiers-Houston SD 1,100/K-12
2020 W Pike St 15342 724-746-1400
John George, supt. Fax 746-3971
www.chbucs.k12.pa.us/
Chartiers-Houston JSHS 500/7-12
2050 W Pike St 15342 724-745-3350
Philip Mary, prin. Fax 745-3495

Houtzdale, Clearfield, Pop. 791
Moshannon Valley SD 900/K-12
4934 Green Acre Rd 16651 814-378-7609
John Zesiger, supt. Fax 378-7100
www.movalley.org
Moshannon Valley JSHS 400/7-12
4934 Green Acre Rd 16651 814-378-7616
Fax 378-5205

Hughesville, Lycoming, Pop. 2,101
Area Vocational Technical School
Supt. — None
Lycoming CTC Vo/Tech
293 Cemetery St 17737 570-584-2300
Eric Butler, prin.

East Lycoming SD 1,700/PK-12
349 Cemetery St 17737 570-584-2131
Michael Pawlik, supt. Fax 584-5701
www.eastlycoming.net
Hughesville JSHS 800/7-12
349 Cemetery St 17737 570-584-5111
Ron Lorson, prin. Fax 584-5378

Hummelstown, Dauphin, Pop. 4,481
Lower Dauphin SD 3,800/K-12
291 E Main St 17036 717-566-5300
Dr. Sherri L. Smith, supt. Fax 566-3670
www.ldsd.org
Lower Dauphin HS 1,200/9-12
201 S Hanover St 17036 717-566-5330
Justin Hanula, prin. Fax 566-3970
Lower Dauphin MS 900/6-8
251 Quarry Rd 17036 717-566-5310
Daniel Berra, prin. Fax 566-5383
Price S, 101 E High St 17036 50/Alt
Dr. David Wuestner, prin. 717-566-5326

Lancaster Mennonite S 300/K-12
1525 Sand Hill Rd 17036 717-533-4900
J. Richard Thomas, supt. Fax 835-0256

Hunker, Westmoreland, Pop. 283

Armbrust Christian Academy 100/PK-12
7786 State Route 819 15639 724-925-3830
Susan Stoner, head sch Fax 925-2523

Huntingdon, Huntingdon, Pop. 6,994
Huntingdon Area SD 2,000/K-12
2400 Cassady Ave Ste 2 16652 814-643-4140
Fred Foster, supt. Fax 643-6244
www.hasd.tiu.k12.pa.us/
Huntingdon Area HS 600/9-12
2400 Cassady Ave 16652 814-643-1080
Deborah Luffy, prin. Fax 643-3800
Huntingdon Area MS 500/6-8
2500 Cassady Ave 16652 814-643-2900
Deborah Luffy, prin. Fax 643-6513

DuBois Business College Post-Sec.
1001 Moore St 16652 814-641-0440
Juniata College Post-Sec.
1700 Moore St 16652 814-641-3000

Huntingdon Valley, Montgomery, Pop. 10,000
Lower Moreland Township SD 2,200/K-12
2551 Murray Ave 19006 215-938-0270
Dr. Marykay Feeley, supt. Fax 947-6933
www.lmtsd.org
Lower Moreland HS 700/9-12
555 Red Lion Rd 19006 215-938-0220
Bill Miles, prin. Fax 947-0333
Murray Avenue MS 500/6-8
2551 Murray Ave 19006 215-938-0230
Jennifer Dilks, prin. Fax 947-3697

Huntingdon Valley Christian Academy 100/PK-10
1845 Byberry Rd 19006 215-947-6595

Immaculata, Chester

Immaculata University Post-Sec.
1145 King Rd 19345 610-647-4400

Imperial, Allegheny, Pop. 2,507
West Allegheny SD 3,300/K-12
PO Box 55 15126 724-695-3422
Dr. Jerri Lynn Lippert, supt. Fax 695-3788
www.westasd.org
West Allegheny HS 1,100/9-12
205 W Allegheny Rd 15126 724-695-5245
Daniel Smith, prin. Fax 695-8690
West Allegheny MS 800/6-8
207 W Allegheny Rd 15126 724-695-8979
Frank Hernandez, prin. Fax 695-8211

Indiana, Indiana, Pop. 13,787
Area Vocational Technical School
Supt. — None
Indiana County Technology Center Vo/Tech
441 Hamill Rd 15701 724-349-6700
Carol Fry, dir.

Indiana Area SD 2,200/PK-12
501 E Pike Rd 15701 724-463-8713
Dale Kirsch, supt. Fax 463-0868
www.iasd.cc
Indiana Area JHS 600/6-8
245 N 5th St 15701 724-463-8568
Michael Minnick, prin. Fax 463-2133
Indiana Area SHS 800/9-12
450 N 5th St 15701 724-463-8562
Wade McElheny, prin. Fax 463-9709

Cambria-Rowe Business College Post-Sec.
422 S 13th St 15701 724-463-0222
Indiana University of Pennsylvania Post-Sec.
1011 South Dr 15705 724-357-2100
Seeds of Faith Christian Academy 100/PK-12
640 Church St 15701 724-463-7719
Erica Parks, admin. Fax 463-8097

Industry, Beaver, Pop. 1,815
Western Beaver County SD
Supt. — See Midland
Western Beaver County JSHS 400/6-12
216 Engle Rd 15052 724-643-8500
David Brandon, prin. Fax 643-8504

Irwin, Westmoreland, Pop. 3,935
Hempfield Area SD
Supt. — See Greensburg
West Hempfield MS 500/6-8
156 Northumberland Dr 15642 724-850-2140
Aaron Steinly, prin. Fax 850-2141

Jamestown, Mercer, Pop. 614
Jamestown Area SD 500/K-12
PO Box 217 16134 724-932-5557
Tracy Reiser, supt. Fax 932-5632
www.jamestown.k12.pa.us
Jamestown Area JSHS 300/7-12
PO Box 217 16134 724-932-3186
Brian Keyser, prin.

Jamison, Bucks
Area Vocational Technical School
Supt. — None
Middle Bucks Institute of Tech Vo/Tech
2740 York Rd 18929 215-343-2480
Kathryn Strouse, hdmstr. Fax 343-8626

Jeannette, Westmoreland, Pop. 9,284
Jeannette CSD 900/K-12
800 Florida Ave 15644 724-523-5497
Matthew Hutcheson, supt. Fax 523-3289
www.jeannette.k12.pa.us/
Jeannette HS 300/9-12
800 Florida Ave 15644 724-523-5591
Patricia Rozycki, prin. Fax 523-2313

Penn-Trafford SD
Supt. — See Harrison City
Penn MS 600/6-8
11 Penn Middle Way 15644 724-744-4431
James Simpson, prin. Fax 744-1215

Jefferson, Greene, Pop. 979
Jefferson-Morgan SD 800/PK-12
PO Box 158 15344 724-883-2310
Donna Furnier, supt. Fax 883-4942
www.jmsd.org/
Jefferson-Morgan MSHS 400/7-12
PO Box 158 15344 724-883-2310
Joseph Orr, prin. Fax 883-3786

Jefferson Hills, Allegheny, Pop. 9,642
Area Vocational Technical School
Supt. — None
Steel Center for Career and Technical Ed Vo/Tech
565 N Lewis Run Rd 15025 412-469-3200
Kevin Rice, prin. Fax 469-2196

West Jefferson Hills SD 2,800/K-12
835 Old Clairton Rd 15025 412-655-8450
Elizabeth H. Wheat, supt. Fax 655-9544
www.wjhsd.net
Jefferson HS 900/9-12
310 Old Clairton Rd 15025 412-655-8610
Christopher Sefcheck, prin. Fax 655-8618
Other Schools – See Pittsburgh

Jenkintown, Montgomery, Pop. 4,346
Jenkintown SD 600/K-12
325 Highland Ave 19046 215-885-3722
Dr. Timothy Wade, supt. Fax 885-2090
www.jenkintown.org/
Jenkintown JSHS 300/7-12
325 Highland Ave 19046 215-884-1801
Thomas Roller, prin. Fax 885-2090

Abington Friends S 700/PK-12
575 Washington Ln 19046 215-886-4350
Richard Nourie, head sch Fax 886-9143
Manor College Post-Sec.
700 Fox Chase Rd 19046 215-885-2360
St. Basil Academy 300/9-12
711 Fox Chase Rd 19046 215-885-3771
Gwen Cote, prin. Fax 885-4025

Jersey Shore, Lycoming, Pop. 4,319
Jersey Shore Area SD 2,600/K-12
175 A and P Dr 17740 570-398-1561
Dr. Jill T. Wenrich Ed.D., supt. Fax 398-5089
www.jsasd.k12.pa.us
Jersey Shore Area HS 800/9-12
701 Cemetery St 17740 570-398-7170
Reed Mellinger M.Ed., prin. Fax 398-5612
Jersey Shore Area MS 600/6-8
601 Thompson St 17740 570-398-7400
Laura Milarch M.Ed., prin. Fax 398-5618

Jim Thorpe, Carbon, Pop. 4,724
Area Vocational Technical School
Supt. — None
Carbon Career & Technical Institute Vo/Tech
150 W 13th St 18229 570-325-3682
David Reinbold, prin.

Jim Thorpe Area SD 2,100/K-12
410 Center Ave 18229 570-325-3691
Brian Gasper, supt. Fax 325-3699
www.jimthorpesd.org/
Jim Thorpe Area HS 600/9-12
1 Olympian Way 18229 570-325-3663
Thomas Lesisko, prin. Fax 325-8973

Johnsonburg, Elk, Pop. 2,464
Johnsonburg Area SD 600/PK-12
315 High School Rd 15845 814-965-2536
Dennis Crotzer, supt. Fax 965-5809
www.johnsonburgareaschooldistrict.net
Johnsonburg Area JSHS 300/7-12
315 High School Rd 15845 814-965-2556
Brock Benson, prin. Fax 965-5809

Johnstown, Cambria, Pop. 20,140
Area Vocational Technical School
Supt. — None
Greater Johnstown Career and Tech Center Vo/Tech
445 Schoolhouse Rd 15904 814-266-6073
John Augustine, prin. Fax 269-4394

Conemaugh Valley SD 800/PK-12
1340 William Penn Ave 15906 814-535-5005
David Lehman, supt. Fax 536-8902
www.cvk12.org/
Conemaugh Valley JSHS 400/7-12
1342 William Penn Ave 15906 814-535-5523
Shane Hazenstab, prin. Fax 536-4025

Ferndale Area SD 700/K-12
100 Dartmouth Ave 15905 814-535-1507
Carole Kakabar, supt. Fax 535-8527
www.fasdk12.org
Ferndale Area JSHS 300/7-12
600 Harlan Ave 15905 814-288-5757
Matthew Thomas, prin. Fax 288-5224

Greater Johnstown SD 3,100/PK-12
1091 Broad St 15906 814-533-5650
Dr. James Cekada, supt. Fax 533-5662
www.gjsd.net
Greater Johnstown HS 800/9-12
222 Central Ave 15902 814-533-5601
Michael Dadey, prin. Fax 533-5698
Greater Johnstown MS 600/6-8
280 Decker Ave 15906 814-533-5570
Dino Scarton, prin. Fax 533-5564

Richland SD 1,600/K-12
319 Schoolhouse Rd 15904 814-266-6063
Arnold Nadonley, supt. Fax 266-7349
www.richlandsd.com/
Richland HS 800/7-12
1 Academic Ave 15904 814-266-6081
Brandon Bailey, prin. Fax 269-9506

Westmont Hilltop SD 1,100/K-12
112 Lindberg Ave 15905 814-255-6751
Steve McGee, supt. Fax 255-7735
www.whsd.org
Westmont Hilltop HS 500/7-12
200 Fair Oaks Dr 15905 814-255-8726
Thomas Mitchell, prin. Fax 255-2704

Bishop McCort Catholic HS 400/9-12
25 Osborne St 15905 814-536-8991
Thomas Fleming, prin. Fax 535-4118
Cambria County Christian S 100/PK-12
561 Pike Rd 15909 814-749-7406
Andrew Williams, admin. Fax 749-7028
Cambria-Rowe Business College Post-Sec.
221 Central Ave 15902 814-536-5168
Commonwealth Technical Institute Post-Sec.
727 Goucher St 15905 814-255-8200
Conemaugh Valley Memorial Hospital Post-Sec.
1086 Franklin St 15905 814-534-9118
Divine Mercy Catholic Academy MS 7-8
25 Osborne St 15905 814-536-8991
Keith Kuckenbrod, prin. Fax 535-4118
Greater Johnstown Area Voc Tech School Post-Sec.
445 Schoolhouse Rd 15904 814-266-6073
PA Academy of Cosmetic Arts & Sciences Post-Sec.
2445 Bedford St 15904 814-269-3444
Pennsylvania Highlands Community College Post-Sec.
101 Community College Way 15904 814-262-6400
University of Pittsburgh at Johnstown Post-Sec.
450 Schoolhouse Rd 15904 814-269-7000

Jonestown, Lebanon, Pop. 1,873
Northern Lebanon SD 2,000/K-12
40 Fisher Ave 17038 717-865-2117
Dr. Don Bell, supt. Fax 865-0606
www.norleb.k12.pa.us
Other Schools – See Fredericksburg

Kane, McKean, Pop. 3,695
Kane Area SD 1,200/K-12
400 W Hemlock Ave 16735 814-837-9570
Anna Kearney, supt. Fax 837-7450
www.kasd.net
Kane Area HS 400/9-12
6965 Route 321 16735 814-837-6821
James Fryzlewicz, prin. Fax 837-6158
Kane Area MS 300/6-8
400 W Hemlock Ave 16735 814-837-6030
Todd Stanko, prin. Fax 837-9133

Karns City, Butler, Pop. 209
Karns City Area SD 1,500/K-12
1446 Kittanning Pike 16041 724-756-2030
Eric Ritzert, supt. Fax 756-2121
www.karnscity.k12.pa.us
Karns City JSHS 800/7-12
1446 Kittanning Pike 16041 724-756-2030
Ed Conto, prin. Fax 756-2121

Kennett Square, Chester, Pop. 6,014
Kennett Consolidated SD 4,200/K-12
300 E South St 19348 610-444-6600
Dr. Barry Tomasetti, supt. Fax 444-6614
kcsd.org
Kennett HS 1,200/9-12
100 E South St 19348 610-444-6620
Jeremy Hritz, prin. Fax 444-7013
Other Schools – See Landenberg

Unionville-Chadds Ford SD 4,100/K-12
740 Unionville Rd 19348 610-347-0970
Dr. John Sanville, supt. Fax 347-0976
www.ucfsd.org
Patton MS 1,000/6-8
760 Unionville Rd 19348 610-347-2000
Timothy V. Hoffman, prin. Fax 347-0421
Unionville HS 1,300/9-12
750 Unionville Rd 19348 610-347-1600
James Conley, prin. Fax 347-1890

Kimberton, Chester

Kimberton Waldorf S 300/PK-12
PO Box 350 19442 610-933-3635
Kevin Hughes, dean Fax 935-6985

King of Prussia, Montgomery, Pop. 19,511
Upper Merion Area SD 3,900/K-12
435 Crossfield Rd 19406 610-205-6401
Dr. John Toleno, supt. Fax 205-6433
www.umasd.org
Upper Merion HS 1,100/9-12
440 Crossfield Rd 19406 610-205-3801
Jonathan Bauer, prin. Fax 205-3993
Upper Merion MS 1,200/5-8
450 Keebler Rd 19406 610-205-8801
Dr. Karen Geller, prin. Fax 205-8999

Achieve Test Prep Post-Sec.
1150 1st Ave 19406 267-687-0333
Cortiva Institute - King of Prussia Post-Sec.
211 S Gulph Rd 19406 484-690-1400
DeVry University Post-Sec.
150 Allendale Rd Ste 3250 19406 610-205-3130

Kingsley, Susquehanna
Mountain View SD 1,100/K-12
11748 State Route 106 18826 570-434-2180
Karen Voigt, supt. Fax 434-2404
www.mvsd.net
Mountain View JSHS 500/7-12
11749 State Route 106 18826 570-434-2501
Robert Presley, prin. Fax 434-9582

Kingston, Luzerne, Pop. 12,983
Area Vocational Technical School
Supt. — None
West Side CTC, 75 Evans St 18704 Vo/Tech
Dr. Thomas Viviano, dir. 570-288-8493

Wyoming Valley West SD 4,200/K-12
450 N Maple Ave 18704 570-288-6551
Irvin T. DeRemer, supt. Fax 714-6948
www.wvwsd.org/
Wyoming Valley West MS 1,100/6-8
201 Chester St 18704 570-287-2131
Deborah Troy, prin. Fax 287-6343
Other Schools – See Plymouth

Wyoming Seminary Upper S 400/9-12
201 N Sprague Ave 18704 570-270-2100
Kevin Rea, pres. Fax 270-2199

Kintnersville, Bucks
Palisades SD 1,800/K-12
39 Thomas Free Dr 18930 610-847-5131
Dr. Bridget O'Connell, supt. Fax 847-8116
www.palisadessd.org
Palisades HS 600/9-12
35 Church Hill Rd 18930 610-847-5131
Richard Heffernan, prin. Fax 847-2562
Palisades MS 400/6-8
4710 Durham Rd 18930 610-847-5131
Zachary Fuller, prin. Fax 847-2691

Kinzers, Lancaster
Pequea Valley SD 1,500/K-12
PO Box 130 17535 717-768-5530
Erik Orndorff, supt. Fax 768-7176
www.pequeavalley.org
Pequea Valley HS 500/9-12
PO Box 287 17535 717-768-5500
Arlen Mummau, prin. Fax 768-5523
Pequea Valley IS 300/7-8
PO Box 257 17535 717-768-5535
Sharon Ray, prin. Fax 768-5656

Kittanning, Armstrong, Pop. 3,989
Armstrong SD 3,700/K-12
181 Heritage Park Dr Ste 2 16201 724-548-7200
Chris DeVivo, supt. Fax 548-7201
www.asd.k12.pa.us
Armstrong JSHS 7-12
300 Buffington Dr 16201 724-548-7600
James Rummel, prin.
Other Schools – See Rural Valley

Armstrong County Memorial Hospital Post-Sec.
1 Nolte Dr 16201 724-543-8404
Grace Christian S 100/PK-12
215 Arthur St 16201 724-543-4019
Darlene Edwards, head sch Fax 545-6738
Kittanning Beauty School Post-Sec.
120 Market St 16201 800-833-4247

Knox, Clarion, Pop. 1,139
Keystone SD 1,100/K-12
451 Huston Ave 16232 814-797-5921
Shawn Algoe, supt. Fax 797-2382
www.keyknox.com
Keystone JSHS 500/7-12
700 Beatty Ave 16232 814-797-1261
Brad Wagner, prin. Fax 797-2868

Kutztown, Berks, Pop. 4,969
Kutztown Area SD 1,400/K-12
251 Long Lane Rd 19530 610-683-7361
Katherine Metrick, supt. Fax 683-7230
www.kasd.org
Kutztown Area HS 500/9-12
50 Trexler Ave 19530 610-683-7346
Fax 894-4801
Kutztown Area MS 300/6-8
10 Deisher Ln 19530 610-683-3575
James Brown, prin. Fax 683-5460

Kutztown University of Pennsylvania Post-Sec.
15200 Kutztown Rd 19530 610-683-4000

Lake Ariel, Wayne
Western Wayne SD 2,100/PK-12
1970 Easton Tpke Bldg C 18436 800-321-9973
Joseph Adams, supt. Fax 341-1221
www.westernwayne.org
Western Wayne HS 700/9-12
1970 Easton Tpke Bldg A 18436 800-321-9973
Paul Gregorski, prin.
Western Wayne MS 500/6-8
1970 Easton Tpke Bldg B 18436 800-321-9973
Kristin Donohue, prin.

Canaan Christian Academy 200/PK-12
30 Hemlock Rd 18436 570-937-4848
Michael Boole, prin. Fax 937-4800

Lancaster, Lancaster, Pop. 57,600
Conestoga Valley SD 4,300/K-12
2110 Horseshoe Rd 17601 717-397-2421
Dr. Gerald Huesken, supt. Fax 397-0442
www.conestogavalley.org
Conestoga Valley HS 1,400/9-12
2110 Horseshoe Rd 17601 717-397-5231
Michael Thornton, prin. Fax 397-8841
Conestoga Valley MS 700/7-8
500 Mount Sidney Rd 17602 717-397-1294
Baron Jones, prin. Fax 397-4404

Hempfield SD
Supt. — See Landisville
Centerville MS 600/7-8
865 Centerville Rd 17601 717-898-5580
James Dague, prin. Fax 618-0999

Lampeter-Strasburg SD 3,100/K-12
1600 Book Rd 17602 717-464-3311
Dr. Kevin Peart Ed.D., supt. Fax 464-4699
www.l-spioneers.org
Lampeter-Strasburg HS 1,000/9-12
1600 Book Rd 17602 717-464-3311
Dr. Benjamin Feeney Ed.D., prin. Fax 509-0485
Meylin MS 800/6-8
1600 Book Rd 17602 717-464-3311
Jamie Raum, prin. Fax 509-0289

Lancaster SD 10,700/K-12
251 S Prince St 17603 717-299-2700
Dr. Damaris Rau, supt. Fax 339-6844
www.lancaster.k12.pa.us
Hand MS 500/6-8
431 S Ann St 17602 717-291-6161
Mark Simms, prin. Fax 391-8600
Lincoln MS 500/6-8
1001 Lehigh Ave 17602 717-291-6187
Dr. Josh Keene, prin. Fax 399-6408
McCaskey East HS 9-12
1051 Lehigh Ave 17602 717-291-6172
Bill Jimenez, prin. Fax 391-8601
McCaskey HS 2,500/9-12
445 N Reservoir St 17602 717-291-6211
Bill Jimenez, prin. Fax 390-2567
Phoenix Academy 500/Alt
630 Rockland St 17602 717-735-7860
Aura Heisey, prin. Fax 399-3427
Reynolds MS 600/6-8
605 W Walnut St 17603 717-291-6257
Stephen Sohonyay, prin. Fax 396-6823
Wheatland MS 600/6-8
919 Hamilton Park Dr 17603 717-291-6285
Donald Trost, prin. Fax 399-6411

Manheim Township SD 5,700/K-12
PO Box 5134 17606 717-569-8231
John Nodecker, supt. Fax 569-3729
www.mtwp.net
Manheim Township HS 1,800/9-12
PO Box 5134 17606 717-560-3097
Deborah Mitchell, prin. Fax 569-2806
Manheim Township MS 900/7-8
PO Box 5134 17606 717-560-3111
Karen Evans, prin. Fax 569-1670

Penn Manor SD 4,700/K-12
2950 Charlestown Rd 17603 717-872-9500
Dr. Michael Leichliter, supt. Fax 872-9505
www.pennmanor.net
Manor MS 500/7-8
2950 Charlestown Rd 17603 717-872-9510
Dr. Dana Edwards, prin. Fax 872-9505
Other Schools – See Millersville, Pequea

Consolidated School of Business Post-Sec.
2124 Ambassador Cir 17603 717-394-6211
Empire Beauty School Post-Sec.
1801 Columbia Ave 17603 717-394-8561
Franklin & Marshall College Post-Sec.
PO Box 3003 17604 717-291-3911
Lancaster Bible College Post-Sec.
901 Eden Rd 17601 717-569-7071
Lancaster Country Day S 600/PK-12
725 Hamilton Rd 17603 717-392-2916
Stephen Lisk, head sch Fax 392-0425
Lancaster Co. Christian S - Leola Campus 300/PK-12
2390 New Holland Pike 17601 717-556-0711
Becky Sprenkle, prin. Fax 656-4868
Lancaster General College of Nursing Post-Sec.
410 N Lime St 17602 800-622-5443
Lancaster HS 800/9-12
650 Juliette Ave 17601 717-509-0315
Terry Klugh, prin. Fax 509-0312
Lancaster Mennonite HS 800/6-12
2176 Lincoln Hwy E 17602 717-299-0436
J. Richard Thomas, supt. Fax 299-0823
Lancaster School of Cosmetology Post-Sec.
50 Ranck Ave 17602 717-299-0200
Lancaster Theological Seminary Post-Sec.
555 W James St 17603 717-393-0654
Pennsylvania College of Art and Design Post-Sec.
PO Box 59 17608 717-396-7833
Thaddeus Stevens College of Technology Post-Sec.
750 E King St 17602 717-299-7730
YTI Career Institute Post-Sec.
3050 Hempland Rd 17601 717-295-1100

Landenberg, Chester
Kennett Consolidated SD
Supt. — See Kennett Square
Kennett MS, 195 Sunny Dell Rd 19350 1,000/6-8
Lorenzo DeAngelis, prin. 610-268-5800

Landisville, Lancaster, Pop. 1,881
Hempfield SD 6,800/K-12
200 Church St 17538 717-898-5564
Dr. Brenda Becker, supt. Fax 898-5628
www.hempfieldsd.org
Hempfield HS 2,200/9-12
200 Stanley Ave 17538 717-898-5510
Dr. Wilbur Stout, prin. Fax 618-1210
Landisville Education Center Alt
220 Church St 17538 717-406-3400
Brendan Cregan, prin. Fax 618-1992
Landisville MS 500/7-8
340 Mumma Dr 17538 717-898-5607
Douglas Dandridge, prin. Fax 618-0871
Other Schools – See Lancaster

Langhorne, Bucks, Pop. 1,596
Neshaminy SD 7,700/K-12
2001 Old Lincoln Hwy 19047 215-809-6500
Joseph Jones, supt. Fax 809-6502
www.neshaminy.k12.pa.us
Maple Point MS 1,000/6-8
2250 Langhorne Yardley Rd 19047 215-809-6230
Matthew Sokol, prin.
Neshaminy HS 2,600/9-12
2001 Old Lincoln Hwy 19047 215-809-6102
Dr. Rob McGee Ph.D., prin.
Other Schools – See Feasterville, Levittown

Cairn University Post-Sec.
200 Manor Ave 19047 215-752-5800
Woods Services Post-Sec.
PO Box 36 19047 800-782-3646

Lansdale, Montgomery, Pop. 15,885
Area Vocational Technical School
Supt. — None
North Montco Tech Career Center Vo/Tech
1265 Sumneytown Pike 19446 215-368-1177
Michael Lucas, dir.

North Penn SD 12,700/K-12
401 E Hancock St 19446 215-368-0400
Dr. Curtis Dietrich, supt. Fax 368-3161
www.npenn.org
North Penn HS 3,000/10-12
1340 S Valley Forge Rd 19446 215-368-9800
Todd Bauer, prin. Fax 855-0632
Penndale MS 1,400/7-9
400 Penn St 19446 215-368-2700
Dr. Sean O'Sullivan, prin. Fax 368-6817
Other Schools – See Hatfield, North Wales

Calvary Baptist S 400/PK-12
1380 S Valley Forge Rd 19446 215-368-1100
Randall Thaxton, admin. Fax 368-1003
Calvary Baptist Theological Seminary Post-Sec.
1380 S Valley Forge Rd 19446 215-368-7538
Dock Mennonite Academy 400/9-12
1000 Forty Foot Rd 19446 215-362-2675
Dr. Conrad J. Swartzentruber, supt. Fax 362-2943
Lansdale Catholic HS 800/9-12
700 Lansdale Ave 19446 215-362-6160
Rita McGovern, prin. Fax 362-5746
Lansdale School of Cosmetology Post-Sec.
215 W Main St 19446 215-362-2322

Lansdowne, Delaware, Pop. 10,265
William Penn SD 5,200/K-12
100 Green Ave 19050 610-284-8000
Joseph Bruni, supt. Fax 284-8054
www.williampennsd.org
Penn Wood HS Green Ave Campus 700/11-12
100 Green Ave 19050 610-284-8080
Dr. D. Brandon Cooley, prin. Fax 284-2141
Other Schools – See Darby, Yeadon

Lansford, Carbon, Pop. 3,876
Panther Valley SD 1,000/K-12
1 Panther Way 18232 570-645-4248
Dennis Kergick, supt. Fax 645-6232
www.panthervalley.org/
Panther Valley JSHS 300/7-12
912 Coal Region Way 18232 570-645-2171
Joseph Gunnels, prin. Fax 645-2507

La Plume, Lackawanna

Keystone College Post-Sec.
PO Box 50 18440 570-945-8000

Laporte, Sullivan, Pop. 316
Sullivan County SD 600/K-12
PO Box 240 18626 570-946-8200
Patricia A. Cross, supt. Fax 946-8210
www.sulcosd.k12.pa.us
Sullivan County JSHS 300/7-12
PO Box 98 18626 570-946-7001
Edward J. Pietroski, prin. Fax 946-5070

Latrobe, Westmoreland, Pop. 8,261
Area Vocational Technical School
Supt. — None
Eastern Westmoreland CTC Vo/Tech
4904 State Route 982 15650 724-539-9788
Marie Bowers, dir. Fax 539-1907

Greater Latrobe SD 3,700/K-12
1816 Lincoln Ave 15650 724-539-4200
Judith Swigart, supt. Fax 539-4202
www.glsd.us
Greater Latrobe HS 1,000/9-12
131 High School Rd 15650 724-539-4225
Jon Mains, prin. Fax 539-4295
Greater Latrobe JHS 700/7-8
130 High School Rd 15650 724-539-4265
Matt Shivetts, prin. Fax 539-4223

Latrobe Area Hospital Post-Sec.
101 W 2nd Ave 15650 724-537-1001
St. Vincent College Post-Sec.
300 Fraser Purchase Rd 15650 724-532-6600
St. Vincent Seminary Post-Sec.
300 Fraser Purchase Rd 15650 724-805-2592

Laureldale, Berks, Pop. 3,857
Muhlenberg SD 3,500/K-12
801 E Bellevue Ave 19605 610-921-8000
Dr. Joseph Macharola, supt. Fax 921-8076
www.muhlsdk12.org
Muhlenberg MS 900/7-9
801 E Bellevue Ave 19605 610-921-8034
Jeffery Ebert, prin. Fax 921-8038
Other Schools – See Reading

Lebanon, Lebanon, Pop. 25,113
Area Vocational Technical School
Supt. — None
Lebanon County CTC Vo/Tech
833 Metro Dr 17042 717-273-8551
George Custer, dir. Fax 273-0534

Cornwall-Lebanon SD 4,600/K-12
105 E Evergreen Rd 17042 717-272-2031
Dr. Philip Domencic, supt. Fax 274-2786
www.clsd.k12.pa.us
Cedar Crest HS 1,500/9-12
115 E Evergreen Rd 17042 717-272-2033
Nicole Malinoski, prin. Fax 389-1823
Cedar Crest MS 1,100/6-8
101 E Evergreen Rd 17042 717-272-2032
Dean Bozman, prin. Fax 389-1856

Lebanon SD 4,800/PK-12
1000 S 8th St 17042 717-273-9391
Dr. Marianne Bartley, supt. Fax 270-6778
www.lebanon.k12.pa.us
Lebanon HS 1,200/9-12
1000 S 8th St 17042 717-273-9391
William Giovino, prin. Fax 270-6778
Lebanon MS 1,000/6-8
350 N 8th St 17046 717-273-9391
Dawn Connelly, prin. Fax 270-6859

Empire Beauty School Post-Sec.
1776 Quentin Rd 17042 717-272-3323
Lebanon Catholic S 300/PK-12
1400 Chestnut St 17042 717-273-3731
Rose Kury, prin. Fax 274-5167
New Covenant Christian S 200/PK-12
452 Ebenezer Rd 17046 717-274-2423
James Hubbard, prin. Fax 274-9830

Leechburg, Armstrong, Pop. 2,128
Kiski Area SD 3,700/K-12
250 Hyde Park Rd 15656 724-845-2022
Dr. Timothy Scott, supt. Fax 842-0444
www.kiskiarea.com
Kiski Area HS 1,300/9-12
250 Hyde Park Rd 15656 724-845-8181
Chad Roland, prin. Fax 842-0403
Kiski Area IS 600/7-8
260 Hyde Park Rd 15656 724-845-2219
Michael Cardamone, prin. Fax 845-3208

Leechburg Area SD 800/K-12
210 Penn Ave 15656 724-842-9681
Tiffany Nix M.Ed., supt. Fax 845-2241
www.leechburg.k12.pa.us
Leechburg Area HS 200/9-12
215 1st Ave 15656 724-842-0571
Matthew Kruluts B.S., prin. Fax 845-4761
Leechburg Area JHS 200/7-8
215 1st Ave 15656 724-842-0571
Matthew Kruluts B.S., prin. Fax 845-4761

Leesport, Berks, Pop. 1,904
Area Vocational Technical School
Supt. — None
Berks CTC - West Vo/Tech
1057 County Road 19533 610-374-4073
Christian Hansen, prin. Fax 987-6106

Schuylkill Valley SD 2,000/K-12
929 Lakeshore Dr 19533 610-916-0957
Dr. Warren Mata, supt. Fax 926-3960
www.schuylkillvalley.org/
Schuylkill Valley HS 600/9-12
929 Lakeshore Dr 19533 610-926-1706
Patrick Sasse, prin. Fax 926-8341
Schuylkill Valley MS 600/5-8
114 Ontelaunee Dr 19533 610-926-7111
Michael Mitchell, prin. Fax 926-3321

Leetsdale, Allegheny, Pop. 1,172
Quaker Valley SD 1,900/K-12
100 Leetsdale Industrial Dr 15056 412-749-3600
Dr. Heidi Ondek, supt. Fax 749-3601
www.qvsd.org
Quaker Valley HS 600/9-12
625 Beaver St 15056 412-749-6020
Deborah Riccobelli, prin. Fax 749-1226
Other Schools – See Sewickley

Lehighton, Carbon, Pop. 5,438
Lehighton Area SD 2,400/K-12
1000 Union St 18235 610-377-4490
Jonathan J. Cleaver, supt. Fax 577-0035
www.lehighton.org/
Lehighton Area HS 700/9-12
1 Indian Ln 18235 610-377-6180
Craig Reichl, prin. Fax 377-1852
Lehighton Area MS 700/5-8
301 Beaver Run Rd 18235 610-377-6535
Mark McGalla Ph.D., prin. Fax 377-6503

Lehman, Luzerne
Lake-Lehman SD
Supt. — See Dallas
Lake-Lehman JSHS 900/7-12
PO Box 38 18627 570-675-7458
Douglas Klopp, prin. Fax 674-2951

Penn State Wilkes-Barre Post-Sec.
PO Box PSU 18627 570-675-2171

Lemont Furnace, Fayette, Pop. 807

Penn State Fayette Eberly Campus Post-Sec.
2201 University Dr 15456 724-430-4100

Leola, Lancaster, Pop. 7,126

Veritas Academy 200/PK-12
26 Hillcrest Ave 17540 717-556-0690
G. Tyler Fischer, hdmstr. Fax 556-0736

Lester, Delaware

All-State Career School Post-Sec.
501 Seminole St 19029 610-521-1818

Levittown, Bucks, Pop. 52,008
Bristol Township SD 6,200/K-12
6401 Mill Creek Rd 19057 215-943-3200
Dr. Melanie Gehrens, supt. Fax 949-8889
www.btsd.us
Truman HS 1,500/9-12
3001 Green Ln 19057 215-547-3000
James Moore, prin. Fax 547-4802
Other Schools – See Bristol, Fairless Hills

Neshaminy SD
Supt. — See Langhorne
Sandburg MS 500/6-8
30 Harmony Rd 19056 215-809-6220
Dawn Kelly, prin. Fax 809-6701

Levittown Beauty Academy Post-Sec.
8919 New Falls Rd 19054 215-943-0298

Lewisberry, York, Pop. 357
West Shore SD 7,600/K-12
507 Fishing Creek Rd 17339 717-938-9577
Dr. Todd Stoltz, supt. Fax 938-2779
www.wssd.k12.pa.us
Crossroads MS 700/6-8
535 Fishing Creek Rd 17339 717-932-1295
Christopher Konieczny, prin. Fax 938-3599
Red Land HS 1,100/9-12
560 Fishing Creek Rd 17339 717-938-6561
Holly Sayre, prin. Fax 938-0886
Other Schools – See Camp Hill, New Cumberland

Lewisburg, Union, Pop. 5,667
Lewisburg Area SD 1,900/K-12
1951 Washington Ave 17837 570-523-3220
Cathy Moser, supt. Fax 522-3278
www.dragon.k12.pa.us
Eichhorn MS 400/6-8
2057 Washington Ave 17837 570-523-3220
George Drogin, prin. Fax 522-3331
Lewisburg Area HS 600/9-12
815 Market St 17837 570-523-3220
David Himes, prin. Fax 524-9484

Bucknell University Post-Sec.
1 Dent Dr 17837 570-577-2000

Lewistown, Mifflin, Pop. 8,199
Area Vocational Technical School
Supt. — None
Academy Vo/Tech
700 Pitt St 17044 717-248-3933
Daniel Potutschnig, dir. Fax 248-5148

Mifflin County SD 5,100/K-12
201 8th St 17044 717-248-0148
James Estep, supt. Fax 248-5345
www.mcsdk12.org
Mifflin County HS 1,200/10-12
501 6th St 17044 717-242-0240
Mark Crosson, prin. Fax 447-2600
Mifflin County JHS 900/8-9
700 Cedar St 17044 717-248-5441
Mike Zinobile, prin. Fax 242-5806

Mifflin-Juniata Career & Technology Ctr Post-Sec.
700 Pitt St 17044 717-248-3933

Liberty, Tioga, Pop. 247
Southern Tioga SD
Supt. — See Blossburg

North Penn - Liberty JSHS 200/7-12
8675 Route 414 16930 570-324-2071
Joseph Eglesia, prin. Fax 324-2313

Ligonier, Westmoreland, Pop. 1,565
Ligonier Valley SD 1,600/K-12
339 W Main St 15658 724-238-5696
Dr. Christine Oldham Ed.D., supt. Fax 238-7877
lvsd.k12.pa.us
Ligonier Valley HS 500/9-12
40 Springer Rd 15658 724-238-9531
Timothy Kantor, prin. Fax 238-2675
Ligonier Valley MS 400/6-8
536 Bell Street Ext 15658 724-238-6412
David Steimer, prin. Fax 238-2358

Limerick, Montgomery
Area Vocational Technical School
Supt. — None
Western Montgomery Career/Technology Ctr Vo/Tech
77 Gratersford Rd 19468 610-489-7272
Christopher Moritzen, dir.

Lincoln University, Chester, Pop. 1,678

Lincoln University Post-Sec.
PO Box 179 19352 484-365-8000

Linesville, Crawford, Pop. 1,024
Conneaut SD 1,300/K-12
219 W School Dr 16424 814-683-5900
Jarrin Sperry, supt. Fax 683-4127
www.conneautsd.org
Conneaut Area SHS 300/9-12
302 W School Dr 16424 814-683-5551
David Maskrey, prin. Fax 683-5221
Other Schools – See Conneaut Lake, Conneautville

Lititz, Lancaster, Pop. 9,235
Warwick SD 4,300/K-12
301 W Orange St 17543 717-626-3734
Dr. April Hershey, supt. Fax 626-3850
www.warwicksd.org/
Warwick HS 1,400/9-12
301 W Orange St 17543 717-626-3700
Ryan Axe, prin. Fax 626-6199
Warwick MS 700/7-8
401 Maple St 17543 717-626-3701
Dr. Michael Smith, prin. Fax 627-6089

Linden Hall 200/6-12
212 E Main St 17543 717-626-8512
Michael Waylett, head sch Fax 627-1384
Lititz Christian S 300/PK-12
501 W Lincoln Ave 17543 717-626-9518
Rick Bernhardt, admin. Fax 626-9028
New Haven Mennonite S 100/1-12
225 Crest Rd 17543 717-626-1603
Linford Weaver, prin.

Littlestown, Adams, Pop. 4,373
Littlestown Area SD 1,700/K-12
162 Newark St 17340 717-359-4146
Christopher Bigger, supt. Fax 359-9617
www.lasd.k12.pa.us
Littlestown HS 700/9-12
200 E Myrtle St 17340 717-359-4146
Dr. Matthew Meakin, prin. Fax 359-9461
Maple Avenue MS 500/5-8
75 Maple Ave 17340 717-359-4146
Eric Naylor, prin. Fax 359-9617

Lock Haven, Clinton, Pop. 9,648

Lock Haven University Post-Sec.
401 N Fairview St 17745 570-484-2011

Loretto, Cambria, Pop. 1,282

St. Francis University Post-Sec.
PO Box 600 15940 814-472-3000

Lower Burrell, Westmoreland, Pop. 11,648
Burrell SD 1,800/K-12
1021 Puckety Church Rd 15068 724-334-1406
Shannon Wagner, supt. Fax 334-1429
www.burrell.k12.pa.us
Burrell HS 600/9-12
1021 Puckety Church Rd 15068 724-334-1403
Dr. John Boylan, prin. Fax 334-1420
Huston MS 400/6-8
1020 Puckety Church Rd 15068 724-334-1443
Brian Ferra, prin. Fax 334-1434

Loysburg, Bedford
Northern Bedford County SD 1,000/PK-12
152 NBC Dr 16659 814-766-2221
Todd B. Beatty, supt. Fax 766-3772
www.nbcsd.org/
Northern Bedford County HS 300/9-12
152 NBC Dr 16659 814-766-2221
Michael O'Dellick, prin. Fax 766-3772
Northern Bedford County MS 200/6-8
152 NBC Dr 16659 814-766-2221
Wayne Sherlock, prin. Fax 766-3772

Lykens, Dauphin, Pop. 1,762
Upper Dauphin Area SD 1,300/K-12
5668 State Route 209 17048 717-362-8134
Evan Williams, supt. Fax 362-3050
www.udasd.org/
Upper Dauphin Area MS 400/5-8
5668 State Route 209 17048 717-362-8177
Jared Shade, prin. Fax 362-6567
Other Schools – See Elizabethville

Mc Alisterville, Juniata, Pop. 971
Juniata County SD
Supt. — See Mifflintown
East Juniata JSHS 500/7-12
32944 Route 35 N 17049 717-463-2111
Benjamin Fausey, prin. Fax 463-3268

Juniata Mennonite S | 200/K-12
289 Leonard Hill Rd 17049 | 717-463-2898
Tom Getz, admin. | Fax 884-7876

Mc Clellandtown, Fayette
Albert Gallatin Area SD
Supt. — See Uniontown
Gallatin North MS | 400/6-8
113 College Ave 15458 | 724-737-5423
Randy Wilson, prin. | Fax 737-5312

Mc Connellsburg, Fulton, Pop. 1,183
Area Vocational Technical School
Supt. — None
Fulton County AVTS | Vo/Tech
145 E Cherry St 17233 | 717-485-5813
Tony Payne, dir.

Central Fulton SD | 1,000/PK-12
151 E Cherry St 17233 | 717-485-3183
Dixie Paruch, supt. | Fax 485-5984
www.cfsd.info
Mc Connellsburg HS | 300/9-12
151 E Cherry St 17233 | 717-485-3195
Erich May, prin. | Fax 485-0175
Mc Connellsburg MS | 200/6-8
151 E Cherry St 17233 | 717-485-3195
Erich May, prin. | Fax 485-0175

Mc Donald, Washington, Pop. 2,125
Fort Cherry SD | 1,000/K-12
110 Fort Cherry Rd 15057 | 724-796-1551
Dr. Jill Jacoby, supt. | Fax 796-0065
www.fortcherry.org
Fort Cherry HS | 300/10-12
110 Fort Cherry Rd 15057 | 724-796-1551
Robert N. Motte, prin. | Fax 356-2769
Fort Cherry JHS | 100/7-9
110 Fort Cherry Rd 15057 | 724-796-1551
Daniel Mayer, prin. | Fax 356-2769

South Fayette Township SD | 2,800/K-12
3680 Old Oakdale Rd 15057 | 412-221-4542
Dr. Bille Rondinelli, supt. | Fax 693-2883
www.southfayette.org
South Fayette Township HS | 800/9-12
3640 Old Oakdale Rd 15057 | 412-221-4542
Aaron Skrbin, prin. | Fax 693-9843
South Fayette Township MS | 600/6-8
3700 Old Oakdale Rd 15057 | 412-221-4542
Kristin Deichler, prin. | Fax 693-0860

Mc Keesport, Allegheny, Pop. 18,886
Area Vocational Technical School
Supt. — None
McKeesport Area Tech Center | Vo/Tech
1960 Eden Park Blvd, | 412-664-3664
Dr. Rula Skezas, dir. | Fax 664-3784

McKeesport Area SD | 3,100/K-12
3590 Oneil Blvd, | 412-664-3610
Dr. Rula Skezas, supt. | Fax 664-3638
www.mckasd.net
Founders Hall MS | 500/7-8
3600 Oneil Blvd, | 412-664-3690
Paul Sebelia, prin. | Fax 664-3768
McKeesport Area HS | 1,100/9-12
1960 Eden Park Blvd, | 412-664-3650
Thomas Bauman, prin. | Fax 664-3787

South Allegheny SD | 1,600/PK-12
2743 Washington Blvd, | 412-675-3070
Richard M. Fine, supt. | Fax 672-2836
www.southallegheny.org
South Allegheny MSHS | 800/7-12
2743 Washington Blvd, | 412-675-3070
Jeffrey Solomon, prin. | Fax 673-4903

Penn State Greater Allegheny | Post-Sec.
4000 University Dr 15131 | 412-675-9000
Serra Catholic HS | 400/9-12
200 Hershey Dr, | 412-751-2020
Timothy Chirdon, prin. | Fax 751-3488

Mc Kees Rocks, Allegheny, Pop. 5,853
Montour SD | 2,800/K-12
225 Clever Rd 15136 | 412-490-6500
Michael Ghilani, supt. | Fax 788-1196
www.montourschools.com
Montour HS | 1,000/9-12
223 Clever Rd 15136 | 412-490-6500
Todd Price, prin. | Fax 494-9747
Other Schools – See Coraopolis

Sto-Rox SD | 900/K-12
600 Russellwood Ave 15136 | 412-771-3213
Frank Dalmas, supt. | Fax 771-5205
www.srsd.k12.pa.us
Sto-Rox JSHS | 400/7-12
1105 Valley St 15136 | 412-771-3213
Tim Beck, prin. | Fax 771-8395

Ohio Valley General Hospital | Post-Sec.
25 Heckel Rd 15136 | 412-777-6207
Robinson Township Christian S | 100/PK-12
77 Phillips Ln 15136 | 412-787-5919
Arthur Broadwick, prin. | Fax 787-1558

Mc Murray, Washington, Pop. 4,622
Peters Township SD | 4,300/K-12
631 E McMurray Rd 15317 | 724-941-6251
Dr. Jeannine French, supt. | Fax 941-6565
www.ptsd.k12.pa.us
Peters Township HS | 1,500/9-12
264 E McMurray Rd 15317 | 724-941-6250
Lori Pavlik, prin. | Fax 942-0915
Peters Township MS | 700/7-8
625 E McMurray Rd 15317 | 724-941-2688
Adam Sikorski, prin. | Fax 941-1426

Mc Sherrystown, Adams, Pop. 3,006

Delone Catholic HS | 500/9-12
140 S Oxford Ave 17344 | 717-637-5969
Dr. Maureen Thiec, prin. | Fax 637-0442

Macungie, Lehigh, Pop. 3,024
East Penn SD
Supt. — See Emmaus
Eyer MS, 5616 Buckeye Rd 18062 | 900/6-8
Michael Kelly, prin. | 610-965-1600
Lower Macungie MS | 1,100/6-8
6299 Lower Macungie Rd 18062 | 610-395-8593
Suzanne Vincent, prin. | Fax 398-4385

Salem Christian S | 200/PK-12
8031 Salem Bible Church Rd 18062 | 610-966-5823
Mark Stanton, head sch | Fax 965-8368

Mahanoy City, Schuylkill, Pop. 4,109
Mahanoy Area SD | 1,000/K-12
1 Golden Bear Dr 17948 | 570-773-3443
Dr. Joie Green, supt. | Fax 773-2913
www.mabears.net
Mahanoy Area HS | 300/9-12
1 Golden Bear Dr 17948 | 570-773-3443
Thomas Smith, prin. | Fax 773-4020
Mahanoy Area MS | 300/5-8
1 Golden Bear Dr 17948 | 570-773-3443
Michael Heater, prin. | Fax 773-4034

Malvern, Chester, Pop. 2,955
Great Valley SD | 4,000/K-12
47 Church Rd 19355 | 610-889-2100
Dr. Regina Palubinsky, supt. | Fax 889-2120
www.gvsd.org
Great Valley HS | 1,200/9-12
225 Phoenixville Pike 19355 | 610-889-1900
Michael Flick, prin. | Fax 695-8901
Great Valley MS | 1,000/6-8
255 Phoenixville Pike 19355 | 610-644-6440
Dr. Edward Souders, prin. | Fax 889-1166

Malvern Prep S | 600/6-12
418 S Warren Ave 19355 | 484-595-1100
Christian Talbot, head sch | Fax 595-1124
Penn State Great Valley Grad Prof Stds | Post-Sec.
30 E Swedesford Rd 19355 | 610-648-3200
Phelps S | 100/6-12
583 Sugartown Rd 19355 | 610-644-1754
Daniel Knopp, head sch | Fax 540-0156
Villa Maria Academy | 400/9-12
370 Old Lincoln Hwy 19355 | 610-644-2551
Sr. Regina Ryan, prin. | Fax 644-2866

Manchester, York, Pop. 2,703
Northeastern York SD | 3,700/K-12
41 Harding St 17345 | 717-266-3667
Dr. Stacey Sidle, supt. | Fax 266-5792
www.nesd.k12.pa.us
Northeastern HS | 1,000/9-12
300 High St 17345 | 717-266-3644
Mathew Gay, prin. | Fax 266-0616
Other Schools – See Mount Wolf

Manheim, Lancaster, Pop. 4,777
Manheim Central SD | 2,400/K-12
71 N Hazel St 17545 | 717-664-8540
Dr. Norman Hatten, supt. | Fax 664-8539
www.manheimcentral.org
Manheim Central HS | 900/9-12
400 Adele Ave 17545 | 717-664-8400
Jeffrey Hughes, prin. | Fax 664-8420
Manheim Central MS | 400/7-8
261 White Oak Rd 17545 | 717-664-1700
Scott Richardson, prin. | Fax 664-1859

Mansfield, Tioga, Pop. 3,545
Southern Tioga SD
Supt. — See Blossburg
North Penn - Mansfield JSHS | 400/7-12
73 W Wellsboro St 16933 | 570-662-2674
Bill David, prin. | Fax 662-2808

Mansfield University of Pennsylvania | Post-Sec.
71 S Academy St 16933 | 570-662-4000
New Covenant Academy | 200/PK-12
310 Extension St 16933 | 570-662-2996
Bruce Reagan, admin. | Fax 662-0272

Maple Glen, Montgomery, Pop. 6,682
Upper Dublin SD | 4,300/K-12
1580 Fort Washington Ave 19002 | 215-643-8800
Dr. Deborah Wheeler, supt. | Fax 643-8808
www.udsd.org
Other Schools – See Dresher, Fort Washington

Marienville, Forest, Pop. 3,126
Forest Area SD
Supt. — See Tionesta
East Forest JSHS | 100/7-12
120 W Birch St 16239 | 814-927-6688
Debra Arner, prin. | Fax 927-8452

Marion Center, Indiana, Pop. 450
Marion Center Area SD | 1,400/PK-12
PO Box 156 15759 | 724-397-5551
Clint Weimer, supt. | Fax 397-9144
www.mcasd.net/
Marion Center Area JSHS | 700/7-12
PO Box 209 15759 | 724-397-5551
Matt Jioio, prin. | Fax 397-9162

Markleysburg, Fayette, Pop. 283
Uniontown Area SD
Supt. — See Uniontown
McMullen MS | 200/6-8
4773 National Pike 15459 | 724-329-8811
Tracy Holesapple, prin. | Fax 329-4696

Mar Lin, Schuylkill, Pop. 649
Area Vocational Technical School
Supt. — None
Schuylkill Technology Center - South | Vo/Tech
PO Box 110 17951 | 570-544-4748
Stacey Minahan, admin. | Fax 544-3895

Mars, Butler, Pop. 1,685
Mars Area SD | 3,300/K-12
545 Route 228 16046 | 724-625-1518
Dr. Wesley Shipley, supt. | Fax 625-1060
www.marsk12.org
Mars Area HS | 1,000/9-12
520 Route 228 16046 | 724-625-1581
Lindsay Rosswog, prin. | Fax 625-4541
Mars Area MS | 500/7-8
1775 Three Degree Rd 16046 | 724-625-3145
Todd Kolson, prin. | Fax 625-2147

Martinsburg, Blair, Pop. 1,949
Spring Cove SD
Supt. — See Roaring Spring
Central HS | 500/9-12
718 Central High Rd 16662 | 814-793-2111
David Crumrine, prin. | Fax 793-4942

Meadville, Crawford, Pop. 13,058
Area Vocational Technical School
Supt. — None
Crawford County CTC | Vo/Tech
860 Thurston Rd 16335 | 814-724-6024
Kevin Sprong, dir. | Fax 337-0602

Crawford Central SD | 3,800/K-12
11280 Mercer Pike 16335 | 814-724-3960
Thomas Washington, supt. | Fax 333-8731
www.craw.org
Meadville Area HS | 800/9-12
930 North St 16335 | 814-336-1121
John Higgins, prin. | Fax 337-1486
Meadville Area MS | 500/7-8
974 North St 16335 | 814-333-1188
Scott Lynch, prin. | Fax 333-2799
Other Schools – See Cochranton

Allegheny College | Post-Sec.
520 N Main St 16335 | 814-332-3100
Calvary Baptist Christian Academy | 200/PK-12
543 Randolph St 16335 | 814-724-6606
Daryl Van Norman, admin. | Fax 337-4357
Laurel Technical Institute | Post-Sec.
847 N Main St Ste 204 16335 | 814-724-0700
Precision Manufacturing Institute | Post-Sec.
764 Bessemer St 16335 | 814-333-2415

Mechanicsburg, Cumberland, Pop. 8,802
Area Vocational Technical School
Supt. — None
Cumberland-Perry AVTS | Vo/Tech
110 Old Willow Mill Rd 17050 | 717-697-0354
Justin Bruhn, dir. | Fax 697-0592

Cumberland Valley SD | 8,300/K-12
6746 Carlisle Pike 17050 | 717-697-8261
Frederick Withum, supt. | Fax 506-3302
www.cvschools.org
Cumberland Valley HS | 2,600/9-12
6746 Carlisle Pike 17050 | 717-766-0217
Judy Baumgardner, prin. | Fax 506-3777
Eagle View MS | 900/6-8
6746 Carlisle Pike 17050 | 717-766-0217
John Gallagher, prin. | Fax 506-3806
Good Hope MS | 1,000/6-8
451 Skyport Rd 17050 | 717-761-1865
Jeff Hosenfeld, prin. | Fax 761-5910

Mechanicsburg Area SD | 3,800/K-12
100 E Elmwood Ave 17055 | 717-691-4500
Mark K. Leidy Ed.D., supt. | Fax 691-3438
www.mbgsd.org
Mechanicsburg Area HS | 1,200/9-12
500 S Broad St 17055 | 717-691-4530
David R. Harris, prin. | Fax 691-7632
Mechanicsburg MS | 900/6-8
1750 S Market St 17055 | 717-691-4560
Joel A. Yohn, prin. | Fax 791-7977

Messiah College | Post-Sec.
1 College Ave 17055 | 717-766-2511

Media, Delaware, Pop. 5,231
Rose Tree Media SD | 3,700/K-12
308 N Olive St 19063 | 610-627-6000
James Wigo, supt. | Fax 891-0959
www.rtmsd.org
Penncrest HS | 1,300/9-12
134 Barren Rd 19063 | 610-627-6200
Ralph Harrison, prin. | Fax 891-0898
Springton Lake MS | 800/6-8
1900 N Providence Rd 19063 | 610-627-6500
Dr. Robert Salladino, prin. | Fax 566-8665

Delaware County Community College | Post-Sec.
901 Media Line Rd 19063 | 610-359-5000
Penn State Brandywine | Post-Sec.
25 Yearsley Mill Rd 19063 | 610-892-1200
Pennsylvania Institute of Technology | Post-Sec.
800 Manchester Ave 19063 | 610-892-1500
Williamson Free School of Mech. Trades | Post-Sec.
106 S New Middletown Rd 19063 | 610-566-1776

Melrose Park, Montgomery, Pop. 6,500

Gratz College | Post-Sec.
7605 Old York Rd 19027 | 215-635-7300

Mercer, Mercer, Pop. 1,978
Area Vocational Technical School
Supt. — None

Mercer County Career Center Vo/Tech
776 Greenville Rd 16137 724-662-3000
Rachel Martin, dir. Fax 662-1025

Mercer Area SD 1,200/K-12
545 W Butler St 16137 724-662-5100
Dr. William Gathers, supt. Fax 662-5109
www.mercer.k12.pa.us
Mercer Area HS 400/9-12
545 W Butler St 16137 724-662-5104
Michael Piddington, prin. Fax 662-2993
Mercer Area MS 200/7-8
545 W Butler St 16137 724-662-5104
Michael Piddington, prin. Fax 662-2993

Mercersburg, Franklin, Pop. 1,540
Tuscarora SD 2,600/K-12
100 W Seminary St 17236 717-328-3127
Dr. Nadine Sanders, supt. Fax 328-9316
www.tus.k12.pa.us
Buchanan HS 800/9-12
4773 Fort Loudon Rd 17236 717-328-2146
Rodney Benedick, prin. Fax 328-5428
Buchanan MS 600/6-8
5191 Fort Loudon Rd 17236 717-328-5221
James Carbaugh, prin. Fax 328-9081

Mercersburg Academy 400/9-12
300 E Seminary St 17236 717-328-6173
Katherine Titus, head sch

Merion Station, Montgomery, Pop. 700

Kohelet Yeshiva HS 100/9-12
223 N Highland Ave 19066 610-667-2020
Rabbi Gil Perl, head sch Fax 667-2223
Merion Mercy Academy 500/9-12
511 Montgomery Ave 19066 610-664-6655
Sr. Barbara Buckley, prin. Fax 664-6322

Mertztown, Berks, Pop. 656
Brandywine Heights Area SD
Supt. — See Topton
Brandywine Heights HS 600/9-12
103 Old Topton Rd 19539 610-682-5102
Josh Ziatyk, prin. Fax 682-5139

Meyersdale, Somerset, Pop. 2,169
Meyersdale Area SD 900/K-12
309 Industrial Park Rd 15552 814-634-5123
Dr. Tracey Karlie, supt. Fax 634-0832
www.masd.net
Meyersdale Area HS 300/9-12
1349 Shaw Mines Rd 15552 814-634-5123
John Wiltrout, prin. Fax 634-0832
Meyersdale Area MS 200/6-8
1353 Shaw Mines Rd 15552 814-634-5123
Wayne Miller, prin. Fax 634-0832

Middleburg, Snyder, Pop. 1,296
Midd-West SD 2,100/K-12
568 E Main St 17842 570-837-0046
Richard J. Musselman, supt. Fax 837-3018
www.mwsd.cc
Midd-West HS 800/8-12
540 E Main St 17842 570-837-0046
Cynthia L. Hutchinson, prin. Fax 837-5267

Middletown, Dauphin, Pop. 8,620
Middletown Area SD 2,300/K-12
55 W Water St 17057 717-948-3300
Lori Suski Ed.D., supt. Fax 948-3329
www.raiderweb.org
Middletown Area HS 700/9-12
1155 N Union St 17057 717-948-3333
Michael Carnes, prin. Fax 948-3359
Middletown Area MS 600/6-8
215 Oberlin Rd 17057 717-930-0739
Kevin Cook, prin. Fax 944-0951

Penn State Harrisburg Post-Sec.
777 W Harrisburg Pike 17057 717-948-6250

Midland, Beaver, Pop. 2,534
Western Beaver County SD 700/PK-12
343 Ridgemont Dr 15059 724-643-9310
Dr. Robert Postupac, supt. Fax 643-8048
www.westernbeaver.org
Other Schools – See Industry

Mifflinburg, Union, Pop. 3,516
Mifflinburg Area SD 2,100/K-12
178 Maple St 17844 570-966-8200
Daniel Lichtel, supt. Fax 966-8210
www.mifflinburg.org
Mifflinburg Area HS 600/9-12
75 Market St 17844 570-966-8230
Michelle Shearer, prin. Fax 966-8260
Mifflinburg Area MS 500/6-8
100 Mabel St 17844 570-966-8290
Daryl Hunsberger, prin. Fax 966-8304

Mifflintown, Juniata, Pop. 920
Juniata County SD 3,000/K-12
75 S 7th St 17059 717-436-2111
Keith Yarger, supt. Fax 436-2777
www.jcsdk12.org
Juniata HS 500/9-12
3931 William Penn Hwy 17059 717-436-2193
Edward Apple, prin. Fax 436-2858
Tuscarora JHS 400/6-8
3873 William Penn Hwy 17059 717-436-2165
Aaron Bennett, prin. Fax 436-5999
Other Schools – See Mc Alisterville

Milford, Pike, Pop. 1,003
Delaware Valley SD 4,000/PK-12
236 Route 6 and 209 18337 570-296-1800
Dr. John Bell, supt. Fax 296-3172
www.dvsd.org
Delaware Valley HS 9-10 9-10
256 Route 6 and 209 18337 570-409-2001
Dr. Brian Blaum, prin. Fax 409-2002
Delaware Valley HS 11-12 800/11-12
252 Route 6 and 209 18337 570-296-1850
Dr. Brian Blaum, prin. Fax 296-3160
Delaware Valley MS 500/6-8
258 Route 6 and 209 18337 570-296-1830
Peter Ioppolo, prin. Fax 296-3162
Other Schools – See Dingmans Ferry

Mill Creek, Huntingdon, Pop. 326
Area Vocational Technical School
Supt. — None
Huntingdon County CTC Vo/Tech
PO Box E 17060 814-643-0951
Mary Lou Lebo, prin.

Millersburg, Dauphin, Pop. 2,536
Millersburg Area SD 800/K-12
799 Center St 17061 717-692-2108
Thomas Haupt, supt. Fax 692-2895
www.mlbgsd.k12.pa.us/
Millersburg Area HS 200/9-12
799 Center St 17061 717-692-2108
David Shover, prin. Fax 692-2895
Millersburg Area MS 200/6-8
799 Center St 17061 717-692-2108
Jennifer Wicht, prin. Fax 692-2895

Northern Dauphin Christian S 100/PK-12
PO Box 233 17061 717-692-1940
JoAnn Kieffer, admin. Fax 692-1940

Millerstown, Perry, Pop. 664
Greenwood SD 800/K-12
405 E Sunbury St 17062 717-589-3117
Dr. Nicholas Guarente, supt. Fax 589-1017
www.greenwoodsd.org
Greenwood HS 200/9-12
405 E Sunbury St 17062 717-589-3116
Michele Dubaich, prin. Fax 589-1016
Greenwood MS 200/6-8
405 E Sunbury St 17062 717-589-3116
Michele Dubaich, prin. Fax 589-1016

Millersville, Lancaster, Pop. 8,074
Penn Manor SD
Supt. — See Lancaster
Penn Manor HS 1,700/9-12
PO Box 1001 17551 717-872-9520
Dr. Philip Gale, prin. Fax 872-0934

Millersville University of Pennsylvania Post-Sec.
PO Box 1002 17551 717-872-3024

Mill Hall, Clinton, Pop. 1,602
Area Vocational Technical School
Supt. — None
Keystone Central CTC Vo/Tech
64 Keystone Central Dr 17751 570-748-6584
Scott Owens, prin. Fax 748-5467

Keystone Central SD 4,100/K-12
86 Administration Dr 17751 570-893-4900
Kelly Hastings, supt. Fax 893-4923
www.kcsd.k12.pa.us
Central Mountain HS 1,300/9-12
64 Keystone Central Dr 17751 570-893-4646
Dr. Steve Turchetta, prin. Fax 893-4946
Central Mountain MS 900/6-8
200 Ben Ave 17751 570-726-3141
Justin Evey, prin. Fax 726-7227
Other Schools – See Renovo

Millville, Columbia, Pop. 940
Millville Area SD 700/K-12
PO Box 260 17846 570-458-5538
Cynthia Jenkins, supt. Fax 458-5584
www.millville.k12.pa.us
Millville Area JSHS 300/7-12
PO Box 260 17846 570-458-5538
Eric Stair, prin. Fax 458-5583

Milton, Northumberland, Pop. 6,900
Milton Area SD 2,200/K-12
700 Mahoning St 17847 570-742-7614
Cathy Keegan M.Ed., supt. Fax 742-4523
www.miltonsd.org/
Milton Area HS 600/9-12
700 Mahoning St 17847 570-742-7611
Andrew Rantz, prin. Fax 742-4928
Milton Area MS 500/6-8
700 Mahoning St 17847 570-742-7685
Gregory Scoggins, prin. Fax 742-4857

Meadowbrook Christian S 400/PK-12
363 Stamm Rd 17847 570-742-2638
Rod Baughman M.Ed., admin. Fax 742-4710

Minersville, Schuylkill, Pop. 4,345
Minersville Area SD 1,300/PK-12
PO Box 787 17954 570-544-1400
Carl McBreen, supt. Fax 544-6162
www.battlinminers.com
Minersville Area JSHS 500/7-12
PO Box 787 17954 570-544-1400
James Grabusky, prin. Fax 544-5866

Mohrsville, Berks, Pop. 375

King's Academy 200/PK-12
1562 Main St 19541 610-926-9639
Michelle Goodman, head sch Fax 926-8089

Monaca, Beaver, Pop. 5,641
Area Vocational Technical School
Supt. — None
Beaver County CTC Vo/Tech
145 Poplar Ave 15061 724-728-5800
Robert Edwards, dir. Fax 775-2299

Central Valley SD 2,400/K-12
160 Baker Road Ext 15061 724-775-5600
Nicholas Perry, supt. Fax 775-4302
www.centralvalleysd.org
Central Valley HS 700/9-12
160 Baker Road Ext 15061 724-775-5600
Shawn McCreary, prin. Fax 775-6560
Central Valley MS 500/6-8
1500 Allen Ave 15061 724-775-5600
Brian Dolph, prin. Fax 775-4302

Community College of Beaver County Post-Sec.
1 Campus Dr 15061 724-480-2222
Penn State Beaver Post-Sec.
100 University Dr 15061 724-773-3800

Monessen, Westmoreland, Pop. 7,447
Monessen CSD 800/K-12
1275 Rostraver St 15062 724-684-3600
Dr. Leanne Spazak, supt. Fax 684-6782
monessenschooldistrict.com
Monessen HS 200/9-12
1245 State Rd 15062 724-684-7100
Eric Manko, prin. Fax 684-7925
Monessen MS 200/6-8
1245 State Rd 15062 724-684-6282
Eric Manko, prin. Fax 684-7931

Douglas Education Center Post-Sec.
130 7th St 15062 724-684-3684

Monongahela, Washington, Pop. 4,226
Ringgold SD
Supt. — See New Eagle
Ringgold HS 900/9-12
1 Ram Dr 15063 724-258-2200
Jason Minniti, prin. Fax 258-7360

Monroeville, Allegheny, Pop. 28,591
Area Vocational Technical School
Supt. — None
Forbes Road CTC Vo/Tech
607 Beatty Rd 15146 412-373-8100
Edward McMullen, dir. Fax 373-8106

Gateway SD 3,500/K-12
9000 Gateway Campus Blvd 15146 412-372-5300
Dr. Nina Zetty, supt. Fax 373-5731
www.gatewayk12.org
Gateway HS 1,300/9-12
3000 Gateway Campus Blvd 15146 412-373-5744
Peter Murphy, prin. Fax 373-5872
Gateway MS 600/7-8
4450 Old William Penn Hwy 15146 412-373-5780
Rocco Telli, prin. Fax 373-5794

Career Training Academy Post-Sec.
4314 Old William Penn # 103 15146 412-372-3900
Community College of Allegheny County Post-Sec.
595 Beatty Rd 15146 724-327-1327
Empire Beauty School Post-Sec.
320 Mall Blvd 15146 412-373-7727

Mont Alto, Franklin, Pop. 1,684

Penn State Mont Alto Post-Sec.
1 Campus Dr 17237 717-749-6000

Montgomery, Lycoming, Pop. 1,554
Montgomery Area SD 700/K-12
120 Penn St 17752 570-547-1608
Daphne Bowers, supt. Fax 547-6271
www.montasd.org
Montgomery JSHS 300/7-12
120 Penn St 17752 570-547-1608
Joseph Stoudt, prin. Fax 547-6755

Montoursville, Lycoming, Pop. 4,566
Montoursville Area SD 2,000/K-12
50 N Arch St 17754 570-368-2491
Dr. Timothy Bowers, supt. Fax 368-3501
www.montoursville.k12.pa.us/
McCall MS 600/5-8
600 Willow St 17754 570-368-2441
Jeffrey Moore, prin. Fax 368-3521
Montoursville Area HS 600/9-12
100 N Arch St 17754 570-368-2611
Daniel Taormina, prin. Fax 368-2768

Montrose, Susquehanna, Pop. 1,608
Montrose Area SD 1,400/K-12
273 Meteor Way 18801 570-278-6221
Carol Boyce, supt. Fax 278-4798
www.masd.info
Montrose JSHS 800/7-12
75 Meteor Way 18801 570-278-3731
William King, prin. Fax 278-9143

Moon Township, Allegheny, Pop. 10,187
Moon Area SD 3,700/K-12
8353 University Blvd 15108 412-264-9440
Donna Milanovich, supt. Fax 264-3268
www.moonarea.net
Moon Area HS 1,200/9-12
8353 University Blvd 15108 412-264-9440
Barry Balaski, prin. Fax 264-1271
Moon Area Upper MS 600/7-8
904 Beaver Grade Rd 15108 412-264-9440
Melissa Heasley, prin. Fax 264-3013

Robert Morris University Post-Sec.
6001 University Blvd 15108 412-397-3000

Moosic, Lackawanna, Pop. 5,672

Empire Beauty School Post-Sec.
3370 Birney Ave 18507 570-823-5987

Morgantown, Lancaster, Pop. 817

Conestoga Christian S 200/PK-12
2760 Main St 19543 610-286-0353
Kenneth Parris, admin. Fax 286-0350

Morrisdale, Clearfield, Pop. 747
West Branch Area SD 1,100/K-12
516 Allport Cutoff 16858 814-345-5615
Michelle Dutrow, supt. Fax 345-5220
www.westbranch.org
West Branch Area JSHS 600/7-12
444 Allport Cutoff 16858 814-345-5615
Joseph Holenchik, prin. Fax 345-6116

Morrisville, Bucks, Pop. 8,532
Morrisville Borough SD 600/K-12
550 W Palmer St 19067 215-736-2681
Michael Kopakowski, supt. Fax 736-2413
mv.org
Morrisville MSHS 200/6-12
550 W Palmer St 19067 215-736-5260
Michael Kopakowski, supt. Fax 736-3958

Moscow, Lackawanna, Pop. 2,016
North Pocono SD 3,000/K-12
701 Church St 18444 570-842-7659
Bryan McGraw, supt. Fax 842-0886
www.npsd.org/
North Pocono HS 1,000/9-12
97 Bochicchio Blvd 18444 570-842-7606
Ronald Collins, prin. Fax 842-2163
North Pocono MS 700/6-8
701 Church St 18444 570-842-4588
Edward Bugno, prin. Fax 842-1783

Mountain Top, Luzerne, Pop. 10,876
Crestwood SD 2,900/K-12
281 S Mountain Blvd 18707 570-474-6782
Dave McLaughlin-Smith, supt. Fax 474-2254
www.csdcomets.org/
Crestwood HS 900/9-12
281 S Mountain Blvd 18707 570-474-6782
Christopher Gegaris, prin. Fax 474-1175
Crestwood MS 500/7-8
281 S Mountain Blvd 18707 570-474-6782
Bonnie Gregory, prin. Fax 474-2254

Mount Braddock, Fayette

Pennsylvania Institute of Health & Tech Post-Sec.
PO Box 278 15465 724-437-4600

Mount Carmel, Northumberland, Pop. 5,840
Mt. Carmel Area SD 1,300/PK-12
600 W 5th St 17851 570-339-1500
Bernard Stellar, supt. Fax 339-0487
www.mca.k12.pa.us
Mt. Carmel Area JSHS 400/7-12
600 W 5th St 17851 570-339-1500
Lisa Varano, prin. Fax 339-0487

Mount Joy, Lancaster, Pop. 7,283
Area Vocational Technical School
Supt. — None
Lancaster County CTC-Mt. Joy Vo/Tech
PO Box 537 17552 717-653-3000
David Smith, prin. Fax 653-0901

Donegal SD 2,300/K-12
1051 Koser Rd 17552 717-653-1447
Susan Ursprung Ed.D., supt. Fax 492-1350
www.donegalsd.org
Donegal HS 800/9-12
1025 Koser Rd 17552 717-653-1871
John Felix, prin. Fax 492-1241
Donegal JHS 500/7-8
915 Anderson Ferry Rd 17552 717-928-2900
Judy Haugh, prin. Fax 928-2911

Mount Pleasant, Westmoreland, Pop. 4,419
Mt. Pleasant Area SD 2,100/K-12
271 State St 15666 724-547-4100
Dr. Timothy Gabauer, supt. Fax 547-0629
www.mpasd.net
Mount Pleasant Area HS 700/9-12
265 State St 15666 724-547-4100
John Campbell, prin. Fax 547-0526
Mount Pleasant Area JHS 300/7-8
265 State St 15666 724-547-4100
Robert Gumbita, admin. Fax 547-0526

Mount Union, Huntingdon, Pop. 2,343
Mt. Union Area SD 1,500/K-12
603 N Industrial Dr 17066 814-542-8631
Dr. Brett Gilliland, supt. Fax 542-8633
www.muasd.org/
Mount Union Area HS 400/9-12
706 N Shaver St 17066 814-542-2518
Curt Whitsel, prin. Fax 542-5451
Mount Union JHS 300/7-8
706 N Shaver St 17066 814-542-9311
Amy Smith, prin.

Mountville, Lancaster, Pop. 2,760

Dayspring Christian Academy 200/PK-12
120 College Ave 17554 717-285-2000
Dr. Michael Myers, hdmstr.

Mount Wolf, York, Pop. 1,367
Northeastern York SD
Supt. — See Manchester
Northeastern MS 600/7-8
4855 Board Rd 17347 717-266-3676
Michael Alessandroni, prin. Fax 266-9735

Muncy, Lycoming, Pop. 2,457
Muncy SD 1,000/K-12
206 Sherman St 17756 570-546-3125
Dr. Craig Skaluba, supt. Fax 546-6676
www.muncysd.org
Muncy JSHS 400/7-12
200 W Penn St 17756 570-546-3127
Timothy Welliver, prin. Fax 546-7688

Munhall, Allegheny, Pop. 11,221
Steel Valley SD 1,400/K-12
220 E Oliver Rd 15120 412-464-3600
Edward Wehrer, supt. Fax 464-3626
steelvalleysd.org
Steel Valley HS 500/9-12
3113 Main St 15120 412-464-3600
Lisa Duval, prin. Fax 464-3609
Steel Valley MS 400/5-8
3114 Main St 15120 412-464-3600
Bryan Macuga, admin. Fax 326-0315

Murrysville, Westmoreland, Pop. 19,098
Franklin Regional SD 3,600/K-12
3210 School Rd 15668 724-327-5456
Dr. Gennaro R. Piraino Ed.D., supt. Fax 327-6149
www.franklinregional.k12.pa.us
Franklin Regional HS 1,200/9-12
3200 School Rd 15668 724-327-5456
Ron Suvak, prin. Fax 327-2782
Franklin Regional MS 900/6-8
4660 Old William Penn Hwy 15668 724-327-5456
Andrew Leviski, prin. Fax 733-0949

Myerstown, Lebanon, Pop. 3,030
Eastern Lebanon County SD 2,400/K-12
180 Elco Dr 17067 717-866-7117
Dr. David Zuilkoski Ed.D., supt. Fax 866-7084
www.elcosd.org/
Eastern Lebanon County HS 700/9-12
180 Elco Dr 17067 717-866-7447
Jennifer Haas, prin. Fax 866-7287
Eastern Lebanon County MS 600/6-8
60 Evergreen Dr 17067 717-866-6591
Christine Kassay, prin. Fax 866-5837

Evangelical Theological Seminary Post-Sec.
121 S College St 17067 717-866-5775
Lebanon Valley Christian S 100/1-12
7821 Lancaster Ave 17067 717-933-5171
Wesley Gingrich, prin. Fax 933-1616
Myerstown Mennonite S 100/1-12
739 E Lincoln Ave 17067 717-866-5667
Moses Martin, prin. Fax 866-8652

Nanticoke, Luzerne, Pop. 10,349
Greater Nanticoke Area SD 2,200/K-12
427 Kosciuszko St 18634 570-735-1270
Dr. Ronald Grevera Ed.D., supt. Fax 735-1350
www.gnasd.com
Greater Nanticoke Area HS 800/8-12
425 Kosciuszko St 18634 570-735-7781
Fax 733-1002

Luzerne County Community College Post-Sec.
1333 S Prospect St 18634 570-740-0200

Nanty Glo, Cambria, Pop. 2,702
Blacklick Valley SD 700/PK-12
555 Birch St 15943 814-749-9211
Dr. John Mastillo, supt. Fax 749-8627
www.bvsd.k12.pa.us
Blacklick Valley JSHS 300/7-12
555 Birch St 15943 814-749-9211
Dr. Laura Fisanick, prin. Fax 749-8627

Narberth, Montgomery, Pop. 4,161
Lower Merion SD
Supt. — See Ardmore
Welsh Valley MS 900/6-8
325 Tower Ln 19072 610-658-3920
Chris Hall, prin. Fax 667-4749

Natrona Heights, Allegheny, Pop. 11,400
Highlands SD 2,500/K-12
PO Box 288 15065 724-226-2400
Dr. Michael Bjalobok, supt. Fax 226-8437
www.goldenrams.com
Highlands HS 800/9-12
1500 Pacific Ave 15065 724-226-1000
Catherine Russo, prin. Fax 226-9611
Highlands MS 600/6-8
1350 Broadview Blvd 15065 724-226-0600
Charles Mort, prin. Fax 226-3287

Allegheny Valley Hospital Post-Sec.
1301 Carlisle St 15065 724-226-7000
St. Joseph HS 200/9-12
800 Montana Ave 15065 724-224-5552
Beverly Kaniecki, prin. Fax 224-3205

Nazareth, Northampton, Pop. 5,699
Nazareth Area SD 4,600/K-12
1 Education Plz 18064 610-759-1170
Dr. Dennis L. Riker, supt. Fax 759-9637
www.nazarethasd.org
Nazareth Area HS 1,500/9-12
501 E Center St 18064 610-759-1730
Alan Davis, prin. Fax 746-2599
Nazareth Area MS 700/7-8
94 Friedensthal Ave 18064 610-759-3350
Robert Kern, prin. Fax 759-3725

Needmore, Fulton, Pop. 168

Fulton County Community Christian S 50/PK-12
PO Box 235 17238 717-573-4400
Jennifer Swope, admin. Fax 573-2731

New Berlin, Union, Pop. 870
Area Vocational Technical School
Supt. — None
SUN Area Technology Institute Vo/Tech
815 Market St 17855 570-966-1031
Jennifer Hain, dir. Fax 966-9492

New Bethlehem, Clarion, Pop. 986
Redbank Valley SD 1,100/K-12
920 Broad St 16242 814-275-2426
Michael Drzewiecki, supt. Fax 275-2428
www.redbankvalley.net/
Redbank Valley JSHS 500/7-12
910 Broad St 16242 814-275-2424
Amy Rupp, prin. Fax 275-2428

New Bloomfield, Perry, Pop. 1,237

Carson Long Military Academy 100/6-12
200 N Carlisle St 17068 717-582-2121
Mark Morgan, pres. Fax 582-8763

New Brighton, Beaver, Pop. 5,744
New Brighton Area SD 1,500/K-12
3225 43rd St 15066 724-843-1795
Dr. Joseph Guarino, supt. Fax 843-6144
www.nbasd.org
New Brighton Area HS 500/9-12
3202 43rd St 15066 724-846-1050
Ryan Yates, prin. Fax 846-2204
New Brighton Area MS 300/6-8
901 Penn Ave 15066 724-846-8100
Julian Underwood, prin. Fax 846-2337

New Castle, Lawrence, Pop. 22,422
Area Vocational Technical School
Supt. — None
Lawrence County CTC Vo/Tech
750 Phelps Way 16101 724-658-3583
Regina Hiler, prin. Fax 658-8530

Laurel SD 1,300/K-12
2497 Harlansburg Rd 16101 724-658-8940
Sandra Hennon Ph.D., supt. Fax 658-2992
www.laurel.k12.pa.us
Laurel JSHS 700/7-12
2497 Harlansburg Rd 16101 724-658-9056
Mark Frengel M.D., prin. Fax 658-2992

Neshannock Township SD 1,300/K-12
3834 Mitchell Rd 16105 724-658-4793
Dr. Terence Meehan, supt. Fax 658-1828
www.neshannock.k12.pa.us
Neshannock HS 400/9-12
3834 Mitchell Rd 16105
Luca Passarelli, prin.
Neshannock JHS 200/7-8
3834 Mitchell Rd 16105 724-658-5513
Dr. Tracy McCalla, prin. Fax 657-8169

New Castle Area SD 2,300/PK-12
420 Fern St 16101 724-656-4756
John Sarandrea, supt. Fax 656-4767
www.ncasd.com
New Castle HS 800/9-12
300 E Lincoln Ave 16101 724-656-4700
Richard Litrenta, prin. Fax 658-3916
New Castle JHS 500/7-8
310 E Lincoln Ave 16101 724-656-4700
Carol Morrell, prin. Fax 658-6276

Shenango Area SD 1,200/K-12
2501 Old Pittsburgh Rd 16101 724-658-7287
Dr. Michael Schreck, supt. Fax 658-5370
www.shenango.k12.pa.us
Shenango HS 500/7-12
2550 Ellwood Rd 16101 724-658-5537
Dr. Joseph McCormick, prin. Fax 658-7584

Union Area SD 600/K-12
2106 Camden Ave 16101 724-658-4775
Michael Ross, supt. Fax 658-5151
www.union.k12.pa.us/
Union Area MSHS 300/6-12
2106 Camden Ave 16101 724-658-4501
Robin Nogay, prin. Fax 658-8617

Erie Business Center South Post-Sec.
170 Cascade Galleria 16101 724-658-9066
Jameson Memorial Hosp School of Nursing Post-Sec.
1211 Wilmington Ave 16105 724-656-4240
New Castle School of Beauty Culture Post-Sec.
314 E Washington St 16101 724-654-6611
New Castle School of Trades Post-Sec.
4117 Pulaski Rd 16101 800-837-8299

New Cumberland, Cumberland, Pop. 7,166
West Shore SD
Supt. — See Lewisberry
New Cumberland MS 400/6-8
331 8th St 17070 717-774-0162
Brian Kocsi, prin. Fax 901-9474

New Eagle, Washington, Pop. 2,165
Ringgold SD 2,900/K-12
400 Main St 15067 724-258-9329
Dr. Karen Polkabla, supt. Fax 258-5363
www.ringgold.org
Other Schools – See Finleyville, Monongahela

New Holland, Lancaster, Pop. 5,286
Eastern Lancaster County SD 3,200/K-12
PO Box 609 17557 717-354-1500
Dr. Robert Hollister, supt. Fax 354-1512
www.elanco.org
Garden Spot HS 1,000/9-12
PO Box 609 17557 717-354-1550
Matthew Sanger, prin. Fax 354-1128
Garden Spot MS 500/7-8
PO Box 609 17557 717-354-1560
Jeffrey Starr, prin. Fax 354-1129

New Hope, Bucks, Pop. 2,495
New Hope-Solebury SD 1,500/K-12
180 W Bridge St 18938 215-862-2552
Dr. Stephen M. Yanni, supt. Fax 744-6012
www.nhsd.org

New Hope-Solebury HS 500/9-12
182 W Bridge St 18938 215-862-2028
Stephen Seier, prin. Fax 862-3198
New Hope-Solebury MS 400/6-8
184 W Bridge St 18938 215-862-0608
Dr. Christina Cortellessa, prin. Fax 862-2862

Solebury S 200/7-12
6832 Phillips Mill Rd 18938 215-862-5261
Tom Wilschutz, head sch Fax 862-3366

New Kensington, Westmoreland, Pop. 12,575
Area Vocational Technical School
Supt. — None
Northern Westmoreland CTC Vo/Tech
705 Stevenson Blvd 15068 724-335-9389
Kurt Kiefer, dir. Fax 337-9010

New Kensington-Arnold SD 1,400/PK-12
707 Stevenson Blvd 15068 724-335-4401
Dr. John Pallone J.D., supt. Fax 994-1212
nkasd.com
Valley JSHS 600/7-12
703 Stevenson Blvd 15068 724-337-4536
Patrick Nee, prin. Fax 337-8054

Career Training Academy Post-Sec.
950 5th Ave 15068 724-337-1000
Citizens General Hospital Post-Sec.
651 4th Ave 15068 724-337-5090
Mary Queen of Apostles S 100/4-8
110 Elmtree Rd 15068 724-339-4411
Catherine Collett, prin. Fax 337-6457
Penn State New Kensington Post-Sec.
3550 7th Street Rd 15068 724-334-5466

New Milford, Susquehanna, Pop. 860
Blue Ridge SD 1,000/PK-12
5058 School Rd 18834 570-465-3141
Matthew Button, supt. Fax 465-3148
www.brsd.org
Blue Ridge HS 300/9-12
5058 School Rd 18834 570-465-3144
Matthew Nebzydoski, prin. Fax 465-3148
Blue Ridge MS 200/6-8
5058 School Rd 18834 570-465-3177
Matthew Nebzydoski, prin. Fax 465-3148

New Oxford, Adams, Pop. 1,767
Conewago Valley SD 3,900/K-12
130 Berlin Rd 17350 717-624-2157
Dr. Russell Greenholt, supt. Fax 624-5020
www.conewago.k12.pa.us
New Oxford HS 1,200/9-12
130 Berlin Rd 17350 717-624-2157
Kevin Thomas, prin. Fax 624-5021
New Oxford MS 600/7-8
130 Berlin Rd 17350 717-624-2157
Dr. Gretchen Gates, prin. Fax 624-6560

New Paris, Bedford, Pop. 183
Chestnut Ridge SD
Supt. — See Fishertown
Chestnut Ridge HS 500/8-12
2588 Quaker Valley Rd 15554 814-839-4195
Max Shoemaker, prin. Fax 839-0018

Newport, Perry, Pop. 1,551
Newport SD 1,100/K-12
PO Box 9 17074 717-567-3806
Ryan Neuhard, supt. Fax 567-6468
www.newportsd.org
Newport HS 300/9-12
PO Box 9 17074 717-567-3806
Scott McGrady, prin. Fax 567-2619
Newport MS 300/6-8
PO Box 9 17074 717-567-3806
Bryan Rehmeyer, prin. Fax 567-2619

New Stanton, Westmoreland, Pop. 2,152
Area Vocational Technical School
Supt. — None
Central Westmoreland CTC Vo/Tech
240 Arona Rd 15672 724-925-3532
Brad Elwood, dir. Fax 925-1423

Newtown, Bucks, Pop. 2,215
Council Rock SD 11,200/K-12
30 N Chancellor St 18940 215-944-1000
Dr. Robert Fraser, supt. Fax 944-1031
www.crsd.org
Council Rock HS North 1,800/9-12
62 Swamp Rd 18940 215-944-1300
Susan McCarthy, prin. Fax 944-1387
Newtown MS 900/7-8
116 Richboro Newtown Rd 18940 215-944-2600
Timothy Long, prin. Fax 944-2698
Other Schools – See Holland, Richboro

Bucks County Community College Post-Sec.
275 Swamp Rd 18940 215-968-8000
George S 500/9-12
PO Box 4460 18940 215-579-6547
Samuel Houser Ph.D., head sch Fax 579-6549

Newtown Square, Delaware, Pop. 11,300
Marple Newtown SD 3,300/K-12
40 Media Line Rd 19073 610-359-4256
Dr. Carol Cary, supt. Fax 723-3340
www.mnsd.net
Marple Newtown HS 1,200/9-12
120 Media Line Rd 19073 610-359-4218
Greg Puckett, prin. Fax 356-2194
Other Schools – See Broomall

Delaware County Christian S 500/6-12
462 Malin Rd 19073 610-353-6522
Dr. Timothy Wiens, head sch Fax 356-9684
Episcopal Academy 1,200/PK-12
1785 Bishop White Dr 19073 484-424-1400
Dr. Thomas Locke, hdmstr. Fax 424-1600

New Tripoli, Lehigh, Pop. 887
Northwestern Lehigh SD 2,200/K-12
6493 Route 309 18066 610-298-8661
Dr. Mary Anne Wright Ph.D., supt. Fax 298-8002
www.nwlehighsd.org
Northwestern Lehigh HS 700/9-12
6493 Route 309 18066 610-298-8661
Aileen Yadush, prin. Fax 298-4645
Northwestern Lehigh MS 500/6-8
6636 Northwest Rd 18066 610-298-8661
William Dovico, prin. Fax 298-8178

Newville, Cumberland, Pop. 1,313
Big Spring SD 2,700/K-12
45 Mount Rock Rd 17241 717-776-2000
Richard Fry, supt. Fax 776-4428
www.bigspring.k12.pa.us
Big Spring HS 900/9-12
100 Mount Rock Rd 17241 717-776-2000
William August, prin. Fax 776-2433
Big Spring MS 600/6-8
47 Mount Rock Rd 17241 717-776-2000
Dr. Linda Wilson, prin. Fax 776-2468

New Wilmington, Lawrence, Pop. 2,444
Wilmington Area SD 1,200/K-12
300 Wood St 16142 724-656-8866
Jeffrey Matty, supt. Fax 946-8982
www.wilmington.k12.pa.us
Wilmington Area HS 400/9-12
350 Wood St 16142 724-656-8866
Michael Wright, prin.
Wilmington Area MS 400/5-8
400 Wood St 16142 724-656-8866
George Endrizzi, prin.

Westminster College Post-Sec.
319 S Market St 16172 724-946-7100

Norristown, Montgomery, Pop. 33,250
Norristown Area SD 7,400/PK-12
401 N Whitehall Rd 19403 610-630-5000
Janet Samuels Ph.D., supt. Fax 630-5013
www.nasd.k12.pa.us
East Norriton MS 900/5-8
330 Roland Dr 19401 610-275-6520
Dr. Christina Spink, prin. Fax 272-0531
Eisenhower MS 500/5-8
1601 Markley St 19401 610-277-8720
Christina Taylor, prin. Fax 270-2901
Norristown Area HS 1,800/9-12
1900 Eagle Dr 19403 610-630-5090
Jeffrey Smith, prin. Fax 630-5115
Roosevelt Alternative S 100/Alt
1161 Markley St 19401 610-275-9720
Dr. Carla Queenan, prin. Fax 272-0552
Stewart MS 500/5-8
1315 W Marshall St 19401 610-275-6870
Martina Walls, prin. Fax 272-0560

The Pathway School Post-Sec.
162 Egypt Rd 19403 610-277-0660

Northampton, Northampton, Pop. 9,830
Catasauqua Area SD
Supt. — See Catasauqua
Catasauqua HS 500/9-12
2500 W Bullshead Rd 18067 610-697-0111
David Ascani, prin. Fax 697-0116

Northampton Area SD 5,100/K-12
2014 Laubach Ave 18067 610-262-7811
Joseph Kovalchik, supt. Fax 262-1150
www.nasdschools.org/
Northampton Area HS 1,700/9-12
1619 Laubach Ave 18067 610-262-7812
Robert Steckel, prin. Fax 262-3024
Northampton Area MS 900/6-8
1617 Laubach Ave 18067 610-262-7817
Patrice Turner, prin. Fax 262-6583

North Braddock, Allegheny, Pop. 4,701
Woodland Hills SD 2,300/K-12
531 Jones Ave, 412-731-1300
Alan Johnson, supt. Fax 273-3601
www.whsd.net
Other Schools – See Pittsburgh

North East, Erie, Pop. 4,255
North East SD 1,600/K-12
50 E Division St 16428 814-725-8671
Dr. Frank McClard, supt. Fax 725-9380
www.nesd1.org
North East HS 500/9-12
1901 Freeport Rd 16428 814-725-8671
Regan Tanner, prin. Fax 725-3357
North East MS 400/6-8
1903 Freeport Rd 16428 814-725-8671
Gregory Beardsley, prin. Fax 725-1086

Northern Cambria, Cambria, Pop. 4,022
Northern Cambria SD 1,100/K-12
601 Joseph St 15714 814-948-5481
Joseph Kimmel, supt. Fax 948-6058
www.ncsd.k12.pa.us
Northern Cambria HS 400/9-12
813 35th St 15714 814-948-6800
Rebecca Pupo, prin. Fax 948-9810
Northern Cambria MS 200/6-8
601 Joseph St 15714 814-948-5880
Marilyn Wargo, prin. Fax 948-5561

North Huntingdon, Westmoreland, Pop. 28,158
Norwin SD 5,200/K-12
281 McMahon Dr 15642 724-861-3000
Dr. William Kerr, supt. Fax 863-9467
www.norwinsd.org
Norwin HS 1,600/9-12
251 McMahon Dr 15642 724-861-3005
Timothy Kotch, prin. Fax 861-0581

Norwin MS 800/7-8
10870 Mockingbird Dr 15642 724-863-5707
Robert Suman, prin. Fax 863-5408

Northumberland, Northumberland, Pop. 3,769
Shikellamy SD
Supt. — See Sunbury
Shikellamy MS 400/6-8
545 Permastone Dr 17857 570-286-3736
Dr. Mary Murphy Kahn, prin.

Northumberland Christian S 200/PK-12
351 5th St 17857 570-473-9786
John Rees, prin. Fax 473-8405
Sunbury Christian Academy 100/PK-12
135 Spruce Hollow Rd 17857 570-473-7592
Richard Hennett, admin. Fax 473-7531

North Versailles, Allegheny, Pop. 12,302
East Allegheny SD 900/PK-12
1150 Jacks Run Rd 15137 412-824-8012
Donald MacFann, supt. Fax 824-1062
www.eawildcats.net
East Allegheny JSHS 500/7-12
1150 Jacks Run Rd 15137 412-824-9700
Betsy D'Emidio, prin. Fax 825-4570

North Wales, Montgomery, Pop. 3,136
North Penn SD
Supt. — See Lansdale
Pennbrook MS 900/7-9
1201 N Wales Rd 19454 215-699-9287
Jim Galante, prin. Fax 699-0151

Lansdale School of Business Post-Sec.
290 Wissahickon Ave 19454 215-699-5700

Oakdale, Allegheny, Pop. 1,442
Area Vocational Technical School
Supt. — None
Parkway West CTC Vo/Tech
7101 Steubenville Pike 15071 412-923-1772
Dr. Darby Copeland, dir. Fax 787-7257

Pittsburgh Technical Institute Post-Sec.
1111 McKee Rd 15071 800-784-9675

Oakmont, Allegheny, Pop. 6,258
Riverview SD 1,000/K-12
701 10th St 15139 412-828-1800
Margaret DiNinno, supt. Fax 828-9346
www.rsd.k12.pa.us
Riverview JSHS 500/7-12
100 Hulton Rd 15139 412-828-1800
Eric Hewitt, prin. Fax 828-6296

Oil City, Venango, Pop. 10,397
Area Vocational Technical School
Supt. — None
Venango Technology Center Vo/Tech
1 Vo Tech Dr 16301 814-677-3097
Mario Fontanazza, dir. Fax 676-0075

Oil City Area SD 2,000/K-12
825 Grandview Rd 16301 814-676-1867
Patrick Gavin, supt. Fax 676-2211
www.ocasd.org
Oil City Area MS 700/5-8
8 Lynch Blvd 16301 814-676-5702
Joy Zuck, prin. Fax 676-2306
Oil City HS 700/9-12
10 Lynch Blvd 16301 814-676-2771
Scott Stahl, prin. Fax 677-7256

DuBois Business College Post-Sec.
701 E 3rd St 16301 814-677-1322
Venango Catholic HS 100/9-12
1505 W 1st St 16301 814-677-3098
Rev. T. Shane Mathew, hdmstr. Fax 676-4453
Venango College of Clarion University Post-Sec.
1801 W 1st St 16301 814-676-6591

Old Forge, Lackawanna, Pop. 8,255
Old Forge SD 900/K-12
300 Marion St 18518 570-457-6721
John Rushefski, supt. Fax 457-8389
www.ofsd.cc
Old Forge JSHS 400/7-12
300 Marion St 18518 570-457-6721
Christopher Thomas, prin. Fax 414-0997

Oley, Berks, Pop. 1,277
Area Vocational Technical School
Supt. — None
Berks CTC - East Vo/Tech
3307 Friedensburg Rd 19547 610-987-6201
Ronald Wilson, prin. Fax 987-6106

Oley Valley SD 1,700/K-12
17 Jefferson St 19547 610-987-4100
Dr. Tracy Shank Ed.D., supt. Fax 987-4138
www.oleyvalleysd.org
Oley Valley HS 600/9-12
17 Jefferson St 19547 610-987-4100
Michael Stauffer, prin. Fax 987-4138
Oley Valley MS 400/6-8
3247 Friedensburg Rd 19547 610-987-4100
Daniel Marks, prin. Fax 987-4240

Orefield, Lehigh
Parkland SD
Supt. — See Allentown
Orefield MS 1,100/6-8
2675 PA Route 309 18069 610-351-5750
Todd Gombos, prin. Fax 351-5799

Oreland, Montgomery, Pop. 5,575
Springfield Township SD 2,200/K-12
1901 Paper Mill Rd 19075 215-233-6000
Dr. Nancy Hacker, supt. Fax 233-5815
www.sdst.org

Springfield Township MS 500/6-8
1901 Paper Mill Rd 19075 215-233-6070
Lauren Patterson, prin. Fax 233-6091
Other Schools – See Erdenheim

Orwigsburg, Schuylkill, Pop. 3,077
Blue Mountain SD 2,800/K-12
PO Box 188 17961 570-366-0515
Dr. David Helsel, supt. Fax 366-0838
www.bmsd.org
Blue Mountain MS 700/6-8
PO Box 279 17961 570-366-0546
James McGonigle, prin. Fax 366-2513
Other Schools – See Schuylkill Haven

Oxford, Chester, Pop. 4,949
Oxford Area SD 3,700/K-12
125 Bell Tower Ln 19363 610-932-6600
David Woods, supt. Fax 932-6614
www.oxfordasd.org
Oxford Area HS 1,300/9-12
705 Waterway Rd 19363 610-932-6640
James Canaday, prin. Fax 932-6649
Penn's Grove S 600/7-8
301 S 5th St 19363 610-932-6615
Tami Motes, prin. Fax 932-6619

Palmerton, Carbon, Pop. 5,366
Palmerton Area SD 1,800/K-12
680 4th St 18071 610-826-7101
Scot Engler, supt. Fax 826-4958
www.palmerton.org/
Palmerton Area HS 500/9-12
3525 Fireline Rd 18071 610-826-3155
Paula Husar, prin. Fax 826-4929
Palmerton Area JHS 300/7-8
3529 Fireline Rd 18071 610-826-2492
Richard DeSocio, prin. Fax 826-2366

Palmyra, Lebanon, Pop. 7,238
Palmyra Area SD 3,300/K-12
1125 Park Dr 17078 717-838-3144
Lisa Brown, supt. Fax 838-5105
www.pasd.us
Palmyra Area HS 1,000/9-12
1125 Park Dr 17078 717-838-1331
Dr. Benjamin Ruby, prin. Fax 838-7915
Palmyra Area MS 800/6-8
50 W Cherry St 17078 717-838-1331
Walter Popejoy, prin. Fax 838-4402

Paoli, Chester, Pop. 5,479

Royer-Greaves School for Blind Post-Sec.
118 S Valley Rd 19301

Patton, Cambria, Pop. 1,764
Cambria Heights SD 1,400/PK-12
PO Box 66 16668 814-674-3626
Michael Strasser, supt. Fax 674-5411
www.chsd1.org/
Cambria Heights HS 500/9-12
PO Box 6 16668 814-674-3601
Kenneth Kerchenske, prin. Fax 674-5605
Cambria Heights MS 300/6-8
PO Box 216 16668 814-674-6290
David Caldwell, prin. Fax 674-5054

Pen Argyl, Northampton, Pop. 3,551
Pen Argyl Area SD 1,700/K-12
1620 Teels Rd 18072 610-863-3191
William Haberl Ed.D., supt. Fax 863-7040
www.edline.net/pages/Pen_Argyl_ASD
Pen Argyl Area HS 500/9-12
501 W Laurel Ave 18072 610-863-1293
David Domchek, prin. Fax 863-7660
Wind Gap MS 700/4-8
1620 Teels Rd 18072 610-863-9093
Dr. Terry Barry, prin. Fax 863-3817

Pennsburg, Montgomery, Pop. 3,798
Upper Perkiomen SD 3,300/K-12
2229 E Buck Rd 18073 215-679-7961
Dr. Alexis McGloin, supt. Fax 679-6214
www.upsd.org
Upper Perkiomen HS 900/9-12
2 Walt Rd 18073 215-679-5935
Dr. William Shirk, prin. Fax 679-0911
Other Schools – See East Greenville

Perkiomen S 300/6-12
200 Seminary St 18073 215-679-9511
Mark Devey, hdmstr. Fax 679-5202

Penns Creek, Snyder, Pop. 711

Penn View Christian Academy 100/PK-12
PO Box 970 17862 570-837-1855
Rev. Brent Lenhart, prin. Fax 837-1865

Pequea, Lancaster
Penn Manor SD
Supt. — See Lancaster
Marticville MS 300/7-8
356 Frogtown Rd 17565 717-284-4135
Christine Santaniello, prin. Fax 284-5954

Perkasie, Bucks, Pop. 8,390
Area Vocational Technical School
Supt. — None
Upper Bucks County AVTS Vo/Tech
3115 Ridge Rd 18944 215-795-2911
Bernard Wagenseller, dir. Fax 795-0530

Pennridge SD 7,300/K-12
1200 N 5th St 18944 215-257-5011
Dr. Jacqueline Rattigan, supt. Fax 453-8699
www.pennridge.org
Pennridge Central MS 600/6-8
144 N Walnut St 18944 215-258-0939
Christian Temchatin, prin. Fax 258-0938
Pennridge HS 2,300/9-12
1228 N 5th St 18944 215-453-6944
Gina DeBona, prin. Fax 257-4986
Pennridge North MS 600/6-8
1500 N 5th St 18944 215-453-6932
Dr. Matthew Cole, prin. Fax 453-7867
Pennridge South MS 500/6-8
610 S 5th St 18944 215-257-0467
Dr. Felicia McAllister, prin. Fax 257-3094

Perryopolis, Fayette, Pop. 1,762
Frazier SD 1,200/PK-12
142 Constitution St 15473 724-736-4427
William Henderson, supt. Fax 736-0688
www.frazierschooldistrict.org/pages/frazier_sd
Frazier HS 300/9-12
142 Constitution St 15473 724-736-4426
Jason Pappas, prin. Fax 736-0688
Frazier MS 300/6-8
142 Constitution St 15473 724-736-4428
Michael Turek, prin. Fax 736-0688

Philadelphia, Philadelphia, Pop. 1,493,502
Area Vocational Technical School
Supt. — None
Dobbins AVTS Vo/Tech
2150 W Lehigh Ave 19132 215-227-4421
Dr. Toni Damon, prin. Fax 227-4944
Edison HS Vo/Tech
151 W Luzerne St 19140 215-324-9599
Awilda Ortiz, prin. Fax 329-5824
Kensington Culinary Arts S Vo/Tech
2463 Emerald St 19125 215-291-5185
James Williams, prin. Fax 291-6320
Mastbaum AVTS Vo/Tech
3116 Frankford Ave 19134 215-291-4703
Dr. Warren Bowman, prin. Fax 291-5657
Randolph AVTS Vo/Tech
3101 Henry Ave 19129 215-227-4407
Darryl Overton, prin. Fax 227-8655
Saul Agricultural S Vo/Tech
7100 Henry Ave 19128 215-487-4467
Tamera Conaway, prin. Fax 487-4844
School for Exceptional Adults AVTS Vo/Tech
1400 W Olney Ave 19141 215-299-3699
Swenson Arts & Technology HS Vo/Tech
2750 Red Lion Rd 19114 215-961-2009
Colette Langston, prin. Fax 961-2081

Cheltenham Township SD
Supt. — See Elkins Park
Cedarbrook MS 700/7-8
1331 Ivy Hill Rd 19150 215-881-6423
Russell Bender, prin. Fax 576-5610

Philadelphia CSD 177,900/PK-12
440 N Broad St 19130 215-400-4000
William Hite Ed.D., supt.
www.philasd.org/
Academy at Palumbo 800/9-12
1100 Catharine St 19147 215-351-7618
Kiana Thompson, prin. Fax 351-7685
Alternative Ed Regional Ctr at 440 Alt
440 N Broad St 19130 215-400-4230
Arts Academy at Benjamin Rush 600/9-12
11081 Knights Rd 19154 215-281-2603
Lori DeFields, prin. Fax 281-2674
Baldi MS 1,200/6-8
8801 Verree Rd 19115 215-961-2003
Luke Hostetter, prin. Fax 961-2116
Bartram HS 1,100/9-12
2401 S 67th St 19142 215-492-6450
Abdul-Mubdi Muhammad, prin. Fax 492-6117
Beeber MS 200/7-8
5925 Malvern Ave 19131 215-581-5513
Khary Moody, prin. Fax 581-5694
Bodine HS for International Affairs 500/9-12
1101 N 4th St 19123 215-351-7332
Karen Thomas, prin. Fax 351-7370
Building 21, 2000 N 7th St 19122 9-9
Tara Ranzy, prin. 215-684-2030
Carver HS for Engineering & Science 800/9-12
1600 W Norris St 19121 215-684-5079
Ted Domers, prin. Fax 684-5151
Central HS 2,300/9-12
1700 W Olney Ave 19141 215-276-5262
Tim McKenna, prin. Fax 276-4721
Clemente MS 500/6-8
122 W Erie Ave 19140 215-291-5400
Edward Penn, prin. Fax 291-5421
Constitution HS 400/9-12
18 S 7th St 19106 215-351-7310
Dr. Tom Davidson, prin. Fax 351-7694
Conwell MS 600/5-8
1849 E Clearfield St 19134 215-291-4722
Erica Green, prin. Fax 291-5019
Creative & Performing Arts HS 700/9-12
901 S Broad St 19147 215-952-2462
Joanne Beaver, prin. Fax 952-6472
Fels HS 1,300/9-12
5500 Langdon St 19124 215-537-2516
Shawn McGuigan, prin. Fax 537-2556
Feltonville Arts & Sciences MS 600/6-8
210 E Courtland St 19120 215-456-5603
John Piniat, prin. Fax 456-5614
Frankford HS 1,300/9-12
5000 Oxford Ave 19124 215-537-2519
Michael Calderone, prin. Fax 537-2598
Franklin HS 800/9-12
550 N Broad St 19130 215-299-4662
Greg Haley, prin. Fax 299-7285
Franklin Learning Center 800/Alt
616 N 15th St 19130 215-684-5916
Joyce Hoog, prin. Fax 684-8969
Furness HS 700/9-12
1900 S 3rd St 19148 215-952-6226
Daniel Peou, prin. Fax 952-8635
Girard Academic Music Program 500/5-12
2136 W Ritner St 19145 215-952-8589
Carol Domb, prin. Fax 952-6544
Harding MS 900/6-8
2000 Wakeling St 19124 215-537-2528
Mary Sanchez, prin. Fax 537-2850
High School of the Future 700/9-12
4021 Parkside Ave 19104 215-823-5502
Richard Sherin, prin. Fax 823-5504
Hill-Freedman World Academy 300/6-12
6200 Crittenden St 19138 215-276-5260
Anthony Majewski, prin. Fax 276-5873
Kensington Business & Finance HS 400/9-12
2501 Coral St 19125 215-291-5168
Renato Lajara, prin. Fax 291-5708
Kensington CAPA HS 400/9-12
1901 N Front St 19122 215-291-5010
Lisette Agosto-Clintron, prin. Fax 291-6334
Kensington Health Sciences S Vo/Tech
2463 Emerald St 19125 215-291-5185
James Williams, prin. Fax 291-6320
Kensington Urban Education 300/Alt
2051 E Cumberland St 19125 215-291-5420
Renato Lajara, prin. Fax 291-5427
King HS 1,100/9-12
6100 Stenton Ave 19138 215-276-5253
William Wade, prin. Fax 276-5844
LaBrum MS 200/6-8
10800 Hawley Rd 19154 215-281-2607
William Griffin, prin. Fax 281-5800
Lankenau HS 300/9-12
201 Spring Ln 19128 215-487-4465
Karen Dean, prin. Fax 487-4879
Leeds MS 300/7-8
1100 E Mount Pleasant Ave 19150 215-248-6602
Kala Johnstone, prin. Fax 248-6623
Linc 9-10
122 W Erie Ave 19140 215-291-5432
Bridget Bujak, prin. Fax 291-5449
Lincoln HS 1,600/9-12
3201 Ryan Ave 19136 215-335-5653
Jack Nelson, prin. Fax 335-5997
Masterman MSHS 1,200/5-12
1699 Spring Garden St 19130 215-299-4661
Jessica Brown, prin. Fax 299-3425
Meehan MS 500/7-8
3001 Ryan Ave 19152 215-335-5654
Mary Jackson, prin. Fax 335-5992
Middle Years Alternative-MYA 300/Alt
4725 Fairmount Ave 19139 215-581-5633
Shakae Dupre, prin. Fax 581-5668
Motivation HS 200/9-12
5900 Baltimore Ave 19143 215-471-2906
Rennu Teli, prin. Fax 492-6924
Northeast HS 3,000/9-12
1601 Cottman Ave 19111 215-728-5018
Sharon McCloskey, prin. Fax 728-5004
Overbrook HS 1,000/9-12
5898 Lancaster Ave 19131 215-581-5507
Yvette Jackson, prin. Fax 581-3406
Parkway Center City HS 600/9-12
540 N 13th St 19123 215-351-7095
Karren Dunkley, prin. Fax 351-7097
Parkway Northwest HS 300/9-12
1100 E Mount Pleasant Ave 19150 215-248-6220
Gina Steiner, prin. Fax 248-6015
Parkway West HS 300/9-12
4725 Fairmount Ave 19139 215-581-5510
Dr. Kathleen McCladdie, prin. Fax 581-5600
Penn Treaty MSHS 600/6-12
600 E Thompson St 19125 215-291-4715
Sam Howell, prin. Fax 291-5172
Philadelphia HS for Girls 1,100/9-12
1400 W Olney Ave 19141 215-276-5258
Parthenia Moore, prin. Fax 276-5738
Philadelphia Military Academy 300/9-12
2118 N 13th St 19122 215-684-5091
Patricia Randzo, prin. Fax 684-5507
Robeson HS for Human Services 300/9-12
4125 Ludlow St 19104 215-823-8207
Richard Gordon, prin. Fax 823-8252
Roxborough HS 600/9-12
6498 Ridge Ave 19128 215-487-4464
Dana Jenkins, prin. Fax 487-4843
Sayre HS 500/9-12
5800 Walnut St 19139 215-471-2904
Jamie Eberle, prin. Fax 471-3486
Science Leadership Academy 600/9-12
55 N 22nd St 19103 215-979-5620
Christopher Lehmann, prin. Fax 567-2809
Science Leadership Academy @ Beeber 9-10
5925 Malvern Ave 19131 215-581-2715
Christopher Johnson, prin. Fax 581-2109
South Philadelphia HS 1,000/9-12
2101 S Broad St 19148 215-952-6220
Otis Hackney, prin. Fax 551-2275
Strawberry Mansion HS 400/9-12
3133 Ridge Ave 19121 215-684-5089
Linda Cliatt-Wayman, prin. Fax 684-5380
The U School: Innovative Lab 9-10
2000 N 7th St 19122 215-684-3266
Neil Geyette, prin. Fax 684-2476
Tilden MS 600/6-8
6601 Elmwood Ave 19142 215-492-6454
Brian Johnson, prin. Fax 492-6128
Wagner MS 600/6-8
1701 W Chelten Ave 19126 215-276-5252
Maya Johnstone, prin. Fax 276-5849
Washington HS 1,700/9-12
10175 Bustleton Ave 19116 215-961-2001
Gene Jones, prin. Fax 961-2545
Washington Jr. MS 600/5-8
201 E Olney Ave 19120 215-456-0422
Jovan Moore, prin. Fax 456-2181
West Philadelphia HS 700/9-12
4901 Chestnut St 19139 215-471-2902
Mary Dean, prin. Fax 471-6402
Wilson MS 1,200/6-8
1800 Cottman Ave 19111 215-728-5015
Stefanie Ressler, prin. Fax 728-5051

Workshop HS 100/Alt
221 S Hanson St 19139 215-471-2960
Simon Hauger, prin. Fax 471-2948

Achieve Test Prep Post-Sec.
1015 Chestnut St Ste 515 19107 610-400-1641
Al-Aqsa Islamic Academy 300/PK-12
1501 Germantown Ave 19122 215-765-6660
Claude Crumpton, prin. Fax 765-6640
Albert Einstein Medical Center Post-Sec.
5501 Old York Rd 19141 215-456-7010
American Beauty Academy Post-Sec.
6912 Frankford Ave 19135 215-331-1515
ARAMARK Healthcare Support Services Post-Sec.
1101 Market St Fl 12 19107 610-687-8600
Archbishop Ryan HS 1,600/9-12
11201 Academy Rd 19154 215-637-1800
Joseph McFadden, prin. Fax 637-8833
Aria Health School of Nursing Post-Sec.
4918 Penn St 19124 215-831-6740
Aviation Institute of Maintenance Post-Sec.
3001 Grant Ave 19114 215-676-7700
Brightwood Career Institute Post-Sec.
3010 Market St 19104 215-594-4000
Brightwood Career Institute Post-Sec.
177 Franklin Mills Blvd 19154 215-612-6600
Calvary Christian Academy 1,000/PK-12
13500 Philmont Ave 19116 215-969-1579
Chris Spittal, dir. Fax 969-9732
Chestnut Hill College Post-Sec.
9601 Germantown Ave 19118 215-248-7001
City S, 860 N 24th St 19130 200/PK-12
Jake Becker, head sch 215-765-5363
Community College of Philadelphia Post-Sec.
1700 Spring Garden St 19130 215-751-8000
Crefeld S 100/7-12
8836 Crefeld St 19118 215-242-5545
Dr. George Zeleznik, head sch Fax 242-8869
Curtis Institute of Music Post-Sec.
1726 Locust St 19103 215-893-5252
DeVry University Post-Sec.
1800 JFK Blvd Ste 200 19103 215-568-2911
Drexel University Post-Sec.
3141 Chestnut St 19104 215-895-2000
Empire Beauty School Post-Sec.
4026 Woodhaven Rd 19154 215-637-3700
Empire Beauty School Post-Sec.
1522 Chestnut St 19102 215-568-3980
Faith Tabernacle S 200/1-12
PO Box 46245 19160 215-221-0909
Kenneth Yeager, prin. Fax 229-3204
Father Judge HS 1,100/9-12
3301 Solly Ave 19136 215-338-9494
Rev. James Dalton, prin. Fax 338-0250
Finshing Trades Institute Post-Sec.
2190 Hornig Rd 19116 215-501-0130
First Century Gospel S 200/1-10
6807 Rising Sun Ave 19111 215-742-6615
William Wakefield, prin. Fax 742-7009
Friends Select S 600/PK-12
1651 Benjamin Franklin Pkwy 19103 215-561-5900
Michael Gary, head sch Fax 864-2979
Germantown Friends S 900/K-12
31 W Coulter St 19144 215-951-2300
Dana Weeks, head sch Fax 951-2312
Girard College 500/1-12
2101 S College Ave 19121 215-787-2600
Clarence Armbrister, pres. Fax 787-2725
Hallahan HS 600/9-12
311 N 19th St 19103 215-563-8930
Michelle Beachy, prin. Fax 563-3809
Holy Family University Post-Sec.
9801 Frankford Ave 19114 215-637-7700
Hope Church S 200/PK-12
6707 Old York Rd 19126 215-927-7770
Dr. Raahsahn Bowden, supt. Fax 927-8070
Hussian School of Art Post-Sec.
111 S Indpndnce Mall E #300 19106 215-574-9600
International Christian HS 100/9-12
413 E Tabor Rd 19120 267-900-2000
Ben Brittin, admin. Fax 455-7198
Jean Madeline Educ. Ctr. for Cosmetology Post-Sec.
315A Bainbridge St 19147 215-238-9998
JNA Institute of Culinary Arts Post-Sec.
1212 S Broad St 19146 215-468-8800
LaSalle Academy 100/3-8
1434 N 2nd St 19122 215-739-5804
Teresa Diamond, prin. Fax 739-1664
La Salle University Post-Sec.
1900 W Olney Ave 19141 215-951-1000
Lincoln Technical Institute Post-Sec.
9191 Torresdale Ave 19136 215-335-0800
Lincoln Technical Institute Post-Sec.
3600 Market St 19104 215-382-1553
Lincoln Technical Institute Post-Sec.
2180 Hornig Rd 19116 215-969-0869
Little Flower HS 700/9-12
1000 W Lycoming St 19140 215-455-6900
Sr. Kathleen Klarich, prin. Fax 329-0478
L.T. International Beauty School Post-Sec.
830 N Broad St 19130 215-922-4478
Lutheran Theological Seminary Post-Sec.
7301 Germantown Ave 19119 215-248-4616
Mercy Vocational HS Vo/Tech
2900 W Hunting Park Ave 19129 215-226-1225
Sr. Susan Walsh, prin. Fax 228-6337
Methodist Hospital Post-Sec.
2301 S Broad St 19148 215-952-9402
Metropolitan Career Center Post-Sec.
100 S Broad St Ste 830 19110 215-568-9215
Moore College of Art and Design Post-Sec.
20th St and The Parkway 19103 215-965-4000
Nazareth Academy HS 400/9-12
4001 Grant Ave 19114 215-637-7676
Sr. Mary Joan Jacobs, prin. Fax 637-8523
Nazareth Hospital Post-Sec.
2601 Holme Ave 19152 215-335-6000
Northeastern Hospital School of Nursing Post-Sec.
2301 E Allegheny Ave 19134 215-291-3145
Northeast Prep S 100/7-12
1309 Cottman Ave 19111 215-342-5500
Alan Cissorsky, dir. Fax 342-8866
Orleans Technical Institute Post-Sec.
2770 Red Lion Rd 19114 215-728-4700
Our Mother of Sorrows S 100/4-8
1008 N 48th St 19131 215-473-5828
Sr. Patricia Bonner, prin. Fax 473-3096
Overbrook School for the Blind Post-Sec.
6333 Malvern Ave 19151 215-877-0313
Peirce College Post-Sec.
1420 Pine St 19102 215-545-6400
Penn Charter S 1,000/PK-12
3000 W School House Ln 19144 215-844-3460
Dr. Darryl J. Ford, head sch Fax 843-3939
Pennsylvania Academy of the Fine Arts Post-Sec.
128 N Broad St 19102 215-972-7600
Pennsylvania Hospital Post-Sec.
800 Spruce St 19107 215-829-3312
Pennsylvania School for the Deaf Post-Sec.
100 W School House Ln 19144
Philadelphia Coll. Osteopathic Medicine Post-Sec.
4170 City Ave 19131 215-871-6100
Philadelphia University Post-Sec.
4201 Henry Ave 19144 215-951-2700
Restaurant School at Walnut Hill College Post-Sec.
4207 Walnut St 19104 215-222-4200
Roman Catholic HS 1,100/9-12
301 N Broad St 19107 215-627-1270
Patricia Sticco, prin. Fax 627-4979
Roxborough Memorial Hospital Post-Sec.
5800 Ridge Ave 19128 215-487-4459
St. Hubert HS 700/9-12
7320 Torresdale Ave 19136 215-624-6840
Dr. Joanne Walls, prin. Fax 624-5940
St. James S 5-8
3217 W Clearfield St 19132 215-226-1276
David Kasievich, head sch
St. Joseph's Prep S 1,000/9-12
1733 W Girard Ave 19130 215-978-1950
Jason Zazyczny, prin. Fax 765-1710
St. Joseph's University Post-Sec.
5600 City Ave 19131 610-660-1000
St. Monica S - Senior Campus 200/4-8
2500 S 16th St 19145 215-467-5338
Sr. Mary Matulka, prin. Fax 467-4599
Settlement Music School Post-Sec.
416 Queen St 19147 215-336-0400
Springside Chestnut Hill Academy 500/PK-12
500 W Willow Grove Ave 19118 215-247-4700
Stephen Druggan, head sch Fax 247-8516
SS. John Neumann/Maria Goretti HS 700/9-12
1736 S 10th St 19148 215-465-8437
Kevin Dugan, prin. Fax 462-2410
Star Career Academy Post-Sec.
2371 Welsh Rd 19114 215-969-5877
Talmudical Yeshiva of Philadelphia Post-Sec.
6063 Drexel Rd 19131 215-473-1212
Talmudical Yeshiva of Philadelphia 100/9-12
6063 Drexel Rd 19131 215-477-1000
Temple University Post-Sec.
1801 N Broad St 19122 215-204-7000
The Art Institute of Philadelphia Post-Sec.
1622 Chestnut St 19103 215-567-7080
Thomas Jefferson University Post-Sec.
1020 Walnut St 19107 215-955-6000
University of Pennsylvania Post-Sec.
3451 Walnut St 19104 215-898-5000
University of the Arts Post-Sec.
320 S Broad St 19102 215-717-6000
University of the Sciences Philadelphia Post-Sec.
600 S 43rd St 19104 215-596-8800
West Catholic Preparatory HS 400/9-12
4501 Chestnut St 19139 215-386-2244
James Gallagher, prin. Fax 222-1651
Westminster Theological Seminary Post-Sec.
PO Box 27009 19118 215-887-5511

Philipsburg, Centre, Pop. 2,742
Philipsburg-Osceola Area SD 1,800/K-12
200 Short St 16866 814-342-1050
Dr. Gregg Paladina, supt. Fax 342-7208
www.pomounties.org
Philipsburg-Osceola Area HS 500/9-12
502 Philips St 16866 814-342-1521
Justin Hazelton, prin. Fax 342-7521
Philipsburg-Osceola Area MS 500/5-8
200 Short St 16866 814-342-4906
Susan Pritchard-Harris, prin. Fax 342-7532

Phoenixville, Chester, Pop. 15,988
Area Vocational Technical School
Supt. — None
Technical College HS - Pickering Campus Vo/Tech
1580 Charlestown Rd 19460 610-933-8877
Frank McKnight, prin. Fax 983-0680

Phoenixville Area SD 3,600/K-12
386 City Line Ave 19460 484-927-5000
Dr. Alan Fegley, supt. Fax 983-3729
www.pasd.com
Phoenixville Area HS 1,000/9-12
1200 Gay St 19460 484-927-5100
Dr. Craig Parkinson, prin. Fax 933-6009
Phoenixville Area MS 800/6-8
1000 Purple Pride Pkwy 19460 484-927-5200
Dr. Frank Garritano, prin. Fax 933-6121

Valley Forge Christian College Post-Sec.
1401 Charlestown Rd 19460 610-935-0450

Pine Forge, Berks

Pine Forge Academy 200/9-12
PO Box 338 19548 610-326-5800
Kris Fielder, prin. Fax 326-4260

Pine Grove, Schuylkill, Pop. 2,160
Pine Grove Area SD 1,600/K-12
103 School St 17963 570-345-2731
Fax 345-2790
www.pgasd.com
Pine Grove Area HS 500/9-12
101 School St 17963 570-345-2731
Michael Janicelli, prin. Fax 345-2793
Pine Grove Area MS 500/5-8
105 School St 17963 570-345-2731
Melissa Mekosh, prin. Fax 345-2791

Pittsburgh, Allegheny, Pop. 297,895
Avonworth SD 1,500/K-12
258 Josephs Ln 15237 412-369-8738
Dr. Thomas W. Ralston, supt. Fax 369-8746
www.avonworth.k12.pa.us
Avonworth HS 400/9-12
304 Josephs Ln 15237 412-366-6360
Emily Clare, prin. Fax 366-7603
Avonworth MS 300/6-8
256 Josephs Ln 15237 412-366-9650
Michael Hall, prin. Fax 358-9621

Baldwin-Whitehall SD 4,100/K-12
4900 Curry Rd 15236 412-884-6300
Dr. Randal A. Lutz, supt. Fax 885-7802
www.bwschools.net/
Baldwin HS 1,500/9-12
4653 Clairton Blvd 15236 412-885-7500
Walter Graves, prin. Fax 885-6652
Harrison MS 900/6-8
129 Windvale Dr 15236 412-885-7530
Jill Fleming-Salopek, prin. Fax 885-6766

Brentwood Borough SD 1,200/K-12
3601 Brownsville Rd 15227 412-881-2227
Dr. Amy Burch, supt. Fax 881-1640
www.brentwoodpgh.k12.pa.us
Brentwood HS 400/9-12
3601 Brownsville Rd 15227 412-881-4940
Jason Olexa, prin. Fax 881-4170
Brentwood MS 300/6-8
3601 Brownsville Rd 15227 412-881-4940
David Radcliffe Ph.D., prin. Fax 881-4170

Chartiers Valley SD 3,400/K-12
2030 Swallow Hill Rd 15220 412-429-2201
Dr. Brian White, supt. Fax 429-2237
Other Schools – See Bridgeville

Fox Chapel Area SD 4,200/K-12
611 Field Club Rd 15238 412-963-9600
Dr. Gene Freeman, supt. Fax 967-0697
www.fcasd.edu
Dorseyville MS 1,000/6-8
3732 Saxonburg Blvd 15238 412-767-5343
Jonathan Nauhaus, prin. Fax 767-4255
Fox Chapel Area HS 1,400/9-12
611 Field Club Rd 15238 412-967-2430
Michael Hower, prin. Fax 967-2458

Keystone Oaks SD 2,000/K-12
1000 Kelton Ave 15216 412-571-6000
Dr. William Stropkaj, supt. Fax 571-6006
www.kosd.org
Keystone Oaks HS 700/9-12
1000 Kelton Ave 15216 412-571-6040
Dr. Keith Hartbauer, prin. Fax 571-6043
Keystone Oaks MS 400/6-8
1002 Kelton Ave 15216 412-571-6146
Jeffrey Kattan, prin. Fax 571-6092

Mt. Lebanon SD 5,200/K-12
7 Horsman Dr 15228 412-344-2077
Dr. Timothy Steinhauer, supt. Fax 344-2047
www.mtlsd.org
Jefferson MS 600/6-8
21 Moffett St 15243 412-344-2123
Kelly Szesterniak, prin. Fax 344-1252
Mellon MS 700/6-8
11 Castle Shannon Blvd 15228 412-344-2122
Christopher Wolfson, prin. Fax 344-0590
Mt. Lebanon HS 1,700/9-12
155 Cochran Rd 15228 412-344-2003
Brian McFeeley, prin. Fax 344-2021

North Allegheny SD 8,200/K-12
200 Hillvue Ln 15237 412-366-2100
Dr. Robert Scherrer, supt. Fax 369-5513
www.northallegheny.org
Carson MS 600/6-8
300 Hillvue Ln 15237 412-369-5520
Katherine Jenkins, prin. Fax 630-5819
Ingomar MS 700/6-8
1521 Ingomar Heights Rd 15237 412-358-1470
Heidi Stark, prin. Fax 366-4487
North Allegheny Intermediate HS 1,400/9-10
350 Cumberland Rd 15237 412-369-5530
Dr. Brendan Hyland, prin. Fax 369-4825
Other Schools – See Wexford

North Hills SD 4,200/K-12
135 6th Ave 15229 412-318-1000
Dr. Patrick Mannarino, supt. Fax 318-1084
www.nhsd.net
North Hills HS 1,400/9-12
53 Rochester Rd 15229 412-318-1400
Beth Williams, prin. Fax 318-1403
North Hills MS 700/7-8
55 Rochester Rd 15229 412-318-1450
Dave Lieberman, prin. Fax 318-1453

Northgate SD 1,200/K-12
591 Union Ave 15202 412-732-3300
Dr. Joseph Pasquerilla, supt. Fax 734-8008
www.northgate.k12.pa.us
Northgate MSHS 500/7-12
589 Union Ave 15202 412-732-3300
Bryan Kyle, prin. Fax 734-8086

Penn Hills SD 2,600/PK-12
260 Aster St 15235 412-793-7000
Dr. Nancy Hines, supt. Fax 793-7825
www.phsd.k12.pa.us
Linton MS 1,200/5-8
250 Aster St 15235 412-793-7000
Katie Friend, prin. Fax 795-6087
Penn Hills HS 1,400/9-12
309 Collins Dr 15235 412-793-7000
Eric Kostic, prin. Fax 712-1047

Pittsburgh SD 24,800/PK-12
341 S Bellefield Ave 15213 412-622-3500
Dr. Linda Lane, supt. Fax 622-7920
www.pps.k12.pa.us
Pittsburgh Allderdice HS 1,300/9-12
2409 Shady Ave 15217 412-422-4800
Melissa Friez, prin. Fax 422-4803
Pittsburgh Allegheny 6-8 300/6-8
810 Arch St 15212 412-323-4115
Toni Kendrick, prin. Fax 323-4114
Pittsburgh Arlington 3-8 400/3-8
2500 Jonquil St 15210 412-488-3641
Kevin McGuire, prin. Fax 488-3760
Pittsburgh Arsenal 6-8 200/6-8
220 40th St 15201 412-622-5740
Patti Camper, prin. Fax 622-5743
Pittsburgh Brashear HS 1,400/9-12
590 Crane Ave 15216 412-571-7300
Kimberly Safran, prin. Fax 571-7305
Pittsburgh CAPA 6-12 900/6-12
111 9th St 15222 412-338-6100
Melissa Pearlman, prin. Fax 338-6143
Pittsburgh Carrick HS 800/9-12
125 Parkfield St 15210 412-885-7700
Dennis Chakey, prin. Fax 885-7708
Pittsburgh Classical 6-8 300/6-8
1463 Chartiers Ave 15220 412-928-3110
Valerie Merlo, prin. Fax 928-3106
Pittsburgh Milliones 6-12 500/6-12
3117 Centre Ave 15219 412-622-5900
Derrick Hardy, prin. Fax 622-5925
Pittsburgh Morrow 5-8 5-8
3530 Fleming Ave 15212 412-529-6600
Alivia Clark, prin. Fax 734-6606
Pittsburgh Obama 6-12 900/6-12
515 N Highland Ave 15206 412-622-5980
Dr. Wayne Walters, prin. Fax 622-5983
Pittsburgh Perry HS 800/9-12
3875 Perrysville Ave 15214 412-323-3400
Nina Sacco, prin. Fax 323-3404
Pittsburgh Schiller 6-8 200/6-8
1018 Peralta St 15212 412-323-4190
Paula Heinzman, prin. Fax 323-4192
Pittsburgh Science\Technology Acad 6-12 500/6-12
107 Thackeray St 15213 412-325-7620
Shawn McNeil, prin. Fax 622-5991
Pittsburgh South Brook 6-8 500/6-8
779 Dunster St 15226 412-572-8170
Jennifer McNamara, prin. Fax 572-8177
Pittsburgh South Hills 6-8 600/6-8
595 Crane Ave 15216 412-572-8130
Jacqueline Hale, prin. Fax 572-8148
Pittsburgh Sterrett 6-8 400/6-8
7100 Reynolds St 15208 412-247-7870
Dr. MiChele Holly, prin. Fax 247-7877
Pittsburgh Student Achievement Center 200/Alt
925 Brushton Ave 15208 412-529-7860
Dalhart Dobbs, prin. Fax 529-7926
Pittsburgh Westinghouse Academy 6-12 500/6-12
1101 N Murtland St 15208 412-665-3940
Alexander Herring, prin. Fax 665-4977

Plum Borough SD 3,600/K-12
900 Elicker Rd 15239 412-795-0100
Dr. Timothy Glasspool, supt. Fax 795-9115
www.pbsd.k12.pa.us
O'Block JHS 600/7-8
440 Presque Isle Dr 15239 724-733-2400
Joseph Fishell, prin. Fax 798-6347
Plum HS 1,300/9-12
900 Elicker Rd 15239 412-795-4880
Justin Stephans, prin. Fax 795-6823

Shaler Area SD
Supt. — See Glenshaw
Shaler Area HS 1,500/9-12
381 Wible Run Rd 15209 412-492-1200
Timothy Royall, prin. Fax 684-1076

Upper St. Clair SD
Supt. — See Upper Saint Clair
Ft. Couch MS 700/7-8
515 Fort Couch Rd 15241 412-833-1600
Joseph DeMar, prin. Fax 854-3095
Upper Saint Clair HS 1,400/9-12
1825 Mclaughlin Run Rd 15241 412-833-1600
Dr. Michael Ghilani, prin. Fax 833-4889

West Jefferson Hills SD
Supt. — See Jefferson Hills
Pleasant Hills MS 700/6-8
404 Old Clairton Rd 15236 412-655-8680
Daniel Como, prin. Fax 655-5691

Woodland Hills SD
Supt. — See North Braddock
Woodland Hills JSHS 1,200/8-12
2550 Greensburg Pike 15221 412-244-1100
Kevin Murray, prin. Fax 242-2344

Bidwell Training Center Post-Sec.
1815 Metropolitan St 15233 412-323-4000
Bishop Canevin Catholic HS 400/9-12
2700 Morange Rd 15205 412-922-7400
Kenneth Sinagra, prin. Fax 922-7403
Bradford School Post-Sec.
125 W Station Square # 129 15219 412-391-6710
Brightwood Career Institute Post-Sec.
933 Penn Ave 15222 412-338-4770
Byzantine Catholic Seminary Post-Sec.
3605 Perrysville Ave 15214 412-321-8383
Career Training Academy Post-Sec.
1500 Shoppes Northway Mall 15237 412-367-4000
Carlow University Post-Sec.
3333 5th Ave 15213 412-578-6000
Carnegie Mellon University Post-Sec.
5000 Forbes Ave 15213 412-268-2000
Center for Emergency Medicine/Western PA Post-Sec.
230 McKee Pl # 500 15213 412-647-4665
Central Catholic HS 800/9-12
4720 5th Ave 15213 412-208-3400
Br. Anthony Baginski, prin. Fax 208-0555
Chatham University Post-Sec.
Woodland Rd 15232 412-365-1100
Community College of Allegheny County Post-Sec.
808 Ridge Ave 15212 412-237-2525
Community College of Allegheny County Post-Sec.
8701 Perry Hwy 15237 412-366-7000
Dean Institute of Technology Post-Sec.
1501 W Liberty Ave 15226 412-531-4433
DeVry University Post-Sec.
210 6th Ave Ste 200 15222 412-642-9072
Duquesne University Post-Sec.
600 Forbes Ave 15282 412-396-6000
Ellis S 500/PK-12
6425 5th Ave 15206 412-661-5992
Robin Newham M.Ed., head sch Fax 661-3979
Empire Beauty School Post-Sec.
1000 McKnight Park Dr #1006 15237 800-575-5983
Everest Institute Post-Sec.
100 Forbes Ave # 1200 15222 412-261-4520
Hillel Academy of Pittsburgh 200/K-12
5685 Beacon St 15217 412-521-8131
Rabbi Sam Weinberg, dir. Fax 521-5150
Home for Crippled Children Post-Sec.
1426 Denniston St 15217
Imani Christian Academy 200/K-12
2150 E Hills Dr 15221 412-731-7982
Terri Ayers M.Ed., prin. Fax 731-7343
La Roche College Post-Sec.
9000 Babcock Blvd 15237 412-367-9300
Mercy Hospital School of Nursing Post-Sec.
1401 Blvd of the Allies 15219 412-232-7940
Neighborhood Academy 100/8-12
709 N Aiken Ave 15206 412-362-2001
Rev. Thomas Johnson, head sch Fax 362-2004
North Hills Beauty Academy Post-Sec.
813 W View Park Dr 15229 412-931-8563
Oakland Catholic HS 600/9-12
144 N Craig St 15213 412-682-6633
Marisa Greco, prin. Fax 682-2496
Pennsylvania Gunsmith School Post-Sec.
812 Ohio River Blvd 15202 412-766-1812
Pittsburgh Career Institute Post-Sec.
421 7th Ave 15219 412-281-2600
Pittsburgh Institute of Aeronautics Post-Sec.
PO Box 10897 15236 412-346-2100
Pittsburgh Institute of Mortuary Science Post-Sec.
5808 Baum Blvd 15206 412-362-8500
Pittsburgh Theological Seminary Post-Sec.
616 N Highland Ave 15206 412-362-5610
Point Park University Post-Sec.
201 Wood St 15222 412-391-4100
Point Park Univ.-St. Francis Med. Ctr. Post-Sec.
201 Wood St 15222 412-392-3879
Pressley Ridge School Post-Sec.
530 Marshall Ave 15214 412-442-4468
Reformed Presbyterian Theological Sem. Post-Sec.
7418 Penn Ave 15208 412-731-6000
Rosedale Technical Institute Post-Sec.
215 Beecham Dr Ste 2 15205 412-521-6200
St. Margaret Schools of Nursing Post-Sec.
221 7th St Ste 100 15238 412-784-4980
Seton-LaSalle HS 500/9-12
1000 McNeilly Rd 15226 412-561-3583
Lauren Martin, prin. Fax 561-9097
Shady Side Academy MS 200/6-8
500 Squaw Run Rd E 15238 412-968-3100
Amy Nixon, head sch Fax 968-3008
Shady Side Academy Senior S 500/9-12
423 Fox Chapel Rd 15238 412-968-3000
Sophie Lau, head sch Fax 968-3002
Shadyside Hospital Post-Sec.
5230 Centre Ave 15232 412-622-2010
South Hills Beauty Academy Post-Sec.
3269 W Liberty Ave 15216 412-561-3381
The Art Institute of Pittsburgh Post-Sec.
420 Blvd of the Allies 15219 412-263-6600
Triangle Tech Post-Sec.
1940 Perrysville Ave 15214 412-359-1000
Trinity Christian S 300/K-12
299 Ridge Ave 15221 412-242-8886
Kennedy Henriquez, head sch Fax 242-8859
University Health Center Post-Sec.
300 Halket St 15213 412-641-4664
University of Pittsburgh Post-Sec.
4200 5th Ave 15213 412-624-4141
UPMC School of Medical Imaging Post-Sec.
3434 Forbes Ave 15213 412-647-3528
Vet Tech Institute Post-Sec.
125 7th St 15222 412-391-7021
Vincentian Academy 200/9-12
8100 McKnight Rd 15237 412-364-1616
Rita Canton, prin. Fax 367-5722
Western Pennsylvania Hospital Post-Sec.
4900 Friendship Ave 15224 412-578-5538
Western Pennsylvania School for Blind Post-Sec.
Bayard at Bellefield 15213
Western Pennsylvania School for the Deaf Post-Sec.
300 E Swissvale Ave 15218 412-371-7000
Winchester Thurston S 700/PK-12
555 Morewood Ave 15213 412-578-7500
Gary Niels, hdmstr. Fax 578-7504
Yeshiva S of Pittsburgh 100/PK-12
2100 Wightman St 15217 412-422-7300
Rabbi Yisroel Rosenfeld, dean Fax 422-5930

Pittston, Luzerne, Pop. 7,622
Pittston Area SD 3,300/K-12
5 Stout St 18640 570-654-2415
Dr. Michael Garzella, supt. Fax 654-5548
www.pittstonarea.com
Pittston Area HS 1,000/9-12
5 Stout St 18640 570-654-3541
John Haas, prin. Fax 602-0823
Pittston Area MS 1,000/5-8
120 New St 18640 570-655-2927
Patrick Bilbow, prin. Fax 654-0862

Plains, Luzerne, Pop. 4,288
Wilkes-Barre Area SD
Supt. — See Wilkes Barre
Solomon/Plains JHS 500/7-8
43 Abbott St 18705 570-826-7224
John Woloski, prin. Fax 820-3715

Pleasant Gap, Centre, Pop. 2,844
Area Vocational Technical School
Supt. — None
Central PA Institute of Science & Tech Vo/Tech
540 N Harrison Rd 16823 814-359-2793
Dr. Richard Makin, dir. Fax 359-2599

Plumsteadville, Bucks, Pop. 2,600

Plumstead Christian S - Middle Upper Cps 200/6-12
PO Box 216 18949 215-766-8073
Patrick Fitzpatrick, hdmstr. Fax 766-2033

Plymouth, Luzerne, Pop. 5,852
Wyoming Valley West SD
Supt. — See Kingston
Wyoming Valley West HS 1,300/9-12
150 Wadham St 18651 570-779-5361
David Novrocki, prin. Fax 779-9510

Plymouth Meeting, Montgomery, Pop. 6,092
Area Vocational Technical School
Supt. — None
Central Montco Technical HS Vo/Tech
821 Plymouth Rd 19462 610-277-2301
Walter Slauch, dir.

Colonial SD 4,700/K-12
230 Flourtown Rd 19462 610-834-1670
Dr. Mary Ellen Gorodetzer, supt. Fax 834-7535
www.colonialsd.org
Colonial MS 1,100/6-8
716 Belvoir Rd 19462 610-275-5100
Robert Fahler, prin. Fax 278-2447
Plymouth-Whitemarsh HS 1,500/9-12
201 E Germantown Pike 19462 610-825-1500
Jason Bacani, prin. Fax 832-0766

Pocono Summit, Monroe
Pocono Mountain SD
Supt. — See Swiftwater
Pocono Mountain West HS 1,900/9-12
181 Panther Ln 18346 570-839-7121
Mark Wade, prin. Fax 839-5968
Pocono Mountain West JHS 800/7-8
180 Panther Ln 18346 570-839-7121
Dr. Eric Vogt, prin. Fax 839-7397

Point Marion, Fayette, Pop. 1,152
Albert Gallatin Area SD
Supt. — See Uniontown
Gallatin South MS 400/6-8
224 New Geneva Rd 15474 724-725-5241
Joetta Britvich, prin. Fax 725-5424

Portage, Cambria, Pop. 2,610
Portage Area SD 900/PK-12
84 Mountain Ave 15946 814-736-9636
Eric Zelanko, supt. Fax 736-9634
www.portageareasd.org
Portage Area JSHS 400/7-12
85 Mountain Ave 15946 814-736-9636
Ralph Cecere, prin. Fax 736-9597

Port Allegany, McKean, Pop. 2,134
Area Vocational Technical School
Supt. — None
Seneca Highlands Career & Technical Ctr Vo/Tech
PO Box 219 16743 814-642-2573
James Young, dir.

Port Allegany SD 900/K-12
20 Oak St 16743 814-642-2596
Gary Buchsen, supt. Fax 642-9574
www.pahs.net
Port Allegany JSHS 400/7-12
20 Oak St 16743 814-642-2544
Marc Budd, prin. Fax 642-5082

Portersville, Butler, Pop. 235

Portersville Christian S 200/PK-12
343 E Portersville Rd 16051 724-368-8787
Lee Saunders, head sch Fax 368-3100

Pottstown, Montgomery, Pop. 21,544
Owen J. Roberts SD 5,200/K-12
901 Ridge Rd 19465 610-469-5100
Dr. Michael Christian, supt. Fax 469-0403
www.ojrsd.com
Roberts HS 1,600/9-12
981 Ridge Rd 19465 610-469-5101
Dr. Richard Marchini, prin. Fax 469-5898
Roberts MS 800/7-8
881 Ridge Rd 19465 610-469-5102
Sean Burns, prin. Fax 469-5832

Pottsgrove SD 3,200/K-12
1301 Kauffman Rd 19464 610-327-2277
William Shirk Ed.D., supt. Fax 327-2530
www.pgsd.org
Pottsgrove HS 1,000/9-12
1345 Kauffman Rd 19464 610-326-5105
Dr. William Ziegler, prin. Fax 970-6191

Pottsgrove MS 700/6-8
1351 N Hanover St 19464 610-326-8243
Dr. David Ramage, prin. Fax 718-0581

Pottstown SD 3,100/PK-12
230 Beech St 19464 610-323-8200
Stephen Rodriguez, supt. Fax 326-6540
www.pottstownschools.com
Pottstown HS 800/9-12
750 N Washington St 19464 610-970-6700
Danielle McCoy, prin. Fax 970-1363
Pottstown MS 900/5-8
600 N Franklin St 19464 610-970-6665
David Todd, prin. Fax 970-8738

Antonelli Medical & Professional Inst Post-Sec.
1700 Industrial Hwy 19464 610-323-7270
Coventry Christian S 300/PK-12
699 N Pleasantview Rd 19464 610-326-3320
John Niehls, head sch Fax 948-1780
Empire Beauty School Post-Sec.
141 E High St 19464 610-327-1313
Hill S 500/9-12
717 E High St 19464 610-326-1000
Zachary Lehman, hdmstr. Fax 705-1753
West-Mont Christian Academy 300/K-12
873 S Hanover St 19465 610-326-7690
Dr. James Smock, admin. Fax 326-7126

Pottsville, Schuylkill, Pop. 14,045
Area Vocational Technical School
Supt. — None
Schuylkill Technology Center - Airport Vo/Tech
240 Airport Rd 17901 570-544-4904
Dr. Diane Niederriter, dir.

Pottsville Area SD 2,800/K-12
1501 Laurel Blvd 17901 570-621-2900
Dr. Jeffrey Zweibel, supt. Fax 621-2025
www.pottsville.k12.pa.us/
Lengel MS 800/5-8
1541 Laurel Blvd 17901 570-621-2924
Michael Maley, prin. Fax 621-2999
Pottsville Area HS 1,000/9-12
1600 Elk Ave 17901 570-621-2962
Tiffany Reedy, prin. Fax 621-2036

McCann School of Business & Technology Post-Sec.
2650 Woodglen Rd 17901 570-622-7622
Nativity BVM HS 200/9-12
1 Lawtons Hl 17901 570-622-8110
Lynn Sabol, prin. Fax 622-0454
SchuylKill Health School of Nursing Post-Sec.
420 S Jackson St 17901 570-621-5027

Prospect Park, Delaware, Pop. 6,344
Interboro SD 3,400/K-12
900 Washington Ave 19076 610-461-6700
Bernadette Reiley, supt. Fax 583-1678
www.interborosd.org
Interboro HS 1,100/9-12
500 16th Ave 19076 610-237-6410
Ryan Johnston, prin. Fax 237-8103

Punxsutawney, Jefferson, Pop. 5,912
Punxsutawney Area SD 2,200/K-12
475 Beyer Ave 15767 814-938-5151
Dr. Keith Wolfe, supt. Fax 938-6677
www.punxsy.k12.pa.us/
Punxsutawney Area HS 800/8-12
500 N Findley St 15767 814-938-5151
David London, prin. Fax 938-5101

Punxsutawney Christian S 200/PK-12
216 N Jefferson St 15767 814-938-2295
Lori Galbraith, admin. Fax 938-2251

Quakertown, Bucks, Pop. 8,835
Quakertown Community SD 5,200/K-12
100 Commerce Dr 18951 215-529-2000
William Harner Ph.D., supt. Fax 529-2042
www.qcsd.org
Freshman Center 400/9-9
349 S 9th St 18951 267-371-1200
Erin Oleksa, prin. Fax 371-1201
Milford MS 400/6-8
2255 Allentown Rd 18951 215-529-2210
Dr. Deb Lock, prin. Fax 529-2211
Quakertown Community HS 1,200/10-12
600 Park Ave 18951 215-529-2060
David Finnerty, prin. Fax 529-2061
Strayer MS 800/6-8
1200 Ronald Reagan Dr 18951 215-529-2290
Derek Peiffer, prin. Fax 529-2291

Quakertown Christian S 200/PK-12
50 E Paletown Rd 18951 215-536-6970
Timothy Gray, admin. Fax 536-2115

Quarryville, Lancaster, Pop. 2,535
Solanco SD 3,600/K-12
121 S Hess St 17566 717-786-8401
Dr. Brian A. Bliss, supt. Fax 786-8245
www.solanco.k12.pa.us
Smith MS 400/6-8
645 Kirkwood Pike 17566 717-786-2244
Paul Gladfelter, prin. Fax 786-8796
Solanco HS 1,100/9-12
585 Solanco Rd 17566 717-786-2151
Stephanie Lininger, prin. Fax 786-1808
Swift MS 400/6-8
1866 Robert Fulton Hwy 17566 717-548-2187
Paul Gladfelter, prin. Fax 548-3350

Radnor, Delaware, Pop. 31,300
Radnor Township SD
Supt. — See Wayne
Radnor HS 1,200/9-12
130 King of Prussia Rd 19087 610-293-0855
Daniel Bechtold, prin. Fax 989-9146

Archbishop Carroll HS 1,000/9-12
211 Matsonford Rd 19087 610-688-7610
Andrew Bradley, prin. Fax 688-8326
Cabrini College Post-Sec.
610 King of Prussia Rd 19087 610-902-8100

Reading, Berks, Pop. 86,403
Antietam SD 1,000/K-12
100 Antietam Rd 19606 610-779-0554
Dr. Melissa G. Brewer, supt. Fax 779-4424
www.antietamsd.org
Antietam MSHS 500/7-12
100 Antietam Rd 19606 610-779-3545
Dr. Felice Stern, prin. Fax 779-0378

Area Vocational Technical School
Supt. — None
Reading-Muhlenberg CTC Vo/Tech
2615 Warren Rd 19604 610-921-7300
Gerald Witmer, admin. Fax 921-7367

Exeter Township SD 3,700/K-12
200 Elm St 19606 610-779-0700
Dr. Robert Phillips, supt. Fax 779-7104
www.exeter.k12.pa.us
Exeter Township HS 1,400/9-12
201 E 37th St 19606 610-779-3060
William Cain, prin. Fax 370-0518
Exeter Township JHS 700/7-8
151 E 39th St 19606 610-779-3320
Eric Flamm, prin. Fax 370-0678

Muhlenberg SD
Supt. — See Laureldale
Muhlenberg HS 900/10-12
400 Sharp Ave 19605 610-921-8078
Michael Mish, prin. Fax 921-7925

Reading SD 15,000/PK-12
800 Washington St 19601 610-371-5611
Dr. Khalid Mumin, supt. Fax 371-5971
www.readingsd.org
Reading HS 3,100/10-12
801 N 13th St 19604 610-371-5710
Eric Turman, prin. Fax 371-8723
Reading Intermediate HS 8-9
215 N 12th St 19604 484-258-7365
Alex Brown, prin. Fax 258-7333

Albright College Post-Sec.
PO Box 15234 19612 610-921-2381
Alvernia University Post-Sec.
400 Saint Bernardine St 19607 610-796-8200
Berks Catholic HS 500/9-12
955 E Wyomissing Blvd 19611 610-374-8361
Tony Balistiere, prin. Fax 374-4309
Empire Beauty School Post-Sec.
2302 N 5th Street Hwy 19605 610-372-2777
Fairview Christian S 200/K-12
410 S 14th St 19602 610-372-8826
Jay Fox, prin. Fax 478-0896
Pace Institute Post-Sec.
606 Court St 19601 610-375-1212
Penn State Berks Post-Sec.
PO Box 7009 19610 610-396-6000
Reading Area Community College Post-Sec.
PO Box 1706 19603 610-372-4721
Reading Hospital & Medical Center Post-Sec.
PO Box 16052 19612 610-378-6664
Reading Junior Academy 100/PK-10
309 N Kenhorst Blvd 19607 610-777-8424
Lee Stahl, prin. Fax 603-0129
St. Joseph's Hospital Post-Sec.
PO Box 316 19603 610-378-2000

Red Lion, York, Pop. 6,289
Red Lion Area SD 5,500/K-12
696 Delta Rd 17356 717-244-4518
Dr. Scott Deisley, supt. Fax 244-2196
www.rlasd.net
Red Lion Area JHS 900/7-8
200 Country Club Rd 17356 717-244-1448
Shane Mack, prin. Fax 244-6160
Red Lion Area SHS 1,600/9-12
200 Horace Mann Ave 17356 717-246-1611
Mark Shue, prin. Fax 246-9181

Red Lion Christian S 200/PK-12
105 Springvale Rd 17356 717-244-3905
Steven Schmuck, prin. Fax 246-3738

Renovo, Clinton, Pop. 1,205
Keystone Central SD
Supt. — See Mill Hall
Bucktail Area JSHS 100/7-12
1300 Bucktail Ave 17764 570-923-1166
Betsy Dickey, prin. Fax 923-2233

Reynoldsville, Jefferson, Pop. 2,735
Area Vocational Technical School
Supt. — None
Jefferson County-Dubois AVTS Vo/Tech
576 Vo Tech Rd 15851 814-653-8265
Barry Fillman, dir. Fax 653-8425

Richboro, Bucks, Pop. 6,518
Council Rock SD
Supt. — See Newtown
Richboro MS 500/7-8
98 Upper Holland Rd 18954 215-944-2500
Richard Hollahan, prin. Fax 944-2598

Ridgway, Elk, Pop. 4,043
Ridgway Area SD 900/K-12
PO Box 447 15853 814-773-3146
Robert Rocco, supt. Fax 776-4299
www.ridgwayareaschooldistrict.com
Ridgway Area HS 300/9-12
PO Box 447 15853 814-773-3164
Brice Benson, prin. Fax 776-4247

Ridgway Area MS 200/6-8
PO Box 447 15853 814-773-3156
Brice Benson, prin. Fax 776-4239

Ridley Park, Delaware, Pop. 6,923
Ridley SD
Supt. — See Folsom
Ridley MS 1,300/6-8
400 Free St 19078 610-237-8034
Adam Staples, prin. Fax 237-8032

Rimersburg, Clarion, Pop. 942
Union SD 600/K-12
354 Baker St Ste 2 16248 814-473-6311
Jean McCleary, supt. Fax 473-8201
www.unionsd.net/
Union JSHS 300/7-12
354 Baker St Ste 1 16248 814-473-3121
Mark Schlosser, prin. Fax 473-8201

Roaring Spring, Blair, Pop. 2,566
Spring Cove SD 1,400/K-12
1100 E Main St 16673 814-224-5124
Betsy Baker, supt. Fax 224-5516
scsd.schoolwires.net
Spring Cove MS 400/6-8
185 Spring Cove Dr 16673 814-224-2106
Breanne Venios, prin. Fax 224-2842
Other Schools – See Martinsburg

Robesonia, Berks, Pop. 2,034
Conrad Weiser Area SD 2,700/PK-12
44 Big Spring Rd 19551 610-693-8545
Dr. Randall Grove, supt. Fax 693-8586
www.conradweiser.org
Weiser HS 900/9-12
44 Big Spring Rd 19551 610-693-8528
Robert G. Galtere, prin. Fax 693-8511
Weiser MS 900/5-8
347 E Penn Ave 19551 610-693-8514
R. Kenneth Buck, prin. Fax 693-8543

Rochester, Beaver, Pop. 3,481
Rochester Area SD 800/K-12
540 Reno St 15074 724-775-7500
Dr. Jane W. Bovalino Ed.D., supt. Fax 775-4077
www.rasd.org
Rochester Area HS 200/9-12
540 Reno St 15074 724-775-7500
Michael Damon, prin. Fax 775-9268
Rochester Area MS 200/6-8
540 Reno St 15074 724-775-7500
Michael Damon, prin. Fax 775-9268

Rockwood, Somerset, Pop. 885
Rockwood Area SD 700/K-12
439 Somerset Ave 15557 814-926-4688
Mark Bower, supt. Fax 926-2880
www.rockwoodschools.org
Rockwood Area JSHS 400/7-12
437 Somerset Ave 15557 814-926-4631
Mark Bower, prin. Fax 926-2631

Rome, Bradford, Pop. 437
Northeast Bradford SD 900/K-12
526 Panther Ln 18837 570-744-2521
William J. Clark, supt. Fax 744-2933
www.nebpanthers.com
Northeast Bradford JSHS 400/7-12
526 Panther Ln 18837 570-744-2521
Robert Moore, prin. Fax 744-1445

North Rome Christian S 100/K-12
3376 N Rome Rd 18837 570-247-2800
Lee Ann Carmichael, admin. Fax 247-7288

Rosemont, Montgomery
Lower Merion SD
Supt. — See Ardmore
Harriton HS 1,200/9-12
600 N Ithan Ave 19010 610-658-3950
Scott Eveslage, prin. Fax 525-6771

Hill Top Preparatory S 100/5-12
737 S Ithan Ave 19010 610-527-3230
Tom Needham, head sch Fax 527-7683
Irwin S 700/PK-12
275 S Ithan Ave 19010 610-525-8400
Dr. Wendy Hill, head sch Fax 525-8908
Rosemont College Post-Sec.
1400 Montgomery Ave 19010 610-527-0200

Roseto, Northampton, Pop. 1,552

Faith Christian S 200/K-12
122 Dante St 18013 610-588-3414
Leeann Long, prin. Fax 588-8103

Royersford, Montgomery, Pop. 4,653
Spring-Ford Area SD 7,800/K-12
857 S Lewis Rd 19468 610-705-6000
Dr. David Goodin, supt. Fax 705-6245
www.spring-ford.net
Spring-Ford 9th Grade Center 600/9-9
400 S Lewis Rd 19468 610-705-6011
Dr. Theresa Weidenbaugh, prin. Fax 705-6233
Spring-Ford HS 1,700/10-12
350 S Lewis Rd 19468 610-705-6001
Dr. Patrick Nugent, prin. Fax 705-6258
Spring-Ford MS 8th Grade Center 700/8-8
700 Washington St 19468 610-705-6002
Dr. Michael Siggins, prin. Fax 705-6255

Pope John Paul II HS 800/9-12
181 Rittenhouse Rd 19468 484-975-6500
James Meredith, prin. Fax 792-3082

Ruffs Dale, Westmoreland
Yough SD
Supt. — See Herminie

Yough MS 700/5-8
171 State Route 31 15679 724-872-5164
Kevin Smetak, prin. Fax 872-5319

Rural Valley, Armstrong, Pop. 873
Armstrong SD
Supt. — See Kittanning
West Shamokin JSHS 700/7-12
178 Wolf Dr 16249 724-783-7040
Dr. Stephen Shutters, prin. Fax 783-6747

Russell, Warren, Pop. 1,393
Warren County SD 4,500/K-12
6820 Market St 16345 814-723-6900
Amy J. Stewart, supt.
www.wcsdpa.org
Eisenhower MSHS 500/6-12
3700 Route 957 16345 814-757-8878
Kelly Martin, prin. Fax 757-8516
Other Schools – See Sheffield, Warren, Youngsville

Saegertown, Crawford, Pop. 988
PENNCREST SD 3,200/K-12
PO Box 808 16433 814-763-2323
Michael J. Healey, supt. Fax 763-5129
www.penncrest.org
Saegertown JSHS 600/7-12
18079 Mook Rd 16433 814-763-2615
Thomas Baker, prin. Fax 763-6702
Other Schools – See Cambridge Springs, Guys Mills

Saint Davids, Delaware

Eastern University Post-Sec.
1300 Eagle Rd 19087 610-341-5800

Saint Marys, Elk, Pop. 12,994
Saint Marys Area SD 2,200/K-12
977 S Saint Marys St 15857 814-834-7831
Dr. Brian Toth, supt. Fax 781-2190
smasd.org
Saint Marys Area HS 700/9-12
977 S Saint Marys St 15857 814-834-7831
Joseph Collins, prin. Fax 781-2190
Saint Marys Area MS 500/6-8
979 S Saint Marys St 15857 814-834-7831
James Wortman, prin. Fax 781-2191

Elk County Catholic HS 300/9-12
600 Maurus St 15857 814-834-7800
Sandra Florig, prin. Fax 781-3441
St. Marys Catholic MS 100/6-8
600 Maurus St 15857 814-834-7800
John Schneider, prin. Fax 781-3441

Salisbury, Somerset, Pop. 724
Salisbury-Elk Lick SD 300/PK-12
PO Box 68 15558 814-662-2733
Joseph Renzi, supt. Fax 662-2544
selsd.com
Salisbury-Elk Lick JSHS 100/7-12
PO Box 68 15558 814-662-2741
Kenneth Fusina, prin. Fax 662-2091

Saltsburg, Indiana, Pop. 862
Blairsville-Saltsburg SD
Supt. — See Blairsville
Saltsburg MSHS 400/6-12
84 Trojan Ln 15681 724-639-3547
Tracy Richards, prin. Fax 639-0071

Kiski S 200/9-12
1888 Brett Ln 15681 724-639-3586
Christopher Brueningsen, hdmstr. Fax 639-8596

Sarver, Butler
Freeport Area SD 1,600/K-12
621 S Pike Rd 16055 724-295-5141
Chris DeVivo, supt. Fax 295-3001
www.freeport.k12.pa.us
Freeport Area HS 600/9-12
625 S Pike Rd 16055 724-295-5143
Michael Kleckner, prin. Fax 295-2390
Other Schools – See Freeport

Evangel Heights Christian Academy 200/PK-12
120 Beale Rd 16055 724-295-9199
Fax 295-9009

Saxonburg, Butler, Pop. 1,517
South Butler County SD 2,600/K-12
328 Knoch Rd 16056 724-352-1700
David Zupsic, supt. Fax 352-3622
southbutler.org
Knoch HS 1,000/9-12
345 Knoch Rd 16056 724-352-1700
Todd Trofimuk, prin. Fax 352-0160
Knoch MS 600/6-8
754 Dinnerbell Rd 16056 724-352-1700
Frank Moxie, prin. Fax 352-0170

Saxton, Bedford, Pop. 730
Tussey Mountain SD 1,000/PK-12
199 Front St 16678 814-635-3670
Mark Bollman, supt. Fax 635-3928
www.tmsd.net
Tussey Mountain HS 300/7-12
199 Front St 16678 814-635-2975
Janell Henderson, prin.
Tussey Mountain JHS 200/7-8
199 Front St 16678 814-635-2975
Janell Henderson, prin. Fax 635-3713

Sayre, Bradford, Pop. 5,530
Sayre Area SD 1,100/PK-12
333 W Lockhart St 18840 570-888-7615
Dr. Sherry Griggs Ph.D., supt. Fax 888-8248
www.sayresd.org
Sayre Area JSHS 500/7-12
331 W Lockhart St 18840 570-888-6622
Dayton Handrick, prin. Fax 882-9385

Robert Packer Hospital Post-Sec.
1 Guthrie Sq 18840 570-888-6666

Schnecksville, Lehigh, Pop. 2,900
Area Vocational Technical School
Supt. — None
Lehigh Career & Technical Institute Vo/Tech
4500 Education Park Dr 18078 610-799-1323

Lehigh Carbon Community College Post-Sec.
4525 Education Park Dr 18078 610-799-2121

Schuylkill Haven, Schuylkill, Pop. 5,373
Blue Mountain SD
Supt. — See Orwigsburg
Blue Mountain HS 900/9-12
1076 W Market St 17972 570-366-0511
Kevin Berger, prin. Fax 366-1965

Schuylkill Haven Area SD 1,300/K-12
501 E Main St 17972 570-385-6705
Lorraine Felker, supt. Fax 385-6736
www.shasd.org
Schuylkill Haven Area HS 500/8-12
501 E Main St 17972 570-385-6717
Sarah Yoder, prin. Fax 385-6745

Penn State Schuylkill Post-Sec.
200 University Dr 17972 570-385-6000

Scotland, Franklin, Pop. 1,373

Providence Christian Academy 50/K-12
PO Box 369 17254 717-298-8090
Jeffrey Garner, head sch

Scottdale, Westmoreland, Pop. 4,332
Southmoreland SD 1,900/K-12
200 Scottie Way 15683 724-887-2005
Dr. John Molnar Ed.D., supt. Fax 887-2055
www.southmoreland.net
Southmoreland MS 400/6-8
200 Scottie Way 15683 724-887-2029
Vince Mascia, prin. Fax 887-2032
Other Schools – See Alverton

Scott Township, Allegheny, Pop. 17,118
Lakeland SD 1,500/K-12
1355 Lakeland Dr, 570-254-9485
R. Scott Jeffery, supt. Fax 254-6730
www.lakelandsd.org
Lakeland JSHS 700/7-12
1355 Lakeland Dr, 570-254-9485
James Pivirotto, prin. Fax 254-6730

Scranton, Lackawanna, Pop. 74,482
Area Vocational Technical School
Supt. — None
CTC of Lackawanna County Vo/Tech
3201 Rockwell Ave 18508 570-346-8471
Thomas Baileys, dir. Fax 342-4251

Scranton SD 9,300/PK-12
425 N Washington Ave 18503 570-348-3400
Dr. Alexis Kirijan, admin. Fax 348-3563
www.scrsd.org/
Northeast IS, 721 Adams Ave 18510 800/6-8
Robert Butka, prin. 570-348-3651
Scranton HS 1,800/9-12
63 Munchak Way 18508 570-348-3481
John Coyle, prin. Fax 348-3561
South Scranton IS 500/6-8
355 Maple St 18505 570-348-3631
Melissa McTiernan, prin.
West Scranton HS 900/9-12
1201 Luzerne St 18504 570-348-3616
Robert Gentilezza, prin. Fax 348-3594
West Scranton IS 700/6-8
1401 Fellows St 18504 570-348-3475
Paul Dougherty, prin.

Bais Yaakov of Scranton 50/9-12
1025 Vine St 18510 570-347-5003
Esther Elefant, prin. Fax 353-5003
Bnos Yisroel Girls HS 100/9-12
620 Monroe Ave 18510 570-558-1370
Fortis Institute Post-Sec.
517 Ash St 18509 570-558-1818
Gregory the Great Academy 100/9-12
621 N Bromley Ave 18504 571-295-6244
Sean Fitzpatrick, prin.
Johnson College Post-Sec.
3427 N Main Ave 18508 570-342-6404
Lackawanna College Post-Sec.
501 Vine St 18509 570-961-7810
Marywood University Post-Sec.
2300 Adams Ave 18509 570-348-6211
Penn Foster Career School Post-Sec.
925 Oak St 18515 570-342-7701
St. Clare / St. Paul S - Main Campus 300/3-8
1527 Penn Ave 18509 570-343-7880
Douglas Workman, prin. Fax 343-0069
Scranton Prep S 800/9-12
1000 Wyoming Ave 18509 570-941-7737
Matthew Bernard, prin. Fax 941-6118
Scranton State School for the Deaf Post-Sec.
1800 N Washington Ave 18509
The Commonwealth Medical College Post-Sec.
525 Pine St 18509 570-504-7000
University of Scranton Post-Sec.
800 Linden St 18510 570-941-7400
Yeshiva Beth Moshe Post-Sec.
930 Hickory St 18505 570-346-1747
Yeshiva Beth Moshe 100/9-12
930 Hickory St 18505 570-346-1747
Rabbi Chaim Bressler, prin. Fax 346-2251

Selinsgrove, Snyder, Pop. 5,582
Selinsgrove Area SD 2,700/K-12
401 18th St 17870 570-374-1144
Chad Cohrs, supt. Fax 372-2222
www.seal-pa.org/
Selinsgrove Area HS 800/9-12
500 N Broad St 17870 570-372-2230
Brian Parise, prin. Fax 372-2240
Selinsgrove Area MS 600/6-8
401 18th St 17870 570-372-2250
John Bohle, prin. Fax 372-2251

Susquehanna University Post-Sec.
514 University Ave 17870 570-374-0101

Sellersville, Bucks, Pop. 4,161

Faith Christian Academy 400/K-12
700 N Main St 18960 215-257-4577
Ryan Clymer, hdmstr. Fax 534-0842
Upper Bucks Christian S 300/PK-12
754 E Rockhill Rd 18960 215-536-9200
Josh Scheiderer, admin. Fax 536-2229

Seneca, Venango, Pop. 1,053
Cranberry Area SD 1,100/K-12
3 Education Dr 16346 814-676-5628
William Vonada, supt. Fax 677-5728
www.edline.net/pages/cranberry_area_school_district
Cranberry Area JSHS 500/7-12
1 Education Dr 16346 814-676-8504
Richard Smith, prin. Fax 676-5156

Christian Life Academy 100/PK-12
3973 State Route 257 16346 814-676-9360
Lanny Williams, admin. Fax 676-2908
Northwest Medical Center Post-Sec.
100 Fairfield Dr 16346 814-677-1711

Sewickley, Allegheny, Pop. 3,749
Quaker Valley SD
Supt. — See Leetsdale
Quaker Valley MS 500/6-8
618 Harbaugh St 15143 412-749-5079
Fax 749-9844

Eden Christian Academy - Mt. Nebo Campus 200/7-12
318 Nicholson Rd 15143 412-741-2825
Todd Aiken, prin. Fax 324-1101
Sewickley Academy 700/PK-12
315 Academy Ave 15143 412-741-2230
Kolia John O'Connor, head sch Fax 741-9234
Sewickley Valley Hospital Post-Sec.
700 Blackburn Rd 15143 412-741-6600
The Education Center at Watson Inst. Post-Sec.
301 Campmeeting Rd 15143 412-741-1800

Shamokin Dam, Snyder, Pop. 1,672

Empire Beauty School Post-Sec.
PO Box 397 17876 570-743-1410

Shanksville, Somerset, Pop. 229
Shanksville-Stonycreek SD
Supt. — See Friedens
Shanksville-Stonycreek MSHS 100/6-12
PO Box 128 15560 814-267-4649
Reno Barkman, prin. Fax 267-4372

Sharon, Mercer, Pop. 13,523
Sharon CSD 2,100/K-12
215 Forker Blvd 16146 724-983-4000
Michael Calla, supt. Fax 981-0844
sharoncitysd.schoolwires.com
Sharon HS 500/9-12
1129 E State St 16146 724-983-4030
Mike Fitzgerald, prin. Fax 981-0840
Sharon MS 300/7-8
1129 E State St 16146 724-983-4032
Terry Karsonovich, prin. Fax 983-4050

Laurel Technical Institute Post-Sec.
200 Sterling Ave 16146 724-983-0700
Penn State Shenango Post-Sec.
147 Shenango Ave 16146 724-983-2803
Sharon Regional Health System Post-Sec.
740 E State St 16146 724-983-5603

Sharon Hill, Delaware, Pop. 5,504
Southeast Delco SD
Supt. — See Folcroft
Academy Park HS 1,200/9-12
300 Calcon Hook Rd 19079 610-522-4330
Nathaniel Robinson, prin. Fax 522-4335

Venus Beauty Academy Post-Sec.
1033 Chester Pike 19079 610-586-2500

Sharpsville, Mercer, Pop. 4,343
Sharpsville Area SD 1,300/K-12
701 Pierce Ave 16150 724-962-7874
Dr. Brad Ferko, supt. Fax 962-7873
www.sharpsville.k12.pa.us/
Sharpsville Area HS 400/9-12
301 Blue Devil Way 16150 724-962-7861
Tim Dadich, prin. Fax 962-7730
Sharpsville Area MS 300/6-8
303 Blue Devil Way 16150 724-962-7863
Heidi AbiNader, prin. Fax 962-7891

Sheffield, Warren, Pop. 1,128
Warren County SD
Supt. — See Russell
Sheffield Area MSHS 300/6-12
6760 Route 6 16347 814-968-3720
Kimberly Yourchisin, prin. Fax 968-4233

Shenandoah, Schuylkill, Pop. 5,009
Shenandoah Valley SD 1,100/PK-12
805 W Centre St 17976 570-462-1936
Brian Waite, supt. Fax 462-4611
www.svbluedevils.org
Shenandoah Valley JSHS 500/7-12
805 W Centre St 17976 570-462-1957
Phillip Andras, prin. Fax 462-2982

Shickshinny, Luzerne, Pop. 832
Northwest Area SD 1,000/PK-12
243 Thorne Hill Rd 18655 570-542-4126
James McGovern, supt. Fax 542-0187
www.northwest.k12.pa.us/
Northwest Area MSHS 500/7-12
243 Thorne Hill Rd 18655 570-542-4126
Ryan Miner, prin. Fax 542-7538

Shillington, Berks, Pop. 5,201
Governor Mifflin SD 4,100/K-12
10 S Waverly St 19607 610-775-1461
Dr. Steven Gerhard, supt. Fax 775-6586
www.governormifflinsd.org
Mifflin HS 1,300/9-12
10 S Waverly St 19607 610-775-5089
Steven Murray, prin. Fax 796-7471
Mifflin MS 700/7-8
10 S Waverly St 19607 610-775-1465
Kevin Hohl, prin. Fax 685-3760

Shinglehouse, Potter, Pop. 1,122
Oswayo Valley SD 400/PK-12
277 S Oswayo St 16748 814-260-1700
Dr. Michele Hartzell, supt. Fax 697-7439
www.oswayovalley.com
Oswayo Valley MSHS 200/6-12
318 S Oswayo St 16748 814-260-1701
Douglas Dickerson, prin. Fax 697-6375

Shippensburg, Cumberland, Pop. 5,366
Shippensburg Area SD 3,400/K-12
317 N Morris St 17257 717-530-2700
Beth Bender, supt. Fax 530-2724
www.ship.k12.pa.us
Shippensburg Area HS 1,000/9-12
201 Eberly Dr 17257 717-530-2730
Bruce Levy, prin. Fax 530-2835
Shippensburg Area MS 800/6-8
101 Park Pl W 17257 717-530-2750
David Rice, prin. Fax 530-2757

Shippensburg University Post-Sec.
1871 Old Main Dr 17257 717-477-7447

Shippenville, Clarion, Pop. 476
Area Vocational Technical School
Supt. — None
Clarion County Career Center Vo/Tech
447 Career Ln 16254 814-226-4391
Mike Stahlman, dir. Fax 226-7350

Shiremanstown, Cumberland, Pop. 1,540

West Shore Christian Academy 400/PK-12
201 W Main St 17011 717-737-3550
Joe Diminick, prin. Fax 761-3977

Sidman, Cambria, Pop. 430
Forest Hills SD 1,900/PK-12
PO Box 158 15955 814-487-7613
Edwin Bowser, supt. Fax 487-7775
www.fhrangers.org
Forest Hills HS 500/10-12
PO Box 325 15955 814-487-7613
Curt Vasas, prin. Fax 487-2371
Forest Hills MS 500/7-9
1427 Frankstown Rd 15955 814-487-7613
Fax 495-7367

Sinking Spring, Berks, Pop. 3,938
Wilson SD
Supt. — See West Lawn
Wilson Southern MS 700/6-8
3100 Iroquois Ave 19608 610-670-0180
Dr. Stephen Burnham, prin. Fax 334-6445
Wilson West MS 700/6-8
450 Faust Rd 19608 610-670-0180
Kyle Wetherhold, prin. Fax 334-6440

Slatington, Lehigh, Pop. 4,171
Northern Lehigh SD 1,700/K-12
1201 Shadow Oaks Ln 18080 610-767-9800
Michael Michaels, supt. Fax 767-9809
www.nlsd.org
Northern Lehigh HS 500/9-12
1 Bulldog Ln 18080 610-767-9832
Robert Vlasaty, prin. Fax 767-9848
Northern Lehigh MS 300/7-8
600 Diamond St 18080 610-767-9812
Jill Chamberlain, prin. Fax 767-9850

Slippery Rock, Butler, Pop. 3,557
Slippery Rock Area SD 2,000/K-12
201 Kiester Rd 16057 724-794-2960
Dr. Alfonso Angelucci, supt. Fax 794-2001
www.slipperyrock.k12.pa.us
Slippery Rock Area HS 600/9-12
201 Kiester Rd 16057 724-794-2960
Cory Hake, prin. Fax 794-1952
Slippery Rock Area MS 500/6-8
201 Kiester Rd 16057 724-794-2960
Dr. Jacob Jefferis, prin. Fax 794-6265

Slippery Rock University Post-Sec.
1 Morrow Way 16057 724-738-9000

Smethport, McKean, Pop. 1,646
Smethport Area SD 900/PK-12
414 S Mechanic St 16749 814-887-5543
David E. London, supt. Fax 887-5544
www.smethportschools.com/
Smethport Area JSHS 400/7-12
412 S Mechanic St 16749 814-887-5545
Robert Miller, prin. Fax 887-5546

Somerset, Somerset, Pop. 6,210
Area Vocational Technical School
Supt. — None
Somerset County Technology Center Vo/Tech
281 Technology Dr 15501 814-443-3651
Karen Remick, dir. Fax 445-6716

Somerset Area SD 2,200/PK-12
645 S Columbia Ave Ste 110 15501 814-443-2831
Krista Mathias, supt. Fax 443-1964
sasd.us
Somerset Area HS 700/9-12
645 S Columbia Ave Ste 130 15501 814-443-2831
Scott Shirley, prin. Fax 444-3202
Somerset Area MS 600/6-8
645 S Columbia Ave Ste 120 15501 814-443-2831
Lisa James, prin. Fax 444-3301

Somerset Community Hospital Post-Sec.
225 S Center Ave 15501 814-443-5221

Souderton, Montgomery, Pop. 6,521
Souderton Area SD 6,300/K-12
760 Lower Rd 18964 215-723-6061
Frank Gallagher, supt. Fax 723-8897
www.soudertonsd.org
Indian Crest MS 800/6-8
139 Harleysville Pike 18964 215-723-9193
Jeff Pammer, prin. Fax 723-8897
Souderton Area HS 2,100/9-12
625 Lower Rd 18964 215-723-2808
Dr. Sam Varano, prin. Fax 723-6352
Other Schools – See Harleysville

Southampton, Bucks, Pop. 11,500
Centennial SD
Supt. — See Warminster
Klinger MS 600/6-8
1415 2nd Street Pike 18966 215-364-5950
Travis Bloom, prin. Fax 364-5955

South Canaan, Wayne

St. Tikhon's Orthodox Theological Sem. Post-Sec.
PO Box 130 18459 570-561-1818

South Park, Allegheny
South Park SD 1,900/K-12
2005 Eagle Ridge Dr 15129 412-655-3111
Wayne P. Gdovic, supt. Fax 655-2952
www.sparksd.org
South Park HS 600/9-12
2005 Eagle Ridge Dr 15129 412-655-4900
David Palmer, prin. Fax 655-1463
South Park MS 600/5-8
2500 Stewart Rd 15129 412-831-7200
Kevin Monaghan, prin. Fax 831-7204

South Williamsport, Lycoming, Pop. 6,306
South Williamsport Area SD 1,300/K-12
515 W Central Ave 17702 570-327-1581
Dr. Mark Stamm, supt. Fax 326-0641
www.mounties.k12.pa.us
South Williamsport Area JSHS 600/7-12
700 Percy St 17702 570-326-2684
Jesse Smith, prin. Fax 326-2687

Spring Church, Armstrong
Apollo-Ridge SD
Supt. — See Apollo
Apollo-Ridge HS 400/9-12
1825 State Route 56 15686 724-478-6000
Clint Weimer, prin. Fax 478-9775
Apollo-Ridge MS 300/6-8
1829 State Route 56 15686 724-478-6000
Travis Barta, prin. Fax 478-3730

Springdale, Allegheny, Pop. 3,373
Allegheny Valley SD
Supt. — See Cheswick
Springdale JSHS 500/7-12
501 Butler Rd 15144 724-274-8100
Michele Welter Ed.D., prin. Fax 274-2106

Springfield, Delaware, Pop. 24,160
Springfield SD 3,900/K-12
111 W Leamy Ave 19064 610-938-6000
Dr. Anthony Barber, supt. Fax 938-6005
www.ssdcougars.org
Richardson MS 800/6-8
20 W Woodland Ave 19064 610-938-6300
Daniel Tracy, prin. Fax 938-6305
Springfield HS 1,200/9-12
49 W Leamy Ave 19064 610-938-6100
Joseph Hepp, prin. Fax 938-6105

Cardinal O'Hara HS 1,400/9-12
1701 S Sproul Rd 19064 610-544-3800
Eileen Vice, pres. Fax 544-1189

Spring Grove, York, Pop. 2,145
Spring Grove Area SD 3,800/K-12
100 E College Ave 17362 717-225-4731
Dr. David J. Renaut, supt. Fax 225-6028
www.sgasd.org
Spring Grove Area HS 1,100/9-12
1490 Roth Church Rd 17362 717-225-4731
Dr. Rosemary Cugliari, prin. Fax 225-0736
Spring Grove Area MS 600/7-8
244 Old Hanover Rd 17362 717-225-4731
Dr. Steve Guadagnino, prin. Fax 225-0146

Spring Mills, Centre, Pop. 267
Penns Valley Area SD 1,500/K-12
4528 Penns Valley Rd 16875 814-422-2000
Brian Griffith, supt. Fax 422-8020
www.pennsvalley.org
Penns Valley Area JSHS 700/7-12
4545 Penns Valley Rd 16875 814-422-8854
Dustin Dalton, prin. Fax 422-8280

Springville, Susquehanna
Area Vocational Technical School
Supt. — None
Susquehanna County Career & Tech. Center Vo/Tech
2380 Elk Lake School Rd 18844 570-278-9229
Dr. Alice Davis, dir. Fax 278-3913

Elk Lake SD 1,300/K-12
2380 Elk Lake School Rd 18844 570-278-1106
Dr. Kenneth Cuomo, supt. Fax 278-4838
www.elklakeschool.org
Elk Lake JSHS 600/7-12
2380 Elk Lake School Rd 18844 570-278-1106
Brian Mallery, prin. Fax 278-4838

State College, Centre, Pop. 41,187
State College Area SD 6,700/K-12
131 W Nittany Ave 16801 814-231-1011
Dr. Robert O'Donnell, supt. Fax 231-4130
www.scasd.org
Mount Nittany MS 700/6-8
656 Brandywine Dr 16801 814-272-4050
Brian Ishler, prin. Fax 272-4055
Park Forest MS 800/6-8
2180 School Dr 16803 814-237-5301
Dr. Karen Wiser, prin. Fax 272-0196
State College Area HS 2,300/9-12
653 Westerly Pkwy 16801 814-231-1111
Curtis Johnson, prin. Fax 231-5024

Empire Beauty School Post-Sec.
206 W Hamilton Ave 16801 814-238-1961
Grace Prep HS 100/9-12
848 Science Park Rd 16803 814-867-1177
Jane Auhl, prin. Fax 240-3977
South Hills School of Business & Tech. Post-Sec.
480 Waupelani Dr 16801 814-234-7755

Steelton, Dauphin, Pop. 5,688
Central Dauphin SD
Supt. — See Harrisburg
Swatara MS 600/6-8
1101 Highland St 17113 717-939-9363
Kelly Fowlkes, prin. Fax 939-2156

Steelton-Highspire SD 1,300/K-12
250 Reynders St 17113 717-704-3800
Dr. Ellen Castagneto, supt. Fax 704-3808
www.shsd.k12.pa.us
Steelton-Highspire JSHS 500/7-12
250 Reynders St 17113 717-704-3800
Willie Slade, prin. Fax 704-3808

Stoneboro, Mercer, Pop. 1,041
Lakeview SD 1,200/K-12
2482 Mercer St 16153 724-376-7911
James C. LaScola, supt. Fax 376-7910
www.lakeview.k12.pa.us
Lakeview HS 400/9-12
2482 Mercer St 16153 724-376-7911
Laurie Kantz, prin. Fax 376-7910
Lakeview MS 400/5-8
2482 Mercer St 16153 724-376-7911
David Blakley, prin. Fax 376-7910

Stoystown, Somerset, Pop. 354
North Star SD
Supt. — See Boswell
North Star MS 300/5-8
3598 Whistler Rd 15563 814-893-5616
Cheryl Slade, prin. Fax 893-5922

Strafford, Chester, Pop. 4,500

Woodlynde S 200/K-12
445 Upper Gulph Rd 19087 610-687-9660
Dr. Christopher Fulco Ed.D., head sch Fax 687-4752

Strattanville, Clarion, Pop. 547
Clarion-Limestone Area SD 900/K-12
4091 C L School Rd 16258 814-764-5111
Michael Stimac, supt. Fax 764-5729
www.clasd.net/
Clarion-Limestone JSHS 400/7-12
4091 C L School Rd 16258 814-764-5111
Doug Rodgers, prin. Fax 764-5274

Stroudsburg, Monroe, Pop. 5,412
Stroudsburg Area SD 4,700/K-12
123 Linden St 18360 570-421-1990
Dr. Charles Amuso, supt. Fax 424-5986
www.sburg.org
Stroudsburg HS 1,300/10-12
1100 W Main St 18360 570-421-1991
Jeff Sodl, prin. Fax 424-1383
Stroudsburg JHS 800/8-9
1901 Chipperfield Dr 18360 570-424-4848
Ryan Cron, prin. Fax 424-4839

Stroudsburg School of Cosmetology Post-Sec.
100 N 8th St 18360 570-421-3387

Summerdale, Cumberland

Central Penn College Post-Sec.
PO Box 309 17093 800-759-2727

Sunbury, Northumberland, Pop. 9,716
Shikellamy SD 2,700/K-12
200 Island Blvd 17801 570-286-3720
Brett Misavage, supt. Fax 286-3776
www.shikbraves.org
Shikellamy HS 900/9-12
600 Walnut St 17801 570-286-3700
Michael Egan, prin. Fax 286-3775
Other Schools – See Northumberland

McCann School of Business & Technology Post-Sec.
1147 N 4th St 17801 570-286-3058
Triangle Tech Post-Sec.
191 Performance Rd 17801 570-988-0700

Susquehanna, Susquehanna, Pop. 1,631
Susquehanna Community SD 800/K-12
3192 Turnpike St 18847 570-853-4921
Bronson Stone, supt. Fax 853-3768
www.scschools.org/
Susquehanna Community JSHS 300/7-12
3192 Turnpike St 18847 570-853-4921
Carmella Bullick, prin. Fax 853-3918

Swarthmore, Delaware, Pop. 5,977

Swarthmore College Post-Sec.
500 College Ave 19081 610-328-8000

Swiftwater, Monroe
Pocono Mountain SD 8,300/K-12
PO Box 200 18370 570-839-7121
Dr. Elizabeth Robison, supt. Fax 895-4768
www.pmsd.org
Pocono Mountain East HS 1,600/9-12
PO Box 200 18370 570-839-7121
Daniel Higgins, prin. Fax 839-5934
Pocono Mountain East JHS 700/7-8
PO Box 200 18370 570-839-7121
Dr. Kathy Fanelli, prin. Fax 839-3242
Swiftwater IS 400/7-8
PO Box 200 18370 570-839-7121
Kristine Kunsman, prin. Fax 839-7820
Other Schools – See Pocono Summit

Tamaqua, Schuylkill, Pop. 7,032
Tamaqua Area SD 2,100/K-12
138 W Broad St 18252 570-668-2570
Raymond J. Kinder, supt. Fax 668-6850
www.tamaqua.k12.pa.us
Rush Academy 200/Alt
50 Meadow Ave 18252 570-668-6932
Tammy Recker, dir. Fax 668-6858
Tamaqua Area HS 600/9-12
500 Penn St 18252 570-668-1901
Thomas McCabe, prin. Fax 668-2970
Tamaqua Area MS 500/6-8
502 Penn St 18252 570-668-1210
Christopher Czapla, prin. Fax 668-5027

Marian HS 300/9-12
166 Marian Ave 18252 570-467-3335
Jean Susko, prin. Fax 467-0186

Taylor, Lackawanna, Pop. 6,195
Riverside SD 1,300/K-12
300 Davis St 18517 570-562-2121
Paul Brennan, supt. Fax 562-3205
www.riversidesd.com
Riverside JSHS 700/7-12
310 Davis St 18517 570-562-2121
Joseph Moceyunas, prin. Fax 562-7551

Thorndale, Chester, Pop. 3,357
Coatesville Area SD 7,300/K-12
3030 C G Zinn Rd 19372 610-466-2400
Dr. Cathy Taschner, supt. Fax 383-1426
casd.schoolwires.net
Other Schools – See Coatesville

Three Springs, Huntingdon, Pop. 439
Southern Huntingdon County SD 1,300/K-12
10339 Pogue Rd 17264 814-447-5529
Michael Zinobile, supt. Fax 447-3967
shcsd.org
Southern Huntingdon County MSHS 700/6-12
10339 Pogue Rd 17264 814-447-5529
Michael Adamek, prin. Fax 447-3750

Throop, Lackawanna, Pop. 4,041
Mid Valley SD 1,500/K-12
52 Underwood Rd 18512 570-307-1108
Patrick Sheehan, supt. Fax 307-1107
www.mvsd.us
Mid Valley Secondary Center 500/7-12
52 Underwood Rd 18512 570-307-2180
Chad Vinansky, prin. Fax 307-1912

Tioga, Tioga, Pop. 659
Northern Tioga SD
Supt. — See Elkland
Williamson JSHS 600/7-12
33 Jct Cross Rd 16946 570-827-2191
Kris Kaufman, prin. Fax 827-3557

Tionesta, Forest, Pop. 478
Forest Area SD 500/PK-12
22318 Route 62 Unit 16 16353 814-755-4491
Amanda Hetrick, supt. Fax 755-2426
www.forestareaschools.org/
West Forest JSHS 100/7-12
22318 Route 62 Unit 15 16353 814-755-3611
Elisha Pospisil, prin. Fax 755-2427
Other Schools – See Marienville

North Clarion County SD 600/PK-12
10439 Route 36 16353 814-744-8536
Steven Young, supt. Fax 744-9378
www.northclarion.org
North Clarion County JSHS 300/7-12
10439 Route 36 16353 814-744-8544
Vanessa Weinlein, prin. Fax 744-8762

Titusville, Crawford, Pop. 5,544
Titusville Area SD 2,100/PK-12
301 E Spruce St 16354 814-827-2715
Karen Jez, supt. Fax 827-7761
www.gorockets.org/
Titusville HS 600/9-12
302 E Walnut St 16354 814-827-2715
Philip Knapp, prin. Fax 827-0551
Titusville MS 500/6-8
415 Water St 16354 814-827-2715
Douglas Gifford, prin. Fax 827-0552

University of Pittsburgh at Titusville Post-Sec.
504 E Main St # 287 16354 814-827-4400

Topton, Berks, Pop. 2,055
Brandywine Heights Area SD 1,400/K-12
200 W Weis St 19562 610-682-5100
Andrew Potteiger, supt. Fax 682-5136
www.bhasd.org
Brandywine Heights Intermediate MS 400/4-8
200 W Weis St 19562 610-682-5131
Robert Farina, prin. Fax 682-5105
Other Schools – See Mertztown

Towanda, Bradford, Pop. 2,864
Area Vocational Technical School
Supt. — None
Northern Tier Career Center Vo/Tech
120 Career Center Ln 18848 570-265-8111
Elizabeth Frankhouser, dir. Fax 265-3002

Towanda Area SD 1,600/K-12
410 State St 18848 570-265-9154
Steve Gobble, supt. Fax 265-4881
www.tsd.k12.pa.us
Towanda Area JSHS 700/7-12
1 High School Dr 18848 570-265-2101
Dennis Peachey, prin. Fax 268-2069

Tower City, Schuylkill, Pop. 1,337
Williams Valley SD 1,000/K-12
10330 Route 209 Rd 17980 717-647-2167
Jolene Smith, supt. Fax 647-2055
www.wvschools.net
Williams Valley JSHS 400/7-12
10330 Route 209 Rd 17980 717-647-2167
Tracey Weller, prin. Fax 647-2055

Trafford, Westmoreland, Pop. 3,138
Penn-Trafford SD
Supt. — See Harrison City
Trafford MS 400/6-8
100 Brinton Ave 15085 412-372-6600
Roger Sullivan, prin. Fax 372-1554

Trevose, Bucks, Pop. 3,515

Strayer University Post-Sec.
3600 Horizon Blvd Ste 100 19053 215-354-2700

Troy, Bradford, Pop. 1,340
Troy Area SD 1,500/K-12
68 Fenner Ave 16947 570-297-2750
Charles Young, supt. Fax 297-1600
www.troyareasd.org/
Troy Area JSHS 700/7-12
150 High St 16947 570-297-2176
Susan Shipman, prin. Fax 297-2058

Martha Lloyd School Post-Sec.
66 Lloyd Ln 16947 570-297-2185

Tunkhannock, Wyoming, Pop. 1,809
Tunkhannock Area SD 2,600/K-12
41 Philadelphia Ave 18657 570-836-3111
Michael Healey, supt. Fax 836-2942
www.tasd.net/
Tunkhannock HS 800/9-12
135 Tiger Dr 18657 570-836-8223
Gregory Ellsworth, prin. Fax 836-4719
Tunkhannock MS 800/5-8
200 Franklin Ave 18657 570-836-8235
James Timmons, prin. Fax 836-5796

Turbotville, Northumberland, Pop. 705
Warrior Run SD 1,600/K-12
4800 Susquehanna Trl 17772 570-649-5138
Dr. John Kurelja, supt. Fax 649-5475
www.wrsd.org
Warrior Run HS 500/9-12
4800 Susquehanna Trl 17772 570-649-5166
Patricia Cross, prin. Fax 649-5591
Warrior Run MS 500/5-8
4800 Susquehanna Trl 17772 570-649-5135
Susan Mabus, prin. Fax 649-6173

Tyrone, Blair, Pop. 5,415
Tyrone Area SD 1,900/PK-12
701 Clay Ave 16686 814-684-0710
Cathy Harlow, supt. Fax 684-8408
www.tyrone.k12.pa.us
Tyrone Area HS 500/9-12
1001 Clay Ave 16686 814-684-4240
Thomas Yoder, prin. Fax 684-4245
Tyrone Area MS 600/5-8
1001 Clay Ave 16686 814-684-4240
Kristen N. Pinter, prin. Fax 682-1013

Grier S 300/7-12
PO Box 308 16686 814-684-3000
Gina Borst, head sch Fax 684-2177

Ulysses, Potter, Pop. 619
Northern Potter SD 600/PK-12
745 Northern Potter Rd 16948 814-848-7506
Scott Graham, supt. Fax 848-7431
www.northernpottersd.org
Northern Potter JSHS 300/7-12
763 Northern Potter Rd 16948 814-848-7534
Nathan Jones, prin. Fax 848-9671

Union City, Erie, Pop. 3,286
Union City Area SD 1,200/PK-12
107 Concord St 16438 814-438-3804
Dr. Sandra Myers, supt. Fax 438-2030
www.ucasd.org
Union City HS 300/9-12
105 Concord St 16438 814-438-7673
Melissa Tomcho, prin. Fax 438-8079
Union City MS 300/6-8
105 Concord St 16438 814-438-7673
Melissa Tomcho, prin. Fax 438-8079

Uniontown, Fayette, Pop. 10,023
Albert Gallatin Area SD 3,300/K-12
2625 Morgantown Rd 15401 724-564-7190
Carl Bezjak, supt. Fax 564-7195
www.agasd.org
Gallatin Area HS 1,200/9-12
1119 Township Dr 15401 724-564-2024
Jason Hutchinson, prin. Fax 564-4525
Other Schools – See Mc Clellandtown, Point Marion

Area Vocational Technical School
Supt. — None
Fayette County Career & Technical Inst Vo/Tech
175 Georges Fairchance Rd 15401 724-437-2721
Dr. Edward Jeffreys, prin.

Laurel Highlands SD 3,300/K-12
304 Bailey Ave 15401 724-437-2821
Dr. Jesse Wallace Ed.D., supt. Fax 437-8929
www.lhsd.org
Laurel Highlands HS 1,000/9-12
300 Bailey Ave 15401 724-437-4741
John Diamond, prin. Fax 437-5653
Laurel Highlands MS 800/6-8
18 Hookton Ave 15401 724-437-2865
Mike Rozgony, prin. Fax 437-8518

Uniontown Area SD 2,800/K-12
205 Wilson Ave 15401 724-438-4501
Dr. Charles D. Machesky, supt. Fax 437-7007
uasdraiders.org
Lafayette MS 200/6-8
303 Connellsville St 15401 724-438-3581
Tracey M. Kuchar, prin. Fax 439-5023
Uniontown Area HS 800/9-12
146 E Fayette St 15401 724-439-5000
Robert Manges, prin. Fax 439-5004
Other Schools – See Markleysburg

Chestnut Ridge Christian Academy 100/PK-12
115 Downer Ave 15401 724-439-1090
Patricia D. Cowsert, prin. Fax 439-4540
Laurel Business Institute Post-Sec.
PO Box 877 15401 724-439-4900

University Park, See State College

Penn State The Dickinson School of Law Post-Sec.
Lewis Katz Building 16802 814-865-8900
Penn State University Post-Sec.
201 Old Main 16802 814-865-4700

Upper Darby, See Darby
Upper Darby SD
Supt. — See Drexel Hill
Beverly Hills MS 1,500/6-8
1400 Garrett Rd 19082 610-626-9317
Kelley Simone, prin.

Harris School of Business Post-Sec.
20 S 69th St 19082 484-463-3800
Prism Career Institute Post-Sec.
6800 Market St 19082 610-789-6700

Upper Saint Clair, Allegheny, Pop. 19,692
Upper St. Clair SD 4,100/K-12
1820 McLaughlin Run Rd 15241 412-833-1600
Dr. Patrick O'Toole, supt. Fax 833-5535
www.uscsd.k12.pa.us
Other Schools – See Pittsburgh

Valley View, Schuylkill, Pop. 1,675
Tri-Valley SD 900/K-12
110 W Main St 17983 570-682-9013
Dr. Mark Snyder, supt. Fax 682-9544
www.tri-valley.k12.pa.us
Other Schools – See Hegins

Verona, Allegheny, Pop. 2,433

Redeemer Lutheran S 200/PK-12
700 Idaho Ave 15147 412-793-5884
Gail Holzer, admin.

Villanova, Delaware

Academy of Notre Dame De Namur 500/6-12
560 Sproul Rd 19085 610-687-0650
Jacqueline Coccia, prin. Fax 687-1912
Devereux Foundation in Pennsylvania Post-Sec.
444 Devereux Dr 19085 610-542-3030
Villanova University Post-Sec.
800 E Lancaster Ave 19085 610-519-4500

Wallingford, Delaware
Wallingford-Swarthmore SD 3,500/K-12
200 S Providence Rd 19086 610-892-3470
Dr. Lisa Palmer, supt. Fax 892-3493
www.wssd.org
Strath Haven HS 1,200/9-12
205 S Providence Rd 19086 610-892-3470
Dr. Mary Jo Yannacone, prin. Fax 892-3494
Strath Haven MS 800/6-8
200 S Providence Rd 19086 610-892-3470
George King, prin. Fax 892-3492

Warfordsburg, Fulton
Southern Fulton SD 800/K-12
3072 Great Cove Rd Ste 100 17267 717-294-2203
Tara Will, supt. Fax 294-2207
sfsd.k12.pa.us
Southern Fulton JSHS 400/7-12
13083 Buck Valley Rd 17267 717-294-3251
Meredith Hendershot, prin. Fax 294-6248

Warminster, Bucks, Pop. 32,400
Centennial SD 5,600/K-12
433 Centennial Rd 18974 215-441-6000
Dr. Jennifer Polinchock, admin. Fax 441-5105
www.centennialsd.org
Log College MS 700/6-8
730 Norristown Rd 18974 215-441-6075
Andrew Doster, prin. Fax 441-6073
Tennent HS 1,800/9-12
333 Centennial Rd 18974 215-441-6181
Dr. Dennis Best, prin. Fax 441-6175
Other Schools – See Southampton

Archbishop Wood HS 1,000/9-12
655 York Rd 18974 215-672-5050
Mary Harkins, prin. Fax 672-9572
Automotive Training Center Post-Sec.
900 Johnsville Blvd 18974 888-233-0476
Empire Beauty School Post-Sec.
435 York Rd 18974 215-443-8446

Warren, Warren, Pop. 9,619
Area Vocational Technical School
Supt. — None
Warren County Career Center Vo/Tech
347 E 5th Ave 16365 814-726-1260
James Evers, prin. Fax 726-9673

Warren County SD
Supt. — See Russell
Beaty-Warren MS 500/6-8
2 E 3rd Ave 16365 814-723-5200
Ann Ryan, prin. Fax 723-9503
Warren Area HS 700/9-12
345 E 5th Ave 16365 814-723-3370
Jeffrey Flickner, prin. Fax 726-3126

Warrington, Bucks, Pop. 7,000
Central Bucks SD
Supt. — See Doylestown
Central Bucks SHS - South 1,900/10-12
1100 Folly Rd 18976 267-893-3000
Scott Davidheiser, prin. Fax 893-5824
Tamanend MS 900/7-9
1492 Stuckert Rd 18976 267-893-2900
Cheryl Leatherbarrow, prin. Fax 893-5818

Washington, Washington, Pop. 13,036
Trinity Area SD 3,300/K-12
231 Park Ave 15301 724-223-2000
Michael Lucas, supt. Fax 228-2640
www.trinitypride.org
Trinity HS 1,100/9-12
231 Park Ave 15301 724-225-5380
Thomas Samosky, prin. Fax 228-9057
Trinity MS 800/6-8
50 Scenic Dr 15301 724-228-2112
Michelle Ostrosky, prin. Fax 228-1196

Washington SD 1,500/K-12
311 Allison Ave 15301 724-223-5112
Dr. Roberta DiLorenzo, supt. Fax 223-5050
www.washington.k12.pa.us
Washington HS 400/9-12
201 Allison Ave 15301 724-223-5080
Paul Kostelnik, prin. Fax 223-5046
Washington JHS 200/7-8
201 Allison Ave 15301 724-223-5060
Chet Henderson, prin. Fax 223-5123

Faith Christian S 200/PK-12
524 E Beau St 15301 724-222-5440
Lucy Hall, prin. Fax 222-5442
First Love Christian Academy 50/9-12
150 Sunset Blvd 15301 724-228-3547
Kathleen Miller, supt. Fax 228-3547
Penn Commercial Business/Technical Sch. Post-Sec.
242 Oak Spring Rd 15301 724-222-5330
Washington & Jefferson College Post-Sec.
60 S Lincoln St 15301 724-222-4400
Washington Hospital Post-Sec.
155 Wilson Ave 15301 724-223-3167

Waterfall, Fulton
Forbes Road SD 400/K-12
159 Red Bird Dr 16689 814-685-3866
Mark Loucks, supt. Fax 685-3159
www.frsd.k12.pa.us
Forbes Road JSHS 200/7-12
159 Red Bird Dr 16689 814-685-3866
Maria Scott, prin. Fax 685-3159

Waterford, Erie, Pop. 1,509
Fort LeBoeuf SD 2,100/K-12
PO Box 810 16441 814-796-2638
Richard Emerick, supt. Fax 796-6459
www.fortleboeuf.net
Fort LeBoeuf HS 700/9-12
931 N High St 16441 814-796-2616
Martin Rimpa, prin. Fax 796-2141
Fort LeBoeuf MS 500/6-8
PO Box 516 16441 814-796-2681
Brent Holt, prin. Fax 796-4712

Wayne, Delaware
Radnor Township SD 3,600/K-12
135 S Wayne Ave 19087 610-688-8100
Dr. Michael Kelly, supt. Fax 687-3318
www.rtsd.org/
Radnor MS 800/6-8
150 Louella Ave 19087 610-386-6300
Esther Purnell, prin. Fax 688-2491
Other Schools – See Radnor

Tredyffrin-Easttown SD 6,500/K-12
940 W Valley Rd Ste 1700 19087 610-240-1900
Dr. Richard Gusick, supt. Fax 240-1965
www.tesd.net/
Valley Forge MS 1,000/5-8
105 W Walker Rd 19087 610-240-1300
Matthew Gibson, prin. Fax 240-1325
Other Schools – See Berwyn

Palmer Theological Seminary Post-Sec.
1300 Eagle Rd 19087 610-896-5000
Valley Forge Military Academy 300/7-12
1001 Eagle Rd 19087 610-989-1200
Sandra Young, head sch Fax 989-1545
Valley Forge Military Academy & College Post-Sec.
1001 Eagle Rd 19087 610-989-1200

Waynesboro, Franklin, Pop. 10,360
Waynesboro Area SD 4,400/K-12
210 Clayton Ave 17268 717-762-1191
Sherran Diller, supt. Fax 762-0028
www.wasd.k12.pa.us
Waynesboro Area HS 1,300/9-12
550 E 2nd St 17268 717-762-1191
Steve Pappas, prin. Fax 762-3787
Waynesboro Area MS 700/7-8
702 E 2nd St 17268 717-762-1191
Aaron Taylor, prin. Fax 762-6566

Waynesburg, Greene, Pop. 4,116
Area Vocational Technical School
Supt. — None
Greene County CTC Vo/Tech
60 Zimmerman Dr 15370 724-627-3106
Karen Pflugh, dir.

Central Greene SD 1,900/K-12
PO Box 472 15370 724-627-8151
Brian Uplinger, supt. Fax 627-9591
www.cgsd.org
Bell MS 400/6-8
126 E Lincoln St 15370 724-852-2722
John Lipscomb, prin. Fax 627-0637
Waynesburg Central HS 600/9-12
30 Zimmerman Dr 15370 724-852-1050
Robert Stephenson, prin. Fax 852-2109

West Greene SD 500/K-12
1367 Hargus Creek Rd 15370 724-499-5183
Thelma Szarell, supt. Fax 499-5623
www.wgsd.org
West Greene MSHS 100/7-12
1352 Hargus Creek Rd 15370 724-499-5051
Scott Sakai, prin. Fax 499-5492

Waynesburg University Post-Sec.
51 W College St 15370 724-627-8191

Weatherly, Carbon, Pop. 2,496
Weatherly Area SD 600/K-12
602 6th St 18255 570-427-8681
Thomas McLaughlin, supt. Fax 427-8918
www.weatherlysd.org
Weatherly Area HS 200/9-12
601 6th St 18255 570-427-8521
Amanda Zaremba, prin. Fax 427-4642
Weatherly Area MS 200/6-8
602 6th St 18255 570-427-8689
Sandra Slavick, prin. Fax 427-8918

Wellsboro, Tioga, Pop. 3,220
Wellsboro Area SD 1,500/K-12
227 Nichols St 16901 570-724-4424
Dr. Brenda Freeman, supt. Fax 724-5103
www.wellsborosd.org
Butler MS 500/5-8
9 Nichols St 16901 570-724-2306
Michael Pietropola, prin. Fax 724-4143
Wellsboro Area HS 500/9-12
225 Nichols St 16901 570-724-3547
Robert Kreger, prin. Fax 724-3027

West Chester, Chester, Pop. 18,141
West Chester Area SD 11,700/K-12
829 Paoli Pike 19380 484-266-1000
Dr. James R. Scanlon, supt. Fax 266-1175
www.wcasd.net
Fugett MS 900/6-8
500 Ellis Ln 19380 484-266-2900
Le Roy G. Whitehead, prin. Fax 266-2999
Peirce MS 800/6-8
1314 Burke Rd 19380 484-266-2500
Geoffrey Mills, prin. Fax 266-2599
Stetson MS 900/6-8
1060 Wilmington Pike 19382 484-266-2700
Dr. Charles A. Cognato, prin. Fax 266-2799
West Chester Bayard Rustin HS 1,300/9-12
1100 Shiloh Rd 19382 484-266-4300
Michael Marano, prin. Fax 266-4399
West Chester East HS 1,300/9-12
450 Ellis Ln 19380 484-266-3800
Kevin Fagan, prin. Fax 266-3899
West Chester Henderson HS 1,300/9-12
400 Montgomery Ave 19380 484-266-3300
Dr. Jason P. Sherlock, prin. Fax 266-3399

Devereux Kanner Center Post-Sec.
390 E Boot Rd 19380 866-532-2212
West Chester Christian S 100/K-12
1237 Paoli Pike 19380 610-692-3700
Andrew Mosier, prin. Fax 631-0132
West Chester University of Pennsylvania Post-Sec.
S High St 19383 610-436-1000
Westtown S 700/PK-12
975 Westtown Rd 19382 610-399-0123
Fax 399-3760

Westfield, Tioga, Pop. 1,060
Northern Tioga SD
Supt. — See Elkland
Cowanesque Valley JSHS 400/7-12
51 N Fork Rd 16950 814-367-2233
Matthew Sottolano, prin. Fax 367-5874

West Grove, Chester, Pop. 2,811
Area Vocational Technical School
Supt. — None
Technical College HS - Pennocks Bridge Vo/Tech
280 Pennocks Bridge Rd 19390 610-345-1800
Michael Katch, prin. Fax 345-1803

Avon Grove SD 5,100/K-12
375 S Jennersville Rd 19390 610-869-2441
Dr. Michael Marchese, supt. Fax 869-8651
www.avongrove.org/
Avon Grove HS 1,800/9-12
257 State Rd 19390 610-869-2446
Thomas Alexander, prin. Fax 869-4511
Engle MS 900/7-8
107 Schoolhouse Rd 19390 610-869-3022
Michael Berardi, prin. Fax 869-0827

West Lawn, Berks, Pop. 1,678
Wilson SD 5,500/K-12
2601 Grandview Blvd 19609 610-670-0180
Dr. Curt Baker, supt. Fax 334-6430
www.wilsonsd.org
Wilson HS 1,900/9-12
2601 Grandview Blvd 19609 610-670-0180
Chris Trickett, prin. Fax 670-9101
Other Schools – See Sinking Spring

West Middlesex, Mercer, Pop. 850
West Middlesex Area SD 800/K-12
3591 Sharon Rd 16159 724-634-3030
Dr. David Foley, supt. Fax 528-0380
www.wmasd.k12.pa.us
West Middlesex JSHS 300/7-12
3591 Sharon Rd 16159 724-634-3030
Kevin Briggs, prin. Fax 528-0380

West Mifflin, Allegheny, Pop. 19,950
West Mifflin Area SD 3,000/PK-12
1020 Lebanon Rd # 250 15122 412-466-9131
Dr. Daniel Castagna, supt. Fax 466-9260
www.wmasd.org
West Mifflin Area HS 1,100/9-12
91 Commonwealth Ave 15122 412-466-9131
Phillip Woods, prin. Fax 466-4595
West Mifflin Area MS 1,100/4-8
81 Commonwealth Ave 15122 412-466-9131
Brian Plichta, prin. Fax 466-0836

All-State Career School Post-Sec.
1200 Lebanon Rd 15122 412-823-1818
Community College of Allegheny County Post-Sec.
1750 Clairton Rd 15122 412-469-1100
Cornerstone Christian Prep Academy 200/PK-12
1900 Clairton Rd 15122 412-466-1919
Cindi R. McCall, dir. Fax 466-0303
Empire Beauty School Post-Sec.
2393 Mountain View Dr 15122 800-575-5983

Westover, Clearfield, Pop. 390
Harmony Area SD 300/PK-12
5239 Ridge Rd 16692 814-845-7918
Dr. Jill M. Dillon, supt. Fax 845-2305
www.harmonyowls.com/
Harmony Area JSHS 100/7-12
5239 Ridge Rd 16692 814-845-7918
Terry Young, prin. Fax 845-2305

West Sunbury, Butler, Pop. 190
Moniteau SD 1,300/K-12
1810 W Sunbury Rd 16061 724-637-2117
George S. Svolos, supt. Fax 637-3862
www.moniteau.k12.pa.us
Moniteau JSHS 600/7-12
1810 W Sunbury Rd 16061 724-637-2091
Lance Fox, prin. Fax 637-3878

Wexford, Allegheny
North Allegheny SD
Supt. — See Pittsburgh
Marshall MS 600/6-8
5145 Wexford Run Rd 15090 724-934-6060
Daniel Swoger, prin. Fax 935-2474
North Allegheny SHS 1,300/11-12
10375 Perry Hwy 15090 724-934-7200
John Kreider, prin. Fax 935-5846

Whitehall, Lehigh, Pop. 13,797
Whitehall-Coplay SD 4,200/K-12
2940 MacArthur Rd 18052 610-439-1431
Dr. Lorie Hackett, supt. Fax 435-0124
www.whitehallcoplay.org/districtsite/
Whitehall-Coplay MS 1,000/6-8
2930 Zephyr Blvd 18052 610-439-1439
Peter Bugbee, prin. Fax 740-9308
Whitehall HS 1,400/9-12
3800 Mechanicsville Rd 18052 610-437-5081
Nathan Davidson, prin. Fax 820-7520

Empire Beauty School Post-Sec.
1634 MacArthur Rd 18052 610-776-8908

Wilkes Barre, Luzerne, Pop. 40,594
Area Vocational Technical School
Supt. — None
Wilkes-Barre Area CTC Vo/Tech
PO Box 1699 18705 570-822-4131
Peter Halesey, dir. Fax 823-4304

Wilkes-Barre Area SD 6,900/K-12
730 S Main St 18702 570-826-7131
Dr. Bernard Prevuznak, supt. Fax 829-5031
www.wbasd.k12.pa.us
Coughlin HS 1,000/9-12
80 N Washington St 18701 570-826-7201
Patrick Patte, prin. Fax 826-7252
G.A.R. Memorial JSHS 900/7-12
250 S Grant St 18702 570-826-7165
Colleen Robatin, prin. Fax 826-7164
Meyers JSHS 900/7-12
341 Carey Ave 18702 570-826-7145
Michael Elias, prin. Fax 820-3770
Other Schools – See Plains

Academy of Creative Hair Design Post-Sec.
125 N Wilkes Barre Blvd 18702 570-825-8363
CDE Career Institute Post-Sec.
100 N Wilkes Barre Ste 100 18702 570-823-3891
Holy Redeemer HS 600/9-12
159 S Pennsylvania Ave 18701 570-829-2424
Anita Sirak, prin. Fax 829-4412
King's College Post-Sec.
133 N River St 18711 570-208-5900
McCann School of Business & Technology Post-Sec.
264 Highland Park Blvd 18702 570-235-2200
Rock Solid Academy 50/K-12
106 S Lehigh St 18708 570-696-5466
Lauren Dennis, head sch Fax 696-2413
Wilkes Barre General Hospital Post-Sec.
575 N River St 18764 570-829-8111
Wilkes University Post-Sec.
84 W South St 18766 570-408-5000

Williamsburg, Blair, Pop. 1,244
Williamsburg Community SD 500/K-12
515 W 3rd St 16693 814-832-2125
Lisa Murgas M.Ed., supt. Fax 832-3657
www.williamsburg.k12.pa.us/
Williamsburg Community JSHS 200/7-12
515 W 3rd St 16693 814-832-2125
Travis Lee M.Ed., prin. Fax 832-0115

Williamsport, Lycoming, Pop. 28,270
Loyalsock Township SD 1,500/K-12
1605 Four Mile Dr 17701 570-326-6508
Gerald McLaughlin, supt. Fax 326-0770
www.loyalsocklancers.org
Loyalsock Township HS 400/9-12
1801 Loyalsock Dr 17701 570-326-3581
Dr. Matthew Reitz, prin. Fax 322-3952
Loyalsock Township MS 400/6-8
2101 Loyalsock Dr 17701 570-323-9439
Charles Greevy, prin. Fax 323-5303

Williamsport Area SD 5,100/K-12
2780 W 4th St 17701 570-327-5500
Don Adams, supt. Fax 327-8122
www.wasd.org
Williamsport Area HS 1,500/9-12
2990 W 4th St 17701 570-323-8411
Brandon Pardoe, prin. Fax 322-4150
Williamsport Area MS 800/7-8
2800 W 4th St 17701 570-323-6177
Reginald Fatherly, prin. Fax 326-6851

Divine Providence Hospital Post-Sec.
1100 Grampian Blvd 17701 570-326-8101
Empire Beauty School Post-Sec.
1808 E 3rd St 17701 570-322-8243
Lycoming College Post-Sec.
700 College Pl 17701 570-321-4000
Pennsylvania College of Technology Post-Sec.
1 College Ave 17701 570-326-3761
St. John Neumann Regional Academy 200/7-12
901 Penn St 17701 570-323-9953
Richard Cummings, prin. Fax 321-7146
Williamsport Hospital Post-Sec.
777 Rural Ave 17701 570-326-8101

Willow Grove, Montgomery, Pop. 15,410
Area Vocational Technical School
Supt. — None
Eastern Center for Arts & Technology Vo/Tech
3075 Terwood Rd 19090 215-784-4800
Thomas Allen, dir. Fax 784-4801

Upper Moreland Township SD 3,100/K-12
2900 Terwood Rd 19090 215-830-1511
Robert Milrod Ph.D., supt. Fax 659-3421
www.umtsd.org/
Upper Moreland HS 1,000/9-12
3000 Terwood Rd 19090 215-830-1500
Joseph Carracappa, prin. Fax 830-1581
Other Schools – See Hatboro

Willow Hill, Franklin
Fannett-Metal SD 400/K-12
PO Box 91 17271 717-349-7172
David Burkett, supt. Fax 349-2748
fmtigers.org
Fannett-Metal MSHS 200/6-12
PO Box 91 17271 717-349-2363
Adam Whitsel, prin. Fax 349-2173

Willow Street, Lancaster, Pop. 7,536
Area Vocational Technical School
Supt. — None
Lancaster County CTC-Willow Street Vo/Tech
PO Box 527 17584 717-464-7050
James Catino, dir. Fax 464-9518

Lancaster County Career & Technology Ctr Post-Sec.
1730 Hans Herr Dr 17584 717-464-7050

Windber, Somerset, Pop. 4,117
Windber Area SD 1,200/PK-12
2301 Graham Ave 15963 814-467-5551
Rick Huffman, supt. Fax 467-4208
www.windberschools.org
Windber Area HS 300/9-12
2301 Graham Ave 15963 814-467-4567
Ric Lucas, prin. Fax 467-0677
Windber Area MS 300/6-8
2301 Graham Ave 15963 814-467-4620
Ric Lucas, prin. Fax 467-6218

Wingate, Centre
Bald Eagle Area SD 1,800/K-12
751 S Eagle Valley Rd 16823 814-355-4860
Jeffrey Miles, supt. Fax 355-1028
www.beasd.org
Bald Eagle Area MSHS 1,000/6-12
751 S Eagle Valley Rd 16823 814-355-4868
John Tobias, prin. Fax 355-2146

Wormleysburg, Cumberland, Pop. 3,002

Harrisburg Academy 400/PK-12
10 Erford Rd 17043 717-763-7811
Dr. James Newman, head sch Fax 975-0894

Wrightsville, York, Pop. 2,269
Eastern York SD 2,500/K-12
PO Box 150 17368 717-252-1555
Dr. Darla Pianowski, supt. Fax 478-6000
www.eyork.k12.pa.us/
Eastern York HS 700/9-12
PO Box 2002 17368 717-252-1551
Dr. Timothy Mitzel, prin. Fax 252-4808
Eastern York MS 600/6-8
PO Box 2003 17368 717-252-3400
Dr. Paula Westerman, prin. Fax 252-4891

Wyalusing, Bradford, Pop. 591
Wyalusing Area SD 1,300/K-12
PO Box 157 18853 570-746-1600
Dr. Jason Bottiglierie, supt. Fax 746-0281
www.wyalusingrams.com/
Wyalusing Valley JSHS 600/7-12
11364 Wyalusing New Albany 18853 570-746-1218
Gary Otis, prin. Fax 746-2053

Wyncote, Montgomery, Pop. 2,980
Cheltenham Township SD
Supt. — See Elkins Park
Cheltenham HS 1,500/9-12
500 Rices Mill Rd 19095 215-517-3700
Iris Parker, prin. Fax 517-3771

Bishop McDevitt HS 700/9-12
125 Royal Ave 19095 215-887-5575
Mary Kirby, prin. Fax 887-1371
Reconstructionist Rabbinical College Post-Sec.
1299 Church Rd 19095 215-576-0800

Wynnewood, Montgomery, Pop. 7,800

Friends' Central S - Upper Campus 600/6-12
1101 City Ave 19096 610-649-7440
Craig Sellers, hdmstr. Fax 649-5669
Lankenau Hospital Post-Sec.
100 E Lancaster Ave 19096 610-526-3019
St. Charles Borromeo Seminary Post-Sec.
100 E Wynnewood Rd 19096 610-667-3394

Wyomissing, Berks, Pop. 10,332
Wyomissing Area SD 1,900/K-12
630 Evans Ave 19610 610-374-0739
Julia Vicente, supt. Fax 374-0948
www.wyoarea.org/
Wyomissing Area JSHS 900/7-12
630 Evans Ave 19610 610-374-0739
Dr. Corey Jones, prin. Fax 374-6012

Berks Technical Institute Post-Sec.
2205 Ridgewood Rd 19610 610-372-1722

Yardley, Bucks, Pop. 2,392
Pennsbury SD
Supt. — See Fallsington
Boehm MS 700/6-8
866 Big Oak Rd 19067 215-428-4220
Theresa Ricci, prin. Fax 428-9605
Penn MS 1,000/6-8
1524 Derbyshire Rd 19067 215-428-4280
Christopher Becker, prin. Fax 428-1549
Pennwood MS 900/6-8
1523 Makefield Rd 19067 215-428-4237
Elizabeth Aldridge, prin. Fax 428-4265

Yeadon, Delaware, Pop. 11,214
William Penn SD
Supt. — See Lansdowne
Penn Wood HS Cypress Street Campus 800/9-10
600 Cypress St 19050 610-626-3223
Dr. D. Brandon Cooley, prin. Fax 284-8061

York, York, Pop. 41,931
Area Vocational Technical School
Supt. — None
York County School of Technology Vo/Tech
2179 S Queen St 17402 717-741-0820
Dr. David Thomas, dir. Fax 741-0694

Central York SD 5,800/K-12
775 Marion Rd 17406 717-846-6789
Dr. Michael Snell, supt. Fax 840-0451
www.cysd.k12.pa.us
Central York HS 1,700/9-12
601 Mundis Mill Rd 17406 717-846-6789
Ryan Caufman, prin. Fax 848-4684
Central York MS 1,000/7-8
1950 N Hills Rd 17406 717-846-6789
Edmund McManama, prin.

West York Area SD 2,300/K-12
2605 W Market St 17404 717-792-2796
Dr. Emilie Lonardi, supt. Fax 792-5114
www.wyasd.k12.pa.us
West York Area HS 900/9-12
1800 Bannister St 17404 717-845-6634
Janet May, prin. Fax 846-9691
West York Area MS 700/6-8
1700 Bannister St 17404 717-845-1671
Brad Sterner, prin. Fax 845-9083

York CSD 3,500/K-12
PO Box 1927 17405 717-845-3571
Dr. Eric Holmes, supt. Fax 849-1394
www.ycs.k12.pa.us
Penn HS 900/9-12
101 W College Ave 17401 717-849-1218
Brandon Carter, prin. Fax 848-1143

York Suburban SD 2,800/K-12
1800 Hollywood Dr 17403 717-885-1210
Dr. Michele Merkle, supt. Fax 885-1211
www.yssd.org/
York Suburban HS 900/9-12
1800 Hollywood Dr 17403 717-885-1270
Dr. Brian Ellis, prin. Fax 885-1271
York Suburban MS 700/6-8
455 Sundale Dr 17402 717-885-1260
Dr. Scott Krauser, prin. Fax 885-1261

Art Institute of York - Pennsylvania Post-Sec.
1409 Williams Rd 17402 717-755-2300
Baltimore School of Massage-York Campus Post-Sec.
170 Red Rock Rd 17406 717-268-1881
Bible Baptist Christian Academy 100/PK-12
4190 N Susquehanna Trl 17404 717-266-2544
Christian S of York 300/PK-12
907 Greenbriar Rd 17404 717-767-6842
Kevin Hofer, hdmstr. Fax 767-4904
Consolidated School of Business Post-Sec.
1605 Clugston Rd 17404 717-764-9550
Empire Beauty School Post-Sec.
2592 Eastern Blvd 17402 717-600-8111
Motorcycle Technology Center Post-Sec.
52 Grumbacher Rd 17406 717-767-4300
Penn State York Post-Sec.
1031 Edgecomb Ave 17403 717-771-4000
York Catholic HS 600/7-12
601 E Springettsbury Ave 17403 717-846-8871
Katie Seufert, prin. Fax 843-4588
York College of Pennsylvania Post-Sec.
441 Country Club Rd 17403 717-846-7788
York Country Day S 200/PK-12
1000 Indian Rock Dam Rd 17403 717-815-6700
Dr. Christine Heine, head sch Fax 815-6769
York Hospital Post-Sec.
1001 S George St 17403 717-851-2942
Yorktowne Business Institute Post-Sec.
W 7th Ave 17404 717-846-5000
YTI Career Institute Post-Sec.
1405 Williams Rd 17402 717-757-1100

York Springs, Adams, Pop. 827
Bermudian Springs SD 2,000/K-12
7335 Carlisle Pike 17372 717-528-4113
Dr. Shane Hotchkiss, supt. Fax 528-7981
www.bermudian.org
Bermudian Springs HS 600/9-12
7335 Carlisle Pike 17372 717-528-5127
Jon DeFoe, prin. Fax 528-4149
Bermudian Springs MS 600/5-8
7335 Carlisle Pike 17372 717-528-5137
Dr. Wade Hunt, prin. Fax 528-0034

Youngsville, Warren, Pop. 1,716
Warren County SD
Supt. — See Russell
Youngsville HS 300/8-12
227 College St 16371 814-563-7573
Amy Beers, prin. Fax 563-4459

Warren County Christian S 50/K-12
165 Mead Run Rd 16371 814-563-4457
Konrad Kerr, admin. Fax 563-7647

Youngwood, Westmoreland, Pop. 3,014

Westmoreland County Community College Post-Sec.
145 Pavilion Ln 15697 724-925-4000

Zieglerville, Montgomery
Perkiomen Valley SD
Supt. — See Collegeville
Perkiomen Valley West MS 600/6-8
220 Big Rd 19492 484-977-7210
Dr. Kim Boyd, prin. Fax 977-7212

RHODE ISLAND

RHODE ISLAND DEPARTMENT OF EDUCATION

255 Westminster St, Providence 02903-3414
Telephone 401-222-4600
Fax 401-277-6178
Website http://www.ride.ri.gov

Commissioner of Education Dr. Ken Wagner

RHODE ISLAND BOARD OF REGENTS

255 Westminster St, Providence 02903-3414

Chairperson Barbara Cottam

PUBLIC, PRIVATE AND CATHOLIC SECONDARY SCHOOLS

Barrington, Bristol, Pop. 15,849
Barrington SD 3,300/PK-12
PO Box 95 02806 401-245-5000
Michael Messore, supt. Fax 245-5003
barringtonschools.org
Barrington HS 1,000/9-12
220 Lincoln Ave 02806 401-247-3150
Joseph Hurley, prin. Fax 245-6170
Barrington MS 800/6-8
261 Middle Hwy 02806 401-247-3160
Dr. Andrew Anderson, prin. Fax 247-3164

Barrington Christian Academy 200/K-12
9 Old County Rd 02806 401-246-0113
Sean Hunley, head sch Fax 246-2540
St. Andrew's S 200/6-12
63 Federal Rd 02806 401-246-1230
David Tinagero, hdmstr. Fax 246-0510

Block Island, Washington
New Shoreham SD 100/K-12
PO Box 1890 02807 401-466-7732
Dr. Judith Lundsten, supt. Fax 466-3249
blockislandschool.net/
Block Island S 100/K-12
PO Box 1890 02807 401-466-5600
Kristine Monje, prin. Fax 466-5610

Bristol, Bristol, Pop. 21,625
Bristol Warren Regional SD 3,400/PK-12
151 State St 02809 401-253-4000
Mario Andrade Ed.D., supt. Fax 253-1740
www.bw.k12.ri.us
Mt. Hope HS 1,000/9-12
199 Chestnut St 02809 401-254-5980
Don Rebello, prin. Fax 254-5925
Other Schools – See Warren

Roger Williams University Post-Sec.
1 Old Ferry Rd 02809 401-253-1040

Central Falls, Providence, Pop. 18,222
Central Falls SD 2,700/PK-12
949 Dexter St 02863 401-727-7700
Victor Capellan, supt. Fax 727-7722
www.cfschools.net/
Calcutt MS 600/5-8
112 Washington St 02863 401-727-7726
Buddy Comet, prin. Fax 724-0870
Central Falls HS 700/9-12
24 Summer St 02863 401-727-7710
Troy Silvia, prin. Fax 727-6157

Coventry, Kent, Pop. 31,083
Coventry SD 5,000/PK-12
1675 Flat River Rd 02816 401-822-9400
Craig Levis, supt. Fax 822-9406
www.coventryschools.net
Career & Technical Center Vo/Tech
40 Reservoir Rd 02816 401-822-9499
Lori Ferguson, dir. Fax 822-9492
Coventry HS 1,600/9-12
40 Reservoir Rd 02816 401-822-9499
Michael Hobin, prin. Fax 822-9492
Feinstein MS of Coventry 1,200/6-8
15 Foster Dr 02816 401-822-9426
Dr. Arthur Lisi, prin. Fax 822-9469

Cranston, Providence, Pop. 78,728
Cranston SD 10,500/PK-12
845 Park Ave 02910 401-270-8000
Jeannine Nota-Masse, supt. Fax 270-8703
www.cpsed.net
Bain MS 400/6-8
135 Gansett Ave 02910 401-270-8010
Jeffrey Taylor, prin. Fax 270-8567
Cranston Area Career & Technical Center Vo/Tech
100 Metropolitan Ave 02920 401-270-8070
Gerry Auth, prin. Fax 270-8611
Cranston HS East 1,600/9-12
899 Park Ave 02910 401-270-8126
Sean Kelly, prin. Fax 270-8509
Cranston HS West 1,500/9-12
80 Metropolitan Ave 02920 401-270-8049
Thomas Barbieri, prin. Fax 270-8526
Hope Highlands MS 400/6-8
300 Hope Rd 02921 401-270-8148
Alexander Kanelos, prin. Fax 270-8706
Park View MS 500/6-8
25 Park View Blvd 02910 401-270-8090
Michael Crudale, prin. Fax 270-8527
Western Hills MS 700/6-8
400 Phenix Ave 02920 401-270-8030
Tim Vesey, prin. Fax 270-8635

Cumberland, Providence
Cumberland SD 4,500/PK-12
2602 Mendon Rd 02864 401-658-1600
Robert Mitchell, supt. Fax 658-4620
www.cumberlandschools.org/
Cumberland HS 1,300/9-12
2600 Mendon Rd 02864 401-658-2600
Alan Tenreiro, prin. Fax 658-3124
McCourt MS 400/6-8
45 Highland Ave 02864 401-725-2092
Jason Masterson Ed.D., prin. Fax 723-1188
North Cumberland MS 600/6-8
400 Nate Whipple Hwy 02864 401-333-6306
Bethany Coughlin, prin. Fax 333-1926

East Greenwich, Kent, Pop. 11,865
East Greenwich SD 2,400/PK-12
111 Peirce St 02818 401-398-1201
Victor Mercurio, supt. Fax 886-3203
www.egsd.net
Cole MS 600/6-8
100 Cedar Ave 02818 401-886-3248
Alexis Meyer, prin. Fax 886-3283
East Greenwich HS 700/9-12
300 Avenger Dr 02818 401-886-3292
Michael Podraza, prin. Fax 885-1336

New England Institute of Technology Post-Sec.
One New England Tech Blvd 02818 401-467-7744
Rocky Hill S 300/PK-12
530 Ives Rd 02818 401-884-9070
James Tracy Ph.D., head sch Fax 885-4985

East Providence, Providence, Pop. 44,064
East Providence SD 5,200/PK-12
145 Taunton Ave 02914 401-435-7500
Kim Mercer, supt. Fax 435-7507
www.epschoolsri.com/
East Providence Career & Technical Ctr Vo/Tech
1998 Pawtucket Ave 02914 401-435-7815
Karen Mellen, dir. Fax 435-7854
East Providence HS 1,500/9-12
2000 Pawtucket Ave 02914 401-435-7806
Shani Wallace, prin. Fax 435-7864
Martin MS 600/6-8
111 Brown St 02914 401-435-7819
Dr. Sandra Forand, prin. Fax 435-7851
Other Schools – See Riverside

Providence Country Day S 200/6-12
660 Waterman Ave 02914 401-438-5170
Vince Watchorn, head sch Fax 435-4514
St. Mary Academy-Bay View 700/PK-12
3070 Pawtucket Ave 02915 401-434-0113
Colleen Gribbin, prin. Fax 434-4756

Exeter, Washington

Montessori Pathways S 4-9
567 South County Trl # 307 02822 401-295-0677
Tara Smith Ph.D., head sch Fax 295-1677

Greenville, Providence, Pop. 8,588

Mater Ecclesiae College Post-Sec.
60 Austin Ave 02828 401-949-2820
Overbrook Academy 100/6-9
60 Austin Ave 02828 401-349-3444

Harrisville, Providence, Pop. 1,581
Burrillville SD 2,400/PK-12
2300 Broncos Hwy 02830 401-568-1301
Dr. Frank Pallotta, supt. Fax 568-4111
www.bsd-ri.net/
Burrillville HS 700/9-12
425 East Ave 02830 401-568-1310
Dr. Michael Whaley, prin. Fax 568-1363
Burrillville MS 600/6-8
2220 Broncos Hwy 02830 401-568-1320
Kathryn Lord, prin. Fax 568-1317

Jamestown, Newport, Pop. 4,999
Jamestown SD 500/PK-8
76 Melrose Ave 02835 401-423-7020
Dr. Carol Ann Blanchette, supt. Fax 423-7022
jsd-ri.schoolloop.com
Lawn S 200/5-8
55 Lawn Ave 02835 401-423-7010
Nathaniel Edmonds, prin. Fax 423-7012

Johnston, Providence, Pop. 26,542
Johnston SD 3,100/PK-12
10 Memorial Ave 02919 401-233-1900
Dr. Bernard DiLullo, supt. Fax 233-1907
www.johnstonschools.org
Ferri MS 700/6-8
10 Memorial Ave 02919 401-233-1930
Matthew Tsonos, admin. Fax 233-1943
Johnston SHS 900/9-12
345 Cherry Hill Rd 02919 401-233-1920
Dennis Morrell, prin. Fax 233-0031

Kingston, Washington, Pop. 6,817

University of Rhode Island 02881 Post-Sec.
401-874-1000

Lincoln, Providence, Pop. 18,045
Lincoln SD 3,100/PK-12
1624 Lonsdale Ave 02865 401-721-3300
Georgia Fortunato, supt. Fax 728-5482
www.lincolnps.org/
Lincoln HS 1,000/9-12
135 Old River Rd 02865 401-334-7500
Kevin McNamara, prin. Fax 334-8753
Lincoln MS 700/6-8
152 Jenckes Hill Rd 02865 401-721-3400
Heidi Godowski, prin. Fax 721-3428

Rhode Island Technical Schools
Supt. — None
Davies Career-Technical HS Vo/Tech
50 Jenckes Hill Rd 02865 401-728-1500
Victoria Garrick, prin. Fax 728-8910

Lincoln Technical Institute Post-Sec.
622 George Washington Hwy 02865 401-334-2430

Middletown, Newport, Pop. 3,400
Middletown SD 2,100/PK-12
26 Oliphant Ln 02842 401-849-2122
Rosemarie Kraeger, supt. Fax 849-0202
www.mpsri.net/
Gaudet MS 700/4-8
1113 Aquidneck Ave 02842 401-846-6395
Beth Hayes, prin. Fax 847-7580
Middletown HS 700/9-12
130 Valley Rd 02842 401-846-7250
Gail Abromitis, prin. Fax 849-7170

St. George's S 400/9-12
372 Purgatory Rd 02842 401-847-7565
Eric Peterson, head sch Fax 842-6677

Narragansett, Washington, Pop. 3,721
Narragansett SD 1,400/PK-12
25 5th Ave 02882 401-792-9450
Katherine Sipala, supt. Fax 792-9439
www.narragansett.k12.ri.us
Narragansett HS 400/9-12
245 S Pier Rd 02882 401-792-9400
Daniel Warner, prin. Fax 792-9410
Narragansett Pier MS 400/5-8
235 S Pier Rd 02882 401-792-9430
Marianne Kirby, prin. Fax 792-9436

Newport, Newport, Pop. 23,495
Newport SD 2,000/PK-12
15 Wickham Rd 02840 401-847-2100
Colleen Jermain Ed.D., supt. Fax 849-0170
www.npsri.net
Newport Area Career & Technical Center Vo/Tech
15 Wickham Rd 02840 401-847-2100
Christianne Fisher, dir. Fax 849-0170
Rogers HS 500/9-12
15 Wickham Rd 02840 401-847-6235
Jeff Goss, prin. Fax 849-3295
Thompson MS 600/5-8
55 Broadway 02840 401-847-1493
Jaime Crowley, prin. Fax 849-3426

Rhode Island Technical Schools
Supt. — None
MET East Bay Campus Vo/Tech
115 Girard Ave 02840 401-849-7711
Brad Martin, prin. Fax 846-5703

International Yacht Restoration School Post-Sec.
449 Thames St 02840 401-848-5777
Salve Regina University Post-Sec.
100 Ochre Point Ave 02840 401-847-6650

North Kingstown, Washington, Pop. 2,800
North Kingstown SD 4,200/PK-12
100 Romano Vineyard Way 02852 401-268-6200
Philip Auger, supt. Fax 268-6405
www.nksd.net
Davisville Academy 200/Alt
50 East Ct 02852 401-398-8100
Karen Skerry, prin. Fax 398-7114
Davisville MS 500/6-8
200 School St 02852 401-541-6300
Ruthanne Logan, prin. Fax 541-6310
North Kingstown HS 1,400/9-12
150 Fairway Dr 02852 401-268-6236
Denise Mancieri, prin. Fax 268-6210
Wickford MS 400/6-8
250 Tower Hill Rd 02852 401-268-6470
Terry Merkel, prin. Fax 268-6480

North Providence, Providence, Pop. 32,500
North Providence SD 3,400/PK-12
2240 Mineral Spring Ave 02911 401-233-1100
Melinda A. Smith M.Ed., supt. Fax 233-1106
www.northprovschools.org
Birchwood MS 400/6-8
10 Birchwood Dr 02904 401-233-1120
Melissa Goho, prin. Fax 353-6903
North Providence HS 1,000/9-12
1828 Mineral Spring Ave 02904 401-233-1150
Joseph Goho, prin. Fax 233-1166
Ricci MS 400/6-8
51 Intervale Ave 02911 401-233-1170
Thomas Mellen, prin. Fax 232-5421

St. Joseph's Hospital Post-Sec.
200 High Service Ave 02904 401-456-3050

North Scituate, Providence
Foster-Glocester Regional SD 1,200/6-12
91 Anan Wade Rd 02857 401-710-7500
Michael Barnes Ph.D., supt. Fax 710-9825
www.fg.k12.ri.us/
Ponaganset HS 700/9-12
137 Anan Wade Rd 02857 401-710-7500
Renee Palazzo, prin. Fax 647-5743
Ponaganset MS 500/6-8
7 Rustic Hill Rd 02857 401-710-7500
Patricia Marcotte, prin. Fax 647-1792

Scituate SD 1,400/PK-12
PO Box 188 02857 401-647-4100
Dr. Lawrence P. Filippelli, supt. Fax 647-4102
www.scituateri.net
Scituate HS 500/9-12
94 Trimtown Rd 02857 401-647-4120
Dr. Michael Hassell, prin. Fax 647-4126
Scituate MS 400/6-8
94 Trimtown Rd 02857 401-647-4123
Michael Zajac, prin. Fax 647-4104

North Smithfield, Providence, Pop. 10,497
North Smithfield SD
Supt. — See Slatersville
North Smithfield HS 500/9-12
412 Greenville Rd 02896 401-766-2500
Timothy McGee, prin. Fax 765-8629
North Smithfield MS 400/6-8
1850 Providence Pike 02896 401-597-6100
John Lahar, prin. Fax 597-6121

Pawtucket, Providence, Pop. 64,391
Pawtucket SD 8,500/PK-12
PO Box 388 02862 401-729-6300
Patti DiCenso, supt. Fax 727-1641
www.psdri.net
Goff JHS 400/7-8
974 Newport Ave 02861 401-729-6500
Lisa Benedetti-Ramzi, prin. Fax 721-2105
Jenks JHS 400/7-8
350 Division St 02860 401-729-6520
Elizabeth Fasteson, prin. Fax 729-6523
Pawtucket Learning Academy Alt
286 Main St 02860 401-721-2127
Dr. Linda Gifford, prin. Fax 729-2126
Shea HS 900/9-12
485 East Ave 02860 401-729-6445
Donald Miller, prin. Fax 729-6454
Slater JHS 500/7-8
281 Mineral Spring Ave 02860 401-729-6480
Dr. Jacqueline Ash, prin. Fax 729-6490
Tolman HS 1,000/9-12
150 Exchange St 02860 401-729-6400
Christopher Savastano, prin. Fax 729-6407

Walsh S for the Arts 200/9-12
350 Division St 02860 401-721-2148
Elizabeth Fasteson, prin. Fax 721-2147

New England Tractor Trailer Training Post-Sec.
600 Mshssuck Valley Ind Hwy 02860 401-725-1220
Newport School of Hairdressing Post-Sec.
226 Main St 02860 401-725-6882
St. Raphael Academy 400/9-12
123 Walcott St 02860 401-723-8100
Daniel Richard, prin. Fax 723-8740

Portsmouth, Newport, Pop. 3,600
Portsmouth SD 2,600/PK-12
29 Middle Rd 02871 401-683-1039
Ana C. Riley, supt. Fax 683-5204
www.portsmouthschoolsri.org
Portsmouth HS 1,000/9-12
120 Education Ln 02871 401-683-2124
Joseph Amaral, prin. Fax 683-1096
Portsmouth MS 1,000/4-8
125 Jepson Ln 02871 401-849-3700
Joseph Amaral, prin. Fax 841-8420

Aquidneck Island Christian Academy 100/K-12
321 E Main Rd 02871 401-849-5550
Joshua White, hdmstr. Fax 849-6811
Portsmouth Abbey S 400/9-12
285 Corys Ln 02871 401-683-2000
Daniel McDonough, hdmstr. Fax 643-1388

Providence, Providence, Pop. 170,517
Providence SD 23,400/PK-12
797 Westminster St 02903 401-456-9100
Christopher Maher, supt. Fax 456-9252
www.providenceschools.org
Alvarez HS 500/9-12
375 Adelaide Ave 02907 401-456-0676
Janice Hawkins, prin. Fax 456-0679
Bishop MS 700/6-8
101 Sessions St 02906 401-456-9344
Kimberly Luca, prin. Fax 456-9110
Central HS 1,100/9-12
70 Fricker St 02903 401-456-9111
Julia Carlson, prin. Fax 456-9113
Classical HS 1,100/9-12
770 Westminster St 02903 401-456-9145
Scott Barr, prin. Fax 456-9155
DelSesto MS 1,000/6-8
152 Springfield St 02909 401-278-0557
Arzinia Gill, prin. Fax 278-0564
E-Cubed Academy 300/9-12
812 Branch Ave 02904 401-456-0694
Regina Winkfield, prin. Fax 456-0696
Greene MS 1,000/6-8
721 Chalkstone Ave 02908 401-456-9347
Dr. Nicole Mathis, prin. Fax 453-8630
Hope HS 900/9-12
324 Hope St 02906 401-456-9161
John Hunt, prin. Fax 456-1747
Hopkins MS 600/6-8
480 Charles St 02904 401-456-9203
Gloria Jackson, prin. Fax 456-9226
Mt. Pleasant HS 900/9-12
434 Mount Pleasant Ave 02908 401-456-9181
Christopher Coleman, prin. Fax 453-8655
Providence Career And Technical Academy Vo/Tech
41 Fricker St 02903 401-456-9136
Wobberson Torchon, dir. Fax 456-9172
Sanchez Educational Complex 600/9-12
182 Thurbers Ave 02905 401-456-1781
Michaela Keegan, prin. Fax 456-1782
Stuart MS 800/6-8
188 Princeton Ave 02907 401-456-9340
Scott Sutherland, prin. Fax 453-8659
West Broadway MS 6-8
29 Bainbridge Ave 02909 401-456-1733
William Black, prin. Fax 278-0527
Williams MS 800/6-8
278 Thurbers Ave 02905 401-456-9355
Jennifer Vorro, prin. Fax 453-8631

Rhode Island Technical Schools
Supt. — None
MET Equality S Vo/Tech
325 Public St 02905 401-752-2610
Steven Bartholomew, prin. Fax 752-2612
MET Justice Campus Vo/Tech
325 Public St 02905 401-752-2630
Janet Vilanueva-Williams, prin. Fax 752-2612
MET Liberty S Vo/Tech
325 Public St 02905 401-752-2680
Arthur Baraf, prin. Fax 752-2612
MET Peace Street Campus Vo/Tech
362 Dexter St 02907 401-752-3400
Chantel Wylie, prin. Fax 752-3425
MET Unity S Vo/Tech
325 Public St 02905 401-752-2650
Alin Bennett, prin. Fax 752-2612
Other Schools – See Lincoln RI, Newport RI

Brown S 800/PK-12
250 Lloyd Ave 02906 401-831-7350
Matt Glendinning, head sch Fax 455-0084
Brown University Post-Sec.
1 Prospect St 02912 401-863-1000
Community Preparatory S 100/3-8
126 Somerset St 02907 401-521-9696
Empire Beauty School Post-Sec.
151 Broadway 02903 401-272-4300
Johnson & Wales University Post-Sec.
8 Abbott Park Pl 02903 401-598-1000
LaSalle Academy 1,500/7-12
612 Academy Ave 02908 401-351-7750
Donald Kavanagh, prin. Fax 444-1782

Lincoln S 400/PK-12
301 Butler Ave 02906 401-331-9696
Suzanne Fogarty, head sch Fax 751-6670
Providence College Post-Sec.
1 Cunningham Sq 02918 401-865-1000
Providence Hebrew Day S 200/PK-12
450 Elmgrove Ave 02906 401-331-5327
Rhode Island College Post-Sec.
600 Mount Pleasant Ave 02908 401-456-8000
Rhode Island Hospital Post-Sec.
593 Eddy St 02903 401-444-5123
Rhode Island School of Design Post-Sec.
2 College St 02903 401-454-6100
St. Patrick Academy 100/9-12
244 Smith St 02908 401-421-9300
Bruce Daigle, prin. Fax 421-0810
San Miguel S 100/5-8
525 Branch Ave 02904 401-467-9777
Carol Soltys, dean Fax 785-4976
School One 100/9-12
220 University Ave 02906 401-331-2497
Jennifer Borman, head sch Fax 421-8869
Wheeler S 800/PK-12
216 Hope St 02906 401-421-8100
Dr. Dan Miller, head sch Fax 751-7674
Women & Infants Hospital Post-Sec.
101 Dudley St 02905 401-274-1100

Riverside, See East Providence
East Providence SD
Supt. — See East Providence
Riverside MS 600/6-8
179 Forbes St 02915 401-433-6230
Cheri Guerra, prin. Fax 433-6261

Slatersville, Providence
North Smithfield SD 1,700/PK-12
PO Box 72 02876 401-769-5492
Stephen Lindberg, supt. Fax 769-5493
www.northsmithfieldschools.com/
Other Schools – See North Smithfield

Smithfield, Providence, Pop. 19,163
Smithfield SD 2,400/PK-12
49 Farnum Pike 02917 401-231-6606
Robert O'Brien, supt. Fax 232-0870
www.smithfield-ps.org
Gallagher MS 600/6-8
10 Indian Run Trl 02917 401-949-2056
Laurie Beauvais, prin. Fax 949-5697
Smithfield HS 800/9-12
90 Pleasant View Ave 02917 401-949-2050
Daniel Kelley, prin. Fax 949-2052

Bryant University Post-Sec.
1150 Douglas Pike 02917 401-232-6000

Tiverton, Newport, Pop. 7,434
Tiverton SD 1,800/K-12
100 N Brayton Rd 02878 401-624-8476
William Rearick, supt. Fax 624-4086
www.tivertonschools.org
Tiverton HS 500/9-12
100 N Brayton Rd 02878 401-624-8494
Christopher Ashley, prin. Fax 624-8495
Tiverton MS 600/5-8
10 Quintal Dr 02878 401-624-6668
Laurie Dias-Mitchell, prin. Fax 624-6669

Wakefield, Washington, Pop. 8,226
South Kingstown SD 3,400/PK-12
307 Curtis Corner Rd 02879 401-360-1300
Dr. Kristen Stringfellow Ed.D., supt. Fax 360-1330
www.skschools.net/
Academic Success Academy Alt
153 School St 02879 401-360-1818
Curtis Corner MS 500/7-8
301 Curtis Corner Rd 02879 401-360-1333
Patricia Aull, prin. Fax 360-1334
South Kingstown HS 1,100/9-12
215 Columbia St 02879 401-360-1000
Robert Mezzanotte, prin. Fax 360-1465

Prout S 600/9-12
4640 Tower Hill Rd 02879 401-789-9262
David Estes, prin. Fax 782-2262

Warren, Bristol, Pop. 11,385
Bristol Warren Regional SD
Supt. — See Bristol
Kickemuit MS 700/6-8
525 Child St 02885 401-245-2010
Jared Vance, prin. Fax 254-5960

Warwick, Kent, Pop. 81,173
Warwick SD 8,400/PK-12
34 Warwick Lake Ave 02889 401-734-3000
Philip Thornton, supt. Fax 734-3003
www.warwickschools.org
Pilgrim HS 1,000/9-12
111 Pilgrim Pkwy 02888 401-734-3250
Gerald Habershaw, prin. Fax 734-3264
Toll Gate HS 1,000/9-12
575 Centerville Rd Ste 1 02886 401-734-3300
Stephen Chrabaszcz, prin. Fax 734-3314
Veterans JHS 1,000/7-8
2401 W Shore Rd 02889 401-734-3200
David Tober, prin. Fax 734-3214
Warwick Area Career & Technical Center Vo/Tech
575 Centerville Rd 02886 401-734-3150
William McCaffrey, dir. Fax 734-3160
Winman JHS 500/7-8
575 Centerville Rd 02886 401-734-3375
Joanne Pelletier, prin. Fax 734-3385

Bishop Hendricken HS 900/9-12
2615 Warwick Ave 02889 401-739-3450
Joseph Brennan, prin. Fax 732-8261

Community College of Rhode Island | Post-Sec.
400 East Ave 02886 | 401-825-1000
Warwick Academy of Beauty Culture | Post-Sec.
1276 Bald Hill Rd Unit 100 02886 | 401-737-4946

Westerly, Washington, Pop. 17,600

Westerly SD | 2,900/PK-12
23 Highland Ave 02891 | 401-315-1500
Roy Seitsinger Ph.D., supt. | Fax 348-2707
www.westerly.k12.ri.us
Westerly HS | 900/PK-PK, 9-
23 Ward Ave 02891 | 401-596-2109
Todd Grimes, prin. | Fax 315-1586
Westerly MS | 900/5-8
10 Sandy Hill Rd 02891 | 401-348-2750
Paula Fusco, prin. | Fax 348-2752

West Greenwich, Kent, Pop. 3,492

Exeter-West Greenwich Regional SD | 1,600/PK-12
940 Nooseneck Hill Rd 02817 | 401-397-5125
James Erinakes M.Ed., supt. | Fax 397-2407
www.ewg.k12.ri.us
Exeter-West Greenwich Regional HS | 500/9-12
930 Nooseneck Hill Rd 02817 | 401-397-6893
Susan Chandler, prin. | Fax 392-0134
Exeter-West Greenwich Regional JHS | 300/7-8
930 Nooseneck Hill Rd 02817 | 401-397-6897
Mary Slattery, prin. | Fax 392-0109

West Warwick, Kent, Pop. 29,600

West Warwick SD | 3,400/PK-12
10 Harris Ave 02893 | 401-821-1180
Karen A. Tarasevich, supt. | Fax 822-8463
www.westwarwickpublicschools.com/
Deering MS | 1,000/5-8
2 Webster Knight Dr 02893 | 401-822-8445
Jeffrey Guiot, prin. | Fax 822-8474
West Warwick HS | 900/9-12
Webster Knight Dr 02893 | 401-821-6596
Phillip Solomon, prin. | Fax 822-8473

Ridley-Lowell Business & Technology Inst | Post-Sec.
186 Providence St 02893 | 844-256-4781

Wood River Junction, Washington

Chariho Regional SD | 3,400/PK-12
455A Switch Rd 02894 | 401-364-7575
Barry Ricci, supt. | Fax 415-6076
www.chariho.k12.ri.us/
Chariho Area Career & Technical Center | Vo/Tech
459 Switch Rd 02894 | 401-364-6869
Susan Votto, dir. | Fax 364-1191
Chariho Regional HS | 1,200/9-12
453 Switch Rd 02894 | 401-364-7778
Laurie Weber, prin. | Fax 415-0436
Chariho Regional MS | 1,000/5-8
455b Switch Rd 02894 | 401-364-0651
Gregory Zenion, prin. | Fax 223-4925
RYSE | 50/Alt
459 Switch Rd 02894 | 401-315-2880
Carolyn Garlick, dir. | Fax 223-9651

Woonsocket, Providence, Pop. 39,726

Woonsocket SD | 5,800/PK-12
108 High St 02895 | 401-767-4600
Patrick McGee, supt. | Fax 767-4607
www.woonsocketschools.com/
Woonsocket Area Career & Tech. Center | Vo/Tech
400 Aylsworth Ave 02895 | 401-767-4662
William Webb, dir. | Fax 767-4665
Woonsocket HS | 1,600/9-12
777 Cass Ave 02895 | 401-767-4700
Carnell Henderson, prin. | Fax 767-4748
Woonsocket MS at Hamlet | 1,200/6-8
60 Florence Dr 02895 | 401-235-6110
Steve Boss, prin.
Woonsocket MS at Villa Nova | 6-8
240 Florence Dr 02895 | 401-235-6125
Steve Boss, prin.

Good Shepherd Regional S | 200/3-8
1210 Mendon Rd 02895 | 401-767-5906
Jennifer DeOliveira, prin. | Fax 767-5905
Mt. St. Charles Academy | 900/6-12
800 Logee St 02895 | 401-769-0310
Edwin Burke, prin. | Fax 762-2327

SOUTH CAROLINA

SOUTH CAROLINA DEPARTMENT OF EDUCATION
1429 Senate St Ste 100, Columbia 29201-3730
Telephone 803-734-8500
Fax 803-734-3389
Website ed.sc.gov/

Superintendent of Education Molly Spearman

SOUTH CAROLINA BOARD OF EDUCATION
1429 Senate St Ste 100, Columbia 29201-3730

Chairperson Michael Brenan

PUBLIC, PRIVATE AND CATHOLIC SECONDARY SCHOOLS

Abbeville, Abbeville, Pop. 5,157
Abbeville County SD 3,100/PK-12
400 Greenville St 29620 864-366-5427
Dr. Jonathan Phipps, supt. Fax 366-8531
www.acsdsc.org
Abbeville County Career Center Vo/Tech
100 Old Calhoun Falls Rd 29620 864-366-9069
Dorinda Bell-Dunlap, dir. Fax 366-4774
Abbeville HS 600/9-12
701 Washington St 29620 864-366-5916
Charles Costner, prin. Fax 366-4939
Wright MS 400/6-8
111 Highway 71 29620 864-366-5998
Skip Hopkins, prin. Fax 366-4282
Other Schools – See Due West

Aiken, Aiken, Pop. 29,094
Aiken County SD 23,900/PK-12
1000 Brookhaven Dr 29803 803-641-2428
Sean Alford Ph.D., supt. Fax 642-8903
www.acpsd.net
Aiken HS 1,400/9-12
449 Rutland Dr NW 29801 803-641-2500
Garen Cofer, prin. Fax 641-2501
Aiken MS 600/6-8
101 Gator Ln 29801 803-641-2570
Scott Floyd, prin. Fax 641-2578
Kennedy MS 1,000/6-8
274 E Pine Log Rd 29803 803-641-2470
Teresa Mitchem, prin. Fax 641-2405
Pinecrest Center Alt
1050 Pinecrest Ave 29801 803-641-2680
Jamie Creasy, coord. Fax 641-2681
Schofield MS 700/6-8
224 Kershaw St NE 29801 803-641-2770
Dr. Lloydette Young, prin. Fax 641-2529
Silver Bluff HS 600/9-12
64 Desoto Dr 29803 803-652-8100
Collette Johnson, prin. Fax 652-8104
South Aiken HS 1,500/9-12
232 E Pine Log Rd 29803 803-641-2600
Jill Jett, prin. Fax 641-2607
Other Schools – See Graniteville, Jackson, Monetta, New Ellenton, North Augusta, Wagener, Warrenville

---

Aiken School of Cosmetology Post-Sec.
225 Richland Ave E 29801 803-644-7133
Aiken Technical College Post-Sec.
PO Box 696 29802 803-593-9231
Lacy Cosmetology School Post-Sec.
3084 Whiskey Rd 29803 803-648-6181
South Aiken Baptist Christian S 400/PK-12
980 Dougherty Rd 29803 803-648-7871
University of South Carolina Post-Sec.
471 University Pkwy 29801 803-648-6851

Allendale, Allendale, Pop. 3,449

University of South Carolina Post-Sec.
PO Box 617 29810 803-584-3446

Anderson, Anderson, Pop. 26,180
Anderson SD 3
Supt. — See Iva
Anderson County Alternative S Alt
805 E Whitner St 29624 864-260-4888
Randolph Dillingham, dir. Fax 260-4004

Anderson SD 4
Supt. — See Pendleton
Pendleton HS 800/9-12
7324 Highway 187 29625 864-403-2100
Brian Couch, prin. Fax 646-8066

Anderson SD 5 12,800/PK-12
PO Box 439 29622 864-260-5000
Thomas Wilson, supt. Fax 260-5074
www.anderson5.net
Anderson College & Career Acad 700/6-8
2302 Dobbins Bridge Rd 29626 864-716-3890
Leonard Galloway, prin. Fax 716-4070
Anderson V Career Campus Vo/Tech
1225 S McDuffie St 29624 864-260-5160
Cecil Bonner, prin. Fax 260-5685
Glenview MS of Choice 700/6-8
2725 Old Williamston Rd 29621 864-716-4060
Walter Mayfield, prin. Fax 716-3883
Hanna HS IB World S 1,800/9-12
2600 N Highway 81 29621 864-260-5110
Shawn Tobin, prin. Fax 260-5213
Lakeside MS of Inquiry & Innovation 500/6-8
315 Pearman Dairy Rd 29625 864-260-5135
Tiffany Osborne, prin. Fax 260-5885
McCants MS IB World S 700/6-8
2123 Marchbanks Ave 29621 864-260-5145
Leigh Burton, prin. Fax 260-5846
Southwood Academy of the Arts 400/6-8
1110 Southwood St 29624 864-260-5205
Jamie Smith, prin. Fax 964-2607
Westside HS Early College Academy 1,700/9-12
806 Pearman Dairy Rd 29625 864-260-5230
Kory Roberts, prin. Fax 260-5007

Anderson Christian S 200/PK-12
3902 Liberty Hwy 29621 864-224-7309
Dr. Michelle Cutler, admin. Fax 224-1085
Anderson Memorial Hospital Post-Sec.
800 N Fant St 29621 864-261-1109
Anderson University Post-Sec.
316 Boulevard 29621 864-231-2000
Forrest College Post-Sec.
601 E River St 29624 864-225-7653
Montessori S of Anderson 200/PK-12
280 Sam McGee Rd 29621 864-226-5344
Vance Jenkins, admin. Fax 231-6562
New Covenant S 200/PK-12
303 Simpson Rd 29621 864-224-5675

Andrews, Georgetown, Pop. 2,842
Georgetown County SD
Supt. — See Georgetown
Andrews HS 500/9-12
12890 County Line Rd 29510 843-264-3414
Dr. Michelle Greene, prin. Fax 264-3326
Rosemary MS 500/6-8
12804 County Line Rd 29510 843-264-9780
LaTanya Goodson, prin. Fax 264-9787

Aynor, Horry, Pop. 554
Horry County SD
Supt. — See Conway
Aynor HS 800/9-12
201 Jordanville Rd 29511 843-488-7100
Michael McCracken, prin. Fax 488-7101

Bamberg, Bamberg, Pop. 3,560
Bamberg SD 1 900/PK-12
3830 Faust St 29003 803-245-3053
Phyllis Schwarting, supt. Fax 245-3056
www.bamberg1.com
Bamberg-Ehrhardt HS 400/9-12
267 Red Raider Dr 29003 803-245-3030
Randall Maxwell, prin. Fax 245-6502
Bamberg-Ehrhardt MS 200/7-8
897 North St 29003 803-245-3058
Dr. Sandra Glover Ed.D., prin. Fax 245-6501

Barnwell, Barnwell, Pop. 4,670
Barnwell SD 45 2,500/PK-12
770 Hagood Ave 29812 803-541-1300
J.H. Grissom, supt. Fax 541-1348
www.barnwell45.org
Barnwell HS 700/9-12
474 Jackson St 29812 803-541-1390
Franklin McCormack, prin. Fax 541-0726
Guinyard-Butler MS 400/7-8
779 Allen St 29812 803-541-1370
Dr. Jessica Brabham-James, prin. Fax 541-1306

Batesburg, Lexington, Pop. 5,296
Lexington County SD 3 2,000/PK-12
338 W Columbia Ave 29006 803-532-4423
Dr. Randall Gary, supt. Fax 532-8000
www.lex3.org
Batesburg-Leesville HS 500/9-12
600 Summerland Ave 29006 803-532-9251
Raymond Padgett, prin. Fax 532-3232
Batesburg-Leesville MS 400/6-8
425 Shealy Rd 29006 803-532-3831
Sharah Clark, prin. Fax 532-8021

King Academy 200/K-12
1046 Sardis Rd 29006 803-532-6682

Beaufort, Beaufort, Pop. 12,089
Beaufort County SD 20,300/PK-12
PO Box 309 29901 843-322-2300
Dr. Jeffrey Moss, supt. Fax 322-2330
www.beaufort.k12.sc.us
Battery Creek HS 800/9-12
1 Blue Dolphin Dr 29906 843-322-5500
Edmond Burnes, prin. Fax 322-5608
Beaufort HS 1,300/9-12
84 Sea Island Pkwy, 843-322-2000
Corey Murphy, prin. Fax 322-2158
Beaufort MS 600/6-8
2501 Mossy Oaks Rd 29902 843-322-5700
Carole Ingram, prin. Fax 322-5723
Islands Academy Alt
2900 Mink Point Blvd 29902 843-322-0733
Susan Guillen, prin. Fax 322-0734
Ladys Island MS 600/6-8
30 Cougar Dr, 843-322-3100
Gregory Hall, prin. Fax 322-3179
Adult Education S Adult
1300 King St 29902 843-322-0780
Dr. Juanita Murrell, prin. Fax 322-0803
Other Schools – See Bluffton, Hilton Head Island, Seabrook

Beaufort Academy 300/PK-12
240 Sams Point Rd, 843-524-3393
Stephen Schools, head sch Fax 524-1171
Beaufort Christian S 100/PK-12
378 Parris Island Gtwy 29906 843-525-0635
Rev. Douglas Wadsworth, admin. Fax 525-0635
Technical College of the Lowcountry Post-Sec.
921 Ribaut Rd 29902 843-525-8211

Belton, Anderson, Pop. 4,063
Anderson SD 2
Supt. — See Honea Path
Belton MS 500/6-8
102 Cherokee Rd 29627 864-338-6595
Josh Burton, prin. Fax 338-3301

Bennettsville, Marlboro, Pop. 8,964
Marlboro County SD 4,100/PK-12
PO Box 947 29512 843-479-4016
Dr. Helena Tillar, supt. Fax 479-5944
www.marlboro.k12.sc.us
Marlboro County HS 1,200/9-12
951 Fayetteville Avenue Ext 29512 843-479-5900
Dr. Andrea Hampton, prin. Fax 479-5916
Other Schools – See Clio

Marlboro Academy 200/K-12
1035 Bennettsville Fire Twr 29512 843-479-6501
Joseph Critcher, hdmstr. Fax 479-1941

Bishopville, Lee, Pop. 3,442
Lee County SD 2,300/PK-12
PO Box 507 29010 803-484-5327
Dr. Wanda Andrews, supt. Fax 484-9107
www.leeschoolsk12.org
Lee Central HS 600/9-12
1800 Wisacky Hwy 29010 803-428-4010
Robert Hemby, prin. Fax 428-4062
Lee Central MS 500/6-8
41 Charlenes Ln 29010 803-428-2100
Tonya Addison, prin. Fax 428-2174
Lee County Academic Learning Center 100/Alt
123 E College St 29010 803-483-0111
John Haynesworth, dir. Fax 483-0113
Lee County Career & Technology Center Vo/Tech
521 Park St 29010 803-484-5327
Betty Lowery, coord. Fax 484-4171

Lee Academy 400/K-12
630 Cousar St 29010 803-484-5532
Maria Watson, head sch Fax 484-9491

Blacksburg, Cherokee, Pop. 1,800
Cherokee County SD
Supt. — See Gaffney
Blacksburg HS 500/9-12
201 W Ramseur Dr 29702 864-839-6371
Craig Bramlett, prin. Fax 839-2960
Blacksburg MS 400/6-8
101 London St 29702 864-206-6829
Virgil Hampton, prin. Fax 839-2390

Blackville, Barnwell, Pop. 2,378
Area Vocational Schools
Supt. — None
Barnwell County Career Center | Vo/Tech
5214 Reynolds Rd 29817 | 803-259-5512
H. Samuel McKay, dir. | Fax 541-4701

Barnwell SD 19 | 800/PK-12
297 Pascallas St 29817 | 803-284-5605
Fax 284-4417
www.barnwell19.k12.sc.us
Blackville-Hilda HS | 200/9-12
PO Box 245 29817 | 803-284-5700
Sterling Harris, prin. | Fax 284-3766
Blackville-Hilda JHS | 100/7-8
PO Box 245 29817 | 803-284-5900
Sterling Harris, prin. | Fax 284-0961

Barnwell Christian S | 100/1-12
5675 SC Highway 70 29817 | 803-259-2100
Patrick Heatwole, admin. | Fax 259-2100
Davis Academy | 200/K-12
5061 Hilda Rd 29817 | 803-284-2476

Bluffton, Beaufort, Pop. 12,248
Beaufort County SD
Supt. — See Beaufort
Bluffton HS | 1,200/9-12
12 HE McCracken Cir 29910 | 843-706-8800
Denise Garison, prin. | Fax 706-8819
Bluffton MS | 1,100/6-8
30 New Mustang Dr 29910 | 843-707-0700
Patricia Freda, prin. | Fax 707-8117
May River HS | 9-12
601 New Riverside Rd 29910 | 843-836-4900
Todd Bornscheuer, prin.
McCracken MS | 1,000/8-9
250 HE McCracken Cir 29910 | 843-706-8700
Jerry Henderson, prin. | Fax 706-8778

Professional Golfers Career College | Post-Sec.
4454 Bluffton Park Cres 200 29910 | 843-757-9611
University of South Carolina | Post-Sec.
1 University Blvd, | 843-208-8000

Blythewood, Richland, Pop. 2,008
Richland SD 2
Supt. — See Columbia
Blythewood Academy | Alt
501 Main St 29016 | 803-691-6890
Dr. Perry Mills, prin. | Fax 691-4396
Blythewood HS | 1,700/9-12
10901 Wilson Blvd 29016 | 803-691-4090
Dr. Brenda Hafner, prin. | Fax 691-4097
Blythewood MS | 700/6-8
2351 Longtown Rd E 29016 | 803-691-6850
Karis Mazyck, prin. | Fax 691-6860
Kelly Mill MS | 900/6-8
1141 Kelly Mill Rd 29016 | 803-691-7210
Mark Sims, prin. | Fax 691-7212
Muller Road MS | 700/6-8
1031 Muller Rd 29016 | 803-691-6851
Sean Bishton, prin. | Fax 738-7531
Westwood HS | 1,300/9-12
180 Turkey Farm Rd 29016 | 803-691-4049
Dr. Cheryl Guy, prin. | Fax 738-7520

Boiling Springs, Spartanburg, Pop. 8,098
Spartanburg SD 2
Supt. — See Chesnee
Boiling Springs HS 9th Grade Campus | 600/9-9
3655 Boiling Springs Rd 29316 | 864-578-2610
Kristi Woodall, prin. | Fax 578-2620
Boiling Springs HS | 1,700/10-12
2251 Old Furnace Rd 29316 | 864-578-8465
Chuck Gordon, prin. | Fax 578-6825

Branchville, Orangeburg, Pop. 1,014
Orangeburg County Consolidated SD 4
Supt. — See Cope
Branchville HS | 300/7-12
PO Box 188 29432 | 803-274-8875
David Hess, prin. | Fax 274-8645

Camden, Kershaw, Pop. 6,772
Kershaw County SD | 10,500/PK-12
2029 W Dekalb St 29020 | 803-432-8416
Dr. Frank Morgan, supt. | Fax 425-8918
www.kcsdschools.com
Applied Technical Education Campus | Vo/Tech
874 Vocational Ln 29020 | 803-425-8982
Gordon Morris, dir. | Fax 425-8983
Camden HS | 1,000/9-12
1022 Ehrenclou Dr 29020 | 803-425-8930
Dan Matthews, prin. | Fax 424-2861
Camden MS | 700/6-8
902 McRae Rd 29020 | 803-425-8975
Byron Johnson, prin. | Fax 425-7867
Continuous Learning Center | Alt
1109 Campbell St 29020 | 803-425-7712
Tommy Gladden, dir. | Fax 425-7713
Kershaw County Adult Education | Adult
874 Vocational Ln 29020 | 803-425-8980
Weyland Burns, dir. | Fax 425-8988
Other Schools – See Elgin, Kershaw, Lugoff

Camden Military Academy | 300/7-12
520 Highway 1 N 29020 | 800-948-6291
Robert Casey Robinson, admin. | Fax 425-1020

Campobello, Spartanburg, Pop. 498
Spartanburg SD 1 | 5,000/PK-12
PO Box 218 29322 | 864-472-2846
Dr. Ron Garner, supt. | Fax 472-4118
www.spart1.org/do/
Landrum HS | 600/9-12
18818 Asheville Hwy 29322 | 864-457-2606
Jason McCraw, prin. | Fax 468-4004
Other Schools – See Inman, Landrum

Cayce, Lexington, Pop. 12,278
Lexington County SD 2
Supt. — See West Columbia
Brookland-Cayce HS | 1,000/9-12
1300 State St 29033 | 803-791-5000
Gregg Morton, prin. | Fax 739-4970
Busbee Creative Arts Academy | 300/6-8
501 Bulldog Blvd 29033 | 803-739-4070
Dr. Dixon Brooks, prin. | Fax 739-4133

Central, Pickens, Pop. 5,067
Pickens County SD
Supt. — See Easley
Daniel HS | 1,000/9-12
140 Blue and Gold Blvd 29630 | 864-397-2900
Josh Young, prin. | Fax 654-9608
Edwards MS | 800/6-8
1157 Madden Bridge Rd 29630 | 864-397-4200
Jeff Duncan, prin. | Fax 624-4426

Southern Wesleyan University | Post-Sec.
PO Box 1020 29630 | 864-644-5000

Chapin, Lexington, Pop. 1,420
SD Five of Lexington & Richland Counties
Supt. — See Irmo
Academy for Success | Alt
11629 Broad River Rd 29036 | 803-575-5300
Dr. Terrance Alridge, prin. | Fax 575-5320
Center for Advanced Technical Studies | 9-12
916 Mount Vernon Church Rd 29036
Dr. Bob Couch, dir. | 803-476-8000
Chapin HS | 1,200/9-12
300 Columbia Ave 29036 | 803-575-5400
Dr. Akil Ross, prin. | Fax 575-5420
Chapin MS | 1,100/6-8
1130 Old Lexington Hwy 29036 | 803-575-5700
Anna Miller, prin. | Fax 575-5721
Spring Hill HS | 600/9-12
11629 Broad River Rd 29036 | 803-476-8700
Dr. Michael Lofton, prin. | Fax 476-8720

Charleston, Charleston, Pop. 118,351
Charleston County SD | 45,100/PK-12
75 Calhoun St Fl 2 29401 | 843-937-6300
Dr. Gerrita Postlewait, supt. | Fax 937-6307
www.charleston.k12.sc.us
Academic Magnet HS | 600/9-12
5109 W Enterprise St Ste A 29405 | 843-746-1300
Judith Peterson, prin. | Fax 746-1310
Burke HS | 300/9-12
244 President St 29403 | 843-579-4815
Maurice Cannon, prin. | Fax 579-4855
Clark Corporate Academy | 100/Alt
1087 E Montague ve 29405 | 843-746-6519
Toshawnka Mahone, dir. | Fax 746-6519
Ft. Johnson MS | 500/6-8
1825 Camp Rd 29412 | 843-762-2740
David Parler, prin. | Fax 762-6212
James Island MS | 400/6-8
1484 Camp Rd 29412 | 843-762-2784
Andreas Westergaard, prin. | Fax 762-6209
Simmons Pinckney MS | 6-8
244 President St 29403 | 843-724-7789
Nathan Nelson, prin. | Fax 579-4363
West Ashley HS | 1,800/9-12
4060 Wildcat Blvd 29414 | 843-573-1201
William Runyon, prin. | Fax 573-1223
West Ashley MS | 300/6-8
1776 William Kennerty Dr 29407 | 843-763-1546
LaCarma Brown-McMillan, prin. | Fax 852-6557
Williams MS | 600/6-8
640 Butte St 29414 | 843-763-1529
Kevin Smith, prin. | Fax 763-5955
Other Schools – See Hollywood, Johns Island, Mount Pleasant, North Charleston

---

Academy of Cosmetology | Post-Sec.
5117 Dorchester Rd 29418 | 843-552-3241
Ashley Hall | 700/PK-12
172 Rutledge Ave 29403 | 843-722-4088
Jill Muti, head sch | Fax 720-2868
Bishop England HS | 800/9-12
363 Seven Farms Dr 29492 | 843-849-9599
Patrick Finneran, prin. | Fax 849-9221
Charleston Cosmetology Institute | Post-Sec.
8484 Dorchester Rd 29420 | 843-552-3670
Charleston School of Law | Post-Sec.
PO Box 535 29402 | 843-329-1000
Charleston Southern University | Post-Sec.
9200 University Blvd 29406 | 843-863-7000
College of Charleston | Post-Sec.
66 George St 29424 | 843-805-5507
First Baptist S of Charleston | 500/PK-12
48 Meeting St 29401 | 843-722-6646
Medical University of South Carolina | Post-Sec.
171 Ashley Ave 29425 | 843-792-2300
Porter-Gaud S | 900/1-12
300 Albemarle Rd 29407 | 843-556-3620
D. DuBose Egleston B.S., head sch | Fax 556-7404
The Art Institute of Charleston | Post-Sec.
24 N Market St 29401 | 866-211-0107
The Citadel | Post-Sec.
171 Moultrie St 29409 | 843-225-3294
Trident Technical College | Post-Sec.
PO Box 118067 29423 | 843-574-6111

Cheraw, Chesterfield, Pop. 5,741
Chesterfield County SD
Supt. — See Chesterfield
Cheraw HS | 700/9-12
649 Chesterfield Hwy 29520 | 843-921-1000
Jason Bryant, prin. | Fax 921-1006
Long MS | 500/6-8
1010 W Greene St 29520 | 843-921-1010
Virginia Sorrow, prin. | Fax 921-1017

Northeastern Technical College | Post-Sec.
1201 Chesterfield Hwy 29520 | 843-921-6900

Chesnee, Spartanburg, Pop. 845
Spartanburg SD 2 | 9,400/K-12
3231 Old Furnace Rd 29323 | 864-578-0128
Scott Mercer, supt. | Fax 578-8924
www.spartanburg2.k12.sc.us
Chesnee HS | 600/9-12
795 S Alabama Ave 29323 | 864-461-7318
Thomas Ezell, prin. | Fax 461-4137
Chesnee MS | 500/6-8
805 S Alabama Ave 29323 | 864-461-3900
Rob Hayes, prin. | Fax 461-3950
Rainbow Lake MS | 700/6-8
1951 Riveroak Rd 29323 | 864-253-5700
Greg Lovelace, prin. | Fax 253-5701
Other Schools – See Boiling Springs, Inman

Chester, Chester, Pop. 5,520
Chester County SD | 5,500/PK-12
509 District Office Dr 29706 | 803-385-6122
Angela H. Bain Ph.D., supt. | Fax 581-6965
www.chester.k12.sc.us/
Chester County Career Center | Vo/Tech
1324 J A Cochran Byp 29706 | 803-377-1991
Thomas Barr, dir. | Fax 581-0912
Chester HS | 800/9-12
1330 J A Cochran Byp 29706 | 803-377-3161
Duane Graham Ed.D., prin. | Fax 581-2363
Chester MS | 700/6-8
1014 McCandless Rd 29706 | 803-377-8192
Sheka Houston, prin. | Fax 581-1875
Other Schools – See Great Falls, Richburg

Chesterfield, Chesterfield, Pop. 1,462
Chesterfield County SD | 7,400/PK-12
401 West Blvd 29709 | 843-623-2175
Dr. Harrison Goodwin, supt. | Fax 623-3434
www.chesterfieldschools.org
Chesterfield HS | 500/9-12
401 N Page St 29709 | 843-623-2161
Scott Radkin, prin. | Fax 623-2050
Chesterfield-Ruby MS | 400/6-8
14445 Highway 9 29709 | 843-623-9401
Neil Adams, prin. | Fax 623-9429
Palmetto Learning Center | Alt
116 Edwards Rd 29709 | 843-623-5101
Thomas Brewer, coord. | Fax 623-5105
Other Schools – See Cheraw, Jefferson, Mc Bee, Pageland

Clemson, Pickens, Pop. 13,699

Clemson University | Post-Sec.
105 Sikes Hall 29634 | 864-656-3311

Clinton, Laurens, Pop. 8,368
Laurens County SD 56 | 3,100/PK-12
211 N Broad St Ste B 29325 | 864-833-0800
Dr. David O'Shields, supt. | Fax 833-0804
www.laurens56.k12.sc.us
Clinton HS | 900/9-12
18132 Highway 72 E 29325 | 864-833-0817
Maureen Tiller, prin. | Fax 833-0825
Clinton MS | 700/6-8
800 N Adair St 29325 | 864-833-0807
Brenda Romines, prin. | Fax 833-0810

Presbyterian College | Post-Sec.
503 S Broad St 29325 | 864-833-2820

Clio, Marlboro, Pop. 720
Marlboro County SD
Supt. — See Bennettsville
Marlboro School of Discovery | 200/Alt
PO Box 517 29525 | 843-586-8376
Toma Dees, prin. | Fax 586-9078

Clover, York, Pop. 5,008
Clover SD 2 | 6,900/PK-12
604 Bethel St 29710 | 803-810-8005
Dr. Marc Sosne, supt. | Fax 222-8010
www.clover2.k12.sc.us
Blue Eagle Academy | Alt
300 Clinton Ave 29710 | 803-810-8420
Hezekiah Massey, dir. | Fax 222-8042
Clover HS | 2,000/9-12
1625 Highway 55 E 29710 | 803-810-8200
Rodney Ruth, prin. | Fax 222-8021
Clover MS | 700/6-8
1555 Highway 55 E 29710 | 803-810-8300
Calub Courtwright, prin. | Fax 222-8034
Oakridge MS | 900/6-8
5650 Highway 557 29710 | 803-631-8000
William Largen, prin. | Fax 631-8102

Columbia, Richland, Pop. 126,841
Richland SD 1 | 24,300/PK-12
1616 Richland St 29201 | 803-231-7000
Dr. Craig Witherspoon, supt. | Fax 231-7502
www.richlandone.org/
Alcorn MS | 300/6-8
5125 Fairfield Rd 29203 | 803-735-3439
Sonji Leach, prin. | Fax 735-3487
Columbia HS | 700/9-12
1701 Westchester Dr 29210 | 803-731-8950
Shenequa Coles, prin. | Fax 731-8953
Crayton MS | 1,100/6-8
5000 Clemson Ave 29206 | 803-738-7224
Susan Childs, prin. | Fax 738-7901
Dreher HS | 1,100/9-12
3319 Millwood Ave 29205 | 803-253-7000
Jeanne Stiglbauer, prin. | Fax 253-7007
Eau Claire HS | 600/9-12
4800 Monticello Rd 29203 | 803-735-7600
Neshunda Walters, prin. | Fax 735-7629
Flora HS | 1,300/9-12
1 Falcon Dr 29204 | 803-738-7300
Richard McClure, prin. | Fax 738-7307
Gibbes MS | 300/6-8
500 Summerlea Dr 29203 | 803-343-2942
Ericka Hursey, prin. | Fax 733-3040
Hand MS | 900/6-8
2600 Wheat St 29205 | 803-343-2947
Brian Goins, prin. | Fax 733-6173
Heyward Career & Technology Center | Vo/Tech
3560 Lynhaven Dr 29204 | 803-735-3343
Sherry Rivers, prin. | Fax 691-4253
Johnson HS | 400/9-12
2219 Barhamville Rd 29204 | 803-253-7092
Dr. Veronica Scott, prin. | Fax 253-5713

Keenan HS 700/9-12
361 Pisgah Church Rd 29203 803-714-2500
Alvin Pressley, prin. Fax 714-2593
Olympia Learning Center Alt
621 Bluff Rd 29201 803-400-1650
Nathan White, prin. Fax 400-1700
Perry MS 300/6-8
2600 Barhamville Rd 29204 803-256-6347
Dr. Robin Coletrain, prin. Fax 255-2262
St. Andrews MS 700/6-8
1231 Bluefield Dr 29210 803-731-8910
Derrick Glover, prin. Fax 731-8913
Sanders MS 400/6-8
3455 Pine Belt Rd 29204 803-738-7575
Andrenna Smith, prin. Fax 738-7566
Adult Education Adult
2612 Covenant Rd 29204 803-343-2935
Marva Coates, dir. Fax 212-1453
Other Schools – See Hopkins

Richland SD 2 26,600/PK-12
6831 Brookfield Rd 29206 803-787-1910
Debra Hamm Ph.D., supt. Fax 738-3334
www.richland2.org
Dent MS 1,300/6-8
2721 Decker Blvd 29206 803-699-2750
Tamala Ashford, prin. Fax 699-2754
Longleaf MS 700/6-8
1160 Longreen Pkwy 29229 803-691-4870
Angela Thom, prin. Fax 691-4043
Richland Northeast HS 1,500/9-12
7500 Brookfield Rd 29223 803-699-2800
Dr. Sabrina Suber, prin. Fax 699-3679
Ridge View HS 1,500/9-12
4801 Hard Scrabble Rd 29229 803-699-2999
Dr. Brenda Mack-Foxworth, prin. Fax 699-2888
Spring Valley HS 2,000/9-12
120 Sparkleberry Ln 29229 803-699-3500
Jeff Temoney, prin. Fax 699-3541
Summit Parkway MS 900/6-8
200 Summit Pkwy 29229 803-699-3580
Andrew Barbone, prin. Fax 699-3682
Wright MS 1,100/6-8
2740 Alpine Rd 29223 803-736-8740
Mary Paige Wylie, prin. Fax 736-8798
Rogers Adult Continuing Center Adult
750 Old Clemson Rd 29229 803-736-8787
Bobby Cunningham, prin. Fax 736-8785
Other Schools – See Blythewood

SD Five of Lexington & Richland Counties
Supt. — See Irmo
Irmo HS 1,600/9-12
6671 Saint Andrews Rd 29212 803-476-3000
David Riegel, prin. Fax 476-3020
Irmo MS 900/6-8
6051 Wescott Rd 29212 803-476-3600
Robert Jackson, prin. Fax 476-3620

Allen University Post-Sec.
1530 Harden St 29204 803-376-5700
Baptist Medical Center Post-Sec.
1519 Marion St 29201 803-771-5042
Benedict College Post-Sec.
1600 Harden St 29204 803-253-5000
Cardinal Newman HS 400/7-12
2945 Alpine Rd 29223 803-888-1631
Jacquie Kasprowski, prin. Fax 782-9314
Centura College Post-Sec.
7500 Two Notch Rd 29223 803-754-7544
Columbia Biblical Seminary Post-Sec.
7435 Monticello Rd 29203 800-777-2227
Columbia College Post-Sec.
1301 Columbia College Dr 29203 800-277-1301
Columbia International University Post-Sec.
7435 Monticello Rd 29203 803-754-4100
Covenant Classical Christian S 100/K-12
3120 Covenant Rd 29204 803-787-0225
Kevin Bolen, admin. Fax 782-7309
ECPI University Post-Sec.
250 Berryhill Rd Ste 300 29210 803-772-3333
Fortis College Post-Sec.
246 Stoneridge Dr Ste 101 29210 803-678-4800
Hammond S 900/PK-12
854 Galway Ln 29209 803-776-0295
Christopher Angel, prin. Fax 776-0122
Heathwood Hall Episcopal S 500/PK-12
3000 S Beltline Blvd 29201 803-765-2309
Chris Hinchey, head sch Fax 748-4755
Kenneth Shuler's School of Cosmetology Post-Sec.
449 Saint Andrews Rd 29210 803-772-6042
Lippen S 500/PK-12
7401 Monticello Rd 29203 803-807-4100
Chip Jones, hdmstr. Fax 744-1387
Lutheran Theological Southern Seminary Post-Sec.
4201 N Main St 29203 803-786-5150
Midlands Technical College Post-Sec.
PO Box 2408 29202 803-738-8324
National Ctr for Credibility Assessment Post-Sec.
7540 Pickens Ave 29207 803-751-9100
Remington College Columbia Post-Sec.
607 Bush River Rd 29210 803-214-9000
Southeastern Institute Post-Sec.
1420 Colonial Life Blvd #80 29210 803-798-8800
South University Post-Sec.
9 Science Ct 29203 803-799-9082
Strayer University Post-Sec.
200 Center Point Cir # 300 29210 803-750-2500
University of South Carolina 29208 Post-Sec.
803-777-7700
Virginia College Post-Sec.
7201 Two Notch Rd 29223 803-509-7100
W.L. Bonner College Post-Sec.
4430 Argent Ct 29203 803-754-3950

Conway, Horry, Pop. 16,872
Horry County SD 41,200/PK-12
PO Box 260005 29528 843-488-6700
Dr. Rick Maxey, supt. Fax 488-6722
www.horrycountyschools.net
Academy for Technology and Academics Vo/Tech
5639 Highway 701 N 29526 843-488-6600
Jayson Powers, prin. Fax 488-6601
Black Water MS 800/6-8
900 E Cox Ferry Rd 29526 843-903-8440
Candace Lane, prin. Fax 903-8441
Conway HS 1,500/9-12
2301 Church St 29526 843-488-0662
Lee James, prin. Fax 488-0686
Conway MS 600/6-8
1104 Elm St 29526 843-488-6040
Regina Treadwell-Pertell, prin. Fax 488-0611
Early College HS 400/9-12
PO Box 261966 29528 843-349-3131
Kandi Fleming-Jones, dir. Fax 347-2498
Horry County Education Center Alt
2694 Highway 905 29526 843-488-7500
Maurice Murphy, prin. Fax 488-7501
Scholars Academy 9-12
104 Chanticleer Dr E 29528 843-349-4117
Norman McQueen, prin. Fax 347-2869
Whittemore Park MS 700/6-8
1808 Rhue St 29527 843-488-0669
Quintina Livingston, prin. Fax 488-0665
Other Schools – See Aynor, Galivants Ferry, Green Sea, Little River, Loris, Murrells Inlet, Myrtle Beach

---

Coastal Carolina University Post-Sec.
PO Box 261954 29528 843-347-3161
Conway Christian S 200/PK-12
PO Box 1245 29528 843-365-2005
Horry-Georgetown Technical College Post-Sec.
PO Box 261966 29528 843-347-3186
Miller-Motte Technical College Post-Sec.
2451 E Highway 501 29526 843-591-1100

Cope, Orangeburg, Pop. 75
Orangeburg County Consolidated SD 4 4,000/PK-12
PO Box 68 29038 803-534-8081
Dr. Tim Newman, supt. Fax 531-5614
www.ocsd4sc.net
Cope Area Career Center Vo/Tech
6052 Slab Landing Rd 29038 803-534-7661
Sandra Jameson, prin. Fax 535-4301
STAR Center for Learning 100/Alt
6064 Slab Landing Rd 29038 803-533-1783
Belinda Johnson, dir. Fax 533-1785
Other Schools – See Branchville, Cordova, Neeses

Cordova, Orangeburg, Pop. 167
Orangeburg County Consolidated SD 4
Supt. — See Cope
Carver-Edisto MS 600/6-8
PO Box 65 29039 803-534-3554
Jeannie Monson, prin. Fax 535-0937
Edisto HS 800/9-12
PO Box 101 29039 803-536-1553
Dr. Shannon Gibson, prin. Fax 531-5615

Cowpens, Spartanburg, Pop. 2,133
Spartanburg SD 3
Supt. — See Glendale
Cowpens MS 500/6-8
150 Foster St 29330 864-279-6400
Cynthia James, prin. Fax 279-6410

Cross, Berkeley
Berkeley County SD
Supt. — See Moncks Corner
Cross HS 300/7-12
1293 Old Highway 6 29436 843-899-8900
Senfronia Smith, prin. Fax 899-8910

Dalzell, Sumter, Pop. 2,975
Sumter SD
Supt. — See Sumter
Hillcrest MS 400/6-8
4355 Peach Orchard Rd 29040 803-499-3341
Tarsha Staggers, prin. Fax 499-3353

Darlington, Darlington, Pop. 6,253
Darlington County SD 10,200/PK-12
PO Box 1117 29540 843-398-5100
Dr. Eddie Ingram, supt. Fax 398-5198
www.darlington.k12.sc.us
Darlington Co. Institute of Technology Vo/Tech
160 Pinedale Dr 29532 843-398-4796
Robbie Smith, dir. Fax 395-1044
Darlington County Intervention S Alt
100 Magnolia St 29532 843-393-5617
Zenobia Edwards, dir. Fax 398-2640
Darlington HS 1,100/9-12
525 Spring St 29532 843-398-2730
Dr. Gregory Harrison, prin. Fax 398-2739
Darlington MS 1,000/6-8
150 Pinedale Dr 29532 843-398-5088
Eddie Shuler, prin. Fax 398-3390
Mayo HS for Math Science & Technology 400/9-12
405 Chestnut St 29532 843-398-2650
Arlene Wallace, prin. Fax 398-2647
Other Schools – See Hartsville, Lamar

Trinity-Byrnes Collegiate S 100/7-12
5001 Hoffmeyer Rd 29532 843-395-9124
Ed Hoffman, head sch Fax 395-6495

Denmark, Bamberg, Pop. 3,519
Bamberg SD 2 700/PK-12
62 Holly Ave 29042 803-793-3346
Dr. Thelma Sojourner, supt. Fax 793-2006
www.denmarkolarschooldistrict2.org
Denmark-Olar HS 200/9-12
197 Viking Cir 29042 803-793-3307
Mickey Pringle, prin. Fax 793-2004
Denmark-Olar MS 100/6-8
45 Green St 29042 803-793-3383
Daryl Brockington, prin. Fax 793-2038

Denmark Technical College Post-Sec.
PO Box 327 29042 803-793-5176
Voorhees College Post-Sec.
PO Box 678 29042 803-780-1234

Dillon, Dillon, Pop. 6,694
Area Vocational Schools
Supt. — None
Dillon County Technology Center Vo/Tech
PO Box 1130 29536 843-774-5143
Jerry Strickland, prin. Fax 774-7711

Dillon SD Four 4,100/PK-12
1738 Highway 301 N 29536 843-774-1200
D. Ray Rogers, supt. Fax 774-1203
www.dillon.k12.sc.us
Dillon HS 900/9-12
1730 Highway 301 N 29536 843-774-1230
Dr. Shawn Johnson, prin. Fax 774-1234
Dillon MS 500/6-8
1803 Joan Dr 29536 843-774-1212
Rodney Cook, prin. Fax 841-3616
Other Schools – See Lake View

Dillon Christian S 300/K-12
PO Box 151 29536 843-841-1000

Dorchester, Dorchester
Area Vocational Schools
Supt. — None
Dorchester Co. Career & Technology Ctr Vo/Tech
507 Schoolhouse Rd 29437 843-563-2361
James Villeponteaux, prin. Fax 563-9038
Other Schools – See Blackville SC, Dillon SC, Manning SC, Ridgeland SC, Williamston SC

Dorchester SD 4
Supt. — See Saint George
Harleyville-Ridgeville MS 200/6-8
1650 E Main St 29437 843-462-2470
Shannon Stephens, admin. Fax 462-2479
Woodland HS 600/9-12
4128 Highway 78 29437 843-563-5956
Bernard Utsey, prin. Fax 563-5997

Due West, Abbeville, Pop. 1,226
Abbeville County SD
Supt. — See Abbeville
Dixie HS 400/8-12
1 Haynes St 29639 864-379-2186
Lori Brownlee-Brewton, prin. Fax 379-8187

Erskine College Post-Sec.
PO Box 338 29639 864-379-2131

Duncan, Spartanburg, Pop. 3,086
Spartanburg SD 5 7,600/K-12
PO Box 307 29334 864-949-2350
Dr. Scott Turner, supt. Fax 439-0051
www.spart5.net
Byrnes Freshman Academy 600/9-9
PO Box 277 29334 864-949-2320
Pat Monteith, prin. Fax 949-2328
Byrnes HS 1,600/10-12
PO Box 187 29334 864-949-2355
Dr. Jeff Rogers, prin. Fax 949-2362
Florence Chapel MS 600/7-8
290 Shoals Rd 29334 864-949-2310
Tammy White, prin. Fax 949-2315
Other Schools – See Lyman

Easley, Pickens, Pop. 19,670
Pickens County SD 15,800/K-12
1348 Griffin Mill Rd 29640 864-397-1000
Dr. Danny Merck, supt. Fax 850-5205
www.pickens.k12.sc.us
Dacusville MS 400/6-8
899 Thomas Mill Rd 29640 864-397-3525
Wanda Tharpe, prin. Fax 850-2094
Easley HS 1,700/9-12
154 Green Wave Blvd 29642 864-397-3100
Gary Culler, prin. Fax 855-8194
Gettys MS 1,400/6-8
510 S Pendleton St 29640 864-397-3900
Michael Cory, prin. Fax 855-1268
Adult Learning Center Adult
106 Glazner St 29640 864-397-3825
Dr. Mary Gaston, dir. Fax 850-8116
Other Schools – See Central, Liberty, Pickens

Ehrhardt, Bamberg, Pop. 541

Jackson Academy 100/PK-12
7054 Broxton Bridge 29081 803-245-4810
Jamee Barnes, head sch Fax 245-5460

Elgin, Kershaw, Pop. 1,286
Kershaw County SD
Supt. — See Camden
Stover MS 700/6-8
1649 Smyrna Rd 29045 803-438-7414
Mike Garity, prin. Fax 438-7014

Estill, Hampton, Pop. 2,023
Hampton SD 2 900/PK-12
PO Box 1028 29918 803-625-5000
Dr. Beverly Gurley, supt. Fax 625-2573
www.hampton2.k12.sc.us
Estill HS 300/9-12
PO Box 757 29918 803-625-5100
Kamar Lee, prin. Fax 625-4695
Estill MS 200/6-8
PO Box 817 29918 803-625-5200
Kamar Lee, prin. Fax 625-3588

Henry Academy 300/PK-12
8766 Savannah Hwy 29918 803-625-2440
Kim Miller, admin. Fax 625-3110

Fairfax, Allendale, Pop. 2,023
Allendale County SD 900/PK-12
3249 Allendale Fairfax Hwy 29827 803-584-4603
Leila Williams, supt. Fax 584-5303
www.acs.k12.sc.us
Allendale-Fairfax HS 400/9-12
3581 Allendale Fairfax Hwy 29827 803-584-2311
Senaca Baines, prin. Fax 584-1787
Allendale-Fairfax MS 200/7-8
3581 Allendale Fairfax Hwy 29827 803-584-3489
Darlene Hall, prin. Fax 584-5331

Florence, Florence, Pop. 36,588
Florence County SD One 17,500/PK-12
319 S Dargan St 29506 843-673-1106
Randy Bridges, supt. Fax 292-1003
www.fsd1.org
Beck Learning Center 7-12
1001 W Sumter St 29501 843-679-6768
Dr. Floyd Creech, dir.
Florence Career Ctr Vo/Tech
126 E Howe Springs Rd 29505 843-664-8465
Alphonso Bradley, dir. Fax 413-4688
Rush Academy Alt
1201 E Ashby Rd 29506 843-664-8911
Cedrick Kennedy, prin.
Sneed MS 1,000/7-8
1102 S Ebenezer Rd 29501 843-673-1199
Hayley Cagle, prin. Fax 679-6890
South Florence HS 1,600/9-12
3200 S Irby St 29505 843-664-8190
Carol Hill, prin. Fax 664-8184
Southside MS 900/7-8
200 E Howe Springs Rd 29505 843-664-8467
Craig Washington, prin. Fax 673-5766
West Florence HS 1,700/9-12
221 N Beltline Dr 29501 843-664-8472
Pamela Quick, prin. Fax 664-8475
Williams MS 700/7-8
1119 N Irby St 29501 843-664-8162
Pam Johnson, prin. Fax 664-8178
Wilson HS 1,100/9-12
1411 E Old Marion Hwy 29506 843-664-8440
Dr. Eric Robinson, prin. Fax 664-8176
Poynor Adult and Community Education Ctr Adult
301 S Dargan St 29506 843-664-8152
Til Morisey, dir. Fax 664-8155

Florence Christian S 700/PK-12
2308 S Irby St 29505 843-662-0454
Florence-Darlington Technical College Post-Sec.
PO Box 100548 29502 843-661-8324
Francis Marion University Post-Sec.
PO Box 100547 29502 843-661-1362
King's Academy 300/PK-12
1015 S Ebenezer Rd 29501 843-661-7464
David Wolff, head sch Fax 661-7647
Maranatha Christian S 300/PK-12
2624 W Palmetto St 29501 843-665-6395
McLeod Regional Medical Center Post-Sec.
555 E Cheves St 29506 843-667-2297
Virgina College Post-Sec.
2400 David H McLeod Blvd 29501 843-407-2200

Fort Mill, York, Pop. 10,605
Fort Mill SD 11,400/K-12
2233 Deerfield Dr 29715 803-548-2527
James Epps Ph.D., supt. Fax 547-4696
www.fortmillschools.org
Fort Mill HS 1,800/9-12
215 Highway 21 Byp 29715 803-548-1900
Dee Christopher, prin. Fax 548-1911
Fort Mill MS 600/6-8
200 Springfield Pkwy 29715 803-547-5553
Greg Norton, prin. Fax 548-2911
Nation Ford HS 1,700/9-12
1400 A O Jones Blvd 29715 803-835-0000
Jason Johns, prin. Fax 835-0010
Springfield MS 700/6-8
1711 Springfield Pkwy 29715 803-548-8199
Keith Griffin, prin. Fax 547-1013
Other Schools – See Tega Cay

Gaffney, Cherokee, Pop. 12,231
Cherokee County SD 9,100/PK-12
PO Box 460 29342 864-206-2201
Dr. Quincie Moore, supt. Fax 902-3541
www.cherokee1.k12.sc.us
Cherokee Technology Center Vo/Tech
3206 Cherokee Ave 29340 864-489-3191
Lane Carter, prin. Fax 487-1287
Copeland Community Learning Center Alt
243 Allison Dr 29341 864-206-6992
LaTunya Means, prin. Fax 487-1238
Ewing MS 400/6-8
171 E Junior High Rd 29340 864-206-2449
Dr. Denise Wooten, prin. Fax 489-8534
Gaffney HS 2,000/9-12
149 Twin Lake Rd 29341 864-902-3600
Dr. RaaShad Fitzpatrick, prin. Fax 902-3628
Gaffney MS 700/6-8
805 E Frederick St 29340 864-206-6129
Dr. Shirley Sealy, prin. Fax 902-3637
Granard MS 600/6-8
815 W Rutledge Ave 29341 864-206-2302
Dr. Mark Bunch, prin. Fax 488-1553
Adult & Community Education Adult
243 Allison Dr 29341 864-487-7152
Lisa Hannon, prin. Fax 487-1260
Other Schools – See Blacksburg

Limestone College Post-Sec.
1115 College Dr 29340 864-489-7151

Galivants Ferry, Horry
Horry County SD
Supt. — See Conway
Aynor MS 600/6-8
400 Frye Rd 29544 843-358-6000
Robbie Watkins, prin. Fax 358-5065

Gaston, Lexington, Pop. 1,599
Lexington County SD 4
Supt. — See Swansea
Sandhills MS 500/7-8
582 Meadowfield Rd 29053 803-490-7005
Patricia Carter, prin.

Georgetown, Georgetown, Pop. 9,055
Georgetown County SD 9,700/PK-12
2018 Church St 29440 843-436-7000
Dr. Randy Dozier, supt. Fax 436-7171
www.gcsd.k12.sc.us
Georgetown HS 900/9-12
2500 Anthuan Maybank St 29440 843-546-8516
Craig Evans, prin. Fax 546-8521
Georgetown MS 900/6-8
2400 Anthuan Maybank St 29440 843-527-4495
Seth Hillman, prin. Fax 527-2290
Howard Adult Center & Optional S Adult
500 S Kaminski St 29440 843-546-0219
James Ferdon, dir. Fax 527-0236
Other Schools – See Andrews, Hemingway, Pawleys Island

Gilbert, Lexington, Pop. 564
Lexington County SD 1
Supt. — See Lexington
Gilbert HS 900/9-12
840 Main St 29054 803-821-1900
Ann O'Cain, prin. Fax 821-1903
Gilbert MS 700/6-8
120 Rikard Cir 29054 803-821-1700
Dr. Benji Ricard, prin. Fax 821-1703

Glendale, Spartanburg, Pop. 305
Spartanburg SD 3 2,900/PK-12
PO Box 267 29346 864-279-6000
Kenny Blackwood, supt. Fax 279-6010
www.spartanburg3.org/
Other Schools – See Cowpens, Pacolet, Spartanburg

Goose Creek, Berkeley, Pop. 34,642
Berkeley County SD
Supt. — See Moncks Corner
Goose Creek HS 1,800/9-12
1137 Red Bank Rd 29445 843-553-5300
Jimmy Huskey, prin. Fax 820-4064
Marrington MS of the Arts 400/6-8
109 Gearing St 29445 843-572-0313
Dara Harrop, prin. Fax 820-4063
Sedgefield MS 1,000/6-8
131 Charles B Gibson Blvd 29445 843-797-2620
Shameka Washington, prin. Fax 820-5401
Stratford HS 1,800/9-12
951 Crowfield Blvd 29445 843-820-4000
Heather Taylor, prin. Fax 820-4042
Westview MS 900/6-8
101 Westview Dr 29445 843-572-1700
Sharon Perry M.Ed., prin. Fax 820-3728

Graniteville, Aiken, Pop. 2,553
Aiken County SD
Supt. — See Aiken
Byrd Learning Center Alt
1 Willis Cir 29829 803-663-4920
Pat Keating, admin. Fax 663-4921
Leavelle-McCampbell MS 500/6-8
82 Canal St 29829 803-663-4300
Michelle Padgett, prin. Fax 663-4302
Midland Valley HS 1,300/9-12
227 Mustang Dr 29829 803-593-7100
Carl White, prin. Fax 593-7106
Aiken County Adult Education Adult
1 Willis Cir 29829 – Pat Keating, dir. 803-663-4920

Great Falls, Chester, Pop. 1,942
Chester County SD
Supt. — See Chester
Great Falls HS 300/9-12
411 Sunset Ave 29055 803-482-2210
Brenda Fort, prin. Fax 482-4896
Great Falls MS 200/6-8
409 Sunset Ave 29055 803-482-2220
Brenda Fort, prin. Fax 482-6025

Greeleyville, Williamsburg, Pop. 428
Williamsburg County SD
Supt. — See Kingstree
Murray HS 300/9-12
222 C E Murray Blvd 29056 843-426-2121
Allen Keels, prin. Fax 426-2151
Murray MS 100/6-8
222A C E Murray Blvd 29056 843-426-2121
Valeria Brown, prin. Fax 426-2151

Green Sea, Horry
Horry County SD
Supt. — See Conway
Green Sea-Floyds JSHS 600/6-12
4990 Tulip Grove Rd 29545 843-392-3131
Dr. Andrea Pridgen, prin. Fax 392-9805

Greenville, Greenville, Pop. 57,469
Anderson SD 1
Supt. — See Williamston
Powdersville HS 800/9-12
145 Hood Rd 29611 864-312-5641
Dr. Robby Roach, prin. Fax 312-5640
Powdersville MS 600/6-8
135 Hood Rd 29611 864-269-1821
Todd Binnicker, prin. Fax 269-0795

Greenville County SD 75,900/PK-12
PO Box 2848 29602 864-355-3100
W. Burke Royster, supt. Fax 241-4195
www.greenville.k12.sc.us/
Beck Academy 1,100/6-8
901 Woodruff Rd 29607 864-355-1400
Jennifer Meisten, prin. Fax 355-1490
Berea HS 1,000/9-12
201 Burdine Dr 29617 864-355-1600
Mike Noel, prin. Fax 355-1625
Berea MS 700/6-8
151 Berea Middle School Rd 29617 864-355-1700
Robin Mill, prin. Fax 355-1777
Carolina Academy 700/9-12
2725 Anderson Rd 29611 864-355-2300
Michael Delaney, prin. Fax 355-2375
Donaldson Career Center Vo/Tech
100 Vocational Dr 29605 864-355-4650
Andy Laye, prin. Fax 355-4683
Enoree Career Center Vo/Tech
108 Scalybark Rd 29617 864-355-7400
Brana Myers, prin. Fax 355-7407
Fine Arts Center 400/11-12
102 Pine Knoll Dr 29609 864-355-2550
Dr. Roy Fluhrer, prin. Fax 355-2579
Fisher MS 6-8
700 Millennium Blvd 29607 864-452-0800
Jane Garraux, prin. Fax 452-0890
Golden Strip Career Ctr Vo/Tech
1120 E Butler Rd 29607 864-355-1050
J.F. Lucas, prin. Fax 355-1058
Greenville Early College 6-12
225 S Pleasantburg Dr 29607 864-355-7560
Dr. Tiffany Estes, prin. Fax 355-9815
Greenville High Academy 1,400/9-12
1 Vardry St 29601 864-355-5500
Jason Warren, prin. Fax 355-5492
Greenville Middle Academy 800/6-8
339 Lowndes Ave 29607 864-355-5600
Nicky Andrews, prin. Fax 355-5682
Hampton HS 1,600/9-12
100 Pine Knoll Dr 29609 864-355-0100
Eric Williams, prin. Fax 355-0194
High School Alternative Program 100/Alt
206 Wilkins St 29605 864-355-5180
Stuart Holcombe, admin. Fax 355-5185
Hughes Academy 900/6-8
122 Deoyley Ave 29605 864-355-6200
Andrew Hooker, prin. Fax 355-6275
Lakeview MS 500/6-8
3801 Old Buncombe Rd 29617 864-355-6400
LaTonya Copeland, prin. Fax 355-6416
League Academy 800/6-8
125 Twin Lake Rd 29609 864-355-8100
Mary Leslie Anderson, prin. Fax 355-8160
Mann Academy 1,700/9-12
160 Fairforest Way 29607 864-355-6300
Charles Mayfield, prin. Fax 355-6329
Sevier MS 700/6-8
1000 Piedmont Park Rd 29609 864-355-8200
Karen Kapp, prin. Fax 355-8255
Southside HS 800/9-12
6630 Frontage Rd 29605 864-355-8700
Bradley Griffith, prin. Fax 355-8798
Star Academy - Donaldson Alt
100 Vocational Dr 29605 864-355-4669
Shakeria McCullough, admin. Fax 355-4683
Star Academy - Enoree Vo/Tech
108 Scalybark Rd 29617 864-355-7401
Shakeria McCullough, dir. Fax 355-7404
Tanglewood MS 600/6-8
44 Merriwoods Dr 29611 864-355-4500
William Price, prin. Fax 355-4512
Adult Education/Lifelong Learning Adult
206 Wilkins St 29605 864-355-6088
Dr. Chuck Welch, prin. Fax 355-6077
Other Schools – See Greer, Mauldin, Piedmont, Simpsonville, Taylors, Travelers Rest

State Supported Schools
Supt. — None
Governors S for the Arts & Humanities 200/9-12
15 University St 29601 864-282-3777
Julie Allen, prin. Fax 241-1235

Academy of Hair Technology Post-Sec.
3715 E North St Ste F 29615 864-322-0300
Bob Jones University Post-Sec.
1700 Wade Hampton Blvd 29614 864-242-5100
Christ Church Episcopal S 1,000/K-12
245 Cavalier Dr 29607 864-299-1522
Dr. Leonard Kupersmith, hdmstr. Fax 299-8861
ECPI University Post-Sec.
1001 Keys Dr # 100 29615 864-288-2828
Furman University Post-Sec.
3300 Poinsett Hwy 29613 864-294-2000
Greenville Technical College Post-Sec.
PO Box 5616 29606 864-250-8000
Hampton Park Christian S 500/PK-12
875 State Park Rd 29609 864-233-0556
Dr. Kevin Priest, admin. Fax 235-5621
Jones Academy 1,300/PK-12
1700 Wade Hampton Blvd 29614 864-770-1395
St. Joseph's HS 400/9-12
100 Saint Josephs Dr 29607 864-234-9009
Keith Kiser, hdmstr. Fax 234-5516
Shannon Forest Christian S 400/PK-12
829 Garlington Rd 29615 864-678-5107
Craig Bouvier, head sch Fax 281-9372
Strayer University Post-Sec.
555 N Pleasantburg Dr # 300 29607 864-250-7000
University of SC School of Medicine Post-Sec.
607 Grove Rd 29605 864-455-7992
Virginia College Post-Sec.
78 Global Dr Ste 200 29607 864-679-4900

Greenwood, Greenwood, Pop. 22,959
Greenwood SD 50 9,200/PK-12
PO Box 248 29648 864-941-5400
Dr. Darrell Johnson, supt. Fax 941-5427
www.gwd50.org
Brewer MS 700/6-8
1000 Emerald Rd 29646 864-941-5500
Corey Collington, prin. Fax 941-5527
Emerald HS 900/9-12
150 Bypass 225 29646 864-941-5730
Brad Nickles, prin. Fax 941-3487
Genesis Education Center Alt
400 Glenwood St 29649 864-941-5460
Damian Coleman, prin.
Greenwood HS 1,600/9-12
1816 Cokesbury Rd 29649 864-941-5600
Chad Evans, prin. Fax 941-5498
Northside MS 700/6-8
431 Deadfall Rd W 29649 864-941-5780
Cyndi Storer, prin. Fax 941-3434
Russell Technology Center Vo/Tech
601 Northside Dr E 29649 864-941-5750
Bonnie Corbitt, prin. Fax 941-5375
Westview MS 700/6-8
1410 W Alexander Rd 29646 864-229-4301
Dr. Steve Glenn, prin. Fax 229-4827

Charzanne Beauty College Post-Sec.
1549 Highway 72 E 29649 864-223-7321
Greenwood Christian S 300/PK-12
2026 Woodlawn Rd 29649 864-229-2427
Lander University Post-Sec.
320 Stanley Ave 29649 864-388-8000

Palmetto Christian Academy of Greenwood 100/PK-12
308 Deadfall Rd W 29649 864-223-0391
Joan Gore, prin. Fax 396-5316
Piedmont Technical College Post-Sec.
PO Box 1467 29648 864-941-8324

Greer, Greenville, Pop. 25,060
Greenville County SD
Supt. — See Greenville
Blue Ridge HS 1,200/8-12
2151 Fews Chapel Rd 29651 864-355-1800
Reena Watson, prin. Fax 355-1821
Blue Ridge MS 1,000/6-8
2423 E Tyger Bridge Rd 29651 864-355-1900
Rebecca Greene, prin. Fax 355-1966
Bonds Career Center Vo/Tech
505 N Main St 29650 864-355-8080
Mike Parris, prin. Fax 355-8264
Greer HS 1,100/9-12
3000 E Gap Creek Rd 29651 864-355-5700
Justin Ludley, prin. Fax 355-5725
Greer MS 1,000/6-8
3032 E Gap Creek Rd 29651 864-355-5800
Daniel Bruce, prin. Fax 355-5880
Riverside HS 1,600/9-12
794 Hammett Bridge Rd 29650 864-355-7800
Andy Crowley, prin. Fax 355-7898
Riverside MS 1,200/6-8
615 Hammett Bridge Rd 29650 864-355-7900
Kate Malone, prin. Fax 355-7918

Hanahan, Berkeley, Pop. 17,513
Berkeley County SD
Supt. — See Moncks Corner
Hanahan HS 1,000/9-12
6015 Murray Dr 29410 843-820-3710
Ric Raycroft, prin. Fax 820-3716
Hanahan MS 900/5-8
5815 Murray Dr 29410 843-820-3800
Robin Rogers, prin. Fax 820-3804
Fishburne Educational Center Adult
6215 Murray Dr 29410 843-820-3742
Dr. Paulette Walker, coord. Fax 820-3826

Hardeeville, Jasper, Pop. 2,902
Jasper County SD
Supt. — See Ridgeland
Hardeeville-Ridgeland MS 300/6-8
150 Hurricane Vly 29927 843-310-1898
Eric Jeffcoat, prin. Fax 784-2167

Harleyville, Dorchester, Pop. 670
Dorchester SD 4
Supt. — See Saint George
Odyssey Educational Center Alt
145 Hill St 29448 843-462-2270
Catherine Yates, prin. Fax 462-2275

Hartsville, Darlington, Pop. 7,682
Darlington County SD
Supt. — See Darlington
Hartsville HS 1,200/9-12
701 Lewellyn Ave 29550 843-383-3700
Dr. Charlie Burry, prin. Fax 857-3715
Hartsville MS 1,200/6-8
1427 14th St 29550 843-857-3000
Brian Hickman, prin. Fax 857-4510

State Supported Schools
Supt. — None
Governers S of Science/Math 200/11-12
401 Railroad Ave 29550 843-383-3900
Dr. Murray Brockman, pres. Fax 383-3903

Coker College Post-Sec.
300 E College Ave 29550 843-383-8000

Hemingway, Williamsburg, Pop. 449
Georgetown County SD
Supt. — See Georgetown
Carvers Bay HS 400/9-12
13002 Choppee Rd 29554 843-545-5837
Richard Neal, prin. Fax 558-6927
Carvers Bay MS 300/6-8
13000 Choppee Rd 29554 843-545-0918
Comeletia Pyatt, prin. Fax 558-6937

Williamsburg County SD
Supt. — See Kingstree
Hemingway Career and Technology Center Vo/Tech
1593 Hemingway Hwy 29554 843-558-5813
Torrance Wilson, admin. Fax 558-5991
Hemingway HS 400/9-12
402 S Main St 29554 843-558-9413
Glen Kennedy, prin. Fax 558-9335
Hemingway M.B. Lee MS 200/6-8
400 S Main St 29554 843-558-2721
Delaney Frierson, prin. Fax 558-0792

Hilton Head Island, Beaufort, Pop. 36,811
Beaufort County SD
Supt. — See Beaufort
Hilton Head Island HS 1,300/9-12
70 Wilborn Rd 29926 843-689-4800
Elizabeth O'Nan, prin. Fax 689-4947
Hilton Head Island MS 1,000/6-8
55 Wilborn Rd 29926 843-689-4500
Neodria Brown, prin. Fax 689-4600

Heritage Academy 100/6-12
11 New Orleans Rd 29928 866-925-5528
Hilton Head Christian Academy 400/PK-12
55 Gardner Dr 29926 843-681-2878
Hilton Head Preparatory S 400/PK-12
8 Fox Grape Rd 29928 843-671-2286
Jon Hopman, hdmstr. Fax 671-7624

Holly Hill, Orangeburg, Pop. 1,261
Orangeburg County Consolidated SD 3 3,000/PK-12
PO Box 98 29059 803-496-3288
Dr. Jesulon Gibbs-Brown, supt. Fax 496-5850
www.obg3.k12.sc.us
Holly Hill-Roberts MS 500/6-8
PO Box 879 29059 803-496-3818
Cardacia Green, prin. Fax 496-7584

Other Schools – See Santee

Holly Hill Academy 300/K-12
PO Box 757 29059 803-496-3243

Hollywood, Charleston, Pop. 4,680
Charleston County SD
Supt. — See Charleston
Baptist Hill HS 400/6-12
5117 Baptist Hill Rd 29449 843-889-2276
Vanessa Brown, prin. Fax 889-2101

Honea Path, Anderson, Pop. 3,518
Anderson SD 2 3,600/PK-12
10990 Belton Honea Path Hwy 29654 864-369-7364
Dr. Richard Rosenberger, supt. Fax 369-4006
www.anderson2.k12.sc.us
Belton-Honea Path HS 1,100/9-12
11000 Belton Honea Path Hwy 29654 864-369-7382
Lester McCall, prin. Fax 369-4011
Honea Path MS 300/6-8
107 Brock Ave 29654 864-369-7641
Dr. John Snead, prin. Fax 369-4034
Other Schools – See Belton

Hopkins, Richland, Pop. 2,838
Richland SD 1
Supt. — See Columbia
Hopkins MS 500/6-8
1601 Clarkson Rd 29061 803-695-3331
Bobbie Hartwell, prin. Fax 695-3320
Lower Richland HS 1,200/9-12
2615 Lower Richland Blvd 29061 803-695-3000
Rose Pelzer, prin. Fax 695-3062
Southeast MS 500/6-8
731 Horrell Hill Rd 29061 803-695-5700
Inger Ferguson, prin. Fax 695-5703

Indian Land, Lancaster
Lancaster County SD
Supt. — See Lancaster
Indian Land HS 800/9-12
8063 River Rd, 803-547-7571
David Shamble, prin. Fax 547-7366
Indian Land MS 700/6-8
8361 Charlotte Hwy, 803-578-2500
Chris Thorpe, prin. Fax 578-2549

Inman, Spartanburg, Pop. 2,273
Spartanburg SD 1
Supt. — See Campobello
Chapman HS 900/9-12
PO Box 389 29349 864-472-2836
Ty Dawkins, prin. Fax 472-0914
Mabry MS 400/7-8
35 Oakland Ave 29349 864-472-8402
Shelley Brown, prin. Fax 472-7438
Swofford Career Center Vo/Tech
5620 Highway 11 29349 864-592-2790
Scott Simpkins, dir. Fax 592-1469

Spartanburg SD 2
Supt. — See Chesnee
Boiling Springs MS 1,100/6-8
4801 Highway 9 29349 864-578-5954
Penny Atkinson, prin. Fax 599-5489

Irmo, Richland, Pop. 10,848
SD Five of Lexington & Richland Counties 16,300/PK-12
1020 Dutch Fork Rd 29063 803-476-8000
Dr. Stephen Hefner, supt. Fax 476-8217
www.lexrich5.org/
Dutch Fork HS 1,900/9-12
1400 Old Tamah Rd 29063 803-476-3300
Dr. Greg Owings, prin. Fax 476-3320
Dutch Fork MS 1,100/7-8
1528 Old Tamah Rd 29063 803-476-4800
Dr. Gerald Gary, prin. Fax 476-4820
Other Schools – See Chapin, Columbia

Iva, Anderson, Pop. 1,209
Anderson SD 3 2,600/PK-12
PO Box 118 29655 864-348-6196
Kathy Hipp, supt. Fax 348-6198
www.anderson3.k12.sc.us
Crescent HS 800/9-12
9104 Highway 81 S 29655 864-352-6175
Barry Jacks, prin. Fax 352-2308
Other Schools – See Anderson, Starr

Jackson, Aiken, Pop. 1,680
Aiken County SD
Supt. — See Aiken
Jackson MS 300/6-8
18731 Atomic Rd 29831 803-279-3525
Jason Holt, prin. Fax 471-2202

Jefferson, Chesterfield, Pop. 722
Chesterfield County SD
Supt. — See Chesterfield
New Heights MS 500/6-8
5738 Highway 151 29718 843-658-6830
Dr. Nikki Miller, prin. Fax 658-6812

Johns Island, Charleston
Charleston County SD
Supt. — See Charleston
Haut Gap MS 500/5-8
1861 Bohicket Rd 29455 843-559-6418
Travis Benintendo, prin. Fax 559-6439
St. Johns HS 300/9-12
1518 Main Rd 29455 843-559-6400
Andre Dukes, prin. Fax 559-6409

Charleston Collegiate S 200/PK-12
2024 Academy Rd 29455 843-559-5506
Hacker Burr, head sch Fax 559-6172

Johnsonville, Florence, Pop. 1,455
Florence County SD Five 1,400/PK-12
PO Box 98 29555 843-386-2358
Robert Smiley, supt. Fax 386-3139
www.flo5.k12.sc.us
Johnsonville HS 400/9-12
237 S Georgetown Hwy 29555 843-386-2707
Sam Tuten, prin. Fax 386-9058
Johnsonville MS 400/5-8
PO Box 67 29555 843-386-2066
Randy Willis, prin. Fax 386-3786

Johnston, Edgefield, Pop. 2,346
Edgefield County SD 3,800/PK-12
3 Par Dr 29832 803-275-4601
Robert Maddox, supt. Fax 275-4426
www.edgefield.k12.sc.us
JET MS 500/6-8
1095 Columbia Rd 29832 803-275-1997
Debbie Courtney, prin. Fax 275-1783
Thurmond Career Center Vo/Tech
17 Par Dr 29832 803-275-1767
Arthur Northrop, dir. Fax 275-1766
Thurmond HS 800/9-12
1131 Columbia Rd 29832 803-275-1768
Dr. Robert Ross, prin. Fax 275-1764
Other Schools – See North Augusta

Wardlaw Academy 200/PK-12
1296 Columbia Rd 29832 803-275-4794

Kershaw, Lancaster, Pop. 1,779
Kershaw County SD
Supt. — See Camden
North Central HS 500/9-12
3000 Lockhart Rd 29067 803-432-9858
David Branham, prin. Fax 425-8992
North Central MS 400/6-8
805 Keys Ln 29067 803-424-2740
Burch Richardson Ed.D., prin. Fax 424-2742

Lancaster County SD
Supt. — See Lancaster
Jackson HS 600/9-12
6925 Kershaw Camden Hwy 29067 803-475-2381
Alex Dabney, prin. Fax 475-7317
Jackson MS 500/6-8
6865 Kershaw Camden Hwy 29067 803-475-6021
Daryl Hinson, prin. Fax 475-8256

Kingstree, Williamsburg, Pop. 3,310
Williamsburg County SD 3,900/PK-12
PO Box 1067 29556 843-355-5571
Carrie Brock, supt. Fax 355-3213
www.wcsd.k12.sc.us
Kingstree HS 600/9-12
616 Martin Luther King Ave 29556 843-355-6525
Dr. Deonia Simmons, prin. Fax 355-7019
Kingstree Middle Magnet S 500/6-8
710 3rd Ave 29556 843-355-1506
James Carraway, prin. Fax 355-9207
Other Schools – See Greeleyville, Hemingway

Williamsburg Academy 400/K-12
1000 Sandy Bay Rd 29556 843-355-9400
Williamsburg Technical College Post-Sec.
601 Martin Luther King Ave 29556 843-355-4110

Ladson, Berkeley, Pop. 13,352
Berkeley County SD
Supt. — See Moncks Corner
College Park MS 800/6-8
713 College Park Rd 29456 843-553-8300
Ingrid Dukes M.Ed., prin. Fax 820-4026
Sangaree MS 800/6-8
1050 Discovery Dr 29456 843-821-4028
Margaret Day, prin. Fax 871-8974

Dorchester SD 2
Supt. — See Summerville
Oakbrook MS 1,000/6-8
286 Old Fort Dr 29456 843-873-9750
Brandon Pitcher, prin. Fax 821-3931

William-Randolph Christian Prep S 50/K-10
9659 Jamison Rd 29456 843-212-4289
Dr. Stephanie Wallace M.Ed., prin. Fax 771-0569

Lake City, Florence, Pop. 6,625
Florence County SD Three 2,600/PK-12
PO Box 1389 29560 843-374-8652
Laura Hickson, supt. Fax 374-2946
fsd3.org
Lake City HS 900/9-12
PO Box 1569 29560 843-374-3321
Ned Blake, prin. Fax 374-3138
McNair JHS 300/7-8
PO Box 1209 29560 843-374-8651
Kristi Anderson, prin. Fax 374-8504

Carolina Academy 200/PK-12
351 N Country Club Rd 29560 843-374-5485

Lake View, Dillon, Pop. 805
Dillon SD Four
Supt. — See Dillon
Lake View JSHS 400/6-12
PO Box 624 29563 843-759-3009
Edison Arnette, prin. Fax 759-3015

Lamar, Darlington, Pop. 980
Darlington County SD
Supt. — See Darlington
Lamar HS 300/9-12
216 N Darlington Ave 29069 843-326-7500
Kathy Gainey, prin. Fax 326-7507
Spaulding MS 300/6-8
400 Cartersville Hwy 29069 843-326-7626
Chrissy Jones, prin. Fax 326-7656

Lancaster, Lancaster, Pop. 8,450
Lancaster County SD 12,000/PK-12
300 S Catawba St 29720 803-286-6972
Dr. Gene Moore, supt. Fax 416-8860
www.lancastercsd.com
Buford HS 600/9-12
4290 Tabernacle Rd 29720 803-286-7068
Rodney Miller, prin. Fax 286-8147
Buford MS 500/6-8
1890 N Rocky River Rd 29720 803-285-8473
Sheri Wells, prin. Fax 283-2023

Lancaster High Career Center — Vo/Tech
625 Normandy Rd 29720 — 803-285-7404
Dr. Joe Keenan, prin. — Fax 285-2720
Lancaster HS — 1,400/9-12
617 Normandy Rd 29720 — 803-283-2001
Dr. Joseph Keenan, prin. — Fax 286-6962
Rucker MS — 600/6-8
422 Old Dixie Rd 29720 — 803-416-8555
Anita Watts, prin. — Fax 285-1534
South MS — 600/6-8
1551 Billings Dr 29720 — 803-283-8416
Joyce Crimminger, prin. — Fax 283-8417
Adult Education — Adult
610 E Meeting St 29720 — 803-285-7660
Dr. Kim Linton, dir. — Fax 285-9281
Other Schools – See Indian Land, Kershaw

University of South Carolina — Post-Sec.
PO Box 889 29721 — 803-313-7000

Landrum, Spartanburg, Pop. 2,337
Spartanburg SD 1
Supt. — See Campobello
Landrum MS — 200/6-8
104 Redland Rd 29356 — 864-457-2629
Tucker Hamrick, prin. — Fax 457-5372

Latta, Dillon, Pop. 1,366
Latta SD — 1,200/PK-12
205 King St 29565 — 843-752-7101
Dr. John Kirby, supt. — Fax 752-2081
www.dillon3.k12.sc.us
Latta HS — 400/9-12
618 N Richardson St 29565 — 843-752-5751
Leigh Darby Sloan, prin. — Fax 752-2707
Latta MS — 400/5-8
612 N Richardson St 29565 — 843-752-7117
Debra Morris, prin. — Fax 752-2722

Laurens, Laurens, Pop. 9,035
Laurens SD 55 — 5,500/PK-12
301 Hillcrest Dr 29360 — 864-984-3568
Dr. Billy Strickland, supt. — Fax 984-8100
www.laurens55.k12.sc.us/
Laurens District 55 HS — 1,600/9-12
5058 Highway 76 W 29360 — 864-682-3151
Sonya Bryant, prin. — Fax 682-7426
Laurens MS — 400/6-8
1035 W Main St 29360 — 864-984-2400
Dr. Rhett Harris, prin. — Fax 984-6013
Sanders MS — 300/6-8
609 Green St 29360 — 864-984-0354
Lacresha Byrd, prin. — Fax 984-2452

Laurens Academy — 200/PK-12
PO Box 425 29360 — 864-682-2324

Lexington, Lexington, Pop. 17,606
Lexington County SD 1 — 23,600/K-12
PO Box 1869 29071 — 803-821-1000
Dr. Greg Little, supt. — Fax 821-1010
www.lexington1.net
Carolina Springs MS — 800/6-8
6180 Platt Springs Rd 29073 — 803-821-4900
Dr. Brice Cockfield, prin. — Fax 821-4903
Focus Program Alternative Learning Ctr — Alt
420 Hendrix St 29072 — 803-821-1300
Chris Rabon, coord. — Fax 821-1303
Lexington HS — 1,900/9-12
2463 Augusta Hwy 29072 — 803-821-3400
Melissa Rawl, prin. — Fax 821-3403
Lexington MS — 800/6-8
702 N Lake Dr 29072 — 803-821-3700
Gloria Nester, prin. — Fax 821-3703
Lexington Technology Center — Vo/Tech
2421 Augusta Hwy 29072 — 803-821-3000
Bryan Hearn, dir. — Fax 821-3003
Meadow Glen MS — 900/6-8
440 Ginny Ln 29072 — 803-821-0600
Dr. Bill Coon, prin. — Fax 821-0603
Pleasant Hill MS — 1,000/6-8
660 Rawl Rd 29072 — 803-821-2700
Dr. Thomas Rivers, prin. — Fax 821-2703
River Bluff HS — 1,500/9-12
320 Corley Mill Rd 29072 — 803-821-0702
Dr. Luke Clamp, prin. — Fax 821-0703
White Knoll HS — 2,000/9-12
5643 Platt Springs Rd 29073 — 803-821-5200
Edward Daughtrey, prin. — Fax 821-5203
Other Schools – See Gilbert, Pelion, West Columbia

Northside Christian Academy — PK-12
4347 Sunset Blvd 29072 — 803-520-5656
Rev. Scott Crede, head sch — Fax 520-5661

Liberty, Pickens, Pop. 3,217
Pickens County SD
Supt. — See Easley
Liberty HS — 700/9-12
124 Red Devil Dr 29657 — 864-397-2600
Josh Oxendine, prin. — Fax 843-5828
Liberty MS — 500/6-8
125 Falcon Ln 29657 — 864-397-3400
Dr. Tim Mullis, prin. — Fax 843-5857
Pickens County Career & Technology Ctr — Vo/Tech
990 Chastain Rd 29657 — 864-397-4500
Ken Hitchcock, dir. — Fax 843-9064

Little River, Horry, Pop. 8,858
Horry County SD
Supt. — See Conway
North Myrtle Beach HS — 1,300/9-12
3750 Sea Mountain Hwy 29566 — 843-399-6171
Trevor Strawderman, prin. — Fax 399-6509
North Myrtle Beach MS — 1,100/6-8
11240 Highway 90 29566 — 843-399-6136
James LaPier, prin. — Fax 399-2233

Longs, Horry

North Myrtle Beach Christian S — 100/PK-12
9535 Highway 90 29568 — 843-399-7181
Benjamin Rhodes, hdmstr. — Fax 399-7183

Loris, Horry, Pop. 2,350
Horry County SD
Supt. — See Conway
Loris HS — 800/9-12
301 Loris Lions Rd 29569 — 843-390-6800
Dirk Gurley, prin. — Fax 390-6801
Loris MS — 700/6-8
5209 Highway 66 29569 — 843-756-2181
Ann Hall, prin. — Fax 756-0522

Lugoff, Kershaw, Pop. 7,335
Kershaw County SD
Supt. — See Camden
Lugoff-Elgin HS — 1,600/9-12
1284 Highway 1 S 29078 — 803-438-3481
Worth Thomasson, prin. — Fax 438-8005
Lugoff-Elgin MS — 700/6-8
1244 Highway 1 S 29078 — 803-438-3591
Karen Bullard, prin. — Fax 438-8027

Lyman, Spartanburg, Pop. 3,187
Spartanburg SD 5
Supt. — See Duncan
Hill MS — 600/7-8
PO Box 1329 29365 — 864-949-2370
Terry Glasgow, prin. — Fax 949-2369

Mc Bee, Chesterfield, Pop. 855
Chesterfield County SD
Supt. — See Chesterfield
Mc Bee HS — 500/7-12
PO Box 218 29101 — 843-335-8251
Dennis McDaniel, prin. — Fax 335-6515

Mc Cormick, McCormick, Pop. 2,752
McCormick County SD — 800/PK-12
821 N Mine St 29835 — 864-852-2435
Don Doggett, supt. — Fax 852-2883
www.mccormick.k12.sc.us
McCormick HS — 200/9-12
6981 SC Highway 28 S 29835 — 864-443-0040
Steve English, prin. — Fax 443-0049
McCormick MS — 200/6-8
6979 SC Highway 28 S 29835 — 864-443-2243
Gena Wideman, prin. — Fax 443-3298

Manning, Clarendon, Pop. 4,077
Area Vocational Schools
Supt. — None
Dubose Career Center — Vo/Tech
3351 Sumter Hwy 29102 — 803-473-2531
Susan Anderson, prin. — Fax 473-4320

Clarendon SD 2 — 3,000/PK-12
PO Box 1252 29102 — 803-435-4435
John Tindal, supt. — Fax 435-8172
www.clarendon2.k12.sc.us
Manning HS — 800/9-12
2155 Paxville Hwy 29102 — 803-435-4417
Preston Threatt, prin. — Fax 435-4404
Manning JHS — 400/7-8
1101 WL Hamilton Rd 29102 — 803-435-8195
Terrie Ard, prin. — Fax 435-6848

Laurence Manning Academy — 1,000/PK-12
PO Box 278 29102 — 803-435-2114
Dr. Spencer Jordan, prin. — Fax 435-9154

Marion, Marion, Pop. 6,862
Marion County SD — 5,200/PK-12
719 N Main St 29571 — 843-423-1811
Dr. Kandace Bethea, supt. — Fax 423-8328
www.marion.k12.sc.us
Creek Bridge HS — 300/6-12
6641 S Highway 41 29571 — 843-362-3500
Darryl Woodberry, prin. — Fax 362-3506
Johnakin MS — 600/6-8
601 Gurley St 29571 — 843-423-8360
Rebecca Ford, prin. — Fax 423-8383
Marion HS — 800/9-12
1205 S Main St 29571 — 843-423-2571
Daris Gore, prin. — Fax 423-8330
Other Schools – See Mullins

Mauldin, Greenville, Pop. 22,445
Greenville County SD
Supt. — See Greenville
Mauldin HS — 2,200/9-12
701 E Butler Rd 29662 — 864-355-6500
Scott Rhymer, prin. — Fax 355-6657

Moncks Corner, Berkeley, Pop. 7,746
Berkeley County SD — 31,600/PK-12
PO Box 608 29461 — 843-899-8600
Brenda Blackburn, supt. — Fax 899-8791
www.bcsdschools.net
Berkeley Alternative S — Alt
106 S Live Oak Dr 29461 — 843-899-8830
Don Brown, prin. — Fax 899-8817
Berkeley County Middle College HS — 100/11-12
1001 S Live Oak Dr 29461 — 843-899-8111
Claire Freeman, prin. — Fax 899-8113
Berkeley HS — 1,300/9-12
406 W Main St 29461 — 843-899-8800
Steven Steele, prin. — Fax 899-8810
Berkeley MS — 1,100/6-8
320 N Live Oak Dr 29461 — 843-899-8840
Mike Wilkerson, prin. — Fax 899-8846
Macedonia MS — 400/6-8
200 Macedonia Foxes Cir 29461 — 843-899-8940
Don Walton, prin. — Fax 899-8929
Berkeley Educational Center — Adult
113 E Main St 29461 — 843-899-8635
Fax 899-8764
Other Schools – See Cross, Goose Creek, Hanahan, Ladson, Saint Stephen, Summerville

---

St. John's Christian Academy — 300/PK-12
204 W Main St 29461 — 843-761-8539
Dr. Eric Denton, hdmstr. — Fax 899-5514

Monetta, Aiken, Pop. 227
Aiken County SD
Supt. — See Aiken

Ridge Spring-Monetta MSHS — 200/6-12
10 J P Kneece Dr 29105 — 803-685-2100
Kyle Blankenship, prin. — Fax 685-2108

Moore, Spartanburg
Spartanburg County SD 6
Supt. — See Roebuck
Anderson Applied Technology Center — Vo/Tech
PO Box 248 29369 — 864-576-5020
Sherri Yarborough, prin. — Fax 576-8642
Dawkins MS — 900/6-8
1300 E Blackstock Rd 29369 — 864-576-8088
Jay Seegars, prin. — Fax 595-2418

Mount Pleasant, Charleston, Pop. 67,140
Charleston County SD
Supt. — See Charleston
Cario MS — 1,300/6-8
3500 Thomas Cario Blvd 29466 — 843-856-4595
Sharon Randall, prin. — Fax 856-4599
Laing MS of Science & Technology — 700/6-8
2705 Bulrush Basket Ln 29466 — 843-849-2809
James Whitehair, prin. — Fax 849-2895
Moultrie MS — 800/6-8
645 Coleman Blvd 29464 — 843-849-2819
Ryan Cumback, prin. — Fax 849-2899
Wando HS — 3,700/9-12
1000 Warrior Way 29466 — 843-849-2830
Dr. Sherry Eppelsheimer, prin. — Fax 849-2890

Coastal Christian Preparatory S — 300/PK-12
681 McCants Dr 29464 — 843-884-3663
Dr. David Piccolo, head sch — Fax 884-9608
Palmetto Christian Academy — 500/PK-12
361 Egypt Rd 29464 — 843-881-9967
J. D. Zubia, hdmstr. — Fax 881-4662

Mullins, Marion, Pop. 4,600
Marion County SD
Supt. — See Marion
Academy of Careers and Technology — Vo/Tech
2697 E Highway 76 29574 — 843-423-1941
Darrell Jameson, dir. — Fax 423-1943
Mullins HS — 500/9-12
747 Millers Rd 29574 — 843-464-3710
Michael Stone, prin. — Fax 464-3717
Palmetto MS — 400/6-8
305 ONeal St 29574 — 843-464-3730
Sam Whack, prin. — Fax 464-3736

Pee Dee Academy — 400/PK-12
PO Box 449 29574 — 843-423-1771

Murrells Inlet, Horry, Pop. 7,501
Horry County SD
Supt. — See Conway
St. James HS — 1,400/9-12
10800 Highway 707 29576 — 843-650-5600
Vann Pennell, prin. — Fax 650-1004

Myrtle Beach, Horry, Pop. 26,336
Horry County SD
Supt. — See Conway
Academy for Arts Science & Technology — Vo/Tech
895 International Dr 29579 — 843-903-8460
Robin Jones, prin. — Fax 903-8461
Carolina Forest HS — 2,100/9-12
700 Gardner Lacy Rd 29579 — 843-236-7997
Gaye Driggers, prin. — Fax 236-7504
Forestbrook MS — 1,100/6-8
4430 Gator Ln 29588 — 843-236-7300
Beverly Holt-Pilkey, prin. — Fax 236-8065
Myrtle Beach HS — 1,200/9-12
3302 Robert M Grissom Pkwy 29577 — 843-448-7149
John Washburn, prin. — Fax 445-2036
Myrtle Beach MS — 1,000/6-8
950 Seahawk Way 29577 — 843-448-3932
Dr. Janice Christy, prin. — Fax 448-1182
Ocean Bay MS — 1,200/6-8
905 International Dr 29579 — 843-903-8420
Barbara McGinnis, prin. — Fax 903-8421
St. James MS — 1,200/6-8
9775 Saint James Rd 29588 — 843-650-5543
Dr. Dwight Boykin, prin. — Fax 650-5610
Socastee HS — 1,500/9-12
4900 Socastee Blvd 29588 — 843-293-2513
Dr. Paul Browning, prin. — Fax 293-3393

Calvary Christian S — 200/PK-12
4511 Dick Pond Rd 29588 — 843-650-2829
Christian Academy of Myrtle Beach — 400/K-12
291 Ronald McNair Blvd 29579 — 843-236-6222
Nancy Henry, head sch — Fax 236-2262
Golf Academy of America — Post-Sec.
3268 Waccamaw Blvd 29579 — 800-342-7342
Pittsburgh Institute of Aeronautics — Post-Sec.
1038 Shine Ave 29577 — 800-444-1440
Risen Christ Lutheran S — 100/PK-12
10595 Highway 17 N 29572 — 843-272-8163
Sean E. O'Connor, prin. — Fax 272-4039
St. Elizabeth Ann Seton HS — 9-9
1300 Carolina Forest Blvd 29579 — 843-839-2245
Ted Hanes, admin.
Strand College of Hair Design — Post-Sec.
423 79th Ave N 29572 — 843-449-1017

Neeses, Orangeburg, Pop. 371
Orangeburg County Consolidated SD 4
Supt. — See Cope
Hunter-Kinard-Tyler HS — 300/7-12
7066 Norway Rd 29107 — 803-263-4832
Mark Dean, prin. — Fax 263-4467

Newberry, Newberry, Pop. 10,123
Newberry County SD — 5,800/PK-12
PO Box 718 29108 — 803-321-2600
Bennie Bennett, supt. — Fax 321-2604
www.newberry.k12.sc.us/
Newberry County Career Ctr — Vo/Tech
3413 Main St 29108 — 803-321-2674
Beverly Leslie, prin. — Fax 321-2676
Newberry HS — 800/9-12
3113 Main St 29108 — 803-321-2621
Vance Jones, prin. — Fax 321-2633

Newberry MS 700/6-8
125 ONeal St 29108 803-321-2640
Kimberly Hamilton, prin. Fax 321-2647
Other Schools – See Prosperity, Whitmire

Newberry Academy 200/PK-12
2055 Smith Rd 29108 803-276-2760
Newberry College Post-Sec.
2100 College St 29108 800-845-4955

New Ellenton, Aiken, Pop. 1,998
Aiken County SD
Supt. — See Aiken
New Ellenton MS 200/6-8
814 Main St S 29809 803-652-8200
Shunte Dugar, prin. Fax 652-8203

Ninety Six, Greenwood, Pop. 1,979
Greenwood SD 52 1,700/PK-12
605 Johnston Rd 29666 864-543-3100
Dr. Sharon Wall, supt. Fax 543-3704
www.greenwood52.org
Edgewood MS 400/6-8
644 S Cambridge St 29666 864-543-3511
Scott Parker, prin. Fax 543-4994
Ninety Six HS 500/9-12
640 S Cambridge St 29666 864-543-2911
Rex Ward, prin. Fax 543-3132

North, Orangeburg, Pop. 730
Orangeburg Consolidated SD 5
Supt. — See Orangeburg
North MSHS 300/6-12
692 Cromer Ave 29112 803-247-2541
Charles Gregory, prin. Fax 247-5090

North Augusta, Aiken, Pop. 20,954
Aiken County SD
Supt. — See Aiken
Knox MS 700/6-8
1804 Wells Rd 29841 803-442-6300
Kyle Smith, prin. Fax 442-6302
North Augusta HS 1,500/9-12
2000 Knobcone Ave 29841 803-442-6100
John Murphy, prin. Fax 442-6127
North Augusta MS 700/6-8
725 Old Edgefield Rd 29841 803-442-6200
Phyllis Gamble, prin. Fax 442-6202

Edgefield County SD
Supt. — See Johnston
Merriwether MS 400/6-8
430 Murrah Rd 29860 803-279-2511
Derrick Forrest, prin. Fax 279-1710

Kenneth Shuler's School of Cosmetology Post-Sec.
736 Martintown Rd 29841 803-278-1200
Victory Christian S 100/K-12
620 W Martintown Rd 29841 803-278-0125

North Charleston, Charleston, Pop. 95,273
Charleston County SD
Supt. — See Charleston
ARMS Academy at Morningside 6-8
1999 Singley St 29405 843-745-2000
Stephanie Flock, prin. Fax 745-7191
Charleston County S of the Arts 1,100/6-12
5109 W Enterprise St 29405 843-529-4990
Dr. Shannon Cook, prin. Fax 529-4991
EXCEL Academy at Morningside 700/6-8
1999 Singley St 29405 843-745-2000
Stephanie Flock, prin. Fax 745-7191
Garrett Academy of Technology Vo/Tech
2731 Gordon St 29405 843-745-7126
Charity Summers, prin. Fax 529-3914
Jenkins Creative Learning Center 200/Alt
2670 Bonds Ave 29405 843-747-6609
Dana Hancock, prin. Fax 746-7438
Liberty Hill Academy 100/Alt
5025 W Enterprise St 29405 843-566-8892
Christopher Haynes, prin. Fax 566-8897
Military Magnet Academy 500/6-12
2950 Carner Ave 29405 843-745-7102
Anderson Townsend, prin. Fax 566-7791
North Charleston HS 500/9-12
1087 E Montague Ave 29405 843-745-7140
Robert Grimm, prin. Fax 566-1954
Northwoods MS 900/6-8
7763 Northside Dr 29420 843-764-2212
Dr. Roy Jones, prin. Fax 569-5466
Stall HS 1,200/9-12
3625 Ashley Phosphate Rd 29418 843-764-2200
Kim Wilson, prin. Fax 764-2240
Zucker Science MS 500/6-8
6401 Dorchester Rd 29418 843-767-8383
Jacob Perlmutter, prin. Fax 207-3073

Dorchester SD 2
Supt. — See Summerville
Fort Dorchester HS 2,000/9-12
8500 Patriot Blvd 29420 843-760-4450
Berkley Postell, prin. Fax 760-4852
River Oaks MS 1,000/6-8
8642 River Oaks Dr 29420 843-695-2470
Scott Matthews, prin. Fax 695-2475

Cathedral Academy 300/K-12
PO Box 41129, 843-760-1192
Chris Bateman, head sch Fax 760-1197
Centura College Post-Sec.
8088 Rivers Ave 29406 843-569-0889
ECPI University Post-Sec.
7410 Northside Dr Ste G101 29420 843-414-0350
Miller-Motte Technical College Post-Sec.
8085 Rivers Ave Ste E 29406 843-574-0101
Southeastern Institute Post-Sec.
4600 Goer Dr Ste 105 29406 843-747-1279
Virginia College Post-Sec.
6185 Rivers Ave 29406 843-614-4300

Orangeburg, Orangeburg, Pop. 13,823
Orangeburg Consolidated SD 5 6,500/PK-12
578 Ellis Ave 29115 803-534-5454
Dr. Jesse Washington, supt. Fax 533-7953
www.ocsd5schools.org
Clark MS 700/6-8
919 Bennett St 29115 803-531-2200
Rodney Zimmerman, prin. Fax 533-6503
Howard MS 400/6-8
1255 Belleville Rd 29115 803-534-5470
Eric Brown, prin. Fax 535-1606
Orangeburg-Wilkinson HS 1,200/9-12
601 Bruin Pkwy 29118 803-534-6180
Dr. Stephen Peters, prin. Fax 533-6310
Technology Center Vo/Tech
3720 Magnolia St 29118 803-536-4473
Dr. Cleve Pilot, prin. Fax 533-6365
Other Schools – See North, Rowesville

Claflin University Post-Sec.
400 Magnolia St 29115 803-535-5000
Orangeburg-Calhoun Technical College Post-Sec.
3250 Saint Matthews Rd 29118 803-536-0311
Orangeburg Preparatory S 800/PK-12
2651 North Rd 29118 803-534-7970
South Carolina State University Post-Sec.
300 College Ave 29115 803-536-7000
Southern Methodist College Post-Sec.
541 Broughton St 29115 803-534-7826

Pacolet, Spartanburg, Pop. 2,212
Spartanburg SD 3
Supt. — See Glendale
Middle School of Pacolet 200/6-8
850 Sunny Acres Rd 29372 864-279-6600
Max Deaton, prin. Fax 279-6610

Pageland, Chesterfield, Pop. 2,713
Chesterfield County SD
Supt. — See Chesterfield
Central HS 600/9-12
200 Zion Church Rd 29728 843-672-6115
Dr. Juddson Starling, prin. Fax 672-2694

South Pointe Christian S 200/PK-12
PO Box 188 29728 843-672-2760
Larry Stinson, head sch Fax 672-3913

Pamplico, Florence, Pop. 1,212
Florence County SD 2 1,200/PK-12
2121 S Pamplico Hwy 29583 843-493-2502
Neal Vincent, supt. Fax 493-1912
www.flo2.k12.sc.us/
Hannah-Pamplico HS 400/9-12
2055 S Pamplico Hwy 29583 843-493-5781
Timothy Gibbs, prin. Fax 493-5424

Pawleys Island, Georgetown, Pop. 101
Georgetown County SD
Supt. — See Georgetown
Waccamaw HS 800/9-12
2412 Kings River Rd 29585 843-237-9899
Dr. David Hammel, prin. Fax 237-9883
Waccamaw MS 500/7-8
247 Wildcat Way 29585 843-237-0106
Jamie Curry, prin. Fax 237-0237

Lowcountry Preparatory S 100/K-12
300 Blue Stem Dr 29585 843-237-4147
Scott Gibson, head sch Fax 237-4147
Pawleys Island Christian Academy 100/PK-12
10304 Ocean Hwy 29585 843-237-9293

Pelion, Lexington, Pop. 671
Lexington County SD 1
Supt. — See Lexington
Pelion HS 800/9-12
600 Lydia Dr 29123 803-821-2200
Clark Cooper, prin. Fax 821-2203
Pelion MS 600/6-8
758 Magnolia St 29123 803-821-2300
Jeffrey Matthews, prin. Fax 821-2303

Pendleton, Anderson, Pop. 2,884
Anderson SD 4 2,800/K-12
PO Box 545 29670 864-403-2000
Dr. Joanne Avery Ph.D., supt. Fax 403-2029
www.anderson4.org
Riverside MS 500/7-8
458 Riverside St 29670 864-403-2200
Dr. Kevin Black, prin. Fax 646-8025
Other Schools – See Anderson

Tri-County Technical College Post-Sec.
PO Box 587 29670 864-646-8361

Pickens, Pickens, Pop. 3,062
Pickens County SD
Supt. — See Easley
Pickens HS 1,400/9-12
150 Blue Flame Dr 29671 864-397-3600
Corey Willimon, prin. Fax 898-5611
Pickens MS 800/6-8
140 Torch Dr 29671 864-397-4100
Reggia Stapleton, prin. Fax 878-9224

Lakeview Christian S 200/PK-12
107 Mauldin Lake Rd 29671 864-878-6959
Rev. Mike Belcher, admin. Fax 878-6927

Piedmont, Greenville, Pop. 5,025
Anderson SD 1
Supt. — See Williamston
Wren HS 1,100/9-12
905 Wren School Rd 29673 864-850-5900
Nichole Boseman, prin. Fax 850-5929
Wren MS 800/6-8
1010 Wren School Rd 29673 864-850-5930
Robin Fulbright, prin. Fax 850-5941

Greenville County SD
Supt. — See Greenville
Woodmont HS 1,700/9-12
2831 W Georgia Rd 29673 864-355-8600
Darryl Imperati, prin. Fax 355-8695
Woodmont MS 700/6-8
325 N Flat Rock Rd 29673 864-355-8500
Greg Scott, prin. Fax 355-8587

Prosperity, Newberry, Pop. 1,173
Newberry County SD
Supt. — See Newberry
Mid-Carolina HS 800/9-12
377 Cy Schumpert Rd 29127 803-364-2134
Ray Cooper, prin. Fax 364-4395
Mid-Carolina MS 600/6-8
6794 US Highway 76 29127 803-364-3634
Deedee Westwood, prin. Fax 364-4877

Rembert, Sumter, Pop. 296

Sumter Academy 400/PK-12
5265 Camden Hwy 29128 803-499-3378

Richburg, Chester, Pop. 273
Chester County SD
Supt. — See Chester
Lewisville HS 400/9-12
3971 Lewisville High School 29729 803-789-5131
James Knox, prin. Fax 789-3188
Lewisville MS 300/6-8
PO Box 280 29729 803-789-5858
Cedrick Tidwell, prin. Fax 789-6159

Ridgeland, Jasper, Pop. 4,009
Area Vocational Schools
Supt. — None
Beaufort-Jasper Acad Career Excellence Vo/Tech
80 Lowcountry Dr 29936 843-987-8107
Dr. Jerry Henderson, dir. Fax 987-1343

Jasper County SD 2,500/PK-12
10942 N Jacob Smart Blvd 29936 843-717-1100
Larry Heath, supt. Fax 717-1199
www.jcsd.net
Ridgeland-Hardeeville HS 700/9-12
250 Jaguar Trl 29936 843-489-8844
Dr. Karen Parker, prin. Fax 717-3275
Other Schools – See Hardeeville

Heyward Academy 300/PK-12
1727 Malphrus Rd 29936 843-726-3673
Marilyn Davis, head sch Fax 726-5773
John Paul II Catholic S 7-10
4211 N Okatie Hwy 29936 843-645-3838
Walter Dupre, prin. Fax 645-3839

Ridgeville, Dorchester, Pop. 1,972
Dorchester SD 2
Supt. — See Summerville
Givhans Community S Alt
273 Highway 61 29472 843-832-1264
Joyce Dearing, prin. Fax 821-3944

Rock Hill, York, Pop. 64,898
Rock Hill SD 3 17,600/PK-12
PO Box 10072 29731 803-981-1000
Dr. Kelly U. Pew, supt. Fax 981-1094
www.rock-hill.k12.sc.us
Castle Heights MS 800/6-8
2382 Fire Tower Rd 29730 803-981-1400
John Kirell, prin. Fax 981-1430
Dutchman Creek MS 900/6-8
4757 Mount Gallant Rd 29732 803-985-1700
Dr. Norris Williams, prin. Fax 985-1740
Northwestern HS 1,800/9-12
2503 W Main St 29732 803-981-1200
James Blake, prin. Fax 981-1250
Phoenix Academy Alt
1234 Flint Street Ext 29730 803-981-1975
Dr. Walter Wolff, dir. Fax 981-1396
Rawlinson Road MS 600/6-8
2631 W Main St 29732 803-981-1500
Dr. Jean Dickson, prin. Fax 981-1532
Rebound Alternative S Alt
1234 Flint Street Ext 29730 803-981-1087
Dr. Walter Wolff, dir. Fax 981-1259
Renaissance Academy Alt
1234 Flint Street Ext 29730 803-985-3737
Dr. Walter Wolff, admin. Fax 981-1396
Rock Hill Applied Technology Center Vo/Tech
2399 W Main St 29732 803-981-1100
Don Gillman, dir. Fax 981-1125
Rock Hill HS 2,000/9-12
320 W Springdale Rd 29730 803-981-1300
Ozzie Ahl, prin. Fax 981-1343
Saluda Trail MS 800/6-8
2300 Saluda Rd 29730 803-981-1800
Elissa Cox, prin. Fax 981-1888
South Pointe HS 1,300/9-12
801 Neely Rd 29730 803-980-2100
Dr. Al Leonard, prin. Fax 980-2105
Sullivan MS 800/6-8
1825 Eden Ter 29730 803-981-1450
Shane Goodwin, prin. Fax 981-1456
Adult & Community Education Adult
1234 Flint Street Ext 29730 803-981-1375
Dr. Sandy Andrews, dir. Fax 981-1397

Clinton College Post-Sec.
1029 Crawford Rd 29730 803-327-7402
Westminster Catawba Christian S 500/PK-12
2650 India Hook Rd 29732 803-366-4119
Scott Dillon, head sch Fax 328-5465
Winthrop University Post-Sec.
701 W Oakland Ave 29733 803-323-2211
York Technical College Post-Sec.
452 Anderson Rd S 29730 803-327-8000

Roebuck, Spartanburg, Pop. 2,173
Spartanburg County SD 6 12,000/PK-12
1390 Cavalier Way 29376 864-576-4212
Dr. Darryl Owings, supt. Fax 574-6265
www.spart6.org

Dorman HS 2,400/10-12
1050 Cavalier Way 29376 864-582-4347
Ken Kiser, prin. Fax 587-8738
Dorman HS - Freshman Campus 900/9-9
1225 Cavalier Way 29376 864-582-3479
Mark Smith, prin. Fax 342-8997
Gable MS 800/6-8
198 Otts Shoals Rd 29376 864-576-3500
Matt Talley, prin. Fax 595-2428
Other Schools – See Moore, Spartanburg

Rowesville, Orangeburg, Pop. 302
Orangeburg Consolidated SD 5
Supt. — See Orangeburg
Bethune-Bowman MSHS 400/6-12
4857 Charleston Hwy 29133 803-516-6011
Lakekia Lewis, prin. Fax 516-6013

Saint George, Dorchester, Pop. 2,077
Dorchester SD 4 2,300/PK-12
500 Ridge St 29477 843-563-4535
Dr. Morris Ravenell, supt. Fax 563-9269
www.dorchester4.k12.sc.us
Saint George MS 300/6-8
600 Minus St 29477 843-563-3171
Jeffery Thompson, prin. Fax 563-5936
Other Schools – See Dorchester, Harleyville

Dorchester Academy 300/PK-12
234 Academy Rd 29477 843-563-9511

Saint Matthews, Calhoun, Pop. 2,002
Calhoun County SD 1,800/PK-12
PO Box 215 29135 803-655-7310
Dr. Steve Wilson, supt. Fax 655-7393
www.ccpsonline.net/
Calhoun County HS 500/9-12
150 Saints Ave 29135 803-874-3071
Cynthia Johnson, prin. Fax 655-5948

Calhoun Academy 400/PK-12
PO Box 526 29135 803-874-2734
Mims Taylor, hdmstr. Fax 655-5096

Saint Stephen, Berkeley, Pop. 1,670
Berkeley County SD
Supt. — See Moncks Corner
Saint Stephen MS 300/6-8
225 Carolina Dr 29479 843-567-3128
Brenda Fleming, prin. Fax 567-8162
Timberland HS 700/9-12
1418 Gravel Hill Rd 29479 843-567-8110
Kerry Daugherty, prin. Fax 567-8116

Saluda, Saluda, Pop. 3,519
Saluda SD 2,200/PK-12
404 N Wise Rd 29138 864-445-8441
David M. Mathis Ed.D., supt. Fax 445-9598
www.saludaschools.org
Saluda HS 600/9-12
160 Ivory Key Rd 29138 864-445-3011
Sarah Longshore, prin. Fax 445-3542
Saluda MS 500/6-8
140 Ivory Key Rd 29138 864-445-3767
Don Hardie, prin. Fax 445-3980

Santee, Orangeburg, Pop. 941
Orangeburg County Consolidated SD 3
Supt. — See Holly Hill
Lake Marion HS 800/9-12
PO Box 650 29142 803-854-9213
Rose Pelzer, prin. Fax 854-5202

Seabrook, Beaufort
Beaufort County SD
Supt. — See Beaufort
Whale Branch Early College HS 500/9-12
169 Detour Rd 29940 843-466-2700
Mona Lise Dickson, prin. Fax 846-6827
Whale Branch MS 400/5-8
2009 Trask Pkwy 29940 843-466-3000
Chad Cox, prin. Fax 466-3087

Seneca, Oconee, Pop. 7,931
Oconee County SD
Supt. — See Walhalla
Hamilton Career Center Vo/Tech
100 Vocational Dr 29672 864-886-4425
Michael Pearson, prin. Fax 886-4426
Seneca HS 900/9-12
100 Bobcat Rdg 29678 864-886-4460
Cliff Roberts, prin. Fax 886-4457
Seneca MS 800/6-8
810 W South 4th St 29678 864-886-4455
Al LeRoy, prin. Fax 886-4452

Oconee Christian Academy 100/PK-12
150 His Way Cir 29672 864-882-6925
Harold Dean Bare, head sch Fax 882-7217

Simpsonville, Greenville, Pop. 17,848
Greenville County SD
Supt. — See Greenville
Bryson MS 1,100/6-8
3657 S Industrial Dr 29681 864-355-2100
Dr. Adrienne Davenport, prin. Fax 355-2194
Chandler MS 700/6-8
4231 Fork Shoals Rd 29680 864-452-0300
Jeffrey Jenkins, prin. Fax 452-0365
Hillcrest HS 2,100/9-12
3665 S Industrial Dr 29681 864-355-3500
G. Bryan Skipper, prin. Fax 355-3382
Hillcrest MS 1,000/6-8
510 Garrison Rd 29681 864-355-6100
Kelli Farmer, prin. Fax 355-6120
Mauldin MS 1,200/6-8
1190 Holland Rd 29681 864-355-6770
Chris Killan, prin. Fax 355-6988

Greenville Classical Academy 100/K-12
2519 Woodruff Rd 29681 864-329-9884
Eric Woernle, prin. Fax 987-9015

Southside Christian S 1,100/PK-12
2211 Woodruff Rd 29681 864-234-7595
Dr. Sam Barfell, supt. Fax 234-7048

Spartanburg, Spartanburg, Pop. 36,415
Spartanburg County SD 6
Supt. — See Roebuck
Fairforest MS 800/6-8
4120 N Blackstock Rd 29301 864-576-1270
Dean Ledford, prin. Fax 576-2600

Spartanburg SD 3
Supt. — See Glendale
Broome HS 900/9-12
381 Cherry Hill Rd 29307 864-279-6700
Rodney Graves, prin. Fax 279-6710

Spartanburg SD 7 7,300/PK-12
PO Box 970 29304 864-594-4400
Dr. Russell W. Booker, supt. Fax 594-4406
www.spart7.org
Carver MS 500/6-8
467 S Church St 29306 864-594-4435
Nicole Thompson, prin. Fax 594-6144
McCracken MS 700/6-8
300 Webber Rd 29307 864-594-4457
Margaret Peach, prin. Fax 596-8418
Morgan Technology Center Vo/Tech
201 Zion Hill Rd 29307 864-579-2810
Bill Price, prin. Fax 579-7392
Spartanburg County Alternative S Alt
364 Successful Way 29303 864-594-4482
Paul Hughes, prin. Fax 594-6154
Spartanburg HS Freshman Academy 500/9-9
50 Emory Rd 29307 864-594-4513
Jada Kidd, dir. Fax 594-4518
Spartanburg SHS 1,300/10-12
500 Dupre Dr 29307 864-594-4410
Jeff Stevens, prin. Fax 594-6142

Converse College Post-Sec.
580 E Main St 29302 864-596-9000
Oakbrook Preparatory S 400/K-12
190 Lincoln School Rd 29301 864-587-2060
Sherman College of Chiropractic Post-Sec.
PO Box 1452 29304 864-578-8770
South Carolina School for Deaf and Blind Post-Sec.
355 Cedar Springs Rd 29302 864-577-7557
Spartanburg Christian Academy 500/PK-12
8740 Asheville Hwy 29316 864-578-4238
Robert McDonald, hdmstr. Fax 542-1846
Spartanburg Community College Post-Sec.
PO Box 4386 29305 864-592-4800
Spartanburg Day S 400/PK-12
1701 Skylyn Dr 29307 864-582-7539
Rachel Deems, head sch Fax 582-7530
Spartanburg Methodist College Post-Sec.
1000 Powell Mill Rd 29301 864-587-4000
University of South Carolina Post-Sec.
800 University Way 29303 864-503-5000
Virginia College Post-Sec.
8150 Warren H Abernathy Hwy 29301 864-504-3200
Westgate Christian S 200/PK-12
1990 Old Reidville Rd 29301 864-576-4953
Wofford College Post-Sec.
429 N Church St 29303 864-597-4000

Starr, Anderson, Pop. 170
Anderson SD 3
Supt. — See Iva
Starr-Iva MS 600/6-8
1034 Rainey Rd 29684 864-352-6146
Daniel Crawford, prin. Fax 352-2095

Summerton, Clarendon, Pop. 994
Clarendon SD 1 800/PK-12
PO Box 38 29148 803-485-2325
Dr. Rose Wilder, supt. Fax 485-2822
www.clarendon1.k12.sc.us
Scott's Branch HS 200/9-12
9253 Alex Harvin Hwy 29148 803-574-2100
Dr. Gwendolyn Harris, prin. Fax 478-7659
Scott's Branch MS 100/7-8
9253 Alex Harvin Hwy 29148 803-574-2100
Dr. Gwendolyn Harris, prin. Fax 478-7659

Clarendon Hall S 200/PK-12
PO Box 609 29148 803-485-3550
Phillip Rizzo, hdmstr. Fax 485-3205

Summerville, Dorchester, Pop. 42,232
Berkeley County SD
Supt. — See Moncks Corner
Cane Bay HS 1,500/9-12
1624 State Rd, 843-899-8786
Dr. Lee Westberry, prin. Fax 899-8789
Cane Bay MS 700/5-8
1175 Cane Bay Blvd, 843-899-1857
Carol Beckmann-Bartlett, prin. Fax 899-1861

Dorchester SD 2 23,800/K-12
102 Greenwave Blvd 29483 843-873-2901
Joseph Pye, supt. Fax 821-4053
www.edlinesites.net/pages/Dorchester_County_SD
Alston MS 900/6-8
500 Bryan St 29483 843-873-3890
Thad Schmenk, prin. Fax 821-3978
Ashley Ridge HS 2,100/9-12
9800 Delemar Hwy 29485 843-695-4900
Karen Radcliffe, prin. Fax 695-4905
DuBose MS 1,100/6-8
1005 DuBose School Rd 29483 843-875-7012
Ted Brinkley, prin. Fax 821-3995
Gregg MS 1,100/6-8
500 Greenwave Blvd 29483 843-871-3150
Will Wilson, prin. Fax 821-3992
Rollings MS of the Arts 700/6-8
815 S Main St 29483 843-873-3610
Dr. Kathy Sobolewski, prin. Fax 821-3985
Summerville HS 2,800/9-12
1101 Boone Hill Rd 29483 843-873-6460
Kenneth Farrell, prin. Fax 821-3989

Adult Education Adult
1325-A Boone Hill Dr 29483 843-873-7372
Mona Caudle, dir.
Other Schools – See Ladson, North Charleston, Ridgeville

Faith Christian S 300/PK-12
337 Farmington Rd, 843-873-8464
David Freberg, head sch Fax 923-6806
Northwood Academy 400/6-12
104 Charger Dr, 843-764-2285
Dr. Darlene Anderson, prin. Fax 764-3713
Pinewood Preparatory S 800/PK-12
1114 Orangeburg Rd 29483 843-873-1643
Stephen Mandell, hdmstr. Fax 821-4257
Ridge Christian Academy 200/PK-12
2168 Ridge Church Rd 29483 843-873-9856

Sumter, Sumter, Pop. 39,747
Sumter SD 16,800/PK-12
1345 Wilson Hall Rd 29150 803-469-6900
Dr. J. Frank Baker, supt. Fax 469-3769
sumterschools.net
Alice Drive MS 800/6-8
40 Miller Rd 29150 803-775-0821
Jeannie Pressley, prin. Fax 778-2929
Bates MS 700/6-8
715 Estate St 29150 803-775-0711
Dr. Ayesha Hunter, prin. Fax 775-0715
Brewington Academy Alt
4300 E Brewington Rd 29153 803-495-8069
Robert Barth, prin. Fax 495-8068
Chestnut Oaks MS 500/6-8
1200 Oswego Hwy 29153 803-775-7272
Dr. Maggie Wright, prin. Fax 775-7601
Crestwood HS 1,200/9-12
2000 Oswego Hwy 29153 803-469-6200
Dr. Shirley Gamble, prin. Fax 469-7678
Ebenezer MS 400/6-8
3440 Ebenezer Rd 29153 803-469-8571
Marlene DeWit, prin. Fax 469-8575
Furman MS 900/6-8
3400 Bethel Church Rd 29154 803-481-8519
Michael Riggins, prin. Fax 481-8923
Lakewood HS 1,100/9-12
350 Old Manning Rd 29150 803-506-2700
John Michalik, prin. Fax 506-2712
Mayewood MS 200/6-8
4300 E Brewington Rd 29153 803-495-8014
Anita Hunter, prin. Fax 495-8016
Sumter Career and Technology Center Vo/Tech
2612 McCrays Mill Rd 29154 803-481-8575
Dr. Shirrie Miller, dir. Fax 481-4232
Sumter HS 2,300/9-12
2580 McCrays Mill Rd 29154 803-481-4480
Nicholas Pearson, prin. Fax 481-4021
Sumter Adult Ed Center Adult
905 N Main St 29150 803-778-6432
Sharon Teigue, dir. Fax 775-4665
Other Schools – See Dalzell

Central Carolina Technical College Post-Sec.
506 N Guignard Dr 29150 803-778-1961
Morris College Post-Sec.
100 W College St 29150 803-934-3200
St. Francis Xavier HS 50/9-12
15 School St 29150 803-773-0210
Kristi Doyle, prin. Fax 775-0119
Sumter Beauty College Post-Sec.
921 Carolina Ave 29150 803-773-7311
Sumter Christian S 200/PK-12
420 S Pike W 29150 803-773-1902
Rev. Ron Davis, admin. Fax 775-1676
University of South Carolina Post-Sec.
200 Miller Rd 29150 803-775-8727
Wilson Hall 800/PK-12
520 Wilson Hall Rd 29150 803-469-3475

Swansea, Lexington, Pop. 808
Lexington County SD 4 3,300/PK-12
607 E 5th St 29160 803-490-7000
Dr. Linda Lavender, supt.
www.lexington4.net
Swansea HS Freshman Academy 50/9-9
1195 I W Hutto Rd 29160 803-490-7006
Shaun Jacques, prin.
Swansea SHS, 500 E 1st St 29160 600/10-12
Craig Baker, prin. 803-490-7007
Other Schools – See Gaston

Taylors, Greenville, Pop. 21,240
Greenville County SD
Supt. — See Greenville
Eastside HS 1,400/9-12
1300 Brushy Creek Rd 29687 864-355-2800
Mike Thorne, prin. Fax 355-2992
Northwood MS 900/6-8
710 Ikes Rd 29687 864-355-7000
Treva Lee, prin. Fax 355-7077

Tega Cay, York, Pop. 7,516
Fort Mill SD
Supt. — See Fort Mill
Gold Hill MS 700/6-8
1025 Dave Gibson Blvd 29708 803-548-8300
Matthew Wallace, prin. Fax 548-8322

Tigerville, Greenville, Pop. 1,267

North Greenville University Post-Sec.
PO Box 1892 29688 864-977-7000

Timmonsville, Florence, Pop. 2,312
Florence County SD Four 700/PK-12
304 Kemper St 29161 843-346-3956
Zona W. Jefferson, supt. Fax 346-5159
www.florence4.k12.sc.us
Johnson MS 200/6-8
304 Kemper St 29161 843-346-4586
Tonya Addison, prin. Fax 346-5159
Timmonsville HS 200/9-12
304 Kemper St 29161 843-346-4586
Tonya Addison, prin. Fax 346-5416

Timmonsville Adult Education Center — Adult
304 Kemper St 29161 — 843-346-3956
Gloria Q. Bracey, coord. — Fax 346-5159

Travelers Rest, Greenville, Pop. 4,504
Greenville County SD
Supt. — See Greenville
Northwest MS — 800/6-8
1606 Geer Hwy 29690 — 864-355-6900
David McDonald, prin. — Fax 355-6920
Travelers Rest HS — 1,200/9-12
301 N Main St 29690 — 864-355-0000
Louis Lavely, prin. — Fax 355-0088

Turbeville, Clarendon, Pop. 765
Clarendon SD 3 — 1,200/PK-12
PO Box 270 29162 — 843-659-2188
Connie Dennis Ph.D., supt. — Fax 659-3204
www.clarendon3.org/
East Clarendon MSHS — 700/6-12
PO Box 153 29162 — 843-659-2187
Jason Cook, prin. — Fax 659-2192

Union, Union, Pop. 8,281
Union County SD — 3,800/K-12
PO Box 907 29379 — 864-429-1740
William F. Roach Ph.D., supt. — Fax 429-1745
www.union.k12.sc.us
Sims MS — 700/6-8
2200 Whitmire Hwy 29379 — 864-429-1755
Eric Childers, prin. — Fax 429-2811
Union County HS — 1,200/9-12
1163 Lakeside Dr 29379 — 864-429-1750
Dr. Shannon Gibson, prin. — Fax 429-5401

University of South Carolina — Post-Sec.
PO Box 729 29379 — 864-429-8728

Varnville, Hampton, Pop. 2,133
Hampton SD 1 — 2,400/PK-12
372 Pine St E 29944 — 803-943-4576
Doug McTeer, supt. — Fax 943-5943
www.hampton1.org
Hampton HS — 700/9-12
115 Airport Rd 29944 — 803-943-3568
Bonnie Wilson, prin. — Fax 943-5036
North District MS — 400/7-8
PO Box 368 29944 — 803-943-3507
Patricia Brantley, prin. — Fax 943-4074

Wagener, Aiken, Pop. 778
Aiken County SD
Supt. — See Aiken
Corbett MS — 200/6-8
10 Corbett Cir 29164 — 803-564-1050
Sonya Colvin, prin. — Fax 564-1058
Wagener-Salley HS — 300/9-12
272 Main St S 29164 — 803-564-1100
Ute Aadland, prin. — Fax 564-1109

Walhalla, Oconee, Pop. 4,200
Oconee County SD — 10,900/PK-12
414 S Pine St 29691 — 864-886-4400
Dr. Michael Thorsland, supt. — Fax 886-4408
www.oconee.k12.sc.us
Oconee Academy — Alt
177 Razorback Ln 29691 — 864-886-4431
Tracey Long, coord. — Fax 886-4432
Walhalla HS — 1,000/9-12
4701 N Highway 11 29691 — 864-886-4490
Steve Garrett, prin. — Fax 886-4488
Walhalla MS — 800/6-8
151 Razorback Ln 29691 — 864-886-4485
Scott Dixon, prin. — Fax 886-4483
Other Schools – See Seneca, Westminster

Walterboro, Colleton, Pop. 5,325
Colleton County SD — 6,100/PK-12
213 N Jefferies Blvd 29488 — 843-782-4510
Dr. Franklin Foster, supt. — Fax 549-2606
colletonsd.org
Colleton County HS — 1,600/9-12
150 Cougar Nation Dr 29488 — 843-782-0031
Dr. Melissa Crosby, prin. — Fax 782-0042
Colleton MS — 1,500/6-8
1379 Tuskegee Airmen Dr 29488 — 843-782-0040
Matthew Brantley, prin. — Fax 782-0041
Thunderbolt Career & Technology Center — Vo/Tech
1069 Thunderbolt Dr 29488 — 843-782-4514
Mr William Hayden, dir. — Fax 538-3009
Adult Education — Adult
609 Colleton Loop 29488 — 843-782-0018
Lynn Jones, dir. — Fax 549-6285

Colleton Prep Academy — 200/PK-12
PO Box 1426 29488 — 843-538-8959
Jill Burttram, head sch — Fax 538-8260
Cosmetic Arts Institute — Post-Sec.
1789 Hampton St 29488 — 843-549-8587

Ware Shoals, Greenwood, Pop. 2,149
Greenwood SD 51 — 800/PK-12
56 S Greenwood Ave 29692 — 864-456-7496
Dr. Fay Sprouse, supt.
www.gwd51.org
Ware Shoals HS — 300/9-12
56 S Greenwood Ave 29692 — 864-456-7923
Paul Anderson, prin. — Fax 456-2370
Ware Shoals MS — 100/5-8
45 W Main St 29692 — 864-456-2711
Nancy Brown, prin. — Fax 456-2153

Warrenville, Aiken, Pop. 1,205
Aiken County SD
Supt. — See Aiken
Aiken County Career & Technical Center — Vo/Tech
2455 Jefferson Davis Hwy 29851 — 803-593-7300
William Hudson, dir. — Fax 593-7115
Langley-Bath-Clearwater MS — 600/6-8
29 Lions Trl 29851 — 803-593-7260
Brenda DeLoache, prin. — Fax 593-7119

West Columbia, Lexington, Pop. 14,742
Lexington County SD 1
Supt. — See Lexington
White Knoll MS — 800/6-8
116 White Knoll Way 29170 — 803-821-4300
Guy Smith, prin. — Fax 821-4303

Lexington County SD 2 — 8,800/PK-12
715 9th St 29169 — 803-796-4708
Dr. William B. James Ph.D., supt. — Fax 739-4063
www.lex2.org/
Airport HS — 1,300/9-12
1315 Boston Ave 29170 — 803-822-5600
Brad Coleman, prin. — Fax 822-5665
Fulmer MS — 700/6-8
1614 Walterboro St 29170 — 803-822-5660
Megan Carrero, prin. — Fax 822-5664
Northside MS — 600/6-8
157 Cougar Dr 29169 — 803-739-4190
Lisa Davis, prin. — Fax 739-3188
Pair Education Center — Alt
2325 Platt Springs Rd 29169 — 803-739-4085
Christina R. Hall, prin. — Fax 739-3195
Pine Ridge MS — 500/6-8
735 Pine Ridge Dr 29172 — 803-755-7400
Dr. David Basile, prin. — Fax 755-7449
Other Schools – See Cayce

State Supported Schools
Supt. — None
Gray Opportunity S — 9-12
3300 W Campus Rd 29170 — 803-896-6480
Pat Smith, dir. — Fax 896-6463

Westminster, Oconee, Pop. 2,380
Oconee County SD
Supt. — See Walhalla
West-Oak HS — 1,000/9-12
130 Warrior Ln 29693 — 864-886-4530
Kurt Kreuzberger, prin. — Fax 886-4527
West Oak MS — 700/6-8
501 Westminster Hwy 29693 — 864-886-4525
Jami Verderosa, prin. — Fax 886-4524

Foothills Christian S — 100/K-12
126 Robin Rd 29693 — 864-647-1220
Joe Mullet, prin.

Whitmire, Newberry, Pop. 1,424
Newberry County SD
Supt. — See Newberry
Whitmire Community S — 300/K-12
2597 Hwy 66 29178 — 803-694-2320
Joey Haney, prin. — Fax 694-3835

Williamston, Anderson, Pop. 3,887
Anderson SD 1 — 9,400/PK-12
PO Box 99 29697 — 864-847-7344
David Havird, supt. — Fax 847-3543
www.anderson1.k12.sc.us
Palmetto HS — 1,000/9-12
804 N Hamilton St 29697 — 864-847-7311
Robert Roach, prin. — Fax 847-3532
Palmetto MS — 800/6-8
803 N Hamilton St 29697 — 864-847-4333
Barry Knight, prin. — Fax 847-3529
Other Schools – See Greenville, Piedmont

Area Vocational Schools
Supt. — None
Career & Technology Center — Vo/Tech
702 Belton Hwy 29697 — 864-847-4121
Dr. Hollie Harrell, dir. — Fax 847-3539

Williston, Barnwell, Pop. 3,095
Williston SD 29 — 1,000/PK-12
12255 Main St 29853 — 803-266-7878
Dr. Missoura G. Ashe, supt. — Fax 266-3879
www.williston.k12.sc.us
Williston-Elko HS — 300/9-12
12233 Main St 29853 — 803-266-3110
Alison Brady, prin. — Fax 266-5489
Williston-Elko MS — 200/6-8
12333 Main St 29853 — 803-266-3430
Greg Sweet, prin. — Fax 266-7623

Winnsboro, Fairfield, Pop. 3,508
Fairfield County SD — 3,100/PK-12
PO Box 622 29180 — 803-635-4607
Dr. J.R. Green, supt. — Fax 635-6578
www.fairfield.k12.sc.us
Fairfield Career & Technology Center — Vo/Tech
790 US Highway 321 Byp S 29180 — 803-635-5506
Christopher Dinkins, prin. — Fax 635-9958
Fairfield Central HS — 800/9-12
836 US Highway 321 Byp S 29180 — 803-635-1441
Tracie Swilley, prin. — Fax 635-3997
Fairfield MS — 400/7-8
728 US Highway 321 Byp S 29180 — 803-635-4270
Dr. Robin Hardy, prin. — Fax 635-9108
Gordon Odyssey Academy — 200/Alt
560 Fairfield St 29180 — 803-635-4859
LaNisha Tindal Ed.D., dir. — Fax 635-5835

Winn Academy — 300/PK-12
PO Box 390 29180 — 803-635-5494
Brandy Mullennax M.Ed., head sch — Fax 635-4310

Woodruff, Spartanburg, Pop. 3,990
Spartanburg SD 4 — 2,800/PK-12
118 McEdco Rd 29388 — 864-476-3186
Dr. W. Rallie Liston, supt. — Fax 476-8616
www.spartanburg4.org
Woodruff HS — 800/9-12
710 Cross Anchor Rd 29388 — 864-476-7045
Dr. Aaron Fulmer, prin. — Fax 476-7224
Woodruff MS — 600/6-8
205 SJ Workman Hwy 29388 — 864-476-3150
Denise Brown, prin. — Fax 476-6036

York, York, Pop. 7,594
York SD 1 — 5,100/PK-12
PO Box 770 29745 — 803-684-9916
Dr. Vernon Prosser, supt. — Fax 684-1903
www.york.k12.sc.us
Johnson Technology Center — Vo/Tech
275 E Alexander Love Hwy 29745 — 803-684-1910
Carrie Bolin, dir. — Fax 684-1913
York Comprehensive HS — 1,500/9-12
275 E Alexander Love Hwy 29745 — 803-684-2336
Chris Black, prin. — Fax 684-1932
York MS — 800/7-8
1010 Devinney Rd 29745 — 803-684-5008
Richard Ball, prin. — Fax 684-1916
York One Academy — Alt
37 Pinckney St 29745 — 803-684-2381
Shelton Clinton, prin. — Fax 684-1932

SOUTH DAKOTA

SOUTH DAKOTA DEPARTMENT OF EDUCATION

800 Governors Dr, Pierre 57501-2235
Telephone 605-773-3134
Fax 605-773-6139
Website doe.sd.gov/

Secretary of Education Dr. Melody Schopp

SOUTH DAKOTA BOARD OF EDUCATION

700 Governors Dr, Pierre 57501-2291

President Donald Kirkegaard

EDUCATIONAL COOPERATIVES

Educational Service Agency Region 2
Joan Frevik, supt. 605-367-7680
715 E 14th St, Sioux Falls 57104 Fax 367-6036
www.edec.org

Mid Central Educational Cooperative
Robert Krietlow, dir. 605-337-2636
PO Box 228, Platte 57369 Fax 337-2271
midcentral-coop.org

NE Educational Services Cooperatives
Gerald Aberle, dir. 605-783-3607
310 5th St, Hayti 57241

Northwest Area Schools
Quinn Lenk, dir. 605-466-2206
PO Box 35, Isabel 57633 Fax 466-2207
www.nwascoop.org

Southeast Area Cooperative
Tricia West, dir. 605-763-5096
1109 W Cedar St, Beresford 57004 Fax 763-2206
southeastareacoop.org

PUBLIC, PRIVATE AND CATHOLIC SECONDARY SCHOOLS

Aberdeen, Brown, Pop. 25,591
Aberdeen SD 6-1 4,200/K-12
1224 S 3rd St 57401 605-725-7100
Dr. Becky Guffin, supt. Fax 725-7199
www.aberdeen.k12.sd.us
A-Tec Academy Vo/Tech
2014 Melgaard Rd 57401 605-725-8281
Scott Pudwill, dir.
Central HS 1,200/9-12
2200 S Roosevelt St 57401 605-725-8100
Jason Uttermark, prin. Fax 725-8199
Holgate MS 500/6-8
2200 N Dakota St 57401 605-725-7700
Dr. Greg Aas, prin. Fax 725-7799
Simmons MS 500/6-8
1300 S 3rd St 57401 605-725-7900
Colleen Murley, prin. Fax 725-7999

Aberdeen Christian S 200/PK-12
1500 N Highway 281 57401 605-225-2053
Eric Kline, supt. Fax 226-2106
Northern State University Post-Sec.
1200 S Jay St 57401 605-626-3011
Presentation College Post-Sec.
1500 N Main St 57401 800-437-6060
Roncalli HS 300/7-12
1400 N Dakota St 57401 605-226-7440
Ed Mitzel, prin. Fax 226-0616
St. Luke's Midland Regional Medical Ctr. Post-Sec.
305 S State St 57401 605-622-5230
South Dakota School Visually Handicapped Post-Sec.
423 17th Ave SE 57401 605-626-2580

Alcester, Union, Pop. 801
Alcester-Hudson SD 61-1 300/PK-12
PO Box 198 57001 605-934-1890
Tim Rhead, supt. Fax 934-1936
www.alcester-hudson.k12.sd.us
Alcester-Hudson HS 100/9-12
PO Box 198 57001 605-934-1890
LeeAnn Haisch, prin. Fax 934-1936
Alcester-Hudson JHS 100/7-8
PO Box 198 57001 605-934-1890
LeeAnn Haisch, prin. Fax 934-1936

Alexandria, Hanson, Pop. 613
Hanson SD 30-1 400/PK-12
PO Box 490 57311 605-239-4387
James Bridge, supt. Fax 239-4293
www.hanson.k12.sd.us/
Hanson HS 100/9-12
PO Box 490 57311 605-239-4387
Ray Slaba, prin. Fax 239-4293
Hanson MS 100/6-8
PO Box 490 57311 605-239-4387
Ray Slaba, prin. Fax 239-4293
Other Schools – See Mitchell

Arlington, Kingsbury, Pop. 909
Arlington SD 38-1 300/PK-12
PO Box 359 57212 605-983-5597
Justin Downes, supt. Fax 983-2820
www.arlington.k12.sd.us
Arlington HS 100/9-12
PO Box 359 57212 605-983-5598
Rhonda Gross, prin. Fax 983-4652
Arlington JHS 50/7-8
PO Box 359 57212 605-983-5598
Rhonda Gross, prin. Fax 983-4652

Oldham-Ramona SD 39-5
Supt. — See Ramona
Spring Lake Colony HS 50/9-12
21727 452nd Ave 57212 605-482-8244
Tom Ludens, prin. Fax 482-8282

Armour, Douglas, Pop. 693
Armour SD 21-1 200/K-12
PO Box 640 57313 605-724-2153
Andrea Powell, supt. Fax 724-2977
www.armour.k12.sd.us/
Armour HS 100/9-12
PO Box 640 57313 605-724-2153
Brad Preheim, prin. Fax 724-2799
Armour MS 50/6-8
PO Box 640 57313 605-724-2698
Andrea Powell, prin. Fax 724-2799

Avon, Bon Homme, Pop. 586
Avon SD 4-1 300/PK-12
PO Box 407 57315 605-286-3291
Tom Culver, supt. Fax 286-3712
www.avon.k12.sd.us
Avon HS 100/9-12
PO Box 407 57315 605-286-3291
James Stubkjaer, prin. Fax 286-3510
Avon JHS 50/7-8
PO Box 407 57315 605-286-3291
James Stubkjaer, prin. Fax 286-3510

Baltic, Minnehaha, Pop. 1,070
Baltic SD 49-1 500/PK-12
PO Box 309 57003 605-529-5464
Robert Sittig, supt. Fax 529-5443
www.balticschool.org
Baltic HS 100/9-12
PO Box 309 57003 605-529-5461
James Aisenbrey, prin. Fax 529-5467
Baltic MS 100/6-8
PO Box 309 57003 605-529-5461
James Aisenbrey, prin. Fax 529-5467

Batesland, Shannon, Pop. 108
Oglala Lakota County SD 65-1 1,500/PK-8
PO Box 109 57716 605-288-1921
Dr. Julie Ertz, supt. Fax 288-1814
www.shannon.ws
Other Schools – See Pine Ridge, Porcupine

Belle Fourche, Butte, Pop. 5,472
Belle Fourche SD 9-1 1,400/K-12
2305 13th Ave 57717 605-723-3355
Dr. Steve Willard, supt. Fax 723-3366
www.bellefourcheschools.org
Belle Fourche Education Connection 50/Alt
2305 13th Ave 57717 605-723-0955
Mathew Raba, prin. Fax 723-0941
Belle Fourche HS 400/9-12
2305 13th Ave 57717 605-723-3350
Mathew Raba, prin. Fax 723-3357
Belle Fourche MS 400/5-8
2305 13th Ave 57717 605-723-3367
Kevin Smidt, prin. Fax 723-3374

Beresford, Union, Pop. 1,991
Beresford SD 61-2 600/PK-12
301 W Maple St 57004 605-763-4293
Brian Field, supt. Fax 763-5305
www.beresford.k12.sd.us/
Beresford HS 200/9-12
301 W Maple St 57004 605-763-2145
Dustin Degen, prin. Fax 763-5305
Beresford MS 200/6-8
205 W Maple St 57004 605-763-2139
Dustin Degen, prin. Fax 763-5305

Big Stone City, Grant, Pop. 465
Big Stone CSD 25-1 100/PK-8
655 Walnut St 57216 605-862-8108
Christopher Folk, supt. Fax 862-8640
bigstonecitylions.weebly.com
Big Stone City JHS 50/6-8
655 Walnut St 57216 605-862-8108
Shelley Haggerty, prin. Fax 862-8640

Bison, Perkins, Pop. 326
Bison SD 52-1 100/K-12
PO Box 9 57620 605-244-5961
Marilyn Azevedo, supt. Fax 244-5276
www.bison.k12.sd.us/
Bison HS 100/9-12
PO Box 9 57620 605-244-5271
Marilyn Azevedo, supt. Fax 244-5276
Bison JHS 50/7-8
PO Box 9 57620 605-244-5271
Marilyn Azevedo, supt. Fax 244-5276

Bonesteel, Gregory, Pop. 272
South Central SD 26-5 100/PK-12
401 Birdsell St 57317 605-654-2314
Brad Peters, supt.
southcentral.k12.sd.us
South Central HS 50/9-12
401 Birdsell St 57317 605-654-2314
Dr. Cheryl Thaler, supt.
South Central MS 50/6-8
401 Birdsell St 57317 605-654-2314
Dr. Cheryl Thaler, supt.

Bowdle, Edmunds, Pop. 501
Bowdle SD 22-1 100/K-12
PO Box 563 57428 605-285-6272
Justin Birchem, supt. Fax 285-6830
www.bowdle.k12.sd.us
Bowdle HS 50/9-12
PO Box 563 57428 605-285-6590
Justin Birchem, prin. Fax 285-6830
Bowdle JHS 50/7-8
PO Box 563 57428 605-285-6590
Justin Birchem, prin. Fax 285-6830

Box Elder, Pennington, Pop. 7,381
Douglas SD 51-1 2,700/PK-12
400 Patriot Dr 57719 605-923-0000
Alan Kerr, supt. Fax 923-0018
www.dsdk12.net
Douglas HS 700/9-12
420 Patriot Dr 57719 605-923-0030
Bud Gusso, prin. Fax 923-0031
Douglas MS 600/6-8
401 Tower Rd 57719 605-923-0050
Dan Baldwin, prin. Fax 923-0051

Brandon, Minnehaha, Pop. 8,690
Brandon Valley SD 49-2 3,200/PK-12
300 S Splitrock Blvd 57005 605-582-2049
Dr. Jarod Larson, supt. Fax 582-7456
brandonvalleyschools.com
Brandon Valley HS 1,000/9-12
301 S Splitrock Blvd 57005 605-582-3211
Dr. Gregg Talcott, prin. Fax 582-2652
Brandon Valley MS 500/7-8
700 E Holly Blvd 57005 605-582-3214
Brad Thorson, prin. Fax 582-7206

Bridgewater, McCook, Pop. 491
Bridgewater-Emery SD 30-3 300/PK-12
PO Box 350 57319 605-729-2541
Jason Bailey, supt. Fax 449-4270
www.bridgewater-emery.k12.sd.us/
Other Schools – See Emery

Britton, Marshall, Pop. 1,232
Britton-Hecla SD 45-4 500/PK-12
PO Box 190 57430 605-448-2234
Steve Benson, supt. Fax 448-5994
www.britton.k12.sd.us

Britton-Hecla HS 200/9-12
PO Box 190 57430 605-448-2234
Carrie James, prin. Fax 448-5994
Britton-Hecla JHS 50/7-8
PO Box 190 57430 605-448-2234
Carrie James, prin. Fax 448-5994

Brookings, Brookings, Pop. 21,716
Brookings SD 5-1 3,200/K-12
2130 8th St S 57006 605-696-4700
Dr. Klint Willert, supt. Fax 696-4704
www.brookings.k12.sd.us
Brookings HS 900/9-12
530 Elm Ave 57006 605-696-4100
Paul vonFischer, prin. Fax 696-4128
Mickelson MS 700/6-8
1801 12th St S 57006 605-696-4500
Tim Steffensen, prin. Fax 696-4506

South Dakota State University 57007 Post-Sec.
605-688-4151

Buffalo, Harding, Pop. 328
Harding County SD 31-1 200/K-12
PO Box 367 57720 605-375-3241
Josh Page, supt. Fax 375-3246
www.hardingcounty.k12.sd.us
Harding County HS 100/9-12
PO Box 367 57720 605-375-3241
Kelly Messmer, prin. Fax 375-3246
Harding County MS 50/6-8
PO Box 367 57720 605-375-3241
Kelly Messmer, prin. Fax 375-3246

Burke, Gregory, Pop. 594
Burke SD 26-2 200/PK-12
PO Box 382 57523 605-775-2644
Erik Person, supt. Fax 775-2468
www.burke.k12.sd.us
Burke HS 100/9-12
PO Box 382 57523 605-775-2645
Mark Otten, prin. Fax 775-2468
Burke MS 50/7-8
PO Box 382 57523 605-775-2645
Mark Otten, prin. Fax 775-2468

Canistota, McCook, Pop. 646
Canistota SD 43-1 200/K-12
PO Box 8 57012 605-296-3458
Larry Nebelsick, supt. Fax 296-3158
www.canistota.k12.sd.us
Canistota HS 100/9-12
PO Box 8 57012 605-296-3458
Lenny Schroeder, prin. Fax 296-3158
Canistota MS 50/6-8
PO Box 8 57012 605-296-3458
Lenny Schroeder, prin. Fax 296-3158

Canton, Lincoln, Pop. 3,010
Canton SD 41-1 900/PK-12
800 N Main St 57013 605-764-2706
Terry Gerber, supt. Fax 764-2700
www.canton.k12.sd.us
Canton HS 300/9-12
800 N Main St 57013 605-764-2706
Russell Townsend, prin. Fax 764-2700
Canton MS 200/6-8
800 N Main St 57013 605-764-2706
Russell Townsend, prin. Fax 764-2700

Castlewood, Hamlin, Pop. 623
Castlewood SD 28-1 300/PK-12
310 E Harry St 57223 605-793-2497
Keith Fodness, supt. Fax 793-2679
www.castlewood.k12.sd.us/
Castlewood HS 100/9-12
310 E Harry St 57223 605-793-2497
Keith Fodness, prin. Fax 793-2679
Castlewood JHS 50/7-8
310 E Harry St 57223 605-793-2497
Keith Fodness, prin. Fax 793-2679

Centerville, Turner, Pop. 877
Centerville SD 60-1 200/PK-12
PO Box 100 57014 605-563-2291
Tim Hagedorn, supt. Fax 563-2615
www.centerville.k12.sd.us
Centerville HS 100/9-12
PO Box 100 57014 605-563-2291
Doug Edberg, prin. Fax 563-2615
Centerville JHS 100/5-8
PO Box 100 57014 605-563-2291
Doug Edberg, prin. Fax 563-2615

Chamberlain, Brule, Pop. 2,326
Chamberlain SD 7-1 900/PK-12
PO Box 119 57325 605-234-4477
Debra Johnson, supt. Fax 234-4479
www.chamberlain.k12.sd.us
Chamberlain HS 300/9-12
PO Box 119 57325 605-234-4467
Rick Pearson, prin. Fax 234-4479
Chamberlain JHS 100/7-8
PO Box 119 57325 605-234-4467
Rick Pearson, prin. Fax 234-4479

Chester, Lake, Pop. 257
Chester Area SD 39-1 600/PK-12
PO Box 159 57016 605-489-2411
Heath Larson, supt. Fax 489-2413
www.chester.k12.sd.us
Chester HS 100/9-12
PO Box 159 57016 605-489-2411
Julie Eppard, prin. Fax 489-2413
Chester MS 100/6-8
PO Box 159 57016 605-489-2411
Julie Eppard, prin. Fax 489-2413
High Plains Alternative S 50/Alt
PO Box 159 57016 605-489-2411
Amy Larson, prin. Fax 489-2413

Clark, Clark, Pop. 1,130
Clark SD 12-2 400/PK-12
220 N Clinton St 57225 605-532-3605
Luanne Warren, supt. Fax 532-3600
clark.k12.sd.us/
Clark HS 100/9-12
220 N Clinton St 57225 605-532-3605
Jerry Hartley, prin. Fax 532-3600
Clark MS 100/5-8
220 N Clinton St 57225 605-532-3604
Jerry Hartley, prin. Fax 532-3600

Clear Lake, Deuel, Pop. 1,256
Deuel SD 19-4 500/PK-12
PO Box 770 57226 605-874-2161
Dean Christensen, supt. Fax 874-8585
www.deuel.k12.sd.us/
Clear Lake MS 100/6-8
PO Box 770 57226 605-874-2162
Eric Bass, prin. Fax 874-8585
Deuel HS 100/9-12
PO Box 770 57226 605-874-2163
Eric Bass, prin. Fax 874-8585

Colman, Moody, Pop. 586
Colman-Egan SD 50-5 200/K-12
200 S Loban Ave 57017 605-534-3534
Tracey Olson, supt. Fax 534-3670
www.colman-egan.k12.sd.us
Colman-Egan HS 100/9-12
200 S Loban Ave 57017 605-534-3534
Scott Hemmer, prin. Fax 534-3670
Colman-Egan JHS 50/7-8
200 S Loban Ave 57017 605-534-3534
Scott Hemmer, prin. Fax 534-3670

Colome, Tripp, Pop. 291
Colome SD 59-3 200/PK-12
PO Box 367 57528 605-842-1624
Ryan Orrock, supt. Fax 842-0783
www.colome.k12.sd.us
Colome HS 100/9-12
PO Box 367 57528 605-842-1624
Anna LaDeaux, prin. Fax 842-0783
Colome JHS 50/6-8
PO Box 367 57528 605-842-1624
Anna LaDeaux, prin. Fax 842-0783

Colton, Minnehaha, Pop. 682
Tri-Valley SD 49-6 800/PK-12
46450 252nd St 57018 605-446-3538
Mike Lodmel, supt. Fax 446-3520
www.tri-valley.k12.sd.us/
Tri-Valley HS 200/9-12
46450 252nd St 57018 605-446-3538
Tim Pflanz, prin. Fax 446-3520
Tri-Valley JHS 100/7-8
46450 252nd St 57018 605-446-3538
Tim Pflanz, prin. Fax 446-3520

Corsica, Douglas, Pop. 584
Corsica-Stickney SD 21-3 100/PK-12
120 S Napoleon Ave 57328 605-946-5475
Scott Muckey, supt. Fax 946-5607
corsica-stickney.k12.sd.us
Corsica-Stickney HS 50/7-12
120 S Napoleon Ave 57328 605-946-5475
Andrew Fergen, prin. Fax 946-5607

Dakota Christian S 100/PK-12
37614 SD Highway 44 57328 605-243-2211
Donald Mitchell, admin. Fax 243-2379

Custer, Custer, Pop. 2,043
Custer SD 16-1 800/PK-12
527 Montgomery St 57730 605-673-3154
Mark Naugle, supt. Fax 673-5607
www.csd.k12.sd.us
Custer JSHS 300/7-12
1645 Wild Cat Ln 57730 605-673-4473
Orion Thompson, prin. Fax 673-4710

Dell Rapids, Minnehaha, Pop. 3,605
Dell Rapids SD 49-3 900/K-12
1216 N Garfield Ave 57022 605-428-5473
Summer Schultz, supt. Fax 428-5609
dr-k12.org
Dell Rapids HS 300/9-12
1216 N Garfield Ave 57022 605-428-5473
Kimberly Kludt, prin. Fax 428-5609
Dell Rapids MS 300/5-8
1216 N Garfield Ave 57022 605-428-5473
Fran Ruesink, prin. Fax 428-5609

St. Mary JSHS 100/7-12
812 N State Ave 57022 605-428-5591
Casey Michel, prin. Fax 428-5377

De Smet, Kingsbury, Pop. 1,084
De Smet SD 38-2 300/K-12
PO Box 157 57231 605-854-3423
Abi Van Regenmorter, supt. Fax 854-9138
www.desmet.k12.sd.us
De Smet HS 100/9-12
PO Box 157 57231 605-854-3423
Mike Warne, prin. Fax 854-9138
De Smet MS 100/6-8
PO Box 157 57231 605-854-3423
Mike Warne, prin. Fax 854-9138

Dewey, Custer
Elk Mountain SD 16-2 50/K-12
10222 Valley Rd 57735 605-749-2258
Curt Voight, admin. Fax 749-2258
Elk Mountain S 50/K-12
10222 Valley Rd 57735 605-749-2258
Curt Voight, admin. Fax 749-2258

Doland, Spink, Pop. 180
Doland SD 56-2 200/K-12
PO Box 385 57436 605-635-6302
Jim Hulscher, supt. Fax 635-6504
www.doland.k12.sd.us/
Doland HS 50/9-12
PO Box 385 57436 605-635-6241
Jim Hulscher, prin. Fax 635-6504
Doland JHS 50/7-8
PO Box 385 57436 605-635-6241
Jim Hulscher, prin. Fax 635-6504

Dupree, Ziebach, Pop. 511
Dupree SD 64-2 400/PK-12
PO Box 10 57623 605-365-5140
Brian Shanks, supt. Fax 365-5514
www.dupree.k12.sd.us
Dupree HS 100/9-12
PO Box 10 57623 605-365-5140
Pandi Pittman, prin. Fax 365-5514
Dupree JHS 100/7-8
PO Box 10 57623 605-365-5140
Pandi Pittman, prin. Fax 365-5514

Eagle Butte, Dewey, Pop. 1,279
Eagle Butte SD 20-1 300/K-12
PO Box 260 57625 605-964-4911
Carol Veit, supt. Fax 964-4912
ceb.k12.sd.us
Eagle Butte HS 50/9-12
PO Box 672 57625 605-964-8744
Dora Gwin, prin. Fax 964-8700
Eagle Butte JHS 50/7-8
PO Box 672 57625 605-964-7841
Dr. Kathie Bowker, prin. Fax 964-1224
E.A.G.L.E. Center 100/Alt
PO Box 672 57625 605-964-8773
Dr. Vicki Birkeland, prin. Fax 964-1218

Edgemont, Fall River, Pop. 746
Edgemont SD 23-1 200/K-12
PO Box 29 57735 605-662-7294
Dave Cortney, supt. Fax 662-7721
edgemont.k12.sd.us
Edgemont HS 50/9-12
PO Box 29 57735 605-662-7254
Dave Cortney, admin. Fax 662-7721

Elk Point, Union, Pop. 1,939
Elk Point-Jefferson SD 61-7 700/PK-12
PO Box 578 57025 605-356-5950
Sheri Hardman, supt. Fax 356-5953
www.epj.k12.sd.us
Elk Point-Jefferson HS 200/9-12
PO Box 578 57025 605-356-5900
Travis Aslesen, prin. Fax 356-5999
Elk Point-Jefferson MS 100/6-8
PO Box 578 57025 605-356-5900
Travis Aslesen, prin. Fax 356-5999

Elkton, Brookings, Pop. 721
Elkton SD 5-3 300/PK-12
PO Box 190 57026 605-542-2541
Brian Jandahl, supt. Fax 542-4441
elkton.k12.sd.us
Elkton HS 100/9-12
PO Box 190 57026 605-542-2541
Kelly Neill, prin. Fax 542-4441
Elkton JHS 100/7-8
PO Box 190 57026 605-542-2541
Kelly Neill, prin. Fax 542-4441

Ellsworth AFB, Meade, Pop. 7,017

National American University Post-Sec.
1000 Ellsworth St Ste 2400B 57706 605-718-6550

Emery, Hanson, Pop. 443
Bridgewater-Emery SD 30-3
Supt. — See Bridgewater
Bridgewater-Emery HS 100/9-12
130 N 6th St 57332 605-449-4271
Christena Schultz, prin. Fax 449-4270
Bridgewater-Emery MS 100/6-8
130 N 6th St 57332 605-449-4271
Christena Schultz, prin. Fax 449-4270

Estelline, Hamlin, Pop. 763
Estelline SD 28-2 300/K-12
PO Box 306 57234 605-873-2201
Jim Lentz, supt. Fax 873-2102
www.estellineschool.com
Estelline HS 100/7-12
PO Box 306 57234 605-873-2201
Jim Lentz, prin. Fax 873-2102
Estelline JHS 50/7-8
PO Box 306 57234 605-873-2203
Jim Lentz, prin. Fax 873-2102

Ethan, Davison, Pop. 328
Ethan SD 17-1 300/PK-12
PO Box 169 57334 605-227-4211
Terry Eckstaine, supt. Fax 227-4236
www.ethan.k12.sd.us/
Ethan HS 100/9-12
PO Box 169 57334 605-227-4211
Tim Hawkins, prin. Fax 227-4236
Ethan JHS 50/7-8
PO Box 169 57334 605-227-4211
Tim Hawkins, prin. Fax 227-4236

Eureka, McPherson, Pop. 856
Eureka SD 44-1 200/PK-12
PO Box 10 57437 605-284-2875
Bo Beck, supt. Fax 284-2810
www.eureka.k12.sd.us/
Eureka HS 50/9-12
PO Box 10 57437 605-284-2875
Bo Beck, prin. Fax 284-2810
Eureka MS 50/6-8
PO Box 10 57437 605-284-2875
Bo Beck, prin. Fax 284-2810

Faith, Meade, Pop. 405
Faith SD 46-2 200/PK-12
PO Box 619 57626 605-967-2152
Kelly Daughters, supt. Fax 967-2153
www.faith.k12.sd.us/
Faith HS 100/9-12
PO Box 619 57626 605-967-2152
Kelly Daughters, supt. Fax 967-2153
Faith JHS 50/7-8
PO Box 619 57626 605-967-2152
Don Kraemer, supt. Fax 967-2153

Faulkton, Faulk, Pop. 724
Faulkton Area SD 24-4 300/K-12
PO Box 308 57438 605-598-6266
Derek Barrios, supt. Fax 598-6666
www.faulkton.k12.sd.us
Faulkton HS 100/9-12
PO Box 308 57438 605-598-6266
Craig Cassens, prin. Fax 598-6666
Faulkton JHS 50/7-8
PO Box 308 57438 605-598-6266
Craig Cassens, prin. Fax 598-6666

Flandreau, Moody, Pop. 2,264
Flandreau SD 50-3 600/K-12
600 W Community Dr 57028 605-997-3263
Rick Weber, supt. Fax 997-2457
www.flandreau.k12.sd.us
Flandreau HS 200/9-12
600 W Community Dr 57028 605-997-2455
Margo Heinert, prin. Fax 997-2457
Flandreau MS 100/6-8
700 W Community Dr 57028 605-997-2705
Brian Relf, prin. Fax 997-2457

Florence, Codington, Pop. 370
Florence SD 14-1 200/PK-12
PO Box 66 57235 605-758-2412
Gary Leighton, supt. Fax 758-2433
www.florence.k12.sd.us/
Florence HS 100/9-12
PO Box 66 57235 605-758-2412
Gary Leighton, prin. Fax 758-2433
Florence JHS 50/7-8
PO Box 66 57235 605-758-2412
Gary Leighton, prin. Fax 758-2433

Forestburg, Sanborn, Pop. 70
Sanborn Central SD 55-5 200/PK-12
40405 SD Highway 34 57314 605-495-4183
Justin Siemsen, supt. Fax 495-4185
www.sanborncentral.com
Sanborn Central HS 100/9-12
40405 SD Highway 34 57314 605-495-4183
Justin Siemsen, prin. Fax 495-4185
Sanborn Central MS 50/6-8
40405 SD Highway 34 57314 605-495-4183
Connie Vermeulen, prin. Fax 495-4185

Fort Pierre, Stanley, Pop. 2,009
Stanley County SD 57-1 300/K-12
PO Box 370 57532 605-223-7741
Joel Price, supt. Fax 223-7750
www.stanleycounty.k12.sd.us
Stanley County MSHS 100/6-12
PO Box 370 57532 605-223-7743
Thomas O'Boyle M.S., prin. Fax 223-7751

Frederick, Brown, Pop. 197
Frederick Area SD 6-2 200/PK-12
PO Box 486 57441 605-329-2145
Knute Reierson, supt. Fax 329-2722
www.frederickarea.k12.sd.us
Frederick HS 100/9-12
PO Box 486 57441 605-329-2145
Jessica Ringgenberg, prin. Fax 329-2722
Frederick JHS 50/7-8
PO Box 486 57441 605-329-2145
Jessica Ringgenberg, prin. Fax 329-2722

Freeman, Hutchinson, Pop. 1,290
Freeman SD 33-1 300/PK-12
PO Box 220 57029 605-925-4214
Don Hotchkiss, supt. Fax 925-4814
www.freeman.k12.sd.us
Freeman HS 100/9-12
PO Box 220 57029 605-925-4214
Kevin Kunz, prin. Fax 925-4814
Freeman JHS 50/7-8
PO Box 220 57029 605-925-4214
Kevin Kunz, prin. Fax 925-4814

Freeman Academy 100/1-12
PO Box 1000 57029 605-925-4237

Garretson, Minnehaha, Pop. 1,155
Garretson SD 49-4 500/PK-12
PO Box C 57030 605-594-3451
Guy Johnson, supt. Fax 594-3443
www.garretson.k12.sd.us/
Garretson HS 100/9-12
PO Box C 57030 605-594-3452
Chris Long, prin. Fax 594-3443
Garretson MS 100/6-8
PO Box C 57030 605-594-3452
Chris Long, prin. Fax 594-3443

Gayville, Yankton, Pop. 403
Gayville-Volin SD 63-1 300/K-12
PO Box 158 57031 605-267-4476
Jason Selchert, supt. Fax 267-4294
www.gayvillevolin.k12.sd.us/
Gayville-Volin HS 100/9-12
PO Box 158 57031 605-267-4476
Tom Rice, prin. Fax 267-4294
Gayville-Volin MS 50/7-8
PO Box 158 57031 605-267-4476
Tom Rice, prin. Fax 267-4294

Gettysburg, Potter, Pop. 1,150
Gettysburg SD 53-1 300/K-12
100 E King Ave 57442 605-765-2436
Chip Sundberg, supt. Fax 765-2249
www.gettysburg.k12.sd.us
Gettysburg HS 100/9-12
100 E King Ave 57442 605-765-2436
Wendy Smith, prin. Fax 765-2249
Gettysburg JHS 50/7-8
100 E King Ave 57442 605-765-2436
Wendy Smith, prin. Fax 765-2249

Gregory, Gregory, Pop. 1,270
Gregory SD 26-4 400/K-12
PO Box 438 57533 605-835-9651
Sara Klein, supt. Fax 835-8146
www.gregory.k12.sd.us/
Gregory HS 100/9-12
PO Box 438 57533 605-835-9672
Jeff Determan, prin. Fax 835-8146
Gregory JHS 50/7-8
PO Box 438 57533 605-835-8771
Jeff Determan, prin. Fax 835-8744

Groton, Brown, Pop. 1,444
Groton Area SD 6-6 600/PK-12
PO Box 410 57445 605-397-2351
Joe Schwan, supt. Fax 397-8453
www.grotonarea.com/
Groton HS 200/9-12
PO Box 410 57445 605-397-8381
Anna Schwan, prin. Fax 397-8453
Groton MS 100/6-8
PO Box 410 57445 605-397-8381
Anna Schwan, prin. Fax 397-8453

Harrisburg, Lincoln, Pop. 4,018
Harrisburg SD 41-2 3,300/PK-12
PO Box 187 57032 605-743-2567
James Holbeck, supt. Fax 743-2569
harrisburgdistrict41-2.org
Harrisburg HS 600/9-12
1300 W Willow St 57032 605-743-2567
Kevin Lein, prin. Fax 743-9040
Harrisburg South MS 300/6-8
600 S Cliff Ave 57032 605-743-2567
Darren Ellwein, prin. Fax 743-5630
Other Schools – See Sioux Falls

Hartford, Minnehaha, Pop. 2,498
West Central SD 49-7 1,300/PK-12
PO Box 730 57033 605-528-3217
Dr. Jeff Danielsen, supt. Fax 528-3219
www.westcentral.k12.sd.us/
West Central HS 300/9-12
PO Box 730 57033 605-528-6236
Melinda Jensen, prin. Fax 528-6217
West Central MS 300/6-8
PO Box 730 57033 605-528-3799
Mark Rockafellow, prin. Fax 528-3702

Hayti, Hamlin, Pop. 381
Hamlin SD 28-3 800/PK-12
44577 188th St 57241 605-783-3631
Patrick Kraning, supt. Fax 783-3632
www.hamlin.k12.sd.us
Hamlin HS 200/9-12
44577 188th St 57241 605-783-3644
Jeff Sheehan, prin. Fax 783-3360
Hamlin MS 200/6-8
44577 188th St 57241 605-783-3644
Jeff Sheehan, prin. Fax 783-3632

Henry, Codington, Pop. 264
Henry SD 14-2 200/K-12
PO Box 8 57243 605-532-5364
Steve Zirbel, supt. Fax 532-3795
www.henry.k12.sd.us/
Henry HS 100/9-12
PO Box 8 57243 605-532-5364
Philip Schonebaum, prin. Fax 532-3795
Henry MS 50/5-8
PO Box 8 57243 605-532-5364
Philip Schonebaum, prin. Fax 532-3795

Herreid, Campbell, Pop. 436
Herreid SD 10-1 100/K-12
PO Box 276 57632 605-437-2263
Jeff Kosters, supt. Fax 437-2264
herreid.k12.sd.us
Herreid HS 50/9-12
PO Box 276 57632 605-437-2263
Jeff Kosters, supt. Fax 437-2264
Herreid MS 50/6-8
PO Box 276 57632 605-437-2263
Jeff Kosters, supt. Fax 437-2264

Highmore, Hyde, Pop. 788
Highmore-Harrold SD 34-2 300/PK-12
PO Box 416 57345 605-852-2275
Quinton Cermak, supt. Fax 852-2295
www.highmore.k12.sd.us
Highmore HS 100/9-12
PO Box 416 57345 605-852-2275
Quinton Cermak M.Ed., prin. Fax 852-2295
Highmore JHS 50/7-8
PO Box 416 57345 605-852-2275
Quinton Cermak M.Ed., prin. Fax 852-2295

Hill City, Pennington, Pop. 926
Hill City SD 51-2 500/PK-12
PO Box 659 57745 605-574-3030
Mike Hanson, supt. Fax 574-3031
hillcity.sd.schoolwebpages.com
Hill City HS 200/9-12
PO Box 659 57745 605-574-3000
Todd Satter, prin. Fax 574-3040
Hill City MS 100/6-8
PO Box 659 57745 605-574-3032
Blake Gardner, prin. Fax 574-3044

Hot Springs, Fall River, Pop. 3,587
Hot Springs SD 23-2 800/PK-12
1609 University Ave 57747 605-745-4145
Kevin Coles, supt. Fax 745-4178
www.hssd.k12.sd.us
Hot Springs HS 300/9-12
1609 University Ave 57747 605-745-4147
Mary Weiss, prin. Fax 745-4166
Hot Springs MS 200/6-8
1609 University Ave 57747 605-745-4146
Liz Baker, prin. Fax 745-6389

Hoven, Potter, Pop. 401
Hoven SD 53-2 100/PK-12
PO Box 128 57450 605-948-2252
Bob Graham, supt. Fax 948-2477
www.hoven.k12.sd.us
Hoven HS 50/9-12
PO Box 128 57450 605-948-2252
Bob Graham, prin. Fax 948-2477
Hoven JHS 50/7-8
PO Box 128 57450 605-948-2252
Dr. Pat Jones, prin. Fax 948-2477

Howard, Miner, Pop. 846
Howard SD 48-3 400/PK-12
500 N Section Line St 57349 605-772-5515
Todd Lee, supt. Fax 772-5516
www.howard.k12.sd.us
Howard HS 100/9-12
500 N Section Line St 57349 605-772-5515
Todd Lee, prin. Fax 772-5516
Howard JHS 50/7-8
500 N Section Line St 57349 605-772-5515
Todd Lee, prin. Fax 772-5516

Hurley, Turner, Pop. 413
Viborg-Hurley SD 60-6
Supt. — See Viborg
Viborg-Hurley MS 50/5-8
PO Box 278 57036 605-238-5221
Brett Mellem, prin. Fax 238-5223

Huron, Beadle, Pop. 12,413
Huron SD 2-2 1,600/K-12
PO Box 949 57350 605-353-6990
Terry Nebelsick Ed.D., supt. Fax 353-6994
www.huron.k12.sd.us
Huron HS 700/9-12
PO Box 949 57350 605-353-7800
Mike Radke, prin. Fax 353-7807
Huron MS 500/6-8
PO Box 949 57350 605-353-6900
Michael Taplett, prin. Fax 353-6913

James Valley Christian S 300/PK-12
1550 Dakota Ave N 57350 605-352-7737
Brian Held, admin. Fax 352-9893

Ipswich, Edmunds, Pop. 945
Ipswich SD 22-6 400/PK-12
PO Box 306 57451 605-426-6571
Trent Osborne, supt. Fax 426-6029
www.ipswich.k12.sd.us
Ipswich HS 100/9-12
PO Box 306 57451 605-426-6571
Trent Osborne, prin. Fax 426-6029
Ipswich MS 100/6-8
PO Box 306 57451 605-426-6571
Mathew Pollock, prin. Fax 426-6029

Irene, Yankton, Pop. 419
Irene-Wakonda SD 13-3 300/PK-12
PO Box 5 57037 605-263-3311
David Hutchison, supt. Fax 263-3316
www.irene-wakonda.k12.sd.us/
Irene-Wakonda JSHS 100/7-12
PO Box 5 57037 605-263-3311
Bruce Bailey, prin. Fax 263-3316

Iroquois, Kingsbury, Pop. 263
Iroquois SD 2-3 300/PK-12
111 E Washita St 57353 605-546-2210
Mike Ruth, supt. Fax 546-8540
www.iroquois.k12.sd.us/
Iroquois HS 100/9-12
111 E Washita St 57353 605-546-2426
Rick Soma, prin. Fax 546-8540
Iroquois MS 50/6-8
111 E Washita St 57353 605-546-2426
Rick Soma, prin. Fax 546-8540

Kadoka, Jackson, Pop. 622
Kadoka Area SD 35-2 400/PK-12
PO Box 99 57543 605-837-2175
Jamie Hermann, supt. Fax 837-2176
www.kadoka.k12.sd.us
Kadoka HS 100/9-12
PO Box 99 57543 605-837-2172
Mikaela O'Bryan, prin. Fax 837-2176

Kennebec, Lyman, Pop. 232
Lyman SD 42-1
Supt. — See Presho
Lyman MS 100/6-8
PO Box 188 57544 605-869-2213
Rene Lillebo, prin. Fax 869-2283

Kimball, Brule, Pop. 698
Kimball SD 7-2 300/PK-12
PO Box 479 57355 605-778-6232
Jeff Rieckman, supt. Fax 778-6393
www.kimball.k12.sd.us
Grass Ranch HS 50/9-12
PO Box 479 57355 605-778-6231
Matt Dykstra, prin. Fax 778-6393
Kimball HS 100/9-12
PO Box 479 57355 605-778-6232
Matt Dykstra, prin. Fax 778-6393
Kimball MS 100/5-8
PO Box 479 57355 605-778-6231
Matt Dykstra, prin. Fax 778-6393

Kyle, Shannon, Pop. 840

Oglala Lakota College Post-Sec.
PO Box 490 57752 605-455-6000

Lake Andes, Charles Mix, Pop. 832
Andes Central SD 11-1 400/PK-12
PO Box 40 57356 605-487-7671
Debera Lucas, supt. Fax 487-7051
www.andescentral.k12.sd.us/
Andes Central HS 100/9-12
PO Box 40 57356 605-487-7671
Rocky Brinkman, prin. Fax 487-7051
Andes Central JHS 50/7-8
PO Box 40 57356 605-487-7671
Rocky Brinkman, prin. Fax 487-7051

Lake Preston, Kingsbury, Pop. 595
Lake Preston SD 38-3 200/K-12
300 1st St NE 57249 605-847-4455
Tim Casper, supt. Fax 847-4311
www.lakepreston.k12.sd.us

Lake Preston HS 100/9-12
300 1st St NE 57249 605-847-4455
Tim Casper, prin. Fax 847-4311
Lake Preston JHS 50/7-8
300 1st St NE 57249 605-847-4455
Tim Casper, prin. Fax 847-4311

Langford, Marshall, Pop. 312
Langford SD 45-5 200/PK-12
PO Box 127 57454 605-493-6454
Monte Nipp, supt. Fax 493-6447
www.langford.k12.sd.us/
Langford HS 100/9-12
PO Box 127 57454 605-493-6454
Toni Brown, prin. Fax 493-6447
Langford MS 50/6-8
PO Box 127 57454 605-493-6454
Toni Brown, prin. Fax 493-6447

Lead, Lawrence, Pop. 3,058
Lead-Deadwood SD 40-1 800/PK-12
320 S Main St 57754 605-717-3890
Dr. Dan Leikvold, supt. Fax 717-2813
www.lead-deadwood.k12.sd.us/
Lead-Deadwood HS 200/9-12
320 S Main St 57754 605-717-3899
Tony Biesiot, prin. Fax 717-2815
Lead-Deadwood MS 200/6-8
234 S Main St 57754 605-717-3898
Jay Beagle, prin. Fax 717-2821
Other Schools – See Nemo

Lemmon, Perkins, Pop. 1,211
Lemmon SD 52-4 200/PK-12
209 3rd St W 57638 605-374-3762
Craig Johnson, supt. Fax 374-3562
www.lemmon.k12.sd.us
Lemmon HS 100/9-12
209 3rd St W 57638 605-374-3762
Craig Johnson, prin. Fax 374-3562
Lemmon JHS 50/7-8
209 3rd St W 57638 605-374-3784
Craig Johnson, prin. Fax 374-3562

Lennox, Lincoln, Pop. 2,100
Lennox SD 41-4 900/PK-12
PO Box 38 57039 605-647-2203
Chad Conaway, supt. Fax 647-2201
www.lennox.k12.sd.us
Lennox HS 300/9-12
PO Box 38 57039 605-647-2203
Chad Allison, prin. Fax 647-6045
Lennox JHS 100/7-8
PO Box 38 57039 605-647-2203
Chad Allison, prin. Fax 647-2502

Leola, McPherson, Pop. 451
Leola SD 44-2 200/K-12
PO Box 350 57456 605-439-3477
Brian Heupel, supt. Fax 439-3206
www.leola.k12.sd.us/
Leola HS 50/9-12
PO Box 350 57456 605-439-3477
Beverly Myer, prin. Fax 439-3206
Leola JHS 50/6-8
PO Box 350 57456 605-439-3477
Beverly Myer, prin. Fax 439-3206

Mc Intosh, Corson, Pop. 167
Mc Intosh SD 15-1 200/PK-12
PO Box 80 57641 605-273-4298
Rob Davis, supt. Fax 273-4531
www.mcintosh.k12.sd.us/
Mc Intosh HS 100/9-12
PO Box 80 57641 605-273-4298
Rob Davis, prin. Fax 273-4531
Mc Intosh JHS 50/7-8
PO Box 80 57641 605-273-4298
Rob Davis, prin. Fax 273-4531

Mc Laughlin, Corson, Pop. 634
Mc Laughlin SD 15-2 500/PK-12
PO Box 880 57642 605-823-4484
Scott Lepke, supt. Fax 823-4886
www.mclaughlin.k12.sd.us
McLaughlin HS 100/9-12
PO Box 880 57642 605-823-4484
Jeremy Hurd, prin. Fax 823-4481
McLaughlin MS 100/6-8
PO Box 880 57642 605-823-4484
Jeremy Hurd, prin. Fax 823-4481

Madison, Lake, Pop. 6,389
Madison Central SD 39-2 1,100/K-12
800 NE 9th St 57042 605-256-7700
Joel Jorgenson, supt. Fax 256-7711
www.madison.k12.sd.us
Madison HS 400/9-12
800 NE 9th St 57042 605-256-7706
Adam Shaw, prin. Fax 256-7711
Madison MS 300/6-8
830 NE 9th St 57042 605-256-7717
Cotton Koch, prin. Fax 256-7728

Dakota State University Post-Sec.
820 N Washington Ave 57042 605-256-5111

Marion, Turner, Pop. 780
Marion SD 60-3 200/PK-12
PO Box 207 57043 605-648-3615
E. David Colberg, supt. Fax 648-3652
marion.k12.sd.us
Marion HS 100/9-12
PO Box 207 57043 605-648-3615
Katie Minster, prin. Fax 648-3617
Marion MS 50/6-8
PO Box 207 57043 605-648-3615
Katie Minster, prin. Fax 648-3617

Martin, Bennett, Pop. 986
Bennett County SD 3-1 500/PK-12
PO Box 580 57551 605-685-6697
Stacy Halverson, supt. Fax 685-6694
www.bennettco.k12.sd.us/
Bennett County HS 200/9-12
PO Box 580 57551 605-685-6330
Nicholas Redden, prin. Fax 685-6935
Bennett County JHS 100/7-8
PO Box 580 57551 605-685-6343
Belinda Ready, prin. Fax 685-6935

Mellette, Spink, Pop. 205
Northwestern Area SD 56-7 300/PK-12
221 3rd St 57461 605-887-3467
Ryan Bruns, supt. Fax 887-3101
www.northwestern.k12.sd.us
Northwestern HS 100/9-12
221 3rd St 57461 605-887-3467
Richard Osborn, prin. Fax 887-3101
Northwestern MS 100/6-8
221 3rd St 57461 605-887-3467
Richard Osborn, prin. Fax 887-3101

Menno, Hutchinson, Pop. 603
Menno SD 33-2 300/PK-12
PO Box 346 57045 605-387-5161
Dr. Charlene Crosswait, supt. Fax 387-5171
www.menno.k12.sd.us/
Menno HS 100/9-12
PO Box 346 57045 605-387-5161
Cameron Kerkhove, prin. Fax 387-5171
Menno MS 50/6-8
PO Box 346 57045 605-387-5161
Cameron Kerkhove, prin. Fax 387-5171

Milbank, Grant, Pop. 3,335
Milbank SD 25-4 900/K-12
1001 E Park Ave 57252 605-432-5579
Tim Graf, supt. Fax 432-4137
www.milbankschooldistrict.com
Milbank HS 300/9-12
1001 E Park Ave 57252 605-432-5546
Dan Snaza, prin. Fax 432-5514
Milbank MS 200/6-8
1001 E Park Ave 57252 605-432-5519
Kristopher Evje, dean Fax 432-4137

Miller, Hand, Pop. 1,475
Miller SD 29-4 400/PK-12
PO Box 257 57362 605-853-2614
Dan Trefz, supt. Fax 853-3041
www.miller.k12.sd.us/
Miller HS 100/9-12
PO Box 257 57362 605-853-2455
Steve Schumacher, prin. Fax 853-3041
Miller JHS 100/7-8
PO Box 257 57362 605-853-2455
Steve Schumacher, prin. Fax 853-3041

Sunshine Bible Academy 100/K-12
400 Sunshine Dr 57362 605-853-3071
Jason Watson, supt. Fax 853-3072

Mission, Todd, Pop. 1,157
Todd County SD 66-1 2,200/K-12
PO Box 87 57555 605-856-3501
Dr. Karen Whitney, supt. Fax 856-2449
www.tcsdk12.org/
Todd County HS 400/9-12
PO Box 726 57555 605-856-3503
Cheryl Whirlwind Soldier, prin. Fax 856-4723
Todd County MS 400/6-8
PO Box 248 57555 605-856-3504
Linda Bordeaux, prin. Fax 856-2032

Sinte Gleska University Post-Sec.
PO Box 105 57555 605-856-5880

Mitchell, Davison, Pop. 15,009
Hanson SD 30-1
Supt. — See Alexandria
Hanson Colony Alternative HS 50/Alt
41659 256th St 57301 605-239-4387
Ray Slaba, prin. Fax 239-4293

Mitchell SD 17-2 2,800/K-12
821 N Capital St 57301 605-995-3010
Dr. Joseph Graves, supt. Fax 995-3089
mitchell.k12.sd.us
Mitchell Career & Technical Educ Academy 9-12
821 N Capital St 57301 605-995-7533
Denise Hoffman, dir. Fax 995-3099
Mitchell HS 800/9-12
920 N Capital St 57301 605-995-3034
Joe Childs, prin. Fax 995-3047
Mitchell MS 600/6-8
800 W 10th Ave 57301 605-995-3051
Justin Zajic, prin. Fax 995-3037
Mitchell Technical Institute Vo/Tech
1800 E Spruce St 57301 800-684-1969
Doug Greenway, dir. Fax 995-3083
Second Chance HS 100/Alt
821 N Capital St 57301 605-995-7509
Shane Thill, dir. Fax 995-8095

Dakota Wesleyan University Post-Sec.
1200 W University Ave 57301 605-995-2600
Mitchell Christian S 200/PK-12
805 W 18th Ave 57301 605-996-8861
Dr. Gary Cookson, prin. Fax 996-3642
Mitchell Technical Institute Post-Sec.
1800 E Spruce St 57301 800-684-1969
Queen of Peace Hospital Post-Sec.
5th & Foster 57301 605-995-2250

Mobridge, Walworth, Pop. 3,357
Mobridge-Pollock SD 62-6 700/PK-12
1107 1st Ave E 57601 605-845-9200
Tim Frederick, supt. Fax 845-3455
www.mobridge-pollock.k12.sd.us/
Mobridge-Pollock HS 200/9-12
1107 1st Ave E 57601 605-845-9200
Michael Busch, prin. Fax 845-3455
Mobridge-Pollock MS 200/6-8
1107 1st Ave E 57601 605-845-9200
Erin Dale, prin. Fax 845-3455

Montrose, McCook, Pop. 466
Montrose SD 43-2 200/K-12
309 S Church Ave 57048 605-363-5025
Lonny Johnson, supt. Fax 363-3513
www.montroseschool.k12.sd.us
Montrose HS 100/9-12
309 S Church Ave 57048 605-363-5025
Lonny Johnson, prin. Fax 363-3513
Montrose JHS 50/6-8
309 S Church Ave 57048 605-363-5025
Sam Jacobs, prin. Fax 363-3513

Mount Vernon, Davison, Pop. 457
Mount Vernon SD 17-3 200/PK-12
PO Box 46 57363 605-236-5237
Patrick Mikkonen, supt. Fax 236-5604
www.mtvernon.k12.sd.us
Mount Vernon HS 100/9-12
PO Box 46 57363 605-236-5237
Patrick Mikkonen, prin. Fax 236-5604
Mount Vernon MS 50/6-8
PO Box 46 57363 605-236-5237
Fax 236-5604

Murdo, Jones, Pop. 476
Jones County SD 37-3 200/PK-12
PO Box 109 57559 605-669-2297
Lorrie Esmay, supt. Fax 669-3248
jonesco.k12.sd.us
Jones County HS 100/9-12
PO Box 109 57559 605-669-2258
Missy Valburg, dean Fax 669-2904
Jones County MS 50/7-8
PO Box 109 57559 605-669-2258
Missy Valburg, dean Fax 669-2904

Nemo, Lawrence
Lead-Deadwood SD 40-1
Supt. — See Lead
Career & Technical Education Campus Vo/Tech
PO Box 110 57759 605-578-2371
Bonnie Fuller, dir. Fax 578-1157

Newell, Butte, Pop. 575
Newell SD 9-2 300/PK-12
PO Box 99 57760 605-456-2393
Robin Dutt, supt. Fax 456-2395
www.newell.k12.sd.us
Newell HS 100/9-12
PO Box 99 57760 605-456-2393
Jennifer Nehl, prin. Fax 456-2395
Newell MS 100/6-8
PO Box 99 57760 605-456-0102
Jennifer Nehl, prin. Fax 456-2395

New Underwood, Pennington, Pop. 640
New Underwood SD 51-3 300/K-12
PO Box 128 57761 605-754-6485
George Seiler, supt. Fax 754-6492
www.newunderwood.k12.sd.us
New Underwood HS 100/9-12
PO Box 128 57761 605-754-6485
George Seiler, prin. Fax 754-6492
New Underwood JHS 50/7-8
PO Box 128 57761 605-754-6485
Barb Paulson, prin. Fax 754-6492

North Sioux City, Union, Pop. 2,476
Dakota Valley SD 61-8 1,000/K-12
1150 Northshore Dr 57049 605-422-3800
Dr. Jerry Rasmussen, supt. Fax 422-3807
www.dakotavalley.k12.sd.us
Dakota Valley HS 300/9-12
1150 Northshore Dr 57049 605-422-3820
Erik Sommervold, prin. Fax 422-3827
Dakota Valley MS 200/6-8
1150 Northshore Dr 57049 605-422-3830
Harlan Halverson, prin. Fax 422-3837

Oelrichs, Fall River, Pop. 123
Oelrichs SD 23-3 100/K-12
PO Box 65 57763 605-535-2631
Dr. Mitch Stone, supt. Fax 535-2046
www.oelrichs.k12.sd.us
Oelrichs HS 100/9-12
PO Box 65 57763 605-535-2631
LuAnn Werdel, prin. Fax 535-2046
Oelrichs JHS 50/6-8
PO Box 65 57763 605-535-2631
LuAnn Werdel, prin. Fax 535-2046

Onida, Sully, Pop. 643
Agar-Blunt-Onida SD 58-3 300/K-12
PO Box 205 57564 605-258-2618
Kevin Pickner, supt. Fax 258-2361
www.abo.k12.sd.us
Sully Buttes HS 100/9-12
PO Box 205 57564 605-258-2618
Jeremy Chicoine, prin. Fax 258-2361
Sully Buttes JHS 50/7-8
PO Box 205 57564 605-258-2618
Jeremy Chicoine, prin. Fax 258-2361

Parker, Turner, Pop. 1,005
Parker SD 60-4 400/K-12
PO Box 517 57053 605-297-3456
Dr. Donavan DeBoer, supt. Fax 297-4381
parker.k12.sd.us
Parker HS 100/9-12
PO Box 517 57053 605-297-3456
Bill Leberman, prin. Fax 297-4381
Parker JHS 100/7-8
PO Box 517 57053 605-297-3456
Bill Leberman, prin. Fax 297-4381

Parkston, Hutchinson, Pop. 1,496
Parkston SD 33-3 600/PK-12
102C S Chapman Dr 57366 605-928-3368
Shayne McIntosh, supt. Fax 928-7284
www.parkston.k12.sd.us
Parkston HS 200/9-12
102A S Chapman Dr 57366 605-928-3368
Eric Norden, prin. Fax 928-4032
Parkston JHS 100/7-8
102A S Chapman Dr 57366 605-928-3368
Eric Norden, prin. Fax 928-4032

Philip, Haakon, Pop. 760
Haakon SD 27-1 300/PK-12
PO Box 730 57567 605-859-2679
Keven Morehart, supt. Fax 859-3005
www.philip.k12.sd.us
Philip HS 100/9-12
PO Box 730 57567 605-859-2680
Mandie Menzel, prin. Fax 859-3550
Philip MS 100/7-8
PO Box 730 57567 605-859-2680
Mandie Menzel, prin. Fax 859-3550

Pierre, Hughes, Pop. 13,369
Pierre SD 32-2 2,600/PK-12
211 S Poplar Ave 57501 605-773-7300
Dr. Kelly Glodt, supt. Fax 773-7304
www.pierre.k12.sd.us
Morse MS 600/6-8
309 E Capitol Ave 57501 605-773-7330
Dr. Kyley Cumbow, prin. Fax 773-7338
Riggs HS 800/9-12
1010 E Broadway Ave 57501 605-773-7350
Kevin Mutchelknaus, prin. Fax 773-7357

Pine Ridge, Shannon, Pop. 3,284
Oglala Lakota County SD 65-1
Supt. — See Batesland
Wolf Creek Upper ES 200/5-8
PO Box 469 57770 605-867-5174
Darrell Eagle Bull, prin. Fax 867-5067

Red Cloud Indian S 200/PK-12
100 Mission Dr 57770 605-867-5888
Bob Brave Heart, supt. Fax 867-2528

Plankinton, Aurora, Pop. 706
Plankinton SD 1-1 300/PK-12
PO Box 190 57368 605-942-7743
Steve Randall, supt. Fax 942-7453
www.plankinton.k12.sd.us
Plankinton HS 100/9-12
PO Box 190 57368 605-942-7743
Steve Randall, admin. Fax 942-7453
Plankinton JHS 50/7-8
PO Box 190 57368 605-942-7743
Steve Randall, admin. Fax 942-7453

Platte, Charles Mix, Pop. 1,219
Platte-Geddes SD 11-5 500/PK-12
PO Box 140 57369 605-337-3391
Joel Bailey, supt. Fax 337-2549
www.platte-geddes.k12.sd.us/
Platte HS 100/9-12
PO Box 140 57369 605-337-3391
Steve Randall, prin. Fax 337-2549
Platte JHS 100/7-8
PO Box 140 57369 605-337-3391
Steve Randall, prin. Fax 337-2549

Porcupine, Shannon, Pop. 1,058
Oglala Lakota County SD 65-1
Supt. — See Batesland
Rockyford Upper ES 200/5-8
HC 49 Box 175 57772 605-455-6300
Monica Whirlwind Horse, prin. Fax 455-2091

Presho, Lyman, Pop. 489
Lyman SD 42-1 400/PK-12
PO Box 1000 57568 605-895-2579
Lynn Vlasman, supt. Fax 895-2216
www.lyman.k12.sd.us/
Lyman HS 100/9-12
PO Box 1000 57568 605-895-2579
Jon Boer, prin. Fax 895-2216
Other Schools – See Kennebec

Ramona, Lake, Pop. 174
Oldham-Ramona SD 39-5 100/PK-12
PO Box 8 57054 605-482-8244
Tom Ludens, supt. Fax 482-8282
www.oldhamramona.k12.sd.us
Oldham-Ramona HS 50/9-12
PO Box 8 57054 605-482-8244
Tom Ludens, prin. Fax 482-8282
Oldham-Ramona JHS 50/7-8
PO Box 8 57054 605-482-8244
Tom Ludens, prin. Fax 482-8282
Other Schools – See Arlington

Rapid City, Pennington, Pop. 65,557
Rapid City Area SD 51-4 13,400/PK-12
300 6th St 57701 605-394-4031
Dr. Lori Simon, supt. Fax 394-2514
www.rcas.org
Central HS 1,800/9-12
433 N Mount Rushmore Rd 57701 605-394-4023
Mike Talley, prin. Fax 355-3041
East MS 600/6-8
4860 Homestead St 57703 605-394-4092
Scott Phares, prin. Fax 394-6935
North MS 500/6-8
1501 N Maple Ave 57701 605-394-4042
Jackie Talley, prin. Fax 394-6120
Rapid City HS 400/Alt
601 Columbus St 57701 605-394-4048
Shane Heilman, prin. Fax 394-6941
South MS 700/6-8
2 Indiana St 57701 605-394-4024
Larry Stevens, prin. Fax 394-5834
Southwest MS 700/6-8
4501 Park Dr 57702 605-394-6792
Robin Gillespie, prin. Fax 355-3095
Stevens HS 1,400/9-12
4215 Raider Rd 57702 605-394-4051
John Julius, prin. Fax 394-1820
West MS 700/6-8
1003 Soo San Dr 57702 605-394-4033
Dan Conrad, prin. Fax 394-1889

Black Hills Beauty College Post-Sec.
623 Saint Joseph St 57701 605-342-0697
Black Hills Lutheran S 50/6-12
PO Box 3034 57709 605-721-0760
Lacey Hoogland, admin.
National American University Post-Sec.
5301 S Highway 16 57701 605-394-4800
Rapid City Christian HS 100/6-12
23757 Arena Dr 57702 605-341-3377
Julie Hewitt, admin. Fax 341-2248
Rapid City Regional Hospital Post-Sec.
353 Fairmont Blvd 57701 605-341-8100
St. Thomas More HS 300/9-12
300 Fairmont Blvd 57701 605-343-8484
Wayne Sullivan, prin. Fax 343-1315
St. Thomas More MS 200/6-8
424 Fairmont Blvd 57701 605-348-1477
Mary Helen Olsen, prin. Fax 342-4367
South Dakota School Mines and Technology Post-Sec.
501 E Saint Joseph St 57701 605-394-2511
Western Dakota Technical Institute Post-Sec.
800 Mickelson Dr 57703 605-394-4034

Redfield, Spink, Pop. 2,312
Redfield SD 56-4 700/PK-12
PO Box 560 57469 605-472-4520
Shad Storley, supt. Fax 472-4525
www.redfield.k12.sd.us
Mickelson Alternative Program 50/Alt
PO Box 560 57469 605-472-4520
Brenda Stover, prin. Fax 472-4525
Redfield HS 200/9-12
PO Box 560 57469 605-472-4520
Rob Lewis, prin. Fax 472-4525
Redfield JHS 100/7-8
PO Box 560 57469 605-472-4520
Rob Lewis, prin. Fax 472-4525

Revillo, Grant, Pop. 117
Grant-Deuel SD 25-3 100/PK-12
16370 482nd Ave 57259 605-623-4241
Allen W. Stewart M.Ed., supt. Fax 623-4215
www.grant-deuel.k12.sd.us/
Grant-Deuel HS 50/9-12
16370 482nd Ave 57259 605-623-4241
Allen W. Stewart M.Ed., supt. Fax 623-4215
Grant-Deuel JHS 50/6-8
16370 482nd Ave 57259 605-623-4241
Allen W. Stewart M.Ed., supt. Fax 623-4215

Roscoe, Edmunds, Pop. 323
Edmunds Central SD 22-5 100/PK-12
PO Box 317 57471 605-287-4251
Karen Fox, supt. Fax 287-4813
www.echs.k12.sd.us
Edmunds Central HS 50/9-12
PO Box 317 57471 605-287-4251
Karen Fox, prin. Fax 287-4813
Edmunds Central MS 50/6-8
PO Box 317 57471 605-287-4251
Karen Fox, prin. Fax 287-4813

Rosholt, Roberts, Pop. 406
Rosholt SD 54-4 200/PK-12
PO Box 106 57260 605-537-4283
Teresa Appel, supt. Fax 537-4285
www.rosholt.k12.sd.us/
Rosholt HS 100/9-12
PO Box 106 57260 605-537-4278
Spencer Oland, prin. Fax 537-4285
Rosholt JHS 50/7-8
PO Box 106 57260 605-537-4278
Spencer Oland, prin. Fax 537-4285

Rutland, Lake
Rutland SD 39-4 100/PK-12
102 School St 57057 605-586-4352
Peter Books, supt. Fax 586-4343
www.rutland.k12.sd.us
Rutland HS 50/9-12
102 School St 57057 605-586-4352
Peter Books, supt. Fax 586-4343
Rutland JHS 50/6-8
102 School St 57057 605-586-4352
Kathleen Trower, lead tchr. Fax 586-4343

Salem, McCook, Pop. 1,343
McCook Central SD 43-7 400/PK-12
PO Box 310 57058 605-425-2264
Dr. Dan Swartos, supt. Fax 425-2079
www.mccookcentral.k12.sd.us/
McCook Central HS 100/9-12
PO Box 310 57058 605-425-2264
Brad Seamer, prin. Fax 425-2079
McCook Central MS 100/5-8
PO Box 310 57058 605-425-2264
Brad Seamer, prin. Fax 425-2079

Scotland, Bon Homme, Pop. 830
Scotland SD 4-3 300/PK-12
711 4th St 57059 605-583-2237
Damon Alvey, supt. Fax 583-2239
www.scotland.k12.sd.us
Scotland HS 100/9-12
711 4th St 57059 605-583-2237
Chris McGregor, prin. Fax 583-2239
Scotland MS 50/6-8
711 4th St 57059 605-583-2237
Chris McGregor, prin. Fax 583-2239

Selby, Walworth, Pop. 634
Selby Area SD 62-5 200/PK-12
PO Box 324 57472 605-649-7818
Darrel McFarland, supt. Fax 649-7282
www.selby.k12.sd.us/
Selby Area HS 100/9-12
PO Box 324 57472 605-649-7818
Yvette Houck, prin. Fax 649-7282
Selby Area JHS 50/7-8
PO Box 324 57472 605-649-7818
Yvette Houck, prin. Fax 649-7282

Sioux Falls, Minnehaha, Pop. 150,371
Harrisburg SD 41-2
Supt. — See Harrisburg
Harrisburg North MS 400/6-8
2201 W 95th St 57108 605-743-2567
Micah Fesler, prin. Fax 275-9140
Sioux Falls SD 49-5 22,300/PK-12
201 E 38th St 57105 605-367-7900
Dr. Brian Maher, supt. Fax 367-4637
www.sf.k12.sd.us
Axtell Park S 400/Alt
201 N West Ave 57104 605-367-7647
Erika Paladino-Hazlett, admin. Fax 367-8326
Career and Technical Education Academy Vo/Tech
4700 W Career Cir 57107 605-367-5504
Jim Kayl, prin. Fax 367-5508
Edison MS 900/6-8
2101 S West Ave 57105 605-367-7643
Steve Griffith, prin. Fax 367-8457
Henry MS 1,100/6-8
2200 S 5th Ave 57105 605-367-7639
Darryl Walker, prin. Fax 367-7693
Lincoln HS 1,900/9-12
2900 S Cliff Ave 57105 605-367-7990
Val Fox, prin. Fax 367-8492
McGovern MS 700/6-8
6221 W Maple St 57107 605-367-4440
Lynn Gillette, prin. Fax 367-4434
Memorial MS 1,100/6-8
1401 S Sertoma Ave 57106 605-362-2785
Carrie Aaron, prin. Fax 362-2790
Roosevelt HS 2,100/9-12
6600 W 41st St 57106 605-362-2860
Tim Hazlett, prin. Fax 362-2883
MS Immersion Center 50/Alt
6221 W Maple St 57107 605-367-4440
Lynn Gillette, prin. Fax 367-4434
Sioux Falls New Technology HS 300/9-12
2205 N Career Ave 57107 605-367-5850
Dolly Ellwein, prin. Fax 367-5852
Washington HS 2,000/9-12
501 N Sycamore Ave 57110 605-367-7970
Daniel Conrad, prin. Fax 367-8494
Whittier MS 1,000/6-8
930 E 6th St 57103 605-367-7620
Twaine Fink, prin. Fax 367-8357

Augustana College Post-Sec.
2001 S Summit Ave 57197 605-274-0770
Globe University Post-Sec.
5101 S Broadband Ln 57108 605-977-0705
Kilian Community College Post-Sec.
300 E 6th St 57103 605-221-3100
Lutheran HS of Sioux Falls 50/9-12
5000 S Western Ave 57108 605-275-2024
Derek Bult, prin. Fax 275-2034
McKennan Hospital Post-Sec.
800 E 21st St 57105 605-339-8113
National American University Post-Sec.
5801 S Corporate Pl 57108 605-336-4600
O'Gorman HS 700/9-12
3201 S Kiwanis Ave 57105 605-336-3644
Kyle Groos, prin. Fax 336-9272
O'Gorman JHS 400/7-8
3100 W 41st St 57105 605-988-0546
Wade Charron, prin. Fax 336-9839
Sioux Falls Christian S 400/PK-12
6120 S Charger Cir 57108 605-334-1422
Jay Woudstra, supt. Fax 334-6928
Sioux Falls Seminary Post-Sec.
2100 S Summit Ave 57105 605-336-6588
Sioux Valley Hospital Post-Sec.
PO Box 5039 57117 605-333-6424
South Dakota School for the Deaf Post-Sec.
2001 E 8th St 57103 605-367-5200
Southeast Technical Institute Post-Sec.
2320 N Career Ave 57107 605-367-7624
Stewart School Post-Sec.
604 N West Ave 57104 605-336-2775
University of Sioux Falls Post-Sec.
1101 W 22nd St 57105 605-331-5000

Sisseton, Roberts, Pop. 2,369
Sisseton SD 54-2 900/K-12
516 8th Ave W 57262 605-698-7613
Dr. Neil Terhune, supt. Fax 698-3032
www.sisseton.k12.sd.us/
Sisseton HS 300/9-12
516 8th Ave W 57262 605-698-7613
Jim Frederick, prin. Fax 698-7353
Sisseton MS 200/6-8
516 8th Ave W 57262 605-698-7613
Tammy Meyer, prin. Fax 698-7487

Sisseton-Wahpeton College Post-Sec.
PO Box 689 57262 605-698-3966

Spearfish, Lawrence, Pop. 10,283
Spearfish SD 40-2 2,200/PK-12
525 E Illinois St 57783 605-717-1201
Kirk Easton, supt. Fax 717-1200
www.spearfish.k12.sd.us
Spearfish HS 600/9-12
525 E Illinois St 57783 605-717-1212
Steve Morford, prin. Fax 717-1211
Spearfish MS 500/6-8
525 E Illinois St 57783 605-717-1215
Don Lyon, prin. Fax 717-1252

Black Hills State University Post-Sec.
1200 University St 57799 605-642-6011
Spearfish Classical Christian S 100/PK-12
PO Box 723 57783 605-717-4019

Sturgis, Meade, Pop. 6,462
Meade SD 46-1 2,600/K-12
1230 Douglas St 57785 605-347-2523
Donald Kirkegaard, supt. Fax 347-0005
meade.k12.sd.us
Sturgis Brown HS 700/9-12
12930 SD Highway 34 57785 605-347-2686
Pete Wilson, prin. Fax 347-0225
Sturgis Williams MS 500/6-8
1425 Cedar St 57785 605-347-5232
Ann Monnast, prin. Fax 720-0190
Other Schools – See Union Center

Summit, Roberts, Pop. 270
Summit SD 54-6 200/PK-12
PO Box 791 57266 605-398-6211
Kurt Jensen, supt. Fax 398-6311
www.summit.k12.sd.us
Summit HS 50/9-12
PO Box 791 57266 605-398-6211
Kurt Jensen, prin. Fax 398-6311

Tabor, Bon Homme, Pop. 415
Bon Homme SD 4-2
Supt. — See Tyndall
Hutterische Colony Alternative HS 50/Alt
31232 Colony Rd 57063 605-589-3387
Cory Lambley, prin. Fax 589-3468

Tea, Lincoln, Pop. 3,745
Tea Area SD 41-5 1,600/K-12
PO Box 488 57064 605-498-2700
Jennifer Lowery, supt. Fax 498-2702
www.teaschools.k12.sd.us
Tea Area HS 400/9-12
PO Box 488 57064 605-498-2700
Collin Knudson, prin. Fax 498-0280
Tea Area MS 300/6-8
PO Box 488 57064 605-498-2700
Chris Fechner, prin. Fax 498-0280

Timber Lake, Dewey, Pop. 419
Timber Lake SD 20-3 400/K-12
PO Box 1000 57656 605-865-3654
Dan Martin, supt. Fax 865-3294
www.tls.new.rschooltoday.com
Timber Lake HS 100/9-12
PO Box 1000 57656 605-865-3654
Julie Marshall, prin. Fax 865-3294
Timber Lake MS 100/6-8
PO Box 1000 57656 605-865-3654
Julie Marshall, prin. Fax 865-3294

Tripp, Hutchinson, Pop. 645
Tripp-Delmont SD 33-5 200/PK-12
PO Box 430 57376 605-935-6766
Gail Swenson, supt. Fax 935-6507
www.tridel.k12.sd.us/
Tripp-Delmont HS 100/9-12
PO Box 430 57376 605-935-6766
Gail Swenson, prin. Fax 935-6507

Tulare, Spink, Pop. 205
Hitchcock-Tulare SD 56-6 200/PK-12
PO Box 108 57476 605-266-2151
Jeff Clark, supt. Fax 266-2160
www.hitchcock-tulare.k12.sd.us/
Hitchcock-Tulare HS 100/9-12
PO Box 108 57476 605-596-4171
Clint Nelson, prin. Fax 596-4150
Hitchcock-Tulare JHS 50/7-8
PO Box 108 57476 605-596-4171
Bill Barrie, prin. Fax 596-4150

Tyndall, Bon Homme, Pop. 1,060
Bon Homme SD 4-2 500/PK-12
PO Box 28 57066 605-589-3388
Dr. Mike Elsberry, supt. Fax 589-3468
www.bonhomme.k12.sd.us/
Bon Homme HS 200/9-12
PO Box 28 57066 605-589-3387
Cory Lambley, prin. Fax 589-3468
Bon Homme MS 100/6-8
PO Box 28 57066 605-589-3387
cory lambley, prin. Fax 589-3468
Other Schools – See Tabor

Union Center, Meade
Meade SD 46-1
Supt. — See Sturgis
Union Center S 50/6-8
1700 SD Highway 34 57787 605-269-2264
Bev Rosenboom, prin. Fax 269-2099

Vermillion, Clay, Pop. 10,331
Vermillion SD 13-1 1,200/PK-12
17 Prospect St 57069 605-677-7000
Dr. Mark Froke, supt. Fax 677-7002
www.vermillion.k12.sd.us
Vermillion Area Alternative Education Alt
840 E Cherry St 57069 605-677-7000
Terri Trumm, dir.
Vermillion HS 300/9-12
1001 E Main St 57069 605-677-7035
Curt Cameron, prin. Fax 677-7042
Vermillion MS 300/6-8
422 Princeton St 57069 605-677-7025
Tim Koehler, prin. Fax 677-7028

University of South Dakota Post-Sec.
414 E Clark St 57069 605-677-5011

Viborg, Turner, Pop. 777
Viborg-Hurley SD 60-6 300/PK-12
PO Box 397 57070 605-766-5418
Peggy Petersen, supt. Fax 766-5635
www.viborg-hurley.k12.sd.us
Viborg-Hurley HS 100/9-12
PO Box 397 57070 605-766-5418
Cory Jensen, prin. Fax 766-5635
Other Schools – See Hurley

Volga, Brookings, Pop. 1,762
Sioux Valley SD 5-5 600/PK-12
PO Box 278 57071 605-627-5657
Laura Schuster, supt. Fax 627-5291
www.svs.k12.sd.us/
Sioux Valley HS 200/9-12
PO Box 278 57071 605-627-5657
Belinda Miller, prin. Fax 627-5291
Sioux Valley MS 100/6-8
PO Box 278 57071 605-627-5657
Belinda Miller, prin. Fax 627-5291

Wagner, Charles Mix, Pop. 1,520
Wagner Community SD 11-4 900/PK-12
101 Walnut Ave SW 57380 605-384-3677
Linda Foos, supt. Fax 384-3678
www.wagner.k12.sd.us/
Wagner HS 200/9-12
101 Walnut Ave SW 57380 605-384-5426
Neil Goter, prin. Fax 384-3200
Wagner MS 200/5-8
101 Walnut Ave SW 57380 605-384-3913
Steve Petry, prin. Fax 384-3678

Wakpala, Corson
Smee SD 15-3 200/PK-12
PO Box B 57658 605-845-3040
Jay Shillingstad, supt. Fax 845-7244
www.smee.k12.sd.us
Wakpala HS 50/9-12
PO Box B 57658 605-845-3040
Barry Mann, prin. Fax 845-7244
Wakpala MS 50/6-8
PO Box B 57658 605-845-3040
Barry Mann, prin. Fax 845-7244

Wall, Pennington, Pop. 739
Wall SD 51-5 200/K-12
PO Box 414 57790 605-279-2156
Cooper Garnos, supt. Fax 279-2613
www.wall.k12.sd.us
Wall HS 100/9-12
PO Box 414 57790 605-279-2156
Cooper Garnos, prin. Fax 279-2613
Wall MS 50/7-8
PO Box 414 57790 605-279-2156
Cooper Garnos, prin. Fax 279-2613

Warner, Brown, Pop. 453
Warner SD 6-5 300/K-12
PO Box 20 57479 605-225-6397
Michael Kroll, supt. Fax 225-0007
www.warner.k12.sd.us/
Warner HS 100/9-12
PO Box 20 57479 605-225-6194
Roby Johnson, prin. Fax 225-0007
Warner MS 100/6-8
PO Box 20 57479 605-225-6194
Michael Kroll, prin. Fax 225-0007

Watertown, Codington, Pop. 21,216
Northeast Technical HSD
1311 3rd Ave NE 57201 605-882-6380
Bert Falak M.Ed., dir. Fax 882-6381
northeasttechnicalhighschool.k12.sd.us
Northeast Technical HS Vo/Tech
1311 3rd Ave NE 57201 605-882-6380
Bert Falak M.Ed., dir. Fax 882-6381

Watertown SD 14-4 3,900/PK-12
PO Box 730 57201 605-882-6312
Dr. Lesli Jutting, supt. Fax 882-6327
www.watertown.k12.sd.us/
Watertown HS 1,100/9-12
200 9th St NE 57201 605-882-6316
Dr. Michael Butts, prin. Fax 882-6327
Watertown MS 600/7-8
1700 11th St NE 57201 605-882-6370
Dr. Todd Brist, prin. Fax 886-6372

Great Plains Lutheran HS 100/9-12
1200 Luther Ln NE 57201 605-886-0672
Rev. David Maertz, pres. Fax 882-9089
Lake Area Technical Institute Post-Sec.
PO Box 730 57201 605-882-5284

Waubay, Day, Pop. 561
Waubay SD 18-3 200/PK-12
202 W School Rd 57273 605-947-4529
Dean Jones M.A., supt. Fax 947-4243
www.waubay.k12.sd.us/
Waubay HS 100/9-12
202 W School Rd 57273 605-947-4529
Dean Jones M.A., prin. Fax 947-4243
Waubay MS 50/6-8
202 W School Rd 57273 605-947-4529
Dean Jones M.A., prin. Fax 947-4243

Waverly, Codington, Pop. 37
Waverly SD 14-5 200/PK-12
319 Mary Pl, 605-886-9174
John Bjorkman, supt. Fax 886-6630
www.waverly.k12.sd.us
Waverly/South Shore HS 100/9-12
319 Mary Pl, 605-886-9174
Mitchell Reed, prin. Fax 886-6630
Waverly/South Shore MS 50/6-8
319 Mary Pl, 605-886-9174
John Bjorkman, prin. Fax 886-6630

Webster, Day, Pop. 1,853
Webster Area SD 18-4 500/PK-12
102 E 9th Ave 57274 605-345-3548
Dr. James Block, supt. Fax 345-4421
www.webster.k12.sd.us/
Webster Area HS 200/9-12
102 E 9th Ave 57274 605-345-4653
James Block, prin. Fax 345-4421
Webster Area MS 100/6-8
102 E 9th Ave 57274 605-345-4651
Craig Case, prin. Fax 345-4421

Wessington Springs, Jerauld, Pop. 954
Wessington Springs SD 36-2 300/PK-12
PO Box 449 57382 605-539-9391
Lance Witte, supt. Fax 539-1029
www.wessingtonsprings.k12.sd.us
Wessington Springs HS 100/9-12
PO Box 449 57382 605-539-9391
Jason Kolousek, prin. Fax 539-1029
Wessington Springs JHS 50/7-8
PO Box 449 57382 605-539-9311
Jason Kolousek, prin. Fax 539-1029

White, Brookings, Pop. 482
Deubrook Area SD 5-6 300/K-12
PO Box 346 57276 605-629-1100
Kevin Keenaghan, supt. Fax 629-3701
www.deubrook.com
Deubrook JSHS 100/7-12
PO Box 346 57276 605-629-1114
Paul Nepodal, prin. Fax 629-3701

White Lake, Aurora, Pop. 368
White Lake SD 1-3 100/PK-12
PO Box 246 57383 605-249-2251
Robert Schroeder, supt. Fax 249-2725
www.whitelake.k12.sd.us/
White Lake HS 50/9-12
PO Box 246 57383 605-249-2251
Robert Schroeder, prin. Fax 249-2725
White Lake JHS 50/7-8
PO Box 246 57383 605-249-2251
Robert Schroeder, prin. Fax 249-2725

White River, Mellette, Pop. 529
White River SD 47-1 400/PK-12
PO Box 273 57579 605-259-3311
Thomas Cameron, supt. Fax 259-3133
www.whiteriver.k12.sd.us/
White River HS 100/9-12
PO Box 273 57579 605-259-3135
Peri Strain, prin. Fax 259-3133
White River MS 100/6-8
PO Box 273 57579 605-259-3135
Kendra Becker, prin. Fax 259-3133

Willow Lake, Clark, Pop. 262
Willow Lake SD 12-3 200/PK-12
PO Box 170 57278 605-625-5945
Scott Klaudt, supt. Fax 625-3103
www.willowlake.k12.sd.us
Willow Lake HS 100/9-12
PO Box 170 57278 605-625-5945
Hector Serna, prin. Fax 625-3103
Willow Lake MS 50/6-8
PO Box 170 57278 605-625-5945
Hector Serna, prin. Fax 625-3103

Wilmot, Roberts, Pop. 481
Wilmot SD 54-7 200/PK-12
PO Box 100 57279 605-938-4647
Larry Hulscher, supt. Fax 938-4185
www.wilmot.k12.sd.us
Wilmot HS 100/9-12
PO Box 100 57279 605-938-4647
Larry Hulscher, prin. Fax 938-4185
Wilmot MS 50/6-8
PO Box 100 57279 605-938-4647
Mike Schmidt, prin. Fax 938-4185

Winner, Tripp, Pop. 2,819
Winner SD 59-2 500/K-12
PO Box 231 57580 605-842-8101
Bruce Carrier, supt. Fax 842-8120
www.winner.k12.sd.us
Winner MSHS 200/6-12
PO Box 231 57580 605-842-8125
Gerald Witte, prin. Fax 842-8121

Wolsey, Beadle, Pop. 376
Wolsey-Wessington SD 2-6 300/K-12
375 Ash St SE 57384 605-883-4221
James Cutshaw, supt. Fax 883-4720
www.wolsey-wessington.k12.sd.us
Wolsey-Wessington HS 100/9-12
375 Ash St SE 57384 605-883-4221
James Cutshaw, prin. Fax 883-4720
Wolsey-Wessington MS 100/6-8
375 Ash St SE 57384 605-883-4221
Carol Rowen, prin. Fax 883-4720

Woonsocket, Sanborn, Pop. 652
Woonsocket SD 55-4 200/PK-12
PO Box 428 57385 605-796-4431
Dr. Rodrick Weber, supt. Fax 796-4352
www.woonsocket.k12.sd.us/
Woonsocket HS 100/9-12
PO Box 428 57385 605-796-4431
Dr. Rodrick Weber, prin. Fax 796-4352

Yankton, Yankton, Pop. 14,259
Yankton SD 63-3 2,800/PK-12
PO Box 738 57078 605-665-3998
Dr. Wayne Kindle, supt. Fax 665-1422
www.ysd.k12.sd.us
Alternative Learning Center Alt
PO Box 738 57078 605-665-2073
Dr. Jennifer Johnke, prin. Fax 655-5948
Yankton HS 900/9-12
PO Box 738 57078 605-665-2073
Dr. Jennifer Johnke, prin. Fax 655-5948
Yankton MS 600/6-8
PO Box 738 57078 605-665-2419
Todd Dvoracek, prin. Fax 665-6239

Mt. Marty College Post-Sec.
1105 W 8th St 57078 605-668-1545
Sacred Heart Hospital Post-Sec.
501 Summit St 57078 605-655-9371
Sacred Heart MS 5-8
504 Capitol St 57078 605-665-1808
Dr. Tim Mulhair, prin. Fax 260-9787

TENNESSEE

TENNESSEE DEPARTMENT OF EDUCATION
710 James Robertson Pkwy, Nashville 37243-1219
Telephone 615-741-2731
Fax 615-532-4791
Website tn.gov/education

Commissioner of Education Candice McQueen

TENNESSEE BOARD OF EDUCATION
710 James Robertson Pkwy, Nashville 37243-1219

Executive Director Dr. Sara Heyburn

PUBLIC, PRIVATE AND CATHOLIC SECONDARY SCHOOLS

Adamsville, McNairy, Pop. 2,170
McNairy County SD
Supt. — See Selmer
Adamsville JSHS 700/7-12
PO Box 407 38310 731-632-3273
Greg Martin, prin. Fax 632-3080

Afton, Greene
Greene County SD
Supt. — See Greeneville
Chuckey-Doak HS 600/9-12
365 Ripley Island Rd 37616 423-798-2636
Shelly Smith, prin. Fax 639-5761
Chuckey Doak MS 500/6-8
120 Chuckey Doak Rd 37616 423-787-2038
Steve Broyles, prin. Fax 787-2096

Alamo, Crockett, Pop. 2,420
Crockett County SD 2,000/PK-12
102 N Cavalier Dr 38001 731-696-2604
Robert Mullins, supt. Fax 696-4734
www.ccschools.net
Crockett County HS 800/9-12
402 Highway 88 38001 731-696-4525
Jared Foust, prin. Fax 696-3124
Crockett County MS 600/6-8
497 N Cavalier Dr 38001 731-696-5583
Bobby McLaughlin, prin. Fax 696-2034

Alcoa, Blount, Pop. 8,239
Alcoa CSD 1,900/PK-12
524 Faraday St 37701 865-984-0531
Dr. Brian Bell, supt. Fax 984-5832
www.alcoaschools.net/
Alcoa HS 500/9-12
1205 Lodge St 37701 865-982-4631
Becky Stone, prin. Fax 380-2240
Alcoa MS 500/6-8
532 Faraday St 37701 865-982-5211
Dr. Scott Porter, prin. Fax 380-2533

Algood, Putnam, Pop. 3,428
Putnam County SD
Supt. — See Cookeville
Algood MS 800/PK-PK, 5-
540 Dry Valley Rd, Cookeville TN 38506
931-537-6141
Tim Martin, prin. Fax 537-3700

Allardt, Fentress, Pop. 632
Fentress County SD
Supt. — See Jamestown
Fentress County Adult HS Adult
220 Portland Ave 38504 931-752-8316
David Garrett, lead tchr. Fax 879-7428

Altamont, Grundy, Pop. 1,042
Grundy County SD 2,300/PK-12
PO Box 97 37301 931-692-3467
Dr. William Childers Ed.D., dir. Fax 692-2188
www.grundycoschools.com
Other Schools – See Coalmont

Antioch, Davidson
Metropolitan Nashville SD
Supt. — See Nashville
Antioch HS 2,000/9-12
1900 Hobson Pike 37013 615-641-5400
Dr. Keiva Wiley, prin. Fax 641-5422
Antioch MS 700/5-8
5050 Blue Hole Rd 37013 615-333-5642
Celia Conley, prin. Fax 333-5053
Apollo MS 800/5-8
631 Richards Rd 37013 615-333-5025
Shawn Lawrence, prin. Fax 333-5029
Cane Ridge HS 1,700/9-12
12848 Old Hickory Blvd 37013 615-687-4000
Michel Sanchez-Wall, prin. Fax 641-5007
Kennedy MS Prep 800/5-8
2087 Hobson Pike 37013 615-501-7900
Dr. Sam Braden, prin.
Marshall MS, 5832 Pettus Rd 37013 800/5-8
Roderick Webb, prin. 615-941-7515
Academy at Hickory Hollow Adult
5248 Hickory Hollow Pkwy 37013 615-687-4028
Billy Fellman, prin.

Ezell-Harding Christian S 600/PK-12
574 Bell Rd 37013 615-367-0532
Belvia Pruitt, prin. Fax 399-8747
Jon Nave University of Cosmetology Post-Sec.
5510 Crossings Cir 37013 - -
Lighthouse Christian S 600/PK-12
5100 Blue Hole Rd 37013 615-331-6286

Arlington, Shelby, Pop. 11,290
Arlington Community SD 5,000/K-12
5475 Airline Rd 38002 901-389-2497
Tamara Mason, supt. Fax 389-2498
www.acsk-12.org
Arlington HS 2,400/9-12
5475 Airline Rd 38002 901-867-1541
Chris Duncan, prin. Fax 867-1546
Arlington MS 1,100/6-8
5470 Lamb Rd 38002 901-867-6015
Dr. Allison Clark, prin. Fax 867-7080

Bartlett CSD
Supt. — See Bartlett
Bartlett Ninth Grade Academy 9-9
4734 Shadowlawn Rd 38002 901-373-2654
John McDonald, prin. Fax 373-1363

Shelby County SD
Supt. — See Memphis
Bolton HS 1,900/9-12
7323 Brunswick Rd 38002 901-416-1435
Chad Stevens, prin. Fax 416-1432

Macon Road Baptist S - East 400/K-12
11015 Highway 64 38002 901-867-8161

Ashland City, Cheatham, Pop. 4,449
Cheatham County SD 6,600/PK-12
102 Elizabeth St 37015 615-792-5664
Stacy Brinkley, dir. Fax 792-2551
www.cheathamcountyschools.net
Cheatham County Central HS 600/9-12
1 Cub Cir 37015 615-792-5641
Stephen Wenning, prin. Fax 792-2090
Cheatham MS 700/5-8
700 Scoutview Rd 37015 615-792-2334
Linda Owen, prin. Fax 792-2337
Riverside Academy Alt
102 Elizabeth St 37015 615-792-5664
Jo Jones, prin. Fax 792-2551
Other Schools – See Kingston Springs, Pleasant View

Athens, McMinn, Pop. 13,106
Athens CSD 1,700/PK-8
943 Crestway Dr 37303 423-745-2863
Dr. Melanie Miller, dir. Fax 745-9041
www.athenscityschools.net
Athens City MS 500/6-8
200 Keith Ln 37303 423-745-1177
Michael Simmons, prin. Fax 745-9679

McMinn County SD 5,900/PK-12
3 S Hill St 37303 423-745-1612
Mickey Blevins Ed.D., dir. Fax 744-1641
www.mcminn.k12.tn.us
McMinn County Career Technical Center Vo/Tech
3 S Hill St 37303 423-745-1612
Mickey Blevins, prin. Fax 744-1641
McMinn County HS 1,500/9-12
2215 Congress Pkwy S 37303 423-745-4142
John Burroughs, prin. Fax 745-0584
Other Schools – See Englewood

Christ's Legacy Academy 100/K-12
964 County Road 180 37303 423-649-0040
Dr. Shane Arnold Ph.D., head sch
Fairview Christian Academy 100/PK-12
261 County Road 439 37303 423-745-6781
Liberty Christian S 100/K-12
PO Box 1555 37371 423-745-9248
Tennessee Technology Center at Athens Post-Sec.
PO Box 848 37371 423-744-2814
Tennessee Wesleyan College Post-Sec.
204 E College St 37303 423-745-7504

Atwood, Carroll, Pop. 925
West Carroll Special SD 1,000/PK-12
1415 State Route 77 38220 731-662-4200
Eric Williams, dir. Fax 662-4250
www.wcssd.org
West Carroll JSHS 500/7-12
760 State Route 77 38220 731-662-7116
Lex Suite, prin. Fax 662-4198

Bartlett, Shelby, Pop. 53,815
Bartlett CSD 7,900/K-12
5650 Woodlawn St 38134 901-202-0855
David Stephens, supt. Fax 202-0854
www.bartlettschools.org
Appling MS 700/6-8
3700 Appling Rd 38133 901-373-1410
Dr. Keshia McMickens, prin. Fax 373-1360
Bartlett HS 1,700/10-12
5688 Woodlawn St 38134 901-373-2620
Tim Jones, prin. Fax 373-2624
Bon Lin MS 600/6-8
3862 N Germantown Rd 38133 901-347-1520
Cody Duncan, prin. Fax 347-1491
Elmore Park MS 600/6-8
6330 Althorne Rd 38134 901-373-2642
Ethan Randle, prin. Fax 373-1361
Other Schools – See Arlington

Shelby County SD
Supt. — See Memphis
Renaissance Academy Lakeside Alt
2911 Brunswick Rd 38133 901-377-4700
Tyria Butler, admin.

National College of Business & Tech Post-Sec.
5760 Stage Rd 38134 901-213-1681

Baxter, Putnam, Pop. 1,354
Putnam County SD
Supt. — See Cookeville
Upperman HS 700/9-12
6950 Nashville Hwy 38544 931-858-3112
Billy Stepp, prin. Fax 858-4641
Upperman MS 5-8
6700 Nashville Hwy 38544 931-858-6601
. Billy Stepp, admin. Fax 858-6637

Bell Buckle, Bedford, Pop. 495

Webb S 300/6-12
PO Box 488 37020 931-389-6003
Raymond Broadhead, head sch Fax 389-6657

Benton, Polk, Pop. 1,374
Polk County SD 2,600/PK-12
PO Box 665 37307 423-299-0471
James Jones, dir. Fax 338-2691
www.polk-schools.com
Chilhowee MS 400/6-8
PO Box 977 37307 423-338-3102
Connie Dunn, prin. Fax 338-3158
Polk County HS 600/9-12
PO Box 188 37307 423-299-0078
Jason Bell, prin. Fax 338-4521
Other Schools – See Copperhill

Big Sandy, Benton, Pop. 553
Benton County SD
Supt. — See Camden
Big Sandy S 300/K-12
13305 Highway 69A 38221 731-593-3221
Marty Caruthers, prin. Fax 593-3245

Blountville, Sullivan, Pop. 3,052
Sullivan County SD 10,500/PK-12
PO Box 306 37617 423-354-1000
Evelyn Rafalowski, supt. Fax 354-1004
www.sullivank12.net
Blountville MS 300/6-8
1651 Blountville Blvd 37617 423-354-1600
Michael Wilson, prin. Fax 354-1606
Holston MS 400/6-8
2348 Highway 75 37617 423-354-1500
Bill Miller, prin. Fax 354-1505

Sullivan Central HS 1,000/9-12
131 Shipley Ferry Rd 37617 423-354-1200
Mark Foster, prin. Fax 354-1206
Other Schools – See Bluff City, Bristol, Kingsport

Northeast State Community College Post-Sec.
PO Box 246 37617 423-323-3191
Tri-Cities Christian S 400/PK-12
1500 Highway 75 37617 423-323-7128

Bluff City, Sullivan, Pop. 1,717
Sullivan County SD
Supt. — See Blountville
Bluff City MS 400/6-8
337 Carter St 37618 423-354-1801
Greg Stallcup, prin. Fax 354-1818
Sullivan East HS 900/9-12
4180 Weaver Pike 37618 423-354-1900
Angie Buckles, prin. Fax 354-1906

Bolivar, Hardeman, Pop. 5,360
Hardeman County SD 4,000/PK-12
10815 Old Highway 64 38008 731-658-2510
Warner Ross, dir. Fax 658-2061
www.hardemancountyschools.org
Bolivar MS 400/6-8
915 Pruitt St 38008 731-658-3656
Mary Ann Polk, prin. Fax 658-6625
Central HS 800/9-12
313 Harris St 38008 731-658-3151
Fred Kessler, prin. Fax 658-6697
Other Schools – See Middleton

Bradford, Gibson, Pop. 1,036
Bradford Special SD 500/PK-12
PO Box 220 38316 731-742-3180
Dan Black, supt. Fax 742-3994
www.bradfordssd.schoolinsites.com
Bradford JSHS 200/7-12
136 Highway 45 S 38316 731-742-3729
Shane Paschall, prin. Fax 742-3088

Brentwood, Williamson, Pop. 36,506
Williamson County SD
Supt. — See Franklin
Brentwood HS 1,600/9-12
5304 Murray Ln 37027 615-472-4220
Kevin Keidel, prin. Fax 472-4241
Brentwood MS 1,300/6-8
5324 Murray Ln 37027 615-472-4250
Dr. Brandon Barkley, prin. Fax 472-4263
Ravenwood HS 2,000/9-12
1724 Wilson Pike 37027 615-472-4800
Dr. Pam Vaden, prin. Fax 472-4821
Sunset MS 800/6-8
200 Sunset Trl 37027 615-472-5040
Dr. Tim Brown, prin. Fax 472-5050
Woodland MS 800/6-8
1500 Volunteer Pkwy 37027 615-472-4930
Priscilla Fizer, prin. Fax 472-4941

Brentwood Academy 800/6-12
219 Granny White Pike 37027 615-373-0611
Curt Masters, hdmstr. Fax 377-3709
Currey Ingram Academy 300/K-12
6544 Murray Ln 37027 615-507-3242
Dr. Jeffrey Mitchell, head sch Fax 507-3170

Brighton, Tipton, Pop. 2,690
Tipton County SD
Supt. — See Covington
Brighton HS 1,400/9-12
8045 Highway 51 S 38011 901-837-5800
Christie Huffman, prin. Fax 837-5829
Brighton MS 1,000/6-8
7785 Highway 51 S 38011 901-837-5600
Sabrina Sneed-Mathews, prin. Fax 837-5625

Bristol, Sullivan, Pop. 26,322
Bristol CSD 4,000/PK-12
615 Martin Luther King Blvd 37620 423-652-9451
Dr. Gary Lilly, dir. Fax 652-9238
www.btcs.org
Tennessee HS 1,200/9-12
1112 Edgemont Ave 37620 423-652-9494
Mary Rouse, prin. Fax 652-9327
Vance MS 600/7-8
815 Edgemont Ave 37620 423-652-9449
Dr. Amy Scott, prin. Fax 652-9297

Sullivan County SD
Supt. — See Blountville
Holston Valley MS 200/6-8
1717 Bristol Caverns Hwy 37620 423-354-1880
Jess Lockhart, prin. Fax 354-1891

King University Post-Sec.
1350 King College Rd 37620 423-968-1187
National College of Business & Tech Post-Sec.
1328 Highway 11 W 37620 423-878-4440

Brownsville, Haywood, Pop. 10,196
Haywood County SD 3,300/PK-12
900 E Main St 38012 731-772-9613
Teresa Russell, dir. Fax 772-3275
www.haywoodschools.com
Haywood HS 900/9-12
1175 E College St 38012 731-772-1845
Dr. Jerry Pyron, prin. Fax 772-6079
Haywood JHS 800/6-8
1201 Haralson St 38012 731-772-3265
Yvette Blue, prin. Fax 772-3352

Bruceton, Carroll, Pop. 1,455
Hollow Rock-Bruceton Special SD 700/PK-12
29590 Broad St 38317 731-418-4180
David Duncan, supt. Fax 418-4188
www.hrbedu.org
Central HS, 29590 Broad St 38317 200/9-12
Joe Norval, prin. 731-418-4189
Central MS 100/6-8
29590 Broad St 38317 731-418-4167
Joe Norval, prin. Fax 418-4188

Buchanan, Henry
Henry County SD
Supt. — See Paris
Lakewood MS 300/6-8
6745 Highway 79 N Ste B 38222 731-644-1600
Mike Bell, prin. Fax 644-0680

Byrdstown, Pickett, Pop. 803
Pickett County SD 800/PK-12
141 Skyline Dr 38549 931-864-3123
Diane Elder, supt. Fax 864-7185
pickett.k12tn.net/
Pickett County HS 200/9-12
130 Skyline Dr 38549 931-864-3422
Jane Winningham, prin. Fax 864-6297

Camden, Benton, Pop. 3,542
Benton County SD 2,300/PK-12
197 Briarwood St 38320 731-584-6111
Mark Florence, supt. Fax 584-8142
www.bcos.org
Benton County Career/Technical Center Vo/Tech
155 Schools Dr 38320 731-584-4492
Dr. Randy Shannon, prin. Fax 584-1864
Camden Central HS 600/9-12
115 Schools Dr 38320 731-584-7254
Shawn McDowell, prin. Fax 584-2799
Camden JHS 400/6-8
75 Schools Dr 38320 731-584-4518
Michelle Leonard, prin. Fax 584-5958
Other Schools – See Big Sandy

Carthage, Smith, Pop. 2,267
Smith County SD 3,200/PK-12
126 Smith Co Middle Schl Ln 37030 615-735-9625
Barry Smith, dir. Fax 735-8271
www.smithcoedu.com
Smith County HS 600/9-12
312 Fite Ave E 37030 615-735-9219
Jeanie Hix, prin. Fax 735-9049
Smith County MS 400/5-8
134 Smith Co Mid School Ln 37030 615-735-8277
Mike Lytle, prin. Fax 735-8255
Other Schools – See Gordonsville

Cedar Hill, Robertson, Pop. 308
Robertson County SD
Supt. — See Springfield
Byrns HS 600/6-12
7025 Highway 41 N 37032 615-696-2251
Doug Haskins, prin. Fax 696-0526

Celina, Clay, Pop. 1,478
Clay County SD 1,100/PK-12
PO Box 469 38551 931-243-3310
Matt Eldridge, dir. Fax 243-3706
www.clayedu.com
Clay County HS 300/9-12
860 Clay County Hwy 38551 931-243-2340
Melissa White, prin. Fax 243-2376

Centerville, Hickman, Pop. 3,602
Hickman County SD 3,600/PK-12
115 Murphree Ave 37033 931-729-3391
Michelle Gilbert, dir. Fax 729-3834
www.hickmank12.org
Hickman County HS 600/9-12
1645 Bulldog Blvd 37033 931-729-2616
Philip Jacobs, prin. Fax 729-2925
Hickman County MS 400/6-8
1639 Bulldog Blvd 37033 931-729-4234
Jeremy Qualls, prin. Fax 729-5688
Other Schools – See Lyles

Chapel Hill, Marshall, Pop. 1,427
Marshall County SD
Supt. — See Lewisburg
Forrest MSHS 800/7-12
310 N Horton Pkwy 37034 931-246-4733
Davy McClaran, prin. Fax 246-4732

Charleston, Bradley, Pop. 646

Candies Creek Academy 100/K-12
294 Old Eureka Rd NW 37310 423-790-5660

Charlotte, Dickson, Pop. 1,221
Dickson County SD
Supt. — See Dickson
Charlotte MS 500/6-8
250 Humphries St 37036 615-740-6060
Dr. Justin Barden, prin. Fax 789-7033
Creek Wood HS 900/9-12
3499 Highway 47 N 37036 615-740-6000
Polly Spencer, prin. Fax 441-2868
New Directions Academy 100/Alt
4000 Highway 48 N 37036 615-740-6070
Karen Willey, prin. Fax 789-7032

Chattanooga, Hamilton, Pop. 164,861
Hamilton County SD 42,200/PK-12
3074 Hickory Valley Rd 37421 423-209-8400
Rick Smith, supt. Fax 209-8601
www.hcde.org
Brainerd HS 600/9-12
1020 N Moore Rd 37411 423-855-2615
Uras Agee, prin. Fax 855-2651
Chattanooga HS Center for Creative Arts 600/6-12
1301 Dallas Rd 37405 423-209-5929
Deborah Smith, prin. Fax 209-5930
Collegiate HS at Chattanooga State 100/10-12
4501 Amnicola Hwy 37406 423-697-4492
Dr. Sonja Rich, prin. Fax 697-2676
Dalewood MS 300/6-8
1300 Shallowford Rd 37411 423-493-0323
Christian Earl, prin. Fax 493-0327
East Lake Academy of Fine Arts 500/6-8
2700 E 34th St 37407 423-493-0334
Lakesha Carson, prin. Fax 493-0343
East Ridge HS 800/9-12
4320 Bennett Rd 37412 423-867-6200
Tamera Helton, prin. Fax 867-6220
East Ridge MS 700/6-8
4400 Bennett Rd 37412 423-867-6214
Steven Robinson, prin. Fax 867-6226
Howard HS Vo/Tech
2500 S Market St 37408 423-209-5868
Zac Brown, prin. Fax 209-5869
Lookout Valley MSHS 400/6-12
350 Lookout High St 37419 423-825-7352
Derrick Rushworth, prin. Fax 821-7951
Normal Park Museum Magnet S 200/6-8
1219 W Mississippi Ave 37405 423-209-5900
Jill Levine, prin. Fax 209-5901
Orchard Knob MS 400/6-8
500 N Highland Park Ave 37404 423-493-7793
Crystal Sorrells, prin. Fax 493-7795
Red Bank HS 700/9-12
640 Morrison Springs Rd 37415 423-874-1900
Dr. Justin Robertson, prin. Fax 874-1924
Red Bank MS 600/6-8
3701 Tom Weathers Dr 37415 423-874-1908
John Pierce, prin. Fax 874-1938
STEM S Chattanooga 100/9-12
4501 Amnicola Hwy 37406 423-531-6270
Dr. Tony Donen, prin. Fax 531-6268
Tyner Academy 600/9-12
6836 Tyner Rd 37421 423-855-2635
Carol Goss, prin. Fax 855-9417
Tyner Middle Academy 500/6-8
6837 Tyner Rd 37421 423-855-2648
Mark Smith, prin. Fax 855-2699
Washington Alternative Learning Center 50/Alt
7821 Hancock Rd 37416 423-893-3520
Dr. Rodney Knox, prin. Fax 893-3521
Other Schools – See Harrison, Hixson, Ooltewah, Sale Creek, Signal Mountain, Soddy Daisy

---

Baylor S 1,100/6-12
171 Baylor School Rd 37405 423-267-8505
Scott Wilson, hdmstr. Fax 265-4276
Boyd-Buchanan S 900/PK-12
4650 Buccaneer Trl 37411 423-622-6177
Calvary Christian S 200/PK-12
4601 North Ter 37411 423-622-2181
Clif Roth, admin.
Chattanooga Christian S 1,200/PK-12
3354 Charger Dr 37409 423-265-6411
Chad Dirkse, pres. Fax 756-4044
Chattanooga College Post-Sec.
248 Northgate Mall Dr 37415 423-624-0078
Chattanooga State Community College Post-Sec.
4501 Amnicola Hwy 37406 423-697-4400
Girls Preparatory S 600/6-12
PO Box 4736 37405 423-634-7600
Dr. Autumn Graves, head sch Fax 634-7643
Grace Baptist Academy 600/PK-12
7815 Shallowford Rd 37421 423-892-8224
Matt Pollock, hdmstr. Fax 892-1194
Hamilton Heights Christian Academy 100/9-12
2201 Hickory Valley Rd 37421 423-894-0597
Rev. Duke Stone, admin. Fax 894-4259
McCallie S 900/6-12
500 Dodds Ave 37404 423-624-8300
Lee Burns, hdmstr. Fax 493-5690
Miller-Motte Technical College Post-Sec.
6020 Shallowford Rd Ste 100 37421 423-510-9675
Notre Dame HS 400/9-12
2701 Vermont Ave 37404 423-624-4618
George Valadie, pres. Fax 624-4621
Richmont Graduate University Post-Sec.
1815 McCallie Ave 37404 423-266-4574
Silverdale Baptist Academy 1,000/PK-12
7236 Bonny Oaks Dr 37421 423-892-2319
Rebecca Hansard, hdmstr. Fax 648-7600
Tennessee Temple University Post-Sec.
1815 Union Ave 37404 800-553-4050
University of Tennessee Post-Sec.
615 McCallie Ave 37403 423-425-4111
Virginia College Post-Sec.
721 Eastgate Loop 37411 423-893-2000

Christiana, Rutherford
Rutherford County SD
Supt. — See Murfreesboro
Christiana MS 900/6-8
4675 Shelbyville Pike 37037 615-904-3885
Bob Horne, prin. Fax 904-3886

Church Hill, Hawkins, Pop. 6,688
Hawkins County SD
Supt. — See Rogersville
Church Hill MS 400/7-8
211 Oak St 37642 423-357-3051
Scott Jones, prin. Fax 357-9873
Volunteer HS 1,200/9-12
1050 Volunteer St 37642 423-357-3641
Bobby Wines, prin. Fax 357-6694

Clarkrange, Fentress, Pop. 575
Fentress County SD
Supt. — See Jamestown
Clarkrange HS 300/9-12
5801 S York Hwy 38553 931-863-3143
Marty Walker, prin. Fax 863-3981

Clarksville, Montgomery, Pop. 126,966
Clarksville-Montgomery County SD 30,700/PK-12
621 Gracey Ave 37040 931-648-5600
Dr. B.J. Worthington, dir. Fax 648-5612
www.cmcss.net

Alternative S Alt
430 Greenwood Ave 37040 931-542-5057
Kim Sigears, prin. Fax 503-3411
Clarksville HS 1,300/9-12
151 Richview Rd 37043 931-648-5690
Jean Luna, prin. Fax 648-5624
Kenwood HS 1,100/9-12
251 E Pine Mountain Rd 37042 931-905-7900
Hal Bedell, prin. Fax 905-7906
Kenwood MS 900/6-8
241 E Pine Mountain Rd 37042 931-553-2080
Marlon Heaston, prin. Fax 552-3080
Middle College HS at APSU 100/9-12
PO Box 4654 37044 931-221-1350
Melissa Champion-Emerson, prin. Fax 221-1360
New Providence MS 1,100/6-8
146 Cunningham Ln 37042 931-648-5655
Laura Barnett, prin. Fax 503-3409
Northeast HS 1,200/9-12
3701 Trenton Rd 37040 931-648-5640
Garry Chadwell, prin. Fax 647-6025
Northeast MS 1,100/6-8
3703 Trenton Rd 37040 931-648-5665
Tracy Hollinger, prin. Fax 503-3410
Northwest HS 1,200/9-12
800 Lafayette Rd 37042 931-648-5675
Dr. Theresa Muckleroy, prin. Fax 648-0094
Richview MS 1,000/6-8
2350 Memorial Drive Ext 37043 931-648-5620
Lisa Clark, prin. Fax 551-8111
Rossview HS 1,400/9-12
1237 Rossview Rd 37043 931-553-2070
Frank Myers, prin. Fax 503-3419
Rossview MS 1,200/6-8
2265 Cardinal Ln 37043 931-920-6150
Christina Harris, prin. Fax 920-6147
STEM Academy 9-12
251 E Pine Mountain Rd 37042 931-905-7900
Christi Fordham, admin. Fax 905-7906
West Creek HS 1,200/9-12
1210 W Creek Coyote Trl 37042 931-503-1788
Christopher Neidigh, prin. Fax 503-1802
West Creek MS 1,000/6-8
1200 W Creek Coyote Trl 37042 931-503-3288
Bryan Feldman, prin. Fax 503-3296
Other Schools – See Cunningham

Austin Peay State University Post-Sec.
601 College St 37044 931-221-7011
Clarksville Academy 600/PK-12
710 N 2nd St 37040 931-647-6311
Clarksville Christian S 100/PK-12
505 Highway 76 37043 931-647-8180
Amanda Binkley, prin. Fax 741-0953
Draughons Junior College Post-Sec.
2691 Trenton Rd 37040 931-552-7600
Miller-Motte Technical College Post-Sec.
1820 Business Park Dr 37040 931-553-0071
North Central Institute Post-Sec.
168 Jack Miller Blvd 37042 931-431-9700
Queen City College Post-Sec.
1594 Fort Campbell Blvd 37042 931-645-2361

Cleveland, Bradley, Pop. 40,418
Bradley County SD 10,200/PK-12
800 S Lee Hwy 37311 423-476-0620
Dr. Linda Cash, dir. Fax 476-0485
www.bradleyschools.org
Bradley Central HS 1,700/9-12
1000 S Lee Hwy 37311 423-476-0650
Todd Shoemaker, prin. Fax 476-0613
Goal Academy 50/Alt
209 Sunset Dr NW 37312 423-476-0699
Kyle Page, prin. Fax 478-8829
Lake Forest MS 1,100/6-8
610 Kile Lake Rd SE 37323 423-478-8821
Ritchie Stevenson, prin. Fax 478-8832
Ocoee MS 1,300/6-8
2250 N Ocoee St 37311 423-476-0630
Ron Spangler, prin. Fax 476-0588
Walker Valley HS 1,500/9-12
750 Lauderdale Mem Hwy NW 37312 423-336-1383
Nat Akiona, prin. Fax 336-1578
REACH Adult HS Adult
1450 Strawberry Ln NE 37311 423-473-8473
Fax 473-8483

Cleveland CSD 5,200/K-12
4300 Mouse Creek Rd NW 37312 423-472-9571
Dr. Russell Dyer, dir. Fax 472-3390
www.clevelandschools.org
Cleveland HS 1,400/9-12
850 Raider Dr NW 37312 423-478-1113
Autumn O'Bryan, prin. Fax 559-1560
Cleveland MS 1,200/6-8
3635 Georgetown Rd NW 37312 423-479-9641
Dr. Leneda Laing, prin. Fax 479-9553
Denning Center of Technology and Careers Vo/Tech
350 Central Ave NW 37311 423-339-0902
Barbra Ector, prin. Fax 559-9477

Cleveland Christian S 100/K-12
695 S Ocoee St 37311 423-476-2642
Cleveland State Community College Post-Sec.
PO Box 3570 37320 423-472-7141
Franklin Academy Post-Sec.
1605 Professional Park Dr N 37312 423-476-3742
Lee University Post-Sec.
1120 N Ocoee St 37311 800-533-9930
Pentecostal Theological Seminary Post-Sec.
900 Walker St NE 37311 423-478-1131
Tennessee Christian Preparatory S 200/PK-12
4995 N Lee Hwy 37312 423-559-8939

Clifton, Wayne, Pop. 2,664
Wayne County SD
Supt. — See Waynesboro
Hughes S 400/PK-12
PO Box A 38425 931-676-3325
Greg Morris, prin. Fax 676-3903

Clinton, Anderson, Pop. 9,667
Anderson County SD 6,800/PK-12
101 S Main St 37716 865-463-2800
Dr. Tim Parrott, supt. Fax 457-9157
www2.acs.ac
Anderson County Career & Technical Ctr Vo/Tech
140 Maverick Cir 37716 865-457-4205
Robbie Herrell, prin. Fax 457-1715
Anderson County HS 1,100/9-12
130 Maverick Cir 37716 865-457-4716
Andrea Russell, prin. Fax 457-3398
Clinch River Community S 100/Alt
160 Maverick Cir 37716 865-457-7462
Darren Leach, prin. Fax 457-6546
Clinton HS 1,100/9-12
425 Dragon Dr 37716 865-457-2611
Caleb Tipton, prin. Fax 457-8805
Clinton MS 700/6-8
110 N Hicks St 37716 865-457-3451
RaeAnn Owens, prin. Fax 457-9486
Other Schools – See Lake City, Norris, Oliver Springs

Coalfield, Morgan, Pop. 2,425
Morgan County SD
Supt. — See Wartburg
Coalfield S 500/K-12
PO Box 98 37719 865-435-7332
Matthew Murphy, prin. Fax 435-2646

Coalmont, Grundy, Pop. 825
Grundy County SD
Supt. — See Altamont
Grundy County HS 700/9-12
24970 SR 108 37313 931-692-5400
Jamie Ruehling, prin. Fax 692-5403

Collegedale, Hamilton, Pop. 8,113

Collegedale Academy 400/9-12
PO Box 628 37315 423-396-2124
Brent Baldwin M.Ed., prin. Fax 396-3363
Collegedale Adventist MS 50/6-8
PO Box 598 37315 423-396-3020
Southern Adventist University Post-Sec.
PO Box 370 37315 423-236-2000

Collierville, Shelby, Pop. 43,413
Collierville SD, 146 College St 38017 7,800/PK-12
John Aitken, supt. 901-861-7000
www.colliervilleschools.org
Collierville HS 1,900/9-12
1101 New Byhalia Rd 38017 901-853-3310
Chip Blanchard, prin. Fax 853-3313
Collierville MS 900/6-8
580 Quinn Rd 38017 901-853-3320
Roger Jones, prin. Fax 853-3327
Schilling Farms MS 1,000/6-8
935 Colbert St S 38017 901-854-2345
Beth Robbins, prin. Fax 854-8200

St. George's Independent S Collierville 700/6-12
1880 Wolf River Blvd 38017 901-457-2000
J. Ross Peters, head sch Fax 457-2121

Collinwood, Wayne, Pop. 979
Wayne County SD
Supt. — See Waynesboro
Collinwood HS 300/9-12
401 N Trojan Blvd 38450 931-724-4316
Benita Smith, prin. Fax 724-4488
Collinwood MS 300/5-8
300 4th Ave N 38450 931-724-9510
Rob Vandiver, prin. Fax 924-2519

Columbia, Maury, Pop. 33,976
Maury County SD 12,000/PK-12
501 W 8th St 38401 931-388-8403
Dr. Chris Marczak, dir. Fax 840-4410
www.mauryk12.org
Columbia Central HS 1,300/9-12
921 Lion Pkwy 38401 931-381-2222
Roger White, prin. Fax 381-6434
Cox MS 800/5-8
633 Bear Creek Pike 38401 931-840-3902
Tim Webb, prin. Fax 840-3903
Porter S Alt
1101 Bridge St 38401 931-381-1474
Robert Busch, admin. Fax 840-4432
Spring Hill HS 900/9-12
1 Raider Ln 38401 931-486-2207
Dr. Christine Potts, prin. Fax 486-3113
Whitthorne MS 900/5-8
915 Lion Pkwy 38401 931-388-2558
Linda Lester, prin. Fax 380-4684
Other Schools – See Culleoka, Hampshire, Mount Pleasant, Santa Fe, Spring Hill

---

Agathos Classical S 100/PK-12
1201 Mapleash Ave 38401 931-388-0556
Ted Trainor, hdmstr. Fax 388-0538
Columbia Academy 600/PK-12
1101 W 7th St 38401 931-388-5363
Columbia State Community College Post-Sec.
1665 Hampshire Pike 38401 931-540-2722
Zion Christian Academy 500/PK-12
6901 Old Zion Rd 38401 931-388-5731
Don Wahlman, hdmstr. Fax 388-5842

Cookeville, Putnam, Pop. 29,908
Putnam County SD 10,000/PK-12
1400 E Spring St 38506 931-526-9777
Jerry S. Boyd, dir. Fax 528-6942
www.pcsstn.com
Cookeville HS 2,200/PK-PK, 9-
1 Cavalier Dr 38501 931-520-2287
Edward L. Ward, prin. Fax 520-2268
Prescott South MS 700/5-8
1859 S Jefferson Ave 38506 931-528-3647
Trey Upchurch, prin. Fax 520-2019
Trace MS 700/5-8
230 Raider Dr 38501 931-520-2200
Michael Miehls, prin. Fax 520-2204
White Plains Academy 100/Alt
288 E Main St 38506 931-537-3862
Joe Matheney, prin. Fax 537-3062
Adult Learning Center Adult
286 E Main St 38506 931-528-8685
Robyn Nabors, prin. Fax 537-2516
Other Schools – See Algood, Baxter, Monterey

Fortis Institute Post-Sec.
1025 Highway 111 38501 931-526-3660
Genesis Career College Post-Sec.
880 E 10th St Ste A 38501 931-526-8735
Highland Rim Academy 100/K-12
PO Box 3022 38502 931-526-4472
Nick Duncan, hdmstr.
Mister Wayne's Sch of Unisex Hair Design Post-Sec.
170 S Willow Ave 38501 931-526-1478
Tennessee Technological University Post-Sec.
1 William L Jones Dr 38505 931-372-3101

Copperhill, Polk, Pop. 348
Polk County SD
Supt. — See Benton
Copper Basin HS 400/7-12
300 Cougar Dr 37317 423-496-3291
Dr. Jared Bigham, prin. Fax 496-5308

Cordova, Shelby
Shelby County SD
Supt. — See Memphis
Cordova HS 1,800/9-12
1800 Berryhill Rd 38016 901-416-4540
Kymberli Chandler, prin. Fax 416-4545
Cordova MS 900/6-8
900 N Sanga Rd 38018 901-416-2189
Stephanie Beach, prin. Fax 416-2191
Dexter MS 500/5-8
6998 Raleigh LaGrange Rd 38018 901-416-0360
Dr. Phyllis Jones, prin. Fax 373-3378
Mt. Pisgah MS 600/6-8
1444 Pisgah Rd 38016 901-416-2620
LaVonda Jones, prin. Fax 756-2306

Evangelical Christian MSHS 700/6-12
PO Box 1030 38088 901-754-7217
Dan Peterson, head sch Fax 754-8123
First Assembly Christian S 800/PK-12
8650 Walnut Grove Rd 38018 901-458-5543
L'Ecole Culinaire Post-Sec.
1245 N Germantown Pkwy 38016 901-754-7115
Mid-America Baptist Theological Seminary Post-Sec.
2095 Appling Rd 38016 901-751-8453
St. Benedict HS 800/9-12
8250 Varnavas Dr 38016 901-260-2840
Sondra Morris, prin. Fax 260-2850

Cornersville, Marshall, Pop. 1,184
Marshall County SD
Supt. — See Lewisburg
Cornersville JSHS 400/7-12
323 S Main St 37047 931-246-4170
Brent Adcox, prin. Fax 246-4153

Corryton, Knox, Pop. 100
Knox County SD
Supt. — See Knoxville
Gibbs HS 1,100/9-12
7628 Tazewell Pike 37721 865-689-9130
Tom Brown, prin. Fax 689-9128

Cosby, Cocke
Cocke County SD
Supt. — See Newport
Cosby HS 400/9-12
3320 Cosby Hwy 37722 423-487-5602
Patrick O'Neil, prin. Fax 487-5502

Covington, Tipton, Pop. 8,910
Tipton County SD 11,600/PK-12
1580 Highway 51 S 38019 901-476-7148
Dr. William Bibb, dir. Fax 476-4870
www.tipton-county.com
Covington HS 700/9-12
803 S College St 38019 901-475-5850
Mark McClain, prin. Fax 476-5778
Crestview MS 600/6-8
201 Mark Walker Dr 38019 901-475-5900
Steve Maclin, prin. Fax 475-2607
Tipton Co. Alternative Learning Center 100/Alt
800 Bert Johnston Ave 38019 901-837-5755
Steve Zurhellen, prin. Fax 476-4612
Other Schools – See Brighton, Munford

Tennessee Technology Center at Covington Post-Sec.
1600 Highway 51 S 38019 901-475-2526

Cowan, Franklin, Pop. 1,690
Franklin County SD
Supt. — See Winchester
South MS 400/6-8
601 Cumberland St W 37318 931-967-7355
Derrick Crutchfield, prin. Fax 967-1413

Cross Plains, Robertson, Pop. 1,691
Robertson County SD
Supt. — See Springfield
East Robertson HS 700/6-12
158 Kilgore Trce 37049 615-654-2191
Mary Cook, prin. Fax 654-4563

Crossville, Cumberland, Pop. 10,670
Cumberland County SD 7,400/PK-12
368 Fourth St 38555 931-484-6135
Donald Andrews, supt. Fax 484-6491
ccschools.k12tn.net/
Cumberland County HS 1,100/9-12
660 Stanley St 38555 931-484-6194
Jon Hall, prin. Fax 456-6872
Stone Memorial HS 1,100/9-12
2800 Cook Rd 38571 931-484-5767
Scott Maddox, prin. Fax 484-4801

Christian Academy of the Cumberlands 100/PK-12
325 Braun St 38555 931-707-9540
Darci Bernabei, prin. Fax 707-9545
Tennessee Technology Center Crossville Post-Sec.
910 Miller Ave 38555 931-484-7502

Crump, Hardin, Pop. 1,405

Tennessee Technology Center at Crump Post-Sec.
PO Box 89 38327 731-632-3393

Culleoka, Maury
Maury County SD
Supt. — See Columbia
Culleoka S 1,000/PK-12
1921 Warrior Way 38451 931-987-2511
Penny Love, prin. Fax 987-2594

Hopewell Church Covenant Family S 50/1-12
3886 Hopewell Rd 38451 931-505-1624
Thomas Vierra, prin. Fax 523-3217

Cumberland Gap, Claiborne, Pop. 477
Claiborne County SD
Supt. — See Tazewell
Cumberland Gap HS 600/9-12
661 Old Jacksboro Pike 37724 423-869-9964
Linda Keck, prin. Fax 869-4352

Cunningham, Montgomery
Clarksville-Montgomery County SD
Supt. — See Clarksville
Montgomery Central HS 1,000/9-12
3955 Highway 48 37052 931-387-3201
Christy Houston, prin. Fax 387-4578
Montgomery Central MS 800/6-8
3941 Highway 48 37052 931-387-2575
Dee-Etta Whitlock, prin. Fax 387-3391

Dandridge, Jefferson, Pop. 2,785
Jefferson County SD 8,100/PK-12
PO Box 190 37725 865-397-3194
Dr. Charles Edmonds, dir. Fax 397-3301
jc-schools.net/
Jefferson County HS 2,100/9-12
115 W Dumplin Valley Rd 37725 865-397-3182
Dr. Scott Walker, prin. Fax 397-4121
Maury MS 600/6-8
965 Maury Cir 37725 865-397-3424
Michelle Walker, prin. Fax 397-4253
Other Schools – See Jefferson City

Dayton, Rhea, Pop. 7,052
Rhea County SD 4,500/PK-12
305 California Ave 37321 423-775-7812
Jerry Levengood, dir. Fax 775-7831
www.rheacounty.org
Other Schools – See Evensville, Spring City

Bryan College Post-Sec.
721 Bryan Dr 37321 423-775-2041
Laurelbrook Academy 100/9-12
114 Campus Dr 37321 423-775-3339
Oxford Graduate School Post-Sec.
500 Oxford Dr 37321 423-775-6596

Decatur, Meigs, Pop. 1,593
Meigs County SD 1,800/PK-12
345 N Main St 37322 423-334-5793
Donald Roberts, supt. Fax 334-1462
www.meigscounty.net
Meigs County HS 500/9-12
PO Box 1182 37322 423-334-5797
Clint Baker, prin. Fax 334-5732
Meigs MS 400/6-8
564 N Main St 37322 423-334-9187
Ronald Woods, prin. Fax 334-1353

Decaturville, Decatur, Pop. 853
Decatur County SD 1,600/PK-12
PO Box 369 38329 731-852-2391
Branson Townsend, supt. Fax 852-2960
www.decaturcountyschools.org
Riverside HS 400/9-12
4250 Highway 641 S 38329 731-852-3941
Hugh Smith, prin. Fax 852-3955
Other Schools – See Parsons

Dickson, Dickson, Pop. 14,179
Dickson County SD 8,800/PK-12
817 N Charlotte St 37055 615-446-7571
Dr. Danny Weeks, dir. Fax 441-1375
www.dicksoncountyschools.org
Dickson County HS 1,500/9-12
509 Henslee Dr 37055 615-446-9003
Joey Holley, prin. Fax 441-4135
Dickson MS 1,200/6-8
401 E College St 37055 615-446-2273
William Burton, prin. Fax 441-4139
Other Schools – See Charlotte, White Bluff

Tennessee Technology Center at Dickson Post-Sec.
740 Highway 46 S 37055 615-441-6220

Dover, Stewart, Pop. 1,392
Stewart County SD 2,100/PK-12
PO Box 433 37058 931-232-5176
Leta Joiner, dir. Fax 232-5390
stewartcountyschools.net
Stewart County HS 700/9-12
120 Robertson Hill Rd 37058 931-232-5179
Michael Craig, prin. Fax 232-3119
Stewart County MS 500/6-8
PO Box 1001 37058 931-232-9112
Steve Nolen, prin. Fax 232-4608

Dresden, Weakley, Pop. 2,945
Weakley County SD 4,500/PK-12
8319 Highway 22 Ste A 38225 731-364-2247
Randy Frazier, supt. Fax 364-2662
www.weakleycountyschools.com
Dresden HS 400/9-12
7150 Highway 22 38225 731-364-2949
Charles West, prin. Fax 364-5328
Dresden MS 400/5-8
759 Linden St Ste A 38225 731-364-2407
David Lewellen, prin. Fax 364-5840
Weakley County Adult Learning Center Adult
8250 Highway 22 38225 731-364-5481
Mark Maddox, dir. Fax 364-3580
Other Schools – See Gleason, Greenfield, Martin

Dunlap, Sequatchie, Pop. 4,760
Bledsoe County SD
Supt. — See Pikeville
Bledsoe County Vocational Center Vo/Tech
26297 US 127 37327 423-554-3293
Steve Reel, dir. Fax 554-3142

Sequatchie County SD 2,300/PK-12
PO Box 488 37327 423-949-3617
Michael L. Swafford, dir. Fax 949-5257
sequatchieschools.net
Sequatchie County HS 700/9-12
PO Box 759 37327 423-949-2154
Tommy Layne, prin. Fax 949-4696
Sequatchie County MS 700/5-8
PO Box 789 37327 423-949-4149
Devona Smith, prin. Fax 949-4140

Sequatchie Valley Preparatory Academy 50/K-12
1050 Ray Hixson Rd 37327 423-554-4677
Robert Young, admin. Fax 554-4398

Dyer, Gibson, Pop. 2,288
Gibson County Special SD 4,000/PK-12
PO Box 60 38330 731-692-3803
Eddie Pruett, dir. Fax 692-4375
www.gcssd.org
Gibson County HS 500/9-12
PO Box 190 38330 731-692-3616
Jim Hughes, prin. Fax 692-2123
Other Schools – See Medina

Dyersburg, Dyer, Pop. 16,802
Dyer County SD 3,800/PK-12
159 Everett Ave 38024 731-285-6712
Dr. Dwight Hedge, dir. Fax 286-6721
www.dyercs.net
Three Oaks MS 500/6-8
3200 Upper Finley Rd 38024 731-285-3100
Laura Brimm, prin. Fax 285-3360
Other Schools – See Newbern

Dyersburg CSD 2,800/PK-12
509 Lake Rd 38024 731-286-3600
Neel Durbin, dir. Fax 286-2754
www.dyersburgcityschools.org/
Dyersburg HS 800/9-12
125 US Highway 51 Byp W 38024 731-286-3630
Kim Worley, prin. Fax 286-2209
Dyersburg MS 600/6-8
400 Frank Maynard Dr 38024 731-286-3625
Cal Johnson, prin. Fax 286-3624

Dyersburg State Community College Post-Sec.
1510 Lake Rd 38024 731-286-3200

Eads, Shelby

Briarcrest Christian S 300/PK-12
76 S Houston Levee Rd 38028 901-765-4600
Steve Simpson, hdmstr. Fax 765-4667

Eagleville, Rutherford, Pop. 600
Rutherford County SD
Supt. — See Murfreesboro
Eagleville S 900/PK-12
500 Old Highway 99 37060 615-904-6710
Bill Tollett, prin. Fax 274-6859

Elizabethton, Carter, Pop. 13,969
Carter County SD 5,600/PK-12
305 Academy St 37643 423-547-4000
Dr. Kevin Ward Ed.D., dir. Fax 542-7560
carter.k12.tn.us
Happy Valley HS 600/9-12
121 Warpath Ln 37643 423-547-4094
Terry Hubbard, prin. Fax 547-4083
Happy Valley MS 500/5-8
163 Warpath Ln 37643 423-547-4070
Jonathan Minton, prin. Fax 547-8352
Siam Learning Center 50/Alt
2453 Siam Rd 37643 423-547-4050
C.B. Hardin, prin. Fax 547-4061
Unaka HS 300/9-12
119 Robinson Ln 37643 423-474-4100
Betsy Oliver, prin. Fax 474-4108
Other Schools – See Hampton, Roan Mountain

Elizabethton CSD 2,500/PK-12
804 S Watauga Ave 37643 423-547-8000
Dr. Corey R. Gardenhour, supt. Fax 547-8929
www.ecschools.net
Dugger JHS 600/6-8
306 W E St 37643 423-547-8025
Randy Little, prin. Fax 547-8021
Elizabethton HS 800/9-12
907 Jason Witten Way 37643 423-547-8015
Joshua Boatman, prin. Fax 547-8016

Tennessee Technology Center Elizabethton Post-Sec.
426 Highway 91 37643 423-543-0070

Englewood, McMinn, Pop. 1,491
McMinn County SD
Supt. — See Athens
Central HS 700/9-12
145 County Road 461 37329 423-263-5541
Lori Hutchinson, prin. Fax 263-0399

Erin, Houston, Pop. 1,288
Houston County SD 1,400/PK-12
PO Box 209 37061 931-289-4148
Cathy Harvey, dir. Fax 289-5543
www.houston.k12.tn.us
Houston County HS 400/9-12
2500 Highway 149 37061 931-289-4447
Linda Jolly, prin. Fax 289-4924
Houston County MS 300/6-8
3460 W Main St 37061 931-289-5591
Anita Gray, prin. Fax 289-5599
Houston County Adult S Adult
2500 Highway 149 37061 931-289-5525
Linda McDonough, prin.

Erwin, Unicoi, Pop. 6,036
Unicoi County SD 2,600/PK-12
100 Nolichucky Ave 37650 423-743-1600
John English, dir. Fax 743-1615
www.unicoischools.com/
Unicoi County Career & Technical S Vo/Tech
100 Okolona Dr 37650 423-743-1639
Fax 743-1671
Unicoi County HS 800/9-12
700 S Mohawk Dr 37650 423-743-1632
Chris Bogart, prin. Fax 743-1636
Unicoi County MS 600/6-8
599 S Mohawk Dr 37650 423-735-0236
Jordan Simmons, prin. Fax 735-0728

Evensville, Rhea
Rhea County SD
Supt. — See Dayton
Rhea County HS 1,500/9-12
885 Eagle Ln 37332 423-775-7821
Jesse Messimer, prin. Fax 775-7889
Rhea County MS 700/6-8
405 Pierce Rd 37332 423-775-7821
Doug Keylon, prin. Fax 775-7823

Fairview, Williamson, Pop. 7,635
Williamson County SD
Supt. — See Franklin
Fairview HS 600/9-12
2595 Fairview Blvd 37062 615-472-4400
Dr. Juli Oyer, prin. Fax 472-4421
Fairview MS 600/6-8
7200 Cumberland Dr 37062 615-472-4430
Heather Hayes, prin. Fax 472-4441

Fayetteville, Lincoln, Pop. 6,705
Fayetteville CSD 1,500/PK-12
110 Elk Ave S Ste 200 37334 931-433-5542
Dr. Janine M. Wilson Ed.D., supt. Fax 433-7499
www.fcsboe.org
Fayetteville HS 300/9-12
1800 Wilson Pkwy Ste A 37334 931-433-3158
Eric Jones, prin. Fax 433-4611
Fayetteville MS 400/5-8
1800 Wilson Pkwy Ste A 37334 931-438-2533
Steve Giffin, prin. Fax 438-2539

Lincoln County SD 4,100/PK-12
206 Davidson St E 37334 931-433-3565
Bill Heath, dir. Fax 433-7397
www.lcdoe.org
Lincoln County HS 900/10-12
1233 Huntsville Hwy 37334 931-433-6505
Sarah Wallace, prin. Fax 438-1490
Ninth Grade Academy 300/9-9
900 Main Ave S 37334 931-433-6156
Spring Brindley, prin. Fax 438-2465

Fayetteville College of Cosmetology Post-Sec.
201 College St W 37334 931-433-1305
Riverside Christian Academy 400/PK-12
PO Box 617 37334 931-438-4722

Franklin, Williamson, Pop. 61,495
Franklin Special SD 3,800/PK-8
507 New Highway 96 W 37064 615-794-6624
Dr. David Snowden Ph.D., supt. Fax 790-4716
www.fssd.org
Freedom MS 600/7-8
750 New Highway 96 W 37064 615-794-0987
Dr. Kristi Jefferson Ed.D., prin. Fax 790-4742
Poplar Grove MS 400/5-8
2959 Del Rio Pike 37069 615-790-4721
Chris Treadway, prin. Fax 790-4730

Williamson County SD 34,000/PK-12
1320 W Main St Ste 202 37064 615-472-4000
Dr. Michael Looney, supt. Fax 472-4190
www.wcs.edu
Centennial HS 1,700/9-12
5050 Mallory Ln 37067 615-472-4270
Dr. Leigh Webb, prin. Fax 472-4291

Franklin HS 1,800/9-12
810 Hillsboro Rd 37064 615-472-4450
Willie Dickerson, prin. Fax 472-4478
Grassland MS 900/6-8
2390 Hillsboro Rd 37069 615-472-4500
Darren Kennedy, prin. Fax 472-4511
Page HS 900/9-12
6281 Arno Rd 37064 615-472-4730
Shane Pantall, prin. Fax 472-4751
Page MS 1,000/6-8
6262 Arno Rd 37064 615-472-4760
Dr. Eric Lifsey, prin. Fax 472-4771
Renaissance HS 100/9-12
108 Everbright St 37064 615-472-4670
Dr. Brian Bass, prin. Fax 472-4675
Other Schools – See Brentwood, Fairview, Nolensville, Spring Hill, Thompsons Station

---

Battle Ground Academy 900/K-12
336 Ernest Rice Ln 37069 615-794-3501
William F. Kesler, head sch Fax 567-8360
Classical Academy of Franklin 200/PK-10
810 Del Rio Pike 37064 615-790-8556
Eric Van Gorden, head sch Fax 790-8617
Comenius S 900/K-12
PO Box 1601 37065 615-528-3778
Jeff Dokkestul, prin. Fax 528-9432
Franklin Christian Academy 100/5-12
PO Box 157 37065 615-599-9229
Hugh Harris, hdmstr. Fax 599-9441
Franklin Classical S 100/K-12
PO Box 1601 37065 615-528-3777
Jeff Dokkestul, prin. Fax 528-9432
Grace Christian Academy 200/PK-12
3279 Southall Rd 37064 615-591-3017
Robbie Mason, hdmstr.
O'More College of Design Post-Sec.
423 S Margin St 37064 615-794-4254
Williamson Christian College Post-Sec.
274 Mallory Station Rd 37067 615-771-7821

Friendsville, Blount, Pop. 902
Blount County SD
Supt. — See Maryville
Union Grove MS 800/6-8
334 S Old Grey Ridge Rd 37737 865-980-1320
Alicia Lail, prin. Fax 980-1323

Gainesboro, Jackson, Pop. 959
Jackson County SD 1,600/PK-12
711 School Dr 38562 931-268-0268
Joe Barlow, dir. Fax 268-3647
volweb.utk.edu/school/jackson/
Jackson County HS 500/9-12
190 Blue Devil Ln 38562 931-268-9771
Charles Breidert, prin. Fax 268-9433
Jackson County MS 500/PK-PK, 4-
170 Blue Devil Ln 38562 931-268-9779
Gail Myers, prin. Fax 268-9413

Gallatin, Sumner, Pop. 29,705
Sumner County SD 28,200/PK-12
695 E Main St 37066 615-451-5200
Dr. Del Phillips, dir. Fax 451-5216
www.sumnerschools.org
Fisher Alternative S 100/Alt
455 N Boyers Ave 37066 615-451-6558
Bob Gideon, prin. Fax 451-5290
Gallatin HS 1,400/9-12
700 Dan P Herron Dr 37066 615-452-2621
Dr. Ron Becker, prin. Fax 451-5426
Rucker-Stewart MS 700/6-8
350 Hancock St 37066 615-452-1734
Bryan Adams, prin. Fax 451-5297
Shafer MS 600/6-8
240 Albert Gallatin Ave 37066 615-452-9100
David Hallman, prin. Fax 451-6545
Station Camp HS 1,500/9-12
1040 Bison Trl 37066 615-451-6551
Art Crook, prin. Fax 451-6556
Station Camp MS 700/6-8
281 Big Station Camp Blvd 37066 615-206-0116
Mike Brown, prin. Fax 206-0165
Sumner County Middle College HS 9-12
1480 Nashville Pike 37066 615-230-3470
Brad Schreiner, prin.
Wilson HS, 685 E Main St 37066 50/9-12
Jennifer Holdren, prin. 615-230-6948
Other Schools – See Hendersonville, Portland, Westmoreland, White House

---

Volunteer State Community College Post-Sec.
1480 Nashville Pike 37066 615-452-8600

Gatlinburg, Sevier, Pop. 3,902
Sevier County SD
Supt. — See Sevierville
Gatlinburg-Pittman HS 600/9-12
150 Proffitt Rd 37738 865-436-5637
Tony Ogle, prin. Fax 436-2567

Germantown, Shelby, Pop. 38,412
Germantown Municipal SD 5,100/K-12
6685 Poplar Ave Ste 202 38138 901-752-7900
Jason Manuel, supt. Fax 757-6479
www.gmsdk12.org
Houston HS 1,700/9-12
9755 Wolf River Blvd 38139 901-756-2370
Kyle Cherry, prin. Fax 756-2377
Houston MS 900/6-8
9400 Wolf River Blvd 38139 901-756-2366
Liz Dias, prin. Fax 756-2346

Shelby County SD
Supt. — See Memphis
Germantown HS 2,100/9-12
7653 Poplar Pike 38138 901-416-0955
Barbara Harmon, prin. Fax 416-0963
Germantown MS 700/6-8
7925 CD Smith Rd 38138 901-416-0950
Amie Marsh, prin. Fax 416-0952

Gleason, Weakley, Pop. 1,427
Weakley County SD
Supt. — See Dresden
Gleason S 500/PK-12
9299 State Championship Dr 38229 731-648-5351
Trish Price, prin. Fax 648-9199

Goodlettsville, Davidson, Pop. 15,590
Metropolitan Nashville SD
Supt. — See Nashville
Goodlettsville MS 500/5-8
300 S Main St 37072 615-859-8956
Beatriz Salgado, prin. Fax 859-8961

Gordonsville, Smith, Pop. 1,200
Smith County SD
Supt. — See Carthage
Gordonsville HS 500/7-12
110 Main St E 38563 615-683-8245
Ronnie Scudder, prin. Fax 683-5193

Gray, Washington, Pop. 1,206
Washington County SD
Supt. — See Jonesborough
Boone HS 1,400/9-12
1440 Suncrest Dr 37615 423-477-1600
Roger Jackson, prin. Fax 477-1625

Greenback, Loudon, Pop. 1,059
Loudon County SD
Supt. — See Loudon
Greenback S 600/PK-12
6945 Morganton Rd 37742 865-856-3028
Mike Casteel, prin. Fax 856-8379

Greenbrier, Robertson, Pop. 6,354
Robertson County SD
Supt. — See Springfield
Greenbrier HS 800/9-12
126 Cuniff Dr 37073 615-643-4526
Dr. Katie Osborne, prin. Fax 643-8873
Greenbrier MS 600/6-8
2450 Highway 41 S 37073 615-643-7823
Kathy Carroll, prin. Fax 643-4580

Dayspring Academy 100/PK-12
2838 Heights Circle Dr 37073 615-672-9650

Greeneville, Greene, Pop. 14,821
Greene County SD 7,300/PK-12
910 W Summer St 37743 423-639-4194
David McLain, dir. Fax 639-1615
www.greenek12.org
North Greene HS 400/9-12
4675 Old Baileyton Rd 37745 423-234-1752
Amanda Weems, prin. Fax 234-3103
South Greene HS 500/9-12
7469 Asheville Hwy 37743 423-639-3790
Dr. Cindy Bowman, prin. Fax 636-3791
Other Schools – See Afton, Mosheim

Greeneville CSD 2,800/PK-12
PO Box 1420 37744 423-787-8000
Dr. Jeff Moorhouse, dir. Fax 638-2540
www.gcschools.net
Greeneville HS 900/9-12
210 Tusculum Blvd 37745 423-787-8030
Patrick Fraley, prin. Fax 787-8028
Greeneville MS 600/6-8
433 E Vann Rd 37743 423-639-7841
Heather Boegemann, prin. Fax 639-4112
Greeneville/Greene Co. Ctr for Technology Vo/Tech
1121 Hal Henard Rd 37743 423-639-0171
Jerry Ayers, prin. Fax 639-0176

Greeneville Adventist Academy 100/K-12
305 Takoma Ave 37743 423-639-2011
Tusculum College Post-Sec.
60 Shiloh Rd 37745 423-636-7300

Greenfield, Weakley, Pop. 2,162
Weakley County SD
Supt. — See Dresden
Greenfield S 600/PK-12
319 W Main St 38230 731-235-3424
Don McCurley, prin. Fax 235-3480

Gruetli Laager, Grundy, Pop. 1,795

Faith Missionary Academy 100/K-12
495 Red Barn Rd 37339 931-779-3338

Halls, Lauderdale, Pop. 2,218
Lauderdale County SD
Supt. — See Ripley
Halls HS 400/9-12
800 W Tigrett St 38040 731-836-9642
Andy Pugh, prin. Fax 836-1072
Halls JHS 200/7-8
800 W Tigrett St 38040 731-836-5579
Michael Blackwood, prin. Fax 836-5555

Hampshire, Maury
Maury County SD
Supt. — See Columbia
Hampshire S 300/K-12
4235 Old State Rd 38461 931-285-2300
Sonya Booker Cathey, prin. Fax 285-2612

Hampton, Carter
Carter County SD
Supt. — See Elizabethton
Hampton HS 500/9-12
766 First Ave 37658 423-725-5200
Jeff Bradley, prin. Fax 725-5204

Harriman, Roane, Pop. 6,223
Roane County SD
Supt. — See Kingston
Harriman HS 300/9-12
920 N Roane St 37748 865-882-1821
Scott Calahan, prin. Fax 882-6479
Harriman MS 300/6-8
1025 Cumberland St 37748 865-882-1727
Leslie Smith, prin. Fax 882-6285
Midtown Educational Center 50/Alt
3096 Roane State Hwy 37748 865-882-0242
Chris Johnson, prin. Fax 882-7734

Roane State Community College Post-Sec.
276 Patton Ln 37748 865-354-3000
Tennessee Technology Center at Harriman Post-Sec.
PO Box 1109 37748 865-882-6703

Harrison, Hamilton, Pop. 7,602
Hamilton County SD
Supt. — See Chattanooga
Brown MS 500/6-8
5716 Highway 58 37341 423-344-1439
Jane Reynolds, prin. Fax 344-1471
Central HS 900/9-12
5728 Highway 58 37341 423-344-1447
Ronald King, prin. Fax 344-1470

Harrogate, Claiborne, Pop. 4,333
Claiborne County SD
Supt. — See Tazewell
Livesay MS 300/5-8
PO Box 460 37752 423-869-4663
Karyn Clark, prin. Fax 869-8389

Lincoln Memorial University Post-Sec.
6965 Cumberland Gap Pkwy 37752 423-869-3611
White Academy 100/5-12
6965 Cumberland Gap Pkwy 37752 423-869-6234

Hartsville, Trousdale, Pop. 2,373
Trousdale County SD 1,200/K-12
103 Lock Six Rd 37074 615-374-2193
Clint Satterfield, dir. Fax 374-1108
www.tcschools.org
Satterfield MS 300/6-8
210 Damascus St 37074 615-374-2748
Amanda Gregory, prin. Fax 374-2602
Trousdale County HS 400/9-12
262 McMurry Blvd W 37074 615-374-2201
Teresa Dickerson, prin. Fax 374-1120

Tennessee Technology Center Hartsville Post-Sec.
716 McMurry Blvd E 37074 615-374-2147

Henderson, Chester, Pop. 6,177
Chester County SD 2,800/PK-12
PO Box 327 38340 731-989-5134
Troy Kilzer, supt. Fax 989-4755
www.chestercountyschools.org
Chester County HS 800/9-12
552 E Main St 38340 731-989-8125
Dr. Ricky Catlett, prin. Fax 989-8131
Chester County JHS 700/6-8
930 E Main St 38340 731-989-8135
Kris Todd, prin. Fax 989-8137

Freed-Hardeman University Post-Sec.
158 E Main St 38340 731-989-6000

Hendersonville, Sumner, Pop. 50,488
Sumner County SD
Supt. — See Gallatin
Beech HS 1,300/9-12
3126 Long Hollow Pike 37075 615-824-6200
Kenny Powell, prin. Fax 264-6553
Ellis MS 600/6-8
100 Indian Lake Rd 37075 615-264-6093
Darren Frank, prin. Fax 264-5800
Hawkins MS 500/6-8
487A Walton Ferry Rd 37075 615-824-3456
Mitch Flood, prin. Fax 264-6003
Hendersonville HS 1,500/9-12
123 Cherokee Rd 37075 615-824-6162
Bob Cotter, prin. Fax 264-6027
Hunter MS 700/6-8
2101 New Hope Rd 37075 615-822-4720
Ahmed White, prin. Fax 264-6036
Hyde Magnet S 700/K-12
128 Township Dr 37075 615-264-6543
Todd Stinson, prin. Fax 264-6546
Knox Doss MS 600/6-8
1338 Drakes Creek Rd 37075 615-824-8383
Kenny Powell, prin. Fax 824-8448

Hendersonville Christian Academy 300/PK-12
355 Old Shackle Island Rd 37075 615-824-1550
Pope John Paul II HS 600/9-12
117 Caldwell Dr 37075 615-822-2375
Faustin Weber, hdmstr. Fax 822-6226

Hermitage, See Nashville
Metropolitan Nashville SD
Supt. — See Nashville
DuPont Tyler MS 700/5-8
431 Tyler Dr 37076 615-885-8827
Dr. Bianca Jefferson, prin. Fax 847-7322

Hixson, See Chattanooga
Hamilton County SD
Supt. — See Chattanooga
Hixson HS 900/9-12
5705 Middle Valley Rd 37343 423-847-4800
Lee Sims, prin. Fax 847-4801
Hixson MS 700/6-8
5681 Old Hixson Pike 37343 423-847-4810
Leangela Rogers, prin. Fax 847-4811

Loftis MS 600/6-8
8611 Columbus Rd 37343 423-843-4749
Brentley Eller, prin. Fax 843-4758

Berean Academy 300/PK-12
441 Berean Ln 37343 423-877-1288

Hohenwald, Lewis, Pop. 3,706
Lewis County SD 1,900/PK-12
206 S Court St 38462 931-796-3264
Benny Pace, supt. Fax 796-5127
www.lewis.k12.tn.us
Lewis County HS 600/9-12
818 W Main St 38462 931-796-4085
Allen Trull, prin. Fax 796-1172
Lewis County MS 400/6-8
207 S Court St 38462 931-796-4586
Steve Edwards, prin. Fax 796-7601

Tennessee Technology Center at Hohenwald Post-Sec.
813 W Main St 38462 931-796-5351

Humboldt, Gibson, Pop. 8,376
Humboldt CSD 900/PK-12
2602 Viking Dr 38343 731-784-2652
Dr. Versie Hamlett, supt. Fax 784-2480
www.humboldtschools.com
Humboldt HS 300/7-12
2600 Viking Dr 38343 731-784-2781
James Walker, prin. Fax 784-8536

Huntingdon, Carroll, Pop. 3,896
Carroll County SD
PO Box 799 38344 731-986-4482
Johnny McAdams, supt. Fax 986-0198
www.carrollschools.com
Carroll County Technical Center Vo/Tech
1235 Buena Vista Rd 38344 731-986-8908
Dennis Stokes, prin. Fax 986-3200

Huntingdon Special SD 1,200/PK-12
585 High St 38344 731-986-2222
Pat Dillahunty, supt. Fax 986-4365
www.huntingdonschools.net
Huntingdon HS 400/9-12
475 Mustang Dr 38344 731-986-8223
Dr. Jonathan Kee, prin. Fax 986-4031
Huntingdon MS 400/4-8
199 Browning Ave 38344 731-986-4544
Scott Carter, prin. Fax 986-8689

South Carroll County Special SD 400/PK-12
145 Clarksburg Rd 38344 731-986-4534
Dr. Tony Tucker, supt. Fax 986-4562
www.rocketsonline.org
Clarksburg S 400/PK-12
145 Clarksburg Rd 38344 731-986-3165
Angela Bartholomew, prin. Fax 986-4562

Huntland, Franklin, Pop. 866
Franklin County SD
Supt. — See Winchester
Huntland S 700/PK-12
400 Gore St 37345 931-469-7506
Ken Bishop, prin. Fax 469-0590

Huntsville, Scott, Pop. 1,235
Scott County SD 3,100/PK-12
PO Box 37 37756 423-663-2159
Bill Hall, supt. Fax 663-9682
www.scottcounty.net
Huntsville MS 300/5-8
3101 Baker Hwy 37756 423-663-2192
Donna Goodman, prin. Fax 663-2967
Scott HS 800/9-12
400 Scott High Dr 37756 423-663-2801
Melissa Rector, prin. Fax 663-2368

Tennessee Technology Center Oneida/Hunts Post-Sec.
355 Scott High Dr 37756 423-663-4900

Jacksboro, Campbell, Pop. 2,000
Campbell County SD 5,900/PK-12
172 Valley St 37757 423-562-8377
Larry Nidiffer, dir. Fax 566-7562
www.campbell.k12.tn.us
Campbell County Comprehensive HS 1,300/9-12
150 Cougar Ln 37757 423-562-8308
Jamie Wheeler, prin. Fax 566-2019
Jacksboro MS 500/6-8
150 Eagle Cir 37757 423-562-3773
Jennifer Fields, prin. Fax 562-8994
Other Schools – See Jellico, La Follette

Tennessee Technology Center at Jacksboro Post-Sec.
PO Box 419 37757 423-566-9629

Jackson, Madison, Pop. 64,311
Jackson-Madison County SD 11,300/PK-12
310 N Parkway 38305 731-664-2592
Verna Ruffin, supt. Fax 664-2502
www.jmcss.org
Jackson Central-Merry Early College HS 700/9-12
332 Lane Ave 38301 731-664-2575
Jason Bridgeman, prin.
Liberty Technology Magnet HS Vo/Tech
3470 Ridgecrest Road Ext 38305 731-423-9086
Dr. June Murry, prin. Fax 424-3445
Madison Academic Magnet S 500/9-12
179 Allen Ave 38301 731-427-3501
Janice Epperson, prin. Fax 427-3587
Northeast MS 500/6-8
2665 Christmasville Rd 38305 731-422-6687
Teresa Tritt, prin. Fax 423-1805
North Parkway MS 500/6-8
1341 N Parkway 38305 731-427-3384
Tracey Vowell, prin. Fax 427-2591
North Side HS 1,000/9-12
3066 N Highland Ave 38305 731-668-3171
Ricky Catlett, prin. Fax 661-9756
Parkview Learning Center 50/Alt
905 E Chester St 38301 731-427-2841
Jason Newman, prin. Fax 427-2529
South Side HS 700/9-12
84 Harts Bridge Rd 38301 731-422-9923
Anita Tucker, prin. Fax 423-3411
West Bemis MS 400/6-8
230 D St 38301 731-988-3810
Dr. Nancy Hutchison, prin. Fax 988-3814

Augustine S 100/PK-12
1171 Old Humboldt Rd 38305 731-660-6822
Donna Nelson, admin. Fax 660-6833
Jackson Christian S 800/PK-12
832 Country Club Ln 38305 731-668-8055
Dr. Mark Benton, pres. Fax 324-4957
Jackson State Community College Post-Sec.
2046 N Parkway 38301 731-424-3520
Lane College Post-Sec.
545 Lane Ave 38301 731-426-7500
Sacred Heart of Jesus & Mary HS 9-12
185 Greenfield Dr 38305 731-660-4774
Ann Keyl, prin. Fax 984-7200
Tennessee Technology Center at Jackson Post-Sec.
2468 Technology Center Dr 38301 731-424-0691
Trinity Christian Academy 700/PK-12
10 Windy City Rd 38305 731-668-8500
Jon Holley, head sch Fax 668-3232
Union University Post-Sec.
1050 Union University Dr 38305 731-668-1818
University S of Jackson 1,100/PK-12
232 McClellan Rd 38305 731-664-0812
Stuart Hirstein, hdmstr. Fax 664-5046
West Tennessee Business College Post-Sec.
1186 Highway 45 Byp 38301 800-737-9822

Jamestown, Fentress, Pop. 1,935
Alvin C. York Institute 700/9-12
701 N Main St 38556 931-879-8101
Phil Brannon, supt. Fax 879-2147
www2.york.k12.tn.us/
York Institute 700/9-12
701 N Main St 38556 931-879-8101
Phil Brannon, prin. Fax 879-2147

Fentress County SD 2,400/PK-12
1011 Old Highway 127 S 38556 931-879-9218
Mike Jones, dir. Fax 879-4050
www.fentress.k12tn.net
Other Schools – See Allardt, Clarkrange

Jasper, Marion, Pop. 3,248
Marion County SD 4,300/PK-12
204 Betsy Pack Dr 37347 423-942-3434
Mark Griffith, supt. Fax 942-4210
www.marionschools.org/
Central Prep Academy Alt
230 Ridley Ave 37347 423-805-9861
Jennifer Rector, prin. Fax 805-9861
Jasper MS 500/5-8
601 Elm Ave 37347 423-942-6251
Ramona McEntyre, prin. Fax 942-0141
Marion County HS 500/9-12
160 Ridley Ave 37347 423-942-5120
Larry Ziegler, prin. Fax 942-5544
Other Schools – See South Pittsburg, Whitwell

Jefferson City, Jefferson, Pop. 7,885
Jefferson County SD
Supt. — See Dandridge
Jefferson MS 600/6-8
361 W Broadway Blvd 37760 865-475-6133
Joel Sanford, prin. Fax 471-6878

Carson-Newman University Post-Sec.
1646 Russell Ave 37760 865-471-2000

Jellico, Campbell, Pop. 2,326
Campbell County SD
Supt. — See Jacksboro
Collins Learning Institute Alt
141 High School Ln 37762 423-784-9455
Harold Sanders, prin.
Jellico HS 400/9-12
141 High School Ln 37762 423-784-9455
Dr. Donna Singley, prin. Fax 784-9456

Joelton, See Nashville
Metropolitan Nashville SD
Supt. — See Nashville
Joelton MS Prep 300/5-8
3500 Old Clarksville Pike 37080 615-876-5100
Todd Irving, prin.

Johnson City, Washington, Pop. 61,881
Johnson City SD 7,800/PK-12
PO Box 1517 37605 423-434-5200
Dr. Richard Bales, supt. Fax 218-4968
www.jcschools.org
Liberty Bell MS 1,200/7-8
806 Morningside Dr 37604 423-232-2192
Tammy Pearce, prin.
Science Hill Career Technical Center Vo/Tech
251 Cotty Jones Dr 37604 423-232-2200
Dr. Julia Decker, dir. Fax 461-1695
Science Hill HS 2,200/9-12
1509 John Exum Pkwy 37604 423-232-2190
Melanie Riden-Bacon, prin. Fax 434-5570

Washington County SD
Supt. — See Jonesborough
Asbury Optional HS Alt
2002 Indian Ridge Rd 37604 423-434-4900
Kari Arnold, prin. Fax 434-4902
Boones Creek MS 300/5-8
4352 N Roan St 37615 423-283-3520
Mike Edmonds, prin. Fax 283-3524

East Tennessee State University Post-Sec.
807 University Pkwy 37614 423-439-1000
Emmanuel School of Religion Post-Sec.
1 Walker Dr 37601 423-926-1186
Providence Academy 500/K-12
2788 Carroll Creek Rd 37615 423-854-9819
Jerry Williams, admin. Fax 854-8958

Jonesborough, Washington, Pop. 4,977
Washington County SD 8,900/PK-12
405 W College St 37659 423-753-1100
Ronald Dykes, dir. Fax 753-1114
www.wcde.org
Crockett HS 1,300/9-12
684 Old State Route 34 37659 423-753-1150
Andy Hare, prin. Fax 753-1167
Jonesborough MS 400/5-8
308 Forrest Dr 37659 423-753-1190
Terry Crowe, prin. Fax 753-1570
Other Schools – See Gray, Johnson City

Kingsport, Sullivan, Pop. 47,353
Kingsport CSD 7,200/PK-12
400 Clinchfield St Ste 200 37660 423-378-2100
Dr. Lyle Ailshie, supt. Fax 378-2120
www.k12k.com/
D-B EXCEL at Cora Cox Academy 50/Alt
520 Myrtle St 37660 423-378-2185
Shanna Hensley, prin. Fax 378-2187
Dobyns-Bennett HS 2,000/9-12
1800 Legion Dr 37664 423-378-8400
Dr. Chris Hampton, prin. Fax 378-8535
Robinson MS 900/6-8
1517 Jessee St 37664 423-378-2200
Brian Partin, prin. Fax 378-2220
Sevier MS 800/6-8
1200 Wateree St 37660 423-378-2450
Dr. Holly Flora, prin. Fax 378-2430

Sullivan County SD
Supt. — See Blountville
Colonial Heights MS 500/6-8
415 Lebanon Rd 37663 423-354-1360
Bill Dunham, prin. Fax 354-1365
Sullivan North HS 600/9-12
2533 N John B Dennis Hwy 37660 423-354-1400
Brent Palmer, prin. Fax 354-1406
Sullivan North MS 300/6-8
2533 N John B Dennis Hwy 37660 423-354-1750
Wayne King, admin. Fax 354-1459
Sullivan South HS 900/9-12
1236 Moreland Dr 37664 423-354-1300
Greg Harvey, prin. Fax 354-1306

Appalachian Christian S 50/K-12
1044 New Beason Well Rd 37660 423-288-3352
Br. Newl Dotson, prin.
Cedar View Christian School 200/PK-12
PO Box 143 37662 423-245-6341

Kingston, Roane, Pop. 5,854
Roane County SD 6,700/PK-12
105 Bluff Rd 37763 865-376-5592
Dr. Leah Watkins Ed.D., dir. Fax 376-1284
www.roaneschools.com
Cherokee MS 500/6-8
200 Paint Rock Ferry Rd 37763 865-376-9281
Elizabeth Rose, prin. Fax 376-8525
Midway HS 300/9-12
530 Loudon Hwy 37763 865-376-5645
Scott Mason, prin. Fax 376-8516
Roane County HS 700/9-12
540 W Cumberland St 37763 865-376-6534
Lance Duff, prin. Fax 376-8530
Other Schools – See Harriman, Oliver Springs, Rockwood, Ten Mile

Kingston Springs, Cheatham, Pop. 2,732
Cheatham County SD
Supt. — See Ashland City
Harpeth HS 600/9-12
170 E Kingston Springs Rd 37082 615-952-2811
Dr. Ryan Longnecker, prin. Fax 952-5013
Harpeth MS 600/5-8
170 Harpeth View Trl 37082 615-952-2293
Scott Adkins, prin. Fax 952-4527

Knoxville, Knox, Pop. 174,475
Knox County SD 58,000/PK-12
PO Box 2188 37901 865-594-1800
Dr. James McIntyre, dir. Fax 594-1627
knoxschools.org
Austin-East HS 600/9-12
2800 Martin Luther King Jr 37914 865-594-3792
Benny Perry, prin. Fax 594-1165
Bearden HS 1,900/9-12
8352 Kingston Pike 37919 865-539-7800
Dr. John Bartlett, prin. Fax 539-7805
Bearden MS 1,200/6-8
1000 Francis Rd 37909 865-539-7839
Sonya Winstead, prin. Fax 539-7851
Byington-Solway Technology Center Vo/Tech
2700 Byington Solway Rd 37931 865-693-3511
David Bell, admin. Fax 694-7094
Cedar Bluff MS 600/6-8
707 N Cedar Bluff Rd 37923 865-539-7891
Christine Oehler, prin. Fax 539-7792
Central HS 1,200/9-12
5321 Jacksboro Pike 37918 865-689-1400
Jody Goins, prin. Fax 689-1403
Farragut HS 1,700/9-12
11237 Kingston Pike, 865-966-9775
Mike Reynolds, prin. Fax 671-7120

Farragut MS 1,400/6-8
200 W End Ave, 865-966-9756
Danny Trent, prin. Fax 671-7048
Fulton HS 1,000/9-12
2509 N Broadway St 37917 865-594-1240
Rob Speas, prin. Fax 594-1228
Gresham MS 800/6-8
500 Gresham Rd 37918 865-689-1430
Donna Parker, prin. Fax 689-7437
Halls HS 1,300/9-12
4321 E Emory Rd 37938 865-922-7757
Mark Duff, prin. Fax 925-7700
Halls MS 1,200/6-8
4317 E Emory Rd 37938 865-922-7494
Tim Wiegenstein, prin. Fax 925-7439
Hardin Valley Academy 1,900/9-12
11345 Hardin Valley Rd 37932 865-690-9690
Sallee Reynolds, prin. Fax 690-9260
Holston MS 900/6-8
600 N Chilhowee Dr 37924 865-594-1300
Ashley Jessie, prin. Fax 594-4429
Karns HS 1,200/9-12
2710 Byington Solway Rd 37931 865-539-8670
Kim Towe, prin. Fax 539-8679
Karns MS 1,400/6-8
2925 Gray Hendrix Rd 37931 865-539-7732
Brad Corum, prin. Fax 539-7745
Kelley Volunteer Academy 100/Alt
3001 Knoxville Center Dr 37924 865-525-0069
Alan Hill, prin. Fax 525-2666
L & N STEM Academy 300/10-12
401 Henley St 37902 865-329-8440
Becky Ashe, prin. Fax 329-8457
Lincon Park Technology & Trade Center Vo/Tech
535 Chickamauga Ave 37917 865-281-2600
Rick Bise, dir. Fax 689-1456
North Knox Vocational Center Vo/Tech
7411 Ledgerwood Rd 37938 865-922-7576
Fax 925-7551
Northwest MS 800/6-8
5301 Pleasant Ridge Rd 37912 865-594-1345
Dr. Karen Loy, prin. Fax 594-1339
South-Doyle HS 1,200/9-12
2020 Tipton Station Rd 37920 865-577-4475
Tim Berry, prin. Fax 577-4540
South-Doyle MS 1,100/6-8
3900 Decatur Dr 37920 865-579-2133
Beth Blevins, prin. Fax 579-2128
Vine MS 300/6-8
1807 Martin Luther King Jr 37915 865-594-4461
Cindy White, prin. Fax 594-1702
West HS 1,200/9-12
3300 Sutherland Ave 37919 865-594-4477
Katherine Banner, prin. Fax 594-4486
West Valley MS 1,200/6-8
9118 George Williams Rd 37922 865-539-5145
Renee Kelly, prin. Fax 539-5155
Whittle Springs MS 500/6-8
2700 White Oak Ln 37917 865-594-4474
Nadriene Jackson, prin. Fax 594-1132
Yoakley S 100/Alt
4415 Washington Pike 37917 865-594-3790
Tom Watson, prin. Fax 594-3770
Knox County Adult HS Adult
3001 Knoxville Center Dr 37924 865-594-8718
Nancy Seely, prin.
Other Schools – See Corryton, Powell, Strawberry Plains

Apostolic Christian S 100/K-12
5020 Pleasant Ridge Rd 37912 865-523-5261
Berean Christian S 400/PK-12
2329 Prosser Rd 37914 865-521-6054
George Waller M.A., hdmstr. Fax 522-5063
Christian Academy of Knoxville 1,000/PK-12
529 Academy Way 37923 865-690-4721
Robert Neu, head sch Fax 690-4752
Concord Christian S 400/K-12
11704 Kingston Pike, 865-966-8858
Ruston Pierce, head sch Fax 288-1617
Fort Sanders School of Nursing Post-Sec.
9821 Cogdill Rd Ste 2 37932
Fountainhead College of Technology Post-Sec.
10208 Technology Dr 37932 865-688-9422
Freedom Christian Academy 200/PK-12
PO Box 6010 37914 865-525-7807
Melanie Stipes, prin. Fax 246-3423
Grace Christian Academy 900/K-12
5914 Beaver Ridge Rd 37931 865-691-3427
Rob Hammond, head sch Fax 342-3827
Huntington College of Health Sciences Post-Sec.
117 Legacy View Way 37918 865-524-8079
Johnson University Post-Sec.
7900 Johnson Dr 37998 865-573-4517
Knoxville Adventist S 100/K-10
3615 Kingston Pike 37919 865-522-9929
Geoffrey White, prin. Fax 522-8263
Knoxville Catholic HS 700/9-12
9245 Fox Lonas Rd 37923 865-560-0313
Dickie Sompayrac Ed.D., pres. Fax 560-0314
Knoxville Christian S 200/PK-12
11549 Snyder Rd 37932 865-966-7060
Jarra Snyder, prin. Fax 671-2148
National College of Business & Tech Post-Sec.
8415 Kingston Pike 37919 865-539-2011
Paideia Academy 200/PK-12
10825 Yarnell Rd 37932 865-670-0440
Mark Hamilton, hdmstr. Fax 474-1476
Pellissippi State Community College Post-Sec.
PO Box 22990 37933 865-694-6400
Reuben Allen College Post-Sec.
120 Center Park Dr 37922 865-966-0400
River's Edge Christian Academy 300/PK-12
PO Box 31733 37930 865-693-6779
Brian Beemer, admin. Fax 317-2443
South College Post-Sec.
3904 Lonas Dr 37909 865-251-1800

Tennessee School for the Deaf Post-Sec.
2725 Island Home Blvd 37920 865-594-6022
Tennessee School of Beauty Post-Sec.
4704 Western Ave 37921 865-588-7878
Tennessee Technology Center at Knoxville Post-Sec.
1100 Liberty St 37919 865-546-5567
University of Tennessee Knoxville Post-Sec.
320 Student Services Bldg 37996 865-974-1000
University of Tennessee Medical Center Post-Sec.
1924 Alcoa Hwy 37920 865-546-5567
Virginia College Post-Sec.
5003 N Broadway St 37918 865-745-4500
Webb S of Knoxville 1,100/PK-12
9800 Webb School Ln 37923 865-693-0011
Michael McBrien, pres. Fax 691-8057
West End Academy PK-12
5311 McKamey Rd 37921 865-690-1720

Kodak, Sevier
Sevier County SD
Supt. — See Sevierville
Northview Junior Academy 200/7-9
2719 Northview Academy Ln 37764 865-933-5880
Kevin DeBow, prin. Fax 933-4018
Northview Senior Academy 600/10-12
2719 Northview Academy Ln 37764 865-933-5880
Greg Clark, prin. Fax 933-4018

Lafayette, Macon, Pop. 4,440
Macon County SD 3,800/PK-12
501 College St 37083 615-666-2125
Tony Boles, dir. Fax 666-7878
www.maconcountyschools.com
Macon County HS 900/9-12
2550 Days Rd 37083 615-666-4320
B.J. West, prin. Fax 666-4757
Macon County JHS 700/6-8
1003 Highway 52 Byp E 37083 615-666-7545
Jamie Kelley, prin. Fax 666-9264
Other Schools – See Red Boiling Springs

Lighthouse Academy 300/PK-12
5576 Highway 52 W 37083 615-666-7151

La Follette, Campbell, Pop. 7,339
Campbell County SD
Supt. — See Jacksboro
La Follette MS 500/6-8
1309 E Central Ave 37766 423-562-8448
Howard St. John, prin. Fax 562-2107
Campbell County Adult HS Adult
318 W Beech St 37766 423-566-5436
Dr. Rita Goins, prin. Fax 562-5219

Lake City, Anderson, Pop. 1,756
Anderson County SD
Supt. — See Clinton
Lake City MS 300/6-8
1132 S Main St 37769 865-426-2609
Kelvin McCullom, prin. Fax 426-9319

La Vergne, Rutherford, Pop. 31,758
Rutherford County SD
Supt. — See Murfreesboro
La Vergne HS 1,800/9-12
250 Wolverine Trl 37086 615-904-3870
Dirk Ash, prin. Fax 904-3871
La Vergne MS 1,000/6-8
382 Stones River Rd 37086 615-904-3877
Cary Holman, prin. Fax 904-3878

Lawrenceburg, Lawrence, Pop. 10,194
Lawrence County SD 6,800/PK-12
700 Mahr Ave 38464 931-762-3581
Dr. Johnny McDaniel, supt. Fax 762-7299
www.lcss.us
Coffman MS 400/7-8
111 Lafayette Ave 38464 931-762-6395
Sarah Cope, prin. Fax 762-7176
Lawrence County HS 1,100/9-12
1800 Springer Rd 38464 931-762-9412
Michael Adkins, prin. Fax 766-0761
LCSS Career-Technical Education Vo/Tech
700 Mahr Ave 38464 931-762-2273
Barnett Education Center Adult
610 Mahr Ave 38464 931-762-5251
Other Schools – See Loretto, Summertown

Lebanon, Wilson, Pop. 25,677
Lebanon Special SD 3,800/PK-8
701 Coles Ferry Pike 37087 615-449-6060
Scott Benson, dir. Fax 449-5673
www.lssd.org
Baird MS 600/6-8
131 WJB Pride Ln 37087 615-444-2190
Pam Sampson, prin. Fax 453-2690
Winfree Bryant MS 600/6-8
1213 Leeville Pike 37090 615-449-4560
Becky Kegley, prin. Fax 449-4590

Wilson County SD 16,900/PK-12
351 Stumpy Ln 37090 615-444-3282
Dr. Donna Wright, dir. Fax 449-3858
www.wcschools.com
Lebanon HS 1,700/9-12
500 Blue Devil Blvd 37087 615-444-9610
Michael Walters, prin. Fax 443-1373
MAP Academy Alt
205 Stumpy Ln 37090 615-453-3400
Rick Miller, prin. Fax 453-3401
Wilson Central HS 1,800/9-12
419 Wildcat Way 37090 615-453-4600
Travis Mayfield, prin. Fax 453-4610
Adult Basic Education Adult
107 N Greenwood St 37087 615-443-8731
Betty Byrd, dir. Fax 453-2529
Wilson County Adult HS Adult
207 J Branham Dr 37087 615-443-7199
Mary Ashby, prin. Fax 443-2690
Other Schools – See Mount Juliet, Watertown

Cumberland University Post-Sec.
1 Cumberland Sq 37087 615-444-2562
Friendship Christian S 500/PK-12
5400 Coles Ferry Pike 37087 615-449-1573
Jon Shoulders, pres. Fax 449-2769

Lenoir City, Loudon, Pop. 8,520
Lenoir CSD 2,400/PK-12
200 E Broadway St 37771 865-986-8058
Dr. Jeanne Barker, dir. Fax 988-6732
www.lenoircityschools.com/
Lenoir City HS 1,300/9-12
1485 Old Highway 95 37771 865-986-2072
Chip Orr, prin. Fax 988-2054
Lenoir City Intermediate MS 600/4-8
2141 Harrison Ave 37771 865-986-2038
Brandee Hoglund, prin. Fax 988-1964

Loudon County SD
Supt. — See Loudon
North MS 800/5-8
421 Hickory Creek Rd 37771 865-986-9944
Mattthew Tinker, prin. Fax 988-9089

Crossroads Christian Academy 100/PK-12
1963 Martel Rd 37772 865-986-9823

Lewisburg, Marshall, Pop. 10,852
Marshall County SD 5,000/PK-12
700 Jones Cir 37091 931-359-1581
Jackie Abernathy, dir. Fax 270-8816
www.k12marshall.net
Lewisburg MS 500/7-8
500 Tiger Blvd 37091 931-359-1265
Randy Hubbell, prin. Fax 359-4030
Marshall County HS 800/9-12
597 W Ellington Pkwy 37091 931-359-1549
John Bush, prin. Fax 359-4784
Spot Lowe Vocational S Vo/Tech
1771 Jason Maxwell Blvd 37091 931-359-4911
Lyn Stacey, dir. Fax 359-3041
Other Schools – See Chapel Hill, Cornersville

Lexington, Henderson, Pop. 7,427
Henderson County SD 4,000/PK-12
35 E Wilson St 38351 731-968-3661
Steve Wilkinson, dir. Fax 968-9457
hcschoolstn.org
Lexington HS 900/9-12
284 White St 38351 731-968-2961
Steve Lindsey, prin. Fax 968-9399
Other Schools – See Reagan

Lexington CSD 1,000/PK-8
99 Monroe Ave 38351 731-967-5591
Susan Bunch, dir. Fax 967-0794
www.caywood.org
Lexington MS 300/6-8
112 Airways Dr 38351 731-968-8457
Beth Deere, prin. Fax 967-7130

Linden, Perry, Pop. 889
Perry County SD 1,200/PK-12
857 Squirrel Hollow Dr 37096 931-589-2102
Eric Lomax, dir. Fax 589-5110
www.perrycountyschools.us
Linden MS 200/5-8
130 College Ave 37096 931-589-5000
Brent Cunningham, prin. Fax 589-3685
Perry County HS 400/9-12
1056 Squirrel Hollow Dr 37096 931-589-2831
Michael Rhodes, prin. Fax 589-5063

Livingston, Overton, Pop. 4,018
Overton County SD 3,300/K-12
302 Zachary St 38570 931-823-1287
Terry Webb, dir. Fax 823-4673
www.overtoncountyschools.net
Livingston Academy HS 1,000/9-12
120 Melvin Johnson Dr 38570 931-823-5911
Leslie Riddle, prin. Fax 823-8626
Livingston MS 300/5-8
216 Bilbrey St 38570 931-823-5917
Doug Smith, prin. Fax 823-7549
Reach Academy 50/Alt
312 W Broad St 38570 931-823-9388
cindy prater, prin. Fax 823-4673
Overton Adult HS Adult
112 Bussell St 38570 931-823-7761
Marsha Wyatt, admin. Fax 823-8852

Tennessee Technology Center Livingston Post-Sec.
740 Hl Tech Dr 38570 931-823-5525

Loretto, Lawrence, Pop. 1,696
Lawrence County SD
Supt. — See Lawrenceburg
Loretto HS 500/9-12
525 2nd Ave S 38469 931-853-4324
Dr. Jennifer Littleton, prin. Fax 853-4340

Loudon, Loudon, Pop. 5,315
Loudon County SD 4,900/PK-12
100 River Rd 37774 865-458-5411
Jason Vance, dir. Fax 458-6138
www.loudoncounty.org/
Ft. Loudoun MS 300/6-8
1083 Mulberry St 37774 865-458-2026
Christie Amburn, prin. Fax 458-6611
Loudon HS 700/9-12
1039 Mulberry St 37774 865-458-4326
Cheri Parrish, prin. Fax 458-0717
Other Schools – See Greenback, Lenoir City

Lyles, Hickman, Pop. 722
Hickman County SD
Supt. — See Centerville

East Hickman HS 600/9-12
7700 Highway 7 37098 931-670-1366
Bruce Jackson, prin. Fax 670-1039
East Hickman MS 400/6-8
9414 E Eagle Dr 37098 931-670-4237
Julia Thomasson, prin. Fax 670-4239

Lynchburg, Moore, Pop. 5,241
Moore County SD 900/K-12
PO Box 219 37352 931-759-7303
Chad Moorehead, dir. Fax 759-6386
www.moorecountyschools.net
Moore County JSHS 400/7-12
1502 Lynchburg Hwy 37352 931-759-4231
Brantley Smith, prin. Fax 759-6390

Motlow State Community College Post-Sec.
PO Box 8500 37352 931-393-1500

Lynnville, Giles, Pop. 286
Giles County SD
Supt. — See Pulaski
Richland MSHS 700/5-12
10610 Columbia Hwy 38472 931-527-3577
Micah Landers, prin. Fax 527-3720

Mc Ewen, Humphreys, Pop. 1,735
Humphreys County SD
Supt. — See Waverly
Mc Ewen HS 300/9-12
335 Melrose St 37101 931-582-6950
Jerry Honea, prin. Fax 582-6952
McEwen JHS 200/6-8
365 Melrose St 37101 931-582-8417
T. Coleman, prin. Fax 582-8418

Mc Kenzie, Carroll, Pop. 5,208
Mc Kenzie Special SD 1,400/PK-12
114 Bell Ave 38201 731-352-2246
Lynn Watkins, dir. Fax 352-7550
www.mckenzieschools.org
Mc Kenzie HS 400/9-12
23292 Highway 22 38201 731-352-2133
Tim Watkins, prin. Fax 352-1424
Mc Kenzie MS 400/5-8
80 Woodrow Ave 38201 731-352-2792
Dorethea Royle, prin. Fax 352-4709

Bethel University Post-Sec.
325 Cherry Ave 38201 731-352-4000
Tennessee Technology Center at Mc Kenzie Post-Sec.
16940 Highland Dr 38201 731-352-5364

Mc Minnville, Warren, Pop. 13,384
Warren County SD 6,600/PK-12
2548 Morrison St 37110 931-668-4022
John R. Cox, dir. Fax 815-2685
www.warrenschools.com
Warren Academy 50/Alt
421 N Spring St 37110 931-473-8723
Frank Fisher, prin. Fax 473-6094
Warren County HS 1,800/9-12
199 Pioneer Ln 37110 931-668-5858
Jimmy Walker, prin. Fax 668-5801
Warren County MS 900/6-8
200 Caldwell St 37110 931-473-6557
Gerald Tidwell, prin. Fax 473-2432

Boyd Christian S 100/PK-12
806 Morrison St 37110 931-473-9631
Covenant Academy 100/PK-12
1079 Country Club Dr 37110 931-668-6185
Tennessee Technology Center Mc Minnville Post-Sec.
241 Vo Tech Dr 37110 931-473-5587

Madison, See Nashville
Metropolitan Nashville SD
Supt. — See Nashville
Madison MS Prep 800/5-8
300 W Old Hickory Blvd 37115 615-684-4018
Jackie Freeman, prin. Fax 612-3664

Goodpasture Christian S 900/PK-12
619 W Due West Ave 37115 615-868-2600
Ricky Perry, pres. Fax 865-1766
Madison Academy 100/9-12
100 Academy Rd 37115 615-865-4055
Middle Tennessee School of Anesthesia Post-Sec.
PO Box 417 37116 615-732-7662
Miller-Motte Technical College Post-Sec.
1515 Gallatin Pike N 37115 615-859-8090
Nashville College of Medical Careers Post-Sec.
1556 Crestview Dr 37115 615-868-2963
National College of Business & Tech Post-Sec.
900 Madison Sq 37115 615-612-3015
Nossi College of Art Post-Sec.
590 Cheron Rd 37115 615-514-2787
Volunteer Beauty Academy Post-Sec.
1793 Gallatin Pike N 37115 615-860-4200

Madisonville, Monroe, Pop. 4,500
Monroe County SD 5,400/PK-12
205 Oak Grove Rd 37354 423-442-2373
Tim Blankenship, dir. Fax 442-1389
www.monroe.k12.tn.us/
Madisonville MS 600/6-8
175 Oak Grove Rd 37354 423-442-4137
Sheryl Debity, prin. Fax 442-9338
Sequoyah HS 1,000/9-12
3128 Highway 411 37354 423-442-9230
Debi Tipton, prin. Fax 442-5520
Other Schools – See Sweetwater, Tellico Plains, Vonore

Hiwassee College Post-Sec.
225 Hiwassee College Dr 37354 423-442-2001

Manchester, Coffee, Pop. 9,924
Coffee County SD 4,100/PK-12
1343 McArthur St 37355 931-723-5150
Dr. LaDonna McFall, dir. Fax 723-5153
www.coffeecountyschools.com/
Coffee County Central HS 1,200/10-12
100 Red Raider Dr 37355 931-723-5159
Joey Vaughn, prin. Fax 723-5161
Coffee County Koss Center 50/Alt
1756 McMinnville Hwy 37355 931-723-5189
Major Shelton, prin. Fax 723-5172
Coffee County MS 1,000/6-8
3063 Woodbury Hwy 37355 931-723-5177
Kimberly Aaron, prin. Fax 723-5180
Coffee County Raider Academy 9-9
865 McMinnville Hwy 37355 931-723-3309
Angela Gribble, prin. Fax 723-8273

Manchester CSD 1,300/PK-8
215 E Fort St 37355 931-728-2316
Sandra Morris, supt. Fax 728-7075
www.manchestercitysch.org
Westwood MS 400/6-8
505 E Taylor St 37355 931-728-2071
Chad Fletcher, prin. Fax 728-0962

Martin, Weakley, Pop. 11,280
Weakley County SD
Supt. — See Dresden
Martin MS 400/6-8
700 Fowler Rd 38237 731-587-2346
Nate Holmes, prin. Fax 588-0529
Westview HS 600/9-12
8161 Highway 45 S 38237 731-587-4202
Jeromy Davidson, prin. Fax 588-0806

University of Tennessee Post-Sec.
554 University Ct 38237 731-881-7000

Maryville, Blount, Pop. 26,990
Blount County SD 11,300/PK-12
831 Grandview Dr 37803 865-984-1212
Rob Britt, dir. Fax 980-1002
www.blountk12.org
Blount 9th Grade Academy 500/9-9
1126 William Blount Dr 37801 865-984-5500
Chris Merrit, prin. Fax 980-1183
Blount HS 1,300/10-12
219 County Farm Rd 37801 865-984-5500
Rob Clark, prin. Fax 977-0153
Carpenters MS 700/6-8
920 Huffstetler Rd 37803 865-980-1414
Jon Young, prin. Fax 980-1404
Eagleton MS 400/6-8
2610 Cinema Dr 37804 865-982-3211
Tony Schultz, prin. Fax 982-4203
Everett Learning Opportunity Center 100/Alt
1500 Jett Rd 37804 865-984-9420
Danny Galyon, prin. Fax 984-7189
Heritage HS 1,500/9-12
3741 E Lamar Alexander Pkwy 37804 865-984-8110
Jake Jones, prin. Fax 984-0147
Heritage MS 800/6-8
3737 E Lamar Alexander Pkwy 37804 865-980-1300
Dr. Steve Moser, prin. Fax 980-1281
Other Schools – See Friendsville

Maryville CSD 5,100/PK-12
833 Lawrence Ave 37803 865-982-7121
Dr. Mike Winstead, supt. Fax 977-5055
www.maryville-schools.org
Maryville HS 1,100/10-12
825 Lawrence Ave 37803 865-982-1132
Greg Roach, prin. Fax 983-1440
Maryville JHS 900/8-9
805 Montvale Station Rd 37803 865-983-2070
Lisa McGinley, prin. Fax 977-9413

Apostolic Christian Academy 100/PK-12
1331 William Blount Dr 37801 865-984-0046
Maryville Christian S 400/PK-12
2525 Morganton Rd 37801 865-681-3205
Kris Schottleutner, admin. Fax 681-4086
Maryville College Post-Sec.
502 E Lamar Alexander Pkwy 37804 865-981-8000

Maynardville, Union, Pop. 2,385
Union County SD 5,600/PK-12
PO Box 10 37807 865-992-5466
Dr. James Carter, dir. Fax 992-0126
www.ucps.org
Maynard MS 700/6-8
PO Box 669 37807 865-992-1030
Greg Clay, prin. Fax 992-1060
Union County Alternative Learning Center 50/Alt
PO Box 609 37807 865-992-7747
Chris Price, prin. Fax 992-9076
Union County HS 800/9-12
150 Main St 37807 865-992-5232
Carmen Murphy, prin. Fax 992-5724

Medina, Gibson, Pop. 3,452
Gibson County Special SD
Supt. — See Dyer
Medina MS 1,100/3-8
PO Box 369 38355 731-783-1962
Steve Maloan, prin. Fax 783-1964
South Gibson County HS 700/9-12
PO Box 249 38355 731-783-0999
Phil Rogers, prin. Fax 783-0011

Memphis, Shelby, Pop. 639,057
Achievement SD 7,400/PK-12
477 S Main St Fl 4 38103 901-260-9649
Malika Anderson, supt.
www.achievementschooldistrict.org
Pathways in Education Alt
4701 Elvis Presley Blvd 38116 901-433-9422
James Bacchus, admin.
Pathways in Education - Memphis Frayser Alt
3156 Thomas St 38127 901-308-8471
James Bacchus, admin.
Westside Achievement MS 500/6-8
3389 Dawn Dr 38127 901-416-3700
Michael Brown, prin. Fax 416-3701

Shelby County SD 106,700/PK-12
160 S Hollywood St 38112 901-321-2500
Dorsey Hopson, supt. Fax 321-2501
www.scsk12.org/
American Way MS 800/6-8
3805 American Way 38118 901-416-1250
Lisa Maclin-Love, prin. Fax 416-1251
Bellevue MS 500/6-8
575 S Bellevue Blvd 38104 901-416-4488
Kevin Malone, prin. Fax 416-4490
Bond MS 1,100/6-8
2737 Kate Bond Rd 38133 901-416-0640
Christopher Murrah, prin. Fax 416-7962
Carver HS 500/9-12
1591 Pennsylvania St 38109 901-416-7594
Dr. Alvin Harris, prin. Fax 416-2235
Central HS 1,800/9-12
306 S Bellevue Blvd 38104 901-416-4500
Gregory McCullough, prin. Fax 416-4506
Chickasaw MS 400/6-8
4060 Westmont Rd 38109 901-416-8134
Veda Turner, prin. Fax 416-8139
Colonial MS 1,200/6-8
1370 Colonial Rd 38117 901-416-8980
Marty Pettigrew, prin. Fax 416-8996
Craigmont HS 1,100/9-12
3333 Covington Pike 38128 901-416-4312
Dr. Tisha Durrah, prin. Fax 416-7675
Craigmont MS 800/6-8
3455 Covington Pike 38128 901-416-7780
LaTrenda Hicks, prin. Fax 416-1454
Douglass HS 700/9-12
3200 Mount Olive Rd 38108 901-416-0990
Janet Thompson, prin. Fax 416-9887
East HS 900/9-12
3206 Poplar Ave 38111 901-416-6160
Dr. Marilyn Hillard, prin. Fax 416-6161
Geeter MS 400/6-8
4649 Horn Lake Rd 38109 901-416-8157
Lori Oduyoye, prin. Fax 416-8160
Georgian Hills MS 300/6-8
3925 Denver St 38127 901-416-3740
Ticada Guyton, prin. Fax 416-6500
Grandview Heights MS 400/6-8
2342 Clifton Ave 38127 901-416-3940
Deartis Barber, prin. Fax 416-3923
Hamilton HS 900/9-12
1363 E Person Ave 38106 901-416-7838
Monekea Smith, prin. Fax 416-7829
Hamilton MS 400/6-8
1478 Wilson St 38106 901-416-7832
Kelly Henderson, prin. Fax 416-3314
Hamilton Success Academy Alt
1478 Wilson St 38106 901-416-7949
Dr. James Suggs, prin. Fax 416-7948
Havenview MS 900/6-8
1481 Hester Rd 38116 901-416-3092
Michael Bates, prin. Fax 416-3093
Hickory Ridge MS 900/6-8
3920 Ridgeway Rd 38115 901-416-9337
Cedric Smith, prin. Fax 416-9210
Highland Oaks MS 900/6-8
5600 Meadowbriar Trl 38125 901-416-0340
Monica Bates, prin. Fax 416-0345
Kingsbury Career Technology Center Vo/Tech
1328 N Graham St 38122 901-416-6000
Timothy Batts, prin. Fax 416-6003
Kingsbury HS 1,100/9-12
1270 N Graham St 38122 901-416-6060
Dr. Terry Ross, prin. Fax 416-6061
Kingsbury MS 400/6-8
1276 N Graham St 38122 901-416-6040
Tarcia Gilliam-Parrish, prin. Fax 416-6058
Kirby HS 1,500/9-12
4080 Kirby Pkwy 38115 901-416-1960
Daniel Jack, prin. Fax 416-1968
Manassas HS 600/9-12
1111 N Manassas St 38107 901-416-3244
James Griffin, prin. Fax 416-3248
Melrose HS 1,000/9-12
2870 Deadrick Ave 38114 901-416-5974
Mark Neal, prin. Fax 416-5984
Memphis Health Careers Academy 100/Alt
80 W Olive Ave 38106 901-416-1950
Brenda Diaz Williams, prin. Fax 416-1951
Messick Career & Technology Center Vo/Tech
703 S Greer St 38111 901-416-4840
Rochelle Griffin, prin. Fax 416-4842
Middle College SHS 200/10-12
750 E Parkway S 38104 901-416-4550
Docia Generette, prin. Fax 416-4555
Mitchell HS 600/9-12
658 W Mitchell Rd 38109 901-416-8174
Kelvin Meeks, prin. Fax 416-8176
MLK Student Transition Academy 200/Alt
620 S Lauderdale 38126 901-416-7320
Clarence Daniel, prin. Fax 416-7259
Northeast Prep Academy 300/Alt
968 N Mendenhall Rd 38122 901-416-2132
Kenneth Dickerson, prin. Fax 416-2157
Northside HS 400/9-12
1212 Vollintine Ave 38107 901-416-4582
Vincent Thompson, prin. Fax 416-9813
Northwest Prep Academy 500/Alt
1266 Poplar Ave 38104 901-416-4400
Roger Jones, prin. Fax 416-4683
Oakhaven HS 500/9-12
3125 Ladbrook Rd 38118 901-416-2300
Dr. Melanie Black, prin. Fax 416-2301

Oakhaven MS 200/6-8
3125 Ladbrook Rd 38118 901-416-2380
Shari Meeks, prin. Fax 416-9780
Overton HS 1,300/9-12
1770 Lanier Ln 38117 901-416-2136
Greg Billings, prin. Fax 416-2135
Price Middle College HS 200/9-12
807 Walker Ave 38126 901-435-1765
Sandra Barnes, prin. Fax 435-1779
Raleigh-Egypt HS 1,000/9-12
3970 Voltaire Ave 38128 901-416-4108
James Griffin, prin. Fax 416-4143
Ridgeway HS 1,200/9-12
2009 Ridgeway Rd 38119 901-416-8820
Dr. Jonathan Stencel, prin. Fax 416-2199
Ridgeway MS 800/6-8
6333 Quince Rd 38119 901-416-1588
Corey Williams, prin. Fax 416-1477
Sheffield Career & Tech Center Vo/Tech
4350 Chuck Ave 38118 901-416-2340
Charles Grove, prin. Fax 416-2394
Sheffield HS 1,000/9-12
4315 Sheffield Ave 38118 901-416-2370
Anthony Frigo, prin. Fax 416-2407
Sherwood MS 600/6-8
3480 Rhodes Ave 38111 901-416-4870
Corey Kelly, prin. Fax 416-4881
Smith STEAM Academy 300/6-8
750 E Parkway S 38104 901-416-4536
Lischa Brooks, prin. Fax 416-4539
Southwest Career & Technology Center Vo/Tech
3746 Horn Lake Rd 38109 901-416-8186
Leroy McClain, prin. Fax 416-8188
Southwest Prep Academy 200/Alt
1237 College St 38106 901-416-7884
Tyria Butler, prin. Fax 416-7886
Southwind HS 1,700/9-12
7900 E Shelby Dr 38125 901-416-3250
Dr. Terrence Brown, prin. Fax 752-2898
Treadwell MS 400/6-8
920 N Highland St 38122 901-416-6100
Roger Faulkner, prin. Fax 416-6133
Trezevant Career & Tech Center Vo/Tech
3224 Range Line Rd 38127 901-416-3800
Eleanor Thomas, prin. Fax 416-3839
Trezevant HS 700/9-12
3350 N Trezevant St 38127 901-416-3760
Dr. Mario Willis, prin. Fax 416-3761
Walker MS 600/6-8
1900 E Raines Rd 38116 901-416-1030
Dr. Terrence Brittenum, prin. Fax 416-1075
Washington HS 500/6-12
715 S Lauderdale St 38126 901-416-7240
Alisha Kiner, prin. Fax 416-7228
Westwood HS 600/9-12
4480 Westmont Rd 38109 901-416-8000
Julia Callaway, prin. Fax 416-8027
Whitehaven HS 2,100/9-12
4851 Elvis Presley Blvd 38116 901-416-3000
Dr. Vincent Hunter, prin. Fax 416-3058
White Station HS 2,300/9-12
514 S Perkins Rd 38117 901-416-8880
David Mansfield, prin. Fax 416-8910
White Station MS 900/6-8
5465 Mason Rd 38120 901-416-2184
Shawn Page, prin. Fax 416-2187
Wooddale HS 1,500/9-12
5151 Scottsdale Ave 38118 901-416-2440
Otis Clayton, prin. Fax 416-2476
Other Schools – See Arlington, Bartlett, Cordova, Germantown, Millington

---

All Saints Bible College Post-Sec.
930 Mason St 38126 901-322-0120
Anthem College Post-Sec.
5865 Shelby Oaks Cir #100 38134 901-432-3800
Baptist College of Health Sciences Post-Sec.
1003 Monroe Ave 38104 901-575-2247
Baptist Memorial Hospital Post-Sec.
350 N Humphreys Blvd #EagB2 38103
901-227-5121
Central Baptist S 200/PK-12
5470 Raleigh LaGrange Rd 38134 901-386-8161
Christian Brothers HS 800/9-12
5900 Walnut Grove Rd 38120 901-261-4900
Chris Fay, prin. Fax 261-4909
Christian Brothers University Post-Sec.
650 E Parkway S 38104 901-321-3000
Collegiate S of Memphis 300/9-12
3353 Faxon Ave 38122 901-591-8200
Concorde Career College Post-Sec.
5100 Poplar Ave Ste 132 38137 901-761-9494
Creative Life Preparatory S 50/PK-12
1222 Riverside Blvd 38106 901-775-0304
Dr. Carolyn Bibbs, pres. Fax 946-5433
DeVry University Post-Sec.
6401 Poplar Ave Ste 600 38119 901-537-2560
Gateway Christian S 1,300/1-12
4070 Macon Rd 38122 901-458-4276
Donna Bumgardner, prin. Fax 323-0914
Harding Academy of Memphis 500/7-12
1100 Cherry Rd 38117 901-767-4494
Trent Williamson, head sch Fax 763-4494
Harding School of Theology Post-Sec.
1000 Cherry Rd 38117 901-761-1350
Hutchison S 900/PK-12
1740 Ridgeway Rd 38119 901-761-2220
Dr. Annette Smith Ed.D., head sch Fax 432-6655
Immaculate Conception Cathedral S 200/PK-12
1695 Central Ave 38104 901-725-2705
Tracey Ford, prin. Fax 725-2701
Lausanne Collegiate S 800/PK-12
1381 W Massey Rd 38120 901-474-1000
Stuart McCathie, hdmstr. Fax 474-1010
Le Moyne-Owen College Post-Sec.
807 Walker Ave 38126 901-435-1000
Margolin Hebrew Academy 200/PK-12
390 S White Station Rd 38117 901-682-2400
Rabbi Benjy Owen, head sch Fax 767-1871
Massage Institute of Memphis Post-Sec.
2076 Union Ave Ste 202 38104 901-726-4665
Memphis Catholic MSHS 200/7-12
61 N McLean Blvd 38104 901-276-1221
Kevin Kimberly, prin. Fax 725-1447
Memphis College of Art Post-Sec.
1930 Poplar Ave 38104 901-272-5100
Memphis Junior Academy 100/PK-12
50 N Mendenhall Rd 38117 901-683-1061
Tracy Fry, prin. Fax 683-1012
Memphis Theological Seminary Post-Sec.
168 E Parkway S 38104 901-458-8232
Memphis University S 700/7-12
6191 Park Ave 38119 901-260-1300
Ellis Haguewood, hdmstr. Fax 260-1301
Methodist Hospital Post-Sec.
1265 Union Ave 38104 901-726-8274
Mid-South Christian College Post-Sec.
3097 Knight Rd 38118 901-375-4400
National College of Business & Tech Post-Sec.
2576 Thousand Oaks Blvd 38118 901-363-9046
New Wave Hair Academy Post-Sec.
3250 Coleman Rd 38128 901-323-6100
New Wave Hair Academy Post-Sec.
804 S Highland St 38111 901-320-9283
Plaza Beauty School Post-Sec.
4682 Spottswood Ave 38117 901-761-4445
Pleasant View S 200/PK-12
1888 Bartlett Rd 38134 901-380-0122
Dr. Mohammed Malley, prin. Fax 380-1527
Remington College Post-Sec.
2710 Nonconnah Blvd # 160 38132 901-345-1000
Rhodes College Post-Sec.
2000 N Parkway 38112 901-843-3000
St. Agnes Academy/St. Dominic S 400/PK-12
4830 Walnut Grove Rd 38117 901-767-1356
Tom Hood, pres. Fax 435-5866
St. Mary's Episcopal S 800/PK-12
60 Perkins Ext 38117 901-537-1472
Albert L. Throckmorton, head sch Fax 682-0119
Southern College of Optometry Post-Sec.
1245 Madison Ave 38104 901-722-3200
Southern Institute of Cosmetology Post-Sec.
4030 Muirfield Dr 38125 - -
Southern Institute of Cosmetology Post-Sec.
3099 S Perkins Rd 38118 901-363-3553
Southwest Tennessee Community College Post-Sec.
PO Box 780 38101 901-333-5000
Strayer University Post-Sec.
2620 Thousand Oaks Ste 1100 38118 901-369-0835
Strayer University Post-Sec.
7275 Appling Farms Pkwy 38133 901-251-7100
Tennessee Academy of Cosmetology Post-Sec.
7041 Stage Rd Ste 101 38133 901-382-9085
Tennessee Academy of Cosmetology Post-Sec.
7020 E Shelby Dr Ste 104 38125 901-757-4166
Tennessee Technology Center at Memphis Post-Sec.
550 Alabama Ave 38105 901-543-6100
The Beauty Institute Post-Sec.
568 Colonial Rd 38117 901-761-1888
University of Memphis 38152 Post-Sec.
901-678-2000
Univ. of Tennessee Health Science Center Post-Sec.
800 Madison Ave 38163 901-448-5500
Vatterott Career College Post-Sec.
6991 Appling Farms Pkwy 38133 901-372-2399
Vatterott College Post-Sec.
2655 Dividend Dr 38132 901-761-5730
Visible Music College Post-Sec.
200 Madison Ave 38103 901-381-3939
Westminster Academy 300/PK-12
2500 Ridgeway Rd 38119 901-380-9192
Ralph Janikowsky, hdmstr. Fax 405-2019
William Moore College of Technology Post-Sec.
1200 Poplar Ave 38104 901-726-1977
Word of Faith Christian Academy 100/PK-12
3528 Sharpe Ave 38111 901-744-4061

Middleton, Hardeman, Pop. 695
Hardeman County SD
Supt. — See Bolivar
Middleton HS 500/7-12
138 Florida Ave 38052 731-376-8391
Darlene Cardwell, prin. Fax 376-8157

Milan, Gibson, Pop. 7,701
Milan Special SD 2,100/PK-12
1165 S Main St 38358 731-686-0844
Judy McGregor, dir. Fax 686-8781
www.milanssd.org
Milan HS 600/9-12
7060 E Van Hook St 38358 731-686-0841
Kris Todd, prin. Fax 686-9829
Milan MS 700/5-8
4040 Middle Rd 38358 731-686-7232
Sam Rhodes, prin. Fax 723-8872

Arnold's Beauty School Post-Sec.
1179 S 2nd St 38358 731-686-7351

Milligan College, Carter

Milligan College Post-Sec.
PO Box 500 37682 423-461-8700

Millington, Shelby, Pop. 9,878
Millington Municipal SD 2,800/PK-12
5020 2nd Ave 38053 901-873-5680
Dr. David Roper, dir. Fax 873-5699
www.millingtonschools.org
Millington Central HS 1,300/9-12
8050 West St 38053 901-873-8100
Clint Durley, prin. Fax 873-8105
Millington MS 500/6-8
4964 Cuba Millington Rd 38053 901-873-8130
Selina Sparkman, prin. Fax 873-8136
Shelby County SD
Supt. — See Memphis
Renaissance Academy North Alt
4885 Bill Knight Rd 38053 901-873-8146
David Matykiewicz, prin.
Woodstock MS 500/6-8
5885 Woodstock Cuba Rd 38053 901-416-4180
Eric Linsy, prin. Fax 416-4182

Faith Heritage Christian Academy 100/PK-12
PO Box 157 38083 901-872-0828
Lighthouse Christian Academy 200/PK-12
3660 Shelby Rd 38053 901-873-3353
Tipton-Rosemark Academy 600/PK-12
8696 Rosemark Rd 38053 901-829-6500
John Scott, head sch Fax 829-4477

Monterey, Putnam, Pop. 2,832
Putnam County SD
Supt. — See Cookeville
Monterey HS 300/7-12
710 Commercial Ave S 38574 931-839-2970
Sonja Farley, prin. Fax 839-6070

Morristown, Hamblen, Pop. 28,494
Hamblen County SD 10,000/K-12
210 E Morris Blvd 37813 423-586-7700
Dr. Dale Lynch, dir. Fax 586-7747
www.hcboe.net
Lincoln Heights MS 500/6-8
219 Lincoln Ave 37813 423-581-3200
Joe Ely, prin. Fax 585-3763
Meadowview MS 500/6-8
1623 Meadowview Ln 37814 423-581-6360
Dominique Salaciak, prin. Fax 585-3771
Miller Boyd Alternative S 50/Alt
376 Snyder Rd 37813 423-585-3785
Calvin Decker, prin. Fax 585-3786
Morristown-Hamblen HS East 1,400/9-12
1 Hurricane Ln 37813 423-586-2543
Gary Johnson, prin. Fax 585-3779
Morristown-Hamblen HS West 1,400/9-12
1 Trojan Trl 37813 423-581-1600
Dr. Jeff Moorhouse, prin. Fax 585-3791
West View MS 600/6-8
1 Indian Path 37813 423-581-2407
Rebekah Patrick, prin. Fax 585-3807
Other Schools – See Whitesburg

Cornerstone Academy 200/PK-12
260 Jacobs Rd 37813 423-307-1189
Ben Holland, hdmstr.
Tennessee Technology Center Morristown Post-Sec.
821 W Louise Ave 37813 423-586-5771
Walters State Community College Post-Sec.
500 S Davy Crockett Pkwy 37813 423-585-2600

Mosheim, Greene, Pop. 2,337
Greene County SD
Supt. — See Greeneville
West Greene HS 600/9-12
275 W Greene Dr 37818 423-422-4061
Steven Tunnell, prin. Fax 638-3180

Mountain City, Johnson, Pop. 2,508
Johnson County SD 2,300/PK-12
211 N Church St 37683 423-727-2640
Dr. Mischelle Simcox, dir. Fax 727-2663
jocoed.net
Johnson County Career & Technical S Vo/Tech
348 Fairground Ln 37683 423-727-1860
Herbie Adams, prin. Fax 727-2693
Johnson County HS 700/9-12
290 Fairground Hill 37683 423-727-2620
Lisa Arnold, prin. Fax 727-2677
Johnson County MS 300/7-8
278 Fairground Hill 37683 423-727-2600
Edna Miller, prin. Fax 727-4141

Mount Juliet, Wilson, Pop. 23,208
Wilson County SD
Supt. — See Lebanon
Mount Juliet HS 2,000/9-12
1800 Curd Rd 37122 615-758-5606
Mel Brown, prin. Fax 758-5645
Mount Juliet MS 1,500/6-8
3565 N Mount Juliet Rd 37122 615-754-6688
Tim Bell, prin. Fax 754-7566
West Wilson MS 1,100/6-8
935 N Mount Juliet Rd 37122 615-758-5152
Wendell Marlowe, prin. Fax 758-5283

Heritage Christian Academy - Mt. Juliet 300/K-12
PO Box 1135 37121 615-604-0564
Mt. Juliet Christian Academy 500/PK-12
735 N Mount Juliet Rd 37122 615-758-2427
Dr. Mike Lee, head sch Fax 758-3662

Mount Pleasant, Maury, Pop. 4,471
Maury County SD
Supt. — See Columbia
Mount Pleasant HS 400/9-12
600 Greenwood St 38474 931-379-5583
Dr. John Gunn, prin. Fax 379-2093
Mt. Pleasant MS of Visual/Performing Art 400/5-8
410 Gray Ln 38474 931-379-1100
Kevin Eady, prin. Fax 379-1108

Munford, Tipton, Pop. 5,823
Tipton County SD
Supt. — See Covington
Munford HS 1,300/9-12
1080 McLaughlin Dr 38058 901-837-5701
Courtney Fee, prin. Fax 837-5729

Munford MS 900/6-8
100 Education Ave 38058 901-837-1700
Vicki Shipley, prin. Fax 837-5749

Murfreesboro, Rutherford, Pop. 106,177
Rutherford County SD 41,400/PK-12
2240 Southpark Dr 37128 615-893-5812
Don Odom, dir. Fax 898-7940
www.rcs.k12.tn.us
Blackman HS 2,000/9-12
3956 Blaze Dr 37128 615-904-3850
Gail Vick, prin. Fax 904-3851
Blackman MS 1,200/6-8
3945 Blaze Dr 37128 615-904-3860
Will Shelton, prin. Fax 904-3861
Central Magnet S 1,200/6-12
701 E Main St 37130 615-904-6789
Dr. John Ash, prin. Fax 904-6788
Holloway HS 100/9-12
619 S Highland Ave 37130 615-890-6004
Sumatra Drayton, prin. Fax 904-7508
McKee Alternative S 50/Alt
2623 Halls Hill Pike 37130 615-890-2282
Mary Jo Yeager, prin. Fax 898-7726
Oakland HS 1,900/9-12
2225 Patriot Dr 37130 615-904-3780
Bill Spurlock, prin. Fax 904-3781
Oakland MS 1,100/6-8
853 Dejarnette Ln 37130 615-904-6760
Kim Edwards, prin. Fax 904-6761
Riverdale HS 1,900/9-12
802 Warrior Dr 37128 615-890-6450
Tom Nolan, prin. Fax 890-9790
Siegel HS 1,800/9-12
3300 Siegel Rd 37129 615-904-3800
Jason Bridgeman, prin. Fax 904-3801
Siegel MS 1,100/6-8
355 W Thompson Ln 37129 615-904-3830
Tom Delbridge, prin. Fax 904-3831
Whitworth-Buchanan MS 700/6-8
5555 Manchester Pike 37127 615-904-6765
Avy Seymore, prin. Fax 904-6766
Other Schools – See Christiana, Eagleville, La Vergne, Rockvale, Smyrna

---

Daymar Institute Post-Sec.
415 Golden Bear Ct 37128 615-217-9347
Franklin Road Christian S 300/PK-12
3124 Franklin Rd 37128 615-890-0894
Kenton Kramer, admin. Fax 893-2837
Middle Tennessee Christian S 700/PK-12
100 E MTCS Rd 37129 615-893-0601
Dr. Robert Sain, pres. Fax 895-8815
Middle Tennessee State University Post-Sec.
1301 E Main St 37132 615-898-2300
Providence Christian Academy 300/PK-12
410 Dejarnette Ln 37130 615-904-0902
Dr. Bill Mott, hdmstr. Fax 904-0859
Redeemer Classical Academy 100/K-12
PO Box 12169 37129 615-904-0350
Tennessee Technology Center Murfreesboro Post-Sec.
1303 Old Fort Pkwy 37129 615-898-8010

Nashville, Davidson, Pop. 588,359
Metropolitan Nashville SD 79,600/PK-12
2601 Bransford Ave 37204 615-259-4636
Shawn Joseph, dir. Fax 214-8897
www.mnps.org
Allen MS Prep 500/5-8
500 Spence Ln 37210 615-291-6385
Kisha Stinson-Cox, prin. Fax 291-6066
Bass Learning Center Alt
5200 Delaware Ave 37209 615-298-3278
Henry Johnson, prin.
Baxter MS 400/5-8
350 Hart Ln 37207 615-262-6710
Miriam Harrington, prin. Fax 262-6743
Bellevue MS 700/5-8
655 Colice Jeanne Rd 37221 615-662-3000
Mark Pittman, prin. Fax 662-5728
Cohn Learning Center 100/Alt
4805 Park Ave 37209 615-298-6617
Debbie Booker, prin.
Creswell MS of the Arts 500/5-8
3500 John Mallette Dr 37218 615-291-6515
Trellaney Lane, prin. Fax 291-5326
Croft Design Center MS 700/5-8
482 Elysian Fields Rd 37211 615-332-0217
Dr. Jeremy Lewis, prin. Fax 333-5650
Donelson MS 700/5-8
110 Stewarts Ferry Pike 37214 615-884-4080
Jennifer Rheinecker, prin. Fax 885-8970
Early Museum Magnet MS Prep 500/5-8
1000 Cass St 37208 615-291-6369
Rise Pope, prin. Fax 298-8497
East Nashville Magnet HS 700/9-12
110 Gallatin Ave 37206 615-262-6947
Steve Ball, prin. Fax 262-3972
East Nashville Magnet MS Prep 5-8
2000 Greenwood Ave 37206 615-262-6670
Paul Brunette, prin.
Glencliff HS 1,400/9-12
160 Antioch Pike 37211 615-333-5070
Clint Wilson, prin. Fax 333-5003
Gra-Mar MS Prep 400/5-8
575 Joyce Ln 37216 615-262-6685
Sonya Brooks, prin. Fax 262-6901
Haynes Health/Medical Science Design Ctr 200/5-8
510 W Trinity Ln 37207 615-262-6688
Dr. Canidra Henderson, prin. Fax 298-8084
Head MS Magnet Prep 600/5-8
1830 Jo Johnston Ave 37203 615-329-8160
Dr. Tonja Williams, prin. Fax 321-8389
Hill MS 600/5-8
150 Davidson Rd 37205 615-353-2020
Connie Gwinn, prin. Fax 884-4028
Hillsboro HS 1,200/9-12
3812 Hillsboro Pike 37215 615-298-8400
Dr. Andrew Shuler Pelham, prin. Fax 353-1159
Hillwood HS 1,200/9-12
400 Davidson Rd 37205 615-353-2025
Dr. Steve Chauncy, prin. Fax 298-8402
Hume-Fogg Academic Magnet HS 900/9-12
700 Broadway 37203 615-291-6300
Dr. Kellie Hargis, prin. Fax 291-6065
Hunters Lane HS 1,600/9-12
1150 Hunters Ln 37207 615-860-1401
Dr. Susan Kessler, prin. Fax 291-6304
Johnson Alternative Learning Center 100/Alt
1200 2nd Ave S 37210 615-749-3067
Dr. Sharon Braden, prin. Fax 749-3076
King Magnet JSHS 1,200/7-12
613 17th Ave N 37203 615-329-8400
Dr. Angela McShepard-Ray, prin. Fax 501-7907
Litton MS 300/5-8
4601 Hedgewood Dr 37216 615-262-6700
Chara Rand, prin. Fax 262-6995
Maplewood HS 1,000/9-12
401 Walton Ln 37216 615-262-6770
Dr. Keely Jones-Mason, prin. Fax 262-6772
McGavock Comprehensive HS 2,300/9-12
3150 Mcgavock Pike 37214 615-885-8850
Robbin Wall, prin. Fax 885-8900
McKissack MS Prep 400/5-8
915 38th Ave N 37209 615-329-8170
Thomas Chappelle, prin. Fax 329-8183
McMurray MS 700/5-8
520 McMurray Dr 37211 615-333-5126
T-Shaka Coverson, prin. Fax 333-5125
Meigs Magnet MS 700/5-8
713 Ramsey St 37206 615-271-3222
Dr. Samuel Underwood, prin. Fax 271-3223
Middle College HS 100/10-12
120 White Bridge Pike 37209 615-353-3742
Roderick Manuel, prin.
Moore MS 600/5-8
4425 Granny White Pike 37204 615-298-8095
Dr. Gary Hughes, prin. Fax 298-8452
Nashville Big Picture HS 200/9-12
160 Rural Ave 37209 615-353-2081
Chaerea Denning-Snorten, prin.
Nashville S of the Arts 600/9-12
1250 Foster Ave 37210 615-291-6600
Dr. Gregory Stewart, prin. Fax 271-1767
Oliver MS Prep 800/5-8
6211 Nolensville Pike 37211 615-332-3011
Jeanna Collins, prin. Fax 332-3019
Overton HS 1,800/9-12
4820 Franklin Pike 37220 615-333-5135
Dr. Jill Pittman, prin. Fax 333-5141
Pearl-Cohn Entertainment Magnet HS 900/9-12
904 26th Ave N 37208 615-329-8150
Dr. Sonia Stewart, prin. Fax 329-8192
Rose Park Math/Science MS 400/5-8
1025 9th Ave S 37203 615-291-6405
Robert Blankenship, prin. Fax 262-6717
Stratford STEM HS 700/9-12
1800 Stratford Ave 37216 615-242-6730
Michael Steele, prin. Fax 885-8929
Stratford STEM MS 5-8
1800 Stratford Ave 37216 615-262-6670
Dr. Janet Wallace, prin.
Two Rivers MS Prep 600/5-8
2991 Mcgavock Pike 37214 615-885-8931
Dr. Shelly Dunaway, prin. Fax 333-5641
West End MS Prep 500/5-8
3529 W End Ave 37205 615-298-8425
Dr. Craig Hammond, prin.
Wright MS 900/5-8
180 McCall St 37211 615-333-5189
Dr. Erin Anderson, prin. Fax 333-5635
Academy at Old Cockrill HS Adult
610 49th Ave N 37209 615-298-2294
Carl Carter, prin.
Academy at Opry Mills HS Adult
437 Opry Mills Dr 37214 615-810-8306
Carmon Brown, prin.
Other Schools – See Antioch, Goodlettsville, Hermitage, Joelton, Madison, Old Hickory, Whites Creek

---

American Baptist College Post-Sec.
1800 Baptist World Ctr Dr 37207 615-256-1463
Anthem Career College Post-Sec.
560 Royal Pkwy 37214 615-232-3700
Aquinas College Post-Sec.
4210 Harding Pike 37205 615-297-7545
Argosy University / Nashville Post-Sec.
100 Centerview Dr Ste 225 37214 615-525-2800
Art Institute of Tennessee - Nashville Post-Sec.
100 Centerview Dr Ste 250 37214 866-747-5770
Belmont University Post-Sec.
1900 Belmont Blvd 37212 615-460-6000
Brightwood College Post-Sec.
750 Envious Ln 37217 615-279-8300
Christ Presbyterian Academy 1,000/PK-12
2323A Old Hickory Blvd 37215 615-373-9550
Davidson Academy 700/PK-12
1414 Old Hickory Blvd 37207 615-860-5300
Tim Johnson M.Ed., hdmstr. Fax 868-7918
Daymar Institute Post-Sec.
340 Plus Park Blvd 37217 615-361-7555
DeVry University Post-Sec.
3343 Perimeter Hill Dr #200 37211 615-445-3456
Diamond Council of America Post-Sec.
3212 W End Ave Ste 202 37203 615-385-5301
Donelson Christian Academy 800/PK-12
300 Danyacrest Dr 37214 615-883-2926
Ensworth S 1,100/K-12
211 Ensworth Pl 37205 615-383-0661
David Braemer, head sch Fax 269-4840
Father Ryan HS 900/9-12
700 Norwood Dr 37204 615-383-4200
Paul Davis, prin. Fax 383-9056
Fisk University Post-Sec.
1000 17th Ave N 37208 615-329-8500
Franklin Road Academy 800/PK-12
4700 Franklin Pike 37220 615-832-8845
Sean Casey, head sch Fax 834-4137
Harpeth Hall S 700/5-12
3801 Hobbs Rd 37215 615-297-9543
Stephanie Balmer, head sch Fax 297-0480
John A. Gupton College Post-Sec.
1616 Church St 37203 615-327-3927
Lincoln College of Technology Post-Sec.
1524 Gallatin Ave 37206 615-226-3990
Lipscomb Academy 1,300/PK-12
3901 Granny White Pike 37204 615-966-1600
Greg J. Glenn, head sch Fax 966-7633
Lipscomb University Post-Sec.
1 University Park Dr 37204 800-333-4358
Meharry Medical College Post-Sec.
1005 Dr DB Todd Jr Blvd 37208 615-327-6111
Mind Body Institute Post-Sec.
2416 Music Valley Dr # 119 37214 615-360-8554
Montgomery Bell Academy 700/7-12
4001 Harding Pike 37205 615-298-5514
Bradford Gioia, hdmstr. Fax 297-0271
Nashville Christian S 600/PK-12
7555 Sawyer Brown Rd 37221 615-356-5600
Nashville State Community College Post-Sec.
120 White Bridge Pike 37209 615-353-3333
National College of Business & Tech. Post-Sec.
1638 Bell Rd 37211 615-333-3344
Remington College Post-Sec.
441 Donelson Pike Ste 150 37214 615-889-5520
SAE Institute Nashville Post-Sec.
7 Music Cir N 37203 615-244-5848
St. Cecilia Academy 300/9-12
4210 Harding Pike Ste 2 37205 615-298-4525
Sr. Anne Catherine Burleigh, prin. Fax 783-0561
St. Thomas Hospital Post-Sec.
PO Box 380 37202 615-222-2111
Seminary Ext. Independent Study Inst. Post-Sec.
901 Commerce St Ste 500 37203 800-229-4612
Strayer University Post-Sec.
1809 Dabbs Ave 37210 615-871-2260
Tennessee School for the Blind Post-Sec.
115 Stewarts Ferry Pike 37214 615-231-7300
Tennessee State University Post-Sec.
3500 John A Merritt Blvd 37209 615-963-5000
Tennessee Technology Center at Nashville Post-Sec.
100 White Bridge Pike 37209 615-425-5500
Trevecca Nazarene University Post-Sec.
333 Murfreesboro Pike 37210 615-248-1200
University S of Nashville 1,000/K-12
2000 Edgehill Ave 37212 615-321-8000
Dr. Vincent Durnan, dir. Fax 321-0889
Vanderbilt University Post-Sec.
2301 Vanderbilt Pl 37235 615-322-7311
Watkins College of Art Design and Film Post-Sec.
2298 Rosa L Parks Blvd 37228 615-383-4848
Welch College Post-Sec.
3606 W End Ave 37205 615-844-5000

Newbern, Dyer, Pop. 3,269
Dyer County SD
Supt. — See Dyersburg
Dyer County HS 1,100/9-12
1000 W Main St 38059 731-627-2229
Peggy Dodds, prin. Fax 627-2152
Northview MS 400/6-8
820 Williams St 38059 731-627-3713
Anthony Jones, prin. Fax 627-4823

Tennessee Technology Center at Newbern Post-Sec.
340 Washington St 38059 731-627-2511

Newport, Cocke, Pop. 6,817
Cocke County SD 4,800/PK-12
305 Hedrick Dr 37821 423-623-7821
Manney Moore, dir. Fax 625-3947
www.cocke.k12.tn.us
Cocke County Alternative S Alt
345 Hedrick Dr 37821 423-625-9768
Bryan Douglas, prin. Fax 625-1807
Cocke County HS 1,200/9-12
216 Hedrick Dr 37821 423-623-8718
Gail Burchette, prin. Fax 623-1213
Hooper Career & Technical Center Vo/Tech
210 Hedrick Dr 37821 423-623-6072
Tracy Beets, prin. Fax 623-6070
Cocke County Adult School Adult
345 Hedrick Dr 37821 423-625-3427
Bryan Douglas, prin. Fax 625-3421
Other Schools – See Cosby

New Tazewell, Claiborne, Pop. 2,986
Claiborne County SD
Supt. — See Tazewell
Claiborne HS 800/9-12
815 Davis Dr 37825 423-626-3532
Taylor Sewell, prin. Fax 626-3555

Nolensville, Williamson, Pop. 5,749
Williamson County SD
Supt. — See Franklin
Mill Creek MS, 200 York Trl 37135 6-8
Kari Miller, admin. 615-472-5250
Nolensville HS 9-10
1600 Summerlyn Dr 37135 615-472-5200
Dr. Bill Harlin, admin.

Norris, Anderson, Pop. 1,472
Anderson County SD
Supt. — See Clinton
Norris MS 500/6-8
PO Box 980 37828 865-494-7171
Jeff Harshbarger, prin. Fax 494-6693

Oakdale, Morgan, Pop. 205
Morgan County SD
Supt. — See Wartburg

Oakdale S 600/K-12
225 Clifty Creek Rd 37829 423-369-3885
Heath Snow, prin. Fax 369-2821

Oakland, Fayette, Pop. 6,569
Fayette County SD
Supt. — See Somerville
West JHS 400/6-8
13100 Highway 194 38060 901-465-9213
Stephanie Neal, prin. Fax 465-1599

Oak Ridge, Anderson, Pop. 28,500
Oak Ridge CSD 4,700/PK-12
PO Box 6588 37831 865-425-9001
Dr. Bruce Borchers, dir. Fax 425-9070
www.ortn.edu
Jefferson MS 700/5-8
200 Fairbanks Rd 37830 865-425-9301
Phil Cox, prin. Fax 425-9339
Oak Ridge HS 1,400/9-12
1450 Oak Ridge Tpke 37830 865-425-9601
Martin McDonald, prin. Fax 425-9678
Robertsville MS 700/5-8
245 Robertsville Rd 37830 865-425-9201
Bruce Lay, prin. Fax 425-9236

Old Hickory, See Nashville
Metropolitan Nashville SD
Supt. — See Nashville
DuPont Hadley MS 600/5-8
1901 Old Hickory Blvd 37138 615-847-7300
Dr. Kevin Armstrong, prin. Fax 847-7311

Academy for G.O.D. K-12
401 Center St 37138 615-722-7107
Betsy Johnson, prin. Fax 246-2719

Oliver Springs, Morgan, Pop. 3,166
Anderson County SD
Supt. — See Clinton
Norwood MS 200/6-8
803 E Tri County Blvd 37840 865-435-7749
Dan Jenkins, prin. Fax 435-5426

Roane County SD
Supt. — See Kingston
Oliver Springs HS 400/9-12
419 Kingston Ave 37840 865-435-7216
Justin Nivens, prin. Fax 435-6774
Oliver Springs MS 300/6-8
317 Roane St 37840 865-435-0011
Nancy Wilson, prin. Fax 435-1621

Faith Christian Academy 50/PK-12
864 Poplar Creek Rd 37840 828-435-0670
Dr. Paul Cates, prin. Fax 435-0670

Oneida, Scott, Pop. 3,699
Oneida Special SD 1,300/PK-12
PO Box 4819 37841 423-569-8912
Dr. Jeanny Hatfield Ph.D., dir. Fax 569-2201
www.oneidaschools.org/
Oneida HS 400/9-12
372 N Main St 37841 423-569-8818
Kevin Byrd, prin. Fax 569-1681
Oneida MS 300/6-8
376 N Main St 37841 423-569-2468
Kelly Posey, prin. Fax 569-5977

Ooltewah, Hamilton, Pop. 676
Hamilton County SD
Supt. — See Chattanooga
East Hamilton MSHS 1,800/6-12
2015 Ooltewah Ringgold Rd 37363 423-893-3535
Gail Chuy, prin. Fax 893-3536
Hamilton County HS 100/Alt
9050 Career Ln 37363 423-344-1433
Gary Kuehn, prin. Fax 344-1434
Hunter MS 700/6-8
6810 Teal Ln 37363 423-344-1474
Robert Alford, prin. Fax 344-1485
Ooltewah HS 1,400/9-12
6123 Mountain View Rd 37363 423-238-5221
Mark Bean, prin. Fax 238-5871
Ooltewah MS 900/6-8
5100 Ooltewah Ringgold Rd 37363 423-238-5732
Chrissy Easterly, prin. Fax 238-5735

Paris, Henry, Pop. 9,926
Henry County SD 3,100/PK-12
217 Grove Blvd 38242 731-642-9733
Dr. Brian Norton, dir. Fax 642-8073
www.henryk12.net/
Grove S 300/9-9
215 Grove Blvd 38242 731-642-4586
Samuel Tharpe, prin. Fax 642-4577
Henry County HS 1,000/10-12
315 S Wilson St 38242 731-642-5232
Dr. Michele Webb, prin. Fax 642-5240
Other Schools – See Buchanan

Paris Special SD 1,800/PK-8
1219 Highway 641 S 38242 731-642-9322
Mike Brown, supt. Fax 642-9327
www.parisssd.org/
Inman MS 500/6-8
400 Harrison St 38242 731-642-8131
Jason Scarbrough, prin. Fax 642-8209

Tennessee Technology Center at Paris Post-Sec.
312 S Wilson St 38242 731-644-7365

Parsons, Decatur, Pop. 2,355
Decatur County SD
Supt. — See Decaturville
Decatur County MS 500/5-8
2740 Highway 641 S 38363 731-847-6510
Chris Villaflor, prin. Fax 847-6572

Pigeon Forge, Sevier, Pop. 5,787
Sevier County SD
Supt. — See Sevierville
Pigeon Forge HS 700/9-12
414 Tiger Dr 37863 865-774-5790
Ben Clabo, prin. Fax 774-5798
Pigeon Forge MS 600/5-8
300 Wears Valley Rd 37863 865-453-2401
Scott Hensley, prin. Fax 453-0799

Pikeville, Bledsoe, Pop. 1,590
Bledsoe County SD 2,000/PK-12
478 Spring St 37367 423-447-2914
Jennifer Terry, dir. Fax 447-7135
bledsoecounty.schoolinsites.com/
Bledsoe County HS 600/9-12
877 Main St 37367 423-447-6851
Linda Pickett, prin. Fax 447-6286
Bledsoe County MS 400/6-8
PO Box 147 37367 423-447-3212
Melissa Reel, prin. Fax 447-3085
Other Schools – See Dunlap

Pleasant View, Cheatham, Pop. 4,108
Cheatham County SD
Supt. — See Ashland City
Sycamore HS 800/9-12
1021 Old Clarksville Pike 37146 615-746-5013
Ramona Fritts, prin. Fax 746-3653
Sycamore MS 800/5-8
1025 Old Clarksville Pike 37146 615-746-8852
Lisa Young, prin. Fax 746-5770

Pleasant View Christian S 300/PK-12
160 Hicks Edgen Rd 37146 615-746-8555
Rusty Campbell, admin. Fax 746-2646

Portland, Sumner, Pop. 11,308
Sumner County SD
Supt. — See Gallatin
Middle Technical College HS @ Portland 9-12
602 SBroadway 37148 615-745-3126
Phillip Campbell, prin.
Portland East MS 400/6-8
604 S Broadway St 37148 615-325-4146
Jackson Howell, prin. Fax 325-5320
Portland HS 1,100/9-12
600 College St 37148 615-325-9201
David Woods, prin. Fax 325-5302
Portland West MS 500/6-8
110 Nolan Private Dr 37148 615-325-8066
Cam MacLean, prin. Fax 325-4073

Highland Academy 100/9-12
211 Highland Circle Dr 37148 615-325-2036

Powell, Knox, Pop. 7,534
Knox County SD
Supt. — See Knoxville
Powell HS 1,400/9-12
2136 W Emory Rd 37849 865-938-2171
Nathan Langlois, prin. Fax 947-2805
Powell MS 1,000/6-8
3329 W Emory Rd 37849 865-938-9008
Gary Critselous, prin. Fax 947-4357

First Baptist Academy 300/K-12
7706 Ewing Rd 37849 865-947-8503
Matt Mercer, hdmstr. Fax 961-6525
Temple Baptist Academy 200/PK-12
1700 W Beaver Creek Dr 37849 865-938-8180
David Whitaker, prin. Fax 938-8147
The Crown College of the Bible Post-Sec.
2307 W Beaver Creek Dr 37849 865-938-8186

Pulaski, Giles, Pop. 7,654
Giles County SD 4,000/PK-12
270 Richland Dr 38478 931-363-4558
Philip Wright, dir. Fax 363-8975
www.giles-lea.giles.k12.tn.us
Bridgeforth MS 400/6-8
1051 Bridgeforth Cir 38478 931-363-7526
Cathie White, prin. Fax 424-7021
Giles County HS 900/9-12
200 Sheila Frost Dr 38478 931-363-6532
Mark Cardin, prin. Fax 424-7010
Other Schools – See Lynnville

Martin Methodist College Post-Sec.
433 W Madison St 38478 931-363-9800
Tennessee Technology Center at Pulaski Post-Sec.
PO Box 614 38478 931-424-4014

Reagan, Henderson
Henderson County SD
Supt. — See Lexington
Scotts Hill HS 500/9-12
7871 Highway 100 38368 731-602-6112
Beverly Ivy, prin. Fax 602-6118

Red Boiling Springs, Macon, Pop. 1,106
Macon County SD
Supt. — See Lafayette
Red Boiling Springs JSHS 300/6-12
415 Hillcrest Dr 37150 615-699-3125
Don Jones, prin. Fax 699-3371

Ripley, Lauderdale, Pop. 8,322
Lauderdale County SD 4,600/PK-12
PO Box 350 38063 731-635-2941
Joey Hassell, supt. Fax 635-7985
www.lced.net
Lauderdale MS 700/6-8
309 Charles Griggs St 38063 731-635-1391
Latonya Jackson, prin. Fax 635-0028
Ripley HS 900/9-12
254 S Jefferson St 38063 731-635-2642
Joe Bridges, prin. Fax 635-7151
Other Schools – See Halls

Tennessee Technology Center at Ripley Post-Sec.
127 Industrial Dr 38063 731-635-3368

Roan Mountain, Carter, Pop. 1,355
Carter County SD
Supt. — See Elizabethton
Cloudland JSHS 300/7-12
476 Cloudland Dr 37687 423-772-5300
Randy Birchfield, prin. Fax 772-5309

Rockvale, Rutherford
Rutherford County SD
Supt. — See Murfreesboro
Rockvale MS 1,000/6-8
6543 Highway 99 37153 615-904-6745
Fred Barlow, prin. Fax 904-6746

Rockwood, Roane, Pop. 5,395
Roane County SD
Supt. — See Kingston
Rockwood HS 400/9-12
512 W Rockwood St 37854 865-354-0882
Shannon Cawood, prin. Fax 354-5170
Rockwood MS 400/6-8
434 W Rockwood St 37854 865-354-0931
Amanda Evans, prin. Fax 354-5160

Rogersville, Hawkins, Pop. 4,364
Hawkins County SD 7,300/PK-12
200 N Depot St 37857 423-272-7629
Steve Starnes, dir. Fax 272-2207
www.hck12.net
Cherokee HS 1,100/9-12
2927 Highway 66 S 37857 423-272-6507
Thomas Floyd, prin. Fax 272-3556
Rogersville MS 500/6-8
958 E Mckinney Ave 37857 423-272-7603
Jim Ailshie, prin. Fax 272-0185
Other Schools – See Church Hill, Sneedville, Surgoinsville

Rossville, Fayette, Pop. 656

Rossville Christian Academy 300/K-12
PO Box 369 38066 901-853-0200

Rutledge, Grainger, Pop. 1,113
Grainger County SD 3,700/PK-12
PO Box 38 37861 865-828-3611
Edwin Jarnagin, dir. Fax 828-4357
www.grainger.k12.tn.us/
Grainger Academy 50/Alt
232 Pioneer Dr 37861 865-828-6330
Kip Combs, prin. Fax 828-3364
Grainger HS 900/9-12
2201 Highway 11W S 37861 865-828-5291
Mark Briscoe, prin. Fax 828-4828
Rutledge MS 500/7-8
140 Pioneer Dr 37861 865-828-3366
Lynn Jones, prin. Fax 828-3364
Grainger County Adult S Adult
PO Box 38 37861 865-828-3611
Dr. James Atkins, prin. Fax 828-4357
Other Schools – See Washburn

Sale Creek, Hamilton, Pop. 2,811
Hamilton County SD
Supt. — See Chattanooga
Sale Creek MSHS 500/6-12
211 Patterson Rd 37373 423-332-8819
Tobin Davidson, prin. Fax 332-8847

Santa Fe, Maury
Maury County SD
Supt. — See Columbia
Santa Fe S 700/PK-12
2629 Santa Fe Pike 38482 931-682-2172
Leigh Ann Willey, prin. Fax 682-2606

Savannah, Hardin, Pop. 6,820
Hardin County SD 3,700/PK-12
155 Guinn St 38372 731-925-3943
Michael Davis, dir. Fax 925-7313
www.hardincountyschools.net
Hardin County HS 1,100/9-12
1170 Pickwick St 38372 731-925-3976
William McAdams, prin. Fax 925-7407
Hardin County MS 700/6-8
299 Lacefield Dr 38372 731-925-9037
Steve Haffly, prin. Fax 925-0253

Selmer, McNairy, Pop. 4,308
McNairy County SD 4,200/K-12
170 W Court Ave 38375 731-645-3267
John Prince, dir. Fax 645-8085
www.mcnairy.org
McNairy Central HS 800/9-12
493 High School Rd 38375 731-645-3226
Cecil Stroup, prin. Fax 645-8014
Selmer MS 400/5-8
635 E Poplar Ave 38375 731-645-7977
Dr. Brenda Armstrong, prin. Fax 645-6377
Other Schools – See Adamsville

Styles and Profiles Beauty College Post-Sec.
119 S 2nd St 38375 731-645-9728

Sevierville, Sevier, Pop. 14,595
Sevier County SD 14,900/PK-12
226 Cedar St 37862 865-453-4671
Dr. Jack Parton, supt. Fax 522-1497
www.sevier.org
Alternative Learning Center 50/Alt
2540 Boyds Creek Hwy 37876 865-453-8338
Jason Kerley, prin. Fax 453-7875
Hardin Academy 100/9-12
2540 Boyds Creek Hwy 37876 865-453-8338
Jason Kerley, prin.

Sevier County HS 1,600/9-12
1200 Dolly Parton Pkwy 37862 865-453-5525
Toby Ward, prin. Fax 428-5867
Sevierville MS 600/6-8
520 High St 37862 865-453-0311
Donna Rolen, prin. Fax 428-2316
Whites Adult HS Adult
226 Cedar St 37862 865-429-1492
Curtis Clabo, prin. Fax 774-4564
Other Schools – See Gatlinburg, Kodak, Pigeon Forge, Seymour

Christian Academy of the Smokies 100/PK-12
1625 Old Newport Hwy 37862 865-774-0012
Smokey Mountain Trucking Institute Post-Sec.
3173 Newport Hwy 37876 800-495-4056

Sewanee, Franklin, Pop. 2,295

St. Andrew's-Sewanee S 300/6-12
290 Quintard Rd 37375 931-598-5651
Karl J. Sjolund, head sch Fax 914-1224
Sewanee The University of the South Post-Sec.
735 University Ave 37383 931-598-1000

Seymour, Sevier, Pop. 10,811
Sevier County SD
Supt. — See Sevierville
Seymour HS 1,200/9-12
732 Boyds Creek Hwy 37865 865-577-7040
Kristy Wallen, prin. Fax 579-1492
Seymour MS 700/6-8
737 Boyds Creek Hwy 37865 865-579-0730
David Loy, prin. Fax 579-0905

King's Academy 500/PK-12
202 Smothers Rd 37865 865-573-8321
Dr. Walter Grubb, hdmstr. Fax 573-8323
Seymour Community Christian S 100/PK-12
PO Box 849 37865 865-577-5500
Patrick Koster, admin. Fax 577-2646

Shelbyville, Bedford, Pop. 19,855
Bedford County SD 8,300/PK-12
500 Madison St 37160 931-684-3284
Don Embry, supt. Fax 684-1133
www.bedfordk12tn.com/
Harris MS 1,000/6-8
570 Eagle Blvd 37160 931-684-5195
James Sullivan, prin. Fax 685-9455
Shelbyville Central HS 1,200/9-12
401 Eagle Blvd 37160 931-684-5672
Whit Taylor, prin. Fax 684-9359
Other Schools – See Unionville, Wartrace

Tennessee Technology Center Shelbyville Post-Sec.
1405 Madison St 37160 931-685-5013

Signal Mountain, Hamilton, Pop. 7,474
Hamilton County SD
Supt. — See Chattanooga
Signal Mountain MSHS 1,300/6-12
2650 Sam Powell Trl 37377 423-886-0880
Robin Copp, prin. Fax 886-0881

Smithville, DeKalb, Pop. 4,481
DeKalb County SD 3,000/PK-12
110 S Public Sq 37166 615-597-4084
Patrick Cripps, supt. Fax 597-6326
www.dekalbschools.net
DeKalb County HS 800/9-12
1130 W Broad St 37166 615-597-4094
Kathy Bryant, prin. Fax 597-8104
DeKalb MS 600/6-8
1132 W Broad St 37166 615-597-7987
Randy Jennings, prin. Fax 597-2640

Smyrna, Rutherford, Pop. 39,070
Rutherford County SD
Supt. — See Murfreesboro
Rock Springs MS 1,000/6-8
3301 Rock Springs Rd 37167 615-904-3825
Chris Treadway, prin. Fax 904-3826
Smyrna HS 1,800/9-12
100 Bulldog Dr 37167 615-904-3865
Rick Powell, prin. Fax 904-3866
Smyrna MS 1,000/6-8
712 Hazelwood Dr 37167 615-904-3845
Jeannie Fitzpatrick, prin. Fax 904-3846
Smyrna West Alternative S 50/Alt
12619 Old Nashville Hwy 37167 615-904-3856
Kay Davenport, prin. Fax 904-3857
Stewart's Creek HS 1,400/9-12
301 Red Hawk Blvd 37167 615-904-6771
Dr. Clark Harrell, prin. Fax 904-6772
Stewarts Creek MS 900/6-8
400 Red Hawk Blvd 37167 615-904-6700
Larry Creasy, prin. Fax 904-6701

Lancaster Christian Academy 500/PK-12
150 Soccer Way 37167 615-223-0451

Sneedville, Hancock, Pop. 1,364
Hancock County SD 1,000/K-12
PO Box 629 37869 423-733-2591
Anthony Seal, dir. Fax 733-8757
www.hancockcountyschools.com
Hancock County MSHS 500/6-12
2700 Main St 37869 423-733-4611
Brian Greene, prin. Fax 733-1427

Hawkins County SD
Supt. — See Rogersville
Clinch S 100/K-12
1540 Clinch Valley Rd 37869 423-272-3202
George Barton, prin. Fax 272-3207

Soddy Daisy, Hamilton, Pop. 12,577
Hamilton County SD
Supt. — See Chattanooga
Sequoya HS Vo/Tech
9517 W Ridge Trail Rd 37379 423-843-4707
Todd Jackson, prin. Fax 843-4719
Soddy Daisy HS 1,200/9-12
618 Sequoyah Access Rd 37379 423-332-8828
Daniel Gilbert, prin. Fax 332-8831
Soddy Daisy MS 500/6-8
200 Turner Rd 37379 423-332-8800
Blake Freeman, prin. Fax 332-8810

Somerville, Fayette, Pop. 3,069
Fayette County SD 3,100/PK-12
PO Box 9 38068 901-465-5260
Dr. Lonnie Harris, supt. Fax 466-0078
www.fcsk12.net
East JHS 400/6-8
400 Leach Dr 38068 901-465-3151
Kathy Redditt, prin. Fax 465-5084
Fayette-Ware HS 900/9-12
13520 Highway 59 38068 901-465-9838
Diane Watkins, prin. Fax 465-1377
Other Schools – See Oakland

Fayette Academy 700/PK-12
PO Box 130 38068 901-465-3241
Courtney Burnette, head sch Fax 465-2141

South Fulton, Obion, Pop. 2,320
Obion County SD
Supt. — See Union City
South Fulton MSHS 400/6-12
1302 John C Jones Pkwy 38257 731-479-1441
Kimberly Jackson, prin. Fax 479-0586

South Pittsburg, Marion, Pop. 2,934
Marion County SD
Supt. — See Jasper
South Pittsburg JSHS 400/7-12
717 Elm Ave 37380 423-837-7561
Danny Wilson, prin. Fax 837-4532

Richard CSD 300/PK-12
1620 Hamilton Ave 37380 423-837-7282
Cindy Blevins, dir. Fax 837-0641
www.richardhardy.org
Hardy Memorial S 300/PK-12
1620 Hamilton Ave 37380 423-837-7282
Beth Webb, prin. Fax 837-0641

Sparta, White, Pop. 4,841
White County SD 4,100/PK-12
136 Baker St 38583 931-836-2229
Sandra Crouch, dir. Fax 836-8128
www.whitecoschools.net
White County HS 1,200/9-12
267 Allen Dr 38583 931-836-3214
Grant Swallows, prin. Fax 836-6295
White County MS 900/6-8
300 Turn Table Rd 38583 931-738-9238
Craig Lynn, prin. Fax 738-9271

Spencer, Van Buren, Pop. 1,580
Van Buren County SD 800/PK-12
PO Box 98 38585 931-946-2242
Cheryl Cole, dir. Fax 946-2858
www.vanburenschools.org
Van Buren County JSHS 400/6-12
337 Sparta St 38585 931-946-2442
Jamie Simmons, prin. Fax 946-2265

Spring City, Rhea, Pop. 1,936
Rhea County SD
Supt. — See Dayton
Spring City MS 300/6-8
751 Wassom Memorial Hwy 37381 423-365-9105
Tina Stinnette, prin. Fax 365-9102

Springfield, Robertson, Pop. 16,188
Robertson County SD 11,500/PK-12
PO Box 130 37172 615-384-5588
Mike Davis, dir. Fax 384-9749
www.rcstn.net/
Coopertown MS 500/4-8
3820 Highway 49 W 37172 615-382-4166
Lewis Walling, prin. Fax 382-4171
Robertson County Alternative Program Alt
800 M S Couts Blvd 37172 615-382-2328
Nancy Williams, prin. Fax 382-2328
Springfield HS 1,100/9-12
5240 Highway 76 E 37172 615-384-3516
Teresa Leavitt, prin. Fax 384-5484
Springfield MS 600/6-8
715 5th Ave W 37172 615-384-4821
Dr. Grant Bell, prin. Fax 382-7890
Other Schools – See Cedar Hill, Cross Plains, Greenbrier, White House

---

South Haven Christian S 400/PK-12
112 Academy Dr 37172 615-384-5073
Dr. Steve Blaser, admin. Fax 425-2403

Spring Hill, Maury, Pop. 28,520
Maury County SD
Supt. — See Columbia
Spring Hill MS 800/5-8
3501 Cleburne Rd 37174 931-451-1531
Shanda Sparrow, prin. Fax 486-3954
Northfield Academy Adult
500 Northfield Ln 37174 931-486-1134
Dianne Kirk, coord. Fax 840-4410

Williamson County SD
Supt. — See Franklin
Spring Station MS 1,100/6-8
1000 Spring Station Dr 37174 615-472-5080
Paula Pulliam, prin. Fax 472-5091

Summit HS 1,200/9-12
2830 Twin Lakes Dr 37174 615-472-5100
Sarah Lamb, prin. Fax 472-5121

Strawberry Plains, Jefferson
Knox County SD
Supt. — See Knoxville
Carter HS 900/9-12
210 N Carter School Rd 37871 865-933-3434
Ryan Siebe, prin. Fax 932-8180
Carter MS 800/6-8
204 N Carter School Rd 37871 865-933-3426
Michael Derrick, prin. Fax 932-8170

Blue Springs Christian Academy 50/PK-12
3265 Blue Springs Rd 37871 865-932-7603
Don Ingram, admin.

Summertown, Lawrence, Pop. 852
Lawrence County SD
Supt. — See Lawrenceburg
Summertown JSHS 600/7-12
411 W College St 38483 931-964-3539
Brent Long, prin. Fax 964-3302

Sunbright, Morgan, Pop. 550
Morgan County SD
Supt. — See Wartburg
Sunbright S 600/K-12
PO Box 129 37872 423-628-2244
Ron Treadway, prin. Fax 628-2120

Surgoinsville, Hawkins, Pop. 1,786
Hawkins County SD
Supt. — See Rogersville
Surgoinsville MS 300/5-8
1044 Main St 37873 423-345-2252
Dr. Rodney Roberson, prin. Fax 345-3598

Sweetwater, Monroe, Pop. 5,664
Monroe County SD
Supt. — See Madisonville
Sweetwater HS 500/9-12
414 S High St 37874 423-337-7881
Eric Weaver, prin. Fax 337-0685

Sweetwater CSD 1,600/PK-8
PO Box 231 37874 423-337-7051
Rodney Boruff, supt. Fax 337-7051
www.compurdy.com/scs2/
Sweetwater JHS 300/7-8
1013 Cannon Ave 37874 423-337-7336
Jaime Downs, prin. Fax 337-7360

Cross Creek Christian S 200/PK-12
501 E North St 37874 423-337-9330
Melissa Whitfield, admin. Fax 337-9335

Tazewell, Claiborne, Pop. 2,172
Claiborne County SD 4,700/PK-12
PO Box 179 37879 423-626-3543
Connie Holdway, dir. Fax 626-5945
www.clairbornecountyschools.com
Soldiers Memorial MS 500/5-8
1510 Legion St 37879 423-626-3531
Lisa Jessie, prin. Fax 626-2151
Claiborne Adult HS Adult
PO Box 600 37879 423-626-8222
Starla Ray, prin. Fax 626-5945
Other Schools – See Cumberland Gap, Harrogate, New Tazewell

Tellico Plains, Monroe, Pop. 866
Monroe County SD
Supt. — See Madisonville
Tellico Plains HS 500/9-12
9180 Highway 68 37385 423-253-2530
Russell Harris, prin. Fax 253-2541
Tellico Plains JHS 300/5-8
120 Old High School Rd 37385 423-253-2250
Ruthie Hunt, prin. Fax 253-7824

Ten Mile, Roane
Roane County SD
Supt. — See Kingston
Midway MS 200/6-8
104 Dogtown Rd 37880 865-717-5464
Amy Cawood, prin. Fax 376-0948

Thompsons Station, Williamson, Pop. 2,172
Williamson County SD
Supt. — See Franklin
Heritage MS 900/6-8
4803 Columbia Pike 37179 615-472-4540
Dr. Dana Finch, prin. Fax 472-4553
Independence HS 1,300/9-12
1776 Declaration Way 37179 615-472-4600
Dr. Niki Patton, prin. Fax 472-4621

Tiptonville, Lake, Pop. 4,409
Lake County SD 900/PK-12
819 McBride St 38079 731-253-6601
Sherry Darnell, supt. Fax 253-7111
www.lcfalcons.net
Lake County HS 200/9-12
300 Cochran St 38079 731-253-7733
Preston Caldwell, prin. Fax 253-7766

Trenton, Gibson, Pop. 4,197
Trenton Special SD 1,400/PK-12
201 W 10th St 38382 731-855-1191
Sandra Harper, supt. Fax 855-1414
www.trentonssd.org
Peabody HS 400/9-12
2069 US Highway 45 Byp N 38382 731-855-2601
Tim Haney, prin. Fax 855-1217
Trenton Rosenwald MS 400/5-8
2065 US Highway 45 Byp S 38382 731-855-2422
Paul Pillow, prin. Fax 855-1826

Troy, Obion, Pop. 1,363
Obion County SD
Supt. — See Union City
Career Technology Center Vo/Tech
528 N US Highway 51 38260 731-536-4688
George Leake, prin. Fax 536-0469
Obion County Central HS 900/9-12
528 N US Highway 51 38260 731-536-4688
Greg Barclay, prin. Fax 536-0469

Tullahoma, Coffee, Pop. 18,247
Tullahoma CSD 3,500/PK-12
510 S Jackson St 37388 931-454-2600
Dr. Dan Lawson, dir. Fax 454-2642
www.tcsedu.net
East MS 400/6-8
908 Country Club Dr 37388 931-454-2632
Charles Lawson, prin. Fax 454-2660
Tullahoma HS 1,100/9-12
927 N Jackson St 37388 931-454-2620
Kathy Rose, prin. Fax 454-2662
West MS 400/6-8
90 Hermitage Dr 37388 931-454-2605
Dr. Mickey Shuran, prin. Fax 454-2661

Union City, Obion, Pop. 10,735
Obion County SD 3,900/PK-12
1700 N 5th St 38261 731-885-9743
Russell J. Davis, dir. Fax 885-4902
www.ocboe.com
Other Schools – See South Fulton, Troy

Union CSD 1,500/PK-12
PO Box 749 38281 731-885-3922
Gary Houston, dir. Fax 885-6033
www.tornadotouch.net
Union City HS 300/9-12
1305 High School Dr 38261 731-885-2373
Wesley Kennedy, prin. Fax 885-5011
Union City MS 400/6-8
1111 High School Dr 38261 731-885-2901
Michael Paul Miller, prin. Fax 885-3677

Unionville, Bedford, Pop. 1,363
Bedford County SD
Supt. — See Shelbyville
Community HS 500/9-12
100 Community Xing 37180 931-685-1418
Robert Ralston, prin. Fax 294-2107
Community MS 400/6-8
3470 Highway 41A N 37180 931-685-1426
Tony Garrette, prin. Fax 294-5126

Vonore, Monroe, Pop. 1,458
Monroe County SD
Supt. — See Madisonville
Vonore MS 200/5-8
414 Hall St 37885 423-884-2730
Matt Conley, prin. Fax 884-2731

Wartburg, Morgan, Pop. 898
Morgan County SD 3,100/K-12
136 Flat Fork Rd 37887 423-346-6214
Dr. Ronald Wilson, supt. Fax 346-6043
mcsed.net/
Central HS 400/9-12
1119 Knoxville Hwy 37887 423-346-6616
Carol Staten, prin. Fax 346-5665
Central MS 300/6-8
146 Liberty Rd 37887 423-346-2800
Dr. Lisa Bunch, prin. Fax 346-2805
Morgan County Career & Technical Center Vo/Tech
132 Flat Fork Rd 37887 423-346-6285
Dr. Joseph Miller, prin. Fax 346-5857
Other Schools – See Coalfield, Oakdale, Sunbright

Wartrace, Bedford, Pop. 637
Bedford County SD
Supt. — See Shelbyville
Cascade HS 600/9-12
1165 Bell Buckle Wartrace 37183 931-389-9389
Tim Harwell, prin. Fax 389-6223
Cascade MS 300/6-8
1165 Bell Buckle Wartrace 37183 931-389-9389
David Parker, prin. Fax 389-6223

Washburn, Grainger
Grainger County SD
Supt. — See Rutledge
Washburn S 600/PK-12
7925 Highway 131 37888 865-497-2557
Ginny McElhaney, prin. Fax 497-2934

Watertown, Wilson, Pop. 1,450
Wilson County SD
Supt. — See Lebanon
Watertown HS 400/9-12
9360 Sparta Pike 37184 615-237-3434
Jeff Luttrell, prin. Fax 237-3030
Watertown MS 300/6-8
515 W Main St 37184 615-237-4000
Michael Pigg, prin. Fax 237-3643

Waverly, Humphreys, Pop. 4,056
Humphreys County SD 3,000/PK-12
2443 Highway 70 E 37185 931-296-2568
James Long, supt. Fax 296-6501
www.hcss.org
Humphreys County Vocational Center Vo/Tech
1327 Highway 70 W 37185 931-296-7867
Lori Dell, dir. Fax 296-7252
Waverly Central HS 600/9-12
1325 Highway 70 W 37185 931-296-3911
Robert Martin, prin. Fax 296-2575
Waverly JHS 500/4-8
520 E Main St 37185 931-296-4514
Andy Daniels, prin. Fax 296-6507
Other Schools – See Mc Ewen

Waynesboro, Wayne, Pop. 2,423
Wayne County SD 2,500/PK-12
PO Box 658 38485 931-722-3548
Marlon Davis, dir. Fax 722-7579
www.waynetn.net/
Wayne County HS 300/9-12
707 S Main St 38485 931-722-3238
Ryan Franks, prin. Fax 722-7641
Wayne County Technology Center Vo/Tech
703 S Main St 38485 931-722-5495
Beverly Hall, prin. Fax 722-5496
Waynesboro MS 300/5-8
PO Box 657 38485 931-722-5545
Jason Morris, prin. Fax 722-3953
Other Schools – See Clifton, Collinwood

Westmoreland, Sumner, Pop. 2,182
Sumner County SD
Supt. — See Gallatin
Westmoreland HS 500/9-12
4300 Hawkins Dr 37186 615-644-2280
Rick Duffer, prin. Fax 644-3395
Westmoreland MS 400/6-8
4128 Hawkins Dr 37186 615-644-3003
Danny Robinson, prin. Fax 644-5584

White Bluff, Dickson, Pop. 3,171
Dickson County SD
Supt. — See Dickson
James MS 300/6-8
3030 Trace Creek Rd 37187 615-740-5770
Jan Ford, prin. Fax 797-6401

White House, Sumner, Pop. 10,123
Robertson County SD
Supt. — See Springfield
White House-Heritage HS 900/7-12
7744 Highway 76 E 37188 615-672-0311
Mary Jo Holmes, prin. Fax 672-7178

Sumner County SD
Supt. — See Gallatin
White House HS 900/9-12
508 Tyree Springs Rd 37188 615-672-3761
Scott Langford, prin. Fax 672-6404
White House MS 700/6-8
2020 Highway 31 W 37188 615-672-4379
Jerry Apple, prin. Fax 672-6409

Christian Community Schools 300/PK-12
506 Hester Dr 37188 615-672-6949
Mark Massey, dir. Fax 616-1330

Whitesburg, Hamblen
Hamblen County SD
Supt. — See Morristown
East Ridge MS 600/6-8
6595 Saint Clair Rd 37891 423-581-3041
James Templin, prin. Fax 585-3765

Whites Creek, See Nashville
Metropolitan Nashville SD
Supt. — See Nashville
Whites Creek HS 800/9-12
7277 Old Hickory Blvd 37189 615-876-5132
Dr. James Bailey, prin. Fax 321-8720

Edwards Classical Academy 100/K-11
4479 Jackson Rd 37189 615-876-7291
Ryan Boomershine, hdmstr.

Whiteville, Hardeman, Pop. 4,622

Tennessee Technology Center Whiteville Post-Sec.
1685 US Highway 64 38075 731-254-8521

Whitwell, Marion, Pop. 1,684
Marion County SD
Supt. — See Jasper
Whitwell HS 400/9-12
200 Tiger Trl 37397 423-658-5141
Teena Casseday, prin. Fax 658-0313
Whitwell MS 400/5-8
1 Butterfly Ln 37397 423-658-5635
Kim Headrick, prin. Fax 658-6949

Winchester, Franklin, Pop. 8,370
Franklin County SD 5,800/PK-12
215 S College St 37398 931-967-0626
Dr. Amie W. Lonas, supt. Fax 967-7832
www.fcstn.net
Franklin County HS 1,500/9-12
833 Bypass Rd 37398 931-967-2821
Dr. Roger Alsup, prin. Fax 967-6945
North MS 700/6-8
2990 Decherd Blvd 37398 931-967-5323
Leah Harrell, prin. Fax 967-1413
Other Schools – See Cowan, Huntland

Woodbury, Cannon, Pop. 2,647
Cannon County SD 2,100/PK-12
301 W Main St Ste 100 37190 615-563-5752
Barbara Parker, supt. Fax 563-2716
www.ccstn.com/
Cannon County HS 600/9-12
1 Lion Dr 37190 615-563-2144
Mike Jones, prin. Fax 563-8068

TEXAS

TEXAS EDUCATION AGENCY
1701 Congress Ave, Austin 78701-1494
Telephone 512-463-9734
Fax 512-463-9838
Website tea.texas.gov/

Commissioner of Education Mike Morath

TEXAS BOARD OF EDUCATION
1701 Congress Ave, Austin 78701-1402

Chairperson Donna Bahorich

REGIONAL EDUCATION SERVICE CENTERS (RESC)

Region 1 ESC
Dr. Cornelia Gonzalez, dir. 956-984-6000
1900 W Schunior St, Edinburg Fax 984-7655
www.esc1.net

Region 2 ESC
Dr. Rick Alvarado Ph.D., dir. 361-561-8400
209 N Water St Fax 883-3442
Corpus Christi 78401
www.esc2.net

Region 3 ESC
Dr. Patricia Shafer, dir. 361-573-0731
1905 Leary Ln, Victoria 77901 Fax 576-4804
www.esc3.net/

Region 4 ESC
Dr. Pam Wells, dir. 713-462-7708
7145 W Tidwell Rd, Houston 77092 Fax 744-6514
www.esc4.net/

Region 5 ESC
Dr. Danny Lovett, dir. 409-951-1700
350 Pine St Ste 500 Fax 951-1800
Beaumont 77701
www.esc5.net

Region 6 ESC
Michael Holland, dir. 936-435-8400
3332 Montgomery Rd Fax 295-1447
Huntsville 77340
www.esc6.net

Region 7 ESC
Elizabeth Abernethy, dir. 903-988-6700
1909 N Longview St, Kilgore 75662 Fax 988-6708
www.esc7.net/

Region 8 ESC
Dr. David Fitts, dir. 903-572-8551
4845 US Highway 271 N Fax 575-2611
Pittsburg 75686
www.reg8.net

Region 9 ESC
Wes Pierce, dir. 940-322-6928
301 Loop 11, Wichita Falls 76306 Fax 767-3836
www.esc9.net

Region 10 ESC
Dr. Gordon Taylor, dir. 972-348-1700
400 E Spring Valley Rd Fax 231-3642
Richardson 75081
www.region10.org/

Region 11 ESC
Dr. Clyde Steelman, dir. 817-740-3600
1451 S Cherry Ln Fax 740-7600
Fort Worth 76108
www.esc11.net

Region 12 ESC
Dr. Jerry Maze, dir. 254-297-1212
PO Box 23409, Waco 76702 Fax 666-0823
www.esc12.net

Region 13 ESC
Rich Elsasser, dir. 512-919-5313
5701 Springdale Rd, Austin 78723 Fax 919-5374
www4.esc13.net

Region 14 ESC
Ronnie Kincaid, dir. 325-675-8600
1850 State Highway 351 Fax 675-8659
Abilene 79601
www.esc14.net/

Region 15 ESC
Scot Goen, dir. 325-658-6571
PO Box 5199, San Angelo 76902 Fax 655-4823
www.netxv.net/

Region 16 ESC
Ray Cogburn, dir. 806-677-5000
5800 Bell St, Amarillo 79109 Fax 677-5001
www.esc16.net

Region 17 ESC
Dr. Kyle Wargo, dir. 806-792-4000
1111 W Loop 289, Lubbock 79416 Fax 792-1523
www.esc17.net/

Region 18 ESC
John Thomas, dir. 432-563-2380
PO Box 60580, Midland 79711 Fax 567-3290
www.esc18.net

Region 19 ESC
Dr. Armando Aguirre, dir. 915-780-1919
PO Box 971127, El Paso 79997 Fax 780-6537
www.esc19.net/

Region 20 ESC
Dr. Ronald Beard, dir. 210-370-5200
1314 Hines, San Antonio 78208 Fax 370-5750
www.esc20.net

PUBLIC, PRIVATE AND CATHOLIC SECONDARY SCHOOLS

Abbott, Hill, Pop. 355

Abbott ISD 300/PK-12
PO Box 226 76621 254-582-3011
Richard Edison, supt. Fax 582-5430
www.abbottisd.org

Abbott S 300/PK-12
PO Box 226 76621 254-582-3011
Eric Pustejovsky, prin. Fax 582-5430

Abernathy, Hale, Pop. 2,787

Abernathy ISD 800/PK-12
505 7th St 79311 806-298-4940
Glen Teal Ed.D., supt. Fax 298-2400
www.abernathyisd.com

Abernathy HS 200/9-12
505 7th St 79311 806-298-4902
Gary Pugh, prin. Fax 298-4653

Abernathy JHS 200/6-8
505 7th St 79311 806-298-4921
Kelly Priest, prin. Fax 298-4775

Abilene, Taylor, Pop. 114,633

Abilene ISD 16,600/PK-12
PO Box 981 79604 325-677-1444
Dr. David Young, supt. Fax 794-1325
www.abileneisd.org

Abilene HS 1,900/9-12
2800 N 6th St 79603 325-677-1731
Robert Morrison, prin. Fax 794-1387

Academy for Tech/Eng/Math/Science 300/9-12
650 US Highway 80 E 79601 325-794-4140
Dr. Ketta Garduno, dir. Fax 794-1341

Clack MS 800/6-8
1610 Corsicana Ave 79605 325-692-1961
Todd Bramwell, prin. Fax 794-1371

Cooper HS 1,800/9-12
3639 Sayles Blvd 79605 325-691-1000
Dr. Karen Munoz, prin. Fax 794-1375

Craig MS 1,000/6-8
702 S Judge Ely Blvd 79602 325-794-4100
Daniel Dukes, prin. Fax 794-1385

Holland Medical HS 9-12
2442 Cedar St 79601 325-794-4120
Lyndsey Williamson, prin. Fax 794-1377

Jefferson Opportunity Center 50/Alt
1741 S 14th St 79602 325-794-4150
Jane Allred, admin. Fax 794-1367

Madison MS 900/6-8
3145 Barrow St 79605 325-692-5661
Tina Wyatt, prin. Fax 794-1313

Mann MS 900/6-8
2545 Mimosa Dr 79603 325-672-8493
Kathy Walker, prin. Fax 794-1374

Woodson Center for Excellence 200/Alt
342 Cockerell Dr 79601 325-671-4736
Jaime Tindall, prin. Fax 794-1377

Adult Learning Center Adult
1929 S 11th St 79602 325-671-4419
Mignon Lawson, dir. Fax 794-1327

Wylie ISD 3,800/PK-12
6251 Buffalo Gap Rd 79606 325-692-4353
Joey Light, supt. Fax 695-3438
www.wyliebulldogs.org

Wylie HS 1,000/9-12
4502 Antilley Rd 79606 325-690-1181
Tommy Vaughn, prin. Fax 690-0320

Wylie JHS 600/6-8
4010 Beltway S 79606 325-695-1910
Rob Goodenough, prin. Fax 692-5786

Abilene Christian S 300/PK-12
2550 N Judge Ely Blvd 79601 325-672-9200
Kirk Wade, pres. Fax 672-1262

Abilene Christian University Post-Sec.
ACU Box 29000 79699 325-674-2000

Hardin-Simmons University Post-Sec.
2200 Hickory St 79698 325-670-1000

Hendrick Medical Center Post-Sec.
1900 Pine St 79601 325-670-2201

McMurry University Post-Sec.
1 McMurry Sta 79697 325-793-3800

Sovereign Grace Classical Academy 50/K-12
831 N Judge Ely Blvd 79601 325-260-8734

Texas College of Cosmetology Post-Sec.
117 Sayles Blvd 79605 325-677-0532

Ackerly, Dawson, Pop. 220

Sands Consolidated ISD 200/PK-12
PO Box 218 79713 432-353-4888
Wayne Henderson, supt. Fax 353-4650
sands.esc17.net

Sands S 200/PK-12
PO Box 218 79713 432-353-4888
Lenny Morrow, prin. Fax 353-4650

Addison, Dallas, Pop. 12,782

Greenhill S 1,300/PK-12
4141 Spring Valley Rd 75001 972-628-5400
Scott Griggs, head sch Fax 404-8217

Trinity Christian Academy 1,500/PK-12
17001 Addison Rd 75001 972-931-8325
David Delph, hdmstr. Fax 931-8923

Adrian, Oldham, Pop. 165

Adrian ISD 100/PK-12
PO Box 189 79001 806-538-6203
Mike Winter, supt. Fax 538-6291
www.adrianisd.net

Adrian S 100/PK-12
PO Box 189 79001 806-538-6203
Maritssa Flores, prin. Fax 538-6291

Afton, Dickens

Patton Springs ISD 100/PK-12
PO Box 32 79220 806-689-2220
Bryan White, supt. Fax 689-2253
pattonsprings.net

Patton Springs S 100/PK-12
PO Box 32 79220 806-689-2220
Bryan White, prin. Fax 689-2253

Agua Dulce, Nueces, Pop. 795

Agua Dulce ISD 400/PK-12
PO Box 250 78330 361-998-2542
Wayne Kelly, supt. Fax 998-2816
www.adisd.net

Agua Dulce JSHS 200/6-12
PO Box 250 78330 361-998-2214
Guadalupe Martinez, prin. Fax 998-2994

Alamo, Hidalgo, Pop. 18,315

Pharr-San Juan-Alamo ISD
Supt. — See Pharr

Alamo MS 700/6-8
1819 W US Highway 83 78516 956-354-2550
Yolanda Gomez, prin. Fax 354-3188

Murphy MS 1,000/6-8
924 Sioux Rd 78516 956-354-2530
Lizette Longoria, prin. Fax 354-3224
Pharr-San Juan-Alamo Memorial HS 1,900/9-12
800 S Alamo Rd 78516 956-354-2420
Juan Garza, prin. Fax 354-3124

Valley Christian Heritage S 100/PK-12
932 N Alamo Rd 78516 956-787-9743

Alba, Wood, Pop. 497
Alba-Golden ISD 800/PK-12
1373 County Road 2377 75410 903-768-2472
Dwayne Ellis, supt. Fax 768-2593
www.agisd.com
Alba-Golden JSHS 400/6-12
1373 County Road 2377 75410 903-768-2472
Michael Mize, prin. Fax 768-2303

Albany, Shackelford, Pop. 1,992
Albany ISD 500/PK-12
PO Box 2050 76430 325-762-2823
Shane Fields, supt. Fax 762-3876
www.albanyisd.net
Albany JSHS 200/7-12
PO Box 2050 76430 325-762-3974
Kevin Hill, prin. Fax 762-3850

Aledo, Parker, Pop. 2,690
Aledo ISD 4,500/PK-12
1008 Bailey Ranch Rd 76008 817-441-8327
Dr. Derek Citty, supt. Fax 441-5144
aledo.schoolfusion.us
Aledo HS 1,100/10-12
1000 Bailey Ranch Rd 76008 817-441-8711
Dan Peterson, prin. Fax 441-5136
Aledo Learning Center 50/Alt
1016 Bailey Ranch Rd 76008 817-441-5176
Cheryl Jones, prin. Fax 441-9488
Aledo MS 700/7-8
416 S FM 1187 76008 817-441-5198
Mandy Musselwhite, prin. Fax 441-5133
Daniel 9th Grade Campus 400/9-9
990 Bailey Ranch Rd 76008 817-441-4504
Angela Tims, prin. Fax 441-2146

Alice, Jim Wells, Pop. 19,053
Alice ISD 5,400/PK-12
2 Coyote Trl 78332 361-664-0981
Dr. Grace Everett, supt. Fax 660-2113
www.aliceisd.net
Adams MS 800/7-8
901 E 3rd St 78332 361-660-2055
Dr. Judy Holmgreen, prin. Fax 660-2094
Alice HS 1,500/9-12
1 Coyote Trl 78332 361-664-0126
Dr. Alex Gonzalez, prin. Fax 660-2115

Alice Christian S 50/K-12
1200 N Stadium Rd 78332 361-668-6636
Sammy Garcia, prin. Fax 668-0840

Allen, Collin, Pop. 82,168
Allen ISD 20,300/PK-12
PO Box 13 75013 972-727-0511
Dr. Jenny Preston, supt. Fax 727-0500
www.allenisd.org
Allen SHS 4,400/10-12
300 Rivercrest Blvd 75002 972-727-0400
Dr. Jason Johnston, prin. Fax 727-0515
Curtis MS 1,100/7-8
1530 Rivercrest Blvd 75002 972-727-0340
Sonya Pitcock, prin. Fax 727-0345
Dillard Special Achievement Center Alt
610 E Bethany Dr 75002 972-727-7163
Eric Pacheco, dir. Fax 727-7162
Ereckson MS 1,100/7-8
450 Tatum Dr 75013 972-747-3308
Leslie Norris, prin. Fax 747-3311
Ford MS 900/7-8
630 Park Place Dr 75002 972-727-0590
Matt Russell, prin. Fax 727-0596
Lowery Freshman Center 1,600/9-9
601 E Main St 75002 972-396-6975
Jill Stafford, prin. Fax 396-6981

Lovejoy ISD 3,700/K-12
259 Country Club Rd 75002 469-742-8000
Ted Moore, supt. Fax 742-8001
www.lovejoyisd.net/
Other Schools – See Lucas

Alpine, Brewster, Pop. 5,819
Alpine ISD 1,000/PK-12
704 W Sul Ross Ave 79830 432-837-7700
Becky Watley, supt. Fax 837-7740
www.alpine.esc18.net
Alpine HS 300/9-12
300 E Hendryx Ave 79830 432-837-7710
Panchi Scown, prin. Fax 837-9813
Alpine MS 300/5-8
801 Middle School Dr 79830 432-837-7720
Justin Gonzales, prin. Fax 837-9814

Sul Ross State University Post-Sec.
PO Box C114 79832 432-837-8032

Altair, Colorado
Rice Consolidated ISD 1,200/PK-12
PO Box 338 77412 979-234-3531
Bill Hefner, supt. Fax 234-3409
www.ricecisd.org
Rice HS 300/9-12
PO Box 338 77412 979-234-3531
Eric Grogan, prin. Fax 234-5901
Rice JHS 200/6-8
PO Box 338 77412 979-234-3531
John Post, prin. Fax 234-3191
Other Schools – See Eagle Lake

Alto, Cherokee, Pop. 1,204
Alto ISD 600/PK-12
244 County Road 2429 75925 936-858-7101
Kerry Birdwell, supt. Fax 858-2101
www.alto.esc7.net/
Alto HS 200/9-12
248 County Road 2429 75925 936-858-7110
Scott Walters, prin. Fax 858-4387
Alto MS 200/5-8
240 County Road 2429 75925 936-858-7140
Kelly West, prin. Fax 858-4579

Alton, Hidalgo, Pop. 12,339
La Joya ISD
Supt. — See La Joya
Trevino MS 900/6-8
301 S Inspiration Blvd, 956-581-3050
Jose T. Garcia, prin. Fax 581-3099

Mission Consolidated ISD
Supt. — See Mission
Alton Memorial JHS 900/6-8
521 S Los Ebanos Blvd, 956-323-5000
Sylvia Garcia, prin. Fax 323-5045

Alvarado, Johnson, Pop. 3,699
Alvarado ISD 3,400/PK-12
PO Box 387 76009 817-783-6800
Dr. Kenneth Estes, supt. Fax 783-3844
www.alvaradoisd.net/
Alvarado HS 1,000/9-12
PO Box 387 76009 817-783-6940
Chris Magee, prin. Fax 783-6944
Alvarado JHS 500/7-8
PO Box 387 76009 817-783-6840
Melodye Brooks, prin. Fax 783-6844

Alvin, Brazoria, Pop. 23,976
Alvin ISD 20,000/PK-12
301 E House St 77511 281-388-1130
Dr. Buck Gilcrease, supt. Fax 388-2719
www.alvinisd.net
Alvin HS 2,500/9-12
802 S Johnson St 77511 281-245-3000
Dr. Johnny Briseno, prin. Fax 331-3053
Alvin JHS 800/6-8
2300 W South St 77511 281-245-2770
Leroy Castro, prin. Fax 331-5926
ASSETS Learning Center 200/Alt
605 W House St 77511 281-331-1690
Elizabeth Garcia, dir. Fax 331-1667
Fairview JHS 900/6-8
2600 County Road 190 77511 281-245-3100
Greg Bingham, prin. Fax 245-3213
Harby JHS 700/6-8
1500 Heights Rd 77511 281-585-6626
Juan Gonzales, prin. Fax 388-2247
Other Schools – See Manvel, Pearland

Alvin Community College Post-Sec.
3110 Mustang Rd 77511 281-756-3500
Living Stones Christian S 200/PK-12
1407 Victory Ln 77511 281-331-0086
Jessica Sanders, admin. Fax 331-6747

Alvord, Wise, Pop. 1,324
Alvord ISD 700/PK-12
PO Box 70 76225 940-427-5975
Dr. Randy Brown, supt. Fax 427-2313
www.alvordisd.net
Alvord HS 200/9-12
PO Box 70 76225 940-427-9643
Dr. Rhett King, prin. Fax 427-9648
Alvord MS 200/6-8
PO Box 70 76225 940-427-5511
Michael Thurman, prin. Fax 427-2461

Amarillo, Potter, Pop. 187,598
Amarillo ISD 32,500/PK-12
7200 W Interstate 40 79106 806-326-1000
Dr. Dana West, supt. Fax 354-4378
www.amaisd.org
Amarillo Area Ctr for Advanced Learning 50/Alt
1100 N Forest St 79106 806-326-2800
Jay Barrett, prin. Fax 371-6100
Amarillo HS 2,200/9-12
4225 Danbury Dr 79109 806-326-2000
Chad Huseman, prin. Fax 354-5092
Austin MS 800/6-8
1808 Wimberly Rd 79109 806-326-3000
David Manchee, prin. Fax 356-4802
Bonham MS 800/6-8
5600 SW 49th Ave 79109 806-326-3100
David Vincent, prin. Fax 356-4865
Bowie MS 700/7-8
2901 Tee Anchor Blvd 79104 806-326-3200
John Smith, prin. Fax 371-6016
Caprock HS 1,900/9-12
3001 E 34th Ave 79103 806-326-2200
David Bishop, prin. Fax 371-6042
Crockett MS 900/6-8
4720 Floyd Ave 79106 806-326-3300
Lisa Loan, prin. Fax 356-4873
de Zavala MS 400/5-8
2801 N Coulter St 79124 806-326-3400
Alan Nickson, prin. Fax 354-4286
Fannin MS 600/6-8
4627 S Rusk St 79110 806-326-3500
Nathan Culwell, prin. Fax 354-4588
Houston MS 800/6-8
815 S Independence St 79106 806-326-3600
Renee Mott, prin. Fax 371-5577
Mann MS 400/7-8
610 N Buchanan St 79107 806-326-3700
Tammie Villarreal, prin. Fax 371-5617
North Heights Alternative S 400/Alt
607 N Hughes St 79107 806-326-2850
Mark Leach, prin. Fax 371-5715
Palo Duro HS 1,900/9-12
1400 N Grant St 79107 806-326-2400
Amy Dorris, prin. Fax 381-7166
Tascosa HS 2,200/9-12
3921 Westlawn St 79102 806-326-2600
David Bishop, prin. Fax 356-4805
Travis MS 700/7-8
2815 Martin Rd 79107 806-326-3800
Jennifer Wilkerson, prin. Fax 381-7207

Canyon ISD
Supt. — See Canyon
Midway Alternative HS 100/Alt
13501 Bell St 79118 806-677-2455
Shawn Neeley, prin. Fax 677-2459
Randall HS 1,500/9-12
5800 Attebury Dr 79118 806-677-2333
Steve Williams, prin. Fax 677-2329
Westover Park JHS 900/7-8
7200 Pinnacle Dr 79119 806-677-2420
Doug Voran, prin. Fax 677-2439
Youth Center S 100/Alt
9300 S Georgia St 79118 806-677-2450
Shawn Neeley, prin. Fax 468-5714

Highland Park ISD 900/PK-12
PO Box 30430 79120 806-335-2823
Jimmy Hannon, supt. Fax 335-3547
www.hpisd.net
Highland Park HS 300/9-12
PO Box 30430 79120 806-335-2821
Tim Landon, prin. Fax 335-3215
Highland Park MS 200/6-8
PO Box 30430 79120 806-335-2821
Tim Landon, prin. Fax 335-3215

River Road ISD 1,400/PK-12
9500 N US Highway 287 79108 806-381-7800
Richard Kelley, supt. Fax 381-1357
www.rrisd.net
River Road HS 400/9-12
101 W Mobley St 79108 806-383-8867
Mike Cheverier, prin. Fax 381-7818
River Road MS 200/7-8
9500 N US Highway 287 79108 806-383-8721
Penny Rosson, prin. Fax 381-7815

Amarillo College Post-Sec.
PO Box 447 79178 806-371-5000
Ascension Academy 200/6-12
PO Box 50729 79159 806-342-0515
Exposito School of Hair Design Post-Sec.
3710 Mockingbird Ln 79109 806-355-9111
Holy Cross Catholic Academy 100/6-12
4110 S Bonham St 79110 806-355-9637
Angi Seidenberger, head sch Fax 353-9520
Milan Institute Post-Sec.
7001 W Interstate 40 79106 806-353-3500
Milan Institute of Cosmetology Post-Sec.
2400 SE 27th Ave 79103 806-371-7600
San Jacinto Christian Academy 400/PK-12
PO Box 3428 79116 806-372-2285
Randy Down, supt. Fax 376-6712
Vista College Post-Sec.
3440 Bell St Unit 100 79109 866-442-4197

Amherst, Lamb, Pop. 712
Amherst ISD 200/PK-12
PO Box 248 79312 806-246-3221
Joel Rodgers, supt. Fax 246-3494
www.amherstisd.com
Amherst S 200/PK-12
PO Box 248 79312 806-246-3221
Joel Rodgers, prin. Fax 246-3649

Anahuac, Chambers, Pop. 2,205
Anahuac ISD 1,200/PK-12
PO Box 369 77514 409-267-3600
James Hopper, supt. Fax 267-3855
www.anahuacisd.net
Anahuac HS 300/9-12
PO Box 1560 77514 409-267-2010
Eric Humphrey, prin. Fax 267-5192
Anahuac MS 300/6-8
PO Box 849 77514 409-267-2040
Tammy Duhon, prin. Fax 267-2046

Anderson, Grimes, Pop. 220
Anderson - Shiro Consolidated ISD 800/PK-12
458 FM 149 Rd W 77830 936-873-4500
Scott Beene, supt. Fax 873-4515
www.ascisd.net
Anderson - Shiro JSHS 400/6-12
458 FM 149 Rd W 77830 936-873-4550
Dr. Chase Thomas, prin. Fax 873-4575

Andrews, Andrews, Pop. 10,989
Andrews ISD 3,800/PK-12
405 NW 3rd St 79714 432-523-3640
Bobby Azam, supt. Fax 523-3343
www.andrews.esc18.net
Andrews Education Center 50/Alt
405 NW 3rd St 79714 432-523-3640
Charlie Falcon, prin. Fax 524-1989
Andrews HS 900/9-12
405 NW 3rd St 79714 432-523-3640
Kyle Clark, prin. Fax 523-6807
Andrews MS 800/6-8
405 NW 3rd St 79714 432-523-3640
Chris Dulin, prin. Fax 524-1904

Angleton, Brazoria, Pop. 18,559
Angleton ISD 6,500/PK-12
1900 N Downing Rd 77515 979-864-8000
Patricia Montgomery Ed.D., supt. Fax 864-8070
www.angletonisd.net/
Angleton HS 1,800/9-12
1 Campus Dr 77515 979-864-8001
Jerry Crowell, prin. Fax 864-8090

Angleton JHS 1,500/6-8
1201 W Henderson Rd 77515 979-849-8206
Doreen Martinez, prin. Fax 864-8675

Angleton Christian S 100/PK-12
3133 N Valderas St 77515 979-864-3842
Gordon Smith, head sch Fax 864-3843

Anna, Collin, Pop. 8,055
Anna ISD 2,600/PK-12
501 S Sherley Ave 75409 972-924-1000
Pete Slaughter, supt. Fax 924-1001
www.annaisd.org
Anna HS 600/9-12
501 S Sherley Ave 75409 972-924-1100
Gerald Springer, prin. Fax 924-1101
Anna MS 600/6-8
501 S Sherley Ave 75409 972-924-1200
Tressi Brown, prin. Fax 924-1201

Anson, Jones, Pop. 2,396
Anson ISD 700/PK-12
1431 Commercial Ave 79501 325-823-3671
Jay Baccus, supt. Fax 823-4444
www.ansontigers.com
Anson HS 200/9-12
1509 Commercial Ave 79501 325-823-2404
Troy Hinds, prin. Fax 823-2514
Anson MS 200/6-8
1120 Avenue M 79501 325-823-2771
David Hagler, prin. Fax 823-3667

Anthony, El Paso, Pop. 4,964
Anthony ISD 800/PK-12
840 6th St 79821 915-886-6500
Dr. Steven Saldivar, supt. Fax 886-2420
www.anthonyisd.net
Anthony HS 200/9-12
825 Wildcat Dr 79821 915-886-6550
Oscar Troncoso, prin. Fax 886-3875
Anthony MS 200/6-8
813 6th St 79821 915-886-6530
Oscar Troncoso, prin. Fax 886-3875

Anton, Hockley, Pop. 1,117
Anton ISD 300/PK-12
PO Box 309 79313 806-997-2301
Dwight Rice, supt. Fax 997-2062
www.antonisd.org
Anton S 300/PK-12
PO Box 309 79313 806-997-2301
Dwight Rice, admin. Fax 997-2062

Apple Springs, Trinity
Apple Springs ISD 200/PK-12
PO Box 125 75926 936-831-3344
Cody Moree, supt. Fax 831-2824
www.asisd.com/
Apple Springs JSHS 100/7-12
PO Box 125 75926 936-831-2241
Kevin Plotts, prin. Fax 831-2824

Aquilla, Hill, Pop. 108
Aquilla ISD 300/PK-12
404 N Richards 76622 254-694-3770
David Edison, supt. Fax 694-6237
www.aquillaisd.net
Aquilla S 300/PK-12
404 N Richards 76622 254-694-3770
Andrew Christian, prin. Fax 694-6237

Aransas Pass, San Patricio, Pop. 8,090
Aransas Pass ISD 1,900/PK-12
2300 McMullen Ln Ste 600 78336 361-758-3466
Mark Kemp, supt. Fax 758-2962
www.apisd.org
Aransas Pass HS 500/9-12
450 S Avenue A 78336 361-758-3248
Wayne Bennett, prin. Fax 758-3251
Blunt MS 400/6-8
2103 Demory Ln 78336 361-758-2711
Martha Rose, prin. Fax 758-4690

Archer City, Archer, Pop. 1,806
Archer City ISD 500/PK-12
PO Box 926 76351 940-574-4536
C.D. Knobloch, supt. Fax 574-4051
www.archercityisd.net
Archer City JSHS 200/7-12
PO Box 926 76351 940-574-4713
Vance Morris, prin. Fax 574-4051

Argyle, Denton, Pop. 3,241
Argyle ISD 1,700/PK-12
800 Eagle Dr 76226 940-464-7241
Dr. Telena Wright, supt. Fax 464-7297
www.argyleisd.com
Argyle HS 700/9-12
800 Eagle Dr 76226 940-262-7777
James Hill, prin. Fax 262-7783
Argyle MS 300/6-8
800 Eagle Dr 76226 940-246-2126
Scott Gibson, prin. Fax 246-2128

Denton ISD
Supt. — See Denton
Harpool MS 1,000/6-8
9601 Stacee Ln 76226 940-369-1700
Jeff Smith, prin. Fax 241-1342

Liberty Christian S 1,300/PK-12
1301 S US Highway 377 76226 940-294-2000
Dr. Rodney Haire, pres. Fax 294-2045

Arlington, Tarrant, Pop. 357,280
Arlington ISD 61,600/PK-12
1203 W Pioneer Pkwy 76013 682-867-4611
Dr. Marcelo Cavazos, supt. Fax 459-7299
www.aisd.net
Arlington Collegiate HS at TCC-SE 9-12
2224 Southeast Pkwy 76018 817-515-3550
Dr. Ben Bholan, prin. Fax 515-3540
Arlington HS 2,900/9-12
818 W Park Row Dr 76013 682-867-8100
Shahveer Dhalla, prin. Fax 867-8119
Bailey JHS 800/7-8
2411 Winewood Ln 76013 682-867-0700
Tiffany Benavides, prin. Fax 867-0708
Barnett JHS 900/7-8
2101 E Sublett Rd 76018 682-867-5000
Stephanie Hawthorne, prin. Fax 419-5005
Boles JHS 700/7-8
3900 SW Green Oaks Blvd 76017 682-867-8000
Jeff Provence, prin. Fax 561-8005
Bowie HS 3,000/9-12
2101 Highbank Dr 76018 682-867-4400
Bill Manley, prin. Fax 867-4406
Carter JHS 1,100/7-8
701 Tharp St 76010 682-867-1700
Reny Lizardo, prin. Fax 867-1721
Gunn JHS 500/7-8
3000 S Fielder Rd 76015 682-867-5400
Juan Villarreal, prin. Fax 867-5405
Houston HS 3,300/9-12
2000 Sam Houston Dr 76014 682-867-8200
Fernando Benavides, prin. Fax 867-6290
Lamar HS 2,900/9-12
1400 W Lamar Blvd 76012 682-867-8300
Andrew Hagman, prin. Fax 867-6959
Martin HS 3,300/9-12
4501 W Pleasant Ridge Rd 76016 682-867-8600
Marlene Roddy, prin. Fax 867-8609
Newcomer Center 200/Alt
600 SE Green Oaks Blvd 76018 682-867-7100
Christy Strybosch, prin. Fax 867-7146
Nichols JHS 800/7-8
2201 Ascension Blvd 76006 682-867-2600
Julie Harcrow, prin. Fax 801-2605
Ousley JHS 600/7-8
950 Southeast Pkwy 76018 682-867-5700
Lora Thurston, prin. Fax 419-5705
Seguin HS 1,700/9-12
7001 Silo Rd 76002 682-867-6700
Sam Nix, prin. Fax 867-6705
Shackelford JHS 700/7-8
2000 N Fielder Rd 76012 682-867-3600
Jerod Zahn, prin. Fax 801-3605
Turning Point Alternative HS 100/Alt
5618 W Arkansas Ln 76016 682-867-3000
Ray Borden, prin. Fax 867-3045
Turning Point Alternative JHS 50/Alt
2209 N Davis Dr 76012 682-867-3050
Linda Williams, prin. Fax 459-7331
Venture Alternative HS 300/Alt
4900 W Arkansas Ln 76016 682-867-6400
Beverley McReynolds, prin. Fax 867-6441
Workman JHS 600/7-8
701 E Arbrook Blvd 76014 682-867-1200
Inelda Acosta, prin. Fax 419-1205
Young JHS 800/7-8
3200 Woodside Dr 76016 682-867-3400
Kelly Hastings, prin. Fax 492-3405

Mansfield ISD
Supt. — See Mansfield
Coble MS 700/7-8
1200 Ballweg Rd 76002 682-314-4900
Winston Gipson, prin. Fax 453-7331
Howard MS 900/7-8
7501 Calendar Rd 76001 682-314-1050
Dr. Maria Gamell, prin. Fax 561-3840
Summit HS 1,900/9-12
1071 Turner Warnell Rd 76001 682-314-0800
Dr. Charlotte Ford, prin. Fax 473-5732
Timberview HS 1,600/9-12
7700 S Watson Rd 76002 682-314-1300
Derrell Douglas, prin. Fax 472-2978

Arlington Baptist College Post-Sec.
3001 W Division St 76012 817-461-8741
Arlington Medical Institute Post-Sec.
1001 NE Green Oaks Ste 190 76006 817-265-0706
B.H. Carroll Theological Institute Post-Sec.
301 S Center St Ste 100 76010 817-274-4284
Brightwood College Post-Sec.
2241 S Watson Rd Bldg 200 76010 972-623-4700
Burton Adventist Academy 300/PK-12
4611 Kelly Elliott Rd 76017 817-572-0081
Concorde Career Institute Post-Sec.
600 E Lamar Blvd Ste 200 76011 817-261-1594
Everest College Post-Sec.
300 Six Flags Dr Ste 100 76011 817-652-7790
Grace Preparatory Academy 400/K-12
PO Box 170958 76003 817-557-3399
Northstar S 100/7-12
4620 Park Springs Blvd 76017 817-478-5825
Lisa Odom, dir.
Oakridge S 900/PK-12
5900 W Pioneer Pkwy 76013 817-451-4994
Jon Kellam, hdmstr. Fax 457-6681
Ogle School of Hair Design Post-Sec.
2200 W Park Row Dr Ste 106 76013 888-820-4224
Pantego Christian Academy 800/PK-12
2201 W Park Row Dr 76013 817-460-3315
Dr. Jeffrey Potts, pres. Fax 459-4687
St. Paul's Preparatory Academy 200/PK-12
6900 US 287 Hwy 76001 817-561-3500
Gayla Rockwell, prin. Fax 561-3408
Tarrant County College Post-Sec.
2100 Southeast Pkwy 76018 817-515-8223
Texas Center for Massage Therapy Post-Sec.
808 W Interstate 20 Ste 100 76017 682-999-3150
Triumph Leadership Academy 76014 200/K-12
Shawn King, prin. 817-394-3100
Fax 394-3101

University of Texas Post-Sec.
701 S Nedderman Dr 76019 817-272-2011

Arp, Smith, Pop. 957
Arp ISD 900/PK-12
PO Box 70 75750 903-859-8482
Dwight Thomas, supt. Fax 859-2621
home.arpisd.org
Arp HS 300/9-12
PO Box 70 75750 903-859-4917
Shannon Arrington, prin. Fax 859-1541
Arp JHS 200/6-8
PO Box 70 75750 903-859-4936
Bryan Hurst, prin. Fax 859-3980

Aspermont, Stonewall, Pop. 909
Aspermont ISD 200/PK-12
PO Box 549 79502 940-989-3355
Tim Bartram, supt. Fax 989-3353
www.aspermontisd.com
Aspermont JSHS 100/6-12
PO Box 549 79502 940-989-2707
Zach Morris, prin. Fax 989-3486

Atascosa, Bexar
Southwest ISD
Supt. — See San Antonio
McNair MS 1,100/6-8
11553 Old Pearsall Rd 78002 210-622-4480
Joseph Guidry, prin. Fax 622-4481

Athens, Henderson, Pop. 12,562
Athens ISD 3,400/PK-12
104 Hawn St 75751 903-677-6900
Blake Stiles, supt. Fax 677-6908
www.athensisd.net
Athens HS 1,000/9-12
708 E College St 75751 903-677-6920
Jami Ivey, prin. Fax 677-6925
Athens MS 700/6-8
6800 State Highway 19 S 75751 903-677-3030
Ginger Morrison, prin. Fax 677-2111

Trinity Valley Community College Post-Sec.
100 Cardinal St 75751 903-677-8822

Atlanta, Cass, Pop. 5,585
Atlanta ISD 1,800/PK-12
106 W Main St 75551 903-796-4194
Sidney Harrist, supt. Fax 799-1004
www.atlisd.net
Atlanta HS 600/9-12
705 Rabbit Blvd 75551 903-796-4411
Nancy Rinehart, prin. Fax 799-1033
Atlanta MS 500/5-8
600 High School Ln 75551 903-796-7928
Jay Wylie, prin. Fax 799-1021

Aubrey, Denton, Pop. 2,543
Aubrey ISD 1,900/PK-12
415 Tisdell Ln 76227 940-668-0060
Dr. David Belding, supt. Fax 365-2627
www.aubreyisd.net
Aubrey HS 500/9-12
510 Spring Hill Rd 76227 940-668-3900
Dr. Shannon Saylor, prin. Fax 668-3903
Aubrey MS 500/5-8
815 W Sherman Dr 76227 940-668-0200
Karen Wright, prin. Fax 365-3135

Denton ISD
Supt. — See Denton
Braswell HS 9-12
26750 University Dr 76227 972-347-7700
Dr. Lesli Guajardo, prin.
Navo MS 1,000/6-8
1701 Navo Rd 76227 972-347-7500
Dr. Mario Layne, prin. Fax 346-2562

Austin, Travis, Pop. 774,864
Austin ISD 83,600/PK-12
1111 W 6th St 78703 512-414-1700
Dr. Paul Cruz, supt. Fax 414-1707
www.austinisd.org
Akins HS 2,600/9-12
10701 S 1st St 78748 512-841-9900
Brandi Hosack, prin. Fax 841-9903
Alternative Learning Center 100/Alt
901 Neal St 78702 512-414-2554
Carol Chapman, prin. Fax 476-2809
Anderson HS 2,200/9-12
8403 Mesa Dr 78759 512-414-2538
Sammilu Harrison, prin. Fax 338-1293
Austin HS 2,100/9-12
1715 W Cesar Chavez St 78703 512-414-2505
Amy Taylor, prin. Fax 414-7373
Bailey MS 900/6-8
4020 Lost Oasis Holw 78739 512-414-4990
John Rocha, prin. Fax 292-0898
Bedichek MS 1,000/6-8
6800 Bill Hughes Rd 78745 512-414-3265
Michael Herbin, prin. Fax 444-4382
Bowie HS 2,900/9-12
4103 W Slaughter Ln 78749 512-414-5247
Susan Leos, prin. Fax 292-0527
Burnet MS 1,100/6-8
8401 Hathaway Dr 78757 512-414-3225
Gavino Barrera, prin. Fax 452-0695
Covington MS 700/6-8
3700 Convict Hill Rd 78749 512-414-3276
Shannon Sellstrom, prin. Fax 892-4547
Crockett HS 1,600/9-12
5601 Manchaca Rd 78745 512-414-2532
Sissy Camacho, prin. Fax 447-0489
Dobie MS 700/6-8
1200 E Rundberg Ln 78753 512-414-3270
Jesse De La Huerta, prin. Fax 836-8411
Eastside Memorial HS 500/9-12
1012 Arthur Stiles Rd 78721 512-414-5810
Bryan Miller, prin. Fax 841-5935

Fulmore MS 1,000/6-8
201 E Mary St 78704 512-414-3207
Lisa Bush, prin. Fax 441-3129
Garcia Young Men's Leadership Academy 500/6-8
7414 Johnny Morris Rd 78724 512-841-9400
Sterlin McGruder, prin. Fax 841-9401
Garza Independence HS 200/11-12
1600 Chicon St 78702 512-414-8600
Dr. Linda Webb, prin. Fax 414-8610
Gorzycki MS 1,300/6-8
7412 W Slaughter Ln 78749 512-841-8600
Cathryn Mitchell, prin. Fax 841-8601
GPA at Lanier HS 200/Alt
1201 Payton Gin Rd 78758 512-414-2893
Fax 832-1203
GPA at Travis Alt
1211 E Oltorf St 78704 512-414-6635
Fax 707-0050
Henry MS 1,000/6-8
2610 W 10th St 78703 512-414-3229
Karen Aidman, prin. Fax 477-7428
International HS 300/9-10
1012 Arthur Stiles Rd 78721 512-414-6817
Leticia Vega, dir. Fax 841-5621
Johnson Early College HS 800/9-12
7309 Lazy Creek Dr 78724 512-414-2543
Sheila Henry, prin. Fax 929-3955
Kealing MS 1,100/6-8
1607 Pennsylvania Ave 78702 512-414-3214
Kenisha Coburn, prin. Fax 478-9133
Lamar MS 700/6-8
6201 Wynona Ave 78757 512-414-3217
George Llewellyn, prin. Fax 467-6862
Lanier HS 1,600/9-12
1201 Payton Gin Rd 78758 512-414-2514
Ryan Hopkins, prin. Fax 832-1203
Liberal Arts & Science Academy 1,000/9-12
7309 Lazy Creek Dr 78724 512-414-5272
Stacia Crescenzi, dir. Fax 414-6050
Martin MS 600/6-8
1601 Haskell St 78702 512-414-3243
Monica DeLaGarza-Conness, prin. Fax 320-0125
McCallum HS 1,600/9-12
5600 Sunshine Dr 78756 512-414-2519
Michael Garrison, prin. Fax 453-2599
Mendez MS 900/6-8
5106 Village Square Dr 78744 512-414-3284
Kathy Ryan, prin. Fax 442-5738
Murchison MS 1,400/6-8
3700 N Hills Dr 78731 512-414-3254
Rebekah Van Ryn, prin. Fax 343-1710
Paredes MS 1,100/6-8
10100 S Mary Moore Searight 78748 512-841-6800
Valeria Torres-Solis, prin. Fax 841-7036
Reagan HS 1,100/9-12
7104 Berkman Dr 78752 512-414-2523
Anabel Garza, prin. Fax 452-7089
Richards S for Young Women Leaders 700/6-12
2206 Prather Ln 78704 512-414-3236
Jeanne Goka-DuBose, prin. Fax 441-5208
Small MS 1,000/6-8
4801 Monterey Oaks Blvd 78749 512-841-6700
Matthew Nelson, prin. Fax 841-6703
Travis HS 1,400/9-12
1211 E Oltorf St 78704 512-414-2527
Ty Davidson, prin. Fax 707-0050
Webb MS 700/6-8
601 E Saint Johns Ave 78752 512-414-3258
Raul Sanchez, prin. Fax 452-9683

Del Valle ISD
Supt. — See Del Valle
Dailey MS 800/6-8
14000 Westall 78725 512-386-3600
Mario Palacios, prin. Fax 386-3630
Ojeda MS 1,000/6-8
4900 McKinney Falls Pkwy 78744 512-386-3500
Sarah Reuwsaat, prin. Fax 386-3505

Eanes ISD 8,000/PK-12
601 Camp Craft Rd 78746 512-732-9001
Dr. Tom Leonard, supt. Fax 732-9005
www.eanesisd.net
Hill Country MS 1,000/6-8
1300 Walsh Tarlton Ln 78746 512-732-9220
Kathleen Sullivan, prin. Fax 732-9229
Westlake HS 2,600/9-12
4100 Westbank Dr 78746 512-732-9280
Steve Ramsey, prin. Fax 732-9289
West Ridge MS 900/6-8
9201 Scenic Bluff Dr 78733 512-732-9240
Kendall Still, prin. Fax 732-9249
Other Schools – See West Lake Hills

Lake Travis ISD 8,300/PK-12
3322 Ranch Road 620 S 78738 512-533-6000
Brad Lancaster, supt. Fax 533-6001
www.ltisdschools.org/
Hudson Bend MS 900/6-8
15600 Lariat Trl 78734 512-533-6400
Mark Robinson, prin. Fax 533-6401
Lake Travis HS 2,400/9-12
3324 Ranch Road 620 S 78738 512-533-6100
Gordon Butler, prin. Fax 533-6102
Other Schools – See Spicewood

Leander ISD
Supt. — See Leander
Canyon Ridge MS 1,200/6-8
12601 Country Trl 78732 512-570-3500
Susan Sullivan, prin. Fax 570-3505
Four Points MS 600/6-8
9700 McNeil Dr 78750 512-570-3700
Dr. Joe Ciccarelli, prin. Fax 570-3705
Vandegrift HS 1,900/9-12
9500 McNeil Dr 78750 512-570-2300
Charlie Little, prin. Fax 570-2305

Manor ISD
Supt. — See Manor
Decker MS 900/6-8
8104 Decker Ln 78724 512-278-4630
Jon Bailey, prin. Fax 278-4654

Pflugerville ISD
Supt. — See Pflugerville
Connally HS 1,900/9-12
13212 N Lamar Blvd 78753 512-594-0800
Kermit Ward, prin. Fax 594-0805
Dessau MS 800/6-8
12900 Dessau Rd 78754 512-594-2600
Jeremy LeJeune, prin. Fax 594-2605
Westview MS 900/6-8
1805 Scofield Ln 78727 512-594-2200
Amanda Johnson, prin. Fax 594-2205

Round Rock ISD
Supt. — See Round Rock
Canyon Vista MS 1,300/6-8
8455 Spicewood Springs Rd 78759 512-464-8100
Nicole Hagerty, prin. Fax 464-8210
Cedar Valley MS 1,300/6-8
8139 Racine Trl 78717 512-428-2300
Matt Groff, prin. Fax 428-2420
Deerpark MS 900/6-8
8849 Anderson Mill Rd 78729 512-464-6600
Jonathan Smith, prin. Fax 464-6740
Grisham MS 700/6-8
10805 School House Ln 78750 512-428-2650
Kim Winters, prin. Fax 428-2790
McNeil HS 2,500/9-12
5720 McNeil Dr 78729 512-464-6300
Courtney Acosta, prin. Fax 464-6550
Pearson Ranch MS 6-8
8901 Pearson Ranch Rd 78717 512-464-5000
Fax 464-5090
Westwood HS 2,600/9-12
12400 Mellow Meadow Dr 78750 512-464-4000
Mario Acosta, prin. Fax 464-4020

ACE Academy 200/PK-12
3901 Shoal Creek Blvd 78756 512-206-4070
AESA Prep Academy 100/2-12
14101 Canonade 78737 512-774-4822
A New Beginning School of Massage Post-Sec.
2525 Wallingwood Dr # 1501 78746 512-306-0975
AOMA Graduate School of Integrative Med Post-Sec.
4701 W Gate Blvd 78745 512-454-1188
ATA College Prep 50/6-12
6800 Spanish Oaks Club Blvd 78738 512-276-2271
Carol Hagar, head sch Fax 276-2272
Austin Community College Post-Sec.
5930 Middle Fiskville Rd 78752 512-223-7000
Austin Graduate School of Theology Post-Sec.
7640 Guadalupe St 78752 512-476-2772
Austin Montessori S - Gaines Creek Cmps 50/7-9
5006 Sunset Trl 78745 512-892-0826
Austin Peace Academy 200/PK-12
5110 Manor Rd 78723 512-926-1737
Diana Abdi, prin. Fax 926-9688
Austin Presbyterian Theological Seminary Post-Sec.
100 E 27th St 78705 512-404-4800
Austin Waldorf S 400/K-12
8700 South View Rd 78737 512-288-5942
Baldwin Beauty School - North Post-Sec.
8440 Burnet Rd 78757 512-458-4127
Baldwin Beauty School - South Post-Sec.
3005 S Lamar Blvd Ste 103 78704 512-441-6898
Brentwood Christian S 700/PK-12
11908 N Lamar Blvd 78753 512-835-5983
Jay Burcham, pres. Fax 835-2184
Capitol City Careers Post-Sec.
5424 W Highway 290 Ste 200 78735 512-892-2640
Capitol City Trade and Technical School Post-Sec.
205 E Riverside Dr 78704 512-444-3257
Career Point College Post-Sec.
9001 N Interstate 35 78753 210-265-6530
Concordia University Texas Post-Sec.
11400 Concordia Univ Dr 78726 512-313-3000
DeVry University Post-Sec.
11044 Research Blvd # B100 78759 512-231-2500
Escoffier School of Culinary Arts Post-Sec.
6020 Dillard Cir Ste B 78752 512-451-5743
Everest Institute Post-Sec.
9100 E Highway 290 # 100 78724 512-928-1933
Headwaters S 200/PK-12
801 Rio Grande St 78701 512-480-8142
Ted Graf, head sch Fax 480-0278
Hill Country Christian S of Austin 500/PK-12
12124 Ranch Road 620 N 78750 512-331-7036
Tim Hillen, hdmstr. Fax 257-4190
Huntington-Surrey S 50/8-12
5206 Balcones Dr 78731 512-478-4743
Huston-Tillotson University Post-Sec.
900 Chicon St 78702 512-505-3000
Hyde Park HS - Quarries Campus 200/9-12
PO Box 4486 78765 512-465-8333
Kirby Hall S 200/PK-12
306 W 29th St 78705 512-474-1770
Kussad Institute of Court Reporting Post-Sec.
2800 S Interstate 35 # 110 78704 512-443-7286
Le Cordon Bleu College of Culinary Arts Post-Sec.
3110 Esperanza Xing Ste 100 78758 512-837-2665
Mediatech Institute Post-Sec.
4719 S Congress Ave 78745 512-447-2002
Rawson Saunders School 100/1-12
2614 A Exposition Blvd 78703 512-476-8382
Laura Steinbach M.Ed., head sch Fax 476-1132
Regents S of Austin 900/K-12
3230 Travis Country Cir 78735 512-899-8095
Rod Gilbert, head sch Fax 899-8623
Renaissance Academy 200/PK-12
14401 Owen-Tech Blvd 78728 512-252-2277
St. Andrew's Episcopal S 300/9-12
5901 Southwest Pkwy 78735 512-299-9700
Sean Murphy, head sch Fax 299-9660
St. Domic Savio Catholic HS 300/9-12
9300 Neenah Ave 78717 512-388-8846
Morgan Daniels, prin. Fax 388-1335
St. Edward's University Post-Sec.
3001 S Congress Ave 78704 512-448-8400
St. Michael's Catholic Academy 400/9-12
3000 Barton Creek Blvd 78735 512-328-2323
Dr. Dawn Nichols, head sch Fax 328-2327
St. Stephen's Episcopal S 700/6-12
6500 Saint Stephens Dr 78746 512-327-1213
Chris Gunnin, head sch Fax 327-6771
San Juan Diego Catholic HS 100/8-12
800 Herndon Ln 78704 512-804-1935
Berenice Anderson, prin. Fax 804-1937
Seminary of the Southwest Post-Sec.
PO Box 2247 78768 512-472-4133
Southern Careers Institute Post-Sec.
2301 S Congress Ave Ste 27 78704 512-448-4795
Texas Health and Science University Post-Sec.
4005 Manchaca Rd 78704 512-444-8082
The College of Health Care Professions Post-Sec.
6505 Airport Blvd Ste 102 78752 512-892-2835
University of Texas at Austin Post-Sec.
1 University Sta 78712 512-471-3434
Veritas Academy 500/PK-12
PO Box 90517 78709 512-891-1673
Virginia College Austin Post-Sec.
6301 E Highway 290 78723 512-371-3500

Avalon, Ellis
Avalon ISD 300/PK-12
PO Box 455 76623 972-627-3251
Dr. David Del Bosque, supt. Fax 627-3220
www.avalonisd.net
Avalon S 300/PK-12
PO Box 455 76623 972-627-3251
Khristopher Marshall, prin. Fax 627-3220

Avery, Red River, Pop. 482
Avery ISD 300/PK-12
150 San Antonio St 75554 903-684-3460
Kelly Burns, supt. Fax 684-3294
www.averyisd.net/
Avery HS 100/9-12
150 San Antonio St 75554 903-684-3431
Daniel Pritchett, prin. Fax 684-3294
Avery MS 100/6-8
150 San Antonio St 75554 903-684-3079
Daniel Pritchett, prin. Fax 684-3294

Avinger, Cass, Pop. 437
Avinger ISD 200/PK-12
245 Conner 75630 903-562-1355
Jacquelyn Smith, supt. Fax 562-1271
www.avingerisd.net/
Avinger S 200/PK-12
245 Conner 75630 903-562-1355
Terry Giddens, prin. Fax 562-1271

Avoca, Jones
Lueders-Avoca ISD
Supt. — See Lueders
Lueders-Avoca HS 50/9-12
8762 County Road 604 79503 325-773-2785
Bob Spikes, supt. Fax 773-3072

Axtell, McLennan
Axtell ISD 700/PK-12
308 Ottawa 76624 254-863-5301
Dr. J.R. Proctor, supt. Fax 863-5651
www.axtellisd.net
Axtell HS 200/9-12
308 Ottawa 76624 254-863-5301
Dale Monsey, prin. Fax 863-5651
Axtell MS 200/6-8
308 Ottawa 76624 254-863-5301
Dale Monsey, prin. Fax 863-5651

Azle, Tarrant, Pop. 10,777
Azle ISD 5,900/PK-12
300 Roe St 76020 817-444-3235
Ray Lea, supt. Fax 444-6866
www.azleisd.net
Azle HS 1,700/9-12
1200 Boyd Rd 76020 817-444-5555
Randy Cobb, prin. Fax 444-8884
Azle JHS 500/7-8
201 School St 76020 817-444-2564
Brian Roberts, prin. Fax 270-0880
Forte JHS 400/7-8
479 Sandy Beach Rd 76020 817-270-1133
Dianne Boone, prin. Fax 270-1157

Azle Christian S 100/PK-12
1801 S Stewart St 76020 817-444-9964
Shery Rushing, admin. Fax 444-9914

Baird, Callahan, Pop. 1,483
Baird ISD 300/PK-12
PO Box 1147 79504 325-854-1400
Jarod Bellar, supt. Fax 854-2058
www.bairdisd.net
Baird HS 100/9-12
PO Box 1147 79504 325-854-1400
Perry Simmons, prin. Fax 854-2808
Baird JHS 100/6-8
PO Box 1147 79504 325-854-1400
Cynthia Bessent, prin. Fax 854-2808

Balch Springs, Dallas, Pop. 23,383
Dallas ISD
Supt. — See Dallas
Young Womens STEAM Academy 1,400/6-8
710 Cheyenne Rd 75180 972-892-5800
Christie Samuel, prin.

Ballinger, Runnels, Pop. 3,731
Ballinger ISD 1,000/PK-12
PO Box 231 76821 325-365-3588
Jeff Butts, admin. Fax 365-5920
www.ballingerisd.net
Ballinger HS 300/9-12
PO Box 231 76821 325-365-3547
Robert Webb, prin. Fax 365-5422
Ballinger JHS 200/6-8
PO Box 231 76821 325-365-3537
Stacy Tucker, prin. Fax 365-5420

Balmorhea, Reeves, Pop. 479
Balmorhea ISD 200/PK-12
PO Box 368 79718 432-375-2223
Manuel Espino, supt. Fax 375-2511
www.bisdbears.esc18.net
Balmorhea S 200/PK-12
PO Box 368 79718 432-375-2223
Teri Barragan, prin. Fax 375-2511

Bandera, Bandera, Pop. 852
Bandera ISD 2,400/PK-12
PO Box 727 78003 830-796-3313
Regina Howell, supt. Fax 796-6238
www.banderaisd.net
Bandera HS 700/9-12
PO Box 727 78003 830-796-6254
Sergio Menchaca, prin. Fax 796-6251
Bandera MS 500/6-8
PO Box 727 78003 830-796-6270
Donald Tosh, prin. Fax 796-6277

Bangs, Brown, Pop. 1,570
Bangs ISD 1,100/PK-12
PO Box 969 76823 325-752-6612
Tony Truelove, supt. Fax 752-6253
www.bangsisd.net
Bangs HS 300/9-12
PO Box 969 76823 325-752-6822
Randy Lancaster, prin. Fax 752-7028
Bangs MS 300/5-8
PO Box 969 76823 325-752-6088
Scott Patrick, prin. Fax 752-6253

Banquete, Nueces, Pop. 721
Banquete ISD 900/PK-12
PO Box 369 78339 361-387-2551
Dr. Max Thompson, supt. Fax 387-7188
www.banqueteisd.esc2.net/
Banquete HS 300/9-12
PO Box 369 78339 361-387-8588
Nancy Mooney, prin. Fax 767-6504
Banquete JHS 200/6-8
PO Box 369 78339 361-387-6504
Ramiro Pena, prin. Fax 387-7051

Barksdale, Edwards
Nueces Canyon Consolidated ISD 300/K-12
PO Box 118 78828 830-234-3514
Kristi Powers, supt. Fax 234-3435
www.nccisd.net/
Nueces Canyon JSHS 100/7-12
PO Box 118 78828 830-234-3524
Luci Harmon, prin. Fax 234-4129

Bartlett, Bell, Pop. 1,605
Bartlett ISD 400/PK-12
PO Box 170 76511 254-527-4247
Travis Edwards, supt. Fax 527-3340
www.bartlett.txed.net
Bartlett S 400/PK-12
PO Box 170 76511 254-527-4247
Angie Peace, prin. Fax 527-3340

Bastrop, Bastrop, Pop. 7,084
Bastrop ISD 9,600/PK-12
906 Farm St 78602 512-772-7100
Steve Murray, supt. Fax 321-7469
www.bisdtx.org/
Bastrop HS 1,200/9-12
1614 Chambers St 78602 512-772-7200
Bradley Brown, prin. Fax 321-7502
Bastrop MS 700/7-8
725 Old Austin Hwy 78602 512-772-7400
Dr. Christopher Julian, prin. Fax 321-1557
Colorado River Collegiate Academy 9-12
1602 Hill St 78602 512-772-7230
Martin Conrardy, prin.
Gateway Alternative S 50/Alt
1019 Lovers Ln 78602 512-772-7820
Patricia Alford, prin. Fax 332-0498
Genesis HS 100/Alt
1602 Hill St 78602 512-772-7230
Martin Conrardy, prin. Fax 321-3212
Other Schools – See Cedar Creek

Bay City, Matagorda, Pop. 17,441
Bay City ISD 3,600/PK-12
PO Box 2510 77404 979-245-5766
Keith Brown, supt. Fax 245-3175
www.bcblackcats.net
Bay City HS 1,000/9-12
400 7th St 77414 979-245-5771
Chris Townsend, prin. Fax 245-1220
Bay City JHS 800/6-8
1507 Sycamore Ave 77414 979-245-6345
Dr. Keely Coufal, prin. Fax 245-1419

Baytown, Harris, Pop. 70,920
Barbers Hill ISD
Supt. — See Mont Belvieu
Barbers Hill MS South 6-8
9600 Eagle Dr, 281-576-2221
Dennis Wagner, prin. Fax 576-3350
Goose Creek Consolidated ISD 22,200/PK-12
PO Box 30 77522 281-420-4800
Randal O'Brien, supt. Fax 420-4815
www.gccisd.net
Baytown JHS 800/6-8
7707 Bayway Dr 77520 281-420-4560
Matthew Bolinger, prin. Fax 420-4908
Cedar Bayou JHS 1,000/6-8
2610 Elvinta St 77520 281-420-4570
Michael Curl, prin. Fax 420-4569
Gentry JHS 1,000/6-8
1919 E Archer Rd 77521 281-420-4590
Murrell Stewart, prin. Fax 420-4909
Goose Creek Memorial HS 1,800/9-12
6001 E Wallisville Rd 77521 281-421-4400
Susan Jackson, prin. Fax 421-4444
Hyland Center 200/Alt
1906 Decker Dr 77520 281-420-4555
Michelle Verdun, prin. Fax 420-4558
Impact Early College HS 400/9-12
200 Lee Dr 77520 281-420-4802
Laura Reyes, prin. Fax 556-5781
Lee HS 1,400/9-12
1809 Market St 77520 281-420-4535
Joseph Farnsworth, prin. Fax 420-4548
Mann JHS 1,000/6-8
310 S Highway 146 77520 281-420-4585
Erica Tran, prin. Fax 420-4664
Sterling HS 2,300/9-12
300 W Baker Rd 77521 281-420-4500
Nathan Chaddick, prin. Fax 420-4974
Stuart Career Center Vo/Tech
300 YMCA Dr 77521 281-420-4550
Renea Dillon, dir. Fax 420-4553
Other Schools – See Highlands

Baytown Christian Academy 200/PK-12
5555 N Main St 77521 281-421-4150
Lee College Post-Sec.
PO Box 818 77522 281-427-5611

Beaumont, Jefferson, Pop. 116,638
Beaumont ISD 19,400/PK-12
3395 Harrison Ave 77706 409-617-5000
Dr. John Frossard, supt. Fax 617-5184
www.bmtisd.com
Austin Innovation Center 100/9-12
3410 Austin St 77706 409-617-6600
Kristi Fuselier, prin.
Beaumont Early College HS 9-12
3410 Austin St 77706 409-617-6600
Kristi Fuselier, prin. Fax 617-6624
Brown Center 100/Alt
3410 Austin St 77706 409-617-5720
Wayne Wells, prin. Fax 617-5738
Central HS 1,700/9-12
88 Jaguar Dr 77702 409-617-5300
Ronald Jackson, prin. Fax 617-5396
King MS 300/6-8
1400 Avenue A 77701 409-617-5850
Dion Varnado, prin. Fax 617-5873
Marshall MS 800/6-8
6455 Gladys Ave 77706 409-617-5900
Brandon Basinger, prin. Fax 617-5924
Odom Academy 800/6-8
2550 W Virginia St 77705 409-617-5925
Tillie Hickman, prin. Fax 617-5949
Ozen HS 1,100/9-12
3443 Fannett Rd 77705 409-617-5400
Donna Prudomme, prin. Fax 617-5496
Pathways Learning Center 100/Alt
3410 Austin St 77706 409-617-5700
Wayne Wells, prin. Fax 617-5718
Smith MS 600/6-8
4415 Concord Rd 77703 409-617-5825
Lachandra Cobb, prin. Fax 617-5848
South Park MS 400/6-8
4500 Highland Ave 77705 409-617-5875
Calvin Rice, prin. Fax 617-5899
Taylor Career Center Vo/Tech
2330 North St 77702 409-617-5740
Michael Shelton, prin. Fax 617-5759
Vincent MS 700/6-8
350 Eldridge Dr 77707 409-617-5950
Lydia Bahnsen, prin. Fax 617-5974
West Brook HS 2,400/9-12
8750 Phelan Blvd 77706 409-617-5500
Diana Valdez, prin. Fax 617-5582

Hamshire-Fannett ISD
Supt. — See Hamshire
Hamshire-Fannett MS 300/7-8
11375 Dugat Rd 77705 409-794-2361
Shawn Clubb, prin. Fax 794-3042

Baptist Hospital of Southeast Texas Post-Sec.
3030 Fannin St Ste A 77701 409-212-5724
Brightwood College Post-Sec.
6115 Eastex Fwy 77706 409-347-5900
Lamar Institute of Technology Post-Sec.
PO Box 10043 77710 409-880-8321
Lamar University Post-Sec.
PO Box 10009 77710 409-880-7011
Legacy Christian Academy 300/PK-12
8200 Highway 105 77713 409-924-0500
Jon Cregor, dir. Fax 924-0953
Monsignor Kelly Catholic HS 400/9-12
5950 Kelly Dr 77707 409-866-2351
Roger Bemis, prin. Fax 866-0917
St. Elizabeth Hospital Post-Sec.
2830 Calder St 77702 409-892-7171
Vista College Post-Sec.
3871 Stagg Dr Ste 194 77701 409-291-4900

Beckville, Panola, Pop. 830
Beckville ISD 700/PK-12
PO Box 37 75631 903-678-3311
Devin Tate, supt. Fax 678-2157
www.beckvilleisd.net/
Beckville HS 200/9-12
PO Box 37 75631 903-678-3591
Phillip Works, prin. Fax 678-3645
Beckville JHS 200/6-8
PO Box 37 75631 903-678-3851
Loretta Blair, prin. Fax 678-3827

Bedford, Tarrant, Pop. 45,838
Hurst-Euless-Bedford ISD 22,100/PK-12
1849 Central Dr Ste A 76022 817-283-4461
Steven Chapman, supt. Fax 354-3311
www.hebisd.edu
Bedford JHS 800/7-9
325 Carolyn Dr 76021 817-788-3101
Michael Martinak, prin. Fax 788-3105
Buinger Career & Technical Education Acd Vo/Tech
1849E Central Dr 76022 817-354-3542
Lisa Karr, prin. Fax 354-3546
Harwood JHS 1,000/7-9
3000 Martin Dr 76021 817-354-3360
Dr. Toby Givens, prin. Fax 354-3369
Other Schools – See Euless, Hurst

Beeville, Bee, Pop. 12,739
Beeville ISD 3,400/PK-12
201 N Saint Marys St 78102 361-358-7111
Dr. Marc Puig, supt. Fax 362-6046
www.beevilleisd.net
Jones HS 1,000/9-12
1902 N Adams St 78102 361-362-6000
DeeDee Bernal, prin. Fax 362-6016
Moreno MS 600/7-8
301 N Minnesota St 78102 361-358-6262
Joni Barber, prin. Fax 362-6092

Coastal Bend College Post-Sec.
3800 Charco Rd 78102 361-358-2838

Bellaire, Harris, Pop. 16,508
Houston ISD
Supt. — See Houston
Bellaire HS 3,600/9-12
5100 Maple St 77401 713-295-3704
Michael McDonough, prin. Fax 295-3763
Pin Oak MS 1,200/6-8
4601 Glenmont St 77401 713-295-6500
Rita Graves, prin. Fax 295-6511

Episcopal HS 700/9-12
4650 Bissonnet St 77401 713-512-3400
Ned Smith, head sch Fax 512-3603
Post Oak S 400/PK-12
4600 Bissonnet St 77401 713-661-6688
Maura Joyce, head sch Fax 661-4959

Bellevue, Clay, Pop. 360
Bellevue ISD 100/K-12
PO Box 38 76228 940-928-2104
Dean Gilstrap, supt. Fax 928-2583
www.bellevueisd.org/
Bellevue S 100/K-12
PO Box 38 76228 940-928-2104
Michael Qualls, prin. Fax 928-2583

Bells, Grayson, Pop. 1,356
Bells ISD 800/PK-12
1550 Ole Ambrose Rd 75414 903-965-7721
Joe Moore, supt. Fax 965-7036
bellsisd.net/
Bells HS 200/9-12
1500 Ole Ambrose Rd 75414 903-965-7315
Josh Weger, prin. Fax 965-5205
Prichard JHS 200/6-8
1510 Ole Ambrose Rd 75414 903-965-4835
Will Steger, prin. Fax 965-7428

Bellville, Austin, Pop. 4,068
Bellville ISD 2,100/PK-12
518 S Mathews St 77418 979-865-3133
Mike Coker, supt. Fax 865-8591
www.bellvilleisd.org
Bellville HS 600/9-12
518 S Mathews St 77418 979-865-3681
Dr. Michael Coopersmith, prin. Fax 865-7080
Bellville JHS 500/6-8
518 S Mathews St 77418 979-865-5966
Natalie Jones, prin. Fax 865-7060
Spicer Alternative Education Center Alt
518 S Mathews St 77418 979-865-7095
Sean McEnerney, coord. Fax 865-7094

Faith Academy 200/PK-12
12177 Highway 36 77418 979-865-1811
Merlene Byler, head sch Fax 865-2454

Belton, Bell, Pop. 17,870
Belton ISD 8,700/PK-12
PO Box 269 76513 254-215-2000
Dr. Susan Kincannon, supt. Fax 215-2001
www.bisd.net
Belton HS 2,600/9-12
600 Lake Rd 76513 254-215-2200
Chris DuBois, prin. Fax 215-2201
Belton New Tech HS @ Waskow 300/9-12
320 N Blair St 76513 254-215-2500
Jill Ross, prin. Fax 215-2501
South Belton MS 800/6-8
805 Sage Brush 76513 254-215-3000
Keonna White, prin. Fax 215-3001
Other Schools – See Temple

Providence Preparatory S 200/PK-12
506 N Main St 76513 254-307-1165

University of Mary Hardin-Baylor — Post-Sec.
900 College St 76513 — 254-295-8642

Benavides, Duval, Pop. 1,353
Benavides ISD — 400/PK-12
PO Box P 78341 — 361-256-3003
Adell Cueva, supt. — Fax 256-3002
www.benavidesisd.net
Benavides JSHS — 200/7-12
PO Box P 78341 — 361-256-3040
Marco Ramirez, prin. — Fax 256-3043

Ben Bolt, Jim Wells
Ben Bolt-Palito Blanco ISD — 600/PK-12
PO Box 547 78342 — 361-664-9904
Dr. Timothy Little, supt. — Fax 668-0446
www.bbpbschools.net
Ben Bolt MS — 200/4-8
PO Box 547 78342 — 361-664-9568
Fernando Galvan, prin. — Fax 664-5235
Ben Bolt-Palito Blanco HS — 200/9-12
PO Box 547 78342 — 361-664-9822
Terry Young, prin. — Fax 664-5481

Benbrook, Tarrant, Pop. 20,889
Fort Worth ISD
Supt. — See Fort Worth
Benbrook JSHS — 700/6-12
201 Overcrest Dr 76126 — 817-815-7100
Richard Penland, prin. — Fax 815-7150
Leonard MS — 800/6-8
8900 Chapin Rd 76116 — 817-815-6200
Cathy Williams-Ridley, prin. — Fax 815-6250
Western Hills HS — 1,400/9-12
3600 Boston Ave 76116 — 817-815-6000
James Wellman, prin. — Fax 815-6050

Benjamin, Knox, Pop. 256
Benjamin ISD — 100/K-12
PO Box 166 79505 — 940-459-2231
Olivia Gloria, supt. — Fax 459-2007
www.benjaminisd.net/
Benjamin S — 100/K-12
PO Box 166 79505 — 940-459-2231
Olivia Gloria, prin. — Fax 459-2007

Ben Wheeler, Van Zandt
Martins Mill ISD — 500/PK-12
301 FM 1861 75754 — 903-479-3872
James Oliver, supt. — Fax 479-3711
www.martinsmillisd.net
Martins Mill HS — 200/7-12
301 FM 1861 75754 — 903-479-3234
Don Layton, prin. — Fax 479-3486

Big Lake, Reagan, Pop. 2,917
Reagan County ISD — 900/PK-12
1111 E 12th St 76932 — 325-884-3705
Steve Long, supt. — Fax 884-3021
www.rcisd.net
Reagan County HS — 300/9-12
1111 E 12th St 76932 — 325-884-3714
Kara Garlitz, prin. — Fax 884-5759
Reagan County MS — 200/6-8
500 N Pennsylvania Ave 76932 — 325-884-3728
David Kohutek, prin. — Fax 884-2327

Big Sandy, Upshur, Pop. 1,325
Big Sandy ISD — 700/PK-12
PO Box 598 75755 — 903-636-5287
Jay Ratcliff, supt. — Fax 636-5111
www.bigsandyisd.org
Big Sandy HS — 200/9-12
PO Box 598 75755 — 903-636-5287
Cindy Bauter, prin. — Fax 636-5111
Big Sandy JHS — 200/6-8
PO Box 598 75755 — 903-636-5287
Lance Morrow, prin. — Fax 636-5111

Harmony ISD — 1,000/PK-12
9788 State Highway 154 W 75755 — 903-725-5492
Dennis Glenn, supt. — Fax 725-6737
www.harmonyisd.net
Harmony HS — 300/9-12
9788 State Highway 154 W 75755 — 903-725-5495
Michael Alphin, prin. — Fax 725-7079
Harmony JHS — 200/6-8
9788 State Highway 154 W 75755 — 903-725-5485
Pamela Beall, prin. — Fax 725-7270

Big Spring, Howard, Pop. 26,933
Big Spring ISD — 3,500/PK-12
708 E 11th Pl 79720 — 432-264-3600
Chris Wigington, supt. — Fax 264-3646
www.bsisd.esc18.net
Big Spring HS — 900/9-12
708 E 11th Pl 79720 — 432-264-3641
Erin White, prin. — Fax 264-4113
Big Spring JHS — 600/7-8
708 E 11th Pl 79720 — 432-264-4135
Rebecca Otto, prin. — Fax 264-4196
D.A.E.P. — Alt
708 E 11th Pl 79720 — 432-264-3641
Bert Otto, prin. — Fax 264-4113

Howard College — Post-Sec.
1001 N Birdwell Ln 79720 — 432-264-5000
Scenic Mountain Medical Center — Post-Sec.
1601 W 11th Pl 79720 — 432-263-1211

Bishop, Nueces, Pop. 3,126
Bishop Consolidated ISD — 1,300/PK-12
719 E 6th St 78343 — 361-584-3591
Dr. Andrea Kuyatt, supt. — Fax 584-3147
www.bishopcisd.net
Bishop HS — 400/9-12
100 Badger Ln 78343 — 361-584-2547
Ray Garza, prin. — Fax 584-2549
Luehrs JHS — 200/7-8
717 E 6th St 78343 — 361-584-3576
Debbie Garcia, prin. — Fax 584-3577

Blackwell, Nolan, Pop. 309
Blackwell Consolidated ISD — 100/PK-12
PO Box 505 79506 — 325-282-2311
Abe Gott, supt. — Fax 282-2027
www.blackwellhornets.org
Blackwell S — 100/PK-12
PO Box 505 79506 — 325-282-2311
Bryan Shipman, prin. — Fax 282-2027

Blanco, Blanco, Pop. 1,722
Blanco ISD — 1,000/PK-12
814 11th St 78606 — 830-833-4414
Dr. Buck Ford, supt. — Fax 833-2019
www.blancoisd.com
Blanco HS — 300/9-12
814 11th St 78606 — 830-833-4337
Keitha St. Clair, prin. — Fax 833-5028
Blanco MS — 200/6-8
814 11th St 78606 — 830-833-5570
Dr. Kathryn Korelich, prin. — Fax 833-2507

Blanket, Brown, Pop. 382
Blanket ISD — 200/K-12
901 Avenue H 76432 — 325-748-5311
David Whisenhunt, supt. — Fax 748-3391
www.blanketisd.net
Blanket HS — 100/9-12
901 Avenue H 76432 — 325-748-5311
Kay Ribble, prin. — Fax 748-2110

Bloomburg, Cass, Pop. 398
Bloomburg ISD — 300/PK-12
307 W Cypress St 75556 — 903-728-5216
Brian Stroman, supt. — Fax 728-5399
www.bloomburgisd.net
Bloomburg HS — 100/6-12
307 W Cypress St 75556 — 903-728-5216
Andrew Rankin, prin. — Fax 728-5399

Blooming Grove, Navarro, Pop. 812
Blooming Grove ISD — 900/PK-12
PO Box 258 76626 — 903-695-2541
Marshall Harrison, supt. — Fax 695-2594
www.bgisd.org
Blooming Grove HS — 300/9-12
PO Box 258 76626 — 903-695-2541
Jack Lee, prin. — Fax 695-2594
Blooming Grove JHS — 200/6-8
PO Box 258 76626 — 903-695-4201
Doyle Bell, prin. — Fax 695-4601

Bloomington, Victoria, Pop. 2,445
Bloomington ISD
Supt. — See Victoria
Bloomington HS — 200/9-12
PO Box 158 77951 — 361-333-8011
Lina Moore, prin. — Fax 333-8015
Bloomington MS — 200/6-8
PO Box 158 77951 — 361-333-8008
Abbie Barnett, prin. — Fax 333-8010

Blue Ridge, Collin, Pop. 807
Blue Ridge ISD — 700/PK-12
318 School St 75424 — 972-752-5554
John Wink, supt. — Fax 752-9084
brisd.net
Blue Ridge HS — 200/9-12
11020 County Road 504 75424 — 972-752-5554
Anthony Figueroa, prin. — Fax 752-5361
Blue Ridge MS — 200/6-8
710 Tiger Pride Cir 75424 — 972-752-5554
Danny Henderson, prin. — Fax 752-5363

Blum, Hill, Pop. 439
Blum ISD — 400/PK-12
PO Box 520 76627 — 254-874-5231
Jeff Sanders, supt. — Fax 874-5233
www.blumisd.net
Blum JSHS — 200/6-12
PO Box 520 76627 — 254-874-5231
Traci Bellomy, prin. — Fax 874-5233

Boerne, Kendall, Pop. 10,349
Boerne ISD — 6,700/PK-12
123 Johns Rd 78006 — 830-357-2000
David Stelmazewski, supt. — Fax 357-2009
www.boerne-isd.net
Boerne Academy — Alt
210 Live Oak St 78006 — 830-357-2925
Cory Bell, admin. — Fax 357-2919
Boerne HS — 1,000/9-12
1 Greyhound Ln 78006 — 830-357-2200
Natalie Farber, prin. — Fax 357-2299
Boerne MS - North — 500/6-8
240 Johns Rd 78006 — 830-357-3100
Tommy Hungate, prin. — Fax 357-3199
Boerne MS - South — 700/6-8
10 Cascade Caverns Rd 78015 — 830-357-3300
Georgia Franks, prin. — Fax 357-3399
Boerne-Samuel V. Champion HS — 1,400/9-12
201 Charger Blvd 78006 — 830-357-2600
Dr. Jodi Spoor, prin. — Fax 357-2699

Blessed Hope Academy — 100/9-12
28604 Interstate 10 W 78006 — 210-697-9191
Alice Ashcraft, dir. — Fax 755-2339
Geneva S of Boerne — 500/K-12
113 Cascade Caverns Rd 78015 — 830-775-6101
Vanguard Christian Institute — 100/PK-12
43360 Interstate 10 W 78006 — 830-537-5244
Rhonda Tracy, admin. — Fax 537-5785

Bogata, Red River, Pop. 1,141
Rivercrest ISD — 700/PK-12
4100 US Highway 271 S 75417 — 903-632-5205
Stanley Jessee, supt. — Fax 632-4691
www.rivercrestisd.net
Rivercrest HS — 200/9-12
4126 US Highway 271 S 75417 — 903-632-5204
Ronny Alsup, prin. — Fax 632-5231
Rivercrest JHS — 200/6-8
4100 US Highway 271 S 75417 — 903-632-0878
Lee Wilson, prin. — Fax 632-4691

Boling, Wharton, Pop. 1,118
Boling ISD — 1,100/PK-12
PO Box 160 77420 — 979-657-2770
Wade Stidevent, supt. — Fax 657-3265
www.bolingisd.net
Boling HS — 300/9-12
PO Box 119 77420 — 979-657-2816
Keith Jedlicka, prin. — Fax 657-2026
Iago JHS — 300/6-8
PO Box 89 77420 — 979-657-2826
Brett Pohler, prin. — Fax 657-2828

Bonham, Fannin, Pop. 9,979
Bonham ISD — 1,800/PK-12
1005 Chestnut St 75418 — 903-583-5526
Dr. Marvin Beaty, supt. — Fax 583-8463
www.bonhamisd.org/
Bonham HS — 500/9-12
1002 War Path St 75418 — 903-583-5567
Ryan Prock, prin. — Fax 583-5560
Rather JHS — 300/7-8
1201 N Main St 75418 — 903-583-7474
Traci Daniel, prin. — Fax 583-3713

Booker, Lipscomb, Pop. 1,488
Booker ISD — 400/PK-12
PO Box 288 79005 — 806-658-4501
Walter Cox, supt. — Fax 658-4503
www.bookerisd.net/
Booker JSHS — 200/6-12
PO Box 288 79005 — 806-658-4521
Brian Holt, prin. — Fax 658-4503

Borger, Hutchinson, Pop. 13,012
Borger ISD — 2,800/PK-12
200 E 9th St 79007 — 806-273-1000
Chance Welch, supt. — Fax 273-1066
www.borgerisd.net
Borger HS — 800/9-12
600 W 1st St 79007 — 806-273-1029
Matt Ammerman, prin. — Fax 273-1036
Borger MS — 600/6-8
1321 S Florida St 79007 — 806-273-1037
Michael Cano, prin. — Fax 273-1069

Frank Phillips College — Post-Sec.
PO Box 5118 79008 — 806-457-4200

Bovina, Parmer, Pop. 1,863
Bovina ISD — 500/PK-12
PO Box 70 79009 — 806-251-1336
Denise Anderson, supt. — Fax 251-1578
www.bovinaisd.org
Bovina HS — 100/9-12
PO Box 70 79009 — 806-251-1317
Steve Arias, prin. — Fax 251-1002
Bovina MS — 100/6-8
PO Box 70 79009 — 806-251-1336
Mark Barnes, prin. — Fax 251-1578

Bowie, Montague, Pop. 5,161
Bowie ISD — 1,700/PK-12
PO Box 1168 76230 — 940-872-1151
Steven Monkres, supt. — Fax 872-5979
www.bowieisd.net/
Bowie HS — 400/9-12
341 US Highway 287 N Access 76230 — 940-872-1154
Blake Enlow, prin. — Fax 872-1299
Bowie JHS — 400/6-8
501 E Tarrant St 76230 — 940-872-1152
Hector Madrigal, prin. — Fax 872-8921

Gold-Burg ISD — 100/PK-12
468 Prater Rd 76230 — 940-872-3562
Roger Ellis, supt. — Fax 872-5933
www.goldburgisd.net
Gold-Burg S — 100/PK-12
468 Prater Rd 76230 — 940-872-3562
Jay Johnson, prin. — Fax 872-5933

Boyd, Wise, Pop. 1,184
Boyd ISD — 1,200/PK-12
PO Box 92308 76023 — 940-433-2327
Ted West, supt. — Fax 433-9569
www.boydisd.net
Boyd HS — 400/9-12
PO Box 92308 76023 — 940-433-2327
Barbara Stice, prin. — Fax 433-9593
Boyd MS — 200/7-8
PO Box 92308 76023 — 940-433-2327
James McDonald, prin. — Fax 433-9568

Boys Ranch, Oldham, Pop. 281
Boys Ranch ISD — 300/K-12
PO Box 219 79010 — 806-534-2221
Kenneth Brown, supt. — Fax 534-2384
www.boysranchisd.org/
Blakemore MS — 100/6-8
PO Box 219 79010 — 806-534-2361
Brandon Sanders, prin. — Fax 534-0041
Boys Ranch HS — 200/9-12
PO Box 219 79010 — 806-534-0032
Mark Kellogg, prin. — Fax 534-0033
STARR Academy — 50/Alt
PO Box 219 79010 — 806-533-1413
Shelly Allen, prin. — Fax 533-2220

Brackettville, Kinney, Pop. 1,675
Brackett ISD — 600/PK-12
PO Box 586 78832 — 830-563-2491
Kevin Newsom, supt. — Fax 563-9264
www.brackettisd.net/
Brackett HS — 200/9-12
PO Box 586 78832 — 830-563-2480
Daron Worrell, prin. — Fax 563-3213

Brackett JHS 100/6-8
PO Box 586 78832 830-563-2480
Christy Price, prin. Fax 563-9559

Brady, McCulloch, Pop. 5,490
Brady ISD 1,300/PK-12
1003 W 11th St 76825 325-597-2301
Johnny Clawson, supt. Fax 597-3984
www.bradyisd.org
Brady HS 400/9-12
1003 W 11th St 76825 325-597-2491
Russell Baldwin, prin. Fax 597-2147
Brady MS 300/6-8
1003 W 11th St 76825 325-597-8110
Shona Moore, prin. Fax 597-4166

Brazoria, Brazoria, Pop. 2,978
Columbia-Brazoria ISD
Supt. — See West Columbia
West Brazos JHS 500/7-8
111 Roustabout Dr 77422 979-799-1730
Robert McReynolds, prin. Fax 798-8000

Breckenridge, Stephens, Pop. 5,738
Breckenridge ISD 1,500/PK-12
PO Box 1738 76424 254-522-9600
Timothy Seymore, supt. Fax 522-9600
www.breckenridgeisd.org
Breckenridge HS 400/9-12
500 W Lindsey St 76424 254-212-4730
Bryan Dieterich, prin. Fax 212-4730
Breckenridge JHS 200/7-8
502 W Lindsey St 76424 254-212-4311
Michelene Etzel, prin. Fax 212-4311

Bremond, Robertson, Pop. 926
Bremond ISD 400/PK-12
601 W Collins St 76629 254-746-7145
Daryl Stuard, supt. Fax 746-7726
www.bremondisd.net
Bremond HS 100/9-12
601 W Collins St 76629 254-746-7145
Harold Schroeder, prin. Fax 746-7726
Bremond MS 100/6-8
601 W Collins St 76629 254-746-7145
John Burnett, prin. Fax 746-7726

Brenham, Washington, Pop. 15,543
Brenham ISD 4,900/PK-12
PO Box 1147 77834 979-277-3700
Walter Jackson Ed.D., supt. Fax 277-3701
www.brenhamisd.net
Brenham HS 1,400/9-12
525 A H Ehrig Dr 77833 979-277-3800
Joe Chandler, prin. Fax 277-3801
Brenham JHS 800/7-8
1200 Carlee Dr 77833 979-277-3830
Bryan Bryant, prin. Fax 277-3831
PRIDE Academy 50/Alt
1301 S Market St 77833 979-277-3890
Allan Colvin, prin. Fax 277-3891

Blinn College Post-Sec.
902 College Ave 77833 979-830-4000
Brenham Christian Academy 50/PK-12
2111 S Blue Bell Rd 77833 979-830-8480
Dr. Charles Loyd, head sch Fax 830-1687

Bridge City, Orange, Pop. 7,734
Bridge City ISD 2,800/PK-12
1031 W Round Bunch Rd 77611 409-735-1500
Todd Lintzen, supt. Fax 735-1512
www.bridgecityisd.net
Bridge City HS 800/9-12
2690 Texas Ave 77611 409-735-1501
Elisha Bell, prin. Fax 735-1519
Bridge City MS 600/6-8
300 Bower Dr 77611 409-735-1513
Lydia Gonzales, prin. Fax 735-1517

Bridgeport, Wise, Pop. 5,936
Bridgeport ISD 2,100/PK-12
2107 15th St 76426 940-683-5124
Eddie Bland, supt. Fax 683-4268
www.bridgeportisd.net
Alternative Learning Center Alt
1101 17th St 76426 940-683-1830
Karl Little, prin. Fax 683-3582
Bridgeport HS 600/9-12
1 Maroon Dr 76426 940-683-4064
Jaime Sturdivant, prin. Fax 683-4014
Bridgeport MS 500/6-8
702 17th St 76426 940-683-2273
Travis Whisenant, prin. Fax 683-5812

Briscoe, Wheeler
Fort Elliott Consolidated ISD 100/PK-12
PO Box 138 79011 806-375-2454
Brad Slatton, supt. Fax 375-2327
www.fecisd.net
Ft. Elliott JSHS 100/6-12
PO Box 138 79011 806-375-2454
Benny Barnett, prin. Fax 375-2327

Broaddus, San Augustine, Pop. 202
Broaddus ISD 400/PK-12
PO Box 58 75929 936-872-3041
Shane McGown, supt. Fax 872-3699
www.broaddusisd.net
Broaddus JSHS 200/6-12
PO Box 58 75929 936-872-3610
Brad Hranicky, prin. Fax 872-9020

Brock, Parker
Brock ISD 1,000/K-12
410 Eagle Spirit Ln 76087 817-594-7642
Scott Drillette, supt. Fax 599-3246
www.brockisd.net
Brock HS 300/9-12
400 Eagle Spirit Ln 76087 817-596-7425
Rick Howell, prin. Fax 594-2509
Brock MS 200/5-8
300 Grindstone Rd 76087 817-594-3195
Ingia Saxton, prin. Fax 594-3191

Bronte, Coke, Pop. 986
Bronte ISD 300/PK-12
PO Box 670 76933 325-473-2511
Tim Siler, supt. Fax 473-2313
www.bronteisd.net
Bronte JSHS 100/7-12
PO Box 670 76933 325-473-2521
Josh Barton, prin. Fax 473-2022

Brookeland, Sabine
Brookeland ISD 400/PK-12
187 Wildcat Walk 75931 409-698-2677
Kevin McCugh, supt. Fax 698-2533
www.brookelandisd.net
Brookeland JSHS 200/6-12
187 Wildcat Walk 75931 409-698-2413
Charlotte Odom, prin. Fax 698-2891

Brookesmith, Brown
Brookesmith ISD 200/PK-12
PO Box 706 76827 325-643-3023
Guy Birdwell, supt. Fax 643-3378
www.brookesmithisd.net/
Brookesmith S 200/PK-12
PO Box 706 76827 325-643-3023
Guy Birdwell, supt. Fax 643-3378

Brookshire, Waller, Pop. 4,653
Royal ISD
Supt. — See Pattison
Royal HS 500/9-12
34499 Royal Rd 77423 281-934-2215
Dr. Ostrova McGary, prin. Fax 934-2866
Royal JHS 400/6-8
2520 Durkin Rd 77423 281-934-2241
Justin Johnston, prin. Fax 934-2329
Royal STEM Academy 200/3-8
2500 Durkin Rd 77423 281-934-3181
K.T. Trimbur-Glenn, admin. Fax 934-3186

Brownfield, Terry, Pop. 9,594
Brownfield ISD 1,800/PK-12
601 E Tahoka Rd 79316 806-637-2591
Tanya Monroe, supt. Fax 637-9208
www.brownfieldisd.net
Brownfield Education Center 50/Alt
321 School Dr 79316 905-555-3533
Chris Edwards, prin. Fax 555-7836
Brownfield HS 400/9-12
701 Cub Dr 79316 806-637-4523
Paul Coronado, prin. Fax 637-3801
Brownfield MS 400/6-8
1001 E Broadway St 79316 806-637-7521
Jerry Estrada, prin. Fax 637-2919

Brownsboro, Henderson, Pop. 1,031
Brownsboro ISD 2,800/PK-12
PO Box 465 75756 903-852-3701
Tommy Hunter, supt. Fax 852-3957
www.gobearsgo.net
Brownsboro HS 800/9-12
PO Box 465 75756 903-852-2321
Brandon Jones, prin. Fax 852-5195
Brownsboro JHS 400/7-8
PO Box 465 75756 903-852-6931
Bradley Robertson, prin. Fax 852-5238

Brownsville, Cameron, Pop. 174,679
Brownsville ISD 49,100/PK-12
1900 Price Rd 78521 956-548-8000
Dr. Esperanza Zendejas, supt. Fax 548-8010
www.bisd.us
Besteiro MS 900/6-8
6280 Southmost Rd 78521 956-544-3900
Kathleen Jimenez, prin. Fax 544-3946
Brownsville Academic Center Alt
3308 Robindale Rd 78526 956-504-6305
Felipe Reyes, prin. Fax 831-8267
Brownsville Early College HS 300/9-12
343 Ringgold Rd 78520 956-698-1476
Acacia Ameel, prin. Fax 548-8842
Brownsville Learning Academy Alt
4350 Morrison Rd 78526 956-982-2860
Dawn Hall, prin. Fax 982-3028
Cummings MS 700/6-8
1800 Cummings Pl 78520 956-548-8630
Teresa Nunez, prin. Fax 548-8218
Faulk MS 900/6-8
2000 Roosevelt St 78521 956-548-8500
Benita Villarreal, prin. Fax 548-8507
Garcia MS 1,100/6-8
5701 FM 802 78526 956-832-6300
Noe Garcia, prin. Fax 832-6304
Hanna HS 2,700/9-12
2615 E Price Rd 78521 956-548-7600
Dr. Norma Ibarra-Cantu, prin. Fax 548-7603
Lopez HS 2,100/9-12
3205 S Dakota Ave 78521 956-982-7400
Dahlia Aguilar, prin. Fax 982-7499
Lucio MS 1,100/6-8
300 N Vermillion Ave 78521 956-831-4550
Mary Solis, prin. Fax 838-2298
Manzano MS 900/6-8
2580 W Alton Gloor Blvd 78520 956-548-9800
Marisol Trevino, prin. Fax 548-6772
Oliveira MS 1,200/6-8
444 Land O Lakes Dr 78521 956-548-8530
Cynthia Castro, prin. Fax 544-3968
Pace HS 1,900/9-12
314 W Los Ebanos Blvd 78520 956-548-7700
Rose Longoria, prin. Fax 548-7710
Perkins MS 1,100/6-8
4750 Austin Rd 78521 956-831-8770
Beatriz Hernandez, prin. Fax 831-8789
Porter HS 2,000/9-12
3500 International Blvd 78521 956-548-7800
Hector Hernandez, prin. Fax 982-2892
Rivera HS 2,300/9-12
6955 FM 802 78526 956-831-8700
Aimee Garza-Limon, prin. Fax 831-8705
Stell MS 1,100/6-8
1105 E Los Ebanos Blvd 78520 956-548-8560
Liz Valdez, prin. Fax 546-2579
Stillman MS 900/6-8
2977 W Tandy Rd 78520 956-698-1000
Eduardo Martinez, prin. Fax 350-3231
Vela MS 1,000/6-8
4905 Paredes Line Rd 78526 956-548-7770
Joel Wood, prin. Fax 548-7780
Veterans Memorial HS 2,200/9-12
4550 US Highway 281 78520 956-574-5600
Dr. Linda Gallegos, prin. Fax 452-1341

Brightwood College Post-Sec.
1900 N Expressway 78521 956-547-8200
Coram Deo Classical Academy 50/1-11
1175 W Price Rd Ste 3 78520 956-459-7162
First Baptist S 300/PK-12
1600 Boca Chica Blvd 78520 956-542-4854
Terry Roberts, supt. Fax 542-6188
Guadalupe Regional MS 100/6-8
1214 Lincoln St 78521 956-504-5568
Maria Alvarado, prin. Fax 504-9393
St. Joseph Academy 700/7-12
101 Saint Joseph Dr 78520 956-542-3581
Melissa Valadez, prin. Fax 542-4748
University of Texas at Brownsville Post-Sec.
1 W University Blvd 78520 956-882-8200
Valley Christian HS 100/9-12
PO Box 4220 78523 956-542-5222
Gail Hanson, prin. Fax 544-0038

Brownwood, Brown, Pop. 19,003
Brownwood ISD 3,500/PK-12
PO Box 730 76804 325-643-5644
Dr. Joe Young, supt. Fax 643-5640
www.brownwoodisd.org
Brownwood HS 900/9-12
2100 Slayden St 76801 325-646-9549
Mitchell Moore, prin. Fax 643-1965
Brownwood MS 500/7-8
1600 Calvert Rd 76801 325-646-9545
Bryan Allen, prin. Fax 646-3785

Howard Payne University Post-Sec.
1000 Fisk Ave 76801 325-646-2502
Victory Life Academy 100/PK-12
PO Box 940 76804 325-641-2223
Cathy Roberts, supt. Fax 641-8063

Bruni, Webb, Pop. 377
Webb Consolidated ISD 300/PK-12
PO Box 206 78344 361-747-5415
Heriberto Gonzalez, supt. Fax 747-5202
webbcisd.org
Bruni HS 100/9-12
PO Box 206 78344 361-747-5415
Humberto Soliz, prin. Fax 747-5301
Bruni MS 100/6-8
PO Box 206 78344 361-747-5415
Sandra Castillo, prin. Fax 747-5298

Bryan, Brazos, Pop. 75,248
Bryan ISD 15,400/PK-12
101 N Texas Ave 77803 979-209-1000
Dr. Tim Rocka, supt. Fax 209-1004
www.bryanisd.org
Austin MS 800/6-8
801 S Ennis St 77803 979-209-6700
Brandon Jayroe, prin. Fax 209-6741
Bryan Collegiate HS 300/9-12
1901 E Villa Maria Rd 77802 979-209-2790
Christina Richardson, prin. Fax 209-2704
Bryan HS 1,900/9-12
3450 Campus Dr 77802 979-209-2400
Lane Buban, prin. Fax 209-2402
Davila MS 600/6-8
2751 N Earl Rudder Fwy 77803 979-209-7150
Shannon McGehee, prin. Fax 209-7151
Harris S 400/Alt
1305 Memorial Dr 77802 979-209-2812
Michael Watts, prin. Fax 209-2813
Long MS 1,100/6-8
1106 N Harvey Mitchell Pkwy 77803 979-209-6500
Cody Satterfield, prin. Fax 209-6566
Rayburn MS 800/6-8
1048 N Earl Rudder Fwy 77802 979-209-6600
Walter Hunt, prin. Fax 209-6611
Rudder HS 1,400/9-12
3251 Austins Colony Pkwy 77808 979-209-7900
Bennie Mayes, prin. Fax 209-7901

Allen Academy 300/PK-12
3201 Boonville Rd 77802 979-776-0731
Dr. Matthew Rush, head sch Fax 774-7769
Brazos Christian S 400/PK-12
3000 W Villa Maria Rd 77807 979-823-1000
Dr. Jeff McMaster, hdmstr. Fax 823-1774
Brazos Valley Cornerstone Christian Acad 100/K-12
3200 Cavitt Ave 77801 979-694-8200
Charlie & Sue's School of Hair Design Post-Sec.
1711 Briarcrest Dr 77802 979-776-4375
St. Joseph Catholic HS 200/6-12
600 S Coulter Dr 77803 979-822-6641
Jim Rike, prin. Fax 779-2810
St. Michael's Episcopal S 100/PK-12
2500 S College Ave 77801 979-822-2715
Jenny Morris, head sch Fax 823-4971
Still Creek Christian Academy 100/K-12
6055 Hearne Rd 77808 979-589-1816
James Inmon, prin. Fax 589-2152

Texas A&M University Health Science Ctr Post-Sec.
8441 State Highway 47 #3100 77807 979-436-9100

Bryson, Jack, Pop. 518
Bryson ISD 200/PK-12
300 N McCloud St 76427 940-392-3281
David Stout, supt. Fax 392-2086
www.brysonisd.net
Bryson S 200/PK-12
300 N McCloud St 76427 940-392-3281
Eric Wilson, prin. Fax 392-2086

Buckholts, Milam, Pop. 513
Buckholts ISD 200/PK-12
PO Box 248 76518 254-593-2744
Nancy Sandlin, supt. Fax 593-2270
www.buckholtsisd.net
Buckholts S 200/PK-12
PO Box 248 76518 254-593-2744
Myron Spencer, prin. Fax 593-2270

Buda, Hays, Pop. 7,167
Hays Consolidated ISD
Supt. — See Kyle
Barton MS 900/6-8
4950 Jack C Hays Trl 78610 512-268-1472
Teri Eubank, prin. Fax 268-1610
Dahlstrom MS 900/6-8
3600 FM 967 78610 512-268-8441
Rod Trevino, prin. Fax 295-5346
Hays HS 2,300/9-12
4800 Jack C Hays Trl 78610 512-268-2911
David Pierce, prin. Fax 268-1394
Impact Center 100/Alt
4125 FM 967 78610 512-268-8473
Sylvia Villejo, prin. Fax 295-5006
Live Oak Academy 100/Alt
4820 Jack C Hays Trl 78610 512-268-8462
Dr. Michael Watson, prin. Fax 268-4142
McCormick MS 6-8
5700 Dacy Ln 78610 512-268-8508
Thad Gittens, prin. Fax 295-4696

Buffalo, Leon, Pop. 1,845
Buffalo ISD 900/PK-12
708 Cedar Creek Rd 75831 903-322-3765
Lacy Freeman, supt. Fax 322-3091
www.buffaloisd.net
Buffalo HS 300/9-12
1724 N Buffalo Ave 75831 903-322-4243
Tracy Gleghorn, prin. Fax 322-5806
Buffalo JHS 300/3-8
335 Bison Trl 75831 903-322-4340
Greg Kennedy, prin. Fax 322-4803

Bullard, Smith, Pop. 2,447
Bullard ISD 2,300/PK-12
PO Box 250 75757 903-894-6639
Todd Schneider, supt. Fax 894-9291
www.bullardisd.net
Bullard HS 700/9-12
PO Box 250 75757 903-894-3272
Scott Franks, prin. Fax 894-3051
Bullard MS 400/7-8
PO Box 250 75757 903-894-6533
Cheryl Hendrix, prin. Fax 894-7592

Brook Hill S 500/PK-12
1051 N Houston St 75757 903-894-5000
Rod Fletcher, head sch Fax 894-6332

Bulverde, Comal, Pop. 4,570

Bracken Christian S 300/PK-12
670 Old Boerne Rd 78163 830-438-3211
Ed Thomas, supt. Fax 980-2327
Gloria Deo Academy 100/PK-12
1100 Bulverde Rd 78163 830-980-8511
Jamie King, head sch Fax 438-2179

Buna, Jasper, Pop. 2,103
Buna ISD 1,500/PK-12
PO Box 1087 77612 409-994-5101
Dr. Steve Hyden, supt. Fax 994-4808
www.bunaisd.net
Buna HS 400/9-12
PO Box 1087 77612 409-994-4811
Roy Farias, prin. Fax 994-4818
Buna JHS 400/6-8
PO Box 1087 77612 409-994-4860
Amber Flowers, prin. Fax 994-4808

Burkburnett, Wichita, Pop. 10,638
Burkburnett ISD 3,500/PK-12
416 Glendale St 76354 940-569-3326
Tylor Chaplin, supt. Fax 569-4776
www.burkburnettisd.org
Burkburnett HS 900/9-12
109 W Kramer Rd 76354 940-569-1411
Brad Owen, prin. Fax 569-1512
Burkburnett MS 700/6-8
108 S Avenue D 76354 940-569-3381
Scott Slater, prin. Fax 569-7116
Gateway Alternative Education Center 50/Alt
200 E 3rd St 76354 940-569-0850
Del Hardaway, admin. Fax 569-3030

Burke, Angelina, Pop. 734

Crimson Christian Academy 50/K-12
7020 S Highway 59, 936-639-1222
Jan Allbritton, admin.
Crimson Christian Academy K-12
7020 S US Highway 59, 936-639-1222
Jan Allbritton, admin.

Burkeville, Newton
Burkeville ISD 200/PK-12
PO Box 218 75932 409-565-2201
Dr. Brant Graham, supt. Fax 565-2012
www.burkevilleisd.org
Burkeville JSHS 100/7-12
PO Box 218 75932 409-565-2201
Dr. Keri Launius, prin. Fax 565-2461

Burleson, Johnson, Pop. 36,116
Burleson ISD 11,400/PK-12
1160 SW Wilshire Blvd 76028 817-245-1000
Dr. Bret Jimerson, supt. Fax 447-5737
www.burlesonisd.net
Burleson Collegiate HS 100/9-9
201 S Hurst Rd Ste 100 76028 817-245-1600
Roxanne Higgins, prin.
Burleson HS 1,500/9-12
100 Elk Dr 76028 817-245-0000
Wayne Leek, prin. Fax 447-5796
Centennial HS 1,600/9-12
201 S Hurst Rd 76028 817-245-0250
Jimmy Neal, prin. Fax 447-2152
Crossroads HS 100/Alt
505 Pleasant Manor Ave 76028 817-245-0500
Mekasha Brown, prin. Fax 447-5889
Hughes MS 1,200/6-8
316 SW Thomas St 76028 817-245-0600
Ben Renner, prin. Fax 447-5748
Kerr MS 1,200/6-8
517 SW Johnson Ave 76028 817-245-0750
Dr. Miller Beaird, prin. Fax 447-5742
STEAM MS, 201 S Hurst Rd 76028 600/6-8
Brandon Johnson, prin. 817-245-1000

Burnet, Burnet, Pop. 5,927
Burnet Consolidated ISD 3,200/PK-12
208 E Brier Ln 78611 512-756-2124
Keith McBurnett, supt. Fax 756-7498
www.burnetcisd.net
Burnet HS 900/9-12
1000 The Green Mile Rd 78611 512-756-6193
Casey Burkhart, prin. Fax 756-4553
Burnet MS 700/6-8
1401 N Main St 78611 512-756-6182
Steve Grant, prin. Fax 756-7955
Quest HS 50/Alt
607 N Vanderveer 78611 512-756-6747
Douglas Marvin Ed.D., prin. Fax 756-6289

Burton, Washington, Pop. 298
Burton ISD 400/PK-12
PO Box 37 77835 979-289-3131
Dr. Edna Kennedy, supt. Fax 289-3076
www.burtonisd.net
Burton JSHS 200/7-12
PO Box 499 77835 979-289-3830
Karen Steenken, prin. Fax 289-4609

Bushland, Potter
Bushland ISD 1,500/PK-12
PO Box 60 79012 806-359-6683
Don Wood, supt. Fax 359-6769
www.bushlandisd.net
Bushland HS 500/9-12
PO Box 60 79012 806-359-6683
Rick Davis, prin. Fax 322-1180
Bushland MS 400/5-8
PO Box 60 79012 806-359-5418
Jack Turner, prin. Fax 355-2841

Bynum, Hill, Pop. 197
Bynum ISD 200/PK-12
PO Box 68 76631 254-623-4251
Larry Mynarcik, supt. Fax 623-4290
www.bynumisd.net/
Bynum S 200/PK-12
PO Box 68 76631 254-623-4251
Lyndsey Pederson, prin. Fax 623-4290

Caddo Mills, Hunt, Pop. 1,323
Caddo Mills ISD 1,500/PK-12
PO Box 160 75135 903-527-6056
Vicki Payne, supt. Fax 527-4883
www.caddomillsisd.org/caddomillsisd/site/default.asp
Caddo Mills HS 400/9-12
PO Box 160 75135 903-527-3164
Jana Everett, prin. Fax 527-4772
Caddo Mills MS 400/6-8
PO Box 160 75135 903-527-3161
Anne Payne, prin. Fax 527-2379

Caldwell, Burleson, Pop. 4,063
Caldwell ISD 1,800/PK-12
203 N Gray St 77836 979-567-2400
Andrew Peters, supt. Fax 567-9876
caldwellisd.net
Caldwell HS 500/9-12
203 N Gray St 77836 979-567-2401
Vicki Ochs, prin. Fax 567-6735
Caldwell MS 400/6-8
203 N Gray St 77836 979-567-2402
Nathan Goodlett, prin. Fax 567-7433

Callisburg, Cooke, Pop. 352
Callisburg ISD 1,200/PK-12
148 Dozier St, 940-665-0540
Steve Clugston, supt. Fax 668-2706
www.cisdtx.net
Callisburg HS 300/9-12
148 Dozier St, 940-665-0961
Tommy Cummings, prin. Fax 665-2849
Callisburg MS 300/6-8
148 Dozier St, 940-665-0961
Bronwyn Werts, prin. Fax 665-2849

Calvert, Robertson, Pop. 1,179
Calvert ISD 200/PK-12
PO Box 7 77837 979-364-2824
Maxie Morgan, supt. Fax 364-2468
www.calvertisd.com/
Calvert S 200/PK-12
PO Box 7 77837 979-364-2824
Tom Kelly, prin. Fax 364-2468

Cameron, Milam, Pop. 5,512
Cameron ISD 1,700/PK-12
PO Box 712 76520 254-697-3512
Allan Sapp, supt. Fax 697-2448
www.cameronisd.net
Cameron JHS 400/6-8
PO Box 712 76520 254-697-2131
Wendy Mahan, prin. Fax 605-0379
Yoe HS 400/9-12
PO Box 712 76520 254-697-3902
Kenneth Driska, prin. Fax 605-0413

Campbell, Hunt, Pop. 622
Campbell ISD 400/PK-12
480 N Patterson St 75422 903-862-3259
Mark Keahey, supt. Fax 862-2222
www.campbellisd.org
Campbell JSHS 200/6-12
480 N Patterson St 75422 903-862-3257
James Daugherty, admin. Fax 862-3547

Canadian, Hemphill, Pop. 2,631
Canadian ISD 1,000/PK-12
800 Hillside Ave 79014 806-323-5393
Kyle Lynch, supt. Fax 323-8143
www.canadianisd.net
Canadian HS 200/9-12
800 Hillside Ave 79014 806-323-5373
Lynn Pulliam, prin. Fax 323-9345
Canadian MS 200/6-8
800 Hillside Ave 79014 806-323-5351
Bruce Bryant, prin. Fax 323-8791

Canton, Van Zandt, Pop. 3,519
Canton ISD 2,100/PK-12
1045 S Buffalo St 75103 903-567-4179
Jay Tullos, supt. Fax 567-2370
www.cantonisd.net
Canton HS 600/9-12
1110 W Highway 243 75103 903-567-6561
Jarrod Bitter, prin. Fax 567-6562
Canton JHS 500/6-8
1115 S Buffalo St 75103 903-567-4329
Amy Autry, prin. Fax 567-1298

Canutillo, El Paso, Pop. 6,297
Canutillo ISD
Supt. — See El Paso
Alderete MS 700/6-8
PO Box 100 79835 915-877-6600
Geoffrey Kimble, prin. Fax 877-6607
Canutillo MS 700/6-8
PO Box 100 79835 915-877-7900
Mark Paz, prin. Fax 877-7907

Canyon, Randall, Pop. 13,164
Canyon ISD 9,400/PK-12
PO Box 899 79015 806-677-2600
Darryl Flusche, supt. Fax 677-2659
www.canyonisd.net
Canyon HS 1,200/9-12
1701 23rd St 79015 806-677-2740
Tim Gilliland, prin. Fax 677-2779
Canyon JHS 600/7-8
910 9th Ave 79015 806-677-2700
Kirk Kear, prin. Fax 677-2739
Other Schools – See Amarillo

West Texas A&M University Post-Sec.
2501 4th Ave 79016 806-651-0000

Carmine, Fayette, Pop. 250
Round Top - Carmine ISD 300/PK-12
PO Box 385 78932 979-249-3200
Adren Pilger, supt. Fax 249-4084
www.rtcisd.net
Round Top - Carmine HS 100/7-12
PO Box 385 78932 979-278-3252
Brandon Schovajsa, prin. Fax 278-3063

Carrizo Springs, Dimmit, Pop. 5,350
Carrizo Springs Consolidated ISD 2,200/PK-12
300 N 7th St 78834 830-876-2473
Dr. Jesse Salazar, supt. Fax 876-9700
www.cscisd.net
Carrizo Springs HS 600/9-12
300 N 7th St 78834 830-876-9393
Michelle Gonzalez, prin. Fax 876-3052
Carrizo Springs JHS 400/7-8
300 N 7th St 78834 830-876-2496
Maria Villarreal, prin. Fax 876-3655

Carrollton, Denton, Pop. 116,719
Carrollton-Farmers Branch ISD 26,200/PK-12
PO Box 115186 75011 972-968-6100
Dr. Bobby Burns, supt. Fax 968-6210
www.cfbisd.edu
Blalack MS 1,000/6-8
1706 E Peters Colony Rd 75007 972-968-3500
Dr. Lance Hamlin, prin. Fax 968-3510
Creekview HS 1,900/9-12
3201 Old Denton Rd 75007 972-968-4800
Joe LaPuma, prin. Fax 968-4810
Grimes Education Center 100/Alt
1745 Hutton Dr 75006 972-968-5600
Bob Tipton, prin. Fax 968-5610
Perry MS 1,000/6-8
1709 E Belt Line Rd 75006 972-968-4400
Asheley Brown, prin. Fax 968-4410
Polk MS 1,100/6-8
2001 Kelly Blvd 75006 972-968-4600
Kelly O'Sullivan, prin. Fax 968-4610
Salazar S 100/Alt
2416 Keller Springs Rd 75006 972-968-5600
Melissa Wesley, prin. Fax 968-5610

Smith HS 2,000/9-12
2335 N Josey Ln 75006 972-968-5200
Joe Pouncy, prin. Fax 968-5210
Turner HS 2,100/9-12
1600 S Josey Ln Bldg 1 75006 972-968-5400
Brooke Hall, prin. Fax 968-5410
Other Schools – See Dallas, Farmers Branch, Irving

Lewisville ISD
Supt. — See Flower Mound
Arbor Creek MS 900/6-8
2109 Arbor Creek Dr 75010 469-713-5971
Joanie Finch, prin. Fax 350-9163
Creek Valley MS 700/6-8
4109 Creek Valley Blvd 75010 469-713-5184
Nicole Jund, prin. Fax 350-9172
Hebron HS 2,200/10-12
4207 Plano Pkwy 75010 469-713-5183
Scot Finch, prin. Fax 350-9255
Hebron Ninth Grade Center 50/9-9
4211 Plano Pkwy 75010 469-713-5996
Amanda Werneke, prin. Fax 626-1630

Carrollton Christian Academy 300/K-12
2205 E Hebron Pkwy 75010 972-242-6688
Elaine Marchant, prin. Fax 245-0321
Prince of Peace Christian S 900/PK-12
4004 Midway Rd 75007 972-447-0532
Chris Hahn, hdmstr. Fax 267-4202
Toni & Guy Hairdressing Academy Post-Sec.
2810 E Trinity Mills Rd 75006 972-416-8396

Carthage, Panola, Pop. 6,679
Carthage ISD 2,700/PK-12
1 Bulldog Dr 75633 903-693-3806
Dr. J. Glenn Hambrick Ed.D., supt. Fax 693-3650
www.carthageisd.org
Carthage HS 700/9-12
1 Bulldog Dr 75633 903-693-2552
Otis Amy, prin. Fax 693-9752
Carthage JHS 400/7-8
1 Bulldog Dr 75633 903-693-2751
Mike Baysinger, prin. Fax 693-9582

Panola College Post-Sec.
1109 W Panola St 75633 903-693-2000

Castroville, Medina, Pop. 2,662
Medina Valley ISD 3,900/PK-12
8449 FM 471 S 78009 830-931-2243
Dr. Kenneth Rohrbach, supt. Fax 931-4050
www.mvisd.com
Medina Valley HS 1,100/9-12
8365 FM 471 S 78009 830-931-2243
Dwight McHazlett, prin. Fax 931-0371
Medina Valley MS 900/6-8
8395 FM 471 S 78009 830-931-2243
Justin Russell, prin. Fax 931-3258

Cayuga, Anderson
Cayuga ISD 600/PK-12
PO Box 427 75832 903-928-2102
Dr. Rick Webb, supt. Fax 928-2646
www.cayugaisd.com
Cayuga HS 200/9-12
PO Box 427 75832 903-928-2294
Russell Holden, prin. Fax 928-2646
Cayuga MS 100/6-8
PO Box 427 75832 903-928-2699
Sherri McInnis, prin. Fax 928-2646

Cedar Creek, Bastrop
Bastrop ISD
Supt. — See Bastrop
Cedar Creek HS 1,400/9-12
793 Union Chapel Rd 78612 512-772-7300
Bridgette Cornelius, prin. Fax 772-7930
Cedar Creek MS 800/7-8
125 Voss Pkwy 78612 512-772-7425
Edgar Rincon, prin. Fax 332-2631

Cedar Hill, Dallas, Pop. 44,182
Cedar Hill ISD 6,600/PK-12
285 Uptown Blvd Ste 300 75104 972-291-1581
Orlando Riddick, supt. Fax 291-5231
www.chisd.net
Cedar Hill Collegiate Academy MS 6-8
1533 High Pointe Ln 75104 469-272-2021
Jackie Fagan, prin.
Cedar Hill SHS 1,600/10-12
1 Longhorn Blvd 75104 469-272-2000
Michael McDonald, prin. Fax 293-7125
Coleman MS 600/6-8
1208 E Pleasant Run Rd 75104 972-293-4505
Jason Miller, prin. Fax 272-9445
Ninth Grade Center 500/9-9
1515 W Belt Line Rd 75104 469-272-2050
Dr. Denise Roache-Davis, prin. Fax 272-3443
Permenter MS 600/6-8
431 W Parkerville Rd 75104 972-291-5270
Tonya Haddox, prin. Fax 291-5296

Northwood University Post-Sec.
1114 W FM 1382 75104 800-622-9000
Trinity Christian S 600/PK-12
1231 E Pleasant Run Rd 75104 972-291-2505

Cedar Park, Williamson, Pop. 47,764
Leander ISD
Supt. — See Leander
Cedar Park HS 1,800/9-12
2150 Cypress Creek Rd 78613 512-570-1200
John Sloan, prin. Fax 570-1205
Cedar Park MS 1,400/6-8
2100 Sunchase Blvd 78613 512-570-3100
Sandra Stewart, prin. Fax 570-3105
Henry MS 1,300/6-8
100 N Vista Ridge Pkwy 78613 512-570-3400
Dr. David Ellis, prin. Fax 570-3405
Running Brushy MS 1,300/6-8
2303 N Lakeline Blvd 78613 512-570-3300
Jim Rose, prin. Fax 570-3305
Vista Ridge HS 2,000/9-12
200 S Vista Ridge Pkwy 78613 512-570-1800
Paul Johnson, prin. Fax 570-1805

Summit Christian Academy of Cedar Park 300/PK-12
2121 Cypress Creek Rd 78613 512-250-1369
Shannon Dare, hdmstr. Fax 257-1851

Celeste, Hunt, Pop. 800
Celeste ISD 500/PK-12
PO Box 67 75423 903-568-4825
Brad Connelly, supt. Fax 568-4495
www.celesteisd.org/
Celeste HS 100/9-12
PO Box 67 75423 903-568-4721
James Branam, prin. Fax 568-4115
Celeste JHS 100/6-8
PO Box 67 75423 903-568-4721
Staci Beadles, prin. Fax 568-4277

Celina, Collin, Pop. 5,948
Celina ISD 2,100/PK-12
205 S Colorado St 75009 469-742-9100
Rick DeMasters, supt. Fax 382-3607
www.celinaisd.com
Celina HS 600/9-12
3455 N Preston Rd 75009 469-742-9102
David Wilson, prin. Fax 382-4830
Celina JHS 300/7-8
710 E Pecan St 75009 469-742-9101
Russell McDaniel, prin. Fax 382-4258

Center, Shelby, Pop. 5,149
Center ISD 2,800/PK-12
PO Box 1689 75935 936-598-5642
James Hockenberry, supt. Fax 598-1515
www.centerisd.org/
Center HS 700/9-12
658 Rough Rider Dr 75935 936-598-6173
Matthew Gregory, prin. Fax 598-1557
Center MS 600/6-8
302 Kennedy St 75935 936-598-5619
Jake Henson, prin. Fax 598-1534

Center Point, Kerr
Center Point ISD 600/PK-12
PO Box 377 78010 830-634-2171
Cody Newcomb, supt. Fax 634-2254
www.cpisd.net
Center Point HS 200/9-12
PO Box 377 78010 830-634-2244
Keith Mills, prin. Fax 634-7430
Center Point MS 100/6-8
PO Box 377 78010 830-634-2533
Keith Mills, prin. Fax 634-7825

Centerville, Leon, Pop. 862
Centerville ISD 700/PK-12
813 S Commerce St 75833 903-536-7812
Jason Jeitz, supt. Fax 536-7148
www.centerville.k12.tx.us
Centerville JSHS 300/7-12
813 S Commerce St 75833 903-536-2935
Dan Parker, prin. Fax 536-3133

Channelview, Harris, Pop. 37,941
Channelview ISD 9,000/PK-12
828 Sheldon Rd 77530 281-452-8002
Greg Ollis, supt. Fax 452-8001
www.cvisd.org
Channelview HS 1,600/10-12
1100 Sheldon Rd 77530 281-452-1450
Cindi Ollis, prin. Fax 457-7346
Endeavor S 100/Alt
915 Sheldon Rd 77530 281-457-0086
Mark Sims, prin. Fax 860-3826
Johnson JHS 1,000/6-8
15500 Proctor St 77530 281-452-8030
Jules Pichon, prin. Fax 452-1022
Kolarik 9th Grade Center 800/9-9
1120 Sheldon Rd 77530 713-378-3400
Cindi Ollis, prin. Fax 378-3498
Other Schools – See Houston

Channing, Hartley, Pop. 363
Channing ISD 100/PK-12
PO Box A 79018 806-235-3719
Robert McLain, supt. Fax 235-2609
www.channingisd.net/
Channing S 100/PK-12
PO Box A 79018 806-235-3719
Forrest Herbert, prin. Fax 235-2609

Charlotte, Atascosa, Pop. 1,708
Charlotte ISD 500/PK-12
PO Box 489 78011 830-277-1431
Mario Sotelo, supt. Fax 277-1551
www.charlotteisd.net
Charlotte HS 100/9-12
PO Box 489 78011 830-277-1432
Denise Cruz, prin. Fax 277-1605
Charlotte MS 200/5-8
PO Box 489 78011 830-277-1646
Roger Solis, prin. Fax 277-1654

Cherokee, San Saba
Cherokee ISD 100/K-12
PO Box 100 76832 325-622-4298
Eldon Franco, supt. Fax 622-4430
www.cherokeeisd.net
Cherokee S 100/K-12
PO Box 100 76832 325-622-4298
Randy Gartman, prin. Fax 622-4430

Chester, Tyler, Pop. 312
Chester ISD 200/PK-12
273 Yellow Jacket Dr 75936 936-969-2371
Cory Hines, supt. Fax 969-2080
www.chesterisd.com
Chester JSHS 100/6-12
273 Yellow Jacket Dr 75936 936-969-2353
Cory Hines, supt. Fax 969-2080

Chico, Wise, Pop. 994
Chico ISD 600/PK-12
PO Box 95 76431 940-644-2228
Don Elsom, supt. Fax 644-5642
www.chicoisdtx.net
Chico HS 200/9-12
PO Box 95 76431 940-644-5783
Randy Brawner, prin. Fax 644-5876
Chico MS 100/6-8
PO Box 95 76431 940-644-5550
Karen Woodruff, prin. Fax 644-5642

Childress, Childress, Pop. 6,037
Childress ISD 1,100/PK-12
PO Box 179 79201 940-937-2501
Rick Teran, supt. Fax 937-2938
www.childressisd.net/
Childress HS 300/9-12
800 Avenue J NW 79201 940-937-6131
Paige Steed, prin. Fax 937-2039
Childress JHS 200/6-8
700 Commerce St 79201 940-937-3641
Marsha Meacham, prin. Fax 937-8427

Chillicothe, Hardeman, Pop. 698
Chillicothe ISD 200/PK-12
PO Box 418 79225 940-852-5391
Todd Wilson, supt. Fax 852-5269
cisd-tx.net
Chillicothe JSHS 100/7-12
PO Box 550 79225 940-852-5391
Tony Martinez, prin. Fax 852-5465

Chilton, Falls, Pop. 896
Chilton ISD 500/PK-12
PO Box 488 76632 254-546-1200
Brandon Hubbard, supt. Fax 546-1201
www.chiltonisd.org
Chilton JSHS 300/6-12
PO Box 488 76632 254-546-1200
Brandon Hubbard, prin. Fax 546-1201

China Spring, McLennan, Pop. 1,276
China Spring ISD 2,400/PK-12
PO Box 250 76633 254-836-1115
Marc Faulkner, supt. Fax 836-0559
www.chinaspringisd.net
China Spring HS 700/9-12
7301 N River Xing 76633 254-836-1771
Max Rutherford, prin. Fax 836-1418
China Spring MS 400/7-8
7201 N River Xing 76633 254-836-4611
Mike Kelly, prin. Fax 836-4777

Chireno, Nacogdoches, Pop. 378
Chireno ISD 300/PK-12
PO Box 85 75937 936-362-2132
Tim Norman, supt. Fax 362-2490
www.chirenoisd.org/
Chireno JSHS 100/7-12
PO Box 85 75937 936-362-2132
Brandy Gray, prin. Fax 362-9331

Christoval, Tom Green, Pop. 503
Christoval ISD 500/K-12
PO Box 162 76935 325-896-2520
Dr. David Walker, supt. Fax 896-7405
www.christovalisd.org
Christoval JSHS 300/6-12
PO Box 162 76935 325-896-2355
John Choate, prin. Fax 896-2671

Cibolo, Guadalupe, Pop. 14,799
Schertz-Cibolo-Universal City ISD
Supt. — See Schertz
Dobie JHS 1,100/7-8
395 W Borgfeld Rd 78108 210-619-4100
Vernon Simmons, prin. Fax 619-4142
Steele HS 100/9-12
1300 FM 1103 78108 210-619-4000
Julie Knox, prin. Fax 619-4057

Cisco, Eastland, Pop. 3,863
Cisco ISD 900/PK-12
PO Box 1645 76437 254-442-3056
Kelly West, supt. Fax 442-1412
www.ciscoisd.net/
Cisco HS 300/9-12
PO Box 1645 76437 254-442-3051
Craig Kent, prin. Fax 442-2516
Cisco JHS 200/6-8
PO Box 1645 76437 254-442-3004
Mark Lewis, prin. Fax 442-1832
Cisco Learning Center 50/Alt
PO Box 1645 76437 254-442-4852
Julie Patterson, prin. Fax 442-1917

Cisco College Post-Sec.
101 College Hts 76437 254-442-5000

Clarendon, Donley, Pop. 1,994
Clarendon ISD 500/PK-12
PO Box 610 79226 806-874-2062
Michael Norrell, supt. Fax 874-2579
www.clarendonisd.net
Clarendon HS 100/9-12
PO Box 610 79226 806-874-2181
Larry Jeffers, prin. Fax 874-3428
Clarendon JHS 100/6-8
PO Box 610 79226 806-874-3232
John Taylor, prin. Fax 874-9748

Clarendon College Post-Sec.
PO Box 968 79226 806-874-3571

Clarksville, Red River, Pop. 3,231
Clarksville ISD 500/PK-12
1500 W Main St 75426 903-427-3891
Dr. Pamela Bryant Ed.D., supt. Fax 427-5071
www.clarksvilleisd.net
Clarksville MSHS 200/6-12
1500 W Main St 75426 903-427-3891
David Lee, prin. Fax 427-5116

Claude, Armstrong, Pop. 1,174
Claude ISD 400/PK-12
PO Box 209 79019 806-226-7331
Jeff Byrd, supt. Fax 226-2244
www.claudeisd.net/
Claude JSHS 200/6-12
PO Box 209 79019 806-226-2191
Derek Daniel, prin. Fax 226-2244

Cleburne, Johnson, Pop. 28,861
Cleburne ISD 6,500/PK-12
505 N Ridgeway Dr Ste 100 76033 817-202-1100
Dr. Kyle Heath, supt. Fax 202-1460
www.cleburne.k12.tx.us/
Cleburne HS 1,700/9-12
1501 Harlin Dr 76033 817-202-1200
LeAnn Downs, prin. Fax 202-1470
Smith MS 700/6-8
1710 Country Club Rd 76033 817-202-1500
William Allen, prin. Fax 202-1475
TEAM 100/Alt
1005 S Anglin St 76031 817-202-2160
Georganne Storm, prin. Fax 202-1489
Wheat MS 700/6-8
810 N Colonial Dr 76033 817-202-1300
Suzanne Keesee, prin. Fax 202-1479

Cleburne Christian Academy 100/K-12
PO Box 2017 76033 817-641-2857

Cleveland, Liberty, Pop. 7,571
Cleveland ISD 3,800/PK-12
316 E Dallas St 77327 281-592-8717
Dr. Darrell Myers, supt. Fax 592-8283
www.clevelandisd.org
Cleveland HS 900/9-12
1600 E Houston St 77327 281-592-8752
Stephen McCanless, prin. Fax 592-7485
Cleveland MS 600/7-8
2000 E Houston St 77327 281-593-1148
Glenn Barnes, prin. Fax 593-3040
Disciplinary Alternative Education Prgrm Alt
200 Charles St 77327 281-432-0478
Victor Fulton, prin. Fax 432-0538
Douglass Learning Academy 100/Alt
900 Sam Wiley Dr 77327 281-592-7595
Sandy Williamson, prin. Fax 432-2754

Tarkington ISD 1,900/PK-12
2770 FM 163 Rd 77327 281-592-8781
Kevin Weldon, supt. Fax 592-3969
www.tarkingtonisd.net/
Tarkington HS 600/9-12
2770 FM 163 Rd 77327 281-592-7739
Daniel Barton, prin. Fax 592-0693
Tarkington MS 500/6-8
2770 FM 163 Rd 77327 281-592-7737
Michael Kelley, prin. Fax 592-5241

Clifton, Bosque, Pop. 3,399
Clifton ISD 1,000/PK-12
1102 Key St 76634 254-675-2827
Rhoda White, supt. Fax 675-4351
www.cliftonisd.org
Clifton HS 300/9-12
1101 N Avenue Q 76634 254-675-1845
Becky Burnett, prin. Fax 675-8002
Clifton MS 200/6-8
1102 Key St 76634 254-675-1855
Andy Ball, prin. Fax 675-2005

Clint, El Paso, Pop. 926
Clint ISD
Supt. — See El Paso
Clint HS 600/9-12
13890 Alameda Ave 79836 915-926-8300
Garrett Ritchey, prin. Fax 851-5375
Clint ISD Early College Academy 100/9-12
13100 Alameda Ave 79836 915-926-8100
Edmond Martinez, prin. Fax 851-3459
Clint JHS 500/6-8
12625 Alameda Ave 79836 915-926-8000
Josephine A. Guzman, prin. Fax 851-3895

Clute, Brazoria, Pop. 11,087
Brazosport ISD 11,900/PK-12
301 W Brazoswood Dr 77531 979-730-7000
Danny Massey, supt. Fax 266-2409
www.brazosportisd.net
Brazoswood HS 2,400/9-12
302 W Brazoswood Dr 77531 979-730-7300
Tracie Phillips, prin. Fax 266-2447
Clute IS 900/5-8
421 E Main St 77531 979-730-7230
Chris Loftin, prin. Fax 730-7363
Lighthouse Learning Center 50/Alt
1035 Dixie Dr 77531 979-730-7340
Dr. Lisa Land, prin. Fax 730-7369
Other Schools – See Freeport, Lake Jackson

Clyde, Callahan, Pop. 3,655
Clyde Consolidated ISD 1,500/PK-12
PO Box 479 79510 325-893-4222
Keith Scharnhorst, supt. Fax 893-4024
www.clyde.esc14.net
Clyde HS 400/9-12
500 N Hays Rd 79510 325-893-2161
Gregg Wilson, prin. Fax 893-2993
Clyde JHS 400/6-8
211 S 3rd St W 79510 325-893-5788
Kenneth Berry, prin. Fax 893-2134

Eula ISD 300/PK-12
6040 FM 603 79510 325-529-3186
Tim Kelley, supt. Fax 529-4461
www.eulaisd.us
Eula JSHS 100/7-12
6040 FM 603 79510 325-529-3605
Candilyn Smith, prin. Fax 529-5534

Coahoma, Howard, Pop. 815
Coahoma ISD 900/PK-12
600 N Main St 79511 432-394-5000
Dr. Amy Jacobs, supt. Fax 394-4302
www.coahomaisd.com/
Coahoma HS 200/9-12
606 N Main St 79511 432-394-5000
Charlotte Stovall, prin. Fax 394-4301
Coahoma JHS 200/6-8
501 High School Dr 79511 432-394-5000
Ashley Roberts, prin. Fax 394-4419

Coldspring, San Jacinto, Pop. 837
Coldspring-Oakhurst Consolidated ISD 1,500/PK-12
PO Box 39 77331 936-653-1115
Dr. Leland Moore, supt. Fax 653-2197
www.cocisd.org
Coldspring-Oakhurst HS 500/9-12
PO Box 39 77331 936-653-1140
Donna Thompson, prin. Fax 653-3687
Lincoln JHS 300/6-8
PO Box 39 77331 936-653-1166
Todd White, prin. Fax 653-3688

Coleman, Coleman, Pop. 4,660
Coleman ISD 800/PK-12
PO Box 900 76834 325-625-3575
Skip McCambridge, supt. Fax 625-4751
www.colemanisd.org
Coleman HS 300/9-12
201 15th St 76834 325-625-2156
Diana Dobbins, prin. Fax 625-4557
Coleman JHS 200/5-8
301 15th St 76834 325-625-3593
Amy Flippin, prin. Fax 625-3358

College Station, Brazos, Pop. 92,151
College Station ISD 11,700/PK-12
1812 Welsh Ave 77840 979-764-5400
Dr. Clark Ealy Ph.D., supt. Fax 764-5535
www.csisd.org
A & M Consolidated HS 2,000/9-12
1801 Harvey Mitchell Pkwy S 77840 979-764-5500
Gwen Elder, prin. Fax 693-0212
A & M Consolidated MS 900/7-8
105 Holik St 77840 979-764-5575
Jeff Mann, prin. Fax 764-5577
Alternative Education Programs 100/Alt
105 Timber St 77840 979-764-5540
Margie Martinez, prin. Fax 764-5564
College Station HS 1,200/9-12
4002 Victoria Ave 77845 979-694-5800
Tiffany Parkerson, prin. Fax 394-5865
College Station MS 900/7-8
900 Rock Prairie Rd 77845 979-764-5545
Oliver Hadnot, prin. Fax 764-5557
College View HS 9-12
1300 George Bush Dr 77840 979-764-5540
Dr. Margie Martinez, prin. Fax 764-5564

Texas A&M University 77843 Post-Sec.
979-845-3211

Colleyville, Tarrant, Pop. 22,415
Grapevine-Colleyville ISD
Supt. — See Grapevine
BRIDGES S 100/Alt
5800 Colleyville Blvd 76034 817-251-5474
Dr. Lynda Burr, prin. Fax 581-4893
Colleyville Heritage HS 2,300/9-12
5401 Heritage Ave 76034 817-305-4700
Lance Groppel, prin. Fax 358-4765
Colleyville MS 700/6-8
1100 Bogart Dr 76034 817-305-4900
David Arencibia, prin. Fax 498-9764
Heritage MS 900/6-8
5300 Heritage Ave 76034 817-305-4790
Scott Saettel, prin. Fax 267-9929
Vista Alternative Learning Center Alt
5800 Colleyville Blvd 76034 817-251-5466
Roger Alzamora, prin. Fax 251-5466

Covenant Christian Academy 600/PK-12
901 Cheek Sparger Rd 76034 817-281-4333
Keith Castello, hdmstr. Fax 334-0367

Collinsville, Grayson, Pop. 1,601
Collinsville ISD 400/PK-12
PO Box 49 76233 903-429-6272
Mark Dykes, supt. Fax 429-6665
www.collinsvilleisd.org
Collinsville JSHS 200/7-12
PO Box 49 76233 903-429-6164
David Johnson, prin. Fax 429-6493

Colmesneil, Tyler, Pop. 588
Colmesneil ISD 400/PK-12
PO Box 37 75938 409-837-5757
Angela Matterson, supt. Fax 837-9107
www.colmesneilisd.net
Colmesneil JSHS 200/7-12
PO Box 37 75938 409-837-2225
Walter McAlpin, prin. Fax 837-9107

Colorado City, Mitchell, Pop. 4,115
Colorado ISD 1,000/PK-12
PO Box 1268 79512 325-728-5312
Reggy Spencer, supt. Fax 728-1015
www.ccity.esc14.net
Colorado HS 300/9-12
1500 Lone Wolf Blvd 79512 325-728-3424
Mark Merrell, prin. Fax 728-1083
Colorado MS 200/6-8
1244 E 10th St 79512 325-728-2673
Robby Russell, prin. Fax 728-1051

Columbus, Colorado, Pop. 3,623
Columbus ISD 1,600/PK-12
105 Cardinal Ln 78934 979-732-5704
Brian Morris, supt. Fax 732-5960
www.columbusisd.org
Columbus Alternative S 50/Alt
1421 Austin St 78934 979-732-2963
Michael Koehl, prin. Fax 732-8862
Columbus HS 500/9-12
103 Cardinal Ln 78934 979-732-5746
Robert Russell, prin. Fax 732-8862
Columbus JHS 400/6-8
702 Rampart St 78934 979-732-2891
Gary leopold, prin. Fax 732-9081

Comanche, Comanche, Pop. 4,301
Comanche ISD 1,000/PK-12
1414 N Austin St 76442 325-356-2727
Gary Speegle, supt. Fax 356-2312
www.comancheisd.net
Comanche HS 300/9-12
1600 N Austin St 76442 325-356-2581
Vinson Pierce, prin. Fax 356-2658
Jeffries JHS 200/6-8
1 Valley Forge St 76442 325-356-5220
Joseph Simmons, prin. Fax 356-1949

Comfort, Kendall, Pop. 2,348
Comfort ISD 1,100/PK-12
PO Box 398 78013 830-995-6400
Leslie Vann, supt. Fax 995-2236
www.comfort.txed.net
Comfort HS 300/9-12
PO Box 280 78013 830-995-6430
Katherine Kuenstler, prin. Fax 995-2261
Comfort MS 300/6-8
PO Box 187 78013 830-995-6420
Josh Limmer, prin. Fax 995-2248

Commerce, Hunt, Pop. 7,851
Commerce ISD 1,500/PK-12
3315 Washington St 75428 903-886-3755
Charles Alderman, supt. Fax 886-6025
www.commerceisd.org
Commerce HS 400/9-12
3315 Washington St 75428 903-886-3756
Steve Drummond, prin. Fax 886-6209
Commerce MS 300/6-8
3315 Washington St 75428 903-886-3795
Dr. Shenequa Miller, prin. Fax 886-6102

Texas A&M University Commerce Post-Sec.
PO Box 3011 75429 903-886-5102

Como, Hopkins, Pop. 696
Como-Pickton Consolidated ISD 700/PK-12
PO Box 18 75431 903-488-3671
Dr. Kay Handlin, supt. Fax 488-3133
www.cpcisd.net
Como-Pickton S 700/PK-12
PO Box 18 75431 903-488-3671
Dustin Carr, prin. Fax 488-3133

Comstock, Val Verde
Comstock ISD 200/K-12
PO Box 905 78837 432-292-4444
Orlie Wolfenbarger, supt. Fax 292-4436
www.comstockisd.net/
Comstock S 200/K-12
PO Box 905 78837 432-292-4444
Travis Grubbs, prin. Fax 292-4436

Conroe, Montgomery, Pop. 55,526
Conroe ISD 54,600/PK-12
3205 W Davis St 77304 936-709-7751
Dr. Don Stockton, supt. Fax 709-9701
www.conroeisd.net
Academy for Science & Health Professions 9-12
3200 W Davis St 77304 936-709-5731
Dr. Mike Papadimitriou, hdmstr. Fax 709-5842
Caney Creek HS 1,900/9-12
13470 FM 1485 Rd 77306 936-709-2000
Trish McClure, prin. Fax 709-2099
Conroe HS 9th Grade Campus 900/9-9
400 Sgt Ed Holcomb Blvd N 77304 936-709-4000
Bryan Gorka, prin. Fax 709-4099
Conroe SHS 2,500/10-12
3200 W Davis St 77304 936-709-5700
Dr. Mark Weatherly, prin. Fax 709-5655
Hauke Academic Alternative HS 200/Alt
701 N 3rd St 77301 936-709-3420
Paula Nicolini, prin. Fax 709-3499
Irons JHS 1,000/7-8
16780 Needham Rd 77385 936-709-8500
Jeff Fuller, prin. Fax 709-8599
Moorehead JHS 1,100/7-8
13475 FM 1485 Rd 77306 936-709-2400
Dr. Jeff Stichler, prin. Fax 709-2499
Oak Ridge 9th Grade Campus 900/9-9
27310 Oak Ridge School Rd 77385 281-465-5000
Anthony Livecchi, prin. Fax 465-5099
Oak Ridge SHS 2,400/10-12
27330 Oak Ridge School Rd 77385 832-592-5300
Tommy Johnson, prin. Fax 592-5544
Peet JHS 1,200/7-8
1895 Longmire Rd 77304 936-709-3700
Tasha Smith, prin. Fax 709-3828

Washington JHS 600/7-8
507 Dr Martin Luther King 77301 936-709-7400
Hartwell Brown, prin. Fax 709-7492
Other Schools – See Spring, The Woodlands

Adventist Christian Academy of Texas 100/PK-12
3601 S Loop 336 E 77301 936-756-5078
Jerry Walters, prin. Fax 365-1764
Calvary Baptist S 200/PK-12
3401 N Frazier St 77303 936-756-0743
Rev. Mark Parker, admin. Fax 756-0764
Covenant Christian S 300/PK-12
4503 Interstate 45 N 77304 936-890-8080
Dr. Glenn Slater, head sch Fax 890-5343
Lifestyle Christian S 100/K-12
3993 Interstate 45 N 77304 936-756-9383
Montie Mansur, prin. Fax 760-3003
Lone Star College - Montgomery Post-Sec.
3200 College Park Dr 77384 936-273-7000
PCAL Christian S 100/PK-12
9268 Highway 242 77385 936-273-6464
Rodman American School 100/PK-12
14030 Park Ave, 936-321-8800

Converse, Bexar, Pop. 17,584
Judson ISD
Supt. — See Live Oak
Judson CARE Adacemy 50/Alt
102 School St 78109 210-619-0330
Aida Nava, prin. Fax 658-2206
Judson HS 3,400/9-12
9142 FM 78 78109 210-945-1100
Jesus Hernandez, prin. Fax 659-4359
Judson MS 1,000/6-8
9695 Schaefer Rd 78109 210-357-0801
Liza Guerrero, prin. Fax 659-8769
Judson STEM Academy 100/6-8
9695 Schaefer Rd 78109 210-945-1159
Dawn Worley, dir.
Thompson Learning Center 50/Alt
PO Box 369 78109 210-945-5053
Joe Gonzalez, prin. Fax 945-7525

Coolidge, Limestone, Pop. 937
Coolidge ISD 300/PK-12
PO Box 70 76635 254-786-4612
Dr. Robert Lowry, supt. Fax 786-4835
www.coolidge.k12.tx.us
Coolidge HS 100/6-12
PO Box 70 76635 254-786-4822
Justin Cox, prin. Fax 786-4835

Cooper, Delta, Pop. 1,923
Cooper ISD 800/PK-12
PO Box 478 75432 903-395-2111
Denicia Hohenberger, supt. Fax 395-2117
www.cooperisd.net/
Cooper HS 200/9-12
PO Box 429 75432 903-395-2111
Richard Roan, prin. Fax 395-2382
Cooper JHS 200/6-8
PO Box 429 75432 903-395-2111
Julie Silman, prin. Fax 395-2382

Coppell, Dallas, Pop. 37,827
Coppell ISD 11,400/PK-12
200 S Denton Tap Rd 75019 214-496-6000
Dr. Mike Waldrip, supt. Fax 496-6036
www.coppellisd.com
Coppell HS 3,100/9-12
185 W Parkway Blvd 75019 214-496-6100
Mike Jasso, prin. Fax 496-6166
Coppell MS East 800/6-8
400 Mockingbird Ln 75019 214-496-6600
Laura Springer, prin. Fax 496-6603
Coppell MS North 900/6-8
120 Natches Trce 75019 214-496-7100
Amanda Ziaer, prin. Fax 496-7103
Coppell MS West 1,000/6-8
1301 Wrangler Cir 75019 214-496-8600
Emily Froese, prin. Fax 496-8606
New Tech HS @ Coppell 400/9-12
113 Samuel Blvd 75019 214-496-5900
Steffany Batik, prin. Fax 496-5906

Copperas Cove, Coryell, Pop. 30,055
Copperas Cove ISD 7,500/PK-12
703 W Avenue D 76522 254-547-1227
Dr. Joe Burns, supt. Fax 547-7060
www.ccisd.com
Copperas Cove HS 2,200/9-12
400 S 25th St 76522 254-547-2534
Miguel Timarky, prin. Fax 547-9870
Copperas Cove JHS 800/6-8
702 Sunny Ave 76522 254-547-6959
Randy Troub, prin. Fax 518-2620
Crossroads HS 50/Alt
306 E Avenue E 76522 254-547-9164
James Irick, prin. Fax 547-4039
Lee JHS 800/6-8
1205 Courtney Ln 76522 254-542-7877
Kayleen Love, prin. Fax 542-8103

Corinth, Denton, Pop. 19,502
Denton ISD
Supt. — See Denton
Crownover MS 900/6-8
1901 Creekside Dr 76210 940-369-4700
Jason Rainey, prin. Fax 321-0502

Lake Dallas ISD
Supt. — See Lake Dallas
Lake Dallas HS 1,300/9-12
3016 Parkridge Dr 76210 940-497-4031
Kristi Strickland, prin. Fax 497-1524

Corpus Christi, Nueces, Pop. 301,876
Calallen ISD 4,100/PK-12
4205 Wildcat Dr 78410 361-242-5600
Dr. Arturo Almendarez, supt. Fax 242-5620
www.calallen.org
Calallen HS 1,200/9-12
4001 Wildcat Dr 78410 361-242-5626
Yvonne Marquez-Neth, prin. Fax 242-5632
Calallen MS 900/6-8
4602 Cornett Dr 78410 361-242-5672
Marcos Flores, prin. Fax 242-0628

Corpus Christi ISD 39,100/PK-12
PO Box 110 78403 361-695-7200
Dr. Roland Hernandez, supt. Fax 886-9109
www.ccisd.us
Adkins MS 6-8
2402 Ennis Joslin Rd 78414 361-878-3800
Norma Cullum, prin. Fax 878-3828
Baker MS 1,000/6-8
3445 Pecan St 78411 361-878-4600
John Dobbins, prin. Fax 878-1834
Branch Acad for Career & Tech Education 100/9-12
3902 Morgan Ave 78405 361-878-4780
Browne MS 800/6-8
4301 Schanen Blvd 78413 361-878-4270
John Trevino, prin. Fax 878-1836
Carroll HS 2,200/9-12
5301 Weber Rd 78411 361-878-5140
Kelly Manlove, prin. Fax 878-2403
Coles HS & Education Ctr 300/Alt
924 Winnebago St 78401 361-844-0432
Monica Bayarena, prin. Fax 844-0436
Cullen Place MS 500/6-8
5225 Greely Dr 78412 361-878-2960
George Lerma, prin. Fax 994-3624
Cunningham MS 600/6-8
4321 Prescott St 78416 361-878-4630
Sandy Salinas-Deleon, prin. Fax 878-1838
Driscoll MS 800/6-8
3501 Kenwood Dr 78408 361-878-4660
Bruce Wilson, prin. Fax 886-9890
Grant MS 1,200/6-8
4350 Aaron Dr 78413 361-878-3740
Carla Rosa-Villarreal, prin. Fax 878-1871
Haas MS 600/6-8
6630 McArdle Rd 78412 361-878-4240
Dr. Lynda DeLeon, prin. Fax 994-3626
Hamlin MS 700/6-8
3900 Hamlin Dr 78411 361-878-4210
Tommy Whitehead, prin. Fax 878-1839
Kaffie MS 1,200/6-8
5922 Brockhampton St 78414 361-878-3700
Patti Heiland, prin. Fax 994-3604
King HS 2,500/9-12
5225 Gollihar Rd 78412 361-906-3400
Elizabeth Perez, prin. Fax 994-6918
Martin Special Emphasis S 700/6-8
3502 Greenwood Dr 78416 361-878-4690
Javier Granados, prin. Fax 878-2455
Miller HS 1,200/9-12
1 Battlin Buc Blvd 78408 361-878-5100
Stella Torres, prin. Fax 883-1928
Moody HS 1,700/9-12
1818 Trojan Dr 78416 361-878-7340
Dr. Sandra Clement, prin. Fax 857-8253
Ray HS 2,000/9-12
1002 Texan Trl 78411 361-878-7300
Cissy Perez, prin. Fax 852-6528
South Park MS 500/6-8
3001 McArdle Rd 78415 361-878-4720
Anna Marie Fuentes, prin. Fax 878-1844
Student Support Center 100/Alt
4401 Greenwood Dr 78416 361-878-2840
Douglas Cross, prin. Fax 878-1437
Veterans Memorial HS 9-12
3750 Cimarron Blvd 78414 361-878-7900
Kim James, prin. Fax 878-7910

Flour Bluff ISD 5,800/PK-12
2505 Waldron Rd 78418 361-694-9000
Brian Schuss, supt. Fax 694-9800
flourbluffschools.us
Flour Bluff HS 1,900/9-12
2505 Waldron Rd 78418 361-694-9100
James Crenshaw, prin. Fax 694-9802
Flour Bluff JHS 1,000/7-8
2505 Waldron Rd 78418 361-694-9300
Cindy Holder, prin. Fax 694-9803

London ISD 800/PK-12
1306 FM 43 78415 361-855-0092
David Freeman, supt. Fax 855-0198
www.londonisd.net
London HS 100/9-12
1306 FM 43 78415 361-855-0092
Rebecca Hitchcock, prin. Fax 855-0198
London MS 300/5-8
1306 FM 43 78415 361-855-0092
Amanda Barmore, prin. Fax 855-0098

Tuloso-Midway ISD 3,500/PK-12
PO Box 10900 78460 361-903-6400
Dr. Sue Nelson, supt. Fax 241-5836
www.tmisd.us
Tuloso-Midway HS 1,200/9-12
PO Box 10900 78460 361-903-6700
Ann Bartosh, prin. Fax 241-4258
Tuloso-Midway MS 900/6-8
PO Box 10900 78460 361-903-6600
Adriana Tagle, prin. Fax 242-9829

West Oso ISD 1,900/PK-12
5050 Rockford Dr 78416 361-806-5900
Conrado Garcia, supt. Fax 225-8308
www.westosoisd.net
West Oso HS 500/9-12
754 Flato Rd 78405 361-806-5960
Belinda Gamez, prin. Fax 299-3111
West Oso JHS 500/6-8
5202 Bear Ln 78405 361-806-5950
Terry Avery, prin. Fax 299-3111

Annapolis Christian Academy 200/PK-12
3875 S Staples St 78411 361-991-6004
Arlington Heights Christian S 200/PK-12
9550 Leopard St 78410 361-241-0090
Leanne Isom, admin. Fax 242-9284
Bishop Garriga MS 200/6-8
3114 Saratoga Blvd 78415 361-851-0853
Rene Gonzalez, prin. Fax 853-5145
Brightwood College Post-Sec.
1620 S Padre Island Dr #600 78416 361-852-2900
Coggin Memorial S 50/PK-10
6645 Downing St 78414 361-991-6968
Del Mar College Post-Sec.
101 Baldwin Blvd 78404 361-698-1200
Incarnate Word Academy 200/6-8
2917 Austin St 78404 361-883-0857
Adolfo Garza, prin. Fax 882-9193
Incarnate Word Academy 300/9-12
2910 S Alameda St 78404 361-883-0857
Jose Torres, prin. Fax 881-8742
Institute of Cosmetic Arts and Science Post-Sec.
1105 Airline Rd 78412 361-991-8868
St. John Paul II HS 400/9-12
3036 Saratoga Blvd 78415 361-855-5744
Perry LeGrange M.Ed., prin. Fax 855-1343
Southern Careers Institute Post-Sec.
2422 Airline Rd 78414 361-857-5700
South Texas Barber College Post-Sec.
3917 Ayers St 78415 361-855-0262
South Texas Vocational Technical Inst Post-Sec.
2000 S Padre Island Dr 78416 361-232-5057
Texas A&M University Corpus Christi Post-Sec.
6300 Ocean Dr 78412 361-825-5700

Corrigan, Polk, Pop. 1,578
Corrigan-Camden ISD 900/PK-12
504 S Home St 75939 936-398-4040
Sherry Hughes, supt. Fax 398-4616
www.ccisdtx.com
Corrigan-Camden HS 300/9-12
504 S Home St 75939 936-398-2341
Susan Torrez, prin. Fax 398-4928
Corrigan-Camden JHS 100/6-8
504 S Home St 75939 936-398-2341
Robert Elliott, prin. Fax 398-4928

Corsicana, Navarro, Pop. 23,195
Corsicana ISD 6,000/PK-12
2200 W 4th Ave 75110 903-874-7441
Dr. Diane Frost Ph.D., supt. Fax 602-8515
www.cisd.org
Collins MS 900/7-8
1500 Dobbins Rd 75110 903-872-3979
Darla Nolen, prin. Fax 874-1423
Corsicana HS 1,600/9-12
3701 W State Highway 22 75110 903-874-8211
Shade Boulware, prin. Fax 874-7403

Mildred ISD 700/K-12
5475 S US Highway 287 75109 903-872-6505
Shannon Baker, supt. Fax 872-1341
www.mildredisd.org
Mildred JSHS 400/6-12
5475 S US Highway 287 75109 903-872-0392
Aaron Tidwell, prin. Fax 641-0356

Navarro College Post-Sec.
3200 W 7th Ave 75110 903-874-6501

Cotton Center, Hale
Cotton Center ISD 100/PK-12
PO Box 350 79021 806-879-2160
Jeff Kirby M.Ed., supt. Fax 879-2175
www.cottoncenterisd.org
Cotton Center S 100/PK-12
PO Box 350 79021 806-879-2176
Jeff Kirby, prin. Fax 879-2175

Cotulla, LaSalle, Pop. 3,594
Cotulla ISD 1,400/PK-12
310 N Main St 78014 830-879-3073
Dr. Jack Seals, supt. Fax 879-3609
www.cotullaisd.org
Cotulla HS 300/9-12
310 N Main St 78014 830-879-2374
Scott Norris, prin. Fax 879-4302
Newman MS 300/6-8
310 N Main St 78014 830-879-2224
Dr. Brenda Jirasek, prin. Fax 879-4357

Covington, Hill, Pop. 269
Covington ISD 300/PK-12
501 N Main 76636 254-854-2215
Diane Innis, supt. Fax 854-2272
www.covingtonisd.org/
Covington S 300/PK-12
501 N Main 76636 254-854-2215
Sherry Abbott, prin. Fax 854-2272

Crandall, Kaufman, Pop. 2,834
Crandall ISD 3,200/PK-12
PO Box 128 75114 972-427-6000
Dr. Robert Jolly, supt. Fax 427-6036
www.crandall-isd.net
Crandall Alternative Center 50/Alt
PO Box 400 75114 972-472-6100
Emily Christensen, prin.
Crandall HS 900/9-12
PO Box 520 75114 972-427-8030
Jeannia Dykman, prin. Fax 427-8234
Crandall MS 700/6-8
PO Box 490 75114 972-427-6080
Amy McAfee, prin. Fax 427-8031

Crane, Crane, Pop. 3,329
Crane ISD 1,100/PK-12
511 W 8th St 79731 432-558-1022
Jim Rumage, supt. Fax 558-1025
www.craneisd.com/css/home.htm
Crane HS 300/9-12
511 W 8th St 79731 432-558-1030
Ramon Berzoza, prin. Fax 558-1056
Crane MS 300/6-8
511 W 8th St 79731 432-558-1040
Lori Schulze, prin. Fax 558-1046

Cranfills Gap, Bosque, Pop. 280
Cranfills Gap ISD 100/PK-12
PO Box 67 76637 254-597-2505
Vincent Gilbert, supt. Fax 597-0001
www.cranfillsgapisd.net
Cranfills Gap S 100/PK-12
PO Box 67 76637 254-597-2505
Monti Parchman, prin. Fax 597-0001

Crawford, McLennan, Pop. 703
Crawford ISD 600/K-12
200 Pirate Dr 76638 254-486-2381
Kenneth Hall, supt. Fax 486-2198
www.crawford-isd.net
Crawford HS 300/7-12
200 Pirate Dr 76638 254-486-2381
Don Harris, prin. Fax 486-2198

Crockett, Houston, Pop. 6,873
Crockett ISD 1,300/PK-12
1400 W Austin St 75835 936-544-2125
Terry Myers, supt. Fax 544-5727
www.crockettisd.net
Crockett Alternative Campus 50/Alt
1400 W Austin St 75835 936-546-5972
Mecheal Abbs, prin. Fax 546-0721
Crockett HS 300/9-12
1400 W Austin St 75835 936-544-2193
Deborah Revels, prin. Fax 546-0104
Crockett JHS 300/6-8
1400 W Austin St 75835 936-544-2125
Michael Woodard, prin. Fax 544-4164

Crosby, Harris, Pop. 2,268
Crosby ISD 5,200/PK-12
706 Runneburg Rd 77532 281-328-9200
Keith Moore Ed.D., supt. Fax 328-9208
www.crosbyisd.org
Crosby HS 1,500/9-12
14703 FM 2100 Rd 77532 281-328-9237
Terry Perkins, prin. Fax 328-9219
Crosby MS 800/7-8
14705 FM 2100 Rd 77532 281-328-9264
Dustin Bromley, prin. Fax 328-9356

Crosbyton, Crosby, Pop. 1,731
Crosbyton Consolidated ISD 300/PK-12
204 S Harrison St 79322 806-675-7331
Shawn Mason, supt. Fax 675-2409
www.crosbyton.k12.tx.us
Crosbyton Secondary S 100/6-12
204 S Harrison St 79322 806-675-7331
Glen Hill, prin. Fax 675-1049

Cross Plains, Callahan, Pop. 974
Cross Plains ISD 300/PK-12
700 N Main St 76443 254-725-6121
Phil Mitchell, supt. Fax 725-6559
www.crossplains.esc14.net/
Cross Plains JSHS 100/7-12
700 N Main St 76443 254-725-6121
Brad Jones, prin. Fax 725-6559

Crowell, Foard, Pop. 945
Crowell ISD 200/PK-12
PO Box 239 79227 940-684-1403
Pam Norwood, supt. Fax 684-1616
www.crowellisd.net
Crowell HS 100/9-12
PO Box 239 79227 940-684-1331
Pam Norwood, admin. Fax 684-1616

Crowley, Tarrant, Pop. 12,575
Crowley ISD 15,000/PK-12
PO Box 688 76036 817-297-5800
Dr. Dan Powell, supt. Fax 297-5805
www.crowleyisdtx.org/
Crowley 9th Grade Campus 500/9-9
1016 FM 1187 W 76036 817-297-5845
Christopher White, prin. Fax 297-5847
Crowley HS 1,400/10-12
1005 W Main St 76036 817-297-5810
Robert Gillies, prin. Fax 297-5854
Crowley Learning Center Alt
PO Box 688 76036 817-297-6992
Roger Corn, prin. Fax 297-4087
Johnson Career & Tech Center Vo/Tech
1033 McCart Ave 76036 817-297-3018
Kady Donaghey, dir. Fax 297-1839
Stevens MS 900/7-8
940 N Crowley Rd 76036 817-297-5840
Kimberly Buckhalton, prin. Fax 297-5850
Summer Creek MS 800/7-8
10236 Summercreek Dr 76036 817-297-5090
Cayla Grossman, prin. Fax 297-5094
Other Schools – See Fort Worth

Nazarene Christian Academy 400/K-12
2001 E Main St 76036 817-297-7003
Kathie Starks M.Ed., prin. Fax 297-1509

Crystal City, Zavala, Pop. 7,131
Crystal City ISD 2,100/PK-12
805 E Crockett St 78839 830-374-2367
Imelda Allen, supt. Fax 374-8004
www.crystalcityisd.org
Alternative S, 805 E Crockett St 78839 Alt
Janie Ramirez Flanagan, admin. 830-374-9840
Crystal City HS 500/9-12
805 E Crockett St 78839 830-374-2341
Gabriel Garcia, prin. Fax 374-8012
Fly JHS 300/7-8
805 E Crockett St 78839 830-374-2371
Sarah Garcia, prin. Fax 374-8060

Cuero, DeWitt, Pop. 6,679
Cuero ISD 2,000/PK-12
960 E Broadway St 77954 361-275-1900
Dr. Ben Colwell, supt. Fax 275-2981
www.cueroisd.org
Cuero HS 600/9-12
920 E Broadway St 77954 361-275-1900
Paul Fleener, prin. Fax 275-2430
Cuero JHS 400/6-8
608 Jr High Dr 77954 361-275-1900
Kim Fleener, prin. Fax 275-6912

Cumby, Hopkins, Pop. 769
Cumby ISD 400/PK-12
303 Sayle St 75433 903-994-2260
Shelly Slaughter, supt. Fax 994-2399
www.cumbyisd.net
Cumby HS 200/7-12
303 Sayle St 75433 903-994-2260
Jennifer Dracos, prin. Fax 994-2510

Miller Grove ISD 300/PK-12
7819 Farm Road 275 S 75433 903-459-3288
Steve Johnson, supt. Fax 459-3744
www.mgisd.net
Miller Grove S 300/PK-12
7819 Farm Road 275 S 75433 903-459-3288
Gary Billingsley, prin. Fax 459-3744

Cushing, Nacogdoches, Pop. 594
Cushing ISD 500/PK-12
PO Box 337 75760 936-326-4890
Michael Davis, supt. Fax 326-4115
www.cushingisd.org
Cushing MSHS 300/6-12
PO Box 337 75760 936-326-4890
Andy Gresham, prin. Fax 326-4131

Cypress, Harris
Cypress-Fairbanks ISD
Supt. — See Houston
Anthony MS 6-8
10215 Greenhouse Rd 77433 281-373-5660
Sherma Duck, prin. Fax 373-5661
Arnold MS 1,600/6-8
11111 Telge Rd 77429 281-897-4700
Jodi Matteson, prin. Fax 807-8610
Carlton Vocational Center Vo/Tech
13550 Woods Spillane Blvd 77429 281-213-1950
Rhonda Turns, dir. Fax 213-1951
Cy-Fair HS 3,500/9-12
22602 Hempstead Hwy 77429 281-897-4600
Mike Smith, prin. Fax 517-6530
Cypress Park HS 9-12
7425 Westgreen Blvd 77433 346-227-6000
Chris Hecker, prin.
Cypress Ranch HS 3,300/9-12
10700 Fry Rd 77433 281-373-2300
Robert Hull, prin. Fax 213-1979
Cypress Springs HS 2,700/9-12
7909 Fry Rd 77433 281-345-3000
Dr. Cheryl Henry, prin. Fax 345-3010
Cypress Woods HS 3,200/9-12
13550 Woods Spillane Blvd 77429 281-213-1800
Gary Kinninger, prin. Fax 213-1827
Goodson MS 1,200/6-8
17333 Huffmeister Rd 77429 281-373-2350
Sheri McCaig, prin. Fax 373-2355
Hamilton MS 1,500/6-8
12330 Kluge Rd 77429 281-320-7000
Kim Sempe, prin. Fax 320-7021
Hopper MS 1,400/6-8
7811 Fry Rd 77433 281-463-5353
Wendi Whitthaus, prin. Fax 463-5354
Salyards MS 1,500/6-8
21757 Fairfield Place Dr 77433 281-373-2400
Liz Wood, prin. Fax 373-2425
Smith MS 1,900/6-8
10300 Warner Smith Blvd 77433 281-213-1010
Susan Higgins, prin. Fax 213-1020
Spillane MS 1,300/6-8
13403 Woods Spillane Blvd 77429 281-213-1645
Michael Maness, prin. Fax 213-1799

Connection S of Houston 100/K-12
15815 House Hahl Rd 77433 832-544-6031
Kathleen Wrobleske, head sch Fax 286-3088
Covenant Academy 200/K-12
11711 Telge Rd 77429 281-373-2233
Leslie Collins, head sch Fax 588-8227
Lone Star College Cyfair Post-Sec.
9191 Barker Cypress Rd 77433 281-290-3200
Oaks Adventist Christian S 100/PK-12
11735 Grant Rd 77429 713-896-0071

Daingerfield, Morris, Pop. 2,512
Daingerfield-Lone Star ISD 1,100/PK-12
200 Tiger Dr 75638 903-645-2239
Sandra Quarles, supt. Fax 645-2137
www.dlisd.org
Daingerfield HS 300/9-12
202 Tiger Dr 75638 903-645-3968
Ryan Carroll, prin. Fax 645-7662
Daingerfield JHS 200/6-8
200 Texas St 75638 903-645-2261
Linda Rhymes, prin. Fax 645-4010

Daisetta, Liberty, Pop. 957
Hull-Daisetta ISD 500/PK-12
PO Box 477 77533 936-536-6321
Mary Huckabay, supt. Fax 536-6251
www.hdisd.net/
Hull-Daisetta HS 200/9-12
PO Box 477 77533 936-536-6321
Quinn Godwin, prin. Fax 536-3839
Hull-Daisetta JHS 100/7-8
PO Box 477 77533 936-536-6321
Quinn Godwin, prin. Fax 536-3839

Dalhart, Dallam, Pop. 7,836
Dalhart ISD 1,800/PK-12
701 E 10th St 79022 806-244-7810
John Massey, supt. Fax 244-7822
www.dalhartisd.org
Dalhart HS 500/9-12
701 E 10th St 79022 806-244-7300
Kevin Douglas, prin. Fax 244-7307
Dalhart JHS 400/6-8
701 E 10th St 79022 806-244-7825
Shannon Marshall, prin. Fax 244-7835
XIT Secondary S 50/Alt
701 E 10th St 79022 806-244-7340
Sarah Nutter, prin. Fax 244-7345

Dallardsville, Polk
Big Sandy ISD 500/PK-12
PO Box 188 77332 936-563-1000
Eric Carpenter, supt. Fax 563-1010
www.bigsandyisd.net
Other Schools – See Livingston

Dallas, Dallas, Pop. 1,183,449
Carrollton-Farmers Branch ISD
Supt. — See Carrollton
Long MS 800/6-8
2525 Frankford Rd 75287 972-968-4100
Charde Dockery, prin. Fax 968-4110

Dallas ISD 156,100/PK-12
3700 Ross Ave 75204 972-925-3700
Michael Hinojosa Ed.D., supt. Fax 925-3201
www.dallasisd.org
Adams HS 1,800/9-12
2101 Millmar Dr 75228 972-502-4900
Richard Kastl, prin. Fax 502-4901
Adamson HS 1,400/9-12
309 E 9th St 75203 972-749-1400
Janie Ortega, prin. Fax 749-1401
Angelou HS 50/Alt
4528 Rusk Ave 75204 972-749-2200
Lynn Smith, prin. Fax 749-2264
Atwell Law Academy 1,000/6-8
1303 Reynoldston Ln 75232 972-794-6400
Selena Deboskie, prin. Fax 794-6401
Browne MS 700/7-8
3333 Sprague Dr 75233 972-502-2500
Jonathan Smith, prin. Fax 502-2501
Carter HS 1,000/9-12
1819 W Wheatland Rd 75232 214-932-5700
Fred Davis, prin. Fax 932-5701
Cary MS 600/6-8
3978 Killion Dr 75229 972-502-7600
Ben Dickerson, prin. Fax 502-7601
Collins-Sorrells S of Educ & Social Srvc 300/9-12
1201 E 8th St 75203 972-925-5940
Shelia Brown, prin. Fax 925-5901
Comstock MS 600/7-8
7044 Hodde St 75217 972-794-1300
Willie Johnson, prin. Fax 794-1301
Conrad HS 1,200/9-12
7502 Fair Oaks Ave 75231 972-502-2300
Anthony Mays, prin. Fax 502-2301
Dade Learning Center 800/6-8
2727 Al Lipscomb Way 75215 972-749-3800
Al Way, prin. Fax 749-3801
Dallas Environmental Science Academy 400/6-8
3635 Greenleaf St 75212 972-794-3950
Diana Nunez, prin. Fax 794-3951
Edison MS 600/6-8
2940 Singleton Blvd 75212 972-794-4100
Luis Valdez, prin. Fax 794-4101
Franklin MS 1,000/6-8
6920 Meadow Rd 75230 972-502-7100
Joseph Sotelo, prin. Fax 502-7101
Garcia MS, 700 E 8th St 75203 900/6-8
Gary Auld, prin. 972-502-5500
Garza Early College HS 400/9-12
4849 W Illinois Ave Rm W53A 75211 214-860-3680
Marcario Hernandez, prin. Fax 860-3639
Gaston MS 1,100/6-8
9565 Mercer Dr 75228 972-502-5400
Sharon Stauss, prin. Fax 502-5401
Gilliam Collegiate Academy 400/9-12
1700 E Camp Wisdom Rd 75241 214-925-1400
LaKeiah Cheatham, prin. Fax 925-1401
Greiner Exploratory Arts Academy 1,500/6-8
501 S Edgefield Ave 75208 972-925-7100
Yvonne Rojas, prin. Fax 925-7101
Hillcrest HS 1,200/9-12
9924 Hillcrest Rd 75230 972-502-6800
Christopher Bayer, prin. Fax 502-6801
Hill MS 900/6-8
505 Easton Rd 75218 972-502-5700
Candice Ruiz, prin. Fax 502-5701
Holmes Classical Academy 800/6-8
2001 E Kiest Blvd 75216 972-925-8500
Sharron Jackson, prin. Fax 925-8501
Holmes MS 1,200/6-8
2939 Saint Rita Dr 75233 214-932-7800
Barbara Moham, prin. Fax 932-7801
Innovation Design Emtrepreneurship Acad 9-12
4800 Ross Ave 75204 972-794-6800
Sarah Ritsema, prin.
Jefferson HS 1,500/9-12
4001 Walnut Hill Ln 75229 972-502-7300
Sandi Massey, prin. Fax 502-7301
Kennedy-Curry MS 700/6-8
6605 Sebring Dr 75241 972-925-1600
David Welch, prin.

Kimball HS 1,300/9-12
3606 S Westmoreland Rd 75233 972-502-2100
Earl Jones, prin. Fax 502-2101
Lang MS, 1678 Chenault St 75228 1,000/6-8
Kimberly Robinson, prin. 972-925-2400
Lassiter Early College HS 200/9-12
701 Elm St 75202 214-860-2356
Michael St. Ama, prin. Fax 860-2359
Learning Alt Ctr for Empowering Youth 100/Alt
4949 Village Fair Dr 75224 972-925-7060
Marlon Brooks, prin. Fax 925-7061
Lincoln Humanities/Communications HS 500/9-12
2826 Hatcher St 75215 972-925-7600
Johanna Weaver, prin. Fax 925-7601
Longfellow Career Academy 400/6-8
5314 Boaz St 75209 972-749-5400
Lorena Hernandez, prin. Fax 749-5401
Long MS 1,300/6-8
6116 Reiger Ave 75214 972-502-4700
Chandra Hooper-Barnett, prin. Fax 502-4701
Madison HS 500/9-12
3000 Mrtn Lthr King Jr Blvd 75215 972-925-2800
Marian Willard, prin. Fax 925-2801
Manns Education Center 100/Alt
3313 S Beckley Ave 75224 972-932-7300
Letice Portley, prin.
Marsh Preparatory Academy 1,200/6-8
3838 Crown Shore Dr 75244 972-502-6600
Martha Bujanda, prin. Fax 502-6601
Medrano MS 900/6-8
9815 Brockbank Dr 75220 972-925-1300
Theresa Sigurdson, prin. Fax 925-1301
Molina HS 2,000/9-12
2355 Duncanville Rd 75211 972-502-1000
Terry Rodriguez, prin. Fax 502-1001
Multiple Careers Magnet HS Vo/Tech
4528 Rusk Ave 75204 972-925-2200
Lynn Smith, prin. Fax 925-2201
North Dallas HS 1,300/9-12
3120 N Haskell Ave 75204 972-925-1500
Blanca Rodriguez, prin. Fax 925-1501
Obama Male Leadership Academy 300/6-12
4730 S Lancaster Rd 75216 972-749-2100
Michael Bland, prin. Fax 749-2101
Patton Academic Center 200/Alt
3313 S Beckley Ave 75224 214-932-5160
Leslie Swann, prin. Fax 932-5149
Piedmont Global Academy 6-8
7625 Hume Dr 75227 972-749-4100
LaTonya Lockhart, prin. Fax 749-4101
Pinkston HS 900/9-12
2200 Dennison St 75212 972-502-2700
Dwain Simmons, prin. Fax 502-2701
Quintanilla MS 800/7-8
2700 Remond Dr 75211 972-502-3200
Salem Hussain, prin. Fax 502-3201
Rangel Young Women's Leadership S 300/6-12
1718 Robert B Cullum Blvd 75210 972-749-5200
Lisa Curry, prin. Fax 749-5201
Richards MS 1,200/6-8
3831 N Prairie Creek Rd 75227 972-892-5400
Francine Taylor, prin.
Roosevelt HS 700/9-12
525 Bonnie View Rd 75203 972-925-6800
Brian DeVeaux, prin. Fax 925-6801
Rusk MS 700/6-8
2929 Inwood Rd 75235 972-925-2000
Julio Perez, prin. Fax 925-2001
Samuell HS 1,700/9-12
8928 Palisade Dr 75217 972-892-5100
Jennifer Tecklenburg, prin. Fax 892-5101
Sanders Magnet Center for Law 400/9-12
1201 E 8th St Ste 203 75203 972-925-5950
Garet Feimster, prin. Fax 925-6010
School Community Guidance Center 100/Alt
4949 Village Fair Dr 75224 972-925-7020
Marlon Brooks, prin. Fax 925-7021
School for the Talented & Gifted 200/9-12
1201 E 8th St Ste 216 75203 972-925-5970
Ben Mackey, prin. Fax 925-6018
School of Business & Management 500/9-12
1201 E 8th St Ste 241 75203 972-925-5920
Michelle Broughton, prin. Fax 925-5901
School of Health Professions 500/9-12
1201 E 8th St Ste 281 75203 972-925-5930
LaSandra Sanders, prin. Fax 925-6007
School of Science & Engineering HS 400/9-12
1201 E 8th St 75203 972-925-5960
Tiffany Huitt, prin. Fax 925-6016
Seagoville HS 1,200/9-12
15920 Seagoville Rd 75253 972-892-5900
Angela West, prin. Fax 892-5901
Seagoville MS 1,100/6-8
950 N Woody Rd 75253 972-892-7100
Javier Chaparro, prin. Fax 892-7101
Skyline HS 4,700/9-12
7777 Forney Rd 75227 972-502-3400
Janice Lombardi, prin. Fax 502-3401
Smith New Tech HS 400/9-12
3030 Stag Rd 75241 214-932-7600
Jamelle Choice, prin. Fax 932-7601
South Oak Cliff HS 1,200/9-12
3601 S Marsalis Ave 75216 214-932-7000
Elvis Williams, prin. Fax 932-7001
Spence Talented/Gifted Academy 1,000/6-8
4001 Capitol Ave 75204 972-925-2300
Deardra Hayes-Whigham, prin. Fax 925-2301
Spruce HS 1,400/9-12
9733 Old Seagoville Rd 75217 972-892-5500
Danielle Petters, prin. Fax 892-5501
STEAM MS at Hulcy 6-8
9339 S Polk St 75232 214-932-7400
Jonica Crowder-Lockwood, prin.
Stockard MS 900/7-8
2300 S Ravinia Dr 75211 972-794-5700
Adam Varrassi, prin. Fax 794-5701

Storey MS 700/6-8
3000 Maryland Ave 75216 972-925-8700
JoAnn Jackson, prin. Fax 925-8701
Sunset HS 2,100/9-12
2120 W Jefferson Blvd 75208 972-502-1500
Claudia Vega, prin. Fax 502-1501
Tasby MS 900/6-8
7001 Fair Oaks Ave 75231 972-502-1900
Audrey de la Cruz, prin. Fax 502-1901
Travis Academy 100/4-8
3001 McKinney Ave 75204 972-794-7500
Mari Smith, prin. Fax 794-7501
Walker MS 800/6-8
12532 Nuestra Dr 75230 972-502-6100
Dr. Laura Stout, prin. Fax 502-6101
Washington Performing & Visual Arts HS 900/9-12
2501 Flora St 75201 972-925-1200
Scott Rudes, prin. Fax 925-1201
White HS 2,300/9-12
4505 Ridgeside Dr 75244 972-502-6200
Michelle Thompson, prin. Fax 502-6201
Wilmer-Hutchins HS 900/9-12
5520 Langdon Rd 75241 972-925-2900
Tamika Prentiss Barnett, prin.
Wilson HS 1,700/9-12
100 S Glasgow Dr 75214 972-502-4400
Steve Ewing, prin. Fax 502-4401
Young Mens Leadership Academy Florence 800/6-8
1625 N Masters Dr 75217 972-749-6000
Dawn Walker, prin. Fax 749-6001
Zumwalt MS 500/6-8
2445 E Ledbetter Dr 75216 972-749-3600
Troy Tyson, prin. Fax 749-3601
Evening Academy Adult
7777 Forney Rd 75227 972-502-3458
Fax 502-3633

Other Schools – See Balch Springs

Duncanville ISD
Supt. — See Duncanville
Kennemer MS 700/7-8
7101 W Wheatland Rd 75249 972-708-3600
Brandee King, prin. Fax 708-3636

Highland Park ISD 7,000/PK-12
7015 Westchester Dr 75205 214-780-3000
Dr. Tom Trigg, supt. Fax 780-3099
www.hpisd.org
Highland Park Alternative Education Ctr Alt
4220 Emerson Ave 75205 214-780-3700
Walter Kelly, prin. Fax 780-3799
Highland Park HS 2,100/9-12
4220 Emerson Ave 75205 214-780-3700
Walter Kelly, prin. Fax 780-3799
Highland Park MS 1,100/7-8
3555 Granada Ave 75205 214-780-3600
Dr. Laurie Hitzelberger, prin. Fax 780-3699

Plano ISD
Supt. — See Plano
Frankford MS 1,100/6-8
7706 Osage Plaza Pkwy 75252 469-752-5200
Shurandia Holden, prin. Fax 752-5201

Richardson ISD
Supt. — See Richardson
Forest Meadow JHS 700/7-8
9373 Whitehurst Dr 75243 469-593-1500
Kerri Jones, prin. Fax 593-1461
Lake Highlands Freshman Center 800/9-9
10200 White Rock Trl 75238 469-593-1300
Bill Gallo, prin. Fax 593-1327
Lake Highlands HS 1,700/10-12
9449 Church Rd 75238 469-593-1000
Frank Miller, prin. Fax 593-1030
Lake Highlands JHS 800/7-8
10301 Walnut Hill Ln 75238 469-593-1600
Veronica Escalante, prin. Fax 593-1606
Liberty JHS 700/7-9
10330 Lawler Rd 75243 469-593-7888
Doug Planey, prin. Fax 593-7764
Parkhill JHS 600/7-9
16500 Shadybank Dr 75248 469-593-5600
Farrah Smock, prin. Fax 593-5500
Westwood Magnet JHS 700/7-9
7630 Arapaho Rd 75248 469-593-3600
Jennie Bates, prin. Fax 593-3508

Argosy University/Dallas Post-Sec.
5001 Lyndon B Johnson # 176 75244 214-890-9900
Art Institute of Dallas Post-Sec.
8080 Park Ln Ste 100 75231 214-692-8080
Bending Oaks HS 50/8-12
11884 Greenville Ave # 120 75243 972-669-0000
Bishop Dunne Catholic S 600/6-12
3900 Rugged Dr 75224 214-339-6561
Kate Dailey, pres. Fax 339-1438
Bishop Lynch HS 1,100/9-12
9750 Ferguson Rd 75228 214-324-3607
Chris Rebuck, pres. Fax 324-3600
Brightwood College Post-Sec.
12005 Ford Rd Ste 100 75234 972-385-1446
Cambridge S of Dallas 100/6-12
3877 Walnut Hill Ln 75229 214-357-2995
Dr. Paul Wolfe, hdmstr. Fax 357-0880
Choices Leadership Academy 50/5-8
18106 Marsh Ln 75287 972-662-0665
Concorde Career College Post-Sec.
12606 Greenville Ave # 130 75243 469-221-3400
Cornerstone Crossroads Academy 50/10-12
PO Box 151062 75315 214-426-3282
Dr. Kristi Lichtenberg, admin. Fax 741-0066
Court Reporting Institute of Dallas Post-Sec.
1341 W Mockingbird Ln #200E 75247 214-350-9722
Covenant S 500/K-12
7300 Valley View Ln 75240 214-358-5818
Dr. Robert Woods, head sch Fax 358-5809

Cristo Rey Dallas Prep 9-9
1064 N Saint Augustine Dr 75217 214-888-5057
Kelby Woodard, admin.
Criswell College Post-Sec.
4010 Gaston Ave 75246 214-821-5433
Dallas Baptist University Post-Sec.
3000 Mountain Creek Pkwy 75211 214-333-7100
Dallas Barber and Stylist College Post-Sec.
9357 Forest Ln 75243 214-575-2168
Dallas Christian Academy 100/PK-12
4025 N Central Expy 75204 214-528-6327
Dallas Christian College Post-Sec.
2700 Christian Pkwy 75234 972-241-3371
Dallas Institute of Funeral Service Post-Sec.
3909 S Buckner Blvd 75227 214-388-5466
Dallas Lutheran HS 200/7-12
8494 Stults Rd 75243 214-349-8912
David Bangert, dir. Fax 340-3095
Dallas Nursing Institute Post-Sec.
12170 Abrams Rd Ste 200 75243 888-201-8806
Dallas Theological Seminary Post-Sec.
3909 Swiss Ave 75204 214-887-5504
El Centro College Post-Sec.
801 Main St 75202 214-860-2000
Episcopal S of Dallas 700/5-12
4100 Merrell Rd 75229 214-358-4368
Meredyth Cole, head sch Fax 357-1232
Everest College Post-Sec.
6080 N Central Expy 75206 214-234-4850
First Baptist Academy 300/PK-12
1606 Patterson St 75201 214-969-7861
Golf Academy of America Post-Sec.
1861 Valley View Ln Ste 100 75234 972-763-8100
Graduate Institute of Applied Linguistic Post-Sec.
7500 W Camp Wisdom Rd 75236 972-708-7340
Hockaday S 1,100/PK-12
11600 Welch Rd 75229 214-363-6311
Elizabeth Lee, head sch Fax 360-6563
Jesuit College Preparatory S 1,100/9-12
12345 Inwood Rd 75244 972-387-8700
Mike Earsing, pres. Fax 661-9349
KD Studio - Actors Conservatory Post-Sec.
2600 N Stemmons Fwy Ste 117 75207 214-638-0484
Lakehill Prep S 400/K-12
2720 Hillside Dr 75214 214-826-2931
Roger Perry, hdmstr. Fax 826-4623
Lawyer's Assistant School of Dallas Post-Sec.
8150 N Central Expy # M2240 75206 214-777-6433
Le Cordon Bleu Inst of Culinary Arts Post-Sec.
11830 Webb Chapel Rd # 1200 75234
214-647-8500
Lighthouse College Post-Sec.
9400 N Central Expy Ste 200 75231 214-368-3680
Mediatech Institute Post-Sec.
13370 Branch View Ln # 135 75234 866-498-1122
Mesorah HS for Girls 50/9-12
12712 Park Central Dr #B190 75251 214-420-1990
MJ's Beauty Academy Post-Sec.
3939 S Polk St Ste 505 75224 214-374-7500
Mountain View College Post-Sec.
4849 W Illinois Ave 75211 214-860-8680
Neilson Beauty College Post-Sec.
416 W Jefferson Blvd 75208 214-941-8756
Ogle School of Hair Design Post-Sec.
6333 E Mockingbird Ln #201 75214 214-821-0819
Parish Episcopal S 1,100/PK-12
4101 Sigma Rd 75244 972-239-8011
David Monaco, head sch Fax 991-1237
Parker University Post-Sec.
2540 Walnut Hill Ln 75229 972-438-6932
Paul Quinn College Post-Sec.
3837 Simpson Stuart Rd 75241 214-376-1000
PCI Health Training Center Post-Sec.
8101 John W Carpenter Fwy 75247 214-380-4322
Presbyterian Hospital Post-Sec.
8200 Walnut Hill Ln 75231 214-345-7558
Redeemer Seminary Post-Sec.
6060 N Central Expy Ste 700 75206 214-528-8600
Richland College Post-Sec.
12800 Abrams Rd 75243 972-238-6100
St. Marks S of Texas 900/1-12
10600 Preston Rd 75230 214-346-8000
David Dini, hdmstr. Fax 346-8002
St. Timothy School 50/PK-12
4333 Cole Ave 75205 214-521-6062
Sanford-Brown College Post-Sec.
1250 W Mockingbird Ln # 150 75247 214-459-8490
Southern Methodist University Post-Sec.
PO Box 750100 75275 214-768-2000
Sterling Health Center Post-Sec.
17084 Dallas Pkwy 75248 972-991-9293
Texas A&M Univ.-Baylor Coll. Dentistry Post-Sec.
3302 Gaston Ave 75246 214-828-8100
Texas Barber Colleges & Hairstyling Sch Post-Sec.
5148 S Lancaster Rd 75241 214-943-7255
Texas Torah Institute 50/9-12
6506 Frankford Rd 75252 214-250-4888
Texas Women's Univ Pickens Inst Health Post-Sec.
5500 Southwestern Medical 75235 214-689-6500
Tint School of Makeup & Cosmetology Post-Sec.
10909 Webb Chapel Rd # 129 75229 214-956-0088
Tyler Street Christian Academy 200/PK-12
915 W 9th St 75208 214-941-9717
Dr. Karen Egger, supt. Fax 941-0324
University of North Texas at Dallas Post-Sec.
7300 University Hills Blvd 75241 972-780-3600
University of Texas S.W. Medical Center Post-Sec.
5323 Harry Hines Blvd 75390 214-648-3111
Ursuline Academy 800/9-12
4900 Walnut Hill Ln 75229 469-232-1800
Gretchen Kane, pres. Fax 232-1836
Velma B's Beauty Academy Post-Sec.
1511 S Ewing Ave 75216 214-942-1541
Wade College Dallas Market Center Post-Sec.
1950 N Stemmons Ste 4080 75207 800-624-4850
West Coast University Post-Sec.
8435 N Stemmons Fwy 75247 214-453-4533

Westwood S 300/PK-12
14340 Proton Rd 75244 972-239-8598
Heather Lourcey, head sch Fax 239-1028
Winston S 200/K-12
5707 Royal Ln 75229 214-691-6950
Rebbie Evans, head sch Fax 691-1509
Yavneh Academy of Dallas 100/9-12
12324 Merit Dr 75251 214-295-3500

Danbury, Brazoria, Pop. 1,690
Danbury ISD 700/PK-12
PO Box 378 77534 979-922-1218
Greg Anderson, supt. Fax 922-8246
www.danburyisd.org
Danbury HS 200/9-12
PO Box 377 77534 979-922-1226
Jon Hill, prin. Fax 922-1051
Danbury MS 100/6-8
PO Box 586 77534 979-922-1226
Jon Hill, prin. Fax 922-1051

Darrouzett, Lipscomb, Pop. 347
Darrouzett ISD 100/PK-12
PO Box 98 79024 806-624-2221
Troy Humphrey, supt. Fax 624-4361
www.darrouzettisd.net
Darrouzett S 100/PK-12
PO Box 98 79024 806-624-2221
Troy Humphrey, prin. Fax 624-4361

Dawson, Navarro, Pop. 793
Dawson ISD 500/PK-12
199 N School Ave 76639 254-578-1031
Stacy Henderson, supt. Fax 578-1721
www.dawsonisd.net/
Dawson HS 200/7-12
199 N School Ave 76639 254-578-1031
Robert Bray, prin. Fax 578-1721

Dayton, Liberty, Pop. 7,114
Dayton ISD 4,700/PK-12
PO Box 248 77535 936-258-2667
Dr. Jessica Johnson, supt. Fax 258-5616
www.daytonisd.net
Dayton HS 1,400/9-12
PO Box 248 77535 936-258-2510
Geoff McCracken, prin. Fax 257-4047
Nottingham Alternative Educ Ctr Alt
PO Box 248 77535 936-257-4100
Stacie Lott, prin. Fax 257-4110
Wilson JHS 800/6-8
PO Box 248 77535 936-258-2309
Benicia Bendele, prin. Fax 257-4109

Decatur, Wise, Pop. 6,000
Decatur ISD 2,700/PK-12
307 S Cates St 76234 940-393-7100
Rod Townsend, supt. Fax 627-3141
www.decaturisd.us/
Decatur HS 900/9-12
750 E Eagle Smt 76234 940-393-7200
Jeff Russell, prin. Fax 627-3669
McCarroll MS 500/6-8
1201 W Thompson St 76234 940-393-7300
Dewayne Tamplen, prin. Fax 627-2497

Victory Christian Academy 200/PK-12
PO Box 32 76234 940-626-4730

Deer Park, Harris, Pop. 31,669
Deer Park ISD 15,700/PK-12
2800 Texas Ave 77536 832-668-7000
Victor White, supt. Fax 930-4638
www.dpisd.org
Bonnette JHS 800/6-8
5010 W Pasadena Blvd 77536 832-668-7700
Paul Moore, prin. Fax 930-4756
Deer Park HS - North Campus 3,800/9-9
402 Ivy Ave 77536 832-668-7300
Ernie Salazar, prin. Fax 930-4840
Deer Park HS - South Campus 3,000/10-12
710 W San Augustine St 77536 832-668-7200
Steve Corry, prin. Fax 930-4894
Deer Park JHS 800/6-8
410 E 9th St 77536 832-668-7500
Dr. Tiffany Regan, prin. Fax 930-4726
Wolters Accelerated HS Alt
204 Ivy Ave 77536 832-668-7400
Clyde Skarke, prin. Fax 930-0525
Other Schools – See Pasadena

De Kalb, Bowie, Pop. 1,672
De Kalb ISD 800/PK-12
101 Maple St 75559 903-667-2566
Dr. John Booth, supt. Fax 667-3791
www.dekalbisd.net
De Kalb HS 200/9-12
152 Maple St 75559 903-667-2422
Neilan Hensley, prin. Fax 667-4086
De Kalb MS 200/5-8
929 W Grizzley St 75559 903-667-2834
Clayton Little, prin. Fax 667-5509

De Leon, Comanche, Pop. 2,226
De Leon ISD 600/PK-12
425 S Texas St 76444 254-893-8210
Dr. Dana Marable Ph.D., supt. Fax 893-8214
www.deleonisd.net
De Leon HS 200/9-12
425 S Texas St 76444 254-893-8240
Liesa Nowlin, prin. Fax 893-4985
Perkins MS 200/6-8
425 S Texas St 76444 254-893-8230
Liesa Nowlin, prin. Fax 893-8234

Dell City, Hudspeth, Pop. 357
Dell City ISD 100/K-12
PO Box 37 79837 915-964-2663
Fabian Gomez, supt. Fax 964-2473
dellcity.schoolwires.com
Dell City S 100/K-12
PO Box 37 79837 915-964-2663
Jody Kotys, prin. Fax 964-2473

Del Rio, Val Verde, Pop. 35,427
San Felipe-Del Rio Consolidated ISD 10,700/PK-12
PO Box 428002 78842 830-778-4000
Carlos Rios Ed.D., supt. Fax 774-9892
www.sfdr-cisd.org
Blended Academy 8-12
PO Box 428002 78842 830-778-4680
Alma Flores, prin.
Del Rio Freshman S 800/9-9
PO Box 428002 78842 830-778-4400
Tomas Cabello, prin. Fax 774-9873
Del Rio HS 2,000/10-12
PO Box 428002 78842 830-778-4329
Dr. Jose Perez, prin. Fax 774-9320
Del Rio MS 1,500/7-8
PO Box 428002 78842 830-778-4530
Jorge Limon, prin. Fax 778-4912

Del Valle, Travis
Del Valle ISD 11,600/PK-12
5301 Ross Rd 78617 512-386-3000
Kelly Crook Ph.D., supt. Fax 386-3015
delvalle.tx.schoolwebpages.com/
Del Valle HS 2,700/9-12
5201 Ross Rd 78617 512-386-3200
David Williams, prin. Fax 386-3205
Del Valle MS 900/6-8
5500 Ross Rd 78617 512-386-3400
James Cruz, prin. Fax 386-3440
Del Valle Opportunity Center 200/Alt
5301 Ross Rd Ste B 78617 512-386-3300
Ray Macias, prin. Fax 386-3316
Other Schools – See Austin

Denison, Grayson, Pop. 22,067
Denison ISD 3,500/PK-12
1201 S Rusk Ave 75020 903-462-7000
Dr. Henry Scott, supt. Fax 462-7002
www.denisonisd.net
Denison HS 1,200/9-12
4200 N State Highway 91 75020 903-462-7125
Dr. Cavin Boettger, prin. Fax 462-7217
Pathways HS 50/Alt
318 W Morgan St 75020 903-462-7150
Lance SanMillan, prin. Fax 462-7220
Scott MS 7-8
1901 S Mirick Ave 75020 903-462-7180
John Parker, prin. Fax 462-7342

Sherman ISD
Supt. — See Sherman
Perrin Learning Center 100/Alt
81 Vandenburg Dr 75020 903-891-6680
Jim May, prin. Fax 786-4766

Grayson College Post-Sec.
6101 FM 691 75020 903-465-6030

Denton, Denton, Pop. 110,797
Denton ISD 26,100/PK-12
1307 N Locust St 76201 940-369-0000
Dr. Jamie Wilson, supt. Fax 369-4982
www.dentonisd.org
Calhoun MS 700/6-8
709 W Congress St 76201 940-369-2400
Paul Martinez, prin. Fax 369-4939
Davis S 100/Alt
1125 Davis St 76209 940-369-4050
Jeff Tinch, prin. Fax 369-4966
Denton HS 2,100/9-12
1007 Fulton St 76201 940-369-2000
Dan Ford, prin. Fax 369-4953
Guyer HS 2,300/9-12
7501 Teasley Ln 76210 940-369-1000
Shaun Perry, prin. Fax 369-4965
LaGrone Advanced Technology Complex Vo/Tech
1504 Long Rd 76207 940-369-4850
Marcus Bourland, prin. Fax 380-0243
McMath MS 700/6-8
1900 Jason Dr 76205 940-369-3300
Dr. Debra Nobles, prin. Fax 369-4946
Moore HS 100/Alt
815 Cross Timber St 76205 940-369-4000
Beth Kelly, prin. Fax 369-4957
Ryan HS 2,300/9-12
5101 E McKinney St 76208 940-369-3000
Vernon Reeves, prin. Fax 369-4960
Strickland MS 900/6-8
324 E Windsor Dr 76209 940-369-4200
Kathleen Carmona, prin. Fax 369-4950
Other Schools – See Argyle, Aubrey, Corinth, Shady Shores

Denton Calvary Academy 200/K-12
PO Box 2414 76202 940-320-1944
Northwest Lineman Training Center Post-Sec.
5110 Dakota Ln 76207 940-383-1000
Selwyn College Preparatory S 200/K-12
3333 W University Dr 76207 940-382-6771
Deb Hof M.S., head sch Fax 383-0704
Texas Woman's University Post-Sec.
PO Box 425589 76204 940-898-2000
University of North Texas Post-Sec.
1155 Union Cir # 311277 76203 940-565-2000

Denver City, Yoakum, Pop. 4,445
Denver City ISD 1,200/PK-12
501 Mustang Dr 79323 806-592-5900
Gary Davis, supt. Fax 592-5909
www.dcisd.org
Denver City HS 400/9-12
601 Mustang Dr 79323 806-592-5950
Rick Martinez, prin. Fax 592-5959
Gravitt JHS 400/6-8
419 Mustang Dr 79323 806-592-5940
Billy Moore, prin. Fax 592-5949

DeSoto, Dallas, Pop. 48,350
De Soto ISD 7,600/PK-12
200 E Belt Line Rd 75115 972-223-6666
Dr. David Harris, supt. Fax 274-8209
www.desotoisd.org
DeSoto Alternative Education Center 50/Alt
200 E Belt Line Rd 75115 972-223-2242
Homer Webb, admin. Fax 230-1735
De Soto East MS 600/6-8
601 E Belt Line Rd 75115 972-223-0690
Brandon Ward, prin. Fax 274-8156
De Soto HS 2,200/9-12
600 Eagle Dr 75115 972-230-0726
Arista Owens-McGowan, prin. Fax 274-8115
De Soto West MS 700/6-8
800 N Westmoreland Rd 75115 972-230-1820
James McBride, prin. Fax 274-8183
WINGS Drop Out Recovery Alt
200 E Belt Line Rd 75115 972-274-8219
Homer Webb, prin. Fax 274-8246
Other Schools – See Glenn Heights

Canterbury Episcopal S 300/PK-12
1708 N Westmoreland Rd 75115 972-572-7200
Sandy Doerge, head sch Fax 572-7400
PC Center Post-Sec.
1229 E Pleasant Run Rd 75115 972-224-9800

Detroit, Red River, Pop. 712
Detroit ISD 500/PK-12
110 E Garner St 75436 903-674-6131
Brian Howie, supt. Fax 674-2478
www.detroiteagles.net
Detroit HS 100/9-12
110 E Garner St 75436 903-674-2646
Jonathan Lloyd, prin. Fax 674-2206
Detroit JHS 100/6-8
110 E Garner St 75436 903-674-2646
Ella Duran, prin. Fax 674-2206

Devers, Liberty, Pop. 439
Devers ISD 200/PK-8
PO Box 488 77538 936-549-7135
Elizabeth A. Harris, supt. Fax 549-7595
www.deversisd.net
Devers JHS 50/6-8
PO Box 488 77538 936-549-7591
Elizabeth A. Harris, admin. Fax 549-7595

Devine, Medina, Pop. 4,321
Devine ISD 2,000/PK-12
605 W Hondo Ave 78016 830-851-0795
Scott Sostarich, supt. Fax 663-6706
www.devineisd.org
Devine HS 600/9-12
1225 W Hondo Ave 78016 830-851-0895
Derrick Byrd, prin. Fax 663-6792
Devine MS 400/6-8
400 Cardinal Dr 78016 830-851-0695
Kandi Darnell, prin. Fax 663-6769

Deweyville, Newton, Pop. 997
Deweyville ISD 700/PK-12
PO Box 408 77614 409-746-2731
Kevin Clark, supt. Fax 746-3360
www.deweyvilleisd.com
Other Schools – See Orange

D Hanis, Medina, Pop. 845
D'Hanis ISD 300/PK-12
PO Box 307 78850 830-363-7216
Scott Higgins, supt. Fax 363-7390
www.dhanisisd.net/
D'Hanis MSHS 300/PK-12
PO Box 307 78850 830-363-7217
Kurt Schumacher, prin. Fax 363-7390

Diana, Upshur
New Diana ISD 1,000/PK-12
1373 US Highway 259 S 75640 903-663-8000
Carl Key, supt. Fax 241-7393
www.ndisd.org
New Diana HS 300/9-12
11826 State Highway 154 E 75640 903-663-8001
Jenifer Politi, prin. Fax 663-2200
New Diana MS 200/6-8
11854 State Highway 154 E 75640 903-663-8002
Joaquin Guerero, prin. Fax 663-1812

Diboll, Angelina, Pop. 4,716
Diboll ISD 2,000/PK-12
PO Box 550 75941 936-829-4718
Vicki Thomas, supt. Fax 829-5558
www.dibollisd.com
Diboll HS 500/9-12
1000 Lumberjack Dr 75941 936-829-5626
John Clements, prin. Fax 829-5708
Diboll JHS 300/7-8
403 Dennis St 75941 936-829-5225
Mark Kettering, prin. Fax 829-5848

Dickinson, Galveston, Pop. 18,370
Dickinson ISD 10,000/PK-12
PO Box Z 77539 281-229-6000
Vicki Mims, supt. Fax 229-6011
www.dickinsonisd.org
Dickinson Continuation Center 100/Alt
2805 Oak Park St 77539 281-229-6350
Wendy Chide, prin. Fax 229-6351
Dickinson HS 2,600/9-12
3800 Baker Dr 77539 281-229-6400
Dr. Billye Smith, prin. Fax 229-6401
McAdams JHS 1,400/7-8
11415 Hughes Rd 77539 281-229-7100
Rachelle Joseph, prin. Fax 229-7101

Pine Drive Christian S 200/PK-12
705 FM 517 Rd E 77539 281-534-4881
Frances Templeton, admin. Fax 534-4318

Dilley, Frio, Pop. 3,879
Dilley ISD 1,000/PK-12
245 W FM 117 78017 830-965-1912
Clint McLain, supt. Fax 965-4069
dilleyisd.net
Dilley HS 300/9-12
245 W FM 117 78017 830-965-1814
Jadie Matthew, prin. Fax 965-1276
Harper MS 200/6-8
245 W FM 117 78017 830-965-2195
Jennifer Torres, prin. Fax 965-2171

Dime Box, Lee
Dime Box ISD 100/PK-12
PO Box 157 77853 979-884-2324
David Rains, supt. Fax 884-0106
www.dimeboxisd.net
Dime Box HS 100/7-12
PO Box 157 77853 979-884-3366
James Lynn Ponder, prin. Fax 884-0106

Dimmitt, Castro, Pop. 4,377
Dimmitt ISD 1,200/PK-12
608 W Halsell St 79027 806-647-3101
Bryan Davis, supt. Fax 647-5433
www.dimmittisd.net
Dimmitt HS 300/9-12
1405 Western Cir 79027 806-647-3105
Rick McKay, prin. Fax 647-5795
Dimmitt MS 400/5-8
1505 Western Cir 79027 806-647-3108
Tiffany Seaton, prin. Fax 647-2996

Dodd City, Fannin, Pop. 356
Dodd City ISD 400/PK-12
602 N Main St 75438 903-583-7585
Craig Reed, supt. Fax 583-9545
www.doddcityisd.org
Dodd City S 400/PK-12
602 N Main St 75438 903-583-7585
Jason Crow, prin. Fax 583-9545

Donna, Hidalgo, Pop. 15,775
Donna ISD 15,400/PK-12
116 N 10th St 78537 956-464-1600
Fernando Castillo, supt. Fax 464-1752
www.donnaisd.net
Donna HS 1,900/9-12
116 N 10th St 78537 956-464-1700
Nancy Castillo, prin. Fax 464-1629
Donna North HS, 116 N 10th St 78537 1,600/9-12
Belinda Vega, prin. 956-464-4190
Excel Academy, 116 N 10th St 78537 100/Alt
Emmy De La Garza, prin. 956-464-1771
Sauceda MS 800/6-8
116 N 10th St 78537 956-464-1360
Adela Troncoso, prin. Fax 464-1349
Solis MS 700/6-8
116 N 10th St 78537 956-464-1650
Mary Lou Rodriguez, prin. Fax 464-1649
3D Academy 100/Alt
116 N 10th St 78537 956-464-1771
Lydia Lugo, prin. Fax 464-2375
Todd MS 900/6-8
116 N 10th St 78537 956-464-1800
Labrado DeHoyos, prin. Fax 464-1824
Veterans MS 900/6-8
116 N 10th St 78537 956-464-1350
Claudia Guerrero, prin. Fax 464-1356

Douglass, Nacogdoches
Douglass ISD 400/K-12
PO Box 38 75943 936-569-9804
Walter Peddy, supt. Fax 569-9446
www.douglassisd.com
Douglass S 400/K-12
PO Box 38 75943 936-569-9804
Jeffrey Roquemore, prin. Fax 569-9446

Dripping Springs, Hays, Pop. 1,763
Dripping Springs ISD 5,100/PK-12
PO Box 479 78620 512-858-3002
Bruce Gearing Ed.D., supt. Fax 858-3099
www.dsisdtx.us
Dripping Springs HS 1,500/9-12
PO Box 479 78620 512-858-3100
Joe Burns, prin. Fax 858-3199
Dripping Springs MS 1,200/6-8
PO Box 479 78620 512-858-3400
Jason Certain, prin. Fax 858-3499

Dripping Springs Christian Academy 50/PK-12
800 W Hwy 290 Bldg C # 100 78620 512-858-9738
Becky Welborn, head sch
King's Academy 50/K-11
PO Box 39 78620 512-858-4700
John Russell, head sch Fax 686-3305

Dublin, Erath, Pop. 3,617
Dublin ISD 1,200/PK-12
PO Box 169 76446 254-445-3341
Rodney Schneider, supt. Fax 445-3345
www.dublinisd.us
Dublin HS 500/7-12
PO Box 169 76446 254-445-0362
Keith Owen, prin. Fax 445-1706

Dumas, Moore, Pop. 14,542
Dumas ISD 4,600/PK-12
PO Box 615 79029 806-935-6461
Monty Hysinger, supt. Fax 935-6275
www.dumasisd.org
Dumas HS 1,100/9-12
PO Box 695 79029 806-935-4151
Brett Beesley, prin. Fax 934-1433
Dumas JHS 600/7-8
PO Box 697 79029 806-935-4155
Kurt Baxter, prin. Fax 934-1434
North Plains Opportunity Center 100/Alt
PO Box 696 79029 806-935-8774
Carl Clements, admin. Fax 935-6376

Duncanville, Dallas, Pop. 38,022
Duncanville ISD 13,100/PK-12
710 S Cedar Ridge Dr 75137 972-708-2000
Dr. Marc Smith, supt. Fax 708-2020
www.duncanvilleisd.org
Byrd MS 700/7-8
1040 W Wheatland Rd 75116 972-708-3400
Kendria Davis-Martin, prin. Fax 708-3434
Duncanville HS 4,000/9-12
900 W Camp Wisdom Rd 75116 972-708-3700
Tia Simmons, prin. Fax 708-3737
PACE HS 100/Alt
502 E Freeman St 75116 972-708-2470
Keith Butcher, prin. Fax 708-2474
Reed MS 500/7-8
530 E Freeman St 75116 972-708-3500
Dr. Ryan McCoy, prin. Fax 708-3535
Summit Learning Center 100/Alt
900 S Cedar Ridge Dr #300A 75137 972-708-2570
Dwight Weaver, prin. Fax 708-2585
Other Schools – See Dallas

State Beauty Academy Post-Sec.
663 Oriole Blvd 75116 972-298-0100

Eagle Lake, Colorado, Pop. 3,613
Rice Consolidated ISD
Supt. — See Altair
Rice Challenge Academy 100/Alt
600 Hwy 3013 W 77434 979-234-3531
Lisa Krenek, prin.

Eagle Pass, Maverick, Pop. 26,203
Eagle Pass ISD 15,000/PK-12
1420 Eidson Rd 78852 830-773-5181
Gilberto Gonzalez, supt. Fax 773-7252
www.eaglepassisd.net
Eagle Pass HS 2,300/9-12
2020 2nd St 78852 830-773-2381
Valeriano Moreno, prin. Fax 758-1795
Eagle Pass JHS 1,200/7-8
1750 N Bibb Ave 78852 830-758-7037
Mario Escobar, prin. Fax 757-1278
Memorial JHS 1,100/7-8
1800 Lewis St 78852 830-758-7053
Maria Sumpter, prin. Fax 773-8900
Winn HS 2,000/9-12
265 Foster Maldonado Blvd 78852 830-757-0828
Jesus Diaz-Wever, prin. Fax 757-3268

Southwest School Post-Sec.
272 Commercial St 78852 830-773-1373

Early, Brown, Pop. 2,720
Early ISD 1,200/PK-12
PO Box 3315, Brownwood TX 76803 325-646-7934
Wes Beck, supt. Fax 646-9238
www.earlyisd.net
Early HS 300/9-12
PO Box 3315, Brownwood TX 76803 325-643-4593
Jennifer Kent, prin. Fax 646-4061
Early MS 300/6-8
PO Box 3315, Brownwood TX 76803 325-643-5665
Robert Weyman, prin. Fax 646-9972

Earth, Lamb, Pop. 1,057
Springlake-Earth ISD 400/PK-12
PO Box 130 79031 806-257-3310
Denver Crum, supt. Fax 257-3927
www.springlake-earth.org
Springlake-Earth HS 100/8-12
PO Box 130 79031 806-257-3819
Cindy Furr, prin. Fax 257-3370

East Bernard, Wharton, Pop. 2,255
East Bernard ISD 1,000/PK-12
723 College St 77435 979-335-7519
Courtney Hudgins, supt. Fax 335-6561
www.ebisd.org
East Bernard HS 300/9-12
723 College St 77435 979-335-7519
Jay Janczak, prin. Fax 335-6085
East Bernard JHS 300/5-8
723 College St 77435 979-335-7519
Emmett Tugwell M.Ed., prin. Fax 335-6415

Eastland, Eastland, Pop. 3,922
Eastland ISD 1,100/PK-12
PO Box 31 76448 254-631-5120
Jason Cochran, supt. Fax 631-5126
www.eastlandisd.net/
Eastland HS 300/9-12
PO Box 31 76448 254-631-5000
Steven Valkenaar, prin. Fax 631-5025
Eastland MS 300/6-8
PO Box 31 76448 254-631-5040
Jason Henry, prin. Fax 631-5049

Ector, Fannin, Pop. 677
Ector ISD 300/PK-12
PO Box 128 75439 903-961-2355
Gary Bohannon, supt. Fax 961-2110
www.ectorisd.net
Ector HS 100/7-12
PO Box 128 75439 903-961-2076
Brad Evans, prin. Fax 961-2356

Edcouch, Hidalgo, Pop. 3,161
Edcouch-Elsa ISD 4,800/PK-12
PO Box 127 78538 956-262-6000
Dr. Richard Rivera, supt. Fax 262-6032
www.eeisd.org
Other Schools – See Elsa

Eddy, McLennan, Pop. 1,113
Bruceville-Eddy ISD 800/PK-12
1 Eagle Dr 76524 254-859-5525
Richard Kilgore, supt. Fax 859-4023
www.beisd.net
Bruceville-Eddy HS 200/9-12
1 Eagle Dr 76524 254-859-5848
Joe Woodard, prin. Fax 859-5001
Bruceville-Eddy MS 100/7-8
1 Eagle Dr 76524 254-859-5525
Mike Hawkins, prin. Fax 859-3207
Other Schools – See Waco

Eden, Concho, Pop. 2,753
Eden Consolidated ISD 200/K-12
PO Box 988 76837 325-869-4121
Kent Coker, supt. Fax 869-5210
www.edencisd.net
Eden JSHS 100/6-12
PO Box 988 76837 325-869-4121
Rebecca Bunger, prin. Fax 869-5023

Edgewood, Van Zandt, Pop. 1,419
Edgewood ISD 900/PK-12
804 E Pine St 75117 903-896-4332
Emmett Baker, supt. Fax 896-7056
www.edgewood-isd.net
Edgewood HS 300/9-12
804 E Pine St 75117 903-896-4856
Jerri Wehmeyer, prin. Fax 896-1050
Edgewood MS 200/6-8
804 E Pine St 75117 903-896-1530
Kristin Prater, prin. Fax 896-7056

Edinburg, Hidalgo, Pop. 76,876
Edinburg Consolidated ISD 34,000/PK-12
PO Box 990 78540 956-289-2300
Dr. Rene Gutierrez, supt. Fax 383-3576
www.ecisd.us/
Barrientes MS 1,300/6-8
PO Box 990 78540 956-289-2430
Robert Lopez, prin. Fax 316-7749
Economedes HS 2,500/9-12
PO Box 990 78540 956-289-2450
Anthony Garza, prin. Fax 385-3050
Edinburg Alternative Education Academy Alt
PO Box 990 78540 956-289-2598
David Rivera, prin. Fax 316-7391
Edinburg HS 2,200/9-12
PO Box 990 78540 956-289-2400
Yesenia Molina, prin. Fax 386-1225
Edinburg North HS 2,600/9-12
PO Box 990 78540 956-289-2500
Mark Micallef, prin. Fax 316-7712
Edinburg South MS 1,500/6-8
PO Box 990 78540 956-289-2415
Dr. Mary Garza, prin. Fax 316-8817
Garza MS 1,100/6-8
PO Box 990 78540 956-289-2480
Anibal Gorena, prin. Fax 316-3109
Harwell MS 1,400/6-8
PO Box 990 78540 956-289-2440
Dr. Raul D'Lorm, prin. Fax 316-7303
Longoria MS 1,000/6-8
PO Box 990 78540 956-289-2486
Jorge Botello, prin. Fax 381-6442
Memorial MS 1,200/6-8
PO Box 990 78540 956-289-2470
Fermin Gonzalez, prin. Fax 316-7581
Vela HS 2,000/9-12
PO Box 990 78540 956-289-2650
Sylvia Ledesma, prin. Fax 383-3576
Vision Academy of Excellence Alt
PO Box 990 78540 956-289-2584
Ernestina Cano, prin. Fax 287-0812

South Texas ISD
Supt. — See Mercedes
South Texas Business Educ &Tech Academy 600/9-12
510 S Sugar Rd 78539 956-383-1684
Dr. Nora Casarez, prin. Fax 383-8544
South Texas Preparatory Academy 600/7-8
724 S Sugar Rd 78539 956-381-5522
Ana Castro, prin. Fax 381-1177

Rio Grande Bible Institute Post-Sec.
4300 S US Highway 281 78539 956-380-8100
University of Texas Pan American Post-Sec.
1201 W University Dr 78539 866-441-8812

Edna, Jackson, Pop. 5,438
Edna ISD 1,600/PK-12
601 N Wells 77957 361-782-3573
Robert O'Connor, supt. Fax 781-1002
www.ednaisd.org
Edna Alternative Center 50/Alt
112 W Ash St 77957 361-782-9051
Sonya Proper, prin.
Edna HS 400/9-12
1303 W Gayle St 77957 361-782-5255
Demetric Wells, prin. Fax 781-1014
Edna JHS 300/6-8
505 W Gayle St 77957 361-782-2351
Brandie Roe, prin. Fax 781-1025

Edna Christian Academy 50/PK-12
PO Box 885 77957 361-782-2052
Rev. Darrell Clark, prin.

El Campo, Wharton, Pop. 11,547
El Campo ISD 3,600/PK-12
700 W Norris St 77437 979-543-6771
Kelly Waters M.Ed., supt. Fax 543-1670
www.ecisd.org
El Campo HS 1,000/9-12
600 W Norris St 77437 979-543-6341
Rich DuBroc, prin. Fax 543-2528

El Campo MS 800/6-8
4010 FM 2765 Rd 77437 979-543-6362
Mark Freeman, prin. Fax 541-5210

Eldorado, Schleicher, Pop. 1,941
Schleicher ISD 600/PK-12
PO Box W 76936 325-853-2514
Robert Gibson, supt. Fax 853-2695
www.scisd.net
Eldorado HS 200/9-12
PO Box W 76936 325-853-2514
Ernest Reynolds, prin. Fax 853-2710
Eldorado MS 200/5-8
PO Box W 76936 325-853-2514
Ezra Walling, prin. Fax 853-2895

Electra, Wichita, Pop. 2,739
Electra ISD 300/PK-12
PO Box 231 76360 940-495-3683
Scott Hogue, supt. Fax 495-3945
www.electraisd.net
Electra JSHS 200/7-12
400 E Roosevelt Ave 76360 940-495-2218
Michael Stevens, prin. Fax 495-3303

Elgin, Bastrop, Pop. 7,996
Elgin ISD 4,200/PK-12
PO Box 351 78621 512-281-3434
Dr. Jodi Duron, supt. Fax 285-5388
www.elginisd.net
Elgin HS 1,200/9-12
14000 County Line Rd 78621 512-281-3438
Cheryl Koury, prin. Fax 281-9804
Elgin MS 900/6-8
1351 N Avenue C 78621 512-281-3382
Riza Cooper, prin. Fax 281-9781
Phoenix HS 50/Alt
902 W 2nd St 78621 512-281-9774
Mike Adams, prin. Fax 281-9862

Elkhart, Anderson, Pop. 1,338
Elkhart ISD 1,200/PK-12
301 E Parker St 75839 903-764-2952
Dr. Ray DeSpain, supt. Fax 764-2466
www.elkhartisd.org/
Elkhart HS 400/9-12
301 E Parker St 75839 903-764-5161
Jason Ives, prin. Fax 764-8288
Elkhart MS 300/6-8
301 E Parker St 75839 903-764-2459
Ron Mays, prin. Fax 764-8287

Slocum ISD 300/PK-12
5765 E State Highway 294 75839 903-478-3624
Cliff Lasiter, supt. Fax 478-3030
www.slocumisd.org
Slocum HS 100/9-12
5765 E State Highway 294 75839 903-478-3624
Errin Deer, prin. Fax 478-3030

Elmaton, Matagorda
Tidehaven ISD, PO Box 129 77440 800/PK-12
Dr. Andrew Seigrist, supt. 979-843-4302
www.tidehavenisd.com
Tidehaven HS, PO Box 159 77440 200/9-12
Patrick Talbert, prin. 979-843-4310
Tidehaven IS, PO Box 130 77440 200/6-8
Patrick Talbert, prin. 979-843-4320

Elm Mott, McLennan
Connally ISD
Supt. — See Waco
Connally JHS 500/6-8
100 Hancock Dr 76640 254-296-7700
Jeremy Ferrero, prin. Fax 829-2354

El Paso, El Paso, Pop. 643,027
Canutillo ISD 6,000/PK-12
7965 Artcraft Rd 79932 915-877-7400
Dr. Pedro Galaviz, supt. Fax 877-7414
www.canutillo-isd.org
Canutillo HS 1,600/9-12
6675 S Desert Blvd 79932 915-877-7800
Teresa Clapsaddle, prin. Fax 877-7807
Other Schools – See Canutillo

Clint ISD 11,800/PK-12
14521 Horizon Blvd 79928 915-926-4000
Juan Martinez, supt. Fax 926-4009
www.clintweb.net
East Montana MS 700/6-8
3490 Ascension Rd 79938 915-926-5200
Dr. Juanita Guerra, prin. Fax 855-0821
Estrada JHS 900/8-9
851 Darrington Rd 79928 915-926-4800
Lorraine Vidales, prin. Fax 852-2455
Horizon HS 1,100/9-12
14651 Horizon Blvd 79928 915-926-4200
Elena Acosta, prin. Fax 852-0357
Mountain View HS 800/9-12
14964 Greg Dr 79938 915-926-5000
Paul Harrington, prin. Fax 855-2503
Other Schools – See Clint

El Paso ISD 60,900/PK-12
PO Box 20100 79998 915-230-2000
Juan Cabrera, supt. Fax 887-5484
www.episd.org
Andress HS 1,800/9-12
5400 Sun Valley Dr 79924 915-236-4000
Robert Ortega, prin. Fax 757-6443
Armendariz MS 800/6-8
2231 Arizona Ave 79930 915-546-9012
Lorenzo Munoz, prin. Fax 577-0848
Austin HS 1,500/9-12
3500 Memphis Ave 79930 915-587-2500
Craig Kehrwald, prin. Fax 566-7360
Bassett MS 700/6-8
4400 Elm St 79930 915-231-2260
Michelle Kirkland, prin. Fax 565-1562

Bowie HS 1,200/9-12
801 S San Marcial St 79905 915-496-8200
Michael Warmack, prin. Fax 532-1918
Brown MS 900/6-8
7820 Helen Of Troy Dr 79912 915-774-4080
Carmen Solis-Rodriguez, prin. Fax 581-6424
Burges HS 1,400/9-12
7800 Edgemere Blvd 79925 915-780-1100
Randall Woods, prin. Fax 771-6914
Canyon Hills MS 800/6-8
8930 Eclipse St 79904 915-231-2240
Jennifer DeGraaf, prin. Fax 757-8067
Center for Career & Technology Education Vo/Tech
1170 N Walnut St 79930 915-236-7900
Matthew Farley, prin. Fax 544-5976
Chapin HS 1,900/9-12
7000 Dyer St 79904 915-832-6730
Robert Marsh, prin. Fax 565-9716
Charles MS 700/6-8
4909 Trojan Dr 79924 915-236-6550
David Zamora, prin. Fax 821-0505
College Career and Technology Academy Alt
2851 Grant Ave 79930 915-236-7000
Adan Lopez, prin. Fax 585-4789
Coronado HS 2,600/9-12
100 Champions Pl 79912 915-236-2000
Angela Henderson, prin. Fax 587-6458
Delta Academy 100/Alt
6400 Delta Dr 79905 915-774-0447
Ernie Watts, admin. Fax 881-1245
El Paso HS 1,300/9-12
800 E Schuster Ave 79902 915-496-8300
Kristine Ferret, prin. Fax 532-2008
Franklin HS 2,800/9-12
900 N Resler Dr 79912 915-236-2200
Rose Ann Martinez, prin. Fax 587-4094
Guillen MS 900/6-8
900 S Cotton St 79901 915-496-4620
Teresa Zamarripa, prin. Fax 532-1143
Henderson MS 800/6-8
5505 Robert Alva Ave 79905 915-887-3080
Elizabeth Maldonado, prin. Fax 772-3425
Hornedo MS 1,200/6-8
6101 High Ridge Dr 79912 915-881-2900
Micaela Varela, prin. Fax 581-7371
Irvin HS 1,500/9-12
9465 Roanoke Dr 79924 915-587-3500
Jennifer DeGraaf, prin. Fax 757-6450
Jefferson HS 1,100/9-12
4700 Alameda Ave 79905 915-496-8010
Federico Rojas, prin. Fax 532-2033
Lafarelle Alternative MS 50/Alt
320 S Campbell 79901 915-751-7186
Ernesto Pena, prin. Fax 751-1316
Lincoln MS 1,000/6-8
500 Mulberry Ave 79932 915-231-2180
Heidi Appel, prin. Fax 581-1371
Magoffin MS 800/6-8
4931 Hercules Ave 79904 915-774-4040
Rogelio Segovia, prin. Fax 757-7675
Morehead MS 800/6-8
5625 Confetti Dr 79912 915-231-2140
Armando Gallegos, prin. Fax 587-5355
Occupational Center Vo/Tech
5300 Warriors Dr 79932 915-230-2870
Fax 584-2940
Richardson MS 700/6-8
11350 Loma Franklin Dr 79934 915-822-8829
Joseph Manago, prin. Fax 822-8812
Ross MS 1,000/6-8
6101 Hughey Cir 79925 915-887-3060
Jason Yturralde, prin. Fax 771-6792
Silva Health Magnet HS 600/9-12
121 Val Verde St 79905 915-496-8100
Federico Rojas, prin. Fax 533-3695
Telles Academy 100/Alt
320 S Campbell St 79901 915-496-4600
Christian James, prin. Fax 532-0540
Terrace Hills MS 700/6-8
4835 Blossom Ave 79924 915-231-2120
Christopher Smith, prin. Fax 759-0615
Transmountain Early College HS 400/9-12
9570 Gateway Blvd N 79924 915-832-4270
Robert Pancoast, prin. Fax 751-2011
Wiggs MS 900/6-8
1300 Circle Dr 79902 915-231-2100
Timothy Luther, prin. Fax 533-2902
San Jacinto Adult Learning Center Adult
1216 Olive Ave 79901 915-230-3200
Arturo Gonzalez, admin. Fax 544-7163

Socorro ISD 45,900/PK-12
12440 Rojas Dr 79928 915-937-0000
Jose Espinoza Ed.D., supt. Fax 851-7572
www.sisd.net
Americas HS 2,300/9-12
12101 Pellicano Dr 79936 915-937-2800
Patricia Cuevas, prin. Fax 855-6898
Clarke MS 1,000/6-8
1515 Bob Hope Dr 79936 915-937-5600
Thomas Redlinger, prin. Fax 857-3765
Eastlake HS 1,800/9-12
13000 Emerald Pass Ave 79928 915-937-3600
Gilbert Martinez, prin. Fax 937-3799
El Dorado HS 2,600/9-12
12401 Edgemere Blvd 79938 915-937-3200
Cynthia Retana, prin. Fax 851-7820
Ensor MS 1,000/6-8
13600 Ryderwood Dr 79928 915-937-6000
Naomi Esparza, prin. Fax 851-7590
Hernando MS 900/6-8
3451 Rich Beem 79938 915-937-9800
Venessa Betancourt, prin. Fax 937-9898
K.E.Y.S. Academy 100/Alt
12380 Pine Springs Dr 79928 915-937-4000
Dr. Magdalena Aguilar, prin. Fax 937-4006

Mission Early College HS 500/9-12
10700 Gateway Blvd E 79927 915-937-1200
Jason Long, prin. Fax 860-2935
Montwood HS 2,700/9-12
12000 Montwood Dr 79936 915-937-2400
Rosa Mireles-Menchaca, prin. Fax 937-2422
Montwood MS 800/6-8
11710 Pebble Hills Blvd 79936 915-937-5800
Sylvia Esparza, prin. Fax 856-9909
Options HS 200/Alt
12380 Pine Springs Dr 79928 915-937-1300
Dr. Magdalena Aguilar, prin. Fax 859-2603
Pebble Hills HS 2,800/9-12
14400 Pebble Hills Blvd 79938 915-937-9400
Malessa Parham, prin. Fax 851-7912
Puentes MS 600/6-8
3216 Tim Foster 79938 915-937-9200
Monica Castro, prin. Fax 851-7855
Sanchez MS 700/6-8
321 N Rio Vista Rd 79927 915-937-5200
Rosa Barrio, prin. Fax 859-6636
Slider MS 800/6-8
11700 School Ln 79936 915-937-5400
Enrique Herrera, prin. Fax 857-5804
Socorro HS 2,500/9-12
10150 Alameda Ave 79927 915-937-2000
Federico Tovar, prin. Fax 937-2394
Socorro MS 600/6-8
321 Bovee Rd 79927 915-937-5000
Jonathan Valdez, prin. Fax 859-6955
Sun Ridge MS 900/6-8
2210 Sun Country Dr 79938 915-937-6600
Ignacio Estorga, prin. Fax 851-7730

Ysleta ISD 42,200/PK-12
9600 Sims Dr 79925 915-434-0000
Dr. Xavier De La Torre, supt. Fax 591-4144
www.yisd.net
Bel Air HS 2,100/9-12
731 N Yarbrough Dr 79915 915-434-2000
Charles Garcia, prin. Fax 593-6110
Bel Air MS 500/7-8
8040 Yermoland Dr 79907 915-434-2200
Dana DeRouen, prin. Fax 591-9439
Camino Real MS 700/6-8
9393 Alameda Ave 79907 915-434-8300
Ida Resendez-Perales, prin. Fax 858-3743
Chavez Academy 100/Alt
7814 Alameda Ave 79915 915-434-9600
Graciela Martinez, prin. Fax 779-2068
Del Valle HS 1,800/9-12
950 Bordeaux Dr 79907 915-434-3000
Antonio Acuna, prin. Fax 858-1427
Desert View MS 500/6-8
1641 Billie Marie Dr 79936 915-434-5300
Maryann Olivas, prin. Fax 591-9327
Eastwood HS 2,300/9-12
2430 Mcrae Blvd 79925 915-434-4000
Armenia Smith, prin. Fax 594-8014
Eastwood MS 1,000/7-8
2612 Chaswood St 79935 915-434-4300
James Boatright, prin. Fax 591-9426
Hanks HS 1,800/9-12
2001 N Lee Trevino Dr 79936 915-434-5000
Gloria Spencer, prin. Fax 598-4621
Indian Ridge MS 800/6-8
11201 Pebble Hills Blvd 79936 915-434-5400
Pauline Muela, prin. Fax 591-9447
Parkland HS 1,300/9-12
5932 Quail Ave 79924 915-434-6000
Dr. Darryl Hensen, prin. Fax 434-6291
Parkland MS 1,200/6-8
6045 Nova Way 79924 915-434-6300
Javier Selgado, prin. Fax 757-6608
Plato Academy 200/Alt
8441 Alameda Ave 79907 915-434-9000
Michael Martinez, prin. Fax 434-9080
Rio Bravo MS 500/6-8
525 Greggerson Dr 79907 915-434-8400
Dr. Sandra Calzada, prin. Fax 872-0269
Riverside HS 1,200/9-12
301 Midway Dr 79915 915-434-7000
Daniel Gurany, prin. Fax 779-6983
Riverside MS 600/7-8
7615 Mimosa Ave 79915 915-434-7300
Jonathan Valdez, prin. Fax 772-7549
Tejas School of Choice 200/Alt
7500 Alpha Ave 79915 915-434-9900
Dr. Lucy Lozano-Lerma, prin. Fax 772-8366
Valle Verde Early College HS 400/9-12
919 Hunter Dr 79915 915-434-1500
Paul Covey, prin. Fax 594-7112
Valley View MS 700/6-8
8660 N Loop Dr 79907 915-434-3300
Penny Bankston, prin. Fax 858-3615
Ysleta HS 1,400/9-12
8600 Alameda Ave 79907 915-434-8000
Silvia Rendon, prin. Fax 858-3299
Ysleta MS 600/6-8
8691 Independence Dr 79907 915-434-8200
Homero Silva, prin. Fax 858-0261
Ysleta Community Learning Center Adult
121 Padres Dr 79907 915-434-9400
Louis Martinez, prin. Fax 858-6307

Anamarc College Post-Sec.
3210 Dyer St 79930 915-351-8100
Anamarc College Post-Sec.
8720 Gateway Blvd E Ste D 79907 915-351-8100
Brightwood College Post-Sec.
8360 Burnham Rd Ste 100 79907 915-595-1935
Cathedral HS 500/9-12
1309 N Stanton St 79902 915-532-3238
Aurora Lujan M.P., prin. Fax 533-8248
El Paso Community College Post-Sec.
PO Box 20500 79998 915-831-2000

Faith Christian Academy 500/PK-12
8960 Escobar Dr 79907 915-594-3305
Shannon Nieman, supt. Fax 593-5474
Father Yermo HS 200/9-12
250 Washington St 79905 915-533-3185
Sr. Karina Tapia, prin. Fax 544-0738
Immanuel Christian S 600/PK-12
1201 Hawkins Blvd 79925 915-778-6160
John Davis, head sch Fax 772-8207
International Business College Post-Sec.
5700 Cromo Dr 79912 915-842-0422
International Business College Post-Sec.
1155 N Zaragoza Rd Ste 100 79907 915-859-0422
iTEC Preparatory Academy 9-12
5450 Hurd Pl 79912 915-581-5600
Tim Rall, hdmstr. Fax 581-5612
Jesus Chapel S 200/PK-12
10200 Album Ave 79925 915-591-9330
Alba Wilcox, prin. Fax 593-1113
Loretto Academy 700/PK-12
1300 Hardaway St 79903 915-566-8400
Abe Ramirez, prin. Fax 564-0563
North Loop Christian Academy 50/PK-12
8617 N Loop Dr 79907 915-872-9435
Valerie Devine, dir.
Patterson Institute 200/7-12
517 S Florence St 79901 915-533-8286
Pipo Academy of Hair Design Post-Sec.
3000 Pershing Dr 79903 915-565-3491
Radford S 100/PK-12
2001 Radford St 79903 915-565-2737
Southwest University at El Paso Post-Sec.
1414 Geronimo Dr 79925 915-778-4001
Tri-State Cosmetology Institute Post-Sec.
601 N Cotton St Ste 5 79902 915-585-8777
Tri-State Cosmetology Institute Post-Sec.
6800 Gateway Blvd E Ste 4A 79915 915-778-1741
University of Texas at El Paso Post-Sec.
500 W University Ave 79968 915-747-5000
Vista College Post-Sec.
6101 Montana Ave 79925 866-442-4197
Western Technical College Post-Sec.
9624 Plaza Cir 79927 915-532-3737
Western Technical College Post-Sec.
9451 Diana Dr 79924 915-566-9621

Elsa, Hidalgo, Pop. 5,655
Edcouch-Elsa ISD
Supt. — See Edcouch
Edcouch-Elsa HS 1,300/9-12
401 N Yellowjacket Dr 78543 956-262-6944
Miguel Castillo, prin. Fax 262-9018
Truan JHS 800/7-8
E 9th St 78543 956-262-6082
Aldo Vidal, prin. Fax 262-6079

Elysian Fields, Harrison
Elysian Fields ISD 1,000/PK-12
PO Box 120 75642 903-633-2420
Maynard Chapman, supt. Fax 633-2498
www.efisd.net
Elysian Fields HS 300/9-12
PO Box 120 75642 903-633-2420
Jack Parker, prin. Fax 633-2498
Elysian Fields MS 200/6-8
PO Box 120 75642 903-633-2420
Brandon Goswick, prin. Fax 633-2326

Emory, Rains, Pop. 1,215
Rains ISD 1,600/PK-12
PO Box 247 75440 903-473-2222
John Rouse, supt. Fax 473-3053
www.rainsisd.org
Rains HS 500/9-12
PO Box 247 75440 903-473-2222
Randell Wellman, prin. Fax 473-5584
Rains JHS 400/6-8
PO Box 247 75440 903-473-2222
Gina Hildebrandt, prin. Fax 473-5162

Ennis, Ellis, Pop. 18,329
Ennis ISD 5,700/PK-12
PO Box 1420 75120 972-872-7000
Dr. John Chapman, supt. Fax 875-8667
www.ennis.k12.tx.us
Ennis HS 1,600/9-12
2301 Ensign Rd 75119 972-872-3500
David Averett, prin. Fax 875-6337
Ennis JHS 800/7-8
3101 Ensign Rd 75119 972-872-3850
Wade Bishop, prin. Fax 875-9044

Era, Cooke
Era ISD 400/K-12
108 Hargrove St 76238 940-665-5961
Jeremy Thompson, supt. Fax 665-5311
www.eraisd.net
Era JSHS 200/7-12
108 Hargrove St 76238 940-665-5961
Jereme Dietz, prin. Fax 665-5311

Euless, Tarrant, Pop. 48,852
Hurst-Euless-Bedford ISD
Supt. — See Bedford
Alternative Education Program 50/Alt
1100 Raider Dr Ste 100 76040 817-354-3398
Damon Emery, coord. Fax 358-5001
Central JHS 1,000/7-9
3191 W Pipeline Rd 76040 817-354-3350
Randy Belcher, prin. Fax 354-3357
Euless JHS 1,000/7-9
306 Airport Fwy 76039 817-354-3340
Sonya Stanton, prin. Fax 354-3345
KEYS HS 100/Alt
1100 Raider Dr Ste 100 76040 817-354-3580
Janet Joseph, prin. Fax 354-3586
Trinity HS 2,400/10-12
500 N Industrial Blvd 76039 817-571-0271
Micheal Harris, prin. Fax 354-3322

Messenger College Post-Sec.
400 S Industrial Blvd 76040 817-554-5950

Eustace, Henderson, Pop. 976
Eustace ISD 1,500/PK-12
PO Box 188 75124 903-425-5151
Dr. Coy Holcombe, supt. Fax 425-5147
www.eustaceisd.net
Eustace HS 400/9-12
PO Box 188 75124 903-425-5161
Chris Whorton, prin. Fax 425-5227
Eustace MS 300/6-8
PO Box 188 75124 903-425-5171
Truman Oakley, prin. Fax 425-5146

Evadale, Jasper, Pop. 1,471
Evadale ISD 500/PK-12
PO Box 497 77615 409-276-1337
Gary Fairchild, supt. Fax 276-1908
www.evadalek12.net
Evadale HS 200/9-12
PO Box 497 77615 409-276-1337
Rusty Minyard, prin. Fax 276-1050
Evadale JHS 100/6-8
PO Box 497 77615 409-276-1337
Cheryl Jones, prin. Fax 276-1588

Evant, Coryell, Pop. 421
Evant ISD 200/PK-12
PO Box 339 76525 254-471-5536
James Slone, supt. Fax 471-5629
www.evantisd.org/
Evant HS 100/7-12
PO Box 339 76525 254-471-5536
Craig Taylor, prin. Fax 471-5629

Everman, Tarrant, Pop. 6,051
Everman ISD 5,500/PK-12
608 Townley Dr 76140 817-568-3500
Curtis Amos, supt. Fax 568-3508
www.eisd.org
Baxter JHS 800/7-8
3038 Shelby Rd 76140 817-568-3530
Kentrel Phillips, prin. Fax 568-3594
Everman Academy HS 1,300/9-12
300 Shelby Rd 76140 817-568-3520
Martin DeHoyos, prin. Fax 568-3516
Everman HS, 1000 S Race St 76140 50/9-12
Dr. Melvin Bedford, prin. 817-568-5200

Fabens, El Paso, Pop. 8,249
Fabens ISD 2,400/PK-12
PO Box 697 79838 915-765-2600
Poncho Garcia, supt. Fax 764-2968
www.fabensisd.net/
Fabens HS 700/9-12
PO Box 697 79838 915-765-2620
Ruben Carrillo, prin. Fax 764-4953
Fabens MS 500/6-8
PO Box 697 79838 915-765-2630
Dr. Joe Keith, prin. Fax 764-7263

Fairfield, Freestone, Pop. 2,920
Fairfield ISD 1,800/PK-12
615 Post Oak Rd 75840 903-389-2532
Melissa Cox, supt. Fax 389-7050
www.fairfieldisd.net
Fairfield HS 500/9-12
615 Post Oak Rd 75840 903-389-4177
Von Wade M.Ed., prin. Fax 389-5453
Fairfield JHS 400/6-8
615 Post Oak Rd 75840 903-389-4210
Bryan Gawryszewski M.Ed., prin. Fax 389-5454

Falfurrias, Brooks, Pop. 4,970
Brooks County ISD 1,500/PK-12
PO Box 589 78355 361-325-8000
Dr. Maria Casas, supt. Fax 325-1913
www.bcisdistrict.net
Falfurrias HS 400/9-12
PO Box 589 78355 361-325-8091
Dr. Cynthia Perez, prin. Fax 325-8158
Falfurrias JHS 300/6-8
PO Box 589 78355 361-325-8071
Maria Vidaurri, prin. Fax 325-8156

Falls City, Karnes, Pop. 604
Falls City ISD 400/K-12
PO Box 399 78113 830-254-3551
Todd Pawelek, supt. Fax 254-3354
www.fcisd.net
Falls City JSHS 200/7-12
PO Box 399 78113 830-254-3551
Christy Blocker, prin. Fax 254-3354

Farmers Branch, Dallas, Pop. 28,241
Carrollton-Farmers Branch ISD
Supt. — See Carrollton
Field MS 900/6-8
13551 Dennis Ln 75234 972-968-3900
Stephanie Jimenez, prin. Fax 968-3910

Brookhaven College Post-Sec.
3939 Valley View Ln 75244 972-860-4700

Farmersville, Collin, Pop. 3,235
Farmersville ISD 1,500/PK-12
501A State Highway 78 N 75442 972-782-6601
Jeff Adams, supt. Fax 784-7293
www.farmersvilleisd.net
Farmersville HS 400/9-12
499 State Highway 78 N 75442 972-782-7757
Wayne Callaway, prin. Fax 782-7245
Farmersville JHS 400/6-8
501 State Highway 78 N 75442 972-782-6202
Dr. Josh Martin, prin. Fax 782-7029

Farwell, Parmer, Pop. 1,360
Farwell ISD 500/PK-12
PO Box F 79325 806-481-3371
Kelly Lusk, supt. Fax 481-9275
www.farwellschools.org
Farwell HS 100/9-12
PO Box F 79325 806-481-3351
Coby Norman, prin. Fax 481-3531
Farwell JHS 100/6-8
PO Box F 79325 806-481-9260
Kristy White, prin. Fax 481-9258

Fayetteville, Fayette, Pop. 257
Fayetteville ISD 200/PK-12
PO Box 129 78940 979-378-4242
Jeff Harvey, supt. Fax 378-4246
www.fayettevilleisd.net
Fayetteville S 200/PK-12
PO Box 129 78940 979-378-4242
Brynn Lopez, prin. Fax 378-4246

Ferris, Ellis, Pop. 2,412
Ferris ISD 2,300/PK-12
PO Box 459 75125 972-544-3858
James Hartman, supt. Fax 544-2784
www.ferrisisd.org
Ferris HS 700/9-12
PO Box 461 75125 972-544-3737
Kevin Dixon, prin. Fax 544-2029
Ferris JHS 400/6-8
PO Box 459 75125 972-544-2279
Rhonda Renner, prin. Fax 544-2281

Fischer, Comal
Comal ISD
Supt. — See New Braunfels
Canyon Lake HS 900/9-12
8555 FM 32 78623 830-885-1700
Blake Hays, prin. Fax 885-1701

Flatonia, Fayette, Pop. 1,376
Flatonia ISD 600/PK-12
PO Box 189 78941 361-865-2941
Beverly Mikulenka, supt. Fax 865-2940
www.flatoniaisd.net
Flatonia HS 300/7-12
PO Box 189 78941 361-865-2941
Chris Sodek, prin. Fax 865-2944
Whispering Hills Achievement Center 50/Alt
PO Box 189 78941 361-865-2941
Robin Branecky, prin. Fax 865-2940

Florence, Williamson, Pop. 1,128
Florence ISD 1,000/PK-12
306 College Ave 76527 254-793-2850
Paul Michalewicz, supt. Fax 793-3055
florenceisd.net
Florence HS 300/9-12
401 County Road 970 76527 254-793-2495
Steve Elder, prin. Fax 793-3784
Florence MS 200/6-8
718 S Patterson 76527 254-793-2504
Catherine Beckerley, prin. Fax 793-3054

Floresville, Wilson, Pop. 6,407
Floresville ISD 3,800/PK-12
1200 5th St 78114 830-393-5300
Sherri Bays Ed.D., supt. Fax 393-5399
www.fisd.us
Floresville Alternative S 50/Alt
335 Alternative Ln 78114 830-393-5368
Angela Garcia, prin. Fax 393-5706
Floresville HS 1,100/9-12
1813 Tiger Ln 78114 830-393-5370
Michael Schroller, prin. Fax 393-5719
Floresville MS 900/6-8
2601 B St 78114 830-393-5350
Marcia Gonzales, prin. Fax 393-5339

Flower Mound, Denton, Pop. 63,499
Lewisville ISD 49,700/PK-12
1800 Timber Creek Rd 75028 469-713-5200
Kevin Rogers Ed.D., supt. Fax 350-9500
www.lisd.net
Downing MS 700/6-8
5555 Bridlewood Blvd 75028 469-713-5962
Lisa Lingren, prin. Fax 350-9176
Flower Mound 9th Grade Campus 9-9
3411A Peters Colony Rd 75022 469-713-5999
Will Skelton, prin.
Flower Mound HS 2,400/10-12
3411 Peters Colony Rd 75022 469-713-5192
Sonya Lail, prin. Fax 350-9237
Forestwood MS 700/6-8
2810 Morriss Rd 75028 469-713-5972
Dave Tickner, prin. Fax 350-9184
Lamar MS 800/6-8
4000 Timber Creek Rd 75028 469-713-5966
Rebecca Clark, prin. Fax 350-9204
Marcus 9th Grade Campus 9-9
5707A Morriss Rd 75028 469-713-5998
Chantell Upshaw, prin.
Marcus HS 2,400/10-12
5707 Morriss Rd 75028 469-713-5196
Gary Shafferman, prin. Fax 350-9313
McKamy MS 1,100/6-8
2401 Old Settlers Rd 75022 469-713-5991
Kelly Knight, prin. Fax 350-9477
Shadow Ridge MS 800/6-8
2050 Aberdeen Dr 75028 469-713-5984
Gary Gibson, prin. Fax 350-9215
Other Schools – See Carrollton, Highland Village, Lewisville, The Colony

---

Coram Deo Academy 1,100/PK-12
4900 Wichita Trl 75022 972-237-0232
Temple Christian Academy 200/K-12
2501 Northshore Blvd 75028 972-874-8700

Floydada, Floyd, Pop. 3,029
Floydada ISD 700/PK-12
226 W California St 79235 806-983-3498
Dr. Gilbert Trevino, supt. Fax 983-5739
www.floydadaisd.esc17.net
Floydada HS 200/9-12
618 Whirlwind Aly 79235 806-983-2340
Wayne Morren, prin.
Floydada JHS 100/7-8
618 Whirlwind Aly 79235 806-983-4961
Wayne Morren, prin. Fax 983-5739

Follett, Lipscomb, Pop. 459
Follett ISD 200/PK-12
PO Box 28 79034 806-653-2301
George Auld, supt. Fax 653-2036
www.follettisd.net
Follett S 200/PK-12
PO Box 28 79034 806-653-2301
Brianna Ethridge, prin. Fax 653-2036

Forestburg, Montague
Forestburg ISD 200/PK-12
PO Box 415 76239 940-964-2323
John Metzler, supt. Fax 964-2531
www.forestburgisd.net
Forestburg S 200/PK-12
PO Box 415 76239 940-964-2323
Randy Seeds, prin. Fax 964-2531

Forney, Kaufman, Pop. 14,459
Forney ISD 8,600/PK-12
600 S Bois d Arc St 75126 972-564-4055
Suzanne McWilliams, supt. Fax 552-3038
www.forneyisd.net
Brown MS 700/7-8
1050 Windmill Farms Blvd 75126 972-564-3967
Dr. Stephen Chapman, prin. Fax 355-1099
Forney HS 1,400/9-12
800 FM 741 75126 972-564-3890
Stephen Whiffen, prin. Fax 564-5616
North Forney HS 1,200/9-12
6170 Falcon Way 75126 972-762-4159
Courtney Peck, prin. Fax 355-0311
Warren MS 700/7-8
811 S Bois D Arc St 75126 469-762-4156
Joseph Pouncy, prin. Fax 552-1693

Forsan, Howard, Pop. 209
Forsan ISD 700/PK-12
PO Box 689 79733 432-457-2223
Randy Johnson, supt. Fax 457-2225
forsan.esc18.net
Forsan JSHS 400/6-12
PO Box 689 79733 432-457-2223
Terry McDonald, prin. Fax 457-2225

Fort Davis, Jeff Davis, Pop. 1,186
Fort Davis ISD 200/PK-12
PO Box 1339 79734 432-426-4440
Graydon Hicks, supt. Fax 426-3841
www.fdisd.com
Fort Davis JSHS 100/6-12
PO Box 1339 79734 432-426-4444
Luane Porter, prin. Fax 426-4449

Fort Hancock, Hudspeth, Pop. 1,741
Fort Hancock ISD 500/PK-12
PO Box 98 79839 915-769-3811
Jose Franco, supt. Fax 769-3940
www.forthancockisd.net
Fort Hancock HS 100/9-12
PO Box 98 79839 915-769-3811
Lorena Molinar, prin. Fax 769-0044
Fort Hancock MS 100/6-8
PO Box 98 79839 915-769-3811
Daniel Medina, prin. Fax 769-0045

Fort Hood, Bell, Pop. 27,754
Killeen ISD
Supt. — See Killeen
Killeen Early College HS 9-12
51000 Tank Destroyer Blvd 76544 254-336-0260
Kathleen Burke, prin. Fax 336-0271
Murphy MS 500/6-8
53393 Sun Dance Dr 76544 254-336-6530
Mike Quinn, prin. Fax 336-6579

Fort Stockton, Pecos, Pop. 8,231
Fort Stockton ISD 2,400/PK-12
101 W Division St 79735 432-336-4000
Ralph Traynham, supt. Fax 336-4008
www.fsisd.net/
Fort Stockton HS 600/9-12
101 W Division St 79735 432-336-4101
Gil-Ray Madrid, prin. Fax 336-4113
Fort Stockton MS 500/6-8
101 W Division St 79735 432-336-4131
Roy Alvarado, prin. Fax 336-4136

Fort Worth, Tarrant, Pop. 728,297
Castleberry ISD 3,900/PK-12
5228 Ohio Garden Rd 76114 817-252-2000
John Ramos, supt. Fax 252-2097
www.castleberryisd.net
Castleberry HS 900/9-12
215 Churchill Rd 76114 817-252-2100
Dr. Amy Ellis, prin. Fax 252-2199
Marsh MS 900/6-8
415 Hagg Dr 76114 817-252-2200
Derrick Spurlock, prin. Fax 738-3454
TRUCE Learning Center 50/Alt
1101 Merritt St 76114 817-252-2490
Wanda Byther, prin. Fax 252-2498
Other Schools – See River Oaks

Crowley ISD
Supt. — See Crowley
Crowley MS 700/7-8
3800 W Risinger Rd 76123 817-370-5650
Omarion Brown, prin. Fax 370-5656
North Crowley 9th Grade Campus 600/9-9
4630 McPherson Blvd 76123 817-297-5896
Daryle Moffett, prin. Fax 297-5878
North Crowley HS 1,700/10-12
9100 S Hulen St 76123 817-263-1250
Stefani Allen, prin. Fax 263-1282

Eagle Mountain.-Saginaw ISD 18,000/PK-12
1200 Old Decatur Rd 76179 817-232-0880
Jim Chadwell Ed.D., supt. Fax 847-6124
www.emsisd.com
Boswell HS 1,700/9-12
5805 W Bailey Boswell Rd 76179 817-237-3314
Nika Davis, prin. Fax 238-8706
Chisholm Trail HS 1,300/9-12
3100 NW College Dr 76179 817-232-7112
Dr. Dana Barnes, prin. Fax 232-7110
Creekview MS 700/6-8
6716 Bob Hanger St 76179 817-237-4261
Anthe Anagnostis, prin. Fax 237-2387
Highland MS 900/6-8
1001 E Bailey Boswell Rd 76131 817-847-5143
Karen Pressley, prin. Fax 847-1922
Hollenstein Career and Technology Center Vo/Tech
5501 Marine Creek Pkwy 76179 817-306-1925
Dana Eldredge, dir. Fax 306-1327
Prairie Vista MS 900/6-8
8000 Comanche Springs Dr 76131 817-847-9210
Anna King, prin. Fax 847-4255
Watson HS 100/Alt
5901 Hereford Dr 76179 817-238-7925
Melanie Stitt, prin. Fax 237-0753
Wayside MS 900/6-8
1300 Old Decatur Rd 76179 817-232-0541
Jason Sneed, prin. Fax 232-2391
Willkie MS 900/6-8
6129 Texas Shiner Dr 76179 817-237-9631
Daniel Knowles, prin. Fax 237-9643
Other Schools – See Saginaw

Fort Worth ISD 83,000/PK-12
100 N University Dr 76107 817-814-2000
Dr. Kent Scribner, supt. Fax 871-2112
www.fwisd.org
Applied Learning Academy 300/Alt
7060 Camp Bowie Blvd 76116 817-815-5500
Alice Buckley, prin. Fax 815-5550
Arlington Heights HS 1,800/9-12
4501 West Fwy 76107 817-815-1000
Sarah Weeks, prin. Fax 815-1050
Carter-Riverside HS 1,200/9-12
3301 Yucca Ave 76111 817-814-9000
Greg Ruthart, prin. Fax 814-9050
Daggett MS 400/6-8
1108 Carlock St 76110 817-814-5200
Monica Garrett, prin. Fax 814-5250
Diamond Hill-Jarvis HS 900/9-12
1411 Maydell St 76106 817-815-0097
James Garcia, prin. Fax 815-0050
Dunbar HS 800/9-12
5700 Ramey Ave 76112 817-815-3000
Sajade Miller, prin. Fax 815-3050
Eastern Hills HS 1,300/9-12
5701 Shelton St 76112 817-815-4000
Chad McCarty, prin. Fax 815-4050
Elder MS 1,200/6-8
709 NW 21st St 76164 817-814-4100
Ronald Schultze, prin. Fax 814-4150
Forest Oak MS 800/6-8
3221 Pecos St 76119 817-815-8200
Paula Woods, prin. Fax 815-8250
Fort Worth ISD Collegiate HS 9-12
5301 Campus Dr 76119 817-815-4402
Lisa Castillo, prin. Fax 815-4208
Handley MS 500/6-8
2801 Patino Rd 76112 817-815-4200
Cheryl Johnson, prin. Fax 815-4250
International Newcomer Academy 400/Alt
7060 Camp Bowie Blvd 76116 817-815-5600
Rodrigo Durbin, prin. Fax 815-5650
Jacquet MS 500/7-8
2501 Stalcup Rd 76119 817-815-3500
Ricky Brown, prin. Fax 815-3550
James MS 1,100/6-8
1101 Nashville Ave 76105 817-814-0200
Joycelyn Barnett, prin. Fax 814-0250
Kirkpatrick MS 500/6-8
3201 Refugio Ave 76106 817-814-4200
Nick Torrez, prin. Fax 814-4250
Marine Creek Collegiate HS 9-12
4801 Marine Creek Pkwy 76179 817-515-7784
Benjamin Leos, prin. Fax 515-7094
McClung MS 800/6-8
3000 Forest Ave 76112 817-815-5300
Norbert Whitaker, prin. Fax 815-5350
McLean MS 1,000/7-8
3816 Stadium Dr 76109 817-814-5300
Melissa Bryan, prin. Fax 814-8350
Meacham MS 700/6-8
3600 Weber St 76106 817-815-0200
Thomas Fraire, prin. Fax 815-0250
Meadowbrook MS 500/6-8
2001 Ederville Rd S 76103 817-815-4300
Katrina Smith, prin. Fax 815-4350
Metro Opportunity S Vo/Tech
2720 Cullen St 76107 817-814-6700
Gerald Magin, prin. Fax 814-6750
Monnig MS 500/6-8
3136 Bigham Blvd 76116 817-815-1200
Ron Rhone, prin. Fax 815-1250
Morningside MS 700/6-8
2751 Mississippi Ave 76104 817-815-8300
Angele Hodges, prin. Fax 815-8350
North Side HS 1,600/9-12
2211 Mckinley Ave 76164 817-814-4000
Antonio Martinez, prin. Fax 814-4050
Paschal HS 2,700/9-12
3001 Forest Park Blvd 76110 817-814-5000
Terri Mossige, prin. Fax 814-5050
Polytechnic HS Vo/Tech
1300 Conner Ave 76105 817-814-0000
Joshua Delich, prin. Fax 814-0050
Riverside MS 1,100/6-8
1600 Bolton St 76111 817-814-9200
Roberto Santana, prin. Fax 814-9250
Rosemont MS 900/7-8
1501 W Seminary Dr 76115 817-814-7200
Oscar Adams, prin. Fax 814-7250
South Hills HS 1,700/9-12
6101 Mccart Ave 76133 817-814-7000
Dorothy Gomez, prin. Fax 814-7050
Southwest HS 1,300/9-12
4100 Altamesa Blvd 76133 817-814-8000
John Engel, prin. Fax 814-8050
Stripling MS 700/6-8
2100 Clover Ln 76107 817-815-1300
Keri Flores, prin. Fax 815-1350
Success HS 200/Alt
1003 W Cannon St 76104 817-815-2700
Ingrid Williams, prin. Fax 815-2750
Texas Academy of Biomedical Sciences 300/9-12
3813 Valentine St 76107 817-815-2300
Troy Langston, prin. Fax 815-2350
Trimble Technical HS Vo/Tech
1003 W Cannon St 76104 817-815-2500
Omar Ramos, prin. Fax 815-2550
Wedgwood MS 900/7-8
3909 Wilkie Way 76133 817-814-8200
Brian Rosatelli, prin. Fax 814-8250
World Languages Institute 6-8
1066 W Magnolia Ave 76104 817-815-2200
Guadalupe Barreto, prin. Fax 815-2250
Wyatt HS 1,300/9-12
2400 E Seminary Dr 76119 817-815-8000
Mario Layne, prin. Fax 815-8050
Young Men's Leadership Academy 200/6-12
5100 Willie St 76105 817-815-3400
Rodney White, prin. Fax 815-3450
Young Women's Leadership Academy 300/6-12
401 E 8th St 76102 817-815-2400
Tamara Albury, prin. Fax 815-2450
Other Schools – See Benbrook

Keller ISD
Supt. — See Keller
Central HS 2,500/9-12
9450 Ray White Rd, 817-744-2000
David Hinson, prin. Fax 744-2252
Fossil Hill MS 1,000/7-8
3821 Staghorn Cir S 76137 817-744-3050
Jennifer Gonzales, prin. Fax 847-6990
Fossil Ridge HS 2,200/9-12
4101 Thompson Rd, 817-744-1700
David Hadley, prin. Fax 337-3407
Hillwood MS 1,200/7-8
8250 Parkwood Hill Blvd 76137 817-744-3350
Kathleen Eckert, prin. Fax 581-1810
Timber Creek HS 2,800/9-12
12350 Timberland Blvd, 817-744-2300
Donnie Bartlett, prin. Fax 744-2338
Timberview MS 1,100/5-8
10300 Old Denton Rd, 817-744-2600
Carrie Jackson, prin. Fax 744-2638
Trinity Springs MS 1,000/7-8
3550 Keller Hicks Rd, 817-744-3500
Justin Barrett, prin. Fax 744-3538

Lake Worth ISD
Supt. — See Lake Worth
Collins MS 500/7-8
3651 Santos Dr 76106 817-306-4250
Kathy Harmon, prin. Fax 624-7058

White Settlement ISD 6,600/PK-12
401 S Cherry Ln 76108 817-367-1300
Frank Molinar, supt. Fax 367-1351
www.wsisd.com/
Brewer HS 1,700/9-12
1025 W Loop 820 N 76108 817-367-1200
Pam Turner, prin. Fax 367-1242
DAEP/Mesa HS 50/Alt
1000 S Cherry Ln Ste A 76108 817-367-1364
Jennifer Heddins, prin. Fax 367-1366
Other Schools – See White Settlement

Alliance Christian Academy PK-10
13105 Harmon Rd 76177 817-439-8425
Dr. Christy Wilson, head sch Fax 840-7657
All Saints' Episcopal S 900/PK-12
9700 Saints Cir 76108 817-560-5700
Dr. Thaddeus Bird, head sch Fax 560-9805
Anderson Private S 50/PK-12
14900 White Settlement Rd 76108 817-448-8484
Bethesda Christian S 400/K-12
4700 N Beach St 76137 817-281-6446
Vicki Vaughn, admin. Fax 581-5123
Brightwood College Post-Sec.
2001 Beach St Ste 201 76103 817-413-2000
Brite Divinity School Post-Sec.
2925 Princeton St 76109 817-257-7575
Calvary Christian Academy 400/PK-12
1401 Oakhurst Scenic Dr 76111 817-332-3351
Sue Tidwell, admin. Fax 332-4621
Cassata HS 200/9-12
1400 Hemphill St 76104 817-926-1745
Chuck McKone, pres. Fax 926-3132
Christian Life Preparatory S 200/K-12
5253 Altamesa Blvd 76123 817-293-1500
Zachary Henry, head sch Fax 503-3092
Covenant Classical S 200/K-12
1701 Wind Star Way 76108 817-820-0884
DeVry University Post-Sec.
301 Commerce St Ste 2000 76102 817-810-9114

Everest College Post-Sec.
5237 N Riverside Dr Ste 100 76137 817-838-3000
Everest College Post-Sec.
4200 South Fwy Ste 1940 76115 817-566-7700
Fort Worth Beauty School Post-Sec.
6785 Camp Bowie Blvd # 100 76116 817-924-4289
Fort Worth Country Day S 1,100/K-12
4200 Country Day Ln 76109 817-302-3209
Eric Lombardi, head sch Fax 377-3425
Harris Hospital Post-Sec.
1301 Pennsylvania Ave 76104 817-878-2106
Harvest Christian Academy 300/PK-12
7200 Denton Hwy 76148 817-485-1660
Terry Caywood, hdmstr. Fax 514-6279
ITOP Christian Academy K-12
2010 E Lancaster Ave 76103 817-885-8875
JPS Inst. for Health Career Development Post-Sec.
2400 Circle Dr 76119 817-920-7380
Lake Country Christian S 400/PK-12
7050 Lake Country Dr 76179 817-236-8703
Nancy Purtell, head sch Fax 236-1103
Nolan HS 1,000/9-12
4501 Bridge St 76103 817-457-2920
Benedict Reyes, prin. Fax 496-9775
Ogle School of Hair Design Post-Sec.
6125 Interstate 20 Ste 128 76132 817-294-2950
Pathway Christian Academy 50/K-12
7460 McCart Ave 76133 817-370-7000
Steve Allen, hdmstr.
Remington College Post-Sec.
300 E Loop 820 76112 817-451-0017
St. Peter's Classical S 100/PK-12
7601 Bellaire Dr S 76132 817-294-0124
Jeanette Johnson, head sch Fax 288-0180
Southwest Christian Prep S 400/7-12
6901 Altamesa Blvd 76123 817-294-9596
Brian Johnson, head sch Fax 292-3644
Southwestern Baptist Theological Sem. Post-Sec.
PO Box 22000 76122 817-923-1921
Tarrant County College Post-Sec.
5301 Campus Dr 76119 817-515-8223
Tarrant County College Post-Sec.
4801 Marine Creek Pkwy 76179 817-515-8223
Temple Christian S 800/PK-12
6824 Randol Mill Rd 76120 817-457-0770
Dorothy Stringer, supt. Fax 457-0777
Texas Christian University Post-Sec.
2800 S University Dr 76129 817-257-7000
Texas Wesleyan University Post-Sec.
1201 Wesleyan St 76105 817-531-4444
Trinity Baptist Temple Academy 100/PK-12
6045 WJ Boaz Rd 76179 817-237-4255
Gregg Jones, prin. Fax 237-5233
Trinity Valley S 1,000/K-12
7500 Dutch Branch Rd 76132 817-321-0100
Ian Craig, head sch Fax 321-0105
University of N Texas Health Science Ctr Post-Sec.
3500 Camp Bowie Blvd 76107 817-735-2000

Franklin, Robertson, Pop. 1,547
Franklin ISD 1,000/PK-12
PO Box 909 77856 979-828-7000
Timothy Bret Lowry, supt. Fax 828-1910
www.franklinisd.net/
Franklin HS 300/9-12
PO Box 909 77856 979-828-7100
Russell White, prin. Fax 828-3364
Franklin MS 200/5-8
PO Box 909 77856 979-828-7200
Susan Nelson, prin. Fax 828-7207

Frankston, Anderson, Pop. 1,210
Frankston ISD 800/PK-12
PO Box 428 75763 903-876-2556
John Allen, supt. Fax 876-4558
www.frankstonisd.net
Frankston HS 200/9-12
PO Box 428 75763 903-876-3219
Donny Lee, prin. Fax 876-4558
Frankston MS 200/6-8
PO Box 428 75763 903-876-2215
Melissa McIntire, prin. Fax 876-4558

Fredericksburg, Gillespie, Pop. 10,449
Fredericksburg ISD 2,900/PK-12
234 Friendship Ln 78624 830-997-9551
Dr. Eric Wright, supt. Fax 997-6164
www.fisd.org/
Fredericksburg HS 1,000/9-12
1107 S State Highway 16 78624 830-997-7551
Ralf Halderman, prin. Fax 997-8583
Fredericksburg MS 600/6-8
110 W Travis St 78624 830-997-7657
Missy Stevens, prin. Fax 997-1927
G.C.L.C. 50/Alt
1110 S Adams St 78624 830-997-9788
Blaine Hahn, prin. Fax 997-9788

Ambleside S of Fredericksburg PK-12
106 S Edison St 78624 830-990-9059
Heritage S 200/K-12
310 Smokehouse Rd 78624 830-997-6597
Christopher Acton, head sch Fax 997-4900

Freeport, Brazoria, Pop. 11,851
Brazosport ISD
Supt. — See Clute
Brazosport HS 1,000/9-12
PO Box Z 77542 979-730-7260
Rita Pintavalle, prin. Fax 730-7366
Freeport IS 600/7-8
PO Box Z 77542 979-730-7240
Brooke Merritt, prin. Fax 237-6329

Freer, Duval, Pop. 2,808
Freer ISD 800/PK-12
PO Box 240 78357 361-394-6025
Steve Van Matre, supt. Fax 394-5005
www.freerisd.org/
Freer HS 200/9-12
PO Box 240 78357 361-394-6717
Conrad Cantu, prin. Fax 394-5046
Freer JHS 200/6-8
PO Box 240 78357 361-394-7102
Rosalva Campos, prin. Fax 394-5016

Friendswood, Galveston, Pop. 35,202
Clear Creek ISD
Supt. — See League City
Brookside IS 800/6-8
3535 E FM 528 Rd 77546 281-284-3600
Lauren Ambeau, prin. Fax 284-3605
Clear Brook HS 2,400/9-12
4607 FM 2351 Rd 77546 281-284-2100
Michele Staley, prin. Fax 284-2105
Westbrook IS 1,100/6-8
302 W El Dorado Blvd 77546 281-284-3800
Stephanie McBride, prin. Fax 284-3805

Friendswood ISD 5,900/PK-12
302 Laurel Dr 77546 281-482-1267
Trish Hanks, supt. Fax 996-2513
www.fisdk12.net
Friendswood HS 2,200/9-12
702 Greenbriar Ave 77546 281-482-3413
Mark Griffon, prin. Fax 996-2523
Friendswood JHS 1,500/6-8
1000 Manison Pkwy 77546 281-996-6200
Dana Drew, prin. Fax 996-6262

Brightwood College Post-Sec.
3208 E FM 528 Rd 77546 281-648-0880

Friona, Parmer, Pop. 4,104
Friona ISD 1,200/PK-12
909 E 11th St 79035 806-250-2747
Dr. Pamela Nelson-Ray, supt. Fax 250-3805
www.frionaisd.com
Friona HS 300/9-12
909 E 11th St 79035 806-250-3951
Erika Montana, prin. Fax 259-2281
Friona JHS 300/6-8
909 E 11th St 79035 806-250-2788
Mark Sundre, prin. Fax 250-8155

Frisco, Collin, Pop. 113,923
Frisco ISD 46,000/PK-12
5515 Ohio Dr 75035 469-633-6000
Dr. Jeremy Lyon, supt. Fax 633-6050
www.friscoisd.org
Career Technology Education Center Vo/Tech
9889 Wade Blvd 75035 469-633-6780
Dianna Manuel, prin. Fax 633-6790
Clark MS 900/6-8
4600 Colby Dr 75035 469-633-4600
Charese Duffey, prin. Fax 633-4650
Cobb MS 900/6-8
9400 Teel Pkwy, 469-633-4300
Kecia Theodore, prin. Fax 633-4310
Frisco Centennial HS 2,200/9-12
6901 Coit Rd 75035 469-633-5600
Alicia Maphies, prin. Fax 633-5650
Frisco HS 1,900/9-12
6401 Parkwood Blvd 75034 469-633-5500
Erin Miller, prin. Fax 633-5550
Griffin MS 700/6-8
3703 Eldorado Pkwy, 469-633-4900
Elizabeth Holcomb, prin. Fax 633-4950
Heritage HS 2,000/9-12
14040 Eldorado Pkwy 75035 469-633-5900
Mark Mimms, prin. Fax 633-5950
Hunt MS 700/6-8
4900 Legendary Dr 75034 469-633-5200
Danny Barrentine, prin. Fax 633-5210
Independence HS 9-12
10555 Independence Pkwy 75035 469-633-5400
Alan Waligura, prin. Fax 633-5450
Lebanon Trail HS 9-12
5151 Ohio Dr 75035 469-633-6600
Devin Padavil, prin. Fax 663-6657
Liberty HS 2,200/9-12
15250 Rolater Rd 75035 469-633-5800
Scott Warstler, prin. Fax 633-5850
Lone Star HS 1,200/9-12
2606 Panther Creek Pkwy, 469-633-5300
Karen Kraft, prin. Fax 633-5350
Maus MS 800/6-8
12175 Coit Rd 75035 469-633-5250
Chakosha Powell, prin. Fax 633-5260
Pearson MS 6-8
2323 Stonebrook Pkwy 75034 469-633-4450
Jamie Wisneski, prin. Fax 633-4460
Pioneer Heritage MS 900/6-8
1649 High Shoals Dr 75034 469-633-4700
Rocky Agan, prin. Fax 633-4750
Reedy HS 9-12
3003 Stonebrook Pkwy 75034 469-633-6400
Karen LeCocq, prin. Fax 633-6450
Roach MS 900/6-8
12499 Independence Pkwy 75035 469-633-5000
Terri Gladden, prin. Fax 633-5010
Stafford MS 1,000/6-8
2288 Little River Rd, 469-633-5100
Robin Scott, prin. Fax 633-5110
Staley MS 700/6-8
6927 Stadium Ln, 469-633-4500
Anita Lightfoot, prin. Fax 633-4550
Student Opportunity Center Alt
6928 Maple St, 469-633-6700
Sue Kirk, prin. Fax 633-6750
Trent MS 6-8
13131 Coleto Creek Dr, 469-633-4400
Shawn Perry, prin. Fax 633-4410
Vandeventer MS 900/6-8
6075 Independence Pkwy 75035 469-633-4350
Paige Hoes, prin. Fax 633-4360
Wakeland HS 2,000/9-12
10700 Legacy Dr, 469-633-5700
Donna Edge, prin. Fax 633-5750
Wester MS 900/6-8
12293 Shepherds Hill Ln 75035 469-633-4800
Richard Manuel, prin. Fax 633-4850
Other Schools – See Mc Kinney, Plano

Collin College Post-Sec.
9700 Wade Blvd 75035 972-377-1790
Legacy Christian Academy 900/PK-12
5000 Academy Dr 75034 469-633-1330
Bill McGee, hdmstr. Fax 633-1348

Fritch, Hutchinson, Pop. 2,086
Sanford-Fritch ISD 800/PK-12
PO Box 1290 79036 806-857-3122
Jim McClellan, supt. Fax 857-3795
www.sfisd.net
Sanford-Fritch HS 200/9-12
PO Box 1290 79036 806-857-3121
Jason Garrison, prin. Fax 857-9147
Sanford-Fritch JHS 200/6-8
PO Box 1290 79036 806-857-9268
Edith Allen, prin. Fax 857-9431

Frost, Navarro, Pop. 641
Frost ISD 400/PK-12
PO Box K 76641 903-682-2711
Duane Limbaugh, supt. Fax 682-2107
www.frostisd.org
Frost JSHS 200/6-12
PO Box K 76641 903-682-2541
Karen Lane, prin. Fax 682-2107

Fruitvale, Van Zandt, Pop. 408
Fruitvale ISD 400/PK-12
PO Box 77 75127 903-896-1191
Rebecca Bain, supt. Fax 896-1011
www.fruitvaleisd.com
Fruitvale HS 100/9-12
PO Box 77 75127 903-896-4363
Charles Harford, prin. Fax 896-1011
Fruitvale MS 100/6-8
PO Box 77 75127 903-896-4363
Charles Harford, prin. Fax 896-1011

Fulshear, Fort Bend, Pop. 1,120
Lamar Consolidated ISD
Supt. — See Rosenberg
Fulshear HS 9-10
9302 Bois D Arc Ln 77441 832-223-0000
Daniel Ward, prin.
Leaman JHS 6-8
9320 Bois D Arc Ln 77441 832-223-0000
Mike Semmler, prin.

Gail, Borden, Pop. 230
Borden County ISD 300/K-12
PO Box 95 79738 806-756-4313
Billy Collins, supt. Fax 756-4310
www.bcisd.net/
Borden S 300/K-12
PO Box 95 79738 806-756-4313
Bart McMeans, prin. Fax 756-4310

Gainesville, Cooke, Pop. 15,668
Gainesville ISD 2,400/PK-12
800 S Morris St 76240 940-665-4362
Jeffrey L. Brasher, supt. Fax 665-4473
www.gainesvilleisd.org
Gainesville HS 700/9-12
2201 S Interstate 35 76240 940-665-5528
Melissa Hutchison, prin. Fax 612-2795
Gainesville JHS 400/7-8
1201 S Lindsay St 76240 940-665-4062
Mary Patterson, prin. Fax 665-1432

North Central Texas College Post-Sec.
1525 W California St 76240 940-668-7731

Galena Park, Harris, Pop. 10,842
Galena Park ISD
Supt. — See Houston
Galena Park HS 2,000/9-12
1000 Keene St 77547 832-386-2800
Tony Gardea, prin. Fax 386-2802
Galena Park MS 1,000/6-8
400 Keene St 77547 832-386-1700
Shaunte Morris, prin. Fax 386-1738

Galveston, Galveston, Pop. 47,004
Galveston ISD 6,400/PK-12
PO Box 660 77553 409-766-5100
Dr. Kelli Moulton, supt. Fax 762-8391
www.gisd.org
Austin Magnet MS 500/5-8
1514 Avenue N 1/2 77550 409-761-3500
Cathy Vanness, prin. Fax 765-5946
Ball HS 1,800/9-12
4115 Avenue O 77550 409-766-5700
Joe Pillar, prin. Fax 766-5738
Central MS 300/7-8
3014 Sealy St 77550 409-761-6200
Cheryl Rutledge, dir. Fax 770-0649

Galveston College Post-Sec.
4015 Avenue Q 77550 409-944-4242
O'Connell College Preparatory HS 100/9-12
1320 Tremont St 77550 409-765-5534
Patti Abbott, prin. Fax 765-5536
Texas A&M University Galveston Post-Sec.
PO Box 1675 77553 409-740-4400
University of Texas Medical Branch Post-Sec.
301 University Blvd 77555 409-772-1011

Ganado, Jackson, Pop. 1,997
Ganado ISD 700/PK-12
PO Box 1200 77962 361-771-4200
Dr. John Hardwick Ed.D., supt. Fax 771-2280
www.ganadoisd.org
Ganado HS 200/9-12
PO Box 1200 77962 361-771-4300
Andy Bridges, prin. Fax 771-2280
Ganado JHS 200/6-8
PO Box 1200 77962 361-771-4309
Joey Rosalez, prin. Fax 771-4310

Garden City, Glasscock, Pop. 334
Glasscock County ISD 300/PK-12
PO Box 9 79739 432-354-2230
Tom Weeaks, supt. Fax 354-2503
www.gckats.net
Glasscock County JSHS 100/7-12
PO Box 9 79739 432-354-2244
Wayland Pierce, prin. Fax 354-2503

Garland, Dallas, Pop. 223,158
Garland ISD 57,200/PK-12
PO Box 469026 75046 972-494-8201
Dr. Bob Morrison, supt. Fax 485-4928
www.garlandisd.net
Austin Academy for Excellence MS 900/6-8
1125 Beverly Dr 75040 972-926-2620
Holly Muzzicato, prin. Fax 926-2633
Bussey MS 900/6-8
1204 Travis St 75040 972-494-8391
Mary Garcia, prin. Fax 494-8971
Classical Center at Brandenburg MS 1,200/6-8
626 Nickens Rd 75043 972-926-2630
Elise Mosty, prin. Fax 926-2633
Garland Alternative Education Center 100/Alt
2015 S Country Club Rd 75041 972-926-2691
Dr. Kim Lozada, prin. Fax 926-2692
Garland HS 2,600/9-12
310 S Garland Ave 75040 972-494-8492
Atticus Wisener, prin. Fax 494-8415
Houston MS 1,100/6-8
2232 Sussex Dr 75041 972-926-2640
Don Hernandez, prin. Fax 926-2647
Jackson Tech Center for Math & Science 1,200/6-8
1310 Bobbie Ln 75042 972-494-8362
David Dunphy, prin. Fax 494-8802
Lakeview Centennial HS 2,400/9-12
3505 Hayman Dr 75043 972-240-3740
Maresa Bailey, prin. Fax 240-3750
Lyles MS 900/6-8
4655 S Country Club Rd 75043 972-240-3720
Lisa Oleson, prin. Fax 240-3723
Memorial Pathway Academy 100/Alt
2825 S 1st St 75041 972-926-2650
Jim Thomas, prin. Fax 926-2651
Naaman Forest HS 2,200/9-12
4843 Naaman Forest Blvd 75040 972-675-3091
Erika Crump, prin. Fax 675-3100
North Garland HS 2,300/9-12
2109 W Buckingham Rd 75042 972-675-3120
Glenda Williams, prin. Fax 675-3145
O'Banion MS 1,100/6-8
700 Birchwood Dr 75043 972-279-6103
John Tucci, prin. Fax 613-9532
Sellers MS 800/6-8
1009 Mars Dr 75040 972-494-8337
Vikki Mahagan, prin. Fax 494-8607
South Garland HS 2,000/9-12
600 Colonel Dr 75043 972-926-2700
Tracy Curtis, prin. Fax 926-2727
Webb MS 1,100/6-8
1610 Spring Creek Dr 75040 972-675-3080
Kenneth Washington, prin. Fax 675-3089
Other Schools – See Rowlett, Sachse

Amberton University Post-Sec.
1700 Eastgate Dr 75041 972-279-6511
Brighter Horizons Academy 700/PK-12
3145 Medical Plaza Dr 75044 972-675-2062
Garland Christian Academy 300/PK-12
1516 Lavon Dr 75040 972-487-0043
Cathey Ondrusek, admin. Fax 276-4079
International Beauty College #3 Post-Sec.
1225 Belt Line Rd Ste 7 75040 972-530-1103
Remington College Post-Sec.
1800 Eastgate Dr 75041 972-686-7878

Garrison, Nacogdoches, Pop. 884
Garrison ISD 700/PK-12
459 N US Highway 59 75946 936-347-7000
Richard Cooper, supt. Fax 347-2529
www.garrisonisd.com
Garrison HS 200/9-12
459 N US Highway 59 75946 936-347-7030
Reid Spivey, prin. Fax 347-7059
Garrison MS 200/6-8
459 N US Highway 59 75946 936-347-7020
Clark Bynum, prin. Fax 347-7004

Gary, Panola
Gary ISD 500/PK-12
132 Bobcat Trl 75643 903-685-2291
Todd Greer, supt. Fax 685-2639
www.garyisd.org
Gary S 500/PK-12
132 Bobcat Trl 75643 903-685-2291
Tony Wood, prin. Fax 685-2639

Gatesville, Coryell, Pop. 15,526
Gatesville ISD 2,600/PK-12
311 S Lovers Ln 76528 254-865-7251
Eric Penrod, supt. Fax 865-2279
www.gatesvilleisd.org
Gatesville HS 800/9-12
311 S Lovers Ln 76528 254-865-8281
Shane Webb, prin. Fax 865-2293
Gatesville JHS 500/7-8
311 S Lovers Ln 76528 254-865-8271
Cindy Venable, prin. Fax 865-2252

Georgetown, Williamson, Pop. 46,741
Georgetown ISD 10,500/PK-12
603 Lakeway Dr 78628 512-943-5000
Dr. Fred Brent, supt. Fax 943-5004
www.georgetownisd.org
Benold MS 900/6-8
3407 Northwest Blvd 78628 512-943-5090
Leslie Michalik, prin. Fax 943-5099
Forbes MS 700/6-8
1911 NE Inner Loop 78626 512-943-5150
Leonard Rhoads, prin. Fax 943-5159
Georgetown Alternative Program 50/Alt
502 Patriot Way 78626 512-943-5196
Louis Garza, prin. Fax 943-5197
Georgetown East View HS 1,400/9-12
4490 E University Ave 78626 512-943-1800
Dr. Dave Denny, prin. Fax 943-1819
Georgetown HS 1,800/9-12
2211 N Austin Ave 78626 512-943-5100
Cade Smith, prin. Fax 943-5109
Richarte HS 100/Alt
2295 N Austin Ave 78626 512-943-5120
Marsha Winship, prin. Fax 943-5121
Tippit MS 800/6-8
1601 Leander Rd 78628 512-943-5040
Brian Dawson, prin. Fax 943-5049

Grace Academy 200/K-12
225 Grace Blvd, 512-864-9500
Southwestern University Post-Sec.
1001 E University Ave 78626 512-863-6511

George West, Live Oak, Pop. 2,431
George West ISD 1,100/PK-12
913 Houston St 78022 361-449-1914
Ty Sparks, supt. Fax 449-1426
www.gwisd.esc2.net/
George West HS 300/9-12
1013 Houston St 78022 361-449-1914
Richard Waterhouse, prin. Fax 449-3128
George West JHS 200/7-8
900 Houston St 78022 361-449-1914
Ashley Lowe, prin. Fax 449-3909

Giddings, Lee, Pop. 4,822
Giddings ISD 1,900/PK-12
PO Box 389 78942 979-542-2854
Roger Dees, supt. Fax 542-9264
www.giddings.txed.net
Giddings HS 600/9-12
PO Box 389 78942 979-542-3351
Chad Rood, prin. Fax 542-5312
Giddings MS 400/6-8
PO Box 389 78942 979-542-2057
Charlotte Penn, prin. Fax 542-3941

Gilmer, Upshur, Pop. 4,805
Gilmer ISD 2,500/PK-12
500 S Trinity St 75644 903-841-7400
Rick Albritton, supt. Fax 843-5279
www.gilmerisd.org
Bruce JHS 300/7-8
111 Bruce St 75645 903-841-7600
Bill Bradshaw, prin. Fax 843-6108
Gilmer HS 700/9-12
850 Buffalo St 75644 903-841-7500
Brian Bowman, prin. Fax 843-2171

Union Hill ISD 300/PK-12
2197 FM 2088 75644 903-762-2140
Dr. Troy Batts, supt. Fax 762-6845
www.uhisd.com
Union Hill HS 100/7-12
2197 FM 2088 75644 903-762-2138
Troy Batts, prin. Fax 762-6845

Gladewater, Gregg, Pop. 6,285
Gladewater ISD 1,600/PK-12
500 W Quitman Ave 75647 903-845-6991
Dr. Jerry Richardson, supt. Fax 845-6994
www.gladewaterisd.com
Gladewater HS 500/9-12
2201 W Gay Ave 75647 903-845-5591
Darryl Dans, prin. Fax 845-3694
Gladewater MS 400/6-8
414 S Loop 485 75647 903-845-2243
Chris Langford, prin. Fax 844-1738

Sabine ISD 1,400/PK-12
5424 FM 1252 W 75647 903-984-8564
Stacey Bryce, supt. Fax 984-6108
www.sabineisd.org
Sabine HS 400/9-12
5424 FM 1252 W 75647 903-984-8587
Eddie Shawn, prin. Fax 986-1103
Sabine MS 300/6-8
5424 FM 1252 W 75647 903-984-4767
Bill Middendorf, prin. Fax 984-8823

Union Grove ISD 600/PK-12
PO Box 1447 75647 903-845-5509
Brian Gray, supt. Fax 845-6178
www.ugisd.org
Union Grove JSHS 200/7-12
PO Box 1447 75647 903-845-5506
Kelly Moore, prin. Fax 845-3003

Glenn Heights, Dallas, Pop. 11,061
De Soto ISD
Supt. — See DeSoto
McCowan MS 900/6-8
1500 Majestic Meadows Dr 75154 972-274-8090
Sissy Lowe, prin. Fax 274-8099

Glen Rose, Somervell, Pop. 2,402
Glen Rose ISD 1,700/PK-12
PO Box 2129 76043 254-898-3900
Wayne Rotan, supt. Fax 897-3651
www.grisd.net
Glen Rose HS 500/9-12
PO Box 2129 76043 254-898-3800
Kelly Shackelford, prin. Fax 897-9871
Glen Rose JHS 400/6-8
PO Box 2129 76043 254-898-3700
Jason Pounds, prin. Fax 897-4059

Godley, Johnson, Pop. 999
Godley ISD 1,700/PK-12
313 N Pearson St 76044 817-389-2536
Dr. Rich Dear, supt. Fax 389-2543
www.godleyisd.net/
Godley HS 500/9-12
9401 N Highway 171 76044 817-389-2265
Leigh Brown, prin. Fax 389-4455
Godley MS 300/7-8
409 N Pearson St 76044 817-389-2121
David Williams, prin. Fax 389-4357

Goldthwaite, Mills, Pop. 1,857
Goldthwaite ISD 600/PK-12
PO Box 608 76844 325-648-3531
Ronny Wright, supt. Fax 648-2456
www.goldisd.net/
Goldthwaite HS 200/9-12
PO Box 608 76844 325-648-3081
Rusty Hollingsworth, prin. Fax 648-2325
Goldthwaite MS 100/6-8
PO Box 608 76844 325-648-3630
Landon Sanderson, prin. Fax 648-3571

Goliad, Goliad, Pop. 1,901
Goliad ISD 900/PK-12
PO Box 830 77963 361-645-3259
Dave Plymale, supt. Fax 645-3614
www.goliadisd.org
Goliad HS 400/9-12
PO Box 830 77963 361-645-3257
Russell Kowalik, prin. Fax 645-8039
Goliad MS 200/7-8
PO Box 830 77963 361-645-3146
Mary Tippin, prin. Fax 645-8040

Gonzales, Gonzales, Pop. 7,175
Gonzales ISD 2,500/PK-12
PO Box 157 78629 830-672-9551
Kimberly Strozier Ed.D., supt. Fax 672-7159
www.gonzalesisd.net
Gonzales HS 700/9-12
1801 N Sarah DeWitt Dr 78629 830-672-7535
Michael Garcia, prin. Fax 672-8273
Gonzales JHS 400/7-8
426 N College St 78629 830-672-8641
Wanda Fryer, prin. Fax 672-6466

Goodrich, Polk, Pop. 267
Goodrich ISD 200/PK-12
PO Box 789 77335 936-365-1100
Dr. Gary Bates, supt. Fax 365-3518
www.goodrichisd.net
Goodrich HS 100/9-12
PO Box 789 77335 936-365-1100
Lara Devillier, prin. Fax 365-2371
Goodrich MS 50/6-8
PO Box 789 77335 936-365-1100
Lara Devillier, prin. Fax 365-2371

Gordon, Palo Pinto, Pop. 475
Gordon ISD 200/PK-12
PO Box 47 76453 254-693-5582
Eric Hough, supt. Fax 693-5503
www.gordonisd.net
Gordon S 200/PK-12
PO Box 47 76453 254-693-5342
Holly Campbell, prin. Fax 693-5503

Gorman, Eastland, Pop. 1,079
Gorman ISD 300/PK-12
PO Box 8 76454 254-734-3171
Fax 734-3393
www.gormanisd.net
Gorman HS 100/9-12
PO Box 8 76454 254-734-3171
Vanessa Oakley, prin. Fax 734-3425
Gorman MS 100/6-8
PO Box 8 76454 254-734-3171
Vanessa Oakley, prin. Fax 734-4729

Graford, Palo Pinto, Pop. 570
Graford ISD 300/PK-12
400 W Division Ave 76449 940-664-3101
Dennis Holt, supt. Fax 664-2123
www.grafordisd.net
Graford JSHS 100/7-12
400 W Division Ave 76449 940-664-3101
Lori Henderson, prin. Fax 664-2026

Graham, Young, Pop. 8,817
Graham ISD 2,600/PK-12
400 3rd St 76450 940-549-0595
Sonny Cruse, supt. Fax 549-8656
www.grahamisd.com
Graham HS 700/9-12
1000 Brazos St 76450 940-549-1504
Joe Gordy, prin. Fax 549-4031
Graham JHS 600/6-8
1000 2nd St 76450 940-549-2002
Ginger Robbins, prin. Fax 549-6991
Graham Learning Center 50/Alt
1000 Brazos St 76450 940-549-1504
Anne Routon, prin. Fax 549-4031

Granbury, Hood, Pop. 7,903
Granbury ISD 6,100/PK-12
600 W Pearl St 76048 817-408-4000
James Largent Ed.D., supt. Fax 408-4014
www.granburyisd.org
Acton MS 800/6-8
1300 James Rd 76049 817-408-4800
Jimmy Dawson, prin. Fax 408-4849
Granbury HS 1,400/9-12
2000 W Pearl St 76048 817-408-4600
Jeremy Ross, prin. Fax 408-4699
Granbury MS 700/6-8
2000 Crossland Rd 76048 817-408-4850
Pat Yelverton, prin. Fax 408-4899
STARS Accelerated HS 100/Alt
301 N Hannaford St 76048 817-408-4450
Ginna Marks, prin. Fax 408-4164

Cornerstone Christian Academy 100/PK-12
1905 W Pearl St Ste 105 76048 817-573-6485
Marci Martinez, admin. Fax 573-7604
North Central Texas Academy 200/PK-12
3846 N Highway 144 76048 254-897-4822
Todd Shipman, pres. Fax 897-7650

Grandfalls, Ward, Pop. 353
Grandfalls-Royalty ISD 100/PK-12
PO Box 10 79742 432-547-2266
Joe Helms, supt. Fax 547-2960
www.grisd.com
Grandfalls-Royalty S 100/PK-12
PO Box 10 79742 432-547-2266
Steven Parker, prin. Fax 547-2960

Grand Prairie, Dallas, Pop. 172,425
Grand Prairie ISD 27,600/PK-12
PO Box 531170 75053 972-264-6141
Dr. Susan Simpson Hull, supt. Fax 237-5440
www.gpisd.org
Adams MS 600/6-8
833 W Tarrant Rd 75050 972-262-1934
Darwert Johnson, prin. Fax 522-3099
Crosswinds HS 300/Alt
1100 N Carrier Pkwy 75050 972-522-2950
Dr. Suzy Meyer, prin. Fax 522-2999
Dubiski Career HS Vo/Tech
2990 S State Highway 161 75052 972-343-7800
Kristin Booth, prin. Fax 343-7899
Fannin MS 800/6-8
301 NE 28th St 75050 972-262-8668
Whitney Carlisle, prin. Fax 343-4799
Grand Prairie Early College HS 9-12
102 Gopher Blvd 75050
Kristen Watson, chncllr.
Grand Prairie Fine Arts Academy 400/6-12
102 High School Dr 75050 972-237-5603
Maria Schell, prin. Fax 343-6399
Grand Prairie SHS 2,500/9-12
101 High School Dr 75050 972-809-5711
Lorimer Arendse, prin. Fax 809-5775
HOPE Academy 100/8-8
1502 College St 75050 972-522-3400
Dr. Suzy Meyer, prin. Fax 343-3499
Jackson MS 1,000/6-8
3504 Corn Valley Rd 75052 972-343-7500
Robert Wallace, prin. Fax 343-7599
Johnson DAEP 100/Alt
650 Stonewall Dr 75052 972-262-7244
Kerry Rapier, prin. Fax 264-9479
Reagan MS 700/6-8
4616 Bardin Rd 75052 972-522-7300
Apryl Baylor, prin. Fax 522-7399
South Grand Prairie Early College HS 9-12
305 W Warrior Trl 75052
Dr. Joanna Slaton, chncllr.
South Grand Prairie HS 9th Grade Campus 800/9-9
305 W Warrior Trl 75052 972-264-1769
Donna Grant, prin. Fax 642-7902
South Grand Prairie SHS 2,300/10-12
301 W Warrior Trl 75052 972-343-1500
Donna Grant, prin. Fax 642-7902
Truman MS 600/6-8
1501 Coffeyville Trl 75052 972-641-7676
Letycia Fowler, prin. Fax 522-3999
Young Mens Leadership Academy 1,000/6-8
2205 SE 4th St 75051 972-264-8651
Avesgus Tetterton, prin. Fax 522-3699
Young Womens Leadership Academy 1,100/6-12
1204 E Marshall Dr 75051 972-343-7400
Patty Cunningham, prin. Fax 343-7499

Arlington Career Institute Post-Sec.
901 E Avenue K 75050 972-647-1607
Jones Beauty College #2 Post-Sec.
311 W Pioneer Pkwy 75051 972-237-1988
Lincoln College of Technology Post-Sec.
2915 Alouette Dr 75052 972-660-5701

Grand Saline, Van Zandt, Pop. 3,102
Grand Saline ISD 1,100/PK-12
400 Stadium Dr 75140 903-962-7546
Micah Lewis, supt. Fax 962-7464
www.grandsalineisd.net
Grand Saline HS 300/9-12
500 Stadium Dr 75140 903-962-7533
Ricky LaPrade, prin. Fax 962-7482
Grand Saline MS 200/6-8
400 Stadium Dr 75140 903-962-7537
Duane Petty, prin. Fax 962-7474

Grandview, Johnson, Pop. 1,542
Grandview ISD 900/PK-12
PO Box 310 76050 817-866-4500
Joe Perrin, supt. Fax 866-3351
www.gvisd.org
Grandview HS 400/9-12
PO Box 310 76050 817-866-4520
Kirby Basham, prin. Fax 866-2645
Grandview JHS 200/6-8
PO Box 310 76050 817-866-4660
Jeff Hudson, prin. Fax 866-3912

Granger, Williamson, Pop. 1,404
Granger ISD 400/PK-12
PO Box 578 76530 512-859-2613
Randy Willis, supt. Fax 859-2446
www.grangerisd.net
Granger S 400/PK-12
PO Box 578 76530 512-859-2173
Mike Abbott, prin. Fax 859-2446

Grapeland, Houston, Pop. 1,478
Grapeland ISD 500/PK-12
PO Box 249 75844 936-687-4619
Gregg Spivey, supt. Fax 687-4624
www.grapelandisd.net
Grapeland HS 200/9-12
PO Box 249 75844 936-687-4661
Rick Frauenberger, prin. Fax 687-9739
Grapeland JHS 100/6-8
PO Box 249 75844 936-687-2351
Rick Frauenberger, admin. Fax 687-5285

Grapevine, Tarrant, Pop. 45,499
Grapevine-Colleyville ISD 13,600/PK-12
3051 Ira E Woods Ave 76051 817-251-5200
Dr. Robin Ryan, supt. Fax 251-5375
www.gcisd-k12.org
Cross Timbers MS 800/6-8
2301 Pool Rd 76051 817-251-5320
Alex Fingers, prin. Fax 424-4296
Grapevine HS 2,100/9-12
3223 Mustang Dr 76051 817-251-5210
David Denning, prin. Fax 481-5957
Grapevine MS 700/6-8
301 Pony Pkwy 76051 817-251-5660
Linda Young, prin. Fax 424-1626
Other Schools – See Colleyville, Hurst

Grapevine Faith Christian S 800/PK-12
729 E Dallas Rdd 76051 817-442-9144
Dr. Ed Smith Ed.D., pres. Fax 442-9904
Novus Academy 100/1-12
204 N Dooley St 76051 817-488-4555

Greenville, Hunt, Pop. 25,073
Greenville ISD 4,700/PK-12
4004 Moulton St 75401 903-457-2500
Donald Jefferies, supt. Fax 457-2504
www.greenvilleisd.com
Greenville HS 1,100/9-12
3515 Lions Lair Rd 75402 903-457-2550
Heath Jarvis, prin. Fax 455-5158
Greenville MS 600/7-8
3611 Texas St 75401 903-457-2620
David Gish, prin. Fax 457-2628
Houston Education Center 100/Alt
3923 Henry St 75401 903-457-2688
Chip Gregory, prin. Fax 457-2689

Greenville Christian S 200/PK-12
8420 Jack Finney Blvd 75402 903-454-1111
Steven Bowers, hdmstr. Fax 455-8470

Groesbeck, Limestone, Pop. 4,255
Groesbeck ISD 1,300/PK-12
PO Box 559 76642 254-729-4100
Dr. Harold Ramm, supt. Fax 729-5167
www.groesbeckisd.net
Groesbeck HS 500/9-12
1202 N Ellis St 76642 254-729-4101
Keri Allen, prin. Fax 729-5458
Groesbeck MS 300/7-8
410 Elwood Enge Dr 76642 254-729-4102
Dayne Duncan, prin. Fax 729-8763

Groom, Carson, Pop. 567
Groom ISD 100/PK-12
PO Box 598 79039 806-248-7557
Jay Lamb, supt. Fax 248-7949
www.groomisd.net
Groom S 100/PK-12
PO Box 598 79039 806-248-7474
Jay Lamb, prin. Fax 248-7949

Groves, Jefferson, Pop. 15,978
Port Neches-Groves ISD
Supt. — See Port Neches
Groves MS 600/6-8
5201 Wilson St 77619 409-962-0225
James Arnett, prin. Fax 963-1898

Groveton, Trinity, Pop. 1,043
Centerville ISD 100/PK-12
10327 N State Highway 94 75845 936-642-1597
Mark Brown, supt. Fax 642-2810
www.centervilleisd.net
Centerville JSHS 100/7-12
10327 N State Highway 94 75845 936-642-1597
Andja Sailer, prin. Fax 642-2810

Groveton ISD 700/PK-12
PO Box 728 75845 936-642-1473
Don Hamilton, supt. Fax 642-1628
www.grovetonisd.net
Groveton JSHS 400/6-12
PO Box 700 75845 936-642-1128
Bryan Finch, prin. Fax 642-1616

Grulla, Starr, Pop. 1,621
Rio Grande City ISD
Supt. — See Rio Grande City
Grulla MS 800/6-8
PO Box 338 78548 956-487-5558
Julio Eguia, prin. Fax 487-5633

Gruver, Hansford, Pop. 1,190
Gruver ISD 400/PK-12
PO Box 650 79040 806-733-2001
Troy Seagler, supt. Fax 733-5416
www.gruverisd.net
Gruver HS 100/9-12
PO Box 747 79040 806-733-2477
Nita Hudson, prin. Fax 733-2596
Gruver JHS 100/5-8
PO Box 709 79040 806-733-2081
Wade Callaway, prin. Fax 733-5523

Gunter, Grayson, Pop. 1,485
Gunter ISD 800/PK-12
PO Box 109 75058 903-433-4750
Dr. Jill Siler, supt. Fax 433-1053
www.gunterisd.org
Gunter HS 300/9-12
PO Box 109 75058 903-433-1542
Chris Dodd, prin. Fax 433-1492
Gunter MS 200/5-8
PO Box 109 75058 903-433-1545
Kim Patterson, prin. Fax 433-9306

Gustine, Comanche, Pop. 473
Gustine ISD 200/PK-12
503 W Main St 76455 325-667-7303
Patti Blue, supt. Fax 667-7281
www.gustine.esc14.net/
Gustine S 200/PK-12
503 W Main St 76455 325-667-7303
Patti Blue, prin. Fax 667-0203

Guthrie, King, Pop. 160
Guthrie Common SD 100/PK-12
PO Box 70 79236 806-596-4466
Kevin Chisum, supt. Fax 596-4519
www.guthriejags.com
Guthrie S 100/PK-12
PO Box 70 79236 806-596-4466
Jodie Reel, prin. Fax 596-4519

Hale Center, Hale, Pop. 2,231
Hale Center ISD 700/PK-12
PO Box 1210 79041 806-839-2451
Steven Pyburn, supt. Fax 839-2195
www.hcisdowls.net
Carr MS 200/5-8
PO Box 1210 79041 806-839-2141
Jimmi Johnson, prin. Fax 839-4417
Hale Center HS 200/9-12
PO Box 1210 79041 806-839-2452
Alan Berry, prin. Fax 839-2059

Hallettsville, Lavaca, Pop. 2,529
Hallettsville ISD 1,000/PK-12
PO Box 368 77964 361-798-2242
Dr. JoAnn Bludau, supt. Fax 798-5902
www.hisdbrahmas.org
Hallettsville HS 300/9-12
PO Box 368 77964 361-798-2242
Darrin Bickham, prin. Fax 798-9297
Hallettsville JHS 300/5-8
PO Box 368 77964 361-798-2242
Sophie Teltschik, prin. Fax 798-3573

Sacred Heart S 300/PK-12
313 S Texana St 77964 361-798-4251
Kevin Haas, prin. Fax 798-4970

Hallsville, Harrison, Pop. 3,526
Hallsville ISD 4,800/PK-12
PO Box 810 75650 903-668-5990
Jeff Collum, supt. Fax 668-5990
www.hisd.com
Hallsville DAEP Alt
PO Box 810 75650 903-668-5990
Jesse Casey, prin. Fax 668-5990
Hallsville HS 1,400/9-12
PO Box 810 75650 903-668-5990
Lindsey Slaten, prin. Fax 668-5990
Hallsville JHS 1,100/6-8
PO Box 810 75650 903-668-5990
Amy Whittle, prin. Fax 668-5990

Haltom City, Tarrant, Pop. 41,719
Birdville ISD 24,300/PK-12
6125 E Belknap St 76117 817-847-5700
Dr. Darrell Brown, supt. Fax 547-5530
www.birdvilleschools.net
Haltom HS 2,700/9-12
5501 Haltom Rd 76137 817-547-6000
David Hamilton, prin. Fax 547-6352
Haltom MS 900/6-8
5000 Hires Ln 76117 817-547-4000
Dr. Jill Balzer, prin. Fax 831-5778
North Oaks MS 600/6-8
4800 Jordan Park Dr 76117 817-547-4600
Dr. Jennifer Klaerner, prin. Fax 581-5352
Shannon HS 50/Alt
6010 Walker St 76117 817-547-5400
David Williams, prin. Fax 831-5847
Other Schools – See North Richland Hills, Richland Hills, Watauga

Hamilton, Hamilton, Pop. 3,076
Hamilton ISD 700/PK-12
400 S College St 76531 254-386-3149
Clay Tarpley, supt. Fax 386-8885
hamiltonisd.org
Hamilton HS 200/9-12
611 S College St 76531 254-386-8167
Louis Lowe, prin. Fax 386-4677
Hamilton JHS 200/6-8
400 S College St 76531 254-386-8168
Mona Gloff, prin. Fax 386-8885

Hamlin, Jones, Pop. 2,109
Hamlin ISD 400/PK-12
PO Box 338 79520 325-576-2722
Brock Cartwright, supt. Fax 576-2152
www.hamlin.esc14.net
Hamlin JSHS 100/7-12
450 SW Avenue F 79520 325-576-3624
Nick McCollister, prin. Fax 576-3926

Hamshire, Jefferson
Hamshire-Fannett ISD 1,700/PK-12
PO Box 223 77622 409-243-2133
Dwaine Augustine Ed.D., supt. Fax 243-3437
www.hfisd.net
Hamshire-Fannett HS 600/9-12
PO Box 223 77622 409-243-2512
Jon Burris, prin. Fax 243-2518
Other Schools – See Beaumont

Happy, Swisher, Pop. 670
Happy ISD 200/PK-12
PO Box 458 79042 806-558-5331
Ray Keith, supt. Fax 558-2070
www.happyisd.net
Happy HS 100/7-12
PO Box 458 79042 806-558-5311
Ray Keith, prin. Fax 558-4301

Hardin, Liberty, Pop. 804
Hardin ISD 1,300/PK-12
PO Box 330 77561 936-298-2112
Bob Parker, supt. Fax 298-9161
www.hardinisd.net/
Hardin HS 300/9-12
PO Box 330 77561 936-298-2118
Richard Ressler, prin. Fax 298-3612
Hardin JHS 200/7-8
PO Box 330 77561 936-298-2054
Dr. Bryan Taulton, prin. Fax 298-3264

Harker Heights, Bell, Pop. 25,289
Killeen ISD
Supt. — See Killeen
Eastern Hills MS 800/6-8
300 Indian Trl 76548 254-336-1100
Jeremy Key, prin. Fax 336-1115
Harker Heights HS 2,300/9-12
1001 E FM 2410 Rd 76548 254-336-0800
Larry Brazzil, prin. Fax 336-0829
Union Grove MS 900/6-8
101 E Iowa Dr 76548 254-336-6580
Dagmar Harris, prin. Fax 336-6593

Harleton, Harrison
Harleton ISD 700/PK-12
PO Box 510 75651 903-777-2372
Dr. Craig Coleman, supt. Fax 777-2406
www.harletonisd.net/
Harleton HS 200/9-12
PO Box 710 75651 903-777-2711
Tonya Knowlton, prin. Fax 777-2547
Harleton JHS 200/6-8
PO Box 610 75651 903-777-3010
Paul Davis, prin. Fax 777-3009

Harlingen, Cameron, Pop. 64,588
Harlingen Consolidated ISD 18,300/PK-12
407 N 77 Sunshine Strip 78550 956-430-9500
Dr. Arturo Cavazos, supt. Fax 430-9514
www.hcisd.org
Cano Freshman Academy 1,300/9-9
1701 W Lozano St 78550 956-430-4900
Vivian Bauer, prin. Fax 427-3772
Coakley MS 800/6-8
1402 S 6th St 78550 956-427-3000
Pedro Sanchez, prin. Fax 427-3006
Early College HS 300/9-12
2510 Pecan St Bldg R 78550 956-430-9690
Dr. Pamela Flores, prin. Fax 430-9693
Gutierrez MS 800/6-8
3205 Wilson Rd 78552 956-430-4400
Mike Reyes, prin. Fax 430-4480
Harlingen HS 1,900/10-12
1201 Marshall St 78550 956-427-3600
Imelda Munivez, prin. Fax 427-3792
Harlingen HS South 1,500/10-12
1701 Dixieland Rd 78552 956-427-3800
Fernando Reyes, admin. Fax 427-3995
Harlingen S of Health Professions 8-9
2302 N 21st St 78550 956-430-4078
Tina Garza, prin. Fax 430-9717
Keys Academy 100/Alt
2809 N 7th St 78550 956-427-3220
Isidoro Nieto, prin. Fax 427-3223
Memorial MS 800/6-8
1901 Rio Hondo Rd 78550 956-427-3020
Alex Gonzalez, prin. Fax 427-3024
Secondary Education Alternative Center 100/Alt
1310 Sam Houston Dr 78550 956-427-3210
Daniel Araiza, prin. Fax 430-4487
Vela MS 800/6-8
801 S Palm Blvd 78552 956-427-3479
Tony Gonzales, prin. Fax 427-3549
Vernon MS 700/6-8
125 S 13th St 78550 956-427-3040
Gracie Gutierrez, prin. Fax 427-3046

Marine Military Academy 200/8-12
320 Iwo Jima Blvd 78550 956-423-6006
Col R. Glenn Hill, supt. Fax 421-9273
Texas State Technical College Post-Sec.
1902 Loop 499 N 78550 956-364-4000
University of Cosmetology Arts & Science Post-Sec.
913 N 13th St 78550 956-412-1212

Harper, Gillespie, Pop. 1,183
Harper ISD 500/PK-12
PO Box 68 78631 830-864-4044
Chris Stevenson, supt. Fax 864-4060
www.harper.txed.net/
Harper HS 200/9-12
PO Box 68 78631 830-864-4044
Dean Eckert, prin. Fax 864-4748
Harper MS 100/5-8
PO Box 68 78631 830-864-4044
Bonnie Stewart, prin. Fax 864-4748

Harrold, Wilbarger
Harrold ISD 100/K-12
18106 Stewart St 76364 940-886-2213
David Thweatt, supt. Fax 886-2215
www.harroldisd.net/
Harrold S 100/K-12
18106 Stewart St 76364 940-886-2213
Craig Templeton, prin. Fax 886-2215

Hart, Castro, Pop. 1,112
Hart ISD 200/PK-12
PO Box 490 79043 806-938-2143
David Cox, supt. Fax 938-2610
www.hartisd.net
Hart JSHS 100/6-12
PO Box 490 79043 806-938-2141
Ramona Neudorf, prin. Fax 938-2610

Hartley, Hartley, Pop. 536
Hartley ISD 200/PK-12
PO Box 408 79044 806-365-4458
Scott Vincent, supt. Fax 365-4459
www.hartleyisd.net
Hartley S 200/PK-12
PO Box 408 79044 806-365-4458
Scott Vincent, supt. Fax 365-4459

Haskell, Haskell, Pop. 3,278
Haskell Consolidated ISD 600/PK-12
PO Box 937 79521 940-864-2602
Bill Alcorn, supt. Fax 864-8096
www.haskell.esc14.net/
Haskell HS 200/9-12
PO Box 937 79521 940-864-8535
Jeff York, prin. Fax 864-3977
Haskell JHS 100/6-8
PO Box 937 79521 940-864-5981
Kent Colley, prin. Fax 864-5982

Paint Creek ISD 100/PK-12
4485 FM 600 79521 940-864-2868
Dr. Cheryl Floyd, supt. Fax 863-4488
www.paintcreek.esc14.net
Paint Creek S 100/PK-12
4485 FM 600 79521 940-864-2868
Roy Gardner, prin. Fax 863-4488

Haslet, Tarrant, Pop. 1,481
Northwest ISD
Supt. — See Justin
Eaton HS, 1350 Eagle Blvd 76052 9-12
Dr. Carri Eddy, prin. 817-698-3955
Wilson MS 800/6-8
14250 Sendera Ranch Blvd 76052 817-698-7900
Mike Blankenship, prin. Fax 698-7970

Legacy Classical Christian Academy 50/PK-12
PO Box 416 76052 817-363-3652
Belinda Henson, admin.

Hawkins, Wood, Pop. 1,237
Hawkins ISD 700/PK-12
PO Box 1430 75765 903-769-2181
Morris Lyon, supt. Fax 769-0505
www.hawkinsisd.org
Hawkins HS 200/9-12
PO Box 1430 75765 903-769-0571
Cindy Thatcher, prin. Fax 769-0573
Hawkins MS 200/6-8
PO Box 1430 75765 903-769-0552
Jason Boyd, prin. Fax 769-0583

Jarvis Christian College Post-Sec.
Highway 80 E PR 7631 75765 903-730-4890

Hawley, Jones, Pop. 626
Hawley ISD 700/PK-12
PO Box 440 79525 325-537-2214
Jimmy J. Burns, supt. Fax 537-2265
www.hawley.esc14.net
Hawley HS 200/9-12
PO Box 440 79525 325-537-2722
Nikki Grisham, prin. Fax 537-2265
Hawley MS 200/6-8
PO Box 440 79525 325-537-2070
Chad Hoffman, prin. Fax 537-2265

Hearne, Robertson, Pop. 4,418
Hearne ISD 900/PK-12
900 Wheelock St 77859 979-279-3200
Dr. Adrain Johnson, supt. Fax 279-3631
www.hearneisd.com
Hearne HS 200/9-12
1201 W Brown St 77859 979-279-2332
Joslyn Pierce, prin. Fax 279-8006
Hearne JHS 100/7-8
1201B W Brown St 77859 979-279-2449
Jannie Mitchell, prin. Fax 279-8033

Heath, Rockwall, Pop. 6,837
Rockwall ISD
Supt. — See Rockwall
Rockwall-Heath HS 2,100/9-12
801 Laurence Dr 75032 972-772-2474
Dr. Tom Maglisceau, prin. Fax 698-2608

Fulton S 200/PK-12
1626 Smirl Dr 75032 972-772-4445
Dr. Letha Hopkins, head sch Fax 772-9558

Hebbronville, Jim Hogg, Pop. 4,553
Jim Hogg County ISD 1,100/PK-12
PO Box 880 78361 361-527-3203
Juan Maldonado, supt. Fax 527-4928
www.jhcisdpk12.org
Hebbronville HS 300/9-12
PO Box 880 78361 361-527-3203
Eric Salinas, prin. Fax 527-5989
Hebbronville JHS 200/6-8
PO Box 880 78361 361-527-3203
Ray Garza, prin. Fax 527-5986

Hedley, Donley, Pop. 328
Hedley ISD 100/PK-12
PO Box 69 79237 806-856-5323
Colby Waldrop, supt. Fax 856-5372
www.hedleyisd.net
Hedley S 100/PK-12
PO Box 69 79237 806-856-5323
Reida Penman, prin. Fax 856-5372

Helotes, Bexar, Pop. 7,218
Northside ISD
Supt. — See San Antonio
O'Connor HS 3,000/9-12
12221 Leslie Rd 78023 210-397-4800
Jacqueline Horras, prin. Fax 695-4804

Hemphill, Sabine, Pop. 1,176
Hemphill ISD 900/PK-12
PO Box 1950 75948 409-787-3371
Reese Briggs, supt. Fax 787-4005
www.hemphill.esc7.net
Hemphill HS 300/9-12
PO Box 1950 75948 409-787-3371
Marc Griffin, prin. Fax 787-1259
Hemphill MS 300/5-8
PO Box 1950 75948 409-787-3371
Jeremy McDaniel, prin. Fax 787-4005

Hempstead, Waller, Pop. 5,718
Hempstead ISD 1,100/PK-12
PO Box 1007 77445 979-826-3304
Dr. Angela Gutsch, supt. Fax 826-5510
www.hempsteadisd.org
Hempstead HS 400/9-12
PO Box 1007 77445 979-826-3331
Eric Mullens, prin. Fax 826-4779
Hempstead MS 400/6-8
PO Box 1007 77445 979-826-5570
Kimberly White, prin. Fax 826-5583

Henderson, Rusk, Pop. 13,557
Carlisle ISD 700/PK-12
8960 FM 13 W 75654 903-861-3801
Michael Payne, supt. Fax 861-3932
www.carlisleisd.org
Carlisle HS 200/9-12
8960 FM 13 W 75654 903-861-3811
Sarah Baker, prin. Fax 861-0100
Carlisle JHS 100/6-8
8960 FM 13 W 75654 903-861-3811
Jennifer Gholson, prin. Fax 861-0100

Henderson ISD 3,500/PK-12
PO Box 728 75653 903-655-5000
Keith Boles, supt. Fax 657-9271
www.hendersonisd.org/
Henderson HS 900/9-12
PO Box 728 75653 903-655-5500
Terry Everitt, prin. Fax 657-7604
Henderson MS 800/6-8
PO Box 728 75653 903-655-5400
Hardy Dotson, prin. Fax 657-6499

Full Armor Christian Academy 100/K-12
PO Box 2035 75653 903-655-8489
Tricia Hall, head sch Fax 657-8267

Henrietta, Clay, Pop. 3,103
Henrietta ISD 900/PK-12
1801 E Crafton St 76365 940-720-7900
Jeff McClure, supt. Fax 538-7505
www.henrietta-isd.net
Henrietta HS 300/9-12
1700 E Crafton St 76365 940-720-7930
Michael Smiley, prin. Fax 538-7535
Henrietta JHS 200/6-8
308 E Gilbert St 76365 940-720-7920
Randy Zamzow, prin. Fax 538-7525

Midway ISD 100/PK-12
12142 State Highway 148 S 76365 940-476-2215
Alan Umholtz, supt. Fax 476-2226
www2.esc9.net/midway
Midway S 100/PK-12
12142 State Highway 148 S 76365 940-476-2222
Cherry Johnston, prin. Fax 476-2226

Hereford, Deaf Smith, Pop. 15,284
Hereford ISD 4,300/PK-12
601 N 25 Mile Ave 79045 806-363-7600
Dr. Rodney Hutto, supt. Fax 363-7647
www.herefordisd.net
Hereford Center for Accelerated Learning 50/Alt
239 Avenue H 79045 806-363-7720
Tony Barker, prin.
Hereford HS 1,100/9-12
200 Avenue F 79045 806-363-7620
Richard Sauceda, prin. Fax 363-7688
Hereford Preparatory Academy 300/8-8
704 La Plata St 79045 806-363-7740
Amy Clifton, prin. Fax 363-7699

Hermleigh, Scurry, Pop. 343
Hermleigh ISD 200/PK-12
8010 Business 84 H 79526 325-863-2772
Brent Dawson, supt. Fax 863-2713
www.hermleigh.esc14.net

Hermleigh S 200/PK-12
8010 Business 84 H 79526 325-863-2482
Eddie Richardson, prin. Fax 863-2713

Hewitt, McLennan, Pop. 13,309
Midway ISD
Supt. — See Woodway
Midway MS 1,200/7-8
800 N Hewitt Dr 76643 254-761-5680
Dr. Herbert Cox, prin. Fax 761-5775

Hico, Hamilton, Pop. 1,369
Hico ISD 500/PK-12
PO Box 218 76457 254-796-2181
Jon Hartgraves, supt. Fax 796-2446
www.hico-isd.net
Hico Secondary S 300/6-12
PO Box 218 76457 254-796-2184
Shelli Stegall, prin. Fax 796-2446

Hidalgo, Hidalgo, Pop. 11,192
Hidalgo ISD 3,200/PK-12
PO Box 8220 78557 956-843-4401
Edward Blaha, supt. Fax 843-3343
www.hidalgo-isd.com
Diaz JHS 700/6-8
PO Box 8220 78557 956-843-4350
Celia Martinez, prin. Fax 843-3198
Hidalgo Academy 50/Alt
PO Box 8220 78557 956-843-4390
Ana Lee Mancha, prin. Fax 843-3339
Hidalgo Early College HS 900/9-12
PO Box 8220 78557 956-843-4300
Judith Dimas, prin. Fax 843-3322

Higgins, Lipscomb, Pop. 392
Higgins ISD 100/PK-12
PO Box 218 79046 806-852-2631
Steve James, supt. Fax 852-3502
www.higginsisd.net
Higgins S 100/PK-12
PO Box 218 79046 806-852-2631
Steve James, supt. Fax 852-3502

High Island, Galveston
High Island ISD 100/PK-12
PO Box 246 77623 409-286-5317
D'Ann Cathriner-Vonderau Ed.D., supt. Fax 286-5351
www.highislandisd.com
High Island HS 100/9-12
PO Box 246 77623 409-286-5314
Amanda Jackson, prin. Fax 286-2120
High Island MS 50/6-8
PO Box 246 77623 409-286-5314
Fax 286-2120

Highlands, Harris, Pop. 7,443
Goose Creek Consolidated ISD
Supt. — See Baytown
Highlands JHS 1,100/6-8
1212 E Wallisville Rd 77562 281-420-4695
Gary Guy, prin. Fax 426-4301
POINT Alternative Center 100/Alt
401 Jones Rd 77562 281-240-4630
Tricia Times, prin. Fax 426-2680

Chinquapin Preparatory S 200/6-12
2615 E Wallisville Rd 77562 281-426-5551
Dr. Laura Henry, prin. Fax 426-5553

Highland Village, Denton, Pop. 14,764
Lewisville ISD
Supt. — See Flower Mound
Briarhill MS 1,000/6-8
2100 Briarhill Blvd 75077 469-713-5975
Chris Mattingly, prin. Fax 350-9167

Hillsboro, Hill, Pop. 8,341
Hillsboro ISD 1,900/PK-12
121 E Franklin St 76645 254-582-8585
Vicki Adams, supt. Fax 582-4165
www.hillsboroisd.org
Hillsboro HS 500/9-12
1600 Abbott Ave 76645 254-582-4100
Keith Hannah, prin. Fax 582-4108
Hillsboro JHS 300/6-8
210 E Walnut St 76645 254-582-4120
Cathryn Patterson, prin. Fax 582-4122

Hill College Post-Sec.
112 Lamar Dr 76645 254-659-7500

Hitchcock, Galveston, Pop. 6,879
Hitchcock ISD 1,100/PK-12
7801 Neville Ave 77563 409-316-6545
Carla Vickroy, supt. Fax 986-5141
www.hitchcockisd.org
Crosby MS 200/6-8
6625 FM 2004 Rd 77563 409-316-6542
Patrick Faour, prin. Fax 986-9254
Hitchcock HS 300/9-12
6629 FM 2004 Rd 77563 409-316-6544
Kellie Edmundson, prin. Fax 986-9339

Holland, Bell, Pop. 1,111
Holland ISD 600/PK-12
PO Box 217 76534 254-657-0175
Cindy Gunn, supt. Fax 657-0172
www.hollandisd.org
Holland HS 200/9-12
PO Box 217 76534 254-657-2523
Britt Gordon, prin. Fax 657-2250
Holland MS 200/6-8
PO Box 217 76534 254-657-2224
Leah Smith, prin. Fax 657-2872

Holliday, Archer, Pop. 1,747
Holliday ISD 900/PK-12
PO Box 689 76366 940-586-1281
Dr. Kevin Dyes, supt. Fax 586-1492
www.hollidayisd.net
Holliday HS 300/9-12
PO Box 947 76366 940-586-1624
Bruce Patterson, prin. Fax 586-9501
Holliday MS 200/6-8
PO Box 977 76366 940-586-1314
Kelly Carver, prin. Fax 586-4480

Hondo, Medina, Pop. 8,749
Hondo ISD 2,200/PK-12
PO Box 308 78861 830-426-3027
Dr. A'Lann Truelock, supt. Fax 426-7683
www.hondoisd.net
Hondo HS 600/9-12
2603 Avenue H 78861 830-426-3341
Robert Knight, prin. Fax 426-7690
McDowell MS 500/6-8
1602 27th St S 78861 830-426-2261
Scott Backus, prin. Fax 426-7624

Honey Grove, Fannin, Pop. 1,640
Honey Grove ISD 600/PK-12
1206 17th St 75446 903-378-2264
Todd Morrison, supt. Fax 378-2991
www.honeygroveisd.net/
Honey Grove HS 200/9-12
1206 17th St 75446 903-378-2264
Tammy Mariani, prin. Fax 378-3050
Honey Grove MS 100/6-8
1206 17th St 75446 903-378-2264
Lee Frost, prin. Fax 378-2095

Hooks, Bowie, Pop. 2,693
Hooks ISD 900/PK-12
100 E 5th St 75561 903-547-6077
Shane Krueger, supt. Fax 547-2943
www.hooksisd.net
Hooks HS 300/9-12
401 E Avenue A 75561 903-547-2215
Danny Garrett, prin. Fax 547-6514
Hooks JHS 300/5-8
3921 FM 560 75561 903-547-2568
Craig Mahar, prin. Fax 547-2595

Houston, Harris, Pop. 2,071,912
Aldine ISD 66,300/PK-12
2520 WW Thorne Blvd 77073 281-449-1011
Dr. Wanda Bamberg, supt. Fax 449-4911
www.aldineisd.org
Aldine Education Center 200/Alt
1702 Aldine Bender Rd 77032 281-985-6685
James Metcalf, prin. Fax 985-6688
Aldine MS 900/7-8
14908 Aldine Westfield Rd 77032 281-985-6580
Marcus Pruitt, prin. Fax 985-6480
Aldine Ninth Grade S 800/9-9
10650 North Fwy 77037 281-878-6800
Jennifer Merryman, prin. Fax 878-6824
Aldine SHS 2,200/10-12
11101 Airline Dr 77037 281-448-5231
Walter Stewart, prin. Fax 878-0641
Carver Magnet HS 900/9-12
2100 S Victory Dr 77088 281-878-0310
Anthony Watkins, prin. Fax 591-8579
Davis Ninth Grade S 900/9-9
12211 Ella Blvd 77067 281-873-1800
Heather Kirk, prin. Fax 539-4044
Davis SHS 1,500/10-12
12525 Ella Blvd 77067 281-539-4070
Thomas Colwell, prin. Fax 539-4075
Drew Academy 600/7-8
1910 W Little York Rd 77091 281-878-0360
Earnest Washington, prin. Fax 447-4694
Eisenhower Ninth Grade S 600/9-9
3550 W Gulf Bank Rd 77088 281-878-7700
LaTonia Amerson, prin. Fax 878-7736
Eisenhower SHS 1,900/10-12
7922 Antoine Dr 77088 281-878-0900
Benjamin Ibarra, prin. Fax 448-2936
Grantham Academy 1,100/7-8
13300 Chrisman Rd 77039 281-985-6590
Jessica Scott, prin. Fax 985-6595
Hall Center for Education 300/Alt
15014 Aldine Westfield Rd 77032 281-985-7446
Pertricia Ross, prin. Fax 985-7453
Hambrick MS 1,000/7-8
4600 Aldine Mail Rd 77039 281-985-6570
Rebecca Hoyt, prin. Fax 442-9036
Hoffman MS 700/7-8
6101 W Little York Rd 77091 713-613-7670
Rosalyn Sweat, prin. Fax 613-7675
Lewis MS 1,000/7-8
21255 W Hardy Rd 77073 281-209-8257
Cassandra Bell, prin. Fax 209-8267
MacArthur Ninth Grade S 1,000/9-9
12111 Gloger St 77039 281-985-7400
D'Ann Delgado, prin. Fax 985-7423
MacArthur SHS 2,500/10-12
4400 Aldine Mail Rd 77039 281-985-6330
Craig Mullenix, prin. Fax 985-6294
Nimitz Ninth Grade S 600/9-9
2425 WW Thorne Blvd 77073 281-209-8200
Tonya Landry, prin. Fax 209-8220
Nimitz SHS 1,700/10-12
2005 WW Thorne Blvd 77073 281-443-7480
Dr. Crystal Watson-Barrow, prin. Fax 233-4331
Plummer MS 900/7-8
11429 Spears Rd 77067 281-539-4000
Andrea Cain, prin. Fax 539-4017
Shotwell MS 1,100/7-8
6515 Trail Valley Way 77086 281-878-0960
Shirley Seals, prin. Fax 591-8564
Stovall MS 1,000/7-8
11201 Airline Dr 77037 281-878-0670
Elsa Wright, prin. Fax 448-0636
Victory Early College HS 400/9-12
4141 Victory Dr 77088 281-810-5675
Phyllis Cormier, prin. Fax 810-5698
Other Schools – See Humble

Alief ISD 45,800/PK-12
4250 Cook Rd 77072 281-498-8110
H.D. Chambers, supt. Fax 498-8730
www.aliefisd.net
Albright MS 1,300/7-8
6315 Winkleman Rd 77083 281-983-8411
Lori Wyatt, prin. Fax 983-8443
Alief Early College HS 400/9-12
2811 Hayes Rd Ste A 77082 281-988-3010
Kerry Beth Johnson, prin. Fax 988-3066
Alief Learning Center 100/Alt
4427 Belle Park Dr 77072 281-983-8000
Mary Wilson, prin. Fax 983-7701
Alief MS 700/7-8
4415 Cook Rd 77072 281-983-8422
David Lopez, prin. Fax 983-8053
Alief Taylor HS 2,900/9-12
7555 Howell Sugar Land Rd 77083 281-988-3500
Mary Williams, prin. Fax 561-7214
Crossroads Alternative Technology S 50/Alt
12360 Bear Ram Rd 77072 281-988-3266
Tremayne Wickliffe, prin. Fax 988-3277
Elsik HS 2,800/10-12
12601 High Star Dr 77072 281-988-3150
Tina Elzy, prin. Fax 530-7058
Elsik Ninth Grade Center 1,200/9-9
6767 S Dairy Ashford Rd 77072 281-988-3239
Vinson Lewis, prin. Fax 988-3319
Hastings HS 2,700/10-12
4410 Cook Rd 77072 281-498-8110
Patrick Cherry, prin. Fax 561-5763
Hastings Ninth Grade Center 1,200/9-9
6750 Cook Rd 77072 281-988-3139
Janie Saxton, prin. Fax 988-3419
Holub MS 900/7-8
9515 S Dairy Ashford Rd 77099 281-983-8433
Pauline Beckley, prin. Fax 983-8398
Kerr HS 800/9-12
8150 Howell Sugar Land Rd 77083 281-983-8484
Greg Freeman, prin. Fax 983-8014
Killough MS 1,000/7-8
7600 Synott Rd 77083 281-983-8444
Bryan Brown, prin. Fax 983-8067
O'Donnell MS 1,300/6-8
14041 Alief Clodine Rd 77082 281-495-6000
Amador Velasquez, prin. Fax 568-5029
Olle MS 1,100/7-8
9200 Boone Rd 77099 281-983-8455
Nelda Billescas, prin. Fax 983-8077
S.O.A.R. Adult
12360 Bear Ram Rd 77072 281-988-3266
Kathleen Jameson, prin. Fax 988-3277

Channelview ISD
Supt. — See Channelview
Aguirre JHS 900/6-8
15726 Wallisville Rd 77049 281-860-3300
Eric Lathan, prin. Fax 860-3320

Clear Creek ISD
Supt. — See League City
Clear Lake HS 2,400/9-12
2929 Bay Area Blvd 77058 281-284-1900
Karen Engle, prin. Fax 284-1905
Clear Lake IS 1,000/6-8
15545 El Camino Real 77062 281-284-3200
Michael Alvarez, prin. Fax 284-3205
Space Center IS 1,100/6-8
17400 Saturn Ln 77058 281-284-3300
Lonnie Leal, prin. Fax 284-3305

Cypress-Fairbanks ISD 110,100/PK-12
PO Box 692003 77269 281-897-4000
Dr. Mark Henry, supt. Fax 897-4125
www.cfisd.net
Adaptive Behavior Center Alt
12508 Windfern Rd 77064 281-897-4174
Chad Perry, dir. Fax 517-2884
Alternative Learning Center - East Alt
12508 Windfern Rd 77064 281-897-4171
Laurie Snyder, prin. Fax 897-4170
Aragon MS 1,600/6-8
16823 West Rd 77095 281-856-5100
Maria Mamaux, prin. Fax 856-5105
Bleyl MS 1,600/6-8
10800 Mills Rd 77070 281-897-4340
Stacia Carew, prin. Fax 897-4353
Campbell MS 1,200/6-8
11415 Bobcat Rd 77064 281-897-4300
Laura Perry, prin. Fax 807-8634
Cook MS 1,600/6-8
9111 Wheatland Dr 77064 281-897-4400
Sherma Duck, prin. Fax 897-3850
Cypress Creek HS 3,300/9-12
9815 Grant Rd 77070 281-897-4200
Vicki Snokhous, prin. Fax 807-8925
Cypress Falls HS 3,500/9-12
9811 Huffmeister Rd 77095 281-856-1000
Becky Denton, prin. Fax 856-1445
Cypress Ridge HS 3,000/9-12
7900 N Eldridge Pkwy 77041 713-807-8000
Stephanie Meshell, prin. Fax 807-8045
Dean MS 1,500/6-8
14104 Reo St 77040 713-460-6153
Heather Bergman, prin. Fax 460-6197
Jersey Village HS 3,400/9-12
7600 Solomon St 77040 713-896-3400
Ralph Funk, prin. Fax 896-3438
Kahla MS 1,500/6-8
16212 W Little York Rd 77084 281-345-3260
Ana Martin, prin. Fax 345-5275
Labay MS 1,500/6-8
15435 Willow River Dr 77095 281-463-5800
Lanette Bellamy, prin. Fax 463-5804
Langham Creek HS 3,100/9-12
17610 FM 529 Rd 77095 281-463-5400
David Hughes, prin. Fax 345-3153

Truitt MS 1,400/6-8
6600 Addicks Satsuma Rd 77084 281-856-1100
Teresa Baranowski, prin. Fax 856-1104
Watkins MS 1,300/6-8
4800 Cairnvillage St 77084 281-463-5850
Dr. Jose Martinez, prin. Fax 856-1565
Windfern HS of Choice 200/Alt
12630 Windfern Rd 77064 281-807-8684
Martha Strother, prin. Fax 807-8693
Other Schools – See Cypress, Katy

Fort Bend ISD
Supt. — See Sugar Land
Hodges Bend MS 1,200/6-8
16510 Bissonnet St 77083 281-634-3000
Dr. Ashley Causey, prin. Fax 634-3028
McAuliffe MS 800/6-8
16650 S Post Oak Rd 77053 281-634-3360
Mary Brewster, prin. Fax 634-3393
Willowridge HS 1,300/9-12
16301 Chimney Rock Rd 77053 281-634-2450
Thomas Graham, prin. Fax 634-2513

Galena Park ISD 22,500/PK-12
14705 Woodforest Blvd 77015 832-386-1000
Dr. Angi Williams, supt. Fax 386-1298
www.galenaparkisd.com
Accelerated Center for Education Alt
13801 Hollypark Dr 77015 832-386-3670
Julien Guillory, prin. Fax 386-3671
Center for Success Alt
13801 Hollypark Dr 77015 832-386-3630
Julien Guillory, prin. Fax 386-3631
Cunningham MS 900/7-8
14110 Wallisville Rd 77049 832-386-4470
David Pierson, prin. Fax 386-4471
North Shore 9th Grade Center 1,200/9-9
13501 Hollypark Dr 77015 832-386-3400
Jason Bollich, prin. Fax 386-3401
North Shore MS 1,300/7-8
120 Castlegory Rd 77015 832-386-2600
James Cline, prin. Fax 386-2643
North Shore SHS 3,400/10-12
353 N Castlegory Rd 77049 832-386-4100
Dr. Joe Coleman, prin. Fax 386-4101
Woodland Acres MS 500/6-8
12947 Myrtle Ln 77015 832-386-4700
Lee Ramirez, prin. Fax 386-4701
Other Schools – See Galena Park

Houston ISD 211,000/PK-12
4400 W 18th St 77092 713-556-6000
Richard Carranza, supt. Fax 556-6323
www.houstonisd.org
Attucks MS 500/6-8
4330 Bellfort St 77051 713-732-3670
Renita Perry, prin. Fax 732-3677
Austin HS 1,700/9-12
1700 Dumble St 77023 713-924-1600
Steve Guerrero, prin. Fax 923-3157
Baylor College of Medicine Academy 200/6-8
2610 Elgin St 77004 713-942-1932
Jyoti Malhan, prin. Fax 942-1943
Beechnut Academy 200/6-12
7055 Beechnut St 77074 713-394-3500
Patrice Grovey, prin. Fax 777-4011
Black MS 800/6-8
1575 Chantilly Ln 77018 713-613-2505
Paolo Castagnoli, prin. Fax 613-2233
Burbank MS 1,400/6-8
315 Berry Rd 77022 713-696-2720
David Knittle, prin. Fax 696-2723
Carnegie-Vanguard HS 600/9-12
1501 Taft St 77019 713-732-3690
Ramon Moss, prin. Fax 732-3694
Challenge Early College HS 500/9-12
5601 West Loop S 77081 713-664-9712
Tonya Miller, prin. Fax 664-9780
Chavez HS 3,000/9-12
8501 Howard Dr 77017 713-495-6950
Rene Sanchez, prin. Fax 495-6988
Clifton MS 900/6-8
6001 Golden Forest Dr 77092 713-613-2516
Rosa Cruz-Gaona, prin. Fax 613-2523
Community Services 100/Alt
1102 Telephone Rd 77023 713-967-5285
Stephen MacLauchlan, prin. Fax 967-5223
Cullen MS 700/6-8
6900 Scott St 77021 713-746-8180
Clayton Crook, prin. Fax 746-8181
Deady MS 900/6-8
2500 Broadway St 77012 713-845-7411
Richard Smith, prin. Fax 649-5816
DeBakey Health Professions HS 800/9-12
3100 Shenandoah St 77021 713-741-2410
Agnes Perry, prin. Fax 746-5211
East Early College HS 500/9-12
220 N Milby St 77003 713-847-4809
Tamera Bolden, prin. Fax 847-4813
Eastwood Academy 400/9-12
1315 Dumble St 77023 713-924-1697
Brandi Lira, prin. Fax 924-1715
Edison MS 700/6-8
6901 Avenue I 77011 713-924-1800
Mayra Hernandez, prin. Fax 924-1316
Energy Institute 200/9-12
1808 Sampson St 77003 713-802-4620
Lori Lambropoulos, prin. Fax 556-9840
Fleming MS 500/6-8
4910 Collingsworth St 77026 713-671-4170
Sabrina Cuby-King, prin. Fax 671-4176
Fondren MS 800/6-8
6333 S Braeswood Blvd 77096 713-778-3360
Monique Lewis, prin. Fax 778-3362
Fonville MS 1,100/6-8
725 E Little York Rd 77076 713-696-2825
Paula Pierre, prin. Fax 696-2829
Forest Brook MS 1,000/6-8
7525 Tidwell Rd 77016 713-631-7720
Tannisha Gentry, prin. Fax 636-4114
Furr HS 900/9-12
520 Mercury Dr 77013 713-675-1118
Dr. Bertie Simmons, prin. Fax 671-3612
Hamilton MS 1,300/6-8
139 E 20th St 77008 713-802-4725
Wendy Hampton, prin. Fax 802-4731
Harper Alternative S 50/Alt
4425 N Shepherd Dr 77018 713-802-4760
Raymond Glass, prin. Fax 802-4768
Hartman MS 1,400/6-8
7111 Westover St 77087 713-845-7435
Geovanny Ponce, prin. Fax 847-4706
HCC Life Skills 50/Alt
1301 Alabama St 77004 713-718-6882
Susan Hurta, prin. Fax 718-6815
Heights HS 2,200/9-12
413 E 13th St 77008 713-865-4400
Connie Berger, prin. Fax 802-4749
Henry MS 900/6-8
10702 E Hardy Rd 77093 713-696-2650
Kenneth Brantley, prin. Fax 696-2657
High School Ahead Academy 300/6-8
5320 Yale St 77091 713-696-2643
Yolanda Jones, prin. Fax 696-2999
Hogg MS 700/6-8
1100 Merrill St 77009 713-802-4700
Angela Sugarek, prin. Fax 802-4708
Holland MS 700/6-8
1600 Gellhorn Dr 77029 713-671-3860
Lashonda Bilbo-Ervin, prin. Fax 671-3874
Houston Acad for International Studies 400/9-12
1810 Stuart St 77004 713-942-1430
Melissa Jacobs, prin. Fax 942-1433
HS for Law Enforcement/Criminal Justice 500/9-12
4701 Dickson St 77007 713-867-5100
Carol Mosteit, prin. Fax 802-4600
HS for Performing & Visual Arts 700/9-12
4001 Stanford St 77006 713-942-1960
Robert Allen, prin. Fax 942-1968
Houston Math Science Tech Ctr 2,600/9-12
9400 Irvington Blvd 77076 713-696-0200
Alan Summers, prin. Fax 696-8984
Jones Futures Academy 400/9-12
7414 Saint Lo Rd 77033 713-733-1111
Geovanny Ponce, prin. Fax 732-3450
Jordan HS for Careers Vo/Tech
5800 Eastex Fwy 77026 713-636-6900
John McAlpine, prin. Fax 636-6917
Kashmere HS 500/9-12
6900 Wileyvale Rd 77028 713-636-6400
Nancy Blackwell, prin. Fax 636-6433
Key MS 700/6-8
4000 Kelley St 77026 713-636-6000
Joseph Williams, prin. Fax 636-6008
Lamar HS 3,200/9-12
3325 Westheimer Rd 77098 713-522-5960
James McSwain, prin. Fax 535-3769
Lanier MS 1,400/6-8
2600 Woodhead St 77098 713-942-1900
Felicia Adams, prin. Fax 942-1907
Las Americas MS 200/4-8
6501 Bellaire Blvd 77074 713-773-5300
Maria Moreno, prin. Fax 773-5303
Lawson MS 1,100/6-8
14000 Stancliff St 77045 713-434-5600
Tynette Guinn, prin. Fax 434-5608
Leland College Prep 300/6-12
1510 Jensen Dr 77020 713-226-2668
Dameion Crook, prin. Fax 226-4923
Liberty HS 500/9-12
6400 Southwest Fwy Ste A 77074 713-458-5555
Monico Rivas, prin. Fax 458-5567
Long Academy 1,000/6-12
6501 Bellaire Blvd 77074 713-778-3380
Marcela Baez, prin. Fax 778-3387
Madison HS 2,000/9-12
13719 White Heather Dr 77045 713-433-9801
Orlando Reyna, prin. Fax 434-5242
Marshall MS 1,000/6-8
1115 Noble St 77009 713-226-2600
Michael Harrison, prin. Fax 226-2605
McReynolds MS 600/6-8
5910 Market St 77020 713-671-3650
Steven Stapleton, prin. Fax 671-3657
Meyerland MS 1,700/6-8
10410 Manhattan Dr 77096 713-726-3616
Wenden Sanders, prin. Fax 726-3622
Middle College HS at Fraga 200/Alt
301 N Drennan St 77003 713-718-6740
Angelica Vega, prin.
Middle College HS at Gulfton 200/Alt
5407 Gulfton St 77081 713-662-2551
Diana del Pilar, prin. Fax 662-2572
Milby HS 2,100/9-12
7414 Saint Lo Rd 77033 713-928-7401
Roy de la Garza, prin. Fax 928-7474
Navarro MS 900/6-8
5100 Polk St 77023 713-924-1760
Kelly Pichon, prin. Fax 924-1768
North Forest HS 1,000/9-12
10725 Mesa Dr 77078 713-636-4300
Richard Fernandez, prin. Fax 636-8116
North Houston Early College HS 400/9-12
8001 Fulton St 77022 713-696-6168
Angela Lundy-Jackson, prin. Fax 696-6172
Northside HS 1,700/9-12
1101 Quitman St 77009 713-226-4900
Julissa Martinez, prin. Fax 226-4999
Ortiz MS 1,000/6-8
6767 Telephone Rd 77061 713-845-5650
Noelia Longoria, prin. Fax 845-5646
Pershing MS 1,700/6-8
3838 Blue Bonnet Blvd 77025 713-295-5240
Steven Shetzer, prin. Fax 295-5252
Project Chrysalis MS 200/6-8
4528 Leeland St 77023 713-924-1700
Jose Covarrubia, prin. Fax 924-1704
Pro-Vision S 100/5-12
4590 Wilmington St 77051 713-748-0030
Fax 748-0037
Reach Charter S 300/9-12
520 Mercury Dr 77013 713-671-4515
Bertie Simmons, prin. Fax 675-1118
Revere MS 1,200/6-8
10502 Briar Forest Dr 77042 713-917-3500
Christian Delariva, prin. Fax 917-3505
Rogers S 800/K-12
5840 San Felipe St 77057 713-917-3565
David Muzyka, prin. Fax 917-3555
Scarborough HS 700/9-12
4141 Costa Rica Rd 77092 713-613-2200
Diego Linares, prin. Fax 613-2205
Sharpstown HS 1,400/9-12
7504 Bissonnet St 77074 713-771-7215
Daniel DeLeon, prin. Fax 773-6103
Sharpstown International S 1,100/6-12
8330 Triola Ln 77036 713-778-3440
Thuy Le-Thai, prin. Fax 778-3444
Soar Center 200/Alt
4400 W 18th St 77092 713-556-7025
Sowmya Kumar, prin. Fax 556-7099
South Early College HS 50/10-12
1930 Airport Blvd 77051 713-732-3623
Steven Gourrier, prin. Fax 732-3425
Sterling HS 800/9-12
11625 Martindale Rd 77048 713-991-0510
Justin Fuentes, prin. Fax 991-8111
Stevenson MS 1,400/6-8
9595 Winkler Dr 77017 713-943-5700
Ruth Ruiz, prin. Fax 943-5711
Sugar Grove MS 700/6-8
8405 Bonhomme Rd 77074 713-271-0214
Lynett Hookfin, prin. Fax 771-9342
Tanglewood MS 600/6-8
5215 San Felipe St 77056 713-625-1411
Gretchen Kasper-Hoffman, prin. Fax 625-1415
Thomas MS 500/6-8
5655 Selinsky Rd 77048 713-732-3500
Connie Smith, prin. Fax 732-3511
Waltrip HS 1,600/9-12
1900 W 34th St 77018 713-688-1361
Edward Mitchell, prin. Fax 957-7743
Washington HS 800/9-12
119 E 39th St 77018 713-696-6600
Carlos Phillips, prin. Fax 696-6657
Welch MS 900/6-8
11544 S Gessner Rd 77071 713-778-3300
Inge Garibaldi, prin. Fax 995-6067
West Briar MS 1,200/6-8
13733 Brimhurst Dr 77077 281-368-2140
Keeley Simpson, prin. Fax 368-2194
Westbury HS 2,100/9-12
11911 Chimney Rock Rd 77035 713-723-6015
Susan Monaghan, prin. Fax 726-2165
Westside HS 2,800/9-12
14201 Briar Forest Dr 77077 281-920-8000
Marguerite Stewart, prin. Fax 920-8059
Wheatley HS 900/9-12
4801 Providence St 77020 713-671-3900
Shirley Rose, prin. Fax 671-3951
Williams Charter MS 500/6-8
6100 Knox St 77091 713-696-2600
Corey Seymour, prin. Fax 696-2604
Wisdom HS 1,400/9-12
6529 Beverlyhill St 77057 713-787-1700
Jonathan Trinh, prin. Fax 787-1723
Worthing HS 600/9-12
9215 Scott St 77051 713-733-3433
Duane Clark, prin. Fax 731-5537
Yates HS 1,000/9-12
3703 Sampson St 77004 713-748-5400
Kenneth Davis, prin. Fax 746-8206
Young Womens College Preparatory Academy 500/6-12
1906 Cleburne St 77004 713-942-1441
Delesa O'Dell-Thomas, prin. Fax 942-1448
Other Schools – See Bellaire

Humble ISD
Supt. — See Humble
Quest Early College HS 300/9-12
1700 Wilson Rd, 281-775-0866
Ginger Noyes, prin. Fax 641-6017
Summer Creek HS 2,300/9-12
14000 Weckford Blvd 77044 281-641-5400
Nolan Correa, prin. Fax 641-5417
Woodcreek MS 1,200/6-8
14600 Woodson Park Dr 77044 281-641-5200
Brent McDonald, prin. Fax 641-5217

Katy ISD
Supt. — See Katy
Mayde Creek HS 2,700/9-12
19202 Groeschke Rd 77084 281-237-3000
Ronnie Edwards, prin. Fax 644-1721
Mayde Creek JHS 1,100/6-8
2700 Greenhouse Rd 77084 281-237-3900
Dr. David Paz, prin. Fax 644-1650

Klein ISD
Supt. — See Klein
Klein Forest HS 3,500/9-12
11400 Misty Valley Dr 77066 832-484-4500
Jeff Bailey, prin. Fax 484-7801
Klein IS 1,200/6-8
4710 W Mount Houston Rd 77088 832-249-4900
Bob Anderson, prin. Fax 249-4046
Ulrich IS 1,100/6-8
10103 Spring Cypress Rd 77070 832-375-7500
Leslie Kompelien, prin. Fax 375-7599
Vistas HS Program Alt
12550 Bammel North Houston 77066 832-484-7650
Peggy Ekster, dir. Fax 484-7697

Wunderlich IS 1,500/6-8
11800 Misty Valley Dr 77066 832-249-5200
Dr. Chris Ruggerio, prin. Fax 249-4050

Pasadena ISD
Supt. — See Pasadena
Beverly Hills IS 1,000/6-8
11111 Beamer Rd 77089 713-740-0420
Stacy Barber, prin. Fax 740-4051
Dobie HS 3,800/9-12
10220 Blackhawk Blvd 77089 713-740-0370
Franklin Moses, prin. Fax 740-4158
Lewis Career and Technical HS Vo/Tech
1348 Genoa Red Bluff Rd 77034 713-740-5320
Steve Fleming, prin. Fax 740-5910
Queens IS 700/6-8
1452 Queens St 77017 713-740-0470
Troy Jones, prin. Fax 740-4102
Roberts MS, 13402 Conklin Ln 77034 6-8
Jorly Thomas, prin. 713-740-5390
Thompson IS 1,000/6-8
11309 Sagedowne Ln 77089 713-740-0510
Melissa Allen, prin. Fax 740-4083

Sheldon ISD 8,000/PK-12
11411 C E King Pkwy 77044 281-727-2000
King Davis, supt. Fax 727-2085
www.sheldonisd.com
King HS 1,800/9-12
8540 C E King Pkwy 77044 281-727-3500
Demetrius McCall, prin. Fax 459-7346
King MS 900/6-8
8530 C E King Pkwy 77044 281-727-4300
Alicia Martin, prin. Fax 459-7452
Null MS 900/6-8
12117 Garrett Rd 77044 281-436-2800
Leroy Bradley, prin. Fax 436-2875
Sheldon Early College HS 300/9-12
8540 C E King Pkwy 77044 281-727-3043
Marcia Herrera, dean

Spring Branch ISD 35,100/PK-12
955 Campbell Rd 77024 713-464-1511
Scott Muri Ed.D., supt. Fax 365-4664
www.springbranchisd.com
Guthrie Center for Excellence Vo/Tech
10660 Hammerly Blvd 77043 713-251-1300
Joe Kolenda, prin. Fax 251-1315
Landrum MS 800/6-8
2200 Ridgecrest Dr 77055 713-251-3700
Steven Speyrer, prin. Fax 251-3715
Memorial HS 2,600/9-12
935 Echo Ln 77024 713-251-2500
Lisa Weir, prin. Fax 251-2515
Memorial MS 1,400/6-8
12550 Vindon Dr 77024 713-251-3900
Daniel Bauer, prin. Fax 251-3915
Northbrook HS 2,100/9-12
1 Raider Cir 77080 713-251-2800
Randolph Adami, prin. Fax 251-2915
Northbrook MS 900/6-8
3030 Rosefield Dr 77080 713-251-4100
Sarah Guerrero, prin. Fax 251-4102
Spring Branch MS 1,200/6-8
1000 Piney Point Rd 77024 713-251-4400
Bryan Williams, prin. Fax 251-4415
Spring Forest MS 800/6-8
14240 Memorial Dr 77079 713-251-4600
Dr. Kaye Williams, prin. Fax 251-4615
Spring Oaks MS 800/6-8
2150 Shadowdale Dr 77043 713-251-4800
Paul Suess, prin. Fax 251-4815
Spring Woods HS 2,100/9-12
2045 Gessner Rd 77080 713-251-3100
Jennifer Collier, prin. Fax 251-3130
Spring Woods MS 900/6-8
9810 Neuens Rd 77080 713-251-5000
Deborah Silber, prin. Fax 251-5015
Stratford HS 2,000/9-12
14555 Fern Dr 77079 713-251-3400
Robert Gex, prin. Fax 251-3420

Spring ISD 36,500/PK-12
16717 Ella Blvd 77090 281-891-6000
Dr. Rodney Watson, supt. Fax 891-6006
www.springisd.org
Bammel MS 1,300/6-8
16711 Ella Blvd 77090 281-891-7900
La'Quesha Grigsby, prin. Fax 891-7901
Claughton MS 1,200/6-8
3000 Spears Rd 77067 281-891-7950
Demonica Amerson, prin. Fax 891-7951
DeKaney HS 2,700/9-12
22351 Imperial Valley Dr 77073 281-891-7260
David Baxter, prin. Fax 891-7261
Roberson MS 1,100/6-8
1500 Southridge 77090 281-891-7700
Tracey Walker, prin. Fax 891-7701
Spring Early College Academy 300/9-12
14450 T C Jester 77014 281-891-6880
Dr. Rene Garganta, prin. Fax 891-6881
Wells MS 1,300/6-8
4033 Gladeridge Dr 77068 281-891-7750
Henri Lewi, prin. Fax 891-7751
Westfield HS 3,200/9-12
16713 Ella Blvd 77090 281-891-7130
Alonzo Reynolds, prin. Fax 891-7131
Other Schools – See Spring

Aerosim Flight Academy Post-Sec.
12711 Blume Ave 77034 281-481-4700
Alexander-Smith Academy 100/9-12
10255 Richmond Ave Ste 100 77042 713-266-0920
Alfred G. Glassell School of Art Post-Sec.
PO Box 6826 77265 713-639-7500
Al-Hadi S of Accelerative Learning 300/PK-12
2313 S Voss Rd 77057 713-787-5000
Dr. Humaira Bokhari, prin. Fax 513-5315
American College of Acupuncture Post-Sec.
9100 Park West Dr 77063 713-780-9777
American InterContinental University Post-Sec.
9999 Richmond Ave 77042 832-201-3600
Anthem College Post-Sec.
70 FM 1960 Rd W 77090 888-852-7272
Art Institute of Houston Post-Sec.
4140 Southwest Fwy 77027 713-623-2040
Astrodome Career Center Post-Sec.
2656 S Loop W Ste 380 77054 713-664-5300
Aviation Institute of Maintenance Post-Sec.
7651 Airport Blvd 77061 713-644-7777
Awty International S 1,300/PK-12
7455 Awty School Ln 77055 713-686-4850
Lisa Darling, head sch Fax 686-4956
Banff S 100/PK-12
13726 Cutten Rd 77069 281-444-9326
Deborah Wasser, prin. Fax 444-3632
Baylor College of Medicine Post-Sec.
1 Baylor Plz 77030 713-798-4951
Behold! Beauty Academy Post-Sec.
3823 Charleston St 77021 713-635-5252
Ben Taub Hospital Post-Sec.
2525 Holly Hall St 77054 713-746-6400
Beren Academy 300/PK-12
11333 Cliffwood Dr 77035 713-723-7170
Bridge S 300/6-12
3333 Bering Dr 77057 713-974-2066
Brightwood College Post-Sec.
711 E Airtex Dr 77073 281-443-8900
Center for Advanced Legal Studies Post-Sec.
3910 Kirby Dr Ste 200 77098 713-529-2778
Chamberlain College of Nursing Post-Sec.
11025 Equity Dr 77041 713-277-9800
Champion Beauty College Post-Sec.
3920 FM 1960 Ste 210 77068 281-583-9117
Clear Lake Christian S 300/K-12
14325 Crescent Landing Dr 77062 281-488-4883
Dr. Bruce Guillot M.S., prin. Fax 480-3287
College of Biblical Studies Post-Sec.
7000 Regency Square Blvd 77036 713-785-5995
Commonwealth Institute / Funeral Service Post-Sec.
415 Barren Springs Dr 77090 281-873-0262
Cristo Rey Jesuit HS 300/9-12
6700 Mount Carmel St 77087 281-501-1298
David Garcia-Prats, prin. Fax 501-3485
Culinary Institute LeNotre Post-Sec.
7070 Allensby St 77022 713-692-0077
Cypress Christian S 600/K-12
11123 Cypress N Houston Rd 77065 281-469-8829
Stephen Novotny J.D., dir. Fax 469-6040
Darul Arqam North PK-12
11815 Adel Rd 77067 281-583-1984
DeVry University Post-Sec.
5051 Westheimer Rd Ste 500 77056 713-850-0888
DeVry University Post-Sec.
11125 Equity Dr 77041 713-973-3100
Duchesne Academy HS 300/9-12
10202 Memorial Dr 77024 713-468-8211
Don Cramp, prin. Fax 465-9809
Elim Christian S 50/K-12
5151 Addicks Satsuma Rd 77084 281-855-3546
Dianne Hornor, prin.
Emery/Weiner S 500/6-12
9825 Stella Link Rd 77025 832-204-5900
Stuart Dow, head sch Fax 204-5910
Eternity Christian S 100/PK-12
1122 West Rd 77038 281-999-5107
Fax 999-0107
Everest Institute Post-Sec.
255 Northpoint Dr Ste 100 77060 281-447-7037
Everest Institute Post-Sec.
9700 Bissonnet St Ste 1400 77036 713-772-4200
Everest Institute Post-Sec.
7151 Office City Dr Ste 100 77087 713-645-7404
Family Christian Academy 300/PK-12
14718 Woodford Dr 77015 713-455-4483
John Bohacek, admin. Fax 450-3730
Fortis College Post-Sec.
6220 Westpark Dr Ste 180 77057 713-266-6594
Fortis College Post-Sec.
450 N Sam Houston Pkwy #200 77060
713-332-0062
Franklin Beauty School #2 Post-Sec.
4965 Martin Luther King 77021 713-645-9060
Gulf Coast Regional Blood Center Post-Sec.
1400 La Concha Ln 77054 713-790-1200
Holy Trinity Episcopal S 100/PK-12
11810 Lockwood Rd 77044 281-459-4323
Jeff Matthews, head sch Fax 459-4302
Houston Baptist University Post-Sec.
7502 Fondren Rd 77074 281-649-3000
Houston Christian HS 500/9-12
2700 W Sam Houston Pkwy N 77043 713-580-6000
Dr. Steve Livingston, head sch Fax 580-6001
Houston Community College Post-Sec.
3100 Main St 77002 713-718-2000
Houston Graduate School of Theology Post-Sec.
2501 Central Pkwy Ste A19 77092 713-942-9505
Houston Quran Academy 200/PK-12
1902 Baker Rd 77094 281-717-4622
Houston Training School Post-Sec.
6630 Gulf Fwy 77087 713-649-5050
ICC Technical Institute Post-Sec.
3333 Fannin St Ste 203 77004 713-522-7799
Iman Academy Southwest 400/1-12
6240 Highway 6 S 77083 281-498-1345
Incarnate Word Academy 300/9-12
609 Crawford St 77002 713-227-3637
Dr. Mary Aamodt, prin. Fax 227-1014
Institute of Cosmetology Post-Sec.
7011 Harwin Dr Ste 100 77036 713-783-9988
Jay's Technical Institute Post-Sec.
11910 Fondren Meadow Dr 77071 713-772-2410
Kinkaid S 1,400/PK-12
201 Kinkaid School Dr 77024 713-782-1640
Andrew Martire Ed.D., hdmstr. Fax 782-3543
Lone Star College - North Harris Post-Sec.
2700 WW Thorne Blvd 77073 281-618-5400
Lone Star College - University Park Post-Sec.
20515 State Highway 249 77070 281-290-2600
Lutheran HS North 300/9-12
1130 W 34th St 77018 713-880-3131
Dana Gerard, head sch Fax 880-5447
Lutheran South Academy 800/PK-12
12555 Ryewater Dr 77089 281-464-8299
Sheila Psencik, head sch Fax 464-6119
Mediatech Institute Post-Sec.
3324 Walnut Bend Ln 77042 832-242-3426
Memorial Hall S 50/4-12
2501 Central Pkwy Ste A19 77092 713-688-5566
Kimberly Taylor, hdmstr. Fax 956-9751
Memorial Hospital System Post-Sec.
7737 Southwest Fwy 77074 713-776-5100
Memorial Private HS 50/6-12
14333 Fern Dr 77079 713-759-2288
Methodist Hospital Post-Sec.
6565 Fannin St 77030 713-441-2599
MIAT Institute of Technology Post-Sec.
533 Northpark Central Dr 77073 713-401-3399
North American College Post-Sec.
3203 N Sam Houston Pkwy W 77038 832-230-5555
Northland Christian S 600/PK-12
4363 Sylvanfield Dr 77014 281-440-1060
Northwest Educational Center Post-Sec.
2910 Antoine Dr Ste B100 77092 713-680-2929
Our Redeemer Lutheran North S 50/6-12
215 Rittenhouse St 77076 713-694-0332
Fax 699-1032
Page Parkes Center of Modeling & Acting Post-Sec.
1130 Silber Rd Ste 200 77055 713-807-8200
Professional Career Training Institute Post-Sec.
227 Airtex Dr 77090 832-484-9100
Rainard S for Gifted Students 100/PK-12
11059 Timberline Rd 77043 713-647-7246
Remington College - Houston Post-Sec.
3110 Hayes Rd Ste 380 77082 281-899-1240
Remington College North Houston Post-Sec.
11310 Greens Crossing # 300 77067 281-885-4450
Rice University Post-Sec.
PO Box 1892 77251 713-348-0000
Royal Beauty Careers Post-Sec.
5020 FM 1960 Rd W Ste A12 77069 281-580-2554
St. Agnes Academy 900/9-12
9000 Bellaire Blvd 77036 713-219-5400
Sr. Jane Meyer, head sch Fax 219-5499
St. John's S 1,300/K-12
2401 Claremont Ln 77019 713-850-0222
Mark Desjardins, hdmstr. Fax 622-2309
St. Michael's Learning Academy 9-12
6220 Westpark Dr St 180 77057 713-977-0566
St. Pius X HS 700/9-12
811 W Donovan St 77091 713-692-3581
Carmen Armistead, head sch Fax 692-5725
St. Stephen's Episcopal School Houston 200/PK-12
1800 Sul Ross St 77098 713-821-9100
David Coe M.S., head sch Fax 821-9156
St. Thomas' Episcopal S 600/PK-12
4900 Jackwood St 77096 713-666-3111
Michael Cusack, hdmstr. Fax 668-3887
St. Thomas HS 700/9-12
4500 Memorial Dr 77007 713-864-6348
Fr. Kevin Storey, prin. Fax 864-5750
Sanford-Brown College Post-Sec.
9999 Richmond Ave 77042 713-779-1110
San Jacinto College Post-Sec.
5800 Uvalde Rd 77049 281-458-4050
San Jacinto College Post-Sec.
13735 Beamer Rd 77089 281-484-1900
School of Automotive Machinists Post-Sec.
1911 Antoine Dr 77055 713-683-3817
School of the Woods 400/PK-12
1321 Wirt Rd 77055 713-686-8811
Second Baptist S 1,100/PK-12
6410 Woodway Dr 77057 713-365-2310
Dr. Jeff D. Williams, head sch Fax 365-2355
South Texas College of Law Post-Sec.
1303 San Jacinto St 77002 713-659-8040
Southwest Christian Academy 200/K-12
7400 Eldridge Pkwy 77083 281-561-7400
Paula Thurmond, prin. Fax 561-9823
Strake Jesuit College Prep S 900/9-12
8900 Bellaire Blvd 77036 713-774-7651
Ken Lojo, prin. Fax 774-6427
Tenney S 100/6-12
3500 S Gessner Rd 77063 713-783-6990
Texas Barber Colleges & Hairstyling Sch Post-Sec.
9275 Richmond Ave Ste 184 77063 713-953-0262
Texas Christian S 200/PK-12
17810 Kieth Harrow Blvd 77084 281-550-6060
Beckie Soliz, head sch Fax 550-2400
Texas Health School Post-Sec.
11211 Katy Fwy Ste 170 77079 713-932-9333
Texas Heart Institute Post-Sec.
PO Box 20345 77225 713-791-4026
Texas Southern University Post-Sec.
3100 Cleburne St 77004 713-313-7011
Texas Woman's University Post-Sec.
6700 Fannin St 77030 713-794-2000
The College of Health Care Professions Post-Sec.
240 Northwest Mall 77092 713-425-3100
The Ocean Corporation Post-Sec.
10840 Rockley Rd 77099 281-530-0202
Torah Girls Academy 50/9-12
10101 Fondren Rd Ste 136 77096 713-936-0644
Rabbi Yehoshua Wender, dean
Trend Barber College Post-Sec.
7725 W Bellfort St 77071 713-721-0000
Trinity Classical School of Houston 400/PK-10
7941 Katy Freeway #110 77024 281-656-1880
Neil Anderson, head sch Fax 893-6134
Tulsa Welding School and Technology Ctr Post-Sec.
243 Greens Rd 77060 918-613-1085
Universal Technical Institute Post-Sec.
721 Lockhaven Dr 77073 800-510-5072

University of Houston Post-Sec.
4800 Calhoun Rd 77204 713-743-1000
University of Houston-Clear Lake Post-Sec.
2700 Bay Area Blvd 77058 281-283-7600
University of Houston-Downtown Post-Sec.
1 Main St 77002 713-221-8000
University of St. Thomas Post-Sec.
3800 Montrose Blvd 77006 713-522-7911
University of Texas Anderson Cancer Ctr. Post-Sec.
1515 Holcombe Blvd Unit 2 77030 713-792-6161
University of TX Health Science Center Post-Sec.
PO Box 20036 77225 713-500-4472
Veterans Affairs Medical Center Post-Sec.
2002 Holcombe Blvd 77030 713-794-7100
Vet Tech Institute Post-Sec.
4669 Southwest Fwy 77027 800-275-2736
Village S 900/PK-12
13077 Westella Dr 77077 281-496-7900
Westbury Christian S 500/PK-12
10420 Hillcroft St 77096 713-551-8100
Western Academy 100/3-8
1511 Butlercrest St 77080 713-461-7000
Xavier Educational Academy 100/5-12
3642 University Blvd # 101 77005 832-533-2652
Richard De La Cuadra, prin.

Howe, Grayson, Pop. 2,551
Howe ISD 1,100/PK-12
105 W Tutt St 75459 903-532-3228
Kevin Wilson, supt. Fax 532-3205
www.howeisd.net
Howe HS 300/9-12
200 Ponderosa Rd 75459 903-532-3236
Michael Smiley, prin. Fax 532-3237
Howe MS 300/5-8
300 Beatrice St 75459 903-532-3286
Clay Wilson, prin. Fax 532-3287

Hubbard, Hill, Pop. 1,406
Hubbard ISD 400/PK-12
PO Box 218 76648 254-576-2564
Dr. Stu Musick, supt. Fax 576-5019
www.hubbardisd.com
Hubbard HS 100/9-12
PO Box 218 76648 254-576-2549
James Wright, prin. Fax 576-2477
Hubbard MS 100/6-8
PO Box 218 76648 254-576-2758
James Wright, prin. Fax 576-5017

Huffman, Harris
Huffman ISD 2,800/PK-12
PO Box 2390 77336 281-324-1871
Dr. Benny Soileau Ed.D., supt. Fax 324-4319
www.huffmanisd.net
Hargrave HS 1,000/9-12
PO Box 2390 77336 281-324-1845
Brandon Perry, prin. Fax 324-3368
Huffman MS 800/6-8
PO Box 2390 77336 281-324-2598
Adam Skinner, prin. Fax 324-2710

Hughes Springs, Cass, Pop. 1,726
Hughes Springs ISD 1,200/PK-12
871 Taylor St 75656 903-639-3800
Sarah Dildine, supt. Fax 639-2624
www.hsisd.net
Hughes Springs HS 300/9-12
701 Russell 75656 903-639-3841
Brian Nation, prin. Fax 639-3928
Hughes Springs JHS 300/6-8
609 Russell 75656 903-639-3812
Randy Stuard, prin. Fax 639-3929

Humble, Harris, Pop. 14,835
Aldine ISD
Supt. — See Houston
Teague MS 900/7-8
21700 Rayford Rd 77338 281-233-4310
Sonya Hicks, prin. Fax 233-4318

Humble ISD 38,100/PK-12
PO Box 2000 77347 281-641-1000
Dr. Elizabeth Fagen, supt. Fax 641-1050
www.humble.k12.tx.us
Atascocita HS 3,100/9-12
13300 Will Clayton Pkwy 77346 281-641-7500
Bill Daniels, prin. Fax 641-7713
Atascocita MS 1,100/6-8
18810 W Lake Houston Pkwy 77346 281-641-4600
Karl Koehler, prin. Fax 641-4617
Cambridge S Alt
18901 Timber Forest Dr 77346 281-641-7445
David Hays, prin. Fax 641-7399
Career & Technology Education Center Vo/Tech
9155 Will Clayton Pkwy 77338 281-641-7950
Dr. Marley Morris, dir. Fax 641-7967
Humble HS 1,600/9-12
1700 Wilson Rd 77338 281-641-6300
Donna Ullrich, prin. Fax 641-6517
Humble MS 1,200/6-8
11207 Will Clayton Pkwy 77346 281-641-4000
Henry Phipps, prin. Fax 641-4117
PACE Program 100/Alt
18901 Timber Forest Dr 77346 281-641-7400
Tammy Alexander, prin. Fax 641-7482
Sterling MS 900/6-8
1131 Wilson Rd 77338 281-641-6000
Damico Bartley, prin. Fax 641-6017
Timberwood MS 1,300/6-8
18450 Timber Forest Dr 77346 281-641-3800
Kenneth Buck, prin. Fax 641-3817
Other Schools – See Houston, Kingwood

Humble Christian S 300/PK-12
16202 Old Humble Rd 77396 281-441-1313
Ted Howell, admin. Fax 441-1329

Huntington, Angelina, Pop. 2,087
Huntington ISD 1,800/PK-12
PO Box 328 75949 936-876-4287
David Flowers, supt. Fax 876-3212
www.huntingtonisd.com/
Huntington HS 500/9-12
PO Box 328 75949 936-876-4150
Shane Stover, prin. Fax 876-4009
Huntington MS 400/6-8
PO Box 328 75949 936-876-4722
Matt Clifton, prin. Fax 876-4009
Pride Alternative S 100/Alt
PO Box 328 75949 936-876-4287
Andy Trekell, dir. Fax 876-4352

Huntsville, Walker, Pop. 38,042
Huntsville ISD 6,500/PK-12
441 FM 2821 Rd E 77320 936-435-6300
Dr. Howell Wright Ed.D., supt. Fax 435-6648
www.huntsville-isd.org
Huntsville HS 1,700/9-12
441 FM 2821 Rd E 77320 936-435-6100
Justin Grimes, prin. Fax 435-6621
Mance Park MS 900/7-8
441 FM 2821 Rd E 77320 936-435-6400
Samantha Mullens, prin. Fax 435-6617

Alpha Omega Academy 400/K-12
PO Box 8419 77340 936-438-8833
Paul Davidhizar, hdmstr. Fax 438-8844
Sam Houston State University Post-Sec.
1806 Avenue J 77340 936-294-1111
Summit Christian Academy 100/PK-12
PO Box 1590 77342 936-295-9601
Joyce Kumba, prin. Fax 295-9236

Hurst, Tarrant, Pop. 36,447
Grapevine-Colleyville ISD
Supt. — See Grapevine
GCISD Collegiate Academy 100/9-9
828 W Harwood Rd 76054
Bobbe Knutz, admin.

Hurst-Euless-Bedford ISD
Supt. — See Bedford
Bell HS 2,100/10-12
1601 Brown Trl 76054 817-282-2551
Jim Bannister, prin. Fax 285-3200
Hurst JHS 1,100/7-9
500 Harmon Rd 76053 817-285-3220
Elizabeth Russo, prin. Fax 285-3225

Ogle School of Hair Design Post-Sec.
720 Arcadia St Apt B 76053 817-284-9231
Tarrant County College Post-Sec.
828 W Harwood Rd 76054 817-515-8223

Hutto, Williamson, Pop. 14,315
Hutto ISD 5,900/PK-12
200 College St 78634 512-759-3771
Dr. Douglas Killian, supt. Fax 759-4797
www.hipponation.org
Farley MS 700/6-8
303 County Road 137 78634 512-759-2050
Jorge Franco, prin. Fax 759-2033
Hutto HS 1,500/9-12
101 FM 685 78634 512-759-4700
Roy Christian, prin. Fax 759-4757
Hutto MS 700/6-8
1005 Exchange Blvd 78634 512-759-4541
Elizabeth Anderson, prin. Fax 759-4753

Idalou, Lubbock, Pop. 2,236
Idalou ISD 1,000/PK-12
PO Box 1338 79329 806-892-1900
Jim Waller, supt. Fax 892-3204
www.idalouisd.net/
Idalou HS 300/9-12
PO Box 1558 79329 806-892-1900
Janet Thornton, prin. Fax 892-2690
Idalou MS 300/5-8
PO Box 1343 79329 806-892-1900
Josh Damron, prin. Fax 892-2388

Imperial, Pecos, Pop. 277
Buena Vista ISD 200/PK-12
PO Box 310 79743 432-536-2225
Mark Dominguez, supt. Fax 536-2469
www.bvisd.net
Buena Vista S 200/PK-12
PO Box 310 79743 432-536-2225
Julian Castillo, prin. Fax 536-2469

Ingleside, San Patricio, Pop. 9,243
Ingleside ISD 2,300/PK-12
PO Box 1320 78362 361-776-7631
Troy Mircovich, supt. Fax 776-0267
www.inglesideisd.org
Ingleside HS 600/9-12
2807 Mustang Dr 78362 361-776-2712
Dawn Whidden, prin. Fax 776-5200
Taylor JHS 400/7-8
2739 Mustang Dr 78362 361-776-2232
Heather Waugh, prin. Fax 776-2192

Ingram, Kerr, Pop. 1,786
Ingram ISD 1,000/PK-12
510 College St 78025 830-367-5517
Dr. Robert Templeton, supt. Fax 367-5631
www.ingramisd.net
Ingram MS 200/6-8
510 College St 78025 830-367-4111
Mindy Merkel, prin. Fax 367-7335
Ingram-Tom Moore HS 300/9-12
510 College St 78025 830-367-4111
Justin Crittenden, prin. Fax 367-7332

Iola, Grimes, Pop. 393
Iola ISD 500/PK-12
PO Box 159 77861 936-394-2361
Dr. Chad Jones, supt. Fax 394-2132
www.iolaisd.net
Iola JSHS 200/7-12
PO Box 159 77861 936-394-2361
Scott Martindale, prin. Fax 394-4700

Iowa Park, Wichita, Pop. 6,289
Iowa Park Consolidated ISD 1,800/PK-12
PO Box 898 76367 940-592-4193
Steve Moody, supt. Fax 592-2136
www.ipcisd.net/
George MS 400/6-8
412 E Cash St 76367 940-592-2196
Darla Biddy, prin. Fax 592-2801
Iowa Park HS 500/9-12
1 Bob Dawson Dr 76367 940-592-2144
Leah Russell, prin. Fax 592-2583

Ira, Scurry
Ira ISD 300/K-12
6143 W FM 1606 79527 325-573-2629
Jay Waller, supt. Fax 573-5825
www.ira.esc14.net/
Ira S 300/K-12
6123 W FM 1606 79527 325-573-2628
Dale Jones, prin. Fax 573-5825

Iraan, Pecos, Pop. 1,225
Iraan-Sheffield ISD 600/PK-12
PO Box 486 79744 432-639-2512
Kevin Allen, supt. Fax 639-2501
isisd.net
Iraan HS 100/9-12
PO Box 486 79744 432-639-2512
Jim Baum, prin. Fax 639-2501
Iraan JHS 100/6-8
PO Box 486 79744 432-639-2512
Michael Meek, prin. Fax 639-2501
Other Schools – See Sheffield

Iredell, Bosque, Pop. 338
Iredell ISD 100/PK-12
PO Box 39 76649 254-364-2411
Patrick Murphy, supt. Fax 364-2206
www.iredell-isd.com
Iredell S 100/PK-12
PO Box 39 76649 254-364-2411
Patrick Murphy, prin. Fax 364-2206

Irving, Dallas, Pop. 212,044
Carrollton-Farmers Branch ISD
Supt. — See Carrollton
Bush MS 700/6-8
515 Cowboys Pkwy 75063 972-968-3700
Matt Warnock, prin. Fax 968-3710
Ranchview HS 800/9-12
8401 Valley Ranch Pkwy E 75063 972-968-5000
Sherie Skruch, prin. Fax 968-5010

Irving ISD 35,300/PK-12
PO Box 152637 75015 972-600-5000
Dr. Jose L. Parra, supt. Fax 215-5201
www.irvingisd.net
Austin MS 1,000/6-8
825 E Union Bower Rd 75061 972-600-3100
Toscha Reeves, prin. Fax 721-3105
Bowie MS 1,000/6-8
600 E 6th St 75060 972-600-3000
Jennifer Anderson, prin. Fax 721-3044
Cardwell Career Preparatory Center 400/Alt
101 E Union Bower Rd 75061 972-600-6140
Maurice Evans, prin. Fax 273-6188
Crockett MS 800/6-8
2431 Hancock St 75061 972-600-4700
Francisco Miranda, prin. Fax 313-4770
de Zavala MS 800/6-8
707 W Pioneer Dr 75061 972-600-6000
Anika Horgan, prin. Fax 273-8924
Houston MS 900/6-8
3033 Country Club Dr W 75038 972-600-7500
Jeffrey Dorman, prin. Fax 261-2399
Irving HS 2,400/9-12
900 N O Connor Rd 75061 972-600-6300
Ahna Gomez, prin. Fax 273-8319
Johnson MS 1,000/6-8
3601 W Pioneer Dr 75061 972-600-0500
Raymie Ramsey, prin. Fax 986-6830
Lamar MS 800/6-8
219 Crandall Rd 75060 972-600-4400
Joe Moreno, prin. Fax 313-4499
MacArthur HS 2,700/9-12
3700 N MacArthur Blvd 75062 972-600-7200
Daniel Cummings, prin. Fax 261-2298
Nimitz HS 2,400/9-12
100 W Oakdale Rd 75060 972-600-5700
Curtis Mauricio, prin. Fax 273-8610
Singley Academy 1,700/9-12
4601 N MacArthur Blvd 75038 972-600-5300
Dr. Andre Smith, prin. Fax 258-5301
Travis MS 1,000/6-8
1600 Finley Rd 75062 972-600-0100
Laurie Gilcrease, prin. Fax 261-2450
Wheeler Transitional Center 50/Alt
1600 E Shady Grove Rd 75060 972-600-3750
Nancy Atkinson, prin. Fax 554-3769

Anthem College Post-Sec.
4250 N Belt Line Rd 75038 888-852-7272
Aviation Institute of Maintenance Post-Sec.
400 E Airport Fwy 75062 214-333-9711
Cistercian Preparatory S 400/5-12
3660 Cistercian Rd 75039 469-499-5400
Fr. Paul McCormick, hdmstr. Fax 499-5440
DeVry University Post-Sec.
4800 Regent Blvd 75063 972-929-6777

Highlands S 400/PK-12
1451 E Northgate Dr 75062 972-554-1980
Gerard Doyle, prin. Fax 721-1691
Islamic S of Irving 500/PK-12
2555 Esters Rd 75062 972-812-2230
Muhammad Diwan, supt. Fax 257-8640
North Lake College Post-Sec.
5001 N MacArthur Blvd 75038 972-273-3000
StoneGate Christian Academy 100/PK-12
2833 W Shady Grove Rd 75060 972-790-0070
Rhonda Tuttle, prin. Fax 790-6560
Tint School of Makeup & Cosmetology Post-Sec.
2716 W Irving Blvd 75061 972-513-1176
Universal Technical Institute Post-Sec.
5151 Regent Blvd 75063 877-873-1080
University of Dallas Post-Sec.
1845 E Northgate Dr 75062 972-721-5000

Italy, Ellis, Pop. 1,835
Italy ISD 500/PK-12
300 College 76651 972-483-1815
Lee Joffre, supt. Fax 483-6152
www.italyisd.info/
Italy JSHS 200/6-12
300 College 76651 972-483-7411
Eric Janszen, prin. Fax 483-1500

Itasca, Hill, Pop. 1,623
Itasca ISD 600/PK-12
123 N College St 76055 254-687-2922
Jim Malone, supt. Fax 687-2637
www.itascaisd.org
Itasca HS 200/9-12
123 N College St 76055 254-687-2922
Mark Parsons, prin. Fax 687-2637
Itasca MS 200/5-8
208 N Files St 76055 254-687-2922
Kristi Sargent, prin. Fax 687-2637

Ivanhoe, Fannin, Pop. 869
Sam Rayburn ISD 500/PK-12
9363 E FM 273 75447 903-664-2255
Cole McClendon, supt. Fax 664-2406
www.srisd.org
Rayburn JSHS 200/7-12
9363 E FM 273 75447 903-664-2165
Wendy Keeton, prin. Fax 664-2407

Jacksboro, Jack, Pop. 4,489
Jacksboro ISD 1,000/PK-12
750 W Belknap St 76458 940-567-7203
Dwain Milam, supt. Fax 567-2214
www.jacksboroisd.net/
Jacksboro HS 300/9-12
1400 N Main St 76458 940-567-7204
Brad Burnett, prin. Fax 567-6028
Jacksboro MS 200/6-8
812 W Belknap St 76458 940-567-7205
Sara Mathis, prin. Fax 567-2681

Jacksonville, Cherokee, Pop. 14,356
Jacksonville ISD 4,900/PK-12
PO Box 631 75766 903-586-6511
Dr. Chad Kelly, supt. Fax 586-3133
www.jisd.org
Compass Center 50/Alt
PO Box 631 75766 903-589-3926
Timothy Ricker, prin. Fax 586-7158
Jacksonville HS 1,200/9-12
PO Box 631 75766 903-586-3661
Karen Kubara, prin. Fax 586-8229
Jacksonville MS 700/7-8
PO Box 631 75766 903-586-3686
Holly Searcy, prin. Fax 586-8071

Baptist Missionary Theological Seminary Post-Sec.
PO Box 670 75766 903-586-2501
Jacksonville College Post-Sec.
105 B J Albritton Dr 75766 903-586-2518

Jarrell, Williamson, Pop. 971
Jarrell ISD 900/PK-12
PO Box 9 76537 512-746-2124
Dr. Bill Chapman, supt. Fax 746-2518
www.jarrellisd.org
Jarrell HS 300/9-12
PO Box 9 76537 512-746-2188
Lindsie Almquist, prin. Fax 746-2183
Jarrell MS 300/6-8
PO Box 9 76537 512-746-4180
Abbe Lester, prin. Fax 746-4280

Jasper, Jasper, Pop. 7,490
Jasper ISD 2,000/PK-12
128 Park Ln 75951 409-384-2401
Dr. Bobby Baker, supt. Fax 382-1084
www.jasperisd.net
Jasper HS 700/9-12
400 Bulldog Ave 75951 409-384-3242
Lydia Bean, prin. Fax 382-1310
Jasper JHS 400/6-8
211 2nd St 75951 409-384-3585
John Seybold, prin. Fax 382-1160

Jayton, Kent, Pop. 530
Jayton-Girard ISD 100/PK-12
PO Box 168 79528 806-237-2991
Trig Overbo, supt. Fax 237-2670
www.jaytonjaybirds.com
Jayton S 100/PK-12
PO Box 168 79528 806-237-2991
Lyle Lackey, prin. Fax 237-2670

Jefferson, Marion, Pop. 2,067
Jefferson ISD 1,200/PK-12
1600 Martin Luther King Dr 75657 903-665-2461
Rob Barnwell, supt. Fax 665-7367
jeffersonisd.org/
Jefferson HS 300/9-12
1 Bulldog Dr 75657 903-665-2461
Michael Walker, prin. Fax 665-2146
Jefferson JHS 300/5-8
804 N Alley St 75657 903-665-2461
Clint Coyne, prin. Fax 665-7149

Jewett, Leon, Pop. 1,158
Leon ISD 700/PK-12
12168 US Highway 79 75846 903-626-1400
Mike Baldree, supt. Fax 626-1420
www.leonisd.net/
Leon HS 200/9-12
12168 US Highway 79 75846 903-626-1475
Jay Winn, prin. Fax 626-1490
Leon JHS 200/6-8
12168 US Highway 79 75846 903-626-1450
J.D. Foley, prin. Fax 626-1455

Joaquin, Shelby, Pop. 818
Joaquin ISD 800/PK-12
11109 US Highway 84 E 75954 936-269-3128
Phil Worsham, supt. Fax 269-3615
www.joaquinisd.net/
Joaquin HS 200/9-12
11109 US Highway 84 E 75954 936-269-3128
James Jackson, prin. Fax 269-9123
Joaquin JHS 200/6-8
11109 US Highway 84 E 75954 936-269-3128
Terri Gray, prin. Fax 269-9123

Johnson City, Blanco, Pop. 1,640
Johnson City ISD 700/K-12
PO Box 498 78636 830-868-7410
David Shanley, supt. Fax 868-7375
johnsoncity.tx.schoolwebpages.com/
Johnson HS 200/9-12
PO Box 498 78636 830-868-4025
Julie Storer, prin. Fax 868-9244
Johnson MS 200/5-8
PO Box 498 78636 830-868-9025
Cammie Ockman, prin. Fax 868-7375

Jonesboro, Coryell
Jonesboro ISD 200/PK-12
PO Box 125 76538 254-463-2111
Matt Dossey, supt. Fax 463-2275
www.jonesboroisd.net
Jonesboro S 200/PK-12
PO Box 125 76538 254-463-2111
Kendra Gustin, admin. Fax 463-2275

Joshua, Johnson, Pop. 5,826
Joshua ISD 5,000/PK-12
PO Box 40 76058 817-202-2500
Fran Marek, supt. Fax 641-2738
www.joshuaisd.org
Joshua HS Ninth Grade Campus 400/9-9
1035 S Broadway St 76058 817-202-2500
Kenny Bodine, prin. Fax 556-4640
Joshua SHS 1,000/10-12
909 S Broadway St 76058 817-202-2500
Mick Cochran, prin. Fax 556-3404
Loflin MS 800/7-8
6801 FM 1902 76058 817-202-2500
Damon Patterson, prin. Fax 202-9140
New Horizon HS 50/Alt
603 Plum St 76058 817-202-2500
Kenny Bodine, prin. Fax 202-8948

Joshua Christian Academy 100/PK-12
PO Box 1379 76058 817-295-7377

Jourdanton, Atascosa, Pop. 3,848
Jourdanton ISD 1,500/PK-12
200 Zanderson Ave 78026 830-769-3548
Theresa McAllister, supt. Fax 769-3272
www.jourdantonisd.net
Jourdanton HS 500/9-12
200 Zanderson Ave 78026 830-769-2350
Keith Chapman, prin. Fax 769-3065
Jourdanton JHS 400/6-8
200 Zanderson Ave 78026 830-769-2234
Robert Rutkowski, prin. Fax 769-2998

Junction, Kimble, Pop. 2,554
Junction ISD 700/PK-12
1700 College St 76849 325-446-3510
Renee Schulze, supt. Fax 446-4413
www.junctionisd.net
Junction HS 200/9-12
1700 College St 76849 325-446-3326
Dana Davis, prin. Fax 446-8206
Junction MS 100/6-8
1700 College St 76849 325-446-2464
Joe Jones, prin. Fax 446-2255

Justin, Denton, Pop. 3,207
Northwest ISD 18,800/PK-12
2001 Texan Dr 76247 817-215-0000
Ryder Warren Ed.D., supt. Fax 215-0170
www.nisdtx.org
Northwest HS 2,700/9-12
2301 Texan Dr 76247 817-215-0200
Jason Childress, prin. Fax 215-0262
Pike MS 800/6-8
2200 Texan Dr 76247 817-215-0400
Christopher Jones, prin. Fax 215-0425
Other Schools – See Haslet, Rhome, Roanoke, Trophy Club

Karnes City, Karnes, Pop. 3,027
Karnes City ISD 800/PK-12
314 N Highway 123 78118 830-780-2321
Jeanette Winn, supt. Fax 780-3823
www.kcisd.net
Karnes City HS 300/9-12
400 N Highway 123 78118 830-780-2321
Brian Uriegas, prin. Fax 780-4352
Karnes City JHS 200/6-8
410 N Highway 123 78118 830-780-2321
Theresa Molina, prin. Fax 780-4382

Katy, Harris, Pop. 13,902
Cypress-Fairbanks ISD
Supt. — See Houston
Alternative Learning Center - West Alt
19350 Rebel Yell Dr 77449 281-855-4310
Stacie Wicke, prin. Fax 855-4307
Cypress Lakes HS 3,500/9-12
5750 Greenhouse Rd 77449 281-856-3800
Sarah Harty, prin. Fax 856-3808
Thornton MS 1,300/6-8
19802 Kieth Harrow Blvd 77449 281-856-1500
Reginald Mitchell, prin. Fax 856-1548

Katy ISD 65,800/PK-12
PO Box 159 77492 281-396-6000
Dr. Lance Hindt, supt. Fax 644-1800
www.katyisd.org
Beckendorff JHS 1,700/6-8
8200 S Fry Rd 77494 281-237-8800
Dr. Ethan Crowell, prin. Fax 644-1635
Beck JHS 1,100/6-8
5200 S Fry Rd 77450 281-237-3300
Carra Flemming, prin. Fax 644-1630
Cardiff JHS 1,000/6-8
3900 Dayflower Dr 77449 281-234-0600
Bryan Rounds, prin. Fax 644-1855
Cinco Ranch HS 3,200/9-12
23440 Cinco Ranch Blvd 77494 281-237-7000
James Cross, prin. Fax 644-1735
Cinco Ranch JHS 1,200/6-8
23420 Cinco Ranch Blvd 77494 281-237-7300
Elizabeth Nicklas, prin. Fax 644-1640
Katy HS 2,900/9-12
6331 Highway Blvd 77494 281-237-6700
Dr. Rick Hull, prin. Fax 644-1702
Katy JHS 1,400/6-8
5350 Franz Rd 77493 281-237-6800
Dr. Jake Leblanc, prin. Fax 644-1645
McDonald JHS 1,000/6-8
3635 Lakes of Bridgewater 77449 281-237-5300
Dr. Kenneth Cummings, prin. Fax 644-1655
McMeans JHS 1,100/6-8
21000 Westheimer Pkwy 77450 281-237-8000
Dr. Susan Rice, prin. Fax 644-1660
Memorial Parkway JHS 900/6-8
21203 Highland Knolls Dr 77450 281-237-5800
Emily Craig, prin. Fax 644-1665
Miller Career and Technology Ctr Vo/Tech
1734 Katyland Dr 77493 281-237-6300
Dr. Anna Webb-Storey, prin. Fax 644-1775
Morton Ranch HS 3,300/9-12
21000 Franz Rd 77449 281-237-7800
Julie Hinson, prin. Fax 644-1747
Morton Ranch JHS 1,300/6-8
2498 N Mason Rd 77449 281-237-7400
Sanee Bell, prin. Fax 644-1670
Opportunity Awareness Center Alt
1732 Katyland Dr 77493 281-237-6350
Kerri Finnesand, prin. Fax 644-1780
Raines HS 50/Alt
1732 Katyland Dr 77493 281-237-1500
Kerri Finnesand, prin. Fax 644-1780
Seven Lake JHS 1,600/6-8
6026 Katy Gaston Rd 77494 281-234-2100
Dr. Imelda Medrano, prin. Fax 644-1885
Seven Lakes HS 3,600/9-12
9251 S Fry Rd 77494 281-237-2800
Ted Vierling, prin. Fax 644-1791
Taylor HS 2,900/9-12
20700 Kingsland Blvd 77450 281-237-3100
Jeff Stocks, prin. Fax 644-1760
Tays JHS 6-8
26721 Hawks Prairie Blvd 77494 281-234-2400
Dr. Kris Mitzner, prin. Fax 644-1945
Tompkins HS 800/9-12
4400 Falcon Landing Blvd 77494 281-234-1000
Mark Grisdale, prin. Fax 644-1910
West Memorial JHS 700/6-8
22311 Provincial Blvd 77450 281-237-6400
Gina Cobb, prin. Fax 644-1675
WoodCreek JHS 1,600/6-8
1801 WoodCreek Bend Ln 77494 281-234-0800
Melinda Stone, prin. Fax 644-1860
Other Schools – See Houston

Faith West Academy 600/PK-12
2225 Porter Rd 77493 281-391-5683
Mary Strickland, prin. Fax 391-2606
St. John XXIII HS 400/9-12
1800 W Grand Pkwy N 77449 281-693-1000
Matthew Oelkers, prin. Fax 693-1001

Kaufman, Kaufman, Pop. 6,619
Kaufman ISD 3,900/PK-12
1000 S Houston St 75142 972-932-2622
Dr. Lori Blaylock, supt. Fax 932-3325
www.kaufmanisd.net
Campbell HS 50/Alt
4814 County Road 151 75142 972-932-8789
Gary Campbell, prin. Fax 932-2278
Kaufman HS 1,000/9-12
3205 S Houston St 75142 972-932-2811
Amy Keith, prin. Fax 932-1948
Norman JHS 600/7-8
3701 S Houston St 75142 972-932-2410
Jeremy Melton, prin. Fax 932-7771

Kaufman Christian S 100/PK-12
401 N Shannon St 75142 972-932-6111
Christy Butler, admin. Fax 962-6111

Keene, Johnson, Pop. 5,659
Keene ISD 900/PK-12
PO Box 656 76059 817-774-5200
Ricky Stephens, supt. Fax 774-5400
www.keeneisd.org/
Keene Alternative Learning Center 50/Alt
PO Box 656 76059 817-774-5370
Ted O'Neil, prin. Fax 774-5405
Keene HS 300/9-12
PO Box 656 76059 817-774-5220
Sandra Denning, prin. Fax 774-5401
Keene JHS 200/6-8
PO Box 656 76059 817-774-5270
Billie Hopps, prin. Fax 774-5402

Chisholm Trail Academy 200/9-12
PO Box 717 76059 817-641-6626
Southwestern Adventist University Post-Sec.
PO Box 567 76059 817-645-3921

Keller, Tarrant, Pop. 38,916
Keller ISD 33,800/PK-12
350 Keller Pkwy 76248 817-744-1000
Randy Reid, supt. Fax 744-1263
www.kellerisd.net
Indian Springs MS 900/7-8
305 Bursey Rd 76248 817-744-3200
Sandy Troudt, prin. Fax 431-4432
Keller HS 2,600/9-12
601 Pate Orr Rd N 76248 817-744-1400
Dr. Michael Nasra, prin. Fax 337-3362
Keller Learning Center 100/Alt
250 College Ave 76248 817-744-4465
Christy Johnson, prin. Fax 744-4464
Keller MS 900/7-8
300 College Ave 76248 817-744-2900
Sandra Chapa, prin. Fax 377-3512
Other Schools – See Fort Worth

Messiah Lutheran Classical Academy 100/PK-10
1308 Whitley Rd 76248 817-431-5486
Erika Mildred, hdmstr. Fax 431-8536
Toni & Guy Hairdressing Academy Post-Sec.
1185 S Main St 76248 817-697-3037

Kemp, Kaufman, Pop. 1,139
Kemp ISD 1,400/PK-12
905 S Main St 75143 903-498-1394
Phil Edwards, supt. Fax 498-1315
kemp.ednet10.net
Kemp HS 400/9-12
220 State Highway 274 75143 903-498-9222
Marietta Maxwell, prin. Fax 498-9275
Kemp JHS 400/6-8
1000 Tolosa Rd 75143 903-498-1343
Clay Tracy, prin. Fax 498-1359

Kenedy, Karnes, Pop. 3,282
Kenedy ISD 700/PK-12
401 FM 719 78119 830-583-4100
Travis McClellan, supt. Fax 583-9950
www.kenedy.isd.tenet.edu
Kenedy HS 200/9-12
401 FM 719 78119 830-583-4100
Timmothy Casner, prin. Fax 583-9126
Kenedy MS 200/6-8
401 FM 719 78119 830-583-4100
Dr. Richard Cardin, prin. Fax 583-9519

Kennard, Houston, Pop. 331
Kennard ISD 300/PK-12
304 State Highway 7 E 75847 936-655-2161
Malinda Lindsey, supt. Fax 655-2327
www.kennardisd.net
Kennard JSHS 100/7-12
304 State Highway 7 E 75847 936-655-2121
Dr. Lesa Whaley, prin. Fax 655-2327

Kennedale, Tarrant, Pop. 6,631
Kennedale ISD 3,200/PK-12
PO Box 467 76060 817-563-8000
Gary Dugger, supt. Fax 483-3610
www.kennedaleisd.net
Kennedale HS 1,000/9-12
PO Box 1208 76060 817-563-8100
Justin Marchel, prin. Fax 563-3718
Kennedale JHS 500/7-8
PO Box 489 76060 817-563-8200
Michael Cagle, prin. Fax 483-3655

Fellowship Academy 200/PK-12
PO Box 738 76060 817-483-2400
Monica Collier, admin. Fax 483-2404

Kerens, Navarro, Pop. 1,548
Kerens ISD 600/PK-12
200 Bobcat Ln 75144 903-396-2924
Jason Adams, supt. Fax 396-2334
www.kerensisd.org
Kerens S 600/PK-12
200 Bobcat Ln 75144 903-396-2931
Gayle White, prin. Fax 396-2334

Kermit, Winkler, Pop. 5,630
Kermit ISD 1,300/PK-12
601 S Poplar St 79745 432-586-1000
Denise Shetter, supt. Fax 586-1016
www.kisd.esc18.net
Kermit HS 400/9-12
601 S Poplar St 79745 432-586-1050
Brandon Enos, prin. Fax 586-1055
Kermit JHS 300/5-8
601 S Poplar St 79745 432-586-1040
Melanie Gimble, prin. Fax 586-1045

Kerrville, Kerr, Pop. 22,087
Kerrville ISD 5,000/PK-12
1009 Barnett St 78028 830-257-2200
Wady Ivy, supt. Fax 257-2249
www.kerrvilleisd.net
Hill Country HS 50/Alt
1200 Sidney Baker St 78028 830-257-2232
Steve Schwarz, prin. Fax 792-5020
Peterson MS 700/7-8
1607 Sidney Baker St 78028 830-257-2204
Donna Jenschke, prin. Fax 257-1300
Tivy HS 1,400/9-12
3250 Loop 534 78028 830-257-2212
Jarrett Jachade, prin. Fax 895-3575

Conlee's College of Cosmetology Post-Sec.
320 W Water St Ste E 78028 830-896-2380
Our Lady of the Hills Catholic HS 100/9-12
235 Peterson Farm Rd 78028 830-895-0501
Therese Schwarz, prin. Fax 895-3470
Schreiner University Post-Sec.
2100 Memorial Blvd 78028 830-896-5411

Kilgore, Gregg, Pop. 12,762
Kilgore ISD 4,000/PK-12
301 N Kilgore St 75662 903-988-3900
Cara Cooke, supt. Fax 983-3212
www.kisd.org
Kilgore Alternative Education Center 50/Alt
301 N Kilgore St 75662 903-988-3921
Julie Hope, coord. Fax 984-0571
Kilgore HS 1,000/9-12
301 N Kilgore St 75662 903-988-3901
Greg Brown, prin. Fax 984-0571
Kilgore MS 900/6-8
301 N Kilgore St 75662 903-988-3902
April Cox, prin. Fax 984-6225

Kilgore College Post-Sec.
1100 Broadway Blvd 75662 903-984-8531

Killeen, Bell, Pop. 120,349
Killeen ISD 40,700/PK-12
PO Box 967 76540 254-336-0000
Dr. John Craft, supt. Fax 526-0010
www.killeenisd.org
Ellison HS 2,500/9-12
909 E Elms Rd 76542 254-336-0600
David Dominguez, prin. Fax 336-0606
Gateway Complex 100/Alt
4100 Zephyr Rd 76543 254-336-1690
Christopher Halpayne, prin. Fax 336-1698
Killeen HS 2,200/9-12
500 N 38th St 76543 254-336-7208
Susan Buckley, prin. Fax 336-0413
KISD Career Center Vo/Tech
1320 Stagecoach Rd 76542 254-336-3804
Alison Belliveau, dir. Fax 336-2303
Liberty Hill MS 900/6-8
4500 Kit Carson Trl 76542 254-336-1370
Jorge Soldevila, prin. Fax 336-1403
Live Oak Ridge MS 800/6-8
2600 Robinett Rd 76549 254-336-2490
Wanda Stidom, prin. Fax 336-2498
Manor MS 700/6-8
1700 S W S Young Dr 76543 254-336-1310
Jennifer Washington, prin. Fax 336-1317
Nolan MS 700/6-8
505 E Jasper Dr 76541 254-336-1150
Lolly Garcia, prin. Fax 336-1162
Palo Alto MS 900/6-8
2301 W Elms Rd 76549 254-336-1200
Matt Widacki, prin. Fax 336-1217
Patterson MS 1,100/6-8
8383 W Trimmier Rd 76542 254-336-7100
Jill Balzer, prin. Fax 336-7136
Rancier MS 700/6-8
3301 Hilliard Ave 76543 254-336-1250
Micah Wells, prin. Fax 336-1254
Shoemaker HS 2,200/9-12
3302 S Clear Creek Rd 76549 254-336-0900
Sandra Forsythe, prin. Fax 336-0937
STEM Academy 9-12
3302 S Clear Creek Rd 76549 254-336-0900
Fax 520-1118
Other Schools – See Fort Hood, Harker Heights

Central Texas College Post-Sec.
PO Box 1800 76540 254-526-7161
Memorial Christian Academy 300/PK-12
PO Box 11269 76547 254-526-5403
Dr. Barbara Carpenter, head sch Fax 634-2030
Texas A&M University Central Texas Post-Sec.
1001 Leadership Pl 76549 254-519-5400

Kingsville, Kleberg, Pop. 25,996
Kingsville ISD 3,400/PK-12
PO Box 871 78364 361-592-3387
Carol G. Perez Ed.D., supt. Fax 595-7805
www.kingsvilleisd.com
King HS 900/9-12
PO Box 871 78364 361-595-8600
Jose Mireles, prin. Fax 595-9170
Memorial MS 500/7-8
PO Box 871 78364 361-595-8675
Dr. Alys Williams, prin. Fax 592-4198
Pogue Options Alternative Academy 50/9-12
PO Box 871 78364 361-595-9137
Diana Guerrero-Pena, prin.

Ricardo ISD 700/PK-8
138 W County Road 2160 78363 361-592-6465
Dr. Maria Canales, supt. Fax 592-3101
www.ricardoisd.us
Ricardo MS 300/5-8
138 W County Road 2160 78363 361-592-6465
Dr. Cynthia Flores, prin. Fax 593-0707

Santa Gertrudis ISD 600/PK-12
PO Box 592 78364 361-384-5087
Dr. Corey Seymour, supt. Fax 592-7736
www.sgisd.net
Santa Gertrudis Academy 300/9-12
PO Box 592 78364 361-384-5041
Les Dragon, prin. Fax 592-5335

Presbyterian Pan American S 200/9-12
PO Box 1578 78364 361-592-4307
Texas A&M University Kingsville Post-Sec.
700 University Blvd 78363 361-593-2111

Kingwood, Harris, Pop. 37,397
Humble ISD
Supt. — See Humble
Creekwood MS 1,100/6-8
3603 W Lake Houston Pkwy 77339 281-641-4400
Walt Winicki, prin. Fax 641-4417
Kingwood HS 2,600/9-12
2701 Kingwood Dr 77339 281-641-6900
Ted Landry, prin. Fax 641-7217
Kingwood MS 1,000/6-8
2407 Pine Terrace Dr 77339 281-641-4200
Bob Atteberry, prin. Fax 641-4217
Kingwood Park HS 1,700/9-12
4015 Woodland Hills Dr 77339 281-641-6600
Lisa Drabing, prin. Fax 641-6617
Riverwood MS 1,100/6-8
2910 High Valley Dr 77345 281-641-4800
Donnie Bodron, prin. Fax 641-4817

Christian Life Center Academy 200/PK-12
806 Russell Palmer Rd 77339 281-319-0077
Rev. Richard Rodriguez, admin. Fax 319-4523
Covenant Preparatory S 7-12
3939 Glade Valley Dr 77339 281-312-6437
Bradley Baggett, head sch
Lone Star College - Kingwood Post-Sec.
20000 Kingwood Dr 77339 281-312-1600

Kirbyville, Jasper, Pop. 2,112
Kirbyville Consolidated ISD 1,300/PK-12
206 E Main St 75956 409-423-2284
Richard Hazlewood, supt. Fax 423-2367
www.kirbyvillecisd.org/
Kirbyville HS 400/9-12
100 E Wildcat Dr 75956 409-423-7500
Dennis Reeves, prin. Fax 423-5313
Kirbyville JHS 200/6-8
2200 S Margaret Ave 75956 409-420-0692
Eric Cormier, prin. Fax 423-6654

Klein, Harris, Pop. 12,000
Klein ISD 48,600/PK-12
7200 Spring Cypress Rd 77379 832-249-4000
Dr. Bret Champion, supt. Fax 249-4015
www.kleinisd.net
Doerre IS 1,200/6-8
18218 Theiss Mail Route Rd 77379 832-249-5700
Fax 249-4054
Kleb IS 1,400/6-8
7425 Louetta Rd 77379 832-249-5500
Clay Huggins, prin. Fax 249-4053
Klein Annex - Alternative Education 100/Alt
7302 Kleingreen Ln 77379 832-249-4800
Brian Marr, dir. Fax 249-4045
Klein HS 3,800/9-12
16715 Stuebner Airline Rd 77379 832-484-4000
Jessica Haddox, prin. Fax 484-7821
Krimmel IS 1,100/6-8
7070 FM 2920 Rd 77379 832-375-7200
Scott Crowe, prin. Fax 375-7150
Strack IS 1,200/6-8
18027 Kuykendahl Rd Ste S 77379 832-249-5400
Andrea Comer, prin. Fax 249-4051
Other Schools – See Houston, Spring

Knippa, Uvalde, Pop. 688
Knippa ISD 400/PK-12
PO Box 99 78870 830-934-2176
Jeff Cottrill, supt. Fax 934-2490
www.knippaisd.net
Knippa S 400/PK-12
PO Box 99 78870 830-934-2177
Jeff Cottrill, prin. Fax 934-2490

Knox City, Knox, Pop. 1,121
Knox City-O'Brien Consolidated ISD 300/PK-12
606 E Main St 79529 940-657-3521
Louis Baty, supt. Fax 657-3379
www.knoxcityschools.net
Knox City HS 100/9-12
606 E Main St 79529 940-657-3565
Colin Howeth, prin. Fax 657-3379
Other Schools – See O Brien

Kopperl, Bosque
Kopperl ISD 200/PK-12
PO Box 67 76652 254-889-3502
Kenneth Bateman, supt. Fax 889-3443
www.kopperlisd.org
Kopperl S 200/PK-12
PO Box 67 76652 254-889-3502
Katrina Adcock, prin. Fax 889-3443

Kountze, Hardin, Pop. 2,103
Kountze ISD 1,200/PK-12
PO Box 460 77625 409-246-3352
John Ferguson, supt. Fax 246-3217
kountzeisd.org
Kountze HS 400/9-12
PO Box 460 77625 409-246-3474
Dr. Chet Deaver, prin. Fax 246-8180
Kountze MS 200/7-8
PO Box 460 77625 409-246-3551
Thomas Cooley, prin. Fax 246-8907

Kress, Swisher, Pop. 707
Kress ISD 200/PK-12
200 E 5th St 79052 806-684-2652
Doug Setliff, supt. Fax 684-2687
www.kressonline.net
Kress JSHS 100/7-12
200 E 5th St 79052 806-684-2651
Leah Zeigler, prin. Fax 684-2687

Krum, Denton, Pop. 4,096
Krum ISD 2,000/PK-12
1200 Bobcat Blvd 76249 940-482-6000
Cody Carroll, supt. Fax 482-3929
www.krumisd.net
Krum HS 500/9-12
1200 Bobcat Blvd 76249 940-482-2601
Michelle Pieniazek, prin. Fax 482-2997
Krum MS 400/6-8
1200 Bobcat Blvd 76249 940-482-2602
Shelly Enloe, prin. Fax 482-6299

Kyle, Hays, Pop. 27,512
Hays Consolidated ISD 17,200/PK-12
21003 Interstate 35 78640 512-268-2141
Michael McKie, supt. Fax 268-2147
www.hayscisd.net
Chapa MS 700/6-8
3311 Dacy Ln 78640 512-268-8500
Lisa Walls, prin. Fax 295-7824
Lehman HS 2,200/9-12
1700 Lehman Rd 78640 512-268-8454
Denisha Presley, prin. Fax 268-2146
Simon MS 600/6-8
3839 E FM 150 78640 512-268-8507
Dr. Jose Puga, prin. Fax 268-4146
Wallace MS 800/6-8
1500 W Center St 78640 512-268-2891
Sarah Hodges, prin. Fax 268-1853
Other Schools – See Buda

Ladonia, Fannin, Pop. 606
Fannindel ISD 200/PK-12
601 W Main St 75449 903-367-7251
Jack Ellis, supt. Fax 367-7252
www.fannindel.net
Fannindel HS 100/6-12
601 W Main St 75449 903-367-7251
Robert Milton M.S., prin. Fax 367-7252

La Feria, Cameron, Pop. 7,287
La Feria ISD 3,600/PK-12
PO Box 1159 78559 956-797-8300
Rey Villarreal, supt. Fax 797-3737
www.laferiaisd.org/
Green JHS 500/7-8
PO Box 1159 78559 956-797-8400
Michael Torres, prin. Fax 797-2157
La Feria Academy 100/Alt
PO Box 1159 78559 956-797-8360
Carlos Verduzco, prin. Fax 797-1583
La Feria HS 900/9-12
PO Box 1159 78559 956-797-8370
Isaac Rodriguez, prin. Fax 797-9374

Lago Vista, Travis, Pop. 5,961
Lago Vista ISD 1,300/PK-12
PO Box 4929 78645 512-267-8300
Darren Webb, supt. Fax 267-8304
www.lagovistaisd.net
Lago Vista HS 400/9-12
PO Box 4929 78645 512-267-8300
Heather Stoner, prin. Fax 267-8304
Lago Vista MS 300/6-8
PO Box 4929 78645 512-267-8300
Paul Thailing, prin. Fax 267-8329

La Grange, Fayette, Pop. 4,573
La Grange ISD 1,500/PK-12
PO Box 100 78945 979-968-7000
William D. Wagner, supt. Fax 968-8155
www.lgisd.net/
La Grange HS 600/9-12
PO Box 100 78945 979-968-4800
John Pineda, prin. Fax 968-6744
La Grange MS 300/7-8
PO Box 100 78945 979-968-4747
Cliff Kinder, prin. Fax 968-6419

La Joya, Hidalgo, Pop. 3,984
La Joya ISD 29,900/PK-12
200 W Expressway 83 78560 956-323-2000
Dr. Alda T. Benavides, supt. Fax 323-2010
www.lajoyaisd.net/
Academy of Health Science Professionals 9-11
801 N Coyote Dr 78560 956-580-5900
Le-Ann Alaniz, prin. Fax 580-5960
Carter Early College HS 400/9-12
603 N Coyote Dr 78560 956-584-4842
Sylvia Sepulveda, prin. Fax 584-4843
College and Career Center Alt
603 N College Dr 78560 956-519-4031
Ronny Cabrera, dir. Fax 519-4030
De Zavala MS 700/6-8
603 Tabasco Rd 78560 956-580-5472
Magda Villarreal, prin. Fax 580-5494
HOPE Academy 100/Alt
101 E Expressway 83 78560 956-580-6121
Lindolfo Zamora, prin. Fax 580-6125
La Joya Early College HS 9-12
801 N Coyote Dr 78560 956-323-2935
Domingo Villarreal, prin. Fax 519-4046
La Joya HS 2,400/9-12
604 N Coyote Dr 78560 956-580-5100
Antonio Cano, prin. Fax 580-5103
LaJoya ISD West Academy 200/Alt
801 N Coyote Dr 78560 956-580-5900
Norma Garcia, prin. Fax 580-5960
Salinas STEM Early College HS 200/9-12
801 N Coyote Dr 78560 956-580-5912
Diana Garcia, prin. Fax 584-0844

Other Schools – See Alton, Mission, Palmview, Penitas

Lake Dallas, Denton, Pop. 6,973
Lake Dallas ISD 4,000/PK-12
PO Box 548 75065 940-497-4039
Gayle Stinson, supt. Fax 497-3737
www.ldisd.net
Lake Dallas MS 900/6-8
PO Box 548 75065 940-497-4037
Jim Parker, prin. Fax 497-4028
Other Schools – See Corinth

Lake Jackson, Brazoria, Pop. 26,471
Brazosport ISD
Supt. — See Clute
Lake Jackson IS 900/7-8
100 Oyster Creek Dr 77566 979-730-7250
Susan Wood, prin. Fax 292-2804

Brazosport Christian S 200/PK-12
200 Willow Dr Ste B 77566 979-297-0563
Stephen Meier, head sch Fax 297-8455
Brazosport College Post-Sec.
500 College Dr 77566 979-230-3000

Lake Worth, Tarrant, Pop. 4,497
Lake Worth ISD 3,200/PK-12
6805 Telephone Rd 76135 817-306-4200
John Hebert, supt. Fax 237-2583
www.lwisd.org
Lake Worth HS 700/9-12
4210 Boat Club Rd 76135 817-306-4200
Dr. Bob Koerner, prin. Fax 237-0697
Other Schools – See Fort Worth

La Marque, Galveston, Pop. 14,302
Texas City ISD
Supt. — See Texas City
La Marque HS 600/9-12
397 Duroux Rd 77568 409-938-4261
Ricky Nicholson, prin. Fax 908-5036
La Marque MS, 1431 Bayou Rd 77568 5-8
Dr. Florence Adkins, prin. 409-938-4286

Lamesa, Dawson, Pop. 9,364
Klondike ISD 300/PK-12
2911 County Road H 79331 806-462-7334
Steve McLaren, supt. Fax 462-7333
klondike.esc17.net
Klondike S 300/PK-12
2911 County Road H 79331 806-462-7332
Tony Bushong, prin. Fax 462-7333

Lamesa ISD 2,100/PK-12
PO Box 261 79331 806-872-5461
Jim Knight, supt. Fax 872-6220
www.lamesa.esc17.net
Lamesa HS 500/9-12
PO Box 261 79331 806-872-8385
Chris Riggins, prin. Fax 872-6608
Lamesa MS 500/6-8
PO Box 261 79331 806-872-8301
Jesse Galdean, prin. Fax 872-2949
Lamesa Success Academy 50/Alt
PO Box 261 79331 806-872-5410
Brad Froman, admin. Fax 872-6220

Lampasas, Lampasas, Pop. 6,551
Lampasas ISD 3,400/PK-12
207 W 8th St 76550 512-556-6224
Chane Rascoe Ed.D., supt. Fax 556-8711
www.lampasas.k12.tx.us
Lampasas HS 1,000/9-12
207 W 8th St 76550 512-564-2310
Mark Kehoe, prin. Fax 564-2406
Lampasas MS 800/6-8
207 W 8th St 76550 512-556-3101
Dana Holcomb, prin. Fax 556-0245

Lancaster, Dallas, Pop. 35,843
Lancaster ISD 6,800/PK-12
422 S Centre Ave 75146 972-218-1400
Dr. Michael McFarland, supt. Fax 218-1401
www.lancasterisd.org
Hall Learning Center Alt
602 E 2nd St 75146 972-218-1441
Eleanor Webb, prin. Fax 218-1442
Lancaster HS 1,700/9-12
200 E Wintergreen Rd 75134 972-218-1800
Joseph Showell, prin. Fax 218-5797
Lancaster MS 1,000/7-8
822 W Pleasant Run Rd 75146 972-218-1660
Shon Joseph, prin. Fax 218-3080

Cedar Valley College Post-Sec.
3030 N Dallas Ave 75134 972-860-8201

Laneville, Rusk
Laneville ISD 200/PK-12
7415 FM 1798 W 75667 903-863-5353
Teresa Shelton, supt. Fax 863-2736
www.lanevilleisd.org
Laneville S 200/PK-12
7415 FM 1798 W 75667 903-863-5353
Joshua Tremont, prin. Fax 863-2376

La Porte, Harris, Pop. 33,263
La Porte ISD 7,600/PK-12
1002 San Jacinto St 77571 281-604-7000
Lloyd Graham, supt. Fax 604-7010
www.lpisd.org
Dewalt Alternative S 100/Alt
1002 San Jacinto St 77571 281-604-6900
Debbie Stewart, prin. Fax 604-6904
La Porte HS 2,200/9-12
1002 San Jacinto St 77571 281-604-7500
Todd Schoppe, prin. Fax 604-7516
La Porte JHS 600/7-8
1002 San Jacinto St 77571 281-604-6600
Candace Pohl, prin. Fax 604-6605

Lomax JHS 600/7-8
1002 San Jacinto St 77571 281-604-6700
Dr. Larry Gerhart, prin. Fax 604-6730

La Pryor, Zavala, Pop. 1,634
La Pryor ISD 500/PK-12
PO Box 519 78872 830-365-4000
Matthew McHazlett, supt. Fax 365-4006
www.lapryor.net
La Pryor HS 200/7-12
PO Box 519 78872 830-365-4007
Tony Dominguez, prin. Fax 365-4026

Laredo, Webb, Pop. 235,714
Laredo ISD 24,900/PK-12
1702 Houston St 78040 956-273-1000
Dr. A. Marcus Nelson, supt. Fax 273-1403
www.laredoisd.org/
Cantu Health Science Magnet S 9-12
2002 San Bernardo Ave 78040 956-273-7100
Geraldina Arredondo, dir. Fax 273-7395
Christen MS 1,400/6-8
2001 Santa Maria Ave 78040 956-273-6400
Lizzy Newsome, prin. Fax 795-3732
Cigarroa HS 1,400/9-12
2600 Zacatecas St 78046 956-273-6800
Laura Flores, prin. Fax 795-3814
Cigarroa MS 1,400/6-8
2600 Palo Blanco St 78046 956-273-6100
Jose Cerda, prin. Fax 718-2208
Lamar MS 1,400/6-8
1818 N Arkansas Ave 78043 956-273-6200
Margarita Taboada, prin. Fax 795-3766
Lara Academy 100/Alt
2901 E Travis St 78043 956-273-7900
Robert Chaney, prin. Fax 726-0350
Martin HS 1,900/9-12
2002 San Bernardo Ave 78040 956-273-7100
Guillermo Pro, prin. Fax 795-3860
Memorial MS 800/6-8
2002 Marcella Ave 78040 956-273-6600
Sandra Garcia, prin. Fax 795-3780
Nixon HS 1,900/9-12
2000 E Plum St 78043 956-273-7400
Dr. Gerardo Cruz, prin. Fax 795-3844
Perez S for Engineering & Technology 9-12
2600 Zacatecas St 78046 956-273-6800
Alfredo Perez, prin. Fax 273-7095
Trevino S of Communications & Fine Arts 9-12
2102 E Lyon 78043 956-273-7800
Dr. Martha Villarreal, prin. Fax 273-7895
Valdez HS Alt
2502 Galveston St 78043 956-273-8000
Melissa Valdez, prin. Fax 273-8095

Texas A&M International University ISD 11-12
5201 University Blvd 78041 956-326-2860
Dr. Patricia Uribe, supt. Fax 326-2864
www.tamiu.edu/coas/theacademy
Texas Academy of International & STEM 11-12
5201 University Blvd 78041 956-326-2860
Dr. Patricia Uribe, dir. Fax 326-2863

United ISD 42,500/PK-12
201 Lindenwood Dr 78045 956-473-6201
Roberto J. Santos, supt. Fax 728-8691
www.uisd.net
Alexander HS 2,800/9-12
3600 E Del Mar Blvd 78041 956-473-5800
Ernesto Sandoval, prin. Fax 473-5999
Alexander Magnet HS 9-12
3600 E Del Mar Blvd 78041 956-473-5866
Elvira Gaona, dean Fax 473-5998
Bruni-Vergar MS 900/6-8
5910 Saint Luke 78046 956-473-6600
Clare G. Flores, prin. Fax 473-6699
Clark MS 800/6-8
500 W Hillside Rd 78041 956-473-7500
Melissa Chapa Ramirez, prin. Fax 473-7599
Garcia MS 500/6-8
499 Pena Dr 78046 956-473-5000
Clotilde Gamez, prin. Fax 473-5099
Gonzalez MS 1,200/6-8
5208 Santa Claudia 78043 956-473-7000
Patricia Perez, prin. Fax 473-7099
Johnson HS 2,600/9-12
5626 Cielito Lindo 78046 956-473-5100
Armando Salazar, prin. Fax 473-5281
Los Obispos MS 1,000/6-8
4801 S Ejido Ave 78046 956-473-7800
Jessica C. Salazar, prin. Fax 473-1899
Trautmann MS 1,800/6-8
8501 Curly Ln 78045 956-473-7400
Leticia Menchaca, prin. Fax 473-7499
United 9th Grade Campus 9-9
8800 McPherson Rd 78045 956-473-2400
Arlene Trevino, dean Fax 473-2499
United HS 3,100/10-12
2811 United Ave 78045 956-473-5600
Alberto Aleman, prin. Fax 473-1980
United Magnet HS 9-12
2811 United Ave 78045 956-473-5627
Maria Isabel Alarcon, dean Fax 473-1981
United MS 1,100/6-8
700 E Del Mar Blvd 78041 956-473-7300
Rebecca Morales, prin. Fax 473-7399
United S.T.E.P. Academy 100/Alt
1600 Espejo Molina Rd 78046 956-473-6500
Gerardo Rodriguez, dir. Fax 473-6599
United South HS 3,100/9-12
4001 Los Presidentes Ave 78046 956-473-5400
Adriana P. Ramirez, prin. Fax 473-5599
United South Magnet HS 9-12
4001 Los Presidentes Ave 78046 956-473-5440
Sinneh Koroma, dean Fax 473-5598
United South MS 1,400/6-8
3707 Los Presidentes Ave 78046 956-473-7700
Martha Alvarez, prin. Fax 473-7799

Washington MS 1,300/6-8
10306 Riverbank Dr 78045 956-473-7600
Beth Porter, prin. Fax 473-7699

Brightwood College Post-Sec.
6410 McPherson Rd 78041 956-717-5909
Laredo Community College Post-Sec.
1 W End Washington St 78040 956-722-0521
St. Augustine HS 400/9-12
1300 Galveston St 78040 956-724-8131
Olga Gentry, prin. Fax 725-9241
Texas A&M International University Post-Sec.
5201 University Blvd 78041 956-326-2000

LaRue, Henderson
La Poynor ISD 500/PK-12
13155 US Highway 175 E 75770 903-876-4057
James Young, supt. Fax 876-4541
www.lapoynorisd.net/
La Poynor HS 100/9-12
13155 US Highway 175 E 75770 903-876-2373
Garland Willis, prin. Fax 876-2374
La Poynor JHS 100/6-8
13155 US Highway 175 E 75770 903-876-2373
Garland Willis, prin. Fax 876-2374

Lasara, Willacy, Pop. 1,039
Lasara ISD 500/PK-12
PO Box 57 78561 956-642-3598
Sara Alvarado, supt. Fax 642-3546
www.lasaraisd.net/
Lasara HS 100/9-12
PO Box 57 78561 956-642-3271
Alejos Salazar, prin. Fax 642-3546

Latexo, Houston, Pop. 319
Latexo ISD 500/PK-12
PO Box 975 75849 936-544-5664
Dr. Stacy Easterly, supt. Fax 544-5332
www.latexoisd.net
Latexo JSHS 200/7-12
PO Box 975 75849 936-544-5664
Kris Whisenant, prin. Fax 544-8456

La Vernia, Wilson, Pop. 1,011
La Vernia ISD 3,100/PK-12
13600 US Highway 87 W 78121 830-779-6600
Dr. Jose Moreno, supt. Fax 779-2304
www.lvisd.org
La Vernia HS 1,000/9-12
225 Bluebonnet Rd 78121 830-779-6630
Kimberley Martin, prin. Fax 779-3218
La Vernia JHS 800/6-8
195 Bluebonnet Rd 78121 830-779-6650
Anthony Kosub, prin. Fax 779-6651

La Villa, Hidalgo, Pop. 1,955
La Villa ISD 600/PK-12
PO Box 9 78562 956-262-4755
Dr. Jose A. Cervantes, supt. Fax 262-7323
www.lavillaisd.org
La Villa Early College HS 200/9-12
PO Box 9 78562 956-262-4715
Dr. Sandra Nieto, prin. Fax 262-9798
La Villa MS 100/6-8
PO Box 9 78562 956-262-4760
Nancy Benavides, prin. Fax 262-5243

Lazbuddie, Parmer
Lazbuddie ISD 200/PK-12
PO Box 9 79053 806-965-2156
Steve Wolf, supt. Fax 965-2892
www.lazbuddieisd.org
Lazbuddie S 200/PK-12
PO Box 9 79053 806-965-2152
Ken Hoskins, prin. Fax 965-2892

League City, Galveston, Pop. 81,913
Clear Creek ISD 39,900/PK-12
PO Box 799 77574 281-284-0000
Dr. Greg Smith, supt. Fax 284-0005
www.ccisd.net
Bayside IS 700/6-8
4430 Village Way 77573 281-284-3000
James Thomas, prin. Fax 284-3005
Clear Creek HS 2,200/9-12
2305 E Main St 77573 281-284-1700
James Majewski, prin. Fax 284-1705
Clear Creek IS 800/6-8
2451 E Main St 77573 281-284-2300
Marshall Ponce, prin. Fax 284-2305
Clear Falls HS 2,400/9-12
4380 Village Way 77573 281-284-1100
Paul House, prin. Fax 284-1106
Clear Path Alternative S 200/Alt
400 S Kansas Ave 77573 281-284-1600
Jerry Herd, prin. Fax 284-1605
Clear Springs HS 2,300/9-12
501 Palomino St 77573 281-284-1300
Gail Love, prin. Fax 284-1305
Creekside IS 800/6-8
4320 W Main St 77573 281-284-3500
Peter Caterina, prin. Fax 284-3505
League City IS 900/6-8
2588 Webster St 77573 281-284-3400
Kimberly Brouillard, prin. Fax 284-3405
Victory Lakes IS 900/6-8
2880 W Walker St 77573 281-284-3700
Adam Douglas, prin. Fax 284-3705
Other Schools – See Friendswood, Houston, Seabrook

Bay Area Christian S 700/PK-12
4800 W Main St 77573 281-332-4814
Jason Nave, head sch Fax 554-5495
Devereux-Texas Treatment Network Post-Sec.
1150 Devereux Dr 77573 800-373-0011

Leakey, Real, Pop. 417
Leakey ISD 300/PK-12
PO Box 1129 78873 830-232-5595
Dr. Barbara Skipper, supt. Fax 232-5535
www.leakeyisd.org
Leakey S 300/PK-12
PO Box 1129 78873 830-232-5595
Gerald Lugaresi, prin. Fax 232-5535

Leander, Williamson, Pop. 25,831
Leander ISD 35,400/PK-12
PO Box 218 78646 512-570-0000
Dr. Dan Troxell, supt. Fax 570-0054
www.leanderisd.org
Glenn HS 9-12
1320 Collaborative Way 78641 512-570-1400
Arturo Lomeli, prin. Fax 570-1405
Leander Extended Opportunity Center Alt
300 S West Dr 78641 512-570-2230
Cathy White, prin. Fax 570-2234
Leander HS 2,000/9-12
3301 S Bagdad Rd 78641 512-570-1000
Tiffany Spicer, prin. Fax 570-1005
Leander MS 800/6-8
410 S West Dr 78641 512-570-3200
Mark Koller, prin. Fax 570-3205
New Hope HS 50/Alt
401 S West Dr 78641 512-570-2200
Barbara Spelman, prin. Fax 570-2204
Rouse HS 2,100/9-12
1222 Raider Way 78641 512-570-2000
Christine Simpson, prin. Fax 570-2005
Stiles MS 800/6-8
3250 Barley Rd 78641 512-570-3800
Susan Cole, prin. Fax 570-3805
Wiley MS 1,000/6-8
1526 Raider Way 78641 512-570-3600
Chris Simpson, prin. Fax 570-3605
Other Schools – See Austin, Cedar Park

Sterling Classical S 200/PK-12
11880 Old 2243 W Ste 700 78641 512-259-2722

Lefors, Gray, Pop. 490
Lefors ISD 200/PK-12
PO Box 390 79054 806-835-2533
Joe Waldron, supt. Fax 835-2238
www.leforsisd.net
Lefors S 200/PK-12
PO Box 390 79054 806-835-2533
Kelley Porter, prin. Fax 835-2238

Leggett, Polk
Leggett ISD 200/PK-12
PO Box 68 77350 936-398-2804
Jana Lowe, supt. Fax 398-2078
www.leggettisd.net
Leggett JSHS 100/7-12
PO Box 68 77350 936-398-2412
Jana Lowe, prin. Fax 398-0889

Lenorah, Martin
Grady ISD 200/PK-12
3500 FM 829 79749 432-459-2444
Leandro Gonzales, supt. Fax 459-2729
grady.tx.schoolwebpages.com
Grady S 200/PK-12
3500 FM 829 79749 432-459-2445
Gary Jones, prin. Fax 459-2729

Leonard, Fannin, Pop. 1,933
Leonard ISD 900/PK-12
1 Tiger Aly 75452 903-587-2318
Larry LaFavers, supt. Fax 587-2845
www.leonardisd.net
Leonard HS 300/9-12
1 Tiger Aly 75452 903-587-3556
Chris Mason, prin. Fax 587-8011
Leonard JHS 200/6-8
1 Tiger Aly 75452 903-587-2315
Tammy Hutchings, prin. Fax 587-2228

Levelland, Hockley, Pop. 13,427
Levelland ISD 3,100/PK-12
704 11th St 79336 806-894-9628
Jeff Northern, supt. Fax 894-2583
www.levellandisd.net
Levelland HS 800/9-12
704 11th St 79336 806-894-8515
Robbie Phillips, prin. Fax 894-6029
Levelland MS 600/6-8
704 11th St 79336 806-894-6355
John Clanton, prin. Fax 894-8935

South Plains College Post-Sec.
1401 College Ave 79336 806-894-9611

Lewisville, Denton, Pop. 93,105
Lewisville ISD
Supt. — See Flower Mound
Career Center East Vo/Tech
2553 FM 544 75056 469-713-5211
Jeff Wagley, prin. Fax 626-1640
Delay MS 900/6-8
2103 Savage Ln 75057 469-713-5191
Jim Baker, prin. Fax 350-9174
Durham MS 800/6-8
2075 S Edmonds Ln 75067 469-713-5963
Brian McCoo, prin. Fax 350-9182
Hedrick MS 700/6-8
1526 Bellaire Blvd 75067 469-713-5188
Barbara Hamric, prin. Fax 350-9196
Huffines MS 900/6-8
1440 N Valley Pkwy 75077 469-713-5990
Estella Rupard, prin. Fax 350-9199
Jackson Career Center Vo/Tech
1597 S Edmonds Ln 75067 469-713-5186
Randall Holder, prin. Fax 350-9342
Killian MS 900/6-8
2561 FM 544 75056 469-713-5977
Deanne Angonia, prin. Fax 350-9200
Lewisville HS 1,800/11-12
1098 W Main St 75067 469-713-5190
Jeffrey Kajs, prin. Fax 350-9291
Lewisville HS Harmon Campus 1,200/9-10
1250 W Round Grove Rd 75067 469-713-5201
Tony Fontana, prin. Fax 626-1680
Lewisville HS Killough Campus 1,000/9-10
1301 Summit Ave 75077 469-713-5987
Pam Flores, prin. Fax 350-9304
Lewisville Learning Center 200/Alt
1601 S Edmonds Ln 75067 469-713-5185
Angela Deaton, prin. Fax 350-9350
Night HS Adult
1601 S Edmonds Ln 75067 469-948-7665
Michael Todd, admin. Fax 350-9588

Lakeland Christian Academy 600/PK-12
397 S Stemmons Fwy 75067 972-219-3939
Terry Campbell, supt. Fax 219-9601
Willow Bend Academy 100/5-12
101 E Southwest Pkwy # 101 75067 972-436-3839
Connie Hayes, prin. Fax 436-3930

Lexington, Lee, Pop. 1,158
Lexington ISD 900/PK-12
8731 N Highway 77 78947 979-773-2254
Dr. Brad Schnautz, supt. Fax 773-4455
www.lexingtonisd.net
Lexington HS 300/9-12
8731 N Highway 77 78947 979-773-2255
Sarah Garrison, prin. Fax 773-4455
Lexington MS 200/6-8
8731 N Highway 77 78947 979-773-2255
William Paul, prin. Fax 773-4455

Liberty, Liberty, Pop. 8,274
Liberty ISD, 1600 Grand Ave 77575 2,100/PK-12
Dr. Cody Abshier, supt. 936-336-7213
www.libertyisd.net
Liberty HS 600/9-12
2615 Jefferson Dr 77575 936-336-6483
Dr. Chad Barrett, prin. Fax 336-3931
Liberty MS 400/6-8
2515 Jefferson Dr 77575 936-336-3582
Rhonda Smith, prin. Fax 336-1021

Liberty Hill, Williamson, Pop. 951
Liberty Hill ISD 3,000/PK-12
301 Forrest St 78642 512-260-5580
Dr. Rob Hart, supt. Fax 260-5581
www.libertyhill.txed.net
Liberty Hill HS 1,000/9-12
16500 W State Highway 29 78642 512-260-5500
Mario Bye, prin. Fax 260-5510
Liberty Hill JHS 500/7-8
13125 W State Highway 29 78642 512-379-3300
Annette Coe, prin. Fax 379-3310

Fortis Academy 200/PK-12
PO Box 580 78642 512-432-5152
Fax 778-5944

Lindale, Smith, Pop. 4,737
Lindale ISD 3,800/PK-12
PO Box 370 75771 903-881-4000
Stan Surratt, supt. Fax 881-4004
www.lindaleeagles.org
Lindale HS 1,100/9-12
PO Box 370 75771 903-881-4050
Valerie Payne, prin. Fax 882-2813
Lindale JHS 600/7-8
PO Box 370 75771 903-881-4150
Jeremy Chilek, prin. Fax 881-4049

Mercy Ships Academy 50/PK-12
15862 Highway 110 N 75771 903-939-7183
Brian Blackburn, admin. Fax 939-7065

Linden, Cass, Pop. 1,960
Linden-Kildare Consolidated ISD 800/PK-12
205 Kildare Rd 75563 903-756-5027
Trevor Rogers, supt. Fax 756-7242
www.lkcisd.net
Linden-Kildare HS 200/9-12
205 Kildare Rd 75563 903-756-7026
Keri Winters, prin. Fax 756-8512
Stephens JHS 200/6-8
205 Kildare Rd 75563 903-756-5381
Randall Wright, prin. Fax 756-8832

Lindsay, Cooke, Pop. 1,000
Lindsay ISD 500/K-12
PO Box 145 76250 940-668-8923
Larry Smith, supt. Fax 668-2662
www.lindsayisd.org
Lindsay HS 200/7-12
PO Box 145 76250 940-668-8474
Steven Cope, prin. Fax 665-1637

Lingleville, Erath
Lingleville ISD 200/PK-12
PO Box 134 76461 254-968-2596
Curt Haley, supt. Fax 965-5821
www.lingleville.us
Lingleville S 200/PK-12
PO Box 134 76461 254-968-2596
Cheryl Hudson, prin. Fax 965-5821

Lipan, Hood, Pop. 426
Lipan ISD 300/PK-8
211 N Kickapoo St 76462 254-646-2266
Cindy Edwards, supt. Fax 646-3499
www.lipanindians.net/
Lipan JHS 50/7-8
211 N Kickapoo St 76462 254-646-2266
Steve Bryant, prin. Fax 646-3499

Little Elm, Denton, Pop. 25,208
Little Elm ISD, PO Box 6000 75068 — 6,600/PK-12
Lowell Strike, supt. — 972-947-9340
www.leisd.ws
Lakeside MS — 1,000/7-8
400 Lobo Ln 75068 — 972-947-9445
Clint Miller, prin. — Fax 947-9332
Little Elm HS — 1,700/9-12
1900 Walker Ln 75068 — 972-947-9443
Renee Pentecost, prin. — Fax 947-9333

Littlefield, Lamb, Pop. 6,333
Littlefield ISD — 1,400/PK-12
1207 E 14th St 79339 — 806-385-4150
Robert Dillard, supt. — Fax 385-4195
www.littlefield.k12.tx.us
Littlefield HS — 400/9-12
1207 E 14th St 79339 — 806-385-4150
Ricky Hobbs, prin. — Fax 385-4191
Littlefield JHS — 300/6-8
1207 E 14th St 79339 — 806-385-4150
Trevor Edgemon, prin. — Fax 385-4192

Little River, Bell, Pop. 1,936
Academy ISD — 1,000/PK-12
704 E Main St 76554 — 254-982-4304
Kevin Sprinkles, supt. — Fax 982-0023
www.academyisd.net
Academy HS — 400/9-12
602 E Main St 76554 — 254-982-4201
Alex Remschel, prin. — Fax 982-4420
Academy MS — 300/6-8
501 E Main St 76554 — 254-982-4620
Stephen Ash, prin. — Fax 982-4776
Bell County Alternative S — Alt
706 E Rio Poco 76554 — 254-982-3505
Terry Day, prin. — Fax 982-3506

Live Oak, Bexar, Pop. 12,703
Judson ISD — 23,500/PK-12
8012 Shin Oak Dr 78233 — 210-945-5100
Dr. Carl Montoya, supt. — Fax 945-6900
www.judsonisd.org
Judson Early College Academy — 400/9-12
8230 Palisades Dr 78148 — 210-619-0200
Michael McFalls, prin. — Fax 659-1990
Other Schools – See Converse, San Antonio, Universal City

Livingston, Polk, Pop. 5,275
Big Sandy ISD
Supt. — See Dallardsville
Big Sandy S — 500/PK-12
FM 1276 77351 — 936-563-1000
Kevin Foster, prin. — Fax 563-1010

Livingston ISD — 4,000/PK-12
PO Box 1297 77351 — 936-328-2100
Dr. Brent Hawkins, supt. — Fax 328-2109
www.livingstonisd.com
Alternative Education Program — Alt
1 Lions Ave 77351 — 936-328-2353
Karen Maxey, prin. — Fax 328-2352
Livingston HS — 1,100/9-12
400 FM 350 S 77351 — 936-967-1600
Brandon Boyd, prin. — Fax 967-8603
Livingston HS Academy — Alt
400 FM 350 S 77351 — 936-967-1600
Lana Smith, prin. — Fax 967-8603
Livingston JHS — 900/6-8
1801 Highway 59 Loop N 77351 — 936-328-2120
Alice Clayton, prin. — Fax 328-2139

Llano, Llano, Pop. 3,210
Llano ISD — 1,800/PK-12
1400 Oatman St 78643 — 325-247-4747
Casey Callahan, supt. — Fax 247-5623
www.llanoisd.org
Llano HS — 500/9-12
2509 S State Highway 16 78643 — 325-248-2200
Jenifer Neatherlin, prin. — Fax 247-2122
Llano JHS — 400/6-8
400 E State Highway 71 78643 — 325-247-4659
Todd Keele, prin. — Fax 247-5821

Llano Christian Academy — 100/PK-12
PO Box 728 78643 — 325-247-4942
Dr. Alice Smith, hdmstr.

Lockhart, Caldwell, Pop. 12,574
Lockhart ISD — 5,100/PK-12
PO Box 120 78644 — 512-398-0000
Tina Knudsen, supt. — Fax 398-0025
www.lockhartisd.org
Lockhart HS — 1,000/10-12
1 Lion Country Dr 78644 — 512-398-0300
Deanna Juarez, prin. — Fax 398-0302
Lockhart HS Freshman Campus — 400/9-9
419 Bois DArc St 78644 — 512-398-0170
Mark Estrada, prin. — Fax 398-0226
Lockhart JHS — 1,100/6-8
500 City Line Rd 78644 — 512-398-0770
Lori Davis, prin. — Fax 398-0772
Pride HS — 50/Alt
1503 N Colorado St 78644 — 512-398-0130
Laurie Lay, prin. — Fax 398-0132

Lockney, Floyd, Pop. 1,837
Lockney ISD — 500/PK-12
PO Box 428 79241 — 806-652-2115
Phil Cotham, supt. — Fax 652-4920
www.lockneyisd.net
Lockney HS — 200/9-12
PO Box 1058 79241 — 806-652-3325
Todd Hallmark, prin. — Fax 652-4920
Lockney JHS — 100/6-8
PO Box 550 79241 — 806-652-2236
Craig Setliff, prin. — Fax 652-4920

Lohn, McCulloch
Lohn ISD — 100/PK-12
PO Box 277 76852 — 325-344-5749
Leon Freeman, supt. — Fax 344-5789
www.lohnisd.net
Lohn S — 100/PK-12
PO Box 277 76852 — 325-344-5749
Dr. Steve Coston, prin. — Fax 344-5790

Lometa, Lampasas, Pop. 834
Lometa ISD — 300/PK-12
PO Box 250 76853 — 512-752-3384
David Fisher, supt. — Fax 752-3424
www.lometaisd.net
Lometa S — 300/PK-12
PO Box 250 76853 — 512-752-3384
Jamie Smart, prin. — Fax 752-3424

Lone Oak, Hunt, Pop. 584
Lone Oak ISD — 1,000/PK-12
8162 US Highway 69 S 75453 — 903-662-5427
Lance Campbell, supt. — Fax 662-5290
www.loisd.net
Lone Oak HS — 300/9-12
8204 US Highway 69 S 75453 — 903-662-0981
Jeff Hicks, prin. — Fax 662-0984
Lone Oak MS — 200/6-8
8160 US Highway 69 S 75453 — 903-662-5121
Dr. Shannon Wilhite, prin. — Fax 662-5017

Longview, Gregg, Pop. 79,235
Longview ISD — 8,600/PK-12
PO Box 3268 75606 — 903-381-2200
Dr. James Wilcox, supt. — Fax 753-5389
www.lisd.org
Forest Park MS — 500/6-8
PO Box 3268 75606 — 903-446-2510
Shay Thompson, prin. — Fax 446-2501
Foster MS — 800/6-8
PO Box 3268 75606 — 903-446-2710
John York, prin. — Fax 758-2052
Judson MS — 500/6-8
PO Box 3268 75606 — 903-446-2610
William Houff, prin. — Fax 663-0275
LEAD Academy, PO Box 3268 75606 — 100/8-12
Kristi Means, prin. — 903-381-3921
Longview HS — 1,900/9-12
PO Box 3268 75606 — 903-663-1301
James Brewer, prin. — Fax 663-7180

Pine Tree ISD — 5,000/PK-12
PO Box 5878 75608 — 903-295-5000
Dr. Teresa Farler, supt. — Fax 295-5004
www.ptisd.org
ExCEL HS — 100/9-12
PO Box 5878 75608 — 903-295-6753
Tyrance Barnett, prin. — Fax 295-5145
PACE Alternative Discipline Center — 300/Alt
PO Box 5878 75608 — 903-295-5130
Shalonda Adams, prin. — Fax 295-5145
Pine Tree HS — 1,200/9-12
PO Box 5878 75608 — 903-295-5031
Cindy Gabehart, prin. — Fax 295-5029
Pine Tree JHS — 700/7-8
PO Box 5878 75608 — 903-295-5081
Vanessa Robinson, prin. — Fax 295-5082

Spring Hill ISD — 1,900/PK-12
3101 Spring Hill Rd 75605 — 903-759-4404
Steven Snell, supt. — Fax 297-0141
www.shisd.net
Spring Hill HS — 500/9-12
3101 Spring Hill Rd 75605 — 903-446-3300
Denny Lind, prin. — Fax 323-7766
Spring Hill JHS — 400/6-8
3101 Spring Hill Rd 75605 — 903-323-7718
Michael Moore, prin. — Fax 323-7765

Christian Heritage S — 200/PK-12
2715 FM 1844 75605 — 903-663-4151
Doug Carr, hdmstr. — Fax 663-4587
East Texas Christian S — 200/PK-12
PO Box 8053 75607 — 903-757-7891
Dr. Renee Sawyer, admin. — Fax 619-0349
Le Tourneau University — Post-Sec.
PO Box 7001 75607 — 903-233-3000
Longview Christian S — 200/K-12
1236 Pegues Pl 75601 — 903-297-3501
Ben Cammack, admin. — Fax 212-2541
St. Mary's Catholic S — 200/PK-12
405 Hollybrook Dr 75605 — 903-753-1657
Amy Allen, prin. — Fax 758-7347
Trinity S of Texas — 300/PK-12
215 N Teague St 75601 — 903-753-0612
Gary Whitwell, head sch — Fax 753-4812
Vista College — Post-Sec.
1905 W Loop 281 Ste 21 75604 — 866-442-4197

Loop, Gaines, Pop. 223
Loop ISD — 100/PK-12
PO Box 917 79342 — 806-487-6411
Dick Van Hoose, supt. — Fax 487-6416
www.loopisd.net/
Loop S — 100/PK-12
PO Box 917 79342 — 806-487-6411
Dick Van Hoose, supt. — Fax 487-6416

Loraine, Mitchell, Pop. 595
Loraine ISD — 200/PK-12
PO Box 457 79532 — 325-737-2225
Brandon McDowell, supt. — Fax 737-2701
www.loraine.esc14.net
Loraine S — 200/PK-12
PO Box 457 79532 — 325-737-2225
James Womack, prin. — Fax 737-2019

Lorena, McLennan, Pop. 1,682
Lorena ISD — 1,400/PK-12
PO Box 97 76655 — 254-857-3239
Dr. Sandra Talbert, supt. — Fax 857-4533
www.lorenaisd.net
Lorena HS — 500/9-12
PO Box 97 76655 — 254-857-4604
Kevin Johnson, prin. — Fax 857-3883
Lorena MS — 400/6-8
PO Box 97 76655 — 254-857-4621
Dr. Celia Drews, prin. — Fax 857-3419

Lorenzo, Crosby, Pop. 1,134
Lorenzo ISD — 300/PK-12
PO Box 520 79343 — 806-634-5591
Oran Hamilton, supt. — Fax 634-5928
www.lorenzoisd.net
Lorenzo JSHS — 100/7-12
PO Box 520 79343 — 806-634-5592
Matt Birdwell, prin. — Fax 634-5788

Los Fresnos, Cameron, Pop. 5,528
Los Fresnos Consolidated ISD — 10,400/PK-12
PO Box 309 78566 — 956-254-5010
Gonzalo Salazar, supt. — Fax 233-4031
www.lfcisd.net
Los Cuates MS — 900/6-8
PO Box 309 78566 — 956-254-5182
Yliana Gonzalez, prin. — Fax 233-6265
Los Fresnos HS — 2,000/10-12
PO Box 309 78566 — 956-254-5300
Justin Stumbaugh, prin. — Fax 233-3570
Reseca MS — 900/6-8
PO Box 309 78566 — 956-254-5159
Elizabeth Swantner, prin. — Fax 233-6209
Other Schools – See San Benito

Lott, Falls, Pop. 750
Rosebud-Lott ISD — 500/PK-12
1789 US Highway 77 76656 — 254-583-4510
Dr. Steve Brownlee, supt. — Fax 583-4469
www.rlisd.org
Rosebud-Lott HS — 200/9-12
1789 US Highway 77 76656 — 254-583-7967
Todd Williams, prin. — Fax 583-1130
Rosebud-Lott MS — 100/7-8
1789 US Highway 77 76656 — 254-583-7962
Todd Williams, prin. — Fax 583-2904
Other Schools – See Rosebud

Louise, Wharton, Pop. 991
Louise ISD — 500/PK-12
PO Box 97 77455 — 979-648-2982
Dr. Garth Oliver, supt. — Fax 648-2520
louiseisd.net
Louise HS — 100/9-12
PO Box 97 77455 — 979-648-2202
Donna Kutac, prin. — Fax 648-2142
Louise JHS — 100/6-8
PO Box 97 77455 — 979-648-2262
Brady Peterson, prin. — Fax 648-2520

Lovelady, Houston, Pop. 635
Lovelady ISD — 500/PK-12
PO Box 99 75851 — 936-636-7616
Dr. Micah Dyer, supt. — Fax 636-2212
www.loveladyisd.net
Lovelady JSHS — 200/7-12
PO Box 280 75851 — 936-636-7636
Michael King, prin. — Fax 636-2305

Lubbock, Lubbock, Pop. 226,600
Frenship ISD
Supt. — See Wolfforth
Heritage MS — 800/6-8
6110 73rd St 79424 — 806-794-9400
Greg Hernandez, prin. — Fax 793-8956
Reese Education Center — 100/Alt
9421 4th St 79416 — 806-885-4910
Farley Reeves, prin. — Fax 885-2442
Terra Vista MS — 600/6-8
1111 Upland Ave 79416 — 806-796-0076
Brent Lowrey, prin. — Fax 796-1540

Lubbock ISD — 27,500/PK-12
1628 19th St 79401 — 806-219-0000
Dr. Berhl Robertson, supt. — Fax 766-1210
www.lubbockisd.org
Atkins MS — 600/6-8
5401 Avenue U 79412 — 806-766-1522
Chris Huber, prin. — Fax 766-2226
Cavazos MS — 600/6-8
210 N University Ave 79415 — 806-219-3200
Marti Makuta, prin. — Fax 766-6627
Coronado HS — 2,100/9-12
4910 29th Dr 79410 — 806-219-1100
Jerry Adams, prin. — Fax 766-0560
Dunbar College Preparatory Academy — 600/6-8
2010 E 26th St 79404 — 806-766-1300
Lori Alexander, prin. — Fax 766-1320
Estacado HS — 700/9-12
1504 E Itasca St 79403 — 806-219-1400
Angelica Wilbanks, prin. — Fax 766-1952
Evans MS — 900/6-8
4211 58th St 79413 — 806-219-3600
Flo Touchstone, prin. — Fax 766-0570
Hutchinson MS — 800/6-8
3102 Canton Ave 79410 — 806-219-3800
Heidi Dye, prin. — Fax 766-0538
Irons MS — 700/6-8
5214 79th St 79424 — 806-219-4000
Philip Riewe, prin. — Fax 766-2070
Lubbock HS — 2,000/9-12
2004 19th St 79401 — 806-219-1600
Doug Young, prin. — Fax 766-1469
MacKenzie MS — 700/6-8
5402 12th St 79416 — 806-219-4200
John Martinez, prin. — Fax 766-0510

Martin ATC Vo/Tech
3201 Avenue Q 79411 806-219-2800
Charlotte Sessom, coord. Fax 766-6675
Matthews Alternative HS 200/Alt
417 N Akron Ave 79415 806-216-2600
Carolyn Thompson, prin. Fax 766-1532
Monterey HS 2,100/9-12
3211 47th St 79413 806-219-1900
Les Purkeypile, prin. Fax 766-0509
Slaton MS 600/6-8
1602 32nd St 79411 806-219-4400
Damon McCall, prin. Fax 766-1571
Talkington S for Young Women Leaders 400/6-12
415 N Ivory Ave 79403 806-219-2200
Berta Fogerson, prin. Fax 766-1738
Wilson MS 500/6-8
4402 31st St 79410 806-219-4600
Kelly Brownfield, prin. Fax 766-0814

Lubbock-Cooper ISD 5,000/PK-12
16302 Loop 493 79423 806-863-7100
Keith Bryant, supt. Fax 863-3130
www.lcisd.net
Lubbock-Cooper Bush MS 600/6-8
3425 118th St 79423 806-776-0750
Edna Parr, prin. Fax 776-0751
Lubbock-Cooper HS 1,100/9-12
16302 Loop 493 79423 806-863-7105
Angie Inklebarger, prin. Fax 863-2877
Lubbock-Cooper MS 500/6-8
16302 Loop 493 79423 806-863-7104
Tami Gunset, prin. Fax 863-7163
Lubbock-Cooper New Hope Academy Alt
16302 Loop 493 79423 806-778-4749
Dave Paschall, prin.

Roosevelt ISD 1,100/PK-12
1406 County Road 3300 79403 806-842-3282
Dallas Grimes, supt. Fax 842-3266
www.roosevelt.k12.tx.us/
Roosevelt HS 300/9-12
1406 County Road 3300 79403 806-842-3283
Jimmy Ledbetter, prin. Fax 842-3931
Roosevelt JHS 200/6-8
1406 County Road 3300 79403 806-842-3218
Tim Crane, prin. Fax 842-3337

All Saints Episcopal S 300/PK-11
3222 103rd St 79423 806-745-7701
Christ the King Cathedral S 300/PK-12
4011 54th St 79413 806-795-8283
Christine Wanjura, prin. Fax 795-9715
Covenant Sch. of Nursing & Allied Health Post-Sec.
2002 W Loop 289 Ste 120 79407 806-797-0955
Kingdom Preparatory Academy 200/PK-12
PO Box 64028 79464 806-767-9334
Lubbock Christian S 300/PK-12
2604 Dover Ave 79407 806-796-8700
Lubbock Christian University Post-Sec.
5601 19th St 79407 806-796-8800
Lubbock Hair Academy Post-Sec.
2844 34th St 79410 806-795-0806
Lubbock Junior Academy 50/K-10
PO Box 6277 79493 806-795-4481
Methodist Hospital Post-Sec.
3615 19th St 79410 806-792-1011
Southcrest Christian S 300/PK-12
3801 S Loop 289 79423 806-797-7400
Linda Merriott M.Ed., supt. Fax 776-0546
South Plains College Post-Sec.
819 S Gilbert Dr 79416 806-885-3048
Texas Tech University Post-Sec.
PO Box 45005 79409 806-742-2011
Texas Tech University Health Science Ctr Post-Sec.
3601 4th St 79430 806-743-1000
Trinity Christian JSHS 300/4-12
6701 University Ave 79413 806-791-6583
Tyler Neal, prin. Fax 745-8461
Virginia College Post-Sec.
5005 50th St 79414 806-784-1900
Vista College Post-Sec.
4620 50th St 79414 866-442-4197

Lucas, Collin, Pop. 5,074
Lovejoy ISD
Supt. — See Allen
Lovejoy HS 1,200/9-12
2350 Estates Pkwy, 469-742-8700
Chris Mayfield, prin. Fax 742-8701
Willow Springs MS 700/7-8
1101 W Lucas Rd, 469-702-8500
Kent Messer, prin. Fax 702-8501

Lueders, Jones, Pop. 342
Lueders-Avoca ISD 100/PK-12
334 Vandeventer St 79533 325-228-4211
Bob Spikes, supt. Fax 228-4513
www.laisd.esc14.net
Other Schools – See Avoca

Lufkin, Angelina, Pop. 34,621
Hudson ISD 2,800/PK-12
6735 Ted Trout Dr 75904 936-875-3351
Mary Ann Whiteker, supt. Fax 875-9209
www.hudsonisd.org
Hudson HS 800/9-12
6735 Ted Trout Dr 75904 936-875-9232
John Courtney, prin. Fax 875-9307
Hudson MS 600/6-8
6735 Ted Trout Dr 75904 936-875-9292
Richard Crenshaw, prin. Fax 875-9317

Lufkin ISD 8,300/PK-12
PO Box 1407 75902 936-634-6696
Dr. LaTonya Goffney, supt. Fax 634-8864
www.lufkinisd.org
Alternative S Alt
PO Box 1407 75902 936-632-7203
Drew Huffty, prin. Fax 632-7209
Angelina County Coop Early College HS 9-12
101 N Cotton Sq 75902 936-633-5344
June Burrow, dir.
Lufkin HS 2,100/9-12
309 S Medford Dr 75901 936-632-7721
Kurt Stephens, prin. Fax 632-8132
Lufkin MS 1,700/6-8
900 E Denman Ave 75901 936-630-4444
Jesus Gomez, prin. Fax 632-4444

Zavalla ISD
Supt. — See Zavalla
Stubblefield Learning Center 50/Alt
208 N John Redditt Dr 75904 936-897-2271

Academy of Hair Design Post-Sec.
512 S Chestnut St 75901 936-634-8440
Angelina College Post-Sec.
PO Box 1768 75902 936-639-1301

Luling, Caldwell, Pop. 5,365
Luling ISD 1,500/PK-12
212 E Bowie St 78648 830-875-3191
Tim Glover, supt. Fax 875-3193
www.luling.txed.net
Gerdes JHS 300/6-8
214 E Bowie St 78648 830-875-2121
Ernie Amaton, prin. Fax 875-5482
Luling HS 400/9-12
218 E Travis St 78648 830-875-2458
Sameera DeLeon, prin. Fax 875-2751

Lumberton, Hardin, Pop. 11,830
Lumberton ISD 3,800/PK-12
121 S Main St 77657 409-923-7580
John Valastro, supt. Fax 755-7848
www.lumberton.k12.tx.us
Lumberton HS 1,100/9-12
103 S LHS Dr 77657 409-923-7890
Darwin Davis, prin. Fax 755-6576
Lumberton MS 600/7-8
123 S Main St 77657 409-923-7581
Leanna Stringer, prin. Fax 751-0641

Lyford, Willacy, Pop. 2,606
Lyford Consolidated ISD 1,600/PK-12
PO Box 220 78569 956-347-3900
Eduardo Infante, supt. Fax 347-5588
www.lyfordcisd.net
Lyford HS 500/9-12
PO Box 220 78569 956-347-3909
Veronica Sanches, prin. Fax 347-5034
Lyford MS 300/6-8
PO Box 220 78569 956-347-3910
Jose Escamilla, prin. Fax 347-2351

Lytle, Atascosa, Pop. 2,470
Lytle ISD 1,800/PK-12
PO Box 745 78052 830-709-5100
Michelle Carroll Smith, supt. Fax 709-5104
lytleisd.com
Lytle HS 500/9-12
PO Box 190 78052 830-709-5105
Loretta Zavala, prin. Fax 709-5107
Lytle JHS 400/6-8
PO Box 825 78052 830-709-5115
Kenneth Dykes, prin. Fax 709-5119

Mabank, Kaufman, Pop. 2,981
Mabank ISD 3,400/PK-12
310 E Market St 75147 903-880-1300
Dr. Russell Marshall, supt. Fax 880-1303
www.mabankisd.net
Mabank Academy Alt
310 E Market St 75147 903-880-1600
Jes Satterwhite, prin. Fax 880-1603
Mabank DAEP Alt
310 E Market St 75147 903-880-1600
Jes Satterwhite, prin. Fax 880-1603
Mabank HS 1,000/9-12
310 E Market St 75147 903-880-1600
Jes Satterwhite, prin. Fax 880-1603
Mabank JHS 500/7-8
310 E Market St 75147 903-880-1670
Barbie Conrad, prin. Fax 880-1673

Mc Allen, Hidalgo, Pop. 129,344
McAllen ISD 25,200/PK-12
2000 N 23rd St 78501 956-618-6000
Jose Gonzalez, supt. Fax 686-8362
www.mcallenisd.org
Achieve Early College HS 400/9-12
3200 Pecan Blvd 78501 956-872-1653
Dr. Esmer Munoz, prin. Fax 872-1650
Brown MS 900/6-8
2700 S Ware Rd 78503 956-632-8700
Alfredo Gutierrez, prin. Fax 632-8709
Cathey MS 1,000/6-8
1800 N Cynthia St 78501 956-971-4300
Melvin L. Benford, prin. Fax 632-2811
De Leon MS 700/6-8
4201 N 29th Ln 78504 956-632-8800
Philip Grossweiler, prin. Fax 632-8805
Fossum MS 800/6-8
7800 N Ware Rd 78504 956-971-1105
Monica Kaufmann, prin. Fax 618-9718
Instruction & Guidance Center 100/Alt
2604 Galveston Ave 78501 956-971-4393
Fernando Gutierrez, prin. Fax 971-4294
Lamar Academy 100/Alt
1009 N 10th St 78501 956-632-3222
Cindy Pena, prin. Fax 632-3662
Lincoln MS 700/6-8
1601 N 27th St 78501 956-971-4200
Maribelle Elizondo, prin. Fax 971-4273
McAllen HS 2,200/9-12
2021 La Vista Ave 78501 956-632-3100
Albert Canales, prin. Fax 632-3114
Memorial HS 2,200/9-12
101 E Hackberry Ave 78501 956-632-5201
Pedro Alvarez, prin. Fax 632-5226
Morris MS 900/6-8
1400 Trenton Rd 78504 956-618-7300
Brian McClenny, prin. Fax 632-3666
Rowe HS 2,200/9-12
2101 N Ware Rd 78501 956-632-5100
Paz Elizondo, prin. Fax 632-5121
Travis MS 700/6-8
600 W Houston Ave 78501 956-971-4242
Efrain Amaya, prin. Fax 632-8454

Sharyland ISD
Supt. — See Mission
Sharyland North JHS 800/7-8
5100 W Dove Ave 78504 956-686-1415
Lorene Bazan, prin. Fax 668-0425

Brightwood College Post-Sec.
1500 S Jackson Rd 78503 956-630-1499
Covenant Christian Academy 500/PK-12
4201 N Ware Rd 78504 956-686-7886
Milton Gonzalez, prin. Fax 686-9470
South Texas Christian Academy 300/PK-12
7001 N Ware Rd 78504 956-682-1117
South Texas College Post-Sec.
3201 Pecan Blvd 78501 956-872-8311
South Texas Vocational-Technical Inst. Post-Sec.
2400 Daffodil Ave 78501 956-631-1107
Taylor Christian S 50/PK-12
2021 W Jackson Ave 78501 956-686-7574
Laura Vaca M.Ed., dir. Fax 682-4945
University of Cosmetology Arts & Science Post-Sec.
8401 N 10th St 78504 956-687-9444

Mc Camey, Upton, Pop. 1,870
Mc Camey ISD 500/PK-12
PO Box 1069 79752 432-652-3666
Ronnie Golson, supt. Fax 652-4219
www.mcisd.esc18.net
Mc Camey HS 200/9-12
PO Box 1069 79752 432-652-3666
Michael Valencia, prin. Fax 652-4245
Mc Camey MS 100/5-8
PO Box 1069 79752 432-652-3666
Blanca Smith, prin. Fax 652-4246

Mc Dade, Bastrop, Pop. 682
Mc Dade ISD 200/PK-12
PO Box 400 78650 512-273-2522
Barbara Marchbanks, supt. Fax 273-2101
www.mcdadeisd.com/
Mc Dade HS 7-12
PO Box 400 78650 512-273-2522
Paul Smith, prin. Fax 273-2021

Mc Gregor, McLennan, Pop. 4,934
Mc Gregor ISD 1,000/PK-12
PO Box 356 76657 254-840-2828
Kevin Houchin, supt. Fax 840-4077
www.mcgregor-isd.org
Isbill JHS 300/6-8
PO Box 356 76657 254-840-3251
Paul Miller, prin. Fax 840-3572
Mc Gregor HS 400/9-12
PO Box 356 76657 254-840-2853
Robert White, prin. Fax 840-2489

Mc Kinney, Collin, Pop. 128,217
Frisco ISD
Supt. — See Frisco
Scoggins MS 700/6-8
7070 Stacy Rd 75070 469-633-5150
Barbara Warner, prin. Fax 633-5160

Mc Kinney ISD 24,500/PK-12
1 Duvall St 75069 469-302-4000
Dr. Rick McDaniel, supt. Fax 302-4071
www.mckinneyisd.net
Cockrill MS 1,400/6-8
1351 Hardin Rd 75071 469-302-7900
Dr. Amber Epperson, prin. Fax 302-7901
Dowell MS 1,200/6-8
301 Ridge Rd 75070 469-302-6700
Holly Rogers, prin. Fax 302-6701
Evans MS 1,500/6-8
6998 Eldorado Pkwy 75070 469-302-7100
Darla Jackson, prin. Fax 302-7101
Faubion MS 900/6-8
2000 Rollins St 75069 469-302-6900
Jimmy Bowser, prin. Fax 302-6901
Johnson MS 900/6-8
3400 Community Ave 75071 469-302-4900
Mitch Curry, prin. Fax 302-4901
Mc Kinney Boyd HS 3,000/9-12
600 N Lake Forest Dr 75071 469-302-5400
Dr. Jennifer Peirson, prin. Fax 302-5401
Mc Kinney HS 2,100/9-12
1400 Wilson Creek Pkwy 75069 469-302-5700
Alan Arbabi, prin. Fax 302-5701
Mc Kinney North HS 2,000/9-12
2550 Wilmeth Rd 75071 469-302-4300
Jae Gaskill, prin. Fax 302-4301
Serenity HS 50/Alt
2100 W White Ave 75069 469-302-7830
Stephen Issa, prin. Fax 302-7831

Collin College Post-Sec.
2200 W University Dr 75071 972-548-6790
Cornerstone Christian Academy 300/PK-12
PO Box 3143 75070 214-491-5700
Dr. Jeff Guleserian, hdmstr.
McKinney Christian Academy 500/PK-12
3601 Bois D Arc Rd 75071 214-544-2658
Bob Lovelady, head sch Fax 542-5056
North Texas Christian Academy 100/PK-12
3201 N Central Expy 75071 214-544-1794

Mc Lean, Gray, Pop. 771
McLean ISD 200/PK-12
PO Box 90 79057 806-779-2571
Oscar Muniz, supt. Fax 779-2248
www.mcleanisd.com
McLean S 200/PK-12
PO Box 90 79057 806-779-2671
Raymond Glass, prin. Fax 779-2248

Mc Leod, Cass
Mc Leod ISD 400/PK-12
PO Box 350 75565 903-796-7181
Cathy May, supt. Fax 796-8443
www.mcleodisd.net
Mc Leod HS 100/9-12
PO Box 350 75565 903-796-7181
Jim Spurlin, prin. Fax 796-8443
Mc Leod MS 100/6-8
PO Box 350 75565 903-796-7181
Jim Spurlin, prin. Fax 796-8443

Madisonville, Madison, Pop. 4,327
Madisonville Consolidated ISD 2,300/PK-12
PO Box 879 77864 936-348-2797
Keith Smith, supt. Fax 348-2751
www.madisonvillecisd.org
Madisonville HS 600/9-12
PO Box 879 77864 936-348-2721
Heath Brown, prin. Fax 348-5753
Madisonville JHS 500/6-8
PO Box 819 77864 936-348-3587
Dr. Chad Moorhead, prin. Fax 348-5603

Magnolia, Montgomery, Pop. 1,381
Magnolia ISD 12,100/PK-12
PO Box 88 77353 281-356-3571
Dr. Todd Stephens Ph.D., supt. Fax 356-1328
www.magnoliaisd.org
Alpha Academy 100/Alt
PO Box 329 77353 281-252-2265
Dean Frederick, prin. Fax 252-2268
Bear Branch JHS 900/7-8
PO Box 606 77353 281-356-6088
Ben King Ed.D., prin. Fax 252-2060
Magnolia HS 1,700/9-12
PO Box 428 77353 281-356-3572
Mike Metz, prin. Fax 252-2092
Magnolia JHS 1,000/7-8
PO Box 476 77353 281-356-1327
David Slater, prin. Fax 252-2125
Magnolia West HS 1,800/9-12
PO Box 426 77353 281-252-2550
Brandon Garza Ed.D., prin. Fax 252-2560

Malakoff, Henderson, Pop. 2,275
Cross Roads ISD 600/PK-12
14434 FM 59 75148 903-489-2001
Richard Tedder, supt. Fax 489-2527
www.crossroadsisd.org
Cross Roads HS 200/9-12
14434 FM 59 75148 903-489-1275
John Miller, prin. Fax 489-0054
Cross Roads JHS 200/6-8
14434 FM 59 75148 903-489-2667
Julie Koepp, prin. Fax 489-3840

Malakoff ISD 1,300/PK-12
1308 FM 3062 75148 903-489-1152
Randy Perry, supt. Fax 489-2566
www.malakoffisd.org/
Malakoff Alternative Program 50/Alt
1209 W Royall Blvd 75148 903-489-4132
Danielle Copeland, prin. Fax 489-3239
Malakoff HS 400/9-12
15201 FM 3062 75148 903-489-1527
Martin Brumit, prin. Fax 489-0971
Malakoff MS 300/6-8
106 N Cedar St 75148 903-489-0264
Quintin Watkins, prin. Fax 489-1812

Manor, Travis, Pop. 4,931
Manor ISD 8,600/PK-12
10335 US Highway 290 E 78653 512-278-4000
Royce Avery, supt. Fax 278-4017
www.manorisd.net
Manor Excel Academy 100/Alt
600 E Parsons St 78653 512-278-4075
Dayna Anthony-Swain, prin. Fax 278-4859
Manor HS 1,600/9-12
12700 Gregg Manor Rd 78653 512-278-4800
Dr. Keith Brooks, prin. Fax 278-4803
Manor MS 900/6-8
12900 Gregg Manor Rd 78653 512-278-4600
Davin Vogler, prin. Fax 278-4285
Manor New Tech HS 400/9-12
10323 US Highway 290 E 78653 512-278-4875
Bobby Garcia, prin. Fax 278-4880
Other Schools – See Austin

Mansfield, Tarrant, Pop. 55,102
Mansfield ISD 30,800/PK-12
605 E Broad St 76063 817-299-6300
Dr. Jim Vaszauskas, supt. Fax 473-5465
www.mansfieldisd.org
Barber Career Tech Academy Vo/Tech
1120 W Debbie Ln 76063 682-314-1600
Catherine Hudgins, prin. Fax 453-6840
Jobe MS 800/7-8
2491 Gertie Barrett Rd 76063 682-314-4400
Elizabeth Hostin, prin. Fax 561-3899
Jones MS 1,000/7-8
4500 E Broad St 76063 682-314-4600
Travis Moore, prin. Fax 453-7380
Lake Ridge HS 9-12
101 N Day Miar Rd 76063 682-314-0400
Dr. Vonda Nunley, prin. Fax 548-2110
Legacy HS 1,900/9-12
1263 N Main St 76063 682-314-0600
Dr. Shelly Butler, prin. Fax 453-7653
Mansfield Frontier HS 200/9-12
1120 W Debbie Ln 76063 682-314-1600
Catherine Hudgins, prin. Fax 453-6840
Mansfield HS 2,300/9-12
3001 E Broad St 76063 682-314-0100
Jennifer Young, prin. Fax 473-5424
Phoenix Academy 100/Alt
902 E Broad St 76063 682-314-1700
Regenia Crane, prin. Fax 473-5477
Wester MS 900/7-8
1520 N Walnut Creek Dr 76063 817-314-1800
Jennifer Powers, prin. Fax 453-7213
Worley MS 900/7-8
500 Pleasant Ridge Dr 76063 682-314-5100
Dr. Julia McMains, prin. Fax 473-5623
Other Schools – See Arlington

Manvel, Brazoria, Pop. 5,107
Alvin ISD
Supt. — See Alvin
Manvel HS 2,500/9-12
19601 Highway 6 77578 281-245-2232
Dr. Roberto Martinez, prin. Fax 245-2268
Manvel JHS 6-8
7302 McCoy Rd 77578 281-245-3700
Raymond Root, prin. Fax 692-9078
Rodeo Palms JHS 900/6-8
101 Palm Desert Dr 77578 281-245-2078
Aeniqua Flowers, prin. Fax 489-8169

Marathon, Brewster, Pop. 427
Marathon ISD 50/PK-12
PO Box 416 79842 432-386-4431
Dr. Guadalupe Singh, supt. Fax 386-4395
www.marathonisd.net
Marathon S 50/PK-12
PO Box 416 79842 432-386-4431
Dr. Guadalupe Singh, admin. Fax 386-4395

Marble Falls, Burnet, Pop. 5,987
Marble Falls ISD 4,000/PK-12
1800 Colt Cir 78654 830-693-4357
Dr. Chris Allen, supt. Fax 693-5685
www.marblefallsisd.org
Falls Career HS Vo/Tech
1800 Colt Cir 78654 830-798-3621
Peggy Little, admin. Fax 798-3636
Marble Falls HS 1,100/9-12
2101 Mustang Dr 78654 830-693-4375
Manuel Lunoff, prin. Fax 693-6079
Marble Falls MS 900/6-8
1511 Pony Dr 78654 830-693-4439
Roger Barr, prin. Fax 693-7788

Faith Academy of Marble Falls 200/K-12
PO Box 1240 78654 830-798-1333
Joseph Rispoli, admin. Fax 798-1332
Living Word Academy 50/1-12
918 2nd St 78654 – Robert Hill, prin. 830-693-3339

Marfa, Presidio, Pop. 1,967
Marfa ISD 300/PK-12
PO Box T 79843 432-729-5500
Oscar Aguero, supt. Fax 729-4310
marfaisd.org
Marfa JSHS 200/6-12
PO Box T 79843 432-729-5500
Amy White, prin. Fax 729-4053

Marion, Guadalupe, Pop. 1,060
Marion ISD 1,300/PK-12
PO Box 189 78124 830-914-2803
Kelly Walters, supt. Fax 420-3268
www.marionisd.net
Marion HS 400/9-12
PO Box 189 78124 830-914-2803
Elizardo Hernandez, prin. Fax 420-3639
Marion MS 300/6-8
PO Box 189 78124 830-914-2803
Jon Lindholm, prin. Fax 420-3206

Marlin, Falls, Pop. 5,913
Marlin ISD 1,000/PK-12
130 Coleman St 76661 254-883-3585
Michael Seabolt, supt. Fax 883-6612
www.marlinisd.org
Marlin HS 200/9-12
1400 Capps St 76661 254-883-2394
Remy Godfrey, prin. Fax 883-3470
Marlin MS 200/6-8
678 Success Dr 76661 254-883-9241
Patti Ward, prin. Fax 883-2839

Marshall, Harrison, Pop. 23,237
Marshall ISD 5,500/PK-12
1305 E Pinecrest Dr 75670 903-927-8700
Dr. Jerry Gibson, supt. Fax 935-0203
www.marshallisd.com
Marshall HS 1,400/9-12
1900 Maverick Dr 75670 903-927-8800
Katina Brown, prin. Fax 938-7052
Marshall JHS 800/7-8
700 W Houston St 75670 903-927-8830
Jason Black, prin. Fax 927-8837

East Texas Baptist University Post-Sec.
1 Tiger Dr 75670 903-935-7963
Texas State Technical College Post-Sec.
2650 E End Blvd S 75672 903-935-1010
Wiley College Post-Sec.
711 Wiley Ave 75670 903-927-3300

Mart, McLennan, Pop. 2,183
Mart ISD 500/PK-12
700 E Navarro Ave 76664 254-876-2523
Leonard Williams, supt. Fax 876-3028
www.martisd.org
Mart HS 200/9-12
700 E Navarro Ave 76664 254-876-2574
Betsy Burnett, prin. Fax 876-2576
Mart MS 100/5-8
700 E Navarro Ave 76664 254-876-2762
Dr. Tawnya Nail, prin. Fax 876-2317

Mason, Mason, Pop. 2,094
Mason ISD 700/PK-12
PO Box 410 76856 325-347-1144
John Schumacher, supt. Fax 294-4412
www.masonisd.net
Mason HS 200/9-12
PO Box 410 76856 325-347-1122
Chris Habecker, prin. Fax 347-8247
Mason JHS 200/5-8
PO Box 410 76856 325-347-1122
Lauren Walch, prin. Fax 347-5461

Matador, Motley, Pop. 605
Motley County ISD 200/PK-12
PO Box 310 79244 806-347-2676
William Cochran, supt. Fax 347-2871
www.motleyco.org
Motley County S 200/PK-12
PO Box 310 79244 806-347-2676
Tim Hill, prin. Fax 347-2871

Mathis, San Patricio, Pop. 4,929
Mathis ISD 1,700/PK-12
PO Box 1179 78368 361-547-3378
Benny Hernandez, supt. Fax 547-4198
www.mathisisd.org
Mathis HS 400/9-12
PO Box 1179 78368 361-547-3322
Albert Arismendi, prin. Fax 547-4139
Mathis MS 400/6-8
PO Box 1179 78368 361-547-2381
Randy Tiemman, prin. Fax 547-4156

Maud, Bowie, Pop. 1,042
Maud ISD 500/PK-12
PO Box 1028 75567 903-585-2219
Charles Martin, supt. Fax 585-5451
www.maudisd.net
Maud S 500/PK-12
PO Box 1028 75567 903-585-2219
David Hedges, prin. Fax 585-5451

May, Brown
May ISD 300/PK-12
3400 E County Road 411 76857 254-259-2091
Mike Carter, supt. Fax 259-3514
www.mayisd.com
May JSHS 100/7-12
3400 E County Road 411 76857 254-259-2131
Steven Howard, prin. Fax 259-2706

Maypearl, Ellis, Pop. 920
Maypearl ISD 1,100/PK-12
PO Box 40 76064 972-435-1000
Ritchie Bowling M.Ed., supt. Fax 435-1001
www.maypearlisd.org
Maypearl HS 300/9-12
PO Box 40 76064 972-435-1020
Lesley Austin, prin. Fax 435-1021
Maypearl JHS 200/7-8
PO Box 40 76064 972-435-1015
Dennis Mitchell, prin. Fax 435-1016

Meadow, Terry, Pop. 593
Meadow ISD 300/PK-12
604 4th St 79345 806-539-2246
Darrian Dover, supt. Fax 539-2529
www.meadowisd.net
Meadow HS 100/6-12
604 4th St 79345 806-539-2222
Steve Reynolds, prin. Fax 539-2334

Medina, Bandera, Pop. 3,931
Medina ISD 100/PK-12
PO Box 1470 78055 830-589-2855
Penny White, supt. Fax 589-7150
www.medinaisd.org
Medina S 100/PK-12
PO Box 1470 78055 830-589-2851
Dr. Sarah McCrae, prin. Fax 589-7150

Melissa, Collin, Pop. 4,615
Melissa ISD 1,800/PK-12
1904 Cooper St 75454 972-837-2411
Keith Murphy, supt. Fax 837-4233
www.melissaisd.org
Melissa HS 500/9-12
3150 Cardinal Dr 75454 972-837-4216
Kenneth Wooten, prin. Fax 837-4381
Melissa MS 300/6-8
2950 Cardinal Dr 75454 972-837-4355
Jim Miller, prin. Fax 837-4497

Memphis, Hall, Pop. 2,281
Memphis ISD 500/PK-12
PO Box 460 79245 806-259-5900
Kent Lemons, supt. Fax 259-2515
www.memphisisd.net
Memphis HS 200/9-12
PO Box 460 79245 806-259-5910
Dick Hutcherson, prin. Fax 259-3026
Memphis MS 100/6-8
PO Box 460 79245 806-259-5920
Kennith Hardin, prin. Fax 259-2051

Menard, Menard, Pop. 1,468
Menard ISD 300/PK-12
PO Box 729 76859 325-396-2404
amy bannowsky, supt. Fax 396-2143
www.menardisd.net
Menard HS 100/9-12
PO Box 729 76859 325-396-2513
Joe Jones, prin. Fax 396-2053

Menard JHS 100/6-8
PO Box 729 76859 325-396-2348
Cordelia Kothmann, admin. Fax 396-2761

Mercedes, Hidalgo, Pop. 15,537
Mercedes ISD 5,300/PK-12
PO Box 419 78570 956-514-2000
Dr. Daniel Trevino, supt. Fax 514-2033
www.misdtx.net
Chacon MS 900/6-8
PO Box 419 78570 956-514-2200
Orlando Rodriguez, prin. Fax 514-2212
Harrell MS 6-8
PO Box 419 78570 956-825-5140
Javier De Anda, prin. Fax 514-2323
Mercedes Academic Academy 100/Alt
PO Box 419 78570 956-825-5076
Heather Garza, dir. Fax 514-2171
Mercedes Early College HS 300/9-12
PO Box 419 78570 956-825-5180
Jeanne Venecia, prin. Fax 514-2175
Mercedes HS 1,000/9-12
PO Box 419 78570 956-514-2100
Patricia Masso, prin. Fax 514-2111

South Texas ISD 3,400/7-12
100 Med High Dr 78570 956-565-2454
Marla Guerra Ed.D., supt. Fax 565-9129
www.stisd.net
Science Academy of South Texas 800/9-12
900 Med High Dr 78570 956-565-4620
Irma Castillo, prin. Fax 565-9112
South Texas HS for Health Professions 800/9-12
700 Med High Dr 78570 956-565-2237
Barbara Heater, prin. Fax 565-4039
Other Schools – See Edinburg, Olmito, San Benito

Meridian, Bosque, Pop. 1,479
Meridian ISD 500/PK-12
PO Box 349 76665 254-435-2081
Dr. John Horak, supt. Fax 435-2025
www.meridianisd.org
Meridian JSHS 300/6-12
PO Box 349 76665 254-435-2723
Paul Booth, prin. Fax 435-2199

Merit, Hunt
Bland ISD 600/PK-12
PO Box 216 75458 903-776-2239
Rick Tidwell, supt. Fax 776-2240
www.blandisd.net
Bland HS 200/9-12
PO Box 216 75458 903-776-2239
Dustin Evans, prin. Fax 776-2426
Bland MS 100/6-8
PO Box 216 75458 903-776-2239
Jason Hammack, prin. Fax 527-5491

Merkel, Taylor, Pop. 2,564
Merkel ISD 800/PK-12
PO Box 430 79536 325-928-5813
Bryan Allen, supt. Fax 928-3910
www.merkel.esc14.net
Merkel HS 300/9-12
PO Box 430 79536 325-928-4667
Casey Hodges, prin. Fax 928-4684
Merkel MS 200/6-8
PO Box 430 79536 325-928-5511
Casey Stone, prin. Fax 928-3138

Mertzon, Irion, Pop. 768
Irion County ISD 300/PK-12
PO Box 469 76941 325-835-6111
Billy Barnett, supt. Fax 835-2017
www.irion-isd.org
Irion County MSHS 200/7-12
PO Box 469 76941 325-835-2881
Shannon Chapman, prin. Fax 835-2298

Mesquite, Dallas, Pop. 137,317
Mesquite ISD 39,500/PK-12
405 E Davis St 75149 972-288-6411
Dr. David Vroonland, supt. Fax 882-7787
www.mesquiteisd.org
Agnew MS 800/7-8
729 Wilkinson Dr 75149 972-882-5750
Donna Gallegos, prin. Fax 882-5760
Berry MS 900/6-8
2675 Bear Dr 75181 972-882-5850
Gerald Sarpy, prin. Fax 882-5888
Horn HS 2,200/9-12
3300 E Cartwright Rd 75181 972-882-5200
Bruce Perkins, prin. Fax 882-5291
Kimbrough MS 900/7-8
3900 N Galloway Ave 75150 972-882-5900
Chris Brott, prin. Fax 882-5942
McDonald MS 1,000/7-8
2930 N Town East Blvd 75150 972-882-5700
Debra Bassinger, prin. Fax 882-5710
Mesquite Academy 200/Alt
2704 Motley Dr 75150 972-882-7570
Connie Boone, prin. Fax 882-7579
Mesquite HS 2,800/9-12
300 E Davis St 75149 972-882-7800
Kevin Samples, prin. Fax 882-7876
New MS 800/7-8
3700 S Belt Line Rd 75181 972-882-5600
Stacy Carpenter, prin. Fax 882-5620
North Mesquite HS 2,600/9-12
18201 Lyndon B Johnson Fwy 75150 972-882-7900
Douglas Barber, prin. Fax 882-7908
Poteet HS 1,700/9-12
3300 Poteet Dr 75150 972-882-5300
Taylor Morris, prin. Fax 882-5353
Terry MS 900/6-8
2351 Edwards Church Rd 75181 972-882-5650
Danny Taylor, prin. Fax 882-5660
Vanston MS 800/7-8
3230 Karla Dr 75150 972-882-5801
Emilio Duran, prin. Fax 882-5848
West Mesquite HS 2,000/9-12
2500 Memorial Blvd 75149 972-882-7600
Alesia Austin, prin. Fax 882-7611
Wilkinson MS 900/6-8
2100 Crest Park Dr 75149 972-882-5950
Leslie Feinglas, prin. Fax 882-5988

Carrington College Post-Sec.
3733 W Emporium Cir 75150 972-682-2800
Dallas Christian S 600/PK-12
1515 Republic Pkwy 75150 972-270-5495
Eastfield College Post-Sec.
3737 Motley Dr 75150 214-860-7100
Hands On Therapy School Post-Sec.
1804 N Galloway Ave 75149 972-285-6133
Metroplex Beauty School Post-Sec.
519 N Galloway Ave 75149 972-288-5485

Mexia, Limestone, Pop. 7,378
Mexia ISD 1,700/PK-12
PO Box 2000 76667 254-562-4000
Dr. Sharon Ross, supt. Fax 562-4007
mexia.schoolfusion.us
Mexia HS 500/9-12
PO Box 2000 76667 254-562-4010
Larry Adair, prin. Fax 562-2142
Mexia JHS 400/6-8
PO Box 2000 76667 254-562-4020
Thurman Brown, prin. Fax 562-5053
Mexia S of Choice 50/Alt
PO Box 2000 76667 254-562-4023
John Schaefer, prin. Fax 562-4024

Miami, Roberts, Pop. 592
Miami ISD 200/PK-12
PO Box 368 79059 806-868-3971
Donna Gill, supt. Fax 868-3171
www.miamiisd.net
Miami S 200/PK-12
PO Box 368 79059 806-868-3971
Randall Hall, prin. Fax 868-3171

Midland, Midland, Pop. 109,776
Greenwood ISD 1,800/PK-12
2700 FM 1379 79706 432-685-7800
Ariel Elliott, supt. Fax 685-7804
www.greenwood.esc18.net
Brooks MS 500/5-8
2700 FM 1379 79706 432-683-6461
John-Paul Huber, prin. Fax 685-7804
Greenwood HS 500/9-12
2700 FM 1379 79706 432-253-6686
Stacy Jones, prin. Fax 685-7814

Midland ISD 23,400/PK-12
615 W Missouri Ave 79701 432-240-1000
Rod Schroder, supt. Fax 689-1976
www.midlandisd.net
Abell JHS 900/7-8
3201 Heritage Blvd 79707 432-689-6200
Jennifer Seybert, prin. Fax 689-6217
Advanced Technology Center Vo/Tech
3200 W Cuthbert Ave 79701 432-681-6312
Kim Evans, dir.
Alamo JHS 800/7-8
3800 Storey Ave 79703 432-689-1700
Leann Dumas, prin. Fax 689-1712
Coleman HS 100/Alt
1600 E Golf Course Rd 79701 432-689-5000
David Moore, prin. Fax 689-5016
Early College at Midland College 300/9-12
3600 N Garfield St 79705 432-685-4641
Renee Aldrin, prin. Fax 685-4669
Goddard JHS 1,000/7-8
2500 Haynes Dr 79705 432-689-1300
Shelly King, prin. Fax 689-1321
Lee Freshman HS 800/9-9
1400 E Oak Ave 79705 432-689-1250
Bobby Stults, prin. Fax 689-1253
Lee SHS 2,000/10-12
3500 Neely Ave 79707 432-689-1600
Stan VanHoozer, prin. Fax 689-1647
Midland Freshman HS 800/9-9
100 E Gist Ave 79701 432-689-1200
Shannon Torres, prin. Fax 689-1209
Midland SHS 2,000/10-12
906 W Illinois Ave 79701 432-689-1100
Carlin Grammer, prin. Fax 689-1144
San Jacinto JHS 700/7-8
1400 N N St 79701 432-689-1350
Deborah Kendricks, prin. Fax 689-1385

Midland Christian S 1,200/PK-12
2001 Culver Dr 79705 432-694-1661
Midland College Post-Sec.
3600 N Garfield St 79705 432-685-4500
Trinity S of Midland 500/PK-12
3500 W Wadley Ave 79707 432-697-3281
Rev. Walter Prehn Ph.D., head sch Fax 697-7403

Midlothian, Ellis, Pop. 17,760
Midlothian ISD 7,700/PK-12
100 Walter Stephenson Rd 76065 972-775-8296
Dr. Lane Ledbetter, supt. Fax 775-1757
www.misd.gs
Midlothian Heritage HS 9-12
4000 FM 1387 76065 972-775-6509
Krista Tipton, prin. Fax 775-7841
Midlothian HS 2,300/9-12
923 S 9th St 76065 972-775-8237
Dr. Al Hemmle, prin. Fax 775-3178
Seale MS 900/6-8
700 George Hopper Rd 76065 972-775-6145
Coy Tipton, prin. Fax 775-1502
Walnut Grove MS 1,000/6-8
990 N Walnut Grove Rd 76065 972-775-5355
Brian Blackwell, prin. Fax 775-8127

Milano, Milam, Pop. 425
Milano ISD 400/PK-12
PO Box 145 76556 512-455-2533
Robert Westbrook, supt. Fax 455-9311
www.milanoisd.net
Milano HS 200/9-12
PO Box 145 76556 512-455-9333
Tracy Brewer, prin. Fax 455-9336
Milano JHS 100/6-8
PO Box 145 76556 512-455-6701
Tracy Brewer, prin. Fax 455-9186

Miles, Runnels, Pop. 823
Miles ISD 400/PK-12
PO Box 308 76861 325-468-2861
Robert Gibson, supt. Fax 468-2179
www.milesisd.net
Miles JSHS 200/7-12
PO Box 308 76861 325-468-2861
Robin Graves, prin. Fax 468-2179

Milford, Ellis, Pop. 717
Milford ISD 200/PK-12
PO Box 545 76670 972-493-2911
Don Clingenpeel, supt. Fax 493-2429
www.milfordisd.org
Milford S 200/PK-12
PO Box 545 76670 972-493-2921
Don Clingenpeel, prin. Fax 493-4600

Millsap, Parker, Pop. 400
Millsap ISD 800/PK-12
201 E Brazos St 76066 940-682-3100
Deann Lee, supt. Fax 682-4476
www.millsapisd.net
Millsap HS 200/9-12
600 Bulldog Dr 76066 940-682-4994
Tammy Addison, prin. Fax 682-4035
Millsap MS 200/6-8
301 E Brazos St 76066 940-682-4994
Jeff Clark, prin. Fax 682-4476

Mineola, Wood, Pop. 4,457
Mineola ISD 1,600/PK-12
1000 W Loop 564 75773 903-569-2448
Kim Tunnell, supt. Fax 569-5155
www.mineolaisd.net
Mineola HS 400/9-12
1000 W Loop 564 75773 903-569-3000
David Sauer, prin. Fax 569-1930
Mineola MS 400/6-8
1000 W Loop 564 75773 903-569-5338
Mike Sorenson, prin. Fax 569-5339

Mineral Wells, Palo Pinto, Pop. 16,580
Mineral Wells ISD 3,300/PK-12
906 SW 5th Ave 76067 940-325-6404
John Kuhn, supt. Fax 325-6378
www.mwisd.net/
Mineral Wells Academy 50/Alt
3810 Ram Blvd 76067 940-325-3033
Jeff Smith, admin. Fax 325-6044
Mineral Wells HS 900/9-12
3801 Ram Blvd 76067 940-325-4408
Jon Almeida, prin. Fax 325-7623
Mineral Wells JHS 500/7-8
1301 SE 14th Ave 76067 940-325-0711
Wendell Barker, prin. Fax 328-0450

Community Christian S 100/PK-12
2501 Garrett Morris Pkwy 76067 940-328-1333
Doug Jefferson, admin. Fax 328-1277

Mission, Hidalgo, Pop. 76,804
La Joya ISD
Supt. — See La Joya
Chavez MS 900/6-8
78 Showers Rd 78572 956-580-6182
Daniel Villarreal, prin. Fax 580-6169
Garcia MS 800/6-8
933 Paula St, 956-584-0800
Santana Galven, prin. Fax 584-0817
Juarez-Lincoln HS 2,300/9-12
7801 W Mile 7 Rd, 956-519-4150
Maria I. Solis, prin. Fax 519-4160
LaJoya ISD East Academy Alt
2916 W Mile 3 Rd, 956-519-5746
Ricardo Estrada, prin. Fax 519-5752
Memorial MS 700/6-8
2610 N Moorefield Rd, 956-580-6087
Rolando Rios, prin. Fax 580-6084
Richards MS 900/6-8
7005 Ann Richards Rd 78572 956-519-5710
Thomas Ocana, prin. Fax 519-5726
Salinas MS 800/6-8
6101 N Bentsen Palm Dr, 956-584-6355
Dr. Antonio Uresti, prin. Fax 584-6356

Mission Consolidated ISD 15,200/PK-12
1201 Bryce Dr 78572 956-323-5505
Dr. Ricardo Lopez, supt. Fax 323-5634
www.mcisd.net
Mission Collegiate HS 200/9-12
1201 Bryce Dr 78572 956-323-6120
Orlando Farias, prin.
Mission HS 1,900/9-12
1201 Bryce Dr 78572 956-323-5700
Edilberto Flores, prin. Fax 323-5890
Mission JHS 900/6-8
1201 Bryce Dr 78572 956-323-3300
Ada Castillo, prin. Fax 323-3338
Roosevelt Alternative S 50/Alt
1201 Bryce Dr 78572 956-323-3900
Eduardo Alaniz, prin. Fax 323-3925
Veterans Memorial HS 1,800/9-12
1201 Bryce Dr 78572 956-323-3000
Fidel Garza, prin. Fax 323-3280
White JHS 900/6-8
1201 Bryce Dr 78572 956-323-3600
Brenda Betancourt, prin. Fax 323-3632

Other Schools – See Alton, Palmhurst

Sharyland ISD 10,300/PK-12
1106 N Shary Rd 78572 956-580-5200
Dr. Robert O'Connor, supt. Fax 585-2972
www.sharylandisd.org
Gray JHS 800/7-8
1106 N Shary Rd 78572 956-580-5333
Lori Ann Garza, prin. Fax 580-5346
Sharyland Advanced Academic Academy 9-12
1106 N Shary Rd 78572 956-584-6467
Ivan Karr, prin.
Sharyland HS 3,300/9-12
1106 N Shary Rd 78572 956-580-5300
Carolyn Mendiola, prin. Fax 580-5311
Sharyland Pioneer HS 9-12
1106 N Shary Rd 78572 956-271-1600
James Heath, prin.
Other Schools – See Mc Allen

Juan Diego Academy 50/9-12
PO Box 3888 78573 956-583-2752
Bob Schmidt, prin. Fax 583-3782

Missouri City, Fort Bend, Pop. 65,862
Fort Bend ISD
Supt. — See Sugar Land
Baines MS 1,500/6-8
9000 Sienna Ranch Rd 77459 281-634-6870
Jennifer Roberts, prin. Fax 634-6880
Elkins HS 2,000/9-12
7007 Knights Ct 77459 281-634-2600
Deidra Lyons-Lewis, prin. Fax 634-2674
Hightower HS 2,300/9-12
3333 Hurricane Ln 77459 281-634-5240
Fred Richardson, prin. Fax 634-5333
Lake Olympia MS 1,200/6-8
3100 Lake Olympia Pkwy 77459 281-634-3520
Deirdre Holloway, prin. Fax 634-3549
Marshall HS 1,300/9-12
1220 Buffalo Run 77489 281-634-6630
Alfred Holland, prin. Fax 634-6650
Missouri City MS 1,200/6-8
202 Martin Ln 77489 281-634-3440
Jerrie Kammerman, prin. Fax 634-3473
Progressive HS Alt
1555 Independence Blvd 77489 281-634-2900
Dr. Cory Collins, prin. Fax 634-2913
Quail Valley MS 1,300/6-8
3019 FM 1092 Rd 77459 281-634-3600
Karissa Ogle, prin. Fax 634-3632
Ridge Point HS 1,900/9-12
500 Waters Lake Blvd 77459 281-327-5200
Leonard Brogan, prin. Fax 327-5201

Monahans, Ward, Pop. 6,896
Monahans-Wickett-Pyote ISD 2,200/PK-12
606 S Betty Ave 79756 432-943-6711
Kellye Riley, supt. Fax 943-2307
www.mwpisd.esc18.net
Monahans Education Center 50/Alt
813 S Alice Ave 79756 432-943-2019
Chad Smith, prin. Fax 943-2593
Monahans HS 500/9-12
809 S Betty Ave 79756 432-943-2519
Patty Dominguez, prin. Fax 943-3327
Walker JHS 300/7-8
800 S Faye Ave 79756 432-943-4622
Mayna Benavides, prin. Fax 943-3723

Mont Belvieu, Chambers, Pop. 3,784
Barbers Hill ISD 4,000/PK-12
PO Box 1108 77580 281-576-2221
Greg Poole, supt. Fax 576-3410
www.bhisd.net/
Barbers Hill HS 1,400/9-12
PO Box 1108 77580 281-576-2221
Rick Kana, prin. Fax 576-3356
Barbers Hill MS North 800/6-8
PO Box 1108 77580 281-576-2221
Lance Murphy, prin. Fax 576-3353
Eagle Positive Intervention Center Alt
PO Box 1108 77580 281-576-2221
Daniel Andrews, prin. Fax 576-3422
Other Schools – See Baytown

Monte Alto, Hidalgo, Pop. 1,914
Monte Alto ISD 1,000/PK-12
25149 1st St 78538 956-262-1381
Olivia Almanza, supt. Fax 262-5535
www.montealtoisd.org
Monte Alto HS 200/9-12
25149 1st St 78538 956-262-1381
Sabrina Franco, admin. Fax 262-5535
Monte Alto MS 200/6-8
25149 1st St 78538 956-262-1374
JImmy Padilla, prin. Fax 262-1377

Montgomery, Montgomery, Pop. 621
Montgomery ISD 7,500/PK-12
PO Box 1475 77356 936-276-2000
Dr. Beau Rees, supt. Fax 276-2101
www.misd.org
Montgomery HS 2,200/9-12
22825 Highway 105 W 77356 936-276-3000
Phil Eaton, prin. Fax 276-3001
Montgomery JHS 1,300/7-8
19000 Stewart Creek Rd 77356 936-276-3300
Angie Chapman, prin. Fax 276-3301

Moody, McLennan, Pop. 1,359
Moody ISD 700/PK-12
12084A S Lone Star Pkwy 76557 254-853-2172
Gary Martel, supt. Fax 853-2886
www.moodyisd.org
Moody HS 200/9-12
11862 S Lone Star Pkwy 76557 254-853-3622
Andrew Miller, prin. Fax 853-3822
Moody MS 200/5-8
107 Coralee Ln 76557 254-853-2182
Eric Cox, prin. Fax 853-2886

Moran, Shackelford, Pop. 270
Moran ISD 100/PK-12
PO Box 98 76464 325-945-3101
Danny Freeman, supt. Fax 945-2741
www.moran.esc14.net
Moran S 100/PK-12
PO Box 98 76464 325-945-3101
Danny Freeman, prin. Fax 945-2741

Morgan, Bosque, Pop. 480
Morgan ISD 100/PK-12
PO Box 300 76671 254-635-2311
John Bryant, supt. Fax 635-2224
www.morganisd.org
Morgan S 100/PK-12
PO Box 300 76671 254-635-2311
Juan Ramirez, prin. Fax 635-2224

Morton, Cochran, Pop. 1,996
Morton ISD 400/PK-12
500 Champion Dr 79346 806-266-5505
Vicki Rice, supt. Fax 266-5449
www.mortonisd.net/
Morton HS 100/9-12
500 Champion Dr 79346 806-266-5505
Glen Smith, prin. Fax 266-5780
Morton JHS 100/6-8
500 Champion Dr 79346 806-266-5505
Glen Smith, prin. Fax 266-5739

Moulton, Lavaca, Pop. 877
Moulton ISD 300/K-12
PO Box C 77975 361-596-4609
Todd Grandjean, supt. Fax 596-7578
www.moultonisd.net
Moulton JSHS 100/7-12
PO Box C 77975 361-596-4691
Jamie Dornak, prin. Fax 596-7119

Mount Calm, Hill, Pop. 312
Mount Calm ISD 100/PK-12
PO Box 105 76673 254-993-2611
Barbara Lane, supt. Fax 993-1022
www.mcisd1.org
Mount Calm S 100/PK-12
PO Box 105 76673 254-993-2611
Pamela Taylor, prin. Fax 993-1022

Mount Enterprise, Rusk, Pop. 445
Mount Enterprise ISD 400/PK-12
301 NW 3rd St 75681 903-822-3721
Byron Jordan, supt. Fax 822-3633
www.meisd.esc7.net
Mount Enterprise JSHS 200/6-12
301 NW 3rd St 75681 903-822-3721
Chance Mays, prin. Fax 822-3633

Mount Pleasant, Titus, Pop. 15,466
Chapel Hill ISD 1,000/PK-12
1069 County Road 4660 75455 903-572-8096
Marc Levesque, supt. Fax 572-1086
www.chisddevils.com
Chapel Hill HS 300/9-12
1069 County Road 4660 75455 903-572-1086
Marcus Ysasi, prin. Fax 572-3850
Chapel Hill JHS 200/6-8
1069 County Road 4660 75455 903-572-1086
Mike Clifton, prin. Fax 572-9747

Mount Pleasant ISD 5,400/PK-12
PO Box 1117 75456 903-575-2000
Judd Marshall, supt. Fax 575-2014
www.mpisd.net
Mount Pleasant HS 1,500/9-12
PO Box 1117 75456 903-575-2020
Dustin Cook, prin. Fax 575-2036
Mount Pleasant JHS 700/7-8
PO Box 1117 75456 903-575-2110
Kelli Glenn, prin. Fax 575-2117

Northeast Texas Community College Post-Sec.
PO Box 1307 75456 903-434-8100

Mount Vernon, Franklin, Pop. 2,608
Mount Vernon ISD 1,600/PK-12
501 Texas Highway 37 75457 903-537-2546
Gregg Weiss, supt. Fax 537-4784
www.mtvernonisd.net/pages/MVISD
Mount Vernon HS 400/9-12
501 Texas Highway 37 75457 903-537-3700
Barry Baker, prin. Fax 537-2536
Mount Vernon JHS 200/7-8
501 Texas Highway 37 75457 903-537-2267
Craig Watson, prin. Fax 537-3601

Muenster, Cooke, Pop. 1,534
Muenster ISD 500/PK-12
PO Box 608 76252 940-759-2281
Steven Self, supt. Fax 759-5200
www.muensterisd.net
Muenster HS 200/7-12
PO Box 608 76252 940-759-2281
John York, prin. Fax 759-4614

Sacred Heart S 200/PK-12
153 E 6th St 76252 940-759-2511
Elizabeth Bartush, prin. Fax 759-4422

Muleshoe, Bailey, Pop. 5,137
Muleshoe ISD 1,500/PK-12
514 W Avenue G 79347 806-272-7400
Dr. R.L. Richards, supt. Fax 272-4120
www.muleshoeisd.net
Muleshoe HS 300/9-12
514 W Avenue G 79347 806-272-7303
Steve Myatt, prin. Fax 272-7574
Watson JHS 300/6-8
514 W Avenue G 79347 806-272-7349
Melvin Nusser, prin. Fax 272-4983

Mullin, Mills, Pop. 179
Mullin ISD 100/PK-12
PO Box 128 76864 325-985-3374
Kristi Mickelson, supt. Fax 985-3915
www.mullinisd.net
Mullin HS 50/7-12
PO Box 128 76864 325-985-3374
Joe Branham, admin. Fax 985-3372

Mumford, Robertson
Mumford ISD 600/PK-12
9755 FM 50, 979-279-3678
Pete Bienski, supt. Fax 279-5044
www.mumford.k12.tx.us
Mumford JSHS 200/7-12
9755 FM 50, 979-279-3678
Pete Bienski, prin. Fax 279-5044

Munday, Knox, Pop. 1,285
Munday Consolidated ISD 400/PK-12
PO Box 300 76371 940-422-4241
Dr. Skip Casey, supt. Fax 422-5331
www.esc9.net/munday
Munday Secondary S 200/7-12
PO Box 300 76371 940-422-4321
John Berry, prin. Fax 422-5331

Murphy, Collin, Pop. 17,219
Plano ISD
Supt. — See Plano
McMillen HS 1,200/9-10
750 N Murphy Rd 75094 469-752-8600
Brian Lyons, prin. Fax 752-8601
Murphy MS 1,200/6-8
620 N Murphy Rd 75094 469-752-7000
Matthew Conrad, prin. Fax 752-7001

Nacogdoches, Nacogdoches, Pop. 32,466
Central Heights ISD 1,100/PK-12
10317 US Highway 259 75965 936-564-2681
Bryan Lee, supt. Fax 569-6889
www.centralhts.org
Central Heights HS 300/9-12
10317 US Highway 259 75965 936-552-3408
David Russell, prin. Fax 560-2016
Central Heights MS 300/6-8
10317 US Highway 259 75965 936-552-3441
Andrew Binford, prin. Fax 564-0177

Martinsville ISD 400/PK-12
12952 E State Highway 7 75961 936-564-3455
David Simmons, supt. Fax 569-0498
www.martinsvilleisd.com
Martinsville S 400/PK-12
12952 E State Highway 7 75961 936-564-3455
Monty Pepper, prin. Fax 569-0498

Nacogdoches ISD 6,600/PK-12
PO Box 631521 75963 936-569-5000
Sandra Dowdy, supt. Fax 569-5797
www.nacisd.org
McMichael MS 800/6-8
PO Box 631521 75963 936-552-0519
Tim Mullican, prin. Fax 552-0523
Moses MS 600/6-8
PO Box 631521 75963 936-569-5001
Fletcher Wilson, prin. Fax 569-5031
Nacogdoches HS 1,600/9-12
PO Box 631521 75963 936-564-2466
Dr. Michael O'Guin, prin. Fax 560-8162
Rector Technical HS 100/Alt
PO Box 631521 75963 936-569-3175
Jerry Winfield, prin. Fax 569-5775

Regents Academy 100/PK-12
200 NE Stallings Dr 75961 936-559-7343
David Bryant, hdmstr.
Stephen F. Austin State University Post-Sec.
1936 North St 75965 936-468-3401

Natalia, Medina, Pop. 1,422
Natalia ISD 1,100/PK-12
PO Box 548 78059 830-663-4416
Dr. Hensley Cone, supt. Fax 663-4186
www.nataliaisd.net
Natalia HS 300/9-12
PO Box 548 78059 830-663-4417
Jane Harris, prin. Fax 663-6410
Natalia JHS 200/6-8
PO Box 548 78059 830-663-4027
Edgar Camacho, prin. Fax 663-2347

Navasota, Grimes, Pop. 6,996
Navasota ISD 3,100/PK-12
PO Box 511 77868 936-825-4200
Rory Gesch, supt. Fax 825-4297
www.navasotaisd.org
Bizzell Academy, PO Box 511 77868 50/Alt
Kristi Jones, prin. 936-825-4296
Navasota HS 700/9-12
PO Box 511 77868 936-825-4250
Derek Bowman, prin. Fax 825-4293
Navasota JHS 700/6-8
PO Box 511 77868 936-825-4225
Melody Hudspeth, prin. Fax 825-4260

Nazareth, Castro, Pop. 311
Nazareth ISD 200/PK-12
PO Box 189 79063 806-945-2231
Glen Waldo, supt. Fax 945-2431
www.nazarethisd.net/
Nazareth S 200/PK-12
PO Box 189 79063 806-945-2231
Jeanie Birkenfeld, prin. Fax 945-2431

Neches, Anderson
Neches ISD 400/PK-12
PO Box 310 75779 903-584-3311
Randy Snider, supt. Fax 584-3686
www.nechesisd.com
Other Schools – See Palestine

Nederland, Jefferson, Pop. 17,344
Nederland ISD 5,000/PK-12
220 N 17th St 77627 409-724-2391
Dr. Robin Perez, supt. Fax 724-4280
www.nederland.k12.tx.us
Alternative S Alt
220 N 17th St 77627 409-727-5241
Karen Bussell, prin. Fax 724-4236
Central MS 700/5-8
220 N 17th St 77627 409-727-5765
Charles Jehlen, prin. Fax 724-4275
Nederland HS 1,600/9-12
220 N 17th St 77627 409-727-2741
Dr. Steven Beagle, prin. Fax 726-2679
Wilson MS 800/5-8
220 N 17th St 77627 409-727-6224
Scott Clemmons, prin. Fax 726-2699

Faris Computer School Post-Sec.
1119 Kent Ave 77627 409-722-4072

Needville, Fort Bend, Pop. 2,792
Needville ISD 2,800/PK-12
PO Box 412 77461 979-793-4308
Curtis Rhodes, supt. Fax 793-3823
www.needvilleisd.com
Needville HS 800/9-12
PO Box 412 77461 979-793-4158
Steve Adamson, prin. Fax 793-5590
Needville JHS 500/7-8
PO Box 412 77461 979-793-4250
Karen Smart, prin. Fax 793-4575

Nevada, Collin, Pop. 815
Community ISD 1,700/PK-12
PO Box 400 75173 972-843-8400
Roosevelt Nivens, supt. Fax 843-8401
www.communityisd.org
Community HS 500/9-12
PO Box 400 75173 972-843-8414
Kenda Willingham, prin. Fax 843-8415
Edge MS 400/6-8
PO Box 400 75173 972-843-8411
David Girardi, prin. Fax 843-8412

Newark, Wise, Pop. 987

Victory in Christ Classical Luth Academy 50/PK-12
508 Main St 76071 817-489-5400
Ruth Rohloff, prin.

New Boston, Bowie, Pop. 4,450
New Boston ISD 1,400/PK-12
201 Rice St 75570 903-628-2521
Dr. Rose Mary Neshyba, supt. Fax 628-8990
www.nbschools.net
New Boston HS 400/9-12
1 W Lion Dr 75570 903-628-6551
Dr. Don Mathis, prin. Fax 628-3695
New Boston MS 300/6-8
1215 N State Highway 8 75570 903-628-6588
Denise Davis, prin. Fax 628-5132

New Braunfels, Comal, Pop. 57,097
Comal ISD 19,200/PK-12
1404 N Interstate 35 78130 830-221-2000
Andrew Kim, supt. Fax 221-2001
www.comalisd.org
Canyon HS 2,200/9-12
1510 N Interstate 35 78130 830-221-2400
Alison Smith, prin. Fax 221-2401
Canyon MS 1,000/6-8
2014 FM 1101 78130 830-221-2300
Fred Steubing, prin. Fax 221-2301
Church Hill MS 900/6-8
1275 N Business IH 35 78130 830-221-2800
Scott Hammond, prin. Fax 221-2801
Memorial Early College HS 100/9-12
1419 N Business IH 35 78130 830-221-2900
Nick Smith, prin. Fax 221-2901
Mountain Valley MS 700/6-8
1165 Sattler Rd 78132 830-885-1300
Kristy Castilleja, prin. Fax 885-1301
Other Schools – See Fischer, Spring Branch

New Braunfels ISD 8,000/PK-12
PO Box 311688 78131 830-643-5700
Randy Moczygemba, supt. Fax 643-5701
www.nbisd.org/
Learning Center 100/Alt
902 W San Antonio St 78130 830-627-6960
Jerry Clark, admin. Fax 627-6961
New Braunfels 9th Grade Center 700/9-9
659 S Guenther Ave 78130 830-643-5700
Jeff Lightsey, prin.
New Braunfels HS 1,700/10-12
2551 Loop 337 78130 830-627-6000
Kara Bock, prin. Fax 627-6001
New Braunfels MS 700/7-8
656 S Guenther Ave 78130 830-627-6270
Greg Hughes, prin. Fax 627-6271
Oakrun MS 1,000/6-8
415 Oak Run Pt 78132 830-627-6400
Shana Behling, prin. Fax 627-6401

New Braunfels Christian Academy 400/PK-12
220 FM 1863 78132 830-629-1821
Jill R. White M.Ed., head sch Fax 639-1880
St. John Paul II Catholic HS 100/9-12
6720 FM 482 78132 830-643-0802
Andrew Iliff, prin. Fax 643-0806

New Caney, Montgomery, Pop. 3,000
New Caney ISD 11,700/PK-12
21580 Loop 494 77357 281-577-8600
Kenn Franklin, supt. Fax 354-2639
www.newcaneyisd.org
Infinity Early College HS 100/9-12
22500 Eagle Dr 77357 281-577-8600
Rebecca Martin, prin.
Keefer Crossing MS 1,000/7-8
20350 FM 1485 Rd 77357 281-577-8840
Andy Pearson, prin. Fax 399-9859
Learning Center 50/Alt
20419 FM 1485 Rd 77357 281-577-2850
Jeremy Harris, prin. Fax 354-4137
New Caney HS 1,500/9-12
21650 Loop 494 77357 281-577-2800
David Loyacano, prin. Fax 354-0186
Other Schools – See Porter

Newcastle, Young, Pop. 582
Newcastle ISD 200/PK-12
PO Box 129 76372 940-846-3551
Ty Spitzer, supt. Fax 846-3452
www.newcastle-isd.net
Newcastle S 200/PK-12
PO Box 129 76372 940-846-3531
Ty Spitzer, admin. Fax 846-3452

New Deal, Lubbock, Pop. 782
New Deal ISD 700/PK-12
PO Box 280 79350 806-746-5833
Jimmy Noland, supt. Fax 746-5707
www.ndisd.net
New Deal HS 200/9-12
PO Box 250 79350 806-746-5933
Matt Reed, prin. Fax 746-5544
New Deal MS 200/5-8
PO Box 308 79350 806-746-6633
Rebecca Cooper, prin. Fax 746-5244

New Home, Lynn, Pop. 334
New Home ISD 300/PK-12
225 N Main St, 806-924-7543
Shane Fiedler, supt. Fax 924-7520
www.newhomeisd.org
New Home S 300/PK-12
225 N Main St, 806-924-7543
Koby Abney, prin. Fax 924-7520

New London, Rusk, Pop. 978
West Rusk ISD 1,000/PK-12
PO Box 168 75682 903-392-7850
Lawrence Coleman, supt. Fax 392-7866
www.westrusk.esc7.net
West Rusk HS 300/9-12
PO Box 168 75682 903-392-7854
Jake Jackson, prin. Fax 895-7866
West Rusk JHS 300/6-8
PO Box 168 75682 903-392-7855
Brian Keith, prin. Fax 392-7866

New Summerfield, Cherokee, Pop. 1,102
New Summerfield ISD 500/PK-12
PO Box 6 75780 903-726-3306
Dr. Brian Nichols, supt. Fax 726-3405
www.nsisd.sprnet.org
New Summerfield S 500/PK-12
PO Box 6 75780 903-726-3306
Josh Faucett, supt. Fax 726-3405

Newton, Newton, Pop. 2,458
Newton ISD 1,100/PK-12
720 Rusk St 75966 409-420-6600
Michelle Barrow, supt. Fax 379-5130
www.newtonisd.net
Newton HS 300/9-12
720 Rusk St 75966 409-420-6600
Tim Kenebrew, prin. Fax 379-3321
Newton MS 300/6-8
720 Rusk St 75966 409-420-6600
Judy Holleman, prin. Fax 379-5082

New Waverly, Walker, Pop. 1,019
New Waverly ISD 900/PK-12
355 Front St 77358 936-344-6751
Dr. Darol Hail, supt. Fax 344-2438
www.new-waverly.k12.tx.us
New Waverly HS 300/9-12
355 Front St 77358 936-344-6451
Kris Drane, prin. Fax 344-6113
New Waverly JHS 200/6-8
355 Front St 77358 936-344-2246
Dudley Hawkes, prin. Fax 344-8313

Nixon, Gonzales, Pop. 2,375
Nixon-Smiley Consolidated ISD 1,100/PK-12
PO Box 400 78140 830-582-1536
Cathy L. Lauer Ph.D., supt. Fax 582-1920
www.nixonsmiley.net
Nixon-Smiley HS 300/9-12
PO Box 400 78140 830-582-1536
Dr. Wendy Fuller, prin. Fax 582-2168
Nixon-Smiley MS 300/5-8
PO Box 400 78140 830-582-1536
Jane Dwyer, prin. Fax 582-2258

Nocona, Montague, Pop. 3,004
Nocona ISD 800/PK-12
220 Clay St 76255 940-825-3267
Dr. Vickie Gearheart, supt. Fax 825-4945
www.noconaisd.net/
Nocona HS 300/9-12
220 Clay St 76255 940-825-3264
Stephenie Wright, prin. Fax 825-7270
Nocona MS 200/6-8
220 Clay St 76255 940-825-3121
Amy Murphey, prin. Fax 825-6151

Prairie Valley ISD 100/PK-12
12920 FM 103 76255 940-825-4425
W. Tucker, supt. Fax 825-4650
www.prairievalleyisd.net/
Prairie Valley JSHS 100/6-12
12920 FM 103 76255 940-825-4425
Lisa Sadler, prin. Fax 825-4650

Nordheim, DeWitt, Pop. 305
Nordheim ISD 200/PK-12
500 Broadway 78141 361-938-5211
Kevin Wilson, supt. Fax 938-5266
www.nordheimisd.org
Nordheim S 200/PK-12
500 Broadway 78141 361-938-5211
Lisa Karnei, prin. Fax 938-5266

Normangee, Leon, Pop. 671
Normangee ISD 500/PK-12
PO Box 219 77871 936-396-3111
Luke Allison, supt. Fax 396-3112
www.normangeeisd.org
Normangee HS 200/9-12
PO Box 219 77871 936-396-6111
Teddy Clevenger, prin. Fax 396-6879
Normangee MS 100/6-8
PO Box 219 77871 936-396-6111
Teddy Clevenger, prin. Fax 396-6879

North Richland Hills, Tarrant, Pop. 62,179
Birdville ISD
Supt. — See Haltom City
Birdville Center of Tech & Advanced Lrng Vo/Tech
7020 Mid Cities Blvd 76180 817-547-3800
Dr. Linda Anderson, dir. Fax 503-8965
Birdville HS 2,000/9-12
9100 Mid Cities Blvd 76180 817-547-8000
Jason Wells, prin. Fax 547-8009
North Richland MS 900/6-8
4800 Rufe Snow Dr 76180 817-547-4200
Ernie Valamides, prin. Fax 581-5372
North Ridge MS 800/6-8
7332 Douglas Ln 76182 817-547-5200
Steve Ellis, prin. Fax 581-5460
Richland HS 2,200/9-12
5201 Holiday Ln 76180 817-547-7000
Carla Rix, prin. Fax 581-5454
Smithfield MS 800/6-8
8400 Main St 76182 817-547-5000
Kyle Pekurney, prin. Fax 581-5480

Fort Worth Christian S 900/PK-12
6200 Holiday Ln 76180 817-520-6200
Young Academy K-12
8521 Davis Blvd 76182 817-427-4888
Kathy Lyda, head sch

North Zulch, Madison
North Zulch ISD 400/PK-12
PO Box 158 77872 936-399-1000
Doug Devine, supt. Fax 399-2025
www.nzisd.org
North Zulch JSHS 200/7-12
PO Box 158 77872 936-399-1030
Rick Panter, prin. Fax 399-2038

Oak Ridge North, Montgomery, Pop. 3,010

Sojourn Academy 100/PK-12
27420 Robinson Rd, 281-298-5800
Jess Larson, head sch Fax 292-2818

Oakwood, Leon, Pop. 506
Oakwood ISD 200/PK-12
631 N Holly St 75855 903-545-2600
Jackie Thomason, supt. Fax 545-2310
www.oakwoodisd.net
Oakwood JSHS 100/7-12
631 N Holly St 75855 903-545-2140
Tina Rayborn, prin. Fax 545-1820

O Brien, Haskell, Pop. 105
Knox City-O'Brien Consolidated ISD
Supt. — See Knox City
O'Brien MS 100/5-8
711 9th St 79539 940-657-3731
Mark Tucker, prin. Fax 657-3379

Odem, San Patricio, Pop. 2,386
Odem-Edroy ISD 1,000/PK-12
1 Owl Sq 78370 361-368-8121
Dr. Lisa Gonzales, supt. Fax 368-2879
www.oeisd.org/
Odem HS 300/9-12
1 Owl Sq 78370 361-368-8121
Ann Ewing, prin. Fax 368-3781
Odem JHS 200/6-8
1 Owl Sq 78370 361-368-8121
Traci Fryar, prin. Fax 368-2033

Odessa, Ector, Pop. 98,924
Ector County ISD 26,600/PK-12
PO Box 3912 79760 432-456-0000
Tom Crowe, supt. Fax 456-9878
www.ectorcountyisd.org
Alternative Education Center 50/Alt
PO Box 3912 79760 432-456-0049
Charles Quintela, prin. Fax 456-0048
Bonham MS 900/6-8
PO Box 3912 79760 432-456-0429
David Steele, prin. Fax 456-0428
Bowie JHS 700/6-8
PO Box 3912 79760 432-456-0439
Mark Ferrer, prin. Fax 456-0438
Crockett MS 600/6-8
PO Box 3912 79760 432-456-0449
Mauricio Marquez, prin. Fax 456-0448
Ector MS 1,100/6-8
PO Box 3912 79760 432-456-0479
Kendra Herrera, prin. Fax 456-0478

Falcon Early College HS 100/9-12
PO Box 3912 79760 432-456-9879
Lindsey Lumpkin, prin. Fax 456-9878
New Tech Odessa HS 400/9-12
PO Box 3912 79760 432-456-6989
Betsabe Salcido, prin. Fax 456-6988
Nimitz MS 800/6-8
PO Box 3912 79760 432-456-0469
Teresa Willison, prin. Fax 456-0468
Odessa Career & Tech Early College HS Vo/Tech
PO Box 3912 79760 432-456-6400
Linda Wilder, prin. Fax 456-6401
Odessa SHS 2,500/10-12
PO Box 3912 79760 432-456-0029
Gregory Nelson, prin. Fax 456-0028
Permian SHS 2,200/10-12
PO Box 3912 79760 432-456-0039
James Ramage, prin. Fax 456-0038
Wilson & Young Medal of Honor MS 500/6-8
PO Box 3912 79760 432-456-0459
Yolanda Hernandez, prin. Fax 456-0458

UTPB STEM Academy K-12
4901 E University Blvd 79762 432-552-2580
Fax 552-2581
utpbstemacademy.org
UTPB STEM Academy K-12
4901 E University Blvd 79762 432-552-2580
Oscar Rendon, prin. Fax 552-2581

Odessa College Post-Sec.
201 W University Blvd 79764 432-335-6400
University of Texas of the Permian Basin Post-Sec.
4901 E University Blvd 79762 432-552-2020

O Donnell, Lynn, Pop. 817
O'Donnell ISD 100/PK-12
PO Box 487 79351 806-428-3241
Cathy Amonett Ed.D., supt. Fax 428-3395
odonnell.esc17.net
O'Donnell S 100/PK-12
PO Box 487 79351 806-428-3247
Cody White, prin. Fax 428-3395

Oglesby, Coryell, Pop. 480
Oglesby ISD 200/PK-12
125 College Ave 76561 254-456-2271
Jason Jones, supt. Fax 456-2522
www.oglesbyisd.net
Oglesby S 200/PK-12
125 College Ave 76561 254-456-2271
Jason Jones, supt. Fax 456-2916

Olmito, Cameron
South Texas ISD
Supt. — See Mercedes
South Texas Acad for Medical Professions 500/9-12
10650 N Expressway 77/83 78575 956-214-6100
Harry Goette, prin. Fax 214-8046

Olney, Young, Pop. 3,242
Olney ISD 700/PK-12
809 W Hamilton St 76374 940-564-3519
Dr. Greg Roach, supt. Fax 564-5205
www.olneyisd.net
Olney HS 200/9-12
704 W Grove St 76374 940-564-5637
Matt Caffey, prin. Fax 564-5733
Olney JHS 100/6-8
300 S Avenue H 76374 940-564-3517
Gunter Rodriguez, prin. Fax 564-8824

Olton, Lamb, Pop. 2,197
Olton ISD 600/PK-12
PO Box 388 79064 806-285-2641
Charles McIver, supt. Fax 285-2724
www.oltonisd.net
Olton HS 200/9-12
PO Box 667 79064 806-285-2691
Kenny Eudy, prin. Fax 285-3316
Olton JHS 200/6-8
PO Box 509 79064 806-285-2681
Brian Hunt, prin. Fax 285-3348

Omaha, Morris, Pop. 1,001
Pewitt Consolidated ISD 1,000/PK-12
PO Box 1106 75571 903-884-2804
Dr. Andy Reddock, supt. Fax 884-2866
www.pewittcisd.net
Pewitt HS 300/9-12
PO Box 1106 75571 903-884-2293
Scot Wright, prin. Fax 884-3111
Pewitt JHS 200/6-8
PO Box 1106 75571 903-884-2505
Tom Giles, prin. Fax 884-2142

Onalaska, Polk, Pop. 1,736
Onalaska ISD 900/PK-12
PO Box 2289 77360 936-646-1000
Lynn Redden, supt. Fax 646-2605
www.onalaskaisd.net
Onalaska JSHS 400/7-12
PO Box 2289 77360 936-646-1020
Anthony Roberts, prin. Fax 646-1022

Orange, Orange, Pop. 18,289
Deweyville ISD
Supt. — See Deweyville
Deweyville JSHS 300/7-12
171 State Highway 12 W 77632 409-746-2685
Dr. Brad Haeggquist, prin. Fax 746-9343

Little Cypress-Mauriceville Cons ISD 3,300/PK-12
6586 FM 1130 77632 409-883-2232
Dr. Pauline Hargrove, supt. Fax 883-3509
www.lcmcisd.org/
Alternative Education Center Alt
7565 Highway 87 N 77632 409-670-4635
Steve Lisbony, admin.
Little Cypress JHS 500/6-8
6765 FM 1130 77632 409-883-2317
Ryan DuBose, prin. Fax 883-5044
Little Cypress-Mauriceville HS 1,000/9-12
7327 Highway 87 N 77632 409-886-5821
Todd Loupe, prin. Fax 886-5762
Mauriceville MS 300/6-8
19952 FM 1130 77632 409-745-3970
Kim Cox, prin. Fax 745-3383

West Orange-Cove Consolidated ISD 2,400/PK-12
PO Box 1107 77631 409-882-5500
Rickie R. Harris, supt. Fax 882-5452
www.woccisd.net
West Orange-Stark MS 500/6-8
PO Box 1107 77631 409-882-5520
Anthony Moten, prin. Fax 882-5545
Other Schools – See West Orange

Baptist Hospital Post-Sec.
608 Strickland Dr 77630 409-883-9361
Community Christian S 200/PK-12
3400 Martin Luther King Jr 77632 409-883-4531
Laurie Beard M.Ed., prin. Fax 883-8855
Lamar State College Orange Post-Sec.
410 W Front St 77630 409-883-7750

Orangefield, Orange
Orangefield ISD 1,800/PK-12
PO Box 228 77639 409-735-5337
Dr. Stephen D. Patterson, supt. Fax 735-2080
www.orangefieldisd.net
Orangefield HS 500/9-12
PO Box 228 77639 409-735-3851
Zach Quinn, prin. Fax 697-2301
Orangefield JHS 500/5-8
PO Box 228 77639 409-735-6737
Deena VanPelt, prin. Fax 792-9605

Orange Grove, Jim Wells, Pop. 1,306
Orange Grove ISD 1,900/PK-12
PO Box 534 78372 361-384-2495
Lynn Burton, supt. Fax 384-2148
www.ogisd.net
Orange Grove HS 500/9-12
PO Box 534 78372 361-384-2330
Gildardo Salazar, prin. Fax 384-0206
Orange Grove JHS 400/6-8
PO Box 534 78372 361-384-2323
Carlos Flores, prin. Fax 384-9579

Ore City, Upshur, Pop. 1,130
Ore City ISD 800/PK-12
100 Rebel Rd N 75683 903-968-3300
Lynn Heflin, supt. Fax 968-3797
www.ocisd.net
Ore City HS 200/9-12
100 Rebel Rd N 75683 903-968-3300
Nathan Heflin, prin. Fax 968-8726
Ore City JHS 200/6-8
100 Rebel Rd N 75683 903-968-3300
Selenia Cato, prin. Fax 968-4913

Overton, Rusk, Pop. 2,503
Leveretts Chapel ISD 300/PK-12
8956 State Highway 42/135 N 75684 903-834-6675
Donna Johnson, supt. Fax 834-6602
www.leverettschapelisd.net
Leveretts Chapel HS 100/9-12
8956 State Highway 42/135 N 75684 903-834-3181
Matt Everett, prin. Fax 834-6602
Leveretts Chapel JHS 100/6-8
8956 State Highway 42/135 N 75684 903-834-3181
Nikki Saxton, prin. Fax 834-6602

Overton ISD 500/PK-12
PO Box 130 75684 903-834-6145
Stephen DuBose, supt. Fax 834-6755
www.overtonisd.net
Overton HS 200/9-12
PO Box 130 75684 903-834-6143
Cindy Bundrick, prin. Fax 834-3246
Overton MS 100/6-8
PO Box 130 75684 903-834-6146
Cindy Bundrick, prin. Fax 834-3256

Ovilla, Ellis, Pop. 3,449

Ovilla Christian S 400/PK-12
3251 Ovilla Rd 75154 972-617-1177
Ron Clyde, hdmstr. Fax 218-0135

Ozona, Crockett, Pop. 3,206
Crockett County Consolidated SD 800/PK-12
PO Box 400 76943 325-392-5501
Raul Chavarria, supt. Fax 392-5177
www.ozonaschools.net
Ozona HS 200/9-12
PO Box 400 76943 325-392-5501
Ronny Clayton, prin. Fax 392-5177
Ozona MS 200/6-8
PO Box 400 76943 325-392-5501
Tamara McWilliams, prin. Fax 392-5177

Paducah, Cottle, Pop. 1,174
Paducah ISD 200/PK-12
PO Box P 79248 806-492-3524
Brian Patterson, supt. Fax 492-2432
www.paducahisd.org
Paducah S 200/PK-12
810 Goodwin Ave 79248 806-492-2009
Will Flemons, prin. Fax 492-2193

Paint Rock, Concho, Pop. 270
Paint Rock ISD 200/PK-12
PO Box 277 76866 325-732-4314
Ron Cline, supt. Fax 732-4384
www.paintrockisd.net
Paint Rock S 200/PK-12
PO Box 277 76866 325-732-4314
Ron Cline, prin. Fax 732-4384

Palacios, Matagorda, Pop. 4,670
Palacios ISD 1,500/PK-12
1209 12th St 77465 361-972-5491
Alexandro Flores, supt. Fax 972-3567
www.palaciosisd.org
Palacios HS 400/9-12
100 Shark Dr 77465 361-972-2571
Stephanie Garcia, prin. Fax 972-6287
Palacios JHS 200/7-8
200 Shark Dr 77465 361-972-2417
Buddy Kelley, prin. Fax 972-6372

Palestine, Anderson, Pop. 18,404
Neches ISD
Supt. — See Neches
Neches HS 100/9-12
1509 County Road 346 75803 903-584-3443
Trent Cook, prin. Fax 584-3686

Palestine ISD 3,300/PK-12
1007 E Park Ave 75801 903-731-8000
Jason Marshall, supt. Fax 766-4983
www.palestineschools.org/
Palestine HS 800/9-12
1600 S Loop 256 75801 903-731-8005
William Stewart, prin. Fax 839-6489
Palestine JHS 400/7-8
233 Ben Milam Dr 75801 903-731-8008
Stephen Cooksey, prin. Fax 655-0731

Westwood ISD 1,600/PK-12
PO Box 260 75802 903-729-1776
Wade Stanford, supt. Fax 729-3696
www.westwoodisd.net
Westwood HS 400/9-12
PO Box 260 75802 903-729-1773
Kyle Lock, prin. Fax 729-8695
Westwood JHS 200/7-8
PO Box 260 75802 903-723-0423
Sonya Brown, prin. Fax 723-6765

Palmer, Ellis, Pop. 1,973
Palmer ISD 1,100/PK-12
PO Box 790 75152 972-449-3389
Kevin Noack, supt. Fax 845-2112
www.palmer-isd.org
Palmer HS 300/9-12
PO Box 790 75152 972-449-3487
Brian Warner, prin. Fax 845-3517
Palmer MS 400/5-8
PO Box 790 75152 972-449-3319
Kristin Middlebrooks, prin. Fax 845-3380

Palmhurst, Hidalgo, Pop. 2,600
Mission Consolidated ISD
Supt. — See Mission
Cantu JHS 800/6-8
5101 N Stewart Rd 78572 956-323-7800
Ana Lisa Flores, prin. Fax 323-7880

Palmview, Hidalgo, Pop. 5,455
La Joya ISD
Supt. — See La Joya
Palmview HS 2,200/9-12
3901 N La Homa Rd, 956-519-5779
Yvonne Flores Ayala, prin. Fax 323-2775

Pampa, Gray, Pop. 17,739
Pampa ISD 3,700/PK-12
1233 N Hobart St 79065 806-669-4700
Tanya Larkin, supt. Fax 665-0506
www.pampaisd.net
Pampa HS 900/9-12
111 E Harvester Ave 79065 806-669-4800
Hugh Piatt, prin. Fax 669-4826
Pampa JHS 800/6-8
4000 Bad Cattle Company Rd 79065 806-669-4901
Jennifer Studebaker, prin. Fax 669-4742
Pampa Learning Center 50/Alt
400 N Faulkner St 79065 806-669-4750
Carrie Williams, prin. Fax 669-4734

Panhandle, Carson, Pop. 2,431
Panhandle ISD 700/PK-12
PO Box 1030 79068 806-537-3568
Blair Brown, supt. Fax 537-5553
www.panhandleisd.net
Panhandle HS 200/9-12
PO Box 1030 79068 806-537-3897
Robin Fulce, prin. Fax 537-3476
Panhandle JHS 100/6-8
PO Box 1030 79068 806-537-3541
Blair Brown, prin. Fax 537-5725

Paradise, Wise, Pop. 438
Paradise ISD 1,100/PK-12
338 School House Rd 76073 940-969-5000
Mac Edwards, supt. Fax 969-5008
www.pisd.net
Paradise HS 300/9-12
338 School House Rd 76073 940-969-5010
Mark Mathis, prin. Fax 969-5009
Paradise MS 300/6-8
338 School House Rd 76073 940-969-5034
Greg Fletcher, prin. Fax 969-5025

Paris, Lamar, Pop. 24,458
Chisum ISD 900/PK-12
3250 S Church St 75462 903-737-2830
Tommy Chalaire, supt. Fax 737-2831
www.chisumisd.org
Chisum HS 300/9-12
3250 S Church St 75462 903-737-2800
Clint Miller, prin. Fax 737-2831
Chisum MS 200/6-8
3250 S Church St 75462 903-737-2806
Aaron Bridges, prin. Fax 737-2831

North Lamar ISD 2,900/PK-12
3201 Lewis Ln 75460 903-737-2000
John McCullough, supt. Fax 669-0129
www.northlamar.net
North Lamar HS 800/9-12
3201 Lewis Ln 75460 903-737-2011
Clint Hildreth, prin. Fax 669-0119
Stone MS 700/6-8
3201 Lewis Ln 75460 903-737-2041
Kelli Stewart, prin. Fax 669-0149

Paris ISD 3,400/PK-12
1920 Clarksville St 75460 903-737-7473
Paul Jones, supt. Fax 737-7484
www.parisisd.net
Paris HS 900/9-12
2255 S Collegiate Dr 75460 903-737-7400
Chris Vaughn, prin. Fax 737-7515
Paris JHS 500/7-8
2400 Jefferson Rd 75460 903-737-7434
Stephen Long, prin. Fax 737-7534
Travis HS of Choice 50/Alt
3270 Graham St 75460 903-737-7560
Joan Moore, prin. Fax 737-7574

Paris Junior College Post-Sec.
2400 Clarksville St 75460 903-785-7661
Trinity Christian Academy 100/PK-12
2190 Farm Road 79 75460 903-785-9557
Glen Martin, dir. Fax 785-7372

Pasadena, Harris, Pop. 147,777
Deer Park ISD
Supt. — See Deer Park
Deepwater JHS 600/6-8
501 Glenmore Dr 77503 832-668-7600
Scott Davis, prin. Fax 475-6138
Fairmont JHS 800/6-8
4911 Holly Bay Ct 77505 832-668-7800
Neil Munro, prin. Fax 998-4456

Pasadena ISD 53,900/PK-12
1515 Cherrybrook Ln 77502 713-740-0000
Deeann Powell, supt. Fax 740-4042
www.pasadenaisd.org
Bondy IS 1,000/6-8
5101 Keith Rd 77505 713-740-0430
Roneka Lee, prin. Fax 740-4152
Guidance Center Alt
3010 Bayshore Blvd 77502 713-740-0792
Robert Sayavedra, prin. Fax 740-4108
Jackson IS 800/6-8
1020 Thomas Ave 77506 713-740-0440
Paula Sword, prin. Fax 740-4109
Kendrick MS, 3000 Watters 77504 6-8
Melissa Messenger, prin. 713-740-5380
Miller IS 900/6-8
1002 Fairmont Pkwy 77504 713-740-0450
Vanessa Reyes, prin. Fax 740-4106
Park View IS 1,000/6-8
3003 Dabney Dr 77502 713-740-0460
Rob Hasson, prin. Fax 740-4115
Pasadena HS 2,500/9-12
206 Shaver St 77506 713-740-0310
Joe Saavedra, prin. Fax 740-4085
Pasadena Memorial HS 3,000/9-12
4410 Crenshaw Rd 77504 713-740-0390
Jeremy Richardson, prin. Fax 740-4156
Rayburn HS 2,900/9-12
2121 Cherrybrook Ln 77502 713-740-0330
Robert Stock, prin. Fax 740-4157
San Jacinto IS 600/6-8
3600 Red Bluff Rd 77503 713-740-0480
Dianna Walker, prin. Fax 740-4153
Southmore IS 900/6-8
2000 Patricia Ln 77502 713-740-0500
Derek Moody, prin. Fax 740-4154
Sullivan MS, 1112 Queens Rd 77502 6-8
Kelly Cook, prin. 713-740-5420
Summit S 100/Alt
1838 E Sam Houston Pkwy S 77503 713-740-0290
Robert DeWolfe, prin. Fax 740-4049
Tegeler Career Center Vo/Tech
4949 Burke Rd 77504 713-740-0410
Jean Cain, prin. Fax 740-4077
Community S Adult
1838A E Sam Houston Pkwy S 77503 713-740-0298
Tom Swan, admin. Fax 740-4048
Other Schools – See Houston, South Houston

Faith Christian Academy K-12
3519 Burke Rd 77504 713-943-9978
First Baptist Christian Academy 400/PK-12
7500 Fairmont Pkwy 77505 281-991-9191
Freddie Cullins, head sch Fax 991-7092
Interactive Learning Systems Post-Sec.
213 W Southmore Ave 77502 713-920-1120
San Jacinto College Post-Sec.
8060 Spencer Hwy 77505 281-476-1501
Texas Chiropractic College Post-Sec.
5912 Spencer Hwy 77505 281-487-1170

Pattison, Waller, Pop. 462
Royal ISD 2,400/PK-12
PO Box 489 77466 281-934-2248
Stacy Ackley, supt. Fax 934-2846
www.royal-isd.net
Other Schools – See Brookshire

Pattonville, Lamar
Prairiland ISD 1,100/PK-12
466 Farm Road 196 75468 903-652-6476
Jeff Ballard, supt. Fax 652-3738
www.prairiland.net
Prairiland HS 300/9-12
466 Farm Road 196 75468 903-652-5681
Jason Hostetler, prin. Fax 652-6400
Prairiland JHS 200/6-8
466 Farm Road 196 75468 903-652-5681
Leslie Watson, prin. Fax 652-3232

Pearland, Brazoria, Pop. 89,386
Alvin ISD
Supt. — See Alvin
Ryan JHS 1,200/6-8
11500 Shadow Creek Pkwy 77584 281-245-3210
Christina Lovette, prin. Fax 245-3221
Shadow Creek HS 9-12
11850 Broadway St 77584 281-388-1130
Kelly Hestand, prin.

Pearland ISD, PO Box 7 77588 20,000/PK-12
John Kelly Ph.D., supt. 281-485-3203
www.pearlandisd.org
Dawson HS, 2050 Cullen Blvd 77581 2,100/9-12
Kelly Holt, prin. 281-412-8800
Miller JHS, 3301 Manvel Rd 77584 900/7-8
Kim Brooks, prin. 281-997-3900
PACE Center 100/Alt
2314 Old Alvin Rd 77581 281-412-1599
John Palombo, prin.
Pearland HS, 3775 S Main St 77581 2,900/9-12
Larry Berger, prin. 281-997-7445
Pearland JHS East 700/7-8
2315 Old Alvin Rd 77581 281-485-2481
Annette Chambliss, prin.
Pearland JHS South 800/7-8
4719 Bailey Rd 77584 281-727-1500
Jason Frerking, prin.
Pearland JHS West 800/7-8
2337 N Galveston Ave 77581 281-412-1222
Dana Miles, prin.
Turner HS, 4717 Bailey Rd 77584 700/9-12
Dr. Jennifer Morrow, prin. 281-727-1600

Eagle Heights Christian Academy 300/PK-12
3005 Pearland Pkwy 77581 281-485-6330
John Stahl, prin. Fax 485-8682

Pearsall, Frio, Pop. 9,098
Pearsall ISD 2,100/PK-12
318 Berry Ranch Rd 78061 830-334-8001
Dr. Nobert Rodriguez, supt. Fax 334-8007
www.pearsallisd.org
Pearsall HS 600/9-12
1990 Maverick Dr 78061 830-334-8011
Varghese Panachakunnil, prin. Fax 334-5018
Pearsall JHS 600/6-8
607 E Alabama St 78061 830-334-8021
Sharon Neumann, prin. Fax 334-8025

Pecos, Reeves, Pop. 8,754
Pecos-Barstow-Toyah ISD 2,300/PK-12
PO Box 869 79772 432-447-7201
Jim Haley, supt. Fax 447-7262
www.pbtisd.esc18.net
Crockett MS 500/6-8
PO Box 869 79772 432-447-7461
Jennifer Guillory, prin. Fax 447-4853
Pecos HS 600/9-12
PO Box 869 79772 432-447-7400
Artemio Ontiveros, prin. Fax 447-9055

Penelope, Hill, Pop. 198
Penelope ISD 200/PK-12
PO Box 68 76676 254-533-2215
Scot Kelley, supt. Fax 533-2262
www.penelopeisd.org/
Penelope S 200/PK-12
PO Box 68 76676 254-533-2215
Scot Kelley, supt. Fax 533-2262

Penitas, Hidalgo, Pop. 4,401
La Joya ISD
Supt. — See La Joya
Saenz MS 700/6-8
39200 Mile 7 Rd 78576 956-519-4007
Belen Martinez, prin. Fax 519-4016

Pep, Hockley, Pop. 85
Whiteface Consolidated ISD
Supt. — See Whiteface
P E P Alternative Co-op S 50/Alt
PO Box 394 79353 806-933-4499
Judy Williams, prin. Fax 933-4699

Perrin, Jack, Pop. 396
Perrin-Whitt Consolidated ISD 300/PK-12
216 N Benson St 76486 940-798-3718
Cliff Gilmore, supt. Fax 798-3071
www.pwcisd.net
Perrin JSHS 200/7-12
216 N Benson St 76486 940-798-3845
Karrie Wilhoit, prin. Fax 798-3071

Perryton, Ochiltree, Pop. 8,746
Perryton ISD 2,400/PK-12
PO Box 1048 79070 806-435-5478
Robert Hall, supt. Fax 435-4689
www.perrytonisd.com
Perryton HS 600/9-12
PO Box 1048 79070 806-435-3633
James Mireles, prin. Fax 435-2602
Perryton JHS 500/6-8
PO Box 1048 79070 806-435-3601
Janet Slaughter, prin. Fax 435-3624
Top-of-Texas Accelerated Education Ctr 50/Alt
PO Box 1048 79070 806-434-0389
Ludi Martin, prin. Fax 434-0402

Petersburg, Hale, Pop. 1,201
Petersburg ISD 300/PK-12
PO Box 160 79250 806-667-3585
Drew Howard, supt. Fax 667-3463
www.petersburgisd.net
Petersburg JSHS 100/7-12
PO Box 160 79250 806-667-3574
Ritchie Tarbet, prin. Fax 667-3463

Petrolia, Clay, Pop. 676
Petrolia ISD 500/PK-12
PO Box 176 76377 940-524-3555
Derrith Welch, supt. Fax 524-3370
www.petroliaisd.org
Petrolia JSHS 200/7-12
PO Box 176 76377 940-524-3264
Wade Wesley, prin. Fax 524-3215

Pettus, Bee, Pop. 551
Pettus ISD 400/PK-12
PO Box D 78146 361-375-2296
Jaime Velasco, supt. Fax 375-2295
www.pettusisd.com
Pettus HS 200/6-12
PO Box D 78146 361-375-2296
Ricky DeLeon, prin. Fax 375-2565

Pflugerville, Travis, Pop. 45,841
Pflugerville ISD 23,600/PK-12
1401 Pecan St W 78660 512-594-0000
Alex Torrez Ph.D., supt. Fax 594-0005
www.pfisd.net
Cele MS 700/6-8
6000 Cele Rd 78660 512-594-3000
Brian Ernest, prin. Fax 594-3005
Hendrickson HS 2,600/9-12
19201 Colorado Sand Dr 78660 512-594-1100
Daniel Garcia, prin. Fax 594-1105
Kelly Lane MS 1,000/6-8
18900 Falcon Pointe Blvd 78660 512-594-2800
Dina Schaefer, prin. Fax 594-2805
PACE Alt
1401B Pecan St W 78660 512-594-1900
Mike Harvey, prin. Fax 594-1905
Park Crest MS 900/6-8
1500 N Railroad Ave 78660 512-594-2400
Zachary Kleypas, prin. Fax 594-2405
Pflugerville HS 2,200/9-12
1301 Pecan St W 78660 512-594-0500
Kirk Wrinkle, prin. Fax 594-0505
Pflugerville MS 1,100/6-8
1600 Settlers Valley Dr 78660 512-594-2000
Robert Stell, prin. Fax 594-2005
Provan Opportunity Center 200/Alt
1401 Pecan St W Ste A 78660 512-594-3600
Jeff Black, prin. Fax 594-3605
Other Schools – See Austin

Pharr, Hidalgo, Pop. 70,290
Pharr-San Juan-Alamo ISD 31,400/PK-12
PO Box 1150 78577 956-354-2000
Dr. Daniel King, supt. Fax 702-5648
www.psjaisd.us/
Buell Central DAEP 200/Alt
218 E Juarez Ave 78577 956-354-2500
Mario Bracamontes, prin. Fax 354-3110
College Career & Technology Academy 200/Alt
1100 E US Highway 83 78577 956-784-8515
Darcia Cuellar, prin. Fax 354-3112
Escalante MS 600/6-8
6123 S Cage Blvd 78577 956-354-2670
Rafael Gonzalez, prin. Fax 354-3200
Johnson MS 900/6-8
500 E Sioux Rd 78577 956-354-2590
Linda Soto, prin. Fax 354-3212
Kennedy MS 800/6-8
600 W Hall Acres Rd 78577 956-354-2650
Luis Villarreal, prin. Fax 354-3206
Liberty MS 1,000/6-8
1212 S Fir St 78577 956-354-2610
Alfredo Carrillo, prin. Fax 354-3218
Pharr-San Juan-Alamo North Early Coll HS 2,100/9-12
500 E Nolana Loop 78577 956-354-2360
Liza Diaz, prin. Fax 354-3140
Pharr-San Juan-Alamo Sonia Sotomayor HS 100/Alt
1200 E Polk Ave 78577 956-354-2510
Rosie Rakay, prin. Fax 354-3120
Pharr-San Juan-Alamo SW Early College HS 1,700/9-12
300 E Rancho Blanco Rd 78577 956-354-2480
Ranulfo Marquez, prin. Fax 354-3172
PSJA Thomas Jefferson Early College HS 500/9-12
714 E US Highway 83 78577 956-784-8525
Virna Bazan, prin. Fax 354-3100
Other Schools – See Alamo, San Juan

Valley View ISD 4,600/PK-12
9701 S Jackson Rd 78577 956-340-1000
Rolando Ramirez, supt. Fax 843-8688
www.vviewisd.net
Valley View Early College Campus 600/8-9
9701 S Jackson Rd 78577 956-340-1200
Tammie Garcia, prin. Fax 213-8438
Valley View HS 1,100/9-12
9701 S Jackson Rd 78577 956-340-1500
Jesus Garza, prin. Fax 843-8195
Valley View T-STEM Early College HS 50/9-12
9701 S Jackson Rd 78577 956-340-1500
Gustavo Guzman, prin. Fax 843-8195

Oratory Academy 700/PK-12
1407 W Moore Rd 78577 956-781-3056
Fr. Leo Daniels, head sch Fax 787-1516
Southern Careers Institute Post-Sec.
1500 N Jackson Rd 78577 956-687-1415

Pilot Point, Denton, Pop. 3,793
Pilot Point ISD 1,400/PK-12
829 S Harrison St 76258 940-686-8700
Dan Gist, supt. Fax 686-8705
www.pilotpointisd.com
Pilot Point HS 400/9-12
1300 N Washington St 76258 940-686-8740
Jason Southard, prin. Fax 686-8745
Pilot Point MS - J. Earl Selz Campus 200/7-8
828 S Harrison St 76258 940-686-8730
Zane Stapp, prin. Fax 686-8735

Pineland, Sabine, Pop. 835
West Sabine ISD 700/PK-12
PO Box 869 75968 409-584-2655
Mike Pate, supt. Fax 584-2139
www.westsabineisd.net
West Sabine JSHS 400/6-12
PO Box 869 75968 409-584-2525
Ryan Fuller, prin. Fax 584-2695

Pittsburg, Camp, Pop. 4,399
Pittsburg ISD 2,500/PK-12
PO Box 1189 75686 903-856-3628
Judy Pollan, supt. Fax 856-0269
pittsburgisd.net
Pittsburg HS 700/9-12
300 N Texas St 75686 903-856-3646
Jonathan Hill, prin. Fax 855-3325
Pittsburg JHS 300/7-8
313 Broach St 75686 903-856-6432
Terri Brown, prin. Fax 855-3357

Plains, Yoakum, Pop. 1,468
Plains ISD 400/PK-12
PO Box 479 79355 806-456-7401
Dr. Stephanie Howard, supt. Fax 456-4325
plainsisd.net/
Plains HS 100/9-12
PO Box 479 79355 806-456-7498
Benjamin Taylor, prin. Fax 456-4325
Plains MS 100/6-8
PO Box 479 79355 806-456-7490
Benjamin Taylor, prin. Fax 456-4325

Plainview, Hale, Pop. 21,983
Plainview ISD 5,200/PK-12
PO Box 1540 79073 806-293-6000
Dr. Rocky Kirk, supt. Fax 296-4014
www.plainviewisd.org
Ash S 100/Alt
908 Ash St 79072 806-293-6010
Rodney Wallace, dir. Fax 296-4183
Coronado MS 400/6-8
2501 Joliet St 79072 806-293-6020
Andrew Hannon, prin. Fax 296-4169
Estacado MS 400/6-8
2200 W 20th St 79072 806-293-6015
Ritchie Thornton, prin. Fax 290-4109
Plainview HS 1,400/9-12
1501 Quincy St 79072 806-293-6005
Tye Rogers, prin. Fax 296-4069

Plainview Christian Academy 200/PK-12
310 S Ennis St 79072 806-296-6034
Karen Earhart, admin. Fax 686-0988
Wayland Baptist University Post-Sec.
1900 W 7th St 79072 806-291-1000

Plano, Collin, Pop. 253,492
Frisco ISD
Supt. — See Frisco
Fowler MS 900/6-8
3801 McDermott Rd 75025 469-633-5050
Donnie Wiseman, prin. Fax 633-5060

Plano ISD 54,100/PK-12
2700 W 15th St 75075 469-752-8100
Dr. Brian Binggeli, supt. Fax 752-8096
www.pisd.edu
Academy HS 9-12
1701 Alma Dr 75075 972-905-8100
Lynn Ojeda, prin. Fax 752-8068
Armstrong MS 700/6-8
3805 Timberline Dr 75074 469-752-4600
Melissa Blank, prin. Fax 752-4601
Bowman MS 800/6-8
2501 Jupiter Rd 75074 469-752-4800
Kristopher Vernon, prin. Fax 752-4801
Carpenter MS 800/6-8
3905 Rainier Rd 75023 469-752-5000
Courtney Washington, prin. Fax 752-5001
Clark HS 1,600/9-10
523 W Spring Creek Pkwy 75023 469-752-7200
Janis Williams, prin. Fax 752-7201
Guinn Special Programs Center Alt
2221 Legacy Dr 75023 469-752-6900
Sharon Bradley, prin. Fax 752-6901
Haggard MS 900/6-8
2832 Parkhaven Dr 75075 469-752-5400
Julie-Anne Dean, prin. Fax 752-5401
Hendrick MS 800/6-8
7400 Red River Dr 75025 469-752-5600
Lisa Long, prin. Fax 752-5601
Jasper HS 1,500/9-10
6800 Archgate Dr 75024 469-752-7400
Dr. Matthew Endsley, prin. Fax 752-7401
Otto MS 1,000/6-8
504 N Star Rd 75074 469-752-8500
Antoine Spencer, prin. Fax 752-8501
Plano East SHS 2,700/11-12
3000 Los Rios Blvd 75074 469-752-9000
George King, prin. Fax 752-9001
Plano SHS 2,600/11-12
2200 Independence Pkwy 75075 469-752-9300
Sarah Watkins, prin. Fax 752-9301
Plano West SHS 2,600/11-12
5601 W Parker Rd 75093 469-752-9600
Kathy King, prin. Fax 752-9601
Renner MS 1,300/6-8
5701 W Parker Rd 75093 469-752-5800
Sonja Pegram, prin. Fax 752-5801
Rice MS 1,200/6-8
8500 Gifford Dr 75025 469-752-6000
Chris Glasscock, prin. Fax 752-6001
Robinson MS 1,000/6-8
6701 Preston Meadow Dr 75024 469-752-6200
Billie Jean Lee, prin. Fax 752-6201
Schimelpfenig MS 1,000/6-8
2400 Maumelle Dr 75023 469-752-6400
Dr. Brant Perry, prin. Fax 752-6401
Shepton HS 1,500/9-10
5505 W Plano Pkwy 75093 469-752-7600
Jeffrey Banner, prin. Fax 752-7601
Vines HS 1,200/9-10
1401 Highedge Dr 75075 469-752-7800
Shauna Sanchez, prin. Fax 752-7801
Williams HS 1,100/9-10
1717 17th St 75074 469-752-8300
Gloria Martinez, prin. Fax 752-8301
Wilson MS 900/6-8
1001 Custer Rd 75075 469-752-6700
Selenda Sager, prin. Fax 752-6701
Other Schools – See Dallas, Murphy

Bethany Christian S 100/PK-12
3300 W Parker Rd 75075 972-596-5811
Dr. Marvin Effa, prin. Fax 596-5814
Collin College Post-Sec.
2800 E Spring Creek Pkwy 75074 972-881-5790
Coram Deo Academy 300/PK-12
9645 Independence Pkwy 75025 972-854-1300
Bill Rector, prin.
Faith Lutheran S 100/PK-12
1701 E Park Blvd 75074 972-423-7448
Rev. Stephen Kieser, hdmstr. Fax 423-9618
John Paul II HS 600/9-12
900 Coit Rd 75075 972-867-0005
Thomas Poore, pres. Fax 867-7555
Prestonwood Christian Academy 1,400/PK-12
6801 W Park Blvd 75093 972-820-5300
Dr. Larry Taylor, head sch Fax 930-4008
St. Timothy Christian Academy 50/K-12
1501 H Ave 75074 972-509-7822
Margaret Whitaker, head sch Fax 509-7829
Spring Creek Academy 200/K-12
6000 Custer Rd 75023 972-517-6730
Erin Thomas, dir. Fax 517-8750
Willow Bend Academy 200/5-12
2220 Coit Rd Ste 500 75075 972-599-7882
Yorktown Education 100/K-12
5170 Village Creek Dr 75093 972-521-8610
Randall Reiners, head sch Fax 484-3696

Pleasanton, Atascosa, Pop. 8,878
Pleasanton ISD 3,200/PK-12
831 Stadium Dr 78064 830-569-1200
Matthew Mann, supt. Fax 569-2171
www.pisd.us
Pleasanton HS 1,000/9-12
831 Stadium Dr 78064 830-569-1250
Twila Guajardo, prin. Fax 569-4747
Pleasanton JHS 500/7-8
831 Stadium Dr 78064 830-569-1280
Jennifer Garcia, prin. Fax 569-1290

Pollok, Angelina
Central ISD 1,600/PK-12
7622 N US Highway 69 75969 936-853-2216
Dr. Allen Garner, supt. Fax 853-2215
www.centralisd.com
Central HS 500/9-12
7622 N US Highway 69 75969 936-853-2167
Justin Risner, prin. Fax 853-2208
Central JHS 500/5-8
7622 N US Highway 69 75969 936-853-2115
Ronnie Musgrove, prin. Fax 853-2348

Ponder, Denton, Pop. 1,372
Ponder ISD 1,300/PK-12
400 W Bailey St 76259 940-479-8200
Bruce Yeager, supt. Fax 479-8209
www.ponderisd.net
Ponder HS 400/9-12
400 W Bailey St 76259 940-479-8210
Shawn Simmons, prin. Fax 479-8219
Ponder JHS 300/6-8
400 W Bailey St 76259 940-479-8220
Ted Heers, prin. Fax 479-8229

Poolville, Parker
Poolville ISD 500/PK-12
PO Box 96 76487 817-594-4452
Jimmie Dobbs, supt. Fax 594-2651
www.poolville.net
Poolville HS 200/9-12
1001 Lone Star Rd 76487 817-599-5134
Shari John, prin. Fax 599-5171
Poolville JHS 100/6-8
PO Box 96 76487 817-594-4539
Matt Scott, prin. Fax 594-0081

Port Aransas, Nueces, Pop. 3,435
Port Aransas ISD 500/PK-12
100 S Station St 78373 361-749-1205
Sharon McKinney, supt. Fax 749-1215
www.paisd.net
Brundrett MS 100/6-8
100 S Station St 78373 361-749-1209
James Garrett, prin. Fax 749-1218
Port Aransas HS 200/9-12
100 S Station St 78373 361-749-1206
Sharon McKinney, prin. Fax 749-1219

Port Arthur, Jefferson, Pop. 53,210
Port Arthur ISD 8,700/PK-12
PO Box 1388 77641 409-989-6100
Dr. Mark Porterie Ed.D., supt. Fax 989-6229
www.paisd.org
Career and Technical Education Vo/Tech
3501 Sgt Lucien Adams Blvd 77642 409-989-4750
Dr. Glenn Mitchell, prin. Fax 983-2204
Jefferson MS 1,100/6-8
2200 Jefferson Dr 77642 409-984-4860
Randy Lupton, prin. Fax 960-6057
Lincoln MS 800/6-8
1023 Abe Lincoln Ave 77640 409-984-8700
LaSonya Baptiste, prin. Fax 982-2847
Memorial 9th Grade Academy 600/9-9
2441 61st St 77640 409-736-1521
Gloria Dodson, prin. Fax 736-0267
Memorial HS 1,500/10-12
3501 Sgt Lucien Adams Blvd 77642 409-984-4000
Dr. Glenn Mitchell, prin. Fax 985-3376
Port Arthur Alternative Center Alt
PO Box 1388 77641 409-984-8650
Luther Thompson, prin. Fax 962-6013

Lamar State College Port Arthur Post-Sec.
1500 Procter St 77640 409-983-4921

Porter, Montgomery, Pop. 7,000
New Caney ISD
Supt. — See New Caney
New Caney MS 1,000/6-8
22784 Highway 59 77365 281-577-8860
Bryan Applegate, prin. Fax 354-8725
Porter HS 1,600/9-12
22625 Sandy Ln 77365 281-577-5900
Dr. Ken Hodgkinson, prin. Fax 577-9175
White Oak MS 900/7-8
24161 Briar Berry Ln 77365 281-577-8800
Roger McAdoo, prin. Fax 354-5186
Woodridge Forest MS 6-8
4540 Woodridge Pkwy 77365 281-577-8800
Michelle Marable, admin.

Port Isabel, Cameron, Pop. 4,982
Point Isabel ISD 2,600/PK-12
101 Port Rd 78578 956-943-0000
Dr. Lisa Garcia, supt. Fax 943-0014
www.pi-isd.net/
Port Isabel HS 700/9-12
101 Port Rd 78578 956-943-0030
Dr. William Roach, prin. Fax 943-0648
Port Isabel JHS 600/6-8
101 Port Rd 78578 956-943-0060
Nancy Gonzalez, prin. Fax 943-0055

Portland, San Patricio, Pop. 14,859
Gregory-Portland ISD 4,200/PK-12
608 College St 78374 361-777-1091
Dr. Paul Clore, supt. Fax 777-1093
www.g-pisd.org
Gregory-Portland HS 1,400/9-12
4601 Wildcat Dr 78374 361-777-4251
Kyde Eddleman, prin. Fax 777-4272
Gregory-Portland JHS 700/7-8
4600 Wildcat Dr 78374 361-777-4042
Gabe Alvarado, prin. Fax 643-3187

Port Lavaca, Calhoun, Pop. 12,146
Calhoun County ISD 4,300/PK-12
525 N Commerce St 77979 361-552-9728
Dr. James B. Cowley, supt. Fax 551-2648
www.calcoisd.org
Calhoun HS 1,200/9-12
201 Sandcrab Blvd 77979 361-552-3775
Nicole Amason, prin. Fax 551-2620
Hope HS 50/Alt
900 N Virginia St 77979 361-552-7084
Dwana Finster, prin. Fax 551-2677
Travis MS 900/6-8
705 N Nueces St 77979 361-552-3784
Michael Torres, prin. Fax 551-2692

Port Neches, Jefferson, Pop. 12,912
Port Neches-Groves ISD 4,800/PK-12
620 Avenue C 77651 409-722-4244
Dr. Rodney Cavness, supt. Fax 724-7864
www.pngisd.org
Alternative Education Center 50/Alt
1810 Port Neches Ave 77651 409-722-5924
Dr. Marc Keith, admin. Fax 724-1448
Port Neches-Groves HS 1,400/9-12
1401 Merriman St 77651 409-729-7644
Dr. Scott Ryan Ed.D., prin. Fax 722-7371
Port Neches MS 600/6-8
749 Central Dr 77651 409-722-8115
Kyle Hooper, prin. Fax 727-8342
Other Schools – See Groves

Post, Garza, Pop. 5,351
Post ISD 900/PK-12
501 S Avenue K 79356 806-495-3343
Mike Comeaux, supt. Fax 495-2945
www.postisd.net
Post HS 200/9-12
307 W 4th St 79356 806-495-2770
Marvin Self, prin. Fax 495-2792
Post MS 200/6-8
405 W 8th St 79356 806-495-2874
Robert Wilson, prin. Fax 495-2426

Poteet, Atascosa, Pop. 3,241
Poteet ISD 1,800/PK-12
PO Box 138 78065 830-742-3567
Andres Castillo, supt. Fax 742-3332
www.poteet.k12.tx.us
Poteet HS 500/9-12
PO Box 138 78065 830-742-3522
Debbie Akers, prin. Fax 742-8497
Poteet JHS 400/6-8
PO Box 138 78065 830-742-3571
Destiny Barrera, prin. Fax 742-8495

Poth, Wilson, Pop. 1,900
Poth ISD 800/PK-12
PO Box 250 78147 830-484-3330
Paula Renken, supt. Fax 484-2961
www.pothisd.us
Poth HS 200/9-12
PO Box 250 78147 830-484-3322
Todd Pawelek, prin. Fax 484-3304
Poth JHS 200/6-8
PO Box 250 78147 830-484-3323
Todd Deaver, prin. Fax 484-3682

Pottsboro, Grayson, Pop. 2,115
Pottsboro ISD 1,200/PK-12
PO Box 555 75076 903-771-0083
Dr. Kevin Matthews, supt. Fax 786-9085
www.pottsboroisd.org
Pottsboro HS 400/9-12
PO Box 555 75076 903-771-0085
Greg Wright, prin. Fax 786-6349
Pottsboro MS 300/5-8
PO Box 555 75076 903-771-2982
John Reves, prin. Fax 786-4902

Prairie Lea, Caldwell
Prairie Lea ISD 200/PK-12
PO Box 9 78661 512-488-2370
Larry Markert, supt. Fax 488-9006
www.plisd.net
Prairie Lea S 200/PK-12
PO Box 9 78661 512-488-2328
Larry Markert, prin. Fax 488-2425

Prairie View, Waller, Pop. 5,483

Prairie View A&M University Post-Sec.
PO Box 519 77446 936-261-3311

Premont, Jim Wells, Pop. 2,649
Premont ISD 600/PK-12
PO Box 530 78375 361-348-3915
Ernest Singleton, supt. Fax 348-2882
www.premontisd.net
Premont HS 200/7-12
PO Box B 78375 361-348-3915
Michael Gonzalez, prin. Fax 348-2914

Presidio, Presidio, Pop. 4,416
Presidio ISD 1,200/PK-12
PO Box 1401 79845 432-229-3275
Dennis McEntire, supt. Fax 229-4228
www.presidio-isd.net
Franco MS 200/6-8
PO Box 1401 79845 432-229-3113
Dr. Edgar Tibayan, prin. Fax 229-4087
Presidio HS 300/9-12
PO Box 1401 79845 432-229-3365
Santos Lujan, prin. Fax 229-4625

Priddy, Mills
Priddy ISD 100/K-12
PO Box 40 76870 325-966-3323
Adrianne Burden, supt. Fax 966-3380
www.priddyisd.net
Priddy S 100/K-12
PO Box 40 76870 325-966-3323
Adrianne Burden, prin. Fax 966-3380

Princeton, Collin, Pop. 6,693
Princeton ISD 4,100/PK-12
321 Panther Pkwy 75407 469-952-5400
Philip Anthony, supt. Fax 736-3505
www.princetonisd.net
Clark JHS 500/7-8
301 Panther Pkwy 75407 469-952-5400
Casey Gunnels, prin. Fax 736-5903
Princeton HS 1,000/9-12
1000 E Princeton Dr 75407 469-952-5400
James Lovelady, prin. Fax 736-5902

Progreso, Hidalgo, Pop. 5,505
Progreso ISD 2,000/PK-12
PO Box 610 78579 956-565-3002
Martin Cuellar, supt. Fax 565-2128
progresoisd.wix.com/pisd
Progreso HS 500/9-12
PO Box 610 78579 956-565-4142
Diana Williams, prin. Fax 565-6029
Thompson MS 300/7-8
PO Box 610 78579 956-565-6539
Yulia Molina, prin. Fax 565-5412

Prosper, Collin, Pop. 9,238
Prosper ISD 5,600/PK-12
605 E 7th St 75078 469-219-2000
Drew Watkins Ed.D., supt. Fax 346-9247
www.prosper-isd.net
Prosper HS 1,600/9-12
301 Eagle Dr 75078 469-219-2180
Greg Wright, prin. Fax 346-9246
Reynolds MS 900/6-8
700 N Coleman St 75078 469-219-2165
Greg Bradley, prin. Fax 346-2455
Rogers MS 500/6-8
1001 S Coit Rd 75078 469-219-2150
Todd Shirley, prin. Fax 346-9248

Grace Classical 100/K-12
4255 E Prosper Trl 75078 469-287-7111
Robert A. Armstrong M.A., head sch Fax 632-1728

Quanah, Hardeman, Pop. 2,586
Quanah ISD 500/PK-12
PO Box 150 79252 940-663-2281
Ryan Turner, supt. Fax 663-2875
www.qisd.net
Quanah HS 200/9-12
PO Box 150 79252 940-663-2791
Rusty Brawley, prin. Fax 663-6447
Travis MS 100/6-8
PO Box 150 79252 940-663-2226
Gayle McKinley, prin. Fax 663-6361

Queen City, Cass, Pop. 1,456
Queen City ISD 1,000/PK-12
PO Box 128 75572 903-796-8256
Charlotte Williams, supt. Fax 796-0248
www.qcisd.net
Queen City HS 300/9-12
PO Box 128 75572 903-796-8259
Carla Dupree, prin. Fax 796-8258
Upchurch MS 300/5-8
PO Box 128 75572 903-796-6412
Steve Holmes, prin. Fax 796-0834

Quinlan, Hunt, Pop. 1,373
Boles ISD 500/PK-12
9777 FM 2101 75474 903-883-4464
Dr. Graham Sweeney, supt. Fax 883-4531
www.bolesisd.com
Boles HS 200/9-12
9777 FM 2101 75474 903-883-2918
Jill Thomason, prin. Fax 883-5109
Boles MS 200/5-8
9777 FM 2101 75474 903-883-4464
Gordon Jordan, prin. Fax 883-3097

Quinlan ISD 2,600/PK-12
401 E Richmond 75474 903-356-1200
Dr. Debra Crosby, supt. Fax 356-1201
www.quinlanisd.net
Ford HS 700/9-12
10064 Business Highway 34 S 75474 903-356-1600
Dr. Donald Merkel, prin. Fax 356-1699
Thompson MS 600/6-8
423 Panther Path 75474 903-356-1500
Brian Kinsworthy, prin. Fax 356-2414

Quitman, Wood, Pop. 1,780
Quitman ISD 1,100/PK-12
1201 E Goode St 75783 903-763-5000
Rhonda Turner, supt. Fax 763-2710
www.quitmanisd.net/
Quitman HS 300/9-12
1101 E Goode St 75783 903-763-5000
Dana Hamrick, prin. Fax 763-2589
Quitman JHS 200/6-8
1101 E Goode St 75783 903-763-5000
Angela Brown, prin. Fax 763-5526

Ralls, Crosby, Pop. 1,930
Ralls ISD 500/PK-12
1082 4th St 79357 806-253-2509
Chris Wade, supt. Fax 253-2508
rallsisd.org
Ralls HS 100/9-12
1082 4th St 79357 806-253-2571
Miguel Salazar, prin. Fax 253-2609
Ralls MS 100/6-8
1082 4th St 79357 806-253-2549
Jeremy Griffith, prin. Fax 253-4031
Recovery Educational Campus 50/Alt
1082 4th St 79357 806-253-2571
Miguel Salazar, prin. Fax 253-2609

Randolph AFB, Bexar, Pop. 1,177
Randolph Field ISD 1,200/PK-12
Building 1225 78148 210-357-2300
Lance Johnson, supt. Fax 357-2469
www.rfisd.net
Randolph HS 300/9-12
Building 1225 78148 210-357-2400
Mark Malone Ed.D., prin. Fax 357-2475
Randolph MS 300/6-8
Building 1225 78148 210-357-2400
Merrie Fox, prin. Fax 357-2475

Ranger, Eastland, Pop. 2,441
Ranger ISD 400/PK-12
1842 E Loop 254 76470 254-647-1187
Mike Thompson, supt. Fax 647-5215
www.ranger.esc14.net
Ranger HS 100/9-12
1842 E Loop 254 76470 254-647-3216
Karen Saunders, prin. Fax 647-1895
Ranger MS 6-8
1842 E Loop 254 76470 254-647-3216
Jessie Ellerbe, prin. Fax 647-1895

Ranger College Post-Sec.
1100 College Cir 76470 254-647-3234

Rankin, Upton, Pop. 776
Rankin ISD 200/PK-12
PO Box 90 79778 432-693-2461
Keith Richardson, supt. Fax 693-2353
www.rankinisd.net
Rankin JSHS 100/7-12
PO Box 90 79778 432-693-1161
Samuel Wyatt, prin. Fax 693-2453

Raymondville, Willacy, Pop. 11,257
Raymondville ISD 2,200/PK-12
419 FM 3168 78580 956-689-8176
Johnny Pineda, supt. Fax 689-0201
www.raymondvilleisd.org/
Green MS 500/6-8
419 FM 3168 78580 956-689-8171
Raul Valdez, prin. Fax 689-5330
Raymondville HS 500/9-12
419 FM 3168 78580 956-689-8170
Cris Flores, prin. Fax 689-8152
Raymondville Options Academic Academy 100/Alt
419 FM 3168 78580 956-689-8185
Frank Garcia, prin.

Red Oak, Ellis, Pop. 10,592
Red Oak ISD 5,200/PK-12
PO Box 9000 75154 972-617-2941
Dr. J. Scott Niven, supt. Fax 617-4333
www.redoakisd.org
Red Oak HS 1,800/9-12
PO Box 9000 75154 972-617-3535
Dr. Doug Funk, prin. Fax 617-4796
Red Oak MS 900/6-8
PO Box 9000 75154 972-617-0066
Cristi Watts, prin. Fax 617-4786

Redwater, Bowie, Pop. 1,037
Redwater ISD 1,100/PK-12
PO Box 347 75573 903-671-3481
Dr. Kathy Allen, supt. Fax 671-2019
www.redwaterisd.org
Redwater HS 300/9-12
PO Box 347 75573 903-671-3421
Rhonda Roberts, prin. Fax 671-3259
Redwater JHS 200/7-8
PO Box 347 75573 903-671-3227
Lee Ann Corbin, prin. Fax 671-9921

Refugio, Refugio, Pop. 2,860
Refugio ISD 700/PK-12
212 W Vance St 78377 361-526-2325
Jack Gaskins, supt. Fax 526-2326
www.refugioisd.net/
Refugio HS 200/9-12
212 W Vance St 78377 361-526-2344
Melissa Gonzales, prin. Fax 526-1075
Refugio JHS, 212 W Vance St 78377 100/7-8
Melissa Gonzales, prin. 361-526-2434

Rhome, Wise, Pop. 1,498
Northwest ISD
Supt. — See Justin
Chisholm Trail MS 900/6-8
583 FM 3433 76078 817-215-0600
Justin Vercher, prin. Fax 215-0648

Rice, Ellis, Pop. 908
Rice ISD 900/PK-12
1302 SW McKinney St 75155 903-326-4287
Lynn Jantzen, supt. Fax 326-4164
www.rice-isd.org
Rice HS 300/9-12
1400 SW McKinney St 75155 903-326-4502
Mike Richardson, prin. Fax 326-5042
Rice IS 400/3-8
1402 SW McKinney St 75155 903-326-4190
Robert Allen, prin. Fax 326-4620

Richards, Grimes
Richards ISD 100/PK-12
9477 Panther Dr 77873 936-851-2364
Martey Ainsworth, supt. Fax 851-2210
www.richardsisd.net
Richards JSHS 100/7-12
9477 Panther Dr 77873 936-851-2364
William Boyce, prin. Fax 851-2210

Richardson, Dallas, Pop. 96,979
Richardson ISD 36,100/PK-12
400 S Greenville Ave 75081 469-593-0000
Jeannie Stone Ed.D., supt. Fax 593-0402
www.risd.org
Apollo JHS 600/7-9
1600 Apollo Rd 75081 469-593-7900
Deanna Wallace, prin. Fax 593-7911
Berkner HS 1,800/10-12
1600 E Spring Valley Rd 75081 469-593-7000
Henry Hall, prin. Fax 593-7211
Berkner STEM Academy 9-12
1600 E Spring Valley Rd 75081 469-593-7008
Austin Gunter, prin. Fax 593-7211
McAuliffe Learning Center 50/Alt
900 S Greenville Ave 75081 469-593-5800
Carmen Steward, prin. Fax 593-5805
Pearce HS 1,600/10-12
1600 N Coit Rd 75080 469-593-5000
Michael Evans, prin. Fax 593-5169
Richardson HS 1,800/10-12
1250 W Belt Line Rd 75080 469-593-3000
Charles Bruner, prin. Fax 593-3010
Richardson-North JHS 600/7-9
1820 N Floyd Rd 75080 469-593-5400
Josh Eason, prin. Fax 593-5434
Richardson-West JHS Tech Magnet 800/7-9
1309 Holly Dr 75080 469-593-3700
Fax 593-3666
Other Schools – See Dallas

Alexander S 50/7-12
409 International Pkwy 75081 972-690-9210
Andrew Cody M.Ed., prin. Fax 690-9284
Canyon Creek Christian Academy 200/PK-12
2800 Custer Pkwy 75080 972-231-4890
Carolyn Stratton, head sch Fax 234-8414
DeVry University Post-Sec.
2201 N Central Expy Ste 200 75080 972-792-7450
IANT Quranic Academy 200/K-12
840 Abrams Rd 75081 972-231-8451
North Dallas Adventist Academy 200/PK-12
302 Centennial Blvd 75081 972-234-6322
Orton Varona, head sch Fax 234-6325
PCI Health Training Center Post-Sec.
1300 International Pkwy 75081 214-380-4322
Salam Academy PK-12
1515 Blake Dr 75081 972-704-4373
University of Texas at Dallas Post-Sec.
800 W Campbell Rd 75080 972-883-2111

Richland Hills, Tarrant, Pop. 7,627
Birdville ISD
Supt. — See Haltom City
Richland MS 600/6-8
7400 Hovenkamp Ave 76118 817-547-4400
James Whitfield, prin. Fax 595-5139

Richland Springs, San Saba, Pop. 332
Richland Springs ISD 100/PK-12
700 W Coyote Trl 76871 325-452-3524
Don Fowler, supt. Fax 452-3230
www.rscoyotes.net
Richland Springs S 100/PK-12
700 W Coyote Trl 76871 325-452-3427
Don Fowler, prin. Fax 452-3580

Richmond, Fort Bend, Pop. 11,601
Fort Bend ISD
Supt. — See Sugar Land
Bowie MS 900/6-8
700 Plantation Dr 77406 281-327-6200
Brian Shillingburg, prin. Fax 327-6201
Bush HS 2,100/9-12
6707 FM 1464 Rd, 281-634-6060
Dr. Cecilia Crear, prin. Fax 634-6066
Crockett MS 800/6-8
19001 Beechnut St, 281-634-6380
Tonya Curtis, prin. Fax 327-6380
Travis HS 2,400/9-12
11111 Harlem Rd 77406 281-634-7000
Julie Diaz, prin. Fax 634-7010

Lamar Consolidated ISD
Supt. — See Rosenberg
Briscoe JHS 1,100/7-8
4300 FM 723 Rd 77406 832-223-4000
Juan Pineda, prin. Fax 223-4001
Foster HS 2,000/9-12
4400 FM 723 Rd 77406 832-223-3800
Gerard Kipping, prin. Fax 223-3801
George Ranch HS 2,100/9-12
8181 FM 762 Rd 77469 832-223-4200
Dr. Fred Black, prin. Fax 223-4201
Reading JHS 1,100/7-8
8101 FM 762 Rd 77469 832-223-4400
Juan Nava, prin. Fax 223-4401

Calvary Episcopal Preparatory 200/PK-12
1201 Austin St 77469 281-342-3161
Malcolm Smith, hdmstr. Fax 232-9449

Richwood, Brazoria, Pop. 3,442

Foundation Prep S 50/3-12
2400 Brazosport Blvd N, Clute TX 77531
Kathy Vickers, admin. 979-265-1111

Riesel, McLennan, Pop. 994
Riesel ISD 600/PK-12
600 E Frederick St 76682 254-896-5000
Brian Garner, supt. Fax 896-2981
www.rieselisd.org
Riesel JSHS 300/7-12
600 E Frederick St 76682 254-896-3171
Brandon Cope, prin. Fax 896-2981

Rio Grande City, Starr, Pop. 13,814
Rio Grande City ISD 10,900/PK-12
1 S Fort Ringgold St 78582 956-716-6700
Alfredo Garcia, supt. Fax 487-8506
www.rgccisd.org
Grulla HS 1,000/9-12
6884 E Highway 83 78582 956-487-7278
Guadalupe Garza, prin. Fax 487-4312
Preparatory for Early College HS 9-12
144 N FM 3167 78582 956-352-6349
Tina Gorena, prin. Fax 352-6387
Ringgold MS 800/6-8
1 S Fort Ringgold St 78582 956-716-6849
Jorge Pena, prin. Fax 716-6807
Rio Grande City HS 2,000/9-12
144 N FM 3167 78582 956-488-6000
Ricardo Saenz, prin. Fax 488-6050
Veterans MS 900/6-8
2700 W Eisenhower St 78582 956-488-0252
Maricela Garcia, prin. Fax 488-0261
Other Schools – See Grulla

Roma ISD
Supt. — See Roma
Barrera MS 700/6-8
258 N FM 649 78582 956-486-2670
Rodrigo Bazan, prin. Fax 486-2607

Rio Hondo, Cameron, Pop. 2,354
Rio Hondo ISD 2,200/PK-12
215 W Colorado St 78583 956-748-1000
Ismael Garcia, supt. Fax 748-1038
www.riohondoisd.net
Rio Hondo HS 600/9-12
215 W Colorado St 78583 956-748-1200
Elizabeth Valdez, prin. Fax 748-1204
Rio Hondo JHS 500/6-8
215 W Colorado St 78583 956-748-1150
Asael Ruvalcaba, prin. Fax 748-1154

Rio Vista, Johnson, Pop. 866
Rio Vista ISD 700/PK-12
PO Box 369 76093 817-373-2009
Tim Wright, supt. Fax 373-2076
www.rvisd.net
Rio Vista HS 200/9-12
PO Box 369 76093 817-373-2669
Tony Martin, prin. Fax 373-3047
Rio Vista MS 200/6-8
PO Box 369 76093 817-373-2009
Jaylynn Cauthen, prin. Fax 373-3046

Rising Star, Eastland, Pop. 829
Rising Star ISD 200/PK-12
PO Box 37 76471 254-643-1986
Mary Jane Atkins, supt. Fax 643-1922
www.risingstarisd.org
Rising Star JSHS 100/7-12
PO Box 37 76471 254-643-1981
Mary Jane Atkins, admin. Fax 643-1981

River Oaks, Tarrant, Pop. 7,362
Castleberry ISD
Supt. — See Fort Worth
REACH HS 50/Alt
1101 Merritt St 76114 817-252-2390
Wanda Mitchell, prin. Fax 252-2398

Riviera, Kleberg, Pop. 688
Riviera ISD 400/PK-12
203 Seahawk Dr 78379 361-296-3101
Karen Unterbrink, supt. Fax 296-3108
www.rivieraisd.us
Kaufer HS 200/7-12
203 Seahawk Dr 78379 361-296-3607
Cindy Pelagio, prin. Fax 296-3845

Roanoke, Denton, Pop. 5,845
Northwest ISD
Supt. — See Justin
Steele Accelerated HS 100/9-12
606 N Walnut St 76262 817-698-5800
Robin Ellis, prin. Fax 698-5840
Tidwell MS 1,000/6-8
3937 Haslet Roanoke Rd 76262 817-698-5900
Kim Barker, prin. Fax 698-5870

Robert Lee, Coke, Pop. 1,034
Robert Lee ISD 200/PK-12
1323 W Hamilton St 76945 325-453-4555
Dr. Aaron Hood, supt. Fax 453-2326
www.rlisd.net
Robert Lee HS 100/7-12
1323 W Hamilton St 76945 325-453-4557
David O'Dell, prin. Fax 453-2326

Robinson, McLennan, Pop. 10,380
Robinson ISD 2,300/PK-12
500 W Lyndale Ave 76706 254-662-0194
Dr. Michael Hope, supt. Fax 662-0215
www.risdweb.org
Robinson HS 700/9-12
500 W Lyndale Ave 76706 254-662-3840
Russ Meggs, prin. Fax 662-4007
Robinson JHS 500/6-8
500 W Lyndale Ave 76706 254-662-3843
Shelly Chudej, prin. Fax 662-1845

Robstown, Nueces, Pop. 11,474
Robstown ISD 2,600/PK-12
801 N 1st St 78380 361-767-6600
Dr. Maria Vidaurri, supt. Fax 387-6311
www.robstownisd.org/
Robstown HS 700/9-12
609 Highway 44 78380 361-387-5999
Sylvia Romero, prin. Fax 387-6702
Salazar Crossroads Academy Alt
701 N 1st St 78380 361-767-6600
Lorena Ceballos, prin.
Seale JHS 500/6-8
401 E Avenue G 78380 361-767-6631
Anita Taylor, prin. Fax 387-6202

Roby, Fisher, Pop. 640
Roby Consolidated ISD 200/PK-12
PO Box 519 79543 325-776-2222
Heath Dickson, supt. Fax 776-2823
www.robycisd.org
Roby HS 100/9-12
PO Box 519 79543 325-776-2223
Jason Carter, prin. Fax 776-2823

Rochelle, McCulloch
Rochelle ISD 200/PK-12
PO Box 167 76872 325-243-5224
Steve Butler, supt. Fax 243-5283
www.rochelleisd.net
Rochelle S 200/PK-12
PO Box 167 76872 325-243-5224
Jym Dennis, prin. Fax 243-5283

Rockdale, Milam, Pop. 5,537
Rockdale ISD 1,600/PK-12
PO Box 632 76567 512-430-6000
Denise Monzingo, supt. Fax 446-3460
www.rockdaleisd.net
Rockdale HS 500/9-12
PO Box 632 76567 512-430-6140
Tiffany Commerford, prin. Fax 446-3512
Rockdale JHS 300/6-8
PO Box 632 76567 512-430-6100
April Eschberger, prin. Fax 446-2597

Rockport, Aransas, Pop. 8,668
Aransas County ISD 3,200/PK-12
PO Box 907 78381 361-790-2212
Joseph Patek, supt. Fax 790-2299
www.acisd.org
Rockport-Fulton HS 900/9-12
PO Box 907 78381 361-790-2220
Scott Rogers, prin. Fax 790-2206
Rockport-Fulton MS 800/6-8
PO Box 907 78381 361-790-2230
Michael Hannum, prin. Fax 790-2030

Rocksprings, Edwards, Pop. 1,182
Rocksprings ISD 300/PK-12
PO Box 157 78880 830-683-4137
David Velky, supt. Fax 683-4141
www.rockspringsisd.net
Rocksprings HS 100/9-12
PO Box 157 78880 830-683-4136
Sandra VanWinkle, prin. Fax 683-4141

Rockwall, Rockwall, Pop. 36,881
Rockwall ISD 14,400/PK-12
1050 Williams St 75087 972-771-0605
Dr. John Villarreal, supt. Fax 771-2637
www.rockwallisd.com
Cain MS 900/7-8
6620 FM 3097 75032 972-772-1170
Megan Gist, prin. Fax 772-2414
Rockwall HS 2,300/9-12
901 W Yellowjacket Ln 75087 972-771-7339
Dr. Courtney Gober, prin. Fax 772-2099
Rockwall Quest Academy 50/Alt
1050 Williams St 75087 972-772-2077
Derrice Randle, prin. Fax 772-1055

Utley MS 700/7-8
1201 T L Townsend Dr 75087 972-771-5281
Todd Bradford, prin. Fax 772-1164
Williams MS 800/7-8
625 E FM 552 75087 972-771-8313
David Blake, prin. Fax 772-2033
Other Schools – See Heath

Heritage Christian Academy 300/PK-12
1408 S Goliad St 75087 972-772-3003
Dr. Brad Helmer, hdmstr. Fax 772-3770

Rogers, Bell, Pop. 1,192
Rogers ISD 900/PK-12
1 Eagle Dr 76569 254-642-3802
Dr. Don Hancock Ed.D., supt. Fax 642-3851
www.rogersisd.org
Rogers HS 300/9-12
1 Eagle Dr 76569 254-642-3224
Lee Vi Moses, prin. Fax 642-3037
Rogers MS 200/6-8
1 Eagle Dr 76569 254-642-3011
Lucinda Smith, prin. Fax 642-0033

Roma, Starr, Pop. 9,764
Roma ISD 6,500/PK-12
PO Box 187 78584 956-849-1377
Carlos Guzman, supt. Fax 849-3118
www.romaisd.com/
ALAS/I & G Center 50/Alt
PO Box 187 78584 956-849-2803
Maria Ramirez, prin. Fax 849-4421
Roma HS 1,700/9-12
PO Box 187 78584 956-849-1333
Marissa Belmontes, prin. Fax 849-2655
Roma MS 700/6-8
PO Box 187 78584 956-849-1434
Nicolasa Sarabia, prin. Fax 849-1895
Other Schools – See Rio Grande City

Ropesville, Hockley, Pop. 433
Ropes ISD 300/PK-12
304 Ranch Rd 79358 806-562-4031
Joel Willmon, supt. Fax 562-4059
www.ropesisd.us
Ropes JSHS 200/6-12
304 Ranch Rd 79358 806-562-4031
Tim Carter, prin. Fax 562-4059

Roscoe, Nolan, Pop. 1,308
Highland ISD 200/PK-12
6625 FM 608 79545 325-766-3652
Duane Hyde, supt. Fax 766-2281
www.highland.esc14.net/
Highland S 200/PK-12
6625 FM 608 79545 325-766-3652
Duane Hyde, supt. Fax 766-3869

Roscoe Collegiate ISD 500/PK-12
PO Box 579 79545 325-766-3629
Dr. Kim Alexander, supt. Fax 766-3138
www.roscoe.esc14.net
Roscoe JSHS 200/6-12
PO Box 10 79545 325-766-3327
Edward Morales, prin. Fax 766-3419

Rosebud, Falls, Pop. 1,384
Rosebud-Lott ISD
Supt. — See Lott
Rosebud-Lott Learning Center 50/Alt
PO Box 638 76570 254-583-7967
Bill Jackson, prin. Fax 583-1130

Rosenberg, Fort Bend, Pop. 30,297
Lamar Consolidated ISD 27,600/PK-12
3911 Avenue I 77471 832-223-0000
Dr. Thomas Randle, supt. Fax 223-0002
www.lcisd.org
Alternative Learning Center 100/Alt
1708 Avenue M 77471 832-223-0900
Randall Donnell, admin. Fax 223-0901
George JHS 1,000/7-8
4601 Airport Ave 77471 832-223-3600
Eric Nicholie, prin. Fax 223-3601
Lamar Consolidated HS 1,500/9-12
4606 Mustang Ave 77471 832-223-3000
Dr. Michael Milstead, prin. Fax 223-3001
Lamar JHS 800/7-8
4814 Mustang Ave 77471 832-223-3200
Creighton Jaster, prin. Fax 223-3201
Terry HS 1,700/9-12
5500 Avenue N 77471 832-223-3400
Andree Osagie, prin. Fax 223-3401
Other Schools – See Fulshear, Richmond

Living Water Christian S 100/PK-10
4808 Airport Ave 77471 281-238-8946
Gamila Frank, prin. Fax 342-9951

Rosharon, Brazoria, Pop. 1,128
Fort Bend ISD
Supt. — See Sugar Land
Ferndell Henry Center for Learning 50/Alt
7447 FM 521 Rd 77583 281-327-6000
Trevor Lemon, prin. Fax 327-6001

Rotan, Fisher, Pop. 1,488
Rotan ISD 200/PK-12
102 N McKinley Ave 79546 325-735-2332
Greg Decker, supt. Fax 735-2686
www.rotan.org
Rotan JSHS 100/6-12
102 N McKinley Ave 79546 325-735-3041
Jody Helms, prin. Fax 735-2520

Round Rock, Williamson, Pop. 97,480
Round Rock ISD 46,100/PK-12
1311 Round Rock Ave 78681 512-464-5000
Steve Flores Ph.D., supt. Fax 464-5090
www.roundrockisd.org

Cedar Ridge HS 2,800/9-12
2801 Gattis School Rd 78664 512-704-0100
Lynette Thomas, prin. Fax 704-0280
Chisholm Trail MS 1,100/6-8
500 Oakridge Dr 78681 512-428-2500
Steven Swain, prin. Fax 428-2629
Early College HS 9-12
4400 College Park Dr, 512-704-1650
Clarissa Rodriguez, prin.
Fulkes MS 800/6-8
300 W Anderson Ave 78664 512-428-3100
Nancy Guererro, prin. Fax 428-3240
Hernandez MS 900/6-8
1901 Sunrise Rd 78664 512-424-8800
Nachelle Scott, prin. Fax 424-8940
Hopewell MS 900/6-8
1535 Gulf Way, 512-464-5200
Karl Waggoner, prin. Fax 464-5349
Ridgeview MS 1,400/6-8
2000 Via Sonoma Dr, 512-424-8400
Travis Mutscher, prin. Fax 424-8540
Round Rock HS 2,900/9-12
201 Deepwood Dr 78681 512-464-6000
Natalie Nichols, prin. Fax 464-6190
Stony Point HS 2,400/9-12
1801 Tiger Trl 78664 512-428-7000
Anthony Watson, prin. Fax 428-7280
Success HS 100/Alt
500 Gattis School Rd 78664 512-428-7291
Thomasine Stewart, dir. Fax 428-7280
Walsh MS 1,400/6-8
3850 Walsh Ranch Blvd 78681 512-704-0800
Brenda Agnew, prin. Fax 704-0940
Other Schools – See Austin

Concordia HS 100/9-12
1500 Royston Ln Ste A 78664 512-248-2547
Steve Glandorf, prin. Fax 252-3839
Round Rock Christian Academy 500/PK-12
301 N Lake Creek Dr Ste A 78681 512-255-4491
Rebecca Blauser, head sch Fax 255-6043

Rowlett, Dallas, Pop. 55,115
Garland ISD
Supt. — See Garland
Coyle MS 1,200/6-8
4500 Skyline Dr 75088 972-475-3711
Nikketta Wilson, prin. Fax 412-7222
Rowlett HS 2,700/9-12
4700 President George Bush 75088 972-463-1712
Michelle Bounds, prin. Fax 412-2951
Schrade MS 1,200/6-8
6201 Danridge Rd 75089 972-463-8790
Rachael Brown, prin. Fax 463-8793

Roxton, Lamar, Pop. 632
Roxton ISD 200/PK-12
PO Box 307 75477 903-346-3213
Kelly R. Pickle, supt. Fax 346-3356
www.roxtonisd.org
Roxton S 200/PK-12
PO Box 307 75477 903-346-3213
Dustin Smyers, prin. Fax 346-3356

Royse City, Rockwall, Pop. 9,169
Royse City ISD 5,000/PK-12
PO Box 479 75189 972-636-2413
Kevin Worthy, supt. Fax 635-7037
www.rcisd.org
Brownling Academy 50/Alt
PO Box 479 75189 972-635-5077
Lloyd Blaine, prin. Fax 635-2504
Royse City HS 1,400/9-12
PO Box 479 75189 972-636-9991
Dr. Sean Walker, prin. Fax 635-2906
Royse City MS 800/7-8
PO Box 479 75189 972-636-9544
Jere Craighead, prin. Fax 635-5093

Rule, Haskell, Pop. 627
Rule ISD 100/PK-12
1100 Union Ave 79547 940-997-2521
Rick Moeller, supt. Fax 997-2446
www.rule.esc14.net
Rule S 100/PK-12
1100 Union Ave 79547 940-997-2246
Tim Holt, prin. Fax 997-2446

Runge, Karnes, Pop. 1,025
Runge ISD 300/PK-12
PO Box 158 78151 830-239-4315
Dr. Bakewell Barron, supt. Fax 239-4816
www.rungeisd.org
Runge JSHS 100/6-12
PO Box 158 78151 830-239-4315
Anna Gonzalez, prin. Fax 239-4816

Rusk, Cherokee, Pop. 5,468
Rusk ISD 2,200/PK-12
203 E 7th St 75785 903-683-5592
Scott Davis, supt. Fax 683-2104
www.ruskisd.net
Rusk HS 600/9-12
203 E 7th St 75785 903-683-5401
Scott Schwartz, prin. Fax 683-6090
Rusk JHS 500/6-8
203 E 7th St 75785 903-683-2502
John Burkhalter, prin. Fax 683-4363

Sabinal, Uvalde, Pop. 1,672
Sabinal ISD 500/PK-12
PO Box 338 78881 830-988-2472
Richard Grill, supt. Fax 988-7151
www.sabinalisd.net
Sabinal HS 200/9-12
PO Box 338 78881 830-988-2475
Luciano Castro, prin. Fax 988-7170
Sabinal JHS 200/6-8
PO Box 338 78881 830-988-2475
Luciano Castro, prin. Fax 988-7170

Sabine Pass, Jefferson
Sabine Pass ISD 400/PK-12
PO Box 1148 77655 409-971-2321
Kristi Heid, supt. Fax 971-2120
www.sabinepass.net
Sabine Pass S 400/PK-12
PO Box 1148 77655 409-971-2321
Kristi Heid, admin. Fax 971-2120

Sachse, Dallas, Pop. 19,902
Garland ISD
Supt. — See Garland
Hudson MS 1,200/6-8
4405 Hudson Park 75048 972-675-3070
Jennifer Benavides, prin. Fax 675-3077
Sachse HS 2,800/9-12
3901 Miles Rd 75048 972-414-7450
Shae Creel, prin. Fax 414-7458

Sadler, Grayson, Pop. 336
S&S Consolidated ISD 900/PK-12
PO Box 837 76264 903-564-6051
Roger Reed, supt. Fax 564-3492
www.sscisd.net
S&S Consolidated HS 300/9-12
PO Box 837 76264 903-564-3768
Mark Youree, prin. Fax 564-7308
S&S Consolidated MS 200/6-8
PO Box 837 76264 903-564-7626
Lance Johnson, prin. Fax 564-7857

Saginaw, Tarrant, Pop. 19,433
Eagle Mountain.-Saginaw ISD
Supt. — See Fort Worth
Saginaw HS 1,900/9-12
800 N Blue Mound Rd 76131 817-306-0914
Patrick Torres, prin. Fax 306-1344

Saint Jo, Montague, Pop. 1,027
Saint Jo ISD 300/PK-12
PO Box L 76265 940-995-2668
Curtis Eldridge, supt. Fax 995-2024
www.saintjoisd.net
Saint Jo JSHS 100/7-12
PO Box L 76265 940-995-2532
Katie Morman, prin. Fax 995-2087

Salado, Bell, Pop. 2,113
Salado ISD 1,500/PK-12
PO Box 98 76571 254-947-5479
Dr. Michael Novotny, supt. Fax 947-5605
www.saladoisd.org
Salado HS 500/9-12
PO Box 98 76571 254-947-5429
Ross Sproul, prin. Fax 947-6984
Salado JHS 200/7-8
PO Box 98 76571 254-947-6935
Marvin Rainwater, prin. Fax 947-6934

Saltillo, Hopkins
Saltillo ISD 300/PK-12
PO Box 269 75478 903-537-2386
David Stickels, supt. Fax 537-2191
www.saltilloisd.net
Saltillo S 300/PK-12
PO Box 269 75478 903-537-2386
David Stickels, admin. Fax 537-2191

San Angelo, Tom Green, Pop. 91,751
Grape Creek ISD 1,100/PK-12
8207 US Highway 87 N 76901 325-658-7823
Angie Smetana, supt. Fax 658-8719
www.grapecreekisd.net/
Grape Creek HS 300/9-12
8207 US Highway 87 N 76901 325-653-1852
Roger Henderson, prin. Fax 653-3568
Grape Creek MS 200/6-8
8207 US Highway 87 N 76901 325-655-1735
Tim Jetton, prin. Fax 657-2997

San Angelo ISD 14,600/PK-12
1621 University Ave 76904 325-947-3700
Dr. Carl Dethloff, supt. Fax 947-3771
www.saisd.org
Carver Learning Center 50/Alt
301 W 9th St 76903 325-659-3648
Jennifer Crutchfield, prin. Fax 657-4087
Central Freshman Campus 700/9-9
218 N Oakes St 76903 325-659-3576
Tim Reid, prin. Fax 659-3583
Central HS 2,000/10-12
655 Caddo St 76901 325-659-3400
Bill Waters, prin. Fax 659-3413
Glenn MS 1,200/6-8
2201 University Ave 76904 325-947-3841
Michael Kalnbach, prin. Fax 947-3847
Lake View HS 1,200/9-12
900 E 43rd St 76903 325-659-3500
Monte Althaus, prin. Fax 653-8661
Lee MS 1,000/6-8
2500 Sherwood Way 76901 325-947-3871
Rikke Black, prin. Fax 947-3890
Lincoln MS 1,000/6-8
255 Lake View Heroes Dr 76903 325-659-3550
Ginger Luther, prin. Fax 659-3559

Wall ISD
Supt. — See Wall
Fairview Alternative Educational Coop 50/Alt
2405 Fairview School Rd 76904 325-651-7656
Albert Johnson, prin.

Ambleside S of San Angelo 100/PK-12
511 W Harris Ave 76903 325-659-1654
Angelo State University Post-Sec.
2601 W Avenue N 76909 800-946-8627
Cornerstone Christian S 200/PK-12
1502 N Jefferson St 76901 325-655-3439
Cynthia Robinson, admin. Fax 658-8998
San Angelo Christian Academy 100/PK-12
518 Country Club Rd 76904 325-651-8363
Jennifer Rackley, admin. Fax 651-1682
Shannon West Texas Memorial Hospital Post-Sec.
120 E Harris Ave 76903 325-653-6741

San Antonio, Bexar, Pop. 1,308,790
Alamo Heights ISD 4,800/PK-12
7101 Broadway St 78209 210-824-2483
Dr. Kevin Brown, supt. Fax 822-2221
www.ahisd.net
Alamo Heights HS 1,500/9-12
6900 Broadway St 78209 210-820-8850
Dr. Cordell Jones, prin. Fax 832-5777
Alamo Heights JHS 1,100/6-8
7607 N New Braunfels Ave 78209 210-824-3231
Laura Ancira, prin. Fax 832-5825

East Central ISD 9,700/PK-12
6634 New Sulphur Springs Rd 78263 210-648-7861
Roland Toscano, supt. Fax 648-0931
www.ecisd.net
Bexar County Learning Center 100/Alt
3621 Farm Rd 78223 210-335-1745
Raye Lynn White, prin. Fax 335-1746
East Central Heritage MS 1,100/6-8
8004 New Sulphur Springs Rd 78263 210-648-4546
Mary Alice McCulloch, prin. Fax 648-3501
East Central HS 2,800/9-12
7173 FM 1628 78263 210-649-2951
Shane McKay, prin. Fax 649-2752
Legacy MS 1,200/6-8
5903 SE Loop 410 78222 210-648-3118
Damon Trainer, prin. Fax 648-1068

Edgewood ISD 12,200/PK-12
5358 W Commerce St 78237 210-444-4500
Dr. Sylvester Perez, supt. Fax 444-4602
www.eisd.net
Brentwood MS 800/6-8
1626 Thompson Pl 78226 210-444-7675
Georgia Neuman, prin. Fax 444-7698
Edgewood Fine Arts Academy 100/9-12
607 SW 34th St 78237 210-444-7925
Patricia Zamora, dir. Fax 444-7973
Frey Alternative Education Complex 100/Alt
900 S San Eduardo Ave 78237 210-444-8230
Mary Inco, admin. Fax 444-8233
Garcia MS 800/6-8
3306 Ruiz St 78228 210-444-8075
Daniel Pina, prin. Fax 444-8098
Kennedy HS 1,400/9-12
1922 S General McMullen Dr 78226 210-444-8040
Zelene Aragon, prin. Fax 444-8020
Memorial HS 1,300/9-12
1227 Memorial St 78228 210-444-8300
Bryan Norwood, prin. Fax 444-8336
Wrenn MS 800/6-8
627 S Acme Rd 78237 210-444-8475
Nicole Cannon, prin. Fax 444-8498

Fort Sam Houston ISD 1,500/PK-12
4005 Winans Rd 78234 210-368-8701
Dr. Gail Siller, supt. Fax 368-8741
www.fshisd.net
Cole MSHS 700/6-12
4001 Winans Rd 78234 210-368-8730
Dr. Isabell Clayton, prin. Fax 368-8731

Harlandale ISD 15,200/PK-12
102 Genevieve Dr 78214 210-989-4300
Reynaldo Madrigal, supt. Fax 921-4356
www.harlandale.net
Harlandale HS 2,000/9-12
114 E Gerald Ave 78214 210-989-1000
Fred Anthony, prin. Fax 924-2335
Harlandale MS 900/6-8
300 W Huff Ave 78214 210-989-2000
Ricardo Marroquin, prin. Fax 977-8764
Kingsborough MS 600/6-8
422 E Ashley Rd 78221 210-989-2200
William Hall, prin. Fax 977-9463
Leal MS 800/6-8
743 W Southcross Blvd 78211 210-989-2400
Geraldine Balleza, prin. Fax 977-1459
McCollum HS 1,800/9-12
500 W Formosa Blvd 78221 210-989-1500
Jacob Garcia, prin. Fax 989-1580
STEM Early College HS 9-12
4040 Apollo St 78214 210-989-4557
Dr. Eddie Rodriguez, prin. Fax 921-4480
Tejeda Academy 200/Alt
12121 SE Loop 410 78221 210-989-4900
Ricardo Salmon, prin. Fax 977-1628
Wells MS 700/6-8
422 W Hutchins Pl 78221 210-989-2600
Jessica Gipprich, prin. Fax 923-5126

Judson ISD
Supt. — See Live Oak
Judson Learning Academy 100/Alt
6909 N Loop 1604 E Ste 2010 78247 210-651-4080
LaTanya Baker, prin. Fax 651-6834
Kirby MS 900/6-8
5441 Seguin Rd 78219 210-661-1140
Jerome Johnson, prin. Fax 662-9275
Metzger MS 900/6-8
7475 Binz Engleman Rd 78244 210-662-2210
Tracey Valree, prin. Fax 662-8390
Veterans Memorial HS 9-12
7618 Evans Rd 78266 210-619-0220
Christina Clark, prin. Fax 945-6990
Wagner HS 2,200/9-12
3000 N Foster Rd 78244 210-662-5000
Mary Duhart-Toppen, prin. Fax 662-9896
Woodlake Hills MS 900/6-8
6625 Woodlake Pkwy 78244 210-661-1110
Daniel Brooks, prin. Fax 666-0169

Lackland ISD 900/PK-12
2460 Kenly Ave Bldg 8265 78236 210-357-5000
Dr. Burnie L. Roper, supt. Fax 357-5050
www.lacklandisd.net/

Stacey JSHS 300/7-12
2460 Kenly Ave Bldg 8265 78236 210-357-5100
Hunter Shelby, prin. Fax 357-5109

North East ISD 67,500/PK-12
8961 Tesoro Dr 78217 210-407-0000
Dr. Brian Gottardy, supt. Fax 804-7017
www.neisd.net

Academy of Creative Education 100/Alt
3736 Perrin Central Bldg 2 78217 210-407-0740
Christopher Throm, prin. Fax 657-8976

Automotive Technology Academy Vo/Tech
3736 Perrin Central Blvd 78217 210-407-0742
Justin Missildine, dir. Fax 637-4992

Bradley MS 1,200/6-8
14819 Heimer Rd 78232 210-356-2600
Todd Bloomer, prin. Fax 491-8314

Bush MS 1,600/6-8
1500 Evans Rd 78258 210-356-2900
Gary Comalander, prin. Fax 491-8471

Churchill HS 2,900/9-12
12049 Blanco Rd 78216 210-356-0000
Justin Oxley, prin. Fax 442-0879

Design and Technology Academy 9-12
5110 Walzem Rd 78218 210-356-2237
Christina Mank-Allen, dir. Fax 650-1285

Driscoll MS 900/6-8
17150 Jones Maltsberger Rd 78247 210-356-3200
Steven Zimmerman, prin. Fax 491-6467

Eisenhower MS 1,200/6-8
8231 Blanco Rd 78216 210-356-3500
John Smith, prin. Fax 442-0537

Electrical Systems Technology S Vo/Tech
2923 MacArthur Vw 78217 210-356-7697
Stephen Albert, prin. Fax 650-1195

Engineering & Technologies Academy 9-12
5110 Walzem Rd 78218 210-356-2317
Robert Lozano, dir. Fax 650-1227

Garner MS 1,000/6-8
4302 Harry Wurzbach Rd 78209 210-805-5100
David Crowe, prin. Fax 805-5138

Harris MS 1,400/6-8
5300 Knollcreek 78247 210-356-4100
Jeremi Niehoff, prin. Fax 657-8892

Hill MS 6-8
21314 Bulverde Rd 78259 210-356-8000
Alan Rochkus, prin. Fax 494-2380

International HS of America 500/9-12
1400 Jackson Keller Rd 78213 210-356-0900
Steven Magadance, dir. Fax 442-0409

Jackson MS 1,000/6-8
4538 Vance Jackson Rd 78230 210-356-4400
Erin Deason, prin. Fax 442-0580

Johnson HS 2,900/9-12
23203 Bulverde Rd 78259 210-356-0400
John Mehlbrech, prin. Fax 356-0430

Krueger MS, 438 Lanark Dr 78218 1,200/6-8
Cynthia Rubio, prin. 210-356-4700

Lee HS 2,500/9-12
1400 Jackson Keller Rd 78213 210-356-0800
Nicole Franco, prin. Fax 442-0325

Lopez MS 1,500/6-8
23103 Hardy Oak Blvd 78258 210-356-5000
Eric Wernli, prin. Fax 481-4072

MacArthur HS 2,600/9-12
2923 MacArthur Vw 78217 210-650-1100
Peter Martinez, prin. Fax 650-1195

Madison HS 3,300/9-12
5005 Stahl Rd 78247 210-356-1400
Debra Aceves-Torres, prin. Fax 637-4435

Nimitz MS 1,000/6-8
5426 Blanco Rd 78216 210-442-0450
Dana Stolhandske, prin. Fax 442-0489

North East Alternative Center 100/Alt
103 W Rampart Dr 78216 210-356-7400
Bill Fish, dir. Fax 442-0623

North East S of the Arts 9-12
1400 Jackson Keller Rd 78213 210-356-1033
Ernie Ramirez, dir. Fax 442-2507

Reagan HS 3,000/9-12
19000 Ronald Reagan 78258 210-356-1800
Brenda Shelton, prin. Fax 482-2222

Roosevelt HS 2,900/9-12
5110 Walzem Rd 78218 210-356-2200
Melvin Echard, prin. Fax 650-1291

STEM Academy Lee 9-12
1400 Jackson Keller Rd 78213 210-356-1001
Dr. Melissa Alcala, dir. Fax 442-0327

STEM Academy Nimitz 6-8
5426 Blanco Rd 78216 210-356-5501
Dr. Melissa Alcala, dir. Fax 442-0476

Tejeda MS 1,500/6-8
2909 E Evans Rd 78259 210-356-5600
John Bojescul, prin. Fax 482-2277

White MS 900/6-8
7800 Midcrown Dr 78218 210-650-1400
Brent Brummet, prin. Fax 650-1443

Wood MS 1,100/6-8
14800 Judson Rd 78233 210-650-1300
Marcus Alvarez, prin. Fax 650-1309

Evening HS Adult
3736 Perrin Central Blvd #4 78217 210-407-0743
Garry Hardcastle, prin. Fax 637-4992

Northside ISD 100,700/PK-12
5900 Evers Rd 78238 210-397-8500
Dr. Brian Woods, supt. Fax 706-8772
nisd.net

Bernal MS 6-8
14045 Bella Vista Pl 78253 210-398-1900
Glenda Munson, prin. Fax 679-8216

Brandeis HS 2,600/9-12
13011 Kyle Seale Pkwy 78249 210-397-8200
Dr. Geri Berger, prin. Fax 561-2000

Brennan HS 2,200/9-12
2400 Cottonwood Way 78253 210-398-1250
Gerardo Marquez, prin. Fax 645-3311

Briscoe MS 1,300/6-8
4265 Lone Star Pkwy 78253 210-398-1100
Christina Rather, prin. Fax 674-0220

Business Careers HS 9-12
6500 Ingram Rd 78238 210-397-7070
Randy Neuenfeldt, prin. Fax 706-7076

Chavez Excel Academy 100/Alt
6500 Ingram Rd 78238 210-397-8120
Darren Calvert, prin. Fax 522-8953

Clark HS 2,800/9-12
5150 De Zavala Rd 78249 210-397-5150
Dr. Jerry Woods, prin. Fax 561-5250

Communications Arts HS 9-12
11600 W FM 471 78253 210-397-6043
Lisa Baker, prin. Fax 688-6092

Connally MS 1,100/6-8
8661 Silent Sunrise 78250 210-397-1000
Cornelius Phelps, prin. Fax 257-1004

Construction Careers Academy Vo/Tech
9411 W Military Dr 78251 210-397-4294
Phillip Edge, prin.

Folks MS 600/6-8
9855 Swayback Rnch 78254 210-398-1600
Barry Perez, prin. Fax 257-3060

Garcia MS 1,500/6-8
14900 Kyle Seale Pkwy 78255 210-397-8400
Tracy Wernli, prin. Fax 695-3830

Harlan HS, 14350 FM 471 78253 9-12
Robert Harris, prin.

Health Careers HS 900/9-12
4646 Hamilton Wolfe Rd 78229 210-397-5400
Linda Burk, prin. Fax 617-5423

Hobby MS 1,000/6-8
11843 Vance Jackson Rd 78230 210-397-6300
Lawrence Carranco, prin. Fax 690-6332

Holmes HS 2,700/9-12
6500 Ingram Rd 78238 210-397-7000
Ada Bohlken, prin. Fax 706-7030

Holmgreen Center 100/Alt
8580 Ewing Halsell Dr 78229 210-397-5460
Sharon Spencer, prin. Fax 617-5476

Jay HS 2,900/9-12
7611 Marbach Rd 78227 210-397-2700
Jay Sumpter, prin. Fax 678-2753

Jay Science and Engineering Academy 9-12
7611 Marbach Rd 78227 210-397-2773
Gretchen Bley, prin. Fax 678-2753

Jefferson MS 1,500/6-8
10900 Shaenfield Rd 78254 210-397-3700
Kevin Kearns, prin. Fax 257-4988

Jones MS 1,200/6-8
1256 Pinn Rd 78227 210-397-2100
Michella Wheat, prin. Fax 678-2113

Jordan MS 1,400/6-8
1725 Richland Hills Dr 78251 210-397-6150
Anabel Romero, prin. Fax 523-4876

Luna MS 1,200/6-8
200 Grosenbacher Rd N 78253 210-397-5300
Lisa Richard, prin. Fax 645-5246

Marshall HS 2,600/9-12
8000 Lobo Ln 78240 210-397-7100
Susan Cleveland, prin. Fax 706-7175

Neff MS 1,200/6-8
5227 Evers Rd 78238 210-397-4100
Yvonne Correa, prin. Fax 523-4566

Northside Alternative HS 100/Alt
144 Hunt Ln 78245 210-397-7080
Dr. Darrell Rice, prin. Fax 706-7086

Northside Alternative MS North 50/Alt
11937 W Interstate 10 78230 210-397-2070
Dr. Karen Petersen, prin. Fax 561-2074

Northside Alternative MS South 50/Alt
5223 Blessing St 78228 210-397-6900
Dr. Karen Petersen, prin. Fax 431-6901

Pease MS 1,200/6-8
201 Hunt Ln 78245 210-397-2950
Katherine Lyssy, prin. Fax 678-2974

Rawlinson MS 1,200/6-8
14100 Vance Jackson Rd 78249 210-397-4900
Mark Rustan, prin. Fax 767-4055

Rayburn MS 1,000/6-8
1400 Cedarhurst Dr 78227 210-397-2150
Dr. Scott McKenzie, prin. Fax 678-2181

Ross MS 1,100/6-8
3630 Callaghan Rd 78228 210-397-6350
Lisa McConoghy, prin. Fax 431-6383

Rudder MS 1,000/6-8
6558 Horn Blvd 78240 210-397-5000
Dr. Mary Jewell, prin. Fax 561-5022

Stevens HS 2,900/9-12
600 N Ellison Dr 78251 210-397-6450
Harold Maldonado, prin. Fax 257-4304

Stevenson MS 1,400/6-8
8403 Tezel Rd 78254 210-397-7300
Chuck Baldridge, prin. Fax 706-7336

Stinson MS 1,200/6-8
13200 Skyhawk Dr 78249 210-397-3600
Lourdes Medina, prin. Fax 561-3609

Taft HS 2,800/9-12
11600 W FM 471 78253 210-397-6000
Tommy Garcia, prin. Fax 688-6072

Vale MS 1,400/6-8
2120 N Ellison Dr 78251 210-397-5700
Dana Gilbert-Perry, prin. Fax 257-1000

Warren HS 3,000/9-12
9411 W Military Dr 78251 210-397-4200
David Empson, prin. Fax 257-4246

Zachry MS 1,000/6-8
9410 Timber Path 78250 210-397-7400
Susan Allain, prin. Fax 706-7432

Other Schools – See Helotes

San Antonio ISD 49,900/PK-12
141 Lavaca St 78210 210-554-2200
Pedro Martinez, supt.
www.saisd.net

Advanced Learning Academy 4-12
637 N Main Ave 78205 210-738-9730
Kathy Bieser, prin. Fax 224-8792

Brackenridge HS 1,900/9-12
400 Eagleland Dr 78210 210-228-1200
Yesenia Cordova, prin. Fax 534-9770

Burbank HS 1,300/9-12
1002 Edwards 78204 210-228-1210
Miguel Elizondo, prin. Fax 533-4394

Cooper Academy at Navarro 200/Alt
623 S Pecos 78207 210-226-3042
Robert Loveland, prin. Fax 223-9031

Davis MS 600/6-8
4702 E Houston St 78220 210-978-7920
Julio Garcia, prin. Fax 662-8189

Edison HS 1,700/9-12
701 Santa Monica 78212 210-738-9720
Charles Munoz, prin. Fax 738-2408

Estrada Achievement Center 100/Alt
1112 S Zarzamora St 78207 210-438-6820
Donnie Whited, prin. Fax 227-8656

Fox Tech HS Vo/Tech
637 N Main Ave 78205 210-738-9730
Kathy Bieser, prin. Fax 224-8792

Highlands HS 1,700/9-12
3118 Elgin Ave 78210 210-438-6800
Dr. Luz Martinez, prin. Fax 337-2567

Houston HS 900/9-12
4635 E Houston St 78220 210-978-7900
Darnell White, prin. Fax 666-2915

Jefferson HS 1,800/9-12
723 Donaldson Ave 78201 210-438-6570
Orlando Vera, prin. Fax 738-2406

Lanier HS 1,700/9-12
1514 W Cesar E Chavez Blvd 78207 210-978-7910
Laura Cooper, prin. Fax 224-9516

Longfellow MS 1,000/6-8
1130 E Sunshine Dr 78228 210-438-6520
Dr. Aurora Terry, prin. Fax 433-0375

Page MS 400/6-8
401 Berkshire Ave 78210 210-228-1230
Dr. Edward Garcia, prin. Fax 533-7369

Pickett Academy 50/Alt
1931 E Houston St 78202 210-438-6825
Mary Olison, prin. Fax 212-3997

Poe MS 700/6-8
814 Aransas Ave 78210 210-228-1235
Miriam Aguilar Guevara, prin. Fax 534-7299

Rogers MS 600/6-8
314 Galway St 78223 210-438-6840
Justin Turner, prin. Fax 333-7954

St. Phillips Early College HS 9-12
1801 Martin Luther King Dr 78203 210-486-2406
Dr. Derrick Thomas, prin. Fax 228-3094

Tafolla MS 800/6-8
1303 W Cesar E Chavez Blvd 78207 210-978-7930
Jeff Price, prin. Fax 227-7044

Twain MS 400/7-8
2411 San Pedro Ave 78212 210-738-9745
Ricky Flores, prin. Fax 738-0518

Wheatley MS 300/7-8
415 Gabriel 78202 210-738-9750
Sandra Galinzoga, prin. Fax 227-9972

Young Mens Leadership Academy 4-8
545 S WW White Rd 78220 210-354-9652
Derrick Brown, prin. Fax 228-3070

South San Antonio ISD 9,900/PK-12
5622 Ray Ellison Blvd 78242 210-977-7000
Dr. Abelardo Saavedra, supt. Fax 977-7021
www.southsanisd.net

Alternative S, 324 Fenfield Ave 78211 50/Alt
Henry Yzaguirre, prin. 210-977-7508

Career Education Center Vo/Tech
2615 Navajo St 78224 210-977-7350
Charles Ervin, coord. Fax 977-7356

Dwight MS 500/6-8
2454 W Southcross Blvd 78211 210-977-7300
Yvonne Hernandez, prin. Fax 977-7316

Kazen MS 500/6-8
1520 Gillette Blvd 78224 210-977-7150
Joseph Carranza, prin. Fax 977-7155

Shepard MS 600/6-8
5558 Ray Ellison Blvd 78242 210-623-1875
Chriselda Bazaldua, prin. Fax 623-1894

South San Antonio HS 2,400/9-12
2515 Bobcat Ln 78224 210-977-7400
Lee Hernandez, prin. Fax 977-7430

Zamora MS 600/6-8
8638 Larkia St 78224 210-977-7278
Rosanna Carmona-Mercado, prin. Fax 977-7285

Southside ISD 5,100/PK-12
1460 Martinez Losoya Rd 78221 210-882-1600
Mark E. Eads, supt. Fax 626-0101
www.southsideisd.org/

Matthey MS 800/7-8
1460 Martinez Losoya Rd 78221 210-882-1601
Staci Weaver, prin. Fax 626-0113

Southside HS 1,300/9-12
1460 Martinez Losoya Rd 78221 210-882-1606
Nate Session, prin. Fax 626-0119

Southwest ISD 13,000/PK-12
11914 Dragon Ln 78252 210-622-4300
Dr. Lloyd Verstuyft, supt. Fax 622-4301
www.swisd.net/

McAuliffe MS 1,000/6-8
11914 Dragon Ln 78252 210-623-6260
Adrian Ramirez, prin. Fax 623-6261

Scobee MS 1,000/6-8
11914 Dragon Ln 78252 210-645-7500
Darin Kasper, prin. Fax 645-7501

Southwest Academy 200/Alt
11914 Dragon Ln 78252 210-622-4750
Juan Perez, prin. Fax 622-9502
Southwest HS 3,300/9-12
11914 Dragon Ln 78252 210-622-4500
Paul Black, prin. Fax 622-4501
Other Schools – See Atascosa, Von Ormy

Achievers' Center for Education 50/5-12
5084 De Zavala Rd 78249 210-690-7359
Anne Zuber, admin. Fax 690-7307
Antonian College Preparatory HS 800/9-12
6425 West Ave 78213 210-344-9265
Tim Petersen, prin. Fax 344-9267
Atonement Academy 600/PK-12
15415 Red Robin Rd 78255 210-695-2240
John Markovetz, hdmstr. Fax 695-9679
Baptist Health System-Sch of Health Prof Post-Sec.
8400 Datapoint Dr 78229 210-297-9636
Baptist University of the Americas Post-Sec.
8019 S Panam Expy 78224 210-924-4338
Brightwood College Post-Sec.
7142 San Pedro Ave Ste 100 78216 210-733-0777
Brightwood College Post-Sec.
6441 NW Loop 410 78238 210-308-8584
Cancer Therapy & Research Center Post-Sec.
7979 Wurzbach Rd 78229 210-450-5664
Career Point College Post-Sec.
4522 Fredericksburg Rd #A22 78201 210-732-3000
Central Catholic HS 600/9-12
1403 N Saint Marys St 78215 210-225-6794
Michael Wohlfarth, prin. Fax 227-9353
Christian Academy of San Antonio 600/PK-12
325 Castroville Rd 78207 210-436-2277
Pamela Payne, supt. Fax 436-2210
Christian S at Castle Hills 400/PK-12
2216 NW Military Hwy 78213 210-878-1000
Michael Pinkston, supt.
Concorde Career College Post-Sec.
4803 NW Loop 410 Ste 200 78229 210-428-2000
Cornerstone Christian S 700/PK-12
4802 Vance Jackson Rd 78230 210-979-9203
Dr. Jerry Eshleman, supt. Fax 340-0940
Culinary Institute of America Post-Sec.
312 Pearl Pkwy Bldg 2 #2102 78215 210-554-6400
Everest Institute Post-Sec.
6550 1st Park Ten Blvd 78213 210-732-7800
Hallmark College Post-Sec.
10401 W Interstate 10 78230 210-690-9000
Hallmark College of Aeronautics Post-Sec.
8901 Wetmore Rd 78216 210-826-1000
Holy Cross of San Antonio 400/6-12
426 N San Felipe Ave 78228 210-433-9395
Henry Galindo, prin. Fax 433-2117
Incarnate Word HS 500/9-12
727 E Hildebrand Ave 78212 210-829-3100
Jennifer Salazar, prin. Fax 829-3120
Keystone S 400/PK-12
119 E Craig Pl 78212 210-735-4022
Brian Yager, head sch Fax 732-4905
Lamson Institute Post-Sec.
5819 NW Loop 410 Ste 160 78238 210-520-1800
Legacy Christian Academy 200/PK-12
2255 Horal St 78227 210-674-0490
Pedro Garza, prin. Fax 674-3615
Lutheran HS of San Antonio 100/9-12
18104 Babcock Rd 78255 210-694-4962
Patrick Maynard, prin. Fax 694-9150
Milan Institute Post-Sec.
6804 Ingram Rd 78238 210-647-5100
Milan Institute of Cosmetology Post-Sec.
605 SW Military Dr 78221 210-922-5900
Mims Classic Beauty College Post-Sec.
5121 Blanco Rd 78216 210-344-2041
New Life Christian Academy 200/PK-12
6601 W US Highway 90 78227 210-679-6001
Anthony Jackson, prin. Fax 679-6080
Northwest Vista College Post-Sec.
3535 N Ellison Dr 78251 210-486-4000
Oblate School of Theology Post-Sec.
285 Oblate Dr 78216 210-341-1366
Our Lady of the Lake University Post-Sec.
411 SW 24th St 78207 210-434-6711
Palo Alto College Post-Sec.
1400 W Villaret Blvd 78224 210-486-3000
Providence Catholic S 400/6-12
1215 N Saint Marys St 78215 210-224-6651
Alicia Garcia, prin. Fax 224-6214
Quest College Post-Sec.
5430 Fredericksburg Rd #310 78229 210-366-2701
River City Believers Academy 100/PK-12
16765 Lookout Rd 78233 210-656-2999
Tracy Smith, prin. Fax 496-2888
St. Anthony Catholic HS 400/9-12
3200 McCullough Ave 78212 210-832-5600
Rene Escobedo Ed.D., prin. Fax 832-5615
St. Gerard Catholic HS 100/9-12
521 S New Braunfels Ave 78203 210-533-8061
Michelle Mendez, prin. Fax 533-3697
St. Mary's Hall 500/PK-12
9401 Starcrest Dr 78217 210-483-9100
Jonathan Eades, head sch Fax 483-9299
St. Mary's University Post-Sec.
1 Camino Santa Maria St 78228 210-436-3011
St. Phillip's College Post-Sec.
1801 Martin Luther King Dr 78203 210-486-2000
San Antonio Beauty College #3 Post-Sec.
4130 Naco Perrin Blvd 78217 210-654-9734
San Antonio Beauty College #4 Post-Sec.
2423 Jamar St # 2 78226 210-433-7222
San Antonio Christian S 500/PK-12
19202 Redland Rd 78259 210-340-1864
Dr. William Walters, supt. Fax 340-0461
San Antonio College Post-Sec.
1300 San Pedro Ave 78212 210-486-0000
Sanford-Brown College Post-Sec.
4511 Horizon Hill Blvd 78229 210-246-7700
Scenic Hills Christian Academy 50/PK-11
11223 Bandera Rd 78250 210-523-2312
Jon Dickerson, prin.
Southern Careers Institute Post-Sec.
238 SW Military Dr Ste 101 78221 210-271-0096
South Texas Vocational Technical Inst Post-Sec.
734 SE Military Dr 78214 888-822-4046
Southwest School Post-Sec.
602 W Southcross Blvd 78221 210-921-0951
Southwest School Post-Sec.
2402 San Pedro Ave 78212 210-225-7287
Texas A&M University San Antonio Post-Sec.
1 University Way 78224 210-784-1000
Texas Health and Science University Post-Sec.
9240 Guilbeau Rd Ste 102 78250 210-509-8080
TMI - The Episcopal S of Texas 400/6-12
20955 W Tejas Trl 78257 210-698-7171
Dr. John W. Cooper, head sch Fax 698-0715
Trinity Christian Academy 200/K-12
5401 N Loop 1604 E 78247 210-653-2800
Sharon Ausbury, prin. Fax 653-0303
Trinity University Post-Sec.
1 Trinity Pl 78212 210-999-7011
University Hospital Post-Sec.
4502 Medical Dr 78229 210-616-2000
University of Texas at San Antonio Post-Sec.
1 UTSA Cir 78249 210-458-4011
University of Texas Health Science Ctr. Post-Sec.
7703 Floyd Curl Dr 78229 210-567-7000
University of the Incarnate Word Post-Sec.
4301 Broadway St 78209 210-829-6000
Winston S San Antonio 100/K-12
8565 Ewing Halsell Dr 78229 210-615-6544
Dr. Charles Karulak, hdmstr. Fax 615-6627

San Augustine, San Augustine, Pop. 2,090
San Augustine ISD 800/PK-12
1002 Barrett St 75972 936-275-2306
Dr. Virginia Liepman, supt. Fax 275-9776
www.saisd.us
San Augustine MSHS 200/6-12
1002 Barrett St 75972 936-275-9603
Leasa Dunn, prin. Fax 275-9829

San Benito, Cameron, Pop. 24,199
Los Fresnos Consolidated ISD
Supt. — See Los Fresnos
Liberty Memorial MS 800/6-8
31579 FM 2893 78586 956-233-3900
Annice Garza, prin. Fax 233-1074
Los Fresnos United HS 900/9-9
33790 FM 803 78586 956-254-5250
Jennifer Stumbaugh, prin. Fax 399-2047

San Benito Consolidated ISD 10,900/PK-12
240 N Crockett St 78586 956-361-6100
Dr. Adrian Vega, supt. Fax 361-6115
www.sbcisd.net
Cabaza MS 900/6-8
2901 Shafer Rd 78586 956-361-6600
Lupita Monsellaves, prin. Fax 361-6608
Callandret Positive Redirection Center 50/Alt
305 Doherty St 78586 956-361-6275
Ray Saldana, prin. Fax 361-6278
Gateway Academy 50/Alt
600 N Austin St 78586 956-361-6446
Rolando Guerra, prin. Fax 399-7985
Jordan MS 900/6-8
700 N McCullough St 78586 956-361-6650
Alfredo Perez, prin. Fax 361-6658
San Benito HS 2,000/10-12
450 S Williams Rd 78586 956-361-6500
Henry Sanchez, prin. Fax 361-6579
San Benito Riverside MS 700/6-8
35428 Padilla St 78586 956-361-6940
Amy Rodriguez, prin. Fax 361-6948
San Benito Veterans Memorial Academy 800/9-9
2115 N Williams Rd 78586 956-276-6000
Gilbert Galvan, prin. Fax 276-6008

South Texas ISD
Supt. — See Mercedes
Rising Scholars Academy of South Texas 7-8
151 S Helen Moore Rd 78586 956-399-4358
Carrie Sauceda, prin. Fax 399-3570

South Texas Training Center Post-Sec.
1901 W US Highway 77 78586 956-399-9698

Sanderson, Terrell, Pop. 834
Terrell County ISD 100/PK-12
PO Box 747 79848 432-345-2515
Amanda Magallan, supt. Fax 345-2404
www.terrell.esc18.net
Sanderson HS 100/5-12
PO Box 747 79848 432-345-2515
Amanda Magallan, prin. Fax 345-2670

San Diego, Duval, Pop. 4,473
San Diego ISD 1,300/PK-12
609 W Labbe St 78384 361-279-3382
Dr. Samuel Bueno, supt. Fax 279-1830
www.sdisd.esc2.net
Jaime JHS 300/6-8
609 W Labbe St 78384 361-279-3382
Yvonne Munoz, prin. Fax 279-3139
San Diego HS 400/9-12
609 W Labbe St 78384 361-279-3382
Mary Garcia, prin. Fax 279-5098

San Elizario, El Paso, Pop. 13,596
San Elizario ISD 4,100/PK-12
PO Box 920 79849 915-872-3900
Sylvia Hopp, supt. Fax 872-3903
www.seisd.net
Garcia-Enriquez MS 600/7-8
PO Box 920 79849 915-872-3960
April Marioni, prin. Fax 872-3961
San Elizario HS 1,100/9-12
PO Box 920 79849 915-872-3970
Maribel Guillen, prin. Fax 872-3971

Sanger, Denton, Pop. 6,799
Sanger ISD 2,700/PK-12
601 Elm St 76266 940-458-7438
Kent Crutsinger, supt. Fax 458-5140
www.sangerisd.net/
Sanger HS 800/9-12
100 Indian Ln 76266 940-458-7497
Dr. Chris Granger, prin. Fax 458-4637
Sanger MS 500/7-8
105 Berry St 76266 940-458-7916
Sally Herrell, prin. Fax 458-5111
Tutt HS 50/Alt
404 Hughes St 76266 940-458-5701
Dr. Ann Hughes, prin. Fax 458-5759

San Isidro, Starr, Pop. 240
San Isidro ISD 300/PK-12
PO Box 10 78588 956-481-3110
Mario Alvarado, supt. Fax 481-3930
www.sanisidroisd.org
San Isidro HS 100/9-12
PO Box 10 78588 956-481-3110
Anna Garcia, prin. Fax 481-3950

San Juan, Hidalgo, Pop. 33,835
Pharr-San Juan-Alamo ISD
Supt. — See Pharr
Austin MS 700/6-8
804 S Stewart Rd 78589 956-354-2570
Liza Navarro, prin. Fax 354-3194
Pharr-San Juan-Alamo Early College HS 1,700/9-12
805 Ridge Rd 78589 956-354-2300
Alejandro Elias, prin. Fax 354-3156
Pharr-San Juan-Alamo E. Ballew CTE HS 200/Alt
715 S Standard Ave 78589 956-354-2520
Stella Sanchez, prin. Fax 354-3116
Yzaguirre MS 900/6-8
605 E FM 495 78589 956-354-2630
Rebecca Luna, prin. Fax 354-3230

San Marcos, Hays, Pop. 44,109
San Marcos Consolidated ISD 7,600/PK-12
PO Box 1087 78667 512-393-6700
Michael Cardona, supt. Fax 393-6709
www.smcisd.net
Goodnight MS 1,000/6-8
PO Box 1087 78667 512-393-6550
Rose Pearson, prin. Fax 393-6560
Lamar - Phoenix Learning Center Alt
PO Box 1087 78667 512-393-6932
Judy Mitchell, prin. Fax 393-6999
Miller MS 700/6-8
PO Box 1087 78667 512-393-6660
Richard Duvall, prin. Fax 393-6602
San Marcos HS 2,100/9-12
PO Box 1087 78667 512-393-6300
Kelli Lopez, prin. Fax 393-6893

Gary Job Corps Center Post-Sec.
PO Box 967 78667 512-396-6561
San Marcos Academy 300/6-12
2801 Ranch Road 12 78666 512-753-8000
Jimmie Scott, pres. Fax 753-8031
San Marcos Adventist Academy 100/PK-10
1523 Old Ranch Road 12 78666 512-392-9475
Texas State University San Marcos Post-Sec.
601 University Dr 78666 512-245-2111

San Perlita, Willacy, Pop. 573
San Perlita ISD 300/PK-12
PO Box 37 78590 956-248-5563
Albert Pena, supt. Fax 248-5561
www.spisd.org
San Perlita HS 100/9-12
PO Box 37 78590 956-248-5250
Adrian Montemayor, prin. Fax 248-5103
San Perlita MS 100/6-8
PO Box 37 78590 956-248-5250
Adrian Montemayor, prin. Fax 248-5103

San Saba, San Saba, Pop. 3,082
San Saba ISD 700/PK-12
808 W Wallace St 76877 325-372-3771
Leigh Ann Glaze, supt. Fax 372-5977
www.san-saba.net
San Saba HS 200/9-12
808 W Wallace St 76877 325-372-3786
Dr. Scott Snyder, prin. Fax 372-3478
San Saba MS 200/5-8
808 W Wallace St 76877 325-372-3200
Dave Lewis, prin. Fax 372-5228

Santa Anna, Coleman, Pop. 1,086
Santa Anna ISD 200/PK-12
701 Bowie St 76878 325-348-3136
David Robinett, supt. Fax 348-3141
santaanna.netxv.net
Santa Anna HS 100/7-12
701 Bowie St 76878 325-348-3137
Laurie Hunter, prin. Fax 348-3149

Santa Fe, Galveston, Pop. 12,112
Santa Fe ISD 4,600/PK-12
PO Box 370 77510 409-925-9001
Dr. Leigh Wall, supt. Fax 925-4002
www.sfisd.org/
Santa Fe HS 1,400/9-12
PO Box 370 77510 409-925-2700
Rachel Blundell, prin. Fax 925-2773
Santa Fe JHS 1,100/6-8
PO Box 370 77510 409-925-9300
Kimberly Ross, prin. Fax 927-4106

Santa Maria, Cameron, Pop. 732
Santa Maria ISD 700/PK-12
PO Box 448 78592 956-565-6308
Maria Chavez, supt. Fax 565-0598
www.smisd.net
Santa Maria HS 200/9-12
PO Box 448 78592 956-565-9144
Cindy Taylor, prin. Fax 514-1968
Santa Maria MS 200/6-8
PO Box 448 78592 956-565-6309
Michael Abeyta, prin. Fax 565-6720

Santa Rosa, Cameron, Pop. 2,866
Santa Rosa ISD 1,200/PK-12
PO Box 368 78593 956-636-9800
Heriberto Villarreal, supt. Fax 636-1439
www.srtx.org
Nelson MS 200/6-8
PO Box 368 78593 956-636-9850
John Gray, prin. Fax 636-1519
Santa Rosa HS 400/9-12
PO Box 368 78593 956-636-9830
Rebecca Corpus, prin. Fax 636-1496

Santo, Palo Pinto
Santo ISD 500/PK-12
PO Box 67 76472 940-769-2835
Greg Gilbert, supt. Fax 769-3116
www.santoisd.net/
Santo JSHS 300/6-12
PO Box 67 76472 940-769-3847
Darla Henry, prin. Fax 769-2796

Saratoga, Hardin
West Hardin County Consolidated ISD 400/PK-12
39227 Highway 105 77585 936-274-5061
John Andrus, supt. Fax 274-4321
westhardin.org
West Hardin MSHS 200/7-12
39227 Highway 105 77585 936-274-5061
Cindy Moss, prin. Fax 274-5671

Savoy, Fannin, Pop. 820
Savoy ISD 300/PK-12
302 W Hayes St 75479 903-965-5262
Brian Neal, supt. Fax 965-7282
www.savoyisd.org
Savoy JSHS 100/7-12
302 W Hayes St 75479 903-965-4024
Mike Smith, prin. Fax 965-5608

Schertz, Guadalupe, Pop. 30,563
Schertz-Cibolo-Universal City ISD 14,100/PK-12
1060 Elbel Rd 78154 210-945-6200
Greg Gibson Ed.D., supt. Fax 945-6292
www.scuc.txed.net
Clemens HS 2,200/9-12
1001 Elbel Rd 78154 210-945-6501
Melissa Sosa, prin. Fax 945-6590
Corbett JHS 1,100/7-8
12000 Ray Corbett Dr 78154 210-619-4150
David Knox, prin. Fax 619-4190
Steele Enhanced Learning Center 2,200/Alt
204 Wright Ave 78154 210-945-6401
Jana Cervates, prin. Fax 945-6410
Other Schools – See Cibolo

Schulenburg, Fayette, Pop. 2,828
Schulenburg ISD 700/PK-12
521 North St 78956 979-743-3448
Lisa Meysembourg, supt. Fax 743-4721
www.schulenburg.txed.net
Schulenburg HS 200/9-12
150 College St 78956 979-743-3605
Charles Henke, prin. Fax 743-4721
Schulenburg JHS 200/6-8
512 North St 78956 979-743-4295
Britina Pesak, admin. Fax 743-3540

Scurry, Kaufman, Pop. 668
Scurry-Rosser ISD 1,000/PK-12
10705 S State Highway 34 75158 972-452-8823
James Sanders, supt. Fax 452-8586
www.scurry-rosser.com
Scurry-Rosser HS 300/9-12
8321 S State Highway 34 75158 972-452-8823
Christian Reed, prin. Fax 452-3694
Scurry-Rosser MS 400/4-8
10729 S State Highway 34 75158 972-452-8823
Grant Miller, prin. Fax 452-8902

Seabrook, Harris, Pop. 11,727
Clear Creek ISD
Supt. — See League City
Seabrook IS 1,000/6-8
2401 N Meyer Ave 77586 281-284-3100
David Williams, prin. Fax 284-3105

Seagraves, Gaines, Pop. 2,405
Seagraves ISD 600/PK-12
PO Box 577 79359 806-387-2035
Dr. Kevin Spiller, supt. Fax 387-2944
www.seagravesisd.net/
Seagraves HS 200/9-12
PO Box 1505 79359 806-387-2520
Josh Goen, prin. Fax 387-2944
Seagraves JHS 100/6-8
PO Box 938 79359 806-387-2646
Glenn Thompson, prin. Fax 387-2451

Sealy, Austin, Pop. 5,953
Sealy ISD 2,800/PK-12
939 Tiger Ln 77474 979-885-3516
Sheryl Moore, supt. Fax 885-6457
www.sealyisd.com
Sealy HS 800/9-12
2372 Championship Dr 77474 979-885-3515
Megan Oliver, prin. Fax 987-3398
Sealy JHS 600/6-8
939 Tiger Ln 77474 979-885-3292
Lisa Svoboda, prin. Fax 877-0743

Seguin, Guadalupe, Pop. 24,967
Navarro ISD 1,700/PK-12
6450 N State Highway 123 78155 830-372-1930
Dee Carter, supt. Fax 372-1853
www.nisd.us
Navarro HS 500/9-12
6350 N State Highway 123 78155 830-372-1931
Gary Haass, prin. Fax 401-5570
Navarro JHS 300/7-8
6450 N State Highway 123 78155 830-401-5550
Luke Morales, prin. Fax 379-3135

Seguin ISD 6,900/PK-12
1221 E Kingsbury St 78155 830-401-8600
Stetson Roane, supt. Fax 379-0392
www.seguin.k12.tx.us
Barnes MS 500/6-8
1539 Joe Carrillo Blvd 78155 830-379-4717
Michael Garza, prin. Fax 379-4239
Briesemeister MS 500/6-8
1616 W Court St 78155 830-379-0600
Elisa Carter, prin. Fax 379-0615
Burges Alternative S 50/Alt
225 N Saunders St 78155 830-401-1261
Wade Cherry, prin. Fax 379-0088
Mercer-Blumberg Learning Center 200/Alt
1205 E Kingsbury St 78155 830-401-8690
Jay Law, prin. Fax 379-1362
Seguin HS 1,800/9-12
815 Lamar 78155 830-372-5770
Hector Esquivel, prin. Fax 372-9851

Lifegate Christian S 200/K-12
395 Lifegate Ln 78155 830-372-0850
Kendra Thomas, prin. Fax 372-0895
Seguin Beauty College Post-Sec.
102 E Court St 78155 830-372-0935
Texas Lutheran University Post-Sec.
1000 W Court St 78155 830-372-8000

Seminole, Gaines, Pop. 6,373
Seminole ISD 2,700/PK-12
207 SW 6th St 79360 432-758-3662
Gary Laramore, supt. Fax 758-9833
www.seminoleisd.net
Seminole HS 700/9-12
2100 NW Avenue D 79360 432-758-5873
Robert Chappell, prin. Fax 758-8146
Seminole JHS 600/6-8
600 NW Avenue J 79360 432-758-9431
Daylan Sellers, prin. Fax 758-5795
Seminole Success Center 50/Alt
206 SW 3rd St 79360 432-758-2772
Seth Davis, prin. Fax 758-3625

Seymour, Baylor, Pop. 2,715
Seymour ISD 600/PK-12
409 W Idaho St 76380 940-889-3525
Dr. John Baker, supt. Fax 889-5340
www.seymour-isd.net
Seymour HS 200/9-12
409 W Idaho St 76380 940-889-2947
Brian Bibb, prin. Fax 889-1045
Seymour MS 200/5-8
409 W Idaho St 76380 940-889-4548
Morris Davis, prin. Fax 889-4962

Shady Shores, Denton, Pop. 2,560
Denton ISD
Supt. — See Denton
Myers MS 700/6-8
131 N Garza Rd 76208 940-369-1500
Angela Ricks, prin. Fax 498-0050

Shallowater, Lubbock, Pop. 2,469
Shallowater ISD 1,600/PK-12
1100 Avenue K 79363 806-832-4531
Dr. Kenny Border, supt. Fax 832-4350
www.shallowaterisd.net
Shallowater HS 400/9-12
1100 Avenue K 79363 806-832-4531
Tom Johnson, prin. Fax 832-4523
Shallowater MS 500/5-8
1100 Avenue K 79363 806-832-4531
Dr. Aron Strickland, prin. Fax 832-5543

Shamrock, Wheeler, Pop. 1,874
Shamrock ISD 400/PK-12
100 S Illinois St 79079 806-256-3492
Kenneth Shields, supt. Fax 256-3628
www.shamrockisd.net
Shamrock HS 100/9-12
100 S Illinois St 79079 806-256-2241
Brandon Mahler, prin. Fax 256-3628
Shamrock JHS 50/6-8
100 S Illinois St 79079 806-256-3492
Ed Berngen, admin. Fax 256-3628

Sheffield, Pecos
Iraan-Sheffield ISD
Supt. — See Iraan
Challenge HS 100/Alt
1 Schoolhouse Rd 79781 432-836-4572
Dr. Candra Cade, prin. Fax 836-4691

Shelbyville, Shelby
Shelbyville ISD 800/PK-12
PO Box 325 75973 936-598-2641
Dr. Ray West, supt. Fax 598-6842
www.shelbyville.k12.tx.us
Shelbyville S 800/PK-12
PO Box 325 75973 936-598-7323
Mario Osby, prin. Fax 598-6842

Shenandoah, Montgomery, Pop. 2,111

Aveda Institute Post-Sec.
19241 David Memorial Dr 77385 936-539-6770

Shepherd, San Jacinto, Pop. 2,281
Shepherd ISD 1,900/PK-12
1401 S Byrd Ave 77371 936-628-3396
Steve Pierce, supt. Fax 628-3841
www.shepherdisd.net/
Shepherd HS 500/9-12
1401 S Byrd Ave 77371 936-628-3371
Jimmy Meekins, prin. Fax 628-6986
Shepherd MS 500/6-8
1401 S Byrd Ave 77371 936-628-3377
Michael Smith, prin. Fax 628-6749

Sherman, Grayson, Pop. 37,575
Sherman ISD 7,100/PK-12
2701 N Loy Lake Rd 75090 903-891-6400
Dr. David Hicks, supt. Fax 891-6407
www.shermanisd.net
Piner MS 1,000/7-8
402 W Pecan St 75090 903-891-6470
Clinton Petty, prin. Fax 891-6475
Sherman HS 1,700/9-12
2201 E Lamar St 75090 903-891-6440
Chris Mogan, prin. Fax 891-6446
Other Schools – See Denison

Austin College Post-Sec.
900 N Grand Ave 75090 903-813-2000
Diamonds Cosmetology College Post-Sec.
1950 N Grand Ave 75090 903-891-0758
Texoma Christian S 300/PK-12
3500 W Houston St 75092 903-893-7076
Jeff Burley, head sch Fax 891-8486

Shiner, Lavaca, Pop. 2,046
Shiner ISD 600/PK-12
PO Box 804 77984 361-594-3121
Trey Lawrence, supt. Fax 594-3925
www.shinerisd.net
Shiner JSHS 300/7-12
PO Box 804 77984 361-594-3131
Brad Oden, prin. Fax 594-4295

Shiner Catholic S 300/PK-12
PO Box 725 77984 361-594-2313
Neely Yackel, prin. Fax 594-8599

Sidney, Comanche
Sidney ISD 100/PK-12
PO Box 190 76474 254-842-5500
Doug Bowden, supt. Fax 842-5731
www.sidney.esc14.net/
Sidney S 100/PK-12
PO Box 190 76474 254-842-5500
James Rucker, prin. Fax 842-5731

Sierra Blanca, Hudspeth, Pop. 550
Sierra Blanca ISD 100/K-12
PO Box 308 79851 915-369-3741
Evelyn Loeffler, supt. Fax 369-2605
www.sierrablancaisd.net
Sierra Blanca S 100/K-12
PO Box 308 79851 915-369-2781
Mark Rolf, prin. Fax 369-2605

Silsbee, Hardin, Pop. 6,524
Silsbee ISD 2,200/PK-12
415 Highway 327 W 77656 409-980-7800
Richard Bain, supt. Fax 980-7897
www.silsbeeisd.org
Edwards-Johnson Memorial Silsbee MS 600/6-8
1140 Highway 327 E 77656 409-980-7800
Sunee Stephens, prin. Fax 980-7875
Silsbee HS 800/9-12
1575 US Highway 96 N 77656 409-980-7800
Paul Trevino, prin. Fax 980-7881

Southeast Texas Career Institute Post-Sec.
975 Highway 327 E Ste 150 77656 409-386-2020

Silverton, Briscoe, Pop. 724
Silverton ISD 200/PK-12
PO Box 608 79257 806-823-2476
Michelle Francis, supt. Fax 823-2276
www.silvertonisd.net
Silverton S 200/PK-12
PO Box 608 79257 806-823-2476
Michelle Francis, supt. Fax 823-2276

Simms, Bowie
Simms ISD 500/PK-12
PO Box 9 75574 903-543-2219
Rex Burks, supt. Fax 543-2512
www.simmsisd.net/
Bowie HS 200/9-12
PO Box 9 75574 903-543-2219
Lisa Hudgeons, prin. Fax 543-2512
Bowie MS 100/6-8
PO Box 9 75574 903-543-2219
Lisa Hudgeons, prin. Fax 543-2512

Sinton, San Patricio, Pop. 5,646
Sinton ISD 2,200/PK-12
PO Box 1337 78387 361-364-6800
Pari Whitten, supt. Fax 364-6905
www.sintonisd.net/
Sinton HS 700/9-12
400 N Pirate Blvd 78387 361-364-6650
Daniel Smith, prin. Fax 364-6668
Smith MS 500/6-8
900 S San Patricio St 78387 361-364-6840
Jennifer Davis, prin. Fax 364-6856

Skidmore, Bee, Pop. 917
Skidmore-Tynan ISD 800/K-12
224 W Main St 78389 361-287-3426
Dr. Randy Hoyer, supt. Fax 287-3442
www.stbobcats.net

Skidmore-Tynan HS 200/9-12
224 W Main St 78389 361-287-3426
Hank Looney, prin. Fax 287-0146
Skidmore-Tynan JHS 200/6-8
224 W Main St 78389 361-287-3426
Dana Scott, prin. Fax 287-0714

Slaton, Lubbock, Pop. 6,048
Slaton ISD 1,300/PK-12
140 E Panhandle St 79364 806-828-6591
Julee Becker, supt. Fax 828-5506
www.slatonisd.net/
Slaton HS 400/9-12
105 N 20th St 79364 806-828-5833
Shaye Murphy, prin. Fax 828-1229
Slaton JHS 300/6-8
300 W Jean St 79364 806-828-6583
Jim Andrus, prin. Fax 828-2080

Slidell, Wise
Slidell ISD 200/PK-12
PO Box 69 76267 940-466-3118
Greg Enis, supt. Fax 466-3062
www.slidellisd.net
Slidell JSHS 100/6-12
PO Box 69 76267 940-466-3118
Marty Hair, prin. Fax 466-3607

Smithville, Bastrop, Pop. 3,753
Smithville ISD 1,800/PK-12
PO Box 479 78957 512-237-2487
Dr. Rock McNulty, supt. Fax 237-2775
www.smithvilleisd.org
Smithville HS 500/9-12
PO Box 479 78957 512-237-2451
Kenneth Parker, prin. Fax 237-5643
Smithville JHS 400/6-8
PO Box 479 78957 512-237-2407
Dr. Bethany Logan, prin. Fax 237-5624

Smyer, Hockley, Pop. 469
Smyer ISD 400/PK-12
PO Box 206 79367 806-234-2935
Dane Kerns, supt. Fax 234-2411
www.smyer-isd.org
Smyer JSHS 200/7-12
PO Box 206 79367 806-234-2935
William Black, prin. Fax 234-2411

Snook, Burleson, Pop. 502
Snook ISD 400/PK-12
PO Box 87 77878 979-272-8307
Brenda Krchnak, supt. Fax 272-5041
www.snookisd.org
Snook Secondary S 100/6-12
PO Box 87 77878 979-272-8307
Dr. Kenzie Bond, prin. Fax 272-5041

Snyder, Scurry, Pop. 11,101
Snyder ISD 2,100/PK-12
2901 37th St 79549 325-574-8900
Jim Kirkland, supt. Fax 573-9025
www.snyderisd.net
Snyder HS 700/9-12
2901 37th St 79549 325-574-8800
Chris Yeschecke, prin. Fax 573-9500
Snyder JHS 600/6-8
2901 37th St 79549 325-574-8700
Jorge Mendez, prin. Fax 574-6024

Western Texas College Post-Sec.
6200 College Ave 79549 325-573-8511

Somerset, Bexar, Pop. 1,624
Somerset ISD 4,000/PK-12
PO Box 279 78069 866-852-9858
Dr. Saul Hinojosa, supt. Fax 852-9860
www.sisdk12.net
Early College Leadership Academy 9-12
PO Box 279 78069 855-999-4634
Brandon Van Vleck, prin.
Somerset HS 1,100/9-12
PO Box 279 78069 866-852-9861
Angela Martinez, prin. Fax 667-2608
Other Schools – See Von Ormy

Somerville, Burleson, Pop. 1,362
Somerville ISD 500/PK-12
PO Box 997 77879 979-596-2153
Charles Camarillo, supt. Fax 596-1778
www.somervilleisd.org
Somerville Secondary S 200/7-12
PO Box 997 77879 979-596-1534
Dan Garza, prin. Fax 596-1778

Sonora, Sutton, Pop. 3,018
Sonora ISD 900/PK-12
807 S Concho Ave 76950 325-387-6940
Ross Aschenbeck, supt. Fax 387-5090
www.sonoraisd.net
Sonora HS 300/9-12
807 S Concho Ave 76950 325-387-6940
Sean Leamon, prin. Fax 387-5348
Sonora JHS 200/6-8
807 S Concho Ave 76950 325-387-6940
Brandon Duncan, prin. Fax 387-2007

Sour Lake, Hardin, Pop. 1,788
Hardin-Jefferson ISD 2,100/PK-12
PO Box 490 77659 409-981-6400
Shannon Holmes Ed.D., supt. Fax 287-2283
www.hjisd.net/
Hardin-Jefferson HS 600/9-12
PO Box 639 77659 409-981-6430
Patrick Brown, prin.
Henderson MS, PO Box 649 77659 500/6-8
Darrell Westfall, prin. 409-981-6420

South Houston, Harris, Pop. 16,918
Pasadena ISD
Supt. — See Pasadena
South Houston HS 2,500/9-12
3820 S Shaver St 77587 713-740-0350
Andrea Wenke, prin. Fax 740-4155
South Houston IS 900/6-8
900 College Ave 77587 713-740-0490
Laura Gomez, prin. Fax 740-4097

Southlake, Tarrant, Pop. 26,042
Carroll ISD 7,800/PK-12
2400 N Carroll Ave 76092 817-949-8282
Dr. David J. Faltys, supt. Fax 949-8228
www.southlakecarroll.edu
Carroll HS 1,300/9-10
800 N White Chapel Blvd 76092 817-949-5600
Paul Giamanco, prin. Fax 949-5656
Carroll MS 700/7-8
1800 Kirkwood Blvd 76092 817-949-5400
Stephanie Mangels, prin. Fax 949-5454
Carroll SHS 1,300/11-12
1501 W Southlake Blvd 76092 817-949-5800
M. Shawn Duhon, prin. Fax 949-5858
Dawson MS 700/7-8
400 S Kimball Ave 76092 817-949-5500
Ryan Wilson, prin. Fax 949-5555

Clariden S 100/PK-12
100 Clariden Ranch Rd 76092 682-237-0400

Southland, Garza
Southland ISD 200/PK-12
190 Eighth St 79364 806-996-5599
Wynn Robinson, supt. Fax 996-5342
www.southlandisd.net
Southland S 200/PK-12
190 Eighth St 79364 806-996-5339
Wynn Robinson, admin. Fax 996-5595

Spearman, Hansford, Pop. 3,341
Spearman ISD 900/PK-12
403 E 11th Ave 79081 806-659-3233
Wm. Clay Montgomery, supt. Fax 659-2079
www.spearmanisd.net
Spearman HS 200/9-12
403 E 11th Ave 79081 806-659-2584
Kelly Carrell, prin. Fax 659-3824
Spearman JHS 200/6-8
313 W 5th Ave 79081 806-659-2563
Shane Whiteley, prin. Fax 659-2243

Spicewood, Burnet
Lake Travis ISD
Supt. — See Austin
Lake Travis MS 1,000/6-8
4932 Bee Creek Rd 78669 512-533-6200
Jodie Villemaire, prin. Fax 533-6201

Splendora, Montgomery, Pop. 1,597
Splendora ISD 3,200/PK-12
23419 FM 2090 Rd 77372 281-689-3128
Dr. Michael Say, supt. Fax 689-7509
www.splendoraisd.org/
Splendora HS 1,000/9-12
23747 FM 2090 Rd 77372 281-689-8008
John DeBrock, prin. Fax 689-8675
Splendora JHS 500/6-8
23411 FM 2090 Rd 77372 281-689-6343
Kent Broussard, prin. Fax 689-8702

Spring, Harris, Pop. 53,043
Conroe ISD
Supt. — See Conroe
York JHS 900/7-8
3515 Waterbend Cv 77386 832-592-8600
Dr. Christopher Povich, prin. Fax 592-8684

Klein ISD
Supt. — See Klein
Hildebrandt IS 1,100/6-8
22800 Hildebrandt Rd 77389 832-249-5100
Joffrey Jones, prin. Fax 249-4068
Klein Collins HS 3,500/9-12
20811 Ella Blvd 77388 832-484-5500
Randy Kirk, prin. Fax 484-7811
Klein Oak HS 3,800/9-12
22603 Northcrest Dr 77389 832-484-5000
Dr. Brian Greeney, prin. Fax 484-7831
Schindewolf IS 1,300/6-8
20903 Ella Blvd 77388 832-249-5900
Dr. Curtis Simmons, prin. Fax 249-4072

Spring ISD
Supt. — See Houston
Bailey MS 1,200/6-8
3377 James Leo Dr 77373 281-891-8000
Tarrynce Robinson, prin. Fax 891-8001
Dueitt MS 1,000/6-8
1 Eagle Xing 77373 281-891-7800
Dr. Benjamin Bostick, prin. Fax 891-7801
Spring HS 3,500/9-12
19428 Interstate 45 77373 281-891-7000
Diaka R. Carter, prin. Fax 891-7001
Twin Creeks MS 1,000/6-8
27100 Cypresswood Dr 77373 281-891-7850
Dario Villota, prin. Fax 891-7851
Wunsche HS Vo/Tech
900 Wunsche Loop 77373 281-891-7650
Bob Thompson, prin. Fax 891-7651

Cunae International S 100/PK-12
5655 Creekside Forest Dr 77389 281-516-3770
Anji Price, dir.
Founders Christian S 100/K-10
24724 Aldine Westfield Rd 77373 281-602-8006
Joe Jones, head sch Fax 403-2420
Frassati Catholic HS 9-12
22151 Frassati Way 77389 832-616-3217
Sr. John Paul Myers, prin. Fax 907-0675
Providence Classical S PK-12
18100 Stuebner Airline Rd 77379 281-320-0500

Spring Branch, Comal
Comal ISD
Supt. — See New Braunfels
Smithson Valley HS 2,300/9-12
14001 State Highway 46 W 78070 830-885-1000
Michael Wahl, prin. Fax 885-1001
Smithson Valley MS 1,000/6-8
6101 FM 311 78070 830-885-1200
Michael Keranen, prin. Fax 885-1201
Spring Branch MS 1,000/6-8
21053 State Highway 46 W 78070 830-885-8800
Chris Smith, prin. Fax 885-8801

Springtown, Parker, Pop. 2,624
Springtown ISD 3,400/PK-12
301 E 5th St 76082 817-220-1700
Mike Kelley, supt. Fax 523-5766
www.springtownisd.net
Springtown HS 900/9-12
915 W Highway 199 76082 817-220-3888
Scott McPherson, prin. Fax 523-5290
Springtown MS 500/7-8
500 Pojo Dr 76082 817-220-7455
Mark Wilson, prin. Fax 220-2395

Spur, Dickens, Pop. 1,312
Spur ISD 300/PK-12
PO Box 250 79370 806-271-3272
Loretta Velez, supt. Fax 271-4575
www.spurbulldogs.com
Spur MSHS 100/6-12
PO Box 250 79370 806-271-3385
Craig Hamilton, prin. Fax 271-4575

Spurger, Tyler
Spurger ISD 400/PK-12
PO Box 38 77660 409-429-3464
Kendall Smith, supt. Fax 429-3770
www.spurgerisd.org
Spurger HS 100/7-12
PO Box 38 77660 409-429-3464
Ronald Ford, prin. Fax 429-3770

Stafford, Fort Bend, Pop. 17,344
Stafford Municipal SD 3,500/PK-12
1625 Staffordshire Rd 77477 281-261-9200
Dr. Robert Bostic, supt. Fax 261-9249
www.staffordmsd.org
Stafford Alternative Education Center Alt
1625 Staffordshire Rd 77477 281-261-9280
Carlotta Allen, admin. Fax 208-6118
Stafford HS 1,000/9-12
1625 Staffordshire Rd 77477 281-261-9239
Misti Morgan, prin. Fax 261-9347
Stafford MS 500/7-8
1625 Staffordshire Rd 77477 281-261-9215
Andre Roberson, prin. Fax 261-9349

Stamford, Jones, Pop. 3,075
Stamford ISD 700/PK-12
507 S Orient St 79553 325-773-2705
Shaun Barnett, supt. Fax 773-5684
www.stamford.esc14.net
Stamford HS 200/9-12
507 S Orient St 79553 325-773-2701
Greg London, prin. Fax 773-4015
Stamford MS 100/6-8
507 S Orient St 79553 325-773-2651
Kevin White, prin. Fax 773-4052

Stanton, Martin, Pop. 2,466
Stanton ISD 900/PK-12
PO Box 730 79782 432-756-2244
David Carr, supt. Fax 756-2052
www.stanton.esc18.net/
Stanton HS 200/9-12
PO Box 730 79782 432-756-3326
Mark Cotton, prin. Fax 756-2248
Stanton MS 200/6-8
PO Box 730 79782 432-756-2544
Albert Chavez, prin. Fax 756-2502

Stephenville, Erath, Pop. 16,950
Huckabay ISD 200/K-12
200 County Road 421 76401 254-968-8476
Troy Roberts, supt. Fax 965-3740
www.hisd.us
Huckabay S 200/K-12
200 County Road 421 76401 254-968-5274
Nick Heupel, prin. Fax 965-3740

Stephenville ISD 3,700/PK-12
2655 W Overhill Dr 76401 254-968-7990
Matt Underwood, supt. Fax 968-5942
www.sville.us
Henderson JHS 600/7-8
2798 W Frey St 76401 254-968-6967
Donna Ward, prin. Fax 965-7018
Stephenville HS 1,000/9-12
2650 W Overhill Dr 76401 254-968-4141
Stephanie Traweek, prin. Fax 968-4897

Stephenville Beauty College Post-Sec.
951 S Lillian St 76401 254-968-2111
Tarleton State University Post-Sec.
PO Box T0001 76402 254-968-9000

Sterling City, Sterling, Pop. 875
Sterling City ISD 300/K-12
PO Box 786 76951 325-378-4781
Bob Rauch, supt. Fax 378-2283
www.sterlingcityisd.net
Sterling City HS 100/6-12
PO Box 786 76951 325-378-5821
Ty Stevens, prin. Fax 378-2087

Stinnett, Hutchinson, Pop. 1,860
Plemons-Stinnett-Phillips Cons ISD 600/PK-12
PO Box 3440 79083 806-878-2858
Bill Wiggins, supt. Fax 878-3585
www.pspcisd.net

West Texas HS 200/9-12
PO Box 3440 79083 806-878-2456
Kent Torbert, prin. Fax 878-3585
West Texas MS 200/6-8
PO Box 3440 79083 806-878-2247
Kevin Freriks, prin. Fax 878-3585

Stockdale, Wilson, Pop. 1,428
Stockdale ISD 800/K-12
PO Box 7 78160 830-996-3551
Paul Darilek, supt. Fax 996-1071
www.stockdaleisd.net
Stockdale HS 200/9-12
PO Box 7 78160 830-996-3103
Sandy Lynn, prin. Fax 996-1046
Stockdale JHS 200/6-8
PO Box 7 78160 830-996-3153
Sharon Dunn, prin. Fax 996-3055

Stratford, Sherman, Pop. 2,009
Stratford ISD 600/PK-12
PO Box 108 79084 806-366-3300
Jerry Birdsong, supt. Fax 366-3304
www.stratfordisd.net
Stratford HS 200/9-12
PO Box 108 79084 806-366-3330
Phillip Hanna, prin. Fax 366-3304
Stratford JHS 200/5-8
PO Box 108 79084 806-366-3320
Clint Seward, prin. Fax 366-3307

Strawn, Palo Pinto, Pop. 647
Strawn ISD 200/PK-12
PO Box 428 76475 254-672-5313
Richard Mitchell, supt. Fax 672-5662
www.strawnschool.net
Strawn S 200/PK-12
PO Box 428 76475 254-672-5776
Richard Mitchell, prin. Fax 672-5662

Sudan, Lamb, Pop. 949
Sudan ISD 400/PK-12
PO Box 249 79371 806-227-2431
Scott Harrell, supt. Fax 227-2146
www.sudanisd.net
Sudan JSHS 200/8-12
PO Box 659 79371 806-227-2431
Gordon Martin, prin. Fax 227-2121

Sugar Land, Fort Bend, Pop. 76,889
Fort Bend ISD 70,700/PK-12
16431 Lexington Blvd 77479 281-634-1000
Charles Dupre Ed.D., supt. Fax 634-1700
www.fortbendisd.com
Austin HS 2,300/9-12
3434 Pheasant Creek Dr, 281-634-2000
Mary Ellen Eidson, prin. Fax 634-2074
Clements HS 2,500/9-12
4200 Elkins Rd 77479 281-634-2150
David Yaffie, prin. Fax 634-2168
Dulles HS 2,200/9-12
550 Dulles Ave 77478 281-634-5600
Dr. Jennifer Nichols, prin. Fax 634-5681
Dulles MS 1,200/6-8
500 Dulles Ave 77478 281-634-5750
Dee Knox, prin. Fax 634-5781
First Colony MS 1,200/6-8
3225 Austin Pkwy 77479 281-634-3240
Sarah Laberge, prin. Fax 634-3267
Fort Settlement MS 1,200/6-8
5440 Elkins Rd 77479 281-634-6440
Michael Hejducek, prin. Fax 634-6456
Garcia MS 1,200/6-8
18550 Old Richmond Rd, 281-634-3160
Dr. Rizvan Quadri, prin. Fax 634-3166
Kempner HS 2,300/9-12
14777 Voss Rd, 281-634-2300
Chris Morgan, prin. Fax 634-2378
Sartartia MS 1,300/6-8
8125 Homeward Way 77479 281-634-6310
Melissa King-Knowles, prin. Fax 634-6373
Sugar Land MS 1,300/6-8
321 7th St, 281-634-3080
Keith Fickel, prin. Fax 634-3108
Technical Education Center Vo/Tech
540 Dulles Ave 77478 281-634-5671
Kennith Kendziora, admin. Fax 634-5700
Other Schools – See Houston, Missouri City, Richmond, Rosharon

---

Ft. Bend Christian Academy 800/PK-12
1250 7th St 77478 281-263-9175
David Pitre Ph.D., head sch Fax 263-9147
Logos Preparatory S K-12
PO Box 16340 77496 281-565-6467
Trent Internationale S 200/PK-12
2553 Cordes Dr 77479 281-980-5800
Huda Ahmed, prin. Fax 980-6106

Sulphur Bluff, Hopkins
Sulphur Bluff ISD 200/PK-12
PO Box 30 75481 903-945-2460
Dustin Carr, supt. Fax 945-2459
www.sulphurbluffisd.net/
Sulphur Bluff S 200/PK-12
PO Box 30 75481 903-945-2460
Amy Northcutt, prin. Fax 945-2459

Sulphur Springs, Hopkins, Pop. 15,115
North Hopkins ISD 500/PK-12
1994 Farm Road 71 W 75482 903-945-2192
Dr. Darin Jolly, supt. Fax 945-2531
www.northhopkins.net
North Hopkins JSHS 200/6-12
1994 Farm Road 71 W 75482 903-945-2192
Rob Stanley, prin. Fax 945-2531

Sulphur Springs ISD 4,200/PK-12
631 Connally St 75482 903-885-2153
Michael Lamb, supt. Fax 439-6162
www.ssisd.net/
Sulphur Springs HS 1,100/9-12
1200 Connally St 75482 903-885-2158
Derek Driver, prin. Fax 439-6116
Sulphur Springs MS 1,000/6-8
832 Wildcat Way 75482 903-885-7741
Jena Williams, prin. Fax 439-6126

Sundown, Hockley, Pop. 1,386
Sundown ISD 700/PK-12
PO Box 1110 79372 806-229-3021
Scott Marshall, supt. Fax 229-2004
www.sundownisd.com
Sundown HS 100/9-12
PO Box 1110 79372 806-229-2511
Brent Evans, prin. Fax 229-2004
Sundown MS 200/6-8
PO Box 1110 79372 806-229-4691
Eddie Carter, prin. Fax 229-2004

Sunnyvale, Dallas, Pop. 5,012
Sunnyvale ISD 1,400/PK-12
417 E Tripp Rd 75182 972-226-5974
Doug Williams, supt. Fax 226-6882
www.sunnyvaleisd.com
Sunnyvale HS 400/9-12
222 N Collins Rd 75182 972-203-4600
Ron Sterling, prin. Fax 226-2854
Sunnyvale MS 400/5-8
216 N Collins Rd 75182 972-226-2922
Carmen Ayo, prin. Fax 226-0982

Grace Fellowship Christian S 100/PK-12
3052 N Belt Line Rd 75182 972-226-4499

Sunray, Moore, Pop. 1,899
Sunray ISD 500/PK-12
PO Box 240 79086 806-948-4411
Brian Thompson, supt. Fax 948-5274
www.sunrayisd.net
Sunray HS 200/9-12
PO Box 240 79086 806-948-5515
Sid Whiteley, prin. Fax 948-5399
Sunray MS 200/5-8
PO Box 240 79086 806-948-4444
Pam Keisling, prin. Fax 948-4208

Sweeny, Brazoria, Pop. 3,645
Sweeny ISD 1,900/PK-12
1310 N Elm St 77480 979-491-8000
Randy Miksch, supt. Fax 491-8030
www.sweenyisd.org
Sweeny HS 600/9-12
1310 N Elm St 77480 979-491-8100
Robert Morrison, prin. Fax 491-8171
Sweeny JHS 500/6-8
1310 N Elm St 77480 979-491-8200
Michael Saul, prin. Fax 491-8274

Sweetwater, Nolan, Pop. 10,784
Sweetwater ISD 2,200/PK-12
207 Musgrove St 79556 325-235-8601
Terry Pittman, supt. Fax 235-5561
www.sweetwaterisd.net/
Sweetwater HS 500/9-12
1205 Ragland St 79556 325-235-4371
Dr. Ron Morris, prin. Fax 235-4861
Sweetwater MS 500/6-8
305 Lamar St 79556 325-236-6303
Jeff Withrow, prin. Fax 236-6941

Texas State Technical College Post-Sec.
300 Homer K Taylor Dr 79556 325-235-7300

Taft, San Patricio, Pop. 3,018
Taft ISD 1,100/PK-12
400 College St 78390 361-528-2636
Jose Lopez, supt. Fax 528-2223
www.taftisd.net
Taft HS 300/9-12
502 Rincon Rd 78390 361-528-2636
Angel Lopez, prin. Fax 528-3918
Taft JHS 200/6-8
727 McIntyre Ave 78390 361-528-2636
Christine Acosta, prin. Fax 528-5477

Tahoka, Lynn, Pop. 2,660
Tahoka ISD 600/PK-12
PO Box 1230 79373 806-561-4105
Dr. George McFarland, supt. Fax 561-4160
www.tahokaisd.us
Tahoka HS 200/9-12
PO Box 1500 79373 806-561-4538
Jeffrey Perez, prin. Fax 561-6082
Tahoka MS 100/6-8
PO Box 1500 79373 806-561-4538
Kelly Kieth, prin. Fax 561-6082

Tatum, Rusk, Pop. 1,369
Tatum ISD 1,600/PK-12
PO Box 808 75691 903-947-6482
Dr. Dee Hartt Ed.D., supt. Fax 947-3295
www.tatumisd.org
Tatum HS 500/9-12
PO Box 808 75691 903-947-6482
Allen Koch, prin. Fax 947-6206
Tatum MS 400/6-8
PO Box 808 75691 903-947-6482
Kevin Smith, prin. Fax 947-3295

Taylor, Williamson, Pop. 14,982
Taylor ISD 3,100/PK-12
3101 N Main St Ste 104 76574 512-365-1391
Jerry Vaughn, supt. Fax 365-3800
www.taylorisd.org

Taylor HS 1,000/9-12
355 FM 973 76574 512-365-1291
Andrew Maddox, prin. Fax 365-9334
Taylor MS 700/6-8
304 Carlos Parker Blvd NW 76574 512-365-8591
Hector Martinez, prin. Fax 365-8589

Teague, Freestone, Pop. 3,527
Teague ISD 1,300/PK-12
420 N 10th Ave 75860 254-739-1300
Dr. Nate Carman, supt. Fax 739-5223
www.teagueisd.org
Teague HS 300/9-12
420 N 10th Ave 75860 254-739-1500
Chris Skinner, prin. Fax 739-2724
Teague JHS 300/6-8
420 N 10th Ave 75860 254-739-1450
Drake Paris, prin. Fax 739-5896
Teague Lion Academy Alt
420 N 10th Ave 75860 254-739-1444
Cathy Schmidt, prin.

Temple, Bell, Pop. 64,746
Belton ISD
Supt. — See Belton
Lake Belton MS 800/6-8
8818 Tarver Dr 76502 254-215-2900
Kris Hobson, prin. Fax 215-2901
North Belton MS 6-8
7907 Prairie View Rd 76502 254-316-5200
Joe Brown, prin. Fax 316-5201

Temple ISD 8,000/PK-12
PO Box 788 76503 254-215-8473
Dr. Robin Battershell, supt. Fax 215-6783
www.tisd.org
Bonham MS 500/6-8
4600 Midway Dr 76502 254-215-6600
Sandra Atmar, prin. Fax 215-6634
Edwards Academy 100/Alt
1414 W Barton Ave 76504 254-215-6944
Phillip Perry, prin. Fax 215-6946
Lamar MS 600/6-8
2120 N 1st St 76501 254-215-6444
Billy Madden, prin. Fax 215-6483
Temple HS 1,900/9-12
415 N 31st St 76504 254-215-7000
Dr. Jason Mayo, prin. Fax 899-6926
Travis Science Academy 700/6-8
1551 S 25th St 76504 254-215-6300
Kristina Carter, prin. Fax 215-6352
Wheatley Alternative Education Center 100/Alt
515 E Avenue D 76501 254-215-5665
Carl Pleasant, prin. Fax 215-5673

Central Texas Beauty College Post-Sec.
2010 S 57th St 76504 254-773-9911
Central Texas Christian S 600/PK-12
4141 W FM 93 76502 254-939-5700
Brian Littlefield, head sch Fax 939-5769
Holy Trinity Catholic HS 100/9-12
6608 W Adams Ave 76502 254-771-0787
Blake Evans, prin. Fax 771-2285
Scott & White Memorial Hospital & Clinic Post-Sec.
2401 S 31st St 76508 254-724-5177
Temple College Post-Sec.
2600 S 1st St 76504 254-298-8282

Tenaha, Shelby, Pop. 1,146
Tenaha ISD 600/PK-12
PO Box 318 75974 936-248-5000
Scott Tyner, supt. Fax 248-3902
www.tenahaisd.com/
Tenaha HS 300/6-12
PO Box 318 75974 936-248-5000
Judy Monroe, prin. Fax 248-3626

Terlingua, Brewster, Pop. 54
Terlingua Common SD 50/K-12
PO Box 256 79852 432-371-2281
Bobbie Jones, supt. Fax 371-2245
www.terlinguacsd.com
Big Bend S 50/K-12
PO Box 256 79852 432-371-2281
Bobbie Jones, admin. Fax 371-2245

Terrell, Kaufman, Pop. 15,583
Terrell ISD 4,200/PK-12
700 N Catherine St 75160 972-563-7504
Amanda Magallan, supt. Fax 563-1406
www.terrellisd.org
Alternative Education Center 50/Alt
305 W College St 75160 972-563-6319
Tracie Pritchett, prin. Fax 563-4786
Furlough MS 600/7-8
1351 Colquitt Rd 75160 972-563-7501
Jay Thompson, prin. Fax 563-5721
Phoenix Center Alt
204 W High St 75160 972-551-5796
Terrell HS 1,000/9-12
400 Poetry Rd 75160 972-563-7525
Dr. Juan Solis, prin. Fax 563-6318

Poetry Community Christian S 200/K-12
18688 FM 986 75160 972-563-7227
Dr. Anne Horan, admin. Fax 563-0025
Southwestern Christian College Post-Sec.
PO Box 10 75160 972-524-3341

Texarkana, Bowie, Pop. 35,750
Liberty-Eylau ISD 2,300/PK-12
2901 Leopard Dr 75501 903-832-1535
Ronnie Thompson, supt. Fax 838-9444
www.leisd.net
Liberty-Eylau HS 700/9-12
2905 Leopard Dr 75501 903-832-1535
Kendrick Smith, prin. Fax 831-6113

Liberty-Eylau MS 400/5-8
5555 Leopard Dr 75501 903-838-5555
Jeff Wright, prin. Fax 832-6700
Liberty-Eylau S of Success 50/Alt
766 Macedonia Rd 75501 903-831-5767
Barry Baker, prin. Fax 838-0493

Pleasant Grove ISD 2,000/PK-12
8500 N Kings Hwy 75503 903-831-4086
Dr. Jason Smith, supt. Fax 831-4435
www.pgisd.net
Pleasant Grove HS 600/9-12
5406 McKnight Rd 75503 903-832-8005
Darren Williams, prin. Fax 832-5381
Pleasant Grove MS 500/6-8
5605 Cooks Ln 75503 903-831-4295
Linda Erie, prin. Fax 831-5501

Red Lick ISD 500/K-8
3511 N FM 2148 75503 903-838-8230
Nick Blain, supt. Fax 831-6134
www.redlickisd.com
Red Lick MS 200/5-8
3511 N FM 2148 75503 903-838-6006
Jason Dempsey, prin. Fax 831-6134

Texarkana ISD 7,100/PK-12
4241 Summerhill Rd 75503 903-794-3651
Paul Norton, supt. Fax 792-2632
www.txkisd.net
Options S 100/Alt
3201 Lincoln Ave 75503 903-793-5632
Amy Doss, prin. Fax 798-2131
Texas HS 1,900/9-12
4001 Summerhill Rd 75503 903-794-3891
Brad Bailey, prin. Fax 792-8971
Texas MS 1,500/6-8
2100 College Dr 75503 903-793-5631
Tim Lambert, prin. Fax 792-2935

Texarkana College Post-Sec.
2500 N Robison Rd 75501 903-823-3456
Texas A&M University Texarkana Post-Sec.
7101 University Ave 75503 903-223-3000
Wadley Regional Medical Center Post-Sec.
1000 Pine St 75501 903-798-8000

Texas City, Galveston, Pop. 44,454
Texas City ISD 7,200/PK-12
PO Box 1150 77592 409-916-0100
Cynthia Lusignolo Ed.D., supt. Fax 942-2655
www.tcisd.org
Blocker MS 900/7-8
1800 9th Ave N 77590 409-916-0700
Julie Southworth, prin. Fax 942-2755
Texas City HS 1,800/9-12
1431 9th Ave N 77590 409-916-0800
Holly LaRoe, prin. Fax 942-2672
Wilson Alternative S 50/Alt
1508 6th St N 77590 409-916-0280
Joy Toney, prin. Fax 942-2462
Other Schools – See La Marque

College of the Mainland Post-Sec.
1200 N Amburn Rd 77591 409-938-1211

Texline, Dallam, Pop. 485
Texline ISD 100/K-12
PO Box 60 79087 806-362-4667
Jody Johnson, supt. Fax 362-4538
www.texlineisd.net
Texline S 100/K-12
PO Box 60 79087 806-362-4284
Terrell Jones, prin. Fax 362-4938

The Colony, Denton, Pop. 35,324
Lewisville ISD
Supt. — See Flower Mound
Griffin MS 700/6-8
5105 N Colony Blvd 75056 469-713-5973
Amy Boughten, prin. Fax 350-9187
Lakeview MS 800/6-8
4300 Keys Dr 75056 469-713-5974
Jeremy Turner, prin. Fax 350-9202
The Colony HS 2,000/9-12
4301 Blair Oaks Dr 75056 469-713-5178
Tim Baxter, prin. Fax 350-9336

The Woodlands, Montgomery, Pop. 92,202
Conroe ISD
Supt. — See Conroe
Academy of Science & Technology 9-12
3701 College Park Dr 77384 936-709-3250
Dr. Susan Caffery, hdmstr. Fax 709-3299
Knox JHS 1,300/7-8
12104 Sawmill Rd 77380 832-592-8400
Joe Daw, prin. Fax 592-8410
McCullough JHS 2,300/7-8
3800 S Panther Creek Dr 77381 832-592-5100
Chris McCord, prin. Fax 592-5116
The Woodlands College Park SHS 2,700/9-12
3701 College Park Dr 77384 936-709-3000
Dr. Mark Murrell, prin. Fax 709-3019
The Woodlands HS Ninth Grade Campus 1,100/9-9
10010 Branch Crossing Dr 77382 832-592-8200
Jill Houser, prin. Fax 592-8202
The Woodlands SHS 3,100/10-12
6101 Research Forest Dr 77381 936-709-1200
Gregg Colschen, prin. Fax 709-1299

Tomball ISD
Supt. — See Tomball
Creekside Park JHS 6-8
8711 Creekside Green Dr, 281-357-3282
Chris Scott, prin. Fax 516-9606

Cooper S 1,000/PK-12
1 John Cooper Dr 77381 281-367-0900
Michael Maher, head sch Fax 292-9201
Esprit International S 100/PK-12
4890 W Panther Creek Dr 77381 281-298-9200
Grace School of Theology Post-Sec.
PO Box 7477 77387 877-476-8674
Legacy Preparatory Christian Academy 200/PK-12
9768 Research Forest Dr, 936-337-2000
Woodlands Christian Academy 400/PK-12
5800 Academy Way 77384 936-273-2555
Julie Ambler, head sch Fax 271-3115

Thorndale, Milam, Pop. 1,329
Thorndale ISD 600/PK-12
PO Box 870 76577 512-898-2538
Adam Ivy, supt. Fax 898-5356
www.thorndale.txed.net
Thorndale HS 200/9-12
PO Box 870 76577 512-898-2321
Orlando Vargas, prin. Fax 898-5558
Thorndale MS 200/6-8
PO Box 870 76577 512-898-2670
Lee Hafley, prin. Fax 898-5505

Thrall, Williamson, Pop. 832
Thrall ISD 500/K-12
201 S Bounds St 76578 512-898-0062
Tommy Hooker, supt. Fax 898-5349
www.thrallisd.com
Thrall MSHS 200/6-12
201 S Bounds St 76578 512-898-5193
Travis Dube, prin. Fax 898-2132

Three Rivers, Live Oak, Pop. 1,845
Three Rivers ISD 600/PK-12
351 S School Rd 78071 361-786-3626
Dr. Mary Springs, supt. Fax 786-2555
www.trisd.org
Three Rivers JSHS 300/7-12
351A S School Rd 78071 361-786-3531
Charles Odom, prin. Fax 786-2555

Throckmorton, Throckmorton, Pop. 823
Throckmorton ISD 100/PK-12
210 College St 76483 940-849-2411
Ken Baugh, supt. Fax 849-3345
www.throck.org
Throckmorton S 100/PK-12
210 College St 76483 940-849-2421
David Farquhar, prin. Fax 849-3345

Tilden, McMullen, Pop. 261
McMullen County ISD 200/PK-12
PO Box 359 78072 361-274-2000
Dave Underwood, supt. Fax 274-3665
www.mcisd.us
McMullen County S 200/PK-12
PO Box 359 78072 361-274-2000
Joe Timms, prin. Fax 274-3580

Timpson, Shelby, Pop. 1,144
Timpson ISD 600/PK-12
PO Box 370 75975 936-254-2463
Mid Johnson, supt. Fax 254-3878
www.timpsonisd.com
Timpson HS 100/9-12
PO Box 370 75975 936-254-3125
Ronald Lindgren, prin. Fax 254-3263
Timpson MS 200/6-8
PO Box 370 75975 936-254-2078
Calvin Smith, prin. Fax 254-2355

Tioga, Grayson, Pop. 788
Tioga ISD 300/PK-12
PO Box 159 76271 940-437-2366
Dr. Charles Holloway, supt. Fax 437-9986
www.tiogaisd.net/
Tioga S 300/PK-12
PO Box 159 76271 940-437-2366
Josh Ballinger, prin. Fax 437-9986

Tivoli, Refugio, Pop. 475
Austwell-Tivoli ISD 200/K-12
207 Redfish St 77990 361-286-3212
Dr. Antonio Aguirre, supt. Fax 286-3637
www.atisd.net
Austwell-Tivoli JSHS 100/7-12
207 Redfish St 77990 361-286-3582
Stephen Maldonado, prin. Fax 286-3637

Tolar, Hood, Pop. 677
Tolar ISD 700/PK-12
PO Box 368 76476 254-835-4718
Travis Stilwell, supt. Fax 835-4704
www.tolarisd.org
Tolar HS 200/9-12
PO Box 368 76476 254-835-4316
Brad Morgan, prin. Fax 835-4237
Tolar JHS 200/6-8
PO Box 368 76476 254-835-5207
Lindsay Morgan, prin. Fax 835-5208

Tomball, Harris, Pop. 10,569
Tomball ISD 13,400/PK-12
310 S Cherry St 77375 281-357-3100
Huey Kinchen, supt. Fax 357-3128
www.tomballisd.net
Tomball Alternative Education Center Alt
1302 Keefer Rd 77375 281-357-3281
Becky Dale, prin. Fax 357-3291
Tomball HS 1,600/9-12
30330 Quinn Rd 77375 281-357-3220
Greg Quinn, prin. Fax 357-3248
Tomball JHS 800/7-8
30403 Quinn Rd 77375 281-357-3000
Chad Allman, prin. Fax 357-3027
Tomball Memorial HS 1,800/9-12
19100 Northpointe Ridge Ln 77377 281-357-3230
Chad Smith, prin. Fax 357-3240
Willow Wood JHS 1,000/7-8
11770 Gregson Rd 77377 281-357-3030
Robert Frost, prin. Fax 357-3045
Other Schools – See The Woodlands

Concordia Lutheran HS 400/9-12
700 E Main St 77375 281-351-2547
Joel Bode, head sch Fax 255-8806
Lone Star College - Tomball Post-Sec.
30555 State Highway 249 77375 281-351-3300
Rosehill Christian S 400/PK-12
19830 FM 2920 Rd 77377 281-351-8114
Dean Unsicker, head sch Fax 516-3418
Woodlands Preparatory S 300/PK-12
27440 Kuykendahl Rd 77375 281-516-0600
Arthur Tyler, head sch Fax 516-1155

Tom Bean, Grayson, Pop. 1,019
Tom Bean ISD 700/K-12
PO Box 128 75489 903-546-6076
Eddie White, supt. Fax 546-6104
www.tbisd.org
Tom Bean HS 200/9-12
PO Box 128 75489 903-546-6319
Dr. Susan Foster, prin. Fax 546-6319
Tom Bean MS 200/6-8
PO Box 128 75489 903-546-6161
Julie Cummings, prin. Fax 546-6798

Tornillo, El Paso, Pop. 1,568
Tornillo ISD 1,100/PK-12
PO Box 170 79853 915-765-3000
Dr. Jeannie Meza-Chavez, supt. Fax 765-3099
www.tisd.us/
Tornillo HS 400/9-12
PO Box 170 79853 915-765-3500
Mauro Guerrero, prin. Fax 765-3599
Tornillo JHS 200/6-8
PO Box 170 79853 915-765-3400
Marco Tristan, prin. Fax 765-3499

Trent, Taylor, Pop. 330
Trent ISD 200/PK-12
PO Box 105 79561 325-862-6125
Leanna West, supt. Fax 862-6448
www.trent.esc14.net
Trent S 200/PK-12
PO Box 105 79561 325-862-6125
Leanna West, admin. Fax 862-6448

Trenton, Fannin, Pop. 627
Trenton ISD 500/PK-12
PO Box 5 75490 903-989-2245
Rick Foreman, supt. Fax 989-2767
www.trentonisd.com
Trenton HS 200/9-12
PO Box 5 75490 903-989-2242
Rick Foreman, prin. Fax 989-2767
Trenton MS 100/5-8
PO Box 5 75490 903-989-2243
Trent Hamilton, prin. Fax 989-5173

Trinidad, Henderson, Pop. 863
Trinidad ISD 200/PK-12
105 W Eaton St 75163 903-778-2673
Corey Jenkins, supt. Fax 778-4120
www.trinidadisd.com
Trinidad S 200/PK-12
105 W Eaton St 75163 903-778-2673
Corey Jenkins, admin. Fax 778-4120

Trinity, Trinity, Pop. 2,644
Trinity ISD 1,200/PK-12
PO Box 752 75862 936-594-3569
John Kaufman, supt. Fax 594-8425
www.trinityisd.net
Trinity HS 300/9-12
PO Box 752 75862 936-594-3560
Eric Kelley, prin. Fax 594-2162
Trinity MS 300/6-8
PO Box 752 75862 936-594-2321
Brittaney Cassidy, prin. Fax 594-3041

Trophy Club, Denton, Pop. 7,926
Northwest ISD
Supt. — See Justin
Medlin MS 1,000/6-8
601 Parkview Dr 76262 817-215-0500
Dr. Eric Drewery, prin. Fax 215-0548
Nelson HS 2,300/9-12
2775 Bobcat Blvd 76262 817-698-5600
Dr. Ron Myers, prin. Fax 698-5670

Troup, Smith, Pop. 1,837
Troup ISD 1,100/PK-12
PO Box 578 75789 903-842-3067
Stuart Bird, supt. Fax 842-4563
www.troupisd.org
Troup HS 300/9-12
PO Box 578 75789 903-842-3065
David Smith, prin. Fax 842-4563
Troup MS 300/6-8
PO Box 578 75789 903-842-3081
Ava Johnson, prin. Fax 842-4563

Troy, Bell, Pop. 1,625
Troy ISD 1,400/PK-12
PO Box 409 76579 254-938-2595
Neil Jeter, supt. Fax 938-7323
www.troyisd.org
Mays MS 300/6-8
PO Box 409 76579 254-938-2543
Michelle Jolliff, prin. Fax 938-2880
Troy HS 400/9-12
PO Box 409 76579 254-938-2561
Randy Hicks, prin. Fax 938-2328

Tulia, Swisher, Pop. 4,912
Tulia ISD 1,100/PK-12
702 NW 8th St 79088 806-995-4591
Steve Post, supt. Fax 995-3169
www.tuliaisd.net
Tulia HS 300/9-12
501 Hornet Pl 79088 806-995-2759
Mike Allison, prin. Fax 995-4413

Tulia JHS 200/6-8
421 NE 3rd St 79088 806-995-4842
Casey McBroom, prin. Fax 995-4498

Turkey, Hall, Pop. 416
Turkey-Quitaque ISD 200/PK-12
11826 Highway 86 79261 806-455-1411
Jackie Jenkins, supt. Fax 455-1718
www.valleypatriots.com
Valley S 200/PK-12
11826 Highway 86 79261 806-455-1411
Jerry Smith, prin. Fax 455-1718

Tuscola, Taylor, Pop. 734
Jim Ned Consolidated ISD 1,100/PK-12
PO Box 9 79562 325-554-7500
Bobby Easterling, supt. Fax 554-7740
www.jimned.esc14.net
Jim Ned HS 300/9-12
PO Box 9 79562 325-554-7755
David Hogan, prin. Fax 554-7550
Jim Ned MS 300/6-8
PO Box 9 79562 325-554-7870
Jay Wise, prin. Fax 554-7750

Tyler, Smith, Pop. 95,596
Chapel Hill ISD 3,500/PK-12
11134 County Road 2249 75707 903-566-2441
Donni Cook Ed.D., supt. Fax 566-8469
www.chapelhillisd.org
Chapel Hill HS 1,000/9-12
13172 State Highway 64 E 75707 903-566-2311
Jeff Hogg, prin. Fax 565-5155
Chapel Hill MS 800/6-8
13174 State Highway 64 E 75707 903-566-1491
Debbie Black, prin. Fax 565-5125

Tyler ISD 17,500/PK-12
PO Box 2035 75710 903-262-1000
Dr. Marty Crawford, supt. Fax 262-1178
www.tylerisd.org
Boulter Creative Arts Magnet S 600/6-8
2926 Garden Valley Rd 75702 903-262-1390
Rodney Curry, prin. Fax 262-1392
Dogan MS 500/6-8
2621 N Border Ave 75702 903-262-1450
Vanessa Holmes, prin. Fax 262-1451
Hogg MS 600/6-8
920 S Broadway Ave 75701 903-262-1500
Eddie Dunn, prin. Fax 262-1501
Hubbard MS 800/6-8
1300 Hubbard Dr 75703 903-262-1560
Kevin Blain, prin. Fax 262-1566
Lee HS 2,600/9-12
411 E Southeast Loop 323 75701 903-262-2625
Daniel Crawford, prin. Fax 262-2630
Moore MST Magnet MS 900/6-8
2101 Devine St 75701 903-262-1640
Claude Lane, prin. Fax 262-1648
Three Lakes MS 6-8
2445 Three Lakes Pkwy 75703 903-952-4400
Christopher Blake, prin.
Tyler HS 2,000/9-12
1120 N Northwest Loop 323 75702 903-262-2850
Kenneth Gay, prin. Fax 262-2852

All Saints Episcopal S 700/PK-12
2695 S Southwest Loop 323 75701 903-579-6000
Randal Brown, head sch Fax 579-6002
Bishop Gorman Regional Catholic MSHS 400/6-12
1405 E Southeast Loop 323 75701 903-561-2424
Jim Franz, prin. Fax 561-2645
Christian Heritage S 100/K-12
961 County Road 1143 75704 903-593-2702
Calvin Todd, admin. Fax 531-2226
East Texas Christian Academy 300/PK-12
2448 Roy Rd 75707 903-561-8642
Good Shepherd S 100/PK-12
2525 Old Jacksonville Rd 75701 903-592-4045
Walter Banek, head sch Fax 596-7149
Grace Community S Upper Campus 600/6-12
3001 University Blvd 75701 903-566-5661
Jay Ferguson, hdmstr. Fax 566-5639
King's Academy Christian S 100/K-12
7330 S Broadway Ave 75703 903-534-9992
Erin Baggs, admin. Fax 526-7929
Star College of Cosmetology Post-Sec.
520 E Front St 75702 903-596-7860
Texas College Post-Sec.
2404 N Grand Ave 75702 903-593-8311
Tyler Junior College Post-Sec.
PO Box 9020 75711 903-510-2200
University of Texas at Tyler Post-Sec.
3900 University Blvd 75701 903-566-7000

Universal City, Bexar, Pop. 18,038
Judson ISD
Supt. — See Live Oak
Kitty Hawk MS 1,300/6-8
840 Old Cimarron Trl 78148 210-945-1220
Beverly Broom, prin. Fax 659-0687

First Baptist Academy 500/PK-12
1401 Pat Booker Rd 78148 210-658-5331
Christine Povolish, hdmstr. Fax 658-7024

Utopia, Uvalde, Pop. 224
Utopia ISD 200/PK-12
PO Box 880 78884 830-966-1928
John Walts, supt. Fax 966-6162
www.utopiaisd.net
Utopia S 200/PK-12
PO Box 880 78884 830-966-3339
Ken Mueller, prin. Fax 966-6162

Uvalde, Uvalde, Pop. 15,676
Uvalde Consolidated ISD 4,800/PK-12
PO Box 1909 78802 830-278-6655
Jeanette Ball, supt. Fax 591-4909
www.ucisd.net
Morales JHS 400/8-8
PO Box 1909 78802 830-591-2980
Michelle Rodriguez, prin. Fax 591-2975
Uvalde HS 1,300/9-12
PO Box 1909 78802 830-591-2950
Elizabeth Sandoval, prin. Fax 591-2960

Southwest School Post-Sec.
122 W North St 78801 830-278-4103
Southwest Texas Junior College Post-Sec.
2401 Garner Field Rd 78801 830-278-4401
Uvalde Classical Academy 100/PK-12
PO Box 2004 78802 830-591-2242
Amanda Dockal, head sch Fax 591-2242

Valentine, Jeff Davis, Pop. 134
Valentine ISD 50/PK-12
PO Box 188 79854 432-467-2671
Debbie Engle, supt. Fax 467-2004
www.valentineisd.com
Valentine S 50/PK-12
PO Box 188 79854 432-467-2671
Fax 467-2004

Valera, Coleman
Panther Creek Consolidated ISD 100/PK-12
129 Private Road 3421 76884 325-357-4506
Dwin Nanny, supt. Fax 357-4470
www.pcreek.net
Panther Creek S 100/PK-12
129 Private Road 3421 76884 325-357-4449
Dwin Nanny, admin. Fax 357-4470

Valley Mills, Bosque, Pop. 1,193
Valley Mills ISD 600/PK-12
PO Box 518 76689 254-932-5210
Dr. Judi Whitis, supt. Fax 932-6601
www.vmisd.net
Valley Mills HS 200/9-12
PO Box 518 76689 254-932-5251
Jason Sansom, prin. Fax 932-6601
Valley Mills JHS 100/7-8
PO Box 518 76689 254-932-5251
Jason Sansom, prin. Fax 932-6601

Valley View, Cooke, Pop. 748
Valley View ISD 700/PK-12
106 Newton St 76272 940-726-3659
William Stokes, supt. Fax 726-3614
www.vvisd.net
Valley View HS 200/9-12
106 Newton St 76272 940-726-3522
Chris Heskett, prin. Fax 726-3862
Valley View MS 200/5-8
106 Newton St 76272 940-726-3244
Jesse Newton, prin. Fax 726-3786

Van, Van Zandt, Pop. 2,615
Van ISD 2,300/PK-12
PO Box 697 75790 903-963-8328
Don Dunn, supt. Fax 963-8799
www.vanschools.org
Van HS 700/9-12
PO Box 697 75790 903-963-8623
Jeff Hutchins, prin. Fax 963-5591
Van JHS 400/7-8
PO Box 697 75790 903-963-8321
Richard Pride, prin. Fax 963-3277

Van Alstyne, Grayson, Pop. 2,993
Van Alstyne ISD 1,300/PK-12
549 Miller Ln 75495 903-482-8802
Dr. John Spies, supt. Fax 482-6086
www.vanalstyneisd.org
Van Alstyne HS 400/9-12
1722 N Waco St 75495 903-482-8803
Jeremiah Johnson, prin. Fax 482-8887
Van Alstyne MS 400/5-8
1314 N Waco St 75495 903-482-8804
Ryan Coleman, prin. Fax 482-8890

Kingdom Country Academy K-12
PO Box 1423 75495 903-267-1273
Karen Love, prin.

Vanderbilt, Jackson, Pop. 392
Industrial ISD 1,200/PK-12
PO Box 369 77991 361-284-3226
Anthony Williams, supt. Fax 284-3349
www.industrialisd.org
Industrial HS 400/9-12
PO Box 399 77991 361-284-3226
Jim Green, prin. Fax 284-3328
Industrial JHS 300/6-8
PO Box 367 77991 361-284-3226
Caleb McCain, prin. Fax 284-3049

Van Horn, Culberson, Pop. 2,041
Culberson County-Allamore ISD 300/PK-12
PO Box 899 79855 432-283-2245
Dalia Benavides, supt. Fax 283-9062
www.ccaisd.net/
Van Horn S 300/PK-12
PO Box 899 79855 432-283-2245
Kittie Gibson, prin. Fax 283-9062

Van Vleck, Matagorda, Pop. 1,828
Van Vleck ISD 900/PK-12
142 S 4th St 77482 979-245-8518
John O'Brien, supt. Fax 245-1214
www.vvisd.org
Herman MS 200/6-8
719 1st St 77482 979-245-6401
David Holubec, prin. Fax 245-8538

Van Vleck HS 300/9-12
133 S 4th St 77482 979-245-4664
Brandon Hood, prin. Fax 244-3485

Vega, Oldham, Pop. 874
Vega ISD 300/K-12
PO Box 190 79092 806-267-2123
Dr. Paul Uttley, supt. Fax 267-2146
www.vegalonghorn.com
Vega HS 200/7-12
PO Box 190 79092 806-267-2126
Kassidy Rosas, prin. Fax 267-2146

Venus, Johnson, Pop. 2,914
Venus ISD 1,900/PK-12
100 Student Dr 76084 972-366-3448
Dr. Renee Warner, supt. Fax 366-8742
www.venusisd.net
Venus HS 500/9-12
12 Bulldog Dr 76084 972-366-8815
Randall Buck, prin. Fax 366-8919
Venus MS 400/6-8
1 Bulldog Dr 76084 972-366-3358
Kimberly Buck, prin. Fax 366-1740

Veribest, Tom Green
Veribest ISD 300/PK-12
PO Box 490 76886 325-655-4912
Bobby Fryar, supt. Fax 655-3355
www.veribestisd.net
Veribest HS 100/7-12
PO Box 490 76886 325-655-2851
Jim Meredith, prin. Fax 653-0551

Vernon, Wilbarger, Pop. 10,848
Northside ISD 200/K-12
18040 US Highway 283 76384 940-552-2551
Jack Coody, supt. Fax 553-4919
www.northsideisd.us
Northside S 200/K-12
18040 US Highway 283 76384 940-552-2551
Mark Haught, prin. Fax 553-4913

Vernon ISD 2,100/PK-12
1713 Wilbarger St 76384 940-553-1900
Gary Harrell, supt. Fax 553-3802
www.vernonisd.org
Vernon HS 500/9-12
2102 Yucca Ln 76384 940-553-3377
Lynn Anderson, prin. Fax 553-4531
Vernon MS 500/6-8
2200 Yamparika St 76384 940-552-6231
Michael Campos, prin. Fax 552-0504

Vernon College Post-Sec.
4400 College Dr 76384 940-552-6291

Victoria, Victoria, Pop. 61,923
Bloomington ISD 900/PK-12
2875 FM 616 77905 361-333-8016
Delores Warnell, supt. Fax 333-8026
www.bisd-tx.org/
Other Schools – See Bloomington

Victoria ISD 14,900/PK-12
PO Box 1759 77902 361-576-3131
Dr. Robert Jaklich Ed.D., supt. Fax 788-9643
www.visd.net/
Cade MS 800/6-8
PO Box 1759 77902 361-788-2840
Jill Lau, prin. Fax 788-2886
Career and Technology Institute Vo/Tech
PO Box 1759 77902 361-788-9288
Dena Pilsner, prin. Fax 788-9656
Howell MS 800/6-8
PO Box 1759 77902 361-578-1561
Jo Beth Jones, prin. Fax 788-9547
Liberty Academy 200/9-12
PO Box 1759 77902 361-788-9650
Sheila Garcia, prin. Fax 788-9700
Mitchell Guidance Center 100/Alt
PO Box 1759 77902 361-788-9658
Tedrick Valentine, prin. Fax 788-9665
Stroman MS 800/6-8
PO Box 1759 77902 361-578-2711
Dawn Maroney, prin. Fax 788-9800
Victoria Area Ctr for Advanced Learning 9-12
PO Box 1759 77902 361-788-9650
Sheila Garcia, prin. Fax 788-9649
Victoria East HS 1,800/9-12
PO Box 1759 77902 361-788-2820
Clark Motley, prin. Fax 788-2826
Victoria West HS 1,700/9-12
PO Box 1759 77902 361-788-2830
Debbie Crick, prin. Fax 788-2836
Welder MS 700/6-8
PO Box 1759 77902 361-575-4553
Richard Wright, prin. Fax 788-9629

Citizens Medical Center Post-Sec.
2701 Hospital Dr 77901 361-573-9181
Devereux-Texas Treatment Network Post-Sec.
120 David Wade Dr 77902 800-383-5000
Faith Academy 400/PK-12
PO Box 4824 77903 361-572-4568
Dr. Chris Royael, supt. Fax 573-5058
St. Joseph HS 300/9-12
110 E Red River St 77901 361-573-2446
Thomas Maj, prin. Fax 573-4221
Texas Vocational School Post-Sec.
1921 E Red River St 77901 361-575-4768
University of Houston-Victoria Post-Sec.
3007 N Ben Wilson St 77901 361-570-4848
Victoria Beauty College Post-Sec.
1508 N Laurent St 77901 361-575-4526
Victoria College Post-Sec.
2200 E Red River St 77901 361-573-3291

Vidor, Orange, Pop. 10,443
Vidor ISD 5,000/PK-12
120 E Bolivar St 77662 409-951-8700
Dr. Jay Killgo, supt. Fax 769-0093
www.vidorisd.org/
AIM Center HS 100/Alt
690 Orange St 77662 409-951-8780
Roxanne Manuel, prin. Fax 769-0443
Vidor HS 1,400/9-12
500 Orange St 77662 409-951-8902
Travis Maines, prin. Fax 769-6767
Vidor JHS 800/7-8
945 N Tram Rd 77662 409-951-8970
Dr. Debra Jordan, prin. Fax 769-6754

Von Ormy, Bexar, Pop. 1,084
Somerset ISD
Supt. — See Somerset
Somerset JHS 600/7-8
4730 W Loop 1604 78073 866-852-9862
Melissa Holguin, prin. Fax 448-2738

Southwest ISD
Supt. — See San Antonio
Resnik MS 6-8
4495 SW Verano Pkwy 78073 210-623-6589
Odilia Martinez, prin. Fax 623-2700

Waco, McLennan, Pop. 122,806
Bosqueville ISD 600/PK-12
7636 Rock Creek Rd 76708 254-757-3113
James Skeeler, supt. Fax 752-4909
www.bosquevilleisd.org
Bosqueville HS 200/9-12
7636 Rock Creek Rd 76708 254-752-8513
Cliff Heath, prin. Fax 752-0326
Bosqueville MS 100/6-8
7636 Rock Creek Rd 76708 254-759-7077
Sara Mynarcik, prin. Fax 752-5459

Bruceville-Eddy ISD
Supt. — See Eddy
Axtell/Bruceville-Eddy Learning Center 50/Alt
2601 Franklin Ave 76710 254-753-3422
Grady Fulbright, prin. Fax 753-3602

Connally ISD 1,900/PK-12
200 Cadet Way 76705 254-296-6460
Wesley Holt, supt. Fax 412-5530
www.connally.org
Connally Early College HS 9-12
200 Cadet Way 76705 254-296-6460
Hermann Pereira, prin. Fax 412-5530
Connally HS 600/9-12
900 N Lacy Dr 76705 254-296-6700
Jill Talamantez, prin. Fax 412-5549
Other Schools – See Elm Mott

Gholson ISD 200/PK-12
137 Hamilton Dr 76705 254-829-1528
Pamela Brown, supt. Fax 829-0054
www.gholsonisd.org
Gholson S 200/PK-12
137 Hamilton Dr 76705 254-829-1528
Heather McCartney, prin. Fax 829-0054

La Vega ISD 2,900/PK-12
400 E Loop 340 76705 254-799-4963
Dr. Sharon Shields, supt. Fax 799-8642
www.lavegaisd.org
La Vega HS 700/9-12
555 N Loop 340 76705 254-799-4951
Chuck Klander, prin. Fax 799-0720
La Vega JHS George Dixon Campus 400/7-8
4401 Orchard Ln 76705 254-799-2428
Chris Borland, prin. Fax 799-8943

Midway ISD
Supt. — See Woodway
Midway HS 2,200/9-12
8200 Mars Dr 76712 254-761-5650
Dr. Brent Merritt, prin. Fax 761-5770

Waco ISD 14,300/PK-12
PO Box 27 76703 254-755-9473
Bonny Cain Ed.D., supt. Fax 755-9690
www.wacoisd.org
ATLAS Academy 6-8
6100 Tennyson Dr 76710 254-754-5491
Sandra Gibson, dean Fax 750-3576
Brazos HS Credit Recovery 200/Alt
3005 Edna Ave 76708 254-754-9422
Daphanie Latchison, prin. Fax 757-6298
Carver MS 500/6-8
1601 J J Flewellen Rd 76704 254-757-0787
Alonza McAdoo, prin. Fax 750-3442
Chavez MS 900/6-8
700 S 15th St 76706 254-750-3736
Kimberly Hamilton, prin. Fax 750-3739
Greater Waco Advanced Health Care Acad Vo/Tech
7200 Viking Dr 76710 254-399-6654
Krystal Wilson, dir. Fax 741-4984
Greater Waco Advanced Manufacturing Acad Vo/Tech
2401 J J Flewellen Rd 76704 254-412-7900
Brandon Cope, dir. Fax 412-7917
Tennyson MS 800/6-8
6100 Tennyson Dr 76710 254-772-1440
Lisa Hall, prin. Fax 741-4970
University HS 1,500/9-12
3201 S New Rd 76706 254-756-1843
Dr. William Shepard, prin. Fax 750-3709
Waco HS 1,700/9-12
2020 N 42nd St 76710 254-776-1150
Ed Love, prin. Fax 741-4815
Wiley Opportunity Center 100/Alt
1030 E Live Oak St 76704 254-757-3829
Larry Curtis, prin. Fax 750-3772

Baylor University Post-Sec.
1 Bear Pl Unit 97056 76798 254-710-1011
Live Oak Classical S 200/PK-12
PO Box 647 76703 254-714-1007
Alison Moffatt, head sch Fax 714-1150
McLennan Community College Post-Sec.
1400 College Dr 76708 254-299-8000
New Creation Adventist S 50/K-10
800 W State Highway 6 76712 254-772-8775
Reicher Catholic HS 200/9-12
2102 N 23rd St 76708 254-752-8349
Mindy Taylor, prin. Fax 752-8408
Texas Christian Academy 200/6-12
4600 Sanger Ave 76710 254-772-5474
Texas State Technical College Post-Sec.
3801 Campus Dr 76705 254-799-3611
Vanguard College Preparatory S 100/7-12
2517 Mount Carmel Dr 76710 254-772-8111
Bill Borg, head sch Fax 772-8263

Waelder, Gonzales, Pop. 1,062
Waelder ISD 300/PK-12
PO Box 247 78959 830-788-7161
Daniel Fuller, supt. Fax 788-7429
www.waelderisd.org
Waelder S 300/PK-12
PO Box 247 78959 830-788-7151
Dr. Ron Lilie, prin. Fax 788-7323

Wall, Tom Green
Wall ISD, PO Box 259 76957 1,100/K-12
Russell Dacy, supt. 325-651-7790
www.wallisd.net
Wall HS, PO Box 259 76957 300/9-12
Ryan Snowden, prin. 325-651-7790
Wall MS, PO Box 259 76957 300/6-8
Matt Rivers, prin. 325-651-7790
Other Schools – See San Angelo

Waller, Waller, Pop. 2,288
Waller ISD 5,900/PK-12
2214 Waller St 77484 936-931-3685
Danny Twardowski, supt. Fax 372-5576
www.wallerisd.net
Schultz JHS 700/6-8
19010 Stokes Rd 77484 936-931-9103
Stephanie Fletcher, prin. Fax 372-9302
Waller HS 1,600/9-12
20950 Fields Store Rd 77484 936-372-3654
Dr. Brian Merrell, prin. Fax 372-4114
Waller JHS 700/6-8
2402 Waller St 77484 936-931-1353
Eric Meldahl, prin. Fax 931-4044

Wallis, Austin, Pop. 1,240
Brazos ISD 800/PK-12
PO Box 819 77485 979-478-6551
Earl Jarrett, supt. Fax 478-6413
www.brazosisd.net/
Brazos HS 200/9-12
PO Box 458 77485 979-478-6000
Mary McCarthy, prin. Fax 478-6002
Brazos MS 200/6-8
PO Box 879 77485 979-478-6814
Clay Hudgins, prin. Fax 478-2574
Prairie Harbor Alternative S Alt
PO Box 819 77485 979-217-1581
Jamie Bates, prin. Fax 217-1607

Walnut Springs, Bosque, Pop. 805
Walnut Springs ISD 200/PK-12
PO Box 63 76690 254-797-2133
Pat Garrett, supt. Fax 797-2191
www.walnutspringsisd.net
Walnut Springs S 200/PK-12
PO Box 63 76690 254-797-2133
Michele Garza, prin. Fax 797-2191

Warren, Tyler, Pop. 751
Warren ISD 1,300/PK-12
PO Box 69 77664 409-547-2241
Brad McEachern, supt. Fax 547-3405
www.warrenisd.net
Warren HS 400/9-12
PO Box 190 77664 409-547-2243
James Swinney, prin. Fax 547-0214
Warren JHS 300/6-8
PO Box 205 77664 409-547-2241
Kristina Wiedman, prin. Fax 547-2740

Waskom, Harrison, Pop. 2,131
Waskom ISD 900/PK-12
PO Box 748 75692 903-687-3361
Jimmy Cox, supt. Fax 687-3253
www.waskomisd.net
Waskom HS 300/9-12
PO Box 748 75692 903-687-3361
Kassie Watson, prin. Fax 687-2897
Waskom MS 300/5-8
PO Box 748 75692 903-687-3361
Bonita Cherry, prin. Fax 687-3372

Watauga, Tarrant, Pop. 22,948
Birdville ISD
Supt. — See Haltom City
Watauga MS 700/6-8
6300 Maurie Dr 76148 817-547-4800
Shannon Houston, prin. Fax 581-5369

Water Valley, Tom Green
Water Valley ISD 300/PK-12
PO Box 250 76958 325-484-2478
Larry J. Taylor, supt. Fax 484-3359
www.wvisd.net/
Water Valley JSHS 100/7-12
PO Box 250 76958 325-484-2424
Scott Edmondson, prin. Fax 484-3359

Waxahachie, Ellis, Pop. 29,212
Waxahachie ISD 7,800/PK-12
411 N Gibson St 75165 972-923-4631
Jeremy Glenn Ed.D., supt. Fax 923-4759
www.wisd.org
Finley JHS 800/6-8
2401 Brown St 75165 972-923-4680
Adan Casas, prin. Fax 923-4687
Howard JHS 900/6-8
265 Broadhead Rd 75165 972-923-4771
Jacob Perry, prin. Fax 923-3817
Waxahachie Challenge Academy Alt
614 N Getzendaner St 75165 972-923-4695
Ryan Cavazos, prin. Fax 923-4717
Waxahachie Global HS 400/9-12
600 W 2nd St 75165 972-923-4761
Ken Lynch, prin. Fax 923-4738
Waxahachie HS 2,000/9-12
1000 N Highway 77 75165 972-923-4600
Al Benskin, prin. Fax 923-4617
Waxahachie HS of Choice 100/Alt
614 N Getzendaner St 75165 972-923-4758
Ryan Cavazos, prin. Fax 923-4717

Southwestern Assemblies of God Univ. Post-Sec.
1200 Sycamore St 75165 972-937-4010
Waxahachie Preparatory Academy 100/K-12
PO Box P 75168 972-937-0440
Scott Marks, admin. Fax 937-5033

Weatherford, Parker, Pop. 24,879
Peaster ISD 900/PK-12
3602 Harwell Lake Rd 76088 817-341-5000
Matt Adams, supt. Fax 341-5003
www.peaster.net
Peaster HS 300/9-12
3600 Harwell Lake Rd 76088 817-341-5000
Chris Pennington, prin. Fax 341-5027
Peaster MS 200/7-8
8512 FM Road 920 76088 817-341-5000
Darren Grudt, prin. Fax 341-5052

Weatherford ISD 7,700/PK-12
1100 Longhorn Dr 76086 817-598-2800
Dr. Jeffrey Hanks, supt. Fax 598-2955
www.weatherfordisd.com
Hall MS 600/7-8
902 Charles St 76086 817-598-2822
Jeanette McNeely, prin. Fax 598-2854
Tison MS 600/7-8
102 Meadowview Rd 76087 817-598-2960
Carolyn Harrison, prin. Fax 598-2963
Weatherford HS 1,600/10-12
2121 Bethel Rd 76087 817-598-2847
Kristy Dowd, prin. Fax 598-2881
Weatherford Ninth Grade Center 600/9-9
1007 S Main St 76086 817-598-2847
Kristy Dowd, prin. Fax 598-2928

Couts Christian Academy 200/PK-12
802 N Elm St 76086 817-599-8601
Amy Nesler, admin. Fax 594-5516
Weatherford Christian S 200/PK-12
111 E Columbia St 76086 817-596-7807
Courtney McKeown, head sch Fax 596-0529
Weatherford College Post-Sec.
225 College Park Dr 76086 817-594-5471

Webster, Harris, Pop. 10,170

Remington College Houston Southeast Post-Sec.
20985 Interstate 45 S 77598 800-560-6192

Weimar, Colorado, Pop. 2,127
Weimar ISD 600/PK-12
506 W Main St 78962 979-725-9504
Jon Wunderlich, supt. Fax 725-8737
www.weimarisd.org/
Weimar HS 200/9-12
506 W Main St 78962 979-725-9504
Darrin Bickham, prin. Fax 725-8737
Weimar JHS 200/5-8
101 N West St 78962 979-725-9515
Stacey Heger, prin. Fax 725-8383

Welch, Dawson, Pop. 221
Dawson ISD 200/PK-12
PO Box 180 79377 806-489-7568
Johnny Tubb, supt. Fax 489-7463
www.dawsonisd.us
Dawson S 200/PK-12
PO Box 180 79377 806-489-7461
Jeff Fleenor, prin. Fax 489-7463

Wellington, Collingsworth, Pop. 2,160
Wellington ISD 600/PK-12
609 15th St 79095 806-447-3102
Kurt Ashmore, supt. Fax 447-5124
www.wellingtonisd.net
Wellington HS 200/9-12
811 15th St 79095 806-447-3172
Jermaine Cantu, prin. Fax 447-9012
Wellington JHS 100/6-8
1504 Amarillo St 79095 806-447-3152
Tim Webb, prin. Fax 447-5089

Wellman, Terry, Pop. 202
Wellman-Union Consolidated ISD 200/PK-12
PO Box 69 79378 806-637-4910
Aaron Waldrip, supt. Fax 637-2585
wellman.esc17.net
Wellman-Union HS 100/6-12
PO Box 129 79378 806-637-4619
Michael Norman, prin. Fax 637-2585

Wells, Cherokee, Pop. 772
Wells ISD 300/PK-12
PO Box 469 75976 936-867-4466
James Moore, supt. Fax 867-4497
www.wells.esc7.net
Wells HS 100/7-12
PO Box 469 75976 936-867-4400
Gary Applewhite, prin. Fax 867-4497

Weslaco, Hidalgo, Pop. 35,580
Weslaco ISD 17,200/PK-12
PO Box 266 78599 956-969-6500
Fax 969-2664
www.wisd.us
Central MS 1,000/6-8
503 E 6th St 78596 956-969-6710
Patricia Munoz, prin. Fax 969-0779
CTE - Early College HS 100/9-9
PO Box 266 78599 956-969-6742
Dr. Olga Estrada, prin. Fax 969-6643
Cuellar MS 800/6-8
1201 S Bridge Ave 78596 956-969-6720
Freddy Rodriguez, prin. Fax 973-9797
Garza MS 1,100/6-8
1111 W Sugar Cane Dr 78599 956-969-6774
John Garlic, prin. Fax 447-0484
Hoge MS 1,000/6-8
2302 N International Blvd 78596 956-969-6730
Pablo Vallejo, prin. Fax 514-0903
Horton Alternative Education Program Alt
PO Box 266 78599 956-969-6916
Sergio Garcia, prin. Fax 969-6782
South Palms Garden HS 100/Alt
3907 Camino Real Viejo 78596 956-969-6621
Fax 565-5994
Weslaco East HS 2,200/9-12
810 S Pleasantview Dr 78596 956-969-6950
Dr. Raul Cantu, prin. Fax 968-8693
Weslaco HS 2,500/9-12
1005 W Pike Blvd 78596 956-969-6700
Yvett Morales, prin. Fax 968-8008

Advanced Barber College and Hair Design Post-Sec.
2818 S International Blvd 78596 956-969-0341
South Texas Vocational-Technical Inst. Post-Sec.
2419 Haggar St 78599 956-969-1564

West, McLennan, Pop. 2,777
West ISD 1,300/PK-12
801 N Reagan St 76691 254-951-2000
David Truitt, supt. Fax 826-7503
www.westisd.net/
West HS 400/9-12
801 N Reagan St 76691 254-981-2050
Don Snook, prin. Fax 826-7514
West MS 300/6-8
801 N Reagan St 76691 254-981-2120
Michele Scott, prin. Fax 826-7524

Westbrook, Mitchell, Pop. 253
Westbrook ISD 300/PK-12
PO Box 99 79565 325-644-2311
Todd Burleson, supt. Fax 644-5101
www.westbrookisd.com
Colorado City Alternative S Alt
PO Box 99 79565 325-644-2311
Cassie Petty, prin. Fax 644-5101
Westbrook S 300/PK-12
PO Box 99 79565 325-644-2311
Cassie Petty, prin. Fax 644-5101

West Columbia, Brazoria, Pop. 3,841
Columbia-Brazoria ISD 3,000/PK-12
PO Box 158 77486 979-345-5147
Steven Galloway, supt. Fax 345-4890
www.cbisd.com
Columbia HS 800/9-12
PO Box 158 77486 979-799-1720
Robert Mowles, prin. Fax 345-6785
Other Schools – See Brazoria

West Lake Hills, Travis, Pop. 3,003
Eanes ISD
Supt. — See Austin
Westlake Alternative S Alt
601 Camp Craft Rd 78746 512-327-2203

West Orange, Orange, Pop. 3,387
West Orange-Cove Consolidated ISD
Supt. — See Orange
West Orange-Stark HS 600/9-12
1400 Newton St 77630 409-882-5570
Rod Anderson, prin. Fax 882-5573

Wharton, Wharton, Pop. 8,727
Wharton ISD 1,800/PK-12
2100 N Fulton St 77488 979-532-6201
Tina Herrington, supt. Fax 532-6228
www.whartonisd.net
Wharton HS 500/9-12
1 Tiger Ave 77488 979-532-6800
Mark Anglin, prin. Fax 532-6807
Wharton JHS 300/7-8
1120 N Rusk St 77488 979-532-6840
Dr. Keith Brooks, prin. Fax 532-6849

Wharton County Junior College Post-Sec.
911 E Boling Hwy 77488 979-532-4560

Wheeler, Wheeler, Pop. 1,576
Kelton ISD 100/PK-12
16703 FM 2697 79096 806-826-5795
Doug Rice, supt. Fax 826-3601
keltonisd.com
Kelton S 100/PK-12
16703 FM 2697 79096 806-826-5795
Johnny James, prin. Fax 826-3601

Wheeler ISD 500/PK-12
PO Box 1010 79096 806-826-5241
Bryan Markham, supt. Fax 826-3118
www.wheelerschools.net
Wheeler S 500/PK-12
PO Box 1010 79096 806-826-5534
Mike Bailey, prin. Fax 826-3118

White Deer, Carson, Pop. 983
White Deer ISD 300/PK-12
PO Box 517 79097 806-883-2311
Karl Vaughn, supt. Fax 883-2321
www.whitedeerisd.net/
White Deer JSHS 100/7-12
PO Box 248 79097 806-883-2311
Darla Forney, prin. Fax 883-5029

Whiteface, Cochran, Pop. 442
Whiteface Consolidated ISD 400/PK-12
PO Box 7 79379 806-287-1154
Dr. Cassidy McBrayer, supt. Fax 287-1131
www.whitefaceschool.net
Whiteface JSHS 200/6-12
PO Box 7 79379 806-287-1104
Chris Mendez, prin. Fax 287-1131
Other Schools – See Pep

Whitehouse, Smith, Pop. 7,533
Whitehouse ISD 4,600/PK-12
106 Wildcat Dr 75791 903-839-5500
Dr. Christopher Moran, supt. Fax 839-5515
www.whitehouseisd.org
Whitehouse HS 1,400/9-12
901 E Main St 75791 903-839-5551
Jonathan Campbell, prin. Fax 839-5530
Whitehouse JHS 700/7-8
108 Wildcat Dr 75791 903-839-5590
Josh Garred, prin. Fax 839-5518

White Oak, Gregg, Pop. 6,394
White Oak ISD 1,400/PK-12
200 S White Oak Rd 75693 903-291-2000
Michael Gilbert, supt. Fax 291-2222
www.woisd.net
White Oak HS 400/9-12
200 S White Oak Rd 75693 903-291-2000
Donna Jennings, prin. Fax 291-2034
White Oak MS 300/6-8
200 S White Oak Rd 75693 903-291-2050
Rebecca Balboa, prin. Fax 291-2035

Whitesboro, Grayson, Pop. 3,755
Whitesboro ISD 1,600/PK-12
115 4th St 76273 903-564-4200
Ryan Harper, supt. Fax 564-9303
www.whitesboroisd.org
Whitesboro HS 400/9-12
1 Bearcat Dr 76273 903-564-4208
Marlene Monk, prin. Fax 564-4288
Whitesboro MS 400/6-8
600 4th St 76273 903-564-4240
Ted Beal, prin. Fax 564-5939

White Settlement, Tarrant, Pop. 15,816
White Settlement ISD
Supt. — See Fort Worth
Brewer MS 1,000/7-8
1000 S Cherry Ln 76108 817-367-1267
Sherri Kottwitz, prin. Fax 367-1268

Whitewright, Grayson, Pop. 1,571
Whitewright ISD 800/PK-12
PO Box 888 75491 903-364-2155
Steve Arthur, supt. Fax 364-2839
whitewrightisd.com
Whitewright HS 200/9-12
PO Box 888 75491 903-364-2535
Steve Morrow, prin. Fax 364-2579
Whitewright MS 200/6-8
PO Box 888 75491 903-364-2151
Bobby Worthy, prin. Fax 364-5263

Whitharral, Hockley
Whitharral ISD 200/K-12
PO Box 225 79380 806-299-1184
Ed Sharp, supt. Fax 299-1257
www.whitharralisd.org/
Whitharral S 200/K-12
PO Box 225 79380 806-299-1135
Carla Kristinek, prin. Fax 299-1257

Whitney, Hill, Pop. 2,048
Whitney ISD 1,500/PK-12
PO Box 518 76692 254-694-2254
Gene Solis, supt. Fax 694-4001
www.whitney.k12.tx.us
Whitney HS 400/9-12
PO Box 518 76692 254-694-3457
Amy Leech, prin. Fax 694-4206
Whitney MS 300/6-8
PO Box 518 76692 254-694-3446
Wayne Redding, prin. Fax 694-2064

Wichita Falls, Wichita, Pop. 102,278
City View ISD 1,000/PK-12
1025 City View Dr 76306 940-855-4042
Steve Harris, supt. Fax 851-8889
www.cityview-isd.net/
City View JSHS 400/7-12
1600 City View Dr 76306 940-855-7511
Daryl Frazier, prin. Fax 851-5027

Wichita Falls ISD 12,500/PK-12
PO Box 97533 76307 940-235-1000
Michael Kuhrt, supt. Fax 720-3228
www.wfisd.net
Barwise MS 400/6-8
3807 Kemp Blvd 76308 940-235-1108
Cody Blair, prin. Fax 235-1109
Denver Alternative Center Alt
1823 5th St 76301 940-235-1101
Linda Nichols, prin. Fax 235-1102
Harrell Accelerated Learning Center 50/Alt
3115 5th St 76301 940-235-1096
Gena Woodard, prin. Fax 235-1097
Hirschi HS 700/9-12
3106 Borton St 76306 940-235-1070
Doug Albus, prin. Fax 235-1300
Kirby JHS 400/7-8
1715 Loop 11 76306 940-235-1113
Troy Farris, prin. Fax 235-1114
McNiel MS 700/7-8
4712 Barnett Rd 76310 940-235-1118
Tania Rushing, prin. Fax 235-1119
Rider HS 1,700/9-12
4611 Cypress Ave 76310 940-235-1077
Dee Palmore, prin. Fax 235-1301
Wichita Falls HS 1,300/9-12
2149 Avenue H 76309 940-235-1084
Christy Nash, prin. Fax 235-1302

Christ Academy 200/PK-12
5105 Stone Lake Dr 76310 940-692-2853
Dr. Jerry Meadows, hdmstr. Fax 692-2657
Midwestern State University Post-Sec.
3410 Taft Blvd 76308 940-397-4000
Notre Dame S 200/PK-12
2821 Lansing Blvd 76309 940-692-6041
Michael Edghill, prin. Fax 692-2811
United Regional Health Care System Post-Sec.
1600 11th St 76301 940-764-3187
Wichita Christian S 300/K-12
1615 Midwestern Pkwy 76302 940-763-1347

Willis, Montgomery, Pop. 5,574
Willis ISD 6,800/PK-12
204 W Rogers St 77378 936-856-1200
Dr. Tim Harkrider, supt. Fax 856-5182
www.willisisd.org/
Brabham MS 800/6-8
10000 FM 830 Rd 77318 936-890-2312
Tiffany Mathews, prin. Fax 856-2910
Lucas MS 800/6-8
1304 N Campbell St 77378 936-856-1274
Kim Sprayberry, prin. Fax 856-1065
Stubblefield Academy 50/Alt
207 Philpot St 77378 936-856-1288
Tanya Maddin, prin. Fax 890-0312
Willis HS 1,800/9-12
1201 FM 830 Rd 77378 936-856-1250
Travis Utecht, prin. Fax 856-3391

Willow Park, Parker, Pop. 3,938

Trinity Christian Academy 400/PK-12
4954 E IH-20 Service Rd S 76087 817-441-5897
Michael Skaggs, head sch Fax 441-9063

Wills Point, Van Zandt, Pop. 3,473
Wills Point ISD 2,500/PK-12
338 W North Commerce St 75169 903-873-5100
Scott Caloss, supt. Fax 873-2462
www.wpisd.com
Wills Point HS 700/9-12
1800 W South Commerce St 75169 903-873-2371
Jeffrey Smith, prin. Fax 873-6008
Wills Point JHS 400/7-8
200 Tiger Dr 75169 903-873-4924
Casey Cochran, prin. Fax 873-4873

Wilson, Lynn, Pop. 487
Wilson ISD 100/PK-12
PO Box 9 79381 806-628-6271
Jerry Burger, supt. Fax 628-6441
www.wilson.esc17.net
Wilson S 100/PK-12
PO Box 9 79381 806-628-6271
Richard Soliz, prin. Fax 628-6441

Wimberley, Hays, Pop. 2,602
Wimberley ISD 2,100/PK-12
951 FM 2325 78676 512-847-2414
Dwain York, supt. Fax 847-2142
www.wimberleyisd.net
Danforth JHS 500/6-8
200 Texan Blvd 78676 512-847-2181
Greg Howard, prin. Fax 847-7897
Wimberley HS 700/9-12
100 Carney Ln 78676 512-847-5729
Jason Valentine, prin. Fax 847-7269

Windcrest, Bexar, Pop. 5,256

Milan Institute of Cosmetology Post-Sec.
5403 Walzem Rd 78218 210-656-1991

Windthorst, Archer, Pop. 398
Windthorst ISD 500/PK-12
PO Box 190 76389 940-423-6688
Don Windham, supt. Fax 423-6505
www.windthorstisd.net
Windhorst JHS 100/6-8
PO Box 190 76389 940-423-6605
Darla Tackett, prin. Fax 423-6505
Windthorst HS 200/9-12
PO Box 190 76389 940-423-6680
Lonnie Hise, prin. Fax 423-6505

Wink, Winkler, Pop. 931
Wink-Loving ISD 400/PK-12
PO Box 637 79789 432-527-3880
Dr. Dewitt Smith, supt. Fax 527-3505
www.wlisd.net
Wink JSHS 100/7-12
PO Box 637 79789 432-527-3880
Scotty Carman, prin. Fax 527-3505

Winnie, Chambers, Pop. 3,222
East Chambers ISD 1,400/PK-12
1955 State Highway 124 77665 409-296-6100
Scott Campbell, supt. Fax 296-3528
www.eastchambers.net
East Chambers HS 400/9-12
234 E Buccaneer Dr 77665 409-296-6100
Adam Bramlett, prin. Fax 296-9596

East Chambers JHS 200/7-8
1931 State Highway 124 77665 409-296-6100
Lou Ann Rainey, prin. Fax 296-2724

Winnsboro, Wood, Pop. 3,395
Winnsboro ISD 1,500/PK-12
207 E Pine St 75494 903-342-3737
Susan Morton, supt. Fax 342-3380
www.winnsboroisd.org
Memorial MS 400/5-8
505 S Chestnut St 75494 903-342-5711
Jeff Akin, prin. Fax 342-6689
Winnsboro HS 400/9-12
409 Newsome St 75494 903-342-3641
David Pinnell, prin. Fax 342-3645

Winona, Smith, Pop. 574
Winona ISD 1,000/PK-12
611 Wildcat Dr 75792 903-939-4001
Cody Mize, supt. Fax 877-9387
www.winonaisd.org
Winona HS 300/9-12
611 Wildcat Dr 75792 903-939-4100
Damenion Miller, prin. Fax 939-4199
Winona MS 200/6-8
611 Wildcat Dr 75792 903-939-4040
Brian Lowe, prin. Fax 877-9150

Winters, Runnels, Pop. 2,547
Winters ISD 600/PK-12
603 N Heights St 79567 325-754-5574
Bruce Davis, supt. Fax 754-5374
www.wintersisd.org
Winters HS 100/9-12
603 N Heights St 79567 325-754-5516
Sammy Tullous, prin. Fax 754-5085
Winters JHS 100/6-8
603 N Heights St 79567 325-754-5518
Terry Payne, prin. Fax 754-5085

Woden, Nacogdoches
Woden ISD 800/PK-12
PO Box 100 75978 936-564-2073
Brady Taylor, supt. Fax 564-1250
www.wodenisd.org/
Woden HS 200/9-12
PO Box 100 75978 936-564-7903
Dr. Justin Keeling, prin. Fax 462-4962
Woden JHS 200/6-8
PO Box 100 75978 936-564-2481
Dr. Jerry Meador, prin. Fax 462-4982

Wolfe City, Hunt, Pop. 1,375
Wolfe City ISD 600/PK-12
505 W Dallas St 75496 903-496-7333
Vernon Richardson, supt. Fax 496-7905
www.wcisd.net
Wolfe City HS 200/9-12
8353 State Highway 34 N 75496 903-496-7333
Chris Sheets, prin. Fax 496-7124
Wolfe City MS 200/6-8
PO Box L 75496 903-496-7333
Melanie Williams, prin. Fax 496-2112

Wolfforth, Lubbock, Pop. 3,636
Frenship ISD 8,300/PK-12
PO Box 100 79382 806-866-9541
Dr. Michelle McCord, supt. Fax 866-4135
www.frenship.us
Frenship HS 2,100/9-12
PO Box 100 79382 806-866-4440
Kim Spicer, prin. Fax 866-9370
Frenship MS 600/6-8
PO Box 100 79382 806-866-4464
Jerry Jerabek, prin. Fax 866-2181
Other Schools – See Lubbock

Woodsboro, Refugio, Pop. 1,498
Woodsboro ISD 500/PK-12
PO Box 770 78393 361-543-4518
Jeff Dyer, supt. Fax 543-4856
www.wisd.net
Woodsboro Secondary S 200/6-12
PO Box 770 78393 361-543-4521
Linda Garza, prin. Fax 543-5140

Woodson, Throckmorton, Pop. 262
Woodson ISD 100/PK-12
PO Box 287 76491 940-345-6528
Gordon Thomas, supt. Fax 345-6549
www.woodsonisd.net
Woodson S 100/PK-12
PO Box 287 76491 940-345-6521
Casey Adams, prin. Fax 345-6549

Woodville, Tyler, Pop. 2,545
Woodville ISD 1,300/PK-12
505 N Charlton St 75979 409-283-3752
Glen Conner, supt. Fax 283-7962
www.woodvilleeagles.org
Woodville HS 300/9-12
505 N Charlton St 75979 409-283-3714
Morgan Wright, prin. Fax 331-3427
Woodville MS 300/6-8
505 N Charlton St 75979 409-283-7109
Eric Holton, prin. Fax 331-3418

Woodway, McLennan, Pop. 8,360
Midway ISD 7,500/PK-12
13885 Woodway Dr 76712 254-761-5610
George Kazanas Ed.D., supt. Fax 761-5789
www.midwayisd.org/
Other Schools – See Hewitt, Waco

Wortham, Freestone, Pop. 1,060
Wortham ISD 500/PK-12
PO Box 247 76693 254-765-3095
David Allen, supt. Fax 765-3473
www.worthamisd.org
Wortham HS 100/9-12
PO Box 247 76693 254-765-3094
David Hayes, prin. Fax 765-3085
Wortham MS 100/6-8
PO Box 247 76693 254-765-3523
David Hayes, prin. Fax 765-3512

Wylie, Dallas, Pop. 40,460
Wylie ISD 14,300/PK-12
PO Box 490 75098 972-429-3000
Dr. David Vinson, supt. Fax 442-5368
www.wylieisd.net
Achieve Academy 50/Alt
PO Box 490 75098 972-429-2390
Melissa True, prin. Fax 941-9213
Burnett JHS 700/7-8
PO Box 490 75098 972-429-3200
Ryan Bickley, prin. Fax 442-1447
Cooper JHS 700/7-8
PO Box 490 75098 972-429-3250
Shawn Miller, prin. Fax 941-9175
McMillan JHS 700/7-8
PO Box 490 75098 972-429-3225
Jon Peters, prin. Fax 941-6372
Wylie East HS 1,700/9-12
PO Box 490 75098 972-429-3150
Mike Williams, prin. Fax 442-2874
Wylie HS 2,000/9-12
PO Box 490 75098 972-429-3100
Virdie Montgomery, prin. Fax 442-1879

Wylie Preparatory Academy 300/K-12
4110 Skyview Ct 75098 972-442-1388
Brenda Kirby, admin. Fax 429-3568

Yantis, Wood, Pop. 386
Yantis ISD 400/PK-12
105 W Oak St 75497 903-383-2463
Dr. Peter Running, supt. Fax 383-7620
www.yantisisd.net
Yantis HS 200/6-12
105 W Oak St 75497 903-383-2463
Jerry Brem, prin. Fax 383-3075

Yoakum, Lavaca, Pop. 5,752
Yoakum ISD 1,600/PK-12
315 E Gonzales St 77995 361-293-3162
Tom Kelley, supt. Fax 293-6678
www.yoakumisd.net/
Yoakum HS 500/9-12
100 Poth St 77995 361-293-3442
Chris Wegener, prin. Fax 293-2145
Yoakum JHS 300/6-8
103 McKinnon St 77995 361-293-3111
Patrick Frank, prin. Fax 293-5787

Yorktown, DeWitt, Pop. 2,079
Yorktown ISD 500/PK-12
PO Box 487 78164 361-564-2252
Chad Gee, supt. Fax 564-2254
www.yisd.org
Yorktown HS 100/9-12
PO Box 487 78164 361-564-2252
Carlos Garza, prin. Fax 564-2274
Yorktown JHS 100/6-8
PO Box 487 78164 361-564-2252
Carlos Garza, prin. Fax 564-2289

Zapata, Zapata, Pop. 5,080
Zapata County ISD 3,600/PK-12
PO Box 158 78076 956-765-6546
Roberto Hein, supt. Fax 765-8350
www.zcisd.org
Zapata HS 900/9-12
PO Box 3750 78076 956-765-0280
Gerardo Garcia, prin. Fax 765-0274
Zapata MS 700/6-8
PO Box 3636 78076 956-765-6542
Elsa Martinez, prin. Fax 765-9204

Zavalla, Angelina, Pop. 708
Zavalla ISD 400/PK-12
431 E Main St 75980 936-897-2271
Ricky Oliver, supt. Fax 897-2674
www.zavallaisd.org
Zavalla JSHS 200/6-12
431 E Main St 75980 936-897-2301
Kathy Caton, prin. Fax 897-2674
Other Schools – See Lufkin

Zephyr, Brown
Zephyr ISD 200/PK-12
11625 County Road 281 76890 325-739-5331
Stanton Marwitz, supt. Fax 739-5906
zephyr.netxv.net
Zephyr S 200/PK-12
11625 County Road 281 76890 325-739-5331
DeeAnna Blanton, prin. Fax 739-2126

UTAH

UTAH OFFICE OF EDUCATION
PO Box 144200, Salt Lake City 84114-4200
Telephone 801-538-7500
Fax 801-538-7768
Website http://www.schools.utah.gov/main/

Superintendent of Public Instruction Dr. Sydnee Dickson

UTAH BOARD OF EDUCATION
250 E 500 S, Salt Lake City 84111-3204

Chairperson

REGIONAL SERVICE CENTERS (RSC)

Central Utah Educational Services
Jason Strate, dir. 435-896-4469
820 N Main St, Richfield 84701 Fax 896-4767
www.mycues.org

Northeastern Utah Educational Services
Duke Mossman, dir. 435-654-1921
35 S Main St, Heber City 84032 Fax 654-2403
www.nucenter.org

Southeast Educational Service Center
J.J. Grant, dir. 435-637-1173
685 E 200 S, Price 84501 Fax 637-1178
seschools.org

Southwest Educational Development Ctr
Edna LaMarca, dir. 435-586-2865
520 W 800 S, Cedar City 84720 Fax 586-2868
www.sedc.k12.ut.us

PUBLIC, PRIVATE AND CATHOLIC SECONDARY SCHOOLS

Alpine, Utah, Pop. 9,390
Alpine SD
Supt. — See American Fork
Timberline MS 1,300/7-9
500 W Canyon Crest Rd 84004 801-610-8765
Peter Glahn, prin. Fax 763-7045

Altamont, Duchesne, Pop. 222
Duchesne SD
Supt. — See Duchesne
Altamont JSHS 300/7-12
PO Box 130 84001 435-738-1345
Dean Wilson, prin. Fax 738-1370

American Fork, Utah, Pop. 25,678
Alpine SD 72,000/K-12
575 N 100 E 84003 801-610-8400
Sam Jarman, supt. Fax 610-8516
alpineschools.org
American Fork JHS 2,000/7-9
20 W 1120 N 84003 801-610-8750
Jeff Schoonover, prin. Fax 756-8407
American Fork SHS 2,100/10-12
510 N 600 E 84003 801-610-8800
Dan Weishar, prin. Fax 756-8575
Alpine Adult S Adult
778 E Bamberger Dr 84003 801-610-8188
Fax 756-1518
Other Schools – See Alpine, Eagle Mountain, Highland, Lehi, Lindon, Orem, Pleasant Grove, Saratoga Sprngs

---

American Heritage S 500/K-12
736 N 1100 E 84003 801-642-0055

Beaver, Beaver, Pop. 3,076
Beaver SD 1,500/K-12
PO Box 31 84713 435-438-2291
Dr. Ray Terry, supt. Fax 438-5898
www.beaver.k12.ut.us
Beaver HS 500/7-12
PO Box 71 84713 435-438-2301
Brady Fails, prin. Fax 438-1519
Other Schools – See Milford

Bicknell, Wayne, Pop. 324
Wayne SD 500/K-12
PO Box 127 84715 435-425-3813
Dr. John M. Fahey Ed.D., supt. Fax 425-3806
www.waynesd.org
Wayne HS 200/9-12
PO Box 217 84715 435-425-3411
Mary Bray, prin. Fax 425-3480
Wayne MS 100/6-8
PO Box 128 84715 435-425-3421
Lance Peterson, prin. Fax 425-3130

Big Water, Kane, Pop. 468
Kane SD
Supt. — See Kanab
Big Water HS 50/7-12
PO Box 410126 84741 435-675-5821
Andrew Roundy, prin. Fax 675-5821

Blanding, San Juan, Pop. 3,283
San Juan SD 3,000/K-12
200 N Main St 84511 435-678-1200
Edward Lyman, supt. Fax 678-1272
www.sjsd.org
Lyman MS 300/6-8
535 N 100 E 84511 435-678-1398
Aaron Brewer, prin. Fax 678-1399
San Juan HS 400/9-12
311 Bronco Blvd 84511 435-678-1301
Bob Peterson, prin. Fax 678-1396
Other Schools – See Montezuma Creek, Monticello, Monument Valley

Bountiful, Davis, Pop. 41,539
Davis SD
Supt. — See Farmington
Bountiful JHS 600/7-9
30 W 400 N 84010 801-402-6000
Kathy Ashton, prin. Fax 402-6001
Bountiful SHS 1,500/10-12
695 Orchard Dr 84010 801-402-3900
Dr. Gregory Wilkey, prin. Fax 402-3901
Millcreek JHS 700/7-9
245 E 1000 S 84010 801-402-6200
Brock Jackman, prin. Fax 402-6201
Mueller Park JHS 700/7-9
955 Mueller Park Rd 84010 801-402-6300
Deanne Kapetanov, prin. Fax 402-6301
South Davis JHS 1,100/7-9
298 W 2600 S 84010 801-402-6400
Jeff Jorgensen, prin. Fax 402-6401
Viewmont SHS 1,800/10-12
120 W 1000 N 84010 801-402-4200
Jason Smith, prin. Fax 402-4201

Brigham City, Box Elder, Pop. 17,553
Box Elder SD 11,300/PK-12
960 S Main St 84302 435-734-4800
Dr. Ronald Tolman, supt. Fax 734-4833
www.besd.net
Box Elder MS 1,000/8-9
18 S 500 E 84302 435-734-4880
Keith Mecham, prin. Fax 734-4885
Box Elder SHS 1,400/10-12
380 S 600 W 84302 435-734-4840
Gary Allen, prin. Fax 734-4846
Young Community HS 100/Alt
230 W 200 S 84302 435-734-4834
Jamie Kent, prin. Fax 734-4860
Other Schools – See Garland, Grouse Creek, Park Valley

Castle Dale, Emery, Pop. 1,623
Emery County SD
Supt. — See Huntington
Emery SHS 400/10-12
PO Box 499 84513 435-381-2689
Steven Gordon, prin. Fax 381-5370

Cedar City, Iron, Pop. 28,202
Iron SD 6,300/K-12
2077 W Royal Hunte Dr 84720 435-586-2804
Dr. Shannon Dulaney, supt. Fax 586-2815
irondistrict.org
Adult HS/Southwest Education Academy 100/Alt
510 W 800 S 84720 435-586-2870
Steve Schofield, prin. Fax 586-2815
Canyon View HS 1,100/9-12
166 W 1925 N 84721 435-586-2813
Rich Nielsen, prin. Fax 586-2849
Canyon View MS 900/6-8
1865 N Main St 84721 435-586-2830
Conrad Aitken, prin. Fax 586-2837
Cedar HS 1,100/9-12
703 W 600 S 84720 435-586-2820
John Dodds, prin. Fax 586-2826
Cedar MS 900/6-8
2215 W Royal Hunte Dr 84720 435-586-2810
Bylynda Murray, prin. Fax 586-2829
Foothill HS 50/Alt
270 E 1600 N 84721 435-867-2513
Steve Schofield, prin. Fax 586-2815
Other Schools – See Parowan

Southern Utah University Post-Sec.
351 W Center St 84720 435-586-7700
Southwest Applied Technology College Post-Sec.
510 W 800 S 84720 435-586-2899

Centerville, Davis, Pop. 15,086
Davis SD
Supt. — See Farmington
Centerville JHS 1,000/7-9
625 S Main St 84014 801-402-6100
Spencer Hansen, prin. Fax 402-6101

Clearfield, Davis, Pop. 28,950
Davis SD
Supt. — See Farmington
Clearfield SHS 1,700/10-12
931 S 1000 E 84015 801-402-8200
Suzi Jensen, prin. Fax 402-8336
North Davis JHS 1,000/7-9
835 S State St 84015 801-402-6500
Chris Keime, prin. Fax 402-6501

Vista College Post-Sec.
1785 E 1450 S Ste 300 84015 866-442-4197

Coalville, Summit, Pop. 1,348
North Summit SD 1,000/PK-12
PO Box 497 84017 435-336-5654
Jerre Holmes, supt. Fax 336-2401
www.nsummit.org
North Summit HS 300/9-12
PO Box 497 84017 435-336-5656
Russell Hendry, prin. Fax 336-0309
North Summit MS 300/5-8
PO Box 497 84017 435-336-5678
Brett Richins, prin. Fax 336-4474

Cottonwood Heights, Salt Lake, Pop. 32,636
Canyons SD
Supt. — See Sandy
Brighton HS 2,100/9-12
2220 E Bengal Blvd, 801-826-5800
Charisse Hilton, prin. Fax 826-5809
Butler MS 900/6-8
7530 S 2700 E, 801-826-6800
Paula Logan, prin. Fax 826-6809

Delta, Millard, Pop. 3,399
Millard SD 2,600/PK-12
285 E 450 N 84624 435-864-1000
David Styler, supt. Fax 864-5684
www.millardk12.org
Delta HS 500/9-12
10 W 300 N 84624 435-864-5610
Teresa Thompson, prin. Fax 864-5619
Delta MS 400/6-8
251 E 300 N 84624 435-864-5660
Rebecca Callister, prin. Fax 864-5669
Delta Technical Center Vo/Tech
305 E 200 N 84624 435-864-5710
Dean Fowles, dir. Fax 864-5719
Other Schools – See Fillmore, Garrison

Draper, Salt Lake, Pop. 41,208
Canyons SD
Supt. — See Sandy
Corner Canyon HS 1,800/9-12
12943 S 700 E 84020 801-826-6400
Darrell Jensen, prin. Fax 826-6409
Draper Park MS 1,400/6-8
13133 S 1300 E 84020 801-826-6900
Mary Anderson, prin. Fax 826-6909

Ameritech College Post-Sec.
12257 Business Park Dr #108 84020 801-816-1444
Argosy University / Salt Lake City Post-Sec.
121 W Election Rd Ste 300 84020 801-601-5000
Art Institute of Salt Lake City Post-Sec.
121 W Election Rd 84020 801-601-4700

Juan Diego Catholic HS 800/9-12
300 E 11800 S 84020 801-984-7602
Galey Colosimo, prin. Fax 984-7601
St. John the Baptist MS 400/6-8
300 E 11800 S 84020 801-984-7613
Patrick Reeder, prin. Fax 984-7649

Duchesne, Duchesne, Pop. 1,664
Duchesne SD 5,100/K-12
PO Box 446 84021 435-738-1240
Dr. David Brotherson, supt. Fax 738-1254
www.dcsd.org
Duchesne JSHS 300/7-12
PO Box 330 84021 435-738-1260
Stan Young, prin. Fax 738-1261
Other Schools – See Altamont, Roosevelt, Tabiona

Dugway, Tooele, Pop. 749
Tooele County SD
Supt. — See Tooele
Dugway JSHS 100/7-12
5020 5th St 84022 435-831-4566
Jeff Wyatt, prin. Fax 831-4951
Dugway S 100/K-12
Bldg 5010 School St 84022 435-831-4090
Jeff Wyatt, prin. Fax 831-4091

Eagle Mountain, Utah, Pop. 20,745
Alpine SD
Supt. — See American Fork
Frontier MS 1,300/7-9
1427 E Mid Valley Rd, 801-610-8777
Scott Sumner, prin. Fax 789-3800

Eden, Weber, Pop. 593
Weber SD
Supt. — See Ogden
Snowcrest JHS 300/7-9
2755 N Highway 162 84310 801-476-5360
Curtis VandenBosch, prin. Fax 476-5399

Enterprise, Washington, Pop. 1,701
Washington County SD
Supt. — See Saint George
Enterprise JSHS 400/7-12
PO Box 460 84725 435-878-2248
Rick Palmer, prin. Fax 878-2479

Ephraim, Sanpete, Pop. 5,963
South Sanpete SD
Supt. — See Manti
Ephraim MS 500/6-8
555 S 100 E 84627 435-283-4037
Timothy Miller, prin. Fax 283-4885

Snow College Post-Sec.
150 College Ave 84627 435-283-7000

Escalante, Garfield, Pop. 794
Garfield SD
Supt. — See Panguitch
Escalante HS 100/7-12
PO Box 228 84726 435-826-4205
Chip Sharpe, prin. Fax 826-4231

Eureka, Juab, Pop. 666
Tintic SD 300/PK-12
PO Box 210 84628 435-433-6363
Kodey Hughes, supt. Fax 433-6643
www.tintic.k12.ut.us
Tintic JSHS 100/7-12
PO Box 230 84628 435-433-6939
Greg Thornock, admin. Fax 433-6845
Other Schools – See Trout Creek

Farmington, Davis, Pop. 17,985
Davis SD 68,800/PK-12
PO Box 588 84025 801-402-5261
Dr. W. Bryan Bowles, supt. Fax 402-5249
www.davis.k12.ut.us
Farmington JHS 900/7-9
150 S 200 W 84025 801-402-6900
Brent Stephens, prin. Fax 402-6901
Other Schools – See Bountiful, Centerville, Clearfield, Kaysville, Layton, Sunset, Syracuse, West Point, Woods Cross

Ferron, Emery, Pop. 1,614
Emery County SD
Supt. — See Huntington
San Rafael JHS 300/7-9
PO Box 790 84523 435-384-2335
Doug Mecham, prin. Fax 384-3354

Fillmore, Millard, Pop. 2,397
Millard SD
Supt. — See Delta
Fillmore MS 300/5-8
435 S 500 W 84631 435-743-5660
Dennis Alldredge, prin. Fax 743-5669
Millard HS 300/9-12
200 Eagle Ave 84631 435-743-5610
George Richardson, prin. Fax 743-5619

Garland, Box Elder, Pop. 2,370
Box Elder SD
Supt. — See Brigham City
Bear River MS 700/8-9
300 E 1500 S 84312 435-257-2540
Eldon Petersen, prin. Fax 257-3945
Bear River SHS 900/10-12
1450 S Main St 84312 435-257-2500
Kristi Capener, prin. Fax 257-3899

Garrison, Millard
Millard SD
Supt. — See Delta
EskDale HS 50/9-12
1000 Circle Dr 84728 435-855-2148
Nomi Sheppard, lead tchr. Fax 855-2148
Garrison 7th & 8th S 50/7-8
1000 Circle Dr 84728 435-855-2148
Nomi Sheppard, lead tchr. Fax 855-2148

Grantsville, Tooele, Pop. 8,741
Tooele County SD
Supt. — See Tooele
Grantsville HS 800/9-12
155 E Cherry St 84029 435-884-4500
Mark Ernst, prin. Fax 884-4519
Grantsville JHS 400/7-8
318 S Hale St 84029 435-884-4510
Charles Mohler, prin. Fax 884-4513

Green River, Emery, Pop. 946
Emery County SD
Supt. — See Huntington
Green River JSHS 100/7-12
PO Box 450 84525 435-564-3461
Kayce Fluckey, prin. Fax 564-8259

Grouse Creek, Box Elder
Box Elder SD
Supt. — See Brigham City
Grouse Creek S 50/K-10
PO Box 16 84313 435-747-7321
Viola Foy, lead tchr. Fax 747-7182

Gunnison, Sanpete, Pop. 3,235
South Sanpete SD
Supt. — See Manti
Gunnison Valley HS 300/9-12
PO Box 460 84634 435-528-7256
Trevor Powell, prin. Fax 528-3556
Gunnison Valley MS 300/6-8
PO Box 1090 84634 435-528-5337
Alan Peterson, prin. Fax 528-5397

Harrisville, Weber, Pop. 5,477
Weber SD
Supt. — See Ogden
Orion JHS 1,000/7-9
370 W 2000 N, 801-452-4700
Chris Earnest, prin. Fax 452-4777

Heber City, Wasatch, Pop. 11,241
Wasatch SD 5,800/K-12
101 E 200 N 84032 435-654-0280
Paul Sweat, supt. Fax 654-4714
www.wasatch.edu/
Rocky Mountain MS 900/7-8
800 School House Way 84032 435-654-9350
Justin Kelly, prin. Fax 654-9343
Wasatch HS 1,700/9-12
930 S 500 E 84032 435-654-0640
Shawn Kelly, prin. Fax 654-3011
Wasatch HS North Campus Adult
180 E 600 S 84032 435-654-4231
Jacki Burnham, prin. Fax 654-9465

Helper, Carbon, Pop. 2,166
Carbon SD
Supt. — See Price
Helper MS 100/6-8
151 Uintah St 84526 435-472-5441
Mika Salas, prin. Fax 472-3502

Herriman, Salt Lake, Pop. 21,297
Jordan SD
Supt. — See West Jordan
Copper Mountain MS 1,100/7-9
12106 S Anthem Park Blvd, 801-412-1200
Cody Curtis, prin. Fax 412-1230
Fort Herriman MS 1,300/7-9
14058 S Mirabella Dr, 801-412-2450
Rodney Shaw, prin. Fax 412-2460
Herriman HS 2,400/10-12
11917 S 6000 W, 801-567-8530
James Birch, prin. Fax 567-8545

Highland, Utah, Pop. 15,197
Alpine SD
Supt. — See American Fork
Lone Peak SHS 2,300/10-12
10189 N 4800 W 84003 801-610-8810
Rhonda Bromley, prin. Fax 763-7064
Mountain Ridge JHS 1,400/7-9
5525 W 10400 N 84003 801-610-8758
Mark Whitaker, prin. Fax 763-7018

Hildale, Washington, Pop. 2,719
Washington County SD
Supt. — See Saint George
Water Canyon S PK-12
250 W Newel Ave 84784 435-668-2847
Darin Thomas, prin.

Holladay, Salt Lake
Granite SD
Supt. — See Salt Lake City
Bonneville JHS 900/7-9
5330 S 1660 E 84117 385-646-5124
Rocky Lambourne, prin. Fax 646-5127
Olympus JHS 800/7-9
2217 E Murray Holladay Rd 84117 385-646-5224
Doug Wagstaff, prin. Fax 646-5227

Huntington, Emery, Pop. 2,105
Emery County SD 2,300/PK-12
PO Box 120 84528 435-687-9846
Larry Davis, supt. Fax 687-9849
emerycsd.org
Canyon View JHS 200/7-9
PO Box 250 84528 435-687-2265
Yvonne Jensen, prin. Fax 687-9546
Other Schools – See Castle Dale, Ferron, Green River

Hurricane, Washington, Pop. 13,404
Washington County SD
Supt. — See Saint George
Hurricane HS 900/10-12
345 W Tiger Blvd 84737 435-635-3280
Jody Rich, prin. Fax 635-3719
Hurricane MS 600/8-9
395 N 200 W 84737 435-635-4634
Jan Goodwin, prin. Fax 635-4663

Hyrum, Cache, Pop. 7,476
Cache County SD
Supt. — See North Logan
Mountain Crest HS 1,700/9-12
255 S 800 E 84319 435-245-6093
Teri Cutler, prin. Fax 245-3818
South Cache JHS 1,300/8-9
10 S 480 W 84319 435-245-6433
Lance Robins, prin. Fax 245-6662

Junction, Piute, Pop. 190
Piute County SD 300/PK-12
PO Box 69 84740 435-577-2912
Shane Erickson, supt. Fax 577-2561
www.piutek12.org
Piute JSHS 200/7-12
PO Box 9 84740 435-577-2912
Kennedy Sylvester, lead tchr. Fax 577-2512

Kamas, Summit, Pop. 1,803
South Summit SD 1,500/PK-12
285 E 400 S 84036 435-783-4301
Dr. Shad Sorenson, supt. Fax 783-4501
www.ssummit.org
South Summit HS 400/9-12
45 S 300 E 84036 435-783-4313
Wade Woolstenhulme, prin. Fax 783-4765
South Summit MS 500/5-8
355 E 300 S 84036 435-783-4341
Steve Camp, prin. Fax 783-2787

Kanab, Kane, Pop. 4,263
Kane SD 1,200/K-12
746 S 175 E 84741 435-644-2555
Ben Dalton, supt. Fax 644-2509
www.kane.k12.ut.us
Kanab HS 300/9-12
59 Cowboy Dr 84741 435-644-5821
Brenan Jackson, prin. Fax 644-5242
Kanab MS 100/7-8
690 Cowboy Way 84741 435-644-5800
Mandie Luce, prin. Fax 644-5121
Other Schools – See Big Water, Lake Powell, Orderville

Kaysville, Davis, Pop. 26,897
Davis SD
Supt. — See Farmington
Canyon Heights S 100/Alt
525 E 300 S 84037 801-402-0720
Marci Flocken, prin. Fax 402-0551
Centennial JHS 1,200/7-9
740 S Sunset Dr 84037 801-402-0100
Aaron Hogge, prin. Fax 402-0101
Davis Applied Technology College Vo/Tech
550 E 300 S 84037 801-593-2500
Mike Bouwhuis, dir. Fax 593-2400
Davis SHS 2,400/10-12
325 S Main St 84037 801-402-8800
Rich Swanson, prin. Fax 402-8801
Fairfield JHS 1,100/7-9
951 N Fairfield Rd 84037 801-402-7000
Bryon Nielsen, prin. Fax 402-7001
Kaysville JHS 1,000/7-9
100 E 350 S 84037 801-402-7200
Curtis Stromberg, prin. Fax 402-7201
Mountain HS 200/Alt
490 S 500 E 84037 801-402-0450
Kathleen Chronister, prin. Fax 402-0451

Davis Applied Technology College Post-Sec.
550 E 300 S 84037 801-593-2500

Kearns, Salt Lake, Pop. 34,126
Granite SD
Supt. — See Salt Lake City
Jefferson JHS 1,100/7-9
5850 S 5600 W 84118 385-646-5194
Jared Reynolds, prin. Fax 646-5195
Kearns JHS 900/7-9
4040 W Sams Blvd 84118 385-646-5204
Scott Bell, prin. Fax 646-5206
Kearns SHS 1,600/10-12
5525 S Cougar Ln 84118 385-646-5380
Maile Loo, prin. Fax 646-5382

Lake Powell, San Juan, Pop. 15
Kane SD
Supt. — See Kanab
Lake Powell HS 50/7-12
1000 Ferry Rd 84533 435-684-2268
Gordon Miller, prin. Fax 684-3821

Laketown, Rich, Pop. 240
Rich SD
Supt. — See Randolph
Rich MS 100/6-8
PO Box 129 84038 435-946-3359
Kip Motta, prin. Fax 946-3366

Layton, Davis, Pop. 65,397
Davis SD
Supt. — See Farmington
Central Davis JHS 900/7-9
663 Church St 84041 801-402-7100
T.J. Barker, prin. Fax 402-7101
Layton SHS 1,800/10-12
440 Lancer Ln 84041 801-402-4800
Ryck Astle, prin. Fax 402-4801
Legacy JHS 800/7-8
411 N 3200 W 84041 801-402-4700
Chadli Bodily, prin. Fax 402-4701
North Layton JHS 900/7-9
1100 W Antelope Dr 84041 801-402-6600
Ed Campbell, prin. Fax 402-6601
Northridge SHS 1,700/10-12
2430 N Hill Field Rd 84041 801-402-8500
Brian Hunt, prin. Fax 402-8501

Eagle Gate College Post-Sec.
915 N 400 W 84041 801-546-7500
Fran Brown College of Beauty Post-Sec.
587 N Main St 84041 801-546-6166
Layton Christian Academy 500/PK-12
2352 E Highway 193 84040 801-771-7141
Greg Miller, admin. Fax 771-0921

Lehi, Utah, Pop. 46,111
Alpine SD
Supt. — See American Fork

Lehi JHS 1,400/7-9
700 E Cedar Hollow Rd 84043 801-768-7010
Kevin Thomas, prin. Fax 768-7016
Lehi SHS 2,200/10-12
180 N 500 E 84043 801-610-8805
David Mower, prin. Fax 768-7007
Skyridge SHS, 3000 N Center 84043 10-12
Joel Perkins, prin. 801-610-8820
Willowcreek MS 1,500/7-9
2275 W 300 N 84043 801-610-8766
Jarom Becar, prin. Fax 766-5168

Mountainland Applied Technology College Post-Sec.
2301 N Ashton Blvd 84043 801-753-6282

Lindon, Utah, Pop. 9,825
Alpine SD
Supt. — See American Fork
Oak Canyon JHS 1,200/7-9
111 S 725 E 84042 801-610-8138
Doug Webb, prin. Fax 785-8768

Evan's Hairstyling College Post-Sec.
284 W 200 N 84042 801-224-6034

Logan, Cache, Pop. 47,175
Cache County SD
Supt. — See North Logan
Cache HS 100/Alt
265 W 1400 N 84341 435-755-0716
Sheri Hansen, prin. Fax 755-0721

Logan CSD 6,100/PK-12
101 W Center St 84321 435-755-2300
Frank Schofield, supt. Fax 755-2311
www.loganschools.org
Logan HS 1,700/9-12
162 W 100 S 84321 435-755-2380
Kenneth Auld, prin. Fax 755-2387
Logan South Campus 100/Alt
325 W 400 S 84321 435-755-2395
Larry Comadena, dean Fax 755-2396
Mt. Logan MS 1,300/6-8
875 N 200 E 84321 435-755-2370
Daryl Guymon, prin. Fax 755-2370

Bridgerland Applied Technology Center Post-Sec.
1301 N 600 W 84321 435-753-6780
Mountain Ridge Helicopters Post-Sec.
2500 N 900 W Fl 15 84321 435-752-3828
New Horizons Beauty College Post-Sec.
550 N Main St Ste 115 84321 435-753-9779
Stevens Henager College Post-Sec.
755 S Main St 84321 435-752-0903
Utah State University Post-Sec.
1400 Old Main Hl 84322 435-797-1000

Magna, Salt Lake, Pop. 25,413
Granite SD
Supt. — See Salt Lake City
Cyprus SHS 1,700/10-12
8623 W 3000 S 84044 385-646-5300
Rob McDaniel, prin. Fax 646-5303
Matheson JHS 1,200/7-9
3650 S Montclair St 84044 385-646-5290
Dawn Hauser, prin. Fax 646-5299

Stansbury Academy 100/8-12
8265 W 2700 S 84044 801-243-1636
Dr. R. Craig Pace Ph.D., prin. Fax 243-1636

Manila, Daggett, Pop. 308
Daggett SD 200/PK-12
PO Box 249 84046 435-784-3174
Bruce Northcott, supt. Fax 784-3920
www.dsdf.org
Manila JSHS 100/7-12
PO Box 249 84046 435-784-3174
Guy Gonder, prin. Fax 784-3271

Manti, Sanpete, Pop. 3,220
South Sanpete SD 3,300/PK-12
39 S Main St 84642 435-835-2261
Kent Larsen, supt. Fax 835-2265
www.ssanpete.org/
Manti HS 600/9-12
100 W 500 N 84642 435-835-2281
George Henrie, prin. Fax 835-2285
Other Schools – See Ephraim, Gunnison

Mapleton, Utah, Pop. 7,784
Nebo SD
Supt. — See Spanish Fork
Mapleton JHS 1,300/7-9
362 E 1200 N 84664 801-489-2892
RaShel Anderson, prin. Fax 489-2899

Midvale, Salt Lake, Pop. 27,166
Canyons SD
Supt. — See Sandy
Hillcrest HS 2,300/9-12
7350 S 900 E 84047 801-826-6000
Gregory Leavitt, prin. Fax 826-6009
Midvale MS 900/6-8
7852 S Pioneer St 84047 801-826-7300
Wendy Dau, prin. Fax 826-7309

Kendall's Academy of Beauty Arts/Science Post-Sec.
7353 S 900 E 84047 801-561-5610

Milford, Beaver, Pop. 1,385
Beaver SD
Supt. — See Beaver
Milford HS 200/7-12
PO Box 159 84751 435-387-2751
David Cluff, prin. Fax 387-2494

Millville, Cache, Pop. 1,804
Cache County SD
Supt. — See North Logan
Ridgeline HS 1,300/9-12
180 N 300 W 84326 435-792-7780
Robert Henke, prin. Fax 753-2168

Moab, Grand, Pop. 4,967
Grand SD 1,500/PK-12
264 S 400 E 84532 435-259-5317
Dr. Scott Crane, supt. Fax 259-6212
www.grandschools.org
Arches Education Center Alt
608 S 400 E 84532 435-719-4840
Ron Dolphin, admin.
Grand County HS 500/9-12
608 S 400 E 84532 435-259-8931
Stephen Hren, prin. Fax 259-4191
Grand County MS 200/7-8
439 S 100 E 84532 435-259-7158
Melinda Snow, prin. Fax 259-6221

Monroe, Sevier, Pop. 2,221
Sevier SD
Supt. — See Richfield
South Sevier HS 400/9-12
430 W 100 S 84754 435-527-4651
Randy Madsen, prin. Fax 527-4653
South Sevier MS 300/6-8
300 E Center St 84754 435-527-4607
Michael Willes, prin. Fax 527-4636

Montezuma Creek, San Juan, Pop. 332
San Juan SD
Supt. — See Blanding, UT
Whitehorse HS 300/7-12
PO Box 660 84534 435-678-1209
Kim Schaefer, prin. Fax 678-1252

Monticello, San Juan, Pop. 1,935
San Juan SD
Supt. — See Blanding, UT
Monticello JSHS 300/7-12
PO Box 69 84535 435-678-1130
Lewis Whitaker, prin. Fax 678-1150

Monument Valley, San Juan
San Juan SD
Supt. — See Blanding, UT
Monument Valley JSHS 200/7-12
PO Box 360008 84536 435-678-1208
Spencer Singer, prin. Fax 678-1258

Morgan, Morgan, Pop. 3,652
Morgan SD 2,600/PK-12
PO Box 530 84050 801-829-3411
Dr. Doug Jacobs, supt. Fax 829-3531
www.morgansd.org
Morgan HS 800/9-12
PO Box 917 84050 801-829-3418
Crae Wilson, prin. Fax 829-6553
Morgan MS 600/6-8
PO Box 470 84050 801-829-3467
Reynold Hoopes, prin. Fax 829-0645

Moroni, Sanpete, Pop. 1,398
North Sanpete SD
Supt. — See Mount Pleasant
North Sanpete MS 400/7-8
PO Box 307 84646 435-436-8206
ODee Hansen, prin. Fax 436-8208

Mount Pleasant, Sanpete, Pop. 3,193
North Sanpete SD 2,300/PK-12
220 E 700 S 84647 435-462-2485
Dr. Sam Ray, supt. Fax 462-2480
www.nsanpete.org
North Sanpete HS 600/9-12
390 E 700 S 84647 435-462-2452
Nan Ault, prin. Fax 462-3112
Other Schools – See Moroni

Wasatch Academy 300/8-12
120 S 100 W 84647 435-462-1400
Joseph Loftin, hdmstr. Fax 462-1450

Murray, Salt Lake, Pop. 45,548
Granite SD
Supt. — See Salt Lake City
Cottonwood SHS 1,500/10-12
5715 S 1300 E 84121 385-646-5264
Terri Roylance, prin. Fax 646-5266

Murray CSD
Supt. — See Salt Lake City
Hillcrest JHS 700/7-9
178 E 5300 S 84107 801-264-7442
Jennifer Covington, prin. Fax 264-4820
Murray SHS 1,400/10-12
5440 S State St 84107 801-264-7460
Dr. John Goldhardt, prin. Fax 264-7461
Riverview JHS 800/7-9
751 W Tripp Ln 84123 801-264-7446
Jim Bouwman, prin. Fax 264-7458

Cameo College of Essential Beauty Post-Sec.
124 E 5770 S 84107 801-484-6173
Eagle Gate College Post-Sec.
5588 S Green St 84123 801-333-8100
Mt. Vernon Academy 100/K-12
184 E Vine St 84107 801-266-5521

Nephi, Juab, Pop. 5,328
Juab SD 2,300/K-12
346 E 600 N 84648 435-623-1940
Rick Robins, supt. Fax 623-1941
www.juabsd.org
Juab HS 700/9-12
802 N 650 E 84648 435-623-1764
Royd Darrington, prin. Fax 623-1772
Juab JHS 300/7-8
555 E 800 N 84648 435-623-1541
Ken Rowley, prin. Fax 623-4995

North Logan, Cache, Pop. 8,096
Cache County SD 16,700/K-12
2063 N 1200 E 84341 435-752-3925
Dr. Steven Norton, supt. Fax 753-2168
www.ccsdut.org
Other Schools – See Hyrum, Logan, Millville, Richmond, Smithfield

North Ogden, Weber, Pop. 17,100
Weber SD
Supt. — See Ogden
North Ogden JHS 700/7-9
575 E 2900 N 84414 801-452-4800
Wendy Long, prin. Fax 452-4839

Ogden, Weber, Pop. 80,717
Ogden CSD 12,400/K-12
1950 Monroe Blvd 84401 801-737-7300
Sandy Coroles, supt. Fax 627-7654
www.ogdensd.org
Highland JHS 900/7-9
325 Gramercy Ave 84404 801-737-7700
Stacey Briggs, prin. Fax 625-8860
Lomond HS 1,200/10-12
1080 9th St 84404 801-737-7900
Dale Wilkinson, prin. Fax 625-1138
Mound Fort JHS 700/7-9
1400 Mound Fort Dr 84404 801-737-7800
Bryan Becherini, prin. Fax 625-8993
Mt. Ogden JHS 900/7-9
3260 Harrison Blvd 84403 801-737-8600
Tracy Van de Venter, prin. Fax 627-7641
Ogden HS 1,300/10-12
2828 Harrison Blvd 84403 801-737-8673
Luke Rasmussen, prin. Fax 392-7338
Washington Alternative HS 200/Alt
455 28th St 84401 801-737-7400
Benjamin Carrier, prin. Fax 625-1171

Weber SD 30,300/K-12
5320 Adams Avenue Pkwy 84405 801-476-7800
Jeff Stephens, supt. Fax 476-7893
www.wsd.net
Bell JHS 700/7-9
165 W 5100 S 84405 801-452-4600
Lenn Ward, prin. Fax 452-4639
Bonneville SHS 1,400/10-12
251 E 4800 S 84405 801-452-4050
Larry Hadley, prin. Fax 476-1837
South Ogden JHS 900/7-9
650 E 5700 S 84405 801-452-4460
Michele Parry, prin. Fax 452-4499
Two Rivers HS 200/Alt
955 W 12th St 84404 801-476-3920
Jeff Marchant, prin. Fax 476-3940
Wahlquist JHS 1,100/7-9
2656 N 2400 W 84404 801-452-4640
Sue Sweet, prin. Fax 452-4679
Weber Innovation HS 10-12
1007 W 12th St 84404 801-476-6500
Reid Newey, prin. Fax 476-6519
Weber SHS 1,900/10-12
430 W Weber High Dr 84414 801-476-3700
Velden Wardle, prin. Fax 476-3799
Other Schools – See Eden, Harrisville, North Ogden, Plain City, Roy, West Haven

Marinello School of Beauty Post-Sec.
3721 S 250 W 84405 801-394-5718
Nightingale College Post-Sec.
4155 Harrison Blvd Ste 100 84403 801-689-2160
Ogden-Weber Applied Technology College Post-Sec.
200 N Washington Blvd 84404 801-627-8300
St. Joseph's HS 200/9-12
1790 Lake St 84401 801-394-1515
Clay Jones, prin. Fax 394-6428
Stevens Henager College Post-Sec.
PO Box 9428 84409 801-392-1471
Utah Schools for the Deaf and the Blind Post-Sec.
742 Harrison Blvd 84404 801-629-4700
Weber State University Post-Sec.
1001 University Cir 84408 801-626-6000

Orderville, Kane, Pop. 575
Kane SD
Supt. — See Kanab
Valley HS 100/7-12
PO Box 128 84758 435-648-2278
Jim Wood, prin. Fax 648-2366

Orem, Utah, Pop. 85,397
Alpine SD
Supt. — See American Fork
Alpine Summit 50/Alt
1581 W 1000 S 84058 801-610-8183
Lynn Gerratt, dir. Fax 227-7831
Canyon View JHS 1,200/7-9
655 E 950 N 84097 801-610-8130
Wade Lott, prin. Fax 227-8706
Lakeridge JHS 1,200/7-9
951 S 400 W 84058 801-610-8134
Kathy Knudsen, prin. Fax 227-2490
Mountain View SHS 1,300/10-12
665 W Center St 84057 801-610-8160
Taran Chun, prin. Fax 227-8764
Orem JHS 900/7-9
765 N 600 W 84057 801-610-8142
Brian Jolley, prin. Fax 227-8796
Orem SHS 1,200/10-12
175 S 400 E 84097 801-610-8165
Mike Browning, prin. Fax 227-8774
Polaris HS Alt
1551 W 1000 S 84058 801-610-8180
Lori Thorn, prin. Fax 227-2447
Timpanogos SHS 1,400/10-12
1450 N 200 E 84057 801-610-8175
Dr. Joe Jensen, prin. Fax 223-3134

Stevens Henager College Post-Sec.
1476 Sandhill Rd 84058 801-373-0285
Utah College of Dental Hygiene Post-Sec.
1176 S 1480 W 84058 801-426-8234
Utah Valley University Post-Sec.
800 W University Pkwy 84058 801-863-8000

Panguitch, Garfield, Pop. 1,509
Garfield SD 900/K-12
PO Box 398 84759 435-676-8821
Tracy Davis, supt. Fax 676-8266
www.garfk12.org

Panguitch HS 100/9-12
PO Box 393 84759 435-676-8805
Russ Torgersen, prin. Fax 676-8521
Panguitch MS 100/7-8
PO Box 393 84759 435-676-8225
Russ Torgersen, prin. Fax 676-2518
Other Schools – See Escalante, Tropic

Park City, Summit, Pop. 7,439
Park City SD 4,700/K-12
2700 Kearns Blvd 84060 435-645-5600
Ember Conley, supt. Fax 645-5609
www.pcschools.us
Park City Learning Center 100/Alt
2400 Kearns Blvd 84060 435-645-5626
Tracy Sjostrom, prin. Fax 645-5627
Park City SHS 1,100/10-12
1750 Kearns Blvd 84060 435-645-5650
Bob O'Connor, prin. Fax 645-5659
Treasure Mountain International S 800/8-9
2530 Kearns Blvd 84060 435-645-5640
Emily Sutherland, prin. Fax 645-5649

Park Valley, Box Elder
Box Elder SD
Supt. — See Brigham City
Park Valley S 50/K-10
788 Education Dr 84329 435-871-4411
Melissa Morris, lead tchr. Fax 871-4444

Parowan, Iron, Pop. 2,772
Iron SD
Supt. — See Cedar City
Parowan HS 300/7-12
PO Box 337 84761 435-477-3366
Roy Mathews, prin. Fax 477-3743

Payson, Utah, Pop. 18,014
Nebo SD
Supt. — See Spanish Fork
Mt. Nebo JHS 700/7-9
851 W 450 S 84651 801-465-6040
Troy Peterson, prin. Fax 465-6045
Payson JHS 1,000/7-9
1025 Highway 198 84651 801-465-6015
Carl Swenson, prin. Fax 465-6023
Payson SHS 1,200/10-12
1050 S Main St 84651 801-465-6025
Ben Ford, prin. Fax 465-6067

Plain City, Weber, Pop. 5,416
Weber SD
Supt. — See Ogden
Fremont SHS 1,900/10-12
1900 N 4700 W 84404 801-452-4000
Rod Belnap, prin. Fax 452-4049

Pleasant Grove, Utah, Pop. 32,692
Alpine SD
Supt. — See American Fork
Pleasant Grove JHS 1,500/7-9
810 N 100 E 84062 801-610-8146
Todd Dalley, prin. Fax 785-8743
Pleasant Grove SHS 2,000/10-12
700 E 200 S 84062 801-610-8170
Steve Stewart, prin. Fax 785-8744

Liahona Preparatory Academy 200/PK-12
2464 W 450 S 84062 801-785-7850

Price, Carbon, Pop. 8,585
Carbon SD 2,900/K-12
251 W 400 N 84501 435-637-1732
Steve Carlsen, supt. Fax 637-9417
www.carbonschools.org
Carbon HS 600/9-12
750 E 400 N 84501 435-637-2463
Bruce Bean, prin. Fax 637-4127
Lighthouse HS 100/Alt
251 W 400 N 84501 435-637-7540
Karlene Bianco, prin. Fax 637-4019
Mont Harmon MS 400/6-8
60 W 400 N 84501 435-637-0510
Seth Allred, prin. Fax 637-6074
Other Schools – See Helper

Utah State University Eastern Post-Sec.
451 E 400 N 84501 435-613-5000

Provo, Utah, Pop. 108,411
Provo CSD 14,300/PK-12
280 W 940 N 84604 801-374-4800
Keith C. Rittel, supt. Fax 374-4808
www.provo.edu
Centennial MS 1,000/7-8
305 E 2320 N 84604 801-374-4621
Gaye Gibbs, prin. Fax 374-4626
Dixon MS 800/7-8
750 W 200 N 84601 801-374-4980
Jarod Sites, prin. Fax 374-4884
Independence HS 300/Alt
636 Independence Ave 84601 801-374-4920
Chris Sorensen, prin. Fax 370-4614
Oak Springs S 50/Alt
1300 E Center St 84606 801-374-4858
Dennis Meyers, prin. Fax 374-4999
Provo HS 1,700/9-12
1125 N University Ave 84604 801-373-6550
Karen Brown, prin. Fax 374-4880
Timpview HS 2,000/9-12
3570 Timpview Dr 84604 801-221-9720
Fidel Montero, prin. Fax 224-4210
East Bay Post HS Adult
515 E 1860 S 84606 801-374-4874
Bryce Vellinga, admin. Fax 374-4872
Provo Adult Education Adult
636 N Independence Ave 84604 801-374-4840
Anita Craven, coord. Fax 374-4816

AmeriTech College Post-Sec.
2035 N 550 W 84604 801-377-2900
Brigham Young University 84602 Post-Sec.
801-422-4636
Dallas Roberts Academy of Hair Design Post-Sec.
1700 N State St Ste 18 84604 801-375-1501
Provo College Post-Sec.
1450 W 820 N 84601 801-818-8900
Rocky Mountain Univ of Health Profession Post-Sec.
561 E 1860 S 84606 801-375-5125
Utah Valley Regional Medical Center Post-Sec.
1034 N 500 W 84604 801-373-7850
Von Curtis Academy of Hair Design Post-Sec.
480 N 900 E 84606 801-374-5111

Randolph, Rich, Pop. 458
Rich SD 500/K-12
PO Box 67 84064 435-793-2135
Dale Lamborn, supt. Fax 793-2136
www.richschool.org
Rich HS 100/9-12
PO Box 278 84064 435-793-2365
Rick Larsen, prin. Fax 793-2375
Other Schools – See Laketown

Richfield, Sevier, Pop. 7,458
Sevier SD 4,800/PK-12
180 E 600 N 84701 435-896-8214
Cade Douglas, supt. Fax 896-8804
www.seviersd.org
Cedar Ridge HS 100/Alt
555 W 100 N 84701 435-896-9464
George Chappell, prin. Fax 896-9475
Red Hills MS 500/6-8
400 S 600 W 84701 435-896-6421
Selena Terry, prin. Fax 896-6423
Richfield HS 600/9-12
495 W Center St 84701 435-896-8247
Brent Gubler, prin. Fax 896-8246
Other Schools – See Monroe, Salina

Richmond, Cache, Pop. 2,447
Cache County SD
Supt. — See North Logan
North Cache JHS 1,100/8-9
157 W 600 S 84333 435-258-2452
Terry Williams, prin. Fax 258-5437

Riverton, Salt Lake, Pop. 37,974
Jordan SD
Supt. — See West Jordan
Jordan Academy for Tech & Careers South Vo/Tech
12723 S Park Ave 84065 801-412-1300
Nicole Plenert, admin. Fax 412-1350
Oquirrh Hills MS 1,200/7-9
12949 S 2700 W 84065 801-412-2350
Michael Glenn, prin. Fax 412-2370
Riverton HS 2,100/10-12
12476 S 2700 W 84065 801-256-5800
Carolyn Gough, prin. Fax 256-5880
South Hills MS 1,000/7-9
13508 S 4000 W 84065 801-412-2400
Ben Jameson, prin. Fax 412-2430

Roosevelt, Duchesne, Pop. 5,853
Duchesne SD
Supt. — See Duchesne
Roosevelt JHS 700/6-8
350 W 200 S 84066 435-725-4585
Mike Ross, prin. Fax 725-4622
Union HS 900/9-12
135 N Union St Ste 124-3 84066 435-725-4525
Rick Nielsen, prin. Fax 725-4576

Uintah Basin Applied Technology College Post-Sec.
1100 E Lagoon St 84066 435-722-6900

Roy, Weber, Pop. 35,969
Weber SD
Supt. — See Ogden
Roy JHS 900/7-9
5400 S 2100 W 84067 801-476-5260
Matt Williams, prin. Fax 476-5299
Roy SHS 1,700/10-12
2150 W 4800 S 84067 801-476-3600
Kirt Swalberg, prin. Fax 476-3699
Sand Ridge JHS 800/7-9
2075 W 4600 S 84067 801-476-5320
Scott Elliot, prin. Fax 476-5359

Saint George, Washington, Pop. 70,848
Washington County SD 26,500/PK-12
121 W Tabernacle St 84770 435-673-3553
Larry Bergeson, supt. Fax 673-3216
www.washk12.org
Desert Hills HS 1,200/10-12
828 Desert Hills Dr 84790 435-674-0885
Rusty Taylor, prin. Fax 674-2606
Desert Hills MS 900/8-9
936 Desert Hills Dr 84790 435-628-0001
Brian Stevenson, prin. Fax 674-6477
Dixie HS 1,100/10-12
350 E 700 S 84770 435-673-4682
Sharla Campbell, prin. Fax 673-2384
Dixie MS 800/7-9
825 S 100 E 84770 435-628-0441
Tim Lowe, prin. Fax 674-6467
Millcreek HS 200/10-12
2410 E Riverside Dr 84790 435-628-2462
Russell Holmes, prin. Fax 628-8206
Pine View HS 1,000/10-12
2850 E 750 N 84790 435-628-5255
Mike Mees, prin. Fax 628-0327
Pine View MS 800/8-9
2145 E 130 N 84790 435-628-7915
Steve Gustaveson, prin. Fax 634-0470
Snow Canyon HS 1,100/10-12
1385 Lava Flow Dr 84770 435-634-1967
Warren Brooks, prin. Fax 634-1130
Snow Canyon MS 900/8-9
1215 Lava Flow Dr 84770 435-674-6474
Brad Bench, prin. Fax 628-3289
Other Schools – See Enterprise, Hildale, Hurricane

Dixie Applied Technology College Post-Sec.
1506 S Silicon Way 84770 435-674-8400
Dixie State College of Utah Post-Sec.
225 S 700 E 84770 435-652-7500
Evan's Hairstyling College Post-Sec.
955 E Tabernacle St 84770 435-673-6128
Hairitage Hair Academy Post-Sec.
900 S Bluff St Ste 9 84770 435-673-5233
Stevens-Henager College Post-Sec.
720 S River Rd Ste C130 84790 435-628-9150

Salem, Utah, Pop. 6,343
Nebo SD
Supt. — See Spanish Fork
Salem Hills SHS 1,300/10-12
150 Skyhawk Blvd 84653 801-423-3200
Bart Peery, prin. Fax 423-3206
Salem JHS 900/7-9
598 N Main St 84653 801-423-6550
Robert Fleming, prin. Fax 423-6558

Salina, Sevier, Pop. 2,467
Sevier SD
Supt. — See Richfield
North Sevier HS 300/9-12
350 W 400 N 84654 435-529-3717
Jade Shepherd, prin. Fax 529-7910
North Sevier MS 300/6-8
135 N 100 W 84654 435-529-3841
Rod Hinck, prin. Fax 529-7377

Salt Lake City, Salt Lake, Pop. 178,350
Granite SD 67,200/PK-12
2500 S State St 84115 385-646-5000
Dr. Martin Bates, supt. Fax 646-4207
www.graniteschools.org
Churchill JHS 600/7-9
3450 E Oakview Dr 84124 385-646-5144
Josh LeRoy, prin. Fax 646-5147
Evergreen JHS 800/7-9
3401 S 2000 E 84109 385-646-5164
Wesley Cutler, prin. Fax 646-5165
Granite Park JHS 700/7-9
3031 S 200 E 84115 385-646-5174
Daniel Stirland, prin. Fax 646-5175
Granite Peaks Alternative HS 300/Alt
501 E 3900 S 84107 385-646-4666
Christine Straatman, dir. Fax 646-4667
Granite Technical Institute Vo/Tech
2500 S State St 84115 385-646-4350
Devon Hartley, prin. Fax 646-4347
Olympus SHS 1,600/10-12
4055 S 2300 E 84124 385-646-5400
Steve Perschon, prin. Fax 646-5405
Skyline SHS 1,400/10-12
3251 E 3760 S 84109 385-646-5420
Doug Bingham, prin. Fax 646-5422
Wasatch JHS 900/7-9
3750 S 3100 E 84109 385-646-5244
John Anderson, prin. Fax 646-5246
Other Schools – See Holladay, Kearns, Magna, Murray, Taylorsville, West Valley

Murray CSD 6,400/K-12
5102 S Commerce Dr 84107 801-264-7400
Dr. Steven Hirase, supt. Fax 264-7456
www.murrayschools.org
Other Schools – See Murray

Salt Lake City SD 24,900/PK-12
440 E 100 S 84111 801-578-8599
Dr. Alexa Cunningham, supt. Fax 578-8248
www.slcschools.org
Bryant MS 400/7-8
40 S 800 E 84102 801-578-8118
James Yapias, prin. Fax 578-8125
Clayton MS 700/7-8
1470 S 1900 E 84108 801-481-4810
Linda Richins, prin. Fax 481-4884
East HS 1,900/9-12
840 S 1300 E 84102 801-583-1661
Greg Maughan, prin. Fax 584-2927
Glendale MS 800/6-8
1430 W Andrew Ave 84104 801-974-8319
Chris Gesteland, prin. Fax 974-8356
Highland HS 1,600/9-12
2166 S 1700 E 84106 801-484-4343
Chris Jensen, prin. Fax 481-4893
Hillside MS 500/7-8
1825 S Nevada St 84108 801-481-4828
Jane Bernston, prin. Fax 481-4831
Horizonte Instruction & Training Center 600/Alt
1234 S Main St 84101 801-578-8574
Joshua Bell, prin. Fax 578-8577
Innovations Early College HS 200/9-12
1633 S Edison St 84115 801-481-4946
Kenneth Grover, prin. Fax 584-2927
Northwest MS 800/7-8
1730 W 1700 N 84116 801-578-8547
Rachel Nance, prin. Fax 578-8558
West HS 2,300/9-12
241 N 300 W 84103 801-578-8500
Paul Sagers, prin. Fax 578-8516

Broadview Entertainment Arts University Post-Sec.
240 Morris Ave 84115 801-300-4300
Eagle Gate College Post-Sec.
405 S Main St 84111 801-333-7120
Fortis College Post-Sec.
3949 S 700 E Ste 150 84107 801-713-0915
Independence University Post-Sec.
4021 S 700 E Ste 400 84107 800-972-5149
Intermountain Christian S 300/PK-12
6515 S Lion Ln 84121 801-365-0370
Mitch Menning, head sch Fax 942-8813
Judge Memorial Catholic HS 700/9-12
650 S 1100 E 84102 801-363-8895
Patrick Lambert, prin. Fax 521-3920
Kendall's Academy of Beauty Arts/Science Post-Sec.
2230 S 700 E 84106 801-486-0101
Latter Day Saints Business College Post-Sec.
95 N 300 W Fl 8th 84101 801-524-8100
Midwives College of Utah Post-Sec.
1174 E Graystone Way Ste 2 84106 801-649-5230
Myotherapy College of Utah Post-Sec.
336 Bugatti Dr 84115 801-484-7624
Neumont University Post-Sec.
143 S Main St 84111 888-638-6668

Realms of Inquiry S 50/6-12
4998 S Galleria Dr 84123 801-467-5911
Reid S 100/PK-12
2965 E 3435 S 84109 801-466-4214
Dr. Ethna R. Reid, prin. Fax 466-4214
Rowland Hall HS 300/9-12
843 S Lincoln St 84102 801-355-7494
Alan Sparrow, head sch Fax 355-0474
Rowland Hall MS 200/6-8
970 E 800 S 84102 801-355-0272
Alan Sparrow, head sch Fax 355-0474
Salt Lake Community College Post-Sec.
4600 S Redwood Rd 84123 801-957-4111
Skin Works School of Advanced Skin Care Post-Sec.
2121 Nowell Cir 84115 801-530-0001
Stevens Henager College Post-Sec.
383 W Vine St 84123 801-531-1180
University of Utah Post-Sec.
201 S 1460 E 84112 801-581-7200
Veterans Affairs Medical Center Post-Sec.
500 Foothill Dr 84148 801-582-1565
Western Governors University Post-Sec.
4001 S 700 E Ste 700 84107 801-274-3280
Westminster College Post-Sec.
1840 S 1300 E 84105 801-484-7651

Sandy, Salt Lake, Pop. 85,199
Canyons SD 33,900/K-12
9361 S 300 E 84070 801-826-5000
Dr. James Briscoe, supt. Fax 826-5053
www.canyonsdistrict.org
Albion MS 900/6-8
2755 E Newcastle Dr 84093 801-826-6700
Molly Hart, prin. Fax 826-6709
Alta HS 1,800/9-12
11055 S 1000 E 84094 801-826-5600
Brian McGill, prin. Fax 826-5609
CTEC Vo/Tech
825 E 9085 S 84094 801-826-6600
Ken Spurlock, prin. Fax 826-6609
Diamond Ridge HS 9-12
825 E 9085 S 84094 801-826-9900
Amy Boettger, prin.
Eastmont MS 900/6-8
10100 S 1300 E 84094 801-826-7000
Stacy Kurtzhals, prin. Fax 826-7009
Indian Hills MS 1,100/6-8
1180 E Sanders Rd 84094 801-826-7100
Doug Graham, prin. Fax 826-7109
Jordan HS 2,200/9-12
95 E Beetdigger Blvd 84070 801-826-6200
Tom Sherwood, prin. Fax 826-6209
Mt. Jordan MS 700/6-8
9351 S Mountaineer Ln 84070 801-826-7400
Cindy Hanson, prin. Fax 826-7409
Union MS 900/6-8
615 E 8000 S 84070 801-826-7500
Kelly Tauteoli, prin. Fax 826-7509
Entrada HS Adult
825 E 9085 S 84094 801-826-6670
Amy Boettger, dir. Fax 826-6679
Other Schools – See Cottonwood Heights, Draper, Midvale

DeVry University Post-Sec.
9350 S 150 E Ste 420 84070 801-565-5110
Francois D. Hair Design Academy Post-Sec.
11339 S 700 E 84070 801-561-2244
Waterford S 900/PK-12
1480 E 9400 S 84093 801-816-2201
Andrew Menke, head sch Fax 523-6229

Saratoga Sprngs, Utah, Pop. 17,223
Alpine SD
Supt. — See American Fork
Vista Heights MS 1,500/7-9
484 W Pony Express Pkwy, 801-610-8770
Todd Dawson, prin. Fax 768-4226
Westlake HS 1,900/9-12
99 N 200 W, 801-610-8815
Gary Twitchell, prin. Fax 768-1068

Smithfield, Cache, Pop. 9,375
Cache County SD
Supt. — See North Logan
Sky View SHS 1,600/10-12
520 S 250 E 84335 435-563-6273
Michael Monson, prin. Fax 563-9534

South Jordan, Salt Lake, Pop. 49,075
Jordan SD
Supt. — See West Jordan
Bingham HS 2,400/10-12
2160 W South Jordan Pkwy 84095 801-256-5100
Christen Richards-Khong, prin. Fax 256-5151
Elk Ridge MS 1,000/7-9
3659 W 9800 S, 801-412-2800
Wyatt Bentley, prin. Fax 412-2830
South Jordan MS 1,500/7-9
10245 S 2700 W 84095 801-412-2900
Shawn McLeod, prin. Fax 412-2930
Valley HS 400/Alt
325 W 11000 S 84095 801-572-7035
Sharon Jensen, prin. Fax 572-7038

American Heritage of South Jordan 300/K-12
11100 S Redwood Rd 84095 801-254-3882

Spanish Fork, Utah, Pop. 33,849
Nebo SD 31,200/PK-12
350 S Main St 84660 801-354-7400
Rick Nielsen, supt. Fax 798-4010
www.nebo.edu
Diamond Fork JHS 1,100/7-9
50 N 900 E 84660 801-798-4052
Brenda Burr, prin. Fax 798-4098
Landmark/Cornerstone HS 300/Alt
612 S Main St 84660 801-798-4030
Lynn Mecham, prin. Fax 798-4044
Maple Mountain SHS 1,300/10-12
51 N 2550 E 84660 801-794-6740
John Penrod, prin. Fax 794-6744
Spanish Fork JHS 1,100/7-9
600 S 820 E 84660 801-798-4075
Matt Christensen, prin. Fax 798-4097
Spanish Fork SHS 1,200/10-12
99 N 300 W 84660 801-798-4060
David McKee, prin. Fax 798-4004
Other Schools – See Mapleton, Payson, Salem, Springville

Springville, Utah, Pop. 28,786
Nebo SD
Supt. — See Spanish Fork
Legacy S 50/Alt
105 S 400 E 84663 801-489-2840
Susan Boothe, prin. Fax 489-2808
Springville JHS 1,000/7-9
189 S 1470 E 84663 801-489-2880
Ryan McGuire, prin. Fax 489-2838
Springville SHS 1,400/10-12
1205 E 900 S 84663 801-489-2870
Everett Kelepolo, prin. Fax 489-2806

Meridian S 200/7-12
1440 W Center St 84663 801-900-6017

Stansbury Park, Tooele, Pop. 5,041
Tooele County SD
Supt. — See Tooele
Stansbury HS 1,600/9-12
5300 Aberdeen Ln 84074 435-882-2479
Gailynn Warr, prin. Fax 882-4049

Sunset, Davis, Pop. 4,981
Davis SD
Supt. — See Farmington
Sunset JHS 900/7-9
1610 N 250 W 84015 801-402-6700
Jonathan Gochberg, prin. Fax 402-6701

Syracuse, Davis, Pop. 23,777
Davis SD
Supt. — See Farmington
Syracuse JHS 1,100/7-9
1450 S 2000 W 84075 801-402-6800
Dr. Kenneth Hadlock, prin. Fax 402-6801
Syracuse SHS 2,000/10-12
665 S 2000 W 84075 801-402-7900
Wendy Nelson, prin. Fax 402-7901

Tabiona, Duchesne, Pop. 166
Duchesne SD
Supt. — See Duchesne
Tabiona HS 100/7-12
PO Box 470 84072 435-738-1320
Darrin Jenkins, prin. Fax 738-1332

Taylorsville, Salt Lake, Pop. 56,089
Granite SD
Supt. — See Salt Lake City
Bennion JHS 1,000/7-9
6055 S 2700 W, 385-646-5114
Rod Horton, prin. Fax 646-5115
Eisenhower JHS 1,000/7-9
4351 S Redwood Rd 84123 385-646-5154
Mark Ellermeier, prin. Fax 646-5158
Hartvigsen S 200/Alt
1510 W 5400 S 84123 385-646-4585
Janice Wayman, prin. Fax 646-4256
Taylorsville SHS 1,700/10-12
5225 S Redwood Rd 84123 385-646-5455
Dr. Garett Muse, prin. Fax 646-5457

Tooele, Tooele, Pop. 30,935
Tooele County SD 14,300/K-12
92 Lodestone Way 84074 435-833-1900
Scott Rogers, supt. Fax 833-1912
tooeleschools.org/SitePages/Home.aspx
Blue Peak HS 100/Alt
211 Tooele Blvd 84074 435-833-8700
Bryce Eardley, prin. Fax 833-8785
Johnsen JHS 900/7-8
2152 N 400 W 84074 435-833-1939
Jared Small, prin. Fax 843-3816
Tooele HS 1,500/9-12
301 W Vine St 84074 435-833-1978
Jeff Hamm, prin. Fax 833-1984
Tooele JHS 800/7-8
411 W Vine St 84074 435-833-1921
Bill Gochis, prin. Fax 833-1923
Other Schools – See Dugway, Grantsville, Stansbury Park, Wendover

Tooele Applied Technology College Post-Sec.
66 W Vine St 84074 435-248-1800

Tropic, Garfield, Pop. 524
Garfield SD
Supt. — See Panguitch
Bryce Valley HS 100/7-12
PO Box 70 84776 435-679-8835
Jeff Brinkerhoff, prin. Fax 679-8539

Trout Creek, Tooele
Tintic SD
Supt. — See Eureka
West Desert JSHS 50/7-12
440 Pony Express Rd 84083 435-693-3112
Daniel Kimball, head sch Fax 693-3109

Vernal, Uintah, Pop. 8,901
Uintah SD 7,600/PK-12
635 W 200 S 84078 435-781-3100
Mark Dockins Ed.D., supt. Fax 781-3107
www.uintah.net/
Uintah HS 1,200/9-12
1880 W 500 N 84078 435-781-3110
Julie Wilde, prin. Fax 781-3117
Uintah MS 1,000/6-8
161 N 1000 W 84078 435-781-3130
Kathleen Hawkins, prin. Fax 781-3134
Vernal MS 1,000/6-8
721 W 100 S 84078 435-781-3140
Mistalyn Leis, prin. Fax 781-3143
Ashley Valley Education Center Adult
559 N 1700 W 84078 435-781-4675
Andrea McKea, admin. Fax 781-4679

Wendover, Tooele, Pop. 1,381
Tooele County SD
Supt. — See Tooele
Wendover JSHS 200/7-12
PO Box 610 84083 435-665-2343
Clint Spindler, prin. Fax 665-7706

West Haven, Weber, Pop. 10,042
Weber SD
Supt. — See Ogden
Rocky Mountain JHS 1,000/7-9
4350 W 4800 S 84401 801-476-5220
Nicole Meibos, prin. Fax 476-5259

West Jordan, Salt Lake, Pop. 99,828
Jordan SD 52,900/K-12
7387 S Campus View Dr 84084 801-567-8100
Dr. Patrice Johnson, supt. Fax 567-8064
www.jordandistrict.org
Copper Hills HS 2,500/10-12
5445 W New Bingham Hwy, 801-256-5300
Todd Quarnberg, prin. Fax 256-5393
Jensen MS 800/7-9
8105 S 3200 W 84088 801-412-2850
Bryan Leggat, prin. Fax 412-2875
Jordan Academy for Tech & Careers North Vo/Tech
9301 S Wights Fort Rd 84088 801-256-5900
Chris Titus, prin. Fax 256-5930
Sunset Ridge MS 1,500/7-9
8292 S Skyline Arch Dr, 801-412-2475
Larry Urry, prin. Fax 412-2490
West Hills MS 1,400/7-9
8270 S Grizzly Way, 801-412-2300
Stacy Evans, prin. Fax 412-2327
West Jordan HS 1,700/10-12
8136 S 2700 W 84088 801-256-5600
Michael Kochevar, prin. Fax 256-5670
West Jordan MS 1,000/7-9
7550 S Redwood Rd 84084 801-412-2100
Dixie Crowther, prin. Fax 412-2140
Southpointe Adult HS Adult
9301 S Wights Fort Rd 84088 801-256-5954
Allen Arko, coord. Fax 256-5992
Other Schools – See Herriman, Riverton, South Jordan

Broadview University Post-Sec.
1902 W 7800 S 84088 801-304-4224
Broadview University Post-Sec.
1902 W 7800 S 84088 801-822-5800

West Point, Davis, Pop. 9,305
Davis SD
Supt. — See Farmington
West Point JHS 1,200/7-9
2775 W 550 N 84015 801-402-8100
Jed Johansen, prin. Fax 402-8101

West Valley, Salt Lake, Pop. 122,084
Granite SD
Supt. — See Salt Lake City
Granger SHS 2,100/10-12
3580 S 3600 W 84119 385-646-5320
Dr. David Dunn, prin. Fax 646-5322
Hunter JHS 1,100/7-9
6131 W Wending Ln 84128 385-646-5184
Carol Carroll, prin. Fax 646-5185
Hunter SHS 2,100/10-12
4200 S 5600 W 84120 385-646-5360
Craig Stauffer, prin. Fax 646-5495
Kennedy JHS 1,000/7-9
4495 S 4800 W 84120 385-646-5214
Mary Anne Stevens, prin. Fax 646-5215
Valley JHS 600/7-9
4195 S 3200 W 84119 385-646-5234
Ike Spencer, prin. Fax 646-5235
West Lake JHS 900/7-9
3400 S 3450 W 84119 385-646-5254
Tyler Howe, prin. Fax 646-5259

Everest College Post-Sec.
3280 W 3500 S 84119 801-840-4800
Premier Hair Academy Post-Sec.
4062 S 4000 W 84120 801-966-8414

Woods Cross, Davis, Pop. 9,426
Davis SD
Supt. — See Farmington
Woods Cross SHS 1,300/10-12
600 W 2200 S 84010 801-402-4500
John Haning, prin. Fax 402-4501

VERMONT

VERMONT DEPARTMENT OF EDUCATION
120 State St, Montpelier 05620-0002
Telephone 802-828-3135
Fax 802-828-3140
Website http://www.state.vt.us/educ/

Secretary of Education Rebecca Holcombe

VERMONT BOARD OF EDUCATION
120 State St, Montpelier 05620-0002

Chairperson Stephan Morse

PUBLIC, PRIVATE AND CATHOLIC SECONDARY SCHOOLS

Arlington, Bennington, Pop. 1,195
Battenkill Valley Supervisory Union 400/K-12
530A E Arlington Rd 05250 802-375-9744
Judith Pullinen, supt. Fax 375-2368
www.bvsu.org
Arlington Memorial HS 200/6-12
529 E Arlington Rd 05250 802-375-2589
Christopher Barnes, prin. Fax 375-1547

Barre, Washington, Pop. 8,882
Barre Supervisory Union 2,500/PK-12
120 Ayers St 05641 802-476-5011
John Pandolfo, supt. Fax 476-4944
www.bsuvt.org/
Spaulding HS 700/9-12
155 Ayers St 05641 802-476-4811
Tom Sedore, prin. Fax 479-4535

VT Technical Centers
Supt. — None
Barre Technical Center Vo/Tech
155 Ayers St 05641 802-476-6237
Penny Chamberlin, prin. Fax 476-4045

Central Vermont Academy 50/K-12
317 Vine St 05641 802-479-0868

Barton, Orleans, Pop. 727
Orleans Central Supervisory Union 1,100/PK-12
130 Kinsey Rd 05822 802-525-1204
Donald Van Nostrand, supt. Fax 525-1276
www.ocsu.org
Other Schools – See Orleans

Bellows Falls, Windham, Pop. 3,056
Windham Northeast Supervisory Union 1,200/K-12
25 Cherry St 05101 802-463-9958
Christopher Kibbe, supt. Fax 463-9705
www.wnesu.org
Bellows Falls MS 200/5-8
15 School St 05101 802-463-4366
Karen Bukowski, prin. Fax 463-9738
Bellows Falls Union HS 300/9-12
PO Box 429 05101 802-463-3944
Christopher Hodsden, prin. Fax 463-9322

Bennington, Bennington, Pop. 8,960
Southwest Vermont Supervisory Union 2,800/K-12
246 S Stream Rd 05201 802-447-7501
James Culkeen, supt. Fax 447-0475
www.svsu.org
Mt. Anthony Union HS 1,000/9-12
301 Park St 05201 802-447-7511
Suzanne Maguire, prin. Fax 442-1260
Mt. Anthony Union MS 600/6-8
747 East Rd 05201 802-447-7541
Tim Payne, prin. Fax 442-1262

VT Technical Centers
Supt. — None
SW VT Career Development Center Vo/Tech
321 Park St 05201 802-447-0220
Fax 442-1745

Bennington College Post-Sec.
1 College Dr 05201 802-442-5401
Grace Christian S 200/PK-12
104 Kocher Dr 05201 802-447-2233
Shawn Smith, admin. Fax 442-8403
Southern Vermont College Post-Sec.
982 Mansion Dr 05201 802-447-4000

Bethel, Windsor, Pop. 558
White River Valley Supervisory Union
Supt. — See South Royalton
Whitcomb JSHS 100/7-12
273 Pleasant St 05032 802-234-9966
Owen Bradley, prin. Fax 234-5779

Bradford, Orange, Pop. 774
Orange East Supervisory Union 1,300/K-12
530 Waits River Rd 05033 802-222-5216
Beth Cobb, supt. Fax 222-4451
www.oesu.org
Oxbow HS 400/7-12
36 Oxbow Dr 05033 802-222-5214
Dr. Doug Harris, prin. Fax 222-5847

VT Technical Centers
Supt. — None
River Bend Career & Tech Center Vo/Tech
PO Box 618 05033 802-222-5212
Robert St. Pierre, admin. Fax 222-4621

Brandon, Rutland, Pop. 1,631
Rutland Northeast Supervisory Union 1,500/PK-12
49 Court Dr 05733 802-247-5757
Jeanne Collins, supt. Fax 247-5548
www.rnesu.org
Otter Valley Union HS 500/7-12
2997 Franklin St 05733 802-247-6833
James Avery, prin. Fax 247-4627

Brattleboro, Windham, Pop. 7,206
VT Technical Centers
Supt. — None
Windham Regional Career Center Vo/Tech
45 Career Cir 05301 802-451-3900
Michael Burnett, dir. Fax 451-3933

Windham Southeast Supervisory Union 2,400/K-12
53 Green St 05301 802-254-3730
Ron Stahley, supt. Fax 254-3733
www.wssu.k12.vt.us
Brattleboro Area MS 300/7-8
109 Sunny Acres Rd 05301 802-451-3500
Keith Lyman, prin. Fax 451-3502
Brattleboro Union HS 800/9-12
131 Fairground Rd 05301 802-451-3400
Steve Perrin, prin. Fax 451-3935

Austine School for the Deaf Post-Sec.
60 Austine Dr 05301 802-258-9522
St. Michael S 100/PK-10
48 Walnut St 05301 802-254-6320
Elaine Beam, prin. Fax 254-5229
SIT Post-Sec.
PO Box 676 05302 802-257-7751
The William Center Post-Sec.
209 Austine Dr 05301 802-258-9537
Union Institute & University Post-Sec.
3 University Way Ste 3 05301 800-871-8165

Bristol, Addison, Pop. 1,992
Addison Northeast Supervisory Union 1,600/PK-12
72 Munsill Ave Ste 601 05443 802-453-3657
Patrick Reen, supt. Fax 453-2029
www.anesu.org
Mt. Abraham Union MSHS 28 800/7-12
220 Airport Dr 05443 802-453-2333
Jessica Barewicz, prin. Fax 453-4359

Burlington, Chittenden, Pop. 41,355
Burlington SD 3,700/PK-12
150 Colchester Ave 05401 802-865-5332
Yaw Obeng, supt. Fax 864-8501
www.bsdvt.org/
Burlington HS 1,100/9-12
52 Institute Rd, 802-864-8411
Tracy Racicot, prin. Fax 864-8408
Edmunds MS 400/6-8
275 Main St 05401 802-864-8486
Bonnie Johnson-Aten, prin. Fax 864-2218
Horizon S Alt
14 S Williams St 05401 802-864-8496
Lynn Kennedy, dir. Fax 864-2213
Hunt MS 400/6-8
1364 North Ave, 802-864-8469
Len Phelan, prin. Fax 864-8467

VT Technical Centers
Supt. — None
Burlington Technical Center Vo/Tech
52 Institute Rd, 802-864-8426
Tracy Racicot, dir. Fax 864-8521

Burlington College Post-Sec.
351 North Ave 05401 802-862-9616
Champlain College Post-Sec.
PO Box 670 05402 802-860-2700
Fletcher Allen Health Care Post-Sec.
111 Colchester Ave 05401 802-847-5133
Rock Point S 50/9-12
1 Rock Point Rd, 802-863-1104
C.J. Spirito, head sch Fax 863-6628
University of Vermont Post-Sec.
194 S Prospect St 05401 802-656-3131

Cabot, Washington, Pop. 226
Washington NE Supervisory Union
Supt. — See Plainfield
Cabot S 200/PK-12
25 Common Rd 05647 802-563-2289
David Schilling, prin. Fax 563-6089

Canaan, Essex, Pop. 390
Essex North Supervisory Union 200/PK-12
PO Box 100 05903 802-266-3330
Christopher Masson, supt. Fax 266-7085
www.essexnorth.org
Canaan S 200/PK-12
99 School St 05903 802-266-8910
Deborah Lynch, prin. Fax 266-7068

Castleton, Rutland, Pop. 1,470
Addison-Rutland Supervisory Union
Supt. — See Fair Haven
Castleton Village S 100/6-8
PO Box 68 05735 802-468-2203
Linda Peltier, prin. Fax 468-5131

Castleton State College Post-Sec.
86 Seminary St 05735 802-468-5611

Chelsea, Orange
White River Valley Supervisory Union
Supt. — See South Royalton
Chelsea S 200/K-12
6 School St 05038 802-685-4551
Mark Blount, prin. Fax 685-3310

Chester, Windsor, Pop. 997
Two Rivers Supervisory Union
Supt. — See Ludlow
Green Mountain Union MSHS 300/7-12
716 VT Route 103 S 05143 802-875-2146
Thomas Ferenc, prin. Fax 875-3183

Colchester, Chittenden
Colchester SD 2,200/PK-12
PO Box 27 05446 802-264-5999
Amy Minor, supt. Fax 863-4774
www.csdvt.org
Colchester HS 700/9-12
PO Box 900 05446 802-264-5700
Heather Baron, prin. Fax 264-5757
Colchester MS 400/6-8
PO Box 30 05446 802-264-5800
Michele Cote, prin. Fax 264-5858

St. Michael's College Post-Sec.
1 Winooski Park 05439 802-654-2000

Concord, Essex, Pop. 268
Essex-Caledonia Supervisory Union 400/PK-8
PO Box 255 05824 802-695-3373
Brian Rayburn, supt. Fax 695-1334
ecsuvt.org.p9.hostingprod.com
Other Schools – See Gilman

Craftsbury Common, Orleans
Orleans Southwest Supervisory Union
Supt. — See Hardwick
Craftsbury S 200/K-12
PO Box 73 05827 802-586-2541
Merri Greenia, prin. Fax 586-7524

Sterling College Post-Sec.
PO Box 72 05827 802-586-7711

Danville, Caledonia, Pop. 378
Caledonia Central Supervisory Union 700/PK-12
PO Box 216 05828 802-684-3801
Dr. Mathew Forest, supt. Fax 684-1190
www.ccsuonline.org
Danville S 400/PK-12
148 Peacham Rd 05828 802-684-3651
Kerin Hoffman, prin. Fax 684-1192

Derby, Orleans, Pop. 595
North Country Supervisory Union
Supt. — See Newport
North Country Union JHS 300/7-8
57 Jr High Dr 05829 802-766-2276
Nicole Corbett, prin. Fax 766-2287

Dorset, Bennington, Pop. 249

Long Trail S 200/6-12
1045 Kirby Hollow Rd 05251 802-867-5717
Steven Dear, head sch Fax 867-4525

Duxbury, See Waterbury
Washington West Supervisory Union
Supt. — See Waitsfield
Crossett Brook MS 300/5-8
5672 VT Route 100 05676 802-244-6100
Tom Drake, prin. Fax 244-6899

East Burke, Caledonia, Pop. 132

Burke Mountain Academy 50/8-12
PO Box 78 05832 802-626-5607

Enosburg Falls, Franklin, Pop. 1,309
Franklin Northeast Supervisory Union
Supt. — See Richford
Enosburg Falls HS 300/9-12
PO Box 417 05450 802-933-7777
Erik Remmers, prin. Fax 933-5375
Enosburg Falls MS 100/6-8
PO Box 417 05450 802-933-7777
Rachel Reynolds, prin. Fax 933-5013

VT Technical Centers
Supt. — None
Cold Hollow Career Center Vo/Tech
PO Box 530 05450 802-933-4003
Nathan Demar, dir. Fax 933-2431

Essex Junction, Chittenden, Pop. 9,092
Chittenden Central Supervisory Union 2,600/PK-12
51 Park St 05452 802-879-5579
Judith DeNova, supt. Fax 878-1370
www.ccsuvt.org
Essex HS 1,300/9-12
2 Educational Dr 05452 802-879-7121
Robert Reardon, prin. Fax 879-5503
Lawton MS 400/6-8
104 Maple St 05452 802-878-1388
Laurie Singer, prin. Fax 879-8175

Essex Town SD 1,300/PK-8
58 Founders Rd 05452 802-878-8168
Mark Andrews, supt. Fax 878-5190
www.etsdvt.org
Essex MS 400/6-8
60 Founders Rd 05452 802-879-7173
Kevin Briggs, prin. Fax 879-1363

VT Technical Centers
Supt. — None
Essex Technical Center Vo/Tech
2 Educational Dr Ste 200 05452 802-879-5558
Robert Travers, dir. Fax 879-5593

Fairfax, Franklin
Franklin West Supervisory Union 1,300/PK-12
4497 Highbridge Rd 05454 802-370-3113
Ned Kirsch, supt. Fax 370-3115
www.fwsu.org
Bellows Free Academy Fairfax 600/PK-12
75 Hunt St 05454 802-849-6711
Thomas Walsh, prin. Fax 849-2611

Fair Haven, Rutland, Pop. 2,236
Addison-Rutland Supervisory Union 1,400/PK-12
49 Main St 05743 802-265-4905
Ronald Ryan, supt. Fax 265-2158
www.arsu.org
Fair Haven Union HS 400/9-12
33 Mechanic St 05743 802-265-4966
Brett Blanchard, prin. Fax 265-3602
Other Schools – See Castleton

Gilman, Essex
Essex-Caledonia Supervisory Union
Supt. — See Concord
Gilman MS 50/5-8
PO Box 97 05904 802-892-5969
Cheryl McVetty, prin. Fax 892-9045

Hardwick, Caledonia, Pop. 1,309
Orleans Southwest Supervisory Union 1,000/K-12
PO Box 338 05843 802-472-6531
Joanne LeBlanc, supt. Fax 472-6250
www.ossu.org/
Hazen Union JSHS 400/7-12
PO Box 368 05843 802-472-6511
Mike Moriarty, prin. Fax 472-3327
Other Schools – See Craftsbury Common

Hinesburg, Chittenden, Pop. 642
Chittenden South Supervisory Union
Supt. — See Shelburne
Champlain Valley Union HS 15 1,200/9-12
369 CVU Rd 05461 802-482-7100
Jeff Evans, prin. Fax 482-7108

Hyde Park, Lamoille, Pop. 449
Lamoille North Supervisory Union 1,900/PK-12
96 Cricket Hill Rd 05655 802-888-3142
Catherine Gallagher, supt. Fax 888-7908
lnsu.cloudaccess.net
Green Mountain Technology & Career Ctr Vo/Tech
738 VT 15 W 05655 802-888-4447
Sherry Lussier, dir. Fax 888-7368
Lamoille Union HS 600/9-12
736 VT 15 W 05655 802-888-4261
Brian Schaffer, prin. Fax 888-2997
Lamoille Union MS 200/7-8
736 VT 15 W 05655 802-851-1300
Wendy Savery, prin. Fax 851-1397

Jericho, Chittenden, Pop. 1,303
Chittenden East Supervisory Union
Supt. — See Richmond
Browns River MS 400/5-8
20 River Rd 05465 802-899-3711
Kevin Hamilton, prin. Fax 899-4281
Mt. Mansfield Union HS 800/9-12
211 Browns Trace Rd 05465 802-899-4690
Michael Weston, prin. Fax 899-2904

Johnson, Lamoille, Pop. 1,395

Johnson State College Post-Sec.
337 College Hl 05656 802-635-2356

Killington, Rutland

Killington Mountain S 50/6-12
2708 Killington Rd 05751 802-422-5671

Ludlow, Windsor, Pop. 795
Two Rivers Supervisory Union 1,100/PK-12
609 Route 103 S 05149 802-875-3365
Meg Powden, supt. Fax 875-6439
su.trsu.org/
Black River MSHS 200/7-12
43 Main St 05149 802-228-4721
Shannon Martin, prin. Fax 228-7233
Other Schools – See Chester

Lyndon Center, Caledonia
VT Technical Centers
Supt. — None
Lyndon Institute Technical Center Vo/Tech
PO Box 127 05850 802-626-3357
Daren Houck, head sch Fax 626-9345

Lyndonville, Caledonia, Pop. 1,188

Lyndon State College Post-Sec.
PO Box 919 05851 802-626-6200

Manchester, Bennington, Pop. 746

Burr and Burton Academy 700/9-12
PO Box 498 05254 802-362-1775
Mark Tashjian, hdmstr. Fax 362-0574

Marlboro, Windham

Marlboro College Post-Sec.
PO Box A 05344 802-257-4333

Middlebury, Addison, Pop. 6,363
Addison Central Supervisory Union 1,700/PK-12
49 Charles Ave 05753 802-382-1274
Dr. Peter Burrows, supt. Fax 388-0024
www.addisoncentralsu.org
Middlebury Union HS 600/9-12
73 Charles Ave 05753 802-382-1500
Fax 382-1101
Middlebury Union MS 300/7-8
48 Deerfield Ln 05753 802-382-1600
Patrick Reen, prin. Fax 382-1215

VT Technical Centers
Supt. — None
Hannaford Career Center Vo/Tech
51 Charles Ave 05753 802-382-1012
D. Lynn Coale, prin. Fax 388-2591

Middlebury College 05753 Post-Sec.
802-443-5000

Milton, Chittenden, Pop. 1,843
Milton Town SD 1,700/PK-12
42 Herrick Ave 05468 802-893-5400
Ann Bradshaw, supt. Fax 893-3213
www.mtsd-vt.org
Milton HS 500/9-12
17 Rebecca Lander Dr 05468 802-893-5400
Anne Blake, prin. Fax 893-3247
Milton MS 400/6-8
42 Herrick Ave 05468 802-893-5400
Becky Day, prin. Fax 893-3213

Montpelier, Washington, Pop. 7,675
Montpelier SD 900/PK-12
5 High School Dr Unit 1 05602 802-223-9796
Dr. Brian Ricca, supt. Fax 223-9795
www.mpsvt.org/
Main Street MS 200/5-8
170 Main St 05602 802-223-3404
Pamela Arnold, prin. Fax 223-9225
Montpelier HS 300/9-12
5 High School Dr 05602 802-225-8000
Michael McRaith, prin. Fax 223-9227

Washington Central Supervisory Union 1,600/PK-12
1130 Gallison Hill Rd 05602 802-229-0553
William Kimball, supt. Fax 229-2761
www.wcsuonline.org
Union 32 JSHS 800/7-12
930 Gallison Hill Rd 05602 802-229-0321
Steven Dellinger-Pate, prin. Fax 223-7411

Community College of Vermont Post-Sec.
PO Box 489 05601 802-828-2800
New England Culinary Institute Post-Sec.
56 College St 05602 877-223-6324
Union Institute & University Post-Sec.
62 Ridge St Ste 2 05602 802-828-8500
Vermont College of Fine Arts Post-Sec.
36 College St 05602 802-828-8600

Morrisville, Lamoille, Pop. 1,933
Lamoille South Supervisory Union 1,600/K-12
46 Copley Ave 05661 802-888-4541
Tracy Wrend, supt. Fax 888-6710
www.lamoillesouthsu.org
Peoples Academy 300/9-12
202 Copley Ave 05661 802-888-4600
Phil Grant, prin. Fax 888-6726
Peoples Academy MS 300/5-8
202 Copley Ave 05661 802-888-1402
Karen Weeks, prin. Fax 888-6488
Other Schools – See Stowe

Newport, Orleans, Pop. 4,495
North Country Supervisory Union 2,700/PK-12
121 Duchess Ave Ste A 05855 802-334-5847
John A. Castle, supt. Fax 334-6528
www.ncsuvt.org
North Country Union HS 800/9-12
PO Box 725 05855 802-334-7921
Anita Mayhew, prin. Fax 334-1618
Other Schools – See Derby

VT Technical Centers
Supt. — None
North Country Career Center Vo/Tech
PO Box 705 05855 802-334-5469
Eileen Illuzzi, prin. Fax 334-3492

United Christian Academy 100/K-12
65 School St 05855 802-334-3112
John Carpenter, head sch Fax 334-2305

North Clarendon, Rutland
Rutland South Supervisory Union 900/PK-12
64 Grange Hall Rd 05759 802-775-3264
Dave Younce, supt. Fax 775-8063
www.rssu.org/
Mill River Union JSHS 500/7-12
2321 Middle Rd 05759 802-775-1925
Andy Pomeroy, prin. Fax 775-6447

Northfield, Washington, Pop. 2,049
Washington South Supervisory Union 600/PK-12
37 Cross St Ste 1 05663 802-485-7755
Laurie Gossens, supt. Fax 485-3348
www.wssu.org
Northfield MSHS 300/6-12
37 Cross St Ste 1 05663 802-485-4500
Ryan Parkman, prin. Fax 485-4440

Norwich University Post-Sec.
158 Harmon Dr 05663 802-485-2000

Orleans, Orleans, Pop. 796
Orleans Central Supervisory Union
Supt. — See Barton
Lake Region Union HS 300/9-12
317 Lake Region Rd 05860 802-754-6521
Andre Messier, prin. Fax 754-2780

Plainfield, Washington, Pop. 393
Washington NE Supervisory Union 600/PK-12
PO Box 470 05667 802-454-9924
Nancy Thomas, supt. Fax 454-9934
Twinfield Union S 400/PK-12
106 Nasmith Brook Rd 05667 802-426-3213
Mark Mooney, prin. Fax 426-4085
Other Schools – See Cabot

Goddard College Post-Sec.
123 Pitkin Rd 05667 802-454-8311
Initiative: A Vermont Waldorf HS 9-12
PO Box 95 05667 802-454-1053

Poultney, Rutland, Pop. 1,589
Rutland Southwest Supervisory Union 600/PK-12
168 York St 05764 802-287-5286
Joan Paustian Ed.D., supt. Fax 287-2284
www.rswsu.org
Poultney HS 200/7-12
154 E Main St 05764 802-287-5861
Jim Frail, prin. Fax 287-2304

Green Mountain College Post-Sec.
1 Brennan Cir 05764 802-287-8000

Proctor, Rutland
Rutland Central Supervisory Union
Supt. — See Rutland
Proctor JSHS 100/7-12
4 Park St 05765 802-459-3353
Adam Rosenberg, prin. Fax 459-6323

Putney, Windham, Pop. 508

Landmark College Post-Sec.
1 River Rd S 05346 802-387-4767
Putney S 200/9-12
418 Houghton Brook Rd 05346 802-387-5566
Emily Jones, head sch Fax 387-6278

Randolph, Orange, Pop. 1,947
Orange Southwest Supervisory Union 1,100/PK-12
24 Central St 05060 802-728-5052
Dr. Brent Kay, supt. Fax 728-4844
www.orangesouthwest.org
Randolph Union JSHS 400/7-12
15 Forest St 05060 802-728-3397
David Barnett, prin. Fax 728-6703

VT Technical Centers
Supt. — None
Randolph Technical Career Center Vo/Tech
17 Forest St 05060 802-728-9595
Jason Gingold, dir. Fax 728-9596

Randolph Center, Orange

Vermont Technical College Post-Sec.
PO Box 500 05061 802-728-1000

Richford, Franklin, Pop. 1,314
Franklin Northeast Supervisory Union 1,600/PK-12
PO Box 130 05476 802-848-7661
Jay Nichols, supt. Fax 848-3531
fnesu.net
Richford JSHS 200/6-12
1 Corliss Hts 05476 802-848-7416
Beth O'Brien, prin. Fax 848-3210
Other Schools – See Enosburg Falls

Richmond, Chittenden, Pop. 707
Chittenden East Supervisory Union 2,700/PK-12
PO Box 282 05477 802-434-2128
John Alberghini, supt. Fax 434-2196
www.cesu.k12.vt.us
Camels Hump MS 400/5-8
173 School St 05477 802-434-2188
Mark Carbone, prin. Fax 434-2192
Other Schools – See Jericho

Rochester, Windsor, Pop. 297
White River Valley Supervisory Union
Supt. — See South Royalton
Rochester S 100/K-12
222 S Main St 05767 802-767-3161
Daniella Stamm, prin. Fax 767-1130

Rutland, Rutland, Pop. 16,220
Rutland Central Supervisory Union 1,000/PK-12
16 Evelyn St 05701 802-775-4342
Dr. Debra Taylor, supt. Fax 775-7319
www.rcsu.org
Other Schools – See Proctor, West Rutland

Rutland City SD 2,200/K-12
6 Church St 05701 802-773-1900
Mary Moran, supt. Fax 773-1927
rutlandcitypublicschools.org/
Rutland HS, 22 Stratton Rd 05701 900/9-12
William Olsen, prin. 802-773-1955
Rutland MS 300/7-8
67 Library Ave 05701 802-773-1960
Wilfred Cunningham, prin. Fax 773-1914

VT Technical Centers
Supt. — None
Stafford Technical Center Vo/Tech
8 Stratton Rd 05701 802-770-1033
Glenn Olson, dir. Fax 770-1066

College of Saint Joseph Post-Sec.
71 Clement Rd 05701 802-773-5900
Mt. St. Joseph Academy 100/9-12
127 Convent Ave 05701 802-775-0151
Sarah Fortier, prin. Fax 775-0424
Rutland Area Christian S 100/PK-12
112 Lincoln Ave 05701 802-775-0709
Dia Lind, prin. Fax 786-0111
Rutland Regional Medical Center Post-Sec.
160 Allen St 05701 802-775-7111

Saint Albans, Franklin, Pop. 6,736
Franklin Central Supervisory Union 2,800/PK-12
28 Catherine St 05478 802-524-2600
Dr. Kevin Dirth, supt. Fax 524-1540
www.fcsuvt.org
Bellows Free Academy 1,000/9-12
71 S Main St 05478 802-527-6555
Chris Mosca, prin. Fax 527-6402

VT Technical Centers
Supt. — None
Northwest Technical Center Vo/Tech
71 S Main St 05478 802-527-6517
Leann Wright, dir. Fax 527-6469

Direct Learning International Post-Sec.
PO Box 846 05478 800-489-4114

Saint Johnsbury, Caledonia, Pop. 6,424

St. Johnsbury Academy 900/9-12
PO Box 906 05819 802-748-8171
Tom Lovett, hdmstr. Fax 748-2358

Saxtons River, Windham, Pop. 550

Vermont Academy 200/9-12
PO Box 500 05154 802-869-6200
Sean Brennan, head sch Fax 869-6242

Sharon, Windsor

Sharon Academy 200/7-12
PO Box 207 05065 802-763-2500
Michael Livingston, prin. Fax 763-2502

Shelburne, Chittenden, Pop. 581
Chittenden South Supervisory Union 3,100/PK-12
5420 Shelburne Rd Ste 300 05482 802-383-1234
Elaine Pinckney, supt. Fax 383-1242
www.cssu.org/
Other Schools – See Hinesburg

Lake Champlain Waldorf HS 50/9-12
122 Bostwick Rd 05482 802-495-0834
Addie Hall, admin. Fax 497-2842

South Burlington, Chittenden, Pop. 17,544
South Burlington SD 2,400/K-12
550 Dorset St 05403 802-652-7250
David Young, supt. Fax 652-7257
www.sbschools.net
South Burlington HS 900/9-12
550 Dorset St 05403 802-652-7000
Patrick Burke, prin. Fax 652-7006
Tuttle MS 600/6-8
500 Dorset St 05403 802-652-7100
Karsten Schlenter, prin. Fax 652-7152

Advanced Welding Institute Post-Sec.
2 Green Tree Dr Ste 3 05403 802-660-0600
O'Briens Training Center Post-Sec.
1233 Shelburne Rd Ste 200 05403 802-658-9591
Rice Memorial HS 400/9-12
99 Proctor Ave 05403 802-862-6521
Sr. Laura Della Santa, prin. Fax 864-9931
Vermont Commons S 100/6-12
75 Green Mountain Dr 05403 802-865-8084
Dexter Mahaffey Ph.D., head sch Fax 865-2429

South Duxbury, Washington
Washington West Supervisory Union
Supt. — See Waitsfield
Harwood Union HS 500/7-12
458 VT Route 100 05660 802-244-5186
Lisa Atwood, prin. Fax 882-1199

South Royalton, Windsor, Pop. 674
White River Valley Supervisory Union 1,300/PK-12
461 Waterman Rd 05068 802-763-8840
Bruce Labs, supt. Fax 763-3235
wrvsu.org
South Royalton S 400/PK-12
223 S Windsor St 05068 802-763-8844
Dean Stearns, prin. Fax 763-3233
Other Schools – See Bethel, Chelsea, Rochester

Vermont Law School Post-Sec.
PO Box 96 05068 802-831-1000

Springfield, Windsor, Pop. 3,895
Springfield SD 1,300/K-12
60 Park St 05156 802-885-5141
Zachary McLaughlin, supt. Fax 885-8169
www.ssdvt.org
Gateway S Alt
13 Fairground Rd 05156 802-885-3477
Nancy Wiese, coord. Fax 885-3473
Riverside MS 300/6-8
13 Fairground Rd 05156 802-885-8490
Becky Read, prin. Fax 885-8442
Springfield HS 500/9-12
303 South St 05156 802-885-7900
Bob Thibault, prin. Fax 885-4459

VT Technical Centers
Supt. — None
River Valley Technical Center Vo/Tech
307 South St 05156 802-885-8300
Scott Farr, dir. Fax 885-8454

Stowe, Lamoille, Pop. 492
Lamoille South Supervisory Union
Supt. — See Morrisville
Stowe HS 200/9-12
413 Barrows Rd 05672 802-253-7229
Jeff Maher, prin. Fax 253-6911
Stowe MS 200/6-8
413 Barrows Rd 05672 802-253-6913
Dan Morrison, prin. Fax 253-5314

Stratton Mountain, Windham, Pop. 50

Stratton Mountain S 100/7-12
7 World Cup Cir 05155 802-297-1886
Christopher Kaltsas, hdmstr. Fax 297-0020

Swanton, Franklin, Pop. 2,303
Franklin Northwest Supervisory Union 2,100/PK-12
100 Robin Hood Dr 05488 802-868-4967
Winton Goodrich, supt. Fax 868-4265
www.fnwsu.org
Missisquoi Valley Union MSHS 900/7-12
100 Thunderbird Dr 05488 802-868-7311
Dennis Hill, prin. Fax 868-3129

Thetford, Orange

Thetford Academy 300/7-12
PO Box 190 05074 802-785-4805

Townshend, Windham
Windham Central Supervisory Union 900/PK-12
1219 VT Route 30 05353 802-365-9510
William Anton, supt. Fax 365-7934
www.windhamcentral.org
Leland & Gray Union HS 400/7-12
PO Box 128 05353 802-365-7355
Dr. Robert Thibault, prin. Fax 365-4126

Vergennes, Addison, Pop. 2,536
Addison Northwest Supervisory Union 1,000/K-12
11 Main St Ste B100 05491 802-877-3332
JoAn Canning, supt. Fax 877-3628
www.anwsu.org
Vergennes Union HS 500/7-12
50 Monkton Rd 05491 802-877-2938
Stephanie Taylor, prin. Fax 877-2558

Waitsfield, Washington, Pop. 162
Washington West Supervisory Union 1,800/PK-12
340 Mad River Park Ste 7 05673 802-496-2272
Brigid Nease, supt. Fax 496-6515
www.wwsu.org/
Other Schools – See Duxbury, South Duxbury

Green Mountain Valley S 100/8-12
271 Moulton Rd 05673 802-496-2150
Tim Harris, head sch Fax 496-6819

Websterville, Washington, Pop. 545

Websterville Baptist Christian S 100/PK-12
PO Box 1 05678 802-479-0141

Wells River, Orange, Pop. 387
Blue Mountain SD 400/PK-12
2420 Route 302 05081 802-757-2766
Emilie Knisley, supt. Fax 757-2790
www.bmuschool.org
Blue Mountain Union S 21 400/PK-12
2420 Route 302 05081 802-757-2711
Scott Blood, prin. Fax 757-3894

West Dover, Windham

Mount Snow Academy 100/6-12
25 Mt Snow Rd 05356 802-464-1100
Todd Ormiston, head sch

West Rutland, Rutland, Pop. 2,007
Rutland Central Supervisory Union
Supt. — See Rutland
West Rutland S 300/PK-12
713 Main St 05777 802-438-2288
Joseph Fleming, prin. Fax 438-5708

White River Junction, Windsor, Pop. 2,238
Hartford SD 1,600/PK-12
73 Highland Ave 05001 802-295-8600
Tom DeBalsi, supt. Fax 295-8602
www.hsdvt.com
Hartford HS 600/9-12
37 Highland Ave 05001 802-295-8610
Joseph Collea, prin. Fax 295-8611
Hartford Memorial MS 300/6-8
245 Highland Ave 05001 802-295-8640
John Grant, prin. Fax 295-8641

VT Technical Centers
Supt. — None
Hartford Area Career & Technology Center Vo/Tech
1 Gifford Rd 05001 802-295-8630
Doug Heavisides, dir. Fax 295-8631

Mid Vermont Christian S 100/PK-12
399 W Gilson Ave 05001 802-295-6800
Robert Bracy M.Ed., hdmstr. Fax 295-3748

Whitingham, Windham
Windham Southwest Supervisory Union
Supt. — See Wilmington
Twin Valley MSHS 200/6-12
4299 VT Route 100 05361 802-368-2880
Thomas Fitzgerald, prin. Fax 368-7382

Williamstown, Orange
Orange North Supervisory Union 800/PK-12
111B Brush Hill Rd 05679 802-433-5818
Susette Bollard, supt. Fax 433-5825
www.onsu.org/
Williamstown MSHS 300/6-12
120 Hebert Rd 05679 802-433-5350
Scott Lang, prin. Fax 433-1037

Williston, Chittenden
Williston SD 1,100/PK-8
195 Central School Dr 05495 802-878-2762
Greg Marino, supt. Fax 871-6101
www.wsdvt.org
Williston Central S 700/3-8
195 Central School Dr 05495 802-878-2762
Jackie Parks, admin. Fax 871-6101

Northern Vermont Regional Day Program Post-Sec.
195 Central School Dr 05495 802-879-4787
Vermont College of Cosmetology Post-Sec.
400 Cornerstone Dr Ste 220 05495 802-863-4666

Wilmington, Windham, Pop. 457
Windham Southwest Supervisory Union 500/PK-12
1 School St 05363 802-464-1300
Christopher Pratt Ed.D., supt. Fax 464-1303
www.windhamsw.k12.vt.us/
Other Schools – See Whitingham

Windsor, Windsor, Pop. 2,011
Windsor Southeast Supervisory Union 1,100/K-12
105 Main St Ste 200 05089 802-674-2144
David Baker, supt. Fax 674-6357
wsesu.net
Windsor HS 300/7-12
19 Ascutney St 05089 802-674-6344
Tiffany Cassano, prin. Fax 674-9802

Winooski, Chittenden, Pop. 7,032
Winooski SD 800/PK-12
60 Normand St 05404 802-655-0485
Sean McMannon, supt. Fax 655-7602
www.wsdschools.org
Winooski HS 200/9-12
60 Normand St 05404 802-655-3530
Leon Wheeler, prin. Fax 655-6538
Winooski MS 200/6-8
60 Normand St 05404 802-655-3530
Leon Wheeler, prin. Fax 655-6538

Woodstock, Windsor, Pop. 897
Windsor Central Supervisory Union 900/PK-12
70 Amsden Way 05091 802-457-1213
Alice Worth, supt. Fax 457-2989
www.wcsu.net/
Woodstock Union HS 400/9-12
100 Amsden Way 05091 802-457-1317
Garon Smail, prin. Fax 457-1850
Woodstock Union MS 100/7-8
100 Amsden Way 05091 802-457-1330
Dana Peterson, prin. Fax 457-5048

VIRGINIA

VIRGINIA DEPARTMENT OF EDUCATION
PO Box 2120, Richmond 23218-2120
Telephone 804-225-2020
Fax 804-371-2099
Website http://www.pen.k12.va.us

Secretary of Public Instruction Dr. Dietra Trent

VIRGINIA BOARD OF EDUCATION
PO Box 2120, Richmond 23218-2120

President Billy Cannaday

PUBLIC, PRIVATE AND CATHOLIC SECONDARY SCHOOLS

Abingdon, Washington, Pop. 8,107
Regional Academic Governors SD
Supt. — See Richmond
Holton Governor's S 10-12
PO Box 1987 24212 276-619-4326
Danny Dixon, dir. Fax 619-4309

Washington County SD 7,400/PK-12
812 Thompson Dr 24210 276-739-3000
Dr. Brian Ratliff, supt. Fax 628-1874
www.wcs.k12.va.us
Abingdon HS 900/9-12
705 Thompson Dr 24210 276-739-3200
Jimmy King, prin. Fax 628-1897
Stanley MS 700/6-8
297 Stanley St 24210 276-739-3300
Scott Allen, prin. Fax 676-1945
Washington Co. Career & Tech Educ Ctr Vo/Tech
255 Stanley St 24210 276-739-3100
Brian Johnson, prin. Fax 623-4126
Other Schools – See Bristol, Damascus, Glade Spring

Cornerstone Christian Academy 200/PK-12
PO Box 2228 24212 276-623-7164
Dr. Clay Brinson, head sch Fax 628-2481
Virginia Highlands Community College Post-Sec.
PO Box 828 24212 276-739-2400
Washington County Adult Skill Center Post-Sec.
848 Thompson Dr 24210 276-676-1948

Accomac, Accomack, Pop. 513
Accomack County SD 5,200/PK-12
PO Box 330 23301 757-787-5754
Dr. Michael Glascoe, supt. Fax 787-2951
www.accomack.k12.va.us
Other Schools – See Chincoteague, Oak Hall, Onley, Tangier

Afton, Nelson

Afton Christian S 50/PK-12
9357 Critzers Shop Rd 22920 540-456-6853
Lori Knight, head sch Fax 456-6236

Alberta, Brunswick, Pop. 294

Southside Virginia Community College Post-Sec.
109 Campus Dr 23821 434-949-1000

Aldie, Loudoun
Loudoun County SD
Supt. — See Ashburn
Champe HS 1,000/9-12
41535 Sacred Mountain St 20105 703-722-2680
John Gabriel, prin. Fax 722-2681
Mercer MS 1,000/6-8
42149 Greenstone Dr 20105 703-957-4340
Robert Phillips, prin. Fax 444-8068

Alexandria, Alexandria, Pop. 135,858
Alexandria CSD 12,000/PK-12
1340 Braddock Pl 22314 703-619-8000
Alvin Crawley Ed.D., supt. Fax 619-8090
www.acps.k12.va.us
Hammond MS 500/6-8
4646 Seminary Rd 22304 703-461-4100
Meilin Jao, prin. Fax 461-4111
Washington MS 600/6-8
1005 Mount Vernon Ave 22301 703-706-4500
Jesse Mazur, prin. Fax 299-7597
Williams HS 2,400/10-12
3330 King St 22302 703-824-6800
Jesse Dingle Ed.D., prin. Fax 824-6826
Williams HS - Howard Campus 800/9-9
3801 W Braddock Rd 22302 703-824-6750
jesse.dingle Ed.D., prin. Fax 824-6781

Fairfax County SD
Supt. — See Falls Church
Bryant Alternative HS 300/Alt
2709 Popkins Ln 22306 703-660-2100
William Hunt, admin. Fax 660-2097
Edison HS 1,800/9-12
5801 Franconia Rd 22310 703-924-8000
Pamela Brumfield, prin. Fax 924-8097
Glasgow MS 1,500/6-8
4101 Fairfax Pkwy 22312 703-813-8700
Shawn DeRose, prin. Fax 813-8797
Hayfield JSHS 2,800/7-12
7630 Telegraph Rd 22315 703-924-7400
Tracey Phillips, prin. Fax 924-7497
Holmes MS 1,000/6-8
6525 Montrose St 22312 703-658-5900
Roberto Pamas, prin. Fax 658-5997
Jefferson HS 1,800/9-12
6560 Braddock Rd 22312 703-750-8300
Dr. Evan Glazer, prin. Fax 750-5010
Montrose Alternative Learning Center Alt
6525 Montrose St 22312 703-658-5800
Susan Lee, admin.
Mount Vernon HS 2,000/9-12
8515 Old Mount Vernon Rd 22309 703-619-3100
Nardos King, prin. Fax 619-3197
Sandburg MS 1,300/7-8
8428 Fort Hunt Rd 22308 703-799-6100
Terrence Yarborough, prin. Fax 799-6197
Twain MS 900/7-8
4700 Franconia Rd 22310 703-313-3700
Baek Chong, prin. Fax 313-3797
West Potomac HS 2,400/9-12
6500 Quander Rd 22307 703-718-2500
Alexander Case, prin. Fax 718-2597
Whitman MS 1,000/7-8
2500 Parkers Ln 22306 703-660-2400
Roger Vanderhye, prin. Fax 660-2497

Regional Academic Governors SD
Supt. — See Richmond
Jefferson Science & Tech HS 1,900/9-12
6560 Braddock Rd 22312 703-750-8300
Dr. Evan Glazer, prin. Fax 750-5036

Bishop Ireton HS 800/9-12
201 Cambridge Rd 22314 703-751-7606
Dr. Thomas Curry, head sch Fax 212-8173
Commonwealth Academy 100/3-12
1321 Leslie Ave 22301 703-548-6912
Peri-Anne Chobot Ed.D., head sch Fax 548-6914
Episcopal HS 400/9-12
1200 N Quaker Ln 22302 703-933-3000
Charles M. Stillwell, hdmstr. Fax 933-3017
Gardner S, 4913 Franconia Rd 22310 6-12
Erick Johnson, head sch 703-822-9300
Global Health College Post-Sec.
25 S Quaker Ln 22314 703-212-7410
Metropolitan S of the Arts Academy 7-12
5665 Barclay Dr Ste 4 22315 703-399-0444
Michelle Collier, dir. Fax 373-2700
Protestant Episcopal Theologcl. Seminary Post-Sec.
3737 Seminary Rd 22304 703-370-6600
St. Stephen's & St. Agnes S 1,100/PK-12
1000 Saint Stephens Rd 22304 703-751-2700
Kirsten Adams, head sch Fax 751-7142
Stratford University Post-Sec.
2900 Eisenhower Ave 22314 571-699-3200

Altavista, Campbell, Pop. 3,366
Campbell County SD
Supt. — See Rustburg
Altavista JSHS 700/6-12
904 Bedford Ave 24517 434-369-4768
Ty Gafford, prin. Fax 369-5191

Amelia Court House, Amelia, Pop. 1,087
Amelia County SD 1,800/PK-12
8701 Otterburn Rd Ste 101 23002 804-561-2621
Dr. Jack McKinley, supt. Fax 561-3057
www.amelia.k12.va.us
Amelia County HS 600/9-12
8500 Otterburn Rd 23002 804-561-2101
Tommy Moon, prin. Fax 561-4567
Amelia County MS 500/5-8
8740 Otterburn Rd 23002 804-561-4422
Dr. Sarah Tanner-Anderson, prin. Fax 561-6525

Amelia Academy 200/PK-12
PO Box 106 23002 804-561-2270

Amherst, Amherst, Pop. 2,173
Amherst County SD 4,300/PK-12
PO Box 1257 24521 434-946-9387
Dr. Steven Nichols, supt. Fax 946-9346
www.amherst.k12.va.us
Amherst County HS 1,300/9-12
139 Lancer Ln 24521 434-946-2898
William Wells, prin. Fax 946-2263
Amherst MS 400/6-8
165 Gordons Fairgrounds Rd 24521 434-946-0691
Christie Cundiff, prin. Fax 946-0258
Other Schools – See Madison Heights

Annandale, Fairfax, Pop. 39,850
Fairfax County SD
Supt. — See Falls Church
Annandale HS 2,300/9-12
4700 Medford Dr 22003 703-642-4100
Tim Thomas, prin. Fax 642-4197
Poe MS 900/6-8
7000 Cindy Ln 22003 703-813-3800
Maria Eck, prin. Fax 813-3897

---

iGlobal University Post-Sec.
7700 Little River Tpke #600 22003 703-941-2020
Northern Virginia Community College Post-Sec.
8333 Little River Tpke 22003 703-323-3000
Springfield Beauty Academy Post-Sec.
4223 Annandale Rd 22003 703-256-5662
University of Northern Virginia Post-Sec.
7601 Little River Tpke 22003 703-941-0949
Washington Baptist University Post-Sec.
4300 Evergreen Ln 22003 703-333-5904
Westwood College - Annandale Post-Sec.
7619 Little River Tpke #500 22003 703-642-3770

Appomattox, Appomattox, Pop. 1,694
Appomattox County SD 2,300/PK-12
PO Box 548 24522 434-352-8251
Dorinda Grasty Ed.D., supt. Fax 352-0883
www.appomattox.schoolfusion.us
Appomattox HS 700/9-12
198 Evergreen Ave 24522 434-352-7146
Dr. Francis Moreno, prin. Fax 352-0822
Appomattox MS 500/6-8
2020 Church St 24522 434-352-8257
Cheryl Servis, prin. Fax 352-5621

Appomattox Christian Academy 50/PK-12
PO Box 517 24522 434-352-7373
Cornerstone Christian Academy 100/PK-12
PO Box 897 24522 434-352-2345
Dr. Geoffrey Hubler, prin. Fax 352-2345

Arlington, Arlington, Pop. 201,587
Arlington County SD 24,300/PK-12
1426 N Quincy St 22207 703-228-6000
Dr. Patrick Murphy, supt. Fax 228-6188
www.apsva.us
Arlington Career Center Vo/Tech
816 S Walter Reed Dr 22204 703-228-5800
Margaret Chung, prin. Fax 228-5815
Arlington Community HS 200/Alt
800 S Walter Reed Dr 22204 703-228-5350
Dr. Barbara Thompson, prin. Fax 522-2437
Governors Career and Technical Academy Vo/Tech
816 S Walter Reed Dr 22204 703-323-2263
Gunston MS 800/6-8
2700 S Lang St 22206 703-228-6900
Dr. Lori Wiggins, prin. Fax 519-9183
Jefferson MS 900/6-8
125 S Old Glebe Rd 22204 703-228-5900
Keisha Boggan, prin. Fax 979-3744
Kenmore MS 900/6-8
200 S Carlin Springs Rd 22204 703-228-6800
David McBride, prin. Fax 998-3069
Langston HS Continuation Alt
2121 N Culpeper St 22207 703-228-5295
Cleveland James, prin. Fax 807-0614
New Directions S Alt
2847 Wilson Blvd 22201 703-228-2117
Philip Bonar, prin. Fax 875-8920
Swanson MS 1,100/6-8
5800 Washington Blvd 22205 703-228-5500
Bridget Loft, prin. Fax 536-2775

Wakefield HS 1,700/9-12
1325 S Dinwiddie St 22206 703-228-6700
Dr. Christian Willmore, prin. Fax 228-6760
Washington-Lee HS 2,200/9-12
1301 N Stafford St 22201 703-228-6200
Gregg Robertson, prin. Fax 524-9814
Williamsburg MS 1,100/6-8
3600 N Harrison St 22207 703-228-5450
Gordon Laurie, prin. Fax 536-2870
Woodland Secondary Program 600/Alt
4100 Vacation Ln 22207 703-228-6363
Casey Robinson, prin. Fax 558-0317
Yorktown HS 1,900/9-12
5200 Yorktown Blvd 22207 703-228-5400
Dr. Raymond Pasi, prin. Fax 228-5409

Argosy University/Washington DC Post-Sec.
1550 Wilson Blvd Ste 600 22209 703-526-5800
Art Institute of Washington Post-Sec.
1820 Fort Myer Dr 22209 703-358-9550
Bishop Denis J. O'Connell HS 1,200/9-12
6600 Little Falls Rd 22213 703-237-1400
Joseph Vorbach Ph.D., head sch Fax 237-1412
Chamberlain College of Nursing Post-Sec.
2450 Crystal Dr 22202 703-416-7300
Court Reporting Institute of Arlington Post-Sec.
4300 Wilson Blvd Ste 140 22203 703-875-1200
DeVry University Post-Sec.
2450 Crystal Dr 22202 703-414-4000
Graham Webb Intl. Academy of Hair Post-Sec.
1621 N Kent St # 1617LL 22209 703-243-9322
Institute for the Psychological Sciences Post-Sec.
2001 Jefferson Davis # 511 22202 703-416-1441
Keller Graduate School Post-Sec.
2450 Crystal Dr 22202 703-414-4000
Marymount University Post-Sec.
2807 N Glebe Rd 22207 703-522-5600
University of Management and Technology Post-Sec.
1901 Fort Myer Dr Ste 700 22209 703-516-0035
Westwood College - Ballston Post-Sec.
4420 Fairfax Dr 22203 703-243-3900

Ashburn, Loudoun, Pop. 41,992
Loudoun County SD 70,400/PK-12
21000 Education Ct 20148 571-252-1000
Dr. Eric Williams, supt. Fax 252-1003
www.lcps.org/
Briar Woods HS 2,200/9-12
22525 Belmont Ridge Rd 20148 703-957-4400
Chris O'Rourke, prin. Fax 542-5923
Broad Run HS 1,900/9-12
21670 Ashburn Rd 20147 571-252-2300
David Spage, prin. Fax 252-2301
Eagle Ridge MS 1,200/6-8
42901 Waxpool Rd 20148 571-252-2140
Scott Phillips, prin. Fax 779-8977
Farmwell Station MS 1,300/6-8
44281 Gloucester Pkwy 20147 571-252-2320
Sherryl Loya, prin. Fax 771-6495
Rock Ridge HS 9-12
43460 Loudoun Reserve Dr 20148 703-996-2100
John Duellman, prin. Fax 996-2101
Stone Bridge HS 1,800/9-12
43100 Hay Rd 20147 571-252-2200
Matthew Wilburn, prin. Fax 252-2201
Stone Hill MS 1,600/6-8
23415 Evergreen Ridge Dr 20148 703-957-4420
Kathryn Clark, prin. Fax 223-0585
Trailside MS 6-8
20325 Claiborne Pkwy 20147 571-252-2280
Bridget Beichler, prin. Fax 724-1086
Other Schools – See Aldie, Chantilly, Hamilton, Leesburg, Potomac Falls, Purcellville, South Riding, Sterling

---

Loudoun S for the Gifted 50/6-12
PO Box 618 20146 703-956-5020
Susan Talbott, dir. Fax 291-4873
Strayer University Post-Sec.
45150 Russell Branch Pkwy 20147 703-729-8800
Virginia Academy 600/PK-12
19790 Ashburn Rd 20147 571-209-5500
Michael Taylor, supt. Fax 209-5845

Ashland, Hanover, Pop. 7,029
Hanover County SD 17,800/K-12
200 Berkley St 23005 804-365-4500
Dr. Michael Gill, supt. Fax 365-4680
www.hcps.us
Henry HS 1,500/9-12
12449 W Patrick Henry Rd 23005 804-365-8000
Elizabeth Smith, prin. Fax 365-8027
Liberty MS 1,100/6-8
13496 Liberty School Rd 23005 804-365-8060
Donald Latham, prin. Fax 365-8061
Other Schools – See Mechanicsville

Randolph-Macon College Post-Sec.
PO Box 5005 23005 804-752-7200

Axton, Henry

Carlisle S 500/PK-12
300 Carlisle Rd 24054 276-632-7288
Thomas Hudgins, head sch Fax 632-9545

Bassett, Henry, Pop. 1,078
Henry County SD
Supt. — See Collinsville
Bassett HS 1,200/9-12
85 Riverside Dr 24055 276-629-1731
John Gibbs, prin. Fax 629-9329

Bastian, Bland
Bland County SD 400/PK-12
361 Bears Trl 24314 276-688-3361
Dr. Chris Stacy, supt. Fax 688-4659
www.bland.k12.va.us
Other Schools – See Rocky Gap

Bealeton, Fauquier, Pop. 4,295
Fauquier County SD
Supt. — See Warrenton
Cedar-Lee MS 600/6-8
11138 Marsh Rd 22712 540-422-7430
David Lee, prin. Fax 422-7449
Liberty HS 1,200/9-12
6300 Independence Ave 22712 540-422-7630
Sam Cox, prin. Fax 422-7389

Bedford, Bedford, Pop. 6,098
Bedford County SD 9,700/K-12
PO Box 748 24523 540-586-1045
Dr. Douglas Schuch, supt. Fax 586-7703
bedford.sharpschool.net
Alternative Education Center Alt
600 Edmund St 24523 540-586-3517
Tracy Piestrak, admin.
Bedford MS 600/6-8
503 Longwood Ave 24523 540-586-7735
Rhetta Watkins, prin. Fax 586-4957
Bedford Science and Technology Center Vo/Tech
600 Edmund St 24523 540-586-3933
Kim Halterman, admin. Fax 586-7711
Governors Health Science Academy Vo/Tech
600 Edmund St 24523 540-586-3933
Kim Halterman, admin. Fax 586-7711
Liberty HS 900/9-12
100 Minute Man Dr 24523 540-586-2541
Dr. Kathleen Dills, prin. Fax 586-7720
Other Schools – See Forest, Moneta

Ben Hur, Lee
Lee County SD
Supt. — See Jonesville
Lee County Career & Technical Center Vo/Tech
PO Box 100 24218 276-346-1960
James Graham, prin. Fax 346-2831

Bent Mountain, Roanoke

Bent Mountain Christian Academy 50/K-12
PO Box 66 24059 540-494-8356
Karen Scott, admin. Fax 929-9028

Berryville, Clarke, Pop. 4,082
Clarke County SD 2,300/PK-12
309 W Main St 22611 540-955-6100
Chuck Bishop, supt. Fax 955-6109
www.clarke.k12.va.us
Clarke County HS 700/9-12
627 Mosby Blvd 22611 540-955-6130
Dana Waring, prin. Fax 955-6139
Johnson-Williams MS 400/6-8
200 Swan Ave 22611 540-955-6160
Evan Robb, prin. Fax 955-6169

Big Stone Gap, Wise, Pop. 5,523
Wise County SD
Supt. — See Wise
Powell Valley MS 500/5-8
3137 2nd Ave E 24219 276-523-0195
Paul Clendenon, prin. Fax 523-4762
Union HS 700/9-12
322 Powell Valley Rd 24219 276-523-1290
Dan Roop, prin. Fax 523-6804

Mountain Empire Community College Post-Sec.
3441 Mountain Empire Rd 24219 276-523-2400

Blacksburg, Montgomery, Pop. 41,455
Montgomery County SD
Supt. — See Christiansburg
Blacksburg HS 1,100/9-12
3401 Bruin Ln 24060 540-951-5706
Brian Kitts, prin. Fax 951-5714
Blacksburg MS 800/6-8
3109 Prices Fork Rd 24060 540-951-5800
Amanda Weidner, prin. Fax 951-5808

Dayspring Christian Academy 300/K-12
PO Box 909 24063 540-552-7777
William Hampton, admin. Fax 552-7778
Edward Via College of Osteopathic Med. Post-Sec.
2265 Kraft Dr 24060 540-231-4000
Virginia Polytechnic Inst. & State Univ. Post-Sec.
24061 540-231-6000

Blackstone, Nottoway, Pop. 3,575

Kenston Forest S 300/PK-12
75 Ridge Rd 23824 434-292-7218

Bluefield, Tazewell, Pop. 5,359
Tazewell County SD
Supt. — See Tazewell
Graham HS 600/9-12
210 Valleydale St 24605 276-326-1235
Cynthia Beavers, prin. Fax 326-1128
Graham MS 400/6-8
1 Academic Cir 24605 276-326-1101
Lee Salyers, prin. Fax 322-1409

Bluefield College Post-Sec.
3000 College Dr 24605 276-326-3682

Bowling Green, Caroline, Pop. 1,090
Caroline County SD 4,400/PK-12
16261 Richmond Tpke 22427 804-633-5088
Dr. George Parker, supt. Fax 633-5563
www.ccps.us
Other Schools – See Milford

Boydton, Mecklenburg, Pop. 430
Mecklenburg County SD 4,600/PK-12
PO Box 190 23917 434-738-6111
Dr. Janet Crawley, supt. Fax 738-6679
www.mcpsweb.org
Other Schools – See Skipwith, South Hill

Bridgewater, Rockingham, Pop. 5,553
Rockingham County SD
Supt. — See Harrisonburg
Ashby HS 1,000/9-12
800 N Main St 22812 540-828-2008
Phil Judd, prin. Fax 828-4764

Blue Ridge Christian S 200/PK-12
PO Box 207 22812 540-828-2233
Karen Shomo, head sch Fax 828-4372
Bridgewater College Post-Sec.
402 E College St 22812 540-828-8000

Bristol, Bristol, Pop. 17,490
Bristol CSD 2,300/PK-12
220 Lee St 24201 276-821-5600
Gary Ritchie, supt. Fax 821-5601
www.bvps.org/
Virginia HS 700/9-12
1200 Long Crescent Dr 24201 276-821-5858
Ronnie Collins, prin. Fax 821-5851
Virginia MS 500/6-8
501 Piedmont Ave 24201 276-821-5660
Bo Love, prin. Fax 821-5661

Washington County SD
Supt. — See Abingdon
Battle HS 600/9-12
21264 Battle Hill Dr 24202 276-642-5300
Randy Poole, prin. Fax 645-2386
Wallace MS 500/6-8
13077 Wallace Pike 24202 276-642-5400
David Lambert, prin. Fax 645-2365

Graham Bible College Post-Sec.
PO Box 1630 24203 423-968-4201
Southeast Culinary & Hospitality College Post-Sec.
100 Piedmont Ave 24201 276-591-5699
Virginia Intermont College Post-Sec.
1013 Moore St 24201 276-669-6101

Bristow, Prince William
Prince William County SD
Supt. — See Manassas
Marsteller MS 1,500/6-8
14000 Sudley Manor Dr 20136 703-393-7608
Roberta Knetter, prin. Fax 530-6327

Broadway, Rockingham, Pop. 3,640
Rockingham County SD
Supt. — See Harrisonburg
Broadway HS 1,000/9-12
269 Gobbler Dr 22815 540-896-7081
Donna Abernathy, prin. Fax 896-2640
Hillyard MS 800/6-8
226 Hawks Hill Dr 22815 540-896-8961
Dave Baker, prin. Fax 896-6641

Buchanan, Botetourt, Pop. 1,142
Botetourt County SD
Supt. — See Fincastle
James River HS 600/9-12
9906 Springwood Rd 24066 540-254-1121
James Talbott, prin. Fax 254-2765

Buckingham, Buckingham, Pop. 370
Buckingham County SD 2,200/PK-12
15595 W James Anderson Hwy 23921 434-969-6100
Dr. Cecil Snead, supt. Fax 969-1176
www.bcpschools.org
Buckingham County HS 600/9-12
78 Knights Rd 23921 434-969-6160
Rudy Roethel, prin. Fax 969-3209
Buckingham County MS 400/6-8
1184 High School Rd 23921 434-969-1044
J.B. Heslip, prin. Fax 969-4290

Buena Vista, Buena Vista, Pop. 6,530
Buena Vista CSD 1,000/K-12
2329 Chestnut Ave Ste A 24416 540-261-2129
Dr. John Keeler, supt. Fax 261-2967
www.bvcps.net
McCluer HS 400/8-12
100 Bradford Dr 24416 540-261-2127
Anna Graham, prin. Fax 261-1828

Southern Virginia University Post-Sec.
1 University Hill Dr 24416 540-261-8400

Bumpass, Louisa

Piedmont Christian S 100/PK-12
2382 Bethany Church Rd 23024 540-872-3543
Marsha Badertscher, head sch Fax 872-3873

Burke, Fairfax, Pop. 39,726
Fairfax County SD
Supt. — See Falls Church
Lake Braddock JSHS 4,100/7-12
9200 Burke Lake Rd 22015 703-426-1000
David Thomas, prin. Fax 426-1093

Carson, Prince George
Jointly Operated Vo Tech SD
Supt. — None - Lolita Hall, dir.
Rowanty Technical Center Vo/Tech
20000 Rowanty Rd 23830 434-246-5741
Fax 246-5721

Castlewood, Russell, Pop. 2,028
Russell County SD
Supt. — See Lebanon
Castlewood HS 400/8-12
304 Blue Devil Cir 24224 276-762-9449
Lila Jenkins, prin. Fax 762-9418

Learning Center 100/PK-11
PO Box 133 24224 276-762-5700
Ken Johnson, admin. Fax 762-7116

Centreville, Fairfax, Pop. 68,513
Fairfax County SD
Supt. — See Falls Church
Mountain View Alternative HS 200/Alt
5775 Spindle Ct 20121 703-522-6840
Kimberly Thomas, admin.
Stone MS 800/7-8
5500 Sully Park Dr 20120 703-631-5500
Amielia Mitchell, prin. Fax 631-5598

Ad Fontes Academy 200/K-12
PO Box 916 20122 571-345-4755
Columbia College Post-Sec.
5940 Centreville Crest Ln 20121 703-266-0508

Chantilly, Fairfax, Pop. 22,194
Fairfax County SD
Supt. — See Falls Church
Chantilly Governor's STEM Academy 9-12
4201 Stringfellow Rd 20151 703-222-7460
Virginia Muller, prin. Fax 222-7497
Chantilly HS 2,700/9-12
4201 Stringfellow Rd 20151 703-222-8100
Teresa Johnson, prin. Fax 222-8197
Franklin MS 900/7-8
3300 Lees Corner Rd 20151 703-904-5100
Sharon Eisenberg, prin. Fax 904-5197
Rocky Run MS 1,100/7-8
4400 Stringfellow Rd 20151 703-802-7700
Anthony Terrell, prin. Fax 802-7797
Westfield HS 2,800/9-12
4700 Stonecroft Blvd 20151 703-488-6300
Anthony Copeland, prin. Fax 488-6397

Loudoun County SD
Supt. — See Ashburn
Lunsford MS 1,400/6-8
26020 Ticonderoga Rd 20152 703-722-2660
Carrie Simms, prin. Fax 327-2420

Auburn S 50/K-12
3800 Concorde Pkwy 20151 703-793-9353
Heather Hargrave M.Ed., head sch Fax 793-9355

Charles City, Charles City, Pop. 131
Charles City County SD 600/PK-12
10910 Courthouse Rd 23030 804-652-4612
Dr. David Gaston, supt. Fax 829-6723
www.ccps.net
Charles City HS 200/7-12
10039 Courthouse Rd 23030 804-829-9249
Panagiotis Tsigaridas, prin. Fax 829-2644

Charlotte Court House, Charlotte, Pop. 538
Charlotte County SD 1,900/PK-12
PO Box 790 23923 434-542-5151
Nancy Leonard, supt. Fax 542-4261
www.ccpsk12.org
Central MS 400/6-8
PO Box 748 23923 434-542-4536
Michael Haskins, prin. Fax 542-4630
Randolph-Henry HS 600/9-12
PO Box 668 23923 434-542-4111
Robbie Mason, prin. Fax 542-4114

Charlottesville, Charlottesville, Pop. 42,217
Albemarle County SD 13,500/PK-12
401 McIntire Rd 22902 434-296-5826
Dr. Pamela Moran, supt. Fax 296-5869
www.k12albemarle.org/
Albemarle HS 1,900/9-12
2775 Hydraulic Rd 22901 434-975-9300
Jay Thomas, prin. Fax 974-4335
Burley MS 600/6-8
901 Rose Hill Dr 22903 434-295-5101
James Asher, prin. Fax 984-4975
Health and Medical Sciences Academy 9-12
1400 Independence Way 22902 434-244-3100
Kitina Dudley, dir.
Jouett MS 600/6-8
210 Lambs Ln 22901 434-975-9320
Kathryn Baylor, prin. Fax 975-9325
Math Engineering and Science Academy 9-12
2775 Hydraulic Rd 22901 434-975-9300
Tony Wayne, dir. Fax 974-4335
Monticello HS 1,100/9-12
1400 Independence Way 22902 434-244-3100
Dr. Jesse Turner, prin. Fax 244-3104
Murray HS 100/Alt
1200 Forest St 22903 434-296-3090
Ashby Kindler, prin. Fax 979-6479
Sutherland MS 600/6-8
2801 Powell Creek Dr 22911 434-975-0599
Rick Vrhovac, prin. Fax 975-0852
Walton MS 400/6-8
4217 Red Hill Rd 22903 434-977-5615
Josh Walton, prin. Fax 296-6648
Other Schools – See Crozet

Charlottesville CSD 4,300/PK-12
1562 Dairy Rd 22903 434-245-2400
Dr. Rosa Atkins, supt. Fax 245-2603
charlottesvilleschools.org
Buford MS 500/7-8
1000 Cherry Ave 22903 434-245-2411
Eric Johnson, prin. Fax 245-2611
Charlottesville HS 1,200/9-12
1400 Melbourne Rd 22901 434-245-2410
Dr. Eric Irizarry, prin. Fax 245-2610
Lugo-McGinness Academy Alt
341 11th St NW 22903 434-245-2406
Stephanie Carter, admin.

Jointly Operated Vo Tech SD
Supt. — None - Lolita Hall, dir.
Charlottsville-Albemarle Tech Center Vo/Tech
1000 Rio Road East 22901 434-973-4461
Bruce Bosselman, dir. Fax 973-4876

American National University Post-Sec.
3926 Seminole Trl 22911 434-220-7960
Covenant S 500/PK-12
175 Hickory St 22902 434-220-7329
George Sanker, hdmstr. Fax 979-3204
Miller S of Albemarle 200/8-12
1000 Samuel Miller Loop 22903 434-823-4805
Sam Hale, admin. Fax 823-6617
Piedmont Virginia Community College Post-Sec.
501 College Dr 22902 434-977-3900
Regents S of Charlottesville 100/K-10
3045 Ivy Rd 22903 434-293-0633
St. Anne's-Belfield S 900/PK-12
2132 Ivy Rd 22903 434-296-5106
David Lourie, hdmstr. Fax 979-1486
Tandem Friends S 200/5-12
279 Tandem Ln 22902 434-296-1303
Ed Hollinger, hdmstr. Fax 296-1886
University of Virginia Post-Sec.
PO Box 400160 22904 434-924-0311
Virginia School of Massage Post-Sec.
153 Zan Rd 22901 434-293-4031

Chatham, Pittsylvania, Pop. 1,254
Pittsylvania County SD 9,200/PK-12
PO Box 232 24531 434-432-2761
Dr. Mark R. Jones, supt. Fax 432-9560
www.pcs.k12.va.us
Chatham HS 700/9-12
100 Chatham Cavalier Cir 24531 434-432-8305
Randy Foster, prin. Fax 432-8351
Chatham MS 500/6-8
11650 US Highway 29 24531 434-432-2169
Julia Woodward, prin. Fax 432-2842
Pittsylvania Career Tech Vo/Tech
11700 US Highway 29 24531 434-432-9416
Angela Rigney, prin. Fax 432-0516
Regional Alternative Center Alt
956 Woodlawn Academy Rd 24531 434-432-8185
Deborah Powell, prin. Fax 432-8186
Other Schools – See Dry Fork, Gretna, Ringgold

Chatham Hall S 100/9-12
800 Chatham Hall Cir 24531 434-432-2941
Suzanne Buck, head sch Fax 432-1002
Hargrave Military Academy 200/7-12
200 Military Dr 24531 434-432-2481
Don Broome, pres. Fax 432-3129

Chesapeake, Chesapeake, Pop. 216,170
Chesapeake CSD 39,000/K-12
PO Box 16496 23328 757-547-0165
Dr. James Roberts, supt. Fax 547-0196
www.cpschools.com/
Chesapeake Alternative S Alt
605 Providence Rd 23325 757-578-7046
Dr. Penny Schultz, prin. Fax 578-7068
Chesapeake Center Science & Tech Vo/Tech
1617 Cedar Rd 23322 757-547-0134
Shonda Pittman-Windham, prin. Fax 547-2391
Crestwood MS 600/6-8
1420 Great Bridge Blvd 23320 757-494-7560
Michael Ward, prin. Fax 494-7599
Deep Creek HS 1,400/9-12
2900 Margaret Booker Dr 23323 757-558-5302
Page Bagley, prin. Fax 558-5305
Deep Creek MS 500/6-8
1955 Deal Dr 23323 757-558-5321
Dr. Muriel Barefield, prin. Fax 558-5320
Governors STEM Academy 9-12
2007 Grizzly Trl 23323 757-558-4493
Karen Black, coord.
Grassfield HS 2,000/9-12
2007 Grizzly Trl 23323 757-558-4749
Michael Perez, prin. Fax 558-9240
Great Bridge HS 1,400/9-12
301 Hanbury Rd W 23322 757-482-5191
Jeffrey Johnson, prin. Fax 482-5559
Great Bridge MS 1,300/6-8
441 Battlefield Blvd S 23322 757-482-5128
Craig Mills, prin. Fax 482-0210
Greenbrier MS 900/6-8
1016 Greenbrier Pkwy 23320 757-548-5309
Dr. Michael Mustain, prin. Fax 548-8921
Hickory HS 1,800/9-12
1996 Hawk Blvd 23322 757-421-4295
Alfredia Turner, prin. Fax 421-2190
Hickory MS 1,500/6-8
1997 Hawk Blvd 23322 757-421-0468
Dr. Deborah Hutchens, prin. Fax 421-0475
Indian River HS 1,700/9-12
1969 Braves Trl 23325 757-578-7000
Naomi Dunbar, prin. Fax 578-7004
Indian River MS 800/6-8
2300 Old Greenbrier Rd 23325 757-578-7030
Terre Werts, prin. Fax 578-7036
Jolliff MS 800/6-8
1021 Jolliff Rd 23321 757-465-5246
Quentin Hicks, prin. Fax 465-1646
Owens MS 1,100/6-8
1997 Horseback Run 23323 757-558-5382
Amber Dortch, prin. Fax 558-5386
Smith HS 2,100/9-12
1994 Tiger Dr 23320 757-548-0696
Paul Joseph, prin. Fax 548-0531
Smith MS 1,000/6-8
2500 Rodgers St 23324 757-494-7590
Judith Thurston, prin. Fax 494-7680
Western Branch HS 2,200/9-12
1968 Bruin Pl 23321 757-638-7900
Dr. Thomas Whitley, prin. Fax 638-7904
Western Branch MS 900/6-8
4201 Hawksley Dr 23321 757-638-7920
Dr. Samuel Khoshaba, prin. Fax 638-7926

Atlantic Shores Christian S 300/7-12
1217 Centerville Tpke N 23320 757-479-9598
Gary Carlson, head sch Fax 479-5311
Aviation Institute of Maintenance Post-Sec.
2211 S Military Hwy 23320 757-363-2121
Centura College Post-Sec.
932 Ventures Way 23320 757-549-2121
DeVry University Post-Sec.
1317 Executive Blvd Ste 100 23320 757-382-5680
Everest College Post-Sec.
825 Greenbrier Cir Ste 100 23320 757-361-3900
Greenbrier Christian Academy 600/PK-12
311 Kempsville Rd 23320 757-547-9595
Dr. Ron White, supt. Fax 547-9569
Sentara College of Health Sciences Post-Sec.
1441 Crossways Blvd Ste 105 23320 757-388-2900
StoneBridge S 300/PK-12
PO Box 9247 23321 757-488-2214
Kathy Rader, head sch Fax 465-7637
Strayer University Post-Sec.
676 Independence Pkwy # 300 23320 757-382-9900
Tidewater Community College Post-Sec.
1428 Cedar Rd 23322 757-822-5100
Veritas Christian Academy 100/PK-12
1208 Centerville Tpke N 23320 757-410-5095

Chester, Chesterfield, Pop. 20,491
Chesterfield County SD
Supt. — See Chesterfield
Carver College & Career Academy 300/Alt
12400 Branders Bridge Rd 23831 804-768-6182
Dr. Ken Butta, prin. Fax 768-6171
Carver MS 1,100/6-8
3800 Cougar Trl 23831 804-524-3620
Dr. John Murray, prin. Fax 520-0189
Dale HS 2,300/9-12
3626 W Hundred Rd 23831 804-768-6245
Pamela Lunsden, prin. Fax 768-6256
Davis MS 1,200/6-8
601 Corvus Ct 23836 804-541-4700
Ed Maynes, prin. Fax 530-2717

John Tyler Community College Post-Sec.
13101 Jefferson Davis Hwy 23831 804-796-4000
Life Christian Academy 100/PK-12
16801 Harrowgate Rd 23831 804-526-5941
Rev. Michael Cherry, admin. Fax 526-3582

Chesterfield, Chesterfield
Chesterfield County SD 59,200/PK-12
PO Box 10 23832 804-748-1405
Dr. Marcus Newsome, supt. Fax 796-7178
mychesterfieldschools.com
Bird HS 1,900/9-12
10301 Courthouse Rd 23832 804-768-6110
Dr. Laura Hebert, prin. Fax 768-6117
Chesterfield Technical Center Vo/Tech
10101 Courthouse Rd 23832 804-768-6160
Dr. Colleen Bryant, prin. Fax 768-6164
Matoaca HS 1,900/9-12
17700 Longhouse Ln 23838 804-590-3108
Belinda Merriman, prin. Fax 590-3022
Other Schools – See Chester, Matoaca, Midlothian, N Chesterfield

---

Guardian Christian Academy 300/PK-11
6851 Courthouse Rd 23832 804-715-3210
Glenda Paul, dir. Fax 715-3237
Richmond Christian S 300/PK-12
6511 Belmont Rd 23832 804-276-3193
Cliff Williams, head sch Fax 276-9106

Chilhowie, Smyth, Pop. 1,774
Smyth County SD
Supt. — See Marion
Chilhowie HS 500/9-12
PO Box 2280 24319 276-646-8966
Mike Sturgill, prin. Fax 646-5951
Chilhowie MS 300/6-8
PO Box 5018 24319 276-646-3942
Sam Blevins, prin. Fax 646-0210

Chincoteague, Accomack, Pop. 2,859
Accomack County SD
Supt. — See Accomac
Chincoteague HS 300/6-12
4586 Main St 23336 757-336-6166
Warren Holland, prin. Fax 336-1902

Christchurch, Middlesex

Christchurch S 200/9-12
49 Seahorse Ln 23031 804-758-2306
John Byers, hdmstr. Fax 758-0721

Christiansburg, Montgomery, Pop. 20,645
Montgomery County SD 9,700/PK-12
750 Imperial St 24073 540-382-5100
Brenda Blackburn, supt. Fax 381-6127
www.mcps.org
Christiansburg HS 1,100/9-12
100 Independence Blvd 24073 540-382-5178
Dr. Kevin Siers, prin. Fax 381-6525
Christiansburg MS 800/6-8
1205 Buffalo Dr 24073 540-394-2180
Jason Garretson, prin. Fax 394-2197
Montgomery Central Alt
208 College St 24073 540-381-6100
Larry Lowe, prin. Fax 381-6185
Other Schools – See Blacksburg, Elliston, Riner, Shawsville

Clifton, Fairfax, Pop. 280
Fairfax County SD
Supt. — See Falls Church
Centreville HS 2,400/9-12
6001 Union Mill Rd 20124 703-802-5400
David Jagels, prin. Fax 802-5497
Liberty MS 1,100/7-8
6801 Union Mill Rd 20124 703-988-8100
Catherine Cipperly, prin. Fax 988-8197

Clifton Forge, Alleghany, Pop. 3,785
Regional Academic Governors SD
Supt. — See Richmond
Jackson River Governor's HS 11-12
PO Box 1000 24422 540-863-2872
Eddie Graham, dir. Fax 863-2915

Dabney S. Lancaster Community College Post-Sec.
PO Box 1000 24422 540-863-2800

Clintwood, Dickenson, Pop. 1,403
Dickenson County SD 2,200/PK-12
PO Box 1127 24228 276-926-4643
Haydee Robinson, supt. Fax 926-6374
www.dickenson.k12.va.us
Ridgeview HS 700/9-12
310 Wolf Pack Way 24228 276-835-1600
Rodney Compton, prin.
Ridgeview MS 500/6-8
320 Wolf Pack Way 24228 276-835-1601
John Whitner, prin.

Cloverdale, Botetourt, Pop. 3,095
Botetourt County SD
Supt. — See Fincastle
Read Mountain MS 700/6-8
182 Orchard Hill Dr 24077 540-966-8655
Beth Mast, prin. Fax 966-8656

Coeburn, Wise, Pop. 2,115
Wise County SD
Supt. — See Wise
Coeburn MS 400/5-8
PO Box 670 24230 276-395-2135
Angie Clendenon, prin. Fax 395-5453
Eastside HS 400/9-12
PO Box 2036 24230 276-395-3389
Bryan Crutchfield, prin. Fax 395-5167

Collinsville, Henry, Pop. 7,233
Henry County SD 7,400/PK-12
PO Box 8958 24078 276-634-4700
Dr. Jared Cotton, supt. Fax 638-2925
www.henry.k12.va.us
Fieldale-Collinsville MS 900/6-8
645 Miles Rd 24078 276-647-3841
Corbin Campbell, prin. Fax 647-4090
Other Schools – See Bassett, Martinsville, Ridgeway

Colonial Beach, Westmoreland, Pop. 3,440
Colonial Beach SD 600/PK-12
16 Irving Ave N 22443 804-224-0906
Dr. Kevin Newman, supt. Fax 224-8357
www.cbschools.net
Colonial Beach HS 200/8-12
100 1st St 22443 804-224-7166
Jennifer Grigsby, prin. Fax 224-7465

Colonial Heights, Colonial Heights, Pop. 17,059
Colonial Heights CSD 2,800/K-12
512 Boulevard, 804-524-3400
Dr. Joseph Cox, supt. Fax 526-4524
www.colonialhts.net
Colonial Heights HS 900/9-12
3600 Conduit Rd, 804-524-3405
Kristin Janssen, prin. Fax 520-7222
Colonial Heights MS 700/6-8
500 Conduit Rd, 804-524-3420
William Hortz, prin. Fax 526-9288

Courtland, Southampton, Pop. 1,266
Southhampton County SD 2,900/PK-12
PO Box 96 23837 757-653-2692
Dr. Alvera Parrish, supt. Fax 653-9422
www.southampton.k12.va.us/
Southampton HS 800/9-12
23350 Southampton Pkwy 23837 757-653-2751
Allene Atkinson, prin. Fax 653-0414
Southampton MS 600/6-8
23450 Southampton Pkwy 23837 757-653-9250
Darian Bell, prin. Fax 653-7251
Southampton Technical Career Center Vo/Tech
23450 Southampton Pkwy 23837 757-653-9170
Linda Adams, admin. Fax 653-9404

Southampton Academy 300/PK-12
26495 Old Plank Rd 23837 757-653-2512

Covington, Covington, Pop. 5,839
Alleghany County SD
Supt. — See Low Moor
Alleghany HS 900/9-12
210 Mountaineer Dr 24426 540-863-1700
Dwayne Ross, prin. Fax 863-1705
Clifton MS 600/6-8
1000 Riverview Farm Rd 24426 540-863-1726
Kim Crandall, prin. Fax 863-1731

Covington CSD 1,000/PK-12
340 E Walnut St 24426 540-965-1400
Thomas Long, supt. Fax 965-1404
www.covingtoncityschools.us
Covington HS 300/8-12
606 S Lexington Ave 24426 540-965-1410
Dr. Shannon Fuhrman, prin.

Jointly Operated Vo Tech SD
Supt. — None – Lolita Hall, dir.
Jackson River Tech Center Vo/Tech
105 E Country Club Ln 24426 540-862-1308
Glenn Spangler, dir. Fax 862-3592

Crewe, Nottoway, Pop. 2,296
Nottoway County SD
Supt. — See Nottoway
Nottoway HS 700/9-12
5267 Old Nottoway Rd 23930 434-292-5373
Dr. Daisy Hicks, prin. Fax 292-3021
Nottoway MS 300/7-8
5279 Old Nottoway Rd 23930 434-292-5375
Roger Coleman, prin. Fax 292-7479

Crozet, Albemarle, Pop. 5,475
Albemarle County SD
Supt. — See Charlottesville
Environmental Studies Academy 9-12
5941 Rockfish Gap Tpke 22932 434-823-8700
Adam Mulcahy, dir. Fax 823-8711
Henley MS 800/6-8
5880 Rockfish Gap Tpke 22932 434-823-4393
Dr. Beth Costa, prin. Fax 823-2711
Western Albemarle HS 1,000/9-12
5941 Rockfish Gap Tpke 22932 434-823-8700
Darah Bonham, prin. Fax 823-8711

Crozier, Goochland

Salem Christian S 100/PK-12
1700 Cardwell Rd 23039 804-784-4174
Todd Brooking, prin. Fax 784-0432

Culpeper, Culpeper, Pop. 15,837
Culpeper County SD 7,900/K-12
450 Radio Ln 22701 540-825-3677
Dr. Anthony S. Brads, supt. Fax 829-2111
www.culpeperschools.org
Binns MS 800/6-8
205 E Grandview Ave 22701 540-825-6894
Sherri Harkness, prin. Fax 829-9926
Culpeper County HS 1,100/9-12
14240 Achievement Dr 22701 540-825-8310
Jeff Dietz, prin. Fax 829-6615
Culpeper County MS 1,100/6-8
14300 Achievement Dr 22701 540-825-4140
Cathy Timmons, prin. Fax 825-7543
Eastern View HS 1,200/9-12
16332 Cyclone Way 22701 540-825-0621
E.G. Bradshaw, prin. Fax 825-9802

Cumberland, Cumberland, Pop. 383
Cumberland County SD 1,400/PK-12
PO Box 170 23040 804-492-4212
Dr. Amy Griffin Ed.D., supt. Fax 492-9869
www.cucps.k12.va.us
Cumberland HS 400/9-12
PO Box 140 23040 804-492-4212
Jeff Scales, prin. Fax 492-9871
Cumberland MS 400/5-8
PO Box 184 23040 804-492-4212
Jeff Dingeldein, prin. Fax 492-9868

Daleville, Botetourt, Pop. 2,539
Botetourt County SD
Supt. — See Fincastle
Lord Botetourt HS 1,100/9-12
1435 Roanoke Rd 24083 540-992-1261
Andy Dewease, prin. Fax 992-8381
STEM - Health Academy 9-12
57 S Center Dr 24083 540-992-3658
Stacey Jones, contact

Damascus, Washington, Pop. 807
Washington County SD
Supt. — See Abingdon
Damascus MS 200/6-8
32101 Government Rd 24236 276-739-4100
Scott Keith, prin. Fax 475-4032
Holston HS 300/9-12
21308 Monroe Rd 24236 276-739-4000
Kendra Honaker, prin. Fax 475-4024

Danville, Danville, Pop. 42,537
Danville CSD 6,300/PK-12
PO Box 9600 24543 434-799-6400
Stanley Jones, supt. Fax 799-5008
www.danvillepublicschools.org
Bonner MS 800/6-8
300 Apollo Ave 24540 434-799-6446
Daphne Wall, prin. Fax 797-8867
Galileo Magnet HS 200/9-12
230 S Ridge St 24541 434-773-8186
Jay Lancaster, prin. Fax 773-8188
Langston Focus S 100/Alt
228 Cleveland St 24541 434-799-5249
Jocelyn Fitzgerald, prin. Fax 797-8925
Washington HS 1,400/9-12
701 Broad St 24541 434-799-6410
Randall Stokes, prin. Fax 799-5251
Westwood MS 600/6-8
500 Apollo Ave 24540 434-797-8860
Joseph Baez, prin. Fax 797-8874
Adult & Continuing Education Center Adult
141 Goode St 24541 434-799-6471
Jackie Rochford, coord. Fax 797-8869

American National University Post-Sec.
336 Old Riverside Dr 24541 434-793-6822
Averett University Post-Sec.
420 W Main St 24541 434-791-5600
Danville Community College Post-Sec.
1008 S Main St 24541 434-797-2222
Danville Regional Medical Center Post-Sec.
142 S Main St 24541 434-799-4510
Westover Christian Academy 400/PK-12
5665 Riverside Dr 24541 434-822-0800
Dr. Terry Moffitt, admin. Fax 822-0441

Dayton, Rockingham, Pop. 1,520
Rockingham County SD
Supt. — See Harrisonburg
Dayton Learning Center Alt
PO Box 10 22821 540-879-2831
Emily Holloway, prin. Fax 879-2578
Pence MS 800/6-8
375 Bowman Rd 22821 540-879-2535
Camala Kite, prin. Fax 879-2179

Dendron, Surry, Pop. 267
Surry County SD
Supt. — See Surry
Jackson MS 300/5-8
4255 New Design Rd 23839 757-267-2810
Trina Craddox, prin. Fax 267-0809

Surry County HS 300/9-12
1675 Hollybush Rd 23839 757-267-2211
Giron Wooden, prin. Fax 267-2978

Dinwiddie, Dinwiddie
Dinwiddie County SD 4,400/K-12
PO Box 7 23841 804-469-4190
William Clark, supt. Fax 469-4197
www.dinwiddie.k12.va.us
Dinwiddie County HS 1,400/9-12
PO Box 299 23841 804-469-4280
Randall Johnson, prin. Fax 469-4293
Dinwiddie County MS 1,000/6-8
PO Box 340 23841 804-469-5430
Jason Chandler, prin. Fax 469-3389

Disputanta, Prince George
Prince George County SD
Supt. — See Prince George
Prince George Education Center Alt
11455 Prince George Dr 23842 804-733-2748
Mattie Thweatt, prin. Fax 733-2749

Dry Fork, Pittsylvania
Pittsylvania County SD
Supt. — See Chatham
Tunstall HS 900/9-12
100 Trojan Cir 24549 434-724-7111
Brian Boles, prin. Fax 724-4588
Tunstall MS 700/6-8
1160 Tunstall High Rd 24549 434-724-7086
Deborah Stowe, prin. Fax 724-7907

Dublin, Pulaski, Pop. 2,500
Pulaski County SD
Supt. — See Pulaski
Dublin MS 600/6-8
650 Giles Ave 24084 540-643-0367
Adam Joyce, prin. Fax 674-0813
Pulaski County HS 1,400/9-12
5414 Cougar Trail Rd 24084 540-643-0747
Michael Grim, prin. Fax 674-4722

New River Community College Post-Sec.
PO Box 1127 24084 540-674-3600

Duffield, Scott, Pop. 90
Scott County SD
Supt. — See Gate City
Rye Cove HS 300/8-12
164 Eagles Nest Ln 24244 276-940-2701
Dr. Travis Nickels, prin. Fax 940-2277

Dumfries, Prince William, Pop. 4,762
Prince William County SD
Supt. — See Manassas
Potomac HS 1,700/9-12
3401 Panther Pride Dr 22026 703-441-4200
Michael Wright, prin. Fax 441-4497
Potomac MS 1,200/6-8
3130 Panther Pride Dr 22026 703-221-4996
Kevin Smith, prin. Fax 221-4998

St. John Paul the Great HS 500/9-12
17700 Dominican Dr 22026 703-445-0300
Sr. Mary Keller, prin. Fax 445-0301

Eastville, Northampton, Pop. 300
Northampton County SD
Supt. — See Machipongo
Northampton HS 400/9-12
PO Box 38 23347 757-678-5151
Michael Myers, prin. Fax 678-5244
Northampton MS 300/7-8
PO Box 38 23347 757-678-5151
Laurel Crenshaw, prin. Fax 678-5244

Elkton, Rockingham, Pop. 2,698
Rockingham County SD
Supt. — See Harrisonburg
East Rockingham HS 700/9-12
250 Eagle Rock Rd 22827 540-298-7450
Eric Baylor, prin. Fax 298-7462
Elkton MS 500/6-8
21063 Blue and Gold Dr 22827 540-298-1228
Dr. Ramona Pence, prin. Fax 298-0029

Elliston, Montgomery, Pop. 900
Montgomery County SD
Supt. — See Christiansburg
Eastern Montgomery HS 300/9-12
4695 Crozier Rd 24087 540-268-3010
Daniel Knott, prin. Fax 268-3012

Emory, Washington, Pop. 1,238

Emory & Henry College Post-Sec.
PO Box 947 24327 276-944-4121

Emporia, Emporia, Pop. 5,846
Greensville County SD 2,600/PK-12
105 Ruffin St 23847 434-634-3748
Dr. Angela Wilson, supt. Fax 634-3495
www.gcps1.com
Greensville County HS 700/9-12
403 Harding St 23847 434-634-2195
Michelle Burton, prin.
Wyatt MS 600/6-8
206 Slagles Lake Rd 23847 434-634-5159
Medicus Riddick, prin. Fax 634-0442

Ewing, Lee, Pop. 438
Lee County SD
Supt. — See Jonesville
Walker HS 300/8-12
126 Blue Gray Rd 24248 276-445-4111
Ron Earley, prin. Fax 445-3046

Exmore, Northampton, Pop. 1,433

Broadwater Academy 300/PK-12
PO Box 546 23350 757-442-9041

Fairfax, Fairfax, Pop. 21,900
Fairfax County SD
Supt. — See Falls Church
Fairfax HS 2,700/9-12
3501 Rebel Run 22030 703-219-2200
David Goldfarb, prin. Fax 219-2297
Frost MS 1,100/7-8
4101 Pickett Rd 22032 703-426-5700
Eric McCann, prin. Fax 426-5797
Lanier MS 1,200/7-8
3801 Jermantown Rd 22030 703-934-2400
Erin Lenart, prin. Fax 934-2497
Robinson JSHS 4,000/7-12
5035 Sideburn Rd 22032 703-426-2100
Matthew Eline, prin. Fax 426-2197
Woodson HS 2,200/9-12
9525 Main St 22031 703-503-4600
Scott Poole, prin. Fax 503-4697
Fairfax County Adult HS Adult
4105 Whitacre Rd 22032 703-503-6407
Brad Rickel, prin.

Columbia College Post-Sec.
8300 Merrifield Ave 22031 703-206-0508
George Mason University Post-Sec.
4400 University Dr 22030 703-993-1000
New S of Northern Virginia 100/4-12
9431 Silver King Ct 22031 703-691-3040
John Potter M.S., hdmstr. Fax 691-3041
Paul VI HS 900/9-12
10675 Fairfax Blvd 22030 703-352-0925
Ginny Colwell, head sch Fax 273-9845
Trinity Christian S 700/K-12
11204 Braddock Rd 22030 703-273-8787
Dr. David Vanderpoel, hdmstr. Fax 501-6744
Virginia International University Post-Sec.
11200 Waples Mill Rd # 360 22030 703-591-7042

Falls Church, Falls Church, Pop. 11,898
Fairfax County SD 181,400/PK-12
8115 Gatehouse Rd 22042 703-423-1000
Dr. Karen Garza, supt. Fax 423-1007
www.fcps.edu
Falls Church HS 1,700/9-12
7521 Jaguar Trl 22042 703-207-4000
Michael Yohe, prin. Fax 207-4097
Jackson MS 1,300/7-8
3020 Gallows Rd 22042 703-204-8100
Chad Lehman, prin. Fax 204-8197
Longfellow MS 1,300/7-8
2000 Westmoreland St 22043 703-533-2600
Carole Kihm, prin. Fax 533-2697
Marshall HS 1,800/9-12
7731 Leesburg Pike 22043 703-714-5400
Jeffrey Litz, prin. Fax 714-5497
Stuart HS 1,900/9-12
3301 Peace Valley Ln 22044 703-824-3900
Penny Gros, prin. Fax 824-3997
Fairfax County Adult HS Adult
7510 Lisle Ave 22043 703-506-2251
Robert Landon, admin.
Other Schools – See Alexandria, Annandale, Burke, Centreville, Chantilly, Clifton, Fairfax, Herndon, Lorton, Mc Lean, Reston, Springfield, Vienna

Falls Church CSD 2,400/K-12
800 W Broad St Ste 203 22046 703-248-5600
Dr. Toni Jones, supt. Fax 248-5613
www.fccps.org/
Henderson MS 500/6-8
7130 Leesburg Pike 22043 703-720-5700
Ty Harris, prin. Fax 720-5710
Mason HS 800/9-12
7124 Leesburg Pike 22043 703-248-5500
Matt Hills, prin. Fax 248-5533

California University of Management/Sci Post-Sec.
400 N Washington St 22046 703-663-8088
Child Development Ctr. of Northern VA Post-Sec.
111 N Cherry St 22046
Fairfax Hospital Post-Sec.
3300 Gallows Rd 22042 703-698-3371
J Leland Center for Theological Studies Post-Sec.
1306 N Highland St 22201 703-812-4757
MedTech College Post-Sec.
6565 Arlington Blvd Ste 100 22042 703-237-6200
Standard Healthcare Services Coll of Nrg Post-Sec.
1073 W Broad St Ste 201 22046 703-891-1787
Stratford University Post-Sec.
7777 Leesburg Pike Ste 100S 22043 703-821-8570
Trinity S at Meadow View 200/7-12
2849 Meadow View Rd 22042 703-876-1920

Falmouth, Stafford, Pop. 4,116
Stafford County SD
Supt. — See Stafford
Drew MS 500/6-8
501 Cambridge St 22405 540-371-1415
Tammara Hanna, prin. Fax 371-1447

Farmville, Prince Edward, Pop. 8,093
Prince Edward County SD 2,200/K-12
35 Eagle Dr 23901 434-315-2100
Dr. K. David Smith, supt. Fax 392-1911
www.pecps.k12.va.us
Prince Edward County Career & Tech Ed Vo/Tech
35 Eagle Dr 23901 434-315-2140
Dr. Brad Bryant, prin. Fax 392-9018
Prince Edward County HS 700/9-12
35 Eagle Dr 23901 434-315-2130
Zoltan Kerestely, prin. Fax 392-1901
Prince Edward MS 700/5-8
35 Eagle Dr 23901 434-315-2120
Tammy Hurt, prin. Fax 392-4286

Fuqua S, PO Box 328 23901 400/PK-12
John Melton, head sch 434-392-4131
Longwood University Post-Sec.
201 High St 23909 434-395-2000

New Life Christian Academy 100/PK-12
9 Mahan Rd 23901 434-392-6236

Ferrum, Franklin, Pop. 1,932

Ferrum College Post-Sec.
PO Box 1000 24088 540-365-2121

Fincastle, Botetourt, Pop. 352
Botetourt County SD 5,400/PK-12
143 Poor Farm Rd 24090 540-473-8263
John S. Busher, supt. Fax 473-8298
www.bcps.k12.va.us
Botetourt Technical Education Center Vo/Tech
253 Poor Farm Rd 24090 540-473-8216
James Bradshaw, prin. Fax 473-8376
Central Academy MS 500/6-8
367 Poor Farm Rd 24090 540-473-8333
Tim McClung, prin. Fax 473-8398
Other Schools – See Buchanan, Cloverdale, Daleville

Fishersville, Augusta, Pop. 7,346
Augusta County SD
Supt. — See Verona
Wilson Memorial HS 800/9-12
189 Hornet Rd 22939 540-886-4286
Dr. Kelly Troxell, prin. Fax 886-4611
Wilson MS 600/6-8
232 Hornet Rd 22939 540-245-5185
Donald Curtis, prin. Fax 245-5189

Jointly Operated Vo Tech SD
Supt. — None – Lolita Hall, dir.
Valley Vocational Tech Center Vo/Tech
49 Hornet Rd 22939 540-245-5002
Laura Tait, prin. Fax 885-0407

Regional Academic Governors SD
Supt. — See Richmond
Shenandoah Valley Governor's S 11-12
49 Hornet Rd 22939 540-245-5088
Lee Ann Whitesell, dir. Fax 886-6476

Augusta Health Post-Sec.
PO Box 1000 22939 540-332-4539

Flint Hill, Rappahannock, Pop. 207

Wakefield Country Day S 200/PK-12
PO Box 739 22627 540-635-8555

Floyd, Floyd, Pop. 419
Floyd County SD 2,100/PK-12
140 Harris Hart Rd NE 24091 540-745-9400
Dr. Kevin W. Harris Ed.D., supt. Fax 745-9496
www.floyd.k12.va.us
Floyd County HS 800/8-12
721 Baker St SE 24091 540-745-9450
Scott Watson, prin. Fax 745-9481

Forest, Bedford, Pop. 9,010
Bedford County SD
Supt. — See Bedford
Forest MS 1,000/6-8
100 Ashwood Dr 24551 434-525-6630
Scott Simmons, prin. Fax 525-1284
Jefferson Forest HS 1,400/9-12
1 Cavalier Cir 24551 434-525-2674
Dr. LeeAnn Calvert, prin. Fax 525-0106

Timberlake Christian S 400/PK-12
202 Horizon Dr 24551 434-237-5943
Jeff Abbett, admin. Fax 239-3319

Fork Union, Fluvanna

Fork Union Military Academy 400/6-12
PO Box 278 23055 434-842-3212
J. Scott Burhoe, pres. Fax 842-4300

Fort Defiance, Augusta
Augusta County SD
Supt. — See Verona
Fort Defiance HS 800/9-12
195 Fort Defiance Rd 24437 540-245-5050
Larry Landes, prin. Fax 245-5054
Stewart MS 600/6-8
118 Fort Defiance Rd 24437 540-245-5046
Brenda Walton, prin. Fax 245-5049

Franklin, Southampton, Pop. 8,431
Franklin CSD 1,300/PK-12
207 W 2nd Ave 23851 757-569-8111
Dr. Willie J. Bell, supt. Fax 516-1015
www.franklincity.k12.va.us
Franklin HS 300/9-12
310 Crescent Dr 23851 757-562-5187
Ronnie Watson, prin. Fax 562-3656
King MS 300/6-8
501 Charles St 23851 757-562-4631
Lisa B. Francis, prin. Fax 562-0231

Paul D. Camp Community College Post-Sec.
100 N College Dr 23851 757-569-6700

Fredericksburg, Fredericksburg, Pop. 23,462
Fredericksburg CSD 3,500/PK-12
817 Princess Anne St 22401 540-372-1130
Dr. David Melton, supt. Fax 372-1111
www.cityschools.com
Monroe HS 900/9-12
2300 Washington Ave 22401 540-372-1100
Dr. Taneshia Rachal, prin. Fax 373-8643
Walker-Grant MS 700/6-8
1 Learning Ln 22401 540-372-1145
Melanie Kay-Wyatt, prin. Fax 891-5449

Regional Academic Governors SD
Supt. — See Richmond
Commonwealth Governor's HS 9-12
12301 Spotswood Furnace Rd 22407 540-548-1278
Merri Kae Vanderploeg, dir. Fax 548-1736

Spotsylvania County SD 23,500/PK-12
8020 River Stone Dr 22407 540-834-2500
Scott Baker Ed.D., supt. Fax 834-2550
www.spotsylvania.k12.va.us
Battlefield MS 800/6-8
11120 Leavells Rd 22407 540-786-4400
Sheila Smith, prin. Fax 786-7109
Chancellor HS 1,300/9-12
6300 Harrison Rd 22407 540-786-2606
Jacqueline Bass-Fortune, prin. Fax 786-1176
Chancellor MS 900/6-8
6320 Harrison Rd 22407 540-786-8099
Cynthia Franzen, prin. Fax 785-9392
Freedom MS 900/6-8
7315 Smith Station Rd 22407 540-548-1030
Alan Jacobs, prin. Fax 786-0782
Massaponax HS 1,800/9-12
8201 Jefferson Davis Hwy 22407 540-710-0419
Dr. Joe Pisani, prin. Fax 710-1596
Riverbend HS 1,900/9-12
12301 Spotswood Furnace Rd 22407 540-548-4051
Dr. Troy Wright, prin. Fax 548-2964
Other Schools – See Spotsylvania

Stafford County SD
Supt. — See Stafford
Dixon-Smith MS 800/6-8
503 Deacon Rd 22405 540-899-0860
Lisa Besceglia, prin. Fax 899-0881
Gayle MS 900/6-8
100 Panther Dr 22406 540-373-0383
Robin Lloyd, prin. Fax 373-8856
Stafford HS 1,900/9-12
63 Stafford Indians Ln 22405 540-371-7200
Joe Lewis, prin. Fax 371-2389

Career Training Solutions Post-Sec.
10304 Spotsylvania Ave #400 22408 540-373-2200
Faith Baptist S 300/PK-12
4105 Plank Rd 22407 540-786-4953
Curtis Tomlin, admin. Fax 786-3380
Fredericksburg Academy 400/PK-12
10800 Academy Dr 22408 540-898-0020
Karen Moschetto, head sch Fax 898-0440
Fredericksburg Christian Upper S 500/6-12
9400 Thornton Rolling Rd 22408 540-371-3852
Richard Yost, supt. Fax 371-4121
Mary Washington Hospital Post-Sec.
1001 Sam Perry Blvd 22401 540-899-1565
St. Michael the Archangel HS 9-12
6301 Campus Dr 22407 540-548-8748
Isaac Kassock, prin. Fax 548-8864
University of Mary Washington Post-Sec.
1301 College Ave 22401 540-654-1000
Virginia Baptist College Post-Sec.
4105 Plank Rd 22407 540-785-5440

Front Royal, Warren, Pop. 14,067
Warren County SD 5,400/K-12
210 N Commerce Ave 22630 540-635-2171
L. Gregory Drescher, supt. Fax 636-4195
www.wcps.k12.va.us
Skyline HS 1,100/8-12
151 Skyline Vista Dr 22630 540-631-0366
Michael Smith, prin. Fax 635-4026
Warren County HS 1,000/8-12
155 Westminster Dr 22630 540-635-4144
Ernestine Jordan, prin. Fax 636-3244

Christendom College Post-Sec.
134 Christendom Dr 22630 540-636-2900
Front Royal Christian S 100/PK-12
80 N Lake Ave 22630 540-635-6799
Fax 635-6152
Randolph-Macon Academy 400/6-12
200 Academy Dr 22630 540-636-5200
David Wesley, pres. Fax 636-5344

Gainesville, Prince William, Pop. 11,049
Prince William County SD
Supt. — See Manassas
Bull Run MS 1,100/6-8
6308 Catharpin Rd 20155 703-753-9969
Matthew Phythian, prin. Fax 753-9610
Gainesville MS 1,300/6-8
8001 Limestone Dr 20155 703-753-2997
Catherine Porter-Lucas, prin. Fax 753-4331

Galax, Galax, Pop. 6,941
Galax CSD 1,300/K-12
223 Long St 24333 276-236-2911
Bill Sturgill, supt. Fax 236-5776
www.gcps.k12.va.us/
Galax JSHS 500/8-12
200 Maroon Tide Dr 24333 276-236-2991
Justin Iroler, prin. Fax 236-8011

Gate City, Scott, Pop. 2,016
Scott County SD 3,800/PK-12
340 East Jackson St 24251 276-386-6118
John Ferguson, supt. Fax 386-2684
scott.k12.va.us
Gate City HS 500/10-12
178 Harry Fry Dr 24251 276-386-7522
Michael Lane, prin. Fax 386-2695
Gate City MS 600/7-9
170 Harry Fry Dr 24251 276-386-6065
Reagan Mullins, prin. Fax 386-2556
Scott County Career & Technical Center Vo/Tech
150 Broadwater Ave 24251 276-386-6515
Ralph Quesinberry, prin. Fax 386-2852
Other Schools – See Duffield, Nickelsville

Glade Spring, Washington, Pop. 1,443
Washington County SD
Supt. — See Abingdon
Glade Spring MS 300/6-8
33474 Stagecoach Rd 24340 276-739-3800
Kelly Holmes, prin. Fax 429-4211
Henry HS 400/9-12
31437 Hillman Hwy 24340 276-739-3700
Andrew Hockett, prin. Fax 944-2125

Glen Allen, Henrico, Pop. 14,427
Henrico County SD
Supt. — See Richmond
Academy at Virginia Randolph 300/Alt
2204 Mountain Rd 23060 804-261-5085
Jesse Casey, prin. Fax 261-5087
Center for Education & Human Development 9-12
10700 Staples Mill Rd 23060 804-501-3300
Ryan Conway, prin.
Center for Information Technology 9-12
4801 Twin Hickory Rd 23059 804-364-8000
Lynne Norris, prin.
Deep Run HS 1,600/9-12
4801 Twin Hickory Rd 23059 804-364-8000
Leonard Pritchard, prin. Fax 364-0887
Glen Allen HS 1,700/9-12
10700 Staples Mill Rd 23060 804-501-3300
Dr. Gwen Miller, prin. Fax 501-3309
Holman MS 900/6-8
600 Concourse Blvd 23059 804-346-1300
Brian Fellows Ph.D., prin. Fax 346-1309
Hungary Creek MS 1,000/6-8
4909 Francistown Rd 23060 804-527-2640
Robert Moose, prin. Fax 527-2642
Short Pump MS 800/6-8
4701 Pouncey Tract Rd 23059 804-360-0800
Thomas McAuley, prin. Fax 360-0808

ECPI University Post-Sec.
4305 Cox Rd 23060 804-934-0100
Stratford University Post-Sec.
11104 W Broad St 23060 804-290-4231

Glenns, Middlesex

Rappahannock Community College Post-Sec.
12745 College Dr 23149 804-758-6700

Gloucester, Gloucester
Gloucester County SD 5,600/PK-12
6099 T C Walker Rd 23061 804-693-5300
Dr. Walter Clemons, supt. Fax 693-6275
gets.gc.k12.va.us
Gloucester HS 1,800/9-12
6680 Short Ln 23061 804-693-2526
Nate Collins, prin. Fax 693-7685
Page MS 500/6-8
5198 T C Walker Rd 23061 804-693-2540
Patricia McMahon, prin. Fax 693-2111
Peasley MS 800/6-8
2885 Hickory Fork Rd 23061 804-693-1499
Craig Reed, prin. Fax 693-1497

Gloucester Point, Gloucester, Pop. 9,193

College of William and Mary Post-Sec.
PO Box 1346 23062 804-684-7000

Goochland, Goochland, Pop. 840
Goochland County SD 2,400/PK-12
PO Box 169 23063 804-556-5630
Jeremy Raley, supt. Fax 556-3847
goochlandschools.org
Goochland HS 800/9-12
3250A River Rd W 23063 804-556-5322
Chris Collier, prin. Fax 556-6485
Goochland MS 600/6-8
3250B River Rd W 23063 804-556-5320
Jennifer Rucker, prin. Fax 556-6223

Great Falls, Fairfax, Pop. 14,902

AVI Career Training Post-Sec.
10130 Colvin Run Rd Ste A 22066 703-759-2200

Gretna, Pittsylvania, Pop. 1,254
Pittsylvania County SD
Supt. — See Chatham
Gretna HS 600/9-12
100 Gretna Hawk Cir 24557 434-656-2246
Stacey Oakes, prin. Fax 656-3045
Gretna MS 500/6-8
201 Coffey St 24557 434-656-2217
Vera Glass, prin. Fax 656-6122

Grundy, Buchanan, Pop. 1,011
Buchanan County SD 3,100/PK-12
1176 Booth Branch Rd 24614 276-935-4551
Tommy Justus, supt. Fax 935-7150
www.buc.k12.va.us
Buchanan County Tech & Career Center Vo/Tech
1124 Almarine Dr 24614 276-935-4541
Sue Cook, prin. Fax 935-4682
Grundy HS 500/9-12
1300 Golden Wave Dr 24614 276-935-2106
Leslie Horne, prin. Fax 935-8602
Other Schools – See Honaker, Hurley, Pilgrims Knob

Appalachian School of Law Post-Sec.
PO Box 2825 24614 800-895-7411

Halifax, Halifax, Pop. 1,298
Halifax County SD 5,500/PK-12
PO Box 1849 24558 434-476-2171
Dr. Merle Herndon, supt. Fax 476-1858
www.halifax.k12.va.us
Halifax County Career Center Vo/Tech
PO Box 1849 24558 434-476-5515
Faye Bruce, admin. Fax 476-5527
Other Schools – See South Boston

Hamilton, Loudoun, Pop. 498
Loudoun County SD
Supt. — See Ashburn
Harmony MS 1,100/6-8
38174 W Colonial Hwy 20158 540-751-2500
Eric Stewart, prin. Fax 751-2501

The Catholic Distance University Post-Sec.
120 E Colonial Hwy 20158 888-254-4238

Hampden Sydney, Prince Edward, Pop. 1,436

Hampden-Sydney College Post-Sec.
1 College Rd 23943 434-223-6000

Hampton, Hampton, Pop. 132,850
Hampton CSD 21,100/PK-12
1 Franklin St 23669 757-727-2000
Dr. Jeffrey Smith, supt. Fax 727-2002
www.hampton.k12.va.us
Architecture & Applied Arts Academy 9-12
522 Woodland Rd 23669 757-850-5000
Jeffrey Mordica, prin.
Bethel HS 1,800/9-12
1067 Big Bethel Rd 23666 757-825-4400
Ralph Saunders, prin. Fax 825-4465
Campus at Lee Alt
1646 Briarfield Rd 23669 757-727-1327
Myra Chambers, dir. Fax 268-3304
Davis MS 700/6-8
1435 Todds Ln 23666 757-825-4520
Violet Whiteman, prin. Fax 825-4533
Eaton MS 700/6-8
2108 Cunningham Dr 23666 757-825-4540
Sharon Slater, prin. Fax 825-4551
Governors Health Science Academy Vo/Tech
1067 Big Bethel Rd 23666 757-825-4400
Ralph Saunders, prin.
Hampton HS 1,600/9-12
1491 W Queen St 23669 757-825-4430
Tiffany Hardy, prin. Fax 825-4711
Jones Magnet MS 600/6-8
1819 Nickerson Blvd 23663 757-850-7900
Dr. Daniel Bowling, prin. Fax 850-5395
Kecoughtan HS 1,700/9-12
522 Woodland Rd 23669 757-850-5000
Jeffrey Mordica, prin. Fax 850-5153
Lindsay MS 700/6-8
1636 Briarfield Rd 23661 757-825-4560
Chevese Thomas, prin. Fax 825-4839
Phoebus HS 1,100/9-12
100 Ireland St 23663 757-727-1000
Mark Hudson, prin. Fax 727-0981
Spratley Gifted Center 600/3-8
339 Woodland Rd 23669 757-850-5032
Dr. Kenneth Crum, prin. Fax 850-5186
Syms MS 1,000/6-8
170 Fox Hill Rd 23669 757-850-5050
Michael Blount, prin. Fax 850-5413

Jointly Operated Vo Tech SD
Supt. — None - Lolita Hall, dir.
New Horizons Career & Tech-Butler Farm Vo/Tech
520 Butler Farm Rd 23666 757-766-1100
Dewey Ray, prin. Fax 766-3591

Newport News CSD
Supt. — See Newport News
New Horizons Alt
520 Butler Farm Rd 23666 757-766-1100
David Creamer, prin. Fax 766-3591

Regional Academic Governors SD
Supt. — See Richmond
New Horizons Governor's S Science/Tech. 11-12
520 Butler Farm Rd 23666 757-766-1100
Vikki Wismer, dir. Fax 224-5421

Bethel College Post-Sec.
1705 Todds Ln 23666 757-826-1883
Bryant & Stratton College Post-Sec.
4410 Claiborne Sq E Ste 233 23666 757-896-6001
Faith Outreach Education Center 100/PK-12
3105 W Mercury Blvd 23666 757-838-8949
Rev. Bobby Hartman, admin. Fax 838-4434
Hampton Christian Academy 200/PK-12
2419 N Armistead Ave 23666 757-838-7538
Meredith Cowley, head sch Fax 827-8067
Hampton University 23669 Post-Sec.
757-727-5000
Riverside Academy Post-Sec.
2244 Executive Dr 23666 757-315-3683
Thomas Nelson Community College Post-Sec.
99 Thomas Nelson Dr 23666 757-825-2700
Virginia School of Hair Design Post-Sec.
101 W Queens Way 23669 757-722-0211

Harrisonburg, Harrisonburg, Pop. 47,739
Harrisonburg CSD 5,200/K-12
1 Court Sq 22802 540-434-9916
Scott Kizner, supt. Fax 434-5196
www.harrisonburg.k12.va.us
Harrisonburg HS 1,400/9-12
1001 Garbers Church Rd 22801 540-433-2651
Cynthia Prieto, prin. Fax 433-3595
Harrison MS 800/5-8
1311 W Market St 22801 540-434-1949
Don Vale, prin. Fax 434-4052
Skyline MS 700/5-8
470 Linda Ln 22802 540-434-6862
Daniel Kirwan, prin. Fax 434-6453

Jointly Operated Vo Tech SD
Supt. — None - Lolita Hall, dir.
Massanutten Tech Center Vo/Tech
325 Pleasant Valley Rd 22801 540-434-5961
Marshall Price, dir. Fax 434-1402

Rockingham County SD 11,900/PK-12
100 Mount Clinton Pike 22802 540-564-3200
Dr. Carol Fenn, supt. Fax 564-3241
www.rockingham.k12.va.us/
Other Schools – See Bridgewater, Broadway, Dayton, Elkton, Penn Laird

---

American National University Post-Sec.
1515 Country Club Rd 22802 540-432-0943
Eastern Mennonite S 400/K-12
801 Parkwood Dr 22802 540-236-6000
Dr. Paul Leaman, head sch Fax 236-6028
Eastern Mennonite University Post-Sec.
1200 Park Rd 22802 540-432-4000
James Madison University Post-Sec.
800 S Main St 22807 540-568-6211
Rockingham Memorial Hospital Post-Sec.
235 Cantrell Ave 22801 540-564-5407

Haymarket, Prince William, Pop. 1,713
Prince William County SD
Supt. — See Manassas
Battlefield HS 2,500/9-12
15000 Graduation Dr 20169 571-261-4400
Amy Ethridge-Conti, prin. Fax 261-4411
Reagan MS 1,300/6-8
15801 Tanning House Pl 20169 571-402-3500
Alfie Turner, prin. Fax 782-1638

Heathsville, Northumberland, Pop. 142
Northumberland County SD
Supt. — See Lottsburg
Northumberland HS 400/9-12
201 Academic Ln 22473 804-580-5192
Dr. Travis Burns, prin.
Northumberland MS 300/6-8
175 Academic Ln 22473 804-580-5753
Michael Ransome, prin.

Herndon, Fairfax, Pop. 22,605
Fairfax County SD
Supt. — See Falls Church
Carson MS 1,300/7-8
13618 McLearen Rd 20171 703-925-3600
Gordon Stokes, prin. Fax 925-3697
Herndon HS 2,200/9-12
700 Bennett St 20170 703-810-2200
William Bates, prin. Fax 810-2262
Herndon MS 1,000/7-8
901 Locust St 20170 703-904-4800
Justine Klena, prin. Fax 904-4897

Oak Hill Christian S 100/PK-12
13525 Dulles Technology Dr 20171 703-796-6887
Temple Baptist S 200/PK-12
1545 Dranesville Rd 20170 703-437-7400
Dr. Samuel Dalton, admin. Fax 437-7430

Highland Springs, Henrico, Pop. 15,359
Henrico County SD
Supt. — See Richmond
Advance College Academy 9-12
15 S Oak Ave 23075 804-328-4000
Allen Riddle, prin.
Center for Engineering 9-12
15 S Oak Ave 23075 804-328-4000
Billy Batkins, prin.
Highland Springs HS 1,700/9-12
15 S Oak Ave 23075 804-328-4000
Pamela Bell, prin. Fax 328-4013
Highland Springs Technical Center Vo/Tech
100 Tech Dr 23075 804-328-4075
William Crowder, prin. Fax 328-4074
Highland Springs Adult Ed Center Adult
201 E Nine Mile Rd 23075 804-328-4095
Gregory Lawson, prin.

Hillsville, Carroll, Pop. 2,663
Carroll County SD 4,000/PK-12
605 Pine St Ste 9 24343 276-728-3191
Dr. Strader Blankenship, supt. Fax 728-3195
www.ccpsd.k12.va.us
Blue Ridge Crossroads Governor's Academy Vo/Tech
100 Cavs Ln 24343 276-728-2125
Roland Hall, coord.
Carroll County HS 1,200/9-12
100 Cavs Ln 24343 276-728-2125
Charles Thompson, prin. Fax 728-9067
Carroll County MS 900/6-8
1036 N Main St 24343 276-728-2382
Marc Quesenberry, prin. Fax 728-4089
Regional Alternative Education Center Alt
205 Oak St 24343 276-728-9055
Jessee Woods, prin.

Honaker, Russell, Pop. 1,440
Buchanan County SD
Supt. — See Grundy
Council HS 100/8-12
7802 Helen Henderson Hwy 24260 276-859-2627
Chris Hagerman, prin. Fax 859-6227

Russell County SD
Supt. — See Lebanon
Honaker HS 500/8-12
PO Box 764 24260 276-873-6363
Tony Bush, prin. Fax 873-7252

Hopewell, Hopewell, Pop. 21,953
Hopewell CSD 4,300/PK-12
103 N 12th Ave 23860 804-541-6400
Dr. Melody Hackney, supt. Fax 541-6401
www.hopewell.k12.va.us
Hopewell HS 1,100/9-12
400 S Mesa Dr 23860 804-541-6402
Thomas M. Pond, prin. Fax 541-6403
Woodson MS 900/6-8
1000 Winston Churchill Dr 23860 804-541-6404
Shannon Royster, prin. Fax 541-6405

West End Christian S 200/PK-12
1600 Atlantic St 23860 804-458-6142
Amy Griggs, prin. Fax 458-7183

Hot Springs, Bath, Pop. 727
Bath County SD
Supt. — See Warm Springs
Bath County HS 300/8-12
464 Charger Ln 24445 540-839-2431
Sarah Rowe, prin. Fax 839-3290

Hurley, Buchanan
Buchanan County SD
Supt. — See Grundy
Hurley HS 200/8-12
6339 Hurley Rd 24620 276-566-7642
Pam Dotson, prin. Fax 566-7127

Hurt, Pittsylvania, Pop. 1,295

Faith Christian Academy 200/PK-12
PO Box 670 24563 434-324-8276
Bruce Devers, admin. Fax 324-8279

Independence, Grayson, Pop. 933
Grayson County SD 1,700/PK-12
PO Box 888 24348 276-773-2832
Kelly Wilmore, supt. Fax 773-2939
www.grayson.k12.va.us
Grayson County Career & Technical Center Vo/Tech
PO Box 707 24348 276-773-2951
Angie Lawson, prin. Fax 773-2396
Grayson County HS 600/9-12
PO Box 828 24348 276-773-2131
Robbie Patton, prin. Fax 773-2682
Independence MS 200/6-8
PO Box 155 24348 276-773-3020
Jamey Hale, prin. Fax 773-0479

Isle of Wight, Isle of Wight

Isle of Wight Academy 600/PK-12
PO Box 105 23397 757-357-3866

Jetersville, Nottoway
Jointly Operated Vo Tech SD
Supt. — None - Lolita Hall, dir.
Amelia-Nottoway Technical Center Vo/Tech
148 Votech Rd 23083 434-645-7854
Mary Tisdale, dir. Fax 645-1044

Nottoway County SD
Supt. — See Nottoway
Piedmont Alternative S Alt
148 Votech Rd 23083 434-645-7854
Mary Tisdale, dir. Fax 645-1044

Jonesville, Lee, Pop. 1,025
Lee County SD 3,400/PK-12
153 School Board Pl 24263 276-346-2107
Mark Carter, supt. Fax 346-0307
www.leectysch.com/
Jonesville MS 200/6-8
160 Bulldog Cir 24263 276-346-1011
Dr. Lynn Metcalfe, prin. Fax 346-1411
Lee HS 700/9-12
200 General Ln 24263 276-346-0173
Michelle Warner, prin. Fax 346-4032
Other Schools – See Ben Hur, Ewing, Pennington Gap

Kenbridge, Lunenburg, Pop. 1,244
Lunenburg County SD 1,600/PK-12
PO Box 710 23944 434-676-2467
Charles Berkley, supt. Fax 676-1000
www.lun.k12.va.us
Other Schools – See Victoria

Keysville, Charlotte, Pop. 820
Regional Academic Governors SD
Supt. — See Richmond
Governor's S of Southside VA 11-12
200 Daniel Rd 23947 434-736-2086
Karen Puckett, dir. Fax 736-2082

Southside Virginia Community College Post-Sec.
200 Daniel Rd 23947 434-736-2018

Kilmarnock, Lancaster, Pop. 1,466
Lancaster County SD
Supt. — See Weems
Lancaster MS 500/4-8
191 School St 22482 804-462-5100
Jessica Davis, prin. Fax 435-0589

King and Queen Court House, King and Queen, Pop. 84
King & Queen County SD 800/PK-12
PO Box 97 23085 804-785-5981
Dr. Carol Carter, supt. Fax 785-5686
www.kqps.net
Central HS 200/8-12
17024 The Trail 23085 804-785-6102
Antione Monroe, prin. Fax 785-5129

King George, King George, Pop. 4,296
King George County SD 4,200/K-12
PO Box 1239 22485 540-775-5833
Dr. Robert B. Benson, supt. Fax 775-2165
www.kgcs.k12.va.us
King George HS 1,300/9-12
10100 Foxes Way 22485 540-775-3535
Dr. Jesse Boyd, prin. Fax 775-8426
King George MS 600/7-8
8246 Dahlgren Rd 22485 540-775-2331
Jennifer Collins, prin. Fax 775-0263

King William, King William, Pop. 228
King William County SD 2,200/PK-12
PO Box 185 23086 804-769-3434
Dr. Mark Jones, supt. Fax 769-3312
www.kwcps.k12.va.us
Hamilton-Holmes MS 500/6-8
18444 King William Rd 23086 804-769-3434
Beverly Young, prin.
King William HS, 80 Cavalier Dr 23086 600/9-12
Dr. Stanley Waskiewicz, prin. 804-769-3434

Lancaster, Lancaster
Lancaster County SD
Supt. — See Weems
Lancaster HS 400/9-12
PO Box 790 22503 804-462-5177
Erskine Morgan, prin. Fax 462-5100

Lawrenceville, Brunswick, Pop. 1,414
Brunswick County SD 1,900/PK-12
1718 Farmers Field Rd 23868 434-848-3138
Dora Wynn M.Ed., supt. Fax 848-4001
www.brunswickcps.org
Brunswick HS 600/9-12
2171 Lawrenceville Plank Rd 23868 434-848-2716
Christopher Coleman, prin. Fax 848-6303
Russell MS 400/6-8
19400 Christanna Hwy 23868 434-848-2132
Dr. Virginia Berry, prin. Fax 848-6201

Brunswick Academy 300/PK-12
2100 Planters Rd 23868 434-848-2220

Lebanon, Russell, Pop. 3,395
Russell County SD 4,200/PK-12
PO Box 8 24266 276-889-6500
Dr. Greg Brown, supt. Fax 889-6508
www.russell.k12.va.us
Lebanon HS 600/8-12
PO Box 217 24266 276-889-6539
Joseph Long, prin. Fax 889-0622
Russell County Alternative Center Alt
PO Box 8 24266 276-889-6521
Michael Roberson, prin. Fax 889-6527
Russell County Career & Technology Ctr Vo/Tech
PO Box 849 24266 276-889-6550
Jennifer Fields, prin. Fax 889-4470
Other Schools – See Castlewood, Honaker

Leesburg, Loudoun, Pop. 41,241
Loudoun County SD
Supt. — See Ashburn
Academy of Engineering and Technology 9-12
801 N King St 20176 571-252-1970
Dr. Tinell Priddy, prin. Fax 252-1975
Belmont Ridge MS 1,500/6-8
19045 Upper Belmont Pl 20176 571-252-2220
Ryan Hitchman, prin. Fax 669-1455
Douglass S Alt
407 E Market St 20176 571-252-2060
Marianne Turner, prin. Fax 771-6555
Harper Park MS 1,000/6-8
701 Potomac Station Dr NE 20176 571-252-2820
Elizabeth Robinson, prin. Fax 779-8867
Heritage HS 1,200/9-12
520 Evergreen Mill Rd SE 20175 571-252-2800
Jeffrey Adam, prin. Fax 252-2801
Loudoun County HS 1,400/9-12
415 Dry Mill Rd SW 20175 571-252-2000
Dr. Michelle Luttrell, prin. Fax 252-2001
Monroe Technology Center Vo/Tech
715 Childrens Center Rd SW 20175 571-252-2080
Timothy Flynn, prin. Fax 771-6563
Riverside HS 9-12
19019 Upper Belmont Pl 20176 703-554-8900
Doug Anderson, prin. Fax 858-7910
Simpson MS 1,000/6-8
490 Evergreen Mill Rd SE 20175 571-252-2840
Chad Runfola, prin. Fax 771-6643
Smart's Mill MS 1,100/6-8
850 N King St 20176 571-252-2030
William Waldman, prin. Fax 669-1485
Tuscarora HS 1,900/9-12
801 N King St 20176 571-252-1900
Pamela Croft, prin. Fax 252-1901

Lexington, Lexington, Pop. 6,907
Lexington CSD 500/K-8
300 Diamond St 24450 540-463-7146
Scott Jefferies, supt. Fax 464-5230
www.lexedu.org
Lylburn-Downing MS 200/6-8
302 Diamond St 24450 540-463-3532
Steven Eckstrom, prin.

Rockbridge County SD 2,800/PK-12
2893 Collierstown Rd 24450 540-463-7386
John Reynolds, supt. Fax 463-7823
www.rockbridge.k12.va.us/
Maury River MS 500/6-8
600 Waddell St 24450 540-463-3129
Randy Walters, prin. Fax 464-4838
Rockbridge County HS 1,000/9-12
143 Greenhouse Rd 24450 540-463-5555
Haywood Hand, prin. Fax 463-6152

Rockbridge Christian Academy 100/PK-12
PO Box 570 24450 540-463-5456
Mary Phillips, admin. Fax 463-3485
Virginia Military Institute Post-Sec.
319 Letcher Ave 24450 540-464-7230
Washington and Lee University Post-Sec.
204 W Washington St 24450 540-458-8400

Locust Grove, Orange
Orange County SD
Supt. — See Orange
Locust Grove MS 600/6-8
6368 Flat Run Rd 22508 540-661-4480
Michael Jamerson, prin. Fax 854-6430

Germanna Community College Post-Sec.
2130 Germanna Hwy 22508 540-423-9030

Locust Hill, Middlesex
Middlesex County SD
Supt. — See Saluda
St. Clare Walker MS 300/6-8
PO Box 9 23092 804-758-2561
Dr. Tracy Seitz, prin. Fax 758-0834

Lorton, Fairfax, Pop. 17,779
Fairfax County SD
Supt. — See Falls Church
South County HS 2,100/9-12
8501 Silverbrook Rd 22079 703-446-1600
Matt Ragone, prin. Fax 446-1697
South County MS 1,100/7-8
8700 Laurel Crest Dr 22079 703-690-5500
Marsha Manning, prin. Fax 690-5597

Lottsburg, Northumberland
Northumberland County SD 1,400/PK-12
2172 Northumberland Hwy 22511 804-529-6134
Dr. Rebecca Gates, supt. Fax 529-6449
www.nucps.net
Other Schools – See Heathsville

Lovingston, Nelson, Pop. 495
Nelson County SD 2,000/PK-12
PO Box 276 22949 434-260-7646
Dr. Jeff Comer, supt. Fax 263-7115
www.nelson.k12.va.us
Nelson County HS 600/9-12
6919 Thomas Nelson Hwy 22949 434-263-8317
Janell Stinnett, prin. Fax 263-5987
Nelson MS 400/6-8
6925 Thomas Nelson Hwy 22949 434-263-4801
Dr. Roger Dunnick, prin. Fax 263-4483

Low Moor, Alleghany, Pop. 252
Alleghany County SD 2,400/K-12
PO Box 140 24457 540-863-1800
Eugene Kotulka, supt. Fax 863-1804
www.alleghany.k12.va.us/
Other Schools – See Covington

Luray, Page, Pop. 4,837
Page County SD 3,500/PK-12
735 W Main St 22835 540-743-6533
Donna Whitley-Smith, supt. Fax 743-7784
www.pagecounty.k12.va.us
Luray HS 500/9-12
243 Bulldog Dr 22835 540-743-3800
Clint Runyan, prin. Fax 743-5524
Luray MS 400/6-8
14 Luray Ave 22835 540-843-2660
Kelly Lawton, prin. Fax 743-1709
Page County Technical Ctr Vo/Tech
525 Middleburg Rd 22835 540-778-7282
Roger Mello, prin. Fax 778-4272
Other Schools – See Shenandoah

Lynchburg, Lynchburg, Pop. 73,910
Campbell County SD
Supt. — See Rustburg
Brookville HS 1,000/9-12
100 Laxton Rd 24502 434-239-2636
Tom Cole, prin. Fax 239-6706
Brookville MS 700/6-8
320 Bee Dr 24502 434-239-9267
Edwin Martin, prin. Fax 237-8974

Lynchburg CSD 8,600/PK-12
PO Box 2497 24505 434-515-5000
Dr. Scott S. Brabrand, supt. Fax 846-1500
www.lcsedu.net
Dunbar MS for Innovation 600/6-8
1200 Polk St 24504 434-515-5310
Kacey M. Crabbe, prin. Fax 522-3727
Fort Hill Community S Alt
1350 Liggates Rd 24502 434-515-5150
Cathy L. Viar, coord. Fax 522-2322
Glass HS 1,400/9-12
2111 Memorial Ave 24501 434-515-5370
Dr. Tracy S. Richardson, prin. Fax 522-3741
Heritage HS 1,000/9-12
3020 Wards Ferry Rd 24502 434-515-5400
Timothy T. Beatty, prin. Fax 582-1137
Linkhorne MS 600/6-8
2525 Linkhorne Dr 24503 434-515-5330
Nancy Claudio, prin. Fax 384-2810
Sandusky MS 600/6-8
805 Chinook Pl 24502 434-515-5350
Leverne L. Marshall, prin. Fax 582-1183
XLR8 STEM Academy 11-12
3506 Wards Rd 24502 434-832-7731
Susan W. Cash, dir.
Adult Learning Center Adult
1200 Polk St 24504 434-515-5160
Howard Brown, lead tchr. Fax 522-2320

Regional Academic Governors SD
Supt. — See Richmond
Central VA Governor's S Science & Tech 11-12
3020 Wards Ferry Rd 24502 434-477-5980
Dr. Steven Smith, dir. Fax 239-4140

American National University Post-Sec.
104 Candlewood Ct 24502 434-239-3500
Centra College of Nursing Post-Sec.
905 Lakeside Dr Ste A 24501 434-200-3070
Central Virginia Community College Post-Sec.
3506 Wards Rd 24502 434-832-7600
Doss Junior Academy 100/K-12
19 George St 24502 434-237-1899
Holy Cross Regional S 200/PK-12
2125 Langhorne Rd 24501 434-847-5436
Mary Sherry, prin. Fax 847-4156
Liberty Christian Academy 2,000/PK-12
100 Mountain View Rd 24502 434-832-2000
John Patterson, supt. Fax 832-2027
Liberty University Post-Sec.
1971 University Blvd 24502 434-582-2000
Lynchburg College Post-Sec.
1501 Lakeside Dr 24501 434-544-8100

Lynchburg General Hosp School of Nursing Post-Sec.
1901 Tate Springs Rd 24501 434-947-3070
Miller-Motte Technical College Post-Sec.
1011 Creekside Ln 24502 434-239-5222
New Covenant S 400/K-12
122 Fleetwood Dr 24501 434-847-8313
Randolph College Post-Sec.
2500 Rivermont Ave 24503 434-947-8000
Virginia Episcopal S 200/9-12
400 V E S RD 24503 434-385-3600
Tommy Battle, hdmstr. Fax 385-3603
Virginia University of Lynchburg Post-Sec.
2058 Garfield Ave 24501 434-528-5276

Machipongo, Northampton
Northampton County SD 1,700/PK-12
7207 Young St 23405 757-678-5151
Charles E. Lawrence, supt. Fax 678-7267
www.ncpsk12.com
TECH Center Alt
7207 Young St 23405 757-678-5151
Melinda Phillips, prin. Fax 678-7267
Other Schools – See Eastville

Mc Lean, Fairfax, Pop. 46,663
Fairfax County SD
Supt. — See Falls Church
Cooper MS 800/7-8
977 Balls Hill Rd 22101 703-442-5800
Arlene Randall, prin. Fax 442-5897
Langley HS 2,000/9-12
6520 Georgetown Pike 22101 703-287-2700
Fred Amico, prin. Fax 287-2797
Mc Lean HS 2,100/9-12
1633 Davidson Rd 22101 703-714-5700
Ellen Reilly, prin. Fax 714-5797

Madeira S 300/9-12
8328 Georgetown Pike 22102 703-556-8200
Pilar Cabeza de Vaca, head sch Fax 821-2845
Oakcrest S 200/6-12
850 Balls Hill Rd 22101 703-790-5450
Mary Ortiz Ph.D., head sch Fax 790-5380
Potomac S 1,000/K-12
1301 Potomac School Rd 22101 703-356-4100
John Kowalik, head sch Fax 883-9031
Reformed Theological Seminary Post-Sec.
1651 Old Meadow Rd Ste 300 22102 703-448-3393

Madison, Madison, Pop. 214
Madison County SD 1,900/PK-12
60 School Board Ct 22727 540-948-3780
Dr. Matthew Eberhardt, supt. Fax 948-6988
www2.madisonschools.k12.va.us
Madison County HS 600/9-12
68 Mountaineer Ln 22727 540-948-3785
Gary Wintersgill, prin. Fax 948-4425
Wetsel MS 400/6-8
186 Mountaineer Ln 22727 540-948-3783
Donald Dodson, prin. Fax 948-4809

Madison Heights, Amherst, Pop. 11,015
Amherst County SD
Supt. — See Amherst
Monelison MS 600/6-8
257 Trojan Rd 24572 434-846-1307
Regina Phillips, prin. Fax 846-5318

Temple Christian S 300/PK-12
PO Box 970 24572 434-846-0024

Manassas, Manassas, Pop. 36,735
Manassas CSD 7,100/K-12
PO Box 520 20108 571-377-6000
Dr. Catherine Magouyrk, supt. Fax 257-8801
www.mcpsva.org
Johnson Learning Center Alt
9051 Tudor Ln 20110 571-377-7250
Dr. Lukisa Barrera-Gibbs, prin. Fax 257-8844
Metz JHS 1,000/7-8
9700 Fairview Ave 20110 571-377-6800
Kimberly Buckheit, prin. Fax 257-8615
Osbourn HS 2,100/9-12
9005 Tudor Ln 20110 571-377-7000
Cathy Benner, prin. Fax 530-0937

Prince William County SD 85,100/PK-12
PO Box 389 20108 703-791-7200
Steven Walts Ed.D., supt. Fax 791-8033
www.pwcs.edu
Benton MS 1,300/6-8
7411 Hoadly Rd 20112 703-791-0727
Denise Huebner, prin. Fax 791-0977
Jackson HS 2,500/9-12
8820 Rixlew Ln 20109 703-365-2900
Richard Nichols, prin. Fax 365-6984
New Directions Alternative S Alt
8886 Rixlew Ln 20109 703-393-7261
Robert Eichorn, prin. Fax 393-3083
Osbourn Park HS 2,800/9-12
8909 Euclid Ave 20111 703-365-6500
Neil Beech, prin. Fax 365-6798
Parkside MS 1,200/6-8
8602 Mathis Ave 20110 703-361-3106
Mary Jane Boynton, prin. Fax 361-8993
Saunders MS 1,100/6-8
13557 Spriggs Rd 20112 703-670-9188
Sheila Huckestein, prin. Fax 670-3078
Stonewall MS 1,200/6-8
10100 Lomond Dr 20109 703-361-3185
John Miller, prin. Fax 368-1266
Other Schools – See Bristow, Dumfries, Gainesville, Haymarket, Manassas Park, Nokesville, Triangle, Woodbridge

Regional Academic Governors SD
Supt. — See Richmond
Governor's S @ Innovation Park 11-12
10910 University Blvd 20110 703-993-7027
Karen Dalfrey Ph.D., dir. Fax 993-7025

American Military University Post-Sec.
10110 Battleview Pkwy # 114 20109 703-330-5398
American National University Post-Sec.
9705 Liberia Ave Ste 299 20010 703-962-9657
Aviation Institute of Maintenance Post-Sec.
10640 Davidson Pl 20109 703-257-5515
ECPI University Post-Sec.
10021 Balls Ford Rd # 100 20109 703-330-5300
Seton S 400/7-12
9314 Maple St 20110 703-368-3220
Anne Carroll, dir. Fax 393-1199
Strayer University Post-Sec.
9990 Battleview Pkwy 20109 703-330-8400

Manassas Park, Manassas Park, Pop. 13,791
Manassas Park CSD 3,200/PK-12
1 Park Center Ct Ste A 20111 703-335-8850
Dr. C. Bruce McDade, supt. Fax 361-4583
www.mpark.net
Manassas Park HS 800/9-12
8200 Euclid Ave 20111 703-361-9131
Dr. Debbie Bergeron, prin. Fax 330-1218
Manassas Park MS 800/6-8
8202 Euclid Ave 20111 703-361-1510
Pam Kalso, prin. Fax 331-3538

Prince William County SD
Supt. — See Manassas
New Dominion Alternative S Alt
8220 Conner Dr 20111 703-361-9808
Michael Lint, prin. Fax 361-2864

Marion, Smyth, Pop. 5,878
Smyth County SD 4,800/PK-12
121 Bagley Cir Ste 300 24354 276-783-3791
Dr. Michael Robinson, supt. Fax 783-3291
www.scsb.org
Marion MS 500/6-8
134 Wilden St 24354 276-783-4466
Damon Mazoff, prin. Fax 783-4952
Marion SHS 700/9-12
848 Stage St 24354 276-783-4731
Mike Davidson, prin. Fax 783-4117
Smyth Career & Technology Center Vo/Tech
147 Fox Valley Rd 24354 276-646-8117
Songia Widener, prin. Fax 646-4009
Other Schools – See Chilhowie, Saltville

Martinsville, Martinsville, Pop. 13,595
Henry County SD
Supt. — See Collinsville
Laurel Park MS 800/6-8
280 Laurel Park Ave 24112 276-632-7216
Jo Ellen Hylton, prin. Fax 632-4865
Center for Community Learning Adult
340 Ridgedale Dr 24112 276-638-1668
Lynn Fitzgibbons, coord. Fax 638-3942

Martinsville CSD 2,100/PK-12
PO Box 5548 24115 276-403-5820
Pamela Heath, supt. Fax 403-5825
www.martinsville.k12.va.us
Martinsville HS 600/9-12
351 Commonwealth Blvd E 24112 276-403-5870
Angela Weinerth, prin. Fax 632-1516
Martinsville MS 500/5-8
201 Brown St 24112 276-403-5886
Cynthia Tarpley, prin. Fax 638-4140

Regional Academic Governors SD
Supt. — See Richmond
Piedmont Governor's S for Math/Sci/Tech 11-12
PO Box 984 24114 276-403-5624
Brian Pace, prin. Fax 403-5638

American National University Post-Sec.
905 Memorial Blvd N 24112 276-632-5621
Patrick Henry Community College Post-Sec.
645 Patriot Ave 24112 276-638-8777

Mathews, Mathews, Pop. 530
Mathews County SD 1,100/K-12
PO Box 369 23109 804-725-3909
Nancy Welch, supt. Fax 725-3951
www.mathews.k12.va.us
Hunter MS 300/5-8
PO Box 339 23109 804-725-2434
Laurel Byrd, prin. Fax 725-2337
Mathews HS 400/9-12
PO Box 38 23109 804-725-3702
Dr. Toni Childress, prin. Fax 725-5778

Matoaca, Chesterfield, Pop. 2,359
Chesterfield County SD
Supt. — See Chesterfield
Matoaca MS 1,100/6-8
6001 Hickory Rd 23803 804-590-3110
Dr. Gayle Hines, prin. Fax 590-9378

Max Meadows, Wythe, Pop. 559
Wythe County SD
Supt. — See Wytheville
Ft. Chiswell HS 500/9-12
1 Pioneer Trl 24360 276-637-3437
Rocky Baker, prin. Fax 637-6316
Ft. Chiswell MS 400/6-8
101 Pioneer Trl 24360 276-637-4400
Brett Booher, prin. Fax 637-4452

Mechanicsville, Hanover, Pop. 35,793
Hanover County SD
Supt. — See Ashland
Atlee HS 1,600/9-12
9414 Atlee Station Rd 23116 804-723-2100
Dr. John Wheeler, prin. Fax 723-2131
Chickahominy MS 1,200/6-8
9450 Atlee Station Rd 23116 804-723-2160
Mark Beckett, prin. Fax 723-2191
Georgetown S Alt
10000 Learning Ln 23116 804-723-3460
Brian Ford, admin. Fax 723-3470
Hanover Center for Trades and Technology Vo/Tech
10002 Learning Ln 23116 804-723-2020
Justin Roerink, prin. Fax 723-2039
Hanover HS 1,300/9-12
10307 Chamberlayne Rd 23116 804-723-3700
Kristina Reece, prin. Fax 723-3759
Jackson MS 1,100/6-8
8021 Lee Davis Rd 23111 804-723-2260
Dr. Quentin Ballard, prin. Fax 723-2261
Lee-Davis HS 1,600/9-12
7052 Mechanicsville Tpke 23111 804-723-2200
Charles Stevens, prin. Fax 723-2202
Oak Knoll MS 900/6-8
10295 Chamberlayne Rd 23116 804-365-4740
Caroline Harris, prin. Fax 365-4741

Grace Christian S 6-12
PO Box 215 23111 804-730-7300
Kathryn Bremner M.Ed., head sch Fax 559-9503

Melfa, Accomack, Pop. 396

Eastern Shore Community College Post-Sec.
29300 Lankford Hwy 23410 757-789-1789

Middleburg, Loudoun, Pop. 655

Foxcroft S 100/9-12
PO Box 5555 20118 540-687-5555
Catherine McGehee, head sch Fax 687-8061
Middleburg Academy 200/8-12
35321 Notre Dame Ln 20117 540-687-5581
Colley Bell, head sch Fax 687-3103

Middletown, Frederick, Pop. 1,237

Lord Fairfax Community College Post-Sec.
173 Skirmisher Ln 22645 540-868-7000

Midland, Fauquier, Pop. 218
Fauquier County SD
Supt. — See Warrenton
Southeastern Alternative S Alt
4484 Catlett Rd 22728 540-422-7390
Dr. Shelly Neibauer, prin. Fax 422-7409

Midlothian, Chesterfield
Chesterfield County SD
Supt. — See Chesterfield
Bailey Bridge MS 1,400/6-8
12501 Bailey Bridge Rd 23112 804-739-6200
Kume Goranson, prin. Fax 739-6211
Career and Technical Center @ Hull Vo/Tech
13900 Hull Street Rd 23112 804-639-8668
Brian Russell, prin. Fax 639-6394
Clover Hill HS 1,900/9-12
13301 Kelly Green Ln 23112 804-639-4940
Dr. Deborah Marks, prin. Fax 739-5000
Cosby HS 2,100/9-12
14300 Fox Club Pkwy 23112 804-639-8340
Dr. Brenda Mayo, prin. Fax 639-8357
James River HS 2,100/9-12
3700 James River Rd 23113 804-378-2420
Jeff Ellick, prin. Fax 379-2695
Manchester HS 1,900/9-12
12601 Bailey Bridge Rd 23112 804-739-6275
Pete Koste, prin. Fax 739-6340
Midlothian HS 1,500/9-12
401 Charter Colony Pkwy 23114 804-378-2440
Shawn Abel, prin. Fax 378-2450
Midlothian MS 1,200/6-8
13501 Midlothian Tpke 23113 804-378-2460
Dr. Patrick Stanfield, prin. Fax 378-7556
Robious MS 1,300/6-8
2701 Robious Crossing Dr 23113 804-378-2510
Dr. Patrick Held, prin. Fax 378-2519
Swift Creek MS 1,000/6-8
3700 Old Hundred Rd S 23112 804-739-6315
Dr. James Frye, prin. Fax 739-6322
Tomahawk Creek MS 1,300/6-8
1600 Learning Place Loop 23114 804-378-7120
Dr. David Ellena, prin. Fax 794-2672

Empire Beauty School Post-Sec.
10807 Hull Street Rd 23112 800-575-5983
Millwood S 200/PK-12
15100 Millwood School Ln 23112 804-639-3200
Dr. Louise Bagwell-Robinson, head sch Fax 639-6930

Milford, Caroline
Caroline County SD
Supt. — See Bowling Green
Caroline HS 1,200/9-12
19155 Rogers Clark Blvd 22514 804-633-9886
Jeff Wick, prin. Fax 633-2435
Caroline MS 1,000/6-8
13325 Devils Three Jump Rd 22514 804-633-6561
Angela Wright, prin. Fax 633-9014

Mineral, Louisa, Pop. 464
Louisa County SD 4,800/PK-12
953 Davis Hwy 23117 540-894-5115
J. Douglas Straley, supt. Fax 894-0252
www.lcps.k12.va.us
Louisa HS 1,400/9-12
757 Davis Hwy 23117 540-894-5436
Lee Downey, prin. Fax 894-0534
Louisa MS 1,100/6-8
1009 Davis Hwy 23117 540-894-5457
Todd Weidow, prin. Fax 894-5096

Moneta, Bedford
Bedford County SD
Supt. — See Bedford
Staunton River HS 1,100/9-12
1095 Golden Eagle Dr 24121 540-297-7151
Dr. Joshua Cornett, prin. Fax 297-4514
Staunton River MS 700/6-8
1293 Golden Eagle Dr 24121 540-297-4152
Dr. Karen Woodford, prin. Fax 297-4076

Monterey, Highland, Pop. 147
Highland County SD 200/PK-12
PO Box 250 24465 540-468-6300
Dr. Thomas Schott Ed.D., supt. Fax 468-6306
www.highland.k12.va.us
Highland JSHS 100/6-12
PO Box 430 24465 540-468-6320
Tim Good, prin. Fax 468-6332

Montross, Westmoreland, Pop. 382
Westmoreland County SD 1,700/PK-12
141 Opal Ln 22520 804-493-8018
Rebecca Lowry, supt. Fax 493-9323
division.wmlcps.org
Montross MS 400/6-8
8884 Menokin Rd 22520 804-493-9818
Jane Geyer, prin. Fax 493-0918
Washington & Lee HS 500/9-12
16380 Kings Hwy 22520 804-493-8015
Dashan Turner, prin. Fax 493-0243

Mount Jackson, Shenandoah, Pop. 1,975
Regional Academic Governors SD
Supt. — See Richmond
Massanutten Regional Governor's S 11-12
6375 Main St 22842 540-477-3226
Susan Fream, dir. Fax 477-3523

Shenandoah County SD
Supt. — See Woodstock
Triplett Tech Vo/Tech
6375 Main St 22842 540-477-3161
Connie Pangle, prin. Fax 477-2402

Mouth of Wilson, Grayson

Oak Hill Academy 100/8-12
2635 Oak Hill Rd 24363 276-579-2619
Dr. Michael Groves, pres. Fax 579-4722

Narrows, Giles, Pop. 2,019
Giles County SD
Supt. — See Pearisburg
Narrows HS 300/8-12
1 Green Wave Ln 24124 540-726-2384
Brian Bowles, prin. Fax 726-2775

Naruna, Campbell
Campbell County SD
Supt. — See Rustburg
Campbell JSHS 500/6-12
PO Box 7 24576 434-376-2015
Dabney Hanson, prin. Fax 376-5859

New Castle, Craig, Pop. 151
Craig County SD 700/PK-12
PO Box 245 24127 540-864-5191
Jeanette Warwick, supt. Fax 864-6885
www.craig.k12.va.us
Craig County MSHS 400/6-12
25239 Craigs Creek Rd 24127 540-864-5185
Robert Stump, prin. Fax 864-5636

New Kent, New Kent, Pop. 227
Jointly Operated Vo Tech SD
Supt. — None - Lolita Hall, dir.
Bridging Comm Reg Career & Technical Ctr Vo/Tech
7930 New Chipping Ln 23124 804-966-8575
Dr. Stephen Trexler, prin. Fax 966-8769

New Kent County SD 3,000/PK-12
PO Box 110 23124 804-966-9650
Dr. David Myers, supt. Fax 966-8556
www.newkentschools.org
New Kent County HS 900/9-12
7365 Egypt Rd 23124 804-966-9671
Chris Valdrighi, prin. Fax 966-2773
New Kent County MS 700/6-8
7501 Egypt Rd 23124 804-966-9655
Sammy Fudge, prin. Fax 966-2703

New Market, Shenandoah, Pop. 2,116

Shenandoah Valley Academy 200/9-12
234 W Lee Hwy 22844 540-740-3161
Donald Short, prin. Fax 740-3336

Newport News, Newport News, Pop. 174,010
Jointly Operated Vo Tech SD
Supt. — None - Lolita Hall, dir.
New Horizons Career & Tech-Woodside Vo/Tech
13400 Woodside Ln 23608 757-874-4444
Bruce Schaffer, prin. Fax 872-8951

Newport News CSD 29,600/PK-12
12465 Warwick Blvd 23606 757-591-4500
Dr. Ashby Kilgore, supt.
www.sbo.nn.k12.va.us
Achievable Dream MSHS 500/6-12
5720 Marshall Ave 23605 757-283-7820
Marylin Sinclair-White, prin. Fax 283-7844
Aviation Academy Vo/Tech
902B Bland Blvd 23602 757-886-2745
Dr. Aaron Smith, dir. Fax 877-5647
Crittenden MS 800/6-8
6158 Jefferson Ave 23605 757-591-4900
Felicia Barnett, prin. Fax 838-8261
Denbigh HS 1,400/9-12
259 Denbigh Blvd 23608 757-886-7700
Dr. Eleanor Blowe, prin. Fax 872-6542
Dozier MS 1,100/6-8
432 Industrial Park Dr 23608 757-888-3300
Lisa Gatz, prin. Fax 887-3662
Enterprise Academy Alt
813 Diligence Dr Ste 110 23606 757-591-4971
Dr. Darwin Mills, prin. Fax 873-3507
Gildersleeve MS 1,100/6-8
1 Minton Dr 23606 757-591-4862
Courtney Mompoint, prin. Fax 596-2059
Governors STEM Academy 9-12
5800 Marshall Ave 23605 757-928-6100
Heritage HS 1,300/9-12
5800 Marshall Ave 23605 757-928-6100
Shameka Gerald, prin. Fax 247-9058
Hines MS 900/6-8
561 McLawhorne Dr 23601 757-591-4878
Dr. Amanda Corbin-Staton, prin. Fax 591-0119
Huntington MS 600/6-8
3401 Orcutt Ave 23607 757-928-6846
Cleo Holloway, prin. Fax 245-8451
Menchville HS 1,600/9-12
275 Menchville Rd 23602 757-886-7722
Robert Surry, prin. Fax 875-0648
New Horizons Alt
13400 Woodside Ln 23608 757-874-4444
Bruce Schaffer, prin. Fax 872-8951
Passage MS 1,000/6-8
400 Atkinson Way 23608 757-886-7600
Janelle Spitz, prin. Fax 886-7661
Point Option Alternative S Alt
813 Diligence Dr Ste 100 23606 757-591-7408
Michael Bonfiglio, dir. Fax 865-4508
Warwick HS 1,500/9-12
51 Copeland Ln 23601 757-591-4700
Dr. Rory Stapleton, prin. Fax 596-7415
Washington MS 400/6-8
3700 Chestnut Ave 23607 757-928-6860
Sean Callender, prin. Fax 247-1119
Woodside HS 2,000/9-12
13450 Woodside Ln 23608 757-886-7530
Sean Callender, prin. Fax 877-0480
Other Schools – See Hampton

Apprentice School Post-Sec.
4101 Washington Ave 23607 757-380-3809
Centura College Post-Sec.
616 Denbigh Blvd 23608 757-874-2121
Christopher Newport University Post-Sec.
1 Avenue of the Arts 23606 757-594-7000
Denbigh Baptist Christian S 300/PK-12
13010 Mitchell Point Rd 23602 757-249-2654
Robert Law, admin. Fax 249-9480
Everest College Post-Sec.
803 Diligence Dr 23606 757-873-1111
Hampton Roads Academy 600/PK-12
739 Academy Ln 23602 757-884-9100
Peter Mertz, hdmstr. Fax 884-9137
Medical Careers Institute Post-Sec.
1001 Omni Blvd Ste 305 23606 866-708-6174
Peninsula Catholic HS 300/8-12
600 Harpersville Rd 23601 757-596-7247
Janine Franklin, prin. Fax 591-9718
Riverside School of Health Careers Post-Sec.
316 Main St 23601 757-240-2200
Stratford University Post-Sec.
836 J Clyde Morris Blve 23601 757-873-4235

Nickelsville, Scott, Pop. 382
Scott County SD
Supt. — See Gate City
Twin Springs HS 300/8-12
273 Titan Ln 24271 276-479-2185
Jordan Mullins, prin. Fax 479-3103

Nokesville, Prince William, Pop. 1,327
Fauquier County SD
Supt. — See Warrenton
Kettle Run HS 1,200/9-12
7403 Academic Ave 20181 540-422-7330
Major Warner, prin. Fax 422-7359

Prince William County SD
Supt. — See Manassas
Brentsville District HS 900/9-12
12109 Aden Rd 20181 703-594-2161
Katherine Meints, prin. Fax 594-2365
Patriot HS 2,600/9-12
10504 Kettle Run Rd 20181 703-594-3020
Michael Bishop Ed.D., prin. Fax 594-3022

Norfolk, Norfolk, Pop. 234,855
Norfolk CSD 31,300/PK-12
PO Box 1357 23501 757-628-3830
Dr. Melinda Boone, supt. Fax 628-3820
www.nps.k12.va.us
Academy of Discovery at Lakewood 3-8
1701 Alsace Ave 23509 757-628-2477
Thomas Smigiel, prin. Fax 628-2486
Academy of Intl Studies at Rosemont 100/6-8
1330 Branch Rd 23513 757-852-4610
Dr. Lynnell Gibson, prin. Fax 852-4615
Azalea Gardens MS 900/6-8
7721 Azalea Garden Rd 23518 757-531-3000
Dr. Reuthenia Clark, prin. Fax 531-3013
Blair MS 1,200/6-8
730 Spotswood Ave 23517 757-628-2400
Dr. Mark Makovec, prin. Fax 628-2422
Granby HS 2,000/9-12
7101 Granby St 23505 757-451-4110
Ted Daughtrey, prin. Fax 451-4118
Lake Taylor HS 1,300/9-12
1384 Kempsville Rd 23502 757-892-3200
Dr. Reba Miller, prin. Fax 892-3210
Lake Taylor MS 900/6-8
1380 Kempsville Rd 23502 757-892-3230
Craig Reed, prin. Fax 892-3240
Madison Alternative S Alt
3700 Bowdens Ferry Rd 23508 757-628-3417
Leesa Mundell, coord. Fax 628-3406
Maury HS 1,600/9-12
322 Shirley Ave 23517 757-628-3344
Karen Berg, prin. Fax 628-3359
Norfolk Technical Center Vo/Tech
1330 N Military Hwy 23502 757-892-3300
Kevin Monroe, coord. Fax 892-3305
Northside MS 800/6-8
8720 Granby St 23503 757-531-3150
Richard Fraley, prin. Fax 531-3144
Norview HS 1,800/9-12
6501 Chesapeake Blvd 23513 757-852-4500
Dr. Marjorie Stealey, prin. Fax 852-4511
Norview MS 1,100/6-8
6325 Sewells Point Rd 23513 757-852-4600
Walter Brower, prin. Fax 852-4590
Ruffner Academy 800/6-8
610 May Ave 23504 757-628-2466
Sallie Cooke, prin. Fax 628-2465
Washington HS 1,200/9-12
1111 Park Ave 23504 757-628-3575
Adrian Day, prin. Fax 628-3566
Granby Evening School Adult
7101 Granby St 23505 757-451-4110
Brandon Bell, prin. Fax 451-4049

Regional Academic Governors SD
Supt. — See Richmond
Governor's S for the Arts 400/9-12
254 Granby St # 2 23510 757-451-4711
Dr. Andrea Warren, dir. Fax 451-4715

Bina HS 50/9-12
425 Washington Park 23517 757-627-2462
Centura College Post-Sec.
7020 N Military Hwy 23518 757-853-2121
De Paul Medical Center Post-Sec.
150 Kingsley Ln 23505 757-489-5120
Eastern Virginia Medical School Post-Sec.
PO Box 1980 23501 757-446-5600
Fortis College Post-Sec.
6300 Center Dr Ste 100 23502 757-499-5447
Norfolk Academy 1,200/1-12
1585 Wesleyan Dr 23502 757-461-6236
Dennis Manning, hdmstr. Fax 455-3181
Norfolk Christian S 500/6-12
255 Thole St 23505 757-423-5770
Norfolk Collegiate S 400/6-12
7336 Granby St 23505 757-480-2885
Scott Kennedy, hdmstr. Fax 588-8655
Norfolk State University Post-Sec.
700 Park Ave 23504 757-823-8600
Ocean View Christian Academy 50/PK-12
9504 Selby Pl 23503 757-583-1808
Amy Dunnavant, prin. Fax 583-5706
Old Dominion University Post-Sec.
5115 Hampton Blvd 23529 757-683-3000
Tidewater Community College Post-Sec.
121 College Pl 23510 757-822-1122
Tidewater Tech Post-Sec.
5301 E Princess Anne Rd 23502 757-858-8324
Virginia Wesleyan College Post-Sec.
1584 Wesleyan Dr 23502 757-455-3200
Wards Corner Beauty Academy Post-Sec.
7525 Tidewater Dr Ste 200 23505 757-583-3300
Yeshiva Aish Kodesh 50/9-12
612 Colonial Ave 23507 757-623-6070

N Chesterfield, Chesterfield
Chesterfield County SD
Supt. — See Chesterfield
Falling Creek MS 1,200/6-8
4724 Hopkins Rd, 804-743-3640
Melanie Knowles, prin. Fax 743-3644
Manchester MS 1,400/6-8
7401 Hull Street Rd, 804-674-1385
Sarah Fraher, prin. Fax 674-1394
Meadowbrook HS 1,600/9-12
4901 Cogbill Rd, 804-743-3675
Andrew Mey, prin. Fax 743-3686
Monacan HS 1,400/9-12
11501 Smoketree Dr, 804-378-2480
William Broyles, prin. Fax 378-2489
Providence MS 800/6-8
900 Starlight Ln, 804-674-1355
Dr. Derek Wasnock, prin. Fax 674-1361
Salem Church MS 900/6-8
9700 Salem Church Rd, 804-768-6225
Dr. Greg Ecroyd, prin. Fax 768-6230

Bryant & Stratton College Post-Sec.
8141 Hull Street Rd, 804-745-2444
Centura College Post-Sec.
7914 Midlothian Tpke, 804-330-0111
Southside Baptist Christian S 100/K-12
411 Branchway, 804-745-8699
Rev. Reginald Stinson, head sch Fax 591-2833
Virginia College Post-Sec.
7200 Midlothian Tpke, 804-977-5100

Norton, Norton, Pop. 3,857
Norton CSD 800/PK-12
PO Box 498 24273 276-679-2330
Dr. Keith Perrigan, supt. Fax 679-4315
www.nortoncityschools.org/
Burton HS 300/8-12
109 11th St SW 24273 276-679-2554
Aaron Williams, prin. Fax 679-2664

Wise County SD
Supt. — See Wise
Central HS 700/9-12
301 Industrial Park Rd 24273 276-328-8015
Charles Collins, prin. Fax 328-8316

Nottoway, Nottoway
Nottoway County SD 2,300/PK-12
10321 E Colonial Trail Hwy 23955 434-645-9596
Dr. Daniel Grounard, supt. Fax 645-1266
www.nottowayschools.org/
Other Schools – See Crewe, Jetersville

Oak Hall, Accomack, Pop. 245
Accomack County SD
Supt. — See Accomac
Arcadia HS 600/9-12
8210 Lankford Hwy 23416 757-824-5613
Rose Taylor, prin. Fax 824-0767
Arcadia MS 500/6-8
PO Box 220 23416 757-824-4862
Brian Tupper, prin. Fax 824-6618
Badger Vocational Education Center North Vo/Tech
PO Box 69 23416 757-824-6386
Rose Taylor, dir. Fax 824-0767

Oakton, Fairfax, Pop. 32,914

Dominion Christian S 200/K-12
10922 Vale Rd 22124 703-758-1055
Flint Hill S 1,100/PK-12
3320 Jermantown Rd 22124 703-584-2300
John Thomas, hdmstr. Fax 584-2369

Oakwood, Buchanan

Appalachian College of Pharmacy Post-Sec.
1060 Dragon Rd 24631 276-498-4190

Onley, Accomack, Pop. 509
Accomack County SD
Supt. — See Accomac
Badger Vocational Education Center South Vo/Tech
PO Box 302 23418 757-787-4522
Brian Patterson, dir. Fax 787-2194
Nandua HS 700/9-12
26350 Lankford Hwy 23418 757-787-4514
Brian Patterson, prin. Fax 787-2194
Nandua MS 500/6-8
20330 Warrior Dr 23418 757-787-7037
John Killmon, prin. Fax 787-8807

Orange, Orange, Pop. 4,610
Orange County SD 5,000/K-12
200 Dailey Dr 22960 540-661-4550
Dr. Brenda Tanner, supt. Fax 661-4599
www.ocss-va.org
Orange County HS 1,500/9-12
201 Selma Rd 22960 540-661-4300
Kelly Guempel, prin. Fax 661-4299
Prospect Heights MS 500/6-8
202 Dailey Dr 22960 540-661-4400
Renee Bourke, prin. Fax 661-4399
Other Schools – See Locust Grove

Palmyra, Fluvanna, Pop. 102
Fluvanna County SD 3,700/PK-12
14455 James Madison Hwy 22963 434-589-8208
Gena Keller, supt. Fax 589-5393
www.fluco.org
Fluvanna County HS 1,400/8-12
1918 Thomas Jefferson Pkwy 22963 434-589-3666
James Barlow, prin. Fax 591-2075

Regional Academic Governors SD
Supt. — See Richmond
Blue Ridge Virtual Governor's HS 9-12
14455 James Madison Hwy 22963 434-589-8208
Marc Carraway, dir. Fax 589-2248

Pearisburg, Giles, Pop. 2,771
Giles County SD 2,500/PK-12
151 School Rd 24134 540-921-1421
Dr. Terry Arbogast, supt. Fax 921-1424
sbo.gilesk12.org
Giles County Technology Center Vo/Tech
1827 Wenonah Ave 24134 540-921-1166
Mark Husband, prin. Fax 921-3906
Giles HS 700/8-12
1825 Wenonah Ave 24134 540-921-1711
Ross Matney, prin. Fax 921-3861
Other Schools – See Narrows

Pennington Gap, Lee, Pop. 1,760
Lee County SD
Supt. — See Jonesville
Pennington MS 400/6-8
201 Middle School Dr 24277 276-546-1453
Jerry Hounshell, prin. Fax 546-3515

Penn Laird, Rockingham
Rockingham County SD
Supt. — See Harrisonburg
Montevideo MS 700/6-8
7648 McGaheysville Rd 22846 540-289-3401
Drew Miller, prin. Fax 289-3601
Spotswood HS 900/9-12
368 Blazer Dr 22846 540-289-3100
Robert Dansey, prin. Fax 289-3301

Petersburg, Petersburg, Pop. 31,887
Petersburg CSD 4,800/PK-12
255 E South Blvd 23805 804-732-0510
Dr. Joseph Melvin, supt. Fax 732-0514
www.petersburg.k12.va.us
Blandford Program Mathematics Humanities 300/Alt
816 E Bank St 23803 804-862-7078
Wayne Carter, coord. Fax 862-7198
Johns JHS 600/8-9
3101 Homestead Dr 23805 804-862-7020
Shannon Washington, prin. Fax 862-5434
Petersburg HS 800/10-12
3101 Johnson Rd 23805 804-861-4884
Alicia Fields, prin. Fax 862-7188
Pittman Alternative S Alt
35 Pine St 23803 804-862-7207
Gloria Graves, coord.

Regional Academic Governors SD
Supt. — See Richmond
Appomattox Reg. Governor's S Arts/Tech 400/9-12
512 W Washington St 23803 804-722-0200
Dr. James Victory, dir. Fax 722-0201

Richard Bland College Post-Sec.
11301 Johnson Rd 23805 804-862-6100
Southside Regional Medical Center Post-Sec.
737 S Sycamore St 23803 804-765-5800
Virginia State University Post-Sec.
1 Hayden Dr 23806 804-524-5000

Pilgrims Knob, Buchanan
Buchanan County SD
Supt. — See Grundy
Twin Valley HS 300/8-12
PO Box 190 24634 276-259-7818
Rick Goodman, prin. Fax 259-6147

Poquoson, Poquoson, Pop. 11,990
Poquoson CSD 2,100/PK-12
500 City Hall Ave 23662 757-868-3055
Dr. Jennifer Parish, supt. Fax 868-3107
www.poquoson.k12.va.us
Poquoson HS 800/9-12
51 Odd Rd 23662 757-868-7123
Brandon Ratliff, prin. Fax 868-3141
Poquoson MS 500/6-8
985 Poquoson Ave 23662 757-868-6031
Todd Perelli, prin. Fax 868-4220

Portsmouth, Portsmouth, Pop. 93,145
Portsmouth CSD 15,000/PK-12
PO Box 998 23705 757-393-8751
Dr. Elie Bracy, supt. Fax 393-5236
ppsk12.us
Churchland HS 1,400/9-12
4301 Cedar Ln 23703 757-686-2500
Shawn Millaci, prin. Fax 686-2504
Churchland MS 900/7-8
4051 River Shore Rd 23703 757-686-2512
Barbara Kimzey, prin. Fax 686-2515
Cradock MS 600/7-8
21 Alden Ave 23702 757-393-8788
Sonya Harrell, prin. Fax 393-5020
New Directions Center Alt
2801 Turnpike Rd 23707 757-393-8728
Horace Lambert, prin. Fax 393-5351
Norcom HS 1,200/9-12
1801 London Blvd 23704 757-393-5442
Dr. Laguna Foster, prin. Fax 393-5449
Waters MS 600/7-8
600 Roosevelt Blvd 23701 757-558-2813
Alice Graham, prin. Fax 485-2829
Wilson HS 1,400/9-12
1401 Elmhurst Ln 23701 757-465-2907
Timothy Johnson, prin. Fax 405-1335
Adult Education Adult
2801 Turnpike Rd 23707 757-393-8822
Barbara Shears-Walker, coord. Fax 393-5246
EXCEL Campus Adult
1401 Elmhurst Ln 23701 757-465-2958
Timothy Johnson, prin. Fax 465-2913

Alliance Christian Academy 200/PK-12
5809 Portsmouth Blvd 23701 757-488-5552
Kimberley Johnson, admin. Fax 488-3192
Hicks Academy of Beauty Culture Post-Sec.
904 Loudoun Ave 23707 757-399-2400
Portsmouth Christian S 700/PK-12
3214 Elliott Ave 23702 757-393-0725
Nancy Stafford, admin. Fax 397-7487
Tidewater Community College Post-Sec.
120 Campus Dr 23701 757-822-2124

Potomac Falls, Loudoun
Loudoun County SD
Supt. — See Ashburn
Potomac Falls HS 1,600/9-12
46400 Algonkian Pkwy 20165 571-434-3200
Dr. Elizabeth Noto, prin. Fax 434-3201

Powhatan, Powhatan
Powhatan County SD 3,200/PK-12
2320 Skaggs Rd 23139 804-598-5700
Dr. Eric Jones, supt. Fax 598-5705
www.powhatan.k12.va.us
Pocahontas MS 300/6-8
4290 Anderson Hwy 23139 804-598-5720
Dr. Lynne Prince, prin. Fax 598-1485
Powhatan HS 1,400/9-12
1800 Judes Ferry Rd 23139 804-598-5710
Dr. Mike Massa, prin. Fax 598-0036

Blessed Sacrament S 300/PK-12
2501 Academy Rd 23139 804-598-4211
Paula Ledbetter, prin. Fax 598-1053

Prince George, Prince George, Pop. 2,019
Prince George County SD 6,400/PK-12
PO Box 400 23875 804-733-2700
Renee P. Williams, supt. Fax 733-2737
pgs.k12.va.us
Clements JHS 1,000/8-9
7800 Laurel Spring Rd 23875 804-733-2730
Christine Romig, prin. Fax 733-3783
Prince George SHS 1,300/10-12
7801 Laurel Spring Rd 23875 804-733-2720
Michael Nelson, prin. Fax 861-4530
Other Schools – See Disputanta

Pulaski, Pulaski, Pop. 8,916
Pulaski County SD 4,500/PK-12
202 N Washington Ave 24301 540-994-2550
Chris Stafford, supt. Fax 994-2552
www.pcva.us
Pulaski MS 400/6-8
500 Pico Ter 24301 540-643-0767
Mary Rash, prin. Fax 980-8571
Other Schools – See Dublin

Regional Academic Governors SD
Supt. — See Richmond
SW VA Governor's S Science Math & Tech 11-12
100 Northwood Dr 24301 540-440-5502
Rebecca Phillips, dir. Fax 994-5841

Purcellville, Loudoun, Pop. 7,498
Loudoun County SD
Supt. — See Ashburn
Blue Ridge MS 900/6-8
551 E A St 20132 540-751-2520
Brion Bell, prin. Fax 338-6823
Loudoun Valley HS 1,200/9-12
340 N Maple Ave 20132 540-751-2400
Susan Ross, prin. Fax 751-2401
Woodgrove HS 1,500/9-12
36811 Allder School Rd 20132 540-751-2600
William Shipp, prin. Fax 751-2601

Patrick Henry College Post-Sec.
10 Patrick Henry Cir 20132 540-338-1776

Quicksburg, Shenandoah
Shenandoah County SD
Supt. — See Woodstock
Jackson HS 500/9-12
150 Stonewall Ln 22847 540-477-2732
Michael Dorman, prin. Fax 477-2098
North Fork MS 300/6-8
1018 Caverns Rd 22847 540-477-2953
Todd Lynn, prin. Fax 477-2562

Radford, Radford, Pop. 16,003
Radford CSD 1,600/PK-12
1612 Wadsworth St 24141 540-731-3647
Robert Graham, supt. Fax 731-4419
www.rcps.org/
Dalton IS 300/7-8
60 Dalton Dr 24141 540-731-3651
Greg Payne, prin. Fax 731-5033
Radford HS 500/9-12
50 Dalton Dr 24141 540-731-3649
W. Jeff Smith, prin. Fax 731-4427

Radford University Post-Sec.
801 E Main St 24142 540-831-5000

Reston, Fairfax, Pop. 56,325
Fairfax County SD
Supt. — See Falls Church
Hughes MS 1,000/7-8
11401 Ridge Heights Rd 20191 703-715-3600
Aimee Monticchio, prin. Fax 715-3697
South Lakes HS 2,400/9-12
11400 South Lakes Dr 20191 703-715-4500
Kimberly Retzer, prin. Fax 715-4597

AKS Massage School Post-Sec.
11793 Indian Ridge Rd 20191 703-304-1146

Richlands, Tazewell, Pop. 5,766
Tazewell County SD
Supt. — See Tazewell
Richlands HS 700/9-12
138 Tornado Aly 24641 276-964-4602
Kimberly Ringstaff, prin. Fax 963-1049
Richlands MS 600/6-8
185 Learning Ln 24641 276-963-5370
Glayde Brown, prin. Fax 963-0210

Southwest Virginia Community College Post-Sec.
PO Box SVCC 24641 276-964-2555

Richmond, Richmond, Pop. 200,073
Henrico County SD 49,800/PK-12
PO Box 23120 23223 804-652-3600
Dr. Patrick Kinlaw, supt. Fax 652-3856
henricoschools.us
Advance College Academy 9-12
2910 N Parham Rd 23294 804-527-4600
Sheralyne Tierseron, prin.
Brookland MS 1,100/6-8
9200 Lydell Dr 23228 804-261-5000
Nicholas Barlett, prin. Fax 261-5003
Byrd MS 1,000/6-8
9400 Quioccasin Rd 23238 804-750-2630
Cheri Guempel, prin. Fax 750-2629
Center for Communications 9-12
7053 Messer Rd 23231 804-226-8700
Beverly Lanier, prin.
Center for Medical Sciences 9-12
2101 Pump Rd 23238 804-750-2600
Todd Phillips, prin.
Center for the Arts 9-12
302 Azalea Ave 23227 804-228-2718
Dr. Stephanie Poxon, prin. Fax 228-2754
Center for the Humanities 9-12
8301 Hungary Spring Rd 23228 804-756-3000
Bruce Marr, prin.
Center for World Languages 9-12
2910 N Parham Rd 23294 804-527-4618
Dr. Anne Fano, prin. Fax 527-4611
Ctr for Leadrshp Govt & Global Economics 9-12
8701 Three Chopt Rd 23229 804-673-3700
Robert Peck, prin.
Fairfield MS 1,000/6-8
5121 Nine Mile Rd 23223 804-328-4020
Art Raymond, prin. Fax 328-4031
Freeman HS 1,700/9-12
8701 Three Chopt Rd 23229 804-673-3700
Anne Poates, prin. Fax 673-3713
Godwin HS 1,800/9-12
2101 Pump Rd 23238 804-750-2600
Elizabeth Armbruster, prin. Fax 750-2611
Henrico HS 1,700/9-12
302 Azalea Ave 23227 804-228-2700
Dr. Hebert Monroe, prin. Fax 228-2715
Hermitage HS 1,600/9-12
8301 Hungary Spring Rd 23228 804-756-3000
Andrew Armstrong, prin. Fax 672-1501
Hermitage Technical Center Vo/Tech
8301 Hungary Spring Rd 23228 804-756-3020
Terrie Allsbrooks, prin. Fax 756-3025
Moody MS 1,000/6-8
7800 Woodman Rd 23228 804-261-5015
Paul Llewellyn, prin. Fax 261-5024
Pocahontas MS 900/6-8
12000 Three Chopt Rd 23233 804-364-0830
Kimberly Sigler, prin. Fax 364-0847
Rolfe MS 1,000/6-8
6901 Messer Rd 23231 804-226-8730
Michael Jackson, prin. Fax 226-8739
Tuckahoe MS 1,100/6-8
9000 Three Chopt Rd 23229 804-673-3720
Ann Greene, prin. Fax 673-3731
Tucker HS 1,500/9-12
2910 N Parham Rd 23294 804-527-4600
Dr. Robert Lowerre, prin. Fax 527-4618

Varina HS 1,700/9-12
•7053 Messer Rd 23231 804-226-8700
Ann Marie Seely, prin. Fax 226-8706
Wilder MS 900/6-8
6900 Wilkinson Rd 23227 804-515-1100
Solomon Jefferson, prin. Fax 515-1110
Mt. Vernon Adult Ed Complex Adult
7850 Carousel Ln 23294 804-527-4660
Gregory Lawson M.Ed., admin.
Other Schools – See Glen Allen, Highland Springs, Sandston

Regional Academic Governors SD 2,600/9-12
PO Box 2120 23218 804-225-2884
Dr. Donna Poland, admin. Fax 786-5466
www.doe.virginia.gov/instruction/governors_school_programs
Walker Governor's S for Gov & Int Study 9-12
1000 N Lombardy St 23220 804-354-6800
Jeff McGee Ph.D., dir. Fax 354-6939
Other Schools – See Abingdon, Alexandria, Clifton Forge, Fishersville, Fredericksburg, Hampton, Keysville, Lynchburg, Manassas, Martinsville, Mount Jackson, Norfolk, Palmyra, Petersburg, Pulaski, Roanoke, Tappahannock, Warrenton

Richmond CSD 22,700/PK-12
301 N 9th St 23219 804-780-7700
Dr. Dana Bedden, supt. Fax 780-4122
www.richmond.k12.va.us
Armstrong HS 1,000/9-12
2300 Cool Ln 23223 804-780-4449
April Hawkins, prin. Fax 780-4485
Binford MS 200/6-8
1701 Floyd Ave 23220 804-780-6231
Tyrus Lyles, prin. Fax 780-6057
Boushall MS 600/6-8
3400 Hopkins Rd 23234 804-780-5016
Widad Abed, prin. Fax 780-5396
Brown MS 800/6-8
6300 Jahnke Rd 23225 804-319-3013
Jonathan Morris, prin. Fax 319-3009
Elkhardt-Thompson MS 500/6-8
7825 Forest Hill Ave 23225 804-272-7554
Joi Lowery, prin. Fax 560-5115
Franklin Military Academy 300/6-12
701 N 37th St 23223 804-780-8526
Sheron Carter-Gunter, prin. Fax 780-8054
Henderson MS 600/6-8
4319 Old Brook Rd 23227 804-780-8288
Deberry Goodwin, prin. Fax 228-5357
Hill MS 500/6-8
3400 Patterson Ave 23221 804-780-6107
LaShante Knight, prin. Fax 780-8754
Huguenot HS 1,300/9-12
7945 Forest Hill Ave 23225 804-320-7967
Jafar Barakat, prin. Fax 560-9103
Jefferson HS 900/9-12
4100 W Grace St 23230 804-780-6028
Candance Veney-Chaplin, prin. Fax 780-6295
King MS 600/6-8
1000 Mosby St 23223 804-780-8011
Dr. Valerie Harris, prin. Fax 780-5590
Marshall HS 800/9-12
4225 Old Brook Rd 23227 804-780-6052
Beverly Britt, prin. Fax 780-4991
MathScience Innovation Center K-12
2401 Hartman St 23223 804-343-6525
Julia Cothran Ed.D., prin. Fax 780-4454
Open HS 200/9-12
600 S Pine St 23220 804-780-4661
Pete Glessman, prin. Fax 780-4865
Richmond Alternative S 200/Alt
119 W Leigh St 23220 804-780-4388
Dana Hawes, prin. Fax 780-8184
Richmond Career Educ & Employment Acad 50/Alt
4314 Crutchfield St 23225 804-780-5037
Maurice Burton, prin.
Richmond Community HS 200/9-12
201 E Brookland Park Blvd 23222 804-285-1015
J. Austin Brown, prin. Fax 282-1303
Richmond Technical Center North Vo/Tech
2015 Seddon Way 23230 804-780-6272
Nancy Holmes, prin. Fax 780-6040
Richmond Technical Center South Vo/Tech
2020 Westwood Ave 23230 804-780-6237
Nancy Holmes, prin. Fax 780-6061
Wythe HS 900/9-12
4314 Crutchfield St 23225 804-780-5037
Reva Green, prin. Fax 780-5043

Al Madina S of Richmond PK-12
PO Box 13103 23225 804-330-4888
Dr. Farah Radwan, prin. Fax 330-4889
Banner Christian S 200/K-12
1501 S Providence Rd 23236 804-276-5200
Dr. Thomas Burkett, hdmstr. Fax 276-7620
Baptist Theological Seminary Post-Sec.
8040 Villa Park Dr Ste 250 23228 804-355-8135
Benedictine HS 300/9-12
12829 River Rd 23238 804-708-9500
Jesse Grapes, hdmstr.
Bon Secours Memorial College of Nursing Post-Sec.
8550 Magellan Pkwy Ste 1100 23227 804-627-5300
Church Hill Academy 9-12
2010 Carlisle Ave 23231 804-222-8760
Rev. Gina Maio, prin.
Collegiate S 1,600/PK-12
103 N Mooreland Rd 23229 804-741-7077
Stephen Hickman, hdmstr. Fax 741-9797
Cooper Episcopal S 100/4-8
2124 N 29th St 23223 804-822-6610
Mike Maruca, head sch Fax 447-5784
East End Christian Academy 50/PK-12
3294 Britton Rd 23231 804-795-9266
Suzanne Helland, dir. Fax 795-2222
ECPI University Post-Sec.
800 Moorefield Park Dr 23236 804-330-5533
Elijah House Academy 200/PK-12
6627 Jahnke Rd Ste B 23225 804-755-7051
Jesse Kell, head sch Fax 377-6800
Fortis College Post-Sec.
2000 Westmoreland St Ste A 23230 804-323-1020
Grove Christian S 200/PK-12
8701 Ridge Rd 23229 804-741-2860
Julia Lloyd, admin. Fax 754-8534
J. Sargeant Reynolds Community College Post-Sec.
PO Box 85622 23285 804-371-3000
Medical Careers Institute Post-Sec.
2809 Emerywood Pkwy 23294 877-338-0006
Orchard House S 100/5-8
500 N Allen Ave 23220 804-228-2436
Susanne Gregory, dir. Fax 228-1069
Precious Blessing Academy 50/PK-12
4823 Bryce Ln 23224 804-232-7180
Lois Bias, dean Fax 232-2490
Richmond Academy 100/PK-12
12285 Patterson Ave 23238 804-784-0036
Nancy Melashenko, prin. Fax 784-1558
St. Catherine's S 900/PK-12
6001 Grove Ave 23226 804-288-2804
Dr. Terrie Scheckelhoff Ph.D., head sch Fax 285-8169
St. Christopher's S 1,000/PK-12
711 Saint Christophers Rd 23226 804-282-3185
Mason Lecky, head sch Fax 285-3914
St. Gertrude HS 300/9-12
3215 Stuart Ave 23221 804-358-9114
Renata Rafferty, head sch Fax 355-5682
St. Mary's Hospital Post-Sec.
5801 Bremo Rd 23226 804-285-2011
Steward S 600/PK-12
11600 Gayton Rd 23238 804-740-3394
G. Daniel Frank, head sch Fax 740-1464
Tawheed Prep S 6-12
1202 Oak St 23220 804-344-3350
Trinity Episcopal S 400/8-12
3850 Pittaway Dr 23235 804-272-5864
Rob Short, head sch Fax 272-4652
Union Presbyterian Seminary Post-Sec.
3401 Brook Rd 23227 804-355-0671
University of Richmond Post-Sec.
28 Westhampton Way 23173 804-289-8000
Veritas S 300/PK-12
3400 Brook Rd 23227 804-272-9517
Keith Nix, head sch Fax 272-9518
Virginia Commonwealth University Post-Sec.
901 W Franklin St 23284 804-828-0100
Virginia Home for Boys & Girls Post-Sec.
8716 W Broad St 23294 804-270-6566
Virginia School for the Deaf and Blind Post-Sec.
PO Box 2120 23218 757-247-2058
Virginia Union University Post-Sec.
1500 N Lombardy St 23220 804-257-5600
Yeshiva of Virginia 50/9-12
6801 Patterson Ave 23226 804-288-7610

Ridgeway, Henry, Pop. 734
Henry County SD
Supt. — See Collinsville
Magna Vista HS 900/9-12
701 Magna Vista School Rd 24148 276-956-3147
JaMese Black, prin. Fax 956-1401

Riner, Montgomery, Pop. 845
Montgomery County SD
Supt. — See Christiansburg
Auburn HS 400/9-12
1650 Auburn School Dr 24149 540-382-5160
Carl Pauli, prin. Fax 381-6110
Auburn MS 300/6-8
4163 Riner Rd 24149 540-382-5165
Guylene Wood-Setzer, prin. Fax 381-6562

Ringgold, Pittsylvania
Pittsylvania County SD
Supt. — See Chatham
Dan River HS 700/9-12
100 Wildcat Circle 24586 434-822-7081
Steven D. Mayhew, prin. Fax 822-7347
Dan River MS 500/6-8
5875 Kentuck Rd 24586 434-822-6027
Emily Reynolds, prin. Fax 822-6548

Roanoke, Roanoke, Pop. 94,517
Regional Academic Governors SD
Supt. — See Richmond
Roanoke Valley Governor's S Science/Tech 9-12
2104 Grandin Rd SW 24015 540-853-2116
Dr. John Kowalski, dir. Fax 853-1056

Roanoke CSD 13,500/PK-12
PO Box 13145 24031 540-853-2502
Dr. Rita Bishop, supt. Fax 853-2951
www.rcps.info
Addison MS 600/6-8
1220 5th St NW 24016 540-853-2681
Robert Johnson, prin. Fax 853-1424
Breckinridge MS 500/6-8
3901 Williamson Rd NW 24012 540-853-2251
Tracey Anderson, prin. Fax 853-6505
Fleming HS 1,400/9-12
3649 Ferncliff Ave NW 24017 540-853-2781
Archie Freeman, admin.
Forest Park Academy Alt
2730 Melrose Ave NW 24017 540-853-2923
Eric Anderson, admin. Fax 853-1773
Henry HS 1,900/9-12
2102 Grandin Rd SW 24015 540-853-2255
Joseph Jablonski, prin. Fax 853-1575
Jackson MS 600/6-8
1004 Montrose Ave SE 24013 540-853-6040
Christian Kish, prin. Fax 853-6027
Madison MS 600/6-8
1160 Overland Rd SW 24015 540-853-2351
Whitney Johnson, prin. Fax 853-1050
Roanoke Technical Education Center Vo/Tech
2200 Grandin Rd SW 24015 540-853-2803
Kathleen Duncan, prin. Fax 853-1062
Taylor Learning Academy Alt
3229 Williamson Rd NW 24012 540-853-1461
Elizabeth Williams, prin. Fax 853-1216
Wilson MS 500/6-8
1813 Carter Rd SW 24015 540-853-2358
Rosalind Henderson, prin. Fax 853-2004

Roanoke County SD 14,000/K-12
5937 Cove Rd 24019 540-562-3700
Dr. Gregory Killough, supt. Fax 562-3994
www.rcs.k12.va.us
Cave Spring HS 1,000/9-12
3712 Chaparral Dr 24018 540-772-7550
Steve Spangler, prin. Fax 772-2107
Cave Spring MS 700/6-8
4880 Brambleton Ave 24018 540-772-7560
Fiona Hill, prin. Fax 772-2195
Hidden Valley HS 1,000/9-12
5000 Titan Trl 24018 540-776-7320
Rhonda Stegall, prin. Fax 776-7322
Hidden Valley MS 600/6-8
4902 Hidden Valley School 24018 540-772-7570
Mike Riley, prin. Fax 772-7519
Northside HS 1,000/9-12
6758 Northside High School 24019 540-561-8155
Frank Dent, prin. Fax 561-8160
Northside MS 700/6-8
6810 Northside High School 24019 540-561-8145
Lori Wimbush, prin. Fax 561-8152
Other Schools – See Salem, Vinton

BarPalma Beauty Careers Academy Post-Sec.
3535 Franklin Rd SW Ste D 24014 540-343-0153
Community HS 50/8-12
302 Campbell Ave SE 24013 540-345-1688
Faith Christian S 300/PK-12
3585 Buck Mountain Rd 24018 540-769-5200
Peter Baur, hdmstr. Fax 769-6030
Hollins University Post-Sec.
PO Box 9707 24020 540-362-6000
Jefferson College of Health Sciences Post-Sec.
101 Elm Ave SE 24013 540-985-8483
Miller-Motte Technical College Post-Sec.
4444 Electric Rd Ste A 24018 540-597-1010
North Cross S 500/PK-12
4254 Colonial Ave 24018 540-989-6641
Dr. Christian Proctor, head sch Fax 989-7299
Parkway Christian Academy 300/PK-12
3230 King St NE 24012 540-982-2400
Angela Goodwin, prin. Fax 982-2005
Roanoke Catholic S 500/PK-12
621 N Jefferson St 24016 540-982-3532
Patrick Patterson, prin. Fax 345-0785
Roanoke Valley Christian S 300/PK-12
PO Box 7010 24019 540-366-2432
Rick Brown, admin. Fax 366-9719
Skyline College Post-Sec.
5234 Airport Rd NW 24012 540-563-8000
University of Fairfax Post-Sec.
1818 Electric Rd 24018 888-980-9151
Virgina Tech Carilion School of Medicine Post-Sec.
2 Riverside Cir Ste M140 24016 540-526-2500
Virginia Western Community College Post-Sec.
PO Box 14007 24038 540-857-8922

Rocky Gap, Bland
Bland County SD
Supt. — See Bastian
Bland County HS 200/7-12
PO Box 9 24366 276-928-1100
Temple Musser, prin. Fax 928-1988

Rocky Mount, Franklin, Pop. 4,700
Franklin County SD 7,400/PK-12
25 Bernard Rd 24151 540-483-5138
W. Mark Church Ph.D., supt. Fax 483-5806
www.frco.k12.va.us
Franklin County HS 2,100/9-12
700 Tanyard Rd 24151 540-483-0221
Jonathan Crutchfield, prin. Fax 483-5149
Franklin MS West 900/7-8
225 Middle School Rd 24151 540-483-5105
Dr. Bernice Cobbs, prin. Fax 483-5585
Gereau Center Vo/Tech
150 Technology Dr 24151 540-483-5446
Jerome Johnson, prin. Fax 483-5788
Adult Education Center Adult
50 Claiborne Ave 24151 540-483-0179
Debbie Hamrick, coord. Fax 483-1297

Christian Heritage Academy 100/PK-12
625 Glennwood Dr 24151 540-483-5855
Deke Andrews, head sch Fax 483-9355

Rural Retreat, Wythe, Pop. 1,472
Wythe County SD
Supt. — See Wytheville
Rural Retreat HS 300/9-12
321 E Buck Ave 24368 276-686-4143
Dyer Jackson, prin. Fax 686-4601
Rural Retreat MS 300/6-8
325 E Buck Ave 24368 276-686-5200
Shannon Vaught, prin. Fax 686-4944

Rustburg, Campbell, Pop. 1,389
Campbell County SD 8,300/PK-12
PO Box 99 24588 434-332-3458
Dr. Robert Johnson, supt. Fax 528-1655
www.campbell.k12.va.us
Campbell Technical Center Vo/Tech
194 Dennis Riddle Dr 24588 434-821-6213
Jon Hardie, prin. Fax 821-2808
Cornerstone Learning Center Alt
194 Dennis Riddle Dr 24588 434-477-5583
Denton Sisk, dir. Fax 821-4512
Rustburg HS 800/9-12
PO Box 830 24588 434-332-5171
Clayton Stanley, prin. Fax 332-1187

Rustburg MS 700/6-8
PO Box 130 24588 434-332-5141
Katherine Bowles, prin. Fax 332-2058
Other Schools – See Altavista, Lynchburg, Naruna

Ruther Glen, Caroline

Carmel S 100/PK-12
PO Box 605 22546 804-448-3288
Carolyn Williamson, head sch Fax 448-3146

Saint George, Greene

Blue Ridge S 200/9-12
273 Mayo Dr, 434-985-2811
William Darrin, hdmstr. Fax 985-7215

Salem, Salem, Pop. 24,439
Roanoke County SD
Supt. — See Roanoke
Burton Center for Arts and Technology Vo/Tech
1760 Roanoke Blvd 24153 540-857-5000
Jason Suhr, prin. Fax 857-5061
Glenvar HS 600/9-12
4549 Malus Dr 24153 540-387-6536
Joseph Hafey, prin. Fax 387-6347
Glenvar MS 400/6-8
4555 Malus Dr 24153 540-387-6322
Jamie Soltis, prin. Fax 387-6283

Salem CSD 3,800/PK-12
510 S College Ave 24153 540-389-0130
Dr. H. Alan Seibert, supt. Fax 389-4135
www.salem.k12.va.us
Lewis MS 900/6-8
616 S College Ave 24153 540-387-2513
Dr. Forest Jones, prin. Fax 389-8914
Salem HS 1,200/9-12
400 Spartan Dr 24153 540-387-2437
Scott Habeeb, prin. Fax 387-2543

American National University Post-Sec.
1813 E Main St 24153 540-986-1800
Roanoke College Post-Sec.
221 College Ln 24153 540-375-2500

Saltville, Smyth, Pop. 2,062
Smyth County SD
Supt. — See Marion
Northwood HS 300/9-12
PO Box Y 24370 276-496-7751
Stan Dunham, prin. Fax 496-3216
Northwood MS 200/6-8
156 Long Hollow Rd 24370 276-624-3341
Marianne Blevins, prin. Fax 624-3535

Saluda, Middlesex, Pop. 753
Middlesex County SD 1,200/PK-12
PO Box 205 23149 804-758-2277
Dr. Peter Gretz, supt. Fax 758-3727
www.mcps.k12.va.us/
Middlesex HS 300/9-12
PO Box 206 23149 804-758-2132
Jeannie Duke, prin. Fax 758-2786
Other Schools – See Locust Hill

Sandston, Henrico, Pop. 7,426
Henrico County SD
Supt. — See Richmond
Elko MS 900/6-8
5901 Elko Rd 23150 804-328-4110
Dominique Friend, prin. Fax 328-4115

New Bridge Academy 100/K-12
5701 Elko Rd 23150 804-737-7833
Rev. J.D. Sluss, admin. Fax 737-1181

Shawsville, Montgomery, Pop. 1,291
Montgomery County SD
Supt. — See Christiansburg
Shawsville MS 200/6-8
4179 Oldtown Rd 24162 540-268-2262
David Dickinson, prin. Fax 268-1868

Shenandoah, Page, Pop. 2,351
Page County SD
Supt. — See Luray
Page County HS 600/9-12
184 Panther Dr 22849 540-652-8712
David Cale, prin. Fax 652-8308
Page County MS 400/6-8
198 Panther Dr 22849 540-652-3400
Lance Moran, prin. Fax 652-8308

Skipwith, Mecklenburg
Mecklenburg County SD
Supt. — See Boydton
Bluestone HS 600/9-12
6825 Skipwith Rd 23968 434-372-5177
Pauline Keeton, prin. Fax 372-5217
Bluestone MS 400/6-8
250 Middle School Rd 23968 434-372-3266
Mary Shores, prin. Fax 372-3362

Smithfield, Isle of Wight, Pop. 7,922
Isle of Wight County SD 5,500/PK-12
820 W Main St 23430 757-357-4393
Dr. James Thornton M.Ed., supt. Fax 357-0849
www.iwcs.k12.va.us
Smithfield HS 1,300/9-12
14171 Turner Dr 23430 757-357-3108
Casey Roberts, prin. Fax 357-7253
Smithfield MS 600/7-8
14175 Turner Dr 23430 757-365-4100
Fred Eng, prin. Fax 365-4222
Other Schools – See Windsor

South Boston, Halifax, Pop. 8,032
Halifax County SD
Supt. — See Halifax
Halifax HS 1,700/9-12
PO Box 310 24592 434-572-4977
Michael Lewis, prin. Fax 572-2675
Halifax MS 1,200/6-8
1011 Middle School Cir 24592 434-572-4100
Magie Wilkerson, prin. Fax 572-4106

South Hill, Mecklenburg, Pop. 4,561
Mecklenburg County SD
Supt. — See Boydton
Park View HS 800/9-12
205 Park View Cir 23970 434-447-3435
Paige Kindley, prin. Fax 447-7876
Park View MS 600/6-8
365 Dockery Rd 23970 434-447-3761
Mark Mabey, prin. Fax 447-4920

South Riding, Loudoun, Pop. 23,365
Loudoun County SD
Supt. — See Ashburn
Freedom HS 1,400/9-12
25450 Riding Center Dr 20152 703-957-4300
Doug Fulton, prin. Fax 542-2086

Spotsylvania, Spotsylvania
Spotsylvania County SD
Supt. — See Fredericksburg
Courtland HS 1,200/9-12
6701 Smith Station Rd 22553 540-898-4445
Clifton Conway, prin. Fax 898-4458
Ni River MS 700/6-8
11632 Catharpin Rd 22553 540-785-3990
Scott Belako, prin. Fax 785-0658
Post Oak MS 800/6-8
6959 Courthouse Rd, 540-582-7517
Karen Foster, prin. Fax 582-7510
Spotsylvania Career & Technical Center Vo/Tech
6713 Smith Station Rd 22553 540-898-2655
Meghan O'Connor, prin. Fax 891-1784
Spotsylvania HS 1,100/9-12
6975 Courthouse Rd, 540-582-3882
Rusty Davis, prin. Fax 582-3890
Spotsylvania MS 800/6-8
8801 Courthouse Rd 22553 540-582-6341
Lane Byrd, prin. Fax 582-3207
Thornburg MS 700/6-8
6929 N Roxbury Mill Rd, 540-582-7600
Kirk Tower, prin. Fax 582-7606

Springfield, Fairfax, Pop. 29,504
Fairfax County SD
Supt. — See Falls Church
Irving MS 1,000/7-8
8100 Old Keene Mill Rd 22152 703-912-4500
Danny Little, prin. Fax 912-4597
Key MS 800/7-8
6402 Franconia Rd 22150 703-313-3900
Christopher Larrick, prin. Fax 313-3997
Lee HS 1,800/9-12
6540 Franconia Rd 22150 703-924-8300
Deirdre Lavery, prin. Fax 924-8397
West Springfield HS 2,300/9-12
6100 Rolling Rd 22152 703-913-3800
Michael Mukai, prin. Fax 913-3897

Accotink Academy Post-Sec.
8519 Tuttle Rd 22152
GW Community S 50/9-12
9001 Braddock Rd Ste 111 22151 703-978-7208

Stafford, Stafford
Stafford County SD 27,100/PK-12
31 Stafford Ave 22554 540-658-6000
Dr. W. Bruce Benson, supt. Fax 658-5963
stafford.schoolfusion.us
Brooke Point HS 1,700/9-12
1700 Courthouse Rd 22554 540-658-6080
Scott McClellan, prin. Fax 658-6072
Colonial Forge HS 2,000/9-12
550 Courthouse Rd 22554 540-658-6115
Greg Daniel, prin. Fax 658-6120
Heim MS 900/6-8
320 Telegraph Rd 22554 540-658-5910
Mary McGraw, prin. Fax 658-0329
Mountain View HS 1,800/9-12
2135 Mountain View Rd, 540-658-6840
James Stemple, prin. Fax 658-6855
North Stafford HS 1,700/9-12
839 Garrisonville Rd 22554 540-658-6150
Thomas Nichols, prin. Fax 658-6158
Poole MS 800/6-8
800 Eustace Rd 22554 540-658-6190
Robert Bingham, prin. Fax 658-6176
Stafford MS 500/6-8
101 Spartan Dr 22554 540-658-6210
Mark Smith, prin. Fax 658-6204
Thompson MS 1,100/6-8
75 Walpole St 22554 540-658-6420
Andrew Grider, prin. Fax 658-6430
Wright MS 800/6-8
100 Wood Dr, 540-658-6240
William Boatwright, prin. Fax 658-6238
Other Schools – See Falmouth, Fredericksburg

Grace Preparatory S 100/PK-12
2202 Jefferson Davis Hwy 22554 540-657-4500

Stanardsville, Greene, Pop. 363
Greene County SD 3,100/PK-12
PO Box 1140 22973 434-939-9000
Dr. Andrea Whitmarsh, supt. Fax 985-4686
www.greenecountyschools.com
Greene County Technical Education Center Vo/Tech
10415 Spotswood Trl 22973 434-939-9005
Scott Lucas, prin. Fax 985-2071
Monroe HS 900/9-12
254 Monroe Dr 22973 434-939-9004
Kyle Pursel, prin. Fax 985-1461
Monroe MS 700/6-8
148 Monroe Dr 22973 434-939-9003
Katie Brunelle, prin. Fax 985-1359

Staunton, Staunton, Pop. 23,179
Augusta County SD
Supt. — See Verona
Beverley Manor MS 700/6-8
58 Cedar Green Rd 24401 540-886-5806
Dr. Sarah Melton, prin. Fax 886-4019
Riverheads HS 500/9-12
19 Howardsville Rd 24401 540-337-1921
Max Lowe, prin. Fax 337-0258

Staunton CSD 2,600/K-12
116 W Beverley St 24401 540-332-3920
Dr. Linda Reviea, supt. Fax 332-3924
www.staunton.k12.va.us
Genesis Alternative Education Alt
1751 Shutterlee Mill Rd 24401 540-332-3934
Robert Craft, dir. Fax 332-3973
Lee HS 700/9-12
1200 N Coalter St 24401 540-332-3926
Dr. Mark Rowicki, prin. Fax 332-3994
Shelburne MS 600/6-8
300 Grubert Ave 24401 540-332-3930
Jennifer Morris, prin. Fax 332-3933

Grace Christian HS 100/9-12
19 S Market St 24401 540-886-9109
Brian Fitzgerald, prin. Fax 886-5958
Mary Baldwin College Post-Sec.
PO Box 1500 24402 540-887-7019
Staunton School of Cosmetology Post-Sec.
PO Box 2385 24402 540-885-0808
Stuart Hall S 200/6-12
PO Box 210 24402 540-885-0356
Mark Eastham, head sch Fax 886-2275
Virginia School for the Deaf and Blind Post-Sec.
PO Box 2069 24402 540-332-9000

Stephens City, Frederick, Pop. 1,772
Frederick County SD
Supt. — See Winchester
Aylor MS 700/6-8
901 Aylor Rd 22655 540-869-3736
David Rudy, prin. Fax 867-2756
Sherando HS 1,500/9-12
185 S Warrior Dr 22655 540-869-0060
John Nelson, prin. Fax 869-5183

Shenandoah Valley Christian Academy 200/PK-12
PO Box 1360 22655 540-869-4600
Julie Curry, supt. Fax 869-4679

Sterling, Loudoun, Pop. 26,953
Loudoun County SD
Supt. — See Ashburn
Dominion HS 1,400/9-12
21326 Augusta Dr 20164 571-434-4400
Dr. W. John Brewer, prin. Fax 434-4401
Park View HS 1,300/9-12
400 W Laurel Ave 20164 571-434-4500
Kirk Dolson, prin. Fax 434-4501
River Bend MS 1,200/6-8
46240 Algonkian Pkwy 20165 571-434-3220
David Shaffer, prin. Fax 444-7578
Seneca Ridge MS 1,000/6-8
98 Seneca Ridge Dr 20164 571-434-4420
Katy Garvey, prin. Fax 444-7567
Sterling MS 1,000/6-8
201 W Holly Ave 20164 571-434-4520
Gus Martinez, prin. Fax 444-7492

Strasburg, Shenandoah, Pop. 6,272
Shenandoah County SD
Supt. — See Woodstock
Signal Knob MS 500/6-8
687 Sandy Hook Rd 22657 540-465-3422
Christopher Cook, prin. Fax 465-5412
Strasburg HS 700/9-12
250 Ram Dr 22657 540-465-5195
Morgan Saeler, prin. Fax 465-5461

Stuart, Patrick, Pop. 1,391
Patrick County SD 2,800/PK-12
PO Box 346 24171 276-694-3163
William Sroufe Ed.D., supt. Fax 694-3170
www.patrick.k12.va.us
Patrick County HS 1,000/8-12
215 Cougar Ln 24171 276-694-7137
Trey Cox, prin. Fax 694-6997

Stuarts Draft, Augusta, Pop. 9,108
Augusta County SD
Supt. — See Verona
Stuarts Draft HS 700/9-12
1028 Augusta Farms Rd 24477 540-946-7600
James Nycum, prin. Fax 946-7605
Stuarts Draft MS 500/6-8
1088 Augusta Farms Rd 24477 540-946-7611
Scott Musick, prin. Fax 946-7613

Ridgeview Christian S 100/PK-12
PO Box 477 24477 540-337-1025
Jeremy Woody, prin.

Suffolk, Suffolk, Pop. 82,776
Jointly Operated Vo Tech SD
Supt. — None - Lolita Hall, dir.
Pruden Center for Industry/Technology Vo/Tech
4169 Pruden Blvd 23434 757-925-5651
Andre Skinner, dir. Fax 925-5639

Suffolk CSD 14,200/PK-12
100 N Main St 23434 757-925-6750
Dr. Deran Whitney, supt. Fax 925-6751
www.spsk12.net/
Forest Glen MS 400/6-8
200 Forest Glen Dr 23434 757-925-5780
Melvin Bradshaw, prin. Fax 925-5557
Kennedy MS 600/6-8
2325 E Washington St 23434 757-934-6212
Vivian Covington, prin. Fax 925-5594

King's Fork HS 1,500/9-12
351 Kings Fork Rd 23434 757-923-5240
Ron Leigh Ed.D., prin. Fax 923-5242
King's Fork MS 1,000/6-8
350 Kings Fork Rd 23434 757-923-5246
Jennifer Presson, prin. Fax 925-5754
Lakeland HS 1,100/9-12
214 Kenyon Rd 23434 757-925-5790
Douglas Wagoner, prin. Fax 925-5599
Nansemond River HS 1,500/9-12
3301 Nansemond Pkwy 23434 757-923-4101
Thomas McLemore, prin. Fax 538-5430
Turlington Woods S Alt
629 Turlington Rd 23434 757-934-6215
Kinsey Bynum, prin. Fax 925-5583
Yeates MS 1,100/6-8
4901 Bennetts Pasture Rd 23435 757-923-4105
Daniel O'Leary, prin. Fax 538-5416

Nansemond-Suffolk Academy 800/PK-12
3373 Pruden Blvd 23434 757-539-8789
Deborah Russell, head sch Fax 934-8363
Suffolk Beauty Academy Post-Sec.
860 Portsmouth Blvd 23434 757-934-0656
Suffolk Christian Academy 200/K-12
3488 Godwin Blvd 23434 757-925-4461
Tamra VanDorn, hdmstr. Fax 924-1194

Surry, Surry, Pop. 239
Surry County SD 900/PK-12
PO Box 317 23883 757-294-5229
Michael Thornton, supt. Fax 294-5263
www.surryschools.net
Other Schools – See Dendron

Sussex, Sussex, Pop. 256
Sussex County SD 1,100/K-12
21302 Sussex Dr 23884 434-246-1099
Arthur Jarrett Ed.D., supt. Fax 246-8214
www.sussex.k12.va.us
Sussex Central HS 300/9-12
21394 Sussex Dr 23884 434-246-6051
Alvina Matthews, prin. Fax 246-5503
Sussex Central MS 300/6-8
21356 Sussex Dr 23884 434-246-2251
Morris Taylor, prin. Fax 246-8912

Sweet Briar, Amherst

Sweet Briar College Post-Sec.
134 Chapel Rd 24595 434-381-6100

Swoope, Augusta
Augusta County SD
Supt. — See Verona
Buffalo Gap HS 500/9-12
1800 Buffalo Gap Hwy 24479 540-337-6021
Dr. Ian Marshall, prin. Fax 337-6236

Tangier, Accomack, Pop. 722
Accomack County SD
Supt. — See Accomac
Tangier S 100/K-12
PO Box 245 23440 757-891-2234
Dr. Nina Pruitt, prin. Fax 891-2572

Tappahannock, Essex, Pop. 2,335
Essex County SD 1,600/PK-12
PO Box 756 22560 804-443-4366
Dr. Scott Burckbuchler, supt. Fax 443-4498
www.essex.k12.va.us
Essex HS 500/9-12
PO Box 1006 22560 804-443-4301
Andrew Hipple, prin. Fax 443-4272
Essex IS 500/5-8
PO Box 609 22560 804-443-3040
Heather Gentry, prin. Fax 445-1079

Regional Academic Governors SD
Supt. — See Richmond
Chesapeake Bay Governor's S 10-12
PO Box 1410 22560 804-443-0267
Terri Perkins, dir. Fax 443-4039

St. Margaret's S 100/8-12
PO Box 158 22560 804-443-3357
Cathy Sgroi, head sch Fax 443-1832

Tazewell, Tazewell, Pop. 4,565
Tazewell County SD 6,300/PK-12
209 W Fincastle Tpke 24651 276-988-5511
George Brown, supt. Fax 988-6765
tazewell.k12.va.us
Tazewell County Career Technical Center Vo/Tech
260 Advantage Dr 24651 276-988-2529
Rodney Gillespie, prin. Fax 988-5494
Tazewell HS 600/9-12
167 Cosby Ln 24651 276-988-6502
Timothy Hollar, prin. Fax 988-3263
Tazewell MS 500/6-8
367 Hope St 24651 276-988-6513
Buffie Crabtree, prin. Fax 988-2363
Other Schools – See Bluefield, Richlands

The Plains, Fauquier, Pop. 213
Fauquier County SD
Supt. — See Warrenton
Marshall MS 500/6-8
4048 Zulla Rd 20198 540-422-7450
David Graham, prin. Fax 422-7469

Wakefield S 400/PK-12
PO Box 107 20198 540-253-7600
David Colon, hdmstr. Fax 253-5492

Toano, James City
Williamsburg-James City County SD
Supt. — See Williamsburg
Toano MS 700/6-8
7817 Richmond Rd 23168 757-566-4251
Tracey Jones, prin. Fax 566-3006

Triangle, Prince William, Pop. 7,762
Prince William County SD
Supt. — See Manassas
Graham Park MS 900/6-8
3613 Graham Park Rd 22172 703-221-2118
Maria Ramadane, prin. Fax 221-1079

Verona, Augusta, Pop. 4,194
Augusta County SD 10,400/K-12
PO Box 960 24482 540-245-5100
Dr. Eric Bond, supt. Fax 245-5115
www.augusta.k12.va.us
Other Schools – See Fishersville, Fort Defiance, Staunton, Stuarts Draft, Swoope

Victoria, Lunenburg, Pop. 1,693
Lunenburg County SD
Supt. — See Kenbridge
Central HS 400/9-12
131 K V Rd 23974 434-696-2137
John Long, prin. Fax 696-1322
Lunenburg MS 400/6-8
583 Tomlinson Rd 23974 434-696-2161
Dr. Sharon Stanislause, prin. Fax 696-2162

Vienna, Fairfax, Pop. 15,197
Fairfax County SD
Supt. — See Falls Church
Kilmer MS 1,300/7-8
8100 Wolftrap Rd 22182 703-846-8800
Ronald James, prin. Fax 846-8897
Madison HS 2,000/9-12
2500 James Madison Dr 22181 703-319-2300
Dan Meier, prin. Fax 319-2397
Oakton HS 2,200/9-12
2900 Sutton Rd 22181 703-319-2700
John Banbury, prin. Fax 319-2797
Thoreau MS 800/7-8
2505 Cedar Ln 22180 703-846-8000
Greg Hood, prin. Fax 846-8097

Fairfax Christian S 200/K-12
1624 Hunter Mill Rd 22182 703-759-5100
Jo Thoburn, pres. Fax 759-2143
National Personal Training Institute Post-Sec.
8500 Leesburg Pike Ste 308 22182 703-988-6528
Silk Road Academy 100/K-12
810 Hillcrest Dr 22180 571-252-3472
Bethany Walker, head sch
University of North America Post-Sec.
8618 Westwood Center Dr 22182 571-633-9651
University of the Potomac Post-Sec.
2070 Chain Bridge Rd # G100 22182 703-709-5875
Vienna Adventist Academy 100/PK-12
340 Courthouse Rd SW 22180 703-938-6200
Dwight Morgan, prin. Fax 938-3934

Vinton, Roanoke, Pop. 7,942
Roanoke County SD
Supt. — See Roanoke
Byrd HS 1,200/9-12
2902 E Washington Ave 24179 540-890-3090
Dr. Richard Turner, prin. Fax 890-7568
Byrd MS 800/6-8
2910 E Washington Ave 24179 540-890-1035
Tammy Newcomb, prin. Fax 890-0703

Mineral Springs Christian S 100/PK-10
1030 Bible Ln 24179 540-890-4465
Kim Morris, admin. Fax 890-3185

Virginia Beach, Virginia Beach, Pop. 422,328
Virginia Beach CSD 69,500/PK-12
PO Box 6038 23456 757-263-1000
Dr. Aaron Spence, supt. Fax 263-1397
www.vbschools.com/
Advanced Technology Center Vo/Tech
1800 College Cres, 757-648-5800
Michael Taylor, dir. Fax 468-4235
Bayside HS 1,900/9-12
4960 Haygood Rd 23455 757-648-5200
James Miller, prin. Fax 473-5123
Bayside MS 700/7-8
965 Newtown Rd 23462 757-648-4400
Dr. Paula Johnson, prin. Fax 473-5185
Brandon MS 1,200/6-8
1700 Pope St 23464 757-648-4450
Dr. Christy McQueeney, prin. Fax 366-4550
Corporate Landing MS 1,300/6-8
1597 Corporate Landing Pkwy 23454 757-648-4500
Freddie Alarcon, prin. Fax 437-6487
Cox HS 1,900/9-12
2425 Shorehaven Dr 23454 757-648-5250
Dr. Randi Riesbeck, prin. Fax 496-6731
First Colonial HS 2,000/9-12
1272 Mill Dam Rd 23454 757-648-5300
Dr. Nancy Farrell, prin. Fax 496-6719
Great Neck MS 1,100/6-8
1848 N Great Neck Rd 23454 757-648-4550
Dr. Eugene Soltner, prin. Fax 496-6774
Green Run HS 1,700/9-12
1700 Dahlia Dr, 757-648-5350
Todd Tarkenton, prin. Fax 431-4153
Independence MS 1,300/6-8
1370 Dunstan Ln 23455 757-648-4600
Carey Manugo, prin. Fax 460-0508
Kellam HS 1,800/9-12
2665 West Neck Rd 23456 757-648-5100
Bruce Biehl, prin. Fax 648-5133
Kempsville HS 1,600/9-12
5194 Chief Trl 23464 757-648-5450
William Harris, prin. Fax 474-7919
Kempsville MS 800/6-8
860 Churchill Dr 23464 757-648-4700
Dr. Patti Jenkins, prin. Fax 474-8449
Landstown HS 2,300/9-12
2001 Concert Dr 23456 757-648-5500
Dr. Brian Matney, prin. Fax 468-1860

Landstown MS 1,500/6-8
2204 Recreation Dr 23456 757-648-4750
John Parkman, prin. Fax 430-3247
Larkspur MS 1,700/6-8
4696 Princess Anne Rd 23462 757-648-4800
Melanie Hamblin, prin. Fax 474-8598
Lynnhaven MS 1,000/6-8
1250 Bayne Dr 23454 757-648-4850
Dr. Violet Hoyle, prin. Fax 496-6793
Ocean Lakes HS 2,200/9-12
885 Schumann Dr 23454 757-648-5550
Dr. Cheryl Askew, prin. Fax 721-4309
Plaza MS 1,100/6-8
3080 S Lynnhaven Rd 23452 757-648-4900
Rodney Burnsworth, prin. Fax 431-5331
Princess Anne HS 1,800/9-12
4400 Virginia Beach Blvd 23462 757-648-5600
Dr. Daniel Smith, prin. Fax 473-5004
Princess Anne MS 1,500/6-8
2323 Holland Rd, 757-648-4950
Alex Bergren, prin. Fax 430-0972
Renaissance Academy Alt
5100 Cleveland St 23462 757-648-6000
Kay Thomas, prin. Fax 473-5111
Salem HS 1,800/9-12
1993 Sundevil Dr 23464 757-648-5650
Matthew Delaney, prin. Fax 474-0100
Salem MS 1,000/6-8
2380 Lynnhaven Pkwy 23464 757-648-5000
Dr. James Smith, prin. Fax 474-8467
Tallwood HS 2,000/9-12
1668 Kempsville Rd 23464 757-648-5700
Dr. James Avila, prin. Fax 479-5534
Technical & Career Education Center Vo/Tech
2925 North Landing Rd 23456 757-648-5850
David Swanger, dir. Fax 427-5558
Virginia Beach MS 900/6-8
600 25th St 23451 757-648-5050
Dr. Sandra Brown, prin. Fax 437-4708
Adult Learning Center Adult
5100 Cleveland St 23462 757-648-6050
Paul Palonbo, dir. Fax 648-6078

Advanced Technology Institute Post-Sec.
5700 Southern Blvd # 100 23462 757-490-1241
Atlantic University Post-Sec.
215 67th St 23451 757-631-8101
Bishop Sullivan Catholic HS 400/9-12
4552 Princess Anne Rd 23462 757-467-2881
Dennis Price, prin. Fax 467-0284
Bryant & Stratton College Post-Sec.
301 Centre Pointe Dr 23462 757-499-7900
Cape Henry Collegiate 900/PK-12
1320 Mill Dam Rd 23454 757-481-2446
Dr. Christopher S. Garran, head sch Fax 481-9194
Centura College Post-Sec.
2697 Dean Dr Ste 100 23452 757-340-2121
ECPI University Post-Sec.
5555 Greenwich Rd Ste 300 23462 757-671-7171
Gateway Christian Academy PK-12
5473 Virginia Beach Blvd 23462 757-499-6551
OakTree Academy 200/PK-12
817 Kempsville Rd 23464 757-248-9560
Terri Turley, dir. Fax 248-9594
Regent University Post-Sec.
1000 Regent University Dr 23464 757-352-4127
Rudy & Kelly Academy of Hair & Nails Post-Sec.
1920 Centerville Tpke # 114 23464 757-473-0994
Stratford University Post-Sec.
555 S Independence Blvd 23452 757-497-4466
Tidewater Community College Post-Sec.
1700 College Cres, 757-822-7100
Virginia Beach Friends S 100/PK-12
1537 Laskin Rd 23451 757-428-7534
Linda Serrette, head sch Fax 428-7511
Virginia Beach Theological Seminary Post-Sec.
2221 Centerville Tpke 23464 757-479-3706

Wakefield, Sussex, Pop. 921

Tidewater Academy 200/PK-12
217 W Church St 23888 757-899-5401

Warm Springs, Bath, Pop. 122
Bath County SD 600/PK-12
PO Box 67 24484 540-839-2722
Sue Hirsh, supt. Fax 839-3040
www.bath.k12.va.us
Other Schools – See Hot Springs

Warrenton, Fauquier, Pop. 9,361
Fauquier County SD 11,100/PK-12
320 Hospital Dr Ste 40 20186 540-422-7000
Dr. David Jeck, supt. Fax 422-7057
www.fcps1.org
Auburn MS 600/6-8
7270 Riley Rd 20187 540-422-7410
Steve Kadilak, prin. Fax 422-7429
Fauquier HS 1,200/9-12
705 Waterloo Rd 20186 540-422-7300
Clarence Burton, prin. Fax 347-0089
Taylor MS 400/6-8
350 E Shirley Ave 20186 540-422-7470
Ruth Nelson, prin. Fax 422-7489
Warrenton MS 500/6-8
244 Waterloo St 20186 540-422-7490
Barbara Bannister, prin. Fax 422-7509
Other Schools – See Bealeton, Midland, Nokesville, The Plains

Regional Academic Governors SD
Supt. — See Richmond
Mountain Vista Governor's S 11-12
6480 College St 20187 540-347-6237
Dr. Rosanne Williamson, prin. Fax 266-3617

Covenant Christian Academy 100/K-10
6317 Vint Hill Rd 20187 540-680-4111
Amber Sabia, head sch

Highland S 500/PK-12
597 Broadview Ave 20186 540-878-2700
Henry Berg, head sch Fax 878-2731
Providence Christian Academy 100/PK-12
6872 Watson Ct 20187 540-349-4989
Rev. Young Shin, hdmstr. Fax 349-3915

Warsaw, Richmond, Pop. 1,495
Jointly Operated Vo Tech SD
Supt. — None - Lolita Hall, dir.
Northern Neck Technical Center Vo/Tech
13946 History Land Hwy 22572 804-333-4940
Bernard Davis, prin. Fax 333-0538

Richmond County SD 900/K-12
PO Box 1507 22572 804-333-3681
James Smith Ed.D., supt. Fax 333-5586
www.richmond-county.k12.va.us
Rappahannock HS 400/8-12
6914 Richmond Rd 22572 804-333-3551
David Ferguson, prin. Fax 333-5186

Washington, Rappahannock, Pop. 133
Rappahannock County SD 900/K-12
6 School House Rd 22747 540-227-0023
Donna Matthews, supt. Fax 987-8896
www.rappahannockschools.us
Rappahannock County HS 400/8-12
12576 Lee Hwy 22747 540-227-0745
Michael Tupper, prin. Fax 987-9331

Waynesboro, Waynesboro, Pop. 20,421
Waynesboro CSD 3,200/PK-12
301 Pine Ave 22980 540-946-4600
Dr. Jeffrey Cassell, supt. Fax 946-4608
www.waynesboro.k12.va.us
Collins MS 600/6-8
1625 Ivy St 22980 540-946-4635
Janet Buchheit, prin. Fax 946-4642
Waynesboro HS 900/9-12
1200 W Main St 22980 540-946-4616
Tim Teachey, prin. Fax 946-4621

Fishburne Military S 100/7-12
225 S Wayne Ave 22980 540-946-7700

Weems, Lancaster
Lancaster County SD 1,300/PK-12
2330 Irvington Rd 22576 804-462-5100
Steve Parker, supt. Fax 435-3309
www.lcs.k12.va.us
Other Schools – See Kilmarnock, Lancaster

West Point, King William, Pop. 3,232
West Point SD 800/PK-12
PO Box T 23181 804-843-4368
Laura Abel, supt. Fax 843-4421
www.wpschools.net
West Point HS 300/9-12
2700 Mattaponi Ave 23181 804-843-3630
Mark Dorsey, prin. Fax 843-3406
West Point MS 200/6-8
1040 Thompson Ave 23181 804-843-9810
Nathan Leach, prin. Fax 843-9812

Weyers Cave, Augusta, Pop. 2,429

Blue Ridge Community College Post-Sec.
PO Box 80 24486 540-234-9261

Williamsburg, Williamsburg, Pop. 13,648
Williamsburg-James City County SD 11,000/K-12
PO Box 8783 23187 757-603-6400
Steven Constantino Ed.D., supt.
wjccschools.org/web/
Berkeley MS 900/6-8
1118 Ironbound Rd 23188 757-229-8051
Amour Mickel, prin. Fax 229-6133
Hornsby MS 900/6-8
850 Jolly Pond Rd 23188 757-565-9400
Jessica Ellison, prin. Fax 565-9401
Jamestown HS 1,300/9-12
3751 John Tyler Hwy 23185 757-259-3600
Dr. Cathy Worley, prin. Fax 259-3759
Lafayette HS 1,200/9-12
4460 Longhill Rd 23188 757-565-0373
Anita Swinton, prin. Fax 565-4268
Warhill HS 1,100/9-12
4615 Opportunity Way 23188 757-565-4615
Dr. Jeffrey Carroll, prin. Fax 565-9101
Other Schools – See Toano

York County SD
Supt. — See Yorktown
Bruton HS 600/9-12
185 E Rochambeau Dr 23188 757-220-4050
Arletha Dockery, prin. Fax 220-4090
Queens Lake MS 400/6-8
124 W Queens Dr 23185 757-220-4080
Scott Meadows, prin. Fax 220-4074
School of the Arts 9-12
185 E Rochambeau Dr 23188 757-220-4050
Arletha Dockery, prin. Fax 369-2611

College of William and Mary Post-Sec.
PO Box 8795 23187 757-221-4000

Providence Classical S 200/K-12
6000 Easter Cir 23188 757-565-2900
Susan Oweis, head sch Fax 565-3720
Walsingham Academy Upper S 200/8-12
PO Box 8702 23187 757-229-6026
Sr. Mary Jeanne Osterle, prin. Fax 259-1401
Williamsburg Christian Academy 200/PK-12
101 School House Ln 23188 757-220-1978
Dr. David Breslin, head sch Fax 741-4009

Winchester, Winchester, Pop. 25,545
Frederick County SD 13,100/K-12
PO Box 3508 22604 540-662-3888
Dr. David Sovine, supt. Fax 722-2788
www.frederick.k12.va.us
Byrd MS 900/6-8
134 Rosa Ln 22602 540-662-0500
Teresa Ritenour, prin. Fax 662-7790
Frederick County MS 700/6-8
4661 N Frederick Pike 22603 540-888-4296
Susan Brinkmeier, prin. Fax 888-3101
Howard Center Vo/Tech
156 Dowell J Cir 22602 540-662-8997
Janelle Ball-Brooks, dir. Fax 662-9112
Millbrook HS 1,300/9-12
251 First Woods Dr 22603 540-545-2800
Carolyn Butler, prin. Fax 545-7962
Wood HS 1,300/9-12
161 Apple Pie Ridge Rd 22603 540-667-5226
Joseph Salyer, prin. Fax 667-3154
Wood MS 900/6-8
1313 Amherst St 22601 540-667-7500
Grant Javersak, prin. Fax 667-7500
Other Schools – See Stephens City

Winchester CSD 4,200/PK-12
PO Box 551 22604 540-667-4253
Dr. Jason Van Heukelum, supt. Fax 667-4253
www.wps.k12.va.us
Handley HS 1,200/9-12
PO Box 910 22604 540-662-3471
Michael Dufrene, prin. Fax 722-6722
Morgan MS 1,300/5-8
48 S Purcell Ave 22601 540-667-7171
Jerry Putt, prin. Fax 723-8897

Grafton School Post-Sec.
PO Box 2500 22604 540-542-0200
Mountain View Christian Academy 100/K-12
153 Narrow Ln 22602 540-868-1231
Dr. Minta Hardman, admin. Fax 869-8976
Shenandoah University Post-Sec.
1460 University Dr 22601 540-665-4500
Winchester Memorial Hospital Post-Sec.
PO Box 3340 22604 540-722-8000

Windsor, Isle of Wight, Pop. 2,598
Isle of Wight County SD
Supt. — See Smithfield
Tyler MS 400/6-8
23320 N Court St 23487 757-242-3229
Jessica Harding, prin. Fax 242-8105
Windsor HS 500/9-12
24 Church St 23487 757-242-6172
Daniel Soderholm, prin. Fax 242-4948

Wirtz, Franklin

Smith Mountain Lake Christian Academy 50/PK-12
2485 Lost Mountain Rd # B 24184 540-719-1192
Lincoln Bryan, admin. Fax 721-4627

Wise, Wise, Pop. 3,248
Wise County SD 6,200/PK-12
PO Box 1217 24293 276-328-8017
Greg Mullins, dir. Fax 328-3350
www.wisek12.org
Addington MS 500/5-8
PO Box 977 24293 276-328-8821
Greg Jessee, prin. Fax 328-2044
Wise County Career-Technical Center Vo/Tech
PO Box 1218 24293 276-328-6113
Larry Hamilton, prin. Fax 328-4443
Other Schools – See Big Stone Gap, Coeburn, Norton

University of Virginia College at Wise Post-Sec.
1 College Ave 24293 276-328-0100
Wise County Christian S 100/PK-12
PO Box 3297 24293 276-328-3297
Eddie Mullins, admin. Fax 328-3248

Woodberry Forest, Madison

Woodberry Forest S 400/9-12
898 Woodberry Forest Rd 22989 540-672-3900
Dr. Byron Hulsey, hdmstr. Fax 672-0928

Woodbridge, Prince William, Pop. 3,887
Prince William County SD
Supt. — See Manassas
Beville MS 1,100/6-8
4901 Dale Blvd 22193 703-878-2593
Timothy Keenan, prin. Fax 730-1274
Forest Park HS 2,400/9-12
15721 Forest Park Dr 22193 703-583-3200
Richard Martinez, prin. Fax 583-6867
Freedom HS 2,000/9-12
15201 Neabsco Mills Rd 22191 703-583-1405
Inez Bryant, prin. Fax 583-8705
Gar-Field HS 2,500/9-12
14000 Smoketown Rd 22192 703-730-7000
Dr. Cherif Sadki, prin. Fax 730-7197
Godwin MS 1,100/6-8
14800 Darbydale Ave 22193 703-670-6166
Jehovanni Mitchell, prin. Fax 670-9888
Hylton HS 2,400/9-12
14051 Spriggs Rd 22193 703-580-4000
David Cassady, prin. Fax 580-4299
Lake Ridge MS 1,200/6-8
12350 Mohican Rd 22192 703-494-5154
Christie Taylor, prin. Fax 494-8246
Lynn MS 1,000/6-8
1650 Prince William Pkwy 22191 703-494-5157
Jorge Neves, prin. Fax 491-5141
Rippon MS 1,200/6-8
15101 Blackburn Rd 22191 703-491-2171
Gail Stone, prin. Fax 491-2487
Woodbridge HS 2,900/9-12
3001 Old Bridge Rd 22192 703-497-8000
David Huckestein, prin. Fax 497-8117
Woodbridge MS 1,200/6-8
2201 York Dr 22191 703-494-3181
Skyles Calhoun, prin. Fax 491-1441

Christ Chapel Academy 600/PK-12
13909 Smoketown Rd 22192 703-670-3822
Rev. Paul Miklich, admin. Fax 897-7905
Everest College Post-Sec.
14555 Potomac Mills Rd 22192 571-408-2100
Heritage Christian S 400/PK-12
14510 Spriggs Rd 22193 703-680-6629
Stratford University Post-Sec.
14349 Gideon Dr 22192 703-897-1982

Woodstock, Shenandoah, Pop. 5,017
Shenandoah County SD 6,200/PK-12
600 N Main St Ste 200 22664 540-459-6222
Dr. Mark Johnston, supt. Fax 459-6707
www.shenandoah.k12.va.us
Central HS 800/9-12
1147 Susan Ave 22664 540-459-2161
Melissa Hensley, prin. Fax 459-5932
Muhlenberg MS 600/6-8
1251 Susan Ave 22664 540-459-2941
Mandy Roller, prin. Fax 459-5965
Other Schools – See Mount Jackson, Quicksburg, Strasburg

Massanutten Military Academy 100/6-12
614 S Main St 22664 540-459-2167
Dr. David Skipper, head sch Fax 459-5421

Wytheville, Wythe, Pop. 8,065
Wythe County SD 4,300/PK-12
1570 W Reservoir St 24382 276-228-5411
Dr. Jeff Perry, supt. Fax 228-9192
wcps.wythe.k12.va.us
Scott Memorial MS 300/6-8
950 S 7th St 24382 276-228-2851
Brad Haga, prin. Fax 228-8261
Wythe Co. Technical Center Vo/Tech
1505 W Spiller St 24382 276-228-5481
Anthony Sykes, prin. Fax 228-8254
Wythe HS 400/9-12
1 Maroon Way 24382 276-228-3157
Dante Lee, prin. Fax 228-4124
Other Schools – See Max Meadows, Rural Retreat

Wytheville Community College Post-Sec.
1000 E Main St 24382 276-223-4700

Yorktown, York, Pop. 195
York County SD 12,300/PK-12
302 Dare Rd 23692 757-898-0300
Dr. Victor Shandor, supt. Fax 890-0771
www.yorkcountyschools.org
Grafton HS 1,200/9-12
403 Grafton Dr 23692 757-898-0530
Royce Hart, prin. Fax 898-0533
Grafton MS 900/6-8
405 Grafton Dr 23692 757-898-0525
Paul Rice, prin. Fax 898-0534
Tabb HS 1,100/9-12
4431 Big Bethel Rd 23693 757-867-7400
Angela Seiders, prin. Fax 867-7414
Tabb MS 900/6-8
300 Yorktown Rd 23693 757-898-0320
Heather Young, prin. Fax 867-7425
York HS 1,100/9-12
9300 George Washington Mem 23692 757-898-0354
Dr. Shannon Butler, prin. Fax 898-8235
Yorktown MS 800/6-8
11201 George Washington Mem 23690 757-898-0360
Susan Hutton, prin. Fax 898-0412
Other Schools – See Williamsburg

Summit Christian Academy 100/7-12
4209 Big Bethel Rd 23693 757-867-7005
Tim Grimes, hdmstr.

WASHINGTON

WASHINGTON DEPARTMENT OF EDUCATION
PO Box 47200, Olympia 98504-7200
Telephone 360-725-6000
Fax 360-753-6712
Website http://www.k12.wa.us

Superintendent of Public Instruction Chris Reykdal

WASHINGTON BOARD OF EDUCATION
PO Box 47206, Olympia 98504-7206

Executive Director

EDUCATIONAL SERVICE DISTRICTS (ESD)

North Central ESD 171
Dr. Richard McBride, supt. 509-665-2610
PO Box 1847, Wenatchee 98807 Fax 662-9027
www.ncesd.org
Northeast Washington ESD 101
Dr. Michael Dunn, supt. 509-789-3800
4202 S Regal St, Spokane 99223 Fax 789-3780
www.esd101.net
Northwest ESD 189
Dr. Gerald Jenkins, supt. 360-299-4000
1601 R Ave, Anacortes 98221 Fax 299-4070
www.nwesd.org/

Olympic ESD 114
Greg Lynch, supt. 360-479-0993
105 National Ave N Fax 478-6869
Bremerton 98312
www.oesd.wednet.edu
ESD 123
Bruce Hawkins, supt. 509-547-8441
3918 W Court St, Pasco 99301 Fax 544-5795
www.esd123.org
Puget Sound ESD
John Welch, supt. 800-917-7600
800 Oakesdale Ave SW Fax 917-7777
Renton 98057
www.psesd.org

ESD 113
Dana Anderson, supt. 360-464-6700
6005 Tyee Dr SW, Tumwater 98512 Fax 464-6900
www.esd113.org
ESD 112
Dr. Tim Merlino, supt. 360-750-7500
2500 NE 65th Ave Fax 750-9706
Vancouver 98661
www.esd112.org
ESD 105
Steve Myers, supt. 509-575-2885
33 S 2nd Ave, Yakima 98902 Fax 575-2918
www.esd105.org/

PUBLIC, PRIVATE AND CATHOLIC SECONDARY SCHOOLS

Aberdeen, Grays Harbor, Pop. 16,223
Aberdeen SD 5 3,300/PK-12
216 N G St 98520 360-538-2000
Dr. Thomas Opstad Ed.D., supt. Fax 538-2014
www.asd5.org
Aberdeen HS 900/9-12
410 N G St 98520 360-538-2040
Sherri Northington, prin. Fax 538-2046
Harbor HS 100/Alt
300 N Williams St 98520 360-538-2180
Derek Cook, prin. Fax 538-2183
Miller JHS 500/7-8
100 E Lindstrom St 98520 360-538-2100
Lisa Griebel, prin. Fax 538-2106
Twin Harbors Skills Center Vo/Tech
410 N G St 98520 360-538-2038
Lynn Green, dir. Fax 538-2057

Wishkah Valley SD 117 100/K-12
4640 Wishkah Rd 98520 360-532-3128
Dennis Johnson, supt. Fax 533-4638
www.wishkah.org
Wishkah Valley S 100/K-12
4640 Wishkah Rd 98520 360-532-3128
Dennis Johnson, supt. Fax 533-4638

Grays Harbor College Post-Sec.
1620 Edward P Smith Dr 98520 360-532-9020

Amanda Park, Grays Harbor, Pop. 240
Lake Quinault SD 97 200/K-12
PO Box 38 98526 360-288-2260
Rich DuBois, supt. Fax 288-2732
www.lakequinaultschools.org
Lake Quinault MSHS 100/6-12
PO Box 38 98526 360-288-2414
Keith Samplawski, prin. Fax 288-2209

Amboy, Clark, Pop. 1,593
Battle Ground SD 119
Supt. — See Brush Prairie
Amboy MS 600/5-8
22115 NE Chelatchie Rd 98601 360-885-6050
Michael Maloney, prin. Fax 885-6055

Anacortes, Skagit, Pop. 15,315
Anacortes SD 103 2,700/PK-12
2200 M Ave 98221 360-293-1200
Dr. Mark Wenzel, supt. Fax 293-1222
www.asd103.org
Anacortes HS 900/9-12
1600 20th St 98221 360-293-2166
Jon Ronngren, prin. Fax 293-0744
Anacortes MS 400/7-8
2202 M Ave 98221 360-293-1230
Patrick Harrington, prin. Fax 293-1231
Cap Sante HS 50/Alt
1717 J Ave 98221 360-293-1225
Kecia Fox, admin. Fax 293-0744
Other Schools – See Mount Vernon

Arlington, Snohomish, Pop. 17,235
Arlington SD 16 6,200/PK-12
315 N French Ave 98223 360-618-6200
Dr. Chrys Sweeting Ed.D., supt. Fax 618-6221
www.asd.wednet.edu
Arlington HS 1,600/9-12
18821 Crown Ridge Blvd 98223 360-618-6300
Brian Beckley, prin. Fax 618-6310
Haller MS 700/6-8
600 E 1st St 98223 360-618-6400
Jeff Larson, prin. Fax 618-6411
Post MS 600/6-8
1220 E 5th St 98223 360-618-6450
Voni Walker, prin. Fax 618-6455
Stillaguamish Valley Learning Center 200/Alt
1215 E 5th St 98223 360-618-6440
Joseph Doucette, prin. Fax 435-1359
Weston HS 100/Alt
4407 172nd St NE 98223 360-618-6340
Will Nelson, prin. Fax 618-6341

Arlington Christian S 50/PK-12
PO Box 3337 98223 360-652-2988
Wendy Tavenner, admin. Fax 652-2921

Asotin, Asotin, Pop. 1,220
Asotin-Anatone SD 420 600/PK-12
PO Box 489 99402 509-243-1100
Dale Bonfield, supt. Fax 243-4251
www.aasd.wednet.edu
Asotin JSHS 300/6-12
PO Box 489 99402 509-243-4151
Jerry Uhling, prin. Fax 243-4090

Auburn, King, Pop. 65,915
Auburn SD 408 14,800/K-12
915 4th St NE 98002 253-931-4900
Dr. Alan Spicciati, supt. Fax 931-8006
www.auburn.wednet.edu
Auburn HS 1,500/9-12
711 E Main St 98002 253-931-4880
Richard Zimmerman, prin. Fax 931-4701
Auburn Mountainview HS 1,500/9-12
28900 124th Ave SE 98092 253-804-4539
Terri Herren, prin. Fax 876-2507
Auburn Riverside HS 1,600/9-12
501 Oravetz Rd SE 98092 253-804-5154
Dave Halford, prin. Fax 804-5168
Cascade MS 700/6-8
1015 24th St NE 98002 253-931-4995
Isaiah Johnson, prin. Fax 833-7580
Mt. Baker MS 900/6-8
620 37th St SE 98002 253-804-4555
Greg Brown, prin. Fax 931-0661
Olympic MS 700/6-8
1825 K St SE 98002 253-931-4966
Jason Hill, prin. Fax 939-2753
Rainier MS 900/6-8
30620 116th Ave SE 98092 253-931-4843
Ben Talbert, prin. Fax 939-4318
West Auburn HS 300/Alt
401 W Main St 98001 253-931-4990
Jon Aarstad, prin. Fax 931-4707

Federal Way SD 210
Supt. — See Federal Way
Jefferson HS 1,700/9-12
4248 S 288th St 98001 253-945-5600
Adrienne Chacon, prin. Fax 945-5656
Kilo MS 500/6-8
4400 S 308th St 98001 253-945-4700
Margaret Peterson, prin. Fax 945-4747
Sequoyah MS 500/6-8
3425 S 360th St 98001 253-945-3670
Mike McCarthy, prin. Fax 945-3699

Auburn Adventist Academy 300/9-12
5000 Auburn Way S 98092 253-939-5000
John Soule, prin. Fax 351-9806
Green River Community College Post-Sec.
12401 SE 320th St 98092 253-833-9111
Rainier Christian MS 100/7-8
20 49th St NE 98002 253-639-7715
Don Garnand, prin. Fax 639-3184

Bainbridge Island, Kitsap, Pop. 22,174
Bainbridge Island SD 303 3,800/PK-12
8489 Madison Ave NE 98110 206-842-4714
Dr. Peter BangKnudsen, supt. Fax 842-2928
www.bisd303.org
Bainbridge HS 1,300/9-12
9330 NE High School Rd 98110 206-842-2634
Duane Fish, prin. Fax 780-1260
Eagle Harbor HS 100/Alt
9530 NE High School Rd 98110 206-780-1646
David Shockley, prin. Fax 855-0511
Woodward MS 500/7-8
9125 Sportsman Club Rd NE 98110 206-842-4787
Mike Florian, prin. Fax 780-4525

Battle Ground, Clark, Pop. 16,976
Battle Ground SD 119
Supt. — See Brush Prairie
Agriculture Science & Environmental Ed Alt
PO Box 200 98604 360-885-5361
Richard Hogg, lead tchr. Fax 885-5365
Battle Ground HS 2,100/9-12
PO Box 200 98604 360-885-6500
Mike Hamilton, prin. Fax 687-6590
CAM Academy 600/Alt
PO Box 200 98604 360-885-6803
Ryan Cowl, prin. Fax 885-6808
Chief Umtuch MS 600/5-8
PO Box 200 98604 360-885-6350
Elizabeth Beattie, prin. Fax 885-6355
Daybreak MS 500/5-8
PO Box 200 98604 360-885-6900
Kevin Palena, prin. Fax 885-6948
River HomeLink 800/Alt
PO Box 200 98604 360-334-8200
Mark Clements, prin. Fax 334-8223
Tukes Valley MS 500/5-8
PO Box 200 98604 360-885-6250
Brian Amundson, prin. Fax 885-6297

Columbia Adventist Academy 100/9-12
11100 NE 189th St 98604 360-687-3161
Firm Foundation Christian S 400/PK-12
1919 SW 25th Ave 98604 360-687-8382
Julie Olson, prin. Fax 687-8799

Belfair, Mason, Pop. 3,769
North Mason SD 403 2,100/PK-12
71 E Campus Dr 98528 360-277-2300
Dana Rosenbach, supt. Fax 277-2320
www.northmasonschools.org
Hawkins MS 400/6-8
300 E Campus Dr 98528 360-277-2302
Thomas Worlund, prin. Fax 277-2324
North Mason HS 700/9-12
200 E Campus Dr 98528 360-277-2303
Chad Collins, prin. Fax 277-2323
PACE Academy 50/Alt
71 E Campus Dr 98528 360-277-2210
Anne Crosby, admin. Fax 277-2320

Bellevue, King, Pop. 117,650
Bellevue SD 405 18,700/PK-12
PO Box 90010 98009 425-456-4000
Dr. J. Tim Mills Ed.D., supt. Fax 456-4176
www.bsd405.org
Bellevue Big Picture S 300/6-12
14844 SE 22nd St 98007 425-456-7800
Bethany Spinler, prin. Fax 456-7805
Bellevue HS 1,500/9-12
10416 Wolverine Way 98004 425-456-7000
Vic Anderson, prin. Fax 456-7005
Chinook MS 900/6-8
2001 98th Ave NE 98004 425-456-6300
Dr. Russell White, prin. Fax 456-6304
Highland MS 500/6-8
15027 Bel Red Rd 98007 425-456-6400
Katie Klug, prin. Fax 456-6499
Interlake HS 1,500/9-12
16245 NE 24th St 98008 425-456-7200
Maria Frieboes-Gee, prin. Fax 456-7215
International S 600/6-12
445 128th Ave SE 98005 425-456-6500
Jennifer Rose, prin. Fax 456-6565
Newport HS 1,700/9-12
4333 Factoria Blvd SE 98006 425-456-7400
Dion Yahoudy, prin. Fax 456-7530
Odle MS 800/6-8
11650 SE 60th St 98006 425-456-6600
Aaron Miller, prin. Fax 456-6616
Sammamish HS 1,000/9-12
100 140th Ave SE 98005 425-456-7600
Scott Powers, prin. Fax 456-7665
Tillicum MS 700/6-8
11650 SE 60th St 98006 425-456-6700
James Peterson, prin. Fax 456-6770
Tyee MS 900/6-8
13630 SE Allen Rd 98006 425-456-6800
Susan Thomas, prin. Fax 456-6801

Academic Institute 50/6-12
2495 140th Ave NE Ste D210 98005 425-401-6844
Bellevue College Post-Sec.
3000 Landerholm Cir SE 98007 425-564-1000
Dartmoor S 100/1-12
2340 130th Ave NE 98005 425-885-6296
Kimm Conroy M.Ed., head sch Fax 885-1137
DeVry University Post-Sec.
600 108th Ave NE Ste 230 98004 425-455-2242
Evergreen Beauty School Post-Sec.
14045 NE 20th St Ste B 98007 425-643-0270
Forest Ridge School of the Sacred Heart 400/5-12
4800 139th Ave SE 98006 425-641-0700
Mark Pierotti, head sch Fax 643-3881

Bellingham, Whatcom, Pop. 77,637
Bellingham SD 501 11,200/PK-12
1306 Dupont St 98225 360-676-6400
Dr. Greg Baker, supt. Fax 676-2793
bellinghamschools.org
Bellingham HS 1,100/9-12
2020 Cornwall Ave 98225 360-676-6575
Linda Miller, prin. Fax 647-6803
Fairhaven MS 600/6-8
110 Parkridge Rd 98225 360-676-6450
Robert Kalahan, prin. Fax 647-6887
Kulshan MS 600/6-8
1250 Kenoyer Dr, 360-676-4886
Meagan Dawson, prin. Fax 647-6892
Options HS 100/Alt
2015 Franklin St 98225 360-647-6871
Byron Gerard, prin. Fax 647-6872
Sehome HS 1,100/9-12
2700 Bill McDonald Pkwy 98225 360-676-6481
Michelle Kuss-Cybula, prin. Fax 647-6863
Shuksan MS 600/6-8
2717 Alderwood Ave 98225 360-676-6454
Amy Carder, prin. Fax 647-6879
Squalicum HS 1,300/9-12
3773 E McLeod Rd 98226 360-676-6471
James Everett, prin. Fax 676-6561
Whatcom MS 600/6-8
810 Halleck St 98225 360-676-6460
Jeffrey Coulter, prin. Fax 647-6881

Ferndale SD 502
Supt. — See Ferndale
Windward HS 200/9-12
5275 Northwest Dr 98226 360-383-9289
Kim Hawes, prin. Fax 383-9152

Meridian SD 505 1,800/PK-12
214 W Laurel Rd 98226 360-398-7111
Tom Churchill, supt. Fax 398-8966
www.meridian.wednet.edu
Meridian HS 500/9-12
194 W Laurel Rd 98226 360-398-8111
Derek Forbes, prin. Fax 398-7720
Other Schools – See Lynden

Bellingham Beauty School Post-Sec.
4192 Meridian St 98226 360-734-1090
Bellingham Technical College Post-Sec.
3028 Lindbergh Ave 98225 360-752-7000
Charter College Bellingham Post-Sec.
410 W Bakerview Rd 98226 360-647-5000
Explorations Academy 50/8-12
PO Box 3014 98227 360-671-8085
Abram Dickerson, head sch
Northwest Indian College Post-Sec.
2522 Kwina Rd 98226 360-676-2772
St. Paul's Academy 400/PK-12
1509 E Victor St 98225 360-733-1750
Toni & Guy Hairdressing Academy Post-Sec.
1411 Railroad Ave 98225 360-676-8444
Western Washington University Post-Sec.
516 High St 98225 360-650-3000
Whatcom Community College Post-Sec.
237 W Kellogg Rd 98226 360-383-3000

Benton City, Benton, Pop. 2,971
Kiona-Benton City SD 52 1,400/PK-12
1105 Dale Ave 99320 509-588-2000
Wade Haun, supt. Fax 588-5580
www.kibesd.org
Kiona-Benton City HS 500/9-12
1105 Dale Ave 99320 509-588-2140
Clay Henry, prin. Fax 588-2651
Kiona-Benton City MS 300/6-8
1105 Dale Ave 99320 509-588-2040
Chuck Feth, prin. Fax 588-2905

Bickleton, Klickitat, Pop. 87
Bickleton SD 203 100/K-12
PO Box 10 99322 509-896-5473
Ric Palmer, supt. Fax 896-2071
www.bickletonschools.org
Bickleton S 100/K-12
PO Box 10 99322 509-896-5473
Ric Palmer, prin. Fax 896-2071

Blaine, Whatcom, Pop. 4,469
Blaine SD 503 2,100/PK-12
765 H St 98230 360-332-5881
Ron Spanjer Ed.D., supt. Fax 332-7568
www.blaine.k12.wa.us
Blaine HS 700/9-12
1055 H St 98230 360-332-6045
Scott Ellis, prin. Fax 332-0333
Blaine MS 500/6-8
975 H St 98230 360-332-8226
Darren Benson, prin. Fax 332-0444

Bonney Lake, Pierce, Pop. 16,669
Sumner SD 320
Supt. — See Sumner
Bonney Lake HS 1,400/9-12
10920 199th Avenue Ct E, 253-891-5700
Cris Turner, prin. Fax 891-5797
Lakeridge MS 600/6-8
5909 Myers Rd E, 253-891-5100
Toby Udager, prin. Fax 891-5145
Mountain View MS 700/6-8
10921 199th Avenue Ct E, 253-891-5200
Curtis Hurst, prin. Fax 891-5245

Bothell, King, Pop. 32,149
Edmonds SD 15
Supt. — See Lynnwood
Lynnwood HS 1,500/9-12
18218 North Rd 98012 425-431-7520
David Golden, prin. Fax 431-7527

Northshore SD 417 20,000/PK-12
3330 Monte Villa Pkwy 98021 425-408-7701
Dr. Michelle Reid Ed.D., supt. Fax 408-7702
www.nsd.org
Bothell SHS 1,600/10-12
9130 NE 180th St 98011 425-408-7000
Bob Stewart, prin. Fax 408-7002
Canyon Park JHS 800/7-9
23723 23rd Ave SE 98021 425-408-6300
Sebastian Ziz, prin. Fax 408-6302
Northshore JHS 700/7-9
12101 NE 160th St 98011 425-408-6700
Tiffany Rodriguez, prin. Fax 408-6702
Secondary Academy for Success 200/Alt
22107 23rd Dr SE 98021 425-408-6600
Donna Tyo, prin. Fax 408-6602
Skyview JHS 900/7-9
21404 35th Ave SE 98021 425-408-6800
Dawn Mark, prin. Fax 408-6802
Other Schools – See Kenmore, Woodinville

Bastyr University Post-Sec.
14500 Juanita Dr NE 98028 425-602-3000
Cascadia Community College Post-Sec.
18345 Campus Way NE 98011 425-352-8000
Cedar Park Christian S - Bothell 1,100/PK-12
16300 112th Ave NE 98011 425-488-9778
Adam Lynch, admin. Fax 483-5765
Woodinville Montessori S - North Creek 300/PK-12
19102 N Creek Pkwy 98011 425-482-3184

Bremerton, Kitsap, Pop. 34,864
Bremerton SD 100-C 5,000/PK-12
134 Marion Ave N 98312 360-473-1000
Dr. Aaron Leavell, supt. Fax 473-1040
www.bremertonschools.org
Bremerton HS 1,200/9-12
1500 13th St 98337 360-473-0800
Monica Sweet, prin. Fax 473-0820
Mountain View MS 800/6-8
2400 Perry Ave 98310 360-473-0600
Michaeleen Gelhaus, prin. Fax 473-0620
Renaissance HS / Open Doors 200/Alt
3400 1st St 98312 360-473-4700
Kristen Morga, prin. Fax 792-1350
West Sound Technical Skills Center Vo/Tech
101 National Ave N 98312 360-473-0550
Shani Watkins, dir. Fax 478-5090

Central Kitsap SD 401
Supt. — See Silverdale
Fairview MS 400/6-8
8107 Central Valley Rd NE 98311 360-662-2600
Iva Scott, prin. Fax 662-2601
Olympic HS 900/9-12
7070 Stampede Blvd NW 98311 360-662-2700
Rebecca Johnson, prin. Fax 662-2701

Crosspoint 200/K-12
4012 Chico Way NW 98312 360-377-7700
Nick Sweeney, admin. Fax 377-7795
Everest College Post-Sec.
155 Washington Ave Ste 200 98337 360-473-1120
Olympic College Post-Sec.
1600 Chester Ave 98337 360-792-6050

Brewster, Okanogan, Pop. 2,353
Brewster SD 111 700/PK-12
PO Box 97 98812 509-689-3418
Eric Driessen, supt. Fax 689-0749
brewsterbears.org
Brewster Alternative S 50/Alt
PO Box 97 98812 509-689-8031
Linda Dezellum, admin. Fax 689-0675
Brewster HS 200/9-12
PO Box 97 98812 509-689-3449
Linda Dezellem, prin. Fax 689-0675
Brewster MS 6-8
PO Box 97 98812 509-689-3449
Greg Austin, admin. Fax 689-0675

Bridgeport, Douglas, Pop. 2,379
Bridgeport SD 75 800/PK-12
PO Box 1060 98813 509-686-5656
Scott Sattler, supt. Fax 686-2221
www.bridgeport.wednet.edu
Aurora HS 50/Alt
PO Box 1060 98813 509-686-8770
Tamra Jackson, prin. Fax 686-9622
Bridgeport HS 200/9-12
PO Box 1060 98813 509-686-8770
Tamra Jackson, prin. Fax 686-9622
Bridgeport MS 200/5-8
PO Box 1060 98813 509-686-9501
Hanna Coffman, dean Fax 686-4052

Brier, Snohomish, Pop. 5,840
Edmonds SD 15
Supt. — See Lynnwood
Brier Terrace MS 600/7-8
22200 Brier Rd 98036 425-431-7834
Alex Alexander, prin. Fax 431-7836

Brush Prairie, Clark, Pop. 2,603
Battle Ground SD 119 13,200/K-12
11104 NE 149th St 98606 360-885-5300
Mark Hottowe, supt. Fax 885-5310
www.battlegroundps.org
Summit View HS 400/Alt
11104 NE 149th St 98606 360-885-5331
Bill Penrose, prin. Fax 885-5402
Other Schools – See Amboy, Battle Ground, Vancouver

Hockinson SD 98 1,500/K-12
17912 NE 159th St 98606 360-448-6400
Sandra Yager, supt. Fax 448-6409
www.hocksd.org
Hockinson HS 700/9-12
16819 NE 159th St 98606 360-448-6450
Colleen Anders, prin. Fax 448-6459
Hockinson MS 500/6-8
15916 NE 182nd Ave 98606 360-448-6440
Brian Lehner, prin. Fax 448-6449

Buckley, Pierce, Pop. 4,221
White River SD 416 3,600/PK-12
PO Box 2050 98321 360-829-0600
Janel Keating, supt. Fax 829-3358
www.whiteriver.wednet.edu
Glacier MS 800/6-8
PO Box 1976 98321 360-829-3395
Robin Cerato, prin. Fax 829-3391
White River HS 1,200/9-12
PO Box 1683 98321 360-829-3352
Cody Mothershead, prin. Fax 829-3351

Rainier School, PO Box 600 98321 Post-Sec.

Burbank, Walla Walla, Pop. 3,235
Columbia SD 400 900/PK-12
755 Maple St 99323 509-547-2136
Dr. Lou Gates, supt. Fax 546-0603
www.csd400.org/
Columbia HS 300/9-12
787 Maple St 99323 509-545-8573
Kyle Miller, prin. Fax 545-6553
Columbia MS 200/6-8
835 Maple St 99323 509-545-8571
Mike Taylor, prin. Fax 547-4277

Burien, King, Pop. 31,292
Highline SD 401 18,600/PK-12
15675 Ambaum Blvd SW 98166 206-631-3000
Dr. Susan Enfield, supt. Fax 631-3393
www.highlineschools.org
Big Picture MSHS 200/7-12
440 S 186th St 98148 206-631-7700
Tim Schlosser, prin. Fax 631-7749
Highline HS 1,300/9-12
225 S 152nd St 98148 206-631-6700
Vicki Fisher, prin. Fax 631-6758
Puget Sound Skills Center Vo/Tech
18010 8th Ave S 98148 206-631-7300
Todd Moorhead, prin. Fax 631-7337
Sylvester MS 600/7-8
16222 Sylvester Rd SW 98166 206-631-6000
Kyle Linman, prin. Fax 631-6064

Other Schools – See Des Moines, SeaTac, Seattle, Tukwila

Academy Northwest / Family Academy 300/K-12
632 SW 150th St 98166 206-246-9227
Denise Sumner, admin. Fax 246-5618
Kennedy HS 900/9-12
140 S 140th St 98168 206-246-0500
Nancy Bradish, prin. Fax 242-0831

Burlington, Skagit, Pop. 8,211
Burlington-Edison SD 100 3,800/K-12
927 E Fairhaven Ave 98233 360-757-3311
Laurel Browning, supt. Fax 755-9198
www.be.wednet.edu/
Burlington-Edison HS 1,100/9-12
301 N Burlington Blvd 98233 360-757-4074
Todd Setterlund, prin. Fax 757-3350
Burlington North Alternative HS 100/Alt
301 N Burlington Blvd 98233 360-757-4074
Todd Setterlund, prin. Fax 757-3350

Skagit Adventist Academy 100/PK-12
530 N Section St 98233 360-755-9261
Gary Brown, prin.

Camas, Clark, Pop. 18,670
Camas SD 117 6,400/K-12
841 NE 22nd Ave 98607 360-335-3000
Mike Nerland, supt. Fax 335-3001
www.camas.wednet.edu/
Camas HS 2,000/9-12
26900 SE 15th St 98607 360-833-5750
Steve Marshall, prin. Fax 833-5751
Hayes Freedom HS 100/9-12
1919 NE Ione St 98607 360-833-5600
Amy Holmes, prin. Fax 833-5601
Liberty MS 700/6-8
1612 NE Garfield St 98607 360-833-5850
Marilyn Boerke, prin. Fax 833-5851
Skyridge MS 900/6-8
5220 NW Parker St 98607 360-833-5800
Aaron Smith, prin. Fax 833-5801

Evergreen SD 114
Supt. — See Vancouver
Union HS 2,100/9-12
6201 NW Friberg Strunk St 98607 360-604-6250
Brian Grimsted, prin. Fax 604-6202

Carnation, King, Pop. 1,754
Riverview SD 407
Supt. — See Duvall
Riverview Learning Center 200/Alt
32302 NE 50th St 98014 425-844-4960
Christopher Mirecki, prin. Fax 844-4962
Tolt MS 700/6-8
3740 Tolt Ave 98014 425-844-4600
Christopher Lupo, prin. Fax 844-4602

Cashmere, Chelan, Pop. 3,023
Cashmere SD 222 1,500/PK-12
210 S Division St 98815 509-782-3355
Glenn Johnson, supt. Fax 782-4747
www.cashmere.wednet.edu
Cashmere HS 500/9-12
329 Tigner Rd 98815 509-782-2914
Tony Boyle, prin. Fax 782-2891
Cashmere MS 500/5-8
300 Tigner Rd 98815 509-782-2001
Sara Graves, prin. Fax 782-2547

Castle Rock, Cowlitz, Pop. 1,912
Castle Rock SD 401 1,300/PK-12
600 Huntington Ave S 98611 360-501-2940
Susan Barker, supt. Fax 501-3140
www.castlerockschools.org
Castle Rock HS 400/9-12
5180 Westside Hwy 98611 360-501-2930
Ryan Greene, prin. Fax 501-2999
Castle Rock MS 300/6-8
615 Front Ave SW 98611 360-501-2920
Tiffany Golden, prin. Fax 501-3125

Cathlamet, Wahkiakum, Pop. 521
Wahkiakum SD 200 400/K-12
PO Box 398 98612 360-795-3971
Bob Garrett, supt. Fax 795-0545
www.wahksd.k12.wa.us
Thomas MS 100/6-8
PO Box 398 98612 360-795-3261
Theresa Libby, prin. Fax 795-3205
Wahkiakum HS 100/9-12
PO Box 398 98612 360-795-3271
Stephanie Leitz, prin. Fax 795-0545

Centralia, Lewis, Pop. 15,816
Centralia SD 401 3,500/K-12
PO Box 610 98531 360-330-7600
Mark Davalos, supt. Fax 330-7604
www.centralia.k12.wa.us
Centralia HS 1,100/9-12
813 Eshom Rd 98531 360-330-7605
Josue Lowe, prin. Fax 330-7616
Centralia MS 600/7-8
901 Johnson Rd 98531 360-330-7619
Heidi Bunker, prin. Fax 330-7622

Centralia Christian S 200/PK-10
PO Box 1209 98531 360-736-7657
Dr. Ann Stout, prin. Fax 807-9161
Centralia College Post-Sec.
600 Centralia College Blvd 98531 360-736-9391

Chattaroy, Spokane
Riverside SD 416 1,400/PK-12
34515 N Newport Hwy 99003 509-464-8201
Dr. Ken Russell, supt. Fax 464-8206
www.riversidesd.org
Riverside Achievement Center 50/Alt
34515 N Newport Hwy 99003 509-464-8478
Lynn Rowse, prin. Fax 464-8479
Riverside HS 500/9-12
4120 E Deer Park Milan Rd 99003 509-464-8550
John McCoy, prin. Fax 464-8556
Riverside MS 400/6-8
3814 E Deer Park Milan Rd 99003 509-464-8450
Michael Syron, prin. Fax 464-8447

Chehalis, Lewis, Pop. 7,074
Adna SD 226 600/K-12
179 Dieckman Rd 98532 360-748-0362
Jim Forrest, supt. Fax 748-9217
www.adnaschools.org
Adna MSHS 400/6-12
121 Adna School Rd 98532 360-748-8552
Kevin Young, prin. Fax 748-1625

Chehalis SD 302 2,800/PK-12
310 SW 16th St 98532 360-807-7200
Ed Rothlin, supt. Fax 748-8899
chehalisschools.org
Chehalis MS 600/6-8
1060 SW 20th St 98532 360-807-7230
Chris Simpson, prin. Fax 740-1849
West HS 1,000/9-12
342 SW 16th St 98532 360-807-7235
Bob Walters, prin. Fax 748-3664

Lewis County Adventist S 100/PK-10
PO Box 1203 98532 360-748-3213

Chelan, Chelan, Pop. 3,828
Lake Chelan SD 129 1,300/K-12
PO Box 369 98816 509-682-3515
Barry DePaoli, supt. Fax 682-5842
www.chelanschools.org
Chelan HS 400/9-12
PO Box 369 98816 509-682-4061
Brad Wilson, prin. Fax 682-5001
Chelan MS 300/6-8
PO Box 369 98816 509-682-4073
Kristin Nelson, prin. Fax 682-5001
Chelan S of Innovation Alt
PO Box 369 98816 509-888-8773
Crosby Carpenter, prin.
Holden Village Community S 50/K-12
PO Box 369 98816 509-682-3515
Karen Crowell, prin. Fax 682-5842

Cheney, Spokane, Pop. 10,120
Cheney SD 360 4,200/PK-12
12414 S Andrus Rd 99004 509-559-4599
Robert Roettger, supt. Fax 559-4508
www.cheneysd.org
Cheney HS 1,200/9-12
460 N 6th St 99004 509-559-4000
Troy Heuett, prin. Fax 559-4005
Cheney MS 500/6-8
740 W Betz Rd 99004 509-559-4400
Mike Stark, prin. Fax 559-4479
Three Springs HS 50/Alt
460 N 6th St 99004 509-559-4521
Ryan Fitzgerald, admin. Fax 559-4582
Other Schools – See Spokane

Eastern Washington University Post-Sec.
526 5th St 99004 509-359-6200

Chewelah, Stevens, Pop. 2,514
Chewelah SD 36 800/PK-12
PO Box 47 99109 509-685-6800
Richard Linehan, supt. Fax 935-8605
www.chewelah.k12.wa.us
Chewelah Alternative HS 50/Alt
PO Box 47 99109 509-685-6800
Jon Symonds, admin. Fax 935-0379
Jenkins JSHS 400/7-12
PO Box 138 99109 509-685-6800
Shawn Anderson, prin. Fax 935-9206

Chimacum, Jefferson
Chimacum SD 49 1,000/K-12
PO Box 278 98325 360-302-5890
Rick Thompson, supt. Fax 732-4336
www.csd49.org
Chimacum HS 300/9-12
PO Box 278 98325 360-302-5900
Whitney Meissner, prin. Fax 732-7359
Chimacum MS 200/6-8
PO Box 278 98325 360-302-5944
David Carthum, prin. Fax 732-6859

Clarkston, Asotin, Pop. 7,028
Clarkston SD J 250-185 2,700/K-12
PO Box 70 99403 509-758-2531
Tim Winter, supt. Fax 758-3326
www.csdk12.org
Clarkston HS 800/9-12
PO Box 370 99403 509-758-5591
Samantha Ogden, prin. Fax 758-2831
Educational Opportunity Center 200/Alt
1284 Chestnut St 99403 509-758-4508
Elece Lockridge, prin. Fax 758-4509
Lincoln MS 400/7-8
1945 4th Ave 99403 509-758-5506
Mike Sperry, prin. Fax 758-7838

Cle Elum, Kittitas, Pop. 1,804
Cle Elum-Roslyn SD 404 900/PK-12
2690 State Route 903 98922 509-649-4850
Gary Wargo, supt. Fax 649-2404
www.cersd.org
Cle Elum-Roslyn HS 300/9-12
2692 State Route 903 98922 509-649-4900
Brett Simpson, prin. Fax 649-3563
Strom MS 200/6-8
2694 State Route 903 98922 509-649-4800
Lara Gregorich-Bennett, prin. Fax 649-3634
Other Schools – See Roslyn

Clyde Hill, King, Pop. 2,918

Bellevue Christian JSHS 500/7-12
1601 98th Ave NE 98004 425-454-4028
Blake DeYoung, prin. Fax 454-4418

Colbert, Spokane
Mead SD 354
Supt. — See Mead
Mountainside MS 700/7-8
4717 E Day Mount Spokane Rd 99005509-465-7400
Craig Busch, prin. Fax 465-7420

Northwest Christian HS 200/9-12
5104 E Bernhill Rd 99005 509-238-4005

Colfax, Whitman, Pop. 2,773
Colfax SD 300 600/K-12
1207 N Morton St 99111 509-397-3042
Jerry Pugh, supt. Fax 397-5835
www.colfax.k12.wa.us
Colfax JSHS 300/7-12
1110 N Morton St 99111 509-397-4368
Carrie Lipe, prin. Fax 397-2414

College Place, Walla Walla, Pop. 8,557
College Place SD 250 900/K-12
1755 S College Ave 99324 509-525-4827
Timothy Payne, supt. Fax 525-3741
www.cpps.org
College Place HS 100/9-12
1755 S College Ave 99324 509-522-3312
Kirk Jameson, prin. Fax 522-3306
Sager MS 300/6-8
1755 S College Ave 99324 509-525-5300
Dale Stopperan, prin. Fax 525-6005

Walla Walla University Post-Sec.
204 S College Ave 99324 509-527-2615
Walla Walla Valley Academy 200/9-12
300 SW Academy Way 99324 509-525-1050

Colton, Whitman, Pop. 412
Colton SD 306 200/K-12
706 Union St 99113 509-229-3385
Nathan Smith, supt. Fax 229-3374
www.colton.k12.wa.us
Colton S 200/K-12
706 Union St 99113 509-229-3386
Nathan Smith, prin. Fax 229-3374

Colville, Stevens, Pop. 4,534
Colville SD 115 1,800/K-12
217 S Hofstetter St 99114 509-684-7850
Pete Lewis, supt. Fax 684-7855
www.colsd.org
Colville HS 600/9-12
154 Highway 20 E 99114 509-684-7800
Kevin Knight, prin. Fax 684-7809
Colville JHS 400/6-8
990 S Cedar St 99114 509-684-7820
Paul Dumas, prin. Fax 684-7825
Panorama S 100/Alt
225 S Hofstetter St 99114 509-684-7840
Kevin Knight, prin. Fax 684-2819

Concrete, Skagit, Pop. 682
Concrete SD 11 400/K-12
45389 Airport Way 98237 360-853-4000
Barbara Hawkings, supt. Fax 853-4004
www.concrete.k12.wa.us
Concrete MSHS 200/7-12
7830 S Superior Ave 98237 360-853-4015
Mike Holbrook, prin. Fax 853-4066
Twin Cedars HS 50/Alt
45389 Airport Way Rm 110 98237 360-853-4015
Mike Holbrook, dir. Fax 853-4066

Connell, Franklin, Pop. 4,122
North Franklin SD J 51-162 2,100/K-12
PO Box 829 99326 509-234-2021
Gregg Taylor, supt. Fax 234-9200
www.nfsd.org
Connell HS 600/9-12
PO Box 829 99326 509-234-2911
Tim Peterson, prin. Fax 234-2921
Olds JHS 300/7-8
PO Box 829 99326 509-234-3931
Jim Jacobs, prin. Fax 234-8171
Palouse Junction HS 50/Alt
PO Box 829 99326 509-234-1055
George Farrah, prin. Fax 234-9200

Cosmopolis, Grays Harbor, Pop. 1,610
North River SD 200 100/PK-12
2867 N River Rd 98537 360-532-3079
David Pickering, supt. Fax 532-1738
www.nr.k12.wa.us/
North River S 100/PK-12
2867 N River Rd 98537 360-532-3079
Sean Pierson, prin. Fax 532-1738

Coulee City, Grant, Pop. 541
Coulee-Hartline SD 151 200/K-12
PO Box 428 99115 509-632-5231
Dr. James Evans, supt. Fax 632-5166
www.achsd.org/chsd.htm
Almira-Coulee-Hartline HS 100/6-12
413 N 4th St 99115 509-632-5231
Dr. James Evans, prin. Fax 632-5166

Coulee Dam, Okanogan, Pop. 1,042
Grand Coulee Dam SD 301J 500/PK-12
110 Stevens Ave 99116 509-633-2143
Dr. Dennis Carlson, supt. Fax 633-2530
www.gcdsd.org
Lake Roosevelt JSHS 200/7-12
505 Crest Dr 99116 509-633-1442
Ronanda Liberty, prin. Fax 633-0356

Coupeville, Island, Pop. 1,760
Coupeville SD 204 900/K-12
501 S Main St 98239 360-678-2400
Dr. Jim Shank, supt. Fax 678-4834
www.coupeville.k12.wa.us
Coupeville HS 300/9-12
501 S Main St 98239 360-678-2410
Duane Baumann, prin. Fax 678-0540
Coupeville MS 200/6-8
501 S Main St 98239 360-678-2410
Duane Baumann, prin. Fax 678-0540

Covington, King, Pop. 16,615
Kent SD 415
Supt. — See Kent
Cedar Heights MS 600/7-8
19640 SE 272nd St 98042 253-373-7620
Heidi Maurer, prin. Fax 373-7628
Kentwood HS 2,000/9-12
25800 164th Ave SE 98042 253-373-7680
John Kniseley, prin. Fax 373-7326
Mattson MS 600/7-8
16400 SE 251st St 98042 253-373-7670
James Schiechl, prin. Fax 373-7673

Tahoma SD 409
Supt. — See Maple Valley
Tahoma SHS 1,800/10-12
18200 SE 240th St 98042 425-413-6200
Terry Duty, prin. Fax 413-6333

Rainier Christian HS 100/9-12
26201 180th Ave SE 98042 253-735-1413
Justin Evans, admin. Fax 887-8234

Cowiche, Yakima, Pop. 418
Highland SD 203 1,200/K-12
PO Box 38 98923 509-678-8630
Mark Anderson, supt. Fax 678-4177
www.highland.wednet.edu/
Highland HS 400/9-12
17000 Summitview Rd 98923 509-678-8800
Brandon Jensen, admin. Fax 678-4140
Highland JHS 200/7-8
17000 Summitview Rd 98923 509-678-8800
Kelly Thorson, prin. Fax 678-4140

Creston, Lincoln, Pop. 228
Creston SD 73 50/PK-12
485 SE E St 99117 509-636-2721
Dr. William Wadlington Ed.D., supt. Fax 636-2910
www.creston.wednet.edu
Creston S 50/PK-12
485 SE E St 99117 509-636-2721
Dr. William Wadlington Ed.D., prin. Fax 636-2910

Curlew, Ferry, Pop. 114
Curlew SD 50 200/PK-12
PO Box 370 99118 509-779-4931
Dr. John Glenewinkel, supt. Fax 779-4938
www.curlew.wednet.edu
Curlew S 200/PK-12
PO Box 370 99118 509-779-4931
Dr. John Glenewinkel, admin. Fax 779-4938

Cusick, Pend Oreille, Pop. 205
Cusick SD 59 300/K-12
305 Monumental Rd 99119 509-445-1125
Don Hawpe, supt. Fax 445-1598
www.cusick.wednet.edu/
Cusick JSHS 100/6-12
305 Monumental Rd 99119 509-445-1125
Stephen Bollinger, admin. Fax 445-1598

Darrington, Snohomish, Pop. 1,303
Darrington SD 330 500/PK-12
PO Box 27 98241 360-436-1323
Dr. Buck Marsh, supt. Fax 436-2045
www.dsd.k12.wa.us
Darrington HS 200/9-12
PO Box 27 98241 360-436-1140
Rachel Quarterman, prin. Fax 436-1089

Davenport, Lincoln, Pop. 1,697
Davenport SD 207 400/PK-12
801 7th St 99122 509-725-1481
Jim Kowalkowski, supt. Fax 725-2260
www.davenport.wednet.edu/
Davenport HS 200/9-12
801 7th St 99122 509-725-4021
Chad Prewitt, prin. Fax 725-2260
Davenport MS 6-8
601 Washington St 99122 509-725-0766
Chad Prewitt, prin. Fax 725-2780

Dayton, Columbia, Pop. 2,459
Dayton SD 2 400/PK-12
609 S 2nd St 99328 509-382-2543
Doug Johnson, supt. Fax 382-2081
www.daytonsd.org
Dayton HS 200/9-12
614 S 3rd St 99328 509-382-4775
Paul Shaber, prin. Fax 382-2081
Dayton MS 100/6-8
614 S 3rd St 99328 509-382-4775
Paul Shaber, prin. Fax 382-2081

Deer Park, Spokane, Pop. 3,505
Deer Park SD 414 2,100/PK-12
PO Box 490 99006 509-464-5500
Travis Hanson, supt. Fax 464-5510
www.dpsd.org
Alternative S Alt
PO Box 550 99006 509-468-3500
Joe Feist, prin. Fax 468-3510
Deer Park HS 700/9-12
PO Box 550 99006 509-468-3500
Joe Feist, prin. Fax 468-3510
Deer Park MS 500/6-8
PO Box 882 99006 509-464-5800
Tim Olietti, prin. Fax 464-5810

Deming, Whatcom, Pop. 349
Mt. Baker SD 507 1,500/K-12
PO Box 95 98244 360-383-2000
Charles Burleigh, supt. Fax 383-2009
www.mtbaker.wednet.edu
Mt. Baker JSHS 600/7-12
PO Box 95 98244 360-383-2015
Matt Durand, prin. Fax 383-2029

Des Moines, King, Pop. 27,680
Highline SD 401
Supt. — See Burien
Mount Rainier HS 1,600/9-12
22450 19th Ave S 98198 206-631-7000
Terry Chapman, prin. Fax 631-7099
Pacific MS 700/7-8
22705 24th Ave S 98198 206-631-5800
Diana Garcia, prin. Fax 631-5860

Kent SD 415
Supt. — See Kent
Kent Mountain View Academy 300/Alt
22420 Military Rd S 98198 253-373-7488
Stephanie Knipp, prin. Fax 373-7490

Highline Community College Post-Sec.
PO Box 98000 98198 206-878-3710

DuPont, Pierce, Pop. 7,501
Steilacoom Historical SD 1
Supt. — See Steilacoom
Pioneer MS 800/6-8
1750 Bobs Hollow Ln 98327 253-583-7200
JoAnne Fernandes, prin. Fax 583-7292

Duvall, King, Pop. 6,458
Riverview SD 407 3,400/PK-12
PO Box 519 98019 425-844-4500
Dr. Anthony L. Smith, supt. Fax 844-4502
www.riverview.wednet.edu
Cedarcrest HS 900/9-12
29000 NE 150th St 98019 425-844-4800
Clarence Lavarias, prin. Fax 844-4802
Other Schools – See Carnation

Easton, Kittitas, Pop. 472
Easton SD 28 100/PK-12
PO Box 8 98925 509-656-2317
Dr. Patrick Dehuff, supt. Fax 656-2585
www.easton.wednet.edu/
Easton S 100/PK-12
PO Box 8 98925 509-656-2317
Dr. Patrick Dehuff, supt. Fax 656-2585

Eastsound, San Juan
Orcas Island SD 137 900/K-12
557 School Rd 98245 360-376-2284
Eric Webb, supt. Fax 376-2283
www.orcasislandschools.org
OASIS K-12, 557 School Rd 98245 500/Alt
Becky Bell, prin. 360-376-1598
Orcas Island HS 100/9-12
715 School Rd 98245 360-376-2287
Kyle Freeman, prin. Fax 376-6078
Orcas Island MS 100/7-8
611 School Rd 98245 360-376-2287
Kyle Freeman, prin. Fax 376-6078

Orcas Christian Day S 100/K-12
PO Box 669 98245 360-376-6683
Tom Roosma, prin. Fax 376-7642

East Wenatchee, Douglas, Pop. 12,915
Eastmont SD 206 5,200/K-12
800 Eastmont Ave 98802 509-884-7169
Dr. Garn Christensen, supt. Fax 884-4210
www.eastmont206.org
Eastmont JHS 900/8-9
905 8th St NE 98802 509-884-2407
David Woods, prin. Fax 884-1988
Eastmont SHS 1,300/10-12
955 3rd St NE 98802 509-884-6665
Lance Noell, prin. Fax 884-8805

Eatonville, Pierce, Pop. 2,651
Eatonville SD 404 1,800/K-12
PO Box 698 98328 360-879-1000
Krestin Bahr, supt. Fax 879-1086
www.eatonville.wednet.edu/
Eatonville HS 600/9-12
PO Box 699 98328 360-879-1200
John Paul Colgan, prin. Fax 879-1284
Eatonville MS 400/6-8
PO Box 910 98328 360-879-1400
Janna Rush, prin. Fax 879-1480

Edgewood, Pierce, Pop. 9,076
Puyallup SD 3
Supt. — See Puyallup
Edgemont JHS 400/7-9
2300 110th Ave E 98372 253-841-8727
Eric Molver, prin. Fax 840-8883

Salvation Christian Academy 200/PK-10
10622 8th St E 98372 253-952-7163
Vadim Hetman, prin. Fax 952-7164

Edmonds, Snohomish, Pop. 38,105
Edmonds SD 15
Supt. — See Lynnwood
Edmonds Heights K-12 S 500/Alt
23200 100th Ave W 98020 425-431-7840
Scott Mauk, prin. Fax 431-7849
Edmonds-Woodway HS 1,600/9-12
7600 212th St SW 98026 425-431-7900
Terrance Mims, prin. Fax 431-7929
Scriber Lake HS 300/Alt
23200 100th Ave W 98020 425-431-7270
Andrea Hillman, prin. Fax 431-7272

Edwall, Lincoln

Christian Heritage S 100/K-12
48009 Ida Ave E 99008 509-236-2224
Brad Cain M.Ed., admin. Fax 236-2412

Ellensburg, Kittitas, Pop. 17,598
Ellensburg SD 401 3,100/K-12
1300 E 3rd Ave 98926 509-925-8000
Dr. Paul Farris, supt. Fax 925-8025
ellensburg.schoolfusion.us
Ellensburg HS 1,000/9-12
1203 E Capitol Ave 98926 509-925-8300
Jeff Ellersick, prin. Fax 925-8305
Excel HS Alt
CWU Michaelson Hall # 122 98926 509-963-2428
Jeff Ellersick, prin.
Morgan MS 700/6-8
400 E 1st Ave 98926 509-925-8200
Michelle Bibich, prin. Fax 925-8202

Central Washington University Post-Sec.
400 E University Way 98926 509-963-1111

Elma, Grays Harbor, Pop. 2,963
Elma SD 68 1,600/PK-12
1235 Monte Elma Rd 98541 360-482-2822
Kevin Acuff, supt. Fax 482-2092
www.elma.wednet.edu
East Grays Harbor HS 50/Alt
1235 Monte Elma Rd 98541 360-482-5086
Linda Meister, prin. Fax 482-2109
Elma HS 600/9-12
1235 Monte Elma Rd 98541 360-482-3121
Darrin Lowry, prin. Fax 482-1200
Elma MS 300/6-8
1235 Monte Elma Rd 98541 360-482-2237
Sunshine Perry, prin. Fax 482-4872

Mary M. Knight SD 311 200/PK-12
2987 W Matlock Brady Rd 98541 360-426-6767
Dr. Ellen Perconti, supt. Fax 427-5516
www.marymknight.com
Knight JSHS 100/7-12
2987 W Matlock Brady Rd 98541 360-426-6767
Dr. Ellen Perconti, admin. Fax 427-5516

Endicott, Whitman, Pop. 289
Endicott SD 308 100/PK-8
308 School Dr 99125 509-657-3523
Gary Wargo, supt. Fax 657-3521
www.sje.wednet.edu/endicott.html
Other Schools – See Saint John

Entiat, Chelan, Pop. 1,090
Entiat SD 127 400/PK-12
2650 Entiat Way 98822 509-784-1800
Dr. Ismael Vivanco, supt. Fax 784-2986
www.entiatschools.org
Entiat Middle & HS 200/6-12
2650 Entiat Way 98822 509-784-1911
Miles Caples, prin. Fax 784-2986

Enumclaw, King, Pop. 10,407
Enumclaw SD 216 4,000/K-12
2929 McDougall Ave 98022 360-802-7100
Michael Nelson, supt. Fax 802-7140
www.enumclaw.wednet.edu/
Enumclaw HS 1,400/9-12
226 Semanski St 98022 360-802-7669
Jill Burnes, prin. Fax 802-7676
Enumclaw MS 500/6-8
550 Semanski St 98022 360-802-7150
Steve Rabb, prin. Fax 802-7224
Thunder Mountain MS 500/6-8
42018 264th Ave SE 98022 360-802-7492
Steven Stoker, prin. Fax 802-7500

Ephrata, Grant, Pop. 7,502
Ephrata SD 165 2,300/K-12
499 C St NW 98823 509-754-2474
Dr. Jerry Simon, supt. Fax 754-4712
www.ephrataschools.org
Ephrata HS 700/9-12
333 4th Ave NW 98823 509-754-5285
Aaron Cummings, prin. Fax 754-4993
Ephrata MS 400/7-8
384 A St SE 98823 509-754-4659
Ken Murray, prin. Fax 754-5625
Sage Hills Alternative S 50/Alt
35 K St SE 98823 509-754-7547
Sharon Scellick, prin. Fax 754-7227

Everett, Snohomish, Pop. 98,083
Everett SD 2 18,800/PK-12
3900 Broadway 98201 425-385-4000
Dr. Gary Cohn, supt. Fax 385-4012
www.everettsd.org
Cascade HS 1,800/9-12
801 E Casino Rd 98203 425-385-6000
Cathy Woods, prin. Fax 385-6002
Eisenhower MS 800/6-8
10200 25th Ave SE 98208 425-385-7500
Stefani Koetje, prin. Fax 385-7502
Everett HS 1,400/9-12
2416 Colby Ave 98201 425-385-4400
Lance Balla, prin. Fax 385-4402
Evergreen MS 1,000/6-8
7621 Beverly Ln 98203 425-385-5700
Christine Avery, prin. Fax 385-5702

Gateway MS — 800/6-8
15404 Silver Firs Dr 98208 — 425-385-6600
Shelley Petillo, prin. — Fax 385-6602
North MS — 700/6-8
2514 Rainier Ave 98201 — 425-385-4800
Mary O'Brien, prin. — Fax 385-4802
Sequoia HS — 300/Alt
3516 Rucker Ave 98201 — 425-385-5100
Kelly Shepherd, prin. — Fax 385-5102
Other Schools – See Mill Creek

Mukilteo SD 6 — 15,700/K-12
9401 Sharon Dr 98204 — 425-356-1274
Dr. Marci Larsen, supt. — Fax 356-1310
www.mukilteo.wednet.edu
ACES HS — 200/Alt
9700 Holly Dr 98204 — 425-366-3900
Marcie Polin, prin. — Fax 366-3902
Explorer MS — 900/6-8
9600 Sharon Dr 98204 — 425-366-5000
Ali Williams, prin. — Fax 366-5002
Mariner HS — 2,100/9-12
200 120th St SW 98204 — 425-366-5700
Brent Kline, prin. — Fax 366-5702
Sno-Isle TECH Skills Center — Vo/Tech
9001 Airport Rd 98204 — 425-348-2220
Dave Rudy, prin. — Fax 356-2201
Voyager MS — 800/6-8
11711 4th Ave W 98204 — 425-366-5300
Wes Bailey, prin. — Fax 366-5302
Other Schools – See Mukilteo

Archbishop Thomas Murphy HS — 500/9-12
12911 39th Ave SE 98208 — 425-379-6363
Steve Schmutz, prin. — Fax 385-2875
Everest College — Post-Sec.
906 SE Evertt Mall Way #600 98208 — 425-789-7960
Everett Community College — Post-Sec.
2000 Tower St 98201 — 425-388-9100
Milan Institute of Cosmetology — Post-Sec.
607 SE Everett Mall Way #5 98208 — 425-353-8193
Montessori S of Snohomish County — 100/PK-12
1804 Puget Dr 98203 — 425-355-1311
Kathleen Gunnell, admin. — Fax 347-1000
Trinity Lutheran College — Post-Sec.
2802 Wetmore Ave 98201 — 425-249-4800

Everson, Whatcom, Pop. 2,414
Nooksack Valley SD 506 — 1,500/PK-12
3326 E Badger Rd 98247 — 360-988-4754
Dr. Mark Johnson, supt. — Fax 988-8983
www.nv.k12.wa.us/
Nooksack Valley HS — 500/9-12
3326 E Badger Rd 98247 — 360-988-2641
Matt Galley, prin. — Fax 988-7058
Other Schools – See Nooksack

Fall City, King, Pop. 1,940
Snoqualmie Valley SD 410
Supt. — See Snoqualmie
Chief Kanim MS — 700/6-8
PO Box 639 98024 — 425-831-8225
Michelle Trifunovic, prin. — Fax 831-8290

Federal Way, King, Pop. 82,130
Federal Way SD 210 — 22,100/PK-12
33330 8th Ave S 98003 — 253-945-2000
Dr. Tammy Campbell, supt. — Fax 945-2001
www.fwps.org
Beamer HS — 1,800/9-12
35999 16th Ave S 98003 — 253-945-2570
Joni Hall, prin. — Fax 945-2599
Decatur HS — 1,400/9-12
2800 SW 320th St 98023 — 253-945-5200
Christina Spencer, prin. — Fax 945-5252
Federal Way Acceleration Academy — Alt
2104 S 314th St Ste 2104 98003 — 253-945-4590
Ashley Barker, prin.
Federal Way HS — 1,600/9-12
30611 16th Ave S 98003 — 253-945-5400
Dr. Matt Oberst, prin. — Fax 945-5454
Federal Way Public Academy — 300/Alt
34620 9th Ave S 98003 — 253-945-3270
Kurt Lauer, prin. — Fax 945-3399
Illahee MS — 700/6-8
36001 1st Ave S 98003 — 253-945-4600
Jerry Warren, prin. — Fax 945-4646
Lakota MS — 800/6-8
1415 SW 314th St 98023 — 253-945-4800
Craig Tutt, prin. — Fax 945-4848
Sacajawea MS — 700/6-8
1101 S Dash Point Rd 98003 — 253-945-4900
Robin Furlan, prin. — Fax 945-4949
Saghalie MS — 500/6-8
33914 19th Ave SW 98023 — 253-945-5000
Joe Kosty, prin. — Fax 945-5050
Truman Campus — 100/Alt
31455 28th Ave S 98003 — 253-945-5800
Dr. Christine Corbley, prin. — Fax 945-5858
Other Schools – See Auburn, Kent

Christian Faith S — 300/PK-12
33645 20th Ave S 98003 — 253-943-2500
Debbie Schindler, head sch — Fax 200-1335
Cortiva Institute - Federal Way — Post-Sec.
2030 S 314th St 98003 — 253-237-5300
DeVry University — Post-Sec.
3600 S 344th Way 98001 — 253-943-2800
Gene Juarez Academy of Beauty — Post-Sec.
2222 S 314th St 98003 — 253-839-6483
Life Academy of Puget Sound — 50/PK-12
414 SW 312th St 98023 — 253-839-7378
Rev. Sue Austin, admin. — Fax 839-1031

Ferndale, Whatcom, Pop. 10,997
Ferndale SD 502 — 4,800/PK-12
PO Box 698 98248 — 360-383-9200
Dr. Linda Quinn Ed.D., supt. — Fax 383-9201
ferndalesd.org
Ferndale HS — 1,400/9-12
PO Box 428 98248 — 360-383-9240
Jeff Gardner, prin. — Fax 383-9242
Horizon MS — 600/6-8
PO Box 1769 98248 — 360-383-9850
Dr. Faye Britt, prin. — Fax 383-9852
Vista MS — 600/6-8
PO Box 1328 98248 — 360-383-9370
Heather Leighton, prin. — Fax 383-9372
Other Schools – See Bellingham

Fife, Pierce, Pop. 8,348
Fife SD 417
Supt. — See Tacoma
Columbia JHS — 600/8-9
2901 54th Ave E 98424 — 253-517-1600
Mark Robinson, prin. — Fax 517-1605

Charter College — Post-Sec.
3700 Pacific Hwy E Ste 407 98424 — 253-252-4200

Forks, Clallam, Pop. 3,383
Quillayute Valley SD 402 — 2,900/PK-12
411 S Spartan Ave 98331 — 360-374-6262
Diana Reaume, supt. — Fax 374-6990
www.qvschools.org
Forks Alternative S — 50/Alt
411 S Spartan Ave 98331 — 360-374-6262
Cindy Feasel, prin. — Fax 374-2360
Forks HS — 300/9-12
261 S Spartan Ave 98331 — 360-374-6262
Cindy Feasel, prin. — Fax 374-9657
Forks JHS, 191 S Spartan Ave 98331 — 7-8
Elena Velasquez, prin. — 360-374-6262

Freeland, Island, Pop. 1,970

Northwest Institute of Literary Arts — Post-Sec.
PO Box 639 98249 — 360-331-0307

Friday Harbor, San Juan, Pop. 2,106
San Juan Island SD 149 — 800/K-12
PO Box 458 98250 — 360-378-4133
Dr. Danna Diaz, supt. — Fax 378-6276
www.sjisd.wednet.edu
Friday Harbor HS — 300/9-12
PO Box 458 98250 — 360-378-5215
Fred Woods, prin. — Fax 378-2647
Friday Harbor MS — 100/7-8
PO Box 458 98250 — 360-378-5214
Fred Woods, prin. — Fax 378-9750
Griffin Bay S — 50/Alt
PO Box 458 98250 — 360-378-3292
Dr. Danna Diaz, admin. — Fax 378-2211

Spring Street International S — 100/5-12
505 Spring St 98250 — 360-378-6393

Garfield, Whitman, Pop. 585
Garfield SD 302 — 100/PK-8
PO Box 398 99130 — 509-635-1331
Zane Wells, supt. — Fax 635-1332
www.garpal.net
Garfield-Palouse MS — 50/6-8
PO Box 398 99130 — 509-635-1331
Zane Wells, prin. — Fax 635-1332

Gig Harbor, Pierce, Pop. 6,870
Peninsula SD 401 — 9,100/PK-12
14015 62nd Ave NW 98332 — 253-530-1000
Robert W. Manahan Ed.D., supt. — Fax 530-1010
www.psd401.net/
Gig Harbor HS — 1,700/9-12
5101 Rosedale St NW 98335 — 253-530-1400
Tom Leacy, prin. — Fax 530-1420
Goodman MS — 600/6-8
3701 38th Ave NW 98335 — 253-530-1600
D.J. Sigurdson, prin. — Fax 530-1620
Harbor Ridge MS — 600/6-8
9010 Prentice Ave 98332 — 253-530-1900
Mike Benoit, prin. — Fax 530-1920
Henderson Bay HS — 200/Alt
8402 Skansie Ave 98332 — 253-530-1700
Brian Tovey, prin. — Fax 530-1720
Kopachuck MS — 600/6-8
10414 56th St NW 98335 — 253-530-4100
Heidi Fedore, prin. — Fax 530-4120
Peninsula HS — 1,500/9-12
14105 Purdy Ln NW 98332 — 253-530-4400
Dave Goodwin, prin. — Fax 530-4420
Other Schools – See Lakebay

Glenwood, Klickitat
Glenwood SD 401 — 50/K-12
PO Box 12 98619 — 509-364-3438
Heather Gimlin, supt. — Fax 364-3689
www.glenwood.k12.wa.us/
Glenwood S — 50/K-12
PO Box 12 98619 — 509-364-3438
Heather Gimlin, supt. — Fax 364-3689

Goldendale, Klickitat, Pop. 3,344
Goldendale SD 404 — 1,000/K-12
604 E Brooks Ave 98620 — 509-773-5177
Mark Heid, supt. — Fax 773-6028
www.goldendaleschools.org
Goldendale HS — 400/9-12
525 E Simcoe Dr 98620 — 509-773-5846
John Westerman, prin. — Fax 773-6900
Goldendale MS — 300/5-8
520 E Collins St 98620 — 509-773-4323
Dave Barta, prin. — Fax 773-4579

Graham, Pierce, Pop. 21,945
Bethel SD 403
Supt. — See Spanaway
Cougar Mountain MS — 600/6-8
5108 260th St E 98338 — 253-683-8000
Bethany Aoki, prin. — Fax 683-8098
Frontier MS — 800/6-8
22110 108th Ave E 98338 — 253-683-8300
Mark Barnes, prin. — Fax 683-8398
Graham-Kapowsin HS — 1,800/9-12
22100 108th Ave E 98338 — 253-683-6100
Matthew Yarkosky, prin. — Fax 683-6198

Grandview, Yakima, Pop. 10,766
Grandview SD 200 — 3,600/PK-12
913 W 2nd St 98930 — 509-882-8500
Kevin Chase, supt. — Fax 882-2029
www.gsd200.org
Compass HS — 100/Alt
913 W 2nd St 98930 — 509-882-8540
Brian Anderson, prin. — Fax 882-2872
Grandview HS — 800/9-12
1601 W 5th St 98930 — 509-882-8750
Kim Casey, prin. — Fax 882-8739
Grandview MS — 800/6-8
1401 W 2nd St 98930 — 509-882-8600
James Heinle, prin. — Fax 882-3538

Granger, Yakima, Pop. 3,222
Granger SD 204 — 1,500/PK-12
701 E Ave 98932 — 509-854-1515
Margarita C. Lopez, supt. — Fax 854-1126
www.gsd.wednet.edu
Granger HS — 400/9-12
701 E Ave 98932 — 509-854-1115
Tricia Anderson, prin. — Fax 854-2757
Granger MS — 500/5-8
701 E Ave 98932 — 509-854-1003
Stephanie Funk, prin. — Fax 854-1083

Granite Falls, Snohomish, Pop. 3,190
Granite Falls SD 332 — 1,600/K-12
205 N Alder St 98252 — 360-691-7717
Linda Hall, supt. — Fax 691-4459
www.gfalls.wednet.edu
Crossroads Alternative HS — 200/Alt
205 N Alder Ave 98252 — 360-283-4407
Bridgette Perrigoue, prin. — Fax 283-4307
Granite Falls HS — 600/9-12
1401 100th St NE 98252 — 360-691-7713
Kevin Davis, prin. — Fax 283-4414
Granite Falls MS — 400/6-8
405 N Alder Ave 98252 — 360-691-7710
Dave Bianchini, prin. — Fax 283-4415

Harrington, Lincoln, Pop. 416
Harrington SD 204 — 100/PK-12
PO Box 204 99134 — 509-253-4331
Justin Bradford M.A., supt. — Fax 456-6306
www.harrsd.k12.wa.us
Harrington JSHS — 50/7-12
PO Box 204 99134 — 509-253-4331
Justin Bradford M.A., admin. — Fax 456-6306

Hoquiam, Grays Harbor, Pop. 8,401
Hoquiam SD 28 — 1,600/PK-12
305 Simpson Ave 98550 — 360-538-8200
Mike Parker, supt. — Fax 538-8202
hoquiam.net
Hoquiam HS — 500/9-12
501 W Emerson Ave 98550 — 360-538-8210
Brock Maxfield, prin. — Fax 538-8212
Hoquiam MS — 400/6-8
200 Spencer St 98550 — 360-538-8220
Traci Sandstrom, prin. — Fax 538-8222

Hunters, Stevens
Columbia SD 206 — 200/PK-12
PO Box 7 99137 — 509-722-3311
Michael Young, supt. — Fax 722-3310
www.columbia206.com
Columbia S — 200/PK-12
PO Box 7 99137 — 509-722-3311
Matt McLain, prin. — Fax 722-3310

Ilwaco, Pacific, Pop. 906
Ocean Beach SD 101
Supt. — See Long Beach
Hilltop S — 5-8
PO Box F 98624 — 360-642-1234
Darin Adams, prin. — Fax 642-1350
Ilwaco HS — 300/9-12
PO Box F 98624 — 360-642-3731
Dave Tobin, prin. — Fax 642-1224

Inchelium, Ferry, Pop. 393
Inchelium SD 70 — 50/K-12
PO Box 285 99138 — 509-722-6181
Kim Spacek, supt. — Fax 722-6192
www.inchelium.wednet.edu
Inchelium S — 50/K-12
PO Box 285 99138 — 509-722-6181
Brian Myers, prin. — Fax 722-6192

Ione, Pend Oreille, Pop. 442
Selkirk SD 70
Supt. — See Metaline Falls
Selkirk MSHS — 100/6-12
10372 Highway 31 99139 — 509-446-3505
Greg Goodnight, prin. — Fax 446-2408

Issaquah, King, Pop. 29,272
Issaquah SD 411 — 18,500/PK-12
565 NW Holly St 98027 — 425-837-7000
Ron Thiele, supt. — Fax 837-7005
www.issaquah.wednet.edu
Beaver Lake MS — 900/6-8
25025 SE 32nd St 98029 — 425-837-4150
Stacy Cho, prin. — Fax 837-4195
Gibson EK HS, 379 1st Pl SE 98027 — Alt
Julia Bamba, prin. — 425-837-6350

Issaquah HS 2,000/9-12
700 2nd Ave SE 98027 425-837-6000
Andrea McCormick, prin. Fax 837-6078
Issaquah MS 800/6-8
600 2nd Ave SE 98027 425-837-6800
Seth Adams, prin. Fax 837-6855
Pacific Cascade MS 900/6-8
24635 SE Issaquah Fall City 98029 425-837-5900
Dana Bailey, prin. Fax 837-5910
Other Schools – See Renton, Sammamish

Joyce, Clallam
Crescent SD 313 200/K-12
PO Box 20 98343 360-928-3311
David Bingham, supt. Fax 928-3066
www.crescentschooldistrict.org
Crescent MSHS 100/6-12
PO Box 20 98343 360-928-3311
Fax 928-3066

Kahlotus, Franklin, Pop. 189
Kahlotus SD 56 100/PK-12
PO Box 69 99335 509-282-3338
Mark Bitzer, supt. Fax 282-3339
www.kahlotussd.org
Kahlotus S 100/PK-12
PO Box 69 99335 509-282-3338
Ron Hopkins, prin. Fax 282-3339

Kalama, Cowlitz, Pop. 2,270
Kalama SD 402 900/K-12
548 China Garden Rd 98625 360-673-5282
Eric Nerison, supt. Fax 673-5228
kalamaschools.org
Kalama MSHS 500/6-12
548 China Garden Rd 98625 360-673-5212
Guy Strot, prin. Fax 673-1280

Kelso, Cowlitz, Pop. 11,473
Kelso SD 458 4,800/PK-12
601 Crawford St 98626 360-501-1900
Glenn Gelbrich, supt. Fax 501-1944
www.kelso.wednet.edu
Coweeman MS 600/6-8
2000 Allen St 98626 360-501-1750
Greg Gardner, prin. Fax 501-1782
Huntington MS 600/6-8
500 Redpath St 98626 360-501-1700
Chris Clark, prin. Fax 501-1723
Kelso HS 1,500/9-12
1904 Allen St 98626 360-501-1800
John Gummel, prin. Fax 501-1843
Loowit HS 50/Alt
2001 Allen St 98626 360-501-1951
John Gummel, prin. Fax 501-1954

Kenmore, King, Pop. 19,563
Northshore SD 417
Supt. — See Bothell
Inglemoor SHS 1,600/10-12
15500 Simonds Rd NE 98028 425-408-7200
Vicki Sherwood, prin. Fax 408-7202
Kenmore JHS 700/7-9
20323 66th Ave NE 98028 425-408-6400
Joshua Sanchez, prin. Fax 408-6402

Kennewick, Benton, Pop. 72,070
Finley SD 53 900/PK-12
224606 E Game Farm Rd 99337 509-586-3217
Lance Hahn, supt. Fax 586-4408
www.finleysd.org
Finley MS 200/6-8
37208 S Finley Rd 99337 509-586-7561
Michael Harrington, prin. Fax 582-8452
River View HS 300/9-12
36509 S Lemon Dr 99337 509-582-2158
Chris Davis, prin. Fax 586-9297

Kennewick SD 17 17,100/PK-12
1000 W 4th Ave 99336 509-222-5000
Dave Bond, supt. Fax 222-5050
www.ksd.org
Chinook MS, 4891 W 27th Ave 99336 6-8
Kevin Pierce, prin. 509-222-7500
Desert Hills MS 1,000/6-8
1701 S Clodfelter Rd 99338 509-222-6600
Steve Jones, prin. Fax 222-6601
Highlands MS 900/6-8
425 S Tweedt St 99336 509-222-6700
Lori McCord, prin. Fax 222-6701
Horse Heaven Hills MS 1,000/6-8
3500 S Vancouver St 99337 509-222-6800
Diana Burns, prin. Fax 222-6801
Kamiakin HS 1,700/9-12
600 N Arthur St 99336 509-222-7000
Chris Chelin, prin. Fax 222-7001
Kennewick HS 1,500/9-12
500 S Dayton St 99336 509-222-7100
Ron King, prin. Fax 222-7101
Legacy HS 200/Alt
202 S Dayton St 99336 509-222-6552
Dennis Boatman, prin. Fax 222-5059
Park MS 900/6-8
1011 W 10th Ave 99336 509-222-6900
Shaun Espe, prin. Fax 222-6901
Phoenix HS 100/9-12
1315 W 4th Ave 99336 509-222-7400
Jill Mulhousen, lead tchr. Fax 222-5153
Southridge HS 1,700/9-12
3520 Southridge Blvd 99338 509-222-7200
Molly Hamaker-Teals, prin. Fax 222-7201
Tri-Tech Vocational Skills Center Vo/Tech
5929 W Metaline Ave 99336 509-222-7300
Paul Randall, prin. Fax 222-7301

Kent, King, Pop. 85,961
Federal Way SD 210
Supt. — See Federal Way
TAF Academy 300/Alt
26720 40th Ave S 98032 253-945-5187
Pam Tuggle, prin. Fax 945-5191
Totem MS 600/6-8
26630 40th Ave S 98032 253-945-5100
Christine Baker, prin. Fax 945-5151

Kent SD 415 27,500/PK-12
12033 SE 256th St 98030 253-373-7000
Dr. Calvin Watts, supt. Fax 373-7231
www.kent.k12.wa.us
iGrad 500/Alt
25668 104th Ave SE, 253-373-4723
Carol Cleveland, prin. Fax 373-7989
Kentlake HS 1,500/9-12
21401 SE Falcon Way 98042 253-373-4900
Dr. Joe Potts, prin. Fax 373-4908
Kent-Meridian HS 2,200/9-12
10020 SE 256th St, 253-373-7405
Dr. Wade Barringer, prin. Fax 373-7411
Kent Phoenix Academy 300/Alt
11000 SE 264th St, 253-373-7542
Merrilee Lyle, prin. Fax 373-7554
Kentridge HS 2,200/9-12
12430 SE 208th St 98031 253-373-7345
Mike Albrecht, prin. Fax 373-7363
Meridian MS 600/7-8
23480 120th Ave SE 98031 253-373-7383
Darice Johnson, prin. Fax 373-7395
Mill Creek MS 900/7-8
620 Central Ave N 98032 253-373-7446
Tammy Unruh, prin. Fax 373-7478
Other Schools – See Covington, Des Moines, Renton

Kettle Falls, Stevens, Pop. 1,505
Kettle Falls SD 212 900/K-12
PO Box 458 99141 509-738-6625
Thaynan Knowlton, supt. Fax 738-6375
www.kfschools.org
Kettle Falls HS 300/9-12
PO Box 458 99141 509-738-6388
James Hill, prin. Fax 738-2670
Kettle Falls MS 200/5-8
PO Box 458 99141 509-738-6014
Tracy Vining, prin. Fax 738-2401

Kingston, Kitsap, Pop. 2,022
North Kitsap SD 400
Supt. — See Poulsbo
Kingston HS 900/9-12
26201 Siyaya Ave NE 98346 360-396-3300
Christy Cole, prin. Fax 396-3941
Kingston MS 600/6-8
9000 NE West Kingston Rd 98346 360-396-3400
Craig Barry, prin. Fax 396-3945

Kirkland, King, Pop. 46,527
Lake Washington SD 414
Supt. — See Redmond
Emerson S 100/K-12
10903 NE 53rd St 98033 425-936-2311
Nell Ballard-Jones, prin. Fax 936-2312
Environmental & Adventure S 100/6-8
8040 NE 132nd St 98034 425-936-2355
Victor Scarpelli, prin. Fax 825-0921
Finn Hill MS 600/6-8
8040 NE 132nd St 98034 425-936-2340
Victor Scarpelli, prin. Fax 814-2955
International Community S 400/6-12
11133 NE 65th St 98033 425-936-2380
Gregory Moncada, prin. Fax 576-1515
Juanita HS 1,300/9-12
10601 NE 132nd St 98034 425-936-1600
Gary Moed, prin. Fax 825-3675
Kamiakin MS 500/6-8
14111 132nd Ave NE 98034 425-936-2400
Joe Joss, prin. Fax 823-2921
Kirkland MS 600/6-8
430 18th Ave 98033 425-936-2420
Deborah McCarson, prin. Fax 889-1589
Lake Washington HS 1,500/9-12
12033 NE 80th St 98033 425-936-1700
Christina Thomas, prin. Fax 576-0539
Northstar MS 100/6-8
10903 NE 53rd St 98033 425-936-2390
Nell Ballard-Jones, prin. Fax 936-2308
WA Network for Innovative Careers Vo/Tech
11605 132nd Ave NE #A108 98034 425-739-8400
Karen Hay, dir. Fax 739-8398

Eastside Preparatory S 200/5-12
10613 NE 38th Pl 98033 425-822-5668
Dr. Terry Macaluso, head sch Fax 822-5648
Lake Washington Institute of Technology Post-Sec.
11605 132nd Ave NE 98034 425-739-8100
Northwest University Post-Sec.
PO Box 579 98083 425-822-8266
Providence Classical Christian S 200/PK-12
11727 NE 118th St 98034 425-774-6622
Ryan Evans, hdmstr. Fax 820-4123
Puget Sound Adventist Academy 100/9-12
5320 108th Ave NE 98033 425-822-7554

Kittitas, Kittitas, Pop. 1,352
Kittitas SD 403 700/K-12
PO Box 599 98934 509-968-3115
Mike Messenger, supt. Fax 968-4730
www.ksd403.org
Kittitas Secondary S 400/6-12
PO Box 599 98934 509-968-3902
Delbert Heistand, prin. Fax 968-3370

Klickitat, Klickitat, Pop. 348
Klickitat SD 402 100/K-12
PO Box 37 98628 509-369-4145
Kevin Davis, supt. Fax 369-3422
www.klickitat.wednet.edu
Klickitat S 100/K-12
PO Box 37 98628 509-369-4145
Kevin Davis, admin. Fax 369-3422

La Center, Clark, Pop. 2,714
La Center SD 101 1,600/K-12
PO Box 1840 98629 360-263-2131
David Holmes, supt. Fax 263-1140
www.lacenterschools.org
La Center HS 500/9-12
PO Box 1780 98629 360-263-1700
Carol Patton, prin. Fax 263-1705
La Center MS 400/6-8
PO Box 1750 98629 360-263-2136
Lauri Landerholm, prin. Fax 263-5936

Lacey, Thurston, Pop. 39,269
North Thurston SD 3 13,900/PK-12
305 College St NE 98516 360-412-4400
Debra J. Clemens, supt. Fax 412-4410
www.nthurston.k12.wa.us
Aspire MS 300/6-8
5900 54th Ave SE 98513 360-412-4730
Courtney Crawford, prin. Fax 412-4739
Chinook MS 900/6-8
4301 6th Ave NE 98516 360-412-4760
Kirsten Rue, prin. Fax 412-4769
Komachin MS 800/6-8
3650 College St SE 98503 360-412-4740
Deborah Sarver, prin. Fax 412-4749
Nisqually MS 600/6-8
8100 Steilacoom Rd SE 98503 360-412-4770
David Crane, prin. Fax 493-2756
North Thurston HS 1,500/9-12
600 Sleater Kinney Rd NE 98506 360-412-4800
Steve Rood, prin. Fax 412-4819
River Ridge HS 1,100/9-12
350 River Ridge Dr SE 98513 360-412-4820
Serenity Malloy, prin. Fax 412-4839
Salish MS 6-8
8605 Campus Glen Dr NE 98516 360-412-4780
Karen Owen, prin. Fax 412-4789
South Sound HS 200/Alt
411 College St NE 98516 360-412-4880
Angela Grizzle, prin. Fax 412-4889
Timberline HS 1,700/9-12
6120 Mullen Rd SE 98503 360-412-4860
Paul Dean, prin. Fax 412-4879

Northwest Christian HS 200/9-12
4710 Park Center Ave NE 98516 360-491-2966
Dr. Terry Ketchum, prin. Fax 491-3086
Pope John Paul II HS 50/9-12
5608 Pacific Ave SE 98503 360-438-7600
Ronald Edwards, prin. Fax 438-7607
St. Martin's University Post-Sec.
5000 Abbey Way SE 98503 360-491-4700

La Conner, Skagit, Pop. 873
La Conner SD 311 600/K-12
PO Box 2103 98257 360-466-3171
Dr. Tim Bruce, supt. Fax 466-3523
www.lcsd.wednet.edu
La Conner HS 200/9-12
PO Box 2103 98257 360-466-3173
Cheryl Sullivan, prin. Fax 466-1062
La Conner MS 100/6-8
PO Box 2103 98257 360-466-4113
Cheryl Sullivan, prin. Fax 466-0153

LaCrosse, Whitman, Pop. 304
LaCrosse SD 126 100/K-12
111 Hill Ave 99143 509-549-3591
Doug Curtis, supt. Fax 549-3529
www.lacrossesd.k12.wa.us
LaCrosse JSHS 50/6-12
111 Hill Ave 99143 509-549-3592
Jeff Pietila, prin. Fax 549-3529

Lakebay, Pierce
Peninsula SD 401
Supt. — See Gig Harbor
Key Penninsula MS 400/6-8
5510 Key Peninsula Hwy N 98349 253-530-4200
Jeri Goebel, prin. Fax 530-4220

Lake Stevens, Snohomish, Pop. 26,753
Lake Stevens SD 4 8,200/PK-12
12309 22nd St NE 98258 425-335-1500
Dr. Amy Beth Cook, supt. Fax 335-1549
www.lkstevens.wednet.edu
Cavelero Mid HS 1,300/8-9
8220 24th St SE 98258 425-335-1630
Mike Snow, prin. Fax 397-9413
Lake Stevens HS 1,800/10-12
2908 113th Ave NE 98258 425-335-1515
Leslie Ivelia, prin. Fax 335-1524

Lake Tapps, Pierce, Pop. 11,482
Dieringer SD 343 1,500/K-8
1320 178th Ave E, 253-862-2537
Dr. Judy Neumeier-Martinson, supt. Fax 862-8472
www.dieringer.wednet.edu
North Tapps MS 500/6-8
20029 12th St E, 253-862-2776
Nate Salisbury, prin. Fax 862-2587

Lakewood, Pierce, Pop. 52,506
Clover Park SD 400 10,700/PK-12
10903 Gravelly Lake Dr SW 98499 253-583-5000
Debbie LeBeau, supt. Fax 583-5198
www.cloverpark.k12.wa.us
Clover Park HS 1,100/9-12
11023 Gravelly Lake Dr SW 98499 253-583-5500
Tim Stults, prin. Fax 583-5508
Harrison Preparatory S 500/6-12
9103 Lakewood Dr SW 98499 253-583-5418
Kevin Rupprecht, prin. Fax 583-5417

Hudtloff MS 700/6-8
8102 Phillips Rd SW 98498 253-583-5400
Cynthia Adams, prin. Fax 583-5408

Lakes HS 1,400/9-12
10320 Farwest Dr SW 98498 253-583-5550
Karen Mauer-Smith, prin. Fax 583-5558

Lochburn MS 600/6-8
5431 Steilacoom Blvd SW 98499 253-583-5420
Greg Willson, prin. Fax 583-5428

Mann MS 400/6-8
11509 Holden Rd SW 98498 253-583-5440
Steve Seberson, prin. Fax 583-5448

Woodbrook MS 500/6-8
14920 Spring St SW 98439 253-583-5460
Nancy LaChapelle, prin. Fax 583-5468

Clover Park Technical College Post-Sec.
4500 Steilacoom Blvd SW 98499 253-589-5800

Pierce College Post-Sec.
9401 Farwest Dr SW 98498 253-964-6500

Lamont, Whitman, Pop. 66

Lamont SD 264 50/5-8
602 Main St 99017 509-257-2463
Joseph Whipple, supt. Fax 257-2316
www.spraguelamont.org

Lamont MS 50/5-8
602 Main St 99017 509-257-2463
Joseph Whipple, admin. Fax 257-2316

Langley, Island, Pop. 1,005

South Whidbey SD 206 1,400/K-12
5520 Maxwelton Rd 98260 360-221-6100
Dr. Josephine Moccia, supt. Fax 221-3835
www.sw.wednet.edu

Langley MS 300/6-8
723 Camano Ave 98260 360-221-5100
Jim McNally, prin. Fax 221-8545

South Whidbey Academy 100/Alt
5520 Maxwelton Rd 98260 360-221-6808
David Pfeiffer, dir. Fax 221-3835

South Whidbey HS 500/9-12
5675 Maxwelton Rd 98260 360-221-4300
John Paton, prin. Fax 221-5797

Island Christian Academy 100/PK-12
PO Box 1048 98260 360-221-0919
Brenda Chittim, dir. Fax 221-1653

Leavenworth, Chelan, Pop. 1,933

Cascade SD 228 1,300/PK-12
330 Evans St 98826 509-548-5885
Bill Motsenbocker, supt. Fax 548-6149
www.cascadesd.org

Cascade HS 400/9-12
10190 Chumstick Hwy 98826 509-548-5277
Elia Daley, prin. Fax 548-7458

Icicle River MS 300/6-8
10195 Titus Rd 98826 509-548-4042
Mike Janski, prin. Fax 548-6646

Lind, Adams, Pop. 553

Lind-Ritzville SD 400/PK-12
PO Box 340 99341 509-677-3481
Matt Ellis, supt. Fax 677-3463
www.lrschools.org

Lind/Ritzville MS 50/6-8
PO Box 340 99341 509-677-3408
Cindy Deska, prin. Fax 677-3420

Other Schools – See Ritzville

Long Beach, Pacific, Pop. 1,362

Ocean Beach SD 101 700/PK-12
PO Box 778 98631 360-642-3739
Jenny Risner, supt. Fax 642-1298
www.ocean.k12.wa.us

Other Schools – See Ilwaco

Longview, Cowlitz, Pop. 35,373

Longview SD 122 6,600/K-12
2715 Lilac St 98632 360-575-7000
Dr. Dan Zorn, supt. Fax 575-7022
www.longview.k12.wa.us

Cascade MS 500/6-8
2821 Parkview Dr 98632 360-577-2701
Chris Rugg, prin. Fax 577-2790

Discovery HS Alt
2742 Harding St 98632 360-575-2926
Jill Diehl, admin. Fax 575-7114

Long HS 1,000/9-12
2903 Nichols Blvd 98632 360-575-7110
Rich Reeves, prin. Fax 575-7112

Monticello MS 500/6-8
1225 28th Ave 98632 360-575-7050
Scott Merzoian, prin. Fax 575-7220

Morris HS 1,000/9-12
1602 Mark Morris Ct 98632 360-575-7770
Philip Suek, prin. Fax 575-7699

Mt. Solo MS 500/6-8
5300 Mt Solo Rd 98632 360-577-2800
Jay Opgrande, prin. Fax 577-2888

Lower Columbia College Post-Sec.
PO Box 3010 98632 360-442-2311

Stylemasters College of Hair Design Post-Sec.
1224 Commerce Ave 98632 360-636-2720

Three Rivers Christian S 100/8-12
2441 42nd Ave 98632 360-636-1600
Erin Hart, admin. Fax 577-5955

Lopez Island, San Juan

Lopez Island SD 144 200/K-12
86 School Rd 98261 360-468-2201
Brian Auckland, supt. Fax 468-2212
www.lopezislandschool.org

Lopez Island MSHS 100/6-12
86 School Rd 98261 360-468-2202
Dave Sather, prin. Fax 468-2212

Lyle, Klickitat, Pop. 484

Lyle SD 406 200/K-12
PO Box 368 98635 509-365-2191
Andrew Kelly, supt. Fax 365-5000
www.lyleschools.org

Lyle HS 100/9-12
PO Box 522 98635 509-365-2211
Andrew Kelly, prin. Fax 365-2665

Lyle MS 50/6-8
PO Box 522 98635 509-365-2211
Andrew Kelly, prin. Fax 365-2665

Lynden, Whatcom, Pop. 11,746

Lynden SD 504 2,700/K-12
1203 Bradley Rd 98264 360-354-4443
Jim Frey, supt. Fax 354-7662
www.lynden.wednet.edu

Lynden HS 900/9-12
1201 Bradley Rd 98264 360-354-4401
Ian Freeman, prin. Fax 354-0991

Lynden MS 600/6-8
516 Main St 98264 360-354-2952
Molly Mitchell-Mumma, prin. Fax 354-6631

Meridian SD 505
Supt. — See Bellingham

Meridian MS 300/6-8
861 Ten Mile Rd 98264 360-398-2291
Gerald Sanderson, prin. Fax 398-8131

Cornerstone Christian S 100/1-12
8872 Northwood Rd 98264 360-318-0663

Lynden Christian HS 300/9-12
515 Drayton St 98264 360-354-3221
Dr. Kevin Kaemingk, prin. Fax 354-1047

Lynden Christian MS 300/5-8
503 Lyncs Dr 98264 360-354-3358
Aaron Bishop, prin. Fax 354-6690

Lynnwood, Snohomish, Pop. 34,119

Edmonds SD 15 19,700/PK-12
20420 68th Ave W 98036 425-431-7000
Christine McDuffie, supt. Fax 431-7006
www.edmonds.wednet.edu

Alderwood MS 700/7-8
1132 172nd St SW 98037 425-431-7579
Erin Murphy, prin. Fax 431-7580

College Place MS 500/7-8
7501 208th St SW 98036 425-431-7451
Sam Yuhan, prin. Fax 431-7449

Meadowdale HS 1,600/9-12
6002 168th St SW 98037 425-431-7650
Kevin Allen, prin. Fax 431-7655

Meadowdale MS 700/7-8
6500 168th St SW 98037 425-431-7707
Joe Webster, prin. Fax 431-7714

Other Schools – See Bothell, Brier, Edmonds, Mountlake Terrace

---

Charter College Post-Sec.
19401 40th Ave W Ste 400 98036 425-275-4900

Edmonds Community College Post-Sec.
20000 68th Ave W 98036 425-640-1459

Mabton, Yakima, Pop. 2,272

Mabton SD 120 800/K-12
PO Box 37 98935 509-894-4852
Minerva Morales, supt. Fax 894-4769
www.msd120.org

Mabton JSHS 300/7-12
PO Box 38 98935 509-894-4951
Caleb Oten, prin. Fax 894-4761

Mansfield, Douglas, Pop. 319

Mansfield SD 207 100/PK-12
PO Box 188 98830 509-683-1012
Cora Nordby, supt. Fax 683-1281
www.mansfield.wednet.edu/

Mansfield S 100/PK-12
PO Box 188 98830 509-683-1012
Cora Nordby, admin. Fax 683-1281

Manson, Chelan, Pop. 1,456

Manson SD 19 700/PK-12
PO Box A 98831 509-687-3140
Matt Charlton, supt. Fax 687-9877
www.manson.org

Manson HS 200/9-12
PO Box A 98831 509-687-9585
Don Vanderholm, prin. Fax 687-6109

Manson MS 100/6-8
PO Box A 98831 509-687-9585
Todd Smith, prin. Fax 687-6109

Maple Valley, King, Pop. 21,591

Tahoma SD 409 7,800/PK-12
25720 Maple Valley Black Di 98038 425-413-3400
Rob Morrow, supt. Fax 413-3455
www.tahomasd.us

Other Schools – See Covington, Ravensdale

Marysville, Snohomish, Pop. 56,950

Lakewood SD 306 2,400/PK-12
17110 16th Dr NE 98271 360-652-4500
Dr. Michael Mack, supt. Fax 652-4502
www.lwsd.wednet.edu

Lakewood HS 800/9-12
17023 11th Ave NE 98271 360-652-4505
Mike Curl, prin. Fax 652-4507

Lakewood MS 500/6-8
16800 16th Dr NE 98271 360-652-4510
Bryan Toutant, prin. Fax 652-4512

Marysville SD 25 10,600/PK-12
4220 80th St NE 98270 360-965-0000
Dr. Becky Berg, supt. Fax 965-0079
www.msd25.org

Academy of Construction & Engineering 400/9-12
8301 84th St NE 98270 360-965-2300
Shawn Stevenson, prin. Fax 965-2304

Arts & Technology HS 300/9-12
7204 27th Ave NE 98271 360-965-2900
Dawn Bechtholdt, prin. Fax 965-2904

Bio Med Academy 400/9-12
8301 84th St NE 98270 360-965-2500
Shawn Stevenson, prin. Fax 965-2504

Cedarcrest MS 900/6-8
6400 88th St NE 98270 360-965-0700
Stephanie Clark, prin. Fax 965-0704

Heritage HS 100/9-12
7204 27th Ave NE 98271 360-965-2800
Shelly Lacy, prin. Fax 965-2804

International S of Communication 400/9-12
8301 84th St NE 98270 360-965-2400
Shawn Stevenson, prin. Fax 965-2404

Marysville MS 800/6-8
4923 67th St NE 98270 360-965-0900
Angela Hansen, prin. Fax 965-0904

Marysville Mountain View HS 200/Alt
7204 27th Ave NE 98271 360-965-3000
Dawn Bechtholdt, prin. Fax 965-3004

Marysville-Pilchuck HS 1,200/9-12
5611 108th St NE 98271 360-965-2000
Rob Lowry, prin. Fax 965-2004

School for the Entrepreneur 400/9-12
8301 84th St NE 98270 360-965-2600
Shawn Stevenson, prin. Fax 965-2604

Tenth Street MS 200/6-8
7204 27th Ave NE 98271 360-965-0400
Sonja Machovina, prin. Fax 965-0404

Totem MS 600/6-8
1605 7th St 98270 360-965-0500
Angela Deldago, prin. Fax 965-0504

Evangel Classical S 50/K-12
9015 44th Dr NE 98270 425-344-2789
Jonathan Sarr, hdmstr.

Grace Academy 300/PK-12
8521 67th Ave NE 98270 360-659-8517
Timothy Lugg, prin. Fax 653-5899

Mattawa, Grant, Pop. 4,417

Wahluke SD 73 2,300/K-12
PO Box 907 99349 509-932-4565
Aaron Chavez, supt. Fax 932-4571
www.wsd73.wednet.edu

Sentinel Technical Alternative HS 50/Alt
PO Box 907 99349 509-932-3133
Mia Benjamin, prin. Fax 932-3320

Wahluke HS 500/9-12
PO Box 907 99349 509-932-4477
Mia Benjamin, prin. Fax 932-4241

Wahluke JHS 500/6-8
PO Box 907 99349 509-932-4455
Andrew Harlow, prin. Fax 932-4282

Mead, Spokane, Pop. 7,091

Mead SD 354 9,100/K-12
2323 E Farwell Rd 99021 509-465-6000
Thomas Rockefeller, supt. Fax 465-6020
www.mead354.org

Mount Spokane HS 1,500/9-12
6015 E Mt Spokane Park Dr 99021 509-465-7200
Darren Nelson, prin. Fax 465-7220

Other Schools – See Colbert, Spokane

Medical Lake, Spokane, Pop. 4,877

Medical Lake SD 326 1,900/PK-12
PO Box 128 99022 509-565-3100
Timothy Ames, supt. Fax 565-3102
www.mlsd.org/

Medical Lake Alternative HS 50/Alt
PO Box 128 99022 509-565-3141
Lyra McGirk, prin. Fax 565-3149

Medical Lake HS 500/9-12
PO Box 128 99022 509-565-3200
Chris Spring, prin. Fax 565-3201

Medical Lake MS 400/6-8
PO Box 128 99022 509-565-3300
Sylvia Campbell, prin. Fax 565-3301

Lakeland Village School Post-Sec.
PO Box 200 99022

Mercer Island, King, Pop. 21,809

Mercer Island SD 400 4,400/K-12
4160 86th Ave SE 98040 206-236-3300
Dr. Gary Plano, supt. Fax 236-3333
www.mercerislandschools.org

Crest Learning Center 100/Alt
4150 86th Ave SE 98040 206-236-3390
Fax 236-4521

Islander MS 1,100/6-8
8225 SE 72nd St 98040 206-236-3413
MaryJo Budzius, prin. Fax 236-3408

Mercer Island HS 1,400/9-12
9100 SE 42nd St 98040 206-236-3350
Vicki Puckett, prin. Fax 236-3358

Northwest Yeshiva HS 100/9-12
5017 90th Ave SE 98040 206-232-5272
Malka Popper, prin. Fax 232-2711

Privett Academy 100/6-12
PO Box 42 98040 206-232-0059

Metaline Falls, Pend Oreille, Pop. 233

Selkirk SD 70 200/PK-12
PO Box 129 99153 509-446-2951
Nancy Lotze, supt. Fax 446-2929
www.selkirk.k12.wa.us

Other Schools – See Ione

Mill Creek, Snohomish, Pop. 17,443

Everett SD 2
Supt. — See Everett

Heatherwood MS 900/6-8
1419 Trillium Blvd SE 98012 425-385-6300
Laura Phillips, prin. Fax 385-6302

Jackson HS 2,000/9-12
1508 136th St SE 98012 425-385-7000
Dave Peters, prin. Fax 385-7002

Monroe, Snohomish, Pop. 16,699
Monroe SD 103 6,300/K-12
200 E Fremont St 98272 360-804-2500
Dr. Fredrika Smith, supt. Fax 804-2529
www.monroe.wednet.edu
Leaders in Learning HS 100/Alt
639 W Main St 98272 360-804-2800
Blake Baird, coord. Fax 804-2819
Monroe HS 1,600/9-12
17001 Tester Rd 98272 360-804-4500
John Lombardi, prin. Fax 804-4699
Park Place MS 800/6-8
1408 W Main St 98272 360-804-4300
Terry Cheshire, prin. Fax 804-4399
Sky Valley Education Center 800/Alt
351 Short Columbia St 98272 360-804-2700
Karen Rosencrans, dir. Fax 804-2759
Other Schools – See Snohomish

Montesano, Grays Harbor, Pop. 3,841
Montesano SD 66 1,200/PK-12
302 N Church St 98563 360-249-3942
Dan Winter, supt. Fax 841-7198
www.monteschools.org
Montesano JSHS 600/7-12
303 N Church St 98563 360-249-4041
Alec Pugh, prin. Fax 841-7527

Morton, Lewis, Pop. 1,107
Morton SD 300/PK-12
PO Box 1219 98356 360-496-5300
John Hannah, supt. Fax 586-3208
www.morton.wednet.edu
Morton JSHS 100/7-12
PO Box 1169 98356 360-496-5137
Josh Stoney, prin. Fax 496-6035

Moses Lake, Grant, Pop. 19,890
Moses Lake SD 161 8,300/PK-12
920 W Ivy Ave 98837 509-766-2650
Dr. Michelle Price, supt. Fax 766-2678
www.moseslakeschools.org
Chief Moses MS 1,000/6-8
1111 E Nelson Rd 98837 509-766-2661
Vicki Swisher, prin. Fax 766-2680
Columbia Basin Technical Skills Center Vo/Tech
900 E Yonezawa Blvd 98837 509-793-7000
Christine Armstrong, dir.
Endeavor MS 300/6-8
6527 Patton Blvd NE 98837 509-766-2667
Ryan Pike, admin. Fax 766-2690
Frontier MS 800/6-8
517 W 3rd Ave 98837 509-766-2662
Greg Kittrell, prin. Fax 766-2663
Moses Lake HS 2,200/9-12
803 Sharon Ave E 98837 509-766-2666
Mark Harris, prin. Fax 766-2682

Wellpinit SD 49
Supt. — See Wellpinit
Columbia Basin Alliance HS 50/Alt
6739 24th St 98837 509-258-4535
Terry Bartolino, prin. Fax 258-7857

Big Bend Community College Post-Sec.
7662 Chanute St NE 98837 509-793-2222
Moses Lake Christian Academy 200/PK-12
1475 Nelson Rd NE Ste A 98837 509-765-9704
Stephanie Voigt, dir. Fax 765-3698

Mossyrock, Lewis, Pop. 745
Mossyrock SD 206 500/K-12
PO Box 478 98564 360-983-3181
Dr. Lisa Grant, supt. Fax 983-8111
www.mossyrockschools.org
Mossyrock Academy 50/Alt
PO Box 478 98564 360-983-3184
Lori Cournyer, prin. Fax 983-3188
Mossyrock JSHS 200/7-12
PO Box 454 98564 360-983-3183
Lori Cournyer, prin. Fax 983-3188

Mountlake Terrace, Snohomish, Pop. 18,701
Edmonds SD 15
Supt. — See Lynnwood
Mountlake Terrace HS 1,200/9-12
21801 44th Ave W 98043 425-431-7776
Greg Schwab, prin. Fax 431-7771

Cedar Park Christian JSHS - Mountlake 100/7-12
23607 54th Ave W 98043 425-774-7773
Al Carpenter, admin. Fax 774-3218

Mount Vernon, Skagit, Pop. 30,973
Anacortes SD 103
Supt. — See Anacortes
Northwest Career & Technical Academy Vo/Tech
2205 W Campus Pl 98273 360-848-0706
Dr. Doug Walker, dir. Fax 848-7586

Mount Vernon SD 320 5,700/K-12
124 E Lawrence St 98273 360-428-6110
Carl Bruner, supt. Fax 428-6172
www.mountvernonschools.org/
LaVenture MS 400/6-8
1200 N Laventure Rd 98273 360-428-6116
Dave Riddle, prin. Fax 428-6189
Mount Baker MS 500/6-8
2310 E Section St 98274 360-428-6127
Jeff Ingrum, prin. Fax 428-6155
Mount Vernon HS 1,900/9-12
314 N 9th St 98273 360-428-6100
Rod Merrell, prin. Fax 428-6152

Mt. Vernon Christian S 300/PK-12
820 W Blackburn Rd 98273 360-424-9157
Jeffrey Droog, supt. Fax 424-9256
Northwest Hair Academy Post-Sec.
615 S 1st St 98273 360-336-6553
Skagit Valley College Post-Sec.
2405 E College Way 98273 360-416-7600

Mukilteo, Snohomish, Pop. 19,401
Mukilteo SD 6
Supt. — See Everett
Harbour Pointe MS 800/6-8
5000 Harbour Pointe Blvd 98275 425-366-5100
Kevin Rohrich, prin. Fax 366-5102
Kamiak HS 2,200/9-12
10801 Harbour Pointe Blvd 98275 425-366-5400
Mike Gallagher, prin. Fax 366-5402
Olympic View MS 800/6-8
2602 Mukilteo Speedway 98275 425-366-5200
Devin McLane, prin. Fax 366-5202

Naches, Yakima, Pop. 787
Naches Valley SD JT3 1,200/K-12
PO Box 99 98937 509-653-2220
Duane Lyons, supt. Fax 653-1211
www.nvsd.org
Naches Valley HS 500/9-12
PO Box 159 98937 509-653-1732
Rich Rouleau, prin. Fax 653-2921
Naches Valley MS 400/5-8
PO Box 39 98937 509-653-1599
Todd Hilmes, prin. Fax 653-2729

Napavine, Lewis, Pop. 1,693
Napavine SD 14 800/PK-12
PO Box 840 98565 360-262-3303
Dr. Richard Jones, supt. Fax 262-9737
www.napa.k12.wa.us
Napavine JSHS 400/7-12
PO Box 357 98565 360-262-3301
Jason Prather, prin. Fax 262-9541

Naselle, Pacific, Pop. 396
Naselle-Grays River Valley SD 155 200/K-12
793 State Route 4 98638 360-484-7121
Dr. Lisa Nelson, supt. Fax 484-3191
www.naselle.wednet.edu
Naselle-Grays River Valley S 100/K-12
793 State Route 4 98638 360-484-7121
Quinn Donlon, prin. Fax 484-3191
Naselle Youth Camp HS 100/Alt
11S Youth Camp Ln 98638 360-484-3269
Gary Flood, prin. Fax 484-7109

Neah Bay, Clallam, Pop. 795
Cape Flattery SD 401
Supt. — See Sekiu
Neah Bay JSHS 200/6-12
PO Box 86 98357 360-645-2221
Jennifer Sikes, prin. Fax 645-2574

Newport, Pend Oreille, Pop. 2,055
Newport SD 56-415 1,000/PK-12
PO Box 70 99156 509-447-3167
Dave Smith, supt. Fax 447-2553
www.newport.wednet.edu
Halstead MS 300/5-8
PO Box 70 99156 509-447-2426
Tony Moser, prin. Fax 447-4914
Newport HS 300/9-12
PO Box 70 99156 509-447-2481
Troy Whittle, prin. Fax 447-4354

Nine Mile Falls, Spokane
Nine Mile Falls SD 325 1,500/PK-12
10110 W Charles Rd 99026 509-340-4300
Brian Talbott, supt. Fax 340-4301
www.9mile.org
Lakeside HS 500/9-12
5909 Highway 291 99026 509-340-4200
Brent Osborn, prin. Fax 340-4201
Lakeside MS 400/6-8
6169 Highway 291 99026 509-340-4100
Jeff Baerwald, prin. Fax 340-4101

Nooksack, Whatcom, Pop. 1,290
Nooksack Valley SD 506
Supt. — See Everson
Nooksack Valley MS 300/6-8
404 W Columbia St 98276 360-966-7561
Joel VanderYacht, prin. Fax 966-7805

North Bend, King, Pop. 5,558
Snoqualmie Valley SD 410
Supt. — See Snoqualmie
Twin Falls MS 700/6-8
46910 SE Middle Fork Rd 98045 425-831-4150
Jeffrey D'Ambrosio, prin. Fax 831-4140
Two Rivers S 100/Alt
330 Ballarat Ave N 98045 425-831-4200
Amy Montanye-Johnson, prin. Fax 831-4210

Northport, Stevens, Pop. 287
Northport SD 211 200/K-12
PO Box 1280 99157 509-732-4251
Don Baribault, supt. Fax 732-6606
www.northportschools.org
Northport HS 100/9-12
PO Box 1280 99157 509-732-4251
Terry Carlson, prin. Fax 732-6606

Oakesdale, Whitman, Pop. 413
Oakesdale SD 324 100/PK-12
PO Box 228 99158 509-285-5296
Dr. Jake Dingman, supt. Fax 285-5121
www.gonighthawks.net
Oakesdale HS 50/7-12
PO Box 228 99158 509-285-5296
Dr. Jake Dingman, supt. Fax 285-5121

Oak Harbor, Island, Pop. 20,413
Oak Harbor SD 201 5,200/PK-12
350 S Oak Harbor St 98277 360-279-5000
Dr. Lance Gibbon, supt. Fax 279-5070
www.ohsd.net
Midway HS Alt
1 Wildcat Way 98277 360-279-5800
Ray Cone, prin. Fax 279-5794
North Whidbey MS 500/6-8
67 NE Izett St 98277 360-279-5500
William Weinsheimer, prin. Fax 279-5516
Oak Harbor HS 1,500/9-12
1 Wildcat Way 98277 360-279-5800
Dwight Lundstrom, prin. Fax 279-5794
Oak Harbor MS 600/6-8
150 SW 6th Ave 98277 360-279-5300
Raenette Wood, prin. Fax 279-5399

North Whidbey Christian HS 7-12
675 E Whidbey Ave 98277 360-675-5352
Rev. Doug Fakkema, admin.

Oakville, Grays Harbor, Pop. 661
Oakville SD 400 300/K-12
PO Box H 98568 360-273-0171
Kathy Lorton, supt. Fax 273-6724
oakvilleschools.org/
Oakville JSHS 100/7-12
PO Box H 98568 360-273-5947
Michael Auton, prin. Fax 273-8229

Ocean Shores, Grays Harbor, Pop. 5,358
North Beach SD 64 600/PK-12
PO Box 159 98569 360-289-2447
Deborah Holcomb, supt. Fax 289-2492
www.northbeachschools.org
North Beach HS 200/9-12
PO Box 969 98569 360-289-3888
Brett Mackey, prin. Fax 289-0996
North Beach JHS 100/7-8
PO Box 969 98569 360-289-3888
Brett Mackey, prin. Fax 289-0996

Odessa, Lincoln, Pop. 895
Odessa SD 105-157-166 J 200/PK-12
PO Box 248 99159 509-982-2668
Dan Read, supt. Fax 982-0163
www.odessa.wednet.edu
Odessa JSHS 100/7-12
PO Box 248 99159 509-982-2111
Jamie Nelson, prin. Fax 982-0163

Okanogan, Okanogan, Pop. 2,464
Okanogan SD 105 1,000/K-12
PO Box 592 98840 509-422-3629
Dr. Richard Johnson, supt. Fax 422-1525
www.oksd.wednet.edu
Okanogan HS 300/9-12
PO Box 592 98840 509-422-3770
Bob Shacklett, prin. Fax 422-3656
Okanogan MS 300/6-8
PO Box 592 98840 509-422-2680
Brett Baum, prin. Fax 422-0068
Other Schools – See Omak

Olympia, Thurston, Pop. 44,308
Olympia SD 111 9,300/PK-12
1113 Legion Way SE 98501 360-596-6100
Dick Cvitanich, supt. Fax 596-6111
osd.wednet.edu
Avanti HS 200/Alt
1113 Legion Way SE 98501 360-596-7900
Michael Velasquez, prin. Fax 596-7901
Capital HS 1,400/9-12
2707 Conger Ave NW 98502 360-596-8000
Curtis Cleveringa, prin. Fax 596-8001
Jefferson MS 400/6-8
2200 Conger Ave NW 98502 360-596-3200
Michael Cimino, prin. Fax 596-3201
Marshall MS 400/6-8
3939 20th Ave NW 98502 360-596-7600
Condee Wood, prin. Fax 596-7601
Olympia HS 1,700/9-12
1302 North St SE 98501 360-596-7000
Matt Grant, prin. Fax 596-7001
Reeves MS 400/6-8
2200 Quince St NE 98506 360-596-3400
Geoff Parks, prin. Fax 596-3401
Washington MS 700/6-8
3100 Cain Rd SE 98501 360-596-3000
Paul Anders, prin. Fax 596-3001

Tumwater SD 33
Supt. — See Tumwater
Secondary Options HS 100/Alt
7741 Littlerock Rd SW 98512 360-709-7760
Jeanette Holocher, lead tchr. Fax 709-7762
West Black Hills HS 900/9-12
7741 Littlerock Rd SW 98512 360-709-7800
Dave Myers, prin. Fax 709-7802

Evergreen State College Post-Sec.
2700 Evergreen Pkwy NW 98505 360-867-6000
NOVA S 100/6-8
2020 22nd Ave SE 98501 360-491-7097
Barbara Hutton, head sch Fax 491-0775
South Puget Sound Community College Post-Sec.
2011 Mottman Rd SW 98512 360-754-7711

Omak, Okanogan, Pop. 4,701
Okanogan SD 105
Supt. — See Okanogan
Okanogan Alternative S 50/Alt
126 S Main St 98841 509-422-3629
Richard Johnson, prin.

Omak SD 19 2,200/PK-12
PO Box 833 98841 509-826-0320
Dr. Erik Swanson, supt. Fax 826-7689
www.omaksd.org
Highlands HS of Omak 50/Alt
PO Box 833 98841 509-826-8504
Wayne Barrett, prin. Fax 826-8532
Omak HS 400/9-12
PO Box 833 98841 509-826-5150
David Kirk, prin. Fax 826-8515
Omak MS 300/6-8
PO Box 833 98841 509-826-2320
Dr. Chris Blackman, prin. Fax 826-7696

Wenatchee Valley College Post-Sec.
116 W Apple Ave 98841 509-422-7800

Onalaska, Lewis, Pop. 606
Onalaska SD 300 600/PK-12
540 Carlisle Ave 98570 360-978-4111
Jeff Davis, supt. Fax 978-4185
www.onysd.wednet.edu
Onalaska HS 200/9-12
540 Carlisle Ave 98570 360-978-4111
Richard Rasanen, prin. Fax 978-4185

Oroville, Okanogan, Pop. 1,653
Oroville SD 410 600/PK-12
816 Juniper St 98844 509-476-2281
Jeff Hardesty, supt. Fax 476-2190
www.oroville.wednet.edu
Oroville JSHS 300/7-12
816 Juniper St 98844 509-476-3612
Kristin Sarmiento, prin. Fax 476-3224

Orting, Pierce, Pop. 6,443
Orting SD 344 2,300/K-12
121 Whitesell St NE 98360 360-893-6500
Dr. Marci Shepard, supt. Fax 893-2300
www.orting.wednet.edu
Orting HS 700/9-12
320 Washington Ave N 98360 360-893-2246
Diane Fox, prin. Fax 893-5701
Orting MS 600/6-8
111 Whitehawk Blvd NW 98360 360-893-3565
Aaron Lee, prin. Fax 893-2919

Othello, Adams, Pop. 7,325
Othello SD 147-163-55 4,000/K-12
1025 S 1st Ave 99344 509-488-2659
Dr. Kenneth C. Hurst, supt. Fax 488-5876
www.othelloschools.org
Desert Oasis HS Alt
825 E Ash St 99344 509-488-4534
Vance Frost, prin. Fax 488-5876
McFarland MS 800/6-8
790 S 10th Ave 99344 509-488-3326
Dennis Adams, prin. Fax 488-6788
Othello HS 1,000/9-12
340 S 7th Ave 99344 509-488-3351
Russell Kovalenko, prin. Fax 488-6779

Palouse, Whitman, Pop. 974
Palouse SD 301 200/PK-12
600 E Alder St 99161 509-878-1921
Calvin Johnson, supt. Fax 878-1948
www.garpal.net
Garfield-Palouse HS 100/9-12
600 E Alder St 99161 509-878-1921
Mike Jones, prin. Fax 878-1675

Pasco, Franklin, Pop. 58,798
Pasco SD 1 15,800/K-12
1215 W Lewis St 99301 509-543-6700
Michelle Whitney, supt. Fax 546-6728
www.psd1.org
Chiawana HS 2,300/9-12
8125 W Argent Rd 99301 509-543-6786
John Wallwork, prin. Fax 543-6730
Delta HS 9-12
5801 Broadmoor Blvd 99301 509-416-7860
Jenny Rodriguez, prin. Fax 416-7861
McLoughlin MS 1,100/7-8
2803 N Road 88 99301 509-547-4542
Dominique Dennis, prin. Fax 543-6797
New Horizons HS 200/Alt
3110 W Argent Rd 99301 509-543-6796
Seth Johnson, prin. Fax 546-2864
Ochoa MS 700/7-8
1801 E Sheppard St 99301 509-543-6742
Jackie Ramirez, prin. Fax 543-6744
Pasco HS 2,000/9-12
1108 N 10th Ave 99301 509-547-5581
Raul Sital, prin. Fax 546-2684
Stevens MS 600/7-8
1120 N 22nd Ave 99301 509-543-6798
Charlotte Stingley, prin. Fax 546-2854

Charter College Pasco Post-Sec.
5278 Outlet Dr 99301 509-546-3900
Columbia Basin College Post-Sec.
2600 N 20th Ave 99301 509-547-0511
Kingspoint Christian S 200/PK-12
7900 W Court St 99301 509-547-6498
Georgia Perkins, admin. Fax 547-6788
Tri Cities Preparatory S 200/9-12
9612 Saint Thomas Dr 99301 509-546-2465
Arlene Jones, prin. Fax 546-2490
Tri-City Adventist S 200/PK-10
4115 W Henry St 99301 509-547-8092
Spencer Hannah, prin. Fax 547-8516

Pateros, Okanogan, Pop. 658
Pateros SD 122 200/K-12
PO Box 98 98846 509-923-2751
Lois Davies, supt. Fax 923-2283
www.pateros.org

Pateros S 200/K-12
PO Box 98 98846 509-923-2343
Michael Hull, prin. Fax 923-2283

Pe Ell, Lewis, Pop. 610
Pe Ell SD 301 300/PK-12
PO Box 368 98572 360-291-3244
Kyle MacDonald, supt. Fax 291-3823
www.peell.k12.wa.us/
Pe Ell S 300/PK-12
PO Box 368 98572 360-291-3244
Kyle MacDonald, supt. Fax 291-3823

Pomeroy, Garfield, Pop. 1,407
Pomeroy SD 110 300/K-12
PO Box 950 99347 509-843-3393
Doug LaMunyan, supt. Fax 843-3046
www.psd.wednet.edu
Pomeroy JSHS 200/7-12
PO Box 950 99347 509-843-1331
Doug LaMunyan, admin. Fax 843-8245

Port Angeles, Clallam, Pop. 18,283
Port Angeles SD 121 3,700/PK-12
216 E 4th St 98362 360-457-8575
Dr. Marc Jackson, supt. Fax 457-4649
www.portangelesschools.org/
Lincoln HS 100/Alt
924 W 9th St 98363 360-452-9502
Cindy Crumb, prin. Fax 417-1993
North Olympic Peninsula Skill Center Vo/Tech
905 W 9th St 98363 360-565-1533
Jody Potter, dir. Fax 417-9068
Port Angeles HS 1,200/9-12
304 E Park Ave 98362 360-452-7602
Jeff Clark, prin. Fax 452-0256
Stevens MS 600/7-8
1139 W 14th St 98363 360-452-5590
Ryan Stevens, prin. Fax 457-5709

Peninsula College Post-Sec.
1502 E Lauridsen Blvd 98362 360-452-9277

Port Hadlock, Jefferson, Pop. 2,742

Northwest School of Wooden Boatbuilding Post-Sec.
42 N Water St 98339 360-385-4948

Port Orchard, Kitsap, Pop. 10,384
South Kitsap SD 402 8,900/K-12
2689 Hoover Ave SE 98366 360-874-7000
Fax 874-7068
www.skitsap.wednet.edu
Cedar Heights JHS 400/6-8
2220 Pottery Ave 98366 360-874-6020
Andrew Cain, prin. Fax 874-6420
Explorer Academy 200/Alt
1723 Wolves Dr 98366 360-443-3605
Pat Oster, prin. Fax 443-3624
Sedgewick JHS 700/7-9
8995 SE Sedgwick Rd 98366 360-874-6090
Daniel Novick, prin. Fax 874-6430
South Kitsap Discovery/Alternative HS 200/Alt
2150 Fircrest Dr SE 98366 360-443-3680
Pat Oster, prin. Fax 443-3704
South Kitsap HS 2,100/9-12
425 Mitchell Ave 98366 360-874-5600
Jerry Holsten, prin. Fax 874-5892
Whitman JHS 700/7-9
1887 Madrona Dr SE 98366 360-874-6160
Brian Carlson, prin. Fax 874-6440

Burley Christian S 100/PK-12
14687 Olympic Dr SE 98367 253-851-8619
Dennis Myers, admin.

Port Townsend, Jefferson, Pop. 8,812
Port Townsend SD 50 1,200/PK-12
1610 Blaine St 98368 360-379-4501
Dr. David Engle, supt. Fax 385-3617
www.ptschools.org
Blue Heron MS 400/4-8
3939 San Juan Ave 98368 360-379-4540
Matthew Holshouser, prin. Fax 379-4548
Port Townsend HS 400/9-12
1500 Van Ness St 98368 360-379-4520
Carrie Ehrhardt, prin. Fax 379-4505

Jefferson Community S 50/7-12
280 Quincy St 98368 360-385-0622

Poulsbo, Kitsap, Pop. 8,738
North Kitsap SD 400 6,100/PK-12
18360 Caldart Ave NE 98370 360-396-3000
Dr. Patrice Page, supt.
www.nkschools.org
North Kitsap HS 1,100/9-12
1780 NE Hostmark St 98370 360-396-3100
Judson Miller, prin. Fax 396-3927
Poulsbo MS 800/6-8
2003 NE Hostmark St 98370 360-396-3200
Josh Emmons, prin. Fax 396-3904
Other Schools – See Kingston

Northwest College of Art and Design Post-Sec.
16301 Creative Dr NE 98370 360-779-9993
West Sound Academy 100/6-12
PO Box 807 98370 360-598-5954
Barrie Hillman, head sch Fax 598-5494

Prescott, Walla Walla, Pop. 314
Prescott SD 402-37 200/K-12
PO Box 65 99348 509-849-2215
Brett Cox, supt. Fax 849-2800
www.prescott.k12.wa.us/
Prescott JSHS 100/7-12
PO Box 65 99348 509-849-2215
Dr. Jodi Thew, prin. Fax 849-2800

Prosser, Benton, Pop. 5,618
Prosser SD 116 2,900/PK-12
1126 Meade Ave Ste A 99350 509-786-3323
Dr. Ray Tolcacher, supt. Fax 786-2062
www.prosserschools.org/
Housel MS 700/6-8
2001 Highland Dr 99350 509-786-1732
Michael Denny, prin. Fax 786-2814
Prosser Falls HS 50/Alt
1500 Grant Ave 99350 509-786-2527
Syndi Duehn, prin. Fax 786-3427
Prosser HS 900/9-12
1203 Prosser Ave 99350 509-786-1224
Kevin Lusk, prin. Fax 786-4227

Pullman, Whitman, Pop. 28,533
Pullman SD 267 2,600/PK-12
240 SE Dexter St 99163 509-332-3581
Bob Maxwell, supt. Fax 336-7202
www.psd267.org
Lincoln MS 600/6-8
315 SE Crestview St 99163 509-334-3411
Cameron Grow, prin. Fax 336-7203
Pullman HS 700/9-12
510 NW Greyhound Way 99163 509-332-1551
Erik Heinz, prin. Fax 332-6868

Pullman Christian S 100/K-12
345 SW Kimball Dr 99163 509-332-3545
Sherri Goetze, prin.
Washington State University Post-Sec.
PO Box 641067 99164 509-335-3564

Puyallup, Pierce, Pop. 35,083
Bethel SD 403
Supt. — See Spanaway
Pierce County Skills Center Vo/Tech
16117 Canyon Rd E 98375 253-683-5950
Michelle Ledbetter, dir. Fax 683-5998

Puyallup SD 3 20,700/K-12
PO Box 370 98371 253-841-1301
Dr. Timothy Yeomans, supt. Fax 840-8959
www.puyallup.k12.wa.us
Aylen JHS 700/7-9
101 15th St SW 98371 253-841-8723
Kevin Mensonides, prin. Fax 840-8856
Ballou JHS 700/7-9
9916 136th St E 98373 253-841-8725
Krista Bates, prin. Fax 840-8819
Emerald Ridge SHS 1,500/10-12
12405 184th St E 98374 253-435-6300
Kevin Hampton, prin. Fax 435-6310
Ferrucci JHS 700/7-9
3213 Wildwood Park Dr 98374 253-841-8756
Brian Fosnick, prin. Fax 840-8855
Glacier View JHS 900/7-9
12807 184th St E 98374 253-840-8922
Jack Widmann, prin. Fax 435-6570
Kalles JHS 900/7-9
501 7th Ave SE 98372 253-841-8729
Guy Kovacs, prin. Fax 840-8984
Puyallup SHS 1,600/10-12
105 7th St SW 98371 253-841-8711
David Sunich, prin. Fax 841-8624
Rogers SHS 1,800/10-12
12801 86th Ave E 98373 253-841-8717
Jason Smith, prin. Fax 840-8802
Stahl JHS 800/7-9
9610 168th Street Ct E 98375 253-840-8881
Troy Hodge, prin. Fax 840-8992
Walker HS 100/Alt
5715 Milwaukee Ave E 98372 253-841-8781
Alicia Nosworthy, prin. Fax 840-8981
Other Schools – See Edgewood

BJ's Beauty & Barber College Post-Sec.
12020 Meridian E Ste G 98373 253-848-1595
Cascade Christian JSHS 500/7-12
811 21st St SE 98372 253-445-9706
Dr. Ken Friesen, prin. Fax 445-0859
Pierce College Post-Sec.
1601 39th Ave SE 98374 253-840-8470

Quilcene, Jefferson, Pop. 571
Quilcene SD 48 300/K-12
PO Box 40 98376 360-765-3363
Wally Lis, supt. Fax 765-3015
www.quilcene.wednet.edu
Crossroads Community S 50/Alt
PO Box 40 98376 360-765-3363
Jenelle Cleland, dir. Fax 765-4183
Quilcene S 200/K-12
PO Box 40 98376 360-765-3363
Dr. Gary Stebbins, prin. Fax 765-4183

Quincy, Grant, Pop. 6,701
Quincy SD 144-101 2,700/K-12
119 J St SW 98848 509-787-4571
John Boyd, supt. Fax 787-4336
www.qsd.wednet.edu
High Tech HS Vo/Tech
404 1st Ave SW 98848 509-787-1678
Kathie Brown, prin. Fax 787-1680
Quincy HS 800/9-12
16 6th Ave SE 98848 509-787-3501
David Talley, prin. Fax 787-8989
Quincy JHS 400/7-8
417 C St SE 98848 509-787-4435
Scott Ramsey, prin. Fax 787-8949

Rainier, Thurston, Pop. 1,719
Rainier SD 307 800/PK-12
PO Box 98 98576 360-446-2207
Bryon Bahr, supt. Fax 446-2918
www.rainier.wednet.edu
Rainier HS 300/9-12
PO Box 98 98576 360-446-2205
John Beckman, prin. Fax 446-2208

Rainier MS 200/6-8
PO Box 98 98576 360-446-2206
John Beckman, prin. Fax 446-7414

Randle, Lewis
White Pass SD 303 400/PK-12
PO Box 188 98377 360-497-3791
Chuck Wyborney, supt. Fax 497-2560
www.whitepass.k12.wa.us
White Pass JSHS 200/7-12
516 Silverbrook Rd 98377 360-497-5816
Chris Schumaker, prin. Fax 497-7773

Ravensdale, King, Pop. 1,086
Tahoma SD 409
Supt. — See Maple Valley
Tahoma JHS 1,200/8-9
25600 SE Summit Landsburg 98051 425-413-5600
Rhonda Ham, prin. Fax 413-5500

Raymond, Pacific, Pop. 2,787
Raymond SD 116 600/PK-12
1016 Commercial St 98577 360-942-3415
Dr. Stephen Holland, supt. Fax 942-3416
www.raymondschooldistrict.org
Raymond JSHS 300/7-12
1016 Commercial St 98577 360-942-3415
Dave Vetter, prin. Fax 942-2504

Willapa Valley SD 160 300/PK-12
22 Viking Way 98577 360-942-5855
Rob Friese, supt. Fax 942-3216
www.willapavalley.org
Willapa Valley JSHS 200/6-12
22 Viking Way 98577 360-942-2006
Nancy Morris, prin. Fax 942-3216

Reardan, Lincoln, Pop. 562
Reardan-Edwall SD 9 600/PK-12
PO Box 225 99029 509-796-2701
Marcus Morgan, supt. Fax 796-4954
www.reardan.net
Reardan JSHS 300/6-12
PO Box 225 99029 509-796-2701
Debi Newsum, prin. Fax 796-4954

Redmond, King, Pop. 51,981
Lake Washington SD 414 25,400/K-12
PO Box 97039 98073 425-936-1200
Dr. Traci Pierce, supt. Fax 936-1213
www.lwsd.org
Evergreen MS 800/6-8
6900 208th Ave NE 98053 425-936-2320
Robert Johnson, prin. Fax 868-0105
Redmond HS 1,900/9-12
17272 NE 104th St 98052 425-936-1800
Jane Todd, prin. Fax 861-7574
Redmond MS 1,000/6-8
10055 166th Ave NE 98052 425-936-2440
Kelly Clapp, prin. Fax 556-9806
Rose Hill MS 600/6-8
13505 NE 75th St 98052 425-936-2460
Erin Bowser, prin. Fax 576-6342
Stella Schola MS 100/6-8
13505 NE 75th St 98052 425-936-2475
Erin Bowser, prin. Fax 936-2476
Other Schools – See Kirkland, Sammamish

Bear Creek S 800/PK-12
8905 208th Ave NE 98053 425-898-1720
Patrick Carruth, hdmstr. Fax 898-1430
DigiPen Institute of Technology Post-Sec.
9931 Willows Rd NE 98052 425-558-0299
Overlake S 500/5-12
20301 NE 108th St 98053 425-868-1000
Matthew Horvat, head sch Fax 868-5771

Renton, King, Pop. 85,890
Issaquah SD 411
Supt. — See Issaquah
Liberty HS 1,200/9-12
16655 SE 136th St 98059 425-837-4800
Sean Martin, prin. Fax 837-4905
Maywood MS 1,000/6-8
14490 168th Ave SE 98059 425-837-6900
Jason Morse, prin. Fax 837-6910

Kent SD 415
Supt. — See Kent
Meeker MS 700/7-8
12600 SE 192nd St 98058 253-373-7284
Shannon Nash, prin. Fax 373-7560
Northwood MS 600/7-8
17007 SE 184th St 98058 253-373-7780
Sherilyn Ulland, prin. Fax 373-7788

Renton SD 403 14,900/K-12
300 SW 7th St 98057 425-204-2300
Dr. Art Jarvis, supt. Fax 204-2456
www.rentonschools.us
Hazen HS 1,500/9-12
1101 Hoquiam Ave NE 98059 425-204-4200
Kate O'Brien, prin. Fax 204-4220
Lindbergh HS 1,300/9-12
16426 128th Ave SE 98058 425-204-3200
Tres Genger, prin. Fax 204-3220
McKnight MS 1,200/6-8
1200 Edmonds Ave NE 98056 425-204-3600
Brian Teppner, prin. Fax 204-3680
Nelsen MS 1,000/6-8
2403 Jones Ave S 98055 425-204-3000
Colin Falk, prin. Fax 204-3079
Renton HS 1,300/9-12
400 S 2nd St 98057 425-204-3400
Giovanna San Martin, prin. Fax 204-3412
Risdon MS, 6928 116th Ave SE 98056 6-8
Craig Cooper, prin. 425-204-2345
Other Schools – See Seattle

Everest College Post-Sec.
981 Powell Ave SW Ste 200 98057 425-255-3281
Pima Medical Institute Post-Sec.
555 S Renton Village Pl 110 98057 425-228-9600
Renton Preparatory Christian S 3-12
200 Mill Ave Ste 110 98057 206-723-5526
Dr. David Zimmerman, prin.
Renton Technical College Post-Sec.
3000 NE 4th St 98056 425-235-2352

Republic, Ferry, Pop. 1,028
Republic SD 309 300/K-12
30306 E Highway 20 99166 509-775-3173
Dr. John Glenewinkel, supt. Fax 775-3712
www.republic.wednet.edu
Republic HS 100/9-12
30306 E Highway 20 99166 509-775-3171
Christopher Burch, admin. Fax 775-1098
Republic JHS 100/7-8
30306 E Highway 20 99166 509-775-3171
Christopher Burch, admin. Fax 775-1098

Richland, Benton, Pop. 46,846
Richland SD 400 11,900/K-12
615 Snow Ave 99352 509-967-6000
Dr. Rick Schulte, supt. Fax 942-2401
www.rsd.edu
Carmichael MS 900/6-8
620 Thayer Dr 99352 509-967-6425
Brian Stadelman, prin. Fax 942-2471
Chief Joseph MS 700/6-8
504 Wilson St, 509-967-6400
Jon Lobdell, prin. Fax 942-2492
Hanford HS 1,700/9-12
450 Hanford St, 509-967-6500
Tory Christensen, prin. Fax 371-2601
Richland HS 1,900/9-12
930 Long Ave 99352 509-967-6535
Tim Praino, prin. Fax 942-2512
River's Edge HS 200/Alt
975 Gillespie St 99352 509-967-6450
Dan Chubb, prin. Fax 942-2598
Other Schools – See West Richland

Liberty Christian S of the Tri-Cities 400/PK-12
2200 Williams Blvd, 509-946-0602
Karen Bjur, prin. Fax 943-5623
Lucas Marc Academy Post-Sec.
71 Gage Blvd 99352 509-591-4979

Ridgefield, Clark, Pop. 4,650
Ridgefield SD 122 2,200/K-12
2724 S Hillhurst Rd 98642 360-619-1301
Dr. Nathan McCann, supt. Fax 619-1397
www.ridgefieldsd.org
Ridgefield HS 700/9-12
2630 S Hillhurst Rd 98642 360-619-1320
Tony VanderMaas, prin. Fax 619-1395
View Ridge MS 300/7-8
510 Pioneer St 98642 360-619-1400
Tony Smith, prin. Fax 619-1459

Cedar Tree Classical Christian S 200/K-12
20601 NE 29th Ave 98642 360-887-0190

Ritzville, Adams, Pop. 1,650
Lind-Ritzville SD
Supt. — See Lind
Lind-Ritzville HS 100/9-12
209 E Wellsandt Rd 99169 509-659-1720
Ronanda Liberty, prin. Fax 659-5140

Rochester, Thurston, Pop. 2,337
Rochester SD 401 2,200/K-12
10140 Highway 12 SW 98579 360-273-5536
Kimberly Fry, supt. Fax 273-5547
www.rochester.wednet.edu
HEART Alternative HS 50/Alt
10140 Highway 12 SW 98579 360-273-5017
Matt Ishler, prin. Fax 273-5017
Rochester HS 600/9-12
19800 Carper Rd SW 98579 360-273-5534
Matt Ishler, prin. Fax 273-2570
Rochester MS 500/6-8
PO Box 398 98579 360-273-5958
Will Maus, prin. Fax 273-2045

Rockford, Spokane, Pop. 465
Freeman SD 358 900/PK-12
15001 S Jackson Rd 99030 509-291-3695
Randy Russell, supt. Fax 291-3636
www.freemansd.org
Freeman HS 300/9-12
14626 S Jackson Rd 99030 509-291-3721
Jim Straw, prin. Fax 291-7337
Freeman MS 200/6-8
15001 S Jackson Rd 99030 509-291-7301
Ben Ferney, prin. Fax 291-8009

Rosalia, Whitman, Pop. 547
Rosalia SD 320 200/PK-12
916 S Josephine Ave 99170 509-523-3061
Larry Keller, supt. Fax 523-3861
www.rosaliaschools.org
Rosalia S 200/PK-12
916 S Josephine Ave 99170 509-523-3061
Darrell Kuhn, prin. Fax 523-3861

Roslyn, Kittitas, Pop. 872
Cle Elum-Roslyn SD 404
Supt. — See Cle Elum
Swiftwater Alternative S 50/Alt
205 W Idaho St 98941 509-649-4990
Mel Blair, prin. Fax 649-2270

Mayflower Christian S PK-12
2nd & Idaho 98941 509-674-5022
Debbie Cernick, admin.

Royal City, Grant, Pop. 2,135
Royal SD 160 1,300/PK-12
PO Box 486 99357 509-346-2222
Rosemarie Search, supt. Fax 346-8746
www.royal.wednet.edu/
Royal HS 400/9-12
PO Box 486 99357 509-346-2256
Matt Ellis, prin. Fax 346-9739
Royal MS 300/7-8
PO Box 486 99357 509-346-2268
David Jaderlund, prin. Fax 346-2269

Saint John, Whitman, Pop. 519
Endicott SD 308
Supt. — See Endicott
Endicott-St. John MS 100/6-8
301 W Nob Hill Rd 99171 509-657-3523
Mark Purvine, prin. Fax 657-3521

St. John SD 322 200/PK-12
301 W Nob Hill Rd 99171 509-648-3336
Suzanne Schmick, supt. Fax 648-3451
www.sje.wednet.edu
St. John-Endicott HS 100/9-12
301 W Nob Hill Rd 99171 509-648-3336
Mark Purvine, prin. Fax 648-3451

Sammamish, King, Pop. 44,087
Issaquah SD 411
Supt. — See Issaquah
Pine Lake MS 800/6-8
3200 228th Ave SE 98075 425-837-5700
Michelle Caponigro, prin. Fax 837-5762
Skyline HS 2,000/9-12
1122 228th Ave SE 98075 425-837-7700
Donna Hood, prin. Fax 837-7705

Lake Washington SD 414
Supt. — See Redmond
Eastlake HS 1,600/9-12
400 228th Ave NE 98074 425-936-1500
Chris Bede, prin. Fax 898-1359
Inglewood MS 1,100/6-8
24120 NE 8th St 98074 425-936-2360
Tim Patterson, prin. Fax 868-0628
Renaissance S of Art & Reasoning 100/6-8
400 228th Ave NE 98074 425-936-1544
Chris Bede, prin. Fax 836-6609
Tesla STEM 9-12
4301 228th Ave SE 98074 425-936-2770
Cindy Dueanas, prin. Fax 869-0014

Eastside Catholic HS 800/6-12
232 228th Ave SE 98074 425-295-3000
Justyna King, prin. Fax 392-5160

SeaTac, King, Pop. 24,721
Highline SD 401
Supt. — See Burien
Academy of Citizenship & Empowerment HS 400/9-12
4424 S 188th St 98188 206-631-6500
Nicole Fitch, prin. Fax 631-6520
Chinook MS 600/7-8
18650 42nd Ave S 98188 206-631-5700
Karin Jones, prin. Fax 631-5770
Global Connections HS 500/9-12
4424 S 188th St Bldg 300 98188 206-631-6550
Nicole Fitch, prin. Fax 631-6522

Seattle Christian S 500/K-12
18301 Military Rd S 98188 206-246-8241
Laird Leavitt, supt. Fax 246-9066

Seattle, King, Pop. 578,438
Highline SD 401
Supt. — See Burien
Arts and Academics Academy 300/9-12
830 SW 116th St 98146 206-631-6250
Jacqueline Downey, prin. Fax 631-6162
Cascade MS 600/7-8
11212 10th Ave SW 98146 206-631-5500
Libby DeBell, prin. Fax 631-5568
Health Sciences & Human Services HS 400/9-12
830 SW 116th St 98146 206-631-6200
Jenni Maughan, prin. Fax 631-6160
New Start HS 100/Alt
814 SW 120th St 98146 206-631-7750
Michael Sita, prin. Fax 631-7780
Technology Engineering Communications HS 300/9-12
830 SW 116th St Bldg 500 98146 206-631-6300
Vanessa Banner, prin. Fax 631-6164

Renton SD 403
Supt. — See Renton
Dimmitt MS 1,000/6-8
12320 80th Ave S 98178 425-204-2800
Gioia Pitts, prin. Fax 204-2812
Secondary Learning Center 300/Alt
7800 S 132nd St 98178 425-204-2100
Ronald Mahan, prin. Fax 204-2111

Seattle SD 1 49,300/PK-12
PO Box 34165 98124 206-252-0000
Dr. Larry Nyland, supt. Fax 252-0102
www.seattleschools.org
Addams MS 300/6-8
11051 34th Ave NE 98125 206-252-4500
Paula Montgomery, prin.
Ballard HS 1,600/9-12
1418 NW 65th St 98117 206-252-1000
Keven Wynkoop, prin. Fax 252-1001
Center S 300/9-12
305 Harrison St 98109 206-252-9850
Oksana Britsova, prin. Fax 252-9851
Cleveland STEM HS 800/9-12
5511 15th Ave S 98108 206-252-7800
George Breland, prin. Fax 252-7801

Denny International MS 900/6-8
2601 SW Kenyon St 98126 206-252-9000
Jeff Clarke, prin. Fax 252-9001
Eckstein MS 1,200/6-8
3003 NE 75th St 98115 206-252-5010
Treena Sterk, prin. Fax 252-5011
Franklin HS 1,300/9-12
3013 S Mount Baker Blvd 98144 206-252-6150
Jennifer Wiley, prin. Fax 252-6151
Garfield HS 1,600/9-12
400 23rd Ave 98122 206-252-2270
Ted Howard, prin. Fax 252-2271
Hale HS 1,100/9-12
10750 30th Ave NE 98125 206-252-3680
Jill Hudson, prin. Fax 262-3681
Hamilton International MS 1,100/6-8
1610 N 41st St 98103 206-252-5810
Tip Blish, prin. Fax 252-5811
Ingraham HS 1,100/9-12
1819 N 135th St 98133 206-252-3880
Martin Floe, prin. Fax 252-3881
Interagency Academy 400/Alt
3528 S Ferdinand St 98118 206-743-3930
Kaaren Andrews, prin. Fax 743-3931
Kurose MS 700/6-8
3928 S Graham St 98118 206-252-7700
Mia Williams, prin. Fax 252-7701
Madison MS 800/6-8
3429 45th Ave SW 98116 206-252-9200
Robert Gary, prin. Fax 252-9201
McClure MS 500/6-8
1915 1st Ave W 98119 206-252-1900
Shannon Conner, prin. Fax 252-1901
Mercer MS 1,000/6-8
1600 S Columbian Way 98108 206-252-8000
Chris Carter, prin. Fax 252-8001
Middle College HS at Seattle University Alt
901 12th Ave 98122 206-720-3078
Jennifer Kniseley, prin. Fax 720-3075
Middle College HS at Univ of WA Alt
PO Box 355845 98195 206-685-3476
Jennifer Kniseley, prin. Fax 616-3664
Middle College HS Northgate Mall Academy 100/Alt
401 NE Northgate Way 98125 206-366-7940
Jennifer Kniseley, prin. Fax 366-7941
NOVA HS 300/9-12
2410 E Cherry St 98122 206-252-3500
Mark Perry, prin. Fax 252-3501
Rainier Beach HS 500/9-12
8815 Seward Park Ave S 98118 206-252-6350
Keith Smith, prin. Fax 252-6351
Roosevelt HS 1,700/9-12
1410 NE 66th St 98115 206-252-4810
Brian Vance, prin. Fax 252-4811
Sealth International HS 1,200/9-12
2600 SW Thistle St 98126 206-252-8550
Aida Fraser-Hammer, prin. Fax 252-8551
Seattle Skills Center Vo/Tech
2445 3rd Ave S 98134 206-252-0730
Dan Golosman, prin.
Seattle World S 200/Alt
1700 E Union St 98112 206-252-2200
Concie Pedroza, prin. Fax 252-2201
South Lake Alternative HS 100/Alt
8601 Rainier Ave S 98118 206-252-6600
Laura Davis Brown, prin. Fax 252-6601
Washington MS 1,200/6-8
2101 S Jackson St 98144 206-252-2600
Susan Follmer, prin. Fax 252-2601
West Seattle HS 1,000/9-12
3000 California Ave SW 98116 206-252-8800
Ruth Medsker, prin. Fax 252-8801
Whitman MS 1,000/6-8
9201 15th Ave NW 98117 206-252-1200
Susan Kleitsch, prin. Fax 252-1201

Antioch University Post-Sec.
2326 6th Ave 98121 206-441-5352
Argosy University/Seattle Post-Sec.
2601A Elliott Ave 98121 206-283-4500
Art Institute of Seattle Post-Sec.
2323 Elliott Ave 98121 206-448-0900
Bainbridge Graduate Institute Post-Sec.
220 2nd Ave S Ste 400 98104 206-855-9559
Bakke Graduate University Post-Sec.
1013 8th Ave Ste 401 98104 206-264-9100
Billings MS 100/6-8
7217 Woodlawn Ave NE 98115 206-547-4614
Anne-Evan Williams, head sch Fax 545-8505
Bishop Blanchet HS 1,000/9-12
8200 Wallingford Ave N 98103 206-527-7711
Polly Skinner, prin. Fax 527-7712
Bush S 600/K-12
3400 E Harrison St 98112 206-322-7978
Percy Abram Ph.D., head sch Fax 860-3876
City University of Seattle Post-Sec.
521 Wall St Ste 100 98121 206-239-4500
Cornish College of the Arts Post-Sec.
1000 Lenora St 98121 800-726-ARTS
Cortiva Institute - Seattle Post-Sec.
425 Pontius Ave N Ste 100 98109 206-282-1233
Divers Institute of Technology Post-Sec.
1341 N Northlake Way 98103 800-634-8377
Everest College Post-Sec.
2111 N Northgate Way 98133 206-440-3090
Explorer West MS 100/6-8
10015 28th Ave SW 98146 206-935-0495
Evan Hundley, head sch Fax 932-7113
Gene Juarez Academy of Beauty Post-Sec.
10715 8th Ave NE 98125 206-365-6900
Holy Names Academy 700/9-12
728 21st Ave E 98112 206-323-4272
Elizabeth Swift, prin. Fax 323-5254
King's HS 400/9-12
19303 Fremont Ave N 98133 206-546-7241
Bob Ruhlman, prin. Fax 546-7214

Lakeside MS 300/5-8
13510 1st Ave NE 98125 206-368-3630
Bernie Noe, hdmstr. Fax 368-3639
Lakeside Upper S 500/9-12
14050 1st Ave NE 98125 206-368-3600
Bernie Noe, head sch Fax 368-3638
Lake Washington Girls MS 100/6-8
810 18th Ave 98122 206-709-3800
Patricia Hearn, head sch Fax 323-9860
North Seattle Community College Post-Sec.
9600 College Way N 98103 206-934-3600
Northwest S 500/6-12
1415 Summit Ave 98122 206-682-7309
Mike McGill, head sch Fax 467-7353
O'Dea HS 400/9-12
802 Terry Ave 98104 206-622-6596
James Walker, prin. Fax 340-4110
Photographic Center Northwest Post-Sec.
900 12th Ave 98122 206-720-7222
Pima Medical Institute Post-Sec.
9709 3rd Ave NE Ste 400 98115 206-322-6100
Sanford-Brown College Post-Sec.
645 Andover Park W 98188 206-575-1865
Seattle Academy of Arts & Sciences 400/6-12
1201 E Union St 98122 206-323-6600
Joe Puggelli, head sch Fax 323-6618
Seattle Central Community College Post-Sec.
1701 Broadway 98122 206-587-3800
Seattle Girls' S 100/5-8
2706 S Jackson St 98144 206-709-2228
Brenda Leaks, head sch Fax 329-1580
Seattle Institute of Oriental Medicine Post-Sec.
444 NE Ravenna Blvd Ste 101 98115 206-517-4541
Seattle Lutheran HS 100/9-12
4100 SW Genesee St 98116 206-937-7722
Dave Meyer, dir. Fax 937-6781
Seattle Nativity S 6-8
2800 S Massachusetts St 98144 206-494-4708
Edward Nelson, dir.
Seattle Pacific University Post-Sec.
3307 3rd Ave W 98119 206-281-2000
Seattle Preparatory S 700/9-12
2400 11th Ave E 98102 206-324-0400
Erin Luby, prin. Fax 323-6509
Seattle School of Theology & Psychology Post-Sec.
2501 Elliott Ave 98121 206-876-6100
Seattle University Post-Sec.
901 12th Ave 98122 206-296-6000
Seattle Waldorf HS 100/9-12
7777 62nd Ave NE 98115 206-522-2644
South Seattle Community College Post-Sec.
6000 16th Ave SW 98106 206-934-5300
University of Washington 98195 Post-Sec.
206-543-2100
University Preparatory Academy 500/6-12
8000 25th Ave NE 98115 206-525-2714
Matt Levinson, head sch Fax 525-9659

Sedro Woolley, Skagit, Pop. 10,288
Sedro-Woolley SD 101 4,300/PK-12
801 Trail Rd 98284 360-855-3500
Phil Brockman, supt. Fax 855-3574
www.swsd.k12.wa.us
Cascade MS 600/7-8
905 McGarigle Rd 98284 360-855-3520
Laura Davis, prin. Fax 855-3521
Sedro-Woolley HS 1,200/9-12
1235 3rd St 98284 360-855-3510
Kerri Carlton, prin. Fax 855-3517
State Street HS 300/Alt
800 State St 98284 360-855-3550
Barb Askland, prin. Fax 855-3551

Sekiu, Clallam, Pop. 27
Cape Flattery SD 401 400/K-12
PO Box 109 98381 360-963-2329
Michelle Parkin, supt. Fax 963-2373
www.capeflattery.wednet.edu
Other Schools – See Neah Bay

Selah, Yakima, Pop. 6,994
Selah SD 119 1,600/PK-12
316 W Naches Ave 98942 509-698-8000
Shane Backlund, supt. Fax 698-8099
www.selah.k12.wa.us
Selah Academy 100/Alt
308 W Naches Ave 98942 509-698-8450
Joe Coscarart, admin. Fax 698-8451
Selah HS 700/9-12
801 N 1st St 98942 509-698-8500
Todd Hilberg, prin. Fax 698-8508
Selah MS 300/6-8
411 N 1st St 98942 509-698-8400
Marc Gallaway, prin. Fax 698-8399

Sequim, Clallam, Pop. 6,414
Sequim SD 323 2,700/K-12
503 N Sequim Ave 98382 360-582-3260
Gary Neal, supt. Fax 683-6303
www.sequim.k12.wa.us
Sequim HS 1,100/9-12
601 N Sequim Ave 98382 360-582-3600
Shawn Langston, prin. Fax 681-8688
Sequim MS 600/6-8
301 W Hendrickson Rd 98382 360-582-3500
Vince Riccobene, prin. Fax 582-9486

Shelton, Mason, Pop. 9,392
Pioneer SD 402 700/PK-8
611 E Agate Rd 98584 360-426-9115
Martin A. Brewer, supt. Fax 426-1036
www.psd402.org
Pioneer MS 400/4-8
611 E Agate Rd 98584 360-426-8291
Bracken Budge, prin. Fax 426-1036

Shelton SD 309 4,200/PK-12
700 S 1st St 98584 360-426-1687
Dr. Alex Apostle, supt. Fax 427-8610
www.sheltonschools.org
Choice HS 200/Alt
807 W Pine St 98584 360-426-7664
Stacey Anderson, prin. Fax 462-1203
Oakland Bay JHS 700/8-9
3301 N Shelton Springs Rd 98584 360-426-7991
Bracken Budge, prin. Fax 427-2940
Shelton HS 1,000/10-12
3737 N Shelton Springs Rd 98584 360-426-4471
Jennifer Deyette, prin. Fax 427-6141

Shoreline, King, Pop. 50,457
Shoreline SD 412 8,800/PK-12
18560 1st Ave NE 98155 206-393-4203
Dr. Rebecca Miner, supt. Fax 393-4204
www.shorelineschools.org
Einstein MS 700/7-8
19343 3rd Ave NW 98177 206-393-4730
Nyla Fritz, prin. Fax 393-4735
Kellogg MS 600/7-8
16045 25th Ave NE 98155 206-393-4783
Heather Hiatt, prin. Fax 393-4780
Shorecrest HS 1,300/9-12
15343 25th Ave NE 98155 206-393-4286
Lisa Gonzalez, prin. Fax 393-4284
Shorewood HS 1,500/9-12
17300 Fremont Ave N 98133 206-393-4372
Bill Dunbar, prin. Fax 393-4711

Greenwood Academy of Hair Design Post-Sec.
18336 Aurora Ave N Ste 103 98133 206-542-1111
King's JHS 200/7-8
19345 Crista Ln N 98133 206-546-7243
Jordana Halkett, prin. Fax 546-7250
Shoreline Christian S 200/PK-12
2400 NE 147th St 98155 206-364-7777
Timothy Visser, admin. Fax 364-0349
Shoreline Community College Post-Sec.
16101 Greenwood Ave N 98133 206-546-4101

Silverdale, Kitsap, Pop. 17,925
Central Kitsap SD 401 9,200/K-12
PO Box 8 98383 360-662-1610
David McVicker, supt. Fax 662-1611
www.ckschools.org
Alternative HS 200/Alt
PO Box 8 98383 360-662-2570
Stuart Crisman, prin. Fax 662-2571
Central Kitsap HS 1,200/9-12
PO Box 8 98383 360-662-2400
Steve Coons, prin. Fax 662-2401
Central Kitsap MS 500/6-8
PO Box 8 98383 360-662-2300
Scott McDaniel, prin. Fax 662-2301
Klahowya Secondary S 900/6-12
PO Box 8 98383 360-662-4000
Jodie Woolf, prin. Fax 662-4001
Ridgetop MS 400/6-8
PO Box 8 98383 360-662-2900
Rusty Willson, prin. Fax 662-2901
Other Schools – See Bremerton

Skykomish, King, Pop. 197
Skykomish SD 404 50/K-12
PO Box 325 98288 360-677-2623
Martin Schmidt, supt. Fax 677-2418
www.skykomishschool.com
Skykomish JSHS 50/7-12
PO Box 325 98288 360-677-2623
Martin Schmidt, admin. Fax 677-2418

Snohomish, Snohomish, Pop. 8,810
Monroe SD 103
Supt. — See Monroe
Hidden River MS 400/6-8
9224 Paradise Lake Rd 98296 360-804-4100
Brett Wille, prin. Fax 804-4199

Snohomish SD 201 10,000/PK-12
1601 Avenue D 98290 360-563-7300
Kent Kultgen Ed.D., supt. Fax 563-7279
www.sno.wednet.edu
AIM HS 200/Alt
525 13th St 98290 360-563-3400
June Shirey, admin. Fax 862-9433
Centennial MS 800/7-8
3000 S Machias Rd 98290 360-563-4525
Dave Sage, prin. Fax 563-4585
Glacier Peak HS 1,700/9-12
7401 144th Pl SE 98296 360-563-7500
Jim Dean, prin. Fax 563-7631
Snohomish HS 1,800/9-12
1316 5th St 98290 360-563-4000
Eric Cahan, prin. Fax 563-4183
Valley View MS 700/7-8
14308 Broadway Ave 98296 360-563-4225
Nancy Rhoades, prin. Fax 563-4236

Snoqualmie, King, Pop. 10,237
Snoqualmie Valley SD 410 6,400/PK-12
PO Box 400 98065 425-831-8000
Joel Aune, supt. Fax 831-8040
www.svsd410.org/
Mount Si HS 1,700/9-12
8651 Meadowbrook Way SE 98065 425-831-8100
John Belcher, prin. Fax 831-8222
Other Schools – See Fall City, North Bend

Soap Lake, Grant, Pop. 1,484
Soap Lake SD 156 500/K-12
410 Ginkgo St S 98851 509-246-1822
Dan McDonald, supt. Fax 246-0669
www.slschools.org
Smokiam Alternative HS 50/Alt
410 Ginkgo St S 98851 509-246-0572
Loris Blair, prin. Fax 246-0669

Soap Lake MSHS 200/6-12
410 Ginkgo St S 98851 509-246-1201
Jacob Bang, prin. Fax 246-1722

South Bend, Pacific, Pop. 1,566
South Bend SD 118 600/PK-12
PO Box 437 98586 360-875-6041
Dr. Jon Tienhaara, supt. Fax 875-6062
www.southbend.wednet.edu
South Bend JSHS 200/7-12
PO Box 437 98586 360-875-5707
Jason Nelson, prin. Fax 875-6036

Spanaway, Pierce, Pop. 24,048
Bethel SD 403 18,100/PK-12
516 176th St E 98387 253-683-6000
Tom Seigel, supt. Fax 683-6019
www.bethelsd.org
Bethel Acceleration Academy Alt
16218 Pacific Ave S 98387 253-267-1045
Gin Hooks, dir.
Bethel HS 1,700/9-12
22215 38th Ave E 98387 253-683-7000
Adam Cox, prin. Fax 683-7098
Bethel MS 700/6-8
22001 38th Ave E 98387 253-683-7200
Julie Shultz-Bartlett, prin. Fax 683-7298
Cedarcrest MS 600/6-8
19120 13th Avenue Ct E 98387 253-683-7500
Scott Martin, prin. Fax 683-7598
Challenger HS 400/Alt
18020 B St E 98387 253-683-6800
Jeff Johnson, prin. Fax 847-2530
Liberty MS 800/6-8
7319 Eustis Hunt Rd 98387 253-683-6500
Tom Mitchell, prin. Fax 683-6598
Spanaway Lake HS 1,700/9-12
1305 168th St E 98387 253-683-5600
Julie Baublits, prin. Fax 683-5698
Other Schools – See Graham, Puyallup, Tacoma

Spangle, Spokane, Pop. 277
Liberty SD 362 400/PK-12
29818 S North Pine Creek Rd 99031 509-624-4415
Kyle Rydell, supt. Fax 245-3288
www.libertysd.us
Liberty HS 100/9-12
6404 E Spangle Waverly Rd 99031 509-245-3229
Aaron Fletcher, prin. Fax 245-3205

Upper Columbia Academy 300/9-12
3025 E Spangle Waverly Rd 99031 509-245-3600

Spokane, Spokane, Pop. 199,521
Cheney SD 360
Supt. — See Cheney
Westwood MS 500/6-8
6120 S Abbott Rd 99224 509-559-4150
Dr. Erika Burden, prin.

Mead SD 354
Supt. — See Mead
Five Mile Prairie S Alt
8621 N Five Mile Rd 99208 509-465-7700
Bruce Olgard, prin. Fax 465-7720
MEAD Alternative HS 100/Alt
529 W Hastings Rd 99218 509-465-6900
Bruce Olgard, prin. Fax 465-6920
Mead HS 1,600/9-12
302 W Hastings Rd 99218 509-465-7000
Teresa Laher, prin. Fax 465-7020
Northwood MS 700/7-8
13120 N Pittsburg St 99208 509-465-7500
Dave Stenersen, prin. Fax 465-7520
Riverpoint Academy 100/9-12
11008 N Newport Hwy 99218 509-465-7900
Moleena Harris, admin.

Spokane SD 81 29,300/PK-12
200 N Bernard St 99201 509-354-5900
Shelley Redinger Ph.D., supt. Fax 354-5959
www.spokaneschools.org
Chase MS 800/7-8
4747 E 37th Ave 99223 509-354-5000
John Andes, prin. Fax 354-5100
Community S at Bancroft 100/Alt
1025 W Spofford Ave 99205 509-354-3810
Dr. Cindy McMahon, prin. Fax 354-3813
Daybreak S 50/Alt
628 S Cowley St 99202 509-624-3227
Richard Miles, prin. Fax 835-4272
Eagle Peak S Alt
6903 E 4th Ave 99212 509-354-7100
Melinda Keberle, prin. Fax 354-7070
Ferris HS 1,700/9-12
3020 E 37th Ave 99223 509-354-6000
Ken Schutz, prin. Fax 354-6161
Garry MS 600/7-8
725 E Joseph Ave 99208 509-354-5200
Robert Reavis, prin. Fax 354-5212
Glover MS 600/7-8
2404 W Longfellow Ave 99205 509-354-5400
Kim Halcro, prin. Fax 354-5399
Lewis & Clark HS 1,900/9-12
521 W 4th Ave 99204 509-354-7000
Marybeth Smith, prin. Fax 354-6969
Medicine Wheel Academy Alt
1300 W Knox Ave 99205 509-354-5693
Pam Austin, prin. Fax 354-5914
NEWTECH Skills Center Vo/Tech
4141 N Regal St 99207 509-354-7470
Karene Duffy, prin. Fax 354-7474
North Central HS 1,300/9-12
1600 N Howard St 99205 509-354-6300
Steve Fisk, prin. Fax 354-6303
On Track Academy 200/Alt
2802 E Rich Ave 99207 509-354-7449
Lisa Mattson, prin. Fax 489-0810
Rogers HS 1,500/9-12
1622 E Wellesley Ave 99207 509-354-6600
Lori Wyborney, prin. Fax 354-6665
Sacajawea MS 800/7-8
401 E 33rd Ave 99203 509-354-5500
Jeremy Ohse, prin. Fax 354-5505
Salk MS 700/7-8
6411 N Alberta St 99208 509-354-5600
Carole Meyer, prin. Fax 354-5542
Shadle Park HS 1,400/9-12
4327 N Ash St 99205 509-354-6700
Julie Lee, prin. Fax 354-6710
Shaw MS 600/7-8
4106 N Cook St 99207 509-354-5800
Jon Swett, prin. Fax 354-5899
TEC at Bryant Alternative S 400/Alt
910 N Ash St 99201 509-354-7810
Suzanne Smith, prin. Fax 354-7816

West Valley SD 363
Supt. — See Spokane Valley
West Valley HS 900/9-12
8301 E Buckeye Ave 99212 509-922-5488
John Custer, prin. Fax 928-3676

All Saints MS 300/PK-PK, 5-
1428 E 33rd Ave 99203 509-624-5712
Katherine Hicks, prin. Fax 624-7752
Carrington College Post-Sec.
10102 E Knox Ave Ste 200 99206 509-532-8888
Glen Dow Academy of Hair Design Post-Sec.
309 W Riverside Ave 99201 509-624-3244
Gonzaga Preparatory S 900/9-12
1224 E Euclid Ave 99207 509-483-8511
Cindy Reopelle, prin. Fax 483-3124
Gonzaga University Post-Sec.
502 E Boone Ave 99258 800-986-9585
Holy Family Hospital Post-Sec.
5633 N Lidgerwood St 99208 509-482-2450
Interface College Post-Sec.
178 S Stevens St 99201 509-467-1727
Northwest HVAC Training Center Post-Sec.
204 E Nora Ave 99207 509-747-8810
Palisades Christian Academy 100/PK-10
1115 N Government Way 99224 509-325-1985
Dan Wister, prin. Fax 324-8904
Sacred Heart Medical Center Post-Sec.
101 W 8th Ave 99204 509-455-3040
St. George's S 400/K-12
2929 W Waikiki Rd 99208 509-466-1636
Joe Kennedy, head sch Fax 467-3258
Spokane Classical Christian S 50/PK-12
7111 N Nine Mile Rd 99208 509-325-2252
Spokane Community College Post-Sec.
1810 N Greene St 99217 509-533-7000
Spokane Falls Community College Post-Sec.
3410 W Fort George Wright 99224 509-533-3500
Summit Christian Academy - Spokane 400/K-12
8913 N Nettleton Ln 99208 509-924-4618
Wes Evans M.Ed., admin. Fax 467-4942
Whitworth University Post-Sec.
300 W Hawthorne Rd 99251 509-777-1000

Spokane Valley, Spokane, Pop. 87,059
Central Valley SD 356 12,600/K-12
19307 E Cataldo Ave, 509-228-5400
Ben Small, supt. Fax 228-5439
www.cvsd.org
Bowdish MS 500/6-8
2109 S Skipworth Rd, 509-228-4700
Ty Larsen, prin. Fax 228-4714
Central Valley HS 2,000/9-12
821 S Sullivan Rd, 509-228-5100
Keri Ames, prin. Fax 228-5109
Evergreen MS 700/6-8
14221 E 16th Ave, 509-228-4780
John Parker, prin. Fax 228-4789
Greenacres MS 800/6-8
17409 E Sprague Ave, 509-228-4860
Vern DiGiovanni, prin. Fax 228-4869
Horizon MS 500/6-8
3915 S Pines Rd, 509-228-4940
Jesse Hardt, prin. Fax 228-4983
Mica Peak HS 100/Alt
15111 E Sprague, 509-228-4050
Kamiel Youseph, prin. Fax 228-4059
North Pines MS 500/6-8
701 N Pines Rd, 509-228-5020
Lora Jackson, prin. Fax 228-5029
University HS 1,700/9-12
12420 E 32nd Ave, 509-228-5240
Keven Frandsen, prin. Fax 228-5249

East Valley SD 361 4,500/K-12
3830 N Sullivan Rd Bldg 1, 509-924-1830
Kelly Shea, supt. Fax 927-9500
www.evsd.org
East Valley HS 1,100/9-12
15711 E Wellesley Ave, 509-927-3200
Jim McAdam, prin. Fax 921-6830
East Valley MS 500/7-8
4920 N Progress Rd, 509-924-9383
Doug Kaplicky, admin. Fax 927-3214
Washington Academy of Arts & Technology 600/Alt
12325 E Grace Ave, 509-241-5001
Frank Brou, prin. Fax 921-5687

West Valley SD 363 3,600/PK-12
PO Box 11739 99211 509-924-2150
Dr. Gene Sementi, supt. Fax 922-5295
www.wvsd.org
Centennial MS 600/6-8
915 N Ella Rd, 509-922-5482
Karen Bromps, prin. Fax 891-9520
Dishman Hills HS 300/Alt
115 S University Rd Ste A, 509-927-1100
Julie Poage, prin. Fax 891-5052
Spokane Valley HS 100/9-12
2011 N Hutchinson Rd, 509-922-5475
Larry Bush, prin. Fax 922-5477
West Valley City MS 200/5-8
8920 E Valleyway Ave, 509-921-2836
Dusty Andres, prin. Fax 921-2849
Other Schools – See Spokane

Oaks-A Classical Christian Academy 300/K-12
PO Box 141146, 509-536-5955
Valley Christian S 200/PK-12
10212 E 9th Ave, 509-924-9131
Derick Tabish, admin. Fax 924-2971

Sprague, Lincoln, Pop. 438
Sprague SD 8 100/K-12
PO Box 305 99032 509-257-2591
Patrick Whipple, supt. Fax 257-2539
www.spraguelamont.org
Sprague HS 50/9-12
PO Box 305 99032 509-257-2511
Bill Ressel, prin. Fax 257-2539

Springdale, Stevens, Pop. 275
Mary Walker SD 207 400/PK-12
PO Box 159 99173 509-258-4534
Kevin Jacka, supt. Fax 258-4707
www.marywalker.org/
Springdale Academy 50/Alt
PO Box 159 99173 509-937-2224
Matthew Cobb, prin.
Springdale MS 100/7-8
PO Box 159 99173 509-258-7357
Matthew Cobb, prin. Fax 258-7756
Walker Alternative HS 50/Alt
PO Box 159 99173 509-258-4533
Matthew Cobb, prin. Fax 258-4555
Walker HS 200/9-12
PO Box 159 99173 509-258-4533
Matthew Cobb, prin. Fax 258-4555

Stanwood, Snohomish, Pop. 6,009
Stanwood-Camano SD 401 4,500/K-12
26920 Pioneer Hwy 98292 360-629-1200
Dr. Jean Shumate, supt. Fax 629-1242
www.stanwood.wednet.edu
Lincoln Hill Academy 50/Alt
7600 272nd St NW 98292 360-629-1340
Ryan Ovenell, prin. Fax 629-1341
Lincoln Hill HS 100/Alt
7600 272nd St NW 98292 360-629-1340
Ryan Ovenell, prin. Fax 629-1341
Port Susan MS 500/6-8
7506 267th St NW 98292 360-629-1360
Dan Johnston, prin. Fax 629-1365
Saratoga S 100/Alt
9307 271st St NW 98292 360-629-1372
Monica McDaniel, lead tchr. Fax 629-1256
Stanwood HS 1,500/9-12
7400 272nd St NW 98292 360-629-1300
Christine DelPozo, prin. Fax 629-1310
Stanwood MS 500/6-8
9405 271st St NW 98292 360-629-1350
Tod Klundt, prin. Fax 629-1354

Steilacoom, Pierce, Pop. 5,521
Steilacoom Historical SD 1 3,100/PK-12
511 Chambers St 98388 253-983-2200
Kathi Weight, supt. Fax 584-7198
www.steilacoom.k12.wa.us
Steilacoom HS 900/9-12
54 Sentinel Dr 98388 253-983-2300
Michael Miller, prin. Fax 983-2393
Other Schools – See DuPont

Stevenson, Skamania, Pop. 1,431
Stevenson-Carson SD 303 900/K-12
PO Box 850 98648 509-427-5674
Karen Douglass, supt. Fax 427-4028
www.scsd.k12.wa.us
Stevenson HS 300/9-12
PO Box 850 98648 509-427-5631
Sarah Marino, prin. Fax 427-5639
Wind River MS 100/7-8
PO Box 850 98648 509-427-5631
Joe Randall, prin. Fax 427-5639

Sultan, Snohomish, Pop. 4,514
Sultan SD 311 1,800/K-12
514 4th St 98294 360-793-9800
Dan Chaplik, supt. Fax 793-9890
www.sultan.k12.wa.us
Sultan HS 500/9-12
13715 310th Ave SE 98294 360-793-9860
Tami Nesting, prin. Fax 793-9864
Sultan MS 400/6-8
301 High Ave 98294 360-793-9850
Nathan Plummer, prin. Fax 793-9859

Sumner, Pierce, Pop. 9,086
Sumner SD 320 8,700/K-12
1202 Wood Ave 98390 253-891-6000
Laurie Dent, supt. Fax 891-6097
www.sumnersd.org
Sumner HS 1,700/9-12
1707 Main St 98390 253-891-5500
Kassie Meath, prin. Fax 891-5585
Sumner MS 700/6-8
1508 Willow St 98390 253-891-5000
Jennifer Williams, prin. Fax 891-5045
Other Schools – See Bonney Lake

Sunnyside, Yakima, Pop. 15,748
Sunnyside SD 201 6,400/K-12
1110 S 6th St 98944 509-837-5851
Kevin McKay, supt. Fax 837-0535
www.sunnysideschools.org
Harrison MS 800/6-8
810 S 16th St 98944 509-837-3601
Robert Bowman, prin. Fax 837-0450

Sierra Vista MS 700/6-8
916 N 16th St 98944 509-836-8500
Doug Rogers, prin. Fax 836-8515
Sunnyside HS 1,800/9-12
1801 E Edison Ave 98944 509-837-2601
Ryan Maxwell, prin. Fax 837-0494

Sunnyside Christian HS 100/9-12
1820 Sheller Rd 98944 509-837-8995
Dean Wagenaar, prin. Fax 837-8895

Tacoma, Pierce, Pop. 182,594
Bethel SD 403
Supt. — See Spanaway
Spanaway MS 700/6-8
15701 B St E 98445 253-683-5400
Tami Nelson, prin. Fax 683-5498

Fife SD 417 3,600/PK-12
5802 20th St E 98424 253-517-1000
Kevin Alfano, supt. Fax 517-1055
www.fifeschools.com
Fife HS 800/10-12
5616 20th St E 98424 253-517-1100
Ron Ness, prin. Fax 517-1105
Other Schools – See Fife

Franklin Pierce SD 402 7,500/PK-12
315 129th St S 98444 253-298-3000
Dr. Frank Hewins, supt. Fax 298-3015
www.fpschools.org
Ford MS 900/6-8
1602 104th St E 98445 253-298-3600
Heather Renner, prin. Fax 298-3615
GATES HS 200/Alt
813 132nd St S 98444 253-298-4000
Valinda Jones, prin. Fax 298-4015
Keithley MS 700/6-8
12324 12th Ave S 98444 253-298-4300
Dr. Tom Edwards, prin. Fax 298-4315
New Pathways Alt
813 132nd St S 98444 253-298-4000
Valinda Jones, prin. Fax 298-4015
Pierce HS 1,100/9-12
11002 18th Ave E 98445 253-298-3800
Ron Hartley, prin. Fax 298-3814
Washington HS 1,000/9-12
12420 Ainsworth Ave S 98444 253-298-4700
James Hester, prin. Fax 298-4715

Tacoma SD 10, PO Box 1357 98401 28,400/PK-12
Carla Santorno, supt. 253-571-1000
www.tacomaschools.org
Baker MS 700/6-8
8001 S J St 98408 253-571-5000
Scott Rich, prin. Fax 571-5091
First Creek MS 800/6-8
1801 E 56th St 98404 253-571-2700
Tammy Larsen, prin. Fax 571-2717
Foss HS 1,000/9-12
2112 S Tyler St 98405 253-571-7300
Lysandra Ness, prin. Fax 571-7466
Giaudrone MS 600/6-8
4902 S Alaska St 98408 253-571-5811
Billy Harris, prin. Fax 571-5812
Gray MS 600/6-8
6229 S Tyler St 98409 253-571-5200
Shaun Martin, prin. Fax 571-5201
iDEA 9-12
6701 S Park Ave 98408 253-571-2555
Lee MS 600/6-8
602 N Sprague Ave 98403 253-571-7700
Christi Brandt, prin. Fax 571-7710
Lincoln HS 1,400/9-12
701 S 37th St 98418 253-571-6700
Patrick Erwin, prin. Fax 571-6789
Mason MS 800/6-8
3901 N 28th St 98407 253-571-7000
Patrice Sulkosky, prin. Fax 571-7091
Meeker MS 600/6-8
4402 Nassau Ave NE 98422 253-571-6500
Timothy Berndt, prin. Fax 571-6503
Mount Tahoma HS 1,400/9-12
4634 S 74th St 98409 253-571-3800
Kevin Kannier, prin. Fax 571-3801
Oakland HS 200/Alt
3319 S Adams St 98409 253-571-5100
Fax 571-5101
Science and Math Institute 500/9-12
5502 Five Mile Dr 98407 253-571-2300
Jon Ketler, prin. Fax 571-2310
Stadium HS 1,700/9-12
111 N E St 98403 253-571-3100
Kevin Ikeda, prin. Fax 571-3101
Stewart HS Alt
1818 Tacoma Ave 98402 253-571-3270
Gregory Eisnaugle, prin. Fax 571-3271
Stewart MS 500/6-8
6501 S 10th St 98465 253-571-4200
Zeek Edmond, prin. Fax 571-4244
Tacoma School of the Arts 500/9-12
PO Box 1357 98402 253-571-7900
Jon Ketler, dir. Fax 571-7901
Truman MS 700/6-8
5801 N 35th St 98407 253-571-5600
Fax 571-5680
Wainwright MS 200/4-8
130 Alameda Ave 98466 253-571-3444
Fax 571-3446
Wilson HS 1,300/9-12
1202 N Orchard St 98406 253-571-6000
Dan Besett, prin. Fax 571-6162

Bates Technical College Post-Sec.
1101 Yakima Ave 98405 253-680-7000
Bellarmine Prep S 1,000/9-12
2300 S Washington St 98405 253-752-7701
Cindy Davis, prin. Fax 756-3887
BJ's Beauty & Barber College Post-Sec.
5239 S Tacoma Way 98409 253-473-4320
Covenant HS 100/9-12
620 S Shirley St 98465 253-759-9570
Richard Hannula, prin. Fax 759-1377
Everest College Post-Sec.
2156 Pacific Ave 98402 253-207-4000
Evergreen Lutheran HS 100/9-12
7306 Waller Rd E 98443 253-946-4488
Ted Klug, prin. Fax 529-9475
Faith Evangelical College & Seminary Post-Sec.
3504 N Pearl St 98407 253-752-2020
Life Christian Academy 600/PK-12
1717 S Union Ave 98405 253-756-5300
Mount Rainier Lutheran HS 100/9-12
12108 Pacific Ave S 98444 253-284-4433
Craig Neumiller, admin. Fax 284-4435
Pacific Lutheran University Post-Sec.
12180 Park Ave S 98447 253-531-6900
Tacoma Baptist S 300/PK-12
2052 S 64th St 98409 253-475-7226
Brad McCain, head sch Fax 471-9949
Tacoma Christian Academy 200/PK-10
2014 S 15th St 98405 253-572-1742
Alex Slobodyanik, prin. Fax 272-3413
Tacoma Community College Post-Sec.
6501 S 19th St 98466 253-566-5000
University of Puget Sound Post-Sec.
1500 N Warner St 98416 253-879-3100
Wright Academy 700/PK-12
7723 Chambers Creek Rd W 98467 253-620-8300
Matt Culberson, head sch Fax 620-8431
Wright S 400/PK-12
827 N Tacoma Ave 98403 253-272-2216
Christian Sullivan, head sch Fax 572-3616

Taholah, Grays Harbor, Pop. 818
Taholah SD 77 100/PK-12
PO Box 249 98587 360-276-4780
Lenora Hall, supt. Fax 276-4370
www.taholah.org
Taholah S 100/PK-12
PO Box 249 98587 360-276-4729
Curtis Cleveringa, prin. Fax 276-4370

Tekoa, Whitman, Pop. 764
Tekoa SD 265 200/PK-12
PO Box 869 99033 509-284-3281
Dr. Connie Kliewer, supt. Fax 284-2045
www.tekoasd.org
Tekoa JSHS 100/7-12
PO Box 869 99033 509-284-3401
Daniel Hutton, prin. Fax 284-5802

Tenino, Thurston, Pop. 1,631
Tenino SD 402 1,200/PK-12
PO Box 4024 98589 360-264-3400
Joe Belmonte, supt. Fax 264-3438
www.teninoschools.org
Tenino HS 400/9-12
PO Box 4024 98589 360-264-3500
Garry Cameron, prin. Fax 264-3538
Tenino MS 300/6-8
PO Box 4024 98589 360-264-3600
John Neal, prin. Fax 264-3638

Thorp, Kittitas, Pop. 235
Thorp SD 400 100/PK-12
PO Box 150 98946 509-964-2107
Dr. Linda Martin, supt. Fax 964-2313
www.thorpschools.org/
Thorp S 100/PK-12
PO Box 150 98946 509-964-2107
Dr. Linda Martin, prin. Fax 964-2313

Toledo, Lewis, Pop. 712
Toledo SD 237 800/PK-12
PO Box 469 98591 360-864-6325
Chris Rust, supt. Fax 864-6326
www.toledoschools.us
Cowlitz Academy 50/Alt
PO Box 469 98591 360-864-2989
Martin Huffman, prin. Fax 864-6326
Toledo HS 300/9-12
PO Box 820 98591 360-864-2391
Martin Huffman, prin. Fax 864-2396
Toledo MS 200/6-8
PO Box 668 98591 360-864-2395
Heather Ogden, prin. Fax 864-8147

Tonasket, Okanogan, Pop. 1,010
Tonasket SD 404 1,200/PK-12
35 Highway 20 98855 509-486-2126
Steve McCullough, supt. Fax 486-1263
www.tonasket.wednet.edu
Tonasket Choice HS 100/Alt
35 Highway 20 98855 509-486-1428
Chelsea Freeman, lead tchr.
Tonasket HS 300/9-12
35 Highway 20 98855 509-486-2161
Brian Ellis, prin. Fax 486-4382
Tonasket MS 200/6-8
35 Highway 20 98855 509-486-2147
Kristi Krieg, prin. Fax 486-1576

Toppenish, Yakima, Pop. 8,831
Toppenish SD 202 3,700/PK-12
306 Bolin Dr 98948 509-865-4455
John M. Cerna, supt. Fax 865-2067
www.toppenish.wednet.edu/
Computer Academy 200/Alt
143 Ward Rd 98948 509-865-3377
Frank Harris, prin. Fax 865-7327
Toppenish HS 800/9-12
141 Ward Rd 98948 509-865-3370
Shawn Myers, prin. Fax 865-3244
Toppenish MS 800/6-8
104 Goldendale Ave 98948 509-865-2730
Larry Davison, prin. Fax 865-7503

Heritage University Post-Sec.
3240 Fort Rd 98948 509-865-8500

Touchet, Walla Walla, Pop. 415
Touchet SD 300 200/K-12
PO Box 135 99360 509-394-2352
Susan Bell, supt. Fax 394-2952
www.touchet.k12.wa.us
Touchet JSHS 200/6-12
PO Box 135 99360 509-394-2352
John Holcomb, prin. Fax 394-2952

Toutle, Cowlitz
Toutle Lake SD 130 600/K-12
5050 Spirit Lake Hwy 98649 360-274-6182
Scott Grabenhorst, supt. Fax 274-7608
www.toutlesd.k12.wa.us
Toutle Lake JSHS 300/7-12
5050 Spirit Lake Hwy 98649 360-274-6132
Chris Byrd, prin. Fax 274-7615

Trout Lake, Klickitat, Pop. 545
Trout Lake SD R-400 100/K-12
PO Box 488 98650 509-395-2571
Doug Dearden, supt. Fax 395-2399
www.troutlake.k12.wa.us/
Trout Lake S 100/K-12
PO Box 488 98650 509-395-2571
Crystal Lanz, prin. Fax 395-2399

Tukwila, King, Pop. 17,643
Highline SD 401
Supt. — See Burien
Raisbeck Aviation HS 400/9-12
9229 E Marginal Way S 98108 206-631-7200
Terese Tipton, prin. Fax 716-0200

Tukwila SD 406 2,900/K-12
4640 S 144th St 98168 206-901-8000
Dr. Nancy Coogan, supt. Fax 901-8016
tukwilaschools.org
Foster HS 900/9-12
4242 S 144th St 98168 206-901-7900
Pat Larson, prin. Fax 901-7907
Showalter MS 700/6-8
4628 S 144th St 98168 206-901-7800
Brett Christopher, prin. Fax 901-7807

Le Cordon Bleu College of Culinary Arts Post-Sec.
360 Corporate Dr N 98188 407-888-4000

Tumwater, Thurston, Pop. 16,544
Tumwater SD 33 6,300/PK-12
621 Linwood Ave SW 98512 360-709-7000
John Bash, supt. Fax 709-7002
www.tumwater.k12.wa.us
Bush MS 500/7-8
2120 83rd Ave SW 98512 360-709-7400
Linda O'Shaughnessy, prin. Fax 709-7402
New Market Skills Center Vo/Tech
7299 New Market St SW 98501 360-570-4500
Kris Blum, dir. Fax 570-4502
Tumwater HS 1,200/9-12
700 Israel Rd SW 98501 360-709-7600
Jeff Broome, prin. Fax 709-7602
Tumwater MS 500/7-8
6335 Littlerock Rd SW 98512 360-709-7500
Jon Wilcox, prin. Fax 709-7502
Other Schools – See Olympia

Twisp, Okanogan, Pop. 890
Methow Valley SD 350
Supt. — See Winthrop
Methow Valley Independent Learning Ctr 50/Alt
220 Highway 20 98856 509-997-8006
Deborah Dekalb, prin. Fax 997-5980

Union Gap, Yakima, Pop. 5,960

La Salle HS 200/9-12
3000 Lightning Way 98903 509-225-2900
Ted Kanelopoulos, prin. Fax 225-2950

University Place, Pierce, Pop. 28,698
University Place SD 83 5,600/K-12
3717 Grandview Dr W 98466 253-566-5600
Jeffery Chamberlin, supt. Fax 566-5607
www.upsd.wednet.edu
Curtis JHS 1,000/8-9
3725 Grandview Dr W 98466 253-566-5670
Jayne Hofstrand, prin. Fax 566-5644
Curtis SHS 1,400/10-12
8425 40th St W 98466 253-566-5710
Tom Adams, prin. Fax 566-5626

Valley, Stevens, Pop. 135
Valley SD 070 1,000/PK-12
3030 Huffman Rd 99181 509-937-2791
Kevin Foster, supt. Fax 937-2691
www.valleysd.org/
Paideia HS 50/9-12
3043 Huffman Rd 99181 509-937-2655
Matthew Cox, prin. Fax 937-2656

Vancouver, Clark, Pop. 153,919
Battle Ground SD 119
Supt. — See Brush Prairie
Laurin MS 600/5-8
13601 NE 97th Ave 98662 360-885-5200
Nick Krause, prin. Fax 885-5205
Pleasant Valley MS 500/5-8
14320 NE 50th Ave 98686 360-885-5500
Tamarah Grigg, prin. Fax 885-5510
Prairie HS 1,400/9-12
11311 NE 119th St 98662 360-885-5000
Travis Drake, prin. Fax 885-5050

Evergreen SD 114 26,000/K-12
PO Box 8910 98668 360-604-4000
John Deeder, supt. Fax 892-5307
www.evergreenps.org/
Cascade MS 900/6-8
PO Box 8910 98668 360-604-3600
Lisa Wagner-Tschirgi, prin. Fax 604-3602
Cascadia Technical Academy Vo/Tech
PO Box 8910 98668 360-604-1050
Mark Mansell, dir. Fax 604-1052
Covington MS 1,100/6-8
PO Box 8910 98668 360-604-6300
Charbonneau Gourde, prin. Fax 604-6302
Evergreen HS 1,800/9-12
PO Box 8910 98668 360-604-3700
Lisa Emmerich, prin. Fax 604-3702
Frontier MS 900/6-8
PO Box 8910 98668 360-604-3200
Griffin Peyton, prin. Fax 604-3202
Heritage HS 2,100/9-12
PO Box 8910 98668 360-604-3400
Derek Garrison, prin. Fax 604-3402
Lacks Health & Bioscience HS 300/9-12
PO Box 8910 98668 360-604-6340
Julie Tumelty, prin. Fax 604-6342
Legacy HS 200/Alt
PO Box 8910 98668 360-604-3900
Heather Fowler, prin. Fax 604-3902
Mountain View HS 1,800/9-12
PO Box 8910 98668 360-604-6100
Matt Johnson, prin. Fax 604-6102
Pacific MS 1,000/6-8
PO Box 8910 98668 360-604-6500
Heather Thiessen, prin. Fax 604-6502
Shahala MS 1,100/6-8
PO Box 8910 98668 360-604-3800
Gregg Brown, prin. Fax 604-3802
Wy' East MS 900/6-8
PO Box 8910 98668 360-604-6400
Caroline Garrett, prin. Fax 604-6402
Other Schools – See Camas

Vancouver SD 37 22,300/K-12
PO Box 8937 98668 360-313-1000
Dr. Steven Webb, supt. Fax 313-1001
www.vansd.org
Alki MS 700/6-8
1800 NW Bliss Rd 98685 360-313-3200
Darci Fronk, prin. Fax 313-3201
Columbia River HS 1,300/9-12
800 NW 99th St 98665 360-313-3900
Alex Otoupal, prin. Fax 313-3901
Discovery MS 700/6-8
800 E 40th St 98663 360-313-3300
Mark Cain, prin. Fax 313-3301
Fir Grove Childrens Center 100/Alt
2920 Falk Rd 98661 360-313-1800
Daniel Bettis, prin. Fax 313-1801
Ft. Vancouver HS 1,400/9-12
5700 E 18th St 98661 360-313-4000
Jody ViDelco, prin. Fax 313-4001
Gaiser MS 900/6-8
3000 NE 99th St 98665 360-313-3400
Mike Lane, prin. Fax 313-3401
Hudson's Bay HS 1,400/9-12
1601 E McLoughlin Blvd 98663 360-313-4400
Val Seeley, prin. Fax 313-4401
Jefferson MS 800/6-8
3000 NW 119th St 98685 360-313-3700
Tom Adams, prin. Fax 313-3701
Lee MS 600/6-8
8500 NW 9th Ave 98665 360-313-3500
Curt Scheidel, prin. Fax 313-3501
Lewis and Clark HS 100/Alt
2901 General Anderson Rd 98661 360-313-4350
Steve Lindblom, prin. Fax 313-4351
McLoughlin MS 900/6-8
5802 MacArthur Blvd 98661 360-313-3600
Travis Boeh, prin. Fax 313-3601
School of Arts & Academics 600/6-12
3101 Main St 98663 360-313-4600
Lori Rotherham, prin. Fax 313-4601
Skyview HS 2,000/9-12
1300 NW 139th St 98685 360-313-4200
James Gray, prin. Fax 313-4201
Vancouver iTech Preparatory S 300/6-12
PO Box 8937 98668 360-313-5200
Christina Iremonger, prin. Fax 313-5201

Charter College Vancouver Post-Sec.
17200 SE Mill Plain Ste 100 98683 360-448-2000
Clark College Post-Sec.
1933 Fort Vancouver Way 98663 360-992-2000
Everest College Post-Sec.
120 NE 136th Ave Ste 130 98684 360-254-3282
Hosanna Christian S 100/PK-12
4120 NE St Johns Rd 98661 360-906-0941
Sue Bishoprick, prin. Fax 694-0224
International Air & Hospitality Academy Post-Sec.
2901 E Mill Plain Blvd 98661 360-695-2500
King's Way Christian S 700/PK-12
3300 NE 78th St 98665 360-574-1613
School of Piano Technology for the Blind Post-Sec.
2510 E Evergreen Blvd 98661 360-693-1511
Seton Catholic HS 100/9-12
9000 NE 64th Ave 98665 360-258-1932
Ed Little, prin. Fax 258-1936
Washington State School for the Blind Post-Sec.
2214 E 13th St 98661
Washington State School for the Deaf Post-Sec.
611 Grand Blvd 98661

Vashon, King, Pop. 10,291
Vashon Island SD 402 1,500/PK-12
PO Box 547 98070 206-463-2121
Michael Soltman, supt. Fax 463-6262
www.vashonsd.org
McMurray MS 400/6-8
9329 SW Cemetery Rd 98070 206-463-9168
Greg Allison, prin. Fax 463-9707
Vashon Island HS 500/9-12
9600 SW 204th St 98070 206-463-9171
Danny Rock, prin. Fax 463-1944

Waitsburg, Walla Walla, Pop. 1,189
Waitsburg SD 401-100 300/K-12
PO Box 217 99361 509-337-6301
Dr. Carol Clarke, supt. Fax 337-6042
www.waitsburgsd.org/
Preston Hall MS 50/6-8
PO Box 217 99361 509-337-9474
Stephanie Wooderchak, prin. Fax 337-6170
Waitsburg HS 100/9-12
PO Box 217 99361 509-337-6351
Stephanie Wooderchak, prin. Fax 337-6551

Walla Walla, Walla Walla, Pop. 30,829
Walla Walla SD 140 6,100/PK-12
364 S Park St 99362 509-527-3000
Wade Smith, supt. Fax 529-7713
www.wwps.org
Garrison MS 600/6-8
906 Chase Ave 99362 509-527-3040
Robert Elizondo, prin. Fax 527-3048
Lincoln Alternative HS 200/Alt
421 S 4th Ave 99362 509-527-3083
Marci Knauft, prin. Fax 527-3011
Pioneer MS 700/6-8
450 Bridge St 99362 509-527-3050
Mira Gobel, prin. Fax 526-5212
Southeast Area Technical Skills Center Vo/Tech
525 Campus Loop 99362 509-526-2000
Dennis Matson, dir. Fax 525-1023
Walla Walla HS 2,000/9-12
800 Abbott Rd 99362 509-527-3020
Pete Peterson, prin. Fax 527-3034

DeSales HS 100/8-12
919 E Sumach St 99362 509-525-3030
Lynne Kuntz, prin. Fax 527-0361
Walla Walla Community College Post-Sec.
500 Tausick Way 99362 509-522-2500
Whitman College Post-Sec.
345 Boyer Ave 99362 509-527-5111

Wapato, Yakima, Pop. 4,948
Wapato SD 207 3,400/PK-12
PO Box 38 98951 509-877-4181
Becky Imler, supt. Fax 877-6077
www.wapatosd.org
PACE HS 100/Alt
310 S Wasco Ave 98951 509-877-6138
Gary Babcock, prin. Fax 877-6164
Wapato HS 800/9-12
1202 S Camas Ave 98951 509-877-3138
Eric Diener, prin. Fax 877-5079
Wapato MS 800/6-8
1309 Kateri Ln 98951 509-877-2173
Anna Keifer, prin. Fax 877-6232

Warden, Grant, Pop. 2,646
Warden SD 146-161 1,000/PK-12
101 W Beck Way 98857 509-349-2366
Dr. David LaBounty, supt. Fax 349-2367
www.warden.wednet.edu
Warden HS 300/9-12
101 W Beck Way 98857 509-349-2581
Courtney McCoy, prin. Fax 349-2531
Warden MS 200/6-8
101 W Beck Way 98857 509-349-2902
Trever Summers, prin. Fax 349-2531

Washougal, Clark, Pop. 13,617
Washougal SD 112-6 3,200/K-12
4855 Evergreen Way 98671 360-954-3000
Mike Stromme, supt. Fax 835-7776
www.washougal.k12.wa.us
Canyon Creek MS 300/6-8
9731 Washougal River Rd 98671 360-954-3500
Sandi Christensen, prin. Fax 837-1500
Excelsior HS 100/Alt
1401 39th St 98671 360-954-3300
Carol Boyden, prin. Fax 835-1182
Jemtegaard MS 500/6-8
35300 SE Evergreen Hwy 98671 360-954-3400
David Cooke, prin. Fax 835-9145
Washougal HS 900/9-12
1201 39th St 98671 360-954-3100
Aaron Hansen, prin. Fax 835-3968

Washtucna, Adams, Pop. 206
Washtucna SD 109-43 100/K-12
730 E Booth Ave 99371 509-646-3237
Vance Alan Wing, supt. Fax 646-3249
www.tucna.wednet.edu
Washtucna S 100/K-12
730 E Booth Ave 99371 509-646-3237
Vance Alan Wing, prin. Fax 646-3249

Waterville, Douglas, Pop. 1,124
Waterville SD 209 300/K-12
PO Box 490 98858 509-745-8584
Fax 745-9073
www.waterville.wednet.edu/
Waterville JSHS 200/6-12
PO Box 490 98858 509-745-8583
Tabatha Mires, prin. Fax 745-9073

Wellpinit, Stevens
Wellpinit SD 49 400/K-12
PO Box 390 99040 509-258-4535
John Adkins, supt. Fax 258-4065
www.wellpinit.org
Wellpinit Alliance HS 50/Alt
PO Box 390 99040 509-258-4535
Terry Bartolino, prin. Fax 258-7378
Wellpinit HS 100/9-12
PO Box 390 99040 509-258-4535
Kristopher Herda, prin. Fax 258-7378
Wellpinit MS 100/6-8
PO Box 390 99040 509-258-4535
Kristopher Herda, prin. Fax 258-7378
Other Schools – See Moses Lake, White Swan

Wenatchee, Chelan, Pop. 31,295
Wenatchee SD 246 7,700/K-12
PO Box 1767 98807 509-663-8161
Brian Flones, supt. Fax 663-3082
www.wenatcheeschools.org
Foothills MS 600/6-8
1410 Maple St 98801 509-664-8961
Mark Goveia, prin. Fax 663-6610
Orchard MS 500/6-8
1024 Orchard Ave 98801 509-662-7745
Taunya Brown, prin. Fax 663-8042
Pioneer MS 700/6-8
1620 Russell St 98801 509-663-7171
Rob Cline, prin. Fax 663-0453
Valley Academy of Learning 200/Alt
1911 N Wenatchee Ave 98801 509-662-6417
Greg Lovercamp, admin. Fax 663-4597
Wenatchee HS 2,100/9-12
1101 Millerdale Ave 98801 509-663-8117
Eric Anderson, prin. Fax 663-2573
Wenatchee Valley Technical Skills Center Vo/Tech
327 E Penny Rd Ste D 98801 509-662-8827
Pete Jelsing, dir. Fax 662-5993
Westside HS 300/Alt
1510 9th St 98801 509-663-7947
Kory Kalahar, prin. Fax 664-3005

Academy of Hair Design Post-Sec.
208 S Wenatchee Ave 98801 509-662-9082
Cascade Christian Academy 200/PK-12
600 N Western Ave 98801 509-662-2723
River Academy 200/PK-12
PO Box 4485 98807 509-665-2415
Eric DeVries, hdmstr. Fax 662-9235
Wenatchee Valley College Post-Sec.
1300 5th St 98801 509-682-6800

Westport, Grays Harbor, Pop. 2,036
Ocosta SD 172 700/PK-12
2580 S Montesano St 98595 360-268-9125
Dr. Paula Akerlund, supt. Fax 268-2540
Ocosta JSHS 300/7-12
2580 S Montesano St 98595 360-268-9125
Brian Hunter, prin. Fax 268-0908

West Richland, Benton, Pop. 11,498
Richland SD 400
Supt. — See Richland
Enterprise MS 1,000/6-8
5200 Paradise Dr 99353 509-967-6200
Jennifer Klauss, prin. Fax 967-5685

White Salmon, Klickitat, Pop. 2,180
White Salmon Valley SD 405-17 1,100/K-12
PO Box 157 98672 509-493-1500
Dr. Jerry Lewis, supt. Fax 493-2275
www.whitesalmonschools.org/
Columbia HS 400/9-12
PO Box 1339 98672 509-493-1970
Craig McKee, prin. Fax 493-4182
Henkle MS 200/7-8
PO Box 1309 98672 509-493-1502
Haley Ortega, prin. Fax 493-3385
White Salmon Academy 50/Alt
1455 NW Bruin Country Rd 98672 509-493-1970
Craig McKee, prin. Fax 493-4182

White Swan, Yakima, Pop. 779
Mount Adams SD 209 1,000/PK-12
PO Box 578 98952 509-874-2611
Dr. Curt Guaglianone, supt. Fax 874-2960
www.masd209.org
Mount Adams MS 100/7-8
PO Box 578 98952 509-874-8626
Joey Castilleja, prin. Fax 874-2646
White Swan HS 300/9-12
PO Box 578 98952 509-874-2324
Joey Castilleja, prin. Fax 874-2646

Wellpinit SD 49
Supt. — See Wellpinit
Fort Simcoe Alliance HS 50/Alt
40 Abella Ln 98952 509-258-4535
Terry Bartolino, prin. Fax 258-7857

Wilbur, Lincoln, Pop. 857
Wilbur SD 200 300/K-12
PO Box 1090 99185 509-647-2221
Steve Gaub, supt. Fax 647-2509
www.wilbur.wednet.edu
Wilbur JSHS 100/7-12
PO Box 1090 99185 509-647-5602
Carla Hudson, prin. Fax 647-2509

Wilson Creek, Grant, Pop. 198
Wilson Creek SD 167-202 100/K-12
PO Box 46 98860 509-345-2541
Gene Nelson, supt. Fax 345-2288
www.wilsoncreek.org
Wilson Creek JSHS 100/7-12
PO Box 46 98860 509-345-2541
Sally Nelson, prin. Fax 345-2288

Winlock, Lewis, Pop. 1,291
Winlock SD 232 700/PK-12
311 NW Fir St 98596 360-785-3582
Shannon Criss, supt. Fax 864-3101
www.winlockschools.org
APOLO Alternative S 50/Alt
311 NW Fir St 98596 360-785-3537
Boyd Calder, prin.

Winlock HS 200/9-12
241 N Military Rd 98596 360-785-3537
Brian Maley, prin. Fax 864-3104
Winlock MS 200/6-8
241 N Military Rd 98596 360-785-3046
Brian Maley, prin. Fax 864-3105

Winthrop, Okanogan, Pop. 390
Methow Valley SD 350 600/PK-12
18 Twin Lakes Rd 98862 509-996-9205
Tom Venable, supt. Fax 996-9208
www.methow.org
Liberty Bell JSHS 300/7-12
18 Twin Lakes Rd 98862 509-996-2215
Deborah Dekalb, prin. Fax 996-3609
Other Schools – See Twisp

Wishram, Klickitat, Pop. 339
Wishram SD 94 100/PK-12
PO Box 8 98673 509-748-2551
Michael Roberts, supt. Fax 748-2127
www.wishramschool.org
Wishram S 100/PK-12
PO Box 8 98673 509-748-2551
Michael Roberts, supt. Fax 748-2127

Woodinville, King, Pop. 10,516
Northshore SD 417
Supt. — See Bothell
Leota JHS 700/7-9
19301 168th Ave NE 98072 425-408-6500
Audee Gregor, prin. Fax 408-6502
Timbercrest JHS 800/7-9
19115 215th Way NE, 425-408-6900
Joe Mismas, prin. Fax 408-6902
Woodinville SHS 1,400/10-12
19819 136th Ave NE 98072 425-408-7400
Kurt Criscione, prin. Fax 408-7402

Chrysalis S 200/K-12
14241 NE Woodinville Duvall 98072 425-481-2228
Karen Fogle, dir. Fax 486-8107

Woodland, Cowlitz, Pop. 5,391
Woodland SD 404 1,600/PK-12
800 2nd St 98674 360-841-2700
Michael Green, supt. Fax 841-2701
www.woodlandschools.org/
Woodland HS 600/9-12
1500 Dike Access Rd 98674 360-841-2800
John Shoup, prin. Fax 841-2801
Woodland MS 300/5-8
755 Park St 98674 360-841-2850
Jake Hall, prin. Fax 841-2851
Woodland TEAM HS 100/Alt
800 3rd St 98674 360-841-2800
Dan Uhlenkott, prin. Fax 841-2801

West Coast Training Post-Sec.
PO Box 970 98674 360-225-6787

Yakima, Yakima, Pop. 89,018
East Valley SD 90 3,000/K-12
2002 Beaudry Rd 98901 509-573-7300
John Schieche, supt. Fax 573-7340
www.evsd90.org
East Valley Central MS 700/6-8
2010 Beaudry Rd 98901 509-573-7500
Matt Toth, prin. Fax 573-7540
East Valley HS 800/9-12
1900 Beaudry Rd 98901 509-573-7400
Dorthea Say, prin. Fax 573-7440

West Valley SD 208 4,900/K-12
8902 Zier Rd 98908 509-972-6000
Dr. Michael Brophy, supt. Fax 972-6025
www.wvsd208.org
West Valley Freshman Campus 400/9-9
9206 Zier Rd 98908 509-972-5600
Ben McMurry, prin. Fax 972-5601
West Valley HS 1,000/10-12
9800 Zier Rd 98908 509-972-5900
Ben McMurry, prin. Fax 972-5901
West Valley JHS 800/7-8
7505 Zier Rd 98908 509-972-5800
William Oppliger, prin. Fax 972-5801

Yakima SD 7 15,900/PK-12
104 N 4th Ave 98902 509-573-7000
Dr. Jack Irion, supt. Fax 573-7181
www.yakimaschools.org/
Davis HS 2,100/9-12
212 S 6th Ave 98902 509-573-2500
Ryan McDaniel, prin. Fax 573-2525
Eisenhower HS 2,000/9-12
611 S 44th Ave 98908 509-573-2600
Jewel Brumley, prin. Fax 573-2626
Franklin MS 900/6-8
410 S 19th Ave 98902 509-573-2100
Sherry Anderson, prin. Fax 573-2121
Lewis & Clark MS 800/6-8
1114 W Pierce St 98902 509-573-2200
Victor Nourani, prin. Fax 573-2222
Stanton Academy 400/Alt
802 River Rd 98902 509-573-1200
Dave Chaplin, prin. Fax 573-1212
Washington MS 700/6-8
510 S 9th St 98901 509-573-2300
Bill Hilton, prin. Fax 573-2323
Wilson MS 800/6-8
902 S 44th Ave 98908 509-573-2400
Ernesto Araiza, prin. Fax 573-2424
Yakima Valley Technical Skills Center Vo/Tech
1120 S 18th St 98901 509-573-5500
Craig Dwight, prin. Fax 834-2041

Pacific Northwest Univ of Health Science Post-Sec.
111 University Pkwy Ste 202 98901 509-452-5100
Perry Technical Institute Post-Sec.
2011 W Washington Ave 98903 509-453-0374
Professional Beauty School Post-Sec.
PO Box 9243 98909 509-877-6443
Riverside Christian S 400/PK-12
721 Keys Rd 98901 509-965-2602
Rick Van Beek, admin. Fax 966-7031
Yakima Adventist Christian S 100/PK-10
1200 City Reservoir Rd 98908 509-966-1933
Renae Young, prin.
Yakima Valley Community College Post-Sec.
PO Box 22520 98907 509-574-4600

Yelm, Thurston, Pop. 6,363
Yelm Community SD 2 5,700/PK-12
PO Box 476 98597 360-458-1900
Brian Wharton, supt. Fax 458-6178
www.ycs.wednet.edu
Ridgeline MS 700/7-9
PO Box 476 98597 360-458-1100
John Johnson, prin. Fax 400-1256
Yelm Extension S 100/Alt
PO Box 476 98597 360-458-2002
Ryan Akiyama, admin. Fax 458-6146
Yelm HS 1,300/10-12
PO Box 476 98597 360-458-7777
Ryan Akiyama, prin. Fax 458-6198
Yelm MS 700/7-9
PO Box 476 98597 360-458-3600
Scot Embrey, prin. Fax 458-6122

Eagle View Christian S 100/PK-12
13036 Morris Rd SE 98597 360-458-3090
Barbara Ballou, prin. Fax 458-4990

Zillah, Yakima, Pop. 2,907
Zillah SD 205 1,300/PK-12
213 4th Ave 98953 509-829-5911
Doug Burge, supt. Fax 829-6290
www.zillahschools.org/
Zillah HS 400/9-12
1602 2nd Ave 98953 509-829-5565
Mike Torres, prin. Fax 829-5285
Zillah MS 200/7-8
1301 Cutler Way 98953 509-829-5511
Tracy Savage, prin. Fax 829-0754

WEST VIRGINIA

WEST VIRGINIA DEPARTMENT OF EDUCATION
1900 Kanawha Blvd E Rm 358, Charleston 25305-0330
Telephone 304-558-2681
Fax 304-558-0048
Website wvde.state.wv.us

State Superintendent of Schools Michael Martirano

WEST VIRGINIA BOARD OF EDUCATION
1900 Kanawha Blvd E Rm 358, Charleston 25305-0009

President Michael Green

REGIONAL EDUCATION SERVICE AGENCIES (RESA)

RESA I
Dr. Robin Lewis, dir. 304-256-4712
400 Neville St, Beckley 25801 Fax 256-4683
resa1.k12.wv.us/
RESA II
Dr. Dee Cockrille, dir. 304-529-6205
2001 McCoy Rd, Huntington 25701 Fax 529-6209
resa2.k12.wv.us/
RESA III
Kelly Watts, dir. 304-766-7655
501 22nd St, Dunbar 25064 Fax 766-7915
resa3.k12.wv.us
RESA IV
David Warvel, dir., 404 Old Main Dr 304-872-6440
Summersville 26651 Fax 872-6442
resa4.k12.wv.us/
RESA V
Joseph Oliverio, dir. 304-485-6513
2507 9th Ave, Parkersburg 26101 Fax 485-6515
resa5.k12.wv.us
RESA VII
Gabriel Devono, dir. 304-624-6554
1201 N 15th St, Clarksburg 26301 Fax 624-5223
resa7.k12.wv.us
RESA VIII
Joan Willard, dir., 109 S College St 304-267-3595
Martinsburg 25401 Fax 267-3599
www.resa8.org
RESA VI
Nick Zervos, dir. 304-243-0440
30 G C and P Rd, Wheeling 26003 Fax 243-0443
resa6.k12.wv.us/

PUBLIC, PRIVATE AND CATHOLIC SECONDARY SCHOOLS

Ansted, Fayette, Pop. 1,400
Fayette County SD
Supt. — See Fayetteville
Ansted MS 200/6-8
PO Box 766 25812 304-658-5170
Richard Petitt, prin. Fax 658-3059

Ashton, Mason
Mason County SD
Supt. — See Point Pleasant
Hannan JSHS 300/7-12
15638 Ashton Upland Rd 25503 304-743-2571
Karen Bare-Oldham, prin. Fax 743-4513

Athens, Mercer, Pop. 1,039

Concord University Post-Sec.
PO Box 1000 24712 800-344-6679

Avondale, McDowell
McDowell County SD
Supt. — See Welch
Sandy River MS 300/6-8
PO Box 419 24811 304-938-2407
Sara Garrett, prin. Fax 938-2418

Baker, Hardy
Hardy County SD
Supt. — See Moorefield
East Hardy HS 200/9-12
PO Box 120 26801 304-897-5948
Jennifer Strawderman, prin. Fax 897-6261

Barboursville, Cabell, Pop. 3,916
Cabell County SD
Supt. — See Huntington
Barboursville MS 800/6-8
1400 Central Ave 25504 304-733-3003
Brent Jarrell, prin. Fax 733-3009

Beaver, Raleigh, Pop. 1,300

Victory Baptist Academy 100/K-12
PO Box 549 25813 304-255-4535

Beckley, Raleigh, Pop. 17,086
Raleigh County SD 12,500/PK-12
105 Adair St 25801 304-256-4500
David Price, supt. Fax 256-4739
boe.rale.k12.wv.us
Academy of Careers and Technology Vo/Tech
390 Stanaford Rd 25801 304-256-4615
Charles Pack, dir. Fax 256-4674
Beckley-Stratton MS 700/6-8
401 Grey Flats Rd 25801 304-256-4616
Rachel Pauley, prin. Fax 256-4763
Park MS 400/6-8
212 Park Ave 25801 304-256-4586
Jacquelin McPeake, prin. Fax 256-4709
Wilson HS 1,300/9-12
400 Stanaford Rd 25801 304-256-4646
Ron Cantley, prin. Fax 256-4642
Other Schools – See Coal City, Glen Daniel, Shady Spring, Sophia

---

New River Community & Technical College Post-Sec.
221 George St Ste 2 25801 304-929-5450
Valley College Post-Sec.
120 New River Town Ctr #C 25801 304-252-9547
Veterans Administration Hospital Post-Sec.
200 Veterans Ave 25801 304-255-2121

Belington, Barbour, Pop. 1,905
Barbour County SD
Supt. — See Philippi
Belington MS 200/6-8
469 Morgantown Pike 26250 304-823-1281
Mary Hovatter, prin. Fax 823-2403

Belle, Kanawha, Pop. 1,248
Kanawha County SD
Supt. — See Charleston
DuPont MS 400/6-8
1 Panther Dr 25015 304-348-1978
Romie Canterbury, prin. Fax 949-1793
Riverside HS 1,200/9-12
1 Warrior Way 25015 304-348-1996
Valery Harper, prin. Fax 348-1921

Belmont, Pleasants, Pop. 892
Pleasants County SD
Supt. — See Saint Marys
Pleasants County MS 400/5-8
510 Riverview Dr 26134 304-299-5275
Lori Barnhart, prin. Fax 665-2451

Berkeley Springs, Morgan, Pop. 614
Morgan County SD 2,500/PK-12
247 Harrison Ave 25411 304-258-2430
David Banks, supt. Fax 258-9146
www.morganschools.net
Berkeley Springs HS 800/9-12
149 Concord Ave 25411 304-258-2871
Mitch Nida, prin. Fax 258-5058
Warm Springs MS 500/6-8
271 Warm Springs Way 25411 304-258-1500
Gene Brock, prin. Fax 258-4600
Other Schools – See Paw Paw

Bethany, Brooke, Pop. 1,014

Bethany College 26032 Post-Sec.
304-829-7000

Blacksville, Monongalia, Pop. 166
Monongalia County SD
Supt. — See Morgantown
Clay-Battelle MSHS 400/6-12
PO Box A 26521 304-432-8208
David Cottrell, prin. Fax 432-8189

Bluefield, Mercer, Pop. 10,213
Mercer County SD
Supt. — See Princeton
Bluefield HS 700/9-12
535 W Cumberland Rd 24701 304-325-9116
Michael Collins, prin. Fax 325-0529
Bluefield MS 600/6-8
2002 Stadium Dr 24701 304-325-2481
Kimberly Miller, prin. Fax 325-2156

Bluefield Regional Medical Center Post-Sec.
500 Cherry St 24701 304-327-1701
Bluefield State College Post-Sec.
219 Rock St 24701 304-327-4000
Valley View SDA S 50/K-12
PO Box 6312 24701 304-325-8679

Bradshaw, McDowell, Pop. 335
McDowell County SD
Supt. — See Welch
Riverview HS 500/9-12
512 Mountaineer Hwy 24817 304-436-8441
Frazier McGuire, prin. Fax 967-2502

Branchland, Lincoln
Lincoln County SD
Supt. — See Hamlin
Guyan Valley MS 300/6-8
5312 McClellan Hwy 25506 304-824-3235
Jonah Adkins, prin. Fax 824-3459

Bridgeport, Harrison, Pop. 8,059
Harrison County SD
Supt. — See Clarksburg
Bridgeport HS 700/9-12
515 Johnson Ave 26330 304-326-7137
Mark DeFazio, prin. Fax 842-6288
Bridgeport MS 600/6-8
413 Johnson Ave 26330 304-326-7142
Carole Crawford, prin. Fax 842-6275

Heritage Christian S 100/PK-12
225 Newton Ave 26330 304-842-1740
Linda Simms, admin. Fax 842-1750
West Virginia Junior College Post-Sec.
176 Thompson Dr 26330 304-842-4007

Buckeye, Pocahontas
Pocahontas County SD
Supt. — See Marlinton
Marlinton MS 200/5-8
1 Copperhead Way 24924 304-799-6773
Joseph Riley, prin. Fax 799-7278

Buckhannon, Upshur, Pop. 5,544
Upshur County SD 3,800/PK-12
102 Smithfield St 26201 304-472-5480
Roy Wager, supt. Fax 472-0258
www.upshurschools.com
Buckhannon-Upshur HS 1,000/9-12
270 BU Dr 26201 304-472-3720
Eddie Vincent, prin. Fax 472-0772
Buckhannon-Upshur MS 900/6-8
553 Route 20 South Rd 26201 304-472-1520
Renee Warner, prin. Fax 472-6864
Eberle Technical Center Vo/Tech
RR 5 Box 2 26201 304-472-1259
Dr. Michael Cutright, dir. Fax 472-3418

West Virginia Wesleyan College Post-Sec.
59 College Ave 26201 304-473-8000

Buffalo, Putnam, Pop. 1,223
Putnam County SD
Supt. — See Winfield
Buffalo HS 300/9-12
3680 Buffalo Rd 25033 304-937-2661
Tawny Stilianoudakis, prin. Fax 937-3470

Bunker Hill, Berkeley
Berkeley County SD
Supt. — See Martinsburg

Musselman MS 1,200/6-8
105 Pride Ave 25413 304-229-1965
James Holland, prin. Fax 229-1967

Cameron, Marshall, Pop. 941
Marshall County SD
Supt. — See Moundsville
Cameron JSHS 300/7-12
2012 Blue and Gold Rd 26033 304-686-3336
Jack Cain, prin. Fax 686-3510

Capon Bridge, Hampshire, Pop. 353
Hampshire County SD
Supt. — See Romney
Capon Bridge MS 300/6-8
PO Box 147 26711 304-856-2534
Ann Downs, prin. Fax 856-3192

Cedar Grove, Kanawha, Pop. 982
Kanawha County SD
Supt. — See Charleston
Cedar Grove MS 200/6-8
PO Box K 25039 304-949-1642
Melissa Lawrence, prin. Fax 949-3418

Ceredo, Wayne, Pop. 1,432
Wayne County SD
Supt. — See Wayne
Ceredo-Kenova MS 200/6-8
PO Box 705 25507 304-453-3588
Tonji Bowen, prin. Fax 453-4420

Chapmanville, Logan, Pop. 1,250
Logan County SD
Supt. — See Logan
Chapmanville HS 700/9-12
200 Vance St 25508 304-855-4522
Katherine Moore, prin. Fax 855-1911
Chapmanville MS 600/5-8
774 Crawley Creek Rd 25508 304-855-8378
Rob Dial, prin. Fax 855-1307

Charleston, Kanawha, Pop. 49,755
Kanawha County SD 28,100/PK-12
200 Elizabeth St 25311 304-348-7770
Ronald Duerring Ed.D., supt. Fax 348-7735
kcs.kana.k12.wv.us
Adams MS 800/6-8
2002 Presidential Dr 25314 304-348-6652
John Moyers, prin. Fax 348-6592
Capital HS 1,300/9-12
1500 Greenbrier St 25311 304-348-6500
Larry Bailey, prin. Fax 348-6509
Carver Career Center Vo/Tech
4799 Midland Dr 25306 304-348-1965
Phil Calvert, prin. Fax 348-1938
Chandler Academy Alt
1900 School St 25387 304-348-6133
Wayman Wilson, prin.
Garnet Career Center Vo/Tech
422 Dickinson St 25301 304-348-6195
Wendy Bailey, prin. Fax 348-6198
Jackson MS 600/6-8
812 Park Ave 25302 304-348-6123
Jessica Austin, prin. Fax 348-1999
Mann MS 500/6-8
4300 MacCorkle Ave SE 25304 304-348-1971
Jon Anderson, prin. Fax 348-6591
Sissonville MS 600/5-8
100 Middle School Ln 25312 304-348-1993
Brian Eddy, prin. Fax 348-6594
Washington HS 1,100/9-12
1522 Tennis Club Rd 25314 304-348-7729
George Aulenbacher, prin. Fax 344-4947
Other Schools – See Belle, Cedar Grove, Clendenin, Cross Lanes, Dunbar, East Bank, Elkview, Nitro, Saint Albans, Sissonville, South Charleston

Carver Career and Tech Education Center Post-Sec.
4799 Midland Dr 25306 304-348-1965
Charleston Catholic HS 400/6-12
1033 Virginia St E 25301 304-342-8415
Colleen Hoyer, prin. Fax 342-1259
Charleston School of Beauty Culture Post-Sec.
210 Capitol St 25301 304-346-9603
Cross Lanes Christian S 300/K-12
5330 Floradale Dr 25313 304-776-5020
Garnet Career Center Post-Sec.
422 Dickinson St 25301 304-348-6195
Kanawha Vlly Community Technical College Post-Sec.
2001 Union Carbide Dr 25303 304-205-6700
University of Charleston Post-Sec.
2300 MacCorkle Ave SE 25304 304-357-4800
West Virginia Junior College Post-Sec.
1000 Virginia St E 25301 304-345-2820

Charles Town, Jefferson, Pop. 5,074
Jefferson County SD 8,800/PK-12
110 Mordington Ave 25414 304-725-9741
Dr. Bondy Gibson, supt. Fax 725-6487
boe.jeff.k12.wv.us
Charles Town MS 700/6-8
193 High St 25414 304-725-7821
Tim Sites, prin. Fax 728-7526
Washington HS 1,100/9-12
300 Washington Patriots Dr 25414 304-885-5110
Judy Marcus, prin. Fax 885-5108
Other Schools – See Harpers Ferry, Shenandoah Junction, Shepherdstown

American Public University Post-Sec.
111 W Congress St 25414 877-755-2787

Charmco, Greenbrier
Greenbrier County SD
Supt. — See Lewisburg
Greenbrier West HS 400/9-12
PO Box 325 25958 304-438-6191
Amy Robertson, prin. Fax 438-9189

Clarksburg, Harrison, Pop. 16,197
Harrison County SD 10,900/PK-12
PO Box 1370 26302 304-624-3325
Dr. Mark Manchin, supt. Fax 624-3361
www.harcoboe.net
Byrd HS 800/9-12
1 Eagle Way 26301 304-326-7200
Steven Gibson, prin. Fax 624-3211
Irving MS 600/6-8
443 Lee Ave 26301 304-326-7420
Susan Ferrell, prin. Fax 624-3388
Liberty HS 600/9-12
1 Mountaineer Dr 26301 304-326-7470
Pamela Knight, prin. Fax 623-3159
Mountaineer MS 500/6-8
2 Mountaineer Dr 26301 304-326-7620
John Rogers, prin. Fax 326-7632
United HS Alt
1349 Shinnston Pike 26301 304-326-7560
Ed Propst, prin. Fax 624-3245
United Technical Center Vo/Tech
251 Marietta St 26301 304-326-7580
Matthew Call, dir. Fax 622-6138
Other Schools – See Bridgeport, Lost Creek, Shinnston

Clarksburg Beauty Academy Post-Sec.
120 S 3rd St 26301 304-624-6475
Emmanuel Christian S 100/PK-12
1318 N 16th St 26301 304-624-6125
Nancy Mercadante, prin. Fax 624-6125
Notre Dame HS 200/7-12
127 E Pike St 26301 304-623-1026
Dr. Carroll Morrison, prin. Fax 623-1026

Clay, Clay, Pop. 483
Clay County SD 2,000/PK-12
PO Box 120 25043 304-587-4266
Kenneth Tanner, supt. Fax 587-4181
www.claycountyschools.org
Clay County HS 500/9-12
PO Box 729 25043 304-587-4226
Melinda Isaacs, prin. Fax 587-2723
Clay County MS 400/6-8
PO Box 489 25043 304-587-2343
Anita Stephenson, prin. Fax 587-2759

Clear Fork, Wyoming
Wyoming County SD
Supt. — See Pineville
Westside HS 600/9-12
HC 65 Box 275 24822 304-682-8965
Keith Stewart, prin. Fax 682-6273

Clendenin, Kanawha, Pop. 1,218
Kanawha County SD
Supt. — See Charleston
Hoover HS 700/9-12
5856 Elk River Rd N 25045 304-965-3394
Michael Kelley, prin. Fax 965-1871

Coal City, Raleigh, Pop. 1,761
Raleigh County SD
Supt. — See Beckley
Independence HS 700/9-12
PO Box 1595 25823 304-683-3228
Johnathan Henry, prin. Fax 683-3834

Craigsville, Nicholas, Pop. 2,184
Nicholas County SD
Supt. — See Summersville
Nicholas County Career and Technical Ctr Vo/Tech
215 Milam Addition Rd 26205 304-742-5416
Thomas Bayless, prin. Fax 742-3953

Crawley, Greenbrier
Greenbrier County SD
Supt. — See Lewisburg
Western Greenbrier MS 300/6-8
315 Timberwolf Dr 24931 304-392-6446
Christy Bailey, prin. Fax 392-6785

Cross Lanes, Kanawha, Pop. 9,816
Kanawha County SD
Supt. — See Charleston
Jackson MS 600/6-8
5445 Big Tyler Rd 25313 304-776-3310
Rhonda Donohoe, prin. Fax 776-3305

Crum, Wayne, Pop. 179
Wayne County SD
Supt. — See Wayne
Crum MS 100/6-8
PO Box 9 25669 304-393-3200
Nona Newsome, prin. Fax 393-4429

Delbarton, Mingo, Pop. 564
Mingo County SD
Supt. — See Williamson
Burch MS 300/5-8
275 Bulldog Blvd 25670 304-475-2700
Leah Wireman, prin. Fax 475-5106
Mingo Central HS 700/9-12
1000 King Coal Hwy 25670 304-426-6603
Theresa Jones, prin.
Mingo County Extended Learning Center Adult
165 Bulldog Blvd 25670 304-475-3347
Thomas Hoffman, prin. Fax 475-3797

Dunbar, Kanawha, Pop. 7,684
Kanawha County SD
Supt. — See Charleston
Dunbar MS 400/6-8
325 27th St 25064 304-766-0363
Donnell Gilliam, prin. Fax 766-0365
Franklin Career & Technical Center Vo/Tech
500 28th St 25064 304-766-0369
Dr. Paula Potter, prin. Fax 766-0371

Dunmore, Pocahontas
Pocahontas County SD
Supt. — See Marlinton
Pocahontas County HS 300/9-12
271 Warrior Way 24934 304-799-6565
Michael Adkins, prin. Fax 799-6893

East Bank, Kanawha, Pop. 953
Kanawha County SD
Supt. — See Charleston
East Bank MS 400/6-8
PO Box 897 25067 304-595-2311
Michael Wilkinson, prin. Fax 595-4676

Eleanor, Putnam, Pop. 1,501
Putnam County SD
Supt. — See Winfield
Putnam Career & Technical Center Vo/Tech
PO Box 640 25070 304-586-3494
C.D. Caldwell, prin. Fax 586-4467
Washington MS 300/6-8
PO Box 660 25070 304-586-2875
Tiauna Slack, prin. Fax 586-3037

Elizabeth, Wirt, Pop. 816
Wirt County SD 1,000/PK-12
PO Box 189 26143 304-275-4279
Mary Jane Pope-Albin, supt. Fax 275-4581
www.edline.net/pages/wirtboe
Wirt County HS 300/9-12
PO Box 219 26143 304-275-4241
Elizabeth Smith, prin. Fax 275-3271
Wirt County MS 300/5-8
PO Box 699 26143 304-275-3977
David Tupper, prin. Fax 275-4257

Elkins, Randolph, Pop. 7,020
Randolph County SD 4,100/PK-12
40 11th St 26241 304-636-9150
Pam Hewitt, supt. Fax 636-9157
boe.rand.k12.wv.us
Elkins HS 800/9-12
100 Kennedy Dr 26241 304-636-9170
Russ Collette, prin. Fax 636-9168
Elkins MS 700/6-8
308 Robert E Lee Ave 26241 304-636-9176
Rich Carr, prin. Fax 636-9178
Randolph Co. Alternative Learning Center 50/Alt
1425 S Davis Ave 26241 304-636-9156
Angela Wilson, prin. Fax 636-9157
Randolph County Technical Center Vo/Tech
200 Kennedy Dr 26241 304-636-9195
John Daniels, prin. Fax 636-9169
Other Schools – See Harman, Mill Creek, Pickens

Davis & Elkins College Post-Sec.
100 Campus Dr 26241 304-637-1900
Highland Adventist S 50/K-12
1 Old Leadsville Rd 26241 304-636-4274

Elkview, Kanawha, Pop. 1,216
Kanawha County SD
Supt. — See Charleston
Elkview MS 800/6-8
5090 Elk River Rd N 25071 304-348-1947
Melissa Lovejoy, prin. Fax 348-6590

Elk Valley Christian S 100/PK-12
58 Mount Pleasant Dr 25071 304-965-7063
Jack Suttle, prin. Fax 965-7064

Ellenboro, Ritchie, Pop. 363
Ritchie County SD
Supt. — See Harrisville
Ritchie County HS 400/9-12
201 Ritchie County School 26346 304-869-3526
Kelly Waggoner, prin. Fax 869-3031
Ritchie County MS 300/6-8
105 Ritchie County School 26346 304-869-3512
Michael Dotson, prin. Fax 869-3519

Fairmont, Marion, Pop. 18,276
Marion County SD 8,000/PK-12
1516 Mary Lou Retton Dr 26554 304-367-2100
Gary Price, supt. Fax 367-2111
www.marionboe.com/
Barnes Learning Center Alt
100 Naomi St 26554 304-367-2127
Travus Oates, prin. Fax 367-2174
East Fairmont HS 700/9-12
1993 Airport Rd 26554 304-367-2140
David Nuzum, prin. Fax 367-2180
East Fairmont MS 400/5-8
221 Mason St 26554 304-367-2123
Jay Michael, prin. Fax 367-2179
Fairmont HS 700/9-12
1 Loop Park Dr 26554 304-367-2150
Karen Finamore, prin. Fax 366-5988
West Fairmont MS 700/5-8
110 10th St 26554 304-366-5631
Lisa Lister, prin. Fax 366-5636
Marion County Adult & Community Educ. Adult
601 Locust Ave 26554 304-363-7323
Donna Metz, prin. Fax 366-2483
Other Schools – See Fairview, Farmington, Mannington, Monongah

Fairmont State University Post-Sec.
1201 Locust Ave 26554 304-367-4892
Pierpont Community & Technical College Post-Sec.
1201 Locust Ave 26554 304-367-4692

Fairview, Marion, Pop. 404
Marion County SD
Supt. — See Fairmont
Fairview MS 100/4-8
17 Jesses Run Rd 26570 304-449-1312
Steve Rodriguez, prin. Fax 449-1305

Farmington, Marion, Pop. 368
Marion County SD
Supt. — See Fairmont

Marion County Technical Center Vo/Tech
2 North Marion Dr 26571 304-986-3590
Raymond Frazier, prin. Fax 986-3440
North Marion HS 800/9-12
1 N Marion Dr 26571 304-986-3063
Russelle DeVito, prin. Fax 986-3086

Fayetteville, Fayette, Pop. 2,872
Fayette County SD 6,800/PK-12
111 Fayette Ave 25840 304-574-1176
Terrence George, supt. Fax 574-3643
www.boe.faye.k12.wv.us
Fayetteville HS 500/7-12
515 W Maple Ave 25840 304-574-0560
Bryan Parsons, prin. Fax 574-0118
Other Schools – See Ansted, Hico, Meadow Bridge, Oak Hill, Smithers

Follansbee, Brooke, Pop. 2,935
Brooke County SD
Supt. — See Wellsburg
Follansbee MS 500/5-8
1400 Main St 26037 304-527-1942
Gregory Rothwell, prin. Fax 527-1954

Fort Gay, Wayne, Pop. 690
Wayne County SD
Supt. — See Wayne
Tolsia HS 400/9-12
1 Rebel Dr 25514 304-648-5566
Reba Sanders-Wallace, prin. Fax 648-8412

Foster, Boone
Boone County SD
Supt. — See Madison
Boone County Career & Tech Ctr Vo/Tech
3505 Daniel Boone Pkwy # B 25081 304-369-4585
Jeffrey Nelson, prin. Fax 369-3692

Boone County Career Center Post-Sec.
3505 Daniel Boone Pkwy # B 25081 304-369-4585
Southern WV Community & Technical Coll. Post-Sec.
3505 Daniel Boone Pkwy # A 25081 304-369-2952

Franklin, Pendleton, Pop. 713
Pendleton County SD 1,000/PK-12
PO Box 888 26807 304-358-2207
Charles Hedrick, supt. Fax 358-2936
pendletoncountyschools.com
Pendleton County MSHS 400/7-12
PO Box 40 26807 304-358-2573
Lori Hull, prin. Fax 358-7701

Future Generations Graduate School Post-Sec.
400 Road Less Traveled Rd 26807 304-358-2000

Gerrardstown, Berkeley
Berkeley County SD
Supt. — See Martinsburg
Mountain Ridge MS 6-8
2771 Gerrardstown Rd 25420 304-229-8833
Dr. Ron Branch, admin. Fax 229-8830

Gilbert, Mingo, Pop. 447
Mingo County SD
Supt. — See Williamson
Gilbert MS 200/5-8
100 Lion Dr 25621 304-664-8197
Daniel Dean, prin. Fax 664-8249

Darrin Christian Academy 100/K-12
PO Box 402 25621 304-664-3763
Kenny Pool, admin. Fax 664-3764

Glen Dale, Marshall, Pop. 1,510
Marshall County SD
Supt. — See Moundsville
Marshall HS 1,100/9-12
1300 Wheeling Ave 26038 304-843-4444
Cassandra Porter, prin. Fax 843-4419

Glen Daniel, Raleigh
Raleigh County SD
Supt. — See Beckley
Liberty HS 600/9-12
PO Box 265 25844 304-934-5306
Lori Knight, prin. Fax 934-5307
Trap Hill MS 500/6-8
665 Coal River Rd 25844 304-934-5392
Jerry Bawgus, prin. Fax 934-5393

Glenville, Gilmer, Pop. 1,501
Gilmer County SD 700/PK-12
809 Medical Dr 26351 304-462-7386
Gabriel DeVono, supt. Fax 462-5103
boe.gilmer.k12.wv.us
Gilmer County JSHS 400/7-12
300 Pine St 26351 304-462-7960
Athanasia Butcher, prin. Fax 462-8578
Other Schools – See Grantsville

Glenville State College Post-Sec.
200 High St 26351 304-462-7361

Grafton, Taylor, Pop. 5,091
Taylor County SD 2,400/PK-12
71 Utt Dr 26354 304-265-2497
Kathleen Green, supt. Fax 265-2508
www.taylorcountyboe.net
Grafton HS 700/9-12
400 Riverside Dr 26354 304-265-3046
Joseph Findley, prin. Fax 265-2156
Taylor County MS 700/5-8
670 Spring Hills Rd 26354 304-265-0722
Matt Keener, prin. Fax 265-4623
Taylor County Vocational Center Vo/Tech
115 Luby St 26354 304-265-1050
Dr. Joseph Findley, prin. Fax 265-1058

Grantsville, Calhoun, Pop. 561
Calhoun County SD
Supt. — See Mount Zion
Calhoun Gilmer Career Center Vo/Tech
5260 E Little Kanawha Hwy 26147 304-354-6151
Bryan Sterns, dir. Fax 354-6154

Gilmer County SD
Supt. — See Glenville
Calhoun-Gilmer Career Center Vo/Tech
5260 E Little Kanawha Hwy 26147 304-354-6151
Bryan Sterns, dir.

Hambleton, Tucker, Pop. 231
Tucker County SD
Supt. — See Parsons
Tucker County HS 300/9-12
116 Mountain Lion Way 26269 304-478-3111
Jay Hamric, prin. Fax 478-3725

Hamlin, Lincoln, Pop. 1,134
Lincoln County SD 3,400/PK-12
10 Marland Ave 25523 304-824-3033
Jeff Midkiff, supt. Fax 824-7947
boe.linc.k12.wv.us
Lincoln HS 900/9-12
81 Lincoln Panther Way 25523 304-824-6000
Dana Snyder, prin. Fax 824-6063
Other Schools – See Branchland

Harman, Randolph, Pop. 143
Randolph County SD
Supt. — See Elkins
Harman S 200/PK-12
PO Box 130 26270 304-227-4114
April Senic, prin. Fax 227-3610

Harpers Ferry, Jefferson, Pop. 283
Jefferson County SD
Supt. — See Charles Town
Harpers Ferry MS 400/6-8
1710 W Washington St 25425 304-535-6357
Eric Vandell, prin. Fax 535-6986

Harrisville, Ritchie, Pop. 1,865
Ritchie County SD 1,500/PK-12
134 S Penn Ave 26362 304-643-2991
Ora Coffman, supt. Fax 643-2994
www.ritchieschools.com
Other Schools – See Ellenboro

Hedgesville, Berkeley, Pop. 311
Berkeley County SD
Supt. — See Martinsburg
Hedgesville HS 1,300/9-12
109 Ridge Rd N 25427 304-754-3354
Ron Lyons, prin. Fax 754-7445
Hedgesville MS 700/6-8
334 School House Dr 25427 304-754-3313
Elizabeth Adams, prin. Fax 754-6613

Hico, Fayette, Pop. 272
Fayette County SD
Supt. — See Fayetteville
Midland Trail HS 300/9-12
PO Box 89 25854 304-658-5184
Diane Blume, prin. Fax 658-5185

Hilltop, Fayette, Pop. 613

Mountainview Christian S 100/PK-12
176 Mountain View Rd 25855 304-465-0502
Rev. Rudell Bloomfield, hdmstr. Fax 465-5484

Hinton, Summers, Pop. 2,623
Summers County SD 1,600/PK-12
116 Main St 25951 304-466-6000
Vicki Hinerman, supt. Fax 466-6008
www.edline.net/pages/summerscountyschools
Summers County HS 400/9-12
1 Bobcat Dr 25951 304-466-6040
Kari Vicars, prin. Fax 466-6044
Summers MS 400/5-8
400 Temple St 25951 304-466-6030
M. Susie Hudson, prin. Fax 466-2271

Hundred, Wetzel, Pop. 296
Wetzel County SD
Supt. — See New Martinsville
Hundred HS 100/9-12
PO Box 830 26575 304-775-5221
Daniel Gottron, prin. Fax 775-2922

Huntington, Cabell, Pop. 47,796
Cabell County SD 12,800/PK-12
2850 5th Ave 25702 304-528-5000
William Smith, supt. Fax 528-5080
www.cabellschools.com
Cabell County Alternative S 50/Alt
2850 5th Ave 25702 304-528-5060
Brenda Scott, prin. Fax 528-5134
Cabell County Career Technology Center Vo/Tech
1035 Norway Ave 25705 304-528-5106
Frank Barnett, prin. Fax 528-5110
Huntington East MS 500/6-8
1 Campbell Dr 25705 304-528-9508
DeLois Perry, prin. Fax 528-5197
Huntington HS 1,600/9-12
1 Highlander Way 25701 304-528-6400
Joedy Cunningham, prin. Fax 528-6422
Huntington MS 600/6-8
925 3rd St 25701 304-528-5180
James Paxton, prin. Fax 528-5215
Other Schools – See Barboursville, Milton, Ona

Wayne County SD
Supt. — See Wayne
Spring Valley HS 1,000/9-12
1 Timberwolf Ln 25704 304-429-1699
Steve Morris, prin. Fax 429-2607

Vinson MS 300/6-8
3851 Piedmont Rd 25704 304-429-1641
Tammy Forbush, prin. Fax 429-6162

Cabell Huntington Hospital Post-Sec.
1340 Hal Greer Blvd 25701 304-526-2111
Covenant S 200/K-12
2400 Johnstown Rd 25701 304-781-6741
Msgr. Shane Artrip, hdmstr. Fax 781-6742
Grace Christian S 200/PK-12
1111 Adams Ave 25704 304-522-8635
Huntington Junior College Post-Sec.
900 5th Ave 25701 304-697-7550
Huntington School of Beauty Culture Post-Sec.
5636 US Route 60 Ste 14 25705 304-736-6289
Marshall University Post-Sec.
1 John Marshall Dr 25755 304-696-3170
Mountwest Community & Technical College Post-Sec.
1 Mountwest Way 25701 866-676-5533
St. Joseph Central HS 100/9-12
600 13th St 25701 304-525-5096
William Archer, prin. Fax 525-0781
St. Mary's Medical Center Post-Sec.
2900 1st Ave 25702 304-526-1270

Hurricane, Putnam, Pop. 6,205
Putnam County SD
Supt. — See Winfield
Hurricane HS 1,100/9-12
3350 Teays Valley Rd 25526 304-562-9851
Richard Campbell, prin. Fax 562-5460
Hurricane MS 1,000/6-8
518 Midland Trl 25526 304-562-9271
Mary Allen, prin. Fax 562-7163

Calvary Baptist Academy 200/K-12
3655 Teays Valley Rd 25526 304-757-6768
Milton Thompson, prin. Fax 757-6777

Institute, Kanawha

West Virginia State University Post-Sec.
PO Box 1000 25112 304-766-3000

Inwood, Berkeley, Pop. 2,871
Berkeley County SD
Supt. — See Martinsburg
Musselman HS 1,400/9-12
126 Excellence Way 25428 304-229-1950
Holly Kleppner, prin. Fax 229-1959

Kenova, Wayne, Pop. 3,199
Wayne County SD
Supt. — See Wayne
Buffalo MS 300/6-8
298 Buffalo Creek Rd 25530 304-429-6062
Elizabeth Ryder, prin. Fax 429-7245

Keyser, Mineral, Pop. 5,316
Mineral County SD 4,200/PK-12
1 Baker Pl 26726 304-788-4200
Shawn Dilly, supt. Fax 788-4204
boe.mine.k12.wv.us/
Keyser HS 700/9-12
1 Tornado Way 26726 304-788-4230
Michael Lewis, prin. Fax 788-4234
Keyser MS 700/5-8
700 Harley O Staggers Sr Dr 26726 304-788-4220
Julie McBee, prin. Fax 788-4225
Mineral County Alternative Program 50/Alt
700 Harley Staggers Dr 26726 304-788-4213
Jenni Woy, prin. Fax 788-4623
Mineral County Technical Center Vo/Tech
600 Harley O Staggers Sr Dr 26726 304-788-4240
Fax 788-4243
Other Schools – See Ridgeley

Potomac State College of West Virginia U Post-Sec.
101 Fort Ave 26726 304-788-6820

Kingwood, Preston, Pop. 2,912
Preston County SD 4,400/PK-12
731 Preston Dr 26537 304-329-0580
Stephen Wotring, supt. Fax 329-0720
www.prestonboe.com
Central Preston MS 300/6-8
64 Wildcat Way 26537 304-329-0033
Karen Ovesney, prin. Fax 329-2389
Preston HS 1,300/9-12
400 Knight Dr 26537 304-329-0400
Dr. David Pastrick, prin. Fax 329-3899

Le Roy, Jackson
Jackson County SD
Supt. — See Ripley
Roane-Jackson Tech Ctr Vo/Tech
9450 Spencer Rd 25252 304-372-7335
Ben Cummings, dir. Fax 372-7336

Lewisburg, Greenbrier, Pop. 3,773
Greenbrier County SD 5,200/PK-12
197 Chestnut St 24901 304-647-6470
Jeff Bryant, supt. Fax 647-6490
www.greenbriercountyschools.org
Greenbrier East HS 1,100/9-12
273 Spartan Ln 24901 304-647-6464
Kelly Huff, prin. Fax 645-2698
Other Schools – See Charmco, Crawley, Ronceverte

West Virginia Sch./Osteopathic Medicine Post-Sec.
400 N Lee St 24901 304-645-6270

Lindside, Monroe
Monroe County SD
Supt. — See Union
Monroe County Technical Center Vo/Tech
RR 1 Box 97 24951 304-753-9971
Tricia King, dir. Fax 753-9792

Monroe HS 500/9-12
RR 1 Box 97-1A 24951 304-753-5182
Lisa Mustain, prin. Fax 753-5184

Logan, Logan, Pop. 1,749
Logan County SD 6,100/PK-12
PO Box 477 25601 304-792-2060
Phyllis Doty, supt. Fax 752-3711
lc2.boe.loga.k12.wv.us
Logan HS 800/9-12
1 Wildcat Way 25601 304-752-6606
Kelly Stanley, prin. Fax 752-6614
Logan MS 700/5-8
14 Wildcat Way 25601 304-752-1804
Ernestine Sutherland, prin. Fax 752-0207
Willis Vo-Tech Center Vo/Tech
PO Box 1747 25601 304-752-4687
David Adkins, prin. Fax 752-2943
Other Schools – See Chapmanville, Mallory, Man

Lost Creek, Harrison, Pop. 482
Harrison County SD
Supt. — See Clarksburg
South Harrison HS 400/9-12
3073 Hawk Hwy 26385 304-326-7440
Dr. Greg Moore, prin. Fax 745-4292
South Harrison MS 300/6-8
3003 Hawk Hwy 26385 304-326-7460
Scott Hage, prin. Fax 745-5587

Mc Mechen, Marshall, Pop. 1,914

Bishop Donahue Memorial HS 100/9-12
325 Logan St 304-233-3850
Thomas Wise, prin. Fax 233-8677

Madison, Boone, Pop. 3,064
Boone County SD 4,200/PK-12
69 Avenue B 25130 304-369-3131
Jeffrey Huffman, supt. Fax 369-0855
www.boonecountyboe.org
Madison MS 500/6-8
404 Riverside Dr W 25130 304-369-4464
Shann Elkins, prin. Fax 369-5800
Scott HS 700/9-12
1 Skyhawk Pl 25130 304-369-3011
Allen Halley, prin. Fax 369-6564
Other Schools – See Foster, Seth, Van

Mallory, Logan, Pop. 1,628
Logan County SD
Supt. — See Logan
Man MS 500/5-8
PO Box 390 25634 304-583-8037
Cynthia Caldwell, prin. Fax 583-8253

Man, Logan, Pop. 759
Logan County SD
Supt. — See Logan
Man HS 400/9-12
800 E McDonald Ave 25635 304-583-6521
Patricia English, prin. Fax 583-6566

Mannington, Marion, Pop. 2,054
Marion County SD
Supt. — See Fairmont
Mannington MS 300/5-8
113 Clarksburg St 26582 304-986-1050
Richard Ott, prin. Fax 986-1747

Marlinton, Pocahontas, Pop. 1,050
Pocahontas County SD 1,100/PK-12
926 5th Ave 24954 304-799-4505
Terrence Beam, supt. Fax 799-4499
pocahontas-k12.wvnet.edu/boe
Other Schools – See Buckeye, Dunmore

Martinsburg, Berkeley, Pop. 16,642
Berkeley County SD 17,300/PK-12
401 S Queen St 25401 304-267-3500
Manny Arvon, supt. Fax 267-3506
berkeleycountyschools.org/
Martinsburg HS 1,300/9-12
701 S Queen St 25401 304-267-3530
Trent Sherman, prin. Fax 267-3536
Martinsburg North MS 600/6-8
250 East Rd, 304-267-3540
Rebekah Eyler, prin. Fax 264-5066
Martinsburg South MS 900/6-8
150 Bulldog Blvd 25401 304-267-3545
Rosa Clark, prin. Fax 264-5062
Rumsey Technical Institute Vo/Tech
3274 Hedgesville Rd, 304-754-7925
Donna VanMetre, dir. Fax 754-7933
Spring Mills HS 800/9-12
499 Campus Dr, 304-274-5141
Marc Arvon, prin. Fax 274-5144
Spring Mills MS 700/6-8
255 Campus Dr, 304-274-5030
Nancy White, prin. Fax 274-3598
Other Schools – See Bunker Hill, Gerrardstown, Hedgesville, Inwood

Blue Ridge Community & Technical College Post-Sec.
13650 Apple Harvest Dr, 304-260-4380
Faith Christian Academy 300/PK-12
138 Greensburg Rd, 304-263-0011
Eric Kerns, admin. Fax 267-0638
International Beauty School Post-Sec.
201 W King St 25401 304-263-4929
Martinsburg College Post-Sec.
341 Aikens Ctr, 304-263-6262
Valley College Post-Sec.
287 Aikens Ctr, 304-263-0979

Mason, Mason, Pop. 951
Mason County SD
Supt. — See Point Pleasant

Wahama JSHS 400/7-12
PO Box 348 25260 304-773-5539
John Bond, prin. Fax 773-5216

Meadow Bridge, Fayette, Pop. 378
Fayette County SD
Supt. — See Fayetteville
Meadow Bridge JSHS 300/7-12
870 Main St 25976 304-484-7917
Stacy White, prin. Fax 484-7921

Middlebourne, Tyler, Pop. 809
Tyler County SD 1,300/PK-12
PO Box 25 26149 304-758-2145
Robin Daquilante, supt. Fax 758-4566
www.tylercountypublicschools.com
Other Schools – See Sistersville

Mill Creek, Randolph, Pop. 718
Randolph County SD
Supt. — See Elkins
Tygarts Valley MSHS 400/7-12
RR 1 Box 290 26280 304-335-4575
Steve Wamsley, prin. Fax 335-6963

Milton, Cabell, Pop. 2,401
Cabell County SD
Supt. — See Huntington
Milton MS 700/6-8
1 Panther Trl 25541 304-743-7308
Deborah Underwood, prin. Fax 743-7324

Monongah, Marion, Pop. 1,032
Marion County SD
Supt. — See Fairmont
Monongah MS 200/5-8
550 Camden Ave 26554 304-367-2164
Steve Malnick, prin. Fax 367-2190

Montgomery, Fayette, Pop. 1,593

Bridgemont Community & Technical College Post-Sec.
619 2nd Ave 25136 304-734-6600
West Virginia University Inst of Tech. Post-Sec.
405 Fayette Pike 25136 888-554-8324

Moorefield, Hardy, Pop. 2,511
Hardy County SD 2,300/PK-12
510 Ashby St 26836 304-530-2348
Dr. Matthew Dotson, supt. Fax 530-2340
www.hardycountyschools.com
Moorefield HS 400/9-12
401 N Main St 26836 304-530-6034
Robert Miller, prin. Fax 530-7569
Moorefield MS 300/6-8
303 Caledonia Heights Rd 26836 304-434-3000
Patrick McGregor, prin. Fax 434-3003
Other Schools – See Baker

Eastern WV Community & Technical College Post-Sec.
316 Eastern Dr 26836 304-434-8000

Morgantown, Monongalia, Pop. 29,068
Monongalia County SD 10,900/PK-12
13 S High St 26501 304-291-9210
Dr. Frank Devono, supt. Fax 291-3015
boe.mono.k12.wv.us
Alternative Learning Center Alt
500 Green Bag Rd Ste G1 26501 304-291-9210
Kim Greene, prin. Fax 296-1379
Monongalia County Tech Education Center Vo/Tech
1000 Mississippi St 26501 304-291-9240
Nancy Napolillo, prin. Fax 291-9247
Morgantown HS 1,700/9-12
109 Wilson Ave 26501 304-291-9260
Paul Mihalko, prin. Fax 291-9263
Mountaineer MS 500/6-8
991 Price St 26505 304-594-1165
Crystal Nantz, prin. Fax 594-1677
South MS 700/6-8
500 E Parkway Dr 26501 304-291-9340
Sandra Brown, prin. Fax 291-9306
Suncrest MS 500/6-8
360 Baldwin St 26505 304-291-9335
Dawna Hicks, prin. Fax 284-9362
University HS 1,200/9-12
131 Bakers Ridge Rd 26508 304-291-9270
Shari Burgess, prin. Fax 291-9248
Westwood MS 400/6-8
670 River Rd 26501 304-291-9300
Leonard Haney, prin. Fax 284-9368
Adult Basic Education Adult
1000 Mississippi St 26501 304-291-9243
Michael Johnston, prin. Fax 291-9247
Other Schools – See Blacksville

Monongalia County Tech Education Center Post-Sec.
1000 Mississippi St 26501 304-291-9240
Morgantown Beauty College Post-Sec.
276 Walnut St 26505 304-292-8475
Trinity Christian S 300/PK-12
200 Trinity Way 26505 304-291-4659
Michelle Stellato, supt. Fax 291-4660
West Virginia Junior College Post-Sec.
148 Willey St 26505 304-296-8282
West Virginia University Post-Sec.
PO Box 6201 26506 304-293-0111
West Virginia University Hospital Post-Sec.
PO Box 8150 26506 304-598-4000

Moundsville, Marshall, Pop. 9,248
Marshall County SD 4,500/PK-12
PO Box 578 26041 304-843-4400
Michael Hince, supt. Fax 843-4409
boe.mars.k12.wv.us
Moundsville MS 500/6-8
223 Tomlinson Ave 26041 304-843-4440
Sandy McAllister, prin. Fax 843-4446
Other Schools – See Cameron, Glen Dale, Wheeling

Mount Gay Shamrock, Logan, Pop. 1,768

Southern WV Community & Technical Coll. Post-Sec.
2900 Dempsey Branch Rd 25637 304-792-7098

Mount Hope, Fayette, Pop. 1,370

Appalachian Bible College Post-Sec.
161 College Dr 25880 304-877-6428

Mount Zion, Calhoun
Calhoun County SD 1,100/PK-12
540 Alan B Mollohan Dr 26151 304-354-7011
Timothy Woodward, supt. Fax 354-7420
www.edline.net/pages/Calhoun_CSD
Calhoun County MSHS 600/5-12
50 Underwood Cir 26151 304-354-6148
Melanie Arthur, prin. Fax 354-7382
Other Schools – See Grantsville

Mullens, Wyoming, Pop. 1,540
Wyoming County SD
Supt. — See Pineville
Mullens MS 200/5-8
801 Moran Ave 25882 304-294-5757
Terri Lea Smith, prin. Fax 294-5762

New Cumberland, Hancock, Pop. 1,085
Hancock County SD 3,100/PK-12
PO Box 1300 26047 304-564-3411
Suzan Smith, supt. Fax 564-3990
boe.hancock.k12.wv.us
Oak Glen HS 500/9-12
195 Golden Bear Dr 26047 304-564-3500
David Smith, prin. Fax 387-2079
Oak Glen MS 600/5-8
39 Golden Bear Dr 26047 304-387-2363
Virginia Greene, prin. Fax 387-4624
Rockefeller Career Center Vo/Tech
80 Rockefeller Cir 26047 304-564-3337
Martin Hudek, dir. Fax 564-4058
Other Schools – See Weirton

New Martinsville, Wetzel, Pop. 5,337
Wetzel County SD 2,700/PK-12
333 Foundry St 26155 304-455-2441
Leatha Williams, supt. Fax 455-3446
www.wetzelcountyschools.com
Magnolia HS 400/9-12
601 Maple Ave 26155 304-455-1990
Kathi Schmalz, prin. Fax 455-5536
Other Schools – See Hundred, Paden City, Pine Grove

New Richmond, Wyoming, Pop. 235
Wyoming County SD
Supt. — See Pineville
Wyoming County East HS 600/9-12
PO Box 390 24867 304-294-5200
Mandy Hylton, prin. Fax 294-5400

Nitro, Kanawha, Pop. 7,083
Kanawha County SD
Supt. — See Charleston
Nitro HS 800/9-12
1300 Park Ave 25143 304-755-4321
Jason Redman, prin. Fax 755-4345

Nutter Fort Stonewood, Harrison, Pop. 1,562

West Virginia Business College Post-Sec.
116 Pennsylvania Ave 26301 304-624-7695

Oak Hill, Fayette, Pop. 7,618
Fayette County SD
Supt. — See Fayetteville
Collins MS 900/5-8
320 W Oyler Ave 25901 304-469-3711
Cynthia Hedrick, prin. Fax 465-1352
Fayette Institute of Technology Vo/Tech
300 W Oyler Ave 25901 304-469-2911
Barry Crist, prin. Fax 469-6963
Oak Hill HS 900/9-12
350 W Oyler Ave 25901 304-469-3551
Tim Payton, prin. Fax 465-1769

Oceana, Wyoming, Pop. 1,373
Wyoming County SD
Supt. — See Pineville
Oceana MS 300/5-8
309 Cook Pkwy 24870 304-682-6296
Shanda Lester, prin. Fax 682-6330

Omar, Logan, Pop. 551

Beth Haven Christian S 100/PK-12
PO Box 620 25638 304-946-4447

Ona, Cabell
Cabell County SD
Supt. — See Huntington
Cabell Midland HS 1,900/9-12
2300 US Route 60 25545 304-743-7400
Lloyd McGuffin, prin. Fax 743-7577

Paden City, Wetzel, Pop. 2,615
Wetzel County SD
Supt. — See New Martinsville
Paden City HS 200/7-12
201 N 4th Ave 26159 304-337-2266
Jason Salva, prin. Fax 337-2290

Parkersburg, Wood, Pop. 30,848
Wood County SD 13,300/PK-12
1210 13th St 26101 304-420-9663
John Flint, supt. Fax 420-9513
woodcountyschoolswv.com
Blennerhassett MS 500/6-8
444 Jewell Rd 26101 304-863-3356
Clint Spencer, prin. Fax 863-3357

Caperton Center for Applied Tech — Vo/Tech
300 Campus Dr 26104 — 304-424-8365
Pier Bocchini, dir. — Fax 424-8366
Edison MS — 700/6-8
1201 Hillcrest St 26101 — 304-420-9525
Jean Mewshaw, prin. — Fax 420-9527
Hamilton MS — 600/6-8
3501 Cadillac Dr 26104 — 304-420-9547
Kevin Campbell, prin. — Fax 420-9567
Parkersburg HS — 1,900/9-12
2101 Dudley Ave 26101 — 304-420-9595
Pam Goots, prin. — Fax 420-9604
Parkersburg South HS — 1,600/9-12
1511 Blizzard Dr 26101 — 304-420-9610
Betsy Patterson, prin. — Fax 420-9607
Van Devender MS — 300/6-8
918 31st St 26104 — 304-420-9645
Darlene Murphy, prin. — Fax 420-9647
Wood County Technical Center — Vo/Tech
1515 Blizzard Dr 26101 — 304-420-9501
Pier Bocchini, dir. — Fax 485-1048
Other Schools – See Vienna, Williamstown

American National University — Post-Sec.
110 Park Shopping Center Dr 26101 — 304-699-3005
Camden Clark Memorial Hospital — Post-Sec.
800 Garfield Ave 26101 — 304-424-2204
Mountain State College — Post-Sec.
1508 Spring St 26101 — 304-485-5487
Parkersburg Catholic HS — 200/7-12
3201 Fairview Ave 26104 — 304-485-6341
Karen Robinson, prin. — Fax 485-4697
West Virginia University at Parkersburg — Post-Sec.
300 Campus Dr 26104 — 304-424-8000

Parsons, Tucker, Pop. 1,472
Tucker County SD — 1,000/PK-12
100 Education Ln 26287 — 304-478-2771
Eddie Campbell Ed.D., supt. — Fax 478-3422
www.tuckercountyschools.com
Other Schools – See Hambleton

Paw Paw, Morgan, Pop. 498
Morgan County SD
Supt. — See Berkeley Springs
Paw Paw JSHS — 100/7-12
60 Pirate Cir 25434 — 304-947-7425
Melinda Kasekamp, prin. — Fax 947-5913

Petersburg, Grant, Pop. 2,438
Grant County SD — 1,800/PK-12
204 Jefferson Ave 26847 — 304-257-1011
Douglas S. Lambert, supt. — Fax 257-2453
grantcountyschools.org
Petersburg JSHS — 700/7-12
207 Viking Dr 26847 — 304-257-1444
Avery Anderson, prin. — Fax 257-5243
South Branch Career & Technical Center — Vo/Tech
401 Pierpont St 26847 — 304-257-1331
Tracy Chenoweth, dir. — Fax 257-2270

Peterstown, Monroe, Pop. 646
Monroe County SD
Supt. — See Union
Peterstown MS — 300/5-8
36 College Dr 24963 — 304-753-4322
Angie Terry, prin. — Fax 753-5376

Philippi, Barbour, Pop. 2,882
Barbour County SD — 2,400/PK-12
45 School St 26416 — 304-457-3030
Jeffrey Woofter, supt. — Fax 457-3559
www.wvschools.com/barbourcountyschools/
Barbour HS — 700/9-12
99 Horseshoe Dr 26416 — 304-457-1360
Mark Lamb, prin. — Fax 457-2658
Philippi MS — 200/6-8
611 Cherry Hill Rd 26416 — 304-457-2999
David Neff, prin. — Fax 457-2561
Other Schools – See Belington

Alderson-Broaddus University — Post-Sec.
101 College Hill Dr 26416 — 304-457-1700

Pickens, Randolph, Pop. 66
Randolph County SD
Supt. — See Elkins
Pickens S — 50/K-12
PO Box 146 26230 — 304-924-5525
Christine Long, prin. — Fax 924-6325

Pine Grove, Wetzel, Pop. 551
Wetzel County SD
Supt. — See New Martinsville
Valley HS — 200/9-12
44 Lumberjack Ln 26419 — 304-889-3151
J.C. Kimble, prin. — Fax 889-2534

Pineville, Wyoming, Pop. 659
Wyoming County SD — 4,200/PK-12
PO Box 69 24874 — 304-732-6262
Frank Blackwell, supt. — Fax 732-7226
boe.wyom.k12.wv.us/
Pineville MS — 300/5-8
PO Box 470 24874 — 304-732-6442
Terry Shumate, prin. — Fax 732-6737
Wyoming County Career & Technical Center — Vo/Tech
1207 Bearhole Rd 24874 — 304-732-8050
Sheila D. Mann, dir. — Fax 732-8332
Other Schools – See Clear Fork, Mullens, New Richmond, Oceana

Poca, Putnam, Pop. 970
Putnam County SD
Supt. — See Winfield
Poca HS — 500/9-12
1 Dot Way 25159 — 304-755-5001
Bradley Knell, prin. — Fax 755-5009
Poca MS — 300/6-8
2884 Charleston Rd 25159 — 304-755-7343
Lynda Rumbaugh, prin. — Fax 755-8930

Point Pleasant, Mason, Pop. 4,266
Mason County SD — 4,300/PK-12
1200 Main St 25550 — 304-675-4540
Jack Cullen, supt. — Fax 675-7226
boe.maso.k12.wv.us
Mason County Career Center — Vo/Tech
281 Scenic Dr 25550 — 304-675-3039
Cheryl Moore, dir. — Fax 675-3413
Point Pleasant MSHS — 1,200/7-12
280 Scenic Dr 25550 — 304-675-1350
William Cottrill, prin. — Fax 675-7480
Other Schools – See Ashton, Mason

Princeton, Mercer, Pop. 6,324
Mercer County SD — 9,900/PK-12
1403 Honaker Ave 24740 — 304-487-1551
Deborah Akers Ed.D., supt. — Fax 425-5844
boe.merc.k12.wv.us
Mercer County Technical Education Ctr — Vo/Tech
1397 Stafford Dr, — 304-425-9551
Linda Cox, dir. — Fax 425-0833
Pikeview HS — 700/9-12
3566 Eads Mill Rd, — 304-384-7586
Mark Godfrey, prin. — Fax 384-7901
Pikeview MS — 600/6-8
3550 Eads Mill Rd, — 304-384-3600
J. Bryan Staten, prin. — Fax 384-3605
Princeton HS — 1,100/9-12
1321 Stafford Dr 24740 — 304-425-8101
Lori Comer, prin. — Fax 425-2823
Princeton MS — 600/6-8
300 N Johnston St 24740 — 304-425-7517
David Lee, prin. — Fax 487-2250
Other Schools – See Bluefield, Rock

American National University — Post-Sec.
421 Hilltop Dr, — 304-431-1600
Mercer Christian Academy — 200/PK-12
314A Oakvale Rd 24740 — 304-425-5671
Rev. Chris Strange, admin. — Fax 487-1263
Valley College — Post-Sec.
616 Harrison St 24740 — 304-425-2323

Prosperity, Raleigh, Pop. 1,474

Greater Beckley Christian S — 200/PK-12
PO Box 670 25909 — 304-255-1571
Charles Atkins, admin. — Fax 582-0341

Ravenswood, Jackson, Pop. 3,825
Jackson County SD
Supt. — See Ripley
Ravenswood HS — 400/9-12
100 Plaza Dr 26164 — 304-273-9301
Jaquetta Hendricks, prin. — Fax 273-9556
Ravenswood MS — 400/6-8
409 Sycamore St 26164 — 304-273-5480
Gary Higginbotham, prin. — Fax 273-5746

Richwood, Nicholas, Pop. 2,006
Nicholas County SD
Supt. — See Summersville
Richwood HS — 400/9-12
1 Valley Ave 26261 — 304-846-2591
Scott Williams, prin. — Fax 846-2684
Richwood MS — 300/6-8
2 Valley Ave 26261 — 304-846-2638
Gene Collins, prin. — Fax 846-9632

Ridgeley, Mineral, Pop. 658
Mineral County SD
Supt. — See Keyser
Frankfort HS — 500/9-12
393 Falcon Way 26753 — 304-726-4767
Joseph Riley, prin. — Fax 726-8597
Frankfort MS — 500/5-8
356 Golden Dr 26753 — 304-726-4339
Patricia Twigg, prin. — Fax 726-4626

Ripley, Jackson, Pop. 3,223
Jackson County SD — 4,900/PK-12
PO Box 770 25271 — 304-372-7300
Blaine C. Hess, supt. — Fax 372-7312
jackson.wv.schoolwebpages.com
Ripley HS — 1,000/9-12
2 School St 25271 — 304-372-7355
William Hosaflook, prin. — Fax 372-7334
Ripley MS — 700/6-8
1 W School St 25271 — 304-372-7350
Dr. Cathryn Carena, prin. — Fax 372-7332
Other Schools – See Le Roy, Ravenswood

Rock, Mercer
Mercer County SD
Supt. — See Princeton
Montcalm HS — 300/7-12
5366 Simmons River Rd 24747 — 304-589-3719
Craig Havens, prin. — Fax 589-7140

Romney, Hampshire, Pop. 1,832
Hampshire County SD — 3,400/PK-12
111 School St 26757 — 304-822-3528
Dr. Jeffrey Crook, supt. — Fax 822-3540
boe.hamp.k12.wv.us
Hampshire County HS Career Training Ctr — Vo/Tech
HC 63 Box 1980 26757 — 304-822-5016
DiAnna Liller, admin. — Fax 822-3220
Hampshire HS — 1,100/9-12
157 Trojan Way 26757 — 304-822-5016
DiAnna Liller, prin. — Fax 822-5760
Romney MS — 400/6-8
296 Calvert Dr 26757 — 304-822-5014
John Watson, prin. — Fax 822-5744
Other Schools – See Capon Bridge

West Virginia Schools/Deaf and Blind — Post-Sec.
26757

Ronceverte, Greenbrier, Pop. 1,742
Greenbrier County SD
Supt. — See Lewisburg
Eastern Greenbrier MS — 900/6-8
403 Knight Dr 24970 — 304-647-6498
Preston Modlin, prin. — Fax 647-3087

Saint Albans, Kanawha, Pop. 10,870
Kanawha County SD
Supt. — See Charleston
Hayes MS — 500/6-8
830 Strawberry Rd 25177 — 304-722-0222
Scott Monty, prin. — Fax 722-0247
McKinley MS — 400/6-8
3000 Kanawha Ter 25177 — 304-722-0218
Amy Scott, prin. — Fax 722-0246
Saint Albans HS — 1,000/9-12
2100 Kanawha Ter 25177 — 304-722-0212
Jeff Kelley, prin. — Fax 722-0211

Mountaineer Beauty College — Post-Sec.
PO Box 547 25177 — 304-727-9999

Saint Marys, Pleasants, Pop. 1,851
Pleasants County SD — 1,200/PK-12
202 Fairview Ave 26170 — 304-684-2215
George Wells, supt. — Fax 684-3569
www.pleasantscountyschools.com
Mid-Ohio Valley Technical Institute — Vo/Tech
2134 N Pleasants Hwy 26170 — 304-684-2464
Ryan Haught, prin. — Fax 684-2544
Saint Marys HS — 400/9-12
2330 N Pleasants Hwy 26170 — 304-684-2421
Jeffrey Sole, prin. — Fax 684-3859
Other Schools – See Belmont

Salem, Harrison, Pop. 1,554

Salem International University — Post-Sec.
PO Box 500 26426 — 888-235-5024

Scott Depot, Putnam

Teays Valley Christian S — 400/K-12
6562 Teays Valley Rd 25560 — 304-757-9550
Jack Davis, supt. — Fax 757-2560

Seth, Boone
Boone County SD
Supt. — See Madison
Sherman HS — 400/9-12
PO Box AB 25181 — 304-837-3301
Todd Barnette, prin. — Fax 837-7529
Sherman JHS — 200/7-8
PO Box AA 25181 — 304-837-3694
Matthew Riggs, prin. — Fax 837-7603

Shady Spring, Raleigh, Pop. 2,968
Raleigh County SD
Supt. — See Beckley
Shady Spring HS — 800/9-12
PO Box 2001 25918 — 304-256-4647
Deanna Massey, prin. — Fax 256-4711
Shady Spring MS — 700/6-8
500 Flat Top Rd 25918 — 304-256-4570
Matthew Bell, prin. — Fax 256-4612

Shenandoah Junction, Jefferson, Pop. 673
Jefferson County SD
Supt. — See Charles Town
Jefferson HS — 1,400/9-12
4141 Flowing Springs Rd 25442 — 304-725-8491
Sherry McCall-Ross, prin. — Fax 728-6590
Wildwood MS — 600/6-8
1209 Shenandoah Junction Rd 25442 — 304-728-4518
Patricia Brockway, prin. — Fax 728-9521

Shepherdstown, Jefferson, Pop. 1,690
Jefferson County SD
Supt. — See Charles Town
Shepherdstown MS — 400/6-8
54 Minden St 25443 — 304-876-6120
Rebecca Horn, prin. — Fax 876-6428

Shepherd University — Post-Sec.
PO Box 5000 25443 — 304-876-5000

Shinnston, Harrison, Pop. 2,173
Harrison County SD
Supt. — See Clarksburg
Lincoln HS — 600/9-12
100 Jerry Toth Dr 26431 — 304-326-7400
James Lopez, prin. — Fax 592-3415
Lincoln MS — 400/6-8
78 Jerry Toth Dr 26431 — 304-326-7540
Lori Scott, prin. — Fax 584-4602

Sissonville, Kanawha, Pop. 4,008
Kanawha County SD
Supt. — See Charleston
Sissonville HS — 600/9-12
6100 Sissonville Dr 25312 — 304-348-1954
Ron Reedy, prin. — Fax 348-6565

Sistersville, Tyler, Pop. 1,391
Tyler County SD
Supt. — See Middlebourne
Tyler Consolidated HS — 400/9-12
1993 Silver Knight Dr 26175 — 304-758-9000
Kent Yoho, prin. — Fax 758-9006
Tyler Consolidated MS — 300/6-8
1993 Silver Knight Dr 26175 — 304-758-9000
Suzette Miller, prin. — Fax 758-9006

Smithers, Fayette, Pop. 800
Fayette County SD
Supt. — See Fayetteville

Valley MSHS 600/6-12
PO Box 459 25186 304-442-8284
Craig Loy, prin. Fax 442-5865

Sophia, Raleigh, Pop. 1,330
Raleigh County SD
Supt. — See Beckley
Independence MS 500/6-8
PO Box 1171 25921 304-683-4542
Teresa Lester, prin. Fax 683-4552

South Charleston, Kanawha, Pop. 13,050
Kanawha County SD
Supt. — See Charleston
South Charleston HS 1,000/9-12
1 Eagle Way 25309 304-766-0352
Michael Arbogast, prin. Fax 768-4663
South Charleston MS 400/6-8
400 3rd Ave 25303 304-348-1918
Henry Graves, prin. Fax 744-4869

Spencer, Roane, Pop. 2,289
Roane County SD 2,300/PK-12
PO Box 609 25276 304-927-6400
Jerry Garner, supt. Fax 927-6402
www.roanecountyschools.com
Roane County HS 700/9-12
1 Raider Way 25276 304-927-6420
Bill Heis, prin. Fax 927-6404
Spencer MS 400/5-8
102 Chapman Ave 25276 304-927-6415
Jacqueline Durst, prin. Fax 927-6416

Summersville, Nicholas, Pop. 3,550
Nicholas County SD 3,900/PK-12
400 Old Main Dr 26651 304-872-3611
Keith Butcher, supt. Fax 872-4626
boe.nich.k12.wv.us
Nicholas County HS 700/9-12
30 Grizzley Ln 26651 304-872-2141
Kendra Rapp, prin. Fax 872-3026
Summersville MS 600/6-8
40 Grizzley Ln 26651 304-872-5092
Kristina Frame, prin. Fax 872-6314
Other Schools – See Craigsville, Richwood

New Life Christian Academy 100/PK-12
899 Broad St 26651 304-872-1148

Sutton, Braxton, Pop. 987
Braxton County SD 2,100/PK-12
98 Carter Braxton Dr 26601 304-765-7101
David Dilly, supt. Fax 765-7148
boe.brax.k12.wv.us/
Braxton County HS 600/9-12
200 Jerry Burton Dr 26601 304-765-7331
Tony Minney, prin. Fax 765-7976
Braxton County MS 300/7-8
100 Carter Braxton Dr 26601 304-765-2644
Michelle Gorby, prin. Fax 765-2696

Union, Monroe, Pop. 551
Monroe County SD 1,800/PK-12
PO Box 330 24983 304-772-3094
Joetta Basile, supt. Fax 772-5020
boe.monr.k12.wv.us
Other Schools – See Lindside, Peterstown

Upperglade, Webster
Webster County SD
Supt. — See Webster Springs
Webster County HS 400/7-12
1 Highlander Dr 26266 304-226-5772
Stacey Cutlip, prin. Fax 226-5792

Van, Boone, Pop. 209
Boone County SD
Supt. — See Madison
Van JSHS 200/6-12
PO Box 100 25206 304-245-8237
Jeffrey Griffith, prin. Fax 245-8695

Vienna, Wood, Pop. 10,628
Wood County SD
Supt. — See Parkersburg
Jackson MS 500/6-8
1601 34th St 26105 304-420-9551
Richard Summers, prin. Fax 295-9954

Ohio Valley University Post-Sec.
1 Campus View Dr 26105 304-865-6000

Wayne, Wayne, Pop. 1,402
Wayne County SD 7,100/PK-12
PO Box 70 25570 304-272-5116
Dr. Steven Paine, supt. Fax 272-6500
boe.wayn.k12.wv.us
Wayne HS 700/9-12
100 Pioneer Rd 25570 304-272-5639
Sara Stapleton, prin. Fax 272-6439
Wayne MS 600/6-8
200 Pioneer Rd 25570 304-272-3227
Beth Webb, prin. Fax 272-5811
Other Schools – See Ceredo, Crum, Fort Gay, Huntington, Kenova

Webster Springs, Webster, Pop. 772
Webster County SD 1,100/PK-12
315 S Main St 26288 304-847-5638
Scott Cochran, supt. Fax 847-2538
boe.webs.k12.wv.us/
Other Schools – See Upperglade

Weirton, Hancock, Pop. 19,434
Hancock County SD
Supt. — See New Cumberland
Weir HS 600/9-12
100 Red Rider Rd 26062 304-748-7600
Dan Enich, prin. Fax 748-7602
Weir MS 600/5-8
125 Sinclair Ave 26062 304-748-6080
Sara Parsons, prin. Fax 748-0847

Madonna HS 200/9-12
150 Michael Way 26062 304-723-0545
Jamie Lesho, prin. Fax 723-0564
West Virginia Northern Community College Post-Sec.
150 Park Ave 26062 304-723-2210

Welch, McDowell, Pop. 2,358
McDowell County SD 3,400/PK-12
30 Central Ave 24801 304-436-8441
Nelson Spencer, supt. Fax 436-4008
boe.mcdo.k12.wv.us
McDowell County Career Technical Center Vo/Tech
PO Box V 24801 304-436-3488
Dennis Jarvis, prin. Fax 436-8063
Mount View MSHS 800/6-12
950 Mount View Rd 24801 304-436-2939
Debra Hall, prin. Fax 436-4714
Other Schools – See Avondale, Bradshaw

Wellsburg, Brooke, Pop. 2,772
Brooke County SD 3,100/PK-12
1201 Pleasant Ave 26070 304-737-3481
Toni Shute, supt. Fax 737-3480
brooke.schoolwires.net
Brooke County Alternative Learning Ctr Alt
102 26th St 26070 304-737-9195
Melissa Figlioli, admin. Fax 737-3481
Brooke HS 1,000/9-12
29 Bruin Dr 26070 304-527-1410
Tim Pannett, prin. Fax 527-3604
Wellsburg MS 400/5-8
1447 Main St 26070 304-737-2922
Jennifer Sisinni, prin. Fax 737-2976
Other Schools – See Follansbee

West Liberty, Ohio, Pop. 1,514

West Liberty University Post-Sec.
208 University Dr 26074 304-336-5000

Weston, Lewis, Pop. 4,051
Lewis County SD 2,500/PK-12
239 Court Ave 26452 304-269-8300
Dr. Joseph Mace, supt. Fax 269-8305
lewisboe.com
Bland MS 800/5-8
358 Court Ave 26452 304-269-8325
Julie Radcliff, prin. Fax 269-8310
Lewis County HS 800/9-12
205 Minuteman Dr 26452 304-269-8315
Derek Lambert, prin. Fax 269-8319

West Union, Doddridge, Pop. 823
Doddridge County SD 1,200/PK-12
1117 WV Route 18 N 26456 304-873-2300
Adam Cheeseman, supt. Fax 873-2210
boe.dodd.k12.wv.us
Doddridge County HS 400/9-12
79 Bulldog Dr 26456 304-873-2521
Dr. Gregory Kuhns, prin. Fax 873-1873
Doddridge County MS 300/5-8
65 Doddridge County School 26456 304-873-2332
Dr. Deborah Kuhns, prin. Fax 873-2541

Wheeling, Ohio, Pop. 27,794
Marshall County SD
Supt. — See Moundsville
Sherrard MS 400/6-8
1000 Fairmont Pike 26003 304-233-3331
Jason Marling, prin. Fax 233-6418

Ohio County SD 5,400/PK-12
2203 National Rd 26003 304-243-0300
Dr. Kimberly S. Miller, supt. Fax 243-0328
wphs.ohio.k12.wv.us/ocbe/
Bridge Street MS 300/6-8
19 Junior Ave 26003 304-243-0381
Joseph Kolb, prin. Fax 243-0385
Triadelphia MS 400/6-8
1636 National Rd 26003 304-243-0387
Ann Coleman, prin. Fax 243-0392
Wheeling MS 200/6-8
3500 Chapline St 26003 304-243-0425
Richard McCardle, prin. Fax 243-0426
Wheeling Park HS 1,600/9-12
1976 Park View Rd 26003 304-243-0400
Amy Minch, prin. Fax 243-0449

Central Catholic HS 200/9-12
75 14th St 26003 304-233-1660
Rebecca Sancomb, prin. Fax 233-3187
Linsly S 500/5-12
60 Knox Ln 26003 304-233-3260
Justin Zimmerman, hdmstr. Fax 232-1975
Ohio Valley Medical Center Post-Sec.
2000 Eoff St 26003 304-234-8294
Scott College of Cosmetology Post-Sec.
1502 Market St 26003 304-232-7798
West Virginia Business College Post-Sec.
1052 Main St 26003 304-232-0361
West Virginia Northern Community College Post-Sec.
1704 Market St 26003 304-233-5900
Wheeling Hospital Post-Sec.
1 Medical Park 26003 304-243-3000
Wheeling Jesuit University Post-Sec.
316 Washington Ave 26003 304-243-2000

Williamson, Mingo, Pop. 3,116
Mingo County SD 4,400/PK-12
RR 2 Box 310 25661 304-235-3333
Dr. Robert Bobbera, supt. Fax 235-3410
mingoboe.us/
Tug Valley HS 400/9-12
555 Panther Ave 25661 304-235-2266
Johnny Branch, prin. Fax 235-2636
Other Schools – See Delbarton, Gilbert

Nolan Christian Academy 50/K-12
30 Nolan St 25661 304-235-3914
Earl White, admin. Fax 235-2919
Southern WV Community & Technical Coll. Post-Sec.
1601 Armory Dr 25661 304-235-6046

Williamstown, Wood, Pop. 2,880
Wood County SD
Supt. — See Parkersburg
Williamstown HS 600/7-12
219 W 5th St 26187 304-375-6151
Pat Peters, prin. Fax 375-6194

Wood County Christian S 300/PK-12
113 W 9th St 26187 304-375-2000
Jane Smith, admin. Fax 375-2000

Winfield, Putnam, Pop. 2,257
Putnam County SD 9,900/PK-12
77 Courthouse Dr 25213 304-586-0500
John Hudson, supt. Fax 586-0553
www.putnamschools.com
Winfield HS 900/9-12
11268 Winfield Rd 25213 304-586-3279
Bruce McGrew, prin. Fax 586-3601
Winfield MS 600/6-8
11883 Winfield Rd 25213 304-586-3072
Dan Rinick, prin. Fax 586-0920
Other Schools – See Buffalo, Eleanor, Hurricane, Poca

WISCONSIN

WISCONSIN DEPARTMENT PUBLIC INSTRUCTION
PO Box 7841, Madison 53707-7841
Telephone 608-266-3390
Fax 608-267-1052
Website dpi.wi.gov

Superintendent of Public Instruction Tony Evers PhD

COOPERATIVE EDUCATIONAL SERVICE AGENCIES (CESA)

CESA 1
Jim Rickabaugh, admin. 262-787-9500
N25W23131 Paul Rd Ste 100 Fax 787-9501
Pewaukee 53072
www.cesa1.k12.wi.us

CESA 2
Gary Albrecht, admin. 262-473-1473
1221 Innovation Dr Fax 472-2269
Whitewater 53190
www.cesa2.org

CESA 3
Joe Price, admin., 1300 Industrial Dr 608-822-3276
Fennimore 53809 Fax 822-3860
www.cesa3.k12.wi.us

CESA 4
Cheryl Gullicksrud, admin. 800-514-3075
923 Garland St E Fax 786-4801
West Salem 54669
www.cesa4.k12.wi.us

CESA 5
Jeremy Biehl, admin. 608-742-8811
626 E Slifer St, Portage 53901 Fax 742-2384
www.cesa5.org/

CESA 6
Dr. Joan Wade, admin. 920-233-2372
2935 Universal Ct, Oshkosh 54904 Fax 236-0580
www.cesa6.org

CESA 7
Jeffery Dickert, admin. 920-492-5960
595 Baeten Rd, Green Bay 54304 Fax 492-5965
www.cesa7.k12.wi.us

CESA 8
Donald Viegut, admin. 920-855-2114
223 W Park St, Gillett 54124 Fax 855-2299
www.cesa8.k12.wi.us

CESA 9
Dr. Karen Wendorf-Heldt, admin. 715-453-2141
PO Box 449, Tomahawk 54487 Fax 453-7519
www.cesa9.org

CESA 10
Mike Haynes, admin. 715-723-0341
725 W Park Ave Fax 720-2070
Chippewa Falls 54729
www.cesa10.k12.wi.us

CESA 11
Jerry Walters, admin. 715-986-2020
225 Ostermann Dr Fax 986-2040
Turtle Lake 54889
www.cesa11.k12.wi.us

CESA 12
Kenneth Kasinski, admin. 715-682-2363
618 Beaser Ave, Ashland 54806 Fax 682-7244
www.cesa12.org

PUBLIC, PRIVATE AND CATHOLIC SECONDARY SCHOOLS

Abbotsford, Clark, Pop. 2,301
Abbotsford SD 700/PK-12
PO Box A 54405 715-223-6715
Cheryl Baker, supt. Fax 223-4239
www.abbotsford.k12.wi.us
Abbotsford MSHS 300/6-12
PO Box 70 54405 715-223-2386
Ryan Bargender, prin. Fax 223-4239
Falcon Enterprise Alternative HS Alt
PO Box A 54405 715-223-0118
Ann Kleiber, prin. Fax 223-0119

Adams, Adams, Pop. 1,940
Adams-Friendship Area SD
Supt. — See Friendship
Adams-Friendship HS 500/9-12
1109 E North St 53910 608-339-3921
Tanya Kotlowski, prin. Fax 339-2569
Adams-Friendship MS 300/6-8
420 N Main St 53910 608-339-4064
Dennis Kaczor, prin. Fax 339-2434

Albany, Green, Pop. 1,005
Albany SD 300/PK-12
400 5th St 53502 608-862-3225
Amy Vesperman, supt. Fax 862-3230
www.albany.k12.wi.us
Albany Community MS 100/6-8
400 5th St 53502 608-862-3135
Connie Gregerson, prin. Fax 862-3230
Albany HS 100/9-12
400 5th St 53502 608-862-3135
Connie Gregerson, prin. Fax 862-3230

Algoma, Kewaunee, Pop. 3,136
Algoma SD 700/PK-12
1715 Division St 54201 920-487-7001
Nicholas Cochart, supt. Fax 487-7016
algomawolves.org
Algoma MSHS 300/7-12
1715 Division St 54201 920-487-7001
Nicholas Cochart, prin. Fax 487-7005

Alma, Buffalo, Pop. 776
Alma SD 300/PK-12
S1618 State Road 35 54610 608-685-4416
Steven Sedlmayr, supt. Fax 685-4446
www.alma.k12.wi.us
Alma HS 100/9-12
S1618 State Road 35 54610 608-685-4416
Steven Sedlmayr, prin. Fax 685-4446

Alma Center, Jackson, Pop. 492
Alma Center-Humbird-Merrillan SD 600/PK-12
PO Box 308 54611 715-964-8271
Paul Fischer, supt. Fax 964-1005
www.achm.k12.wi.us
Lincoln HS 200/9-12
PO Box 308 54611 715-964-5311
Paul Janson, prin. Fax 964-1005
Lincoln JHS 100/7-8
PO Box 308 54611 715-964-5311
Paul Janson, prin. Fax 964-1005

Almond, Portage, Pop. 447
Almond-Bancroft SD 200/PK-12
1336 Elm St 54909 715-366-2941
Dann Boxx, admin. Fax 366-2940
www.abschools.k12.wi.us
Almond-Bancroft S 200/PK-12
1336 Elm St 54909 715-366-2941
Jeff Rykal, prin. Fax 366-2943

Altoona, Eau Claire, Pop. 6,546
Altoona SD 1,600/PK-12
1903 Bartlett Ave 54720 715-839-6032
Dr. Connie Biedron, supt. Fax 839-6066
www.altoona.k12.wi.us
Altoona HS 400/9-12
711 7th St W 54720 715-839-6031
Jason LeMay, prin. Fax 839-6028
Altoona MS 300/6-8
1903 Bartlett Ave 54720 715-839-6030
Dan Peggs, prin. Fax 839-6099

Amery, Polk, Pop. 2,886
Amery SD 1,600/PK-12
543 Minneapolis Ave S 54001 715-268-9771
James Kuchta, admin. Fax 268-7300
www.amerysd.k12.wi.us
Amery HS 500/9-12
555 Minneapolis Ave S 54001 715-268-9771
Shawn Doerfler, prin. Fax 268-7792
Amery MS 300/6-8
501 Minneapolis Ave S 54001 715-268-9771
Thomas Bensen, prin. Fax 268-4967

Amherst, Portage, Pop. 1,031
Tomorrow River SD 1,000/PK-12
357 N Main St 54406 715-824-5521
Dennis Raabe, supt. Fax 824-7177
www.amherst.k12.wi.us
Amherst HS 300/9-12
357 N Main St 54406 715-824-5522
Mark Luetschwager, prin. Fax 824-5454
Amherst MS 200/5-8
357 N Main St 54406 715-824-5524
Phillip Tubbs, prin. Fax 824-5454

Antigo, Langlade, Pop. 8,127
Antigo SD 2,200/PK-12
120 S Dorr St 54409 715-627-4355
Brian Misfeldt Ph.D., supt. Fax 623-3279
www.antigo.k12.wi.us
Antigo HS 800/9-12
1900 10th Ave 54409 715-623-7611
Thomas Zamzow, prin. Fax 623-7624
Antigo MS 500/6-8
815 7th Ave 54409 715-623-4173
Amy Dahms, prin. Fax 627-4982

Appleton, Outagamie, Pop. 71,375
Appleton Area SD 15,900/PK-12
PO Box 2019 54912 920-832-6161
Lee Allinger, supt. Fax 832-1725
www.aasd.k12.wi.us
Appleton East HS 1,300/9-12
2121 E Emmers Dr 54915 920-832-6212
Matt Mineau, prin. Fax 832-4880
Appleton North HS 1,500/9-12
5000 N Ballard Rd 54913 920-832-4300
James Huggins, prin. Fax 832-4301
Appleton West HS 1,100/9-12
610 N Badger Ave 54914 920-832-6219
Greg Hartjes, prin. Fax 832-4198
Einstein MS 500/7-8
324 E Florida Ave 54911 920-832-6240
Dave Mueller, prin. Fax 832-6164
Madison MS 600/7-8
2020 S Carpenter St 54915 920-832-6276
David Torrey, prin. Fax 832-6337
Wilson MS 400/7-8
225 N Badger Ave 54914 920-832-6226
Mark McQuade, prin. Fax 832-4857

Fox Valley Lutheran HS 600/9-12
5300 N Meade St 54913 920-739-4441
Steve Granberg, prin. Fax 739-4418
Fox Valley Technical College Post-Sec.
PO Box 2277 54912 920-735-5600
Gill-Tech Academy of Hair Design Post-Sec.
230 S McCarthy Rd 54914 920-739-8684
Globe University Post-Sec.
5045 W Grande Market Dr 54913 920-364-1100
Lawrence University Post-Sec.
711 E Boldt Way 54911 920-832-7000
Rasmussen College Post-Sec.
3500 E Destination Dr # 100 54915 920-750-5900
St. Elizabeth Hospital Post-Sec.
1506 S Oneida St 54915 920-738-2015
St. Francis Xavier HS 600/9-12
1600 W Prospect Ave 54914 920-733-6632
Mike Mauthe, prin. Fax 733-5513
St. Francis Xavier MS 400/6-8
2626 N Oneida St 54911 920-730-8849
Dave Callan, prin. Fax 730-4147

Arcadia, Trempealeau, Pop. 2,912
Arcadia SD 1,200/PK-12
756 Raider Dr 54612 608-323-3315
Louie Ferguson, supt. Fax 323-2256
www.arcadia.k12.wi.us/
Arcadia HS 300/9-12
756 Raider Dr 54612 608-323-3315
Alan Herman, prin. Fax 323-2256
Arcadia MS 300/5-8
725 Fairfield Ave 54612 608-323-3315
Michele Butler, prin. Fax 323-3188

Argyle, Lafayette, Pop. 857
Argyle SD 300/PK-12
PO Box 256 53504 608-543-3318
Phillip Updike, supt. Fax 543-3868
www.argyle.k12.wi.us
Argyle MSHS 200/6-12
PO Box 256 53504 608-543-3318
Phillip Updike, prin. Fax 543-3868

Ashland, Ashland, Pop. 7,896
Ashland SD 2,200/PK-12
2000 Beaser Ave 54806 715-682-7080
Keith Hilts, supt. Fax 682-7097
www.ashland.k12.wi.us
Ashland HS 700/9-12
1900 Beaser Ave 54806 715-682-7089
Greg Posewitz, prin. Fax 682-2075
Ashland MS 500/6-8
203 11th St E 54806 715-682-7087
Paul Gilbertson, prin. Fax 682-7944

Northland College Post-Sec.
1411 Ellis Ave 54806 715-682-1699
Wisconsin Indianhead Technical College Post-Sec.
2100 Beaser Ave 54806 715-682-4591

Athens, Marathon, Pop. 1,096
Athens SD 400/PK-12
PO Box F 54411 715-257-7511
Timothy Micke, supt. Fax 257-7502
www.athens1.org
Athens HS 200/9-12
PO Box F 54411 715-257-7511
Juli Gauerke, prin. Fax 257-7651
Athens MS 100/6-8
PO Box F 54411 715-257-7511
Juli Gauerke, prin. Fax 257-7651

Auburndale, Wood, Pop. 703
Auburndale SD 900/PK-12
PO Box 139 54412 715-652-2117
Dr. William Greb, supt. Fax 652-2836
www.aubschools.com
Auburndale MSHS 500/6-12
PO Box 190 54412 715-652-2115
James Delikowski, prin. Fax 652-6322

Augusta, Eau Claire, Pop. 1,531
Augusta SD 500/PK-12
E19320 Bartig Rd 54722 715-286-2291
Ryan Nelson, supt. Fax 286-3336
www.augusta.k12.wi.us
Augusta MSHS 200/6-12
E19320 Bartig Rd 54722 715-286-2291
Ken Abel, prin. Fax 286-3393

Baldwin, Saint Croix, Pop. 3,900
Baldwin-Woodville Area SD 1,700/PK-12
550 US Highway 12 54002 715-684-3411
Eric Russell, supt. Fax 684-3168
www.bwsd.k12.wi.us
Baldwin-Woodville HS 500/9-12
1000 13th Ave 54002 715-684-3321
Dave Brandvold, prin. Fax 684-5160
Other Schools – See Woodville

Baldwin Christian S 100/PK-12
896 US Highway 63 54002 715-684-2656

Balsam Lake, Polk, Pop. 991
Unity SD 1,000/PK-12
1908 150th St 54810 715-825-3515
Brandon Robinson, supt. Fax 825-3517
www.unity.k12.wi.us/
Unity HS 300/9-12
1908 150th St 54810 715-825-2131
Jason Cress, prin. Fax 825-4430
Unity MS 300/5-8
1908 150th St 54810 715-825-2101
Elizabeth Jorgensen, prin. Fax 825-4410

Bangor, LaCrosse, Pop. 1,446
Bangor SD 600/PK-12
PO Box 99 54614 608-486-2331
David Laehn, supt. Fax 486-4587
www.bangor.k12.wi.us
Bangor MSHS 300/6-12
PO Box 99 54614 608-486-2331
Don Addington, prin. Fax 486-4587

Baraboo, Sauk, Pop. 11,882
Baraboo SD 2,900/PK-12
423 Linn St 53913 608-355-3950
Dr. Lori Mueller, supt. Fax 355-3960
www.baraboo.k12.wi.us
Baraboo HS 1,000/9-12
1201 Draper St 53913 608-355-3940
Glenn Bildsten, prin. Fax 355-3962
Young MS 700/6-8
1531 Draper St 53913 608-355-3930
John Gunnell, prin. Fax 355-3998

University of Wisconsin Baraboo/Sauk Co. Post-Sec.
1006 Connie Rd 53913 608-355-5230

Barneveld, Iowa, Pop. 1,221
Barneveld SD 400/K-12
PO Box 98 53507 608-924-4711
Brett Stousland, supt. Fax 924-1646
www.barneveld.k12.wi.us
Barneveld MSHS 200/6-12
105 W Douglas St 53507 608-924-4711
Ben Jones, prin. Fax 924-1646

Barron, Barron, Pop. 3,378
Barron Area SD 1,300/PK-12
100 W River Ave 54812 715-537-5612
Craig Broeren, supt. Fax 637-5161
www.barron.k12.wi.us
Barron HS 400/9-12
1050 E Woodland Ave 54812 715-537-5627
Kirk Haugestuen, prin. Fax 637-1603
Riverview MS 400/5-8
135 W River Ave 54812 715-537-5641
Scott Stralka, prin. Fax 637-5373

Bayfield, Bayfield, Pop. 459
Bayfield SD 400/PK-12
300 N 4th St 54814 715-779-3201
Dr. David Aslyn, supt. Fax 779-5268
www.bayfield.k12.wi.us
Bayfield HS 100/9-12
300 N 4th St 54814 715-779-3201
David Aslyn, prin. Fax 779-5226
Bayfield MS 100/6-8
300 N 4th St 54814 715-779-3201
Jeff Gordon, prin. Fax 779-5226

Bayside, Milwaukee, Pop. 4,320
Fox Point Bayside SD
Supt. — See Fox Point
Bayside MS 400/5-8
601 E Ellsworth Ln 53217 414-247-4201
Jodi Hackl, prin. Fax 247-8963

Beaver Dam, Dodge, Pop. 16,040
Beaver Dam SD 3,400/PK-12
705 McKinley St 53916 920-885-7300
Stephen Vessey, supt. Fax 885-7306
www.bdusd.org
Beaver Dam HS 1,000/9-12
500 Gould St 53916 920-885-7313
Crystal Bates, prin. Fax 885-7317
Beaver Dam MS 800/6-8
108 4th St 53916 920-885-7365
John Casper, prin. Fax 885-7415
Smith Learning Academy 50/Alt
400 E Burnett St 53916 920-885-7423
Dan Lueck, prin. Fax 885-7429

Moraine Park Technical College Post-Sec.
700 Gould St 53916 920-887-1441
Wayland Academy 200/9-12
101 N University Ave 53916 920-356-2120
Joseph Lennertz, head sch Fax 887-3373

Belleville, Dane, Pop. 2,367
Belleville SD 1,000/PK-12
625 W Church St 53508 608-835-6120
Pam Yoder, supt. Fax 424-3486
www.belleville.k12.wi.us/
Belleville HS 300/9-12
635 W Church St 53508 608-835-6120
Nate Perry, prin. Fax 424-3692
Belleville MS 100/7-8
625 W Church St 53508 608-835-6120
Nate Perry, prin. Fax 424-3692

Belmont, Lafayette, Pop. 980
Belmont Community SD 400/PK-12
PO Box 348 53510 608-762-5131
Christy Larson, supt. Fax 762-5129
www.belmont.k12.wi.us
Belmont JSHS 200/6-12
PO Box 348 53510 608-762-5131
Mike Beranek, prin. Fax 762-5129

Beloit, Rock, Pop. 35,780
Beloit SD 6,500/K-12
1633 Keeler Ave 53511 608-361-4000
Dr. Thomas Johnson, supt. Fax 361-4122
www.sdb.k12.wi.us
Aldrich IS 600/4-8
1859 Northgate Dr 53511 608-361-3600
Joe Vrydaghs, prin. Fax 361-4122
Beloit Learning Academy 200/Alt
1033 Woodward Ave 53511 608-361-4310
Tina Goecks, prin. Fax 361-4122
Cunningham IS 300/4-8
910 Townline Ave 53511 608-361-2200
Jennifer Fanning, prin. Fax 361-4122
Fruzen IS 700/4-8
2600 Milwaukee Rd 53511 608-361-2000
Mathew Kleinschmidt, prin. Fax 361-4122
McNeel IS 800/4-8
1524 Frederick St 53511 608-361-3800
Anthony Bosco, prin. Fax 361-4122
Memorial HS 1,800/9-12
1225 4th St 53511 608-361-3000
Carole Campbell, prin. Fax 361-4122

School District of Beloit Turner 1,500/PK-12
1237 E Inman Pkwy 53511 608-364-6372
Dr. Dennis McCarthy, supt. Fax 364-6373
www.turnerschools.org/
Turner HS 500/9-12
1231 E Inman Pkwy 53511 608-364-6370
Ryan Bertelsen, prin. Fax 365-4768
Turner MS 400/6-8
1237 E Inman Pkwy 53511 608-364-6367
Cory Everson, prin. Fax 364-6369

Beloit College Post-Sec.
700 College St 53511 608-363-2000
Rock County Christian HS 100/6-12
916 Bushnell St 53511 608-365-7378
Bob Cerniglia, prin. Fax 365-7382

Benton, Lafayette, Pop. 970
Benton SD 300/PK-12
PO Box 7 53803 608-759-4002
Kyle Luedtke, admin. Fax 759-3805
www.benton.k12.wi.us
Benton HS 100/7-12
PO Box 7 53803 608-759-4002
Kyle Luedtke, admin. Fax 759-3805

Berlin, Green Lake, Pop. 5,480
Berlin Area SD 1,700/PK-12
295 E Marquette St 54923 920-361-2004
Dr. Robert Eidahl Ed.D., supt. Fax 361-2170
www.berlin.k12.wi.us
Berlin HS 500/9-12
222 Memorial Dr 54923 920-361-2000
Lynn Mork, prin. Fax 361-2005
Berlin MS 400/6-8
242 Memorial Dr 54923 920-361-2441
Mike Raether, prin. Fax 361-3379

Birchwood, Washburn, Pop. 440
Birchwood SD 400/PK-12
300 S Wilson St 54817 715-354-3471
Diane Johnson, supt. Fax 354-3469
www.birchwood.k12.wi.us
Birchwood HS 100/9-12
300 S Wilson St 54817 715-354-3471
Jeff Stanley, prin. Fax 354-3469
Birchwood MS 50/6-8
300 S Wilson St 54817 715-354-3471
Jeff Stanley, prin. Fax 354-3469

Black River Falls, Jackson, Pop. 3,539
Black River Falls SD 1,600/PK-12
301 N 4th St 54615 715-284-4357
Dr. Shelly Severson, supt. Fax 284-7064
www.brf.org
Black River Falls HS 500/9-12
1200 Pierce St 54615 715-284-4324
Thomas Chambers, prin. Fax 284-7626
Black River Falls MS 400/6-8
1202 Pierce St 54615 715-284-5315
David Roou, prin. Fax 284-0364
Gebhardt S 300/Alt
411 Gebhardt Rd 54615 715-284-5125
Sherry Holt, dir. Fax 284-7472

Blair, Trempealeau, Pop. 1,358
Blair-Taylor SD 600/PK-12
PO Box 107 54616 608-989-2881
Jeff Eide, supt. Fax 989-2451
btsd.k12.wi.us
Blair-Taylor MSHS 300/7-12
PO Box 107 54616 608-989-2525
Dana Eide, prin. Fax 989-9161

Blanchardville, Lafayette, Pop. 822
Pecatonica Area SD 400/PK-12
PO Box 117 53516 608-523-4248
Jill Underly, supt. Fax 523-4286
www.pecatonica.k12.wi.us
Pecatonica JSHS 200/6-12
PO Box 117 53516 608-523-4285
Paul Manriquez, prin. Fax 523-4286

Bloomer, Chippewa, Pop. 3,508
Bloomer SD 1,200/PK-12
1310 17th Ave 54724 715-568-2800
Dr. Mary Randall, supt. Fax 568-5315
www.bloomer.k12.wi.us
Bloomer HS 400/9-12
1310 17th Ave 54724 715-568-5300
Chad Steinmetz, prin. Fax 568-5304
Bloomer MS 300/5-8
600 Jackson St 54724 715-568-1025
Rhonda Herrick, prin. Fax 568-3687

Bonduel, Shawano, Pop. 1,465
Bonduel SD 800/PK-12
PO Box 310 54107 715-758-4860
Patrick Rau, supt. Fax 758-4869
www.bonduel.k12.wi.us
Bonduel HS 300/9-12
PO Box 310 54107 715-758-4850
Jane Wonderling, prin. Fax 758-4859
Bonduel MS 200/6-8
PO Box 310 54107 715-758-4840
Mark Margelofsky, prin. Fax 758-4849

Boscobel, Grant, Pop. 3,210
Boscobel Area SD 800/PK-12
1110 Park St 53805 608-375-4164
Greg Bell, supt. Fax 375-2378
www.boscobel.k12.wi.us
Boscobel HS 200/9-12
300 Brindley St 53805 608-375-4161
Rodney Lewis, prin. Fax 375-2640
Boscobel MS 100/7-8
300 Brindley St 53805 608-375-4161
Rodney Lewis, prin. Fax 375-2640

Bowler, Shawano, Pop. 282
Bowler SD 400/PK-12
500 S Almon St 54416 715-793-4101
Faith Gagnon, supt. Fax 793-1302
www.bowler.k12.wi.us
Bowler JSHS 100/7-12
500 S Almon St 54416 715-793-4101
Kim Ninabuck, prin. Fax 793-1302

Boyceville, Dunn, Pop. 1,080
Boyceville Community SD 800/PK-12
1003 Tiffany St 54725 715-643-3647
Kevin Sipple, supt. Fax 643-3127
www.boyceville.k12.wi.us
Boyceville HS 200/9-12
1003 Tiffany St 54725 715-643-3647
Steven Glocke, prin. Fax 643-2209
Boyceville MS 100/7-8
1003 Tiffany St 54725 715-643-3647
Steven Glocke, prin. Fax 643-2209

Brillion, Calumet, Pop. 3,113
Brillion SD 1,000/PK-12
315 S Main St 54110 920-756-2368
Dominick Madison Ph.D., supt. Fax 756-3705
www.brillionsd.org
Brillion HS 300/9-12
W1101 County Road HR 54110 920-756-9238
Peter Kittel, prin. Fax 756-9427
Brillion MS 200/6-8
315 S Main St 54110 920-756-2166
Bonnie Olson, prin. Fax 756-3705

Brodhead, Green, Pop. 3,270
Brodhead SD 1,000/PK-12
2501 W 5th Ave 53520 608-897-2141
Leonard Lueck, supt. Fax 897-2770
www.brodhead.k12.wi.us
Brodhead HS 300/9-12
2501 W 5th Ave 53520 608-897-2155
James Matthys, prin. Fax 897-3026
Brodhead MS 200/6-8
2100 W 9th Ave 53520 608-897-2184
Dr. Lisa Semrow, prin. Fax 897-2789

Brookfield, Waukesha, Pop. 37,413
Elmbrook SD 6,900/PK-12
PO Box 1830 53008 262-781-3030
Mark Hansen, supt. Fax 790-4095
www.elmbrookschools.org
Brookfield Central HS 1,300/9-12
16900 Gebhardt Rd 53005 262-785-3910
Brett Gruetzmacher, prin. Fax 785-3993
Brookfield East HS 1,300/9-12
3305 Lilly Rd 53005 262-781-3500
Andy Farley, prin. Fax 790-5445
Wisconsin Hills MS 900/6-8
18700 W Wisconsin Ave 53045 262-785-3960
Lisa Rettler, prin. Fax 785-3967

Other Schools – See Elm Grove

Anthem College Post-Sec.
440 S Executive Dr Ste 200 53005 888-852-7272
Brookfield Academy 900/PK-12
3462 N Brookfield Rd 53045 262-783-3200
Ottawa University Post-Sec.
245 S Executive Dr Ste 110 53005 262-879-0200

Brown Deer, Milwaukee, Pop. 11,652
Brown Deer SD 1,100/PK-12
8200 N 60th St 53223 414-371-6750
Dr. Deb Kerr, admin. Fax 371-6751
browndeer.schoolfusion.us
Brown Deer MSHS 800/7-12
8060 N 60th St 53223 414-371-7000
Tosha Womack, prin. Fax 371-7001

Bruce, Rusk, Pop. 772
Bruce SD 500/PK-12
104 W Washington Ave 54819 715-868-2533
Joni Weinert, supt. Fax 868-2534
www.bruce.k12.wi.us
Bruce HS 200/9-12
104 W Washington Ave 54819 715-868-2585
Larry Villiard, prin. Fax 868-2534
Bruce MS 100/6-8
104 W Washington Ave 54819 715-868-2585
Larry Villiard, prin. Fax 868-2534

Brussels, Door
Southern Door SD 1,100/PK-12
2073 County Road DK 54204 920-825-7311
Patricia Vickman, supt. Fax 825-7155
www.southerndoor.k12.wi.us
Southern Door HS 400/9-12
2073 County Road DK 54204 920-825-7333
Steve Bousley, prin. Fax 825-7081
Southern Door MS 200/6-8
2073 County Road DK 54204 920-825-7321
Gary Langenberg, prin. Fax 825-7692

Burlington, Racine, Pop. 10,361
Burlington Area SD 3,100/PK-12
100 N Kane St 53105 262-763-0210
Peter Smet, supt. Fax 763-0215
www.basd.k12.wi.us
Burlington HS 1,200/9-12
400 Mc Canna Pkwy 53105 262-763-0200
Eric Burling, prin. Fax 763-0216
Karcher MS 500/7-8
225 Robert St 53105 262-763-0190
Jill Oelslager, prin. Fax 767-5580

Catholic Central HS 200/9-12
148 McHenry St 53105 262-763-1510
Dave Wieters, prin. Fax 763-1509

Butternut, Ashland, Pop. 367
Butternut SD 100/PK-12
PO Box 247 54514 715-769-3434
Joseph Zirngibl, supt. Fax 769-3712
www.lightatorch.info
Butternut S 100/PK-12
PO Box 247 54514 715-769-3434
Joseph Zirngibl, admin. Fax 769-3712

Cadott, Chippewa, Pop. 1,424
Cadott Community SD 900/PK-12
426 Myrtle St 54727 715-289-3795
Damon Smith, supt. Fax 289-3748
www.cadott.k12.wi.us
Cadott HS 200/9-12
426 Myrtle St 54727 715-289-3795
Matthew McDonough, prin. Fax 289-3085
Cadott JHS 100/7-8
426 Myrtle St 54727 715-289-3795
Matthew McDonough, prin. Fax 289-3085

Cambria, Columbia, Pop. 765
Cambria-Friesland SD 400/PK-12
410 E Edgewater St 53923 920-348-5548
Timothy Raymond, supt. Fax 348-5119
www.cf.k12.wi.us
Cambria-Friesland MSHS 200/6-12
410 E Edgewater St 53923 920-348-5135
Debra Torrison, prin. Fax 348-5119

Cambridge, Dane, Pop. 1,441
Cambridge SD 900/PK-12
403 Blue Jay Way 53523 608-423-4345
Bernard Nikolay, supt. Fax 423-9869
www.cambridge.k12.wi.us
Cambridge HS 300/9-12
403 Blue Jay Way 53523 608-423-3261
Keith Schneider, prin. Fax 423-9598
Nikolay MS 200/6-8
211 South St 53523 608-423-7335
Krista Jones, prin. Fax 423-4499

Cameron, Barron, Pop. 1,761
Cameron SD 1,100/PK-12
PO Box 378 54822 715-458-4560
Joe Leschisin, admin. Fax 458-4822
www.cameron.k12.wi.us
Cameron HS 300/9-12
PO Box 378 54822 715-458-4560
John Meznarich, prin. Fax 458-4236
Cameron MS 300/5-8
PO Box 378 54822 715-458-4560
Hans Schmidt, prin. Fax 458-3436

Campbellsport, Fond du Lac, Pop. 1,998
Campbellsport SD 1,400/PK-12
114 W Sheboygan St 53010 920-533-8381
Paul A. Amundson, admin. Fax 533-5726
www.csd.k12.wi.us
Campbellsport HS 500/9-12
114 W Sheboygan St 53010 920-533-4811
Todd Hencsik, prin. Fax 533-3521
Campbellsport MS 300/6-8
114 W Sheboygan St 53010 920-533-4811
Todd Hencsik, prin. Fax 533-3521

Casco, Kewaunee, Pop. 569
Luxemburg-Casco SD
Supt. — See Luxemburg
Luxemburg-Casco MS 300/7-8
619 Church Ave 54205 920-837-2205
Mike Snowberry, prin. Fax 837-7517

Cashton, Monroe, Pop. 1,094
Cashton SD 600/PK-12
PO Box 129 54619 608-654-5131
David Bell, supt. Fax 654-5136
www.cashton.k12.wi.us
Cashton JSHS 300/6-12
PO Box 129 54619 608-654-5131
Jennifer Butzler, prin. Fax 654-5136

Cassville, Grant, Pop. 939
Cassville SD 200/PK-12
715 E Amelia St 53806 608-725-5116
John Luster, supt. Fax 725-2353
www.cassvillesd.k12.wi.us
Cassville JSHS 100/7-12
715 E Amelia St 53806 608-725-5116
John Luster, prin. Fax 725-2353

Cazenovia, Sauk, Pop. 314
Weston SD 300/PK-12
E2511A County Road S 53924 608-986-2151
Emily Miller, supt. Fax 986-2205
www.weston.k12.wi.us
Weston HS 100/9-12
E2511A County Road S 53924 608-986-2151
Emily Miller, admin. Fax 986-2205
Weston MS 100/6-8
E2511A County Road S 53924 608-986-2151
Emily Miller, admin. Fax 986-2205

Cecil, Shawano, Pop. 563

Wolf River Lutheran HS 50/9-12
PO Box 77 54111 715-745-2400
Caroline Bedroske, dir. Fax 745-2496

Cedarburg, Ozaukee, Pop. 11,308
Cedarburg SD 3,000/K-12
W68N611 Evergreen Blvd 53012 262-376-6100
Todd Bugnacki, supt. Fax 376-6110
www.cedarburg.k12.wi.us
Cedarburg HS 1,100/9-12
W68N611 Evergreen Blvd 53012 262-376-6200
Adam Kurth, prin. Fax 376-6210
Webster MS 700/6-8
W75N624 Wauwatosa Rd 53012 262-376-6500
Tony DeRosa, prin. Fax 376-6510

Cedar Grove, Sheboygan, Pop. 2,097
Cedar Grove-Belgium Area SD 1,100/PK-12
321 N 2nd St 53013 920-668-8686
Dr. Jeanne Courneene, supt. Fax 668-8605
www.cedargrovebelgium.k12.wi.us/
Cedar Grove-Belgium HS 300/9-12
321 N 2nd St 53013 920-668-8686
Josh Ketterhagen, prin. Fax 668-8605
Cedar Grove-Belgium MS 300/5-8
321 N 2nd St 53013 920-668-8518
Jodi Swagel, prin. Fax 668-8566

Chetek, Barron, Pop. 2,205
Chetek-Weyerhaeuser Area SD 900/PK-12
PO Box 6 54728 715-924-2226
Dr. Mark Johnson, supt. Fax 924-2376
www.cwasd.k12.wi.us
Chetek-Weyerhaeuser Area HS 300/9-12
PO Box 6 54728 715-924-3137
Larry Zeman, prin. Fax 924-2921
Chetek-Weyerhaeuser Area MS 200/6-8
PO Box 6 54728 715-924-3136
Larry Zeman, prin. Fax 924-1794

Chilton, Calumet, Pop. 3,890
Chilton SD 1,200/PK-12
530 W Main St 53014 920-849-8109
Susan Kaphingst, supt. Fax 849-4539
www.chilton.k12.wi.us
Chilton HS 400/9-12
530 W Main St 53014 920-849-2358
Ty Breitlow, prin. Fax 849-3998
Chilton MS 400/5-8
530 W Main St 53014 920-849-9152
Matthew Kiel, prin. Fax 849-7210

Chippewa Falls, Chippewa, Pop. 13,496
Chippewa Falls Area USD 4,700/PK-12
1130 Miles St 54729 715-726-2417
Heidi Taylor-Eliopoulos, supt. Fax 726-2781
cfsd.chipfalls.k12.wi.us
Chippewa Falls HS 1,400/9-12
735 Terrill St 54729 715-726-2406
Becky Davis, prin. Fax 726-2792
Chippewa Falls MS 1,100/6-8
750 Tropicana Blvd 54729 715-726-2400
Susan Kern, prin. Fax 726-2789

McDonell Central HS 100/9-12
1316 Bel Air Blvd 54729 715-723-9126
Jeff Heinzen, pres. Fax 723-1501
Notre Dame MS 100/6-8
1316 Bel Air Blvd 54729 715-723-4777
Jeff Heinzen, pres. Fax 723-3353

Clayton, Polk, Pop. 562
Clayton SD 400/PK-12
PO Box 130 54004 715-948-2163
Cathleen Shimon, supt. Fax 948-2362
www.claytonschooldistrict.new.rschooltoday.com
Clayton HS 100/9-12
PO Box 130 54004 715-948-2163
Edward Cerney, prin. Fax 948-2362
Clayton MS 100/6-8
PO Box 130 54004 715-948-2163
Edward Cerney, prin. Fax 948-2362

Clear Lake, Polk, Pop. 1,055
Clear Lake SD 600/PK-12
1101 3rd St SW 54005 715-263-2114
Josh Ernst, admin. Fax 263-2933
www.clwarriors.org
Clear Lake HS 200/9-12
1101 3rd St SW 54005 715-263-2113
Nick Gilles, prin. Fax 263-3550
Clear Lake JHS 100/7-8
1101 3rd St SW 54005 715-263-2113
Nick Gilles, prin. Fax 263-3550

Cleveland, Manitowoc, Pop. 1,481

Lakeshore Technical College Post-Sec.
1290 North Ave 53015 920-693-1000

Clinton, Rock, Pop. 2,131
Clinton Community SD 1,200/PK-12
PO Box 566 53525 608-676-5482
Dr. Randy Refsland, supt. Fax 676-4444
www.clinton.k12.wi.us
Clinton HS 400/9-12
PO Box 566 53525 608-676-2223
Janae Gile, prin. Fax 676-4444
Clinton MS 300/5-8
PO Box 559 53525 608-676-2275
Ben Simmons, prin. Fax 676-5176

Clintonville, Waupaca, Pop. 4,497
Clintonville SD 1,400/PK-12
45 W Green Tree Rd 54929 715-823-7215
Tom O'Toole, supt. Fax 823-1315
www.clintonville.k12.wi.us
Clintonville HS 500/9-12
64 W Green Tree Rd 54929 715-823-7215
Lance Bagstad, prin. Fax 823-1481
Clintonville MS 400/5-8
255 N Main St 54929 715-823-7215
Scott Werfal, prin. Fax 823-1443

Colby, Clark, Pop. 1,841
Colby SD 900/PK-12
PO Box 139 54421 715-223-2301
Dr. Steven Kolden, supt. Fax 223-4539
www.colby.k12.wi.us
Colby HS 300/9-12
PO Box 110 54421 715-223-2338
Marcia Diedrich, prin. Fax 223-4388
Colby MS 200/4-8
PO Box 110 54421 715-223-8869
Jim Hagen, prin. Fax 223-6754

Coleman, Marinette, Pop. 713
Coleman SD 600/PK-12
347 Business 141 N 54112 920-897-4011
Douglas Polomis, supt. Fax 897-4921
www.coleman.k12.wi.us
Coleman HS 200/9-12
343 Business 141 N 54112 920-897-3822
Douglas Polomis, prin. Fax 897-2015

Colfax, Dunn, Pop. 1,143
Colfax SD 900/PK-12
601 University Ave 54730 715-962-3773
William Yingst, supt. Fax 962-4024
www.colfax.k12.wi.us/
Colfax MSHS 400/7-12
601 University Ave 54730 715-962-3155
John Dachel, prin. Fax 962-4024

Columbus, Columbia, Pop. 4,934
Columbus SD 1,300/PK-12
200 W School St 53925 920-623-5950
Annette Deuman, supt. Fax 623-5958
www.columbus.k12.wi.us
Columbus HS 400/9-12
1164 Farnham St 53925 920-623-5956
Jacob Ekern, prin. Fax 623-5959
Columbus MS 400/4-8
400 S Dickason Blvd 53925 920-623-5954
Loren Glasbrenner, prin. Fax 623-5742

Wisconsin Academy 100/9-12
N2355 Du Borg Rd 53925 920-623-3300

Combined Locks, Outagamie, Pop. 3,308
Kimberly Area SD 4,600/PK-12
PO Box 159 54113 920-788-7900
Bob Mayfield Ed.D., supt. Fax 788-7919
www.kimberly.k12.wi.us
Other Schools – See Kimberly

Cornell, Chippewa, Pop. 1,446
Cornell SD 300/PK-12
PO Box 517 54732 715-861-6947
Dr. Paul Schley, supt. Fax 239-6587
www.cornell.k12.wi.us
Cornell MSHS 100/6-12
PO Box 517 54732 715-861-6947
David Elliott, prin. Fax 239-6587

Cottage Grove, Dane, Pop. 6,069
Monona Grove SD
Supt. — See Monona
Glacial Drumlin MS 800/5-8
801 Damascus Trl 53527 608-839-8437
Renee Tennant, prin. Fax 839-8984

Crandon, Forest, Pop. 1,853
Crandon SD 900/PK-12
9750 US Highway 8 W 54520 715-478-3339
Fax 478-5130
www.crandon.k12.wi.us
Crandon HS 200/9-12
9750 US Highway 8 W 54520 715-478-6125
Andy Space, prin. Fax 478-5570

Crandon MS 200/6-8
9750 US Highway 8 W 54520 715-478-6124
Andy Space, prin. Fax 478-5130

Crivitz, Marinette, Pop. 971
Crivitz SD 700/PK-12
400 South Ave 54114 715-854-2721
Patrick Mans, supt. Fax 854-3755
www.crivitz.k12.wi.us
Crivitz HS 200/9-12
400 South Ave 54114 715-854-2721
Jeff Baumann, prin. Fax 854-3755

Cross Plains, Dane, Pop. 3,510
Middleton-Cross Plains Area SD
Supt. — See Middleton
Glacier Creek MS 600/5-8
2800 N Military Rd 53528 608-829-9420
Tim Keeler, prin. Fax 798-5425

Cuba City, Grant, Pop. 2,077
Cuba City SD 700/PK-12
101 N School St 53807 608-744-2847
Roger Kordus, supt. Fax 744-2324
www.cubacity.us
Cuba City HS 200/9-12
101 N School St 53807 608-744-8888
James Boebel, prin. Fax 744-2324

Cudahy, Milwaukee, Pop. 17,945
Cudahy SD 2,400/PK-12
2915 E Ramsey Ave 53110 414-294-7400
Dr. James Heiden, supt. Fax 294-4083
www.cudahy.k12.wi.us/
Cudahy HS 800/9-12
4950 S Lake Dr 53110 414-294-2700
Christopher Haeger, prin. Fax 769-2379
Cudahy MS 400/6-8
5530 S Barland Ave 53110 414-294-2830
Kim Berner, prin. Fax 489-3010

Cumberland, Barron, Pop. 2,141
Cumberland SD 1,000/PK-12
1010 8th Ave 54829 715-822-5124
Dr. Barry Rose, supt. Fax 822-5136
www.cumberland.k12.wi.us
Cumberland HS 300/9-12
1000 8th Ave 54829 715-822-5121
Ritchie Narges, prin. Fax 822-5138
Cumberland MS 300/5-8
980 8th Ave 54829 715-822-5122
Colin Green, prin. Fax 822-5132

Darlington, Lafayette, Pop. 2,431
Darlington Community SD 800/PK-12
11630 Center Hill Rd 53530 608-776-2006
Dr. Denise Wellnitz, supt. Fax 776-3407
www.darlington.k12.wi.us
Darlington HS 200/9-12
11838 Center Hill Rd 53530 608-776-4001
Aaron Lancaster, prin. Fax 776-2378

Deerfield, Dane, Pop. 2,294
Deerfield Community SD 800/PK-12
300 Simonson Blvd 53531 608-764-5431
Michelle Jensen, supt. Fax 764-2556
www.deerfield.k12.wi.us
Deerfield HS 200/9-12
300 Simonson Blvd 53531 608-764-5431
Brad Johnsrud, prin. Fax 764-5433
Deerfield MS 100/7-8
300 Simonson Blvd 53531 608-764-5431
Brad Johnsrud, prin. Fax 764-5433

De Forest, Dane, Pop. 8,802
De Forest Area SD 3,600/PK-12
520 E Holum St 53532 608-842-6500
Eric Runez, supt. Fax 842-6592
www.deforest.k12.wi.us
De Forest Area HS 1,000/9-12
815 Jefferson St 53532 608-842-6600
Machell Schwarz, prin. Fax 842-6615
De Forest Area MS 1,000/5-8
404 Yorktown Rd 53532 608-842-6000
Ann Higgins, prin. Fax 842-6015

Delafield, Waukesha, Pop. 7,026

St. John's Northwestern Military Academy 300/7-12
1101 Genesee St 53018 262-646-3311
Dr. Jack H. Albert, pres. Fax 646-7128

Delavan, Walworth, Pop. 8,369
Delavan-Darien SD 2,400/PK-12
324 Beloit St 53115 262-728-2642
Dr. Robert Crist, supt. Fax 728-5954
www.ddschools.org
Delavan-Darien HS 800/9-12
150 Cumming St 53115 262-728-2642
Mike Kolff, prin. Fax 728-9713
Phoenix MS 500/6-8
414 Beloit St 53115 262-728-2642
Henry Schmelz, prin. Fax 728-0359

Wisconsin School for the Deaf Post-Sec.
309 W Walworth Ave 53115

Denmark, Brown, Pop. 2,098
Denmark SD 1,500/PK-12
450 N Wall St 54208 920-863-4000
Tony Klaubauf, supt. Fax 863-4015
www.denmark.k12.wi.us
Denmark HS 500/9-12
450 N Wall St 54208 920-863-4200
Oran Nehls, prin. Fax 863-8856
Denmark MS 300/6-8
450 N Wall St 54208 920-863-4100
Amy Gleeson, prin. Fax 863-3184

De Pere, Brown, Pop. 23,399
De Pere SD 4,000/K-12
1700 Chicago St 54115 920-337-1032
Benjamin Villarruel, supt. Fax 337-1033
www.depere.k12.wi.us
De Pere HS 1,400/9-12
1700 Chicago St 54115 920-337-1020
Annette Deuman, prin. Fax 337-1041
De Pere MS 700/7-8
700 Swan Rd 54115 920-337-1024
Betty Hartman, prin. Fax 337-1049

West De Pere SD 3,100/PK-12
400 Reid St Ste W 54115 920-337-1393
John Zegers, supt. Fax 337-1398
www.wdpsd.com
West De Pere HS 800/9-12
665 Grant St 54115 920-338-5200
Dr. Russell Gerke, prin. Fax 338-5310
West De Pere MS 600/6-8
1177 S 9th St 54115 920-337-1099
Dr. James Finley, prin. Fax 337-1380

St. Norbert College Post-Sec.
100 Grant St 54115 920-337-3181

De Soto, Vernon, Pop. 286
De Soto Area SD 600/PK-12
615 Main St 54624 608-648-0102
Fax 648-3959
www.desoto.k12.wi.us
De Soto HS 200/9-12
615 Main St 54624 608-648-0100
Linzi Gronning, prin. Fax 648-0117
De Soto MS 100/6-8
615 Main St 54624 608-648-0104
Linzi Gronning, prin. Fax 648-0117

Dodgeville, Iowa, Pop. 4,656
Dodgeville SD 1,300/PK-12
307 N Iowa St 53533 608-935-3307
Dr. Jeffrey Jacobson, supt. Fax 935-3021
www.dsd.k12.wi.us
Dodgeville HS 400/9-12
912 W Chapel St 53533 608-935-3307
Laura Nyberg, prin. Fax 935-9540
Dodgeville MS 300/6-8
951 W Chapel St 53533 608-935-3307
Sally Baxter, prin. Fax 935-9643

Dousman, Waukesha, Pop. 2,279
Kettle Moraine SD
Supt. — See Wales
Kettle Moraine MS 900/6-8
301 E Ottawa Ave 53118 262-965-6500
Michael Comiskey, prin. Fax 965-6506

Drummond, Bayfield, Pop. 153
Drummond Area SD 400/PK-12
PO Box 40 54832 715-739-6669
John Knight, supt. Fax 739-6345
www.dasd.k12.wi.us
Drummond HS 100/9-12
PO Box 40 54832 715-739-6231
Kristine Lamb, prin. Fax 739-6345
Drummond MS 100/7-8
PO Box 40 54832 715-739-6231
Kristine Lamb, prin. Fax 739-6345

Dunbar, Marinette, Pop. 48

Northland International University Post-Sec.
W10085 Pike Plains Rd 54119 715-324-6900

Durand, Pepin, Pop. 1,916
Durand-Arkansaw SD 600/PK-12
PO Box 190 54736 715-672-8919
Greg Doverspike, supt. Fax 672-8930
www.durand.k12.wi.us
Durand MSHS 500/6-12
PO Box 190 54736 715-672-8917
Bill Clouse, prin. Fax 672-8930

Assumption Catholic S Durand Campus 100/4-8
901 W Prospect St 54736 715-672-5617
Mary Lansing, prin. Fax 672-3931

Eagle River, Vilas, Pop. 1,377
Northland Pines SD 1,400/PK-12
1800 Pleasure Island Rd 54521 715-479-6487
Mike Richie Ed.D., supt. Fax 479-7633
www.npsd.k12.wi.us/
Northland Pines HS 400/9-12
1800 Pleasure Island Rd 54521 715-479-4473
Jim Brewer, prin. Fax 479-5808
Northland Pines MS 300/6-8
1700 Pleasure Island Rd 54521 715-479-6479
Dan Marien, prin. Fax 479-7303

Advanced Welding Institute Post-Sec.
8090 State Highway 17 S 54521 715-337-0122

East Troy, Walworth, Pop. 4,231
East Troy Community SD 1,700/PK-12
2043 Division St 53120 262-642-6710
Dr. Christopher Hibner, supt.
www.easttroy.k12.wi.us
East Troy HS 500/9-12
3128 Graydon Ave 53120 262-642-6760
Kevin Kitslaar, prin. Fax 642-6776
East Troy MS 400/6-8
3143 Graydon Ave 53120 262-642-6740
Peter Synes, prin. Fax 642-6743

Eau Claire, Eau Claire, Pop. 64,812
Eau Claire Area SD 10,900/PK-12
500 Main St 54701 715-852-3000
Dr. Mary Ann Hardebeck, supt. Fax 852-3004
www.ecasd.us

DeLong MS 900/6-8
2000 Vine St 54703 715-852-4900
Dr. Tim O'Reilly, prin. Fax 852-4904
Memorial HS 1,700/9-12
2225 Keith St 54701 715-852-6300
Trevor Kohlhepp, prin. Fax 852-6304
North HS 1,300/9-12
1801 Piedmont Rd 54703 715-852-6600
Dave Valk, prin. Fax 852-6604
Northstar MS 600/6-8
2711 Abbe Hill Dr 54703 715-852-5100
Tim Skutley, prin. Fax 852-5104
South MS 800/6-8
2115 Mitscher Ave 54701 715-852-5200
Dianna Zeegers, prin. Fax 852-5204

Chippewa Valley Technical College Post-Sec.
620 W Clairemont Ave 54701 715-833-6200
Globe University Post-Sec.
4955 Bullis Farm Rd 54701 715-855-6600
Immanuel Lutheran HS 100/9-12
501 Grover Rd 54701 715-836-6621
Joel Gullerud, prin. Fax 836-6634
Professional Hair Design Academy Post-Sec.
3408 Mall Dr 54701 715-835-2345
Regis HS 200/9-12
2100 Fenwick Ave 54701 715-830-2271
Paul Pedersen, prin. Fax 830-5461
Regis MS 100/7-8
2100 Fenwick Ave 54701 715-830-2272
Paul Pedersen, prin. Fax 830-5461
Sacred Heart Hospital Post-Sec.
900 W Clairemont Ave 54701 715-839-4131
University of Wisconsin Post-Sec.
PO Box 4004 54702 715-836-2637

Edgar, Marathon, Pop. 1,476
Edgar SD 600/PK-12
PO Box 196 54426 715-352-2351
Cari Guden, supt. Fax 352-3198
www.edgar.k12.wi.us
Edgar HS 200/9-12
PO Box 196 54426 715-352-2352
Jordan Sinz, prin. Fax 352-3198
Edgar MS 100/6-8
PO Box 198 54426 715-352-2727
Jordan Sinz, prin. Fax 352-3022

Edgerton, Rock, Pop. 5,394
Edgerton SD 1,900/PK-12
200 Elm High Dr 53534 608-561-6100
Dr. Dennis Pauli, supt. Fax 884-9327
www.edgerton.k12.wi.us
Edgerton HS 500/9-12
200 Elm High Dr 53534 608-561-6020
Dr. Mark Coombs, prin. Fax 884-7969
Edgerton MS 400/6-8
300 Elm High Dr 53534 608-561-6030
Clark Bretthauer, prin. Fax 884-2279

Oaklawn Academy 200/7-9
432 Liguori Rd 53534 608-884-3425
Fr. Javier Gonzalez, prin. Fax 884-8175

Elcho, Langlade, Pop. 333
Elcho SD 300/PK-12
PO Box 800 54428 715-275-3225
William Fisher, supt. Fax 275-4388
www.elchoschool.org
Elcho HS 100/6-12
PO Box 800 54428 715-275-3707
Shawn Rude, prin. Fax 275-4388

Elkhart Lake, Sheboygan, Pop. 964
Elkhart Lake - Glenbeulah SD 500/PK-12
PO Box 326 53020 920-876-3381
Dr. Ann Buechel-Haack, supt. Fax 876-3511
www.elgs.k12.wi.us/
Elkhart Lake - Glenbeulah HS 200/9-12
PO Box 326 53020 920-876-3381
Jim Brown, prin. Fax 876-3511

Elkhorn, Walworth, Pop. 9,969
Elkhorn Area SD 3,000/K-12
3 N Jackson St 53121 262-723-3160
Jason Tadlock, supt. Fax 723-4652
www.elkhorn.k12.wi.us
Elkhorn Area HS 900/9-12
482 E Geneva St 53121 262-723-4920
Chris Trottier, prin. Fax 723-8092
Elkhorn Area MS 700/6-8
627 E Court St 53121 262-723-6800
Bryan Frost, prin. Fax 723-4967

Gateway Technical College Post-Sec.
400 County Road H 53121 262-741-8200
Wright Graduate University Post-Sec.
N7698 County Road H 53121 855-561-4347

Elk Mound, Dunn, Pop. 858
Elk Mound Area SD 1,200/PK-12
405 University St 54739 715-879-5066
Eric Wright, supt. Fax 879-5846
www.elkmound.k12.wi.us
Elk Mound HS 300/9-12
405 University St 54739 715-879-5521
Paul Weber, prin. Fax 879-5846
Elk Mound MS 400/5-8
302 University St 54739 715-879-5595
Christopher Hahn, prin. Fax 879-5886

Ellsworth, Pierce, Pop. 3,234
Ellsworth Community SD 1,700/PK-12
300 Hillcrest St 54011 715-273-3900
Barry Cain, supt. Fax 273-5775
www.ellsworth.k12.wi.us
Ellsworth HS 500/9-12
323 Hillcrest St 54011 715-273-3904
Mark Stoesz, prin. Fax 273-6824

Ellsworth MS 500/5-8
312 Panther Dr 54011 715-273-3908
Jon Dodge, prin. Fax 273-6834

Elm Grove, Waukesha, Pop. 5,869
Elmbrook SD
Supt. — See Brookfield
Pilgrim Park MS 800/6-8
1500 Pilgrim Pkwy 53122 262-785-3920
Mark Peperkorn, prin. Fax 785-3933

Elmwood, Pierce, Pop. 815
Elmwood SD 300/PK-12
213 S Scott St 54740 715-639-2711
Paul Blanford Ed.D., supt. Fax 639-3110
www.elmwood.k12.wi.us
Elmwood HS 100/9-12
213 S Scott St 54740 715-639-2721
Christopher Segerstrom, prin. Fax 639-3110
Elmwood MS 100/6-8
213 S Scott St 54740 715-639-2721
Christopher Segerstrom, prin. Fax 639-3110

Elroy, Juneau, Pop. 1,424
Royall SD 500/PK-12
1501 Academy St 53929 608-462-2600
Mark Gruen, supt. Fax 462-2618
www.royall.k12.wi.us
Royall MSHS 200/7-12
1501 Academy St 53929 608-462-2600
Scott Uppena, prin. Fax 462-2618

Evansville, Rock, Pop. 4,947
Evansville Community SD 1,700/PK-12
340 Fair St 53536 608-882-5224
Jerry Roth, supt. Fax 882-6564
www.evansville.k12.wi.us
Evansville HS 500/9-12
640 S 5th St 53536 608-882-4600
Scott Everson, prin. Fax 882-6157
McKenna MS 400/6-8
307 S 1st St 53536 608-882-4780
Jason Knott, prin. Fax 882-5744

Fall Creek, Eau Claire, Pop. 1,306
Fall Creek SD 800/PK-12
336 E Hoover Ave 54742 715-877-2123
Dr. Joseph Sanfelippo, supt. Fax 877-2911
www.fallcreek.k12.wi.us
Fall Creek HS 300/9-12
336 E Hoover Ave 54742 715-877-2809
Brian Schulner, prin. Fax 877-2911
Fall Creek MS 200/6-8
336 E Hoover Ave 54742 715-877-2511
Brad LaPoint, prin. Fax 877-2911

Fall River, Columbia, Pop. 1,685
Fall River SD 500/PK-12
PO Box 116 53932 920-484-3333
Michael Garrow, supt. Fax 484-3600
www.fallriver.k12.wi.us
Fall River HS 300/6-12
PO Box 116 53932 920-484-3333
Brian Zacho, prin. Fax 484-3600

Fennimore, Grant, Pop. 2,489
Fennimore Community SD 700/PK-12
1397 9th St 53809 608-822-3243
Jamie Nutter, supt. Fax 822-3250
www.fennimore.k12.wi.us
Fennimore JSHS 300/6-12
510 7th St 53809 608-822-3245
Dan Bredeson, prin. Fax 822-3247

Southwest Wisconsin Technical College Post-Sec.
1800 Bronson Blvd 53809 608-822-3262

Fish Creek, Door
Gibraltar Area SD 600/PK-12
3924 State Highway 42 54212 920-868-3284
Tina Van Meer, supt. Fax 868-2714
www.gibraltar.k12.wi.us
Gibraltar HS 200/9-12
3924 State Highway 42 54212 920-868-3284
Dr. Gereon Methner, prin. Fax 868-2714
Gibraltar MS 100/7-8
3924 State Highway 42 54212 920-868-3284
Dr. Gereon Methner, prin. Fax 868-2714

Fitchburg, Dane, Pop. 24,633
Verona Area SD
Supt. — See Verona
Savanna Oaks MS 500/6-8
5890 Lacy Rd 53711 608-845-4000
Sandy Eskrich, prin. Fax 845-4020

Florence, Florence, Pop. 589
Florence SD 400/PK-12
PO Box 440 54121 715-528-3217
Ben Niehaus, supt. Fax 528-5338
www.myflorence.org
Florence HS 100/9-12
PO Box 440 54121 715-528-3215
Brandon Jerue, admin. Fax 528-5330
Florence MS 50/7-8
PO Box 440 54121 715-528-3215
Brandon Jerue, admin. Fax 528-5338

Fond du Lac, Fond du Lac, Pop. 42,372
Fond du Lac SD 7,400/PK-12
72 W 9th St 54935 920-929-2900
James Sebert Ed.D., supt. Fax 929-6804
www.fonddulac.k12.wi.us
Fond du Lac HS 2,000/9-12
801 Campus Dr 54935 920-929-2740
Michelle Hagen, prin. Fax 929-6964
Sabish MS 500/6-8
100 N Peters Ave 54935 920-929-2800
Torrie Rochon-Luft, prin. Fax 929-2807
Theisen MS 500/6-8
525 E Pioneer Rd 54935 920-929-2850
Brad Nerat, prin. Fax 929-2854
Woodworth MS 500/6-8
101 Morningside Dr 54935 920-929-6900
Steven Hill, prin. Fax 929-6944

Fond du Lac Christian S 100/PK-12
720 Rienzi Rd 54935 920-924-2177
Dr. Wendy Lundberg, admin. Fax 322-9459
Marian University Post-Sec.
45 S National Ave 54935 920-923-7600
Moraine Park Technical College Post-Sec.
235 N National Ave 54935 920-922-8611
St. Mary's Springs Academy 200/PK-12
255 County Road K 54937 920-921-4870
Erin Flood, prin. Fax 921-2786
University of Wisconsin Fond du Lac Post-Sec.
400 University Dr 54935 920-929-1100
Winnebago Lutheran Academy 400/9-12
475 E Merrill Ave 54935 920-921-4930
David Schroeder, prin. Fax 921-4280

Fort Atkinson, Jefferson, Pop. 12,238
Fort Atkinson SD 2,800/PK-12
201 Park St 53538 920-563-7800
Dr. Jeff Zaspel, supt. Fax 563-7809
www.fortschools.org
Fort Atkinson HS 1,000/9-12
925 Lexington Blvd 53538 920-563-7811
Dan Halvorsen, prin. Fax 563-7810
Fort Atkinson MS 600/6-8
310 S 4th St E 53538 920-563-7833
Robert Abbott, prin. Fax 563-7838

Fountain City, Buffalo, Pop. 848
Cochrane-Fountain City SD 700/PK-12
S2770 State Road 35 54629 608-687-7771
Thomas Hiebert, supt. Fax 687-3312
www.cfc.k12.wi.us
Cochrane-Fountain City JSHS 300/7-12
S2770 State Road 35 54629 608-687-4391
Steve Stoppelmoor, prin. Fax 687-6412

Fox Point, Milwaukee, Pop. 6,600
Fox Point Bayside SD 900/PK-8
7300 N Lombardy Rd 53217 414-247-4167
Dr. Robert Kobylski, supt. Fax 351-7164
www.foxbay.k12.wi.us
Other Schools – See Bayside

Maple Dale-Indian Hill SD 500/PK-8
8377 N Port Washington Rd 53217 414-351-7380
Jennifer Wimmer, supt.
www.mapledale.k12.wi.us
Maple Dale S 300/3-8
8377 N Port Washington Rd 53217 414-351-7380
Tim Reymer, prin.

Franklin, Milwaukee, Pop. 34,981
Franklin SD 4,400/PK-12
8255 W Forest Hill Ave 53132 414-529-8220
Steve Patz, supt. Fax 529-8230
www.franklin.k12.wi.us
Forest Park MS 700/7-8
8225 W Forest Hill Ave 53132 414-529-8250
Christopher Reuter, prin. Fax 529-8249
Franklin HS 1,500/9-12
8222 S 51st St 53132 414-423-4640
Michael Nowak, prin. Fax 421-0558

Frederic, Polk, Pop. 1,124
Frederic SD 500/PK-12
1437 Clam Falls Dr 54837 715-327-5630
Josh Robinson, admin. Fax 327-5609
www.frederic.k12.wi.us/
Frederic 6-12 S 200/6-12
1437 Clam Falls Dr 54837 715-327-4223
Ryan Fitzgerald, prin. Fax 327-8655

Fredonia, Ozaukee, Pop. 2,138
Northern Ozaukee SD 1,300/PK-12
401 Highland Dr 53021 262-692-2489
Dave Karrels, supt. Fax 692-6257
www.nosd.edu
Ozaukee HS 200/9-12
401 Highland Dr 53021 262-692-2453
Tom Dorgan, prin. Fax 692-6257
Ozaukee MS 200/6-8
401 Highland Dr 53021 262-692-2463
Charles Schwartz, prin. Fax 692-2313

Freedom, Outagamie
Freedom Area SD 1,600/PK-12
N4021 County Rd E, Kaukauna WI 54130
920-788-7944
Kevin Kilstofte, supt. Fax 788-7949
www.freedomschools.k12.wi.us
Freedom HS 500/9-12
N4021 County Rd E, Kaukauna WI 54130
920-788-7940
Kurt Erickson, prin. Fax 788-7700
Freedom MS 400/6-8
N4021 County Rd E, Kaukauna WI 54130
920-788-7945
Ken Fisher, prin. Fax 788-7701

Friendship, Adams, Pop. 720
Adams-Friendship Area SD 1,600/PK-12
201 W 6th St 53934 608-339-3213
Rick Waski, supt. Fax 339-6213
www.afasd.net
Other Schools – See Adams

Galesville, Trempealeau, Pop. 1,463
Galesville-Ettrick-Trempealeau SD 1,400/PK-12
PO Box 4000 54630 608-582-4657
Aaron Engel, supt. Fax 582-4961
www.getsd.org
Coulee Region HS Alt
16935 N Main St 54630 608-582-2200
Troy White, prin. Fax 582-4263
Gale-Ettrick-Tremp HS 400/9-12
PO Box 4000 54630 608-582-2291
Troy White, prin. Fax 582-4263
Gale-Ettrick-Tremp MS 300/6-8
19650 Prairie Ridge Ln 54630 608-582-3500
Matt Wenthe, prin. Fax 582-3501

Genoa City, Walworth, Pop. 3,006
Genoa City J2 SD 600/PK-8
PO Box 250 53128 262-279-1051
Kellie Bohn, supt. Fax 279-1052
Brookwood MS 300/4-8
PO Box 250 53128 262-279-1053
Pam Larson, prin. Fax 279-1052

Germantown, Washington, Pop. 19,491
Germantown SD 3,900/PK-12
N104W13840 Donges Bay Rd 53022 262-253-3900
Jeff Holmes, supt. Fax 251-6999
www.germantown.k12.wi.us
Germantown HS 1,400/9-12
W180N11501 River Ln 53022 262-253-3400
Joel Farren, prin. Fax 253-3494
Kennedy MS 900/6-8
W160N11836 Crusader Ct 53022 262-253-3450
Susan Climer, prin. Fax 253-3499

Gillett, Oconto, Pop. 1,370
Gillett SD 500/PK-12
PO Box 227 54124 920-855-2137
Todd Carlson, supt. Fax 855-1557
www.gillett.k12.wi.us
Gillett HS 200/9-12
PO Box 227 54124 920-855-2137
Steve Linssen, prin. Fax 855-6600
Gillett MS 100/6-8
PO Box 227 54124 920-855-2137
Steve Linssen, prin. Fax 855-6600

Gilman, Taylor, Pop. 409
Gilman SD 400/PK-12
325 N 5th Ave 54433 715-447-8211
Georgia Kraus, supt. Fax 447-8731
www.gilman.k12.wi.us
Gilman JSHS 200/7-12
325 N 5th Ave 54433 715-447-8211
Daniel Peggs, prin. Fax 447-8731

Gilmanton, Buffalo
Gilmanton SD 200/PK-12
PO Box 28 54743 715-946-3158
Glen Denk, supt. Fax 946-3474
www.ghs.k12.wi.us
Gilmanton HS 100/9-12
PO Box 28 54743 715-946-3158
Kory Rud, prin. Fax 946-3474
Gilmanton MS 50/5-8
PO Box 28 54743 715-946-3158
Kory Rud, prin. Fax 946-3174

Glendale, Milwaukee, Pop. 12,578
Glendale-River Hills SD 1,000/PK-8
2600 W Mill Rd 53209 414-351-7170
Larry Smalley, supt. Fax 434-0109
www.glendale.k12.wi.us
Glen Hills MS 500/4-8
2600 W Mill Rd 53209 414-351-7160
Fax 351-8100

Nicolet UNHSD 1,100/9-12
6701 N Jean Nicolet Rd 53217 414-351-7520
Robert Kobylski, supt. Fax 351-7526
nicolet.k12.wi.us/
Nicolet Union HS 1,100/9-12
6701 N Jean Nicolet Rd 53217 414-351-7524
Greg Kabara, prin. Fax 351-7526

Bryant & Stratton College Post-Sec.
500 W Silver Spring Dr K340 53217 414-961-9600
Columbia College of Nursing Post-Sec.
4425 N Port Washington Rd 53212 414-326-2330

Glenwood City, Saint Croix, Pop. 1,234
Glenwood City SD 700/PK-12
850 Maple St 54013 715-265-4757
Timothy Johnson, supt. Fax 265-4214
www.gcsd.k12.wi.us
Glenwood City HS 200/9-12
850 Maple St 54013 715-265-4266
Patrick Gretzlock, prin. Fax 265-7129
Glenwood City MS 200/6-8
850 Maple St 54013 715-265-4266
Patrick Gretzlock, prin. Fax 265-7129

Glidden, Ashland, Pop. 505
Chequamegon SD
Supt. — See Park Falls
Chequamegon MS 200/6-8
64 S Grant St 54527 715-264-2141
Diana Rein, prin. Fax 264-3413

Goodman, Marinette, Pop. 271
Goodman-Armstrong Creek SD 100/PK-12
PO Box 160 54125 715-336-2575
Cory Hinkel, supt. Fax 336-2576
www.goodman.k12.wi.us
Goodman JSHS 50/6-12
PO Box 160 54125 715-336-2576
Cory Hinkel, prin. Fax 336-2576

Grafton, Ozaukee, Pop. 11,349
Grafton SD 2,100/PK-12
1900 Washington St 53024 262-376-5400
Jeff S. Nelson, supt. Fax 376-5599
www.grafton.k12.wi.us
Grafton HS 700/9-12
1950 Washington St 53024 262-376-5500
Scott Mantei, prin. Fax 376-5510
Long MS 300/6-8
700 Hickory St 53024 262-376-5800
Kevin Deering, prin. Fax 376-5810

Granton, Clark, Pop. 353
Granton Area SD 200/K-12
217 N Main St 54436 715-238-7292
Charles Buckel, supt. Fax 238-7288
www.granton.k12.wi.us
Granton HS 100/6-12
217 N Main St 54436 715-238-7175
Rhonda Opelt, prin. Fax 238-7827

Grantsburg, Burnett, Pop. 1,314
Grantsburg SD 1,400/PK-12
480 E James Ave 54840 715-463-5499
Joni Burgin, supt. Fax 463-2534
www.gk12.net/
Grantsburg HS 300/9-12
480 E James Ave 54840 715-463-2531
Joshua Watt, prin. Fax 463-5068
Grantsburg MS 300/4-8
480 E James Ave 54840 715-463-2455
Bill Morrin, prin. Fax 463-3209

Green Bay, Brown, Pop. 101,558
Ashwaubenon SD 3,300/PK-12
1055 Griffiths Ln 54304 920-492-2900
Brian Hanes, supt. Fax 492-2911
www.ashwaubenon.k12.wi.us
Ashwaubenon HS 1,100/9-12
2391 S Ridge Rd 54304 920-492-2950
Brian Nelsen, prin. Fax 492-2912
Parkview MS 700/6-8
955 Willard Dr 54304 920-492-2940
Kris Hucek, prin. Fax 492-2944

Green Bay Area SD 20,500/PK-12
PO Box 23387 54305 920-448-2000
Dr. Michelle Langenfeld, supt. Fax 448-3562
www.gbaps.org/
East HS 1,200/9-12
1415 E Walnut St 54301 920-448-2090
Lori Frerk, prin. Fax 448-2166
Edison MS 1,100/6-8
442 Alpine Dr 54302 920-391-2450
Jonathon Wiebel, prin. Fax 391-2531
Franklin MS 700/6-8
1233 Lore Ln 54303 920-492-2670
Jackie Hauser, prin. Fax 492-5563
Lombardi MS 900/6-8
1520 S Point Rd 54313 920-492-2625
Jim Van Abel, prin. Fax 492-5564
Minoka-Hill S Alt
325 N Roosevelt St 54301 920-448-2150
Aaron Norris, prin. Fax 448-3562
Preble HS 2,200/9-12
2222 Deckner Ave 54302 920-391-2400
Natasha Rowell, prin. Fax 391-2530
Southwest HS 1,200/9-12
1331 Packerland Dr 54304 920-492-2650
Rod Bohm, prin. Fax 492-5561
Washington MS 800/6-8
314 S Baird St 54301 920-448-2095
Margaret Lardinois, prin. Fax 448-3551
West HS 1,000/9-12
966 Shawano Ave 54303 920-492-2600
Mark Flaten, prin. Fax 492-2641

Howard-Suamico SD 5,900/PK-12
2706 Lineville Rd 54313 920-662-7878
Damian LaCroix, supt. Fax 662-9777
www.hssd.k12.wi.us
Bay Port HS 1,800/9-12
2710 Lineville Rd 54313 920-662-7000
Michael Frieder, prin. Fax 662-7291
Bay View MS 800/7-8
1217 Cardinal Ln 54313 920-662-8196
Steve Meyers, prin. Fax 662-7979

Bellin College Post-Sec.
3201 Eaton Rd 54311 920-433-6699
Bellin Hospital Post-Sec.
PO Box 23400 54305 920-433-3497
Empire Beauty School Post-Sec.
2575 W Mason St 54303 920-494-1430
Globe University Post-Sec.
2620 Development Dr 54311 920-264-1600
Green Bay Adventist Junior Academy 50/K-10
1422 Shawano Ave 54303 920-494-2741
Kiana Binford, prin. Fax 494-6507
Northeastern Wisconsin Lutheran HS 100/9-12
1311 S Robinson Ave 54311 920-469-6810
Chris Nelson, dir. Fax 469-2200
Northeast Wisconsin Technical College Post-Sec.
PO Box 19042 54307 920-498-5444
Notre Dame De La Baie Academy 700/9-12
610 Maryhill Dr 54303 920-429-6100
John Ravizza, prin. Fax 429-6168
Providence Academy 100/PK-12
1420 Division St 54303 920-592-0890
Rasmussen College Post-Sec.
904 S Taylor St Ste 100 54303 920-593-8400
St. Vincent Hospital Post-Sec.
PO Box 13508 54307 920-433-8155
University of Wisconsin Post-Sec.
2420 Nicolet Dr 54311 920-465-2000
Wisconsin College of Cosmetology Post-Sec.
PO Box 28257 54324 920-336-8888

Greendale, Milwaukee, Pop. 13,859
Greendale SD 2,600/PK-12
6815 Southway 53129 414-423-2700
Dr. Gary Kiltz, supt. Fax 423-2723
www.greendale.k12.wi.us
Greendale HS 900/9-12
6801 Southway 53129 414-423-0110
Steven Lodes, prin. Fax 423-1667
Greendale MS 600/6-8
6800 Schoolway 53129 414-423-2800
John Weiss, prin. Fax 423-2806

Luther HS 300/9-12
5201 S 76th St 53129 414-421-4000
Dr. Wayne Jensen, prin. Fax 421-4071

Greenfield, Milwaukee, Pop. 36,124
Greenfield SD 3,900/PK-12
4850 S 60th St 53220 414-855-2050
Lisa Elliott, supt. Fax 855-2051
www.greenfield.k12.wi.us
Greenfield HS 1,400/9-12
4800 S 60th St 53220 414-281-6200
Paul Thusius, prin. Fax 281-8860
Greenfield MS 800/6-8
3200 W Barnard Ave 53221 414-282-4700
Brad Iding, prin. Fax 282-1017

Whitnall SD 2,400/PK-12
5000 S 116th St 53228 414-525-8400
Dr. Lisa Olson, supt. Fax 525-8401
www.whitnall.com
Whitnall HS 800/9-12
5000 S 116th St 53228 414-525-8500
Jacquelyn Winter, prin. Fax 525-8501
Whitnall MS 500/6-8
5025 S 116th St 53228 414-525-8650
Lynn LeRoy, prin. Fax 525-8651

Green Lake, Green Lake, Pop. 956
Green Lake SD 300/PK-12
PO Box 369 54941 920-294-6411
Ken Bates, supt. Fax 294-6589
www.glsd.k12.wi.us
Green Lake JSHS 100/7-12
PO Box 369 54941 920-294-6411
Mary Allen, prin. Fax 294-6589

Greenville, Outagamie
Hortonville SD
Supt. — See Hortonville
Greenville MS 600/5-8
N1450 Fawn Ridge Dr 54942 920-757-7140
Travis Lawrence, prin. Fax 757-7141

Greenwood, Clark, Pop. 1,021
Greenwood SD 400/PK-12
PO Box 310 54437 715-267-6101
Todd Felhofer, supt. Fax 267-6113
www.greenwood.k12.wi.us/
Greenwood MSHS 200/7-12
PO Box 310 54437 715-267-6101
Todd C. Fischer, prin. Fax 267-6113

Gresham, Shawano, Pop. 545
Gresham SD 200/PK-12
501 Schabow St 54128 715-787-3211
Keary Mattson, supt. Fax 787-3951
www.gresham.k12.wi.us/
Gresham HS 100/9-12
501 Schabow St 54128 715-787-3211
Keary Mattson, prin. Fax 787-3951

Hales Corners, Milwaukee, Pop. 7,616

Sacred Heart School of Theology Post-Sec.
PO Box 429 53130 414-425-8300

Hammond, Saint Croix, Pop. 1,895
St. Croix Central SD 1,600/PK-12
PO Box 118 54015 715-796-2256
Tim Widiker, supt. Fax 796-2460
www.scc.k12.wi.us
St. Croix Central HS 400/9-12
1751 Broadway St 54015 715-796-5383
Kurt Soderberg, prin. Fax 796-5662
St. Croix Central MS 400/5-8
PO Box 118 54015 715-796-2256
Scott Woodington, prin. Fax 796-2460

Hartford, Washington, Pop. 14,070
Hartford J1 SD 1,800/PK-8
402 W Sumner St 53027 262-673-3155
Dr. Mark Smits, admin. Fax 673-3548
www.hartfordjt1.k12.wi.us
Central MS 500/6-8
1100 Cedar St 53027 262-673-8040
Joe Viste, prin. Fax 673-7596

Hartford UNHSD 1,400/9-12
805 Cedar St 53027 262-670-3200
Attila Weninger, supt. Fax 673-8943
www.huhs.org
Hartford Union HS 1,400/9-12
805 Cedar St 53027 262-670-3200
Daniel Dobner, prin. Fax 673-8943

Hartland, Waukesha, Pop. 8,992
Arrowhead UNHSD 2,300/9-12
700 North Ave 53029 262-369-3611
Laura Myrah, supt. Fax 367-7406
www.arrowheadschools.org
Arrowhead Union HS 2,300/9-12
700 North Ave 53029 262-369-3611
Gregg Wieczorek, prin. Fax 367-4693

Hartland-Lakeside J3 SD 1,200/PK-8
800 E North Shore Dr 53029 262-369-6700
Dr. Glenn Schilling, supt. Fax 369-6755
www.hartlake.org
North Shore MS 300/6-8
800 N Shore Dr 53029 262-369-6767
Michele Schmidt, prin. Fax 369-6766

Lake Country Lutheran HS 200/9-12
401 Campus Dr 53029 262-367-8600
Dwayne Jobst, prin. Fax 367-0611
University Lake S 300/PK-12
PO Box 290 53029 262-367-6011
Ron Smyczek, head sch Fax 367-3146

Hayward, Sawyer, Pop. 2,245
Hayward Community SD 1,900/PK-12
15930 W 5th St 54843 715-634-2619
Craig Olson, supt. Fax 634-3560
www.hayward.k12.wi.us
Hayward HS 600/9-12
15930 W 5th St 54843 715-634-2619
Todd Johnson, prin. Fax 634-2761
Hayward MS 400/6-8
15930 W 5th St 54843 715-634-2619
Hugh Duffy, prin. Fax 634-9953

Lac Courte Oreilles Ojibwa Comm College Post-Sec.
13466 W Trepania Rd 54843 715-634-4790

Hazel Green, Grant, Pop. 1,238
Southwestern Wisconsin SD 600/PK-12
PO Box 368 53811 608-854-2261
John Costello, supt. Fax 854-2305
www.swsd.k12.wi.us
Southwestern Wisconsin HS 200/9-12
PO Box 368 53811 608-854-2261
Cynthia Lacey, prin. Fax 854-2315

Hilbert, Calumet, Pop. 1,124
Hilbert SD 400/PK-12
PO Box 390 54129 920-853-3558
Anthony Sweere, supt. Fax 853-7030
www.hilbert.k12.wi.us
Hilbert HS 200/9-12
PO Box 390 54129 920-853-3558
Anthony Sweere, prin. Fax 853-7030
Hilbert MS 100/5-8
PO Box 390 54129 920-853-3558
Anthony Sweere, prin. Fax 853-7030

Hillsboro, Vernon, Pop. 1,405
Hillsboro SD 500/PK-12
PO Box 526 54634 608-489-2221
Curt Bisarek, supt. Fax 489-2811
www.hillsboro.k12.wi.us
Hillsboro MSHS 300/6-12
PO Box 526 54634 608-489-2221
Chris Koopman, prin. Fax 489-2811

Holcombe, Chippewa, Pop. 266
Lake Holcombe SD 100/PK-12
27331 262nd Ave 54745 715-595-4241
Jeffrey Mastin, supt. Fax 595-6383
www.lakeholcombe.k12.wi.us
Lake Holcombe S 100/PK-12
27331 262nd Ave 54745 715-595-4241
Mark Porter, prin. Fax 595-6383

Holmen, LaCrosse, Pop. 8,875
Holmen SD 3,900/PK-12
1019 McHugh Rd 54636 608-526-6610
Dr. Kristin Mueller, supt. Fax 526-1333
www.holmen.k12.wi.us
Holmen HS 1,100/9-12
1001 McHugh Rd 54636 608-526-3372
Robert Baer, prin. Fax 526-9446
Holmen MS 800/6-8
502 N Main St 54636 608-526-3391
Ryan Vogler, prin. Fax 526-6716

Horicon, Dodge, Pop. 3,609
Horicon SD 700/PK-12
611 Mill St 53032 920-485-2898
Richard Appel, supt. Fax 485-3601
www.horicon.k12.wi.us
Horicon JHS 100/7-8
841 Gray St 53032 920-485-4441
Teresa Graven, prin. Fax 485-3244
Horicon SHS 200/9-12
841 Gray St 53032 920-485-4441
Teresa Graven, prin. Fax 485-3244

Mountain Top Christian Academy 50/PK-12
W3941 State Road 33 53032 920-485-6630
Stacy Nummerdor, admin. Fax 485-0236

Hortonville, Outagamie, Pop. 2,685
Hortonville SD 3,400/PK-12
PO Box 70 54944 920-779-7900
Dr. Heidi Schmidt, supt. Fax 779-7903
www.hasd.org
Hortonville HS 1,100/9-12
155 Warner St 54944 920-779-7933
Todd Timm, prin. Fax 779-7935
Hortonville MS 400/5-8
220 Warner St 54944 920-779-7922
Steven Gromala, prin. Fax 779-7923
Other Schools – See Greenville

Howards Grove, Sheboygan, Pop. 3,170
Howards Grove SD 800/K-12
403 Audubon Rd 53083 920-565-4454
Christopher Peterson, supt. Fax 565-4461
www.hgsd.k12.wi.us
Howards Grove HS 300/9-12
401 Audubon Rd 53083 920-565-4450
Scott Fritz, prin. Fax 565-4451
Howards Grove MS 300/5-8
506 Kennedy Ave 53083 920-565-4452
Andy Hansen, prin. Fax 565-4460

Hudson, Saint Croix, Pop. 12,505
Hudson SD 5,600/PK-12
644 Brakke Dr 54016 715-377-3700
Dr. Nick Ouellette, supt. Fax 377-3726
www.hudsonraiders.org
Hudson HS 1,700/9-12
1501 Vine St 54016 715-377-3800
Peg Shoemaker, prin. Fax 377-3801
Hudson MS 1,300/6-8
1300 Carmichael Rd 54016 715-377-3820
Ann Mitchell, prin. Fax 377-3821

Hurley, Iron, Pop. 1,529
Hurley SD 300/PK-12
5503 W Range View Dr 54534 715-561-4900
Christopher Patritto, supt. Fax 561-4953
www.hurley.k12.wi.us
Hurley S 300/PK-12
5503 W Range View Dr 54534 715-561-4900
Melissa Oja, prin. Fax 561-4157

Hustisford, Dodge, Pop. 1,121
Hustisford SD 400/PK-12
PO Box 326 53034 920-349-8109
Heather Cramer Ph.D., supt. Fax 349-3716
www.hustisford.k12.wi.us
Hustisford JSHS 200/6-12
PO Box 326 53034 920-349-3261
Meg Perron, prin. Fax 349-8495

Independence, Trempealeau, Pop. 1,329
Independence SD 400/PK-12
23786 Indee Blvd 54747 715-985-3172
Barry Schmitt, supt. Fax 985-2303
www.indps.k12.wi.us
Independence HS 100/9-12
23786 Indee Blvd 54747 715-985-3172
Barry Schmitt, prin. Fax 985-2303

Iola, Waupaca, Pop. 1,297
Iola-Scandinavia SD 700/PK-12
450 Division St 54945 715-445-2411
David C. Dyb Ed.D., supt. Fax 445-4468
www.iola.k12.wi.us
Iola-Scandinavia MSHS 400/7-12
540 S Jackson St 54945 715-445-2411
Sara Anderson, prin. Fax 445-5119

Jackson, Washington, Pop. 6,685

Kettle Moraine Lutheran HS 400/9-12
3399 Division Rd 53037 262-677-4051
David Bartelt, supt. Fax 677-4290
Living Word Lutheran HS 200/9-12
2230 Living Word Ln 53037 262-677-9353
Dave Miskimen, prin. Fax 677-8357

Janesville, Rock, Pop. 62,455
Janesville SD 10,400/PK-12
527 S Franklin St, 608-743-5000
Dr. Karen Schulte, supt. Fax 743-5110
www.janesville.k12.wi.us
Craig HS 1,600/9-12
401 S Randall Ave 53545 608-743-5200
Dr. Alison Bjoin, prin. Fax 743-5150
Edison MS 700/6-8
1649 S Chatham St 53546 608-743-5900
James Lemire, prin. Fax 743-5910
Franklin MS 600/6-8
450 N Crosby Ave, 608-743-6000
Charles Urness Ph.D., prin. Fax 743-6010
Marshall MS 900/6-8
25 S Pontiac Dr 53545 608-743-6200
Synthia Taylor, prin. Fax 743-6210
Parker HS 1,400/9-12
3125 Mineral Point Ave, 608-743-5600
Chris Laue, prin. Fax 743-5550

Blackhawk Technical College Post-Sec.
PO Box 5009 53547 608-758-6900
University of Wisconsin Rock County Post-Sec.
2909 Kellogg Ave 53546 608-758-6565
WI School for Visually Handicapped Post-Sec.
1700 W State St 53546 608-758-6100

Jefferson, Jefferson, Pop. 7,891
Jefferson SD 1,900/PK-12
206 S Taft Ave 53549 920-675-1000
Mark Rollefsonm, supt. Fax 675-1020
www.sdoj.org
Jefferson HS 600/9-12
700 W Milwaukee St 53549 920-675-1100
Stephen Dinkel, prin. Fax 675-1120
Jefferson MS 400/6-8
501 S Taft Ave 53549 920-675-1300
David Wallace, prin. Fax 675-1320

St. Coletta School, RR 1 Box 43 53549 Post-Sec.

Johnson Creek, Jefferson, Pop. 2,707
Johnson Creek SD 600/PK-12
PO Box 39 53038 920-699-2811
Michael Garvey Ph.D., supt. Fax 699-2801
www.johnsoncreek.k12.wi.us/
Johnson Creek MSHS 300/5-12
PO Box 39 53038 920-699-3481
Neil O'Connell, prin. Fax 699-3566

Juda, Green, Pop. 357
Juda SD 300/PK-12
N2385 Spring St 53550 608-934-5251
Traci Davis, supt. Fax 934-5254
www.judaschool.com
Juda HS 100/9-12
N2385 Spring St 53550 608-934-5251
Traci Davis, prin. Fax 934-5254

Juneau, Dodge, Pop. 2,802
Dodgeland SD 800/PK-12
401 S Western Ave 53039 920-386-4404
Annette Thompson, supt. Fax 386-4498
www.dodgeland.k12.wi.us
Dodgeland HS 300/9-12
401 S Western Ave 53039 920-386-4404
Jeffrey Sauer, prin. Fax 386-2601
Dodgeland MS 200/6-8
401 S Western Ave 53039 920-386-4404
Marcia Modaff, prin. Fax 386-0345

Kaukauna, Outagamie, Pop. 15,244
Kaukauna Area SD 3,900/PK-12
1701 County Road CE 54130 920-766-6100
Mark Duerwaechter, admin. Fax 766-6104
www.kaukauna.k12.wi.us
Kaukauna HS 1,100/9-12
1701 County Road CE 54130 920-766-6113
Mike Werbowsky, prin. Fax 766-6157
River View MS 1,100/5-8
101 Oak St 54130 920-766-6111
Dan Joseph, prin. Fax 766-6109

Kenosha, Kenosha, Pop. 96,606
Kenosha SD 21,900/PK-12
3600 52nd St 53144 262-359-6300
Dr. Sue Savaglio-Jarvis, supt. Fax 359-7672
www.kusd.edu
Bradford HS 1,500/9-12
3700 Washington Rd 53144 262-359-6200
Dr. Kurt Sinclair, prin. Fax 359-5948
Bullen MS 800/6-8
2804 39th Ave 53144 262-359-4460
Andy Baumgart, prin. Fax 359-4487
Hillcrest S 50/Alt
4616 24th St 53144 262-359-6118
Eitan Benzaquen, prin. Fax 359-7870
Indian Trail HS & Academy 2,200/9-12
6800 60th St 53144 262-359-8700
Maria Kotz, prin. Fax 359-8756
Lance MS 1,000/6-8
4515 80th St 53142 262-359-2240
Chad Dahlk, prin. Fax 359-2184
Lincoln MS 800/6-8
6729 18th Ave 53143 262-359-6296
Star Daley, prin. Fax 359-5966
Mahone MS 1,100/6-8
6900 60th St 53144 262-359-8100
Terri Huck, prin. Fax 359-6851
Reuther Central HS 400/Alt
913 57th St 53140 262-359-6160
Karen Walters, prin. Fax 359-6281
Tremper HS 1,800/9-12
8560 26th Ave 53143 262-359-2200
Richard Aiello, prin. Fax 359-2187
Washington MS 600/6-8
811 Washington Rd 53140 262-359-6291
Curtiss Tolefree, prin. Fax 359-6056
Other Schools – See Pleasant Prairie

Carthage College Post-Sec.
2001 Alford Park Dr 53140 262-551-8500
Christian Life S 800/PK-12
10700 75th St 53142 262-694-3900
Rev. Susan Nelson, supt. Fax 694-3312
Gateway Technical College Post-Sec.
3520 30th Ave 53144 262-564-2200
St. Joseph Catholic Academy 500/6-12
2401 69th St 53143 262-654-8651
Karen Earle, prin. Fax 654-1615
University of Wisconsin Post-Sec.
PO Box 2000 53141 262-595-2345

Keshena, Menominee, Pop. 1,238
Menominee Indian SD 800/PK-12
PO Box 1330 54135 715-799-3824
Wendell Waukau, supt. Fax 799-4659
www.misd.k12.wi.us
Menominee Indian HS 300/9-12
PO Box 850 54135 715-799-3846
James Reif, prin. Fax 799-5558
Other Schools – See Neopit

College of Menominee Nation Post-Sec.
PO Box 1179 54135 715-799-5600

Kewaskum, Washington, Pop. 3,967
Kewaskum SD 1,800/PK-12
PO Box 37 53040 262-626-8427
James Smasal, supt. Fax 626-2961
www.kewaskumschools.org
Kewaskum Career Academy Vo/Tech
PO Box 426 53040 262-626-8427
Scott Jornlin, prin. Fax 626-4702
Kewaskum HS 600/9-12
PO Box 426 53040 262-626-8427
William Loss, prin. Fax 626-4214
Kewaskum MS 400/6-8
PO Box 432 53040 262-626-8427
Julie Skelton, prin. Fax 626-4214

Kewaunee, Kewaunee, Pop. 2,918
Kewaunee SD 1,000/PK-12
915 2nd St 54216 920-388-3230
Karen Treml, supt. Fax 388-5174
www.kewaunee.k12.wi.us
Kewaunee HS 300/9-12
911 3rd St 54216 920-388-2951
Michael Holtz, prin. Fax 388-5165
Kewaunee MS 200/6-8
921 3rd St 54216 920-388-2458
Kacy Rohr, prin. Fax 388-5696
Lakeshore Alternative S 50/Alt
915 2nd St 54216 920-388-3230
Michael Holtz, prin. Fax 388-5174

Kiel, Manitowoc, Pop. 3,708
Kiel Area SD 1,300/PK-12
PO Box 201 53042 920-894-2266
Dr. Louise Blankenheim, supt. Fax 894-5100
www.kiel.k12.wi.us/
Kiel HS 400/9-12
PO Box 218 53042 920-894-2263
Heidi Dorner, prin. Fax 894-5101
Kiel MS 400/5-8
PO Box 197 53042 920-894-2264
Dr. Deborah Sixel, prin. Fax 894-5100

Kieler, Grant, Pop. 494

Holy Ghost/Immaculate Conception S 50/4-8
PO Box 129 53812 608-568-7220
Fax 568-3811

Kimberly, Outagamie, Pop. 6,394
Kimberly Area SD
Supt. — See Combined Locks
Gerritts MS 700/7-8
545 S John St 54136 920-788-7905
Eric Brinkmann, prin. Fax 788-7914
Kimberly HS 1,400/9-12
1662 E Kennedy Ave 54136 920-687-3024
Michael Rietveld, prin. Fax 687-3029

Kohler, Sheboygan, Pop. 2,103
Kohler SD 800/PK-12
333 Upper Rd 53044 920-803-7200
Quynh Trueblood, supt. Fax 459-2930
www.kohlerpublicschools.org/
Kohler HS 200/9-12
333 Upper Rd 53044 920-803-7202
Timothy Brown, prin. Fax 459-2930
Kohler MS 200/6-8
333 Upper Rd 53044 920-803-7202
Timothy Brown, prin. Fax 459-2930

La Crosse, LaCrosse, Pop. 50,284
La Crosse SD 6,800/PK-12
807 East Ave S 54601 608-789-7600
Randy Nelson, supt. Fax 789-7960
www.lacrosseschools.org/
Central HS 1,100/9-12
1801 Losey Blvd S 54601 608-789-7900
Jeffrey Fleig, prin. Fax 789-7931
Lincoln MS 400/6-8
510 9th St S 54601 608-789-7780
Melissa Murray, prin. Fax 789-7181
Logan HS 800/9-12
1500 Ranger Dr 54603 608-789-7700
Dr. Deborah Markos, prin. Fax 789-7711
Logan MS 400/6-8
1450 Avon St 54603 608-789-7740
Jay Pica, prin. Fax 789-7754
Longfellow MS 500/6-8
1900 Denton St 54601 608-789-7670
Penny Reedy, prin. Fax 789-7975
7 Rivers Community HS Alt
807 East Ave S 54601 608-789-8940
Penny Reedy, prin.

Aquinas HS 400/9-12
315 11th St S 54601 608-784-0287
Ted Knutson, prin. Fax 782-8851
Aquinas MS South Campus 100/7-8
315 11th St S 54601 608-784-0156
Patricia Kosmatka, prin. Fax 784-0229
Gunderson Medical Foundation Post-Sec.
1836 South Ave 54601 608-782-7300
Providence Academy 100/PK-12
716 Windsor St 54603 608-784-6167
University of Wisconsin La Crosse Post-Sec.
1725 State St 54601 608-785-8000
Viterbo University Post-Sec.
900 Viterbo Dr 54601 608-796-3000
Western Technical College Post-Sec.
400 7th St N 54601 608-785-9200

Ladysmith, Rusk, Pop. 3,376
Ladysmith SD 800/PK-12
1700 Edgewood Ave E 54848 715-532-5277
Paul Uhren, supt. Fax 532-7445
ladysmith.k12.wi.us
Ladysmith HS 300/9-12
1700 Edgewood Ave E 54848 715-532-5531
Robert Lecheler, prin. Fax 532-5961
Ladysmith MS 200/6-8
1700 Edgewood Ave E 54848 715-532-5252
Andrew Grimm, prin. Fax 532-7455

La Farge, Vernon, Pop. 740
La Farge SD 200/PK-12
301 W Adams St 54639 608-625-0107
Shawn Donovan, supt. Fax 625-0118
www.lafarge.k12.wi.us/
La Farge HS 100/9-12
301 W Adams St 54639 608-625-2400
Angela Egge, prin. Fax 625-0152
La Farge MS 50/6-8
301 W Adams St 54639 608-625-2400
Angela Egge, prin. Fax 625-0152

Lake Geneva, Walworth, Pop. 7,583
Lake Geneva J1 SD 2,200/PK-8
208 E South St 53147 262-348-1000
James Gottinger, supt. Fax 248-9704
www.lakegenevaschools.com
Lake Geneva MS 700/6-8
600 N Bloomfield Rd 53147 262-348-3000
Drew Halbesma, prin. Fax 348-3092

Lake Geneva-Genoa City UHSD 1,500/9-12
208 E South St 53147 262-348-1000
Dr. James Gottinger, supt. Fax 248-9704
www.lakegenevaschools.com
Badger HS 1,500/9-12
220 E South St 53147 262-348-2000
Bob Kopydlowski, prin. Fax 248-6178

Lake Mills, Jefferson, Pop. 5,657
Lake Mills Area SD 1,500/PK-12
120 E Lake Park Pl 53551 920-648-2215
Dean Sanders, supt. Fax 648-5795
www.lakemills.k12.wi.us
Lake Mills HS 400/9-12
615 Catlin Dr 53551 920-648-2355
Pamela Streich, prin. Fax 648-2357
Lake Mills MS 400/5-8
318 College St 53551 920-648-2358
Jennifer Nicholson, prin. Fax 648-8928

Lakeside Lutheran HS 400/9-12
231 Woodland Beach Rd 53551 920-648-2321
James Grasby, prin. Fax 648-5625

Lancaster, Grant, Pop. 3,854
Lancaster Community SD 900/PK-12
925 W Maple St 53813 608-723-2175
Rob Wagner, supt. Fax 723-6397
www.lancastersd.k12.wi.us
Lancaster HS 300/9-12
806 E Elm St 53813 608-723-2173
Mark Uppena, prin. Fax 723-2441
Lancaster MS 200/6-8
802 E Elm St 53813 608-723-6425
Mark Uppena, prin. Fax 723-6731

Land O Lakes, Vilas

Conserve S 50/10-11
5400 N Black Oak Lake Rd 54540 715-547-1300
Stefan Anderson, hdmstr. Fax 547-1386

Laona, Forest, Pop. 574
Laona SD 200/PK-12
5216 Forest Ave 54541 715-674-2143
Larry Palubicki, supt. Fax 674-5904
www.laona.k12.wi.us
Laona JSHS 100/7-12
5216 Forest Ave 54541 715-674-2143
Jim Bradley, prin. Fax 674-5904

Lena, Oconto, Pop. 558
Lena SD 400/PK-12
304 E Main St 54139 920-829-5703
Ben Pytleski, supt. Fax 829-5122
www.lena.k12.wi.us
Alternative S 50/Alt
304 E Main St 54139 920-829-5703
James Torzala, prin. Fax 829-5122
Lena HS 100/9-12
304 E Main St 54139 920-829-5244
James Torzala, prin. Fax 829-5122
Lena MS 100/6-8
304 E Main St 54139 920-829-5244
James Torzala, prin. Fax 829-5122

Little Chute, Outagamie, Pop. 10,339
Little Chute Area SD 1,500/PK-12
325 Meulemans St Ste A 54140 920-788-7605
David Botz, supt. Fax 788-7603
www.littlechute.k12.wi.us
Little Chute HS 400/9-12
1402 Freedom Rd 54140 920-788-7600
Daniel Valentyn, prin. Fax 788-7841
Little Chute MS 200/7-8
325 Meulemans St Ste B 54140 920-788-7607
Lori Van Handel, prin. Fax 788-7615

Livingston, Iowa, Pop. 663
Iowa-Grant SD 800/PK-12
498 County Road IG 53554 608-943-6311
Linda Erickson, supt. Fax 943-8438
www.igs.k12.wi.us
Iowa-Grant HS 200/9-12
462 County Road IG 53554 608-943-6312
Chris Gotto, prin. Fax 943-8707

Lodi, Columbia, Pop. 3,022
Lodi SD 1,500/PK-12
115 School St 53555 608-592-3851
Charles Pursell, supt. Fax 592-3852
www.lodi.k12.wi.us
Lodi HS 500/9-12
1100 Sauk St 53555 608-592-3853
Vincent Breunig, prin. Fax 592-1045
Lodi MS 400/6-8
900 Sauk St 53555 608-592-3854
Joe Prosek, prin. Fax 592-1035

Lomira, Dodge, Pop. 2,408
Lomira SD 1,000/PK-12
PO Box 919 53048 920-269-4396
Robert Lloyd, admin. Fax 269-4996
www.lomira.k12.wi.us/
Lomira HS 400/9-12
PO Box 919 53048 920-269-4396
Debra Janke, prin. Fax 269-4128
Lomira MS 300/6-8
PO Box 919 53048 920-269-4396
Robert Lloyd, prin. Fax 269-4996

Loyal, Clark, Pop. 1,258
Loyal SD 500/PK-12
PO Box 10 54446 715-255-8552
Cale Jackson, supt. Fax 255-8553
www.loyal.k12.wi.us
Loyal HS 200/9-12
PO Box 10 54446 715-255-8511
Christopher Lindner, prin. Fax 255-8553
Loyal JHS 100/7-8
PO Box 10 54446 715-255-8511
Christopher Lindner, prin. Fax 255-8553

Luck, Polk, Pop. 1,101
Luck SD 500/PK-12
810 S 7th St 54853 715-472-2152
Christopher Schultz, supt. Fax 472-2159
www.lucksd.k12.wi.us
Luck JSHS 200/7-12
810 S 7th St 54853 715-472-2151
Brad Werner, prin. Fax 472-2159

Luxemburg, Kewaunee, Pop. 2,502
Luxemburg-Casco SD 1,900/PK-12
PO Box 70 54217 920-845-2391
Glenn Schlender, supt. Fax 845-5871
www.luxcasco.k12.wi.us
Luxemburg-Casco HS 600/9-12
PO Box 410 54217 920-845-2336
Fax 845-2280

Other Schools – See Casco

Mc Farland, Dane, Pop. 7,692
Mc Farland SD 4,200/PK-12
5101 Farwell St 53558 608-838-3169
Andrew Briddell Ph.D., admin. Fax 838-3074
www.mcfarland.k12.wi.us
Indian Mound MS 500/6-8
6330 Exchange St 53558 608-838-8980
Erin Tarnutzer, prin. Fax 838-4588
Mc Farland HS 700/9-12
5103 Farwell St 53558 608-838-3166
Jeff Finstad, prin. Fax 838-4562

Madison, Dane, Pop. 226,807
Madison Metro SD 25,300/PK-12
545 W Dayton St 53703 608-663-1879
Jennifer Cheatham, supt. Fax 204-0342
www.madison.k12.wi.us
Black Hawk MS 400/6-8
1402 Wyoming Way 53704 608-204-4360
Kenya Walker, prin. Fax 204-0368
Cherokee Heights MS 500/6-8
4301 Cherokee Dr 53711 608-204-1240
Kevin Brown, prin. Fax 204-0378
East HS 1,600/9-12
2222 E Washington Ave 53704 608-204-1600
Michael Hernandez, prin. Fax 204-0388
Hamilton MS 800/6-8
4801 Waukesha St 53705 608-204-4620
Jessica Taylor, prin. Fax 204-0417
Innovative & Alternative Education 50/Alt
1045 E Dayton St 53703 608-204-4220
Karyn Stocks-Glover, prin. Fax 204-1580
Jefferson MS 600/6-8
101 S Gammon Rd 53717 608-663-6403
Issac Kirkwood, prin. Fax 442-2193
LaFollette HS 1,500/9-12
702 Pflaum Rd 53716 608-204-3600
Sean Storch, prin. Fax 204-0435
Memorial HS 1,800/9-12
201 S Gammon Rd 53717 608-663-5990
Jay Affeldt, prin. Fax 442-2197
O'Keeffe MS 400/6-8
510 S Thornton Ave 53703 608-204-6820
Tony Dugas, prin. Fax 204-0561
Sennett MS 600/6-8
502 Pflaum Rd 53716 608-204-1920
Tremayne Clardy, prin. Fax 204-0495
Shabazz-City HS 100/Alt
1601 N Sherman Ave 53704 608-204-2440
Aric Soderbloom, prin. Fax 204-0503
Sherman MS 400/6-8
1610 Ruskin St 53704 608-204-2100
Kristin Foreman, prin. Fax 204-0501
Spring Harbor MS 300/6-8
1110 Spring Harbor Dr 53705 608-204-1100
Pam Waite, prin. Fax 204-0509
Toki MS 500/6-8
5606 Russett Rd 53711 608-204-4740
Nicole Schaefer, prin. Fax 204-0523
West HS 2,000/9-12
30 Ash St 53726 608-204-4100
Beth Thompson, prin. Fax 204-0529
Whitehorse MS 500/6-8
218 Schenk St 53714 608-204-4480
Deborah Ptak, prin. Fax 204-0538

Abundant Life Christian S 300/K-12
4901 E Buckeye Rd 53716 608-221-1520
Doug Butler, prin. Fax 221-8572
Edgewood College Post-Sec.
1000 Edgewood College Dr 53711 608-663-4861
Edgewood HS 600/9-12
2219 Monroe St 53711 608-257-1023
Robert Growney, prin. Fax 257-9133
Empire Beauty School Post-Sec.
6414 Odana Rd 53719 608-270-0188
Globe University Post-Sec.
4901 Eastpark Blvd 53718 608-216-9400
Herzing University Post-Sec.
5218 E Terrace Dr 53718 608-249-6611
Madison Area Technical College Post-Sec.
1701 Wright St 53704 608-246-6100
Madison Media Institute Post-Sec.
2702 Agriculture Dr 53718 608-663-2000
St. Ambose Academy 100/6-12
602 Everglade Dr 53717 608-827-5863
Scott Schmiesing, prin.
University of Wisconsin Post-Sec.
500 Lincoln Dr 53706 608-262-1234

Manawa, Waupaca, Pop. 1,362
Manawa SD 700/PK-12
800 Beech St 54949 920-596-2525
Dr. Melanie Oppor, supt. Fax 596-5308
www.manawaschools.org
Little Wolf JSHS 300/7-12
515 E 4th St 54949 920-596-5800
Daniel Wolfgram, prin. Fax 596-2655

Manitowoc, Manitowoc, Pop. 33,258
Manitowoc SD 5,200/PK-12
PO Box 1657 54221 920-686-4777
Mark Holzman, supt. Fax 686-4780
www.manitowocpublicschools.org
Lincoln SHS 1,200/10-12
1433 S 8th St 54220 920-683-4861
Luke Valitchka, prin. Fax 683-4845
Washington JHS 600/7-9
2101 Division St 54220 920-683-4857
Kathleen Lemberger, prin. Fax 683-7989
Wilson JHS 500/7-9
1201 N 11th St 54220 920-683-4859
Lee Thennes, prin. Fax 683-7988

Empire Beauty School Post-Sec.
1034 S 18th St 54220 920-684-3028
Manitowoc Lutheran HS 200/9-12
4045 Lancer Cir 54220 920-682-0215
Ryan Rathje, prin. Fax 682-2363

Roncalli HS 400/9-12
2000 Mirro Dr 54220 920-682-8801
Tim Olson, prin. Fax 686-8110
St. Francis of Assisi MS 200/6-8
2109 Marshall St 54220 920-683-6884
Steve Thiele, prin. Fax 683-6882
Silver Lake College of the Holy Family Post-Sec.
2406 S Alverno Rd 54220 920-684-6691
University of Wisconsin Manitowoc Post-Sec.
705 Viebahn St 54220 920-683-4700

Maple, Douglas
Maple SD 1,400/PK-12
PO Box 188 54854 715-363-2431
Dr. Sara Croney, supt. Fax 363-2191
www.nw-tigers.org
Northwestern HS 400/9-12
PO Box 218 54854 715-363-2434
Mark Carlson, prin. Fax 363-2523
Other Schools – See Poplar

Marathon, Marathon, Pop. 1,520
Marathon City SD 700/PK-12
PO Box 37 54448 715-443-2226
Richard Parks, supt. Fax 443-2611
www.marathon.k12.wi.us
Marathon HS 200/9-12
PO Box 37 54448 715-443-2226
David Beranek, prin. Fax 443-2611

Marinette, Marinette, Pop. 10,850
Marinette SD 2,100/PK-12
2139 Pierce Ave 54143 715-735-1400
Dr. Wendy Dzurick, supt. Fax 732-7930
www.marinette.k12.wi.us
Marinette HS 600/9-12
2135 Pierce Ave 54143 715-735-1300
Justine Braatz, prin. Fax 732-7929
Marinette MS 600/5-8
1011 Water St 54143 715-735-1500
Michael Whisler, prin. Fax 732-7939

Northeast Wisconsin Technical College Post-Sec.
1601 University Dr 54143 715-735-9361
St. Thomas Aquinas Academy 100/PK-12
1200 Main St 54143 715-735-7481
Peter Mayhew, admin. Fax 735-3375
University of Wisconsin Marinette Post-Sec.
750 W Bay Shore St 54143 715-735-4300

Marion, Waupaca, Pop. 1,253
Marion SD 500/PK-12
1001 N Main St 54950 715-754-2511
James Bena, supt. Fax 754-4508
www.marion.k12.wi.us
Marion JSHS 200/7-12
105 School St 54950 715-754-5273
Daniel Breitrick, prin. Fax 754-1350

Markesan, Green Lake, Pop. 1,472
Markesan SD 700/PK-12
PO Box 248 53946 920-398-2373
Duane Bark, supt. Fax 398-3281
www.markesan.k12.wi.us
Markesan HS 200/9-12
PO Box 248 53946 920-398-2373
John Koopman, prin. Fax 398-3281
Markesan MS 200/6-8
PO Box 248 53946 920-398-2373
John Koopman, prin. Fax 398-3281

Marshall, Dane, Pop. 3,813
Marshall SD 1,200/PK-12
PO Box 76 53559 608-655-3466
Dr. Barb Sramek, supt. Fax 655-4481
www.marshall.k12.wi.us
Marshall HS 400/9-12
PO Box 76 53559 608-655-1310
Brian Sniff, prin. Fax 655-3046
Marshall MS 200/7-8
PO Box 76 53559 608-655-1571
Lisa Blochwitz, prin. Fax 655-1591

Marshfield, Wood, Pop. 18,924
Marshfield SD 3,800/PK-12
1010 E 4th St 54449 715-387-1101
Dr. Deirdre Wells, supt. Fax 387-0133
www.marshfieldschools.org
Marshfield HS 1,200/9-12
1401 E Becker Rd 54449 715-387-8464
Steve Sukawaty, prin. Fax 384-3589
Marshfield MS 600/7-8
900 E 4th St 54449 715-387-1249
David Schoepke, prin. Fax 384-9269

Columbus HS 100/9-12
710 S Columbus Ave 54449 715-387-1177
Steven VanWhye, prin. Fax 384-4535
Columbus MS 100/6-8
710 S Columbus Ave 54449 715-387-1177
Steven VanWhye, prin. Fax 384-4535
Marshfield Clinic/St. Josephs Hospital Post-Sec.
1000 N Oak Ave 54449 715-221-6332
Mid-State Technical College Post-Sec.
2600 W 5th St 54449 715-387-2538
St. Joseph Hospital/Marshfield Clinic Post-Sec.
611 N Saint Joseph Ave 54449 715-387-1713
Univ. of Wisconsin - Marshfield/Wood Co. Post-Sec.
2000 W 5th St 54449 715-389-6530

Mauston, Juneau, Pop. 4,366
Mauston SD 1,500/PK-12
510 Grayside Ave 53948 608-847-5451
Dr. Christine M. Weymouth, supt. Fax 847-4635
www.maustonschools.org
Mauston HS 500/9-12
800 Grayside Ave 53948 608-847-4410
Jim Dillin, prin. Fax 847-4802
Olson MS 300/6-8
508 Grayside Ave 53948 608-847-6603
Brian Bauer, prin. Fax 847-4925

Mayville, Dodge, Pop. 5,113
Mayville SD 1,300/PK-12
N8210 State Road 28 53050 920-387-7963
Scott Sabol, supt. Fax 387-7979
www.mayvilleschools.com
Mayville HS 400/9-12
500 N Clark St 53050 920-387-7960
Robert Clark, prin. Fax 387-7977
Mayville MS 500/3-8
445 N Henninger St 53050 920-387-7970
John Schlender, prin. Fax 387-7974

Mazomanie, Dane, Pop. 1,638
Wisconsin Heights SD 700/PK-12
10173 US Highway 14 53560 608-767-2595
Randy Freese Ed.D., supt. Fax 767-3579
www.wisheights.k12.wi.us
Wisconsin Heights HS 200/9-12
10173 US Highway 14 53560 608-767-2586
Asta Sepetys, prin. Fax 767-2062
Wisconsin Heights MS 200/6-8
10173 US Highway 14 53560 608-767-2586
Asta Sepetys, prin. Fax 767-2062

Medford, Taylor, Pop. 4,279
Medford Area SD 2,200/PK-12
124 W State St 54451 715-748-4620
Patrick Sullivan, supt. Fax 748-6839
www.medford.k12.wi.us
Medford Alternative HS Alt
624 College St 54451 715-748-4620
Kellie Keene, lead tchr.
Medford HS 600/9-12
1015 W Broadway Ave 54451 715-748-5951
Jill Lybert, prin. Fax 748-6438
Medford MS 600/5-8
509 Clark St 54451 715-748-2516
Al Leonard, prin. Fax 748-1213

Mellen, Ashland, Pop. 725
Mellen SD 300/PK-12
PO Box 500 54546 715-274-3601
Michael Cox, supt. Fax 274-3715
www.mellendiggers.org
Mellen HS 100/9-12
PO Box 500 54546 715-274-3601
Maija Alexandrou, prin. Fax 274-3715

Melrose, Jackson, Pop. 499
Melrose-Mindoro SD 800/PK-12
N181 State Hwy 108 54642 608-488-2201
Del DeBerg, supt. Fax 488-2805
www.mel-min.k12.wi.us
Melrose-Mindoro HS 200/9-12
N181 State Hwy 108 54642 608-488-2201
Jeff Arzt, prin. Fax 488-2805

Menasha, Winnebago, Pop. 17,081
Menasha JSD 3,600/PK-12
PO Box 360 54952 920-967-1400
Chris VanderHeyden, supt. Fax 751-5038
www.mjsd.k12.wi.us
Maplewood MS 800/6-8
1600 Midway Rd 54952 920-967-1600
Dr. Bev Sturke, prin. Fax 832-5837
Menasha HS 1,000/9-12
420 7th St 54952 920-967-1800
Dr. Lawrence Haase, prin. Fax 751-5223

University of Wisconsin Fox Valley Post-Sec.
1478 Midway Rd 54952 920-832-2600

Menomonee Falls, Waukesha, Pop. 35,186
Menomonee Falls SD 4,200/PK-12
W156N8480 Pilgrim Rd 53051 262-255-8440
Patricia Greco, supt. Fax 255-8461
www.sdmfschools.org
Menomonee Falls HS 1,500/9-12
W142N8101 Merrimac Dr 53051 262-255-8444
Corey Golla, prin. Fax 255-8377
North MS 900/6-8
N88W16750 Garfield Dr 53051 262-255-8450
Lynn Grimm, prin. Fax 255-8475

Bethlehem Lutheran S - South 100/5-8
N84W15252 Menomonee Ave 53051 262-251-3120
Daryl Weber, prin. Fax 251-4679
Calvary Baptist S 200/PK-12
N84W19049 Menomonee Ave 53051 262-251-0328

Menomonie, Dunn, Pop. 15,977
Menomonie Area SD 3,100/K-12
215 Pine Ave NE 54751 715-232-1642
Joe Zydowsky, supt. Fax 232-1317
www.msd.k12.wi.us
Menomonie HS 1,000/9-12
1715 5th St W 54751 715-232-2606
David Munoz, prin. Fax 232-2629
Menomonie MS 700/6-8
920 21st St SE 54751 715-232-1673
Stacey Everson, prin. Fax 232-5486

University of Wisconsin Post-Sec.
712 Broadway St S 54751 715-232-1122

Mequon, Ozaukee, Pop. 22,848
Mequon-Thiensville SD 3,500/PK-12
5000 W Mequon Rd 53092 262-238-8500
Demond Means, supt. Fax 238-8520
www.mtsd.k12.wi.us
Homestead HS 1,300/9-12
5000 W Mequon Rd 53092 262-238-5646
Brett Bowers, prin. Fax 238-5633
Lake Shore MS 400/6-8
11036 N Range Line Rd 53092 262-238-7613
Kate Dunning, prin. Fax 238-7650
Steffen MS 400/6-8
6633 W Steffen Dr 53092 262-238-4706
Deborah Anderson, prin. Fax 238-4740

Concordia University Post-Sec.
12800 N Lake Shore Dr 53097 262-243-5700
Milwaukee Area Technical College Post-Sec.
5555 W Highland Rd 53092 262-238-2200

Mercer, Iron, Pop. 516
Mercer SD 100/PK-12
2690 W Margaret St 54547 715-476-2154
Erik Torkelson, supt. Fax 476-2587
www.mercer.k12.wi.us
Mercer S 100/PK-12
2690 W Margaret St 54547 715-476-2154
Erik Torkelson, admin. Fax 476-2587

Merrill, Lincoln, Pop. 9,553
Merrill Area SD 3,500/PK-12
1111 N Sales St 54452 715-536-4581
Walter Leipart, supt. Fax 536-1788
www.maps.k12.wi.us
Merrill HS 900/9-12
1201 N Sales St 54452 715-536-4594
Shannon Murray, prin. Fax 536-5504
Prairie River MS 600/6-8
106 N Polk St 54452 715-536-9593
Gerald Beyer, prin. Fax 536-6378

Merton, Waukesha, Pop. 3,309
Merton Community SD 800/PK-8
PO Box 15 53056 262-538-2227
Ronald Russ, supt. Fax 538-3937
www.merton.k12.wi.us
Merton IS 400/5-8
PO Box 15 53056 262-538-1130
Jay Posick, prin. Fax 538-4978

Middleton, Dane, Pop. 17,031
Middleton-Cross Plains Area SD 5,900/PK-12
7106 South Ave 53562 608-829-9000
Dr. Donald Johnson, supt. Fax 836-1536
www.mcpasd.k12.wi.us
Kromrey MS 700/5-8
7009 Donna Dr 53562 608-829-9530
Steve Soeteber, prin. Fax 831-8388
Middleton HS 2,000/9-12
2100 Bristol St 53562 608-829-9660
Dr. Stephen Plank, prin. Fax 831-1995
Other Schools – See Cross Plains

Globe University Post-Sec.
1345 Deming Way 53562 608-830-6900

Milton, Rock, Pop. 5,493
Milton SD 3,400/PK-12
448 E High St 53563 608-868-9200
Timothy J. Schigur, supt. Fax 868-9215
www.milton.k12.wi.us
Milton HS 1,000/9-12
114 W High St 53563 608-868-9300
Jeremy Bilhorn, prin. Fax 868-9399
Milton MS 500/7-8
20 E Madison Ave 53563 608-868-9350
Laura Jennaro, prin. Fax 868-9269

Milwaukee, Milwaukee, Pop. 580,512
Milwaukee SD 75,400/PK-12
PO Box 2181 53201 414-475-8393
Dr. Darienne Driver, supt. Fax 475-8595
www.milwaukee.k12.wi.us
ASSATA 100/Alt
3517 W Courtland Ave 53209 414-345-6113
Carlotta Pritchett, prin. Fax 345-9893
Audubon Technology & Communication Ctr 600/6-8
3300 S 39th St 53215 414-902-7800
Leon Groce, prin. Fax 902-7815
Audubon Technology & Communication HS 300/9-12
3300 S 39th St 53215 414-902-7806
Leon Groce, prin. Fax 902-7869
Banner Prep HS of Milwaukee 50/Alt
4610 W State St 53208 414-461-9561
Karen Huff, admin. Fax 461-9846
Bay View HS 700/9-12
2751 S Lenox St 53207 414-294-2400
Aaron Shapiro, prin. Fax 294-2415
Bradley Tech & Trade HS Vo/Tech
700 S 4th St 53204 414-212-2400
Jineen McLemore-Torres, prin. Fax 212-2415
Groppi HS 200/Alt
1312 N 27th St 53208 414-934-8200
Joel Eul, prin. Fax 934-8215
Hamilton HS 1,700/9-12
6215 W Warnimont Ave 53220 414-327-9300
Rosana Mateo, prin. Fax 327-9315
King International HS 1,500/9-12
1801 W Olive St 53209 414-267-0700
Dr. Jennifer Smith, prin. Fax 267-0715
King International MS 400/6-8
4950 N 24th St 53209 414-616-5200
Tamara Ellis, prin.
Lad Lake Synergy MSHS 100/Alt
2820 W Grant St 53215 414-332-2675
Glen Stevens, admin.
Lincoln MS of the Arts 700/6-8
820 E Knapp St 53202 414-212-3300
Ramon Evans, prin. Fax 212-3315
MacDowell Montessori S 700/PK-12
6415 W Mount Vernon Ave 53213 414-935-1400
Andrea Corona, prin. Fax 935-1415
Madison Academic Campus 1,000/9-12
8135 W Florist Ave 53218 414-393-6100
Gregory Ogunbowale, prin. Fax 393-6222
Meir S 500/3-10
1555 N Martin Luther King 53212 414-212-3200
Michelle Morris Carter, prin. Fax 212-3215
Milwaukee HS of the Arts 900/9-12
2300 W Highland Ave 53233 414-934-7000
Barry Applewhite, prin. Fax 934-7015
Milwaukee S of Languages 1,200/6-12
8400 W Burleigh St 53222 414-393-5700
Jennifer Smith, admin. Fax 393-5715
Morse-Marshall S for Gifted and Talented 1,400/6-12
4141 N 64th St 53216 414-393-2300
Larry Farris, prin. Fax 393-2315
New School for Community Services 200/Alt
609 N 8th St 53233 414-298-9390
Hector Rosales, lead tchr. Fax 298-9395
NOVA MSHS 100/Alt
2320 W Burleigh St 53206 414-874-0283
Patricia Bridges, dir. Fax 874-0284
Obama S of Career & Tech Educ 200/K-12
5075 N Sherman Blvd 53209 414-393-4900
Dr. Mateva Harris, prin.
Project STAY 300/Alt
609 N 8th St 53233 414-298-9300
Diane Ludwig, admin. Fax 298-9315
Pulaski HS 1,400/9-12
2500 W Oklahoma Ave 53215 414-902-8900
Lolita Patrick, prin. Fax 902-8915
Reagan Preparatory HS 1,200/9-12
4965 S 20th St 53221 414-304-6100
Michael Roemer, prin. Fax 304-6115
Riverside University HS 1,600/9-12
1615 E Locust St 53211 414-906-4900
Michael Harris, prin. Fax 906-4915
Roosevelt Creative Arts MS 600/6-8
800 W Walnut St 53205 414-267-8800
Keushum Willingham, prin. Fax 267-8815
Shalom HS 100/Alt
1749 N 16th St 53205 414-933-5019
Gwendolyn Spencer, admin. Fax 933-5433
South Division HS 1,200/9-12
1515 W Lapham Blvd 53204 414-902-8300
Jesus Santos, prin. Fax 902-8315
Southeastern Education Center 50/Alt
4050 N 34th St 53216 414-875-9452
Darren Buckley, admin. Fax 875-9004
Vincent HS 1,300/9-12
7501 N Granville Rd 53224 262-236-1200
Zannetta Walker, prin. Fax 236-1254
Washington HS of Info Technology 800/9-12
2525 N Sherman Blvd 53210 414-875-5900
Darrell Williams, prin.
Wedgewood Park International S 800/6-8
6506 W Warnimont Ave 53220 414-604-7800
Suzanne Purpero, prin. Fax 604-7815
WI Consrv Lifelong Learning S 700/K-12
1017 N 12th St 53233 414-304-6800
Lena Patton, prin. Fax 304-6815

West Allis SD 9,700/PK-12
1205 S 70th St Ste 600 53214 414-604-3000
Dr. Martin Lexmond, supt. Fax 256-6314
www.wawmsd.org
Other Schools – See West Allis, West Milwaukee

Alverno College Post-Sec.
PO Box 343922 53234 414-382-6000
Atlas Preparatory Academy 900/PK-12
1039 E Russell Ave 53207 414-385-0771
Aurora Health Care Post-Sec.
3000 W Montana St 53215 414-647-3000
Believers in Christ Christian Academy 200/PK-12
4065 N 25th St 53209 414-444-1146
Candace Covington, prin. Fax 444-5378
Blood Center of SE Wisconsin Post-Sec.
1701 W Wisconsin Ave 53233 414-937-6338
Bryant & Stratton College Post-Sec.
310 W Wisconsin Ave Ste 500 53203 414-276-5200
Bufkin Christian Academy 100/PK-12
827 N 34th St 53208 414-934-8885
Texas Bufkin, admin. Fax 934-8886
Cardinal Stritch University Post-Sec.
6801 N Yates Rd 53217 414-410-4000
Columbia Hospital Post-Sec.
2025 E Newport Ave 53211 414-961-3800
Cristo Rey Jesuit HS 9-12
1215 S 45th St 53214 414-436-4600
Luke Harrison, prin.
Cross Trainers Academy 100/PK-10
1530 W Center Ave 53206 414-935-0500
Jacquelyn Verhulst, admin. Fax 344-6972
Destiny HS 300/9-12
7210 N 76th St 53223 414-353-4430
Kristen Reed, prin. Fax 353-0637
DeVry University Post-Sec.
411 E Wisconsin Ave Ste 300 53202 414-278-7677
Divine Savior-Holy Angels HS 700/9-12
4257 N 100th St 53222 414-462-3742
Dan Quesnell, prin. Fax 466-0590
Early View Academy of Excellence 400/PK-10
7132 W Good Hope Rd 53223 414-431-0001
Eastbrook Academy 400/PK-12
5375 N Green Bay Ave 53209 414-228-7905
Jay Wriedt, head sch Fax 228-9854
Everest College Post-Sec.
1311 N 6th St 53212 414-831-8400
Froedtert Memorial Lutheran Hospital Post-Sec.
PO Box 26099 53226 414-259-2606
Holy Redeemer Christian Academy 500/PK-12
3500 W Mother Daniels Way 53209 414-466-1800
Br. Jatiki Smith, prin. Fax 466-9294
Holy Wisdom Academy West Campus 100/4-8
3344 S 16th St 53215 414-383-3453
Julie Ann Robinson, prin. Fax 672-2645
HOPE Christian HS 200/9-12
3215 N Dr Martin L King Dr 53212 414-264-4476
Tom Schalmo, prin. Fax 264-4592
Kaplan College Post-Sec.
111 W Pleasant St Ste 101 53212 414-225-4610
Kaplan University Post-Sec.
201 W Wisconsin Ave 53203 414-223-2105
Marquette University Post-Sec.
PO Box 1881 53201 414-288-7700
Marquette University HS 1,100/9-12
3401 W Wisconsin Ave 53208 414-933-7220
Jeff Monday, prin. Fax 937-8588
Medical College of Wisconsin Post-Sec.
8701 W Watertown Plank Rd 53226 414-955-8296

Messmer HS 700/9-12
742 W Capitol Dr 53206 414-264-5440
Todd Willems, prin. Fax 264-6430
Milwaukee Area Technical College Post-Sec.
700 W State St 53233 414-297-6282
Milwaukee Career College Post-Sec.
3077 N Mayfair Rd Ste 300 53222 800-754-1009
Milwaukee Institute of Art & Design Post-Sec.
273 E Erie St 53202 414-847-3200
Milwaukee Lutheran HS 600/9-12
9700 W Grantosa Dr 53222 414-461-6000
Adam Kirsch, prin. Fax 461-2733
Milwaukee School of Engineering Post-Sec.
1025 N Broadway 53202 414-277-7300
Milwaukee SDA S 100/K-10
10900 W Mill Rd 53225 414-353-3520
Ken Smith, prin. Fax 353-1451
Mohammed S 200/PK-12
317 W Wright St 53212 414-263-6772
Mt. Lebanon Lutheran S - Omega Campus 100/5-8
8444 W Melvina St 53222 414-463-5030
Jonathan Winkel, dir. Fax 463-5086
Mount Mary University Post-Sec.
2900 N Menomonee River Pkwy 53222
414-258-4810
Nativity Jesuit MS 100/4-8
1515 S 29th St 53215 414-645-1060
Sue Smith, pres. Fax 645-0505
Northwest Catholic S - Upper Campus 200/4-8
8202 W Denver Ave 53223 414-352-6927
Michelle Paris, prin. Fax 352-7258
Notre Dame MS 100/5-8
1420 W Scott St 53204 414-671-3000
Patrick Landry, prin. Fax 671-3170
Pius XI HS 800/9-12
135 N 76th St 53213 414-290-7000
Paul Geise, prin. Fax 290-7001
Prince of Peace MS 300/PK-K, 6-8
1646 S 22nd St 53204 414-645-4922
Patricia Blaszczyk, prin. Fax 645-4940
St. Anthony HS 9-12
4807 S 2nd St 53207 414-763-6352
Laura Gutierrez, prin. Fax 384-1733
St. Anthony MS 6-8
2156 S 4th St 53207 414-810-3858
Katie Petersen, prin. Fax 810-3938
St. Francis Hospital Post-Sec.
3237 S 16th St 53215 414-647-5106
St. Joan Antida HS 300/9-12
1341 N Cass St 53202 414-272-8423
Paul Gessner, head sch Fax 272-3135
St. Luke's Medical Center Post-Sec.
2900 W Oklahoma Ave 53215 414-649-7500
St. Thomas More HS 400/9-12
2601 E Morgan Ave 53207 414-481-8370
Dr. Mark Joerres, prin. Fax 481-3382
Salam S 700/PK-12
4707 S 13th St 53221 414-282-0504
Br. Wanis Shalaby, prin. Fax 282-6959
Tamarack Waldorf S 200/PK-12
1150 E Brady St 53202 414-277-0009
Jean Kacanek, admin. Fax 277-7799
The Art Institute of Wisconsin Post-Sec.
320 E Buffalo St Ste 100 53202 414-978-5000
Torah Academy of Milwaukee 100/9-12
6800 N Green Bay Ave 53209 414-352-6789
Travis Academy 400/PK-12
8616 N Steven Rd 53223 414-342-4950
University of Wisconsin Post-Sec.
PO Box 413 53201 414-229-1122
University S 1,100/PK-12
2100 W Fairy Chasm Rd 53217 414-352-6000
Laura Fuller, admin. Fax 352-8076
Vici Beauty School Post-Sec.
11010 W Hampton Ave 53225 414-464-5002
Wisconsin Conservatory of Music Post-Sec.
1584 N Prospect Ave 53202 414-276-5760
Wisconsin Institute for Torah Study 100/9-12
3288 N Lake Dr 53211 414-963-9317
Wisconsin Lutheran College Post-Sec.
8800 W Bluemound Rd 53226 414-443-8800
Wisconsin Lutheran HS 800/9-12
330 Glenview Ave 53213 414-453-4567
Msgr. Phil Leyrer, prin. Fax 453-3001
WI School of Professional Psychology Post-Sec.
9120 W Hampton Ave Ste 212 53225 414-464-9777
Zablocki VA Medical Center Post-Sec.
5000 W National Ave 53295 414-384-2000

Mineral Point, Iowa, Pop. 2,475
Mineral Point SD 700/PK-12
705 Ross St 53565 608-987-0740
Luke Francois, supt. Fax 987-3766
www.mineralpointschools.org
Mineral Point HS 200/9-12
705 Ross St 53565 608-987-0730
Mitch Wainwright, prin. Fax 987-3766
Mineral Point MS 100/6-8
705 Ross St 53565 608-987-0720
Vickie Dahl, prin. Fax 987-3766

Minocqua, Oneida, Pop. 440
Lakeland UNHSD 700/9-12
9573 State Highway 70 54548 715-356-5252
James Bouche, admin. Fax 356-1892
www.luhs.k12.wi.us
Lakeland HS 700/9-12
9573 State Highway 70 54548 715-356-5252
James Bouche, prin. Fax 356-1892

Mishicot, Manitowoc, Pop. 1,424
Mishicot SD 800/PK-12
PO Box 280 54228 920-755-4633
Colleen Timm, supt. Fax 755-4068
www.mishicot.k12.wi.us
Mishicot HS 300/9-12
PO Box 280 54228 920-755-2311
Thomas Ellenbecker, prin. Fax 755-2390
Mishicot MS 200/6-8
PO Box 280 54228 920-755-2808
Colleen Timm, prin. Fax 755-2390

Mondovi, Buffalo, Pop. 2,751
Mondovi SD, 337 N Jackson St 54755 1,000/PK-12
Greg Corning, supt. 715-926-3684
www.mondovi.k12.wi.us
Mondovi HS 300/9-12
337 N Jackson St 54755 715-926-3656
Mike Bruning, prin. Fax 926-3617
Mondovi MS, 337 N Jackson St 54755 200/6-8
Mike Bruning, prin. 715-926-3656

Monona, Dane, Pop. 7,407
Monona Grove SD 3,100/PK-12
5301 Monona Dr 53716 608-221-7660
Dr. Daniel Olson Ed.D., supt. Fax 221-7688
www.mononagrove.org
Monona Grove HS 900/9-12
4400 Monona Dr 53716 608-221-7666
Dr. Paul Brost, prin. Fax 221-7690
Other Schools – See Cottage Grove

Monroe, Green, Pop. 10,726
Monroe SD 2,500/PK-12
925 16th Ave Ste 3 53566 608-328-7171
Cory Hirsbrunner, supt. Fax 328-7214
www.monroeschools.com
Monroe HS 700/9-12
1600 26th St 53566 608-328-7117
Chris Medenwaldt, prin. Fax 328-7230
Monroe MS 500/6-8
1510 13th St 53566 608-328-7120
Brian Boehm, prin. Fax 328-7224

Paul Mitchell The School Post-Sec.
1015 18th Ave Ste 212 53566 608-329-7004

Montello, Marquette, Pop. 1,476
Montello SD 700/PK-12
222 Forest Ln 53949 608-297-7617
Dr. B. Lynn Brown, supt. Fax 297-7726
www.montelloschools.org
Montello JSHS 300/6-12
222 Forest Ln 53949 608-297-2126
Chuck Harsh, prin. Fax 297-9390

Monticello, Green, Pop. 1,208
Monticello SD 400/PK-12
334 S Main St 53570 608-938-4194
Allen Brokopp, supt. Fax 938-1062
www.monticello.k12.wi.us/
Monticello HS 100/9-12
334 S Main St 53570 608-938-4194
Mark Gustafson, prin. Fax 938-1062
Monticello MS 100/6-8
334 S Main St 53570 608-938-4194
Mark Gustafson, prin. Fax 938-1062

Mosinee, Marathon, Pop. 3,964
Mosinee SD 2,100/PK-12
591 W State Highway 153 54455 715-693-2530
Dr. Ann Schultz, supt. Fax 693-7272
www.mosineeschools.org
Mosinee HS 700/9-12
1000 High St 54455 715-693-2550
Nathan Lehman, prin. Fax 693-1152
Mosinee MS 800/4-8
700 High St 54455 715-693-3660
Joshua Sween, prin. Fax 693-6655

Northland Lutheran HS 100/9-12
2107 Tower Rd 54455 715-359-3400
Ryan Wiechmann, prin. Fax 241-9203
WI Valley Lutheran HS 100/9-12
601 Maple Ridge Rd 54455 715-693-2693
Dave Beringer, admin. Fax 693-5962

Mount Calvary, Fond du Lac, Pop. 757

St. Lawrence Seminary HS 200/9-12
301 Church St 53057 920-753-7500
David Bartel, dean Fax 753-7507

Mount Horeb, Dane, Pop. 6,889
Mount Horeb Area SD 2,400/PK-12
1304 E Lincoln St 53572 608-437-2400
Dr. Steve Salerno, supt. Fax 437-5597
www.mhasd.k12.wi.us
Mount Horeb HS 700/9-12
305 S 8th St 53572 608-437-2400
Michael Werbowsky, prin. Fax 437-4926
Mount Horeb MS 600/6-8
900 E Garfield St 53572 608-437-2400
Paul Christiansen, prin. Fax 437-6227

Mukwonago, Waukesha, Pop. 7,291
Mukwonago SD 4,700/K-12
385 E Veterans Way 53149 262-363-6300
Shawn McNulty, supt. Fax 363-6272
www.masd.k12.wi.us
Mukwonago HS 1,600/9-12
605 W School Rd 53149 262-363-6200
James Darin, prin. Fax 363-6239
Park View MS 800/7-8
930 N Rochester St 53149 262-363-6292
Mark Doome, prin. Fax 363-6320

Norris SD 50/6-12
W247S10395 Center Dr 53149 262-662-5911
Sara Trampf, supt. Fax 662-5502
www.norriscenter.org
Norris JSHS 50/6-12
W247S10395 Center Dr 53149 262-662-5911
Christopher Fountain, prin. Fax 662-5502

Muscoda, Grant, Pop. 1,294
Riverdale SD 600/PK-12
PO Box 66 53573 608-739-3832
Bryce Bird, supt. Fax 739-3751
www.riverdale.k12.wi.us/
Riverdale HS 200/9-12
PO Box 66 53573 608-739-3116
Jonthan Schmidt, prin. Fax 739-4486
Riverdale JHS 100/7-8
235 E Elm St 53573 608-739-3116
Jonathan Schmidt, prin. Fax 739-4486

Muskego, Waukesha, Pop. 23,915
Muskego-Norway SD 4,700/PK-12
S87W18763 Woods Rd 53150 262-971-1800
Dr. Kelly Thompson, supt. Fax 679-5790
www.muskegonorway.org/
Bay Lane MS 700/5-8
S75W16399 Hilltop Dr 53150 262-971-1810
Dawn Zandt, prin. Fax 422-2204
Lake Denoon MS 700/5-8
W216S10586 Crowbar Dr 53150 262-971-1820
Linda O'Bryan, prin. Fax 662-1588
Muskego HS 1,700/9-12
W183S8750 Racine Ave 53150 262-971-1790
Todd Irvine, prin. Fax 679-3534

Nashotah, Waukesha, Pop. 1,378

Nashotah House Post-Sec.
2777 Mission Rd 53058 262-646-6500

Necedah, Juneau, Pop. 904
Necedah Area SD 700/PK-12
1801 S Main St 54646 608-565-2256
Larry Gierach, supt. Fax 565-3201
www.necedahschools.org
Necedah MSHS 400/6-12
1801 S Main St 54646 608-565-2256
Mark Becker, prin. Fax 565-7044

Neenah, Winnebago, Pop. 25,158
Neenah SD 6,200/PK-12
410 S Commercial St 54956 920-751-6800
Mary Pfeiffer Ph.D., supt. Fax 751-6809
www.neenah.k12.wi.us
Neenah HS 2,000/9-12
1275 Tullar Rd 54956 920-751-6900
Brian Wunderlich, prin. Fax 751-7001
Shattuck MS 1,000/7-8
600 Elm St 54956 920-751-6850
Stephanie Phernetton, prin. Fax 751-6899

St. Mary Catholic HS 200/9-12
1050 Zephyr Dr 54956 920-722-7796
Patrick Batey, prin. Fax 722-5940
St. Mary Catholic MS 200/6-8
1000 Zephyr Dr 54956 920-727-0279
Mike Zuleger, prin. Fax 727-1215
Theda Clark Regional Medical Center Post-Sec.
130 2nd St 54956 920-729-2004

Neillsville, Clark, Pop. 2,446
Neillsville SD 1,000/PK-12
614 E 5th St 54456 715-743-3323
John Gaier, supt. Fax 743-8718
www.neillsville.k12.wi.us
Neillsville MSHS 500/7-12
401 Center St 54456 715-743-8738
Craig Ruskin, prin. Fax 743-8714

Nekoosa, Wood, Pop. 2,530
Nekoosa SD 1,300/PK-12
600 S Section St 54457 715-886-8000
Terry Whitmore, supt. Fax 886-8012
www.nekoosasd.net
Alexander MS 400/4-8
540 Birch St 54457 715-886-8040
Jon Sprehn, prin. Fax 886-8097
Nekoosa Academy Alt
500 Cedar St 54457 715-886-8099
Ann Lepak, lead tchr. Fax 886-8191
Nekoosa HS 400/9-12
500 Cedar St 54457 715-886-8060
Mike Kumm, prin. Fax 886-8087

Neopit, Menominee, Pop. 682
Menominee Indian SD
Supt. — See Keshena
Menominee Indian MS 100/6-8
PO Box 9 54150 715-756-2324
Timothy Meyers, prin. Fax 756-2496

Neosho, Dodge, Pop. 566
Herman Neosho Rubicon SD 200/PK-8
201 Center St 53059 920-625-3531
Dennis Kaczor, supt. Fax 625-3536
www.hnrschools.org
Other Schools – See Rubicon

Victory Christian HS 50/9-12
PO Box 46 53059 920-625-3995
Bruce Dickman, prin. Fax 625-3995

New Auburn, Chippewa, Pop. 537
New Auburn SD 300/PK-12
PO Box 110 54757 715-237-2202
Scott Johnson, supt. Fax 237-2350
www.newauburn.k12.wi.us
New Auburn JSHS 100/7-12
PO Box 110 54757 715-237-2505
Cory Martens, prin. Fax 237-2350

New Berlin, Waukesha, Pop. 39,208
New Berlin SD 4,600/K-12
4333 S Sunnyslope Rd 53151 262-789-6200
Joe Garza, supt. Fax 786-0512
www.nbexcellence.org/
Eisenhower MSHS 1,200/7-12
4333 S Sunnyslope Rd 53151 262-789-6300
Matthew Buckley, prin. Fax 789-6313
New Berlin West MSHS 1,200/7-12
18695 W Cleveland Ave 53146 262-789-6400
Michael Fesenmaier, prin. Fax 789-6442

Heritage Christian Schools 500/PK-12
3500 S West Ln 53151 262-432-0333
John Davis, pres. Fax 432-0542

New Glarus, Green, Pop. 2,162
New Glarus SD 800/PK-12
PO Box 7 53574 608-527-2410
Dr. Jennifer Thayer, supt. Fax 527-5101
www.ngsd.k12.wi.us
New Glarus HS 300/9-12
PO Box 7 53574 608-527-2410
Jeff Eichelkraut, prin. Fax 527-5101
New Glarus MS 100/5-8
PO Box 67 53574 608-527-2410
Mark Stateler, prin. Fax 527-5101

New Holstein, Calumet, Pop. 3,214
New Holstein SD 1,100/PK-12
1715 Plymouth St 53061 920-898-5115
Dan Nett, supt. Fax 898-4112
www.nhsd.k12.wi.us
New Holstein HS 300/9-12
1715 Plymouth St 53061 920-898-4256
Rodney Figuero, prin. Fax 898-4112
New Holstein MS 300/6-8
1717 Plymouth St 53061 920-898-4769
Richard Amundson, prin. Fax 898-4810

New Lisbon, Juneau, Pop. 2,524
New Lisbon SD 700/PK-12
500 S Forest St 53950 608-562-3700
Dennis Birr, supt. Fax 562-5333
www.newlisbon.k12.wi.us
New Lisbon JSHS 300/7-12
500 S Forest St 53950 608-562-3700
Gary Syftestad, prin. Fax 562-5333

New London, Waupaca, Pop. 7,241
New London SD 2,500/PK-12
901 W Washington St 54961 920-982-8530
Dr. Kathleen Gwidt, supt. Fax 982-8551
www.newlondon.k12.wi.us
New London HS 800/9-12
1700 Klatt Rd 54961 920-982-8420
Danielle Sievert, prin. Fax 982-8440
New London IS / MS 700/5-8
1000 W Washington St 54961 920-982-8532
Pete Schulz, prin. Fax 982-8605

New Richmond, Saint Croix, Pop. 8,254
New Richmond SD 3,200/PK-12
701 E 11th St 54017 715-243-7411
Patrick Olson, supt. Fax 246-3638
www.newrichmond.k12.wi.us
New Richmond HS 800/9-12
701 E 11th St 54017 715-243-7451
Tom Wissink, prin. Fax 243-7464
New Richmond MS 700/6-8
701 E 11th St 54017 715-243-7472
Doug Hatch, prin. Fax 246-0580

Wisconsin Indianhead Technical College Post-Sec.
1019 S Knowles Ave 54017 715-246-6561

Niagara, Marinette, Pop. 1,609
Niagara SD 500/PK-12
700 Jefferson Ave 54151 715-251-1330
Nathaniel Burklund, supt. Fax 251-4544
www.niagara.k12.wi.us
Niagara JSHS 200/7-12
700 Jefferson Ave 54151 715-251-4541
Kipp Beaudoin, prin. Fax 251-3715

North Fond du Lac, Fond du Lac, Pop. 4,969
North Fond Du Lac SD 1,300/PK-12
225 McKinley St 54937 920-929-3750
Aaron Sadoff, supt. Fax 929-3696
www.nfdl.k12.wi.us
Allen MS 300/6-8
305 Mckinley St 54937 920-929-3754
Adam Broten, prin. Fax 929-3747
Mann HS 400/9-12
325 Mckinley St 54937 920-929-3740
Samantha Freimund, prin. Fax 929-3664

Oak Creek, Milwaukee, Pop. 33,834
Oak Creek-Franklin SD 6,400/PK-12
7630 S 10th St 53154 414-768-5886
Dr. Tim Culver, supt. Fax 768-6172
ocfsd.org
Oak Creek East MS 900/6-8
9330 S Shepard Ave 53154 414-768-6260
Annalee Bennin, prin. Fax 768-6293
Oak Creek HS 2,000/9-12
340 E Puetz Rd 53154 414-768-6100
Michael Read, prin. Fax 768-6130
Oak Creek West MS 500/6-8
8401 S 13th St 53154 414-768-6250
Michael Maxson, prin. Fax 768-6296

Milwaukee Area Technical College Post-Sec.
6665 S Howell Ave 53154 414-571-4500

Oakfield, Fond du Lac, Pop. 1,057
Oakfield SD 500/PK-12
PO Box 99 53065 920-583-4117
Vance Dalzin, supt. Fax 583-4033
www.oakfield.k12.wi.us/
Oakfield HS 100/9-12
PO Box 39 53065 920-583-3141
Carmen Klassy, prin. Fax 583-4673
Oakfield MS 100/6-8
PO Box 39 53065 920-583-3141
Carmen Klassy, prin. Fax 583-4673

Oconomowoc, Waukesha, Pop. 15,586
Oconomowoc Area SD 4,900/K-12
W360N7077 Brown St 53066 262-560-1115
Dr. Roger Rindo, supt.
www.oasd.k12.wi.us
Nature Hill IS 800/5-8
850 N Lake Rd 53066 262-569-4945
Jason Curtis, prin. Fax 569-4958
Oconomowoc HS 1,500/9-12
641 E Forest St 53066 262-560-3100
Dr. Joseph Moylan, prin. Fax 567-8960
Silver Lake IS 700/5-8
555 Oconomowoc Pkwy 53066 262-560-4305
Ellyn Helberg, prin. Fax 560-4318

Oconto, Oconto, Pop. 4,472
Oconto USD 1,000/PK-12
400 Michigan Ave 54153 920-834-7814
Aaron Malczewski, supt. Fax 834-9884
www.oconto.k12.wi.us
Oconto HS 300/9-12
1717 Superior Ave 54153 920-834-7812
Bill Slough, prin. Fax 834-7804
Oconto MS 200/5-8
400 Michigan Ave 54153 920-834-7806
Adam DeWitt, prin. Fax 834-9884

Oconto Falls, Oconto, Pop. 2,850
Oconto Falls SD 1,800/PK-12
200 N Farm Rd 54154 920-848-4471
Dr. Dean Hess, supt. Fax 848-4474
www.ocontofalls.k12.wi.us
Oconto Falls HS 500/9-12
PO Box 988 54154 920-848-4467
Bruce Russell, prin. Fax 846-4444
Washington MS 400/6-8
102 S Washington St 54154 920-846-4463
Stephanie Landreman, prin. Fax 846-4453

Omro, Winnebago, Pop. 3,492
Omro SD 1,300/PK-12
455 Fox Trl 54963 920-685-5666
Fax 685-5757
www.omro.k12.wi.us
Omro HS 400/9-12
455 Fox Trl 54963 920-685-7405
Kelly Spors, prin. Fax 685-7040
Omro MS 300/6-8
455 Fox Trl 54963 920-685-7403
Paul Williams, prin. Fax 685-5757

Onalaska, LaCrosse, Pop. 17,449
Onalaska SD 2,800/PK-12
1821 E Main St 54650 608-781-9700
Dr. Francis E. Finco, supt. Fax 781-9712
www.onalaska.k12.wi.us
Onalaska HS 900/9-12
700 Hilltopper Pl 54650 608-783-4561
Jared Schaffner, prin. Fax 783-0102
Onalaska MS 600/6-8
711 Quincy St 54650 608-783-5366
Jed Kees, prin. Fax 781-8030

Globe University Post-Sec.
2651 Midwest Dr 54650 608-779-2600
Luther HS 300/9-12
1501 Wilson St 54650 608-783-5435
Paul Wichmann, prin. Fax 783-4758
The Salon Professional Academy Post-Sec.
566 Theater Rd 54650 608-781-8772

Ontario, Vernon, Pop. 550
Norwalk-Ontario-Wilton SD 700/PK-12
PO Box 130 54651 608-337-4403
Dr. Kelly Burhop, supt. Fax 337-4348
www.now.k12.wi.us/
Brookwood JSHS 300/7-12
PO Box 130 54651 608-337-4401
Brad Pettit, prin. Fax 337-4348

Oostburg, Sheboygan, Pop. 2,866
Oostburg SD 1,000/PK-12
PO Box 700100 53070 920-564-2346
Kevin Bruggink, supt. Fax 564-6138
oostburg.k12.wi.us
Oostburg HS 300/9-12
PO Box 700100 53070 920-564-2346
Scott Greupink, prin. Fax 564-6138
Oostburg MS 200/6-8
PO Box 700100 53070 920-564-2383
Sherri Stengel, prin. Fax 564-6138

Oregon, Dane, Pop. 9,079
Oregon SD 3,600/K-12
123 E Grove St 53575 608-835-4000
Brian Busler, supt. Fax 835-9509
www.oregonsd.org
Oregon HS 1,100/9-12
456 N Perry Pkwy 53575 608-835-4300
Jim Pliner, prin. Fax 835-7894
Oregon MS 600/7-8
601 Pleasant Oak Dr 53575 608-835-4800
Shannon Anderson, prin. Fax 835-3849

Orfordville, Rock, Pop. 1,432
Parkview SD 500/PK-12
PO Box 250 53576 608-879-2717
Dr. Steve Lutzke, supt. Fax 879-2732
www.parkview.k12.wi.us
Parkview JSHS 300/7-12
408 W Beloit St 53576 608-879-2994
William Trow, prin. Fax 879-9375

Osceola, Polk, Pop. 2,529
Osceola SD 1,800/PK-12
PO Box 128 54020 715-294-4140
Mark Luebker, supt. Fax 294-2428
www.osceola.k12.wi.us
Osceola HS 500/9-12
PO Box 128 54020 715-294-2127
Adam Spiegel, prin. Fax 755-2068
Osceola MS 400/6-8
PO Box 128 54020 715-294-4180
Rebecca Styles, prin. Fax 294-2428

Valley Christian S 50/PK-12
933A 248th St 54020 715-294-3373
Sonja Degerstrom, admin. Fax 294-3373

Oshkosh, Winnebago, Pop. 65,117
Oshkosh Area SD 10,000/PK-12
PO Box 3048 54903 920-424-0395
Stan Mack, supt. Fax 424-0466
www.oshkosh.k12.wi.us
Merrill MS 400/6-8
108 W New York Ave 54901 920-424-0177
Cindy Olson, prin. Fax 424-7512
Oshkosh North HS 1,200/9-12
1100 W Smith Ave 54901 920-424-7000
Jacqueline Schleicher, prin. Fax 424-4054
Oshkosh West HS 1,600/9-12
375 N Eagle St 54902 920-424-4090
Erin Kohl, prin. Fax 424-4950
South Park MS 400/6-8
1551 Delaware St 54902 920-424-0431
Lisa McLaughlin, prin. Fax 424-7513
Stanley MS 400/6-8
915 Hazel St 54901 920-424-0442
Philip Marshall, prin. Fax 424-7515
Tipler MS 300/6-8
325 S Eagle St 54902 920-424-0320
Jay Jones, prin. Fax 424-7514
Traeger MS 500/6-8
3000 W 20th Ave 54904 920-424-0065
Jill Pascarella, prin. Fax 424-7511

Fox Valley Technical College Post-Sec.
150 N Campbell Rd 54902 920-233-9191
Lourdes Academy HS 200/9-12
110 N Sawyer St 54902 920-235-5670
Fax 235-7453
Lourdes Academy MS 200/6-8
110 N Sawyer St 54902 920-235-5670
Fax 235-7453
Mercy Medical Center Post-Sec.
PO Box 3370 54903 920-233-5110
University of Wisconsin Post-Sec.
800 Algoma Blvd 54901 920-424-1234
Valley Christian S 200/PK-12
3450 Vinland St 54901 920-231-9704
Bradley Dunn, admin. Fax 231-9804

Osseo, Trempealeau, Pop. 1,691
Osseo-Fairchild SD 900/PK-12
50851 East St 54758 715-597-3141
William Tourdot Ed.D., supt. Fax 597-3606
www.ofsd.k12.wi.us
Osseo-Fairchild HS 300/9-12
50900 Francis St 54758 715-597-3141
Drew Semingson, prin. Fax 597-3647
Osseo MS 200/6-8
50900 Francis St 54758 715-597-3141
Drew Semingson, prin. Fax 597-3647

Owen, Clark, Pop. 936
Owen-Withee SD 500/PK-12
PO Box 417 54460 715-229-2151
Robert Houts, supt. Fax 229-4322
www.owen-withee.k12.wi.us
Owen-Withee HS 100/9-12
PO Box 417 54460 715-229-2151
Julie Van Ark, prin. Fax 229-4322
Owen-Withee JHS 100/7-8
PO Box 417 54460 715-229-2151
Julie Van Ark, prin. Fax 229-4322

Palmyra, Jefferson, Pop. 1,774
Palmyra-Eagle Area SD 1,000/PK-12
PO Box 901 53156 262-495-7101
Steven Bloom, supt. Fax 495-7151
www.palmyra.k12.wi.us
Palmyra-Eagle HS 300/9-12
PO Box 901 53156 262-495-7101
Kari Timm, prin. Fax 495-7146
Palmyra-Eagle MS 200/7-8
PO Box 901 53156 262-495-7101
Kari Timm, prin. Fax 495-7146

Pardeeville, Columbia, Pop. 2,095
Pardeeville Area SD 800/PK-12
PO Box 130 53954 608-429-2153
Earl Knitt, supt. Fax 429-2277
www.pardeeville.k12.wi.us
Pardeeville HS 300/9-12
PO Box 130 53954 608-429-2153
Jason Lemay, prin. Fax 429-2277
Pardeeville MS 200/5-8
PO Box 130 53954 608-429-2153
Ted Lenz, prin. Fax 429-2277

Park Falls, Price, Pop. 2,367
Chequamegon SD 800/PK-12
420 9th St N 54552 715-762-2474
David Anderson, admin. Fax 762-5469
www.csdk12.net
Chequamegon HS 300/9-12
400 9th St N 54552 715-762-2474
Timothy Kief, prin. Fax 762-5674
Other Schools – See Glidden

Patch Grove, Grant, Pop. 198
River Ridge SD 500/PK-12
PO Box 78 53817 608-994-2715
Jeff Athey, supt. Fax 994-2891
www.rrsd.k12.wi.us
River Ridge MSHS 200/7-12
PO Box 78 53817 608-994-2715
Clay Koenig, prin. Fax 994-2891

Pembine, Marinette, Pop. 189
Beecher-Dunbar-Pembine SD 300/PK-12
PO Box 247 54156 715-324-5314
Chris Metras, supt. Fax 324-5282
www.pembine.k12.wi.us/

Pembine JSHS 100/6-12
PO Box 247 54156 715-324-5314
Chris Metras, admin. Fax 324-5282

Pepin, Pepin, Pop. 835
Pepin Area SD 200/PK-12
PO Box 128 54759 715-442-2391
Bruce Quinton, supt. Fax 442-3607
www.pepin.k12.wi.us
Pepin HS 100/7-12
PO Box 128 54759 715-442-2391
Bruce Quinton, prin. Fax 442-3607

Peshtigo, Marinette, Pop. 3,466
Peshtigo SD 1,300/PK-12
341 N Emery Ave 54157 715-582-3677
Kim Eparvier, supt. Fax 582-3850
www.peshtigo.k12.wi.us
Peshtigo MSHS 600/7-12
380 Green St 54157 715-582-3711
Chad Sodini, prin. Fax 582-0740

Pewaukee, Waukesha, Pop. 8,065
Pewaukee SD 2,800/PK-12
404 Lake St 53072 262-691-2100
Dr. JoAnn Sternke, supt. Fax 691-1052
pewaukee.schoolwires.net
Clark MS 400/7-8
472 Lake St 53072 262-691-2100
Randy Daul, prin. Fax 695-5004
Pewaukee HS 800/9-12
510 Lake St 53072 262-691-2100
Marty Van Hulle, prin. Fax 695-5006

Trinity Academy 100/PK-12
W225N3131 Duplainville Rd 53072 262-695-2933
Waukesha County Technical College Post-Sec.
800 Main St 53072 262-691-5566

Phelps, Vilas
Phelps SD 100/K-12
4451 Old School Rd 54554 715-545-2724
Delnice Hill, supt. Fax 545-3728
www.phelps.k12.wi.us
Phelps HS 50/9-12
4451 Old School Rd 54554 715-545-2724
Jason Pertile, dean Fax 545-3728

Phillips, Price, Pop. 1,454
Phillips SD 800/PK-12
PO Box 70 54555 715-339-2419
Rick Morgan, supt. Fax 339-2416
www.phillips.k12.wi.us/
Phillips HS 300/9-12
PO Box 70 54555 715-339-2141
Colin Hoogland, prin. Fax 339-2144
Phillips MS 200/6-8
PO Box 70 54555 715-339-2141
Colin Hoogland, prin. Fax 339-2144

Pittsville, Wood, Pop. 868
Pittsville SD 600/PK-12
5459 Elementary Ave Ste 2 54466 715-884-6694
Rodney Figueroa, supt. Fax 884-5218
www.pittsville.k12.wi.us
Pittsville HS 200/9-12
5407 1st Ave 54466 715-884-6412
Mark Weddig, prin. Fax 884-2870

Plainfield, Waushara, Pop. 852
Tri-County Area SD 500/PK-12
409 S West St 54966 715-335-6366
Tony Marinack, supt. Fax 335-6365
www.tricounty.k12.wi.us
Tri-County HS 200/7-12
409 S West St 54966 715-335-6366
Nicholas Marti, prin. Fax 335-6322

Platteville, Grant, Pop. 11,124
Platteville SD 1,500/PK-12
780 N 2nd St 53818 608-342-4000
Connie Valenza, supt. Fax 342-4412
www.platteville.k12.wi.us
Platteville HS 400/9-12
710 E Madison St 53818 608-342-4020
Timothy Engh, prin. Fax 342-4427
Platteville MS 500/4-8
40 E Madison St 53818 608-342-4010
Jason Julius, prin. Fax 342-4497

University of Wisconsin Post-Sec.
1 University Plz 53818 608-342-1491

Pleasant Prairie, Kenosha, Pop. 19,418
Kenosha SD
Supt. — See Kenosha
Lakeview Technology Academy Vo/Tech
9449 88th Ave 53158 262-359-8155
William Hittman, prin. Fax 359-8159

Plum City, Pierce, Pop. 598
Plum City SD 300/PK-12
907 Main St 54761 715-647-2591
Mary Baier, supt. Fax 647-3015
www.plumcity.k12.wi.us
Plum City JSHS 200/6-12
907 Main St 54761 715-647-2591
Paul Churchill, prin. Fax 647-3015

Plymouth, Sheboygan, Pop. 8,357
Plymouth SD 2,100/PK-12
125 S Highland Ave 53073 920-892-2661
Carrie Dassow Ph.D., supt. Fax 892-6366
www.plymouth.k12.wi.us
Plymouth HS 800/9-12
125 S Highland Ave 53073 920-893-6911
Jennifer Rauscher, prin. Fax 892-6366
Riverview MS 400/6-8
300 Riverside Cir 53073 920-892-4353
Chris Scudella, prin. Fax 892-5072

Poplar, Douglas, Pop. 589
Maple SD
Supt. — See Maple
Northwestern MS 300/6-8
PO Box 46 54864 715-364-2218
T. Krieg, prin. Fax 364-2540

Portage, Columbia, Pop. 10,179
Portage Community SD 2,400/PK-12
305 E Slifer St 53901 608-742-4879
Charles Poches Ed.D., supt. Fax 742-4950
www.portage.k12.wi.us
Bartels MS 600/6-8
2505 New Pinery Rd 53901 608-742-2165
Robert Meicher, prin. Fax 745-4884
Portage HS 700/9-12
301 E Collins St 53901 608-742-8545
Robin Kvalo, prin. Fax 742-0617

Port Edwards, Wood, Pop. 1,802
Port Edwards SD 400/K-12
801 2nd St 54469 715-887-9000
Kyle Cronan, supt. Fax 887-9040
www.pesd.k12.wi.us
Edwards HS 100/9-12
801 2nd St 54469 715-887-9000
Kyle Cronan, prin. Fax 887-9040
Edwards MS 100/6-8
801 2nd St 54469 715-887-9000
Cara Christy, prin. Fax 887-9040

Port Washington, Ozaukee, Pop. 11,098
Port Washington-Saukville SD 2,700/PK-12
100 W Monroe St 53074 262-268-6000
Michael Weber Ph.D., supt. Fax 268-6020
www.pwssd.k12.wi.us
Jefferson MS 700/5-8
1403 N Holden St 53074 262-268-6100
Arlan Galarowicz, prin. Fax 268-6120
Port Washington HS 900/9-12
427 W Jackson St 53074 262-268-5500
Eric Burke, prin. Fax 268-5520

Port Washington Catholic MS 100/5-8
1802 N Wisconsin St 53074 262-284-2682
Kristine Klein, prin. Fax 284-4168

Port Wing, Bayfield, Pop. 160
South Shore SD 200/PK-12
PO Box 40 54865 715-774-3500
Clendon Gustafson, admin. Fax 774-3569
sshore.org
South Shore JSHS 100/7-12
PO Box 40 54865 715-774-3500
Clendon Gustafson, prin. Fax 774-3569

Potosi, Grant, Pop. 686
Potosi SD 300/PK-12
128 US Highway 61 N 53820 608-763-2162
Ronald Saari, supt. Fax 763-2035
www.potosisd.k12.wi.us
Potosi HS 100/9-12
128 US Highway 61 N 53820 608-763-2161
Mike Uppena, prin. Fax 763-2035
Potosi MS 100/6-8
128 US Highway 61 N 53820 608-763-2162
Mike Uppena, prin. Fax 763-2035

Poynette, Columbia, Pop. 2,497
Poynette SD 1,100/PK-12
PO Box 10 53955 608-635-4347
Matt Shappell, supt. Fax 635-9200
www.poynette.k12.wi.us
Poynette HS 300/9-12
PO Box 10 53955 608-635-4347
Mark Hoernke, prin. Fax 635-9201
Poynette MS 200/6-8
PO Box 10 53955 608-635-4347
Brian Sutton, prin. Fax 635-9233

Prairie du Chien, Crawford, Pop. 5,867
Prairie du Chien Area SD 1,000/PK-12
800 E Crawford St 53821 608-326-3700
Drew Johnson, supt. Fax 326-0000
www.pdc.k12.wi.us
Prairie du Chien HS 400/9-12
800 E Crawford St 53821 608-326-3700
Andy Banasik, prin. Fax 326-3709

Prairie Catholic S - St. John MS 100/5-8
720 S Wacouta Ave 53821 608-326-4400
Wade Marlow, prin. Fax 326-4876

Prairie du Sac, Sauk, Pop. 3,923
Sauk Prairie SD 2,100/PK-12
440 13th St 53578 608-643-5990
Cliff Thompson, supt. Fax 643-6216
www.saukprairieschools.org
Sauk Prairie HS 800/9-12
105 9th St 53578 608-643-5900
Chad Harnisch, prin. Fax 643-5419
Other Schools – See Sauk City

Prairie Farm, Barron, Pop. 472
Prairie Farm SD 300/PK-12
630 River Ave S 54762 715-455-1683
Michael Thomley, supt. Fax 455-1056
www.prairiefarm.k12.wi.us
Prairie Farm HS 100/9-12
630 River Ave S 54762 715-455-1861
Casey Fossum, prin. Fax 455-1869
Prairie Farm MS 100/6-8
630 River Ave S 54762 715-455-1841
Casey Fossum, prin. Fax 455-1869

Prentice, Price, Pop. 653
Prentice SD 300/PK-12
PO Box 110 54556 715-428-2811
Randall Bergman, supt. Fax 428-2815
www.prentice.k12.wi.us
Prentice MSHS 100/5-12
PO Box 110 54556 715-428-2811
Melissa Pilgrim, prin. Fax 428-2815

Prescott, Pierce, Pop. 4,176
Prescott SD 1,200/PK-12
1220 Saint Croix St 54021 715-262-5782
Dr. Rick Spicuzza, supt. Fax 262-5091
www.prescott.k12.wi.us
Prescott HS 400/9-12
1010 Dexter St 54021 715-262-5010
David Vortherms, prin. Fax 262-4888
Prescott MS 300/6-8
125 Elm St N 54021 715-262-5054
Jim Dalluhn, prin. Fax 262-3965

Princeton, Green Lake, Pop. 1,208
Princeton SD 400/PK-12
PO Box 147 54968 920-295-6571
Sam Santacroce, supt. Fax 295-4778
www.princeton.k12.wi.us
Princeton S 400/PK-12
PO Box 147 54968 920-295-6571
Sam Santacroce, prin. Fax 295-4778

Pulaski, Brown, Pop. 3,500
Pulaski Community SD 3,700/PK-12
PO Box 36 54162 920-822-6000
Bec Kurzynske, supt. Fax 822-6005
www.pulaskischools.org
Pulaski Community MS 800/6-8
911 S Saint Augustine St 54162 920-822-6500
Patrick Fullerton, prin. Fax 822-6505
Pulaski HS 1,100/9-12
1040 S Saint Augustine St 54162 920-822-6700
Jeremy Pach, prin. Fax 822-6707

Racine, Racine, Pop. 76,696
Racine USD 19,800/PK-12
3109 Mount Pleasant St 53404 262-635-5600
Dr. Lolli Haws, supt. Fax 631-7121
www.rusd.org
Case HS 1,900/9-12
7345 Washington Ave 53406 262-619-4200
Jody Bloyer, prin. Fax 619-4259
Gilmore MS 700/6-8
2330 Northwestern Ave 53404 262-619-4260
Bryan Wright, prin. Fax 619-4272
Horlick HS 2,100/9-12
2119 Rapids Dr 53404 262-619-4300
Angela Apmann, prin. Fax 619-4390
Jerstad-Agerholm MS 700/6-8
3601 Lasalle St 53402 262-664-6075
Doug Clum, prin. Fax 664-6120
McKinley MS 800/6-8
2340 Mohr Ave 53405 262-664-6150
Cheri Kulland, prin. Fax 664-6196
Mitchell MS 700/6-8
2701 Drexel Ave 53403 262-664-6400
Soren Gajewski, prin. Fax 664-6444
Park HS 1,600/9-12
1901 12th St 53403 262-619-4400
Dennis Christensen, prin. Fax 619-4490
Racine Alternative Education 100/Alt
2405 Northwestern Ave 53404 262-664-6600
Eliot Underhill, dir. Fax 664-6644
Starbuck MS 800/6-8
1516 Ohio St 53405 262-664-6500
Andre Bennett, prin. Fax 664-6510
Walden III MSHS 300/6-12
1012 Center St 53403 262-664-6250
Rob Kreil, dir. Fax 664-6255

All Saints Healthcare System Post-Sec.
1320 Wisconsin Ave 53403 262-636-2846
Gateway Technical College Post-Sec.
1001 Main St 53403 262-619-6200
Midwest College of Oriental Medicine Post-Sec.
6232 Bankers Rd 53403 262-554-2010
Racine Lutheran HS 200/9-12
251 Luedtke Ave 53405 262-637-6538
Dave Burgess, prin. Fax 637-6601
St. Catherine HS 400/6-12
1200 Park Ave 53403 262-632-2785
Christopher Olley, pres. Fax 632-5144

Randolph, Columbia, Pop. 1,798
Randolph SD 500/PK-12
110 Meadowood Dr 53956 920-326-2427
Kevin Knudson, supt. Fax 326-2439
www.rsdwi.org
Randolph HS 200/9-12
110 Meadowood Dr 53956 920-326-2425
Andrew Kohn, prin. Fax 326-2430

Random Lake, Sheboygan, Pop. 1,574
Random Lake SD 900/PK-12
605 Random Lake Rd 53075 920-994-4342
Thomas Malmstadt, supt. Fax 994-4820
www.randomlake.k12.wi.us
Random Lake HS 300/9-12
605 Random Lake Rd 53075 920-994-9193
Adam Englebretson, prin. Fax 994-4820
Random Lake MS 300/5-8
605 Random Lake Rd 53075 920-994-2498
Amanda Jacobson, prin. Fax 994-4820

Reedsburg, Sauk, Pop. 9,120
Reedsburg SD 2,600/PK-12
501 K St 53959 608-524-2016
Thomas Benson, supt. Fax 768-8927
www.rsd.k12.wi.us
Reedsburg Area HS 800/9-12
1100 S Albert Ave 53959 608-768-8928
Rob Taylor, prin. Fax 768-8929
Webb MS 600/6-8
707 N Webb Ave 53959 608-768-8930
Casey Campbell, prin. Fax 768-8931

Reedsville, Manitowoc, Pop. 1,195
Reedsville SD 500/PK-12
340 Manitowoc St 54230 920-754-4341
Tony Butturini, supt. Fax 754-4344
www.reedsville.k12.wi.us
Reedsville HS 200/9-12
340 Manitowoc St 54230 920-754-4341
Tony Butturini, prin. Fax 754-4344

Rhinelander, Oneida, Pop. 7,686
Rhinelander SD 2,300/K-12
665 Coolidge Ave Ste B 54501 715-365-9700
Kelli Jacobi, supt. Fax 365-9713
www.rhinelander.k12.wi.us
Rhinelander HS 800/9-12
665 Coolidge Ave Ste B 54501 715-365-9500
David Ditzler, prin. Fax 365-9568
Williams MS 400/6-8
915 Acacia Ln 54501 715-365-9220
Richard Gretzinger, prin. Fax 365-9296

Nicolet Area Technical College Post-Sec.
PO Box 518 54501 715-365-4410

Rib Lake, Taylor, Pop. 905
Rib Lake SD 500/PK-12
PO Box 278 54470 715-427-3222
Lori Manion, supt. Fax 427-3221
www.riblake.k12.wi.us
Rib Lake HS 100/9-12
PO Box 278 54470 715-427-3220
Rick Cardey, prin. Fax 427-5022
Rib Lake MS 100/6-8
PO Box 278 54470 715-427-5446
Rick Cardey, prin. Fax 427-3221

Rice Lake, Barron, Pop. 8,342
Rice Lake Area SD 2,000/PK-12
700 Augusta St 54868 715-234-9007
Larry Brown, supt. Fax 234-4552
www.ricelake.k12.wi.us
Rice Lake HS 700/9-12
30 S Wisconsin Ave 54868 715-234-2181
Curt Pacholke, prin. Fax 234-6679
Rice Lake MS 600/5-8
204 Cameron Rd 54868 715-234-8156
Josh Tomesh, prin. Fax 234-9439

Univ. of Wisconsin Center-Barron County Post-Sec.
1800 College Dr 54868 715-234-8176
Wisconsin Indianhead Technical College Post-Sec.
1900 College Dr 54868 715-234-7082

Richfield, Washington, Pop. 11,239
Richfield J1 SD 400/PK-8
PO Box 127 53076 262-628-1032
Tara Villalobos, admin. Fax 628-3013
www.richfield.k12.wi.us
Richfield ES 200/3-8
PO Box 127 53076 262-628-1032
Tara Villalobos, admin. Fax 628-3013

Richland Center, Richland, Pop. 5,137
Ithaca SD 400/PK-12
24615 State Hwy 58 53581 608-585-2512
Robert Smudde, admin. Fax 585-2505
www.ithaca.k12.wi.us/
Ithaca HS 100/9-12
24615 State Hwy 58 53581 608-585-2311
Robert Smudde, admin. Fax 585-2505
Ithaca MS 100/6-8
24615 State Hwy 58 53581 608-585-2311
Robert Smudde, admin. Fax 585-2505

Richland SD 1,400/PK-12
1996 US Hwy 14 W 53581 608-647-6106
Jarred Burke, admin. Fax 647-8454
www.richland.k12.wi.us
Richland Center HS 400/9-12
1996 US Hwy 14 W 53581 608-647-6131
Jon Bosworth, prin. Fax 647-8734
Richland MS 300/6-8
1801 State Hwy 80 S 53581 608-647-6381
David Guy, prin. Fax 647-4735

University of Wisconsin Richland Post-Sec.
1200 US Hwy 14 W 53581 608-647-6186

Rio, Columbia, Pop. 1,045
Rio Community SD 500/PK-12
411 Church St 53960 920-992-3141
Mark McGuire, supt. Fax 992-3157
www.rio.k12.wi.us
Rio MSHS 300/6-12
411 Church St 53960 920-992-3141
Dana Tait, prin. Fax 992-3157

Ripon, Fond du Lac, Pop. 7,674
Ripon Area SD 1,800/PK-12
PO Box 991 54971 920-748-4600
Dr. Mary Whitrock, supt. Fax 748-2715
www.ripon.k12.wi.us
Crossroads Alternative Education 50/Alt
PO Box 991 54971 920-748-4616
Anne Lang, admin. Fax 748-4805
Ripon HS 500/9-12
PO Box 991 54971 920-748-4616
Seth Meinel, prin. Fax 748-4622
Ripon MS 200/6-8
PO Box 991 54971 920-748-4638
Thomas Hoh, prin. Fax 748-4653

Ripon College Post-Sec.
PO Box 248 54971 920-748-8115

River Falls, Pierce, Pop. 14,778
River Falls SD 3,200/PK-12
852 E Division St 54022 715-425-1800
Jamie Benson, supt. Fax 425-1804
www.rfsd.k12.wi.us
Meyer MS 700/6-8
230 N 9th St 54022 715-425-1820
Mark Chapin, prin. Fax 425-1823
River Falls HS 1,000/9-12
818 Cemetery Rd 54022 715-425-1830
Kit Luedtke, prin. Fax 425-1827

University of Wisconsin Post-Sec.
410 S 3rd St 54022 715-425-3911

Rosendale, Fond du Lac, Pop. 1,054
Rosendale-Brandon SD 1,000/PK-12
300 W Wisconsin St 54974 920-872-2851
Wayne Weber, supt. Fax 872-2647
www.rbsd.k12.wi.us
Laconia HS 300/9-12
301 W Division St 54974 920-872-2161
Wayne Weber, prin. Fax 872-2777
Rosendale IS 200/4-8
200 S Main St 54974 920-872-2126
John Hokenson, prin. Fax 872-2061

Rosholt, Portage, Pop. 506
Rosholt SD 600/PK-12
PO Box 310 54473 715-677-4542
Marc Christianson, supt. Fax 677-3543
www.rosholt.k12.wi.us
Rosholt HS 200/9-12
PO Box 310 54473 715-677-4541
James Grygleski, prin. Fax 677-6767
Rosholt MS 100/6-8
PO Box 310 54473 715-677-4541
James Grygleski, prin. Fax 677-6767

Rothschild, Marathon, Pop. 5,209

Globe University Post-Sec.
1480 County Road XX 54474 715-301-1300

Rubicon, Dodge
Herman Neosho Rubicon SD
Supt. — See Neosho
Honor IS 100/5-8
N3501 County Road P 53078 262-673-2920
Fax 673-2975

Saint Croix Falls, Polk, Pop. 2,110
St. Croix Falls SD 1,100/PK-12
PO Box 130 54024 715-483-2507
Mark Burandt, supt. Fax 483-3695
www.scf.k12.wi.us
St. Croix Falls HS 300/9-12
PO Box 130 54024 715-483-2507
Peggy Ryan, prin. Fax 483-3695
St. Croix Falls MS 300/5-8
PO Box 130 54024 715-483-2507
Joe Connors, prin. Fax 483-3695

Saint Francis, Milwaukee, Pop. 9,213
St. Francis SD 1,300/PK-12
4225 S Lake Dr 53235 414-747-3900
Blake Peuse, supt. Fax 482-7198
www.sfsd.k12.wi.us
Deer Creek IS 400/4-8
3680 S Kinnickinnic Ave 53235 414-482-8400
Guy Powell, prin. Fax 482-8406
Saint Francis HS 600/9-12
4225 S Lake Dr 53235 414-747-3600
Casey Blochowiak, prin. Fax 747-3605

St. Francis Seminary Post-Sec.
3257 S Lake Dr 53235 414-747-6400

Salem, Kenosha
Central HSD of Westosha 1,200/9-12
PO Box 38 53168 262-843-2321
Dr. Scott Pierce, admin. Fax 843-4069
www.westosha.k12.wi.us
Central-Westosha HS 1,200/9-12
PO Box 38 53168 262-843-2321
Lisa Albrecht, prin. Fax 843-4069

Sauk City, Sauk, Pop. 3,378
Sauk Prairie SD
Supt. — See Prairie du Sac
Sauk Prairie MS 600/6-8
207 Maple St 53583 608-643-5500
Ted Harter, prin. Fax 643-5503

Seneca, Crawford
Seneca SD 300/PK-12
PO Box 34 54654 608-734-3411
David Boland, supt. Fax 734-3430
www.seneca.k12.wi.us
Seneca HS 100/9-12
PO Box 34 54654 608-734-3411
David Boland, prin. Fax 734-3430
Seneca JHS 100/5-8
PO Box 34 54654 608-734-3411
David Boland, prin. Fax 734-3430

Seymour, Outagamie, Pop. 3,392
Seymour Community SD 2,400/PK-12
10 Circle Dr 54165 920-833-2304
Peter Ross, supt. Fax 833-6037
www.seymour.k12.wi.us/
Seymour Community HS 700/9-12
10 Circle Dr 54165 920-833-2306
Tom Mueller, prin. Fax 833-7608
Seymour MS 500/6-8
10 Circle Dr 54165 920-833-7199
Judy Schenk, prin. Fax 833-9376

Shawano, Shawano, Pop. 9,050
Shawano SD 2,600/PK-12
218 County Road B 54166 715-526-3194
Gary Cumberland, supt. Fax 526-6072
www.shawanoschools.com
Shawano Community HS 800/9-12
220 County Road B 54166 715-526-2175
Scott Zwirschitz, prin. Fax 524-8414
Shawano Community MS 500/6-8
1050 S Union St 54166 715-526-2192
Mary Kramer, prin. Fax 526-5037

Sheboygan, Sheboygan, Pop. 48,427
Sheboygan Area SD 10,100/PK-12
830 Virginia Ave 53081 920-459-3500
Joseph Sheehan Ph.D., supt. Fax 459-6487
www.sheboygan.k12.wi.us
Farnsworth MS 600/6-8
1017 Union Ave 53081 920-459-3655
Todd DeBruin, prin. Fax 459-3660
Mann MS 600/6-8
2820 Union Ave 53081 920-459-3666
Vicki Ritchie, prin. Fax 459-3669
North HS 1,500/9-12
1042 School Ave 53083 920-459-3600
Jason Bull, prin. Fax 459-3601
South HS 1,000/9-12
3128 S 12th St 53081 920-459-3637
Mike Trimberger, prin. Fax 459-6733
Urban MS 700/6-8
1226 North Ave 53083 920-459-3680
Ted Distefano, prin. Fax 459-4065

Lakeland College Post-Sec.
PO Box 359 53082 920-565-1000
Sheboygan Area Lutheran HS 200/9-12
3323 University Dr 53081 920-452-3323
Allen Holzheimer, prin. Fax 452-1310
Sheboygan County Christian HS 100/9-12
929 Greenfield Ave 53081 920-458-9981
Ann Steenwyk B.S., prin. Fax 458-9957
University of Wisconsin Sheboygan Post-Sec.
1 University Dr 53081 920-459-6600

Sheboygan Falls, Sheboygan, Pop. 7,719
Sheboygan Falls SD 1,800/PK-12
220 Amherst Ave 53085 920-467-7893
Jean Born, supt. Fax 467-7899
www.sheboyganfalls.k12.wi.us
Sheboygan Falls HS 500/9-12
220 Amherst Ave 53085 920-467-7890
Luke Goral, prin. Fax 467-7825
Sheboygan Falls MS 500/5-8
101 School St 53085 920-467-7880
Meloney Markofski, prin. Fax 467-7885

Shell Lake, Washburn, Pop. 1,340
Shell Lake SD 700/PK-12
271 Highway 63 S 54871 715-468-7816
David Bridenhagen, supt. Fax 468-7812
www.shelllake.k12.wi.us
Shell Lake JSHS 300/7-12
271 Highway 63 S 54871 715-468-7814
Heather Cox, prin. Fax 468-7989

Wisconsin Indianhead Technical College Post-Sec.
505 Pine Ridge Dr 54871 715-468-2815

Shiocton, Outagamie, Pop. 910
Shiocton SD 600/PK-12
PO Box 68 54170 920-986-3351
Nichole Schweitzer, supt. Fax 986-3291
www.shiocton.k12.wi.us
Shiocton HS 200/7-12
PO Box 68 54170 920-986-3351
Kelly Zeinert, prin. Fax 986-3291

Shorewood, Milwaukee, Pop. 12,886
Shorewood SD 2,100/PK-12
1701 E Capitol Dr 53211 414-963-6901
Bryan Davis, supt. Fax 963-6904
www.shorewoodschools.org
Shorewood HS 700/9-12
1701 E Capitol Dr 53211 414-963-6921
Tim Kenney, prin. Fax 961-2819
Shorewood IS 300/7-8
3830 N Morris Blvd 53211 414-963-6951
Michael Joynt, prin. Fax 963-6946

Shullsburg, Lafayette, Pop. 1,223
Shullsburg SD 400/PK-12
444 N Judgement St 53586 608-965-4427
Loras Kruser, admin. Fax 965-3794
www.shullsburg.k12.wi.us
Shullsburg HS 100/9-12
444 N Judgement St 53586 608-965-4427
Joseph Diedrich, prin. Fax 965-3794
Shullsburg JHS 100/6-8
444 N Judgement St 53586 608-965-4427
Joseph Diedrich, prin. Fax 965-3794

Siren, Burnett, Pop. 776
Siren SD 400/PK-12
24022 4th Ave 54872 715-349-2290
Kevin Shetler Ed.D., supt. Fax 349-7476
www.siren.k12.wi.us
Siren HS 200/6-12
24022 4th Ave 54872 715-349-2277
Jason Hinze, prin. Fax 349-7476

Slinger, Washington, Pop. 5,014
Slinger SD 3,100/PK-12
207 Polk St 53086 262-644-9615
Daren Sievers, supt. Fax 644-7514
www.slinger.k12.wi.us
Slinger HS 1,000/9-12
209 Polk St 53086 262-644-5261
Philip Ourada, prin. Fax 644-0479
Slinger MS 700/6-8
521 Olympic Dr 53086 262-644-5226
Dean Goneau, prin. Fax 644-7353

Soldiers Grove, Crawford, Pop. 590
North Crawford SD 500/PK-12
47050 County Road X 54655 608-735-4318
Brandon Munson, supt. Fax 735-4317
www.northcrawford.com
North Crawford HS 200/9-12
47050 County Road X 54655 608-735-4311
Toby Tripalin, prin. Fax 735-4317

Solon Springs, Douglas, Pop. 597
Solon Springs SD 300/PK-12
8993 E Baldwin Ave 54873 715-378-2263
Michael Cox, supt. Fax 378-2073
www.solonk12.net
Solon Springs S 300/PK-12
8993 E Baldwin Ave 54873 715-378-2263
Geraldine Muller, prin. Fax 378-2073

Somers, Kenosha

Shoreland Lutheran HS 300/9-12
PO Box 295 53171 262-859-2595
Paul Scriver M.Ed., prin. Fax 859-2783

Somerset, Saint Croix, Pop. 2,588
Somerset SD 1,600/PK-12
PO Box 100 54025 715-247-3313
Dr. Mark Bezek, supt. Fax 247-5588
www.somerset.k12.wi.us
Somerset HS 500/9-12
PO Box 100 54025 715-247-3355
Chris Moore, prin. Fax 247-3864
Somerset MS 500/5-8
PO Box 100 54025 715-247-4400
Sara Eichten, prin. Fax 247-4437

South Milwaukee, Milwaukee, Pop. 20,823
South Milwaukee SD 3,300/PK-12
901 15th Ave 53172 414-766-5000
Dr. Rita Olson, supt. Fax 766-5005
www.sdsm.k12.wi.us/
South Milwaukee HS 1,100/9-12
801 15th Ave 53172 414-766-5100
Beth Kaminski, prin. Fax 766-5131
South Milwaukee MS 700/6-8
1001 15th Ave 53172 414-766-5800
James Hendrickson, prin. Fax 766-5803

South Wayne, Lafayette, Pop. 489
Black Hawk SD 300/PK-12
PO Box 303 53587 608-439-5400
Dr. William Chambers, supt. Fax 439-1022
www.blackhawk.k12.wi.us
Black Hawk HS 100/6-12
PO Box 303 53587 608-439-5371
Cory Milz, prin. Fax 439-1022

Sparta, Monroe, Pop. 9,396
Sparta Area SD 2,700/PK-12
201 E Franklin St 54656 608-269-3151
John Hendricks, supt. Fax 366-3526
www.spartan.org
Sparta HS 700/9-12
506 N Black River St 54656 608-366-3504
Samuel Russ, prin. Fax 366-3506
Sparta Meadowview MS 500/6-8
1225 N Water St 54656 608-366-3497
Jeffery Krull, prin. Fax 366-3500

Spencer, Marathon, Pop. 1,903
Spencer SD 800/PK-12
PO Box 418 54479 715-659-5347
Michael Endreas, supt. Fax 659-5470
www.spencer.k12.wi.us
Spencer JSHS 400/6-12
PO Box 418 54479 715-659-4211
Jerry Zanotelli, prin. Fax 659-5470

Spooner, Washburn, Pop. 2,637
Spooner Area SD 1,200/PK-12
801 County Highway A 54801 715-635-2171
Fax 635-7174
www.spooner.k12.wi.us
Spooner HS 400/9-12
801 County Highway A 54801 715-635-2172
Sarah Johnson, prin. Fax 635-7074
Spooner MS 300/5-8
750 Oak St 54801 715-635-2173
Bradley Larrabee, prin. Fax 635-7074

Spring Green, Sauk, Pop. 1,601
River Valley SD 1,300/PK-12
660 W Daley St 53588 608-588-2551
Tom Wermuth, supt. Fax 588-2558
www.rvschools.org
River Valley HS 500/9-12
660 Varsity Blvd 53588 608-588-2554
Darby Blakley, prin. Fax 588-2827
River Valley MS 300/6-8
660 W Daley St 53588 608-588-2556
James Radtke, prin. Fax 588-2026

Spring Valley, Pierce, Pop. 1,346
Spring Valley SD 600/PK-12
PO Box 249 54767 715-778-5551
Dr. Donald Haack, supt. Fax 778-4761
www.springvalley.k12.wi.us
Spring Valley MSHS 200/6-12
PO Box 249 54767 715-778-5554
Gretchen Cipriano, prin. Fax 778-5556

Stanley, Chippewa, Pop. 3,592
Stanley-Boyd Area SD 1,000/PK-12
507 E 1st Ave 54768 715-644-5534
James Jones, supt. Fax 644-5584
www.stanleyboyd.k12.wi.us
Stanley-Boyd HS 300/9-12
507 E 1st Ave 54768 715-644-5534
Dave Ludy, prin. Fax 644-6701
Stanley-Boyd MS 200/6-8
507 E 1st Ave 54768 715-644-5715
Dave Ludy, prin. Fax 644-5584

Stevens Point, Portage, Pop. 26,351
Stevens Point Area SD 6,800/PK-12
1900 Polk St 54481 715-345-5456
Craig Gerlach, supt. Fax 345-7302
www.pointschools.net
Fernandez Ctr for Alternative Learning 100/Alt
1025 Clark St 54481 715-345-5592
Jesse Jackson, prin. Fax 345-7374
Franklin JHS 800/7-9
2000 Polk St 54481 715-345-5413
Steve Prokop, prin. Fax 345-5696
Jacobs JHS 800/7-9
2400 Main St 54481 715-345-5422
Dan Dobratz, prin. Fax 345-7340
Stevens Point Area SHS 1,600/10-12
1201 Northpoint Dr 54481 715-345-5400
Jon Vollendorf, prin. Fax 345-5408

Mid-State Technical College Post-Sec.
1001 Centerpoint Dr 54481 715-344-3063
Pacelli Catholic MS 200/6-8
708 1st St 54481 715-344-1890
Ellen Lopas, prin. Fax 342-2005
Pacelli Catholic HS 200/9-12
1301 Maria Dr 54481 715-341-2442
Larry Theiss, prin. Fax 341-6779
Stevens Point Christian Academy 50/K-12
801 County Road HH 54481 715-341-3275
Heidi Uitenbroek, prin. Fax 341-3275
University of Wisconsin Post-Sec.
2100 Main St 54481 715-346-0123

Stockbridge, Calumet, Pop. 630
Stockbridge SD 200/PK-12
PO Box 188 53088 920-439-1782
David Moscinski, supt. Fax 439-1150
www.stockbridge.k12.wi.us/
Stockbridge HS 100/9-12
PO Box 188 53088 920-439-1158
Chad Marx, prin. Fax 439-1150
Stockbridge MS 50/6-8
PO Box 188 53088 920-439-1158
Chad Marx, prin. Fax 439-1150

Stoughton, Dane, Pop. 12,430
Stoughton Area SD 3,200/PK-12
320 North St 53589 608-877-5000
Tim Onsager, admin. Fax 877-5028
www.stoughton.k12.wi.us
River Bluff MS 700/6-8
235 N Forrest St 53589 608-877-5503
Fred Potter, prin. Fax 877-5508
Stoughton HS 1,100/9-12
600 Lincoln Ave 53589 608-877-5601
Mike Kruse, prin. Fax 877-5619

Stratford, Marathon, Pop. 1,570
Stratford SD 900/PK-12
PO Box 7 54484 715-687-3130
Scott Winch, supt. Fax 687-4074
www.stratford.k12.wi.us
Stratford HS 300/9-12
PO Box 7 54484 715-687-4311
Janeen LaBorde, prin. Fax 687-4652
Stratford MS 200/6-8
PO Box 7 54484 715-687-4311
Janeen LaBorde, prin. Fax 687-4652

Strum, Trempealeau, Pop. 1,111
Eleva-Strum SD 600/PK-12
W23597 US Highway 10 54770 715-695-2696
Craig Semingson, admin. Fax 695-3519
www.esschools.k12.wi.us/
Eleva-Strum MSHS 300/7-12
W23597 US Highway 10 54770 715-695-2696
Cory Kulig, prin. Fax 695-3938

Sturgeon Bay, Door, Pop. 9,041
Sevastopol SD 500/PK-12
4550 State Highway 57 54235 920-743-6282
Steve Cromell, supt. Fax 743-4009
www.sevastopol.k12.wi.us
Sevastopol HS 100/9-12
4550 State Highway 57 54235 920-743-6282
Adam Baier, prin. Fax 743-4009
Sevastopol MS 100/6-8
4550 State Highway 57 54235 920-743-6282
Adam Baier, prin. Fax 743-4009

Sturgeon Bay SD 1,200/PK-12
1230 Michigan St 54235 920-746-2800
Daniel Tjernagel, supt. Fax 746-3888
www.sturbay.k12.wi.us
Sturgeon Bay HS 400/9-12
1230 Michigan St 54235 920-746-2800
Robert Nickel, prin. Fax 746-3888
Walker MS 300/6-8
19 N 14th Ave 54235 920-746-2810
Randy Watermolen, prin. Fax 746-3885

Northeast Wisconsin Technical College Post-Sec.
229 N 14th Ave 54235 920-746-4900

Sun Prairie, Dane, Pop. 28,546
Sun Prairie Area SD 7,100/PK-12
501 S Bird St 53590 608-834-6500
Dr. Brad Saron, supt. Fax 834-6555
www.spasd.k12.wi.us
Cardinal Heights Upper MS 1,100/8-9
220 Kroncke Dr 53590 608-318-8000
Ryan Ruggles, prin. Fax 318-8192
Prairie Phoenix Academy 100/Alt
160 South St 53590 608-834-6900
Lisa Bollinger, prin. Fax 834-6992
Sun Prairie HS 1,500/10-12
888 Grove St 53590 608-834-6700
Lisa Heipp, prin. Fax 834-6792

Diesel Truck Driver Training School Post-Sec.
7190 Elder Ln 53590 608-837-7800

Superior, Douglas, Pop. 26,443
Superior SD 4,600/PK-12
3025 Tower Ave 54880 715-394-8700
Janna Stevens, supt. Fax 394-8708
www.superior.k12.wi.us
Superior HS 1,400/9-12
2600 Catlin Ave 54880 715-394-8720
Kent Bergum, prin. Fax 394-8760
Superior MS 900/6-8
3626 Hammond Ave 54880 715-394-8740
Richard Flaherty, prin. Fax 395-8483

Maranatha Academy 100/PK-12
4916 S State Road 35 54880 715-399-8757
Keith Russell, admin. Fax 399-8758
University of Wisconsin Post-Sec.
PO Box 2000 54880 715-394-8101
Wisconsin Indianhead Technical College Post-Sec.
600 N 21st St 54880 715-394-6677

Suring, Oconto, Pop. 532
Suring SD 400/PK-12
PO Box 158 54174 920-842-2178
Kelly Casper, supt. Fax 842-4570
www.suring.k12.wi.us
Suring HS 100/9-12
PO Box 158 54174 920-842-2182
Pamela Berg, prin. Fax 842-4570

Sussex, Waukesha, Pop. 10,416
Hamilton SD 4,700/PK-12
W220N6151 Town Line Rd 53089 262-246-1973
Dr. Paul Mielke, supt. Fax 246-6552
www.hamilton.k12.wi.us
Hamilton HS 1,400/9-12
W220N6151 Town Line Rd 53089 262-246-6471
Candis Mongan, prin. Fax 246-1885
Templeton MS 1,100/6-8
N59W22490 Silver Spring Dr 53089 262-246-6477
Brad Hoffmann, prin. Fax 246-0465

Thorp, Clark, Pop. 1,612
Thorp SD 600/PK-12
PO Box 449 54771 715-669-5401
James Montgomery, admin. Fax 669-5403
www.thorp.k12.wi.us/
Thorp HS 200/9-12
PO Box 449 54771 715-669-5401
Bill Hass, prin. Fax 669-5403

Three Lakes, Oneida, Pop. 604
Three Lakes SD 500/PK-12
6930 W School St 54562 715-546-3496
Dr. George Karling, supt. Fax 546-8125
www.threelakessd.k12.wi.us
Three Lakes JSHS 200/7-12
6930 W School St 54562 715-546-3321
Eugene Welhoefer, prin. Fax 546-2828

Tigerton, Shawano, Pop. 725
Tigerton SD 200/PK-12
PO Box 10 54486 715-535-4000
Dr. Wayne Johnson, admin. Fax 535-4010
www.tigerton.k12.wi.us
Tigerton MSHS 100/6-12
PO Box 40 54486 715-535-4001
Dr. Wayne Johnson, admin. Fax 535-1355

Tomah, Monroe, Pop. 8,916
Tomah Area SD 2,900/PK-12
129 W Clifton St 54660 608-374-7004
Cindy Zahrte, supt. Fax 372-5087
www.tomah.k12.wi.us
Kupper Learning Center 100/Alt
1310 Townline Rd 54660 608-374-7020
Paul Skofronick, admin. Fax 374-8710
Tomah HS 900/9-12
901 Lincoln Ave 54660 608-374-7358
Robert Joyce, prin. Fax 374-7290
Tomah MS 600/6-8
612 Hollister Ave 54660 608-374-7885
Steven Buss, prin. Fax 374-7303

Tomahawk, Lincoln, Pop. 3,356
Tomahawk SD 1,300/PK-12
1048 E King Rd 54487 715-453-5551
Cheryl Baker, supt. Fax 453-6736
www.tomahawk.k12.wi.us
Tomahawk HS 400/9-12
1048 E King Rd 54487 715-453-2106
Scott Swenty, prin. Fax 453-1437
Tomahawk MS 300/6-8
1048 E King Rd 54487 715-453-5371
Trisha Detert, prin. Fax 453-9630

Tony, Rusk, Pop. 113
Flambeau SD 500/PK-12
PO Box 86 54563 715-532-3183
Rich Hanson, supt. Fax 532-5405
www.flambeau.k12.wi.us
Flambeau MSHS 200/6-12
PO Box 86 54563 715-532-3183
Erica Schley, prin. Fax 532-5405

Turtle Lake, Barron, Pop. 1,031
Turtle Lake SD 400/PK-12
205 Oak St 54889 715-986-2597
Kent Kindschy, admin. Fax 986-2444
www.turtlelake.k12.wi.us
Turtle Lake HS 100/9-12
205 Oak St 54889 715-986-4470
Brian Buck, prin. Fax 986-2444

Two Rivers, Manitowoc, Pop. 11,594
Two Rivers SD 1,700/PK-12
4521 Lincoln Ave 54241 920-793-4560
Lisa Quistorf, supt. Fax 793-4014
www.trschools.k12.wi.us
Clarke MS 500/5-8
4608 Bellevue Pl 54241 920-794-1614
Tim Wester, prin. Fax 793-1819
Two Rivers HS 500/9-12
4519 Lincoln Ave 54241 920-793-2291
Larry Schlosser, prin. Fax 793-5068

Union Grove, Racine, Pop. 4,851
Union Grove UNHSD 1,000/9-12
3433 S Colony Ave 53182 262-878-4427
Alan Mollerskov, supt. Fax 878-3291
www.ug.k12.wi.us

Union Grove HS 1,000/9-12
3433 S Colony Ave 53182 262-878-2434
Thomas Hermann, prin. Fax 878-4056

Union Grove Christian S 100/PK-12
417 15th Ave 53182 262-878-1264

Valders, Manitowoc, Pop. 958
Valders Area SD 1,000/K-12
138 E Wilson St 54245 920-775-9500
Debra Hunt, supt. Fax 775-9509
www.valders.k12.wi.us
Valders HS 400/9-12
201 E Wilson St 54245 920-775-9530
Julie Laabs, prin. Fax 775-9509
Valders MS 300/5-8
138 Jefferson St 54245 920-775-9520
Kelly Isselmann, prin. Fax 775-9509

Verona, Dane, Pop. 10,419
Verona Area SD 5,200/PK-12
700 N Main St 53593 608-845-4300
Dean Gorrell, supt. Fax 845-4321
www.verona.k12.wi.us
Badger Ridge MS 500/6-8
740 N Main St 53593 608-845-4100
Michael Murphy, prin. Fax 845-4120
Verona Area HS 1,500/9-12
300 Richard St 53593 608-845-4400
Pam Hammen, prin. Fax 845-4420
Other Schools – See Fitchburg

Viola, Vernon, Pop. 694
Kickapoo Area SD 500/PK-12
S6520 State Highway 131 54664 608-627-0101
Douglas Olsen, supt. Fax 627-0118
www.kickapoo.k12.wi.us
Kickapoo MSHS 200/6-12
S6520 State Highway 131 54664 608-627-0100
Aaron Mithum, prin. Fax 627-0132

Viroqua, Vernon, Pop. 4,314
Viroqua Area SD 1,200/PK-12
115 N Education Ave 54665 608-637-1186
Dr. Kehl Arnson, supt. Fax 637-8554
www.viroqua.k12.wi.us
Viroqua HS 300/9-12
100 Blackhawk Dr 54665 608-637-3191
Katherine Klos, prin. Fax 637-8034
Viroqua MS 300/5-8
100 Blackhawk Dr 54665 608-637-3171
John Schneider, prin. Fax 637-8034

Cornerstone Christian Academy 50/PK-12
S3655 Duncan Ln 54665 608-634-4102
Jim Schweitzer, admin. Fax 634-4162
Youth Initiative HS 50/9-12
500 E Jefferson St Ste 302 54665 608-637-6445

Wabeno, Forest, Pop. 550
Wabeno Area SD 500/PK-12
PO Box 460 54566 715-473-2592
Jennifer Vogler, supt. Fax 473-5201
www.wabeno.k12.wi.us
Wabeno JSHS 200/7-12
PO Box 460 54566 715-473-5122
William Taylor, prin. Fax 473-3406

Wales, Waukesha, Pop. 2,532
Kettle Moraine SD 4,000/PK-12
563 A J Allen Cir 53183 262-968-6300
Patricia Deklotz, supt. Fax 968-6390
www.kmsd.edu/
Kettle Moraine HS 1,300/9-12
349 N Oak Crest Dr 53183 262-968-6200
Jeffrey Walters, prin. Fax 968-6217
Other Schools – See Dousman

Walworth, Walworth, Pop. 2,799
Big Foot UNHSD 500/9-12
PO Box 99 53184 262-275-2116
Dorothy Kaufmann, admin. Fax 275-5117
www.bigfoot.k12.wi.us
Big Foot Union HS 500/9-12
PO Box 99 53184 262-275-2116
Dorothy J. Kaufmann, admin. Fax 275-5117

Washburn, Bayfield, Pop. 2,031
Washburn SD 600/PK-12
PO Box 730 54891 715-373-6188
Dr. Thomas Wiatr, supt. Fax 373-5877
www.washburn.k12.wi.us
Washburn HS 200/9-12
PO Box 730 54891 715-373-6188
Heidi King, prin. Fax 373-5877
Washburn MS 100/6-8
PO Box 730 54891 715-373-6199
Al Krause, prin. Fax 373-0586

Washington Island, Door
Washington SD 100/K-12
888 Main Rd 54246 920-847-2507
Mati Palm-Leis, supt. Fax 847-2865
www.island.k12.wi.us
Washington Island HS 50/9-12
888 Main Rd 54246 920-847-2507
Dr. Mati M. Palm-Leis, admin. Fax 847-2865

Waterford, Racine, Pop. 5,327
Waterford Graded JSD 1 1,500/K-8
819 W Main St 53185 262-514-8250
Ed Brzinski, supt. Fax 514-8251
www.waterford.k12.wi.us
Fox River MS 400/7-8
921 W Main St 53185 262-514-8240
Darlene Markle, prin. Fax 514-8241

Waterford UNHSD 1,000/9-12
507 W Main St 53185 262-534-9059
Keith Brandstetter, supt. Fax 534-6871
www.waterforduhs.k12.wi.us
Waterford Union HS 1,000/9-12
100 Field Dr 53185 262-534-3189
Daniel Foster, prin. Fax 534-4971

Waterloo, Jefferson, Pop. 3,304
Waterloo SD 700/PK-12
813 N Monroe St 53594 920-478-3633
Brian Henning, admin. Fax 478-3821
www.waterloo.k12.wi.us
Waterloo HS 300/9-12
813 N Monroe St 53594 920-478-2171
Brad Donner, prin. Fax 478-9539
Waterloo IS/MS 100/5-8
813 N Monroe St 53594 920-478-2696
Shannon Karcher, prin. Fax 478-3987

Watertown, Jefferson, Pop. 23,579
Watertown Unified SD 3,800/PK-12
111 Dodge St 53094 920-262-1460
Cassandra Schug, supt. Fax 262-1469
www.watertown.k12.wi.us
Riverside MS 800/6-8
131 Hall St 53094 920-262-1480
Jonathan Rouse, prin. Fax 262-1468
Watertown HS 1,300/9-12
825 Endevour Dr 53098 920-262-7500
William Loss, prin. Fax 262-7545

Luther Preparatory S 400/9-12
1300 Western Ave 53094 920-261-4352
Matthew Crass, pres. Fax 262-8118
Maranatha Baptist Academy 100/9-12
745 W Main St 53094 920-206-2366
Maranatha Baptist Bible Coll & Seminary Post-Sec.
745 W Main St 53094 920-261-9300
Trinity-St. Luke's Lutheran S 100/5-8
303 Clark St 53094 920-206-1844
James Moeller, prin. Fax 206-1750

Waukesha, Waukesha, Pop. 69,639
Waukesha SD 13,200/PK-12
222 Maple Ave 53186 262-970-1000
Todd Gray, supt. Fax 970-1021
www.waukesha.k12.wi.us
Butler MS 900/6-8
310 N Hine Ave 53188 262-970-2900
Jason Sadowski, prin. Fax 970-2920
Horning MS 800/6-8
2000 Wolf Rd 53186 262-970-3300
Mark Wegner, prin. Fax 970-3320
North HS 1,100/9-12
2222 Michigan Ave 53188 262-970-3500
Rebecca Newcomer, prin. Fax 970-3520
Paul MS 600/6-8
400 N Grand Ave 53186 262-970-3100
Rob Bennett, prin. Fax 970-3120
South HS 1,100/9-12
401 E Roberta Ave 53186 262-970-3705
Timothy Joynt, prin. Fax 970-3720
West HS 1,200/9-12
3301 Saylesville Rd 53189 262-970-3900
David LaBorde, prin. Fax 970-3920

Carroll University Post-Sec.
100 N East Ave 53186 262-547-1211
Catholic Memorial HS 700/9-12
601 E College Ave 53186 262-542-7101
Robert Hall, prin. Fax 542-1633
DeVry University Post-Sec.
N14W23833 Stone Ridge Dr 53188 262-347-2911
St. Joseph MS 200/6-8
818 N East Ave 53186 262-896-2930
Joseph Heinecke, prin. Fax 896-2935
University of Wisconsin Waukesha Post-Sec.
1500 N University Dr 53188 262-521-5200

Waunakee, Dane, Pop. 11,963
Waunakee Community SD 3,800/PK-12
905 Bethel Cir 53597 608-849-2000
Randy Guttenberg, supt. Fax 849-2350
www.waunakee.k12.wi.us
Waunakee HS 1,200/9-12
301 Community Dr 53597 608-849-2100
Brian Kersten, prin. Fax 849-2164
Waunakee MS 600/7-8
1001 South St 53597 608-849-2060
Marcy Peters-Felice, prin. Fax 849-2088

Madison Country Day S 300/PK-12
5606 River Rd 53597 608-850-6000
Ben Hebebrand, head sch Fax 850-6006

Waupaca, Waupaca, Pop. 6,011
Waupaca SD 2,200/PK-12
515 School St 54981 715-258-4121
David Poeschl, supt. Fax 258-4125
www.waupaca.k12.wi.us/
Waupaca HS 700/9-12
E2325 King Rd 54981 715-258-4131
Robert Becker, prin. Fax 258-4135
Waupaca MS 700/5-8
1149 Shoemaker Rd 54981 715-258-4140
Ben Rayome, prin. Fax 256-5681

Waupun, Dodge, Pop. 11,240
Waupun Area SD 1,600/PK-12
950 Wilcox St 53963 920-324-9341
Tonya Gubin, supt. Fax 324-2630
www.waupun.k12.wi.us
Waupun Area JSHS 600/7-12
801 E Lincoln St 53963 920-324-5591
Jeff Finstad, prin. Fax 324-6980

Central Wisconsin Christian S 300/PK-12
301 Fox Lake Rd 53963 920-324-4233
Mark Buteyn, admin. Fax 324-5036

Wausau, Marathon, Pop. 38,312
Wausau SD 8,100/PK-12
PO Box 359 54402 715-261-0500
Dr. Kathleen Williams, supt. Fax 261-2503
www.wausauschools.org/
Mann MS 800/6-8
3101 N 13th St 54403 715-261-0725
Julie Sprague, prin. Fax 261-2035
Muir MS 900/6-8
1400 Stewart Ave 54401 715-261-0100
Larry Mancl, prin. Fax 261-2461
Wausau East HS 1,100/9-12
2607 N 18th St 54403 715-261-0650
Bradley Peck, prin. Fax 845-2913
Wausau West HS 1,400/9-12
1200 W Wausau Ave 54401 715-261-0850
Jeb Steckbauer, prin. Fax 261-3260

Faith Christian Academy 100/PK-12
225 S 28th Ave 54401 715-842-0797
Dave Wysong, admin. Fax 842-1042
Newman Catholic MSHS 300/6-12
1130 W Bridge St 54401 715-845-8274
Daniel Sullivan, prin. Fax 842-1302
Northcentral Technical College Post-Sec.
1000 W Campus Dr 54401 715-675-3331
Rasmussen College Post-Sec.
1101 Westwood Dr 54401 715-841-8000
State College of Beauty Culture Post-Sec.
1930 Grand Ave 54403 715-849-5368
University of Wisconsin Marathon County Post-Sec.
518 S 7th Ave 54401 715-261-6235
Wausau Hospital Center Post-Sec.
333 Pine Ridge Blvd 54401 715-847-2117

Wausaukee, Marinette, Pop. 563
Wausaukee SD 500/PK-12
PO Box 258 54177 715-856-5153
Bob Berndt, supt. Fax 856-6592
www.wausaukee.k12.wi.us
Wausaukee HS 200/9-12
PO Box 258 54177 715-856-5151
Jared Deschane, prin. Fax 856-6592
Wausaukee JHS 100/7-8
PO Box 258 54177 715-856-5151
Jared Deschane, prin. Fax 856-6592

Wautoma, Waushara, Pop. 2,182
Wautoma Area SD 1,400/PK-12
PO Box 870 54982 920-787-7112
Jeff Kasuboski, supt. Fax 787-1389
www.wautomasd.org
Parkside MS 500/4-8
PO Box 870 54982 920-787-4577
Deb Premo, prin. Fax 787-7336
Wautoma HS 400/9-12
PO Box 870 54982 920-787-3354
Tom Rheinheimer, prin. Fax 787-1513

Wauwatosa, Milwaukee, Pop. 45,454
Wauwatosa SD 7,100/PK-12
12121 W North Ave 53226 414-773-1000
Phil Ertl, supt. Fax 773-1019
www.wauwatosaschools.org
East HS 1,200/9-12
7500 Milwaukee Ave 53213 414-773-2000
Nick Hughes, prin. Fax 773-2020
Longfellow MS 800/6-8
7600 W North Ave 53213 414-773-2400
Mark Carter, prin. Fax 773-2420
West HS 1,000/9-12
11400 W Center St 53222 414-773-3000
Frank Calarco, prin. Fax 773-3020
Whitman MS 700/6-8
11100 W Center St 53222 414-773-2600
Jeff Keranen, prin. Fax 773-2620

Bryant & Stratton College Post-Sec.
10950 W Potter Rd 53226 414-302-7000

Wauzeka, Crawford, Pop. 697
Wauzeka-Steuben SD 200/PK-12
301 E Main St 53826 608-875-5311
Robert Sailer, supt. Fax 875-5100
www.wauzeka.k12.wi.us
Wauzeka-Steuben S 200/PK-12
301 E Main St 53826 608-875-5311
Robert Sailer, prin. Fax 875-5100

Webster, Burnett, Pop. 634
Webster SD 700/PK-12
PO Box 9 54893 715-866-4391
Jim Erickson, supt. Fax 866-4283
www.webster.k12.wi.us
Webster HS 200/9-12
PO Box 9 54893 715-866-4281
Josh Hetfeld, prin. Fax 866-4377
Webster MS 200/5-8
PO Box 9 54893 715-866-4282
Diana Lesneski, prin. Fax 866-4377

West Allis, Milwaukee, Pop. 59,182
West Allis SD
Supt. — See Milwaukee
Central HS 1,400/9-12
8516 W Lincoln Ave 53227 414-604-3110
Dr. Amy VanDeuren, prin. Fax 546-5536
Hale HS 1,600/9-12
11601 W Lincoln Ave 53227 414-604-3210
Matthew Lesar, prin. Fax 546-5734
Lane IS 6-8
1300 S 109th St 53214 414-329-6610
Bob Antholine, prin. Fax 259-0306
Lincoln IS 400/6-8
7815 W Lapham St 53214 414-604-4210
Liz Kayzar, prin. Fax 777-7256
West Allis West Milwaukee Learning Ctr 200/Alt
1135 S 70th St 53214 414-604-3510
Jason Grabner, prin. Fax 454-0293

Wright IS 1,100/6-8
9501 W Cleveland Ave 53227 414-604-3410
Jeff Thomson, prin. Fax 546-5785

Grace Christian Academy 200/PK-12
8420 W Beloit Rd 53227 414-327-4200
Cynthia Hummitzsch, admin. Fax 327-4386
Milwaukee Area Technical College Post-Sec.
1200 S 71st St 53214 414-456-5500

West Bend, Washington, Pop. 30,669
West Bend SD 5,400/PK-12
735 S Main St 53095 262-335-5435
Erik Olson, supt. Fax 335-5470
www.west-bend.k12.wi.us
Badger MS 600/7-8
727 S 6th Ave 53095 262-335-5456
Dave Uelmen, prin. Fax 306-4380
East HS 1,200/9-12
1305 E Decorah Rd 53095 262-335-5532
Bill Greymont, prin. Fax 335-8242
West HS 1,100/9-12
1305 E Decorah Rd 53095 262-335-5587
Bill Greymont, prin. Fax 335-8251

Moraine Park Technical College Post-Sec.
2151 N Main St 53090 262-335-5706
University of Wisconsin Washington Co Post-Sec.
400 S University Dr 53095 262-335-5200

Westby, Vernon, Pop. 2,182
Westby Area SD 1,100/PK-12
206 West Ave S 54667 608-634-0101
Charles Norton, supt. Fax 634-0118
www.westby.k12.wi.us
Westby Area HS 300/9-12
206 West Ave S 54667 608-634-3101
Karl Stoker, prin. Fax 634-0123
Westby Area MS 300/5-8
206 West Ave S 54667 608-634-0200
Mike Weninger, prin. Fax 634-0218

Westfield, Marquette, Pop. 1,241
Westfield SD 1,100/PK-12
N7046 County Road M 53964 608-296-2107
John Eyerly, supt. Fax 296-2938
www.westfield.k12.wi.us
Westfield Area HS 300/9-12
N7046 County Road M 53964 608-296-2141
David Moody, prin. Fax 296-2293
Westfield Area MS 200/7-8
N7046 County Road M 53964 608-296-2141
David Moody, prin. Fax 296-2293

West Milwaukee, Milwaukee, Pop. 4,109
West Allis SD
Supt. — See Milwaukee
West Milwaukee IS 500/6-8
5104 W Greenfield Ave 53214 414-604-3310
Jeffery Taylor, prin. Fax 389-3815

Weston, Marathon, Pop. 12,921
D.C. Everest Area SD 5,600/PK-12
6300 Alderson St 54476 715-359-4221
Kristine Gilmore, supt. Fax 359-2056
www.dce.k12.wi.us
D.C. Everest HS 1,300/10-12
6500 Alderson St 54476 715-359-6561
Thomas Johansen, prin. Fax 355-7220
D.C. Everest JHS 800/8-9
1000 Machmueller St 54476 715-359-0511
Jason McFarlane, prin. Fax 359-9395

West Salem, LaCrosse, Pop. 4,740
West Salem SD 1,800/PK-12
405 Hamlin St E 54669 608-786-0700
Troy Gunderson, supt. Fax 786-2960
www.wsalem.k12.wi.us
West Salem HS 600/9-12
490 Mark St N 54669 608-786-1220
Josh Mallicoat, prin. Fax 786-1273
West Salem MS 400/6-8
450 Mark St N 54669 608-786-2090
Ben Wopat, prin. Fax 786-1081

Coulee Christian S 200/PK-12
230 Garland St W 54669 608-786-3004
Dr. Tammy Chandler, admin. Fax 786-3005

Weyauwega, Waupaca, Pop. 1,882
Weyauwega-Fremont SD 900/PK-12
PO Box 580 54983 920-867-8800
Scott Bleck, supt. Fax 867-8815
www.wegafremont.k12.wi.us
Weyauwega-Fremont HS 300/9-12
PO Box 580 54983 920-867-8950
Jeremy Schroeder, prin. Fax 867-8975
Weyauwega-Fremont MS 200/6-8
PO Box 580 54983 920-867-8850
Jeremy Schroeder, prin. Fax 867-8875

Whitefish Bay, Milwaukee, Pop. 13,847
Whitefish Bay SD 3,100/PK-12
1200 E Fairmount Ave 53217 414-963-3921
John Thomsen, supt. Fax 963-3959
www.wfbschools.com
Whitefish Bay HS 1,000/9-12
1200 E Fairmount Ave 53217 414-963-3928
Amy Levek, prin. Fax 963-3870
Whitefish Bay MS 600/6-8
1144 E Henry Clay St 53217 414-963-6800
Mike O'Connor, prin. Fax 963-6808

Dominican HS 300/9-12
120 E Silver Spring Dr 53217 414-332-1170
Edward Foy, prin. Fax 332-4101

Whitehall, Trempealeau, Pop. 1,550
Whitehall SD 500/PK-12
19121 Hobson St 54773 715-538-4374
Michael Beighley, supt. Fax 538-4639
www.whitehallsd.k12.wi.us
Whitehall Memorial MSHS 200/7-12
PO Box 37 54773 715-538-4364
Mike Beighley, prin. Fax 538-4639

White Lake, Langlade, Pop. 352
White Lake SD 200/PK-12
PO Box 67 54491 715-882-8421
William Fisher, supt. Fax 882-2914
www.whitelake.k12.wi.us
White Lake JSHS 100/7-12
PO Box 67 54491 715-882-2361
Glenda Boldig, prin. Fax 882-2914

Whitewater, Walworth, Pop. 14,180
Whitewater USD 1,800/PK-12
419 S Elizabeth St 53190 262-472-8700
Dr. Mark Elworthy, supt. Fax 472-8710
www.wwusd.org
Whitewater HS 500/9-12
534 S Elizabeth St 53190 262-472-8100
Doug Parker, prin. Fax 472-8181
Whitewater MS 400/6-8
401 S Elizabeth St 53190 262-472-8300
Dr. Tanya Wojciechowicz, prin. Fax 472-8310

University of Wisconsin Post-Sec.
800 W Main St 53190 262-472-1234

Wild Rose, Waushara, Pop. 719
Wild Rose SD 600/PK-12
PO Box 276 54984 920-622-4203
Craig Hayes, supt. Fax 622-4604
www.wildrose.k12.wi.us
Wild Rose MSHS 300/6-12
PO Box 276 54984 920-622-4201
Chris Nelson, prin. Fax 622-4801

Williams Bay, Walworth, Pop. 2,540
Williams Bay SD 600/PK-12
PO Box 1410 53191 262-245-1575
Dr. Wayne Anderson, supt. Fax 245-5877
www.williamsbayschool.org
Williams Bay HS 100/9-12
PO Box 1410 53191 262-245-6224
Dr. William White, prin. Fax 245-5877
Williams Bay MS 100/6-8
PO Box 1410 53191 262-245-6224
Dr. William White, prin. Fax 245-5877

Faith Christian S 200/PK-12
PO Box 1230 53191 262-245-9404
Jim McCormick, head sch Fax 245-0128
G Williams College of Aurora University Post-Sec.
PO Box 210 53191 262-245-5531

Wilmot, Kenosha, Pop. 442
Wilmot UNHSD 1,100/9-12
PO Box 8 53192 262-862-9005
Daniel S. Kopp, admin. Fax 862-6413
www.wilmothighschool.com
Wilmot HS 1,100/9-12
PO Box 8 53192 262-862-2351
Dr. John LaFleur, prin. Fax 862-6929

Wind Point, Racine, Pop. 1,708

Prairie S 700/PK-12
4050 Lighthouse Dr, 262-752-2500
Dr. Nat Coffman, head sch Fax 752-2517

Winneconne, Winnebago, Pop. 2,364
Winneconne Community SD 1,500/PK-12
PO Box 5000 54986 920-582-5802
Margaret Larson, supt. Fax 582-5816
www.winneconne.k12.wi.us
Winneconne HS 500/9-12
PO Box 5000 54986 920-582-5810
Leah Michaud, prin. Fax 582-5813
Winneconne MS 400/6-8
PO Box 5000 54986 920-582-5800
Todd Schroeder, prin. Fax 582-5812

Winter, Sawyer, Pop. 305
Winter SD 300/PK-12
PO Box 310 54896 715-266-3301
Kurt Lindau, admin. Fax 266-2216
www.winter.k12.wi.us/
Winter HS 100/9-12
PO Box 310 54896 715-266-3301
Kurt Lindau, admin. Fax 266-9221
Winter MS 100/6-8
PO Box 310 54896 715-266-6701
Kurt Lindau, admin. Fax 266-2216

Wisconsin Dells, Columbia, Pop. 2,648
Wisconsin Dells SD 1,800/PK-12
811 County Road H 53965 608-254-7769
Terrance Slack, supt. Fax 254-8058
www.sdwd.k12.wi.us
Spring Hill MS 300/6-8
300 Vine St 53965 608-253-2467
Julie Ennis, prin. Fax 254-6397
Wisconsin Dells HS 500/9-12
520 Race St 53965 608-253-1461
Hugh Gaston, prin. Fax 254-6288

Wisconsin Rapids, Wood, Pop. 18,141
Wisconsin Rapids SD 5,300/PK-12
510 Peach St 54494 715-424-6700
Colleen Dickmann, supt. Fax 422-6070
www.wrps.org
East JHS 800/8-9
311 Lincoln St 54494 715-424-6730
Kevin Yeske, prin. Fax 422-6270
Lincoln SHS 1,200/10-12
1801 16th St S 54494 715-424-6750
Ronald Rasmussen, prin. Fax 422-6097
River Cities HS 100/Alt
2390 48th St S 54494 715-424-6798
Matthew Green, prin. Fax 422-6370

Assumption HS 200/9-12
445 Chestnut St 54494 715-422-0910
Paul Klinkhammer, prin. Fax 422-0912
Assumption MS 100/6-8
440 Mead St 54494 715-422-0950
Joan Bond, prin. Fax 422-0955
Mid-State Technical College Post-Sec.
500 32nd St N 54494 715-422-5300

Wittenberg, Shawano, Pop. 1,064
Wittenberg-Birnamwood SD 1,200/PK-12
400 W Grand Ave 54499 715-253-2213
Garrett Rogowski, supt. Fax 253-3588
www.wittbirn.k12.wi.us/
Wittenberg-Birnamwood HS 400/9-12
400 W Grand Ave 54499 715-253-2211
Jill Sharp, prin. Fax 253-3588

Wonewoc, Juneau, Pop. 810
Wonewoc-Union Center SD 300/PK-12
101 School Rd 53968 608-464-3165
Sharon Ennis, supt. Fax 464-3325
www.wc.k12.wi.us
Wonewoc HS 100/9-12
101 School Rd 53968 608-464-3165
Michelle Noll, prin. Fax 464-3325
Wonewoc JHS 50/6-8
101 School Rd 53968 608-464-3165
Michelle Noll, prin. Fax 464-3325

Woodville, Saint Croix, Pop. 1,320
Baldwin-Woodville Area SD
Supt. — See Baldwin
Viking MS 500/5-8
500 Southside Dr 54028 715-698-2456
Scott Benoy, prin. Fax 698-3315

Wrightstown, Brown, Pop. 2,803
Wrightstown Community SD 1,400/PK-12
PO Box 128 54180 920-532-5551
Carla Buboltz, supt. Fax 532-4664
www.wrightstown.k12.wi.us
Wrightstown HS 500/9-12
PO Box 128 54180 920-532-0525
Scott Thompson, prin. Fax 532-0860
Wrightstown MS 400/5-8
PO Box 128 54180 920-532-5553
Lee Mierow, prin. Fax 532-3869

WYOMING

WYOMING DEPARTMENT OF EDUCATION
2300 Capitol Ave, Cheyenne 82001-3644
Telephone 307-777-7673
Fax 307-777-6234
Website edu.wyoming.gov

Superintendent of Public Instruction Jillian Balow

WYOMING BOARD OF EDUCATION
2300 Capitol Ave, Cheyenne 82001-3644

Chairperson Pete Gosar

BOARDS OF COOPERATIVE EDUCATIONAL SERVICES (BOCES)

Big Horn County SD 2 BOCES
Rhonda Savage, dir. 307-548-6466
502 Hampshire Ave, Lovell 82431
Carbon Co. Higher Education Center BOCES
David Throgmorton Ph.D., dir. 307-328-9274
812 E Murray St, Rawlins 82301 Fax 324-3338
www.cchec.org
Carbon County SD 2 BOCES
Melissa Donough, dir. 307-326-5271
PO Box 1530, Saratoga 82331 Fax 326-8089
www.crb2.k12.wy.us/boces/
Central Wyoming BOCES
Jeana Lam-Pickett, admin. 307-268-3309
125 College Dr, Casper 82601 Fax 268-2611
www.caspercollege.edu/boces/index.html
Eastern Wyoming BOCES
Mike Durfee, dir. 307-532-8346
3200 W C St, Torrington 82240 Fax 532-8229
Fremont County BOCES
Sandy Barton, dir. 307-856-2028
320 W Main St, Riverton 82501 Fax 856-4058
www.fcboces.org

Northeast Wyoming BOCES
Julie Cudmore, dir. 307-682-0231
410 N Miller Ave, Gillette 82716 Fax 686-7628
www.newboces.com/
Northwest Wyoming BOCES
Carolyn Conner, dir. 307-864-2171
PO Box 112, Thermopolis 82443 Fax 864-9463
www.nwboces.com/
Oyster Ridge BOCES
Bridget Stewart, dir. 307-877-6958
20 Adaville Dr, Diamondville 83116 Fax 828-9040
www.kemmereroutreach.com
Park County SD 1 BOCES
Ingrid Eickstedt, dir. 307-754-6469
231 W 6th St Bldg 25, Powell 82435 Fax 754-7839
www.morelearningfun.org
Region V BOCES
Doris Woodbury, dir. 307-733-8210
PO Box 899, Wilson 83014 Fax 733-8462
boces5.org

Sublette BOCES
Ward Wise, dir. 307-367-6873
PO Box 977, Pinedale 82941 Fax 367-6634
www.subletteboces.com
Sweetwater BOCES
Bernadine Craft Ph.D., dir. 307-382-1607
PO Box 428, Rock Springs 82902 Fax 382-1875
www.westernwyoming.edu/services/boces/
Teton BOCES
Scott Crisp, prin. 307-732-3700
PO Box 568, Jackson 83001
Uinta BOCES
Michael Williams, dir. 307-789-5742
1013 W Cheyenne Dr Unit A Fax 789-7975
Evanston 82930
www.uintaeducation.org
Uinta County SD #4 & #6 BOCES
Karla Behunin, dir. 307-782-6401
PO Box 130, Mountain View 82939 Fax 782-7410
www.westernwyoming.edu/distance/vlc/
Western Sublette 9 BOCES
Angie Clifford, dir. 307-276-5522
PO Box 706, Big Piney 83113 Fax 276-3480
www.sublette9boces.org

PUBLIC, PRIVATE AND CATHOLIC SECONDARY SCHOOLS

Afton, Lincoln, Pop. 1,881
Lincoln County SD 2 2,600/K-12
222 E 4th Ave 83110 307-885-3811
Alan Allred, supt. Fax 885-9562
www.lcsd2.org
Star Valley HS 700/9-12
444 W Swift Creek Ln 83110 307-885-7847
Homer Bennett, prin. Fax 885-3299
Star Valley MS 400/7-8
999 Warrior Way 83110 307-885-5208
Steve Burch, prin. Fax 885-0472
Swift Creek HS 50/Alt
222 E 4th Ave 83110 307-885-7139
Tyler Jack, prin. Fax 885-9562
Other Schools – See Cokeville

Baggs, Carbon, Pop. 438
Carbon County SD 1
Supt. — See Rawlins
Little Snake River Valley S 200/K-12
PO Box 9 82321 307-383-2185
Joel Thomas, prin. Fax 383-2184

Basin, Big Horn, Pop. 1,274
Big Horn County SD 4 300/K-12
PO Box 151 82410 307-568-2684
Roy Hoyt Ed.D., supt. Fax 568-2654
www.bgh4.org
Riverside HS 100/9-12
PO Box 151 82410 307-568-2416
Tony Anson, prin. Fax 568-2415
Other Schools – See Manderson

Big Horn, Sheridan, Pop. 487
Sheridan County SD 1
Supt. — See Ranchester
Big Horn HS 200/9-12
PO Box 490 82833 307-674-8190
Ben Smith, prin. Fax 672-5306
Big Horn MS 100/6-8
PO Box 490 82833 307-674-8190
Richard Welch, prin. Fax 672-5306

Big Piney, Sublette, Pop. 550
Sublette County SD 9 700/K-12
PO Box 769 83113 307-276-3322
Kevin Garvey, supt. Fax 276-3731
www.sublette9.org
Big Piney HS 200/9-12
PO Box 769 83113 307-276-3324
Jeff Makelky, prin. Fax 276-3480
Big Piney MS 200/6-8
PO Box 769 83113 307-276-3315
Stanley Dodds, prin. Fax 276-5209

Buffalo, Johnson, Pop. 4,536
Johnson County SD 1 1,300/K-12
601 W Lott St 82834 307-684-9571
Gerry Chase, supt. Fax 684-5182
www.jcsd1.k12.wy.us
Buffalo HS 300/9-12
29891 Old Highway 87 82834 307-684-2269
Chad Bourgeois, prin. Fax 684-9481
Clear Creek MS 200/6-8
361 W Gatchell St 82834 307-684-5594
Darren Schmidt, prin. Fax 684-9096
Other Schools – See Kaycee

Burlington, Big Horn, Pop. 287
Big Horn County SD 1
Supt. — See Cowley
Burlington HS 100/9-12
PO Box 9 82411 307-762-3334
Matt Davidson, prin. Fax 762-3604
Burlington MS 50/7-8
PO Box 9 82411 307-762-3334
Matt Davidson, prin. Fax 762-3604

Burns, Laramie, Pop. 295
Laramie County SD 2
Supt. — See Pine Bluffs
Burns JSHS 300/7-12
PO Box 160 82053 307-245-4100
Bobby Dishman, prin. Fax 547-3583

Casper, Natrona, Pop. 54,284
Natrona County SD 1 12,800/PK-12
970 N Glenn Rd 82601 307-253-5200
Steve Hopkins, supt. Fax 253-5330
www.natronaschools.org/
Casper Classical Academy 400/6-9
900 S Beverly St 82609 307-253-3160
Marie Puryear, prin. Fax 253-2286
Centennial JHS 600/6-8
1421 Waterford 82609 307-253-2900
Mike Britt, prin. Fax 253-2891
CY MS 800/6-9
2900 Cyclone Blvd 82604 307-253-2700
Valerie Braughton, prin. Fax 253-2683
Frontier MS 100/6-8
900 S Beverly St 82609 307-253-2300
Casey Cloninger, prin. Fax 253-2286
Morgan JHS 800/6-8
1440 S Elm St 82601 307-253-2500
Steve Ellbogen, prin. Fax 253-2411
Natrona County HS 1,700/9-12
930 S Elm St 82601 307-253-1700
Shannon Harris, prin. Fax 253-1507
Pathways Innovation Center Vo/Tech
3000 Independence Ct 82604 307-253-1451
Chad Sharpe, admin.

Roosevelt HS 100/Alt
3000 Independence Ct 82604 307-253-1400
Shawna Trujillo, prin. Fax 253-1450
Star Lane Center Alt
1400 S Fairdale Ave 82601 307-253-3100
Chad Sharpe, prin. Fax 253-3117
Transitions Learning Center Alt
920 S Beverly St 82604 307-253-4350
Chris Bolender, prin. Fax 253-4321
Walsh HS 1,700/9-12
3500 E 12th St 82609 307-253-2000
Brad Diller, prin. Fax 253-2066
Other Schools – See Midwest

Casper College Post-Sec.
125 College Dr 82601 307-268-2110
SAGE Technical Service Truck Driving Sch Post-Sec.
2368 Oil Dr 82604 800-307-0242
Wyoming School for the Deaf Post-Sec.
539 Payne Ave 82609

Cheyenne, Laramie, Pop. 58,048
Laramie County SD 1 13,600/K-12
2810 House Ave 82001 307-771-2100
John Lyttle, supt. Fax 771-2364
www.laramie1.org
Carey JHS 700/7-8
1780 E Pershing Blvd 82001 307-771-2580
Derek Nissen, prin. Fax 771-2578
Central HS 1,200/9-12
5500 Education Dr 82009 307-771-2680
Fred George, prin. Fax 771-2699
East HS 1,500/9-12
2800 E Pershing Blvd 82001 307-771-2663
Samuel Mirich, prin. Fax 771-2679
Johnson JHS 700/7-8
1236 W Allison Rd 82007 307-771-2640
Brian Cox, prin. Fax 771-2660
McCormick JHS 600/7-8
6000 Education Dr 82009 307-771-2650
Jeff Conine, prin. Fax 771-2661
South HS 1,000/9-12
1213 W Allison Rd 82007 307-771-2410
Philip Thompson, prin. Fax 771-2420
Triumph HS 200/Alt
1250 W College Dr 82007 307-771-2500
Michael Helenbolt, prin. Fax 771-2508

Cheeks Intl Academy of Beauty Culture Post-Sec.
207 W 18th St 82001 307-637-8700
CollegeAmerica Post-Sec.
6101 Yellowstone Rd Ste 101 82009 307-632-7048
Institute of Business & Medical Careers Post-Sec.
1854 Dell Range Blvd 82009 307-433-8363
Laramie County Community College Post-Sec.
1400 E College Dr 82007 307-778-5222

Chugwater, Platte, Pop. 210
Platte County SD 1
Supt. — See Wheatland
Chugwater HS 50/9-12
406 5th St 82210 307-422-3501
Tom Waring, prin. Fax 422-3433
Chugwater JHS 50/7-8
406 5th St 82210 307-422-3501
Tom Waring, prin. Fax 422-3433

Clearmont, Sheridan, Pop. 141
Sheridan County SD 3 100/K-12
PO Box 125 82835 307-758-4412
Charles Auzqui, supt. Fax 758-4444
www.sheridan3.com
Arvada-Clearmont HS 50/9-12
PO Box 125 82835 307-758-4412
Christy Wright, prin. Fax 758-4444
Arvada-Clearmont JHS 50/7-8
PO Box 125 82835 307-758-4412
Christy Wright, prin. Fax 758-4444

Cody, Park, Pop. 9,367
Park County SD 6 2,100/K-12
919 Cody Ave 82414 307-587-4253
Ray Schulte, supt. Fax 527-5762
www.park6.org
Cody HS 700/9-12
919 Cody Ave 82414 307-587-4251
Barton Bailey, prin. Fax 587-9369
Cody MS 500/6-8
919 Cody Ave 82414 307-587-4273
Tim Foley, prin. Fax 587-3547
Heart Mountain Academy Alt
919 Cody Ave 82414 307-527-1028
Jeremiah Johnston, prin.

West Park Hospital Post-Sec.
707 Sheridan Ave 82414 307-527-7501

Cokeville, Lincoln, Pop. 533
Lincoln County SD 2
Supt. — See Afton
Cokeville JSHS 100/7-12
PO Box 220 83114 307-279-3273
Brian Toomer, prin. Fax 279-3221

Cowley, Big Horn, Pop. 654
Big Horn County SD 1 1,000/PK-12
PO Box 688 82420 307-548-2254
Shon Hocker, supt. Fax 548-7610
bighorn1.com
Rocky Mountain HS 300/9-12
PO Box 280 82420 307-548-2723
Tim Winland, prin. Fax 548-6452
Rocky Mountain MS 200/6-8
PO Box 280 82420 307-548-2723
Tim Winland, prin. Fax 548-6452
Other Schools – See Burlington

Dayton, Sheridan, Pop. 749
Sheridan County SD 1
Supt. — See Ranchester
Tongue River HS 100/9-12
PO Box 408 82836 307-655-2236
Mark Fritz, prin. Fax 655-9798

Diamondville, Lincoln, Pop. 720
Lincoln County SD 1 400/K-12
PO Box 335 83116 307-877-9095
Teresa Chaulk, supt. Fax 877-9638
www.lcsd1.k12.wy.us
Other Schools – See Kemmerer

Douglas, Converse, Pop. 6,039
Converse County SD 1 1,700/K-12
615 Hamilton St 82633 307-358-2942
Dr. Dan Espeland, supt. Fax 358-3934
converse1schools.org
Douglas HS 500/9-12
615 Hamilton St 82633 307-358-2940
Dan Edwards, prin. Fax 358-2737
Douglas MS 400/6-8
615 Hamilton St 82633 307-358-9771
Ryan Mackey, prin. Fax 358-5315

Dubois, Fremont, Pop. 957
Fremont County SD 2 200/K-12
PO Box 188 82513 307-455-5545
Martha Gale, supt. Fax 455-2178
www.fremont2.org/
Dubois HS 50/9-12
PO Box 188 82513 307-455-5524
Brandon Farris, prin. Fax 455-2654
Dubois MS 50/6-8
PO Box 188 82513 307-455-5524
Brandon Farris, prin. Fax 455-2654

Encampment, Carbon, Pop. 445
Carbon County SD 2
Supt. — See Saratoga
Encampment S 200/K-12
PO Box 277 82325 307-327-5442
Michael Erickson, prin. Fax 327-5142

Ethete, Fremont, Pop. 1,530
Fremont County SD 14 600/PK-12
638 Blue Sky Hwy 82520 307-332-3904
Owen St. Clair, supt. Fax 332-7567
www.fremont14.k12.wy.us
Wyoming Indian HS 200/9-12
638 Blue Sky Hwy 82520 307-332-9765
Pamela Gambler, prin. Fax 335-7739
Wyoming Indian MS 100/6-8
638 Blue Sky Hwy 82520 307-332-9765
Scott Gion, prin.

Evanston, Uinta, Pop. 12,128
Uinta County SD 1 2,900/K-12
PO Box 6002 82931 307-789-7571
Ryan Thomas, supt. Fax 789-6225
www.uinta1.com
Davis MS 300/6-8
PO Box 6002 82931 307-789-8096
Chris Brown, prin. Fax 789-3386
Evanston HS 800/9-12
PO Box 6002 82931 307-789-0757
Merle Lester, prin. Fax 789-7447
Evanston MS 300/6-8
PO Box 6002 82931 307-789-5499
Eric Christenot, prin. Fax 789-7972
Horizon Alternative S 100/Alt
PO Box 6002 82931 307-789-0122
Shad Hamilton, prin. Fax 789-2522

Farson, Sweetwater, Pop. 309
Sweetwater County SD 1
Supt. — See Rock Springs
Farson-Eden HS 50/9-12
PO Box 400 82932 307-273-9301
Michael Estes, prin. Fax 273-9313
Farson-Eden MS 50/6-8
PO Box 400 82932 307-273-9301
Michael Estes, prin. Fax 273-9313

Fort Washakie, Fremont, Pop. 1,730
Fremont County SD 21 500/PK-12
90 Ethete Rd 82514 307-332-5983
H. Terry Ebert, supt. Fax 332-7267
www.fortwashakieschool.com
Fort Washakie HS 50/9-12
90 Ethete Rd 82514 307-332-0142
Shad Hamilton, prin. Fax 335-8020
Fort Washakie MS 100/7-8
90 Ethete Rd 82514 307-332-2380
George Mirich, prin. Fax 332-3597

Gillette, Campbell, Pop. 28,659
Campbell County SD 1 8,800/K-12
PO Box 3033 82717 307-682-5171
Dr. Boyd Brown, supt. Fax 682-6619
www.campbellcountyschools.net/
Campbell County HS North 1,500/10-12
1000 Camel Dr 82716 307-682-7247
Troy Zickefoose, prin. Fax 682-3914
Campbell County HS South 9-12
4001 Saunders Blvd 82718 307-687-7733
Dennis Holmes, prin.
Sage Valley JHS 1,000/7-9
1000 W Lakeway Rd 82718 307-682-2225
Terry Quinn, prin. Fax 687-7614
Twin Spruce JHS 900/7-9
100 E 7th St 82716 307-682-3144
Dana Lyman, prin. Fax 686-1969
Westwood HS 100/Alt
7 Opportunity Spur 82718 307-682-9809
Kelly Morehead, prin. Fax 686-7566
Other Schools – See Wright

Gillette College Post-Sec.
300 W Sinclair St 82718 307-686-0254
Heritage Christian S 100/PK-12
510 Wall Street Ct 82718 307-686-1392
Jenn VerBurg, head sch Fax 257-7256

Glendo, Platte, Pop. 203
Platte County SD 1
Supt. — See Wheatland
Glendo HS 50/9-12
305 N Paige Ave 82213 307-735-4471
Stanetta Twiford, prin. Fax 735-4220
Glendo JHS 50/7-8
305 N Paige Ave 82213 307-735-4471
Stanetta Twiford, prin. Fax 735-4220

Glenrock, Converse, Pop. 2,551
Converse County SD 2 600/K-12
PO Box 1300 82637 307-436-5331
Kirk Hughes, supt. Fax 436-8235
www.cnv2.k12.wy.us/
Glenrock HS 200/9-12
PO Box 1300 82637 307-436-9201
Scott James, prin. Fax 436-8517
Glenrock Intermediate MS 100/5-8
PO Box 1300 82637 307-436-9258
Coley Shadrick, prin. Fax 436-7507

Green River, Sweetwater, Pop. 12,356
Sweetwater County SD 2 2,700/K-12
320 Monroe Ave 82935 307-872-5500
Donna Little-Kaumo, supt. Fax 872-5518
www.swcsd2.org
Expedition Academy 50/10-12
351 Monroe Ave 82935 307-872-4800
Ralph Obray, prin. Fax 872-4797
Green River HS 800/9-12
1615 Hitching Post Dr 82935 307-872-4747
Darren Howard, prin. Fax 872-4758
Lincoln MS 400/7-8
350 Monroe Ave 82935 307-872-4400
Matt Mikkelsen, prin. Fax 872-4477

Greybull, Big Horn, Pop. 1,834
Big Horn County SD 3 500/K-12
640 8th Ave N 82426 307-765-4756
Dr. Barry Bryant, supt. Fax 765-4617
www.greybullschools.com
Greybull HS 200/9-12
640 8th Ave N 82426 307-765-2537
Ty Flock, prin. Fax 765-2870
Greybull MS 100/6-8
640 8th Ave N 82426 307-765-4492
Joel Rogers, prin. Fax 765-2586

Guernsey, Platte, Pop. 1,136
Platte County SD 2 200/K-12
PO Box 189 82214 307-836-2735
Mike Beard, supt. Fax 836-2450
www.guernseysunrise.org
Guernsey-Sunrise HS 100/9-12
PO Box 189 82214 307-836-2745
Kyle Gunderson, prin. Fax 836-2450
Guernsey-Sunrise JHS 50/7-8
PO Box 189 82214 307-836-2745
Kyle Gunderson, prin. Fax 836-2450

Hanna, Carbon, Pop. 829
Carbon County SD 2
Supt. — See Saratoga
Hanna-Elk Mountain-Medicine Bow JSHS 100/7-12
PO Box 810 82327 307-325-6545
Steven Priest, prin. Fax 325-9223

Hulett, Crook, Pop. 375
Crook County SD 1
Supt. — See Sundance
Hulett S 200/K-12
PO Box 127 82720 307-467-5231
Linda Wolfskill, prin. Fax 467-5280

Jackson, Teton, Pop. 9,432
Teton County SD 1 2,600/K-12
PO Box 568 83001 307-733-2704
Gillian Chapman Ed.D., supt. Fax 734-1219
www.tcsd.org
Jackson Hole HS 600/9-12
PO Box 568 83001 307-732-3700
Dr. Scott Crisp, prin. Fax 732-3720
Jackson Hole MS 600/6-8
PO Box 568 83001 307-733-4234
Debbie Pfortmiller, prin. Fax 733-4254
Summit HS 100/9-12
PO Box 568 83001 307-733-9116
Beth Auge, prin. Fax 739-8922

Journeys S 200/PK-12
700 Coyote Canyon Rd 83001 307-733-1313
Nancy Lang, head sch Fax 733-7560

Kaycee, Johnson, Pop. 260
Johnson County SD 1
Supt. — See Buffalo
Kaycee K-12 S 100/K-12
PO Box 6 82639 307-738-2573
Andrea Gilbert, prin. Fax 738-2495

Kemmerer, Lincoln, Pop. 2,635
Lincoln County SD 1
Supt. — See Diamondville
Kemmerer JSHS 200/7-12
1525 3rd West Ave 83101 307-877-6991
Orlen Zempel, prin. Fax 877-4117
New Frontier HS 50/Alt
1004 Elk St 83101 307-877-5819
David Gardner, prin. Fax 877-5644

Lander, Fremont, Pop. 7,311
Fremont County SD 1 1,700/K-12
863 Sweetwater St 82520 307-332-4711
Dave Barker, supt. Fax 332-6671
www.landerschools.org
Lander MS 400/6-8
755 Jefferson St 82520 307-332-4040
Julie Shanley, prin. Fax 332-0435
Lander Valley HS 500/9-12
350 Baldwin Creek Rd 82520 307-332-3640
Brad Neuendorf, prin. Fax 332-2861
Pathfinder HS 50/Alt
626 Washington St 82520 307-335-7050
Ely Sixbey, lead tchr. Fax 335-8695

Wyoming State Training School Post-Sec.
8204 State Highway 789 82520 307-332-5302

Laramie, Albany, Pop. 30,183
Albany County SD 1 3,500/PK-12
1948 E Grand Ave 82070 307-721-4400
Dr. Jubal C. Yennie, supt. Fax 721-4408
www.acsd1.org
Laramie HS 700/9-12
1710 Boulder Dr 82070 307-721-4420
Stacy Bush, prin. Fax 721-4419
Laramie JHS 600/6-8
1355 N 22nd St 82072 307-721-4430
Debra Fisher, prin. Fax 721-4435
Whiting HS 50/Alt
801 S 24th St 82070 307-721-4449
Jeff Lewis, prin. Fax 721-4519
Other Schools – See Rock River

University of Wyoming Post-Sec.
1000 E University Ave 82071 307-766-1121
WyoTech Post-Sec.
4373 N 3rd St 82072 307-742-3776

Lingle, Goshen, Pop. 467
Goshen County SD 1
Supt. — See Torrington
Lingle-Ft. Laramie HS 100/9-12
PO Box 379 82223 307-837-2296
Rick Cotant, prin. Fax 837-3025
Lingle-Ft. Laramie MS 100/6-8
PO Box 379 82223 307-837-2283
Rick Cotant, prin. Fax 837-2057

Lovell, Big Horn, Pop. 2,347
Big Horn County SD 2 700/K-12
502 Hampshire Ave 82431 307-548-2259
Dr. Rick Woodford, supt. Fax 548-7555
www.bgh2.k12.wy.us/
Lovell HS 200/9-12
502 Hampshire Ave 82431 307-548-2256
Scott O'Tremba, prin. Fax 548-9452
Lovell MS 100/6-8
325 W 9th St 82431 307-548-6553
Douglas Hazen, prin. Fax 548-6136

Lusk, Niobrara, Pop. 1,541
Niobrara County SD 1 700/PK-12
PO Box 629 82225 307-334-3793
Aaron Carr, supt. Fax 334-0126
www.lusk.k12.wy.us
Niobrara County HS 400/9-12
PO Box 1050 82225 307-334-3320
Marty Wood, prin. Fax 334-2331

Lyman, Uinta, Pop. 2,090
Uinta County SD 6 700/K-12
PO Box 1090 82937 307-786-4100
Colby Gull, supt. Fax 787-3241
www.uinta6.k12.wy.us/
Lyman HS 200/9-12
PO Box 1090 82937 307-786-4100
Todd Limoges, prin. Fax 787-3241
Lyman IS 200/5-8
PO Box 1090 82937 307-786-4100
Michael Olson, prin. Fax 787-3241

Manderson, Big Horn, Pop. 112
Big Horn County SD 4
Supt. — See Basin
Cloud Peak MS 100/5-8
PO Box 97 82432 307-568-2846
Shane Schaffner, prin. Fax 568-3885

Meeteetse, Park, Pop. 325
Park County SD 16 100/K-12
PO Box 218 82433 307-868-2501
Jay Curtis, supt. Fax 868-9264
www.park16.org
Meeteetse S 100/K-12
PO Box 218 82433 307-868-2501
Cory Dziowgo, prin. Fax 868-9264

Midwest, Natrona, Pop. 395
Natrona County SD 1
Supt. — See Casper
Midwest S 200/PK-12
256 Lewis 82643 307-253-3500
Chris Tobin, prin. Fax 253-3520

Moorcroft, Crook, Pop. 998
Crook County SD 1
Supt. — See Sundance
Moorcroft HS 200/9-12
PO Box 129 82721 307-756-3446
Becky Waters, prin. Fax 756-3724

Mountain View, Uinta, Pop. 1,273
Uinta County SD 4 600/K-12
PO Box 130 82939 307-782-3377
Jeff Newton, supt. Fax 782-6879
www.uinta4.com
Mountain View HS 200/9-12
PO Box 130 82939 307-782-6340
Ben Carr, prin. Fax 782-6967
Mountain View MS 200/6-8
PO Box 130 82939 307-782-6338
Lane Stratton, prin. Fax 782-6876

Newcastle, Weston, Pop. 3,468
Weston County SD 1 800/K-12
116 Casper Ave 82701 307-746-4451
Brad LaCroix, supt. Fax 746-3289
www.weston1.k12.wy.us
Newcastle HS 300/9-12
116 Casper Ave 82701 307-746-2713
Tracy Ragland, prin. Fax 746-2350
Newcastle MS 200/6-8
116 Casper Ave 82701 307-746-2746
Todd Quigley, prin. Fax 746-4983

Pavillion, Fremont, Pop. 225
Fremont County SD 6 400/PK-12
PO Box 10 82523 307-856-7970
Diana Clapp, supt. Fax 856-3385
www.fre6.k12.wy.us/
Wind River HS 100/9-12
PO Box 10 82523 307-856-7970
Ceatriss Wall, prin. Fax 856-8641
Wind River Learning Academy Alt
PO Box 10 82523 307-856-7970
Ceatriss Wall, prin. Fax 856-8641
Wind River MS 100/6-8
PO Box 10 82523 307-856-7970
Orvin Jenks, prin. Fax 856-8641

Pine Bluffs, Laramie, Pop. 1,114
Laramie County SD 2 1,000/K-12
PO Box 489 82082 307-245-4050
Jon Abrams, supt. Fax 245-3561
laramie2.org
Pine Bluffs JSHS 200/7-12
PO Box 520 82082 307-245-4000
Todd Sweeter, prin. Fax 245-3144
Other Schools – See Burns

Pinedale, Sublette, Pop. 1,999
Sublette County SD 1 1,000/K-12
PO Box 549 82941 307-367-2139
Jay Harnack, supt. Fax 367-4626
www.sub1.org
Pinedale HS 300/9-12
PO Box 549 82941 307-367-2137
Fax 367-2611
Pinedale MS 200/6-8
PO Box 549 82941 307-367-2821
Jeryl Fluckiger, prin. Fax 367-4217
Skyline HS Alt
PO Box 549 82941 307-367-2137
Eric Makelky, prin. Fax 367-2611

Powell, Park, Pop. 6,232
Park County SD 1 1,700/K-12
160 N Evarts St 82435 307-764-6186
Kevin Mitchell, supt. Fax 764-6156
www.park1.net
Powell HS 500/9-12
160 N Evarts St 82435 307-764-6181
Jim Kuhn, prin. Fax 764-6151
Powell MS 400/6-8
160 N Evarts St 82435 307-764-6185
Jason Sleep, prin. Fax 764-6155

Shoshone Learning Center 50/Alt
160 N Evarts St 82435 307-764-6187
Ginger Sleep, prin. Fax 764-6157

Northwest College Post-Sec.
231 W 6th St 82435 307-754-6000

Ranchester, Sheridan, Pop. 853
Sheridan County SD 1 1,000/K-12
PO Box 819 82839 307-655-9541
Marty Kobza, supt. Fax 655-9477
www.sheridan.k12.wy.us/
Tongue River MS 100/6-8
PO Box 879 82839 307-655-9533
Pete Kilbride, prin. Fax 655-9894
Other Schools – See Big Horn, Dayton

Rawlins, Carbon, Pop. 9,144
Carbon Co. Higher Education Center BOCES
812 E Murray St 82301 307-328-9274
David Throgmorton Ph.D., dir. Fax 324-3338
www.cchec.org
Vocational Campus Vo/Tech
1650 Harshman 82301 307-328-9204
Fax 328-9273

Carbon County SD 1 1,800/K-12
615 Rodeo St 82301 307-328-9200
Fletcher Turcato, supt. Fax 328-9258
www.crb1.net
Cooperative HS 50/Alt
615 Rodeo St 82301 307-328-9250
Mark Gaines, prin. Fax 328-9258
Rawlins HS 400/9-12
1401 Colorado St 82301 307-328-9280
Tom Weed, prin. Fax 328-9286
Rawlins MS 400/6-8
1001 Brooks St 82301 307-328-9201
Kevin O'Dea, prin. Fax 328-9226
Other Schools – See Baggs

Riverton, Fremont, Pop. 10,330
Fremont County SD 25 2,600/K-12
121 N 5th St W 82501 307-856-9407
Terry Snyder, supt. Fax 856-3390
www.fremont25.org
Riverton HS 800/9-12
121 N 5th St W 82501 307-856-9491
John Griffith, prin. Fax 856-2333
Riverton MS 500/6-8
121 N 5th St W 82501 307-856-9443
Cheryl Mowry, prin. Fax 857-1695

Central Wyoming College Post-Sec.
2660 Peck Ave 82501 307-855-2000

Rock River, Albany, Pop. 236
Albany County SD 1
Supt. — See Laramie
Rock River S 50/K-12
PO Box 128 82083 307-378-2271
Wade Fiscus, prin. Fax 378-2505

Rock Springs, Sweetwater, Pop. 22,670
Sweetwater County SD 1 5,500/K-12
PO Box 1089 82902 307-352-3400
Kelly McGovern, supt. Fax 352-3411
www.sweetwater1.org
Black Butte HS Alt
PO Box 1089 82902 307-352-3290
Michael Maloney, prin. Fax 503-3192
Rock Springs HS 1,400/9-12
PO Box 1089 82902 307-352-3440
Darrin Peppard, prin. Fax 315-2632
Rock Springs JHS 800/7-8
PO Box 1089 82902 307-352-3474
Tina Johnson, prin. Fax 316-5634
Other Schools – See Farson, Wamsutter

Western Wyoming Community College Post-Sec.
2500 College Dr 82901 307-382-1600

Saratoga, Carbon, Pop. 1,658
Carbon County SD 2 700/K-12
PO Box 1530 82331 307-326-5271
Dr. Jim Copeland, supt. Fax 326-8089
www.crb2.k12.wy.us
Saratoga MSHS 100/7-12
PO Box 1710 82331 307-326-5246
Linda Butler, prin. Fax 326-9607
Other Schools – See Encampment, Hanna

Sheridan, Sheridan, Pop. 17,182
Sheridan County SD 2 3,300/K-12
PO Box 919 82801 307-674-7405
Craig Dougherty, supt. Fax 674-5041
www.scsd2.com/
Fort Mackenzie HS 50/Alt
1301 Avon St 82801 307-673-8730
Troy Lake, prin. Fax 673-8732
Sheridan HS 900/9-12
1056 Long Dr 82801 307-672-2495
Brent Leibach, prin. Fax 672-8071
Sheridan JHS 700/6-8
500 Lewis St 82801 307-672-9745
Mitch Craft, prin. Fax 672-5311
Wright Place 50/Alt
1301 Avon St 82801 307-673-8730
Troy Lake, prin. Fax 673-8732

Sheridan College Post-Sec.
PO Box 1500 82801 307-674-6446

Shoshoni, Fremont, Pop. 645
Fremont County SD 24 400/PK-12
404 Wrangler Way 82649 307-876-2583
Bruce Thoren, supt. Fax 876-2469
www.fremont24.com/
Shoshoni HS 100/9-12
404 Wrangler Way 82649 307-876-2576
Carl Rice, prin. Fax 876-9325
Shoshoni JHS 100/7-8
404 Wrangler Way 82649 307-876-2576
Carl Rice, prin. Fax 876-9325

Sundance, Crook, Pop. 1,174
Crook County SD 1 1,000/K-12
PO Box 830 82729 307-283-2299
Mark Broderson, supt. Fax 283-1810
www.crook1.com
Bear Lodge HS, PO Box 1160 82729 50/Alt
Teresa Brown, prin. 307-283-2144
Sundance JSHS 200/7-12
PO Box 850 82729 307-283-1007
James O'Connor, prin. Fax 283-2300
Other Schools – See Hulett, Moorcroft

Ten Sleep, Washakie, Pop. 257
Washakie County SD 2 100/K-12
PO Box 105 82442 307-366-2223
Jimmy Phelps, supt. Fax 366-2304
www.wsh2.k12.wy.us
Ten Sleep HS 50/9-12
PO Box 105 82442 307-366-2233
Russell Budmayr, prin. Fax 366-2304
Ten Sleep MS 50/7-8
PO Box 105 82442 307-366-2233
Russell Budmayr, prin. Fax 366-2304

Thermopolis, Hot Springs, Pop. 2,973
Hot Springs County SD 1 600/K-12
415 Springview St 82443 307-864-6515
Dustin Hunt, supt. Fax 864-6615
www.hotsprings1.org
Hot Springs County HS 200/9-12
415 Springview St 82443 307-864-6511
Scott Shoop, prin. Fax 864-3970
Thermopolis MS 200/5-8
415 Springview St 82443 307-864-6551
Breez Daniels, prin. Fax 864-6608

Torrington, Goshen, Pop. 6,432
Goshen County SD 1 1,700/K-12
626 W 25th Ave 82240 307-532-2171
Jean Chrostoski, supt. Fax 532-7085
www.goshen1.org
Torrington HS 400/9-12
2400 W C St 82240 307-532-7101
Jim English, prin. Fax 532-2696
Torrington MS 300/6-8
2742 W E St 82240 307-532-7014
Marvin Haiman, prin. Fax 532-8402
Other Schools – See Lingle, Yoder

Eastern Wyoming College Post-Sec.
3200 W C St 82240 307-532-8200

Upton, Weston, Pop. 1,090
Weston County SD 7 300/K-12
PO Box 470 82730 307-468-2461
Dr. Summer Stephens, supt. Fax 468-2797
www.weston7.org
Upton HS 100/9-12
PO Box 470 82730 307-468-2361
Linda Crawford, prin. Fax 468-2459
Upton MS 100/6-8
PO Box 470 82730 307-468-9331
Clark Coberly, prin. Fax 468-2832

Wamsutter, Sweetwater, Pop. 442
Sweetwater County SD 1
Supt. — See Rock Springs
Desert MS 50/6-8
PO Box 10 82336 307-324-7811
Jared Hardman, prin. Fax 589-1164

Wheatland, Platte, Pop. 3,590
Platte County SD 1 1,000/K-12
1350 Oak St 82201 307-322-3175
Dennis Fischer, supt. Fax 322-2084
platte1.org
Wheatland HS 300/9-12
1350 Oak St 82201 307-322-2075
Frank Jesse, prin. Fax 322-9739
Wheatland MS 200/6-8
1350 Oak St 82201 307-322-1518
Cory Dziowgo, prin. Fax 322-1560
Other Schools – See Chugwater, Glendo

Worland, Washakie, Pop. 5,424
Washakie County SD 1 1,400/K-12
1900 Howell Ave 82401 307-347-9286
David Nicholas, supt. Fax 347-8116
www.wsh1.k12.wy.us
Worland HS 400/9-12
801 S 17th St 82401 307-347-2412
Kevin Smith, prin. Fax 347-8549
Worland MS 300/6-8
2150 Howell Ave 82401 307-347-3233
Ryan Clark, prin. Fax 347-3710

Wright, Campbell, Pop. 1,786
Campbell County SD 1
Supt. — See Gillette
Wright JSHS 200/7-12
PO Box 490 82732 307-464-0140
Hal Johnson, prin. Fax 464-0154

Yoder, Goshen, Pop. 151
Goshen County SD 1
Supt. — See Torrington
Southeast HS 100/9-12
PO Box 160 82244 307-532-7176
Randy Epler, prin. Fax 532-5771
Southeast JHS 100/7-8
PO Box 160 82244 307-532-7176
Randy Epler, prin. Fax 532-5771

CHARTER SCHOOLS

School	Address	City,State	Zip code	Telephone	Fax	Grade	Contact
			Alaska				
Academy Charter S	801 E Arctic Ave	Palmer, AK	99645-6179	907-746-2358	746-2368	K-8	Barbara Gerard
Alaska Native Cultural Charter S	550 Bragaw St	Anchorage, AK	99508-2125	907-742-1370	742-1373	K-8	Sibongile Agerter
American Charter Academy	244 S Sylvan Rd Ste 110	Wasilla, AK	99654	907-352-0150	352-0180	2-12	Becky Huggins
Anvil City Science Academy	PO Box 131	Nome, AK	99762-0131	907-443-6207	443-5144	5-8	Todd Hindman
Aquarian Charter S	1705 W 32nd Ave	Anchorage, AK	99517-2002	907-742-4900	742-4919	K-6	Lucas Saltzman
Aurora Borealis Charter S	705 Frontage Rd Ste A	Kenai, AK	99611-7740	907-283-0292	283-0293	K-8	Cody McCanna
Birchtree Charter S	7107 E Palmer Wasilla Hwy	Palmer, AK	99645-7763	907-745-1831	745-1843	K-8	Cathy Busbey
Chinook Charter S	3002 International St	Fairbanks, AK	99701-7391	907-452-5020	452-5048	K-8	Wendy Demers
Eagle Academy Charter S	10901 Mausel St	Eagle River, AK	99577-8065	907-742-3025	742-3035	K-6	Kitty Logan
Family Partnership Charter S	401 E Fireweed Ln Ste 100	Anchorage, AK	99503-2100	907-742-3700	742-3710	K-12	Deanne Carroll
Fireweed Academy	995 Soundview Ave Ste 2	Homer, AK	99603	907-235-9728	235-8561	K-6	Todd Hindman
Fronteras Spanish Immersion S	2315 N Seward Meridian Pky	Wasilla, AK	99654	907-745-2223	376-2227	K-8	Jennifer Schmidt
Frontier Charter S	400 W Northern Lights Blvd	Anchorage, AK	99503-3877	907-742-1180	742-1188	K-12	Gerald Finkler
Highland Academy Charter S	5530 E Northern Lights Blvd	Anchorage, AK	99504	907-742-1700	742-1711	6-12	Dr. Michael Shapiro
Juneau Community Charter S	10014 Crazy Horse Dr	Juneau, AK	99801-8529	907-586-2526	586-3543	K-8	Cynthia McFeeters
Kaleidoscope S	549 N Forest Dr	Kenai, AK	99611-7410	907-283-0804	283-3786	K-6	Robin Dahlman
Ketchikan Charter S	410 Schoenbar Rd	Ketchikan, AK	99901-6218	907-225-8568	247-8568	K-8	Robert Marshall
Kokrine Charter S	601 Loftus Rd	Fairbanks, AK	99709-3430	907-474-0958	479-2104	7-12	Josh Snow
Midnight Sun Family Learning Center	7362 W Parks Hwy # 714	Wasilla, AK	99623-9300	907-357-6786	373-6786	K-8	Jeanne Troshynski
PAIDEIA Cooperative S	616 W 10th Ave	Anchorage, AK	99501	907-742-4161	742-4165	K-12	Cheryl Huber
Rilke Schule German Schl of Arts & Sci	1846 E 64th Ave	Anchorage, AK	99507	907-742-0900	742-0945	K-8	Christopher Barr
Soldotna Montessori Charter S	162 E Park Ave	Soldotna, AK	99669-7552	907-260-9221	260-9032	K-6	Mary Jo Sanders
Star of the North Secondary S	2945 Monk Ct	North Pole, AK	99705-6129	907-490-9025	490-9021	7-12	Diana Childs
STrEaM Academy	7801 E 32nd Ave	Anchorage, AK	99504	907-742-9000		6-8	Adam Mokelke
Tongass S of Arts & Sciences	410 Schoenbar Rd Ste 202	Ketchikan, AK	99901-6218	907-225-5720	225-8822	PK-6	Marian Gonzales
Twindly Bridge Charter S	141 E Seldon Rd Ste C	Wasilla, AK	99654-3351	907-376-6680	746-6683	K-12	John Weetman
Watershed Charter S	4975 Decathlon Ave	Fairbanks, AK	99709-4514	907-374-9350	374-9360	K-8	Jarrod Decker
Winterberry Charter S	4802 Bryn Mawr Ct	Anchorage, AK	99508	907-742-0139	742-4985	K-8	Lee Young
			Arizona				
AAEC - Estrella Mountain HS	3400 N Dysart Rd	Avondale, AZ	85392-1003	623-535-0754	535-1210	9-12	Dale Nicol
AAEC - Paradise Valley	3775 E Union Hills Dr	Phoenix, AZ	85050-3214	602-569-1101	569-6372	9-12	Dr. Martha Braly
AAEC - Prescott Valley	7500 E Civic Cir	Prescott Valley, AZ	86314-6800	928-775-3200	775-3201	9-12	Patrick Welert
AAEC - Red Mountain Early College HS	2165 N Power Rd	Mesa, AZ	85215-2971	480-854-1504	854-3564	9-12	Ray Gless
AAEC - South Mountain	2002 E Baseline Rd	Phoenix, AZ	85042-6906	602-323-9890	323-9869	9-12	Linda LaFontain
Acacia ES	12955 E Colossal Cave Rd	Vail, AZ	85641-9091	520-879-2200	879-2201	K-5	Terri Brooks
Academy Adventures Midtown ES	3025 N Winstel Blvd	Tucson, AZ	85716-1740	520-777-3757	207-6489	K-5	John Penczar
Academy Adventures PS	3902 N Flowing Wells Rd	Tucson, AZ	85705-2403	520-407-1200	407-1201	K-5	Dayna Arnold
Academy Del Sol - Hope	6740 S Santa Clara Ave	Tucson, AZ	85756-6450	520-325-2800	325-2811	K-8	
Academy Del Sol - Midtown	4525 E Broadway Blvd	Tucson, AZ	85711-3509	520-325-2800	325-2812	K-8	Jason Riegert
Academy Del Sol - Star Valley	7102 W Valley Crest Pl	Tucson, AZ	85757-8709	520-789-7733		K-8	Jason Reigert
Academy of Building Industries	1547 E Lipan Blvd	Fort Mohave, AZ	86426-6031	928-788-2601	788-2610	9-12	Jean Thomas
Academy of Excellence	425 N 36th St	Phoenix, AZ	85008-6303	602-389-4271	389-4278	K-8	Dr. Eula Dean
Academy of Math & Science	1557 W Prince Rd	Tucson, AZ	85705-3023	520-293-2676	888-1732	K-12	Tatyana Chayka
Academy of Math & Science Camelback	6633 Camelback Rd	Phoenix, AZ	85033	520-295-9069	594-8078	K-8	Debbie Yarbrough
Academy of Mathematics and Science South	3335 W Flower St	Phoenix, AZ	85017-4802	520-887-5392		K-8	Brynn Embley
Academy of Tucson ES	9209 E Wrightstown Rd	Tucson, AZ	85715-5514	520-886-6076	886-6575	K-4	Carole Rostash M.Ed.
Academy of Tucson HS	10720 E 22nd St	Tucson, AZ	85748-7029	520-733-0096	733-0097	9-12	Jose Garcia
Academy of Tucson MS	7310 E 22nd St	Tucson, AZ	85710-6427	520-749-1413	749-2824	5-8	Larry Speta
Academy With Community Partners	433 N Hall	Mesa, AZ	85203-7407	480-833-0068	833-8966	9-12	Margaret Williamson M.A.
Accelerated Learning Center	4105 E Shea Blvd	Phoenix, AZ	85028-3525	602-485-0309	485-9356	9-12	Frank Canady Ed.D.
Accelerated Schools	5245 N Camino De Oeste	Tucson, AZ	85745-8925	520-743-2256	743-2417	PK-12	David Jones
ACCLAIM Academy	7624 W Indian School Rd	Phoenix, AZ	85033-3009	623-691-0919	691-6091	K-8	Jose Martinez
ACE Charter HS - North	1929 N Stone Ave	Tucson, AZ	85705-5642	520-623-5843	791-9893	9-12	Jay Slauter
Acorn Montessori Charter S	8556 E Loos Dr	Prescott Valley, AZ	86314-6455	928-772-5778	775-8654	2-8	Cynthia Johnson
Acorn Montessori Charter S - West	7555 E Long Look Dr	Prescott Valley, AZ	86314-5507	928-775-0238	775-8654	PK-1	Cynthia Johnson
Adams Traditional Academy	2323 W Parkside Ln	Phoenix, AZ	85027-1256	602-938-5517	938-1179	PK-8	Sharon Malone
Adventure S	5757 E Pima St	Tucson, AZ	85712-5609	520-296-0656	721-4472	K-5	Brian Henderson
Aim Higher College Prep Academy	4848 S 2nd St	Phoenix, AZ	85040-2122	602-243-7788	243-7799	7-12	
All Aboard Charter S	5827 N 35th Ave	Phoenix, AZ	85017-1915	602-433-0500	973-8208	K-5	Rhonda Newton
Alta Vista Charter HS	5040 S Campbell Ave	Tucson, AZ	85706-1510	520-294-4922	294-4933	9-12	Alicia Alvarez
Ambassador Academy	3820 E Ray Rd Ste 8	Phoenix, AZ	85044-7159	480-961-2214	993-3222	K-8	Dr. Elba Reyes
American Heritage Academy	2030 E Cherry St	Cottonwood, AZ	86326-6963	928-634-2144	634-9053	K-12	Eric Evans
American Heritage Academy	132 W General Crook Trl	Camp Verde, AZ	86322-8575	928-567-0462	567-0464	K-8	Darrell White
American Leadership Academy	4507 S Mountain Rd	Mesa, AZ	85212-7010	480-420-2110	420-2109	K-6	Paul Sinclair
American Leadership Academy	650 W Combs Rd	Queen Creek, AZ	85140-9014	480-344-9899	420-2103	K-6	Christina Schubert
American Leadership Academy	850 W Combs Rd	Queen Creek, AZ	85140-9015	480-344-9898	344-9849	7-12	Bill Guttery
American Leadership Academy	23908 S Hawes Rd	Queen Creek, AZ	85142-9505	480-987-4500	882-1330	7-12	Tommy Roberts
American Leadership Academy	19843 E Chandler Hts Rd	Queen Creek, AZ	85142	480-420-2150	888-8595	K-6	Dan Provonsha
American Leadership Academy	34696 N Village Ln	San Tan Valley, AZ	85142-4495	480-420-2100	729-6003	K-6	Chad McLeod
American Leadership Academy	4380 N Hunt Hwy	Florence, AZ	85132	480-344-9800	518-5245	K-6	Stuart Enkey
American Leadership Academy	3155 S San Tan Village Pkwy	Gilbert, AZ	85295-0857	480-988-3204	988-3280	K-6	Robert Brown
Amerischools Academy - Camelback	1333 W Camelback Rd	Phoenix, AZ	85013-2106	602-532-0100	532-9964	K-8	Pam Eklund
Amerischools Academy - Country Club	1150 N Country Club Rd	Tucson, AZ	85716-3942	520-620-1100	624-4376	K-8	Jordan Krause
Amerischools Academy - Yuma North	1220 S 4th Ave	Yuma, AZ	85364-4624	928-919-7203	919-7205	K-6	Patrick Koppinger
Amerischools Academy - Yuma South	2098 S 3rd Ave	Yuma, AZ	85364-6425	928-329-1100	329-9177	K-6	Ashley Fox
Anthem Preparatory Academy	39808 N Gavilan Peak Pkwy	Anthem, AZ	85086-2523	623-465-4776	465-4832	K-12	Alison Westerlind
Apache Trail HS	945 W Apache Trl	Apache Junction, AZ	85120-5409	480-288-0337	288-0340	9-12	Terra Kasapo
Archway Classical Academy - Arete	4525 E Baseline Rd	Gilbert, AZ	85234-2986	480-422-4233		K-5	Neil Gillingham
Archway Classical Academy - Chandler	1951 N Alma School Rd	Chandler, AZ	85224-2840	480-855-6474	855-7475	K-5	Leanne Fawcett
Archway Classical Academy - Cicero	7205 N Pima Rd	Scottsdale, AZ	85258-4027	480-424-1790		K-5	Dr. Mark Discher
Archway Classical Academy - Glendale	23276 N 83rd Ave	Peoria, AZ	85383-1621	623-866-4710		K-5	Jack Kersting
Archway Classical Academy - Lincoln	2250 S Gilbert Rd	Chandler, AZ	85286-1588	480-424-1798		K-5	Dr. Benjamin Mitchell
Archway Classical Academy - N Phoenix	13613 N Cave Creek Rd Ste C	Phoenix, AZ	85022-5137	602-996-4355	889-0187	K-5	David Denton
Archway Classical Academy - Scottsdale	7496 E Tierra Buena Ln	Scottsdale, AZ	85260-1613	480-776-0413	889-7014	K-4	Lisa Armstrong
Archway Classical Academy - Trivium East	14130 W McDowell Rd	Goodyear, AZ	85395-2514	623-414-4883	889-6286	K-5	Heather Washburn
Archway Classical Academy - Trivium West	2001 N Bullard Ave	Goodyear, AZ	85395-3372	623-414-4883		K-5	Theresa Kruegar
Archway Classical Academy - Veritas	3102 N 56th St Ste 100	Phoenix, AZ	85018-6606	602-489-7341	263-7997	K-5	Dr. Mary Jeffries
Arete Preparatory Academy	4525 E Baseline Rd	Gilbert, AZ	85234-2986	480-222-4233	222-4234	6-12	Robert Wagner
Arizona Academy of Science	1875 N Central Ave	Phoenix, AZ	85004-1507	602-253-1199	595-8693	K-8	
AZ Call-A-Teen Center of Excellence	649 N 6th Ave	Phoenix, AZ	85003-1659	602-252-6721	252-2952	9-12	Sharlet Barnett
Arizona Charter Academy	16025 N Dysart Rd	Surprise, AZ	85374-4062	623-974-4959	974-4840	K-12	Heather Henderson
Arizona City ES	12115 W Benito Dr	Arizona City, AZ	85123	520-466-2450		PK-8	
Arizona College Prep Academy	3434 E Broadway Blvd	Tucson, AZ	85710	520-722-1200	722-0052	K-8	Charlene Mendoza
Arizona Collegiate HS	3161 N 33rd Ave	Phoenix, AZ	85017-4818	623-498-8200	269-2970	9-12	Michael Dunbar
AZ Compass Prep and Arts S	2020 N Arizona Ave	Chandler, AZ	85225	480-779-2000	779-2100	7-12	Claudia McKim M.Ed.
AZ Connections Academy	335 E Germann Rd Ste 140	Gilbert, AZ	85297-2920	480-782-5842	323-2905	K-12	Kerri Wright
AZ Conservatory for Arts & Academics	16454 N 28th Ave	Phoenix, AZ	85053-7534	623-878-0986	776-7956	K-5	Christopher Lalley
AZ Conservatory for Arts & Academics	2820 W Kelton Ln	Phoenix, AZ	85053-3028	602-266-4278	978-2764	6-12	Holly Foged
Arizona Language Preparatory	4645 E Marilyn Rd	Phoenix, AZ	85032-4839	602-996-1595		K-4	Sara Hecht
Arizona School for the Arts	1410 N 3rd St	Phoenix, AZ	85004-1608	602-257-1444	252-7795	5-12	Dr. Leah Fregulia
Arizona Virtual Academy	99 E Virginia Ave Ste 200	Phoenix, AZ	85004-1195	866-476-1320	595-6874	K-12	Kelly Van Sande
Arroyo ES	4535 W Cholla St	Glendale, AZ	85304-3535	602-896-5100	896-5120	K-8	Philip Liles
Arts Academy at Estrella Mountain	2504 S 91st Ave	Tolleson, AZ	85353-8921	623-227-0769	936-5337	PK-8	Ronald Alexander
Arts Academy at Scottsdale	6140 E Thunderbird Rd	Scottsdale, AZ	85254-3863	480-376-3190	998-4029	K-6	Charles Boebinger
ASU Preparatory Academy	735 E Fillmore St	Phoenix, AZ	85006-3324	602-257-4843	257-4852	K-8	David Lujan
ASU Prep Polytechnic HS	7350 E Unity Ave	Mesa, AZ	85212-6043	480-727-5750		9-12	Chrystal Keller
Athlos Traditional Academy	3201 S Gilbert Rd	Chandler, AZ	85286-5193	480-270-5422	237-5780	K-8	Nicole McMillian
Avalon Charter School	1045 S San Marcos Dr	Apache Junction, AZ	85120-6337	480-671-4584	671-4586	K-8	
AZTEC HS	2330 W 28th St	Yuma, AZ	85364-6954	928-314-1900	726-2826	9-12	Molly Kelly
BASIS Ahwatukee	10210 S 50th Pl	Phoenix, AZ	85044-5209	480-659-2294	696-3607	4-12	Kristen Jordison
Basis Chandler	1800 E Chandler Blvd	Chandler, AZ	85225-5109	480-907-6072	907-6624	5-12	Stephanie Terrell

School	Address	City,State	Zip code	Telephone	Fax	Grade	Contact
BASIS Flagstaff	1700 N Gemini Dr	Flagstaff, AZ	86001-1600	928-774-5502	774-5503	5-12	Sean Clark
BASIS Mesa	5010 S Eastmark Pkwy	Mesa, AZ	85212-8165	602-239-4807	822-1259	4-12	Matt Fritzmiller
BASIS Oro Valley	11155 N Oracle Rd	Oro Valley, AZ	85737-5606	520-308-5220	308-5078	6-12	Michelle Mason
BASIS Peoria	25950 N Lake Pleasant Pkwy	Peoria, AZ	85383-1434	623-215-4920	566-9109	5-12	Mark Allen
BASIS Phoenix	11850 N 32nd St	Phoenix, AZ	85028-1200	602-595-9870	595-9820	5-12	Petra Pajtas
BASIS Phoenix Central PS	201 E Indianola Ave	Phoenix, AZ	85012	602-559-5399	283-7500	K-8	Sharon Elisco
BASIS Prescott	1901 Prescott Lakes Pkwy	Prescott, AZ	86301-7806	928-277-0334	458-5562	5-12	Becky Ratliff
BASIS Scottsdale	10400 N 128th St	Scottsdale, AZ	85259	480-451-7500	451-4555	5-12	Elizabeth McConaghy
BASIS - Tucson	3825 E 2nd St	Tucson, AZ	85716-4368	520-326-6367	326-6359	K-6	Roberto Ramirez
BASIS Tucson North	5740 E River Rd	Tucson, AZ	85750-1915	520-326-3444		5-12	Erin Paradis
Benchmark S	4120 E Acoma Dr	Phoenix, AZ	85032-4753	602-765-3582	765-1932	K-6	Barbara Darroch
Bennett Academy	2930 W Bethany Home Rd	Phoenix, AZ	85017-1615	602-943-1317	943-0280	K-8	Dr. Nancy Bennett
Bennett Academy - Venture	1535 W Dunlap Ave	Phoenix, AZ	85021-2953	602-242-4220		K-5	Shawn Lane
Berean Academy	1169 N Colombo Ave	Sierra Vista, AZ	85635	520-459-4113	459-4121	K-12	Mark Bennett
Blueprint HS	670 N Arizona Ave Ste 1	Chandler, AZ	85225	480-892-0235	892-0236	9-12	Robert Rodenbaugh
Bradley Academy of Excellence	PO Box 6060	Goodyear, AZ	85338-0618	800-993-1458	932-9904	PK-8	Laura Couret
Bright Beginnings S	400 N Andersen Blvd	Chandler, AZ	85224-8273	480-821-1404	821-1463	PK-6	Karen Edris
Burke Basic S	131 E Southern Ave	Mesa, AZ	85210-5355	480-964-4602	964-6566	K-6	Glen Gaddie
Butterfield ES	44150 W Maricopa Casa Grand	Maricopa, AZ	85138-5900	520-568-6100	568-6109	K-6	Janel Hildick
Calibre Academy Surprise	15688 W Acoma Dr	Surprise, AZ	85379-5652	623-556-2179	547-2806	K-8	Rebecca Venegas
Cambridge Academy - Mesa Campus	9412 E Brown Rd	Mesa, AZ	85207-4338	480-641-2828	325-2365	K-6	Amy Monarrez
Cambridge Academy - Queen Creek	20365 E Ocotillo Rd	Queen Creek, AZ	85142-9508	480-987-3577	987-4281	K-8	Tyler Knowles
Camelback Academy	7634 W Camelback Rd	Glendale, AZ	85303-5627	623-247-2204	247-1113	K-8	Karen Kordon
Camino Montessori	44301 W Maricopa Ave	Maricopa, AZ	85138-5902	520-868-6145	868-6149	PK-6	Judith Webster
Candeo Schools	9965 W Calle Lejos	Peoria, AZ	85383-1117	623-979-6500	979-6510	K-8	Dr. Stephanie Musser Ed.D.
Canyon Pointe Academy	4941 W Union Hills Dr	Glendale, AZ	85308-1486	602-896-1166	896-1164	K-6	Suzanne Smailagic
Canyon Rose Academy	3686 W Orange Grove Rd #192	Tucson, AZ	85741	520-797-4884	797-8868	9-12	Christopher Golston
Canyon View Prep Academy	9030 E Florentine Rd	Prescott Valley, AZ	86314-8973	928-775-5115	775-6253	9-12	Debra Slagle
Carden of Tucson S	5260 N Royal Palm Dr	Tucson, AZ	85705-1148	520-293-6661	408-7366	K-8	Bette Jeppson
Career Success HS - Duffy Campus	2550 E Jefferson St	Phoenix, AZ	85034-2637	602-393-4200	393-4205	9-12	Mike McCarthy
Career Success HS - Main Campus	3816 N 27th Ave	Phoenix, AZ	85017-4703	602-285-5525	285-0026	9-12	Kelly Sheick
Career Success JSHS - North Phoenix	2325 E Bell Rd	Phoenix, AZ	85022	602-687-8282	687-8283	7-12	Eric Pawlak
Career Success S - Sage Campus	3120 N 32nd St	Phoenix, AZ	85018-6202	602-955-0355	955-4805	K-8	Kurt Walker
Carpe Diem E-Learning Community S	3777 W 22nd Ln	Yuma, AZ	85364-5905	928-317-3113	317-0828	7-12	Jon Larson
CASA Academy	1500 W Maryland Ave	Phoenix, AZ	85015-1401	602-892-5022	892-5023	K-3	Tacey Clayton
Caurus Academy	41900 N 42nd Ave	Anthem, AZ	85086-1595	623-551-5083	551-5679	K-8	Dameon Blair M.S.
Center for Academic Success ES	900 Carmelita Dr	Sierra Vista, AZ	85635-1927	520-458-4200	458-1409	K-8	Stephen Huff
Center for Academic Success ES	1415 F Ave	Douglas, AZ	85607-1655	520-805-1558	458-1409	K-8	Marcela Munguia
Center for Academic Success HS	900 Carmelita Dr	Sierra Vista, AZ	85635-1927	520-458-4200	458-6396	9-12	Stephen Huff
Center for Academic Success HS	510 N G Ave	Douglas, AZ	85607-2822	520-364-2616	417-0973	9-12	Marcela Munguia
Center for Educational Excellence	1700 E Elliot Rd Ste 9	Tempe, AZ	85284-1631	480-632-1940	632-1398	K-8	Stacey Cochran
Challenge Charter S	5801 W Greenbriar Dr	Glendale, AZ	85308-3847	602-938-5411	938-5393	K-6	Wendy Miller
Challenger Basic S	1315 N Greenfield Rd	Gilbert, AZ	85234-2813	480-830-1750	830-1763	K-6	Brad Tobin
Champion Schools	7900 S Jesse Owens Pkwy	Phoenix, AZ	85042	602-341-6527	341-6529	K-8	Carolyn Sawyer
Chandler Preparatory Academy	1951 N Alma School Rd	Chandler, AZ	85224-2840	480-855-5410	855-7789	6-12	Helen Hayes
Changemaker HS	1300 S Belvedere Ave	Tucson, AZ	85711-5701	520-615-2200	615-2112	9-12	Judith Anderson
Children First Academy - Phoenix	1648 S 16th St	Phoenix, AZ	85034-5340	602-712-0500	712-0506	K-10	Rachael Lay
Children First Academy - Tempe	1460 S Horne	Mesa, AZ	85204	480-557-6211	557-6249	K-8	Jevon Lewis
Children Reaching for the Sky Prep	1844 S Alvernon Way	Tucson, AZ	85711-5607	520-790-8400	620-6570	K-5	Lee Griffin
Cicero Preparatory Academy	7205 N Pima Rd	Scottsdale, AZ	85258	480-424-1790	434-6614	6-9	Dr. Mark Discher
City HS	48 E Pennington St	Tucson, AZ	85701-1535	520-623-7223	547-0680	9-12	Brett Goble
Civano Community S	10625 E Drexel Rd	Tucson, AZ	85747-6120	520-879-1700	879-1701	K-5	Connie Erickson
Compass HS	PO Box 17810	Tucson, AZ	85731-7810	520-296-4070	296-4103	9-12	John Ferguson
Concordia Charter S	142 N Date	Mesa, AZ	85201-6419	480-461-0555	461-0556	K-6	Mike McCarthy
Concordia Charter S - Navajo Mission	1/4 Mile E of Highway 191	Round Rock, AZ	86547	928-787-2869	787-2867	K-3	Esther Davis
Cooley MS	1100 S Recker Rd	Gilbert, AZ	85296	480-279-8300	279-8305	7-8	Shawn Varner
Copper Canyon Academy	7785 W Peoria Ave	Peoria, AZ	85345-5922	623-930-1734	930-8709	K-8	Ed MacDonald
Copper Point HS	732 W Roger Rd	Tucson, AZ	85705	520-624-7169	624-7169	6-12	Dustie Gunn-Ader
Cornerstone Charter S	7107 N Black Canyon Hwy	Phoenix, AZ	85021-7619	602-595-2198	242-2398	9-12	Casey Weiss
Country Gardens Charter S	6313 W Southern Ave	Laveen, AZ	85339-2916	602-237-3741	237-3892	K-12	Goldie Burge
Crestview College Prep HS	2616 E Greenway Rd	Phoenix, AZ	85032-4320	602-765-8470	765-8471	9-12	Kristin Schaefer
Crown Charter S	PO Box 363	Litchfield Park, AZ	85340-0363	623-535-9300	535-5410	K-6	James Shade
Crown Point HS	4802 N 59th Ave	Phoenix, AZ	85033-1702	623-845-0781	849-2840	9-12	Claudia Ramirez
Deer Valley Academy	18424 N 51st Ave	Glendale, AZ	85308-1443	602-467-6874	467-6955	9-12	Barbara Dalicandro
Desert Cove ES	11020 N 28th St	Phoenix, AZ	85028-2500	602-449-3400	449-3405	K-6	Stacey Orest
Desert Heights Charter S	5821 W Beverly Ln	Glendale, AZ	85306-1801	602-896-2900	467-9540	K-8	Katherine Miller
Desert Heights Preparatory Academy	3540 W Union Hills Dr	Glendale, AZ	85308-2402	602-896-2900	467-9540	5-12	Chelsey Peitz
Desert Hills HS	1515 S Val Vista Dr	Gilbert, AZ	85296-3854	480-813-1151	813-1161	9-12	Greg Garland
Desert Marigold S	6210 S 28th St	Phoenix, AZ	85042-4715	602-243-6909	243-6933	PK-12	Charles Burkum
Desert Pointe Academy	7785 W Peoria Ave	Peoria, AZ	85345-5922	623-930-1734	930-8709	9-12	Ed McDonald
Desert Rose Academy	326 W Fort Lowell Rd	Tucson, AZ	85705	520-797-4884	797-8868	9-12	Michael Lee
Desert Sky Community S	1350 N Arcadia Ave	Tucson, AZ	85712-4706	520-745-3888	745-5110	K-5	Shelly Adrian
Desert Springs Academy	10129 E Speedway Blvd	Tucson, AZ	85748	520-321-1709	321-9316	K-8	Sandra Shoffner
Desert Springs Preparatory ES	6010 E Acoma Dr	Scottsdale, AZ	85254-2599	602-449-7100	449-7105	PK-6	Raquel Scott
Desert Star Academy	5635 Hwy 95	Fort Mohave, AZ	86426	928-770-4523		PK-6	Margie Montgomery
Desert Star Community S	1240 S Recycler Rd	Cornville, AZ	86325-5224	928-282-0171	284-9565	K-8	Cheryl LeBlanc
Desert View Academy	2363 S Kennedy Ln	Yuma, AZ	85365	928-314-1102	314-1086	K-6	Deb Wiegel
Destiny S	798 E Prickly Pear Dr	Globe, AZ	85501-2395	928-425-0925	425-0927	K-8	Scott Williamson
Digital Technology Academy	1250 W Continental Rd	Green Valley, AZ	85614	520-219-4383		K-8	
DINE Southwest HS	HC 63 Box 303	Winslow, AZ	86047-9424	928-657-3272	657-3272	9-12	Lucinda Honani
Discovery Plus Academy	PO Box 1089	Pima, AZ	85543-1089	928-485-2498	485-2508	K-5	DeeAnn Williams
Dobson Academy	PO Box 6070	Chandler, AZ	85246-6070	480-855-6325	855-6323	K-8	Dr. Phil Adams
EAGLE College Prep: Maryvale	3950 N 53rd Ave	Phoenix, AZ	85031-3011	602-638-0820	638-0821	K-8	Yesenia Fitzhugh
EAGLE College Prep: Mesa	1619 E Main St	Mesa, AZ	85203-9017	602-638-0802	638-0806	K-8	Tracy Allen
EAGLE College Prep S	2450 W South Mountain Ave	Phoenix, AZ	85041-7601	602-323-5400	323-5401	K-8	Crystal Danzy
EAGLE Harmony S	2435 E Pecan Rd	Phoenix, AZ	85040-3632	602-268-1212	237-5140	K-8	Ebony Johnson
Eastpointe HS	8495 E Broadway Blvd	Tucson, AZ	85710-4009	520-731-8180	731-8179	9-12	
East Valley Academy	855 W 8th Ave	Mesa, AZ	85210-3401	480-981-2008	641-4473	9-12	Pat Goolsby
Edge Charter S - Himmel Park	2555 E 1st St	Tucson, AZ	85716-4152	520-881-1389	881-0852	9-12	Rob Pecharich
Edge Charter S - Northwest	231 W Giaconda Way	Tucson, AZ	85704-4341	520-877-9179	881-0852	9-12	Rob Pecharich
EdOptions HS	2150 E Southern Ave	Tempe, AZ	85282-7504	480-621-3365		9-12	William Sawner
Educational Opportunity Center	3818 W 16th St	Yuma, AZ	85364-4107	928-329-0990	783-0886	9-12	
EduPreneurship Student Center	7801 N 27th Ave	Phoenix, AZ	85051-6675	602-973-8998	973-5510	K-8	Deborah Salas
Edu-Prize S	4567 W Roberts Rd	Queen Creek, AZ	85142-7511	480-888-1610		1-6	
Edu-Prize S	580 W Melody Ave	Gilbert, AZ	85233-1418	480-813-9537	813-6742	K-8	Dr. Robbie McCamman
E-Institute at Avondale	1035 E Van Buren St	Avondale, AZ	85323-1552	623-760-9061	760-9068	9-12	Curtis Gardner
E-Institute at Metro	9201 N 29th Ave	Phoenix, AZ	85051-3468	602-439-5026	889-0351	9-12	Eric Luthi
E-Institute at Surprise	16578 W Greenway Rd Ste 204	Surprise, AZ	85388-2184	623-544-9285	546-9540	9-12	Casey Robertson
E-Institute at Union Hills	3515 W Union Hills Dr	Glendale, AZ	85308-2429	602-843-3891	843-4375	9-12	Rick Wolff
E-Institute Charter HS at Grovers	4744 W Grovers Ave	Glendale, AZ	85308	602-621-4398	889-0351	9-12	Rick Wolff M.Ed.
E-Institute HS at Buckeye	6213 S Miller Rd	Buckeye, AZ	85326-1256	623-505-7118	505-3594	9-12	Marty Acosta
El Dorado HS	2200 N Arizona Ave Ste 17	Chandler, AZ	85225-3452	480-726-9536	726-9543	9-12	Dave Miller
El Dorado HS	2200 N Arizona Ave	Chandler, AZ	85225-3450	480-726-9536		9-12	Dave Miller
Empower Collegiate Academy	2411 W Colter St	Phoenix, AZ	85015	602-283-5720		9-12	Brian Holman
Encore Arts Academy	7618 E University Dr	Mesa, AZ	85207	480-981-1500	641-4473	K-8	Kathy Tolman
Estrella HS	510 N Central Ave	Avondale, AZ	85323-1909	623-932-6561	932-1263	9-12	Jon Kronstedt
Ethos Academy	8801 N 43rd Ave	Phoenix, AZ	85051	623-262-1202	931-5357	PK-6	Tim Boykin
Farm at Mission Montessori Academy	4530 E Gold Dust Ave	Phoenix, AZ	85028-4221	602-466-1153		4-8	
Fireside ES	3725 E Lone Cactus Dr	Phoenix, AZ	85050-8360	602-449-4700	449-4705	K-6	Teresa Simmons
Flagstaff Arts and Leadership Academy	3401 N Fort Valley Rd	Flagstaff, AZ	86001-8388	928-779-7223	779-7041	7-12	Laura Kelly
Flagstaff Junior Academy	306 W Cedar Ave	Flagstaff, AZ	86001-1413	928-774-6007	774-7268	PK-8	Thomas Drumm
Foothills Academy	7191 E Ashler Hills Dr	Scottsdale, AZ	85266-9300	480-488-5583	488-6902	K-12	Dr. Donald Senneville
Fountain Hills Charter S	PO Box 18419	Fountain Hills, AZ	85269-8419	480-837-0046	837-0024	K-8	Lynda Rice
Franklin Charter S - Crismon	22120 E Queen Creek Rd	Queen Creek, AZ	85142-9830	480-987-0722	987-3517	K-6	Shalisa Arnold
Franklin Charter S - Gilbert	1475 S Val Vista Dr	Gilbert, AZ	85296	480-632-0722	632-8716	K-6	Diana Dana
Franklin Charter S - Power	22951 S Power Rd	Queen Creek, AZ	85142	480-677-8400	677-8555	K-6	Adrienne Lamb
Franklin HS	18864 E Germann Rd	Queen Creek, AZ	85142-7338	480-558-1197	659-5354	7-12	Mark McAfee
Franklin Phonetic PS Sunnyslope	9317 N 2nd St	Phoenix, AZ	85020	602-870-6674		K-5	Debra Denette
Franklin Phonetic S	6116 E State Route 69	Prescott Valley, AZ	86314-2806	928-775-6747	775-6740	K-8	Christina Gabaldon M.A.
Freedom Academy North	28700 N Pima Rd	Scottsdale, AZ	85266-9008	602-424-0771	424-0773	K-6	Veronica Gatling
Freedom Academy South	3916 E Paradise Ln	Phoenix, AZ	85032-3232	602-424-0771	424-0773	K-8	Linda Hoffman
Freire Freedom S	47 E Pennington St	Tucson, AZ	85701-1533	520-352-0057	352-0058	6-8	Joann Groh
Freire Freedom S	300 E University Blvd	Tucson, AZ	85705-6929	520-906-7552	624-7518	6-8	JoAnn Groh
Friendly House Academia Del Pueblo S	201 E Durango St	Phoenix, AZ	85004-2913	602-258-4353	416-7375	K-8	Gabriel Sandoval
Future Investment MS	1854 S Alvernon Way	Tucson, AZ	85711-5607	520-747-3733	745-2848	6-8	Lee Griffin
GateWay Early College HS	108 N 40th St	Phoenix, AZ	85034-1704	602-286-8762	286-8752	9-12	
GEM Charter S	1704 N Center St	Mesa, AZ	85201-2223	480-833-2622	833-2655	K-6	Nelleke van Savooyen

School	Address	City,State	Zip code	Telephone	Fax	Grade	Contact
Genesis Academy	525 E McDowell Rd	Phoenix, AZ	85004-1537	602-254-8090	254-8094	9-12	Karen Callahan
Gervin Prep Academy	2801 E Southern Ave	Phoenix, AZ	85040-3604	480-219-2121	633-6787	6-8	Gregory Copeland
Gilbert Arts Academy	862 E Elliot Rd	Gilbert, AZ	85234-6912	480-325-6100	632-2077	K-6	Lauren Arnold
Gilbert Early College HS	717 W Ray Rd # 101	Gilbert, AZ	85233-8443	480-545-8011	558-7038	7-12	Lori Anderson
Girls Leadership Academy	715 W Mariposa St	Phoenix, AZ	85013-2449	602-274-7318	274-7549	6-12	Kellie Warren
Glendale Preparatory Academy	23276 N 83rd Ave Ste 1	Peoria, AZ	85383-1621	623-889-0822	889-0825	6-12	Brandon Crowe
Glendale Preparatory Academy	7201 W Beardsley Rd	Glendale, AZ	85308-5673	602-889-0822	889-0825	6-12	Brandon Crowe
Glenview College Prep HS	3802 W Maryland Ave	Phoenix, AZ	85019-1541	602-841-1221	841-1364	9-12	Chris Ecton
Gowan Science Academy	1590 S Avenue C	Yuma, AZ	85364-4118	928-539-1200	539-1299	K-6	Jamie Haines
Grand Canyon College Prep Charter S	5301 S McClintock Dr	Tempe, AZ	85283-2234	480-233-3622	491-7096	6-12	David Gordon
Grande Innovation Academy	950 N Peart Rd	Casa Grande, AZ	85122-5403	520-381-2360	876-0492	K-5	Patty Messer
Great Expectations Academy	1466 W Camino Antigua	Sahuarita, AZ	85629-9720	520-399-2121	399-2123	K-8	Mark Phillips
Ha:San Prep & Leadership Charter S	1333 E 10th St	Tucson, AZ	85719-5808	520-882-8826	882-8651	9-12	James Merino
Happy Valley S	7140 W Happy Valley Rd	Peoria, AZ	85383-3255	623-376-2900	376-9030	K-6	James Born
Happy Valley S East	266 E Westbrooke Rd	San Tan Valley, AZ	85140-8961	480-888-1342	888-8450	K-6	Jared Palmer
Harvest Preparatory Academy	350 E 18th St	Yuma, AZ	85364-5723	928-782-2052	819-5976	K-12	Dr. Deborah Ybarra
Harvest Preparatory Academy Goodyear	14900 W Van Buren St	Goodyear, AZ	85338-3002	602-708-2334	236-3248	K-8	Tara Walters
Harvest Preparatory Academy - San Luis	1044 N 10th Ave	San Luis, AZ	85349	928-782-2052	819-5976	K-5	
Havasu Preparatory Academy	3155 Maricopa Ave	Lk Havasu Cty, AZ	86406	928-854-4011	453-4042	K-8	Amy Hanon
Haven Montessori S	621 W Clay Ave	Flagstaff, AZ	86001-6221	928-522-0985	774-7412	K-K	Elisa McKnight
Hayes HS	PO Box 10899	Bapchule, AZ	85121-0105	520-315-5100	315-5115	9-12	Crispin Zamudio
Hearn Academy	17606 N 7th Ave	Phoenix, AZ	85023-1567	602-896-9160	896-1997	K-8	Gaye Leo
Heritage Academy	32 S Center St	Mesa, AZ	85210-1306	480-969-5641	969-6972	7-12	Earl Taylor
Heritage Academy - Laveen	4275 W Baseline Rd	Laveen, AZ	85339-1880	602-290-8546	926-2656	9-12	Kim Ellsworth
Heritage Academy - Queen Creek	19630 Germann Rd	Queen Creek, AZ	85242	480-461-4400	452-0833	9-12	Spencer Bowers
Heritage ES	6805 N 125th Ave	Glendale, AZ	85307-2402	623-935-1931	935-1931	K-8	Justin Dye
Heritage ES - Williams Campus	790 E Rodeo Rd	Williams, AZ	86046-9653	928-635-3998	635-3999	K-5	Kaytie Thies
Hermosa Montessori Charter S	12051 E Fort Lowell Rd	Tucson, AZ	85749-9702	520-749-5518	749-6087	K-8	Sheila Stolov
Hiaki HS	4747 W Calle Vicam	Tucson, AZ	85757-8860	520-883-5051		9-12	
Highland Free S	510 S Highland Ave	Tucson, AZ	85719-6427	520-623-0104	903-1318	K-6	Nicholas Sofka
Hillcrest Academy	3761 S Power Rd	Mesa, AZ	85212-3634	480-325-8950	353-2832	K-12	Jerad Hunsaker
Hirsch Academy	6535 E Osborn Rd	Scottsdale, AZ	85251-6026	480-488-9362		K-4	
Holsteiner Agricultural S	44400 W Honeycutt Rd	Maricopa, AZ	85138-2944	520-568-8620		K-6	Tanya Graysmark
Hope HS	7620 W Lower Buckeye Rd	Phoenix, AZ	85043-7433	623-772-8013	772-8021	9-12	Krissyn Sumare
Hope HS Online	5651 W Talavi Blvd Ste 170	Glendale, AZ	85306-1893	602-674-8344	943-9700	7-12	Erin Horn
Horizon Community Learning Center	16233 S 48th St	Phoenix, AZ	85048-0801	480-659-3000	659-3022	K-12	Betsy Fera
Huachuca Mountain ES	3555 E Fry Blvd	Sierra Vista, AZ	85635-2972	520-515-2960	515-2966	K-6	Karen Kukuchka
Humanities & Sciences Academy	1105 E Broadway Rd	Tempe, AZ	85282-1505	480-317-5900	829-4999	9-12	Sue Durkin
Humanities & Sciences HS	5201 N 7th St	Phoenix, AZ	85014-2802	602-650-1333	650-1881	9-12	Michael Curd
Imagine Avondale ES	950 N Eliseo Felix Jr Way	Avondale, AZ	85323-1202	602-344-1730	344-1740	PK-8	Kim Agnew
Imagine Charter S at Bell Canyon	18052 N Black Canyon Hwy	Phoenix, AZ	85053-1715	602-547-7920	547-7923	K-8	Joshua Jordan
Imagine Charter S at Camelback	5050 N 19th Ave	Phoenix, AZ	85015-3205	602-344-4620	344-4630	K-8	Mary Ann Hartwick
Imagine Charter S at Cortez Park	3535 W Dunlap Ave	Phoenix, AZ	85051-5303	602-589-9840	589-9841	K-8	Jason Whitaker
Imagine Charter S at Desert West	6738 W McDowell Rd	Phoenix, AZ	85035-4642	602-344-7150	344-7160	K-8	Bill Heintz
Imagine Charter S at East Mesa	9701 E Southern Ave	Mesa, AZ	85209-3769	480-355-6830	355-6840	K-9	Melynda Hache
Imagine Charter S at Rosefield	12050 N Bullard Ave	Surprise, AZ	85379-6325	623-344-4300	344-4310	K-8	James Mecca
Imagine Charter S at Tempe	1538 E Southern Ave	Tempe, AZ	85282-5687	480-355-1640	355-1650	K-6	Selethia Benn
Imagine Charter S at West Gilbert	2061 S Gilbert Rd	Gilbert, AZ	85295-4620	480-855-2700	855-2701	K-8	Matt Rawley
Imagine Coolidge ES	1290 W Vah Ki Inn Rd	Coolidge, AZ	85128-9314	520-723-5391	723-5491	K-8	Freddie Villalon
Imagine Prep at Surprise	14850 N 156th Ave	Surprise, AZ	85379-5653	623-344-1770	214-1083	7-12	Chris McComb
Imagine Prep - Superstition	1843 W 16th Ave	Apache Junction, AZ	85120-6967	480-355-0530	355-0540	6-12	Frank Stirpe
Incito S	877 N Sarival Ave	Goodyear, AZ	85338-2316	623-398-6868		K-8	April Black
Integrity Education Centre	515 E Continental Dr	Tempe, AZ	85281-1057	480-731-4829	945-2008	K-12	
Intelli School - Glendale	13806 N 51st Ave	Glendale, AZ	85306-4834	602-564-7210	564-7301	9-12	Patricia Shaw
Intelli School - Main	1727 N Arizona Ave Ste 5	Chandler, AZ	85225-7084	480-855-5318	855-5904	9-12	Jonathan Owen
Intelli School - Metro Center	3327 W Peoria Ave	Phoenix, AZ	85029-4605	602-564-7240	564-7241	9-12	Patricia Shaw
Intelli School - Paradise Valley	1427 E Bell Rd Ste 102	Phoenix, AZ	85022-2712	602-564-7280	564-7281	9-12	Patricia Shaw
International Commerce HS	5201 N 7th St	Phoenix, AZ	85014-2802	602-650-1333	650-1777	9-12	
International Commerce HS	1105 E Broadway Rd	Tempe, AZ	85282-1505	480-317-5900	829-4999	9-12	
iSchool 2020	3777 W 22nd Ln	Yuma, AZ	85364-5905	928-317-3113	783-3473	9-12	Ryan Hackmann
Jefferson Academy of Advanced Learning	40 S 11th St	Show Low, AZ	85901-6001	928-537-5432	537-0440	K-12	Sandy Stewart
Jefferson Preparatory HS	16635 N 51st Ave	Glendale, AZ	85306	602-595-2990	595-2440	7-12	Tawnya Mecham
Keystone Montessori Charter S	1025 E Liberty Ln	Phoenix, AZ	85048-8462	480-460-7312	283-8402	K-9	Cindy Maschoff
Khalsa Montessori S	2536 N 3rd St	Phoenix, AZ	85004-1308	602-252-3759	252-1890	K-6	Keerat Giordano
Khalsa Montessori S	3701 E River Rd	Tucson, AZ	85718-6633	520-529-3611	615-0625	K-8	Nirvair Khalsa
Kingman Academy of Learning HS	3420 N Burbank St	Kingman, AZ	86409-3105	928-681-2900	681-2424	9-12	Jeff Martin
Kingman Academy of Learning IS	3419 Harrison St	Kingman, AZ	86409-3604	928-681-3200	681-2424	3-5	Stacy Matthews
Kingman Academy of Learning MS	3269 Harrison St	Kingman, AZ	86409-3679	928-692-5265	681-2424	6-8	Dawn Day
Kingman Academy of Learning PS	3400 N Burbank St	Kingman, AZ	86409-3105	928-692-2500	692-2505	K-2	Trudi Bradley
La Paloma Academy	2050 N Wilmot Rd	Tucson, AZ	85712-3039	520-721-4205	721-4263	K-8	Brendan Ewald
La Paloma Academy - Lakeside	8140 E Golf Links Rd	Tucson, AZ	85730-1229	520-733-7373	733-7392	K-8	Sean Watins
La Paloma Academy South	5660 S 12th Ave	Tucson, AZ	85706-3102	520-807-9668		K-8	Paul Bummer
Larkspur ES	2430 E Larkspur Dr	Phoenix, AZ	85032	602-449-3300	449-3305	K-6	Jamie Roberson
Las Puertas Community S	4560 S Coach Dr	Tucson, AZ	85714-3429	520-546-9296		6-9	
La Tierra Community S	124 N Virginia St	Prescott, AZ	86301-3224	928-445-5100		K-6	Lenka Studnicka Ph.D.
Leading Edge Academy at East Mesa	10115 E University Dr	Mesa, AZ	85207-7210	480-984-5645	627-3634	K-6	Chad Kobold
Leading Edge Academy -ES	717 W Ray Rd	Gilbert, AZ	85233-8443	480-545-6646		K-6	Lori Anderson
Leading Edge Academy - Maricopa	18700 N Porter Rd	Maricopa, AZ	85138-4220	520-568-7800		K-6	Mathew Reese
Leading Edge Academy - Queen Creek	4815 W Hunt Hwy	Queen Creek, AZ	85142-3271	480-655-6787	655-6788	K-12	Steve Butcher
Leading Edge Academy San Tan	7377 W Hunt Hwy	Queen Creek, AZ	85142-7451	480-882-1631		6-12	Nick Schuerman
Learning Foundation & Performing Arts	5761 E Brown Rd	Mesa, AZ	85205-4400	480-807-1100	807-1190	K-12	Nikki Triggs
Learning Foundation & Performing Arts S	3939 E Warner Rd	Gilbert, AZ	85296-0500	480-240-8025		K-6	Evelyn Taylor
Learning Foundation & Performing Arts S	1120 S Gilbert Rd	Gilbert, AZ	85296-3465	480-635-9400	635-1907	K-12	Robert Villa
Learning Foundation Performing Arts S	851 N Stapley Dr	Mesa, AZ	85203-5644	480-834-6202	834-3991	K-12	Jeannine Rucker
Legacy Traditional Charter S	2747 S Recker Rd	Gilbert, AZ	85295-7851	480-397-9260	223-6453	K-8	Claudia McKim
Legacy Traditional S - Avondale Campus	12320 W Van Buren St	Avondale, AZ	85323-5238	623-344-0330	932-7848	K-8	Michelle Hart
Legacy Traditional S - Casa Grande	1274 E ONeil Dr	Casa Grande, AZ	85122	520-421-2323	421-4443	K-8	Jennifer Hackett M.Ed.
Legacy Traditional S - Laveen Campus	7900 S 43rd Ave	Laveen, AZ	85339-3023	623-344-0472	237-0477	K-8	
Legacy Traditional S - Maricopa	17760 Regent Dr	Maricopa, AZ	85138	520-423-9999	423-9997	K-8	Amy Sundeen M.Ed.
Legacy Traditional S - Northwest Tucson	3500 W Cortaro Farms Rd	Tucson, AZ	85742-7808	520-505-3640	579-6833	K-8	Christine Fitzsimmons M.Ed
Legacy Traditional S - Queen Creek	41800 N Barnes Pkwy	San Tan Valley, AZ	85140-6638	480-655-5553	655-5558	K-8	Marie Wilson M.Ed.
Legacy Traditional S - Surprise	14506 W Sweetwater Ave	Surprise, AZ	85379-4290	623-299-9820	299-9821	K-8	Brandi Adams-Bressler
Leman Academy of Excellence	7720 N Silverbell Rd	Tucson, AZ	85743	520-639-8080	395-1352	K-8	
Leman Academy of Excellence	1000 E Wilcox Dr	Sierra Vista, AZ	85635-2622	877-235-3626	395-1352	K-6	
Leman Academy of Excellence	3761 S Power Rd	Mesa, AZ	85212-3634	877-235-3626	395-1352	K-6	
Liberty Arts Academy	3015 S Power Rd	Mesa, AZ	85212-3000	480-830-3444	830-4335	K-6	Julia Angel
Liberty HS	1300 E Cedar St	Globe, AZ	85501-1731	928-402-8024	402-8358	9-12	
Liberty Traditional Charter S	4027 N 45th Ave	Phoenix, AZ	85031-2840	602-442-8791	353-9270	K-8	Jeremy Parker
Liberty Traditonal S - Saddleback	3715 N Washington Ave	Douglas, AZ	85607-3602	520-364-6311		K-4	Edward Mealy
Lifelong Learning Academy	3295 W Orange Grove Rd	Tucson, AZ	85741-2937	520-219-4383	544-0220	K-8	
Life Skills Center of Arizona	8123 N 35th Ave Ste 2	Phoenix, AZ	85051-9403	602-242-6400	242-6823	9-12	
Lincoln Preparatory Academy	2250 S Gilbert Rd	Chandler, AZ	85286-1588	480-424-1796		6-8	Dr. Benjamin Mitchell
Lincoln Traditional S	10444 N 39th Ave	Phoenix, AZ	85051-1179	602-896-6300	896-6320	K-8	Tara Mayole
Madison Highland Prep S	1431 E Campbell Ave	Phoenix, AZ	85014	602-745-3800	745-3899	9-11	Kerry Clark
Madison Preparatory S	5815 S Mcclintock Dr	Tempe, AZ	85283-3227	480-345-2306	345-0059	7-12	David Batchelder
Maricopa ES	44150 W Maricopa Casa Grand	Maricopa, AZ	85138-5900	520-568-5160	568-5166	K-6	Dr. Jennifer Robinson
Maricopa Wells MS	44150 W Maricopa Casa Grand	Maricopa, AZ	85138-5900	520-568-7100	568-7104	7-8	Rick Abel
Maryvale Preparatory Academy	6301 W Indian School Rd	Phoenix, AZ	85033-3326	602-247-6095	889-6282	K-5	Mac Esau
Masada Charter S	PO Box 2277	Colorado City, AZ	86021-2277	928-875-2525	875-2526	K-9	Leanne Timpson
Math & Science Success Academy	434 W Lerdo Rd	Tucson, AZ	85756-6655	520-751-2783	888-1732	K-12	Adriana Rodriguez
Maya HS	3660 W Glendale Ave	Phoenix, AZ	85051-8335	602-242-3442	242-5255	9-12	John Anderson
Mesa Arts Academy	221 W 6th Ave	Mesa, AZ	85210-2446	480-844-3965	844-0205	K-8	Sue Douglas
Mesquite ES	9455 E Rita Rd	Tucson, AZ	85747-6300	520-879-2100	879-2101	K-5	Diane Samorano
Metropolitan Arts Institute	1700 N 7th Ave Ste 100	Phoenix, AZ	85007-1760	602-258-9500	258-9504	9-12	Matthew Baker
Mexicayotl Charter S	667 N 7th Ave	Tucson, AZ	85705-8336	520-624-4018	287-0037	K-8	Corina Aguirre
Midtown HS	7318 W Lynwood St	Phoenix, AZ	85035-4542	623-936-8682	936-8559	9-12	John White
Midtown PS	4735 N 19th Ave	Phoenix, AZ	85015-3725	602-265-5133	604-2337	K-5	Judy White
Milestones Charter S	4707 E Robert E Lee St	Phoenix, AZ	85032-9529	602-404-1009	404-5456	K-8	Tara Cabardo
Mingus Springs Charter S	3600 Sunset Dr	Chino Valley, AZ	86323-5054	928-636-4766	636-5149	K-8	Dawn Gonzales
Mission Heights Prep HS	1376 E Cottonwood Ln	Casa Grande, AZ	85122-2971	520-836-9383		9-12	Drew Goodson
Mission Montessori Academy	4530 E Gold Dust Ave	Phoenix, AZ	85028-4221	602-466-1153		7-8	Joslyn Maike
Mission Montessori del Cielo	5550 E Mercer Ln	Scottsdale, AZ	85254-4737	480-284-8000	284-8875	PK-K	
Mission Montessori del Jardin	5550 E Mercer Ln	Scottsdale, AZ	85254-4737	480-699-4950	314-3346	1-3	
Mission Montessori del Norte	5550 E Mercer Ln	Scottsdale, AZ	85254-4737	480-840-1609	840-1676	4-6	Dr. Lalit Ecka
Mission Montessori on the Desert	5550 E Mercer Ln	Scottsdale, AZ	85254-4737	480-860-4330	657-3715	PK-K	
Mohave Accelerated ES	625 Marina Blvd	Bullhead City, AZ	86442	928-704-9345	704-4977	K-5	Sandy Smith
Mohave Accelerated ES East	945 Thumb Butte Rd	Bullhead City, AZ	86442	928-704-9345	704-4977	K-5	Jeremy Klingensmith

School	Address	City,State	Zip code	Telephone	Fax	Grade	Contact
Mohave Accelerated Learning Center	625 Marina Blvd	Bullhead City, AZ	86442-5414	928-704-9345	704-4977	6-12	Valorie Merrigan
Montessori Academy	6050 N Invergordon Rd	Paradise Valley, AZ	85253-5248	480-945-1121	874-2928	K-8	Juli Newman
Montessori Charter S of Flagstaff	850 N Locust St	Flagstaff, AZ	86001-3343	928-226-1212	774-0337	K-8	Kim Loaiza
Montessori Charter S of Flagstaff-Cedar	2212 E Cedar Ave	Flagstaff, AZ	86004	928-774-1600	774-0424	7-8	Marlane Spencer
Montessori Childrens House	2400 W Datsi St	Camp Verde, AZ	86322-8412	928-567-1878	567-2107	K-K	Janet Taylor
Montessori Day Charter S - Mountainside	9215 N 14th St	Phoenix, AZ	85020-2713	602-943-7672	395-0271	K-8	Pat Freeman
Montessori Day S - Chandler Lakeshore	1700 W Warner Rd	Chandler, AZ	85224-2676	480-730-8886	730-9072	PK-6	Theresa Averill
Montessori de Santa Cruz Charter S	PO Box 4706	Tubac, AZ	85646-4706	520-398-0536	398-0776	PK-6	Mary Gilbert
Montessori Education Centre Charter S	2834 E Southern Ave	Mesa, AZ	85204-5517	480-926-8375	503-0515	PK-6	Tammy Whiting
Montessori Education Ctr - Charter S N	815 N Gilbert Rd	Mesa, AZ	85203-5805	480-964-1381	668-5457	PK-6	Rachel Lichtenbergher
Montessori House Charter S	2415 N Terrace Cir	Mesa, AZ	85203-1220	480-464-2800	464-2836	K-6	Sherie Richardson
Montessori Schoolhouse	1301 E Fort Lowell Rd	Tucson, AZ	85719-2239	520-319-8668	881-4096	K-5	Michael Ebner
Mosaica Online HS	3738 N 16th St	Phoenix, AZ	85016-5915	602-282-0240		9-12	Justin Schmitt
Mountain Oak Charter S	1455 Willow Creek Rd	Prescott, AZ	86301-1438	928-541-7700	445-1301	K-8	Cynthia Roe
Mountain Rose Academy	3686 W Orange Grove Rd	Tucson, AZ	85741	520-797-4884	797-8868	9-12	Jennifer Haley
Mountain S	311 W Cattle Drive Trl	Flagstaff, AZ	86005-7060	928-779-2392	773-3246	PK-5	Gina Andress
Mountain View Preparatory S	1 N Willard St	Cottonwood, AZ	86326	928-649-8144	649-8145	K-8	Stephanie Jones
Mt. Turnbull Academy	PO Box 129	Bylas, AZ	85530-0129	928-475-3050	475-3051	9-12	Jayson Stanley
New Horizon S for the Performing Arts	446 E Broadway Rd	Mesa, AZ	85204-2020	480-655-7444	655-8220	K-6	Jim Wyler
New School for the Arts	1216 E Apache Blvd	Tempe, AZ	85281-6005	480-481-9235	970-6625	6-12	Katy Cardenas
New World Educational Center Charter S	5818 N 7th St	Phoenix, AZ	85014-5806	602-238-9577	238-9210	K-12	Jesus Armenta
NFL YET College Prep Academy	4848 S 2nd St	Phoenix, AZ	85040-2122	602-243-7788	243-7799	7-12	
Northern AZ Academy for Career Dev.	PO Box 125	Taylor, AZ	85939-0125	928-536-4222	536-4441	9-12	Scott Moore
Northern AZ Academy for Career Dev.	502 Airport Rd	Winslow, AZ	86047-5400	928-289-3329	289-4485	9-12	
Northland Preparatory Academy	3300 E Sparrow Ave	Flagstaff, AZ	86004-6703	928-214-8776	214-8778	7-12	Toni Keberlein
North Phoenix Preparatory Academy	13613 N Cave Creek Rd Ste F	Phoenix, AZ	85022-5137	602-996-4355	889-0161	6-9	Kevin Topper
North Pointe Preparatory S	10215 N 43rd Ave	Phoenix, AZ	85051-1025	623-209-0017	209-0021	7-12	Richard Gow
Northpoint Expeditionary Learning Acad	551 1st St	Prescott, AZ	86301-2501	928-717-3272	717-2316	9-12	Charles Mentken
North Star Charter S	10720 W Indian School Rd	Phoenix, AZ	85037-5722	623-907-2661	907-2501	9-12	Kurt Huzar
Nosotros Academy	440 N Grande Ave	Tucson, AZ	85745-2703	520-624-1023	624-7999	3-12	Paul Felix
Odyssey Institute for Advanced Studies	1495 S Verrado Way	Buckeye, AZ	85326	623-327-1757		6-12	Mary Daniels
Odyssey Preparatory Academy	6500 S Apache Rd	Buckeye, AZ	85326	623-327-3111	327-0554	K-5	Kenneth Olson
Odyssey Preparatory Academy	17532 W Harrison St	Goodyear, AZ	85338-8000	623-882-1140	882-1196	K-6	Liz Douglass
Old Vail MS	13299 E Colossal Cave Rd	Vail, AZ	85641-9090	520-879-2400	879-2401	6-8	Dr. Laurie Emery
Ombudsman Charter S - East	3943 E Thomas Rd	Phoenix, AZ	85018-7511	602-840-2997	840-1402	6-12	Emily Langfeldt
Ombudsman Charter S - East II	4041 E Thomas Rd Ste 106	Phoenix, AZ	85018-7528	602-667-7759	667-7793	9-12	
Ombudsman Charter S - Metro	4220 W Northern Ave	Phoenix, AZ	85051-5753	602-840-2997	842-6157	6-12	
Ombudsman Charter S - Northeast	3242 E Bell Rd	Phoenix, AZ	85032-2727	602-485-9872	367-0367	6-12	
Ombudsman Charter S - Northwest	9516 W Peoria Ave	Peoria, AZ	85345-6139	602-840-2997	840-1402	6-12	Emily Langfeldt
Ombudsman Charter S - Valencia	1686 W Valencia Rd Ste 100	Tucson, AZ	85746-6065	520-573-5858	807-9333	6-12	Emily Langfeldt
Ombudsman Charter S - West	2909 W Bell Rd	Glendale, AZ	85308	602-840-2997	840-1402	6-12	Emily Langfeldt
Omega Alpha Academy	1402 N San Antonio Ave	Douglas, AZ	85607-2434	520-805-1261	805-1272	K-12	Jose Frisby
Open Doors Community S	13644 N Sandario Rd	Marana, AZ	85653-8580	520-744-2484		K-8	Mary Franco
Orangewood S	7337 N 19th Ave	Phoenix, AZ	85021-7998	602-347-2900	347-2920	K-8	Colleen Mahoney
PACE Preparatory Academy	6711 E 2nd St	Prescott Valley, AZ	86314	928-775-9675	775-9673	9-12	Mary Augustinovich
Paideia Academy of South Phoenix	7777 S 15th Ter	Phoenix, AZ	85042-6754	602-343-3040	381-9029	PK-6	Dr. Brian Winsor
Painted Rock Academy	14800 N 25th Dr	Phoenix, AZ	85023-5002	602-466-8855		K-8	Britainy McMillan
Pan-American Charter ES	3001 W Indian School Rd	Phoenix, AZ	85017-4151	602-266-3989	266-3979	K-8	Marta Pasos
Paradise Education Center	15533 W Paradise Ln	Surprise, AZ	85374-5851	623-975-2646	975-2841	K-8	Allison Gonzales
Paradise Honors HS	12775 N 175th Ave	Surprise, AZ	85388	623-546-7200	975-4380	9-12	Mike Sears
Paragon Science Academy	2975 W Linda Ln	Chandler, AZ	85224	480-814-1600	814-1661	K-12	Selim Tanyeri M.Ed.
Paramount Academy	11039 W Olive Ave	Peoria, AZ	85345-9200	623-977-0614	977-0615	K-8	Melody Ward
Park View MS	9030 E Florentine Rd	Prescott Valley, AZ	86314-8973	928-775-5115	775-6253	6-8	Debra Slagle
Patagonia Montessori S	PO Box 628	Patagonia, AZ	85624-0628	520-394-9530	394-2864	PK-8	Jessi Beebe
Pathfinder Academy	2906 N Boulder Canyon	Mesa, AZ	85207-1066	480-986-7071	986-9858	K-8	Susan Stradling
Patriot Academy	19023 E San Tan Blvd	Queen Creek, AZ	85142-9705	480-279-4780	807-1209	K-8	Jay Brown
Paulden Community S	24850 N Naples St	Paulden, AZ	86334-2839	928-636-1430	636-3087	K-8	James Sexton
Payson Center for Success HS	514 W Wade	Payson, AZ	85541-4886	928-472-2011	472-2039	9-12	
Peak S	2016 N 1st St Ste A	Flagstaff, AZ	86004-4241	928-779-0771	779-0774	K-8	Paula Drossman
Peoria Accelerated HS	8885 W Peoria Ave	Peoria, AZ	85345-6442	623-979-0031	979-0113	9-12	Amanda Bachler
Phoenix Advantage Charter S	3738 N 16th St	Phoenix, AZ	85016-5915	602-263-8777		K-8	Leanne Bowley
Phoenix College Prep Academy	1202 W Thomas Rd	Phoenix, AZ	85013-4208	602-285-7998	285-7697	9-12	
Phoenix Collegiate Academy	5610 S Central Ave	Phoenix, AZ	85040-3090	602-268-9900	268-9911	2-12	Rachel Bennett Yanof
Phoenix School of Academic Excellence	5310 N 12th St	Phoenix, AZ	85014-2903	602-241-7876	424-0281	7-12	Julie Palma
Pillar Academy of Business & Finance	1589 E Plantation Rd	Mohave Valley, AZ	86440	928-346-3925	346-3930	9-12	
Pima Partnership S	1346 N Stone Ave	Tucson, AZ	85705-7338	520-326-2528	326-2527	7-12	
Pima Rose Academy	1690 W Irvington Rd	Tucson, AZ	85746	520-797-4884	797-8868	9-12	Joanne Vigilant
Pima Vocational HS - Downtown	175 W Irvington Rd	Tucson, AZ	85714	520-243-1745		9-12	
Pima Vocational HS Northwest	5025 W Ina Rd	Tucson, AZ	85743-9751	520-443-6469		9-12	Gloria Proo
Pine Forest Charter S	2257 E Cedar Ave	Flagstaff, AZ	86004	928-779-9880	779-9792	K-8	Michael Heffernan
Pinnacle HS - Casa Grande	2510 N Trekell Rd	Casa Grande, AZ	85122-1007	520-423-2380	423-2383	9-12	
Pinnacle HS - Mesa	151 N Centennial Way	Mesa, AZ	85201-6734	480-668-5003	668-5005	9-12	
Pinnacle HS - Nogales	2055 N Grand Ave	Nogales, AZ	85621-1038	520-281-5109	281-5132	9-12	
Pinnacle HS - Tempe E	1712 E Guadalupe Rd Ste 101	Tempe, AZ	85283-3983	480-785-7776	785-7778	9-12	
Pinnacle HS - Tempe W	2224 W Southern Ave Ste 2	Tempe, AZ	85282-4345	602-414-0950	414-0927	9-12	
Pinnacle Peak ES	7690 E Williams Dr	Scottsdale, AZ	85255-4801	602-449-6700	449-6705	K-6	Lora Herbein
Pinnacle Pointe Academy	6753 W Pinnacle Peak Rd	Glendale, AZ	85310-5301	623-537-3535	537-4433	K-6	Suzanne Smailagic
Pinnacle Virtual HS	3225 S Hardy Dr	Tempe, AZ	85282-3394	480-755-8222	755-8111	7-12	
Pioneer Preparatory S	6510 W Clarendon Ave	Phoenix, AZ	85033-4001	623-933-3733	252-0022	K-6	Tony Best
Polytechnic ES	6859 E Rembrandt Ave	Mesa, AZ	85212	480-727-5700	727-5701	K-6	Claudia Mendoza
PPEP TEC - Chavez Learning Center	PO Box 6779	San Luis, AZ	85349	928-627-8550	627-8980	9-12	Angelica Sanchez
PPEP TEC - Fernandez Learning Center	1840 E Benson Hwy	Tucson, AZ	85714-1770	520-889-8276	741-4369	9-12	
PPEP TEC - Paul Learning Center	220 E Florence Blvd	Casa Grande, AZ	85122-4031	520-836-6549	836-0290	9-12	Leticia Lujan
PPEP TEC - Powell Learning Center	4116 Avenida Cochise Ste F	Sierra Vista, AZ	85635-5843	520-458-8205	458-8293	9-12	
PPEP TEC - Raul H. Castro Learning Ctr	1122 N G Ave	Douglas, AZ	85607-1927	520-364-4405	364-1405	9-12	Raul Torrez
PPEP TEC - Soltero Learning Center	8677 E Golf Links Rd	Tucson, AZ	85730-1315	520-290-9167	290-9220	9-12	Randy Kempton
PPEP TEC - Yepez Learning Center	201 N Bingham Ave	Somerton, AZ	85350	928-627-9648	627-9197	9-12	Gloria Rodriguez
Precision Academy	7318 W Lynwood St	Phoenix, AZ	85035-4542	623-936-8682	936-8559	9-12	Dr. Caroline White
Premier Charter HS	7544 W Indian School Rd	Phoenix, AZ	85033-3030	623-245-1500	245-1506	9-12	Debbie Petersen
Prescott Valley S	PO Box 27348	Prescott Valley, AZ	86312-7348	928-772-8744	775-4457	K-12	Monika Fuller
Presidio S	1695 E Fort Lowell Rd	Tucson, AZ	85719-2319	520-881-5222	881-5522	K-12	Mindy White
Primavera Online HS	2471 N Arizona Ave Ste 1	Chandler, AZ	85225-1394	480-456-6678	355-2100	7-12	Mori Creamer
Pueblo Del Sol ES	3555 E Fry Blvd	Sierra Vista, AZ	85635-2972	520-515-2970	515-2973	K-6	Tom Yarborough
Quail Run ES	3303 E Utopia Rd	Phoenix, AZ	85050-3900	602-449-4400	449-4405	K-6	Marta Maynard
Quest HS	217 E Olympic Dr	Phoenix, AZ	85042	480-831-6057	831-6095	9-12	Melissa Barnett
RCB Medical Arts Academy	6049 N 43rd Ave	Phoenix, AZ	85019-1641	602-973-6018	589-1349	9-12	Steven Durand
Reyes Maria Ruiz Leadership Academy	4848 S 2nd St	Phoenix, AZ	85040-2122	602-243-7788	243-7799	K-6	Armando Ruiz
Ridgeline Academy	33625 N North Valley Pkwy	Phoenix, AZ	85085-4229	623-223-1335		K-6	Keven Barker
Rimrock Public HS	3705 Beaver Creek Rd	Rimrock, AZ	86335	928-567-9213	567-9304	9-12	Kathleen McCabe
Rincon Vista MS	10770 E Bilby Rd	Tucson, AZ	85747-5999	520-879-3200	879-3201	6-8	Cristela Cardenas
Rising S	7444 E Broadway Blvd	Tucson, AZ	85710-1411	520-730-2657		6-12	George Rising Ph.D.
Riverbend Preparatory S	5625 S 51st Ave	Laveen, AZ	85339	602-285-3003	285-5560	K-8	John Paquin
Royal Palm MS	8520 N 19th Ave	Phoenix, AZ	85021-4293	602-347-3200	347-3220	6-8	Heidi Keefer
RSD HS - Blended Learning Academy	13615 N 35th Ave	Phoenix, AZ	85029-1243	602-993-5225	993-0506	9-12	Red Davis
SABIS International	1903 E Roeser Rd	Phoenix, AZ	85040-3341	602-305-8865	323-5526	K-8	Goldie LaPorte
Saddleback ES	44150 W Maricopa Casa Grand	Maricopa, AZ	85138-5900	520-568-6110	568-6119	PK-6	Felicia Williams
Sage Academy	1055 E Hearn Rd	Scottsdale, AZ	85254	602-485-3402	485-7874	K-8	
Sandpiper ES	6724 E Hearn Rd	Scottsdale, AZ	85254-3332	602-449-6300	449-6305	K-6	Diana Cameron
San Pedro Valley HS	360 S Patagonia St	Benson, AZ	85602-6533	520-720-6726	720-6702	9-12	Richard Connet
Santa Cruz ES	44150 W Maricopa Casa Grand	Maricopa, AZ	85138-5900	520-568-5170	568-5176	K-6	Dr. Loraine Conley
San Tan Charter S	3959 E Elliot Rd	Gilbert, AZ	85234-4345	480-222-0811	539-1028	PK-12	Dr. Kristofer Sippel
Santa Rosa ES	44150 W Maricopa Casa Grand	Maricopa, AZ	85138	520-568-6152	568-6155	K-6	Eva Safranek
Satori Charter S	3727 N 1st Ave	Tucson, AZ	85719-1609	520-293-7555	293-7020	2-8	Jesse Ramos
Scottsdale Country Day S	10460 N 56th St	Scottsdale, AZ	85253-1133	480-452-5777		K-6	Steve Prahcharov
Scottsdale Preparatory Academy	16537 N 92nd St	Scottsdale, AZ	85260-1528	480-776-1970	776-1975	5-12	Alison Chaney
Sedona Charter S	165 Kachina Dr	Sedona, AZ	86336-4303	928-204-6464	204-6486	K-8	Alice Madar
Self Development Charter S	1515 E Indian School Rd	Phoenix, AZ	85014-4901	480-830-8006		K-8	
Self Development Charter S	1709 N Greenfield Rd	Mesa, AZ	85205-3103	480-641-2640	641-2678	K-8	Anjum Majeed
Seneca Preparatory Academy	601 E Fort Lowell Blvd	Tucson, AZ	85705	520-721-5289		K-5	
Sequoia Charter ES	1460 S Horne	Mesa, AZ	85204-5760	480-890-4002		K-6	Donna Driggers
Sequoia Charter Secondary S	1460 S Horne	Mesa, AZ	85204-5760	480-649-7737	649-0711	9-12	LaRonda Lugo
Sequoia Choice Precision S	3906 E Broadway Rd	Phoenix, AZ	85040-2996	602-453-3661	453-3667	9-12	
Sequoia Choice S - AZ Distance Learning	2331 N Horne	Mesa, AZ	85203	480-461-3222	890-4106	K-12	Cindy Chleborad
Sequoia ES	1460 S Horne	Mesa, AZ	85204-5760	480-890-4002	890-4107	K-6	Donna Driggers
Sequoia Lehi ES	2331 N Horne	Mesa, AZ	85203-1823	480-397-9890	397-4003	PK-6	S. Paschal
Sequoia Pathfinder Academy	4816 S Eastmark Pkwy	Mesa, AZ	85212-8179	480-351-8070	351-8407	K-6	Juliane Hillock
Sequoia Pathway Academy	19265 N Porter Rd	Maricopa, AZ	85138-4053	520-568-9333	568-9444	K-12	Matthew Metcalf

School	Address	City,State	Zip code	Telephone	Fax	Grade	Contact
Sequoia S for the Deaf & Hard of Hearing	1460 S Horne	Mesa, AZ	85204-5760	480-890-4001	890-4113	K-12	Heather Laine
Sequoia STAR Academy	323 N Gilbert Rd	Mesa, AZ	85203-8262	480-834-7400	834-7402	7-12	Lynn McConnell
Sequoia Village S	982 Full House Ln	Show Low, AZ	85901-4042	928-537-1208	537-4275	K-12	Mindy Savoia M.Ed.
Shelby S	249 W Standage Dr	Payson, AZ	85541	928-478-4706	478-0681	K-10	Ezra Stuyvesant
Sky Islands S	6000 E 14th St	Tucson, AZ	85711	520-382-9210	382-5888	9-12	Dr. Shari Popen
Skyline District 5 S	PO Box 10858	Bapchule, AZ	85121-0104	520-315-3236	315-3233	5-12	Vaughn Flannigan
Skyline Prep HS	7500 S 40th St	Phoenix, AZ	85042	602-343-4980	343-4996	9-12	Tonya Bridges-Brown M.A.
Skyview HS	4290 S Miller Rd	Buckeye, AZ	85326-6307	623-386-6799	327-9636	9-12	Danielle Calderon
Skyview S	125 S Rush St	Prescott, AZ	86303-4432	928-776-1730	776-1742	K-8	Scott McCreery
Sonoran Desert S	6724 S Kings Ranch Rd	Gold Canyon, AZ	85118-2963	480-396-5463	396-4980	5-12	Patricia Dalman
Sonoran Science Academy - Broadway	6880 E Broadway Blvd	Tucson, AZ	85710-2818	520-751-2401	751-2451	K-8	Erdal Kocak
Sonoran Science Academy - Davis Monthan	5741 E Ironwood St	Tucson, AZ	85708-1429	520-300-5699	207-7698	6-12	Peggy Fontenot M.Ed.
Sonoran Science Academy - Peoria	17667 N 91st Ave	Peoria, AZ	85382	623-776-9344	933-8001	K-8	Barbara Stabenow
Sonoran Science Academy - Phoenix	4837 E McDowell Rd	Phoenix, AZ	85008-4225	602-244-9855	244-9856	K-12	Jim Satterlee
Sonoran Science Academy - Tucson	2325 W Sunset Rd	Tucson, AZ	85741-3809	520-665-3400	665-3420	K-12	Dr. Adnan Doyuran Ph.D.
Sonoran Sky ES	12990 N 75th St	Scottsdale, AZ	85260-4746	602-449-6500	449-6505	PK-6	Robert Dawson
Southern Arizona Community Academy	2470 N Tucson Blvd	Tucson, AZ	85716-2469	520-319-6113	319-6115	9-12	Abelardo Cubillas
Southgate Academy	7842 E Wrightstown Rd	Tucson, AZ	85715	520-741-7900	741-7901	K-12	Sherry Matyjasik
South Mountain Preparatory Academy	449 E Southern Ave	Phoenix, AZ	85040-3045	602-953-2933		K-3	
South Phoenix Prep and Arts School	7450 S 40th St	Phoenix, AZ	85042	877-225-8711		PK-4	Jackie Zander M.Ed.
South Pointe Charter ES	2033 E Southern Ave	Phoenix, AZ	85040-3344	602-276-1943	276-2726	K-6	Darwin Russell
South Pointe HS	8325 S Central Ave	Phoenix, AZ	85042-6576	602-243-0600	243-0800	9-12	Larry McGill
South Pointe JHS	217 E Olympic Dr	Phoenix, AZ	85042	602-243-8496	276-5244	6-8	Melissa Barnett
South Ridge HS	1122 S 67th Ave	Phoenix, AZ	85043-4417	623-247-0106	247-0527	9-12	Melissa Rivers
Southside Community S	2701 S Campbell Ave	Tucson, AZ	85713-5080	520-623-7102	623-7125	6-12	Laura LaFave
South Valley Prep and Arts Academy	7500 S 40th St	Phoenix, AZ	85042	877-225-2118	437-2901	5-8	Tasha Gant M.Ed.
South Verde Technology Magnet S	410 Camp Lincoln Rd	Camp Verde, AZ	86322-7494	928-567-8076	567-8093	9-12	Steve King
Southwest Leadership Academy	4301 W Fillmore St	Phoenix, AZ	85043-2908	602-265-2000		9-12	Dr. Gregory Fowler
STAR S	145 Leupp Rd	Flagstaff, AZ	86004-8501	928-415-4157	225-2179	K-8	Dr. Mark Sorenson
StarShine Academy Creative Community	3535 E McDowell Rd	Phoenix, AZ	85008-3847	602-957-9557	956-0065	K-12	Todd Peapenburg
Starshine Fay Landrum Academy	1902 W Roeser Rd	Phoenix, AZ	85041	602-237-6030		K-12	
STEM Academy Polytechnic	6110 S Sagewood St	Mesa, AZ	85212	480-727-5750		5-8	
Stepping Stones Academy	35812 N 7th St	Phoenix, AZ	85086-7410	623-465-4910	587-8514	PK-8	Dedre Stewart-Alliger
Step Up S	44 E 5th St	Mesa, AZ	85201-5901	480-344-2600	850-0004	K-8	
Student Choice HS	1833 N Scottsdale Rd	Tempe, AZ	85281-1563	480-947-9511	947-9624	9-12	Catherine McAllister
Student Choice HS - Peoria	8194 W Deer Valley Rd	Peoria, AZ	85382-2127	623-242-2722	566-1634	9-12	Joy McCain
Summit HS	728 E Mcdowell Rd	Phoenix, AZ	85006-2518	602-258-8959	258-8953	9-12	James Sigman
Sun Valley Charter S	5806 S 35th Pl	Phoenix, AZ	85040-2844	602-692-4914	612-2196	K-6	Tanae Morrison M.Ed.
Sun Valley HS	1143 S Lindsay Rd	Mesa, AZ	85204-6298	480-497-4800	497-1314	9-12	Joe Procopio
Sweetwater S	4602 W Sweetwater Ave	Glendale, AZ	85304-1505	602-896-6500	896-6520	K-8	Luanne Herman
SySTEM Phoenix	1301 E Almeria Rd	Phoenix, AZ	85006-2509	602-710-1873		6-12	Angelica Cruz
Taylion Virtual Academy	4744 W Grovers Ave	Glendale, AZ	85308-3453	855-297-2466	889-7806	9-12	Charlene Shores
Teleos Preparatory Academy	1401 E Jefferson St	Phoenix, AZ	85034-2315	602-275-5455	275-5954	K-8	Brian Taylor
Telesis Preparatory Academy	2598 Starlite Ln	Lk Havasu Cty, AZ	86403-4946	928-855-8661	855-9302	K-12	Sandra Breece Ed.D.
Tempe Preparatory Academy	1251 E Southern Ave	Tempe, AZ	85282-5605	480-839-3402	755-0546	6-12	Dr. Wayne Porter
Thoman Air and Space Academy	730 W Calle Arroyo Sur	Green Valley, AZ	85614-5883	520-219-4383		K-8	Mary Lou Klem
Toltecali Academy	251 W Irvington Rd	Tucson, AZ	85714-3054	520-882-3029	882-3041	9-12	
Tri-City College Prep HS	5522 Side Rd	Prescott, AZ	86301-8483	928-777-0403	777-0402	9-12	Keri Milliken
Triumphant Learning Center	201 E Main St	Safford, AZ	85546-2051	928-348-8422	348-8423	K-8	Robin Dutt
Trivium Preparatory Academy	2001 N Bullard Ave	Goodyear, AZ	85395-3372	623-866-4730	866-4729	6-10	Heidi Vasiloff
Tucson Collegiate Prep	40 W Fort Lowell Rd	Tucson, AZ	85705-3810	520-870-1670		6-8	Steve Campbell
Tucson Country Day S	9239 E Wrightstown Rd	Tucson, AZ	85715-5514	520-296-0883	290-1521	K-8	Dr. Deborah Anders
Tucson International Academy	2700 W Broadway Blvd	Tucson, AZ	85745-1715	520-792-3255	792-3245	K-12	Miguel Montemayor
Tucson International Academy East Campus	2700 W Broadway Blvd	Tucson, AZ	85745-1715	520-792-3255	792-3245	K-10	Peter Meehan
Tucson International Academy - Midvale	2700 W Broadway Blvd	Tucson, AZ	85745-1715	520-792-3255	792-3245	K-12	Valarie Enriquez
Tucson International Academy West Campus	2700 W Broadway Blvd	Tucson, AZ	85745-1715	520-792-3255	792-3245	K-12	Valerie Enriquez
Tucson Preparatory S	104 E Prince Rd	Tucson, AZ	85705-3666	520-622-4185	622-4755	9-12	Jody Sullivan
Vail Academy and HS	7762 E Science Park Dr	Tucson, AZ	85747	520-879-1902	879-1901	K-12	Dennis Barger
Valley Academy - Charter S	1520 W Rose Garden Ln	Phoenix, AZ	85027-3529	623-516-7747	516-2703	PK-8	Victoria Wilber M.Ed.
Valley Preparatory Academy	2150 E Southern Ave	Tempe, AZ	85282-7504	480-621-5382		9-12	Jennifer Womack
Val Vista Academy	4120 S Val Vista Dr	Gilbert, AZ	85297-4607	480-656-5555	689-5952	K-8	Dr. Gary Londer
Vector Prep and Arts Academy	2020 N Arizona Ave	Chandler, AZ	85225	480-779-2000	779-2100	K-6	Deborah Coleman M.Ed.
Verde Valley Montessori Charter S	PO Box 2678	Cottonwood, AZ	86326-2509	928-634-3288	634-9781	PK-8	Maryann Green
Veritas Preparatory Academy	3102 N 56th St Ste 200	Phoenix, AZ	85018-6606	602-263-1128	263-7997	6-12	David Dean
Victory HS	PO Box 8374	Phoenix, AZ	85066-8374	602-243-7583	243-7563	9-12	Dr. Shirley Branham
Villa Montessori - Phoenix	2802 E Meadowbrook Ave	Phoenix, AZ	85016-4939	602-955-2210	381-4017	K-8	Margo O'Neill
Vision Charter S	5901 S Santa Cruz Calle	Tucson, AZ	85709-0001	520-444-0241	741-8123	9-12	
Visions Unlimited Academy	1275 E Barney Ln	Benson, AZ	85602-7955	520-586-8691	586-3074	K-8	Richard Valentine
Vista College Preparatory S	812 S 6th Ave	Phoenix, AZ	85003-2528	602-374-7159	374-8201	K-5	Julia Meyerson
Vista Grove Preparatory Academy	2929 E McKellips Rd	Mesa, AZ	85213-3128	480-924-1500	924-0552	PK-9	Abelardo Batista
Washington Academy	1945 S 1st St E	Snowflake, AZ	85937-5374	928-440-6228		K-8	Kathleen Danielson
Webster Basic S	5399 N Pima Rd	Scottsdale, AZ	85250-2620	480-291-6900	291-6901	K-6	Jessica Friedermann
Webster Basic S	7301 E Baseline Rd	Mesa, AZ	85209-4907	480-986-2335	373-9176	PK-6	Jessica Friedermann
Western S of Science and Technology	6515 W Indian School Rd	Phoenix, AZ	85033-3330	623-249-3900	243-9030	7-9	Aaron Dille
Westland S	4141 N 67th Ave	Phoenix, AZ	85033-3314	623-247-6456	247-6520	K-12	
West Phoenix HS	3835 W Thomas Rd	Phoenix, AZ	85019-4434	602-269-1110	269-1112	9-12	Alex Horton
Whispering Wind Academy	15844 N 43rd St	Phoenix, AZ	85032-4124	602-449-7300	449-7305	K-6	Johnny Brownlie
Willow Creek Charter S	2100 Willow Creek Rd	Prescott, AZ	86301-5391	928-776-1212	776-0009	K-8	Terese Soto
Young Scholars Academy	1501 E Valencia Rd	Bullhead City, AZ	86426-5218	928-704-1100	704-1177	K-8	Tonnie Smith
YouthWorks Charter HS	1915 E 36th St	Tucson, AZ	85713	520-623-5843		9-12	Kelvin Strozier
Arkansas							
Academic Center of Excellence	21 Funtastic Dr	Cabot, AR	72023-6005	501-743-3520	843-0283	7-12	Michele Evans
Arkansas Arts Academy	1110 W Poplar St	Rogers, AR	72756	479-636-2272	636-5447	K-8	Matt Young
Arkansas Arts Academy	1110 W Poplar St	Rogers, AR	72756	479-631-2787	899-6479	9-12	Barbara Padgett
Arkansas Virtual Academy	4702 W Commercial Dr Ste B3	No Little Rock, AR	72116-7073	501-664-4225	664-4226	K-11	Dr. Scott Sides
Brunson New Vision Charter S	PO Box 1210	Warren, AR	71671-1210	870-226-2351	226-8541	4-5	Regina Scroggins
Capital City Lighthouse Charter S	3901 Virginia Dr	No Little Rock, AR	72118-4265	501-313-2901	313-2910	K-5	Eric Dailey
Cloverdale Magnet MS	6300 Hinkson Rd	Little Rock, AR	72209-4712	501-447-2500	447-2501	6-8	Wanda Ruffins
Covenant Keepers Charter S	5615 Geyer Springs Rd	Little Rock, AR	72209-1812	501-682-7550	682-7577	6-8	Dr. Valerie Tatum
Cross County Elementary Technology Acad	2622 Highway 42	Cherry Valley, AR	72324-8674	870-588-3337	588-4454	K-6	Mindy Searcy
Cross County HS A New Tech S	21 County Road 215	Cherry Valley, AR	72324-8957	870-588-3337	588-4606	7-12	Stephen Prince
Eastside New Vision Charter S	PO Box 1210	Warren, AR	71671-1210	870-226-6761	226-8538	K-3	Sara Weaver
eStem Public Charter ES	112 W 3rd St	Little Rock, AR	72201-2702	501-748-9200	975-4092	K-4	Jessi Forster
eStem Public Charter HS	123 W 3rd St	Little Rock, AR	72201-2701	501-748-9335	748-9370	9-12	Johnecia Howard
eStem Public Charter MS	112 W 3rd St	Little Rock, AR	72201-2702	501-748-9200	975-4092	5-8	Jessi Forster
Exalt Academy Of Southwest Little Rock	6111 W 83rd St	Little Rock, AR	72209-4637	501-568-3279	568-3286	K-2	Tina Long
Flightline Upper Academy	1030 Cannon Dr	No Little Rock, AR	72114	501-988-1085	988-1090	5-8	Evan McGrew
Forrest City College Preparatory	637 S Washington St	Forrest City, AR	72335-3845	870-677-6766	633-0602	5-5	Marcus Nelson
Haas Hall Academy	2600 SE J St	Bentonville, AR	72712	479-268-3424	250-9292	7-12	Dr. Rod Wittenberg
Haas Hall Academy	3880 N Front St	Fayetteville, AR	72703-5130	479-966-4930	966-4932	7-12	Dr. Martin Schoppmeyer
Hope Academy of Public Services	601 W 6th St	Hope, AR	71801	870-777-3454		5-8	Carol Duke
Imboden Area Charter S	PO Box 297	Imboden, AR	72434-0297	870-869-3015	869-3016	K-8	Judy Warren
Jacksonville Lighthouse Charter S	251 N 1st St	Jacksonville, AR	72076-4462	501-985-1200	985-1201	K-6	Norman Whitfield
Jacksonville Lighthouse Coll Prep Acad	251 N 1st St	Jacksonville, AR	72076-4462	501-985-1228	985-1233	7-12	Will Felton
Jacksonville Lighthouse Flightline S	Bldg 1030 Cannon Dr	Jacksonville, AR	72099-0001	501-988-1085	988-1090	5-8	Evan McGrew
KIPP Blytheville College Preparatory S	1200 Byrum Rd	Blytheville, AR	72315-8119	870-780-6333	780-6310	5-8	Maisie Wright
KIPP Blytheville Collegiate HS	1200 Byrum Rd	Blytheville, AR	72315-8119	870-780-6333	780-6310	9-12	Maisie Wright
KIPP Delta College Preparatory S	514 Missouri	Helena, AR	72342-3751	870-753-9444	753-9450	5-8	Heather Johnson
KIPP Delta Collegiate High School	320 Missouri	Helena, AR	72342-3709	870-338-8138	338-8623	9-12	Stephanie Bennetts
KIPP Delta Elementary Literacy Academy	215 Cherry St	Helena, AR	72342	870-753-9800	753-9801	K-4	Todd Dixon
Lisa Academy	21 Corporate Hill Dr	Little Rock, AR	72205-4537	501-227-4942	227-4952	6-12	Ilker Fidan
Lisa Academy-North Little Rock	5410 Landers Rd	No Little Rock, AR	72117-1935	501-945-2727	945-2728	K-12	Fatih Bogrek
Little Rock Prep Academy	6711 W Markham St	Little Rock, AR	72205	501-683-1855	683-1847	K-8	Jennifer McMahan
Maumelle Charter ES	900 Edgewood Dr	Maumelle, AR	72113	501-803-0666	803-9748	K-6	Paula Newton
Maumelle Charter HS	600 Edgewood Dr	Maumelle, AR	72113	501-851-3333	851-2599	7-12	Rob McGill
Miner Academy	800 School St	Bauxite, AR	72011-9143	501-557-5453	557-2235	6-12	Joshua Harrison
Northwest Arkansas Classical Academy	1302 Melissa Dr Ste 100	Bentonville, AR	72712-7942	479-715-6676		K-8	Susan Provenza
Osceola STEM Academy	112 N School St	Osceola, AR	72370-2413	870-563-2150	622-1025	5-8	Christel Smith
Ozark Montessori Academy	922 E Emma Ave	Springdale, AR	72764-4503	479-935-9992	439-9235	K-7	Christine Silano
Pea Ridge Manufacturing & Business Acad	781 W Pickens Rd	Pea Ridge, AR	72751-2519	800-451-1241	431-6332	11-12	Charley Clark
Pine Bluff Lighthouse Charter S	708 W 2nd Ave	Pine Bluff, AR	71601-4002	870-534-0277	534-0263	K-8	Brent Mitchell
Premier HS of Little Rock	1621 Dr Martin Luther King	Little Rock, AR	72202-6068	501-246-3161	677-0271	9-12	Mia Meadows
Quest MS of Pine Bluff	308 S Blake St	Pine Bluff, AR	71601-3622	870-536-1009		5-8	Arnold Robertson
Quest MS of West Little Rock	1815 Rahling Rd	Little Rock, AR	72223-4677	501-821-0382	437-0487	6-8	Chris Stevens
Rockbridge Montessori Charter S	108 W Roosevelt Rd	Little Rock, AR	72206-2246	501-404-9549	508-5740	K-8	Shannon Nuckols

School	Address	City,State	Zip code	Telephone	Fax	Grade	Contact
Scott Charter S	15306 Alexander Rd	Scott, AR	72142-9781	501-961-1744		K-6	
SIATech Little Rock	6724 Interstate 30	Little Rock, AR	72209-3157	501-562-0039	562-7671	9-12	Katie Tatum
Warren HS A Conversion Charter S	PO Box 1210	Warren, AR	71671-1210	870-226-6736	226-8527	9-12	Bryan Cornish
Warren MS A Conversion Charter S	PO Box 1210	Warren, AR	71671-1210	870-226-2484	226-8511	6-8	Kathryn Cornish
Washington Academy Charter S	3512 Grand Ave	Texarkana, AR	71854-2232	870-772-4792	774-2185	7-12	Terry Taylor
California							
Abraxis Charter HS	PO Box 2587	Santa Rosa, CA	95405-0587	707-539-2897	539-2778	9-12	Martin Wilkes
Acacia Charter ES	1016 E Bianchi Rd	Stockton, CA	95210	209-477-7013	477-7015	K-5	Patricia Lingerfelt
Acacia Charter MS	1605 E March Ln	Stockton, CA	95210-5667	209-477-7014	956-2182	6-8	Theresa Johnson
Academia Avance Charter S	PO Box 42095	Los Angeles, CA	90042-0095	323-230-7270	652-0994	6-12	Ricardo Mireles
Academia Moderna	2410 Broadway	Walnut Park, CA	90255-6342	323-923-0383	923-0380	K-5	Carrie Checca
Academies of the Antelope Valley	6300 W Avenue L	Lancaster, CA	93536-4540			7-12	Chris Grado
Academy for Academic Excellence	17500 Mana Rd	Apple Valley, CA	92307-2181	760-946-5414	242-6398	K-12	Lisa Lamb
Academy of Alameda ES	401 Pacific Ave	Alameda, CA	94501-1837	510-748-4017	523-5304	K-5	Nora Bullock
Academy of Alameda MS	401 Pacific Ave	Alameda, CA	94501-1837	510-214-2460	523-5801	6-8	Matt Huxley
Academy of Business Law & Education	6515 Inglewood Ave	Stockton, CA	95207-3871	209-478-1600	235-2986	9-12	Matthew George
Academy of Careers & Exploration	PO Box 249	Helendale, CA	92342-0249	760-952-2396	952-1178	7-12	William Brown
Academy of Personalized Learning	2195 Larkspur Ln	Redding, CA	96002	530-222-9275		K-12	Patricia Dougherty
Academy of Science and Engineering	5753 Rodeo Rd	Los Angeles, CA	90016	323-545-1100	545-1102	9-11	Teresa Henderson-Johnson
Accelerated Achievement Academy	1059 N State St	Ukiah, CA	95482-3413	707-463-7080	463-7085	4-12	Selah Sawyer
Accelerated Charter ES	3914 S Main St	Los Angeles, CA	90011	323-846-6694	846-0686	K-6	Susan Raudry
Accelerated Charter HS	4136 N Mooney Blvd	Tulare, CA	93274	559-688-2021	687-7317	9-12	Wendi Powell
Accelerated S	4000 S Main St	Los Angeles, CA	90037-1022	323-235-6343	235-6346	K-8	Francis Reading
ACE Charter HS	1776 Educational Park Dr	San Jose, CA	95133-1703	408-251-1362	251-1366	9-12	Jahsve Worthy
ACE Charter HS	570 Airport Way	Camarillo, CA	93010-8500	805-437-1410	437-1491	9-12	Joseph Clausi
ACE Charter S	1665 Santee Dr	San Jose, CA	95122	408-426-6361		5-7	Cesar Torrico
ACE I Empower Academy	625 S Sunset Ave	San Jose, CA	95116	408-729-3920		5-8	Greg Lippman
ACE Inspire Axademy	1155 E Julian St	San Jose, CA	95112	408-295-6008	295-3584	5-8	Marcela Miranda
Achieve Academy	303 Hegenberger Rd Ste 301	Oakland, CA	94621-1419	510-904-6440	904-6761	4-5	Lucy Schmidt
Achieve Charter S of Paradise	771 Elliott Rd	Paradise, CA	95969-3913	530-872-4100	872-4105	K-8	Casey Taylor
Adams Academy	1 Sierra Gate Plz	Roseville, CA	95678	916-780-6800	888-1343	K-12	Heather Brown
Adelante Charter S of Santa Barbara	1102 E Yanonali St	Santa Barbara, CA	93103-2704	805-966-7392	966-7243	PK-6	Juanita Hernandez
Advanced Learning Academy	335 E Walnut St	Santa Ana, CA	92701-5928	714-480-4300	480-4399	K-8	Kimberly Garcia
Alameda Community Learning Center	1900 3rd St	Alameda, CA	94501-1851	510-521-7123	521-7350	6-12	Patti Wilczek
Alder Grove Charter S	714 F St	Eureka, CA	95501-1036	707-268-0854	268-0813	K-12	J. Allen-San Giovanni
Alexander Science Center	3737 S Figueroa St	Los Angeles, CA	90007-4366	213-746-1995	746-7443	K-5	Norma Spencer
Alianza Charter S	115 Casserly Rd	Watsonville, CA	95076-8645	831-728-6333	728-6947	K-8	Rafael Ramirez
Alliance 6-12 College Ready Academy	8755 Woodman Ave	Arleta, CA	91331	818-962-3648		6-12	Jonathan Tiongco
Alliance Alice Baxter College-Ready HS	461 W 9th St	San Pedro, CA	90731-3211	310-221-0430		9-12	Robert Canosa-Carr
Alliance Bloomfield Technology HS	7907 Santa Fe Ave	Huntington Park, CA	90255-6630	323-537-2060	537-2044	9-12	Ani Meymerian
Alliance College-Ready Middle Academy 12	100 E 49th St	Los Angeles, CA	90011	323-238-7270		6-8	Robin Manly
Alliance College-Ready Middle Academy 8	113 S Rowan Ave	Los Angeles, CA	90063	323-269-2156		6-8	Melissa Chew
Alliance College-Ready Middle Academy 9	5886 Compton Ave	Los Angeles, CA	90001-1345	323-484-0450		6-8	Omar Reyes
Alliance Collins Family College-Ready HS	2071 Saturn Ave	Huntington Park, CA	90255-3635	323-923-1588	923-1589	9-12	Robert Delfino
Alliance Gertz-Ressler HS	2023 S Union Ave	Los Angeles, CA	90007-1326	213-745-8141	745-8142	9-12	Howard Lappin
Alliance Health Services Academy HS	10616 S Western Ave	Los Angeles, CA	90047	323-972-9010	905-1578	9-12	Carla McCullough
Alliance Leadership Middle Academy	2941 W 70th St	Los Angeles, CA	90043-4420	323-920-4388		6-8	Joy May-Harris
Alliance Morgan McKinzie HS	110 S Townsend Ave	Los Angeles, CA	90063	323-526-8198	526-8438	9-12	Arthur Sanchez
Alliance Neuwirth Leadership Academy	4610 S Main St	Los Angeles, CA	90037-2736	323-342-2874	342-2875	9-12	Miguel Gamboa
Alliance Ouchi-O'Donovan 6-12 Complex	5356 5th Ave	Los Angeles, CA	90043-2622	323-596-2290	596-2295	6-12	Dea Tramble
Alliance Ted Tajima HS	1552 W Rockwood St	Los Angeles, CA	90026	213-241-8533	943-4931	9-12	Carmen Vazquez-Mancini
All Tribes American Indian Charter S	PO Box 1432	Valley Center, CA	92082-1432	760-749-5982	749-4153	PK-12	Mary Ann Donohue
Almond Acres Charter Academy	1601 L St	San Miguel, CA	93451-9107	805-467-2095	467-2098	K-8	Bob Bourgault
Alpha: Cindy Avitia HS	1881 Cunningham Ave	San Jose, CA	95122-1712	408-758-1195	791-1558	9-10	Will Eden
Alpha: Jose Hernandez MS	1601 Cunningham Ave	San Jose, CA	95122-2314	408-780-0831		6-8	Hope Evans
Alpha Charter S	7900 Eloise Ave	Elverta, CA	95626-9217	916-991-2244	991-0271	9-12	Michael Borgaard
Alpha I Blanca Alvarado MS	1601 Cunningham Ave	San Jose, CA	95122	408-780-0831		6-7	John Glover
Alta Vista Charter S	11988 Hesperia Rd Ste B	Hesperia, CA	92345	760-947-0006		K-12	Kenneth Larson
Alta Vista Community Charter S	173 Oak St	Auburn, CA	95603-4318	530-745-1220	885-7066	K-5	Camille Taylor
Alternative Coop Education Charter S	400 Hemlock St	Vacaville, CA	95688	707-453-6245	448-7933	K-6	Jennifer Buzolich
Alternatives in Action	6221 E 17th St	Oakland, CA	94621	510-285-6290	285-6294	9-12	Patricia Murillo
Alvarado Academy	26247 Ellis St	Madera, CA	93638-0813	559-675-2070	675-2074	K-8	Dr. Nicolas Retana
Alvina Charter ES	295 W Saginaw Ave	Caruthers, CA	93609-9710	559-864-9411	864-1808	K-8	Mike Iribarren
Ambassador Sanchez Charter S	5659 E Kings Canyon Rd	Fresno, CA	93727-4641	559-470-8222		9-12	David Petropulos
American Indian Charter HS	746 Grand Ave	Oakland, CA	94607	510-482-6000	482-6002	9-12	Joel Julien
American Indian Charter S II	171 12th St	Oakland, CA	94607-4900	510-893-8701	893-0345	K-8	Elston Perry
American River Charter S	6620 Wentworth Springs Rd	Georgetown, CA	95634	530-333-8340	333-8346	K-12	Sally Dyck
Americas Finest Charter S	730 45th St	San Diego, CA	92102-3619	619-694-4790	794-2762	K-8	Jan Perry
Anahuacalmecac Intl University Prep S	4736 Huntington Dr S	Los Angeles, CA	90032-1942	323-352-3148	352-8758	K-12	
Anderson New Technology HS	2098 North St	Anderson, CA	96007-3477	530-365-3100	365-2957	9-12	Carol Germano
Animo College Preparatory Academy	2265 E 103rd St	Los Angeles, CA	90002-3132	323-568-4136	568-4190	9-12	James Marin
Animo Ellen Ochoa Charter MS	725 S Indiana St	Los Angeles, CA	90023	323-565-3245		6-8	Marco Duran
Animo Florence-Firestone Charter MS	155 W 69th St	Los Angeles, CA	90003	323-585-3312	565-1610	6-8	Josh Hartford
Animo Inglewood Charter HS	3425 W Manchester Blvd	Inglewood, CA	90305-2101	323-565-2100	565-2109	9-12	Leilani Abulon
Animo Jackie Robinson Charter HS	3500 S Hill St	Los Angeles, CA	90007-4333	323-846-5800	846-8760	9-12	Kristine Botello
Animo James B. Taylor Charter MS	810 E 111th Pl	Los Angeles, CA	90059	323-568-8613	568-8617	6-8	Amber Garcia Bowman
Animo Jefferson Charter MS	1655 E 27th St	Los Angeles, CA	90011	323-232-1857	232-6505	6-8	Edgar Flota
Animo Leadership Charter HS	11044 S Freeman Ave	Inglewood, CA	90304-2418	323-565-4420	565-4421	9-12	Julio Murcia
Animo Mae Jemison Charter MS	12700 Avalon Blvd	Los Angeles, CA	90061-2730	323-565-4450	754-1382	6-8	Meghan Schooler
Animo Pat Brown Charter HS	8255 Beach St	Los Angeles, CA	90001	323-585-3312	585-8985	9-12	Brian Thomas-Reed
Animo Phillis Wheatley Charter MS	12226 S Western Ave	Los Angeles, CA	90047-5240	323-600-6099		6-8	Meghan Maguire
Animo Ralph Bunche Charter HS	1655 E 27th St	Los Angeles, CA	90011-2202	323-232-9436	232-9440	9-12	Nancy Padilla-Flores
Animo South Los Angeles HS	11100 S Western Ave	Los Angeles, CA	90047-4845	323-779-0544	779-0565	9-12	Taiala Carvalho
Animo Venice HS	820 Broadway St	Venice, CA	90291-3408	310-392-8751	392-8752	9-12	Julio Murcia
Animo Watts Charter HS	12628 Avalon Blvd	Los Angeles, CA	90061-2728	323-756-3930	756-3947	9-12	Abraham Devilliers
Animo Western Charter MS	12226 S Western Ave	Los Angeles, CA	90047-5240	323-600-6000	652-1849	6-8	Sonja Johnson
Animo Westside Charter MS	5456 McConnell Ave	Los Angeles, CA	90066-2056	323-565-3251	227-9739	6-8	Lemuel Mosset
Annenberg HS	4000 S Main St	Los Angeles, CA	90037-1022	323-235-6343	235-6346	9-12	Rene Quon
Antelope Valley Learning Academy	1240 Commerce Center Dr	Lancaster, CA	93534-5841	661-952-5520	940-9908	K-12	Erin Wade
Antioch Charter Academy	3325 Hacienda Way	Antioch, CA	94509-5407	925-755-7311	755-7313	K-8	Todd Heller
Antioch Charter Academy II	1201 W 10th St	Antioch, CA	94509-1406	925-755-1252	755-7527	K-8	Todd Heller
Apple Academy Charter S	4920 S Western Ave	Los Angeles, CA	90062-2326	323-348-4276		K-5	Laurie Inman
Aptitud Community Academy at Goss	2475 Van Winkle Ln	San Jose, CA	95116-3758	408-928-7650	928-7651	PK-8	Maria Manzanedo
Ararat Charter S	6555 Sylmar Ave	Van Nuys, CA	91401-6202	818-994-2904	994-8096	K-5	Eduardo Villela
ARISE HS	3301 E 12th St Ste 205	Oakland, CA	94601-2940	510-436-5487	436-5493	9-12	Elizabeth Soilis
Arroyo Paseo Charter HS	3773 El Cajon Blvd	San Diego, CA	92105	619-677-3017	677-3018	9-12	Brian Wickersham
Arroyo Vista Charter S	2491 School House Rd	Chula Vista, CA	91915-2534	619-656-9676	656-1858	K-8	Patricia Roth
Arts in Action Community Charter S	1241 S Soto St	Los Angeles, CA	90023-2666	323-266-4371	266-4371	K-5	Elysa Vargas
Arundel ES	200 Arundel Rd	San Carlos, CA	94070-1945	650-508-7311	508-7314	K-4	Ray Dawley
ASA Charter S	3512 N E St	San Bernardino, CA	92405-2110	909-475-3322	883-2708	K-12	Susan Lucey
Aspire Alexander Twilight College Prep S	2360 El Camino Ave	Sacramento, CA	95821-5611	916-979-1788	979-1796	K-5	Jamie Wallen
Aspire Alexander Twilight Secondary Acad	2360 El Camino Ave	Sacramento, CA	95821-5611	916-979-1788	979-1796	6-12	Robert Spencer
Aspire APEX Academy	444 N American St	Stockton, CA	95202-2129	209-466-3861	466-4290	K-5	Melissa Brookens
Aspire Berkley Maynard Academy	6200 San Pablo Ave	Oakland, CA	94608-2228	510-658-2900	658-1013	K-8	Jay Stack
Aspire Capitol Heights Academy	2520 33rd St	Sacramento, CA	95817-1943	916-739-8520	739-8529	K-8	Stephan Sanders
Aspire College Academy	8030 Atherton St	Oakland, CA	94605	510-562-8030	562-8013	K-5	Jessica Newburn
Aspire East Palo Alto Charter S	1286 Runnymede St	East Palo Alto, CA	94303-1332	650-614-9100	614-9183	K-5	Maricela Wilson
Aspire East Palo Alto Phoenix Academy	1039 Garden St	East Palo Alto, CA	94303	650-325-1460	325-1327	6-12	Elisha Jackson
Aspire Eres Academy	1936 Courtland Ave	Oakland, CA	94601	510-436-9760	436-9765	K-8	Courtney Walker
Aspire Firestone Academy	8929 Kauffman Ave	South Gate, CA	90280-3422	323-249-5740	568-2017	K-5	Dustin Katch
Aspire Gateway Academy	8929 Kauffman Ave	South Gate, CA	90280-3422	323-249-5750	249-5759	K-5	Semi Park
Aspire Golden State College Prep Academy	1009 66th Ave	Oakland, CA	94621	510-567-9631	632-1569	6-12	Greg Dutton
Aspire Inskeep Academy	123 W 59th St	Los Angeles, CA	90003-1103	323-235-8400	232-8030	K-6	Amy Coventry
Aspire Junior Collegiate Academy	6724 S Alameda St	Huntington Park, CA	90255-3617	323-583-5421		K-5	Rachel Garfield
Aspire Langston Hughes Academy	2050 West Ln	Stockton, CA	95205-3358	209-943-2389	943-2901	6-12	Anthony Solina
Aspire Lugo Academy	6100 Carmelita Ave	Huntington Park, CA	90255-4603	323-585-1153	585-1283	K-5	Sandra Kim
Aspire Monarch Academy	1445 101st Ave	Oakland, CA	94603-3207	510-568-3101	655-1222	K-5	Jennifer Green
Aspire Ollin University Prep Academy	2540 E 58th St	Huntington Park, CA	90255-2659	323-277-2901		6-12	Jennifer Garcia
Aspire Pacific College Prep Academy	2565 E 58th St	Huntington Park, CA	90255-2606	323-589-2800	589-2802	10-12	John Zapata
Aspire Port City Academy	2040 West Ln	Stockton, CA	95205-3358	209-943-2389	943-2901	K-5	Shelby Scheideman
Aspire Richmond CA College Prep Academy	3040 Hilltop Mall Rd	Richmond, CA	94806	510-646-1696		6-12	Javier Cabra
Aspire Richmond Technology Academy	3040 Hilltop Mall Rd	Richmond, CA	94806	510-480-0660		K-5	Arlena Ford
Aspire River Oaks Charter S	1801 Pyrenees Ave	Stockton, CA	95210-5207	209-956-8100	956-8102	K-5	Kris Jamison
Aspire Slauson Academy	123 W 59th St	Los Angeles, CA	90003-1103	323-235-8400	232-8030	K-6	Paul Delgado
Aspire Tate Academy	123 W 59th St	Los Angeles, CA	90003-1103	323-235-8400	583-7271	K-6	Ana Martinez

School	Address	City,State	Zip code	Telephone	Fax	Grade	Contact
Aspire Titan Academy	6720 S Alameda St	Huntington Park, CA	90255-3617	323-583-5421	588-7342	K-5	Leilani Lafaurie
Aspire Triumph Technology Academy	3200 62nd Ave	Oakland, CA	94605	510-638-9445	638-0744	K-5	Jessica Chacon
Aspire University Charter S	3313 Coffee Rd	Modesto, CA	95355-1534	209-544-8722	544-8864	K-5	Laura Thompson
Aspire Vanguard College Prep Acad	5255 1st St	Empire, CA	95319	209-269-9977	538-1620	6-12	Salvador Padilla M.A.
Aspire Vincent Shalvey Academy	10038 N Highway 99	Stockton, CA	95212-2127	209-931-5399	931-5185	K-5	Karla Fachner
Assurance Learning Academy	5701 S Western Ave	Los Angeles, CA	90062-2714	323-272-1225	945-2430	K-12	Jeffrey Martineau
Atkinson Academy Charter S	4718 Engle Rd	Carmichael, CA	95608	916-977-3790	977-3793	K-6	James Atkinson
Audeo Charter S	10170 Huennekens St	San Diego, CA	92121-2964	858-678-2050	552-9394	6-12	Tim Tuter
Audeo Charter S II	10170 Huennekens St	San Diego, CA	92121	858-678-2051	552-6660	K-12	Joy Garrity
Aveson Global Leadership Acadmey	1919 Pinecrest Dr	Altadena, CA	91001-2116	626-797-1440	797-1918	6-12	Kate Bean
Aveson School of Leaders	1919 Pinecrest Dr	Altadena, CA	91001-2116	626-797-1440	797-1918	K-5	Kate Bean
Bachrodt Charter Academy	102 Sonora Ave	San Jose, CA	95110-1457	408-535-6211	535-6588	K-5	Rigo Palacios
Ballington Academy for Arts and Science	799 E Rialto Ave	San Bernardino, CA	92408	619-228-2054	282-1300	K-5	Doreen Mulz
Ballington Academy for the Arts/Sciences	1525 W Main St	El Centro, CA	92243-2211	760-353-0140	353-0745	K-6	Doreen Mulz
Banks Charter S	PO Box 80	Pala, CA	92059-0080	760-742-3300	742-3102	K-5	Eric Kosch
Barona Indian Charter S	1095 Barona Rd	Lakeside, CA	92040-1516	619-443-0948	443-7280	K-8	Josh Stepner
Bay Area Technology S	8251 Fontaine St	Oakland, CA	94605-4109	510-382-9932	382-9934	6-12	Hayri Hatipoglu
Baypoint Preparatory Academy	26089 Girard St	Hemet, CA	92544-8701	951-658-1700	658-0723	K-12	Nancy Spencer
Bayshore Prep Charter S	1175 Linda Vista Dr	San Marcos, CA	92078-3811	760-471-0847	736-0275	K-12	Nancy Spencer
Bayside Community Day S	24501 Cactus Ave	Moreno Valley, CA	92553	951-571-7890	571-7891	6-12	Dr. Henry Herreras
Bay View Academy	222 Casa Verde Way	Monterey, CA	93940-3753	831-751-3142		K-5	Catherine Glick
Beacon Classical Academy	2400 Euclid Ave	National City, CA	91950	619-267-1294	267-1297	K-8	Alma Van Nice
Beckford Charter S for Enriched Studies	19130 Tulsa St	Northridge, CA	91326-2645	818-360-1924	832-9831	K-5	Shelly Brower
Bella Mente Montessori Academy	1737 W Vista Way	Vista, CA	92083-2112	760-621-8948	639-0611	K-8	Erin Feeley
Bellevue-Sante Fe Charter S	1401 San Luis Bay Dr	San Luis Obispo, CA	93405-8003	805-595-7169	595-9013	K-6	Brian Getz
Big Picture ES	735 N Glenn Ave	Fresno, CA	93728	559-497-8272	497-5621	K-6	Perry Jensen
Big Picture HS - Fresno	1207 S Trinity St	Fresno, CA	93706-2611	559-420-1234		7-12	Pasquale Catanzarite
Big Sur Charter S	304 Foam St	Monterey, CA	93920	831-667-0203	884-5454	K-12	Shawna Garritson
Binkley ES	4965 Canyon Dr	Santa Rosa, CA	95409-3204	707-539-6060	539-4862	PK-6	Kelly Lister
Birmingham Community HS	17000 Haynes St	Van Nuys, CA	91406-5420	818-758-5200	342-5877	9-12	Bill Parks
Bitney College Prep HS	135 Joerschke Dr	Grass Valley, CA	95945-5249	530-477-1235	272-1091	9-12	Russ Jones
Blue Oak Charter S	450 W East Ave	Chico, CA	95926-7238	530-879-7483	879-7490	K-8	Stephanie Nichols
Bowling Green Chacon Language & Science	6807 Franklin Blvd	Sacramento, CA	95823	916-433-7321	433-7388	PK-6	
Bowling Green McCoy Academy	4211 Turnbridge Dr	Sacramento, CA	95823-1929	916-433-5426	433-5429	K-6	Susan Gibson
Bowman Charter S	13777 Bowman Rd	Auburn, CA	95603-3147	530-885-1974	888-8175	K-8	Kelly Graham
Bridges Academy	1702 McLaughlin Ave	San Jose, CA	95122-2936	408-283-6400	283-6419	7-8	Alex Frontini
BRIDGES Charter S	1335 Calle Bouganvilla	Thousand Oaks, CA	91360-6604	805-492-3560		K-8	Jay Guidetti
Bright Star Secondary Academy	2636 S Mansfield Ave	Los Angeles, CA	90016-3512	424-789-8337		9-12	Corey Taylor
Brittan Acres ES	2000 Belle Ave	San Carlos, CA	94070-3798	650-508-7307	508-7310	PK-3	John Triska
Buckingham Charter Magnet HS	188 Bella Vista Rd Ste B	Vacaville, CA	95687-5413	707-453-7300	453-7303	9-12	Mike Boles
Bullis Charter S	102 W Portola Ave	Los Altos, CA	94022-1210	650-947-4939	947-4989	K-8	Wanny Hersey
Burton Pathways Charter Academy	1414 W Olive Ave	Porterville, CA	93257-3062	559-782-4748	782-4708	9-12	Jan Mekeel
Burton Technology Academy HS	10101 S Broadway	Los Angeles, CA	90003	323-920-6125	920-6950	9-12	Rogelio Sanchez M.Ed.
Butterfield Charter HS	600 W Grand Ave	Porterville, CA	93257-2029	559-782-7057	782-7090	9-12	Staci Phipps
Cain MS	150 Palm Ave	Auburn, CA	95603-3712	530-823-6106	823-0943	6-8	Cindy Giove
Calahan Community Charter S	18722 Knapp St	Northridge, CA	91324-3027	818-886-4612	886-0760	K-5	Michelle Wells
Caliber: Beta Academy	4301 Berk Ave	Richmond, CA	94804	510-685-9886		K-6	Ashlee Gutierrez
Caliber: ChangeMakers Academy	1357 Colusa St	Vallejo, CA	94590	707-563-9827		K-8	Rachael Weingarten
Cali Calmecac Language Academy	9491 Starr Rd	Windsor, CA	95492-9460	707-837-7747	837-7752	K-8	Jeanne Acuna
California Academy for Liberal Studies	7350 N Figueroa St	Los Angeles, CA	90041	213-239-0063	254-4099	6-12	Connie Rivas
California Collegiate Charter S	2009 W Martin Luther King B	Los Angeles, CA	90062	323-450-7290		6-10	Sue Marie Louise Brown
CA Connections Academy @ North Bay	20932 Big Canyon Rd	Middletown, CA	95461-7721	949-306-8498		K-12	Richard Savage
California Connections Academy @ Ripon	580 N Wilma Ave	Ripon, CA	95366	209-253-1208	253-0406	PK-12	Amy Hunt
California Heritage Youthbuild Academy	8544 Airport Rd	Redding, CA	96002	530-378-5254	378-5256	9-12	Cathy Taylor
CA Heritage Youthbuild Academy II	8544 Airport Rd	Redding, CA	96002	530-378-5254	378-5256	9-12	Cathy Clouse-Taylor
California Military Institute	755 N A St	Perris, CA	92570	951-443-2731	943-0473	5-12	Michael Rhodes
California Montessori Project-Amer River	6838 Kermit Ln	Fair Oaks, CA	95628-3048	916-864-0081	864-0084	K-8	RaDene Girola
California Montessori Project-Capitol	2635 Chestnut Hill Dr	Sacramento, CA	95826-2912	916-325-0910	325-0912	K-8	Bernie Evangelista
California Montessori Project-Carmichael	5325 Engle Rd Ste 810	Carmichael, CA	95608	916-971-2430	971-2435	K-8	Julie Miller
California Montessori Project-Elk Grove	8828 Elk Grove Blvd Ste 4	Elk Grove, CA	95624-1875	916-714-9699	714-9703	K-8	Kathleen Merz
California Montessori Project-Orangevale	6545 Beech Ave	Orangevale, CA	95662	916-673-9389	989-1584	K-6	Kim Aldridge
California Montessori Project-Shingl Spr	4645 Buckeye Rd	Shingle Springs, CA	95682-9505	530-672-3095	672-3097	K-8	Kim Zawilski
California Pacific Charter S	PO Box 8	Warner Springs, CA	92086-0008	855-225-7227		K-12	Lisa Newhall
California Prep Sutter 8-12	15898 Central St	Meridian, CA	95957-9517			8-12	Melanie Rodriguez
California Prep Sutter K-7	15898 Central St	Meridian, CA	95957-9517			K-7	Melanie Rodriguez
California STEAM	19191 W Excelsior Ave	Five Points, CA	93624	559-391-4425		K-8	Eli Johnson
California STEAM San Bernardino	83600 Trona Rd	Trona, CA	93562	310-527-1741		K-12	Eli Johnson
California STEAM Sonoma	170 Liberty School Rd	Petaluma, CA	94952	707-527-1741		K-12	Eli Johnson
California Virtual Academies	50 Moreland Rd	Simi Valley, CA	93065-1659	805-581-0202	581-0330	K-12	Katrina Abston
California Virtual Academy @ San Joaquin	2360 Shasta Way	Simi Valley, CA	93065	805-581-0202		K-12	Katrina Abston
Calvert Charter S for Enriched Studies	19850 Delano St	Woodland Hills, CA	91367-3898	818-347-2681	347-5301	K-5	Amanda Evans
Camarillo Academy of Progressive Educ	777 Aileen St	Camarillo, CA	93010	805-384-1415	385-1473	K-8	MaryEllen Lang
Camino Nuevo Academy #2	3400 W 3rd St	Los Angeles, CA	90020	213-736-5542	736-5664	K-8	Alejandra Mayo
Camino Nuevo Academy - Cisneros	1018 Mohawk St	Los Angeles, CA	90026-3131	213-353-5300	596-3878	K-8	Melissa Mendoza
Camino Nuevo Charter Academy	697 S Burlington Ave	Los Angeles, CA	90057-3743	213-736-5542	736-5664	PK-8	Mark Healy
Camino Nuevo Charter HS	1215 Miramar St	Los Angeles, CA	90026-6115	213-240-8700		9-12	Marisol Pineda-Conde
Camino Nuevo Charter HS 2	3500 W Temple St	Los Angeles, CA	90004-3620	213-736-5566	736-5066	9-12	Julie Jhun
Camino Nuevo Charter S Burlington Campus	697 S Burlington Ave	Los Angeles, CA	90057-3743	213-413-4245	413-8553	K-8	Mark Healy
Camino Nuevo ES - Jose Castellanos	1723 Cordova St	Los Angeles, CA	90007-1114	323-730-7160	737-5626	K-5	James Lee
Camino Science & Natural Rsrcs Charter S	3060 Snows Rd	Camino, CA	95709-9578	530-644-2204	644-5412	K-8	Boyd Holler
Camptonville Academy	321 16th St	Marysville, CA	95901-4223	530-742-2786	742-6067	K-12	Christopher Mahurin
Canyon ES	421 Entrada Dr	Santa Monica, CA	90402-1303	310-454-7510	454-7543	K-5	Nicole Sheard
Capistrano Connections Academy	33272 Valle Rd	San Juan Capo, CA	92675-4842	949-461-1667		K-12	Richard Savage
Capitol Collegiate Academy	2118 Meadowview Rd	Sacramento, CA	95832	916-476-5796		K-8	Cristin Fiorelli
Capitol Heights Academy	2520 33rd St	Sacramento, CA	95817	916-739-8520	739-8529	K-5	Dr. Stephan Sanders
Carpenter Community Charter S	3909 Carpenter Ave	Studio City, CA	91604-3732	818-761-4363	508-6724	K-5	Joseph Martinez
Carver S of Arts & Sciences	10101 Systems Pkwy	Sacramento, CA	95827-3007	916-228-5751	228-5760	9-12	Allegra Alessandri
Casa Ramona Academy for Technology	1524 W 7th St	San Bernardino, CA	92411-2508	909-888-3132		K-12	Esther Ramos Estrada
Castlemont Primary Academy	8601 MacArthur Blvd Ste 300	Oakland, CA	94605	510-775-0900	277-9089	K-5	Detra Denully
Castle Rock Charter S	1260 Glenn St	Crescent City, CA	95531-2113	707-464-0390	464-9606	K-12	Jeff Slayton
CCLB Gateway Cities Charter S	3635 Atlantic Ave	Long Beach, CA	90807	562-216-1790	216-1792	9-12	Richard Stroup
Cecil Avenue Math & Science Academy	1430 Cecil Ave	Delano, CA	93215-1444	661-721-5030	721-5097	6-8	Darrell Hennessee
Ceiba College Preparatory Academy	260 W Riverside Dr	Watsonville, CA	95076	831-345-6056	464-3213	6-12	Annie Millar
Celerity Achernar Charter S	310 E El Segundo Blvd	Compton, CA	90222	310-764-1234	868-2517	K-5	Jason Rios
Celerity Cardinal Charter S	7330 Bakman Ave	Sun Valley, CA	91352	323-223-9184	688-3835	K-5	Wilburd Estrada
Celerity Dyad Charter S	4501 Wadsworth Ave	Los Angeles, CA	90011-3637	323-231-1202	231-1255	K-8	Patrick Stickley
Celerity Nascent Charter S	3417 W Jefferson Blvd	Los Angeles, CA	90018-3235	323-732-6613	733-2977	K-8	Sergio Alvarez Ruiz
Celerity Octavia Charter S	3010 Estara Ave	Los Angeles, CA	90065	310-904-2012	843-9912	K-8	Adriana Mungia
Celerity Palmati Charter S	6501 Laurel Canyon Blvd	North Hollywood, CA	91606	818-753-2712	301-2278	K-6	Titchamroeun Son
Celerity Troika Charter S	1495 Colorado Blvd	Los Angeles, CA	90041-2366	323-344-0160	344-0165	K-8	Karina Solis
Centennial College Preparatory Academy	2079 Saturn Ave	Huntington Park, CA	90255-3635	323-826-9616	588-7342	6-7	Jesicah Rolapp
Center for Advanced Learning	4016 S Central Ave	Los Angeles, CA	90011-2708	323-232-0245	223-3675	K-5	Brooke Jackson
Center for Advanced Research Technology	2555 Clovis Ave	Clovis, CA	93612-3901	559-248-7400	248-7423	11-12	Rick Watson
Central California Connections Academy	4020 S Demaree St Ste B	Visalia, CA	93277-9476	559-713-1324	713-1330	K-12	Richard Savage
Central City Value S	221 N Westmoreland Ave	Los Angeles, CA	90004-4815	213-471-4686	385-5127	9-12	Joaquin Arroyo
Century Academy for Excellence	2400 W 85th St	Inglewood, CA	90305-1816	323-752-8834	752-8874	6-8	Giselle Edman
Century Community Charter S	901 Maple St	Inglewood, CA	90301-3823	310-412-2286	412-4085	6-8	Dana Means
Cesar Chavez Language Academy	2750 W Steele Ln	Santa Rosa, CA	95403	707-528-5011	528-5012	K-8	Rebekah Rocha
Charter Alternatives Academy	28050 Road 148	Visalia, CA	93292-9297	559-730-7491	730-7490	7-12	Carlos Peralta
Charter Alternative S	6520 Oak Dell Rd	El Dorado, CA	95623-4322	530-622-6984	621-2543	K-8	David Publicover
Charter Community S and Home Study Acad	6767 Green Valley Rd	Placerville, CA	95667-8984	530-295-2259	642-0492	7-12	David Publicover
Charter HS of Arts Multimedia/Performing	6842 Van Nuys Blvd	Van Nuys, CA	91405-4650	818-994-7614	994-0099	9-12	Christopher Bright Ph.D.
Charter Home School Academy	211 W Tulare Ave	Visalia, CA	93277-4813	559-730-7916	735-8060	K-8	Steve Rodriguez
Charter Montessori Blue Oak Campus	2391 Merrychase Dr	Cameron Park, CA	95682-9094	530-676-0164	676-0758	K-5	Paul Stewart
Charter S of Morgan Hill	9530 Monterey Rd	Morgan Hill, CA	95037-9356	408-463-0618	463-0267	K-8	Paige Cisewski
Charter S of San Diego	10170 Huennekens St	San Diego, CA	92121-2964	858-678-2020	552-6660	7-12	Ginese Quann
Chatsworth Charter HS	10027 Lurline Ave	Chatsworth, CA	91311-3153	818-678-3400	709-6952	9-12	Dr. Timothy Guy Ed.D.
Chawanakee Academy	PO Box 210	O Neals, CA	93645-0210	559-868-4200	868-4222	K-12	Gary Talley
Chicago Park Community Charter S	15725 Mount Olive Rd	Grass Valley, CA	95945-7906	530-346-2153	346-8559	K-8	Dan Zeisler
Chico Country Day S	102 W 11th St	Chico, CA	95928-6006	530-895-2650	895-9159	K-8	Suzanne Michelony
Children of Promise Preparatory Academy	3130 W 111th Pl	Inglewood, CA	90303-2315	310-677-3014	677-1599	K-3	Carleton Lincoln
Children's Community Charter S	6830 Pentz Rd	Paradise, CA	95969-2902	530-877-2227	872-1396	K-8	Emily Mullins
CHIME Institute's Schwarzenegger Cmnty S	19722 Collier St	Woodland Hills, CA	91364-3618	818-346-5100	346-5120	K-8	Jennifer Hill
Chrysalis Charter S	PO Box 709	Palo Cedro, CA	96073-0709	530-547-9726	547-9734	K-8	Irene Salter
Chula Vista Learning Community Charter S	590 K St	Chula Vista, CA	91911-1118	619-426-2885	426-3048	PK-12	Dr. Jorge Ramirez
Cielo Vista Charter S	650 S Paseo Dorotea	Palm Springs, CA	92264-1406	760-416-8250	416-8253	K-6	Devlin Clinton
Cinnabar Charter ES	286 Skillman Ln	Petaluma, CA	94952-1226	707-765-4345	765-4349	PK-8	Tracie Kern

School	Address	City,State	Zip code	Telephone	Fax	Grade	Contact
Circle of Independent Learning	4700 Calaveras Ave	Fremont, CA	94538-1124	510-797-0100	797-0118	K-12	Stephanie Walton
Citizens of the World Charter S	1516 Carlton Way	Los Angeles, CA	90028	323-464-4063	372-3847	PK-8	Dr. Ramona Patrick
Citizens of the World Charter S	11561 Gateway Blvd	Los Angeles, CA	90064	424-248-0544		K-5	Alison Kerr
Citizens of the World Charter S	1316 N Bronson Ave	Hollywood, CA	90028	323-464-4292	464-8292	K-5	Marissa Berman
City Arts & Technology HS	325 La Grande Ave	San Francisco, CA	94112-2866	415-841-2200	695-5326	9-12	Daniel Allen
City Heights Preparatory Academy	3770 Altadena Ave	San Diego, CA	92105-3007	619-795-3137		6-12	Dr. Marnie Nair
City HS	11625 W Pico Blvd	Los Angeles, CA	90064-2908	310-273-2489	273-2499	9-12	Sheri Werner
City Honors Charter HS	120 W Regent St	Inglewood, CA	90301-1225	310-680-4880	680-5144	9-12	Kiwiana Cain
City Language Immersion Charter S	4041 Hilcrest Dr	Los Angeles, CA	90008	323-294-4937	294-4938	K-5	Raul Alarcon
City S	11625 W Pico Blvd	Los Angeles, CA	90064	310-273-2489	273-2499	6-8	Sheri Werner
Civicorps Academy	101 Myrtle St	Oakland, CA	94607-2543	510-992-7800	992-7950	9-12	Tessa Nicholas
Classical Academy	2950 Bear Valley Pkwy S	Escondido, CA	92025-7446	760-546-0101	739-8289	K-8	Cameron Curry
Classical Academy HS	207 E Pennsylvania Ave	Escondido, CA	92025-2808	760-480-9845	739-8289	9-12	Dana Moen
Clayton Valley Charter HS	1101 Alberta Way	Concord, CA	94521-3747	925-682-7474	825-7859	9-12	Jeff Eben
Clear Passage Educational Center	1471 Martin Luther King Jr	Long Beach, CA	90813-2162	888-502-1116		9-12	Vivianna Trujillo
Clemente Charter S	5701 Fishburn Ave	Maywood, CA	90270-2819	323-984-9008		PK-5	Norma Moreno
Cleveland HS	8140 Vanalden Ave	Reseda, CA	91335-1199	818-885-2300	727-0964	9-12	Cindy Duong
Clovis Online S / Enterprise	1655 David E Cook Way	Clovis, CA	93611-0581	559-327-4400	327-4490	K-12	Rees Warne
Coastal Academy Charter	4096 Calle Platino	Oceanside, CA	92056-5805	760-631-4020	631-4027	K-8	Marcy Cashin
Coastal Grove Charter S	PO Box 510	Arcata, CA	95518-0510	707-825-8804	825-1761	K-8	Bettina Eipper
Cole Academy	333 E Walnut St	Santa Ana, CA	92701-5928	714-836-9023	836-9041	K-5	Jon Norton
Coleman Tech HS	3540 Aero Ct	San Diego, CA	92123-1711	858-874-4338	874-5645	9-12	Dr. Neil McCurdy
Colfax Charter ES	11724 Addison St	North Hollywood, CA	91607-3202	818-761-5115	985-6017	K-5	Robyn Friedman
College and Career Preparatory Academy	1669 E Wilshire Ave Ste 603	Santa Ana, CA	92705-4508	714-547-9986		9-12	Byron Fairchild
College Bridge Academy	2824 S Main St	Los Angeles, CA	90007-3334	323-249-7845	249-1170	9-12	Noel Trout
College Preparatory MS	5150 Jackson Dr	La Mesa, CA	91942-9001	619-303-2782	303-3759	5-8	Christina Callaway
College Prep HS	26400 Dartmouth St	Hemet, CA	92544-6302	951-925-5155		12-12	Frank Green
College Ready Middle Academy #4	9719 S Main St	Los Angeles, CA	90003-4135	323-451-3009	455-1655	6-8	Darron Evans
College Ready Middle Academy #5	211 S Avenue 20	Los Angeles, CA	90031-2508	323-352-8034	352-8980	6-8	Laura Galvan
Collegiate Charter HS	312 N Record Ave	Los Angeles, CA	90063-1824	213-304-7077		9-12	Vanessa Jackson
Collins School at Cherry Valley	1001 Cherry St	Petaluma, CA	94952-2065	707-778-4740	778-4839	K-8	Fran Hansell
Come Back Butte Charter S	1859 Bird St	Oroville, CA	95965	530-532-5757		9-12	Karen Stiles
Come Back Kids Charter S	3939 13th St	Riverside, CA	92501-3505	951-826-6454		9-12	Janice Delagrammatikas
Community Charter Early College HS	11500 Eldridge Ave	Lake View Ter, CA	91342-6522	818-485-0951	485-0952	9-12	Dr. Akilah Lyons-Moore
Community Charter MS	11500 Eldridge Ave	Lake View Ter, CA	91342-6522	818-485-0933	485-0940	6-8	Akilah Lyons-Moore
Community Collaborative Charter S	32248 Crown Valley Rd	Acton, CA	93510-2620	760-494-9646	897-7558	K-12	Meghan Freeman
Community Collaborative Charter S	5715 Skvarla Ave	McClellan, CA	95652	916-286-5161	643-2031	K-12	Jon Campbell
Community Magnet ES	11301 Bellagio Rd	Los Angeles, CA	90049-1705	310-476-2281	472-6391	K-5	Carla Cretaro
Community Outreach Academy	5640 Dudley Blvd	McClellan, CA	95652-1034	916-286-1950	640-0227	K-6	Larissa Gonchar
Community Outreach Academy	3800 Bolivar Ave	North Highlands, CA	95660	916-286-1908	286-1992	7-8	Yuliya Hall
Community Preparatory Academy	7511 Raymond Ave	Los Angeles, CA	90044-2430	323-751-1460	704-3045	K-5	Janis Bucknor
Community Roots Academy	29292 Crown Valley Pkwy	Laguna Niguel, CA	92677	949-831-4272		K-8	Jeremy Cavallaro
Community S for Creative Education	2111 International Blvd	Oakland, CA	94606	510-517-0331		PK-8	Dr. Clifford Thompson
Competitive Edge Charter Academy	34450 Stonewood Dr	Yucaipa, CA	92399-6852	909-790-3207	790-8364	K-8	Joe Mead
Connect Community Charter S	635 Oakside Ave	Redwood City, CA	94063-3863	650-562-7190	562-7191	K-8	Alicia Yamashita
Connecting Waters Charter S	12420 Bentley St	Waterford, CA	95386-9158	209-874-9463	874-9531	K-12	Sherri Nelson
Connections VPA Academy	17555 Tuolumne Rd	Tuolumne, CA	95379-9701	209-928-4228	928-1422	7-12	Diana Harford
Conservatory of Vocal/Instrumental Arts	3800 Mountain Blvd	Oakland, CA	94619-1630	510-285-7511		K-8	Gregg Hood
Conservatory Vocal Instrumental Arts HS	12500 Campus Dr	Oakland, CA	94619	510-328-1119		9-12	Valerie Abad
Contra Costa S of Performing Arts	150 N Wiget Ln Ste 203	Walnut Creek, CA	94598	925-690-8600		6-12	Neil McChesney
CORE Butte Charter S	260 Cohasset Rd Ste 120	Chico, CA	95926-2282	530-894-3952	566-9819	K-12	Mary Cox
CORE Placer Charter S	1033 S Auburn St	Colfax, CA	95713-9703	530-346-8340	346-2446	K-12	Alison Garcia
Cornerstone Academy Preparatory	1598 Lucretia Ave	San Jose, CA	95122	408-361-3876		K-6	Valerie Douglass
Corona Charter S	9400 Remick Ave	Pacoima, CA	91331-4223	818-834-5805	834-8075	6-8	Larry Simonsen
Cottonwood Creek Charter S	PO Box 1648	Cottonwood, CA	96022	530-347-7200	347-9375	K-8	Mark Boyle
County Collaborative Charter S	3291 Buckman Springs Rd	Pine Valley, CA	91962-4003	858-472-5222		K-12	Meghan Freeman
Cox Academy	9860 Sunnyside St	Oakland, CA	94603-2750	510-904-6300	904-6730	K-5	Kevin King
Creative Arts Charter S	1601 Turk St	San Francisco, CA	94115-4527	415-749-3509	749-3437	K-8	Jenny Kipp
Creative Connections Arts Academy	7201 Arutas Dr	North Highlands, CA	95660-2809	916-566-1870	566-1871	K-6	Edward Delgado
Creative Connections Arts Academy	6444 Walerga Rd	North Highlands, CA	95660-3945	916-566-3470	566-3505	7-12	Edward Delgado
Credo HS	1290 Southwest Blvd	Rohnert Park, CA	94928-3437	707-664-0600		9-12	Chip Romer
Creekside Charter S	PO Box 2891	Olympic Valley, CA	96146-2891	530-581-1036	581-2012	K-8	Jeff Kraunz
Crenshaw Arts-Technology Charter HS	4120 11th Ave	Los Angeles, CA	90008-3712	323-778-7700	778-7712	9-12	Patricia Smith
Crescent Valley Public Charter S	116 E Main St	Visalia, CA	93291	559-970-5894	243-9102	K-12	Shellie Escobedo
Crescent View Charter West HS	1901 E Shields Ave	Fresno, CA	93726-5318	559-470-8822	225-1205	9-12	Abby Sipes
Crescent View South Charter S	1901 E Shields Ave	Fresno, CA	93726-5318	559-222-8439	222-8430	K-12	Rafael Aguilar
Crossroads Charter S	418 W 8th St	Hanford, CA	93230-4536	559-583-5060	585-7298	K-12	Laurie Blue
Crown Preparatory Academy	2055 W 24th St	Los Angeles, CA	90018-1925	213-448-9747	410-2271	5-8	Matthew DeFord
Cruz Leadership Academy	14265 Story Rd	San Jose, CA	95127-3823	408-729-2281		9-12	Yesenia Marquez
Cypress Charter HS	2039 Merrill St	Santa Cruz, CA	95062-4176	831-477-0302	477-7659	9-12	Daniel Stonebloom
Dailey Charter ES	3135 N Harrison Ave	Fresno, CA	93704-5240	559-248-7060	227-5530	K-5	Gia Shirley
Dantzler Preparatory Academy	5940 S Budlong Ave	Los Angeles, CA	90044	323-290-6968	459-7813	K-5	Akeysha Allen-Goods
Darby Avenue Charter S	10818 Darby Ave	Northridge, CA	91326-3112	818-360-1824	832-9761	K-5	Lucy Lee
Darnall Charter S	6020 Hughes St	San Diego, CA	92115-6520	619-582-1822	287-4732	K-8	Consuelo Manriquez
DaVinci Academy JSHS	1400 E 8th St	Davis, CA	95616	530-757-7154	759-2178	7-12	Tyler Millsap
DaVinci Communications S	12495 Isis Ave	Hawthorne, CA	90250-4147	310-725-5800	643-7659	9-12	Nathan Barrymore
DaVinci Design S	12501 Isis Ave	Hawthorne, CA	90250-4149	310-725-5800	643-7659	9-12	Kate Parsons
DaVinci Health Sciences Charter S	PO Box 8830	Chula Vista, CA	91912-8830	619-420-0066	420-0677	K-8	Josh Stepner
DaVinci Innovation Academy	13500 Aviation Blvd	Hawthorne, CA	90250-6462	310-725-5800	643-7659	K-8	Michelle Rainey
DaVinci Science S	13500 Aviation Blvd	Hawthorne, CA	90250-6462	310-725-5800	643-3013	K-12	Steve Wallis
Dearborn Elementary Charter Academy	9240 Wish Ave	Northridge, CA	91325-2533	818-349-4381	886-2149	K-5	Kimberly Estrada
Dehesa Charter S	1441 Montiel Rd Ste 143	Escondido, CA	92026-2242	760-743-7880	743-7919	K-12	Terri Novacek
De La Hoya Animo Charter HS	1114 S Lorena St	Los Angeles, CA	90023-2915	323-780-1259	780-4862	9-12	Cynthia Ybarra
Delta Bridges Charter S	703 E Swain Rd	Stockton, CA	95207-3146	209-477-4001		K-5	Jeff Tilton
Delta Charter ES	PO Box 127	Clarksburg, CA	95612-0127	916-744-1200	744-1246	K-6	Vanessa Belair
Delta Charter S	343 Soquel Ave	Santa Cruz, CA	95062-2355	831-477-5213	479-6173	9-12	Angela Meeker
Delta Charter S	31400 S Koster Rd	Tracy, CA	95304-8824	209-830-6363	830-9707	K-12	George Vierra
Delta Home Charter S	1301 Durham Ferry Rd	Tracy, CA	95304	209-937-4227	329-4227	K-12	Kellyann Reis
Delta Keys Charter S	722 W March Ln	Stockton, CA	95207	209-830-6363		K-12	Dr. Jeff Tilton
Delta Launch Charter S	722 W March Ln	Stockton, CA	95207-6216	209-830-6363		K-12	Jeff Tilton
Del Vista Math & Science Academy	710 Quincy St	Delano, CA	93215-3044	661-721-5040	721-5087	PK-5	Ana Ruiz
Denair Charter Academy	3460 Lester Rd	Denair, CA	95316-9502	209-634-0917	669-9282	K-12	Brian LaFountain
Denair Elementary Charter Academy	3460 Lester Rd	Denair, CA	95316-9502	209-632-8887		K-5	Lucy Zamora
Desert Sands Charter HS	44130 20th St W	Lancaster, CA	93534-4045	661-942-3357	944-4857	9-12	Jessica Sherlock
Design Tech HS	1800 Rollins Rd	Burlingame, CA	94010-2205	650-394-5157		9-12	Ken Montgomery
Diamond Technology Institute	112 Diamond Dr	Watsonville, CA	95076-3184	831-728-6225	728-6233	11-12	Marci Keller
Diego Hills Charter S	4585 College Ave	San Diego, CA	92115	619-286-0312	286-0791	8-12	Lindsay Reese
Diego Valley Charter S	511 N 2nd St	El Cajon, CA	92021	619-286-0312	286-0791	K-12	Jonelle Godfrey
Discovery Charter Preparatory S	13570 Eldridge Ave	Sylmar, CA	91342	818-897-1187	897-1295	9-12	Karen Smith
Discovery Charter S	1100 Camino Biscay	Chula Vista, CA	91910-7737	619-656-0797	656-3899	K-8	Sandy Du-Song
Discovery Charter S	51 E Beverly Pl	Tracy, CA	95376-3191	209-831-5240	831-5243	5-8	Virginia Stewart
Discovery Charter S	4021 Teale Ave	San Jose, CA	95117-3433	408-243-9800	243-9812	K-8	Debby Perry
Discovery Charter S II	762 Sunset Glen Dr	San Jose, CA	95123	408-300-3158	972-9114	PK-8	Debby Perry
Dixie Canyon Community Charter S	4220 Dixie Canyon Ave	Sherman Oaks, CA	91423-3904	818-784-6283	788-3340	K-5	Gloria Yniguez
Dixon Montessori Charter S	355 N Almond St	Dixon, CA	95620-2702	707-678-8953	676-5215	K-8	Joanne Green
Downtown Charter Academy	2000 Dennison St	Oakland, CA	94606	510-535-1580	535-1597	6-8	Angela Ortega
Downtown College Preparatory	1402 Monterey Hwy	San Jose, CA	95110	408-271-1730	271-1734	9-12	Andria Plasencia
Downtown College Preparatory MS	1155 E Julian St	San Jose, CA	95116-1005	408-271-8120	271-8855	6-8	Pedro Cuevas
Downtown College Prep MS	2800 Ocala Ave	San Jose, CA	95148-1114	408-942-7000	942-7007	6-8	Brandon Jones
Downtown College Prep S	2888 Ocala Ave	San Jose, CA	95148	408-942-7000	742-9000	6-8	Terri Furton
Downtown Value S	950 W Washington Blvd	Los Angeles, CA	90015-3312	213-748-8062	748-8868	K-8	Ana Chavez
Dunham Charter S	4111 Roblar Rd	Petaluma, CA	94952	707-795-5050	795-5166	PK-6	
Dunlap Leadership Academy	39500 Dunlap Rd	Dunlap, CA	93621	559-305-7320	338-2026	9-12	Ron Pack
e3 Civic HS	395 11th Ave 6th Floor	San Diego, CA	92101	619-241-4306		9-12	Helen Griffith
Eagle Peak Montessori S	800 Hutchinson Rd	Walnut Creek, CA	94598-4505	925-946-0994	946-9409	1-8	Michelle Hammons
Early College Acad for Leaders/Scholars	2050 N San Fernando Rd	Los Angeles, CA	90065-1267	323-276-5525	276-5534	9-12	Chanel Young-Smith
East Bay Innovation Academy	3400 Malcolm Ave	Oakland, CA	94605-5353	510-577-9557		6-12	Devin Krugman
East Oakland Leadership Academy	2614 Seminary Ave	Oakland, CA	94605-1570	510-562-5238	562-5239	K-8	Dr. Laura Armstrong
East Palo Alto Academy	1050 Myrtle St	East Palo Alto, CA	94303	650-839-8900	839-8902	9-12	Amika Guillaume
eCademy Charter	1100 Cahill Ave	Turlock, CA	95380	209-669-3410	669-0180	K-12	Gabe Ontiveros
Edison-Bethune Charter Academy	1616 S Fruit Ave	Fresno, CA	93706-2819	559-457-2530	498-0711	PK-6	Rodolfo Garcia
Edison Charter Academy	3531 22nd St	San Francisco, CA	94114-3405	415-970-3330	285-0527	K-8	Adrienne Morrell
Eel River Charter S	PO Box 218	Covelo, CA	95428-0218	707-983-6946	983-6197	K-6	Betty Tuttle
Einstein Academy	3035 Ash St	San Diego, CA	92102-1718	619-795-1190	795-1180	K-5	Greta Bouterse
Einstein Academy Letters Arts Science	11311 Frascati St	Agua Dulce, CA	91390	661-268-1660	268-0209	K-6	Stefanie Council
Einstein Academy MS	458 26th St	San Diego, CA	92102-3026	619-795-1190	795-1180	6-8	David Sciarretta
Einstein Acad for Letters Art & Sciences	8844 Burton Way	Beverly Hills, CA	90211-1724	310-409-2940		K-12	Michael Fishler

School	Address	City,State	Zip code	Telephone	Fax	Grade	Contact
Einstein Acad for Letters Art & Sciences	25443 Orchard Village Rd	Valencia, CA	91355-2935	661-666-3677		K-6	Scott Cusack
Einstein Acad Letters Arts Sci	28141 Kelly Johnson Pkwy	Santa Clarita, CA	91355-5003	661-702-0755	775-0321	7-12	Edward Gika
EJE Academy Charter ES	851 S Johnson Ave	El Cajon, CA	92020-5811	619-401-4150	401-4151	K-8	Delia Pacheco
El Camino Real Charter HS	5440 Valley Circle Blvd	Woodland Hills, CA	91367-5949	818-595-7500	710-9023	9-12	David Fehte
Elevate ES	2285 Murray Ridge Rd	San Diego, CA	92123-3934	858-751-4774	839-3700	K-5	Robert Elliott
Elk Grove Charter S	10065 Atkins Dr	Elk Grove, CA	95757-4309	916-714-1653	714-1721	K-12	Marc Levine
El Oro Way Charter S	12230 El Oro Way	Granada Hills, CA	91344-1609	818-360-2288	360-3264	K-5	SooJoon Choi
El Rancho Charter S	181 S Del Giorgio Rd	Anaheim, CA	92808-1307	714-997-6238	281-8791	7-8	Michele Walker
El Sol Santa Ana Science & Arts Academy	1010 N Broadway	Santa Ana, CA	92701-3408	714-543-0023	543-0026	K-8	Monique Daviss
Emelita Academy Charter S	17931 Hatteras St	Encino, CA	91316-1037	818-342-6353	774-9352	K-5	Elizabeth Mayorga
Emerson MS	1650 Selby Ave	Los Angeles, CA	90024-5716	310-234-3100	474-6517	6-8	Dimone Watson
Emerson Parkside Academy	2625 Josie Ave	Long Beach, CA	90815-1511	562-420-2631	420-7642	K-5	Adilis Vitetta
Empire Springs Charter S	15350 Riverview Rd	Helendale, CA	92342	951-242-8800	252-8801	K-12	Tanya Rogers
Empower Charter S	2230 E Jewett St	San Diego, CA	92111-6013	858-292-1304	292-1358	K-6	Demetria Brown
Enadia ES	22944 Enadia Way	West Hills, CA	91307-2206	818-595-3900	716-7738	K-5	Heather Jeanne
Encino Charter ES	16941 Addison St	Encino, CA	91316-3433	818-784-1762	995-7110	K-5	Marcia Koff
Encore HS for Performing & Visual Arts	16955 Lemon St	Hesperia, CA	92345-5139	760-956-2632	956-7052	7-12	Denise Griffin
Encore HS for the Arts - Riverside	3800 Main St	Riverside, CA	92501-3624	951-824-1358		7-12	Denise Griffin
Endeavor College Prep Charter S	126 Bloom St	Los Angeles, CA	90012-1902	323-947-7311	843-9502	K-8	Edward Morris
Environmental Charter HS	16315 Grevillea Ave	Lawndale, CA	90260-2858	310-214-3400	214-3410	9-12	Alison Diaz
Environmental Charter MS	3600 W Imperial Hwy	Inglewood, CA	90303-2714	310-793-0157	680-9843	6-8	Beth Bernstein-Yamashiro
Environmental Charter MS	812 W 165th Pl	Gardena, CA	90247-5105	310-425-1605	217-1096	6-8	Robert Gloria
Environmental Science & Technology HS	2930 Fletcher Dr	Los Angeles, CA	90065-1407	323-739-0560	739-0565	9-12	Andres Versage
Envision Academy for Arts & Technology	1515 Webster St	Oakland, CA	94612-3355	510-596-8901	596-8905	9-12	Laura Robell
Epic Charter S	100 S Anaheim Blvd	Anaheim, CA	92805	657-220-1000	749-4540	K-12	Paul MacGregor
Epic Charter S	1112 29th Ave	Oakland, CA	94601-2212	510-689-2035	904-6751	6-8	Michael Hatcher
EPIC de Cesar Chavez	410 W J St	Tehachapi, CA	93561-1411	661-822-4381	822-4703	9-12	David Villarino
EPIC S	2945 Ramco St	West Sacramento, CA	95691	916-286-1960		K-8	Summer Sorosinski
Epiphany Prep Charter S	725 N Escondido Blvd	Escondido, CA	92025	760-440-8199		K-4	David Rivera
Epiphany Prep Charter S	6134 Benson Ave	San Diego, CA	92114-4204	619-677-2180		K-8	David Rivera Ed.D.
Equitas Academy 3	2723 W 8th St	Los Angeles, CA	90005	213-201-0440		K-K	Malka Borrego
Equitas Academy Charter S	2723 W 8th St	Los Angeles, CA	90005	213-201-0440	652-4444	5-8	Malka Borrego
Equitas Academy Charter S	1700 W Pico Blvd	Los Angeles, CA	90015-2412	213-201-0440		K-5	Kelli Kilty
Escondido Charter HS	1868 E Valley Pkwy	Escondido, CA	92027-2525	760-737-3154	738-8996	9-12	Denny Snyder
Escuela Popular Accelerated Family Lrng	467 N White Rd	San Jose, CA	95127-1441	408-275-7190	275-7192	K-12	Patricia Reguerin
Escuela Popular HS Academy	149 N White Rd	San Jose, CA	95127-1936	408-275-7191	259-1595	9-12	Gricelda Gonzalez
Everest Public HS	455 5th Ave	Redwood City, CA	94063-3727	650-366-1050	366-1892	9-12	Christopher Lewine
Everest Value S	668 S Catalina St	Los Angeles, CA	90005-1708	213-487-7736		K-8	Christopher Medinger
Evergreen Institute of Excellence	19500 Learning Way	Cottonwood, CA	96022	530-347-3411	347-7954	PK-12	Leila Dumore
Excel Charter Academy	1855 N Main St	Los Angeles, CA	90031-3227	323-222-5010	222-5148	6-8	Dr. Gloria Gasca
Excel Prep Charter S	25560 Alessandro Blvd	Moreno Valley, CA	92553-2921	909-864-6000	864-6100	K-8	Alex Lucero
Excel Prep Charter S - IE	25560 Alessandro Blvd	Moreno Valley, CA	92553-2921	800-940-3918		K-8	Jacquet Dumas
Excelsior Education Center Charter S	18422 Bear Valley Rd # 11	Victorville, CA	92395-5850	760-245-4262	245-4009	7-12	William Flynn
Executive Preparatory Academy of Finance	2814 Manhattan Beach Blvd	Gardena, CA	90249	310-467-4175		9-12	Monique Woodley
Extera Public School	2226 E 3rd St	Los Angeles, CA	90033-3906	323-780-8300	780-8301	K-6	Cristina Gorocica Ed.D.
Extera Public S # 2	1015 S Lorena St	Los Angeles, CA	90023-2222	323-263-3600	263-3633	K-5	Monica Salas
Fairmont Charter ES	1355 Marshall Rd	Vacaville, CA	95687-5519	707-453-6240	447-0759	K-6	Deanna Brownlee
Family First Charter S	4953 Marine Ave	Lawndale, CA	90260-1250	310-263-3204		9-12	Paul Guzman
Family Partnership Home Study Charter S	625 S McClelland	Santa Maria, CA	93454	805-686-5339	686-4658	K-12	Miguel Gonzales
Fammatre Charter ES	2800 New Jersey Ave	San Jose, CA	95124-1556	408-377-5480	377-8751	K-5	Lisa MacFarland
Farnham Charter S	15711 Woodard Rd	San Jose, CA	95124-2697	408-377-3321	377-7237	K-5	Matt Hill
Feaster Charter S	670 Flower St	Chula Vista, CA	91910-1327	619-422-8397	422-4780	K-8	Francisco Velasco
Fenton Avenue Charter S	11828 Gain St	Sylmar, CA	91342-7132	818-896-7482	890-9986	2-5	Stacy Hutter
Fenton Leadership Academy	8926 Sunland Blvd	Sun Valley, CA	91352	818-962-3636		K-2	Wendy Kaufman
Fenton Primary Center	11351 Dronfield Ave	Pacoima, CA	91331-1404	818-896-7482	890-9986	K-1	Richard Parra
Fenton STEM Academy	8926 Sunland Blvd	Sun Valley, CA	91352	818-962-3636		3-5	Jennifer Miller
Finch S	PO Box 428	Orland, CA	95963-0428	530-865-1683	865-1688	K-12	Lisa Morgan
Folsom Cordova Community Charter S	4420 Monhegan Way	Mather, CA	95655	916-294-9190	985-3665	K-8	Jim Cagney
Foothill Leadership Academy	19401 Susan Way	Sonora, CA	95370-9266	209-606-2213		K-8	Ian McVey
Forest Charter S	470 Searls Ave	Nevada City, CA	95959-3030	530-265-4823	265-5037	K-12	Peter Sagebiel
Forest Ranch Charter S	15815 Cedar Creek Rd	Forest Ranch, CA	95942	530-891-3154	891-3155	K-6	Christia Marasco
Forestville Academy	6321 Hwy 116	Forestville, CA	95436-9606	707-887-2279	887-2185	2-8	Phyllis Parisi
Fortune S	6829 Stockton Blvd Ste 380	Sacramento, CA	95823-2396	916-287-4470	287-4477	K-8	Odisa Nyong
Francophone Charter S of Oakland	9736 Lawlor St	Oakland, CA	94605-4735	510-394-4110		K-8	Ben Daoudi
Fremont Charter S	1120 W 22nd St	Merced, CA	95340-3540	209-385-6627	385-6301	K-6	Dawn Walker
Freshwater Charter MS	75 Greenwood Heights Dr	Eureka, CA	95503-9441	707-442-2969	442-9527	7-8	Si Talty
Frontier ES	1854 Mustang Dr	Hanford, CA	93230-9811	559-585-2430	585-2440	K-5	John Raven
Fuenta Nueva Charter S	1730 Janes Rd	Arcata, CA	95521	707-822-3348	822-5862	K-5	Beth Wylie
Fusion Charter S	2217 Geer Rd	Turlock, CA	95382-2407	209-667-0327		7-12	Siobhan Hanna
Futures HS	3701 Stephen Dr	North Highlands, CA	95660-4532	916-286-1902	263-6059	7-12	Nataliya Burko
Gabriella Charter S	1435 Logan St	Los Angeles, CA	90026-3307	213-413-5741	413-5874	K-8	Rhonda Baldenegro
Gardner Charter S	647 E St	Chula Vista, CA	91910-2119	619-934-0300		K-6	Beverly Bautista
GARR Academy of Math & Entrepreneurial	1724 W 53rd St	Los Angeles, CA	90062-2718	323-294-2008	295-3936	K-5	Annitra Edmond
Gates ES	23882 Landisview Ave	Lake Forest, CA	92630-5199	949-837-2260	837-5013	K-6	Yvonne Estling
Gateway Academy	1520 Yosemite Ave	Escalon, CA	95320-1753	209-838-7177	838-6703	K-8	Jennifer Klopatek-Drisco
Gateway College and Career Academy	4800 Magnolia Ave	Riverside, CA	92506	951-222-8934		9-12	Miguel Contreras
Gateway HS	1430 Scott St	San Francisco, CA	94115-3510	415-749-3600	749-2716	9-12	Michael Fuller
Gateway International S	900 Morse Ave	Sacramento, CA	95864-7710	916-286-1985		K-8	Joi Tikoi
Gateway MS	1512 Golden Gate Ave	San Francisco, CA	94115-4515	415-922-1001	922-1055	6-8	Aaron Watson
Gateway to College Academy	680 Sonoma Mountain Pkwy	Petaluma, CA	94954	707-778-4621	778-4822	9-12	Vanessa Shannon
Germain Charter Academy	20730 Germain St	Chatsworth, CA	91311-2418	818-341-5821	882-3599	K-5	Luis Lopez
Gilroy Prep	277 100f Ave	Gilroy, CA	95020	408-337-5445		1-7	Christin Barkas
Girls Athletic Leadership S	15040 Roscoe Blvd	Panorama City, CA	91402	818-593-3620		6-8	Carrie Wagner
Glacier Charter HS	41267 Highway 41	Oakhurst, CA	93644-9403	559-642-1422	642-1592	9-12	Michael Cox
Global College Prep Charter HS	3243 Center Court Ln	Antelope, CA	95843-9111	916-339-4680	339-4684	6-12	Doug Hughey
Global Education Academy	4141 S Figueroa St	Los Angeles, CA	90037-2038	323-232-9588	232-9587	K-5	Craig Merrill
Global Education Academy 2	2020 Oak St	Los Angeles, CA	90007-1307	323-537-7225	232-9587	K-5	David Warken
Global Education Academy MS	1374 W 35th St	Los Angeles, CA	90007	323-641-7283	641-7314	6-8	Rosalind Mickels-Miller
GOALS Academy	412 W Carl Karcher Way	Anaheim, CA	92801	714-563-2390	563-2401	PK-6	Dr. Debra Schroeder Ed.D.
Goethe International Charter S	12500 Braddock Dr	Los Angeles, CA	90066-6808	310-306-3484	306-3245	K-8	Gwenis Laura
Golden Eagle Charter S	2226 S Mount Shasta Blvd #C	Mount Shasta, CA	96067	530-926-5800	926-5826	K-12	Shelly Adams
Golden Oak Montessori S of Hayward	2652 Vergil Ct	Castro Valley, CA	94546-6402	510-931-7868		1-8	Maria Omari
Golden Valley Charter S	3585 Maple St Ste 101	Ventura, CA	93003-3507	805-642-3435	642-3468	K-12	Terri Schiavone
Golden Valley Orchard S	6550 Filbert Ave	Orangevale, CA	95662-4112	916-987-1490	987-1102	K-8	John Baker
Golden Valley River S	9601 Lake Natoma Dr	Orangevale, CA	95662-5099	916-987-6141	987-6741	K-8	Nicole Grant
Gold Rush Charter S	16331 Hidden Valley Rd	Sonora, CA	95370-7926	209-532-9781	532-9234	K-12	Ron Hamilton
Gompers Preparatory Academy	1005 47th St	San Diego, CA	92102-3626	619-263-2171	264-4342	6-12	Vince Riveroll
Gorman Learning Center	1826 Orange Tree Ln	Redlands, CA	92374-2821	909-307-6312	793-5964	K-12	Denice Burchett
Granada Hills Charter HS	10535 Zelzah Ave	Granada Hills, CA	91344-5999	818-360-2361	363-9504	9-12	Brian Bauer
Grass Valley Charter S	225 S Auburn St	Grass Valley, CA	95945-7229	530-273-8723	271-0557	PK-8	Brian Martinez
Gratton ES	4500 S Gratton Rd	Denair, CA	95316-9762	209-632-0505	632-7810	K-8	Shannon Sanford
Greater San Diego Academy	13881 Campo Rd Ste A-5	Jamul, CA	91935-3208	619-669-3050	669-3066	K-12	Catherine Bowes
Great Valley Academy	3200 Tully Rd	Modesto, CA	95350	209-576-2283	576-2838	K-8	Russell Howell
Great Valley Academy - Salida	5901 Sisk Rd	Modesto, CA	95356	209-545-7500	545-7712	K-8	Russell Howell
Greene Academy	2950 W River Dr	Sacramento, CA	95833-3767	916-567-5560		7-12	Leslie Sargent
Green Valley Charter S	947 6th St	Los Banos, CA	93635	209-675-7699		K-7	Andrew Meza
Grimmway Academy	901 Nectarine Ct	Arvin, CA	93203-2424	661-855-8200		K-6	Joanna Kendrick
Grizzly ChalleNGe Charter S	PO Box 3209	San Luis Obispo, CA	93403-3209	805-782-6882	594-6341	10-12	Paul Piette
Grove S	200 Nevada St	Redlands, CA	92373-5385	909-798-7831	307-6464	7-12	Ben Moudry
Guajome Park Academy	2000 N Santa Fe Ave	Vista, CA	92083-1534	760-631-8500	631-8504	K-12	Bob Hampton
Guidance Charter HS	37230 37th St E	Palmdale, CA	93550	661-285-1600	285-1601	7-12	Kamal Al-Khatib
Guidance Charter S	1125 E Palmdale Blvd Ste B	Palmdale, CA	93550-4867	661-272-1701	272-1728	K-6	Kamal Al-Khatib
Hale Charter Academy	23830 Califa St	Woodland Hills, CA	91367-2922	818-313-7400	346-7517	6-8	Christopher Perdigao
Hallmark Charter S	2445 9th St	Sanger, CA	93657-2780	559-524-7170	875-3573	K-12	Alfred Sanchez
Hamlin Charter Academy	22627 Hamlin St	West Hills, CA	91307-3603	818-348-4741	348-3506	K-5	Dana Carter
Harbor Springs Charter S	43466 Business Park Dr	Temecula, CA	92590	866-252-8800	252-8801	K-12	Dr. Kathleen Hermsmeyer
Hardy Brown College Prep	PO Box 1590	San Bernardino, CA	92402	909-884-1410	889-5002	K-8	Toiya Allen
Harmony Magnet Academy	19429 Road 228	Strathmore, CA	93267	559-568-0347	568-1929	9-12	Jeff Brown
Hart-Ransom Academic Charter S	3920 Shoemake Ave	Modesto, CA	95358-8577	209-523-0401	523-1064	PK-12	David Cline M.Ed.
Harvest Ridge Cooperative Charter S	9050 Old State Hwy	Newcastle, CA	95658-9515	916-259-1425	259-1428	K-8	Janet Sutton
Hawking II Charter S	1411 27th St	San Diego, CA	92154	619-628-2651		9-12	Lorena Chavez
Hawking STEAM Charter S	1355 2nd Ave	Chula Vista, CA	91911	619-498-8830		K-12	Carmen Diaz
Hawthorne Math & Science Academy	4467 W Broadway	Hawthorne, CA	90250-3819	310-973-8620	973-8167	9-12	Esau Berumen
Haynes Charter for Enriched Studies	6624 Lockhurst Dr	West Hills, CA	91307-3135	818-716-7310	716-7249	K-5	Barbara Meade
Healdsburg Charter S @ Healdsburg ES	400 1st St	Healdsburg, CA	95448-3939	707-431-3440	431-3592	K-2	Stephanie Feith
Healdsburg Charter S - Fitch Mountain	520 Monte Vista Ave	Healdsburg, CA	95448	707-473-4449	473-4483	3-5	Beth Wolk
Health Careers Academy	931 E Magnolia St	Stockton, CA	95202-1813	209-933-7360		9-12	Traci Miller

School	Address	City,State	Zip code	Telephone	Fax	Grade	Contact
Health Sciences HS & Middle College	3910 University Ave Ste 100	San Diego, CA	92105-7302	619-528-9070	528-9084	10-12	Dr. Sheri Johnson
Health Sciences MS	3910 University Ave Ste 100	San Diego, CA	92105-7302	619-528-9070		6-9	Sheri Johnson
Hearthstone S	2280 6th St	Oroville, CA	95965-3261	530-532-5644	532-5794	K-12	Nick Catomerisios
Heather ES	2757 Melendy Dr	San Carlos, CA	94070-3604	650-508-7303	508-7306	K-4	Pam Jasso
Heights Charter S	2710 Alpine Blvd	Alpine, CA	91901-2276	619-792-9000		K-8	Diana Whyte
Helix Charter HS	7323 University Ave	La Mesa, CA	91942-0555	619-644-1940	462-9266	9-12	Kevin Osborn
Henry HS	230 Harbour Way S	Richmond, CA	94804	510-235-2439	235-2487	9-12	
Heritage Charter S	1855 E Valley Pkwy	Escondido, CA	92027-2517	760-737-3111	737-9322	K-8	Shawn Roner
Heritage Digital Academy Charter MS	2255 E Valley Pkwy	Escondido, CA	92027	760-294-5599		6-8	Jorge Torres
Heritage Peak Charter S	6450 20th St	North Highlands, CA	95660	866-992-9033	348-4325	K-12	Dr. Paul Keefer
Hesby Oaks Leadership Charter S	15530 Hesby St	Encino, CA	91436-1519	818-528-7000	907-0788	K-8	Movses Tarakhchyan
Hickman Charter S	13306 4th St	Hickman, CA	95323-9634	209-874-9070	874-1457	K-8	Paul Gardner
Hickman ES	13306 4th St	Hickman, CA	95323-9634	209-874-1816	874-3721	K-5	Candetta Holdren
Hickman MS	13306 4th St	Hickman, CA	95323-9634	209-556-6540	874-3721	6-8	Candetta Holdren
Higher Learning Academy	2625 Plover St	Sacramento, CA	95815	916-286-5183	643-9893	K-8	Cindy Petersen
Highlands Community Charter S	1333 Grand Ave	Sacramento, CA	95838-3654	916-844-2283	471-0552	1-12	Michael Roessler
High Tech ES	2150 Cushing Rd	San Diego, CA	92106-6189	619-564-6700		K-5	Anne Worrall
High Tech ES Chula Vista	1949 Discovery Falls Dr	Chula Vista, CA	91915-2037	619-591-2550	591-2553	K-5	Stacey Lopaz
High Tech ES North County	1460 W San Marcos Blvd	San Marcos, CA	92078-4017	760-759-2785	759-2788	K-5	Amanda Massey
High Tech Explorer ES	2230 Truxtun Rd Ste A	San Diego, CA	92106-6128	619-795-3600	795-3090	K-5	Briony Chown
High Tech High Media Arts	2230 Truxtun Rd Ste B	San Diego, CA	92106-6128	619-398-8620	758-9568	9-12	Robert Kuhl
High Tech HS Chula Vista	1945 Discovery Falls Dr	Chula Vista, CA	91915-2037	619-591-2500	591-2503	9-12	Lillian Hsu
High Tech HS North County	1420 W San Marcos Blvd	San Marcos, CA	92078-4017	760-759-2700	759-2799	9-12	Isaac Jones
High Tech International HS	2855 Farragut Rd	San Diego, CA	92106-6029	619-398-4900	758-1960	9-12	Brett Peterson
HighTech LA	17111 Victory Blvd	Van Nuys, CA	91406-5455	818-609-2640	881-1754	9-12	Marsha Rybin
High Tech Middle Media Arts	2230 Truxtun Rd Ste B	San Diego, CA	92106-6128	619-398-8640	758-9568	6-8	Casey Salmon
High Tech MS	2359 Truxtun Rd	San Diego, CA	92106-6049	619-814-5060	243-5050	6-8	Nicole Hinostro
High Tech MS Chula Vista	1949 Discovery Falls Dr	Chula Vista, CA	91915-2037	619-591-2530	591-2533	6-8	Melissa Daniels
High Tech MS North County	1460 W San Marcos Blvd	San Marcos, CA	92078-4017	760-759-2750	759-2779	6-8	Juliet Mohnkern
Hollister Prep S	881 Line St	Hollister, CA	95023	831-313-0772		K-8	Heather Parsons
Holly Drive Leadership Academy	4801 Elm St	San Diego, CA	92102-1354	619-266-7333	266-7330	K-8	Alysia Smith
Holt College Prep Academy	3293 Morada Ln	Stockton, CA	95212-3110	209-955-1477	955-1472	6-8	Joseph Williams
Holt College Prep Academy	3201 Morada Ln	Stockton, CA	95212-3110	209-955-1477	955-1472	9-12	Jeff Palmquist
HomeTech Charter S	7126 Skyway	Paradise, CA	95969-3271	530-872-1171	872-1172	K-12	Michael Ervin
Hope Academy	2480 Sebastopol Rd	Santa Rosa, CA	95407	707-528-5272	528-5666	K-6	Matthew Pollack
Hopper STEM Academy	601 Grace Ave	Inglewood, CA	90301-1306	310-910-0230		6-8	Adell Walker
Horizon Charter S	PO Box 489000	Lincoln, CA	95648-9000	916-408-5200	408-5223	K-12	Cynthia Wood Ph.D.
Hume Lake Charter S	64144 Hume Lake Rd	Hume, CA	93628-9600	559-305-7565	305-7707	K-12	Michael Stockdale
ICEF Inglewood Elementary Charter Acad	434 S Grevillea Ave	Inglewood, CA	90301-2300	323-298-6420	293-9092	K-5	Shuron Owens-Lincoln
ICEF Inglewood Middle Charter Academy	304 E Spruce Ave	Inglewood, CA	90301-2711	323-298-6425	293-9092	6-8	Shuron Owens-Lincoln
ICEF Innovation Los Angeles Charter	5029 S Vermont Ave	Los Angeles, CA	90037	323-290-6997		K-5	Charles Lemle
ICEF Vista Academy	4471 Inglewood Blvd	Los Angeles, CA	90066-6209	323-298-6400	317-2839	K-5	Kristen Buczek
ICEF Vista Middle Academy	4471 Inglewood Blvd	Los Angeles, CA	90066-6209	323-298-6400	317-2839	6-8	Kristen Buczek
IFTIN Charter S	5465 El Cajon Blvd	San Diego, CA	92115-3620	619-265-2411	265-2484	K-8	Amal Hersi
iLEAD Hybrid	28050 Hasley Canyon Rd	Castaic, CA	91384	800-925-1502		K-12	Dawn Evenson
iLEAD Lancaster Charter S	254 E Ave K-4	Lancaster, CA	93535	661-722-4287	323-8394	K-8	Kim Etter
Imagine School at Imperial Valley	1150 N Imperial Ave	El Centro, CA	92243-1740	760-592-7250	592-7251	K-7	Grace Jiminez
Imagine S Coachella Valley	84-090 Ave 50	Coachella, CA	92236	760-391-9200		K-2	Blanca Kabeary
Impact Academy of Arts & Technology	2560 Darwin St	Hayward, CA	94545	510-300-1560	300-1565	9-12	Sean McClung
Imperial Beach Charter S	650 Imperial Beach Blvd	Imperial Beach, CA	91932-2706	619-628-5600	628-5680	1-8	Melissa Griffith
Imperial Beach Charter School West	525 3rd St	Imperial Beach, CA	91932-1101	619-628-8900	628-8980	PK-K	Michelle Syverson
Imperial Pathways Charter S	253 E Ross Ave	El Centro, CA	92243	760-312-5500		9-12	Monalisa Vitela
Incubator S	7400 West Manchester	Los Angeles, CA	90045	310-338-2490	338-2496	6-8	Travis Brandy
Independence Charter Academy	PO Box 249	Helendale, CA	92342-0249	760-952-1760	245-1034	K-12	Michael Hayhurst
Independence Charter S	3920 Blue Bird Dr	Modesto, CA	95356-0254	209-545-4415	545-2682	K-8	Ana Garcia
Ingenium Charter MS	7330 Winnetka Ave	Canoga Park, CA	91306	818-309-2777	309-2779	6-8	Cindy Guardado
Ingenium Charter S	22250 Elkwood St	Canoga Park, CA	91304	818-456-4590		K-5	Cindy Guardado
Ingenuity Charter S	6130 Skyline Dr	San Diego, CA	92114-5620	619-487-1163	487-9682	6-12	Dr. Jonathan Dean
Inland Leaders Charter S	12375 California St	Yucaipa, CA	92399	909-446-1100	446-1125	K-8	Michael Gordon
Innovations Academy	10380 Spring Canyon Rd	San Diego, CA	92131-3699	619-271-1414	271-1418	K-8	Christine Kuglen
Innovative Horizons Charter S	1461 N A St	Perris, CA	92570-1968	951-657-0728	940-5103	K-8	Sharill Cortez
Inspire Charter S	33323 Santiago Rd	Acton, CA	93510-1416	760-269-2214	269-2216	K-12	Cris Alcala
Inspire Charter S - Kern	955 Stanislaus St	Maricopa, CA	93252	661-932-1802	932-1804	K-12	Herbert Nichols
Inspire Charter S - North	4305 S Meridian Rd	Meridian, CA	95957	626-932-1802	932-1804	K-12	Herbert Nichols
Inspire Charter S - South	4612 Dehesa Rd	El Cajon, CA	92019-2922	619-784-7481	784-7482	K-12	Herbert Nichols
Inspire School of Arts and Sciences	335 W Sacramento Ave	Chico, CA	95926	530-891-3090	891-3089	9-12	Jerry Crosby
Integrity Charter S	701 National City Blvd	National City, CA	91950-1123	619-336-0808	336-1526	K-8	
Intellectual Virtues Acad of Long Beach	3601 Linden Ave	Long Beach, CA	90807-4001	562-912-7017		6-8	Jacquie Bryant
Intermountain STEM Academy Charter S	13412 Bottle Rock Rd	Cobb, CA	95426	707-928-4873	928-4653	5-8	Tim Gill
International S of Monterey	1720 Yosemite St	Seaside, CA	93955-3914	831-583-2165	899-7653	K-8	Sean Madden
Ipakanni Early College Charter HS	1459 Downer St	Oroville, CA	95965	530-532-1165		6-12	Walter Gramps
IQ Academy California Los Angeles	1830 Nogales St	Rowland Heights, CA	91748-2945	888-997-4722	398-5515	K-12	Katrina Abston
Island Community Day S	1776 6th Avenue Dr	Kingsburg, CA	93631-1701	559-897-1046	897-1265	4-8	Misti Jennings
Island S	7799 21st Ave	Lemoore, CA	93245-9673	559-924-6424	924-0247	K-8	Charlotte Hines
Ivy Academia Entrepreneurial Charter S	7353 Valley Circle Blvd	West Hills, CA	91304-6706	818-449-5900	914-3674	7-12	Caroline Wesley Ed.D.
Ivy Academia Entrepreneurial Charter S	5461 Winnetka Ave	Winnetka, CA	91364	818-716-0771	348-8339	PK-6	Caroline Wesley Ed.D.
Ivy Bound Academy	15355 Morrison St	Sherman Oaks, CA	91403-1514	818-808-0158	808-0157	5-8	Adam Gaunt
Ivy Bound Academy MST Charter MS	20040 Parthenia St	Northridge, CA	91324-3222	818-646-4992	646-4993	5-8	Michelle Pacifici
IvyTech Charter S	6591 Collins Dr	Moorpark, CA	93021-1492	805-222-5188	426-8245	7-12	Jacqueline Gardner
Jacobs High Tech HS	2861 Womble Rd	San Diego, CA	92106-6025	619-243-5000	243-5050	9-12	Kaleb Rashad
Jacoby Creek Charter S	1617 Old Arcata Rd	Bayside, CA	95524-9301	707-822-4896	822-4898	K-8	Melanie Nannizzi
Jardin De la Infancia	307 E 7th St	Los Angeles, CA	90014-2209	213-614-1745	614-2047	K-1	Zuzy Chavez
Jew Academies	1944 Flint Ave	San Jose, CA	95148-1213	408-223-3750	223-7346	K-8	Joseph Nuno
Johnson JHS	1300 Stroud Ave	Kingsburg, CA	93631-1000	559-897-1091	897-6867	7-8	Laura North
Jordan MS	7911 Winnetka Ave	Winnetka, CA	91306	818-882-2496	882-1798	6-8	Dr. Maria Alvarado
Journey S	27102 Foxborough	Aliso Viejo, CA	92656-3377	949-448-7232	448-7256	K-5	Gavin Keller
Juan Bautista de Anza Charter S	2101 S Marina Dr	Salton City, CA	92274-8509	760-767-5850	759-1221	1-12	Dr. Sandra Thorpe
Juarez ES	1450 Marina Way S	Richmond, CA	94804	510-215-7009	215-7016	PK-5	Rocio Gonzalez
Julian Charter S	PO Box 1780	Julian, CA	92036-1780	866-853-0003	765-3849	K-12	Jennifer Cauzza
Justice Street Academy Charter	23350 Justice St	West Hills, CA	91304-4402	818-346-4388	346-4649	K-5	Cynthia Hernandez
Kairos Public School Vacaville Academy	129 Elm St	Vacaville, CA	95688-6925	707-356-9210		K-8	Jared Austin
Kavod Charter ES	3201 Marathon Dr	San Diego, CA	92123-2638	858-386-0887		K-5	Alexa Greenland
Kawana Springs ES	2121 Moraga Dr	Santa Rosa, CA	95404-6114	707-545-4283	573-9065	PK-6	Carolina Castro
Keiller Leadership Academy MS	7270 Lisbon St	San Diego, CA	92114-3007	619-263-9266	262-2217	K-8	Joel Christman
Kenny Charter S	3525 M L King Blvd	Sacramento, CA	95817-3654	916-277-6500	277-6507	K-8	Gail Johnson
Kenter Canyon ES	645 N Kenter Ave	Los Angeles, CA	90049-1999	310-472-5918	472-9738	K-5	Dr. Terry Moren
Kepler Neighborhood S	1537 Fulton St	Fresno, CA	93721	559-495-0849		K-8	Christine Montanez
Kern Workforce 2000 Academy	5801 Sundale Ave	Bakersfield, CA	93309-2924	661-827-3158	396-2987	10-12	Roman Aguilar
Keyes To Learning Charter S	PO Box 519	Keyes, CA	95328-0519	209-634-6467	669-7121	PK-12	Rusty Wynn
Kid Street Learning Center	PO Box 6784	Santa Rosa, CA	95406-0784	707-525-9223	525-9432	K-6	Linda Conklin
Kinetic Academy	721 Utica Ave	Huntingtn Bch, CA	92648	714-465-4565		K-8	Breanne Sarrow
King-Chavez Academy of Excellence	2850 Logan Ave	San Diego, CA	92113-2412	619-232-2825	232-2943	K-8	Jorge Collins
King/Chavez Arts Academy	415 31st St	San Diego, CA	92102-4236	619-525-7320	696-7459	3-5	Sr. Shelley Baca
King/Chavez Athletics Academy	415 31st St	San Diego, CA	92102-4236	619-525-7320	744-3817	3-5	Shelley Baca
King-Chavez Community HS	201 A St	San Diego, CA	92101-4003	619-704-1020	704-1021	9-12	Dr. Kevin Bradshaw
King/Chavez Preparatory Academy	500 30th St	San Diego, CA	92102-3090	619-744-3828	744-3829	6-8	Scott Worthing
King/Chavez Primary Academy	415 31st St	San Diego, CA	92102-4236	619-525-7320	696-7459	K-2	Gerry Guevara
King City Arts Magnet S	415 Pearl St	King City, CA	93930-2919	831-385-5473	385-1016	K-5	Brad Smith
Kings River-Hardwick S	10300 Excelsior Ave	Hanford, CA	93230-9108	559-584-4475	585-1422	K-8	Cathlene Anderson
KIPP Academy of Innovation	5156 Whittier Blvd	Los Angeles, CA	90022	323-406-8000	406-8002	5-8	Alice Lai
KIPP Academy of Opportunity	7019 S Van Ness Ave	Los Angeles, CA	90047-1659	323-778-0125	778-0162	5-8	Tanya Gray
KIPP Adelante Preparatory Academy	1475 6th Ave Ste 100	San Diego, CA	92101-3245	619-233-3242	233-3212	5-8	Monique McKeown
KIPP Bayview Academy	1060 Key Ave	San Francisco, CA	94124-3563	415-467-2522	467-9522	5-8	Sherrye Hubbard
KIPP Bridge Charter S	1700 Market St	Oakland, CA	94607	510-874-7255	874-6796	5-8	Lolita Jackson
KIPP Comienza Community Prep S	6410 Rita Ave	Huntington Park, CA	90255	323-589-1450	589-1716	K-4	D'Anza Smith
KIPP Empower Academy	8466 S Figueroa St	Los Angeles, CA	90003-2729	323-750-2279	750-7902	K-4	Neela Parasnis
KIPP Excelencia Charter S	656 Laurel St	Redwood City, CA	94063	650-465-3616		PK-2	Kyle Shaffer
KIPP Heritage Academy	2545 Sherlock Dr	San Jose, CA	95121	408-318-7256		5-8	Amy Tran
KIPP Ignite Academy	9110 S Central Ave	Los Angeles, CA	90002	323-486-6402	486-6403	K-1	Cassandra Cope
KIPP I Heartwood Charter MS	1250 S King Rd	San Jose, CA	95122-2146	408-926-5477	926-5478	5-8	Susana Mena
Kipp II Prize Preparatory Academy	1250 S King Rd	San Jose, CA	95122-2146	408-251-5600	251-5602	5-8	Autumn Zangrilli
KIPP Iluminar Academy	4800 E Cesar Chavez Ave	Los Angeles, CA	90022	323-800-5218	489-4471	K-4	Mara Bond
KIPP King Collegiate HS	2005 Via Barrett	San Lorenzo, CA	94580-1315	510-828-9509	317-2333	9-12	Kelly Lara
KIPP Los Angeles College Preparatory	2810 Whittier Blvd	Los Angeles, CA	90023-1527	323-264-7737	264-7730	5-8	Carlos Lanuza
KIPP Philosophers Academy	8300 S Central Ave	Los Angeles, CA	90001-3707	323-584-6664	584-6666	5-8	Heidi Kunkel
KIPP Promesa Prep S	207 S Dacotah St	Los Angeles, CA	90063	323-486-6400	486-6401	K-4	Adriana Rodriguez
KIPP Raices Academy	668 S Atlantic Blvd	Los Angeles, CA	90022-3212	323-780-3900	780-3939	K-4	Yesenia Castro

School	Address	City,State	Zip code	Telephone	Fax	Grade	Contact
KIPP San Francisco Bay Academy	1430 Scott St	San Francisco, CA	94115-3510	415-440-4306	440-4308	5-8	Ellen Bray
KIPP San Francisco College Preparatory	1195 Hudson Ave	San Francisco, CA	94124-2488	415-643-6951	826-9182	9-12	Caroline Gifford
KIPP San Jose Collegiate Charter S	1790 Educational Park Dr	San Jose, CA	95133-1703	408-937-3752	937-3755	9-12	Tom Ryan
KIPP Scholar Academy	1729 W MLK Jr Blvd	Los Angeles, CA	90062	323-292-2272	292-2555	5-8	Tiffany Moore
KIPP Sol Academy	4800 E Cesar Chavez Ave	Los Angeles, CA	90022	323-800-5220	800-5221	5-5	
KIPP Summit Academy	2005 Via Barrett	San Lorenzo, CA	94580-1315	510-258-0106	258-0097	5-8	Salome Portugal
KIPP Vida Preparatory Academy	5101 S Western Ave	Los Angeles, CA	90062	323-406-8007	406-8008	K-4	Erendira Flores
Knowledge Enlightens You (KEY) Academy	1570 Ward St	Hayward, CA	94541-3030	510-543-4124	862-0209	K-8	Krista Kastriotis
Lake County International Charter S	PO Box 984	Middletown, CA	95461-0984	707-987-3063	825-9344	K-8	Gwendolyn Maupin-Ahern
Lakeview Charter Academy	11465 Kagel Canyon St	Lake View Ter, CA	91342-6505	818-485-0340	485-0342	6-8	Danny Herrera
Lakeview Charter HS	13361 Glenoaks Blvd	Sylmar, CA	91342-2110	818-356-2591	356-2581	9-12	Adam Almeida
Language Academy	2850 49th St	Sacramento, CA	95817-2303	916-277-7137	277-7141	K-8	Eduardo De Leon
Larchmont Charter ES	1265 N Fairfax Ave	West Hollywood, CA	90046-5205	323-656-6418	656-6407	K-10	Mersedeh Emrani
Lashon Academy	7477 Kester Ave	Van Nuys, CA	91405-1722	818-514-4566	337-0102	K-6	Sara Garcia
La Sierra Academy	1735 E Houston Ave	Visalia, CA	93292-2349	559-733-6963	733-6845	7-12	Anjelica Zermeno
LA's Promise Charter MS 1	1755 W 52nd St	Los Angeles, CA	90062	323-745-4928		6-8	Lori Pawinski
La Tijera Academy of Excellence	1415 N La Tijera Blvd	Inglewood, CA	90302	310-680-5260	419-2537	K-8	Ugema James
Latino College Preparatory Academy	14271 Story Rd	San Jose, CA	95127-3823	408-729-2281	285-5324	9-12	Raul Lomeli
Laurel Preparatory Academy	10170 Huennekens St	San Diego, CA	92121-2964	858-678-4812		6-12	Lynne Alipio
Laurel Tree Charter S	4555 Valley West Blvd	Arcata, CA	95521-4683	707-822-5626	822-5654	K-12	Brenda Sutter
LAVA Charter S	1660 Monroe St	Red Bluff, CA	96080	530-727-9495	727-9498	5-8	John Sheffield
Laverne Elementary Preparatory Academy	PO Box 400880	Hesperia, CA	92340	760-948-4333	948-9333	K-8	Debra Tarver
LaVerne Science & Technology Charter S	250 W La Verne Ave	Pomona, CA	91767-2375	909-397-4684	392-0191	K-6	Dolores Lobaina
La Vida Charter S	16201 N Highway 101	Willits, CA	95490-8724	707-459-6344	459-6377	K-12	Ann Kelly
Lazear Charter Academy	824 29th Ave	Oakland, CA	94601-2205	510-689-2000		K-8	Sarah Morrill
Leadership HS	350 Seneca Ave	San Francisco, CA	94112-3248	415-841-8910	841-8925	9-12	Beth Silbergeld
Leadership Public S - Hayward	28000 Calaroga Ave	Hayward, CA	94545-4600	510-300-1340	372-0396	9-12	Michael DeSousa
Leadership Public S - Richmond	251 S 12th St	Richmond, CA	94801	510-235-4522	588-4593	9-12	Shawn Benjamin
Learning Choice Academy	9950 Scripps Lake Dr	San Diego, CA	92131-1082	619-463-8811	463-8339	K-12	Debi Gooding
Learning for Life Charter S	330 Reservation Rd Ste F	Marina, CA	93933-3286	831-582-9820	582-9825	7-12	Cindy Dotson
Learning Works!	88 N Daisy Ave	Pasadena, CA	91107-3704	626-564-2871	564-2870	7-12	Mikala Rahn
Lemoore Middle College HS	555 College Dr	Lemoore, CA	93245-9248	559-925-3552	925-6059	9-12	Charles Gent
Lemoore University Charter S	100 Vine St	Lemoore, CA	93245-3418	559-924-6890	924-6839	5-8	Crescenciano Camarena
Lennox Math Science & Technology Academy	10319 Firmona Ave	Lennox, CA	90304-1419	310-680-5600	671-5029	9-12	Armando Mena
Libertas College Preparatory Charter S	3875 Dublin Ave	Los Angeles, CA	90008-1945	310-902-6808		4-8	Anna Carlstone-Hurst
Liberty Charter HS	8425 Palm St	Lemon Grove, CA	91945	619-668-2131	668-2133	9-12	Debbie Beyer
Liberty ES	170 Liberty School Rd	Petaluma, CA	94952	707-795-4380	795-6468	PK-6	Chris Rafanelli
Life Learning Academy	651 8th St	San Francisco, CA	94130-1901	415-397-8957	397-9274	9-12	Teri Delane
Lifeline Education Charter S	357 E Palmer St	Compton, CA	90221-2610	310-605-2510	764-4890	6-12	Paula DeGroat
Life Source International Charter S	44339 Beech Ave	Lancaster, CA	93534	661-579-2970	579-2977	K-8	Deberae Culpepper
Lighthouse Community Charter S	444 Hegenberger Rd	Oakland, CA	94621	510-562-8801	562-8803	K-12	Steve Sexton
Lincoln ES	1900 Mariposa St	Kingsburg, CA	93631-2044	559-897-5141	897-3537	2-3	Matt Stovall
Lincoln Street S	1135 Lincoln St	Red Bluff, CA	96080	530-528-7301	529-4120	K-8	Michelle Barnard
Linscott Charter S	220 Elm St	Watsonville, CA	95076-5025	831-728-6301	761-5478	K-8	Julie Wiley
Literacy First Charter S	799 E Washington Ave	El Cajon, CA	92020-5327	619-579-7232	579-5730	K-12	Debbie Beyer
Live Oak Charter S	PO Box 2054	Petaluma, CA	94953-2054	707-762-9020	762-9019	K-8	Matthew Morgan
Livermore Valley Charter HS	2451 Portola Ave	Livermore, CA	94551-1756	925-456-9000	456-9009	9-12	Lynn Lysko
Livermore Valley Charter S	3252 Constitution Dr	Livermore, CA	94551-7567	925-443-1690	443-1692	K-8	Eric Dillie
Locke College Prep Academy	325 E 111th St	Los Angeles, CA	90061	323-420-2067		9-12	Dr. Peggy Gutierrez
Lockhurst Drive Charter ES	6170 Lockhurst Dr	Woodland Hills, CA	91367-1299	818-888-5280	346-0283	K-5	Susan Dacorsi
Lodestar: a Lighthouse Charter S	2433 Coolidge Ave	Oakland, CA	94601	510-209-2166	271-8803	K-12	Yanira Canizales
Loma Vista Charter S	467 E Honolulu St	Lindsay, CA	93247	559-562-5111	562-4637	K-12	Dennis Doane
Loma Vista Immersion Academy	207 Maria Dr	Petaluma, CA	94954-2301	707-765-4302	765-4343	K-6	Jorge Arvizu
Long Valley Charter S	PO Box 7	Doyle, CA	96109-0007	530-827-2395	827-3562	K-12	Sherri Morgan
Loomis Basin Charter S	5438 Laird Rd	Loomis, CA	95650-8916	916-652-2642	652-1809	K-8	Erika Sloane
Los Angeles Academy of Arts & Enterprise	1200 W Collton St Ste 3-320	Los Angeles, CA	90026	213-487-0600	487-0500	6-12	Yolanda Jimenez
Los Angeles International Charter S	625 Coleman Ave	Los Angeles, CA	90042-4903	323-257-1499	257-1497	9-12	Angelique Sims
Los Angeles Leadership Academy	2670 Griffin Ave	Los Angeles, CA	90031-2311	323-381-8484	381-8489	K-8	Antonio Sanchez
Los Angeles Leadership Academy - HS	234 E Avenue 33	Los Angeles, CA	90031-1937	323-227-7719	227-7721	9-12	Roger Lowenstein
Los Feliz Charter S for the Arts	2709 Media Center Dr	Los Angeles, CA	90065-1700	323-539-2810	539-2815	K-6	Linda Lee
LPS College Park Charter S	8601 MacArthur Blvd	Oakland, CA	94605-4037	510-633-0750	291-9783	9-12	Ellen Digiacomo
Luskin Academy	2941 W 70th St	Los Angeles, CA	90043-4420	213-905-1210	905-1215	9-12	Rosalio Medrano
MAAC Community Charter S	1385 3rd Ave	Chula Vista, CA	91911-4302	619-476-0749	476-0913	9-12	Debbie VanEnkevort
Madera County Independent Academy	1105 S Madera Ave	Madera, CA	93637-5576	559-662-4636	675-8313	K-12	Brett Salinas
Magnolia Science Academy	18238 Sherman Way	Reseda, CA	91335-4550	818-609-0507	609-0534	6-12	Mustafa Sahin M.Ed.
Magnolia Science Academy	102 Baker St E	Costa Mesa, CA	92626	714-557-7002	242-1449	K-12	Laura Schlottman
Magnolia Science Academy 2	17125 Victory Blvd	Van Nuys, CA	91406	818-758-0300	758-0333	6-12	Steven Keskinturk
Magnolia Science Academy 3	1254 E Helmick St	Carson, CA	90746	310-637-3806	933-4767	6-12	Dr. John White
Magnolia Science Academy 4	11330 Graham Pl	Los Angeles, CA	90064-3725	310-473-2464	473-2416	6-12	Lisa Ross
Magnolia Science Academy 5	18230 Kittridge St	Reseda, CA	91335	818-219-0676	609-0534	6-9	Brad Plonka
Magnolia Science Academy 6	3754 Dunn Dr	Los Angeles, CA	90034-5805	310-842-8555	842-8558	6-8	John G. Terzi
Magnolia Science Academy 7	18355 Roscoe Blvd	Northridge, CA	91325-4104	818-886-0585	975-5215	K-5	Fatih Metin
Magnolia Science Academy 8	6411 Orchard Ave	Bell, CA	90201-2222	310-826-3925	826-3926	6-8	Jason Hernandez
Magnolia Science Academy - San Diego	6365 Lake Atlin Ave	San Diego, CA	92119-3206	619-644-1300	644-1600	6-8	Gokhan Serce
Making Waves Academy	4123 Lakeside Dr	Richmond, CA	94806-1942	510-262-1511	262-1518	5-12	Evangelina Ward-Jackson
Manzanita Charter MS	461 33rd St	Richmond, CA	94804	510-222-3500	222-3555	6-8	Jim Trombley
Manzanita Public Charter S	991 Mountain View Blvd	Vandenberg AFB, CA	93437-1209	805-734-5600	734-3572	K-6	Suzanne Nicastro
Mare Island Technology Academy HS	2 Positive Pl	Vallejo, CA	94589-1825	707-552-6482	552-0288	6-12	Matt Smith
Maria Montessori Charter Academy	1850 Wildcat Blvd	Rocklin, CA	95765-5471	916-630-1510	624-7305	K-8	Brent Boothby
Marquez Charter S	16821 Marquez Ave	Pacific Plsds, CA	90272-3243	310-454-4019	573-1532	K-5	Benjamin Meritt
Marysville Charter Academy for the Arts	1917 B St	Marysville, CA	95901-3731	530-749-6157	741-7892	7-12	Tim Malone
Math and Science College Preparatory	3200 W Adams Blvd	Los Angeles, CA	90018-1832	323-821-1393	607-1453	9-9	Janette Rodriguez
Mattole Valley Charter S	PO Box 211	Petrolia, CA	95558-0211	707-629-3634	629-3649	PK-12	Richard Graey
McGill School of Success	3025 Fir St	San Diego, CA	92102-1123	619-239-0632	239-1318	K-3	Fredrick Lanuza
Meadows Arts & Technology ES	2000 La Granada Dr	Thousand Oaks, CA	91362-2016	805-495-7037	374-1160	K-5	Brenda Olshever
Merced Scholars Charter S	1850 Wardrobe Ave	Merced, CA	95341-6407	209-381-5165	381-5166	6-12	Mark Pintor
Merkin MS	2023 S Union Ave	Los Angeles, CA	90007-1326	213-748-0141	748-0142	6-8	Meghan Van Pelt
Method Charter S	24620 Jefferson St	Murrieta, CA	92562	951-461-4620		K-12	Jessica Venezia
Method S	317 E Foothill Blvd	Arcadia, CA	91006-2510	626-408-5882		K-12	Jessica Venezia
Metro Charter S	320 W 15th St	Los Angeles, CA	90015-3091	213-377-5708	943-1502	K-5	Kim Clerx
MET Sacramento Charter HS	810 V St	Sacramento, CA	95818-1330	916-264-4700	264-4701	9-12	Vince Wolfe
Mid Valley Alternative Charter S	9895 7th Ave	Hanford, CA	93230-8802	559-583-1149	582-7565	K-8	Todd Barlow
Milagro Charter S	1855 N Main St	Los Angeles, CA	90031-3227	323-223-1786	223-8593	K-5	Sascha Robinett
Millennium Charter HS	51 E Beverly Pl	Tracy, CA	95376-3191	209-831-5240	831-5243	9-12	Virginia Stewart
Millennium Charter HS	901 Blanco Circle	Salinas, CA	93901	831-755-0830		9-12	Mike Murphy
Minarets Charter HS	PO Box 208	O Neals, CA	93645-0208	559-868-8659	868-8686	9-12	Daniel Ching
Mirus Secondary S	14073 Main St Ste 103	Hesperia, CA	92345-4675	760-947-7100	947-7135	7-12	Mary Bixby
Mission Preparatory S	75 Francis St	San Francisco, CA	94112-1924	415-508-9626		K-8	Jane Henzerling
Mission View Charter S	20655 Soledad Canyon Rd #12	Santa Clarita, CA	91351	661-272-1225	945-2430	7-12	Taera Childers
Miwok Valley Language Academy	1010 Saint Francis Dr	Petaluma, CA	94954-5322	707-765-4304	765-4380	K-6	Brett Wilson
Mohan High School	644 W 17th St	Los Angeles, CA	90015-3400	213-342-2870	342-2871	9-12	Loreen Riley
Mojave River Academy	16519 Victor St	Victorville, CA	92395-3965	760-245-3222	245-3774	K-12	Nancy Lewis
Monarch Learning Center	PO Box 992418	Redding, CA	96099-2418	530-247-7307	243-4819	K-8	Patti Davis
Montague Charter Academy	13000 Montague St	Pacoima, CA	91331-4146	818-899-0215	834-9782	K-5	Leonidas Tarca
Monterey Bay Charter S	1004B David Ave	Pacific Grove, CA	93950-5443	831-655-4638	655-4815	K-8	Cassandra Bridge
Monterey County Home Charter S	PO Box 80851	Salinas, CA	93912-0851	831-755-0331	755-0837	K-12	Justin McCollum
Mountain Academy Charter S	201 Memorial Dr	Weaverville, CA	96093	530-623-2861	623-4489	K-12	Fabio Robles
Mountain Home Charter S	41267 Highway 41	Oakhurst, CA	93644-9403	559-642-1422	642-1592	K-8	Michael Cox
Mountain Oaks S	PO Box 1209	San Andreas, CA	95249-1209	209-754-0532	754-3556	K-12	Anne Colman
Mountain View Montessori Charter S	17000 Silica Dr	Victorville, CA	92395	760-843-3303	843-1074	K-6	Gwen Dixon
Mt Lassen Charter S	100 David S Hall St	Herlong, CA	96113	530-252-4313	252-4314	K-6	Patrick Condon
Mueller Charter S	715 I St	Chula Vista, CA	91910-5199	619-422-6192	422-0356	K-9	Dr. Kevin Riley
Muir Charter S	12338 McCourtney Rd	Grass Valley, CA	95949	530-272-4008	366-7349	9-12	Richard Guess
Multicultural Learning Center	7510 De Soto Ave	Canoga Park, CA	91303-1430	818-716-5783	716-1085	K-8	Shirley Aragon
Museum S	211 Maple St	San Diego, CA	92103-6527	619-236-8712	236-8906	K-8	Phil Beaumont
Napa Valley Language Academy	2700 Kilburn Ave	Napa, CA	94558-5623	707-253-3678	259-8427	K-6	Alejandra Uribe
National University Academy	1101 National Dr Ste C	Sacramento, CA	95834-2936	760-630-4080		K-12	Kimberleigh Marro
Natomas Charter S	4600 Blackrock Dr	Sacramento, CA	95835-1250	916-928-5353	928-5333	PK-12	Ting Sun Ph.D.
Natomas-Pacific Pathways Prep	3700 Del Paso Rd	Sacramento, CA	95834-9606	916-567-5740	567-5749	9-12	Tom Rutten
Natomas Pacific Pathways Prep ES	4400 E Commerce Way	Sacramento, CA	95834	916-567-5741	567-5749	K-5	Marcie Dart
Natomas Pacific Pathways Prep MS	3700 Del Paso Rd	Sacramento, CA	95834-9606	916-567-5741	567-5749	6-8	David Hunt
NAVA College Preparatory Academy	1319 E 41st St	Los Angeles, CA	90011-3301	213-846-2203	521-1668	9-12	Gustavo Barrientos
Nea Community Learning Center	1900 3rd St	Alameda, CA	94501-1851	510-748-4008	864-4281	K-12	Annalisa Moore
Nestle Avenue ES	5060 Nestle Ave	Tarzana, CA	91356-4399	818-342-6148	609-9864	K-5	Cheryl Gray-Sortino
Nestor Language Academy Charter S	1455 Hollister St	San Diego, CA	92154-4063	619-628-0900	628-0980	K-8	Guadalupe Avilez
Nevada City Charter S	750 Hoover Ln	Nevada City, CA	95959-2910	530-265-1885	265-1889	K-8	Brynn Bourke
Nevada City S for the Arts	13032 Bitney Springs Rd # 8	Nevada City, CA	95959-9017	530-273-7736	273-1378	PK-8	Holly Pettitt

School	Address	City,State	Zip code	Telephone	Fax	Grade	Contact
NEW Academy Canoga Park	21425 Cohasset St	Canoga Park, CA	91303-1450	818-710-2640	710-2654	PK-5	Patricia Gould
NEW Academy of Science & Arts	379 Loma Dr	Los Angeles, CA	90017-1149	213-413-9183	413-9187	PK-5	Dr. Eric Todd Ed.D.
Newcastle Charter S	8951 Valley View Dr	Newcastle, CA	95658-9723	916-663-3307	663-3524	PK-8	Liz Staton
New Day Academy	30611 Whitmore Rd	Whitmore, CA	96096	530-233-3861	233-3864	K-12	Laura Van Acker
New Designs Charter S	2303 Figueroa Way	Los Angeles, CA	90007-2504	213-765-9084	765-0214	6-12	Stephen Gyesaw
New Designs Charter S - Watts	12714 Avalon Blvd	Los Angeles, CA	90061-2730	323-418-0600	418-1600	6-12	Joseph Ntung
New Heights Charter S	2202 W Martin Luther King	Los Angeles, CA	90008-2723	323-508-0155	508-0156	K-8	Amy Berfield
New Horizons Charter Academy	5955 Lankershim Blvd	North Hollywood, CA	91601-1006	818-655-9602	655-9607	K-8	Richard Thomas
New Jerusalem ES	31400 S Koster Rd	Tracy, CA	95304-9543	209-835-2597	835-2613	K-8	Donald Patzer
New Joseph Bonnheim Community Charter S	7300 Marin Ave	Sacramento, CA	95820-3551	916-643-7400	691-9858	K-6	Christie Wells-Artman
New Los Angeles Charter ES	5421 Rodeo Rd	Los Angeles, CA	90016	323-939-6400	939-6411	K-5	Kate O'Brien
New Los Angeles Charter S	1919 S Burnside Ave	Los Angeles, CA	90016-1114	323-939-6400	939-6411	6-8	Daryl Brook
Newman Leadership Academy	1314 E Date St	San Bernardino, CA	92404-4234	909-522-4461		K-6	Joyce Payne
New Millenium Secondary S	1301 W 182nd St Ste B	Gardena, CA	90248-3322	310-999-6162	999-6163	9-12	Samantha Navarro
New S of San Francisco	2929 19th St	San Francisco, CA	94110-2019	415-401-8489		K-5	Ryan Chapman
New Technology HS	1400 Dickson St	Sacramento, CA	95822-3437	916-433-2839	433-2840	9-12	Kenneth Durham
New Village Girls Academy	147 N Occidental Blvd	Los Angeles, CA	90026-4601	213-385-4015	385-4020	9-12	Dr. Andrea Purcell
New Vision MS	2050 Pacific St	San Bernardino, CA	92404-6179	909-888-8390	888-8470	6-8	Alex Lucero
New West Charter S	1905 Armacost Ave	Los Angeles, CA	90025-5210	310-943-5444	231-3399	6-12	Dr. Sharon Weir
NextGeneration STEAM Academy	18001 Commercial St	Lathrop, CA	95330-8543	209-229-4736		K-8	Leslie Pombo
Nightingale S	1721 Carpenter Rd	Stockton, CA	95206-3809	209-933-7260	234-1850	K-8	Myra Machuca
Nobel MS	9950 Tampa Ave	Northridge, CA	91324-1142	818-773-4700	701-9480	6-8	Derek Horowitz
Nord Country Charter S	5554 California St	Chico, CA	95973-9795	530-891-3138	891-3273	K-6	Kathleen Dahlgren
Northcoast Prep and Performing Arts Acad	PO Box 276	Arcata, CA	95518-0276	707-822-0861	822-0878	6-12	Michael Bazemore
North County Trade Tech HS	1126 N Melrose Dr	Vista, CA	92083-3467	760-598-0782	598-0895	9-12	Doreen Quinn
Northern Summit Academy	3435 Main St	Cottonwood, CA	96022	530-949-0154	472-1127	K-12	Julia Knight
Northern Summit Academy	2877 Childress Dr	Anderson, CA	96007	530-949-0154		K-12	Julia Knight
North Oakland Community Charter S	1000 42nd St	Oakland, CA	94608-3621	510-655-0540	655-1222	K-8	Stephen Ajani
North Valley Pivot Charter School	2550 Lakewest Dr	Chico, CA	95928	877-544-1423		6-12	Jayne Gaskell
Northwest Prep Charter S	2590 Piner Rd	Santa Rosa, CA	95401-4035	707-522-3320	522-3101	7-12	Joyce Hamilton
Norton Space and Aeronautics Academy	503 E Central Ave	San Bernardino, CA	92408-2313	909-386-2300	386-7855	K-12	Guadalupe Girard
NOVA Academy - Coachella	52780 Frederick St	Coachella, CA	92236	714-543-5437	543-5463	9-12	Lisa Hernandez
Nova Academy Early College HS	500 W Santa Ana Blvd	Santa Ana, CA	92706	714-569-0948	569-1693	9-12	Andrea Brumbaugh
Novato Charter S	940 C St	Novato, CA	94949-5060	415-883-4254	883-1859	K-8	Nikki Lloyd
Nueva Esperanza Charter Academy	1218 4th St	San Fernando, CA	91340-2314	818-256-1951	256-2397	6-12	Fidel Ramirez
Nueva Vista Language Academy	120 Garces Hwy	Delano, CA	93215-3328	661-721-5070	721-3638	PK-5	Anamarie Sanchez
Nuview Bridge Early College HS	30401 Reservoir Ave	Nuevo, CA	92567-9361	951-928-8498	928-0186	9-12	Dr. Jason Fowler Ed.D.
N Valley Military Institute Coll Prep	12105 Allegheny St	Sun Valley, CA	91352	818-368-1557	368-1935	6-12	Dr. Mark Ryan
Oakdale Charter HS	1235 E D St	Oakdale, CA	95361-3223	209-848-4361	848-4363	9-12	Dennis Hitch
Oak Grove ES	8760 Bower St	Sebastopol, CA	95472-2450	707-823-5225	829-2614	K-5	Paige Gardner
Oakland Charter Academy	4215 Foothill Blvd	Oakland, CA	94601	510-532-6751	532-6753	6-8	David Camarena
Oakland Charter HS	345 12th St	Oakland, CA	94607	510-893-8700	893-8705	9-12	Raquel Oliva-Gomez
Oakland Military Institute College Prep	3877 Lusk St	Oakland, CA	94608	510-594-3900	597-9886	6-12	Richard Wallis
Oakland S for the Arts	530 18th St	Oakland, CA	94612-1512	510-873-8800	873-8816	6-12	Donn Harris
Oakland Unity HS	6038 Brann St	Oakland, CA	94605-1544	510-635-7170	635-3830	9-12	William Nee
Oakland Unity MS	6038 Brann St	Oakland, CA	94605	510-969-5302		6-8	Damon Grant
Oak Park Prep S	2315 34th St	Sacramento, CA	95817-1211	916-533-4861		7-8	Annie Cervenka
Oasis Charter S	1135 Westridge Pkwy	Salinas, CA	93907-2529	831-424-9003	424-9005	K-6	Dr. Juanita Perea
Obama Charter S	PO Box 72028	Los Angeles, CA	90002	323-566-1965	566-1418	PK-5	Chaleese Norman
Ocean Charter S	12606 Culver Blvd	Los Angeles, CA	90066-6506	310-827-5511	827-2012	K-3	Stephanie Edwards
Ocean Charter S	7400 W Manchester Ave	Los Angeles, CA	90045	310-348-9050	348-9085	4-8	Stephanie Edwards
Ocean Grove Charter S	1166 Broadway Ste Q	Placerville, CA	95667-5745	800-979-4436	295-3583	K-12	Randy Gaschler
Odyssey Charter S	725 W Altadena Dr	Altadena, CA	91001-4103	626-229-0993	229-0586	K-8	Lauren O'Neill
O'Farrell Charter S	6130 Skyline Dr	San Diego, CA	92114-5620	619-263-3009	263-4339	PK-12	Dr. Jonathan Dean
Old Adobe ES	2856 Old Adobe Rd	Petaluma, CA	94954-9546	707-765-4301	765-4334	K-6	Jeff Williamson
Old Town Academy	2120 San Diego Ave	San Diego, CA	92110-2901	619-574-6225	683-2096	K-8	Jon Centofranchi
Olive Grove Charter S	PO Box 370	New Cuyama, CA	93254	805-623-1111	623-8512	K-12	Laura Mudge
Olivet Elementary Charter S	1825 Willowside Rd	Santa Rosa, CA	95401-3923	707-522-3045	522-3047	K-6	Mary Reynolds
one.Charter	800 Douglas Rd	Stockton, CA	95207-3607	209-468-9079	468-4651	7-12	Janine Kaeslin
OnePurpose S	PO Box 24509	San Francisco, CA	94124	415-657-0277		K-5	Antonio Tapia
Open Charter Magnet S	5540 W 77th St	Los Angeles, CA	90045-3214	310-568-0735	568-0904	K-5	Antoinette Cass
Opportunities for Learning	320 N Halstead St	Pasadena, CA	91107	626-814-0161	814-0686	K-12	Jesus Franco
Opportunities for Learning Charter S	18523 Soledad Canyon Rd	Canyon Country, CA	91351-3722	661-424-1337	424-1129	7-12	Jesus Franco
Opportunities for Learning S	33621 Del Obispo St Ste E	Dana Point, CA	92629-2100	949-248-1282	248-2450	K-12	Jesus Franco
Optimist Charter S	6957 N Figueroa St	Los Angeles, CA	90042-1245	323-443-3100		7-12	Lynn DeYoung
Options for Youth - Apple Valley	13675 Niabi Rd	Apple Valley, CA	92308	760-247-6078	961-1723	7-12	Kathy Lento
Options for Youth - Arden	2125 Fulton Ave Ste 100	Sacramento, CA	95825	916-971-3175	971-3186	7-12	Jocelyn Baldwin
Options for Youth Burbank 1	1610 W Burbank Blvd	Burbank, CA	91506-1311	818-566-7525	566-7712	K-12	Jesus Franco
Options for Youth Burbank 2	401 S Glenoaks Blvd	Burbank, CA	91502	818-566-9809	566-9819	7-12	Bill Tynan
Options for Youth Carmichael	5825 Windmill Way	Carmichael, CA	95608-1300	916-485-5155	485-5484	7-12	Jesus Franco
Options for Youth Charter S	405 S San Gabriel Blvd	San Gabriel, CA	91776-1965	626-282-0390	282-0391	7-12	Maricela Frymark
Options for Youth - Chino 1	7011 Schaefer Ave Ste E	Chino, CA	91710	909-465-9529	465-9809	7-12	Wendy Gillespie
Options for Youth - Chino 2	5475 Philadelphia St Ste B	Chino, CA	91710	909-591-6559	591-8438	7-12	Maricela Frymark
Options for Youth - Fontana 1	16981 Foothill Blvd	Fontana, CA	92335	909-357-3168	357-2875	7-12	Wendy Gillespie
Options for Youth - Fontana 2	17216 Slover Ave	Fontana, CA	92337	909-429-0482	429-9212	7-12	Wendy Gillespie
Options for Youth - Hesperia 1	15461 Main St	Hesperia, CA	92345	760-948-3355		7-12	
Options for Youth Irwindale	16023 Arrow Hwy Ste C	Baldwin Park, CA	91706	626-337-9352	337-4503	7-12	Maricela Frymark
Options for Youth La Crescenta	2626 Foothill Blvd	La Crescenta, CA	91214	626-236-2060	236-2062	7-12	Maricela Frymark
Options for Youth North Highlands	3542 A St	North Highlands, CA	95660	916-338-2375	338-2417	7-12	Jocelyn Baldwin
Options for Youth Northridge	19315 Saticoy St	Reseda, CA	91335	818-886-8392	886-8393	7-12	Bill Tynan
Options for Youth - Ontario	3130 Inland Empire Blvd	Ontario, CA	91764	909-476-5959	476-3636	7-12	Maricela Frymark
Options for Youth Orangevale	9470 Madison Ave	Orangevale, CA	95662	916-988-4138	988-4176	7-12	Jocelyn Baldwin
Options for Youth Pomona	695 E Foothill Blvd	Pomona, CA	91767	909-593-2163	596-5627	7-12	Maricela Frymark
Options for Youth - Rancho	9849 Foothill Blvd	Rch Cucamonga, CA	91730	909-466-9082	466-9083	7-12	Jocelyn Baldwin
Options for Youth Rancho Cordova	11088 Olson Dr	Rancho Cordova, CA	95670-5650	916-631-8113	631-8121	7-12	Jocelyn Baldwin
Options for Youth San Bernardino I	985 S E St Ste A	San Bernardino, CA	92408	909-381-6260	381-6230	7-12	Bryan Gillespie
Options for Youth San Bernardino II	1148 E Highland Ave	San Bernardino, CA	92404	909-882-8500	882-8315	7-12	Bryan Gillespie
Options for Youth Sylmar	13752 Foothill Blvd	Sylmar, CA	91342	818-698-4168		7-12	Bill Tynan
Options for Youth - Upland	310 N Mountain Ave	Upland, CA	91786-5115	909-946-0500	946-0506	7-12	Wendy Gillespie
Options for Youth Van Nuys	6628 Van Nuys Blvd	Van Nuys, CA	91405	818-781-9059	781-9067	7-12	Bill Tynan
Options for Youth Victorville - 1	14725 7th St	Victorville, CA	92395	760-955-5525	955-1107	7-12	Kathy Lento
Options for Youth Victorville - 2	11975 Hesperia Rd	Hesperia, CA	92345	760-955-5900	955-5919	7-12	Kathy Lento
Options for Youth Victorville - 3	15378 Ramona Ave	Victorville, CA	92392	760-245-9086		7-12	Kathy Lento
Options for Youth Victorville - 4	15048 Bear Valley Rd Ste E	Victorville, CA	92395	760-241-8300	241-8879	7-12	Kathy Lento
Orange County Academy Science and Arts	29292 Crown Valley Pkwy	Laguna Niguel, CA	92677	949-269-3290		K-8	Doreen Fioretto
Orange County Educational Arts Academy	825 N Broadway	Santa Ana, CA	92701-3423	714-558-2787	558-2775	K-8	Kristin Collins
Orange County HS of the Arts	1010 N Main St	Santa Ana, CA	92701-3602	714-560-0900	664-0463	7-12	Steven Wagner
Orchard View Charter S	700 Watertrough Rd	Sebastopol, CA	95472-3917	707-823-4709	823-6187	K-12	Cathy Stroud
Orcutt Academy	610 Pinal Ave	Orcutt, CA	93455	805-938-8550		K-8	Joe Dana
Orcutt Academy	610 Pinal Ave	Orcutt, CA	93455	805-938-8550	938-8995	9-12	Rhett Carter
Our Community Charter S	10045 Jumilla Ave	Chatsworth, CA	91311	818-350-5000	350-5007	K-8	Lynn Izakowitz
Oxford Preparatory Academy	23000 Via Santa Maria	Mission Viejo, CA	92691-1827	949-305-6111	297-4747	K-8	Jeff Rich
Oxford Preparatory Academy	5862 C St	Chino, CA	91710	909-464-2672	248-0459	PK-8	Andrew Crowe
Oxford Preparatory Academy	22882 Loumont Dr	Lake Forest, CA	92630	949-916-5672	692-2102	K-8	Jeff Rich
Pacific Coast Charter S	294 Green Valley Rd	Watsonville, CA	95076-1300	831-786-2180	786-2192	K-12	Suzanne Smith
Pacific Collegiate Charter S	3004 Mission St	Santa Cruz, CA	95060-5733	831-479-7785	427-5254	7-12	Archie Douglas
Pacific Community Charter S	PO Box 984	Point Arena, CA	95468-0984	707-882-4131	882-4132	K-12	Sigrid Hillscan
Pacific Law Academy	1621 Brookside Rd	Stockton, CA	95207-7804	209-933-7445		9-12	Carol Sanderson
Pacific View Charter S	3670 Ocean Ranch Blvd	Oceanside, CA	92056-2669	760-757-0161	435-2666	K-12	Gina Campbell
Pacific View Charter S	115 Henderson St	Eureka, CA	95501	707-269-9490	269-9491	K-12	James Malloy
Pacoima Charter S	11016 Norris Ave	Pacoima, CA	91331-2598	818-899-0201	890-3812	K-5	Sylvia Fajardo
Pajaro Valley HS	500 Harkins Slough Rd	Watsonville, CA	95076-9453	831-728-8102	728-6944	9-12	Alison Niizawa
Palisades Charter ES	800 Via De La Paz	Pacific Plsds, CA	90272-3617	310-454-3700	459-5627	K-5	Joan Ingle
Palisades Charter HS	15777 Bowdoin St	Pacific Plsds, CA	90272-3523	310-230-6623	454-6076	9-12	Dr. Pamela Magee
Palmdale Aerospace Academy	38060 20th St E	Palmdale, CA	93550-4903	661-273-3680	266-7201	7-12	Dr. Laura Herman
Palm Desert Charter MS	74200 Rutledge Way	Palm Desert, CA	92260-2646	760-862-4320	862-4327	6-8	Sallie Fraser
Paradise Charter MS	6473 Clark Rd	Paradise, CA	95969-3501	530-872-7277	872-2924	6-8	Chris Reid
Paradise Charter S	3361 California Ave	Modesto, CA	95358-8337	209-524-0184	524-0363	K-8	Heath Thomason
Paradise eLearning Academy	5911 Maxwell Dr	Paradise, CA	95969-4023	530-872-6425	872-6418	9-12	Kathleen Blacklock
Paragon Collegiate Academy	1608 Sampson St	Marysville, CA	95901-4314	530-742-2505	763-5772	K-8	Laura Cotney
Para Los Ninos Charter S	1617 E 7th St	Los Angeles, CA	90021-1207	213-239-6605		K-5	Santa Acuna
Para Los Ninos - Gratts ECC	474 Hartford Ave	Los Angeles, CA	90017-1306	213-481-3200	977-5449	PK-2	Dr. Juan Ramirez
Para Los Ninos MS	835 Stanford Ave	Los Angeles, CA	90021-1847	213-896-2640	896-2660	6-8	Sandra Mejia
Paramount Collegiate Academy	4010 El Camino Ave	Sacramento, CA	95821	916-484-1480		6-12	Dawn Douglas
Pasadena Rosebud Academy	3544 Canon Blvd	Altadena, CA	91001-4008	626-797-7704		K-1	Shawn Brumfield Ed.D.
Paseo Grande S	2444 Marconi Ave	Sacramento, CA	95821	916-974-7307		K-12	Dave Petropulos
Pathways Academy Charter	1782 La Costa Meadows # 102	San Marcos, CA	92078	760-494-9646	897-7558	K-12	Meghan Freeman

School	Address	City,State	Zip code	Telephone	Fax	Grade	Contact
Pathways Charter S	150 Professional Center Dr	Rohnert Park, CA	94928-2148	707-585-6510	585-6515	K-12	Dr. Robert Tavonatti
Pathways Community S	8800 S San Pedro St	Los Angeles, CA	90003-3541	323-481-2334		9-12	Erica Hamilton
Pathways ICare Charter S	1020 Sun Down Way	Roseville, CA	95661-4473	916-784-6107	771-0893	K-8	Christina Smith
Pathways to College Charter S	PO Box 402672	Hesperia, CA	92340-2672	760-949-8002	947-9648	K-8	Dr. Sonya Joyner
Peabody Charter S	3018 Calle Noguera	Santa Barbara, CA	93105-2848	805-563-1172	569-7042	K-6	Demian Barnett
Peak to Peak Mountain Charter S	19009 Cerro Noroeste Rd	Pine Mountain C, CA	93222	661-242-3811		K-8	Mindy Moffatt
Penngrove ES	365 Adobe Rd	Penngrove, CA	94951	707-778-4755	778-4831	K-6	Amy Fadeji
Petaluma Accelerated Charter S	110 Ellis St	Petaluma, CA	94952	707-778-4750	778-4789	7-8	Matthew Harris
Phoenix Academy	PO Box 4925	San Rafael, CA	94913-4925	415-491-0581	491-0981	9-12	Raquel Rose
Piner-Olivet Charter S	2707 Francisco Ave	Santa Rosa, CA	95403-1869	707-522-3310	522-3317	7-8	Kim Kern
Pioneer ES	1888 Mustang Dr	Hanford, CA	93230-9811	559-584-8831	584-7049	PK-5	Sharon Cronk
Pioneer MS	101 W Pioneer Way	Hanford, CA	93230-9489	559-584-0112	584-0118	6-8	Jamie Rogers
Pioneer Technical Center	1105 S Madera Ave	Madera, CA	93637-5576	559-664-1600	673-5569	9-12	Leslie Neumeier
Pittman S	701 E Park St	Stockton, CA	95202-2207	209-933-7496	942-2769	K-8	Adrienne Machado
Pivot Online Charter - North Bay	2999 Cleveland Ave Ste D	Santa Rosa, CA	95403-2761	707-843-4676	544-2908	K-12	Jayna Gaskell
Pivot Online Charter S	1030 La Bonita Dr	San Marcos, CA	92078-5292	760-591-0217		6-12	Jayna Gaskell
Plainview Academic Charter Academy	10819 Plainview Ave	Tujunga, CA	91042-1633	818-353-1730	353-6658	K-5	Kenneth Johnson
Plumas Charter S	175 N Mill Creek Rd	Quincy, CA	95971-9678	530-283-3851	283-3841	K-12	Taletha Washburn
Pomelo Community Charter S	7633 March Ave	West Hills, CA	91304-5233	818-887-9700	887-1744	K-5	Andrea Ferber
Port of Los Angeles HS	250 W 5th St	San Pedro, CA	90731-3304	310-832-9201	832-1605	9-12	Gaetano Scotti
Prepa Tec HS	2665 Clarendon Ave	Walnut Park, CA	90255	323-800-2741	923-0380	9-12	Jose Salas
PREPA TEC - Los Angeles	2665 Clarendon Ave	Walnut Park, CA	90255	323-923-0383	923-0380	6-8	Wendy Chaves
Preuss S	9500 Gilman Dr	La Jolla, CA	92093-5004	858-822-3000	822-1620	6-12	Scott Barton
Price Charter MS	2650 New Jersey Ave	San Jose, CA	95124-1520	408-377-2532	377-7406	6-8	Sara Brown
Primary Charter S	51 E Beverly Pl	Tracy, CA	95376-3191	209-831-5240	831-5243	K-4	Virginia Stewart
Primary Years Academy	1540 N Lincoln St	Stockton, CA	95204-5617	209-933-7355	941-4580	K-5	Jean Segura
Provisional Accelerated Learning Academy	PO Box 7100	San Bernardino, CA	92411-0100	909-887-7002	887-8942	9-12	Dwaine Radden
Public Policy Charter S	1701 Browning Blvd	Los Angeles, CA	90062-1302	323-205-7920		5-8	Sonali Tucker
Public Safety Academy	1482 E Enterprise Dr	San Bernardino, CA	92408-0161	909-382-4574		6-12	Jennifer Stickel
PUC Community Charter ES	14019 Sayre St	Sylmar, CA	91342-4265	818-492-1890	492-1881	K-5	Jocelyn Velez
PUC Inspire Charter Academy	919 Eighth St	San Fernando, CA	91340	818-492-1880		6-8	Megan McGarry
Puente Charter S	10000 S Western Ave	Los Angeles, CA	90047	323-756-4921	754-8464	K-K	Jerome Greening
Puente Charter S	501 S Boyle Ave	Los Angeles, CA	90033-3816	323-780-8900		K-K	Jerome Greening
Quail Lake Charter S	4087 N Quail Lake Dr	Clovis, CA	93619-4646	559-524-6720	292-1276	K-8	Kim Labosky
REACH	708 Gravenstein Hwy N	Sebastopol, CA	95472-2808	707-823-8618	829-6285	K-8	Julie Heinsen
REACH Leadership STEAM Academy	4850 Jurupa Ave	Riverside, CA	92504	951-275-8820	275-8829	PK-6	Dr. Virgie Rentie
Reagan ES	1180 Diane Ave	Kingsburg, CA	93631-2830	559-897-6986	897-6987	4-6	Bobby Rodriguez
REALM Charter HS	1222 University Ave	Berkeley, CA	94702-1766	510-665-8300	809-9899	9-12	Victor Diaz
REALM Charter MS	2023 8th St	Berkeley, CA	94710-2026	510-809-9800	809-9899	6-8	Victor Diaz
Redding School of the Arts	955 Inspiration Pl	Redding, CA	96003	530-243-7145	243-4318	K-8	Margaret Johnson
Redwood Academy of Ukiah	PO Box 1383	Ukiah, CA	95482-1383	707-467-0500	467-4942	7-12	Rod Logan
Redwood Coast Montessori	1611 Peninsula Dr	Arcata, CA	95521-9658	707-832-4194	832-4194	K-8	Bryan Little
Redwood Preparatory Charter S	1480 Ross Hill Rd	Fortuna, CA	95540	707-682-6149		PK-8	Krista Croteau
Renaissance Arts Academy	1800 Colorado Blvd	Los Angeles, CA	90041-1340	323-259-5700	259-5718	K-12	P.K. Candaux
Resolute Academy Charter	1265 E 112th St	Los Angeles, CA	90059	323-559-6284		5-8	Natasha Sperstein
Revere Charter MS	1450 Allenford Ave	Los Angeles, CA	90049-3614	310-917-4800	576-7957	6-8	Thomas Tiannucc
Richmond Charter Academy	1450 Marina Way S	Richmond, CA	94804	510-235-2465	235-2487	6-8	Jeff Clinton
Richmond College Prep S	PO Box 2814	Richmond, CA	94802-2814	510-235-2066		K-6	Allie Welch
Ridgecrest Charter S	325 S Downs St	Ridgecrest, CA	93555-4531	760-375-1010	375-7766	K-8	Steve Martinez
Riebli ES	315 Mark West Springs Rd	Santa Rosa, CA	95404-1101	707-524-2980	524-2986	K-6	Patty Dineen
Rincon Valley Charter S	5305 Dupont Dr	Santa Rosa, CA	95409-3843	707-539-3410	537-1791	7-8	Kate Westrich
Rio Valley Charter S	1110 W Kettleman Ln	Lodi, CA	95240	209-368-4934	368-4953	K-12	Marcie Grill
Rise Kohyang HS	1575 W 2nd St	Los Angeles, CA	90026	213-284-2553	256-3974	9-12	Elias Pappas
Rise Kohyang MS	3020 Wilshire Blve Ste 2	Los Angeles, CA	90010	424-789-8338	256-3974	6-8	Eliza Kim
Rising Sun Montessori S	7006 Rossmore Ln	El Dorado Hills, CA	95762	916-936-2333		PK-8	Karl Zierhut
Riverbank Language Academy Charter S	2400 Stanislaus St	Riverbank, CA	95367-2233	209-869-8093	869-0430	K-8	Vanessa Rojas
River Charter S Lighthouse Charter	1500 Park Blvd	West Sacramento, CA	95691-3027	916-744-1212		K-8	Steve Lewis
River Islands Technology Academy	1175 Marina Dr	Lathrop, CA	95330-8586	209-229-4700		K-7	Brenda Scholl
River MS	2447 Old Sonoma Rd	Napa, CA	94558-6006	707-253-6813	258-2800	6-8	Celeste Akiu
River Montessori Charter S	3880 Cypress Dr	Petaluma, CA	94954-5613	707-778-6414	773-5800	1-6	Kelly Mannion
River Oak Charter S	555 Leslie St	Ukiah, CA	95482-5507	707-467-1855	467-1857	K-8	Rima Meechan
River Oaks Academy Charter S	920 Hampshire Rd Ste X	Westlake Vlg, CA	91361	805-777-7999	777-7998	PK-12	Claudia Weintraub
Riverside County Education Academy	44-801 Golf Center Pkwy	Indio, CA	92201	760-863-3111	863-3110	9-12	Santos Campos
Riverside County Education Academy	13730 Perris Blvd	Moreno Valley, CA	92553	951-826-4905		9-12	Santos Campos
Riverside Drive ES	13061 Riverside Dr	Sherman Oaks, CA	91423-2199	818-990-4525	789-4835	K-5	Kesia Doucette
Riverside Preparatory S	PO Box 455	Oro Grande, CA	92368-0455	760-243-5884	843-3766	K-12	JoAnn Baeten
River Springs Charter S	43466 Business Park Dr	Temecula, CA	92590-5526	951-252-8800	252-8801	K-12	Tanya Rogers
River Valley Charter S	9707 1/2 Marilla Dr	Lakeside, CA	92040-2868	619-390-2579	390-2581	7-12	Travis Wall
Roberts Ferry Charter School Academy	101 Roberts Ferry Rd	Waterford, CA	95386-9502	209-874-2331		6-8	Bob Loretelli
Roberts Institute of Learning Charter S	6785 Imperial Ave	San Diego, CA	92114-4317	619-674-6019	546-0274	K-6	Shelia Malveaux
Rocketship Academy Brilliant Minds	2960 Story Road	San Jose, CA	95127	408-708-5650	618-8637	PK-4	Amy Filsinger
Rocketship Alma Academy	198 W Alma Ave	San Jose, CA	95110-3631	877-931-6838	982-3691	K-5	Hana Martinez
Rocketship Discovery Prep S	370 Wooster Ave	San Jose, CA	95116-1095	408-217-8951	217-9251	K-6	Eesir Kaur
Rocketship Fuerza Community Prep	70 S Jackson Ave	San Jose, CA	95116-2506	408-708-5744		K-4	Maricela Guerrero
Rocketship Los Suenos Academy	331 S 34th St	San Jose, CA	95116-2905	877-684-4028	935-6084	K-5	Judy Lavi
Rocketship Mateo Sheedy ES	788 Locust St	San Jose, CA	95110	408-286-3330	286-3331	K-5	Jason Fromoltz
Rocketship Mosaic ES	950 Owsley Ave	San Jose, CA	95122-3109	408-899-2607	899-2613	K-5	Danny Etcheverry
Rocketship Rising Stars	3167 Senter Rd	San Jose, CA	95111	301-789-5469		K-5	Cheye Calvo
Rocketship Si Se Puede Academy	2249 Dobern Ave	San Jose, CA	95116-3405	408-286-3344	286-3331	K-12	Heidy Shinn
Rocketship Spark Academy	683 Sylvandale Ave	San Jose, CA	95111	408-622-6651	622-5748	K-5	Annie Tran
Rocklin Academy	6532 Turnstone Way	Rocklin, CA	95765-5865	916-632-6580	784-3034	K-6	Laura Regan
Rocklin Academy at Meyers Street	5035 Meyers St	Rocklin, CA	95677-2811	916-632-6580	784-3034	K-6	Wendy Mitchell
Rocklin Academy Gateway	6550 Lonetree Blvd	Rocklin, CA	95765-5874	916-632-6580	784-3034	PK-8	Jillyane Antoon
Rocklin Independent Charter Academy	3250 Victory Dr	Rocklin, CA	95765	916-632-3195		K-12	Wayne Hauptman A.B.
Rocky Point Charter S	3500 Tamarack Dr	Redding, CA	96003-1747	530-225-0456	225-0499	K-8	Deborah Stierli
Romero Charter S	1157 S Berendo St	Los Angeles, CA	90006-3301	213-413-9600	413-9699	6-8	Jose Castillo
Roosevelt Community Learning Center	31191 Road 180	Visalia, CA	93292-9585	559-592-9160	592-2927	K-12	Daniel Huecker
Roosevelt ES	1185 10th Ave	Kingsburg, CA	93631-2100	559-897-5193	897-6865	1-1	Shawn Marshall
Rosa Parks Academy	1930 S D St	Stockton, CA	95206-2489	209-944-5590	465-2690	K-5	Natalie June
Roseland Accelerated MS	1777 West Ave	Santa Rosa, CA	95407-7449	707-546-7089	546-0434	7-8	Haley Piazza
Roseland Collegiate Prep	80 Ursuline Rd	Santa Rosa, CA	95403-1729	707-528-1764	528-8605	7-10	Danielle Yount
Roseland University Prep	100 Sebastopol Rd	Santa Rosa, CA	95407-6928	707-566-9990	566-9992	9-12	Sue Reese
Roses in Concrete Community S	4551 Steele St	Oakland, CA	94619-2743	510-698-3794		K-8	Jeff Duncan-Andrade
Sacramento HS	2315 34th St	Sacramento, CA	95817-1299	916-277-6200	277-6370	9-12	Michelle Seijas
Sacramento Valley Charter S	2301 Evergreen Ave	West Sacramento, CA	95691-3009	916-596-6422	564-5764	K-8	Sheila Gibson
St. Hope Public School 7	5201 Strawberry Ln	Sacramento, CA	95820-4815	916-649-7850	277-7039	K-8	Erin Marston
Salmon Creek S	1935 Bohemian Hwy	Occidental, CA	95465-9100	707-874-1205	874-1226	2-8	Rene McBride
Samueli Academy	1901 N Fairview St	Santa Ana, CA	92706	714-619-0245	619-0252	9-12	Rocio Gomez
San Carlos Charter Learning Center	750 Dartmouth Ave	San Carlos, CA	94070-1769	650-508-7343	508-7341	K-8	Stacy Emory
San Diego Cooperative Charter S	7260 Linda Vista Rd	San Diego, CA	92111-6128	858-496-1613	467-9741	K-8	Dr. Sarah Saluta
San Diego Cooperative Charter S 2	PO Box 13926	San Diego, CA	92170	619-840-6993		K-8	Anthony Villasenor
San Diego Cooperative Charter S 2	3550 Logan Ave	San Diego, CA	92113-2712	619-840-6993		K-8	Anthony Vissasenor
San Diego Global Vision Academy	3430 School St	San Diego, CA	92116-3423	619-600-5321	550-3637	K-5	Christine Kane
San Diego Neighborhood Homeschools	3548 Seagate Way Ste 140	Oceanside, CA	92056-2676	760-295-1117	509-4691	K-12	Salvador Leon
San Diego Virtual Charter S	7950 University Ave	La Mesa, CA	91942-5579	619-713-7271	308-6007	7-12	Brennan McLaughlin
Sanger Academy Charter S	2207 9th St	Sanger, CA	93657-2711	559-524-6840	875-8045	K-8	Christy Platt
San Jacinto Valley Academy	480 N San Jacinto Ave	San Jacinto, CA	92583-2729	951-654-6113	644-5083	K-12	Penny Harrison
San Joaquin Building Futures Academy	PO Box 213030	Stockton, CA	95213-9030	209-468-8140	468-4951	9-12	Janine Kaeslin
San Jose Charter Academy	2021 W Alwood St	West Covina, CA	91790-3259	626-856-1693	480-7125	K-8	Erin Shiroma
San Jose Conservation Corps Charter S	1560 Berger Dr	San Jose, CA	95112-2703	408-283-7171		12-12	Stephanie Ogden
San Juan Choices Charter S	4425 Laurelwood Way	Sacramento, CA	95864-0881	916-979-8378		6-12	Tony Oddo
San Lorenzo Valley USD Charter S	325 Marion Ave	Ben Lomond, CA	95005-9403	831-335-0932	336-0131	K-12	Rhonda Schlosser
San Miguel ES	5350 Faught Rd	Santa Rosa, CA	95403-1205	707-524-2960	524-2968	K-6	Patrick Eagle
Santa Barbara Charter S	6100 Stow Canyon Rd	Goleta, CA	93117-1705	805-967-6522	967-6382	PK-8	
Santa Clarita Valley International S	28060 Hasley Canyon Rd	Castaic, CA	91384-4572	661-705-4820	607-0295	K-12	Kimberly Matthes
Santa Monica Blvd Community Charter S	1022 N Van Ness Ave	Los Angeles, CA	90038-3252	323-469-0971	462-4093	K-6	David Riddick
Santa Rosa Academy	27587 La Piedra Rd	Menifee, CA	92584	951-672-2400	672-6060	K-12	Midge James
Santa Rosa Accelerated Charter	4650 Badger Rd	Santa Rosa, CA	95409-2633	707-528-5319	528-5644	5-6	Ed Navarro
Santa Rosa Charter Academy	3838 Eagle Rock Blvd	Los Angeles, CA	90065-3638	323-254-1703	254-0958	6-8	Melody Levine
Santa Rosa Charter S for the Arts	2230 Lomitas Ave	Santa Rosa, CA	95404	707-522-3170	522-3172	K-8	Paul Gaudreau
Santa Rosa French-American Charter S	1350 Sonoma Ave	Santa Rosa, CA	95405	707-522-3161		K-6	Richard Johnstone
Santa Ynez Valley Charter S	PO Box 59	Santa Ynez, CA	93460-0059	805-686-7360	686-7383	K-8	Mark Palmerston
Santiago Charter MS	515 N Rancho Santiago Blvd	Orange, CA	92869-2724	714-997-6366	532-4758	7-8	James D'Agostino
Sartorette Charter S	3850 Woodford Dr	San Jose, CA	95124-3736	408-264-4380	264-1758	K-5	John Hayes
SAVA: Sacramento Academic and Vocational	3141 Dwight Rd Ste 400	Elk Grove, CA	95758-6473	916-428-3200	428-3232	7-12	Morri Elliott
SAVA: Sacramento Academic and Vocational	5330 Power Inn Rd Ste D	Sacramento, CA	95820-6757	916-387-8063	387-0139	7-12	Morri Elliott
SCALE Leadership Academy	13089 Peyton Dr	Chino Hills, CA	91709-6018	888-315-4660		K-12	Lawrence Wynder

School	Address	City,State	Zip code	Telephone	Fax	Grade	Contact
Schaefer Charter S	1370 San Miguel Rd	Santa Rosa, CA	95403-1986	707-522-3015	522-3017	K-6	Gina Silveira
School of Arts and Enterprise	295 N Garey Ave	Pomona, CA	91767-5429	909-622-0699	620-1018	6-12	Lucille Berger
School of Extended Educational Options	1460 E Holt Ave Ste 100	Pomona, CA	91767-5851	909-397-4900	622-2496	7-12	Tom Sweeney
School of Unlimited Learning	2336 Calaveras St	Fresno, CA	93721-1104	559-498-8543	237-0956	9-12	Dr. Mark Wilson
Science and Technology Charter S	PO Box 458	Knights Landing, CA	95645-0458	530-735-6435	735-6155	K-6	Barbara Herms
Sebastopol Independent Charter S	PO Box 1170	Sebastopol, CA	95473-1170	707-824-9700	824-1432	K-8	Chris Topham
Sequoia Charter ES	PO Box 44260	Lemon Cove, CA	93244-0260	559-564-2106	564-2126	K-8	Jeremy Powell
Serna Charter S	19 S Central Ave	Lodi, CA	95240-2901	209-331-7809	331-7997	K-6	Maria Cervantes
Serrania Charter for Enriched Studies	5014 Serrania Ave	Woodland Hills, CA	91364-3350	818-340-6700	592-0565	K-5	Sr. Luis Alvarado M.Ed.
Shasta Charter Academy	307 Park Marina Cir	Redding, CA	96001	530-245-2600	245-2611	9-12	Ben Claassen M.A.
Shenandoah HS	6540 Koki Ln	El Dorado, CA	95623-4328	530-622-6212	622-1071	9-12	Chuck Palmer
Shenandoah Valley MS	10010 Shenandoah Rd	Plymouth, CA	95669	209-257-5334		5-8	
Sherman Oaks Charter S	14755 Greenleaf St	Sherman Oaks, CA	91403-4199	818-784-8283	981-8258	K-5	Judith Dichter
Sherwood Montessori S	1071 E 16th St	Chico, CA	95928	530-513-2296		K-8	Michelle Yezbick
Shiloh Charter School	6633 Paradise Rd	Modesto, CA	95358	209-522-2261	522-2261	3-12	Seth Ehrler
SIATech Charter S	1949 Avenida del Oro	Oceanside, CA	92056-5829	760-945-1227	631-3411	9-12	Dr. Linda Dawson
Sierra Academy of Expeditionary Learning	340 Buena Vista St	Grass Valley, CA	95945-7210	530-268-2200		9-12	Erica Crane
Sierra Charter S	1931 N Fine Ave	Fresno, CA	93727-1534	559-490-4290	490-4292	K-12	Lisa Marasco
Sierra Expeditionary Learning	11603 Donner Pass Rd	Truckee, CA	96161-4953	530-582-3701	582-3703	K-8	David Manahan
Sierra Foothill Charter S	4952 School House Rd	Catheys Valley, CA	95306-9710	209-742-6222	742-6922	K-8	Mindy Bolar
Sierra Montessori Academy	16229 Duggans Rd	Grass Valley, CA	95949-8520	530-268-9990	268-0613	K-8	Henry Bietz
Sierra Vista Charter HS	351 N K St	Tulare, CA	93274	559-687-7384	687-7388	9-12	Tammy Aldaco
Silver Oak HS	951 Palisade St	Hayward, CA	94542-1048	510-370-3334		9-12	Elaine Blasi
Simon Technology Acad HS	10720 Wilmington Ave	Los Angeles, CA	90059-1236	323-744-2122	744-2123	9-12	Dr. Christopher Carr
Six Rivers Charter HS	1720 M St	Arcata, CA	95521-5741	707-825-2428	825-2034	9-12	Ron Perry
Sixth Grade Academy	700 Bantam Way	Petaluma, CA	94952-1709	707-778-4724		6-6	Renee Semik
Sixth Street Prep-STREAM S	12219 Second Ave	Victorville, CA	92395	760-241-0962	241-2497	K-6	Collin Rowe
Skirball MS	603 E 115th St	Los Angeles, CA	90059-2322	323-905-1377	905-1378	6-8	Marco Ibarra
Sky Mountain Charter S	4535 Missouri Flat Rd	Placerville, CA	95667-6846	530-295-3566	295-3583	K-12	Susan Clark
Smidt Technology HS	211 S Avenue 20	Los Angeles, CA	90031-2508	323-352-3206		9-12	Dr. Dean Marolla-Turner
Smythe Academy of Arts & Sciences	2781 Northgate Blvd	Sacramento, CA	95833-2208	916-566-2740	566-3584	PK-6	Ken Dandurand
Smythe Academy of Arts & Sciences	700 Dos Rios St	Sacramento, CA	95811-0434	916-566-3430	566-3531	7-8	Melissa Jewell M.Ed.
SOAR Charter Academy	198 W Mill St	San Bernardino, CA	92408-1402	909-888-3300	888-3310	K-8	Trisha Lancaster
Sol Aureus College Prep Charter S	6620 Gloria Dr	Sacramento, CA	95831-1655	916-421-0600	421-0601	K-8	Norman Hernandez
Soledad Enrichment Action Charter S	222 N Virgil Ave	Los Angeles, CA	90004-3622	213-480-4200	480-4199	9-12	Margaret Godinez
Sonoma Charter S	17202 Highway 12	Sonoma, CA	95476-3667	707-935-4232	935-4207	K-8	Kevin Kassebaum
Sonoma Mountain ES	1900 Rainier Cir	Petaluma, CA	94954-2543	707-765-4305	765-4385	K-6	Michele Gochberg
South Bay Charter S	6077 Loma Ave	Eureka, CA	95503-6869	707-443-4828	444-3690	K-8	Gary Storts
South Sutter Charter S	4535 Missouri Flat Rd Ste1A	Placerville, CA	95667	800-979-4436	295-3583	K-12	Jason Jones
Spark Charter S	739 Morse Ave	Sunnyvale, CA	94085-3010	408-752-2631		K-8	Christopher Mahoney Ed.D.
Spring Creek Matanzas Charter S	1687 Yulupa Ave	Santa Rosa, CA	95405-7778	707-546-6183	528-8027	4-6	Kate Westrich
Spring Creek Matanzas Charter S	4675 Mayette Ave	Santa Rosa, CA	95405-7331	707-545-1771	545-6926	PK-3	Joan Boyce
Squaw Valley Preparatory	PO Box 2891	Olympic Valley, CA	96146-2891	530-581-1036	581-2012	6-12	Jeff Kraunz
Stallworth Charter S	1610 E Main St	Stockton, CA	95205-5521	209-948-4511	943-5218	PK-8	Robin Mooreziad
Stanislaus Alternative Charter S	1120 13th St	Modesto, CA	95354-0950	209-238-6801	238-4216	9-12	Julie Moore
Steele Canyon Charter HS	12440 Campo Rd	Spring Valley, CA	91978-2331	619-660-3500	660-7198	9-12	Don Hohimer
Stella Middle Charter Academy	2636 S Mansfield Ave	Los Angeles, CA	90016-3512	323-406-7155	954-6415	5-6	Darryl Garris
Stellar Charter School	5885 E Bonnyview Rd	Redding, CA	96001-4535	530-245-7730	245-7731	K-12	Heidi Schuler
Stern Math and Science S	5151 State Univ Dr Lot 7	Los Angeles, CA	90032	323-987-2144	987-2149	9-12	Kirsten Woo Ph.D.
Stockton Collegiate International ES	PO Box 2286	Stockton, CA	95201-2286	209-390-9861	390-9862	K-5	Scott Luhn
Stockton Collegiate International S	PO Box 2286	Stockton, CA	95201	209-390-9861	390-9862	6-12	Scott Luhn
Stockton Early College Academy	349 E Vine St	Stockton, CA	95202-1107	209-933-7370	939-9504	9-12	Joshaua Thom
Stockton HS	22 S Van Buren St	Stockton, CA	95203-3118	209-933-7365	469-3740	9-12	Maryann Santella
Stone Bridge S	1680 Los Carneros Ave	Napa, CA	94559-9741	707-252-5522	251-9767	K-8	Bill Bindewald
Stony Point Academy	3223 Primrose Ave	Santa Rosa, CA	95407	707-568-7504		K-10	Lisa Katimbang
STREAM Charter S	479 Oro Dam Blvd E	Oroville, CA	95965-5743	530-534-1633		K-8	Donald Phillips
Success One Charter S	451 S Villa Ave	Willows, CA	95988-2964	530-934-6575		K-5	Susan Domenighini
Summit Charter Academy	2036 E Hatch Rd	Modesto, CA	95351-5142	209-538-8082	538-1620	K-5	Jamey Olney
Summit Charter Academy - Lombardi Campus	1509 Lombardi St	Porterville, CA	93257	559-788-6445	783-9400	K-6	Treasure Weisenberger
Summit Charter Academy - Mathew Campus	175 S Mathew St	Porterville, CA	93257-2710	559-782-5902	782-5907	K-6	Lily Shimer
Summit Charter Collegiate Academy	15550 Redwood St	Porterville, CA	93257	559-788-6440	788-6444	6-12	Krista Gaines-Herrera Ed.D
Summit K2 Charter S	1800 Elm St	El Cerrito, CA	94530	510-435-2032		7-12	Abbie Ridenour
Summit Leadership Academy High Desert	12850 Muscatel St	Hesperia, CA	92344-5566	760-949-9202	949-9257	9-12	Shannon Brandner
Summit Preparatory Charter HS	890 Broadway St	Redwood City, CA	94063-3105	650-556-1110	556-1121	9-12	Penelope Pak
Summit Preparatory Charter S	5100 S Broadway Ave	Los Angeles, CA	90037	323-642-8806		4-8	Arianna Haut
Summit Public S: Rainier	1750 S White Rd	San Jose, CA	95127-4760	408-831-3104	831-3105	9-12	Edwin Avarca
Summit Public S: Shasta	699 Serramonte Blvd	Daly City, CA	94015-4132	650-799-4719	799-4721	9-12	Caitlyn Herman
Summit Public S: Tahoma	285 Blossom Hill Rd	San Jose, CA	95123-2048	408-729-1981	729-3853	9-12	Nicholas Kim
Summit Public School: Denali	495 Mercury Dr	Sunnyvale, CA	94085-4707	669-600-5697		6-12	Kevin Bock
SunRidge Charter S	7285 Hayden Ave	Sebastopol, CA	95472-4359	707-824-2844	824-2861	K-8	Kalen Wood
Sunrise MS	1149 E Julian St	San Jose, CA	95116-1005	877-659-4785		6-8	Teresa Robinson
Sutter Peak Charter Academy	6450 20th St	Rio Linda, CA	95673-3718	866-992-9033		K-12	Heather Marshall
Sycamore Academy Science & Cultural Arts	23151 Palomar St	Wildomar, CA	92595	951-678-5217	678-5932	K-6	Barbara Hale
Sycamore Valley Academy	4230 W Tulare Ave	Visalia, CA	93277	559-622-3236	622-3237	K-8	Ruth Dutton
Sylmar Charter HS	13050 Borden Ave	Sylmar, CA	91342-4299	818-833-3700	364-1037	9-12	James Lee
Synergy Charter Academy	PO Box 78999	Los Angeles, CA	90016-0999	323-235-7960	235-7970	K-5	Kristine Miklos
Synergy Kinetic Academy	PO Box 78999	Los Angeles, CA	90016	323-846-2225	846-2234	6-8	Christine Bradford
Synergy Quantum Academy	PO Box 78999	Los Angeles, CA	90016-0999	323-846-4716	846-4729	9-12	Dr. Phillip Gedeon
Taft Charter HS	5461 Winnetka Ave	Woodland Hills, CA	91364-2548	818-227-3600	592-0877	9-12	Daniel Steiner
Taylion Academy	1184 W 2nd St Ste 101	San Bernardino, CA	92410	909-889-5152	723-1131	K-12	
Taylion High Desert Academy	11336 Bartlett Ave Ste 9	Adelanto, CA	92301	760-843-6622		K-12	Timothy Smith
Taylion San Diego Academy	100 N Rancho Santa Fe Rd	San Marcos, CA	92069-1280	760-295-5564	295-5614	K-12	Timothy Smith
TEACH Academy of Technologies	10045 S Western Ave	Los Angeles, CA	90047	323-777-2068	777-7143	5-8	Dr. Greg Perez
TEACH Tech Charter HS	10000 S Western Ave	Los Angeles, CA	90047-4254	323-750-8471	750-8477	9-12	Frank Williams
TEAM Charter S	600 E Main St	Stockton, CA	95202-3029	209-462-2282		PK-5	Marlesse Cavazos
Tehama eLearning Academy	715 Jackson St Ste B	Red Bluff, CA	96080-3771	530-527-0188	527-0273	6-12	Michelle Barnard
Temecula Preparatory S	35777 Abelia St	Winchester, CA	92596-8450	951-926-6776	926-6797	K-12	Cindy Woodruff
Temecula Valley Charter S	35755 Abelia St	Winchester, CA	92596-8450	951-294-6775	294-6780	K-8	Lois Hastings
Tennenbaum Family Technology HS	2050 N San Fernando Rd	Los Angeles, CA	90065-1267	323-276-5545		9-12	Dr. Abigail Nunez
Thomas Charter HS	101 W Adell St	Madera, CA	93638	559-675-6626	675-6612	9-12	Jessica Montemayor
Thomas Charter S	101 W Adell St	Madera, CA	93638	559-674-1192	674-8955	K-8	Tera Napier
Three Rivers Charter S	1211 Del Mar Dr	Fort Bragg, CA	95437-5641	707-964-1128	964-1003	K-12	Roger Coy
Thrive Public Charter S	4260 54th St	San Diego, CA	92115-6009	619-839-9543		K-8	Nicole Assisi
Tierra Linda MS	750 Dartmouth Ave	San Carlos, CA	94070-1769	650-508-7370	508-7341	5-8	Steven Kaufman
Tierra Pacifica Charter S	986 Bostwick Ln	Santa Cruz, CA	95062-1756	831-462-9404	477-0936	K-8	Linda Lambdin
Today's Fresh Start Charter S	2301 E Rosencrans Ave	Compton, CA	90221	310-631-1502		K-8	Tanya Goff
Today's Fresh Start Charter S	2255 W Adams Blvd	Los Angeles, CA	90018	323-732-6636		K-8	
Today's Fresh Start Charter S	4514 Crenshaw Blvd	Los Angeles, CA	90043	323-293-9826		K-8	
Today's Fresh Start Charter S	3405 W Imperial Hwy	Inglewood, CA	90303	310-680-7599		K-8	Jeanette Parker
Topanga Charter ES	22075 Topanga School Rd	Topanga, CA	90290-3835	310-455-3711	455-3517	K-6	Steven Gediman
Topeka Charter S for Advanced Studies	9815 Topeka Dr	Northridge, CA	91324-1800	818-886-2266	885-7682	K-5	Temika Dixon
Tree of Life Montessori Charter S	PO Box 966	Ukiah, CA	95482-0966	707-462-0913	462-0914	PK-8	Celeste Beck
Trillium Charter S	1464 Spear Ave	Arcata, CA	95521-4882	707-822-4721	822-7054	PK-5	Marianne Keller
Triumph Center for Early Childhood Ed	4104 Martin Luther King Jr	Sacramento, CA	95820-2725	916-731-8200		PK-PK	Allison Ferry
Triumph Charter S	13361 Glenoaks Blvd	Sylmar, CA	91342-2110	818-356-2795	979-6579	6-12	Christine Graves
Trivium Charter S	1600 Berkeley Dr	Lompoc, CA	93436-7105	805-291-1303		K-12	Trisha Vais
Tubman Village Charter S	6880 Mohawk St	San Diego, CA	92115-1728	619-668-8635	668-2480	K-8	Rachel McCoy
Twin Hills Charter MS	1685 Watertrough Rd	Sebastopol, CA	95472-4647	707-823-7446	823-6470	6-8	Catherine Bosch
Twin Ridges Home Study Charter S	111 New Mohawk Rd	Nevada City, CA	95959-3270	530-478-1815	478-0266	K-8	Jenny Travers
Twin Rivers Charter S	2510 Live Oak Blvd	Yuba City, CA	95991	530-755-2872	673-1847	K-8	Karen Villalobos
Uncharted Shores Academy	330 E St	Crescent City, CA	95531-3945	707-464-9828	464-1428	PK-8	Margie Rouge
Union Street Charter S	470 Union St	Arcata, CA	95521-6429	707-822-4845	825-9025	K-5	Rea Erickson
University HS	2611 E Matoian Way MS/UH134	Fresno, CA	93740-0001	559-278-8263	278-0447	9-12	Dr. James Bushman
University Preparation S	550 Temple Ave	Camarillo, CA	93010-4833	805-482-4608	388-5814	PK-5	Charmon Evans
University Preparatory Academy	2315 Canoas Garden Ave	San Jose, CA	95125-2005	408-723-1839	779-0519	7-12	Daniel Ordaz
University Preparatory HS	915 S Mooney Blvd	Visalia, CA	93277-2214	559-730-2529	737-4378	9-12	Eric Thiessen
University Preparatory S	2200 Eureka Way	Redding, CA	96001-0337	530-245-2790	245-2791	6-12	Shelle Peterson
University Preparatory Value HS	700 Wilshire Blvd Fl 4	Los Angeles, CA	90017	213-335-3730		9-12	David Doyle
Urban Corps of San Diego County Charter	3127 Jefferson St	San Diego, CA	92110	619-235-6884		9-12	Dan Thomas
Urban Discovery Academy	840 14th St	San Diego, CA	92101	619-788-4668	688-9796	K-8	Jenni Owen
Urban Montessori Charter S	5328 Brann St	Oakland, CA	94619-3312	510-842-1181	535-3841	K-8	David Castillo
USC College Prep Santa Ana	1010 W 17th St	Santa Ana, CA	92706	212-454-0599		9-12	Evelyn Castro
USC East College Prep	3825 N Mission Rd	Los Angeles, CA	90031-3137	323-285-1441		9-12	Andrew Goltermann
Valdez Leadership Academy	1855 Lucretia Ave	San Jose, CA	95122-3730	408-384-4015	936-3095	9-12	Jeffrey Camarillo
Vallejo Charter S	2833 Tennessee St	Vallejo, CA	94591-6456	707-556-8620	556-8624	K-8	Carla Galbraith
Valley Charter ES	16514 Nordhoff St	North Hills, CA	91343-3724	818-810-6713	810-9667	K-5	Leslie Lainer
Valley Charter HS	108 Campus Way	Modesto, CA	95350-5803	209-238-6800	238-6897	9-12	Michael Berhorst

School	Address	City,State	Zip code	Telephone	Fax	Grade	Contact
Valley Charter MS	6952 Van Nuys Blvd	Van Nuys, CA	91405	818-988-9128	988-9265	6-8	Matthew Rubin
Valley Life Charter S	3737 W Walnut Ave	Visalia, CA	93277-3947	559-761-1299		K-12	Lori Lackey
Valley Oak Charter S	PO Box 878	Ojai, CA	93024-0878	805-640-4421	646-4700	K-12	Laura Fulmer
Valley Oaks Charter S	1300 17th St	Bakersfield, CA	93301-4504	661-852-6750	633-5287	K-12	Deanna Downs
Valley Preparatory Academy	4221 N Hughes Ave	Fresno, CA	93705-1611	559-225-7737	225-0976	K-8	Shelly Lether
Valley View Charter Prep	2453 Grand Canal Blvd	Stockton, CA	95207-8259	916-866-9033	991-5770	K-12	John Mittan
Valor Academy Charter HS	8015 Van Nuys Blvd	Panorama City, CA	91402-6009	323-934-8910	934-8916	9-12	Evelyn Licea
Valor Academy Charter S	9034 Burnet Ave	North Hills, CA	91343	818-830-1700	830-1799	5-8	Maurice Regalado
Valor Academy ES	17081 Devonshire St	Northridge, CA	91325	818-217-2733	934-8916	K-4	May Oey
Van Gogh Charter S	17160 Van Gogh St	Granada Hills, CA	91344-1299	818-360-2141	831-9081	K-5	Pamela Merloni
Vantage Point Charter S	10862 Spenceville Rd	Penn Valley, CA	95946-9625	530-432-5312	432-8744	K-12	Torie F. England
Vaughn Next Century Learning Center	13330 Vaughn St	San Fernando, CA	91340-2216	818-896-7461	834-9036	PK-12	Anita Zepeda
Ventura S of Arts & Global Education	PO Box 392	Ventura, CA	93002-0392	805-648-5503	648-5539	K-8	Mary Galvin
Venture Academy	PO Box 213030	Stockton, CA	95213-9030	209-468-5940	468-9000	K-12	Kathleen Focacci
View Park Accelerated MS	5311 S Crenshaw Blvd	Los Angeles, CA	90043	323-290-6961	290-9271	6-8	Tamarra Lewis
View Park Prep Accelerated Charter ES	3855 W Slauson Ave	Los Angeles, CA	90043-2947	323-290-6950	298-4935	K-5	Leslie Shaw-McGee
View Park Prep Accelerated HS	5701 Crenshaw Blvd	Los Angeles, CA	90043-2409	323-290-6975	881-4924	9-12	Dr. Hurshel Williams
Village Charter Academy	7357 Jordan Ave	Canoga Park, CA	91303-1238	818-716-2887		K-5	Jennifer Clark
Village Charter S	2590 Piner Rd	Santa Rosa, CA	95401-4035	707-524-2848		K-8	Rebecca Ivanoff
Village ES	900 Yulupa Ave	Santa Rosa, CA	95405-7018	707-545-5754	573-0951	K-6	Cecilia Holt
Vincent Academy	2501 Chestnut St	Oakland, CA	94607-2477	510-452-2100	452-2101	K-5	Kate Nicol
Visalia Charter Independent Study	1821 W Meadow Ave	Visalia, CA	93277-2247	559-735-8055	622-3170	9-12	Michele Reid
Visions in Education Charter S	5030 El Camino Ave	Carmichael, CA	95608-4650	916-971-5331	971-5590	K-12	Dr. Jody Graf
Vista Charter MS	2900 W Temple St	Los Angeles, CA	90026-4516	213-201-4000	201-5861	6-8	Jose Miguel Kubes
Vista Heritage Charter MS	2609 W Fifth St	Santa Ana, CA	92703	714-988-2720	201-5861	6-8	Lauri Martin
Vista Oaks Charter S	14301 Byron Hwy	Byron, CA	94514-2515	925-420-6616		K-8	Joy Groen
Vista Real Charter HS	401 S A St Ste 3	Oxnard, CA	93030-5278	805-486-5449	486-5455	9-12	Corrine Manley
Voices Academy at Morgan Hill	16870 Murphy Ave	Morgan Hill, CA	95037	408-763-5770		K-8	Juan Carlos Villasenor
Voices Academy at Mt. Pleasant	14271 Story Rd	San Jose, CA	95127	408-684-3503		K-8	Maria Madrigal
Voices College-Bound Language Academy	715 Hellyer Ave	San Jose, CA	95111	408-361-1960	361-1979	K-8	Charles Miller
Walden Academy	1149 W Wood St	Willows, CA	95988-2614	530-361-6480		PK-5	
Washington Charter S	45768 Portola Ave	Palm Desert, CA	92260-4861	760-862-4350	862-4356	K-5	Allan Lehmann
Washington ES	1501 Ellis St	Kingsburg, CA	93631-1896	559-897-2955	897-6863	PK-K	Jennifer DuPras M.Ed.
Watsonville Charter S of the Arts	75 Whiting Rd	Watsonville, CA	95076-1421	831-728-8123	728-6286	K-8	Amy Thomas
Watts Learning Center	310 W 95th St	Los Angeles, CA	90003-4012	323-754-9900	754-0935	K-5	Kelly Baptiste
Watts Learning Ctr Charter MS	8800 S San Pedro St	Los Angeles, CA	90003-3541	323-565-4800	750-5051	6-8	Gayle Windom
W.E.B. DuBois Charter S	2604 Martin Luther King Blv	Fresno, CA	93706	559-486-1166	486-1199	K-12	Linda Washington
Welby Way Charter ES & Gifted Magnet Ctr	23456 Welby Way	West Hills, CA	91307-3328	818-348-1975	704-8726	K-5	Jennifer Yoo
West Charter S	4600 Lavell Rd	Santa Rosa, CA	95403	707-524-2741	524-2782	K-8	Tracy Kendall
Westchester Secondary Charter S	7001 S St Andrews Pl	Los Angeles, CA	90047	310-216-6800		6-10	Janet Landon
Western Center Academy	2345 Searl Pkwy	Hemet, CA	92543-9706	951-791-0033	791-0032	6-12	Paul Bailey
Western Sierra Collegiate Academy	660 Menlo Dr	Rocklin, CA	95765-3713	916-778-4544	626-5540	7-12	Gregg Moses
Westlake Charter S	3800 Del Paso Rd	Sacramento, CA	95834	916-567-5760	567-5769	K-5	John Eick
West Park Charter Academy	2695 S Valentine Ave	Fresno, CA	93706-9042	559-233-6501	497-1944	K-12	Ramiro Elizondo
West Sacramento Early College Prep S	1504 Fallbrook St	West Sacramento, CA	95691-3622	916-375-7680		6-12	Jessica Anderson
Westside Innovative School House	6550 W 80th St	Los Angeles, CA	90045	310-642-9474	642-9475	K-7	Dr. Chelsie Murphy
Westside Prep Charter S - Eastside	6469 Guthrie St	North Highlands, CA	95660-3944	916-566-1860	566-1861	7-8	Renee Scott-Femenella
Westside Prep Charter S - Frontier	6691 Silverthorne Cir	Sacramento, CA	95842-2654	916-566-1840	566-1841	7-8	Ellen Giffin
Westside Prep Charter S - Westside	6537 W 2nd St	Rio Linda, CA	95673	916-566-1990	566-1991	7-8	Laura Lofgren
Westwood Charter ES	2050 Selby Ave	Los Angeles, CA	90025-6311	310-474-7788	475-1295	K-5	Kathy Flores
Westwood Charter S	PO Box 56	Westwood, CA	96137-0056	877-256-2994	256-2964	K-12	Marty Growdon
Wheatland Charter Academy	123 Beale Hwy	Beale AFB, CA	95903	530-788-0248	788-0518	K-5	Jodie Jacklett
White Oaks ES	1901 White Oak Way	San Carlos, CA	94070-4747	650-508-7317	508-7320	PK-3	Allison Liner
Whitmore Charter HS	PO Box 307	Ceres, CA	95307-0307	209-556-1617	538-7931	9-12	Sarah Olson
Whitmore Charter S	PO Box 307	Ceres, CA	95307-0307	209-556-1610	538-7931	K-8	Sarah Olson
Wilbur Charter S for Enriched Academics	5213 Crebs Ave	Tarzana, CA	91356-4010	818-345-1090	881-8128	K-5	Deborah Plat
Wilder's Preparatory Academy Charter S	830 N La Brea Ave	Inglewood, CA	90302-2206	310-671-5578	671-2424	K-8	Rosalyn S. Robinson
Wildflower Open Classroom	2414 Cohasset Rd	Chico, CA	95926	530-892-1676	892-9317	K-8	Tom Hicks
Willits Charter ES	405 E Commercial St	Willits, CA	95490-3203	707-459-1400	455-6650	K-5	Kara McClellan
Willits Charter S	1431 S Main St	Willits, CA	95490-4309	707-459-5506	459-5576	6-12	Jennifer Lockwood
Willow Creek Academy	636 Nevada St	Sausalito, CA	94965-1654	415-331-7530	331-1622	K-8	Tara Seekins
Willowside MS	5285 Hall Rd	Santa Rosa, CA	95401-5566	707-542-3322	525-4439	6-8	Linsey Gannon
Wilson College Prep S	400 105th Ave	Oakland, CA	94603-2968	510-635-7737	635-7727	6-12	Michelle Cortez
Wonderful College Prep Academy	1942 Randolph St	Delano, CA	93215-1527	661-454-3000	454-3099	6-12	Ricardo Esquivel
Woodlake ES	23231 Hatteras St	Woodland Hills, CA	91367-3199	818-347-7097	883-3953	K-5	Mario Thompson
Woodland Hills Charter S	22201 San Miguel St	Woodland Hills, CA	91364-3039	818-347-9220	347-2365	K-5	Antoinette Brusca
Woodland Star Charter S	17811 Arnold Dr	Sonoma, CA	95476-4019	707-996-3849	996-4369	K-8	Jamie Lloyd
Woodson Charter S	3333 N Bond Ave	Fresno, CA	93726-5712	559-229-3529	229-0459	7-12	Victor Martinez
Woodward Leadership Academy	1777 W Base Line St	San Bernardino, CA	92411-1648	909-266-1762		K-6	Jaqueline Johnson
Wright Charter S	4389 Price Ave	Santa Rosa, CA	95407-6550	707-542-0556	542-0418	K-8	Laurie Whiteside
Yav Pem Suab Academy	7555 S Land Park Dr	Sacramento, CA	95831-3863	916-433-5057	433-5289	K-6	Vince Xiong
Yosemite-Wawona Elementary Charter	7925 Chilnualna Falls Rd	Yosemite NtPk, CA	95389	209-375-6383	375-1029	1-5	Esme McCarthy
Youthbuild Charter S	155 W Washington St	Los Angeles, CA	90015	213-741-2600	741-2628	9-12	Phil Matero
Youth Opportunities Unlimited S	915 W Manchester Ave	Los Angeles, CA	90044-4915	323-789-4731	778-4612	9-12	Maisha James-McIntosh
Yuba City Charter S	256 Wilbur Ave	Yuba City, CA	95991	530-822-9667	822-9629	PK-12	James Ferreira
Yuba County Career Prep Charter S	1104 E St	Marysville, CA	95901-4825	530-741-6025	741-6032	K-12	Rocco Greco
Yuba Environmental Science Charter Acad	PO Box 430	Oregon House, CA	95962-0430	530-692-2210	692-3241	PK-8	Katheryn Smith
Yuba River Charter S	505 Main St	Nevada City, CA	95959-2218	530-265-6060	265-6070	K-8	Ron Charles
Yu Ming Charter S	1086 Alcatraz Ave	Emeryville, CA	94608-1265	415-452-2063	452-2095	K-8	Sue Park

Colorado

School	Address	City,State	Zip code	Telephone	Fax	Grade	Contact
Academy 360	12000 E 47th Ave	Denver, CO	80239	303-574-1360		PK-5	Eric Brucz
Academy Charter S	1551 Prairie Hawk Dr	Castle Rock, CO	80109-7900	303-660-4881	660-6385	K-8	Yvette Brown
Academy for Advanced & Creative Learning	2510 N Chestnut St	Colorado Spgs, CO	80907	719-434-6566	434-9696	K-8	Nikki Myers
Academy of Urban Learning Charter S	2417 W 29th Ave	Denver, CO	80211-3709	303-282-0900	282-0902	9-12	Michelle Kennard
Academy	11800 Lowell Blvd	Westminster, CO	80031-5097	303-289-8088	289-8087	K-12	David Floodeen
ACE Community Challenge Charter S	948 Santa Fe Dr	Denver, CO	80204-3937	303-436-9588	436-0919	8-10	Rachel Ramirez
Addenbrooke Classical Academy	3940 S Teller St	Lakewood, CO	80235	303-989-1336	986-5509	K-12	Charles Wright
Alta Vista Charter ES	PO Box 449	Lamar, CO	81052-0449	719-336-2154	336-0170	K-6	Talara Coen
American Academy	11155 Motsenbocker Rd	Parker, CO	80134	720-292-5600	644-3792	K-8	Erin Kane
American Academy	6971 Mira Vista Ln	Castle Pines, CO	80108	720-292-5200	733-2641	K-8	Erin Kane
Animas HS	PO Box 4414	Durango, CO	81302-4414	970-247-2474	247-2483	9-12	Sean Woytek
Aspen Community Charter S	PO Box 336	Woody Creek, CO	81656-0336	970-923-4080	923-6207	K-8	Jim Gilchrist
Aspen Ridge Prep S	705 Austin Ave	Erie, CO	80516	720-242-6225	294-0573	K-5	Charla Salmeron
Aspen View Academy	2131 Low Meadow Blvd	Castle Rock, CO	80109-8032	720-733-3436	660-5959	PK-8	Jason Edwards
Atlas Preparatory S	1602 S Murray Blvd	Colorado Spgs, CO	80916	719-358-7196	355-1819	5-12	Adam Lenzmeier
Aurora Academy Charter S	10251 E 1st Ave	Aurora, CO	80010-4308	303-367-5983	367-5820	K-8	Pat Leger
Axl Academy	14100 E Jewell Ave	Aurora, CO	80012-5678	303-377-0758	597-1547	PK-8	Brent Reckman
Banning Lewis Ranch Academy	7094 Cottonwood Tree Dr	Colorado Spgs, CO	80927-5000	719-570-0075	522-2900	K-8	Eric Dinnel
Battle Rock Charter S	11351 Road G	Cortez, CO	81321-9569	970-565-3237	564-1140	K-6	Karen Casgrain
Belle Creek Charter S	9290 E 107th Ave	Henderson, CO	80640-8964	303-468-0160	468-0164	K-8	Jackie Fields
Blair Edison Charter S	4905 Cathay St	Denver, CO	80249-8376	303-371-9570	371-8348	K-8	Kristen Lee
Boulder Prep Charter HS	5075 Chaparral Ct	Boulder, CO	80301-3589	303-545-6186	545-6187	9-12	Lili Adeli
Bromley East Charter S	356 Longspur Dr	Brighton, CO	80601-8700	720-685-3297	685-9513	K-8	Lori Sheldon
Caprock Academy	714 24 1/2 Rd	Grand Junction, CO	81505-9628	970-243-1771	243-3612	K-12	Kristin Trezise
Carbondale Community S	PO Box 365	Carbondale, CO	81623-0365	970-963-9647	704-0501	K-8	Tom Penzel
Carbon Valley Academy	4040 Coriolis Way	Frederick, CO	80504-5449	303-774-9555	774-9592	PK-8	Julie Johnson
Cardinal Community Academy	3101 County Road 65	Keenesburg, CO	80643-8604	303-732-9312	732-9314	K-8	April Dowdy
Career Building Academy	1120 Court St	Pueblo, CO	81003-2819	719-546-1740		7-12	Dr. Dana Lambert
Challenge to Excellence Charter S	16995 Carlson Dr	Parker, CO	80134-8000	303-841-9816	840-3246	K-8	Donna Mitchell
Chavez Academy	2500 W 18th St	Pueblo, CO	81003-1152	719-295-1623	295-1625	K-8	Lori Montanez
Chavez Academy	3752 Tennyson St	Denver, CO	80212-1914	303-455-0848	855-7252	K-8	Kamini Patel
Cherry Creek Academy Charter	6260 S Dayton St	Englewood, CO	80111-5203	303-779-8988	779-8817	K-8	Jay Cerny
Children's Kiva Montessori S	510 N Beech St	Cortez, CO	81321-2115	970-564-4850		K-8	Josh Warinner
CIVA Charter S	4635 Northpark Dr	Colorado Spgs, CO	80918-3813	719-633-1306	633-1691	9-12	Randy Zimmerman
Classical Academy Central	1655 Springcrest Rd	Colorado Spgs, CO	80920-1545	719-265-9766	265-1751	K-6	Rebecca DeMeyer
Classical Academy East	12201 Cross Peak Vw	Colorado Spgs, CO	80921	719-282-1181	260-9743	K-6	Amy Nelson
Classical Academy HS	975 Stout Rd	Colorado Spgs, CO	80921-3801	719-484-0091	484-0085	9-12	Sean Shields
Classical Academy JHS	975 Stout Rd	Colorado Spgs, CO	80921-3801	719-484-0091	487-2339	7-8	Hugh DiPretore
Classical Academy North	975 Stout Rd	Colorado Spgs, CO	80921-3801	719-484-0081	484-0078	K-6	Don Stump
Collegiate Academy of Colorado	8420 Sangre De Cristo Rd	Littleton, CO	80127-4201	303-972-7433	932-0695	K-12	Christian Becker
Colorado Calvert Academy	155 Boardwalk Dr Ste 547	Fort Collins, CO	80525-3040	970-232-3317	258-1591	K-8	Elizabeth Davis
Colorado Charter HS	1175 Osage St Ste 100	Denver, CO	80204-3445	303-892-8475	825-3011	10-12	Clark Callahan
Colorado Early Colleges Douglas County	10235 Parkglenn Way	Parker, CO	80138-3870	720-638-6824		9-12	John Etzell
Colorado Early Colleges Fort Collins	4800 Wheaton Dr	Fort Collins, CO	80525-9483	970-377-0044	377-1144	9-12	Sandi Brown
Colorado Springs Charter Academy	2577 N Chelton Rd	Colorado Spgs, CO	80909-1302	719-636-2722	636-2726	K-8	Jacob Murphy

School	Address	City,State	Zip code	Telephone	Fax	Grade	Contact
Colorado Springs Early Colleges	4405 N Chestnut St # E	Colorado Spgs, CO	80907	719-955-4675	260-1253	9-12	Jennifer Daugherty
Colorado Virtual Academy	165 S Union Blvd Ste 777	Lakewood, CO	80228	303-255-4650	504-4072	9-12	Melissa Lambrecht
Community Leadership Academy	6880 Holly St	Commerce City, CO	80022-2536	303-288-2711	288-2714	PK-5	Ron Jajdelski
Community Prep Charter S	332 E Willamette Ave	Colorado Spgs, CO	80903-1116	719-227-8836	227-8897	9-12	Marty Schneider
Compass Academy	2285 S Federal Blvd	Denver, CO	80219	720-424-0096		6-8	Marcia Fulton
Compass Montessori Charter S	10399 W 44th Ave	Wheat Ridge, CO	80033-2701	303-420-8288	420-0139	PK-6	Cameron Gehlen
Compass Montessori Charter S	4441 Salvia St	Golden, CO	80403-1698	303-271-1977	271-1984	PK-12	Seth Webb
Connect Charter S	104 W 7th St	Pueblo, CO	81003	719-542-0224	583-9799	6-8	Jeff Hawkins
Crest Academy	220 W 12th St	Salida, CO	81201-2306	719-539-2977	530-5234	5-8	Karen Lundberg
Crestone Charter S	PO Box 400	Crestone, CO	81131-0400	719-256-4907	256-4908	K-12	Marie-Louise Baker
Crown Pointe Academy	2900 W 86th Ave	Westminster, CO	80031	303-428-1882	428-1938	K-8	Keith Ouweneel
DCS Montessori Charter S	311 E Castle Pines Pkwy	Castle Pines, CO	80108	303-387-5625	387-5626	PK-8	Jeromy Johnson
Denver Justice HS	300 E 9th Ave	Denver, CO	80203	303-480-5610	480-5613	9-12	Gary Losh
Denver Language S	451 Newport St	Denver, CO	80220	303-557-0852	393-6805	K-8	Kathy Benzel
Denver S of Science & Tech-Henry MS	3005 S Golden Way	Denver, CO	80227	303-802-4130		6-8	Lisa Richardson
Denver S of Science & Technology	2000 Valentia St	Denver, CO	80238	303-320-5570	377-5101	9-12	Jeff Desserich
Denver S of Science & Technology	150 S Pearl St	Denver, CO	80209	303-524-6350		9-9	Brad White
Denver S of Science & Technology	2000 Valentia St	Denver, CO	80238	303-320-5570		6-8	Jessica Heesacker
Denver S of Science & Technology-Byers	150 S Pearl St	Denver, CO	80209	303-524-6350	524-6355	6-8	Brad White
Denver S of Science & Technology - CG	8499 Stoll Pl	Denver, CO	80238	303-802-4120	802-4205	6-8	John Clark
Denver S of Science & Technology-Cole HS	3240 N Humboldt St	Denver, CO	80205	303-524-6354		9-12	Rebecca Bloch
Denver S of Science & Technology-Cole MS	1350 E 33rd Ave	Denver, CO	80205	303-524-6354	524-6309	6-8	Shawn Smith
Denver S of Science & Technology CV HS	3111 W Dartmouth Ave	Denver, CO	80236-2842	303-524-6320		9-12	Rebecca Meyer
Denver S of Science & Technology CV MS	3111 W Dartmouth Ave	Denver, CO	80236	720-524-6374		6-8	Erin Dillon
Denver S of Science & Technology - GVR	4800 Telluride St	Denver, CO	80249	303-524-6300	389-7398	9-12	Jenna Kalin
Denver S of Science & Technology - GVR	4800 Telluride St	Denver, CO	80249	303-524-6300		6-8	Caroline Gaudiani
Doral Academy of Colorado	7100 Wadsworth Blvd	Arvada, CO	80003	303-428-8443	389-9367	K-7	Joshua Rau
Downtown Denver Expeditionary S	1860 N Lincoln St	Denver, CO	80203	720-424-2350		K-5	Erin Sciscione
Eagle County Charter Academy	1105 Miller Ranch Rd	Edwards, CO	81632-6425	970-926-0656	926-0786	K-8	Kim Walter
Eagle Ridge Academy	3551 E Southern St	Brighton, CO	80601-0015	303-655-0773	655-9155	9-12	Dr. Ben Ploeger
Early College of Arvada	4905 W 60th Ave	Arvada, CO	80003-6916	720-473-4400	308-4701	6-12	Eric Covington
Excel Academy	11500 W 84th Ave	Arvada, CO	80005-5272	303-467-2295	467-2291	K-8	Lisa Gjellum
Flagstaff Academy	2040 Miller Dr	Longmont, CO	80501-6748	303-651-7900	651-7922	PK-8	Robin Lowe
Fort Collins Montessori S	1900 S Taft Hill Rd	Fort Collins, CO	80526-1227	970-631-8612		PK-3	Frank Vincent
Foundations Academy	340 S 45th Ave	Brighton, CO	80601	303-659-9519	835-7151	K-8	Jerry Martinez
Franklin Academy	2270 Plaza Dr	Highlands Ranch, CO	80129	720-383-4519	974-1738	PK-8	Bob Barber
Free Horizon Montessori S	581 Conference Pl	Golden, CO	80401-5615	303-231-9801	231-9983	PK-8	Kresta Vuolo
Frontier Academy Charter S	2560 W 29th St	Greeley, CO	80631-8507	970-330-1780	330-4334	K-5	Dr. Bradford Every
Frontier Academy Charter S	6530 W 16th St	Greeley, CO	80634-8675	970-339-9153	339-5631	6-12	Dr. Stephen Seedorf
Frontier Charter Academy	418 Yoder St	Calhan, CO	80808-8688	719-347-3156	347-3054	K-8	Karin Gurokovich
Georgetown Community S	PO Box 129	Georgetown, CO	80444	303-569-3277	569-2761	PK-6	Sharon Warren
Girls Athletic Leadership S	750 Galapago St	Denver, CO	80204	303-282-6437	282-6815	6-12	Carrie Donovan
Global Village Academy	403 S Airport Blvd Unit A	Aurora, CO	80017-3900	303-309-6657	317-6538	K-8	Courtney Black
Global Village Academy	555 W 112th Ave	Northglenn, CO	80234	303-446-7100	446-7101	K-8	Nicole Caldwell
Global Village Academy Colorado Springs	1702 N Murray Blvd	Colorado Spgs, CO	80915-1333	719-645-8063	591-6784	K-4	Alicia Welch
Global Village Academy Fort Collins	2130 W Horsetooth Rd	Fort Collins, CO	80526-6436	970-282-3767	282-3766	K-4	Brian Weber
GLOBE Charter S	3302 Alpine Pl	Colorado Spgs, CO	80909	719-630-0577	630-0395	K-6	Heidi Breakey
Gloval Village Academy	18451 Ponderosa Dr	Parker, CO	80134-5782	720-476-8044		K-8	Lance Howard
GOAL Academy	107 W 11th St	Pueblo, CO	81003	877-776-4625	746-2874	9-12	Ken Crowell
Golden View Classical Academy	601 Corporate Cir	Golden, CO	80401-5609	303-598-6700	598-6698	K-12	Robert Garrow
Great Plains Academy	444 E Front St	Byers, CO	80103-9727	720-360-0706	489-3857	K-12	Justin Schmidt
Guffey Community Charter S	PO Box 147	Guffey, CO	80820-0147	719-689-2093	689-3407	PK-8	Pam Moore
Highline Academy Northeast	19451 E Maxwell Pl	Denver, CO	80249	303-454-2706		K-5	Kelly Brandon
Highline Academy Southeast	2170 S Dahlia St	Denver, CO	80222-5106	303-759-7808	759-7809	K-8	Kali Garofoli
High Point Academy	6750 N Dunkirk St	Aurora, CO	80019-2107	303-217-5152	217-5153	PK-8	Keri Melmed
Hope Online Learning Academy Co-op	373 Inverness Pkwy Ste 205	Englewood, CO	80112	720-402-3000	675-3013	K-12	Heather O'Mara
Horizons K-8 School	4545 Sioux Dr	Boulder, CO	80303-3732	720-561-3600	561-3601	K-8	John McCluskey
Huerta Preparatory HS	2727 W 18th St	Pueblo, CO	81003-1185	719-583-1030	545-2389	9-12	Crystal Gallegos
Imagine Charter S at Firestone	5753 Twilight Ave	Firestone, CO	80504	303-772-3711	772-3977	PK-8	Nancy Box
Imagine Classical Academy - Indigo Ranch	6464 Peterson Rd	Colorado Spgs, CO	80923	719-495-7360	495-4239	PK-8	Frank Fowler
Independence Academy	651 29 Rd	Grand Junction, CO	81504	970-254-6850	241-2064	K-8	Damon Lockhart
Indian Peaks Charter S	PO Box 1819	Granby, CO	80446-1819	970-887-3805	887-3829	K-8	Allison Beauvais
Irwin Charter ES - Astrozon Cmps	5525 Astrozon Blvd	Colorado Spgs, CO	80916	719-302-9107	884-0992	K-5	Elizabeth Berg
Irwin Charter ES - Howard Campus	1801 Howard Ave	Colorado Spgs, CO	80909	719-302-9100	632-4178	K-5	Saadia Dumas
Irwin Charter HS	5525 Astrozon Blvd	Colorado Spgs, CO	80916-4226	719-302-9109	576-8071	9-12	Alex Marquez
Irwin Charter MS	5525 Astrozon Blvd	Colorado Spgs, CO	80916-4226	719-302-9108	591-9993	6-8	Holly Varnum
Jefferson Academy	11251 Reed Way	Broomfield, CO	80020-2720	303-887-1992	887-2435	7-12	Heather Grantham
Jefferson Academy	9955 Yarrow St	Broomfield, CO	80021-4048	303-438-1011	438-1046	K-6	Michael Nolan
Juniper Ridge Charter S	640 24 1/2 Rd	Grand Junction, CO	81505-1245	970-639-0884		K-6	Patrick Ebel
Juniper S	PO Box 655	Durango, CO	81302-0655			K-5	
Justice HS	805 Excalibur St	Lafayette, CO	80026	720-277-6480		9-12	Tijani Cole
KIPP Denver Collegiate HS	451 S Tejon St	Denver, CO	80223	303-922-5324	922-9910	9-12	Kurt Pusch
KIPP Montbello College Prep	5290 Kittredge St	Denver, CO	80239	303-307-1970		5-8	Danielle D'Ascenzo
KIPP Montbello ES	19451 E Maxwell Pl	Denver, CO	80249	720-452-2551	570-2066	PK-4	Lindsey Lorehn
KIPP Northeast Denver Leadership Academy	18250 E 51st Ave	Denver, CO	80249	720-452-2570		9-10	Grant Erwin
KIPP Sunshine Peak Academy	375 S Tejon St	Denver, CO	80223-1961	303-623-5772	623-0410	5-8	Emily Yates
Knowledge Quest Academy	705 School House Dr	Milliken, CO	80543-3154	970-587-5742	587-5750	K-8	Linda Spreitzer
Lake George Charter S	PO Box 420	Lake George, CO	80827-0420	719-748-3911	748-8151	PK-6	Bill Fredenburg
Landmark Academy at Reunion	10566 Memphis St	Commerce City, CO	80022	303-287-2901	379-2050	K-8	Jennifer Stengel
Legacy Academy	1975 Legacy Cir	Elizabeth, CO	80107-8330	303-646-2636	646-2635	K-8	Kurt Naber
Liberty Common ES	1725 Sharp Point Dr	Fort Collins, CO	80525-4424	970-482-9800	482-8007	K-6	Keith Churchill
Liberty Common HS	2745 Minnesota Dr	Fort Collins, CO	80525-6794	970-672-5500	672-5499	7-12	Bob Schaffer
Life Skills Center of Colorado Springs	1810 Eastlake Blvd	Colorado Spgs, CO	80910-3422	719-471-0684	471-4392	9-12	Mary Ruben-Clapper
Lincoln Academy	7180 Oak St	Arvada, CO	80004-1416	303-467-5363	467-5367	PK-8	Janelle Johnson
Littleton Academy Charter S	1200 W Mineral Ave	Littleton, CO	80120-4536	303-798-5252	798-0298	K-8	Shelly Russell
Littleton Preparatory Charter S	5301 S Bannock St	Littleton, CO	80120-1742	303-734-1995	734-3620	K-8	Kimberly Ash
Lotus S for Excellence	11001 E Alameda Ave Ste A	Aurora, CO	80012-1034	303-360-0052	360-0071	K-12	Eray Idil
Loveland Classical Charter S	3835 14th St SW	Loveland, CO	80537-6675	970-541-1507	776-9227	K-12	Ian Stout
Maclaren Charter S	303 Austin Bluffs Pkwy	Colorado Spgs, CO	80918-3922	719-313-4488	313-4491	6-12	Mary Faith Hall
Madison Charter Academy	660 Syracuse St	Colorado Spgs, CO	80911-2546	719-391-3977	391-1744	K-6	Dr. Anne Shineman
Magon Academy	5301 Lowell Blvd	Denver, CO	80221-7313	303-412-7610	412-7658	K-8	Kaye Taavialma
Marble Charter S	418 W Main St	Marble, CO	81623	970-963-9550	963-8435	K-10	Amy Rusby
Mesa Valley Community S	2387 Patterson Rd	Grand Junction, CO	81505-1219	970-254-7202	243-3075	K-12	Laurajean Downs
Monarch Montessori of Denver	4895 Peoria St	Denver, CO	80239	303-712-2001	500-0646	K-5	Rob Clemens
Montessori del Mundo	15503 E Mississippi Ave # B	Aurora, CO	80017	720-863-8629		PK-4	Karen Farquharson
Montessori Peaks Academy	9904 W Capri Ave	Littleton, CO	80123-3535	303-972-2627	933-4182	PK-6	Shannon Aasheim
Monument Academy	1150 Village Ridge Pt	Monument, CO	80132-8992	719-481-1950	481-1948	PK-8	Dr. Don Griffin
Mountain MS	108 W 31st St	Durango, CO	81301-4231	970-828-5600		6-8	Shane Voss
Mountain Phoenix Community S	4725 Miller St	Wheat Ridge, CO	80033	303-728-9100	728-9801	PK-8	Dirk Angevine
Mountain Sage Community S	2310 E Prospect Rd Ste A	Fort Collins, CO	80525-9770	970-568-5456	482-1803	K-8	Liv Helmericks
Mountain Song Community S	2904 W Kiowa St	Colorado Spgs, CO	80904	719-203-6364	375-0180	K-8	Raj Solanki
Mountain View Core Knowledge S	890 Field Ave	Canon City, CO	81212-9250	719-275-1980	275-1998	K-8	Karen Sartori
Mountain View Virtual S	7730 E Belleview Ave # AG9	Greenwood Vlg, CO	80111	303-770-1240	771-1210	9-12	Kelly Boren
New America S - Jeffco	5806 W Alameda Ave	Lakewood, CO	80226	303-894-3171	237-4119	9-12	
New America S - Lowry	9125 E 7th Pl	Denver, CO	80230-7111	303-320-9854	363-8083	9-12	Annie Trujillo
New America S - Thornton	8978 Washington St	Thornton, CO	80229-4537	303-991-0130	252-9254	9-12	Mike Epke
New Legacy Charter S	2091 Dayton St	Aurora, CO	80010-1010	303-340-7880		9-12	Jennifer Douglas
New Vision Charter S	2366 E 1st St	Loveland, CO	80537-5906	970-593-6827	461-1947	K-8	Tim Bishop
North Routt Charter S	26990 Eagle Ln	Clark, CO	80428-9702	970-871-6062	871-6067	K-8	Brandon LaChance
North Star Academy	16700 Keystone Blvd	Parker, CO	80134-3544	720-851-7827	851-0976	K-8	Kendra Hossfeld
Odyssey S of Denver	6550 E 21st Ave	Denver, CO	80207	303-316-3944	316-4016	K-8	Marnie Cooke
Paradox Valley Charter S	PO Box 420	Paradox, CO	81429-0420	970-859-7236	859-7235	PK-8	Jon Orris
Parker Core Knowledge Charter S	11661 N Pine Dr	Parker, CO	80138-8022	303-840-7070	840-9785	PK-8	Teri Aplin
Parker Performing Arts S	15035 Compark Blvd	Parker, CO	80134			K-8	
Passage Charter S	703 S 9th St	Montrose, CO	81401-4409	970-249-8066	249-3497	9-12	Corinne Vogenthaler
Paul Academy of Arts & Knowledge	4512 McMurry Ave	Fort Collins, CO	80525-3400	970-226-2800	226-2806	PK-5	James Lewicki
Peak to Peak Charter S	800 Merlin Dr	Lafayette, CO	80026-2146	303-453-4600	453-4613	K-12	Kyle Mathews
Pikes Peak Prep S	525 E Costilla St	Colorado Spgs, CO	80903-3764	719-570-7575	475-0831	K-12	Stephanie Atencio
Pikes Peak S of Expeditionary Learning	11925 Antlers Ridge Dr	Falcon, CO	80831	719-522-2580	522-2585	PK-8	Don Knapp
Pinnacle Charter S	1001 W 84th Ave	Federal Heights, CO	80260-4717	303-450-3985	255-6305	K-12	
Platte River Academy	4085 Lark Sparrow St	Highlands Ranch, CO	80126-5209	303-221-1070	221-1069	K-8	Mike Munier
Power Technical Early College	2525 Canada Dr	Colorado Spgs, CO	80922	719-301-6200		6-12	Rob Daugherty
Prospect Ridge Academy	2555 Preble Creek Pkwy	Broomfield, CO	80023-8096	720-399-0300	545-2163	K-12	April Wilkin
Pueblo S for the Arts & Sciences	2415 Jones Ave	Pueblo, CO	81004	719-404-2680	404-2681	K-8	Brian Repola
REACH	940 Fillmore St	Denver, CO	80206	720-668-9691		PK-3	Jim McDermott
Ridge View Academy	28101 E Quincy Ave	Watkins, CO	80137-9502	303-766-3000	766-2151	9-12	Ed Cope
Ridgeview Classical S	1800 S Lemay Ave	Fort Collins, CO	80525-1240	970-494-4620	494-4625	K-12	Derek Anderson

School	Address	City,State	Zip code	Telephone	Fax	Grade	Contact
RiseUp Community HS	1801 Federal Blvd	Denver, CO	80204	303-587-4713		9-12	Lucas Ketzer
Rocky Mountain Academy of Evergreen	2959 Royale Elk Way	Evergreen, CO	80439-8689	303-670-1070	670-1253	PK-8	Dr. Roberta Harrell
Rocky Mountain Classical Academy	4620 Antelope Ridge Dr	Colorado Spgs, CO	80922-2497	719-622-8000	622-8004	K-8	Christianna Fogler
Rocky Mountain Deaf S	10300 W Nassau Ave	Denver, CO	80235	303-984-5749	984-7290	PK-12	Amy Novotny
Rocky Mountain Prep	7808 Cherry Creek South Dr	Denver, CO	80231	720-863-8920	863-8940	PK-5	Jen Heller
Rocky Mountain Prep S	10455 E 25th Ave	Aurora, CO	80010	720-863-8922	863-8940	PK-5	Caitlin Vaughan
Rocky Mountain Prep Southwest S	911 S Hazel Ct	Denver, CO	80219	720-863-8920		PK-5	Jennifer Reese
Roosevelt Charter Academy	205 Byron Dr	Colorado Spgs, CO	80910-2508	719-637-0311	380-0176	K-5	Steve Tompkins
Roots ES	3475 Holly St	Denver, CO	80207	720-593-1338		K-5	Eve Bunevich
Ross Montessori S	109 Lewies Ln	Carbondale, CO	81623	970-963-7199	963-7342	K-8	Sonya Hemmen M.A.
St. Vrain Montessori Charter S	1055 Delaware Ave	Longmont, CO	80501-6143	303-682-4339	682-8925	PK-6	Katie Torres
Salida Del Sol Academy	111 E 26th St	Greeley, CO	80631	970-347-8223		K-8	Joe Melendez
Salida Montessori Charter S	PO Box 1080	Salida, CO	81201-1080	719-539-4887		K-8	Rafe Quinton
SkyView Academy	6161 Business Center Dr	Highlands Ranch, CO	80130	303-471-8439	470-1903	PK-12	Richard Barrett
SOAR	4800 Telluride St	Denver, CO	80249	720-287-5100	287-5119	K-5	Laurie Godwin
Southwest Early College Charter S	3001 S Federal Blvd	Denver, CO	80236-2711	303-935-5473	935-5591	9-12	Halley Joseph
Southwest Open Charter S	410 N Dolores Rd	Cortez, CO	81321	970-565-1150	565-8770	9-12	Jennifer Carter
Stargate Charter S	3951 Cottonwood Lakes Blvd	Thornton, CO	80241-2187	303-450-3936	450-3941	K-8	Josh Cochran
STEM S and Academy	8773 Ridgeline Blvd	Highlands Ranch, CO	80129	303-683-7836	683-2099	6-12	Dr. Penny Eucker
Stone Creek Charter S	33520 Highway 6	Edwards, CO	81632	970-569-3327	569-3492	K-8	Carrie Kirkutis
STRIVE Prep - Excel	2960 N Speer Blvd	Denver, CO	80211-3795	303-630-0360		9-12	Kate Schrepfer
STRIVE Prep - Federal	2626 W Evans Ave	Denver, CO	80219	303-573-2017		6-8	Libby Miller
STRIVE Prep - GVR	4800 Telluride St	Denver, CO	80249	303-999-2893		6-8	Jessica Savage
STRIVE Prep - Kepner	911 S Hazel Ct	Denver, CO	80219	720-485-6394		6-6	Katie Ryan
STRIVE Prep - Lake	1820 Lowell Blvd	Denver, CO	80204	303-551-7200	551-7207	6-8	Susan Morris
STRIVE Prep - Montbello	5000 Crown Blvd	Denver, CO	80239	303-999-3825		6-8	Vachon Brackett
STRIVE Prep - Rise	18250 E 51st Ave	Denver, CO	80249	720-485-6393		9-9	Elisha Roberts
STRIVE Prep - Ruby Hill	2626 W Evans Ave	Denver, CO	80219	720-460-2800		K-3	Alexa Mason
STRIVE Prep - SMART	3201 W Arizona Ave	Denver, CO	80219-3941	303-962-9880		9-12	Antonio Vigil
STRIVE Prep - Sunnyside	4735 Pecos St	Denver, CO	80211	720-723-2000		6-8	Jessica Tillis
STRIVE Prep - Westwood	3201 W Arizona Ave	Denver, CO	80219	303-962-9880	962-9886	6-8	Kathleen Esparza
Summit MS	4655 Hanover Ave	Boulder, CO	80305-6036	720-561-3900	561-3901	6-8	Adam Galvin
Swallows Charter Academy	278 S McCulloch Blvd	Pueblo West, CO	81007-2844	719-547-1627	547-2509	K-12	Dr. Cindy Compton
TCA College Pathways	12201 Cross Peak Vw	Colorado Spgs, CO	80921-3438	719-494-0631	484-0087	7-12	Steve Wright
Twin Peaks Charter Academy	340 S Sunset St	Longmont, CO	80501	303-772-7286	494-3611	K-12	Joe Mehsling
Two Rivers Community S	PO Box 188	Glenwood Spgs, CO	81602-0188	970-384-5200		K-8	Adriana Ayala-Hire Ed.D.
Two Roads Charter S	6980 Pierce St	Arvada, CO	80003-3646	303-423-3377	467-6955	K-12	Wendy Noel
Union Colony Prep ES	1051 29th Street Rd	Evans, CO	80620	970-673-4997	353-2271	K-6	Ken Wildenstein
Union Colony Prep S	2000 Clubhouse Dr	Greeley, CO	80634-3643	970-673-4546	330-7604	7-12	Lance Mosness
University Preparatory S	2409 Arapahoe St	Denver, CO	80205-2614	303-292-0463	296-2844	K-3	David Singer
University Prep - Steele St	3230 E 38th Ave	Denver, CO	80205-3726	303-292-0463		K-5	Jessica Valsechi
University Schools	6525 W 18th St	Greeley, CO	80634	970-506-7000	506-7070	K-12	Dr. Sherry Gerner
Vanguard Classical S	801 Yosemite St	Denver, CO	80230	303-691-2384	226-5529	K-8	Peggy Downs
Vanguard Classical S	17101 E Ohio Dr	Aurora, CO	80017	303-338-4110	338-4129	K-12	Peggy Downs
Vanguard S	1832 S Wahsatch Ave	Colorado Spgs, CO	80905-2341	719-471-1999	634-4180	K-4	Ward Barr
Vanguard S	1605 S Corona Ave	Colorado Spgs, CO	80905-2571	719-471-1999	634-4180	7-12	Colin Mullaney
Venture Prep Charter S	2900 Richard Allen Ct	Denver, CO	80205	303-893-0805	320-7665	9-12	Erin Quigley
Victory Prep Academy	5701 Quebec St	Commerce City, CO	80022-4821	303-288-6111		6-12	Ron Jajdelski
Vision Charter Academy	1080 Pioneer Rd	Delta, CO	81416	970-874-8226	874-8336	K-8	Willyn Webb
Vista Charter S	PO Box 10000	Montrose, CO	81402-9701	970-249-4470	252-3354	9-12	Beth Sass
Westgate Community S	12500 Washington St	Thornton, CO	80241	303-425-0967	452-4519	K-12	Sharon Collins
West Ridge Academy	6200 W 20th St	Greeley, CO	80634-9675	970-330-3671	330-3679	K-9	Russ Spicer
Wilson Academy	8300 W 94th Ave	Westminster, CO	80021-4590	303-431-3694	423-4388	PK-8	Carole Bartusiak
Windsor Charter Academy	680 Academy Ct	Windsor, CO	80550-3101	970-674-5020	674-5017	K-12	Rebecca Teeples
World Compass Academy	2490 S Perry St	Castle Rock, CO	80104	303-814-5200	688-9543	PK-5	Lance Howard
Wyatt Academy	3620 N Franklin St	Denver, CO	80205-3325	303-292-5515	292-5111	K-8	Joe Taylor

Connecticut

School	Address	City,State	Zip code	Telephone	Fax	Grade	Contact
Achievement First Amistad HS	580 Dixwell Ave	New Haven, CT	06511-1744	203-772-1092	772-1784	9-12	Claire Polcarck
Achievement First Bridgeport Academy	529 Noble Ave	Bridgeport, CT	06608-1803	203-333-9128	333-9142	5-8	Challa Flemming
Achievement First Bridgeport Academy	655 Stillman St	Bridgeport, CT	06608-1331	203-338-0593	338-0714	K-4	Christina Pares
Achievement First Hartford Academy ES	305 Greenfield St	Hartford, CT	06112-1826	860-695-6560	242-6457	K-4	Ernest Peterson
Achievement First Hartford Academy HS	305 Greenfield St	Hartford, CT	06112-1826	860-695-6680	722-8138	9-12	Emily Banks
Achievement First Hartford Academy MS	305 Greenfield St	Hartford, CT	06112-1826	860-695-6760	242-6457	5-8	Sorby Grant
Achievement First Summit S	85 Edwards St	Hartford, CT	06120	860-695-6200	722-8805	5-8	Benjamin Cruse
Amistad Academy ES	130 Edgewood Ave	New Haven, CT	06511-4520	203-772-7000	772-2520	K-4	Amanda Alonzy
Amistad Academy MS	130 Edgewood Ave	New Haven, CT	06511-4520	203-772-7000	776-0229	5-8	Katie Poynter
Bridge Academy	160 Pulaski St	Bridgeport, CT	06608	203-336-9999	336-9852	7-12	Timothy Dutton
Common Ground HS	358 Springside Ave	New Haven, CT	06515-1024	203-389-4333	389-7458	9-12	Lizanne Cox
Dickerson's Jumoke Academy ES	250 Blue Hills Ave	Hartford, CT	06112	860-527-0575		PK-4	Dr. Michael Finley
Elm City College Preparatory ES	407 James St	New Haven, CT	06513-3016	203-772-7010	498-0712	K-4	Andrew Poole
Elm City College Preparatory MS	794 Dixwell Ave	New Haven, CT	06511-1035	203-772-5332	772-3641	5-8	Chris Friedline
Elm City Montessori S	375 Quinnipiac Ave	New Haven, CT	06513-4455	203-903-4031	490-2316	PK-5	Dr. Alissa Levy
Explorations Charter S	71 Spencer St	Winsted, CT	06098-1128	860-738-9070	738-9092	9-12	Jill Johnson
Great Oaks Charter S	510 Barnum Ave	Bridgeport, CT	06608-2432	203-870-8188	870-8189	6-12	Monica Filppu
Highville Charter S	1 Science Park	Hamden, CT	06511-1963	203-287-0528	497-9899	PK-10	Craig Drazek
Integrated Day Charter S	68 Thermos Ave	Norwich, CT	06360-6957	860-892-1900	892-1902	PK-8	Anna James
Interdistrict S for Arts & Communication	190 Governor Winthrop Blvd	New London, CT	06320-6612	860-447-1003	447-0470	6-8	David C. Howes
Jumoke Academy Honors SMaRT	339 Blue Hills Ave	Hartford, CT	06112	860-527-0575	286-1137	5-8	Iris Gomero
Jumokoe Academy Honors	875 Asylum Ave	Hartford, CT	06105	860-527-0575	286-1137	5-8	Nichelle Woodson
Milner S	104 Vine St	Hartford, CT	06112-2295	860-695-4380	278-4694	PK-8	Karen Lott
New Beginnings Family Academy	184 Garden St	Bridgeport, CT	06605-1213	203-384-2897	384-2898	PK-8	Ronelle Swagerty
Odyssey Community S	579 Middle Tpke W	Manchester, CT	06040-2728	860-645-1234	533-0324	K-8	Elaine Stancliffe
Park City Prep Charter S	1550 State St	Bridgeport, CT	06605-2009	203-953-3766	953-3771	5-8	Bruce Ravage
Side by Side Charter S	10 Chestnut St	Norwalk, CT	06854-2928	203-857-0306	838-2666	PK-8	Matthew Nittoly
Stamford Academy	229 North St	Stamford, CT	06901-1112	203-324-6300	324-6310	9-12	David Williams
Trailblazers Academy	83 Lockwood Ave	Stamford, CT	06902-4201	203-977-5690	977-5688	6-8	Michael Duggan
Washington Academy	240 Greene St	New Haven, CT	06511-6934	203-691-6535	777-7614	K-3	John Taylor

Delaware

School	Address	City,State	Zip code	Telephone	Fax	Grade	Contact
Academia Antonia Alonso	1200 N French St	Wilmington, DE	19884-0012	302-660-4760	660-4761	K-2	Dr. Mark Phelps
Academy of Dover Charter S	104 Saulsbury Rd	Dover, DE	19904-2705	302-674-0684	674-3894	K-5	Cheri Marshall
Campus Community S	350 Pear St	Dover, DE	19904-3016	302-736-0403	736-5330	K-8	Catherine Balsley Ed.D.
Charter S of Wilmington	100 N DuPont Rd	Wilmington, DE	19807-3106	302-651-2727	652-1246	9-12	Samuel Paoli
Delaware Acad of Pub Safety & Security	801 N DuPont Hwy	New Castle, DE	19720-2544	302-322-6050	322-4029	9-12	Herbert Sheldon
Delaware Design-Lab HS	179 Stanton Christiana Rd	Newark, DE	19702-1619	215-820-7547		9-12	Dr. Cristina C. Alvarez
Delaware MET	920 N French St	Wilmington, DE	19801	302-654-7050	654-7055	9-12	
Delaware Military Academy	112 Middleboro Rd	Wilmington, DE	19804-1621	302-998-0745	998-3521	9-12	Anthony Pullella
Early College HS at DE State University	1570 N DuPont Hwy	Dover, DE	19901-2215	302-678-3247	857-4456	9-12	Dr. Evelyn Edney
East Side Charter S	3000 N Claymont St	Wilmington, DE	19802-2807	302-762-5834	762-3864	PK-8	Aaron Bass
Edison Charter S	2200 N Locust St	Wilmington, DE	19802-4429	302-778-1101	778-2232	K-8	Salome Thomas-El
Family Foundations Academy	1101 Delaware St	New Castle, DE	19720-6033	302-324-8901	324-8908	K-8	Dr. Lamont Browne
First State Military Academy	355 W Duck Creek Rd	Clayton, DE	19938-7712	302-223-2150		9-10	Patrick Gallucci
First State Montessori Academy	1000 N French St	Wilmington, DE	19801-3331	302-576-1500	576-1501	K-6	Courtney Fox
Freire Charter S	201 W 14th St	Wilmington, DE	19801-1114	302-407-4800	654-1125	8-10	Paul Ramirez
Gateway Lab S	2501 Centerville Rd	Wilmington, DE	19808-1603	302-633-4091	633-5680	3-8	Tim Griffiths
Great Oaks Charter S - Wilmington	1200 N French St	Wilmington, DE	19801-3239	302-660-4790		6-6	Kia Childs
Kuumba Academy Charter S	1200 N French St	Wilmington, DE	19801-3239	302-472-6450	472-6452	K-8	Sally Maldonado
Las Americas Aspira Academy	326 Ruthar Dr	Newark, DE	19711-8017	302-292-1463	292-1291	K-8	Margaret Lopez Waite
MOT Charter S	1156 Levels Rd	Middletown, DE	19709-7700	302-376-5125	376-5120	K-10	Linda Jennings
Newark Charter S	200 McIntire Dr	Newark, DE	19711-3568	302-369-2001	368-3460	K-12	Gregory Meece
Odyssey Charter HS	4319 Lancaster Pike	Wilmington, DE	19805	302-516-8000	780-5962	9-12	Dr. Nick Manolakos
Odyssey Charter S Lower Campus	4319 Lancaster Pike	Wilmington, DE	19805	302-994-6490	780-5962	K-5	Dr. Nick Manolakos
Odyssey Charter S Upper Campus	4319 Lancaster Pike	Wilmington, DE	19805	302-655-6490	780-5962	6-8	Dr. Nick Manolakos
Positive Outcomes Charter S	3337 S Dupont Hwy	Camden, DE	19934-1378	302-697-8805	697-8813	6-12	Edward Emmett
Prestige Academy	1121 Thatcher St	Wilmington, DE	19802-5135	302-762-3240	762-4782	5-8	Cordie Greenlea
Providence Creek Academy Charter S	PO Box 265	Clayton, DE	19938-0265	302-653-6276	653-7850	K-8	Audrey Erschen
Sussex Academy of Arts and Sciences	21150 Airport Rd	Georgetown, DE	19947-5573	302-856-3636	856-3376	6-12	Patricia Oliphant Ed.D.

District Of Columbia

School	Address	City,State	Zip code	Telephone	Fax	Grade	Contact
Academy of Hope Charter S	2315 18th Pl	Washington, DC	20018	202-269-6623	269-6632	Adult	Lecester Johnson
Academy of Hope Public Charter S	421 Alabama Ave SE	Washington, DC	20032-1517	202-269-6623		Adult	Lecester Johnson
Achievement Preparatory Academy	908 Wahler Pl SE	Washington, DC	20032-4000	202-562-1214	562-1219	PK-3	Jake Lappi
Achievement Prep MS	908 Wahler Pl	Washington, DC	20032	202-562-1214	562-1219	4-8	Shantelle Wright
Angelou Charter HS	5600 E Capitol St NE	Washington, DC	20019-6739	202-379-4335	315-3995	9-12	Tameika Ashford

School	Address	City,State	Zip code	Telephone	Fax	Grade	Contact
Angelou Charter S - Young Adult	5600 E Capitol St NE	Washington, DC	20019	202-289-8898	315-3995	Adult	Dr. Sean Yisrael
AppleTree Early Learning - Columbia Hts	2750 14th St NW	Washington, DC	20009	202-667-9490		PK-PK	Melissa Guillen
AppleTree Early Learning-Douglass Knoll	2017 Savannah Ter SE	Washington, DC	20020	202-629-2545	629-2548	PK-PK	Charlie Crabtree
AppleTree Early Learning - Lincoln Park	138 12th St NE	Washington, DC	20002	202-621-6581	621-6584	PK-PK	Raquel Carson
AppleTree Early Learning - Oklahoma Ave	330 21st St NE	Washington, DC	20002	202-629-2179	629-2189	PK-PK	Allison Waddy
AppleTree Early Learning - Parklands	2011 Savannah St SE	Washington, DC	20020	202-889-0643	506-1894	PK-PK	Niesha Cumberpatch
AppleTree Early Learning - Southwest	801 7th St SW	Washington, DC	20024	202-506-9190	646-0510	PK-PK	
Basis DC Charter S	410 8th St NW	Washington, DC	20004	202-393-5437	803-5764	5-12	Tim Eyerman
Bethune Day Academy	5412 16th St NW	Washington, DC	20011	202-459-4710	536-2670	PK-8	Linda McKay
Breakthrough Montessori Charter S	1244 Taylor St NW	Washington, DC	20011			PK-PK	Keith Whitescarver
Bridges Public Charter S	100 Gallatin St NE	Washington, DC	20011	202-545-0515	545-0517	PK-4	Kristine Rigley
Briya Charter S	100 Gallatin St	Washington, DC	20011	202-232-7777		PK-Ad	
Briya Charter S	4300 13th St NW	Washington, DC	20011	202-797-7337		PK-Ad	
Briya Charter S	1755 Newton St NW	Washington, DC	20010-1823	202-797-7337		PK-12	Christie McKay
Briya Charter S	3912 Georgia Ave NW	Washington, DC	20011-5861	202-545-2020	797-8470	PK-12	Christie McKay
Briya Charter S	2333 Ontario Rd NW	Washington, DC	20009-2627	202-232-7777		PK-12	Christie McKay
Capital City Public Charter S	100 Peabody St NW	Washington, DC	20011	202-808-9800	387-7074	PK-12	Karen Dresden
Cedar Tree Academy	701 Howard Rd SE	Washington, DC	20020	202-610-4193	610-2845	PK-K	Dr. Latonya Henderson
Center City Pub Charter S - Brightwood	6008 Georgia Ave NW	Washington, DC	20011	202-723-3322	291-0219	PK-8	Rachel Tommelleo
Center City Pub Charter S - Capitol Hill	1503 E Capitol St SE	Washington, DC	20003-1508	202-547-7556	547-5686	PK-8	Valery Dragon
Center City Pub Charter S - Congress Hts	220 Highview Pl SE	Washington, DC	20032	202-562-7070	547-5829	PK-8	Niya White
Center City Public Charter S - Petworth	510 Webster St NW	Washington, DC	20011	202-726-9212	726-3378	PK-8	Nazo Burgy
Center City Public Charter S - Shaw	711 N St NW	Washington, DC	20001	202-234-1093	462-6875	PK-8	Brandy Tyson
Center City Public Charter S - Trinidad	1217 W Virginia Ave NE	Washington, DC	20002-3817	202-723-3322	398-4832	PK-8	Vernetta Christian
Chavez - Capitol Hill HS	709 12th St SE	Washington, DC	20003	202-547-3424	547-2507	9-12	Oriel Robinson-Taylor
Chavez - Parkside MSHS	3701 Hayes St NE	Washington, DC	20019-1702	202-398-2230	398-2535	6-12	William Massey
Chavez Prep MS	770 Kenyon St NW	Washington, DC	20010	202-723-3975	723-3976	6-8	Courtney Miller
Children's Guild DC	2146 24th Pl NE	Washington, DC	20018	202-774-5442		K-8	Nakia Nicholson
City Arts & Prep Charter S	705 Edgewood St NE Fl 2	Washington, DC	20017-3341	202-269-4646	403-3222	PK-8	Andrew Kirkland
Community College Prep Academy	500 19th St NE	Washington, DC	20006	202-610-5780		Adult	Connie Spinner
Community College Prep Academy	2405 Martin L King Ave SE	Washington, DC	20020	202-610-5780		Adult	C. Vanessa Spinner
Creative Minds International Charter S	3700 N Capitol St NW	Washington, DC	20011	202-588-0370	588-0263	PK-6	Dr. Golnar Abedin
Democracy Prep Congress Hts Charter S	3100 Martin L King Ave SE	Washington, DC	20032	202-561-0860	561-0864	PK-7	Benjamin Feit
DC Bilingual Public Charter S	33 Riggs Rd NE	Washington, DC	20011	202-750-6674	745-2562	PK-5	Daniela Anello
District of Columbia International S	PO Box 43250	Washington, DC	20010	202-459-4790	787-3995	6-8	Simon Rodberg
DC Prep Charter ES - Anacostia	1102 W St SE	Washington, DC	20020-5737	202-729-3500	889-2785	PK-3	Maria-Teresa Duvall
DC Prep Charter ES - Benning	100 41st St NE	Washington, DC	20019-3308	202-398-2838	398-2839	PK-6	Maura Englender
DC Prep Charter ES - Edgewood	707 Edgewood St NE	Washington, DC	20017	202-635-4411	635-4412	PK-3	Avise Hayes
DC Prep Charter MS - Edgewood	701 Edgewood St NE	Washington, DC	20017	202-832-5700	832-5701	4-8	Rachel McClam
DC Scholars Charter S	5601 E Capitol St SE	Washington, DC	20019	202-559-6138	618-9396	PK-5	Rebecca Crouch
Eagle Academy Charter S	1017 New Jersey Ave SE	Washington, DC	20003	202-459-6825	479-6796	PK-3	Sabrina Ogilvie
Eagle Academy Charter S - Congress Hts.	3400 Wheeler Rd SE	Washington, DC	20032	202-544-2646	544-0187	PK-3	Melanie Leonard
Early Childhood Academy	4025 9th St SE	Washington, DC	20032-6051	202-373-0035	373-5586	PK-3	Wendy Edwards
Excel Academy Public Charter S	2501 M L K Jr SE	Washington, DC	20020	202-373-0097	373-0477	PK-8	Dana Bogle
Friendship Charter MS - Woodridge	2959 Carlton Ave NE	Washington, DC	20018-2615	202-635-6500	635-6481	4-8	Felicia Owo
Friendship Charter S Armstrong	1400 1st St NW	Washington, DC	20002	202-572-1070		PK-5	Jeffrey Scanlon
Friendship Charter S - Blow-Pierce	725 19th St NE	Washington, DC	20002-4713	202-572-1070	399-6157	PK-8	Dr. Jeffrey Grant
Friendship Charter S - Chamberlain	1345 Potomac Ave SE	Washington, DC	20003-4411	202-547-5800	547-4554	PK-8	Morrise Harbour
Friendship Charter S - Online	120 Q St NE	Washington, DC	20002-2100	202-281-1700	281-1799	K-12	
Friendship Charter S - Southeast Academy	645 Milwaukee Pl SE	Washington, DC	20032-2606	202-562-1980	562-0726	PK-5	David Lawery
Friendship Charter S - Technology Prep	645 Milwaukee Pl SE	Washington, DC	20032	202-562-1980	562-1817	6-12	Peggy Jones
Friendship Collegiate Academy	2507 Martin Luther King Ave	Washington, DC	20032	202-552-5700	373-0955	6-12	Mary Dunnock
Goodwill Excel Center	1776 G St NW	Washington, DC	20006	202-839-3650		9-12	Catherine Meloy
Harmony DC Public Charter S	62 T St NE	Washington, DC	20002	202-529-7500	529-7501	K-6	
Haynes Public Charter S	4501 Kansas Ave NW	Washington, DC	20011	202-706-5838	706-5832	PK-12	Phyllis Hedlund
Haynes Public Charter S	3600 Georgia Ave NW	Washington, DC	20010	202-667-4446	667-8811	5-8	Myron Long
Howard University MS of Math & Science	405 Howard Pl NW	Washington, DC	20059-0001	202-806-7725	865-0271	6-8	Kathryn Procope
Ideal Academy	6130 N Capitol St NW	Washington, DC	20011-1405	202-729-6660	729-6677	PK-8	George Rutherford Ph.D.
IDEA Public Charter HS	1027 45th St NE	Washington, DC	20019-3802	202-399-4750	399-4387	9-12	Lanette Bacchus
Imagine Hope Community Charter - Lamond	6200 Kansas Ave NE	Washington, DC	20011	202-722-4421	722-4431	PK-6	Diana Tharpe
Imagine Hope Community Charter - Tolson	2917 8th St NE	Washington, DC	20017-1669	202-832-7370	832-7644	PK-8	Camille Darden
Ingenuity Prep Charter S	4600 Livingston Rd SE	Washington, DC	20032	202-374-8458		PK-2	Aaron Cuny
Inspired Teaching S	200 Douglas St NE	Washington, DC	20002	202-248-6825	248-6939	PK-8	Deborah Williams
Kingsman Academy	1375 E St NE	Washington, DC	20002-5429	202-547-1028	547-1272	6-12	Shannon Hodge
KIPP DC: AIM Academy	2600 Douglass Pl SE	Washington, DC	20020	202-678-5477	678-4383	5-8	Kimberly Neal
KIPP DC: Arts and Technology Academy	5300 Blaine St NE	Washington, DC	20019	202-398-6811		PK-K	Allison Artis
KIPP DC: College Preparatory	1401 Brentwood Pkwy NE	Washington, DC	20002	202-678-2527	678-0082	9-12	Jessica Cunningham
KIPP DC: Connect Academy	1375 Mount Olivet Rd NE	Washington, DC	20002-2509	202-396-5477	223-4504	PK-K	Donny Tiengtum
KIPP DC: Discover Academy	2600 Douglass Pl SE	Washington, DC	20020	202-678-7735	678-0085	PK-K	Philonda Johnson
KIPP DC: Grow Academy	421 P St NW	Washington, DC	20001-2417	202-986-4769	986-1625	PK-K	Lauren Ellis
KIPP DC: Heights Academy	2600 Douglass Pl SE	Washington, DC	20020	202-610-5323	610-6555	1-4	Gaelen Gallagher
KIPP DC: KEY Academy	4801 Benning Rd SE	Washington, DC	20019-6145	202-582-5477	582-0152	5-8	David Ayala
KIPP DC: LEAD Academy	421 P St NW	Washington, DC	20001	202-223-4505	223-4504	1-3	Mekia Love
KIPP DC: LEAP Academy	4801 Benning Rd SE	Washington, DC	20019-6145	202-582-5327	582-4680	PK-PK	Abraham Clayman
KIPP DC: Promise Academy	4801 Benning Rd SE	Washington, DC	20019	202-265-7766	582-4686	1-4	Andhra Lutz
KIPP DC: Spring Academy	1375 Mount Olivet Rd NE	Washington, DC	20002-2509	202-397-5477	223-4504	K-4	Lindsey Hoy
KIPP DC: Valor Academy	5300 Blaine St NE	Washington, DC	20019-6665			5-8	Gillian Connor
KIPP DC: WILL Academy	421 P St NW	Washington, DC	20001-2417	202-328-9455	328-9457	4-8	Tiffanie Williams
KIPP DC Northeast Academy	1375 Mount Olivet Rd NE	Washington, DC	20002-2509	202-398-5477		5-7	John Barnhardt
KIPP DC Quest Academy	5300 Blaine St NE	Washington, DC	20019	202-397-5477		1-4	John Petersen
Latin American Montessori Bilingual S	1375 Missouri Ave NW	Washington, DC	20011-1862	202-525-5105	722-4125	PK-5	Cristina Encinas
Latin American Montessori Bilingual S	1800 Perry St NE	Washington, DC	20018	202-525-5105	621-8621	PK-5	Cristina Encinas
LAYC Career Academy	3047 15th St NW	Washington, DC	20009-4211	202-319-2228	462-5696	Adult	Nicole Hanrahan
Lee Montessori Public Charter S	3025 4th St NE	Washington, DC	20017	202-779-9740	318-0763	PK-2	Megan Hubbard
Marshall Academy	2427 M L K Jr Ave SE	Washington, DC	20020	202-563-6862	563-6946	9-12	Melanie Sala
Meridian Public Charter S	3031 14th St NW	Washington, DC	20009	202-387-9830	387-7605	PK-8	Candice Bobo
Monument Academy	500 19th St NE	Washington, DC	20002	202-545-3180		5-6	Marlene Magrino
Mundo Verde Bilingual Charter S	30 P St NW	Washington, DC	20001	202-750-7060	667-4811	PK-5	Kristin Scotchmer
National Collegiate Prep Charter HS	4600 Livingston Rd SE	Washington, DC	20032	202-832-7737	832-7736	9-12	Cordelia Postell
Next Step Public Charter S	3047 15th St NW	Washington, DC	20009	202-319-2249	234-0001	Adult	Arturo Martinez
Paul - International HS	5800 8th St NW	Washington, DC	20011-1900	202-291-7499	291-7495	6-12	Jami Dunham
Perry Street Preparatory S	1800 Perry St NE	Washington, DC	20018	202-529-4400	526-2214	PK-8	Rachel Crouch
Rocketship Public Charter S	2335 Raynolds Pl SE	Washington, DC	20020-3246	877-806-0920		PK-3	
Roots Public Charter S	15 Kennedy St NW	Washington, DC	20011-5201	202-882-8073	882-8075	PK-8	Dr. Bernida Thompson
Rosario International Public Charter S	1100 Harvard St NW	Washington, DC	20009-5356	202-797-4700	232-6442	Adult	Holly-Ann Freso-Moore
Rosario International Public Charter S	514 V St NE	Washington, DC	20002	202-734-4900		6-8	Karen Rivas
St. Coletta Special Education Charter S	1901 Independence Ave SE	Washington, DC	20003-1733	202-350-8680	350-8699	PK-12	Janice Corazza
SEED Public Charter S	4300 C St SE	Washington, DC	20019-4100	202-248-7773	248-3021	6-12	Dr. Adrian Manuel
Sela Charter S	6015 Chillum Pl NE	Washington, DC	20011	202-670-7352		PK-3	Natalie Smith
Shining Stars Montessori Academy	1240 Randolph St NE	Washington, DC	20017	202-723-1467	319-2309	PK-3	Regina Rodriguez
Somerset Prep Academy	3301 Wheeler Rd SE	Washington, DC	20032	202-562-9104	457-1980	6-10	Lauren Catalano
Stokes Charter S	3700 Oakview Ter NE	Washington, DC	20017	202-265-7237	265-4656	PK-5	Erika Bryant
Two Rivers Public Charter S	1234 4th St NE	Washington, DC	20002-3432	202-543-8477	543-8479	6-8	Elaine Hou
Two Rivers Public Charter S	1227 4th St NE	Washington, DC	20002-3431	202-546-4477	546-0869	PK-8	Maggie Bello
Two Rivers Public Charter S - Young	820 26th St NE	Washington, DC	20002-3262	202-388-1360		PK-1	Maggie Bello
Washington Latin Public Charter S	5200 2nd St NW	Washington, DC	20011	202-223-1111	723-1171	5-12	Peter Anderson
Washington MST Public Charter HS	1920 Bladensburg Rd NE	Washington, DC	20002-1812	202-636-8011	636-3495	9-12	N'Deye Diagne
Washington Yu Ying Public Charter S	220 Taylor St NE	Washington, DC	20017-1009	202-635-1950	635-1960	PK-5	Maquita Alexander
Wright Charter S	770 M St SE	Washington, DC	20003-3609	202-388-1011	388-5197	8-12	Dr. Marco Clark
YouthBuild Public Charter S	3014 14th St NW	Washington, DC	20009-6819	202-319-0141	518-0618	Adult	Andrew Touchette

Florida

School	Address	City,State	Zip code	Telephone	Fax	Grade	Contact
Academic Solutions Academy	4099 N Pine Island Rd	Sunrise, FL	33351-6548	954-572-6600	572-6444	9-12	Andrew Kinlock
Academic Solutions Academy	2000 W Commercial Blvd	Fort Lauderdale, FL	33309	954-572-6600	572-6444	9-12	Andrew Kinlock
AcadeMir Charter MS	5800 SW 135th Ave	Miami, FL	33183	305-967-8492	392-1928	6-8	Karla Rodriguez
AcadeMir Charter S Preparatory	19185 SW 127th Ave	Miami, FL	33177	305-964-7542	964-7458	K-5	Dr. Mary Gonzalez-Ledo
AcadeMir Charter S West	14880 SW 26th St	Miami, FL	33185	305-485-9911	485-9944	K-5	Olivia Bernal
AcadeMir Prep Academy	10870 SW 113th Pl	Miami, FL	33176	305-596-4149	596-4151	K-5	Karla Rodriguez
Academy at the Farm	9500 Alex Lange Way	Dade City, FL	33525-8213	352-588-9737	588-0508	K-8	Ray Polk
Academy Da Vinci	1060 Keene Rd	Dunedin, FL	34698-6300	727-298-2778	502-6065	K-5	Lucy Foran
Academy for Positive Learning Charter S	1200 N Dixie Hwy	Lake Worth, FL	33460-2123	561-585-6104	585-7849	K-8	Renatta Adan-Espinoza
Academy of Environmental Science	12695 W Fort Island Trl	Crystal River, FL	34429-5290	352-795-8793	249-2100	9-12	Sandy Balfour
Academy of International Education	1080 La Baron Dr	Miami Springs, FL	33166-6064	305-883-3900	883-3901	K-8	Vera Hirsh
Acceleration MS	3365 Seminole Ave	Fort Myers, FL	33916	239-400-1818	689-8511	6-8	Dr. Patricia Lightner
Access Charter S	6000 E Colonial Dr	Orlando, FL	32807	321-319-0640	319-0643	6-12	Roger Watkins
Achievement Academy - Bartow	695 E Summerlin St	Bartow, FL	33830-4848	863-533-0690	534-0798	PK-PK	Cindi Parker-Pearson

School	Address	City,State	Zip code	Telephone	Fax	Grade	Contact
Achievement Academy - Lakeland	716 E Bella Vista St	Lakeland, FL	33805-3009	863-683-6504	688-9292	PK-PK	Cindi Parker-Pearson
Achievement Academy - Winter Haven	2211 28th St NW	Winter Haven, FL	33881-1807	863-965-7586	968-5016	PK-PK	Cindi Parker-Pearson
Adler ES	4515 38th Ave N	St Petersburg, FL	33713	727-329-9545	522-2854	K-6	Yuri Yamashita
Advantage Academy	304 W Prosser Dr	Plant City, FL	33563-6975	813-567-0801	441-0272	K-8	Keith Miller
Advantage Academy at Waterstone	855 Waterstone Way	Homestead, FL	33033-5941	305-248-6206	248-6208	K-8	Nancy Roque
Advantage Academy Santa Fe	9790 SW 107th Ct	Miami, FL	33176	786-228-5309	718-1921	K-5	Teresita Nieves
Alachua Learning Center	PO Box 1389	Alachua, FL	32616	386-418-2080	418-4116	K-8	Krishna Rivera
Alee Academy Charter S	1705 E County Road 44	Eustis, FL	32736-2500	352-357-9426	357-8426	9-12	
Allen Leadership Academy	940 Caliph St	Opa Locka, FL	33054-3507	305-615-2977	615-3032	K-5	Latoya Robinson
Aloma Charter HS	495 N Semoran Blvd Ste 8	Winter Park, FL	32792	407-657-4343	657-4317	9-12	Jacqueline Evans
Alpha Charter S of Excellence	1217 SW 4th St	Miami, FL	33135	305-643-2132	642-3717	K-5	Isabel Navas
Alpha International Academy	121 S 24th Ave	Hollywood, FL	33020	954-505-7974	505-7976	K-5	Wayne Neunie
Altoona S	42630 State Road 19	Altoona, FL	32702-9638	352-669-3444	669-3407	K-5	Walter Schmidt
AMI Kids Emerald Coast	207 4th St SE	Ft Walton Bch, FL	32548-5636	850-244-2711	244-2171	6-12	Audra Ray
Andrews HS	3500 N Andrews Ave Ext	Pompano Beach, FL	33064	954-944-4123	784-3681	9-12	Eunice Casey
Apalachicola Bay Charter S	98 12th St	Apalachicola, FL	32320-2003	850-653-1222	653-1857	K-8	Chimene Johnson
Archimedean Academy	12425 SW 72nd St	Miami, FL	33183-2513	305-279-6572	675-8448	K-5	Christina Briz
Archimedean Middle Conservatory	12425 SW 72nd St	Miami, FL	33183-2513	305-279-6572	675-8448	6-8	Vasiliki Moysidis
Archimedean Upper Conservatory	12425 SW 72nd St	Miami, FL	33183	305-279-6572	675-8448	9-12	Demetrios Demopoulos
Ascend Career Academy	5251 Coconut Creek Pkwy	Margate, FL	33063-3962	954-978-4555		9-12	Vincent Alessi
ASPIRA Arts DECO	1 NE 19th St	Miami, FL	33132-1030	305-576-1512	576-0810	6-8	Maria Caceres
ASPIRA Leadership and College Prep	13330 SW 288th St	Homestead, FL	33033	305-246-1111	246-1433	K-8	Antonio Cejas
ASPIRA Raul Martinez Charter S	13300 Memorial Hwy	North Miami, FL	33161-3940	305-893-8050	891-6055	6-9	Kenneth Feria
Aspire Charter Academy	928 Malone Dr	Orlando, FL	32810	407-297-9955		K-5	
Athenian Academy of Pasco	3118 Seven Springs Blvd	New Port Richey, FL	34655-3340	727-372-0200	376-1916	K-8	Evan Markowitz
Athenian Academy	2289 N Hercules Ave	Clearwater, FL	33763-2326	727-298-2718	298-2719	K-8	Kathy Hershelman
Atlantic Montessori Charter S	9893 Pines Blvd	Pembroke Pines, FL	33024-6164	754-263-2700	263-2596	K-3	Juana Garcia
Atlantic Montessori Charter S	2550 S Flamingo Rd	Davie, FL	33325	954-790-8943	399-9787	PK-5	Juana Garcia
Avant Garde Academy	2025 McKinley St	Hollywood, FL	33020	954-816-6153	800-2715	K-8	Dr. Steven Blinder
Avant Garde Academy	3540 Pleasant Hill Rd	Kissimmee, FL	34746	407-944-4464	368-6048	K-8	Yesenia Cantillo
Avant Garde Academy of Osceola	2880 N Orange Blossom Trl	Kissimmee, FL	34741	321-697-3800	386-7357	6-12	Tiffany Hughes
Aventura City of Excellence Charter S	3333 NE 188th St	Aventura, FL	33180-2933	305-466-1499	466-1339	K-8	Julie Alm
Bay Haven Charter Academy	2501 Hawks Landing Blvd	Panama City, FL	32405-6658	850-248-3500	248-3514	PK-8	Jamie Vickers
Beacon College Preparatory	13400 NW 28th Ave	Opa Locka, FL	33054-4842	786-353-6109		PK-5	Patrick Evans
Beasley Technical Academy	13830 Jetport Commerce Pkwy	Fort Myers, FL	33913	239-476-9100	561-9864	9-12	Dr. Joseph Torregrasso
Believers Academy	5840 Corporate Way Ste 100	West Palm Beach, FL	33407-2040	561-340-2507	340-2510	9-12	Lori Dyer
Bellalago Charter Academy	3651 Pleasant Hill Rd	Kissimmee, FL	34746-2935	407-933-1690	933-2143	K-8	Wendy Honeycutt
Bell Creek Academy	13221 Boyette Rd	Riverview, FL	33569	813-793-6075	413-2985	6-12	Dr. Margaret Fahringer
Belle Glade Excel	555 SW 16th St	Belle Glade, FL	33430	561-257-5210	983-8020	K-5	Altoria Henley
Belmont Academy	496 SW Ring Ct	Lake City, FL	32025	386-487-0487	755-7989	PK-12	Ron Barker
Berkley Accelerated MS	5316 Berkley Rd	Auburndale, FL	33823-8493	863-984-2400	984-2411	6-8	Jill Bolender
Berkley ES	5240 Berkley Rd	Auburndale, FL	33823-8491	863-968-5024	968-5026	PK-5	Gayle Thomas
Beulah Academy of Science	8633 Beulah Rd	Pensacola, FL	32526-5203	850-944-2822	944-2848	6-8	Sherry Bailey
Big Pine Academy	30220 Overseas Hwy	Big Pine Key, FL	33043-3357	305-872-1266	872-1265	PK-7	Cathy Hoffman
Biscayne HS	1680 Dunn Ave Ste 8	Jacksonville, FL	32218	904-423-8855		9-12	Erica Williams
Boca Raton Charter S	269 NE 14th St	Boca Raton, FL	33432	561-750-0437	750-7880	K-5	Louise Nelson
Bok Academy	13901 Hwy 27	Lake Wales, FL	33859-2570	863-638-1010	638-1212	6-8	Damien Moses
Bonita Springs Charter S	25380 Bernwood Dr	Bonita Springs, FL	34135-7850	239-992-6932	992-7359	K-8	Carissa Carroll
Boulware Springs Charter S	1303 NE 23rd Ave	Gainesville, FL	32609-3822	352-215-2175		K-5	Kay Abbitt
Bridgeprep Academy Greater Miami	137 NE 19th St	Miami, FL	33132	786-477-4372	446-8714	K-5	Ana Natali
Bridgeprep Academy Interamerican	621 Beacom Blvd	Miami, FL	33135	305-643-4833	643-4832	K-8	Mitzie Ortiz
Bridgeprep Academy of Arts & Minds	3138 Commodore Plz	Miami, FL	33133-5814	305-448-1100	448-9737	9-12	Antonietta DiGirolamo
BridgePrep Academy of Hollywood Hills	1400 N 46th Ave	Hollywood, FL	33021	954-362-8268	362-8271	K-5	Kai Walker
Bridgeprep Academy of Tampa	2418 W Swann Ave	Tampa, FL	33609-4712	813-258-5652	258-5654	K-8	Christine Harris
Bridgeprep Academy of Village Green	13300 SW 120th St	Miami, FL	33186	305-253-8775	429-1058	K-8	Paricia Garcia
BridgePrep Academy - Orlando	5710 La Costa Dr	Orlando, FL	32807	321-775-2119		K-6	Dr. Joy Gordon Fernandez
Bridgeprep Academy South	10700 SW 56th St	Miami, FL	33165-7044	305-271-3109	271-5315	K-8	Patricia Perez
Bright Futures Academy	10350 Riverside Dr	Palm Bch Gdns, FL	33410	561-253-7504	658-0565	K-8	Ashley Slone
Brooks-DeBartolo Collegiate HS	10948 N Central Ave	Tampa, FL	33612	813-971-5600	971-5656	9-12	Kristine Bennett
Brooksville Engineering Science Tech.	835 School St	Brooksville, FL	34601-4006	352-544-2373		9-12	Andre Buford
Broward Math and Science S	6101 NW 31st St	Margate, FL	33063	954-969-8488	756-8053	K-12	Ali Gumus
Burns Science & Technology Charter S	160 Ridge Rd	Oak Hill, FL	32759-9773	386-210-4915	210-4922	K-8	Dr. Janet McGee
Byrneville Charter S	1600 Byrneville Rd	Century, FL	32535-3640	850-256-6350	256-6357	K-5	Dee Wolfe-Sullivan
Campus Charter S	3815 Curtis Blvd	Port Saint John, FL	32927	321-633-8234		K-6	Greg Gerard
Canoe Creek Charter Academy	3600 Canoe Creek Rd	Saint Cloud, FL	34772-9132	407-891-7320	891-7330	PK-8	Julie Ramirez
Cape Coral Charter S	76 Mid Cape Ter	Cape Coral, FL	33991-2008	239-995-0904	995-0369	PK-8	Bonnie Brett
Capstone Academy	4901 W Fairfield Dr	Pensacola, FL	32506-4111	850-458-7735	455-7754	PK-K	Charles Thomas
Capstone Academy Milton Charter S	5308 Stewart St	Milton, FL	32570-4736	850-626-3091	626-3093	PK-PK	Claire Errington
Caring & Sharing Charter S	PO Box 5936	Gainesville, FL	32627-5936	352-372-1004	372-0894	PK-6	Curtis Peterson
Central Charter S	4515 N State Road 7	Laud Lakes, FL	33319-5883	954-735-6295	735-6232	K-8	Tonya Dix
Central Florida Leadership Academy	427 N Primrose Dr	Orlando, FL	32803-5012	407-480-2352	289-5204	6-11	Tiffany Ward
Central HS	700 W 23rd St Bldg H	Panama City, FL	32405-3936	850-215-0770	763-7613	9-12	Jeremy Knapp
Chain of Lakes Collegiate HS	999 Avenue H NE	Winter Haven, FL	33881-4256	863-298-6800	298-6801	11-12	Bridget Fetter
Championship Academy	3367 N University Dr	Davie, FL	33328	954-362-3415	640-9678	K-8	Paulina Reyna
Championship Academy	1100 Hillcrest Dr	Hollywood, FL	33021	954-924-8006	924-8044	K-12	Savitria Guthrie
Chancery High Charter	7001 S Orange Blossom Trl	Orlando, FL	32809	407-850-9791	850-9856	9-12	Michael Showalter
Channelside Academy of Math & Science	1029 E Twiggs St	Tampa, FL	33602-3527	813-579-9649	463-2439	K-8	Suzanne Elder
Charter HS of the Americas	970 W Flagler St	Miami, FL	33130	305-325-1001	324-9934	9-12	Barbara Sanchez
Charter S of Excellence - Davie	2801 N University Dr	Pembroke Pines, FL	33024	954-433-8838	433-8636	K-5	Jennifer Jaynes
Charter S of Excellence - Ft Lauderdale	1217 SE 3rd Ave	Fort Lauderdale, FL	33316-1905	954-522-2997	522-3159	K-5	Lisa Castro
Charter S of Excellence Riverland	3550 Davie Blvd	Fort Lauderdale, FL	33312-3438	954-581-0167	581-0195	K-5	Rosa Dyer
Charter School of Excellence Tamarac	7595 NW 61st St	Tamarac, FL	33321	954-721-8902	721-8908	K-5	Racquel Lipscomb
Chautauqua Learn & Serve Charter S	1118 Magnolia Ave	Panama City, FL	32401-2815	850-785-5056	785-5071	9-Adu	Cynthia McCauley
Children's Reading Center	7901 Saint Johns Ave	Palatka, FL	32177	386-328-9990	328-9949	K-5	Jacqueline England
Chiles Academy	868 George W Engram Blvd	Daytona Beach, FL	32114-1859	386-322-6102	258-4681	6-12	Anne Ferguson
Choices in Learning Charter S	1100 E State Road 434	Winter Springs, FL	32708-2773	407-302-1005	542-5553	K-5	Janet Kearney
City of Hialeah Education Academy	2590 W 76th St	Hialeah, FL	33016-6888	305-362-4006	362-7006	6-12	Carlos Alvarez
City of Palms Charter HS	2830 Winkler Ave Ste 201	Fort Myers, FL	33916	239-561-6611	561-6230	9-12	Sarah White
City of Pembroke Pines Central ES	12350 Sheridan St	Pembroke Pines, FL	33026-3813	954-322-3330	322-3389	K-8	Sean Chance
City of Pembroke Pines Charter HS	17189 Sheridan St	Pembroke Pines, FL	33331-1934	954-538-3700	538-3715	6-12	Peter Bayer
City of Pembroke Pines East ES	10801 Pembroke Rd	Pembroke Pines, FL	33025-1707	954-443-4800	443-4811	K-5	Kenneth Bass
City of Pembroke Pines West ES	1680 SW 184th Ave	Pembroke Pines, FL	33029-6120	954-450-6990	443-4820	K-5	Michael Castellano
City of Pembroke Pines West MS	18500 Pembroke Rd	Pembroke Pines, FL	33029-6108	954-443-4847	447-1691	6-8	Michael Castellano
Clark Advanced Learning Center	2400 SE Salerno Rd	Stuart, FL	34997-6505	772-419-5750	419-5760	10-12	Debra Kohuth
Classical Preparatory Charter S	16500 Lyceum Way	Spring Hill, FL	34610	727-803-7903		K-10	Ben Davis
Clay Charter Academy	1417 Red Apple Rd	Middleburg, FL	32068	904-276-9515	406-1608	K-8	Angela Galyan
C.O.A.S.T. Charter S	PO Box 338	Saint Marks, FL	32355-0338	850-925-6344	925-6396	PK-8	Alyssa Higgins
Collegiate HS at NW FL State College	100 College Blvd E	Niceville, FL	32578-1347	850-729-4949	729-4950	10-12	Anthony Boyer
Community Charter S of Excellence	11604 N 15th St	Tampa, FL	33612	813-931-5500	971-5232	K-8	Matthew Torano M.Ed.
Compass Middle Charter S	550 E Clower St	Bartow, FL	33830-6403	863-519-8701	519-8704	5-8	Anita Fine
Connections Educ Ctr of the Palm Beaches	5841 Corporate Way Ste 10	West Palm Beach, FL	33407	561-328-6044		K-8	Debra Johnson
Coral Reef Montessori Academy	10853 SW 216th St	Cutler Ridge, FL	33170-3146	305-255-0064	255-4085	K-8	Lucy Canzoneri-Golden
Coral Springs Charter S	3205 N University Dr	Coral Springs, FL	33065-4115	954-340-4100	340-4111	6-12	Gary Springer
Cornerstone Academy Charter S	5903 Randolph Ave	Orlando, FL	32809-4241	407-608-7171		K-8	Renee Pancoast
Cornerstone Academy HS	5903 Randolph Ave	Orlando, FL	32809	407-608-7171	608-7172	9-12	Renee Pancoast
Coronado HS	3057 Cleveland Ave	Fort Myers, FL	33901	239-337-9140	337-9141	9-12	Joelle Lyman
Countryside Montessori Charter S	5852 Ehren Cutoff	Land O Lakes, FL	34639-3428	813-996-0991	996-0993	1-8	Dr. Michael Rom
Crossroad Academy Charter S	470 Strong Rd	Quincy, FL	32351-6006	850-875-9626	875-1403	PK-12	Kevin Forehand
Cypress Junction Montessori	PO Box 102	Winter Haven, FL	33882	863-259-1490		K-8	Casey Moyer-Caswell
Dayspring Academy ES	8911 Timber Oaks Ave	Port Richey, FL	34668-2426	727-862-8600	868-5175	K-5	Brenda Garcia
Dayspring Academy Secondary	9509 Palm Ave	Port Richey, FL	34668-4647	727-847-9003	848-8774	6-12	Tim Greenier
Discovery Academy at Lake Alfred	1000 N Buena Vista Dr	Lake Alfred, FL	33850-2031	863-295-5955	956-5089	6-8	Kevin Warren
Discovery Academy of Science	1120 Curlew Rd	Dunedin, FL	34698	727-369-6361	499-6828	2-6	Emre Akbaba
Discovery Academy of Science	1380 Pinehurst Rd	Dunedin, FL	34698	727-330-2424	499-6828	K-1	Megan Holland
Discovery HS	640 Evenhouse Rd	Lake Alfred, FL	33850	863-268-7178	956-5089	9-12	Carol Fulks
Doctors Charter S of Miami Shores	11301 NW 5th Ave	Miami Shores, FL	33168-3343	305-754-2381	751-5833	6-12	Dr. Kelly Andrews
Dolphin Park HS	3206 S University Dr	Miramar, FL	33025-3007	954-433-1573	433-1589	9-12	Vanessia Blackshire
Doral Academy	2450 NW 97th Ave	Doral, FL	33172-2308	305-597-9999	591-2669	K-5	Eleonora Cuesta
Doral Academy HS	11100 NW 27th St	Doral, FL	33172-5001	305-597-9950	477-6762	9-12	Carlos Ferrals
Doral Academy Preparatory MS	2601 NW 112th Ave	Doral, FL	33172-1804	305-591-0020	591-9251	6-8	Carlos Ferrals
Doral International Academy	6700 NW 104th Ave	Doral, FL	33178	786-270-2088	221-2238	K-8	Victoria Gomez
Doral Performing Arts\Entertainment Acad	11100 NW 27th St	Doral, FL	33172	305-597-9950	591-9251	9-12	Carlos Ferralls
Downtown Doral Charter ES	8390 NW 53rd St	Doral, FL	33166	305-569-2223	569-2226	K-3	Jeanette Isenberg
Downtown Miami Charter S	305 NW 3rd Ave	Miami, FL	33128-1606	305-579-2112	579-2115	K-6	Dr. Rebecca Dinda
Duval Charter Scholars Academy	100 Scholars Way	Jacksonville, FL	32216	904-724-1536	721-5381	K-8	Carin White
Duval Charter S at Baymeadows	7510 Baymeadows Way	Jacksonville, FL	32256	904-638-7947	466-4101	K-12	Kim Stidham
Duval Charter S at Flagler Center	12755 Flagler Center Blvd	Jacksonville, FL	32258-2610	904-899-1010	899-1011	K-8	Adam Cross

School	Address	City,State	Zip code	Telephone	Fax	Grade	Contact
Duval Charter S at Mandarin	5209 Shad Rd	Jacksonville, FL	32257-2005	904-440-2901	440-2902	K-8	Dawn Lamb
Duval Charter S at Southside	8680 A C Skinner Pkwy	Jacksonville, FL	32256-6985	904-423-5348	423-5349	K-8	Ashley Doty
Duval Charter S at Westside	9238 103rd St	Jacksonville, FL	32210-8610	904-421-0250	423-2601	K-8	Tania Woods
Eagle Arts Academy	1000 Wellington Trce	Wellington, FL	33414	561-412-4087		K-6	Michael Smith
Eagles Nest Charter Academy	3698 NW 15th St	Lauderhill, FL	33311	954-635-2308	990-6921	K-8	Christine Mentis
Early Beginnings Academy	1411 NW 14th Ave	Miami, FL	33125-1616	305-325-1080	325-1044	PK-2	Makeesha Coleman
Easter Seals Charter S	1219 Dunn Ave	Daytona Beach, FL	32114-2405	386-255-4568	258-7677	PK-PK	April Leopold
Econ River Charter HS	14180 E Colonial Dr	Orlando, FL	32826	407-790-2143		9-12	Isabel Villanueva
Educational Horizons Charter S	1281 S Wickham Rd	West Melbourne, FL	32904-2450	321-729-0786	802-6823	K-6	Cynthia Thomas
Ed Venture Charter S	117 East Coast Ave	Hypoluxo, FL	33462	561-582-1454	547-9682	9-12	Patricia Ryan
Einstein S	5910 SW Archer Rd	Gainesville, FL	32608	352-335-4321	335-1575	2-8	Christine Aurelio
Enterprise HS	2461 N McMullen Booth Rd	Clearwater, FL	33759-1305	727-474-1237	725-3470	9-12	Donna Hulbert
Escambia Charter S	391 90 9 Ranch Rd	Cantonment, FL	32533-9098	850-937-0500	968-5605	9-12	Jerome Chisholm
Everest Charter S	10044 W McNab Rd	Tamarac, FL	33321	954-532-3015	876-1696	K-8	Raul Baez
Everglades Preparatory Academy	360 E Main St Bldg C	Pahokee, FL	33476-1800	561-924-3002	924-3013	9-12	Edna Stephens M.Ed.
Everglades Preparatory Academy	2251 E Mowry Dr	Homestead, FL	33033-4913	786-601-1969	377-5759	6-12	Aimee Leyva
Excelsior Charter Academy	3520 NW 191st St	Miami Gardens, FL	33056-2900	786-565-9188	623-0900	K-9	Janell Wyartt
Excelsior Charter S of Broward	10066 W McNab Rd	Tamarac, FL	33321	954-726-5227	722-2451	K-5	Cristina Reynolds
Excelsior Language Academy of Hialeah	369 E 10th St	Hialeah, FL	33010-4131	305-897-9004	883-5279	PK-8	Clint Duvo
Expressions Learning Arts Academy	5408 SW 13th St	Gainesville, FL	32608-5038	352-373-5223	373-6327	K-5	Juniper DiGiovanni M.Ed.
Fair Babson Park ES	815 N Scenic Hwy	Babson Park, FL	33827-9795	863-678-4664	678-4669	PK-5	Elizabeth Tyler
Flagler HS	1951 W Copans Rd	Pompano Beach, FL	33064-1549	754-220-7899	973-3199	9-12	Stuart Morgan-Graham
Florida Autism Center of Excellence	6310 E Sligh Ave	Tampa, FL	33617-9107	813-985-3223	985-3199	PK-12	Annie Russell
Florida Cyber Charter Academy	9143 Philips Hwy Ste 590	Jaxville Bch, FL	32256	904-247-3268	719-1645	9-12	Bridget White
Florida Futures Academy North	1760 N Congress Ave	West Palm Beach, FL	33409	561-215-0933		9-12	Carolyn Taylor
Florida Futures Academy South	8160 Okeechobee Blvd	West Palm Beach, FL	33411	561-215-0933		9-12	Carolyn Taylor
Florida International Academy	13400 NW 28th Ave	Opa Locka, FL	33054-4842	305-685-8190	688-1745	K-8	Sonia Mitchell
Florida SIA Tech at Gainesville	7022 NW 10th Pl	Gainesville, FL	32605-3147	352-333-7952	333-7953	9-12	Christal Blue
Florida Southwestern Collegiate HS	8099 College Pkwy	Fort Myers, FL	33919-5566	239-432-6767	433-6912	9-12	Dr. Brian Botts
Focus Academy	304 Druid Hills Rd	Temple Terrace, FL	33617	813-443-5558	443-5630	9-12	Sara Capwell
Four Corners Charter S	9100 Teacher Ln	Davenport, FL	33897-6212	407-787-4300	787-4331	K-5	Denise Thompson
Four Courners Upper S	9160 Bella Citta Blvd	Davenport, FL	33896	407-589-4600	589-4601	6-12	Denise Thompson
Franklin Academy	7882 S Military Trl	Boynton Beach, FL	33436	561-767-4700	952-6925	K-8	Christopher Glinton
Franklin Academy	4500 NW 103rd Ave	Sunrise, FL	33351	954-206-0850	497-3296	K-8	Sergio Delgado
Franklin Academy	18800 Pines Blvd	Pembroke Pines, FL	33029-1310	954-703-2294	436-2861	K-8	Elena Diaz
Franklin Academy	5651 Hood Rd	Palm Bch Gdns, FL	33418-1572	561-348-2525		K-8	Ivy Bernardo
Franklin Academy	6301 S Flamingo Rd	Cooper City, FL	33330	954-780-5533	252-8147	K-8	Doug Piper
Galileo S for Gifted Learning	3900 E State Road 46	Sanford, FL	32771	321-249-9221	878-0791	K-8	Michelle Nunez
Gamla Charter S	8600 Jog Rd	Boynton Beach, FL	33472	561-742-8017	742-8018	K-8	Elanit Weizman
Gamla Charter S	11155 SW 112th Ave	Miami, FL	33176	305-596-6266	596-6964	K-8	Dr. Gur Berman
Gamla Charter S North Broward	2620 Hollywood Blvd	Hollywood, FL	33020-4807	954-342-4064	342-4107	K-8	Sharon Miller
Gamla Charter School South Broward	6511 W Sunrise Blvd	Plantation, FL	33313	954-587-8348	587-8347	K-8	Christine Cardoso
Gamla Preparatory Academy	2650 Van Buren St	Hollywood, FL	33020	954-924-6495	924-6496	6-12	Monique Machado
Gardens S of Technology Arts	9153 Roan Ln	Palm Bch Gdns, FL	33403	561-290-7661	449-3470	K-8	Dr. Kevin Kovacs
Gateway Charter ES	12850 Commonwealth Dr	Fort Myers, FL	33913-8039	239-768-5048	768-5710	K-8	Sara Abraham M.Ed.
Gateway Charter HS	12770 Gateway Blvd	Fort Myers, FL	33913-8654	239-768-3350	768-3874	9-12	Sara Abraham
Genesis Preparatory S	207 NW 23rd Ave	Gainesville, FL	32609-3604	352-379-1188	379-1142	K-3	Charmaine Henry
Gibson Charter S	1682 NW 4th Ave	Miami, FL	33136-1507	305-438-0895	438-0896	K-8	Fareed Khan
Glades Academy	7368 State Road 15	Pahokee, FL	33476	561-924-9402	924-9279	K-8	Vinnisha Jones
Global Outreach Charter Academy	9570 Regency Square Blvd	Jacksonville, FL	32225-9104	904-551-7104	551-7120	K-8	Tangia Anderson
Goodwill L.I.F.E. Academy	5100 Tice St Ste D	Fort Myers, FL	33905-5203	239-334-4434	334-4439	6-12	Lynn Pottorf
Governors Charter Academy	4351 Mahan Dr	Tallahassee, FL	32308-5724	850-391-5259	391-5260	K-6	Dr. Adriane Peters
Green Springs HS	3555 NW 7th St	Miami, FL	33125-4015	305-720-2996	541-5559	9-12	Enrique Palma
Greentree Preparatory Charter S	750 NW 180th Ter	Pembroke Pines, FL	33029-2826	954-780-8733	430-7706	K-5	Rosa Pou
G-STAR School of the Arts	2030 S Congress Ave	Palm Springs, FL	33406	561-967-2023	963-8975	9-12	Kim Collins M.Ed.
Gulf Coast Acad of Science & Technology	10444 Tillery Rd	Spring Hill, FL	34608-3706	352-688-5092	688-5095	6-8	Nevin Siefert
Gulf Coast Charter Academy South	215 Airport Pulling Rd N	Naples, FL	34104	239-784-1539	263-4443	K-8	Gwen DaPore
Gulf Coast MS	2139 Deborah Dr	Spring Hill, FL	34609-3827	352-666-5790	666-5792	6-8	Dave Schoelles
Gulfstream Goodwill LIFE Academy	3800 S Congress Ave	Boynton Beach, FL	33426-8424	561-259-1000	259-1011	9-12	Cindy Maunder
Harlem Heights Community Charter S	15570 Hagie Dr	Fort Myers, FL	33908	239-482-7706	204-3009	K-3	Kristin Vollmer
Harris Preparatory Academy	1408 E Blount St	Pensacola, FL	32503-5620	850-432-2273	432-4624	K-5	Celestine Lewis
Hartridge Academy	1400 US Highway 92	Winter Haven, FL	33881-8137	863-956-4434	956-3267	K-5	Debra Richards
Hawn Charter School of the Arts	565 S Lakeview Dr Unit 110	Lake Helen, FL	32744	386-228-3900	228-3901	K-8	Kelly Conway M.A.
Healthy Learning Academy	13505 W Newberry Rd	Newberry, FL	32669-2752	352-372-2279	372-1665	K-5	Anni Egan
Henderson Hammock Charter S	10322 Henderson Rd	Tampa, FL	33625	813-739-6633	739-6681	K-8	Lane Morris
Highly Inquisitive & Versatile Ed	5855 NW 171st St	Miami, FL	33015-4607	305-231-4888	231-4881	K-8	Carlos Gonzalez
Hillcrest ES	1051 State Road 60 E	Lake Wales, FL	33853-4258	863-678-4216	678-4086	PK-5	Jennifer Barrow
Hillsborough Academy of Math & Science	9659 W Waters Ave	Tampa, FL	33635-1500	813-793-6085	413-2984	K-8	Cristina Fuentes
Hollywood Academy of Arts & Science	1705 Van Buren St	Hollywood, FL	33020-5125	954-925-6404	925-8123	K-8	Mark Hage
Hope Center for Autism Charter S	1695 SE Indian St	Stuart, FL	34997-4962	772-334-3288	334-2203	PK-2	Joanne Sweazey
Hope Charter S	1550 E Crown Point Rd	Ocoee, FL	34761-3722	407-656-4673	264-6960	K-8	Crystal Yoakum
Horizon Charter S of Tampa	7235 W Hillsborough Ave	Tampa, FL	33634	813-887-3800	885-9626	K-8	Sheila Thomley
Imagine Charter S at Broward	9001 Westview Dr	Coral Springs, FL	33067-2869	954-255-0020	255-1336	K-8	Maria Tracy
Imagine Charter S at Lakewood Ranch	10535 Portal Xing	Bradenton, FL	34211	941-750-0966	750-0966	PK-8	Selenia Quinones
Imagine Charter S at North Lauderdale	1395 S State Road 7	N Lauderdale, FL	33068-4023	954-973-8900	974-5588	K-5	Erin Kelly
Imagine Charter S at North Manatee	9275 49th Ave E	Palmetto, FL	34221	941-981-5345	981-5349	K-8	Dawn Patterson
Imagine Charter S at Town Center	775 Town Center Blvd	Palm Coast, FL	32164-2520	386-586-0100	586-2784	PK-8	James Menard
Imagine Charter S at West Melbourne	3355 Imagine Way	West Melbourne, FL	32904	321-768-6200	768-6300	PK-6	Brian DeGonzague
Imagine Charter S at Weston	2500 Glades Cir	Weston, FL	33327-2253	954-659-3600	659-3620	K-8	Nadine Laham
Imagine Charter S Nau Campus	4402 SW Yamada Dr	Port St Lucie, FL	34953	772-237-8600	237-8620	K-8	Melissa Adams
Imagine MSHS at North Port	2757 Sycamore St	North Port, FL	34289	941-426-2050	423-8252	6-12	Cher Gardner
Imagine S at Evening Rose	3611 Austin Davis Ave	Tallahassee, FL	32308	850-877-5187	877-6463	K-6	Linda John
Imagine S at Land O' Lakes	2940 Sunlake Blvd	Land O Lakes, FL	34638	813-428-7444	428-7445	K-8	Aimee Williams
Imagine S at North Port	1000 Innovation Ave	North Port, FL	34289-9308	941-426-2050	423-8252	K-5	Aleischa Coover
Imagine S at Palmer Ranch	6220 McIntosh Rd	Sarasota, FL	34238-2965	941-257-1125	923-1124	K-8	Alisa Wright
Imagine S - Chancellor Campus	3333 High Ridge Rd	Boynton Beach, FL	33426-8745	561-585-1189	585-1166	K-8	Susan Onori
Imagine S Plantation Campus	8200 Peters Rd	Plantation, FL	33324-3201	954-358-4200	472-1994	K-8	Ethiel Calvo
Imagine South Lake Charter S	2750 Hartwood Marsh Rd	Clermont, FL	34711	352-243-2960	243-2967	K-8	Kathleen Dial
Imagine South Vero Charter S	6000 4th St	Vero Beach, FL	32968	772-567-2728	410-0329	K-8	Chris Rock
IMater Academy	600 W 20th St	Hialeah, FL	33010	305-884-6320	884-6321	PK-5	Elizabeth Poveda
iMater Academy MSHS	651 W 20th St	Hialeah, FL	33010	305-805-5722	805-5723	6-12	Teresa M. Santalo
Immokalee Community S	123 N 4th St	Immokalee, FL	34142	239-867-3223	867-3224	K-6	Dr. Zulaika Quintero
Independence Academy	12902 E US Highway 92	Dover, FL	33527	813-473-8600	441-7160	K-8	Shane Clark
Indian River Charter HS	6055 College Ln	Vero Beach, FL	32966-1285	772-567-6600	567-6338	9-12	Cynthia Trevino-Aversa
Inlet Grove Community HS	600 W 28th St	Riviera Beach, FL	33404	561-881-4600	881-4668	9-12	John Myszkowski
Innovation Charter S	600 SW 3rd St	Pompano Beach, FL	33060	954-715-1777		K-5	Tiffanie Holm
Innovations MS	2768 N Hiawassee Rd	Orlando, FL	32818	407-429-7901		6-8	Adrienne Crayton Brown
Integrated Science and Asian Culture	301 Westward Dr	Miami Springs, FL	33166	305-863-8030	863-8031	K-8	Eleonora Cuesta
International S of Broward	3100 NW 75th Ave	Hollywood, FL	33024-2355	954-987-2026	987-7261	6-12	Dr. Jacquelyne Hoy
International Studies Charter S	2480 SW 8th St	Miami, FL	33135-3016	305-643-2955	643-2956	6-12	Victoriano Rodriguez
International Studies Virtual Academy	11100 NW 27th St	Doral, FL	33172	305-591-0020	591-9251	6-12	Victorino Rodriguez
Island Park HS	16520 S Tamiami Trl Ste 190	Fort Myers, FL	33908-5349	239-204-5965	243-0043	9-12	A.J. Nauss
Island S	PO Box 1090	Boca Grande, FL	33921-1090	941-964-8016	964-8017	K-5	Jean Thompson
Island Village Montessori S Sarasota	11011 Clark Rd	Sarasota, FL	34241	941-954-4999	925-0267	K-6	Cindy Hoffman
Island Village Montessori S Venice	2001 Pinebrook Rd	Venice, FL	34292-1560	941-484-4999	484-2150	PK-12	Jason Hunter
Jackson Preparatory S	546 Mary Esther Blvd	Ft Walton Bch, FL	32548	850-833-3321	833-3292	K-8	Kaye McKinley
Jewel Charter Academy	705 Blake Ave	Cocoa, FL	32922	321-634-5462	634-5465	K-8	Thomas Cole
JFK Charter S	4696 Davis Rd	Lake Worth, FL	33461-5204	561-868-6100	963-4697	K-7	Sharon Hench
Just Arts and Management Charter MS	2450 NW 97th Ave	Doral, FL	33172	305-597-9999	591-2669	6-8	Eleonara Cuesta
Just for Girls Academy	1011 21st St E	Bradenton, FL	34208	941-243-3954	243-3963	K-5	Deanna Smith
Keys Gate Charter HS	2325 SE 28th Ave	Homestead, FL	33035	786-272-9600	272-9601	9-12	Corinne Baez
Keys Gate Charter S	2000 SE 28th Ave	Homestead, FL	33035-2102	305-230-1616	230-1347	K-8	Corinne Baez
Key West Collegiate Charter S	5901 College Rd	Key West, FL	33040-4315	305-296-5927	809-3191	9-12	Cory Oliver
Key West Montessori Charter S	1400 United St	Key West, FL	33040-3400	305-293-1400		1-6	Lynn Barras
Kids Community College Charter S -Orange	1475 E Silver Star Rd	Ocoee, FL	34761	407-982-2421	203-3867	K-5	Keri Hefferin
Kids Community College - Riverview South	10030 Mathog Rd	Riverview, FL	33578	813-671-1440	553-1719	K-8	Karen Seder
Kids Community College SE Charter S	11519 McMullen Rd	Riverview, FL	33569	813-699-4600	671-1245	K-6	Martha Caballero
Kidz Choice Charter S	1800 N Douglas Rd	Pembroke Pines, FL	33024-3200	954-251-2419	260-5935	K-5	Lilly Swanson
Kings Kids Academy of Health Sciences	3000 N 34th St	Tampa, FL	33605-2250	813-238-4900	238-6700	K-5	Lillia Stroud
KIPP Impact MS	1440 McDuff Ave N	Jacksonville, FL	32254-2035	904-683-6643	683-9895	5-8	Warren Buck
KIPP Jacksonville	1440 McDuff Ave N	Jacksonville, FL	32254	904-683-6643	683-9895	K-2	Kim Davidson
KIPP VOICE ES	1440 McDuff Ave N	Jacksonville, FL	32254-2035	904-683-6643	683-9895	K-4	Kimberly Davidson
Kissimmee Charter Academy	2850 Bill Beck Blvd	Kissimmee, FL	34744-4073	407-847-1400	847-1401	PK-8	Lori McCarley
Lake Eola Charter S	135 N Magnolia Ave	Orlando, FL	32801-2301	407-246-0900	246-6334	K-8	Veronica Denoia
Lakeland Montessori MS	800 E Palmetto St	Lakeland, FL	33801-5529	863-413-0003	812-4689	7-8	Heather Manrow
Lakeland Montessori Schoolhouse	1124 N Lake Parker Ave	Lakeland, FL	33805-4725	863-413-0003	413-0006	PK-6	Heather Manrow
Lake Wales HS	1 Highlander Way	Lake Wales, FL	33853-3334	863-678-4222	678-4064	9-12	Donna Dunson

School	Address	City,State	Zip code	Telephone	Fax	Grade	Contact
Lauderhill HS	4131 NW 16th St	Lauderhill, FL	33313-5810	954-731-2585	731-2587	9-12	Sharard Walker
LBA Academy	13835 NW 97th Ave	Hialeah, FL	33018-1213	305-827-3022	827-3023	9-12	Chayma Gomez
Learning Center at the Els Center	18370 Limestone Creek Rd	Jupiter, FL	33458	561-640-0270		PK-8	Stacie Routt
Learning Gate Community S	16215 Hanna Rd	Lutz, FL	33549-5701	813-948-4190	948-7587	K-8	Michelle Mason
Learning Lodge Academy	5844 Pine Hill Rd	Port Richey, FL	34668-6616	727-389-0067		K-5	Kerrie Cuffe
Learning Path Academy	1340 Kenwood Rd	West Palm Beach, FL	33401-7408	561-832-0232	370-6869	PK-5	Isis Rosso
Legacy Charter HS	1550 E Crown Point Rd	Ocoee, FL	34761-3722	407-656-4673	264-6960	9-12	Roberta VanHouten
Legacy Preparatory Academy	302 E Linebaugh Ave	Tampa, FL	33612	813-253-0053	253-0182	K-8	Yolanda Capers
Legends Academy Charter S	3032 Monte Carlo Trl	Orlando, FL	32805-4354	407-985-5195	650-8355	K-12	
Lincoln-Marti Charter S	3500 W 84th St	Hialeah, FL	33018-4945	305-827-8080	827-8004	K-8	Yaimy Fernandez
Lincoln-Marti Charter S	970 W Flagler St	Miami, FL	33130	305-325-1001	324-9934	K-12	Barbara Sanchez
Lincoln-Marti Charter S	2244 Fortune Rd	Kissimmee, FL	34744	407-530-5000	518-9047	K-2	
Lincoln-Marti Charter S - International	103 E Lucy St	Florida City, FL	33034	305-242-3330	242-3331	K-8	Barbara Sanchez
Literacy Leadership Technology Academy	6771 Madison Ave	Tampa, FL	33619-6836	813-234-0940	234-0946	K-8	Lesley Logan
Lone Star HS	8050 Lone Star Rd Ste 1	Jacksonville, FL	32211-6227	904-725-5998	724-3172	9-12	LaShanda Roberts
Lutz Preparatory S	17951 N US Highway 41	Lutz, FL	33549	813-428-7100	428-7061	K-8	Bonnie Guertin
Magnolia Montessori Academy	1540 New Jersey Rd	Lakeland, FL	33803-2409	863-797-4991		K-5	Aurielle Hollinger
Main Street HS	1100 N Main St	Kissimmee, FL	34744	321-250-1871	846-0816	9-12	Veronica Torres
Manatee Charter S	4550 30th St E	Bradenton, FL	34203	941-465-4296	465-4297	K-8	Deborah Tracy
Manatee S for the Arts	700 Haben Blvd	Palmetto, FL	34221-4173	941-721-6800	721-6805	6-12	Dr. Bill Jones
Manatee S of Arts and Sciences	3700 32nd St W	Bradenton, FL	34205-2708	941-755-5012	755-7934	PK-6	Richard Ramsey
Marco Island Academy	2255 San Marco Rd	Marco Island, FL	34145-6925	239-393-5133	393-5143	9-12	Melissa Scott
Marco Island Charter MS	1401 Trinidad Ave	Marco Island, FL	34145-3949	239-377-3200	377-3201	6-8	George Abounader
Marion Charter MS	3233 SE Maricamp Rd	Ocala, FL	34471-6292	352-812-7960		6-8	Mary Pinson
Marion Charter S	39 Cedar Rd	Ocala, FL	34472-8331	352-687-2100	687-2700	K-5	Michelle Axson
Marion Military Academy	3443 SW 20th St	Ocala, FL	34474-2809	352-291-6600	291-6601	9-12	Tom Adair
Mascotte Conversion Charter ES	460 Midway Ave	Mascotte, FL	34753-8800	352-429-2294	429-4836	PK-5	Radean Johnson
Mason Classical Academy	3073 Horseshoe Dr S Ste 104	Naples, FL	34104-6145	239-227-2838	201-2056	K-12	David Hull
Mater Academy	8003 NW 103rd St	Hialeah Gardens, FL	33016	305-698-9900	698-3822	3-5	Cecilia Guilarte
Mater Academy	8625 Byron Ave	Miami Beach, FL	33141-4834	305-864-2889	864-2890	K-12	Marisol Gomez
Mater Academy at Mount Sinai	4300 Alton Rd	Miami Beach, FL	33140-2948	305-604-1453	604-1454	K-8	Eileen Hernandez
Mater Academy Bay	22025 SW 87th Ave	Cutler Bay, FL	33190	305-269-5989	969-5990	K-5	Brenda Cruz
Mater Academy Charter MSHS	7901 NW 103rd St	Hialeah Gardens, FL	33016-2419	305-828-1886	828-6175	6-12	Judith Marty
Mater Academy East Charter HS	998 SW 1st St	Miami, FL	33130-1112	305-324-6963	324-6966	6-12	Jenney Aguirre
Mater Academy East Charter S	450 SW 4th St	Miami, FL	33130-1410	305-324-4667	324-6580	K-5	Beatrice Riera
Mater Academy HS International Studies	795 NW 32nd St	Miami, FL	33127-3645	305-634-0445	634-0446	9-12	Ileana Melian
Mater Academy Lakes HS	17300 NW 87th Ave	Hialeah, FL	33015-3516	305-698-8000	698-1800	6-12	Rene Rovirosa
Mater Academy of International Studies	795 NW 32nd St	Miami, FL	33127-3645	305-634-0445	634-0446	K-8	Ileana Melian
Mater Academy PS	7700 NW 98th St	Hialeah Gardens, FL	33016	305-698-9900	698-3822	PK-2	Cecilia Guilarte
Mater Brighton Lakes Academy	3200 Pleasant Hill Rd	Kissimmee, FL	34746	407-931-0325	931-0326	K-8	Carmen Cangemi
Mater Gardens Academy	9010 NW 178th Ln	Hialeah, FL	33018-6548	305-512-9775	512-3708	K-8	Lourdes Isla-Marrero
Mater Grove Academy	2805 SW 32nd Ave	Miami, FL	33133-3431	305-442-4992	442-4993	K-8	Sheila Caleo-Gonzalez
Mater International Academy	3405 NW 27th Ave	Miami, FL	33142	305-638-8016	638-8017	K-1	Olga Camarena
Mater Performing Arts Academy	7901 NW 103rd St	Hialeah Gardens, FL	33016-2419	305-828-1886	828-6175	9-12	Judith Marty
Mater Virtual Academy	17300 NW 87th Ave	Hialeah, FL	33015	305-512-3917	512-3712	6-12	Ofelia Alvarez
Mavericks HS at Palm Springs	3525 S Congress Ave	Palm Springs, FL	33461	561-623-6935	641-6370	9-12	DeAnna Allen
Mavericks HS of North Miami-Dade County	16150 NE 17th Ave	N Miami Beach, FL	33162-4744	786-629-7053	949-5604	9-12	Alejandro Madrigal
Mavericks HS of South Miami-Dade County	698 N Homestead Blvd	Homestead, FL	33030-6207	305-909-6307	248-2913	9-12	Daniel Walke
McAuliffe Charter ES	2817 SW 3rd Ln	Cape Coral, FL	33991-1151	239-283-4511	282-0376	PK-5	Jacquelin Collins
Mc Intosh Area Charter S	PO Box 769	Mc Intosh, FL	32664-0769	352-591-9797	591-9747	K-5	Jolene Vining
McKeel Academy of Technology	1810 W Parker St	Lakeland, FL	33815-1243	863-499-2818	603-6339	6-12	Joyce Powell
McKeel Central Academy	411 N Florida Ave	Lakeland, FL	33801-4803	863-499-1287	688-1607	K-5	Michele Spurgeon
Melrose HS	2744 Davie Blvd	Fort Lauderdale, FL	33312	954-681-4096	797-4446	9-12	Tona Coley
Miami Arts Charter S	3900 Biscayne Blvd	Miami, FL	33137-3721	305-763-6257	740-5670	6-12	Alfredo de la Rosa
Miami Childrens Museum Charter S	980 MacArthur Cswy	Miami, FL	33132-1604	305-329-3758	329-3767	K-2	Nina Cortina
Miami Community Charter HS	18720 SW 352nd St	Florida City, FL	33034-4580	786-243-9981	217-6804	9-12	Dr. Jila Rezaie
Miami Community Charter MS	18720 SW 352nd St	Florida City, FL	33034	786-243-9981	217-6804	6-8	Dr. Jila Rezaie
Miami Community Charter S	101 S Redland Rd	Florida City, FL	33034-4630	305-245-2552	245-2527	K-5	Dr. Jila Rezaie
Micanopy Area Cooperative S	802 NW Seminary Ave	Micanopy, FL	32667-8500	352-466-0990	466-4090	PK-5	Brenda Maynard
Micanopy MS	PO Box 109	Micanopy, FL	32667-0109	352-466-1090	466-1030	6-9	Tara Lowe-Phillips
Milburn Academy - Deland	913 E New York Ave	DeLand, FL	32724	386-738-9150	738-9151	9-12	Art Sands
Milburn Academy	1031 Mason Ave	Daytona Beach, FL	32117	386-304-0086	304-0087	9-12	Art Sands
Minneola Conversion Charter ES	320 E Pearl St	Minneola, FL	34715	352-394-2600	394-2079	K-5	Sherry Watts
Montessori Academy of Early Enrichment	6300 Lake Worth Rd	Greenacres, FL	33463-3006	561-649-0004	649-0964	PK-5	Jean Ranck
Montessori of Winter Garden Charter S	855 E Plant St Ste 600	Winter Garden, FL	34787-3164	407-654-2045	654-2046	PK-6	
MYcroSchool Citrus Charter HS	3612 W Educational Path	Lecanto, FL	34461	352-527-0900	527-0814	9-12	Danita Smith
MYcroSchool Gainesville	2209 NW 13th St	Gainesville, FL	32609-3426	352-379-2902	379-2956	9-12	Randy Starling
MYcroSchool Jacksonville	1584 Normandy Village Pkwy	Jacksonville, FL	32221	904-783-3611	783-3703	9-12	Randy Hudspeth
MYcroSchool Pinellas HS	840 3rd Ave S	St Petersburg, FL	33701	727-825-3710	825-3751	9-12	Steven Humphries
Nap Ford Community Charter S	325 N Parramore Ave	Orlando, FL	32801-1402	407-245-8711	245-8712	PK-5	Jennifer Porter-Smith
Nature Coast MS	6830 NW 140th St	Chiefland, FL	32626-8271	352-490-0700	490-0702	6-8	Charles Bowe
New Beginnings HS	3425 Lake Alfred Rd	Winter Haven, FL	33881	863-298-5666	298-5675	6-12	Terri Nelson
New Dimensions HS	4900 Old Pleasant Hill Rd	Kissimmee, FL	34759-3430	407-870-9949	870-8976	9-12	Dr. Jacqueline Grimm
New Life Charter Academy	3260 Stirling Rd	Hollywood, FL	33021-2031	954-381-5199	734-6408	K-5	Shirley Brunache
New Springs S	2410 E Busch Blvd	Tampa, FL	33612	813-933-5025	527-9982	K-8	Oguz Tekin
Nixon Academy	1780 Mercy Dr	Orlando, FL	32808	407-412-6968		K-5	Stacey Mahoney
North Bay Haven Charter Academy	1104A Balboa Ave	Panama City, FL	32401-2017	850-248-0205	215-0644	K-5	Michael McLaughlin
North Bay Haven Charter MSHS	1 Buccaneer Dr	Panama City, FL	32404-8940	850-248-0801	248-1201	6-12	Michael McLaughlin
North Broward Academy of Excellence	8200 SW 17th St	N Lauderdale, FL	33068-4101	954-718-2211	718-2215	K-5	Staci Valbrun
North Broward Academy of Excellence MS	8200 SW 17th St	N Lauderdale, FL	33068-4101	954-718-2211	718-2215	6-8	Staci Valbrun
North County Charter S	6640 Old Dixie Hwy	Vero Beach, FL	32967	772-794-1941	794-1945	K-5	Dr. Jessica Keaton
Northern Palms Charter HS	13251 N Cleveland Ave	N Ft Myers, FL	33903	239-997-9987	997-9981	9-12	Bernadette Graham
North Gardens HS	4692 NW 183rd St	Miami Gardens, FL	33055-3054	786-528-6308	621-1611	9-12	Neisha Mack-Freeman
North Nicholas HS	428 SW Pine Island Rd	Cape Coral, FL	33991-1916	239-242-4230	242-4231	9-12	Janet Morris
North Park HS	3400 NW 135th St	Opa Locka, FL	33054-4708	305-720-2995	953-3289	9-12	Michael Sell
North University HS	4800 N University Dr	Lauderhill, FL	33351-5746	954-746-4483	741-8113	9-12	Frank Gaines
Oak Creek Charter S of Bonita Springs	28011 Performance Ln	Bonita Springs, FL	34135	239-498-6864	495-7178	K-8	Jose Rubio
Oakland Avenue Charter S	456 E Oakland Ave	Oakland, FL	34760-8844	407-877-2039	877-6222	K-5	Pamela Wolfcale
Oasis Charter ES	3415 Oasis Blvd	Cape Coral, FL	33914-4924	239-542-1577	549-7662	K-5	Donnie Hopper
Oasis Charter HS	3519 Oasis Blvd	Cape Coral, FL	33914-4914	239-541-1167	541-1590	9-12	Shannon Treece
Oasis Charter MS	3507 Oasis Blvd	Cape Coral, FL	33914	239-945-1999	540-7677	6-8	Keith Graham
Oasis MS	4304 32nd St W	Bradenton, FL	34205	941-749-1979	714-7333	6-8	Edna Bailey
Oasis Preparatory Academy	5200 W South St	Orlando, FL	32811	407-930-2581		K-5	Christopher Essex
Ocean Studies Charter S	92295 Overseas Hwy	Tavernier, FL	33070	305-852-7700		K-3	Jennifer Flores
Odyssey Charter ES	1755 Eldron Blvd SE	Palm Bay, FL	32909-6832	321-733-0442	733-1178	K-6	Wendi Nolder
Odyssey Charter JSHS	1350 Wyoming Dr SE	Palm Bay, FL	32909-5757	321-345-4117	327-7261	7-12	Dr. Monica Knight
Odyssey Preparatory Academy	1350 Wyoming Dr SE	Palm Bay, FL	32909-5757	321-345-4117		PK-6	Constance Ortiz
Okaloosa Academy	720 Lovejoy Rd NW	Ft Walton Bch, FL	32548-3833	850-864-3133	834-4305	6-12	Ray Sansom
One Room S House Project	4180 NE 15th St	Gainesville, FL	32609-2011	352-376-4014	376-3345	K-8	Eric Torres
Orange County Preparatory Academy	10250 University Blvd	Orlando, FL	32817	407-440-9293	960-2662	K-8	Nicole Duslak
Orlando Science Charter ES	2611 Technology Dr	Orlando, FL	32804-8003	407-253-7304	253-7305	PK-5	Michael Singleton
Orlando Science Charter MSHS	2427 Lynx Ln	Orlando, FL	32804	407-253-7304	253-7305	6-12	Abdulaziz Yalcin
Osceola Science Charter S	2880 N Orange Blossom Trl	Kissimmee, FL	34744	407-864-8296	253-7305	K-8	
Our Children's Academy	555 Burns Ave	Lake Wales, FL	33853-3335	863-679-3338	679-3944	PK-8	Debra Johnson
Palm Acres Charter HS	507 Sunshine Blvd	Lehigh Acres, FL	33971	239-333-3300	368-1330	9-12	Sarah White
Palm Bay Academy	2112 Palm Bay Rd NE	Palm Bay, FL	32905-2915	321-984-2710	984-0799	K-5	Madhu Longani
Palm Bay Charter MS	635 Community College SE	Palm Bay, FL	32909	321-726-9005	726-3938	6-8	Jerry RunnerSmith
Palm Bay Language Immersion S	1465 Troutman Blvd NE	Palm Bay, FL	32905	321-723-4218	953-5160	K-3	Madhu Longani
Palm Bay Preparatory Academy	700 W 23rd St	Panama City, FL	32405-3936	850-215-0770	763-7613	6-12	Kathy Fontaine
Palm Beach Maritime Academy	600 S East Coast Ave	Lantana, FL	33462	561-578-5700	337-3400	K-8	Marie Turchiaro
Palm Beach Maritime Academy HS	1518 Lantana Rd	Lantana, FL	33462-1538	561-547-3775	540-5177	9-12	Marie Turchiaro
Palm Beach S for Autism	8480 Lantana Rd	Lake Worth, FL	33467	561-533-9917	533-9918	PK-12	Olive Balbosa
Palmetto Charter S	1601 17th St W	Palmetto, FL	34221-6151	941-723-3711	729-5805	K-8	Brian Bustle
Palm Glades Preparatory HS	22655 SW 112th Ave	Miami, FL	33170	786-272-2269	446-8956	6-12	Archalena Coats
Palm Harbor Academy	95 Old Kings Rd N	Palm Coast, FL	32137-8227	386-447-9692		K-5	Donna Kargel
Palm Pointe Educ Research S at Tradition	10680 SW Academic Way	Port St Lucie, FL	34987	772-345-3245	345-3244	K-8	Kathleen Perez
Panacea Prep\Eagles Nest Charter S	201 N University Dr	Coral Springs, FL	33071	954-341-5550	341-5557	K-8	Stacey Mahoney
Paragon Academy of Technology	502 N 28th Ave	Hollywood, FL	33020-3811	954-925-0155	925-0209	6-8	Dr. Steven Montes
Paramount Charter S	7100 W Oakland Park Blvd	Sunrise, FL	33313	954-372-6325	944-5903	K-8	Corey Montgomery
Passport S	5221 Curry Ford Rd	Orlando, FL	32812-8741	407-658-9900	658-9911	K-8	Dr. Osvaldo Garcia
Pathways Academy	4850 N State Road 7	Laud Lakes, FL	33319	954-739-6166	333-3853	K-8	Dr. Candice Maharaj
Patriot Oaks Academy	475 Longleaf Pine Pkwy	Saint Johns, FL	32259-7306	904-547-4050		K-8	Emily Harrison
Pemayetv Emahakv Charter S	100 E Harney Pond Rd NE	Okeechobee, FL	34974-2867	863-467-2501	467-8610	PK-8	Brian Greseth
Pembroke Academy Pines MSHS	5000 SW 207th Ter	Pembroke Pines, FL	33332	954-315-0770	315-0769	6-12	Dr. Arlene Valdes
Pembroke Pines FSU Charter ES	601 SW 172nd Ave	Pembroke Pines, FL	33029-4003	954-499-4244	499-3016	K-5	Dr. Lisa Libidinsky
Pensacola Beach ES	900 Via De Luna Dr	Pensacola Beach, FL	32561-2262	850-934-4020	934-4040	K-5	Jeff Castleberry
Pepin Academies	10530 Lake Saint Charles Bl	Riverview, FL	33578-4595	813-677-6700	677-6755	3-12	Dr. Craig Butz

School	Address	City,State	Zip code	Telephone	Fax	Grade	Contact
Pepin Academies	3916 E Hillsborough Ave	Tampa, FL	33610-4542	813-236-1755	236-1195	3-12	Dr. Craig Butz
Pepin Academies - Pasco	9804 Little Rd	New Port Richey, FL	34654	727-233-2961	233-2963	3-12	Celeste Kellar
Performing Arts Academy	1324 Kingsley Ave	Orange Park, FL	32073	904-269-0039		K-5	Jacqueline Ottosen
Pineapple Cove Classical Academy	6162 Minton Rd NW	Palm Bay, FL	32907	321-802-9500	802-9933	K-8	Dr. Kelly Gunter
Pinecrest Academy North Charter S	10207 W Flagler St	Miami, FL	33174	305-553-9762	553-9763	K-8	Victoria Larrauri
Pinecrest Academy - South Campus	15130 SW 80th St	Miami, FL	33193-1302	305-386-0800	386-6298	K-5	Elaine Clemente
Pinecrest Cove Academy	4101 SW 107th Ave	Miami, FL	33165-4814	305-480-2097	207-1897	K-8	Susie Dopico
Pinecrest Creek Charter S	1100 Lee Rd	Orlando, FL	32810-5847	407-757-2706	757-2711	K-5	
Pinecrest Glades Academy	15250 SW 8th St	Miami, FL	33194	305-229-6949		K-12	Carrie Montano
Pinecrest Preparatory Academy	14301 SW 42nd St	Miami, FL	33175-7832	305-207-1027	207-1897	K-5	Ana Diaz
Pinecrest Preparatory Academy HS	14901 SW 42nd St	Miami, FL	33185-4535	305-559-8583	559-8584	6-12	Maria Nunez
Pinecrest Preparatory S Orlando	8503 Daetwyler Dr	Orlando, FL	32827-5018	407-856-8359	856-8361	K-8	Yasmeen Khan
Pinellas Academy of Math and Science	1775 S Highland Ave	Largo, FL	33756-1847	727-330-9449	581-9205	K-8	Linda Schwerer
Pinellas Preparatory Academy	2300 Belcher Rd S Ste 100	Largo, FL	33771-4257	727-536-3600	536-3661	4-8	Amanda Matsumoto
Pinellas Primary Academy	2300 Belcher Rd S	Largo, FL	33771-4257	727-536-3600	536-3661	PK-3	Nancy Walker
Pinellas Westcoast Academy & HS	21810 US Highway 19 N	Clearwater, FL	33765	727-475-1256	725-3395	6-12	Edward Erikson
Pivot Charter HS	2675 Winkler Ave Ste 200	Fort Myers, FL	33901-9328	239-243-8266	689-5474	6-12	Joy Moore
Pivot Charter S	3020 S Falkenburg Rd	Riverview, FL	33578-2562	813-626-6724	626-6712	6-12	Elizabeth Bretz
Pivot Charter S	8129 N Pine Island Rd	Tamarac, FL	33321	954-720-3001	722-5578	6-12	Nicole Scarpaci
Plato Academy	8812 Old County Road 54	New Port Richey, FL	34653	727-877-2437		K-2	Jennifer Perez
Plato Academy Clearwater	2045 Palmetto St	Clearwater, FL	33765	727-228-9517	228-9518	PK-8	Dawn Parker
Plato Academy Largo	7100 142nd Ave	Largo, FL	33771	727-228-9952	228-9953	K-8	Veronica Han-G
Plato Academy Palm Harbor	1601 Curlew Rd	Palm Harbor, FL	34683	727-228-6850	228-6851	K-8	Stephen Donnelly
Plato Academy Pinellas Park	9200 49th St N	Pinellas Park, FL	33782	727-521-7260	521-7261	K-3	Carrie Aranzabal
Plato Academy St. Petersburg	3901 Park St N	St Petersburg, FL	33709	727-521-7258	521-7259	K-8	Michelle West
Plato Academy Seminole	10888 126th Ave	Largo, FL	33778	727-228-9950	228-9951	K-8	Karen Staab
Plato Academy Tarpon Springs	2795 Keystone Rd	Tarpon Springs, FL	34688	727-939-6413	939-6414	K-8	Danielle Turro
Polk Avenue ES	110 E Polk Ave	Lake Wales, FL	33853-4199	863-678-4244	678-4680	PK-5	Gail Quam
Polk Pre-Collegiate Academy	5316 Berkley Rd	Auburndale, FL	33823-8493	863-984-2400	984-2411	9-10	Cathy Carver
Polk State College Collegiate HS	3425 Winter Lake Rd	Lakeland, FL	33803	863-669-2322	669-2944	11-12	Rick Jeffries
Polk State Lakeland Gateway to Coll HS	3425 Winter Lake Rd	Lakeland, FL	33803	863-669-2322	669-2330	11-12	Corey Barnes
Potentials Charter S	1201 Australian Ave	Riviera Beach, FL	33404-6635	561-842-3213	863-4352	PK-5	Bairbre Flood
Princeton House Charter S	1166 Lee Rd	Orlando, FL	32810-5847	407-523-7121	523-7187	PK-5	Kim Gelalia
Prosperitas Leadership Academy Charter	4504 S Orange Blossom Trl	Orlando, FL	32839	407-854-3945	854-3955	9-12	Nadia Pierre
Putnam Academy of Arts and Sciences	310 S Palm Ave	Palatka, FL	32177-4161	386-326-4212	326-6235	6-8	Curtis Ellis
Putnam EDGE HS	PO Box 1258	Palatka, FL	32178-1258	386-385-7292		9-12	Lisa Parsons
Quantum HS	1275 Gateway Blvd	Boynton Beach, FL	33426-8302	561-293-2971	277-0590	9-12	Dr. Joy Hicks-Gomez
RAMZ Academy Miami	2609 NW 7th St	Miami, FL	33125-3022	786-445-5697	642-8624	K-5	Dr. Maybelline Truesdell
RCMA Leadership Academy	18236 S US Highway 301	Wimauma, FL	33598-4307	813-672-5159	633-6119	6-8	Mark Haggett
RCMA Wimauma Academy	18240 S US Highway 301	Wimauma, FL	33598-4307	813-672-5159	633-6119	K-5	Mark Haggett
Reading Edge Academy	2975 Enterprise Rd	DeBary, FL	32713-2708	386-668-8911	668-8443	K-5	Margaret Comardo
Renaissance Charter S	300 NW Cashmere Blvd	Port St Lucie, FL	34986	772-344-5982	344-5985	K-8	Nicole Luicci
Renaissance Charter S at Central Palm	6696 S Military Trl	Lake Worth, FL	33463-7501	561-209-7106	209-7107	K-8	Jackson Self
Renaissance Charter S at Chickasaw Trail	8203 Valencia College Ln	Orlando, FL	32825-3242	321-206-0662	206-0664	K-8	Cindy Townsend
Renaissance Charter S at Cooper City	2800 N Palm Ave	Cooper City, FL	33026-3500	954-668-2500	668-2980	K-8	Amanda Delgado
Renaissance Charter S at Coral Springs	6250 W Sample Rd	Coral Springs, FL	33067-3176	954-369-1179	780-5411	K-8	Diana Sierra-Krumrie
Renaissance Charter S at Crown Point	83 West Rd	Ocoee, FL	34761	407-573-1080	573-1081	K-8	Brett Taylor
Renaissance Charter S at Cypress	8151 Okeechobee Blvd	West Palm Beach, FL	33411-2048	561-282-5860		K-8	Rachel Mellion
Renaissance Charter S at Goldenrod	6004 S Goldenrod Rd	Orlando, FL	32822	321-536-2952	536-2953	K-8	Nate Mariano
Renaissance Charter S at Hunter's Creek	4140 Town Center Blvd	Orlando, FL	32837	321-206-3103	206-3104	K-8	Jose Roberto Acosta
Renaissance Charter S at Palms West	12031 Southern Blvd	Ryl Palm Bch, FL	33470-4994	561-214-6782	214-6783	K-8	Steve Epstein
Renaissance Charter S at Pines	10501 Pines Blvd	Pembroke Pines, FL	33026-6006	954-862-1283	862-1284	K-8	Daniel Verdier
Renaissance Charter S at Plantation	6701 W Sunrise Blvd	Plantation, FL	33313-6039	954-556-9700	556-9701	K-8	Lori Butler
Renaissance Charter S at Poinciana	5125 Robert McLane Blvd	Kissimmee, FL	34758	407-569-0639	569-0640	K-8	Angela Feliciano
Renaissance Charter S at Summit	2001 Summit Blvd	West Palm Beach, FL	33406-4439	561-228-5240	228-5241	K-8	Heather Czeskleba
Renaissance Charter S at Tapestry	2510 W Carroll St	Kissimmee, FL	34741	407-569-0163	569-0164	K-8	Jodi Evans
Renaissance Charter S at Tradition	10900 SW Tradition Pkwy	Fort Pierce, FL	34987	772-236-2180	236-2181	K-8	Stacy Schmit
Renaissance Charter S at University	8399 N University Dr	Tamarac, FL	33321-1711	954-414-0996	414-0998	K-8	LaShonda White
Renaissance Charter S at Wellington	3220 S State Road 7	Wellington, FL	33449-8037	561-228-5242		K-8	Andrea Reilly
Renaissance Charter S at West Palm Beach	1889 Palm Beach Lakes Blvd	West Palm Beach, FL	33409-3501	561-839-1994	839-1995	K-8	Michael Lupton
Renaissance Elementary Charter S	10651 NW 19th St	Doral, FL	33172-2536	305-591-2225	591-2984	K-5	Maria Torres
Renaissance Learning Academy	1310 N Congress Ave	West Palm Beach, FL	33409	561-296-1776	296-1791	9-12	Toby Honsberger
Renaissance Middle Charter S	8360 NW 33rd St	Doral, FL	33122	305-728-4622	401-1978	6-8	Maria Torres
Resilience Charter S	1717 NE 9th St Bldg A	Gainesville, FL	32609	352-745-3690		6-12	Lea Fox
Ridgeview Global Studies Academy	1000 Dunson Rd	Davenport, FL	33896-8383	863-419-3171	419-3172	K-7	Ralph Frier
RISE Academy S of Science and Technology	6101 NW 31st St	Margate, FL	33063	954-968-7977	968-8386	K-8	Dr. Carmella Morton
Rising Leaders Academy	1527 Lincoln Ave	Panama City, FL	32405	850-215-0844	215-1711	K-12	Suha Jaber
River City Science Academy	7565 Beach Blvd	Jacksonville, FL	32216-3003	904-855-8010	855-8014	6-12	Ozan Sipahioglu
River City Science Academy Elementary	7555 Beach Blvd	Jacksonville, FL	32216	904-855-8010	727-9245	K-5	Jamey Hough
River City Science Academy - Innovations	8313 Baycenter Rd	Jacksonville, FL	32256-7415	904-647-5110	551-0821	K-8	Mesut Erdogan
River City Science at Mandarin	10911 Old St	Jacksonville, FL	32257	904-440-5339		K-8	Alaaddin Akgul
Riviera Beach Maritime Academy	251 W 11th St	Riviera Beach, FL	33404-7534	561-841-7600	841-7626	9-12	Tonya Hicks
Round Lake Conversion Charter ES	31333 Round Lake Rd	Mount Dora, FL	32757-9599	352-385-4399	735-1860	PK-5	Linda Bartberger
Rowlett Academy for Arts & Communication	3500 9th St E	Bradenton, FL	34208-4516	941-708-6100	708-6109	K-5	Kim Penman
Royal Palm Charter S	7135 Babcock St SE	Palm Bay, FL	32909-5462	321-723-0650	722-1117	K-8	Shannon Shupe
St. Augustine Public Montessori S	7 Williams St	Saint Augustine, FL	32084-2878	904-342-5350	342-5354	1-6	Judi Dunlap
St. Cloud Prep Academy	3101 Progress Ln	Saint Cloud, FL	34769	407-593-6601	891-0145	K-8	Michele Quinn
St. Johns Community Campus	62 Cuna St	Saint Augustine, FL	32084-3684	904-209-6842		9-12	Lynne Funcheon
Saint Peter's Academy	4250 38th Ave	Vero Beach, FL	32967-1711	772-562-1963	567-8361	PK-6	Ruth Jefferson
St. Petersburg Collegiate HS	PO Box 13489	St Petersburg, FL	33733-3489	727-341-4610	341-4226	10-12	Starla Metz
SALTech Charter HS	4811 Payne Stewart Dr	Jacksonville, FL	32209	904-328-5001	768-8618	9-12	Michael LaRoche
Samsula Academy	248 N Samsula Dr	New Smyrna, FL	32168-8762	386-423-6650	423-6651	K-5	Peggy Comardo
San Jose Academy	4072 Sunbeam Rd	Jacksonville, FL	32257	904-425-1725	683-9101	6-12	Alan Hall
Sarasota Academy of the Arts	4466 Fruitville Rd	Sarasota, FL	34232-1926	941-377-2278	404-4492	K-8	Cecilia Blankenship
Sarasota Military Academy	801 Orange Ave	Sarasota, FL	34236-4116	941-926-1700	926-1701	9-12	Robin Livingston
Sarasota Military Academy Prep	3101 Bethel Ln	Sarasota, FL	34240	941-877-7737	877-7738	6-8	Thomas Vara
Sarasota S of Arts & Sciences	645 Central Ave	Sarasota, FL	34236-4016	941-330-1855	330-1835	6-8	Tara Tahmosh-Newell
Sarasota Suncoast Academy	8084 Hawkins Rd	Sarasota, FL	34241-9300	941-924-4242	924-8282	K-5	Steve Crump
S for Accelerated Lrng & Technologies	4811 Payne Stewart Dr	Jacksonville, FL	32209-9208	904-328-5003	768-8618	9-12	Michael LaRoche
School of Arts & Sciences	3208 Thomasville Rd	Tallahassee, FL	32308-7904	850-386-6566	386-8183	K-8	Julie Fredrickson
School of Success Academy	6974 Wilson Blvd	Jacksonville, FL	32210-3663	904-573-0880	573-0889	6-8	Genell Mills
Sculptor Charter S	1301 Armstrong Dr	Titusville, FL	32780-7907	321-264-4000	264-4011	K-8	Patricia O'Sullivan
Seacoast Collegiate HS	109 Greenway Trl	Santa Rsa Bch, FL	32459-5415	850-200-4170		9-11	Jonathan Davignon
Seacoast Charter Academy	9100 Regency Square Blvd N	Jacksonville, FL	32211-8103	904-562-4780	726-0249	K-5	Marla Stremmel
Seagull Academy for Independent Living	6250 N Military Trl	Riviera Beach, FL	33407	561-540-8110	540-8331	6-12	Linda Moore
Seaside Community Charter S	2630 State Road A1A	Jacksonville, FL	32233	904-853-6287	485-8448	K-5	Sharon Sanders
Seaside Neighborhood S	PO Box 4610	Santa Rsa Bch, FL	32459-4610	850-231-0396	231-4725	5-8	Kim Mixon
Sebastian Charter JHS	782 Wave St	Sebastian, FL	32958-5049	772-388-8838	388-8815	6-8	Marvel Nolan
Seed S of Miami	15800 NW 42nd Ave	Miami Gardens, FL	33054-6155	855-818-7333	503-7033	6-12	Kara Locke
Seminole Heights Charter HS	4006 N Florida Ave	Tampa, FL	33603	813-234-0809	236-2406	9-12	Robert Schodt
Seminole Science Charter S	3580 N US Highway 17/92	Lake Mary, FL	32746	407-864-8296	253-7305	K-8	
Sheeler Charter HS	871 E Semoran Blvd	Apopka, FL	32703	407-886-1825	886-7482	9-12	Leon Wilson
Sigsbee Charter S	939 Felton Rd	Key West, FL	33040-6798	305-294-1861	292-6869	PK-5	Elisa Jannes
Six Mile Charter Academy	6851 Lancer Ave	Fort Myers, FL	33912-4334	239-768-9375	225-2477	K-8	Eric Lewis
Sky Academy Englewood	881 S River Rd	Englewood, FL	34223	941-999-4775	999-4796	6-8	John Bailey
Sky Academy Venice	705 Center Rd	Venice, FL	34285-4808	941-244-2626	244-2319	6-8	Steve Smith
Somerset Academy	20801 Johnson St	Pembroke Pines, FL	33029	954-442-0233	442-0813	K-5	Bernardo Montero
Somerset Academy	18491 SW 134th Ave	Miami, FL	33177-2923	305-969-6074	969-6077	K-5	Suzette Ruiz
Somerset Academy Bay	9500 SW 97th Ave	Miami, FL	33176-2827	305-274-0682	274-0683	K-8	Salli Hernandez
Somerset Academy Boca	333 SW 4th Ave	Boca Raton, FL	33432	561-393-1091	393-1092	K-8	Daniel Shourds
Somerset Academy Canyons HS	9385 Boynton Beach Blvd	Boynton Beach, FL	33472	561-732-8252	732-8253	6-12	Bonnie May
Somerset Academy Central Miramar Campus	9300 Pembroke Rd	Miramar, FL	33025-1640	954-435-1570	435-1571	K-12	Athena Guillen
Somerset Academy Davie	3788 Davie Rd	Davie, FL	33314	954-584-5528	584-5598	K-5	Dina Miller
Somerset Academy Eagle Campus	8711 Lone Star Rd	Jacksonville, FL	32211	904-551-3292	551-3293	K-5	LaTatia Ray
Somerset Academy East Prep & Hollywood	2000 S State Road 7	Miramar, FL	33023	954-987-7890	987-7891	K-5	Dr. Mary Stuart
Somerset Academy HS	20805 Johnson St	Pembroke Pines, FL	33029-1916	954-442-0233	442-0813	9-12	Bernardo Montero
Somerset Academy Key	959 SE 6th Ave	Deerfield Beach, FL	33441	954-481-0602	481-0603	6-12	Dennis Mulrooney
Somerset Academy Lakes	2845 Summit Blvd	West Palm Beach, FL	33406	561-641-4449	360-2452	K-2	Shannine Sadesky
Somerset Academy MS	18491 SW 134th Ave	Miami, FL	33177-2923	305-969-6074	969-6077	6-8	Suzette Ruiz
Somerset Academy MS	20803 Johnson St	Pembroke Pines, FL	33029-1916	954-442-0233	442-0813	6-8	Bernardo Montero
Somerset Academy Miramar	12601 Somerset Blvd	Miramar, FL	33027-5898	305-829-2406	829-4477	PK-8	Alexandra Prieto
Somerset Academy Pompano	1101 NW 33rd St	Pompano Beach, FL	33064	954-946-4144	946-4005	K-8	Dr. Donna Kaye
Somerset Academy Silver Palms	23255 SW 115th Ave	Homestead, FL	33032-4505	305-257-3737	257-3751	K-12	Kerri Rodriguez
Somerset Academy South Homestead	300 SE 1st Dr	Homestead, FL	33030-7307	305-245-6108	245-6109	K-12	Layda Morales
Somerset Academy South Miami	5876 SW 68th St	South Miami, FL	33143-3693	305-740-0509	740-0510	K-8	Kim Guilarte
Somerset Arts Conservatory	20807 Johnson St	Pembroke Pines, FL	33029	954-442-0233	442-0813	9-12	Bernardo Montero
Somerset City Arts Conservatory	47 NW 16 St	Homestead, FL	33030	305-246-4949	249-4919	K-6	Idalia Suarez

School	Address	City,State	Zip code	Telephone	Fax	Grade	Contact
Somerset College Prep Academy	501 NW University Blvd	Port St Lucie, FL	34986	772-343-7028	343-7029	9-12	Erika Rains
Somerset Gables Academy	624 Anastasia Ave	Coral Gables, FL	33134-6404	305-442-8626	442-8627	K-8	Suzette Ruiz
Somerset Miramar South S	12425 SW 53rd St	Miramar, FL	33027-5493	305-829-2406	829-4477	K-5	Alexandra Prieto
Somerset Oaks Academy	1000 Old Dixie Hwy	Homestead, FL	33030	305-247-3939	247-3994	K-8	Idalia Suarez
Somerset Pines Academy	901 NE 33rd St	Pompano Beach, FL	33064-5231	954-786-5980	786-5981	K-8	Dr. Donna Kaye
Somerset Preparatory Academy	1429 Broward Rd	Jacksonville, FL	32218-5315	904-503-0661	379-5936	PK-10	David Cook
Somerset Prep North Lauderdale	7101 Kimberly Blvd	N Lauderdale, FL	33068	954-718-5065	718-5066	K-12	Donyale McGhee
Somerset Village Academy	225 NW 29th St	Wilton Manors, FL	33311	954-390-0971	390-0972	K-8	Anthony Marruci
South Broward Montessori Charter S	520 NW 5th St	Hallandale Bch, FL	33009-3314	954-251-1443	251-1820	K-5	Elaine Padron
South Florida Autism Charter S	18305 NW 75th Pl	Hialeah, FL	33015-2957	305-823-2700	823-2705	K-11	Dr. Tamara Ramdeen
South McKeel Academy	2222 Edgewood Dr S	Lakeland, FL	33803-3631	863-510-0044	510-0021	K-7	Kim Benson
Southshore Charter Academy	11667 Big Bend Rd	Riverview, FL	33578	813-769-1209	769-2161	K-8	Kristen Storm-Taylor
South Tech Academy	1300 SW 30th Ave	Boynton Beach, FL	33426-9099	561-369-7004	369-7024	9-12	Ellen Gray
South Tech Preparatory Academy	1325 Gateway Blvd	Boynton Beach, FL	33426-8304	561-318-8087	369-7024	6-8	Nicole Handy
Sports Leadership Academy of Miami	604 NW 12th Ave	Miami, FL	33136	305-326-0003	326-0004	6-12	Francisco Jimenez
Sports Leadership and Management MS	2845 Summit Blvd	West Palm Beach, FL	33406	561-434-2162	360-2452	6-8	Shannine Sadesky
Spring Creek Conversion Charter ES	44440 Spring Creek Rd	Paisley, FL	32767-9063	352-669-3275	669-3762	PK-6	Wesley Locke
State College of Florida Collegiate S	5840 26th St W	Bradenton, FL	34207	941-752-5491	758-4801	6-12	Kelly Monod
Stellar Leadership Academy	7900 NW 27th Ave Ste F-1	Miami, FL	33147-4909	305-693-2273	693-8016	9-12	Dr. Angel Chaisson
Student Leadership Academy	200 Field Ave E	Venice, FL	34285-3936	941-485-5551	485-2694	6-8	Vickie Marble
Summerville Advantage Academy	11575 SW 243rd St	Homestead, FL	33032-7163	305-253-2123	253-4304	K-8	Mary March
Suncoast S for Innovative Studies	845 S School Ave	Sarasota, FL	34237-8039	941-953-4433	953-4435	PK-8	Stephen Evans
SunEd HS	2360 W Oakland Park Blvd	Oakland Park, FL	33311-1410	954-678-3939	485-6243	9-12	DeeEtte Naukana
SunEd HS of North Broward	1121 Banks Rd	Margate, FL	33063-6702	954-246-4004	379-2722	9-12	Tammy Lara
Sunrise HS	424 W Sunrise Blvd	Fort Lauderdale, FL	33311	954-446-9234	522-1539	9-12	Martie Lovely
Sunshine ES	502 N 28th Ave	Hollywood, FL	33020	954-925-0155	925-0209	K-5	Dr. Steven Montes
Sunshine High Charter	6600 Old Winter Garden Rd	Orlando, FL	32835-1218	407-641-4156	886-7482	9-12	Margaret Olmo
Tallahassee S of Math & Science	3434 N Monroe St	Tallahassee, FL	32303-2743	850-681-7827	325-6706	K-8	Ahmet Temel
Team Success S of Excellence	202 13th Ave E	Bradenton, FL	34208-3246	941-714-7260	714-7333	K-8	Aimee Fleming
Terrace Community MS	11734 Jefferson Rd	Thonotosassa, FL	33592-2101	813-987-6555	324-8974	6-8	Tahvia Shaw
Therapeutic Learning Center	2109 ARC Dr	Saint Augustine, FL	32084-0512	904-824-8932	824-8063	PK-PK	Paulette Hudson
Tiger Academy	6079 Bagley Rd	Jacksonville, FL	32209-1805	904-309-6840	309-6867	PK-5	Charles McWhite
Toussaint L'Ouverture HS	301 SW 14th Ave	Delray Beach, FL	33444-1455	561-266-1200	266-1286	9-12	Mandy Freeman
Town and Country Charter HS	7555 W Waters Ave	Tampa, FL	33615	813-902-2858	884-7807	9-12	Porshia Jones
Treasure Village Montessori Charter S	86731 Overseas Hwy	Islamorada, FL	33036-3129	305-852-3482	852-2432	PK-8	Kelly Mangel
Trinity S for Children	2402 W Osborne Ave	Tampa, FL	33603-1434	813-874-2402	874-2412	K-8	Dr. Madeline O'Dea
True North Classical Academy	9393 Sunset Dr	Miami, FL	33173	305-749-5725	271-9052	K-8	Mark Snyder
Turner Learning Academy	2201 SW 42nd Ave	West Park, FL	33023-3456	954-463-8404	463-3566	K-5	Maxine Spence
UCP Charter S Downtown Campus	4680 Lake Under Hill	Orlando, FL	32807	407-852-3300	852-3301	PK-4	Lillian Flores
UCP East Campus	12702 Science Dr	Orlando, FL	32826	407-852-3300	281-0442	PK-5	Anna Morin
UCP Kissimmee/Osceola Campus	1820 Armstrong Blvd	Kissimmee, FL	34741	407-852-3300	932-3480	PK-2	Jim Farren
UCP Lake Mary/Seminole Campus	756 N Sun Dr	Lake Mary, FL	32746	407-852-3300	852-3301	PK-2	Marife Gomez
UCP Pine Hills Charter S	5800 Golf Club Pkwy	Orlando, FL	32808-4800	407-299-5553	299-5520	PK-4	Dr. Karyn Hawkins-Scott
UCP Transitional Learning Academy	3305 S Orange Ave	Orlando, FL	32806	407-852-3300	852-3301	6-12	Stacey Ricketts
UCP West Orange Charter S	1297 Winter Garden Vineland	Winter Garden, FL	34787-6706	407-852-3300	905-0532	K-5	
Unity Charter S of Cape Coral	2107 Santa Barbara Blvd	Cape Coral, FL	33991	239-829-5134	242-0477	K-8	Jennifer Fowler
Unity Charter S of Fort Myers	4740 S Cleveland Ave	Fort Myers, FL	33907	239-333-0766	333-0768	K-8	Stephan Terebieniec
University Academy	1980 Discovery Loop	Panama City, FL	32405-2771	850-481-4410		K-5	Elizabeth Crowe Ph.D.
University Preparatory Academy	2101 N Australian Ave	West Palm Beach, FL	33407-5630	561-670-1138		K-8	Richard Ledgister
Valor Academy of Leadership	4819 Soutel Dr	Jacksonville, FL	32208	904-469-8195	524-8440	6-12	John Taylor
Valrico Lake Advantage Academy	13306 Boyette Rd	Riverview, FL	33569-5741	813-699-5049	413-5191	K-5	Lauren Herbert
Viera Charter S	6206 Breslay Dr	Viera, FL	32940-8418	321-541-1434	608-2322	K-8	Dr. Julie Cady
Village of Excellence Academy	8718 N 46th St	Temple Terrace, FL	33617-6002	813-988-8632	983-0683	K-5	Dr. Cametra Edwards
Village of Excellence Academy MS	4600 E Busch Blvd	Tampa, FL	33617-6008	813-374-9972	304-2202	6-8	Dr. Cametra Edwards
Villages Charter HS	251 Buffalo Trl	The Villages, FL	32162-7176	352-259-3777	259-3850	9-12	Jason Spencer
Villages Charter Intermediate Center	521 Old School Rd	The Villages, FL	32162-7170	352-259-2300	259-2056	2-3	LeAnne Yerk
Villages Charter MS	450 Village Campus Cir	The Villages, FL	32162-7169	352-259-0044	753-1113	6-8	Dr. Peggy Irwin
Villages Charter Primary Center	420 Village Campus Cir	The Villages, FL	32162-7169	352-259-7700	259-7707	K-1	LeAnne Yerk
Virtue Arts & Science Academy	1824 Dean Rd	Jacksonville, FL	32216	904-379-0004	619-1531	6-12	Michelle Knapp
Visible Men Academy Charter S	921 63rd Ave E	Bradenton, FL	34203	941-758-7588		K-8	Neil Phillips
Walton Academy	389 Dorsey Ave	Defuniak Spgs, FL	32435-3013	850-892-3999	892-7854	6-12	David Schmidt
Walton Academy for the Performing Arts	4817 N Florida Ave	Tampa, FL	33603-2117	813-231-9272	231-9271	K-5	Tanika Walton
Waverly Academy	5710 Wesconnett Blvd	Jacksonville, FL	32244	904-647-8552	515-5353	6-8	Fernette Moore
Wayman Academy of the Arts	1176 Labelle St	Jacksonville, FL	32205-6487	904-695-9995	693-1127	K-5	Simaran Bakshi
Wells Charter Academy	2426 Remington Blvd	Kissimmee, FL	34744-8467	407-697-1020	697-1021	K-8	Reagan Hall
West Broward Academy	5281 Coconut Creek Pkwy	Margate, FL	33063	754-702-2320	263-5900	K-8	Jean Reilly
Western Academy Charter S	650 Royal Palm Blvd Ste 300	Ryl Palm Bch, FL	33411	561-792-4123	422-0674	K-8	Linda Terranova
West University Charter HS	11602 N 15th St	Tampa, FL	33612	813-774-4396	971-5011	9-12	Jeffrey Mitchell
Whispering Winds Charter S	2480 NW Old Fannin Rd	Chiefland, FL	32626	352-490-5799	490-7242	K-8	Kimberly Bartley
Wilson ES	306 Florida Ave	Lake Wales, FL	33853-3121	863-678-4211	678-4217	PK-5	Barbara Jones
Winthrop Charter S	6204 Scholars Hill Ln	Riverview, FL	33578-4298	813-235-4811	315-4403	K-8	Terry Johnson
Woodmont Charter S	10402 N 56th St	Temple Terrace, FL	33617-3637	813-708-1596	739-7301	K-8	Latasha Scurry
Woodville MS	1900 Natural Bridge Rd	Tallahassee, FL	32305	850-922-4213	921-4281	6-8	Beth Button
Workforce Advantage Academy	2113 E South St	Orlando, FL	32803-6502	407-898-7228	898-6448	11-12	Belinda Jones
Worthington HS	1711 Worthington Rd	West Palm Beach, FL	33409	561-537-5696	697-4366	9-12	Cassandra Oliver
Youth Co-Op Preparatory Charter S	7700 W 20th Ave	Hialeah Gardens, FL	33016-1859	305-819-8855	819-8455	K-12	Maritza Aragon
Georgia							
Academies of Creative Education	1130 Dahlonega Hwy	Cumming, GA	30040	770-781-3141	888-1193	9-12	Betty Pope
Academy for Advanced Studies	401 E Tomlinson St	McDonough, GA	30253	770-320-7997	610-5853	9-12	John Uesseler
Academy for Classical Education	5665 New Forsyth Rd	Macon, GA	31210-5770	478-238-5757		K-9	Laura Perkins
Amana Academy	285 S Main St	Alpharetta, GA	30009-1937	678-624-0989	624-0892	K-8	Cherisse Campbell
Athens Community Career Academy	440 Dearing Ext Bldg 101	Athens, GA	30606	706-357-5244	353-3877	10-12	Lawrence Harris
Atlanta Classical Academy	3260 Northside Dr NW	Atlanta, GA	30305	404-369-3500	795-1049	K-10	Dr. Terrance Moore
Atlanta Heights Charter S	3712 Martin Luther King Jr	Atlanta, GA	30331-3674	404-472-3003	264-2132	K-8	Nicole Bullen
Atlanta Neighborhood Charter ES	688 Grant St SE	Atlanta, GA	30315-1420	404-624-6226	624-9093	K-5	Lara Zelski
Atlanta Neighborhood Charter MS	820 Essie Ave SE	Atlanta, GA	30316-2425	678-904-0051	904-0052	6-8	Cathey Goodgame
Baconton Community Charter S	260 E Walton St	Baconton, GA	31716-7706	229-787-9999	787-0077	PK-12	Lynn Pinson
Baldwin College and Career Academy	155 GA Highway 49 W	Milledgeville, GA	31061-3600	478-453-6429	453-5060	7-12	Dr. Cloise Williams
Bartow County College & Career Academy	738 Grassdale Rd NW	Cartersville, GA	30121	770-606-5182	606-5890	9-12	Dr. Paul Sabin
Berrien Academy Performance Learning Ctr	1015 Exum Rd	Nashville, GA	31639-2730	229-686-6576	686-6580	9-12	Michele Garner
Bishop Hall Charter S	220 N Pinetree Blvd	Thomasville, GA	31792-3915	229-227-1397	558-9420	9-12	Chris Huckans
Brighten Academy	3264 Brookmont Pkwy	Douglasville, GA	30135	770-615-3680	575-3614	K-8	Lisa McDonald
Cairo HS	455 5th St SE	Cairo, GA	39828-2399	229-377-2222	377-2812	9-12	Christopher Lokey
Carroll County College and Career Acad	1075 Newnan Rd	Carrollton, GA	30116-6435	770-832-8380	830-5037	9-12	Cindy Clanton
Centennial Academy	531 Luckie St NW	Atlanta, GA	30313-2401	404-802-8550	853-4089	K-8	Alison Shelton
Central Educational Center	160 Martin Luther King Dr	Newnan, GA	30263-2331	678-423-2000	423-2008	8-12	Mark Ballou
Chamblee Charter HS	3688 Chamblee Dunwoody Rd	Chamblee, GA	30341-2143	678-676-6902	676-6910	9-12	Dr. Norman Sauce
Charter Conservatory Liberal Arts/Tech.	149 Northside Dr E	Statesboro, GA	30458	912-764-5888	489-8493	6-12	Corliss Reese
Chattahoochie Hills Charter S	9670 Rivertown Rd	Fairburn, GA	30213	678-466-7300	466-7305	K-5	Walt Buttler
Cherokee Charter Academy	2126 Sixes Rd	Canton, GA	30114-8162	678-385-7322	385-7323	K-8	Dr. Scott O'Prey
Chesnut ES Charter	4576 N Peachtree Rd	Dunwoody, GA	30338-5809	678-676-7102	676-7110	PK-5	Veronica Williams
Chestatee Academy	2740 Fran Mar Dr	Gainesville, GA	30506-1136	770-297-6270	297-6275	6-8	Jennifer Kogod
Chestnut Mountain Creative S of Inquiry	4841 Union Church Rd	Flowery Branch, GA	30542-5202	770-967-3121	967-4891	K-5	Wade Pearce
Clear Creek MS	1020 Clear Creek Rd	Ellijay, GA	30536-7898	706-276-5150	276-5151	7-8	David Mashburn
Clubview ES	2836 Edgewood Rd	Columbus, GA	31906-1225	706-565-3017	565-3022	PK-5	Teresa Lawson
Coastal Empire Montessori Charter S	301 Buckhalter Rd	Savannah, GA	31405-6111	912-395-4070	201-5051	PK-5	Stephanie Babcock-Wright
Coweta Charter Academy	6675 Highway 16	Senoia, GA	30276-3345	770-599-0228	599-0556	K-8	Tiffany Pollock
Dekalb Academy of Tech & Environment	1492 Kelton Dr	Stone Mountain, GA	30083-1918	678-999-9290	999-9294	K-8	Dr. Maury Wills
DeKalb PATH Academy	3007 Hermance Dr NE	Atlanta, GA	30319-2627	404-846-3242	846-3243	5-8	Crystal Clarke
DeKalb Prepatory Academy	1402 Austin Dr	Decatur, GA	30032	404-937-2000	937-2020	K-8	Carla Pettis
Destiny Achievers Academy of Excellence	3595 Linecrest Rd	Ellenwood, GA	30294-1839	404-328-0898	328-1294	9-12	Kelvin Griffin
Douglas Co. College & Career Institute	4600 Timber Ridge Dr	Douglasville, GA	30135-1225	770-947-7690	947-3896	9-12	Mandy Johnson
Drew Charter S	301 E Lake Blvd SE	Atlanta, GA	30317-3152	404-687-0001	687-0480	PK-12	Peter McKnight
Dubois Integrity Academy	6479 Church St	Riverdale, GA	30274-2040	770-997-4860		K-2	Dr. Stephanie Payne
Dubois Integrity Academy	6390 Church St	Riverdale, GA	30274-1624	770-994-9527		3-5	Dr. Stephanie Payne
Effingham Career Academy	2940 GA Highway 21 S	Rincon, GA	31326	912-754-5610	754-5611	10-12	Ashley Kieffer
Ellijay ES	32 McCutchen St	Ellijay, GA	30540-3302	706-276-5020	276-5022	2-4	Lauree Pierce
Ellijay PS	196 McCutchen St	Ellijay, GA	30540-3393	706-276-5010	276-5013	PK-1	Stephanie Burnette
Flowery Branch HS	6603 Spout Springs Rd	Flowery Branch, GA	30542	770-967-8000	967-1218	9-12	Dr. Jason Carter
Floyd County College and Career Academy	100 Tom Poe Dr SW	Rome, GA	30161-6776	706-236-1860	236-1862	9-12	Eric Waters
Foothills Charter HS	600 Madison St	Danielsville, GA	30633-7030	706-795-2197		9-12	Renee Padgett
Fulton Academy of Science and Technology	11365 Crabapple Rd	Roswell, GA	30075	678-321-1100		K-6	Annette Higgins M.Ed.
Fulton Leadership Academy	1706 Washington Ave	Atlanta, GA	30344	404-472-3529	472-3520	6-12	Douglas Ward
Furlow Charter S	63 Valley Dr	Americus, GA	31709	229-931-8667		K-8	Valerie Duff
Futral Road ES	180 Futral Rd	Griffin, GA	30224-7454	770-229-3735	233-6001	PK-5	Ben Steele

School	Address	City,State	Zip code	Telephone	Fax	Grade	Contact
Georgia Connections Academy	2763 Meadow Church Rd # 208	Duluth, GA	30097	678-825-3258		K-12	Heather Robinson
Georgia Cyber Academy	1745 Phoenix Blvd Ste 100	Atlanta, GA	30349-5534	404-334-4790	684-8816	K-12	Matt Arkin
Georgia S for Innovation & the Classics	5073 Storey Mill Rd	Hephzibah, GA	30815	706-434-8085	434-8086	K-6	Mary Abbott
Gilmer HS	408 Bobcat Trl	Ellijay, GA	30540-5406	706-276-5080	276-5088	9-12	Eric McFee
Gilmer MS	1860 S Main St	Ellijay, GA	30540-5407	706-276-5030	276-5035	5-6	Larry Walker
Glascock County Consolidated S	1230 Panther Way	Gibson, GA	30810-4238	706-598-2121	598-2611	PK-12	Danny Lovering
GLOBE Academy	2225 Heritage Dr NE	Atlanta, GA	30345	404-464-7040		K-6	Christi Elliott-Earby
Golden Isles Career Academy	4404 Glynco Pkwy	Brunswick, GA	31525-6852	912-280-4000	261-2285	9-12	Dr. Rick Townsend
Graduation Achievement Charter HS	100 Edgewood Ave NE Ste 915	Atlanta, GA	30303-3070	404-937-5735	577-9023	9-12	Dr. Monica Henson
Gwinnett Online Campus	713 Hi Hope Rd	Lawrenceville, GA	30043-4541	770-326-8082	326-8064	4-12	Dr. Christopher Ray
Gwinnett S of Math Science and Tech	970 McElvaney Ln	Lawrenceville, GA	30044-2300	678-518-6700	518-6702	9-12	I.V. Bray
Hampton ES	10 Central Ave	Hampton, GA	30228-2100	770-946-4345	946-3472	K-5	Brian Keefer
Hapeville Charter Career Academy	6045 Buffington Rd	College Park, GA	30349	404-766-0101	941-1102	9-12	Jannard Rainey
Hapeville Charter MS	3535 S Fulton Ave	Hapeville, GA	30354-1701	404-767-7730	767-7706	6-8	Marcia Lowe
Harris Elementary Charter S	2300 Danielsville Rd	Athens, GA	30601-1038	706-357-5203	357-5209	PK-5	Xernona Thomas
Heart of Georgia College & Career Acad	338 W Laurens School Rd	Dublin, GA	31021-1222	478-609-0366		9-12	Tiffany Lofton
Heritage Preparatory Academy	569 M L King Jr Dr NW	Atlanta, GA	30314	678-399-2810		6-8	
Hickory Flat ES	841 Brannan Rd	McDonough, GA	30253-4749	770-898-0107	898-0114	K-5	Marla Surette
Hillcrest ES	1100 Edgewood Dr	Dublin, GA	31021-5599	478-353-8200	353-8201	K-5	Demme McManus
Houston County Career Academy	1311 Corder Rd	Warner Robins, GA	31088-7117	478-322-3280	322-3294	9-12	Sabrina Phelps
Hutchings College & Career Academy	1780 Anthony Rd	Macon, GA	31204	478-779-2550	779-2540	9-12	Barbara Alston
International Academy of Smyrna	2144 S Cobb Dr SE Ste A	Smyrna, GA	30080-1348	678-370-0980	370-0981	K-8	Kari Schrock
International Charter S of Atlanta	1335 Northmeadow Pkwy # 100	Roswell, GA	30076	470-222-7420	360-0032	K-4	Pamela Spalla
International Community S	2418 Wood Trail Ln	Decatur, GA	30033	404-499-8969	499-8968	K-5	Olivia McDonald-Murray
International Studies Magnet ES	2237 Cutts Dr	Albany, GA	31705-3810	229-431-3384	431-3381	K-5	Dr. Zeda George
Ivy Preparatory Academy	3705 Engineering Dr	Norcross, GA	30092-2878	770-342-0089	342-0088	6-8	Chaz Patterson
Ivy Preparatory Academy at Kirkwood	1807 Memorial Dr SE	Atlanta, GA	30317-2103	404-622-2727	622-2725	K-8	Kendra Shipmon
Ivy Prep Young Men's Leadership Academy	1807 Memorial Dr	Atlanta, GA	30317-2103	404-622-2727	622-2725	K-8	
Jenkins-White Charter ES	800 15th Ave	Augusta, GA	30901-4145	706-737-7320	731-7651	PK-5	Lori Johnson
Kennesaw Charter Science & Math Academy	3010 Cobb Pkwy NW	Kennesaw, GA	30152	678-290-9628	290-9638	K-5	Kay Frey
Kindezi S	386 Pine St NE	Atlanta, GA	30308	404-719-4005		K-6	Gilberte Pascal
Kindezi S	1890 Detroit Ave NW	Atlanta, GA	30314	404-671-4900	671-4901	K-8	Hyla-Mone't Penn
Kingsley ES	2051 Brendon Dr	Dunwoody, GA	30338-4599	678-874-8902	874-8910	PK-5	Melanie Pearch
KIPP Atlanta Collegiate S	98 Anderson Ave NW	Atlanta, GA	30314	404-574-5126	574-5129	9-12	David Howland
KIPP South Fulton Academy	1286 Washington Rd	East Point, GA	30344-3537	678-278-0160	278-0165	5-8	Jondre Pryor
KIPP STRIVE Academy	1444 Lucile Ave SW	Atlanta, GA	30310	404-753-1530	753-1532	5-8	Kim Karacalidis
KIPP STRIVE Primary Academy	1444 Lucile Ave SW	Atlanta, GA	30310-1217	404-753-1530	753-1532	K-4	Mini'imah Shaheed
KIPP Vision Academy	660 McWilliams Rd SE	Atlanta, GA	30315-7544	404-537-5252	671-4882	5-8	Tasha Davis
KIPP Vision PS	660 McWilliams Rd SE	Atlanta, GA	30315	404-537-5252	671-4882	K-4	Dr. Wheda Carletos
KIPP WAYS Academy	350 Temple St NW	Atlanta, GA	30314-2721	404-475-1941	475-1946	5-8	Dwight Ho-Sang
KIPP WAYS PS	350 Temple St NW	Atlanta, GA	30314-2721	404-475-1941	475-1946	K-2	Tandi Prillerman
Lake Oconee Academy	1021 Titan Cir	Greensboro, GA	30642-6047	706-454-1562	453-1773	K-8	Otho Tucker Ph.D.
Lamar County College and Career Academy	1 Trojan Way	Barnesville, GA	30204-1544	770-358-8641	358-8649	9-12	Matt Adams
Lanier Charter Career Academy	2719 Tumbling Creek Rd	Gainesville, GA	30504	770-531-2330	450-5978	9-12	David Moody
Latin College Prep	2626 Hogan Rd	East Point, GA	30344	404-669-8060	393-1491	6-8	Andre Mitchell
Latin Grammar S	2626 Hogan Rd	East Point, GA	30344	404-669-8060	393-1491	K-5	Alka Franceschi
Leadership Preparatory Academy	6400 Woodrow Rd	Lithonia, GA	30038	404-665-3100		K-8	Lonnie Hall
Liberty College and Career Academy	245 Darsey Rd	Hinesville, GA	31313	912-876-4904		9-12	Tom Alexander
Macon Charter Academy	PO Box 13433	Macon, GA	31208	478-330-7177		K-8	Dr. Georgia Gary
Main Street Academy	2861 Lakeshore Dr	College Park, GA	30337	404-768-0081	767-2491	K-8	Cheryl Parker
Martin Technology Acad of Math & Science	4216 Martin Rd	Flowery Branch, GA	30542-3509	770-965-1578	965-1668	K-5	Dr. Ley Hathcock
McEver Arts Academy	3265 Montgomery Dr	Gainesville, GA	30504-5515	770-534-7473	531-3055	K-5	Matthew Alexander
Morgan County ES	1640 Buckhead Rd	Madison, GA	30650	706-752-4750	752-4751	3-5	Ty Snyder
Morgan County HS	1231 College Dr	Madison, GA	30650-1499	706-752-4900	752-4901	9-12	Dr. Miki Edwards
Morgan County MS	920 Pearl St	Madison, GA	30650-1056	706-752-4800	752-4801	6-8	Dr. Darrell Stephens
Morgan County PS	993 East Ave	Madison, GA	30650-1498	706-752-4700	752-4701	PK-2	Lisa Daniel
Mountain Education Charter HS	901 Fairview School Rd	Demorest, GA	30535-3017	706-754-4461	754-5181	9-12	Sherrie Whiten
Mountain Education Charter HS	218 School St	Blairsville, GA	30512-3690	706-745-9575	745-3588	9-12	Roy Perrin
Mountain Education Charter HS	4560 Old Highway 76	Blue Ridge, GA	30513-4756	706-632-6100	632-0461	9-12	Lori Chastain
Mountain Education Charter HS	175 Primary School Rd	Ellijay, GA	30540-3666	706-276-5002	276-5008	9-12	Timothy Mount
Mountain Education Charter HS	65 Kenimer St	Cleveland, GA	30528	706-219-4664	219-4665	9-12	
Mountain Education Charter HS	136 Elm St	Cumming, GA	30040-2222	678-965-4971	965-4972	9-12	Janet Spaulding
Mountain Education Charter HS	328 Old Blairsville Rd	Cleveland, GA	30528-1134	706-348-4599	348-4498	9-12	Thomas Slege
Mountain Education Charter HS	121 D B Carroll St	Jasper, GA	30143	706-253-1750	253-1755	9-12	Ron Hunter
Mountain Education Charter HS	86 Adams Cir	Bowman, GA	30624-2126	706-213-4300	245-0407	9-12	Sonya Barnett
Mountain Education Charter HS	1130 Dahlonega Hwy	Cumming, GA	30040-4536	678-965-4971	965-5022	9-12	Kimberly Barnes
Mountain Education Charter HS	2723 Tumbling Creek Rd	Gainesville, GA	30504-5863			9-12	Greg Williams
Mountain Education Charter HS	963 Tiger Connector Rd	Tiger, GA	30576	706-212-4390	782-2188	9-12	Tomy Short
Mountain Education Charter HS	50 Eastanollee Livestock Rd	Eastanollee, GA	30538-2373	706-886-3114	886-3127	9-12	Debbie Gurley
Mountain View ES	350 Calvin Jackson Dr	Ellijay, GA	30540-5589	706-276-5100	276-5102	K-4	Charles Walker
Mount Vernon Exploratory S	4844 Jim Hood Rd	Gainesville, GA	30506-2834	770-983-1759	983-1663	K-5	Jennifer Westbrook
Murphey MS	2216 Bungalow Rd	Augusta, GA	30906	706-737-7350	737-7353	6-8	D'Andrea Jackson
Museum S of Avondale Estates	923 Forrest Blvd	Decatur, GA	30030	404-289-0320		PK-8	Katherine Kelbaugh
New Life Academy of Excellence	4725 River Green Pkwy	Duluth, GA	30096-2567	678-720-9870	720-9875	K-8	Alphonsa Foward
Newton College & Career Academy	144 Ram Dr	Covington, GA	30014-1956	678-625-6769	625-6041	10-12	Chad Walker
North Metro Academy of Performing Arts	182 Hunter St	Norcross, GA	30071	770-903-3400	903-2950	K-8	Dr. Daundria Phillips
Northwest Georgia College & Career Acad	2300 Maddox Chapel Rd NE	Dalton, GA	30721-6645	706-876-3600	876-3602	9-12	David Moeller
Odyssey Charter S	14 Saint John Cir	Newnan, GA	30265-1020	770-251-6111	251-6606	K-8	Andy Geeter
Oglethorpe Charter S	7202 Central Ave	Savannah, GA	31406-4203	912-395-5075	201-7626	6-8	Dr. Kevin Wall
Pataula Charter Academy	PO Box 332	Edison, GA	39846-0332	229-835-3322	835-2233	K-12	Kylie Holley
Peachtree Charter MS	4664 N Peachtree Rd	Atlanta, GA	30338-5811	678-676-7702	676-7710	6-8	Scott Heptinstall
Polk College and Career Academy	612 S College St	Cedartown, GA	30125-3522	770-748-3821		9-12	Dr. Katie Thomas
Putnam County ES	314 S Washington Ave	Eatonton, GA	31024-1126	706-485-5312	923-2808	3-5	Scott Sauls
Putnam County HS	300 War Eagle Rd	Eatonton, GA	31024-2304	706-485-9971	485-3128	9-12	Marc Dastous
Putnam County MS	140 Sparta Hwy	Eatonton, GA	31024-8493	706-485-8547	485-7090	6-8	Jay Homan
Putnam County PS	162 Old Glenwood Springs Rd	Eatonton, GA	31024-6525	706-485-5141	485-4147	PK-2	Dr. Fernando Aker
Rockdale Career Academy	1064 Culpepper Dr SW	Conyers, GA	30094-5985	770-388-5677	388-5678	9-12	Jill Oldham
Sardis Enrichment School	2805 Sardis Rd	Gainesville, GA	30506-2228	770-532-0104	531-3057	PK-5	Neil Yarrington
Savannah Classical Academy	705 E Anderson St	Savannah, GA	31401	912-395-4040		K-12	Benjamin Payne
Sawyer Road ES	840 Sawyer Rd	Marietta, GA	30062-2263	770-429-9923	429-9936	K-5	Susan Graves
Scholars Academy Charter S	6630 Camp St	Riverdale, GA	30274-2404	770-756-9710	629-4755	K-5	
Scintilla Charter Academy	2171 E Park Ave	Valdosta, GA	31602-4436	229-244-5750	333-0283	K-5	Stephanie Mullis
Sedalia Park ES	2230 Lower Roswell Rd	Marietta, GA	30068-3359	770-509-5162	509-5342	K-5	Tiffany Jackson
Skyview HS	5134 Old National Hwy	College Park, GA	30349	404-418-8812		9-12	Byron Foster
Smoke Rise ES	1991 Silver Hill Rd	Stone Mountain, GA	30087-1699	678-874-3602	874-3610	PK-5	Pamela McCloud
South Eastern Early College & Career Acd	413 Pete Phillips Dr	Vidalia, GA	30474	912-293-1318		9-12	Shelly Smith
Spout Springs S of Enrichment	6640 Spout Springs Rd	Flowery Branch, GA	30542-5575	770-967-4860	967-4883	K-5	Arlene Thomas
Taliaferro County S	557 Broad St NW	Crawfordville, GA	30631-2918	706-456-2575	456-2689	PK-12	Jemessyn Foster
Tapestry Charter Public S	PO Box 48082	Atlanta, GA	30362-1082	678-268-6403		6-9	Barbara Boone
Tapestry Charter S	3130 Raymond Dr	Atlanta, GA	30340	470-268-6403	268-6403	6-9	Barbara Boone
THINC Academy	1 College Cir	LaGrange, GA	30240	706-443-5826	523-0266	10-12	Dr. Chris Williams
Tybee Island Maritime Academy	PO Box 1519	Tybee Island, GA	31328-1519	912-395-4060		K-5	Patrick Rossiter
Unidos Dual Language Charter S	4475 Hendrix Dr	Forest Park, GA	30297-1244	678-827-7947	827-7948	K-8	Dr. A. Clifton Myles
Union Point STEAM Academy	1401 Highway 77 N	Union Point, GA	30669-1109	706-486-4117	486-4974	K-7	Ashlie Miller
Utopian Academy for the Arts Charter S	6630 Camp St	Riverdale, GA	30274-2404	770-892-1644	731-2135	6-8	Artesius Miller
Walton HS	1590 Bill Murdock Rd	Marietta, GA	30062-5999	770-578-3225	578-3227	9-12	Judith McNeill
Wauka Mtn Multiple Intelligences Academy	5850 Brookton Lula Rd	Gainesville, GA	30506-2909	770-983-3221	983-1019	PK-5	Pam Doig
Webster County HS	7168 Washington St	Preston, GA	31824-5232	229-828-3365	828-2014	9-12	Janie Downer
Wesley International Academy	211 Memorial Dr SE	Atlanta, GA	30312-2021	678-904-9137	904-9138	K-8	Dr. Keisha Hancock
Westside Atlanta Charter S	1903 Drew Dr NW	Atlanta, GA	30318	404-228-9678		K-5	Delana Reeves
World Language Academy	4670 Winder Hwy	Flowery Branch, GA	30542-3611	770-967-5854	967-3496	PK-4	Britney Bennett
World Language Academy	3215 Poplar Springs Rd	Gainesville, GA	30507	770-533-4004	533-4018	5-8	Brittney Bennett
Wynnton Arts Academy	2303 Wynnton Rd	Columbus, GA	31906-2540	706-748-3147	748-3151	K-5	Carolyn Mull

Hawaii

School	Address	City,State	Zip code	Telephone	Fax	Grade	Contact
Connections New Century Charter S	174 Kamehameha Ave	Hilo, HI	96720-2865	808-961-3664	961-2665	K-12	John Thatcher
Hakipu'u Learning Center	PO Box 1159	Kaneohe, HI	96744-1159	808-235-9155	235-9160	4-12	Charlene Hoe
Halau Ku Mana Charter S	2101 Makiki Heights Dr	Honolulu, HI	96822-2520	808-945-1600	945-1604	4-12	Mahina Duarte
Hawaii Academy of Arts & Science	PO Box 1494	Pahoa, HI	96778-1494	808-965-3730	965-3733	K-12	Steve Hirakami
Hawaii Technology Academy	94-810 Moloalo St	Waipahu, HI	96797-3355	808-676-5444	676-5470	K-12	Leigh Fitzgerald M.Ed.
Innovations Public Charter S	75-5815 Queen Kaahumanu Hwy	Kailua Kona, HI	96740-2013	808-327-6205	327-6209	K-8	Jennifer Hiro
Kamaile Academy	85-180 Ala Akau St	Waianae, HI	96792-2323	808-697-7110	697-7115	PK-12	Anna Winslow
Kanuikapono Charter S	4333 Kukuihale Rd	Anahola, HI	96703	808-822-9032	482-3055	K-12	Ku'uipo Torio
Kanu 'o Ka 'Aina Charter S	PO Box 398	Kamuela, HI	96743-0398	808-887-8144	887-8146	K-12	Allyson Tamura
Ka'u Learning Academy	PO Box 89	Naalehu, HI	96772-0089	808-498-0761		3-6	Kathryn Tydlacka M.Ed.
Ka 'Umeke Ka'eo Public Charter S	222 Desha Ave	Hilo, HI	96720-4815	808-933-3482	933-3488	K-10	Huihui Kanahele-Mossman

School	Address	City,State	Zip code	Telephone	Fax	Grade	Contact
Ka Waihona O Ka Na'auao Charter S	89-195 Farrington Hwy	Waianae, HI	96792-4102	808-620-9030	620-9036	K-8	Alvin Parker
Kawaikini Charter S	3-1821 Kaumualii Hwy Ste J	Lihue, HI	96766	808-632-2032	246-4635	K-12	Samuel Ka'auwai
Ke Ana La'ahana Public Charter S	1500 Kalanianaole Ave	Hilo, HI	96720-4914	808-961-6228	961-6229	7-12	Mapuana Waipa
Ke Kula Ni'ihau Kekaha Public Charter S	8135 Kekaha Rd	Kekaha, HI	96752	808-337-0481	337-1289	PK-12	Haunani Seward
Ke Kula 'O Nawahiokalani'opu'u Charter S	16-120 Opukahaia St	Keaau, HI	96749-8135	808-982-4260	966-7821	K-8	Dr. Kauanoe Kamana
Ke Kula 'O Samuel Kamakau Lab S	46-500 Kuneki St	Kaneohe, HI	96744-3568	808-235-9175	235-9173	PK-12	Dr. Meahilahila Kelling
Kihei Charter S	PO Box 1098	Kihei, HI	96753-1098	808-875-0700	874-6745	K-12	Dan Kuhar
Kona Pacific Public Charter S	PO Box 115	Kealakekua, HI	96750-0115	808-322-4900	322-4906	K-8	Usha Kotner
Kualapu'u Charter ES	PO Box 260	Kualapuu, HI	96757-0260	808-567-6900	567-6906	K-6	Lydia Trinidad
Kua 'O Ka La Public Charter S	14-5322 Kalapana Kapoho Rd	Pahoa, HI	96778-8066	808-965-5098	965-9618	K-12	Susan Osborne
Kula Aupuni Niihau A Kahelelani Aloha	8315 Kekaha Rd	Kekaha, HI	96752	808-337-2022	337-2033	K-12	Hedy Sullivan
Lanikai ES	140 Alala Rd	Kailua, HI	96734-3199	808-266-7844	266-7848	PK-6	Ed Noh
Malama Honua Charter S	41-054 Ehukai St	Waimanalo, HI	96795-1603	808-259-5522		K-2	Denise Espania
Na Wai Ola Public Charter S	181355 Volcano Rd	Mountain View, HI	96771	808-968-2318	968-0778	K-6	Daniel Caluya M.Ed.
SEEQS Charter S	845 22nd Ave	Honolulu, HI	96816-4521	808-677-3377		6-12	Buffy Cushman-Patz
Thompson Academy	1040 Richards St Ste 220	Honolulu, HI	96813-2920	808-441-8000	683-7062	K-12	Diana Oshiro
University Laboratory S	1776 University Ave	Honolulu, HI	96822-2447	808-956-7833	956-7260	K-12	Keoni Jeremiah
Volcano S of Arts & Sciences	PO Box 845	Volcano, HI	96785-0845	808-985-9800	985-9898	K-8	Ardith Renteria
Voyager Charter S	2428 Wilder Ave	Honolulu, HI	96822-2418	808-521-9770	521-9772	K-8	Marybeth Barr
Wai'alae ES	1045 19th Ave	Honolulu, HI	96816-4699	808-733-4880	733-4886	K-5	Wendy Lagareta
Waimea Charter MS	67-1229 Mamalahoa Hwy	Kamuela, HI	96743-8429	808-887-6090	887-6087	6-8	Amy Kendziorski M.Ed.
West Hawaii Explorations Academy	73-4460 Queen Kaahumanu Hwy	Kailua Kona, HI	96740-2632	808-327-4751	327-4750	6-12	Heather Nakakura

Idaho

School	Address	City,State	Zip code	Telephone	Fax	Grade	Contact
Academy	1295 Alpine Ave	Pocatello, ID	83202-3100	208-232-1447	232-1448	K-8	Joel Lovstedt
American Heritage Charter S	1736 S 35th W	Idaho Falls, ID	83402-5691	208-529-6570	529-3344	K-9	Shawn Rose
Another Choice Virtual Charter S	1014 W Hemingway Blvd	Nampa, ID	83651-1733	208-475-4255	475-4274	K-12	Dr. Kelsey Williams
ANSER Charter S	202 E 42nd St	Garden City, ID	83714	208-426-9840	426-9863	K-8	Michelle Dunstan
ARTEC Charter S	202 18th St	Twin Falls, ID	83303	208-732-6346	736-4770	9-12	Claire Major
Bird Charter S	614 S Madison Ave	Sandpoint, ID	83864-8724	208-255-7771	263-9441	6-12	Alan Millar
Blackfoot Charter Community Learning Ctr	2801 Hunters Loop	Blackfoot, ID	83221-6206	208-782-0744	782-1330	K-8	Debbie Steele
Chief Tahgee Elementary Academy	PO Box 217	Fort Hall, ID	83203	208-237-2710	237-1734	K-6	Joel Weaver
Coeur D'Alene Charter Academy	4904 N Duncan Dr	Coeur d Alene, ID	83815-8329	208-676-1667	676-8667	6-12	Dan Nickla y
Compass Charter S	2511 W Cherry Ln	Meridian, ID	83642-1135	208-855-2802	895-0197	K-12	Kelly Trudeau
Falcon Ridge Charter S	278 S Ten Mile Rd	Kuna, ID	83634	208-922-9228	922-4198	K-8	Mark Green
Heritage Academy	500 S Lincoln Ave	Jerome, ID	83338-3027	208-595-1617		K-8	Dr. Christine Ivie
Heritage Community Charter S	1803 E Ustick Rd	Caldwell, ID	83605-6607	208-453-8070	453-8077	K-8	Javier Castaneda
Idaho Arts Charter S	1220 5th St N	Nampa, ID	83687-3416	208-463-4324	468-0572	K-12	Jackie Collins
Idaho College & Career Readiness Academy	1965 S Eagle Rd Ste 150	Meridian, ID	83642-9287	866-917-2420	917-2416	K-12	Monte Pittman
Idaho Connects Online S	12639 W Explorer Dr Ste 185	Boise, ID	83713-1889	208-287-3668	287-3671	6-12	Vickie McCullough
Idaho Digital Learning Academy	PO Box 10017	Boise, ID	83707	208-342-0207	577-4034	K-12	Dr. Cheryl Charlton
Idaho Distance Education Academy	PO Box 338	Deary, ID	83823-0338	208-877-1513	877-1713	K-12	Tera Reeves
Idaho Science and Technology Charter S	21 N 550 W	Blackfoot, ID	83221-5562	208-785-7827	785-9913	6-8	Tami Dortch
Idaho Virtual Academy	1965 S Eagle Rd Ste 190	Meridian, ID	83642-9246	208-322-3559	322-3688	K-12	Kelly Edginton
Inspire Virtual Charter S	600 N Steelhead Way Ste 164	Boise, ID	83704-9620	208-322-4002	322-4008	K-12	Karen Glassman
iSucceed Virtual HS	6148 Discovery Way	Boise, ID	83704	208-375-3116	375-3117	9-12	Katie Allison
iSucceed Virtual HS	6148 N Discovery Way # 120	Boise, ID	83713	208-375-3116	375-3117	9-12	Katie Allison
Jefferson Charter S	1209 Adam Smith Ave	Caldwell, ID	83605-5487	208-455-8772	455-8713	K-12	Chuck Ward
Kootenai Bridge Academy	606 River Ave	Coeur D Alene, ID	83814	208-930-4515	930-4791	11-12	Charles Kenna
Legacy Charter S	4015 Legacy Way	Nampa, ID	83686-5801	208-467-0947	467-0948	K-6	Seth Stallcop
Liberty Charter S	9955 Kris Jensen Ln	Nampa, ID	83686-4742	208-466-7952	466-7961	K-12	Rebecca Stallcop
McKenna Charter HS	675 S Haskett St	Mountain Home, ID	83647-3375	208-580-2449	580-2450	9-12	Larry Slade
Meridian Medical Arts Charter HS	1789 E Heritage Park Ln	Meridian, ID	83646	208-855-4075	855-4081	9-12	Scott Hill
Meridian Technical Charter HS	3800 N Locust Grove Rd	Meridian, ID	83646-5510	208-288-2928	288-5685	9-12	Randy Yadon
Monticello Montessori Charter S	4707 Sweetwater Way	Ammon, ID	83406	208-419-0742	419-0765	K-6	Erica Kemery
Moscow Charter S	1723 E F St	Moscow, ID	83843-9571	208-883-3195	892-3855	K-8	Tony Bonuccelli
North Idaho STEM Charter Academy	PO Box 434	Rathdrum, ID	83858-0434	208-687-8002		K-9	Scott Thomson
North Star Charter S	839 N Linder Rd	Eagle, ID	83616-4427	208-939-9600	939-6090	K-12	Melissa Andersen
North Valley Academy	906 Main St	Gooding, ID	83330-1625	208-934-4567	934-4522	K-12	Gayle DeSmet
Odyssey Charter S	1235 Jones St	Idaho Falls, ID	83401	208-557-3627		6-12	Karl Peterson
Palouse Prairie Charter S	PO Box 9511	Moscow, ID	83843	208-882-3684	882-3689	K-8	Jeneille Branen
Payette River Technical Academy	721 W 12th St Ste A	Emmett, ID	83617	208-365-0985	365-7800	9-12	Patrick Goff
Pocatello Community Charter S	995 S Arthur Ave	Pocatello, ID	83204-3400	208-478-2522	478-2622	K-8	Michael Mendive
Rolling Hills Charter S	8900 Horseshoe Bend Rd	Boise, ID	83714-3859	208-939-5400	939-5401	K-8	Shane Pratt M.Ed.
Sage International S of Boise	1513 Tyrell Ln Ste 110	Boise, ID	83706	208-343-7243	287-0829	K-12	Don Keller
Syringa Mountain S	4021 Glenbrook Dr	Hailey, ID	83333-8516	208-806-2880		K-8	Mende Coblentz
Taylors Crossing Charter S	1445 Wood River Rd	Idaho Falls, ID	83401-5095	208-552-0397	904-3814	K-12	Daniel Wendt
Upper Carmen Charter S	PO Box 33	Carmen, ID	83462-0033	208-756-4590	756-6695	K-6	Sue Smith
Victory Charter S	9779 Kris Jensen Ln	Nampa, ID	83686-4741	208-442-9400	442-9401	K-12	Dr. Marianne Saunders
Village Charter S	219 N Roosevelt St	Boise, ID	83706-1850	208-336-2000	367-1234	K-8	Tony Richard
Vision Charter S	19291 Ward Ln	Caldwell, ID	83605-7936	208-455-9220	455-9121	K-12	Wendy Oldenkamp
White Pine Charter S	2959 John Adams Pkwy	Ammon, ID	83406-4508	208-522-4432	522-4452	K-8	Jeremy Clarke
Xavier Charter S	1218 N College Rd W	Twin Falls, ID	83301-5651	208-734-3947	733-1348	K-12	Gary Moon

Illinois

School	Address	City,State	Zip code	Telephone	Fax	Grade	Contact
Academy for Global Citizenship	4647 W 47th St	Chicago, IL	60632	773-582-1100	582-1101	K-8	Jennifer Moore
ACE Technical Charter HS	5410 S State St	Chicago, IL	60609-6342	773-548-8705	548-8706	9-12	Marvin Talley
Amandla Charter S	6820 S Washtenaw Ave	Chicago, IL	60629	773-535-7150	535-7151	6-12	Alyssa Nickow
Asian Human Services - Passages Charter	1643 W Bryn Mawr Ave	Chicago, IL	60660	773-433-3530	769-3229	PK-8	Maritza Torres
ASPIRA - Antonia Pantoja Alternative HS	3129 N Pulaski Rd	Chicago, IL	60641	773-252-0970	427-0872	10-12	Dr. Martha Zurita
ASPIRA Business and Finance HS	2989 N Milwaukee Ave	Chicago, IL	60618	773-252-0970		9-12	Janie Flores
ASPIRA - Early College HS	3986 W Barry Ave	Chicago, IL	60618	773-252-0970	267-3568	9-12	Raul Guerra
ASPIRA Haugan MS	3729 W Leland Ave	Chicago, IL	60625-5706	773-252-0970	427-0872	6-8	Pablo Ortega
Cambridge Lakes S	900 Wester Blvd	Pingree Grove, IL	60140-2050	847-464-4300	464-0318	PK-8	Julie Skaggs
Catalyst Charter - Maria	6727 S California Ave	Chicago, IL	60629	773-993-1770	993-1771	K-12	Jasmia Fowler
Catalyst Charter S - Circle Rock	5608 W Washington Blvd	Chicago, IL	60644	773-945-5025	626-2345	K-8	Elizabeth Jamison-Dunn
Chicago Collegiate Charter S	11816 S Indiana Ave	Chicago, IL	60628	773-536-9098	264-5792	4-7	Beth Napleton
Chicago International Charter S - Avalon	1501 E 83rd Pl	Chicago, IL	60619-6501	773-721-0858	731-0142	K-8	Brandon Kimble
Chicago International Charter S - Basil	1816 W Garfield Blvd	Chicago, IL	60609-5606	773-778-9455	778-9456	K-8	Elizabeth Tieche
Chicago International Charter S - Bond	13300 S Langley Ave	Chicago, IL	60827	773-468-1300	253-0988	K-6	Tyson Daniel
Chicago International Charter S Longwood	1309 W 95th St	Chicago, IL	60643-1496	773-238-5330	238-5350	3-12	Kenyatta Stansberry
Chicago International Charter S - Loomis	9535 S Loomis St	Chicago, IL	60643	773-429-8955	429-8441	K-2	Lindsey Girard
Chicago International Charter S Prairie	11530 S Prairie Ave	Chicago, IL	60628-5612	773-928-0480	928-6971	K-8	Keith Shaw
Chicago International Charter S - Quest	1443 N Ogden Ave	Chicago, IL	60610	773-565-2100	951-2906	6-12	Ayanna Gore
Chicago International Charter S W Belden	2245 N McVicker Ave	Chicago, IL	60639-2766	773-637-9430	637-9791	K-8	Colleen Collins
Chicago Intl Charter S - Bucktown	2235 N Hamilton Ave	Chicago, IL	60647-3303	773-645-3321	645-3327	K-8	Sophia Halkias
Chicago Intl Charter S - Irving Park	3820 N Spaulding Ave	Chicago, IL	60618-4413	773-433-5000	433-5009	K-8	Karin Breo M.Ed.
Chicago Intl Charter S Northtown	3900 W Peterson Ave Ste 1	Chicago, IL	60659-3162	773-478-3655	478-6029	9-12	Dr. Josh Emmett
Chicago Intl Charter S Ralph Ellison	1817 W 80th St	Chicago, IL	60620-4557	773-478-4434	224-2594	9-12	Kimberly Hinton
Chicago Intl Charter S Washington Park	110 E 61st St	Chicago, IL	60637	773-347-0200	324-3302	K-8	Shaymora Blanks
Chicago Intl Charter S Wrightwood	8130 S California Ave	Chicago, IL	60652-2716	773-434-4575	434-2026	K-8	David Lewis
Chicago Lighthouse Charter School	7847 S Jeffery Ave	Chicago, IL	60649	312-320-9893	285-1564	K-8	Lakisha Thigpen
Chicago Math and Science Academy	7212 N Clark St	Chicago, IL	60626	773-761-8960	761-8961	6-12	Ali Kuran
Chicago Virtual Charter S	38 S Peoria St	Chicago, IL	60607-2628	312-267-4486	676-3689	K-12	Dr. Richard Lebron
Christopher House Charter ES	5235 W Belden St	Chicago, IL	60639	773-922-7542	922-7559	K-3	Kristin Novy
EPIC Academy	8255 S Houston Ave	Chicago, IL	60617-2191	773-535-7930	535-7934	9-12	Matthew King
Erie Charter S	1405 N Washtenaw Ave	Chicago, IL	60622	773-486-7161	486-7234	K-8	Eleanor Nicholson
Excel Academy - Woodlawn	7530 S South Shore Dr	Chicago, IL	60649	773-902-7800	902-7615	9-12	Renee Carter
Foundations College Prep S	1233 W 109th Pl	Chicago, IL	60643	773-298-5800		6-12	Sarah Hunko-Baker
Frazier Preparatory Academy	3711 W Douglas Blvd	Chicago, IL	60623	773-521-1303	521-1365	PK-8	Tiffany Brown
Galapagos Charter S	2605 School St	Rockford, IL	61101-5264	815-708-7946	708-7966	K-8	Michael Lane
Great Lakes Academy Charter S	8401 S Saginaw Ave	Chicago, IL	60617	773-530-3040	530-3039	K-3	Katherin Myers
Horizon Science Academy - SW Charter	5401 S Western Blvd	Chicago, IL	60609	773-498-3355	498-4984	K-10	Matt Yildiz
HSA Belmont Charter S	2456 N Mango Ave	Chicago, IL	60639	773-237-2702	237-2726	K-8	Serdar Kartal
HSA McKinley Park Charter S	2245 W Pershing Rd	Chicago, IL	60609-2211	773-247-8400	247-8401	K-12	Cafer Cengiz
Instituto Health Sciences Career Academy	2520 S Western Ave	Chicago, IL	60608	773-890-8020	376-8573	9-12	Hillyn Sennholtz
Instituto - Justice Lozano	2570 S Blue Island Ave	Chicago, IL	60608-4817	773-890-8060	890-1537	9-12	Christine Diaz
Instituto - Justice Lozano Mastery	2520 S Western Ave	Chicago, IL	60608	773-890-0055	890-1537	9-12	Christine Diaz
Intrinsic Charter HS	4540 W Belmont Ave	Chicago, IL	60641	708-887-2735	887-2812	7-12	Melissa Zaikos
Jackson Charter S	315 Summit St	Rockford, IL	61107	815-316-0093	316-0170	K-8	Angelique Watson
KIPP Ascend MS	1616 S Avers Ave	Chicago, IL	60623-2401	773-521-4399	521-4766	6-8	Lauren Henley
KIPP Ascend PS	1440 S Christiana Ave	Chicago, IL	60623-1734	773-522-1261	522-1185	K-5	Ellen Bhattacharyya
KIPP Bloom College Prep S	5515 S Lowe Ave	Chicago, IL	60621	773-938-8565	783-6910	5-8	Ellen Sale
KIPP Create College Prep S	4818 W Ohio St	Chicago, IL	60644	773-938-8553	287-4548	5-8	Billy Warden
KIPP One Academy	730 N Pulaski Rd	Chicago, IL	60624	773-938-8578		K-K,	Rashid Bell

School	Address	City,State	Zip code	Telephone	Fax	Grade	Contact
LEARN 6 in North Chicago	3131 Sheridan Rd	Great Lakes, IL	60088	847-473-3845	473-2988	K-8	Kelly Tyson
LEARN 7 Charter ES	3021 W Carroll Ave	Chicago, IL	60612	773-584-4350	826-7918	K-5	Margie Smagacz
LEARN 8 Charter MS	3021 W Carroll Ave	Chicago, IL	60612	773-584-4300	826-7933	6-8	David Lewis
LEARN 9 Campus in Waukegan	1200 W Glen Flora Ave	Waukegan, IL	60085	847-377-0690		K-4	Maytee Diez
Learn 10 in North Chicago	3131 Sheridan Rd	Great Lakes, IL	60088	847-473-3845		K-3	Kelly Tyson
LEARN Charter S Campbell Campus	212 S Francisco Ave	Chicago, IL	60612-3618	773-826-0370	826-0109	K-5	Karin McGuire
LEARN Charter S Excel Campus	3021 W Carroll Ave	Chicago, IL	60612-1721	312-243-7001	243-7160	K-5	Sekou Robertson
LEARN Charter S Hunter Perkins Campus	1700 W 83rd St	Chicago, IL	60620-4621	773-488-1634	488-1753	K-7	Jon Bennett
LEARN Charter S - Romano Butler Campus	1132 S Homan Ave	Chicago, IL	60624-4344	773-722-0200	826-0015	PK-8	Robin Johnson
LEARN Charter S - South Chicago Campus	8914 S Buffalo Ave	Chicago, IL	60617	773-722-8577		K-8	Ginger Lumpkin
Legacy Academy for Excellence Charter S	4029 Prairie Rd	Rockford, IL	61102-4501	815-961-1100		K-12	Barbara Forte
Legacy Charter S	4217 W 18th St	Chicago, IL	60623-2325	773-542-1640	542-1699	PK-8	Richard Glass
Legal Prep Charter Academy	4319 W Washington Blvd	Chicago, IL	60624	773-922-7800	386-5796	9-12	Samuel Finkelstein
Little Black Pearl Art and Design Center	1060 E 47th St	Chicago, IL	60653	773-285-1211	285-1633	9-12	Monica Haslip
Locke Charter Academy	3141 W Jackson Blvd	Chicago, IL	60612-2729	773-265-7232	265-7258	PK-8	Patrick Love
Montessori S of Englewood	6936 S Hermitage Ave	Chicago, IL	60636	773-535-9255	535-9590	K-5	Rita Nolan
Morgan ES	420 N Colfax St	Byron, IL	61010-1438	815-234-5491	234-4094	PK-5	Buster Barton
Moving Everest Charter S	416 N Laramie Ave	Chicago, IL	60644	312-683-9695	674-7221	K-2	Mika Krause
Namaste Charter S	3737 S Paulina St	Chicago, IL	60609-2047	773-715-9558	376-6495	K-8	Stephanie Bloom
Noble Academy	1443 N Ogden Ave	Chicago, IL	60610	312-574-1527	575-4217	9-10	Lauren Boros
Noble - Baker College Prep	2710 E 89th St	Chicago, IL	60617	773-535-6340	913-0346	9-12	Vincent Gay
Noble - Butler College Prep	821 E 103rd St	Chicago, IL	60628	773-535-5490	442-0343	9-12	Christopher Goins
Noble - Chicago Bulls College Prep S	2040 W Adams St	Chicago, IL	60612	773-534-7599	850-0192	9-12	Wendy Erskine
Noble - DRW College Prep	931 S Homan Ave	Chicago, IL	60624	773-893-4500	893-4501	9-12	Matthew Kelley
Noble - Gary Comer College Prep	7131 S South Chicago Ave	Chicago, IL	60619	773-729-3969	729-3960	9-12	Estee Kelly
Noble - Golder College Prep	1454 W Superior St	Chicago, IL	60642	312-265-9925	243-8402	9-12	Stephanie Hernandez
Noble - Hansberry College Prep	8748 S Aberdeen St	Chicago, IL	60620	773-729-3400	304-1995	9-12	Lauryn Fullerton
Noble - ITW David Speer Academy	5321 W Grand Ave	Chicago, IL	60639	773-622-7484	304-2700	9-12	Tom Mulder
Noble - Johnson College Prep	6350 S Stewart Ave	Chicago, IL	60621	312-348-1888	278-0449	9-12	Matthew Brown
Noble - Mansueto HS	5101 S Keller	Chicago, IL	60632	773-349-8200	409-0440	9-9	Darko Simunovic
Noble - Muchin College Prep	1 N State St	Chicago, IL	60602	312-445-4680	332-0058	9-12	Emily Mason
Noble - Pritzker College Prep	4131 W Cortland St	Chicago, IL	60639-4923	773-394-2848	394-2931	9-12	Pablo Sierra
Noble - Rauner College Prep	1337 W Ohio St	Chicago, IL	60642-6430	312-226-5345	226-3552	9-12	Jennifer Reid
Noble - Rowe - Clark Math & Science Acad	3645 W Chicago Ave	Chicago, IL	60651-3934	773-242-2212	826-6936	9-12	Brenda Cora
Noble Street College Prep	1010 N Noble St	Chicago, IL	60642	773-862-1449	278-0421	9-12	Ellen Metz
Noble - UIC College Prep	1231 S Damen Ave	Chicago, IL	60608	312-768-4858	496-7149	9-12	Tressie McDonough
North Lawndale College Prep - Christiana	1615 S Christiana Ave	Chicago, IL	60623	773-542-1490	542-1492	9-12	Senita Murphy
North Lawndale College Prep - Collins	1313 S Sacramento Dr	Chicago, IL	60623-2218	773-542-6766	542-6995	8-12	Tim Bouman
Perspectives Charter MS	8131 S May St	Chicago, IL	60620-3007	773-358-6300	358-6399	6-8	Sauda Porter
Perspectives - HS of Technology	8131 S May St	Chicago, IL	60620	773-358-6120	358-6129	9-12	Eron Powell
Perspectives - Joslin HS	1930 S Archer Ave	Chicago, IL	60616-6505	312-225-7400	225-7411	6-12	Stephen Todd
Perspectives - Leadership Academy	8131 S May St	Chicago, IL	60620-3007	773-358-6100	358-6199	6-12	Sarah Severson
Perspectives - Math & Science Academy	3663 S Wabash Ave	Chicago, IL	60653	773-358-6800	358-6055	6-12	Brandy Woodard
Plato Learning Academy	5545 W Harrison St	Chicago, IL	60644	773-413-3090	413-3095	K-8	Charles Williams
Polaris Charter Academy	620 N Sawyer Ave	Chicago, IL	60624-1528	773-534-0820	534-6645	K-8	Michelle Navarre
Prairie Crossing Charter S	1571 Jones Point Rd	Grayslake, IL	60030-3536	847-543-9722	543-9744	K-8	Geoff Deigan
Prologue - Early College HS	1135 N Cleaver St	Chicago, IL	60642	773-935-9925	935-8357	9-12	Walter Perkins
Prologue-Johnston S of Art & Design	1549 W 95th St	Chicago, IL	60643	773-341-2260	341-2922	9-12	Joyce Bowen
Providence Englewood Charter S	6515 S Ashland Ave	Chicago, IL	60636-3003	773-434-0202	434-0196	K-8	Angela Johnson-Williams
Quest Charter Academy	2503 N University St	Peoria, IL	61604-2601	309-402-0030	685-3001	5-12	Dr. Nicole Woods
Robertson Charter S	2240 E Geddes Ave	Decatur, IL	62526-5127	217-428-7072	428-9214	K-8	Niki Fenderson
Rowe ES	1424 N Cleaver St	Chicago, IL	60642	312-445-5870	445-5875	K-8	Tony Sutton
Shabazz Academy	7823 S Ellis Ave	Chicago, IL	60619-3213	773-651-1221	651-0302	K-8	Shannon Mason
SIU East St. Louis Charter S	601 James R Thompson Blvd	E Saint Louis, IL	62201-1129	618-482-8370	482-8372	9-12	Veronica Washington
Sizemore Academy of B Shabazz	6547 S Stewart Ave	Chicago, IL	60621	773-651-1661	651-4125	K-8	Danielle Robinson
Southland College Prep	4601 Sauk Trl	Richton Park, IL	60471-1470	708-748-8105		9-12	Dr. Blondean Davis
Springfield Ball Charter S	2530 E Ash St	Springfield, IL	62703-5600	217-525-3275	525-3316	PK-8	Matthew Fraas
UCCS - Carter Woodson Campus	4444 S Evans Ave	Chicago, IL	60653	773-624-0700	624-0707	6-8	Jarred Brown
UCCS - Donoghue Campus	707 E 37th St	Chicago, IL	60653-1406	773-285-5301	285-5389	PK-5	Errika Baker
UCCS - North Kenwood/Oakland Campus	1119 E 46th St	Chicago, IL	60653-4403	773-536-2399	536-2435	PK-5	Tonya Howell
UCCS - Woodlawn Campus	6420 S University Ave	Chicago, IL	60637-3659	773-752-8101	324-0653	6-12	Kieran Palmer-Klein
UNO Charter Garcia HS	4248 W 47th St	Chicago, IL	60632	773-579-3480	376-5785	9-12	Alex Rock
UNO Charter S - Bartolome De Las Casas	1641 W 16th St	Chicago, IL	60608-2039	312-432-3224	432-1066	K-8	Courtney Mix-Binish
UNO Charter S - Brighton Park	4420 S Fairfield Ave	Chicago, IL	60632	773-455-5434	455-5435	K-8	Laura Castle
UNO Charter S - Carlos Fuentes Campus	2845 W Barry Ave	Chicago, IL	60618-7015	312-279-9826	279-9852	K-8	Joann Tanner
UNO Charter S - Octavio Paz Campus	2651 W 23rd St	Chicago, IL	60608-3609	773-890-1054	890-1069	K-8	Cherise Jones
UNO Charter S - Officer Donald Marquez	2916 W 47th St	Chicago, IL	60632-1907	773-321-2200	321-2250	K-8	Allison Hansen
UNO Charter S - Omar Torres	4248 W 47th St	Chicago, IL	60632	773-579-3475	376-5645	K-8	Christopher Allen
UNO Charter S - Roberto Clemente	2050 N Natchez Ave	Chicago, IL	60707	312-455-5425	455-5456	K-8	Maisha Copeland
UNO Charter S - Rogers Park	7416 N Ridge Blvd	Chicago, IL	60645	312-455-5442	455-5443	K-12	Molly Robinson
UNO Charter S - Rufino Tamayo Campus	5135 S California Ave	Chicago, IL	60632-2124	773-434-6355	434-5036	K-8	Matthew Katz
UNO Charter S - Sandra Cisneros	2744 W Pershing Rd	Chicago, IL	60632	773-376-8830	376-8825	K-8	Adams Sparks
UNO Charter S - Santiago	2510 W Cortez St	Chicago, IL	60622	312-455-5410	455-5411	K-8	Melissa Sweazy
UNO Charter S - Soccer Academy	5050 S Homan Ave	Chicago, IL	60632	312-455-5450	455-5451	PK-8	Sandra Medina-Alba
UNO Charter School - Soccer Academy HS	5025 S Saint Louis Ave	Chicago, IL	60632	312-455-5446	455-5447	9-12	John Loehr
UNO Charter S - SPC Daniel Zizumbo	4248 W 47th St	Chicago, IL	60632	773-579-3470	376-5605	K-8	Christopher Allen
Urban Prep Academy - Englewood HS	6201 S Stewart Ave	Chicago, IL	60621-3247	773-535-9724	535-0012	9-12	Dion Steele
Urban Prep - Bronzeville	521 E 35th St	Chicago, IL	60616	773-624-3444	624-3405	9-12	Conrad Timbers-Ausar
Urban Prep - West HS	1326 W 14th Pl	Chicago, IL	60608	773-534-8860	534-1050	9-12	Patrick Robinson
West Town Academy	500 N Sacramento Blvd	Chicago, IL	60612	312-563-9044	563-9672	10-12	Alicia Schutter
YCCS-Academy of Scholastic Achievement	4651 W Madison St	Chicago, IL	60644-3646	773-921-1315	921-8324	10-12	Nicole Simpson Ed.D.
YCCS-Addams HS	1814 S Union Ave	Chicago, IL	60616-1045	312-563-1746		9-12	Theresa Comparini
YCCS-Albizu Campos HS	2739 W Division St	Chicago, IL	60622-2854	773-342-8022	342-6609	10-12	Danette Sokacich
YCCS-Austin Career Education Center	5352 W Chicago Ave	Chicago, IL	60651-2857	773-626-6988	626-2641	10-12	Anne Gottlieb
YCCS-CCA Academy	1231 S Pulaski Rd	Chicago, IL	60623	773-762-2272	762-2065	10-12	Nahid Zahedi
YCCS-Chatham Academy	9035 S Langley Ave	Chicago, IL	60619	773-651-1500	651-1523	10-12	Lisa Williams
YCCS-Community Youth Development Inst	7836 S Union Ave	Chicago, IL	60620-2409	773-224-2273	224-2214	10-12	Keena Robinson
YCCS-El Cuarto Ano - Association House	1116 N Kedzie Ave	Chicago, IL	60651-4152	773-772-7170	772-8617	10-12	David Piper
YCCS-Harvey Middle College S	10001 S Woodlawn Ave	Chicago, IL	60628-1645	773-291-6518	291-6199	10-12	Mateo Trujillo
YCCS-Houston HS	7847 S Jeffery Blvd	Chicago, IL	60649	773-723-9630	723-9022	10-12	Dionne Kirksey
YCCS-Innovation HS	17 N State St Fl 3	Chicago, IL	60602	312-999-9360	999-9361	10-12	Melissa Cortirla
YCCS-Latino Youth HS	2001 S California Ave	Chicago, IL	60608-2486	773-648-2130	648-2098	10-12	Leticia Fernandez
YCCS-McKinley Lakeside HS	2920 S Wabash Ave	Chicago, IL	60616	312-949-5010	949-5015	10-12	Irma Plaxico
YCCS-Sullivan House Alternative HS	8164 S South Chicago Ave	Chicago, IL	60617-1041	773-978-8680	375-1482	10-12	Dr. Thomas Gattuso
YCCS-Truman Middle College HS	1145 W Wilson Ave	Chicago, IL	60640-6063	773-907-4840	907-4844	10-12	Michelle Yoo
YCCS Virtual HS	1900 W Van Buren St Rm 2417	Chicago, IL	60612	312-429-0027	243-5733	10-12	Mary Bradley
YCCS-Westside Holistic Leadership Acdmy	4909 W Division St	Chicago, IL	60651-3161	773-261-0994	261-1029	10-12	Daisy Lopez
YCCS-Youth Connection Leadership Acdmy	3424 S State St Fl 2	Chicago, IL	60616-5000	312-225-4668	225-4862	10-12	Keisha Davis-Johnson
Young Womens Leadership S	2641 S Calumet Ave	Chicago, IL	60616-2901	312-949-9400	949-9142	8-12	Dr. Vanesa Thompson
YouthBuild McLean County Charter S	360 Wylie Dr Ste 305	Normal, IL	61761	309-454-3898	454-3913	9-12	Suzanne Fitzgerald

Indiana

School	Address	City,State	Zip code	Telephone	Fax	Grade	Contact
ACE Prep Academy	5326 Hillside Ave	Indianapolis, IN	46220	317-744-9847	744-9836	K-5	Anna Shults
Anderson Preparatory Academy	101 W 29th St	Anderson, IN	46016-5209	765-649-8472		K-12	Jill Barker
Aspire Charter Academy	4900 W 15th Ave	Gary, IN	46406	219-944-7400	944-7474	K-8	Rasheeda Green
Avondale Meadows Academy	3980 Meadows Dr	Indianapolis, IN	46205-3114	317-803-3182	803-2367	K-5	Kelly Herron
Bloomington Project S	349 S Walnut St	Bloomington, IN	47401	812-558-0041	334-5873	K-8	Catherine Diersing
Bowman Leadership Academy	975 W 6th Ave	Gary, IN	46402-1708	219-883-4826	883-1331	K-12	Sarita Stevens
Brown Charter Academy	3600 N German Church Rd	Indianapolis, IN	46235-8504	317-891-0730	891-0908	K-8	James Hill
Campagna Academy Charter S	7403 Cline Ave	Schererville, IN	46375-2645	219-322-8614	322-8436	9-12	Elena Dwyre
Canaan Community Academy	8775 N Canaan Main St	Canaan, IN	47224	812-839-0003		K-6	Donna Taylor
Career Academy South Bend	3801 Crescent Cir	South Bend, IN	46628	574-299-9800	288-6125	7-12	Lydia Jagger
Carpe Diem - Meridian	2240 N Meridian St	Indianapolis, IN	46208-5728	317-921-7497	921-7299	6-12	Nathan Storm
Carpe Diem - Northwest	5435 W Pike Plaza Rd	Indianapolis, IN	46254	317-808-8749		6-12	Rosalie Pettigrew
Charter School of the Dunes	7300 Melton Rd	Gary, IN	46403	219-939-9690	939-9031	K-12	Constance Smith
Christel House Academy South	2717 S East St	Indianapolis, IN	46225-2104	317-783-4690	783-4693	K-12	Jenny Reynolds
Christel House Academy West	55 N Tibbs Ave	Indianapolis, IN	46222	317-783-4901	951-2182	K-4	Richard Hunt
Community Montessori S	4102 Saint Joseph Rd	New Albany, IN	47150-9750	812-948-1000	948-0441	PK-12	Barbara Burke-Fondren
Damar Charter Academy	5125 Decatur Blvd	Indianapolis, IN	46241-7511	317-455-2400	455-2447	K-12	Aimee Brown
Decatur Township S for Excellence	5106 S High School Rd	Indianapolis, IN	46221-3606	317-856-0900	856-0143	7-12	Tim VanWanzeele
Discovery Charter S	800 Canonie Dr	Chesterton, IN	46304	219-983-9800	929-5723	K-8	Ernesto Martinez
Donnan Elementary & MS	1202 E Troy Ave	Indianapolis, IN	46203	317-217-1979		K-8	Michael Dunagan
East Chicago Lighthouse Charter S	3916 Pulaski St	East Chicago, IN	46312	219-378-7450	378-9070	K-7	Jessica Beasley
East Chicago Urban Enterprise Academy	1402 E Chicago Ave	East Chicago, IN	46312-3587	219-392-3650	392-3652	K-8	Charlotte Jackson
Enlace Academy	3725 Kiel Ave	Indianapolis, IN	46224	317-383-0607	383-0605	K-6	Kevin Kubacki
Excel Center	630 Nichol Ave	Anderson, IN	46016-1247	317-524-3930	374-0047	9-12	Brandon Marks

School	Address	City,State	Zip code	Telephone	Fax	Grade	Contact
Excel Center	2855 N Franklin Rd	Indianapolis, IN	46219	317-524-3910	429-1015	9-12	Corey Emery
Excel Center	300 N 17 St	Noblesville, IN	46060	317-524-4410	565-5284	K-8	Dr. Steve Dillon
Excel Center	2721 Kenwood Ave	South Bend, IN	46628-1750	574-472-7330	472-7301	9-12	Randy Beachy
Excel Center	3919 Madison Ave	Indianapolis, IN	46227	317-524-4420	275-7879	K-8	Khalilah Palmer
Excel Center	1635 W Michigan St	Indianapolis, IN	46222	317-524-4141	524-4337	9-12	Greg Pryor
Excel Center	101 W Superior St	Kokomo, IN	46901-4658	317-524-3642	457-3367	9-12	Tom Pengelly
Excel Center	615 N 18th St	Lafayette, IN	47904-3413	317-524-3641	420-7916	9-12	Danielle White
Excel Center	1215 S J St	Richmond, IN	47374	317-524-3734	935-7511	9-12	Tyler Stewart
Faulkner Academy	1111 W 2nd St	Marion, IN	46952-3674	765-662-9910	662-9918	K-6	Janice Adams
Gary Lighthouse Charter S	3201 Pierce St	Gary, IN	46408-1100	219-880-1762	884-4858	K-7	Beverly Echols
Gary Middle College	131 E 5th Ave	Gary, IN	46402	219-888-7120	886-6646	9-12	Joseph Arredondo
Geist Montessori S	13942 E 96th St	Mc Cordsville, IN	46055-9811	317-335-1158	335-1265	K-8	Dr. Susan Fries
Global Preparatory Academy	2033 Sugar Grove Ave	Indianapolis, IN	46202	317-226-4244	226-3469	K-8	Mariama Carson
Hammond Academy of Science & Tech	33 Muenich Ct	Hammond, IN	46320-1706	219-852-0500	852-4153	6-12	Dr. Sean Egan
Heritage Institute of Arts & Technology	5681 Harrison St	Merrillville, IN	46410	888-843-4428		K-5	Shelley Fisher Ph.D.
Herron Charter HS	110 E 16th St	Indianapolis, IN	46202-2404	317-231-0010	231-3759	9-12	Janet McNeal
Hoosier Academy	2855 N Franklin Rd	Indianapolis, IN	46219	317-547-1400	547-1500	K-6	Dr. Byron Ernest
Hoosier Academy	2855 N Franklin Rd	Indianapolis, IN	46219	317-495-6494	454-0670	7-12	Christopher Chalker
Hope Academy	8102 Clearvista Pkwy	Indianapolis, IN	46256-1661	317-572-9356	849-1455	9-12	Linda Gagyi
Howe Community HS	4900 Julian Ave	Indianapolis, IN	46201-3755	317-693-1980		7-12	Tyler Small
Indiana College Preparatory S	4050 E 38th St	Indianapolis, IN	46218-1444	317-914-5868		K-8	Ashely Green
Indiana Connections Academy	6640 Intech Blvd Ste 250	Indianapolis, IN	46278	317-818-5590	818-6000	K-12	Melissa Brown
Indiana Math and Science Academy	4575 W 38th St	Indianapolis, IN	46254-3313	317-298-0025	282-0505	K-8	Murat Atlihan
Indiana Math and Science Academy North	7435 N Keystone Ave	Indianapolis, IN	46240-4377	317-259-7300	259-7363	K-12	Onder Secen
Indiana Math and Science Academy South	2710 Bethel Ave	Indianapolis, IN	46203-3103	317-780-1200	780-0400	K-8	Cathy Sparks
Indianapolis Academy of Excellence	1145 E 22nd St	Indianapolis, IN	46202	317-653-4009	653-4008	K-3	Tara Gustin
Indianapolis Lighthouse Charter S	1780 Sloan Ave	Indianapolis, IN	46203-3640	317-351-1534	351-1804	PK-12	Kim Randall
Indianapolis Lighthouse Charter S East	4002 N Franklin Rd	Indianapolis, IN	46226-5297	317-897-2472	897-0302	7-10	Steven Pelych
Indianapolis Metropolitan HS	1635 W Michigan St	Indianapolis, IN	46222-3852	317-524-4638	524-4114	9-12	Jonathan Gates
Indiana Virtual S	500 E 96th St Ste 400	Indianapolis, IN	46240	317-581-5355	581-5399	6-12	Dr. Percy Clark
Insight S of Indiana	2855 N Franklin Rd	Indianapolis, IN	46219	317-495-6494	454-0670	7-12	Kathy Coe
Inspire Academy - A S of Inquiry	2801 E 16th St	Muncie, IN	47302	765-216-7980	216-7798	PK-8	Leslie Draper
Irvington Community S	6705 Julian Ave	Indianapolis, IN	46219-6642	317-357-5359	357-9752	K-12	Tim Mulherin
Johnson Academy	4625 Werling Dr	Fort Wayne, IN	46806-3410	260-441-8727	441-9357	K-5	Dawn Starks
Joshua Academy	1230 E Illinois St	Evansville, IN	47711-5745	812-401-6300	401-6307	K-6	Pamela Decker
Kindezi Academy	3421 N Keystone Ave	Indianapolis, IN	46218-1133	317-226-4269	226-3338	K-6	Kris Walker Guess
Kindezi Academy	3421 N Keystone Ave	Indianapolis, IN	46218	317-226-4269		K-2	Kevin Kubacki
KIPP Indy College Prep MS	1740 E 30th St	Indianapolis, IN	46218	317-547-5477	547-5499	6-8	Nick Perry
KIPP Indy Unite ES	1740 E 30th St	Indianapolis, IN	46218	317-547-5477	547-5499	K-2	Ellen Reuter
Lighthouse College Preparatory Academy	725 Clark Rd	Gary, IN	46406-1822	219-977-9583	977-9725	8-12	Kaitlin Karpinski
Manual HS	2405 Madison Ave	Indianapolis, IN	46225-2106	317-217-1983	396-5399	9-12	Michael Stamper
Marion Academy	2107 N Riley Ave	Indianapolis, IN	46218-3925	317-983-1300	225-4174	6-12	LaToya Black
Marshall Leadership Academy	2310 Weisser Park Ave	Fort Wayne, IN	46803-3462	260-755-0193		K-8	Tameka Wilson
Mays Community Academy	929 E South St	Mays, IN	46155	765-645-5577	645-5230	K-8	Shannon New
Neighbors New Vistas HS	5201 US Highway 6	Portage, IN	46368	219-850-4448	850-4445	9-12	Anna Swope
New Community S	1904 Elmwood Ave	Lafayette, IN	47904-2224	765-420-9617	420-9672	K-8	Trudie Hedrick
Nexus Academy of Indianapolis	6101 N Keystone Ave Ste 302	Indianapolis, IN	46220-2493	317-252-5919	252-5917	9-12	Jamie Brady
Options Charter S	530 W Carmel Dr	Carmel, IN	46032	317-815-2098	846-3806	9-12	Camille Scott
Options Charter S Noblesville	9945 Cumberland Pointe Blvd	Noblesville, IN	46060	317-773-8659	773-9017	6-12	Jacob Brandau
Padua Academy	349 N Warman Ave	Indianapolis, IN	46222-4079	317-636-3739	636-3740	K-8	Cindy Greer
Paramount S of Excellence	3020 Nowland Ave	Indianapolis, IN	46201-1422	317-775-6660	423-0569	K-8	Scott Frye
Phalen @ Francis Scott Key S	3920 Baker Dr	Indianapolis, IN	46235-1619	317-226-4103	226-3730	PK-6	Agnes Ikhiobe Aleobua
Phalen Leadership Academy	2323 N Illinois St	Indianapolis, IN	46208	317-333-6980	924-8383	K-6	Kris Walker-Guess
Renaissance Academy	4093 W US Highway 20	La Porte, IN	46350-8269	219-878-8711	311-8321	PK-8	Kieran McHugh
Rock Creek Community Academy	11525 Highway 31	Sellersburg, IN	47172-9618	812-246-9271	246-0722	K-12	Sara Hauselman
Rural Community Academy	2385 N State Road 63	Sullivan, IN	47882-7152	812-382-4500	382-4055	K-8	Susie Pierce
Seven Oaks Classical S	200 E Association St	Ellettsville, IN	47429	812-935-5003		K-8	Dr. Stephen Shipp
Signature S	610 Main St	Evansville, IN	47708-1618	812-421-1820	421-9189	9-12	Jean Hitchcock
Smith Academy for Excellence	725 W Washington Blvd	Fort Wayne, IN	46802	260-579-6939	424-3846	4-12	Corey Smith
Southeast Neighborhood S of Excellence	1601 Barth Ave	Indianapolis, IN	46203-2743	317-423-0204	631-4401	K-8	Dr. Kristie Sweeney
Steel City Academy	2660 W 35th Ave	Gary, IN	46408			7-9	Christina Hart
Success Academy	3408 Ardmore Trl	South Bend, IN	46628-1302	574-288-5333		PK-4	Dean Fecher
Tindley Accelerated S	3960 Meadows Dr	Indianapolis, IN	46205-3114	317-545-1745	547-4415	9-12	Marcus Robinson
Tindley Collegiate Academy	4020 Meadows Pkwy	Indianapolis, IN	46205	317-777-7740	377-1435	6-8	Kelli Marshall
Tindley Genesis Academy	2540 N Capitol Ave	Indianapolis, IN	46208	317-777-6832	926-0673	K-4	Todd Hawks
Tindley Preparatory Academy	4010 N Sherman Dr	Indianapolis, IN	46226	317-777-6290	546-7224	6-8	Patrick Jones
Tindley Renaissance Academy	4020 Sherman Dr	Indianapolis, IN	46226	317-777-7290	377-1808	K-5	Edward Rangel
Tindley Summit Academy	4002 N Franklin Rd	Indianapolis, IN	46226	317-777-6830	534-3566	K-5	Kirshawndra Davis
21st Century Charter S	556 Washington St	Gary, IN	46402	219-886-9339	886-0869	PK-12	Anthony Cherry
Veritas Academy	530 E Ireland Rd	South Bend, IN	46614-2660	574-287-3230	287-2643	K-8	Germaine Smith
Vision Academy	1751 E Riverside Dr	Indianapolis, IN	46202	317-632-2006	662-3792	K-8	Ian Yearwood
Xavier S of Excellence	3423 S Michigan St	South Bend, IN	46614	574-231-6600	231-6640	K-8	Samantha Smith

Iowa

School	Address	City,State	Zip code	Telephone	Fax	Grade	Contact
Prescott ES	1151 White St	Dubuque, IA	52001-5005	563-552-4200	552-4201	PK-5	Vicki Sullivan
Vista Early College S	621 Tornado Dr	Storm Lake, IA	50588-2277	712-732-8065	732-8068	9-12	Beau Ruleaux
West Central Charter HS	PO Box 54	Maynard, IA	50655-0054	563-637-2283	637-2294	9-12	Stuart Fuhs

Kansas

School	Address	City,State	Zip code	Telephone	Fax	Grade	Contact
Abilene Virtual S	213 N Broadway St	Abilene, KS	67410-2648	785-263-2630		6-12	B. Roth
Caney Valley Charter Academy	601 E Bullpup Blvd	Caney, KS	67333-2543	620-879-9232	879-9232	10-12	Ron Oyler
Erie HS	1400 N Main St	Erie, KS	66733-5006	620-244-3287	244-3290	9-12	Noah Francis
Greeley County JSHS	400 W Lawrence St	Tribune, KS	67879-9636	620-376-4265	376-2465	6-12	Mark Lackey
Hope Street Charter Academy	1900 SW Hope St	Topeka, KS	66604-3984	785-438-4280	271-3684	9-12	Dale Noll
Hugoton Learning Academy	215 W 11th St	Hugoton, KS	67951	620-428-6374	428-6378	7-12	Jennifer Burrows
Insight S of Kansas	16740 W 175th St	Olathe, KS	66062-8984	800-260-0438	664-2796	K-12	Cassandra Barton
Kinsley-Offerle JSHS	716 Colony Ave	Kinsley, KS	67547-1155	620-659-2126	659-2180	7-12	William King
Lawrence Virtual HS	1104 E 1000 Rd	Lawrence, KS	66047-9409	785-832-5620	832-5621	9-12	Keith Wilson
Lawrence Virtual S	1104 E 1000 Rd	Lawrence, KS	66047-9409	785-832-5620	832-5621	K-8	Keith Wilson
Service Valley Charter Academy	PO Box 129	Oswego, KS	67356-0129	620-421-3449	421-3640	K-8	Ray Huff
Smoky Valley Virtual Charter S	121 S Main St	Lindsborg, KS	67456	785-227-4292	227-3610	K-12	Glen Suppes
21st Century Learning Academy	730 S Main St	Greensburg, KS	67054	620-548-2289	548-2389	6-12	Brian Deterding
Walton Rural Life ES	PO Box 140	Walton, KS	67151-0140	620-837-3161	837-5669	K-4	Jason Chalashtari
West Franklin Learning Center	PO Box 407	Williamsburg, KS	66095-0407	785-746-5766		9-12	Braden Anshutz
Yoder Charter S	PO Box 78	Yoder, KS	67585-0078	620-465-2605	465-2307	K-8	Delon Martens

Louisiana

School	Address	City,State	Zip code	Telephone	Fax	Grade	Contact
Acadiana Renaissance Charter Academy	600 Savoy Rd	Youngsville, LA	70592-6384	337-374-1209	374-1210	K-7	Christine Stoudt
Advantage Charter Academy	14740 Plank Rd	Baker, LA	70714-4403	225-774-3111	208-1962	K-6	Dr. Clifford Wallace
Akili Academy of New Orleans	3811 N Galvez St	New Orleans, LA	70117-5503	504-355-4172	355-4176	K-8	Allison Lowe
Algiers Technology Academy	6501 Berkley Dr	New Orleans, LA	70131-5513	504-302-7071	324-6998	9-12	Nia Mitchell
ARISE Academy	3819 Saint Claude Ave	New Orleans, LA	70117-5735	504-615-6354	456-2087	PK-8	Krista Brown
Ashe Charter S	1456 Gardena Dr	New Orleans, LA	70122-1914	504-373-6267	896-4003	K-8	Ryan Bennett
Audubon Charter S	428 Broadway St	New Orleans, LA	70118-3514	504-324-7100	866-1691	PK-3	Latoye Brown
Audubon Charter S	1111 Milan St	New Orleans, LA	70115-2760	504-324-7110	866-1691	4-8	Latoye Brown
Avoyelles Charter S	201 Longfellow Rd	Mansura, LA	71350-4292	318-240-9991	253-4198	K-12	Julie Roy
Baton Rouge Charter Academy at Mid-City	1900 Lobdell Blvd	Baton Rouge, LA	70806-1725	225-663-1057	610-1831	K-8	Tale Lockett
Baton Rouge College Prep Charter S	5300 Monarch Ave Bldg 8	Baton Rouge, LA	70811-5628	225-257-9180		5-12	Kathryn Rice
Baton Rouge University Prep ES	5300 Monarch Ave	Baton Rouge, LA	70811-5628	225-364-9805		K-1	Meghan Turner
Bayou Community Academy	800 E 7th St	Thibodaux, LA	70301-3607	985-446-3011		PK-8	Dr. Melanie Becnel
Beekman Charter S	15190 A M Baker Rd	Bastrop, LA	71220-6408	318-281-1743	283-5100	PK-12	Roy McCoy
Behrman S	715 Opelousas Ave	New Orleans, LA	70114-2449	504-302-7090	309-8042	PK-8	Rene Lewis-Carter
Belle Chasse Academy	100 5th St	Belle Chasse, LA	70037-1002	504-433-5850	433-5590	K-8	Jane Dye
Bricolage Academy	3368 Esplanade Ave	New Orleans, LA	70119-3132	504-539-4505		K-3	Josh Densen
Brown ES	300 RWE Jones St	Grambling, LA	71245-2135	318-274-3118	274-3824	K-5	Rosalind Russell
Capdau Charter S	4621 Canal St	New Orleans, LA	70119-5807	504-872-9257	280-2312	PK-8	Rulonda Green
Capitol HS	1000 N 23rd St	Baton Rouge, LA	70802-3398	225-239-7506	227-2420	9-12	Paul Jackson
Carver Collegiate Academy	3059 Higgins Rd	New Orleans, LA	70126	504-308-3660	754-7980	9-12	Jerel Bryant
Carver Preparatory Academy	5552 Read Blvd	New Orleans, LA	70127	504-308-3660	754-7980	9-12	Benjamin Davis
Celerity Crestworth Charter S	10650 Avenue F	Baton Rouge, LA	70807-2501	225-308-3274	341-6779	6-8	Kimberly Boudreaux
Celerity Dalton Charter S	3605 Ontario St	Baton Rouge, LA	70805	225-357-0244	341-6779	PK-5	Arneisha Brisco
Celerity Lanier Charter S	4705 Lanier Dr	Baton Rouge, LA	70812-4020	225-308-3273	341-6679	PK-5	Alicia Franklin
Children's Charter S	1143 North St	Baton Rouge, LA	70802-4547	225-387-9273	387-9272	PK-5	Eddie Greenup
Clark Leadership Academy	1517 Statesman Rd	Opelousas, LA	70570-2836	337-418-4222	942-4273	5-12	Tiffanie Lewis
Clark Prep HS	1301 N Derbigny St	New Orleans, LA	70116-2213	504-373-6202	827-4538	9-12	Reginald Coleman

School	Address	City,State	Zip code	Telephone	Fax	Grade	Contact
Coghill Accelerated Academy	4617 Mirabeau Ave	New Orleans, LA	70126-3540	504-373-6237	308-3661	PK-8	Aisha Jones
Cohen College Prep MSHS	3520 Dryades St	New Orleans, LA	70115-5331	504-335-0400	617-7200	6-12	Rahel Wondwossen
Community S for Apprenticeship Learning	1555 Madison Ave	Baton Rouge, LA	70802-3460	225-336-1410	336-1414	6-8	LaMont Cole
Craig Charter S	1423 Saint Philip St	New Orleans, LA	70116-2933	504-940-2115		PK-8	Ann Ford
Crescent Leadership Academy	2701 Lawrence St	New Orleans, LA	70114-3013	504-702-5790	702-5791	7-12	Nick Dean
Crocker College Prep	2301 Marengo St	New Orleans, LA	70115-6253	504-335-0404	285-9980	PK-8	Amanda Aiken
Cypress Academy	4238 Saint Charles Ave	New Orleans, LA	70115-4740	504-383-3337		K-2	Bob Berk
D'Arbonne Woods Charter S	9560 Highway 33	Farmerville, LA	71241	318-368-8051	368-8053	K-12	Pam Schooler
Delhi Charter S	6940 Highway 17	Delhi, LA	71232-7021	318-878-0433	878-0434	K-12	Brett Raley
Delta Charter S	300 Lynwood Dr	Ferriday, LA	71334-2038	318-757-3202	757-6497	K-12	William Givens
Democracy Prep Baton Rouge	4055 Prescott Rd	Baton Rouge, LA	70805-5146	225-372-2037	389-6587	K-1	Michelle Gieg
Downsville Charter S	PO Box 8	Downsville, LA	71234-0008	318-982-5318	982-5737	PK-12	Tony Cane
Easton Charter HS	3019 Canal St	New Orleans, LA	70119-6305	504-324-7400	324-7946	9-12	Alexina Medley
Einstein Charter MSHS @Sarah Towles Reed	5316 Michoud Blvd	New Orleans, LA	70129-1435	504-503-0470		6-12	Tiffany Cherrie
Einstein Charter S @ Village de l'Est	5100 Cannes St	New Orleans, LA	70129-1203	504-324-7450	254-4121	PK-5	Sabrina Marsh
Einstein Charter S Sherwood Forest	4801 Maid Marion	New Orleans, LA	70128	504-503-0110		PK-5	Shimon Ancker
Eisenhower ES	3700 Tall Pines Dr	New Orleans, LA	70131-8499	504-302-7109	398-7129	PK-5	Ronicka Briscoe
Encore Academy	4217 Orleans Ave	New Orleans, LA	70119-4605	504-444-2224		PK-8	Terri Smith
Esperanza Charter S	4407 S Carrollton Ave	New Orleans, LA	70119-6823	504-373-6272	488-1813	K-8	Nicole Saulny
Excellence Academy Charter S for Arts	811 Washington St	Monroe, LA	71201	318-350-6855	410-1625	6-8	Christina Gremillion
Fischer Academy	1801 L B Landry Ave	New Orleans, LA	70114-6166	504-302-7111	363-1016	PK-8	Dahme Bolden
Foundation Prep Charter S	7301 Dwyer Rd	New Orleans, LA	70126	504-434-0521		K-6	Myrialis King
Franklin HS	2001 Leon C Simon Dr	New Orleans, LA	70122-3524	504-286-2600	286-2642	9-12	Dr. Pat Widhalm
Gentilly Terrace S	4720 Painters St	New Orleans, LA	70122-5099	504-708-2053	284-5847	PK-8	Edward Brown
GEO Prep Academy of Greater Baton Rouge	4006 Platt Dr	Baton Rouge, LA	70814-4216	225-337-7636	337-0000	K-3	
Glencoe Charter S	4491 Highway 83	Franklin, LA	70538-7500	337-923-6900	923-0982	K-8	Michael Parrie
Grambling State University Lab. HS	407 Central Ave	Grambling, LA	71245-3001	318-274-6153	274-3215	9-12	Sandra Boston
Grambling State University Lab. MS	407 Central Ave	Grambling, LA	71245-3001	318-274-6531	274-3360	6-8	Dr. Pamela Payne
Green Charter S	2319 Valence St	New Orleans, LA	70115-5959	504-304-3532	896-4147	K-8	Ava Lee
Habans Charter ES	3501 Seine St	New Orleans, LA	70114	504-941-1810		PK-8	Kate Mehok
Harney Spirit of Excellence Acad	2503 Willow St	New Orleans, LA	70113-3234	504-373-6230	891-6919	PK-8	Eileen Williams
Harte Charter S	5300 Berkley Dr	New Orleans, LA	70131-7204	504-373-6281	304-1817	K-8	Jamar McKneely
Haynes Charter ES	8600 Elmgrove Garden Dr	Baton Rouge, LA	70807-4712	225-774-1311	774-1323	PK-5	Diana Haynes
Hughes Academy	3519 Trafalgar St	New Orleans, LA	70119-2041	504-373-6251	267-9760	PK-8	Stefan Lallinger
Hynes Charter S	990 Harrison Ave	New Orleans, LA	70124-3833	504-324-7160	488-0213	PK-8	Michelle Douglas
Iberville Charter Academy	24360 Enterprise Blvd	Plaquemine, LA	70764	225-238-7346	238-7347	K-8	D'Lacie Monk
Impact Charter ES	4815 Lavey Ln	Baker, LA	70714-4745	225-308-9565	308-4239	K-5	
Inspire Charter Academy	5454 N Foster Dr	Baton Rouge, LA	70805-3031	225-356-3936		K-8	Lorna Davis
International HS	727 Carondelet St	New Orleans, LA	70130-3705	504-613-5703	566-1142	9-12	Sean Wilson
International S of Louisiana	1400 Camp St	New Orleans, LA	70130-4208	504-654-1088	654-1086	K-8	Melanie Tennyson
International S of Louisiana	8101 Simon St	Metairie, LA	70003-6427	504-934-4875	754-7875	K-8	Melanie Tennyson
Jeff Community S	PO Box 19227	New Orleans, LA	70179-0227	504-373-6258	308-3620	PK-8	Patricia Perkins
Jefferson Chamber Foundation Acad-East	3410 Jefferson Hwy	Jefferson, LA	70121-2630	504-410-3280		8-12	Casey Champion
Jefferson Chamber Foundation Academy	475 Manhattan Blvd	Harvey, LA	70058-4441	504-410-3121	410-3120	9-12	Millie Harris
Jefferson RISE Charter S	501B Lapalco Blvd	Gretna, LA	70056	504-410-5905		6-6	Kathleen Sullivan
Karr Charter HS	3332 Huntlee Dr	New Orleans, LA	70131-7046	504-302-7135	301-2721	9-12	Harold Clay
Kenilworth Science & Technology Charter	7600 Boone Ave	Baton Rouge, LA	70808-6716	225-766-8111	767-9061	6-8	Hasan Suzuk
Kenner Discovery Health Sciences Academy	2504 Maine Ave	Metairie, LA	70003-5445	504-233-4720		PK-8	Patty Glaser Ph.D.
King Charter S for Science & Tech	1617 Caffin Ave	New Orleans, LA	70117-2909	504-940-2243	940-2276	PK-12	Dr. Doris Hicks Ed.D.
KIPP Believe College Prep S	9330 Forshey St	New Orleans, LA	70118-1836	504-304-8857	304-8862	5-8	Luke Naegele
KIPP Believe PS	421 Burdette St	New Orleans, LA	70118-3819	504-266-2050	264-9363	K-4	Sarah Beth Greenberg
KIPP Central City Academy	2514 3rd St	New Orleans, LA	70113-2633	504-609-2283	708-5334	5-8	Alex Jarrell
KIPP Central City PS	2625 Thalia St	New Orleans, LA	70113-2843	504-373-6290	302-9737	K-4	Korbin Johnson
KIPP East Community PS	5500 Piety Dr	New Orleans, LA	70126-2308	504-301-2964		K-4	Jennifer Carey
KIPP Leadership Academy	2300 Saint Claude Ave	New Orleans, LA	70117-8307	504-373-6256	322-3924	K-8	Herneshia Dukes
KIPP McDonogh 15 MS	5500 Piety Dr	New Orleans, LA	70126-2308	504-609-2280	264-5598	5-8	Deanna Reddick
KIPP McDonogh 15 PS	721 Saint Philip St	New Orleans, LA	70116-2713	504-592-8520	592-8515	PK-4	Mark Burton
KIPP Renaissance HS	3820 Saint Claude Ave	New Orleans, LA	70117-5736	504-373-6255	322-3924	9-12	Joey LaRoche
Lafayette Academy	2727 S Carrollton Ave	New Orleans, LA	70118-4338	504-861-8370	861-8369	PK-8	Monica Boudouin
Lafayette Renaissance Charter Academy	205 Vienne Ln	Lafayette, LA	70507-3251	337-706-0066	706-0068	K-7	Erin Gray
Lake Area New Tech Early College HS	6026 Paris Ave	New Orleans, LA	70122-2726	504-267-8811	267-8833	9-12	Darren Lewis
Lake Charles Charter Academy	3160 Power Center Pkwy	Lake Charles, LA	70607	337-475-7900	475-7901	K-8	Dr. Pamela Quebodeaux
Lake Charles College Prep S	2750 Power Center Pkwy	Lake Charles, LA	70607	337-419-2868	419-2867	9-10	Lorette Bass
Lake Forest Charter ES	11110 Lake Forest Blvd	New Orleans, LA	70128	504-826-7140	248-7020	PK-8	Mardele Early
Landry - O.P. Walker HS	1200 L B Landry Ave	New Orleans, LA	70114-2657	504-302-7170	302-7229	9-12	Mary Laurie
Laureate Academy Charter S	3400 6th St	Harvey, LA	70058-2710	504-503-0170		K-1	Claire Heckerman
Linwood Public Charter S	401 W 70th St	Shreveport, LA	71106-3034	318-865-4800	865-0542	6-8	Vickie Carroll
Louisiana Connections Academy	4664 Jamestown Ave	Baton Rouge, LA	70808-3218	225-372-8389	448-2798	K-12	Glenda Jones
Louisiana Key Academy	3172 Government St	Baton Rouge, LA	70806-5624	225-298-1223		1-3	Evelyn Gauthreaux
Louisiana S for Agricultural Sciences	5303 Highway 115	Bunkie, LA	71322-4301	318-346-8029	346-4479	7-12	Dexter Compton
Louisiana Virtual Charter Academy	4962 Florida Blvd	Baton Rouge, LA	70806-4031	877-490-3596		K-12	
Lusher Charter Lower S	7315 Willow St	New Orleans, LA	70118-5232	504-862-5110	866-4292	K-5	Kathleen Riedlinger
Lusher Charter MSHS	5624 Freret St	New Orleans, LA	70115-6547	504-304-3960	861-1839	6-12	Kathleen Riedlinger
Lycee Francais de la Nouvelle Orleans	5951 Patton St	New Orleans, LA	70115-3232	504-620-5500	875-2441	K-6	Keith Bartlett
Madison Preparatory Academy	1555 Madison Ave	Baton Rouge, LA	70802-3460	225-636-5865	336-1414	9-12	Alisa Welsh
MAX Charter S	PO Box 2072	Thibodaux, LA	70310-0001	985-227-9500	227-9515	1-8	Linda Musson Ed.D.
McDonogh 32 S	800 De Armas St	New Orleans, LA	70114-4414	504-302-7144	363-1058	PK-8	Danielle Williams-Woods
McDonogh 42 S	1651 N Tonti St	New Orleans, LA	70119-2540	504-942-3660	942-0731	PK-8	Leslie Williams
Mentorship Academy	339 Florida St	Baton Rouge, LA	70801-1721	225-346-5180		9-12	Robert Webb
Milestone Academy	3774 Gentilly Blvd	New Orleans, LA	70122-6128	504-894-0557	894-0235	K-8	
Moton Charter S	6800 Chef Menteur Hwy	New Orleans, LA	70126	504-245-4400	248-7300	PK-7	Paulette Bruno
Nelson Charter S	3121 Saint Bernard Ave	New Orleans, LA	70119-1916	504-943-1311	304-5160	PK-8	Dr. Chancey Nash Ed.D.
NET Charter HS	1614 Oretha Castle Haley Bl	New Orleans, LA	70113-1311	504-267-9060	267-9059	9-12	Elizabeth Ostberg
New Orleans Charter Science and Math HS	5625 Loyola Ave	New Orleans, LA	70115-5014	504-324-7061	309-4178	9-12	Chana Benenson
New Orleans Military & Maritime Academy	425 OBannon St	New Orleans, LA	70114-1571	504-227-3810	875-4326	9-12	Cecilia Garcia
New Vision Learning Academy	507 Swayze St	Monroe, LA	71201-8130	318-338-9995	338-9987	PK-12	
Northshore Charter S	111 Walker St	Bogalusa, LA	70427-1943	985-732-0005	732-0580	K-12	Marc Merriman
Osborne ES	6701 Curran Blvd	New Orleans, LA	70126-1719	504-400-0614	708-4556	PK-8	Rachel Wong
Plessy Community S	2021 Pauger St	New Orleans, LA	70116	504-503-0055	503-0056	PK-5	Joan Reilly
ReNEW Aaron ES	10200 Curran Blvd	New Orleans, LA	70127-1304	504-367-3307	644-4183	PK-8	Heather Harris
ReNEW Accelerated HS	3649 Laurel St	New Orleans, LA	70115-2549	504-367-3307		9-12	Vasy McCoy
ReNEW Cultural Arts Academy	3128 Constance St	New Orleans, LA	70115-2337	504-324-4207	267-4741	PK-8	Ron Gubitz
ReNEW McDonogh City Park Academy	2733 Esplanade Ave	New Orleans, LA	70119-3332	504-940-1740	940-1780	K-8	Keevis Louis
ReNEW Schaumburg ES	9501 Grant St	New Orleans, LA	70127-4256	504-304-1532	304-1390	PK-8	Laci Blondell
ReNEW SciTech Academy	820 Jackson Ave	New Orleans, LA	70130-4940	504-267-4574	267-0572	PK-8	Disha Jain
Sci Academy	5552 Read Blvd	New Orleans, LA	70127-3143	504-373-6264	324-0171	9-12	Rhonda Dale-Hart
Singleton Charter S	2220 Oretha C Haley Blvd	New Orleans, LA	70113	504-568-3466	569-3378	PK-8	Debra Robertson
Slaughter Community Charter S	2944 Highway 412 W	Slaughter, LA	70777-3232	225-570-8682	570-8694	7-12	Dr. Linda Saucier
South Baton Rouge Charter Academy	9211 Parkway Dr	Baton Rouge, LA	70810-7020	225-349-7489	349-7490	PK-5	Monique Smith
Southwest Louisiana Charter Academy	1700 E McNeese St	Lake Charles, LA	70607-4824	337-475-7910	475-7911	K-8	Dr. LaTonia Harris
Success Preparatory Academy	2011 Bienville St	New Orleans, LA	70112-3313	504-909-6275	571-6317	K-8	Niloy Gangopadhyay
Tallulah Charter S	1206 N Cedar St	Tallulah, LA	71282-2710	318-574-0029	574-0073	PK-5	Keith Wolfe
Tangi Academy Charter S	118 N Richardson St	Hammond, LA	70403	985-269-7695		K-6	
Thrive Baton Rouge	1120 Government St	Baton Rouge, LA	70802-4802	225-239-7820	771-8559	6-12	
Tubman ES	2832 General Meyer Ave	New Orleans, LA	70114-3012	504-227-3800	227-3801	PK-8	Julie Lause
Virtual Academy of Lafourche	639 Harrison St	Thibodaux, LA	70301-2739	985-446-2877	446-2993	K-12	Julie Bourgeois
Vision Academy	4108 Harvey St	Monroe, LA	71203-5746	318-651-3984		9-12	
Wheatley Community S	2300 Dumaine St	New Orleans, LA	70119-3512	504-373-6205	488-4091	PK-8	Diana Archuleta
Williams ES	11755 Dwyer Rd	New Orleans, LA	70128-3454	504-373-6288	245-2796	PK-8	Kelly Batiste
Williams ES	3127 Martin Luther King Jr	New Orleans, LA	70125-3328	504-522-0100	910-1045	K-8	Krystal Hardy
Willow Charter Academy	1818 NE Evangeline Thruway	Lafayette, LA	70501	337-534-8218	205-6195	K-6	Karmen Kynard
Wilson Charter S	3617 General Pershing St	New Orleans, LA	70125-4530	504-373-6274	308-3615	PK-8	Lee Green
Wright Charter S	1426 Napoleon Ave	New Orleans, LA	70115-3958	504-304-3916	896-4095	6-12	Sharon Clark
Young Audiences Charter S	1407 Virgil St	Gretna, LA	70053	504-304-6332	267-4667	PK-6	Brandon House
Maine							
Baxter Academy for Technology & Science	54 York St	Portland, ME	04101-4569	207-699-5500	331-4831	9-12	Michele LaForge
Cornville Regional Charter S	1192 W Ridge Rd	Cornville, ME	04976-6214	207-474-8503	474-8515	K-8	Travis Works
Fiddlehead S of Arts & Sciences	25 Shaker Rd	Gray, ME	04039-9435	207-657-2244		PK-4	Jacinda Cotton-Castro
Harpswell Coastal Academy	29 Burbank Rd	Brunswick, ME	04011	207-833-3229	833-3231	6-12	John D'Anieri
Maine Academy of Natural Sciences	PO Box 159	Hinckley, ME	04944-0159	207-238-4100	238-4107	9-12	Tonya Arnold
Maine Connections Academy	75 John Roberts Rd Ste 11B	South Portland, ME	04106	207-805-3254	541-3990	7-12	Douglas Bourget
Maine Virtual Academy	6 E Chestnut St	Augusta, ME	04330-5758	207-613-8900		7-12	Dr. Melinda Browne
Snow Pond Arts Academy	8 Goldenrod Ln	Sidney, ME	04330	844-476-6976		9-10	
Maryland							

School	Address	City,State	Zip code	Telephone	Fax	Grade	Contact
AFYA Charter MS	2800 Brendan Ave	Baltimore, MD	21213-1213	410-485-2102		6-8	Katie Marts
Baltimore Collegiate S for Boys	1101 Winston Ave	Baltimore, MD	21212	443-642-5320		4-7	John Snowdy
Baltimore International Academy	4410 Frankford Ave	Baltimore, MD	21206-5133	410-426-3650	426-3651	K-8	John Enkiri
Baltimore Leadership S for Young Women	128 W Franklin St	Baltimore, MD	21201-4504	443-642-2048	338-2684	6-12	Chevonne Hall
Baltimore Montessori Charter S	1600 Guilford Ave	Baltimore, MD	21202-2823	410-528-5393	528-8126	PK-8	Allison Shecter
Banneker Blake Academy Arts & Sciences	PO Box 11311	Baltimore, MD	21239	443-642-5420		6-8	Luis Espinoza
Carroll Creek Montessori Charter S	7215 Corporate Ct	Frederick, MD	21703-8488	301-663-7970	663-6107	PK-5	Marilyn Horan
Chesapeake Charter S	20945 Great Mills Rd	Lexington Park, MD	20653-4370	301-863-9585	863-9586	K-8	Angela Funya
Chesapeake Math & IT Academy North	6100 Frost Pl	Laurel, MD	20707	301-350-6051	560-3461	6-12	Mehmet Gunes
Chesapeake Math & IT Academy South	9822 Fallard Ct	Upper Marlboro, MD	20772	240-573-7250	823-9326	6-9	Ali Gurbuz
Chesapeake Math & IT ES	6151 Chevy Chase Dr	Laurel, MD	20707	240-573-7240	776-2322	K-5	N. Riley
Chesapeake Science Point Charter S	7321 Parkway Dr	Hanover, MD	21076	410-757-5277	757-5280	6-12	Erkan Derin
City Neighbors Charter S	4301 Raspe Ave	Baltimore, MD	21206-1913	410-325-2627	325-2489	K-8	Nicholas Brown
City Neighbors Hamilton S	5609 Sefton Ave	Baltimore, MD	21214-2300	443-642-2052	426-0190	K-8	Obidimma Okobi
City Neighbors HS	5609 Sefton Ave	Baltimore, MD	21214	443-642-2119		9-12	Cheyanne Zahrt
City Springs ES	100 S Caroline St	Baltimore, MD	21231-1798	410-396-9165	396-9113	PK-8	Rhonda Richetta
College Park Academy	7501 Adelphi Rd	Hyattsville, MD	20783	240-696-3206	422-0510	6-10	Bernadette Brewster
ConneXions: A Community Based Arts S	2801 N Dukeland St	Baltimore, MD	21216	410-984-1418	669-4418	6-12	Kia Harper
Coppin Academy	2500 W North Ave	Baltimore, MD	21216-3633	410-951-2602	951-2610	9-12	Aisha Almond
Creative City Charter S	2810 Shirley Ave	Baltimore, MD	21215	443-642-3600		K-5	Traci Mathena
Crossroads S	802 S Caroline St	Baltimore, MD	21231	410-276-4924		6-8	Matthew Ebert
Empowerment Academy	851 Braddish Ave	Baltimore, MD	21216-4723	443-984-2381	362-2454	PK-8	Marie Parfait-Davis
Excel Academy	7910 Scott Rd	Landover, MD	20785	301-925-2320		K-8	Diane Kanu
Frederick Classical Charter S	8455 Spires Way Ste CC	Frederick, MD	21701	240-236-1200		K-7	Erica Cummins
Govans ES	5801 York Rd	Baltimore, MD	21212-3616	410-396-6396	547-7840	PK-5	Linda Taylor
Green S	2851 Kentucky Ave	Baltimore, MD	21213-1215	410-488-5312	488-5314	K-5	Kate Primm
Green Street Academy	125 N Hilton St	Baltimore, MD	21229	443-642-2068		6-12	Crystal Harden-Lindsey
Hampstead Hill Academy	500 S Linwood Ave	Baltimore, MD	21224-3856	410-396-9146	396-3637	PK-8	Matthew Hornbeck
Imagine Andrews Charter S	4701 San Antonio Blvd	Andrews AFB, MD	20762	301-350-6002	599-5620	K-8	H. Douglas Rice
Imagine - Foundations at Leeland	14111 Oak Grove Rd	Upper Marlboro, MD	20774-8424	301-383-1899	218-1454	K-8	Lance Pace
Imagine Foundations at Morningside	6900 Ames St	Morningside, MD	20746-3504	301-817-0544	817-0956	K-7	Douglas Gaither
Imagine - Lincoln Public Charter S	4207 Norcross St	Temple Hills, MD	20748	301-808-5600	808-5611	K-8	Dallas Lee
Independence S Local I HS	2801 N Dukeland St	Baltimore, MD	21226	443-642-2504	467-1091	9-12	Dimitric Roseboro
Jackson Charter S	900 Woodbourne Ave	Baltimore, MD	21212	443-320-9499	320-9036	5-8	Damia Thomas
KIPP Harmony Academy	4701 Greenspring Ave	Baltimore, MD	21209	443-642-2027		K-8	Natalia Walter
Midtown Academy	1398 W Mount Royal Ave	Baltimore, MD	21217-4134	410-225-3257	225-3514	K-8	Suzanne Penny
Monarch Academy	2525 Kirk Ave	Baltimore, MD	21218	443-642-2402	254-0201	K-8	Cera Rebello
Monarch Academy Charter S	6730 Baymeadow Dr	Glen Burnie, MD	21060-6412	410-760-2072	760-1321	K-8	Maurine Larkin
Monarch Global Academy Contract S	430 Brock Bridge Rd	Laurel, MD	20724-2472	301-886-8648		K-8	Donna O'Shea
Monocacy Valley Montessori S	217 Dill Ave	Frederick, MD	21701-4905	301-668-5013	668-5015	K-8	Nancy Radkiewicz
Northwood Appold Community Academy	4417 Loch Raven Blvd	Baltimore, MD	21218-1554	410-323-9546	323-1836	K-5	Kim Felton
Patterson Park Charter S	27 N Lakewood Ave	Baltimore, MD	21224-1155	410-558-1230	558-1003	PK-8	Dr. Charles Kramer
Roots and Branches S	1807 Harlem Ave	Baltimore, MD	21217	443-642-2320		K-5	Anne Rossi
Rosemont ES	2777 Presstman St	Baltimore, MD	21216-4025	410-396-0574	545-3298	PK-8	Dwayne Wheeler
Southwest Baltimore Charter S	1300 Herkimer St	Baltimore, MD	21223	443-984-3385	244-0410	K-8	Iffeisha Gordon-Toppin
Templeton Preparatory Academy	1200 Pennsylvania Ave	Baltimore, MD	21217-3045	410-396-0882		PK-5	Evelyn Perry
Tunbridge ES	5504 York Rd	Baltimore, MD	21212	410-323-8692		PK-8	Sheila Adams
Turning Point Academy	7800 Good Luck Rd	Lanham Seabrook, MD	20706-3505	301-552-0164	552-7307	K-8	Rhonda Clomax
Wolfe Street Academy	245 S Wolfe St	Baltimore, MD	21231-2622	410-396-9140	396-8064	PK-5	Mark Gaither
Massachusetts							
Academy of Pacific Rim Charter S	1 Westinghouse Plz	Hyde Park, MA	02136-2077	617-361-0050	361-0045	5-12	Spencer Blasdale
Advanced Math & Science Academy	201 Forest St	Marlborough, MA	01752-3012	508-597-2400	597-2499	6-12	Erin O'Connor
Alma del Mar Charter S	26 Madeira Ave	New Bedford, MA	02746	774-206-6827	206-6833	K-8	Emily Stainer
Amesbury: Amesbury Innovation HS	71 Friend St	Amesbury, MA	01913-2723	978-388-8037	388-8073	9-12	Eryn Maguire
Argosy Collegiate Charter S	263 Hamlet St	Fall River, MA	02724-3342	508-567-4725		6-8	Kristen Pavao
Atlantis Charter S	37 Park St	Fall River, MA	02721-1712	508-672-3537	672-2474	K-12	Robert Beatty
Banneker Charter Public S	21 Notre Dame Ave	Cambridge, MA	02140-2505	617-497-7771	497-4223	PK-6	Sherley Bretous-Carre
Barnstable Comm Horace Mann Charter S	165 Bearses Way	Hyannis, MA	02601	508-790-6485	790-6432	K-3	Dr. Sheila Kukstis
Baystate Academy	2001 Roosevelt Ave	Springfield, MA	01104-1657	413-366-5100	366-5101	6-12	Tim Sneed
Bentley Academy Charter S	25 Memorial Dr	Salem, MA	01970-5651	978-740-1260	740-1164	K-5	Marlena Afonso
Berkshire Arts & Technology Charter S	PO Box 267	Adams, MA	01220-0267	413-743-7311	743-7327	6-12	April West
Boston Collegiate Charter S	11 Mayhew St	Dorchester, MA	02125-1628	617-265-1172	265-1176	5-12	Sarah Morland
Boston Day & Evening Academy	20 Kearsarge Ave	Roxbury, MA	02119-2318	617-635-6789	635-6380	9-12	Alison Hramiec
Boston Green Academy	20 Warren St	Brighton, MA	02135-3602	617-635-9860	635-9858	9-12	Matthew Holzer
Boston Preparatory Charter S	1286 Hyde Park Ave	Hyde Park, MA	02136-2714	617-333-6688	333-6689	6-12	Sharon Liszanckie
Boston Renaissance Charter S	1415 Hyde Park Ave	Hyde Park, MA	02136	617-357-0900	357-0949	K-6	Alexandra Buckmire
Bridge Boston Charter S	2 McLellan St	Dorchester, MA	02121-4011	857-229-1601	674-0861	PK-5	Jennifer Daly
Brooke East Boston Charter S	94 Horace St	East Boston, MA	02128	617-409-5150	567-5295	K-8	Molly Cole
Brooke Mattapan Charter S	150 American Legion Hwy	Dorchester, MA	02124	617-268-1006	474-4612	K-8	Abby Waldman
Brooke Roslindale Charter S	190 Cummins Hwy	Roslindale, MA	02131-3722	617-325-7977	325-2260	K-8	Meghan Parquette
Cape Cod Lighthouse Charter S	195 Route 137	Harwich, MA	02645-1320	774-408-7994	237-9041	6-8	Paul Niles
City on a Hill Charter S	58 Circuit St	Roxbury, MA	02119-1925	617-445-1515	445-9153	9-12	Cristin Berry
City on a Hill Charter S	384 Acushnet Ave	New Bedford, MA	02740-6238	508-985-6400	985-6422	9-12	Kimberly Wall
City on a Hill Charter S	2181 Washington St	Roxbury, MA	02119	617-516-5888	533-9421	9-12	Sonya Pratt
Codman Academy	637 Washington St	Dorchester, MA	02124-3510	617-287-0700	287-9064	K-12	Thabiti Brown
Collegiate Charter S of Lowell	1857 Middlesex St	Lowell, MA	01851	978-458-1399	458-1366	K-6	Frederick Randall
Community Charter S of Cambridge	245 Bent St	Cambridge, MA	02141-2001	617-354-0047	354-3624	6-12	Caleb Hurst-Hiller
Community Day Arlington ES	150 Arlington St	Lawrence, MA	01841	978-722-8311	722-8514	K-4	Ryan Werb
Community Day Charter S	190 Hampshire St	Lawrence, MA	01840-1251	978-722-2583	682-1013	PK-8	Mary Chance
Community Day Charter S Gateway	9 Ballard Way	Lawrence, MA	01843-1045	978-688-4283	688-4370	K-4	
Community Day S R. Kingman Webster	50 Pleasant St	Lawrence, MA	01841-2244	978-686-9327		K-4	
Conservatory Lab Charter S	2120 Dorchester Ave	Dorchester, MA	02124-5617	617-254-8904	254-8909	PK-8	Diana Lam
Davis Leadership Academy Charter S	23 Leonard St	Dorchester, MA	02122-2718	617-474-7950	474-7957	6-8	Karmala Sherwood
Dudley Street Neighborhood S	6 Shirley St	Roxbury, MA	02119-2726	617-227-8055		K-5	Dawn Lewis
Excel Academy Charter S	1150 Saratoga St	East Boston, MA	02128-1228	617-561-1371	963-7162	5-8	Jennifer Gallaspy
Excel Academy - Chelsea	180 2nd St	Chelsea, MA	02150	617-336-9970	516-1676	5-8	Katherine Pereira
Excel Academy - East Boston	58 Moore St	East Boston, MA	02128	617-874-4080	516-1603	5-8	Jocelyn Foulke
Foster Charter S	10 New Bond St	Worcester, MA	01606-2699	508-854-8400	854-8484	K-12	Brian Haas
Four Rivers Charter S	248 Colrain Rd	Greenfield, MA	01301-9701	413-775-4577	775-4578	7-12	Peter Garbus
Foxborough Regional Charter S	131 Central St	Foxboro, MA	02035-2458	508-543-2508	543-7982	K-12	Ronald Griffin
Franklin Classical Charter S	201 Main St	Franklin, MA	02038-1933	508-541-3434	541-5396	K-8	Heather Zolnowski
Freire Social Justice Charter S	PO Box 1009	Holyoke, MA	01041	413-536-3201	536-3206	9-12	Melissa Mirhej
Global Learning Charter S	190 Ashley Blvd	New Bedford, MA	02746-1752	508-991-4105	991-4110	5-12	Dr. Stephen Furtado
Hampden Charter S of Science	20 Johnson Rd	Chicopee, MA	01022	413-593-9090	294-2648	6-12	Tarkan Topcuoglu
Hilltown Cooperative Charter S	1 Industrial Pkwy	Easthampton, MA	01027	413-529-7178	527-1530	K-8	Daniel Klatz
Hill View Montessori Charter S	75 Foundation Ave	Haverhill, MA	01835-6926	978-521-2616	521-2656	K-8	Debra Diggins
Holyoke Community Charter S	2200 Northampton St	Holyoke, MA	01040-3430	413-533-0111	536-5444	K-8	Sonia Pope
Innovation Academy Charter S	72 Tyng Rd	Tyngsboro, MA	01879-2044	978-649-0432	649-6337	5-12	Gregory Orpen
Kennedy Academy for Health Careers	360 Huntington Ave	Boston, MA	02115-5005	617-373-8576	373-7850	9-12	Dr. Caren Walker-Gregory
King Charter S of Excellence	285 Dorset St	Springfield, MA	01108-2821	413-214-7806	214-7838	K-5	Juraye Pierson
KIPP Academy Boston Charter S	384 Warren St	Roxbury, MA	02119-1830	617-238-7300	652-7461	K-8	Nikki Barnes
KIPP Academy Lynn Charter S	90 High Rock St	Lynn, MA	01902-3851	781-598-1609	598-1639	5-12	Drea DeAngelo
KIPP Academy Lynn ES	20 Wheeler St	Lynn, MA	01902	781-558-9263	598-1639	K-1	Eveleen Hsu
Lawrence Family Development Charter S	34 West St	Lawrence, MA	01841-3426	978-689-9863	689-8133	PK-8	Susan Earabino
Leominster Center for Excellence	464 Abbott Ave	Leominster, MA	01453-5446	978-596-6334	534-7775	9-12	Carrie Duff
Libertas Academy Charter S	1 Federal St Building 1	Springfield, MA	01105	413-349-9080	589-4578	6-12	Modesto Montero
Lowell Community Charter S	206 Jackson St	Lowell, MA	01852-2106	978-323-0800	323-4600	K-8	Kathy Egmont
Lowell Middlesex Academy Charter S	67 Middle St	Lowell, MA	01852-1868	978-656-3165	459-0456	9-12	Margaret McDevitt
Marblehead Community Charter S	17 Lime St	Marblehead, MA	01945-2530	781-631-0777	631-0500	4-8	Helena Cullen-Hamzeh
Martha's Vineyard Charter S	PO Box 1150	West Tisbury, MA	02575-1150	508-693-9900	696-9008	K-12	Robert Moore
MATCH Charter S	1001 Commonwealth Ave	Boston, MA	02215-1308	617-232-0300	232-2838	PK-12	Hannah Larkin
McAuliffe Regional Charter S	139 Newbury St Ste 1	Framingham, MA	01701-4591	508-879-9000	879-1066	6-8	Kristin Harrison
Mystic Valley Regional Charter S	770 Salem St	Malden, MA	02148-4415	781-388-0222	321-5688	K-12	Martin Trice
Neighborhood House Charter S	21 Queen St	Dorchester, MA	02122-2509	617-825-0703	825-1829	PK-8	Kate Scott
New Heights Charter S of Brockton	1 Commerce Way	Norwood, MA	02062	781-688-8107	688-8104	6-8	Janice Manning
New Liberty Innovation S	Museum Place Mall Ste 200	Salem, MA	01970	978-825-3470	825-3475	9-12	Jennifer Winsor
Parker Charter Essential S	49 Antietam St	Ayer, MA	01434-5230	978-772-3293	772-3295	7-12	Todd Sumner
Phoenix Academy	15 Union St	Lawrence, MA	01840-1866	978-722-8410	686-3613	9-12	Sarah Caney
Phoenix Charter Academy	59 Nichols St	Chelsea, MA	02150	617-889-3100	889-3144	9-12	Kevin Dean
Phoenix Charter Academy Springfield	65 Lincoln St	Springfield, MA	01105	413-273-1236		9-12	Jacqueline Adam-Taylor
Pioneer Charter S of Science	51 Summer St	Everett, MA	02149-3741	617-389-7277	389-7278	K-12	Sanela Jonuz
Pioneer Charter S of Science II	97 Main St	Saugus, MA	01906	781-666-3907	666-3910	7-12	Vahit Sevinc
Pioneer Valley Chinese Immrsn Charter S	317 Russell St	Hadley, MA	01035	413-582-7040	582-7068	K-12	Kathleen Wang
Pioneer Valley Performing Arts Charter S	15 Mulligan Dr	South Hadley, MA	01075-7511	413-552-1580	552-1594	7-12	Scott Goldman
Prospect Hill Academy Charter S	50 Essex St	Cambridge, MA	02139-2602	617-284-7800	284-7980	K-12	Angela Allen Ph.D.

School	Address	City,State	Zip code	Telephone	Fax	Grade	Contact
Rising Tide Charter S	6 Resnik Rd	Plymouth, MA	02360-4873	508-747-2620	830-9441	5-12	Jill Crafts
River Valley Charter S	2 Perry Way	Newburyport, MA	01950-4001	978-465-0065	465-0119	K-8	Andrew Willemsen
Roxbury Prep HS	86 Wachusett St	Jamaica Plain, MA	02130	617-858-2288		9-12	Shradha Patel
Roxbury Prep Mission Hill Campus	120 Fisher Ave	Roxbury, MA	02120-3320	617-566-2361	566-2373	5-8	Ryan Kelly
Roxbury Prep S Dorchester Campus	206 Magnolia St	Dorchester, MA	02121	617-858-2300	275-5760	5-8	Ryan Kelly
Roxbury Prep S Lucy Stone Campus	22 Regina Rd	Dorchester, MA	02124	617-979-0115	822-7527	5-8	Nikhil Bhatia
SABIS International Charter S	160 Joan St	Springfield, MA	01129-1530	413-783-2600	783-2555	K-12	Karen Reuter
Salem Academy Charter S	45 Congress St	Salem, MA	01970-5579	978-744-2105	744-7246	6-12	Stephanie Callahan
Seven Hills Charter S	51 Gage St	Worcester, MA	01605-3014	508-799-7500	713-0956	K-8	Michael Barth
Silver Hill Horace Mann Charter S	675 Washington St	Haverhill, MA	01832-4523	978-374-3448	374-3461	K-5	Margaret Shepherd
Sizer S	500 Rindge Rd	Fitchburg, MA	01420	978-345-2701	345-9127	7-12	David Perrigo
South Shore Charter S	100 Longwater Cir	Norwell, MA	02061-1650	781-982-4202	982-4201	K-12	Alicia Savage
Springfield Prep Charter S	370 Pine St	Springfield, MA	01105	413-231-2722	215-0004	K-2	Bill Spirer
Sturgis Charter Public S	427 Main St	Hyannis, MA	02601-3905	508-778-1782	771-6785	9-12	Paul Marble
UP Academy	215 Dorchester St	South Boston, MA	02127-2876	617-635-8819	635-8820	6-8	Katy Buckland
UP Academy	60 Allen St	Lawrence, MA	01840-1806	978-722-8159	722-8533	6-8	Komal Bhasin
UP Academy Dorchester	35 Westville St	Dorchester, MA	02124	617-635-8810	635-8815	PK-8	Kate Mahoney
UP Academy Holland	85 Olney St	Dorchester, MA	02121-3535	617-635-8832	220-3023	PK-5	Hillary Casson
UP Academy Kennedy MS	1385 Berkshire Ave	Springfield, MA	01151	413-787-7510	787-7561	6-8	Ryan Kelly
UP Academy Oliver MS	233 Haverhill St	Lawrence, MA	01840-1405	978-242-7446	722-8527	6-8	Dr. Katy Abdelahad
Veritas Preparatory Charter S	370 Pine St	Springfield, MA	01105	413-539-0055	306-5076	5-8	Rachel Romano

Michigan

School	Address	City,State	Zip code	Telephone	Fax	Grade	Contact
Abney Academy - ES	1435 Fulton St E	Grand Rapids, MI	49503-3853	616-454-5541	454-5598	K-5	Charlie Lovelady
Abney Academy - MS	256 Alger St SE	Grand Rapids, MI	49507-3409	616-301-2810	301-2814	6-8	Damon Pitt
Academic and Career Education Academy	884 E Isabella Rd	Midland, MI	48640-8326	989-631-5202	631-4541	9-12	Michelle Zielinski
Academy of Business and Technology	19625 Wood St	Melvindale, MI	48122-2201	313-382-3422	382-3906	6-12	Michael Jackson
Academy of Business and Technology ES	5277 Calhoun St	Dearborn, MI	48126-3203	313-581-2223	581-2247	K-5	Dr. Paul Merritt
Academy of International Studies	3056 Hanley St	Hamtramck, MI	48212-3572	313-873-9900	873-9201	K-8	Dawn Lynk-Jones
Academy of Warren	13943 E 8 Mile Rd	Warren, MI	48089-3351	586-552-8010	552-8014	K-8	Jim Perry
Achieve Charter Acadmey	3250 Denton Rd	Canton, MI	48188-2110	734-397-0960	397-0968	K-7	Jen Conley
Advanced Technology Academy	4801 Oakman Blvd	Dearborn, MI	48126-3755	313-625-4700	582-9407	K-12	Cynthia Anderson
A.G.B.U. Alex & Marie Manoogian S	22001 Northwestern Hwy	Southfield, MI	48075-4081	248-569-2988	569-1346	K-12	Dyana Kezelian
Alternative Educational Acad Ogemaw Co.	2389 S M 76	West Branch, MI	48661-8778	989-362-3006	362-9076	6-12	Dana McGrew
American International Academy	27100 Avondale	Inkster, MI	48141	734-895-7974	331-4260	6-9	Tom White
American International Academy	300 S Henry Ruff	Westland, MI	48186	734-895-7974	331-4260	K-5	Tom White
American Montessori Academy	14800 Middlebelt Rd	Livonia, MI	48154-4031	734-525-7100	525-8952	K-2	David Poirier
American Montessori Academy Upper ES	17175 Olympia	Redford, MI	48240	313-533-0000	533-0005	3-7	Renee Arnot
Ann Arbor Learning Community	3980 Research Park Dr	Ann Arbor, MI	48108-2220	734-477-0340	929-6505	K-8	Abby Kuhn
Arbor Academy	55 Arbor St	Battle Creek, MI	49015-2903	269-963-5851	964-2643	K-6	Allison Gumper
Arbor Preparatory HS	6800 Hitchingham Rd	Ypsilanti, MI	48197-8998	734-961-9700	961-9701	9-12	Ana Salazar
Arts Academy in the Woods	32101 Caroline	Fraser, MI	48026-3209	586-294-0391	294-0617	9-12	Michael Mitchell
Arts & Technology Academy of Pontiac	888 Enterprise Dr	Pontiac, MI	48341-3167	248-452-9309	452-9312	PK-12	Septembra Williams
Augusta Academy	600 W Michigan Ave	Augusta, MI	49012	269-731-5454		K-3	Meadow Nuyen
Bahweting Charter S	1301 Marquette Ave	Sault S Marie, MI	49783-9533	906-635-5055	635-3805	K-8	Dr. Theresa Kallstrom
Battle Creek Area Learning Center	15 Arbor St	Battle Creek, MI	49015-2903	269-565-4782	565-4784	9-12	Timothy Allard
Battle Creek Montessori Academy	399 20th St N	Springfield, MI	49037-4815	269-339-3308	339-3309	PK-8	Jessica Eldridge
Bay-Arenac Community HS	805 Langstaff St	Essexville, MI	48732-1367	989-893-8811	895-7749	9-12	Ryan Donlan
Bay City Academy - Farragut Campus	301 N Farragut St	Bay City, MI	48708	989-414-8254		K-5	Jill Plant
Bay City Academy - Madison Arts Campus	400 N Madison Ave	Bay City, MI	48708	989-414-5480		6-9	Darci Long
Benton Harbor Charter S	455 Riverview Dr	Benton Harbor, MI	49022-5080	269-925-3807	927-3673	PK-8	Tim Harris
Black River Public S	491 Columbia Ave	Holland, MI	49423-4838	616-355-0055	355-0057	K-12	Shannon Brunink
Blended Lrng Acad Credit Recovery HS	1754 E Clark Rd	Lansing, MI	48906-1020	517-574-4667		9-12	Dr. Tim Brannan
Blue Water Middle College Academy	323 Erie St	Port Huron, MI	48060-3812	810-989-5805	989-5848	9-12	Pete Spencer
Boggs S	4141 Mitchell St	Detroit, MI	48207-1620	313-923-2301	923-2300	K-6	Julia Putnam
Bradford Academy	24218 Garner St	Southfield, MI	48033-2900	248-351-0000	356-4770	K-12	Cheryl Paull
Branch Line S	16360 Hubbard St	Livonia, MI	48154-6100	734-335-0663		K-8	Jennifer Wilkins
Bridge Academy	9600 Buffalo St	Hamtramck, MI	48212-3323	313-624-6100	624-6200	PK-8	Dr. Naji Abduljaber Ph.D.
Bridge Academy - West	3105 Carpenter Rd	Detroit, MI	48212	313-462-6200	462-6201	6-8	Mohammed Alsanai
Burton Glen Charter Academy	4171 E Atherton Rd	Burton, MI	48519-1435	810-744-2300	744-2400	K-8	Denesha Rawls-Smith
Byron Center Charter S	9930 Burlingame Ave SW	Byron Center, MI	49315-8631	616-878-4852	878-7196	K-12	Thomas Berriman
Caniff Liberty Academy	2650 Caniff St	Hamtramck, MI	48212-3033	313-872-2000	338-3344	K-8	Rebecca Snoblin
Canton Charter Academy	49100 Ford Rd	Canton, MI	48187-5415	734-453-9517	453-9551	K-8	Kelie Fuller
Canton Preparatory HS	46610 Cherry Hill Rd	Canton, MI	48187	734-656-0003	656-0009	9-10	Aquan Miles
Capstone Academy	3500 John R St	Detroit, MI	48201-2402	313-202-6082	831-3510	4-12	Brian Serafino
Carleton Academy	2001 W Hallett Rd	Hillsdale, MI	49242-1959	517-437-2000	437-2919	K-12	Colleen Gadwood
Carver Academy	14510 2nd Ave	Highland Park, MI	48203-5715	313-865-6024	865-6658	K-8	Dez'arae Adams
CASMAN Alternative Academy	225 9th St	Manistee, MI	49660-3109	231-723-4981	723-1555	7-12	Michelle VanVoorst
Central Academy	2459 S Industrial Hwy	Ann Arbor, MI	48104-6129	734-822-1100	822-1101	PK-12	Dr. Luay Shalabi
Cesar Chavez Academy - Elementary East	4130 Maxwell St	Detroit, MI	48214-1109	313-924-0317	924-0425	K-5	Adasina Philyaw
Chandler Park Academy ES	20200 Kelly Rd	Harper Woods, MI	48225-1203	313-884-8830	884-9130	K-5	Marian Flaggs
Chandler Park Academy HS	20234 Kelly Rd	Harper Woods, MI	48225	313-499-3010	499-3052	9-12	Shaun Black
Chandler Park Academy MS	20100 Kelly Rd	Harper Woods, MI	48225-1201	313-839-9886	839-3221	6-8	Kenneth Williams
Chandler Woods Charter Academy	6895 Samrick Ave NE	Belmont, MI	49306-8844	616-866-6000	866-6001	PK-8	Joe Hammond
Charlevoix Montessori Academy for Arts	115 W Hurlbut St	Charlevoix, MI	49720-1510	231-547-9000	547-9464	K-12	Kali Kondrat
Chatfield S	231 Lake Dr	Lapeer, MI	48446-1661	810-667-8970	667-8983	K-8	Matt Young
Chavez HS	1761 Waterman St	Detroit, MI	48209-2194	313-551-0611	552-0552	9-12	Juan Martinez
Chavez Lower Academy	8126 W Vernor Hwy	Detroit, MI	48209-1524	313-843-9440	297-6948	K-2	Gabriela Jaime
Chavez MS	6782 Goldsmith St	Detroit, MI	48209-2089	313-842-0006	842-0167	6-8	April Jenkins
Chavez Upper ES	4100 Martin St	Detroit, MI	48210-2806	313-361-1083	361-1095	3-5	Thomas Goodley
Cole Academy	1915 W Mount Hope Ave	Lansing, MI	48910-2434	517-372-0038	372-1446	K-6	Brian Shaughnessy
Commonwealth Community Development Acad	13477 Eureka St	Hamtramck, MI	48212-1754	313-366-9470	366-9471	K-8	Angela Moore
Concord Academy - Boyne	401 E Dietz Rd	Boyne City, MI	49712-9653	231-582-0194	582-4214	K-12	Rebekah Leist
Concord Academy-Petoskey	2468 Atkins Rd	Petoskey, MI	49770-9003	231-439-6800	439-6803	K-12	Robert Ollar
Conner Creek Academy East	16911 Eastland St	Roseville, MI	48066-2078	586-779-8055	498-8734	K-6	Karen Smith
Consortium College Preparatory HS	4366 Military St	Detroit, MI	48210-2452	313-964-2339	964-3922	5-12	Jeffrey Maxwell
Cornerstone Health and Technology S	17351 Southfield Rd	Detroit, MI	48235	313-486-4260		9-12	Jared Davis
Cornerstone Jefferson-Douglass Academy	17305 Ashton	Detroit, MI	48219	313-637-3000		K-12	
Countryside Academy	4821 North St	Benton Harbor, MI	49022	269-944-5655	944-5695	K-2	
Countryside Academy	4800 Meadowbrook Rd	Benton Harbor, MI	49022-9629	269-944-3319	944-0242	3-12	Lyn Sperry
Covenant House Academy Central	2959 Martin Luther King Jr	Detroit, MI	48208-2475	313-899-6900	899-6910	9-12	Anna West
Covenant House Academy East	7600 Goethe St	Detroit, MI	48214-1762	313-267-4315	267-4320	9-12	Nathaniel King
Covenant House Academy - Grand Rapids	50 Antoine St SW	Grand Rapids, MI	49507-1002	616-364-2000		9-12	Doreen Mangrum
Covenant House Academy SW	1450 25th St	Detroit, MI	48216-1404	313-297-8720	297-8730	9-12	Jennifer Joubert
Creative Montessori Academy	15100 Northline Rd	Southgate, MI	48195-2408	734-284-5600	281-2637	PK-8	Carol Hutton
Creative Technologies Academy	350 Pine St	Cedar Springs, MI	49319-8680	616-696-4905	696-4920	K-12	Dan George
Crescent Academy	17570 W 12 Mile Rd	Southfield, MI	48076-1905	248-423-4581	423-1027	PK-12	Cherise Cupidore M.Ed.
Crockett Academy	4851 14th St	Detroit, MI	48208-2204	313-896-6078	896-1363	K-12	Monique Woodland-Phillip
Cross Creek Charter Academy	7701 Kalamazoo Ave SE	Byron Center, MI	49315-9534	616-656-4000	656-4001	PK-8	Joe Nieuwkoop
Crossroads Charter Academy	215 N State St	Big Rapids, MI	49307-1444	231-796-6589	796-9874	K-6	Ross Meads
Crossroads Charter Academy	215 Spruce St W	Big Rapids, MI	49307-1471	231-796-9041	796-9790	7-12	Ross Meads
da Vinci Institute	559 Murphy St	Jackson, MI	49202	517-780-9980	780-9747	K-8	Kristi Neelis
da Vinci Institute	2255 Emmons Rd	Jackson, MI	49201-8335	517-796-0031	796-0320	9-12	Sandy Maxson
Dearborn Academy	19310 Ford Rd Ste 2	Dearborn, MI	48128-2403	313-982-1300	982-9087	K-8	Afrin Alavi
DeTour Arts & Technology Academy	202 Division St	De Tour Village, MI	49725-5006	906-297-2011	297-3403	K-12	Brooke Maciag
Detroit Academy of Arts & Sciences	2985 E Jefferson Ave	Detroit, MI	48207-4288	313-259-1744	393-0460	K-6	Turquoise Neal
Detroit Academy of Arts & Sciences	3100 E Jefferson Ave	Detroit, MI	48207-4221	313-259-1704		6-8	Turquoise Neal
Detroit Achievement Academy	7000 W Outer Dr	Detroit, MI	48235-3166	313-468-9518		K-3	Sharon Yaecker-Roesser
Detroit Community ES	12675 Burt Rd	Detroit, MI	48223-3314	313-537-3570	537-6904	K-8	Sharon McPhail
Detroit Community HS	12675 Burt Rd	Detroit, MI	48223-3314	313-537-3570	537-6904	9-12	Sharon McPhail
Detroit Delta Prep Acad Social Justice	3550 John C Lodge Fwy	Detroit, MI	48201-2960	313-638-1444		9-12	Meagan Brown
Detroit Edison Academy	1903 Wilkins St	Detroit, MI	48207-2112	313-833-1100	833-8653	K-12	Ralph Bland
Detroit Enterprise Academy	11224 Kercheval St	Detroit, MI	48214-3323	313-823-5799	823-0342	K-8	Chanavia Patterson
Detroit Innovation Academy	18211 Plymouth Rd	Detroit, MI	48228	313-736-5537	242-1527	K-8	Sherie Manthiram
Detroit Leadership Academy	13550 Virgil St	Detroit, MI	48223	313-242-1500	241-1527	K-5	Pauline Nagle
Detroit Leadership Academy HS	5845 Auburn St	Detroit, MI	48228	313-769-2015	791-7994	6-12	Edwynn Bell
Detroit Merit Academy	1091 Alter Rd	Detroit, MI	48215-2861	313-331-3328	331-3278	PK-8	Sandra Terry-Martin
Detroit Premier Academy	7781 Asbury Park	Detroit, MI	48228-3685	313-945-1472	945-1744	K-8	James Kinsey
Detroit Prep	2411 Iroquois Ave	Detroit, MI	48214			K-1	Jen McMillan
Detroit Public Safety Academy	1250 Rosa Parks Blvd	Detroit, MI	48216-1950	313-965-6916	965-6938	7-12	Isaiah Pettway
Detroit Service Learning Academy	21605 W 7 Mile Rd	Detroit, MI	48219-1810	313-541-7619	541-7656	PK-8	Shannon Smith
Douglass International Acad	21700 Marlow St	Oak Park, MI	48237-2604	248-953-2003		PK-6	Rashid Faisal
Dove Academy of Detroit	20001 Wexford St	Detroit, MI	48234-1807	313-366-9110	366-9130	PK-8	Brandon Slone M.Ed.
Eagle Crest Charter Academy	11950 Riley St	Holland, MI	49424-8553	616-786-2400	786-4692	K-8	Jack DeLeeuw Ed.D.
Eagle's Nest Academy	5005 Cloverlawn Dr	Flint, MI	48504-2084	810-965-1514	787-9160	K-4	Dr. Reginald Flynn
East Arbor Charter Academy	6885 Merritt Rd	Ypsilanti, MI	48197-8958	734-484-5506	547-3078	K-8	Tanesha Newby

School	Address	City,State	Zip code	Telephone	Fax	Grade	Contact
East Shore Leadership Academy	1403 7th St	Port Huron, MI	48060-5903	810-247-0687		K-5	Nancy Gardner
Eaton Academy	21450 Universal Ave	Eastpointe, MI	48021-2969	586-777-1519	777-1527	K-8	Kenis Wallevand
El-Hajj Malik El-Shabazz Academy	1028 W Barnes Ave	Lansing, MI	48910-1308	517-267-8474	484-0095	PK-6	Vincent Price
Ellis Academy	18977 Schaefer Hwy	Detroit, MI	48235-1762	313-927-5395	927-5376	K-8	Michael Johnson
Ellis Academy West	19800 Beech Daly Rd	Redford, MI	48240-1348	313-450-0300	450-0305	K-8	Dr. Ticheal Jones
Endeavor Charter Academy	380 Helmer Rd N	Springfield, MI	49037-7776	269-962-9300	962-9393	K-8	Angela Wyckoff
Excel Charter Academy	4201 Breton Rd SE	Grand Rapids, MI	49512-3857	616-281-9339	281-6707	K-8	Daniel Bartels
Faxon Language Immersion Academy	28555 Middlebelt Rd	Farmingtn Hls, MI	48334-4104	248-702-6272	702-6376	K-8	Rosalie Cohen
Flagship Charter Academy	13661 Wisconsin St	Detroit, MI	48238-2356	313-933-7933	933-9061	K-8	Faren D'Abell
FlexTech HS	7707 Conference Center Dr	Brighton, MI	48114-7334	810-844-3366	229-2331	9-12	Melanie Laber
Flex Tech HS Novi	24245 Karim Blvd	Novi, MI	48375	248-426-8530	426-8557	9-12	Sarah Pazur
Ford Academy: S for Creative Studies	10225 3rd St	Detroit, MI	48202-1287	313-826-1159	731-0400	K-5	Felicia Brimage
Ford Academy	20651 W Warren St	Dearborn Hts, MI	48127-2622	313-436-0020	441-9169	5-12	Dr. Beverly Baroni
Ford Academy	PO Box 1148	Dearborn, MI	48121-1148	313-982-6200	982-6195	9-12	Cora Christmas
Ford Academy/Schl for Creative Studies	485 W Milwaukee St	Detroit, MI	48202-3220	313-481-4000	481-4001	6-12	Dr. Curtis Lewis
Forest Academy	5196 Comstock Ave	Kalamazoo, MI	49048-3476	269-488-2315	488-2317	K-6	Amanda Brown
Fortis Academy	3875 Golfside Rd	Ypsilanti, MI	48197-3726	734-572-3623	572-5792	K-8	Ira Kleiman
Four Corners Montessori Academy	1075 E Gardenia Ave	Madison Heights, MI	48071-3433	248-542-7001	542-7901	PK-8	Chris Schoenherr
Frontier International Academy	13200 Conant St	Hamtramck, MI	48212	313-462-6300	316-4554	6-12	Dr. Mohamad Issa
Gateway to Success Academy	526 N Scottville Rd	Scottville, MI	49454	231-845-0922		6-12	James Bandstra
GEE Edmonson Academy	1300 W Canfield St	Detroit, MI	48201-1006	313-228-0910	447-2533	PK-8	Domini Nailer
GEE White Academy	5161 Charles St	Detroit, MI	48212-2462	313-866-3595	866-3476	PK-8	Felicia Jones M.Ed.
Genesee STEM Academy	5240 Calkins Rd	Flint, MI	48532	810-600-6466	600-6445	K-8	Rita Cheek
Global Heights Academy	23713 Joy Rd	Dearborn Hts, MI	48127-1408	313-624-3400	624-3401	PK-5	Shawn Robson
Global Preparatory Academy	26200 Ridgemont St	Roseville, MI	48066-3270	586-575-9500	491-2556	PK-8	Nicole Woods
Global Tech Academy	1715 E Forest Ave	Ypsilanti, MI	48198-4160	734-390-9625		K-5	Mohamad Issa
Grand Blanc Academy	5135 E Hill Rd	Grand Blanc, MI	48439-7637	810-953-3140	953-3165	K-8	Patty Wood
Grand Rapids Child Discovery Center	409 Lafayette Ave SE	Grand Rapids, MI	49503-5329	616-459-0330	732-4437	K-5	John Robinson
Grand Rapids Ellington Acad Arts & Tech	600 Burton St SE	Grand Rapids, MI	49507-3202	616-241-6300	635-2803	K-12	Cynthia Springer
Grand River Academy	28111 8 Mile Rd	Livonia, MI	48152-2359	248-893-6100	479-1996	K-8	Alan Harper
Grand River Prep HS	650 52nd St SE	Kentwood, MI	49548-5837	616-261-1800	261-1853	9-12	Koree Woodward
Grand Traverse Academy	1245 Hammond Rd E	Traverse City, MI	49686-9000	231-995-0665	995-0880	PK-12	Susan Dameron
Grattan Academy ES	12047 Old Belding Rd NE	Belding, MI	48809-9367	616-691-8999	691-9857	K-5	Elizabeth Kreiner
Grattan Academy HS	9481 Jordan Rd	Greenville, MI	48838-9437	616-754-9360	754-9363	6-12	Tom Kreiner
Greater Heights Academy	3196 W Pasadena Ave	Flint, MI	48504-2330	810-768-3860	768-3865	K-5	Lisa Leimeister
Great Lakes Academy	46312 Woodward Ave	Pontiac, MI	48342-5006	248-334-6434	334-6457	K-8	Aaron Williams
Great Lakes Cyber Academy	2140 University Park # 270	Okemos, MI	48864	517-381-5062	381-5090	6-12	Heather Ballien
Great Oaks Academy	4257 Bart Ave	Warren, MI	48091-1977	586-427-4540	427-4541	K-8	Damon Williams
Greenspire S	1026 Red Dr	Traverse City, MI	49684-4593	231-421-5905	805-1327	6-8	Kevin Kelly
Hamilton Academy	14223 Southampton St	Detroit, MI	48213-3744	313-866-4505	344-7981	K-8	Dr. P. Bilbrew
Hamtramck Academy	11420 Conant St	Hamtramck, MI	48212-3134	313-368-7312	368-7376	K-8	Michael Griffie
Hanley International Academy	2400 Denton St	Hamtramck, MI	48212-3616	313-875-8888	875-8889	PK-8	Shameka McPherson
Heston Academy	1350 N Saint Helen Rd	Saint Helen, MI	48656-9521	989-632-3390	632-3393	PK-12	David Patterson
Highland Park Renaissance Academy	45 E Buena Vista St	Highland Park, MI	48203-3343	313-957-3005	868-0345	PK-12	Carmen Willingham
Highpoint Virtual Academy of Michigan	PO Box 596	Mesick, MI	49668	855-831-0145		K-8	Mary Moorman
Hillsdale Preparatory S	160 Mechanic Rd	Hillsdale, MI	49242-1053	517-437-4625	437-3830	K-8	Stephen Philipp
Holly Academy	820 Academy Rd	Holly, MI	48442-1546	248-634-5554	634-5564	K-8	Julie Kildee
Honey Creek Community S	PO Box 1406	Ann Arbor, MI	48106-1406	734-994-2636	994-2341	K-8	Al Waters
Hope Academy	12121 Broadstreet Ave	Detroit, MI	48204-1550	313-934-0054	934-0074	K-8	Dr. Ronald E. Williams
Hope Academy of West Michigan	240 Brown St SE	Grand Rapids, MI	49507-2502	616-301-8458	264-3346	K-12	Phil Haack
Hope of Detroit Academy	4444 35th St	Detroit, MI	48210	313-897-8720	897-5142	5-10	Alberta Galarza
Hope of Detroit Academy	4443 N Campbell St	Detroit, MI	48210-2520	313-897-8720	897-5142	K-4	Ali Abdel
Huron Academy	36301 Utica Rd	Clinton Twp, MI	48035	586-690-8180		3-7	Mark Talbot
Huron Academy	11401 Metropolitan Pkwy	Sterling Hts, MI	48312-2937	586-446-9170	446-9173	K-2	Mark Talbot
ICademy Global	8485 Homestead Dr	Zeeland, MI	49464-8969	616-748-5637	772-0373	K-12	Brook Drooger
Inkster Preparatory Academy	27355 Woodsfield St	Inkster, MI	48141	313-278-3825		K-2	Shawn Hurt
Innocademy	8485 Homestead Dr	Zeeland, MI	49464-8969	616-748-5637	772-0373	K-12	Brook Drooger
Innocademy Allegan Campus	2611 56th St	Fennville, MI	49408	269-561-4050	772-0373	K-5	Chad Zuber
Insight S of Michigan	6512 Centurion Dr Ste 320	Lansing, MI	48917-8248	877-842-3793		6-12	Marcus Moore
International Academy of Flint	2820 S Saginaw St	Flint, MI	48503-5708	810-600-5000	600-5300	K-12	Kendra Giles
International Academy of Saginaw	1944 Iowa Ave	Saginaw, MI	48601-5213	989-921-1000	921-1001	K-8	Christopher Matheson
Island City Academy	6421 S Clinton Trl	Eaton Rapids, MI	48827-9698	517-663-0111	663-0167	PK-8	William Aaron Warren
Jackson Preparatory & Early College S	2111 Emmons Rd	Jackson, MI	49201-8395	517-768-7093	795-2735	6-12	Shane Malmquist
Jefferson International Academy	60 S Lynn Ave	Waterford, MI	48328	248-682-5000	481-2053	PK-8	Dr. Elizabeth Herron-Ruff
Joy Preparatory Academy	15055 Dexter Ave	Detroit, MI	48238-2124	313-340-0023	340-0678	PK-8	Frances Gardulescu
Kalamazoo Covenant Academy	400 W Crosstown Pkwy	Kalamazoo, MI	49001-2761			9-12	Gretchen LaHaie
Kensington Woods HS	PO Box 206	Lakeland, MI	48143-0206	517-545-0828	545-7588	6-12	Markus Muennix
Keys Grace Academy	27321 Hampden St	Madison Heights, MI	48071-3113	248-629-7700	629-7708	K-12	Lisa Mansour
Keystone Academy	47925 Bemis Rd	Belleville, MI	48111-9760	734-697-9470	697-9471	K-8	Keturah Godfrey
King Education Center	16827 Appoline St	Detroit, MI	48235-4205	313-341-4944	341-7014	K-8	Dr. Constance Price
Kingsbury Country Day S	5000 Hosner Rd	Oxford, MI	48370-1000	248-628-2571	628-3612	PK-8	Tom Mecsey
Knapp Charter Academy	1759 Leffingwell Ave NE	Grand Rapids, MI	49525-4531	616-364-1100	364-9780	PK-8	Dave Turcotte
Lakeside Charter S	3921 Oakland Dr	Kalamazoo, MI	49008-4820	269-202-5536	381-5332	4-12	Steven Laidacker
Lake Superior Academy	8936 S Mackinac Trl	Sault S Marie, MI	49783	906-440-0091		K-3	Susie Schlehuber
Landmark Academy	4800 Lapeer Rd	Kimball, MI	48074-1517	810-982-7210	982-0679	K-12	Debby Wilton
Lansing Charter Academy	3300 Express Ct	Lansing, MI	48910-4370	517-882-9585	882-9587	K-6	Alvin Ward
Laurus Academy	24590 Lahser Rd	Southfield, MI	48033-6040	248-799-8401	799-8404	K-8	Dr. Raul Calderon
Leelanau Montessori Academy	PO Box 838	Suttons Bay, MI	49682-0838	231-271-8609	271-8689	PK-6	Rebecca Creighton
Legacy Charter Academy	4900 E Hildale St	Detroit, MI	48234-2225	313-368-2215	432-2807	K-8	Letoskey Carey
Life Skills Center of Pontiac	142 Auburn Ave	Pontiac, MI	48342-3008	248-322-1163	322-1164	9-12	Keisha Palmer
Life Tech Academy	3101 Technology Blvd Ste A	Lansing, MI	48910	517-325-5469	325-5468	7-12	Thomas Ackerson
Lighthouse Academy	3330 36th St SE	Grand Rapids, MI	49512-2810	616-949-2287	949-2379	K-12	Jamie San Miguel
Lighthouse Academy - North Campus	1260 Ekhart St NE	Grand Rapids, MI	49503-1380	616-965-9700	965-9701	3-12	Todd Penning
Light of the World Academy	550 E Hamburg St	Pinckney, MI	48169-9105	734-720-9760	720-9763	PK-6	Kathy Moorehouse
Lincoln-King Academy	13436 Grove St	Detroit, MI	48235-4222	313-862-2352	862-2462	PK-8	Carolyn Brown
Linden Charter Academy	3244 N Linden Rd	Flint, MI	48504-1753	810-720-0515	720-0626	K-8	Deonna Washington
Livingston Classical Cyber Academy	8877 Main St	Whitmore Lake, MI	48189	734-839-6307		K-9	Cory Merante
MacDowell Preparatory Academy	4201 W Outer Dr	Detroit, MI	48221	313-457-6400	494-8142	PK-7	Lindsie Boykin
Macomb Academy	39092 Garfield Rd	Clinton Twp, MI	48038-2790	586-228-2201	228-2210	12-12	Andrew Wise
Macomb Montessori Academy	14057 E 9 Mile Rd	Warren, MI	48089	586-359-2138	533-2812	K-6	Ashley Ogonowski
Madison Academy	6170 Torrey Rd	Flint, MI	48507-5954	810-655-2949	655-2931	K-6	Tricai Osborne
Madison Academy - HS	3266 S Genesee Rd	Burton, MI	48519	810-875-9050	877-6255	9-12	Joddi Mills
Madison-Carver Academy	19900 McIntyre St	Detroit, MI	48219-1263	313-486-4626		K-8	Pamela Farris
Marshall Academy	18203 Homer Rd	Marshall, MI	49068-8718	269-781-6330	781-8749	K-12	Brent Swan
Merritt Academy	59900 Havenridge Rd	New Haven, MI	48048-1915	586-749-6000	749-8582	PK-12	Nathan Seiferlein
Metro Charter Academy	34800 Ecorse Rd	Romulus, MI	48174-1642	734-641-3200	641-6530	K-8	Shelli Wildfong
Michigan Collegiate MSHS	31300 Ryan Rd	Warren, MI	48092-1354	586-777-5792	698-0392	7-12	Russel Woodruff
Michigan Connections Academy	3950 Heritage Ave Ste 100	Okemos, MI	48864-3389	517-507-5390	507-5389	K-12	Bryan Klochack
Michigan Great Lakes Virtual Academy	50 Filer St Ste F	Manistee, MI	49660-2788	855-380-2480	794-6416	K-12	Kendall Schroeder
Michigan Math & Science Academy	8155 Ritter	Center Line, MI	48015-1452	586-920-2163	920-2164	K-12	Oguzhan Yildiz M.Ed.
Michigan S for the Arts	825 Golf Dr	Pontiac, MI	48341-2354	248-338-2787	499-8843	K-9	Dr. Carl Byerly
Michigan Technical Academy	19940 Mansfield St	Detroit, MI	48235-2332	313-272-1649	272-1849	PK-4	Phillip Price
Michigan Technical Academy	23750 Elmira St	Redford, MI	48239-1485	313-537-9311	537-9312	5-8	James Spruill
Michigan Virtual Academy	678 Front Ave NW	Grand Rapids, MI	49504-5325	877-794-9427	843-5871	K-12	Andrei Nichols
Midland Acad Advanced & Creative Studies	4653 E Bailey Bridge Rd	Midland, MI	48640-8542	989-496-2404	496-2466	K-12	Dr. Kathryn Shick
Mid-Michigan Leadership Academy	730 W Maple St	Lansing, MI	48906-5086	517-485-5379	485-5892	K-8	Tim Tenneriello
Momentum Academy	99 E Woodward Heights Blvd	Hazel Park, MI	48030-1450	248-336-5600	808-6478	PK-8	Kevelin Jones
Morey Montessori Public School Academy	418 W Blanchard Rd	Shepherd, MI	48883-9552	989-866-6741	866-6737	PK-8	Eric Johnson
Mt. Clemens Montessori Academy	1070 Hampton Rd	Mount Clemens, MI	48043-2955	586-465-5545	465-2283	PK-5	Stelgene P'sachoulias
Multicultural Academy	5550 Platt Rd	Ann Arbor, MI	48108-9762	734-677-0732	677-0740	PK-8	Elizabeth Parks M.S.
Murphy Performance Academy	23901 Fenkell St	Detroit, MI	48223-1431	313-494-7585	494-7550	K-8	Malon Harris
Muskegon Covenant Academy	125 Catherine Ave	Muskegon, MI	49442-3331	231-720-3100		9-12	Jim VanBergen
Muskegon Montessori Academy	2950 McCracken St	Norton Shores, MI	49441-3623	231-766-7500	766-7215	K-6	Ali DuBois
New Bedford Academy	6315 Secor Rd	Lambertville, MI	48144-9411	734-854-5437	854-1573	K-8	Greg Sauter
New Beginnings Academy	211 E Michigan Ave	Ypsilanti, MI	48198-5677	734-481-9001	544-2706	K-6	Kenya Crockett
New Branches Charter Academy	3662 Poinsettia Ave SE	Grand Rapids, MI	49508	616-243-6221	243-6221	K-8	Terry Larkin
New Paradigm College Prep S	2450 S Beatrice St	Detroit, MI	48217-1631	313-406-7060		K-5	Tamara Collins
New Paradigm Glazer Academy	2001 La Belle St	Detroit, MI	48238-2941	313-852-1500	852-1499	PK-7	Robert Hines
New Paradigm Loving Academy	1000 Lynn St	Detroit, MI	48211-1081	313-252-3028	866-0989	PK-8	Ronald Newton
New School High	46250 Ann Arbor Rd W	Plymouth, MI	48170	734-386-6601		9-10	Cyndi Burnstein
New Standard Academy	2040 W Carpenter Rd	Flint, MI	48505-1908	810-787-3330		PK-8	Calvin Sims
Nexus Academy of Grand Rapids	801 Broadway Ave NW Ste 225	Grand Rapids, MI	49504-4464	616-458-4992	458-6088	9-12	Daniel McMinn
Nexus Academy of Lansing	2175 University Park Dr	Okemos, MI	48864-3975	517-347-7793	347-7864	9-12	Charles Carver
Nexus Academy of Royal Oak	31333 Southfield Rd Ste 200	Beverly Hills, MI	48025-5440	248-593-8440	593-8264	9-12	Michael Foley
Noor International Academy	37412 Dequindre Rd	Sterling Hts, MI	48310-3503	586-365-5000	365-5001	PK-8	Nawal Hamadeh
North Central Academy	5055 Corey Rd	Mancelona, MI	49659-9467	231-584-2080	584-2082	K-12	Kurt Grangood
Northridge Academy	4100 W Coldwater Rd	Flint, MI	48504	810-785-8811	785-9844	K-8	Latricia Brown M.Ed.

School	Address	City,State	Zip code	Telephone	Fax	Grade	Contact
North Saginaw Charter Academy	2332 Trautner Dr	Saginaw, MI	48604-9593	989-249-5400	249-5800	K-8	Sarah Simpson
North Star Academy	3030 Wright St	Marquette, MI	49855-9649	906-226-0156	226-0167	K-12	Joseph Kukulski
Oakland Academy	6325 Oakland Dr	Portage, MI	49024-2589	269-324-8951	324-8974	PK-6	Henry Winter
Oakland International Academy	6111 Miller St	Detroit, MI	48211-1552	313-925-1000	925-1133	2-4	Ahmed Saber
Oakland International Academy	4001 Miller St	Detroit, MI	48211-1554	313-923-0790	923-0927	PK-1	Ahmed Saber
Oakland International Academy - HS	2619 Florian St	Hamtramck, MI	48212-3452	313-285-8990	784-9438	9-12	Ahmed Saber
Oakland International Academy Middle	8228 Conant St	Detroit, MI	48211-1407	313-347-0246	347-0250	5-8	Ahmed Saber
Oakside Scholars Charter Academy	355 Summit Dr	Waterford, MI	48328-3366	248-706-2000	920-0351	K-8	Kathleen Grinwis
Ojibwe Charter S	11507 W Industrial Dr	Brimley, MI	49715-9087	906-248-2530	248-2532	K-12	Stephanie Vittitow
Old Redford Academy ES	17195 Redford St	Detroit, MI	48219-3259	313-532-7510	543-2055	PK-5	Tomeka Dixon
Old Redford Academy MS	22122 W McNichols Rd	Detroit, MI	48219-3245	313-653-3888	412-2162	6-8	Chavonne McGowan
Old Redford Academy Prep HS	8001 W Outer Dr	Detroit, MI	48235-3293	313-543-3080	543-3129	9-12	Charles Davis M.Ed.
Outlook Academy	2879 116th Ave	Allegan, MI	49010-9004	269-673-2161	673-2361	5-12	Rick Cain
Pansophia Academy	52 Abbott Ave	Coldwater, MI	49036-1430	517-279-4686	279-0089	K-12	Jamie Mueller
Paragon Charter Academy	3750 McCain Rd	Jackson, MI	49201-7675	517-750-9500	750-9501	K-8	Ben Kriesch
Paramount Charter Academy	3624 S Westnedge Ave	Kalamazoo, MI	49008-2969	269-553-6400	553-6401	PK-8	Jodi Donkin
Paris Academy	PO Box 5142	Saginaw, MI	48603	989-401-9101		K-12	
Pathways Academy	11340 E Jefferson Ave	Detroit, MI	48214-3331	734-221-0977		7-12	Nathaniel King
Pathways Global Leadership Academy	30053 Parkwood St	Inkster, MI	48141	313-355-0952	731-0177	9-12	Joseph Gibson
Plymouth Educational Center	1460 E Forest Ave	Detroit, MI	48207-1000	313-831-3280	831-5766	PK-8	LaShanda Thomas
Plymouth Scholars Charter Academy	48484 N Territorial Rd	Plymouth, MI	48170	734-459-6149	864-0341	K-8	Walter Reese
Pollack Academic Center of Excellence	23777 Southfield Rd	Southfield, MI	48075-3458	248-569-1060	569-1403	K-8	Dr. Damian Perry
Pontiac Academy for Excellence	196 Cesar E Chavez Ave	Pontiac, MI	48342	248-745-9420	745-4898	K-12	James Spruill
Presque Isle Academy	20830 Cedar St	Onaway, MI	49765-8600	989-733-6708	733-6701	9-12	Earl Bassett
Prevail Academy	353 Cass Ave	Mount Clemens, MI	48043-2112	586-783-0173	783-0179	K-8	Colleen Furman
Quest Charter Academy	24745 Van Born Rd	Taylor, MI	48180-1221	734-299-0534	299-0577	K-8	Ralph Garza
Reach Academy	25275 Chippendale St	Roseville, MI	48066-3960	586-498-9171	498-9173	K-8	Nicole Young
Redford Service Learning Academy	25940 Grand River Ave	Redford, MI	48240-1435	313-539-4115	539-4660	K-8	Robert Warmack
Regent Park Scholars Charter Academy	15865 E 7 Mile Rd	Detroit, MI	48205-2545	313-371-1300	221-9942	K-8	Crystal Byse
Regents Academy	17715 Brady	Redford, MI	48240	888-473-2408		K-12	Dr. Paula Watkins
Reh Academy	2201 Owen St	Saginaw, MI	48601-3466	989-753-2349	753-1819	PK-8	Kate Scheid
Renaissance Public S Academy	2797 S Isabella Rd	Mount Pleasant, MI	48858-2067	989-773-9889	772-4503	K-8	Lisa Bergman
Richfield Public School Academy	3807 N Center Rd	Flint, MI	48506-2642	810-736-1281	736-2326	PK-8	Pamela Haldy
Ridge Park Charter Academy	4120 Camelot Ridge Dr SE	Grand Rapids, MI	49546-2432	616-222-0093	222-0138	K-8	Emory Wyckoff
Rising Stars Academy	23855 Lawrence	Center Line, MI	48015-1083	586-806-6455	806-6967	12-12	John Commyn
River City Scholars Charter Academy	944 Evergreen St	Grand Rapids, MI	49507	616-248-3390	723-0128	K-8	Holly Hillary
Riverside Academy East	7124 Miller Rd	Dearborn, MI	48126-1918	313-624-3200	624-3201	K-5	Eman Radha
Riverside Academy ECC	7050 Pinehurst St	Dearborn, MI	48126	313-624-3500	624-3501	PK-PK	Constance Robinson
Riverside Academy West	6409 Schaefer Rd	Dearborn, MI	48126-2212	313-624-3600	624-3601	6-12	Ramzi Saab
Rose Leadership Academy	15000 Trojan St	Detroit, MI	48235-1680	313-397-3333	397-4155	9-12	Russell Harris
Ross-Hill Academy ES	3111 Elmwood St	Detroit, MI	48207-2418	313-922-8088	922-2015	K-8	Phyllis Ross
Rutherford Winans Academy	16411 Curtis St	Detroit, MI	48235-3202	313-852-0709	852-0702	PK-5	Karen Abbott
Saginaw Learn to Earn Academy	1000 Tuscola St	Saginaw, MI	48607-1421	989-399-8775		9-12	Brad Gomoluch
Saginaw Preparatory Academy	5173 Lodge St	Saginaw, MI	48601-6829	989-752-9600	752-9618	PK-8	Molly Rundell
St. Clair County Intervention Academy	1170 Michigan Rd	Port Huron, MI	48060-4658	810-966-1649	966-4312	6-12	Troy Peyerk
SER Metro Learning Academy	9215 Michigan Ave	Detroit, MI	48210	313-846-2240		9-12	
South Arbor Charter Academy	8200 Carpenter Rd	Ypsilanti, MI	48197-9173	734-528-2821	528-2829	K-8	Kim Bondy
South Canton Scholars Charter Academy	3085 S Canton Center Rd	Canton, MI	48188-2452	734-398-5658	547-3077	K-8	Sabrina Terenzi
South Pointe Scholars Charter Academy	10550 Geddes Rd	Ypsilanti, MI	48198-9442	734-484-0118	864-0353	K-8	Nancy Kouba
Southwest Detroit Community S	4001 29th St	Detroit, MI	48210	313-782-4422	782-4469	K-8	Frank Donner
Star International Academy	24425 Hass St	Dearborn Hts, MI	48127-3275	313-724-8990	724-8994	PK-12	Ali Bazzi
Starr Detroit Academy	19360 Harper Ave	Harper Woods, MI	48225	313-649-2200	924-5490	K-8	Kimberley Pressley M.Ed.
State Street Academy	1110 State St	Bay City, MI	48706-3669	989-684-6484	684-6202	K-6	Joy Wagner
Stewart Perfomance Academy	13120 Wildemere St	Detroit, MI	48238-3336	313-327-0058		K-8	Detra Coleman
Stockwell Academy	9758 E Highland Rd	Howell, MI	48843-9098	810-632-2200	632-2201	K-8	Jessica Moceri
Stockwell Preparatory Academy	1032 Karl Greimel Dr	Brighton, MI	48116-9471	810-225-9940	225-9941	9-12	Steven Beyer
Success Academy	1620 Ludington St	Escanaba, MI	49829	906-553-7979	553-7981	9-12	Laura Bartel
Success Mile Academy	27300 Dequindre Rd	Warren, MI	48092-2870	586-353-2108	353-2109	K-8	Thomas Gladieux
Success Virtual Learning Center	7188 Avenue B	Vestaburg, MI	48891	989-427-2020	681-8387	9-12	Dr. Frank Sebastian
Summit Academy	PO Box 310	Flat Rock, MI	48134-0310	734-379-6810	379-6745	K-8	Leann Hedke
Summit Academy HS	18601 Middlebelt Rd	Romulus, MI	48174-9290	734-955-1730	955-1737	9-12	Erin Avery
Summit Academy MS	18601 Middlebelt Rd	Romulus, MI	48174-9290	734-955-1712	955-1729	6-8	Leann Hedke
Summit Academy North ES	28697 Sibley Rd	Romulus, MI	48174-9736	734-789-1428	789-1431	K-5	Michael Bravo
Taylor Exemplar Academy	26727 Goddard Rd	Taylor, MI	48180-3912	734-941-7742	941-9641	K-8	Julie Zirille
Taylor International Academy	26555 Franklin Rd	Southfield, MI	48033-5340	248-354-1500	354-1501	PK-8	Robert Davis
Taylor Preparatory HS	9540 Telegraph Rd	Taylor, MI	48180-3356	734-668-2100	668-2101	9-12	Aquan Miles
Three Lakes Academy	W17352 Main St	Curtis, MI	49820	906-586-6631	586-6573	K-7	Susan Pann
Three Oaks Public School Academy	1212 Kingsley St	Muskegon, MI	49442-4025	231-767-3365	777-9815	K-6	Monecia Vasbinder
Timberland Charter Academy	2574 McLaughlin Ave	Muskegon, MI	49442-4439	231-767-9700	767-9710	K-8	Angelia Coleman
Timbuktu Academy	10800 E Canfield St	Detroit, MI	48214-1601	313-823-6000	823-9748	K-8	ChaRhonda Edgerson
Tipton Academy	1615 Belton St	Garden City, MI	48135	734-261-0500	956-6360	PK-8	Suzanne March
Trillium Academy	15740 Racho Blvd	Taylor, MI	48180-5211	734-374-8222	374-5025	K-12	Angela Romanowski
Triumph Academy	3000 Vivian Rd	Monroe, MI	48162-8600	734-240-2610	240-2785	K-8	Amy Tansel
Trix Performance Academy	13700 Bringard Dr	Detroit, MI	48205-1156	313-852-8644	866-8655	K-8	Emily Piccoli
Universal Academy	4833 Ogden St	Detroit, MI	48210-2011	313-581-5006	581-5514	PK-12	Uzma Anjum
Universal Learning Academy	28015 Joy Rd	Westland, MI	48185-5525	734-402-5900	402-5901	PK-12	Michelle Hadous
University Prep Academy Murray ES	435 Amsterdam St	Detroit, MI	48202-3407	313-309-0552	309-0487	PK-5	Kimberly Llorens
University Preparatory Academy HS	600 Antoinette St	Detroit, MI	48202-3457	313-874-4340	874-4470	9-12	Camille Hibbler
University Preparatory Academy MS	5310 Saint Antoine St	Detroit, MI	48202-4131	313-831-0100	831-4197	6-8	Aisha Scott
University Preparatory Acad Thompson ES	957 Holden St	Detroit, MI	48202-3443	313-874-9800	874-9822	K-5	Tamara Johnson
University Prep Science & Math ES	2251 Antietam Ave	Detroit, MI	48207-3879	313-782-4400		K-5	Kimberly Phillips
University Prep Science & Math HS	2664 Franklin St	Detroit, MI	48207-4423	313-393-9166	393-9165	9-12	Zetia Hogan M.Ed.
University Prep Science & Math MS	5100 John R St	Detroit, MI	48202-4061	313-832-8400	833-4816	6-8	Jennifer Spencer
University Yes Academy	PO Box 2716	Detroit, MI	48202-0716	313-270-2556	646-6887	K-12	Joe Kotarski
Vanderbilt Charter Academy	301 W 16th St	Holland, MI	49423-3417	616-820-5050	820-5051	PK-8	Holly Hillary
Vanguard Charter Academy	1620 52nd St SW	Wyoming, MI	49519-9629	616-538-3630	538-3646	K-8	Mark DeJong
Virtual Learning Academy of St. Clair	499 Range Rd	Marysville, MI	48040-2220	810-364-8990	364-7474	9-12	Denice Lapish
Vista Charter Academy	711 32nd St SE	Grand Rapids, MI	49548-2307	616-246-6920	246-6930	K-8	Heather Guerra M.Ed.
Vista Meadows Academy	20651 W Warren St	Dearborn Hts, MI	48127	313-240-4347	441-9169	9-12	Dr. Darryln Harrison
Voyageur Academy	4321 Military St	Detroit, MI	48210-2451	313-361-4180	361-4770	K-6	Aundrea Johnson
Voyageur College Prep	4366 Military Street	Detroit, MI	48210	313-748-4000	897-1760	9-12	Jeff Maxwell
Walden Green Montessori S	17339 Roosevelt Rd	Spring Lake, MI	49456-1253	616-842-4523	842-4522	K-8	Mark Neidlinger
Walker Charter Academy	1801 3 Mile Rd NW	Grand Rapids, MI	49544-1445	616-785-2700	785-0894	K-8	Steve Bagley
Walton Charter Academy	744 E Walton Blvd	Pontiac, MI	48340-1361	248-371-9300	371-1642	K-8	Mona Boersma
Warrendale Charter Academy	19400 Sawyer St	Detroit, MI	48228-3330	313-240-4200	240-4203	K-8	Vondra Glass
Washington-Parks Academy	11685 Appleton	Redford, MI	48239-1445	313-592-6061	242-5156	K-8	Kalyani Bhatt
Washtenaw Technical Middle College	4800 E Huron River Dr	Ann Arbor, MI	48105-9481	734-973-3410	973-3464	10-12	Dr. Karl Covert
Waterford Montessori Academy	4860 Midland Ave	Waterford, MI	48329	248-674-2400	674-2424	PK-6	Theo Papatheodoropoulos
W-A-Y Academy	8701 W Vernor	Detroit, MI	48209	313-444-8082		7-12	Jennifer Hernandez
WAY Academy-Flint	817 E Kearsley St	Flint, MI	48503	810-412-8655	820-2642	6-12	Madeline Black
WAY Academy Washtenaw Campus	555 Briarwood Cir	Ann Arbor, MI	48108	734-249-9929		6-12	Madeline Black
W-A-Y Academy West Campus	19321 W Chicago St	Detroit, MI	48228	313-444-9398		6-12	Demeatrice Brooks
WAY Michigan	407 E Fort St	Detroit, MI	48226-2940	313-444-9292		6-12	Michelle Sarkody
Wells Academy	281 S Fair Ave	Benton Harbor, MI	49022-7219	269-926-2885	926-2923	K-7	Charlie Lovelady
Wellspring Preparatory HS	1031 Page St NE	Grand Rapids, MI	49505-5544	616-235-9500	235-2526	9-12	Jessica Knoth
West MI Academy Environmental Science	4463 Leonard St NW	Grand Rapids, MI	49534-2138	616-791-7454	791-7453	PK-12	Kerri Barrett
West Michigan Acad of Arts & Academics	17350 Hazel St	Spring Lake, MI	49456-1222	616-844-9961	844-9941	PK-8	Cathy Cantu
West Michigan Aviation Academy	5363 44th St SE	Grand Rapids, MI	49512-4093	616-446-8886	957-0491	9-12	Patrick Cwayna
Weston Preparatory Academy	22930 Chippewa St	Detroit, MI	48219-1161	313-387-6038	387-6180	K-8	Yvonne McClean
West Village Academy - South Campus	3530 Westwood St	Dearborn, MI	48124-3100	313-274-9200	274-0062	K-8	Coletta Counts
White Pine Academy	510 Russell St	Leslie, MI	49251-9478	517-589-8961	589-9194	K-8	Keven Numinen
Winans Academy of Performing Arts ES	9740 McKinney St	Detroit, MI	48224-2503	313-640-4610	640-4611	K-8	Tomi Ingram
Windemere Park Charter Academy	3100 W Saginaw St	Lansing, MI	48917-2307	517-327-0700	327-0800	PK-8	Yvonne Thomas
Windover HS	919 Smith Rd	Midland, MI	48640-4164	989-832-0852	839-7699	9-12	Gina Wilson
Woodland Park Academy	2083 E Grand Blanc Rd	Grand Blanc, MI	48439-2700	810-695-4710	695-1658	K-8	Jeremy Brown
Woodland S	7224 Supply Rd	Traverse City, MI	49696-9400	231-947-7474	947-7667	K-8	Nathan Tarsa
Woodward Academy	951 E Lafayette St	Detroit, MI	48207-2999	313-961-2108	963-3501	PK-8	Jeremaine Kyles
WSC Academy	855 Jefferson St	Ypsilanti, MI	48197-5209	734-794-0218	794-0216	9-12	Portia Davis-Mann
Youth Advancement Academy	6750 Chime St	Kalamazoo, MI	49009-6408	269-353-4193	353-4214	9-12	Amber Long
		Minnesota					
Academia Cesar Chavez S	1801 Lacrosse Ave	Saint Paul, MN	55119	651-778-2940	778-2942	PK-6	Bondo Nyembwe
Academic Arts HS	60 Marie Ave E	West Saint Paul, MN	55118-5932	651-457-7427	554-7611	9-12	Krissy Wright
Achieve Language Academy	2169 Stillwater Ave E	Saint Paul, MN	55119-3508	651-738-4875	738-8268	PK-8	Mary Apuli
AFSA HS	100 Vadnais Blvd	Vadnais Heights, MN	55127-4036	651-209-3910	209-3911	9-12	Becky Meyer
AFSA MS	1435 Midway Pkwy	Saint Paul, MN	55108	612-260-2662	493-2088	5-8	Becky Meyer

School	Address	City,State	Zip code	Telephone	Fax	Grade	Contact
Agamim Classical Academy	1503 Boyce St	Hopkins, MN	55343-8549	952-856-2531	856-2728	K-8	Miranda Morton
Arcadia Charter S	1719 Cannon Rd	Northfield, MN	55057-1680	507-663-8806	663-8802	6-12	Patrick Exner
Art and Science Academy	903 6th Avenue Ct NE	Isanti, MN	55040	763-568-4091		K-8	Jill Arendt
Aspen Academy	14825 Zinran Ave	Savage, MN	55378-4557	952-226-5940	226-5949	K-8	Mike McNulty
Athlos Academy St. Cloud	3701 33rd St S	Saint Cloud, MN	56301	320-281-4430		K-6	Kathy Mortensen Ed.D.
Athlos Leadership Academy	10100 Noble Pkwy N	Brooklyn Park, MN	55443-1311	763-777-8942	315-0601	PK-8	Jennifer Geraghty
Augsburg Fairview Academy	2504 Columbus Ave	Minneapolis, MN	55404	612-333-1614	339-2229	9-12	Heidi Anderson
Aurora Charter S	2101 E 26th St	Minneapolis, MN	55404-4102	612-722-1999	870-4287	K-8	Matthew Cisewski
Avalon Charter S	700 Glendale St	Saint Paul, MN	55114-1782	651-649-5495	649-5462	6-12	Carrie Bakken
Banaadir Academy	1130 N 7th St	Minneapolis, MN	55411	612-326-7200	521-4007	K-8	Shawn Fondow
Banaadir South Charter ES	2526 27th Ave S	Minneapolis, MN	55406	612-518-8176	521-4007	K-5	Rani Hayden
Bdote Learning Center	3216 E 29th St	Minneapolis, MN	55406	612-279-6380		K-5	Angela Christian-Nelson
Beacon Academy	9060 Zanzibar Ln N	Maple Grove, MN	55311-1261	763-546-9999	416-3682	K-8	Sean Koster
Best Academy	1300 Olson Memorial Hwy	Minneapolis, MN	55411	612-381-9743		K-8	Hashim Yonis
Birch Grove Community S	PO Box 2383	Tofte, MN	55615-2383	218-663-0170	663-7904	PK-5	Caroline Wood
Bluesky Online Charter S	33 Wentworth Ave E Ste 100	West Saint Paul, MN	55118-3432	651-642-0888	642-0435	7-12	Amy Larsen
Bluffview Montessori S	1321 Gilmore Ave	Winona, MN	55987-2459	507-452-2807	452-6869	K-8	Stephanie Wehman
Bright Water ES	5140 Fremont Ave N	Minneapolis, MN	55430-3419	612-302-3410	302-5911	K-6	Ann Johnson
Cannon River STEM S	1800 14th St NE	Faribault, MN	55021-2508	507-331-7836		K-8	Nalani McCutcheon
Cedar Riverside Community Charter S	1610 S 6th St Ste 100	Minneapolis, MN	55454-1102	612-339-5767	339-2951	K-8	Randy Vetsch
CHOICE Technical Academy	315 S Grove Ave	Owatonna, MN	55060	507-400-4009		7-12	Sara Baird
City Academy	958 Jessie St	Saint Paul, MN	55130-4058	651-298-4624	292-6511	9-12	Milo Cutter
Clarkfield Charter S	301 13th St	Clarkfield, MN	56223	320-669-1995	669-1997	K-6	Kathy Koetter
College Prep Elementary S	355 Randolph Ave	Saint Paul, MN	55102-3762	651-605-2360	605-2369	K-6	Michael Raimondi
Cologne Academy	1221 Village Pkwy	Cologne, MN	55322-9248	952-466-2276	466-4030	K-8	Lynn Gluck-Peterson
Community of Peace Academy	471 Magnolia Ave E	Saint Paul, MN	55130-3849	651-776-5151	771-4841	PK-12	Cara Quinn
Community School of Excellence	170 Rose Ave W	Saint Paul, MN	55117-4437	651-917-0073	917-3717	K-8	Kazoua Kong-Thao
Cornerstone Montessori ES	1611 Ames Ave	Saint Paul, MN	55106-2903	651-774-5000		K-6	Liesl Taylor
Crosslake Community Charter S	36974 County Road 66	Crosslake, MN	56442-2527	218-692-5437	692-5437	K-8	Todd Lyscio
Crosslake Community Online HS	36974 County Road 66	Crosslake, MN	56442-2527	218-692-5437	692-5437	9-12	Todd Lyscio
Cyber Village Academy	768 Hamline Ave S	Saint Paul, MN	55116-2224	651-523-7170	523-7113	K-12	Dave Glick
DaVinci Academy of Arts and Science	13001 Central Ave NE	Blaine, MN	55434-4150	763-754-6577	754-6578	K-8	Debra Lach
Discovery Charter S	4100 66th St E	Inver Grove, MN	55076	651-444-8464	444-8468	K-5	Dan Hurley
Discovery Public S	126 8th St NW	Faribault, MN	55021-4241	507-331-5423	331-2618	6-12	Jim Severson
Discovery Woods Montessori Charter S	604 N 7th St	Brainerd, MN	56401	218-828-8200		K-6	Meg Litts
DREAM Technical Academy	1705 16th Street NE	Willmar, MN	56201	320-262-5640		7-12	Tammie Knick
Dugsi Academy	1091 Snelling Ave N	Saint Paul, MN	55108-2705	651-642-0667	642-0668	K-8	Abdulkadir Osman
Eagle Ridge Academy	11111 Bren Rd W	Minnetonka, MN	55343	952-746-7760	746-7765	K-12	Jason Ulbrich
East Range Academy of Tech & Science	2000 Siegel Blvd	Eveleth, MN	55734-8642	218-744-7965	744-2349	10-12	Judy Youso
E.C.H.O. Charter S	PO Box 158	Echo, MN	56237-0158	507-925-4143	925-4165	K-12	Jason VanEngen
Edvisions Off Campus S	PO Box 307	Henderson, MN	56044-0307	507-248-3101	665-2752	7-12	Gigi Dobosenski
El Colegio Charter S	4137 Bloomington Ave	Minneapolis, MN	55407-3332	612-728-5728	728-5790	9-12	Norma C. Garces
Excell Academy for Higher Learning	6510 Zane Ave N	Brooklyn Park, MN	55429-1571	763-533-0500	533-0508	PK-8	Sabrina Williams
Face to Face Academy	1165 Arcade St	Saint Paul, MN	55106-2615	651-772-5544	772-5621	9-12	Jennifer Plum
Flex Academy	100 W 66th St	Richfield, MN	55423-2371	612-470-0601		5-8	Tora Townsend
Freedom Academy Charter S	2201 Girard Ave N	Minneapolis, MN	55411-2548	612-361-6600		K-5	Toni Wilcox
Friendship Acad of Fine Arts Charter S	2600 E 38th St	Minneapolis, MN	55406	612-879-6703	879-6707	K-6	Dr. Charvez Russell
Glacial Hills ES	PO Box 189	Starbuck, MN	56381-0189	320-239-3840	239-2803	K-6	Deb Mathias
Global Academy	4065 Central Ave NE	Columbia Hts, MN	55421-2917	763-404-8200	781-5260	K-8	Helen Fisk
Goodall Environmental Science Academy	8008 83rd St NW	Maple Lake, MN	55358-2454	952-852-0129	679-7617	6-12	Craig Wignes
Great Expectations S	PO Box 310	Grand Marais, MN	55604-0310	218-387-9322	387-9344	K-8	Peter James
Great River S	1326 Energy Park Dr	Saint Paul, MN	55108-5202	651-305-2780	305-2781	1-12	Samuel O'Brien
Green Isle Community S	PO Box 277	Green Isle, MN	55338-0277	507-326-7144	326-5434	PK-6	Brandy Barrett
Harbor City International S	332 W Michigan St Ste 300	Duluth, MN	55802-1644	218-722-7574	625-6068	9-12	Anne Wise
Harvest Prep S - Seed Academy	1300 Olson Memorial Hwy	Minneapolis, MN	55411-3968	612-381-9743	381-0748	K-4	Rachelle Larson
Hennepin ES	2123 Clinton Ave	Minneapolis, MN	55404	612-843-5050	871-2406	K-6	Dr. Julie Henderson
Hiawatha College Prep	3800 Pleasant Ave	Minneapolis, MN	55409-1578	612-353-4324		5-8	John Kaczorek
Hiawatha Collegiate HS	4640 17th Ave	Minneapolis, MN	55407-4790	612-547-9056		9-12	Nicole Cooley
Hiawatha Leadership Academy	1611 E 46th St	Minneapolis, MN	55407-3669	612-455-4004	248-8947	K-4	Daniela Vasan
Hiawatha Leadership Academy	3810 E 56th St	Minneapolis, MN	55417-2218	612-987-5688	825-4777	PK-4	Eli Kramer
Higher Ground Academy	1381 Marshall Ave	Saint Paul, MN	55104-6353	651-645-1000	645-2100	K-12	Bill Wilson
High School for Recording Arts	1166 University Ave W	Saint Paul, MN	55104-4169	651-287-0890	287-0891	9-12	Anthony Simmons
Hmong College Prep Academy	1515 Brewster St	Saint Paul, MN	55108-2612	651-209-8002	289-1802	K-8	Dr. Christianna Hang
Hmong College Prep Academy HS	1515 Brewster St	Saint Paul, MN	55108-2612	612-209-8002	209-8003	9-12	Dr. Christianna Hang
Hope Community Academy	720 Payne Ave	Saint Paul, MN	55130-4127	651-796-4500	796-4599	K-8	MayChy Vu
International Spanish Language Academy	5959 Shady Oak Rd S	Minnetonka, MN	55343	952-746-6020	746-6023	K-6	Jeremy Perrin
Jeffrey Academy	1550 Summit Ave	Saint Paul, MN	55105-2274	651-414-6000	414-6006	5-8	Jennifer Schiller
Jennings Community Learning Center	2455 University Ave W	Saint Paul, MN	55114-1507	651-649-5403	649-5490	7-12	Bill Zimneiwicz
Kaleidoscope Charter S	7525 Kalland Ave NE	Otsego, MN	55301-9690	763-428-1890	428-1691	K-12	Dr. Brett Wedlund
Kato Public Carter S	110 N 6th St	Mankato, MN	56001-4443	507-387-5524	387-5680	7-12	Claudia Madrigal
KIPP North Star Academy	5034 Oliver Ave N	Minneapolis, MN	55430-3355	612-287-9700	287-9702	5-8	Alvin Abraham
La Crescent Montessori & STEM S	1116 S Oak St	La Crescent, MN	55947-1560	507-895-4054	895-4064	PK-12	Tammy Stremcha
Lafayette Public Charter S	PO Box 125	Lafayette, MN	56054-0125	507-228-8943	228-8288	PK-8	Peter Roufs
Lakes International Language Academy	246 11th Ave SE	Forest Lake, MN	55025	651-464-0771	464-4429	PK-5	Cam Hedlund
Lakes International Language Academy	19850 Fenway Ave N	Forest Lake, MN	55025	651-464-8989	464-8990	6-12	Shannon Peterson
Learning for Leadership Charter	3300 5th St NE	Minneapolis, MN	55418-1165	612-789-9598	789-0547	K-12	Jit Kundan
Level Up Academy	2600 Co Rd E East	White Bear Lake, MN	55110	651-408-5559		K-8	Molly Dandelet
LIFE Prep	930 Geranium Ave E	Saint Paul, MN	55106-2610	651-793-6624	793-6633	PK-6	Bart Johnson
Lincoln International S	2520 Minnehaha Ave	Minneapolis, MN	55404-4118	612-872-8690	879-9557	9-12	Manyi Tambe
Lionsgate Academy	5605 Green Cir Dr	Minnetonka, MN	55343	612-351-4567	737-4007	7-12	Diane Halpin Ph.D.
Loveworks Academy for Arts	2225 Zenith Ave N	Golden Valley, MN	55422-3852	952-522-6830	522-6840	K-8	April Shaw
Main Street S of Performing Arts	1320 Mainstreet	Hopkins, MN	55343-7403	952-224-1340	224-2955	9-12	Matt McFarlane
Mastery S	4021 Thomas Ave N	Minneapolis, MN	55412	612-876-4105		K-4	Paula Bump
Math & Science Academy	8430 Woodbury Xing	Woodbury, MN	55125-9433	651-578-8061	578-7532	6-12	John Gawarecki
Metro Deaf S	1471 Brewster St	Saint Paul, MN	55108-2612	651-224-3995	222-0939	PK-12	Dr. Susan Lane-Outlaw
Metro Schools of MN	2600 E 26th St	Minneapolis, MN	55406-1201	612-722-2555	729-2274	6-12	Farhan Hussein
Milroy Area Charter S	PO Box 10	Milroy, MN	56263	507-336-2563	336-2568	K-4	Heidi Sachariason
Minisinaakwaang Leadership Academy	20930 367th Ln	McGregor, MN	55760	218-768-5301	768-3357	K-12	Paul McGlynn
Minnesota Early Learning Academy	6717 85th Ave N	Brooklyn Park, MN	55445-2255	763-205-4396	999-6988	K-6	Jennifer Mitchell
Minnesota International MS	277 12th Ave N	Minneapolis, MN	55401	612-465-8465		5-8	Faysal Ali
Minnesota Internship Center	1821 University Ave W # 271	Saint Paul, MN	55104	651-288-3152		9-12	Jon Gross
Minnesota Internship Center Charter	2507 Fremont Ave N	Minneapolis, MN	55411-2079	612-238-3022		9-12	Robert Heise
Minnesota Internship Center Charter	2507 Fremont Ave N	Minneapolis, MN	55411-2079	612-238-0758		9-12	Cindy Hahn
Minnesota Internship Center Charter	2507 Fremont Ave N	Minneapolis, MN	55411-2079	612-588-1449		9-12	Jim Morehouse
Minnesota Math and Science Academy	169 Jenks Ave	Saint Paul, MN	55117-5068	651-246-0845	330-1984	K-6	Murat Oguz
Minnesota New Country S	PO Box 488	Henderson, MN	56044-0488	507-248-3353	248-3604	K-12	Jim Wartman
Minnesota Online HS	2314 University Ave W	Saint Paul, MN	55114-1863	800-764-8166	586-2870	9-12	Elissa Raffa
Minnesota Virtual HS	180 5th St E # M10A	Saint Paul, MN	55101-2672	612-746-7977	746-7989	6-12	Bill Glenz
MTCS Connections Academy	1336 Energy Park Dr Ste 100	Saint Paul, MN	55108-5283	651-523-0888	726-2917	K-12	Melissa Gould
MTS ES	1800 2nd St NE	Minneapolis, MN	55418	612-729-9140	789-0446	K-6	Shelia Casey
MTS HS	2872 26th Ave S	Minneapolis, MN	55406	612-722-9013	724-4763	7-12	Larry Ronglien
MTS P.E.A.S.E. Academy	601 13th Ave SE	Minneapolis, MN	55414-1437	612-378-1377	378-4886	9-12	Michael Durchslag
Nasha Shkola Charter S	3500 Williston Rd	Minnetonka, MN	55345	952-746-1880	452-8672	K-8	Paul Kinsley
Natural Science Academy	920 Holley Ave Ste 3	Saint Paul Park, MN	55071-1558	651-925-5050	925-5051	K-5	Kendra Hunding
Naytahwaush Community S	PO Box 8	Naytahwaush, MN	56566-0008	218-935-5025	935-5263	K-6	Terri Anderson
Nerstrand Charter S	PO Box 156	Nerstrand, MN	55053-0156	507-333-6850	333-6870	K-5	Maggie Kiley
New Century Academy	1000 5th Ave SE	Hutchinson, MN	55350	320-234-3660	234-3668	7-12	Jason Becker
New City S	229 13th Ave NE	Minneapolis, MN	55413-1117	612-623-3309	623-3319	K-8	Jitendrapal Kundan
New Discoveries Montessori Academy	1000 5th Ave SE	Hutchinson, MN	55350-7028	320-234-6362	234-6300	K-6	Dave Conrad
New Heights Charter S	614 Mulberry St W	Stillwater, MN	55082-4858	651-439-1962	439-0716	K-12	Thomas Kearney
New Millennium Academy	5105 Brooklyn Blvd	Minneapolis, MN	55429	612-377-6260	377-6261	K-8	Yee Yang
New Summit S	1380 Energy Ln Ste 108	Saint Paul, MN	55108	612-410-4109	305-0891	K-8	Dr. Dido Kotile
Noble Academy	9477 Decatur Dr N	Minneapolis, MN	55445-3400	763-592-7706	592-7707	K-5	Neal Thao
Northeast College Prep Charter S	300 Industrial Blvd NE	Minneapolis, MN	55413	612-248-8240		K-5	Carl Phillips
Northern Lights Community S	PO Box 2829	Warba, MN	55793-2829	218-492-4400	492-4402	6-12	Michael Hamernick
North Lakes Academy	308 15th St SW	Forest Lake, MN	55025-1303	651-982-2688	464-6409	9-12	Cam Stottler
North Lakes Academy	255 7th Ave NW Ste B	Forest Lake, MN	55025-1177	651-982-2773	464-6409	5-8	Andrew Brandt
North Metro Flex Academy	2350 Helen St	North St Paul, MN	55109	612-900-4435		K-4	Therese Privette
North Shore Community S	5926 Ryan Rd	Duluth, MN	55804-9672	218-525-0663	525-0024	K-6	Barry Wolff
North Star Academy	3301 Technology Dr	Duluth, MN	55811	218-728-9556	728-2075	K-8	Bonnie Jorgenson
Northwest Passage HS	11345 Robinson Dr NW	Coon Rapids, MN	55433-4061	763-862-9223	862-9250	9-12	Peter Wieczorek
Nova Classical Academy	1455 Victoria Way	Saint Paul, MN	55102-4213	651-209-6320	209-6325	K-12	Dr. Eric Williams
Odyssey Academy	6201 Noble Ave N	Brooklyn Center, MN	55429	763-971-8200	549-2380	K-8	Melinda Crowley
Oshki Ogimaag Charter S	PO Box 320	Grand Portage, MN	55605-0320	218-475-2112	475-2119	K-6	Anna Deschampe
PACT Charter S	7250 E Ramsey Pkwy	Ramsey, MN	55303-6902	763-712-4200	712-4201	K-12	Tony Simons
Paladin Career and Technical HS	308 Northtown Dr NE	Blaine, MN	55434-1039	763-786-4799	786-4798	9-12	Brandon Wait
Parnassus Preparatory S	11201 96th Ave N	Maple Grove, MN	55369-3676	763-496-1416	898-3977	K-12	Constance Ford

School	Address	City,State	Zip code	Telephone	Fax	Grade	Contact
Partnership Academy	305 E 77th St	Richfield, MN	55423-4312	612-866-3630	866-3640	K-5	Lisa Hendricks
Pillager Area Charter S	PO Box 130	Pillager, MN	56473-0130	218-746-3875	746-3876	9-12	Mark Wolhart
Prairie Creek Community S	27695 Denmark Ave	Northfield, MN	55057-5333	507-645-9640	645-8234	K-5	Simon Tyler
Prairie Seeds Academy	6200 W Broadway Ave	Minneapolis, MN	55428-2826	763-450-1388	450-1389	K-12	Choua Yang
Prodeo Academy	1555 40th Ave NE	Columbia Hts, MN	55421-3103	612-559-4881		K-8	Richard Campion
Raleigh Academy	5905 Raleigh St	Duluth, MN	55807	218-628-0697	628-9924	K-5	Danielle Perich
Ridgeway Community S	35564 County Road 12	Houston, MN	55943-4006	507-454-9566	454-9567	PK-5	Jodi Dansingburg
River's Edge Academy	188 Plato Blvd W	Saint Paul, MN	55107-2021	651-234-0150	234-0159	9-12	Meghan Cavalier
Riverway Learning Community Charter S	1733 W Service Dr Ste 18	Winona, MN	55987-2286	507-474-6120	474-6190	PK-12	Katey Wadewitz
Rochester Beacon Academy	974 Skyline Dr SW	Rochester, MN	55902	507-258-5351		6-12	Kari Weiss
Rochester Math and Science Academy	415 16th St SW	Rochester, MN	55902-2125	507-252-5995		K-8	Abdulkadir Abdulle
Rochester Off Campus Charter HS	2364 Valleyhigh Dr NW	Rochester, MN	55901-7641	507-282-3325	282-0976	9-12	Jay Martini
Rochester STEM Academy	415 16th St SW	Rochester, MN	55902-2125	507-281-2381		9-12	Bryan Rossi Ph.D.
SAGE Academy Charter S	3900 85th Ave N	Brooklyn Park, MN	55443-1908	763-315-4020	315-4028	9-12	Diane Scholten
Saint Cloud Math and Science Academy	136 Division St	Waite Park, MN	56387	320-774-2201	774-2204	K-5	Tammy Bengtson
St. Croix Preparatory Academy	4260 Stagecoach Trl N	Stillwater, MN	55082-1197	651-395-5900	395-5901	K-12	Jon Gutierrez
Saint Paul City S	260 Edmund Ave	Saint Paul, MN	55103-1783	651-225-9177	487-7551	PK-8	Bondo Nyembwe
Saint Paul Conservatory Performing Art	16 5th St W	Saint Paul, MN	55102	651-290-2225	290-9000	9-12	Callie Jacobs
Sankofa Underground North Academy	1200 W Broadway Ave Ste 110	Minneapolis, MN	55411	612-547-6617	208-0382	K-1	AsaleSol Young
Schoolcraft Learning Community S	PO Box 1685	Bemidji, MN	56619-1685	218-586-3284	586-3285	K-8	Scott Anderson
Sejong Academy of Minnesota	1330 Blair Ave N	Saint Paul, MN	55104	651-330-6944	330-7011	PK-8	Brad Tipka
Seven Hills Preparatory Academy	8600 Bloomington Ave	Bloomington, MN	55425-1920	952-426-6000	426-6020	K-5	Carolyn Farrell
Seven Hills Preparatory Academy	1401 W 76th St	Richfield, MN	55423-3852	612-314-7600		6-8	Carl Schlueter
Sojourner Truth Academy	3820 Emerson Ave N	Minneapolis, MN	55412-2039	612-588-3599	588-0217	PK-8	Julie Guy
Southside Family Charter S	4500 Clinton Ave	Minneapolis, MN	55419-5143	612-872-8322	872-0612	K-8	David Nunez
Spectrum 6th Grade Center	11044 Industrial Circle NW	Elk River, MN	55330	763-241-8703		6-6	Vanessa Spark
Spectrum HS	17796 Industrial Cir NW	Elk River, MN	55330-4754	763-241-8703	633-1380	7-12	Vanessa Spark
Spero Academy	1534 6th St NE	Minneapolis, MN	55413-1319	612-465-8600	465-8603	K-5	Curtis Windham
Star of the North Academy Charter S	1562 Viking Blvd NE	East Bethel, MN	55011	763-812-1367		K-8	Lulzim Axhijaj
STEP Academy	835 5th St E	Saint Paul, MN	55106	651-289-6120	457-4692	6-12	Mustafa Ibrahim
Stonebridge World S	4530 Lyndale Ave S	Minneapolis, MN	55419-4802	612-877-7400	877-7444	K-6	Barbara Novy
Stride Academy	1025 18th St N	Saint Cloud, MN	56303	320-230-5340	253-0006	K-3	Brett Fechner
Stride Academy South Campus	3241 Oakham Ln	Saint Cloud, MN	56301-6373	320-230-5340	217-6318	4-8	Donna Nordstrom
Summit Charter S	3109 E 50th St	Minneapolis, MN	55417	612-876-3050		K-6	Madgy Rabeaa
Swan River Montessori Charter S	500 Maple St	Monticello, MN	55362-8878	763-271-7926	295-0075	PK-6	Katie Curtis
TEAM Academy	220 17th Ave NE	Waseca, MN	56093-2753	507-833-8326	833-8327	K-6	Jill Courtney
Tesfa International S	1745 University Ave 1st Fl	Saint Paul, MN	55104	651-717-4844	641-4052	K-6	Rebecca Magnuson
TrekNorth HS	2400 Pine Ridge Ave NW	Bemidji, MN	56601	218-444-1888	444-1893	6-12	Dan McKeon
Trio Wolf Creek Distance Learning	10363 Liberty Ln	Chisago City, MN	55013-5418	651-213-2017	257-0576	4-12	Tracy Quarnstrom
TRUTH Prep Academy	PO Box 28876	Saint Paul, MN	55128	651-401-5380		K-5	Jermaine Cooper
Twin Cities Academy	690 Birmingham St	Saint Paul, MN	55106	651-205-4797	205-4799	6-8	Betsy Lueth
Twin Cities Academy HS	690 Birmingham St	Saint Paul, MN	55106	651-205-4797	205-4799	9-12	Betsy Lueth
Twin Cities German Immersion S	1031 Como Ave	Saint Paul, MN	55103-1021	651-492-7106	330-2270	K-8	Ted Anderson
Twin Cities International ES	277 12th Ave N	Minneapolis, MN	55401-1026	612-821-6470	821-6477	K-4	Abdirashid Warsame
Ubah Medical Academy Charter S	1600 Mainstreet	Hopkins, MN	55343-7409	952-540-2942	540-2950	9-12	Musa Farah
Universal Academy Charter S	1745 University Ave W	Saint Paul, MN	55104	651-442-3124		K-8	Farhiya Einte
Upper Mississippi Academy	426 Osceola Ave S	Saint Paul, MN	55102-3535	651-528-8091	683-2042	6-12	Harry Adler
Urban Academy Charter S	1668 Montreal Ave	Saint Paul, MN	55116-2469	651-215-9419	215-9571	K-6	Mongsher Ly
Venture Academy	315 27th Ave SE	Minneapolis, MN	55414	612-345-9040	294-6737	6-12	Jon Bacal
Vermilion Country S	PO Box 629	Tower, MN	55790-0629	218-753-1246		7-12	Kevin Fitton
Voyageurs Expeditionary S	3724 Bemidji Ave N	Bemidji, MN	56601	218-444-3130	444-3126	6-12	Scott Anderson
Watershed HS	6541 16th Ave S	Minneapolis, MN	55423-1751	612-871-4363	871-1004	9-12	Destiny Sparks
West Side Summit Charter S	497 Humboldt Ave	Saint Paul, MN	55107-2866	651-200-4543		K-8	Ilse Akbar
Woodbury Leadership Academy	600 Weir Dr	Woodbury, MN	55125	651-539-2641	656-3031	K-8	Bert Strassburg
World Learner Charter S	112050 Hundertmark Rd	Chaska, MN	55318-2817	952-368-7398	368-6094	1-8	Deana Siekmann
Yinghua Academy	1616 Buchanan St NE	Minneapolis, MN	55413-1609	612-788-9095	788-9079	K-8	Susan Berg
Mississippi							
Hayes Cooper Center for Math & Science	500 N Martin Luther King	Merigold, MS	38759-9632	662-748-2734	748-2735	PK-6	Renee Lamastus
Midtown Public Charter S	301 Adelle St	Jackson, MS	39202	601-354-7770	487-9319	5-6	Josalyn Filkins
ReImagine Prep	309 W McDowell Rd	Jackson, MS	39204-5523	601-941-0844		6-12	Christina McDonald
Smilow Prep S	787 E Northside Dr	Jackson, MS	39206	601-941-0844		5-5	Victoria Haberman
Missouri							
Academia de Ninos ES	5123 E Truman Rd	Kansas City, MO	64127-2440	816-994-0396	472-1471	K-5	Kimberly Kenyon
Academie Lafayette S	3421 Cherry St	Kansas City, MO	64109-2269	816-888-7400	888-7410	K-3	Heather Royce
Academie Lafayette S	6903 Oak St	Kansas City, MO	64113-2530	816-361-7735	361-5788	4-8	Elimane Mbengue
Academy for Integrated Arts	7910 Troost Ave	Kansas City, MO	64131	816-444-1720	444-1721	K-6	Tricia DeGraff
Academy of Envrnmntl Sci & Math ES	3325 Bell Ave	Saint Louis, MO	63106-1602	314-932-1464		K-5	Anna Westlund
Academy of Envrnmntl Sci & Math MS	3021 Hickory St	Saint Louis, MO	63104-1818	314-345-5673		6-8	CeAndre Perry
Allen Village HS	4251 Bridger Rd	Kansas City, MO	64111-3116	816-931-0177	561-4640	9-12	Phyllis Washington
Allen Village S	706 W 42nd St	Kansas City, MO	64111-3120	816-931-0177	561-4640	K-8	Amy Washington
Alta Vista Charter HS	1524 Paseo Blvd	Kansas City, MO	64127	816-471-2582	221-0012	9-12	Eduardo Mendez
Alta Vista Charter MS	2640 Belleview Ave	Kansas City, MO	64108-2325	816-471-2139	960-4913	6-8	Melody Stutzman
Aspire Academy	5421 Thekla Ave	Saint Louis, MO	63120-2513	314-383-8900	383-8925	PK-6	Sheldon McAfee
Banneker Charter Academy Technology	6401 Rockhill Rd	Kansas City, MO	64131-1122	816-926-9110	363-8721	PK-8	Dr. Marian Brown
Biome S	4471 Olive St	Saint Louis, MO	63108	314-531-0982	737-7187	K-8	Debi Weaver
Brookside Charter S	1815 E 63rd St	Kansas City, MO	64130	816-531-2192	756-3055	K-8	Roger Offield
Carondelet Leadership Academy	7604 Michigan Ave	Saint Louis, MO	63111-3332	314-802-8744	802-8721	K-8	Patrice Coffin
Chinese S	3740 Marine Ave	Saint Louis, MO	63118	314-533-0975		K-5	Dr. Lydia Chen
City Garden Montessori Charter S	1618 Tower Grove Ave	Saint Louis, MO	63110-2206	314-664-7646	664-4997	PK-8	Dr. Nicole Evans Ed.D.
Confluence Academy-Old North St. Louis	3017 N 13th St	Saint Louis, MO	63107-3924	314-241-1110	241-1115	K-6	Sonya Murray
Confluence Academy-South City Campus	4235 S Compton Ave	Saint Louis, MO	63111	314-481-4700	351-0240	PK-8	Pam Davenport
Confluence Prep Academy	310 N 15th St	Saint Louis, MO	63103-2378	314-588-1247	588-1296	9-12	Mike Powers
Crossroads Academy of Kansas City	1015 Central St	Kansas City, MO	64105	816-221-2600	221-2601	K-8	Beverly Leonard
DeLaSalle Charter S	3737 Troost Ave	Kansas City, MO	64109-2658	816-561-4445	561-6106	9-12	Mark Williamson
EAGLE College Prep: Tower Grove East	2900 S Grand Blvd	Saint Louis, MO	63118	314-664-7627	930-2452	K-4	Emily Dittmer
EAGLE College Preparatory S	2617 Shenandoah Ave	Saint Louis, MO	63104	314-664-7627	735-4471	K-4	English Marvin
EAGLE College Preparatory S	3716 Morganford Rd	Saint Louis, MO	63116-1615	314-664-7627	664-6250	K-8	TarynAnn Barry
French S	3740 Marine Ave	Saint Louis, MO	63118	314-533-0975		K-5	Meghan Hill
Frontier S of Excellence	5605 Troost Ave	Kansas City, MO	64110	816-822-1331	822-1332	6-12	
Frontier S of Innovation	6700 Corporate Dr	Kansas City, MO	64120	816-363-1907	363-1165	4-8	Kristin Snyder
Frontier S of Innovation	6700 Corporate Dr	Kansas City, MO	64120	816-363-1907	363-1165	K-3	Rose Dicus
Frontier STEM HS	6455 E Commerce Ave	Kansas City, MO	64120	816-541-8200	399-2747	9-12	Serkan Kilic
Gateway Science Academy	5049 Fyler Ave	Saint Louis, MO	63139-1103	314-261-4361	261-4364	6-12	Matt Sagnak
Gateway Science Academy	6651 Gravois Ave	Saint Louis, MO	63116	314-669-9000	669-9944	K-5	Wendy Gilliam
Gateway Science Academy of St. Louis	6576 Smiley Ave	Saint Louis, MO	63139	314-932-7513	932-7514	K-5	Nuh Celik
Genesis Promise Academy	3800 E 44th St	Kansas City, MO	64130-2168	816-921-0775	921-4268	K-8	Kevin Foster
Grand Center Arts Academy	711 N Grand Blvd	Saint Louis, MO	63103-1029	314-533-1791	371-4630	6-12	Matt Frederickson
Hawthorn Leadership S for Girls	1901 N Kingshighway Blvd	Saint Louis, MO	63113-1123	314-361-5323		6-8	Dr. Robyn Wiens
Hogan Preparatory Academy	6409 Agnes Ave	Kansas City, MO	64132	816-444-4479	444-4268	6-8	Zac Coughlin
Hogan Preparatory Academy	1221 E Meyer Blvd	Kansas City, MO	64131-1207	816-444-3464	363-0473	9-12	Shannon North
Hogan Preparatory Academy	5809 Michigan Ave	Kansas City, MO	64130	816-444-5010	361-2410	K-5	Amber White
Hope Leadership Academy	2800 E Linwood Blvd	Kansas City, MO	64128-1544	816-921-1213	332-6296	K-4	Sean Saunders
International S	3740 Marine Ave	Saint Louis, MO	63118	314-533-0975		6-8	Rob Biesendorfer
Kansas City Neighborhood Academy	1619 E 24th Ter	Kansas City, MO	64108	816-418-1500		PK-3	Dr. Robin Henderson
Kauffman S	6401 Paseo Blvd	Kansas City, MO	64131-1213	816-268-5660	268-5645	5-12	Hannah Lofthus
KIPP Endeavor Academy	PO Box 22624	Kansas City, MO	64113	816-241-3994	241-3339	K-8	Jana Cooper
KIPP Inspire S	1212 N 22nd St	Saint Louis, MO	63106	314-296-3502	696-8925	5-8	Joseph Olwig
KIPP Triumph Academy	955 Arcade Ave	Saint Louis, MO	63112-2702	314-454-9255	249-4328	5-8	Elizabeth Valerio
KIPP Victory Academy	955 Arcade Ave	Saint Louis, MO	63112	314-454-9255		K-4	Jeremy Braun
KIPP Wisdom Academy	2647 Ohio Ave	Saint Louis, MO	63118	314-384-9561	975-0072	K-4	Jacob Shiffrin
Lafayette Preparatory Academy	1900 Lafayette Ave	Saint Louis, MO	63104	314-880-4458	880-4459	K-5	Susan Marino
Lamb ES	1000 Charlotte St	Kansas City, MO	64106-3051	816-842-8040	842-7727	K-8	Jennifer Wilson
La Salle MS	1106 N Jefferson Ave	Saint Louis, MO	63106	314-531-9820	531-4820	5-8	Dr. Phillip Pusateri
Lift for Life Academy	1731 S Broadway	Saint Louis, MO	63104-4050	314-231-2337	231-1299	6-12	David LeMay
New Hope Academy	1001 Bennington Ave	Kansas City, MO	64126	816-595-0800	595-0801	9-12	
North Side Community S	3033 N Euclid Ave	Saint Louis, MO	63115-1632	314-385-4500	385-9538	PK-5	John Grote
Parks ES	3715 Wyoming St	Kansas City, MO	64111-3945	816-753-6700	753-3436	K-4	Joe Palmer
Pathway Academy	2015 E 72nd St	Kansas City, MO	64132	816-631-7100	621-7101	K-5	Joseph Williams
Preclarus Mastery Academy	620 N Grand Blvd	Saint Louis, MO	63103	314-454-0815	338-7435	4-8	Mylai Tenner
Premier Charter S	5279 Fyler Ave	Saint Louis, MO	63139-1300	314-645-9600	645-9700	K-8	Julie Frugo
Quality Hill Academy	1080 Washington St	Kansas City, MO	64105	816-221-3191	221-3192	K-3	Lindsay Yates
St. Louis College Prep	1224 Grattan St	Saint Louis, MO	63104-2922	314-561-3440	667-3477	5-8	Fleischer Lauren
St. Louis College Prep HS	1224 Grattan St	Saint Louis, MO	63104-2922	314-561-3440	667-3477	9-12	Fleischer Lauren

School	Address	City,State	Zip code	Telephone	Fax	Grade	Contact
Scuola Vita Nuova	535 Garfield Ave	Kansas City, MO	64124-1513	816-231-5788	231-5181	K-8	Nicole Goodman
Spanish S	4011 Papin St	Saint Louis, MO	63110-1731	314-533-0597		K-5	Arlene Galve-Salgado
Tolbert Community Academy	3400 Paseo Blvd	Kansas City, MO	64109-2429	816-561-0114	561-1015	K-8	Dr. LaQuanda Carpenter
University Academy	6801 Holmes Rd	Kansas City, MO	64131-1382	816-412-5900	410-0322	K-12	Tony Kline
Nevada							
Academy for Career Education	2800 Vassar St	Reno, NV	89502-3214	775-324-3900	324-3901	9-12	Bob DeRuse
Agassi Academy	1201 W Lake Mead Blvd	Las Vegas, NV	89106-2411	702-948-6000	948-6002	K-12	Chris Smith
Alpine Academy	605 Boxington Way Ste 112	Sparks, NV	89434-6918	775-356-1166	356-1168	9-12	Jill Ross
American Preparatory Academy	8377 W Patrick Ln	Las Vegas, NV	89113	702-970-6800	248-0454	K-11	Christie Olivieri M.S.
Bailey Charter ES	210 Gentry Way	Reno, NV	89502-4209	775-323-6767	323-6799	K-6	Michelle Engebretson
Beacon Academy of Nevada	7360 W Flamingo Rd	Las Vegas, NV	89147-5404	702-726-8600	538-9500	9-12	Tambre Tondryk
Carson Montessori S	2263 Mouton Dr	Carson City, NV	89706-0446	775-887-9500	887-9502	K-6	Jessica Daniels
Coral Academy of Science Charter S	1701 Valley Rd	Reno, NV	89512	775-322-0274	322-1378	K-4	Feyzi Tandogan
Coral Academy of Science Charter S	6275 Neil Rd	Reno, NV	89511	775-829-4601	829-4612	9-12	Feyzi Tandogan
Coral Academy of Science Charter S	1350 E 9th St	Reno, NV	89512-2904	775-323-2332	323-2366	5-8	Feyzi Tandogan
Coral Academy of Science - Las Vegas	8185 Tamarus St	Las Vegas, NV	89123-2464	702-269-8512	269-3258	K-2	Ercan Aydogdu
Coral Academy of Science - Las Vegas	7951 Deer Springs Way	Las Vegas, NV	89131	702-685-4333	385-7525	K-5	
Coral Academy of Science - Las Vegas	42 Baer Dr	Las Vegas, NV	89115	702-643-5121	643-5138	K-5	
Coral Academy of Science - Las Vegas	2150 Windmill Pkwy	Henderson, NV	89074	702-485-3410	722-2718	3-5	Ercan Aydogdu
Coral Academy of Science - Las Vegas	1051 Sandy Ridge Ave	Henderson, NV	89052	702-776-8800	776-8803	6-12	
Delta Academy	818 W Brooks Ave	Las Vegas, NV	89030	702-396-2252	396-0848	7-12	Dr. Kyle Konold
Discovery Charter S	3883 E Mesa Vista Ave	Las Vegas, NV	89120-2036	702-547-5682	547-5685	K-8	Clark Price
Doral Academy Cactus Campus	9025 W Cactus Ave	Las Vegas, NV	89178	702-960-7500	960-7960	K-8	Danielle Marshall
Doral Academy - Fire Mesa	2568 Fire Mesa St	Las Vegas, NV	89128	702-901-4950		K-12	Bridget Bilbray-Phillips
Doral Academy - Red Rock	626 Crossbridge Dr	Las Vegas, NV	89138	702-776-8530		K-12	Bridget Bilbray-Phillips
Doral Academy Saddle Campus	9625 W Saddle Ave	Las Vegas, NV	89147	702-776-6491	802-2638	K-9	Debbie Tomasetti
Elko Institute for Academic Achievement	1031 Railroad St Ste 107	Elko, NV	89801-3975	775-738-3422	738-3488	K-8	Connie Zeller
enCompass Academy	1300 Foster Dr	Reno, NV	89509	775-322-5566	322-5509	9-12	Toby Weidenmayer
Equipo Academy	4131 E Bonanza Rd	Las Vegas, NV	89110-2280	702-907-0432		6-12	Ben Salkowe
Explore Knowledge Academy	5871 Mountain Vista St	Las Vegas, NV	89120-2308	702-870-5032	871-5032	K-12	Abbe Mattson
Founders Academy	4025 N Rancho Dr	Las Vegas, NV	89130-3492	702-998-8368	998-1328	K-10	Timm Petersen
High Desert Montessori Charter S	2590 Orovada St	Reno, NV	89512-2119	775-624-2800	624-2801	PK-9	Tammie Stockton
Honors Academy of Literature	195 N Arlington Ave	Reno, NV	89501	775-737-4084	737-4533	K-8	Dr. Andi Morency
I Can Do Anything Charter HS	1195 Corporate Blvd Ste C	Reno, NV	89502-2363	775-857-1544	857-6825	9-12	Dawn Reid
Imagine S at Mountain View	6610 Grand Montecito Pkwy	Las Vegas, NV	89149	702-253-0251	253-0254	K-6	Dr. Eve Breier
Innovations International Charter S	1600 E Oakey Blvd	Las Vegas, NV	89104-3334	702-216-4337	216-4353	K-6	Dr. Connie Malin
Innovations International Charter S	950 E Sahara Ave	Las Vegas, NV	89104-3022	702-216-4337	216-4353	7-12	Dr. Connie Malin
Leadership Academy of Nevada	7495 W Azure Dr	Las Vegas, NV	89130-4416	702-350-1472	825-2684	6-12	Byron Richardson
Learning Bridge	505 S Pioche Hwy	Ely, NV	89301	775-289-3500	289-3511	K-8	Kristy Sedlacek
Mariposa Dual Language Academy	3875 Glen St	Reno, NV	89502	775-826-4040	826-4030	PK-5	Chris McBride
Mater Academy of Nevada	3445 Mountain Vista St	Las Vegas, NV	89121	702-485-2400	485-3322	PK-8	Renee Fairless
Nevada Connections Academy	555 Double Eagle Ct #2000	Reno, NV	89521	775-826-4200	826-4288	K-12	Steve Werlein
Nevada State HS	233 N Stephanie St	Henderson, NV	89074-8060	702-953-2600	953-2608	11-12	Mark Schumm
Nevada Virtual Academy	4801 S Sandhill Rd	Las Vegas, NV	89121	702-514-4025	407-5055	K-12	Yolanda Hamilton
Oasis Academy	920 W Williams Ave Ste 100	Fallon, NV	89406-2615	775-423-5437	423-5433	K-12	Melissa Mackedon
Odyssey Charter S	2251 S Jones Blvd	Las Vegas, NV	89146-3145	702-257-0578	259-7793	K-12	Tim Lorenz
One Hundred Academy of Excellence	2341 Comstock Dr	North Las Vegas, NV	89032-3512	702-636-2551	636-9475	K-8	Rachelle Conner
Pinecrest Academy	2840 Via Contressa	Henderson, NV	89044	702-473-5777		K-8	Michael O'Dowd
Pinecrest Academy	1385 E Cactus Ave	Las Vegas, NV	89183	702-750-9150	570-6360	K-8	Lucy Keaton
Pinecrest Academy	1360 S Boulder Hwy	Henderson, NV	89015-6958	702-749-3500	749-9995	K-8	Dr. Carrie Buck
Quest Preparatory Academy	7550 W Alexander Rd	Las Vegas, NV	89149	702-631-4751		K-K	Janelle Veith
Quest Preparatory Academy	1300 E Bridger Ave	Las Vegas, NV	89101	702-631-4751		K-5	Janelle Veith
Quest Preparatory Academy	4660 N Rancho Dr	Las Vegas, NV	89130	702-631-4751	548-2225	K-8	Janelle Veith
Rainbow Dreams Academy	950 W Lake Mead Blvd	Las Vegas, NV	89106-2339	702-638-0222	638-0220	K-6	Brenda Jordan
Sierra Nevada Academy	13880 Stead Blvd	Reno, NV	89506-1579	775-677-4500	677-4441	K-8	Dr. Kim Regan
Silver Sands Montessori Charter S	1841 Whitney Mesa Dr	Henderson, NV	89014-2070	702-522-6220	522-6218	K-8	Denise Crosby
Silver State Charter S	788 Fairview Dr	Carson City, NV	89701	775-883-7900	883-9130	9-12	Krystal Hoefling
Somerset Academy of Las Vegas	385 W Centennial Pkwy	North Las Vegas, NV	89084-5801	702-633-5616	633-5628	K-8	Dr. Francine Mayfield
Somerset Academy of Las Vegas	50 N Stephanie St	Henderson, NV	89074	702-998-0500	998-0503	K-8	Reggie Farmer
Somerset Academy of Las Vegas	4650 Losee Rd	North Las Vegas, NV	89081-4208	702-902-5466	902-5444	K-10	Dan Phillips
Somerset Academy of Las Vegas	7058 Sky Pointe Dr	Las Vegas, NV	89131	702-478-8888	776-7216	K-12	Dr. Andre Denson
Sports Leadership & Management Academy	1095 Fielders St	Henderson, NV	89015	702-473-5735	473-5753	6-9	Dan Triana
New Hampshire							
Academy for Science & Design	486 Amherst St Unit 1	Nashua, NH	03063-1282	603-595-4705	262-9163	6-12	Jennifer Cava
Birches Academy of Academics and Art	419 S Broadway	Salem, NH	03079	603-458-6399		K-8	Dr. Dael Angelico-Hart
Cocheco Academy of the Arts	40 Hampshire Cir	Dover, NH	03820	603-742-0700	742-7207	9-12	James Friel M.Ed.
Compass Classical Academy	15 Elkins St	Franklin, NH	03235	603-729-3370		K-6	Judy Tilton
CSI Charter S	26 Washington St	Penacook, NH	03303-1519	603-753-0194	753-0009	11-12	James Gorman
Founders Academy	5 Perimeter Rd	Manchester, NH	03103-3305	603-952-4705	624-0057	6-12	Maureen Mooney
Frost Charter S	PO Box 967	North Conway, NH	03860	603-356-6332		K-8	Ellen Ohlenbusch
Gate City Charter S for the Arts	7 Henry Clay Dr	Merrimack, NH	03054-4847	603-943-5273		K-8	Karin Cevasco
Granite State Arts Academy	19 Keewaydin Dr	Salem, NH	03079	603-912-4944		9-12	Anthony Polito
Great Bay eLearning Charter S	30 Linden St	Exeter, NH	03833-2622	603-775-8638	775-8528	7-12	Peter Stackhouse
Ledyard Charter S	PO Box 327	Lebanon, NH	03766	603-727-4772		9-12	John Higgins
Making Community Connections Charter S	60 Rogers St	Manchester, NH	03103	603-935-7488		6-12	Conor Sands
MC2 Charter S	149 Emerald St Ste UP3	Keene, NH	03431	603-283-0844		9-12	Chris O'Reilly
MicroSociety Academy Charter S	591 W Hollis St	Nashua, NH	03062	603-595-7877		K-6	Amy Bottomley
Mill Falls Charter S	100 William Loeb Dr	Manchester, NH	03109-5309	603-232-5176	518-7489	K-6	Meryl Levin
Mountain Village Charter S	13 Old Route 25	Plymouth, NH	03264	603-536-3900	947-0189	K-8	Alfie Eden Kerr
Next Charter S	5 Hood Rd	Derry, NH	03038	603-437-6398	437-6398	9-12	Joseph Crawford
North Country Charter Academy	260 Cottage St Ste A	Littleton, NH	03561-4137	603-444-1535	444-9843	7-12	Lisa Lavoie
PACE Career Academy	65 Pinewood Rd	Allenstown, NH	03275	603-210-1882	210-2341	9-12	Martin Castle
Polaris Charter S	100 Coolidge Ave	Manchester, NH	03102-3208	603-634-0034	634-0041	K-6	Jennifer Murdock - Smith
Seacoast Charter S	171 Watson Rd	Dover, NH	03820-5820	603-842-5764	842-5415	K-8	Peter Sweet
Strong Foundations Charter S	715 Riverwood Dr	Pembroke, NH	03275-3701	603-225-2715	225-2738	K-8	Beth McClure
Surry Village Charter S	449 Route 12A	Surry, NH	03431	603-357-9700	357-9701	K-8	Dr. Matora Fiorey
TEAMS Charter S	26 Washington St	Penacook, NH	03303-1519	603-753-4022	753-6429	K-8	George Rogers
Virtual Learning Academy	30 Linden St	Exeter, NH	03833-2622	603-778-2500	651-5038	6-12	Stephen Kossakoski
New Jersey							
Academy Charter HS	1725 Main St	South Belmar, NJ	07719-3051	732-681-8377	681-8375	9-12	Dr. Mary Jo McKinley
Academy for Urban Leadership HS	612 Amboy Ave	Perth Amboy, NJ	08861-2578	848-203-3742	203-3948	9-12	Dr. Nestor Collazo
Atlantic Community Charter S	112 S New York Road	Galloway, NJ	08205	609-568-1300		K-8	Jeanine Bethel
Banneker Preparatory Charter S	PO Box 128	Willingboro, NJ	08046-0128	609-531-0158		6-8	Richard Wilson M.A.
BelovED Community Charter S	508 Grand St	Jersey City, NJ	07302	201-630-4700	918-6137	K-6	Kelly Convery
Bergen Arts and Science Charter ES	30 Madonna Pl	Garfield, NJ	07026	862-247-8510	247-8511	K-3	
Bergen Arts and Science Charter HS	43 Maple Ave	Hackensack, NJ	07601	201-968-5039	968-5044	9-12	
Bergen Arts and Science Charter MS	200 MacArthur Ave	Garfield, NJ	07026-1214	973-253-0002	253-0110	4-8	Nihat Guvercin
Bridgeton Charter S	790 E Commerce St	Bridgeton, NJ	08302	856-497-8202		K-2	Mecca Jackson
Burch Charter S of Excellence	100 Linden Ave	Irvington, NJ	07111-2560	973-373-3223	373-3228	PK-5	Dr. Theodore Boler
Camden Academy Charter HS	879 Beideman Ave	Camden, NJ	08105-4227	856-365-1000	365-1005	9-12	Dr. Marvin Jones
Camden Community Charter S	415 N 9th St	Camden, NJ	08102	856-635-0310		K-8	Andrea Surratt
Camden Prep Charter S	1500 S 8th St	Camden, NJ	08104	856-379-4488		K-5	Michael Ambriz
Camden's Pride Charter S	897 N 31st St	Camden, NJ	08105	856-365-1000	966-5383	K-4	Christa Hahn
Camden's Promise Charter S	879 Beideman Ave	Camden, NJ	08105-4227	856-365-1000	365-1005	5-8	Dr. Joseph Conway
Central Jersey College Prep Charter S	17 Schoolhouse Rd	Somerset, NJ	08873-4245	732-302-9991	302-9992	K-12	Tarkan Topcuoglu
ChARTer-TECHnical HS for Performing Arts	413 New Rd	Somers Point, NJ	08244-2143	609-926-7694	926-8472	9-12	Dr. Brian McGuire
Classical Academy Charter S of Clifton	20 Valley Rd	Clifton, NJ	07013-1030	973-278-7707	277-7720	6-8	Vincent DeRosa
College Achieve Charter S	365 Emerson Ave	Plainfield, NJ	07062-1701	908-625-1879	441-9877	K-8	Mike Piscal
Community Charter S of Paterson	75 Spruce St	Paterson, NJ	07501	973-413-2057	345-7623	K-8	Mark Valli
Compass Academy Charter School	23 W Chestnut Ave	Vineland, NJ	08360	856-899-5570	431-7971	K-5	Susan Little
Cramer Hill ES	1033 Cambridge Ave	Camden, NJ	08105	856-726-0027		K-4	
Cresthaven Academy	530 W 7th St	Plainfield, NJ	07060	908-756-1234		K-8	Monica Villafuerte
Discovery Charter S	240 Halsey St	Newark, NJ	07102	973-623-0222	623-0024	4-8	Barbara Weiland
East Orange Community Charter S	99 Washington St	East Orange, NJ	07017-1006	973-996-0400	996-0398	K-4	Harvin Dash
Edison Energysmart Charter S	150 Pierce St 2nd Fl	Somerset, NJ	08873	732-412-7643	412-7645	K-8	Oguz Yildiz
Edwards Academic Charter S	509 Bramhall Ave	Jersey City, NJ	07304-2730	201-433-5300		K-8	James Brewer
Elysian Charter S	1460 Garden St	Hoboken, NJ	07030	201-876-0102	876-9576	K-8	Harry Laub Ph.D.
Empowerment Academy Charter S	508 Grand St	Jersey City, NJ	07302	201-630-4700		K-2	Rhema Dai
Englewood on the Palisades Charter S	65 W Demarest Ave	Englewood, NJ	07631-2316	201-569-9765	568-9576	K-6	Shirl Burns M.Ed.
Environment Comm Opportunity Charter S	817 Carpenter St	Camden, NJ	08102-1132	856-963-2627	963-2628	K-5	Dr. Antoinette Dendtler
Ethical Community Charter S	95 Broadway	Jersey City, NJ	07306-6304	201-984-4151	200-9931	K-7	Marta Bergamini
Foundation Academy Charter IS	363 W State St	Trenton, NJ	08618-5705	609-920-9200	920-9205	3-8	Graig Weiss

School	Address	City,State	Zip code	Telephone	Fax	Grade	Contact
Foundation Collegiate Academy	22 Grand St	Trenton, NJ	08611	609-920-9200	920-9205	9-12	Shavonne McMillan
Freedom Prep Charter S	1000 Atlantic Ave	Camden, NJ	08104	856-962-0766	962-0769	K-11	Ronald Brady
Freire Charter S	PO Box 120	Newark, NJ	07101	973-733-9393	733-9377	9-12	Tauheedah Baker-Jones
Golden Door Charter S	3044 John F Kennedy Blvd	Jersey City, NJ	07306-3604	201-795-4400	795-3308	K-8	Brian Stiles
Gray Charter S	55 Liberty St	Newark, NJ	07102-4815	973-824-6661	824-2296	K-8	Verna Gray
Greater Brunswick Charter S	429 Joyce Kilmer Ave	New Brunswick, NJ	08901-3322	732-448-1052	448-1055	K-8	Donna Medea
Great Futures Charter HS	225 Morris Blvd	Jersey City, NJ	07302	201-716-1520	716-1530	9-11	Dr. Brian Falkowski
Great Oaks Legacy Charter S	24 Maiden Ln	Newark, NJ	07102	973-565-9170		K-12	Jared Taillefer
Hatikvah International Academy Charter S	7 Lexington Ave	East Brunswick, NJ	08816	732-254-8300	254-8380	K-7	Dr. Marcia Grayson
Hoboken Charter S	4 Garden St	Hoboken, NJ	07030	201-963-3280	963-0695	PK-12	Deirdra Grode
Hoboken Dual Language Charter S	123 Jefferson St	Hoboken, NJ	07030	201-427-1458	706-4491	K-7	Jennifer Sargent
Holland Charter S	190 Oliver St	Paterson, NJ	07501-1816	973-345-2212	345-2233	K-8	Christina Scano
Hope Academy Charter S	601 Grand Ave	Asbury Park, NJ	07712-6656	732-988-4227	988-9125	K-8	DaVisha Pratt
Hope Community Charter S	836 S 4th St	Camden, NJ	08103-2047	856-379-3448		K-4	Robin Ruiz
Hudson Arts & Science Charter S	131 Midland Ave	Kearny, NJ	07032	201-955-1818	955-1817	K-5	Nihat Guvercin
International Academy of Atlantic City	25 W Black Horse Pike	Pleasantville, NJ	08232	609-498-6350		K-4	Natakie Chestnut
International Academy of Trenton	31 Chancery Ln	Trenton, NJ	08618	609-759-2005	337-7933	K-5	Dr. Taneisha Spall
International Charter S of Trenton	105 Grand St	Trenton, NJ	08611-2417	609-394-3111	394-3116	K-4	Melissa Benford
Jersey City Community Charter S	128 Danforth Ave	Jersey City, NJ	07305-2626	201-433-2288	433-5803	K-8	Eugene Brown
Jersey City Global Charter S	255 Congress St	Jersey City, NJ	07307	201-636-8540	636-8543	K-5	Nadira Raghunandan
Kingdom Charter S of Leadership	121 W Church St	Blackwood, NJ	08012-3971	856-232-0100		K-6	Wandria McCall-Hampton
KIPP Cooper Norcross	525 Clinton St	Camden, NJ	08103-1223	856-966-9600		K-1	Joanna Belcher
Knowledge A to Z Charter S	1725 Park Blvd	Camden, NJ	08103	856-375-1140	963-1980	K-4	Tishara Landi
Lady Liberty Academy Charter S	746 Sandford Ave	Newark, NJ	07106	973-623-9005	483-0807	K-8	Dr. James Catalano
LEAP Academy University Charter S	549 Cooper St	Camden, NJ	08102-1210	856-614-0400	342-7900	K-12	Manuel Delgado
Learning Community Charter S	2495 John F Kennedy Blvd	Jersey City, NJ	07304-2007	201-332-0900	332-4981	K-8	Colin Hogan
Link Community Charter S	23 Pennsylvania Ave	Newark, NJ	07114-2007	973-642-0529	642-1978	5-8	Kathleen Hester J.D.
Mastery S of Camden North Camden ES	800 Erie St	Camden, NJ	08102	856-726-0026		K-7	
Merit Prepartory Charter S	909 Broad St	Newark, NJ	07102	973-642-4400	367-7706	6-9	Kimberly White
M.E.T.S. Charter S	211 Sherman Ave	Jersey City, NJ	07307-2040	201-526-8500	526-7630	6-12	Ian Fallstich
Millville Public Charter S	1101 Wheaton Ave Ste 220	Millville, NJ	08332	856-506-8143		K-6	Valerie James-Kemp
Newark Educators Community Charter S	9-11 Hill St	Newark, NJ	07102-2642	973-732-3848	732-3847	PK-5	Dina Velez
Newark Prep Charter S	570 Broad St	Newark, NJ	07102-4518	862-307-7010	307-7107	9-12	Henry McNair
New Horizons Community Charter S	45 Hayes St	Newark, NJ	07103	973-848-0400	596-0984	K-6	Andre Hollis
North Star Academy Charter S	10 Washington Pl	Newark, NJ	07102-3106	973-642-0101	642-5800	K-12	Michael Ambriz
Obama Green Charter HS	35 Watchung Ave	Plainfield, NJ	07060-1207	877-643-4064		9-12	Steven King
PACE Charter School of Hamilton	1949 Hamilton Ave	Hamilton, NJ	08619-3736	609-587-2288	587-8483	K-5	Debbie Pontoriero
Passaic Arts and Science Charter S	7 Saint Francis Way	Passaic, NJ	07055	973-928-5544	928-5545	K-10	Nihat Guvercin
Paterson Arts and Science Charter S	202 Union Ave	Paterson, NJ	07502	862-336-1550	336-1551	K-8	Nihat Guvercin
Paterson Charter S for Science and Tech	276 Wabash Ave	Paterson, NJ	07503	973-345-4400	345-4636	K-6	Riza Gurcanli M.Ed.
Paterson Charter S for Science and Tech	196 W Railway Ave	Paterson, NJ	07503	973-247-0600	247-9924	7-12	
People's Preparatory HS	321 Bergen St	Newark, NJ	07103-2639	973-622-1790	622-1453	9-12	Jess Rooney
Phillip's Academy Charter S	47 State St	Paterson, NJ	07501	973-247-8920	624-0102	K-K	Regina Lauricella
Phillip's Academy Charter S	342 Central Ave	Newark, NJ	07103-2808	973-624-0644	624-0102	K-8	Mark Shultz
Pride Academy Charter S	117 Elmwood Ave	East Orange, NJ	07018-2420	973-672-3200	672-3207	5-8	Fiona Thomas
Princeton Charter S	100 Bunn Dr	Princeton, NJ	08540-2821	609-924-0575	924-0282	K-8	Lawrence Patton
Queen City Academy Charter S	815 W 7th St	Plainfield, NJ	07063-1449	908-753-4700	753-4816	K-8	Danielle West
Red Bank Charter S	58 Oakland St	Red Bank, NJ	07701-1104	732-450-2092	936-1923	PK-8	Meredith Pennotti
Ridge & Valley Charter S	1234 State Route 94	Blairstown, NJ	07825-4115	908-362-1114	362-6680	K-8	Nanci Dvorsky
Riverbank Charter S of Excellence	1300 Hornberger Ave	Roebling, NJ	08554-1313	609-499-4321	447-0350	K-3	Beth Kelley
Robeson Charter S for the Humanities	643 Indiana Ave	Trenton, NJ	08638-3821	609-394-7721	394-7720	4-8	Megan Lepore
Roseville Community Charter S	11 Gray St	Newark, NJ	07107-1529	973-908-8057	733-9555	K-1	
Soaring Heights Charter S	1 Romar Ave	Jersey City, NJ	07305-1713	201-434-4800	434-7474	K-8	Claudia Zuorick
Sussex Co. Charter S for Technology	385 N Church Rd	Sparta, NJ	07871-3307	973-383-3250	383-2901	6-8	Noreen Lazariuk
TEAM Academy Charter S	60 Park Pl Ste 802	Newark, NJ	07102-5508	973-705-8326	556-1238	K-12	Joanna Belcher
Teaneck Community Charter S	563 Chestnut Ave	Teaneck, NJ	07666	201-833-9600	833-9225	K-8	Ralph Gallo
Thomas Charter MS	308 S 9th St	Newark, NJ	07103	973-621-0060	792-0066	6-8	Genique Hamilton
Thomas Charter S	370 S 7th St	Newark, NJ	07103-2047	973-621-0060	621-0061	PK-5	Laura Porcaro
Treat Academy Charter S - North	443 Clifton Ave	Newark, NJ	07104-1339	973-482-8811	482-7681	K-8	Theresa Adubato
Treat Academy Chartr S - Central	180 William St	Newark, NJ	07103	973-286-1020	286-1050	K-8	Theresa Adubato
Trenton Stem-to-Civics Charter S	1555 Pennington Rd	Ewing, NJ	08618-1301	609-503-1103		9-12	Dr. Leigh Byron
Union County TEAMS Charter S	515 W 4th St	Plainfield, NJ	07060-4225	908-754-9043	754-7790	K-12	Sheila Thorpe
Unity Charter S	1 Evergreen Pl	Morristown, NJ	07960	973-292-1808	267-9288	K-8	Connie Sanchez
University Academy Charter HS	275 W Side Ave	Jersey City, NJ	07305-1130	201-200-3200	200-3262	9-12	Erie Lugo
University Heights Charter S	74 Hartford St	Newark, NJ	07103-2832	973-623-1965	623-8511	K-8	Tamara Cooper
Varisco-Rogers Charter S	233 Woodside Ave	Newark, NJ	07104-3113	973-481-9001	481-9009	K-8	Teressa Segarra
Village Charter S	101 Sullivan Way	Trenton, NJ	08628-3425	609-695-0110	695-1880	K-8	Keoke Wooten-Johnson
Vineland Public Charter S	2560 Industrial Way	Vineland, NJ	08360	856-691-1004	691-1005	PK-9	Cornelio Sabio

New Mexico

School	Address	City,State	Zip code	Telephone	Fax	Grade	Contact
ABQ Charter Academy	405 Dr Martin Luther King	Albuquerque, NM	87102-3541	505-242-6640	242-6872	9-12	Amy Roble
Academy for Technology and the Classics	74 A Van NU PO	Santa Fe, NM	87508-1465	505-473-4282	467-6513	7-12	Susan Lumley
ACE Leadership HS	1240 Bellamah Ave NW	Albuquerque, NM	87104-2133	505-242-4733	242-2220	9-12	Tori Stephens-Shauger
Albuquerque Institute of Math & Science	933 Bradbury Dr SE	Albuquerque, NM	87106-4374	505-559-4249	243-9235	6-12	Kathy Sandoval-Snider
Albuquerque School of Excellence	13201 Lomas Blvd NE	Albuquerque, NM	87112-7001	505-312-7711	312-7712	1-12	Salih Aykac
Albuquerque Sign Language Academy	620 Lomas Blvd NW	Albuquerque, NM	87102-2080	505-247-1701	247-1704	K-9	Raphael Martinez M.A.
Albuquerque Talent Development Academy	1800 Atrisco Dr NW	Albuquerque, NM	87120	505-503-2465	831-7031	9-12	Gloria Garza
Alma D Arte Charter HS	402 W Court Ave	Las Cruces, NM	88005-2596	575-541-0145	527-5329	9-12	Mark Harshorne
Anansi Charter S	PO Box 1709	El Prado, NM	87529-1709	575-776-2256	776-5561	K-8	Michele Hunt
Anthony Charter S	780 Landers Rd	Anthony, NM	88021-6812	575-882-0600	882-0603	7-12	Abe Armendariz
ASK Academy	4550 Sundt Rd NE	Rio Rancho, NM	87124-7021	505-891-0757	891-2115	6-12	Dan Busse
Biehl Charter HS	123 4th St SW	Albuquerque, NM	87102-3201	505-299-9409	299-9493	9-12	Frank McCulloch
Carinos De Los Ninos S	714 Calle Don Diego	Espanola, NM	87532	505-753-1128	747-3932	K-8	Vernon Jaramillo
Chavez Community S	1325 Palomas Dr SE	Albuquerque, NM	87108-4718	505-877-0558	242-1466	9-12	Tani Arness
Cien Aguas International S	2000 Randolph Rd SE	Albuquerque, NM	87106	505-255-0001	255-0400	K-8	Casey Benavidez
Coral Community Charter S	4401 Silver Ave SE	Albuquerque, NM	87108-2856	505-292-6725		K-4	Donna Eldredge
Corrales International S	5500 Wilshire Ave NE	Albuquerque, NM	87113	505-344-9733	338-1409	K-12	Mark Tolley
Cottonwood Classical Preparatory S	7801 Jefferson St NE	Albuquerque, NM	87109-4351	505-998-1021	341-9510	6-12	Sam Obenshain
Cottonwood Valley Charter S	PO Box 1829	Socorro, NM	87801-1829	575-838-2026	838-2420	K-8	Kim Schaffer
Creative Education Preparatory Institute	4801 Montano Rd NW	Albuquerque, NM	87120-2428	505-314-2374	314-2377	9-12	Elisa Bohannon
Deming Cesar Chavez Charter HS	315 E 1st St	Deming, NM	88030-3104	575-544-8404	544-8755	9-12	
Digital Arts and Technology Academy	1011 Lamberton Pl NE	Albuquerque, NM	87107-1641	505-341-0888	341-0658	9-12	Lisa Myhre
Dorn Community Charter S	1119 Edith Blvd SE	Albuquerque, NM	87102	505-243-1434	243-6943	K-5	Ellen Esquibel-Bellamy
Dream Dine	PO Box 4386	Shiprock, NM	87420-4386	505-948-2014		PK-8	
Duncan Heritage Academy	1900 Atrisco Dr NW	Albuquerque, NM	87120	505-839-4971	831-9027	PK-8	Jesus Moncada
Dzil Dit Looi S of Empowerment	PO Box 52	Navajo, NM	87328-0052	505-488-3170		6-11	Kayla Begay
East Mountain HS	PO Box 340	Sandia Park, NM	87047-0340	505-281-7400	281-4173	9-12	Monique Siedschlag
El Camino Real Charter S	3713 Isleta Blvd SW	Albuquerque, NM	87105-5919	505-314-2212	314-2216	K-12	Paym Greene
Estancia Valley Classical Academy	PO Box 2340	Moriarty, NM	87035-2340	505-832-2223	832-5006	K-12	Tim Thiery
Explore Academy	4001 Jefferson Plz NE	Albuquerque, NM	87109	505-468-1092	468-1098	9-12	Justin Baiardo
GREAT Academy	6001A San Mateo Blvd NE	Albuquerque, NM	87109	505-792-0306	792-0225	9-12	Jasper Matthews
Gutierrez MS	69 Gail Harris Blvd	Roswell, NM	88203	575-347-9703	347-9707	6-8	Joe Andreis
Health Leadership HS	1900 Randolph Rd SE	Albuquerque, NM	87106-4247	505-750-4547		9-12	Blanca Lopez
Horizon Academy - West	3021 Todos Santos St NW	Albuquerque, NM	87120-3601	505-998-0459	998-0463	PK-5	Cynthia Carter
International S at Mesa del Sol	2660 Eastman Ave SE	Albuquerque, NM	87106-9716	505-508-3295	508-3328	K-9	Dr. Sean Joyce
Jefferson Montessori Academy	500 W Church St	Carlsbad, NM	88220-5135	575-234-1703	887-9391	K-12	Cindy Holguin
Kennedy HS	4300 Blake Rd SW	Albuquerque, NM	87121-5179	505-873-1165	242-7444	9-12	Robert Baade
King Community S	8100 Mountain Rd NE	Albuquerque, NM	87110	505-344-0746	344-0789	K-8	Tonya Newton
La Academia de Esperanza	5310 Sequoia Rd NW	Albuquerque, NM	87120-1249	505-764-5500	764-5501	6-12	Steve Wood
La Academia Dolores Huerta	1480 N Main St	Las Cruces, NM	88001-1106	575-526-2984	523-5407	6-8	Octavio Casillas
La Jicarita Community S	14156 State Road 75	Penasco, NM	87553	915-496-7933		K-6	Cindy Arsenault
La Promesa Early Learning Center	7500 La Morada NW	Albuquerque, NM	87120-1765	505-268-3274	268-3276	PK-8	Dr. Analee Maestas
La Resolana Leadership Academy	230 Truman St NE	Albuquerque, NM	87108-1333	505-243-8114	243-8385	6-8	Justina Montoya
Las Montanas Charter S	1405 S Solano Dr	Las Cruces, NM	88001-4235	575-636-2100	527-7686	9-12	Richard Robinson
La Tierra Montessori S of the Arts & Sci	PO Box 1399	Espanola, NM	87532-1399	505-852-0200	852-0326	K-8	Suzanne Lynne
Learning Community Charter S	5555 McLeod Rd NE	Albuquerque, NM	87109-2408	505-332-3200	332-8780	6-12	Viola Martinez
Leopold Charter S	1422 Highway 180 E	Silver City, NM	88061-7837	575-538-2547	388-4970	6-12	Eric Ahner
Lindrith Area Heritage Charter S	PO Box 119	Lindrith, NM	87029-0119	575-774-6669		K-8	Rebecca Gibson M.A.
Los Puentes Charter S	4012 4th St NW	Albuquerque, NM	87107	505-342-5959	341-0836	7-12	Micaela Smith
MASTERS Program	6401 S Richards Ave	Santa Fe, NM	87508	505-428-7320	428-7322	10-12	Anne Salzmann
McCurdy Charter S	PO Box 2250	Espanola, NM	87532-2250	505-692-6090	692-6095	K-12	Janette Archuleta
Media Arts Collaborative Charter S	4401 Central Ave NE	Albuquerque, NM	87108-1209	505-243-1957	268-1651	6-12	Glenna Voigt M.A.
Middle College HS	200 College Rd Ste 9	Gallup, NM	87301	505-722-9945	722-9946	10-12	Connie Torres
Mission Achievement & Success Charter S	1718 Yale Blvd SE	Albuquerque, NM	87106-4286	505-242-3118	243-3062	6-9	JoAnn Myers
Monte Del Sol Charter S	4157 Walking Rain Rd	Santa Fe, NM	87507-0825	505-982-5225	982-5321	7-12	Dr. Robert Jessen
Montessori ES	1730 Montano Rd NW	Albuquerque, NM	87107-3210	505-796-0149	796-0147	K-8	Mary Jane Besante

School	Address	City,State	Zip code	Telephone	Fax	Grade	Contact
Montessori of the Rio Grande Charter S	1650 Gabaldon Dr NW	Albuquerque, NM	87104	505-842-5993	242-2907	PK-5	Dr. Bonnie Dodge Ed.D.
Moreno Valley HS	PO Box 1037	Angel Fire, NM	87710-1037	575-377-3100	377-7263	9-12	Greg Vincent
Mosaic Academy	450 Llano St	Aztec, NM	87410-2201	505-334-6364	334-6364	K-8	Diane Mittler
Mountain Mahogany Community S	5014 4th St NW	Albuquerque, NM	87107-3908	505-341-1424	341-1428	K-8	Baylor DelRosario
Native American Community Academy	1000 Indian School Rd NW	Albuquerque, NM	87104-2304	505-266-0992	266-2905	6-12	Kara Bobroff
New America S - Las Cruces	PO Box 16680	Las Cruces, NM	88004-6680	575-527-9085	527-9153	9-12	Margarita Porter
New America School	1734 Isleta Blvd SW	Albuquerque, NM	87105-4636	505-222-4360	873-2602	9-12	LaTricia Mathis
New Mexico Connections Academy	4001 Office Court Dr # 201	Santa Fe, NM	87507	505-428-2131	424-9092	4-12	Athena Trujillo
New Mexico International School	8650 Alameda Blvd NE	Albuquerque, NM	87122-3794	505-503-7670	503-7989	K-5	Todd Knouse
New Mexico School for the Arts	275 E Alameda St	Santa Fe, NM	87501-2113	505-310-4194	629-4108	9-12	Cindy Montoya
New Mexico Virtual Academy	845 Sullivan Ave	Farmington, NM	87401-7356	505-436-2383	258-4080	6-12	Deborah Jackson
North Valley Academy	7939 4th St NW	Los Ranchos, NM	87114	505-998-0501	998-0505	PK-8	Susan McConnell
Nuestros Valores Charter S	6800 Gonzales Rd SW	Albuquerque, NM	87121	505-873-7758	873-3567	9-12	Monica Aguilar
Public Academy for Performing Arts	11800 Princess Jeanne NE	Albuquerque, NM	87112	505-830-3128	830-9930	6-12	Doreen Winn
Red River Valley Charter S	PO Box 742	Red River, NM	87558-0742	575-754-6117	754-3258	PK-8	Karen Phillips
Rio Gallinas S for Ecology and the Arts	1107 Montezuma St	Las Vegas, NM	87701-3519	505-454-8687	454-8688	K-8	Gerald Garcia
Roots & Wings Community S	HC 81 Box 22	Questa, NM	87556-9712	575-586-2076	586-2087	K-8	Nancy Gonzalez
Sage Montessori Charter S	3831 Midway Pl NE	Albuquerque, NM	87109	505-344-7447	797-4294	K-6	Felix Garcia
SAMS Academy	4100 Aerospace Pkwy NW	Albuquerque, NM	87120-8792	505-338-8601	296-0510	7-12	Coreen Carrillo
San Diego Riverside Charter S	PO Box 99	Jemez Pueblo, NM	87024-0099	575-834-7419	834-9167	K-8	Karen Mayhew
Sandoval Academy of Bilingual Education	483 Arkansas St SE	Rio Rancho, NM	87124-3202	505-803-8444		K-8	Miranda Gonzales
School of Dreams Academy	906 Juan Perea Rd	Los Lunas, NM	87031	505-804-7639	804-7639	PK-12	Michael Ogas
Sena Charter HS	69 Hotel Cir NE	Albuquerque, NM	87123-1202	505-237-2373	237-2380	9-12	Nadine Torres
South Valley Academy	3426 Blake Rd SW	Albuquerque, NM	87105-5009	505-452-3132	452-3133	9-12	Julie Radoslovich
South Valley Preparatory S	2813 Gun Club Rd SW	Albuquerque, NM	87105-6333	505-222-5642	222-5647	6-8	Charlotte Trujillo
Southwest Intermediate Learning Center	10301 Candelaria Rd NE	Albuquerque, NM	87112-1504	505-296-7677	296-0510	7-8	Al Baysinger M.A.
Southwest Primary Learning Center	10301 Candelaria Rd NE	Albuquerque, NM	87112-1504	505-296-7677	296-0510	4-6	Al Baysinger M.A.
Southwest Secondary Learning Center	10301 Candelaria Rd NE	Albuquerque, NM	87112-1504	505-296-7677	296-0510	7-12	Kirk Hartom
Taos Academy	110 Paseo Del Canon W	Taos, NM	87571	575-751-3109	751-3394	5-12	Traci Filiss
Taos Charter S	1303 Paseo Del Canon East	Taos, NM	87571	575-751-7222	751-7546	K-8	Doug Moser
Taos Integrated School of the Arts	PO Box 668	Taos, NM	87571-0668	575-758-7755	758-7766	K-8	Susan Germann
Taos International S	118 Este Es Rd	Taos, NM	87571-6669	575-751-7115		K-8	Nadine Vigil
Taylor Academy	3900 Del Rey Blvd	Las Cruces, NM	88012-7992	575-652-4006	652-4621	K-8	Aine Garcia-Post
Technology Leadership HS	800 20th NW	Albuquerque, NM	87104			9-12	Tony Monfiletto
Tierra Adentro - NM Sch Acedemics/Art	1511 Central Ave NE	Albuquerque, NM	87106-4408	505-967-4720	967-4721	6-12	Veronica Torres
Tierra Encantada Charter S	551 Alarid St	Santa Fe, NM	87501	505-983-3337	983-6637	7-12	Danny Pena
Turqoise Trail ES	13A San Marcos Loop	Santa Fe, NM	87508-7083	505-986-4000	474-7862	PK-6	Dr. Ray Griffin
21st Century Public Academy	6805 Academy Pkwy West NE	Albuquerque, NM	87109	505-254-0280	254-8507	5-8	Mary Tarango
Uplift Community S	406 NM Highway 564	Gallup, NM	87301-4872	505-863-4333	863-4885	K-6	James Cammon
Vista Grande HS	213 Paseo Del Canon E	Taos, NM	87571-6239	575-758-5100	758-5102	9-12	Isabelle St. Onge

New York

School	Address	City,State	Zip code	Telephone	Fax	Grade	Contact
Academic Leadership Charter S	677 E 141st St	Bronx, NY	10454-2815	718-585-4215	585-4837	K-5	Norma Figueroa-Hurwitz
Academy Charter S	117 N Franklin St	Hempstead, NY	11550-1314	516-408-2200	292-2329	K-6	Clarence Williams
Academy of the City Charter S	3614 12th St	Astoria, NY	11106	718-487-9857	785-9592	K-2	Richard Lee
Achievement First Apollo Charter S	350 Linwood St	Brooklyn, NY	11208-2116	718-235-2647	235-2649	K-4	Jesse Balis-Harris
Achievement First Aspire Charter S	982 Hegeman Ave	Brooklyn, NY	11208-4434	718-838-0205	228-8839	K-5	Sarah Kasok
Achievement First Brooklyn HS	1485 Pacific St	Brooklyn, NY	11216-3204	718-363-2260	363-2262	9-12	Chris Bostock
Achievement First Brownsville Charter S	2021 Bergen St	Brooklyn, NY	11233-4801	718-471-2600	342-3458	K-5	Katherine Roger
Achievement First Bushwick Charter S	1300 Greene Ave	Brooklyn, NY	11237-4502	718-471-2560	453-0428	K-12	Michael Rosskamm
Achievement First Crown Heights Charter	790 E New York Ave	Brooklyn, NY	11203-1212	718-774-0762	774-0830	K-12	Camilla Lopez
Achievement First East New York ES	557 Pennsylvania Ave	Brooklyn, NY	11207-5727	718-485-4924	342-5194	K-8	Injy Carpenter
Achievement First Endeavor S	510 Waverly Ave	Brooklyn, NY	11238-2702	718-622-4786	789-1649	K-12	Tom Kaiser
Achievement First Linden ES	800 Van Siclen Ave	Brooklyn, NY	11207-7805	718-471-2700	789-1649	K-4	Amanda Hageman
Achievement First North Brooklyn Prep S	200 Woodbine St	Brooklyn, NY	11221-4748	718-471-2690	402-1818	K-8	Elena Knappen
Albany Community Charter S	65 Krank St	Albany, NY	12202-1150	518-433-1500	433-1501	K-5	S. Neal Currie
Albany Leadership Charter HS for Girls	19 Hackett Blvd	Albany, NY	12208-3407	518-694-5300	694-5307	9-12	Christina Roberts
Amani Charter S	60 S 3rd Ave Ste 1	Mount Vernon, NY	10550-3313	914-668-6450	699-0839	5-8	Debra Stern
Amber Charter S	220 E 106th St	New York, NY	10029-4020	212-534-9667	534-6225	K-5	Dr. Vasthi Acosta
American Dream Charter S	510 E 141st St	Bronx, NY	10454-2753	718-585-3071	227-2760	6-8	Melissa Melkonian
Bedford Stuyvesant Collegiate Charter S	800 Gates Ave	Brooklyn, NY	11221-2203	718-669-7460	669-7771	5-12	Mabel Lajes-Guiteras
Bed-Stuy New Beginnings Charter S	82 Lewis Ave	Brooklyn, NY	11206-7013	718-453-1001	452-2090	K-5	Nicholas Tishuk
Beginning With Children Charter S II	215 Heyward St	Brooklyn, NY	11206-2966	718-302-7700	302-7701	PK-3	Esosa Ogbahon
Boys Prep Charter S of New York	1695 Seward Ave	Bronx, NY	10473-4249	646-783-3589	346-9096	K-5	Kristin Norgrove
Brighter Choice Charter MS for Boys	116 Lake Ave	Albany, NY	12206	518-694-8200	694-5551	5-8	Derick Brown
Brighter Choice Charter MS for Girls	250 Central Ave	Albany, NY	12206	518-694-5550	694-5551	5-8	Marcus Puccioni
Brighter Choice Charter S for Boys	116 N Lake Ave	Albany, NY	12206-2710	518-694-8200	694-8201	K-4	Karen McLean
Brighter Choice Charter S for Girls	250 Central Ave	Albany, NY	12206-2639	518-694-4100	694-4123	K-4	Marcus Puccioni
Brilla College Preparatory Charter S	413 E 144th St	Bronx, NY	10454-1004	347-273-8439		K-5	Kelsey Kopro
Bronx Academy of Promise Charter S	1349 Inwood Ave	Bronx, NY	10452-3222	718-293-6950	681-8225	K-8	Catherine Jackvony
Bronx Charter S for Better Learning	3740 Baychester Ave	Bronx, NY	10466-5031	718-655-6660	655-5555	K-5	Shubert Jacobs
Bronx Charter S for Children	388 Willis Ave	Bronx, NY	10454-1303	718-402-3300	402-3258	K-5	Doreen Land
Bronx Charter S for Excellence	1960 Benedict Ave	Bronx, NY	10462-4402	718-828-7301	828-7302	K-8	Charlene Reid
Bronx Charter S for the Arts	950 Longfellow Ave	Bronx, NY	10474-4809	718-893-1042	893-7910	K-5	Miriam Raccah
Bronx Community Charter S	3170 Webster Ave	Bronx, NY	10467-4902	718-584-1400	944-1405	K-5	Martha Andrews
Bronx Global Learning Institute	750 Concourse Vlg W	Bronx, NY	10451-3865	718-993-1740	993-1965	K-5	Mary Ranero-Cordero
Bronx Lighthouse Charter S	1001 Intervale Ave	Bronx, NY	10459-3151	646-915-0025	915-0037	K-12	Travis Brown
Bronx Preparatory Charter S	3872 3rd Ave	Bronx, NY	10457-8222	718-294-0841	294-2381	5-12	Lourdes Flores
Brooklyn Ascend Lower S	205 Rockaway Pkwy	Brooklyn, NY	11212-3444	718-907-9147	240-9140	K-6	Brandon Sorlie
Brooklyn Charter S	545 Willoughby Ave	Brooklyn, NY	11206-6815	718-302-2085	302-2426	K-5	Omigbade Escayg
Brooklyn Dreams Charter S	259 Parkville Ave	Brooklyn, NY	11230-1310	718-859-8400	586-0347	K-6	Yvette Wilds
Brooklyn East Collegiate Charter S	80 Underhill Ave	Brooklyn, NY	11238-3509	718-250-5760	250-5761	5-8	Eric Green
Brooklyn Excelsior Charter S	856 Quincy St	Brooklyn, NY	11221-3612	718-246-5681	246-5864	K-8	Christopher Petty
Brooklyn LAB Charter S	240 Jay St	Brooklyn, NY	11201-1937	347-429-8439	612-9127	6-8	Eric Tucker Ph.D.
Brooklyn Prospect Charter S	3002 Fort Hamilton Pkwy	Brooklyn, NY	11218-1608	347-889-7041	889-7038	6-12	LaNolia Omowanile
Brooklyn Scholars Charter S	2635 Linden Blvd	Brooklyn, NY	11208-4907	718-348-9360	348-9362	K-8	Desiree Kirton
Brooklyn S of Inquiry	50 Avenue P	Brooklyn, NY	11204-6105	718-621-5730	621-5735	K-8	Donna Taylor
Brooklyn Urban Garden Charter S	500 19th St	Brooklyn, NY	11215-6204	212-437-8318		6-8	Susan Tenner
Broome Street Academy	121 Avenue of the Americas	New York, NY	10013-1510	212-453-0295	966-7253	9-12	Dr. Barbara McKeon
Brownsville Ascend Charter S	1501 Pitkin Ave	Brooklyn, NY	11212	347-294-2600	342-1082	K-8	Erica Murphy
Brownsville Collegiate Charter S	364 Sackman St	Brooklyn, NY	11212-7614	718-636-0370	296-8321	5-9	Anjya Thomas
Buffalo Academy of Science Charter S	190 Franklin St	Buffalo, NY	14202	716-854-2490	854-5039	5-12	Mucahit Polat
Buffalo United Charter S	325 Manhattan Ave	Buffalo, NY	14214-1809	716-835-9862	835-6272	K-8	Tammy Messmer
Bushwick Ascend Charter S	751 Knickerbocker Ave	Brooklyn, NY	11221-5336	718-240-9162	484-0498	K-3	Dellianna Burrows
Canarsie Ascend Charter S	9719 Flatlands Ave	Brooklyn, NY	11236-3729	718-907-0153		K-1	Anastasia Michals
Central Brooklyn Ascend Charter S	465 E 29th St	Brooklyn, NY	11226-7825	718-246-4800		K-5	Michelle Flowers
Central Queens Academy Charter S	5530 Junction Blvd	Elmhurst, NY	11373-4622	718-271-6200	271-6900	5-5	Jesse Tang
Challenge Preparatory Charter S	710 Hartman Ln	Far Rockaway, NY	11691-1849	718-327-1352	327-1361	K-3	Debra Sostre
Charter S for Applied Technologies	2303 Kenmore Ave	Buffalo, NY	14207-1311	716-876-7505	876-9758	K-12	Efrain Martinez
Charter S of Educational Excellence	260 Warburton Ave	Yonkers, NY	10701-2226	914-476-5070	476-2858	K-8	Cindy Lopez
Charter S of Inquiry	404 Edison St	Buffalo, NY	14215	716-833-3250		K-8	
Child Development Center of the Hamptons	110 Stephen Hands Path	East Hampton, NY	11937	631-324-0207	324-4112	K-5	Gerard Cairns
Children's Aid Society Charter S	1919 Prospect Ave	Bronx, NY	10457-6506	347-871-9002	583-6238	K-5	Casey Vier
Citizens of the World Charter S	424 Leonard St	Brooklyn, NY	11222-3908	718-384-1386		K-5	Meredith Cronk
Citizens of the World Charter S	791 Empire Blvd	Brooklyn, NY	11213-5653	718-221-5095		K-5	Liz Rawlins
City Polytechnic HS	105 Tech Pl	Brooklyn, NY	11201	718-875-1473	875-1947	9-12	Yusuf Muhammad
Community Partnership Charter S	241 Emerson Pl	Brooklyn, NY	11205-3808	718-399-3824	399-1495	K-7	Melanie Bryon
Community Roots Charter S	51 Saint Edwards St	Brooklyn, NY	11205-2932	718-858-1629	858-1754	K-6	Allison Keil
Compass Charter S	300 Adelphi St	Brooklyn, NY	11205-4601	718-310-3588	852-4682	K-5	Brooke Peters
Coney Island Prep Public Charter S	501 West Ave	Brooklyn, NY	11224-4220	718-513-6951	513-6955	5-8	Jacob Mnookin
Cultural Arts Academy at Spring Creek	1400 Linden Blvd	Brooklyn, NY	11212	718-683-3300	272-1330	K-5	Dr. Laurie B. Midgette
de Hostos Charter S	938 Clifford Ave	Rochester, NY	14621-4808	585-544-6170	544-3848	K-8	Jeffrey Halsdorfer
Democracy Preparatory Harlem HS	212 W 120th St	New York, NY	10027-6413	212-932-7791	666-3706	9-12	Steve Popper
Democracy Prep Charter HS	222 W 134th St	New York, NY	10030-3002	212-281-3061	281-3064	9-12	Natasha Trivers
Democracy Prep Charter MS	207 W 133rd St	New York, NY	10030-3201	212-281-1248	283-4202	6-8	Zach Siegel
Democracy Prep Endurance Charter S	250 W 127th St	New York, NY	10027-2957	212-316-7602	316-7022	6-8	Margaret Marrer
Discovery Charter S	133 Hoover Dr	Rochester, NY	14615-2603	585-342-4032	342-4003	K-2	Joseph Saia
DREAM Charter S	1991 2nd Ave	New York, NY	10029	212-722-0232	348-5979	K-7	Eve Colavito
Eagle Academy for Young Men III	17110 Linden Blvd	Jamaica, NY	11434-1327	718-480-2600	723-4709	6-8	Matthew Hamilton
East Harlem Scholars Academy	1573 Madison Ave	New York, NY	10029-3819	212-348-2518	348-2848	K-8	Cheyenne Sao Roque
East Harlem Scholars Academy II	2050 2nd Ave	New York, NY	10029-4704	212-831-0650	289-7967	K-8	Steve Corbett
Elmwood Village Charter S	40 Days Park	Buffalo, NY	14201	716-886-4581	348-3707	K-8	Danielle Bruno
Enterprise Charter S	275 Oak St	Buffalo, NY	14203-1643	716-855-2114	855-2967	K-8	Julie Schwab
Equality Charter S	4140 Hutchinson River Pkwy	Bronx, NY	10475-5467	718-320-3032	320-3721	6-8	Caitlin Franco
Equity Project Charter S	549 Audubon Ave	New York, NY	10040	646-254-6451	202-3584	K-K,	Zeke Vanderhoek
Evergreen Charter S	605 Peninsula Blvd	Hempstead, NY	11550-5424	516-292-2060		K-5	Maritza Meyers

School	Address	City,State	Zip code	Telephone	Fax	Grade	Contact
Excellence Boys Charter S	225 Patchen Ave	Brooklyn, NY	11233-1529	718-638-1830	638-2548	K-9	Felix Li
Excellence Girls Charter S	794 Monroe St	Brooklyn, NY	11221-3501	718-638-1875	228-6670	K-4	Nikki Bowen
Explore Charter S	655 Parkside Ave	Brooklyn, NY	11226-1505	718-703-4484	703-8550	K-8	Michal-Anne Jones
Explore Empower Charter S	188 Rochester Ave	Brooklyn, NY	11213-3102	718-771-2090	771-2128	K-5	Christina Cotter
Explore Exceed Charter S	443 Saint Marks Ave	Brooklyn, NY	11238-3707	718-989-6702	701-8328	K-8	Curtis Palmore
Explore Excel Charter S	1077 Remsen Ave	Brooklyn, NY	11236-3451	347-303-3245	272-1827	K-4	Dana Bogle
Fahari Academy Charter S	72 Veronica Pl	Brooklyn, NY	11226-4122	718-215-3185	282-5397	5-9	Stephanie Clagnaz Ed.D.
Family Life Academy Charter S	14 W 170th St	Bronx, NY	10452-3227	718-410-8100	410-8800	K-8	Angel Rodriguez
Family Life Academy Charter S II	296 E 140th St	Bronx, NY	10454-1125	718-410-8100		K-3	Lourdes Arroyo
Family Life Academy Charter S III	370 Gerard Ave	Bronx, NY	10451	718-585-6580		K-5	Andrea Hernandez
Future Leaders Institute	134 W 122nd St	New York, NY	10027-5501	212-678-2868	866-2367	K-8	Dani McPartlin
Genesee Community Charter S	657 East Ave	Rochester, NY	14607-2101	585-697-1960	271-5904	K-6	Lisa Wing
Girls Preparatory Charter S	442 E Houston St	New York, NY	10002-1122	212-388-0241	388-1086	K-8	Anne Lackritz
Girls Preparatory Charter S of the Bronx	681 Kelly St Rm 205	Bronx, NY	10455	718-292-2113	292-5586	PK-5	Sharon Stephens
Girls Prep Bronx Charter MS	890 Cauldwell Ave	Bronx, NY	10456	718-665-6090		6-7	Martha Zornow
Global Community Charter S	2350 5th Ave	New York, NY	10037-1101	646-360-2363	390-6036	K-1	Phyllis Siwiec
Global Concepts Charter S	1001 Ridge Rd	Lackawanna, NY	14218-1755	716-821-1903	821-9563	K-12	Tracy McGee
Grand Concourse Academy Charter S	925 Hutchinson River Pkwy	Bronx, NY	10465	718-684-6505	684-6514	K-7	Ira Victor
Great Oaks Charter S	38 Delancey St	New York, NY	10002	212-233-5152	267-4357	6-8	Antonio Vance
Green Tech High Charter S	99 Slingerland St	Albany, NY	12202	518-694-3400	694-3401	9-12	Dr. Paul Miller
Growing Up Green Charter S	3927 28th St	Long Is City, NY	11101-3728	347-642-4306	642-4310	K-4	Matthew Greenberg
Hahn Expeditionary Learning S	5800 Tilden Ave	Brooklyn, NY	11203	718-629-1204	629-1076	9-12	Veronica Coleman
Harbor Science & Arts Charter S	132 E 111th St	New York, NY	10029-2602	917-261-2700	360-7429	K-8	Joanne Hunt
Harlem Childrens Zone Promise Academy I	245 W 129th St	New York, NY	10027-1953	646-556-6290	368-3621	K-12	Dr. Joseph Cordero
Harlem Childrens Zone Promise Academy II	2005 Madison Ave	New York, NY	10035-1294	646-556-6285	492-1542	K-5	Sheryl Ragland
Harlem Childrens Zone Promise Acad II MS	35 E 125th St	New York, NY	10035-1816	646-437-1481		6-8	Judy Palacios
Harlem Hebrew Language Academy Charter S	147 Saint Nicholas Ave	New York, NY	10026	212-866-4608	537-0280	K-2	Robin Natman
Harlem Link Charter S	20 W 112th St	New York, NY	10026-3902	212-289-3249	289-3686	K-5	Steven Evangelista
Harlem Prep Charter S	240 E 123rd St Frnt 1	New York, NY	10035-2068	212-876-9953	876-9926	K-6	Lindsay Malanga
Harlem Village Academy Charter HS	35 W 124th St	New York, NY	10027-5634	646-812-9200		9-12	Kathleen Portillo
Harlem Village Academy Charter S	244 W 144th St	New York, NY	10030-1202	646-812-9300	548-9576	5-8	Lauren Konigsberg
Harlem Village Acad Ldrshp Charter S	2351 1st Ave	New York, NY	10035-3422	646-812-9490	996-1626	5-8	Kimberly Hayes
Health Sciences Charter S	1140 Ellicott St	Buffalo, NY	14209-1934	716-888-4080	464-7623	9-12	Dr. Hank Stopinski
Hebrew Language Academy Charter S	2186 Mill Ave	Brooklyn, NY	11234-6308	718-377-7200	377-7220	K-4	David Penberg
Heketi Community Charter S	403 Concord Ave	Bronx, NY	10454-1631	718-260-6002	292-7154	K-5	Cynthia Rosario
Hellenic Classical Charter S	646 5th Ave	Brooklyn, NY	11215-5401	718-499-0957	499-0959	K-8	Christine Tettonis
Hyde Leadership Charter S	730 Bryant Ave	Bronx, NY	10474-6006	718-991-5500	842-8616	K-12	Betsy Olney
Hyde Leadership Charter S	330 Alabama Ave	Brooklyn, NY	11207-4005	718-495-5620	495-5827	K-2	Sandra DuPree
Icahn Charter S 1	1525 Brook Ave	Bronx, NY	10457-8005	718-716-8105	214-6596	K-8	Sandra Lugo
Icahn Charter S 2	1640 Bronxdale Ave	Bronx, NY	10462-3302	212-828-6107	828-7308	K-7	Brenda Carrasquillo
Icahn Charter S 3	1500 Pelham Pkwy S	Bronx, NY	10461-1100	718-828-0034	794-2357	K-6	Midga Agosto
Icahn Charter S 4	1500 Pelham Pkwy S	Bronx, NY	10461-1100	718-828-0034	828-0664	K-5	Michelle Allen
Icahn Charter S 5	1500 Pelham Pkwy S	Bronx, NY	10461-1100	718-828-0034	794-2359	K-3	Lawford Cunningham
Icahn Charter S 6	1701 Fulton Ave	Bronx, NY	10457-7546	718-294-1706	583-6194	K-2	Brian Geelan
Icahn Charter S 7	1535 Story Ave	Bronx, NY	10473-4555	718-328-5480	328-5483	K-6	Laura Sullivan
Imagine Me Leadership Charter S	818 Schenck Ave	Brooklyn, NY	11207-7904	347-985-2140	985-2145	K-3	Bevon Thompson
International Leadership Charter HS	2900 Exterior St	Bronx, NY	10463-7103	718-562-2300	562-2235	9-12	Dr. Elaine Lopez
Invictus Preparatory Charter S	370 Fountain Ave	Brooklyn, NY	11208-4304	718-235-1682	235-1685	5-8	Cliff Thomas
Inwood Academy for Leadership Charter S	108 Cooper St	New York, NY	10034-2332	212-304-0103	303-0370	5-7	Christina Reyes
Izquierdo Health & Science Charter S	800 Home St	Bronx, NY	10456-5443	718-378-0490	378-0492	6-10	Richard Burke
Johnson Charter S	15 Jewett Pkwy	Buffalo, NY	14214-2319	716-856-4390		K-4	Wendy Richards
Johnson Charter S	30 Watervliet Ave	Albany, NY	12206-1983	518-432-4300	432-4311	K-4	Tiffani Curtis Ed.D.
Johnson Fruit Belt Community Charter S	15 Jewett Pkwy	Buffalo, NY	14214-2319	716-856-4390	856-4391	K-4	Wendy Richards
King Center Charter S	156 Newburgh Ave	Buffalo, NY	14211-1826	716-891-7912	895-2058	K-8	Antoinette Rhodes
King's Collegiate Charter S	1084 Lenox Rd	Brooklyn, NY	11212-1930	718-342-6047	342-6727	5-8	Scott Schuster
KIPP Academy Charter MS	250 E 156th St	Bronx, NY	10451	718-665-3555	585-7982	5-8	Frank Corcoran
Kipp Academy ES	730 Concourse Vlg W	Bronx, NY	10451-3137	718-943-3737	292-7199	K-4	Tyritia Groves
KIPP A.M.P. Charter S	1224 Park Pl	Brooklyn, NY	11213-2703	718-943-3740	774-3673	5-12	Latasha Williams
KIPP Infinity Charter S	625 W 133rd St	New York, NY	10027-7303	212-991-2626	862-9679	K-8	Allison Holley
KIPP STAR MS	433 W 123rd St	New York, NY	10027-5002	212-991-2650	666-4723	5-8	Stacy Johnson
KIPP Tech Valley Charter S	321 Northern Blvd	Albany, NY	12210	518-694-9494	694-9411	5-8	Don Applyrs
KIPP Washington Heights MS	21 Jumel Pl	New York, NY	10032-4316	212-991-2620	342-2521	5-5	Danny Swersky
La Cima Charter S	800 Gates Ave	Brooklyn, NY	11221-2203	718-443-2136	443-7291	K-5	Andrea Zayas
Launch Expeditionary Learning Charter S	1580 Dean St	Brooklyn, NY	11213-1713	718-221-1064	604-6915	6-8	Geoffrey Roehm
Lavelle Preparatory Charter S	1 Teleport Dr	Staten Island, NY	10311-1003	347-630-1760	466-5746	6-8	Christopher Zilinski
Leadership Preparatory Ocean Hill S	51 Christopher Ave	Brooklyn, NY	11212-8014	718-250-5767	881-9666	K-3	Rachel King
Leadership Prep Bedford Stuy Charter S	141 Macon St	Brooklyn, NY	11216-2206	718-636-0360	636-0747	K-7	Owen Losse
Leadership Prep Brownsville Charter S	985 Rockaway Ave	Brooklyn, NY	11212-5152	718-669-7461	228-6496	K-4	Katie Newton
Leadership Prep Canarsie Charter S	1001 E 100th St	Brooklyn, NY	11236-4415	347-390-0570	534-3881	K-8	Katie Thaeder
Lindsay Wildcat Academy Charter S	17 Battery Pl	New York, NY	10004-1207	212-209-6006	635-3874	9-12	Ronald Tabano
Manhattan Charter S	100 Attorney St	New York, NY	10002-3405	212-533-2743	533-2820	K-5	Genie DePolo
Manhattan Charter S II	220 Henry St	New York, NY	10002-4815	212-964-3792	964-3795	K-1	Joanne Mejias
Merrick Academy-Queens Public Charter S	20701 Jamaica Ave	Queens Village, NY	11428-1544	718-479-3753	479-8108	K-6	Tonya Johnson
MESA Charter HS	231 Palmetto St	Brooklyn, NY	11221	917-257-6876	227-2763	9-12	Arthur Samuels
Metropolitan Lighthouse Charter S	500 Courtlandt Ave	Bronx, NY	10451-5032	718-893-0640	893-0675	K-5	Courtney Russell
Middle Village Prep Charter S	6802 Metropolitan Ave	Middle Village, NY	11379-1622	718-869-2933	821-2498	6-8	Ronald Rivera
Mott Hall Charter S	1260 Franklin Ave	Bronx, NY	10456-3502	718-991-9139	991-9150	6-6	Geovanti Steward
Mott Haven Academy Charter S	170 Brown Pl	Bronx, NY	10454-4140	718-292-7015	292-7823	K-5	Jessica Nauiokas
Neighborhood Charter S of Harlem	132 W 124th St	New York, NY	10027-4919	646-701-7117	484-6652	K-3	Brett Gallini
New American Academy Charter S	9301 Avenue B	Brooklyn, NY	11236	718-385-1709	385-1856	K-4	Lisa Silva
Newburgh Preparatory Charter HS	471 Broadway	Newburgh, NY	12550-5332	845-565-4040	565-4033	9-12	Wendy Wright
New Dawn Charter HS	242 Hoyt St	Brooklyn, NY	11217-2913	347-505-9103	505-2516	9-12	Dr. Sara Asmussen
New Heights Academy Charter S	1818 Amsterdam Ave	New York, NY	10031-1715	212-283-5400	507-9314	5-12	Robert Parkes
New Hope Academy Charter S	475 E 57th St	Brooklyn, NY	11203	718-337-8303	504-3883	K-5	Tamika Stewart
New Roots Charter S	PO Box 936	Ithaca, NY	14851-0936	607-882-9220	882-9230	9-12	Tina Nilsen-Hodges
New Visions Charter HS for Humanities	99 Terrace View Ave	Bronx, NY	10463-5079	718-817-7686	817-7688	9-12	Seth Levin
New Visions Charter HS Humanities III	3000 Avenue X	Brooklyn, NY	11235-1232	718-368-4145		9-12	Porsche Cox
New Visions Charter HS Humanities II	455 Southern Blvd	Bronx, NY	10455-4911	718-665-5380	665-5383	9-12	Richard Gonzlez
New Visions Charter HS II	900 Tinton Ave	Bronx, NY	10456-7411	718-665-3671	645-7409	9-12	Stacey King
New Visions Charter HS Math & Sci III	3000 Avenue X	Brooklyn, NY	11235-1232	718-934-9240	934-9171	9-12	Nissi Jonathan
New Visions Charter HS Math & Science	99 Terrace View Ave	Bronx, NY	10463-5079	718-817-7683	817-7685	9-12	Robert Hiller
New World Preparatory Charter S	26 Sharpe Ave	Staten Island, NY	10302-1234	718-705-8990	442-1583	6-8	Amanda Ainley
New York City Montessori Charter S	423 E 138th St	Bronx, NY	10454-3041	347-226-9094	226-9097	PK-5	Abeku Hayes
New York French American Charter S	311 W 120th St	New York, NY	10027-6128	212-666-4134		K-5	Marc Maurice
Niagara Charter S	2077 Lockport Rd	Niagara Falls, NY	14304-1109	716-297-4520	297-4617	K-6	Darci Novak
Northside Charter HS	424 Leonard St	Brooklyn, NY	11222-3908	347-390-1273	390-1274	9-12	Suzanne Curran
North Side S	1650 Utopia Pkwy	Whitestone, NY	11357-3346	718-229-5050	402-2028	PK-3	Irene Kouba
NYC Autism Charter S	433 E 100th St	New York, NY	10029-6606	212-860-2580	860-2960	K-12	Julie Fisher
NYC Charter HS for AECI	838 Brook Ave	Bronx, NY	10451-4620	646-400-5566	585-4780	9-12	Charles Gallo
Ocean Hill Collegiate Charter S	1137 Herkimer St	Brooklyn, NY	11233-3109	718-250-5765	250-5766	5-6	Hannah Solomon
Opportunity Charter S	240 W 113th St	New York, NY	10026-3306	212-866-6137	665-7436	6-12	Marya Baker
Oracle Charter S	888 Delaware Ave	Buffalo, NY	14209-2008	716-362-3188	362-3187	9-12	John Ashwood
Our World Neighborhood Charter S	3612 35th Ave	Astoria, NY	11106-1227	718-392-3405	392-2840	K-8	Brian Ferguson
PAVE Academy	732 Henry St	Brooklyn, NY	11231-3229	718-858-7813	858-7814	K-5	Spencer Robertson
Peninsula Prep Academy Charter S	611 Beach 19th St	Far Rockaway, NY	11691	347-403-9231	327-2580	K-5	Karen Jones
Professional Preparatory Charter S	616 Quincy St	Brooklyn, NY	11221-1812	718-285-3787	919-0486	K-5	Rafiq Kalam Id-Din
PUC Achieve Charter S	14 Mark St	Rochester, NY	14605-1331	585-471-6219	471-6220	5-6	Arkee Allen
Renaissance Charter HS for Innovation	410 E 100th St	New York, NY	10029-6604	212-722-5871	430-8555	9-12	Stephen Riff
Renaissance Charter S	3559 81st St	Jackson Heights, NY	11372-5033	718-803-0060	803-3785	K-12	Stacey Gauthier
Riverhead Charter S	3685 Middle Country Rd	Calverton, NY	11933-1807	631-369-5800		K-8	Raymond Ankrum
Riverton Street Charter S	11834 Riverton St	Saint Albans, NY	11412	718-481-8200	923-3315	K-8	Andrea Whitehurst
ROADS Charter S I	1495 Herkimer St	Brooklyn, NY	11233-3425	718-280-9819	498-0604	9-12	Kristin Greer
ROADS Charter S II	1010 Rev James A Polite Ave	Bronx, NY	10459-3053	718-861-7515	861-7518	9-12	Chester Asher
Rochdale Early Advantage Charter S	12205 Smith St	Jamaica, NY	11434-2522	718-978-0075	978-0110	K-3	Derrick Dunlap
Rochester Academy Charter S	1777 Latta Rd	Rochester, NY	14612	585-467-9201	467-9250	7-12	Mehmet Demirtas
Rochester Academy Charter S of the Arts	299 Kirk Rd	Rochester, NY	14612-3377	845-826-4586		K-2	Donna Cozine
Rochester Career Mentoring Charter S	30 Hart St Ste 3	Rochester, NY	14605-1100	585-232-1045	262-2479	9-12	Kathleen Denaro
Rochester Prep ES	899 Jay St	Rochester, NY	14611-1219	585-235-0008	235-0014	K-4	Jaimie Brillante
Rochester Prep ES - West Campus	85 Saint Jacob St	Rochester, NY	14621	585-368-5100	368-5091	K-1	Emily Volpe
Rochester Prep MS - Brooks Campus	630 Brooks Ave	Rochester, NY	14619-2255	585-436-8629	436-5985	5-8	Patrick Pastore
Rochester Prep MS - West Campus	432 Chili Ave	Rochester, NY	14611	585-368-5090	368-5091	5-8	Paul Powell
Roosevelt Childrens Academy Charter S	201 Debevoise Ave	Roosevelt, NY	11575	516-867-6202	867-6206	K-8	Sheila Lyle Maxwell
St. Hope Leadership Academy	222 W 134th St	New York, NY	10030-3002	212-283-1204	283-1207	5-8	Constance Bond
Sisulu-Walker Charter S	125 W 115th St	New York, NY	10026-2908	212-663-8216	866-5793	K-5	Michelle Haynes
South Bronx Charter S Intl Culture/Arts	164 Bruckner Blvd	Bronx, NY	10454	718-292-5737	292-1205	K-5	Evelyn Hey
South Bronx Classical Charter S	977 Fox St	Bronx, NY	10459-3320	718-860-4340	860-4125	K-5	Lester Long
South Bronx Classical Charter S II	333 E 135th St	Bronx, NY	10454-4301	718-860-4340	860-4125	K-5	Leena Gyftopoulos

School	Address	City,State	Zip code	Telephone	Fax	Grade	Contact
South Buffalo Charter S	154 S Ogden St	Buffalo, NY	14210-1910	716-826-7213	826-7168	K-8	Brian Wiesinger
Southside Academy Charter S	2200 Onondaga Creek Blvd	Syracuse, NY	13207-2361	315-476-3019	476-6639	K-8	Dr. Ronald Large
Staten Island Community Charter S	309 Saint Pauls Ave	Staten Island, NY	10304	347-857-6981	861-0601	K-3	Dr. Michael Courtney
Success Academy Charter Harlem 1	34 W 118th St	New York, NY	10026-1937	646-747-7170	457-5659	K-7	Danique Loving
Success Academy Charter Harlem 2	144 E 128th St Ste 3	New York, NY	10035-1329	646-442-6600	281-4638	K-5	Noah Green
Success Academy Charter Harlem 3	141 E 111th St	New York, NY	10029-2641	646-747-6700	478-9492	K-5	Richard Seigler
Success Academy Charter Harlem 4	240 W 113th St	New York, NY	10026-3306	646-442-6500	478-9493	K-5	William Loskoch
Success Academy Charter Harlem 5	301 W 140th St	New York, NY	10030-1406	646-380-2580	961-4731	K-3	Molly Cohen
Success Academy Charter S Bed-Stuy 2	211 Throop Ave	Brooklyn, NY	11206-5701	718-704-1439		K-4	Brittany Davis-Roberti
Success Academy Charter S Bed-Stuy 1	70 Tompkins Ave	Brooklyn, NY	11206-5616	718-635-3294	964-6598	K-2	Monica Burris
Success Academy Charter S Bensonhurst	99 Avenue P	Brooklyn, NY	11204-6119	347-514-7082		K-4	Jonathan Dant
Success Academy Charter S Bergen Beach	1420 E 68th St	Brooklyn, NY	11234-5708	347-817-2017		K-4	Jessica Johnson
Success Academy Charter S Bronx 3	968 Cauldwell Ave	Bronx, NY	10456-6804	646-790-2145		K-2	Dan Rojas
Success Academy Charter S Bronx 4	885 Bolton Ave	Bronx, NY	10473-2737	646-558-0043		K-12	Shea Reeder
Success Academy Charter S Bronx 1	339 Morris Ave	Bronx, NY	10451-6122	347-286-7950	479-1192	K-5	Elizabeth Vandlik
Success Academy Charter S Bronx 2	450 Saint Pauls Pl	Bronx, NY	10456-1938	347-286-7966	479-1194	K-8	Vanessa Bangser
Success Academy Charter S Cobble Hill	284 Baltic St	Brooklyn, NY	11201-6402	718-704-1460		K-1	Kerri Tabarcea
Success Academy Charter S Crown Hts	330 Crown St	Brooklyn, NY	11225-3004	646-790-2129		K-4	Kristen Cipriano
Success Academy Charter S Fort Greene	101 Park Ave	Brooklyn, NY	11205-2001	646-790-2137		K-12	Nina Fink
Success Academy Charter S Harlem Central	461 W 131st St	New York, NY	10027	646-569-5900		6-8	Kiah Hufane
Success Academy Charter S Harlem West	215 W 114th St Fl 5	New York, NY	10026-2802	646-569-5920		5-8	Khari Shabazz
Success Academy Charter S Hell's Kitchen	439 W 49th St	New York, NY	10019-7235	646-790-2153		K-5	Michael LaFrancis
Success Academy Charter S Prospect Hts	760 Prospect Pl	Brooklyn, NY	11216-3602	646-790-2121		K-12	Monica Komery
Success Academy Charter S - Rosedale	14765 249th St	Laurelton, NY	11422-2400	347-514-7060		K-4	Christina Danielsen
Success Academy Charter S Springfield Gd	13255 Ridgedale St	Laurelton, NY	11413-1500	347-602-4335		K-4	Michelle Cooper
Success Academy Charter S Upper West	145 W 84th St Fl 2	New York, NY	10024-4614	646-274-1580		K-2	Carrie Roby
Success Academy Charter S Williamsburg	183 S 3rd St Fl 4	Brooklyn, NY	11211-5311	718-704-1419		K-3	Abigail Johnson
Success Academy Charter Washington Hts	701 Fort Washington Ave	New York, NY	10040-3702	646-558-0027		K-4	Kelsey DePalo
Success Academy Union Square	40 Irving Pl	New York, NY	10003-2305	646-790-2161		K-4	Jennifer Waldman
Summit Academy Charter S	27 Huntington St	Brooklyn, NY	11231-1824	718-875-1403	875-1891	6-9	Natasha Campbell
Syracuse Academy of Science Charter S	1001 Park Ave	Syracuse, NY	13204-2125	315-428-8997	428-9109	K-12	Tolga Hayali Ed.D.
Tapestry Charter S	65 Great Arrow Ave	Buffalo, NY	14216-3203	716-204-5883	204-5887	K-12	Lynn Bass
Tech International Charter S	3120 Corlear Ave	Bronx, NY	10463	718-549-1908	240-0363	6-8	Ryan McCabe
True North Troy Preparatory S	2 Polk St	Troy, NY	12180-5512	518-445-3100	445-3101	K-8	Paul Powell
Tubman Charter S	3565 3rd Ave	Bronx, NY	10456-3403	718-537-9912	537-9858	K-8	Cleveland Person
UFT Charter S	800 Van Siclen Ave	Brooklyn, NY	11207-7805	718-927-5540		K-12	Justin Davis
Unity Prep S of Brooklyn	432 Monroe St	Brooklyn, NY	11221-1111	212-437-8372		6-12	Joshua Beauregard
University Preparatory Charter HS	1290 Lake Ave	Rochester, NY	14613-1230	585-672-1280	458-2732	7-12	Dr. Connie Lucchese
University Prep Charter HS	600 Saint Anns Ave	Bronx, NY	10455-2800	718-292-6543	220-8110	9-12	Andrea d'Amato
Urban Choice Charter S	545 Humboldt St	Rochester, NY	14610-1221	585-288-5702	654-9882	K-8	Christina Schermerhorn
Urban Dove Charter S	600 Lafayette Ave	Brooklyn, NY	11216-1020	718-783-8232	783-8239	9-10	Lewis Thomas
Utica Academy of Science Charter S	1214 Lincoln Ave	Utica, NY	13502-4532	315-266-1072	266-1073	6-12	Mustafa Ersoy
Vertus Charter S	21 Humboldt St	Rochester, NY	14609	585-747-8911		9-12	Dr. Leigh McGuigan
VOICE Charter S of NY	3624 12th St	Long Is City, NY	11106-5002	718-786-6213		K-5	Frank Headley
West Buffalo Charter S	113 Lafayette Ave	Buffalo, NY	14213-1349	716-923-1534	768-0980	K-4	Andrea Todoro
Western NY Maritime Charter S	266 Genesee St	Buffalo, NY	14204-1453	716-842-6289	842-4241	9-12	Lawrence Astyk
Westminster Community Charter S	24 Westminster Ave	Buffalo, NY	14215-1614	716-816-3450	838-7458	K-8	Robert Ross
Williamsburg Charter S	198 Varet St	Brooklyn, NY	11206-3703	718-782-9830	782-9834	9-12	Marsha Spampinato
Williamsburg Collegiate Charter S	157 Wilson St	Brooklyn, NY	11211-7706	718-302-4018	881-9978	5-12	Alex Bronson
Young Women's College Prep Charter S	133 Hoover Dr	Rochester, NY	14615	585-254-0320		7-12	Toyia Wilson

North Carolina

School	Address	City,State	Zip code	Telephone	Fax	Grade	Contact
Academy of Moore County	12588 US Highway 15 501	Aberdeen, NC	28315	910-757-0401	757-0403	K-5	Allyson Schoen
A.C.E. Academy	7807 Caldwell Rd	Harrisburg, NC	28075	704-456-7153	626-2655	K-8	Laila Minott
Alpha Academy	PO Box 35476	Fayetteville, NC	28303-0476	910-223-7711	678-9011	K-9	Eugene Slocum
American Renaissance ES	132 E Broad St	Statesville, NC	28677-5852	704-924-8870	873-1398	K-8	Tony Hall
Anderson Creek Club Charter S	4940 Ray Rd	Spring Lake, NC	28390-5097	910-814-9001	814-9002	K-5	Ozie Lee Hall
Arapahoe Charter S	9005 NC Highway 306 S	Arapahoe, NC	28510-9699	252-249-2599	249-1316	K-12	Dr. Dennis Sawyer
Aristotle Preparatory Academy	2461 Arty Ave	Charlotte, NC	28208	704-215-4550		K-4	David Davis
Arts Based S	1380 N Martin Luther King	Winston Salem, NC	27101-3035	336-748-4116	748-4117	K-8	Robin Hollis
ArtSpace Charter S	2030 US 70 Hwy	Swannanoa, NC	28778-8211	828-298-2787	298-6221	K-8	Lori Cozzi
Bear Grass Charter S	6344 E Bear Grass Rd	Williamston, NC	27892-8434	252-789-1010	789-1014	6-12	Donna Moore
Bethany Community MS	181 Bethany Rd	Reidsville, NC	27320-7464	336-951-2500	951-0087	6-8	Vicky Bethel
Bethel Hill Charter S	401 Bethel Hill School Rd	Roxboro, NC	27574-7503	336-599-2823	599-9299	K-5	Stephen Hester
Bradford Preparatory S	2502 Salome Church Rd	Charlotte, NC	28262	704-549-0080	549-0085	K-12	Kelly Painter
Brevard Academy	1110 Hendersonville Hwy	Pisgah Forest, NC	28768	828-885-2665	862-3497	K-8	Richard Duncan
Bridges Academy	2587 Pleasant Ridge Rd	State Road, NC	28676-9318	336-874-2721	874-3804	K-8	Merry Lowe
Brown Leadership Academy	PO Box 1433	Elizabethtown, NC	28337-1433	910-862-2965	862-3054	6-12	Roland McKoy
Cabarrus Charter Academy	7550 Ruben Linker Rd	Concord, NC	28027	704-886-2158	886-2159	6-11	
Cabarrus Charter Academy	355 Poplar Crossing Dr NW	Concord, NC	28027	704-789-2500	789-2501	K-5	Craig Paul
Cape Fear Center for Inquiry	2525 Wonder Way	Wilmington, NC	28401-8014	910-362-0000	362-0048	K-8	Lori Roy
Capitol Encore Academy	126 Hay St	Fayetteville, NC	28301-5650	910-849-0888	491-6786	K-5	Sylvia Adamczyk
Cardinal Charter S	1020 Saint Charles Pl	Cary, NC	27513	919-653-5000	653-6000	K-6	Nicholas Shosho
Carolina International S	9545 Poplar Tent Rd	Concord, NC	28027-9512	704-455-3847	455-4672	K-12	David Kukielski
Carter Community Charter S	1955 W Cornwallis Rd	Durham, NC	27705	919-797-2340	797-2343	K-8	LaManda Pryor
Casa Esperanza Montessori Charter S	2600 Sumner Blvd Ste 130	Raleigh, NC	27616-5146	919-855-9811	855-9813	PK-8	Ibis Nunez
Central Park S for Children	724 Foster St	Durham, NC	27701-2111	919-682-1200	680-6381	K-8	John Heffernan
Central Wake Charter HS	1425 Rock Quarry Rd	Raleigh, NC	27610	919-521-5067	890-3286	9-12	Thomas Hanley
Charlotte Choice Charter S	PO Box 44065	Charlotte, NC	28215	980-272-8306		K-8	Dr. Linda Cruz
Charlotte Lab S	301 E 9th St Ste 100	Charlotte, NC	28202	704-464-3830	223-5005	K-5	Dr. Mary Moss Brown
Charlotte Learning Academy	701 Scaleybark Rd	Charlotte, NC	28209-4744	980-355-2077		6-10	Stacey Rose
Charlotte Secondary S	8601 McAlpine Park Dr	Charlotte, NC	28211-6305	704-295-0137	295-0156	6-12	Nancy Dillon
Charter Day S	7055 Bacons Way NE	Leland, NC	28451-7960	910-655-1214	655-1549	K-8	Steve Smith
Chatham Charter S	PO Box 245	Siler City, NC	27344-0245	919-742-4550	742-2518	K-12	Dr. John Eldridge
Children's Village Academy	PO Box 2206	Kinston, NC	28502-2206	252-939-1958	939-1242	K-8	Jessica Jones
CIS Academy	818 W 3rd St	Pembroke, NC	28372-7307	910-521-1669	521-1670	6-8	Billy Haggans
Clover Garden S	2454 Altamahaw Union Ridge	Burlington, NC	27217-7965	336-586-9440	586-9477	K-12	Walter Finnigan
College Preparatory & Leadership Academy	5700 Riverdale Dr	Jamestown, NC	27282	336-884-0131	883-0109	K-12	Dr. Michelle Johnson
Columbus Charter S	35 Bacons Way	Whiteville, NC	28472-6225	910-641-4042	641-4043	K-8	Steven Smith
Commonwealth HS	5112 Central Ave	Charlotte, NC	28205-5812	704-899-4998	469-4661	9-12	Tom Hanley
Community Charter S	510 S Torrence St	Charlotte, NC	28204-3160	704-377-3180	377-3182	K-5	Oretha Roberts
Community S of Davidson	404 Armour St	Davidson, NC	28036-6905	704-896-6262	896-2025	K-12	Joy Warner
Cornerstone Charter Academy	7800 Airport Center Dr	Greensboro, NC	27409	336-482-3855	482-3857	K-12	Joe Caraher
Corvian Community School	9501 David Taylor Dr	Charlotte, NC	28262	704-717-7550	717-7558	K-7	Stacey Haskell
Crosscreek Charter S	306 Sandalwood Ave	Louisburg, NC	27549-2650	919-497-3198	497-0232	K-8	Robin Jackson
Delany New S for Children	119 Brevard Rd	Asheville, NC	28806-2922	828-236-9441	236-9442	K-8	Buffy Fowler
Dillard Academy	PO Box 1188	Goldsboro, NC	27533-1188	919-581-0166	581-0122	K-6	Hilda Hicks
Douglass Academy	507 N 6th St	Wilmington, NC	28401	910-763-1976	763-1974	K-5	Barbra Jones
East Wake Academy	821 Charter School Way	Zebulon, NC	27597	919-404-0444	404-2377	K-12	Stephen Gay
Endeavor Charter S	4879 One World Way	Wake Forest, NC	27587-5902	919-848-0333	848-8716	K-8	Christi Whiteside
Envision Science Academy	9400 Forum Dr	Raleigh, NC	27615	919-435-4002	307-4308	K-8	Steve Pond
Evergreen Community Charter S	50 Bell Rd	Asheville, NC	28805-1538	828-298-2173	298-2269	K-8	Dr. Susan Mertz
Excelsior Classical Academy	4100 N Roxboro St	Durham, NC	27704	919-907-0410	219-2610	K-5	Cynthia Gadol
Expedition S	437 Dimmocks Mill Rd Ste 33	Hillsborough, NC	27278	919-245-8432		K-8	Tammy Finch
Exploris S: K-8 Learning Community	401 Hillsborough St	Raleigh, NC	27603-1791	919-715-3690	715-2042	K-8	Summer Clayton
Falls Lake Academy	1701 E Lyon Station Rd	Creedmoor, NC	27522	919-964-9003	964-9008	K-10	Amy Hobgood
FernLeaf Community Charter S	58 Howard Gap Rd	Fletcher, NC	28732	828-398-9268	575-5402	K-3	Michael Luplow
Flemington Academy	PO Box 127	Lake Waccamaw, NC	28450	910-646-2237	356-0028	6-12	Tracy Coston M.Ed.
Forsyth Academy	5426 Shattalon Dr	Winston Salem, NC	27106-1919	336-922-1121	922-1033	K-8	Wendy Barajas
Franklin Academy	1127 Chalk Rd	Wake Forest, NC	27587-9150	919-570-8262	570-8241	3-8	Denise Kent
Franklin Academy	604 S Franklin St	Wake Forest, NC	27587-2276	919-554-4911		K-2	Denise Kent
Franklin Academy HS	648 Flaherty Ave	Wake Forest, NC	27587-2290	919-453-5090		9-12	David Mahaley
Franklin S of Innovation	21 Innovation Dr	Asheville, NC	28806	828-318-8140	318-8125	6-12	Michelle Vruwink
Gaston College Preparatory S	320 Pleasant Hill Rd	Gaston, NC	27832-9511	252-308-6932	308-6936	K-12	Tammi Sutton
Gate City Charter Academy	123 Flemingfield Rd	Greensboro, NC	27405	336-617-5900	232-1734	K-5	Corey Moore
Girls Leadership Academy of Wilmington	PO Box 7621	Wilmington, NC	28406	910-338-5258		6-12	Laura Hunter
Global Scholars Academy	311 Dowd St	Durham, NC	27701-2443	919-682-5903	956-8535	K-8	Jason Jowers
Grandfather Academy	PO Box 98	Banner Elk, NC	28604-0098	828-898-5465	898-8513	K-12	Michelle Griffin
Gray Stone Day S	PO Box 650	Misenheimer, NC	28109-0650	704-463-0567	463-0569	9-12	Helen Nance
Greensboro Academy	4049 Battleground Ave	Greensboro, NC	27410-8410	336-286-8404	286-8403	K-8	Doug Hower
Guilford Preparatory Academy	2210 E Cone Blvd	Greensboro, NC	27405-4857	336-954-1344	954-1965	K-8	Robin Buckrham
Haliwa-Saponi Tribal S	130 Haliwa Saponi Trl	Hollister, NC	27844-9390	252-257-5853	257-1093	K-12	Rebecca Arroyo
Hawbridge S	PO Box 40	Saxapahaw, NC	27340	336-376-1122	376-6996	6-12	Dr. Kenneth Moles
Healthy Start Academy	807 W Chapel Hill St	Durham, NC	27701-3112	919-956-5599	688-9027	K-8	Dr. Anthony Chalmers
Henderson Collegiate	1071 Old Epsom Rd	Henderson, NC	27536-5654	252-598-1038	598-1037	4-9	Frank Terranova
Henderson Collegiate HS	906 Health Center Rd	Henderson, NC	27536-5479	252-598-1039		9-12	Jackson Olsen

School	Address	City,State	Zip code	Telephone	Fax	Grade	Contact
Heritage Collegiate Leadership Academy	PO Box 1170	Windsor, NC	27983	252-794-0597	794-0598	K-8	Kashi Bazemore-Hall
Hope Elementary Charter S	1116 N Blount St	Raleigh, NC	27604-1302	919-834-0941	834-9338	K-5	Clarissa Fleming
Howard S for the Arts & Educ	1004 Herring Ave E	Wilson, NC	27893-3311	252-293-4150	293-4151	K-8	Dr. JoAnne Woodard
Institute for Development Young Leaders	1305 W Club Blvd	Durham, NC	27705	919-973-4178	401-8005	K-8	Yvette Munroe
Invest Collegiate	2045 Suttle Ave	Charlotte, NC	28208	704-370-4000	973-7876	K-7	Danah Telfaire
Invest Collegiate-Imagine	1000 Brevard Rd Ste 175	Asheville, NC	28806-2276	828-633-6491	633-6494	K-10	Laura Townley
Iredell Charter Academy	251 Home Improvement St	Troutman, NC	28166	704-508-0104	508-0105	K-6	Dr. Andrea LoPresti
Island Montessori Charter S	6339 Carolina Beach Rd	Wilmington, NC	28412	910-795-4860	707-1201	K-8	Brian Corrigan
Jefferson Classical Academy	2527 US 221A Hwy	Mooresboro, NC	28114-7698	828-657-9998	657-9012	K-12	Joseph Maimone
Joy Charter S	107 S Driver St	Durham, NC	27703-4133	919-908-1600	402-4263	K-8	Mark Bailey
Kannapolis Charter Academy	1911 Concord Lake Rd	Kannapolis, NC	28083	704-273-5310	273-5326	K-8	Katrina Samuels
Kestrel Heights S	4700 S Alston Ave	Durham, NC	27713-4419	919-484-1300	484-1355	K-12	Dr. Mark Tracy
KIPP Academy Charlotte	931 Wilann Dr	Charlotte, NC	28215-2147	704-537-2044	537-2855	K-K,	Tiffany Flowers
KIPP Durham College Preparatory S	1107 Holloway St	Durham, NC	27701	919-307-9118		5-6	Anders Campbell
KIPP Halifax College Prep	515 Becker Dr	Roanoke Rapids, NC	27870-3380	252-410-0277	308-9656	5-8	Marlow Wilkins
Lake Lure Classical Academy	PO Box 6	Lake Lure, NC	28746	828-625-9292	625-9298	K-12	Thomas Keever
Lake Norman Charter S	12435 S Old Statesville Rd	Huntersville, NC	28078-7252	704-948-8600	948-8778	5-12	Shannon Stein
Langtree Charter Academy	154 Foundation Ct	Mooresville, NC	28117	704-705-1698	360-3026	K-10	Van Wade
Learning Center	945 Connahetta St	Murphy, NC	28906-3524	828-835-7240	835-9471	K-8	Mary Jo Dyre
Lincoln Charter S Denver	7834 Galway Ln	Denver, NC	28037	704-483-6611	483-6611	K-12	Jonathan Bryant
Lincoln Charter S Lincolnton	133 Eagle Nest Rd	Lincolnton, NC	28092-7383	704-736-9888		K-8	Jonathan Bryant
Longleaf School of the Arts	207 E Hargett St	Raleigh, NC	27601-1437	919-896-8164	516-0923	9-12	Rachel Davis
Magellan Charter S	9324 Baileywick Rd	Raleigh, NC	27615-1909	919-844-0277	844-3882	3-8	Mary Griffin
Mallard Creek STEM Academy	9142 Browne Rd	Charlotte, NC	28269	980-288-4811	799-3166	K-6	Deanna Smith
Matthews Charter Academy	2332 Mount Harmony Church	Matthews, NC	28105	980-339-5449	321-7058	K-7	Christy Morrin
Metrolina Regional Scholars Academy	5225 77 Center Dr	Charlotte, NC	28217-0708	704-503-1112	503-1183	K-8	Jessica Cuneo
Millennium Charter Academy	500 Old Springs Rd	Mount Airy, NC	27030-3034	336-789-7570	789-8445	K-12	Kirby McCrary
Mountain Community S	613 Glover St	Hendersonville, NC	28792-5451	828-696-8480	696-8451	K-8	Denise Pesce
Mountain Discovery Charter S	890 Jenkins Branch Rd N	Bryson City, NC	28713-4514	828-488-1222	488-0526	K-8	Carter Petty
Mountain Island Charter S	13440 Lucia Riverbend Hwy	Mount Holly, NC	28120-9766	704-827-8840	827-8675	K-12	Justin Matthews
Neuse Charter S	909 E Booker Dairy Rd	Smithfield, NC	27577	919-938-1077	938-1079	K-12	Susan Pullium
New Dimensions S	550 Lenoir Rd	Morganton, NC	28655-2697	828-437-5753	437-2980	K-8	Larry Wilkerson
NC Connections Academy	PO Box 12052	Durham, NC	27709	919-224-4040	361-6321	K-10	Nathan Currie
North Carolina Leadership Academy	PO Box 1728	Kernersville, NC	27285	336-992-2710	992-2714	K-12	Dottie Heath
North Carolina Virtual Academy	4220 NC Highway 55	Durham, NC	27713	919-346-0121	324-6597	K-10	Joel Medley
Northeast Academy of Aerospace Tech	PO Box 2889	Elizabeth City, NC	27906	252-562-0653	338-8546	7-10	Andrew Harris
North East Carolina Prep S	274 Husky Trl	Tarboro, NC	27886	252-641-0464	641-1816	K-12	Thomas Schuck
Notheast Regional S of Biotech Ag	1215 Saint Andrews St	Jamesville, NC	27846-9772	252-792-0241	792-0245	9-12	Hallet Davis
Orange Charter S	920 Corporate Dr	Hillsborough, NC	27278-8557	919-644-6272	644-6275	K-8	Lisa Bair
Oxford Preparatory S	6041 Landis Rd	Oxford, NC	27565-7411	919-690-0360	690-0230	8-12	Andrew Swanner
PAVE SE Raliegh Charter S	3420 Idlewood Village Dr	Raleigh, NC	27610	804-446-4777	800-3054	K-2	Ariana Kanwit
Phoenix Academy	4020 Meeting Way	High Point, NC	27265	336-869-0079	464-2070	K-10	Kimberly Norcross M.Ed.
Piedmont Classical HS	300 NC 68	Greensboro, NC	27409	336-701-2271	283-5340	9-11	Hannah Cobb
Piedmont Community Charter S	PO Box 3706	Gastonia, NC	28054-0038	704-853-2428	853-3689	K-12	Jennifer Purdee
Pine Lake Preparatory S	104 Yellow Wood Cir	Mooresville, NC	28115-6100	704-237-5300	237-5398	K-12	Christopher Terrill
Pinnacle Classical Academy	900 S Post Rd	Shelby, NC	28152	704-740-4040	482-5527	K-9	Robert Brown
Pioneer Springs Community S	9300 Bob Beatty Rd	Charlotte, NC	28269	704-494-0777		K-5	Rebecca Friend
PreEminent Charter S	3815 Rock Quarry Rd	Raleigh, NC	27610-5123	919-235-0511	235-0514	K-8	Melanie Butler-Williams
Quality Education Academy	5012 Lansing Dr Ste D	Winston Salem, NC	27105-3026	336-744-0804	293-0617	K-12	Simon Johnson
Queen City STEM S	PO Box 480064	Charlotte, NC	28269-5300	980-299-6633	299-6634	K-6	Atila Akyurek
Queen's Grant Community S	6400 Matthews Mint Hill Rd	Mint Hill, NC	28227-9323	704-573-6611	943-2395	K-12	Krista Tolchin
Quest Academy	10908 Strickland Rd	Raleigh, NC	27615-1873	919-841-0441	841-0443	K-8	Elizabeth Readmond
Raleigh Charter HS	1307 Glenwood Ave	Raleigh, NC	27605-1216	919-715-1155	715-1176	9-12	Dr. Lisa Huddleston
Reaching All Minds Academy	2703 Holloway St	Durham, NC	27703	919-596-1899	882-8339	K-5	Thomas McKoy
Research Triangle Charter Academy	2418 Ellis Rd	Durham, NC	27703-5543	919-957-7108	957-9698	K-8	Dr. Wayne Muhammad
Research Triangle HS	PO Box 13453	Durham, NC	27709-3453	919-998-6757	998-3402	9-12	Eric Grunden
River Mill Academy	235 Cheeks Ln	Graham, NC	27253	336-229-0909	229-9975	K-12	Jeffrey Dishmon
Rocky Mount Prep S	3334 Bishop Rd	Rocky Mount, NC	27804	252-443-9923	443-9932	K-12	Todd Pipkin
Roxboro Community S	115 Lake Dr	Roxboro, NC	27573-5672	336-597-0020	597-3152	6-12	Natalie Brozy
Sandhills Theatre Arts Renaissance S	140 Southern Dunes Dr	Vass, NC	28394-9218	910-695-1004	695-7322	K-12	Dr. Wesley Graner
Shining Rock Classical Academy	1023 Dellwood Rd	Waynesville, NC	28786	828-738-2665		K-7	Ben Butler
Socrates Academy	3909 Weddington Rd	Matthews, NC	28105	704-321-1711	321-1714	K-8	Sandra Brighton
South Brunswick Charter S	2260 Achievement Ave SE	Bolivia, NC	28422	910-338-4178	338-4179	K-5	Michelle Mena
Southeastern Academy	12251 NC Highway 41 N	Lumberton, NC	28358-6892	910-738-7828	671-8067	PK-8	Kristen Stone
Southern Wake Academy	5108 Old Powell Rd	Holly Springs, NC	27540-9200	919-567-9955	567-9956	6-12	David Thomas
Sterling Montessori Academy	202 Treybrooke Dr	Morrisville, NC	27560-9300	919-462-8889	462-8890	PK-8	Paul Raymond
Stewart Creek HS	2701F Freedom Dr	Charlotte, NC	28208	704-755-5112	960-1726	9-12	Ismael Villafane
Success Institute Charter S	PO Box 1332	Statesville, NC	28687-1332	704-881-0441	881-0870	K-8	Tenna Williams
Sugar Creek Charter S	4101 N Tryon St	Charlotte, NC	28206-2066	704-509-5470	921-1004	K-10	Cheryl Turner
Summerfield Charter Academy	5300 N US 220	Summerfield, NC	27358	336-643-1974	217-8367	K-6	Rudy Swofford
Summit Charter S	370 Mitten Ln	Cashiers, NC	28717-4511	828-743-5755	743-9157	K-8	Danny Howell
Thunderbird Preparatory S	17609 Old Statesville Rd	Cornelius, NC	28031	704-412-1024	445-7754	K-6	Dr. Emmanuel Vincent
Tiller S	1950 US Highway 70 E	Beaufort, NC	28516-7836	252-728-1995	728-3711	K-5	Virginia Jones
Torchlight Academy	3211 Bramer Dr	Raleigh, NC	27604-1603	919-850-9960	850-9961	K-6	Dr. Cynthia McQueen
Triad Math and Science Academy	700 Creek Ridge Rd	Greensboro, NC	27406	336-621-0061	621-0072	K-12	Dr. Guray Taysever
Triangle Math and Science Academy	312 Gregson Dr	Cary, NC	27511-6444	919-388-0077	651-1418	K-12	Mithat Karabulut
Two Rivers Community S	1018 Archie Carroll Rd	Boone, NC	28607-8506	828-262-5411	262-5412	K-8	Dr. David Rizor
Union Academy	675 N M L King Jr Blvd	Monroe, NC	28110-8119	704-283-8883	283-8823	K-12	Dr. Ann Walters
Union Day S	PO Box 1005	Waxhaw, NC	28173	704-256-1494	256-5567	K-3	Ashley Hurley
Union Prep Academy at Indian Trail	2324 Younts Rd	Indian Trail, NC	28079	704-893-3607	893-3608	K-8	Joan Roman
United Community S	1406 Suther Rd	Charlotte, NC	28213	980-819-0555	819-0663	K-2	Erika Hedgepeth
Uwharrie Charter Academy	PO Box 1282	Asheboro, NC	27204-1282	336-610-0813	610-0815	9-12	Heather Soja
Vance Charter S	2090 Ross Mill Rd	Henderson, NC	27536	252-431-0440	436-0688	K-9	Sean Connolly
Veritas Community S	2600 Grimes St	Charlotte, NC	28206	980-677-0101	228-3028	K-4	Katy Ridnouer M.Ed.
Voyager Academy ES	4210 Ben Franklin Blvd	Durham, NC	27704	919-433-3301		K-5	
Voyager Academy HS	4302 Ben Franklin Blvd	Durham, NC	27704	919-433-3301		9-12	
Voyager Academy MS	101 Hock Parc	Durham, NC	27704	919-433-3301	433-3305	6-8	Jennifer Lucas
Wake Forest Charter Academy	1851 Friendship Chapel Rd	Wake Forest, NC	27587-1825	919-263-8673	882-9038	K-6	Amanda Brown
Washington Montessori S	2330 Old Bath Hwy	Washington, NC	27889	252-946-1977	946-5938	K-12	Austin Smigel
Water's Edge Village S	PO Box 215	Corolla, NC	27927-0215	252-453-4502	453-3154	K-6	Meghan Agresto
Wayne Preparatory Academy	600 Tommys Rd	Goldsboro, NC	27530	919-734-8085		K-6	Dr. Todd Forgette
Williams Academy	PO Box 309	Crossnore, NC	28616-0309	828-733-5241	737-7915	K-12	Dr. Cyndi Austin Ed.D.
Willow Oak Montessori S	50101 Governors Dr	Chapel Hill, NC	27517-9257	919-240-7787		1-4	Peter Rubinas
Wilmington Preparatory Academy	134 Cinema Dr	Wilmington, NC	28403-1490	910-799-6776	338-1834	K-8	Kevin Johnson
Wilson Preparatory Academy	2755 Tilghman Rd N	Wilson, NC	27896	252-294-2533	294-2534	K-8	Daryl Woodard
Winterville Charter Academy	4160 Bays Water Rd	Winterville, NC	28590	252-689-6153	360-4576	K-8	Dr. Devon Carson
Woods Charter S	160 Woodland Grove Ln	Chapel Hill, NC	27516-4085	919-960-8353	960-0133	K-12	Cotton Bryan
Woodson S	437 Goldfloss St	Winston Salem, NC	27127-3125	336-723-6838	723-6425	K-12	Ruth Hopkins
Youngsville Academy	PO Box 250	Youngsville, NC	27596	919-556-3609	556-3498	K-2	Larry Henson
Z.E.C.A. School of Arts & Technology	110 Branchwood Dr Ste C	Jacksonville, NC	28546-5900	910-219-8603	219-8604	K-6	Stacey Owens-Howard

Ohio

School	Address	City,State	Zip code	Telephone	Fax	Grade	Contact
A+ Arts Academy	2633 Maybury Rd	Columbus, OH	43205	614-626-2250	626-2258	K-6	Renee Craft
A+ Arts Academy	270 S Napoleon Ave	Columbus, OH	43213	614-338-0767	338-0787	7-8	Vicki Washington
A+ Arts Academy	1395 Fair Ave	Columbus, OH	43205	614-725-1305	725-2305	PK-6	Dr. David Fant
A+ Children's Academy	100 Obetz Rd	Columbus, OH	43207-4031	614-491-3270	492-0035	PK-2	Melinda Hardgrow
Academy For Urban Scholars HS	1808 E Broad St	Columbus, OH	43203	614-545-9890	545-9889	9-12	Roger Fox
Academy of Arts & Sciences	3038 N Leavitt Rd	Lorain, OH	44052	440-244-0156	244-3935	K-12	James Sinclair
Academy of Educational Excellence	728 Parkside Blvd	Toledo, OH	43607-3858	330-382-2280		K-3	
Academy of Urban Scholars	1350 5th Ave Ste 100	Youngstown, OH	44504-1765	330-774-9070	776-9636	9-12	Kevin Ellerbre
Achieve Career Preparatory Academy	3891 Martha Ave	Toledo, OH	43612	419-243-8559	243-8583	8-12	Cindy Wilson
Akron Digital Academy	133 Merriman Rd	Akron, OH	44303	330-237-2200	237-2207	K-12	LaShawn Terrell
Akron Preparatory S	1200 E Market St Ste 3360	Akron, OH	44305	330-247-6232	299-7173	K-8	Heather Stevens
Akros MS	265 Park St	Akron, OH	44304-1305	330-374-6704	374-6713	6-8	Holly Piskula
Allen Academy III	1206 Shuler Ave	Hamilton, OH	45011	513-868-2900	868-0498	K-6	Erin Ramsey
Allen Academy II	184 Salem Ave	Dayton, OH	45406	937-586-9756	586-9764	2-6	Valeria Kerley
Allen Academy	700 Heck Ave	Dayton, OH	45417	937-586-9815	586-0271	7-9	Aundray Brooks
Allen Preparatory S	627 Salem Ave	Dayton, OH	45406-5822	937-278-4201	278-4229	K-1	Yolanda Clark
Alliance Academy of Cincinnati	1712 Duck Creek Rd	Cincinnati, OH	45207-1644	513-751-5555	751-5072	K-8	Elizabeth King
Alternative Education Academy	1830 Adams St	Toledo, OH	43604-4428	330-253-8680	514-8227	K-12	David Bowlin
Apex Academy	16005 Terrace Rd	East Cleveland, OH	44112-2001	216-451-1725	451-1765	K-8	Michael Bean
Arts & College Preparatory Academy	4401 Hilton Corporate Dr	Columbus, OH	43232-3303	614-986-9974	986-9976	9-12	Anthony Gatto
Ashland County Community Academy	716 Union St	Ashland, OH	44805-1823	419-903-0295	903-0341	9-12	Donne Copenhaver
Auglaize County Educational Academy	1130 E Albert St	Lima, OH	45804	419-738-4572	738-4591	K-12	Shawn Brown
Aurora Academy	824 6th St	Toledo, OH	43605	419-693-6841	693-4799	K-8	Latanya Ridley
Autism Academy of Learning	110 Arco Dr Ste 1	Toledo, OH	43607	419-865-7487	865-8360	K-12	James Jones

School	Address	City,State	Zip code	Telephone	Fax	Grade	Contact
Autism Model S	3020 Tremainsville Rd	Toledo, OH	43613-1901	419-897-4400	897-4403	K-12	Mary Walters
Beacon Academy	1379 Garfield Ave SW	Canton, OH	44706	330-941-5852		K-8	Danielle Artl
Beacon Hill Academy	PO Box 285	Mount Eaton, OH	44659-0285	330-359-5600		6-12	Bradley Herman
Bella Academy of Excellence	19114 Bella Dr	Cleveland, OH	44119-3007	216-481-1500	481-4515	K-6	Arun Dutt
Bennett Venture Academy	5130 Bennett Rd	Toledo, OH	43612-3422	419-269-2247	269-2257	K-8	Luis Calderon
Berwyn East Academy	1850 Bostwick Rd	Columbus, OH	43227-3374	614-564-9548		PK-3	Shannan Enoch
Bridges Community Academy	190 Saint Francis Ave	Tiffin, OH	44883-4012	419-455-9295	455-9296	K-12	Dona Kaufman
Broadway Academy	3398 E 55th St	Cleveland, OH	44127-1691	216-271-7747	271-6438	PK-8	Christopher Hammill
Brookwood Academy	2685 E Livingston Ave	Columbus, OH	43209-2961	614-231-1199	235-2280	9-12	Ellen Wristen
Buckeye On-Line School for Success	119 E 5th St	East Liverpool, OH	43920-3030	866-642-9237	385-4535	K-12	Rick Sheppard
Buckeye Preparatory Academy	1414 Gault St	Columbus, OH	43205-2933	614-300-3685	252-7083	K-8	Renee Dunn
Canton College Preparatory S	101 Cleveland Ave NW	Canton, OH	44702	330-455-0498		K-8	Darryl Lindsay
Canton Harbor HS	1731 Grace Ave NE	Canton, OH	44705-2261	330-452-8414	452-8452	9-12	Joseph Cole
Capella HS	5130 Warrensville Center Rd	Maple Heights, OH	44137	216-587-5282		9-12	
Capital HS	640 Harrisburg Pike	Columbus, OH	43223	614-228-2854	228-4679	9-12	Monica Scott
Carpe Diem Charter S	5641 Belmont Ave	Cincinnati, OH	45224	513-363-6600	363-6620	7-12	Tyree Gaines
CASTLE HS	3950 Prospect Ave E	Cleveland, OH	44115	216-443-5400	443-9017	9-12	Carl Kendall
Center for Student Achievement	21 Tropic St	Jackson, OH	45640-1966	740-286-7839	286-7837	9-12	Don Jenkins
Central Academy of Ohio	2727 Kenwood Blvd	Toledo, OH	43606-3216	419-205-9800	205-9899	K-6	Mohamad Issa
Central HS	840 W State St	Columbus, OH	43222	614-362-7530		9-12	Karen Wachter
Chapelside Cleveland Academy	3845 E 131st St	Cleveland, OH	44120-4661	216-283-6589	283-3087	K-8	Tim Spencer
Charles S at Ohio Dominican	1270 Brentnell Ave	Columbus, OH	43219-2017	614-258-8588	258-8584	9-12	Gregory Brown
Chavez College Prep ES	2400 Mock Rd	Columbus, OH	43219	614-299-1007	299-3684	K-5	Jameica Shoultz
Cincinnati College Prep Academy	1425 Linn St	Cincinnati, OH	45214	513-684-0777	684-8888	K-12	Guyton Mathews
Cincinnati Generation Academy	7243 Eastlawn Dr	Cincinnati, OH	45237	513-389-0968	389-0964	K-6	Danielle Bateman
Cincinnati Technology Academy	3800 Glenway Ave	Cincinnati, OH	45205-1436	513-471-7323	386-7931	9-12	Roger Conners
Citizens Academy	10118 Hampden Ave	Cleveland, OH	44108-3538	216-791-4195	791-3013	K-5	Jennifer Taylor
Citizens Academy East	12523 Woodside Ave	Cleveland, OH	44108-2422	216-367-9392	761-7398	K-3	Alicia Levy
Citizens Academy Southeast	17900 Harvard Ave	Cleveland, OH	44128	216-586-3887	561-1121	K-5	Lachelle Dixon-Harris
Citizens Leadership Academy	9711 Lamont Ave	Cleveland, OH	44106-4124	216-229-8185	229-8516	6-8	Shelly Saltzman
City Day Community S	318 S Main St	Dayton, OH	45402-2716	937-223-8130	223-8136	K-8	Paula Leone
Clark Preparatory Academy	501 S Wittenberg Ave	Springfield, OH	44506	937-504-1175		K-8	
Clay Avenue Community S	1030 Clay Ave	Toledo, OH	43608-2167	419-727-9900	727-9902	K-6	Julie McLaughlin
Cleveland Art & Social Science Academy	10701 Shaker Blvd	Cleveland, OH	44104-3752	216-229-3000	229-3182	K-8	Deborah Mays
Cleveland College Preparatory S	4906 Fleet Ave	Cleveland, OH	44105	216-341-1347	341-4466	K-8	
Cliff Park HS	821 N Limestone St	Springfield, OH	45503-3609	937-342-3006		9-12	John Stack
Collinwood Village Academy	716 E 156th St	Cleveland, OH	44110-2408	216-451-4022	451-4040	9-12	Bethany Scott
Colonial Preparatory Academy	2199 5th St SW	Akron, OH	44314-2405	330-752-2792		K-8	David Stiles
Columbus Arts & Tech Academy	2255 Kimberly Pkwy E	Columbus, OH	43232-7210	614-577-0900	866-0300	K-9	Derrick Shelton
Columbus Collegiate Academy	1469 E Main St	Columbus, OH	43205-2152	614-299-5284	299-5303	6-8	Celeste Ferguson
Columbus Collegiate Academy - West	300 Dana Ave	Columbus, OH	43223	614-545-9570	545-9571	K-5	Nathan Parker
Columbus Humanities Arts & Tech Academy	1333 Morse Rd	Columbus, OH	43229-6322	614-261-1200	261-1201	K-8	Latasha Morgan M.Ed.
Columbus Performance & Fitness Academy	274 E 1st Ave Ste 200	Columbus, OH	43201	614-318-0720	375-1995	K-8	Adam Haman
Columbus Prep & Fitness Academy	1258 Demorest Rd	Columbus, OH	43204	614-318-0606	351-9804	K-8	Jeff Luelleman
Columbus Preparatory Academy	3330 Chippewa St	Columbus, OH	43204-1653	614-275-3600	275-3601	K-8	Chad Carr
Cornerstone Academy	6015 E Walnut St	Westerville, OH	43081-9620	614-775-0615	775-0633	K-8	Natalee Long
Coshocton Opportunity S	1205 Cambridge Rd	Coshocton, OH	43812-2741	740-622-3600	623-6860	9-12	Roger Moore
Cruiser Academy	4400 Marketing Pl	Groveport, OH	43125	614-237-8756	237-9308	9-12	Bill Young
Dayton Business Technology HS	348 W 1st St	Dayton, OH	45402	937-225-3989	225-3998	9-12	Greg Stone
Dayton Early College Academy	300 College Park Ave	Dayton, OH	45469-0001	937-229-5780	229-5786	7-12	David Taylor
Dayton Liberty Campus	4401 Dayton Liberty Rd	Dayton, OH	45417-5903	937-262-4080	262-4091	K-8	Dr. Theodore Wallace
Dayton SMART Bilingual Academy	601 S Keowee St	Dayton, OH	45410	937-222-2812	264-8683	K-4	Marvis Meeks
Dayton View Academy	1416 W Riverview Ave	Dayton, OH	45402-6217	937-567-9426	567-9446	K-8	Dr. Theodore Wallace
DECA PREP	200 Homewood Ave	Dayton, OH	45405-4328	937-610-0110	260-4478	K-6	Judy Hennessey Ph.D.
Discovery Academy	2740 W Central Ave	Toledo, OH	43623	419-214-3266		K-6	Noah Campbell
Dohn Community HS	608 E McMillan St	Cincinnati, OH	45206-1926	513-281-6100	281-6103	9-12	Leando Davenport
Douglass Reclamation Academy	3167 Fulton Rd	Cleveland, OH	44109-1465	216-961-5631	961-5637	9-12	Iteisha Jefferson M.Ed.
Eagle Academy	1430 Idaho St	Toledo, OH	43605	419-697-2760	697-2763	6-12	Nicolette Whitson
Eagle Learning Center HS	2665 Navarre Ave	Oregon, OH	43616-3245	419-720-2003	720-2007	9-12	Loren Dirr
Early College Academy	345 E 5th Ave	Columbus, OH	43201-2819	614-298-4742	298-9107	9-12	Jonathan Stevens
East Academy	15720 Kipling Ave	Cleveland, OH	44110-3105	216-383-1214		K-8	Nehemiah Thomas
East Bridge Academy of Excellence	2323 Lake Club Dr	Columbus, OH	43232	614-501-3822		K-6	
East Preparatory Academy	4129 Superior Ave	Cleveland, OH	44103-1129	216-539-0595		K-8	Joy Beasley
Eastside Arts Academy	6700 Lansing Ave	Cleveland, OH	44105-3756	216-441-9830	441-9834	K-5	Katherine Rybak
Edge Academy	92 N Union St	Akron, OH	44304-1347	330-535-4581	535-5074	K-5	Chris Burchfield
Educational Academy for Boys & Girls	1500 W 3rd Ave	Columbus, OH	43212-2843	614-294-3020		K-5	Estella Stephens
Einstein Academy	3550 Crocker Rd	Westlake, OH	44145-6314	440-471-4982	617-6809	9-12	Bruce Thomas
Electronic Classroom of Tomorrow	3700 S High St Ste 95	Columbus, OH	43207-4083	614-492-8884	492-8894	K-12	Ricky Teeters
Elyria Community MS	336 S Logan St	Elyria, OH	44035	440-365-0390	365-0397	6-8	Eric Fortuna
Elyria Community S	300 Abbe Rd N	Elyria, OH	44035-3724	440-366-5225	366-6280	K-5	Eric Fortuna
Emerson Academy of Dayton	501 Hickory St	Dayton, OH	45410-1232	937-223-2889	660-6386	K-8	Allison Foreman
E Prep & Village Prep Charter S	1417 E 36th St	Cleveland, OH	44114-4116	216-456-2070	361-9717	K-8	John McBride
E Prep & Village Prep Charter S	9201 Crane Ave	Cleveland, OH	44105	216-298-1164	341-0106	K-8	Chris O'Brien
Everest HS	1555 Graham Rd	Reynoldsburg, OH	43068-2632	614-367-1980		9-12	Doug Gillum
Fairborn Digital Academy	700 Black Ln	Fairborn, OH	45324-5844	937-879-0511	879-8160	9-12	Erik Tritsch
Findlay Digital Academy	1219 W Main Cross St # 101	Findlay, OH	45840	419-425-3598	425-3588	9-12	Sandra White
Flex HS	115 S Gift St	Columbus, OH	43215	614-610-9749		9-12	Alicia Henry
Focus Learning Academy East	4480 Refugee Rd	Columbus, OH	43232-4459	614-269-0150	269-0151	9-12	Jason Morton
Focus Learning Academy North	4807 Evanswood Dr	Columbus, OH	43229-6285	614-310-0430	310-0469	9-12	Tiffany DeLong-Kocher
Focus Learning Academy Southwest	190 Southwood Ave	Columbus, OH	43207-1133	614-545-2000	545-1995	9-12	Kerry Hill
Focus Learning Acad of Northern Columbus	1880 E Dublin Granville Rd	Columbus, OH	43229-3523	614-547-0920	547-0924	K-8	Travis Budd
Foundation Academy	1050 Wyandotte Ave	Mansfield, OH	44906-1939	419-526-9540	526-9542	K-10	Joann Hipsher
Fox Academy	1505 Jefferson Ave	Toledo, OH	43604-5722	419-720-4500	720-4502	7-12	
Foxfire East Academy	60901 Beech Grove Ln	Cambridge, OH	43725	740-432-5457		9-12	
Foxfire ES	2805 Pinkerton Ln	Zanesville, OH	43701	740-453-4509	455-4084	K-4	Amanda Matthews
Foxfire HS	PO Box 1818	Zanesville, OH	43702	740-453-4509	455-4084	9-12	Todd Whiteman
Foxfire IS	2805 Pinkerton Ln	Zanesville, OH	43701-8593	740-453-4509		5-8	Amanda Matthews
Franklin Local Community S	PO Box 95	Roseville, OH	43777-0095	740-697-7317	697-0793	7-12	Jennifer Woodard
Franklinton Preparatory Academy	40 Chicago Ave	Columbus, OH	43222-1132	614-636-3721		9-12	Martin Griffith
Gate Community S	4060 Sullivant Ave	Columbus, OH	43228	614-501-3820		7-12	Henry Warren
Glass City Academy	1000 Monroe St	Toledo, OH	43604-5954	419-720-6311	720-6315	11-12	Stewart Jesse
Global Ambassadors Language Academy	13442 Lorain Ave	Cleveland, OH	44111	216-315-7942		K-8	Jessica Gilway
Global Village Academy	5720 State Rd	Parma, OH	44134-2565	216-767-5956	767-5653	K-6	Oleh Holowatyj
Goal Digital Academy	890 W 4th St Ste 400	Mansfield, OH	44906-2561	419-521-9008	529-2976	K-12	Patricia Jenkins
Graham Expeditionary MS	140 E 16th Ave	Columbus, OH	43201-1617	614-253-4000	253-4002	5-8	Gregory Brown
Graham PS	140 E 16th Ave	Columbus, OH	43201-1617	614-253-4001	643-5146	K-5	Eileen Meers
Graham S	3950 Indianola Ave	Columbus, OH	43214-3167	614-262-1111	262-5878	9-12	Gregory Brown
Greater Ohio Virtual S	1879 Deerfield Rd	Lebanon, OH	45036	513-695-2924	695-2588	7-12	Shawn E. Lenney
Greater Summit County Early Learning Ctr	2141 Pickle Rd	Akron, OH	44312-4221	330-945-5600		PK-4	Teresa Graves
Great Western Academy	310 N Wilson Rd	Columbus, OH	43204-6221	614-276-1028	276-1049	K-8	Jason Knight
Green Inspiration Academy	4265 Northfield Rd	Highland Hills, OH	44128	216-378-9573	882-0554	K-8	Ginny Schemrich
Groveport Community S	4485 S Hamilton Rd	Groveport, OH	43125-9334	614-574-4100	574-4107	K-8	Dair Foster
Haley S	4901 Galaxy Pkwy	Cleveland, OH	44128-5948	216-581-4259	510-5732	K-6	Richard Hronek
Hamilton Alternative Academy	775 Rathmell Rd	Columbus, OH	43207-4737	614-491-8044	491-5564	K-12	Allyson Price
Hamilton County Math & Science S	2675 Civic Center Dr	Cincinnati, OH	45231-1311	513-728-8620	728-8623	K-8	Dwan Moore M.Ed.
Hardin Community S	400 Decatur St	Kenton, OH	43326-2043	419-673-3210		6-12	Wade Melton
Harrisburg Pike Community S	680 Harrisburg Pike	Columbus, OH	43223	614-223-1510	223-1584	K-6	Laura Holler
Harvard Avenue Performance Academy	12000 Harvard Ave	Cleveland, OH	44105-5444	216-283-5100	283-5762	K-8	Paula Baldwin
HBCU Preparatory School 1	12601 Shaker Blvd	Cleveland, OH	44120-2041	216-812-0244	812-0234	K-12	
HBCU Preparatory School 2	12601 Shaker Blvd	Cleveland, OH	44120-2041	216-426-8601	426-9528	3-5	
Heir Force Community S	150 W Grand Ave	Lima, OH	45801-4006	419-228-9241	228-1555	K-8	Darwin Lofton
Hollingworth S for Talented & Gifted	653 Miami St	Toledo, OH	43605-2277	419-705-3411	720-4923	K-9	Terrence Franklin
Hope Academy for Autism	1628 Niles Rd SE	Warren, OH	44484-5111	330-369-2454	369-2455	K-12	Kimberly Clinkscale
Hope Academy Northcoast Campus	4310 E 71st St	Cleveland, OH	44105-5759	216-429-0232	429-0249	K-8	
Hope Academy Northwest	1441 W 116th St	Cleveland, OH	44102-2301	216-226-6800	226-6805	K-12	
Hope Learning Academy of Toledo	4234 Monroe St	Toledo, OH	43606-1938	419-297-6313	725-9184	K-8	Justin Bryson
Horizon Science Academy Cincinnati	1055 Laidlaw Ave	Cincinnati, OH	45237-5005	513-242-0099	242-2467	K-8	Ergun Sevilmis
Horizon Science Academy Cleveland HS	6000 S Marginal Rd	Cleveland, OH	44103-1078	216-432-3660	432-3670	9-12	Mustafa Ada
Horizon Science Academy Cleveland MS	6100 S Marginal Rd	Cleveland, OH	44103-1043	216-432-9940	432-9941	6-8	
Horizon Science Academy Columbus ES	2835 Morse Rd	Columbus, OH	43231-6033	614-475-4585	475-4587	K-5	Jessica Lindskog
Horizon Science Academy Columbus HS	1070 Morse Rd	Columbus, OH	43229-6290	614-846-7616	846-7696	9-12	
Horizon Science Academy Columbus MS	2350 Morse Rd	Columbus, OH	43229-5801	614-428-6564	428-6574	6-8	Okan Celiker
Horizon Science Academy Dayton	4751 Sue Ann Blvd	Dayton, OH	45415-1171	937-277-1177	277-3090	K-4	Jaime Lierly
Horizon Science Academy Dayton Downtown	121 S Monmouth St	Dayton, OH	45403-2127	937-281-1980	281-1979	K-8	Mustafa Ada
Horizon Science Academy Dayton HS	250 Shoup Mill Rd	Dayton, OH	45415-3517	937-281-1480	281-1481	5-12	Ali Kucuker
Horizon Science Academy - Denison	1700 Denison Ave	Cleveland, OH	44109-2945	216-739-9911	739-9913	K-8	Bulent Akben M.Ed.
Horizon Science Academy Denison ES	2261 Columbus Rd	Cleveland, OH	44113-4230	216-661-8840	661-8850	K-5	Nicole Kratz

School	Address	City,State	Zip code	Telephone	Fax	Grade	Contact
Horizon Science Academy of Lorain	760 Tower Blvd	Lorain, OH	44052-5223	440-282-4277	282-4278	K-12	Fatih Sumer
Horizon Science Academy Springfield	630 S Reynolds Rd	Toledo, OH	43615-6314	419-535-0524	535-0525	K-8	Erin Schreiner
Horizon Science Academy Youngstown	3403 Southern Blvd	Youngstown, OH	44507-2044	330-782-3003	782-3356	K-8	Ferhat Kapki
iLEAD Spring Meadows	1615 Timberwolf Dr	Holland, OH	43528	419-491-7423		PK-6	Tiffany Adamski
IMAC HS	445 Bowman St	Mansfield, OH	44903-1201	419-247-4475	247-3392	9-12	Harold Dean
Imagine Akron Academy	1585 Frederick Blvd	Akron, OH	44320	330-379-1034	379-0489	K-K	Audrea Pettaway
Imagine Columbus Primary Academy	4656 Heaton Rd	Columbus, OH	43229-6612	614-433-7510	433-7515	K-8	Jennifer Keller
Imagine Hill Academy	6145 Hill Ave	Toledo, OH	43615	419-867-8167		K-5	Sarah Carstensen
Imagine Leadership Academy	2405 Romig Rd	Akron, OH	44320-3826	330-848-1100		1-6	Audrea Pettaway
Imagine Woodbury Academy	100 E Woodbury Dr	Dayton, OH	45415	937-277-1710		K-5	Jenna Hundley
Insight School of Ohio	2760 Airport Dr Ste 135	Columbus, OH	43219-2294	614-300-2766	448-2739	9-12	Amanda Conley
Intergenerational S	11327 Shaker Blvd Ste 200	Cleveland, OH	44104-3863	216-721-0120	721-0126	K-8	Dr. Cathy Whitehouse
International Academy of Columbus	2439 Fuji Dr	Columbus, OH	43229	614-794-0643	794-0697	K-8	Dr. Mouhamed Tarazi
Invictus HS	3122 Euclid Ave	Cleveland, OH	44115-2508	216-539-7200	361-3090	9-12	Dean Manke
King Academy Community S	224 W Liberty St	Cincinnati, OH	45202-6990	513-421-7519	421-1770	K-8	Andrea Martinez
KIPP Columbus	2750 Agler Rd	Columbus, OH	43224	614-263-6137	263-6207	5-8	Hannah Powell
Klepinger Road Community S	3650 Klepinger Rd	Dayton, OH	45416-1919	937-610-1710	610-1730	K-8	Melissa McManaway
Lake Erie College Preparatory S	14405 Saint Clair Ave	Cleveland, OH	44110-3433	216-453-4556	268-4951	K-8	Dr. Samuel Lockhart
Lake Erie International HS	11650 Detroit Ave	Cleveland, OH	44102-2320	216-539-7229	651-6174	9-12	John Stack
Lakeland Academy Community S	101 E Main St	Freeport, OH	43973	740-658-1042	658-1062	K-12	Mindy Pittis
Lakeshore Intergenerational S	18025 Marcella Rd	Cleveland, OH	44119-2615	216-586-3872		K-3	Robin Bartley
Lakewood City Academy	1470 Warren Rd	Lakewood, OH	44107-3918	216-529-4037	227-5975	6-12	Terrilynn Bornino-Elwell
Lawrence County Academy	11627 State Route 243	Chesapeake, OH	45619-7962	740-867-6641	867-1371	7-12	Robert Wilds
Liberty Preparatory S	PO Box 374	Smithville, OH	44677-0374	330-669-0055	669-0055	9-12	Brian Hessey
LifeLinks Community S	205 W Crawford St	Van Wert, OH	45891-1903	419-623-5380	238-3974	6-12	Gordon Stemen
LifeSkills Center Columbus North	1900 E Dublin Granville Rd	Columbus, OH	43229-3553	614-891-9041	891-8571	9-12	
Life Skills Center of Canton	1100 Cleveland Ave NW	Canton, OH	44702	330-456-4490		9-12	
Life Skills Center of Cincinnati	2612 Gilbert Ave	Cincinnati, OH	45206-1205	513-475-0222	475-0444	9-12	
Life Skills Center of Dayton	1721 N Main St	Dayton, OH	45405-4143	937-274-2841	274-2873	9-12	
Life Skills Center of Elyria	2015 W River Rd N	Elyria, OH	44035-2309	440-324-1755	324-1723	9-12	
Life Skills Center of North Akron	1458 Brittain Rd	Akron, OH	44310-3641	330-633-5990	633-7005	9-12	
Life Skills Center of Toledo	1830 Adams St	Toledo, OH	43604-4428	419-241-5504	241-9176	9-12	
Life Skills Center of Youngstown	3405 Market St	Youngstown, OH	44507-2009	330-743-6698	743-6702	9-12	
LifeSkills Columbus Southeast	2400 S Hamilton Rd	Columbus, OH	43232-4963	614-863-9175	863-9185	9-12	
Life Skills HS of Cleveland	4600 Carnegie Ave	Cleveland, OH	44103	216-431-7571		9-12	
Life Skills HS of Cleveland	12201 Larchmere Blvd	Shaker Heights, OH	44120-1101	216-421-7587	421-8189	9-12	
Lighthouse Community S	6100 Desmond St	Cincinnati, OH	45227-1897	513-561-7888	561-7818	6-12	Amy Shrock
Lincoln Park Academy	3185 W 41st St	Cleveland, OH	44109	216-263-7008	263-7007	K-8	
Lincoln Preparatory S	4215 Robert Ave	Cleveland, OH	44109-1255	216-772-1336	961-5378	K-8	Maureen Businger
London Academy	40 S Walnut St	London, OH	43140-1246	740-852-5703	852-4609	9-12	Pauline Swan
Lorain Community ES	1110 W 4th St	Lorain, OH	44052-1408	440-204-2130	204-2134	K-4	Melisa Shady
Lorain Community MS	1110 W 4th St	Lorain, OH	44052-1408	440-242-2023	204-2134	5-8	Melisa Shady
Lorain Preparatory Academy	4125 Leavitt Rd # 2	Lorain, OH	44053-2341	440-282-3127	282-3179	3-8	James Sinclair
Madison Ave School of the Arts	1511 Madison Ave	Toledo, OH	43604-4433	419-259-4000	243-1513	K-5	Lindsey Day
Madison Community S	2015 W 95th St	Cleveland, OH	44102-3791	216-651-5212	651-9040	K-8	Melissa Rice
Madisonville SMART ES	4324 Homer Ave	Cincinnati, OH	45227-2943	513-241-1101		K-6	Joe Calloway
Mahoning County HS	100 Debartolo Pl Ste 220	Youngstown, OH	44512-6095	330-965-2860		9-12	Jennifer Whittemore
Mahoning Unlimited Classroom	7401 Market St Rm 519	Youngstown, OH	44512	330-533-8755	729-9349	4-12	Brad Justice
Mahoning Valley Opportunity S	496 Glenwood Ave	Youngstown, OH	44502-1509	330-744-7656	743-9757	9-12	David Macali
Main Preparatory Academy	1035 Clay St	Akron, OH	44301	234-738-1925		6-8	
Mansfield Elective Academy	445 Bowman St	Mansfield, OH	44903-1201	567-247-4475	247-3392	K-9	Deborah Franklin
Marion City Digital Academy	910 E Church St	Marion, OH	43302	740-223-3882	223-3878	K-12	Richard Fogle
Maritime Academy of Toledo	803 Water St	Toledo, OH	43604-1831	419-244-9999	244-9898	5-12	Jodi Johns
Marshall HS	4720 Roosevelt Blvd	Middletown, OH	45044-6250	513-318-7078	425-6951	9-12	Chuck Hall
Marshall HS	13540 Lorain Ave	Cleveland, OH	44111	216-961-9813		9-12	
Massillon Digital Academy	930 17th St NE	Massillon, OH	44646-4853	330-830-3900	830-0953	K-12	Nicki Howard
Menlo Park Academy	14440 Triskett Rd	Cleveland, OH	44111-2263	440-925-6365	925-0698	K-8	Beverley Veccia M.Ed.
Miamisburg Secondary Academy	540 Park Ave	Miamisburg, OH	45342-2854	937-866-3381	865-5250	7-12	Greg Whitehead
Miami Valley Academies	5656 Springboro Pike	Dayton, OH	45449-2806	937-294-4522	294-4545	K-12	Robin Solazzo
Middlebury Academy	88 Kent St	Akron, OH	44305-2544	330-752-2766	940-1339	K-5	Maureen Businger
Middletown Prep & Fitness Academy	816 2nd Ave	Middletown, OH	45044-4201	513-424-6110	424-6121	K-8	Elizabeth Kelliher
Midnimo Cross Cultural Community S	1567 Loretta Ave	Columbus, OH	43211-1507	614-261-7480	261-7481	6-9	Marvis McGowan
Millenium Community ES	3500 Refugee Rd	Columbus, OH	43232-4862	614-255-5585	255-5580	K-8	Tijuana Russell
Mound Street Health Careers Academy	354 Mound St	Dayton, OH	45402-8325	937-223-3041	223-5867	9-12	Ron Cothran
Mound Street IT Careers Academy	354 Mound St	Dayton, OH	45402-8325	937-223-3041	223-5867	9-12	Ron Cothran
Mound Street Military Careers Academy	354 Mound St	Dayton, OH	45402-8325	937-223-3041	223-5867	9-12	Ron Cothran
Mt. Auburn International Academy	244 Southern Ave	Cincinnati, OH	45219-3023	513-241-5500	241-5501	K-12	Wissam Sabbagh
Mt. Healthy Prep & Fitness Academy	7601 Harrison Ave	Mount Healthy, OH	45231-3107	513-587-6280	521-4509	K-8	Timothy Baggs
Near West Intergenerational S	3805 Terrett Ave	Cleveland, OH	44113-2847	216-961-4308		K-6	Brooke King
Newark Digital Academy	255 Woods Ave	Newark, OH	43055-4436	740-328-2022	328-2270	K-12	John Lutz
New Beginnings Academy	4707 Hilton Corporate Dr	Columbus, OH	43232	614-367-0589	367-0921	8-12	Kathleen Keck
New Day Academy	291 E 222nd St Ste 205	Euclid, OH	44123-1718	216-797-1602	797-1604	K-12	Terrance Walton
Nexus Academy of Cleveland	3615 Superior Ave E #4402A	Cleveland, OH	44114	216-361-1314		9-12	Brittiany Sanford
Nexus Academy of Columbus	4689 Hilton Corporate Dr	Columbus, OH	43232	614-866-4761	866-4963	9-12	
Nexus Academy of Toledo	600 Jefferson Ave	Toledo, OH	43604-1071	419-244-8875		9-12	Andrea Weilacher
Noble Academy - Cleveland	1200 E 200th St	Euclid, OH	44117-1111	216-486-8866	486-2846	K-8	
Noble Academy - Columbus	1329 Bethel Rd	Columbus, OH	43220-2611	614-326-0687	326-0691	K-8	Ali Kucuker
North Central Academy	928 W Market St Ste B	Tiffin, OH	44883-2529	419-448-5786	448-5789	6-12	Adam Pittis
North Dayton S of Discovery	3901 Turner Rd	Dayton, OH	45415-3654	937-278-6671	278-6964	K-8	Ronald Albino
Northeast Ohio College Preparatory S	2357 Tremont Ave	Cleveland, OH	44113	216-965-0580	394-0364	K-12	
Northland Prep & Fitness ES	1875 Morse Rd	Columbus, OH	43229-6603	614-318-0600	262-9111	K-8	Ashley Graver
Northmont Secondary Academy	4916 National Rd	Clayton, OH	45315-9714			9-12	George Caras
Northpointe Academy	3648 Victory Ave	Toledo, OH	43607-2564	419-535-1997	244-4205	K-8	Nicholas Jacobs
Norwood Conversion Community S	2132 Williams Ave	Norwood, OH	45212-3806			9-12	John Stacy
Oakstone Community S	5747 Cleveland Ave	Columbus, OH	43231-2831	614-865-9643	865-9649	PK-12	Heather Kronewetter
Ohio College Preparatory S	21100 Southgate Park Blvd	Maple Heights, OH	44137	216-453-4550		K-8	
Ohio Connections Academy	5181 Natorp Blvd Ste 150	Mason, OH	45040-7935	513-234-4900		K-12	Marie Hanna
Ohio Construction Academy	1725 Jetway Blvd	Columbus, OH	43219	614-295-4364		9-12	Jill Adams
Ohio Valley Energy Technology Academy	10692 State Route 150	Rayland, OH	43943	740-769-7395	769-2361	9-12	Mark Miller
Ohio Virtual Academy	1690 Woodlands Dr Ste 200	Maumee, OH	43537-4045	419-482-0948	482-0955	K-12	Dr. Kristin Stewart Ph.D.
Old Brook HS	4877 Pearl Rd	Cleveland, OH	44109	440-319-3370	661-2298	9-12	Jamila Smith
Old Brooklyn Community ES	4430 State Rd	Cleveland, OH	44109-4779	216-661-7888	661-5975	K-4	Cherie Kaiser
Old Brooklyn Community MS	4430 State Rd	Cleveland, OH	44109-4779	216-351-0280	661-5975	5-8	Karil Stohlman
Orion Academy	1798 Queen City Ave	Cincinnati, OH	45214-1427	513-251-6000	251-3851	K-8	Kendell Dorsey
Outreach Academy-Students w/Disabilities	9772 Diagonal Rd	Mantua, OH	44255	330-732-8249	732-2575	K-12	Mary Wideman M.Ed.
Par - Excellence Academy	96 Maholm St	Newark, OH	43055-3906	740-344-7279	344-7272	PK-6	Gisele James
Parma Community ES	7667 Day Dr	Parma, OH	44129	440-888-5490	888-5890	K-3	Brian Belmont
Parma Community HS	5983 W 54th St	Parma, OH	44129	440-887-0319	845-2834	9-12	Linda Geyer
Parma Community MS	5983 W 54th St	Parma, OH	44129	440-845-2587	845-2834	4-8	Linda Geyer
Pathway S of Discovery	173 Avondale Dr	Dayton, OH	45404-2123	937-235-5498	235-5569	K-8	Keith Colbert
Patriot Preparatory Academy	4938 Beatrice Dr	Columbus, OH	43227	614-864-5332	864-5381	K-12	Ted Frissora
Performance Academy of Eastland	2220 S Hamilton Rd	Columbus, OH	43232	614-314-6301	577-1933	K-8	Norbert Tate
Phoenix Academy Community S	1505 Jefferson Ave	Toledo, OH	43604-5722	419-720-4500		7-12	Craig Cotner
Phoenix Community Learning Center	3595 Washington Ave	Cincinnati, OH	45229-2617	513-351-5801	351-5809	K-8	Glenda Brown
Pickerington Community S	7800 Refugee Rd	Pickerington, OH	43147-7987	614-830-2797		9-12	Bobby Blackburn
Pinnacle Academy	860 E 222nd St	Euclid, OH	44123-3317	216-731-0127	731-0688	K-8	Jennifer Littlefield
Pleasant Community Digital S	1105 Owens Rd W	Marion, OH	43302-8421	740-389-4815	389-6985	K-K	Dr. Shelly Dason
Promise Academy	1701 E 13th St	Cleveland, OH	44114-3227	216-443-0500	443-0506	9-12	Dr. Cordelia Harris
Provost Academy Ohio	1335 Dublin Rd	Columbus, OH	43215	614-866-7570		6-12	Naim Sanders
Puritas Community ES	15204 Puritas Ave	Cleveland, OH	44135-2716	216-688-0680	688-0609	K-4	Margaret Colwell
Puritas Community MS	5730 Broadview Rd	Parma, OH	44134-1602	216-688-0680		6-8	Rebecca Keeney
Puritas Community MS	15204 Puritas Ave	Cleveland, OH	44135	216-251-1596	251-3540	5-8	Meg Colwell
QDA HS	400 Mill Ave SE Ste 901	New Phila, OH	44663-3878	330-364-0618	364-0618	K-12	Steve Eckert
Quest Community S	12000 Snow Rd	Parma, OH	44130-9314	216-220-4412		9-12	Dewey Chapman
REACH Academy	2014 Consaul St	Toledo, OH	43605-1412	419-691-4876	691-5184	K-5	Shannon Kane
Renaissance Academy	4300 Kimberly Pkwy N	Columbus, OH	43232	614-866-7277		9-12	Sharice Martin
Richland S of Academic Arts	75 N Walnut St	Mansfield, OH	44902	419-522-8224		K-8	Sandra Sutherland
Ridgedale Community S	3103 Hillman Ford Rd	Morral, OH	43337-9302	740-382-6065	383-6538	K-12	
Rise & Shine Academy	3248 Warsaw St	Toledo, OH	43608	419-244-9900	244-9906	K-6	Tashlai Burney
Rittman Academy	100 Saurer St	Rittman, OH	44270-1259	330-927-7162	927-7405	9-12	Kent Smith
River Gate HS	458 Franklin St SE	Warren, OH	44483-5715	330-392-0231		9-12	Karen Wachter
Riverside Academy	3280 River Rd	Cincinnati, OH	45204-1214	513-921-7777	921-7704	K-8	Arnez Gray
Road to Success Academy	1555 Bryden Rd	Columbus, OH	43205-2149	614-252-4645		9-12	Alicia Henry
Rushmore Academy	2222 Marion-Mount Gilead Rd	Marion, OH	43302	740-387-2043	387-2169	9-12	Steve Vanderhoff
Schnee Learning Center	2222 Issaquah St	Cuyahoga Falls, OH	44221-3704	330-922-1966	945-4059	9-12	Cameron Lazar
Sciotoville Elementary Academy	5523 3rd St	Sciotoville, OH	45662-5401	740-776-2920	776-2916	K-4	Rick Bowman
Sciotoville HS	224 Marshall St	Sciotoville, OH	45662-5549	740-776-6777	776-6812	5-12	Michael Yeagle

School	Address	City,State	Zip code	Telephone	Fax	Grade	Contact
Southern Ohio Academy	522 Glenwood Ave	Sciotoville, OH	45662-5505	740-259-6843		9-12	Patricia Ciraso
South Scioto Academy	2200 Winslow Dr	Columbus, OH	43207	614-445-7684	445-7688	K-8	Courtney Watters
Southside Academy	1400 Oak Hill Ave	Youngstown, OH	44507	330-774-5660	743-1998	K-8	
Springfield Prep & Fitness Academy	1615 Selma Rd	Springfield, OH	45505-4245	937-323-6250	323-6252	K-8	Darren Fansler
Stambaugh Charter Academy	2420 Donald Ave	Youngstown, OH	44509-1306	330-792-4806	787-0278	K-8	Landon Brown
Star Academy of Toledo	5025 Glendale Ave	Toledo, OH	43614-1855	419-720-6330	720-7372	K-8	Julieta Dinkins
STEAM Academy of Akron	1338 Virginia Ave	Akron, OH	44306-3603	330-773-1100		K-5	Nova O'Callaghan
STEAM Academy of Dayton	545 Odlin Ave	Dayton, OH	45405-2743	937-262-7063		9-12	Debra A. Johnson M.Ed.
STEAM Academy of Warren	261 Elm Rd NE	Warren, OH	44483-5003	330-394-3200	394-3600	K-8	Jonathan Natko
STEAM Academy of Warrensville Heights	4700 Richmond Rd	Warrensvl Hts, OH	44128-5984	216-595-2866	595-3180	K-6	Gary Lane
Steel Academy	1570 Creighton Ave	Akron, OH	44310	330-633-1383		6-12	Stephanie Eafford
Stepstone Academy	2121 E 32nd St	Cleveland, OH	44115-2747	440-260-6400	431-7897	K-5	Toni Miller
Stockyard Community ES	3200 W 65th St	Cleveland, OH	44102-5510	216-651-5143	651-9515	K-6	Amber Steele
Stockyard Community MS	3224 W 65th St	Cleveland, OH	44102-5510	216-961-5052	651-9227	7-8	Gregory Cek
Stonebrook Montessori	975 East Blvd	Cleveland, OH	44108	216-644-3012		PK-3	Jacqui Miller
Sullivant Avenue Community S	3435 Sullivant Ave	Columbus, OH	43204-1103	614-308-5991	308-5622	K-6	Jamie Lama
Summit Academy Akron ES	2503 Leland Ave	Akron, OH	44312-2426	330-253-7441	253-7457	K-6	Dawn Presley
Summit Academy Akron HS	464 S Hawkins Ave	Akron, OH	44320-1228	330-434-2343	434-5295	9-12	Shelly Curcic
Summit Academy Akron MS	464 S Hawkins Ave	Akron, OH	44320	330-252-1510	784-8347	7-8	
Summit Academy - Canton HS	2400 Cleveland Ave NW	Canton, OH	44709-3613	330-453-8547	453-8924	9-12	John Fullerman
Summit Academy - Canton S	1620 Market Ave S	Canton, OH	44707	330-458-0393	458-0518	K-8	
Summit Academy Columbus	2521 Fairwood Ave Ste 100	Columbus, OH	43207-2712	614-237-5497	237-6519	K-5	
Summit Academy Community S Cincinnati	1660 Sternblock Ln	Cincinnati, OH	45237-3805	513-321-0561	321-0795	K-8	Megan Fagan
Summit Academy Community S Dayton	4128 Ceder Ridge Rd	Dayton, OH	45414	937-278-4298	278-4613	K-8	Eric Marthaler
Summit Academy Community S for Alt Lrnrs	2140 E 36th St	Lorain, OH	44055-2756	440-277-4110	277-4112	K-5	A.J. Charpentier
Summit Academy Community S - Toledo	1853 South Ave	Toledo, OH	43609-2086	419-385-5730	385-5781	K-8	
Summit Academy Community S Warren	2106 Arbor Ave SE	Warren, OH	44484-5225	330-369-4233	369-4299	K-6	
Summit Academy Community S Xenia	1694 Pawnee Dr	Xenia, OH	45385-4126	937-372-5210	372-5250	K-8	Cassy Stidham
Summit Academy Lorain - Secondary S	1051 E St	Lorain, OH	44052	440-288-0448	288-0997	9-12	Joshua Preece M.Ed.
Summit Academy MS Columbus	2521 Fairwood Ave Ste 200	Columbus, OH	43207	614-237-5497	237-6519	6-8	Cheryl Elliott
Summit Academy MS - Lorain	346 Illinois Ave	Lorain, OH	44052-2106	440-288-0448	288-0997	6-8	Diane Soloman
Summit Academy - Middletown	4700 Central Ave	Middletown, OH	45044-5354	513-422-8540	423-6352	K-6	Megan Bockelman
Summit Academy Middletown HS	7 S Marshall Rd	Middletown, OH	45044-5375	513-420-9767	727-1520	7-12	Beth Varley
Summit Academy Painesville	268 N State St	Painesville, OH	44077-4009	440-358-0877	358-0397	K-9	Frank Cheraso
Summit Academy Parma	5868 Stumph Rd	Parma, OH	44130-1736	440-888-5407	888-5417	K-12	Eric Johnson
Summit Academy S for Alt Learners	1461 Moncrest Dr NW	Warren, OH	44485-1928	330-399-1692	399-1768	7-12	
Summit Academy Secondary S Toledo	2913 S Republic Blvd	Toledo, OH	43615	419-476-7859	476-7763	9-12	Abby Spangler
Summit Academy Toledo Learning Center	5115 Glendale Ave Ste N	Toledo, OH	43614-1801	419-476-0784	476-0763	K-8	Kurt Aey
Summit Academy Transition HS - Cinci	5800 Salvia Ave	Cincinnati, OH	45224-3029	513-541-4000	541-4075	9-12	Christy Brewer
Summit Academy Transition HS Columbus	2521 Fairwood Ave	Columbus, OH	43207	614-880-0714	880-0732	9-12	Trina Moore
Summit Academy Transition HS Dayton	251 Erdiel Dr	Dayton, OH	45415-3632	937-813-8952	813-8596	9-12	Gary Miller
Summit Academy - Youngstown	1400 Oak Hill Ave	Youngstown, OH	44507-1018	330-228-8235	747-0957	8-12	
Summit Academy Youngstown	144 N Schenley Ave	Youngstown, OH	44509-2041	330-259-0421	259-0424	K-7	
Sunbridge S	2105 N McCord Rd	Toledo, OH	43615	419-725-5437	754-2073	9-12	Erica Pharis
T2 Honors Academy	18450 S Miles Rd	Warrensvl Hts, OH	44128-4236	216-510-5458		6-8	India Ford
T.C.P. World Academy	6000 Ridge Ave	Cincinnati, OH	45213-1624	513-531-9500	531-2406	K-6	Karen French
Toledo Prep & Fitness Academy	3001 Hill Ave	Toledo, OH	43607-2932	419-535-3700	535-3701	K-8	Valerie Sandy
Toledo S for the Arts	333 14th St	Toledo, OH	43604-7713	419-246-8732	244-3979	6-12	Martin Porter
Toledo SMART ES	1850 Airport Hwy	Toledo, OH	43609	419-214-3290	214-3294	K-3	Jessica Kuhlman
Tomorrow Center	PO Box 216	Edison, OH	43320-0216	419-946-1900	947-9551	6-12	
Tooba Academy	1950 Morse Rd	Columbus, OH	43229	614-888-8536	888-8496	K-8	
Townsend North Community S	305 S Washington St	Castalia, OH	44824-9263	419-684-5402		9-12	Peter Bartkowiak
Towpath Trail HS	275 W Market St	Akron, OH	44303-2159	234-542-0102		9-12	John Stack
TRECA Digital Academy	100 Executive Dr	Marion, OH	43302-6306	740-389-4798	389-4517	K-12	Adam Clark
Trotwood Preparatory & Fitness Academy	3100 Shiloh Springs Rd	Trotwood, OH	45426-2247	937-854-4100	837-9759	K-8	Alison Foreman
UBAH Math & Reading Academy	3850 Sullivant Ave	Columbus, OH	43228-4327	614-279-6000		K-5	Lance Weber
University Academy	107 S Arlington St	Akron, OH	44306	330-535-7728		K-8	
University of Cleveland Preparatory S	1906 E 40th St	Cleveland, OH	44103	216-361-9720	431-3375	K-8	Kenan Bishop
Urbana Community S	711 Wood St	Urbana, OH	43078-1498	937-653-1478	652-3845	K-12	
Utica Shale Academy of Ohio	38095 State Route 39	Salineville, OH	43945	330-420-5353		9-12	Eric Sampson
Village Preparatory S Willard	2220 W 93rd St	Cleveland, OH	44102	216-586-3892		K-5	John McBride
Virtual Community S of Ohio	340 Waggoner Rd	Reynoldsburg, OH	43068-9707	614-501-2002	386-1560	K-12	Jeff Nelson
Voinovich Reclamation Academy	11801 Buckeye Rd	Cleveland, OH	44120	216-295-1493	295-1576	9-12	Jennifer Morison
Washington Park Community S	4000 Washington Park Blvd	Newburgh Hts, OH	44105-3211	216-271-6055	271-6099	K-8	Helene Jasinski
Watkins Academy	4401 Dayton Liberty Rd	Dayton, OH	45417	937-220-9100		K-8	
West Academy	12913 Bennington Ave	Cleveland, OH	44135-3761	216-251-5450	251-6410	K-8	
West Carrollton Secondary Academy	3400 W Alex Bell Rd	West Carrollton, OH	45449-2819	937-859-5121		11-12	Heather Pinto
West Central Learning Academy	522 W North St	Lima, OH	45801-4215	419-227-9252	227-2511	7-12	Connie Houser
Westpark Community ES	16210 Lorain Ave	Cleveland, OH	44111-5521	216-688-0271	688-0273	K-4	Sheila Delzani
Westpark Community MS	16210 Lorain Ave	Cleveland, OH	44111-5521	216-251-7200	251-0355	5-8	Mindy Kidd
West Preparatory Academy	13111 Crossburn Ave	Cleveland, OH	44135-5017	216-772-1340	898-5894	K-5	Jennifer Heyman
Westside Academy	4330 Clime Rd N	Columbus, OH	43228-3439	614-272-9392	272-8940	K-8	
Westside Community S of the Arts	3727 Bosworth Rd	Cleveland, OH	44111-6037	216-688-1900	688-1902	K-8	Deborah Rotolo
Westwood Preparatory Academy	840 W State St	Columbus, OH	43222	330-510-5400		9-12	Ashley Kaufman
Whitehall Prep & Fitness S	3474 E Livingston Ave	Columbus, OH	43227-2219	614-324-4585	238-3184	K-8	Donnell Drake
Wildwood Environmental Academy	1546 Dartford Rd	Maumee, OH	43537-1374	419-868-9885	868-9981	K-8	Elizabeth Lewin
Winterfield Venture Academy	305 Wenz Rd	Toledo, OH	43615-6244	419-531-3285	531-3637	K-8	Nate Preston
Winton Preparatory Academy	4750 Winton Rd	Cincinnati, OH	45232-1501	513-276-4166		K-8	Lisa Davis
Youngstown Academy of Excellence	1408 Rigby St	Youngstown, OH	44506-1617	330-746-3970	746-3965	K-8	Lawrence Reeves
Youngstown Community ES	50 Essex St	Youngstown, OH	44502-1838	330-746-2240	746-6618	K-6	Dennis L. Rice
YouthBuild Columbus Comm S	1183 Essex Ave	Columbus, OH	43201-2925	614-291-0805	291-0890	9-12	Nkenge Jacobs
Zanesville Community S	920 Moxahala Ave	Zanesville, OH	43701-5533	740-588-5685	455-4331	9-12	Jeffrey Moore
Zenith Academy	4606 Heaton Rd	Columbus, OH	43229-6612	614-888-9943	888-6689	K-9	
Zenith Academy East	2261 S Hamilton Rd	Columbus, OH	43232-4301	614-577-0997	577-0995	K-8	
Zenith Academy West	3385 South Blvd	Columbus, OH	43204	614-272-6300	272-6301	K-9	Asheer Tashfeen

Oklahoma

School	Address	City,State	Zip code	Telephone	Fax	Grade	Contact
ABLE Charter S	4500 N Classen Blvd	Oklahoma City, OK	73118	405-990-2282	673-5338	6-12	Dr. Kenneth Kuczynski
ASTEC Charter S	2401 NW 23rd St Ste 39A	Oklahoma City, OK	73107	405-947-6274	947-0035	6-12	Ronald Grant
Brown Community S	2 S Elgin Ave	Tulsa, OK	74120-1808	918-425-1407	425-6693	K-5	Deborah Brown
College Bound Academy	2525 S 103rd E Ave	Tulsa, OK	74129	918-925-1580		PK-4	Chelsea Vanacore
Collegiate Hall	1142 E 56th St	Tulsa, OK	74105	918-925-1620		4-8	Nikhil Kawlra
Discovery School of Tulsa	4821 S 72nd East Ave	Tulsa, OK	74145-6502	918-960-3131	960-3130	K-8	Maureen Brown
Dove Science Academy	919 NW 23rd St	Oklahoma City, OK	73106-5691	405-524-9762	524-9471	6-12	
Dove Science Academy	280 S Memorial Dr	Tulsa, OK	74112-2202	918-834-3936	834-3352	6-12	Abidin Erez
Dove Science Academy	4901 N Lincoln Blvd	Oklahoma City, OK	73105	405-605-5566	605-5578	K-5	
Epic One on One S	4101 NW 122nd St Ste B	Oklahoma City, OK	73120-8816	405-749-4550	749-4540	PK-12	David Chaney
Harding Charter Preparatory HS	3333 N Shartel Ave	Oklahoma City, OK	73118-7277	405-606-8742	609-1677	9-12	Dr. Mylo Miller
Harding Fine Arts Academy	PO Box 18895	Oklahoma City, OK	73154-0895	405-702-4322	601-0904	9-12	Barry Schmelzenbach
Hughes Academy	1821 E 66th St	Tulsa, OK	74130	918-939-9651		9-12	Dr. Rodney Clark
Hupfeld Academy at Western Village	1508 NW 106th St	Oklahoma City, OK	73114-5214	405-751-1774	752-6833	PK-5	Ruthie Rayner
Independence Charter MS	3232 NW 65th St	Oklahoma City, OK	73116-3512	405-767-3000	767-3007	6-8	Vana Baker
Insight S of Oklahoma	1156 S Douglas Blvd	Midwest City, OK	73130-5237	877-637-2614		7-12	Sheryl Tatum
KIPP Reach College Preparatory	PO Box 776	Oklahoma City, OK	73101	405-425-4622	425-4624	5-8	Tracy McDaniel
KIPP Tulsa Academy	1661 E Virgin St	Tulsa, OK	74106	918-794-8652	794-8712	5-8	Andrew McRae
Lighthouse Charter S	4609 S Santa Fe Ave	Oklahoma City, OK	73109	405-600-7038	602-2102	PK-5	Amanda Kissing
Oklahoma Connections Academy	2425 Nowata Pl	Bartlesville, OK	74006-4741	918-977-3285	331-3629	K-12	Tammy Shepherd
Oklahoma Virtual Charter Academy	1160 S Douglas Blvd	Midwest City, OK	73130	866-467-0848	259-8332	K-12	Sheryl Tatum
Rex Charter ES	500 W Sheridan Ave	Oklahoma City, OK	73102-5001	405-587-8100		PK-3	Joseph Pierce Ed.D.
Sankofa Charter S	111 E 1st St	Tulsa, OK	74103-2816	918-425-1407		6-8	Richard Patterson
Santa Fe South ES	301 SE 38th St	Oklahoma City, OK	73129	405-681-7480	681-7484	K-5	Kim Figueroa
Santa Fe South HS	301 SE 38th St	Oklahoma City, OK	73129-3099	405-631-6100	681-6993	9-12	Lance Seeright
Santa Fe South MS	4712 S Santa Fe Ave	Oklahoma City, OK	73109-7545	405-635-1053	635-0423	6-8	Michael Figueroa
SeeWorth Academy	12600 N Kelley Ave	Oklahoma City, OK	73131-1869	405-475-6400	475-8566	3-12	Stacey Golden
Tsunadeloquasdi Cherokee Immersion S	PO Box 520	Tahlequah, OK	74465-0520	918-453-5400	467-4746	PK-8	Holly Davis
Tulsa Honor Academy	2525 S 101st E Ave	Tulsa, OK	74129	918-833-9420		5-8	Elsie Urueta
Tulsa Legacy Charter S	105 E 63rd St N	Tulsa, OK	74126	918-794-1442	794-1480	PK-4	Carlisha Williams
Tulsa Legacy Charter Upper Academy	6001 N Peoria AVE	Tulsa, OK	74126	918-576-6129		5-7	Carlisha Williams
Tulsa S of Arts and Sciences	1202 W Easton St	Tulsa, OK	74127	918-828-7727	828-7747	7-12	Liesa Smith

Oregon

School	Address	City,State	Zip code	Telephone	Fax	Grade	Contact
Academy for Character Education	195 N 6th St	Cottage Grove, OR	97424-1602	541-942-9707	942-7884	K-12	Starr Sahnow
Academy of Arts and Academics	615 Main St	Springfield, OR	97477	541-744-6728	744-6713	9-12	Mike Fisher
Alliance Charter Academy	16075 Front St	Oregon City, OR	97045	503-785-8556	722-4113	1-12	Nic Chapin
Annex Charter S	402 Annex Rd	Ontario, OR	97914-8010	541-262-3280	262-3578	K-8	Steve Bishop

School	Address	City,State	Zip code	Telephone	Fax	Grade	Contact
Arco Iris Spanish Immersion S	13600 SW Allen Blvd	Beaverton, OR	97005	503-473-0416		1-6	Felicia Giambrone
Arlington ES	PO Box 10	Arlington, OR	97812-0010	541-454-2727	454-2335	K-8	Kevin Hunking
Arlington HS	PO Box 10	Arlington, OR	97812-0010	541-454-2632	454-2137	9-12	Kevin Hunking
Armadillo Technical Institute	PO Box 1560	Phoenix, OR	97535-1560	541-535-3287		4-12	Kim DeCosta
Arthur Academy	13717 SE Division St	Portland, OR	97236-2841	503-252-3753	760-1204	K-5	Jon Luebke
Bend International S	63020 OB Riley Rd	Bend, OR	97703	541-797-7038	797-7039	K-8	Meera Rupp
Bethany Charter S	11824 Hazelgreen Rd NE	Silverton, OR	97381-9626	503-873-4300	873-0143	K-8	Kathy Frank
Bridge Charter Academy	60 S Pioneer St	Lowell, OR	97452	541-543-5339		K-10	John VonDoloski
Burnt River S	PO Box 9	Unity, OR	97884-1000	541-446-3336	446-3581	K-12	Lorrie Andrews
Butte Falls Charter S	PO Box 228	Butte Falls, OR	97522-0228	541-865-3563	865-3217	K-12	Dianne Gorman
Camas Valley S	PO Box 57	Camas Valley, OR	97416-0057	541-445-2131	445-2041	PK-12	Patrick Lee
Career Technical HS	801 SW Highway 101 Ste 404	Lincoln City, OR	97367-2752	541-351-8551	994-7592	9-12	Sean Larson
Cascade Heights Charter S	15301 SE 92nd Ave	Clackamas, OR	97015	503-653-3996	343-4500	K-8	Holly Denman
Center for Advanced Learning	1484 NW Civic Dr	Gresham, OR	97030-5564	503-667-4978	492-1572	11-12	Carol Eagan
Childs Way Charter S	37895 Row River Rd	Culp Creek, OR	97434-9610	541-946-1821	946-2007	5-12	Michael Kerns
City View Charter S	PO Box 1808	Hillsboro, OR	97123-1808	503-844-9424	844-9425	K-8	Jeffrey Hays
Clackamas Academy of Industrial Science	1306 12th St	Oregon City, OR	97045	503-785-7860	785-8396	8-12	Scott Curtis
Clackamas Middle College HS	12021 SE 82nd Ave	Happy Valley, OR	97086-7713	503-518-5925	518-5928	9-12	Dr. Brian Sien Ed.D.
Clackamas Web Academy	8740 SE Sunnybrook Blvd	Clackamas, OR	97015-5737	503-659-4664	659-4994	1-12	Brad Linn
Coburg Community Family Charter S	91274 N Coburg Rd	Coburg, OR	97408	541-790-3408	790-3532	K-5	Laura Ralls
Community Roots S	229 Eureka Ave	Silverton, OR	97381	503-874-4107	874-4108	K-6	Miranda Traegar
Cove S	PO Box 68	Cove, OR	97824-0068	541-568-4424	568-4231	K-12	Bruce Neil
Dallas Community S	788 SW Birch St	Dallas, OR	97338	503-420-4360		K-8	Dennis Schultz
Days Creek Charter S	PO Box 10	Days Creek, OR	97429-0010	541-825-3296	825-3052	K-12	Dr. Mark Angle
EAGLE Charter S	999A Locust St NE	Salem, OR	97301-5496	503-339-7114	990-6909	K-5	Cliff Monroe
EagleRidge Charter HS	677 S 7th St	Klamath Falls, OR	97601-6223	541-884-7627	871-7054	9-12	Donald Peterson
Eddyville Charter S	1 Eddyville School Rd	Eddyville, OR	97343	541-875-2942	875-2491	K-12	Jennifer Johnson
Elkton ES	PO Box 390	Elkton, OR	97436-0390	541-584-2115	584-2113	K-8	Andy Boe
Elkton HS	PO Box 390	Elkton, OR	97436-0390	541-584-2228	584-2227	9-12	Andy Boe
Emerson Charter S	105 NW Park Ave	Portland, OR	97209-3315	503-525-6124	223-4875	K-5	Tara O'Neil
Estacada Early College	PO Box 2631	Estacada, OR	97023-2631	503-630-5001	630-5206	10-12	Joni Tabler
Forest Grove Community S	1914 Pacific Ave	Forest Grove, OR	97116-2326	503-359-4600	359-4622	1-8	Vanessa Gray
Fossil Charter S	PO Box 206	Fossil, OR	97830-0206	541-763-4384	763-4010	K-12	Brad Sperry
Four Rivers Community S	2449 SW 4th Ave	Ontario, OR	97914-1829	541-889-3715	889-3718	K-8	Chelle Robins
Glendale Community Charter S	PO Box E	Glendale, OR	97442-0605	541-832-1801	832-2486	9-12	Brenyl Swanson
Goodall Environmental MS	999B Locust St NE	Salem, OR	97301	503-399-7070	391-4070	6-8	Annie Morton
Gresham Arthur Academy	1890 NE Cleveland Ave	Gresham, OR	97030-4210	503-667-4900	667-4933	K-5	Kandace Burton
Harper Charter S	2987 Harper Westfall Rd	Harper, OR	97906-2008	541-358-2473	358-2488	K-12	Ron Talbot
Hope Chinese Charter S	3500 SW 104th Ave	Beaverton, OR	97005	971-226-7500		K-5	Julie Rickman M.Ed.
Howard Street Charter S	710 Howard St SE	Salem, OR	97302-3098	503-399-3408	375-7861	6-8	Christina Tracy
Imbler Charter S	PO Box 164	Imbler, OR	97841-0164	541-534-5331	534-9560	K-12	Angie Lakey-Campbell
Ione Community Charter S	PO Box 167	Ione, OR	97843-0167	541-422-7131	422-7555	K-12	Henry Ramirez
Ivy S	4212 NE Prescott St	Portland, OR	97218-1632	503-288-8820	288-8894	1-8	Liz Caravaca
Joseph Charter S	PO Box 787	Joseph, OR	97846-2023	541-432-7311	432-1100	K-12	Sherri Kilgore
KairosPDX Learning Academy Charter S	PO Box 12190	Portland, OR	97212-0190	503-567-9820		K-5	Zalika Gardner
Kids Unlimited Academy	821 N Riverside Ave	Medford, OR	97501	541-774-3900	772-3443	K-6	Lynn Eccleston
Kings Valley Charter S	38840 Kings Valley Hwy	Philomath, OR	97370-9750	541-929-2134	929-8179	K-12	Jamon Ellingson
KNOVA Learning Oregon	740 SE 182nd Ave	Portland, OR	97233	503-907-1023	907-1024	K-6	
Le Monde French Immersion ES	2044 E Burnside St	Portland, OR	97214	503-467-7529	548-2190	K-5	Dr. Chantal Martel Ph.D.
Lewis & Clark Montessori Charter S	15600 SE 232nd Dr	Damascus, OR	97089-8172	503-427-0803	855-3017	PK-3	Melissa Harbert
Lighthouse S	62868 School Rd	Coos Bay, OR	97420	541-751-1649	751-1659	K-8	Wade Lester
Logos Public Charter S	400 Earhart St	Medford, OR	97501-7828	541-842-3658	842-1927	K-12	Joe VonDoloski
Lourdes Charter S	39059 Jordan Rd	Scio, OR	97374-9330	503-394-3340		1-8	Linda Duman
Luckiamute Valley Charter S	17475 Bridgeport Rd	Dallas, OR	97338-9458	503-838-1933	606-9879	K-8	Dan Austin
Madrone Trail Charter S	3070 Ross Ln	Central Point, OR	97502	541-842-3657		K-8	Karen Bailey
Metro East Web Academy	1394 NW Civic Dr	Gresham, OR	97030-5569	503-258-4790	258-4791	6-12	David Gray
Milwaukie Academy of the Arts	11300 SE 23rd Ave	Milwaukie, OR	97222-7753	503-353-5843	353-5845	9-12	Tim Taylor
M.I.T.C.H. Charter S	19550 SW 90th Ct	Tualatin, OR	97062-7505	503-639-5757		K-8	Melissa Meyer
Molalla River Academy	16897 S Callahan Rd	Molalla, OR	97038	503-829-6672	759-6672	K-8	Shelley Urben
Mosier Community S	PO Box 307	Mosier, OR	97040-0307	541-478-3321	478-2536	K-8	Brian Schimel
Mountain View Academy	65 S Pioneer St	Lowell, OR	97452-9721	541-937-8405		K-8	Laurie Cardwell
Muddy Creek Charter S	30252 Bellfountain Rd	Corvallis, OR	97333	541-752-0377	752-9481	K-5	Bryan Traylor
Multisensory Learning Academy	22565 NE Halsey St	Fairview, OR	97024	503-405-7868	405-7869	K-8	Sheri Fitzsimmons
Network Charter S	2550 Portland St	Eugene, OR	97405-3127	541-344-1229	344-5118	7-12	Ame Beard
Nixyaawi Community S	PO Box 638	Pendleton, OR	97801-0638	541-429-7900	966-2671	9-12	Ryan Heinrich
North Columbia Academy	28168 Old Rainier Rd	Rainier, OR	97048-3017	503-556-3777	556-3778	9-12	Anne Montgomery
North Powder Charter S	PO Box 10	North Powder, OR	97867-0010	541-898-2244	898-2046	PK-12	Lance Dixon
Opal Charter S	4015 SW Canyon Rd	Portland, OR	97221-2759	503-471-9902	223-6600	K-5	Dr. Kristin Laluk
Optimum Learning Environments Charter S	7905 June Reid Pl NE	Keizer, OR	97303-2559	503-399-5548	399-3469	1-5	Tom Charboneau
Oregon City Service Learning Academy	995 S End Rd	Oregon City, OR	97045-3469	503-785-8445	650-5483	7-12	Tim Graham
Oregon Coast Technology S	1500 16th St	North Bend, OR	97459-2625	541-756-8341	756-1313	7-12	Bill Lucero
Oregon Connections Academy	833 NW Santiam Blvd	Mill City, OR	97360-2101	503-897-2272		K-12	Candyce Farthing
Oregon Trail Academy	36225 SE Proctor Rd	Boring, OR	97009	503-668-5521	668-6250	K-10	Ginger Redlinger
Oregon Virtual Academy	400 Virginia Ave Ste 210	North Bend, OR	97459	541-751-8060	751-8016	K-12	Brandy Osborn
Paisley S	PO Box 97	Paisley, OR	97636-0097	541-943-3111	943-3129	K-12	William Wurtz
Phoenix S of Roseburg	3131 NE Diamond Lake Blvd	Roseburg, OR	97470-3632	541-673-3036	957-5906	8-12	Ron Breyne
Pine Eagle Charter S	375 N Main St	Halfway, OR	97834-8153	541-742-2811	742-2810	K-12	Morgan Gover
Portland Arthur Academy	7507 SE Yamhill St	Portland, OR	97215-2284	503-257-3936	257-3929	K-5	Susan McCool
Portland Village ES	7654 N Delaware Ave	Portland, OR	97217-6417	503-445-0056	445-0058	K-8	Paul Berg
Powell Butte Community Charter S	13650 SW Highway 126	Powell Butte, OR	97753-1604	541-548-1166	548-7635	K-8	Jackie LaFrenz
Prospect Charter S	PO Box 40	Prospect, OR	97536-0040	541-560-3653	560-3644	PK-12	Tim Dexter
Redmond Proficiency Academy	639 SW Forest Ave	Redmond, OR	97756	541-526-0882	516-1160	6-12	Dr. Jon Bullock
Reedsport Community Charter S	2260 Longwood Dr	Reedsport, OR	97467-1167	541-271-2141	271-2143	7-12	Vincent Swagerty
Renaissance Public Academy	PO Box 208	Molalla, OR	97038-0208	503-759-7002	759-7004	4-12	Darrel Camp
Resource Link Charter S	1255 Hemlock Ave	Coos Bay, OR	97420-1298	541-267-1499	266-7314	K-12	Dale Inskeep
Reynolds Arthur Academy	123 SW 21st St	Troutdale, OR	97060	503-465-8882	465-8883	K-6	Chris Arnold
Ridgeline Montessori Public Charter S	4500 W Amazon Dr	Eugene, OR	97405-4652	541-681-9662	681-4394	K-8	
Sage Community S	PO Box 655	Chiloquin, OR	97624-0655	541-783-2533	783-2544	K-8	Anna Fowler
Saint Helens Arthur Academy	33035 Pittsburg Rd	Saint Helens, OR	97051-3305	503-366-7030		K-8	Michael Arthur
Sand Ridge Charter S	30581 Sodaville Mtn Home Rd	Lebanon, OR	97355	541-258-2416	258-1898	K-12	Audrey Cota
Sauvie Island Academy	14445 NW Charlton Rd	Portland, OR	97231-1402	503-621-3426	621-3384	K-8	Darla Meeuwsen
SEI Academy Charter S	3920 N Kerby Ave	Portland, OR	97227-1255	503-249-1721	284-4456	6-8	Timothy Rodgers
Sheridan Allprep Online Academy	PO Box 583	Sheridan, OR	97378-0583	503-843-9330	758-1982	K-12	Jesse Eisenschmidt
Sheridan Japanese S	PO Box 446	Sheridan, OR	97378-0446	503-843-3400	843-7438	4-12	Andrew Scott
Sherwood Charter S	PO Box 1342	Sherwood, OR	97140-1342	503-925-8007	925-8172	K-8	Joy Raboli
Siletz Valley S	PO Box 247	Siletz, OR	97380-0247	541-444-1100	444-2368	K-12	Sam Tupou
Silvies River Charter S	39235 Highway 205	Frenchglen, OR	97736-9704	541-589-2401	722-7129	K-12	Dr. Shawn Farrens
South Columbia Family S	33589 High School Way	Warren, OR	97053	503-366-9009	366-9010	K-12	Ray Brown
Southwest Charter S	0640 SW Bancroft St	Portland, OR	97239-4244	503-244-1697	244-1709	K-8	Suzanne Perry
Springwater Environmental Sciences S	PO Box 3010	Oregon City, OR	97045-0301	503-631-7700	631-7720	K-8	Dawn Bolotow
Summit Learning Charter	PO Box 2631	Estacada, OR	97023	503-630-5001	630-5206	K-12	Sean Gallagher
Sunny Wolf Charter S	PO Box 438	Wolf Creek, OR	97497-0438	541-866-2735	866-2738	K-5	Penelope DiGennaro
Sweet Home Charter S	28721 Liberty Rd	Sweet Home, OR	97386-9776	541-367-1833	367-1839	K-6	Tavia Thornton
Three Rivers Charter S	4975 Willamette Falls Dr	West Linn, OR	97068-3348	503-723-6019	723-6407	4-8	Katherine Holtgraves
Triangle Lake Charter S	20264 Blachly Grange Rd	Blachly, OR	97412-9714	541-925-3262	925-3062	K-12	James Brookins
Trillium Charter S	5420 N Interstate Ave	Portland, OR	97217-4569	503-285-3833	249-0348	K-12	Kieran Connolly
Twin Rivers Charter S	2621 Augusta St	Eugene, OR	97403	541-349-5055		9-12	Stephen Moore
Valley Inquiry Charter S	5774 Hazelgreen Rd NE	Salem, OR	97305	503-399-3150	391-4091	K-5	Lisa Sundseth
Valley S	PO Box 1225	Medford, OR	97501	541-842-3914		6-8	
Village S	3411 Willamette St	Eugene, OR	97405	541-345-7285	242-6874	K-8	Bob Kaminski
West Lane Technology Learning Center	24967 Highway 126	Veneta, OR	97487	541-935-2101	935-8345	9-12	Ron Osibov
Willamette Leadership Academy	34020 B St	Eugene, OR	97405	541-246-2842	246-2841	6-12	Steve Brandom
Woodburn Arthur Academy	575 Gatch St	Woodburn, OR	97071-4927	503-981-5746	981-5742	K-5	Glenn Izer
Woodland Charter S	PO Box 740	Murphy, OR	97533	541-846-4246		1-8	Christopher Green

Pennsylvania

School	Address	City,State	Zip code	Telephone	Fax	Grade	Contact
Achievement House Charter S	600 Eagleview Blvd Ste 1	Exton, PA	19341-1121	484-615-6200	458-1204	7-12	Don Asplen
ACT Academy Cyber Charter HS	2111 Eastburn Ave	Philadelphia, PA	19138-2630	267-297-6231		9-12	
Ad Prima Charter S	3556 Frankford Ave	Philadelphia, PA	19134-2118	215-288-7062	288-8673	K-6	Meghan Allhouse
Ad Prima Charter S	1922 N 63rd St	Philadelphia, PA	19151-2652	215-403-2953	292-4058	K-8	Aldo Cavalli
Agora Cyber Charter S	590 N Gulph Rd	King of Prussia, PA	19406-2800	844-402-4672	254-8939	K-12	Kevin Corcoran
Allen Preparatory Charter S	2601 S 58th St	Philadelphia, PA	19143-6146	215-878-1544	727-0711	5-8	Lawrence Jones
Alliance for Progress Charter S	1630 N 16th St	Philadelphia, PA	19121	215-232-4892	232-4894	4-8	Joanna Hightower
Alliance for Progress Charter S	1821 Cecil B Moore Ave	Philadelphia, PA	19121-3135	215-232-4892	232-4894	K-3	Joanna Hightower
Architecture & Design Charter HS	105 S 7th St	Philadelphia, PA	19106-3324	215-351-2900	351-9458	9-12	Gregory Wright
ARISE Academy Charter HS	2116 E Haines St	Philadelphia, PA	19138-2600	215-563-1656		9-12	Gabriel Kuriloff

School	Address	City,State	Zip code	Telephone	Fax	Grade	Contact
Arts Academy Charter ES	601 W Union St	Allentown, PA	18101-2308	610-657-5388		K-5	Jacqueline Vogel
Arts Academy Charter S	1610 E Emmaus Ave	Allentown, PA	18103-8307	610-351-0234	351-0307	5-8	Jan Labellarte
ASPIRA Bilingual Cyber Charter S	4332 N 5th St	Philadelphia, PA	19140	215-455-1300	455-1300	K-12	Cynthia Cruz-Vega
ASPIRA Olney HS	100 W Duncannon Ave	Philadelphia, PA	19120-3410	215-456-3014	456-3064	9-12	James Thompson
ASPIRA Stetson Charter S	3200 B St	Philadelphia, PA	19134-2202	215-291-4720	291-4168	5-8	Thomas Mullin
Attucks Youth Build Charter S	605 S Duke St	York, PA	17401-3111	717-848-3610	843-3914	9-12	Jacquie Martino-Miller
Avon Grove Charter S	110 State Rd	West Grove, PA	19390-8908	484-667-5000		K-12	Kristen Bishop
Baden Academy Charter S	1016 W State St	Baden, PA	15005-1338	855-590-2227	869-4269	K-5	
Bear Creek Community Charter S	2000 Bear Creek Blvd	Wilkes Barre, PA	18702-9684	570-820-4070	270-6149	K-8	Brian Dugas
Beaver Area Academic Charter S	Gypsy Glen Rd	Beaver, PA	15009	724-774-4022		7-12	Carrie Rowe
Belmont Academy Charter S	907 N 41st St	Philadelphia, PA	19104-1278	215-386-5768	386-5769	K-K	Claire Cohen
Belmont Charter S	4030 Brown St	Philadelphia, PA	19104-4844	215-823-8208	823-8209	1-8	Claire Cohen
Birney Charter S	900 Lindley Ave	Philadelphia, PA	19141-3920	215-456-3000	456-3113	K-8	Kareem Thomas
Boys Latin of Philadelphia Charter S	5501 Cedar Ave	Philadelphia, PA	19143-1929	215-387-5149	387-5159	6-12	Dr. Noah Tennant
Bracetti Academy Charter S	1840 Torresdale Ave	Philadelphia, PA	19124-4418	215-291-4436	291-4985	K-12	Jana Somma
Bucks County Montessori Charter S	219 Tyburn Rd	Fairless Hills, PA	19030-4403	215-428-6700	428-6702	K-6	Brian Long
Byers Charter S	1911 Arch St	Philadelphia, PA	19103-1403	215-972-1700	972-1701	PK-6	Jesse Bean
Capital Area School for the Arts	150 Strawberry Sq	Harrisburg, PA	17101-1815	717-732-8450	732-8451	9-12	Timothy Wendling
Center for Student Learning Charter S	345 Lakeside Dr	Levittown, PA	19054-3933	215-269-7390	269-7395	6-12	Dr. Charles Bonner
Central Pennsylvania Digital Charter S	721 N Juniata St Ste 3	Hollidaysburg, PA	16648-1455	814-682-5258	946-8526	K-12	Angela Boutiller
Centre Learning Community Charter S	2643 W College Ave	State College, PA	16801-2604	814-861-7980	861-8030	5-8	Kosta Dussias
Chester Charter S for the Arts	200 Commerce Dr	Aston, PA	19014-3203	610-859-3010		K-8	Akosua Watts
Chester Community Charter S	214 E 5th St	Chester, PA	19013-4510	610-447-0400	876-5716	K-6	Dr. David Clark
Chester County Family Academy	530 E Union St	West Chester, PA	19382-4206	610-696-5910	696-6324	K-2	Susan Flynn
Circle of Seasons Charter S	8380 Mohr Ln	Fogelsville, PA	18051-1918	610-285-6267		K-5	
City Charter HS	201 Stanwix St	Pittsburgh, PA	15222-1350	412-690-2489	690-2316	9-12	Dr. Ron Sofo
Clemente Charter S	136 S 4th St	Allentown, PA	18102-5445	610-439-5181	435-4731	6-12	Damian Romero
Clemente ES - Charter	462 Walnut St	Allentown, PA	18102	610-435-5334		K-6	Samuel Polanco
Collegium Charter S	435 Creamery Way Ste 300	Exton, PA	19341	610-903-1300	903-1317	K-12	Antoinette Rath
Columbus Charter S	1242 S 13th St	Philadelphia, PA	19147	215-389-6000	389-3732	6-8	Rosemary Dougherty
Columbus Charter S	916 Christian St	Philadelphia, PA	19147-3808	215-925-7400	925-7491	K-5	Rosemary Dougherty
Commonwealth Connections Charter S	4050 Crums Mill Rd	Harrisburg, PA	17112-2827	717-651-7200	651-0670	K-12	Dr. Maurice Flurie
Community Academy of Philadelphia	1100 E Erie Ave	Philadelphia, PA	19124-5424	215-533-6700	533-6722	K-12	Joe Proietta
DeHostos Charter S	6301 N 2nd St	Philadelphia, PA	19120-1522	215-455-2300	455-6312	K-8	
Delaware Valley Charter HS	5201 Old York Rd	Philadelphia, PA	19141-2995	215-455-2550	455-5701	9-12	Dr. Harold Kurtz
Discovery Charter S	4700 Parkside Ave	Philadelphia, PA	19131-4712	215-879-8182	879-9510	K-8	Nina Brevard
Douglass Mastery Charter S	2118 W Norris St	Philadelphia, PA	19121-2100	215-684-5063	684-8916	K-8	Tom Weishaupt
Eastern University Academy Charter S	3300 Henry Ave Ste 2	Philadelphia, PA	19129-1121	215-769-3131	769-3112	7-12	Omar Barlow
Education Plus Academy Cyber Charter S	487 Devon Park Dr	Wayne, PA	19087-1808	215-600-2709	600-3609	K-8	Lydia Jerchau
Environmental Charter S at Frick Park	829 Milton St	Pittsburgh, PA	15218-1005	412-247-7970	247-7971	K-6	Jon McCann
Erie Rise Leadership Academy Charter S	2501 Plum St	Erie, PA	16502-2570	814-520-6468		K-6	Terry Lang
Esperanza Academy Charter HS	301 W Hunting Park Ave	Philadelphia, PA	19140-2625	215-457-3667	457-4381	6-12	David Rossi
Esperanza Cyber Charter S	4261 N 5th St	Philadelphia, PA	19140-2615	215-967-9703		6-12	
Evergreen Community Charter S	PO Box 523	Mountainhome, PA	18342-0523	570-595-6355	595-6038	6-12	Jill Shoesmith
Executive Education Academy Charter S	555 Union Blvd	Allentown, PA	18109-3389	484-841-7044		K-8	Robert Lysek
Fell Charter S	777 Main St	Simpson, PA	18407-1236	570-282-5199	282-0930	K-8	Mary Jo Walsh
First Philadelphia Charter S	4300 Tacony St	Philadelphia, PA	19124-4134	215-743-3100	743-9877	K-12	Myra Mezei
Folk Arts-Cultural Treasures Charter S	1023 Callowhill St	Philadelphia, PA	19123-3704	215-569-2600	569-3985	K-8	Pheng Lim
Franklin Towne Charter ES	4259 Richmond St	Philadelphia, PA	19137-1930	215-289-3389	288-4041	K-8	Patrick Field
Franklin Towne Charter HS	PO Box 310	Philadelphia, PA	19105	215-289-5000	535-8910	9-12	Dr. Joseph Venditti Esq.
Freire Charter HS	2027 Chestnut St	Philadelphia, PA	19103-3307	215-592-4252	557-9051	9-12	Dr. Kelly Davenport
Freire Charter S	1026 Market St	Philadelphia, PA	19107-4205	267-670-7499	670-7740	5-8	Dr. Kelly Davenport
Gardner Multiple Intelligence S	1615 E Elm St	Scranton, PA	18505	570-941-4100	941-7699	K-8	Maria Rozaieski
Gettysburg Montessori Charter S	888 Coleman Rd	Gettysburg, PA	17325	717-334-1120		K-6	Faye Pleso
Gillingham Charter S	915 Howard Ave	Pottsville, PA	17901	570-955-3830		K-12	
Global Leadership Academy	4601 W Girard Ave	Philadelphia, PA	19131-4615	267-295-5700	295-5701	K-8	Dr. Naomi Johnson-Booker
Graystone Academy Charter S	139 Modena Rd	Coatesville, PA	19320-4036	610-383-4311		K-6	Marita Barber
Green Woods Charter S	468 Domino Ln	Philadelphia, PA	19128-4363	215-482-6337		K-8	Jean Wallace
Harambee Institute of Science Technology	640 N 66th St	Philadelphia, PA	19151-3606	215-472-8770	472-9611	K-8	Damond Warren
Hill House Passport Academy Charter S	510 Heldman St	Pittsburgh, PA	15219	412-376-3724		9-12	Dwayne Homa
HOPE for Hyndman Charter S	130 School Dr	Hyndman, PA	15545-8125	814-842-3918	842-6246	K-12	Dr. Thomas Otis
I-Lead Charter S	401 Penn St	Reading, PA	19601-3974	855-453-2327		9-12	Angel Figueroa
Imagine Penn Hills Charter S	200 Penn School Dr	Verona, PA	15147-2850	412-793-6471	793-6473	K-6	Tamara Allen
Imani Education Circle Charter S	5612 Greene St	Philadelphia, PA	19144-2808	215-713-9240	713-9243	K-8	Adrienne Davis
Imhotep Institute Charter HS	6201 N 21 St	Philadelphia, PA	19138-2521	215-438-4140	438-4160	9-12	Cicely Peterson-Mangum
Independence Charter S	1600 Lombard St	Philadelphia, PA	19146-1507	215-238-8000	545-2924	K-8	Ramzy Andrawos
Infinity Charter S	51 Banks St Ste 1	Penbrook, PA	17103-2067	717-238-1880		K-8	Suzanne Gausman
Ketterer Charter S	1133 Village Way	Latrobe, PA	15650-5201	724-537-9110	537-9114	1-12	Eric Guldin
Keystone Academy Charter S	6649 Tulip St	Philadelphia, PA	19135-2835	215-332-2111	332-2840	K-8	John Goulding
Keystone Education Center Charter S	425 S Good Hope Rd	Greenville, PA	16125-8629	724-588-2511	588-2545	6-12	Mike Gentile
Khepera Charter S	926 W Sedgley Ave	Philadelphia, PA	19140-5439	215-843-1700	843-3530	6-8	Verna Holmes
Khepera Charter S	926 W Sedgley Ave	Philadelphia, PA	19140-5439	215-843-1700	843-3530	K-5	Mukasa Afrika
KIPP Dubois Collegiate Academy	5070 Parkside Ave	Philadelphia, PA	19131-4750	215-307-3465	307-3271	9-12	Aaron Bass
KIPP Philadelphia Charter S	2709 N Broad St	Philadelphia, PA	19132-2722	215-227-1728	827-5942	5-8	Ryane Burke
KIPP Philadelphia ES	2409 W Westmoreland St	Philadelphia, PA	19129-1309	267-687-7283	687-7295	K-4	Ben Speicher
KIPP West Philadelphia Prep Charter S	5900 Baltimore Ave	Philadelphia, PA	19143-3129	215-294-2973	294-8707	5-8	Cheshonna Miles
La Academia Charter S	30 N Ann St	Lancaster, PA	17602-3063	717-295-7763	399-6456	6-12	Guillermo Barroso
Laboratory Charter S	5339 Lebanon Ave	Philadelphia, PA	19131	215-877-9881	877-9882	2-8	
Laboratory Charter S	800 N Orianna St	Philadelphia, PA	19123-2250	215-574-1680	574-0622	K-8	Elizabeth Bonner
Lancaster County Academy	1202 Park City Ctr	Lancaster, PA	17601-2724	717-295-2499	392-8603	9-12	Gerald Huesken
Lehigh Valley Academy	1560 Valley Center Pkwy	Bethlehem, PA	18017-2276	610-866-9660		K-12	Susan Mauser
Lehigh Valley Charter HS for the Arts	321 E 3rd St	Bethlehem, PA	18015-1309	610-868-2971	868-1446	9-12	Diane LaBelle
Lehigh Valley Dual Language Charter S	551 Thomas St	Bethlehem, PA	18015-3447	610-419-3120	419-3968	K-6	Lisa Pluchinsky
Lincoln Charter S	559 W King St	York, PA	17401-3776	717-699-1573	846-4031	K-5	Leonard Hart
Lincoln Leadership Academy Charter S	1414 E Cedar St	Allentown, PA	18109-2308	484-860-3300		K-12	Sandra Figueroa-Torres
Lincoln Park Performing Arts Charter S	1 Lincoln Park	Midland, PA	15059-1535	724-643-9004	643-0769	K-12	Patrick Poling
Manchester Academic Charter S	1214 Liverpool St	Pittsburgh, PA	15233-1304	412-322-0585	322-2176	K-8	Vasilios Scoumis
Maritime Academy Charter S	2275 Bridge St	Philadelphia, PA	19137-1300	215-535-4555	535-4398	4-12	Edward Poznek
MaST Community Charter S	1800 Byberry Rd	Philadelphia, PA	19116-3012	215-348-1100	348-1217	K-12	John Swoyer
Mastery Charter HS Hardy Williams Campus	5400 Warrington Ave	Philadelphia, PA	19143-4810	267-499-2100	729-1892	7-10	Lisa Bellamy
Mastery Charter HS - Lenfest Campus	35 S 4th St	Philadelphia, PA	19106-2710	215-922-1902	922-1903	7-12	Steven Kollar
Mastery Charter HS - Pickett Campus	5700 Wayne Ave	Philadelphia, PA	19144-3314	215-866-9000	866-9001	6-12	Jason Kegel
Mastery Charter HS - Shoemaker Campus	5301 Media St	Philadelphia, PA	19131-4035	267-296-7111	296-7112	7-12	Sharif El-Mekki
Mastery Charter HS - Thomas Campus	927 Johnston St	Philadelphia, PA	19148-5016	267-236-0036	236-0030	7-12	Kristy Fruit
Mastery Charter S Clymer Campus	1201 W Rush St	Philadelphia, PA	19133	215-223-2243	227-3697	K-6	Tiffany Holmes
Mastery Charter S Grover Cleveland Cmps	3701 N 19th St	Philadelphia, PA	19140-3555	215-227-5042	893-5290	K-8	Charmaine Collins
Mastery Charter S -Hardy Williams Campus	1712 S 56th St	Philadelphia, PA	19143-5308	215-724-2343	724-2374	K-12	
Mastery Charter S Harrity Campus	5601 Christian St	Philadelphia, PA	19143-2805	215-471-2908	471-3807	PK-8	Stuart Warshawer
Mastery Charter S Mann Campus	5376 W Berks St	Philadelphia, PA	19131-3229	215-581-5616	581-5610	K-6	Stan Bobowski
Mastery Charter S Pastorius	5650 Sprague St	Philadelphia, PA	19138	215-951-5689		K-8	
Mastery Charter S Prep MS	1798 W Hunting Park Ave	Philadelphia, PA	19140-3408	215-227-4408	227-3694	6-8	Raymond Fields
Mastery Charter S Simon Gratz Campus	1798 W Hunting Park Ave	Philadelphia, PA	19140-3408	215-227-4408	227-3694	9-12	Rickia Reid
Mastery Charter S Smedley Campus	1790 Bridge St	Philadelphia, PA	19124-1359	215-537-2523	537-3694	K-6	Brian McLaughlin
Mastery Charter S - Thomas Campus	814 Bigler St	Philadelphia, PA	19148-5023	267-296-7000	236-0030	K-6	Michael Farrell
Math Civics & Sciences Charter S	447 N Broad St	Philadelphia, PA	19123-3643	215-923-4880	923-4859	1-12	Frank Devine
Memphis Street Academy Charter S	2950 Memphis St	Philadelphia, PA	19134-4314	215-291-4709	291-4754	5-8	Aqueelah Ellzy
Montessori Regional Charter S	3750 W 26th St	Erie, PA	16506-2039	814-833-7771	833-1838	K-6	Anthony Pirrello
Multi-Cultural Academy Charter S	3821 N Broad St	Philadelphia, PA	19140-3609	215-227-0513	227-0415	9-12	James Higgins
New Day Charter S	256 S 5th St	Huntingdon, PA	16652-1285	814-643-7112	643-7116	7-12	Steven Fleck
New Foundations Charter S	8001 Torresdale Ave	Philadelphia, PA	19136-2917	215-624-8100	624-0600	K-8	Paul Stadelberger
New Foundations Charter S	4850 Rhawn St	Philadelphia, PA	19136-2935	215-344-6410	624-6817	9-12	Paul Stadelberger
Nittany Valley Charter S	1612 Norma St	State College, PA	16801-6228	814-867-3842	231-0795	K-8	Kara Martin
Northwood Academy	4621 Castor Ave	Philadelphia, PA	19124-3024	215-289-5606	289-5464	K-8	Amy Hollister
Pan American Academy Charter S	2830 N American St	Philadelphia, PA	19133-3517	215-425-1212	423-0871	K-8	Dr. Darcy Russotto
Pantoja Community Charter S	4101 N American St	Philadelphia, PA	19140-2606	215-329-2733	329-2433	K-8	Sandra Gonzalez
Pennsylvania Cyber Charter S	652 Midland Ave	Midland, PA	15059-1433	724-643-1180	643-1963	K-12	Dr. Michael Conti
Pennsylvania Distance Learning Charter S	2100 Corporate Dr Ste 500	Wexford, PA	15090-7647	724-933-7300	933-7655	K-12	Dr. Ed Mandell
Pennsylvania Leadership Charter S	1332 Enterprise Dr	West Chester, PA	19380-5996	610-701-3333		K-12	Dr. James Hanak
PA Learners Online Cyber Charter S	475 E Waterfront Dr	Homestead, PA	15120-1144	412-394-5733		9-12	Dr. David Martin
Pennsylvania Virtual Charter S	630 Park Ave	King of Prussia, PA	19406-1408	610-275-8501	275-1719	K-12	Joanne Jones Barnett
People for People Charter S	800 N Broad St	Philadelphia, PA	19130-2202	215-763-7060	763-6210	K-8	Pri Seebadri
Perseus House Charter S of Excellence	1511 Peach St	Erie, PA	16501-2104	814-480-5914	454-9859	7-12	Dana LaFata
Philadelphia Academy Charter S	1700 Tomlinson Rd	Philadelphia, PA	19116-3848	215-673-3990	673-3341	9-12	Megan Simmons
Philadelphia Academy Charter S	11000 Roosevelt Blvd	Philadelphia, PA	19116-3903	215-676-8320	676-8340	K-8	Allyssa Schmitt
Philadelphia Charter S for the Arts/Sci	1197 Haworth St	Philadelphia, PA	19124-2505	215-537-2520	537-2861	K-8	Michael Rocco
Philadelphia Electrical & Tech Charter S	1420 Chestnut St	Philadelphia, PA	19102-2505	267-514-1823	514-1834	9-12	Erin Dougherty
Philadelphia Montessori Charter S	2227 Island Rd	Philadelphia, PA	19142-1009	215-365-4011	365-4367	K-6	Carrie Kries

School	Address	City,State	Zip code	Telephone	Fax	Grade	Contact
Philadelphia Performing Arts Charter S	2600 S Broad St	Philadelphia, PA	19145-4616	215-551-4000	551-1113	K-5	Angela Puleio
Philadelphia Performing Arts Charter S	2407 S Broad St	Philadelphia, PA	19148-3508	215-551-4000	551-1113	K-1	Angela Puleio
Premier Arts and Science Charter S	500 N 17th St	Harrisburg, PA	17103-1423	717-234-3200		K-5	Steven Rayzer
Preparatory Charter S	1928 Point Breeze Ave	Philadelphia, PA	19145-2612	215-334-6144	334-6147	9-12	Patricia Sack
Propel Charter HS - Andrew Street	605 E 10th Ave	Munhall, PA	15120-1911	412-462-4625	462-6980	9-12	Angela Allie
Propel Charter HS - Braddock Hills	1500 Yost Blvd	Pittsburgh, PA	15221-4822	412-271-4929	271-4905	9-12	Bob Bischoff
Propel Charter S - Braddock Hills	1500 Yost Blvd	Braddock Hills, PA	15221-4822	412-271-3061	271-0865	K-8	Jocelyn Artinger
Propel Charter S - East	1611 Monroeville Ave	Turtle Creek, PA	15145-1652	412-823-0347		K-8	Sandra Gough
Propel Charter S - Hazelwood	5401 Glenwood Ave	Pittsburgh, PA	15207-1847	412-325-7105		K-6	Tina Chekan
Propel Charter S - Homestead	129 E 10th Ave	Homestead, PA	15120-1608	412-464-2604		K-8	Carrie Miller
Propel Charter S - Mc Keesport	2412 Versailles Ave	McKeesport, PA	15132-2037	412-678-7215		K-8	Mike Evans
Propel Charter S - Montour	340 Bilmar Dr	Pittsburgh, PA	15205	412-539-0100	539-0109	K-8	Matt Strine
Propel Charter S - Northside	1805 Buena Vista St	Pittsburgh, PA	15212-3914	412-325-1412	325-1428	K-8	Ariane Watson
Propel Charter S - Pitcairn	435 Agatha St	Pitcairn, PA	15140-1310	412-457-0020		K-8	Robert Bischoff
Renaissance Academy	413 Fairview St	Phoenixville, PA	19460	610-983-4080	983-4096	K-12	Gina Guarino-Buli
Sankofa Academy	446 W Gay St	West Chester, PA	19380-2851	610-696-0333	696-0620	5-12	Dr. LaMont McKim
Sankofa Freedom Academy	2501 Kensington Ave	Philadelphia, PA	19125-1321	215-228-2001	228-2099	K-12	Dr. Ayesha Imani
School Lane Charter S	2400 Bristol Pike	Bensalem, PA	19020-5263	215-245-6055	245-6058	K-10	Karen Schade
Seven Generations Charter S	154 E Minor St	Emmaus, PA	18049-4103	610-421-8844		K-8	Paul Hunter
Souderton Charter S Collaborative	110 E Broad St	Souderton, PA	18964-1276	215-721-4560	721-4071	K-8	Jennifer Arevalo
Southwest Leadership Academy	7101 Paschall Ave	Philadelphia, PA	19142-1031	215-729-1939	729-1976	K-8	Alphonso Evans
Spectrum Charter S	4369 Northern Pike	Monroeville, PA	15146-2807	412-374-8130	374-9629	9-12	Michelle Johnson
Stone Valley Community Charter S	13006 Greenwood Rd	Huntingdon, PA	16652-6030	814-667-2705	667-2231	K-5	Dr. Kim Connelly
Sugar Valley Rural Charter S	236 E Main St	Loganton, PA	17747-9502	570-725-7822	725-7825	K-12	Logan Coney
SusQ-Cyber Charter S	240 Market St Box 1A	Bloomsburg, PA	17815	866-370-1226	245-0246	9-12	Patricia Leighow
Sylvan Heights Science Charter S	915 S 13th St	Harrisburg, PA	17104-3402	717-232-9220	232-9221	K-4	Timothy Hess M.Ed.
Tacony Academy Charter S	1330 Rhawn St	Philadelphia, PA	19111-2802	215-742-5100	742-5200	K-8	Ashley Redfearn-Neswick
Tacony Academy Charter S	6201 Keystone St	Philadelphia, PA	19135-3701	267-388-8656	388-8666	9-12	Naimah Holliday
Thackston Charter MS	625 E Philadelphia St	York, PA	17403-1625	717-846-6160	848-2856	5-8	Denise Butts
Tidioute Community Charter S	241 Main St	Tidioute, PA	16351-1222	814-484-3550	484-3977	K-12	Dr. Doug Allen
21st Century Cyber Charter S	126 Wallace Ave	Downingtown, PA	19335-2600	484-875-5400	875-5404	6-12	Kim McCully
Universal Alcorn Charter S	3200 Dickinson St	Philadelphia, PA	19146-3316	215-952-6219	952-0853	K-8	Sheila Mallory
Universal Audenried Charter HS	3301 Tasker St	Philadelphia, PA	19145-1021	215-952-4801	952-4805	9-12	Blanchard Diavua
Universal Bluford Charter S	5801 Media St	Philadelphia, PA	19131-3824	215-581-5502	581-5725	K-6	Crystal Gary-Nelson
Universal Creighton Charter S	5401 Tabor Ave	Philadelphia, PA	19120-2130	215-537-2531	537-8398	K-8	Wendy Baldwin
Universal Daroff Charter S	5630 Vine St	Philadelphia, PA	19139-1301	215-471-2905	471-3159	K-8	Anna Smith
Universal Institute Charter S	801 S 15th St	Philadelphia, PA	19146-2215	215-732-2876	732-8066	K-8	Jeffrey Williams
Universal Vare Charter MS	2100 S 24th St	Philadelphia, PA	19145-3222	215-952-8611	952-8520	5-8	Craig Metcalfe
Urban Academy Greater Pittsburgh Charter	437 Turrett St	Pittsburgh, PA	15206	412-361-1008	361-1042	K-5	Dr. Gail Edwards
Urban Pathways Charter S	925 Penn Ave	Pittsburgh, PA	15222-3806	412-392-4601	392-4602	K-5	Kimberly Fitzgerald
Vida Charter S	120 E Broadway	Gettysburg, PA	17325	717-334-3643	334-9806	K-6	Martha Davis
Vision Academy Charter S	41 E Baltimore Ave	Lansdowne, PA	19050	484-466-6341	466-2124	K-5	Isik Durmus
West Oak Lane Charter S	7115 Stenton Ave	Philadelphia, PA	19138-1136	215-927-7995	927-7980	K-8	Dr. Debbera Peoples-Lee
West Philadelphia Achievement Charter S	6701 Callowhill St	Philadelphia, PA	19151-3603	215-476-6471	476-6481	K-5	Christine Godfrey
Widener Partnership Charter S	1450 Edgmont Ave	Chester, PA	19013-3943	610-872-1358	872-1794	K-7	Dr. Darlene Davis
Wiley Community Charter S	1446 E Lake Rd	Erie, PA	16507-1936	814-461-9600	461-0226	K-8	Peter Russo
Wissahickon Charter S	4700 Wissahickon Ave	Philadelphia, PA	19144-4252	267-338-1020	338-1030	K-8	Kristi Littell
Wonderland Charter S	2112 Sandy Dr	State College, PA	16803-2282	814-234-5886		K-K	Harold Ohnmeis
World Communications Charter S	512 S Broad St	Philadelphia, PA	19146-1613	215-735-3198	735-3824	6-12	Gamal Sherif Ed.D.
York Academy Regional Charter S	32 W North St	York, PA	17401-2403	717-801-3900	718-1092	K-6	
Young Scholars Charter S	900 N Marshall St	Philadelphia, PA	19123-1307	215-232-9727	232-4542	6-8	Jessika Rao
Young Scholars Kenderton Charter S	1500 W Ontario St	Philadelphia, PA	19140-5012	215-227-4412		K-8	Shakira Smith
Young Scholars of Central PA Charter S	1530 Westerly Pkwy	State College, PA	16801-2848	814-237-9727	237-1517	K-8	Levent Kaya
Young Scholars of Western PA	600 Newport Dr	Pittsburgh, PA	15234-2653	412-668-2064	668-2068	K-6	
YouthBuild Charter S	1231 N Broad St Fl 3	Philadelphia, PA	19122-4023	215-627-8671	763-5774	12-12	Simran Sidhu

Rhode Island

School	Address	City,State	Zip code	Telephone	Fax	Grade	Contact
Academy for Career Exploration	155 Harrison St	Providence, RI	02907	401-456-1738	521-0653	9-12	Mario Cirillo Ph.D.
Achievement 1st Providence Mayoral Acad	370 Hartford Ave	Providence, RI	02909-5104	401-347-1106	633-6677	K-4	Morgan Carter
BEACON Charter HS for the Arts	320 Main St	Woonsocket, RI	02895-3138	401-671-6261	671-6264	9-12	Michael Skeldon
Blackstone Academy	334 Pleasant St	Pawtucket, RI	02860-5289	401-726-1750	726-1753	9-12	Kyleen Carpenter
Blackstone Valley Prep ES 1	291 Broad St	Cumberland, RI	02864-7802	401-335-3133	305-3185	K-4	Kyle Quadros
Blackstone Valley Prep ES 3	3 Fairlawn Way	Lincoln, RI	02865	401-475-2680	475-2415	K-4	Josh Falk
Blackstone Valley Prep ES 2	52 Broad St	Cumberland, RI	02864	401-305-6860	305-6866	K-4	Sara Tucker
Blackstone Valley Prep Mayoral Acad HS	3357 Mendon Rd	Cumberland, RI	02864-2112	401-405-0320	405-0440	9-12	Jonathon Santos Silva
Blackstone Valley Prep Mayoral Acad MS	3 Fairlawn Way	Lincoln, RI	02865	401-475-8829	475-8931	5-8	Joy Souza
Compass S	537 Old North Rd	Kingston, RI	02881-1220	401-788-8322	788-8326	K-8	Brandee Lapisky
Cuffee S	459 Promenade St	Providence, RI	02908-5601	401-453-2626	453-4964	K-12	Chris Haskins
Greene S	94 John Potter Rd	West Greenwich, RI	02817-2099	401-397-8600	397-8700	9-12	Joshua Laplant
Highlander Charter S	42 Lexington Ave	Providence, RI	02907-1716	401-277-2600	277-2603	PK-12	Rose Grant
Hope Academy	1000 Eddy St	Providence, RI	02905-4739	401-533-9192	533-9101	K-1	Raphael Diaz
International Charter S	334 Pleasant St	Pawtucket, RI	02860-5289	401-721-0824	721-0976	K-5	Julie Nora Ph.D.
Kingston Hill Academy	850 Stony Fort Rd	Saunderstown, RI	02874-1003	401-783-8282	783-5656	K-5	Linda Paolillo
Learning Community S	21 Lincoln Ave	Central Falls, RI	02863-2012	401-722-9998	722-0990	K-8	Sarah Friedman
NEL/CPS Construction Career Academy	4 Sharpe Dr	Cranston, RI	02920-4410	401-270-8692	270-8697	9-12	Dennis Curran
Nowell Leadership Academy II	133 Delaine St	Providence, RI	02909-2728	401-751-0405	751-0020	9-12	Jodi LaFauci
Nowell Leadership Academy I	43 Hawes St	Central Falls, RI	02863-3007	401-751-0405	751-0020	9-12	Jodi LaFauci
RI Nurses Institute Middle College	150 Washington St	Providence, RI	02903-3300	401-680-4900	331-5646	10-12	Pamela McCue
RISE Prep Mayoral Academy	1 Social St	Woonsocket, RI	02895-3136	401-765-5127		K-8	
Segue Institute for Learning	325 Cowden St	Central Falls, RI	02863-2145	401-721-0964	721-0984	6-8	Melissa Lourenco
SouthSide Elementary Charter S	126 Somerset St	Providence, RI	02907	401-270-9007		K-2	Wendy Randle
Times2 STEM Academy	50 Fillmore St	Providence, RI	02908-3105	401-272-5094	272-0555	K-12	Rudolph Moseley
Trinity Academy for the Performing Arts	158 Messer St	Providence, RI	02909-1741	401-432-7881	432-7882	7-12	Nanci DeRobbio
Village Green Virtual Charter S	135 Weybosset St	Providence, RI	02903-3803	401-831-2878		9-12	Dr. Robert Pilkington

South Carolina

School	Address	City,State	Zip code	Telephone	Fax	Grade	Contact
Academy for Teaching and Learning	109 Hinton St	Chester, SC	29706-2022	803-385-6334	385-6335	PK-8	Robyn Brakefield
Academy of Hope Charter S	3521 Juniper Bay Rd	Conway, SC	29527-4227	843-397-5719	397-5712	K-8	Melissa McCloud
Aiken Performing Arts Academy	PO Box 418	Aiken, SC	29801	803-644-4824	641-1155	9-12	Keisha Lloyd-Kennedy
Allegro Charter S of Music	120 Broad St	Charleston, SC	29401	843-297-8033	207-4701	6-12	Daniel Neikirk
Anderson V Charter S	1225 S McDuffie St	Anderson, SC	29624-2746	864-260-5538	260-5911	9-12	Katie Brown
Brashier Middle College HS	1830 W Georgia Rd	Simpsonville, SC	29680-7212	864-757-1800	757-1850	9-12	Michael Sinclair
Bridges Preparatory S	PO Box 120	Beaufort, SC	29901	843-982-7737	982-7707	K-8	Dr. Nick Ithomitis
Bridgewater Academy	191 River Landing Blvd	Myrtle Beach, SC	29579-9502	843-236-3689	236-4921	K-8	Steve Wilson
Calhoun Falls Charter S	205 Edgefield St	Calhoun Falls, SC	29628-1018	864-418-8014	418-9379	6-12	Deirdre McCullough
Cape Romain Environmental Educ Charter S	1011 Old Cemetery Rd	Mc Clellanville, SC	29458-9735	843-887-3323	887-3525	PK-8	Margaret Crouch M.Ed.
Carolina School for Inquiry	PO Box 2484	Columbia, SC	29202	803-691-1250	691-1247	PK-6	Victoria Dixon-Mokeba
Carolina Voyager Charter S	721 Wappoo Rd	Charleston, SC	29407	843-203-3891	718-2903	K-4	Dr. Harry Walker
Charleston Charter S for Math & Science	1002 King St	Charleston, SC	29403	843-720-3085	720-3196	6-12	Melissa Frasier
Charleston Development Academy	233 Line St	Charleston, SC	29403-8100	843-722-2689	722-2694	PK-8	Dr. Shaun Johnson
Coastal Leadership Academy	3710 Palmetto Pointe Blvd	Myrtle Beach, SC	29588	843-788-9898	410-4826	9-12	Renee Mathews
Coastal Montessori Charter S	111 Old Plantation Dr	Pawleys Island, SC	29585	843-235-0413	235-0418	1-7	Dr. Nathalie Hunt
Cooper Charter S	4568 Seaboard Rd	Salters, SC	29590-3365	843-387-5426	387-5444	PK-8	Dr. Kerry Singleton
Cyber Academy of South Carolina	330A Pelham Rd	Greenville, SC	29615-3115	855-611-2830	558-0535	K-12	David Crook
Discovery S	302 W Dunlap St	Lancaster, SC	29720-2405	803-285-8430	416-8907	K-5	Tom McDuffie
East Cooper Montessori Charter S	1120 Rifle Range Rd	Mount Pleasant, SC	29464-4229	843-216-2883	216-8880	PK-8	Jody Swanigan
East Point Academy	1340 Knox Abbott Dr	Cayce, SC	29033	803-739-4992	739-4977	PK-6	Dr. Winnie Johnson
Felton Laboratory Charter S	PO Box 2349	Orangeburg, SC	29116-2349	803-536-7034	533-3635	K-8	Dr. Gloria Winkler
Fox Creek HS	165 Shortcut Rd	North Augusta, SC	29860-9123	803-613-9435	613-1533	9-12	Josh Trahan
Garden City Preparatory Academy for Boys	1195 Saint Matthews Rd	Orangeburg, SC	29115-3417	888-448-7641	445-5953	6-7	Kevin Rasberry
Gray Collegiate Academy	3833 Leaphart Rd	West Columbia, SC	29169-2416	803-951-3321	381-9764	9-12	Joedy Moots
GREEN Charter S	1440 Pelham Rd	Greenville, SC	29615-3900	864-288-4134	288-0826	K-8	Adem Dokmeci
Greenville Technical Charter HS	PO Box 5616	Greenville, SC	29606-5616	864-250-8845	250-8846	9-12	Dr. J. Brodie Bricker
Greer Middle College Charter HS	138 W McElhaney Rd	Taylors, SC	29687-5843	864-469-7571	469-7573	9-12	Jimmy Armstrong Ph.D.
High Point Academy	6655 Pottery Rd	Spartanburg, SC	29303-6715	864-316-9788	249-1516	K-12	Lori Manning
Horse Creek Academy	1200 Toolebeck Rd	Aiken, SC	29803	803-226-0160	226-0202	PK-8	Dr. Frank Roberson
Imagine Columbia Leadership Academy	3810 N Main St	Columbia, SC	29203-6443	803-929-1140	929-1145	K-5	Suezan Turknett
James Island Charter HS	1000 Fort Johnson Rd	Charleston, SC	29412-8898	843-762-2754	762-5228	9-12	Richard Gordon
Kennedy Charter S	PO Box 418	Aiken, SC	29801	803-644-4824	641-1155	3-8	Keisha Lloyd-Kennedy
Langston Charter MS	1950 Woodruff Rd	Greenville, SC	29607-5937	864-286-9700	286-9699	6-8	Greg Able
Lead Academy	804 Mauldin Rd	Greenville, SC	29607	864-770-1790	302-1278	5-8	Rodney Johnson
Legacy Charter S Fuller Campus	1613 W Washington St	Greenville, SC	29601	864-214-1600	451-7023	K-4	Virginia Burrows
Legacy Charter S Parker Campus	900 Woodside Ave	Greenville, SC	29611	864-248-0646	283-6444	5-12	Stephen Hampton
Lowcountry Leadership Charter S	5139 Gibson Rd	Hollywood, SC	29449-6181	843-889-5527	889-5529	K-12	Mache Larkin
Lowcountry Montessori S	749 Broad River Dr	Beaufort, SC	29906-6868	843-322-0577	322-0925	K-12	Amy Horn

School	Address	City,State	Zip code	Telephone	Fax	Grade	Contact
Mathis Charter HS	2872 Azalea Dr	N Charleston, SC	29405	843-557-1611	747-5810	9-12	Natrice Henriques
Midlands Middle College	1260 Lexington Dr	West Columbia, SC	29170-2176	803-822-7043	822-7039	11-12	Carole Fearrington
Midlands STEM Institute	112 Crane St	Winnsboro, SC	29180-6941	803-815-1524	815-0072	K-12	Marie Milam
NEXT HS	2000 Wade Hampton Blvd	Greenville, SC	29615-1037	864-214-6398		9-10	
OCSD5 HS for Health Professions	770 Stilton Rd	Orangeburg, SC	29115-3083	803-535-1693	535-1664	9-12	Kimberly Broughton
Orange Grove Charter S	1225 Orange Branch Rd	Charleston, SC	29407-3336	843-763-1520	769-2245	PK-6	John Clendaniel
PALM Charter HS	136 Rodeo Dr	Myrtle Beach, SC	29579	843-903-6600	903-6602	9-12	Avery Moore
Palmetto Academy of Learning and Success	3021 Fred Nash Blvd	Myrtle Beach, SC	29577	843-293-1725		K-8	Courtney Fancher
Palmetto Scholar's Academy	7499 Dorchester Rd	N Charleston, SC	29418-3310	843-300-4118	300-4123	6-12	Dr. Tim Gott
Palmetto S at Children's Attention Home	PO Box 2892	Rock Hill, SC	29732-4892	803-328-6555	327-8618	K-8	Dr. Hugh Wilson
Palmetto Youth Academy	1209 N Douglas St	Florence, SC	29501-0600	843-679-7070	679-7046	1-6	Yvonne Burgess
Pattison's Academy for Comprehensive Ed.	2014 Bees Ferry Rd	Charleston, SC	29414	843-556-1070	556-6742	K-12	Shannon O'Neill
Pee Dee Math Science Technology Academy	101 Docs Dr	Bishopville, SC	29010	803-428-8400	883-8736	K-7	E. Keith Bailey
Phoenix Charter HS	PO Box 170	Alcolu, SC	29001-0170	803-505-6800	505-6801	9-12	Elease Fulton
Presitge Preparatory Academy	2415 Avenue F	N Charleston, SC	29405	843-900-7722		K-4	Joyce Coleman
Provost Academy of South Carolina	200 Arbor Lake Dr Ste 301	Columbia, SC	29223-4504	803-735-9110	753-9878	9-12	Stephanie Cagle
Quest Leadership Academy	29 Ridgeway Dr	Greenville, SC	29605-2454	864-275-0465		PK-4	Calandra Davis
Richland One Middle College S	316 Beltline Blvd	Columbia, SC	29205-3624	803-738-7114	738-7117	11-12	Dr. Tiniece Javis
Richland Two Charter HS	7900 Brookmont Ln	Columbia, SC	29203	803-419-1348	935-1212	9-12	Bobby Cunningham
Riverview Charter S	81 Savannah Hwy	Beaufort, SC	29906	843-379-0123	379-0133	K-8	Alison Thomas
Riverwalk Academy	5750 Mount Gallant Rd	Rock Hill, SC	29732	803-327-8400	454-9031	K-7	Charlie French
Royal Live Oaks Academy Arts & Sciences	PO Box 528	Hardeeville, SC	29927-0528	843-784-2630	784-2623	K-12	Karen Wicks
South Carolina Calvert Academy	3700 Forest Dr Ste 406	Columbia, SC	29204-4010	803-462-0254	462-0326	K-8	Alexandria Gillicrese
SC Connections Academy	220 Stoneridge Dr Ste 403	Columbia, SC	29210-8018	803-212-4712	212-4946	K-12	Amanda Ebel
South Carolina Science Academy	2015 Marion St	Columbia, SC	29201	803-227-6422	391-4902	6-12	Kalu Kalu
SC Virtual Charter School	140 Stoneridge Dr Ste 420	Columbia, SC	29210-8200	803-253-6222	253-6279	K-12	Dr. Cherry Daniel
South Carolina Whitmore S	510 Lexington Ave	Chapin, SC	29036	866-476-6416	476-1646	9-12	John Loveday
Spartanburg Preparatory S	385 S Spring St	Spartanburg, SC	29306-5264	864-621-3882	804-6404	K-9	Dr. John Von Rohr
York Preparatory Academy	1047 Golden Gate Ct	Rock Hill, SC	29732-8878	803-324-4400	496-2083	K-12	Dr. Brian Carpenter
Youth Leadership Academy	698 Concord Church Rd	Pickens, SC	29671	864-898-4511	898-5784	6-8	Sandee Blankenship

Tennessee

School	Address	City,State	Zip code	Telephone	Fax	Grade	Contact
Arrow Academy of Excellence	645 Semmes St	Memphis, TN	38111-2201	901-207-1891		K-3	Raychellet Williamson
Aspire Coleman ES	3210 Raleigh Millington Rd	Memphis, TN	38128-3395	901-416-4306		PK-6	Owen Ricciardi
Aspire Hanley ES #1	680 Hanley St	Memphis, TN	38114-2534	901-416-5958		PK-7	Megan McGrail
Aspire Hanley ES #2	680 Hanley St	Memphis, TN	38114-2534	901-416-5958		PK-6	Sha Fanion
Aurora Collegiate Academy	3804 Given Ave	Memphis, TN	38122-3535	901-249-4615	249-4915	K-5	Grant Monda
Brick Church College Prep S	2835 Brick Church Pike	Nashville, TN	37207	615-806-6317		5-8	Dennis Wolff
Cameron College Prep S	1034 1st Ave S	Nashville, TN	37210-2616	615-806-6320		5-8	Tait Danhausen
Chattanooga Charter School of Excellence	5600 Brainerd Rd	Chattanooga, TN	37411-5310	423-710-1121		K-6	Dr. Marcia Griffin
Chattanooga Girls Leadership Academy	1802 Bailey Ave	Chattanooga, TN	37404-3005	423-702-7230		6-12	Elaine Swoffard Ed.D.
Circles of Success Learning Academy	867 S Parkway E	Memphis, TN	38106-5605	901-322-7978	322-7993	K-5	
City University S Boys Preparatory	1475 E Shelby Dr	Memphis, TN	38116-7225	901-775-2219	775-2044	6-8	Tracie Greer
City University S Girls Preparatory	1475 E Shelby Dr	Memphis, TN	38116-7225	901-775-2219	775-2044	6-8	Tracie Greer
City University S of Independence	1475 E Shelby Dr	Memphis, TN	38116	901-775-2219	775-2044	9-12	Tracie Greer
City University S of Liberal Arts	1475 E Shelby Dr	Memphis, TN	38116	901-775-2219	775-2044	9-12	Tracie Greer
Cornerstone Prep - Denver Campus	1940 Frayser Blvd	Memphis, TN	38127-5618	901-416-3938		K-5	Diana Bey
Cornerstone Prep - Lester Campus	320 Carpenter St	Memphis, TN	38112-4002	901-416-5969	416-5971	PK-6	Angie Cramer
DuBois S of Arts & Technology	4475 S Germantown Rd	Memphis, TN	38125-3449	901-801-6171	801-6170	K-12	Audrey Hudson
DuBois S of Leadership & Public Policy	817 Brownlee Rd	Memphis, TN	38116-6207	901-751-7122	869-4056	K-12	Curtis Weathers
East End Preparatory S	1460 McGavock Pike	Nashville, TN	37216	615-630-7470	630-7490	K-4	Jim Leckrone
Fairley HS	4950 Fairley Rd	Memphis, TN	38109-7399	901-730-8160		9-12	Zach Samson
Freedom Prep Academy - Westwood	778 Parkrose Rd	Memphis, TN	38109	901-259-5959		K-8	Donique Nobles
Freedom Preparatory Academy	5132 Jonetta St	Memphis, TN	38109-7061	901-259-5959	259-5950	6-12	Sundiata Salaam
GRAD Academy	1880 Prospect St	Memphis, TN	38106-6710	901-206-8848		9-12	Dr. Darian Jones
Hillcrest HS	4184 Graceland Dr	Memphis, TN	38116-2655	901-416-3104	416-9432	9-12	
Humes Preparatory Academy - Upper S	659 N Manassas St	Memphis, TN	38107-3902	901-310-1332		6-8	Dr. Johnoson Crutchfield
Intrepid College Prep S	5432 Bell Forge Ln E	Antioch, TN	37013	615-810-8443		5-8	Mia Howard
Ivy Academy Environmental Charter S	8520 Dayton Pike	Soddy Daisy, TN	37379	423-305-7494	305-7496	6-12	Angie Markum
King Preparatory HS	1530 Dellwood Ave	Memphis, TN	38127-7265	901-416-3880		9-12	Kimberly Hopkins-Clark
KIPP: Kirkpatrick ES	1000 Sevier St	Nashville, TN	37206	615-226-4484		K-1	Amy Galloway
KIPP Academy Nashville MS	123 Douglas Ave	Nashville, TN	37207-5155	615-226-4484		5-8	Laura Howarth
KIPP Memphis Academy ES	2248 Shannon Ave	Memphis, TN	38108-1407	901-452-2682		K-2	Jenna Molinski
KIPP Memphis Academy MS	2110 Howell Ave	Memphis, TN	38108-2268	901-791-9793		5-8	Andrew Bobowski
KIPP Memphis Collegiate ES	230 Henry Ave	Memphis, TN	38107-2483	901-791-9391	791-9394	K-4	Grace Williams
KIPP Memphis Collegiate HS	2110 Howell Ave	Memphis, TN	38108-2268	901-791-9792	791-9796	9-10	Richard Bailey
KIPP Memphis Collegiate MS	230 Henry Ave	Memphis, TN	38107-2483	901-791-9390	791-9394	5-8	Grace Williams
KIPP Memphis Preparatory ES	2230 Corry Rd	Memphis, TN	38106-7814	901-577-3330		K-1	Sarah Jensen
KIPP Memphis Preparatory MS	2230 Corry Rd	Memphis, TN	38106-7814	901-881-5128		5-7	Crystal Windless
KIPP Memphis University MS	3966 Sewanee Rd	Memphis, TN	38109-4000	901-577-3300		6-7	Mitch Bartkiewicz
KIPP Nashville College Prep MS	3410 Knight Dr	Nashville, TN	37207	615-226-4484	226-4401	5-7	Nikki Olszewski
KIPP Nashville Collegiate HS	123 Douglas Ave	Nashville, TN	37207-5155	615-226-4484		9-12	Jake Ramsey
Kirby MS	6670 E Raines Rd	Memphis, TN	38115-6610	901-416-1980	416-0974	6-8	Pamela Yancy-Taylor
Klondike Preparatory Academy	1250 Vollintine Ave	Memphis, TN	38107-2826	901-310-1999		K-3	Jennifer Isom
Knowledge Academies	5320 Hickory Hollow Pkwy	Antioch, TN	37013	615-810-8370	877-0502	5-8	Arielle McCallum
Knowledge Academies HS	5320 Hickory Hollow Pkwy	Antioch, TN	37013	615-800-6814	887-0502	9-12	Ariel McCallum
LEAD Academy	2835 Brick Church Pike	Nashville, TN	37207	615-352-1253	327-5425	5-8	
LEAD Academy HS	1034 1st Ave S	Nashville, TN	37210	615-327-5422		9-12	Nic Frank
Leadership Prep Charter S	4190 Elliston Rd	Nashville, TN	38111-7902	901-378-3917		K-5	Valissia Allen
LEAD Prep Southeast	531 Metroplex Dr	Nashville, TN	37211	615-678-0543	800-8272	5-8	Chris Elliott
Lester Prep	320 Carpenter St	Memphis, TN	38112-4002	901-416-3640		6-8	Brearn Wright
Libertas S at Brookmeade	3777 Edenburg Dr	Memphis, TN	38127-4717	901-609-3611		PK-1	Bob Nardo
Liberty Collegiate Academy	3515 Gallatin Pike	Nashville, TN	37216	615-564-1965	650-0912	5-8	
Memphis Academy of Health Sciences	3925 Chelsea Avenue Ext	Memphis, TN	38108-2612	901-382-1441	382-1944	6-12	Dr. Reginald Williams
Memphis Academy of Science & Engineering	1254 Jefferson Ave	Memphis, TN	38104-7229	901-333-1580	333-1582	6-12	Rodrick Gaston
Memphis Business Academy	2450 Frayser Blvd	Memphis, TN	38127-5823	901-353-1475	308-1430	K-5	Marsharee Shaw
Memphis Business Academy HS	3306 Overton Crossing St	Memphis, TN	38127-6549	901-357-8680	357-8681	9-12	Dr. Menthia Clark
Memphis Business Academy MS	3306 Overton Crossing St	Memphis, TN	38127-6549	901-357-2711	357-2442	6-8	Dr. Menthia Clark
Memphis College Prep S	1500 Dunn Ave	Memphis, TN	38106	901-620-6475	620-6476	K-5	Ashley Foxx
Memphis Grizzlies Prep Charter S	168 Jefferson Ave	Memphis, TN	38103-2219	901-474-0955	474-9049	9-12	Parker Couch
Memphis Rise Academy	5130 Raleigh Lagrange Rd	Memphis, TN	38134	901-379-5750		6-12	Jack Vuylsteke
Memphis Scholars Caldwell-Guthrie S	951 Chelsea Ave	Memphis, TN	38107-2034	901-416-3220	416-3211	PK-5	
Memphis Scholars Florida-Kansas	90 W Olive St	Memphis, TN	38106	901-305-9983		K-5	Tom Mcpherson
Memphis Scholars Raleigh-Egypt MS	4215 Alice Ann Dr	Memphis, TN	38128-2204	901-416-4141	416-4110	6-8	
Memphis School of Excellence	4450 S Mendenhall Rd	Memphis, TN	38141	901-367-7814	367-7816	6-12	Muhammet Turkay
Moving Ahead S of Scholars Learning	229 S Danny Thomas Blvd	Memphis, TN	38126-1501	901-528-2337	528-5190	K-3	Kelly Carter
Nashville Academy of Computer Science	3230 Brick Church Pike	Nashville, TN	37207	615-921-5000		5-6	
Nashville Classical Charter S	1310 Ordway Pl	Nashville, TN	37206	615-538-5841		K-2	Charlie Friedman
Nashville Prep Academy	1300 56th Ave N	Nashville, TN	37209	615-921-8440	921-8460	5-8	Arlyn Ilgenfritz
Neelys Bend College Prep	1251 Neelys Bend Rd	Madison, TN	37115	615-860-1477		5-6	Marcus Moye
Neelys Bend ES	1300 Neelys Bend Rd	Madison, TN	37115-5515	615-860-1471		K-4	Dr. Derrick Salter
Neelys Bend MS	1251 Neelys Bend Rd	Madison, TN	37115-5471	615-645-6461		5-8	Marcus Moye
New Vision Academy	297 Plus Park Blvd	Nashville, TN	37217	615-360-1115	361-8545	5-8	Tim Malone
Omni Prep North Pointe Lower S	3333 Old Brownsville Rd	Memphis, TN	38134-8419	901-828-4912	828-4902	K-4	Melissa Schaeffer
Omni Prep North Pointe MS	3333 Old Brownsville Rd	Memphis, TN	38134-8419	901-828-4912	828-4902	5-8	Mary Mitchell
Power Center Academy ES	6120 Winchester Rd	Memphis, TN	38115-4014	901-333-2999		K-5	
Power Center Academy HS	5390 Mendenhall Mall	Memphis, TN	38115-4505	901-310-1331	367-0039	9-12	Dr. Steevon Hunter
Power Center Academy MS	6120 Winchester Rd	Memphis, TN	38115-4014	901-333-6874	367-9682	6-8	Steevon Hunter
Promise Academy	1346 Bryan St	Memphis, TN	38108-2401	901-324-4456	324-4457	K-4	Thomas Beazley
Promise Academy Spring Hill	3796 Frayser Raleigh Rd	Memphis, TN	38128-5235	901-410-0284		PK-2	Patrick Washington
Purpose Preparatory S	220 Venture Cir	Nashville, TN	37228	615-724-0705		K-3	Lagra Newman
RePublic HS	3307 Brick Church Pike	Nashville, TN	37207	615-921-6620		9-9	
Rocketship Nashville Northeast ES	2526 Dickerson Pike	Nashville, TN	37207	615-650-5560		K-4	James Robinson
Rocketship United Academy	320 Plus Park Blvd	Nashville, TN	37217	615-712-7499		K-4	James Robinson
Smithson-Craighead Academy	730 Neelys Bend Rd	Madison, TN	37115	615-228-9886	865-6308	K-4	Janelle Glover
Soulsville Charter S	1115 College St	Memphis, TN	38106-2203	901-261-6366	261-6398	6-12	NeShante Brown
Southern Avenue Charter S	2221 Democrat Rd	Memphis, TN	38132	901-743-7335	743-7677	K-5	Katie Jones
Southern Avenue MS	2185 Democrat Rd	Memphis, TN	38132-1802	901-744-6644	744-6645	6-8	Lytania Black
STAR Academy Charter S	3260 James Rd	Memphis, TN	38128-5351	901-387-5050	387-0798	K-5	Angela Holloway
STEM Prep Academy	1162 Foster Ave	Nashville, TN	37210	615-921-2200		5-8	Dr. Kristen McGraner
STEM Prep HS	1162 Foster Ave	Nashville, TN	37210	615-921-2200		9-12	
Strive Collegiate Academy	3055 Lebanon Pike	Nashville, TN	37214	615-645-6440		5-8	Lakendra Butler
Valor Flagship Academy	4527 Nolensville Pike	Nashville, TN	37211	615-823-7982		5-6	Dr. Travis Commons
Valor Voyager Academy	4527 Nolensville Pike	Nashville, TN	37211	615-823-7982		5-8	Sarah Giblin
Veritas College Preparatory Charter S	1500 Dunn Ave	Memphis, TN	38106	901-526-1900	526-1988	6-8	Nick Getschman
Vision Preparatory Charter S	260 Joubert Ave	Memphis, TN	38109-1828	901-775-1018		K-5	Megan Salemi

School	Address	City,State	Zip code	Telephone	Fax	Grade	Contact
Whitney Achievement ES	1219 Whitney Ave	Memphis, TN	38127-7754	901-416-3949	416-3953	PK-5	Debra Broughton
Wooddale MS	3467 Castleman St	Memphis, TN	38118-4538	901-730-4086	794-9002	6-8	Jacob Edwards
Woods Academy of Innovation	3824 Austin Peay Hwy	Memphis, TN	38128-3722	901-800-1209	627-6081	K-8	Effie Jenkins-Smith

Texas

School	Address	City,State	Zip code	Telephone	Fax	Grade	Contact
A+ Academy	10327 Rylie Rd	Dallas, TX	75217-8240	972-557-5578	557-5807	PK-12	Emma Bruce
Abundant Life Christian S	5130 Casey St	La Marque, TX	77568	409-935-8369	935-3337	PK-12	Cynthia Hallam
Academy of Accelerated Learning	6025 Chimney Rock Rd	Houston, TX	77081-4011	713-773-4766	666-2532	PK-5	Doris Robins
Academy of Accelerated Learning	6711 Bellfort St	Houston, TX	77087-6457	713-645-0336	640-2435	PK-5	Doris Robins
Academy of Careers & Technologies	PO Box 681866	San Antonio, TX	78268-1866	210-226-7568	226-8548	9-12	Akenese Iosefo
Academy of Dallas	1030 Oak Park Dr	Dallas, TX	75232-1238	214-371-9600	371-1053	PK-8	Conrad Hargest
Accelerated Learning Center	721 Omaha Dr	Corpus Christi, TX	78408-2839	361-887-7766	887-6035	PK-12	Maria Garza
Advantage Academy - Grand Prairie East	300 W Pioneer Pkwy	Grand Prairie, TX	75051	214-276-5800	276-5890	8-12	Tammy Bailey
Advantage Academy - Grand Prairie West	955 Freetown Rd	Grand Prairie, TX	75051	214-451-2120	602-2212	PK-7	Christy Drekaj
Advantage Academy - North Duncanville	4009 Joseph Hardin Dr	Dallas, TX	75236-1507	214-276-5880	467-9131	PK-8	Darketsha Williams
Advantage Academy - Waxahachie	701 W Highway 287 Byp	Waxahachie, TX	75165-5163	972-451-2107	937-9876	PK-8	Deb Garten
AIA Houston ES	PO Box 20589	Houston, TX	77225-0589	713-728-9330	283-6190	PK-6	LaShawn Hoskins
AIA Lancaster ES	901 E Belt Line Rd	Lancaster, TX	75146	713-283-6298	283-6190	PK-6	LaShawn Hoskins
AIM College & Career Prep	5200 Avenue N 1/2	Galveston, TX	77551-4729	409-761-6302	770-0918	6-12	Jean Fullen
Alamo Leadership Academy	535 New Laredo Hwy	San Antonio, TX	78211-1978	210-922-1687	922-1630	PK-12	Cheryl Stewart
Alief Montessori Community S	4215 H St	Houston, TX	77072-5380	281-530-9406	530-2233	PK-5	Nancy Chieu
Allen Charter S	5220 Nomas St	Dallas, TX	75212-3229	972-794-5100	794-5101	PK-5	Sheila Ortiz Espinell
Alpha Charter S	701 W State St	Garland, TX	75040-6310	972-272-2173	205-9050	PK-12	Micheal Watkins
Altamira Academy	220 Foremost Dr	Austin, TX	78745-7324	512-953-8301		PK-2	Dan Horn
Ambassadors Preparatory Academy	5001 Avenue U	Galveston, TX	77551	409-762-1115	762-1114	PK-8	Dr. Patricia Williams
Amigos Por Vida-Friends for Life Charter	5503 El Camino Del Rey St	Houston, TX	77081-1805	713-349-9945	349-0671	PK-8	Freddy Delgado
Annunciation Home	3610 Shell Rd	Georgetown, TX	78628-9246	512-864-7755		6-12	Holly Engleman
Aristoi Classical Academy	5618 11th St	Katy, TX	77493-1971	281-391-5003	391-5010	K-11	Brenda Davidson
Arlington Classics Academy	2800 W Arkansas Ln	Arlington, TX	76016-5819	817-274-2008	274-8768	K-2	Melissa Fambrough
Arlington Classics Academy Intermediate	5200 S Bowen Rd	Arlington, TX	76017	817-303-1553	549-0246	3-5	Teri Rodgers
Arlington Classics Academy Middle	5200 S Bowen Rd	Arlington, TX	76017-3756	817-987-1819	549-0246	6-8	Kurtis Flood
Athlos Leadership Academy	4955 Pablo Kisel Blvd	Brownsville, TX	78520	956-509-2690	509-2326	PK-12	Yolanda Cantu
Athlos Leadership Academy	4427 Chandler	San Antonio, TX	78222	210-278-3880	278-3929	PK-12	Hector Gomez
Athlos Leadership Academy - Premier	1515 Goliad Rd	San Antonio, TX	78223	866-894-8581		PK-6	Trina Cardenas
Austin Achieve Public S	5908 Manor Rd	Austin, TX	78723-3631	512-522-4190	727-3788	6-12	John Armbrust
Austin Can Academy Charter S	2406 Rosewood Ave	Austin, TX	78702-2408	512-477-4226	931-8034	9-12	Frank Oakes
Austin Discovery S	8509 FM 969 Ste 200	Austin, TX	78724-5771	512-674-0700	674-3133	K-8	Leigh Moss
Austin State University Charter S	PO Box 6072	Nacogdoches, TX	75962-0001	936-468-5899	468-7015	K-5	Lysa Hagan
Baker-Ripley Charter S	6500 Rookin St	Houston, TX	77074	713-273-3731	273-3797	K-5	Raquel Sosa-Gonzalez
Barkley/Ruiz ES	1111 S Navidad St	San Antonio, TX	78207-6000	210-978-7940	227-4029	PK-5	Jackie Ibarra-Lanford M.Ed
BASIS San Antonio Medical Center	8519 Floyd Curl Dr	San Antonio, TX	78240	210-319-5525	877-9214	5-12	David Hubalik
BASIS San Antonio North Central	318 E Ramsey Rd	San Antonio, TX	78216	210-775-4125		5-10	Abigail Hasberry
Beta Academy	9701 Almeda Genoa Rd	Houston, TX	77075	832-331-2460		K-7	Latisha Andrews
Bexar County Academy	1485 Hillcrest Dr	San Antonio, TX	78228-3900	210-432-8600	432-8667	PK-8	Linda Sleeper
Bonham Academy	925 S Saint Marys St	San Antonio, TX	78205-3410	210-228-3300	223-3899	K-8	Will Webber
Brazos River Charter S	PO Box 949	Nemo, TX	76070-0949	254-898-9226	898-2297	K-12	Bengie Laning
Brazos S for Inquiry & Creativity	1055 W Tidwell Rd	Houston, TX	77091-4349	713-681-1960	681-1979	PK-6	Tiffany Rock
Brazos S for Inquiry & Creativity	6400 Southwest Fwy Ste S	Houston, TX	77074	713-952-4300	952-4305	PK-8	Tiffany Rock
Brazos S for Inquiry & Creativity	410 Bethel Ln	Bryan, TX	77802-1005	979-774-5032	774-5039	PK-8	Christopher Osgood
Briscoe ES	2015 S Flores St	San Antonio, TX	78204-1936	210-228-3305	222-0822	PK-6	D'Les Herron
Brooks Academy Oaks	6070 Babcock Rd	San Antonio, TX	78240	210-998-4458		K-5	Sherrell Coleman
Brooks Academy of Science & Engineering	3803 Lyster Rd	San Antonio, TX	78235-5152	210-633-9006	633-9990	K-12	Sherrell Coleman
Brooks Estrella Academy	8005 Outer Circle Rd	San Antonio, TX	78235	210-257-5175		K-6	Bonnie Salas
Brooks International Studies Academy	134 E Lambert St	San Antonio, TX	78204	210-998-4452		K-7	Patricia Lozano-Landry
Brown-Fellowship Leadership Academy	5701 Red Bird Center Dr	Dallas, TX	75237-1917	972-709-4700	635-6635	3-8	Paula Brown
Brown-Fellowship Leadership S	6901 S Westmoreland Rd	Dallas, TX	75237-2431	972-709-4700	709-6605	PK-2	Paula Brown
Brune Charter S	PO Box 399	Leakey, TX	78873-0399	830-232-7101	232-4279	1-12	Dr. Carmen Boatright
Burnham ES	7310 Bishop Flores Dr	El Paso, TX	79912-1429	915-584-9499	585-8814	K-5	Audrey Shetty
Buzbee Vocational HS	143 Forest Service Road 233	New Waverly, TX	77358	936-344-7235	344-6396	9-12	Will Gollihar
Cailloux-Najim S	PO Box 609	Ingram, TX	78025	830-367-6100	367-2611	1-12	Kelly Bluemel
Calallen Charter HS	46 Cornett Dr	Corpus Christi, TX	78410	361-242-5980	242-5682	10-12	L. Duke
Carpe Diem Innovative S	8038 W Military Dr	San Antonio, TX	78227	210-774-9284		6-12	Valerie Robertson
Carrollton Classical Academy	2400 N Josey Ln	Carrollton, TX	75006-1617	972-245-2900	245-2999	K-5	Stephanie Scott
Cedar Hill Collegiate HS	1515 W Belt Line Rd	Cedar Hill, TX	75104-1603	469-272-2021	293-2652	9-12	Corey Seymour
Cedar Park Charter Academy	201 Buttercup Creek Blvd	Cedar Park, TX	78613	512-331-2980	590-8721	PK-12	Michele Kelsay
Cedars International Academy	8416 N Interstate 35	Austin, TX	78753-6438	512-419-1551	419-1581	PK-8	Heather Rauls
Cedars International HS	6700 Middle Fiskville Rd	Austin, TX	78752	512-956-4406		9-12	
Champions Academy	2113 Cypress Landing Dr	Houston, TX	77090	832-446-6762		K-5	Venora Goodie
Chaparral Star Academy	14046 Summit Dr	Austin, TX	78728-7115	512-989-2672	251-9799	K-12	Marsha Hagin
Chapel Hill Academy	4640 Sycamore School Rd	Fort Worth, TX	76133-7356	817-289-0242	289-3657	PK-5	Victoria Sendejo M.Ed.
Chavez Academy	4613 S Padre Island Dr	Corpus Christi, TX	78411-4413	361-561-5651	561-5654	9-12	Sandra Valencia
Cityscape S	6211 E Grand Ave	Dallas, TX	75223-1425	214-824-4747	824-4447	PK-5	Carol Thorne
Clay Academy	3303 Potters House Way	Dallas, TX	75236-3037	214-467-4143	467-4143	K-8	Ericka Johnson-Allen
Clear Horizons Early College HS	13735 Beamer Rd Box 913	Houston, TX	77089	281-929-4657	284-9960	9-12	Dr. Brett Lemley
Clear View HS	400 S Walnut St	Webster, TX	77598-5120	281-284-1500	284-1505	9-12	Michael Houston
Coastal Village ES	721 10th St	Galveston, TX	77550	409-761-6800	765-5674	PK-4	Cherie Spencer
Coastal Village MS	1110 21st St	Galveston, TX	77550	409-761-6900		5-8	Cherie Spencer
Collegiate HS	101 Baldwin Blvd	Corpus Christi, TX	78404-3805	361-698-2425	698-2427	9-12	Tracie Rodriguez
Compass Academy Charter S	1111 Pagewood Ave	Odessa, TX	79761	432-332-9896	332-8667	PK-12	Mackenzie Atkins
Comquest Academy	207 Peach St	Tomball, TX	77375-4733	281-516-0611	516-9807	7-12	Tanis Stanfield
C.O.R.E. Academy	12707 Cullen Blvd	Houston, TX	77047-2849	713-457-2858		3-9	Nolan Jeffery
Corinth Classical Academy	3600 Meadowview Dr	Corinth, TX	76210	940-497-0148		K-7	Aimee Giacumakis
Cornerstone Academy	8655 Emnora Ln	Houston, TX	77080-6203	713-251-1600	251-1615	6-8	Jill Wright
Corpus Christi College Prep HS	3501 S Padre Island Dr	Corpus Christi, TX	78415-2908	361-225-4240	561-5654	9-12	Stephen Mora
Corpus Christi Montessori S	822 Ayers St	Corpus Christi, TX	78404	361-852-0707	653-2340	PK-8	Cerise Weeks
Cove Charter Academy	2205 FM 3046	Copperas Cove, TX	76522	254-238-8231	247-3931	PK-12	Dr. Mike Anderson
Crosstimbers Academy	PO Box 1327	Weatherford, TX	76086-1327	817-594-6220	594-6227	9-12	David Vance
Cumberland Academy	1340 Shiloh Rd	Tyler, TX	75703	903-581-2890	581-1476	K-5	Andrew Griffith
Cumberland Academy HS	7200 Paluxy Dr	Tyler, TX	75703	903-630-7670		9-12	Kathy Parker
Cumberland Academy MS	1040 Shiloh Rd	Tyler, TX	75703	903-581-2890	581-1476	6-8	Tim Schodowski
Dallas Can Academy Carrollton/Farmers	2720 Hollandale Ln	Farmers Branch, TX	75234-2035	972-243-2178	243-2669	9-12	Amparo Hakemack
Dallas Can Academy - Grant East	2901 Morgan Dr	Dallas, TX	75241-6516	972-228-4226		9-12	Rodney Milliner
Dallas Can Academy - Oak Cliff	325 W 12th St	Dallas, TX	75208-6502	214-943-2244	946-4427	9-12	Faustino Rivas
Dallas Can Academy - Pleasant Grove	1227 N Masters Dr	Dallas, TX	75217-3722	972-225-1194	225-1164	9-12	Mene Khepera
Dallas Can Academy Ross Avenue	4621 Ross Ave	Dallas, TX	75204-4994	214-824-4226	841-7951	9-12	Fernando Vadillo
Da Vinci S for Science and the Arts	785 Southwestern Dr	El Paso, TX	79912-1240	915-584-4024	581-9840	6-12	Richard Harrid
Denton Classical Academy	4420 Country Club Rd	Denton, TX	76210	940-565-8333	919-5316	K-1	Susan Thomas
DePelchin - Richmond Campus	710 S 7th St	Richmond, TX	77469-3445	281-342-4906		K-12	Michael McKenzie
Draw Academy	3920 Stoney Brook Dr	Houston, TX	77063-6406	713-706-3729	706-3711	PK-8	Fernando Donatti
Early College HS	3939 Valley View Ln	Farmers Branch, TX	75244-4906	972-968-6200	968-6210	9-12	Michael Arreola
East Austin College Prep Academy	6002 Jain Ln	Austin, TX	78721	512-287-5000	928-1440	2-6	Jamie Eubanks
East Austin College Prep - MLK Campus	5800 E MLK Blvd	Austin, TX	78721-1737	512-287-5050		7-12	Dr. Ruben Pena
East Fort Worth Montessori Academy	501 Oakland Blvd	Fort Worth, TX	76103-1014	817-496-3003	496-3004	PK-5	Shello Tabb
East Texas Charter S Chadwick Campus	2402 Alpine Rd	Longview, TX	75601	903-753-9400	753-0285	9-12	Terry Lapic
Eden Park Academy	6215 Manchaca Rd Bldg D	Austin, TX	78745-4927	512-383-0613	383-0665	K-6	Johnnie Smith
Edinburg Classical Academy	2110 S McColl Rd	Edinburg, TX	78539	956-720-4361	720-4361	K-8	Dr. Alicia Luna
Education Center International Academy	201 N Erby Campbell Blvd	Royse City, TX	75189	972-636-2600	628-9124	K-8	Tonya Harris
Education Center International Academy	302 N Town East Blvd	Sunnyvale, TX	75182	214-628-9152	628-9124	K-8	Laverna Greenlee
Education Center International Academy	8200 Schrade Rd	Rowlett, TX	75088-4716	972-412-8080	628-9124	K-8	Lisa Hiatt
Ehrhart S	PO Box 7733	Beaumont, TX	77726-7733	409-839-8200	839-8242	PK-8	Corina Long
El Paso Academy East	11000 Argal Ct	El Paso, TX	79935-3712	915-590-8589	590-0052	9-12	Lionel Rubio
El Paso Academy West	201 W Redd Rd	El Paso, TX	79932-1903	915-845-7997	845-7522	9-12	Toni Kreye
El Paso Leadership Academy	1918 Texas Ave	El Paso, TX	79901-1917	915-298-3900		6-8	Omar Yanar
Energized for Excellence Academy	6107 Bissonnet St	Houston, TX	77081	713-773-3600	773-3630	6-8	Arlene Kho
Energized For Excellence ECC	7419 Ashcroft Dr	Houston, TX	77081-6801	713-773-3600	773-3630	PK-PK	Ada Cooper
Energized For Excellence ES	6107 Bissonnet St	Houston, TX	77081-6807	713-773-3600	773-3630	K-5	Jose Cintron
Energized for STEM Academy Central	9220 Jutland Rd	Houston, TX	77033-3905	713-773-3600	773-3630	9-12	Dr. Shavon Clark
Energized For STEM Academy HS West	7419 Ashcroft Dr	Houston, TX	77081-6801	713-773-3600	773-3630	9-12	Shavon Clark
Energized for STEM Academy MS Central	6107 Bissonnet	Houston, TX	77081	713-773-3600	773-3630	6-8	Adrienne Henderson
Energized for STEM Academy West	6107 Bissonnet St	Houston, TX	77081-6807	713-773-3600	773-3630	6-8	Ranier Perez
Evolution Academy Charter S	2414 Spring Cypress Rd	Spring, TX	77388	972-907-3755	907-3605	9-12	Julia Askew
Evolution Academy Charter S	3920 W Cardinal Dr	Beaumont, TX	77705	409-239-5553		9-12	
Evolution Academy Charter S	1101 S Sherman St	Richardson, TX	75081-4852	972-907-3755	907-3765	9-12	Cynthia Jones Trigg
Excel Center	1015 Norwood Park Blvd	Austin, TX	78753	512-531-5500	339-5299	9-12	Theresa Terlik
Excellence in Leadership Academy	915 W Expressway 83	Mission, TX	78572	956-424-9504	585-4673	PK-6	Elizabeth B. Lopez
Focus Learning Academy	2524 W Ledbetter Dr	Dallas, TX	75233	214-467-7751	709-1111	PK-10	Phyllis Johnson

School	Address	City,State	Zip code	Telephone	Fax	Grade	Contact
Ford Academy Alameda S for Art & Design	318 W Houston St	San Antonio, TX	78205-2427	210-226-4031	271-0125	9-12	Wayne Boggs
Fort Worth Academy of Fine Arts	3901 S Hulen St	Fort Worth, TX	76109-3321	817-924-1482	926-9932	3-12	Randy Dean
Fort Worth Can Academy	6620 Westcreek Dr	Fort Worth, TX	76133	817-531-3223		9-12	Ku-Masi Lewis
Fort Worth Can Academy South Campus	1316 E Lancaster Ave	Fort Worth, TX	76102-6634	817-735-1515	735-1465	9-12	William Arevelo
Founders Classical Academy	500 Parker Sq	Flower Mound, TX	75028-7431	972-899-2521		K-5	Sam Vanderplas
Founders Classical Academy	790 Windbell Cir	Mesquite, TX	75149-3116	214-444-7255		K-8	Dr. Shannon Nason
Founders Classical Academy in Dallas	8510 Military Pkwy	Dallas, TX	75227	469-607-6277		K-8	Matthew Stone M.Ed.
Founders Classical Academy in Lewisville	1010 Bellaire Blvd	Lewisville, TX	75067-5650	469-464-3415	524-9980	K-12	Jason Caros
Founders Classical Academy of Leander	1303 Leander Dr	Leander, TX	78641-2037	512-259-0103	532-6503	K-12	Kathleen Arnn
Founders Classical Academy of Schertz	8453 E 1518 N	Schertz, TX	78154	210-510-2618		K-7	Nathanael Rea
Frank Inspire Academy	11216 Bandera Rd	San Antonio, TX	78250-6800	210-638-5900		K-8	Christopher Duke
Garcia Early College HS	5241 University Blvd	Laredo, TX	78041	956-273-7700	795-8185	9-12	Israel Castilla
Garland Can Academy	2256 Arapaho Rd	Garland, TX	75044	972-441-7202		9-12	Dr. Daniel Johnson
Garza-Gonzales Charter S	4129 Greenwood Dr	Corpus Christi, TX	78416-1841	361-881-9988	881-9994	PK-12	Adolfo Chapa
Gateway Academy Sierra Vista	4620 S Lucy	Laredo, TX	78046	956-723-0345	712-1112	9-12	Odie Arambula
Gateway Academy Townlake	1230 Townlake Dr	Laredo, TX	78041-3786	956-722-0747	722-0767	9-12	Raymundo Gonzalez
Gateway Charter Academy	6103 Houston School Rd	Dallas, TX	75241	214-375-2039	375-1842	PK-12	Raymond Edwards
Gateway College Prep S	3360 Westinghouse Rd	Georgetown, TX	78626	512-868-4947	868-4946	K-12	Alan Santucci
Gateway Tech HS	2951 Williams Dr	Georgetown, TX	78628	512-868-5299	868-3744	9-12	Annette Stevenson
GCCLR Institute of Technology	4125 Greenwood Dr	Corpus Christi, TX	78416	361-881-9988	814-1687	PK-12	Adolfo Chapa
Georgetown Charter Academy	302 Serenada Dr	Georgetown, TX	78628-1628	512-863-9236	863-9290	PK-12	Josiah Perkins
Gervin Academy	6944 S Sunbelt Dr	San Antonio, TX	78218-3335	210-568-8800	568-8897	PK-12	Jesse Villanueva M.Ed.
Gervin Technology Center	3030 E Commerce St	San Antonio, TX	78220-1013	210-587-3576	587-3587	10-12	Dorothy Wendorf
Golden Rule Charter S Cockrell Hill	2602 W Illinois Ave	Dallas, TX	75233	214-333-9330	333-9325	PK-8	Jim Wright
Golden Rule Charter S DeSoto	135 W Wintergreen Rd	DeSoto, TX	75115	469-248-4463	248-4471	PK-5	Tonja Frazier
Golden Rule Charter S Grand Prairie	1729 Avenue B	Grand Prairie, TX	75051	214-333-9330	333-9325	PK-6	Jim Wright
Golden Rule Charter S Oak Cliff	2602 W Illinois Ave	Dallas, TX	75233-1002	214-333-9330	333-9325	PK-12	Vicente Delgado
Golden Rule Charter S Pleasant Grove	2602 W Illinois Ave	Dallas, TX	75233	469-341-5783	333-9325	PK-4	Diana Lara
GPISD Uplift at Lee ES	401 E Grand Prairie Rd	Grand Prairie, TX	75051-1945	972-262-6785		K-2	Dani Erbert
Grand Prairie Collegiate Institute	401 E Grand Prairie Rd	Grand Prairie, TX	75051-1945	972-343-3120	343-3159	6-12	Jennifer Ellison
Grand Preparatory S	300 E Church St	Grand Prairie, TX	75050	972-854-0600		K-8	Allen Anderson
Great Hearts Irving	3350 W Story Rd	Irving, TX	75038	469-759-3030		K-8	Philip Althage
Great Hearts Monte Vista	319 E Mulberry Ave	San Antonio, TX	78212	210-888-9485	888-9484	6-9	Peter Crawford
Great Hearts Monte Vista South	211 Belknap Pl	San Antonio, TX	78212	210-888-9485		K-5	Mandi Cannon
Great Hearts Northern Oaks	17223 Jones Maltsberger Rd	San Antonio, TX	78247	210-888-9843		K-8	Trinette Keffer
Hampton Preparatory S	8915 S Hampton Rd	Dallas, TX	75232-6002	972-421-1982	421-1986	K-12	Brady Cooper
Harlingen Leadership Academy	4501 W Expressway 83	Harlingen, TX	78552-3604	956-364-2456	364-2453	PK-5	Cindy Sadler
Harmony S of Achievement	16209 Kieth Harrow Blvd	Houston, TX	77084	281-855-2500	656-8525	K-5	Melissa Knight
Harmony S of Advancement	3171 N Sam Houston Pkwy W	Houston, TX	77038	281-741-8899	741-8006	9-12	Faith Oner
Harmony S of Business-Dallas	8080 President George Bush	Dallas, TX	75252	214-321-0100	919-4352	K-12	Muhammed Gecit
Harmony S of Discovery	6270 Barker Cypress Rd	Houston, TX	77084-1628	281-861-5105	656-8525	K-10	Adnan Karanci
Harmony S of Excellence	2015 SW Loop 410	San Antonio, TX	78227-2534	210-645-7166	645-7178	K-12	Bambi Teaff
Harmony School of Excellence	7340 Gessner Rd	Houston, TX	77040-3144	713-983-8668	983-8667	K-12	Hasan Sazci
Harmony S of Excellence - Austin	2100 E Saint Elmo Rd	Austin, TX	78744	512-693-0000	693-0008	K-12	Engin Dogan
Harmony S of Excellence - Dallas	1024 W Rosemeade Pkwy	Carrollton, TX	75007	469-892-5556	892-5667	6-12	Huseyin Sari
Harmony S of Excellence El Paso	9435 Betel Dr	El Paso, TX	79907	915-307-4412	307-4772	K-8	
Harmony S of Excellence-Endeavor	5668 W Little York Rd	Houston, TX	77091-1123	281-999-8400	999-8404	K-12	Kamil Yilmaz
Harmony S of Exploration	9305 W Sam Houston Pkwy S	Houston, TX	77099	713-831-7406	831-7408	K-3	Nora Morales
Harmony S of Fine Arts and Technology	9115 Kirby Dr	Houston, TX	77054	832-433-7001	433-7083	K-9	Alain Frankiewicz
Harmony S of Ingenuity	10555 Stella Link Rd	Houston, TX	77025	713-664-1020	664-1025	K-12	Recep Yilmaz
Harmony S of Innovation	13522 W Airport Blvd	Sugar Land, TX	77498	281-302-6445	302-6745	7-12	Alpaslan Uzgoren
Harmony S of Innovation	9421 W Sam Houston Pkwy S	Houston, TX	77099-1898	713-541-3030	541-3032	PK-8	Ali Yilmaz
Harmony S of Innovation - Austin	2124 E Saint Elmo Rd	Austin, TX	78744	512-300-0895	330-4225	K-5	Tiffany Molina
Harmony S of Innovation - Dallas	1024 W Rosemeade Pkwy	Carrollton, TX	75007	469-892-5556	892-5667	K-12	Clinton Barnes
Harmony S of Innovation - El Paso	5210 Fairbanks Dr	El Paso, TX	79924	915-757-2929	757-2202	K-12	Riza Gurlek
Harmony S of Innovation - Euless	701 S Industrial Blvd # 115	Euless, TX	76040	817-554-2800	684-9405	K-4	Crystal McAnalley
Harmony S of Innovation-Fort Worth	8100 S Hulen St	Fort Worth, TX	76123	817-386-5505	977-1727	6-12	Mehmet Basoglu
Harmony S of Innovation - Garland	2250 Firewheel Pkwy	Garland, TX	75040	469-814-0059	814-0579	6-12	Murat Tunca
Harmony S of Innovation-Laredo	4608 Daugherty Ave	Laredo, TX	78041	956-568-9495	568-9490	K-12	Gelaldine Salas
Harmony S of Innovation - San Antonio	8125 Glen Mont	San Antonio, TX	78239	210-265-1715	265-5364	K-8	Mert Aykanat
Harmony S of Nature & Athletics	8120 W Camp Wisdom Rd	Dallas, TX	75249-4402	972-296-1000	296-2125	K-12	Bilal Ozen
Harmony S of Political Science	13415 Ranch Road 620 N	Austin, TX	78717	512-284-9880	284-9632	K-8	Ilker Yimaz
Harmony S of Science	5435 S Braeswood Blvd	Houston, TX	77096-4001	713-729-4400	729-6600	K-8	Mehmet Subas
Harmony S of Science - Austin	11800 Stonehollow Dr # 100	Austin, TX	78758	512-821-1700	821-1702	K-8	Allanur Agaberdiyev
Harmony S of Technology	3203 N Sam Houston Pkwy W	Houston, TX	77038	281-444-1555	444-1015	K-8	Sezgin Aydi
Harmony Science Academy	13415 W Bellfort Ave	Sugar Land, TX	77478	713-265-2525	265-2565	PK-6	Afreem Merchant
Harmony Science Academy - Austin	930 E Rundberg Ln	Austin, TX	78753-4826	512-835-7900	835-7901	6-12	Kyle Borel
Harmony Science Academy - Beaumont	4055 Calder Ave	Beaumont, TX	77706-4925	409-838-4000	838-4009	PK-12	Klediol Murati
Harmony Science Academy - Brownsville	1124 Central Blvd	Brownsville, TX	78520	956-574-9555	574-9558	PK-12	Mustafa Altindag
Harmony Science Academy - Bryan	2031 S Texas Ave	Bryan, TX	77802-1834	979-779-2100	779-2110	PK-8	Mehmet Uguz
Harmony Science Academy - Dallas	12005 Forestgate Dr	Dallas, TX	75243	214-954-7277	954-7277	PK-12	Serif Mercan
Harmony Science Academy - El Paso	9405 Betel Dr	El Paso, TX	79907-3457	915-859-4620	859-4630	K-12	Selcuk Bakir
Harmony Science Academy - Euless	701 S Industrial Blvd # 115	Euless, TX	76040	817-354-3000	354-3008	5-12	Maksat Altiyev
Harmony Science Academy - Fort Worth	5651 Westcreek Dr	Fort Worth, TX	76133-2248	817-263-0700	263-0705	K-12	Serena Jackson
Harmony Science Academy - Garland	2302 Firewheel Pkwy	Garland, TX	75040	972-212-4777	212-4778	K-5	Jennifer Hornsby
Harmony Science Academy - Grand Prairie	1102 NW 7th St	Grand Prairie, TX	75050	972-642-9911	642-9922	K-12	Angela Knapp
Harmony Science Academy HS	9431 W Sam Houston Pkwy S	Houston, TX	77099	713-492-0214	383-2839	9-12	
Harmony Science Academy - Katy	22400 Grand Corner Dr	Katy, TX	77494	832-437-3926	437-3927	K-5	Jasmeen Kohli
Harmony Science Academy - Laredo	4401 San Francisco Ave	Laredo, TX	78041-4663	956-712-1177	712-1188	K-12	Mustafa Ayik
Harmony Science Academy - Lubbock	1516 53rd St	Lubbock, TX	79412-2916	806-747-1000	747-1005	K-12	Hakan Simsek
Harmony Science Academy - North Austin	1421 Wells Branch Pkwy #200	Pflugerville, TX	78660	512-251-5000	251-5001	6-12	Fr. Bunyamin Bozdogan
Harmony Science Academy - Odessa	2755 N Grandview Ave	Odessa, TX	79762-6952	432-363-6000	363-6001	K-12	Cetin Demir
Harmony Science Academy - San Antonio	8505 Lakeside Pkwy	San Antonio, TX	78245	210-674-7788	674-7766	K-12	Yasar Cakir
Harmony Science Academy - Waco	1900 N Valley Mills Dr	Waco, TX	76710-2559	254-751-7878	751-7877	K-12	Serkan Beyhan
Harris MS	325 Pruitt Ave	San Antonio, TX	78204-2598	210-228-1220	226-9448	6-8	Dr. Carol Velazquez
Harvest Preparatory Academy	17770 Imperial Valley Dr	Houston, TX	77060	832-446-3138	446-6362	K-6	Michael Blackshire
Hawthorne Academy	115 W Josephine St	San Antonio, TX	78212-4125	210-738-9795	733-1495	K-8	Guadalupe Rodriguez
Heights Preparatory Charter S	2806 Canada Dr	Dallas, TX	75212	214-442-7094	442-7099	K-12	Andrew Baca
Helping Hands Charter S	2200 E 6th St	Austin, TX	78702-3457	512-538-0177	232-9177	K-7	Holly Engleman
Heritage Academy	8750 Fourwinds Dr	San Antonio, TX	78239	210-593-0111		PK-5	Lois Chapa
Highland Park ES	635 Rigsby Ave	San Antonio, TX	78210-3099	210-228-3335	533-8132	PK-5	Dr. Rose Engelbrecht
Highland Park Gifted & Talented Academy	901 E Drexel Ave	San Antonio, TX	78210-3105	210-293-4206	532-3810	PK-6	Martha Kizer
High Point Academy	1256 N Jim Wright Fwy	Wht Settlemt, TX	76108-1048	817-600-6401		K-10	Katie Stellar
Hope ES	4301 32nd St	Port Arthur, TX	77642	409-983-3244	983-6408	PK-5	Bobby Lopez
Hope S	2849 9th Ave	Port Arthur, TX	77642-3961	409-983-3244	983-6408	6-12	Bobby Lopez
Horizon Montessori III - Harlingen	2802 S 77 Sunshine Strip	Harlingen, TX	78550	956-423-8200	423-8207	PK-7	Dr. Patricia Quesada
Horizon Montessori II - Weslaco	1222 W Sugar Cane Dr	Weslaco, TX	78599-3892	956-969-0044	969-0065	PK-8	Valerie Uresti-Reyes
Horizon Montessori I - Mc Allen	221 N Main St	McAllen, TX	78501	956-668-1400	668-1404	PK-8	John Gonzalez
Houston A+ Challenge	2700 Southwest Frwy Ste B	Houston, TX	77098	832-519-9590	840-5616	6-8	Dr. Scott Van Beck
Houston A+ Up University	2700 Southwest Frwy Ste B	Houston, TX	77098	832-519-9590	840-5616	6-8	Gabrielle Gunn
Houston Can Academy - Hobby	9020 Gulf Fwy	Houston, TX	77017-7007	832-379-4226	944-6736	9-12	Yardley Williams
Houston Can Academy - North	3401 Hardy St	Houston, TX	77009-5928	713-659-4226	651-1493	9-12	Roslyn Philpott
Houston Can Academy Southwest	9745 Bissonett Dr Bldg D	Houston, TX	77036	281-931-4324		9-12	Dr. James Troutman
Houston Gateway Acad - Elite Coll Prep	7310 Bowie St	Houston, TX	77012-2904	832-649-2700	649-3092	PK-8	Tiffany Wright
Houston Gateway Academy - Coral Campus	1020 Coral St	Houston, TX	77012-2906	832-649-2700	649-3092	PK-12	Ignacio Arroyo
Houston Gateway Academy - Evergreen	3400 Evergreen Dr	Houston, TX	77087-3715	713-644-8292	649-3092	PK-8	Yuridia Lubiano
Houston Heights HS	1125 Lawrence St	Houston, TX	77008-6651	713-868-9797	868-9750	9-12	Richard Mik
Houston State Univ Charter S	7410 Fry Rd	Cypress, TX	77433	936-294-1103	294-1102	PK-6	Dr. Stacey Edmonson
Huston Academy	680 Peach Orchard Rd	Stephenville, TX	76401-4938	254-965-8883	965-8654	7-12	Carol Taylor
IDEA Academy Alamo	325 State Highway 495	Alamo, TX	78516-6877	956-588-4005	588-4006	K-5	Ana Garza
IDEA Academy Allan	1701 Vargas Rd	Austin, TX	78741	512-646-2800	646-2801	PK-10	Disha Jain
IDEA Academy Brownsville	4395 Paredes Line Rd	Brownsville, TX	78526-1296	956-832-5150	832-5716	K-5	Erica Matamoros
IDEA Academy Carver	217 Robinson Pl	San Antonio, TX	78202-2751	210-223-8885	223-8970	K-5	Guadalupe Diaz
IDEA Academy Donna	401 S 1st St	Donna, TX	78537-3055	956-464-0203	464-8532	PK-5	Sylvia Verdooran
IDEA Academy Eastside	2519 Martin Luther King Dr	San Antonio, TX	78203	210-239-4800	239-4801	K-6	Deion Brown
IDEA Academy Edinburg	2553 N Roegiers Rd	Edinburg, TX	78541-8602	956-287-6100	287-6101	PK-5	Nora Perez
IDEA Academy Frontier	2800 S Dakota Ave	Brownsville, TX	78521-6133	956-541-2002	541-5561	K-5	Dora Villegas
IDEA Academy McAllen	201 N Bentsen Rd	McAllen, TX	78501-8297	956-429-4100	429-4126	K-5	Cassandra Flores
IDEA Academy Mission	1600 S Schuerbach Rd	Mission, TX	78572	956-583-8315	424-3248	K-5	C. Cavazos-Escamilla
IDEA Academy Monterrey Park	222 SW 39th St	San Antonio, TX	78237-1765	210-239-4200		K-3	Martha Short
IDEA Academy North Mission	201 N Bentsen Rd	McAllen, TX	78501	956-424-4300		K-6	Cassandra Flores
IDEA Academy Pharr	600 E Las Milpas Rd	Pharr, TX	78577-9864	956-283-1515	783-1557	PK-5	Sonia Aguilar
IDEA Academy Riverview	30 Palm Blvd	Brownsville, TX	78520	956-832-5900	832-5901	PK-7	Radha Guajardo
IDEA Academy Rundberg	9504 N IH 35	Austin, TX	78753	512-822-4800	822-4801	K-7	Karen Weissinger
IDEA Academy San Benito	2151 Russell Ln	San Benito, TX	78586-8969	956-399-5252	361-9478	K-5	Tricia Noyola
IDEA Academy San Juan	200 N Nebraska Ave	San Juan, TX	78589	956-702-5150	702-4497	K-5	Melissa Finch
IDEA Academy South Flores	6919 S Flores St	San Antonio, TX	78221-1943	210-239-4150		K-5	Hailey McCarthy

School	Address	City,State	Zip code	Telephone	Fax	Grade	Contact
IDEA Academy Walzem	6445 Walzem Rd	San Antonio, TX	78239	210-239-4600	239-4601	K-4	Ryane Burke
IDEA Academy Weslaco	2931 E Sugar Cane Dr	Weslaco, TX	78599-2723	956-351-4100	351-4101	K-5	Jayne Pocquette
IDEA Academy Weslaco Pike	1000 E Pike Blvd	Weslaco, TX	78596	956-351-4850	351-4851	PK-8	Silvia Martinez
IDEA Bluff Springs Academy	1700 E Slaughter Ln	Austin, TX	78744	512-822-4200		K-6	Roberta Rivas
IDEA College Prep Alamo	325 State Highway 495	Alamo, TX	78516-6877	956-588-4005	588-4006	6-12	Israel Ybarra
IDEA College Prep Allan	220 Foremost Dr	Austin, TX	78745	512-646-2800	646-2801	6-12	Nathan Lowry
IDEA College Prep Bluff Springs	1700 E Slaughter Ln	Austin, TX	78744	512-822-4200		6-6	DeAnna Bruce
IDEA College Prep Brownsville	4395 Paredes Line Rd	Brownsville, TX	78526	956-832-5150	832-5716	6-12	Marco Lopez
IDEA College Prep Carver	217 Robinson Pl	San Antonio, TX	78202-2751	210-223-8885	223-8970	6-12	Chang John Yu
IDEA College Prep Donna	401 S 1st St	Donna, TX	78537-3055	956-464-0203	464-8532	6-12	Amanda Canales
IDEA College Prep Edinburg	2553 N Roegiers Rd	Edinburg, TX	78541-8602	956-287-6100	287-6101	6-12	Ramiro Gomez
IDEA College Prep Frontier	2800 S Dakota Ave	Brownsville, TX	78521	956-541-2002	541-5561	6-12	Dora Villegas
IDEA College Prep Judson	13427 Judson Rd	San Antonio, TX	78233	210-529-3600		6-6	Joaquin Hernandez
IDEA College Prep Mays	1210 Horal Rd	San Antonio, TX	78245	210-529-3200		6-6	Gerald Boyd
IDEA College Prep McAllen	201 N Bentsen Rd	McAllen, TX	78501-8297	956-429-4100	429-4126	6-12	Jon Alvarez
IDEA College Prep Mission	1600 S Schuerbach Rd	Mission, TX	78572-1217	956-583-8315	424-3248	6-12	Yvonne Anglada
IDEA College Prep Monterrey Park	222 SW 39th St	San Antonio, TX	78237-1765	210-239-4200		6-6	Curtis Lawrence
IDEA College Prep Pharr	600 E Las Milpas Rd	Pharr, TX	78577-9864	956-283-1515	783-1557	6-12	Claudia Ash
IDEA College Prep San Benito	2151 Russell Ln	San Benito, TX	78586-8969	956-399-5252	361-9478	6-12	Joel Garcia
IDEA College Prep San Juan	600 E Sioux Rd	San Juan, TX	78589-3491	956-588-4021	588-4030	6-12	Andrea Lopez
IDEA College Prep South Flores	6919 S Flores St	San Antonio, TX	78221-1943	210-239-4150		6-8	Constantine Polites
IDEA College Prep Toros	315 E Palm Dr	Edinburg, TX	78539	956-351-4350		9-12	Brad Scott
IDEA College Prep Walzem	6445 Walzem Rd	San Antonio, TX	78239	210-239-4600	239-4601	K-8	Dr. Khalil Graham
IDEA College Prep Weslaco	2931 E Sugar Cane Dr	Weslaco, TX	78599	956-351-4100	351-4101	6-12	Leanna Sarinana
IDEA College Prep Weslaco Pike	1000 E Pike Blvd	Weslaco, TX	78596	956-351-4850	351-4851	6-8	Stephanie Sullenger
IDEA Judson Academy	13427 Judson Rd	San Antonio, TX	78233	210-529-3600		K-2	Hope Williams
IDEA Mays Academy	1210 Horal Dr	San Antonio, TX	78245	210-529-3200		K-2	Carmen Sepulveda
IDEA Quest Academy	14001 N Rooth Rd	Edinburg, TX	78541-4194	956-287-1003	287-2737	K-5	Rosa Chapa
IDEA Quest College Prep S	14001 N Rooth Rd	Edinburg, TX	78541-4194	956-287-1003	287-2737	6-12	Jose De Leon
Imagine International Academy	2860 Virginia Pkwy	Mc Kinney, TX	75071	214-491-1500	491-1504	K-12	Don Menzies
Infinity Preparatory S	1401 S MacArthur Blvd	Irving, TX	75060	469-621-9200		K-11	Mark Foreman
Innovation Academy	3900 University Blvd	Tyler, TX	75799	903-730-3988	617-6814	3-9	Aimee Dennis
Innovation Academy	3201 N Eastman Rd	Longview, TX	75605-5026	903-686-0018	617-6814	3-8	Angela Ladine
Innovation Academy	1820 W Spring St	Palestine, TX	75803-7900	903-480-4070	480-4070	3-8	Becky Rutledge
Inspired for Excellence Academy West	12525 Fondren Rd	Houston, TX	77035	832-834-5295	641-1669	5-8	Leatha Gilmore
Inspired Vision Academy MSHS	8501 Bruton Rd	Dallas, TX	75217-1909	972-285-5758	285-0061	7-12	Nick Kongamnach
Inspired Vision Charter ES	8421 Bohannon Dr	Dallas, TX	75217-1917	214-391-7964	391-7954	PK-6	Dr. Lana Sprayberry-King
International Leadership of Texas ES	3501 S Great Southwest Pkwy	Grand Prairie, TX	75052	469-348-7960		K-8	Valerie Layne
International Leadership of Texas ES	4131 Rufe Snow Dr	N Richlnd Hls, TX	76180	817-345-0926		K-8	Lilia Vasquez
International Leadership of Texas ES	24406 Franz Rd	Katy, TX	77493	281-394-9417		K-8	Dr. Raul Hinojosa
International Leadership of Texas ES	17000 Katy Fwy	Houston, TX	77094	281-599-8004		K-8	Maria Gomez-Rocque M.Ed
International Leadership of Texas ES	3301 N Shiloh Rd	Garland, TX	75044	972-414-8000	495-2405	K-8	Irene Aguilar
International Leadership of Texas ES	4950 S Bowen Rd	Arlington, TX	76017	817-419-9281		K-8	Antonio Verduzco
International Leadership of Texas HS	4413 N Shiloh Rd	Garland, TX	75044	972-414-3414		9-12	Anthony Palagonia
International Leadership of Texas HS	2851 Ragland Rd	Grand Prairie, TX	75052	682-808-5960		9-12	Quentyn Seamster
International Leadership of Texas-Keller	4201 Heritage Trace Pkwy	Fort Worth, TX	76244	817-431-5135	562-8933	9-12	Rodney Cooksy
International Leadership of Texas-Keller	2301 Heritage Trace Pkwy	Fort Worth, TX	76177	817-665-0646	232-8220	K-8	Dr. Dora Renaud
Irving MS	1300 Delgado St	San Antonio, TX	78207-1467	210-738-9740	734-0941	6-8	Dr. Verenice Gutierrez
iSchoolHigh Amarillo	6000 S Georgia St	Amarillo, TX	79118	806-352-0171	397-5456	9-12	Michael Griffin
ISchool High at the Woodlands	3232 College Park Dr	The Woodlands, TX	77384-4500	936-231-8594	861-3810	9-12	
iSchoolHigh Hickory Creek	800 Point Vista Rd Ste 518	Hickory Creek, TX	75065	940-247-2777		9-12	Aaron Wimberly
iSchool STEM	1800 Lakeway Dr Ste 100	Lewisville, TX	75057-6438	972-317-2470	397-1633	9-12	Stephanie Scott
iSchool University Park	20515 State Highway 249	Houston, TX	77070-2764	281-251-5770	643-9673	9-12	Mike Laird
Kandy Stripe Academy	8701 Delilah St	Houston, TX	77033-3827	713-734-4909	731-7890	PK-8	Cassandra Anderson
Kauffman Leadership Academy	314 W Wilson St	Cleburne, TX	76033	682-459-2800		6-12	Dr. Theresa Kauffman
Kelley Charter S	802 Oblate Dr	San Antonio, TX	78216-7330	210-431-9881	253-2198	PK-6	Kathryn Zanin
KI Charter Academy	120 Bert Brown St	San Marcos, TX	78666-5803	512-396-8500	754-3894	1-12	Jerry Lager
King Academy	3501 Martin Luther King Dr	San Antonio, TX	78220-2325	210-978-7935	223-6907	K-8	Natasha Pinnix
Kingsland S	136 Real St	Kingsland, TX	78639	325-388-0020		K-6	Meloni Puishes
Kingsway Leadership Academy	1727 Senator Carlos Truan	Kingsville, TX	78363-6672	210-221-2591	221-2594	PK-8	Noemy Garcia
KIPP 3D Academy	500 Tidwell Rd	Houston, TX	77022-2122	832-230-0566		5-8	Alison Cumbley
KIPP: Pleasant Grove PS	2200 Saint Augustine	Dallas, TX	75227	972-323-4230		PK-4	Dexter Chaney
KIPP Academy MS	10711 Kipp Way Dr	Houston, TX	77099-2675	832-328-1051	328-0178	5-8	Andrew Rubin
KIPP Academy MS West	8500 Highway 6 S	Houston, TX	77083	832-230-0573		5-8	Steven Khadam-Hir
KIPP Aspire Academy	239 Stark St	San Antonio, TX	78204	210-735-7300	735-7305	5-8	Bradley Tarrance
KIPP Austin Academy of Arts & Letters	8509 FM 969 Ste A	Austin, TX	78724-5702	512-501-3640	501-3641	5-8	Kevin Newman
KIPP Austin Beacon Prep	5107 I-35 S Ste A	Austin, TX	78744	512-651-1918	924-2872	5-8	Katie Hayes
KIPP Austin Brave HS	8509 FM 969 Building 676	Austin, TX	78724	512-651-2225		9-12	Stephanie Burns
KIPP Austin College Prep S	8004 Cameron Rd	Austin, TX	78754	512-501-4969	637-6899	5-8	Katie Shapiro
KIPP Austin Collegiate	8509 FM 969 Ste 676	Austin, TX	78724	512-501-3586	501-3587	9-12	Carrie Donovan
KIPP Austin Comunidad	8004 Cameron Rd	Austin, TX	78754	512-501-3911	870-9224	K-4	Justin Scott
KIPP Austin Connections	8509 FM 969 Ste 629	Austin, TX	78724-5713	512-651-5537	870-9537	K-4	Bethany Blevins
KIPP Austin Leadership Elementary	5107 I-35 S Ste A	Austin, TX	78744	512-651-2168		K-4	Nicole Seltman
KIPP Austin Obras	5107 I-35 S Ste A	Austin, TX	78744	512-651-2069		K-4	Matthew Frank
KIPP Austin Vista MS	5107 I-35 S Ste A	Austin, TX	78744	512-651-1921	461-8086	5-8	Laura Farber
KIPP Camino Academy	4343 W Commerce St	San Antonio, TX	78237	210-829-4200	829-4207	5-8	Juan Juarez
KIPP CONNECT S	6700 Bellaire Blvd	Houston, TX	77074	281-879-3023		PK-7	Adam Kutac
KIPP Destiny ES	3663 W Camp Wisdom Rd	Dallas, TX	75237	972-708-8500		K-4	Katie Gilleland
KIPP Destiny MS	3663 W Camp Wisdom Rd	Dallas, TX	75237-2507	972-708-8500		5-8	Esmeralda Cardoso
KIPP DREAM Prep	500 Tidwell Rd	Houston, TX	77022	832-230-6082		PK-4	Haley Simonton-Bonilla
KIPP Esperanza Dual Language Academy	103 Tuleta Dr	San Antonio, TX	78212-3176	210-317-2731		K-K	Michael Shay
KIPP Explore Academy	5402 Lawndale St	Houston, TX	77023	832-230-0547	924-5046	PK-4	Amy Stabile
KIPP Generations Collegiate	500 Tidwell Rd	Houston, TX	77022-2122	832-230-0566	328-0178	9-12	Nancy Flores
KIPP Houston HS	10711 Kipp Way Dr	Houston, TX	77099-2675	832-328-1082	838-4293	9-12	Mohamad Maarouf
KIPP Intrepid Preparatory S	5402 Lawndale St	Houston, TX	77023	281-879-3100	463-7318	6-8	Joy Taluyo
KIPP Legacy Preparatory S	9606 Mesa Dr	Houston, TX	77078-3024	832-230-0567	491-7311	PK-3	Monique Payton
KIPP Liberation College Preparatory S	5400 Martin Luther King	Houston, TX	77021-3010	832-230-0565	842-6689	5-8	Tai Ingram
KIPP Northeast College Preparatory	9680 Mesa Dr	Houston, TX	77078-3015	832-230-0567		9-12	Gillian Quinn-Pineda
KIPP PEACE ES	5400 Martin Luther King	Houston, TX	77021	281-879-3063		PK-4	Lisa Williams
KIPP Poder Academy	128 S Audubon Dr	San Antonio, TX	78212-1520	210-888-6513	888-6515	5-5	Rachel Obermeier
KIPP Polaris Academy for Boys	9636 Mesa Dr	Houston, TX	77078-3024	832-230-0567	633-4783	5-8	Aaron Green
KIPP SHARP College Preparatory Lower S	8430 Westglen Dr	Houston, TX	77063-6312	281-879-3000	915-0074	PK-4	Michelle Bennett
KIPP Sharpstown College Prep	8440 Westpark Dr	Houston, TX	77063	281-879-3005	915-0074	5-8	Rebecca Easterby
KIPP Shine Prep	10711 Kipp Way Dr	Houston, TX	77099-2675	832-328-1051	328-0178	PK-5	Deborah Shifrine
KIPP Spirit College Preparatory S	11000 Scott St	Houston, TX	77047	832-230-0562	731-1644	5-8	Tiffany George-Prados
KIPP Sunnyside HS	11000 Scott St	Houston, TX	77047	832-230-0562	230-0570	9-12	Rian Wright
KIPP Truth Academy	1545 S Ewing Ave	Dallas, TX	75216	214-375-8326	375-2990	4-8	Michael Horne
KIPP Truth ES	3663 W Camp Wisdom Rd	Dallas, TX	75237-2507	214-893-4377		K-4	Katie Hill
KIPP Unity PS	8500 Highway 6 S	Houston, TX	77083-5709	832-230-0572		PK-4	Kaleena Rosenbauer
KIPP University Prep HS	239 Stark St	San Antonio, TX	78204	210-290-8720	290-9427	9-12	Abbey Morton-Garland
KIPP Un Mundo Dual Language Academy	4343 W Commerce St	San Antonio, TX	78237-1625	210-824-1905	485-1393	K-2	Nancy Ocasio
KIPP Voyage Academy for Girls	9616 Mesa Dr	Houston, TX	77078	832-230-0567	491-7311	5-8	Celeste Barretto
KIPP ZENITH Academy	11000 Scott St	Houston, TX	77047	832-230-0562		PK-4	Cassandra Cotman
Kolitz Academy	12500 NW Military Hwy	San Antonio, TX	78231	210-302-6900	302-6913	K-8	Kathryn Davis
Kometzky S	8701 MoPac Expy	Austin, TX	78759	512-471-5280	232-9177	PK-12	Christee Jackson
La Academia de Estrellas	111 S Beckley Ave	Dallas, TX	75203	214-946-8908	946-8777	PK-8	Ivelisse Centeno
La Fe Preparatory S	616 E Father Rahm Ave	El Paso, TX	79901-2912	915-533-4560	533-4175	PK-8	Amy O'Rourke
Laurel Ridge	17720 Corporate Woods Dr	San Antonio, TX	78259-3500	210-491-9400		PK-12	Sally Arnold
Leadership Prep S	8500 Teel Pkwy	Frisco, TX	75034-0525	972-294-6921	294-3416	K-8	Michelle Holland
Lee Academy	1826 Basse Rd	San Antonio, TX	78213	210-431-9881	582-2547	9-12	Valarie Walker
Legacy Preparatory Academy	8510 Military Pkwy	Dallas, TX	75227	469-287-8530	461-0794	K-12	Rebecca Good
Legacy Preparatory Academy	601 Accent Dr	Plano, TX	75075	469-206-2250	461-0794	K-12	Amelia Ahmed
Legacy Ranch	13326 N Highway 183	Gonzales, TX	78629	830-638-5300		K-12	James Hamilton
Liberation Academy	11600 W Airport Blvd	Meadows Place, TX	77477	346-754-5867		K-6	Audrey Sanders
Life S - Cedar Hill ES	129 W Wintergreen Rd	Cedar Hill, TX	75104	972-293-2825	291-2877	K-6	Candace Johnson
Life S - Lancaster ES	950 S Interstate 35 E	Lancaster, TX	75146-3304	972-274-7950	274-7991	K-6	DeWayne Parker
Life S - Mountain Creek ES	5525 W Illinois Ave	Dallas, TX	75211-6612	214-623-0012	467-2857	K-3	Kim Riepe
Life S - Oak Cliff ES	4400 S R L Thornton Fwy	Dallas, TX	75224-5110	214-376-8200	371-0297	K-6	Anita Sanders
Life S - Oak Cliff HS	4400 S R L Thornton Fwy	Dallas, TX	75224	214-413-1612	371-0193	7-12	Roy Watts
Life S - Red Oak ES	777 S Interstate 35 Rd	Red Oak, TX	75154	469-552-9200	617-5767	K-6	Joy Shepherd
Life S - Waxahachie HS	170 Butcher Rd	Waxahachie, TX	75165-6016	469-708-4444	708-4445	9-12	Patrick Harvell
Life S - Waxahachie MS	3295 Highway 77	Waxahachie, TX	75165	972-937-0715	937-0503	7-8	Anne Beckman
Lighthouse Charter S	2718 Frontier Dr	San Antonio, TX	78227-4069	210-674-4100	674-4108	PK-8	Mary Salinas
Lighthouse Charter S	8138 Westshire Dr	San Antonio, TX	78227	210-674-4100	674-4108	PK-12	Mary Salinas
Lindsley Park Community S	7130 Lindsley Ave	Dallas, TX	75223	214-321-9155	321-0702	PK-3	Jan Mallett
LivingWay Leadership Academy	350 Ruben M Torres Blvd	Brownsville, TX	78520	956-554-0999	554-9701	PK-12	Cecilia Septimo
Lone Star Language Academy	5301 Democracy Dr	Plano, TX	75024	972-696-9461		K-6	Nammie Ichilav

School	Address	City,State	Zip code	Telephone	Fax	Grade	Contact
Lowell MS	919 Thompson Pl	San Antonio, TX	78226-1494	210-228-1225	223-6248	6-8	Maribel Rodriguez
Luna Preparatory PS	2020 N Lamar St	Dallas, TX	75202	214-442-7882		K-5	Alieshia Baisy
Luna Preparatory Secondary S	2625 Elm St	Dallas, TX	75226	214-445-3300	445-3299	6-12	Candice Dagnino
Madla Early College HS	1400 W Villaret Blvd	San Antonio, TX	78224-2417	210-486-3686		9-12	Jeff Flores
Magnolia Montessori For All	5100 Pecan Brook Dr	Austin, TX	78724	512-522-2429	291-6242	PK-8	Sara Cotner
Mainland Preparatory Academy	319 Newman Rd	La Marque, TX	77568-3440	409-934-9100	934-9130	K-8	Wilma Green
Manara Academy	8201 Tristar Dr	Irving, TX	75063	972-304-1155	304-1150	K-6	Monica Hall
Manara Leadership Academy	8001 Jetstar Dr Ste 100	Irving, TX	75063	972-304-1155	304-1150	7-12	Adam Flores
Manara STEM Academy	6101 S Collins St	Arlington, TX	76018	972-304-1155	304-1150	K-6	Luis Valdez
Mangum ES	4315 Mangum Rd	Houston, TX	77092	713-688-0505	688-3286	PK-5	Josefa Olivares
Massieu Academy	823 N Center St	Arlington, TX	76011-5859	817-460-0396	460-9867	PK-12	Monica Fox
Mayes Institute	5807 Calhoun Rd	Houston, TX	77021-3301	713-747-5629	747-5683	K-8	Beatrice Mayes
Meadowland Charter S	121 Old San Antonio Rd	Boerne, TX	78006	830-331-4094	331-4096	7-12	Geoff Knitt
Meridian Preparatory S	1801 S Beach St	Fort Worth, TX	76105	817-288-1700	288-1692	K-5	Ginger Cole-Leffel
Meridian S	2555 N Interstate 35	Round Rock, TX	78664-2015	512-660-5230	660-5231	K-12	Rick Fernandez
Methodist Children's Home	1111 Herring Ave	Waco, TX	76708-3642	254-750-1298	750-1307	6-12	Cristy Cunningham
Meyer HS	1020 Elm St Bldg 100	Waco, TX	76704-2277	254-754-2288	754-8002	9-12	Tara Spence
Meyerpark Charter S	PO Box 35616	Houston, TX	77235-5616	713-729-9712	729-9720	K-5	Julia Hutcherson
Midland Academy Charter S	500 N Baird St	Midland, TX	79701-4704	432-686-0003	686-0845	K-12	Janet Wallace
Mid-Valley Academy	1785 W US Highway 77	San Benito, TX	78586	956-276-9930	276-9943	9-12	Nancy Ramirez
Mid-Valley Academy	200 N 17th St	McAllen, TX	78501	956-618-2303	618-2323	9-12	Ramiro Vela
Mid-Valley Academy	103 E 2nd St	Mercedes, TX	78570-2701	956-565-5417	565-8439	9-12	Jennifer McLelland
Mighty Preparatory S	3700 Wichita St	Fort Worth, TX	76119	817-288-3800	288-3799	K-12	Tiffany Starnes
Milburn Academy - Amarillo	4106 SW 51st Ave	Amarillo, TX	79109-6132	806-463-2284	463-2231	9-12	Derek Davis
Milburn Academy -Corpus Christi	5333 Everhart Rd Bldg C	Corpus Christi, TX	78411	361-225-4424	225-4945	9-12	Mario Vasquez
Milburn Academy - Fort Worth	6785 Camp Bowie Blvd	Fort Worth, TX	76116-7158	817-731-7627	731-7628	9-12	Susan Richey
Milburn Academy - Houston	713 E Airtex Dr	Houston, TX	77073	281-209-3505	209-9475	9-12	Valarie Harvick
Milburn Academy - Killeen	802 N 2nd St Bldg G	Killeen, TX	76541-4711	254-634-4444	634-4044	9-12	Jerrod Barton
Milburn Academy - Lubbock	2333 50th St	Lubbock, TX	79412	806-740-0811	740-0804	9-12	Shawn Haseloff
Milburn Academy - North Midland	3303 W Illinois Ave Ste 14	Midland, TX	79703	432-522-7200	522-5201	9-12	Teffanie White
Milburn Academy - Odessa	2419 N County Rd W	Odessa, TX	79763-2677	432-550-7833	550-7884	9-12	Mary Janssen
Milburn Academy - Pasadena	171 Pasadena Town Sq # 353	Pasadena, TX	77506	210-774-1108		9-12	Sonja Williams
Milburn Academy - South Midland	503 E Interstate 20 Ste 110	Midland, TX	79701	432-203-9829	704-5520	9-12	Ronald Medrano
Monticello Academy	4618 San Pedro Ave	San Antonio, TX	78212	210-738-0020	738-0033	K-12	Terri Harrold M.Ed.
Mount Carmel Academy	7155 Ashburn St	Houston, TX	77061-2611	713-643-2008	645-0078	9-12	Maureen Giacchino
Nelms Charter HS	20625 Clay Rd	Katy, TX	77449-5593	281-398-8031	398-8032	9-12	Michael Dean
Nelms Charter MS	20625 Clay Rd	Katy, TX	77449-5593	281-398-8031	398-8032	5-8	Michael Dean
New Frontiers Charter S	4018 S Presa St	San Antonio, TX	78223-1005	210-533-3655	533-5077	K-8	Ruben Pesina
New Horizons S	850 Highway 574 W	Goldthwaite, TX	76844	325-938-5513	938-5512	1-12	Suzanne Rush
Newman International Academy Arlington	2011 S Fielder Rd	Arlington, TX	76013-6255	817-459-8555	394-6155	PK-12	Donna Hart
Newman International Academy at Grace	308 W Park Row Dr	Arlington, TX	76010	817-655-2156		K-5	
Newman International Academy Cedar Hill	1114 FM 1382	Cedar Hill, TX	75104	682-207-5878		PK-12	Subhas Mathew
Newman International Acad of Fort Worth	6801 Meadowbrook Dr	Fort Worth, TX	76112	817-655-2255		PK-3	Miriam Dale Duncan
Newman International Acad of Mansfield	1201 N State Highway 360	Mansfield, TX	76063	817-870-6649		K-4	Keith Shull
New Neighbor Campus	6500 Rookin St	Houston, TX	77074-5019	713-273-3731		K-5	Raquel Sosa-Gonzalez
Nolan Creek S	505 E Avenue C	Belton, TX	76513	254-939-4491		K-5	Ken Wiseman
North Hills S	606 E Royal Ln	Irving, TX	75039-3503	972-501-0645	501-9439	K-12	Heather Periera
Northwest Early College HS	6701 S Desert Blvd	El Paso, TX	79932-8501	915-877-1700	877-7033	9-12	Tracy Speaker
Nova Academy	PO Box 170127	Dallas, TX	75217-0127	214-381-3422	381-3499	PK-3	Donna Houston-Woods
Nova Academy Southeast - Bruton	PO Box 170127	Dallas, TX	75217-0127	214-309-9030	398-6363	PK-6	Donna Houston-Woods
Nova Academy Southeast - Prichard	PO Box 170127	Dallas, TX	75217-0127	972-808-7470	808-7471	K-8	Donna Houston-Woods
NYOS Charter S	1605 Kramer Ln	Austin, TX	78758-4284	512-275-1593	287-5258	PK-3	Terry Berkenhoff
NYOS Charter S	12301 N Lamar Blvd	Austin, TX	78753-1314	512-583-6967	583-6973	4-12	Curtis Wilson
Oak Cliff Faith Family Academy	300 W Kiest Blvd	Dallas, TX	75224	214-375-7682	375-7681	PK-12	Brenda McGeorge
Odyssey Academy - Galveston	2412 61st St	Galveston, TX	77551	409-750-9289	740-3735	PK-12	Jennifer Goodman
Olive Tree Montessori Academy	8601 Randol Mill Rd	Fort Worth, TX	76120	817-460-5000	460-5003	PK-5	Sadia Haq
Olympic Hills Charter S	2200 E 6th St	Austin, TX	78702-3457	512-444-4835	232-9177	K-12	Dottie Goodman
Panola Charter S	PO Box 610	Carthage, TX	75633-0610	903-693-6355	693-6391	8-12	Keith Koonce
Panola Early College HS	PO Box 610	Carthage, TX	75633	903-693-6355	694-2208	8-12	Keith Koonce
PARAMUS Early College HS	602 S Raguet St	Lufkin, TX	75904	936-634-5515	634-5518	9-12	Dr. Merilyn Session
Paseo Del Norte Academy	1599 George Dieter Dr	El Paso, TX	79936	915-298-3637	298-3644	9-12	Maria Baquera
Paso Del Norte Academy - Ysleta	711 N Mesa St	El Paso, TX	79902-3925	915-532-7216	532-2251	9-12	Luis Liano
Pathfinder Camp	20800 FM 150 W	Driftwood, TX	78619-9202	512-858-4258	858-4960	K-12	Melissa Ruffin
Pathways 3H Ranch	110 Youth Ranch Rd # 3H	Mountain Home, TX	78058	830-866-3761	866-3705	6-12	Sally Arnold
Pegasus Charter HS	601 N Akard St Ste 203	Dallas, TX	75201-3303	214-740-9991	740-9799	K-12	Virginia Hart
Phoenix S	3333 Bering Dr	Houston, TX	77057-6718	713-784-6345		K-12	Brett Schriewer
Pinnacle Preparatory S	2510 S Vernon Ave	Dallas, TX	75224	214-442-6100	442-6181	K-6	Katie Leinenkugel
Pioneer Technology & Arts Academy	3100 Oates Dr	Mesquite, TX	75150	972-375-9672	301-2135	6-8	
Pioneer Technology & Arts Academy	300 Aerobic Ln	Greenville, TX	75402	903-257-3920		6-8	
Porter S	PO Box 2053	Wimberley, TX	78676-6953	512-847-6867	847-0737	9-12	Kenn Peters
Por Vida Academy	1135 Mission Rd	San Antonio, TX	78210-4505	210-532-9161	533-5612	9-12	Loren Franckowiak
Positive Solutions Charter S	1325 N Flores St	San Antonio, TX	78212-4900	210-299-1025	299-1052	9-12	Ruby Torres
Premier HS CTE Edinburg	4701 Sugar Rd	Edinburg, TX	78539	956-386-1793		9-12	Nelda Garza
Premier HS of Abilene	3161 S 23rd St	Abilene, TX	79605-5861	325-698-8111	695-5620	9-12	Sue Pond
Premier HS of Amarillo	3242 Hobbs Rd	Amarillo, TX	79109-3213	806-367-5447	315-9506	9-12	Michael Griffin
Premier HS of Austin	1701 W Ben White Blvd #100A	Austin, TX	78704	512-444-8442	673-0058	9-12	Jennifer Kasapi
Premier HS of Beaumont	209 N 11th St	Beaumont, TX	77702-2213	409-835-4303	835-2882	9-12	Bonnie Whitehead
Premier HS of Brownsville	955 Paredes Line Rd	Brownsville, TX	78521-2659	956-550-0084	554-0890	9-12	Norma Sorola
Premier HS of Brownwood/Early	819 Early Blvd	Early, TX	76802	325-643-3735	363-4987	7-12	
Premier HS of Comanche	1008 S Austin St	Comanche, TX	76442	325-356-9673	794-8319	6-12	
Premier HS of Dayton	1709 County Road 611	Dayton, TX	77535-8561	936-257-8017	449-6775	9-12	Ray Moore
Premier HS of Del Rio	1503 Veterans Blvd	Del Rio, TX	78840-3625	830-298-2100	573-0849	9-12	Berta Martinez
Premier HS of East El Paso	8720 Gateway Blvd E Ste E	El Paso, TX	79907	915-633-1598	693-5206	9-12	Dr. Eduardo Servin
Premier HS of El Paso	1035 Belvidere St Ste 116	El Paso, TX	79912	915-581-4300	581-4378	9-12	Dr. Eduardo Servin
Premier HS of Fort Worth	6411 Camp Bowie Blvd Ste B	Fort Worth, TX	76116-5449	817-731-2028	728-0824	9-12	Kelly Kidd
Premier HS of Granbury	919 E US Highway 377 Ste 1	Granbury, TX	76048-1436	817-573-0435	895-9616	9-12	Marsha Grissom
Premier HS of Huntsville	2407 Sam Houston Ave Ste C	Huntsville, TX	77340-5862	936-439-5204	622-9113	9-12	Kevin Nichols
Premier HS of Irving South	1081 W Shady Grove Rd	Irving, TX	75060-5868	972-254-1016	565-1157	9-12	Tiffini Miller
Premier HS of Laredo	2201 Chihuahua St	Laredo, TX	78043-3737	956-723-7788	284-0175	9-12	
Premier HS of Lewisville	1800 Lakeway Dr	Lewisville, TX	75057-6429	972-316-4160		9-12	Debbie Foster
Premier HS of Lindale	17141 State Highway 110 N	Lindale, TX	75771-5933	903-881-9940	882-0183	6-12	
Premier HS of Lubbock	2002 W Loop 289 Ste 121	Lubbock, TX	79407-7701	806-763-1518	763-9310	9-12	Thomas Martin
Premier HS of Midland	4320 W Illinois Ave Ste A	Midland, TX	79703-5591	432-682-0384	682-0897	9-12	Holli Stockstill
Premier HS of Mission	1203 St Claire Blvd	Mission, TX	78572-8465	956-424-9290	859-0140	9-12	Laura Thatcher
Premier HS of New Braunfels	1928 S Seguin Ave Unit 100A	New Braunfels, TX	78130	830-609-6606	319-4382	9-12	Richard Ramirez
Premier HS of North Austin	1835 Kramer Ln Ste A600	Austin, TX	78758-4259	512-832-0965	563-6438	9-12	Manuela Allen
Premier HS of North Houston	14314 Walters Rd	Houston, TX	77014	281-918-4044		9-12	Alexis DelGado
Premier HS of Palmview	406 W Veterans Blvd	Palmview, TX	78572-8327	956-584-8458	584-9807	9-12	Selma Femat
Premier HS of Pflugerville	616 FM 685 Ste 204B	Pflugerville, TX	78660-3681	512-969-5100		6-12	Paulita Zuniga
Premier HS of Pharr	200 E Expressway 83 Ste E	Pharr, TX	78577	956-781-8800	781-7464	9-12	Rosie Zamora
Premier HS of Richardson	1111 Digital Dr Ste 101	Richardson, TX	75081-1948	972-479-9602	885-9621	9-12	Shaina Tackett-Cox
Premier HS of San Antonio	4941 Walzem Rd Ste 8220	San Antonio, TX	78218-2176	210-650-0944		9-12	Berta Martinez
Premier HS of San Juan	1200 E Business 83	San Juan, TX	78589-4758	956-961-4721	961-4724	9-12	Alma Prado
Premier HS of Texarkana	3448 Summerhill Rd	Texarkana, TX	75503	430-200-4385		9-12	Heather McNeill
Premier HS of Tyler	1106 N Glenwood Blvd	Tyler, TX	75702-5059	903-592-5222	592-0324	9-12	Tabatha Ervin
Premier HS of Waco	4720 N 19th St	Waco, TX	76708-1213	254-752-0441	752-0445	9-12	Lisa Linton
Quest MS	1301 Waters Ridge Dr	Lewisville, TX	75057-6022	972-316-6700	316-6705	6-8	Marci Stapp
Quinn Campus MS	1020 Elm St Bldg 100	Waco, TX	76704-2277	254-754-8000	754-8009	5-8	Tyler Ellis
Ramirez Charter S	702 Avenue T	Lubbock, TX	79401-2303	806-219-6500	766-1825	K-5	Nancy Parker
Ranch Academy	3120 VZ County Road 2318	Canton, TX	75103-4671	903-939-8000	200-2918	6-12	Melissa Pardue
Rapoport Academy East	2000 J J Flewellen Rd	Waco, TX	76704-1642	254-799-4191	799-4525	PK-4	Cindy Kubacak
Rapoport Academy North	2200 MacArthur Dr	Waco, TX	76708	254-313-1313		PK-4	Heather Franks
Real Learning Academy	6405 S IH 35	Austin, TX	78744-3401	512-438-7325	383-0665	PK-4	Michelle Stahl
Rhodes MS	3000 Tampico St	San Antonio, TX	78207-6498	210-978-7925	433-7299	6-8	Moises Ortiz
Rhodes S - Northeast	600 Charles St	Humble, TX	77338	281-319-9300	446-2898	PK-8	
Rhodes S - Northshore	12818 Tidwell Rd	Houston, TX	77044	281-459-9797		PK-5	
Rhodes S - Northwest	6601 Antoine Dr	Houston, TX	77091	832-562-2822		K-5	
Rhodes S - Southeast	5874 Bellfort St	Houston, TX	77033	832-962-8181	962-8171	K-5	Dr. Tammi Mitchell
Richland Collegiate HS	12800 Abrams Rd	Dallas, TX	75243-2104	972-761-6888	761-6890	11-12	Donna Walker
Ripley House Charter S	4410 Navigation Blvd	Houston, TX	77011-1036	713-315-6429	547-8201	K-5	Angela Wedlick
Ripley House MS	4414 Navigation Blvd	Houston, TX	77011	713-315-6430		6-8	
Rise Academy	PO Box 2837	Lubbock, TX	79408-2837	806-744-0438	201-7088	PK-8	Richard Baumgartner
Riverside Park ES	202 School St	San Antonio, TX	78210-3940	210-228-3355	534-6987	PK-5	Dr. Cassie McClung
Robbins MS	602 S Raguet St	Lufkin, TX	75904	936-634-5515	634-5518	6-8	JoDee Woodcock
Saenz JHS	1826 Basse Rd	San Antonio, TX	78213	210-431-9881	582-2587	7-8	Valarie Walker
St. Anthony S	3732 Myrtle St	Dallas, TX	75215-3849	214-421-3645	421-7416	K-8	David Ray
St. Mary's Academy Charter S	507 N Filmore St	Beeville, TX	78102-5000	361-358-5601	358-5704	K-8	Hirma Elizondo

School	Address	City,State	Zip code	Telephone	Fax	Grade	Contact
San Antonio Can Academy	1807 Centennial Blvd	San Antonio, TX	78211-1205	210-923-1226	928-3366	9-12	Mark Tribett
San Antonio S for Inquiry & Creativity	4618 San Pedro Ave	San Antonio, TX	78212-1411	210-738-0020	738-0033	K-12	Andrew Dunn
Sanchez HS	6001 Gulf Fwy	Houston, TX	77023-5425	713-926-1112	926-8129	6-12	John DeLaCruz
Save Our Streets Learning Center	1700 Groesbeck St	Bryan, TX	77803	979-703-1810	703-1834	K-5	Becky Tucker
School for the Highly Gifted	2990 S State Highway 161	Grand Prairie, TX	75052-7247	972-343-7864		1-3	Holly Mohler
School of Science and Technology	4737 Saratoga Blvd	Corpus Christi, TX	78413-2117	361-851-2450	851-2475	K-12	Ekrem Demirci
S of Science & Technology Advancement	10550 Westoffice Dr	Houston, TX	77042	713-266-2522	266-2494	PK-8	
School of Science and Technology Alamo	12200 Crownpoint Dr	San Antonio, TX	78233	210-657-6400	657-6401	K-8	Mustafa Kililioglu
School of Science & Technology Discovery	5707 Bandera Rd	Leon Valley, TX	78238	210-543-1111	543-1112	K-8	Yvette Alvarez
School of Science and Technology HS	1450 NE Loop 410	San Antonio, TX	78209-1513	210-804-0222	822-3422	6-12	Celal Keskin
S of Science and Technology Houston	16200 State Highway 249	Houston, TX	77086	346-270-2101	270-2187	K-8	
Sci-Tech Preparatory	6405 S IH-35	Austin, TX	78744	512-220-9120	383-0665	6-12	Mary Brinkman M.Ed.
Scott Collegiate Academy	4116 Avenue N 1/2	Galveston, TX	77550-6957	409-761-6100	765-5946	5-8	Debra Owens
Seashore Learning Center	14493 S Padre Isl PMB 307A	Corpus Christi, TX	78418	361-949-1222	949-6762	PK-4	Genger Holt
Seashore Middle Academy	14493 S Padre Isl PMB 307A	Corpus Christi, TX	78418	361-654-1134	654-1139	5-8	Barbara Beeler
Seguin ES	2400 E Walnut St	Seguin, TX	78155	830-549-5930	433-4534	PK-5	Christine Wilmoth
SER-Ninos Charter S	5815 Alder Dr	Houston, TX	77081-2708	713-667-6145	667-0645	PK-8	Charmaine Constantine
Settlement Home	1600 Payton Gin Rd	Austin, TX	78758-6506	512-836-2150	836-2159	K-12	Mayola Toliver
Shoreline Academy	1220 Gregory St	Taft, TX	78390-3044	361-528-3959	528-2143	7-12	DeAnn Phillips
South Plains Academy	4008 Avenue R	Lubbock, TX	79412-1603	806-744-0330	741-1089	9-12	Jennifer McLelland
Southwest ES	8440 Bissonnet St	Houston, TX	77074-3908	713-988-5839	270-0076	PK-5	Pamela Sailors
Southwest HS	6400 Westpark Dr Ste 200	Houston, TX	77057	713-954-9528	953-0119	9-12	Ralph Butler
Southwest MS	6400 Westpark Dr Ste 200	Houston, TX	77057	713-954-9528	953-0119	6-8	Albert Fernandez
Southwest Preparatory ES NW Campus	4151 Culebra Rd	San Antonio, TX	78228	210-819-7860	438-8253	PK-6	Cheryl Wills-Pacheco
Southwest Preparatory HS NW Campus	6535 Culebra Rd	San Antonio, TX	78238	210-432-2634	432-5482	7-12	Lesley Carr
Southwest Preparatory S NE Campus	1258 Austin Hwy Ste 220	San Antonio, TX	78209-4820	210-829-8017	829-8514	PK-8	Veronica Champion
Southwest Preparatory S SE Campus	735 S WW White Rd	San Antonio, TX	78220-2524	210-333-1403	333-3024	6-12	Michael Tamaren
Southwest Prep S New Directions Campus	1258 Austin Hwy Bldg 2	San Antonio, TX	78209-4891	210-828-2161	826-9962	9-12	Veronica Champion
Step Charter S	11250 S Wilcrest Dr	Houston, TX	77099	281-988-7797		K-8	William Clark
Storm ES	435 Brady Blvd	San Antonio, TX	78207-8001	210-978-8005	224-1998	PK-5	Claudia Ramos
Strinden ES	602 S Raguet St	Lufkin, TX	75904	936-634-5515	634-5518	PK-5	Jennifer Shaw
Summit International Preparatory S	1305 N Center St	Arlington, TX	76011	817-287-5121	287-5132	K-12	Tracy Odom
Tekoa Academy of Accelerated Studies	1408 W Park Ave	Orange, TX	77630-4951	409-886-9864		PK-5	Rhonda Orebo
Tekoa Academy of Accelerated Studies	326 Thomas Blvd	Port Arthur, TX	77640-5242	409-982-5400	982-8498	K-6	Dr. Paula Richardson
Tekoa Academy of Accelerated Studies	327 Thomas Blvd	Port Arthur, TX	77640-5243	409-985-4738		7-12	Dr. Paula Richardson
Temple Charter Academy	7177 Airport Rd	Temple, TX	76502-7142	254-778-8682	853-4144	PK-12	Jason Osburn
Texas Connections Academy at Houston	10550 Richmond Ave Ste 140	Houston, TX	77042-5112	281-661-8293	780-2487	3-12	Lea Ann Lockard
Texas Early College HS	2400 E End Blvd S	Marshall, TX	75672-7402	903-935-4109	935-4067	8-12	Robert Bruce
Texas Education Centers at Aubrey	1851 Oak Grove Pkwy	Little Elm, TX	75068-3240	972-292-3562	292-3563	K-8	Debbie Foster
Texas Education Centers at Denton	4601 IH 35 N	Denton, TX	76210	940-383-1972	383-7655	K-8	James Gandy
Texas Education Centers in Lewisville	968 Raldon St	Lewisville, TX	75067-5229	972-221-3564	221-3576	K-8	Donica Hill
Texas Empowerment Academy	6414 N Hampton Dr	Austin, TX	78723-2043	512-494-1076	494-1009	K-5	David Nowlin
Texas Empowerment Academy	3613 Bluestein Dr	Austin, TX	78721-2900	512-494-1076	494-0199	5-12	David Nowlin
Texas Leadership Charter Acad Arlington	2001 Brown Blvd	Arlington, TX	76006	817-385-9338	861-1242	K-8	Ron Carroll
Texas Leadership Charter Academy Abilene	1840 N 8th St	Abilene, TX	79603	325-480-3500		K-6	Melinda McCarty
Texas Leadership Charter Academy Midland	3300 Thomas Ave	Midland, TX	79703	432-242-7117	262-0994	PK-8	Becky Rejon
Texas NeuroRehabilitation Center	1106 W Dittmar Rd	Austin, TX	78745-6328	512-444-4835	462-6665	K-12	Dottie Goodman
Texas Preparatory S	PO Box 1643	San Marcos, TX	78667-1643	512-928-3000	928-3005	K-6	Daphne McDole
Texas S of the Arts	6025 Village Pkwy	Fort Worth, TX	76134-3430	817-732-8372	732-8373	K-8	Natalie Texada
Texas Serenity Academy	8500 Sweetwater Ln	Houston, TX	77037-2816	281-820-9540	820-6204	K-8	Michelle Foreman
Texas Serenity Academy - Gano	4637 Gano St	Houston, TX	77009	281-258-7700		K-5	Danielle Johnson
Texas Virtual Academy	1955 Lakeway Dr Ste 250B	Lewisville, TX	75057-6436	866-360-0161	506-6777	3-12	Sara Baker
TLC Academy	PO Box 61726	San Angelo, TX	76906-1726	325-652-3200	942-6795	K-12	Dr. Christopher Morrow
Travis Early College HS	1915 N Main Ave	San Antonio, TX	78212	210-738-9830	733-5486	9-12	Adrianna Arredondo
Treetops School International	12500 S Pipeline Rd	Euless, TX	76040-5853	817-283-1771	684-0892	PK-12	Lou Blanchard
Trinity Basin S - 10th St Campus	831 W 10th St	Dallas, TX	75208	214-296-9302	296-9306	PK-4	Candee Martinez
Trinity Basin S - Ewing Campus	808 N Ewing Ave	Dallas, TX	75203-1524	214-942-8846	942-8864	PK-4	Kyla Jaramillo
Trinity Basin S - Jefferson Campus	855 E 8th St	Dallas, TX	75203	214-941-4881	941-4866	5-8	Jennifer Masten
Trinity Basin S - Pafford Campus	101 E Pafford St	Fort Worth, TX	76110	817-840-7501	840-7502	PK-7	Jodi Rebarchek
Trinity Basin S - Panola Campus	4400 Panola Ave	Fort Worth, TX	76103	817-458-4222	946-9194	PK-3	Natasha Forge
Trinity Charter S - Big Sandy Campus	15892 County Road 26	Tyler, TX	75707-2728	512-459-1000	705-2447	6-12	Nicki Cornejo
Trinity Charter S - Bokenkamp Campus	5517 S Alameda St	Corpus Christi, TX	78412	361-992-1412		K-12	Hilda Vega
Trinity Charter S - Chapel Hill Campus	15892 County Road 26	Tyler, TX	75707-2728	903-459-1000	705-2447	K-12	Nicki Cornejo
Trinity Charter S - Krause Center Campus	25752 Kingsland Blvd	Katy, TX	77494-2086	281-392-7505	392-6887	6-12	Sandra Flores
Trinity Charter S - New Hope Campus	1000 N McColl Rd	McAllen, TX	78501	956-435-0700		3-12	
Trinity Charter S - New Life Campus	650 Scarbourough	Canyon Lake, TX	78133-4529	830-964-4390	964-4376	4-12	Kellie Ragland
Trinity Charter S - Pegasus Campus	896 Robin Ranch Rd	Lockhart, TX	78644-4578	512-432-1652	705-2447	3-12	Keely Reynolds
Trinity Charter S - Willow Bend Campus	2902 Highway 31 E	Tyler, TX	75702-8613			K-12	Nicki Cornejo
Trinity Environmental Academy	PO Box 570975	Dallas, TX	75357-0975	972-920-6558	767-0494	PK-12	Michael Hooten
Trivium Academy	2201 E Hebron Pkwy	Carrollton, TX	75010	469-855-5531		K-6	Sheryl Bradley
TSU Charter Lab S	3100 Cleburne St	Houston, TX	77004	713-313-6754	313-6745	K-5	Debbra Collins
Two Dimensions Preparatory Academy	12121 Veterans Memorial Dr	Houston, TX	77067-5237	281-227-4708	232-0032	PK-5	DeAteria Akan
Two Dimensions Preparatory Academy	901 E 10th Ave	Corsicana, TX	75110-6726	281-227-4700	872-2858	PK-K	Shirley Harris
Two Dimensions Preparatory Academy	12330 Vickery St	Houston, TX	77039-3608	281-227-4700	987-7306	PK-4	Jamal Adams
UME Preparatory Academy	3838 Spur 408	Dallas, TX	75236	214-545-6243	709-7951	K-12	Mike Spurlock
UME Preparatory Academy	415 N Cedar Ridge Dr	Duncanville, TX	75116	972-296-0084		K-5	Shannan Horton
Universal Academy	2616 N MacArthur Blvd	Irving, TX	75062-5401	972-255-1800	255-6122	PK-12	Sheraton Duffey
Universal Academy - Flower Mound	1001 E Sandy Lake Rd	Coppell, TX	75019-3112	972-393-5834	255-6122	PK-12	Diane Moshier
University Charter S	2200 E 6th St	Austin, TX	78702-3457	512-495-9705	495-9631	PK-5	Tanya King
University HS	2007 University Ave	Austin, TX	78705-5623	512-382-0072	232-9177	9-12	Julie McElrath Ray
University of Houston Charter S of Tech	3855 Holman St	Houston, TX	77204-6056	713-743-9111	743-9121	K-5	Dr. Carolyn Black
Uplift Gradus Prep	121 Seahawk Dr	DeSoto, TX	75115	214-451-5551		K-3	Sharon Duplantier
Uplift Lee Prep	401 E Grand Prairie Rd	Grand Prairie, TX	75051	972-262-6785		K-3	Dani Erbert
Uplift Mighty Prep S	3700 Mighty Mite Dr	Fort Worth, TX	76105	817-288-3800		K-10	Karen Aikman
Uplift Peak Academy	4600 Bryan St	Dallas, TX	75204	214-821-7325	370-3972	PK-12	Samina Noorani
Uplift Triumph Preparatory S	9411 Hargrove Dr	Dallas, TX	75220-6034	972-590-5100		K-5	Christine Denison
Vanguard Academy Beethoven ES	2215 S Veterans Blvd	Edinburg, TX	78539	956-318-0211	318-0220	PK-4	Norma Espino
Vanguard Academy Charter School	1200 E Kelly Ave	Pharr, TX	78577-5033	956-781-1701	781-8055	PK-12	Charlene Rodriguez
Vanguard Academy II	901 S Athol St	Pharr, TX	78577	956-702-0134	702-0166	PK-5	Angelica Martinez
Vanguard Academy III	155 E Business Highway 83	Alamo, TX	78516-9208	956-702-2548	702-2731	PK-5	Myrna Ramirez
Varnett S - East	PO Box 1457	Houston, TX	77251-1457	713-637-6574	637-8319	PK-5	Gayle Voltz
Varnett S - Northeast	PO Box 1457	Houston, TX	77251-1457	713-631-4396	491-3597	PK-5	Toni Fisher
Varnett S - Southwest	PO Box 1457	Houston, TX	77251-1457	713-723-4699	283-1728	PK-5	Ni'Cole Mukes
Victory Preparatory Academy	6011 W Orem Dr	Houston, TX	77085	713-729-6963	721-1665	9-12	Winston Steele
Victory Preparatory Academy	2903 Jensen Dr	Houston, TX	77026-6019	713-229-0560	250-7074	PK-12	Aben Ellerbee
Village Tech S	535 S Clark Rd	Cedar Hill, TX	75104-2822	972-827-7843	291-1531	PK-12	Robert Johansen
Vista Academy of Amarillo	6000 S Georgia St	Amarillo, TX	79118-8804	806-352-0171	367-5449	K-12	Michael Griffin
Vista Academy of Austin	1504 E 51st St	Austin, TX	78723-3012	512-371-8933	433-9225	K-5	Miriam Spiller-Troilo
Vista Academy of Beaumont	10255 Eastex Fwy Ste 100	Beaumont, TX	77708-1061	409-434-4549	316-2728	K-5	Sherry Hanson
Vista Academy of Crockett	1303 E Houston Ave	Crockett, TX	75835-1749	936-546-0493	546-0034	K-5	Deborah Kelly M.S.
Vista Academy of Dallas	7300 Bruton Rd	Dallas, TX	75217-1447	214-792-9331	792-9334	K-6	
Vista Academy of Elgin	2418 FM 1704	Elgin, TX	78621-5565	512-285-2710	679-2521	K-6	Jenness LaPage
Vista Academy of Garland	3024 Anita Dr	Garland, TX	75041-2708	972-840-1100	840-1105	K-8	Campbell Gillis
Vista Academy of Hickory Creek	800 Point Vista Dr Ste 518	Hickory Creek, TX	75065-7639	940-321-1144	231-9437	K-5	Kimberly Powell
Vista Academy of Humble	901 Wilson Rd	Humble, TX	77338-5104	281-913-5107	655-1476	K-5	Sandra Gonzales
Vista Academy of Huntsville	2407 Sam Houston Ave	Huntsville, TX	77340-5862	936-291-0203	293-8096	K-6	Robbie Harris
Vista Academy of Jasper	1501B S Wheeler St	Jasper, TX	75951-5103	409-489-9222	489-9272	K-8	Laura McMillon
Vista Academy of North Garland	1600 W Campbell Rd	Garland, TX	75044-2300	972-530-7373	679-0860	K-5	Emily Mason
Vista Academy of Pasadena Beta Academy	6109 Fairmont Pkwy	Pasadena, TX	77505-4024	281-372-8999	345-6895	K-4	Latisha Andrews
Vista Academy of Richardson	2101 E Renner Rd	Richardson, TX	75082-2209	972-530-7373		3-6	Emily Mason
Vista Academy of The Woodlands	6565 Research Forest Dr	The Woodlands, TX	77381-6030	936-242-1541	688-8037	K-8	Ferrell Yeokum
Vista Academy of Tyler	3105 University Blvd Ste B	Tyler, TX	75701-6614	903-504-5690	567-2247	K-5	Keith Garcia
Vista Academy of Willis	202 S Thomason St	Willis, TX	77378-8987	936-890-0100	890-0110	K-8	Kurt Goedrich
Vista del Futuro Charter S	7310 Bishop Flores Dr	El Paso, TX	79912-1429	915-855-8143	855-8179	K-6	Yvonne Whitman
Waco Charter S	615 N 25th St	Waco, TX	76707-3443	254-754-8169	754-7389	PK-5	Sabrina Gray
WALIPP-TSU Academy	5220 Scott St	Houston, TX	77004-7922	713-741-3600	741-3603	6-8	Cheryl Lawson
Walker IS	6500 N Interstate 35	San Antonio, TX	78218	210-654-4411	590-0376	PK-6	Cristen Martens M.Ed.
Wallace Accelerated HS	149 S State Highway 208	Colorado City, TX	79512-6603	325-728-2392	728-1025	8-12	Daryl Williams
Waxahachie Faith Family Academy	701 Ovilla Rd	Waxahachie, TX	75167-9430	972-937-3704	937-5806	PK-8	Monica Kramer
Wells Branch Leadership Academy	15201 Burnet Rd	Austin, TX	78728	512-872-8440		PK-12	William Ihlenfeldt
Westchester Acad International Studies	901 Yorkchester Dr	Houston, TX	77079-3446	713-251-1800	251-1815	6-12	Kathy Menotti
Westlake Academy	2600 J T Ottinger Rd	Westlake, TX	76262-8012	817-490-5757	490-5758	K-12	Dr. Mechelle Bryson
Whittier MS	2101 Edison Dr	San Antonio, TX	78201-3499	210-738-9755	735-0704	6-8	Irene Talamantes
Williams House S	107 W Railway St	Lometa, TX	76853	512-752-7501	752-7503	K-12	Stephanie House
Williams Preparatory S	1750 Viceroy Dr	Dallas, TX	75235-2308	214-276-0352	637-6393	K-12	Mauricio Dominguez
Winfree Academy Charter S	2985 S State Highway 360	Grand Prairie, TX	75052-7615	214-204-2030	204-2034	9-12	Corrine Johnson
Winfree Academy Charter S	2550 Beckleymeade Ave # 150	Dallas, TX	75237	469-930-5199	930-5206	9-12	Brad Landis

School	Address	City,State	Zip code	Telephone	Fax	Grade	Contact
Winfree Academy Charter S	1661 Gateway Blvd	Richardson, TX	75080-3530	972-234-9855	234-9975	9-12	David Stubblefield
Winfree Academy Charter S	3110 Skyway Cir S	Irving, TX	75038-4207	972-251-2010	251-4301	9-12	Ridwan Williams
Winfree Academy Charter S	341 Bennett Ln	Lewisville, TX	75057-4801	214-222-2200	222-0201	9-12	Madge Ennis
Winfree Academy Charter S	6311 Boulevard 26 Ste 300	N Richlnd Hls, TX	76180-1595	817-590-2240	590-8724	9-12	Heather Nichols
Wood Charter S at Afton Oaks	620 E Afton Oaks Blvd	San Antonio, TX	78232-1236	210-638-5000	638-5575	5-12	Asa Cuellar
Wood Charter S at Granbury	1300 Crossland Rd	Granbury, TX	76048-5208	210-638-5600	638-5675	4-12	Marc Malloy
Wood Charter S at Hays County	2250 Clovis R Barker Rd	San Marcos, TX	78666	210-638-5400	638-5475	5-12	Kayla Heyward
Wood Charter S at Meridell	12550 W State Highway 29	Liberty Hill, TX	78642	512-528-2462		K-12	Wendy Rollins
Wood Charter S at Rockdale	696 N FM 487	Rockdale, TX	76567-6005	210-638-5700	638-5775	4-12	Raymon Puente
Yes Prep S - Brays Oaks	9000 W Bellfort St	Houston, TX	77031-2410	713-967-8400	778-0917	6-12	Chris Claflin
Yes Prep S - East End	8329 Lawndale St	Houston, TX	77012-3707	713-967-7800	921-2305	6-12	Leah Peters
Yes Prep S - Fifth Ward	1305 Benson St	Houston, TX	77020-4044	713-924-0602	670-0032	6-12	Barbara Campbell
Yes Prep S - Gulfton	6565 De Moss Dr	Houston, TX	77074-5099	713-967-9800	774-1808	6-12	Hugh Guill
Yes Prep S - Northbrook	3030 Rosefield Dr	Houston, TX	77080	713-251-4200	251-4214	6-8	Jermy Jones
Yes Prep S - North Central	13703 Aldine Westfield Rd	Houston, TX	77039-2001	281-227-2044	227-2090	6-12	Bryan Reed
Yes Prep S - North Forest	6602 Winfield Rd	Houston, TX	77050	713-967-8600	636-7895	6-12	Eldridge Gilbert
Yes Prep S - Northside	5215 Jensen Dr	Houston, TX	77026-2514	713-924-0400	589-2502	6-8	Maureen Israel
Yes Prep S - Southeast	353 Crenshaw Rd	Houston, TX	77034-1543	713-967-9400	910-2350	6-12	Charles Schmidt
Yes Prep S - Southside	5515 S Loop E	Houston, TX	77033	713-924-5500		6-6	Chris Claflin
Yes Prep S - Southwest	4411 Anderson Rd	Houston, TX	77053-2307	713-967-9200	413-0003	6-12	Eric Newcomer
Yes Prep S - West	10535 Harwin Dr	Houston, TX	77036	713-967-8200	541-8518	6-12	Ashleigh Fritz
Yes Prep S - White Oak	5620 W Tidwell Rd	Houston, TX	77091-4638	713-924-5200	589-2502	6-12	
Young Learners Charter S	3333 Bering Dr	Houston, TX	77057-6718	713-784-1215	780-2338	PK-K	Lillian Conway
Young Learners S	8432 Bissonnet St	Houston, TX	77074	713-772-7100	772-7104	PK-2	Lillian Conway
Young Scholars Academy of Excellence	1809 Louisiana St	Houston, TX	77002-8013	713-654-1404	654-1401	PK-8	Anella Coleman
Young Womens Leadership Academy	2123 W Huisache Ave	San Antonio, TX	78201-4809	210-438-6525	732-7999	6-12	Delia McLerran
Yzaguirre S for Success	2950 Broadway St	Houston, TX	77017	713-640-3763	454-0893	6-8	Philip Cano
Yzaguirre S for Success	2950 Broadway St	Houston, TX	77017	713-640-3734	454-0893	PK-5	Luisa Martinez
Yzaguirre S for Success	2950 Broadway St	Houston, TX	77017-1706	713-649-6201	641-1853	9-12	Alma Perez-Silva
Yzaguirre S for Success	2255 N Coria St	Brownsville, TX	78520	956-544-7103	542-2667	PK-8	Maria Knosel
Zoe Learning Academy	3229 Hadley St Ste A	Houston, TX	77004	281-968-2962	724-8255	PK-7	Joyce Colquitt
Zoe Learning Academy	202 W Center St	Duncanville, TX	75116-3441	972-296-3335	296-3335	PK-6	Dr. Richard Rose

Utah

School	Address	City,State	Zip code	Telephone	Fax	Grade	Contact
Academy for Math Engineering & Science	5715 S 1300 E	Salt Lake City, UT	84121-1023	801-278-9460	277-3527	9-12	Brett Wilson
American Academy of Innovation	5410 W South Jordan Pkwy	South Jordan, UT	84009	801-810-4786		6-12	Scott Jones
American International S of Utah	4998 S Galleria Dr	Murray, UT	84123	801-989-7191		K-12	Nathan Justis
American Leadership Academy	898 W 1100 S	Spanish Fork, UT	84660-5654	801-794-2226	794-2130	K-12	Richard Morley
American Prep Academy - Accelerated S	3636 W 3100 S	West Valley, UT	84120	385-351-3090	351-3089	K-12	Carolyn Sharette
American Prep Academy - New Americas	1255 W Crystal Ave	West Valley, UT	84119	801-839-3613	839-3626	K-9	Carolyn Sharette
American Preparatory Academy Draper 2	11938 S Lone Peak Pkwy	Draper, UT	84020-6886	801-810-3590	810-3589	K-12	Carolyn Sharette
American Preparatory Academy Draper 1	12892 S Pony Express Rd	Draper, UT	84020	801-553-8500	576-9300	K-6	Carolyn Sharette
American Preparatory Academy - Salem	1195 Elk Ridge Dr	Salem, UT	84653-5521	801-465-4434	465-7808	K-9	Carolyn Sharette
Aristotle Academy	704 S 600 E	American Fork, UT	84003	801-763-7286	756-7037	K-8	Warren Shenk
Ascent Academies of Utah - Farmington	22 S 650 W	Farmington, UT	84025	801-220-2200		K-9	Janice Newton
Ascent Academies of Utah - Lehi	1999 W 900 N	Lehi, UT	84043	801-374-9641		K-9	Tricia Remington
Ascent Academies of Utah - West Jordan	5662 W 8200 S	West Jordan, UT	84081	385-275-0909		K-9	Michael Clark
Athenian Eacademy	765 E 340 S	American Fork, UT	84003	385-715-5400	265-4308	K-12	Matt Throckmorton
Athlos Academy of Utah	12309 S Mustang Trail Way	Herriman, UT	84096	801-809-5206		K-9	Esther Thompson
Bear River Science Academy	75 S 400 W	Logan, UT	84321	435-753-8811	661-6118	K-8	Janet Adams
Beehive Science & Technology Academy	830 E 9400 S	Sandy, UT	84094	801-576-0070	618-4115	6-12	Hanifi Oguz
Bowen Laboratory ES	6700 Old Main Hl	Logan, UT	84322-6700	435-797-3085	797-3668	K-5	Dan Johnson
Canyon Grove Academy	588 W 3300 N	Pleasant Grove, UT	84062	801-785-9300	785-8997	K-9	Sheri Ebert
Canyon Rim Academy	3005 S 2900 E	Salt Lake City, UT	84109	801-474-2066	474-2085	K-6	Merry Fusselman
Channing Hall Charter S	13515 S 150 E	Draper, UT	84020-8602	801-572-2709	571-8786	K-8	Heather Shepherd
City Academy	555 E 200 S	Salt Lake City, UT	84102-2007	801-596-8489	521-4181	7-12	Sonja Woodbury
DaVinci Academy of Science and the Arts	2033 Grant Ave	Ogden, UT	84401-0409	801-409-0700	334-8533	K-12	Fred Donaldson
Dixie Montessori Academy	1160 N 645 W	Washington, UT	84780	435-251-8539	578-0718	K-7	Julie Wand
Dual Immersion Academy	1155 S Glendale Dr	Salt Lake City, UT	84104	801-972-1425	972-9482	PK-8	Angela Fanjul
Early Light Academy	11709 S Vadania Dr	South Jordan, UT	84009	801-302-5988	727-0773	K-9	Sydney Young
East Hollywood HS	2185 S 3600 W	West Valley, UT	84119-1121	801-886-8181	972-9585	9-12	Katrina Walker
Edison Charter S - North	180 E 2600 N	North Logan, UT	84341-1551	435-787-2820	787-0299	K-9	Scott Jackson
Edison Charter S - South	1275 W 2350 S	Nibley, UT	84321-6181	435-752-0123	787-4350	K-9	Melani Kirk
Endeavor Hall Charter S	2614 S Decker Lake Ln	West Valley, UT	84119	801-972-1153	972-1163	K-8	Trudy Jack
Entheos Academy-Kearns	4710 W 6200 S	Kearns, UT	84118	801-417-5444	417-5448	K-9	Eric Robins
Entheos Academy-Magna	2606 S 7200 W	Magna, UT	84044	801-250-5233	250-5240	K-9	Mat Edvik
Esperanza ES	4956 W 3500 S	West Valley, UT	84120	801-305-1450	722-8252	K-6	Eulogio Alejandre
Excelsior Academy	124 E Erda Way	Tooele, UT	84074-9735	435-882-3062	882-4997	K-8	Stephanie Eccles
Fast Forward Charter HS	875 W 1400 N	Logan, UT	84321-6804	435-713-4255	753-9615	9-12	Jill Lowe
Franklin Discovery Academy	320 E Gammon Rd	Vineyard, UT	84058	801-785-6500		K-6	Gil Jarvie
Freedom Preparatory Academy	1190 W 900 N	Provo, UT	84604-3171	801-437-3100	437-3149	K-5	Lynne Herring
Freedom Preparatory Academy Secondary	1761 W 820 N	Provo, UT	84604	801-437-3100	437-3149	7-12	Buddy Ivie
Freedom Preparatoy Academy	426 N 100 W	Vineyard, UT	84058	801-437-3100	437-3149	K-5	Jonathan Kano
Gateway Preparatory Academy	201 E Thoroughbred Way	Enoch, UT	84721	866-867-5558	867-5497	K-8	Andrew Burt
Good Foundations Academy	5101 S 1050 W	Riverdale, UT	84405	801-393-2950	393-2953	K-6	Brent Petersen
Greenwood Charter S	840 N US 89	Harrisville, UT	84404	801-590-2972	689-0331	K-8	Jessie Kidd
Guadalupe S	1385 N 1200 W	Salt Lake City, UT	84116	801-531-6100	531-6106	K-6	Richard Pater
Hancock Charter S	125 N 100 E	Pleasant Grove, UT	84062-2355	801-796-5646	785-4934	K-8	Julie Adamic
Hawthorn Academy - South Jordan Campus	1137 W 11400 S	South Jordan, UT	84095	801-260-3040	254-6677	K-6	Spencer Jacobs
Hawthorn Academy - West Jordan Campus	9062 S 2200 W	West Jordan, UT	84088	801-282-9066	727-0836	K-9	Ryan Dubois
HighMark Charter S	2467 E South Weber Dr	South Weber, UT	84405	801-476-4627	475-5803	K-9	Mary Johnston
Intech Collegiate HS	1787 Research Park Way	North Logan, UT	84341-5600	435-753-7377	753-3775	9-12	Jason Stanger
Itineris Early College HS	8714 S Roy Del Cir	West Jordan, UT	84088	385-800-2140	800-2141	10-12	Renee Edwards
Jefferson Academy	1425 S Angel St	Kaysville, UT	84037	801-593-8200	660-6996	K-6	Nicole Jones
Kairos Academy	1325 W 2200 S	West Valley, UT	84119	385-355-1640		9-12	Brad Lester
Lakeview Academy	527 W 400 N	Saratoga Spgs, UT	84045	801-331-6788	331-6792	K-9	Rick Veasey
Leadership Learning Academy	100 W 2675 N	Layton, UT	84041	801-593-9552	784-5174	K-6	Heidi Bauerle
Legacy Preparatory Academy	1375 W Center St	North Salt Lake, UT	84054-2952	801-936-0555	936-1038	K-4	Karen Holman
Legacy Preparatory Academy	2214 S 1250 W	Woods Cross, UT	84087	801-294-2801		5-9	Priscilla Stringfellow
Lewis Academy	364 N State Road 198	Santaquin, UT	84655	801-754-3376	754-3102	K-6	Diane Nelson
Lincoln Academy	1582 W 3300 N	Pleasant Grove, UT	84062-9041	801-756-2039	785-2109	K-9	Jake Hunt
Lumen Scholar Institute	2342 Coyote St	Eagle Mountain, UT	84005	801-987-9497		K-12	Rebecca Harrison
Maeser Prep Academy	320 W 600 S	Lindon, UT	84042	801-235-9000	235-9010	7-12	Robyn Ellis
Mana Aademy Charter S	2355 S Technology Dr	West Valley, UT	84119	801-972-6262	401-7135	K-12	Fr. Anapesi Kaili
Maria Montessori Academy	2505 N 200 E	Ogden, UT	84414	801-827-0150	827-0145	K-9	Stephanie Speicher
Merit College Prep Academy	1440 W Center St	Springville, UT	84663	801-491-7600	491-7650	7-12	Kim Mitchell
Moab Charter S	358 E 300 S	Moab, UT	84532-2624	435-259-2277	259-6652	K-6	
Monticello Academy	2782 S Corporate Park Dr	West Valley, UT	84120	801-417-8040	417-8041	K-9	Dr. Gregory Cox
Mountain Heights Academy	9067 S 1300 W Ste 204	West Jordan, UT	84088	801-721-6329	670-0032	7-12	DeLaina Tonks
Mountainville Academy	195 S Main St	Alpine, UT	84004-1630	801-756-9805	763-9823	K-9	Janese Vance
Mountain West Montessori Academy	4125 S Foxview Dr	South Jordan, UT	84095	801-566-6962	727-7109	K-9	Amy Pilkington
Navigator Pointe Academy	6844 S Navigator Dr	West Jordan, UT	84084-4405	801-840-1210	840-1236	K-9	Judy Farris
North Davis Preparatory Academy	1765 W Hill Field Rd	Layton, UT	84041-7323	801-547-1809	547-1649	K-9	Ryan Robinson
Northern Utah Acad for Math Engnrg & Sci	2750 University Park Blvd	Layton, UT	84041-9099	801-395-3350	395-3351	10-12	Kelli Booth
North Star Academy	2920 W 14000 S	Bluffdale, UT	84065	801-302-9579	302-9578	K-9	Tana Archer
Odyssey Charter S	738 Quality Dr	American Fork, UT	84003-3309	801-492-8105	763-8743	K-6	Russell Schellhous
Ogden Preparatory Academy	1415 Lincoln Ave	Ogden, UT	84404	801-627-2066	394-2267	K-6	Amie Campbell
Ogden Preparatory Academy	1435 Lincoln Ave	Ogden, UT	84404-5678	801-627-3066	395-2267	7-9	Amie Campbell
Open Classroom	134 D St	Salt Lake City, UT	84103-2640	801-578-8144	578-8218	PK-8	Kathryn Hollicker
Pacific Heritage Academy	1755 W 1100 N	Salt Lake City, UT	84116	801-363-1892	364-4735	K-8	Dirk Matthias
Paradigm HS	11577 S 3600 W	South Jordan, UT	84095	801-676-1018	676-1036	9-12	Fernando Seminario
Pinnacle Canyon Academy	210 N 600 E	Price, UT	84501-2613	435-613-8102	613-8105	K-12	Roberta Hardy
Pioneer HS for the Performing Arts	704 S 600 E	American Fork, UT	84003	801-768-8787		9-12	Shari Bradley
Promontory S of Expeditionary Learning	1051 W 2700 S	Perry, UT	84302-4197	435-919-1900	919-1902	K-8	Jamie McKay
Providence Hall ES	4795 W Patriot Ridge Dr	Herriman, UT	84096	801-727-8260	727-8282	K-6	Jodi Lusty
Providence Hall HS	4557 W Patriot Ridge Dr	Herriman, UT	84096	801-727-8260		9-12	Nate Marshall
Providence Hall JHS	4558 W Patriot Ridge Dr	Herriman, UT	84096	801-727-8260	432-8496	7-8	Brian Fauver
Quest Academy	4862 W 4000 S	West Haven, UT	84401	801-731-9859	731-9860	K-9	Dr. David Bullock
Ranches Academy	7789 N Tawny Owl Cir	Eagle Mountain, UT	84005	801-789-4000	789-4001	K-6	Susie Scherer
Reagan Academy	1143 W Center St	Springville, UT	84663-3028	801-489-7828	491-2829	K-8	Justin Riggs
Renaissance Academy	3435 N 1120 E	Lehi, UT	84043-6538	801-768-4202	768-4295	K-9	Mark Ursic
Rockwell Charter HS	3435 Stonebridge Ln	Eagle Mountain, UT	84005	801-789-7625	789-7628	7-12	Darren Beck
Roots Charter HS	2250 S 1300 W	West Valley, UT	84119	801-573-8719		9-12	Tyler Bastian
Salt Lake Arts Academy	844 S 200 E	Salt Lake City, UT	84111-4203	801-531-1173	531-7726	5-8	Amy Wadsworth
Salt Lake Center for Science Education	1400 W Goodwin Ave	Salt Lake City, UT	84116-1629	801-578-8226	578-8677	6-12	Gina Sanzenbacher
Salt Lake School for the Performing Arts	2291 S 2000 E	Salt Lake City, UT	84106-4138	801-466-6700	485-1707	9-12	Ronald Litteral

School	Address	City,State	Zip code	Telephone	Fax	Grade	Contact
Scholar Academy	928 N 100 E	Tooele, UT	84074	435-566-6957	882-6641	K-6	Sandy Shepard
Soldier Hollow Charter S	2002 Olympic Dr	Midway, UT	84049-6216	435-654-1347	654-1349	K-6	Brenda Hedden
Spectrum Academy	665 Cutler Dr	North Salt Lake, UT	84054	801-936-0318	936-0209	7-12	Christina Guevera
Spectrum Academy	575 Cutler Dr	North Salt Lake, UT	84054	801-936-0318	936-0568	K-6	Christine Manning
Spectrum Academy - Pleasant Grove	867 S 800 W	Pleasant Grove, UT	84062	801-785-9019	899-1635	K-10	Liz Banner
Stegner Academy	980 S Bending River Rd	Salt Lake City, UT	84104	801-884-7950		K-8	Adam Gerlach
Success Academy at SUU	351 W University Blvd	Cedar City, UT	84720	435-865-8790	865-8795	9-12	John Tripp
Success Academy DSU	225 S 700 E	Saint George, UT	84770-3875	435-652-7830	656-4149	10-12	John Tripp
Summit Academy	1285 E 13200 S	Draper, UT	84020-9000	801-572-4166	572-4169	K-8	Tyler Whittle
Summit Academy - Bluffdale	1940 W 14400 S	Bluffdale, UT	84065	801-254-9488		K-8	Odila Conica
Summit Academy HS	14942 S 560 W	Bluffdale, UT	84065	801-495-3272	495-3275	9-12	Ted Mecham
Summit Academy - Independence	15327 S Noell Nelson Dr	Bluffdale, UT	84065	801-987-8755	987-8733	K-8	Lisa Cutler
Syracuse Arts Academy - Antelope	2893 W 1700 S	Syracuse, UT	84075-9838	801-779-2066	779-2087	K-9	Jan Whimpey
Syracuse Arts Academy - North	357 S 1550 W	Syracuse, UT	84075	801-827-0540	774-9270	K-6	Judy Nixon
Terra Academy	267 Aggie Blvd	Vernal, UT	84078	844-322-6562	887-9006	K-12	Cassie Hays
Timpanogos Academy	70 S 100 E	Lindon, UT	84042	801-785-4979	785-9690	K-6	Errol Porter
Tuacahn HS for the Performing Arts	1100 Tuacahn	Ivins, UT	84738-4701	435-652-3201	652-3306	9-12	Dr. Drew Williams
Uintah River HS	PO Box 235	Fort Duchesne, UT	84026-0235	435-725-4088	722-0811	9-12	Ben Pugh
Utah Career Path HS	450 S Simmons Way	Kaysville, UT	84037	801-593-2440	593-2140	9-12	Robyn Bagley
Utah Connections Academy	687 W 700 S Ste E	Woods Cross, UT	84087	801-298-6660	298-6670	K-12	Jeffrey Herr
Utah County Academy of Science	940 W 800 S	Orem, UT	84058-5915	801-863-2222	225-2214	10-12	Dr. Anna Trevino
Utah International Charter S	350 E Baird Cir	Salt Lake City, UT	84115	385-290-1306		7-12	Angela Rowland
Utah Military Academy - Riverdale	5120 S 1050 W	Riverdale, UT	84405	801-689-3013	689-3325	7-12	Matt Throckmorton
Utah Virtual Academy	310 E 4500 S Ste 620	Murray, UT	84107	801-262-4922	262-5086	K-12	Stacey Hutchings
Valley Academy Charter S	539 N 870 W	Hurricane, UT	84737	435-635-0772		K-8	Kevin Dunkley
Vanguard Academy	2650 S Decker Lake Lane	West Valley, UT	84119	801-327-8724	327-8725	7-12	Suzanne Owen
Venture Academy	495 N 1500 W	Ogden, UT	84404	801-393-3900	393-2006	K-12	Dr. Mark Child
Vista at Entrada S	585 E Center St	Ivins, UT	84738	435-673-4110	256-6433	K-8	Samuel Gibbs
Voyage Academy	1891 N 1500 W	Clinton, UT	84015	801-776-4900	776-1966	K-6	Stacee Phillips
Walden S of Liberal Arts	4230 N University Ave	Provo, UT	84604	801-374-1545	374-3397	PK-12	Dr. Lois Bobo
Wasatch Peak Academy	414 Cutler Dr	North Salt Lake, UT	84054-2951	801-936-3066	936-0887	K-6	Emily Swan
Wasatch Waldorf Charter S	1458 E Murray Holladay Rd	Murray, UT	84117	801-871-3950		K-8	Emily Merchant
Washington Academy	2277 S 3000 E	Saint George, UT	84790-8510	435-673-2232	673-0142	K-8	Anya Yeager M.S.
Weber State University Charter Academy	1351 Edvalson St	Ogden, UT	84408	801-626-6271	626-7427	K-K	Camie Bearden M.Ed.
Webster Academy	205 E 400 S	Orem, UT	84058-6311	801-426-6624	426-6645	K-6	Rick Kempton
Weilenmann S of Discovery	4199 Kilby Rd	Park City, UT	84098-5466	435-575-5411	575-5412	K-8	Cindy Phillips
Winter Sports S in Park City	4251 Shadow Mountain Dr	Park City, UT	84098	435-649-8760	649-9087	9-12	Dave Kaufman

Virginia

School	Address	City,State	Zip code	Telephone	Fax	Grade	Contact
Community Public Charter S	1200 Forest St	Charlottesville, VA	22903	434-972-1607	984-4975	6-8	Ashby Kindler
Green Run Collegiate Charter S	1700 Dahlia Dr	Virginia Beach, VA	23453-2199	757-648-5393		9-12	Barbara Winn
Henry S of Science and Arts	611 W 31st St	Richmond, VA	23225-3518	804-888-7061		K-5	Eileen Atkinson
Hillsboro Charter Academy	37110 Charles Town Pike	Purcellville, VA	20132-2942	540-751-2560	771-6732	K-5	Trisha Ybarra-Peters
Middleburg Community Charter S	101 N Madison St	Middleburg, VA	20117-2645	540-687-5048	527-1257	K-5	David Larson
Murray Charter HS	1200 Forest St	Charlottesville, VA	22903-5262	434-296-3090	979-6479	9-12	Ashby Kindler
York River Academy	11201 George Washington Mem	Yorktown, VA	23690-9701	757-898-0516	890-1045	9-12	Walter Cross

Washington

School	Address	City,State	Zip code	Telephone	Fax	Grade	Contact
Excel Charter S	19300 108th Ave SE	Kent, WA	98031-0146	253-487-7530		6-7	Adel Sefrioui

Wisconsin

School	Address	City,State	Zip code	Telephone	Fax	Grade	Contact
Advanced Learning Academy of WI	100 W River Ave	Barron, WI	54812-1052	715-537-5612	637-5161	K-12	Craig Broeren
A L B A	1712 S 32nd St	Milwaukee, WI	53215-2104	414-902-7525	902-7526	PK-5	Brenda Martinez
Alliance Charter ES	215 E Forest Ave	Neenah, WI	54956-2765	920-751-6970	751-6861	K-5	Diane Luft
Alliance HS	850 W Walnut St	Milwaukee, WI	53205-1717	414-267-5400	267-5415	9-12	Tina Owen
ALPS Charter S	325 S Eagle St	Oshkosh, WI	54902-5626	920-424-0320	424-7514	5-8	Jay Jones
Andrews Academy	1225 4th St	Beloit, WI	53511	608-361-3000	361-4122	6-12	Tina Goecks
Appleton Bilingual S	913 N Oneida St	Appleton, WI	54911	920-832-6232	832-6355	K-5	Joel Cannon
Appleton Career Academy	5000 N Ballard Rd	Appleton, WI	54913-8942	920-832-4300	832-4301	9-12	Patrick Lee
Appleton Central HS	PO Box 2019	Appleton, WI	54912-2019	920-832-6136	993-7074	6-12	Justin Heitl
Appleton eSchool	2121 E Emmers Dr	Appleton, WI	54915-3802	920-832-6212	832-4880	7-12	Matt Mineau
Appleton Public Montessori S	1545 E Broadway Dr	Appleton, WI	54915	920-832-6325	832-6322	K-6	Dom Ferrito
Appleton Technical Academy	610 N Badger Ave	Appleton, WI	54914-3405	920-832-6234	832-4198	9-12	Greg Hartjes
ARISE Virtual Academy	450 N Crosby Ave	Janesville, WI	53548-3340	608-743-6654	743-5130	K-12	David Parr
Ashland Charter HS	1900 Beaser Ave	Ashland, WI	54806	715-682-7089	682-2075	9-12	Greg Posewitz
Ashland Elementary Charter S	1101 Binsfield Rd	Ashland, WI	54806-3759	715-682-7823		3-5	Mary Zoesch
Badger Rock MS	501 E Badger Rd	Madison, WI	53713-2120	608-663-1633		6-8	Timothy Bubon
Barron Area Montessori S	808 E Woodland Ave	Barron, WI	54812-1759	715-537-5621	637-9353	PK-4	Tawnee Glinski
Bayshore Community Academy	400 Michigan Ave	Oconto, WI	54153	920-834-7406	834-9884	5-8	Adam DeWitt
Birchwood Blue Hills Charter HS	201 E Birch Ave	Birchwood, WI	54817-8800	715-354-9809	354-3469	7-12	Jeffrey Stanley
Birchwood Public Montessori S	201 E Birch Ave	Birchwood, WI	54817-8800	715-354-9809	354-3469	K-6	Jeffrey Stanley
Bobcat Virtual Academy	300 S Wilson St	Birchwood, WI	54817-8841	715-354-3471		PK-12	Jeffrey Stanley
Bridges Virtual S	1201 N Sales St	Merrill, WI	54452-3171	866-537-2743		K-12	John Hagemeister
Brompton S	7951 36th Ave	Kenosha, WI	53142-2119	262-359-2191	359-2194	K-8	Suzanne Loewen
Bruce - Guadalupe Community S	1028 S 9th St	Milwaukee, WI	53204-1335	414-643-6441	649-9022	K-8	Pascual Rodriguez
Business & Economics Acad of Milwaukee	3620 N 18th St	Milwaukee, WI	53206-2362	414-615-3915	988-6704	PK-8	Alisha Birtha
Capitol West Academy	3939 N 88th St	Milwaukee, WI	53222-2748	414-465-1302	465-1319	PK-8	Donna Niccolai-Weber
C.A.R.E. Charter S	2031 Porter Rd	Plover, WI	54467	715-342-0614	342-0614	7-9	Steve Prokop
Carmen HS of Science and Tech - South	1712 S 32nd St	Milwaukee, WI	53215-2104	414-384-4444	384-4455	9-12	Janis Meinke
Carmen MSHS of Science & Tech - NW	5496 N 72nd St	Milwaukee, WI	53218	414-837-4000		6-12	Kyra VandeBunte
Catalyst Academy	709 S Shawano St	New London, WI	54961-1754	920-982-8686		7-12	Christopher Doran
Catalyst Charter MS	PO Box 991	Ripon, WI	54971-0991	920-748-4638	748-4653	6-8	Thomas Hoh
CAVE	PO Box 378	Cameron, WI	54822-0378	715-458-4560	458-4236	K-12	Jon Griffith
Central City Cyberschool	4301 N 44th St	Milwaukee, WI	53216-1473	414-444-2330	444-2435	K-8	Christine Faltz
Central HS	621 S Water St	Sheboygan, WI	53081-4431	920-459-6746	803-7756	9-12	Duane Simmons
Central Wisconsin STEM Academy	540 Birch St	Nekoosa, WI	54457-1318	715-886-8040		4-7	Jon Sprehn
Central Wisconsin Virtual S	357 N Main St	Amherst, WI	54406-9102	715-824-5522		6-12	Mark Luetschwager
Chippewa Valley Montessori Charter S	400 Cameron St	Eau Claire, WI	54703-5101	715-852-6950	852-6995	PK-5	Todd Johnson
Cirrus Charter HS	301 W Division St	Rosendale, WI	54974-9640	920-872-2161		9-12	Wayne Weber
Clark Street Community S	2429 Clark St	Middleton, WI	53562-2619	608-829-9640		9-12	Jill Gurtner
Class ACT Charter S	400 9th St N	Park Falls, WI	54552-1384	715-762-2474	762-5674	9-12	Timothy Kief
Classical Charter S	3310 N Durkee St	Appleton, WI	54911-1215	920-832-4968	997-1390	K-8	Bernie Mitchell
Community HS	6700 N 80th St	Milwaukee, WI	53223-5506	414-256-8200	256-8215	9-12	Roxane Mayeur
Connects Learning Center	6201 S Barland Ave	Cudahy, WI	53110-2951	414-766-5090	766-5095	9-12	Stacey Adamczyk
CORE 4-Edgerton ES	5145 S 116th St	Hales Corners, WI	53130-1001	414-525-8900	525-8901	PK-PK	Lori Komas
CORE 4-Hales Corners ES	11319 W Godsell Ave	Hales Corners, WI	53130-1817	414-525-8800	525-8801	PK-PK	Lori Komas
Coulee Montessori Charter S	1611 Kane St	La Crosse, WI	54603	608-789-7970	789-0035	PK-8	Laura Huber
Creative Minds Charter S	7450 Titus Dr	Minocqua, WI	54548-9139	715-356-5206	356-1626	3-5	Brent Johnson
Daniels University Preparatory Academy	4834 N Mother Daniels Way	Milwaukee, WI	53209-5981	414-466-1650		K-8	Theresa Adams
D.C. Everest Idea S	4704 Camp Phillips Rd	Weston, WI	54476-1573	715-359-6561		6-12	Steven Pophal
Denmark Community Charter S	450 N Wall St	Denmark, WI	54208-9416	920-863-4153	863-4036	7-12	Melissa Dupke
De Soto Virtual S	615 Main St	De Soto, WI	54624-8644	608-648-0102		K-12	Scott Kelly
Destinations Career Academy of WI	4709 Dale Curtin Dr	Mc Farland, WI	53558	855-475-3218		K-12	Nich Sutherland
Dewey Academy of Learning	1420 Harvey St	Green Bay, WI	54302-1918	920-272-7074	448-3560	9-12	Molly O'Neill
Dimensions of Learning Academy	6218 25th Ave	Kenosha, WI	53143-4370	262-359-6849	359-3134	K-8	Diana Pearson
Discovery Charter S	200 Fuller St	Columbus, WI	53925-1647	920-623-5952	623-6026	K-3	Beth Hellpap
Downtown Montessori Academy	2507 S Graham St	Milwaukee, WI	53207-1609	414-744-6005	744-6007	K-8	Virginia Flynn
eAchieve Academy of Wisconsin	222 Maple Ave	Waukesha, WI	53186-4725	262-970-1074	970-1148	K-12	Rick Nettesheim
Eagleville Elementary Charter S	S101W34511 County Road LO	Eagle, WI	53119	262-363-6258	594-5495	1-6	Ron Schlicht
Early Learning Academy	3871 E Bluestem Dr	Oak Creek, WI	53154-6640	414-768-6220		PK-PK	Christopher Gabrhel
ES for the Arts and Academics	3508 N 21st St	Sheboygan, WI	53083-2807	920-459-0947		K-5	Ted Hamm
Elkhorn Options Virtual Charter S	3 N Jackson St	Elkhorn, WI	53121-1905	262-723-3160	723-4652	K-12	Trisha Spende
Endeavor Charter S	825 Endeavour Dr	Watertown, WI	53098	920-262-7525		9-12	Bob Logan
Enrich Excel Achieve Learning Academy	2607 N 18th St	Wausau, WI	54403-3176	715-261-0636	845-2913	6-12	Dr. Shannon Young
Escuela Verde	3628 W Pierce St	Milwaukee, WI	53215-1030	414-988-7960	988-7961	7-12	Joella Zocher
Exploration Academy	400 N Main St	Verona, WI	53593-1147	608-845-4550		9-12	Pheng Lee
Fairview S	6500 W Kinnickinnic River	Milwaukee, WI	53219-3099	414-546-7700	546-7715	PK-8	Ebbie Wells
Fond du Lac STEM Academy	401 S Military Rd	Fond du Lac, WI	54935-4822	920-906-6722		3-5	Donald Smith
Fond du Lac STEM Institute	401 S Military Rd	Fond du Lac, WI	54935	920-906-6722		6-9	Donald Smith
Forest Lane Community S	222 Forest Ln	Montello, WI	53949-9390	608-297-2128	297-8075	PK-5	John Graf
Foster ES	305 W Foster St	Appleton, WI	54915-1515	920-832-6288	832-4831	K-6	Matt Zimmerman
Fox River Academy	1000 S Mason St	Appleton, WI	54914-5457	920-832-6260	993-1390	1-8	Lori Leschisin
Fox West Academy	220 Warner St	Hortonville, WI	54944-8559	920-779-7929	779-7923	6-8	Steven Gromala
Grandview HS	2745 S 13th st	Milwaukee, WI	53215-3875	414-672-1168	672-1273	9-12	Debi Harry
HACIL	15930 W 5th St	Hayward, WI	54843-7181	715-934-2112	934-8080	PK-12	Crystal Hexum

School	Address	City,State	Zip code	Telephone	Fax	Grade	Contact
Harborside Academy	714 49th St	Kenosha, WI	53140-3353	262-359-8400	359-8450	6-12	William Haithcock
Hartland Fine Arts Leadership Academy	232 Church St	Hartland, WI	53029-1704	262-369-6710	369-6711	K-2	Heather Grindatti
Hawley Environmental S	5610 W Wisconsin Ave	Milwaukee, WI	53213-4258	414-256-8500	256-8515	PK-5	Patricia Cifax
Health Care Academy	115 E 6th St S	Ladysmith, WI	54848-1910	715-532-5531	532-7899	9-12	Robert Lecheler
Highland Community ES	1030 Cardinal Dr	Highland, WI	53543-9791	608-929-4525	929-4527	PK-5	Josh Tarrell
Highland Community HS	1030 Cardinal Dr	Highland, WI	53543-9791	608-929-4525	929-4527	9-12	Josh Tarrell
Highland Community MS	1030 Cardinal Dr	Highland, WI	53543-9791	608-929-4525	929-4527	6-8	Josh Tarrell
Highland Community S	1706 W Highland Ave	Milwaukee, WI	53233-1132	414-342-1412	342-1408	PK-8	Kathy Ronco
High Marq Environmental Charter S	222 Forest Ln	Montello, WI	53949-9390	608-297-2126	297-7726	7-12	Chuck Harsh
HS of Health Sciences	349 N Oak Crest Dr	Wales, WI	53183-9711	262-968-6273		9-11	Stephen Plum
Hines Academy	7151 N 86th St	Milwaukee, WI	53224-4861	414-358-3542	760-4364	PK-8	Precious Washington
Hmong American Peace Academy	4601 N 84th St	Milwaukee, WI	53225-4958	414-383-4944	383-4950	PK-12	Chris Her-Xiong
Honey Creek Continuous Progess Charter S	6701 W Eden Pl	Milwaukee, WI	53220-1335	414-604-7900	604-7915	PK-5	Gitanjali Chawla
Humboldt Park ES	3230 S Adams Ave	Milwaukee, WI	53207-2700	414-294-1700	294-1715	PK-8	Georgia Becker
i4Learning Community S	5760 Mohawk Rd	Campbellsport, WI	53010	262-626-8427	626-4401	PK-5	Joel Dziedzic
IDEAL Charter S	1420 W Goldcrest Ave	Milwaukee, WI	53221-5013	414-267-1600		K-8	Jennifer Carter
IDEAS Academy	830 Virginia Ave	Sheboygan, WI	53081-4427	920-459-0950		9-12	Ted Hamm
IForward: Wisconsin's Online Charter S	480 E James Ave	Grantsburg, WI	54840-7959	855-447-4723	463-2534	6-12	Billy Beesley
iLEAD Charter S	510 Grayside Ave	Mauston, WI	53948-1921	608-847-5451	847-4635	7-12	Gil Saylor
Innovations STEM Academy	1225 N Water St	Sparta, WI	54656-4303	608-366-3497		6-8	Toby Oswald
Island City Academy	980 8th Ave	Cumberland, WI	54829-9188	715-822-5122	822-5132	7-12	Colin Green
Island City Virtual Academy	1010 8th Ave	Cumberland, WI	54829	715-822-5124	822-5136	PK-12	Dr. Barry Rose
JEDI Virtual HS	1221 Innovation Dr	Whitewater, WI	53190	262-473-1469	472-2269	PK-12	Leslie Steinhaus
Journey Charter S	PO Box 991	Ripon, WI	54971-0991	920-748-1550		K-2	Tanya Sanderfoot
Juneau County Charter S	N11003 17th Ave	Necedah, WI	54646	608-565-7494	565-7559	7-12	Amy McMillen
Kaleidoscope Academy	318 E Brewster St	Appleton, WI	54911-3702	920-832-6294	832-4605	6-8	Al Brant
Kenosha e-School	1808 41st Pl	Kenosha, WI	53140-5612	262-359-7715	359-5933	K-12	Dan Tenuta
Kenosha Schl of Enhanced Tech/Curriculum	6811 18th Ave	Kenosha, WI	53143-4932	262-359-3800	359-3850	K-8	Angela Andersson
Kiel eSchool	PO Box 201	Kiel, WI	53042-0201	920-894-5169	894-5100	7-12	Heidi Dorner
KM Explore Charter S	219 N Oak Crest Dr	Wales, WI	53183-9705	262-968-6300		PK-5	Laura Dahm
KM Global S	349 N Oak Crest Dr	Wales, WI	53183-9711	262-968-6273	968-6390	9-12	Michele Koper
La Casa de Esperanza Charter S	410 Arcadian Ave	Waukesha, WI	53186-5005	262-547-0887	547-0735	K-K	Kristy Casey
La Causa Charter S	PO Box 4188	Milwaukee, WI	53204-0188	414-902-1660	902-1676	K-8	Maria Ayala-Smith
La Crosse Design Institute	1900 Denton St	La Crosse, WI	54601	608-789-7670	789-7975	6-8	Penny Reedy
LaCrossroads Charter HS	1801 Losey Blvd S	La Crosse, WI	54601	608-789-7700	789-7711	9-12	Troy McDonald
Lake Country Academy	4101 Technology Pkwy	Sheboygan, WI	53083-6049	920-208-3020	208-3022	PK-8	Shawn Dzwonkowski
Laker Online Virtual Charter S	205 Oak St	Turtle Lake, WI	54889-8929	715-986-4470	986-2444	K-12	Kent Kindschy
Lakeview Montessori S	711 Pine St	Sparta, WI	54656-1947	608-366-3468	366-3473	PK-6	Patrick Olbert
Laurel HS	100 Blackhawk Dr	Viroqua, WI	54665-1315	608-637-3191	637-8034	9-12	Katherine Klos
LEADS Primary Charter S	1410 Waukechon Rd	Shawano, WI	54166-3168	715-524-2134	526-4372	PK-2	Troy Edwards
LIFE Entrepreneurial S	800 N Shore Dr	Hartland, WI	53029-2713	262-369-6767	369-3766	6-8	Michele Schmidt
Lighthouse Learning Academy	4521 Lincoln Ave	Two Rivers, WI	54241	920-793-4560		K-12	Lisa Quistorf
Link2Learn Virtual Charter S	PO Box 6	Chetek, WI	54728	715-924-2226	924-2376	PK-12	Terryn Wingler-Petty
Little Chute Career Pathways	325 Meulemans St Ste A	Little Chute, WI	54140-3300	920-788-7600	788-7841	9-12	Dan Valentyn
Little Chute FLEX Academy	325 Meulemans St Ste B	Little Chute, WI	54140-3300	920-380-9250	788-7603	K-7	David Botz
Lumen Charter HS	PO Box 991	Ripon, WI	54971-0991	920-748-4616	748-4622	9-12	Seth Meinel
Magellan Charter MS	225 N Badger Ave	Appleton, WI	54914-3832	920-832-6226	832-4857	7-8	Debra Moreland
Maple Grove Charter S	290 County Road F	Hamburg, WI	54411-9141	715-536-7684	536-4221	K-5	Heidi Siebert Preul
Marathon Venture Academy	100 Spring Valley Dr	Marathon, WI	54448-3400	715-443-2538		6-8	Sarah Budny
Marshall Charter S	PO Box 76	Marshall, WI	53559-0076	608-655-1310	655-3046	11-12	Brian Sniff
Mauston Montessori Charter S	708 Loomis Dr	Mauston, WI	53948	608-847-5616		PK-3	Lynda Oleinik
McKinley Academy	1010 Huron St	Manitowoc, WI	54220-3314	920-683-4780	683-4782	9-12	Kristin Lee
McKinley Charter S	1266 McKinley Rd	Eau Claire, WI	54703-2220	715-852-6900	852-6904	6-12	Peter Riley
Mead Charter S	241 17th Ave S	Wisc Rapids, WI	54495-2408	715-424-6777	422-6333	PK-6	Margie Dorshorst
Merrill Adult Diploma Academy	1101A N Mill St	Merrill, WI	54452-1179	715-536-1431	539-2769	10-12	Shannon Murray
Merrimac Community Charter S	360 School St	Merrimac, WI	53561-9584	608-493-2217	493-2895	PK-5	Sid Malek
Mighty River Acad of Virtual Education	800 E Crawford St	Pr du Chien, WI	53821-2327	608-326-3703		K-12	Mike Liddell
Milwaukee Academy of Science	2000 W Kilbourn Ave	Milwaukee, WI	53233-1625	414-933-0302	933-1426	PK-12	Judy Merryfield
Milwaukee College Prep - 38th St	2623 N 38th St	Milwaukee, WI	53210-2502	414-445-1000	445-1005	K-8	Maggy Olson
Milwaukee College Prep - Lloyd St	1228 W Lloyd St	Milwaukee, WI	53205-1243	414-264-6000	264-2004	K-8	Andy Vitrano
Milwaukee College Prep S - 36th St	2449 N 36th St	Milwaukee, WI	53210-3040	414-445-8020	445-8167	K-8	Kristen Foster
Milwaukee College Prep S North Campus	1350 W North Ave	Milwaukee, WI	53205-1257	414-264-6600	264-6607	K-8	Michael Morgan
Milwaukee Collegiate Academy	4030 N 29th St	Milwaukee, WI	53216-1816	414-873-4014	873-4344	9-12	Judith Parker
Milwaukee Community Cyber HS	131 S 1st St	Milwaukee, WI	53204	414-308-1230	308-1231	9-12	Jonathan Dorman
Milwaukee Environmental Sciences Charter	6600 W Melvina St	Milwaukee, WI	53216	414-353-3830	353-3834	PK-8	Roseann Lococo
Milwaukee Excellence Charter S	4950 N 24th St	Milwaukee, WI	53209	414-403-5892		6-7	Maurice Thomas
Milwaukee Math & Science Academy	110 W Burleigh St	Milwaukee, WI	53212-2046	414-263-6400	263-6403	PK-8	David Chief
Milwaukee Scholars Charter S	7000 W Florist Ave	Milwaukee, WI	53218-1855	414-393-0197		K-8	Taneka Smith
Monona Grove Liberal Arts Charter S	5301 Monona Dr	Monona, WI	53716-3126	608-316-1924	221-7688	9-12	Kristen Langer
Montello Virtual S	222 Forest Ln	Montello, WI	53949-9390	608-297-2128	297-8075	K-12	John Graf
Montessori ES	421 W Maple St	River Falls, WI	54022	715-425-7645	425-5380	PK-6	Nate Schurman
Mosaic S	830 Virginia Ave	Sheboygan, WI	53081-4427	920-459-0946		6-8	Ted Hamm
New Century Charter S	401 W Verona Ave	Verona, WI	53593-1318	608-845-4900	845-4920	K-5	
New Directions Learning Community	2601 Sullivan Ave	Kaukauna, WI	54130-3564	920-766-6116	766-6122	K-4	Abbey Frischmann
New Horizons for Learning	1701 E Capitol Dr	Shorewood, WI	53211-1911	414-963-6921	961-2819	9-12	Tim Kenney
New Path Charter S	512 Caldwell Ave	Oconto Falls, WI	54154-1138	920-848-4455	848-3899	7-12	Teri Bohm
Next Door Charter S	2545 N 29th St	Milwaukee, WI	53210-3116	414-562-2929	562-1979	PK-K	Kate Linscott
Next Generation Academy	1700 Klatt Rd	New London, WI	54961-8603	920-982-8420	982-8440	6-12	Anne Ferge
Niikuusara Community S	540 Birch St	Nekoosa, WI	54457-1318	715-886-8040	886-8097	4-8	Jon Sprehn
North Division Charter HS	1011 W Center St	Milwaukee, WI	53206-3262	414-267-4900	267-5015	9-12	Stanley McWilliams
Northeast Wisconsin Montessori S	411 E Washington Ave	Cleveland, WI	53015-1517	920-693-8241	693-8357	1-6	Bill Klein
Northern Lakes Regional Academy	33 Ann St	Rice Lake, WI	54868-2265	715-234-9007		9-12	Curt Pacholke
Northern Waters Environmental S	15930 W 5th St	Hayward, WI	54843-7181	715-634-2619	634-9953	6-10	Brittany Roberts
Northland Pines Montessori Learning Ctr	8234 Highway 70 W	Saint Germain, WI	54558-9749	715-542-3632		PK-4	Tony Duffek
North Star Academy	207 N 1st St	Cameron, WI	54822-9703	715-537-5612	637-5161	9-12	Craig Broeren
NorthStar Community Charter S	N14463 Highway 53	Minong, WI	54859-9483	715-466-2297	466-5149	4-8	Curt Zamzow
Northwood ES	N14463 Highway 53	Minong, WI	54859-9483	715-466-2297		PK-5	Curt Zamzow
Northwood MSHS	N14463 Highway 53	Minong, WI	54859-9483	715-466-2297	466-5149	6-12	Curt Zamzow
Northwoods Community ES	9086 County K	Harshaw, WI	54529-9731	715-282-8200	282-8218	K-5	Timothy Howell
Northwoods Community Secondary S	665 Coolidge Ave	Rhinelander, WI	54501-2898	715-365-9660	365-9687	6-12	Will Losch
NOVA Tech	2433 W Roosevelt Dr	Milwaukee, WI	53209-6640	414-301-6592	301-6593	9-12	Scott Campbell
NR4Kids Charter S	701 E 11th St	New Richmond, WI	54017-2399	715-243-7403	246-4278	PK-PK	Mike Ballard
Nuestro Mundo Community S	902 Nichols Rd	Monona, WI	53716-2565	608-663-1079	204-0364	K-5	Josh Forehand
Oakwood Environmental Educ Charter S	1225 N Oakwood Rd	Oshkosh, WI	54904-8456	920-424-0315	424-7591	PK-5	Kirby Schultz
Oconto Falls Alternative Learning Site	320 E Central Ave	Oconto Falls, WI	54154-1456	920-848-4455	848-3899	10-12	Mark Trepanier
Odyssey Charter S	2037 N Elinor St	Appleton, WI	54914-2255	920-832-6250	832-4389	3-6	Kristin Comerford
Oredocker Project S	203 11th St E	Ashland, WI	54806-3245	715-682-7087		6-8	Laura Comer
Osceola Charter Preschool	PO Box 128	Osceola, WI	54020-0128	715-294-3457	294-2428	PK-PK	Peggy Weber
Ouisconsing S of Collaboration	103 Pleasant St	Lodi, WI	53555	608-592-3855	592-2496	3-5	Sherri Endres-Lovell
Park Community Charter S	509 Lawe St	Kaukauna, WI	54130-2021	920-766-6129	766-6544	K-4	Kenneth Kortens
Pathways Charter S	1043 S Main St	West Bend, WI	53095-4655	262-306-7125		7-9	
Penfield Montessori S	1441 N 24th St	Milwaukee, WI	53205	414-999-2330		PK-8	Dr. Sabrina Claude
Phantom Knight S of Opportunity	400 Reid St Ste W	De Pere, WI	54115-2164	920-425-1915	429-1919	7-12	Dr. Jason Lau
Point of Discovery S	1900 W Zinda Dr	Stevens Point, WI	54481	715-345-5566	245-0203	6-8	Dan Lathrop
Portage Academy of Achievement	117 W Franklin St	Portage, WI	53901-1755	608-742-8545	745-0887	9-12	Matt Paulsen
Promethean Charter S	PO Box 247	Butternut, WI	54514-0247	715-769-3434	769-3712	9-12	Joseph Zirngibl
Quest ES	PO Box 991	Ripon, WI	54971-0991	920-748-4695	748-4698	3-5	Randy Hatlen
Racine Civil Leaders Academy	1325 Park Ave	Racine, WI	53403-1848	262-664-8500	664-8524	PK-5	Danielle Dekker
REAL Charter S	5915 Erie St	Racine, WI	53402-1925	262-664-8100	664-8110	6-12	Curt Shircel
Renaissance Charter Alternative Academy	1107 S Wasson Ln	River Falls, WI	54022-2726	715-425-7687	425-7693	9-12	Kit Luedtke
Renaissance S for the Arts	610 N Badger Ave	Appleton, WI	54914-3405	920-832-5708	832-4198	9-12	Todd Kadolph
Richland Online Academy	1996 US Hwy 14 W	Richland Center, WI	53581-1352	608-647-6106		6-12	Caleb Hundt
Rocketship Southside Community Prep	3003 W Cleveland Ave	Milwaukee, WI	53215-2800	414-455-3539	918-8999	K-4	Rodney Lynk
Rock River Charter S	31 W Milwaukee St	Janesville, WI	53548-2911	608-743-5070	752-8430	9-12	Dr. Lisa Peterson
Rock University HS	2909 Kellogg Ave	Janesville, WI	53546-5606	608-758-6512		10-12	Tina Johnson
Rural Virtual Academy	624 College St	Medford, WI	54451	888-801-2666		PK-12	Charlie Heckel
St. Croix Academy of Virtual Education	PO Box 118	Hammond, WI	54015	715-796-5383	796-5662	K-12	Stephani Owens
S for AGricultural & Environmental Study	200 S Depot St	Fox Lake, WI	53933-9625	920-928-3136		PK-8	Bruce McMurry
School for Arts and Performance	349 N Oak Crest Dr	Wales, WI	53183-9711	262-968-6273	968-6217	9-12	Kevin Erickson
School for Early Developmnt & Achievment	2020 W Wells St	Milwaukee, WI	53233-2720	414-937-2024	937-2021	PK-2	Nicola Ciurro
School of Sci Engineering & Technology	PO Box 107	Blair, WI	54616	608-989-9835	989-2451	1-6	Lynn Halvorson
School of Technology & Arts I	1111 7th St S	La Crosse, WI	54601-5474	608-789-7695	789-7030	K-5	Steve Michaels
School of Technology & Arts II	510 9th St S	La Crosse, WI	54601	608-789-7780	789-7181	6-8	Melissa Murray
Shapiro ES	1050 W 18th Ave	Oshkosh, WI	54902-6602	920-424-0164	424-7594	PK-5	Trina Anderson
Shared Journeys Charter S	9004 W Lincoln Ave	West Allis, WI	53227-2452	414-328-6535	545-6230	7-12	Lisa Colla
Sheboygan Leadership Academy	1305 Saint Clair Ave	Sheboygan, WI	53081-3233	920-208-5930		PK-8	Peggy Henseler
SOAR Charter HS	1800 Pleasure Island Rd	Eagle River, WI	54521-8980	715-479-4473		9-12	Scott Foster

School	Address	City,State	Zip code	Telephone	Fax	Grade	Contact
SOAR Charter S	6485 Town Hall Rd	Land O Lakes, WI	54540-9659	715-547-3619		5-12	Scott Foster
Sparta Area Independent Learning S	201 E Franklin St	Sparta, WI	54656-1803	608-366-3430	366-3526	9-12	Bob Sanders
Sparta Charter Preschool	201 E Franklin St	Sparta, WI	54656-1803	608-269-3151	366-3529	PK-PK	Diane Everson-Riley
Sparta High Point Charter S	201 E Franklin St	Sparta, WI	54656-1803	608-366-3151	366-3529	6-12	Peggy Jadack
Spooner Area Virtual Academy	801 County Highway A	Spooner, WI	54801-7429	715-635-2171	635-7174	K-12	Kurt Kunkel
Stellar Collegiate S	1115 S 7th St	Milwaukee, WI	53204	414-210-5707		PK-2	Melissa McGonegle
TAGOS Leadership Academy	1350 N Parker Dr	Janesville, WI	53545-0719	608-743-5071	743-5095	7-12	Dr. Kim Ehrhardt
Tenor High S	840 N Jackson St	Milwaukee, WI	53202-3807	414-431-4371	431-4376	9-12	Tyson Tlachac
Tesla Engineering Charter S	2121 E Emmers Dr	Appleton, WI	54915-3802	920-997-1399	832-4880	9-12	Paul Weisse
Time 4 Learning Charter S	5900 S 51st St	Greendale, WI	53129-2634	414-423-2750		PK-PK	Tracy Flater
Tomah Area Montessori S	1720 Academy Ave	Tomah, WI	54660	608-374-5624	372-5087	PK-3	Tim Gnewikow
Tomorrow River Community Charter S	10186 County Road MM	Amherst Jct, WI	54407-9053	715-281-4776	346-2730	PK-6	
Transitional Skills Center	850 Maple St	Glenwood City, WI	54013-4346	715-265-4266	265-7129	10-12	Timothy Johnson
21st Century eSchool	2429 Clark St	Middleton, WI	53562-2619	608-829-9027	831-5160	K-12	Jill Gurtner
21st Century Prep S	1220 Mound Ave	Racine, WI	53404-3350	262-598-0026	598-0031	PK-8	Arletta Tucker
UCC Acosta MS	615 W Washington St	Milwaukee, WI	53204	414-649-4923	649-1920	6-8	Santiago Navarro
Universal Academy for the College Bound	3872 N 8th St	Milwaukee, WI	53206-3303	414-914-9220		K-5	LaShawnda Holland
Universal Academy for the College Bound	6850 N 53rd St	Milwaukee, WI	53223-5239	414-716-5858		6-8	LaShawnda Holland
Valley New S	10 E College Ave Ste 228	Appleton, WI	54911	920-993-7037	832-1725	7-12	Ben Vogel
Veritas HS	3025 W Oklahoma Ave	Milwaukee, WI	53215-4347	414-389-5575	389-5576	9-12	Sherry Tolkan
Vernon County Area Better Futures HS	100 Blackhawk Dr	Viroqua, WI	54665-1315	608-637-3191	637-8034	10-12	Katherine Klos
Verona Area Core Knowledge Charter S	740 N Main St	Verona, WI	53593-1153	608-845-4130	845-4961	K-8	Rick Kisting
Verona Area International S	5890 Devoro Rd	Fitchburg, WI	53711	608-845-4224	845-4220	K-5	Barbara Drake
Viroqua Area Montessori S	115 N Education Ave	Viroqua, WI	54665	608-637-7071	637-1211	PK-5	Kate Moll
Walworth County Education Alternative HS	400 County Road H	Elkhorn, WI	53121-2035	262-741-8138	741-8131	9-12	Kelly Demerath
Warriner MSHS for Personalized Learning	712 Riverfront Dr Ste 101	Sheboygan, WI	53081-4665	920-459-0945	459-0950	6-12	Duane Simmons
Waukesha Academy of Health Professions	401 E Roberta Ave	Waukesha, WI	53186-6637	262-970-3710	970-3720	9-12	Richard Lehman
Waukesha East Alternative S	1150 Whiterock Ave	Waukesha, WI	53186-4101	262-970-4355	970-4380	9-12	Ryan Galante
Waukesha Engineering Preparatory Academy	401 E Roberta Ave	Waukesha, WI	53186-6637	262-970-3880	970-3720	9-12	Timothy Joynt
Waukesha STEM Academy	114 S Charles St	Waukesha, WI	53186-6202	262-970-2300	970-2320	K-5	James Murray
Waukesha STEM Academy	130 Walton Ave	Waukesha, WI	53186-5904	262-970-2500	970-2520	6-8	James Murray
Waupaca County Charter S	PO Box 457	Weyauwega, WI	54983-0457	920-867-4744		6-12	Wendy Cartledge
Wausau Area Montessori Charter S	3101 N 13th St	Wausau, WI	54403-2317	715-261-0795	261-2035	K-6	Erin Bailey
Wausau EGL Academy	2607 N 18th St	Wausau, WI	54403	715-261-0625	845-5341	9-12	Mike Schwei
Wauwatosa STEM	1060 Glenview Ave	Wauwatosa, WI	53213-3034	414-773-1900	773-1920	K-5	Mike Heun
Westside Academy	1940 N 36th St	Milwaukee, WI	53208-1927	414-934-4400	934-4415	K-8	Tequila Kurth
Whittier ES	4382 S 3rd St	Milwaukee, WI	53207-4968	414-294-1400	294-1415	PK-5	Peggy Mystrow
Wildlands Research Charter S	S1 County Road K	Fall Creek, WI	54742	715-286-4400	877-2234	7-12	Paul Tweed
Windlake Academy	1445 S 32nd St	Milwaukee, WI	53215-1903	414-672-0726	672-2019	4-8	Theresa Yurk
Windlake ES	2433 S 15th St	Milwaukee, WI	53215-3132	414-643-9052	643-0162	K-3	Jim Kotsonis
Wisconsin Connections Academy	350 W Capitol Dr	Appleton, WI	54911	920-993-7076	832-6284	K-12	Michelle Mueller
Wisconsin Virtual Learning	401 Highland Dr	Fredonia, WI	53021-9491	262-692-3988	692-3952	PK-12	Karen O'Donnell
WIVA	4709 Dale Curtin Dr	Mc Farland, WI	53558-8958	608-838-9482	838-9483	K-12	Nicholaus Sutherland
Woodland Progressive Charter S	7450 Titus Dr	Minocqua, WI	54548-9139	715-356-5206	358-2649	6-8	Brent Johnson
Woodlands S	5510 W Blue Mound Rd	Milwaukee, WI	53208-3012	414-475-1600	475-9575	PK-8	Patty Rogers
Woodlands S East	3121 W State St	Milwaukee, WI	53208-3494	414-937-2000	937-3730	PK-4	Maureen Sullivan
Wright Charter MS	1717 Fish Hatchery Rd	Madison, WI	53713-1244	608-204-1340	204-0547	6-8	Angela Crawford

Wyoming

School	Address	City,State	Zip code	Telephone	Fax	Grade	Contact
Arapahoe Charter HS	445 Little Wind Rvr Bottom	Arapahoe, WY	82510	307-856-3795		9-12	Elberta Monroe
Laramie Montessori Charter School	608 S 4th St	Laramie, WY	82070	307-742-9964		K-6	Elizabeth Coffey
Poder Academy	2201 Morrie Ave	Cheyenne, WY	82001	307-632-2248		K-8	Dr. Jayne Smith
Snowy Range Academy	4037 E Grand Ave Ste A	Laramie, WY	82070-5128	307-745-9930	745-9931	K-8	Dawn Wilson

BUREAU OF INDIAN AFFAIRS SCHOOLS

Agency/School	Address	City,State	Zip code	Telephone	Fax	Grade	Enr	Superintendent/Principal
Education Resource Center - Albuquerque	1011 Indian School NW	Albuquerque, NM	87104	505-563-5265	563-5345	K-12	3,300	Tony Dearman
Education Resource Center - Belcourt	School St #16	Belcourt, ND	58316			PK-12	400	
Education Resource Center - Bismarck	3315 University Dr	Bismarck, ND	58504			K-12	300	
Education Resource Center - Chinle	PO Box 6003	Chinle, AZ	86503-6003	928-674-5130	674-5134	K-12	600	Gloria Hale-Showalter
Education Resource Center - Crownpoint	PO Box 848	Crownpoint, NM	87313	505-786-6151	786-6016	K-12	3,800	
Education Resource Center - Flandreau	1132 N Crescent St	Flandreau, SD	57028			K-12	800	
Education Resource Center - Kyle	PO Box 333	Pine Ridge, SD	57770-0333	605-867-1306	867-5610	K-12	1,700	
Education Resource Center - Minneapolis	2001 Killebrew Dr Ste 122	Bloomington, MN	55425	952-851-5427	851-5439	K-12	1,200	
Education Resource Center - Nashville	545 Marriott Dr Ste 700	Nashville, TN	37214	615-564-6500	564-6701	PK-12	2,100	
Education Resource Center - Phoenix	2600 N Central Ave Ste 800	Phoenix, AZ	85004	602-265-1592	265-0293	K-12	100	Jim Hastings
Education Resource Center - Seattle	909 1st Ave Ste 192	Seattle, WA	98104	206-220-7976	220-7981	K-12	1,100	
Education Resource Center - Shiprock	PO Box 3229	Shiprock, NM	87420	505-368-3400	368-3409	K-12	1,800	
Education Resource Center - Tuba City	PO Box 746	Tuba City, AZ	86045-0746	928-283-2218	283-2286	K-12	200	Donald Coffland
Education Resource Center - Window Rock	PO Box 1449	Window Rock, AZ	86515	928-871-5932	871-5945	K-12	1,200	Tamarah Pfeiffer Ph.D.
Bureau of Indian Affairs	1849 C St NW	Washington, DC	20240-0002	202-208-6123	208-3312			Dr. Charles Roessel
Blackwater Community S	3652 E Blackwater School Rd	Coolidge, AZ	85128-6609	520-215-5859	215-5862	K-2		Jack Sharma
Casa Blanca Community S	PO Box 10940	Bapchule, AZ	85121-0105	520-315-3489	315-3505	K-4		Jacque Bradley
Dishchii'bikoh Community S	PO Box 80068	Cibecue, AZ	85911-0068	928-332-2480	332-2341	K-12		Juan Aragon
First Mesa ES	PO Box 750	Polacca, AZ	86042-0750	928-737-2581	737-2323	K-6		Alma Shinquah
Flandreau Indian HS	1132 N Crescent St	Flandreau, SD	57028	605-997-3773	997-2601	9-12		Everall Fox
Gila Crossing S	4665 W Pecos Rd	Laveen, AZ	85339-9009	520-550-4834	550-4252	K-8		Ruben Gonzalez
Hopi Day S	PO Box 42	Kykotsmovi, AZ	86039-0042	928-734-2468	734-2470	K-6		Dianna Wallace
Hopi JSHS	PO Box 337	Keams Canyon, AZ	86034-0356	928-738-5111	738-5333	7-12	500	Alban Naha
Hotevilla-Bacavi Community S	PO Box 48	Hotevilla, AZ	86030-0048	928-734-2462	734-2225	K-8		Lorrie Harding
Isleta ES	1000 Moonlight Dr SW	Albuquerque, NM	87105-8124	505-869-2321	869-1625	K-6	200	Rebecca Vesley
Jemez Day S	PO Box 139	Jemez Pueblo, NM	87024-0139	575-834-7304	834-7081	K-6	100	Freddie Cardenas
Jicarilla Dormitory	PO Box 1009	Dulce, NM	87528-1009	575-759-3101	759-3338	1-12		David Montoya
Keams Canyon ES	PO Box 397	Keams Canyon, AZ	86034-0385	928-738-2385	738-5519	K-6	100	Gary Polacca
Laguna ES	PO Box 191	Laguna, NM	87026-0191	505-552-9200	552-7294	K-5	200	Dr. Kay Morris
Laguna MS	PO Box 268	Laguna, NM	87026-0268	505-552-9091	552-6466	6-8	100	Dr. Natalie Martinez
Mescalero Apache S	PO Box 230	Mescalero, NM	88340-0230	575-464-4431	464-4822	PK-12	500	Sergio Castanon
Moencopi Day S	PO Box 185	Tuba City, AZ	86045-0185	928-283-5361	283-4662	K-6		Rebecca Fred
Ohkay Owingeh Community S	PO Box 1077	San Juan Pueblo, NM	87566-1077	505-852-2154	852-4305	K-8	100	Maxine Ortiz
Pine Hill S	PO Box 220	Pinehill, NM	87357-0220	505-775-3242	775-3241	K-12	300	Grant Clawson
Riverside Indian S	101 Riverside Dr	Anadarko, OK	73005	405-247-6670	247-5529	4-12		Clay Vinyard
Roosevelt S, Theodore	PO Box 567	Fort Apache, AZ	85926-0567	928-338-4464	338-1009	6-8		Ruben Gonzalez
Salt River ES	10005 E Osborn Rd	Scottsdale, AZ	85256-4019	480-362-2400	362-2401	K-6		Cheryl Parker
San Felipe Pueblo S	PO Box 4343	San Felipe Pb, NM	87001	505-867-3365	867-6253	K-8	400	Ruby Montoya
San Ildefonso Day S	36 Tunyo Po	Santa Fe, NM	87506-7258	505-455-2366	455-2155	K-6	50	Julianna Trujillo
Santa Clara Day S	625 Kee St	Espanola, NM	87532-8905	505-753-4406	753-8866	K-6	100	Steve Marsh
Santa Fe Indian S	PO Box 5340	Santa Fe, NM	87502-5340	505-989-6300	989-6317	7-12		Roy Herrera
Second Mesa Day S	PO Box 98	Second Mesa, AZ	86043-0098	928-737-2571	737-2565	K-6	300	Anthony Morrison
Sky City Community S	PO Box 349	Pueblo of Acoma, NM	87034-0349	505-552-6671	552-6672	K-8	200	Yvonne Haven
Taos Day S	PO Box 1850	Taos, NM	87571-1850	575-758-3652	758-1566	K-8	200	Dr. Alfred Taylor
Te Tsu Geh Oweenge S	RR 42 Box 2	Santa Fe, NM	87506	505-982-1516	982-2090	K-6	50	Veronica Martinez
T'siya S, Zia	1000 Borrego Canyon Rd	Zia Pueblo, NM	87053-6104	505-867-3553	867-5079	K-7		Dr. Melanie Haskin
Blackfeet Dormitory	PO Box 627	Browning, MT	59417-0627	406-338-7441	338-5725	1-12		Renee Tatsey
Cheyenne-Eagle Butte S	PO Box 672	Eagle Butte, SD	57625-0672	605-964-8777	964-8776	K-12		Dr. Neil Trottier
Dunseith Day S	PO Box 759	Dunseith, ND	58329-0759	701-263-4636	263-4200	K-8		Michelle Thomas
Ojibwa Indian S	PO Box 600	Belcourt, ND	58316-0600	701-477-3108	477-6039	K-8		Michael Blue
Pine Ridge S	PO Box 1202	Pine Ridge, SD	57770-1202	605-867-5193	867-5482	K-12	400	Mona Miyasato
Jamerson S, Theodore	3315 University Dr	Bismarck, ND	58504-7565	701-530-0677	530-0601	K-8		Francis Azure
Rock Creek Grant S	PO Box 127	Bullhead, SD	57621-0127	605-823-4971	823-4350	K-8		Clyde Naasz
Sitting Bull Day S	PO Box 26	Little Eagle, SD	57639-0026	605-823-4235	823-2292	K-8		Lisa Bielawski

Agency/School	Address	City,State	Zip code	Telephone	Fax	Grade	Enr	Superintendent/Principal
Standing Rock Community S	PO Box 377	Fort Yates, ND	58538-0377	701-854-3461	854-2078	K-12	200	Bernadette Dauenhauer
Tate Topa Tribal S	PO Box 199	Fort Totten, ND	58335-0199	701-766-1400	766-1457	K-8		Jacqueline Thompson
Twin Buttes S	7997 7A St NW	Halliday, ND	58636-4004	701-938-4396	938-4398	K-8	50	Sandra Starr
White Shield S	2 2nd Ave W	Roseglen, ND	58775-6009	701-743-4350	743-4501	K-12	100	John Jankowski
Black Mesa Community S	PO Box 97	Pinon, AZ	86510-0097	928-674-3632	659-8187	K-8	50	Marie Rose
Cottonwood Day S	Navajo Route 4	Chinle, AZ	86503	928-725-3256	725-3243	K-8		Dr. Leclare Salabye-Gishey
Dennehotso Boarding S	PO Box 2570	Dennehotso, AZ	86535-2570	928-658-3201	658-3221	K-8		James Brown
Greasewood Springs Community S	HC 58 Box 60	Ganado, AZ	86505-9706	928-654-3331	654-3384	PK-8	200	Lucinda Godinez
Jeehdeez'a ES	PO Box 1073	Pinon, AZ	86510-1073	928-725-3308	725-3306	K-5		Sylvia Largo
Lukachukai Community S	PO Box 230	Lukachukai, AZ	86507-0230	928-787-4400		K-8		Arthur Ben
Many Farms Community S	PO Box 70	Many Farms, AZ	86538-3070	928-781-6221	781-6376	K-8		Jacqueline Benally
Many Farms HS	PO Box 307	Many Farms, AZ	86538-3307	928-781-6226	781-6355	9-12		Dr. Carmelia Becenti
Nazlini Community S	HC 58 Box 35	Ganado, AZ	86505-9704	928-755-6125	755-3729	K-6	50	Ronald Arias
Pinon Community S	PO Box 159	Pinon, AZ	86510-0159	928-725-3234	725-3232	K-12		Sherry Mitchell
Rock Point Community S	PO Box 560	Rock Point, AZ	86545-0560	928-659-4221	659-4235	K-12		Deanna Dougi
Rough Rock Community S	PO Box 5000-PTT	Chinle, AZ	86503	928-728-3550	728-3502	K-12	300	Dr. Leon Ben
Alamo Navajo Community S	PO Box 5907	Alamo, NM	87825-5907	575-854-2543	854-2545	K-12	300	Karen Bramlett
Baca/Dlo'ay Azhi Community S	PO Box 1809	Prewitt, NM	87045	505-972-2769	972-2310	K-6	300	Timothy Nelson
Borrego Pass S	PO Box 679	Crownpoint, NM	87313-0679	505-786-5237	786-7078	K-8	1,200	John Bach
Ch'ooshgai Community S	PO Box 321	Tohatchi, NM	87325-0321	505-733-2700	733-2703	K-8	400	Maxine Chischilly
Lake Valley Navajo S	PO Box 748	Crownpoint, NM	87313-0748	505-786-5392	786-5956	K-8	100	Tonya Sturgess
Mariano Lake Community S	PO Box 787	Crownpoint, NM	87313-0787	505-786-5265	786-5203	PK-6	100	Charles Sherman
Na NeelZhiin Ji'Olta S	HC 79 Box 9	Cuba, NM	87013-9701	575-731-2272	731-2252	K-8		Kenneth Toledo
Ojo Encino S	HC 79 Box 7	Cuba, NM	87013-9701	505-731-2333	731-2361	K-8	100	Vickie Blackwater
Pueblo Pintado Community S	HC 79 Box 80	Cuba, NM	87013-9600	575-655-3341	655-3342	PK-8	300	Irowena Whitehair
T'iis Ts'ozi Bi'Olta' S	PO Box 178	Crownpoint, NM	87313-0178	505-786-6159	786-6163	K-8	400	Virginia Jumbo
Tohaali' Community S	PO Box 9857	Newcomb, NM	87455-9857	505-789-3201	789-3202	K-8	200	Delores Bitsilly
To'Hajiilee'He S	PO Box 3438	Canoncito, NM	87026-3438	505-908-2426	908-2914	PK-12	300	Dr. Karen Sanchez-Griego
Tse'ii'ahi' Community S	PO Box 828	Crownpoint, NM	87313-0828	505-786-5389	726-5635	K-4	100	
Chickasaw Children's Village	12998 Village Rd	Kingston, OK	73439	580-564-3060	564-3605	1-12		Sallie Wallace
Crow Creek Sioux Tribal S	101 Crow Creek Loop	Stephan, SD	57346	605-852-2455	852-2140	K-12		Marice Ashley
Enemy Swim S	13525 446th Ave	Waubay, SD	57273-5715	605-947-4605	947-4188	PK-8	200	Virginia Dolney
Eufaula Dormitory	716 Swadley Dr	Eufaula, OK	74432-2201	918-689-2522	689-2438	1-12		Denise Honwa
Jones Academy	HC 74 Box 102-5	Hartshorne, OK	74547	918-297-2518	297-2364	1-12	100	Brad Spears
Kickapoo Nation S	PO Box 106	Powhattan, KS	66527-0106	785-474-3365	474-3530	K-12	100	Debra Turner
Lower Brule Day S	PO Box 245	Lower Brule, SD	57548-0245	605-473-0216	473-0217	PK-6		Joel Hovland
Lower Brule HS	PO Box 245	Lower Brule, SD	57548-0245	605-473-5510	473-5207	7-12		Marice Ashley
Marty Indian S	PO Box 187	Marty, SD	57361-0187	605-384-5431	384-5933	K-12		Gina Curran
Meskwaki Settlement S	1610 305th St	Tama, IA	52339	641-484-4990	484-3264	K-12		Carolyn Manard
Sequoyah HS	PO Box 520	Tahlequah, OK	74465	918-453-5400	456-0634	9-12		Leroy Qualls
Takini S	HC 77 Box 537	Howes, SD	57748-9511	605-538-4399	538-4315	K-12		Linda Hunter
Tiospa Zina Tribal S	PO Box 719	Agency Village, SD	57262-0719	605-698-3953	698-7686	K-12	500	Dr. Roger Bordeaux
American Horse S	PO Box 660	Allen, SD	57714-0660	605-455-1209	455-2249	PK-8	300	Dr. Gloria Kitsopoulas
Crazy Horse S	PO Box 260	Wanblee, SD	57577-0260	605-462-6836	462-6510	K-12	300	Silas Blaine
Isna Wica Owayawa-Loneman S	PO Box 50	Oglala, SD	57764-0050	605-867-6875	867-5109	K-8	200	Charles Cuny
Little Wound S	PO Box 500	Kyle, SD	57752-0500	605-455-6150	455-2703	PK-12	900	Charles Cuny
Pierre Indian Learning Center	3001 E Sully Ave	Pierre, SD	57501-4403	605-224-8661	224-8465	1-8		Darrell Jeanotte
Porcupine S	PO Box 180	Porcupine, SD	57772-0180	605-455-6450	867-5480	K-8		Chris Bordeaux
St. Francis Indian S	PO Box 379	Saint Francis, SD	57572-0379	605-747-2299	747-2379	K-12		Richard Bad Milk
St. Stephens Indian S	PO Box 345	Saint Stephens, WY	82524-0345	307-856-4147	856-3742	K-12		Elma Brown
Sicangu Owaye Oti	PO Box 69	Mission, SD	57555	605-856-4486	856-4490	1-12		Nancy Hernandez
Tiospaye Topa S	PO Box 300	Ridgeview, SD	57652-0300	605-733-2290	733-2299	K-12		Brent Mareska
Wounded Knee S	PO Box 350	Manderson, SD	57756-0350	605-867-4350	867-5156	K-8		Alice Phelps
Bug-O-Nay-Ge-Shig S	15353 Silver Eagle Dr NW	Bena, MN	56626-1012	218-665-3000	665-3024	K-12	300	Amanda Norman
Circle of Life S	PO Box 447	White Earth, MN	56591-0447	218-983-4180	983-3767	K-12		Ricky White
Circle of Nations Indian Boarding S	832 8th St N	Wahpeton, ND	58075-3642	701-642-3796	642-1984	1-8		Cheryl Poitra
Fond du Lac Ojibwe S	49 University Rd	Cloquet, MN	55720	218-878-7242	878-7263	K-12		Jennifer Johnson
Lac Courte Oreilles Ojibwa S	8575 N Trepania Rd	Hayward, WI	54843-2205	715-634-8924	634-6058	K-12		Jessica Hutchison
Lumsden Bahweting Anishinabe S, J.K.	1301 Marquette Ave	Sault S Marie, MI	49783-9533	906-635-5055	635-3805	K-8	500	Susan Palmer
Menominee Tribal S	PO Box 39	Neopit, WI	54150-0039	715-756-2354	756-2364	K-8		Lori Corn
Nah Tah Wahsh Public S Academy	N14911 Hannahville Road B 1	Wilson, MI	49896-9612	906-466-2952	466-2556	K-12	200	Tom Miller
Nay Ah Shing S	43651 Oodena Dr	Onamia, MN	56359-2320	320-532-4695	532-4675	K-12		Noah Johnson
Oneida Nation S	PO Box 365	Oneida, WI	54155-0365	920-869-1676	869-1684	PK-12	300	Sharon Mousseau
Ahafachkee S	30290 Josie Billie Hwy	Clewiston, FL	33440	863-983-6348	983-6535	PK-12		Dorothy Cain
Bogue Chitto S	13241 Highway 491 N	Philadelphia, MS	39350-5463	601-389-1000	389-1002	K-8		Larry Robinson
Cherokee Central ES	1582 Ravensford Dr	Cherokee, NC	28719	828-554-5020	554-5035	K-5		Paula Coker
Cherokee Central HS	1582 Ravensford Dr	Cherokee, NC	28719	828-554-5030	554-5033	9-12		Fredrick Hickman
Cherokee Central MS	1582 Ravensford Dr	Cherokee, NC	28719	828-554-5026	554-5029	6-8		Deborah Foerst
Chitimacha Day S	3613 Chitimacha Trl	Jeanerette, LA	70544-8317	337-923-9960	923-7346	K-8	100	Tanya Rosamond
Choctaw Central HS	150 Recreation Rd	Choctaw, MS	39350-7180	601-663-7777	656-7077	9-12	400	Fredrick Hickmon
Choctaw Central MS	150 Recreation Rd	Choctaw, MS	39350-7180	601-656-8938	656-1558	7-8	200	Jackie Harpole
Conehatta S	851 Tushka Rd	Conehatta, MS	39057-2804	601-775-8254	775-9229	PK-8	300	Brian Parkman
Indian Island S	10 Wabanaki Way	Indian Island, ME	04468-1254	207-827-4285	827-3599	PK-8	100	Tracy Nute
Indian Township S	13 School Dr	Princeton, ME	04668-5000	207-796-2362	796-2726	PK-8	100	Mary Anne Spearin
Miccosukee Indian S	PO Box 440021	Miami, FL	33144-0021	305-894-2364	894-2365	K-12	100	Manuel Varela
Pearl River ES	470 Industrial Rd	Choctaw, MS	39350-4256	601-656-9051	656-9054	K-6	700	Suzanne Hyatt
Rafferty S, Beatrice	22 Bayview Dr	Pleasant Point, ME	04667-4111	207-853-6085	853-2483	PK-8	100	Mike Chadwick
Red Water S	106 Braves Blvd	Carthage, MS	39051	601-267-8500	267-5193	K-8		Bobby Boone
Standing Pine ES	538 Highway 487 E	Carthage, MS	39051-6031	601-267-9225	267-9129	K-6		Jason Roberson
Tucker S	126 E Tucker Cir	Philadelphia, MS	39350-8351	601-656-8775	656-9341	K-8		Delnita Jones
Chemawa Indian S	3700 Chemawa Rd NE	Salem, OR	97305-1199	503-399-5721	399-5870	9-12		Lora Braucher
Havasupai S	PO Box 40	Supai, AZ	86435-0040	928-448-2901	448-2108	K-8		Coleen Maldonado
Kennedy S, John F.	PO Box 130	Whiteriver, AZ	85941-0130	928-338-4591	338-4592	K-8		Susan Higgins M.Ed.
San Simon S	HC 1 Box 8292	Sells, AZ	85634-9711	520-362-2231	362-2405	K-8		Frank Rogers
Santa Rosa Day S	HC 1 Box 8400	Sells, AZ	85634-9713	520-361-2276	361-2511	K-8		Maxine Roanhorse-Dineyaz
Santa Rosa Ranch S	HC 2 Box 7570	Sells, AZ	85634-9741	520-383-2359	383-3960	K-8		Jim Hastings
Sherman Indian HS	9010 Magnolia Ave	Riverside, CA	92503-4431	951-276-6325	276-6336	9-12		Mary Yarger
Tohono O'Odham HS	HC 1 Box 8513	Sells, AZ	85634-9735	520-362-2400	362-2265	9-12	100	Michael Krug
Chief Leschi S	5625 52nd St E	Puyallup, WA	98371-3610	253-445-6003	445-2350	K-12		Amy Eveskcige
Couer D'Alene Tribal S	PO Box 338	Desmet, ID	83824-0338	208-686-5808	686-5080	K-8	100	Donavan Chase
Duckwater Shoshone S	PO Box 140002	Duckwater, NV	89314	775-863-0242		K-8	50	
Lummi HS	2334 Lummi View Dr	Bellingham, WA	98226-9277	360-758-4330	758-3152	9-12		Heather Leighton
Lummi Tribal S	2334 Lummi View Dr	Bellingham, WA	98226-9277	360-758-4300	758-3160	K-8		Heather Leighton
Muckleshoot Tribal S	15209 SE 376th St	Auburn, WA	98092	253-931-6709	939-5568	K-12	300	Michael Aaron
Noli S	PO Box 700	San Jacinto, CA	92581-0700	951-654-5596	654-7198	6-12	100	Donovan Post
Northern Cheyenne Tribal S of Busby	PO Box 150	Busby, MT	59016-0150	406-592-3646	592-3645	K-12		Loverty Erickson
Paschal Sherman Indian S	169 N End Omak Lake Rd	Omak, WA	98841-9477	509-422-7590	422-7539	PK-9	200	Tami Hickle
Pyramid Lake HS	PO Box 267	Nixon, NV	89424	775-574-1016	574-1037	7-12		Jake Chapin
Quileute Tribal S	PO Box 39	La Push, WA	98350-0039	360-374-5609	374-5784	K-12		Mark Jacobson
Shoshone Bannock S	PO Box 790	Pocatello, ID	83204-0790	208-238-4200	238-2628	7-12	100	Eric Lords
Two Eagle River S	PO Box 160	Pablo, MT	59855-0160	406-675-0292	675-0294	K-12		Rollie Sullivan
Wa He Lut Indian S	11110 Conine Ave SE	Olympia, WA	98513-9603	360-456-1311	456-1319	K-8	100	Harvey Whitford
Yakima Tribal S	PO Box 151	Toppenish, WA	98948-0151	509-865-4478		8-12	100	Relyn Storm
Aneth Community S	PO Box 600	Montezuma Creek, UT	84534-0600	435-651-3271	651-3272	K-6	200	Brenda Whitehorse
Atsa'Biya'a'zh Community S	PO Box 1809	Shiprock, NM	87420-1809	505-368-2100	368-2076	K-6		Freda Nells
Beclabito Day S	PO Box 1200	Shiprock, NM	87420-1200	928-656-3556	656-3557	K-4		Dr. Gladys Tracy
Cove Day S	PO Box 2000	Red Valley, AZ	86544-2000	928-653-4457	653-4415	K-6	50	Dr. Leo Johnson
Dzilth-Na-O-Dith-Hle Comm S	35 Road 7585 Ste 5003	Bloomfield, NM	87413-4936	505-960-0356		K-12	200	Mike Walker
Hanaa'dli Community S	PO Box 639	Bloomfield, NM	87413	505-325-3411	327-3591	K-12		Janice Yazzie-Montoya
Kayenta Community S	PO Box 188	Kayenta, AZ	86033-0188	928-697-3439	697-3490	K-8		Gloria Hale-Showalter
Kinteel Residential Academy	1600 Lydia Rippey Rd	Aztec, NM	87410	505-334-6565	334-8630	9-12		
Navajo Prep S	1220 W Apache St	Farmington, NM	87401-3886	505-326-6571	327-9213	9-12	300	Betty Ojaye
Nenahnezad Community S	PO Box 337	Fruitland, NM	87416-0337	505-598-6922	960-0970	K-6	200	Nolan Johnson
Red Rock Day S	PO Box 2007	Red Valley, AZ	86544-2007	928-653-4456	653-5711	K-8	200	Dr. Leo Johnson
Sanostee Day S	PO Box 159	Sanostee, NM	87461-0159	505-723-2476	723-2425	K-3	100	David Smith
Shiprock HS	PO Box 1809	Shiprock, NM	87420-1809	505-368-2100	368-2076	7-12	600	Julia Donald
T'iis Nazbas Community S	PO Box 2002	Teec Nos Pos, AZ	86514-2002	928-656-3252	656-3486	K-8	200	Dr. Karina Roessel
Chilchinbeto Community S	PO Box 740	Kayenta, AZ	86033-0740	928-697-3800	697-3448	K-8		Dr. Connie Williams
Dilcon Community S	HC 63 Box G	Winslow, AZ	86047-9414	928-657-3211	657-3213	K-8		William Wachunas
Greyhills Academy HS	PO Box 160	Tuba City, AZ	86045-0160	928-283-6271	283-6604	9-12		Dr. Loren Hudson
Kaibeto Boarding S	PO Box 1420	Kaibeto, AZ	86053	928-673-3480	673-3489	K-8		Phyllis N. Yazzie
KinLani Bordertown Dormitory	901 N Kinlani Dr	Flagstaff, AZ	86001-1585	928-774-5270	556-9683	9-12		Theresa Boone-Schular
Leupp S	Highway 99	Leupp, AZ	86035	928-686-6211	686-6216	K-12		
Little Singer Community S	PO Box AQ	Winslow, AZ	86047-1541	928-686-6108	686-6439	K-6		Etta Shirley
Naa Tsis 'Aan Community S	PO Box 100101	Tonalea, AZ	86044	928-672-2335	672-2609	K-8		Lolita Paddock
Richfield Residential Hall	765 W 1st Ave	Richfield, UT	84701-2436	435-896-5101	896-6157	9-12		Cody Workman
Rocky Ridge Boarding S	PO Box 299	Kykotsmovi, AZ	86039-0299	928-725-3650	725-3655	K-8		Kimberly Dominguez

Agency/School	Address	City,State	Zip code	Telephone	Fax	Grade	Enr	Superintendent/Principal
Seba Dalkai Boarding S	HC 63 Box H	Winslow, AZ	86047-9415	928-657-3208	657-3224	K-9	100	Maye Bigboy
Shonto Preparatory S	PO Box 7900	Shonto, AZ	86054-7900	928-672-3528	672-3505	K-12	100	Lemual Adson
Tonalea Day S	PO Box 39	Tonalea, AZ	86044-0039	928-283-6325	283-5158	K-8		Perfillia Charlie
Tuba City Boarding S	PO Box 187	Tuba City, AZ	86045-0187	928-283-2330	283-2362	K-8		Donald Coffland
Bread Springs Day S	PO Box 1117	Gallup, NM	87305-1117	505-778-5665	778-5692	K-3	100	Nancy Taranto
Chi-Chil'tah Community S	PO Box 278	Vanderwagen, NM	87326-0278	505-778-5574	778-5575	K-8	100	Marlene Tsosie
Crystal Boarding S	PO Box 1288	Navajo, NM	87328	505-777-2385	777-2648	K-6		Alberto Castruita
Hunters Point Boarding S	PO Box 99	Saint Michaels, AZ	86511-0099	928-871-4439	871-4435	K-5	100	Dr. Berdina Tsosie
Kin Dah Lichi'i Olta	PO Box 800	Ganado, AZ	86505-0800	928-755-3707	755-3448	K-6	200	Ora James
Pine Springs Day S	PO Box 4198	Houck, AZ	86505	928-871-4311	871-4341	K-4	100	Lou Ann Jones
Tiisyaakin Residential Hall	1100 W Buffalo St	Holbrook, AZ	86025-2330	928-524-6222	524-2231	9-12		Renee White-Alcott
Wide Ruins Community S	PO Box 309	Chambers, AZ	86502-0309	928-652-3251	652-3252	K-6	100	Dr. Elvira Bitsoi
Wingate ES	PO Box 1	Fort Wingate, NM	87316-0001	505-488-6300	488-6444	PK-8		Dr. Edie Morris
Wingate HS	PO Box 2	Fort Wingate, NM	87316-0002	505-488-6400	488-6444	9-12	500	Gloria Arviso
Winslow Residential Hall	600 N Alfred Ave	Winslow, AZ	86047-3130	928-289-2379		7-12		Isabel Britton

DEPARTMENT OF DEFENSE DEPENDENT SCHOOLS

DEPT. OF DEFENSE DEPENDENT SCHOOLS
4040 Fairfax Dr Fl 9, Arlington, VA 22203-1613
Telephone 703-588-3104
Website http://www.dodea.edu

DEPARTMENT OF DEFENSE DEPENDENT SCHOOLS

District/School	Address	City,State	Zip code	Telephone	Fax	Grade	Enr	Superintendent/Principal
Fort Campbell Dependent SD	**77 Texas Ave**	**Fort Campbell, KY**	**42223-5127**	**270-439-1927**	**439-6992**	**PK-12**	**4,900**	**Dr. Frank Calvano**
Barkley ES	4720 Polk Rd	Fort Campbell, KY	42223-1900	270-439-1951	439-1901	PK-5	600	Ted Turnipseed
Barsanti ES	7409 McAuliffe Loop	Fort Campbell, KY	42223-6025	270-640-1213	431-0519	PK-5	600	Dr. David Martin
Fort Campbell HS	1101 Bastogne Ave	Fort Campbell, KY	42223-5133	270-640-1219	431-9386	9-12	600	Hugh McKinnon
Jackson ES	84 Texas Ave	Fort Campbell, KY	42223	931-431-6211	431-4453	PK-5	700	Linda Shelton
Lincoln ES	84 Texas Ave	Fort Campbell, KY	42223	270-640-1212	439-2335	PK-5	600	Linda Haberman
Lucas ES, Andre	2115 Airborne St	Fort Campbell, KY	42223-5333	270-640-1208	431-5842	PK-5	500	Dr. Suzanne Jones
Mahaffey MS	585 S Carolina Ave	Fort Campbell, KY	42223-5134	270-640-1215	439-3472	6-8	400	Steve Gardner
Marshall ES	75 Texas Ave	Fort Campbell, KY	42223-5135	270-640-1214	439-4382	PK-5	500	Dr. Suzanne Jones
Wassom MS	3066 Forest Rd	Fort Campbell, KY	42223-5272	270-640-1218	439-0249	6-8	300	Kimberly Butts
Fort Knox Community SD	**281 Fayette Ave**	**Fort Knox, KY**	**40121-6201**	**502-624-2345**	**624-3969**	**PK-12**	**1,400**	**Frank Calvano Ed.D.**
Fort Knox HS	266 Maine St	Fort Knox, KY	40121-6800	502-624-6647	624-6171	9-12	400	Gregg Mowen Ed.D.
Macdonald ES	128 McCracken St	Fort Knox, KY	40121-2706	502-624-5650	624-2108	1-5	200	Laura Gibson M.A.
Scott MS	266 Mississippi St	Fort Knox, KY	40121-6814	502-624-2236	624-5433	6-8	300	Youlanda Washington
Ph.D.								
Van Voorhis ES	120 Folger St	Fort Knox, KY	40121-6086	502-624-5854	624-7267	PK-5	500	Sharon McGourty Perkins
Georgia / Alabama Dependent SD	**7441 Custer Rd Bldg 2670**	**Fort Benning, GA**	**31905-9647**	**706-545-7276**	**545-8227**	**PK-8**	**400**	**Dr. Christy Huddleston**
Dexter ES, Herbert J.	99 Yeager Ave	Fort Benning, GA	31905-6522	706-545-3424	545-9106	PK-5		Edwina Smith
Faith MS, Don C.	1375 Ingersoll St	Fort Benning, GA	31905-7200	706-545-0310	545-7800	6-8		Darrell Mood
Fort Rucker ES	PO Box 620279	Fort Rucker, AL	36362-0279	334-255-1607	268-7482	2-6		Dr. Vicki Gilmer
Fort Rucker PS	PO Box 620279	Fort Rucker, AL	36362-0279	334-255-2822	268-7483	PK-1		Dr. Deborah Deas
Loyd ES, Frank R.	5701 Santa Fe Rd	Fort Benning, GA	31905-2724	706-544-8961	544-8972	PK-5		Julita Martinez
Maxwell AFB ES	800 Magnolia Blvd	Maxwell AFB, AL	36112-5922	334-953-7804	953-4339	PK-8	400	Dr. Ronald Knight
McBride ES, Morris R.	700 Custer Rd	Fort Benning, GA	31905-7402	706-544-9411	544-9299	PK-5		Phyllis Parker
Stowers ES, Freddie	7791 Stowers Dr	Fort Benning, GA	31905-3130	706-544-2312	544-2349	PK-5		Debbie Parks
White ES, Edward A.	300 1st Division Rd	Fort Benning, GA	31905-6627	706-545-4623	545-5469	PK-5		Dr. Renee Mallory
Wilson ES, Richard G.	112 Lavoie Ave	Fort Benning, GA	31905-7523	706-545-5723	545-9505	PK-5		Michelle Allen
NY/VA Domestic Dependent School System	**3308 John Quick Rd Ste 201**	**Quantico, VA**	**22134-1752**	**703-630-7012**	**784-3100**	**PK-12**	**700**	**Helen Balilo**
Crossroads ES	3315 Purvis Rd	Quantico, VA	22134-2101	703-630-7065		PK-5	700	Donna Kacmarski
Dahlgren S	6117 Sampson Rd Ste 206	Dahlgren, VA	22448-5121	540-653-8822	653-4591	PK-8		Dr. Jeffrey Duncan
Quantico MSHS	3307 Purvis Rd	Quantico, VA	22134-2198	703-630-7055	784-4851	6-12		Michael Johnson
West Point ES	705A Barry Rd	West Point, NY	10996-1110	845-938-2313	938-3352	PK-4		Denise Webster-Cochenour
West Point MS	705 Barry Rd	West Point, NY	10996-1110	845-938-2923	938-2568	5-8		David Rudy
North Carolina Dependent SD	**PO Box 70089**	**Fort Bragg, NC**	**28307-0089**	**910-907-0228**	**907-1405**	**PK-9**	**4,300**	**Dr. Emily Marsh**
Albritton MS	PO Box 70089	Fort Bragg, NC	28307-0089	910-907-0201	432-4072	6-8	600	Pat Schob
Bitz IS	2028 Bevin St	Camp Lejeune, NC	28547-1436	910-451-2575	451-1475	3-5	400	Dewanda Sholar
Bowley ES	PO Box 70089	Fort Bragg, NC	28307-0089	910-907-0202	907-3513	PK-5	300	Mike Thornburg
Brewster MS	883 Stone St	Camp Lejeune, NC	28547-2501	910-451-2561	451-2600	6-8		Emilio Garza
Butner PS	PO Box 70089	Fort Bragg, NC	28307-0089	910-907-0203	432-8400	PK-2	500	Kim McBroom
Delalio ES	1500 Curtis Rd	Jacksonville, NC	28540-3406	910-449-0601	449-0677	PK-5		Wyonia Chevis
Devers ES	PO Box 70089	Fort Bragg, NC	28307-0089	910-907-0204	396-7374	PK-5	500	Cassandra White
Gordon ES	4200 Percy Blvd	Cameron, NC	28326-9832	910-907-1300	908-3504	PK-5	500	Joel Grim
Hampton PS	PO Box 70089	Fort Bragg, NC	28307-0089	910-907-0205	908-1190	PK-2		Priscilla Joiner
Heroes ES	100 Barnett Way	Camp Lejeune, NC	28547-2552	910-449-8000		PK-5		Kendra White
Irwin IS	PO Box 70089	Fort Bragg, NC	28307-0089	910-907-0206	907-1247	2-5	500	Miriam Breece
Johnson PS	2027 Stone St	Camp Lejeune, NC	28547-2506	910-451-2431	451-2433	PK-2		Andrea Mial
Lejeune HS	835 Stone St	Camp Lejeune, NC	28547-2520	910-451-2451	451-3130	9-12		Eric Steimel
Shughart ES	4800 Camel Rd	Cameron, NC	28326-5056	910-907-0210		PK-5	600	Dr. Carolyn Carr
Shughart MS	4800 Camel Rd	Cameron, NC	28326-5056	910-907-0211	907-2150	6-8	500	Karen Jones
Tarawa Terrace ES	84 Iwo Jima Blvd	Tarawa Terrace, NC	28543-1231	910-450-1635	450-1637	PK-5		Leigh Anne Faulkner
South Carolina / Fort Stewart SD	**376 Davis Ave**	**Fort Stewart, GA**	**31315-1033**	**912-369-6691**	**876-4339**	**PK-6**	**6,100**	**Dr. Samantha Ingram**
Bolden S, Charles Frank	2 Albacore St	Beaufort, SC	29906-3503	843-846-6112	846-9283	3-8	4,000	Dr. Angela Stephens
Brittin ES	2772 Hero Rd	Fort Stewart, GA	31315-1713	912-368-3324	368-3412	PK-6	600	Dr. Theresa Davis
Diamond ES	482 Davis Ave	Fort Stewart, GA	31315-1015	912-876-5797	876-8350	PK-6		Marva Tutt
Elliott ES, Middleton Stuart	345 Elliott Dr	Beaufort, SC	29906-4569	843-846-6982	846-6720	PK-2	300	Latonya Leeks
Galer ES, Robert Edward	221 E Cardinal Ln	Beaufort, SC	29906-3347	843-846-6100	846-1860	PK-2	300	Carol Kipp-Caldwell
Kessler ES, Patrick	1127 Austin Rd	Fort Stewart, GA	31315-5792	912-368-3958	368-5048	PK-6	100	Dr. Djuna Crowder
Murray ES, Charles P.	24 Murray Ave	Fort Stewart, GA	31315-2823	912-369-1576	767-3600	PK-6	200	Talisha Thompson
Pierce Terrace ES	5715 Adams Ct	Columbia, SC	29206-5379	803-782-1772	738-8895	PK-2	300	Dr. Andrea McClain
Pinckney ES, Charles C.	5900 Chesnut Rd	Columbia, SC	29206-5365	803-787-6815	790-2169	3-6	200	Audrey Griffin

CATHOLIC SCHOOL SUPERINTENDENTS

NATIONAL CATHOLIC EDUCATIONAL ASSOC.
1005 N Glebe Rd Ste 525, Arlington, VA 22201-5792
Telephone 800-711-6232
Fax 243-0025
Website ncea.org

Archdiocese/Diocese	Address	City,State	Zip code	Telephone	Fax	Grade	Enr	Superintendent
Diocese of Albany	40 N Main Ave	Albany, NY	12203-1481	518-453-6602	453-6667	PK-12	6,500	Michael Pizzingrillo
Diocese of Alexandria	PO Box 7417	Alexandria, LA	71306-0417	318-445-2401	448-6121	PK-12	2,500	Thomas Roque
Diocese of Allentown	1425 Mountain Dr N	Bethlehem, PA	18015-4722	610-866-0581	867-8702	PK-12	11,900	Philip Fromuth
Diocese of Altoona-Johnstown	933 S Logan Blvd	Hollidaysburg, PA	16648-3035	814-693-1401	696-6725	PK-12	4,400	Sr. Donna Leiden
Diocese of Amarillo	PO Box 5644	Amarillo, TX	79107	806-383-2243	383-8452	PK-12	700	Fr. Robert Busch Ph.D.
Archdiocese of Anchorage	225 Cordova St	Anchorage, AK	99501-2409	907-297-7700	297-3885	PK-12	500	
Diocese of Arlington	200 N Glebe Rd Ste 503	Arlington, VA	22203	703-841-2519	524-8670	PK-12	17,100	Jennifer Bigelow
Archdiocese of Atlanta	2401 Lake Park Dr SE	Smyrna, GA	30080-8859	404-920-7700	920-7701	PK-12	11,900	Dr. Diane Starkovich Ph.D.
Diocese of Austin	6225 E Highway 290	Austin, TX	78723	512-949-2400	949-2520	PK-12	5,100	Dr. Ned Vanders
Diocese of Baker	2450 NE 27th St	Bend, OR	97701-9506	541-382-4701	312-9111	PK-8	600	Dr. Dennis Dempsey
Archdiocese of Baltimore	320 Cathedral St	Baltimore, MD	21201-4421	410-547-5515	539-5566	PK-12	27,400	Dr. Barbara Edmondson
Diocese of Baton Rouge	PO Box 2028	Baton Rouge, LA	70821-2028	225-336-8735	336-8711	PK-12	14,900	Dr. Melanie Verges
Diocese of Beaumont	PO Box 3948	Beaumont, TX	77704-3948	409-924-4328	838-4511	PK-12	1,600	Marcia Stevens
Diocese of Belleville	2620 Lebanon Ave	Belleville, IL	62221-3002	618-235-9601	235-7115	PK-12	5,900	Thomas Posnanski
Diocese of Biloxi	1790 Popps Ferry Rd	Biloxi, MS	39532-2118	228-702-2130	702-2178	PK-12	4,100	Dr. Mike Ladner
Diocese of Birmingham	PO Box 12047	Birmingham, AL	35202-2047	205-838-8303	838-8330	PK-12	5,900	Frances Lawlor
Diocese of Bismarck	218 1st St SE	Minot, ND	58701-3920	701-838-1026		PK-12	2,700	Fr. Justin Waltz
Diocese of Boise	1501 S Federal Way Ste 400	Boise, ID	83705-2591	208-342-1311	342-0224	PK-12	3,000	James Reed
Archdiocese of Boston	66 Brooks Dr	Braintree, MA	02184	617-779-3601	746-5702	PK-12	40,200	Kathleen Mears
Diocese of Bridgeport	238 Jewett Ave	Bridgeport, CT	06606-2892	203-416-1638	372-1961	PK-12	11,100	Dr. Steven Cheeseman
Diocese of Brooklyn	310 Prospect Park W	Brooklyn, NY	11215-6214	718-965-7300	965-7353	PK-12	40,200	Dr. Thomas Chadzutko
Diocese of Brownsville	700 Virgen de San Juan	San Juan, TX	78589-3030	956-784-5051	784-5081	PK-12	3,900	Sr. Cynthia A. Mello M.A.
Diocese of Buffalo	795 Main St	Buffalo, NY	14203-1215	716-847-5520	847-5593	PK-12	14,100	Sr. Carol Cimino Ed.D.
Diocese of Burlington	55 Joy Dr	S Burlington, VT	05403	802-658-6110	658-6112	PK-12	2,100	Lisa Lorenz
Diocese of Camden	631 Market St	Camden, NJ	08102	856-583-6103	756-0225	PK-12	13,800	Mary Boyle M.Ed.
Diocese of Charleston	901 Orange Grove Rd	Charleston, SC	29407	843-261-4096		PK-12	7,000	Sandra Leatherwood
Diocese of Charlotte	1123 S Church St	Charlotte, NC	28203-4003	704-370-3244	370-3380	PK-12	7,800	Dr. Janice Ritter
Diocese of Cheyenne	PO Box 1468	Cheyenne, WY	82003	307-638-1530	637-7936	PK-12	1,000	Vernon Dobelmann
Archdiocese of Chicago	PO Box 1979	Chicago, IL	60690-1979	312-534-5200	534-5295	PK-12	81,700	Jim Rigg Ph.D.
Archdiocese of Cincinnati	100 E 8th St	Cincinnati, OH	45202	513-421-3131	421-6271	PK-12	43,900	Susan Gibbons
Diocese of Cleveland	1404 E 9th St	Cleveland, OH	44114-1735	216-696-6525	579-9655	PK-12	43,900	Christopher Knight
Diocese of Colorado Springs	228 N Cascade Ave	Colorado Spgs, CO	80903-1324	719-636-2345	866-6453	PK-12	1,700	Holly Goodwin
Diocese of Columbus	197 E Gay St	Columbus, OH	43215	614-221-5829	241-2563	PK-12	17,200	Dr. Joe Brettnacher Ph.D.
Diocese of Corpus Christi	PO Box 2620	Corpus Christi, TX	78403-2620	361-882-6191	693-6798	PK-12	3,600	Dr. Rosemary Henry
Diocese of Covington	1125 Madison Ave	Covington, KY	41011	859-392-1500	392-1500	K-12	10,000	Michael Clines
Diocese of Crookston	PO Box 610	Crookston, MN	56716	218-281-4533	281-3328	PK-12	1,300	Tina Stanger
Diocese of Dallas	PO Box 190507	Dallas, TX	75219-0507	214-379-2830	522-1753	PK-12	14,600	Matthew Vereecke Ed.D.
Diocese of Davenport	780 W Central Park Ave	Davenport, IA	52804-1901	563-324-1911	324-5811	PK-12	4,800	Dr. Lee Morrison
Archdiocese of Denver	1300 S Steele St	Denver, CO	80210-2599	303-715-3200	715-2007	PK-12	10,400	Kevin Kijewski J.D.
Diocese of Des Moines	601 Grand Ave	Des Moines, IA	50309-2501	515-237-5013	237-5070	PK-12	6,400	Dr. Tracy Bonday
Archdiocese of Detroit	12 State St	Detroit, MI	48226	313-237-4661	237-5857	PK-12	31,900	Dr. Brian Dougherty
Diocese of Dodge City	PO Box 137	Dodge City, KS	67801-0137	620-227-1513	227-1570	PK-8	900	Trina Delgado
Archdiocese of Dubuque	1229 Mount Loretta Ave	Dubuque, IA	52003-8787	563-556-2580	556-5464	PK-12	11,700	Kimberly Hermsen
Diocese of Duluth	2830 E 4th St	Duluth, MN	55812-1501	218-724-9111	724-1056	PK-8	1,500	Cynthia Zook
Diocese of El Paso	499 Saint Matthews St	El Paso, TX	79907-4214	915-872-8426	872-8464	PK-12	4,100	Sr. Elizabeth Swartz
Diocese of Erie	PO Box 10397	Erie, PA	16514-0397	814-824-1241	824-1239	PK-12	8,100	Dr. Samuel Signorino
Diocese of Evansville	PO Box 4169	Evansville, IN	47724-0169	812-424-5536	424-0973	PK-12	6,700	Dr. Daryl Hagan
Diocese of Fairbanks	PO Box 71620	Fairbanks, AK	99701	907-456-4574	452-5978	K-12	500	Nancy Hanson
Diocese of Fall River	423 Highland Ave	Fall River, MA	02720-3718	508-678-2828	674-4218	PK-12	6,800	Stephen Perla
Diocese of Fargo	5201 Bishops Blvd S Ste A	Fargo, ND	58104-7605	701-356-7907	356-7994	PK-12	2,200	Fr. Andrew Jasinski
Diocese of Fort Worth	800 W Loop 820 S	Fort Worth, TX	76108-2936	817-560-3300	244-8839	PK-12	5,900	Jennifer Pelletier
Diocese of Fresno	1550 N Fresno St	Fresno, CA	93703	559-488-7420	488-7422	PK-12	6,100	Mona Faulkner
Diocese of Ft. Wayne-South Bend	PO Box 390	Fort Wayne, IN	46801-0390	260-422-4611	426-3077	PK-12	12,800	Marsha Jordan
Diocese of Gallup	PO Box 1338	Gallup, NM	87305-1338	505-863-4406	863-2269	PK-12	1,300	Jeanette Suter
Archdiocese of Galveston-Houston	2403 Holcombe Blvd	Houston, TX	77021-2023	713-741-8704	741-7379	PK-12	18,000	Dr. Julie Vogel
Diocese of Gary	9292 Broadway	Merrillville, IN	46410-7088	219-769-9292	738-9034	PK-12	6,200	Dr. Joe Majchrowicz
Diocese of Gaylord	611 W North St	Gaylord, MI	49735-8349	989-732-5147	705-3589	PK-12	3,000	Frank Sander
Diocese of Grand Island	PO Box 996	Grand Island, NE	68802-0996	308-382-6565	382-6569	PK-12	1,500	Gregory Logsdon
Diocese of Grand Rapids	360 Division Ave S Ste 3A	Grand Rapids, MI	49503	616-246-0590	551-5650	PK-12	6,600	David Faber
Diocese of Great Falls-Billings	PO Box 1399	Great Falls, MT	59403-1399	406-727-6683	454-3480	PK-12	2,900	Dr. Timothy Uhl
Diocese of Green Bay	PO Box 23825	Green Bay, WI	54305-3825	920-272-8309	272-8273	PK-12	9,600	Sr. Kay Klackner
Diocese of Greensburg	723 E Pittsburgh St	Greensburg, PA	15601-2697	724-837-0901	837-0857	PK-12	3,300	Dr. Maureen Marsteller
Ph.D.								
Diocese of Harrisburg	4800 Union Deposit Rd	Harrisburg, PA	17111-3710	717-657-4804	657-3790	PK-12	11,300	Livia Riley
Archdiocese of Hartford	467 Bloomfield Ave	Bloomfield, CT	06002-2903	860-242-5573		PK-12	14,700	Dr. Michael Griffin
Diocese of Helena	PO Box 1708	Helena, MT	59601	406-442-5761	442-9047	PK-12	1,200	Dr. Timothy Uhl
Diocese of Honolulu	6301 Pali Hwy	Kaneohe, HI	96744-5224	808-203-6764	261-7022	PK-12	8,600	Michael Rockers Ed.D.
Diocese of Houma-Thibodaux	PO Box 505	Schriever, LA	70395-0505	985-850-3114	850-3225	PK-12	5,600	Marian Fertitta
Archdiocese of Indianapolis	1400 N Meridian St	Indianapolis, IN	46202-2305	317-236-1430	261-3364	PK-12	22,000	Gina Kuntz Fleming
Diocese of Jackson	PO Box 2248	Jackson, MS	39225-2248	601-960-8470	960-8469	PK-12	4,000	Catherine Cook
Diocese of Jefferson City	PO Box 104900	Jefferson City, MO	65110-4900	573-635-9127	635-2286	PK-12	6,900	Sr. Elizabeth Youngs
Diocese of Joliet	16555 Weber Rd	Crest Hill, IL	60403	815-838-2181	838-2182	PK-12	21,700	Rev. John Belmonte Ph.D.
Diocese of Juneau	415 6th St Ste 300	Juneau, AK	99801-1091	907-586-2227	463-3237	PK-6	100	
Diocese of Kalamazoo	215 N Westnedge Ave	Kalamazoo, MI	49007-3760	269-903-0165	349-6440	PK-12	3,100	Margaret Erich
Archdiocese of Kansas City	12615 Parallel Pkwy	Kansas City, KS	66109-3718	913-721-1570	721-5598	PK-12	15,100	Dr. Kathleen O'Hara
Diocese of Kansas City-Saint Joseph	PO Box 419037	Kansas City, MO	64141-6037	816-756-1850	756-1571	PK-12	11,300	Dr. Dan Peters
Diocese of Knoxville	805 S Northshore Dr	Knoxville, TN	37919	865-584-3307	584-4319	PK-12	3,500	Sr. Mary Marta Abbott
Diocese of La Crosse	PO Box 4004	La Crosse, WI	54602-4004	608-788-7707	788-7709	PK-12	7,500	Thomas Reichenbacher
Diocese of Lafayette	PO Box 3387	Lafayette, LA	70502	337-261-5529	261-5572	PK-12	14,400	Anna Larriviere
Diocese of Lafayette-in-Indiana	2300 S 9th St	Lafayette, IN	47909-2400	765-269-4670	269-4671	PK-12	5,100	Peg Dispenzieri
Diocese of Lake Charles	1112 Bilbo St	Lake Charles, LA	70601-5226	337-433-9640	433-9685	PK-12	2,500	Kimberlee Gazzolo
Diocese of Lansing	228 N Walnut St	Lansing, MI	48933	517-342-2482	342-2515	PK-12	9,000	Sean Costello
Diocese of Laredo	1201 Corpus Christi St	Laredo, TX	78040-5354	956-753-5208	753-5203	K-12	2,100	Romeo Rodriguez
Diocese of Las Cruces	1280 Med Park Dr	Las Cruces, NM	88005-3239	575-523-7577	524-3874	PK-8	600	Julie Fracker
Diocese of Las Vegas	PO Box 18316	Las Vegas, NV	89114-8316	702-697-3903	735-8941	K-12	3,900	Catherine Thompson
Diocese of Lexington	1310 W Main St	Lexington, KY	40508-2048	859-253-1993	253-0111	PK-12	3,800	George Pressey
Diocese of Lincoln	PO Box 80328	Lincoln, NE	68501-0328	402-488-2040	488-6525	K-12	6,900	Msgr. John Perkinton
Diocese of Little Rock	PO Box 7565	Little Rock, AR	72217-7565	501-664-0340	603-0518	K-12	6,900	Vernell Bowen M.Ed.
Archdiocese of Los Angeles	3424 Wilshire Blvd	Los Angeles, CA	90010-2241	213-637-7300	637-6140	PK-12	79,000	Dr. Kevin Baxter
Archdiocese of Louisville	1935 Lewiston Dr	Louisville, KY	40216-2523	502-448-8581	448-5518	PK-12	20,000	Leisa Schulz
Diocese of Lubbock	PO Box 98700	Lubbock, TX	79499-8700	806-792-3943	792-8109	PK-12	400	Christine Wanjura
Diocese of Madison	PO Box 44983	Madison, WI	53744-4983	608-821-3180	821-3181	PK-12	7,200	Michael Lancaster
Diocese of Manchester	PO Box 310	Manchester, NH	03105-0310	603-669-3100	669-0377	PK-12	6,700	David Thibault
Diocese of Marquette	1004 Harbor Hills Dr	Marquette, MI	49855	906-227-9127	225-0437	PK-8	1,300	Mark Salisbury
Diocese of Memphis	5825 Shelby Oaks Dr	Memphis, TN	38134-7316	901-373-1219	373-1223	PK-12	6,600	Janet M. Donato
Diocese of Metuchen	146 Metlars Ln	Piscataway, NJ	08854-4303	732-562-2446	562-1016	PK-12	10,300	Ellen Ayoub
Archdiocese of Miami	9401 Biscayne Blvd	Miami Shores, FL	33138-2970	305-762-1076	762-1115	PK-12	33,500	Kim Pryzbylski Ph.D.
Archdiocese of Milwaukee	PO Box 070912	Milwaukee, WI	53207-0912	414-758-2256	769-3408	PK-12	29,800	Dr. Kathleen Cepelka
Archdiocese of Mobile	352 Government St	Mobile, AL	36602	251-438-4611	438-4612	PK-12	6,200	Gwen Byrd
Diocese of Monterey	485 Church St	Monterey, CA	93940-3207	831-373-1608	373-0173	PK-12	4,900	Kathleen Radecke
Diocese of Nashville	2800 McGavock Pike	Nashville, TN	37214-1402	615-352-7218	353-7972	PK-12	6,100	Dr. Therese Williams
Archdiocese of Newark	PO Box 9500	Newark, NJ	07104-0500	973-497-4260	497-4249	PK-12	31,900	Dr. Margaret Dames
Archdiocese of New Orleans	7887 Walmsley Ave	New Orleans, LA	70125-3496	504-866-7916	861-6260	PK-12	36,900	Dr. Jan Lancaster

Archdiocese/Diocese	Address	City,State	Zip code	Telephone	Fax	Grade	Enr	Superintendent
Diocese of New Ulm	1421 6th St N	New Ulm, MN	56073	507-359-2966	354-0268	PK-12	2,200	Karla Cross
Archdiocese of New York	1011 1st Ave Fl 18	New York, NY	10022-4112	212-371-1000	758-3018	PK-12	70,100	Dr. Timothy McNiff
Diocese of Norwich	43 Perkins Ave	Norwich, CT	06360-3643	860-887-4086	887-9371	PK-12	4,400	Henry Fiore
Diocese of Oakland	2121 Harrison St	Oakland, CA	94612-3788	510-628-2154	451-5331	PK-12	17,500	Sr. Barbara Bray
Diocese of Ogdensburg	PO Box 369	Ogdensburg, NY	13669-0369	315-393-2920	314-7296	PK-12	1,900	Sr. Ellen Rose Coughlin
Archdiocese of Oklahoma City	PO Box 32180	Oklahoma City, OK	73123-0380	405-721-5651	709-2811	PK-12	5,000	Diane Floyd
Archdiocese of Omaha	3300 N 60th St	Omaha, NE	68104	402-557-5600	827-3792	PK-12	18,900	Patrick Slattery
Diocese of Orange	13280 Chapman Ave	Garden Grove, CA	92840	714-282-3000	282-5059	PK-12	19,200	Gregory Dhuyvetter
Diocese of Orlando	PO Box 1800	Orlando, FL	32802-1800	407-246-4800	246-4942	PK-12	13,400	Henry Fortier
Diocese of Owensboro	600 Locust St	Owensboro, KY	42301-2130	270-683-1545	683-6883	PK-12	3,900	Jim Mattingly
Diocese of Palm Beach	9995 N Military Trl	West Palm Beach, FL	33410-5497	561-775-9500	775-9556	PK-12	6,100	Gary Gelo
Diocese of Paterson	777 Valley Rd	Clifton, NJ	07013-2205	973-777-8818	779-0083	PK-12	10,300	Mary Baier
Diocese of Pensacola-Tallahassee	PO Box 13284	Pensacola, FL	32591-3284	850-435-3540	436-6424	PK-12	2,700	Michael P. Juhas
Diocese of Peoria	419 NE Madison Ave	Peoria, IL	61603	309-671-1550	671-1579	PK-12	11,200	Sharon Weiss Ed.D.
Archdiocese of Philadelphia	222 N 17th St	Philadelphia, PA	19103-1202	215-587-3700	587-5644	PK-12	69,400	Mary Rochford
Diocese of Phoenix	400 E Monroe St	Phoenix, AZ	85004-2336	602-354-2345	354-2436	PK-12	14,000	MaryBeth Mueller
Diocese of Pittsburgh	111 Blvd of the Allies	Pittsburgh, PA	15222-1618	412-456-3090	456-3098	PK-12	18,900	Michael Latusek Ed.D.
Archdiocese of Portland	2838 E Burnside St	Portland, OR	97214-1895	503-233-8300	236-3683	PK-12	13,400	Br. William Dygert
Diocese of Portland	510 Ocean Ave	Portland, ME	04103-4900	207-773-6471	773-0182	PK-12	2,700	Jim King
Diocese of Providence	1 Cathedral Sq	Providence, RI	02903-3695	401-278-4550	278-4596	PK-12	13,500	Daniel Ferris
Diocese of Pueblo	101 N Greenwood St	Pueblo, CO	81003-3164	719-561-1121	561-2251	PK-12	900	John Brainard M.Ed.
Diocese of Raleigh	7200 Stonehenge Dr	Raleigh, NC	27613	919-821-9749	522-1695	PK-12	8,800	Dr. Michael Fedewa
Rapid City Catholic School System	424 Fairmont Blvd	Rapid City, SD	57701	605-348-1477	342-4367	K-12	1,000	Barb Honeycutt
Diocese of Reno	290 S Arlington Ave Ste 200	Reno, NV	89501-1713	775-326-9430	372-6247	PK-12	1,700	Karen Barreras
Diocese of Richmond	7800 Carousel Ln	Richmond, VA	23294-4201	804-359-5661	358-9159	PK-12	9,200	Ray Honeycutt
Diocese of Rochester	1150 Buffalo Rd	Rochester, NY	14624-1890	585-328-3228	328-3149	PK-12	7,700	Anthony Cook
Diocese of Rockford	PO Box 7044	Rockford, IL	61125-7044	815-399-4300	399-6278	PK-12	14,000	Michael Kagan
Diocese of Rockville Centre	PO Box 9023	Rockville Ctr, NY	11571-9023	516-678-5800	678-7362	PK-12	29,400	Sr. Joanne Callahan
Diocese of Sacramento	2110 Broadway	Sacramento, CA	95818-2518	916-733-0110	733-0120	PK-12	13,500	Lincoln Snyder
Diocese of Saginaw	5800 Weiss St	Saginaw, MI	48603-2762	989-799-7910	399-2257	PK-12	2,700	Mary Ann Deschaine
Diocese of St. Augustine	11625 Old St Augustine Rd	Jacksonville, FL	32258-2056	904-262-3200	596-1042	PK-12	10,200	Rev. Scott Conway
Diocese of St. Cloud	305 7th Ave N Ste 201	Saint Cloud, MN	56303-3633	320-251-0111	251-0259	PK-12	4,900	Linda Kaiser
Archdiocese of St. Louis	20 Archbishop May Dr	Saint Louis, MO	63119	314-792-7300	792-7350	PK-12	41,300	Kurt Nelson
Archdiocese of St. Paul	328 Kellogg Blvd W	Saint Paul, MN	55102-1900	651-291-4500	290-1628	PK-12	31,700	Jason Slattery
Diocese of St. Petersburg	PO Box 40200	St Petersburg, FL	33743-0200	727-347-5539	341-6848	PK-12	12,400	Chris Pastura
Diocese of Salina	PO Box 825	Salina, KS	67402-0825	785-827-8746	827-6133	PK-12	2,400	Dr. Nick Compagnone
Diocese of Salt Lake City	27 C St	Salt Lake City, UT	84103-2302	801-328-8641	328-8643	PK-12	5,500	Mark Longe
Diocese of San Angelo	499 Saint Matthews St	El Paso, TX	79907-4214	915-872-8426	872-8423	PK-8	700	Sr. Elizabeth Ann Swartz
Archdiocese of San Antonio	2718 W Woodlawn Ave	San Antonio, TX	78228-5195	210-734-2620	734-9112	PK-12	12,700	Marti West
Diocese of San Bernardino	1201 E Highland Ave	San Bernardino, CA	92404-4641	909-475-5437	475-5477	PK-12	7,700	Patricia Vesely
Diocese of San Diego	PO Box 85728	San Diego, CA	92186-5728	858-490-8240	490-8272	PK-12	16,100	John Galvan
Archdiocese of San Francisco	1 Peter Yorke Way	San Francisco, CA	94109-6602	415-614-5660	614-5664	PK-12	24,600	Dr. Nina K. Russo
Diocese of San Jose	1150 N 1st St Ste 100	San Jose, CA	95112	408-983-0185	983-0192	PK-12	16,000	Katherine Almazol
Archdiocese of Santa Fe	4000 Saint Josephs Pl NW	Albuquerque, NM	87120-1714	505-831-8173	831-8107	PK-12	5,000	Susan Murphy
Diocese of Santa Rosa	PO Box 1297	Santa Rosa, CA	95402	707-566-3311	566-3382	PK-12	4,500	Linda Norman
Diocese of Savannah	2170 E Victory Dr	Savannah, GA	31404	912-201-4100	201-4101	K-12	5,000	Michelle Kroll
Diocese of Scranton	300 Wyoming Ave	Scranton, PA	18503-1243	570-207-2251	207-2261	PK-12	5,900	Msgr. David L. Tressler
Archdiocese of Seattle	710 9th Ave	Seattle, WA	98104-2017	206-382-4861	654-4651	PK-12	22,700	Dr. Patrick Haggarty
Diocese of Shreveport	3500 Fairfield Ave	Shreveport, LA	71104-4108	318-219-7253	868-5057	PK-12	2,000	Sr. Carol Shively
Diocese of Sioux City	PO Box 3379	Sioux City, IA	51102-3379	712-233-7527	233-7598	PK-12	5,900	Dr. Dan Ryan
Diocese of Sioux Falls	523 N Duluth Ave	Sioux Falls, SD	57104-2714	605-988-3761	988-3746	PK-12	5,000	Katie Mellor
Diocese of Spokane	PO Box 1453	Spokane, WA	99210-1453	509-358-7330	358-7302	PK-12	4,300	Dr. Duane Schafer Ph.D.
Diocese of Springfield-Cape Girardeau	601 S Jefferson Ave	Springfield, MO	65806-3107	417-866-0841	866-1140	PK-12	4,400	Leon Witt
Diocese of Springfield	1615 W Washington St	Springfield, IL	62702-4757	217-698-8500	698-0802	PK-12	10,700	Brandi Borries
Diocese of Springfield	PO Box 1730	Springfield, MA	01102-1730	413-452-0830	452-0555	PK-12	3,200	Sr. M. Andrea Ciszewski
Diocese of Steubenville	PO Box 969	Steubenville, OH	43952-5969	740-282-3631	282-3327	PK-12	2,000	Paul Ward
Diocese of Stockton	212 N San Joaquin St	Stockton, CA	95202	209-466-0636	463-5937	PK-12	4,100	Marian Graham
Diocese of Superior	PO Box 969	Superior, WI	54880-0017	715-392-2937	392-2015	PK-8	2,400	Peggy Schoenfuss
Diocese of Syracuse	240 E Onondaga St	Syracuse, NY	13202-2668	315-470-1450	470-1470	PK-12	5,900	William Crist
Diocese of Toledo	1933 Spielbusch Ave	Toledo, OH	43604-5360	419-244-6711	255-8269	PK-12	18,400	Teresa Richardson
Diocese of Trenton	PO Box 5147	Trenton, NJ	08638-0147	609-406-7400	406-7429	PK-12	19,400	JoAnn Tier
Diocese of Tucson	PO Box 31	Tucson, AZ	85702-0031	520-838-2547	838-2589	PK-12	6,700	Sheri Dahl
Diocese of Tulsa	820 S Boulder Ave	Tulsa, OK	74119-1624	918-582-9177	582-1851	PK-12	4,600	Jim Pohlman
Diocese of Tyler	1015 E Southeast Loop 323	Tyler, TX	75701-9656	903-534-1077	534-1370	PK-12	1,000	Dr. James Klassen
Diocese of Venice in Florida	1000 Pinebrook Rd	Venice, FL	34285-6426	941-484-9543	484-1121	PK-12	4,200	Dr. Kristy Swol
Diocese of Victoria	PO Box 4070	Victoria, TX	77903-4070	361-573-0828	573-5725	PK-12	2,900	Dr. John Quary
Archdiocese of Washington DC	5001 Eastern Ave	Hyattsville, MD	20782-3447	301-853-4500	853-7672	PK-12	27,600	William Ryan
Diocese of Wheeling-Charleston	PO Box 230	Wheeling, WV	26003-0010	304-232-0444	233-8551	PK-12	5,800	Dr. Vincent de Paul Schmidt Ed.D.
Diocese of Wichita	424 N Broadway Ave	Wichita, KS	67202	316-269-3950	269-2486	PK-12	10,400	Bob Voboril
Diocese of Wilmington	1626 N Union St	Wilmington, DE	19806-2540	302-573-3133	573-6945	PK-12	11,600	Louis De Angelo Ed.D.
Diocese of Winona	PO Box 588	Winona, MN	55987-0588	507-454-4643	454-8106	PK-12	5,000	Marsha Stenzel
Diocese of Worcester	49 Elm St	Worcester, MA	01609-2514	508-929-4317	929-4386	PK-12	7,400	Delma Josephson Ph.D.
Diocese of Yakima	5301 Tieton Dr Ste B	Yakima, WA	98908-3479	509-965-7117	966-8334	PK-12	1,700	Rev. Thomas Bunnell
Diocese of Youngstown	144 W Wood St	Youngstown, OH	44503-1030	330-744-8451	744-5099	K-12	6,900	Mary Fiala

LUTHERAN SCHOOL SUPERINTENDENTS

LUTHERAN CHURCH MISSOURI SYNOD
1333 S Kirkwood Rd, Saint Louis, MO 63122-7295
Telephone 800-248-1930

Website http://www.lcms.org

LUTHERAN SCHOOL SUPERINTENDENTS

Region	Address	City,State	Zip code	Telephone	Fax	Superintendent
Atlantic	171 White Plains Rd	Bronxville, NY	10708-1923	914-337-5700	337-7471	Jessica Hinsch Raba
California-Nevada-Hawaii	2772 Constitution Dr Ste A	Livermore, CA	94551-7571	925-245-4000	245-1107	Dr. Robert Newton
Central Illinois	1850 N Grand Ave W	Springfield, IL	62702-1626	217-793-1802	793-1822	Glenn Goeres
Eastern	5111 Main St	Williamsville, NY	14221-5203	716-634-5111	634-5452	Dr. Chris Wicher
English	33100 Freedom Rd	Farmington, MI	48336-4030	248-476-0039	476-0188	Rev. David Stechholz
Florida-Georgia	5850 T G Lee Blvd Ste 500	Orlando, FL	32822-4410	407-857-5556	857-5665	Mark Brink
Indiana	1145 Barr St	Fort Wayne, IN	46802-3135	260-423-1511	423-1514	Dr. Jon Mielke
Iowa East	1100 Blairs Ferry Rd	Marion, IA	52302-3092	319-373-2112	373-9827	Dr. Brian Saunders
Iowa West	409 Kenyon Rd Ste B	Fort Dodge, IA	50501-5718	515-576-7666	576-2323	Dr. Steve Turner
Kansas	1000 SW 10th Ave	Topeka, KS	66604-1104	785-357-4441	357-5071	Jim Bradshaw
Michigan	3773 Geddes Rd	Ann Arbor, MI	48105-3098	734-665-3791	665-0255	Bruce Braun
Mid-South	1675 Wynne Rd	Cordova, TN	38016-4905	901-373-1343	373-4826	Dr. Roger Paavola
Minnesota North	PO Box 604	Brainerd, MN	56401-0604	218-829-1781	829-0037	Rev. Donald Fondow
Minnesota South	14301 Grand Ave	Burnsville, MN	55306-5707	952-435-2550	435-2581	Sean Martens
Missouri	660 Mason Ridge Center Dr	Saint Louis, MO	63141-8557	314-590-6200	590-6201	Alan Freeman
Montana	30 Broadwater Ave	Billings, MT	59101-1826	406-259-2908	259-1305	Rev. Terry Forke
Nebraska	PO Box 407	Seward, NE	68434-0407	888-643-2961	643-2990	Bob Ziegler
New England	400 Wilbraham Rd	Springfield, MA	01109-2723	203-773-1400	783-0909	Rev. Tim Yeadon
New Jersey	1168 Springfield Ave	Mountainside, NJ	07092-2906	908-233-8111	233-3883	Caren Vogt
North Dakota	413 E Avenue D	Bismarck, ND	58501-3949	701-751-3424		Dr. James Baneck
Northern Illinois	2301 S Wolf Rd	Hillside, IL	60162-2211	708-449-3020	449-3026	Mike Zimmer
Northwest	1700 NE Knott St	Portland, OR	97212-3301	503-288-8383	284-2785	Jim Scriven
North Wisconsin	3103 Seymour Ln	Wausau, WI	54401-4049	715-845-8241	845-3836	Rev. Dwayne Lueck
Ohio	PO Box 38277	Olmsted Falls, OH	44138-0277	440-235-2297	235-1970	Travis Grulke
Oklahoma	308 NW 164th St	Edmond, OK	73013-2006	405-348-7600	384-7601	Rev. Barrie Henke

Region	Address	City,State	Zip code	Telephone	Fax	Superintendent
Pacific Southwest	1540 Concordia	Irvine, CA	92612-3203	949-854-3232	854-8140	Rachel Klitzing
Rocky Mountain	14334 E Evans Ave	Aurora, CO	80014-1408	303-695-8001	695-4047	Rev. Allen Anderson
SELC	566 Oak Ridge Rd	Clark, NJ	07066-2124	732-382-7320	382-7512	Rev. Andrew Dzurovcik
South Dakota	PO Box 89110	Sioux Falls, SD	57109-9110	605-361-1514	361-7959	Rev. Scott Sailer
Southeastern	6315 Grovedale Dr	Alexandria, VA	22310-2501	703-971-9371	922-6047	Rev. John Denninger
Southern	100 Mission Dr	Slidell, LA	70460-5221	504-282-2632	871-9696	Glenn Gerber
Southern Illinois	2408 Lebanon Ave	Belleville, IL	62221-2529	618-234-4767	234-4830	Roger Sprengel
South Wisconsin	8100 W Capitol Dr	Milwaukee, WI	53222-1981	414-464-8100	464-0602	Dr. Chris Cody
Texas	7900 E Highway 290	Austin, TX	78724-2402	512-926-4272	926-1006	Dr. William Hinz
Wyoming	2400 S Hickory St	Casper, WY	82604-3471	307-265-9000	234-6629	Rev. John Hill

GENERAL CONFERENCE OF SEVENTH-DAY ADVENTISTS SUPERINTENDENTS

NORTH AMERICAN DIV. OFFICE OF EDUCATION
12501 Old Columbia Pike, Silver Spring, MD 20904-6601
Telephone 301-680-6400
Fax 680-6464
Website http://www.nadadventist.org

GENERAL CONFERENCE OF SEVENTH-DAY ADVENTISTS SUPERINTENDENTS

Conference	Address	City,State	Zip code	Telephone	Fax	Superintendent
Atlantic Union	**PO Box 1189**	**South Lancaster, MA**	**01561-1189**	**978-368-8333**	**368-7948**	**Astrid Thomassian**
Greater New York Conference	PO Box 5029	Manhasset, NY	11030-5029	516-627-9350	627-9272	Marlene Romeo
New York Conference	4930 W Seneca Tpke	Syracuse, NY	13215-2225	315-469-6921	469-6924	Jeremy Garlock
Northeastern Conference	11550 Merrick Blvd	Jamaica, NY	11434-1852	718-291-8006	739-5133	Viola Chapman
Northern New England Conference	479 Main St	Westbrook, ME	04092-4330	207-797-3760	797-2851	Trevor Schlisner
Southern New England Conference	PO Box 1169	South Lancaster, MA	01561-1169	978-365-4551	365-3838	Pat Giese
Columbia Union Conference	**5427 Twin Knolls Rd**	**Columbia, MD**	**21045-3247**	**410-997-3414**	**596-6758**	**Donovan Ross**
Allegheny East Conference	767 Douglass Dr	Boyertown, PA	19512-7775	610-326-4610	326-3946	Judy Dent
Allegheny West Conference	1339 E Broad St	Columbus, OH	43205-1503	614-252-5271	252-3246	Dr. William Cox
Chesapeake Conference	6600 Martin Rd	Columbia, MD	21044-3999	410-995-1910	995-1434	Jacqueline Messenger
Mountain View Conference	1400 Liberty St	Parkersburg, WV	26101-4124	304-422-4581	422-4582	Larry Boggess
New Jersey Conference	2303 Brunswick Ave	Lawrenceville, NJ	08648-4410	609-802-0840	396-9273	Sadrail Saint-Ulysse
Ohio Conference	PO Box 1230	Mount Vernon, OH	43050-8230	740-397-4665	397-1648	Ken Knudsen
Pennsylvania Conference	720 Museum Rd	Reading, PA	19611-1429	610-374-8331	374-9331	Jeff Bovee
Potomac Conference	606 Greenville Ave	Staunton, VA	24401-4881	540-886-0771	886-5734	Keith Hallam
Lake Union Conference	**PO Box 287**	**Berrien Springs, MI**	**49103-0287**	**269-473-8200**	**471-7920**	**Linda Fuchs**
Illinois Conference	619 Plainfield Rd	Willowbrook, IL	60527-8438	630-856-2890	734-0929	
Indiana Conference	15205 Westfield Blvd	Carmel, IN	46032-8000	317-844-6201	571-9281	Herb Wrate
Lake Region Conference	8517 S State St	Chicago, IL	60619-5697	773-846-2661	846-5309	Renee Humphreys
Michigan Conference	PO Box 24187	Lansing, MI	48909-4187	517-316-1550	316-1501	Diane Barlow
Wisconsin Conference	PO Box 100	Fall River, WI	53932-0100	920-484-6555	484-6550	Linda Rosen
Mid-America Union Conference	**PO Box 6128**	**Lincoln, NE**	**68506-0128**	**402-484-3000**	**483-4453**	**John Kriegelstein**
Central States Conference	3301 Parallel Pkwy	Kansas City, KS	66104-4354	913-371-1071	371-1609	Judith Mason
Dakota Conference	7200 N Washington St	Bismarck, ND	58503-6301	701-751-6177	751-6178	Gerard Ban
Iowa-Missouri Conference	PO Box 65665	West Des Moines, IA	50265-0665	515-223-1197	223-5692	Dr. Joseph Allison
Kansas-Nebraska Conference	3440 SW Urish Rd	Topeka, KS	66614-4601	785-478-4726	478-1000	Gary Kruger
Minnesota Conference	7384 Kirkwood Ct	Maple Grove, MN	55369	763-424-8923	424-9576	Connie McCormick
Rocky Mountain Conference	2520 S Downing St	Denver, CO	80210-5818	303-282-3650	733-1843	Lonnie Hetterle
North Pacific Union Conference	**5709 N 20th St**	**Ridgefield, WA**	**98642-7724**	**360-857-7027**	**857-7127**	**Dennis Plubell**
Alaska Conference	6100 OMalley Rd	Anchorage, AK	99507-6958	907-346-1004	346-3279	Laurie Hosey
Idaho Conference	7777 W Fairview Ave	Boise, ID	83704-8418	208-375-7524	375-7526	Patrick Frey
Montana Conference	175 Canyon View Rd	Bozeman, MT	59715-0607	406-587-3101	587-1598	Phil Hudema
Oregon Conference	19800 Oatfield Rd	Gladstone, OR	97027-2546	503-850-3500	654-5657	Gale Crosby
Upper Columbia Conference	3715 S Grove Rd	Spokane, WA	99224-6090	509-838-2761	838-4882	Larry Marsh
Washington Conference	32229 Weyerhaeuser Way S	Federal Way, WA	98001-9347	253-681-6008	681-6009	Archie Harris
Pacific Union Conference	**PO Box 5005**	**Westlake Vlg, CA**	**91359-5005**	**805-413-7314**	**413-7319**	**Berit von Pohle**
Arizona Conference	PO Box 12340	Scottsdale, AZ	85267-2340	480-991-6777	991-4833	Gus Martin
Central California Conference	PO Box 770	Clovis, CA	93613-0770	559-347-3059	347-3054	David Gillham
Hawaii Conference	2728 Pali Hwy	Honolulu, HI	96817-1485	808-595-7591	595-2345	Miki Akeo Nelson
Nevada-Utah Conference	10475 Double R Blvd	Reno, NV	89521-8905	775-322-6929	322-9371	Eileen White
Northern California Conference	PO Box 23165	Pleasant Hill, CA	94523-0165	925-603-5061	599-1304	Bill Keresoma
Southeastern California Conference	PO Box 79990	Riverside, CA	92513-1990	951-509-2307	509-2392	Donald Dudley
Southern California Conference	PO Box 969	Glendale, CA	91209-0969	818-546-8400	546-8454	Dr. Harold Crook
Southern Union Conference	**PO Box 923868**	**Norcross, GA**	**30010-3868**	**770-408-1800**	**408-1801**	**Debra Fryson**
Carolina Conference	PO Box 44270	Charlotte, NC	28215-0043	704-596-3200	596-5775	Gary Rouse
Florida Conference	PO Box 2626	Winter Park, FL	32790-2626	407-644-5000	644-7550	Frank Runnels Ed.D.
Georgia-Cumberland Conference	PO Box 12000	Calhoun, GA	30703-7001	706-629-7951	625-3684	Kevin Kossick
Gulf States Conference	PO Box 240249	Montgomery, AL	36124-0249	334-272-7493	272-7987	Stan Hobbs
Kentucky-Tennessee Conference	PO Box 1088	Goodlettsville, TN	37070-1088	615-859-1391	859-2120	Stephen Bralley
South Atlantic Conference	3978 Memorial Dr	Decatur, GA	30032-2205	404-792-0535	792-7817	Dr. James Lamb
South Central Conference	PO Box 78767	Nashville, TN	37207-8767	615-226-6500	262-9141	Sharon Lewis
Southeastern Conference	1701 Robie Ave	Mount Dora, FL	32757-6339	352-735-3142	735-3562	Barbara Davis
Southwestern Union Conference	**PO Box 4000**	**Burleson, TX**	**76097-1630**	**817-295-0476**	**447-2443**	**Randy Gilliam**
Arkansas-Louisiana Conference	PO Box 31000	Shreveport, LA	71130-1000	318-631-6240	631-7611	Steve Burton
Oklahoma Conference	PO Box 32098	Oklahoma City, OK	73123-0298	405-721-6110	721-7594	Jack Francisco
Southwest Region Conference	PO Box 226289	Dallas, TX	75222-6289	214-943-4491	946-2528	Buford Griffith
Texas Conference	PO Box 800	Alvarado, TX	76009-0800	817-790-2255	783-5266	John Hopps
Texico Conference	PO Box 1366	Corrales, NM	87048-1366	505-244-1611	244-1811	Derral Reeve